ONE POWERFUL BRAND, DOING ONE THING BETTER — REACHING NEWSPAPER DECISION MAKERS

EDITOR & PUBLISHER

Penetrating Editorial, Strategic Business Ideas and Practical Solutions

editorandpublisher.com

EDITOR & PUBLISHER ®

97th Annual
Newspaper
DATABOOK™
The Encyclopedia of the Newspaper Industry

BOOK 1: DAILIES
2018

Editorial: 18475 Bandilier Circle, Fountain Valley, CA 92708 – (949) 660-6150; Fax (949) 660-6172
Customer Service: (888) 732-7323

97th ANNUAL
Newspaper
DATABOOK

Published annually by Editor & Publisher, the oldest publishers' and advertisers' periodical in the United States

With which has been merged: **The Journalist**, establisher March 22, 1884; **Newspaperdom**, March 22, 1892; **The Fourth Estate**, March 1, 1894; **Editor & Publisher**, June 29, 1901; **Advertising**, January 22, 1925.

CORPORATE OFFICES	*(949) 660-6150*
	FAX (949) 660-6172
EDITOR-IN-CHIEF	*Jeff Fleming*
	jeff@editorandpublisher.com
MANAGING EDITOR	*Nu Yang*
	nu@editorandpublisher.com
ART DIRECTOR	*Meredith Ewell*
	meredith@editorandpublisher.com
SALES & MARKETING	*Wendy MacDonald*, ext. 231
CONSULTANT	*wendy@editorandpublisher.com*
SUBSCRIPTION	
SERVICES	*(888) 732-7323*
CIRCULATION	*Rick Avila*, ext. 254
MANAGER	*rick@editorandpublisher.com*
CIRCULATION	*Emily Wells*, ext. 225
ASSISTANTS	*Dustin Nguyen*, ext. 255
ACCOUNTING	*Kym Bashford*, ext. 213
	kym@editorandpublisher.com

EDITORIAL & ADVERTISING MAILING ADDRESS
18475 BANDILIER CIRCLE, FOUNTAIN VALLEY, CA 92708

WWW.EDITORANDPUBLISHER.COM

Editor & Publisher is printed in the U.S.A.

DUNCAN McINTOSH CO.
FOUNDED BY:

Editor and Publisher • *Duncan McIntosh Jr.*
Co-Publisher • *Teresa Ybarra McIntosh (1942-2011)*

18475 Bandilier Circle, Fountain Valley, CA 92708, (949) 660-6150; fax (949) 660-6172; www.editorandpublisher.com;

ISBN 1-930732-69-4 (Book 1)   ISBN 1-930732-70-8 (Book 2)

Letter from the Publisher...

Welcome to the 2018 edition of the *Editor & Publisher Newspaper DataBook*. The *2018 DataBook* offers countless facts about the newspaper industry including their online and digital products.

The entries in this directory are designed and organized to give you the information you need about newspapers -- fast. The directory is also available electronically on the web at www.editorandpublisher.com/databook, enabling you to search, retrieve and export data for your own personal use.

The *DataBook* in print is divided into two volumes with the following content. Book I features detailed listings for U.S. and Canadian daily newspapers (publishing four or more times a week), including contact information, personnel, circulation, advertising rates, mechanical specifications, commodity consumption and equipment. Users will also find listings of U.S. and Canadian daily newspaper groups; syndicates and news services; both conventional and interactive companies offering products and services to the industry; associations; newspaper brokers and appraisers; advertising representatives; and much more. The Who's Where directory of industry professionals with phone numbers, titles, and company names for both Dailies and Weeklies is contained in the final section of this book. Book II contains the Weekly newspapers, those publishing three or fewer days a week.

As of January 1, 2018, daily newspapers in the United States numbered 1,277. Total U.S. Daily newspaper circulation was 29.2 million. The number of U.S. Sunday newspapers totaled 857 with circulation of 33.2 million. Additional information can be found in the Ready Reckoner charts, which appear on pages iv through vi of this front section.

Editor & Publisher thanks the people of the newspaper industry and in businesses supporting the industry for their help in providing us with accurate information for the 97th annual edition of the *Editor & Publisher Newspaper DataBook*. Please continue to direct questions, comments and suggestions to us at rick@editorandpublisher.com.

Sincerely,

Duncan McIntosh
Publisher

TABLE OF CONTENTS
2018 EDITOR & PUBLISHER® NEWSPAPER DATABOOK®

BOOK 1: DAILIES

BASIC DATA FOR ADVERTISING SPACE BUYERS

Morning

Period Ended	Total number of papers	Total net circulation	Total column inch rate	millinch rate	Relation of millinch rate to the preceeding 2 years
12/31/17	947	26,190,248	$98,912.03	$3,776.67	increase $572.82 + 17.88%
12/31/16	939	30,356,515	$98,912.03	$3,258.35	increase $720.41 + 28.39%
12/31/15	972	25,475,799	$80,232.92	$3,149.37	increase $1344.13 + 74.45%
12/31/14	953	36,765,040	$70,841.07	$1,926.51	increase $170.23 + 8.84%
12/31/13	980	36,975,153	$62,264.89	$1,683.97	decrease $81.66 - 4.62%
12/31/12	985	38,723,356	$70,808.91	$1,828.58	increase $263.29 + 16.82%
12/31/11	980	41,562,085	$70,767.01	$1,702.68	increase $261.60 + 15.36%
12/31/09	869	43,421,084	$62,001.81 (40,795,519 AM plus 2,625,565 PM through combinations)	$1,427.90	increase $17.39 + 1.22%
12/31/08	872	42,939,680	$62,445.50 (42,757,749 AM plus 181,931 PM through combinations)	$1,454.26	increase $129.54 + 8.91%
12/31/07	867	44,745,057	$61,155.81 (44,547,744 AM plus 197,313 PM through combinations)	$1,366.76	increase $114.08 + 8.35%
12/31/06	833	45,708,175	$58,628.68 (45,441,416 AM plus 266,729 PM through combinations)	$1,262.67	increase $129.00 + 10.06%
12/31/05	817	46,402,988	$56,736.35 (46,122,614 AM plus 280,734 PM through combinations)	$1,222.69	increase $167.70 + 13.72%
12/31/04	814	47,483,349	$51,502.53 (46,887,490 AM plus 595,859 PM through combinations)	$1,084.64	increase $75.54 + 6.97%
12/31/03	787	47,614,150	$48,820.93 (46,930,215 AM plus 683,935 PM through combinations)	$1,025.34	increase $48.34 + 4.71%
12/31/02	777	47,314,102	$46,617.77 (46,617,163 AM plus 696,939 PM through combinations)	$992.85	increase $51.50 + 5.20%

Afternoon

Period Ended	Total number of papers	Total net circulation	Total column inch rate	millinch rate	Relation of millinch rate to the preceeding 2 years
12/31/17	356	2,995,167	$8,645.71	$2,866.55	increase $11.63 + 0.40%
12/31/16	369	3,062,643	$8,645.71	$2,822.96	increase $21.66 + 0.77%
12/31/15	389	3,167,576	$9,271.17	$2,926.89	increase $294.60 + 11.19%
12/31/14	402	3,654,749	$9,791.10	$2,675.71	increase $604.66 + 22.60%
12/31/13	444	3,736,932	$9,674.44	$2,588.87	increase $912.35 + 54.42%
12/31/12	442	4,709,613	$7,315.09	$1,553.22	decrease $284.74 - 15.49%
12/31/11	470	4,543,326	$8,177.16	$1,799.82	decrease $19.70 - 1.08%
12/31/09	528	6,413,488	$12,032.42 (5,482,151 PM plus 931,337 AM through combinations)	$1,876.10	decrease $108.79 - 5.80%
12/31/08	546	6,858,369	$12,090.92 (5,839,770 PM plus 1,018,559 AM through combinations)	$1,762.94	decrease $60.23 - 3.42%
12/31/07	565	7,238,621	$12,824.47 (6,193,856 PM plus 1,044,765 AM through combinations)	$1,771.67	increase $186.46 + 10.52%
12/31/06	614	8,436,773	$13,783.60 (6,887,784 PM plus 1,548,989 AM through combinations)	$1,633.75	increase $162.56 + 9.95%
12/31/05	645	8,159,398	$12,538.29 (7,222,429 PM plus 936,969 AM through combinations)	$1,536.67	increase $169.71 + 11.05%
12/31/04	653	9,327,047	$13,111.15 (7,738,648 PM plus 1,588,399 AM through combinations)	$1,405.71	increase $116.50 + 8.29%
12/31/03	680	9,987,734	$13,265.68 (8,255,136 PM plus 1,732,598 AM through combinations)	$1,328.20	increase $24.81 + 1.87%
12/31/02	692	10,334,154	$12,919.94 (8,568,994 PM plus 1,765,160 AM through combinations)	$1,250.22	decrease $79.02 - 6.32%

Sunday

Period Ended	Total number of papers	Total net circulation	Total column inch rate	millinch rate	Relation of millinch rate to the preceeding 2 years
12/31/17	857	33,159,908			
12/31/16	866	37,771,075			
12/31/15	904	34,237,037			
12/31/14	923	42,750,613			
12/31/13	934	43,292,426			
12/31/12	981	44,821,529			
12/31/11	1015	50,880,930			
12/31/09	919	46,895,201	$75,207.37 (46,849,960 Sunday plus 45,241 AM and PM through combinations)	$1,603.70	increase $106.90 + 6.67%
12/31/08	902	49,162,344	$75,630.08 (49,114,892 Sunday plus 47,452 AM and PM through combinations)	$1,538.37	increase $142.32 + 9.25%
12/31/07	907	51,347,859	$74,722.80 (51,246,332 Sunday plus 101,527 AM and PM through combinations)	$1,455.23	increase $154.84 + 10.64%
12/31/06	907	53,279,897	$71,227.96 (53,175,299 Sunday plus 104,598 AM and PM through combinations)	$1,336.86	increase $157.63 + 13.37%
12/31/05	914	55,376,702	$69,991.16 (55,270,361 Sunday plus 106,321 AM and PM through combinations)	$1,263.91	increase $200.08 + 15.83%
12/31/04	915	57,862,287	$63,332.56 (57,753,013 Sunday plus 109,274 AM and PM through combinations)	$1,094.54	increase $86.99 + 7.94%
12/31/03	917	58,883,978	$60,834.09 (58,494,695 Sunday plus 459,188 AM and PM through combinations)	$1,033.12	increase $75.97 + 7.35%
12/31/02	913	59,680,781	$58,613.95 (58,780,299 Sunday plus 900,482 AM and PM through combinations)	$982.12	increase $90.80 + 9.30%

READY RECKONER OF ADVERTISING RATES AND CIRCULATIONS - CANADA

95 daily newspapers (69 morning, 26 evening) and 20 Sunday

Number of newspapers as of January 1, 2018 with circulations mainly as reported for six months ended September 30, 2017

PROVINCE	Population Statistics Canada July 2017 (est.)	AMs	PMs	Total	AM Circulation	Inch rates including all combinations	PM Circulation	Inch rates including all combinations	Total AM & PM Circulation	Minimum rates for AM & PM coverage
					MORNING PAPERS NET CIRCULATION SEPT 30, 2017		AFTERNOON PAPERS NET CIRCULATIOON SEPT 30, 2017		TOTALS	
Alberta	4,318,772	8	2	10	239,194	$21.57	11,537	$3.98	250,731	$25.55
British Columbia	4,849,442	7	4	11	322,764	$10.33	9,869	$21.98	332,633	$32.31
Manitoba	1,346,993	3	1	4	94,654	$12.64	2,382	$0.00	97,036	$12.64
New Brunswick	760,744	4	0	4	91,877	$10.48	0	$0.00	91,877	$10.48
Newfoundland and Labrado	527,613	2	0	2	14,726	$2.80	0	$0.00	14,726	$2.80
Nova Scotia	957,470	2	2	4	111,269	$273.48	0	$0.00	111,269	$273.48
Ontario	14,318,750	27	16	43	961,243	$1,221.79	119,625	$23.32	1,080,868	$1,245.11
Prince Edward Island	152,768	2	0	2	19,627	$2.13	0	$0.00	19,627	$2.13
Quebec	8,439,925	10	0	10	799,465	$7,122.75	0	$0.00	799,465	$7,122.75
Saskatchewan	1,169,752	2	2	4	71,549	$8.44	12,389	$3.69	83,938	$12.13
Yukon Territory	38,825	0	1	1	0	$0.00	1,359	$17.00	1,359	$17.00
TOTALS	36,881,054	69	26	95	2,726,368	$8,686.41	157,161	$69.97	2,883,529	$8,756.38

SUNDAY PAPERS NET CIRCULATION SEPT 30, 2017

PROVINCE	Number of Papers	Sunday Circulation
Alberta	4	78,241
British Columbia	4	176,149
Manitoba	1	16,786
New Brunswick	0	0
Newfoundland and Labrado	0	0
Nova Scotia	1	97,283
Ontario	5	295,192
Prince Edward Island	0	0
Quebec	5	621,315
Saskatchewan	0	0
Yukon Territory	0	0
TOTALS	20	1,284,966

READY RECKONER OF ADVERTISING RATES AND CIRCULATIONS
1,277 daily newspapers (947 morning, 356 evening and including 26 all-day) and 857 Sunday
Number of newspapers as of Jan. 1, 2018 with circulation as reported for six months primarily ending on Sept. 30, 2017

STATE	NUMBER OF DAILY NEWSPAPERS				MORNING PAPERS NET CIRCULATION SEPT. 30, 2017		AFTERNOON PAPERS NET CIRCULATION SEPT. 30, 2017		TOTALS		SUNDAY PAPERS NET CIRCULATION SEPT. 30, 2017	
	Population 2017 (est.)	AMs	PMs	Total	AM Circulation	Inch rates including all combinations	PM Circulation	Inch rates including all combinations	Total AM & PM Circulation	Minimum rates for AM & PM coverage	Number of papers	Sunday circulation
Alabama	4,874,747	20	1	21	201,396	$520.45	4,200	$9.95	205,596	$530.40	14	201,505
* Alaska	739,795	5	3	7	44,205	$147.19	22,000	$98.65	66,205	$235.84	4	56,640
Arizona	7,016,270	12	0	12	313,977	$917.90	0	$0.00	313,977	$917.90	10	449,507
Arkansas	3,004,279	16	9	25	244,459	$638.13	34,527	$108.58	278,986	$646.71	16	285,367
* California	39,536,653	63	6	68	2,062,127	$5,786.29	256,526	$125.70	2,318,653	$5,911.99	52	3,123,641
* Colorado	5,607,154	23	7	28	549,958	$1,339.08	13,195	$70.66	563,153	$1,409.74	17	647,817
Connecticut	3,588,184	16	2	18	296,879	$1,029.79	30,465	$72.15	327,344	$1,101.94	14	423,385
Delaware	961,939	2	0	2	73,582	$476.00	0	$0.00	73,582	$476.00	2	91,590
* District of Columbia	693,972	3	1	3	533,794	$420.50	33,574	$312.50	567,368	$733.00	1	522,055
Florida	20,984,400	37	0	37	1,372,413	$3,506.04	0	$0.00	1,372,413	$3,506.04	34	1,926,385
Georgia	10,429,379	26	3	29	422,481	$1,169.48	28,603	$47.75	451,084	$1,217.23	21	559,432
Hawaii	1,427,538	6	0	6	199,801	$347.75	0	$0.00	199,801	$347.75	5	213,788
Idaho	1,716,943	11	1	12	140,975	$198.11	5,000	$14.00	145,975	$212.11	10	227,554
* Illinois	12,802,023	35	22	56	1,066,846	$3,170.54	135,849	$316.99	1,202,695	$3,487.53	30	1,450,368
* Indiana	6,666,818	46	23	66	553,900	$1,325.46	170,499	$261.65	724,399	$1,587.11	30	771,152
* Iowa	3,145,711	18	20	33	241,081	$791.05	106,082	$357.53	347,163	$1,148.58	13	350,787
Kansas	2,913,123	14	15	29	159,224	$431.58	67,523	$145.38	226,747	$576.96	12	175,595
* Kentucky	4,454,189	15	7	21	272,080	$403.00	53,695	$106.40	325,775	$509.40	15	364,542
Louisiana	4,684,333	11	8	19	211,221	$504.63	49,208	$110.61	260,429	$615.24	13	275,016
Maine	1,335,907	5	2	7	98,581	$408.45	13,876	$32.00	112,457	$440.45	4	89,003
Maryland	6,052,177	9	0	9	237,295	$2,048.28	0	$0.00	237,295	$2,048.28	8	378,844
* Massachusetts	6,859,819	19	13	30	606,058	$14,843.94	159,314	$351.19	765,372	$15,195.13	17	722,540
Michigan	9,962,311	27	20	47	477,359	$1,141.23	280,927	$689.87	758,286	$1,831.10	24	829,968
Minnesota	5,576,606	17	5	22	580,528	$774.23	45,260	$128.40	625,788	$902.63	14	839,965
Mississippi	2,984,100	9	8	17	125,425	$367.74	56,410	$116.26	181,835	$484.00	16	187,519
Missouri	6,113,532	22	14	36	406,161	$22,910.60	160,787	$167.79	566,948	$23,078.39	17	561,610
Montana	1,050,493	8	3	11	191,764	$275.65	10,406	$28.70	202,170	$304.35	8	191,470
Nebraska	1,920,076	7	8	15	239,575	$337.60	51,407	$124.80	290,982	$462.40	6	291,241
Nevada	2,998,039	5	0	5	274,653	$813.30	0	$0.00	274,653	$813.30	4	308,097
New Hampshire	1,342,795	9	1	10	114,719	$183.59	7,081	$13.60	121,800	$197.19	6	106,737
* New Jersey	9,005,644	16	1	16	682,242	$1,871.45	5,235	$15.60	687,477	$1,887.05	14	867,805
New Mexico	2,088,070	12	3	15	162,066	$201.57	19,270	$43.64	181,336	$245.21	12	183,339
* New York	19,849,399	42	15	55	3,508,479	$17,997.42	172,424	$443.59	3,680,903	$18,441.01	39	4,305,584
North Carolina	10,273,419	39	5	44	619,673	$1,497.47	44,911	$100.50	664,584	$1,597.97	39	768,470
North Dakota	755,393	7	3	10	100,575	$194.44	7,004	$26.39	107,579	$220.83	7	107,975
Ohio	11,658,609	54	27	81	1,079,254	$2,806.21	186,747	$1,241.42	1,266,001	$4,047.63	45	1,394,621
Oklahoma	3,930,864	20	13	33	267,056	$723.55	67,839	$155.15	334,895	$878.70	25	364,302
* Oregon	4,142,776	9	8	16	214,079	$467.39	135,132	$252.36	349,211	$719.75	11	365,560
Pennsylvania	12,805,537	53	17	70	1,243,302	$14,254.91	129,874	$768.58	1,373,176	$15,023.49	47	1,748,546
Puerto Rico	3,337,177	0	0	0	0	$0.00	0	$0.00	0	$0.00	0	0
* Rhode Island	1,059,639	5	1	5	84,847	$364.51	474	$7.02	85,321	$371.53	2	89,638
South Carolina	5,024,369	15	1	16	294,397	$1,186.37	6,409	$12.50	300,806	$1,198.87	14	359,349
South Dakota	869,666	6	5	11	77,086	$209.14	24,492	$68.51	101,578	$277.65	5	76,116
* Tennessee	6,715,984	15	11	25	355,454	$452.30	108,696	$164.77	464,150	$617.07	18	544,393
Texas	28,304,596	54	13	67	1,284,883	$2,689.48	57,430	$158.29	1,342,313	$2,847.77	61	1,798,727
Utah	3,101,833	6	0	6	179,857	$582.80	0	$0.00	179,857	$582.80	6	285,121
Vermont	623,657	7	1	8	52,809	$188.40	5,695	$20.00	58,504	$208.40	4	44,977
* Virginia	8,470,020	20	1	20	2,516,315	$1,036.29	22,858	$28.65	2,539,173	$1,064.94	17	1,654,561
Washington	7,405,743	15	5	20	518,333	$837.59	37,852	$94.65	556,185	$932.24	16	685,866
West Virginia	1,815,857	11	6	17	156,929	$486.76	44,216	$157.22	201,145	$643.98	12	209,645
* Wisconsin	5,795,483	19	15	32	430,674	$1,062.20	104,993	$369.19	535,667	$1,431.39	20	620,401
Wyoming	579,315				49,421	$114.36	17,202	$40.75	66,623	$155.11	6	61,792
TOTALS	329,056,355	947	356	1,277	26,190,248	$116,352.19	2,995,167	$7,969.89	29,185,415	$124,322.08	857	33,159,908

* Indicates population groups including one or more of the 26 all-day newspapers counted both in AM & PM columns, but only once in the total

Circulation for these papers is equally divided between AMs & PMs

CIRCULATION OF U.S. DAILY NEWSPAPERS BY CIRCULATION GROUPS

Circulation	NUMBER OF DAILY NEWSPAPERS AMs	PMs	Total	MORNING PAPERS NET CIRCULATION SEPT. 30, 2017 AM Circulation	Inch rates including all combinations	AFTERNOON PAPERS NET CIRCULATION SEPT. 30, 2017 PM Circulation	Inch rates including all combinations	TOTALS Total AM & PM Circulation	Minimum rates for AM & PM coverage	SUNDAY PAPERS NET CIRCULATION SEPT. 30, 2017 Number of papers	Sunday circulation
More than 1,000,000	2	0	2	3,192,369	$2,033.05	0	$0.00	3,192,369	$2,033.05	3	3,334,907
500,001 - 1,000,000	1	0	1	513,776	$563.00	0	$0.00	513,776	$563.00	3	2,035,397
* 100,001 - 500,000	8	1	8	2,564,461	$9,237.59	226,397	$0.00	2,790,858	$9,237.59	65	13,106,485
* 50,001 - 100,000	45	3	46	6,344,570	$36,419.53	245,895	$233.60	6,590,465	$36,653.13	55	3,880,110
* 25,001 - 50,000	48	3	50	3,311,148	$20,735.70	160,975	$362.61	3,472,123	$21,098.31	123	4,344,849
* 10,001 - 25,000	96	10	103	3,273,659	$8,012.19	260,812	$423.06	3,534,471	$8,435.25	296	4,827,565
* 5,001 - 10,000	293	38	328	4,566,428	$12,088.53	547,754	$1,125.93	5,114,182	$13,214.46	185	1,352,011
* 5,000 or less	454	301	739	2,423,831	$27,262.58	1,553,340	$5,824.67	3,977,171	$33,087.25	127	278,584
TOTALS	947	356	1,277	26,190,242	$116,352.17	2,995,173	$7,969.87	29,185,415	$124,322.04	857	33,159,908

*Indicates population groups including one or more of the 26 all-day newspapers counted both in AM & PM columns, but only once in the total

Circulation for these papers is equally divided between AMs & PMs

NEWSPAPER ADVERTISING

A SUMMARY OF NEWSPAPER ADVERTISING TRENDS COMPILED BY EDITOR & PUBLISHER FROM MEDIA RECORDS AND NAA REPORTS

LINAGE TOTALS - 1963 to 1970

Note: Figures from 1963 to 1970 are in thousands of lines; department store advertising is included in retail figures.

YEAR	RETAIL	DEPARTMENT STORE	GENERAL	AUTOMOTIVE	FINANCIAL	CLASSIFIED	TOTAL ADVERTISING
1963	1,442,817	508,402	261,747	141,877	53,588	695,888	2,595,917
1964	1,673,186	593,476	292,549	159,729	60,067	787,135	2,973,466
1965	1,776,702	627,924	288,528	170,366	63,350	858,631	3,157,577
1966	1,863,633	652,845	310,287	182,894	73,184	924,255	3,354,253
1967	1,897,081	657,266	297,106	158,506	69,946	878,114	3,300,753
1968	1,917,404	625,691	296,134	170,958	72,838	923,724	3,381,058
1969	2,003,022	629,340	300,080	173,623	81,677	1,017,084	3,575,486
1970	2,014,880	613,212	275,156	161,570	74,907	917,262	3,443,775

DOLLAR OUTLAY - 1971 to 2013

Note: On Jan. 1, 1971, the Media Records base was increased to 64 from 52 cities, and the terms from it's report "Total Agate Lines" to "Dollar Outlay." Numbers are in thousands of dollars; department store advertising is included in retail figures.

YEAR	RETAIL	DEPARTMENT STORE	GENERAL	AUTOMOTIVE	FINANCIAL	CLASSIFIED	TOTAL ADVERTISING
1971	1,807,304	536,930	455,356	100,765	103,099	751,652	3,218,176
1972	2,004,666	567,833	504,377	102,514	122,137	914,868	3,648,562
1973	2,044,095	561,770	479,183	99,783	138,898	1,024,153	3,786,112
1974	2,078,760	562,583	491,508	104,191	126,023	966,673	3,767,155
1975	2,363,965	634,965	547,099	93,264	130,810	982,229	4,117,367
1976	3,129,474	793,497	752,267	144,538	147,394	1,522,474	5,696,147
1977	3,129,474	793,497	752,267	144,538	147,394	1,522,474	5,696,147
1978	3,579,933	871,250	826,614	151,004	201,670	1,884,505	6,643,726
1979	3,959,802	891,902	937,792	192,961	236,771	2,201,717	7,529,043
1980	4,396,320	954,411	1,122,701	183,568	297,962	2,191,773	8,192,324
1981	5,067,750	1,092,674	1,379,698	225,627	387,152	2,514,923	9,575,150
1982	5,282,855	1,151,824	1,419,610	265,013	398,732	2,497,840	9,864,050
1983	5,028,265	1,140,450	1,482,434	248,470	327,427	2,698,155	9,784,751
1984	12,784,000		3,081,000			7,657,000	23,522,000
1985	13,443,000		3,352,000			8,375,000	25,170,000
1986	14,311,000		3,376,000			9,303,000	26,990,000

Note: Since 1984, the dollar volume has been supplied by the newspaper advertising bureau, now part of Newspaper Association of America. The large increase in all subsequent years occurs because these figures include all newspapers nationwide.

YEAR	RETAIL	DEPARTMENT STORE	GENERAL	AUTOMOTIVE	FINANCIAL	CLASSIFIED	TOTAL ADVERTISING
1987	15,227,000		3,494,000			10,691,000	29,412,000
1988	15,790,000		3,821,000			11,586,000	31,197,000
1989	16,504,000		3,948,000			11,916,000	32,368,000
1990	16,652,000		4,122,000			11,506,000	32,280,000
1991	15,839,000		3,924,000			10,587,000	30,350,000
1992	16,041,000		3,834,000			10,764,000	30,639,000
1993	16,859,000		3,853,000			11,157,000	31,869,000
1994	17,496,000		4,149,000			12,464,000	34,109,000
1995	18,099,000		4,251,000			13,742,000	36,092,000
1996	18,344,000		4,667,000			15,065,000	38,076,000
1997	19,242,000		5,315,000			16,773,000	41,330,000
1998	20,331,000		5,721,000			17,873,000	43,925,000
1999	20,907,000		6,732,000			18,650,000	46,289,000
2000	21,409,000		7,653,000			19,608,000	48,670,000
2001	20,679,000		7,004,000			16,622,000	44,305,000
2002	20,994,000		7,210,000			15,898,000	44,102,000
2003	21,341,000		7,797,000			15,801,000	44,939,000
2004	22,012,000		8,083,000			16,608,000	46,703,000
2005	22,187,000		7,910,000			17,312,000	47,409,000
2006	22,120,910		7,504,895			16,985,536	46,611,341
2007	21,018,000		7,005,000			14,186,000	42,209,000
2008	18,768,570		5,995,934			9,975,014	34,739,518
2009	14,218,000		4,424,000			6,179,000	24,821,000
2010	12,926,051		4,221,075			5,648,110	22,795,236
2011	11,887,000		3,777,000			5,028,000	20,692,000
2012	10,984,000		3,335,000			4,626,000	18,945,000

* To present a truer picture of advertising trends, all linage carried in the three metropolitan New York City dailies that struck for 90 days August to November 1978 has been excluded from 1978 totals and 1977 figures have been correspondingly adjusted.

* Source: Research Department of the Newspaper Association of America, 4/13.

CIRCULATION OF DAILY NEWSPAPERS OF CANADA BY CIRCULATION GROUPS

Circulation	NUMBER OF DAILY NEWSPAPERS AMs	PMs	Total	MORNING PAPERS NET CIRCULATION SEPT 30, 2017 AM Circulation	Inch rates including all combinations	AFTERNOON PAPERS NET CIRCULATIOON SEPT 30, 2017 PM Circulation	Inch rates including all combinations	TOTALS Total AM & PM Circulation	Minimum rates for AM & PM coverage	SUNDAY PAPERS NET CIRCULATION SEPT 30, 2017 Number of Papers	Sunday Circulation
More than 500,000	0	0	0		$0.00	0	$0.00	0	$0.00	0	0
250,001 - 500,000	1	0	1	257,656	$503.00	0	$0.00	257,656	$503.00	0	0
100,001 - 250,000	4	0	4	641,371	$890.76	0	$0.00	641,371	$890.76	2	335,290
50,001 - 100,000	14	0	14	1,086,313	$6,554.72	0	$0.00	1,086,313	$6,554.72	6	514,789
25,001 - 50,000	10	0	10	351,846	$201.30	0	$0.00	351,846	$201.30	4	118,762
10,001 - 25,000	16	3	19	269,726	$190.79	33,810	$4.94	303,536	$195.73	3	43,180
10,000 or less	24	23	47	119,456	$345.84	123,351	$65.03	242,807	$410.87	5	8,986
TOTALS	69	26	95	2,726,368	$8,686.41	157,161	$69.97	2,883,529	$8,756.38	20	1,021,007

U.S. AND CANADIAN MULTINEWSPAPER CITIES

Note: This list includes 43 cities in the United States and 8 cities in Canada as of Jan 1, 2016. Newspapers publishing under the 8 joint operating agreements are indicated with a (*). The 2 U.S. cities and 1 Canadian city with newspapers of common ownership are indicated by an (+). The national newspapers are not included.

TUCSON, AZ
Arizona Daily Star (m-mon to fri;m-sat;S)
The Daily Territorial (m-mon to fri)

LOS ANGELES, CA
La Opinion (all day-mon to fri;m-sat;S)
Los Angeles Times (m-mon to fri;m-sat;S)
News-Press (m-wed to fri;m-sat;S)

MONROVIA, CA
San Gabriel Valley Tribune (m-mon to fri;m-sat;S)+
The Whittier Daily News (m-tues to fri;m-sat;S)

SAN FRANCISCO, CA
San Francisco Chronicle (m-mon to fri;m-sat;S)
The Examiner (m-mon to fri;S)

TORRANCE, CA
Daily Breeze (m-mon to fri;m-sat;S)
Pasadena Star-News (m-mon to fri;m-sat;S)

VICTORVILLE, CA
Daily Press (m-mon to fri;m-sat;S)
Desert Dispatch (m-mon to fri;m-sat)

VISALIA, CA
Tulare Advance-Register (m-mon to fri;m-sat)
Visalia Times-Delta (m-mon to fri;m-sat;S)

ASPEN, CO
Aspen Daily News (m-mon to fri;m-sat;S)
The Aspen Times (m-mon to fri;m-sat;S)

BOULDER, CO
Colorado Daily (m-mon to fri)
Daily Camera (m-mon to fri;m-sat;S)*

WASHINGTON, DC
Washington Post Express (m-mon to fri)
The Washington Post (m-mon to fri;m-sat;S)

GAINESVILLE, FL
The Gainesville Sun (m-mon to fri;m-sat;S)
The Independent Florida Alligator (m-mon to fri)

ATLANTA, GA
Atlanta Journal-Constitution (m-mon to fri;m-sat;S)
Fulton County Daily Report (m-mon to fri;m-sat;S)

HONOLULU, HI
Honolulu Star-Advertiser (m-mon to fri;m-sat;S)
USA Today Hawaii Edition (m-mon to fri)

AURORA, IL
Daily Southtown (m-mon to fri;m-S)+
The Courier-News (m-mon to fri;m-S)

CHICAGO, IL
Chicago Sun-Times (m-mon to fri;m-sat;S)
Chicago Tribune (m-mon to fri;m-sat;S)
The Beacon News (m-mon to fri;m-S)
The Herald News (m-mon to fri;m-S)

HARRISBURG, IL
Eldorado Daily Journal (e-mon to fri)
The Daily Register (e-mon to fri)

CRAWFORDSVILLE, IN
Journal Review (m-mon to fri)

The Paper of Montgomery County (all day-mon to fri;m-sat)

BOSTON, MA
Boston Herald (m-mon to fri;m-sat;S)
Metro Boston (m-mon to fri)
The Boston Globe (m-mon to fri;m-sat;S)

BALTIMORE, MD
The Baltimore Sun (m-mon to fri;m-sat;S)
The Daily Record (m-mon to fri)

CLINTON TOWNSHIP, MI
The Daily Tribune (m-wed to fri;m-sat;S)
The Macomb Daily (m-mon to fri;m-sat;S)

DETROIT, MI
Detroit Free Press (m-mon to fri;m-S)
The Detroit News (m-mon to fri;m-sat;m-S)*

NILES, MI
Dowagiac Daily News (m-mon to fri)
Niles Daily Star (m-mon to fri)

COLUMBIA, MO
Columbia Daily Tribune (e-mon to fri;m-sat;S)
Columbia Missourian (m-mon to thur;m-S)

SOMERVILLE, NJ
Courier News (m-mon to fri;m-sat;S)+
Home News Tribune (m-mon to fri;m-sat;S)

TRENTON, NJ
The Times (m-mon to fri;m-sat;S)
The Trentonian (m-mon to fri;m-sat;S)

GALLUP, NM
Messenger (m-mon to fri;m-sat)
Gallup Independent (e-mon to fri;m-sat)

BROOKLYN, NY
El Diario La Prensa (m-mon to fri;m-sat;S)
New York Daily Challenge (m-mon to fri;m-sat;S)

HUDSON, NY
The Daily Mail (m-tues to fri;m-sat)+
Register-Star (m-tues to fri;m-sat;S)

NEW YORK, NY
amNew York (m-mon to fri)
Metro New York (m-mon to fri)
New York Daily News (m-mon to fri;m-sat;S)
New York Post (m-mon to fri;m-sat;S)
The New York Times (m-mon to fri;m-sat;S)
The Wall Street Journal (m-mon to fri;m-sat)

ROCHESTER, NY
The Daily Record (m-mon to fri)
Democrat and Chronicle (m-mon to fri;m-sat;S)

FREMONT, OH
News-Herald (e-mon to fri; m-sat;S)
The News-Messenger (e-mon to fri;m-sat;S)

MANSFIELD, OH
Telegraph-Forum (m-mon to fri; m-sat)+
News Journal (m-mon to fri;m-sat;S)

STEUBENVILLE, OH
Herald-Star (e-mon to fri; m-sat;S)
Weirton Daily times (e-mon to fri;m-sat;S)

XENIA, OH
Fairborn Daily Herald (m-tues to fri;m-sat)
Xenia Daily Gazette (m-tues to fri;m-sat)

MEDFORD, OR
The Ashland Daily Tidings (m-mon to fri;m-sat;S)

Mail Tribune (m-mon to fri;m-sat;S)

LANSDALE, PA
The Reporter (m-mon to fri;m-sat;S)
The Times Herald (m-mon to fri;m-sat;S)

PHILADELPHIA, PA
Metro Philadelphia (m-mon to fri)
Philadelphia Inquirer, Daily News & Philly.com (m-mon to fri;m-sat;S)

WILKES BARRE, PA
The Citizens'Voice (m-mon to fri;m-sat;S)
Times Leader (m-mon to fri;m-sat;S)

YORK, PA
The York Dispatch (e-mon to fri)*
York Daily Record/York Sunday News (m-mon to fri;S)*

BLUFFTON, SC
The Beaufort Gazette (m-mon to fri;m-sat;S)+
The Island Packet (m-mon to fri;m-sat;S)

MEMPHIS, TN
The Daily News (m-mon to fri)
The Commercial Appeal (m-mon to fri;m-sat;S)

SALT LAKE CITY, UT
Deseret News (m-mon to fri;m-sat;S)
The Salt Lake Tribune (m-mon to fri;S)

SEATTLE, WA
Seattle Daily Journal of Commerce (m-mon to fri;m-sat)
The Seattle Times (m-mon to fri;m-sat;S)

CANADA

CALGARY, AB
Calgary Herald (m-mon to fri;m-sat)
Metro Calgary (m-mon to fri;m-sat;S)
The Calgary Sun (m-mon to fri;m-sat;S)

EDMONTON, AB
Edmonton Journal (m-mon to fri;m-sat)
The Edmonton Sun (m-mon to fri;m-sat;S)

VANCOUVER, BC
The Province (m-mon to fri;S)+
The Vancouver Sun (m-mon to fri;m-sat)*

WINNIPEG, MB
The Winnipeg Sun (m-mon to fri;m-sat;S)
Winnipeg Free Press (m-mon to fri;m-sat)

OTTAWA, ON
Le Droit (m-mon to fri;m-sat)
The Ottawa Citizen (m-mon to fri;m-sat)
The Ottawa Sun (m-mon to fri;m-sat;S)

TORONTO, ON
National Post (m-mon to fri;m-sat)
The Epoch Times (m-mon to fri;m-sat;S)
The Globe and Mail (m-mon to fri;m-sat;S)
The Toronto Sun (m-mon to fri;m-sat;S)
Toronto Star (m-mon to fri;m-sat;S)

MONTREAL, QC
La Presse (m-mon to fri;m-sat)
Le Devoir (m-mon to fri;m-sat)
Le Journal de Montreal (m-mon to fri;m-sat;S)
Montreal Gazette (m-mon to fri;m-sat)

SHERBROOKE, QC
La Tribune (m-mon to fri;m-sat)
The Record (m-mon to fri)

TOP 100 DAILY NEWSPAPERS IN THE U.S.

Mc Lean (VA) USA TODAY (m-mon to fri) 2081202
New York (NY) The Wall Street Journal (m-mon to fri) 1111167
New York (NY) The New York Times (m-mon to fri) 513776
Los Angeles (CA) Los Angeles Times (All day-mon to fri) 452793
New York (NY) New York Post (m-mon to fri) 425365
Chicago (IL) Chicago Tribune (m-mon to fri) 419864
Washington (DC) The Washington Post (m-mon to fri) 349586
Melville (NY) Newsday (m-mon to fri) 309047
Denver (CO) The Denver Post (m-mon to fri) 285027
Minneapolis (MN) Star Tribune (m-mon to fri) 278013
New York (NY) New York Daily News (m-mon to fri) 271163
Houston (TX) Houston Chronicle (m-mon to fri) 225120
Boston (MA) The Boston Globe (m-mon to fri) 224286
Dallas (TX) The Dallas Morning News (m-mon to fri) 223553
St Petersburg (FL) Tampa Bay Times (m-mon to fri) 219920
Philadelphia (PA) Philadelphia Inquirer,
Daily News & Philly.com (m-mon to fri) 203986
Seattle (WA) The Seattle Times (m-mon to fri) 185749
New York (NY) amNew York (m-mon to fri) 184583
Phoenix (AZ) The Arizona Republic (m-mon to fri) 183849
Brooklyn (OH) The Plain Dealer (m-mon to fri) 179224
San Francisco (CA) San Francisco Chronicle (m-mon to fri) 170471
Saint Paul (MN) St. Paul Pioneer Press (m-mon to fri) 165768
Newark (NJ) The Star-Ledger (m-mon to fri) 161963
Detroit (MI) Detroit Free Press (m-mon to fri) 156321
Clinton (PA) Pittsburgh Post-Gazette (m-mon to fri) 153738
San Diego (CA) The San Diego Union-Tribune (m-mon to fri) 153132
Milwaukee (WI) Milwaukee Journal Sentinel (m-mon to fri) 152944
Honolulu (HI) Honolulu Star-Advertiser (m-mon to fri) 151585
Washington (DC) Washington Post Express (m-mon to fri) 150634
Kansas City (MO) The Kansas City Star (m-mon to fri) 143237
Portland (OR) The Oregonian (All day-mon to fri) 143220
San Jose (CA) The Mercury News (m-mon to fri) 141005
Sacramento (CA) The Sacramento Bee (m-mon to fri) 140167
Atlanta (GA) Atlanta Journal-Constitution (m-mon to fri) 139864
Rockaway (NJ) Herald News (m-mon to fri) 138904
Saint Louis (MO) St. Louis Post-Dispatch (m-mon to fri) 135705
Chicago (IL) Chicago Sun-Times (m-mon to fri) 134874
Henderson (NV) Las Vegas Sun (m-mon to fri) 127648
Woodland Park (NJ) The Record (m-mon to fri) 125038
Little Rock (AR) Arkansas Democrat-Gazette (m-mon to fri) 124041
Orlando (FL) Orlando Sentinel (m-mon to fri) 121799
Buffalo (NY) The Buffalo News (All day-mon to fri) 119226
Santa Ana (CA) The Orange County Register (m-mon to fri) 116250
Columbia (MO) Columbia Daily Tribune (e-mon to fri) 114672
Walnut Creek (CA) East Bay Times (m-mon to fri) 113068
Indianapolis (IN) The Indianapolis Star (m-mon to fri) 109121
Greensburg (PA) Tribune-Review (m-mon to fri) 108810
Louisville (KY) The Courier-Journal (m-mon to fri) 108363
Hartford (CT) The Hartford Courant (m-mon to fri) 107410
Norfolk (VA) The Virginian-Pilot (m-mon to fri) 106913

Las Vegas (NV) Las Vegas Review-Journal (m-mon to fri) 106702
Baltimore (MD) The Baltimore Sun (m-mon to fri) 106443
Columbus (OH) The Columbus Dispatch (m-mon to fri) 105055
Oklahoma City (OK) The Oklahoman (m-mon to fri) 102742
Fort Worth (TX) Fort Worth Star-Telegram (m-mon to fri) 101680
Omaha (NE) Omaha World-Herald (m-mon to fri) 101287
Raleigh (NC) The News & Observer (m-mon to fri) 100395
Cincinnati (OH) The Cincinnati Enquirer (m-mon to fri) 98890
Charlotte (NC) The Charlotte Observer (m-mon to fri) 97755
Fort Lauderdale (FL) South Florida Sun-Sentinel (m-mon to fri) 97653
Austin (TX) Austin American-Statesman (m-mon to fri) 97205
Doral (FL) Miami Herald (m-mon to fri) 95416
Richmond (VA) Richmond Times-Dispatch (m-mon to fri) 86824
Boston (MA) Boston Herald (m-mon to fri) 86567
Bozeman (MT) Bozeman Daily Chronicle (m-tues to fri) 86567
San Antonio (TX) San Antonio Express-News (m-mon to fri) 86366
Albuquerque (NM) Albuquerque Journal (m-mon to fri) 83795
Detroit (MI) The Detroit News (m-mon to fri) 80145
Baton Rouge (LA) The Advocate (m-mon to fri) 79123
Salt Lake City (UT) The Salt Lake Tribune (m-mon to fri) 78417
Des Moines (IA) The Des Moines Register (m-mon to fri) 74573
West Palm Beach (FL) The Palm Beach Post (m-mon to fri) 73037
Arlington Heights (IL) Daily Herald (m-mon to fri) 72106
Riverside (CA) The Press-Enterprise (m-mon to fri) 71870
Fresno (CA) The Fresno Bee (m-mon to fri) 71831
Rochester (NY) Democrat and Chronicle (m-mon to fri) 71630
Spokane (WA) The Spokesman-Review (m-mon to fri) 71127
Nashville (TN) The Tennessean (m-mon to fri) 70760
Grand Rapids (MI) The Grand Rapids Press (e-mon to fri) 70120
Syracuse (NY) The Post-Standard (m-mon to fri) 69951
Toledo (OH) The Blade (m-mon to fri) 69118
Grand Island (NE) The Grand Island Independent (m-mon to fri) 69003
Washington (DC) The Washington Times (All day-mon to fri) 67148
Allentown (PA) The Morning Call (m-mon to fri) 66288
Franklin (OH) Dayton Daily News (m-mon to fri) 65835
New Castle (DE) The News Journal (m-mon to fri) 64711
Providence (RI) The Providence Journal (m-mon to fri) 64432
Akron (OH) Akron Beacon Journal (m-mon to fri) 62974
Madison (WI) Wisconsin State Journal, Madison (m-mon to fri) 62868
Chattanooga (TN) Chattanooga Times Free Press (m-mon to fri) 62403
Knoxville (TN) Knoxville News Sentinel (m-mon to fri) 62002
Tucson (AZ) Arizona Daily Star (m-mon to fri) 59343
Memphis (TN) The Commercial Appeal (m-mon to fri) 59325
Neptune (NJ) Asbury Park Press (m-mon to fri) 59174
Boston (MA) Metro Boston (m-mon to fri) 57804
Fort Wayne (IN) The News-Sentinel (e-mon to fri) 57281
Brooklyn (NY) New York Daily Challenge (m-mon to fri) 56544
Lexington (KY) Lexington Herald-Leader (m-mon to fri) 56426
Tulsa (OK) Tulsa World (m-mon to fri) 56381
Sarasota (FL) Sarasota Herald-Tribune (m-mon to fri) 55109

TOP 10 DAILY NEWSPAPERS IN CANADA

Montreal (QC) La Presse (m-mon to fri) 257656
Toronto (ON) The Globe and Mail (m-mon to fri) 213520
Montreal (QC) Le Journal de Montreal (m-mon to fri) 171560
Toronto (ON) Toronto Star (m-mon to fri) 132896
Vancouver (BC) The Vancouver Sun (m-mon to fri) 123395

Vancouver (BC) The Province (m-mon to fri) 99515
Halifax (NS) The Chronicle Herald (m-mon to fri) 88893
Ottawa (ON) The Ottawa Citizen (m-mon to fri) 88577
Toronto (ON) The Toronto Sun (m-mon to fri) 86462
Calgary (AB) Calgary Herald (m-mon to fri) 82670

TOP 100 SUNDAY NEWSPAPERS IN THE U.S.

New York (NY) The Wall Street Journal	1145230
Mc Lean (VA) USA TODAY	1113840
New York (NY) The New York Times	1075837
Los Angeles (CA) Los Angeles Times	792673
Chicago (IL) Chicago Tribune	720669
Washington (DC) The Washington Post	522055
Minneapolis (MN) Star Tribune	452362
New York (NY) New York Post	399569
Denver (CO) The Denver Post	395910
St Petersburg (FL) Tampa Bay Times	370983
Philadelphia (PA) Philadelphia Inquirer, Daily News & Philly.com	363700
Melville (NY) Newsday	345925
Houston (TX) Houston Chronicle	345214
New York (NY) New York Daily News	336367
Boston (MA) The Boston Globe	323524
Dallas (TX) The Dallas Morning News	303045
Phoenix (AZ) The Arizona Republic	296039
Seattle (WA) The Seattle Times	284633
Detroit (MI) Detroit Free Press	273141
Atlanta (GA) Atlanta Journal-Constitution	269437
Brooklyn (OH) The Plain Dealer	248273
Newark (NJ) The Star-Ledger	244884
Saint Paul (MN) St. Paul Pioneer Press	244742
Milwaukee (WI) Milwaukee Journal Sentinel	238247
San Francisco (CA) San Francisco Chronicle	237204
San Diego (CA) The San Diego Union-Tribune	233718
Baltimore (MD) The Baltimore Sun	230588
Clinton (PA) Pittsburgh Post-Gazette	230164
Kansas City (MO) The Kansas City Star	225460
Santa Ana (CA) The Orange County Register	207947
Greensburg (PA) Tribune-Review	200592
Saint Louis (MO) St. Louis Post-Dispatch	197933
Sacramento (CA) The Sacramento Bee	195495
San Jose (CA) The Mercury News	190850
Orlando (FL) Orlando Sentinel	187646
Columbus (OH) The Columbus Dispatch	183341
Buffalo (NY) The Buffalo News	180776
Fort Lauderdale (FL) South Florida Sun-Sentinel	180220
Fort Worth (TX) Fort Worth Star-Telegram	175585
Portland (OR) The Oregonian	173736
Hartford (CT) The Hartford Courant	171592
Indianapolis (IN) The Indianapolis Star	170943
Little Rock (AR) Arkansas Democrat-Gazette	166945
Honolulu (HI) Honolulu Star-Advertiser	165538
Woodland Park (NJ) The Record	158818
Louisville (KY) The Courier-Journal	151598
Cincinnati (OH) The Cincinnati Enquirer	150603
San Antonio (TX) San Antonio Express-News	149636
Rockaway (NJ) Herald News	146759
Chicago (IL) Chicago Sun-Times	141549
Raleigh (NC) The News & Observer	139034
Norfolk (VA) The Virginian-Pilot	139013
Henderson (NV) Las Vegas Sun	138209
Charlotte (NC) The Charlotte Observer	137639
Walnut Creek (CA) East Bay Times	135131
Riverside (CA) The Press-Enterprise	133042
Doral (FL) Miami Herald	129096
Las Vegas (NV) Las Vegas Review-Journal	128403
Oklahoma City (OK) The Oklahoman	127247
Omaha (NE) Omaha World-Herald	123805
Austin (TX) Austin American-Statesman	120408
Des Moines (IA) The Des Moines Register	119129
Allentown (PA) The Morning Call	115938
Nashville (TN) The Tennessean	115459
Salt Lake City (UT) Deseret News	113840
Syracuse (NY) The Post-Standard	113704
Grand Rapids (MI) The Grand Rapids Press	111963
Richmond (VA) Richmond Times-Dispatch	111642
Albuquerque (NM) Albuquerque Journal	106803
Rochester (NY) Democrat and Chronicle	103112
Toledo (OH) The Blade	102637
Franklin (OH) Dayton Daily News	99859
West Palm Beach (FL) The Palm Beach Post	97198
Memphis (TN) The Commercial Appeal	95738
Neptune (NJ) Asbury Park Press	91925
Salt Lake City (UT) The Salt Lake Tribune	91879
Albany (NY) Times Union	91814
Grand Island (NE) The Grand Island Independent	91321
Baton Rouge (LA) The Advocate	90118
Fresno (CA) The Fresno Bee	89205
Providence (RI) The Providence Journal	84239
Tucson (AZ) Arizona Daily Star	82978
Madison (WI) Wisconsin State Journal, Madison	81273
Newport News (VA) Daily Press	80965
Fort Wayne (IN) The News-Sentinel	80879
Akron (OH) Akron Beacon Journal	80634
Knoxville (TN) Knoxville News Sentinel	78962
Arlington Heights (IL) Daily Herald	78786
New Castle (DE) The News Journal	78607
Jacksonville (FL) The Florida Times-Union	78045
Lexington (KY) Lexington Herald-Leader	76877
Boston (MA) Boston Herald	76798
Bozeman (MT) Bozeman Daily Chronicle	76798
Spokane (WA) The Spokesman-Review	76654
Tulsa (OK) Tulsa World	75040
Tacoma (WA) The News Tribune	74653
Springfield (MA) The Republican	74226
Sarasota (FL) Sarasota Herald-Tribune	69974
Lancaster (PA) LNP	68057
Port Saint Lucie (FL) St. Lucie News Tribune	66322

TOP 10 SUNDAY NEWSPAPERS IN CANADA

Montreal (QC) La Presse	263959
Montreal (QC) Le Journal de Montreal	176638
Toronto (ON) Toronto Star	158652
Vancouver (BC) The Province	112608
Halifax (NS) The Chronicle Herald	97283
Toronto (ON) The Toronto Sun	95172
Vanier (QC) Le Journal de Quebec	80947
Quebec (QC) Le Soleil	72202
Victoria (BC) Victoria Times Colonist	56577
Calgary (AB) The Calgary Sun	35700

MECHANICAL EQUIPMENT — ABBREVIATIONS

COMPOSITION

TYPESETTERS

AG — Agfa-Gevaert
AU — Autologic
AX — Automix
Bg — Bobst Graphic
COM — Compugraphic
Dy — Dymo
F — Fairchild
Fi — Filmotype
Fo — Fotosetter
Fr — Friden
HCM — Hell/HCM
Hd — Headliner
HI — Harris
Ik — Itek
Jus — Justowriter
L — Lanston
LC — Linofilm Composer
M — Mergenthaler
Ma — Morisawa
MGD — MGD-Rockwell
MON — Monotype
Ph — Photon
Pr — Protype
Pt — Photo Typositor
So — Simmons-Owega
SP — Star Parts
Sr — Singer
ST — Stripprinter
TC — Titus Communications
V — Varityper
Va — Varisystems
VG — Visual Graphics

FRONT-END HARDWARE & SOFTWARE

ACT — Automated Complete Typesetting
AG — Agfa-Gevaert
AP — Associated Press
APP — Apple
AT — Atex
AU — Autologic
AX — Automix
BD — Berthold NA
Bee — Beehive
BF — Basic 4
Bg — Bobst Graphic
BR — Bunker Ramo
Bs — Burroughs
C — Chemco
CD — Crosfield Data Systems
CDS — Computer Double Screen
CJ — Collier-Jackson
CM — Cincinnati Milacron
COM — Compugraphic
CPU — Computext
Cp — CompuScan
CS — Computer Services
CSI — Computer Systems Inc.
Cx — Camex
Da — Datapoint
DD — Delta Data
DEC — Digital Equipment Corp.
DL — Data Logic
DS — Data Disc
DTI — Digital Technology International
Dy — Dymo
ECR — ECRM
EKI — Electric Knowledge Inc.
En — Entrex
ES — Evans & Southerland
ESE — Editorial System Engineering Co.
FSI — Freedom Systems Integrators
Gn — Genisis
HAS — Hastech
Hel — Hell
HI — Harris
HP — Hewlett Packard
Hw — Honeywell
Hx — Hendrix
Hz — Hazeltine
IBM — International Business Machines

III — Information International Inc.
Ik — Itek
In — Infotron
INS — Independent Network Services
ISSI — Integrated Software Systems Inc.
KC — Key Corp.
Kk — Kodak
Lf — Leaf Systems
LIP — Logicon-Intercomp
Lk — Lektromedia
LNS — Lee Newspapers Services
LS — Lear-Siegler
M — Mergenthaler
Mac — Macintosh
MD — Micro Data
MeD — Mega Data
MGD — MGD-Rockwell
Mh — Mohr
Mk — Mycro-Tek
MON — Monotype
MPS — Morris Publishing Systems
Mx — Memorex
NEC — Newspaper Electronics Corp.
NW — Neasi-Weber
Omn — Omnitext
Omo — Omron
On — Ontel
Op — Omptimix
OS — One Systems
PBS — Publishing Business Systems
PEP — Perception Electronic

PUBLISHING

PS — Peripheral Systems
QPS — Quark Publishing Systems
Ra — Raytheon
RSK — Radio Shack
RZ — Royal Zenith
SCS — Software Consulting Services
SII — System Integrators Inc.
SMS — Stauffer Media Systems
Syc — Sycor
SyD — Systems Development
TC — Titus Communications
Te — Telcom
TI — Texas Instruments
TM — Teleram
Tr — Teleray
TRW — TRW-Fujitsu
TS — Tal-Star
Tt — Teleterm
Tx — Telex
Uni — Univac
V — Varityper
Va — Varisystems
X — Xerox
XIT — Xitron
ZC — Zentec Corp.

AUDIOTEX

DJ — Dow Jones
TEDS — Toronto Star Edition Design System
TMS — Tribune Media Services
VNN — Voice News Network

OCR READERS

APP — Apple
COM — Compugraphic
Cp — CompuScan
Da — Datatype
Di — Digitek
ECR — ECRM
Hx — Hendrix
M — Mergenthaler
MGD — MGD-Rockwell

PLATE-MAKING

PLATE SYSTEMS

AU — Autologic
B — Brown
CD — Crosfield Data Systems
DiL — DiLitho
DP — DuPont
Dyn — Dynaflex
ECM — EOCOM
F — Fairchild
He — Hercules (Merigraph)
LE — LogEtronics
LP — Laser-Plate
LX — Grace (Letterflex)
Mag — Magnesium
Na — Napp
Nat — National
Rf — Richflex
WL — Western Litho
Z — Zinc

PLATE PROCESSORS

B — Brown
Be — Beach
BM — Ball Metal
CEM — Chemcut
Dow — Dow Chemical
DP — DuPont
Dyn — Dynaflex
He — Hercules (Merigraph)
Ic — Iconics
LG — Laser Graphics
LX — Grace (Letterflex)
MAS — Master
Na — Napp
Nat — National
Nu — nuArc
Ny — Nyloprint
Tas — TasopeSearch
Wd — Wood
WL — Western Litho

CAMERAS

AG — Agfa-Gevaert
B — Brown
Bo — Borrowdale
Br — Bruning
C — Chemco
CL — Clydedale
Co — Consolidated
COM — Compugraphic
DAI — Dainippon
DSA — D.S. America (SCREEN)
ECR — ECRM
Go — Goodkin
Ik — Itek
K — Kenro
Kk — Kodak
Kl — Klimsch
L — Lanston
LE — LogEtronics
MG — ModiGraphic
Nu — nuArc
R — Robertson
Sm — Statmaster
VG — Visual Graphics
W — Western

AUTOMATIC FILM PROCESSORS

AG — Agfa-Gevaert
AU — Autologic
C — Chemo
DP — DuPont
Kk — Kodak
Kr — Kreonite
LE — LogEtronics
P — Pako
WL — Western Litho

COLOR SEPARATION SYSTEMS

AG — Agfa-Gevaert
BKY — Berkey
C — Chemco
Ca — Carlson
Eh — Ehrenreich
Hel — Hell
KFM — K&F Printing Systems International

Kk — Kodak
Lf — Leaf Systems
RZ — Royal Zenith
WDS — Warner MDS

PRESSROOM

DILITHO SYSTEMS

DI — Dahlgren
G — Goss
HI — Harris
In — Inland
RPM — Smith RPM Co.
Ry — Ryco Graphic
T — Taft
Wd — Wood

PRESSES

Bk — Babcock
Cb — Crabtree
FAU — Faustel
Fin — Fincor
FOL — Flex-O-Line
G — Goss
GE — General Electric
H — Hoe
Ha — Hantscho
HAR — Hoe-Aller
HI — Heidelberg-Harris
KB — Koenig & Bauer
KP — King Press
MAN — MAN/Roland USA
MHI — Mitsubishi Heavy Ind.
MOT — Motter
SC — Scott
SLN — Solna
TKS — Tokyo Kikai Seisakusho
Tp — Thatcher-Pacer
Wd — Wood
WPC — Web Press Corp.

PRESS CONVERSION SYSTEMS

KDS — Kidder Stacy
KFM — K&F Printing Systems International
PEC — Publishers Equip. Corp.
PMC — Press Machinery Corp.
RKW — Rockwell
RPM — Smith RPM Co.

REPROPORTIONING SYSTEMS

CS — Combined Services
FLS — Flurographic Services

MAILROOM

STACKERS

BG — Baldwin-Gegenheimer
CH — Cutler-Hammer
DG — Didde Glaser
Fg — Ferag
HI — Heidelberg-Harris
HL — Hall
Id — IDAB
KAN — Kansa
MM — Muller-Martini
MRS — Mailroom Systems
NJP — Nolan Jampol
PPK — Pace Pack
QWI — Quipp
RKW — Rockwell
SH — Sta-Hi
St — Stepper

INSERTERS/STUFFERS

D — Dexter
DG — Didde Glaser
Fg — Ferag
G — Goss
Gr — Graphicart
HI — Harris
I — Insertomatic
KAN — Kansa
KR — Kirk-Rudy
LEG — Leger Inc.

M — Mergenthaler
Mc — McCain
Mg — Magnacratt
MM — Muller-Martini
S — Sheridan
SH — Sta-Hi
St — Stepper

BUNDLE TYERS

AMP — Ampag
Bu — Bunn
Ca — Carlson
Cn — Cranston
Cr — Crawford
CYP — Cypack
Eb — Ebby
Gd — Gerrard
Gs — General Strapping
HL — Hall
Id — IDAB
In — Inland
It — Interlake
J — Jampol
Mc — McCain
Md — MidStates
MLN — Signode
MM — Muller-Martini
MVP — Metaveppa
NJP — Nolan Jampol
OVL — Ovalstrapping
PM — Paper Man
QWI — Quipp
S — Sheridan
Sa — Saxmayer
SHt — SatoHit
Si — Parker-Signode
St — Stepper
Ty — Tyler
Us — USSteel
Ws — Walla Star
WT — Wire-Tyer

ADDRESSERS

Am — Addressograph-Multigraph
AVY — Avery
BH — Bell & Howell
Ch — Cheshire
Dm — Dick Mailer
El — Elliott
Gd — Gerrard
GL — Galley List
Gp — Graphotype
Hw — Honeywell
IBM — International Business Machines
KAN — Kansa
KR — Kirk-Rudy
Mg — Magnacraft
Pa — Pollard-Alling
PB — Pitney-Bowes
Rp — Roto-Strip Printer
RSK — Radio Shack
SC — Scriptomatic
Sp — Speedomat
SRC — Standard Register Co.
St — Stepper
Wm — Wing Mailer

DELIVERY SYSTEMS

CBM — Custom Built Machinery
EDS — EDS-IDAB
Fg — Ferag
FMC — FMC Corp.
KAN — Kansa
RKW — Rockwell
SIH — SI Handling

LIBRARY SYSTEMS

AT — Atex
ATT — AT&T
BH — Bell & Howell
CCC — Capital Cities Communications
DDC — Documaster
DEC — Digital Equipment
GE — General Electric
IBM — International Business Machines

IFK — Info-Ky
IXA — Infotex Assoc.
LIP — Logicon-Intercomp
MED — Mead
QLS — QL Systems
SII — System Integrators Inc.
SMS — Stauffer Media Systems

COMMUNICATIONS

FACSIMILE EQUIPMENT

ABD — AB Dick
Ao — Apeco
AP — Associated Press
ATT — AT&T
CD — Crosfield Digital Systems
CP — Canadian Press
DF — Data Fax
Dm — Daycom
ECM — EOCOM
Hel — Hell
Ho — Hogan
IBM — International Business Machines
III — Information International Inc.
LI — Litcom
Mag — Magnavox
Mh — Muirhead
Px — Pressfax
Q — Quickfax
QWI — Quipp
Rem — Remington
SN — Scanatron
SW — Stewart Warner
Uf — Unifax
UPI — United Press International
VI — Vistatype
Wr — Warwick
Wx — Westrex
X — Xerox

DATA COMMUNICATIONS

AMS — American Satellite
DTG — Datalog
EPT — Epic Technology
GAN — Gandalf Data
Mot — Motorola
XIT — Xitron

BUSINESS COMPUTERS

ALR — Advanced Logic Research
APP — Apple
AT — Atex
ATT — AT&T
Bs — Burroughs
CJ — Collier-Jackson
DEC — Digital Equipment Corp.
DG — Data General
EKI — Electric Knowledge Inc.
HP — Hewlett Packard
Hw — Honeywell
IBM — International Business Machines
Mac — Macintosh
Mk — Mycro-Tek
NEC — Newspaper Electronics Corp.
PBS — Publishing Business Systems
RSK — Radio Shack
TI — Texas Instruments
Uni — Univac
Wa — Wang

The table of abbreviations is for major equipment manufacturers listed in section I & III. Companies not found in the above list are entered in full.

DAILY NEWSPAPERS SOLD IN 2017

Dirks, Van Essen & Murray

Newspaper Mergers, Acquisitions, Appraisals & Consulting

Newspaper	Daily Circ.	Buyer	Seller
Albemarle(NC)StanlyNews&Press*	5,000	Boone Newspapers	CNHI
Alton (IL) Telegraph*	10,600	Hearst Newspapers	Civitas Media
Altus (OK) Times*	1,300	Graystone Media Group	Civitas Media
Anchorage (AK) Alaska Dispatch News	23,300	Binkley family	Alice Rogoff
Aspen (CO) Daily News*	12,500	Paperbag Media	David Danforth
Beaver County (PA) Times	18,000	New Media Investment Group	Calkins Media
Big Rapids (MI) Pioneer	4,800	Hearst Newspapers	Batdorff family
Bucks County (PA) Courier-Times	23,000	New Media Investment Group	Calkins Media
Burlington County (NJ) Times	18,000	New Media Investment Group	Calkins Media
Chicago (IL) Sun-Times	106,300	ST Acquisition Holdings	Wrapports LLC
Clinton (NC) Sampson Independent*	2,300	Champion Media	Civitas Media
Delaware (OH) Gazette*	2,700	AIM Media Midwest	Civitas Media
Dix Communications (5 dailies)	69,600	New Media Investment Group	Dix family
Doylestown (PA) Intelligencer	19,000	New Media Investment Group	Calkins Media
Durant (OK) Daily Democrat*	2,000	Graystone Media Group	Civitas Media
Eau Claire (WI) Leader-Telegram	17,600	Adams Publishing	Graaskamp/Atkinson families
Fairborn (OH) Daily Herald*	1,000	AIM Media Midwest	Civitas Media
Frederick (MD) News-Post	21,100	Ogden Newspapers	Randall family
Gallipolis (OH) Daily Tribune*	1,900	AIM Media Midwest	Civitas Media
Greenville (OH) Daily Advocate*	2,800	AIM Media Midwest	Civitas Media
Hillsboro (OH) Times-Gazette*	2,000	AIM Media Midwest	Civitas Media
Jacksonville (IL) Journal-Courier*	6,600	Hearst Newspapers	Civitas Media
Lanett (AL) Valley Times-News*	5,500	Boone Newspapers	Walls family
Laurinburg (NC) Exchange*	1,900	Champion Media	Civitas Media
Lewiston (ME) Sun Journal	16,100	Reade Brower	Costello family
Lima (OH) News*	19,900	AIM Media Midwest	Civitas Media
Logan (WV) Banner*	1,700	HD Media	Civitas Media
London (OH) Madison Press*	1,500	AIM Media Midwest	Civitas Media
Lumberton (NC) Robesonian*	4,500	Champion Media	Civitas Media
Manistee (MI) News Advocate	4,500	Hearst Newspapers	Batdorff family
Medford (OR) Mail Tribune	15,500	Rosebud Media	New Media Investment Group
Middlesboro (KY) Daily News*	2,100	Boone Newspapers	Civitas Media

DAILY NEWSPAPERS SOLD IN 2017, continued

Dirks, Van Essen & Murray
Newspaper Mergers, Acquisitions, Appraisals & Consulting

Newspaper	Daily Circ.	Buyer	Seller
Middletown (CT) Press*	2,000	Hearst Newspapers	Digital First Media
Moline (IL) Dispatch-Argus*	27,700	Lee Enterprises	Small family
Monroe (WI) Times	3,100	Morris Multimedia	Bliss Communications
Morris Publishing Group (11 dailies)	196,900	New Media Investment Group	Morris Communications
Mount Airy (NC) News*	4,900	Champion Media	Civitas Media
Mount Airy (NC) News	4,900	Adams Publishing	Champion Media
New Haven (CT) Register*	22,100	Hearst Newspapers	Digital First Media
New York (NY) Daily News	184,300	Tronc	Mort Zuckerman
Newport (RI) Daily News*	8,200	New Media Investment Group	Sherman family
Palmdale(CA)AntelopeValleyPress*	9,700	Antelope Valley Press Inc.	Markham family
Pioneer News Group (7 dailies)	78,700	Adams Publishing	Wood/Scripps family
Piqua (OH) Daily Call*	2,700	AIM Media Midwest	Civitas Media
Point Pleasant (WV) Register*	1,600	AIM Media Midwest	Civitas Media
Pomeroy (OH) Daily Sentinel*	1,400	AIM Media Midwest	Civitas Media
Portsmouth (OH) Daily Times*	4,400	AIM Media Midwest	Civitas Media
Rockingham (NC) Daily Journal*	3,100	Champion Media	Civitas Media
Sedalia (MO) Democrat*	5,400	Phillips Media	Civitas Media
Sidney (OH) Daily News*	6,100	AIM Media Midwest	Civitas Media
Sulphur Springs (TX) News-Telegram	4,800	Southern Newspapers	Frailey family
Torrington (CT) Register Citizen*	2,000	Hearst Newspapers	Digital First Media
Troy (OH) Daily News*	3,500	AIM Media Midwest	Civitas Media
Uniontown (PA) Herald-Standard	14,800	Ogden Newspapers	Calkins Media
Urbana (OH) Daily Citizen*	2,800	AIM Media Midwest	Civitas Media
Washington Courthouse (OH) Record-Herald*	2,400	AIM Media Midwest	Civitas Media
Williamson (WV) Daily News*	1,500	HD Media	Civitas Media
Willimantic (CT) Chronicle*	5,100	Central CT Communications	Crosbie family
Wilmington (OH) News-Journal*	2,900	AIM Media Midwest	Civitas Media
Xenia (OH) Daily Gazette*	2,200	AIM Media Midwest	Civitas Media

*Transactions in which DV&M acted as an advisor or representative
Research provided by Dirks, Van Essen & Murray, 1-10-18

Section I

Daily Newspapers Published in the United States and Canada

United States

Canada

DAILY NEWSPAPERS PUBLISHED IN THE UNITED STATES

ALABAMA

ALEXANDER CITY

ALEXANDER CITY OUTLOOK
548 Cherokee Road, Alexander City, Ala., 35010-2503, Tallapoosa; gen tel (256) 234-4281; adv tel (256) 234-4281 ext.15; ed tel (256) 234-4281 ext.23; gen fax (256) 234-6550; adv fax (256) 234-6550; ed fax (256) 234-6550; gen/nat adv e-mail kenneth. boone@alexcityoutlook.com; disp adv e-mail tippy.hunter@alexcityoutlook.com; class adv e-maillinda.ewing@alexcityoutlook.com; ed e-mail austin.nelson@alexcityoutlook.com ; editorgroup@alexcityoutlook.com; web site www.alexcityoutlook.com
Group: Boone Newspapers, Inc.
Published: Tues, Wed, Thur, Fri, Sat
Weekday Frequency: m
Saturday Frequency: m
Circulation: 5,300; 5,300(sat)
Last Audit: Sworn/Estimate/Non-Audited September 30, 2017
Advertising Rate (weekday/saturday): Open inch rate $13.90
News services: Landon Media Group.
Established: 1892
Own Printing Facility?: Yes
Commercial Printers?: Yes
Special Editions: Bridal (Apr); Back-to-School (Aug); Christmas Greetings (Dec); Parade (Feb); Home Town Business (Jan); FYI (Jul); Spring Fashion (Mar); Graduation (May); Gift Guide (Nov); Fall Fashion (Sept).
Special Weekly Sections: Lake Martin Fish Wrapper (Fri); Education (Thur); Automotive (Wed).
Syndicated Publications: Parade (S); American Profile (Weekly).
Pub..................................Kenneth Boone
Circ.Mgr............................David Kendrick
Managing Ed ....Mitch Sneed
Dir of Advert ....Tippy Hunter
Magazine Manag. Ed..................Betsy Iler
Asst. Mag. Ed ....Mia Osborn
Prodn. Mgr. ....Lee Champion
Market. Consultant....................Kim Morse
National Accts. ....Doug Patterson
Sports Ed. ....Robert Hudson
Sports Ed. ....Cathy Higgins
Market Information: TMC.
Mechanical Available: Offset; Black and 3 ROP colors; insert accepted; page cutoffs - 22 3/4.
Mechanical Specifications: Type page 13 x 21 1/2; E - 6 cols, 2 1/16, 1/8 between; A - 6 cols, 2 1/16, 1/8 between; C - 9 cols, 2 1/16, 1/8 between.
Delivery Method: Mail, Newsstand, Carrier, RacksEquipment & Software: PRESSROOM EQUIPMENT: Lines — 5-KP/News King.; MAILROOM EQUIPMENT: Counter Stackers — BG/Count-O-Veyor 104A; Tying Machines — 1/Ca.; CLASSIFIED EQUIPMENT: Hardware — 2-APP/Mac.; EDITORIAL EQUIPMENT: Hardware — 7-APP/ Mac/3-APP/Mac, 2-APP/Mac LaserWriter. PRODUCTION EQUIPMENT: Hardware — Nu; Cameras — CL.

ANDALUSIA

ANDALUSIA STAR-NEWS
207 Dunson St, Andalusia, Ala., 36420-3705, Covington; gen tel (334) 222-2402; ed tel (334) 222-2402; gen fax (334) 222-6597; ed fax (334) 222-6597; gen/nat adv e-mail ruck. ashworth@andalusiastarnews.com; disp adv e-mail ruck.ashworth@andalusiastarnews. com; class adv e-mailruck.ashworth@ andalusiastarnews.com; ed e-mail michele. gerlach@andalusiastarnews.com; web site www.andalusiastarnews.com - 498,200(views) 3,570(visitors)
Group: Boone Newspapers, Inc.
Published: Tues, Wed, Thur, Fri, Sat
Weekday Frequency: m
Saturday Frequency: m
Circulation: 3,395; 3,600(sat)
Last Audit: Sworn/Estimate/Non-Audited September 30, 2017
Advertising Rate (weekday/saturday): Open inch rate $9.80
News services: NEA. **Established:** 1939
Special Editions: Baseball (Apr); Football (Aug); Progress (Feb); Chamber Guide (Jan); Pride In America (Jun); Home Improvement (Mar); Graduation (May).
Special Weekly Sections: Health Page (Fri); Business/Financial Page (Tues); Education (Tues); Education (Wed.).
Syndicated Publications: American Profile (Weekly).
Pub./Ed .... Michele Gerlach
Adv. Mgr.................................. Ruck Ashworth
Prodn. Mgr. ....Chris Love
Office Mgr ....Lisa Rainey
Principal Designer/Magazine Ed ... Kendra Majors
Sports Ed. ....Josh Dutton
Market Information: ADS; TMC.
Mechanical Available: Offset; Black and 3 ROP colors; insert accepted - by request; page cutoffs - 22 7/8.
Mechanical Specifications: Type page 10 x 21

1/2; E - 6 cols
Delivery Method: Mail, Newsstand, Carrier, RacksEquipment & Software: PRESSROOM EQUIPMENT: Lines — 10-KP/News King single width 1994; Folders — KP/KJ 6; Reels & Stands — 6; MAILROOM EQUIPMENT: Counter Stackers — BG/Count-O-Veyor; Inserters & Stuffers — KAN/480; Tying Machines — Wilton; Address Machine — 2/Dispensa-Matic/16.; BUSINESS EQUIPMENT: Dell/PC BUSINESS SOFTWARE: Microsoft/Excel CLASSIFIED EQUIPMENT: Hardware — APP/Mac G3; Printers — APP/Mac LaserWriter 810 Pro, Xante/Accel-a-Writer 8200; CLASSIFIED SOFTWARE: Baseview/Class Manager Plus. DISPLAY EQUIPMENT: Hardware — 2-APP/Mac G3; Printers — APP/ Mac LaserWriter 810 Pro, Xante/Accel-a-Writer 8200; Other Hardware — Lf 35 negative scanner, 2-XYQUEST 270mb drive, 2-XYQUEST 28.8 modem. DISPLAY SOFTWAREAd Make-up Applications — QPS/QuarkXPress 4.0, Adobe/Acrobat 2.1; EDITORIAL EQUIPMENT: Hardware — 6-APP/Mac Quadra 610, 2-APP/Power Mac 8100, 1-APP/Power Mac 8500, 10-APP/ Mac G3, 2-APP/Mac 8500/2-V/Panther 3990 Imagesetter, XYQUEST/270 Mb drive, XYQUEST/28.8 modem, Polaroid/SprintScan 35; Printers — 2-APP/Mac LaserWriter 810 Pr PRODUCTION EQUIPMENT:

Hardware — Nat/Universal 33 Subtractive; Cameras — Horizontal/Clyesdale; Scanners — 2-HP/ScanJet IIcx, 1-Lf/Leafscan 35, 1-Polaroid/Sprintscan 35ES PRODUCTION SOFTWARE: QPS/QuarkXPress 4.0.

ANNISTON

THE ANNISTON STAR
4305 McClellan Blvd, Anniston, Ala., 36206-2812, Calhoun; gen tel (256) 236-1551; adv tel (256) 235-9222; ed tel (256) 235-9556; gen fax (256) 241-1991; adv fax (256) 241-1984; ed fax (256) 241-1991; gen/nat adv e-mail mbergstresser@annistonstar.com; disp adv e-mail mbergstresser@annistonstar. com; class adv e-mailmbergstresser@ annistonstar.com; ed e-mail news@ annistonstar.com; web site www.annistonstar. com; web site 2 twitter.com/annistonstar
Group: Consolidated Publishing Co.
Published: Tues, Wed, Thur, Fri, Sat, Sun
Weekday Frequency: m
Saturday Frequency: m
Circulation: 13,118; 13,118(sat); 15,149(sun)
Last Audit: AAM June 30, 2017
Advertising Rate (weekday/saturday): Open inch rate $40.00
News services: NYT, Tribune **Established:** 1883
Own Printing Facility?: Yes
Commercial Printers?: Yes
Special Editions: Healthy Living
Special Weekly Sections: TV Star (Fri)
Syndicated Publications: Parade (S).
LongLeaf
Chrmn./Pub............................. H. Brandt Ayers
Pres..........................Phillip A. Sanguinetti
VP for Operations...................Robert Jackson
V.P/ Sales & Mktg ....Robert Jackson
Office Manager ....Scott Calhoun
Pro. Mgr. ....Ben Gilreath
Circ. Mgr. ....Dennis Dunn
Online Dir..............................Chris Pittman
Mng. Ed. ....Ben Cunningham
Circ. Mgr. ....Donnie Bowman
Features Ed ....Lisa Davis
Customer Serv Mgr ....Mandy Schlemminger
Columnist................................George Smith
Commentary Ed. ....Phillip Tutor
Photo Ed. ....Trent Penny
Pub./Ed. ....Bob Davis
Market Information: Split run; TMC.
Mechanical Available: Offset; Black and 3 ROP colors; insert accepted; page cutoffs - 22.
Mechanical Specifications: Type page 9.88 x 21
Areas Served: East Alabama
Delivery Method: Mail, Newsstand, Carrier, RacksEquipment & Software: PRESSROOM EQUIPMENT: Lines — 12 DGM 850; Pasters —6 Jardis Pasters MAILROOM EQUIPMENT: Counter Stackers — Quipp 400; Inserters & Stuffers — 1-Mueller/227 GMA SLS 1000; Tying Machines — Dynaric ; BUSINESS EQUIPMENT: IBM/AS-400 CLASSIFIED EQUIPMENT: Hardware — Microsoft/Windows NT Server 4.0; Printers — HP/LaserWriter; CLASSIFIED SOFTWARE: Baseview/Classified. DISPLAY EQUIPMENT: Hardware — Microsoft/NT Server; Printers — HP/LaserWriter; DISPLAY SOFTWAREAd Make-up Applications — Microsoft/Word, APP/Mac Appleshare; Layout Software — MEI. EDITORIAL EQUIPMENT: Hardware — PC LAN, Microsoft/Windows NT Server 4.0; Printers — HP/LaserJet 4MV EDITORIAL SOFTWARE: Microsoft/Windows, Microsoft/ Word. PRODUCTION EQUIPMENT: Hardware — SCREEN PlateRite News 2000 Thermal Platesetter PRODUCTION SOFTWARE: InDesign

ATHENS

THE NEWS-COURIER
410 W Green St, Athens, Ala., 35611-2518, Limestone; gen tel (256) 232-2720; adv tel

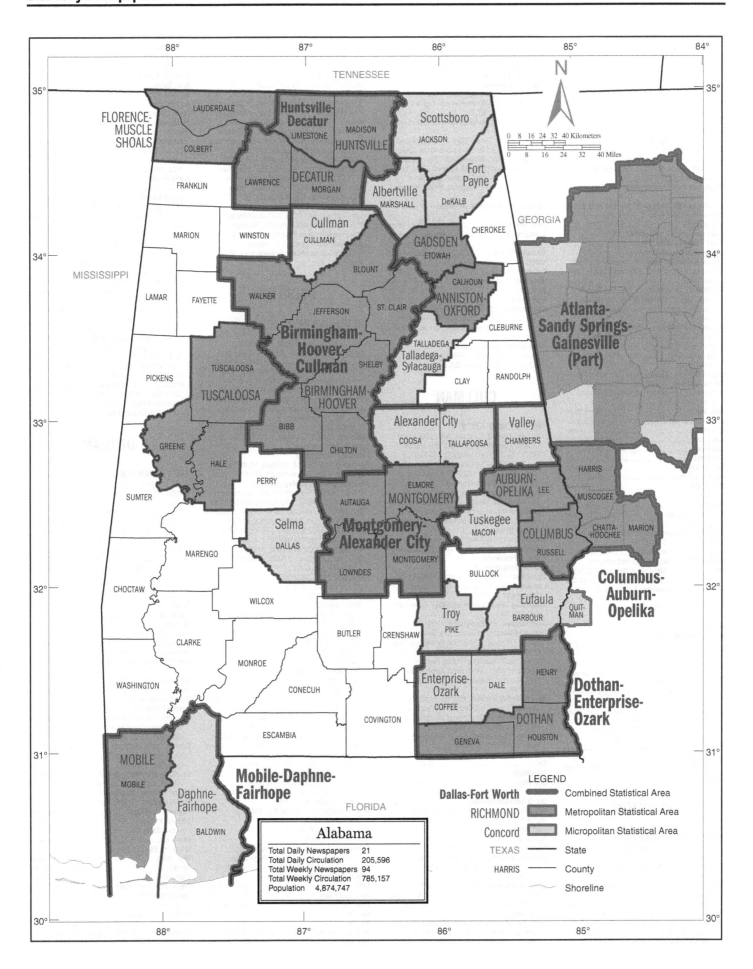

TENNESSEE

FLORENCE-
MUSCLE
SHOALS

LAUDERDALE

COLBERT

FRANKLIN

**Huntsville-
Decatur**

MADISON
LIMESTONE

HUNTSVILLE

Scottsboro

JACKSON

Fort
Payne

DeKALB

GEORGIA

MISSISSIPPI

MARION

LAMAR

FAYETTE

WINSTON

LAWRENCE

DECATUR

MORGAN

Cullman

CULLMAN

Albertville

MARSHALL

GADSDEN

ETOWAH

CHEROKEE

**Atlanta-
Sandy Springs-
Gainesville
(Part)**

BLOUNT

WALKER

JEFFERSON

ST. CLAIR

CALHOUN

**ANNISTON-
OXFORD**

CLEBURNE

PICKENS

TUSCALOOSA

**Birmingham-
Hoover-
Cullman**

SHELBY

TALLADEGA

Talladega-
Sylacauga

TUSCALOOSA

BIBB

**BIRMINGHAM-
HOOVER**

CHILTON

CLAY

RANDOLPH

GREENE

HALE

PERRY

COOSA

Alexander City

TALLAPOOSA

Valley

CHAMBERS

HARRIS

MUSCOGEE

SUMTER

AUTAUGA

ELMORE

MONTGOMERY

**AUBURN-
OPELIKA**

LEE

COLUMBUS

CHATTA-
HOOCHEE

MARION

Selma

DALLAS

**Montgomery-
Alexander City**

Tuskegee

MACON

RUSSELL

**Columbus-
Auburn-
Opelika**

MARENGO

MONTGOMERY

LOWNDES

BULLOCK

CHOCTAW

WILCOX

BUTLER

CRENSHAW

Troy

PIKE

Eufaula

BARBOUR

QUIT-
MAN

CLARKE

MONROE

CONECUH

Enterprise-
Ozark

COFFEE

DALE

HENRY

**Dothan-
Enterprise-
Ozark**

WASHINGTON

ESCAMBIA

COVINGTON

DOTHAN

GENEVA

HOUSTON

MOBILE

MOBILE

Daphne-
Fairhope

BALDWIN

**Mobile-Daphne-
Fairhope**

FLORIDA

N

0 8 16 24 32 40 Kilometers
0 8   16   24   32   40 Miles

LEGEND

Dallas-Fort Worth   Combined Statistical Area

RICHMOND   Metropolitan Statistical Area

Concord   Micropolitan Statistical Area

TEXAS   State

HARRIS   County

Shoreline

Alabama	
Total Daily Newspapers	21
Total Daily Circulation	205,596
Total Weekly Newspapers	94
Total Weekly Circulation	785,157
Population	4,874,747

(256) 232-2720; ed tel (256) 233-2720; gen fax (256) 233-7753; adv fax (256) 771-0207; ed fax (256) 233-7753; gen/nat adv e-mail katherine@athensnews-courier.com; disp adv e-mail katherine@athensnews-courier.com; class adv e-mailkandy@athensnews-courier.com; ed e-mail adam@athensnews-courier.com; web site www.enewscourier.com
- 394,112(views) 187,760(visitors)
Group: Community Newspaper Holdings, Inc.
Published: Tues, Wed, Thur, Fri, Sat
Weekday Frequency: m
Saturday Frequency: m
Circulation: 4,602; 6,380(sat)
Last Audit: Sworn/Estimate/Non-Audited September 30, 2017
Advertising Rate (weekday/saturday): Open inch rate $12.00
Advertising Rate (sunday): Open inch rate $15.00
Online Advertising Rate: $17.50 CPM $20.00 CPM
News services: AP **Established:** 1880
Own Printing Facility?: No
Commercial Printers?: No
Special Weekly Sections: TV Times (Fri); Kid's Corner (Thur); Home Solutions (Tues); Food Day (Wed).
Syndicated Publications: TV Tab (Fri); Relish (Monthly); Spry (Monthly); Athlon Sports (Monthly); American Profile (Weekly); Parade (Sun).
Proprietary Publications: Faith & Family(Jan/April/July/Oct); Limestone Life(Feb/May/Aug/Nov); Boom(March/June/Sept/Dec); TN Valley Agriculture(April/Aug); Blitz (Aug); Class of 20xx (Sept)
Digital Platform - Mobile: Apple, Android
Digital Platform - Tablet: Apple iOS, Android, Windows 7, Blackberry Tablet OS, Kindle, Nook, Kindle Fire
Gen. Mgr. .... Katherine Miller
Accounting Clerk .... Cynthia Gibson
Adv Sales .... Carey Carter
Adv Sales .... Heather Casillas
Adv Sales .... Angie Christopher
Adv Sales .... Angie McElyea
Manag. Editor .... Adam Smith
Ad Production .... Glenda Smith
News Editor .... Lora Scripps
Sports .... Jonathan Deal
Reporter .... Jean Cole
Lifestyles Reporter .... Rebecca Croomes
Copy Editor .... Edd Davis
Audience Development Associate .... Kala Tatum
Customer Service Specialist .... Lisa Hill
Classified Sales Consultant .... Kandy Mathis
Market Information: TMC; Zoned editions.
Mechanical Available: Offset; Black and 3 ROP colors; insert accepted; page cutoffs - 22 3/4.
Mechanical Specifications: Type page 13 x 21 1/2; E - 6 cols, 2 1/16, 1/8 between; A - 6 cols, 2 1/16, 1/8 between; C - 8 cols, 1 3/4, 1/8 between.
Areas Served: Limestone County
Delivery Method: Mail, Newsstand, RacksEquipment & Software: CLASSIFIED EQUIPMENT: Hardware — APP/Mac; COM/4961, COM/2414; Printers — APP/Mac 810; CLASSIFIED SOFTWARE: Baseview. DISPLAY EQUIPMENT: Hardware — APP/Mac G3; Printers — 1-APP/Mac LaserPrinter; DISPLAY SOFTWAREAd Make-up Applications — Multi-Ad/Creator 4.0, Adobe/Photoshop 5.0.; EDITORIAL EQUIPMENT: Hardware — APP/Mac/6-ECR/Autokon; Printers — 1-HP/4MV, 1-APP/Mac 810 EDITORIAL SOFTWARE: QPS/QuarkXPress 4.0, Adobe/Photoshop 5.0. PRODUCTION EQUIPMENT: Hardware — Caere/OmniPage 6.0.

CLANTON

THE CLANTON ADVERTISER

1109 7th St N, Clanton, Ala., 35045-2113, Chilton; gen tel (205) 755-5747; adv tel (205)755-5747 ext 606 ; ext. 604; ed tel (205) 755-5747, ext. 610; gen fax (205) 755-5857; gen/nat adv e-mail zack.bates@clantonadvertiser.com ; brandy.clackley@clantonadvertiser.com; disp adv e-mail zack.bates@clantonadvertiser.com ; brandy.clackley@clantonadvertiser.com; class adv e-mailzack.bates@clantonadvertiser.com ; brandy.clackley@clantonadvertiser.com; ed e-mail stephen.dawkins@clantonadvertiser.com; web site www.clantonadvertiser.com
Group: Boone Newspapers, Inc.
Published: Tues, Wed, Thur, Fri, Sat
Weekday Frequency: m
Saturday Frequency: m
Circulation: 5,000; 5,000(sat); 5,000(sun)
Last Audit: Sworn/Estimate/Non-Audited September 30, 2017
Advertising Rate (weekday/saturday): Open inch rate $11.95
Special Editions: Senior Scene (Apr); Football Preview (Aug); Christmas Greetings (Dec); Progress (Feb); Bridal Guide (Jan); Faces and Places (Jul); Peach Festival (Jun); Life in the South (Mar); Graduating Seniors (May); Christmas Songbook (Nov); Holiday Cookbook (Oct); H
Syndicated Publications: American Profile (Weekly).
Pres/Publisher .... Tim Prince
Managing Editor .... Stephen Dawkins
Prodn. Mgr. .... Jimmy Ruff
Marketing Consul .... Zack Bates
Mailroom mgr .... Scott Mims
Customer Service .... Laura Cleckley
Marketing Consultant .... Brandy Clackley
Staff Writer .... Anthony Richards
Staff Writer .... Emily Reed
Mechanical Specifications: Type page 11 5/8 x 21 1/2; E - 6 cols, 1 5/6, 1/8 between; A - 6 cols, 1 5/6, 1/8 between; C - 10 cols, 1 1/16, 7/64 between.
Areas Served: Chilton County
Equipment & Software: PRESSROOM EQUIPMENT: Lines — G/Community.;

CULLMAN

THE CULLMAN TIMES

300 4th Ave SE, Cullman, Ala., 35055-3611, Cullman; gen tel (256) 734-2131; adv tel (256) 734-2131; ed tel (256) 734-2131; gen fax (256)737-1006; adv fax (256)737-1020; ed fax (256) 736-2972; gen/nat adv e-mail karas@cullmantimes.com; disp adv e-mail karas@cullmantimes.com; class adv e-maildebbiem@cullmantimes.com ; ewilliams@cullmantimes.com ; ed e-mail editor@cullmantimes.com; web site www.cullmantimes.com
Group: Community Newspaper Holdings, Inc.
Published: Mon, Tues, Wed, Thur, Fri, Sat, Sun
Weekday Frequency: m
Saturday Frequency: m
Circulation: 10,000; 10,000(sat); 10,500(sun)
Last Audit: Sworn/Estimate/Non-Audited September 30, 2017
Advertising Rate (weekday/saturday): Open inch rate $16.70
News services: AP. **Established:** 1901
Special Editions: Consumer How To Guide (Apr); Sound Off (Aug); Christmas Greetings (Dec); Bridal Guide (Feb); Prime Times (Jan); Prime Times (Jul); Reader's Choice Awards (Jun); Spring Fashion (Mar); Graduation (May); Alabama Auto Guide (Monthly); Thanksgiving Day (Nov);
Special Weekly Sections: Church Page (Fri); Opinion Page (S); Used Auto Buyers Guide (Sat); Nascar Page (Thur); Outdoors (Tues); Best Food Day-Farm Page (Wed).
Syndicated Publications: Relish (Monthly) American Profile (Weekly).
Pub. .... Terry Connor
Ed. .... David Palmer
Classifieds .... Debbie Miller
Bus. Mgr. .... Pete Lewter
Adv. Dir. .... Laurie Chapman
Dir. of Audience Develp .... Sam Mazzara
News Ed. .... Amanda Shavers-Davies
Digital Ed. .... Trent Moore
Staff Writer .... Tiffeny Owens
Sports Ed. .... Jake Winfrey
Market Information: ADS; TMC.
Mechanical Available: Offset; Black and 3 ROP colors; insert accepted - hi-fi; page cutoffs - 22 3/4.
Mechanical Specifications: Type page 12 x 21 1/2; E - 6 cols, 1 7/8, 1/8 between; A - 6 cols, 1 7/8, 1/8 between; C - 8 cols, 1 1/3, 1/8 between.
Areas Served: Cullman (AL) Equipment & Software: PRESSROOM EQUIPMENT: Lines — 10-HI/Cotrell V-30 1993; Folders — HI/JF-25C (Main), HI/JF-25B (Aux).; MAILROOM EQUIPMENT: Tying Machines — 1/Bu, 1-/Power Strapper; Wrapping Singles — 1-/St; Address Machine - 1-/Am, 1-/KR, 1-KR/4-up head, Prism/Ink Jet.; BUSINESS EQUIPMENT: SUN, E-450 BUSINESS SOFTWARE: PBS, AM 3.0, CMS 3.0 CLASSIFIED EQUIPMENT: Hardware — 4-APP/Mac; Printers — Xante/Accel-a-Writer 8200; CLASSIFIED SOFTWARE: 5-Baseview/Ad Manager Pro, 2-Baseview/Class Flow. DISPLAY EQUIPMENT: Printers — Xante/Accel-a-Writer 8200; DISPLAY SOFTWARELayout Software — 6-APP/Mac. EDITORIAL EQUIPMENT: Hardware — 7-COM/Intrepid, 6-APP/Mac, 8-APP/Mac; Printers — APP/Mac Laser Writer 560, Xante/Accel-a-Writer 8200 EDITORIAL SOFTWARE: Microsoft/Word 6.1, APP/Mac Write Now 4.0, QPS/QuarkXPress. PRODUCTION EQUIPMENT: Hardware — Pre Press/Panther Plus Imagesetter, Gluntz & Jensen/Multi-Line 21; Cameras — 1-R, 1-Cl, Kk/Image Maker; Scanners — APP/Mac II.

DECATUR

THE DECATUR DAILY

201 1st Ave SE, Decatur, Ala., 35601-2333, Morgan; gen tel (256)353-4612; adv tel (256)340-2362; ed tel (256)340-2430; gen fax (256) 340-2411; adv fax (256)340-2358; ed fax (256) 340-2392; gen/nat adv e-mail news@decaturdaily.com; disp adv e-mail Deborah.lemen@decaturdaily.com; class adv e-mailclassifieds@decaturdaily.com; ed e-mail news@decaturdaily.com; web site www.decaturdaily.com
- 1,262,222(views) 554,856(visitors)
Published: Mon, Tues, Wed, Thur, Fri, Sat, Sun
Weekday Frequency: m
Saturday Frequency: m
Circulation: 14,735; 14,735(sat); 18,457(sun)
Last Audit: AAM December 31, 2015
Advertising Rate (weekday/saturday): INVESTMENT PER YEAR: no commitment $23/in, $3000-5000 $19.49/in, $5001-10000 $18.27/in, $10001-30000 $17.92/in, $30001-50000 $17.76/in, $50001-70000 $17.27, $70001-100000 $16.93/in, $100001-130000 $16.84 in, $130001-160000 $16.55/in; $160001-190000 $16.14/in, $190001-230000 $16.04/in ; $230001-270000 $15.87/in ; $270001+ $15.40/in
Advertising Rate (sunday): INVESTMENT PER YEAR: no commitment $25/in ; $3000-5000 $21.38/in ; $5001-10000 $20.10/in ; $10001-30000 $19.59/in ; $30001-50000 $19.44/in ; $50001-70000 $18.91/in ; $70001-$100000 $18.65/in ; $100001-130000 $18.44/in ; $130001-160000 $18.15/in ; $160001-190000 $17.63/in ; $190001-230000 $17.55 ; $230001-270000 $17.37/in ; $270001+ $16.85/in
Online Advertising Rate: Home page(300x250, 100000 imoressions) $1812 ; News Page(300x250, 35000 impressions) $609 ; Business Page(300x250, 15000 impressions) $261 ; Sports Page(300x250, 25000 impressions) $435 ; Living Page(300x250, 25000 impressions) $435 ; Calendar Page(600x250, 25000 impressions) $435 ; Opinions Page(300x250, 25000 impressions) $435 ; Obituaries Page(300x250, 50000 impressions) $870 ; Photo Galleries Page(300x250, 25000 impressions) $435; Run of Site Mobile(300x250, 50000 impressions) $870 ; Run of Site all pages(728x90) $10 CPM
News services: AP, NYT, SHNS, TMS. **Established:** 1912
Own Printing Facility?: Yes
Commercial Printers?: Yes
Special Weekly Sections: Agriculture (Mon); Business Page (S); Church Page (Sat); Building Page (Tues); Shopping Bag (Wed).
Syndicated Publications: Parade (S).
Pub. .... Clint Shelton
Dir., Operations .... Scott Brown
Exec. Ed. .... Don Hudson
Op. Dir. .... Scott Brown
Ad. Dir. .... Craig Hatcher
Mng. Ed. (Online) .... Bruce McLellan
Circ. Mgr. .... Barb McKillip
Bus. Writer .... Eric Flerschauer
Educ. Writer .... Bayne Hughes
Asst. Metro Ed. .... Franklin Harris
Photo Dept. Ed. .... John Godbey
Major Accts Mgr .... Shelia Smith
Asst. Sports Ed .... Michael Wetzel
Art Dept Mgr. .... Stephen Johnson
Ad Sale Exec. .... Michael Hagen
Market Information: TMC; Zoned editions.
Mechanical Available: Offset; Black and 3 ROP colors; insert accepted; page cutoffs - 22 3/4.
Mechanical Specifications: Type page 11 1/2 x 21 1/2; E - 6 cols, 1 15/16, 1/8 between; A - 6 cols, 1 15/16, 1/8 between; C - 10 cols, 1 1/16, 1/16 between.
Areas Served: Decatur and the Tennessee Valley in North Alabama
Delivery Method: CarrierEquipment & Software: PRESSROOM EQUIPMENT: Lines — 7-G/Urbanite, 1-G/3-color unit single width; Reels & Stands — 2; MAILROOM EQUIPMENT: Counter Stackers — QWI/350; Inserters & Stuffers — HI; Tying Machines — Dynaric/NP 1500; Address Machine — KR; BUSINESS EQUIPMENT: IBM/AS-400 BUSINESS SOFTWARE: INSI CLASSIFIED EQUIPMENT: Hardware — APT; Okidata; CLASSIFIED SOFTWARE: APT. DISPLAY EQUIPMENT: Hardware — 7-APP/Mac; Other Hardware — 2-Ultre/4000 Imagesetter DISPLAY SOFTWAREAd Make-up Applications — APT; Layout Software — APT. EDITORIAL EQUIPMENT: Hardware — 10-Compaq/386, 24-AST/286/2-V/XP 1000, 1-Ultre/4000 Imagesetter EDITORIAL SOFTWARE: APT. PRODUCTION EQUIPMENT: Hardware — Adobe/Photoshop 6.0, APP/Mac G3, APP/Mac G4; Cameras — SCREEN; Scanners — Umax/Majicsan PRODUCTION SOFTWARE: APT/ACT, QPS/QuarkXPress 3.32.

DOTHAN

THE DOTHAN EAGLE

227 N Oates St, Dothan, Ala., 36303-4555, Houston; gen tel (334) 792-3141; adv tel (334)702-2600 ; (334) 702-6060 (classified); ed tel (334) 792-3141; gen fax (334) 712-7979; adv fax (334) 793-2040; ed fax (334) 712-7979; gen/nat adv e-mail sales@dothaneagle.com; advertising@dothaneagle.com; disp adv e-mail advertising@dothaneagle.com; class adv e-mailclassifieds@dothaneagle.com; ed e-mail letters@dothaneagle.com; web site www.dothaneagle.com
- 1,000,000(views)
Group: BH Media Group
Published: Mon, Tues, Wed, Thur, Fri, Sat, Sun
Weekday Frequency: m
Saturday Frequency: m
Circulation: 17,870; 17,870(sat); 20,275(sun)
Last Audit: AAM June 30, 2016
Advertising Rate (weekday/saturday): Open inch rate $40.00
Advertising Rate (sunday): Open inch rate $44.00
News services: AP, NEA. **Established:** 1903
Own Printing Facility?: Yes
Special Editions: Wire Grass Outdoors (Monthly); Football Weekend (Nov); Football Weekend (Oct); New Car (Quarterly); Football Weekend (Sept); Golf (Spring); Golf (Summer).
Special Weekly Sections: Home & Garden (Fri); Expanded Business Pages (S); Church Page (Sat); Food (Wed).
Syndicated Publications: Relish (Monthly); USA WEEKEND Magazine (S).
Digital Platform - Mobile: Android
Digital Platform - Tablet: Android
Regional Publisher .... Steve Smith
Editorial Page Ed. .... William Perkins
Regional Sales Dir .... Jerry Morgan
Sports Ed. .... Jon Johnson
Managing Ed. .... Kendall Clinton
Mgr., Mktg. .... Stephanie Madden
News Ed. .... Christie Kulavich
Prodn. Mgr. .... Charlie Gibson
Prodn. Mgr., Pressroom .... Tim Slater
Market Information: Split run; TMC; Zoned editions.
Mechanical Available: Offset; Black and 3 ROP colors; insert accepted; page cutoffs - 22 3/4.
Mechanical Specifications: Type page 13 x 21 1/2; E - 6 cols, 2 1/16, 3/16 between; A - 6

cols, 2 1/16, 3/16 between; C - 9 cols, 1 3/8, 1/16 between.
Areas Served: Houston, Covington, Henry, Barbour, Pike Counties (AL); Holmes, Jackson Counties (FL)
Delivery Method: Newsstand, CarrierEquipment & Software: PRESSROOM EQUIPMENT: Lines — 12-G/Urbanite single width (64 page capacity).; MAILROOM EQUIPMENT: Counter Stackers — 2-Id/2000-4000; Inserters & Stuffers — 8-GMA/Station, GMA/SLS 1000 (DTP); Tying Machines — 1-Dynaric/Auto Strapper; Wrapping Singles — Mailroom Control System MA; Address Machine — KR/320; BUSINESS EQUIPMENT: HP BUSINESS SOFTWARE: Oracle, PBS, ATT, CText, Microsoft/Windows CLASSIFIED EQUIPMENT: Hardware — CText; Printers — V/5300.; DISPLAY EQUIPMENT: Hardware — CText; Printers — V/5300; DISPLAY SOFTWARELayout Software — SCS/Layout 8000. EDITORIAL EQUIPMENT: Hardware — CText; Printers — V/5300. PRODUCTION EQUIPMENT: Hardware — Caere/OmniPage, 2-Tegra/5300 Film device; Cameras — 1-LE/121-V242, 1-R/432; Scanners — 2-Umax, 1-Umax/ PowerLook PRODUCTION SOFTWARE: QPS/QuarkXPress 3.3.

ENTERPRISE

THE ENTERPRISE LEDGER

1110 Boll Weevil Cir, Ste D, Enterprise, Ala., 36330-1390, Coffee; gen tel (334) 347-9533; adv tel (334) 347-9533; ed tel (334) 347-9533; gen fax (334) 347-0825; adv fax (334) 347-0825; ed fax (334) 347-0825; gen/nat adv e-mail news@eprisenow.com; disp adv e-mail LAllgood@eprisenow.com; class adv e-mailclassifieds@eprisenow.com; ed e-mail news@eprisenow.com; web site www.eprisenow.com
Group: BH Media Group
Published: Tues, Wed, Thur, Fri, Sun
Circulation: 7,100; 7,700(sun)
Last Audit: Sworn/Estimate/Non-Audited September 30, 2017
Advertising Rate (weekday/saturday): Open inch rate $15.00 (Tues-Fri)
Advertising Rate (sunday): Open inch rate $15.50
News services: 1898
Special Editions: Home & Garden (April); Fort Rucker Appreciation (May); Class of 20XX, 12 years later (May); Newcomers Guide (July)
Syndicated Publications: Real Estate (Monthly); Apartment Living (Quarterly).
Gen. Mgr./Editor .... Kyle Mooty
News Clerk .... Gwen Black
Account Exec. .... Laren Allgood
Account Exec. .... Mable Ruttlen
Reporter .... Josh Boutwell
Reporter .... Courtney Gilley
Receptionist .... Ginger McClay
Market Information: Split run; TMC; Zoned editions.
Mechanical Available: Offset; Black and 3 ROP colors; insert accepted; page cutoffs - 22 3/4.
Mechanical Specifications: Type page 13 x 21 1/2; E - 6 cols, 2 1/16, 1/8 between; A - 6 cols, 2 1/16, 1/8 between; C - 9 cols, 1 1/2, 1/8 between.
Areas Served: Coffee County and parts of Dale, Geneva, and Covington counties
Delivery Method: Mail, Newsstand, Carrier, Racks

FLORENCE

TIMES DAILY

219 W Tennessee St, Florence, Ala., 35630-5440, Lauderdale; gen tel (256) 766-3434; adv tel (256) 740-5815; ed tel (256) 740-4725; gen fax (256) 740-4700; adv fax (256) 740-4700; ed fax (256) 740-4717; gen/nat adv e-mail melody.bishop@timesdaily.com; disp adv e-mail renita.jimmar@timesdaily.com; class adv e-mailerica.mayfield@timesdaily.com; ed e-mail mike.goens@timesdaily.com; web site www.timesdaily.com
Published: Mon, Tues, Wed, Thur, Fri, Sat, Sun
Weekday Frequency: m
Saturday Frequency: m
Circulation: 20,306; 18,976(sat); 21,555(sun)
Last Audit: AAM June 30, 2015
Advertising Rate (weekday/saturday): Open inch rate $49.10
News services: AP. **Established:** 1890
Own Printing Facility?: Yes
Commercial Printers?: Yes
Special Editions: Explore the Shoals (Apr); High School Football (Aug); Progress (Feb); Money Matters (Jan); Living Here (Jul); Senior Living (Jun); Lawn and Garden (Mar); Graduation (May); High School Basketball (Nov); Readers Choice (Oct).
Shoals Woman (every other month);Tennessee Valley Brides (annual);TNValleyHomefinder (monthly); TNValleyWheels (biweekly)
Special Weekly Sections: Currents (Fri); Best Food Day (Wed).
Syndicated Publications: Shoals Woman (Every other month); Shoals Magazine (Quarterly); USA Weekend (S)Explore the Shoals (AprProgress (Feb); Money Matters (Jan); Living Here (Jul); Senior Living (Jun); Tennessee Valley Brides (annual);TNValleyHomefinder (monthly); TNValleyWheels (biweekly)
Prod. Dir. .... Kevin Blurton
Adv. Dir. .... Melody Bishop
Adv. Mgr., Display .... Renita Jimmar
Pub. .... Darrell R. Sandlin
Exec. Ed. .... Gary Maitland
Dir., ITS/Pre Press Serv. .... Chris Giroir
Controller .... Charlotte Ann Filloramo
TVPCO circ mgr .... Walter Goggins
City Ed. .... Sherhonda Allen
Lifestyle Ed. .... Teri T. Stepleton
News Asst. .... Valerie Sherer
Photo Ed. .... Matthew T. McKean
Sports Ed. .... Gregg Dewalt
Asst. Sports Ed. .... Jeff McIntyre
Online Ed .... Bruce McLellan
Prodn. Mgr., Pre Press .... Lin Reynolds
Pressroom Mgr. .... Mike Roberts
Office Mgr .... Leta Milstead
Market Information: TMC.
Mechanical Available: Offset; Black and 3 ROP colors; insert accepted; page cutoffs - 22.
Mechanical Specifications: Type page 11 x 21; E - 6 cols, 1 15/16, 3/16 between; A - 6 cols, 1 5/8, 3/16 between; C - 9 cols, 11/16, 1/16 between.Equipment & Software: PRESSROOM EQUIPMENT: Folders — 1, 1-G/Urbanite 1997 MAILROOM EQUIPMENT: Counter Stackers — 5-QWI/350-400W; Inserters & Stuffers — NP1472; 632 Inserter; Tying Machines — Power Strap; Dynaric; BUSINESS SOFTWARE: INSI CLASSIFIED EQUIPMENT: Hardware — PC; DISPLAY EQUIPMENT: Hardware — APP/Mac; DISPLAY SOFTWAREAd Make-up Applications — ATS; Layout Software — QPS/QuarkXPress. EDITORIAL EQUIPMENT: Hardware — PC EDITORIAL SOFTWARE: CPU. PRODUCTION EQUIPMENT: Scanners — 1-PixelCraft/8000.

FORT PAYNE

THE TIMES-JOURNAL

811 Greenhill Blvd NW, Fort Payne, Ala., 35967, De Kalb; gen tel (256) 845-2550; adv tel (256) 304-0061; ed tel (256) 304-0053 ; gen fax (256) 845-7459; adv fax (256) 845-7459; ed fax (256) 845-7459; gen/nat adv e-mail lstiefel@times-journal.com; disp adv e-mail composing@times-journal.com; class adv e-mailclassified@times-journal.com; ed e-mail hbuckner@times-journal.com; web site www.times-journal.com
Group: Southern Newspapers Inc.
Published: Tues, Wed, Thur, Fri, Sat
Weekday Frequency: m
Saturday Frequency: m
Circulation: 3,334; 3,334(sat)
Last Audit: CAC March 31, 2015
Advertising Rate (weekday/saturday): Open inch rate $10(per column in). Special rates: $6.45 PCI (20 consec issues), $6.95 PCI(2 issues per week, for 4 consec weeks), $7.65 PCI(1 issue per week, for 13 consec weeks)
Online Advertising Rate: Top Web Leaderboard(728x90): $350/month Run Of Site(6 months), $300/month Run Of Site(1 year); Middle rectangle(300x250): $250/month Run Of Site(6 months), $200/month Run Of Site(1 year), $350/month assigned spot(6 months), $300/month assigned spot(1 year); Leaderboard(728x90): $250/month Run of Site(6 months), $200/month Run of Site(1 year), $350/month assigned spot(6 months), $300/month assigned spot(1 year); Micobar(88x31): $25/month Run Of Site
News services: 1878
Own Printing Facility?: No
Commercial Printers?: No
Syndicated Publications: American Profile (Weekly), USA Weekend (Weekly), The EXTRA (Tues), The Sand Mountain Shopper's Guide(Tues)
Pres./Pub. .... Tricia Clinton Dunne
Advertising Manager .... Linda Stiefel
Classified Representative .... Emily Tipton
Circ. Mgr .... Connie Hughes
Ed. .... Lew Gilliland
Chief Photo .... Melissa Henry
Mng. Ed. .... Bradley Roberts
Market Information: TMC; Zoned editions.
Mechanical Available: Offset; Black and 3 ROP colors; insert accepted; page cutoffs - 21 1/2.
Mechanical Specifications: Type page 13 x 21 1/2; E - 6 cols, 2 1/16, 1/8 between; A - 6 cols, 2 1/16, 1/8 between; C - 6 cols, 2 1/16, 1/8 between.
Areas Served: DeKalb and Fort PayneCounty, Alabama
Delivery Method: Mail, Newsstand, Carrier, RacksEquipment & Software: PRESSROOM EQUIPMENT: Lines — 5-G/Community; MAILROOM EQUIPMENT: Address Machine — 2-Am/1900, 2-El/3101.; BUSINESS EQUIPMENT: IBM CLASSIFIED EQUIPMENT: Hardware — APP/Mac.; DISPLAY EQUIPMENT: Hardware — APP/Mac.; EDITORIAL EQUIPMENT: Hardware — Mk, APP/Mac. PRODUCTION EQUIPMENT: Hardware — 1-WL/30A; Cameras — AG/Repromaster/3800.

GADSDEN

THE GADSDEN TIMES

401 Locust St, Gadsden, Ala., 35901-3737, Etowah; gen tel (256) 549-2000; adv tel (256) 549-2071; ed tel (256) 399-9742; gen fax (256) 549-2013; adv fax (256) 549-2013; ed fax (256) 549-2105; gen/nat adv e-mail tina.peppers@gadsdentimes.com; disp adv e-mail wes.williams@gadsdentimes.com; class adv e-maildana.brown@gadsdentimes.com; ed e-mail ron.reaves@gadsdentimes.com; web site www.gadsdentimes.com - 2,400,000(views)
Group: New Media Investment Group
Published: Mon, Tues, Wed, Thur, Fri, Sat, Sun
Weekday Frequency: m
Saturday Frequency: m
Circulation: 12,597; 12,597(sat); 13,609(sun)
Last Audit: AAM March 31, 2016
Advertising Rate (weekday/saturday): Open inch rate $27.00
Advertising Rate (sunday): Open inch rate $28.00
Online Advertising Rate: Run of site impressions(12 month commitment will receive 10% discount): 1000-49999 $10 per m, 50000-99999 $9 per m, 100000 $8 per m, Home page only $14M
News services: AP **Established:** 1867
Own Printing Facility?: Yes
Commercial Printers?: No
Special Editions: Football (Aug); County Focus Editions (4) (Feb); Home & Garden (Mar); Graduation (May); Basketball (Nov).
Special Weekly Sections: Religious News (Fri); People (Mon); Real Estate (S); Health News (Thur); Home (Tues); Food (Wed).
Syndicated Publications: Parade (S).
Digital Platform - Mobile: Apple
Digital Platform - Tablet: Apple iOS
Pub. .... Glen Porter
Exec. Ed. .... Ron Reaves
Finance Dir .... Richard Davis
Circ.Director .... John Chapman
Photo Dept. Mgr. .... Marc Golden
Travel/Women's Ed. .... Cyndi Nelson
Advert. Dir .... Wes Williams
Assoc. Ed. .... Greg Bailey
Digital Prod .... Michael Rodgers
National Sales-Retail .... Tina Peppers
Market Information: TMC.
Mechanical Available: Offset; Black and 3 ROP colors; insert accepted; page cutoffs - 22 3/4.
Mechanical Specifications: Type page 13 x 21 1/2; E - 6 cols, 2 1/16, 1/8 between; A - 6 cols, 2 1/16, 1/8 between; C - 9 cols, 1 11/32, 3/32 between.
Areas Served: 35901, 35903, 35904 35905, 35906, 35907, 35950, 35951, 35952, 35953, 35954, 35956, 35957, 35959, 35960, 35961, 35962, 35963, 35967, 35968, 35971, 35972, 35973, 35974, 35983, 35986, 35987, 35990, 36250, 36265, 36271, 36272, 36279
Delivery Method: Mail, Newsstand, Carrier, RacksEquipment & Software: PRESSROOM EQUIPMENT: Reels & Stands — 6; BUSINESS EQUIPMENT: ADV/36 CLASSIFIED EQUIPMENT: Hardware — APP/Mac G4; Printers — AU, AG/Accuset; CLASSIFIED SOFTWARE: Baseview. DISPLAY EQUIPMENT: Hardware — APP/Mac G3; Printers — AU, AG/Accuset; Other Hardware — HP/8100N, HP/5M DISPLAY SOFTWAREAd Make-up Applications — Multi-Ad/Creator 3.8; Layout Software — APP/Mac. EDITORIAL EQUIPMENT: Hardware — APP/Mac-SH; Printers — AU, AG/Accuset EDITORIAL SOFTWARE: Baseview. PRODUCTION EQUIPMENT: Hardware — Mac Base/AG Accuset, 1-Konica/K-280, QPS 3.31; Scanners — Mk/SilverScan, Mk/ScanMaker III, Kk, Nikon/Coolscan PRODUCTION SOFTWARE: QPS 4.0.

JASPER

DAILY MOUNTAIN EAGLE

1301 Viking Dr, Jasper, Ala., 35501-4983, Walker; gen tel (205) 221-2840; adv tel (205) 221-2840; ed tel (205) 221-2840; gen fax (205) 221-6203; adv fax (205)221-1815; ed fax (205) 221-6203; gen/nat adv e-mail jerry.geddings@mountaineagle.com; disp adv e-mail jerry.geddings@mountaineagle.com; class adv e-maildonna.hicks@mountaineagle.com; ed e-mail ron.harris@mountaineagle.com; web site www.mountaineagle.com
Group: Cleveland Newspapers, Inc.
Published: Tues, Wed, Thur, Fri, Sat, Sun
Weekday Frequency: m
Saturday Frequency: m
Circulation: 6,628; 6,628(sat); 7,129(sun)
Last Audit: AAM December 31, 2015
Advertising Rate (weekday/saturday): Open inch rate $9.83
Advertising Rate (sunday): Front Page Banner: open rate $299, 13 times $249, 26 times $199. 52 times $179
Online Advertising Rate: Top Banner (728x90), Right Panel(300x250), Bottom Banner(728x90) = $125 per position per month
News services: AP. **Established:** 1872
Special Editions: Atlanta Braves (Apr); Football (Aug); Letters to Santa (Dec); Progress (Feb); Senior Citizen (Jul); Home Folks (Jun); Graduation (May); Gift Guide (Nov); Women's World (Oct); Newcomer's Guide (Sept).
Syndicated Publications: TV Guide (Fri); USA WEEKEND Magazine (S); Business & Industrial Review (Tues); Best Food (Wed); American Profile (Weekly).
Ed./Pub. .... James Phillips
Sports Ed. .... Jonathan Bentley
Office/Credit Mgr. .... Charlotte Caterson
Classified Ad Mgr. .... Sandra Lawson
Prod. Mgr .... Michael Keeton
Circ. Dir. .... Tia Jones
Adv. Dir. .... Jake Aaron
Market Information: ADS; TMC.
Mechanical Available: Offset; Black and 3 ROP colors; insert accepted; page cutoffs - 22 3/4.
Mechanical Specifications: Type page 13 x 21 1/2; E - 6 cols, 5/16, 1/8 between; A - 6 cols, 5/16, 1/8 between; C - 6 cols, 5/16, 1/8 between.
Areas Served: 35501, 35503Equipment & Software: PRESSROOM EQUIPMENT: Lines — 8-WPC/Web Leader; 3-WPC/Quadcolor; Folders — 2-WPC/2:1.; MAILROOM EQUIPMENT: Counter Stackers — 1-BG/Count-O-Veyor; Inserters & Stuffers — 4-DG/320; Tying Machines — 1/Sa;

Address Machine — 1-Ch/730.; EDITORIAL EQUIPMENT: Hardware — Mk/12-Mk. PRODUCTION EQUIPMENT: Hardware — 2-Mk/Ad Touch, 2-APP/Mac LaserWriter Plus; Cameras — 1-R/Corsair, 1-DAI/5161.

LANETT

THE VALLEY TIMES-NEWS

220 N 12th St, Lanett, Ala., 36863-6422, Chambers; gen tel (334) 644-8100; adv tel (334) 644-8100; ed tel (334) 644-8123; gen fax (334) 644-5587; adv fax (334) 644-5587; ed fax (334) 644-5587; gen/nat adv e-mail advertising@valleytimes-news.com; disp adv e-mail advertising@valleytimes-news.com; class adv e-mailclassifieds@valleytimes-news.com; ed e-mail news@valleytimes-news.com; web site www.valleytimes-news.com

Group: The Valley Times-News
Published: Mon, Tues, Wed, Thur, Fri
Weekday Frequency: e
Circulation: 4,200
Last Audit: USPS October 1, 2016
Advertising Rate (weekday/saturday): Open inch rate $9.95
Online Advertising Rate: Banner: $60/Month
News services: AP. **Established:** 1950
Own Printing Facility?: No
Commercial Printers?: No
Special Editions: Christmas Greetings (Dec); Progress (Apr); Cookbook (Nov); Car Care (Oct); Football (Aug).
Special Weekly Sections: Food Section (Wed); Television (Fri). Extensive automobile and real estate advertising(Fri)
Ed. .... Cy Wood
Classified Manager .... Martha Milner
Graphics Ed. .... Kathy Reeves
Sports Ed. .... Scott Sickler
Market Information: TMC.
Mechanical Available: Offset; Black and 3 ROP colors; insert accepted; page cutoffs - 22 3/4.
Mechanical Specifications: Type page 13 x 21 1/2; E - 6 cols, 2 1/8, 1/4 between; A - 6 cols, 2 1/8, 1/4 between; C - 9 cols, 1 1/2, 1/8 between.
Areas Served: West Point, Georgia, & Lanett and Valley (AL)
Delivery Method: Mail, Newsstand, Carrier, RacksEquipment & Software: PRESSROOM EQUIPMENT: Lines — 6-G/Community; Folders — G/2:1; MAILROOM EQUIPMENT: Counter Stackers — 1/BG; Tying Machines — 1-/BG.; BUSINESS EQUIPMENT: 1-RSK/Model III, 1-Bs/B96-40 BUSINESS SOFTWARE: APP/Mac CLASSIFIED EQUIPMENT: Hardware — Mk, PC, APP/Mac; Printers — 2-COM/308 Laser; CLASSIFIED SOFTWARE: Mk. DISPLAY EQUIPMENT: Hardware — APP/Mac, COM, PC; Printers — 2-COM/308; DISPLAY SOFTWAREAd Make-up Applications — Mk, APP/Mac.; EDITORIAL EQUIPMENT: Hardware — Mk, PC; Printers — 2-COM/308 Laser EDITORIAL SOFTWARE: Mk, APP/Mac. PRODUCTION EQUIPMENT: Hardware — 1-LE/LD-1800A; Cameras — Roconex/1-B.

MONTGOMERY

MONTGOMERY ADVERTISER

475 Molton St, Montgomery, Ala., 36104-3523, Montgomery; gen tel (334) 262-1611; adv tel (334) 264-3733; ed tel (334) 261-1524; gen fax (334) 261-1505; adv fax (334) 261-1591; ed fax (334) 261-1505; ed e-mail jearnhardt@gannett.com; web site www.montgomeryadvertiser.com

Group: Gannett
Published: Mon, Tues, Wed, Thur, Fri, Sat, Sun
Weekday Frequency: m
Saturday Frequency: m
Circulation: 20,185; 20,185(sat); 26,266(sun)
Last Audit: AAM March 31, 2017
Advertising Rate (weekday/saturday): Open inch rate $113.04
News services: AP, SHNS, MCT, GNS, PR Newswire. **Established:** 1829
Own Printing Facility?: Yes
Special Editions: Coupon Book (Apr); Game Day College (Aug); SEC Game Day (Dec); Health & Fitness (Feb); Coupon Book (Jan); Hyundai (Jul); Restaurant Guide (Jun); Gulf Coast Tab (Mar); Health & Fitness (May); Holiday Gift Guide (Nov); Coupon Book (Oct); First Methodist Ven
Special Weekly Sections: Religion (Fri); TV Week (S); Home & Garden (Sat); Go (weekly entertainment) (Thur); Health (Tues); Food (Wed).
Syndicated Publications: USA WEEKEND Magazine (S).
Consumer Exper. Dir/Sports Ed .... Brad Zimanek
Content Strategist/Digital Ed. .... Steve Arnold
Exec. Ed. .... Bro Krift
Pres. .... Michael Galvin
Exec/ Asst. .... Debbie Goddard
Adv. Dir. .... Jim Broyles
Market Information: Split run; TMC; Zoned editions.
Mechanical Available: Offset; Black and 3 ROP colors; insert accepted - samples; page cutoffs - 20 1/2.
Mechanical Specifications: Type page 11 5/8 x 20 1/2; E - 6 cols, 1 5/6, 1/8 between; A - 6 cols, 1 5/6, 1/8 between; C - 10 cols, between.
Areas Served: Montgomery, Prattville and the River RegionEquipment & Software: PRESSROOM EQUIPMENT: Folders — G/3:2 (144 page); Pasters —G/RTPReels & Stands — 8-G/3-Arm.; MAILROOM EQUIPMENT: Counter Stackers — 6-QWI/350; Inserters & Stuffers — NP/1472; Tying Machines — 5-Dynaric/NP-2; Wrapping Singles — 1-Bu/Tying Machine, 5-QWI/Viper Bottom Wraps; Address Machine — Barstrom/In-Line; BUSINESS EQUIPMENT: IBM/AS-400 9406-300 BUSINESS SOFTWARE: Microsoft/Office Pro 1997 CLASSIFIED EQUIPMENT: Hardware — 20-Dell/Optiplex, Dell/Power Edge 90; Printers — HP/4si; CLASSIFIED SOFTWARE: Harris/AdPower, HI/CASH 2.1.9. DISPLAY EQUIPMENT: Hardware — 17-APP/Power Mac G4; Printers — HP LaserJet 5, HP LaserJet/8550; Other Hardware — 2-APP/Mac Workgroup DISPLAY SOFTWAREAd Make-up Applications — QPS/QuarkXPress, Adobe/Photoshop 5.5; Layout Software — SCS/Layout 8000. EDITORIAL EQUIPMENT: Hardware — 70-Dell/Optiplex, Sun/Enterprise 450; Printers — HP, Unity/1600 XL, HP/8150 EDITORIAL SOFTWARE: Harris/Newsmaker 2.5, HI/Newsmaker Editorial 3.5. PRODUCTION EQUIPMENT: Hardware — 2-V/Pro Panther 36, 1-V/5300-B; Cameras — 1-C; Scanners — 2-ECR, ScanView/ScanMate 5000 Drum Scanner, Kk/2035S, HP/ScanJet 4C, Nikon/LS 2000 PRODUCTION SOFTWARE: Solaris 2.5, HI/Newsmaker Pagination 4.0.

OPELIKA

OPELIKA-AUBURN NEWS

2901 Society Hill Rd, Opelika, Ala., 36804-4850, Lee; gen tel (334) 749-6271; adv tel (334) 737-2488; ed tel (334) 749-6271; gen fax (334) 749-1228; adv fax (334) 749-1228; ed fax (334) 737-2493; gen/nat adv e-mail shaydel@oanow.com; disp adv e-mail shaydel@oanow.com; class adv e-mailoanewsclassifieds@oanow.com ; crussell@oanow.com; ed e-mail pjohnston@oanow.com; web site www.oanow.com

Group: BH Media Group
Published: Mon, Tues, Wed, Thur, Fri, Sat, Sun
Weekday Frequency: m
Saturday Frequency: m
Circulation: 9,622; 9,622(sat); 10,965(sun)
Last Audit: AAM December 31, 2016
Advertising Rate (weekday/saturday): Open inch rate $31.60
News services: AP. **Established:** 1904
Special Weekly Sections: Best Automotive Days (Fri); Best Real Estate Days (S); Church Page (Sat); Business Pages (Thur); Business Pages (Tues); Living Pages (Wed).
Syndicated Publications: USA WEEKEND Magazine (S).
Pub .... Rex Maynor
Mng. Ed. .... Patrick Johnston
Sports Ed. .... Dana Sulonen
Adv. Dir .... Sheila Haydel
Classified Adv. Mgr .... Crystal Russell
Creative Serv Mgr .... Greg Curry
Circ. Dir .... John Gaddy
Prod. Dir .... H. T. Bear
Market Information: ADS; TMC.
Mechanical Available: Offset; Black and 3 ROP colors; insert accepted; page cutoffs - 22.
Mechanical Specifications: Type page 11 1/2 x 21 1/2; E - 6 cols, 1 3/4, 1/6 between; A - 6 cols, 1 3/4, 1/6 between; C - 6 cols, 1 3/4, 1/6 between.
Areas Served: Auburn, Auburn University, Opelika, Lee County and East Alabama
Delivery Method: MailEquipment & Software: PRESSROOM EQUIPMENT: Lines — 8-G/Community 1976; Folders — SC/499.; MAILROOM EQUIPMENT: Tying Machines — MLN/Sprint.; BUSINESS EQUIPMENT: PBS BUSINESS SOFTWARE: Unix CLASSIFIED EQUIPMENT: Hardware — APP/Mac; CLASSIFIED SOFTWARE: Baseview. DISPLAY EQUIPMENT: Hardware — APP/Mac IIcx; Printers — V; DISPLAY SOFTWAREAd Make-up Applications — Baseview.; EDITORIAL EQUIPMENT: Hardware — APP/Mac; Printers — V EDITORIAL SOFTWARE: QPS/QuarkXPress, Baseview. PRODUCTION EQUIPMENT: Hardware — 1-Nu, Pre Press/Panther Plus; Cameras — Amergraph.

SCOTTSBORO

THE DAILY SENTINEL

701 Veterans Dr, Scottsboro, Ala., 35768-2132, Jackson; gen tel (256) 259-1020; gen fax (256) 259-2709; gen/nat adv e-mail advertising@thedailysentinel.com; disp adv e-mail advertising@thedailysentinel.com; class adv e-maillynn.loy@thedailysentinel.com; ed e-mail dewayne.patterson@thedailysentinel.com; web site www.thedailysentinel.com

Group: Southern Newspapers Inc.
Published: Tues, Wed, Thur, Fri, Sat
Weekday Frequency: m
Saturday Frequency: m
Circulation: 3,044; 3,301(sat)
Last Audit: CAC March 31, 2015
Advertising Rate (weekday/saturday): Open inch rate $10.00
Online Advertising Rate: Call for Rates
News services: AP, TMS. **Established:** 1887
Own Printing Facility?: Yes
Commercial Printers?: Yes
Proprietary Publications:
Jackson - Full Color Glossy Magazine for high-end wage earners
Digital Platform - Mobile: Apple, Android
Digital Platform - Tablet: Apple iOS, Android
Adv. Dir. .... Ken Bonner
Mng. Ed. .... Dewayne Patterson
Sports Ed. .... Jason Bowen
Prodn. Mgr. .... Junior Lewis
Circulation Manager .... Darlene Walker
Classified Sales .... Lynn Loy
Business Mgr. .... Wendy Howell
Graphic Design .... Robert Marousky
Publisher
Brandon Cox
Market Information: Split run; TMC; .
Mechanical Available: Black and 3 ROP colors; insert accepted - cards; page cutoffs - 21 1/2.
Mechanical Specifications: Type page 13 x 21 1/2; E - 6 cols, 2 1/16, 1/8 between; A - 6 cols, 2 1/16, 1/8 between; C - 9 cols, 1 1/2, 1/16 between.
Areas Served: Jackson County (AL)
Delivery Method: Mail, Newsstand, Carrier, RacksEquipment & Software: PRESSROOM EQUIPMENT: 4-KP/Color King 1992; 2-KP/Color 1999.; Press Drive — W/House Motors, GE/Motors MAILROOM EQUIPMENT: Counter Stackers — Mid-Atlantic; Tying Machines — 1/Strapex, 1-/Strapex; Address Machine — 1-/KR.; BUSINESS EQUIPMENT: IBM, Packard Bell/Force I CLASSIFIED EQUIPMENT: Hardware — APP/Mac Quadra 610; CLASSIFIED SOFTWARE: Baseview/Class Manager Plus, Baseview/Fraw. DISPLAY EQUIPMENT: Hardware — APP/Mac Quadra 610; Printers — APP/Mac LaserWriter Pro 810; DISPLAY SOFTWAREAd Make-up Applications — Multi-Ad/Creator, QPS/QuarkXPress.; EDITORIAL EQUIPMENT: Hardware — APP/Mac Quadra 610; Printers — APP/Mac LaserWriter Pro 810 EDITORIAL SOFTWARE: Microsoft/Word, QPS/QuarkXPress. PRODUCTION EQUIPMENT: Hardware — Konica/Imagesetter; Cameras — C/Marathon; Scanners — Ap PRODUCTION SOFTWARE: QPS/QuarkXPress 4.0.

SELMA

THE SELMA TIMES-JOURNAL

1018 Water Ave, Selma, Ala., 36701-4617, Dallas; gen tel (334) 875-2110; gen fax (334) 872-4588; adv fax (334) 875-5896; ed fax (334) 875-5896; gen/nat adv e-mail ads@selmatimesjournal.com; disp adv e-mail ads@selmatimesjournal.com; class adv e-mailmichelle.coleman@selmatimesjournal.com; ed e-mail tim.reeves@selmatimesjournal.com; web site www.selmatimesjournal.com - 400,000(views) 47,000(visitors)

Group: Boone Newspapers, Inc.
Published: Tues, Wed, Thur, Fri, Sat, Sun
Weekday Frequency: m
Saturday Frequency: m
Circulation: 8,500; 8,500(sat); 10,000(sun)
Last Audit: Sworn/Estimate/Non-Audited September 30, 2017
Advertising Rate (weekday/saturday): Open inch rate $15.75
Advertising Rate (sunday): Open inch rate $15.75
News services: AP **Established:** 1827
Own Printing Facility?: Yes
Commercial Printers?: Yes
Special Editions: Battle of Selma (Apr); Kickoff-Football (Aug); Horizons-Progress (Feb); FYI-For Your Information (Jun); Graduation (May); Chamber of Commerce (Nov); Women in Business (Sept); Health & Fitness (Jan); Hoopla (Nov); Pilgrimage (Mar); Industry (Jun); Calender (Dec)
Syndicated Publications: Parade (S).
Pub .... Dennis Palmer
VP/Bus. Mgr. .... Jay Davis
Audience Devt. Mgr .... Tasha Tice
Ed. .... Justin Averette
Prodn. Mgr. .... Fred Scott
Adv. Mgr. .... Tina Yelverton
Acct. Dept Mgr .... Stephanie Reeves
Composition Mgr .... Karen Lawler
News Ed. .... Daniel Evans
Market Information: Split run; TMC; Zoned editions.
Mechanical Available: Offset; Black and 3 ROP colors; insert accepted; page cutoffs - 22 3/4.
Mechanical Specifications: Type page 13 x 21 1/2; E - 6 cols, 2 1/16, 1/8 between; A - 6 cols, 2 1/16, 1/8 between; C - 10 cols, 1 3/8, 1/16 between.
Areas Served: Dallas, Wilcox, Perry Counties
Delivery Method: Mail, Newsstand, Carrier, RacksEquipment & Software: PRESSROOM EQUIPMENT: Lines — 10-KP/News King.; MAILROOM EQUIPMENT: Counter Stackers — 1/BG; Inserters & Stuffers — By hand; Tying Machines — 1-/Bu; Address Machine — 1-/KR.; BUSINESS EQUIPMENT: PC CLASSIFIED EQUIPMENT: Hardware — APP/Mac; APP/Mac; CLASSIFIED SOFTWARE: Baseview 1. DISPLAY SOFTWARELayout Software — 4-APP/Mac. EDITORIAL EQUIPMENT: Hardware — APP/Mac. PRODUCTION EQUIPMENT: Hardware — Kodak, Trendsetter direct to plate

TALLADEGA

THE DAILY HOME

6 Sylacauga Hwy, Talladega, Ala., 35160, Talladega; gen tel (256) 362-1000; adv tel (256) 362-1000; ed tel (256) 362-1000; gen fax (256) 299-2192; adv fax (256) 299-2197; ed fax (256) 362-2192; gen/nat adv e-mail padamson@dailyhome.com; disp adv e-mail padamson@dailyhome.com; class adv e-mailchutto@dailyhome.com; ed e-mail efowler@dailyhome.com; web site www.dailyhome.com

Group: Consolidated Publishing Co.
Published: Tues, Wed, Thur, Fri, Sat, Sun
Weekday Frequency: m

Saturday Frequency: m
Circulation: 9,872; 9,872(sat); 9,872(sun)
Last Audit: Sworn/Estimate/Non-Audited September 30, 2017
Branch Offices: Pell City, AL
Sylacauga, AL
Advertising Rate (weekday/saturday): Open inch rate $15.80
News services: AP. **Established:** 1867
Own Printing Facility?: No
Commercial Printers?: No
Special Editions: Uppdate (February) Football (Aug); Spirit of Christmas (Dec); Vacation Drawing (Feb);Lakeside (monthly) Home & Garden (Mar); Graduation Tab (May); Christmas Gift Guide (Nov); Adopt A Pet Classified Promotion (Oct)
Special Weekly Sections: Religion Page (Sat); Food Page (Wed).
Syndicated Publications: Parade (S).
Digital Platform - Mobile: Apple, Windows
Publisher....Robert Jackson
Webpage Coord.....Jim Smothers
Adv. Dir.....Pam Adamson
Assoc. Ed.....Janice Keith
Adv. Mgr., Retail Sales....Sandy Carden
Classified Mgr.....Carrie Hutto
Circ. Mgr.....Kandi Macy
Sports Ed.....LaVonte Young
Business Mgr....Barbara Wilson
Market Information: ADS; Split run; TMC; Zoned editions.
Mechanical Available: Offset; Black and 3 ROP colors; insert accepted; page cutoffs - 22 3/4.
Mechanical Specifications: Type page 13 x 21 1/2; E - 6 cols, 2 1/16, 1/8 between; A - 6 cols, 2 1/16, 1/8 between; C - 9 cols, 1 3/8, 1/16 between.
Areas Served: Talladega & St. Clair Counties
Delivery Method: Mail, Newsstand, Carrier, RacksEquipment & Software: BUSINESS EQUIPMENT: IBM CLASSIFIED EQUIPMENT: Hardware — APP/Mac; Printers — APP/Mac LaserWriter I; CLASSIFIED SOFTWARE: Baseview. DISPLAY EQUIPMENT: Hardware — APP/Mac; Printers — APP/Mac LaserWriter I; DISPLAY SOFTWAREAd Make-up Applications — Aldus/PageMaker, Microsoft/Word.; EDITORIAL EQUIPMENT: Hardware — APP/Mac/HP/Flatbed Scanner, Polaroid/Film Scanner; Printers — APP/Mac LaserWriter I EDITORIAL SOFTWARE: Aldus/PageMaker, Microsoft/Word, QPS/QuarkXPress. CIRCULATION SOFTWARDTI

TROY

THE TROY MESSENGER

918 S Brundidge St, Troy, Ala., 36081-3222, Pike; gen tel (334) 566-4270; adv tel (334) 670-6306; ed tel (334) 670-6323; gen fax (334) 566-4281; adv fax (334) 566-4281; ed fax (334) 566-4281; gen/nat adv e-mail travis.williams@troymessenger.com; disp adv e-mail brittany.harrison@troymessenger.com; class adv e-mailrachel.hicks@troymessenger.com; ed e-mail robbyn.brooks@troymessenger.com; web site www.troymessenger.com
Group: Boone Newspapers, Inc.
Published: Tues, Wed, Thur, Fri, Sun
Weekday Frequency: m
Circulation: 2,814; 2,814(sun)
Last Audit: Sworn/Estimate/Non-Audited September 30, 2017
Advertising Rate (weekday/saturday): Open inch rate $14.90
News services: NEA. **Established:** 1866
Syndicated Publications: American Profile (Weekly).
Pub.....Stacy Graning
Features Ed.....Jaine Treadwell
Sports Writer....Mike Hensley
Staff Writer....Scottie Brown
Class. Mgr and Bookkeeping....Jessica Stuff
Retail Advert....Travis Williams
Distrb. Mgr....Rennie Raines
Market Information: TMC; Zoned editions.
Mechanical Available: Offset; Black and 3 ROP colors; insert accepted.
Mechanical Specifications: Type page 13 1/2 x 21 1/2; E - 6 cols, 2, 1/4 between; A - 6 cols, 2, 1/4 between; C - 9 cols, 1 5/16, 1/4 between.
Areas Served: Troy and Pike County
Equipment & Software: CLASSIFIED EQUIPMENT: Hardware — Mk.; DISPLAY SOFTWARELayout Software — APP/Mac LC II, Mk/Newswriter. EDITORIAL EQUIPMENT: Hardware — Mk/Newswriter. PRODUCTION EQUIPMENT: Hardware — Mk/LaserWriter.
Note: For printing information see Andalusia Star News.

TUSCALOOSA

THE TUSCALOOSA NEWS

315 28th Ave, Tuscaloosa, Ala., 35401-1022, Tuscaloosa; gen tel (205) 345-0505; adv tel (205) 722-0148; ed tel (866)400-8477; gen fax (205) 349-0802; adv fax (205) 722-0175; ed fax (205) 349-0802; gen/nat adv e-mail chris.powell@tuscaloosanews.com; disp adv e-mail chris.powell@tuscaloosanews.com; class adv e-mailchris.powell@tuscaloosanews.com; ed e-mail michael.james@tuscaloosanews.com; web site www.tuscaloosanews.com
- 2,700,000(views) 428,000(visitors)
Group: New Media Investment Group
Published: Mon, Tues, Wed, Thur, Fri, Sat, Sun
Weekday Frequency: m
Saturday Frequency: m
Circulation: 23,374; 23,042(sat); 27,214(sun)
Last Audit: AAM March 31, 2016
Advertising Rate (weekday/saturday): Open inch rate $51.73
Advertising Rate (sunday): Open inch rate $54.12
Online Advertising Rate: Banner: $10
News services: AP, NYT. **Established:** 1818
Own Printing Facility?: Yes
Commercial Printers?: Yes
Special Editions: University of Alabama Today (Aug); Fall Homes Decorating (Dec); Focus (Feb); Back-to-School (Jul); Family-owned Businesses (Jun); Focus (Mar); Outdoors (May); Parade of Homes (Oct); Outdoors (Sept).
Special Weekly Sections: Church Page (Fri); TV Click (S); Best Food Day (Wed).
Syndicated Publications: Parade (S).
Digital Platform - Mobile: Apple, Android, Windows, Blackberry
Digital Platform - Tablet: Apple iOS, Android, Windows 7, Blackberry Tablet OS, Kindle, Nook, Kindle Fire
Pub.....Jim Rainey
Exec. Ed.....Michael James
Sports Ed.....Tommy Deas
Cust. Serv Mgr....Jessica Sargent
Prodn. Mgr.,....Steven Fowler
Exec Assist.....Carla Gillespie
City Ed.....Ken Roberts
Photo Dept. Mgr.....Robert Sutton
Mng. Ed. (Sports)....Edwin Stanton
Theater/Music Ed.....Mark Cobb
Opns. Dir.....Paul Hass
Creative Serv Dir.....Sam Kirkwood
Prepress/Commercial Print Manager Chuck Jones
Dir of Finance....Steve Hopper
News Clerk....Peggy Skelton Johnson
Adv. Majors Mgr.....Don Wallace
Adv. Retail Mgr.....Chris Powell
Market Information: TMC.
Mechanical Available: Offset; Black and 3 ROP colors; insert accepted - any size; page cutoffs - 22 3/4.
Mechanical Specifications: Type page 13 x 21 1/2; E - 6 cols, 2 1/16, 1/8 between; A - 6 cols, 2 1/16, 1/8 between; C - 9 cols, 1 3/8, 1/16 between.
Areas Served: West Alabama
Delivery Method: Carrier, RacksEquipment & Software: PRESSROOM EQUIPMENT: Lines — 10-G/Urbanite, 1-G/Urbanite (3 color); Pasters —8-Ebway/H535000; Control System — 2; Registration System — KFM/Pin System. MAILROOM EQUIPMENT: Counter Stackers — 3-HL/Monitor; Inserters & Stuffers — 1-S/10-48P; Tying Machines — 1-MLN/ML, 1/Power Strap, 1-MLN/MLEE, 1-Dynaric/NP-2; Address Machine — 1-/KR.; BUSINESS EQUIPMENT: IBM/AS-400 CLASSIFIED EQUIPMENT: Hardware — PC, Microsoft/Windows NT; Printers — HP/5000; CLASSIFIED SOFTWARE: AT/IAS, Computext. DISPLAY EQUIPMENT: Hardware — APP/Mac; Printers — QMS, HP/Color; Other Hardware — X/Scanner, Kk/Scanner DISPLAY SOFTWAREAd Make-up Applications — QPS/QuarkXPress, Adobe/Photoshop; Layout Software — CompuText. EDITORIAL EQUIPMENT: Hardware — PC, Microsoft/Windows NT; Printers — HP/5000 EDITORIAL SOFTWARE: CompuText. PRODUCTION EQUIPMENT: Hardware — 2-COM/9600, 1-Nu/Flip Top FT52UPNS; Cameras — 1-C/Spartan III, 1-R; Scanners — 2-Kk/RFS 2035+, 2-X/11x17 Flatbed PRODUCTION SOFTWARE: CompUtext.

ALASKA

ANCHORAGE

ALASKA DISPATCH NEWS

300 W 31st Ave, Anchorage, Alaska, 99503-3878, Anchorage; gen tel (907) 257-4200; adv tel (907) 257-4504; ed tel (907) 257-4303; gen fax (907) 279-7579; adv fax (907)279-8170; ed fax (907) 258-2157; gen/nat adv e-mail advertising@alaskadispatch.com; disp adv e-mail advertising@alaskadispatch.com; class adv e-mailclassifieds@alaskadispatch.com; ed e-mail newstips@alaskadispatch.com; web site www.adn.com
- 11,547,966(views) 1,528,515(visitors); web site 2 www.showmealaska.net
Group: Alaska Dispatch Publishing LLC
Published: Mon, Tues, Wed, Thur, Fri, Sat, Sun
Weekday Frequency: All day
Saturday Frequency: All day
Circulation: 33,301; 29,110(sat); 34,908(sun)
Last Audit: AAM June 30, 2016
Newspaper Reps: David Hulen, Executive Editor
Roger Weinfurter, VP, Audience Engagement
Advertising Rate (weekday/saturday): Open inch rate $121.60 (Mon-Thur); $122.65 (Fri-Sat)
Advertising Rate (sunday): Open inch rate $147.25
Online Advertising Rate: In-State 300x250 $12-19 CPM; Floorboard $20 CPM; Pencil $21 CPM; Outside Alaska $5 CPM; City-level targeting $2 CPM; Rich media $5 CPM; Day parting $2 CPM; Mobile only $14-25 CPM; Premium positions $1,250-$3,250
News services: NYT, LAT-WP, MCT, RN, CNS, DJ, TMS, UPI. **Established:** 2014
Own Printing Facility?: Yes
Commercial Printers?: Yes
Special Editions: Best of Alaska (Jan); Iditarod (Feb); Back to School (Aug); Holiday Gift Guide (Nov)
Special Weekly Sections: We Alaskans (Sun); Alaska Life (Sun); Play (Fri)
Proprietary Publications: 61º North; Show Me Alaska/Visitors' Guide; We Alaskans; Community Xtra!; Best of Alaska
Digital Platform - Mobile: Apple, Android, Windows
Digital Platform - Tablet: Apple iOS, Kindle, Nook, Kindle Fire
Pub.....Alice Rogoff
Executive Ed.....David Hulen
Advertising Operations Director....Kea Cuaresma
Director, Sales & Special Content....Maia Nolan-Partnow
Executive Vice President....Margy Johnson
VP, Audience Engagement....Roger Weinfurter
VP, Production....Ken Carter
Market Information: ADS; TMC; Zoned editions.
Mechanical Available: Offset; Black and 3 ROP colors; insert accepted; page cutoffs - 21 1/8.
Mechanical Specifications: Type page 11 5/8 x 20 7/8; E - 6 cols, 1 7/8, 3/16 between; A - 6 cols, 1 7/8, 3/16 between; C - 10 cols, 1 7/25, 1/8 between.
Areas Served: Entire state of Alaska
Delivery Method: Mail, Newsstand, Carrier, RacksEquipment & Software: PRESSROOM EQUIPMENT: Lines — 9-G/Headliner offset double width 1986; 4-HL/V-30 Heatset single width 1995; Press Drive — 9-GE/Motors, Fin/Controllers, 2-GE Motor/Fin/Control, 1-GE w/GE/Controllers; Folders — 2-G/3:2 (144 page; MAILROOM EQUIPMENT: Counter Stackers — 4-Hall/HT II, 3-QWI/401; Inserters & Stuffers — 1-HI/14-72, 1-GMA/S-1000, MM/227 5:1; Tying Machines — 1/Power Strap, 2-Signode/Spirit, 4-Dynamic/NP 1500, 2-Signode/LB2000, 2-QWI/Viper, PBS/Insert Management; Address Machine — Addressing machin;
Note: Semiannual Alaska job fairs (April, Sept); Best of Alaska Awards and Showcase (Jan)

FAIRBANKS

FAIRBANKS DAILY NEWS-MINER

200 N Cushman St, Fairbanks, Alaska, 99701-2832, Fairbanks North Star; gen tel (907) 456-6661; adv tel (907) 459-7548; ed tel (907) 459-7572; gen fax (907) 452-5054; adv fax (907) 451-8962; ed fax (907) 452-7917; gen/nat adv e-mail editor@newsminer.com; disp adv e-mail ads@newsminer.com; class adv e-mailads@newsminer.com; ed e-mail newsroom@newsminer.com; web site www.newsminer.com
- 2,700,000(views) 380,000(visitors)
Group: Helen E Snedded Foundation
Published: Mon, Tues, Wed, Thur, Fri, Sat, Sun
Weekday Frequency: m
Saturday Frequency: m
Circulation: 13,356; 13,356(sat); 16,022(sun)
Last Audit: AAM September 30, 2014
Advertising Rate (weekday/saturday): Open inch rate $27.88
Advertising Rate (sunday): Open inch rate $27.88
Online Advertising Rate: Call for current rates.
News services: AP, NYT. **Established:** 1903
Own Printing Facility?: Yes
Special Editions: Building (Apr); Back-to-School (Aug); Christmas Greeter (Dec); Valentine's Day (Feb); Hunting (Jul); Visitor's Guide (Jun); Winter Carnival (Mar); Christmas Shopper (Nov); Winter Survival (Sept).
Special Weekly Sections: Health (Tue); Best Food Day (Wed); Outdoors, Religion Arts, Nightlife (Fri); Youth (Sat); TV, Business (Sun); Entertainment (Daily)
Syndicated Publications: Parade (S).
Digital Platform - Mobile: Apple, Android, Windows, Blackberry
Digital Platform - Tablet: Apple iOS, Android, Blackberry Tablet OS
Gen. Mgr.....Katherine Strle
Mng. Ed.....Rod Boyce
Online Ed.....Julie Strcker
MulitM Acc. Exec.....Danita Swensson
Pub.....Fuller Cowell
Mechanical Available: Offset; Black and 3 ROP colors; insert accepted; page cutoffs - 22 3/4.
Mechanical Specifications: Type page 12 7/8 x 21; E - 6 cols, 2 1/16, 1/8 between; A - 6 cols, 2 1/16, 1/8 between; C - 10 cols, 1 1/4, 1/12 between.
Areas Served: North & West Alaska
Delivery Method: Mail, Newsstand, Carrier, RacksEquipment & Software: PRESSROOM EQUIPMENT: Lines — 11-G/Urbanite; 4-G 1965; 1-G/Urbanite 1996; 1-G/Urbanite 1997; 4-G/Urbanite 1998; Press Drive — 1-HP/75, 1-HP/100; Folders — 1-G/2:1; Reels & Stands — 6-G/Urbanite; Control System — 2; MAILROOM EQUIPMENT: Counter Stackers — QWI/108; Inserters & Stuffers — 1-MM/227, 1-MM/227; Tying Machines — 2-MLN/EE; Wrapping Singles — 1-PRM/720; Address Machine — 1-IBM/AS-400; BUSINESS EQUIPMENT: 1-IBM/AS-400, 15-Gateway, Novell/LAN, Microsoft/Windows NT SQL BUSINESS SOFTWARE: Microsoft/Word, Microsoft/Excel, Libra, Abra Cadabra, Human Resources, Geac/Vision Shift CLASSIFIED EQUIPMENT: Hardware — 15-Pentium/PC; Printers — 3-Okidata; CLASSIFIED SOFTWARE: HI/CASH, Microsoft/Windows 95. DISPLAY EQUIPMENT: Hardware — 2-SCS/Layout 8000; Printers — 1-HP/1600C, 1-Case/Printer, 1-HP/Laserjet 6MP; Other Hardware — 1-HP/Scanjet 6100C DISPLAY SOFTWAREAd Make-up Applications — Multi-Ad/Creator 3.7; Layout Software — 2-SCS/Layout 8000, 5-APP/Power Mac G3. EDITORIAL EQUIPMENT: Hardware — 31-PC 486/1-Lf/AP Leaf Picture Desk, 1-APP/Power Mac G3; Printers — Panasonic, 1-APP/Mac LaserWriter II, Okidata EDITORIAL SOFTWARE: HI/PEN System. PRODUCTION EQUIPMENT: Hardware — TextBridge/Pro 98, 2-Gluntz & Jensen; Cameras — 1-R/16 x 20, 1-W/20

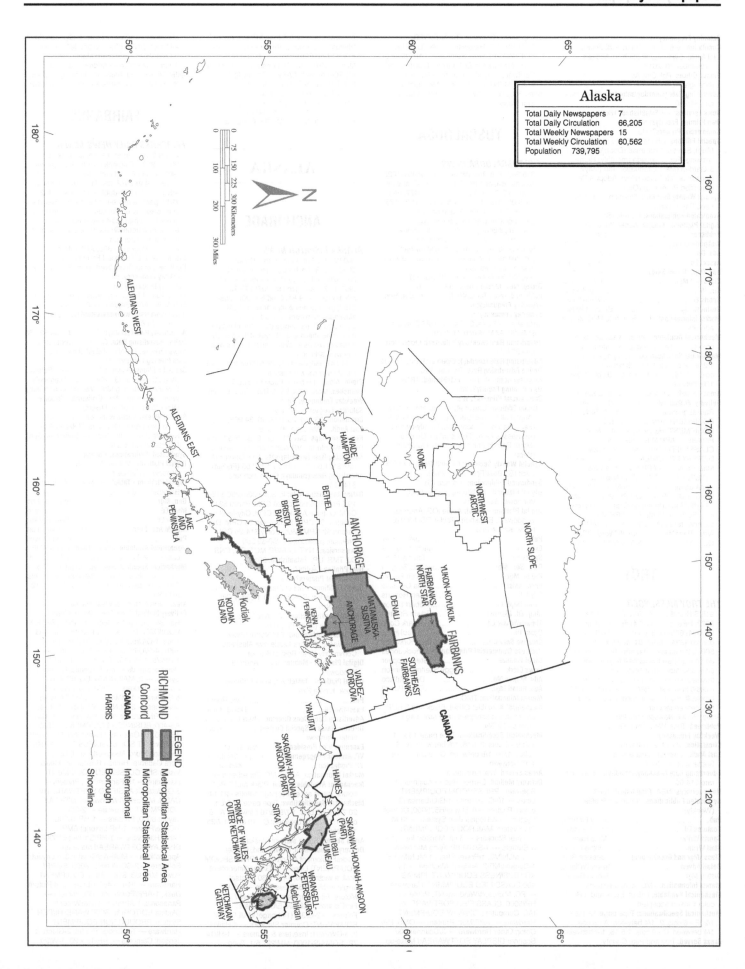

Alaska

Total Daily Newspapers	7
Total Daily Circulation	66,205
Total Weekly Newspapers	15
Total Weekly Circulation	60,562
Population	739,795

LEGEND

Metropolitan Statistical Area

RICHMOND
Concord

Micropolitan Statistical Area

CANADA

International

HARRIS

Borough

Shoreline

x 24; Scanners — 1-ECR/Autokon 8400 PRODUCTION SOFTWARE: HI/XP-21 Images.

JUNEAU

JUNEAU EMPIRE

3100 Channel Dr, Ste 1, Juneau, Alaska, 99801-7837, Juneau; gen tel (907) 586-3740; adv tel (907)523-2290; ed tel (907) 523-2265; gen fax (907) 586-9097; adv fax (907) 586-9097; ed fax (907) 586-3028; gen/nat adv e-mail kathryn.nickerson@juneauempire.com; disp adv e-mail kathryn.nickerson@juneauempire.com; class adv e-mailkathryn.nickerson@juneauempire.com; ed e-mail editor@juneauempire.com; web site www.juneauempire.com
- 1,100,000(views) 216,000(visitors)

Group: GateHouse Media, Inc.
Published: Mon, Tues, Wed, Thur, Fri, Sun
Weekday Frequency: m
Circulation: 4,371
Last Audit: Sworn/Estimate/Non-Audited September 30, 2017
Branch Offices: None
Advertising Rate (weekday/saturday): Open inch rate $22.00
Advertising Rate (sunday): Open inch rate $22.00
Online Advertising Rate: Leaderboard(top banner, 729x90 pixels): $18 per thousand impressions ; Max Ad(right side, 300x600 pixels): $16 per thousand imp ; Position(right side, 160x600 pixels): $15 per thousand imp; In-Story Ad(left side, 300x250 pixels): $15 per thousand imp; Bottom Banner(728x90 pixels): $3 per thousand imp.
News services: AP, MCT. **Established:** 1912
Own Printing Facility?: Yes
Commercial Printers?: Yes
Special Editions: Salmon Derby (Aug); Christmas (Dec); George Washington's Birthday (Feb); Legislature (Jan); Juneau Guide (May); High School Basketball Preview (Nov); Lifestyles (Oct).
Special Weekly Sections: Neighbors (Fri); TV Week (S); Preview (Thur); Spotlight (Tues); Neighbors (Wed).
Syndicated Publications: Juneau Guide - tourism/travel
Proprietary Publications: Capital City Weekly
Digital Platform - Mobile: Apple, Android, Windows
Digital Platform - Tablet: Apple iOS
Bus. Mgr. .... Shane Leavitt
Advertising Manager .... Kathryn Nickerson
Director of Audience .... Abby Lowell
Managing Editor .... Charles Westmoreland
Page Designer .... Sarah Cannard
Production and Commercial Printing .... Kerry Rasmussen
Photographer .... Michael Penn
Circulation Director and Production Director . Brian Naplachowski
Interim Pub. .... Deedie McKenzie
Market Information: ADS.
Mechanical Available: Offset; Black and 3 ROP colors; insert accepted; page cutoffs - 22 1/2.
Mechanical Specifications: Type page 13 x 21; E - 6 cols, 2 1/16, 1/8 between; A - 6 cols, 2 1/16, 1/8 between; C - 8 cols, 1 1/2, 1/8 between.
Areas Served: 99801
Delivery Method: Newsstand, Carrier, RacksEquipment & Software: PRESSROOM EQUIPMENT: Lines — 7-G/Community single width; Folders — 1-G/Community, G/SC (with Balloon former).; MAILROOM EQUIPMENT: Counter Stackers — BG/Count-O-Veyor; Inserters & Stuffers — KAN/8 units & counter; BUSINESS EQUIPMENT: Gateway, IBM/PS2 CLASSIFIED EQUIPMENT: Hardware — Gateway; Printers — Toshiba, Epson; CLASSIFIED SOFTWARE: MPS. DISPLAY EQUIPMENT: Hardware — APP/Macs, APP/Power Mac; Printers — AG/1500, HP/LaserJet 4 Plus; DISPLAY SOFTWAREAd Make-up Applications — Multi-Ad/Creator, QPS/QuarkXPress, InDesign.; EDITORIAL EQUIPMENT: Hardware — Gateway/AG/1500; Printers — APP/Mac II NTX EDITORIAL SOFTWARE: MPS/Tecs 2. PRODUCTION EQUIPMENT: Hardware — 2-M/202N; Cameras — C/Spartan III.

KENAI

PENINSULA CLARION

150 Trading Bay Rd, # 1, Kenai, Alaska, 99611-7716, Kenai Peninsula; gen tel (907) 283-7551; adv tel (907)283-7551; ed tel (907) 335-1251; gen fax (907) 283-3299; adv fax (907) 283-8144; ed fax (907) 283-3299; gen/nat adv e-mail advertising@peninsulaclarion.com; disp adv e-mail advertising@peninsulaclarion.com; class adv e-mailadvertising@peninsulaclarion.com; ed e-mail will.morrow@peninsulaclarion.com; web site www.peninsulaclarion.com; web site 2 alaskajobs.net

Group: GateHouse Media, Inc.
Published: Mon, Tues, Wed, Thur, Fri, Sun
Weekday Frequency: m
Circulation: 5,710; 5,710(sun)
Last Audit: Sworn/Estimate/Non-Audited September 30, 2017
Advertising Rate (weekday/saturday): Open inch rate $21.83
Advertising Rate (sunday): Open inch rate $21.83
Online Advertising Rate: Leaderboard $15; Skyscraper $13
News services: AP. **Established:** 1970
Special Editions: Mother's Day (Apr); Hunting (Aug); Greetings (Dec); Industry (Feb); Fathers' Day (Jun); Recreation Guide (May); Real Estate (Monthly); Coupon Book (Quarterly).
Special Weekly Sections: Community, Neighbors, Seniors (Mon); Schools, Pets (Tue); Grocery, Food (Wed); What's Happening, Entertainment, Business (Thur); Outdoors, Real Estate (Fri); Travel, Inside Alaska, Health, Nutrition, TV, Comics (Sun)
Digital Platform - Mobile: Apple, Android
Digital Platform - Tablet: Apple iOS, Android
Adv. Dir .... Leslie Talent
Mng. Ed. .... Will Morrow
City Ed. Reporter .... Brian Smith
Adv. Rep. .... Stephanie Davidson
Reporter .... Rashah McChesney
Adv. Rep .... Gregory Harrington
Classified Adv. .... Annette Evans-Helle
Circ.Mgr .... Tom Janz
HR .... Jane Rusell
Pub .... Vitto Kleinschmidt
Market Information: TMC.
Mechanical Available: Offset; Black and 3 ROP colors; insert accepted - all; page cutoffs - 21 1/2.
Mechanical Specifications: Type page 13 x 21 1/2; E - 6 cols, 2, 1/6 between; A - 6 cols, 2, 1/6 between; C - 8 cols, 1 1/2, 1/6 between.
Areas Served: Central Peninsula
Delivery Method: Mail, Newsstand, CarrierEquipment & Software: PRESSROOM EQUIPMENT: Lines — 8-G/Offset single width 1992; Press Drive — 2-Fin/60 h.p.; Reels & Stands — 3; MAILROOM EQUIPMENT: Counter Stackers — 1/BG; Inserters & Stuffers — 1-/St; Tying Machines — 3-/Bu; Wrapping Singles — 1-/St; Address Machine — 1-/St; BUSINESS EQUIPMENT: Gateway/EV500 CLASSIFIED EQUIPMENT: Hardware — APP/Mac.; EDITORIAL EQUIPMENT: Hardware — APP/Mac. PRODUCTION EQUIPMENT: Hardware — 2-Nu, XIT/Cadet, ECR/Imagesetter; Cameras — 1-R.

KETCHIKAN

KETCHIKAN DAILY NEWS

501 Dock St, Ketchikan, Alaska, 99901-6411, Ketchikan Gateway; gen tel (907) 225-3157; adv tel (907) 225-3157; ed tel (907) 225-3157; gen fax (907) 225-1096; adv fax (907) 225-1096; ed fax (907) 225-1096; gen/nat adv e-mail kdn@kpunet.net; disp adv e-mail kdn@kpunet.net; class adv e-mailclassifieds@ketchikandailynews.com; ed e-mail news@ketchikandailynews.com; web site www.ketchikandailynews.com

Group: Pioneer Printing Co.
Published: Mon, Tues, Wed, Thur, Fri, Sat
Weekday Frequency: m
Saturday Frequency: m
Circulation: 4,117; 4,117(sat)
Last Audit: Sworn/Estimate/Non-Audited September 30, 2017
Advertising Rate (weekday/saturday): Open inch rate $14.68
Online Advertising Rate: Banner: $40 Skyscraper: $28
News services: AP. **Established:** 1934
Special Editions: Christmas Card Edition (Annually).
Syndicated Publications: First City Scene (Sat).
Co-Pub. .... Lew Williams
Co-Pub. .... Tena Williams
Circ. Mgr. .... Lecile Kiffer
Mng. Ed. .... Terry Miller
Market Information: TMC.
Mechanical Available: Offset; Black and 3 ROP colors; insert accepted - anything; page cutoffs - 22 1/2.
Mechanical Specifications: Type page 13 1/2 x 21; E - 6 cols, 2 1/16, 1/8 between; A - 6 cols, 2 1/16, 1/8 between; C - 9 cols, 1 1/2, 1/16 between.
Areas Served: Entire state of Alaska
Delivery Method: Mail, Newsstand, Carrier, RacksEquipment & Software: PRESSROOM EQUIPMENT: Lines — 3-G/Community; 1-G/Universal; Folders — 1-G/2:1.; MAILROOM EQUIPMENT: Address Machine — 3/Wm.; CLASSIFIED EQUIPMENT: Hardware — Point 4.; EDITORIAL EQUIPMENT: Hardware — APP/Mac. PRODUCTION EQUIPMENT: Hardware — 1-COM/8400, APP/Mac LaserWriter II, COM/3400 Laserprinter; Cameras — 1-R/Vertical.

KODIAK

KODIAK DAILY MIRROR

1419 Selig St, Kodiak, Alaska, 99615-6450, Kodiak Island; gen tel (907) 486-3227; adv tel (907) 486-3227 ext. 613; ext. 628; ed tel (907) 486-3227 ext. 622 ; gen fax (907) 486-3088; adv fax (907)486-3088; ed fax (907)225-3157; gen/nat adv e-mail advertising@kodiakdailymirror.com; disp adv e-mail sales@kodiakdailymirror.com; class adv e-mailclassifieds@kodiakdailymirror.com; ed e-mail editor@kodiakdailymirror.com; web site www.kodiakdailymirror.com
- 130,000(views) 50,000(visitors)

Group: Helen E Snedded Foundation
Published: Mon, Tues, Wed, Thur, Fri
Weekday Frequency: e
Circulation: 2,849
Last Audit: Sworn/Estimate/Non-Audited September 30, 2017
Advertising Rate (weekday/saturday): Open inch rate $14.00 pci
Advertising Rate (sunday): n/a
Online Advertising Rate: Leaderboard - $0.005 CPM
Global - $0.003 CPM
1/2 Global - $0.0018
News services: AP, CNS, TMS. **Established:** 1940
Own Printing Facility?: Yes
Commercial Printers?: No
Special Editions: United States Coast Guard Supplement (Aug); Holiday Gift Guide (Dec); Bear Chronicles (Apr); Graduation (May); ComFish (Mar); Crab Festival (May); Summer Adventures (May); Getting Involved (Mar, Sep); Holiday Greetings (Dec); Joe Floyd Tournament Preview (Jan); Health & Fitness (Feb); Back to School (Aug).
Special Weekly Sections: Fisheries Wrap up (Mon); Gardengate (Mon); Outdoors (Tues).
Publisher .... Richard Harris
Reporter .... Derek Clakston
Circulation .... Janet Baker
Pressroom .... Michael McGee
Business Manager .... Pam Reynolds
Reporter .... Julie Herrmann
Reporter .... Nicole Klauss
Editor .... James Brooks
Office Manager .... Dan Zeleznik
Advertising Sales .... Nicole Clark
Market Information: TMC.
Mechanical Available: Offset; Black and 3 ROP colors; insert accepted - any; page cutoffs - 22 3/4 Folded.
Mechanical Specifications: Type page 11 1/2 x 21; E - 6 cols, 3 3/4, 3/16 between; A - 6 cols, 3 3/4, 3/16 between; C - 6 cols, 3 3/4, 3/16 between.
Areas Served: 01001, 03048, 10021, 26301, 33431, 33630, 34610, 45309, 49038, 50325, 71913, 80202, 83854, 84037, 92116, 94553, 95222, 97007, 97324, 97365, 97365, 98188, 98195, 98199, 98370, 98607, 99337, 99501, 99503, 99504, 99506, 99508, 99515, 99517, 99519, 99521, 99550, 99565, 99577, 99603, 99615, 99619, 99624, 99643, 99644, 99664, 99669, 99685, 99686, 99697, 99701, 99775, 99811
Delivery Method: Mail, Carrier, RacksEquipment & Software: PRESSROOM EQUIPMENT: Lines — 5-G/Community.; BUSINESS EQUIPMENT: Compaq/586-166 BUSINESS SOFTWARE: Synaptic CLASSIFIED EQUIPMENT: Hardware — 1-APP/Mac Mini; CLASSIFIED SOFTWARE: AdManagerPro4 DISPLAY EQUIPMENT: Hardware — APP/iMac; Other Hardware — APP/Mac Mini, APP/iPad (3rd Gen) DISPLAY SOFTWAREAd Make-up Applications — Adobe/Creator, Adobe/InDesign CS4, Adobe/InDesign CS2, Adobe/Photoshop CS2 EDITORIAL EQUIPMENT: Hardware — APP/iMac; Other Hardware — APP/Mac Mini; Printers — HP/LaserJet EDITORIAL SOFTWARE: Microsoft/Word. PRODUCTION EQUIPMENT: Hardware — Nu/Flip Top FT40UP; Cameras — SCREEN/Companica 516.

SITKA

DAILY SITKA SENTINEL

112 Barracks St, Sitka, Alaska, 99835-7532, Sitka; gen tel (907) 747-3219; adv tel (907) 747-3219; ed tel (907) 747-3219; gen fax (907) 747-8898; adv fax (907) 747-8898; ed fax (907) 747-8898; gen/nat adv e-mail susan@sitkasentinel.com; disp adv e-mail susan@sitkasentinel.com; class adv e-mailcyndi@sitkasentinel.com; ed e-mail thad@sitkasentinel.com; web site www.sitkasentinel.com

Group: Verstovia Corp.
Published: Mon, Tues, Wed, Thur, Fri
Weekday Frequency: e
Circulation: 2,501
Last Audit: Sworn/Estimate/Non-Audited September 30, 2017
Advertising Rate (weekday/saturday): Open inch rate $13.85
Online Advertising Rate: Banner: $100/Month; Skyscraper: $65/Month
News services: AP. **Established:** 1940
Own Printing Facility?: Yes
Commercial Printers?: Yes
Special Editions: Back-to-School (Aug); Christmas Greetings (Dec); Boat Show (Mar); Summer Visitors (May); Christmas Shopping Issue (Nov); Moonlight Madness (Oct).
Special Weekly Sections: Sitka Weekend (entertainment, TV schedules, feature stories)
Co-Pub. .... Thad Poulson
Adv. Mgr. .... Susan Mcfadden
Ed. .... Sandy Poulson
Market Information: Only daily serving Sitka, pop. 8,500
Mechanical Available: Offset; Black and 3 ROP colors; insert accepted; page cutoffs - 22 3/4.
Mechanical Specifications: Type page 13 1/2 x 21; E - 6 cols, 2 1/16, 1/8 between; A - 6 cols, 2 1/16, 1/8 between; C - 6 cols, 2 1/16, 1/8 between.
Areas Served: Sitka
Delivery Method: Newsstand, CarrierEquipment & Software: PRESSROOM EQUIPMENT: Lines — 4-G/CommunityECRM 4x CTP MAILROOM EQUIPMENT: Tying Machines — Felins/Paktyer; Address Machine — Wm.; BUSINESS EQUIPMENT: 3-Microsoft/Windows BUSINESS SOFTWARE: Quickbooks CLASSIFIED EQUIPMENT: Hardware — IBM; Printers — HP/Laser Jet, CLASSIFIED SOFTWARE: TC 1.348. Media Span DISPLAY EQUIPMENT: Networked Macs,scanner, copier DISPLAY SOFTWAREAd Make-up Applications — Aldus/PageMaker, Adobe/Illustrator, Adobe/Photo Shop; Layout Software, Media Span ad management — APP/Mac. EDITORIAL EQUIPMENT: Hardware — 10 mac minis and two Windows computers in network. 3 laser printers, scanners, misc. modems, switches and routers EDITORIAL SOFTWARE: Adobe InCopy, Pagemaker, Photoshop, Illustrator, Acrobat,InDesign PRODUCTION

EQUIPMENT: ECRM Mako 4x CTP PRODUCTION SOFTWARE: InDesign CIRCULATION EQUIPMENT: Windows Computers CIRCULATION SOFTWARSatori
Note: Thad

ARIZONA

BULLHEAD CITY

MOHAVE VALLEY DAILY NEWS

2435 Miracle Mile, Bullhead City, Ariz., 86442-7311, Mohave; gen tel 928-763-2505; adv tel (928) 763-2505 ext. 2221; ed tel (928) 763-2505 ext. 5144; gen fax 928-763-2509; adv fax (928) 763-7820; ed fax (928) 763-7820; gen/nat adv e-mail national@nwppub.com; disp adv e-mail national@nwppub.com; class adv e-mailfastclassifieds@nwppub.com; ed e-mail bmcmillen@mohavedailynews.com; web site www.mohavedailynews.com - 365,000(views) 100,000(visitors); web site 2 http://laughlinentertainer.com/; web site 3 www.needlesdesertstar.com
Group: Brehm Communications, Inc.
Published: Mon, Tues, Wed, Thur, Fri, Sun
Weekday Frequency: m
Circulation: 7,006; 7,610(sun)
Last Audit: AAM December 31, 2016
Newspaper Reps: Larry Kendrick (General Manager - Production)
Bill McMillen (City Editor)
Don Orth (General Manager)
Jamie McCorkle (Sales Manager)
Branch Offices: (Needles Desert Star) 800 W. Broadway, Needles CA 92363
Advertising Rate (weekday/saturday): Open inch rate $25.10
Advertising Rate (sunday): $25.10
Online Advertising Rate: Pencil Ad $450(x1) ; Leaderboard $295(x10) ; In-Story Ad $295(x10) ; Skyscraper $175(x10) ; Side title $175(x5)
News services: AP. **Established:** 1963
Own Printing Facility?: Yes
Commercial Printers?: Yes
Special Editions: Resource Guide, January; Dining Out, February; Health & Wellness, March; River Run, April; May, Life on the Colorado; Best Of, June; Newcomer's Guide, October; Happy Holidays, November; Last Minute Gift Guide, December.
Special Weekly Sections: Laughlin Nevada Times (weekly)
Needles Desert Star (weekly)
Boosters (shoppers)
Clippin' the River (TMC)
Colorado River Real Estate Magazine (monthly)
Desert Deals (monthly coupon book)
Syndicated Publications: American Profile (Tuesday)
Proprietary Publications: Laughlin Entertainer
Colorado River Real Estate Magazine
Clippin the River
Boosters
Digital Platform - Mobile: Apple, Android, Windows, Blackberry
Digital Platform - Tablet: Apple iOS, Android, Windows 7, Blackberry Tablet OS, Kindle, Nook, Kindle Fire
City Editor .... Bill McMillen
Sports Ed. ....Daniel McKillop
CTP (Creo).......................................Carlos Ruiz
Circ. Mgr./Classifieds...........................Don Orth
Operations Director...................... Larry Kendrick
Sales Manager .... Jamie McCorkle
Market Information: ADS; TMC.
Mechanical Available: Offset; Black and 3 ROP colors; insert accepted - most; page cutoffs - 22 3/4.
Mechanical Specifications: Type page 13 x 21; E - 6 cols, 1 13/16, 1/6 between; A - 6 cols, 1 13/16, 1/6 between; C - 6 cols, 1 13/16, 1/6 between.
Areas Served: Bullhead City, Fort Mojave, Mohave Valley, Topock, & Golden Shores (Ariz) ; Laughlin (Nev) ; Needles (Calif)
Delivery Method: Mail, Newsstand, Carrier, RacksEquipment & Software: PRESSROOM EQUIPMENT: Lines — 3-WPC/Atlas single width, 1-WPC/Marc 25; 1-WPC/Quad stack single width, 3-WPC/Marc 25; Folders — WPC (1/4-1/2), WPC/Mark 25 1999; Reels & Stands — 4; MAILROOM EQUIPMENT: Tying Machines — MLN/2EE, OVL, It; BUSINESS EQUIPMENT: Qantel BUSINESS SOFTWARE: Quattro/Pro CLASSIFIED EQUIPMENT: Hardware — APP/iMac; Printers — Xante/Accel-a-Writer 8300, Xante/Accel-a-Writer 3G; CLASSIFIED SOFTWARE: Baseview/Ad Manager Pro. DISPLAY EQUIPMENT: Hardware — APP/Mac G4; Printers — Xante/Accel-a-Writer 8300, Xante/Accel-a-Writer 3G; Other Hardware — HP/800 Plotter DISPLAY SOFTWAREAd Make-up Applications — Multi-Ad/Creator 6, Aldus/Freehand 10.0, Adobe/Photoshop 7.0, Adobe/Color Access, Adobe/Illustrator 9.0, Adobe/PageMaker 6.5; EDITORIAL EQUIPMENT: Hardware — APP/Mac; Printers — Xante/Accel-a-Writer 3G, Xante/Accel-a-Writer 8300 EDITORIAL SOFTWARE: Baseview/NewsEdit Pro, QPS, Aldus/Freehand, Adobe/Photoshop, Adobe/Color Access, Baseview. PRODUCTION EQUIPMENT: Hardware — GTS/OLIC, 2-Post Script/Level 3, 2-Pre Press/Panther Pro V; Cameras — B; Scanners — Lf, Microtek, Umax/Flatbed, Nikon/Coolscan LS-2000 PRODUCTION SOFTWARE: Baseview, Quark 4.0.

CASA GRANDE

CASA GRANDE DISPATCH

200 W 2nd St, Casa Grande, Ariz., 85122-4409, Pinal; gen tel (520) 836-7461; adv tel (520) 426-3814; ed tel (520) 423-8611; gen fax (520) 836-0343; adv fax (520) 836-8522; gen/nat adv e-mail ads@trivalleycentral.com; class adv e-mailclassifieds@trivalleycentral.com; ed e-mail dkramerjr@pinalcentral.com; web site www.pinalcentral.com
Group: Casa Grande Valley Newspapers Inc.
Published: Tues, Wed, Thur, Fri, Sat, Sun
Weekday Frequency: m
Saturday Frequency: m
Circulation: 6,252; 6,252(sat); 6,551(sun)
Last Audit: AAM December 31, 2016
Advertising Rate (weekday/saturday): Open inch rate $14.17
News services: AP. **Established:** 1912
Own Printing Facility?: Yes
Commercial Printers?: Yes
Special Editions: Home Improvement (Apr); Back-to-School (Aug); Christmas (Dec); O'Odham Tash (Indian Days) (Feb); Customer Appreciation (Jul); Car Care (Jun); Spring Fashion (Mar); Graduation (May); Real Estate (Monthly); Gift Guide (Nov); Cotton Issue (Oct).
Special Weekly Sections: Tri-Valley Dispatch (Wed).
Syndicated Publications: Pinal Ways (Quarterly); USA WEEKEND Magazine (Sat);
Digital Platform - Tablet: Kindle
Co-Pub./Adv. Dir. ....Kara K. Cooper
Co-Pub./Managing Ed. ....Donovan Kramer Jr.
Data Processing Mgr., Prodn. Systems...........Rob Williams
CFO... Andre Phillips
Prodn. Dir........................................Mark Urseth
Asst. Managing Editor..................... Andy Howell
Special Projects.............................. Zoe Cooper
Circ. Dir. .... Brian Kramer
Sports Ed. .... Ed Petruska
Assignment Ed......................... Shelley Ridenour
Market Information: ADS; TMC.
Mechanical Available: Offset; Black and 3 ROP colors; insert accepted; page cutoffs - 22 3/4.
Mechanical Specifications: Type page 13 x 21 1/2; E - 6 cols, 2 1/16, 1/8 between; A - 6 cols, 2 1/16, 1/8 between; C - 8 cols, 1 9/16, 1/8 between.
Areas Served: 85122, 85194, 85172, 85128, 85147, 85131, 85132, 85139
Delivery Method: Newsstand, CarrierEquipment & Software: PRESSROOM EQUIPMENT: Lines — 13-G/Community; 2, 3; Folders — 2-G/Suburban (with balloon), G/SSC.; MAILROOM EQUIPMENT: Counter Stackers — 2-BG/105; Inserters & Stuffers — 1-KAN/480 Inserter; Tying Machines — 2-MLN/ML2EE; Address Machine — 1/Wm.; BUSINESS EQUIPMENT: GEAC/Vision Shift, Covalent CLASSIFIED EQUIPMENT: Hardware — APP/Mac Quadra 630; Printers — Okidata; CLASSIFIED SOFTWARE: Baseview/Class Manager 3.0.6. DISPLAY EQUIPMENT: Hardware — APP/Power Mac; Printers — APP/Mac LaserWriter Pro 16/600, Xante/Accel-a-Writer 8200, Tektronix/Phaser 300; DISPLAY SOFTWAREAd Make-up Applications — Multi-Ad/Creator 4.0, QPS/QuarkXPress 3.32.; EDITORIAL EQUIPMENT: Hardware — APP/Power Mac, APP/Mac Quadra/Phrasea/Archive (photo/text); Printers — APP/Mac LaserWriter IIq EDITORIAL SOFTWARE: Baseview/NewsEdit Pro IQUE, Baseview/Wire Manager IQ Pro, QPS/QuarkXPress 3.32. PRODUCTION EQUIPMENT: Hardware — Caere/OmniPage Direct, AG/Accuset 1500, AG/Viper RIP, Vista/88; Cameras — 1-DAI/C-260-D PRODUCTION SOFTWARE: QPS/QuarkXPress 3.32.

FLAGSTAFF

ARIZONA DAILY SUN, FLAGSTAFF

1751 S Thompson St, Flagstaff, Ariz., 86001-8716, Coconino; gen tel (928) 774-4545; adv tel (928) 774-4545; ed tel (928) 556-2241; gen fax (928) 773-1934; ed fax (928) 774-4790; gen/nat adv e-mail drowley@azdailysun.com; disp adv e-mail cbrady@azdailysun.com; class adv e-maillsmith@azdailysun.com; ed e-mail news@azdailysun.com; web site www.azdailysun.com - 1,230,000(views) 220,139(visitors)
Group: Lee Enterprises, Inc.
Published: Tues, Wed, Thur, Fri, Sat, Sun
Weekday Frequency: m
Saturday Frequency: m
Circulation: 7,412; 7,212(sat); 8,250(sun)
Last Audit: Sworn/Estimate/Non-Audited September 9, 2017
Newspaper Reps: Zachary Meier
Kevin Moore
Lydia Smith
Advertising Rate (weekday/saturday): Open inch rate $28.40
Advertising Rate (sunday): Open in ch rate $34.08
Online Advertising Rate: $10 CPM ROS big box and leaderboard; Mobile Impression $20 CPM; Interactive Video $250 flat rate; PAW (Pencil Ad with Wrapper) $150/day; Flyerboard 7-day web $35 flat, mobile $25 flat, Combo $50 flat
News services: AP, MCT, TMS, CSM. **Established:** 1883
Own Printing Facility?: Yes
Commercial Printers?: Yes
Special Editions: JANUARY:
Lose to Win
New Year's Special
FEBRUARY:
Valentine's Day
Dining Club Card
MARCH:
St. Patrick's Day
APRIL:
Easter Dining
Health Tabloid
MAY:
Mother's Day
Memorial Day
99 Things
JUNE:
Father's Day
Summer Tourist Guide
Locally Owned
JULY:
Fourth of July
Summer Tourist Guide
AUGUST:
Dining Club Card
Back To School
Summer Tourist Guide
Welcome Back NAU
SEPTEMBER:
Festival of Science
OCTOBER:
Daily Sun Calendar
Best of Flagstaff #1
NOVEMBER:
Women in Business
Thanksgiving
Holiday Shopping
DECEMBER:
Best of Flagstaff #2
Letters to Santa
Last Minute Shopping
Special Weekly Sections: SUNDAY: Health & Medicine
Wednesday TV Book
Syndicated Publications: Athlon (Monthly);Relish (Monthly); Parade (S).
Proprietary Publications: Best of Flagstaff December 2017
Progress Report April 2018
Mountain Living Magazine Monthly
Flagstaff Live Entertainment Guide Weekly
Digital Platform - Mobile: Apple
Digital Platform - Tablet: Apple iOS
Pres./Pub.......................................Don Rowley
Editorial Page Ed. .... Randy Wilson
Prodn. Mgr., Pressroom ....William Smith
Ad Director...................................Colleen Brady
Market Information: TMC.
Mechanical Available: Offset; Black and 3 ROP colors; insert accepted; page cutoffs - 22 3/4.
Mechanical Specifications: Type page 9.8889 x 21 1/2; E - 6 cols, 1.5556, 1/8 between; A - 6 cols, 1.5556, 1/8 between.
Areas Served: 86001,86004, 86015, 86017, 86018, 86040, 86045, 86046, 86047, 86351, 86033, 86023, 86339
Delivery Method: Mail, Newsstand, Carrier, RacksEquipment & Software: PRESSROOM EQUIPMENT: Lines — 15-G/Community (3 stacked units, plus 1-4 high); Press Drive — 2-HP/75; Folders — 1-G/SSC, 1; Reels & Stands — 7 Stands; MAILROOM EQUIPMENT: Counter Stackers — 1-BG/Count-O-Veyor 109; Inserters & Stuffers — 1-Harris 848, 1-KAN/480 ; Tying Machines — Si/Spirit, 2/Oval Strapper; Address Machine — ScrippSat; BUSINESS SOFTWARE: PBS, Phoenix, Falcon CLASSIFIED EQUIPMENT: Hardware — PC; CLASSIFIED SOFTWARE: Mactive. DISPLAY EQUIPMENT: Hardware — APP/Mac; DISPLAY SOFTWARELayout Software — Adobe/InDesign. EDITORIAL EQUIPMENT: Hardware — APP/Mac/APP/Mac II Graphics; Printers — APP/Mac LaserPrinter EDITORIAL SOFTWARE: Baseview, In Design PRODUCTION EQUIPMENT: Hardware — Amerigraph/437, LaserMaster/1200XLO, 2-AU/3850; Scanners — HP/ScanJet IIc PRODUCTION SOFTWARE: In Design, QPS/QuarkXPress, Adobe/Photoshop.

KINGMAN

KINGMAN DAILY MINER

3015 N Stockton Hill Rd, Kingman, Ariz., 86401-4162, Mohave; gen tel (928) 753-6397; adv tel (928) 753-6397; ed tel (928) 753-6397; gen fax (928) 753-5661; adv fax (928) 753-5661; ed fax (928) 753-3796; gen/nat adv e-mail advertising@kdminer.com; disp adv e-mail advertising@kdminer.com; class adv e-mailclassified@kdminer.com; ed e-mail editorial@kdminer.com; web site www.kdminer.com
Group: Western News&Info, Inc.
Published: Mon, Tues, Wed, Thur, Fri, Sun
Weekday Frequency: m
Circulation: 7,969; 8,172(sun)
Last Audit: Sworn/Estimate/Non-Audited September 30, 2017
Advertising Rate (weekday/saturday): Open inch rate $17.92
Advertising Rate (sunday): Open inch rate $19.81
News services: AP, Papert (Landon). **Established:** 1882
Special Editions: Business Showcase (Apr); Back-to-School (Aug); Last Minute Christmas (Dec); Top 10 Stories of the Year (Jan); Soap Box Derby (Jul); Welcome to Kingman (Jun); Home & Garden (Mar); Park & Recreation Book (May); Christmas Kick-Off (Nov); Destination Kingman
Special Weekly Sections: American (Mon);Business, Showcase (Wed); Entertainment (Thur); TV/Entertainment, Religion, School, Homes (Fri); Business, Properties (Sun)
Syndicated Publications: Relish (Monthly); Parade (S); American Profile (Weekly).
Pub..................................... Debbie White-Hoel

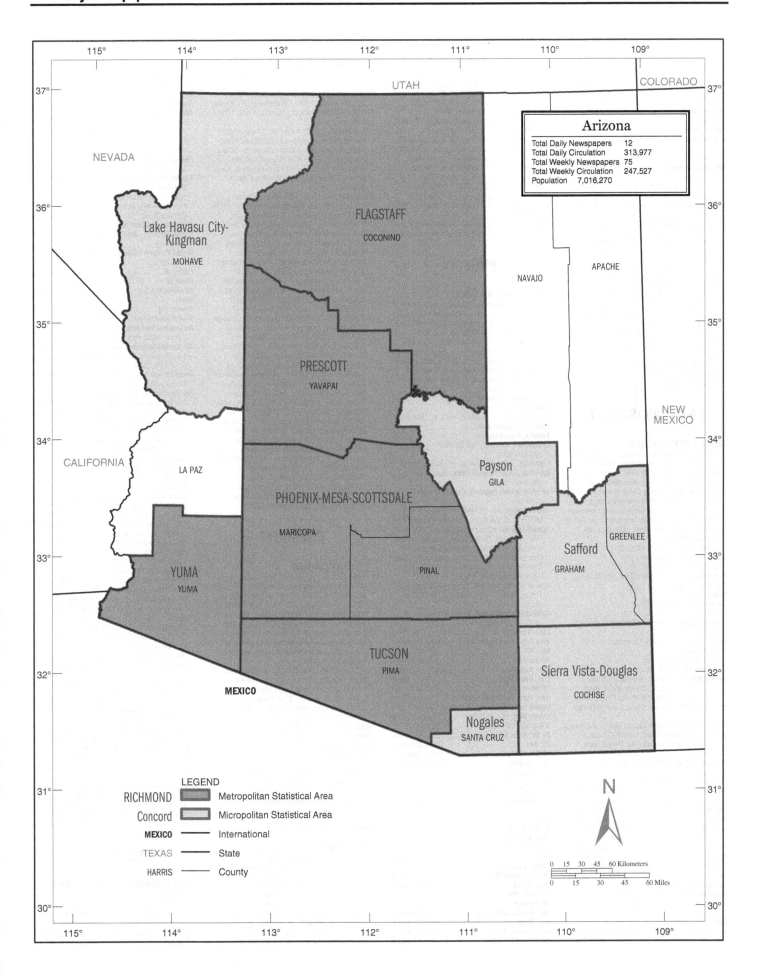

NEVADA

UTAH

COLORADO

Lake Havasu City-Kingman

MOHAVE

FLAGSTAFF

COCONINO

NAVAJO

APACHE

Arizona

Total Daily Newspapers	12
Total Daily Circulation	313,977
Total Weekly Newspapers	75
Total Weekly Circulation	247,527
Population	7,016,270

PRESCOTT

YAVAPAI

NEW MEXICO

CALIFORNIA

LA PAZ

Payson

GILA

PHOENIX-MESA-SCOTTSDALE

MARICOPA

GREENLEE

Safford

GRAHAM

YUMA

YUMA

PINAL

TUCSON

PIMA

Sierra Vista-Douglas

COCHISE

MEXICO

Nogales

SANTA CRUZ

LEGEND

RICHMOND — Metropolitan Statistical Area

Concord — Micropolitan Statistical Area

MEXICO —— International

TEXAS —— State

HARRIS —— County

N

0 15 30 45 60 Kilometers

0 15 30 45 60 Miles

Adv. Dir. .... Colleen Machado
Ed ....Rich Thurlow
Ed ....Mark Borgard
Circ. Dir. ....Kandy Cummins
Prodn. Dir. .... Paul Mauser
News Ed ....Alan Choate
Graphics Mgr. .... Michael Knowlton
Bus. Mgr. ....Nirali Dave
HR Generalist ....Nettie Thorpe
Circ. Mgr. ....Storm Kinion
Market Information: TMC.
Mechanical Available: Offset; Black and 3 ROP colors; insert accepted - poly bags; page cutoffs - 22 3/4.
Mechanical Specifications: Type page 12 1/2 x 21 1/2; E - 6 cols, 1 27/32, 1/8 between; A - 6 cols, 1 27/32, 1/8 between; C - 6 cols, 1 27/32, 1/8 between.
Areas Served: Kingman, Arizona, and Mohave County
Equipment & Software: PRESSROOM EQUIPMENT: Lines — 8-G/Suburban, 8; Folders — G/SC, G/Suburban; Reels & Stands — 2; MAILROOM EQUIPMENT: Counter Stackers — 2-HL/Monitor; Inserters & Stuffers — SH/1372 (12 pocket); Tying Machines — 2-MLN/2A; Address Machine — KR; CLASSIFIED SOFTWARE: CAMS. DISPLAY SOFTWAREAd Make-up Applications — Adobe/Illustrator 2.0, QPS/QuarkXPress 3.1, Adobe/Photoshop 2.5, Multi-Ad/Creator 4.1, Caere/OmniPage.; EDITORIAL SOFTWARE: QPS/QuarkXPress. PRODUCTION EQUIPMENT: Hardware — Caere/OmniPage; Cameras — SCREEN/C-240-D; Scanners — Umax, Polaroid/SprintScan 35 PRODUCTION SOFTWARE: QPS/QuarkXPress.

LAKE HAVASU CITY

TODAY'S NEWS-HERALD

2225 Acoma Blvd W, Lake Havasu City, Ariz., 86403-2907, Mohave; gen tel (928) 453-4237; adv tel (928) 855-2197; ed tel (928) 453-4237; gen fax (928) 855-9892; adv fax (928) 855-9892; ed fax (928) 855-2637; gen/nat adv e-mail ads@havasunews.com; disp adv e-mail ads@havasunews.com; class adv e-mailclassified@havasunews.com; ed e-mail editor@havasunews.com; web site www.havasunews.com
- 366,048(views) 74,000(visitors)
Group: Western News&Info, Inc.
Wick Communications
Published: Mon, Tues, Wed, Thur, Fri, Sun
Weekday Frequency: m
Saturday Frequency: m
Circulation: 8,635; 8,947(sun)
Last Audit: VAC June 30, 2017
Advertising Rate (weekday/saturday): Open inch rate $24.60
Advertising Rate (sunday): Open inch rate $24.60
News services: AP.
Own Printing Facility?: No
Commercial Printers?: No
Special Editions: Holiday Shopping Guide (Dec); Winter Visitor's Guide (Feb); Meet Your Merchant (Mar); Summer Guide (May); Winter Visitor's Guide (Nov); London Bridge Days (Oct).
Special Weekly Sections: Sports (Mon); Business (Tue); Best Food (Wed); Health (Thur); Entertainment, Church (Fri); Real Estate, Comics, TV (Sun)
Syndicated Publications: American Profile (Weekly).
Digital Platform - Mobile: Android
Pres/Pub .... Michael E. Quinn
Controller ....Sandy Stangifer
Adv. Dir. ....Christine Hammers
Sports .... Kevin Baird
Circ. Mgr. ....Alexis Christensen
Bus. Mgr. ....Shannon Engles
Pro. Mgr. ....Cindy Taylor
HR Mgr. ....Chris Walker
Copy Ed ....Gwen Girsdansky
Ed ....Brandon Bowers
Market Information: TMC.
Mechanical Available: Black and 3 ROP colors; insert accepted - envelopes, cards; page cutoffs - 21.
Mechanical Specifications: Type page 13 x 21; E - 6 cols, 2 1/16, 1/4 between; A - 6 cols, 2 1/16, 1/4 between; C - 6 cols, 2 1/16, 1/4 between.
Areas Served: Lake Havasu, AZ
Delivery Method: Mail, Newsstand, Carrier, RacksEquipment & Software: PRESSROOM EQUIPMENT: Lines — Press Control System 1993.; BUSINESS EQUIPMENT: ATT/Unix PC BUSINESS SOFTWARE: Vision Data CLASSIFIED EQUIPMENT: Hardware — 2-APP/Power Mac; CLASSIFIED SOFTWARE: Multi-Ad/CAMS. DISPLAY EQUIPMENT: Hardware — APP/Mac; DISPLAY SOFTWAREAd Make-up Applications — Multi-Ad/Creator.; EDITORIAL EQUIPMENT: Hardware — 12-APP/Mac EDITORIAL SOFTWARE: Microsoft/Word, Aldus/PageMaker, QPS/QuarkXPress. PRODUCTION EQUIPMENT: Hardware — Microtek; Scanners — Microtek/II SI, Microtek PRODUCTION SOFTWARE: QPS/QuarkXPress 3.3.
Note: This paper is equally owned by Western Newspapers Inc. and Wick Communications.

PHOENIX

THE ARIZONA REPUBLIC

200 E Van Buren St, Phoenix, Ariz., 85004-2238, Maricopa; gen tel (602) 444-8000; adv tel (602) 444-8317; ed tel (602) 444-6397; gen fax (602) 444-8044; adv fax (602) 444-8788; ed fax (602) 444-8044; gen/nat adv e-mail tthomas@republicmedia.com; disp adv e-mail tthomas@republicmedia.com; class adv e-mailjmisner@kpnx.com; ed e-mail republicmedia@azcentral.com; web site www.azcentral.com
9,236,651(visitors)
Group: Gannett
Published: Mon, Tues, Wed, Thur, Fri, Sat, Sun
Weekday Frequency: m
Saturday Frequency: m
Circulation: 183,849; 186,224(sat); 296,039(sun)
Last Audit: AAM December 31, 2016
Advertising Rate (weekday/saturday): Open inch rate $495.00
Advertising Rate (sunday): Open inch rate $668.00
News services: AP, LAT-WP, NYT, SHNS, RN, MCT, HN, CSM, GNS, TMS. **Established:** 1890
Special Editions: Working (Apr); Football Extra Preview (Aug); Fiesta/College Bowl Preview (Dec); Spring Training/Baseball Preview (Feb); Phoenix Open (Jan); Mercury/WNBA Preview (Jun); Arizona Inc. (May); Working (Oct); Rep AZ Best (Sept).
Special Weekly Sections: Food (Wed); AZ Living, Things To Do (Thur); Preview (Fri); Travel (Sun)
Syndicated Publications: Vista (Fri); USA WEEKEND Magazine (S).
Exec. Vice Pres./CFO ....Jon Held
Vice Pres., Community Rel ....Gene D'Adamo
Dir., HR .... Mike Spector
Admin. Asst .... Patsy Rivera
Circ. Asst. Dir. ....Jack Saunders
Circ. Opns. Mgr. ....Steve Reed
VP, News Ed. ....Nicole Carroll
Gen. Mgr., Scottsdale Republic ....Mike Ryan
Deputy Ed., Presentation/Sports ...... Tracy Collins
Deputy Mng. Ed., Page One ....Keira Nothaft
A & E Rep. Ed. ....Stacy Sullivan
Sr. VP, News & Audience Dev. ....Randy Lovely
VP, Adv. ....Chris Stegman
VP/Digital Media .... Mike Coleman
VP/Production .... Bob Kotwasinski
Linda Valdez
Keith Holmes
Christina Leonard
Dir.; Automotive ....Christopher Wood
Jeff Myers
Justin Beam
VP Digital Sales .... David Knight
Pres./Gen. Mgr. ....John Misner
Nat'l Adv. Mgr. ....Timothy Thomas
Sr. Dir. ....Cherrill Crosby
Digital Sales Dir. .... Jeff Cook
Digital Content Dir. .... Julia Thompson
Pres. & Pub. ....Mi-Ai Parrish
VP Pres., Adv. ....Chase Rankin
VP, Finance .... Trisha Gosser
Dir., Key Account Sales .... Kevin Martinelli
Dir., Class. Adv. .... Brett Sondrup
Dir., Territory Sales .... Amy Lindsey
Dir., Client Strategy .... Sean Rogers
Dir., Adv. Op .... Craig Ludwig
Market Information: Split run; TMC; Zoned editions.
Mechanical Available: Offset; Black and 3 ROP colors; insert accepted - samples, post-it notes; page cutoffs - 22 3/4.
Mechanical Specifications: Type page 13 x 21 1/2; E - 6 cols, 1 3/4, 1/8 between; A - 6 cols, 1 3/4, 1/8 between; C - 10 cols, 1 1/8, 1/16 between.
Areas Served: The Arizona Republic provides delivery to all zip codes in Maricopa, Pinal, Yavapai, Gila and Graham counties. Select zip codes in Coconino, Navajo, Apache, Greenlee, Cochise and Pima counties. Only small SCS delivery in Mohave, La Paz and Yuma counties.
Delivery Method: Mail, Newsstand, Carrier, RacksEquipment & Software: PRESSROOM EQUIPMENT: Lines — 9-G/Metroliner; 9-G/Metroliner; 9-G/Headliner offset; 9-G/Colorliner; 9-G/Colorliner; 9-G/Colorliner; 9-G/Colorliner; Folders — 7-G/3:2; Reels & Stands — Reels & Stands and Sta; MAILROOM EQUIPMENT: Counter Stackers — 36-HL/Monitor, 1-HL/HT, 4-QWI/351; Inserters & Stuffers — 6/AM Graphics/NP 2299; Tying Machines — 32-/Power Strap, 4-/Dynamics.; BUSINESS EQUIPMENT: Bull/DPS-8000, Sun/2000, 4-Sun/4000 BUSINESS SOFTWARE: Microsoft, Cyborg, Lotus Notes, Oracle:financials, In-house CLASSIFIED EQUIPMENT: Hardware — 2-Sun 4800, PCs; dat*, ME-CLS, Multibox; Printers — HP/Desktops; CLASSIFIED SOFTWARE: PGL, Mactive Adbase 2.24. DISPLAY EQUIPMENT: Hardware — 2-Sun/E4500, APP/Mac; Printers — 2-HP/Laser, Techtronic 780, Xerox, Mosaic Multiples, 6-See-Color; DISPLAY SOFTWAREAd Make-up Applications — Adobe/InDesign CS2, QPS/QuarkXPress 6.5, Adobe/Photoshop CS2, Adobe/Illustrator CS2 11, Adobe/Acrobat-Distiller 7.0, Mosaic/Inspector; EDITORIAL EQUIPMENT: Hardware — Sun/Sparc 4500, CCI; Printers — HP EDITORIAL SOFTWARE: CCI, Microsoft/Word Office. PRODUCTION EQUIPMENT: Hardware — III/Laser Setter, 5-AII/3850 Typesetter, APP/Mac; Scanners — 2-Scitex/Smart Scan PRODUCTION SOFTWARE: CCI.

PRESCOTT

THE DAILY COURIER

1958 Commerce Center Cir, Prescott, Ariz., 86301-4454, Yavapai; gen tel (928) 445-3333; adv tel (928) 776-8122; ed tel (928) 445-3333; gen fax (928) 772-3810; adv fax (928) 445-4756; ed fax (928) 759-5671; gen/nat adv e-mail editorial@prescottaz.com; disp adv e-mail msmith@prescottaz.com; class adv e-mailclassifieds@prescottaz.com; ed e-mail editorial@prescottaz.com; web site www.dcourier.com
- 2,014,719(views) 235,052(visitors); web site 2 http://pvtrib.com/ - 61,247(views) 21,557(visitors); web site 3 http://prescottkudos.com/ - 27,442(views) 12,351(visitors); web site 4http://cvrnews.com/ - 31,304(views) 9,304(visitors)
Group: Western News&Info, Inc.
Published: Mon, Tues, Wed, Thur, Fri, Sat, Sun
Weekday Frequency: m
Saturday Frequency: m
Circulation: 12,534; 12,534(sat); 13,178(sun)
Last Audit: VAC September 30, 2015
Branch Offices: (The Daily Courier) 8307 E. Hwy 69, Ste B, Prescott Valley AZ 86314
Advertising Rate (weekday/saturday): Open inch rate, PCI(per column inch) $25.40, Mon-Thurs and Sat
Advertising Rate (sunday): Open inch rate, PCI $27.80, Fri and Sun
Online Advertising Rate: ROS-Agreement Term I Leaderboard: $300/wk(2 months or less), $231/wk(3-5 months), $185/wk(6-11 months), $131/wk(12 months) ; HalfPage/Wide Skyscraper: $285/wk(2 months or less), $216/wk(3-5 months), $169/wk(6-11 months); $116/wk(12 months); Medium Rectangle: $270/wk(2 months or less), $200/wk(3-5 months); $146/wk(6-11 months), $100/wk(12 months); In-story Medium Rectangle: $216/wk(2 months or less), $169/wk(3-5 months), $139/wk(6-11months), $108/wk(12 months); HomePage Ad: $316/wk(2 months or less), $223/wk(3-5 months), $154/wk(6-11 months), $92/wk(12 months)
News services: Western Newspapers Inc..
Established: 1882
Own Printing Facility?: Yes
Commercial Printers?: Yes
Special Editions: Bride & Groom(Feb); Home Style- Home Improvement(March and Sept); Health Care Focus(April and Oct); Wildwest Frontier Days(June); Celebrations- holiday decorating and entertaining(Nov, Dec)
Special Weekly Sections: Real Estate (Fri); Business (S).
Syndicated Publications: Relish(1st Wed/month), Spry(2nd Wed/month), Parade(Sun), Athlon Sports(3rd Tues/month, counting from the first full week), American Profile(Thurs), and Comics(Sun)
Proprietary Publications: None
Digital Platform - Mobile: Apple, Android, Windows
Digital Platform - Tablet: Apple iOS, Android
City Editor .... Tim Wiederaenders
Prodn. Dir. .... Gary Brinkman
Photo Ed. .... Les Stukenberg
Adv./Graphics Dir. ....Babette Cubitt
Editor .... Robin Layton
Advertising .... Megan Smith
Market Information: ADS; TMC.
Mechanical Available: Offset; Black and 3 ROP colors; insert accepted; page cutoffs - 22.
Mechanical Specifications: Type page 11 3/4 x 21 1/2; E - 6 cols, between; A - 6 cols, between; C - 6 cols, between.
Areas Served: Yavapai County(Prescott Valley, Chino Valley, and Camp Verde)
Delivery Method: Mail, Newsstand, Carrier, RacksEquipment & Software: PRESSROOM EQUIPMENT: Lines — 1-G/Community; 1-DIDDE/UV; Press Drive — 2, 1, 150, 100, 75; Folders — 1-G/Universal 45, 1-G/SSC; Reels & Stands — 6-Enkel/Splicer.; MAILROOM EQUIPMENT: Counter Stackers — 1-HL/Monitor, 1-QWI; Inserters & Stuffers — HI/Sheridan 1372, MM/227; Tying Machines — Strap-Pack/Strapper 35-80 AKN, MLN/ML2-EE, Si/LB 2000, Si/LB 2330; Address Machine — 3/Dispensa-matic; BUSINESS EQUIPMENT: DEC/200, APP/Mac PowerBook 160, APP/Mac PowerBook 550, Mk/ScanMaker IIG Scanner, APP/Mac LaserWriter II NTX, 2-DEC/server, 6-DEC/VT-420 monitor, 2-DEC/VT-220 monitor, DEC/LA-424 Desktop printer, C.Itoh/Dot Matrix Printer, AST/PC, APP/Mac Plus, CLASSIFIED EQUIPMENT: Hardware — 6-APP/Mac Beige G3, 1-APP/Mac 7200/120, 1-APP/Mac Powerbook G3, 1-APP/Apple Design Keyboard, 1-Kensington/Keyboard, 1-APP/Mac Pro Plus Keyboard, 1-APP/Apple 14 Monitor, 1-APP/Apple 17 Monitor, 5-Sony/Monitors; 1-Umax/Astra 2200S S; DISPLAY EQUIPMENT: Hardware — 4-APP/Mac Blue/White G3, 4-APP/Mac Beige G3, 2-APP/Mac G4, 3-APP/Apple Design Keyboards, 2-APP/Mac USB Keyboards, 5-APP/Mac Pro Plus Keyboards, 3-APP/Apple 1705 Monitor, 1-Optiquest/Monitor, 6-Sony/Monitor; Printers — 1-Lexmart C910, 1-Xante/Ac; EDITORIAL EQUIPMENT: Hardware — APP/Mac 19 color monitor/AG/Focus Scanner; Printers — APP/Mac LaserWriter 16-1600 PS EDITORIAL SOFTWARE: Adobe/Photoshop, QPS/QuarkXPress 4.0, Microsoft/Word, Aldus/Freehand. PRODUCTION EQUIPMENT: Hardware — 2-Pre Press/Panther Fast Track CTP, 3-Sony/Monitors, 3-APP/USB Extended Keyboards, 3-APP/USB Optical Mouse PRODUCTION SOFTWARE: Adobe/Acrobat 4.0, MultiAd/Creator2, Flightcheck 4.5r22, Adobe/Illustrator 9.0, Adobe/Indesign 2.0, Insposition 2.5.4, Adob

SIERRA VISTA

WICK COMMUNICATIONS - HERALD/REVIEW

102 Fab Ave, Sierra Vista, Ariz., 85635-1741, Cochise; gen tel (520) 458-9440; adv tel (520) 515-4630; ed tel (520) 515-4610; gen fax (520) 459-0120; gen/nat adv e-mail becky.bjork@myheraldreview.com; class adv

e-mailclassified@myheraldreview.com; ed e-mail editor@myheraldreview.com; web site www.myheraldreview.com
- 535,000(views) 62,000(visitors)
Group: Wick Communications
Published: Tues, Wed, Thur, Fri, Sun
Weekday Frequency: m
Saturday Frequency: m
Circulation: 5,228; 5,809(sun)
Last Audit: VAC September 30, 2017
Advertising Rate (weekday/saturday): Open inch rate $15.25
Advertising Rate (sunday): Open inch rate $16.25
News services: AP, NYT **Established:** 1955
Own Printing Facility?: Yes
Commercial Printers?: Yes
Special Editions: Holiday Sweepstakes (Nov); Vitality Magazine (Quarterly) Chamber Directory (Jan); Back-to-School (Jul); Picture Your Home (Real Estate Magazine) (Monthly); Southeast Arizona Traveler (Oct). Year in Review (Jan.1)
Special Weekly Sections: Religion Page (Thur); Business (Tues); Comics (S); Real Estate (Sun); Taste/Health (Wed); Entertainment (Thu)
Syndicated Publications: American Profile (Tues).
Digital Platform - Mobile: Apple, Android, Windows
Digital Platform - Tablet: Apple iOS, Android, Windows 7
Adv. Dir. .... Becky Bjork
Bus. Mgr. .... Joan Hancock
Opinions Ed. .... Eric Petermann
Asst. Gen. Mgr. .... Pat Wick
Publisher .... Jennifer Sorenson
Market Information: Split run; TMC; Zoned editions.
Mechanical Available: Offset; Black and CMYK; inserts accepted - all; page cutoffs - 21.
Mechanical Specifications: Type page 9 89/100 x 21; E - 6 cols, 1 56/100, 5/6 between; A - 6 cols, 1 56/100, 5/6 between; C - 9 cols, 1, 58/100 between.
Areas Served: 85635, 85650, 85615, 85616, 85636, 85603
Delivery Method: Mail, Newsstand, Carrier, RacksEquipment & Software: PRESSROOM EQUIPMENT: Lines — 15-G/Community; Control System — Perretta; MAILROOM EQUIPMENT: Counter Stackers — BG/ Count-O-Veyor 106; Inserters & Stuffers — 1-HI/Sheridan; Tying Machines - 2-Wilton/ Strap Pack 55-80; Control System — Prism.; BUSINESS EQUIPMENT: DEC BUSINESS SOFTWARE: Vision Data CLASSIFIED EQUIPMENT: Hardware — APP/Mac; Printers — APP/Mac; CLASSIFIED SOFTWARE: Baseview. DISPLAY EQUIPMENT: Hardware — APP/ Mac; Printers — APP/Mac; DISPLAY SOFTWARELayout Software — Adobe/ Creative Suite. EDITORIAL EQUIPMENT: Hardware — APP/Mac; Printers — APP/Mac EDITORIAL SOFTWARE: Baseview.
Adobe Creative Suite
PRODUCTION EQUIPMENT: Hardware — Southern Lithoplate MX33 PRODUCTION SOFTWARE: Adobe/Creative Suite.

SUN CITY

DAILY NEWS-SUN

17220 N Boswell Blvd, Ste 101, Sun City, Ariz., 85373-2065, Maricopa; gen tel (623) 977-8351; adv tel (623)876-2566; ed tel (623) 876-2534; gen fax (623) 876-3699; adv fax (623) 876-2589; ed fax (623) 876-3698; gen/ nat adv e-mail rcarlton@yourwestvalley.com; disp adv e-mail rcarlton@yourwestvalley.com; class adv e-mailtrodgers@yourwestvalley. com; ed e-mail dmccarthy@yourwestvalley. com; web site www.yourwestvalley.com
- 165,000(views) 55,000(visitors)
Group: Independent Newsmedia Inc. Usa
Published: Mon, Tues, Wed, Thur, Fri, Sat
Weekday Frequency: m
Saturday Frequency: m
Circulation: 4,079; 29,275(sat)
Last Audit: CAC June 30, 2016
Advertising Rate (weekday/saturday): Modular sizes open rates: Full $1017, Half $585, Fourth $300, Eighth $172, Twelfth $116
Advertising Rate (sunday): Modular sizes open rates: Full $1017, Half $585, Fourth $300, Eighth $172, Twelfth $116
Online Advertising Rate: Sliding Billboard: Targeted cost $200/day, $500/week, $1800/ moIHome Page Cost $350/day, $600/week, $2100/mo ; Page Curl: Targeted cost $150/ day, $375/week, $1200/mo IHomePage cost $200/day, $500/week, $1800/mo ; Wallpaper: Target cost $300/day, $650/week, $2300/ mo IHomePage cost $425/day, $700/week, $2500/mo ; Floating Post-it: Targeted cost $500/week IHomePage cost $1000/week ; Tower: Targeted cost $125/day, $350/week, $1000/mo IHomePage cost $150/day, $425/ week, $1300/mo ; Expandable(leaderboard/ medium rectangle): ROS cost $15 cpm, targeted cost $18 cpm, homepage cost $22 cpm ; Leaderboard: ROS cost $10 cpm, targeted cost $12 cpm, homepage cost $15; Medium Rectangle: ROS cost $11 cpm, Targeted cost $13 cpm, homepage cost $16 cpm; In-story Medium Rectangle: ROS cost $12 cpm, targeted cost $14 cpm, homepage cost $17 cpm; Interstitial: ROS cost $14cpm, targeted cost $16 cpm
News services: AP, DJ, ONS. **Established:** 1956
Own Printing Facility?: Yes
Commercial Printers?: Yes
Special Editions: Choices (Apr); Funeral Planner (Jun); Spring Home Improvement (Mar); Senior Caregivers (May); Holiday Gift Guides (Nov); Fall Home Improvement (Oct).
Special Weekly Sections: Week's End/Business Review (Sat); Weekender/Entertainment (Thur); Food & Nutrition (Tues); Travel (Wed).
Syndicated Publications: TV/Entertainment (Fri); USA WEEKEND Magazine (Sat).
Pub. .... Marji Ranes
Circulation. Dir. .... Robert Martin
Adv. Dir. .... Penny Bruns
Exec. Ed. .... Dan McCarthy
Sports Ed. .... Rich Bolas
Op. Dir. .... Michael Bergstrom
Bus. Mgr. .... Louis Gobin
Preprint/Warehouse .... Cameron Carranza
Market Information: ADS; TMC.
Mechanical Available: Offset; Black and 3 ROP colors; insert accepted - all; page cutoffs - 22 3/4.
Mechanical Specifications: Type page 11 5/8 x 21 1/2; E - 6 cols, 1 7/8, 1/8 between; A - 6 cols, 1 7/8, 1/8 between; C - 9 cols, 1 7/8, 1/8 between.
Areas Served: Sun City, Sun City West, Sun City Grand, El Mirage, Youngtown, and Surprise
Delivery Method: Mail, Newsstand, Carrier, RacksEquipment & Software: PRESSROOM EQUIPMENT: Lines — 8-G/Urbanite; Folders — 1-G/Urbanite 1000; Reels & Stands — 2-G/High; Registration System — Burgess/Carlson. MAILROOM EQUIPMENT: Counter Stackers — 2-HL/ Quiad; Inserters & Stuffers — GMA; Tying Machines — 2/Dynaric ND1500; Wrapping Singles — Mailroom Control System Lincs/ GMA.; BUSINESS EQUIPMENT: IBM/AS-400, HP/Vectra BUSINESS SOFTWARE: MS/Office CLASSIFIED EQUIPMENT: Hardware — Sun; 1-Umax/Scanner; Printers — 2-HP; CLASSIFIED SOFTWARE: DTI. DISPLAY EQUIPMENT: Hardware — SUN; Printers — 3-HP; Other Hardware — Epson/ Scanner DISPLAY SOFTWAREAd Make-up Applications — DTI; Layout Software — DTI. EDITORIAL EQUIPMENT: Hardware — SUN/2-Canon/Digital Cameras; Printers — 2-HP EDITORIAL SOFTWARE: DTI. PRODUCTION EQUIPMENT: Hardware — NuArc; Cameras — C/Spartan III PRODUCTION SOFTWARE: DTI.

TUCSON

ARIZONA DAILY STAR

4850 S Park Ave, Tucson, Ariz., 85714-1637, Pima; gen tel 520-573-4142; adv tel (520) 573-4366; ed tel (520) 573-4142; gen fax 520-573-4109; adv fax (520) 573-4407 (retail) ; (520) 573-4294 (classified); ed fax (520) 573-4200; gen/nat adv e-mail advertising@ tucson.com; disp adv e-mail advertising@ tucson.com; class adv e-mailadvertising@ tucson.com; ed e-mail mparham@tucson. com; web site www.tucson.com
- 12,066,635(views) 1,137,934(visitors) 1,481,236(visitors)
Group: Lee Enterprises, Inc.
Published: Mon, Tues, Wed, Thur, Fri, Sat, Sun
Weekday Frequency: m
Saturday Frequency: m
Circulation: 59,343; 63,327(sat); 82,978(sun)
Last Audit: AAM December 31, 2016
Advertising Rate (weekday/saturday): Contract Volume(no matter what volume it's $31 for Mon/Tues): open $120.60(daily), $2500- $102.50(daily), $5000- $98(daily), $7500- $92.60(daily), $10000- $88.30(daily), $15000- $85.10(daily), $25000- $82.80(daily), $35000- $80.70(daily), $50000- $78.50(daily), $75000- $76.30(daily), $100000- $74.20(daily), $150000- $72(daily)
Advertising Rate (sunday): Contract volume rate: open $149.10, $2500- $126.50, $5000- $120.90,$7500- $116, $10000- $109.40, $15000- $104.50, $25000- $102.30, $35000- $99, $50000- $96.90, $75000- $93.60, $100000- $91.30, $150000- $88.60
Online Advertising Rate: Skyscraper(160x600): Home Page & Targeted Channel($8), Run-of-site rate($6), Roadblock($12), BT Tuscon($10); Leaderboard(728x90): Home Page & Targeted Channel($10), Run-of-site rate($6), Roadblock($12), BT Tuscon($12); Big Box(300x250): Home Page & Targeted Channel($12), Run-of-site rate($9), Roadblock($15), BT Tuscon($15)
News services: AP, NYT, MCT, SHNS, DJ, DF, TMS. **Established:** 1877
Special Weekly Sections: Caliente (entertainment) (Thurs); TV Week (S); Food & More (Wed).
Syndicated Publications: USA WEEKEND Magazine (Fri). ; Parade(Sun)
Proprietary Publications: Caliente(Thurs); La Estrella de Tucson(Fri
Digital Platform - Mobile: Apple, Android, Windows, Blackberry
Digital Platform - Tablet: Apple iOS, Android, Windows 7, Blackberry Tablet OS
Ed. .... Jill Spitz
VP Finance .... Joel Rohlik
VP Adv. Sales & Mktg. .... Alisha Owens
Dir. Print Ops. .... John Lundgren
Dir. Digital Innovation .... Rob Wisner
Mrktg. Dir. .... Darrell Durham
Dir. IT .... Mike Facemire
Dir. Circ & Consumer Innovation .... Mark Lolwing
Sr. Ed. .... Hipolito R. Corella
Sr. Editor .... Debbie Kornmiller
Copy Chief .... George Campbell
Editorial Page Ed. .... Ann Brown
Editorial Page Ed. .... Maria Parham
Film Critic .... Phil Villarreal
Food/Home Ed. .... Kristen Cook
Health/Medical Ed. .... Stephnie Innes
Starnet Online Ed. .... John Bolton
High School Sports Ed. .... Ryan Finley
Sports Ed. .... Jennin Corner
Science/Technology Ed. .... Norma Coile
News/Research Servs. Dir. .... Elaine Raines
Circ. Distrib. Spec. .... Johnny Childs
Pres./Pub. .... John D'Orlando
Market Information: Split run; TMC; Zoned editions.
Mechanical Available: Offset; Black and 3 ROP colors; insert accepted - single sheet flyers; page cutoffs - 22 3/4.
Mechanical Specifications: Type page 12 x 21 1/2; E - 6 cols, 1 4/5, between; A - 6 cols, 1 4/5, between; C - 10 cols, 1 1/10, between.
Areas Served: Pima County, Cochise County, Santa Cruz County, Pinal County, Graham County
Delivery Method: Mail, Newsstand, RacksEquipment & Software: PRESSROOM EQUIPMENT: Lines — 8-G/Metro 3127A doublewidth (4 half decks); 8-G/Metro 3128A doublewidth (4 half decks); Folders — 4-G/3:2; Reels & Stands — G/Harmonic Drive; Registration System — WPC/Metro Color 4/4 Tower. MAILROOM EQUIPMENT: Counter Stackers — 4-GMA, 3-QWI/400, 4-QWI/500, 2-QWI/500C; Inserters & Stuffers — 1/SLS 1000 10:1, 2-/SLS 3000 22:1, GMA/PTH; Tying Machines — 6-/MLN, 3-/ Power Strap, 2-HI/RS-25; Wrapping Singles — 4-QWI/Bottom Wrap, 4-QWI/Vipers w/ Ink Jet Labe; BUSINESS EQUIPMENT: IBM/AS-400 CLASSIFIED EQUIPMENT: Hardware — Proteon/PC Network; Printers — HP/4000 Laser Jet, Tektronix/Phaser 300; CLASSIFIED SOFTWARE: TECS-2 4.2. DISPLAY EQUIPMENT: Hardware — APP/ Mac, Sun, Microsoft; Printers — DEC/LA 120, Tekronix/Phaser 300, HP/2500C, HP/ LaserJet 4050; DISPLAY SOFTWAREAd Make-up Applications — Baseview/Ad Manager 2.8, QPS/QuarkXPress 4.04; Layout Software — MEI, ALS. EDITORIAL EQUIPMENT: Hardware — MS/NT, APP/ Mac Desktop; Printers — HP/LaserJet IV EDITORIAL SOFTWARE: QPS. PRODUCTION EQUIPMENT: Hardware — 4-APP/Mac Power PC, 2-III/3810 Imagesetter, 3-3850 Sierras; Scanners — Umax/100 PRODUCTION SOFTWARE: HI/8900 Classified 7.6, QPS 2.08.
Note: Advertising is sold in combination with Tucson Citizen (e) for $210.20(d) & $292.10(S). Individual newspaper rates not made available. For detailed production information, see Tucson Newspapers listing.

THE DAILY TERRITORIAL

2900 E Broadway Blvd, Ste 113, Tucson, Ariz., 85716-5344, Pima; gen tel (520) 294-1200; adv tel (520) 294-1200; ed tel (520) 294-1200; gen fax (520) 294-4040; adv fax (520) 294-4040; ed fax (520) 295-4071; gen/nat adv e-mail editor@azbiz.com; disp adv e-mail advertising@azbiz.com; class adv e-mailjahearn@azbiz.com; ed e-mail dhatfield@azbiz.com; web site www.azbiz. com
Group: Wick Communications
Published: Mon, Tues, Wed, Thur, Fri
Weekday Frequency: m
Circulation: 753
Last Audit: Sworn/Estimate/Non-Audited September 30, 2017
Advertising Rate (weekday/saturday): Open inch rate $5.45
News services: American Newspaper Representatives Inc.. **Established:** 1966
Pub. .... Thomas Lee
Adv. Dir. .... Jill A'Hearn
Adv. Mgr., Legal .... Monica Akyol
Circ. Dir. .... Laura Horvath
Ed. .... David Hatfield
Art Dir. .... Andrew Arthur
Prodn. Mgr. .... Greg Day
Mechanical Available: Offset; Black and 3 ROP colors; insert accepted; page cutoffs - 22 3/4.
Mechanical Specifications: Type page 10 1/4 x 13; E - 4 cols, 2 3/8, 1/8 between; A - 4 cols, 2 3/8, 1/8 between; C - 6 cols, 1 1/2, 3/16 between.
Areas Served: 856-857Equipment & Software: PRESSROOM EQUIPMENT: Lines — 6-HI/ V-15A; Atlas/Web Leader 2000; MAILROOM EQUIPMENT: Counter Stackers — BG/ Count-O-Veyor; Tying Machines — 2-Ace/ Tyer; Address Machine — 1-Ch/612.; BUSINESS EQUIPMENT: NCR/LAN Sys CLASSIFIED EQUIPMENT: Hardware — Mk/3000, 1-PC.; DISPLAY EQUIPMENT: Hardware — APP/Mac; Printers — APP/ Mac LaserWriter II, HP/Laserwriter 4MV (11x17); DISPLAY SOFTWAREAd Make-up Applications — Aldus/PageMaker, Aldus/Freehand; Layout Software — Mk. EDITORIAL EQUIPMENT: Hardware — 1-Mk/3000, 10-PC/Mk. PRODUCTION EQUIPMENT: Hardware — Microtek/ Scanmaker Plus, HP/Laserwriter 4MV (11x17), Pre Press/Panther Plus 46; Cameras — 1-SCREEN/Companica-6500D, 1-AG/20 x 24; Scanners — Umax/Powerlook II PRODUCTION SOFTWARE: Adobe/ PageMaker 6.5.

YUMA

YUMA SUN

2055 S Arizona Ave, Yuma, Ariz., 85364-6549, Yuma; gen tel (928) 539-6800; adv tel (928)539-6829; ed tel (928) 539-6862; gen fax (928) 343-1009; adv fax (928) 343-1009; ed fax (928) 782-7369; gen/nat adv e-mail nationals@yumasun.com; disp adv e-mail nationals@yumasun.com; class adv e-mailclassifieds@yumasun.com; ed e-mail news@yumasun.com; web site www. yumasun.com
Group: RISN Operations Inc.
Published: Mon, Tues, Wed, Thur, Fri, Sat, Sun
Weekday Frequency: m

Saturday Frequency: m
Circulation: 10,917; 10,917(sat); 11,973(sun)
Last Audit: CAC June 30, 2017
Advertising Rate (weekday/saturday): Open inch rate $30.01
Advertising Rate (sunday): $34.23
News services: AP. **Established:** 1872
Own Printing Facility?: Yes
Commercial Printers?: Yes
Special Editions: Health Connections (Every other month, odd months); Raising Healthy Yuma Families (4x a year); Yuma's Best (Feb); Ag in Yuma (Mar.); Southwest Living (every other month); Dove Hunting (Aug. or Sept); Visiting in Yuma (Oct.); PAWS pet adoption (monthly). Military Publications-Desert Flightline and Outpost (Every Monday-the two publications alternate); Southwest Services (monthly)
Special Weekly Sections: Business/Financial (S); Religion (Sat); Food (Tues); Business/Financial (Wed).
Syndicated Publications: Parade
Digital Platform - Mobile: Apple, Android, Windows, Blackberry
Digital Platform - Tablet: Apple iOS, Android, Windows 7, Blackberry Tablet OS, Kindle, Nook, Kindle Fire
Editor, Bajo El Sol..........................John Vaughn
Special Content Ed......................... Randy Hoeft
Production Dir. ....David Fornof
Business Mgr................................. Kathy White
Sports Ed. .... Grady Garrett
Nationals Account Manager.................Darlene F
Market Information: TMC/ Marketplace
Mechanical Available: Offset; Black and 3 ROP colors; insert accepted; page cutoffs - 21.
Mechanical Specifications: Type page 11 13/16 x 21; E - 6 cols, 1/6 between; A - 6 cols, 1/6 between; C - 6 cols, 1/6 between.
Areas Served: 85364, 85365, 92283, 85367, 85356, 85352, 85350, 85336, 85349
Delivery Method: Mail, Carrier, RacksEquipment & Software: PRESSROOM EQUIPMENT: Lines — 9-G/Urbanite 1970.; MAILROOM EQUIPMENT: Counter Stackers — 1-Id/2100, 1-MM/CN25; Inserters & Stuffers — 1-MM/Alphaliner 10:1; Tying Machines — 1-MLN/2EE, 1/MLN, 1-Sterling/MR40CH; BUSINESS EQUIPMENT: PCs BUSINESS SOFTWARE: MediaSpan CLASSIFIED EQUIPMENT: Hardware — PCs; Media Span; Printers — HP/4000; CLASSIFIED SOFTWARE: MediaSpan DISPLAY EQUIPMENT: Hardware — PCs; Printers — 1-QMS/1660; DISPLAY SOFTWAREAd Make-up Applications — MediaSpan EDITORIAL EQUIPMENT: Hardware — 30-APP/Mac G3/1-APP/Mac Quadra 605, 1-APP/Mac Quadra 610, SMS/Stauffer Gold, Lf/AP Leaf Picture Desk, 1-Umax/Scanner, 1-Lf/Leafscan, 1-APP/Power Mac 60066, 1-Gateway/7500, 1-APP/Mac Quadra 800, Sun/Microsystems Server, Sybase/Datab EDITORIAL SOFTWARE: MediaSpan PRODUCTION SOFTWARE: MediaSpan
Note: Special Events-Boomers and Beyond, Welcome Back Winter Visitor Bash, Taste of Home

ARKANSAS

ARKADELPHIA

ARKADELPHIA SIFTINGS HERALD

205 S 26th St, Arkadelphia, Ark., 71923-5423, Clark; gen tel (870) 246-5525; adv tel (870) 246-5525; ed tel (870) 246-5525; gen fax (870) 246-6556; adv fax (870) 246-6556; ed fax (870) 246-6556; gen/nat adv e-mail rhaycox@siftingsherald.com; disp adv e-mail rhaycox@siftingsherald.com; class adv e-mailjjones@siftingsherald.com; ed e-mail wledbetter@siftingsherald.com; web site www.siftingsherald.com
Group: New Media Investment Group
Published: Mon, Tues, Wed, Thur, Fri
Weekday Frequency: e
Circulation: 1,600
Last Audit: Sworn/Estimate/Non-Audited September 30, 2017
Advertising Rate (weekday/saturday): Open inch rate $10.05
News services: AP. **Established:** 1899
Own Printing Facility?: Yes
Commercial Printers?: Yes
Syndicated Publications: American Profile (Weekly).
Digital Platform - Mobile: Apple, Android, Windows, Blackberry
Digital Platform - Tablet: Apple iOS, Android, Windows 7, Blackberry Tablet OS, Kindle, Nook, Kindle Fire
Asst. Circ. Mgr.........................Charlie Fetterhoff
Sports Ed. ....Jamal Brown
Sr. Group Pub. ....Ed Graves
Bus. Mgr. ....Marcia Hunt
Market Information: TMC.
Mechanical Available: Offset; Black and 3 ROP colors; insert accepted; page cutoffs - 22 3/4.
Mechanical Specifications: Type page 13 1/2 x 21 1/2; E - 6 cols, 2, 1/6 between; A - 6 cols, 2, 1/6 between; C - 9 cols, 1 1/3, 1/6 between.
Areas Served: Arkadelphia, Clark County and the surrounding area
Delivery Method: Mail, Newsstand, Carrier, RacksEquipment & Software: PRESSROOM EQUIPMENT: Lines — 5-KP/News King.; MAILROOM EQUIPMENT: Tying Machines — Ca/Band-Tyer; Address Machine — Wm.; BUSINESS EQUIPMENT: IBM CLASSIFIED EQUIPMENT: Hardware — APP/Mac; Printers — APP/Mac; CLASSIFIED SOFTWARE: Baseview. DISPLAY EQUIPMENT: Hardware — APP/Mac; Printers — APP/Mac LaserWriter; DISPLAY SOFTWAREAd Make-up Applications — Multi-Ad/Creator.; EDITORIAL EQUIPMENT: Hardware — APP/Mac; Printers — APP/Mac LaserWriter EDITORIAL SOFTWARE: Aldus/PageMaker. PRODUCTION EQUIPMENT: Hardware — Nu; Cameras — SCREEN/Companica 640c.

BATESVILLE

BATESVILLE DAILY GUARD

258 W Main St, Batesville, Ark., 72501-6711, Independence; gen tel (870) 793-2383; adv tel (870) 793-2383; ed tel (870) 793-2383; gen fax (870) 793-9268; adv fax (870) 793-9268; ed fax (870) 793-9268; gen/nat adv e-mail advertising@guardonline.com; disp adv e-mail advertising@guardonline.com; class adv e-mailclassifieds@guardonline.com; ed e-mail news@guardonline.com; web site www.guardonline.com
Published: Mon, Tues, Wed, Thur, Fri
Weekday Frequency: e
Circulation: 9,067
Last Audit: Sworn/Estimate/Non-Audited September 30, 2017
Advertising Rate (weekday/saturday): Open inch rate $10.78
News services: AP. **Established:** 1876
Own Printing Facility?: Yes
Commercial Printers?: Yes
Special Editions: Batesville USA (Apr); Fair Time (Aug); Spirit of Christmas (Dec); Brides (Jan); Father's Day (Jun); Baseball (Mar); Graduation (May); Basketball (Nov); Hunting (Oct).
Special Weekly Sections: Education (Fri); Outdoors (Thur); Business (Tues); Agriculture (Wed).
Syndicated Publications: River Country Tab (Fri); American Profile (Weekly).
Pub...Dr. O.E. Jones
Gen. Mgr...Pat Jones
Circ. Dir. ....Christine Brown
Adv. Ed. Mng. ....Angelia Roberts
Mng. Ed. ....Andrea Bruner
Photo Ed. .... Kris Caraway
Online Mgr. .... J. Ross Jones
Prodn. Mgr., Pressroom..................Don Stitcher
Classified Adv. Mgr........................ Shelly Garth
Mechanical Available: Offset; Black and 2 ROP colors; insert accepted; page cutoffs - 22 3/4.
Mechanical Specifications: Type page 13 x 21; E - 6 cols, 2 1/16, 1/8 between; A - 6 cols, 2 1/16, 1/8 between; C - 6 cols, 2 1/16, 1/8 between.
Areas Served: Batesville (AR) & surrounding area
Delivery Method: Mail, Newsstand, Carrier, RacksEquipment & Software: PRESSROOM EQUIPMENT: Lines — 1-F/20-page.; MAILROOM EQUIPMENT: Tying Machines — 2/Sa.; BUSINESS EQUIPMENT: 3-IBM/Sys 36 CLASSIFIED EQUIPMENT: Hardware — 1-TC.; EDITORIAL EQUIPMENT: Hardware — 8-TC, 1-XIT/Portable XPT II. PRODUCTION EQUIPMENT: Hardware — 3-LC; Cameras — 1-B.

BENTON

THE SALINE COURIER

321 N Market St, Benton, Ark., 72015-3734, Saline; gen tel (501) 315-8228; adv tel (501) 315-8228; ed tel (501) 315-8228; gen fax (501) 315-1230; adv fax (501) 315-1920; ed fax (501) 315-1920; gen/nat adv e-mail news@bentoncourier.com; disp adv e-mail dwills@bentoncourier.com; class adv e-mailclass@bentoncourier.com; ed e-mail news@bentoncourier.com; subscription@bentoncourier.com; web site www.bentoncourier.com
- 90,000(views) 22,000(visitors)
Group: Horizon Publications Inc.
Published: Mon, Tues, Wed, Thur, Fri, Sat, Sun
Weekday Frequency: e
Saturday Frequency: m
Circulation: 5,500; 65(sat); 5,700(sun)
Last Audit: Sworn/Estimate/Non-Audited September 30, 2017
Advertising Rate (weekday/saturday): $12.90, Thurs: $15.90
Advertising Rate (sunday): $12.90
Online Advertising Rate: 20
News services: AP. **Established:** 1876
Own Printing Facility?: Yes
Commercial Printers?: Yes
Special Editions: American Home Week/Home Improvement (Apr); Back-to-School (Aug); Christmas (Dec); Business Profile (Feb); Summer Recreation Guide (Jun); Fashion/Bridal (Mar); Spring Car Care (May); Cooking (Nov); Fall Car Care (Oct); Hunting (Sept).
Special Weekly Sections: Religion (Sat); Living (S); Neighbors (Lifestyle) (Thur); Business (Tues); Food & Good Health (Wed).
Syndicated Publications: TV Magazine (S); American Profile (Weekly).
Digital Platform - Mobile: Apple, Android
Digital Platform - Tablet: Apple iOS, Android
Composing Manager................. Patricia Stuckey
Pub.................................. Kelly Freudensprung
Ed...Josh Briggs
Press Room Mgr. ....Ricky Walters
Market Information: TMC
Mechanical Available: Offset; Black and 3 ROP colors; insert accepted; page cutoffs - 22 3/4.
Mechanical Specifications: Type page 13 x 21 1/2; E - 6 cols, 1 4/5, 1/8 between; A - 6 cols, 1 4/5, 1/8 between; C - 9 cols, 1 11/50, 1/8 between.
Areas Served: 72015, 72019, 72022, 72002, 72011, 72103, 72167
Delivery Method: Newsstand, Carrier, RacksEquipment & Software: PRESSROOM EQUIPMENT: Lines — 8-G/Community.; Alfa-Quest CTP MAILROOM EQUIPMENT: Counter Stackers — 1/BG; Tying Machines — 2-/Bu.; BUSINESS EQUIPMENT: Baseview CLASSIFIED EQUIPMENT: Hardware — 2-APP/Mac; CLASSIFIED SOFTWARE: Baseview/Class. DISPLAY EQUIPMENT: Hardware — APP/Mac II NT; Printers — 2-APP/Mac LaserWriter Plus, V/Imagesetter; DISPLAY SOFTWAREAd Make-up Applications — QPS, Adobe/Photoshop; Layout Software — APP/Mac II, APP/Mac IIcx, APP/Mac IIfx, APP/Mac Quadra 700. EDITORIAL EQUIPMENT: Mac OS 10.6 x 9 EDITORIAL SOFTWARE: NewsEdit Pro, Adobe InCopy, Creative Suites v. 5 PRODUCTION EQUIPMENT: Hardware — V/Imagesetter, 2-APP/Mac Laser, APP/Mac LaserWriter Plus; Cameras — 1-B PRODUCTION SOFTWARE: Scanners — 2-Microtek/Neg. Scanner, APP/Mac Flatbed Scanner.

BLYTHEVILLE

BLYTHEVILLE COURIER NEWS

900 N Broadway St, Blytheville, Ark., 72315-1714, Mississippi; gen tel (870) 763-4461; adv tel (870) 763-4461; ed tel (870) 763-4461; gen fax (870) 763-6874; adv fax (870) 763-6874; ed fax (870) 763-6874; gen/nat adv e-mail sriley@couriernews.net; disp adv e-mail sdelaney@couriernews.net; class adv e-mailsdelaney@couriernews.net; ed e-mail aweld@couriernews.net; web site www.couriernews.net
Group: Rust Communications
Published: Tues, Thur, Fri, Sun
Weekday Frequency: e
Circulation: 2,290; 2,290(sun)
Last Audit: CAC September 30, 2013
Advertising Rate (weekday/saturday): Open inch rate $10.00
News services: AP.
Own Printing Facility?: Yes
Commercial Printers?: Yes
Special Editions: Income Tax (Jan).
Special Weekly Sections: Church Page (Fri); Senior Outlook (Mon); Kids Page (S); Business (Thur); Health & Environment (Tues); Best Food Day (Wed).
Syndicated Publications: TV Magazine (Fri); Relish (Monthly); Color Comics (S).
Pub.... David Tennyson
Adv. Mgr...Harry Dorby
Mng. Ed. ....Mark Brassfield
Ed... Andy Weld
Prodn. Foreman, Pressroom......... Susie Robison
Staff Writer............................. Aaron Fitzpatrick
Market Information: TMC.
Mechanical Available: Offset; Black and 3 ROP colors; insert accepted - all; page cutoffs - 21 1/2.
Mechanical Specifications: Type page 13 1/2 x 21 1/2; E - 6 cols, 2 1/16, 1/8 between; A - 6 cols, 2 1/16, 1/8 between; C - 9 cols, 1 3/8, 1/8 between.
Areas Served: Blytheville Community
Delivery Method: Mail, RacksEquipment & Software: PRESSROOM EQUIPMENT: Lines — 8-G/Community; Folders — 1-G/SC, 1-G/Community.; MAILROOM EQUIPMENT: Tying Machines — 1-Felin/11313, 1-Us/GMH; Address Machine — 1-El/300.; BUSINESS SOFTWARE: Vision Data, Microsoft/Excel CLASSIFIED EQUIPMENT: Hardware — APP/Mac Quadra 605; CLASSIFIED SOFTWARE: Baseview, Microsoft, QPS. DISPLAY EQUIPMENT: Hardware — 2-APP/Mac Quadra 610; Printers — APP/Mac LaserWriter Pro 810; Other Hardware — Microtek/ScanMaker IIG. DISPLAY SOFTWAREAd Make-up Applications — Multi-Ad/Creator 3.6; EDITORIAL EQUIPMENT: Hardware — 2-APP/Mac Power Book, 3-APP/Mac Quadra, 2-APP/Mac Classic/Microtek/ScanMaker; Printers — APP/Mac ImageWriter EDITORIAL SOFTWARE: QPS, Baseview/NewsEdit, Multi-Ad/Creator. PRODUCTION EQUIPMENT: Hardware — Tl/OmniPage; Cameras — 1-R/1975, LE/500 PRODUCTION SOFTWARE: QPS.

CAMDEN

CAMDEN NEWS

113 Madison Ave NE, Camden, Ark., 71701-3514, Ouachita; gen tel (870) 836-8192; adv tel (870) 836-8192; gen fax (870) 837-1414; gen/nat adv e-mail camnews@cablelynx.com; disp adv e-mail advertising@camdenarknews.com; ed e-mail sports@camdenarknews.com; web site www.camdenarknews.com
Group: WEHCO Media, Inc.
Published: Mon, Tues, Wed, Thur, Fri
Weekday Frequency: e
Circulation: 4,342
Last Audit: Sworn/Estimate/Non-Audited September 30, 2017
Advertising Rate (weekday/saturday): Open inch rate $13.10
News services: AP. **Established:** 1920
Special Editions: Industrial Progress (Apr); Football (Aug); Bridal (Jan); Home, Lawn, & Garden (Mar); Cookbook (Oct); Fall Fashion

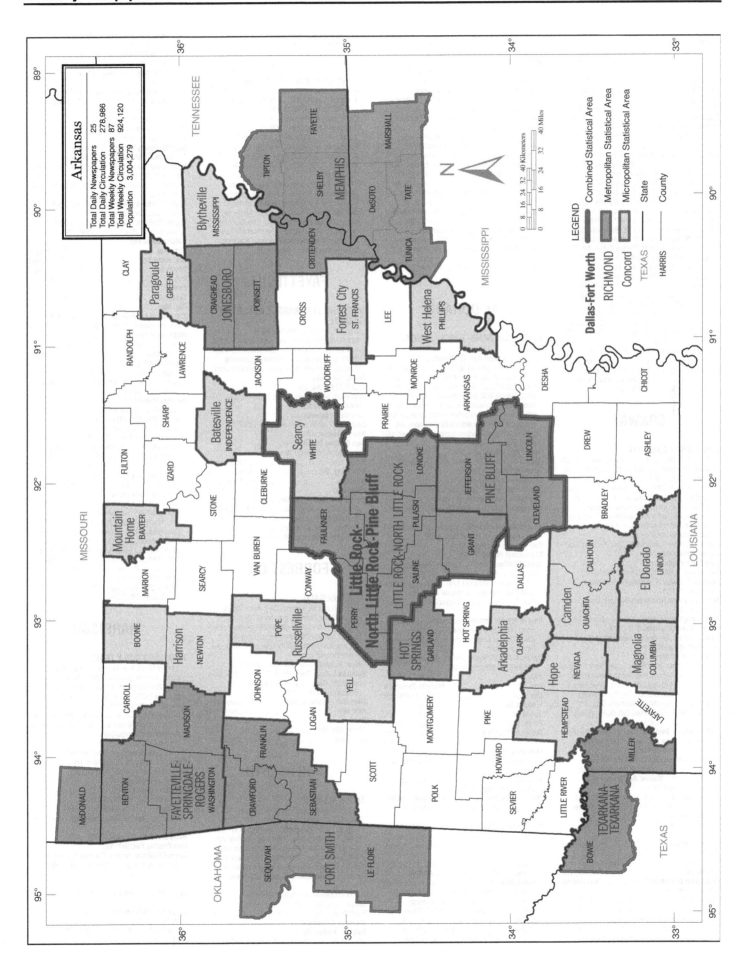

(Sept).

Syndicated Publications: Relish (Monthly); Food (Tues); American Profile (Weekly).
Pub. ....Walter E. Hussman
Gen. Mgr. ....Sue Silliman
Bus. Mgr. ....Pam Hulse
Adv. Mgr. ....Susan Silliman
Circ. Mgr. ....LaDonna Foster
Mng. Ed. ....Jim Edwards
Sports Ed. ....Kelly Blair
Market Information: TMC.
Mechanical Available: Offset; Black and 3 ROP colors; insert accepted.
Mechanical Specifications: Type page 13 x 21 1/2; E - 6 cols, 2 1/16, 1/8 between; A - 6 cols, 2 1/16, 1/8 between; C - 8 cols, 1 3/8, 1/16 between.Equipment & Software: BUSINESS EQUIPMENT: 1-Compaq/386-25, 2-Wyse BUSINESS SOFTWARE: Sun/System CLASSIFIED EQUIPMENT: Hardware — 2-APP/iMac; CLASSIFIED SOFTWARE: Baseview 3.3. DISPLAY EQUIPMENT: Other Hardware — HP/LaserWriter 5MP Plus DISPLAY SOFTWARELayout Software — 1-APP/Super Mac 8500, 20 Color Monitors, Scanners. EDITORIAL EQUIPMENT: Hardware — 7-APP/Mac G4, 7-APP/iMac; Printers — Epson/DXF 5000 3.2 EDITORIAL SOFTWARE: QPS/QuarkXPress 4.1, Baseview. PRODUCTION EQUIPMENT: Hardware — Adobe/Photoshop 6.0, Caere/OmniPage 8.0 PRODUCTION SOFTWARE: QPS/QuarkXPress 4.1.
Note: Subscribers to the Camden News (e) & the Magnolia Banner-News (e) receive the Sunday edition of the El Dorado News-Times (mS). See the El Dorado listing for Sunday circulation & advertising rates.

CONWAY

LOG CABIN DEMOCRAT
1111 Main St, Ste 102, Conway, Ark., 72032-5449, Faulkner; gen tel (501) 327-6621; adv tel (501) 505-1227; ed tel (501) 505-1212; gen fax (501) 327-6787; gen/nat adv e-mail ads@thecabin.net; disp adv e-mail ads@thecabin.net; class adv e-mailclassads@thecabin.net; ed e-mail editorial@thecabin.net; web site www.thecabin.net
Group: GateHouse Media, Inc.
Published: Mon, Tues, Wed, Thur, Fri, Sat, Sun
Weekday Frequency: m
Saturday Frequency: m
Circulation: 5,653; 5,653(sat); 7,319(sun)
Last Audit: Sworn/Estimate/Non-Audited October 1, 2017
Advertising Rate (weekday/saturday): Open inch rate $12.25
Advertising Rate (sunday): Open inch rate $13.75
Online Advertising Rate: $10 CPM
News services: AP, SHNS. **Established:** 1879
Own Printing Facility?: No
Commercial Printers?: No
Special Editions: Toad Suck Daze (Apr); Football (Aug); Last Minute Gift Guide (Dec); Bridal Tab (Feb); Red Tag Sale (Jan); Newcomer's Guide (Jul); June Shopping Spree (Jun); Spring Fashion (Mar); Mother's Day Gift Guide (May); Christmas Gift Guide (Nov); Auto Car Care (Oct)
Special Weekly Sections: Church Directory (Fri); Business Page (S); Best Food Day (Tues); Education Page (Wed).
Syndicated Publications: USA WEEKEND Magazine (S); American Profile (Weekly).
Digital Platform - Mobile: Apple, Android, Windows, Blackberry
Digital Platform - Tablet: Apple iOS, Android, Windows 7, Blackberry Tablet OS, Kindle, Nook, Kindle Fire
Group Controller, HR
Cynthia Crabb
Adv. Production ....Jay Prince
Online Dir. ....Nick Stahl
VP of Sales ....Betsey Barham
VP Audience ....Kelly Sublett
Circulation Operations Mgr ....Ron Garner
Market Information: TMC.
Mechanical Available: Offset; Black and 3 ROP colors; insert accepted; page cutoffs - 21 1/2.
Mechanical Specifications: Type page 15 1/4 x 21 1/2; E - 6 cols, 2 1/16, 1/8 between; A - 6 cols, 2 1/16, 1/8 between; C - 7 cols, 2 1/16,

1/8 between.
Areas Served: 72032, 72033, 72034, 72039, 72047, 72058, 72061, 72106, 72173
Delivery Method: Newsstand, Carrier, RacksEquipment & Software: PRESSROOM EQUIPMENT: Lines — 6-HI/Cotrell; MAILROOM EQUIPMENT: Counter Stackers — Stobb/PI; Inserters & Stuffers — MM/227E; Tying Machines — 1-Bu/63685; Wrapping Singles — 1-Sa/EM, 1-St/730; Address Machine — 1-Wm/28297.; BUSINESS EQUIPMENT: 1-IBM/Sys 34, APP/Mac CLASSIFIED EQUIPMENT: Hardware — 2-Mk, APP/Mac; Printers — Laser; CLASSIFIED SOFTWARE: Baseview/Ad Manager Pro. DISPLAY EQUIPMENT: Printers — HP/LaserJet III; Other Hardware — APP/Mac DISPLAY SOFTWARELayout Software — Dell/3255X. EDITORIAL EQUIPMENT: Hardware — Mk, APP/Mac/APP/Mac; Printers — Laser EDITORIAL SOFTWARE: Baseview/NewsEdit. PRODUCTION EQUIPMENT: Hardware — ECR/PelBox 1245CS, MON/Rip Express 1.02; Cameras — 1-R/480; Scanners — COM PRODUCTION SOFTWARE: Baseview/NewsEdit.

EL DORADO

EL DORADO NEWS-TIMES / SUNDAY NEWS
111 N Madison Ave, El Dorado, Ark., 71730-6124, Union; gen tel (870) 862-6611; adv tel (870) 862-6611; ed tel (870) 862-6611; gen fax (870) 862-5226; adv fax (870) 862-9482; ed fax (870) 862-9482; gen/nat adv e-mail editorial@eldoradonews.com; disp adv e-mail advertising@eldoradonews.com; class adv e-mailclassifieds@eldoradonews.com; ed e-mail editorial@eldoradonews.com; web site www.eldoradonews.com
Group: WEHCO Media, Inc.
Published: Mon, Tues, Wed, Thur, Fri, Sat, Sun
Weekday Frequency: m
Saturday Frequency: m
Circulation: 5,671; 5,671(sat); 5,247(sun)
Last Audit: AAM March 31, 2016
Advertising Rate (weekday/saturday): Open inch rate $23.75
Advertising Rate (sunday): Open inch rate $23.75
News services: AP. **Established:** 1876
Own Printing Facility?: Yes
Commercial Printers?: Yes
Special Editions: Spring Fashion (Apr); Back-to-School (Aug); Progress (Mar); Graduation (May); Senior Health (July); Veterans Section (Oct.); Christmas Catalogue (Nov); Fall Fashion (Sept). Bella Magazine (Feb., May, Oct,)
Special Weekly Sections: Education (Tue); Best Food (Wed); Real Estate (Fri); Religion (Sat); Living, Entertainment (Sun); Business, Finance (Mon)
Syndicated Publications: Relish (Monthly); USA WEEKEND Magazine (S);
Pub. ....Betty Chatham
Adv. Dir. ....Nichole Patterson
Circ. Mgr. ....Danny Leftridge
Features Ed. ....Janice McIntire
Sports Ed. ....Tony Burns
Prodn. Mgr. ....Iva Gail Riser
Business Office Mgr. ....Paula Burson
VP. ....Buddy King
Managing Ed. ....Randal Curtman
Pg. Design Ed. ....Kelsey Womack
J.W. Misenheimer
Man. Ed. ....Madeleine Leroux
Market Information: TMC.
Mechanical Available: Offset; Black and 3 ROP colors; insert accepted; page cutoffs - 21 1/2 inches
Mechanical Specifications: Type page 13 x 21 1/2; E - 6 cols, 1 5/8, 3/16 between; A - 6 cols, 1 5/8, 13/16 between; C - 8 cols, 1 3/16, 1/8 between.
Areas Served: 71730, 71759, 71750, 71765, 71762, 71749, 71758, 71768, 71724,
Delivery Method: Mail, Carrier, RacksEquipment & Software: PRESSROOM EQUIPMENT: Lines — 4-G/Urbanite (8 pgs on each unit).; MAILROOM EQUIPMENT: Counter Stackers — Systems Technology/Count-O-Veyor; Tying Machines — 1-Ca/Band tyer, Sterling; Address Machine — Wm.;

CLASSIFIED EQUIPMENT: Hardware — 3-APP/Mac; HP/Laserjet 4050; CLASSIFIED SOFTWARE: Baseview/Ad Manager Pro 2.05. DISPLAY EQUIPMENT: Hardware — 5-APP/Power Mac G4; Other Hardware — HP/1050E. DISPLAY SOFTWAREAd Make-up Applications — QPS/QuarkXPress 4.1; EDITORIAL EQUIPMENT: Hardware — 5-APP/Mac G4, 12-APP/iMac/Nikon/Cool Scan 4; Printers — 1-Microtek/Flatbed Scanner EDITORIAL SOFTWARE: Baseview 3.2.2. PRODUCTION EQUIPMENT: Hardware — Caere/OmniPage 8.0; Cameras — C/Spartan III; Scanners — Epson/1280 PRODUCTION SOFTWARE: Multi-Ad/Creator 6.0.
Note: The Sunday edition of the El Dorado News-Times (mS) is called The Sunday News. It is a combined edition of the El Dorado News-Times, Camden News (e) & Magnolia Banner-News (e). The Sunday News is distributed to subscribers in Union County, Columbia County and Ouachita County in southern Arkansas.

FAYETTEVILLE

NORTHWEST ARKANSAS DEMOCRAT-GAZETTE
212 N East Ave, Fayetteville, Ark., 72701-5225, Washington; gen tel (479) 442-1700; adv tel (866) 652-4373; adv fax (479) 442-5477; gen/nat adv e-mail keikenberry@nwadg.com; web site www.nwaonline.com
Group: NAN LLC
WEHCO Media, Inc.
Published: Mon, Tues, Wed, Thur, Fri, Sat, Sun
Weekday Frequency: m
Saturday Frequency: m
Last Audit: AAM September 30, 2017
News services: AP.
Own Printing Facility?: Yes
Commercial Printers?: Yes
Pres. ....Todd Nelson
Adv./Mktg. Dir. ....Crystal Costa
Adv. Mgr. ....Kent Eikenberry
Mktg. Mgr. ....Vanessa Wrutz
Delivery Method: Mail, Newsstand, Carrier, RacksEquipment & Software: PRESSROOM EQUIPMENT: Lines — 8-G/Headliner offset; Folders — Hoe/Colormatic 3:2/2:1; Pasters —9-Hoe/Colormatic Auto Paster.

FORREST CITY

TIMES-HERALD
222 N Izard St, Forrest City, Ark., 72335-3324, Saint Francis; gen tel (870) 633-3130; gen fax (870) 633-0599; gen/nat adv e-mail addept@thnews.com; class adv e-mailclassifiedads@thnews.com; web site www.thnews.com
Group: Argent Arkansas News Media
Published: Mon, Tues, Wed, Thur, Fri, Sat, Sun
Last Audit: Sworn/Estimate/Non-Audited September 30, 2017
Reporter. / Photographer ....Caleb Talley
Adv. Mgr. ....Amy Hale
Pub. ....Tamara Johnson
Class. Adv. Mgr. ....Courtney Hunt
Pub. Emer. ....Bonner McCollum

FORT SMITH

TIMES RECORD
3600 Wheeler Ave, Fort Smith, Ark., 72901-6621, Sebastian; gen tel (479) 785-7700; adv tel (479) 785-7700; gen fax (479) 784-0448; adv fax (479) 784-0448; gen/nat adv e-mail jnewman@swtimes.com; disp adv e-mail jnewman@swtimes.com; class adv e-mailjnewman@swtimes.com; ed e-mail mtaylor@swtimes.com; web site www.swtimes.com
 - 900,000(views) 160,000(visitors)
Group: New Media Investment Group
Published: Mon, Tues, Wed, Thur, Fri, Sat, Sun
Weekday Frequency: m
Saturday Frequency: m
Circulation: 18,000; 18,000(sat); 21,180(sun)

Last Audit: Sworn/Estimate/Non-Audited January 29, 2018
Advertising Rate (weekday/saturday): $43.24 (commissionable)
Advertising Rate (sunday): $46.26 (commissionable)
Online Advertising Rate: Solutions Available including OnTarget, SEO, SEM, Facebook, Zip Recruiter, ONO and more
News services: AP. **Established:** 1893
Own Printing Facility?: No
Commercial Printers?: Yes
Special Weekly Sections: OnScreen
Syndicated Publications: USA Weekend
Proprietary Publications: River Valley Advertiser, River Valley Real Estate & Home, Healthy U, Oh Baby, Bridal Planner, Best of Best, Best of Preps
Digital Platform - Mobile: Apple, Android, Windows, Blackberry
Digital Platform - Tablet: Apple iOS, Android, Windows 7, Blackberry Tablet OS
Outside Sales Mgr. ....Julie Newman
Circ. Mgr. ....Glen Hogue
Dig. Sales Mgr. ....Tara Lynch
Sports Ed. ....Brian Sanderford
Pub. ....Crystal Costa
Feat. Ed. ....Steve Peterson
Exec. Ed. ....Mardi Taylor
Dig. Mgr. ....Tara Lynch
Mechanical Available: Offset; Black and 3 ROP colors; insert accepted; page cutoffs - 23 1/2.
Mechanical Specifications: Type page 10"x21; E - 6 cols, 1.52", 1/8 between; A - 6 cols, 1.52", 1/8 between; C - 9 cols, 1.04", 1/8 between.
Areas Served: Crawford, Franklin, Johnson, Logan, Polk, Scott, and Sebastian counties in Arkansas; Haskell, LeFlore and Sequoyah counties in Oklahoma
Delivery Method: Mail, Newsstand, Carrier, RacksEquipment & Software: PRESSROOM EQUIPMENT: 200 lpi G/Cosmo double width; Pasters —6-G/Cosmo. BUSINESS SOFTWARE: Media Plus Advertising CLASSIFIED EQUIPMENT: Macintosh G5 CLASSIFIED SOFTWARE: MediaSpan DISPLAY EQUIPMENT: Hardware — 2-APP/G4, 1-APP/iMac, APP/7200/120; Printers — 2-HP/4050; DISPLAY SOFTWAREAd Make-up Applications — MediaSpan, InDesign CS4 Photoshop CS4; EDITORIAL EQUIPMENT: Hardware — 21-APP/Mac G4, 12-APP/Mac G3, 30-APP/iMac/6-Digital Cameras, 4-Digital Card Readers; Printers — 1-APP/8500, 1-HP/Color 8550 EDITORIAL SOFTWARE: NewsEngin PRODUCTION EQUIPMENT: Hardware — 2-Nu, KFM, Anitic/Plate Processor PRODUCTION SOFTWARE: MediaSpan, QuarkXPress, Adobe CS4 InDesign, Photoshop, Illustrator CIRCULATION SOFTWARCircPro

HARRISON

HARRISON DAILY TIMES
111 W Rush Ave, Harrison, Ark., 72601-4218, Boone; gen tel (870) 741-2325; adv tel (870)743-0624; ed tel (870)743-0601; gen fax (870) 741-5632; gen/nat adv e-mail dailytimes@harrisondaily.com; disp adv e-mail jasono@harrisondaily.com; class adv e-maildebbiel@harrisondaily.com; ed e-mail news@harrisondaily.com; web site www.harrisondaily.com
 - 277,368(views) 44,599(visitors)
Group: Community Publishers, Inc.
Published: Tues, Wed, Thur, Fri, Sat
Weekday Frequency: m
Saturday Frequency: m
Circulation: 5,701; 6,529(sat)
Last Audit: CVC December 31, 2014
Advertising Rate (weekday/saturday): Open inch rate $15.00
News services: AP. **Established:** 1876
Own Printing Facility?: Yes
Special Editions: Health, Fitness & Medical (Monthly). Progress, March, Full Market Coverage (Monthly), Thanksgiving / Black Friday
Special Weekly Sections: TV Magazine-Focus (Fri).
Syndicated Publications: USA WEEKEND Magazine (S).
Digital Platform - Mobile: Apple, Android, Blackberry

Digital Platform - Tablet: Apple iOS, Android, Windows 7, Blackberry Tablet OS, Kindle
Pub. .... Jim Perry
Gen. Mgr. .... Jason Overman
Bus./Finance Ed. .... Donna Braymer
City/Metro Ed. .... James White
Fashion/Style Ed. .... Yvonne Cone
Food Ed. .... Jane Dunlap Christenson
Political/Gov't Ed. .... Lee Dunlap
Mng. Ed. .... Jeff Brasel
Managing Ed. .... Lynn Blevins
Circ. Mgr .... Jim Kennedy
Advertising Manager .... Todd Edwards
Market Information: TMC.
Mechanical Available: Offset; Black and 3 ROP colors; insert accepted; page cutoffs - 22 3/4.
Mechanical Specifications: Type page 11.25 x 20.5, 6 cols.
Areas Served: 72601, 72611, 72615, 72616, 72619, 72644, 72648, 72638, 72641, 72630, 72650, 72662, 72682, 72685, 72687Equipment & Software: PRESSROOM EQUIPMENT: Lines — 7-G/Community (DEV color deck); MAILROOM EQUIPMENT: Tying Machines — 2-/Bu; Wrapping Singles — 1-St/ Collator-tyer (ST-3 unit); Address Machine — 1-/Ch.; BUSINESS EQUIPMENT: 5-RSK, APA CLASSIFIED EQUIPMENT: Hardware — Apple; 2-Mk.; CLASSIFIED SOFTWARE: MediaSpan DISPLAY EQUIPMENT: Hardware — Apple & PC; EDITORIAL EQUIPMENT: Hardware — Mk, APP/Mac/ APP/Mac II, 10-Mk/400, 3-APP/Mac; Printers — 2-APP/Mac LaserWriter 630 Pro, 1-APP/ Mac LaserWriter NTX. PRODUCTION EQUIPMENT: Hardware — Direct to plate.

HOPE

HOPE STAR

522 W 3rd St, Hope, Ark., 71801-5001, Hempstead; gen tel (870) 777-8841; gen fax (870) 777-3311; gen/nat adv e-mail hopestar71802@yahoo.com; disp adv e-mail thaycox@hopestar.com; ed e-mail kmclemore@hopestar.com; web site www.hopestar.com
Group: New Media Investment Group
Published: Mon, Tues, Wed, Thur, Fri
Weekday Frequency: e
Circulation: 3,031
Last Audit: Sworn/Estimate/Non-Audited September 30, 2017
Advertising Rate (weekday/saturday): Open inch rate $15.60
News services: AP. **Established:** 1899
Special Editions: Watermelon Festival (Jul); Progress (Mar); Graduation (May).
Syndicated Publications: Star Time Entertainment (weekly TV section) (Fri); American Profile (Weekly).
Circ. Dir. .... Donnie Hollis
Sr. Group Pub. .... Shane Allen
Bus. Mgr. .... Marsha Hunt
Tim Haycox
Ed. .... Richard Kennedy
Market Information: ADS; TMC.
Mechanical Available: Offset; Black and 3 ROP colors; insert accepted - all; page cutoffs - 22 3/4.
Mechanical Specifications: Type page 13 x 21 1/2; E - 6 cols, 2 1/16, 1/8 between; A - 6 cols, 2 1/16, 1/8 between; C - 6 cols, 2 1/16, 1/8 between.Equipment & Software: PRESSROOM EQUIPMENT: Lines — 5-WPC/Marc 25; Reels & Stands — 5; MAILROOM EQUIPMENT: Counter Stackers — BG/Count-O-Veyor; Tying Machines — 4-Sa/EM10755; Wrapping Singles — 4/Sa; Address Machine — 1-Ch/500, 1-Ch/730.; BUSINESS EQUIPMENT: IBM/Sys 34 CLASSIFIED EQUIPMENT: Hardware — APP/Mac Network.; DISPLAY SOFTWARELayout Software — APP/ Mac. EDITORIAL EQUIPMENT: Hardware — 4-APP/Mac IIci/6-HI/1250, 5-COM/ Computype, 6-APP/Mac Performa; Printers — LaserMaster/XL 1200. PRODUCTION EQUIPMENT: Hardware — APP/Mac LaserWriter NTX; Cameras — 1-B/Caravelle 18 x 24.

HOT SPRINGS

NATIONAL PARK

THE SENTINEL-RECORD

300 Spring St, Hot Springs National Park, Ark., 71901-4148, Garland; gen tel (501) 623-7711; gen fax (501) 623-2984; gen/nat adv e-mail debej@hotsr.com; disp adv e-mail debej@hotsr.com; class adv e-maildebbiel@hotsr.com; ed e-mail editor@hotsr.com; web site www.hotspringssr.com
Group: WEHCO Media, Inc.
Published: Mon, Tues, Wed, Thur, Fri, Sat, Sun
Weekday Frequency: m
Saturday Frequency: m
Circulation: 10,524; 10,524(sat); 11,387(sun)
Last Audit: AAM March 31, 2017
Advertising Rate (weekday/saturday): Open inch rate $33.27 for National
Advertising Rate (sunday): Open inch rate $33.27 for National
News services: AP. **Established:** 1877
Special Editions: Mail-it-Away (Feb); Spring Home Improvement (Mar); Come to Play, Come to Stay (Apr); Ladies' Night Out (Apr); Family Owned Business (May); Readers' Choice (Jun); Back to School (Jul); Senior Resource Guide (Aug); Football (Aug); Hot Springs Village Appreciation Days (Sep); Fall Home Improvement (Oct); Garland County Cares (Oct); Senior Scene (Monthly).
Special Weekly Sections: TV Magazine (S).
Syndicated Publications: Relish (Monthly); USA WEEKEND Magazine (Sat); American Profile (Weekly).
Digital Platform - Mobile: Apple
Digital Platform - Tablet: Apple iOS, Kindle
Pub. .... Walter E. Hussman
Online Ed. .... Mark Gregory
Photo Ed. .... Richard Rasmussen
Photographer .... Alison Harbour
Real Estate Ed. .... Lynda Lampinen
Religion Ed. .... Linda Arneson
Sports Ed. .... Robert Wisener
Prodn. Mgr., Pre Press .... Jimmy Robertson
Adv. Dir. .... Debe Johnson
Circ. Dir. .... Glenn Waits
Gary Troutman
Gen. Mgr. .... Harry Porter
Market Information: TMC.
Mechanical Available: Offset; Black and 3 ROP colors; insert accepted; page cutoffs - 22 3/4.
Mechanical Specifications: Type page 11 5/8 x 21 1/4; E - 6 cols, 1 3/4, 1/8 between; A - 6 cols, 1 3/4, 1/8 between; C - 9 cols, 1 1/4, 1/8 between.
Areas Served: 71901, 71913, 71909, others
Delivery Method: Mail, Newsstand, Carrier, RacksEquipment & Software: PRESSROOM EQUIPMENT: Lines — 7-G/ Urbanite 1967; Reels & Stands — G/7.; MAILROOM EQUIPMENT: Counter Stackers — 2-HL/Monitor, 1-QWI/Sport II; Inserters & Stuffers — 1-KAN/480; Tying Machines — MLN/MLN2A, Si/Portable; BUSINESS EQUIPMENT: IBM BUSINESS SOFTWARE: PBS, Circulation, Ad Management CLASSIFIED EQUIPMENT: Hardware — APP/Mac; Printers — Okidata; CLASSIFIED SOFTWARE: Baseview. DISPLAY EQUIPMENT: Hardware — APP/ Mac; Printers — AG/Accuset 1500; DISPLAY SOFTWAREAd Make-up Applications — Multi-Ad 4.3; Layout Software — Mk/ Ad Manager. EDITORIAL EQUIPMENT: Hardware — APP/Mac EDITORIAL SOFTWARE: Baseview. PRODUCTION EQUIPMENT: Hardware — TI/OmniPage; Scanners — HP PRODUCTION SOFTWARE: QPS 4.1.

JONESBORO

THE JONESBORO SUN

518 Carson St, Jonesboro, Ark., 72401-3128, Craighead; gen tel (870) 935-5525; gen fax (870) 935-5823; adv fax (870) 935-1674; ed fax (870) 935-5823; disp adv e-mail llynn@jonesborosun.com; class adv e-mailsmith@jonesborosun.com; ed e-mail cwessel@jonesborosun.com; web site www.jonesborosun.com
Group: Paxton Media Group, LLC
Published: Mon, Tues, Wed, Thur, Fri, Sat, Sun
Weekday Frequency: m
Saturday Frequency: m
Circulation: 19,830; 19,830(sat); 22,564(sun)
Last Audit: Sworn/Estimate/Non-Audited October 5, 2017
Advertising Rate (weekday/saturday): Open inch rate $27.25
Advertising Rate (sunday): $28.35
News services: AP. **Established:** 1903
Own Printing Facility?: Yes
Commercial Printers?: Yes
Special Editions: Farm Family, NEA Plants, Academic Allstars, ASU Campus Guide, High School Football/Basketball, NEA District Fair, Chamber Leadership, Local Favorites, Sun Outdoors, NEA Harvest, Let's Eat Out, Susan G. Komen Cancer Awareness, Christmas Open House, Jonesboro Concierge Guide
Special Weekly Sections: Lifestyle (S); Church Page (Sat); Food (Wed). Entertainment (Thurs)
Syndicated Publications: TV Guide (S), Athlon Sports, Relish
Pub. .... David Mosesso
Adv. Dir. .... Lisa Lynn
Sports Ed. .... Kevin Turbeville
Production Manager, IT .... Roger Brumley
Controller .... Michael Shain
Circ. Director .... Lorri Householder
Editor .... Chris Wessel
Mng. Ed. .... Waylon Harris
Market Information: TMC.
Mechanical Available: Offset; Black and 3 ROP colors; insert accepted; page cutoffs - 21 1/2.
Mechanical Specifications: Type page 11 x 21 1/2; E - 6 cols, 2, 1/8 between; A - 6 cols, 2, 1/8 between; C - 8 cols, 1 1/2, 1/8 between.
Areas Served: 72005 72019 72031 72043 72067 72076 72101 72104 72112 72118 72143 72160 72183 72201 72206 72211 72313 72315 72320 72324 72330 72347 72350 72351 72354 72358 72365 72370 72377 72386 72387 72391 72395 72396 72401 72403 72404 72410 72411 72412 72413 72414 72415 72416 72417 72419 72421 72422 72425 72426 72427 72428 72429 72430 72431 72432 72433 72434 72435 72436 72437 72438 72440 72441 72442 72443 72444 72445 72447 72449 72450 72451 72453 72454 72455 72456 72457 72458 72459 72460 72461 72462 72464 72465 72466 72467 72469 72470 72471 72472 72473 72474 72475 72476 72478 72479 72482 72501 72503 72513 72519 72522 72529 72530 72532 72542 72543 72554 72560 72653 72654 72703 72756 72921 72956
Delivery Method: Mail, Newsstand, Carrier, RacksEquipment & Software: PRESSROOM EQUIPMENT: Lines — 8-G/Urbanite 1986; Folders — 1-G/2:1; Reels & Stands — 2-G/4 Tier; Control System — 2-1986.; MAILROOM EQUIPMENT: Counter Stackers — Newstack, 1-Id/660, 1-Id/2200; Inserters & Stuffers — HI/1372, W/ARS; Tying Machines — 2/MLN; Address Machine — 1-/KR, 2-/ CYP.; CLASSIFIED SOFTWARE: MediaSpan EDITORIAL SOFTWARE: MediaSpan PRODUCTION SOFTWARE: Prestelligence

LITTLE ROCK

ARKANSAS DEMOCRAT-GAZETTE

121 E Capitol Ave, Little Rock, Ark., 72201-3819, Pulaski; gen tel (501) 378-3400; adv tel (501)378-3434; ed tel (501) 378-3485 ; gen fax (501)378-3863; adv fax (501) 378-3591; ed fax (501) 372-4765; gen/nat adv e-mail dbrowning@arkansasonline.com; disp adv e-mail dbrowning@arkansasonline.com; class adv e-maildbrowning@arkansasonline.com; ed e-mail ffellone@arkansasonline.com; web site www.ardemgaz.com
928,680(visitors)
Group: WEHCO Media, Inc.
Published: Mon, Tues, Wed, Thur, Fri, Sat, Sun
Weekday Frequency: m
Saturday Frequency: m
Circulation: 124,041; 121,475(sat); 166,945(sun)
Last Audit: AAM March 31, 2017
Advertising Rate (weekday/saturday): Open inch rate $248.00
Advertising Rate (sunday): Open inch rate $376.00
News services: 1991
Own Printing Facility?: Yes
Special Weekly Sections: Business, Farm, Style, Weather (Daily); Style (Tue/Sun); Active, Business, Technology (Mon); Best Food Day, Family (Wed); Arkansas Weekend (Thur); Movies (Fri); Home, Garden, Religion (Sat); Dear Abby, high Profile, TV, Real Estate, Book, Travel (Sun)
Pub.
Walter Hussman
Pres./Gen. Mgr. .... Lynn Hamilton
VP, Adv./Mktg .... Scott Stine
V.P./Circulation .... Larry Graham
City Ed. .... Danny Shameer
Online Dir. .... Matthew Costa
State Ed. .... Heidi White
Projects Ed. .... Sonny Albarado
Asst. Managing Ed. .... Barry Arthur
Chief Photographer .... John Sykes
Info. Systems Mgr. .... Eric Gilreath
Online Dir. .... Conan Gallaty
Areas Served: ARKANSAS
Delivery Method: Mail, Newsstand, Carrier, Racks

MAGNOLIA

BANNER-NEWS

130 S Washington, Magnolia, Ark., 71753-3523, Columbia; gen tel (870) 234-5130; gen fax (870) 234-2551; gen/nat adv e-mail cmartin@bannernews.net; disp adv e-mail advertising@bannernews.net; ed e-mail news@bannernews.net; web site www.bannernews.net
Group: WEHCO Media, Inc.
Published: Mon, Tues, Wed, Thur, Fri
Weekday Frequency: e
Circulation: 3,500
Last Audit: Sworn/Estimate/Non-Audited September 30, 2017
Advertising Rate (weekday/saturday): Open inch rate $10.57 retail and $8.95 classified
News services: AP. **Established:** 1878
Own Printing Facility?: No
Commercial Printers?: Yes
Special Editions: Blossom Festival (Apr); Bride (Jan); Progress (May);
Syndicated Publications: Relish (Monthly);
Digital Platform - Mobile: Apple, Android
Digital Platform - Tablet: Apple iOS, Android
Pub. .... Walter E. Hussman
Gen. Mgr. .... Susan Gill
Circ. Mgr. .... Stepahnie Scott
Mng. Ed. .... Dan Marsh
Sports Ed. .... Chris Gilliam
Market Information: TMC.
Mechanical Available: Offset; Black and 3 ROP colors; insert accepted; page cutoffs - 21 1/2.
Mechanical Specifications: 46" web
Areas Served: 71753
Delivery Method: Mail, Newsstand, Carrier, RacksEquipment & Software: MAILROOM EQUIPMENT: Tying Machines — Cyclone; Address Machine — Novell/LAN.; CLASSIFIED SOFTWARE: Baseview. EDITORIAL SOFTWARE: NewsEngin
Note: The Banner-News is printed at the El Dorado News-Times. For detailed production information, see the El Dorado News-Times listing.

MALVERN

MALVERN DAILY RECORD

219 Locust St, Malvern, Ark., 72104-3721, Hot Spring; gen tel (501) 337-7523; adv tel (501) 337-1226 ext. 216; ed tel (501) 337-1226 ext. 215; gen fax (501) 337-1226; gen/nat adv e-mail advertising@malvern-online.com; disp adv e-mail advertising@malvern-online.com; class adv e-mailclassifieds@malvern-online.com; ed e-mail editor@malvern-online.com; web site www.malvern-online.com
Group: Horizon Publications Inc.
Published: Tues, Wed, Thur, Fri, Sat
Weekday Frequency: e
Saturday Frequency: m
Circulation: 2,800; 3,200(sat)
Last Audit: Sworn/Estimate/Non-Audited September 30, 2017
Newspaper Reps: Richard Folds

Branch Offices: NA
Advertising Rate (weekday/saturday): Open inch rate $11.45
News services: AP. **Established:** 1914
Own Printing Facility?: No
Commercial Printers?: No
Special Editions: Christmas (Dec); Progress (Jan); Thanksgiving/Christmas Kick-off (Nov).
Syndicated Publications: Food Days (TUE); Consumer Review (Thur); Food Days (TUE); American Profile (SAT).
Circ. Mgr. ....Kathi Ledbetter
Adv. Dir. ....Michelle Cummins
Pub. ....Richard Folds
Composition Mgr. ....Stephanie Rhea
Business Mgr. ....Kim Taber
Sports Ed. ....Eric Moore
Gov. & City Reporter ....Josh Waddles
Lifestyles Ed. ....Gretchen Ritchey
Market Information: TMC.
Mechanical Available: Offset; Black and 4 ROP colors; insert accepted; page cutoffs - 22 3/4.
Mechanical Specifications: Type page 13 x 21 1/2; E - 6 cols, 2 1/16, 1/8 between; A - 6 cols, 2 1/16, 1/8 between; C - 9 cols, 1 1/3, 1/8 between.
Areas Served: 72104, 71923, 71929, 71941, 72128, 72167, 71913
Delivery Method: Mail, Newsstand, Carrier, RacksEquipment & Software: PRESSROOM EQUIPMENT: NA MAILROOM EQUIPMENT: NA BUSINESS EQUIPMENT: PC BUSINESS SOFTWARE: Ad Manager Pro CLASSIFIED EQUIPMENT: Hardware — APP/Mac; CLASSIFIED SOFTWARE: Ad Manager Pro DISPLAY EQUIPMENT: Printers — APP/Mac DISPLAY SOFTWAREInDesigns EDITORIAL EQUIPMENT: Hardware — APP/Mac EDITORIAL SOFTWARE: InDesign, Photoshop, Adobe Acrobat PRODUCTION EQUIPMENT: Hardware — Nat/A-250; Cameras — B. PRODUCTION SOFTWARE: InDesign, Photoshop, Adobe Acrobat CIRCULATION EQUIPMENT: Mac CIRCULATION SOFTWARCircpro/Newscycle

MARION

THE EVENING TIMES

1010 State Highway 77, Marion, Ark., 72364-9007, Crittenden; gen tel (870) 735-1010; adv tel (870) 735-1010; ed tel (870) 735-1010; gen fax (870) 735-1020; adv fax (870) 735-1020; ed fax (870) 735-1020; gen/nat adv e-mail news@theeveningtimes.com; disp adv e-mail retailadv@theeveningtimes.com; class adv e-mailClassified@theeveningtimes.com; ed e-mail news@theeveningtimes.com; web site www.theeveningtimes.com
Group: Crittenden Publishing Co.
Published: Mon, Tues, Wed, Thur, Fri
Weekday Frequency: m
Circulation: 8,000
Last Audit: Sworn/Estimate/Non-Audited September 30, 2017
Advertising Rate (weekday/saturday): Open inch rate $12.81
News services: 1943
Own Printing Facility?: Yes
Commercial Printers?: Yes
Special Editions: Pigskin Preview (Aug); Christmas Greetings (Dec); Farm Family (Aug.); Valentine Pages (Feb); Progress (March-April); Back-to-School Tab (Jul); Holiday Gift Guide
Syndicated Publications: American Profile (Weekly).
Adv. Dir. ....Nick Coulter
Mike Coulter
Business manager ....Alice Rains
Pub. ....Alex Coulter
Office/Credit Mgr. ....Alice Raines
Managing editor ....Gary Meece
Circ. Mgr. ....Gail Clark
Market Information: TMC.
Mechanical Available: Offset; Black and 3 ROP colors; insert accepted; page cutoffs - 23 3/4.
Mechanical Specifications: Type page 11 3/4 x 21 1/2; E - 6 cols, 1 7/10, 1/8 between; A - 6 cols, 3 3/5, 1/16 between; C - 9 cols, 1 1/10, 1/8 between.
Areas Served: 72303, 72364, 72348, 72301
Delivery Method: Mail, Carrier, RacksEquipment & Software: PRESSROOM EQUIPMENT: Lines — 6-KP/News King 1974; Folders — KP/Newsking; Reels & Stands — 6-Roll/Stands; Control System — GE/SP 200.; MAILROOM EQUIPMENT: Tying Machines — 2/Akebono; Address Machine — St; BUSINESS EQUIPMENT: IBM/386-486, APP/Mac BUSINESS SOFTWARE: QuarkXPress CLASSIFIED EQUIPMENT: Hardware — Baseview/Ad Manager Pro, QPS/QuarkXPress; Printers — ECR; CLASSIFIED SOFTWARE: CText. DISPLAY EQUIPMENT: Printers — Accel-A-Writer, ECR; DISPLAY SOFTWAREAd Make-up Applications — Adobe/PageMaker, Adobe/Photoshop, QPS/QuarkXPress, Adobe/Illustrator; Layout Software — APP/Mac G4, APP/Mac G3, APP/Power Mac 8600. EDITORIAL EQUIPMENT: ; Printers — ECR EDITORIAL SOFTWARE: Baseview/NewsEdit Pro, QPS/QuarkXPress. PRODUCTION EQUIPMENT: Hardware — APP/Mac, PCs; Cameras — C/Spartan III; Scanners — Canon/Flatbed, Canon/Coldscan PRODUCTION SOFTWARE: QPS/QuarkXPress.

MOUNTAIN HOME

THE BAXTER BULLETIN

16 W 6th St, Mountain Home, Ark., 72653-3508, Baxter; gen tel (870) 508-8000; adv tel (870) 508-8078; ed tel (870) 508-8064; gen fax (870) 508-8020; adv fax (870) 508-8020; ed fax (870) 508-8020; gen/nat adv e-mail advertising@baxterbulletin.com; disp adv e-mail classads@baxterbulletin.com; ed e-mail newsroom@baxterbulletin.com; web site www.baxterbulletin.com
- 950,000(views) 126,790(visitors)
Group: Gannett
Published: Mon, Tues, Wed, Thur, Fri, Sat, Sun
Weekday Frequency: m
Saturday Frequency: m
Circulation: 6,490; 7,219(sat); 106(sun)
Last Audit: AAM September 30, 2017
Advertising Rate (weekday/saturday): Open inch rate $12.60
Advertising Rate (sunday): Open inch rate $12.60
Online Advertising Rate: Run of Site: Leaderboard $7, Large Rectangle $8, Half Page $14 ; Base CPM: Billboard $35, Hero Flip $30, Pushdown $40, Pushdown Plus(with rails) $45, Interactive Takeover $55, Active Rails $30
News services: AP, GNS. **Established:** 1901
Special Editions: Health (Apr); Back-to-School (Aug); Letters to Santa (Dec); Baxter County Fact Book (Feb); Chronology (Jan); Home Show (Mar); Twin Lakes Real Estate Guide (Monthly); Christmas Gift Guide (Nov); Baxter County Fair (Sept).
Special Weekly Sections: TV Book (Fri); Technology (Mon); Faith/Religion (Sat); Entertainment (Thur); Health/Fitness (Tues); Food (Wed).
Syndicated Publications: USA WEEKEND Magazine (Sat).
Proprietary Publications: Living Well Magazine(bi-monthly), HomeFinder Magazine(monthly), Fact Book(annually)
Distribution/ Dock Supervisor .....Clyde Anderson
Composing Supervisor ....Tammy House
Features ed. ....Joanne Bratton
Managing Editor ....Sonny Elliott
Editorial page Ed. ....Thomas Garrett
Online Ed. / Food Ed ....Linda Masters
Adv. Dir. ....Adrianne Dunn
Ad. Acct. Relationship Specialist ....Stormi Day
Advertising Acct. Relationship Specialist... Kendra Spencer
Ad. Clerk ....Marsha Meissner
Armando Rios
Exec. Dir. ....Paul Berry
Pres. ....Allen Jones
Reporter ....Scott Liles
Health & Education Rep. ....Billy Jean Louis
Market Information: TMC.
Mechanical Available: Offset; Black and 3 ROP colors; insert accepted; page cutoffs - 22 3/4.
Mechanical Specifications: Type page 11 5/8 x 21; E - 6 cols, 1 5/6, 1/8 between; A - 6 cols, 1 5/6, 1/8 between; C - 6 cols, 1 5/6, 1/8 between.
Areas Served: 65655, 72519, 72531, 72537, 72538, 72544, 72566, 72583, 72585, 72619, 72623, 72626, 72634, 72635, 72642, 72651, 72653, 72658, 72677, 72661, 72687Equipment & Software: PRESSROOM EQUIPMENT: Lines — 6-G/Community, 2-Dauphin/Graphic Units.; MAILROOM EQUIPMENT: Counter Stackers — 1/BG; Inserters & Stuffers — 1-/MM; Tying Machines — 2-/Bu, 1-Samuel/Strapper; Address Machine — 1-KR, 1-Profit Packaging/P3.; BUSINESS EQUIPMENT: 1-IBM/AS-400 CLASSIFIED EQUIPMENT: Hardware — 3-Epson/PC; CLASSIFIED SOFTWARE: Baseview/Ad Manager Pro 2.6. DISPLAY EQUIPMENT: Other Hardware — 3-HI/1420 DISPLAY SOFTWARELayout Software — MEI/Ad Force 4.0. EDITORIAL EQUIPMENT: Hardware — Mk/3000/9-Mk/PC EDITORIAL SOFTWARE: Baseview/NewsEdit Pro 3.5. PRODUCTION EQUIPMENT: Hardware — 2-COM/8400; Cameras — 1-C/Spartan III; Scanners — Umax PRODUCTION SOFTWARE: QPS/QuarkXPress 4.11.

PARAGOULD

PARAGOULD DAILY PRESS

1401 W Hunt St, Paragould, Ark., 72450-3575, Greene; gen tel (870) 239-8562; adv tel (870)239-8562; ed tel (870)239-8562; gen fax (870) 239-3636; adv fax (870) 239-3636; gen/nat adv e-mail bkeller@paragoulddailypress.com; disp adv e-mail advertising@paragoulddailypress.com; class adv e-mailadvertising@paragoulddailypress.com; ed e-mail editor@paragoulddailypress.com; web site www.paragoulddailypress.com
29,131(visitors)
Group: Paxton Media Group, LLC
Published: Tues, Wed, Thur, Fri, Sun
Weekday Frequency: m
Saturday Frequency: m
Circulation: 4,200; 4,200(sun)
Last Audit: Sworn/Estimate/Non-Audited September 30, 2017
Advertising Rate (weekday/saturday): Open inch rate $8.95
Advertising Rate (sunday): $8.95
News services: AP.
Special Editions: Travel (Apr); Fall Fashions (Aug); Christmas (Dec); Loose Caboose Festival (Jul); Family-Owned Business (Jun); Spring Fashions (Mar); Thanksgiving (Nov); Outdoors (Oct); Football (Sept).
Special Weekly Sections: Entertainment (Fri); Weddings (S); Outdoors; Farm (Thur); Business (Tues); Food (Wed).
Sports Ed. ....Mike McKinney
General Manager ....Brenda Keller
Editor ....Steve Gillespie
Market Information: TMC.
Mechanical Available: Offset; Black and 3 ROP colors; insert accepted; page cutoffs - 23 5/16.
Mechanical Specifications: Type page 11 5/8 x 21 1/2; E - 6 cols, 1 5/6, 1/8 between; A - 6 cols, 1 5/6, 1/16 between; C - 9 cols, 1 7/20, 1/8 between.
Areas Served: 72450, 72443, 72436, 72474, 72412, 72439, 72461, 72425, 72454, 72476, 63829Equipment & Software: PRESSROOM EQUIPMENT: Lines — 6-G/Community (balloon former); MAILROOM EQUIPMENT: Tying Machines — 1-Sa/4592; Address Machine — 1-El/3300.; CLASSIFIED EQUIPMENT: Hardware — APP/Mac; Printers — Okidata/Pacemark 3410; CLASSIFIED SOFTWARE: Baseview, QPS. DISPLAY EQUIPMENT: Hardware — 1-APP/Mac G3, 3-APP/Mac G4; Printers — HP/LaserJet 5000N, HP/2500 CM; Other Hardware — APP/Mac G4 Server DISPLAY SOFTWAREAd Make-up Applications — Multi-Ad/Creator, Adobe/Photoshop, Caere/OmniPage; Layout Software — APP/Mac. EDITORIAL EQUIPMENT: Hardware — APP/Mac; Printers — HP/LaserJet 5000N EDITORIAL SOFTWARE: QPS, APP/Appleworks 6.0, QPS/QuarkXPress 4.1, Text Edit Plus. PRODUCTION EQUIPMENT: Hardware — 2-APP/Mac Laser Plus, Pelbox/UR-30, APP/Mac G-3; Cameras — 1-C/Spartan III; Scanners — Nikon/Film Scanner PRODUCTION SOFTWARE: QPS/QuarkXPress 4.1.

PINE BLUFF

PINE BLUFF COMMERCIAL

300 S Beech St, Pine Bluff, Ark., 71601-4039, Jefferson; gen tel (870) 534-3400; adv tel (870) 543-1452; ed tel (870) 543-1456; gen fax (870) 534-0113; adv fax (870) 534-0113; ed fax (870) 534-0113; gen/nat adv e-mail kbrickey@pbcommercial.com; disp adv e-mail pbcads@pbcommercial.com; ed e-mail news@pbcommercial.com; web site www.pbcommercial.com
Group: New Media Investment Group
Published: Tues, Wed, Thur, Fri, Sat, Sun
Weekday Frequency: m
Saturday Frequency: m
Circulation: 6,998; 6,998(sat); 7,320(sun)
Last Audit: CAC September 30, 2016
Advertising Rate (weekday/saturday): Open inch rate $20.70
News services: AP, MCT, NEA.
Special Editions: Good News Tab (Apr); Football Tab (Aug); Wedding Tab (Feb); FYI Community Information Tab (Jul); Garden & Home Improvement (Mar); Wrap It Up Early (Nov); Fall Hunting/Fishing Guide Tab (Sept).
Special Weekly Sections: Weekend Entertainment (Fri); Business News (S); TV (Sat); Business News (Wed).
Syndicated Publications: USA WEEKEND Magazine (S).
News Clerk ....Sandra Hope
Pub. ....Ed Graves
Mng. Ed. ....John Worthen
Circ. Mgr. ....Mae Washington
Adv. Mgr. ....Margie Savage
Class. Mgr. ....Paula Pamplin
Market Information: TMC; Zoned editions.
Mechanical Available: Offset; Black and 3 ROP colors; insert accepted; page cutoffs - 21.
Mechanical Specifications: Type page 11 5/8 x 21; E - 6 cols, 1 4/5, 1/6 between; A - 6 cols, 1 4/5, 1/6 between; C - 9 cols, 1 1/5, 1/6 between.Equipment & Software: PRESSROOM EQUIPMENT: Lines — 9-G/Urbanite; MAILROOM EQUIPMENT: Counter Stackers — QWI/350; Inserters & Stuffers — 2-MM/227; Tying Machines — EAM-Mosca, 1-MLN/2A; Address Machine — 1-KR/211.; BUSINESS EQUIPMENT: 9-HP/917LX3000, Link/MC5 CLASSIFIED EQUIPMENT: Hardware — APP/Mac G3; Printers — Pre Press/Panther Plus, Pre Press/Panther Plus 136, HP/Laser Jet 4MV; CLASSIFIED SOFTWARE: Baseview/Admanager Pro. DISPLAY EQUIPMENT: Printers — Pre Press/Panther Plus, Pre Press/Panther Plus 136, HP/Laser Jet 4MV; DISPLAY SOFTWAREAd Make-up Applications — Aldus/Freehand 6.0, QPS/QuarkXPress 4.0; Layout Software — APP/Mac G-3s. EDITORIAL EQUIPMENT: Hardware — APP/Mac G3; Printers — Pre Press/Panther Plus, Pre Press/Panther Plus 136, HP/Laser Jet 4MV EDITORIAL SOFTWARE: Baseview/NewsEdit PRO 1998. PRODUCTION EQUIPMENT: Hardware — Graham/S-1-27; Cameras — Kk/5060B, C/Marathon; Scanners — 5-Microtek/Scanmaker E6, 5-Vmax, 1-Mirage II PRODUCTION SOFTWARE: Baseview.

RUSSELLVILLE

THE COURIER

201 E 2nd St, Russellville, Ark., 72801-5102, Pope; gen tel (479) 968-5252; adv tel (479) 967-7355; gen fax (479) 968-2832; adv fax (479) 967-9361; ed fax (479) 968-4037; gen/nat adv e-mail michelle@couriernews.com; disp adv e-mail michelle@couriernews.com; class adv e-mailclass1@couriernews.com; ed e-mail info@couriernews.com; web site www.couriernews.com
- 400,000(views) 65,000(visitors)
Group: Paxton Media Group, LLC
Published: Tues, Wed, Thur, Fri, Sat, Sun
Weekday Frequency: m
Saturday Frequency: m
Circulation: 6,000; 6,000(sat); 7,000(sun)
Last Audit: USPS October 15, 2017
Advertising Rate (weekday/saturday): Open inch rate $19.75
Advertising Rate (sunday): $15.65

Online Advertising Rate: $5.00 cpm
News services: AP, **Established:** 1875
Own Printing Facility?: Yes
Commercial Printers?: Yes
Special Editions: Newcomer's Guide (Apr); Football (Aug); Active Lifestyles (Dec); RVL Magazine (Jan); RVL Magazine (Jul); RVL Magazine (Jun); Medical Directory (Mar); Salute to Area Business (May); Gift Guide (Nov); Progress (Oct);
Special Weekly Sections: Church Directory (Fri); Real Estate (S); Business Review (Tues); Best Food Day (Wed). TV Book (Sun)
Syndicated Publications: Relish - monthly (S). Athlon Sports
Digital Platform - Mobile: Apple, Android, Windows
Digital Platform - Tablet: Apple iOS, Android, Kindle
Pub. .... David Meadows
Adv. Dir. .... Michelle Harris
Prod. Mgr. .... David Weaver
Market Information: TMC.
Mechanical Available: Offset; Black and 3 ROP colors; insert accepted; page cutoffs - 22 3/4.
Mechanical Specifications: Type page 12 1/2 x 21 1/2; E - 6 cols, 1 4/5, 1/8 between; A - 6 cols, 1 4/5, 1/8 between; C - 9 cols, 1 1/6, 1/8 between.
Areas Served: 72823, 72837, 72843, 72847, 72858, 72801, 72802, 72824, 72829, 72823, 72834,72842, 72853, 72857, 72830, 72845, 72846
Delivery Method: Mail, Newsstand, Carrier, RacksEquipment & Software: PRESSROOM EQUIPMENT: 8-unit/Urbanite 1993; Folders — G/Quarter, G/Half, G/Upper, G/Lower.; MAILROOM EQUIPMENT: Counter Stackers — 1/BG; Inserting, SLS 1000; Tying Machines — Dynaric; Wrapping Singles — 3-/SA; Address Machine — 2-/KR.; BUSINESS EQUIPMENT: Mac G-5's BUSINESS SOFTWARE: MSSI, Great Plains CLASSIFIED EQUIPMENT: Hardware — 1-APP/Mac G-5 1-APP/Mac G-5 1-APP/Mac G-5610, ; Printers — HP LaswerWriter Plus; CLASSIFIED SOFTWARE: MediaSpan DISPLAY EQUIPMENT: Hardware — G-5's x5 ; Printers — HP Laser Writer; DISPLAY SOFTWARE — MediaSpan; EDITORIAL EQUIPMENT: Hardware — Mac G-5's x 9//300G Flatbed Scanner; Printers — HP Laserwriter
DELL pc's EDITORIAL SOFTWARE: MediaSpan
OS 10
Windows 7 PRODUCTION EQUIPMENT: Hardware — Mac G-5's
MAKO CTP, 2 lines.
NELA punch/bender PRODUCTION SOFTWARE: InDesign.

SEARCY

THE DAILY CITIZEN

723 W Beebe Capps Expy, Searcy, Ark., 72143-6303, White; gen tel (501) 268-8621; adv tel (501) 268-8621; gen fax (501) 268-6277; gen/nat adv e-mail bblack@thedailycitizen.com; disp adv e-mail classifieds@thedailycitizen.com; ed e-mail editor@thedailycitizen.com; web site www.thedailycitizen.com
Group: Paxton Media Group, LLC
Published: Tues, Wed, Thur, Fri, Sat, Sun
Weekday Frequency: m
Saturday Frequency: m
Circulation: 5,686; 5,686(sat); 5,686(sun)
Last Audit: Sworn/Estimate/Non-Audited September 30, 2017
Advertising Rate (weekday/saturday): Open inch rate $13.00
News services: AP, NEA. **Established:** 1854
Special Weekly Sections: Weekend Review (Fri); Business Review (Mon); Business News (S); Business News (Thur); Merchant's Market (Tues); Best Food Day (Wed).
Syndicated Publications: Color Comics (S).
Pub. .... Mike Murphy
Adv. Dir. .... Pat Tullos
Circ. Mgr. .... Jessica Jackson
Ed. .... Jay Strasner
Mng. Ed. .... Warren Watkins
Community Ed. .... Wendy Waring
News Ed. .... Gabe Calzada
Sports Ed. .... Quinton Bagley
Ed. .... Steve Watts
Sports Ed. .... Harrison Keegan
Market Information: TMC.
Mechanical Available: Offset; Black and 3 ROP colors; insert accepted; page cutoffs - 22 7/8.
Mechanical Specifications: Type page 13 x 21 1/2; E - 6 cols, 2 1/16, 1/8 between; A - 6 cols, 2 1/16, 1/8 between; C - 9 cols, 1 3/8, 1/16 between.Equipment & Software: PRESSROOM EQUIPMENT: Lines — 6-HI/V-15A.; MAILROOM EQUIPMENT: Tying Machines — 2/Bu.; BUSINESS EQUIPMENT: APP/Mac II, IBM/PCs CLASSIFIED EQUIPMENT: Hardware — APP/Mac IIs; Printers — APP/Mac LaserPrinters; CLASSIFIED SOFTWARE: Baseview. DISPLAY EQUIPMENT: Hardware — APP/Mac IIs; Printers — APP/Mac LaserPrinters; DISPLAY SOFTWAREAd Make-up Applications — Multi-Ad/Creator.; EDITORIAL EQUIPMENT: Hardware — APP/Mac Classics (networked); Printers — APP/Mac LaserPrinters EDITORIAL SOFTWARE: Baseview. PRODUCTION EQUIPMENT: Hardware — 1-Nat; Cameras — 1-R.

STUTTGART

STUTTGART DAILY LEADER

111 W 6th St, Stuttgart, Ark., 72160-4243, Arkansas; gen tel (870) 673-8533; gen fax (870) 673-3671; gen/nat adv e-mail sales@stuttgartdailyleader.com; disp adv e-mail sales@stuttgartdailyleader.com; class adv e-mailsales@stuttgartdailyleader.com; ed e-mail editor@stuttgartdailyleader.com; web site www.stuttgartdailyleader.com
Group: New Media Investment Group
Published: Mon, Tues, Wed, Thur, Fri
Weekday Frequency: e
Circulation: 2,397
Last Audit: Sworn/Estimate/Non-Audited September 30, 2017
Advertising Rate (weekday/saturday): Open inch rate $15.75
News services: AP, TMS.
Own Printing Facility?: Yes
Special Editions: Summer Baseball, City (June); Farm, Family, Real Estate (July); Back to School, Football, Home, harvest (Aug); Football, Real Estate, Pretty Baby, Home, Hunting Guide (Sept); Football, Homecoming, Red Ribbon Week, Home, Auto, Home Lawn (Oct); Duck Edition, Open House, Shopping, Hometown Holiday, Real Estate, Restaurant Guide (Nov); Countdown to Christmas, Lights Content, Last Minute Shopping, Hometown Holiday (Dec)
Special Weekly Sections: Civic Minded (Mon); Business, Bowling (Tue); Outdoors (Thur); Education, Church (Fri);
Syndicated Publications: TV (Every other week); Fifty-plus (Monthly); American Profile (Weekly).
Digital Platform - Mobile: Apple, Android, Blackberry
Business Mgr. .... Stephanie Tiner
Circ. Mgr. .... Willene Boehn
Managing Editor .... Stephanie Fischer
Senior Publisher .... John Tucker
Composing Director .... April Scott
Press Manager .... Dudley Raper
Pub .... Mitch Bettis
Acct. Exec. .... Danni Jo Bueker
Market Information: TMC.
Mechanical Available: Offset; Black and 3 ROP colors; insert accepted - any; page cutoffs - 22 3/4.
Mechanical Specifications: Type page 13 x 21 1/2; E - 6 cols, 2 1/16, 1/8 between; A - 6 cols, 2 1/16, 1/8 between; C - 9 cols, 1 3/8, 1/16 between.
Areas Served: 72160 (Stuttgart), 72042 (Dewitt), 72003 (Almyra)Equipment & Software: PRESSROOM EQUIPMENT: Lines — 6-G/Community; Folders — G/Suburban.; MAILROOM EQUIPMENT: Tying Machines — Felins/Tying.; CLASSIFIED EQUIPMENT: Hardware — APP/Mac, APP/Power Mac 7200; Umax/Color Scanner, ZIP drive; Printers — APP/Mac NTX, GCC/Elite 600; CLASSIFIED SOFTWARE: Baseview/Class Manager Plus. DISPLAY EQUIPMENT: Hardware — 6-APP/Mac NTX; Printers — GCC/Elite 600, APP/Mac-4/600; Other Hardware — XYQUEST/Xywrite CD-Rom DISPLAY SOFTWAREAd Make-up Applications — QPS/QuarkXPress, Multi-Ad/Creator 6.0; Layout Software — APP/Mac, APP/Power Mac 7200. EDITORIAL EQUIPMENT: Hardware — APP/Mac Performa 6200CD, APP/Power Mac 7200/Umax/Color Scanner; Printers — APP/Mac LaserWriter NTX, GCC/Elite 600, APP/Mac-4/600 EDITORIAL SOFTWARE: QPS/QuarkXPress 3.11, Baseview/NewsEdit. PRODUCTION EQUIPMENT: Hardware — Umax, Adobe/Photoshop; Cameras — 1-SCREEN/Auto film processors PRODUCTION SOFTWARE: QPS/QuarkXPress 3.11.

TEXARKANA

TEXARKANA GAZETTE

101 E Broad St, Texarkana, Ark., 71854-5901, Miller; gen tel (870) 330-7550; adv tel (870)330-7611; ed tel (870)330-7652; gen fax (870) 330-7571; adv fax (870) 330-7571; ed fax (870)330-7571; gen/nat adv e-mail rmeredith@texarkanagazette.com; disp adv e-mail rmeredith@texarkanagazette.com; class adv e-mailwshipp@texarkanagazette.com; ed e-mail lminor@texarkanagazette.com; web site www.texarkanagazette.com - 1,199,898(views) 140,507(visitors)
Group: WEHCO Media, Inc.
Published: Mon, Tues, Wed, Thur, Fri, Sat, Sun
Weekday Frequency: m
Saturday Frequency: m
Circulation: 17,665; 17,665(sat); 18,423(sun)
Last Audit: AAM December 31, 2016
Advertising Rate (weekday/saturday): Open inch rate $47.56
Advertising Rate (sunday): Open inch rate $48.79
News services: AP, TMS, SHNS, CNS, Roll Call Report Syndicate. **Established:** 1875
Own Printing Facility?: Yes
Special Editions: Bridal, Super Bowl (Jan); Valentine (Feb); Home & Garden, Outdoors (Mar); Spring Fashion, Lawn, Garden (Apr); Mother's Day, Progress (May); Newcomer's Guide (Jun); Back to School, Football (Aug); Quality Section, Home Improvement, Race for the Cure (Oct); Holiday Cookbook, Thanksgiving (Nov); Santa's Helper (Dec)
Special Weekly Sections: Best Food Day (Wed); Religion (Sat);
Syndicated Publications: Relish (Monthly); USA WEEKEND Magazine (S); American Profile (Weekly).
Digital Platform - Mobile: Apple
Digital Platform - Tablet: Apple iOS
Adv. Sales Mgr. .... Rick Meredith
Ed. .... Les Minor
City Ed. .... Christy Busby
Editorial Page Ed. .... Russell McDermott
Farm Reporter .... Greg Bischof
Photo Ed. .... Evan Lewis
Gen. Mgr. .... Terri Leifeste
Market Information: ADS; TMC.
Mechanical Available: Headliner Offset; Black and 3 ROP colors; insert accepted; page cutoffs - 22 3/4.
Mechanical Specifications: Type page 11 5/8 x 21 1/2; E - 6 cols, 1 13/16, 1/8 between; A - 6 cols, 1 13/16, 1/8 between; C - 9 cols, 1 1/4, 1/8 between.
Areas Served: 71753, 71801, 71822, 71826, 71832, 71833, 71834, 71836, 71837, 71838, 71839, 71840, 71842, 71845, 71846, 71851, 71852, 71853, 71854, 71855, 71857, 71859, 71860, 71862, 71865, 71866, 75426, 75455, 75501, 75503, 75551, 75554, 75555, 75556, 75559, 75560, 75561, 75563, 75566, 75567, 75568, 75569, 75570, 75571, 75572, 75573, 75574, 75638, 75656
Delivery Method: Mail, Newsstand, Carrier, RacksEquipment & Software: PRESSROOM EQUIPMENT: Lines — 5-G/Headliner Offset 5044-Double Width; Folders — 2-G/2:1.; MAILROOM EQUIPMENT: Counter Stackers — 2/QWI; Inserters & Stuffers — 1372; Tying Machines — 1-MLN/2EE, 2-MLN/2A, Dynaric; Control System — Fincor; Address Machine — 1-Ch/515 (with quarter folder), 1-/WM; BUSINESS EQUIPMENT: Wyse, Dell, APP/Mac, IBM/RS6000 BUSINESS SOFTWARE: Lawson, PBS CLASSIFIED EQUIPMENT: Hardware — 1-Ad/iMac, 1-APP/G4 Mini Tower, 6-APP/iMac; CLASSIFIED SOFTWARE: Baseview/ClassFlow. DISPLAY EQUIPMENT: Hardware — 4-APP/Power Mac G3, 3-APP/Power Mac G4, 2-E-Mac; Printers — APP/Mac LaserWriter 360, Epson/Stylus 18x24 Color Printer, Tektronic/Phaser 560, Cannon/Image Runner 5000, HP/Desinejet 1050C; DISPLAY SOFTWAREAd Make-up Applications — Multi-Ad/Creator, QPS/QuarkXPress, Multi-Ad/Cr; EDITORIAL EQUIPMENT: Hardware — 24-APP/iMac, 2-APP/Mac G3, 1-APP/Mac Power PC 8100, 1-APP/Mac Power PC 8600, Quantum/4000 NAS; Printers — 2-AG/Accuset 1500 with Xitron software RIP EDITORIAL SOFTWARE: QPS/QuarkXPress, Adobe/Photoshop, Baseview 3.2.1, Red Hat Linux 8. PRODUCTION EQUIPMENT: Hardware — 1-Nu/404, 2-AG/Accuset 1500 with Xytron RIP, 1-Glunz & Jensen/550; Cameras — 1-C/Spartan III; Scanners — Microtek/ScanMaker IIXE flatbed color, APP/Mac IIfx, Microtek/FB scanner, Calera/Wordscan, HP/ScanJet (plus flatbed b&w) PRODUCTION SOFTWARE: QPS/

CALIFORNIA

AUBURN

AUBURN JOURNAL

1030 High St, Auburn, Calif., 95603-4707, Placer; gen tel (916) 774-7910; adv tel (530) 852-0225; ed tel (530) 885-6585 ext. 2; gen fax (530) 885-7235; adv fax (530) 885-4511; ed fax (530) 887-1231; gen/nat adv e-mail ajournal@goldcountrymedia.com ; disp adv e-mail mjh@goldcountrymedia.com; class adv e-mailclassifieds@goldcountrymedia.com; ed e-mail ajournal@goldcountrymedia.com; dericr@goldcountrymedia.com; web site www.auburnjournal.com; web site 2 www.goldcountrymedia.com
Group: Brehm Communications, Inc.
Published: Tues, Wed, Thur, Fri, Sun
Weekday Frequency: m
Circulation: 8,101; 8,163(sun)
Last Audit: VAC December 31, 2016
Advertising Rate (weekday/saturday): Open inch rate $21.25
Advertising Rate (sunday): call for pricing
News services: AP, U.S. Suburban Press Inc., TMS, UPI. **Established:** 1872
Own Printing Facility?: Yes
Commercial Printers?: Yes
Syndicated Publications: USA WEEKEND Magazine (S).
Publisher .... Todd Frantz
Brehm Communications, Inc.
Director of Circulations .... Kelly Leibold
Advert Direct. .... Beth O'Brien
Market Information: TMC.
Mechanical Available: Offset; Black and 3 ROP colors; insert accepted - Polybags; page cutoffs - 22.
Mechanical Specifications: Type page 10 x 21; E - 6 cols, 1 9/16, 1/8 between; A - 6 cols, 1 9/16, 1/8 between; C - 6 cols, 1 9/16, 1/8 between.
Areas Served: Placer County
Delivery Method: Mail, Newsstand, Carrier, RacksEquipment & Software: PRESSROOM EQUIPMENT: Lines — 18-G/Community SSC, 2-DGM/430; Press Drive — 4-Fin/75hp; Folders — 2-G/SSC; Reels & Stands — 7; MAILROOM EQUIPMENT: Tying Machines — 2/Bu, 3-Si; Address Machine — KR; BUSINESS EQUIPMENT: Qantel/Q29BS CLASSIFIED EQUIPMENT: Hardware — PC; Printers — 2-LaserMaster, 2-Pre Press/Panther Plus Imagesetter; CLASSIFIED SOFTWARE: APT. DISPLAY EQUIPMENT: Hardware — APP/Mac; Printers — Cannon/Image Class C2100, Xante/Accel-a-Writer 3G; Other Hardware — 4-CD-Rom, 2-ZIP 100, 1-Epson/1600 Scanner DISPLAY SOFTWARELayout Software — Multi-Ad/Creator. EDITORIAL EQUIPMENT:

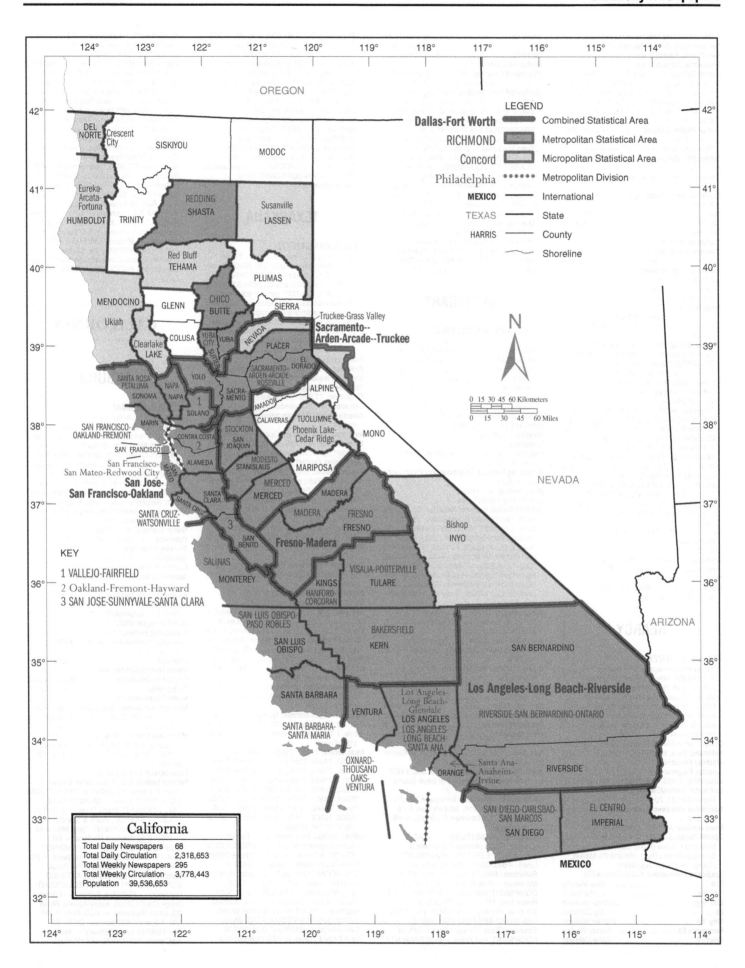

LEGEND

Dallas-Fort Worth	Combined Statistical Area
RICHMOND	Metropolitan Statistical Area
Concord	Micropolitan Statistical Area
Philadelphia	Metropolitan Division
MEXICO	International
TEXAS	State
HARRIS	County
	Shoreline

KEY

1 VALLEJO-FAIRFIELD
2 Oakland-Fremont-Hayward
3 SAN JOSE-SUNNYVALE-SANTA CLARA

California

Total Daily Newspapers	68
Total Daily Circulation	2,318,653
Total Weekly Newspapers	295
Total Weekly Circulation	3,778,443
Population	39,536,653

OREGON

NEVADA

ARIZONA

MEXICO

DEL NORTE
Crescent City
SISKIYOU
MODOC
Eureka-Arcata-Fortuna
HUMBOLDT
TRINITY
REDDING SHASTA
Susanville
LASSEN
Red Bluff
TEHAMA
PLUMAS
MENDOCINO
GLENN
CHICO BUTTE
SIERRA
Ukiah
COLUSA
YUBA CITY
YUBA
NEVADA
Truckee-Grass Valley
Sacramento--Arden-Arcade--Truckee
Clearlake
LAKE
PLACER
SANTA ROSA-PETALUMA
NAPA
YOLO
SACRAMENTO-ARDEN-ARCADE-ROSEVILLE
EL DORADO
SONOMA
NAPA
SACRA-MENTO
ALPINE
SOLANO
AMADOR
MARIN
CALAVERAS
TUOLUMNE
SAN FRANCISCO-OAKLAND-FREMONT
STOCKTON
SAN JOAQUIN
Phoenix Lake-Cedar Ridge
MONO
SAN FRANCISCO
San Francisco-San Mateo-Redwood City
ALAMEDA
MODESTO STANISLAUS
San Jose-San Francisco-Oakland
SAN MATEO
MARIPOSA
SANTA CRUZ-WATSONVILLE
SANTA CLARA
MERCED MERCED
MADERA
SANTA CRUZ
MADERA
FRESNO FRESNO
SAN BENITO
Fresno-Madera
SALINAS
Bishop
INYO
MONTEREY
KINGS
HANFORD-CORCORAN
VISALIA-PORTERVILLE
TULARE
SAN LUIS OBISPO-PASO ROBLES
SAN LUIS OBISPO
BAKERSFIELD
KERN
SAN BERNARDINO
SANTA BARBARA
Los Angeles-Long Beach-Glendale
Los Angeles-Long Beach-Riverside
VENTURA
LOS ANGELES
RIVERSIDE-SAN BERNARDINO-ONTARIO
SANTA BARBARA-SANTA MARIA
LOS ANGELES-LONG BEACH-SANTA ANA
OXNARD-THOUSAND OAKS-VENTURA
Santa Ana-Anaheim-Irvine
ORANGE
RIVERSIDE
SAN DIEGO-CARLSBAD-SAN MARCOS
EL CENTRO
IMPERIAL
SAN DIEGO

Hardware — PC/25-IBM/PC; Printers — 2-LaserMaster/, 2-Pre Press/Panther Plus Imagesetter EDITORIAL SOFTWARE: APT. PRODUCTION EQUIPMENT: Hardware — Caere/OmniPage Pro; Scanners — Umax, Polaroid/SprintScan.
Note: Auburn Journal, Inc. is owned by Brehm Communications Inc.

BAKERSFIELD

THE BAKERSFIELD CALIFORNIAN

1707 Eye St, Bakersfield, Calif., 93301-5208, Kern; gen tel (661) 395-7500; adv tel (661) 395-7500; ed tel (661) 395-7244; gen fax (661) 395-7280; adv fax (661) 395-7406; ed fax (805) 395-7519; gen/nat adv e-mail srockwell@bakersfield.com; disp adv e-mail jwells@bakersfield.com; class adv e-mailjwells@bakersfield.com; ed e-mail JArthur@bakersfield.com; web site www.bakersfield.com
Group: Virginia F. Moorhouse
Published: Mon, Tues, Wed, Thur, Fri, Sat, Sun
Weekday Frequency: m
Saturday Frequency: m
Circulation: 24,634; 27,216(sat); 30,267(sun)
Last Audit: AAM March 31, 2017
Advertising Rate (weekday/saturday): Size 7 $459.00; 1/4 Pg $1486.00; $3448.00 (Sat)
Advertising Rate (sunday): Size 1 $221.00; 1/8 Pg $1725.00; 1/4 Pg $3448.00
Online Advertising Rate: Homepage Leaderboard & Big Box: $18 cpm. Run of Site Leaderboard & Big Box: $10 cpm. Section Specific Leaderboard & Big Box: $15 cpm.
News services: AP, NYT, McClatchy, CSM. **Established:** 1866
Special Editions: Relay for Life ROP Pages (Apr); Holiday Worship (Dec); Wedding Planner (Feb); Kern Life (Jul); Best of Kern County (May); Focus on Living (Monthly); Harvest Home Show (Oct); Kern County Fair Guide (Sept).
Special Weekly Sections: Sports (Mon); Business (Tue); Business, garden, Home, Best Food (Wed); Business, Weekend, Entertainment (Thur); Movies (Fri); Religion, Auto, Homes (Sat); Real Estate, TV, Travel, Best Food (Sun)
Syndicated Publications: Parade (S); Latino Weekly Magazine (Weekly).
Chrmn. of the Board/Pub. .... Ginger F. Moorhouse
Pres. & Chief Exec. Officer .... Michelle Chantry
Asst. Mng. Ed. .... Lois Henry
Exec. Ed. .... Robert Price
Assoc. Pub. .... Virginia Cowenhoven
Design Ed. .... Jarrod Graham
Lifestyles Ed. .... Jennifer Self
Copy/Layout Ed. .... Timothy Heinrichs
Sports Ed. .... Zach Ewing
Prod. Dev. Director .... Benavente Christine
Chief Photographer .... Felix Adamo
S.r Video Producer .... Chris McCullah
Market Information: Split run; TMC.
Mechanical Available: Offset; Black and 3 ROP colors; insert accepted - product samples, donation bags; page cutoffs - 22 1/20.
Mechanical Specifications: Type page 13 x 21; E - 6 cols, 2 1/16, 1/8 between; A - 6 cols, 2 1/16, 1/8 between; C - 10 cols, 1 3/8, 1/8 between.
Areas Served: Kern County
Delivery Method: Mail, Newsstand, Carrier, RacksEquipment & Software: PRESSROOM EQUIPMENT: Lines — 8-TKS/(4 half decks) 1983; Folders — 2-TKS/3:2; MAILROOM EQUIPMENT: Counter Stackers — 3-HL/Monitor; Inserters & Stuffers — Fg/8:1; Tying Machines — Power Strap/PL6; Address Machine — Domino/Jet Array Ink Jet Printer.; BUSINESS EQUIPMENT: Sun/1000E BUSINESS SOFTWARE: PBS CLASSIFIED EQUIPMENT: Hardware — 13-PC; CLASSIFIED SOFTWARE: DTI/Class Speed. DISPLAY EQUIPMENT: Hardware — APP/Mac G4; Printers — HP/DesignJet 75S, HP/5 MU; Other Hardware — Digital Camera, AII/3750 Scanner DISPLAY SOFTWAREAd Make-up Applications — Multi-Ad/Creator, Adobe/Photoshop 4.0; Layout Software — MEI/ALS. EDITORIAL EQUIPMENT: Hardware — APP/Mac, 40-APP/Mac G3, 51-APP/Mac G4; Printers — HP EDITORIAL SOFTWARE: QPS. PRODUCTION EQUIPMENT: Hardware — WL/Lith V, 2-AU/3850, 2-AII, AII/3850; Cameras — C/Spartan III, Walzberg, AG/8200; Scanners — Nikon, Kk PRODUCTION SOFTWARE: QPS/QuarkXPress.

BENICIA

BENICIA HERALD

820 1st St, Benicia, Calif., 94510-3216, Solano; gen tel (707) 745-0733; gen fax (707) 745-8583; gen/nat adv e-mail adsbenicia@yahoo.com; disp adv e-mail adsbenicia@yahoo.com; class adv e-mailadsbenicia@yahoo.com; ed e-mail beniciaherald@gmail.com; web site www.beniciaheraldonline.com
Group: McNaughton Newspapers
Published: Tues, Wed, Thur, Fri, Sun
Weekday Frequency: m
Circulation: 2,707; 2,707(sun)
Last Audit: Sworn/Estimate/Non-Audited September 30, 2017
Advertising Rate (weekday/saturday): Open inch rate $12.60
Advertising Rate (sunday): Open inch rate $12.60
News services: Papert (Landon), U.S. Suburban Press Inc.. **Established:** 1898
Special Weekly Sections: Financial (Tue); Best Food (Wed); Seniors (Thur); Auto, Entertainment, Religion (fri); Real Estate (Sun);
Syndicated Publications: USA WEEKEND Magazine (S).
Adv. Mgr. .... Pam Poppe
Circ. Mgr. .... Joe Smith
Ed. .... Marc Ethier
Pub. .... David Payne
Market Information: TMC.
Mechanical Available: Offset; Black and 3 ROP colors; insert accepted; page cutoffs - 22 1/2.
Mechanical Specifications: Type page 12 1/2 x 21 1/2; E - 6 cols, 2, 1/8 between; A - 6 cols, 2, 1/8 between; C - 8 cols, 1 1/2, 1/8 between.Equipment & Software: BUSINESS EQUIPMENT: IBM/AS-400 CLASSIFIED EQUIPMENT: Hardware — IBM.; DISPLAY SOFTWARELayout Software — APP/Mac AdMaker. EDITORIAL EQUIPMENT: Hardware — APP/Mac EDITORIAL SOFTWARE: QPS/QuarkXPress.

CAMARILLO

VENTURA COUNTY STAR

550 Camarillo Center Dr, Camarillo, Calif., 93010-7700, Ventura; gen tel (805) 437-0000; adv tel (805) 437-0000; ed tel (805) 437-0000; gen fax (805) 437-0465; gen/nat adv e-mail feedback@vcstar.com; disp adv e-mail shanna.cannon@vcstar.com; ed e-mail news@vcstar.com; web site www.vcstar.com - 7,000,000(views) 800,000(visitors)
Group: Gannett
Published: Mon, Tues, Wed, Thur, Fri, Sat, Sun
Weekday Frequency: m
Saturday Frequency: m
Circulation: 35,036; 37,725(sat); 46,279(sun)
Last Audit: AAM March 31, 2017
Advertising Rate (weekday/saturday): $60 pci
Advertising Rate (sunday): $65 pci
News services: AP, NYT, McClatchy, SHNS, MCT, NEA, TMS. **Established:** 1925
Own Printing Facility?: Yes
Commercial Printers?: Yes
Special Editions: Spelling Bee (March);
Star Scholar Awards (April);
Readers' Choice (May);
Eldercare (July);
Living Here (October)
Pink (October)
Special Weekly Sections: Time Out (Fri); CARS (Sat).; Homes (Sun)
Syndicated Publications: Parade (S); Relish, Spry
Digital Platform - Mobile: Apple, Android, Windows, Blackberry
Digital Platform - Tablet: Apple iOS, Android, Blackberry Tablet OS, Kindle, Kindle Fire
Dir., Finance .... Denice Atcheson
Digital Adv. .... Amy Aguilar
Dir., Mktg. .... Monica White
Circ. Dir., Home Delivery .... John Rotter
Mng. Ed. .... John Moore
Asst. Mng. Ed. .... DeAnn Justesen
Bus. Ed. .... Jim Medina
News Ed. .... Darrin Peschka
Dig. Media .... Ray Meese
Reg. Pub. .... Shanna Cannon
VP Adv. .... Natealine Judie
Market Information: TMC
Mechanical Available: Offset; Black and 3 ROP colors; insert accepted; page cutoffs - 22 3/4.
Mechanical Specifications: Type page 10 3/4 x 21 1/2; E - 6 cols, 1 35/50, 1/10 between; A - 6 cols, 1 35/50, 1/10 between; C - 10 cols, 98/100, 1/10 between.
Areas Served: Ventura County, Carpinteria
Delivery Method: Mail, Newsstand, Carrier, RacksEquipment & Software: PRESSROOM EQUIPMENT: Lines — 10-TKS/3 Color Decks double width 1997; Folders — 1-TKS/Folder 3:2; Registration System — ABB/WPC. MAILROOM EQUIPMENT: Counter Stackers — 8-HL/Monitor, Fg, 2-QWI/Dual Halls; Inserters & Stuffers — 2-NP/630, AM Graphics, HI/Finishing System; Tying Machines — 10/Sterling; Control System — Prima; Address Machine — 1-/Domino Jet System.; CLASSIFIED EQUIPMENT: Hardware — Pentium/PCs, Compaq; Printers — HP/4si mx; CLASSIFIED SOFTWARE: AT. DISPLAY EQUIPMENT: Hardware — APP/Power Mac; Printers — Typhoon, HP/755C Plotter, HP/Plotter 2500, QMS 2060; DISPLAY SOFTWAREAd Make-up Applications — QPS/QuarkXPress, Adobe/Photoshop, Adobe/Acrobat, Macromedia/Freehand, Adobe/PDF, Adobe/Illustrator; Layout Software — QPS/QuarkXPress, MEI/ALS, AT. EDITORIAL EQUIPMENT: Hardware — APP/PowerMac, APP/iMacPrinters — HP/4si mx, Data Products/Typhoon 6 EDITORIAL SOFTWARE: QPS, QPS/QuarkXPress 4.04. PRODUCTION EQUIPMENT: Hardware — Offset, 4-MS/NT Dec Alpha RIP; Cameras — 1-C/Spartan III; Scanners — 1-AII/3750, 1-Scitex/Smart 340L PRODUCTION SOFTWARE: QPS, MEI/ALS.

CHICO

CHICO ENTERPRISE-RECORD

400 E Park Ave, Chico, Calif., 95928-7127, Butte; gen tel (530) 891-1234; adv tel (530) 896-7751; ed tel (530) 896-7754; gen fax (530) 342-3617; adv fax (530) 891-9204; ed fax (530) 896-7793; gen/nat adv e-mail chicoer@chicoer.com; disp adv e-mail fcrosthwaite@chicoer.com; class adv e-mailrridgell@chicoer.com; ed e-mail dlittle@chicoer.com; web site www.chicoer.com
Group: Digital First Media
Published: Mon, Tues, Wed, Thur, Fri, Sat, Sun
Weekday Frequency: m
Saturday Frequency: m
Circulation: 18,044; 17,502(sat); 25,379(sun)
Last Audit: AAM September 30, 2015
Advertising Rate (weekday/saturday): Open inch rate $70.39
Advertising Rate (sunday): Open inch rate $72.74
News services: AP, NEA, SHNS. **Established:** 1853
Special Editions: Home & Garden Issue (Apr); University (Aug); Last Minute Gift Guide (Dec); Chico Outlook (Feb); Salute to Agriculture Tab (Mar); Silver Dollar Fair Tab (May); Senior's Tab (Monthly); Christmas Opening (Nov); Health & Wellness Tab (Quarterly); Chico Expo (
Special Weekly Sections: Sports, Lifetsyle, Stock (Daily); Business (Wed/Sat); Best Food (Wed); Home & Garden (Fri); Entertainment (Thur); Church, TV (Sat); Farm news (Sun)
Syndicated Publications: Relish (Monthly); USA WEEKEND Magazine (S); TV Times (Sat).
Controller .... Robert Gardner
Dir., HR .... Maureen Garrity
City Ed. .... Steve Schoonover
Ed. .... Michelle King
Sports Ed. .... Dave Davies
Adv. Dir. .... Fred Crosthwaite
Systems Mgr. .... Ray Kirk
Classified Adv. Mgr. .... Rene Ridgell
Circ. Dir. .... Mazi Kavoosi
Pub. .... Jim Gleim
Market Information: TMC; Zoned editions.
Mechanical Available: Offset Press; Black and 3 ROP colors; insert accepted - flyers printed in-house; page cutoffs - 22.
Mechanical Specifications: Type page 10 1/4 x 21; E - 6 cols, 1 9/16, 1/8 between; A - 6 cols, 1 9/16, 1/8 between; C - 10 cols, 31/32, 1/16 between.
Areas Served: 95926, 95928, 95973, 95938, 95966, 95965, 95969
Delivery Method: Mail, Newsstand, Carrier, RacksEquipment & Software: PRESSROOM EQUIPMENT: Lines — 4-MAN/Uniman 4 x 2 (2 color decks, double width); Pasters —4-MEG. MAILROOM EQUIPMENT: Counter Stackers — 2-HL/Monitor, 1/QWI; Inserters & Stuffers — 2-/MM; Tying Machines — 1-/MLN, I-/It; Address Machine — 3-/Wm.; BUSINESS EQUIPMENT: CJ CLASSIFIED EQUIPMENT: Hardware — APP/Mac; CLASSIFIED SOFTWARE: Baseview. DISPLAY EQUIPMENT: Hardware — APP/Mac; DISPLAY SOFTWARELayout Software — Baseview. EDITORIAL EQUIPMENT: Hardware — APP/Mac EDITORIAL SOFTWARE: Baseview, QPS/QuarkXPress. PRODUCTION EQUIPMENT: Hardware — 2-Pre Press/Panther Imagesetter, 1-OLEC/OV 33 HD; Cameras — 1-R/LE PRODUCTION SOFTWARE: Baseview, QPS/QuarkXPress.

COSTA MESA

DAILY PILOT

1375 Sunflower Ave, Costa Mesa, Calif., 92626-1665, Orange; gen tel (714) 966-4600; adv tel (714) 966-5777; ed tel (714) 966-4600; gen fax (714) 966-4679; adv fax (714) 966-4663; gen/nat adv e-mail dailypilot@latimes.com; disp adv e-mail marissa.contreras-dominguez@latimes.com; ed e-mail John.Canalis@latimes.com; web site www.dailypilot.com
Group: Tronc, Inc.
Published: Wed, Thur, Fri, Sat, Sun
Weekday Frequency: m
Saturday Frequency: m
Circulation: 24,600; 29,500(sat); 29,500(sun)
Last Audit: Sworn/Estimate/Non-Audited September 30, 2017
Advertising Rate (weekday/saturday): Open inch rate $29.90
News services: Papert (Landon), U.S. Suburban Press Inc.. **Established:** 1961
Special Editions: Healthy, Wealthy & Wise (Apr); New Year (Dec); Annual Almanac (Feb); Healthy, Wealthy & Wise (Jan); Healthy, Wealthy & Wise (Jul); Menu Guide (Jun); Toshiba Senior Golf Classic (Mar); Student Design-an-Ad (May); Gift Guide (Nov); Top 103 (Sept).
Special Weekly Sections: Auto Pilot (Sat).
Syndicated Publications: Real Estate (Sat).
Digital Platform - Mobile: Apple, Android
Digital Platform - Tablet: Apple iOS, Android
Exec. Ed. .... John Canalis
City Ed. .... Rob Vardon
Online Ed. .... Ann Haley
Photo Ed. .... Don Leach
Sports Ed. .... Steve Virgen
Community Ed. .... Debbie Zucco
Mechanical Available: Offset; Black and 3 ROP colors; insert accepted - card stock single sheet; page cutoffs - 22 3/4.
Mechanical Specifications: Type page 13 x 21; E - 6 cols, 2 1/16, 1/8 between; A - 6 cols, 2 1/16, 1/8 between; C - 10 cols, 1 3/8, 1/16 between.
Areas Served: Huntington Beach, Seal Beach, Laguna Beach, Newport Beach, Costa Mesa, Corona del MarEquipment & Software: PRESSROOM EQUIPMENT: Lines — 8-HI/N1600; Folders — 1-HI/2:1; Pasters —7-MEG/500; Reels & Stands — 7-MEG/500.; MAILROOM EQUIPMENT: Counter Stackers — 2-Id/NS440; Inserters & Stuffers — 1-S/24P; Tying Machines — 2-MLN/MLN2A; Address Machine — 1-El/8000-1.; BUSINESS EQUIPMENT: HP/3000 BUSINESS SOFTWARE: CJ/OP CLASSIFIED EQUIPMENT: Hardware — PC; Printers — HP/Laser, V/with Tegra Controller; CLASSIFIED SOFTWARE: Intertext. DISPLAY EQUIPMENT: Hardware — APP/Mac 8100; Printers — HP/LaserJet 4MV, APP/Mac LaserWriter 630, HP/8000, Cyclone; Other Hardware — AG/

Accuset 1500 DISPLAY SOFTWAREAd Make-up Applications — Multi-Ad/Creator, QPS/QuarkXPress, Adobe/Photoshop; Layout Software — MEI/ALS. EDITORIAL EQUIPMENT: Hardware — Ik, Dewar/Sys IV, APP/Mac, PC/Output, AG/Accuset 1500; Printers — HP/LaserJet 4MV, HP/LaserJet 5P EDITORIAL SOFTWARE: QPS, Dewar/ System with QuarkXPress. PRODUCTION EQUIPMENT: Hardware — 2-V, 1-Nu/UPNS, 1-BKY/Adlux 5KW; Cameras — 1-Ik/530 Stat camera; Scanners — AG/6100 Stat Camera, Howtek/Color Scanner.

EL CENTRO

IMPERIAL VALLEY PRESS

205 N 8th St, El Centro, Calif., 92243-2301, Imperial; gen tel (760) 337-3400; adv tel (760) 337-3443; ed tel (760) 337-3453; gen fax (760) 353-3003; adv fax (760) 353-3003; ed fax (760) 353-3003; gen/nat adv e-mail circulation@ivpressonline.com; disp adv e-mail advertising@ivpressonline.com; class adv e-mailclassified@ivpressonline.com; ed e-mail rbrown@ivpressonline.com; web site www.ivpressonline.com

Group: ....Imperial Valley News Media Inc.
Published: Mon, Tues, Wed, Thur, Fri, Sat, Sun
Weekday Frequency: e
Saturday Frequency: m
Circulation: 6,761; 6,761(sat); 7,486(sun)
Last Audit: CAC March 31, 2017
Advertising Rate (weekday/saturday): Open inch rate $27.50
News services: AP. **Established:** 1901
Special Editions: Women of Imperial Valley (Aug); California Midwinter Fair (Feb); Inland Empire (Jan); County Progress (Jul); Graduation (Jun); Sweet Onion Festival (May); Business Journal (Monthly); Cattle Call Tab (Oct); Football Preview (Sept).
Special Weekly Sections: Church Page (Fri); Lifestyles (S); Youth Page (Sat); Farm Page (Thur); Food Page (Tues).
Syndicated Publications: Relish (Monthly); TV Plus (TV Guide) (S); American Profile (Tues).
Ed.. Brad Jennings
Sports Ed. ....Mario Renteria
Copy Editor..................................... Sarah Malan
Copy Ed.. Esteban Ortiz
Designer. Copy Ed................... Vincenta Tamayo
Sales Mgr...Norma Lira
Pub.. Belinda Mills
Market Information: ADS; TMC.
Mechanical Available: Offset; Black and 3 ROP colors; insert accepted; page cutoffs - 22 3/4.
Mechanical Specifications: Type page 11 3/5 x 21 1/2; E - 6 cols, 1 4/5, 1/8 between; A - 6 cols, 1 4/5, 1/8 between; C - 9 cols, 1 1/5, 4/5 between.Equipment & Software: PRESSROOM EQUIPMENT: Lines — G/ Urbanite 1061; G/Urbanite 1061; G/Urbanite 1061; G/Urbanite 1061; G/Urbanite 1061; G/ Urbanite 1061; G/Urbanite 1061; Pasters —Folders 1. MAILROOM EQUIPMENT: Counter Stackers — 2/HL; Inserters & Stuffers — 2-/KAN; Tying Machines — Sterling.; BUSINESS EQUIPMENT: Sun/ PC Server BUSINESS SOFTWARE: PBS CLASSIFIED EQUIPMENT: Hardware — PC; Xante; Printers — AG/Imagesetter, Graphic Enterprises/Pro Setter 1000; CLASSIFIED SOFTWARE: ACT. DISPLAY EQUIPMENT: Hardware — PC; Printers — Graphic Enterprises/Pro Setter 1000, LaserMaster/ Unity 1800XL-0; DISPLAY SOFTWAREAd Make-up Applications — Mk/Managing Editor 2.0; Layout Software — MEI/ALS. EDITORIAL EQUIPMENT: Hardware — PC/ AG/Accuset 1000; Printers — 2-Xante/Accel-a-Writer EDITORIAL SOFTWARE: ACT, Microsoft/Word 6.0, QPS/QuarkXPress 3.3. PRODUCTION EQUIPMENT: Hardware — 2-Xante/Accel-a-Writer 8200, AG/Accuset 1000; Cameras — Companica; Scanners — AG/Flatbed PRODUCTION SOFTWARE: QPS/QuarkXPress 4.1.

EUREKA

TIMES-STANDARD

930 6th St, Eureka, Calif., 95501-1112, Humboldt; gen tel (707) 441-0500; adv tel (707) 441-0556; ed tel (707) 441-0507; gen fax (707) 441-0568; adv fax (707) 441-0565; ed fax (707) 441-0501; gen/nat adv e-mail ads@times-standard.com; disp adv e-mail jmarchetti@times-standard.com; class adv e-mailclass@times-standard.com; ed e-mail mvalles@times-standard.com; web site www.times-standard.com
- 470,627(views) 162,320(visitors)

Group: Digital First Media
Published: Tues, Wed, Thur, Fri, Sat, Sun
Weekday Frequency: m
Saturday Frequency: m
Circulation: 8,166; 8,166(sat); 9,564(sun)
Last Audit: Sworn/Estimate/Non-Audited August 31, 2017
Advertising Rate (weekday/saturday): Open inch rate $22.00
Advertising Rate (sunday): Open inch rate $23.10
Online Advertising Rate: $18.00 CPM
News services: AP. **Established:** 1854
Own Printing Facility?: Yes
Commercial Printers?: Yes
Special Editions: North Coast 101 (May); Humboldt County Fair Tab (Aug); Gift Guide (Dec); Spring Bridal (May); Winter Bridal (Jan); Best Of (Mar); Women in Business Tab (Oct); Football Preview (Sept).
Special Weekly Sections: Business & Service Directory, Entertainment/TV Listings, Business, Style (Daily); Business, Seniors (Tue); Business, Food (Wed); Home & Garden (Thur); Business, Art (Fri); On the market, Religion (Sat); Business, Comics (Sun)
Proprietary Publications: Redwood Times - weekly publication in southern Humboldt County. 4000 circ
Digital Platform - Mobile: Apple, Android, Windows
Digital Platform - Tablet: Apple iOS, Android, Windows 7
Mng. Ed. .... Marc Valles
Advertising Director/Production Director....Carmel Bonitatibus
Market Information: ADS; TMC.
Mechanical Available: Offset; Black and 3 ROP colors; insert accepted - bags, samples; page cutoffs - 21 1/2.
Mechanical Specifications: 1 col = 1.56"
2 col = 3.25"
3 col = 4.94"
4 col = 6.63"
5 col = 8.31 "
6 col = 10"
Areas Served: 95501, 95503, 95519, 95521, 95524, 95525, 95528, 95531, 95536, 95540, 95542, 95546, 95547, 95548, 95549, 95551, 95553, 95555, 95556, 95560, 95562, 95563, 95565, 95567, 95570, 95571, 95573
Delivery Method: Mail, Newsstand, Carrier, RacksEquipment & Software: PRESSROOM EQUIPMENT: Lines — 8-G/Urbanite 1990; Folders — G/2:1.; MAILROOM EQUIPMENT: Counter Stackers — 2/MM; Inserters & Stuffers — 2-/MM; Tying Machines — 1-MLN/ ML1EE; Wrapping Singles — 1-Am/1997B; Address Machine — GEAC; BUSINESS EQUIPMENT: NewzWare, GEAC BUSINESS SOFTWARE: Microsoft/Office CLASSIFIED EQUIPMENT: Hardware — 6-APP/ iMac; 4-APP/iMac; Printers — APP/Mac LaserWriter; CLASSIFIED SOFTWARE: Baseview/Ad Manager Pro 2.0. DISPLAY EQUIPMENT: Printers — Konica/Marlin; DISPLAY SOFTWAREAd Make-up Applications — Multi-Ad/Creator 2; Layout Software — 6-APP/Mac G3. EDITORIAL EQUIPMENT: Hardware — 18-Mk, 20-APP/Mac/4-APP/Mac G3 Server; Printers — Canon/Imagerunner 330 EDITORIAL SOFTWARE: QPS/QuarkXPress 6.0. PRODUCTION EQUIPMENT: Hardware — HP/LaserJet 8100N, Epson/Color Printer 7500; Cameras — 1-R/432 Mark II, 1-LE/121 PRODUCTION SOFTWARE: InDesign CS5.5,/QPS/QuarkXPress 6.0, MEI/ALS 2.5, Baseview/NewsEdit Pro 3.2.1.

FAIRFIELD

DAILY REPUBLIC

1250 Texas St, Fairfield, Calif., 94533-5748, Solano; gen tel (707) 425-4646; adv tel (707) 427-6937; ed tel (707) 427-6925; gen fax (707) 425-5924; adv fax (707) 425-5924; ed fax (707) 425-5924; gen/nat adv e-mail tbmcnaughton@dailyrepublic.net; disp adv e-mail bkermoade@dailyrepublic.net; class adv e-mailkmonroe@dailyrepublic.net; ed e-mail gfaison@dailyrepublic.net; web site www.dailyrepublic.com

Group: McNaughton Newspapers
Published: Mon, Wed, Thur, Fri, Sat, Sun
Weekday Frequency: m
Saturday Frequency: m
Circulation: 10,622; 10,622(sat); 11,403(sun)
Last Audit: CAC June 30, 2016
Advertising Rate (weekday/saturday): Open inch rate $24.30
Advertising Rate (sunday): $26.70
News services: AP, NYT, SHNS. **Established:** 1855
Special Editions: American Home Week (Apr); Annual Welcome (Aug); Thanksgiving Morning (Nov); Cookbook (Oct); Solano Seniors (Other); Solano Summer (Summer).
Special Weekly Sections: Automobiles (Fri); Religion (S); Religion (Sat); Best Food Day (Wed).
Syndicated Publications: Relish (Monthly); USA WEEKEND Magazine (S); Real Estate Magazine (Sat); American Profile (Weekly).
Pres./CEO/Pub........................ Foy McNaughton
Adv. Dir..................................... Sharon Guy
Adv. Mgr., Nat'l .... Brian Kermoade
Tailwind Ed. ....Nick DeCicco
Asst. Sports Ed. .... Brian Arnold
Copy Ed................................... Susan Winslow
Design Ed...............................Maureen Fissolo
News Ed....................................... Shawn Miller
Online/Projects Ed. .... Kathleen L'Ecluse
Photo Ed. .... Brad Zweerink
Sports Ed. .... Paul Farmer
IT Dir...Joe Boydston
Opns. Dir.......................... T. Burt McNaughton
Prodn. Foreman, Pressroom........ Larry Mammen
Market Information: TMC.
Mechanical Available: Offset; Black and 3 ROP colors; insert accepted - all types; page cutoffs - 22 3/4.
Mechanical Specifications: Type page 11 7/8 x 21 3/8; E - 6 cols, 1 7/8, 1/8 between; A - 6 cols, 1 7/8, 1/8 between; C - 10 cols, 1 3/16, 1/8 between.
Areas Served: 94533,94534, 94585Equipment & Software: PRESSROOM EQUIPMENT: Lines — 9-G/Urbanite; MAILROOM EQUIPMENT: Counter Stackers — 2-BG/ Count-O-Veyor; Inserters & Stuffers — 2-KAN/480; Tying Machines — 1/MLN; Address Machine — 2-/Am, 1-Ch/725.; BUSINESS EQUIPMENT: 1-IBM, Sun/ Ultra 1 BUSINESS SOFTWARE: Vision Data CLASSIFIED EQUIPMENT: Hardware — 10-APP/Mac; Printers — HP/4MV; CLASSIFIED SOFTWARE: Baseview. DISPLAY EQUIPMENT: Hardware — APP/ Mac G3; DISPLAY SOFTWARELayout Software — 3-COM/Dawn (on-line), 5-APP/ Mac Network. EDITORIAL EQUIPMENT: Hardware — APP/Mac G4, APP/ Mac G3/IPTech/Turbo RIP EDITORIAL SOFTWARE: Baseview/NewsEdit Pro IQUE. PRODUCTION EQUIPMENT: Hardware — 2-Birmy/Setter, 2-Accuset/1000; Cameras — 1-Danagraph; Scanners — 2-Kk/2750, 2-HP/6100 PRODUCTION SOFTWARE: QPS/QuarkXPress 4.12.

FRESNO

THE FRESNO BEE

1626 E St, Fresno, Calif., 93786-0001, Fresno; gen tel (559) 441-6111; adv tel (559) 441-6405; ed tel (559) 441-6307; adv fax (559) 441-6458; ed fax (559) 441-6499; gen/nat adv e-mail mmcdowell@fresnobee.com; disp adv e-mail jcollings@fresnobee.com; class adv e-mailclassads@fresnobee.com; ed e-mail jboren@fresnobee.com; web site www.fresnobee.com
- 7,988,637(views) 1,138,974(visitors)

Group: The McClatchy Company
Published: Mon, Tues, Wed, Thur, Fri, Sat, Sun
Weekday Frequency: m
Saturday Frequency: m
Circulation: 71,831; 75,038(sat); 89,205(sun)
Last Audit: AAM December 31, 2016
Advertising Rate (weekday/saturday): Open inch rate $208.75
Advertising Rate (sunday): Open inch rate $241.75
News services: AFP, AP, NYT, LAT-WP, MCT, SHNS. **Established:** 1922
Special Weekly Sections: Best Food Day (Wed); Entertainment (Fri); Auto, Church, Home, Garden (Sat); Travel, Entertainment, TV, Cable Guide, Business (Sun)
Syndicated Publications: 7 Magazine (Fri); Color Comics (S).
Exe. Ed/Senior V.P .... Jim Boren
Adv. Sr. Vice Pres., Sales/Strategic Mktg. ......John Coakley
V.P. of Digital / Audience development.... Stephen Dana
Asst. to VP & Dir of Audience Devel . Cyndy Kutka
Human Resources Dir ....Mark Ochinero
Dir Audience Dev................. Marshall McDowell
Real Estate,Agencies, Magazines, Medical Valerie Vaz
VP Finance.......................................Mari Wylie
West Reg VP Production...................Jeff Gledhill
VP Custom Pub..........................Valerie Bender
Publisher/Sierra Star...................... Betty E. Linn
Managing Ed .... John Rich
Metro Ed .... Tad Weber
Pres./Pub......................................Tom Cullinan
Market Information: ADS; Split run; TMC; Zoned editions.
Mechanical Available: Flexographic; Black and 3 ROP colors; insert accepted - poly bags; page cutoffs - 22.
Mechanical Specifications: Type page 9 7/8 x 21; E - 6 cols, 1.55, .115 between; A - 6 cols, 1.55, 1/8 between; C - 6 cols, 1.55, .115 between.Equipment & Software: PRESSROOM EQUIPMENT: Lines — 6-MAN/Print Couples, 22-MAN/Flexoman double width 1991; 6-MAN/Print Couples, 22-MAN/Flexoman M double width 1991; 6-MAN/Print Couples, 22-MAN/Flexoman M, 18-1992; Folders — MAN/4:3:2; Pasters —18-HUR/50 Hi Speed Utilized Reel T MAILROOM EQUIPMENT: Counter Stackers — 2/Compass 180, 1-Id/2000, 2-HL/HT; Inserters & Stuffers — 3-HI/1472P; Tying Machines — 4-/Power Strap/PSN-6, 6-/ Samuel Strap; Wrapping Singles — 6-HL/ Bottom Wrap; Address Machine — 1-/ Kirk Rudy, 1-Prism/InkJet Online System; CLASSIFIED EQUIPMENT: Hardware — Tandem/K1004, 3-HP/Apollo 715, 50-HP/ EPC, 2-Sun/Ultra 10; Printers — 6-HP/5000; CLASSIFIED SOFTWARE: Scoop, SII/ SCP, Coyote/XA, SII/Czar II. DISPLAY EQUIPMENT: Hardware — Sun/Sparc Stations, APP/Mac; Printers — All/3850, HP/Design Jet 1055 CM; DISPLAY SOFTWAREAd Make-up Applications — QPS/QuarkXPress, All/Ad Manager; Layout Software — MEI/ALS. EDITORIAL EQUIPMENT: Hardware — 150-HP/Vectra VE8, 30-HP/Kzyzx xu, 12-Sun/E 450/All/ Output Manager NT, 2-DEC; Printers — 2-HP/Design Jet 1055CM, 12-HP/LaserJet 5000 EDITORIAL SOFTWARE: Unisys/ Hermes, Unisys/Wire Center. PRODUCTION EQUIPMENT: Hardware — Na/FP IV, 2-Na/ Flex-V, 5-Loge, 5-III/3850; Cameras — 1-C/ Newspager II, 1-C/Marathon; Scanners — 2-Scitex/Eversmart Pro, 2-Eskofot/Full Page PRODUCTION SOFTWARE: Unisys/ Hermes 5.5.

GRASS VALLEY

THE UNION

464 Sutton Way, Grass Valley, Calif., 95945-4102, Nevada; gen tel (530) 273-9561; adv tel (530) 273-9567; ed tel (530) 477-4249; gen fax (530) 273-1854; adv fax (530) 273-1854; ed fax (530) 477-4292; gen/nat adv e-mail letters@theunion.com; disp adv e-mail ads@theunion.com; ed e-mail letters@theunion.com; web site www.theunion.com
- 700,000(views) 100,000(visitors)

Group: Swift Communications, Inc.
Published: Mon, Tues, Wed, Thur, Fri, Sat
Weekday Frequency: m
Saturday Frequency: m
Circulation: 9,346; 9,346(sat)
Last Audit: CAC December 31, 2016
Advertising Rate (weekday/saturday): Open inch

rate $26.46
Online Advertising Rate: $19.00 CPM
News services: AP. **Established:** 1864
Own Printing Facility?: Yes
Commercial Printers?: Yes
Special Editions: Best of Nevada County (Apr); Fair (Aug); Bride (Jan); Home & Garden (Mar); Football (Sept).
Special Weekly Sections: Business (Mon); Home and Garden (Sat); Family (Thur); Health (Tues); Food (Wed).
Syndicated Publications: American Profile (Weekly).
Proprietary Publications: Prospector (Weekly Entertainment News & Information)
Circ. Dir. .... Steve Schurkey
Ed. ....Brian Hamilton
City Editor ....Liz Kellar
Sports Ed. .... Walter Ford
Mgmt. Info Servs./Online Mgr. .... Tom Harbert
Prodn. Dir. ....Lee Brant
Adv. Mgr. ....Julia Stidham
Circ. Dir. ....Elizabeth Baldwin
Pub. .... Don Rogers
Market Information: TMC.
Mechanical Available: Offset; Black and 3 ROP colors; insert accepted; page cutoffs - 22 3/4.
Mechanical Specifications: Type page 13 x 21 1/2; E - 6 cols, 2 1/16, 1/8 between; A - 6 cols, 2 1/16, 1/8 between; C - 9 cols, 1 3/8, 1/16 between.
Areas Served: 95959, 95945, 95949, 95946, 95602
Delivery Method: Mail, Newsstand, Carrier, RacksEquipment & Software: PRESSROOM EQUIPMENT: Lines — 7-G/Community (2 stack color.); MAILROOM EQUIPMENT: Counter Stackers — 1-BG/MFG; Inserters & Stuffers — 2/MM, MM/227; Tying Machines — 1-/MLN, 1-/Bu.; BUSINESS EQUIPMENT: Sun/Sparc server BUSINESS SOFTWARE: PBS/Media Plus CLASSIFIED EQUIPMENT: Hardware — APP/Mac, APP/iMac; CLASSIFIED SOFTWARE: Baseview/Ad Manager Pro. DISPLAY EQUIPMENT: Hardware — Ethernet/Ap Talk, 7-APP/Mac Centris; DISPLAY SOFTWARELayout Software — APP/Mac. EDITORIAL EQUIPMENT: Hardware — APP/Mac. EDITORIAL SOFTWARE: DTI PRODUCTION EQUIPMENT: Hardware — APP/Mac; Cameras — 1-SCREEN/Ver. PRODUCTION SOFTWARE: DTI CIRCULATION SOFTWARPBS

HANFORD

THE SENTINEL
300 W 6th St, Hanford, Calif., 93230-4518, Kings; gen tel (559) 582-0471; adv tel (559) 582-0471; ed tel (559) 582-0471; gen fax (559) 582-0512; adv fax (559) 582-8631; ed fax (559) 587-1876; gen/nat adv e-mail mlee@hanfordsentinel.com; disp adv e-mail jvikjord@hanfordsentinel.com; class adv e-mailjvikjord@HanfordSentinel.com; ed e-mail editor@hanfordsentinel.com; web site www.hanfordsentinel.com
Group: Lee Enterprises, Inc.
Published: Mon, Tues, Wed, Thur, Fri, Sat
Weekday Frequency: e
Saturday Frequency: e
Circulation: 5,168; 6,188(sat)
Last Audit: AAM March 31, 2016
Advertising Rate (weekday/saturday): Open inch rate $32.50
Advertising Rate (sunday): Open inch rate $34.75
News services: AP. **Established:** 1886
Special Editions: Bridal Tab (Feb); Dairy (Jun); Home Improvement (Mar); Christmas Opening (Nov); Football (Sept); Living in The Valley (Sept); Our Towns (Quarterly)
Special Weekly Sections: Prime Time, Senior (Mon); Best Food Day (Tue); Real Estate (Fri); Church, Farm (Weekend)
Syndicated Publications: Relish (Monthly); USA WEEKEND Magazine (S); Parade (Weekly).
Digital Platform - Mobile: Apple, Android, Windows, Blackberry
Digital Platform - Tablet: Apple iOS, Android, Windows 7, Blackberry Tablet OS, Kindle, Nook, Kindle Fire
City Ed. .... Mark Eiman
Adv. Mgr. ....Victoria Beierschmitt
Editor ....Linda Green

Publisher .... Davis Taylor
Market Information: Split run; TMC.
Mechanical Available: Offset; Black and 3 ROP colors; insert accepted; page cutoffs - 22 3/4.
Mechanical Specifications: Type page 13 x 21 1/2; E - 6 cols, 2 1/16, 1/8 between; A - 6 cols, 2 1/16, 1/8 between; C - 9 cols, 1 3/8, 1/16 between.
Areas Served: 93230, 93245, 93202Equipment & Software: PRESSROOM EQUIPMENT: Lines — 7-G/Community floor, 1-G/Stacked, 4-G/Stacked 4-high; MAILROOM EQUIPMENT: Counter Stackers — 1/Rima; Inserters & Stuffers — 1-MM/227E; Tying Machines — 1-MLN/ML2EE, 1-/Sterling.; BUSINESS EQUIPMENT: 8-Mk/Acer, 2-Dell/Dimensions XPS P200s, HP/Laser Jet BUSINESS SOFTWARE: Lotus, SmartSuite, Microsoft/Office, WordPerfect, CDA CLASSIFIED EQUIPMENT: Hardware — 4-ScrippSat; Printers — QMS/820 Turbo; CLASSIFIED SOFTWARE: Synaptic. DISPLAY EQUIPMENT: Hardware — APP/Mac; Printers — QMS/2060; DISPLAY SOFTWAREAd Make-up Applications — Ad Force; Layout Software — Ad Force, MEI. EDITORIAL EQUIPMENT: Hardware — APP/Mac; Printers — QMS/2060 EDITORIAL SOFTWARE: Baseview/NewsEdit Pro IQUE 3.2.2. PRODUCTION EQUIPMENT: Hardware — 2-AU/APS, 3850 Color Imager, Noritsu, QMS/2060 1800 x 60, ECR/Scriptsetter VRL-36/HS; Cameras — 1-SCREEN/Companica 660c; Scanners — Tecsa/TS2470.

LAKEPORT

LAKE COUNTY RECORD-BEE
2150 S Main St, Lakeport, Calif., 95453-5620, Lake; gen tel (707) 900-2016; adv tel (707) 900-2016; ed tel (707) 900-2016; gen fax (707) 263-0600; gen/nat adv e-mail ahansmith@record-bee.com; disp adv e-mail ahansmith@record-bee.com; class adv e-mailkpinkston@record-bee.com; ed e-mail dfaries@record-bee.com; web site www.record-bee.com
Group: Digital First Media
Published: Tues, Wed, Thur, Fri, Sat
Weekday Frequency: m
Saturday Frequency: m
Circulation: 5,000; 4,821(sat)
Last Audit: AAM June 30, 2017
Newspaper Reps: Kevin McConnell, Publisher; Dave Faries, Managing Editor
Special Weekly Sections: Business (Tue); Health (Wed); Eat+Drink (Thur) Arts, Entertainment (Fri); Real Estate, Religion (Sat)
Sports Ed. .... Brian Sumpter
Production Dir. ....Carol Wilbur
Prodn. Mgr., Mailroom ....Jose Contreras
Pub. ....Kevin McConnell
Adv. Asst. .... Amy Hansmith
Areas Served: 95453, 95435, 95493, 95485, 95464, 95458, 95451, 95426, 95443, 95423, 95424, 95422, 95457, 95467, 95461
Delivery Method: Mail, Newsstand, Carrier, RacksEquipment & Software: MAILROOM EQUIPMENT: ; Address Machine — 1-/Ch; CLASSIFIED EQUIPMENT: LaserWriter 16-600, Okidata/line Printer; DISPLAY EQUIPMENT: Hardware — AG/Studio Star Scanner. DISPLAY SOFTWARE4.1, QPS/QuarkXPress 3.32, Adobe/Photoshop 4.01;

LODI

LODI NEWS-SENTINEL
125 N Church St, Lodi, Calif., 95240-2102, San Joaquin; gen tel (209) 369-2761; adv tel (209) 369-2761; ed tel (209) 369-7035; gen fax (209) 369-1084; adv fax (209) 369-1084; ed fax (209) 369-6706; gen/nat adv e-mail martw@lodinews.com; disp adv e-mail ads@lodinews.com; ed e-mail news@lodinews.com; web site www.lodinews.com
Group: Central Valley News-Sentinel Inc.
Published: Tues, Wed, Thur, Fri, Sat
Weekday Frequency: m
Saturday Frequency: m
Circulation: 8,163; 8,163(sat)
Last Audit: CAC March 31, 2017

Advertising Rate (weekday/saturday): Open inch rate $23.03 (commissionable)
Advertising Rate (sunday): none
News services: AP, MCT **Established:** 1881
Own Printing Facility?: Yes
Commercial Printers?: No
Special Editions: Senior services (Jan); Brides (Feb); Visitors Guide (May); Home Improvement Guide (Jun); How-To Guide (July); Grape & Wine Festival (Sept); Christmas (Dec).
Special Weekly Sections: Business/Stock Market (Fri); Church (Sat); Business/Stock Market (Thur); Business/Stock Market (Tues); Best Food Day (Wed).
Syndicated Publications: USA WEEKEND Magazine (Sat).
Digital Platform - Mobile: Apple, Android, Windows
Digital Platform - Tablet: Apple iOS, Android, Windows 7, Blackberry Tablet OS, Kindle, Nook, Kindle Fire
Bookkeeper ....Stephanie Hiatt
Newsroom Ed .... Scott Howell
Chief Photographer ....Ahbeck Casson
Ed. .... Richard Hanner
Pressroom Foreman .... Chuck Barton
Pub. ....Steven Malkowich
Pub. ....Glenn Stifflemire
Market Information: TMC
Mechanical Available: Offset; Black and 3 ROP colors; insert accepted - coupons; page cutoffs - 22 3/4.
Mechanical Specifications: Type page 10 15/16 x 21 1/2; E - 6 cols, 1 3/4, 3/16 between; A - 6 cols, 1 13/16, 1/8 between; C - 8 cols, 1 1/4, 1/8 between.
Areas Served: 95220, 95227, 95237, 95240, 95242, 95253, 95258, 95632, 95686
Delivery Method: Mail, Newsstand, Carrier, RacksEquipment & Software: PRESSROOM EQUIPMENT: Lines — 6-1979, G/Community single width; 6-1979 Goss Community single width; Folders — 2-G/2:1.; MAILROOM EQUIPMENT: Counter Stackers — 1/KAN; Inserters & Stuffers — 1-KAN/9 station; Tying Machines — 1-/MLN; Address Machine — 1-/St.; BUSINESS EQUIPMENT: Apple BUSINESS SOFTWARE: MYOB CLASSIFIED EQUIPMENT: Hardware — Apple; ECR/Jetsetter 6200; Printers — QMS/2060 Print System; CLASSIFIED SOFTWARE: Baseview/Ad Manager Pro. DISPLAY EQUIPMENT: Hardware — APP/Mac G3; Printers — Xante/Accel-a-Writer 3G; Other Hardware — ECR/Imagesetter VRL 36, ECR/Jetsetter 6200 DISPLAY SOFTWAREAd Make-up Applications — QPS/QuarkXPress 4.0, Multi-Ad/Creator 4.03; Layout Software — MEI/ALS Page Director 2.5. EDITORIAL EQUIPMENT: Hardware — APP/Mac G3/ECR/Jetsetter 6200; Printers — Xante/Accel-a-Writer 3G EDITORIAL SOFTWARE: Baseview/NewsEdit Pro IQUE 3.22. PRODUCTION EQUIPMENT: Hardware — Caere/OmniPage Pro 8.0, Adobe/Photoshop 4.0, Adobe/Photoshop 6.0; Cameras — 1-Acti; Scanners — Microtek/1850 si, 2-Umax/Powerlook II, Polaroid/SprintScan 35, 1-Epson/Expression 636 PRODUCTION SOFTWARE: QPS/QuarkXPress 4.0.

LONG BEACH

PRESS-TELEGRAM
727 Pine Ave, Long Beach, Calif., 90813-4321, Los Angeles; gen tel (562) 435-1161; adv tel (562) 499-1243; ed tel (562) 499-1337; gen fax (562) 499-1277; adv fax (562) 435-5415; ed fax (562) 499-1277; gen/nat adv e-mail online@presstelegram.com; ptnews@presstelegram.com; ed e-mail ptnews@presstelegram.com; web site www.presstelegram.com
Group: Southern California News Group Digital First Media
Published: Mon, Tues, Wed, Thur, Fri, Sat, Sun
Weekday Frequency: m
Saturday Frequency: m
Circulation: 18,227; 18,055(sat); 33,431(sun)
Last Audit: AAM June 30, 2017
Newspaper Reps: Frank Pine, SVP & Executive Editor
Toni Sciacqua, Managing Digital Editor

Rich Archbold, Public Editor
News services: AP **Established:** 1897
Own Printing Facility?: Yes
Commercial Printers?: Yes
Special Editions: Grand Prix (Apr); Back To School (Aug); Chronology (Dec); Love Lines-Class (Feb); Careers and Education (Jan); Millenium Bride (Jul); Father's Day (Jun); Pre-Owned Vehicles (Mar); Grad Tab (May); LB Marathon (Nov); Halloween (Oct); Olympics (Sept).
Special Weekly Sections: Opinion (Sun, Tue-Fri); Business (Thur, Sat); Spotlight (Fri, Sun); Real Estate/Homes (Sat, Sun); Autos/Cars (Fri-Sun); Employment (Mon, Sun); Travel (Sun); Home & Garden (Sat); Health (Sun); Faith (Sat)
Syndicated Publications: Spry (Weekly); Parade (Weekly)
Digital Platform - Mobile: Apple, Android, Windows, Blackberry
Digital Platform - Tablet: Apple iOS, Android, Windows 7, Blackberry Tablet OS, Kindle, Nook, Kindle Fire
Pres. & Pub. ....Ron Hasse
Exec. Ed. .... Frank Pine
Chief Revenue Officer ....Tom Kelly
VP Mktg ....Bill VanLaningham
Chief Fin Officer ....Dan Scofield
VP HR ....Rosemaria Altieri
Retail Sales Mgr. .... Tom Taylor
Sr. Ed. .... Tom Bray
Mng Digital Ed ....Toni Sciacqua
Opinion Ed. ....Brian Calle
VP of Advt. ....Leslie Lindemann
Exec Sports Ed .... Tom Moore
Mechanical Available: Offset; Black and 3 ROP colors; insert accepted; page cutoffs - 21.
Mechanical Specifications: Type page 9.89 x 21; E - 6 cols, 1.56, .10 between; A - 6 cols,1.56, .10 between; C - 10 cols, .938, .054 between.
Areas Served: Artesia, Bell, Bellflower, Carson, Cerritos, Compton, Cypress, Downey, Hawaiian Gardens,
Huntington Park, La Mirada, Lakewood, Long Beach, Los Alamitos, Lynwood, Norwalk, Paramount, Pico Rivera, San Pedro, Santa Fe Springs,
Seal Beach, Signal Hill, South Gate and Wilmington.
Delivery Method: Mail, Newsstand, Carrier, RacksEquipment & Software: BUSINESS EQUIPMENT: HP/3000 Series 967 BUSINESS SOFTWARE: CJ/AIM, Microsoft/Access Window, Adobe/Photoshop 3.01, Adobe/Illustrator, QuarkXPress, CJ/AIM 7.01.G, CJ/Layout 2.01.E, CJ/AD Tracking 5.01.C, CJ/CIS 4.01.H, CJ 2.09.M, CJ 8.02.D, CJ 7.02.D, Microsoft/Office Windo CLASSIFIED EQUIPMENT: Hardware — SII/Tandem; CLASSIFIED SOFTWARE: SII/Czar. DISPLAY EQUIPMENT: Hardware — 16-APP/Mac G4; Other Hardware — Mac DB Server, CJ/Ad Tracking DISPLAY SOFTWAREAd Make-up Applications — APP/Mac, QPS/QuarkXPress; Layout Software — SCS/Layout 8000, SII/IAL. EDITORIAL EQUIPMENT: Hardware — SII/Tandem EDITORIAL SOFTWARE: SII/Editorial. PRODUCTION EQUIPMENT: Hardware — 2-AU/APS6-108C, AU/Soft PIP RIPs, 2-AU/3750; Cameras — 1-C/Newspager, C/Spartan III PRODUCTION SOFTWARE: CSI/1170, SII/INL & IAL.
Note: The Southern California News Group includes the Long Beach Press-Telegram, Los Angeles Daily News, (Ontario) Inland Valley Daily Bulletin, Pasadena Star-News, The Facts (Redlands), The Sun (San Bernardino), San Gabriel Valley Tribune, Whittier Daily News, Orange County Register, Riverside Press-Enterprise, Daily Breeze (Torrance).

LOS ANGELES

LA OPINION
915 Wilshire Blvd, Ste 800, Los Angeles, Calif., 90017-3488, Los Angeles; gen tel (213) 896-2150; adv tel (213) 896-2300; ed tel (213) 896-2333; gen fax (213) 896-2151; adv fax (213) 896-2080; ed fax (213) 896-2171; gen/nat adv e-mail lorena.torres@laopinion.com; disp adv e-mail lorena.torres@laopinion.com; ed e-mail editor@

laopinion.com; web site www.laopinion.com
Group: impreMedia LLC
Published: Mon, Tues, Wed, Thur, Fri, Sat, Sun
Weekday Frequency: m
Saturday Frequency: m
Circulation: 37,998; 29,314(sat); 33,098(sun)
Last Audit: AAM March 31, 2016
Advertising Rate (weekday/saturday): Open inch rate $85.10
News services: AP, EFE, CNS, AFP, NOTIMEX, UPI, PR Newswire, PRWEB **Established:** 1926
Own Printing Facility?: No
Commercial Printers?: Yes
Special Editions: Calendario Torneo (Jan); Calendario Torneo (March); Mujeres Destacadas (March); Dodgers Calendar (April); Angels Calendar (April); Mothers Day (May); Cinco de Mayo (May); MLB All Star (July); 4th of July Special (July); Mexican Soccer League (July); Back to School La Opinion (July/August); Back to School Contigo (August); Fiestas Patrias (Sept); Gift Ideas (Nov); Gift Ideas (Dec).
Special Weekly Sections: Entertainment, life, Style Sports, Business (Daily); Education, Small Business, Employment (Mon); Health, Personal Finance, Legal (Tue); Food, Morgage (wed); Entertainment, Technology, Real Estate (Thur); Auto, Community, marketing (Fri); Auto, Beauty, Fashion, Economy (Sat); Children, Travel, International Business (Sun)
Syndicated Publications: Main News (daily), Ciudad (daily), Negocios (daily), hola LA (Everyday except thurs.), La Vibra (Thursdays) Deportes (daily), Clasificados (daily)
CEO/Pub. .... Monica Lozano
Ed. / Exec. Vice Pres. .... Davan Maharaj
Dir. IT .... Bob Mason
Dir., Local Sales .... Lorena Torres
Mechanical Available: Open Web Offset; Black and 3 ROP colors; insert accepted - upon approval; page cutoffs - 22 3/4.
Mechanical Specifications: Type page 12 1/2 x 21 1/2; E - 6 cols, 1 7/8, 3/16 between; A - 6 cols, 1 7/8, between; C - 10 cols, 1 1/16, between.
Delivery Method: Newsstand, RacksEquipment & Software: PRESSROOM EQUIPMENT: Lines — 10-G/Urbanite U1247 single width; 10-G/Urbanite U1379 single width; Folders — G/Series 1000; Pasters —18-Enkel/Autoweb 2500; Control System — Fin/Consoles.; MAILROOM EQUIPMENT: Counter Stackers — 3/NJP, 1-/EZ; Tying Machines — 2-Bu/ Tristar 210, 5-OVL/415; Address Machine — 1-/BH, Ap/IIe.; BUSINESS EQUIPMENT: PBS/Business System, IBM/380 Risc System, Ricoh Aticio 5500 BUSINESS SOFTWARE: DSI/Papertrack CLASSIFIED EQUIPMENT: Hardware — 52-SII/K-100 Himalaya Risc; Printers — Ricoh Aticio 5500/MC4500; CLASSIFIED SOFTWARE: SII. DISPLAY EQUIPMENT: Hardware — 3-Sun/Sparc 20; Printers — 3-HP/ LaserPrinter; DISPLAY SOFTWAREAd Make-up Applications — DTI/AdSpeed; Layout Software — DTI. EDITORIAL EQUIPMENT: Hardware — 52-SII/K-100 Himalaya Risc/RSK/Tandy 2000; Printers — HP 1050 C Plus, HP Design Jet 1050C EDITORIAL SOFTWARE: SII. PRODUCTION EQUIPMENT: Hardware — 2-COM/8600, 1-ECR/VR 36, 1-ECR/VR 30, 1-AG/Arcus, 1-Pre Press/Panther 62, 1-ECR/Knockout; Cameras — R/500, 1-B/Horizontal; Scanners — 1-Nikon/Slide Scanner, 1-Optronics/ Prosetter Drum Scanner, 1-APP/Mac Quadra 950, 1-APP/Mac Quadra 650.

LOS ANGELES TIMES

2300 E. Imperial Hwy, El Segundo, Calif., 90012-4299, Los Angeles; gen tel (213) 237-5000; adv tel (800) 528-4637 ext. 72769; ed tel (213) 237-7000; gen/nat adv e-mail myad@latimes.com; web site www.latimes.com
- 137,500,000(views) 39,000,000(visitors)
Group: Tribune Publishing, Inc.
Published: Mon, Tues, Wed, Thur, Fri, Sat, Sun
Weekday Frequency: All day
Saturday Frequency: All day
Circulation: 452,793; 470,594(sat); 792,673(sun)
Last Audit: AAM March 31, 2017
Advertising Rate (weekday/saturday): www.latimes.com/mediakit
Advertising Rate (sunday): www.latimes.com/mediakit
Online Advertising Rate: www.latimes.com/mediakit
News services: 1881
Own Printing Facility?: No
Commercial Printers?: Yes
Special Editions: Hoy (Spanish-language), The Envelope, Hot Property, DesignLA, Times Community News
Digital Platform - Mobile: Apple, Android
Digital Platform - Tablet: Apple iOS, Android
VP, Adv. Marketing .... Mike Kechichian
Deputy Managing Ed. Colin Crawford
Asst. Managing Ed. .... Michael Whitley
Senior Counsel Jeff Glasser
Deputy Bureau Chief, Washington D.C. Bob Drogin
Deputy Managing Ed. Michael Whitley, Scott Kraft
Op-Ed Ed. .... Juliet Lapidos
Staff Photographer .... Allen Schaben
Ed. of the Editorial Pages .... Nicholas Goldberg
Sacramento Bureau Chief .... John Myers
Politics, Asst. Managing Ed. .. Christina Bellantoni
Local & CA., Asst. Managing Ed. .... Shelby Grad
Data Desk, Senior Dig. Ed. .... Ben Welsh
News Op., Exec. News Ed. .... James Angius
Executive Chairman ...... Dr. Patrick Soon-Shiong
CEO and Publisher .... Ross Levinsohn
Executive Editor .... Norman Pearlstine
Market Information: www.latimes.com/mediakit
Mechanical Available: www.latimes.com/mediakit
Mechanical Specifications: www.latimes.com/mediakit
Areas Served: Southern California (print edition), Worldwide (online & digital products & editions)
Delivery Method: Newsstand, Carrier, Racks

NEWS-PRESS

202 W 1st St, Fl 2nd, Los Angeles, Calif., 90012-4299, Los Angeles; gen tel (818) 637-3200; adv tel (818) 637-3200; ed tel (818) 637-3200; gen fax (818) 241-1975; adv fax (818) 637-3247; ed fax (818) 241-1975; gen/nat adv e-mail lisa.cosenza@latimes.com; disp adv e-mail Kim.Nguyen2@latimes.com; class adv e-mailJosie.Flores@latimes.com; ed e-mail gnp@latimes.com ; web site www.glendalenewspress.com
- 150,000(views)
Group: Tronc, Inc.
Published: Wed, Thur, Fri, Sat, Sun
Weekday Frequency: m
Saturday Frequency: m
Circulation: 21,754; 36,159(sat)
Last Audit: VAC March 21, 2004
Advertising Rate (weekday/saturday): $30.00
News services: City News Services **Established:** 1905
Digital Platform - Mobile: Apple
Digital Platform - Tablet: Apple iOS, Android
VP/Advertising .... Jeff Young
Dir. Adv. .... Lisa Consenza
Ed. .... Dan Evans
City Ed. .... Mark Kellam
Sports Ed. .... Grant Gordon
Web Ed. .... Sameea Kamal
Feat. Ed. .... Steve Appleford
Mng. Ed. .... Carol Cormaci
Market Information: TMC
Mechanical Available: Offset; Black and 3 ROP colors; insert accepted - preprinted, all; page cutoffs - 22 3/4"
Mechanical Specifications: Type page 13" x 20 3/4"; E - 6 cols, 1 13/16", 1/8" between; A - 6 cols, 1 13/16", 1/8" between; C - 10 cols, 1 1/10", 1/16" between.
Areas Served: Glendale, La Crescenta, Montrose, Verdugo City
Delivery Method: Mail, Carrier, RacksEquipment & Software: DISPLAY SOFTWARELayout Software — Managing Editor/ALS PRODUCTION SOFTWARE: CCI

MANTECA

MANTECA BULLETIN

531 E Yosemite Ave, Manteca, Calif., 95336-5806, San Joaquin; gen tel (209) 249-3500; adv tel (209) 249-3500; ed tel (209) 249-3500; gen fax (209) 249-3559; adv fax (209) 249-3551; ed fax (209) 249-3559; disp adv e-mail ads@mantecabulletin.com; ed e-mail news@mantecabulletin.com; web site www.mantecabulletin.com
Group: Morris Multimedia, Inc.
Published: Mon, Tues, Wed, Thur, Fri, Sat, Sun
Weekday Frequency: m
Saturday Frequency: m
Circulation: 5,350; 5,350(sat); 5,350(sun)
Last Audit: VAC June 1, 2011
Advertising Rate (weekday/saturday): $14.33/inch Open rate
News services: AP; MNCC **Established:** 1908
Own Printing Facility?: Yes
Commercial Printers?: Yes
Special Editions: HS Football Preview (Aug); Pumpkin Fair (Oct); Sidewalk Fair (Apr)
Special Weekly Sections: BulletinExtra On-the-Road (Fridays); Home Guide (Saturday);
Syndicated Publications: American Profile (Weekly); Relish (monthly); Spry (monthly)
Editorial Page Ed. .... Dennis Wyatt
Composing Mgr. .... Kay Garcia
Group Publisher .... Dave Winegarden
Advertising Director .... Chuck Higgs
Circulation Director .... Drew Savage
Business Manager .... Tamara Foreman
Pressroom Manager .... Howard Santiago
City Editor .... Rose Albano-Risso
Sports Editor .... Jonamar Jacinto
I.T. Manager .... Adam Wright
Adv. Mgr. .... Teri Garcia
Circ. Mgr. .... Amy Hitchcock
Group Pub. .... Hank Vander Veen
Market Information: TMC.
Mechanical Available: Offset; Black and 3 ROP colors; insert accepted - all; page cutoffs - 22.
Mechanical Specifications: Type page 12 x 21; E - 6 cols, 1 5/8, 1/8 between; A - 6 cols, 1 7/8, 1/8 between; C - 10 cols, 7/8, 1/8 between.
Areas Served: 95336, 95337, 95330, 95366, 95231, 95206
Delivery Method: Mail, Newsstand, Carrier, RacksEquipment & Software: PRESSROOM EQUIPMENT: Lines — 13-G/Community; Press Drive — Fin/75 h.p., Twin/150 hp; Folders — 1-G/SC.; MAILROOM EQUIPMENT: Counter Stackers — 1-BG/ Count-O-Veyor; Tying Machines — 3/Bu; Address Machine — 1-/Am.; BUSINESS EQUIPMENT: 4-Pentium/network with Microsoft Windows 2000 BUSINESS SOFTWARE: MAS 90 CLASSIFIED EQUIPMENT: Hardware — 6-APP/Mac G3; Printers — APP/Mac Pro 630; CLASSIFIED SOFTWARE: Baseview. DISPLAY EQUIPMENT: Printers — HP/8000N; Other Hardware — HP/800C DesignJet DISPLAY SOFTWAREAd Make-up Applications — QPS/QuarkXPress, Baseview, Adobe/ Photoshop; Layout Software — 6-APP/Mac G4. EDITORIAL EQUIPMENT: Hardware — 10-APP/Mac G3; Printers — HP/LaserJet 4MV EDITORIAL SOFTWARE: Baseview/ NewsEdit Pro. PRODUCTION EQUIPMENT: Hardware — HP/8000N, Pre Press/Panther, Konica/EV Jetsetter 9100; Cameras — 1-B; Scanners — 4-HP, 2-Umax PRODUCTION SOFTWARE: QPS/QuarkXPress.

MARYSVILLE

APPEAL DEMOCRAT

1530 Ellis Lake Dr, Marysville, Calif., 95901-4258, Yuba; gen tel (530) 741-4700; adv tel (530) 749-6556; ed tel (530) 749-6552; gen fax (530) 741-1061; adv fax (530) 749-8394; ed fax (530) 749-8390; gen/nat adv e-mail info@appealdemocrat.com; disp adv e-mail info@appealdemocrat.com; class adv e-mailadclass@appealdemocrat.com; ed e-mail adnewsroom@appealdemocrat.com; web site www.appealdemocrat.com
- 1,529,197(views) 174,360(visitors)
Group: VISTA California News Media. Inc.
Published: Mon, Tues, Wed, Thur, Fri, Sat, Sun
Weekday Frequency: m
Saturday Frequency: m
Circulation: 11,013; 11,013(sat); 11,163(sun)
Last Audit: CAC September 30, 2016
Advertising Rate (weekday/saturday): Open inch rate $27.80
News services: AP, MCT, TMS. **Established:** 1860
Own Printing Facility?: Yes
Commercial Printers?: Yes
Special Editions: Explore (Jan); How To Guide (Apr); Medical Directory (Feb & Aug); New Neighbors (Feb); Brides (Jan); Business Card Directory (Mar); Y-S Fair (Jul); Graduation (Jun); Home Improvement (Mar); Spirit of Freedom (Nov); Inside the Locker Room (Aug); Friday Night Lights (Sep-Nov); Best of Yuba/Sutter (Sept); Pride (Oct); Christmas Kick-Off (Nov-Dec).
Special Weekly Sections: Life (S); Real Estate (Sat); Food (Wed). Entertainment (Thurs)
Syndicated Publications: Parade Magazine (Sunday)
Proprietary Publications: Prospect Magazine (Monthly)
Digital Platform - Mobile: Apple, Android
Digital Platform - Tablet: Apple iOS, Android
Adv. Mgr., Classified .... Nancy Brown
Business Manager Donna Blair
Editor .... Steve Miller
Publisher .... Glenn Stiffemire
Sales & Marketing Director .... Jamie Keith
Circulation Manager .... Lori Wilson
Market Information: TMC.
Mechanical Available: Offset; Black and 3 ROP colors; insert accepted - sample pouch, poly bag; page cutoffs - 22 3/4.
Mechanical Specifications: Type page 11 5/8 x 21 1/2; E - 6 cols, 1 13/16, 1/8 between; A - 6 cols, 1 13/16, 1/8 between; C - 9 cols, 1 3/16, 1/8 between.
Areas Served: Yuba County, Sutter County
Delivery Method: Mail, Newsstand, Carrier, RacksEquipment & Software: PRESSROOM EQUIPMENT: Lines — 8-G/Urbanite (1 color hump) 1986; MAILROOM EQUIPMENT: Counter Stackers — 1-BG/Count-O-Veyor 108; Inserters & Stuffers — 2-MM/227; Tying Machines — 1-MLN/ML2EE, 1-MLN/ Spirit; Wrapping Singles — 1-Id; Control System — 1/HL.; BUSINESS EQUIPMENT: PC BUSINESS SOFTWARE: Great Plains CLASSIFIED EQUIPMENT: Hardware — APP/Mac, Baseview; CLASSIFIED SOFTWARE: Baseview. DISPLAY EQUIPMENT: Hardware — APP/Mac; DISPLAY SOFTWARELayout Software — MEI. EDITORIAL EQUIPMENT: Hardware — APP/Mac, Baseview/APP/Power Mac, HP/8000; Printers — Pre Press/Panther Pro, Varityper EDITORIAL SOFTWARE: Dewar/Sys IV, Baseview. PRODUCTION EQUIPMENT: Hardware — Caere/ OmniPage Pro 7.0.1, Pre Press/Panther Pro 36 Imagesetter; Cameras — C/Spartan III; Scanners — Nikon/Coolscan 35mm PRODUCTION SOFTWARE: Baseview.

MERCED

MERCED SUN-STAR

3033 G St, Merced, Calif., 95340-2108, Merced; gen tel (209) 722-1511; gen fax (209) 385-2468; ed fax (209) 385-2460; gen/nat adv e-mail rperes@mercedsun-star.com; disp adv e-mail rperes@mercedsun-star.com; class adv e-mailmrocci@mercedsun-star.com; ed e-mail editor@mercedsun-star.com; web site www.mercedsun-star.com
- 2,035,479(views) 401,626(visitors)
Group: The McClatchy Company
Published: Mon, Tues, Wed, Thur, Fri, Sat
Weekday Frequency: m
Saturday Frequency: m
Circulation: 9,247; 12,451(sat)
Last Audit: AAM September 30, 2015
News services: AP. **Established:** 1869
Own Printing Facility?: No
Commercial Printers?: No
Special Editions: Senior Scene (Monthly).
Special Weekly Sections: Diversity (Mon); Health, Fitness (Tue); Food, Flavor (Wed); Arts, Entertainment (Thur); Family (Fri); Auto, Church, Pets, Real Estate, TV, Technology, Travel (Sat); Business, Finance (Daily)
Syndicated Publications: Preview/Entertainment (Fri); UC Merced (Quarterly); Parade (S); TV Update (Sat).
Digital Platform - Mobile: Apple, Android, Windows
Digital Platform - Tablet: Apple iOS, Android, Windows 7
Pres./Pub. .... Ken Riddick
Mng. Ed. .... Michelle Morgante
Ops. Dir. .... Michael Rocci

Digital Ed. .... Brian Clark
Digital Content Prod .... Jim Silva
VP Audience Dev .... Maria Ravera
Market Information: ADS; TMC.
Mechanical Available: Offset; Black and 3 ROP colors; insert accepted - card inserts; page cutoffs - 22 3/4.
Mechanical Specifications: Type page 13 x 21; E - 6 cols, 2 1/16, 1/8 between; A - 6 cols, 2 1/16, 1/8 between; C - 9 cols, 1 3/8, 1/16 between.
Areas Served: Merced/Mariposa Counties and Chowchilla in northern Madera County
Delivery Method: Mail, Newsstand, Carrier, RacksEquipment & Software: PRESSROOM EQUIPMENT: Lines — 8-G/Urbanite; Folders — 1-G/2:1.; MAILROOM EQUIPMENT: Counter Stackers — 1-G/Stackmaster; Inserters & Stuffers — 4/MM; Tying Machines — 3-MLN/ML2EE, 1-EAM-Mosca; Address Machine — 2-/KR.; BUSINESS EQUIPMENT: 2-IBM/486 CLASSIFIED EQUIPMENT: Hardware — APP/Mac; Printers — HP/LaserJet; CLASSIFIED SOFTWARE: Baseview. DISPLAY EQUIPMENT: Hardware — IBM; Printers — Okidata/Microline 591; DISPLAY SOFTWAREAd Make-up Applications — Synaptic.; EDITORIAL EQUIPMENT: Hardware — APP/Mac; Printers — HP/LaserJet EDITORIAL SOFTWARE: Baseview. PRODUCTION EQUIPMENT: Hardware — 1-Accuset/800, 1-Konica/CRT Autokon, 1-Konica/K-550; Cameras — 1-C/Spartan I, 1-SCREEN/Companica 650 CR (color); Scanners — Umax/1200, Polaroid/SprintScan, ECR/Autokon PRODUCTION SOFTWARE: Baseview, QPS/QuarkXPress 4.0.

MODESTO

THE MODESTO BEE

1325 H St, Modesto, Calif., 95354-2427, Stanislaus; gen tel (209) 578-2000; adv tel (209) 578-2040; ed tel (209) 578-2343 ; gen fax (209) 578-2095; adv fax (209) 578-2271; ed fax (209) 578-2207; gen/nat adv e-mail ejohnston@modbee.com; disp adv e-mail tritchey@modbee.com; class adv e-maildwhitmore@modbee.com; ed e-mail jfarrow@modbee.com; web site www.modbee.com
- 5,048,509(views) 729,785(visitors)
Group: The McClatchy Company
Published: Mon, Tues, Wed, Thur, Fri, Sat, Sun
Weekday Frequency: m
Saturday Frequency: m
Circulation: 33,992; 34,411(sat); 43,852(sun)
Last Audit: AAM December 31, 2016
Advertising Rate (weekday/saturday): Open inch rate $110.00 (Mon-Fri); $124.00 (Sat)
Advertising Rate (sunday): Open inch rate $124.00
News services: AP, NYT, LAT-WP, MCT, MNS. **Established:** 1884
Own Printing Facility?: Yes
Commercial Printers?: No
Special Weekly Sections: Health (Mon); Workpalce, Pets, Fun, Poker (Tue); Taste, Small Business, bowling, Fishing (Wed); Technology, Teens, High School Sports (Thur); Arts, Entertainment, Auto, Fantasy Sports (Fri); Recreation, Leisure, Home & Garden, Real Estate, Agriculture (Sat); Friends, Family, Comics, Finance, Consumer (Sun)
Syndicated Publications: Parade (S).
Digital Platform - Mobile: Apple, Android, Windows
Digital Platform - Tablet: Apple iOS, Android
Dir., Finance .... Walter E. Kletke
Adv. Vice Pres. .... Tim Ritchey
Adv. Mgr., Inside Sales .... Deanna Whitmore
Circ. Mgr., Acquisition .... Patty Tharp
Circ. Mgr., Distr. .... Craig Mackenzie
Exec. Ed. .... Joe Kieta
Editorial Page Ed. .... Judy Sly
Graphics Dir. .... Jim Lawrence
Health/Medical Reporter .... Ken Carlson
Chief Photographer .... Debbie Noda
Nat'l Sales Coord. .... Peggy Luty
Pres. & Pub. .... Ken Riddick
Market Information: ADS; Split run; TMC; Zoned editions.
Mechanical Specifications: Type page 13 x 21; E - 6 cols, 2 1/16, 1/8 between; A - 6 cols, 2 1/16, 1/8 between; C - 10 cols, 1 1/2, 1/16 between.
Areas Served: Counties: Stanislaus, San Joaquin, Calaveras, Tuolumne, Merced, Mariposa
Delivery Method: Newsstand, Carrier, RacksEquipment & Software: PRESSROOM EQUIPMENT: Lines — 8-G/Flexoliner; Press Drive — Rockwell/Allen Bradley; Folders — 2-G/Sovereign; Reels & Stands — 8-G/CT-50 RTP.; MAILROOM EQUIPMENT: Counter Stackers — 2-HL/HTII, 1-HL/HTII dual carrier, 2-HI/Olympian; Inserters & Stuffers — HI/NP 2299; Tying Machines — 4/Power Strap/PSN5, 1-/Power Strap/PSN6, 1-/MLN; Wrapping Singles — 3-HL/Monarch, 1-/EDS; Control System — HI/Prima; BUSINESS EQUIPMENT: DEC/VAX 4600, PBS/Circulation Mgmt. 3.2 BUSINESS SOFTWARE: CJ CLASSIFIED EQUIPMENT: Hardware — SII/Tandem, 6-Compaq, Tandem; DISPLAY EQUIPMENT: Hardware — 13-APP/Mac G3; Printers — AG; Other Hardware — CNI, AdDesk, Expance EDITORIAL EQUIPMENT: Hardware — 6-Compaq, DEC/Alpha/9-IBM/PC PRODUCTION EQUIPMENT: Hardware — Na/Flex, III, 1-Autologic 3850; Scanners — AG/T2000, Umax

MONROVIA

SAN GABRIEL VALLEY TRIBUNE

605 E Huntington Dr, Ste 100, Monrovia, Calif., 91016-6353, Los Angeles; gen tel (626) 962-8811; adv tel (626) 962-8811; ed tel (626) 544-0811; gen fax (626) 962-8849; adv fax (626) 795-5515; ed fax (626) 338-9157; gen/nat adv e-mail news.tribune@sgvn.com; disp adv e-mail business@sgvn.com; class adv e-mailcarla.asmundson@sgvn.com; ed e-mail steve.hunt@sgvn.com; web site www.sgvtribune.com
Group: Southern California News Group
Published: Mon, Tues, Wed, Thur, Fri, Sat, Sun
Weekday Frequency: m
Saturday Frequency: m
Circulation: 23,230; 22,201(sat); 31,844(sun)
Last Audit: AAM March 31, 2015
Advertising Rate (weekday/saturday): Open inch rate $177.00
Advertising Rate (sunday): Open inch rate $179.00
News services: AP, CNS, MCT, Scripps-McClatchy, BPI, DJ, TMS, NYT. **Established:** 1955
Special Editions: The Body (Apr); Local Business (Aug); The Rose Magazine (Dec); The Body (Jan); Seen Magazine (Jul); Health Beat (Jun); Health Beat (Mar); Water Awareness (May); Holiday Guide (Nov); The Body (Oct); College & Prep Football (Sept).
Special Weekly Sections: Career Site (S); Home Buyer (Sat).
Syndicated Publications: Relish (Monthly); U Magazine (mS) (Other); TV Magazine (S).
Circu.Dir .... Joe Robidoux
Senior Ed. .... Steve Hunt
Mark Welches
VP, Nat'l Sales/Major Retail .... Mickie Sullivan
Market Information: ADS; TMC.
Mechanical Available: Offset; Black and 3 ROP colors; insert accepted; page cutoffs - 22 3/4.
Mechanical Specifications: Type page 11 1/2 x 21 1/4; E - 6 cols, 1 13/16, 1/8 between; A - 6 cols, 1 13/16, 1/8 between; C - 10 cols, 1 1/6, 1/16 between.Equipment & Software: PRESSROOM EQUIPMENT: Lines — 7-G/HO 1989; Reels & Stands — 14; Control System — G/MPCS.; MAILROOM EQUIPMENT: Counter Stackers — 5-Id/2000, 2-Id/440, 1/QWI; Inserters & Stuffers — 4-GMA/SLS 1000; Tying Machines — 8-/Power Strap/PSN5, 2-/Dynaric; Wrapping Singles — Addressing machine 2-Videojet/VMS.; BUSINESS EQUIPMENT: HP/969 BUSINESS SOFTWARE: CJ, Ultipro (Payroll) CLASSIFIED EQUIPMENT: Hardware — 1-SII/Server Net; 27-SII/Coyote 3; Printers — 3-HP; CLASSIFIED SOFTWARE: SII/Czar II. DISPLAY EQUIPMENT: Hardware — 6-APP/Mac, 3-Compaq; Printers — Proofers, HP; DISPLAY SOFTWAREAd Make-up Applications — SII/IAL; Layout Software — SII/IAL, 4-Compaq/Ring Stations. EDITORIAL EQUIPMENT: Hardware — SII/Server Net/75-SII/Coyote 3, 2-SII/PC; Printers — 5-HP EDITORIAL SOFTWARE: SII/Editorial. PRODUCTION EQUIPMENT: Hardware — 2-AIL/3850, 2-Polaroid, QPS; Cameras — 1-Spartan/III, 1-C/Newspager, 1-C/Spartan III; Scanners — 2-Lf/Leafscan 35, 10-Compaq, 2-Polaroid PRODUCTION SOFTWARE: SII/INL 9.2.
Note: The Los Angeles Newspaper Group includes the Long Beach Press-Telegram (mS), Los Angeles Daily News (mS), Ontario Inland Valley Daily Bulletin (mS), Pasadena Star-News (mS), Redlands Daily Facts (eS), San Bernardino County Sun (mS), San Gabriel Valley Tribune

THE WHITTIER DAILY NEWS

605 E Huntington Dr, Ste 100, Monrovia, Calif., 91016-6353, Los Angeles; gen tel (562) 698-0955; adv tel (626) 544-0888; ed tel (562) 567-7543; gen fax (626) 856-2750; gen/nat adv e-mail jon.merendino@langnews.com; ed e-mail news.wdn@sgvn.com; web site www.whittierdailynews.com
Group: Southern California News Group
Published: Tues, Wed, Thur, Fri, Sat, Sun
Weekday Frequency: m
Saturday Frequency: m
Circulation: 9,896; 9,651(sat); 13,901(sun)
Last Audit: AAM March 31, 2015
Advertising Rate (weekday/saturday): Open inch rate $177.00
Advertising Rate (sunday): open inch rate $179.00
News services: AP, CNS, MCT, Scripps-McClatchy, BPI, DJ, NYT, United Media.
Own Printing Facility?: No
Special Editions: Prep Extra (Aug.); The Rose Magazine (Dec); Holiday Guide (Nov); Dining Guide (Sept).
Special Weekly Sections: Career Site (S); New Home Buyer (Sat).
Syndicated Publications: Relish (Monthly); TV Magazine (S).
Digital Platform - Mobile: Apple
Digital Platform - Tablet: Apple iOS
Mng. Ed. .... Steve Hunt
Bus. Ed. .... Kevin Smith
City Editor .... Daniel Tedford
Reporter .... Mike Sprague
Reporter .... Sandra Molina
Peter Fullam
Clerk .... Venusse Navid
Prep Editor .... Fred Robledo
VP, Nat'l Sales/Major Retail .... Mickie Sullivan
Market Information: ADS; TMC.
Mechanical Available: Offset; Black and 3 ROP colors; insert accepted; page cutoffs - 22 3/4.
Mechanical Specifications: Type page 11 1/2 x 21 1/2; E - 6 cols, 1 13/16, 1/8 between; A - 6 cols, 1 13/16, 1/8 between; C - 10 cols, 1 1/16, 1/16 between.
Delivery Method: Newsstand, Carrier, RacksEquipment & Software: PRESSROOM EQUIPMENT: Lines — 7-G/HO 1989; Reels & Stands — 14; Control System — G/MPCS.; MAILROOM EQUIPMENT: Counter Stackers — 5-Id/2000, 2-Id/440, 1/QWI, Id/2000; Inserters & Stuffers — 4-GMA/SLS 1000; Tying Machines — 5-/Power Strap/PSN-5, 2-/Dynaric; Address Machine — 2-Videojet/VMS.; BUSINESS EQUIPMENT: HP/969 BUSINESS SOFTWARE: CJ, Ultipro CLASSIFIED EQUIPMENT: Hardware — 1-SII/ServerNet; 27-SII/Coyote 3; Printers — 3-HP; CLASSIFIED SOFTWARE: SII/Czar II. DISPLAY EQUIPMENT: Hardware — 6-APP/Mac, 3-Compaq; Printers — Proofers, HP; Other Hardware — SII/IAL, 4-Compaq/Ring Station. DISPLAY SOFTWAREAd Make-up Applications — SII/IAL; EDITORIAL EQUIPMENT: Hardware — SII/ServerNet/75-SII/Coyote 35, 2-SII/PC; Printers — 5-HP EDITORIAL SOFTWARE: SII/Editorial. PRODUCTION EQUIPMENT: Hardware — 2-WL, APP/Mac, QPS; Cameras — 1-Spartan/III, 1-C/Newspager, 1-C/Spartan III; Scanners — 2-Lf/Leafscan 35, 10-Compaq, 2-Polaroid PRODUCTION SOFTWARE: SII/INL 9.2.
Note: The Los Angeles Newspaper Group includes the Long Beach Press-Telegram (mS), Los Angeles Daily News (mS), Ontario Inland Valley Daily Bulletin (mS), Pasadena Star-News (mS), Redlands Daily Facts (eS), San Bernardino County Sun (mS), San Gabriel Valley Tri

MONTEREY

THE MONTEREY COUNTY HERALD

2200 Garden Rd, Monterey, Calif., 93940-5329, Monterey; gen tel (831) 372-3311; adv tel (831) 646-4308; ed tel (831) 646-4381; gen fax (831) 648-1126 ; adv fax (831) 648-1126; ed fax (831) 372-8401 ; gen/nat adv e-mail circservices@montereyherald.com; disp adv e-mail dkrolczyk@montereyherald.com; class adv e-mailopenhouses@montereyherald.com; ed e-mail mhcity@montereyherald.com; web site www.montereyherald.com
Group: Digital First Media
Published: Mon, Tues, Wed, Thur, Fri, Sat, Sun
Weekday Frequency: m
Saturday Frequency: m
Circulation: 12,072; 12,072(sat); 13,639(sun)
Last Audit: AAM September 30, 2016
Advertising Rate (weekday/saturday): Open inch rate $73.81
Advertising Rate (sunday): Open inch rate $82.07
News services: AP, LAT-WP, NYT, MCT. **Established:** 1922
Special Editions: Classic Car Weekend (Aug); Holiday Gift Guide (Dec); Wedding Planner (Feb); AT&T Pro-Am Golf (Jan); California Rodeo Salinas (Jul); Discover Carmel Valley 1 (Jun); Senior 1 (Mar); Focus on Salinas (May); Discover Carmel Valley 2 (Nov); Cherry's Jubilee Ca
Special Weekly Sections: Senior, Go Calendar (Mon); Business (Tue); Best Food Day (Wed); Entertainment (Thur); Auto (Fri); Real Estate, Religion, Home & Garden (Sat); Leisure, TV, Health and Science (Sun)
Syndicated Publications: TV Week (S).
CFO .... Juan Jose Sierra
Pub. .... Gary Omernick
Online Ed. .... Lisa Mitchell
Feat. Ed. .... Mike Hale
Political Ed. .... Royal Calkins
Prod. Mgr., Publishing Systems Jeremy Patterson
Prod. Mgr. .... Robert B. Booth
Jeff Mitchell
Ad. Dir. .... Dana Arvig
Market Information: TMC.
Mechanical Available: Flexography; Black and 3 ROP colors; insert accepted; page cutoffs - 22 1/4.
Mechanical Specifications: Type page 13 x 21; E - 6 cols, 2 1/16, 1/8 between; A - 6 cols, 2 1/16, 1/8 between; C - 9 cols, 1 3/8, 1/16 between. Equipment & Software: PRESSROOM EQUIPMENT: Lines — 7-G/Flexoliner 1988; MAILROOM EQUIPMENT: Counter Stackers — 2-MM/310, 1-MM/375, 1-TMSI/Compass 180; Inserters & Stuffers — 2-MM/308 Biliner; Tying Machines — 2/MLN, 2-Sterling/MR45CH.; BUSINESS EQUIPMENT: 1-DEC/VAX-4200, 1-DEC/VAX-4300, 5-APP/Mac, 24-IBM BUSINESS SOFTWARE: CJ/AIM CLASSIFIED EQUIPMENT: Hardware — 22-PC; CLASSIFIED SOFTWARE: DTI/Class, Dewar/Disc Sys III. DISPLAY EQUIPMENT: Hardware — 14-APP/Mac; DISPLAY SOFTWAREAd Make-up Applications — QPS/QuarkXPress.; EDITORIAL EQUIPMENT: Hardware — 10-PC, 25-Visual Display Terminals/2-PrePress/Tegra with 5000 processors & 50001 Imagers; Printers — 1-Dataproducts/LZR EDITORIAL SOFTWARE: Dewar/Disc Sys III. PRODUCTION EQUIPMENT: Hardware — 2-Tegra/Varityper/XP-1000, 2-Tegra/Varityper 5000 RIP, 1-AG/Avantra 25, 1-Bidco, 2-Cascade/RIP; Cameras — 2-C/Spartan III; Scanners — HP/ScanJet Plus, ECR/Autokon 1000DC.

NAPA

NAPA VALLEY REGISTER

1615 Soscol Ave, Napa, Calif., 94559-1901, Napa; gen tel (707) 226-3711; adv tel (707) 257-3003; gen fax (707) 252-0247; adv fax (707) 257-3003; gen/nat adv e-mail napaprod@napanews.com; disp adv e-mail nkostecka@napanews.com; class adv

e-mailvalleyclassifieds@napanews.com; ed e-mail napaopinion@napanews.com; web site www.napavalleyregister.com
Group: Lee Enterprises, Inc.
Published: Mon, Tues, Wed, Thur, Fri, Sat, Sun
Weekday Frequency: m
Saturday Frequency: m
Circulation: 9,854; 10,100(sat); 10,135(sun)
Last Audit: AAM March 31, 2016
Advertising Rate (weekday/saturday): Open inch rate $24.90
Advertising Rate (sunday): Open inch rate $26.90
News services: AP.
Own Printing Facility?: Yes
Commercial Printers?: Yes
Special Editions: Once Upon A Time (Apr); Football (Aug); Wishbooks (Dec); Bridal (Feb); Healthwise (Jan); The Best Years (Jul); County Fair (Jun); Spring Home & Garden (Mar); Napa Solano Home & Garden (May); Auto Showcase (Nov); Transamerica Golf (Oct); Heirlooms (Sept).
Special Weekly Sections: Best Food (Tue); Auto (Fri); Home & Garden, Entertainment (sat); Real Estate (Sun); Business (Daily)
Syndicated Publications: Relish (Monthly); USA WEEKEND Magazine (S).
Adv. Dir..................................Norma Kostecka
Features Ed..............................Sasha Paulsen
Ed...Sean Scully
City Ed......................................Kevin Courtney
Class. Adv. Dir.........................Rodolfo Schwanz
Market Information: Split run; TMC.
Mechanical Available: Offset; Black and 3 ROP colors; insert accepted; page cutoffs - 22 3/4.
Mechanical Specifications: Type page 13 x 21 1/2; E - 6 cols, 1 5/8, 1/8 between; A - 6 cols, 1 7/8, 1/8 between; C - 10 cols, 1 1/8, 1/16 between.Equipment & Software: PRESSROOM EQUIPMENT: Lines — 7-G/Urbanite; MAILROOM EQUIPMENT: Counter Stackers — 1/ BG; Inserters & Stuffers — 2-MM/6:1; Tying Machines — 1-/MLN; Address Machine — American Business Computers.; BUSINESS EQUIPMENT: 6-ScrippSat CLASSIFIED EQUIPMENT: Hardware — 5-ScrippSat; Printers — LaserMaster/ Unity; CLASSIFIED SOFTWARE: Synaptic. DISPLAY EQUIPMENT: Hardware — 5-ScrippSat; Printers — 3-LaserMaster/ Unity; Other Hardware — ScrippSat. DISPLAY SOFTWAREAd Make-up Applications — QPS/QuarkXPress, QPS, Adobe/Photoshop, Archetype/Corel Draw; EDITORIAL EQUIPMENT: Hardware — 25-APP/Mac; Printers — 2-LaserMaster/ Unity 1800 x 60, 2-AU/3850 EDITORIAL SOFTWARE: Baseview. PRODUCTION EQUIPMENT: Hardware — 5-LaserMaster/ Unity; Cameras — 1-MG; Scanners — HP/ ScanJet IIc PRODUCTION SOFTWARE: QPS/QuarkXPress 3.31.

OROVILLE

OROVILLE MERCURY - REGISTER

2124 5th Ave, Oroville, Calif., 95965-5862, Butte; gen tel (530) 896-7751; gen/nat adv e-mail slehman@orovillemr.com; web site www.orovillemr.com
Group: Media News Group
Published: Mon, Tues, Wed, Thur, Fri, Sat, Sun
Circulation: 2,723; 2,703(sat)
Last Audit: AAM September 30, 2015
Local News Editor.................Steve Schoonover
Adv, Exec................................Sandra Lehman
Adv. Dir..................................Fred Crosthwaite
Areas Served: Butte County

PALM SPRINGS

THE DESERT SUN

750 N Gene Autry Trl, Palm Springs, Calif., 92262-5463, Riverside; gen tel (760) 322-8889; adv tel (760) 322-8889; ed tel (760) 778-4637; gen fax (760) 778-4512; adv fax (760) 778-4528; ed fax (760) 778-4654; ed e-mail localnews@desertsun.com; web site www.thedesertsun.com
Group: Gannett
Published: Mon, Tues, Wed, Thur, Fri, Sat, Sun
Weekday Frequency: m
Saturday Frequency: m
Circulation: 28,191; 28,191(sat); 31,900(sun)
Last Audit: AAM March 31, 2017
Advertising Rate (weekday/saturday): Open inch rate $106.75
Advertising Rate (sunday): Open inch rate $113.25
News services: AP, GNS. **Established:** 1927
Special Editions: Home Sweet Home (Apr); Football (Aug); Restaurant Guide (Dec); Riverside County Date Festival (Feb); Bob Hope Golf Classic (Jan); Newsweek & Evert Cup Tennis Championships (Mar); Keeping Cool & Summer Fun (May); Pure Gold Coupons (Monthly); Discover the C
Special Weekly Sections: Desert Living (Sun); Snapshots, Golf (Tue); Food & Drink (Wed); Healthy Living (Thur); Weekend Entertainment (Fri); TV, Home, Real Estate (Sat); Business, Bilingual (Monthly)
Syndicated Publications: Weekend Entertainment Guide (Fri); Desert Magazine (Monthly); TV Magazine (Sat).
Exec. Ed....Greg Burton
Sports Ed......................................Matt Solinsky
Prod..Chris Weddle
Prod..Jose bastidas
Prod..Maire McCain
Market Information: TMC.
Mechanical Available: Offset; Black and 3 ROP colors; insert accepted; page cutoffs - 22 1/16.
Mechanical Specifications: Type page 13 x 21; E - 6 cols, 2, 1/8 between; A - 6 cols, 2, 1/8 between; C - 10 cols, 1 1/5, 1/8 between.

PALMDALE

ANTELOPE VALLEY PRESS

37404 Sierra Hwy, Palmdale, Calif., 93550-9343, Los Angeles; gen tel (661) 273-2700; adv tel (661) 273-2700; ed tel (661)273-2700; gen fax (661) 947-4870; adv fax (661) 947-4870; ed fax (661) 947-4870; gen/nat adv e-mail email@avpress.com; class adv e-mailclassified@avpress.com; ed e-mail sarnold@avpress.com; web site www.avpress.com
Group: Antelope Valley Newspapers Inc
Published: Mon, Tues, Wed, Thur, Fri, Sat, Sun
Weekday Frequency: m
Saturday Frequency: m
Circulation: 8,746; 8,746(sat); 10,865(sun)
Last Audit: VAC May 31, 2017
Advertising Rate (weekday/saturday): Open inch rate $53.30 Daily
Advertising Rate (sunday): $57.38
Online Advertising Rate: additional rate card on request
News services: Metro, AP, TMS, N YT, Bloomberg, CNS, CSM, MCT. **Established:** 1915
Own Printing Facility?: Yes
Commercial Printers?: Yes
Special Editions: Annual Fair (Aug); Annual Future Leaders (Feb); Annual Welcome (Oct) Wedding(Jan)New Vehicles(Oct)
Special Weekly Sections: Automotive (Fri); Real Estate (S); Food (Wed). Business (M-Sun)
Syndicated Publications: Parade (Weekly).Relish monthly
Proprietary Publications: Antelope Valley Lifestyle (Monthly) Real Estate (monthly) Dining and Entertainment(Bi yearly) AV Express(weekly)
Pub.................................William C. Markham
Vice Pres./Gen. Mgr.....................Cherie Bryant
Ed....Charles Bostwick
Bus./Finance Ed...........................James Skeen
Photo Ed....Ron Siddle
Special Sections Ed..................Karen Maeshiro
Prodn. Mgr., Opns........................Dennis Birks
Classified Adv. Dir.......................Mike McMullin
Adv. Dir......................................Mark Sherwood
Market Information: ADS; TMC.
Mechanical Available: Offset; Black and 4 ROP colors; insert accepted; page cutoffs - 22 3/4.
Mechanical Specifications: Type page 22 1/8 x 21 1/2; E - 6 cols, 2 1/16, 1/8 between; A - 6 cols, 2 1/16, 1/8 between; C - 9 cols, 1 3/8, 1/16 between.
Areas Served: 93536, 93551, 93534, 93535, 93550, 93560, 93552, 93543, 93505, 93510, 93501, 93591, 93532, 93553, 93561, 93523, 93516, 93544, 91355, 91390, 91351
Delivery Method: Mail, Newsstand, Carrier, RacksEquipment & Software: PRESSROOM EQUIPMENT: Lines — 10-Goss/Urbanite ; Press Drive — 3-HP/100; Folders — 1-G/ Urbanite 1000 Series; Pasters —7-Enkel/ AutomaticControl System — Goss/Console; Registration System - Duarte/Pin System. EgrafTech Polyneat thermal negative plate processors; Screen PlateRite News 2000 S+Thermal plate recorders MAILROOM EQUIPMENT: Counter Stackers — 3-Id/2100; Inserters & Stuffers — AM Graphics/NP 630; Tying Machines — 2/Dynaric; Control System — Amerigraph/Icon; Address Machine — KR/ Communications.; BUSINESS EQUIPMENT: Dell power edge 2800, Dell power edge 2900 BUSINESS SOFTWARE: PBS, SBS, Edgil, Bellatrix, Global CLASSIFIED EQUIPMENT: Hardware — SunFire V120, StorEdge 330, Sun V440; Mac GA; Printers — HP 2300, HP 1300; CLASSIFIED SOFTWARE: DTI 5.5 DISPLAY EQUIPMENT: Hardware — Quad G5; Printers — HP 8150, HP 755, HP 1055; DISPLAY SOFTWAREAd Make-up Applications — DTI 5.5/In Design; EDITORIAL EQUIPMENT: Hardware — Sun V440, StorEdge 330/Mac G4, Mac G5; Printers — HP 8150 EDITORIAL SOFTWARE: DTI 55/In Copy PRODUCTION EQUIPMENT: Hardware — HP 1055 Color Proofer, 755 Color Proofer, 2 All 3850's Screen platerite news 2000s, Egraftech plate processor; Cameras — 2-C, R/440, 1-C/ Spartan 3; Scanners — Epson 3200 Photo PRODUCTION SOFTWARE: DTI 5.5, Fusion RIP, Highwater Q2 Load balancer, Frist proof pro, DynaStrip 5 page pairer CIRCULATION SOFTWARBelletrix

PORTERVILLE

THE PORTERVILLE RECORDER

115 E Oak Ave, Porterville, Calif., 93257-3807, Tulare; gen tel (559) 784-5000; adv tel (559) 784-5000 ext. 1061; ed tel (559) 784-5000 ext. 1040; gen fax (559) 784-5245; adv fax (559) 784-5245; ed fax (559) 784-1689; gen/nat adv e-mail recorderads@portervillerecorder.com; ed e-mail recorder@portervillerecorder.com; web site www.portervillerecorder.com
- 400,000(views) 60,000(visitors)
Group: RISN Operations Inc.
Published: Mon, Tues, Wed, Thur, Fri, Sat
Weekday Frequency: m
Saturday Frequency: m
Circulation: 5,000; 6,500(sat)
Last Audit: Sworn/Estimate/Non-Audited July 17, 2017
Advertising Rate (weekday/saturday): Modular rates
Online Advertising Rate: $10 cpm
News services: AP, MCT, NEA, TMS. **Established:** 1909
Own Printing Facility?: No
Commercial Printers?: No
Special Editions: Medical Directory (Feb); Bridal (Jan); Readers Choice (Jul); Porterville Fair (May); Holiday Gifts (Nov); Women in Business (Oct); Living Here (Sept); From the Fields (twice a year); Tulare County - In the Shadow of Giants(spring and fall).
Special Weekly Sections: Financial, Health and Fitness (Sat); Arts & Entertainment (Thur); Schools (Tues); Heritage (Weds.).
Syndicated Publications: Parade Magazine (Sat); The Buzz (Mon). American Profile (Mon) Relish (First Wed of month)
Digital Platform - Mobile: Apple, Android
Bus. Mgr....................................Craig Dimmitt
Adv./Mktg. Dir...........................Josie Chapman
Pub./Ed...Rick Elkins
Circ. Dir...Alex Larson
Asst. Circ. Mgr...............................Terry Feagin
Mng. Ed./ Asst. Pub.....................Brian Williams
Market Information: Split run; TMC.
Mechanical Available: Offset; Black and 3 ROP colors; insert accepted; page cutoffs - 22 3/4.
Mechanical Specifications: Type page 13 x 21; E - 6 cols, 2 1/16, 1/8 between; A - 6 cols, 2 1/16, 1/8 between; C - 9 cols, 1 5/16, 1/8 between.
Areas Served: 93257, 93247, 93258, 93265, 93267, 93270
Delivery Method: Mail, Newsstand, Carrier, RacksEquipment & Software: MAILROOM EQUIPMENT: Tying Machines — 2/Us, 1-/ MLN.; BUSINESS EQUIPMENT: 1-Packard Bell/Novell, 3-IBM/PC 80, 2-IBM/30, Novell, 1-Genecom/4440XT, 4-Compaq, 1-Packard Bell/Visionary BUSINESS SOFTWARE: AR 5000 CLASSIFIED EQUIPMENT: Hardware — 4-APP/Mac G3; 1998-APP/Mac G3 Server; Printers — 1-HP/8000, 2-ECR/ Imagesetter; CLASSIFIED SOFTWARE: Baseview/Ad Manager Pro 2.06. DISPLAY EQUIPMENT: Hardware — 4-APP/ Mac 7300; Printers — 1-HP/8000, ECR/ Imagesetter; Other Hardware — 4-Flatbed/ Scanner. DISPLAY SOFTWAREAd Make-up Applications — Indesign CS3, Adobe Suite Products EDITORIAL EQUIPMENT: Hardware — 8-APP/Mac G3, 6-Umax/2-APP/ Mac 8600 Server; Printers — 1-HP/8000, 2-ECR/Imagesetter EDITORIAL SOFTWARE: Baseview/NewsEdit Pro IQ 3.2.3, Indesign CS3 PRODUCTION EQUIPMENT: Hardware — 1-Nu/Plate Burner, APP/Mac Quadra 950; Cameras — Acti/225; Scanners — Flatbed, Nikon PRODUCTION SOFTWARE: Indesign CS3,Adobe Suite Products

RANCHO CUCAMONGA

INLAND VALLEY DAILY BULLETIN

9616 Archibald Ave, Ste 100, Rancho Cucamonga, Calif., 91730-7940, San Bernardino; gen tel (909) 987-6397; adv tel (909) 987-9200; ed tel (909) 987-6360; gen fax (909) 466-0235; adv fax (909) 989-8287; ed fax (909) 948-9038; gen/nat adv e-mail jmaurer@scng.com; disp adv e-mail adv@inlandnewspapers.com; ed e-mail citydesk@inlandnewspapers.com; web site www.dailybulletin.com
- 1,400,000(views) 465,310(visitors)
Group: Southern California News Group
Published: Mon, Tues, Wed, Thur, Fri, Sat, Sun
Weekday Frequency: m
Saturday Frequency: m
Circulation: 16,601; 17,187(sat); 31,205(sun)
Last Audit: AAM June 30, 2017
News services: AP **Established:** 1882
Special Weekly Sections: Opinion (Sun, Tue-Fri); Business (Thurs, Sat); Spotlight (Fri, Sun); Real Estate/Homes (Sat); Autos/Cars (Sat); Employment (Wed, Sun); Travel (Sun); Home & Garden (Sat); Health (Sun); Faith (Sat); TV Listings (Sun)
Syndicated Publications: Spry (Weekly); Parade (Weekly)
Digital Platform - Mobile: Apple, Android, Windows, Blackberry
Digital Platform - Tablet: Apple iOS, Android, Windows 7, Blackberry Tablet OS, Nook, Kindle Fire
Pres./Pub...Ron Hasse
Adv. VP...Jim Maurer
Exec. Ed....Frank Pine
Senior Editor........................Kimberly Guimarin
City Editor..Mike Cruz
Market Information: ADS; TMC; Zoned editions.
Mechanical Available: Offset; Black and 3 ROP colors; insert accepted; page cutoffs - 21.
Mechanical Specifications: Type page 9.89 x 21; E - 6 cols, 1.56, .10 between; A - 6 cols,1.56, .10 between; C - 10 cols, .938, .054 between.
Areas Served: Alta Loma, Chino, Chino Hills, Claremont, Corona, Diamond Bar, Fontana, Jurupa,
La Verne, Montclair, Norco, Ontario, Pomona, Rancho Cucamonga, Rialto, San Dimas and Upland
Delivery Method: Newsstand, Carrier, RacksEquipment & Software: PRESSROOM EQUIPMENT: Lines — 7-MAN/Uniman 4 x 2 double width (4 color decks) 1986; 7-MAN/Uniman 4 X 2 double width (4 color decks) 1988; Folders — 4-MAN/2:1; Pasters —14-MEG, 3. MAILROOM EQUIPMENT: Counter Stackers — 4-HL/ Monitor; Inserters & Stuffers — 2-MM/227S; Tying Machines — 5/MLN.; BUSINESS EQUIPMENT: Unisys/6000-70, HP/3000 927-LX BUSINESS SOFTWARE: Unix 3.0.12-1, Xi/Textspooler 15.1, Progress 5.2E, HP/ MPE XL-IX, Cobol/II-XL, Data General 6.1, CJ, UDMS/Report Writer 4.0 CLASSIFIED EQUIPMENT: Hardware — 22-PC; APP/Mac; Printers — HP/LaserJet 4M Plus, Pre Press/

Panther Pro 46 Imagesetter; CLASSIFIED SOFTWARE: SII. DISPLAY EQUIPMENT: Hardware — APP/Mac Quadra 610, APP/Mac G3, APP/Power Mac 8100, APP/Mac G4; Printers — Pre Press/Panther Pro 46 Imagesetters, HP/750 Color Plotter; DISPLAY SOFTWAREAd Make-up Applications — Aldus/FreeHand 7.0, Microsoft/Works 4.0, Multi-Ad/Creator, Adobe/Illustrator 6.0, Adobe/Photoshop; EDITORIAL EQUIPMENT: Hardware — APP/Mac/APP/Power Mac, APP/Mac G3; Printers — XIT/486 Clipper, APP/Mac LaserWriter Plus IIg, Pre Press/Panther Pro 46, Pre Pres/Panther Laserwriter EDITORIAL SOFTWARE: Baseview, QPS/QuarkXPress. PRODUCTION EQUIPMENT: Hardware — Pre Press/Panther Pro 46, 3-P/7225, 1-P/26RA; Cameras — C/Spartan III; Scanners — ECR/Autokon 1000 PRODUCTION SOFTWARE: Baseview, QPS/QuarkXPress 4.0.

Note: The Southern California News Group includes the Long Beach Press-Telegram, Los Angeles Daily News, (Ontario) Inland Valley Daily Bulletin, Pasadena Star-News, The Facts (Redlands), The Sun (San Bernardino), San Gabriel Valley Tribune, Whittier Daily News, Orange County Register, Riverside Press-Enterprise, Daily Breeze (Torrance).

RED BLUFF

DAILY NEWS

728 Main St, Red Bluff, Calif., 96080-3342, Tehama; gen tel (530) 527-2151; adv tel (530) 527-2151 ext. 3; ed tel (530) 737-5042; gen fax (530) 527-9251; adv fax (530) 527-5774; ed fax (530) 527-9251; gen/nat adv e-mail advertise@redbluffdailynews.com; disp adv e-mail advertise@redbluffdailynews.com; class adv e-mailnsouza@redbluffdailynews.com; ed e-mail editor@redbluffdailynews.com; web site www.redbluffdailynews.com

Group: MediaNews Group
Published: Tues, Wed, Thur, Fri, Sat
Weekday Frequency: m
Saturday Frequency: m
Circulation: 2,925; 3,419(sat)
Last Audit: AAM September 30, 2015
Advertising Rate (weekday/saturday): Open inch rate $20.35
News services: AP, NYT, SHNS. **Established:** 1885
Special Editions: Rodeo (Apr); Back-To-School (Aug); Future Ad Designers (Dec); Red Bluff Today (Feb); Corning Today (Jan); Fourth of July (Jul); Health (Mar); Women (May); Farm/City (Nov); Antiques & Collectables (Oct); Tehama Dist. Fair (Sept).
Special Weekly Sections: Best Food Days, Senior Citizen (Tue); Business (Wed); Highlights, TV, Farm (Sat)
Syndicated Publications: Relish (Monthly); USA WEEKEND Magazine (Sat); American Profile (Weekly).
Pub./Adv. Dir. .... Greg Stevens
Ed. .... Chip Thompson
Circ. Mgr. .... Kathy Hogan
Multi-Media Acc. Exec. .... Gayla Eckels
Market Information: TMC.
Mechanical Available: Offset; Black and 3 ROP colors; insert accepted; page cutoffs - 22 1/2.
Areas Served: Tehama CountyEquipment & Software: PRESSROOM EQUIPMENT: Lines — 4-G/Urbanite (balloon former) 1980; Folders — 1-G/2:1; Reels & Stands — 1980.; MAILROOM EQUIPMENT: Counter Stackers — BG/Count-O-Veyor; Tying Machines — 2/Cyclone.; BUSINESS EQUIPMENT: Brainworks/PCs BUSINESS SOFTWARE: SSPS CLASSIFIED EQUIPMENT: Hardware — 5-APP/Power Mac 7200-90; Printers — 1-Okidata/Pacemark 3410, 1-HP/LaserJet 4MV; CLASSIFIED SOFTWARE: Baseview. DISPLAY EQUIPMENT: Hardware — APP/Power Mac 7200-90; Printers — HP/Laserjet 4MV; DISPLAY SOFTWAREAd Make-up Applications — Baseview, Ad Force; Layout Software — Ad Force. EDITORIAL EQUIPMENT: Hardware — 6-APP/Power Mac 7600-12, 4-APP/Power Mac 7200-90; Printers — HP/LaserJet 4MV EDITORIAL SOFTWARE: Baseview. PRODUCTION EQUIPMENT: Hardware — 2-HP/Laser Jet 4MV, 2-APP/Power Mac 7600-120; Cameras — Acti/Process, 3M/Imager PRODUCTION SOFTWARE: Baseview.

REDDING

RECORD SEARCHLIGHT

1101 Twin View Blvd, Redding, Calif., 96003-1531, Shasta; gen tel 530-225-8250 ; adv tel (530) 225-8241; ed tel (530) 225-8211; gen fax 530-225-8236; adv fax (530) 225-8212; ed fax (530) 225-8236; gen/nat adv e-mail Lynnette.Young@redding.com; class adv e-mailRRSClassified@redding.com; ed e-mail letters@redding.com; web site www.redding.com
771,115(visitors)

Group: Gannett
Published: Mon, Tues, Wed, Thur, Fri, Sat, Sun
Weekday Frequency: m
Saturday Frequency: m
Circulation: 18,528; 17,379(sat); 20,113(sun)
Last Audit: AAM June 30, 2016
Advertising Rate (weekday/saturday): Open inch rate $53.85
Advertising Rate (sunday): Open inch rate $57.60
News services: AP, LAT-WP, McClatchy, SHNS, MCT, TMS. **Established:** 1938
Own Printing Facility?: Yes
Commercial Printers?: Yes
Special Editions: Best of North State - Annual Health Care - Annual
Special Weekly Sections: Business (daily); Education, Computer Technology (Mon); Best Food (Wed); Entertainment, health, Fitness, Outdoors, Arts (Thur); Auto, Key Buys (Fri); Religion, Home & Garden (Sat); Real Estate (Sat/Sun); Travel, Outdoor (Sun)
Syndicated Publications: Parade (S).
Mng. Ed. .... Carole Ferguson
Multimedia Journalist .... Damon Arthur
Photo. .... Andreas Fuhrmann
Ed./VP of New Media Content .... Silas Lyons
Sup. of Press Ops. .... Ronnie Alido
Market Information: ADS; TMC.
Mechanical Available: Offset; Black and 3 ROP colors; insert accepted - all; page cutoffs - 22 3/4.
Mechanical Specifications: Type page 11 1/2 x 21 1/4; E - 6 cols, 1 3/4, 1/8 between; A - 6 cols, 1 3/4, 1/8 between; C - 10 cols, 1 3/32, 1/16 between.
Delivery Method: Mail, Newsstand, Carrier, RacksEquipment & Software: PRESSROOM EQUIPMENT: Lines — 7-HI/N1650 double width 1982; Pasters —7-MEGReels & Stands — 7-MEG.; MAILROOM EQUIPMENT: Counter Stackers — 3/HL; Inserters & Stuffers — GMA/1000; Tying Machines — 2-MLN/2A; Address Machine — KR.; BUSINESS EQUIPMENT: PBS, Sun/Sparc 10 BUSINESS SOFTWARE: PBS/Adv Mgt 2.8, PBS/Circ Mgt 2.7 CLASSIFIED EQUIPMENT: Hardware — PC; Printers — HP; CLASSIFIED SOFTWARE: HI/CASH, Microsoft/Windows. DISPLAY EQUIPMENT: Hardware — PC; Printers — HP/LaserJet 4MV; DISPLAY SOFTWAREAd Make-up Applications — Archetype/Corel Draw 9.0; Layout Software — Archetype/Corel Draw, Microsoft/Windows. EDITORIAL EQUIPMENT: Hardware — PC; Printers — V, TB/GUA 5100, TB/GUA 5380E, HP/LaserJet 4MV EDITORIAL SOFTWARE: Dewar, HI. PRODUCTION EQUIPMENT: Hardware — 2-Amerigraph/Magnum 323, APP/Mac, Kk/RFS 2035 Plus; Cameras — 1-Acti/504-D; Scanners — Scitex/Smart 540, Kk/RFS 2035 Plus PRODUCTION SOFTWARE: HI/NMP.

REDLANDS

THE FACTS (REDLANDS)

19 E Citrus Ave, Ste 102, Redlands, Calif., 92373-4763, San Bernardino; gen tel (909) 793-3221; adv tel (909) 793-3221; ed tel (909) 793-3221; gen fax (909) 793-9588; adv fax (909) 793-9588; ed fax (909) 793-9588; gen/nat adv e-mail ads@redlandsdailyfacts.com; disp adv e-mail ads@redlandsdailyfacts.com; class adv e-mailjmaurer@scng.com; ed e-mail editor@redlandsdailyfacts.com; web site www.redlandsdailyfacts.com
- 487,864(views) 178,252(visitors)

Group: Southern California News Group
Published: Tues, Wed, Thur, Fri, Sat, Sun
Weekday Frequency: m
Saturday Frequency: m
Circulation: 2,949; 3,005(sat); 3,430(sun)
Last Audit: AAM June 30, 2017
Newspaper Reps: Frank Pine, Executive Editor; Kimberly Guimarin, Senior Editor; Jim Maurer, VP of Advertising, Kat Wang, Director of Circulation Operations
News services: AP **Established:** 1890
Special Weekly Sections: Business (Wed), Real Estate (Sun); Autos/Cars (Fri-Sun); Employment (Sun); Travel (Sun); Faith (Thurs, Fri)
Syndicated Publications: Spry (Weekly)
Proprietary Publications: Redlands Extra (Weekly TMC)
Digital Platform - Mobile: Apple, Android, Windows, Blackberry
Digital Platform - Tablet: Apple iOS, Android, Windows 7, Blackberry Tablet OS, Kindle, Nook, Kindle Fire
Managing Editor, Digital Operations Toni Sciacqua
City Editor .... Jessica Keating
Pres./Pub. .... Ron Hasse
Exec. Sports Ed. .... Tom Moore
Executive Editor .... Frank Pine
Mechanical Available: Offset; Black and 3 ROP colors; insert accepted; page cutoffs - 21.
Mechanical Specifications: Type page 9.89 x 21; E - 6 cols, 1.56, .10 between; A - 6 cols,1.56, .10 between; C - 10 cols, .938, .054 between.
Areas Served: Highland, Loma Linda, Mentone, Redlands and Yucaipa.
Delivery Method: Newsstand, Carrier, RacksEquipment & Software: BUSINESS EQUIPMENT: Collier Jackson CLASSIFIED EQUIPMENT: Hardware — PC; CLASSIFIED SOFTWARE: SII. DISPLAY SOFTWARELayout Software — Ad Force. PRODUCTION EQUIPMENT: Hardware — Caere/OmniPage Pro 2.12, 2-NewGen/Turbo PS-480; Scanners — 1-Microtek/600-GS PRODUCTION SOFTWARE: Baseview.
Note: The Southern California News Group includes the Long Beach Press-Telegram, Los Angeles Daily News, (Ontario) Inland Valley Daily Bulletin, Pasadena Star-News, The Facts (Redlands), The Sun (San Bernardino), San Gabriel Valley Tribune, Whittier Daily News, Orange County Register, Riverside Press-Enterprise, Daily Breeze (Torrance).

RIDGECREST

THE DAILY INDEPENDENT

PO Box 7, Ridgecrest, Calif., 93556-0007, Kern; gen tel (760) 375-4481; adv tel (760) 375-4880; ed tel (760) 375-4481; gen fax (760) 375-4880; adv fax (760) 375-4880; ed fax (760) 375-4880; gen/nat adv e-mail pmckay@ridgecrestca.com; disp adv e-mail mlueck@ridgecrestca.com; class adv e-mailcbarrera@ridgecrestca.com; web site www.ridgecrestca.com

Group: New Media Investment Group
Published: Tues, Wed, Thur, Fri, Sat
Weekday Frequency: m
Saturday Frequency: m
Circulation: 7,900; 7,900(sat)
Last Audit: Sworn/Estimate/Non-Audited September 30, 2017
Advertising Rate (weekday/saturday): Open inch rate $11.58
News services: AP.
Special Editions: Christmas Carols & Greetings (Dec); Independent Babies (Jan); Graduation Congratulations (Jun); Home Show (Mar); Spring Car Care (May); Fall Home Improvement (Nov); New Car Buyers Guide (Oct); Fall Sports (Sept).
Special Weekly Sections: Real Estate (Fri); Business (S); Automotive (Thur); Automotive (Tues); Best Food Day (Wed).
Syndicated Publications: American Profile (Weekly).
Pub .... John Watkins
Display Adv. Mgr. .... Paula McKay
Classified Adv. Mgr. .... Rodney Connors
Circ. Mgr. .... Brian Voigt
City Ed. .... Nathaniel Lidle
Sports Ed. .... Cheeto Barrera
Sports Ed. .... Anthony Gentile
Mng. Ed. .... Jack Barnwell
Mng. Ed. .... Aaron Crutchfield
Market Information: Split run; TMC.
Mechanical Available: Offset; Black and 3 ROP colors; insert accepted; page cutoffs - 22 3/4.
Mechanical Specifications: Type page 13 x 21 1/2; E - 6 cols, 2 1/16, 1/8 between; A - 6 cols, 2 1/16, 1/8 between; C - 9 cols, 1 1/3, 1/12 between.Equipment & Software: PRESSROOM EQUIPMENT: Lines — 9-G; Registration System — Duarte/PIN System. MAILROOM EQUIPMENT: Tying Machines — MLN.; BUSINESS EQUIPMENT: PBS CLASSIFIED EQUIPMENT: Hardware — APP/iMac, APP/Mac G4; CLASSIFIED SOFTWARE: Baseview. DISPLAY EQUIPMENT: Hardware — APP/iMac; DISPLAY SOFTWARELayout Software — APP/Mac G4. EDITORIAL EQUIPMENT: Hardware — APP/Mac/2-APP/Mac ci. PRODUCTION EQUIPMENT: Hardware — 1-Nu; Cameras — AG PRODUCTION SOFTWARE: ECR/Panther Pro.

RIVERSIDE

THE PRESS-ENTERPRISE

1825 Chicago Ave, Ste 100, Riverside, Calif., 92507-2373, Riverside; gen tel (951) 684-1200; adv tel (951) 368-9250; ed tel (951) 368-9460; gen fax (951) 368-9023; adv fax (951) 368-9009; ed fax (951) 368-9023; gen/nat adv e-mail adavis@pe.com; disp adv e-mail adavis@pe.com; class adv e-mailclassifieds@pe.com; ed e-mail penews@pe.com; web site www.pe.com
1,199,397(visitors)

Group: Digital First Media
Published: Mon, Tues, Wed, Thur, Fri, Sat, Sun
Weekday Frequency: m
Saturday Frequency: m
Circulation: 71,870; 77,878(sat); 133,042(sun)
Last Audit: AAM March 31, 2015
Advertising Rate (weekday/saturday): Open inch rate $199.00
Advertising Rate (sunday): Open inch rate $211.00
News services: AP, MCT, TMS **Established:** 1878
Own Printing Facility?: Yes
Commercial Printers?: Yes
Special Editions: Readers' Choice, Summer Fun, Holiday Gift Guides (2)
Special Weekly Sections: Senior Lifestyles (Mon); The Guide (Fri); Homes (Sat); Real Estate, Business (Sun)
Digital Platform - Mobile: Apple, Android
Digital Platform - Tablet: Kindle, Nook, Kindle Fire
Photo-Visuals Ed. .... Eric Vilchis
Managing Ed. .... Tom Bray
Ed. .... Nikie Johnson
Columnist .... Cassie MacDuff
Asst. Managing Ed. .... Roger Ruvolo
Metro Ed. .... Mark Acosta
Gen. Mgr./Hispanic Media .... Frank Escobedo
Dir. Multimedia Sales Dev. .... John Kerr
Adv. Dir. .... Anita Davis
Interactive Dev. Dir. .... Paul McAfee
Circ. Mgr., Home Del. .... Mike Kreiser
Pub .... Richard Mirman
Sr. Ed. .... Kimberly Guimarin
Market Information: Split run; TMC; Zoned editions.
Mechanical Available: Offset; Black and 3 ROP colors; insert accepted; page cutoffs - 22.
Mechanical Specifications: Type page 11 5/8 x 21; E - 6 cols, 2 1/16, 1/8 between; A - 6 cols, 2 1/16, 1/8 between; C - 10 cols, 1 3/16, 1/16 between.
Areas Served: Many
Delivery Method: Newsstand, Carrier, RacksEquipment & Software: PRESSROOM EQUIPMENT: Lines — 9-G/HO-Double Width 1987; 9-G/HO-Double Width 1987; 9-G/HO-Double Width 1987; Reels & Stands — 24, 45; Control System — 3-G/MPCS.; MAILROOM EQUIPMENT: Counter Stackers — 7-HL/Monitor, 1-Id/NS660, 5-QWI/400; Inserters & Stuffers — 3-HI/NP 1372, 1-HI/NP 1472; Tying Machines — 8-Si/MLN, 2/Bu, 3-/Sterling, 3-Dynaric/NP 1500; Control System — QWI/Conveyors & Controls, QWI/On-Line; Address Machine

— Addressi; BUSINESS EQUIPMENT: 2-DEC/VAX 6410, 2-DEC/Alpha Server 4000 BUSINESS SOFTWARE: CJ, HP/9000 k570 CLASSIFIED EQUIPMENT: Hardware — CText, IMB/RS 6000 Sybase; CLASSIFIED SOFTWARE: AT, CText. DISPLAY EQUIPMENT: Hardware — All/Ad Manager, APP/Mac, 36-All/Ad Manager 2.6; Printers — Tektronix, HP, Plotter; Other Hardware — III/3725 Illustration Scanner, 1-III/3650 Info Scanner, 2-III/3750 DISPLAY SOFTWAREAd Make-up Applications — Multi-Ad; Layout Software — Aii. EDITORIAL EQUIPMENT: Hardware — 9-AT/Series 60; Printers — Okidata, HP EDITORIAL SOFTWARE: AT 4.67. PRODUCTION EQUIPMENT: Hardware — 3-Glunz & Jensen/35 HD, 2-III/3810 Laser, 1-III/3850 Sierra, 1-III/3850 Sierra, 4-III/3850 SST, 2-III/3850W SST, LE/Max 26; Cameras — 1-C/Marathon, 1-C/Spartan III; Scanners — 2-ECR/Autokon 1000, 1-III/3750.

SACRAMENTO

THE SACRAMENTO BEE

2100 Q St, Sacramento, Calif., 95816-6816, Sacramento; gen tel (916) 321-1485; adv tel (916) 321-1465; ed tel (916) 321-1851; gen fax (916) 326-5576; adv fax (916) 326-5595; gen/nat adv e-mail rmote@sacbee.com; ed e-mail opinion@sacbee.com; web site www.sacbee.com 3,343,258(visitors)

Group: The McClatchy Company
Published: Mon, Tues, Wed, Thur, Fri, Sat, Sun
Weekday Frequency: m
Saturday Frequency: m
Circulation: 140,167; 142,046(sat); 195,495(sun)
Last Audit: AAM December 31, 2016
Advertising Rate (weekday/saturday): $368.00 Gross/Commissionable per column inch
Advertising Rate (sunday): $425.00 Gross/ Commissionable per column inch
Online Advertising Rate: $10.00 (ROS) Net CPM 300x250 size
$7.00 (ROS) Net CPM 728x90 size
$5.00 (ROS) Net CPM 300x100 size
News services: AP, Bloomberg, CT, MCT, LAT-WP, NYT, SHNS, DJ, GNS, HN. **Established:** 1857
Own Printing Facility?: Yes
Commercial Printers?: Yes
Special Weekly Sections: Friday's Ticket (Fri); Travel (S); Home & Garden (Sat); Food & Wine (Wed); Feast (Sunday).
Syndicated Publications: Parade (S).
Digital Platform - Mobile: Apple, Android, Windows
Digital Platform - Tablet: Apple iOS, Android, Kindle, Nook
Pres./Pub. .... Cheryl Dell
Sr. Vice Pres., Finance .... Gary Strong
Vice Pres., HR .... Linda Brooks
Adv. Sr. Vice Pres. .... Francesca Lewis
Adv. Mgr., Market Analysis .... Darrell Kunken
Adv. Mgr., Nat'l .... Suzanne Deegan
VP Audience Development .... Maria Ravera
Audience Admin & Operations Manager .... Mark Montgomery
New Business & Operations Manager .. Gary Pitts
Production Director .... Robert Ford
Director Community affairs .... Pam Dinsmore
Editorial Pages Editor .... Stuart Leavenworth
Executive Editor & Sr. VP News .... Joyce Terhaar
National/Key Account Manager .... Steve Howard
VP, Adv. .... Ryan Mote
Market Information: TMC.
Mechanical Available: Offset; Black and 4 ROP colors; insert accepted; page cutoffs - 22.
Mechanical Specifications: Type page 11 1/2 x 21; E - 6 cols, 1 81/100, 1/8 between; A - 6 cols, 1 81/100, 1/8 between; C - 6 cols, 1 1/10, 1/8 between.
Areas Served: Sacramento (CA)
Sacramento County, Yolo County, Placer County, El Dorado County plus portions of surrounding counties.
Delivery Method: Mail, Newsstand, Carrier, RacksEquipment & Software: PRESSROOM EQUIPMENT: Lines — 11-G/Metroliner (double width) 1981; 11-G/Metroliner (double width) 1981; 11-G/Metroliner (double width) 1981; 36-G/Colorliner couples (double width) 1989; Folders — PPK/ Imperial 3:2; Pasters —9-G/RTPReels & Stands — Reels & Stands and Stands; MAILROOM EQUIPMENT: Counter Stackers — 22-QWI/300, 4-Id/200; Inserters & Stuffers — 6/AM Graphics/2299; Tying Machines — 18-Dynaric/NP-1, 24-Dynaric/ NP-2, 21-Dynaric/PNP-1; Control System — Prima, Denex.; CLASSIFIED EQUIPMENT: Hardware — SII/Sys 55; Printers — HP/ LaserJet; CLASSIFIED SOFTWARE: SII. DISPLAY EQUIPMENT: Printers — 2-HP 25DDCP; Other Hardware — All/Oman NT Royer, OP DISPLAY SOFTWAREAd Make-up Applications — Cx 8.0; Layout Software — Ad Mgr.. EDITORIAL EQUIPMENT: Hardware — PC; Printers — HP/LaserJet EDITORIAL SOFTWARE: Unisys/Hermes 5.5. PRODUCTION EQUIPMENT: Hardware — 3-Aii/3850, 2-Aii/3850 Wide, 1-KFM/Verifier, 1-Nu/Flip Top; Scanners — 2-Eskofot/20245, Scitex/Eversmart PRODUCTION SOFTWARE: Unisys/Hermes 5.5.

SAN BERNARDINO

THE SUN

290 N D St, Ste 101, San Bernardino, Calif., 92401-1711, San Bernardino; gen tel (909) 889-9666; adv tel (909) 386-3950; ed tel (909) 386-3991; adv fax (909) 884-2536; ed fax (909) 885-8741; gen/nat adv e-mail voice@inlandnewspapers.com; disp adv e-mail shawna.federoff@inlandnewspapers.com; ed e-mail citydesk@sbsun.com; web site www.sbsun.com

Group: Southern California News Group
Published: Mon, Tues, Wed, Thur, Fri, Sat, Sun
Weekday Frequency: m
Saturday Frequency: m
Circulation: 48,698; 43,254(sat); 63,041(sun)
Last Audit: AAM September 30, 2012
Advertising Rate (weekday/saturday): Open inch rate $158.00
Advertising Rate (sunday): Open inch rate $182.00
News services: AP, MCT, GNS, SHNS, McClatchy, City News Service. **Established:** 1894
Own Printing Facility?: Yes
Commercial Printers?: Yes
Special Editions: Nursing in the Inland Empire (Nov); Health & Fitness (5 times/yr) (Other); News of the City (Quarterly); Home & Garden (Semi-yearly); Route 66 (Sept).
Special Weekly Sections: Weekend (Fri); Business File (Mon); Business Sunday (S); Home Guide (Sat); Gardening (Tues); Food (Wed).
Syndicated Publications: Relish (Monthly); TV Week (S).
Pres./Pub. .... Ron Hasse
Exec. Ed. .... Frank Pine
Marketing Dir .... Shawna Federoff
VP, Nat'l Sales/Major Retail .... Mickie Sullivan
Sr. Ed. .... Kimberly Guimarin
Market Information: Split run; TMC; Zoned editions.
Mechanical Available: Offset; Black and 3 ROP colors; insert accepted; page cutoffs - 22.
Mechanical Specifications: Type page 12 1/2 x 21; E - 6 cols, 2, 1/8 between; A - 6 cols, 2, 1/8 between; C - 10 cols, 1 1/4, 1/16 between.
Areas Served: 91701 91730 91739 91786 92220 92223 92252 92277 92284 92301 92307 92308 92311 92313 92314 92315 92316 92320 92324 92325 92327 92335 92336 92337 92339 92342 92345 92346 92347 92352 92354 92358 92359 92371 92373 92374 92376 92377 92382 92392 92394 92397 92399 92401 92404 92405 92407 92408 92410 92411
Delivery Method: Mail, Newsstand, Carrier, RacksEquipment & Software: PRESSROOM EQUIPMENT: Lines — 6-G/Headliner Offset (4 wide) 1992; 6-G/Headliner Offset (4 wide) 1992; 6-G/Headliner Offset (4 wide) 1992; Folders — 6-G/3:2 (160 page); Pasters —18-G/CT50; Control System — G/ MPCS.; MAILROOM EQUIPMENT: Counter Stackers — QWI; Inserters & Stuffers — 3/ AM Graphics/NP 1472; Tying Machines — 4-MLN/EM1016A; Control System — QWI; Address Machine — 2-/Ch, 2-Barstrom/on-line; BUSINESS EQUIPMENT: IBM/AS-400 BUSINESS SOFTWARE: WordPerfect, Lotus CLASSIFIED EQUIPMENT: Hardware — AT/ Series 60; MON/Postscript; Printers — MON/ Laser Express; CLASSIFIED SOFTWARE: AT 4.67. DISPLAY EQUIPMENT: Hardware — 14-APP/Mac; Printers — MON/Postscript; DISPLAY SOFTWAREAd Make-up Applications — Multi-Ad/Creator 4.0.1; Layout Software — MEI/ALS 8000. EDITORIAL EQUIPMENT: Hardware — 1-AT/Series 60, 1-HI/Newsmaker 1.6.53/AT, MON/Postscript, APP/Mac Graphics Systems; Printers — MON/Laser Express. PRODUCTION EQUIPMENT: Hardware — WL, 2-Futuro/ Monotype; Cameras — 1-C/Pager II; Scanners — ECR/Autokon 8400, ECR/ Autokon 1000 PRODUCTION SOFTWARE: HI/Newsmaker.
Note: The Los Angeles Newspaper Group includes the Long Beach Press-Telegram (mS), Los Angeles Daily News (mS), Ontario Inland Valley Daily Bulletin (mS), Pasadena Star-News (mS), Redlands Daily Facts (eS), San Bernardino County Sun (mS), San Gabriel Valley Tri

SAN DIEGO

THE SAN DIEGO UNION-TRIBUNE

600 B St, Ste 1201, San Diego, Calif., 92101-4505, San Diego; gen tel (619) 299-3131; adv tel (619) 293-2335; ed tel (619) 293-1211; adv fax (760) 740-5464; ed e-mail letters@sduniontribune.com; web site www.sandiegouniontribune.com

Group: Tribune Publishing, Inc.
Published: Mon, Tues, Wed, Thur, Fri, Sat, Sun
Weekday Frequency: m
Saturday Frequency: m
Circulation: 153,132; 153,132(sat); 233,718(sun)
Last Audit: AAM December 31, 2016
Advertising Rate (weekday/saturday): Open inch rate $459.00
News services: Landon Media & Metro Suburbia, CNS, NYT, MCT, RN, DF, DJ, LAT-WP, NNS, SHNS, TMS. **Established:** 1868
Own Printing Facility?: No
Commercial Printers?: No
Special Editions: San Diego's Best (Aug); Auto Show (Dec); Super Bowl (Feb); NFL Playoffs (Jan); Summer Adventures (Jul); Summer Adventures (Jun); SD Best Ballot (Mar); Passport (May); Holiday Gift Guide (Nov); Dining Guide (Oct); NFL Football Preview (Sept.)
Special Weekly Sections: Health (Tues); Food (Wed); Night & Day (Entertainment Guide) (Thur); Night+Day Weekend, RPM (Fri);Wheels, Home & Garden, New Homes (Sat); SD In-Depth, Arts & Culture, Military (Sun)
Syndicated Publications: Dining Around (Central) (Annually); SD Home (Every other month); SD Health (Other); Fashion Forward (Semi-yearly) Eldercare (annually); Vida Latina (weekly)
Proprietary Publications: Enlace (weekly), Night & Day Street Edition (weekly
Digital Platform - Mobile: Apple, Android, Windows
Digital Platform - Tablet: Apple iOS, Android, Kindle, Kindle Fire
Publisher and Editor in Chief .... Jeff Light
Executive Chairman .... Dr. Patrick Soon-Shiong
Editorial & Opinion Director .... Matthew Hall
Market Information: Split run; TMC; Zoned editions.
Mechanical Available: Offset; Black and 3 ROP colors; insert accepted; page cutoffs - 22.
Mechanical Specifications: Type page 11 1/2 x 21 1/2; E - 6 cols, 1 7/8, 1/6 between; A - 6 cols, 1 7/8, 1/6 between; C - 10 cols, 1 1/10, 1/20 between.
Areas Served: 92007, 92008, 92009, 92010, 92011, 92024, 92054, 92056, 92057, 92058, 92075, 92081, 92083, 92084, 92003, 92025, 92026, 92027, 92028, 92029, 92059, 92060, 92061, 92069, 92078, 92082, 91901, 91902, 91905, 91906, 91910, 91911, 91913, 91914, 91915, 91916, 91917, 91931, 91932, 91934, 91935, 91941, 91942, 91945, 91950, 91962, 91963, 91977, 91978, 91980, 92014, 92019, 92020, 92021, 92037, 92040, 92064, 92067, 92071, 92091, 92101, 92102, 92103, 92104, 92105, 92004, 92036, 92065, 92066, 92070, 92086, 92106, 92107, 92108, 92109, 92110, 92111, 92113, 92114, 92115, 92116, 92117, 92118, 92119, 92120, 92121, 92122, 92123, 92124, 92126, 92127, 92128, 92129, 92130, 92131, 92139, 92154, 92173, 92530, 92532, 92543, 92544, 92545, 92562, 92563, 92583, 92584, 92585, 92586, 92587, 92590, 92591, 92592, 92595, 92596, 92883
Delivery Method: Mail, Newsstand, Carrier, RacksEquipment & Software: MAILROOM EQUIPMENT: Counter Stackers — 23-QWI/350, 2-QWI/SJ400; Inserters & Stuffers — 4-AM Graphic/2299 20:1; Tying Machines — 24-Dynaric/NP2, 1-Dynaric/RLM1; Wrapping Singles — 16-QWI/Cobra, 1-QWI/ Viper; Control System — HI/AMCS, HI/Omni 200E; Address Machine — Addressing; BUSINESS EQUIPMENT: 2-DEC/VAX 7610 BUSINESS SOFTWARE: Microsoft/Office 2000 CLASSIFIED EQUIPMENT: Hardware — Tandem/ServerNet, 185-Pentium; III/ Postscript, SII/Scoop II, SII/SCP Pagination; Printers — HP/LaserJets, APP/Mac LaserWriter; CLASSIFIED SOFTWARE: SII/ Czar II. DISPLAY EQUIPMENT: Hardware — 4-Sparc/20s, 2-DEC/Alpha NFS Servers; Other Hardware — III/Postscript, All/Oman NT 3850 DISPLAY SOFTWAREAd Make-up Applications — Dataflow, Imageflow, Viewflow; Layout Software — Cascade, 20-APP/Mac. EDITORIAL EQUIPMENT: Hardware — Tandem/Clx, 350-Micron/P2/ III/Postscript, All/Oman NT 3850; Printers — HP/LaserJets EDITORIAL SOFTWARE: SII/Sys 55. PRODUCTION EQUIPMENT: Hardware — 7-All/3850, 1-KFM/Twin Drawer, 1-P/26 RA, 1-P/DL 260, 1-P/1800IS, 1-P/26 RT, 2-AG/660, 4-Glunz & Jensen, Konica/28D Processor, 2-LE/LL2218, 1-LE/ LL21D; Scanners — 4-AG/Arcus, 3-All/3750 PRODUCTION SOFTWARE: SII/Classified.

SAN FRANCISCO

SAN FRANCISCO CHRONICLE

901 Mission St, San Francisco, Calif., 94103-3052, San Francisco; gen tel (415) 777-7000; adv tel (415) 777-7272; ed tel (415) 777-7100; adv fax (415) 896-6410; ed fax (415) 348-3080; gen/nat adv e-mail advertise@sfchronicle.com; disp adv e-mail advertise@sfchronicle.com; class adv e-mailDFitzgibbon@sfchronicle.com; ed e-mail metro@schronicle.com; web site www.sfchronicle.com 2,800,000(visitors); web site 2 www.SFGATE.com 29,700,000(visitors)

Group: Hearst Communications, Inc.
Published: Mon, Tues, Wed, Thur, Fri, Sat, Sun
Weekday Frequency: m
Saturday Frequency: m
Circulation: 170,471; 139,798(sat); 237,204(sun)
Last Audit: AAM September 30, 2016
Advertising Rate (weekday/saturday): 1/32 Pg $1180.00; 1/16 $2213.00
Advertising Rate (sunday): 1/32 Pg $1460.00; 1/16 $2738.00
News services: AP, Bloomberg, Getty, MCT, NYT, WP **Established:** 1865
Special Editions: Weddings (Jan); SF Chronicle Wine Competition, Napa Valley (Feb); Spring Fashion (Mar); Rising Star Chefs, Top 100 Restaurants (Apr); Schools, Camps, and Activities Guide (May); Weekend Destinations (Jun); Travel (Jul); Fall Arts Preview, Wine Country Guide (Aug); Fall Fashion (Sept); Warriors Pre-Season, Bar Stars (Oct); Holiday Entertaining, Ski (Nov); Gift Guide (Dec)
Special Weekly Sections: Business, Finance, Art, Entertainment (Daily); Technology (Mon); Home & Garden (Wed); Weekend Datebook (Thur); Cars (Fri); New Homes (Sat); Real Estate, Travel, Hot Jobs, Style, Food+Home (Sun);
Syndicated Publications: Parade (S).
Digital Platform - Mobile: Apple
VP of Cir. .... Mick Cohen
Editor in Chief .... Audrey Cooper
Editorial Page Ed .... John Diaz
Sports Ed. .... Alan Saracevic
Deputy Metro Ed .... Demian Bulwa
Metro Editor .... Trapper Byrne

Photo Ed..Kat Duncan
Assist. Metro Ed...........Suzanne Espinosa Solis
Photo Ed..Nicole Fruge
Arts/Entertain. Ed.................................Leba Hertz
Travel Ed...Spud Hilton
Pub..Jeff Johnson
Deputy Editorial Ed........................Lois Kazakoff
Asst. Metro Ed...........................Terry Robertson
Asst. Sports Ed............................Michael Lerseth
Asst. Metro Ed...............................Mark Lundgren
Asst. Mng. Ed.................................Tim O'Rourke
Movie Ed./Copy Ed.....................Walter Addiego
Mng. Ed., Enterprise....................Michael Gray
Mng. Ed., Digital.........................Fernando Diaz
Business and Tech Ed..................Owen Thomas
VP Marketing................................Sarah Cooney
Market Information: Split run; TMC; Zoned editions.
Mechanical Available: Offset, Heatset Offset; Black and 3 ROP colors; insert accepted - all; page cutoffs - 21 inches
Mechanical Specifications: Image area 10.08" x 20.25"; E - 5 cols, 1.88", 1/6" between cols; A - 6 cols, 1.49", 1/6" between cols; C - 6 cols, 1.49", 1/6" between cols.
Delivery Method: Newsstand, Carrier, RacksEquipment & Software: PRESSROOM EQUIPMENT: Lines — 3-MAN/Roland XXL Triple Wide (3 units 4/4, 1 tower can be split into two 2/2 webs) (1 unit has optional Heatset) (Fremont) 2009; 3-MAN/Roland XXL Triple Wide (3 units 4/4, 1 tower can be split into two 2/2 webs) (1 unit has optional Heatset) (Fremont) 2009; 3-MAN/Roland XXL Triple Wide (3 units 4/4, 1 tower can be split into two 2/2 webs) (1 unit has optional Heatset) (Fremont) 2009width (9 half decks) (Richmond) 1990; Presses 1 & 2 AND Presses 2 & 3 can be duplexed together.; Press 3 has quaterfolding capabilities.; Press Drive — Baumueller; Folders — 3-MAN/Roland 2:5:5 Jaw Folders ; Pasters —12-MAN/RolandReels & Stands — 12-MAN/Roland (4 per press); Control System — MAN/Roland; Registration System — QIPC MAILROOM EQUIPMENT: Counter Stackers — 10-Fg, 4-QWI/Packman; Inserters & Stuffers — 5-Fg (each with 1 press feeder, 2 disc feeders and 10 pocket feeders), 2 MagnaPak 33:1; Tying Machines — 6-Ferag, 10-Ferag Cross Tie, 4-Mosca; Control System — Goss Omnizone; BUSINESS EQUIPMENT: Sun i86, Mac BUSINESS SOFTWARE: Neasi-Weber Admarc, DTI Circulation, Atex AdManager, DPS AdTracker CLASSIFIED EQUIPMENT: Hardware — PC IBM, PC DELL; Linux VM; Printers — HP/LaserJet 1200, HP/LaserJet 3850, HP LaserJet 5M; CLASSIFIED SOFTWARE: Atex AdManager, SCS Classified Pagination DISPLAY EQUIPMENT: Hardware — Apple G5; Printers — Compaq/Pagemarq, AII/3850, HP/4M, HP/5M; Other Hardware — Cezanne/Scanner DISPLAY SOFTWAREAd Make-up Applications — DPS Ad Tracker, OneVision Asura, Agfa Intellitune; Layout Software — Multi-Ad/Creator 8.5.1, QPS/QuarkXPress 4.11. EDITORIAL EQUIPMENT: Hardware — Sun i86, Mac; Printers — HP/DesignJet, HP/LaserJet EDITORIAL SOFTWARE: CCI NewsDesk, AlfaQuest PrintExpress, SCC MediaServer, MEI ALS, NewsColor, Agfa Intellitune PRODUCTION EQUIPMENT: Hardware — 3-Kodak CTP Platemakers, 3-Kodak? Plate Processors, Burgess Plate Handling System

THE EXAMINER
835 Market St Ste 550, Suite 550, San Francisco, Calif., 94103-1906, San Francisco; gen tel (415) 728-4227; adv tel (415) 359-2704; ed tel (415) 728-4227; gen/nat adv e-mail jcurran@sfmediaco.com; disp adv e-mail gzuehls@sfmediaco.com; class adv e-mailgzuehls@sfmediaco.com; ed e-mail gzuehls@sfmediaco.com; web site www.sfexaminer.com
- 1,400,000(views) 490,000(visitors)
Group: Black Press Community News Media
Published: Mon, Tues, Wed, Thur, Fri, Sun
Weekday Frequency: m
Last Audit: VAC September 30, 2015
Advertising Rate (weekday/saturday): $117 pci
Advertising Rate (sunday): $153.19
Online Advertising Rate: $11
News services: 1865
Own Printing Facility?: Yes

Commercial Printers?: Yes
Special Weekly Sections: Health, Art, Nightlife (Thur); Movies (Fri); Real Estate, Food (Sun)
Digital Platform - Mobile: Apple, Android, Windows, Blackberry
Digital Platform - Tablet: Apple iOS, Windows 7, Blackberry Tablet OS, Kindle, Nook, Kindle Fire
Publisher......................................Glenn Zuehls
Market Information: San Francisco 38% San Mateo 49%
Mechanical Specifications: Full page 10.125 x 10.25 inches
Areas Served: San Francisco county and San Mateo County

SAN JOSE

THE MERCURY NEWS
4 N 2nd St, Ste 800, San Jose, Calif., 95113-1317, Santa Clara; gen tel 408-920-5000 ; gen fax (408) 288-8060; gen/nat adv e-mail mturpin@bayareanewsgroup.com; class adv e-mailclassads@bayareanewsgroup.com; web site www.mercurynews.com
Group: Digital First Media
Published: Mon, Tues, Wed, Thur, Fri, Sat, Sun
Weekday Frequency: m
Saturday Frequency: m
Circulation: 141,005; 129,499(sat); 190,850(sun)
Last Audit: AAM September 30, 2016
Own Printing Facility?: Yes
Commercial Printers?: Yes
Pers./Pub.......................................Sharon Ryan
Sr. VP/CFO..............................Lisa Buckingham
Sr. VP/Digital Adv..........................Jason Cross
Editorial Ed..........................Barbara Marshman
City Ed.................................Sandra Gonzales
Delivery Method: Mail, Newsstand, Carrier, Racks

SAN LUIS OBISPO

THE TRIBUNE
3825 S Higuera St, San Luis Obispo, Calif., 93401-7438, San Luis Obispo; gen tel (805) 781-7800; adv tel (805) 781-7831; ed tel (805) 781-7902; gen fax (805) 781-7870; adv fax (805) 781-7871; ed fax (805) 781-7905; gen/nat adv e-mail majoraccounts@thetribunenews.com; disp adv e-mail majoraccounts@thetribunenews.com; class adv e-mailclassifiedsells@thetribunenews.com; ed e-mail letters@thetribunenews.com; web site www.sanluisobispo.com
- 5,409,521(views) 1,023,458(visitors)
Group: The McClatchy Company
Published: Mon, Tues, Wed, Thur, Fri, Sat, Sun
Weekday Frequency: m
Saturday Frequency: m
Circulation: 25,718; 28,351(sat); 29,355(sun)
Last Audit: AAM September 30, 2016
Advertising Rate (weekday/saturday): Open inch rate $30.55 (Mon-Wed); $33.50 (Thur-Sat)
Advertising Rate (sunday): Open inch rate $34.07
Online Advertising Rate: $10 CPM Open Rate (Standard Sizes)
$16 CPM Open Rate (300x600)
$25 CPM Pre-Roll Video
News services: AP, Scripps-McClatchy Western Services, MCT, CNS, LAT-WP, NYT, TMS.
Established: 1869
Own Printing Facility?: No
Commercial Printers?: No
Special Editions: Vintages, Central Coast Beach Towns, Living Here
Special Weekly Sections: Home, Garden, (Wed); Ticket Entertainment (Thur); Real Estate Weekly (Sat); Showcase, Travel,. Arts, Books, Food & Wine, Comics, (Sun)
Syndicated Publications: TV Book, Parade (Sun).
Digital Platform - Mobile: Apple, Android, Windows, Blackberry
Digital Platform - Tablet: Apple iOS, Android, Windows 7, Blackberry Tablet OS
Circulation Manager.........................Cathy Veley
Advert. Opt. Mgr. ....Lori Haynes
Digital Development Director........Sergio Holguin
VP/Exec. Ed.................................Sandra Duerr
Sr. Ed...Joe Tarica
Ticket Ed..Sarah Linn
VP of Advert. ....Valerie Vaz

Pub.. Ken Riddick
Market Information: TMC.
Mechanical Available: Offset; Black and 3 ROP colors; insert accepted; page cutoffs - 21 3/4.
Mechanical Specifications: Type page 9.875 x 20.7"; E - 6 cols, 1 7/8, 1/8 between; A - 6 cols, 1 7/8, 1/8 between; C - 10 cols, 1 1/8, 1/32 between.
Areas Served: 93452, 93428, 93430, 93442, 93402, 93401, 93405, 93451, 93465, 93426, 93446, 93461, 93422, 93432, 93453, 93424, 93449, 93433, 93420, 93445, 93444, 93454
Delivery Method: Carrier, RacksEquipment & Software: PRESSROOM EQUIPMENT: Lines — 14-G/Urbanite single width; Press Drive — 3, 1; Folders — 1, 1; Reels & Stands — 4-G/Urbanite.; MAILROOM EQUIPMENT: Counter Stackers — Quip 500; Inserters & Stuffers — SLS 2000 12:2; Tying Machines — Samual NT 40; Address Machine — Ch; BUSINESS EQUIPMENT: PBS BUSINESS SOFTWARE: PBS/MediaPlus CLASSIFIED EQUIPMENT: Hardware — DTI, APP/Mac Solaris sys; APP/Mac (for Ad Makeup); CLASSIFIED SOFTWARE: DTI. Class Speed Suite v 4.2.3 DISPLAY EQUIPMENT: Hardware — APP/Mac; Printers — 1-APP/Mac LaserWriter Plus; EDITORIAL EQUIPMENT: Hardware — 45-APP/Mac, 3-TI/810/1-HP/33491A; Printers — 3-HP/LaserJet EDITORIAL SOFTWARE: APP/Mac OS, Claris/Works, QPS/QuarkXPress, Adobe/Photoshop. PRODUCTION EQUIPMENT: Hardware — 2-APP/Mac LaserWriter Plus, ECR/45-50, ECR/Jetsetter; Scanners — Epson 4180 PRODUCTION SOFTWARE: MEI/ALS 5.2.0.
Note: 20 Under 40 Event (annually in February)

SAN MATEO

SAN MATEO DAILY JOURNAL
1900 Alameda De Las Pulgas, Ste 112, San Mateo, Calif., 94403-1295, San Mateo; gen tel (650) 344-5200; gen fax (650) 344-5290; gen/nat adv e-mail ads@smdailyjournal.com; class adv e-mailclassifieds@smdailyjournal.com; ed e-mail news@smdailyjournal.com; web site www.smdailyjournal.com
Group: Bigfoot Media, Inc.
Published: Mon, Tues, Wed, Thur, Fri
Weekday Frequency: m
Saturday Frequency: m
Circulation: 14,800; 14,800(sat)
Last Audit: Sworn/Estimate/Non-Audited September 30, 2017
Advertising Rate (weekday/saturday): Open inch rate $25.00
News services: AP. Established: 2000
Special Editions: Easter (Apr); Summer Shopping (Aug); Post-Holiday Clearance (Dec); Valentine's Day (Feb); Post-Holiday Clearance (Jan); Summer Shopping (Jul); Summer Employment (Jun); St. Patrick's Day (Mar); Summer Employment (May); Holiday Gift Guide (Nov); Holiday Emp
Special Weekly Sections: Automotive (Fri); Automotive (Sat); Kids Korner (Thur); Health (Tues); Education Directory (Wed).
Syndicated Publications: Relish (Monthly).
Pub.. Jerry Lee
Ed.. Jon Mays
Copy Ed./Page Designer.............Erik Oeverndiek
Prodn. Mgr. ....Nicola Zeuzem
Mechanical Available: Black; insert accepted; page cutoffs - 16.
Mechanical Specifications: Type page 10 x 15 1/2; E - 5 cols, 1 4/5, between; A - 6 cols, 1 1/2, between; C - 6 cols, 1 1/2, between.
Areas Served: San Francisco Peninsula Equipment & Software: CLASSIFIED EQUIPMENT: Hardware — APP/Mac; CLASSIFIED SOFTWARE: Baseview/AdManager Pro, QPS/QuarkXPress, Adobe/Illustrator, Adobe/Photoshop, Multi-Ad/Creator. DISPLAY EQUIPMENT: Hardware — APP/Mac; DISPLAY SOFTWAREAd Make-up Applications — Baseview/Ad Manager Pro.; EDITORIAL EQUIPMENT: Hardware — APP/Mac EDITORIAL SOFTWARE: QPS/QuarkXPress, Baseview/NewsEdit Pro. PRODUCTION SOFTWARE: QPS/QuarkXPress.

SAN RAFAEL

MARIN INDEPENDENT JOURNAL
4000 Civic Center Dr, Ste 301, San Rafael, Calif., 94903-4129, Marin; gen tel (415) 883-8600; web site marinij.com
Group: Digital First Media
Published: Mon, Tues, Wed, Thur, Fri, Sat, Sun
Last Audit: Sworn/Estimate/Non-Audited September 30, 2017

SANTA ANA

THE ORANGE COUNTY REGISTER
625 N Grand Ave, Santa Ana, Calif., 92701-4347, Orange; gen tel (877) 469-7344; adv tel (714) 796-3845; ed tel (714) 796-7989; gen fax (714) 796-5052; adv fax (714) 558-7544; ed fax (714) 796-3657; gen/nat adv e-mail customerservice@ocregister.com; disp adv e-mail mryan@ocregister.com; class adv e-mailescimeca@ocregister.com; ed e-mail letters@ocregister.com; web site www.ocregister.com
3,649,055(visitors)
Group: Digital First Media
Published: Mon, Tues, Wed, Thur, Fri, Sat, Sun
Weekday Frequency: m
Saturday Frequency: m
Circulation: 116,250; 124,490(sat); 207,947(sun)
Last Audit: AAM March 31, 2017
Advertising Rate (weekday/saturday): Open inch rate $467.51/$381.77
Advertising Rate (sunday): $361.85
News services: AP Established: 1905
Own Printing Facility?: Yes
Commercial Printers?: Yes
Special Editions: LA Auto Show (Jan); Orange County Fair (Jul); Used Car/Auto Service (Jun); Home Beautiful (Mar); Best of Orange County (Sept).
Special Weekly Sections: Home & Garden (Sat); Commentary (S); Food(Thur); Health & Fitness (Wed).
Syndicated Publications: Parade (S).
Proprietary Publications: Santa Ana Register (Thur)
Digital Platform - Mobile: Apple, Android
Digital Platform - Tablet: Apple iOS
**National & Foreign Rep., Senior Ed. ....Gene Harbrecht
Sales Mgr................................Patricia Roberts
Dir. Recruitment....................Elizabeth Stevens
VP, Opinion Page Ed. ....Brian Calle
VP Cir...Bruce Blair
Chief Revenue Officer....................Steve Churm
Bus. Ed...............................Bernard Wolfson
Comm. News Ed...........................Paul Eakins
Feat., Asst. Managing Ed. ....Jefferey Miller
Mag., Asst. Managing Ed. ....Sherry Stern
Op., Asst. Managing Ed.................Steve Green
Page One, Asst. Managing Ed....Andre Mouchard
Photography, Dir......................Michele Cardon
Sr. Ed................................Todd Harmonson
Visuals, Asst. Managing Ed. ....Helayne Perry
Pub. & CEO.................................Ron Hasse
CFO..................................Dan Scofield
Exec. Ed.......................................Frank Pine
VP, Sales....................................Tom Kelly
VP, Op...............................Jon Merendino
VP Ad........................Henry Williamson
Market Information: ADS; Split run; TMC.
Mechanical Available: Offset; Black and 3 ROP colors; insert accepted; page cutoffs - 22 3/4.
Mechanical Specifications: Type page 11 1/2 x 21 1/2; E - 6 cols, 1 3/4, 1/8 between; A - 6 cols, 1 3/4, 1/8 between; C - 10 cols, 1 3/22, 1/8 between.
Areas Served: Orange County, CA
Delivery Method: Newsstand, Carrier, RacksEquipment & Software: PRESSROOM EQUIPMENT: Lines — 11-G/Metro 1979; 11-G/Metro 1979; 11-G/Metro 1982; 11-G/Headliner 1984; 11-G/Headliner 1985; 11-G/Metro 1989; Folders — 2-G/Single, 4-G/Double Out; Pasters —G/Static Belt RIPReels & Stands — G/Y C; MAILROOM EQUIPMENT: Counter Stackers — 5-SH/251, 9-GPS/3000, 2-Id/2000, 2-HL/440; Inserters & Stuffers — 1/MM, GMA/SLS 1000 16:1; Tying Machines — 17-MLN/2E; Wrapping Singles — 3-/Si; Address Machine — 3-/Ch; BUSINESS EQUIPMENT: HP/9000-K570,

IBM/9672, 32-AT/PDPJ BUSINESS SOFTWARE: Admarc, Microsoft/Office 97 Pro Discus, Lawson GL/AD CLASSIFIED EQUIPMENT: Hardware — 12-AT/J-11; Infoswitch/ACD; Printers — Printronix, Okidata; CLASSIFIED SOFTWARE: AT, Mactive. DISPLAY EQUIPMENT: Hardware — Sun/Microsystems; Other Hardware — Infoswitch/ACD DISPLAY SOFTWAREAd Make-up Applications — Unix, III; Layout Software — III. EDITORIAL EQUIPMENT: Hardware — 14-AT/J-11, CCI; Printers — Printronix, Okidata EDITORIAL SOFTWARE: AT. PRODUCTION EQUIPMENT: Hardware — 4-M/L-500, 2-M/L-530, 1-ECR/ScriptSetter IV; Cameras — 1-C/Newspager, R/481, C/Spartan III; Scanners — 2-ECR/Autokon 1000DE, ECR/Autokon All PRODUCTION SOFTWARE: Mactive, CCI.

Note: The Orange County Register operates a separate printing facility in Anaheim.

SANTA BARBARA

SANTA BARBARA NEWS-PRESS

715 Anacapa St, Santa Barbara, Calif., 93101-2203, Santa Barbara; gen tel (805) 564-5200; adv tel (805) 564-5200; ed tel (805)564-5271; gen fax (805) 966-6258; adv fax (805) 966-6258; ed fax (805) 966-6258; gen/nat adv e-mail advertising@newspress.com; disp adv e-mail advertising@newspress.com; class adv e-mailclassad@newspress.com; ed e-mail news@newspress.com; web site www.newspress.com 116,141(visitors)

Group: Ampersand Publishing
Published: Mon, Tues, Wed, Thur, Fri, Sat, Sun
Weekday Frequency: m
Saturday Frequency: m
Circulation: 26,068; 25,199(sat); 25,439(sun)
Last Audit: AAM September 30, 2013
Advertising Rate (weekday/saturday): Open inch rate $63.86
Advertising Rate (sunday): Open inch rate $70.25
News services: AP, NYT, MCT, SHNS, DJ, TMS. **Established:** 1868
Special Editions: Home and Decorator (Apr); Back to School (Aug); Gift Guide (Dec); Weddings (Feb); Business Outlook (Jan); Fiesta (Jul); Fashion (Mar); Chefs (May); The Season Begins (Nov); Surf (Oct); Prep Football (Sept).
Special Weekly Sections: Business, Technology (Mon); Seniors (Tue); Healthy Living (Wed); Best Food (Thur); Entertainment, Arts, Culture, TV (Fri); Religion, Garden (Sat); Travel, Real Estate, Comics, Arts, Books, Perspective (Sun);
Syndicated Publications: USA WEEKEND Magazine (S).
Co-Pub. .... Arthur Von Wiesenberger
Co-Pub. .... Wendy Mccaw
CFO/Dir., Opns. .... Norman Colavincenzo
Dir., Community Rel. .... Graham Brown
Customer Serv. Mgr. .... Jacky Barnard
Mng. Ed. .... Linda Strean
Editorial Page Ed. .... Travis K. Armstrong
Features Ed. .... Gary Robb
Photo/Graphics Ed. .... Len Wood
Sports Columnist .... John Zant
Dir., Systems .... Raul Gil
MIS Mgr. .... Rick Merrick
Web Designer/Developer .... Mary Beckman
Prodn. Dir. .... Bob Yznaga
Prodn. Mgr., Publishing Servs. .... Sharon Moore
Editorial Page Assistant .... Tony Peck
Nat'l Adv. Sales Mgr. .... Ray Rosenthal
Ed. in chief .... Deborah Garcia
Market Information: Split run; TMC.
Mechanical Available: Offset; Black and 3 ROP colors; insert accepted; page cutoffs - 22.
Mechanical Specifications: Type page 13 x 21; E - 6 cols, 2 1/16, 1/8 between; A - 6 cols, 2 1/16, 1/8 between; C - 9 cols, 1 3/8, 1/16 between.Equipment & Software: PRESSROOM EQUIPMENT: Lines — 4-G/Metrocolor (2 towers; 1 mono; 1 HO w/half deck) 1993; Folders — G/3:2 double single delivery 1993; Pasters —5-G/CT-45; Reels & Stands — 5-G/CT-45; Control System — G/MCPS2.; MAILROOM EQUIPMENT: Counter Stackers — 4/QWI; Inserters & Stuffers — 1-HI/NP 630; Tying Machines — 4-/Dynaric; Wrapping Singles — 3-/QWI; Control System — Am/AMCS, MM/Print roll, Davario/Conveyor; Address Machine — 1-/Ch; BUSINESS EQUIPMENT: DEC/VAX BUSINESS SOFTWARE: CJ, MCBA, Microsoft, DTI CLASSIFIED EQUIPMENT: Hardware — APP/Power Mac, Sun/Sparc; Grand Junction/Fast Ethernet Switches; Printers — HP, Dataproducts, III/3850; CLASSIFIED SOFTWARE: DTI/ClassSpeed 4.2. DISPLAY EQUIPMENT: Hardware — DEC/VAX, DTI/AdSpeed, 30-APP/Mac Quadra; Printers — DEC, HP, Dataproducts, Canon/Laser Printer; DISPLAY SOFTWAREAd Make-up Applications — CJ; Layout Software — CJ. EDITORIAL EQUIPMENT: Hardware — APP/PowerMac, Sun/Sparc; Printers — DEC, HP EDITORIAL SOFTWARE: DTI. PRODUCTION EQUIPMENT: Hardware — 2-G, J, III/Graphic Cobe Imager, DTI; Scanners — ECR III/3750, Nikon 35mm, CD, 5-Umax/Flatbed PRODUCTION SOFTWARE: DTI, QPS/QuarkXPress 3.3, Adobe/PageMaker 5.0, Adobe/FreeHand 5.0.

SANTA CLARITA

SANTA CLARITA VALLEY SIGNAL

24000 Creekside Rd, Santa Clarita, Calif., 91355-1726, Los Angeles; gen tel (661) 259-1234; gen fax (661) 254-8068; adv fax (661) 259-2081; ed fax (661) 255-9689; gen/nat adv e-mail info@the-signal.com; web site www.the-signal.com

Group: Paladin Multi-Media
Published: Tues, Wed, Thur, Fri, Sat
Weekday Frequency: m
Saturday Frequency: m
Circulation: 7,021; 10,673(sat)
Last Audit: VAC December 31, 2016
Advertising Rate (weekday/saturday): Open inch rate $39.90
News services: AP. **Established:** 1919
Own Printing Facility?: Yes
Commercial Printers?: Yes
Special Weekly Sections: Entertainment (Fri); Valley Homes (S); Religion (Sat); Lifestyles/Features (Tues); Lifestyles/Features (Wed).
Exec VP .... Russ Briley
Executive Editor .... Jason Schaff
Editorial Ed. .... Lila Littlejohn
Asst. Mng. Ed./Sports Ed. .... Cary Osborne
Senior Writer .... Jim Holt
Pres./Pub. .... Charles Champion
Mng. Ed. .... Jana Adkins
Market Information: TMC.
Mechanical Available: Offset; Black and 3 ROP colors; insert accepted; page cutoffs - 22 3/4.
Mechanical Specifications: Type page 12 x 21 1/4; E - 6 cols, 1 7/8, 1/8 between; A - 6 cols, 1 7/8, 1/8 between; C - 10 cols, 1, 1/8 between.Equipment & Software: BUSINESS EQUIPMENT: PC BUSINESS SOFTWARE: IBM/Acct Mate CLASSIFIED EQUIPMENT: Hardware — APP/Mac; Printers — TI/Omni 800; CLASSIFIED SOFTWARE: Baseview. DISPLAY EQUIPMENT: Hardware — APP/Mac; DISPLAY SOFTWAREAd Make-up Applications — Baseview; Layout Software — Baseview. EDITORIAL EQUIPMENT: Hardware — APP/Mac; Printers — Xante/3 G EDITORIAL SOFTWARE: Baseview. PRODUCTION EQUIPMENT: Hardware — 2-Nu/Flip Top FT52, 1-MAS/Newspeed; Cameras — 1-Acti PRODUCTION SOFTWARE: QPS 4.1.1.

SANTA MARIA

SANTA MARIA TIMES

3200 Skyway Dr, Santa Maria, Calif., 93455-1824, Santa Barbara; gen tel (805) 925-2691; adv tel (888) 422-8822; ed tel (805) 739-2143; gen fax (805) 928-5657; adv fax (805) 928-5657; ed fax (805) 928-5657; gen/nat adv e-mail cschur@santamariatimes.com; disp adv e-mail sedwards@santamariatimes.com; class adv e-mailbcunningham@santamariatimes.com; ed e-mail mcooley@santamariatimes.com; web site www.santamariatimes.com

Group: Lee Enterprises, Inc.
Published: Tues, Wed, Thur, Fri, Sat, Sun
Weekday Frequency: m
Saturday Frequency: m
Circulation: 9,305; 8,965(sat); 9,517(sun)
Last Audit: AAM September 30, 2015
Advertising Rate (weekday/saturday): Open inch rate $36.86
Advertising Rate (sunday): Open inch rate $40.73
News services: AP, GNS, MCT, NYT, SHNS, TMS.
Special Editions: Santa Maria Strawberry Festival (Apr); Readers' Choice (Aug); Last Minute Gift Guide (Dec); Farm & Agriculture (Feb); Wedding Guide (Jan); Mid-State Fair (Jul); Flower Festival (Jun); Personal Improvement (Mar); Fire Safety (May); Coupon Direct (Monthly);
Special Weekly Sections: Entertainment (Wed); Senior (Thur); best Food (Fri); Religion (Sat); Travel (Sun)
Syndicated Publications: Relish (Monthly); USA WEEKEND Magazine (S).
Pres./Pub. .... Cynthia Schur
Circ. Dir. .... Rick Macke
Exec. Ed. .... Tom Bolton
Mng. Ed. .... Marga K. Cooley
Asst. Mng. Ed. .... Len Wood
Online Ed. .... Gary Robb
Sports Ed. .... Elliott Stern
Web Developer .... Jose Aquino
Prodn. Mgr. .... George Fischer
Web Master .... Braxton Carroll
Retail Mgr. .... Sara Edwards
Circ. Mgr. .... Guillermo Tamayo
Market Information: TMC.
Mechanical Available: Offset; Black and 3 ROP colors; insert accepted - upon prior quote only; page cutoffs - 22 3/4.
Mechanical Specifications: Type page 11 5/8 x 21 1/2; E - 6 cols, 1 13/16, 1/8 between; A - 6 cols, 2 1/16, 1/8 between; C - 10 cols, 1 1/32, 1/16 between.Equipment & Software: PRESSROOM EQUIPMENT: Lines — 10-G/Urbanite single width; MAILROOM EQUIPMENT: Counter Stackers — QWI; Inserters & Stuffers — HI/1372; Tying Machines — 2/MLNEE; Address Machine — Wm/from computer lists.; BUSINESS EQUIPMENT: PBS BUSINESS SOFTWARE: PBS: Circ, PBS: Adv CLASSIFIED EQUIPMENT: Hardware — 9-APP/iMac G3; APP/Mac G4 Server; Printers — HP/8150n; CLASSIFIED SOFTWARE: Baseview/Ad Manager Pro. DISPLAY EQUIPMENT: Hardware — 7-APP/Power Mac G3; Printers — 1-QMS/2060; Other Hardware — Baseview. DISPLAY SOFTWAREAd Make-up Applications — QPS/QuarkXPress 4.11; EDITORIAL EQUIPMENT: Hardware — 15-APP/Power Mac G3, 3-APP/Power Mac 7300, 2-APP/Power Mac G4/1-Umax/Astra 4000n Scanner; Printers — 1-QMS/2060 EDITORIAL SOFTWARE: QPS/QuarkXPress 4.11, Adobe/Photoshop 6.0, Macromedia/Freehand 9, Baseview/NewsEdit Pro 3.6.1, SII. PRODUCTION EQUIPMENT: Hardware — 1-Nu PRODUCTION SOFTWARE: QPS/QuarkXPress 4.11, Multi-Ad/Creator 2 6.5.

SANTA MONICA

SANTA MONICA DAILY PRESS

1640 5th St Ste 218, Suite 218, Santa Monica, Calif., 90401-3325, Los Angeles; gen tel 310-458-7737; adv tel (310) 573-8342; ed tel (310) 573-8350; gen fax 310-576-9913; adv fax (310) 576-9913; ed fax (310) 576-9913; gen/nat adv e-mail daniela@smdp.com; disp adv e-mail schwenker@smdp.com; ed e-mail editor@smdp.com; web site www.smdp.com

Published: Mon, Tues, Wed, Thur, Fri, Sat
Weekday Frequency: m
Saturday Frequency: m
Circulation: 12,087; 12,087(sat)
Last Audit: Sworn/Estimate/Non-Audited September 30, 2017
Advertising Rate (weekday/saturday): Open inch rate $24.00
News services: 2001
Pub .... Ross Furukawa
Editor-in-Chief .... Matthew Hall
Staff Writer .... Kelsey Fowler

SANTA ROSA

THE PRESS DEMOCRAT

427 Mendocino Ave, Santa Rosa, Calif., 95401-6313, Sonoma; gen tel (707) 526-8570; adv tel (707) 526-8570; ed tel (707)521-5288; gen fax (707) 526-8549; adv fax (707) 521-5334; ed fax (707)521-5436; gen/nat adv e-mail ken.jaggie@pressdemocrat.com; disp adv e-mail ken.jaggie@pressdemocrat.com; class adv e-mailjennifer.williams@pressdemocrat.com; ed e-mail letters@pressdemo.com; web site www.pressdemocrat.com 551,959(visitors); web site 2 707.pressdemocrat.com; web site 3 www.Petaluma360.com; web site 4www.watchsonomacounty.com

Group: Sonoma Media Investments LLC
Published: Mon, Tues, Wed, Thur, Fri, Sat, Sun
Weekday Frequency: m
Saturday Frequency: m
Circulation: 45,054; 46,803(sat); 50,900(sun)
Last Audit: AAM September 30, 2016
Advertising Rate (weekday/saturday): Open inch rate $120.30
Advertising Rate (sunday): Open inch rate $132.32
News services: NYT, AP, LAT-WP, McClatchy, TMS, **Established:** 1857
Own Printing Facility?: Yes
Commercial Printers?: Yes
Special Weekly Sections: Technology (Mon); Lifestyle, Teen, Classified (Tue); Best Food & Wine Day (Wed); Time Out, Outdoor, Fitness, Wellness (Thur); Entertainment (Fri); Home and Garden, Auto (Sat); Forum, Travel, TV, Real Estate (Sun)
Syndicated Publications: Santa Rosa Magazine (Quarterly); TV Week (S);
Digital Platform - Mobile: Apple, Android
Digital Platform - Tablet: Apple iOS, Kindle
Controller .... Stephen Daniels
Adv. Dir. .... Carolyn McCulligh
Adv. Mgr., Nat'l .... Don Wolff
Dir., Mktg. .... Cindy Butner
Circ. Mgr. .... Dava Amador
Digital Development Director ... Jennifer Williams
Pub. .... Catherine Barnett
Mng. Ed. .... Robert Swofford
Sr. Ed., Presentation .... George Millener
Editorial Page Ed. .... Paul Gullixson
Digital Director .... Greg Retsinas
HR Dir. .... Emily DeBacker
Production Dir. .... Sam Caddle
Heather Irwin
Gen. Mgr. .... Barbara Mitchel
Market Information: ADS; Split run; TMC.
Mechanical Available: Offset; Black and 3 ROP colors; insert accepted; page cutoffs - 22.
Mechanical Specifications: Type page 11 5/8 x 20 3/4; E - 6 cols, 1 13/16, 1/8 between; A - 6 cols, 1 13/16, 1/8 between; C - 6 cols, 1 13/16, 1/8 between.
Areas Served: 95425, 95482, 94508, 94515, 94562, 94567, 94573, 94574, 94576, 95449, 95469, 95470, 95490, 95422, 95443, 95451, 95453, 95457, 95468, 95461, 95467, 95464, 95485, 95493, 95410, 95420, 95421, 95432, 95437, 95445, 95450, 95456, 95459, 95460, 95468, 95480, 95494, 95497, 95423, 95424, 94928, 94931, 94951, 94952, 94954, 95401, 95403, 95404, 95405, 95407, 95409, 95416, 95431, 95433, 95439, 95448, 95472, 95476, 95487, 95492, 94922, 94923, 94929, 94971, 94972, 95419, 95430, 95436, 95441, 95442, 95444, 95446, 95452, 95462, 95465, 95471. 95486
Delivery Method: Mail, Newsstand, Carrier, RacksEquipment & Software: PRESSROOM EQUIPMENT: Lines — 8-G/Headliner (4 decks) 1986; Folders — 2-G/3:2 (144); Pasters —G/RPT. MAILROOM EQUIPMENT: Counter Stackers — 6/QWI; Inserters & Stuffers — 2-/AM Graphics/6305 22/24, 1-/AM Graphics/NP 630 22 hopper, 1-/AM Graphics/NP 630 26 hopper; Tying Machines — 6-/Power Strap/PSN6, 4-/Dynaric; Wrapping Singles — 1-HI/650 Saddle Binder, PowerStrap; BUSINESS EQUIPMENT: IBM/AS-400 Model E50 BUSINESS SOFTWARE: PBS (DTI), Lawson, INSI CLASSIFIED EQUIPMENT: Hardware — Atex, Compaq/Proliant 6000, Compaq, HP; RE/Magazine Production Unit, ; Printers — HP/4000TN; CLASSIFIED SOFTWARE: AT/Advantage

1.4.8305, MEI/CLS, Atex. DISPLAY EQUIPMENT: Hardware — APP/Mac, III/Ad Manager; Other Hardware — SII, Tandem/TXP, SII/Interactive Ad Layout, 1-SII/Tahoe Layout Terminal DISPLAY SOFTWAREAd Make-up Applications — Multi-Ad/Creator, III/Ad Manager, QPS/QuarkXPress, Baseview/Managing Editor CLS; Layout Software — APP/Mac. EDITORIAL EQUIPMENT: Hardware — Unisys/Publishing System, Sun/Server, Compaq/Prosignia/PC; Printers — 5-HP/Laser Jet EDITORIAL SOFTWARE: Unisys 4.0. PRODUCTION EQUIPMENT: Scanners — Nikon, CD, Autokon/1000 PRODUCTION SOFTWARE: MEI/CLS 2.6.

SCOTTS VALLEY

SANTA CRUZ SENTINEL

1800 Green Hills Rd, Ste 210, Scotts Valley, Calif., 95066-4985, Santa Cruz; gen tel (831) 423-4242; adv tel (831) 648-4301; ed tel (831)429-2427 ; gen fax (831) 423-1154; adv fax (831) 423-1154; ed fax (831) 429-9620; gen/nat adv e-mail gomernick@montereyherald.com; disp adv e-mail rpowell@montereyherald.com; ed e-mail news@santacruzsentinel.com; web site www.santacruzsentinel.com
Group: Digital First Media
Published: Mon, Tues, Wed, Thur, Fri, Sat, Sun
Weekday Frequency: m
Saturday Frequency: m
Circulation: 22,448; 21,960(sat); 24,221(sun)
Last Audit: AAM September 30, 2015
Advertising Rate (weekday/saturday): Open inch rate $42.18
News services: AP, McClatchy, NYT. **Established:** 1856
Special Editions: Back to School (Aug); Last Minute Gift Guide (Dec); Forecast (Feb); Bride & Groom (Jan); Wharf to Wharf Race (Jul); Antiques (Jun); Home & Garden (Mar); Holiday Gift Guide (Nov); Employment Digest (Oct); Santa Cruz County Fair (Sept).
Special Weekly Sections: Spotlight-Entertainment & Dining (Fri); Seniors (Mon); Education (S); Sports-Breaking Away (Thur); Best Food Day (Wed).
Syndicated Publications: Relish (Monthly); TV Magazine (S).
Ed...Don Miller
Books Ed.....................................Chris Watson
Bus. Ed.....................................Julie Copeland
City Desk....................................Len La Barth
Feat. Ed................................Marc DesJardins
Ent. Ed.....................................Wallace Baine
Travel Ed...............................Stacey Vreeken
Internet Dir...............................Mike Blaesser
Circ. Mgr...............................Mardi Browning
Pub.......................................Gary Omernick
Market Information: ADS; Split run; TMC.
Mechanical Available: Offset; Black and 3 ROP colors; insert accepted - product samples; page cutoffs - 22 3/4.
Mechanical Specifications: Type page 13 x 21 1/2; E - 6 cols, 2 1/16, 1/8 between; A - 6 cols, 2 1/16, 1/8 between; C - 9 cols, 1 3/8, 1/16 between.Equipment & Software: PRESSROOM EQUIPMENT: Lines — 6-G/Headliner 1985; Reels & Stands — 5; MAILROOM EQUIPMENT: Counter Stackers — 3/QWI; Inserters & Stuffers — 2-GMA/6:1-8:1; Tying Machines — 2-/Power Strap, 1-/OVL.; BUSINESS EQUIPMENT: 1-IBM/AS-400 CLASSIFIED EQUIPMENT: Hardware — IBM/300PL; CLASSIFIED SOFTWARE: Dewarview/Enterprise. DISPLAY EQUIPMENT: Hardware — IBM/300 PL; Printers — HP/LaserJet 4; Other Hardware — 3-SII/Coyote, 1-APP/Power Mac 9500, 3-APP/Power Mac 8100, 1-APP/Mac Centris 650, APP/Mac LaserWriter Pro 810, Unity Turbo XL-O, HP/Pain DISPLAY SOFTWAREAd Make-up Applications — QPS/QuarkXPress 3.32, Microsoft/Word 6.0; EDITORIAL EQUIPMENT: Hardware — IBM/300 PL EDITORIAL SOFTWARE: QPS/QuarkXPress 3.32, Microsoft/Word 6.0, Dewar/View 2.11. PRODUCTION EQUIPMENT: Hardware — 1-WL; Cameras — Ik/550, Ik/555; Scanners — Kk/RFS 2035 PRODUCTION SOFTWARE: QPS/QuarkXPress 3.31.

SONORA

THE UNION DEMOCRAT

84 S Washington St, Sonora, Calif., 95370-4711, Tuolumne; gen tel (209) 532-7151; adv tel (209) 588-4555; ed tel (209) 588-4525; gen fax (209) 532-5139; adv fax (209) 532-5139; ed fax (209) 532-6451; gen/nat adv e-mail ads@uniondemocrat.com; disp adv e-mail ads@uniondemocrat.com; class adv e-mailclass@uniondemocrat.com; ed e-mail newsroom@uniondemocrat.com; letters@uniondemocrat.com; web site www.uniondemocrat.com
- 500,000(views) 40,000(visitors)
Group: Western Communications, Inc.
Published: Mon, Tues, Wed, Thur, Fri
Weekday Frequency: e
Circulation: 7,493; 7,493(sat)
Last Audit: AAM March 31, 2016
Advertising Rate (weekday/saturday): Open inch rate $21.00
News services: AP. **Established:** 1854
Own Printing Facility?: Yes
Commercial Printers?: Yes
Special Editions: MotherLode Fair (Jul); Know It All (Aug); Home & Garden (Apr); MotherLode Roundup (May);Christmas Countdown (Nov/Dec);Recreation Guide (Jan)
Special Weekly Sections: Health, Medicine (Mon); Food, Drink (Tue); Business (Wed); Sierra Living (Thur); Community (Fri)
Syndicated Publications: Parade (Fri)
Bus. Mgr. .... Lynne Fernandez
Adv. Mgr. .... Peggy Pietrowicz
Mng. Ed., Features ....Margie Thompson
Sports Ed. .... Bill Rozak
Coord., Systems/Web .... Derek Rosen
Prodn. Mgr., Opns./Press .... Yochanan Quillen
Circulation Manager .... Sharon Sharp
Interim Publisher............................ Kari Borgen
Pub .... Gary Piech
Editor .... Lyn Riddle
Pub..Wells Andrews
Market Information: Split run; TMC.
Mechanical Available: Web Offset; Black and 3 ROP colors; insert accepted; page cutoffs - 23.
Mechanical Specifications: Standard Broadsheet 6 col. X 21.5"
6 col., 10.63"; 5 col., 8.83"; 4 col., 7.03"; 3 col., 5.23"; 2 col., 3.43"; 1 col., 1.63". 129" on full page. Column gutters, .167"
Areas Served: 95370, 95327, 95383, 95346, 95310, 95321, 95372, 95373,95379
Delivery Method: Mail, Newsstand, Carrier, RacksEquipment & Software: PRESSROOM EQUIPMENT: Lines — 8-G/Community single width.; MAILROOM EQUIPMENT: Tying Machines — Dynaric; Address Machine — Wm.; BUSINESS EQUIPMENT: 7-PC Clone BUSINESS SOFTWARE: PBS CLASSIFIED EQUIPMENT: Hardware — APP/Mac; Printers — V, APP/Mac; DISPLAY EQUIPMENT: Hardware — APP/Mac; Printers — V/Imagesetters, ECR/3650, Pre Press/Panther Plus, Epson/Stylus 3000; Other Hardware — Nikon/35mm Scanner, AG/Arcus II Flatbed Scanner, Umax/Powerlook II DISPLAY SOFTWAREAd Make-up Applications — QPS/QuarkXPress, Adobe/Photoshop, Adobe/Illustrator; Layout Software — Other EDITORIAL EQUIPMENT: Hardware — APP/Mac/Nikon/35mm Scanner, Umax/Powerlook II; Printers — V, APP/Mac, HP EDITORIAL SOFTWARE: Baseview, QPS/QuarkXPress, Adobe/Photoshop, Adobe/Illustrator. PRODUCTION EQUIPMENT: Hardware — Caere/OmniPage Pro, Pre Press/Panther Plus; Cameras — SCREEN/Companica 5161; Scanners — Nikon/LS-1000 PRODUCTION SOFTWARE: QPS/QuarkXPress 4.0.

STOCKTON

THE RECORD

530 E Market St, Stockton, Calif., 95202-3009, San Joaquin; gen tel (209) 943-6397; adv tel (209) 546-8200; ed tel (209) 546-8250; gen fax (209) 546-8186; adv fax (209) 546-8232; ed fax (209) 546-8288; gen/nat adv e-mail advertising@recordnet.com; disp adv e-mail advertising@recordnet.com; class adv e-mailadvertising@recordnet.com; ed e-mail newsroom@recordnet.com; web site www.recordnet.com
- 1,800,000(views) 400,000(visitors)
Group: New Media Investment Group
Published: Mon, Tues, Wed, Thur, Fri, Sat, Sun
Weekday Frequency: m
Saturday Frequency: m
Circulation: 17,871; 17,871(sat); 23,771(sun)
Last Audit: AAM December 31, 2016
Advertising Rate (weekday/saturday): upon request
Advertising Rate (sunday): upon request
Online Advertising Rate: 300x250: $15/1 Month, $12/12 Months.
Leaderboard: $15/1 Month, $12/12 Months.
News services: AP, MCT. **Established:** 1895
Own Printing Facility?: Yes
Commercial Printers?: Yes
Special Editions: Pinnacle (Annually); Outlook 1 (Feb); Holiday Guide (Nov); Best of San Joaquin (Oct).
Special Weekly Sections: Health & Fitness - Mondays; Home & Garden - Tuesdays; Food - Wednesdays; Entertainment - Thursdays; Automotive - Friday; Real Estate - Sat/Sun; Travel - Sunday;
Digital Platform - Mobile: Apple, Android, Windows
Digital Platform - Tablet: Apple iOS
Credit Mgr. ....Claudine Dunham
Adv. Dir. ....Deitra Kenoly
Editor .... Mike Klocke
Mng. Editor .... Donald W. Blount
Online Editor .... Genette Brookshire
Sports Editor .... Bob Highfill
Tech Servs. Mgr. ....Ken Damilano
Safety, Environmental, Maintenance Mgr. ....Jim Frankel
CFO...Charles Scott
Metro Ed. .... Barbara Zumwalt
Press Manager .... David Greenlee
HR Director .... Sandi Johnson
New Media Dir..........................Josh Harmon
Mechanical Available: Offset; Black and full color ROP colors; insert accepted - commercial flyers; page cutoffs - 22 3/4.
Mechanical Specifications: Type page 11 5/8 x 21 1/2; E - 6 cols, 1 5/6, 1/6 between; A - 6 cols, 1 5/6, 1/6 between; C - 10 cols, 1 1/16, 1/12 between.
Areas Served: San Joaquin County
Delivery Method: Newsstand, Carrier, RacksEquipment & Software: PRESSROOM EQUIPMENT: Lines — 10-TKS; Press Drive — 7-ABB; Folders — 1-TKS; Pasters —7-BrockReels & Stands — 7-TKS; Control System — ABB, Brock; Registration System — Quad Tech. MAILROOM EQUIPMENT: Counter Stackers — 2-HI/Olympic NP 500, 2-QWI/Packman; Inserters & Stuffers — 1-HI/1472P; Tying Machines — 2-Dynaric/NP 1500 HS; Control System — G; CLASSIFIED EQUIPMENT: Hardware — Dell/6450 Cluster Server; Hyphen/Mac RIP, OPI/Hyphen; CLASSIFIED SOFTWARE: Mactive/Classified 2.24, SQL/Server 2000. DISPLAY EQUIPMENT: Printers — HP; DISPLAY SOFTWAREAd Make-up Applications — Adobe/Illustrator, Adobe/Photoshop; Layout Software — HI/Jazbox, Managing Editor/ALS 4.2. EDITORIAL EQUIPMENT: Hardware — APP/Mac, PC; Printers — HP, CIRCULATION SOFTWARDTI

TORRANCE

DAILY BREEZE

21250 Hawthorne Blvd, Ste 170, Torrance, Calif., 90503-5514, Los Angeles; gen tel (310) 540-5511; adv tel (310) 540-5511; ed tel (310) 540-5511; gen fax (310) 772-6281; adv fax (310) 543-4796; ed fax (310) 540-6272; gen/nat adv e-mail tom.kelly@langnews.com; disp adv e-mail tom.kelly@langnews.com; class adv e-mailmarilyn.james@dailybreeze.com; ed e-mail newsroom@dailybreeze.com; calendar@dailybreeze.com; web site www.dailybreeze.com
Group: Southern California News Group
Published: Mon, Tues, Wed, Thur, Fri, Sat, Sun
Weekday Frequency: m
Saturday Frequency: m
Circulation: 49,362; 49,144(sat); 61,294(sun)

Last Audit: AAM March 31, 2015
Advertising Rate (weekday/saturday): Call for rates
Advertising Rate (sunday): Call for rates
Online Advertising Rate: Call for rates
News services: AP, City News Service, SHNS, Religion News Service Established: 1894
Own Printing Facility?: No
Commercial Printers?: Yes
Digital Platform - Mobile: Apple, Android
Digital Platform - Tablet: Apple iOS, Android
Pres. & Pub......................................Ron Hasse
Ed...Toni Sciacqua
City Ed.......................................Frank Suraci
Exec. Ed. .... Frank Pine
Dig. News Dir. ....Daniel Tedford
Exec. Sports Ed. ....Tom Moore
Sr. Ed. .... Tom Bray
Mechanical Specifications: http://losangelesnewsgroup.com/production-specs
Areas Served: 90245, 90247, 90248, 90249, 90250, 90254, 90260, 90266, 90274, 90275, 90277, 90278, 90501, 90502, 90503, 90504, 90505, 90506, 90710, 90717, 90731, 90732, 90744, 90745, 90746, 90747
Delivery Method: Mail, Newsstand, Carrier, RacksEquipment & Software: PRESSROOM EQUIPMENT: Lines — Outsourced to Southwest Offset Printing, Gardena, CA;
Note: The Los Angeles Newspaper Group includes the Long Beach Press-Telegram (mS), Los Angeles Daily News (mS), Ontario Inland Valley Daily Bulletin (mS), Pasadena Star-News (mS), Redlands Daily Facts (eS), San Bernardino County Sun (mS), San Gabriel Valley Tribune

PASADENA STAR-NEWS

21250 Hawthorne Blvd, Ste 170, Torrance, Calif., 90503-5514, Los Angeles; gen tel (310) 543-6110; adv tel (310) 543-6110; ed tel (310) 543-6110; gen fax (818) 713-3009; adv fax (818) 713-3009; ed fax (818) 713-3009; gen/nat adv e-mail mickie.sullivan@langnews.com; disp adv e-mail mickie.sullivan@langnews.com; class adv e-mailcarla.asmundson@sgvn.com ; ed e-mail news.star-news@sgvn.com; web site www.pasadenastarnews.com
Group: Southern California News Group
Published: Mon, Tues, Wed, Thur, Fri, Sat, Sun
Weekday Frequency: m
Saturday Frequency: m
Circulation: 24,219; 22,016(sat); 36,581(sun)
Last Audit: AAM September 30, 2012
Advertising Rate (weekday/saturday): Open inch rate $177.00
Advertising Rate (sunday): Open inch rate $179.00
News services: AP, CNS, Scripps-McClatchey, DJ, NYT, TMS.
Special Editions: Earth Day (Apr); Pro Football Tab (Aug); The Rose Magazine (Dec); The Body (Jan); Hot Blues and Cool Jazz (Jul); Health Beat (Jun); Health Beat (Mar); Water Awareness (May); Holiday Guide (Nov); Rodeo Tab (Oct); Think Environmental (Sept).
Special Weekly Sections: Home Buyer (S); Home Buyer (Sat).
Syndicated Publications: Relish (Monthly); USA WEEKEND Magazine (S).
V.P./HR...................................... Gloria Arango
Ed.. Larry Wilson
Bus. Ed. .... Kevin Smith
Pres./Pub....................................Ron Hasse
Frank Pine
Exec. Sports Ed. .... Tom Moore
Market Information: ADS; TMC; Zoned editions.
Mechanical Available: Offset; Black and 3 ROP colors; insert accepted; page cutoffs - 22 3/4.
Mechanical Specifications: Type page 11 1/2 x 21 1/4; E - 6 cols, 1 13/16, 1/8 between; A - 6 cols, 1 13/16, 1/8 between; C - 10 cols, 1 1/16, 1/16 between.Equipment & Software: PRESSROOM EQUIPMENT: Lines — 7-G/HO 1989; Reels & Stands — 14; Control System - G/MPCS.; MAILROOM EQUIPMENT: Counter Stackers — 5-Id/2000, 2-Id/440, 1/QWI; Inserters & Stuffers — 4-GMA/SLS 1000; Tying Machines — 5-/Power Strap/PSN5, 2-/Dynaric; Wrapping Singles — Addressing machine 2-Videojet/VMS.; BUSINESS EQUIPMENT: HP/969 BUSINESS SOFTWARE: CJ, Ultipro (payroll) CLASSIFIED EQUIPMENT: Hardware — 1-SII/ServerNet; 27-SII/Coyote 3; Printers — 3-HP; CLASSIFIED SOFTWARE: SII/

Czarll. DISPLAY EQUIPMENT: Hardware — 6-APP/Mac, 3-Compaq; Printers — Proofers, HP; DISPLAY SOFTWAREAd Make-up Applications — SII/IAL; Layout Software — SII/IAL, 4-Compaq/Ring Stations. EDITORIAL EQUIPMENT: Hardware — SII/ServerNet/75-SII/Coyote, 2-SII/PC 22; Printers — 5-HP EDITORIAL SOFTWARE: SII/Editorial. PRODUCTION EQUIPMENT: Hardware — AP Web Server, APP/Mac, QPS; Cameras — 2-C/Spartan III, 1-C/Newspager; Scanners — 10-Compaq, 2-Lf/Leafscan 35, 2-Polaroid PRODUCTION SOFTWARE: SII/INL 9.2.

Note: The Los Angeles Newspaper Group includes the Long Beach Press-Telegram (mS), Los Angeles Daily News (mS), Ontario Inland Valley Daily Bulletin (mS), Pasadena Star-News (mS), Redlands Daily Facts (eS), San Bernardino County Sun (mS), San Gabriel Valley Tri

UKIAH

THE UKIAH DAILY JOURNAL

617 S State St, Ukiah, Calif., 95482-4912, Mendocino; gen tel (707) 468-3500; adv tel (707) 468-3500; ed tel (707) 468-3500; gen/nat adv e-mail udjemily@ukiahdj.com ; disp adv e-mail udjemily@ukiahdj.com ; class adv e-mailadvertising@record-bee.com ; ed e-mail udj@ukiahdj.com; web site www.ukiahdailyjournal.com
- 600,000(views) 90,000(visitors); web site 2 https://www.facebook.com/pages/The-Ukiah-Daily-Journal/79374461327

Group: Digital First Media
Published: Tues, Wed, Thur, Fri, Sat, Sun
Weekday Frequency: m
Saturday Frequency: m
Circulation: 5,070; 5,070(sat); 5,344(sun)
Last Audit: AAM September 30, 2014
Advertising Rate (weekday/saturday): Open inch rate $16.00 (Mon-Thur); $18.00 (Fri-Sat);
Advertising Rate (sunday): Open inchr ate $18.00
News services: 1860
Own Printing Facility?: No
Commercial Printers?: No
Special Editions: Home & Garden (Apr); Redwood Empire Fair Official Program (Aug); Christmas Songbook (Dec); Auto Show (Feb); Ukiah Lifestyles/Almanac (Jul); Summer Fun Coupon Book (Jun); Holy Week Directory (Mar); Mother's Day Dining/Gift Guide (May); Homemakers School (O
Special Weekly Sections: Best Food Day, Health & Wellness (Tue); Business (Wed); Lifestyle, Arts, Entertainment (Thur); Real Estate, Community (Fri); Religion (Sat); This Was News, Photo, Weddings, Engagements, Births (Sun)
Syndicated Publications: Relish (Monthly); On TV (S); American Profile (Weekly).
Pub.....................Kevin McConnell
Asst. Ed.....................Jody Martinez
Online Ed.....................K.C. Meadows
Webpage Ed.....................Brittany Dashiell
Lake Mendo Group Dig. Dir...........Gail McAlister
Market Information: ADS; TMC.
Mechanical Available: Offset; Black and 3 ROP colors; insert accepted - spadea, gatefolds; page cutoffs - 22 3/4.
Mechanical Specifications: Type page 12 x 21; E - 6 cols, 1 9/10, 1/8 between; A - 6 cols, 1 9/10, 1/8 between; C - 9 cols, 1 1/4, 1/16 between.
Delivery Method: Mail, Newsstand, Carrier, RacksEquipment & Software: BUSINESS EQUIPMENT: Compaq, Samsung, AR, HP, CJ BUSINESS SOFTWARE: Lotus 1-2-3 5.0 CLASSIFIED EQUIPMENT: Hardware — APP/Mac; Printers — APP/Mac LaserWriter Select 360, HP/5000N; CLASSIFIED SOFTWARE: Baseview/Class Manager Pro, Baseview/Class Flow. DISPLAY EQUIPMENT: Printers — HP/5000N; Other Hardware — ReCAs/Co-op system, APP/Mac Performa DISPLAY SOFTWAREAd Make-up Applications — Multi-Ad/Creator 4.0, QPS/QuarkXPress 3.32, Microsoft/Word 5.1, Adobe/Photoshop 3.0, Adobe/Illustrator 7.0, Adobe/Acrobat 4.0; Layout Software — 3-APP/Mac. EDITORIAL EQUIPMENT: Hardware — APP/Mac/Epson/1200C Flatbed Scanner, Nikon/Scanner; Printers — HP/5000N EDITORIAL SOFTWARE: Baseview/NewsEdit. PRODUCTION EQUIPMENT: Hardware — Caere/OmniPage 3.0; Scanners — Epson/1200C Flatbed Scanner, Epson/Flatbed-636, HP/4MV, Nikon/LS1000 PRODUCTION SOFTWARE: QPS/QuarkXPress 3.31, Baseview/Class Flow.

VACAVILLE

THE REPORTER

916 Cotting Ln, Vacaville, Calif., 95688-9338, Solano; gen tel (707) 448-6401; adv tel (707) 453-8109; ed tel (707) 448-2200; gen fax (707) 447-7405; adv fax (707) 447-7405; ed fax (707) 451-5210; gen/nat adv e-mail mhutt@thereporter.com; disp adv e-mail mhutt@thereporter.com; ed e-mail letters@thereporter.com; web site www.thereporter.com

Group: Digital First Media
Published: Mon, Tues, Wed, Thur, Fri, Sat, Sun
Weekday Frequency: m
Saturday Frequency: m
Circulation: 17,221; 16,195(sat); 17,569(sun)
Last Audit: Sworn/Estimate/Non-Audited September 30, 2017
Advertising Rate (weekday/saturday): Open inch rate $20
Advertising Rate (sunday): Open inch rate $22
News services: AP. **Established:** 1883
Special Weekly Sections: Auto (Fri); Home (S); Religion (Sat); Prime Time (Tues); Food (Wed).
Syndicated Publications: Relish (Monthly); USA WEEKEND Magazine (S); American Profile (Weekly).
Pub.....................Jim Gleim
Circ. Mgr.....................Jerry Schoenberg
Adv. Dir.....................Marc Hutt
Features Ed.....................Greg Trott
Prodn. Mgr.....................Brent Dobbier
HR Dir.....................Steffanie Jackson
Managing Ed.....................Matt Miller
Market Information: TMC.
Mechanical Available: Offset; Black and 3 ROP colors; insert accepted; page cutoffs - 22 3/4.
Mechanical Specifications: Type page 13 1/4 x 21; E - 6 cols, 2 1/16, 1/8 between; A - 6 cols, 2 1/16, 1/8 between; C - 10 cols, 1 3/16, 1/8 between.
Areas Served: Solano County
Delivery Method: MailEquipment & Software: PRESSROOM EQUIPMENT: Lines — 7-DEV/Horizon (upper/lower former); Folders — DEV/V50.; MAILROOM EQUIPMENT: Counter Stackers — HL/Monitor, Id/Marathoner; Inserters & Stuffers — GMA/SLS 1000 8:1; Tying Machines — Ace/50, Power Strap/PSN-6; Wrapping Singles — Mailroom Control System Id/Conveyors, Id/Bottom wrap, Id/Truckloaders.; BUSINESS EQUIPMENT: HP/927LX BUSINESS SOFTWARE: CJ/AIM 5.01, CIS 4.01, GL, AP CLASSIFIED EQUIPMENT: Hardware — CText, 12-PC; Printers — APP/Mac LaserWriter Plus; CLASSIFIED SOFTWARE: CText 2.1. DISPLAY EQUIPMENT: Hardware — IBM/486 fileserver, APP/Mac; Printers — V/6000; DISPLAY SOFTWARELayout Software — 8-APP/Mac network. EDITORIAL EQUIPMENT: Hardware — HI; Printers — APP/Mac 810, V/6000. PRODUCTION EQUIPMENT: Hardware — 1-APP/Mac LaserWriter NTX, 1-V/VT-600; Cameras — SCREEN; Scanners — 1-APP/Mac PRODUCTION SOFTWARE: HI/8900.

VALLEJO

VALLEJO TIMES-HERALD

420 Virginia St, Ste 2A, Vallejo, Calif., 94590-6018, Solano; gen tel (707) 644-1141; adv tel (707) 453-8178; ed tel (707) 644-1141; gen fax (707) 553-6851; adv fax (707) 553-6851; ed fax (707) 553-6851; gen/nat adv e-mail sgilroy@timesheraldonline.com; disp adv e-mail dsheely@bayareanewsgroup.com; class adv e-mailsally@thereporter.com; ed e-mail jbungart@timesheraldonline.com; web site www.timesheraldonline.com

Group: Digital First Media
Published: Tues, Wed, Thur, Fri, Sat, Sun
Weekday Frequency: m
Saturday Frequency: m
Circulation: 13,580; 13,199(sat); 13,777(sun)
Last Audit: AAM September 30, 2009
Advertising Rate (weekday/saturday): Open inch rate $20.00
Advertising Rate (sunday): Open inch rate $21.00
News services: AP, SHNS, McClatchy, Bay City News. **Established:** 1875
Own Printing Facility?: Yes
Commercial Printers?: No
Special Editions: Baseball Preview (Apr); I Do-Bridal (Feb); Super Bowl (Jan); Fremont Art & Wine Festival (Jul); Daytrips (May); California Home (Monthly); Grand National Rodeo-Cow Palace (Oct); NFL Preview (Sept).
Special Weekly Sections: Technology (Mon); Life (Tue); Food & Wine (Wed); Eye (Thur); Life (Fri); Home & Garden, Real Estate (Sat); Business, Lifestyle, Travel, TV (Sun)
Syndicated Publications: Relish (Monthly); USA WEEKEND Magazine (S); American Profile (Weekly).
Digital Platform - Mobile: Apple, Android
Digital Platform - Tablet: Apple iOS, Kindle
Pub.....................Jim Gleim
Classified Mgr.....................Sally Schulz
Adv. Dir.....................Matt Miller
Community Ed.....................Richard Freedman
Pre Press Mgr.....................Lisa Lerseth
VP, Sales....................Hernan Ponce
Mng. Ed.....................Jack Bungart
Market Information: TMC.
Mechanical Available: Offset; Black and 3 ROP colors; insert accepted; page cutoffs - 21 1/2.
Mechanical Specifications: Type page 12 x 21 1/2; E - 6 cols, 2, 1/8 between; A - 6 cols, 2, 1/8 between; C - 10 cols, 1 1/8, 3/16 between.
Areas Served: 94590, 94591, 94510
Delivery Method: Newsstand, Carrier, RacksEquipment & Software: PRESSROOM EQUIPMENT: Lines — 13-G/Urbanite, 1-1986; Press Drive — 2-GE/200 LP; Folders — 1-G/900 Series; Reels & Stands — 2; MAILROOM EQUIPMENT: Counter Stackers — 3-QWI/350; Inserters & Stuffers — 2-MM/227, 1/MM; Tying Machines — 1-/OVL, 2-/Power Strap; Address Machine — 1-/Ch.; BUSINESS EQUIPMENT: 1-HP/3000-LX, ALR/Unix BUSINESS SOFTWARE: CJ, Unix/SCO, Progress CLASSIFIED EQUIPMENT: Hardware — APP/Mac; Printers — Lexmark/Optra T; CLASSIFIED SOFTWARE: Baseview. DISPLAY EQUIPMENT: Hardware — APP/Mac; Printers — APP/Mac LaserWriter 8500, 3-APP/Mac LaserWriter 16-600; DISPLAY SOFTWAREAd Make-up Applications — Multi-Ad/Creator 3.8; Layout Software — Page Director/ALS. EDITORIAL EQUIPMENT: Hardware — APP/MacPrinters — APP/Mac 8500, APP/Mac 16-600 EDITORIAL SOFTWARE: Baseview. PRODUCTION EQUIPMENT: Hardware — 2-Nu, Devotec 20; Cameras — 1-C/A2024; Scanners — Polaroid/SprintScan 35, LaCie/Silverscanner III PRODUCTION SOFTWARE: Baseview.

VICTORVILLE

DAILY PRESS

13891 Park Ave, Victorville, Calif., 92392-2435, San Bernardino; gen tel (760) 241-7744; adv tel (760) 951-6288; ed tel (760) 951-6270; gen fax (760) 241-7145; adv fax (760) 241-7145; ed fax (760) 241-7145; gen/nat adv e-mail rlipscomb@vvdailypress.com; disp adv e-mail acallahan@vvdailypress.com; class adv e-mailacallahan@vvdailypress.com; ed e-mail DKeck@vvdailypress.com; web site www.vvdailypress.com

Group: New Media Investment Group
Published: Mon, Tues, Wed, Thur, Fri, Sat, Sun
Weekday Frequency: m
Saturday Frequency: m
Circulation: 13,120; 13,120(sat); 16,989(sun)
Last Audit: CAC December 31, 2016
Advertising Rate (weekday/saturday): Open inch rate $40
News services: 1937
Nat'l/Majors., Adv.....................Leslie Poe
Online Coordinator....................Bryan Kawasaki
Ed.....................Steve Hunt
Adv. Director....................Angie Callahan
Classified Supervisor....................Janet Baldwin
Pub.....................Donnie Welch

DESERT DISPATCH

13891 Park Ave, Victorville, Calif., 92392-2435, San Bernardino; gen tel (760) 256-2257; adv tel (760) 256-2257; ed tel (760) 256-2257; gen fax (760) 256-0685; adv fax (760) 256-0685; ed fax (760) 256-0685; gen/nat adv e-mail acallahan@vvdailypress.com; disp adv e-mail acallahan@vvdailypress.com; class adv e-mailblint@desertdispatch.com; ed e-mail editorial@desertdispatch.com; web site www.desertdispatch.com

Group: LMG National Publishing, Inc.
Published: Mon, Tues, Wed, Thur, Fri, Sat
Weekday Frequency: m
Saturday Frequency: m
Circulation: 1,862; 1,862(sat)
Last Audit: CAC March 31, 2015
Advertising Rate (weekday/saturday): Open inch rate $40
News services: AP. **Established:** 1910
Own Printing Facility?: Yes
Special Editions: Exploring Barstow (Apr); Main St. USA (Aug); Letters to Santa (Dec); Presidents' Day (Feb); Gettysburg Address (Jan); Declaration of Independence (Jul); Parade of Homes (Jun); Battle Colors (Mar); Memorial Day (May); Veterans Day (Nov); Parade of Homes (Oct)
Special Weekly Sections: Real Estate (Fri); Business Page (Mon); Food (Wed).
Syndicated Publications: Weekender Magazine (Fri); On TV (S).
Pub.....................Al Frattura
Ed.....................Steve Hunt
Adv. Dir.....................Bea Lint
Women's Ed.....................Kay Lavato
Mgmt. Info Servs. Mgr.....................Josh Brunton
Online Mgr.....................David Schrimpf
Prodn. Mgr., Composing....................Harry Pontius
Circ. Dir.....................Jackie Parsons
Sports Ed.....................Laura McCusker
City Ed.....................Mike Lamb
Market Information: ADS.
Mechanical Available: Web Offset; Black and 3 ROP colors; insert accepted; page cutoffs - 21 1/2.
Mechanical Specifications: Type page 14 x 22 3/4; E - 6 cols, 2 1/16, 1/8 between; A - 6 cols, 2 1/16, 1/8 between; C - 9 cols, 1 1/3, 1/8 between.
Areas Served: Barstow
Delivery Method: Mail, Newsstand, Carrier, RacksEquipment & Software: BUSINESS SOFTWARE: HPBS CLASSIFIED EQUIPMENT: Printers — TI/Omni800; CLASSIFIED SOFTWARE: Baseview. DISPLAY SOFTWAREAd Make-up Applications — QPS/QuarkXPress, Aldus/PageMaker, Aldus/FreeHand, Claris/MacDraw; Layout Software — APP/Mac, Baseview. EDITORIAL EQUIPMENT: Hardware — Software Baseview, QPS/QuarkXPress. PRODUCTION EQUIPMENT: Hardware — Baseview, QPS/QuarkXPress.
Note: The Barstow Desert Dispatch (mS) has a combination rate of $46.00 with the Victorville Daily Press (mS). The two papers publish a combined Sunday edition, the Press-Dispatch; the combination rate for the Press-Dispatch is $52.00. Individual newspaper rate

VISALIA

TULARE ADVANCE-REGISTER

330 N West St, Visalia, Calif., 93291-6010, Tulare; gen tel 559-735-3200; adv tel (559) 735-3231; ed tel (559) 735-3277; gen fax 559-733-0826; adv fax (559) 735-3396; ed fax (559) 735-3399; gen/nat adv e-mail dygarcia@visaliatimesdelta.com; disp adv e-mail dygarcia@visaliatimesdelta.com; class adv e-maildygarcia@visaliatimesdelta.com; ed e-mail dhayes2@visaliatimesdelta.com; web site www.tulareadvanceregister.com

Group: Gannett
Published: Mon, Tues, Wed, Thur, Fri, Sat
Weekday Frequency: m
Saturday Frequency: m
Circulation: 11,868; 14,935(sat)
Last Audit: AAM September 30, 2014
Advertising Rate (weekday/saturday): Open inch rate $54.09 (Mon-Fri); $60.31 (Sat)
News services: 1882

Commercial Printers?: Yes
Special Editions: Health & Fitness (Jan);World AG Expo (Feb); Job Fair (Apr); Health & Fitness (Apr); Living Here (May); Medical Directory (June); Health & Fitness (July); Tulare County Fair (Sept); Kids Fest (Nov); Get Fit (Dec); Real Estate Plus (Semi-monthly)
Special Weekly Sections: Health, Agriculture (Mon); Best Food, Grocery (Wed); Home (Thur); Choices, Entertainment, Auto (Fri); Real Estate, TV (Sat)
Pres./Pub. .... Paula Goudreau
Circ. Mgr. .... Theresa Simpson
Regional Publisher .... Karen Ferguson
Exec. Ed. .... Silas Lyons
Areas Served: 93274, 93277
Delivery Method: Mail, Newsstand, Carrier, Racks

VISALIA TIMES-DELTA

330 N West St, Visalia, Calif., 93291-6010, Tulare; gen tel (559) 735-3200; adv tel (559) 735-3231; ed tel (559) 735-3277; gen fax (559) 733-0826; adv fax (559) 735-3396; ed fax (559) 735-3399; gen/nat adv e-mail publisher@visaliatimesdelta.com; disp adv e-mail retail@visaliatimesdelta.com; class adv e-mailclassified@visaliatimesdelta.com; ed e-mail news@visaliatimesdelta.com; web site www.visaliatimesdelta.com - 1,174,358(views) 188,553(visitors); web site 2 m.visaliatimesdelta.com - 188,553(views) 23,623(visitors)
Group: Gannett
Published: Mon, Tues, Wed, Thur, Fri, Sat, Sun
Weekday Frequency: m
Saturday Frequency: m
Circulation: 11,646; 13,499(sat); 195(sun)
Last Audit: AAM March 31, 2017
Advertising Rate (weekday/saturday): Open inch rate $54.09 (Mon-Fri); $60.31 (Sat)
Online Advertising Rate: run-of-site:
medium rectangle (300x250) - $10 CPM
leaderboard (728x90) - $10 CPM
half page ad (300x600) - $15 CPM
skyscraper (160x600) - $10 CPM
News services: AP, GNS, NYT, TMS. **Established:** 1859
Own Printing Facility?: Yes
Commercial Printers?: Yes
Special Editions: Health & Fitness (Jan); Health & Fitness (Apr); Living Here (May); Medical Directory (June); Health & Fitness (July); Tulare County Fair (Sept); Real Estate Plus (Semi-monthly)
Special Weekly Sections: Health, Agriculture (Mon); Best Food, Grocery (Wed); Home (Thur); Choices, Entertainment, Auto (Fri); Real Estate, TV (Sat)
Syndicated Publications: Vista (Mon/1x month); USA Weekend(Sat).
Digital Platform - Mobile: Apple, Android
Digital Platform - Tablet: Apple iOS, Android
Pres./Pub. .... Paula Goudreau
City Ed. .... Jim Houck
Prodn. Mgr., Opns. .... David Sutton
Daily Ed. .... Melinda Morales
Adv. Dir. .... Jimmy Fryar
Circ. Sales/Opns. Mgr. .... Michael Skrocki
Media Group Rep. .... Theresa Simpson
VP Finance .... Mari Benko Wylie
Regional Publisher .... Karen Ferguson
Advert Mgr .... Trey Dean
News Ed .... Eric Woomer
Exec. Ed. .... Silas Lyons
Market Information: Split run; TMC.
Mechanical Available: Offset; Black and 3 ROP colors; insert accepted - Poly Bags; page cutoffs - 22.
Mechanical Specifications: .
Areas Served: 93291, 93292, 93277, 93274, 93235, 93221, 93223, 93227, 93247, 93271, 93272, 93286, 93618
Delivery Method: Mail, Newsstand, Carrier, RacksEquipment & Software: PRESSROOM EQUIPMENT: Lines — 10-G/Urbanite 1986; MAILROOM EQUIPMENT: Counter Stackers — 1-QWI/1000, 1-HI/RS25, 1-G/Overstacker, 1-HI/RS25; Inserters & Stuffers — 1-HI/848; Tying Machines - 2/MLN, 1-/MLN; Wrapping Singles — 1-/QWI; Address Machine — 1-/Ch;

WALNUT CREEK

EAST BAY TIMES

175 Lennon Ln Ste 100, Suite 100, Walnut Creek, Calif., 94598-2466, Contra Costa; gen tel (925) 935-2525 ; adv tel (925) 779-7120; ed tel (925) 943-8235; gen fax 925-706-2305; adv fax (925) 754-9483; ed fax (925) 706-2305; gen/nat adv e-mail ccnnewsrelease@bayareanewsgroup.com.; disp adv e-mail rsimmonds@bayareanewsgroup.com; class adv e-mailcctclassifieds@bayareanewsgroup.com; ed e-mail dhatfield@bayareanewsgroup.com; web site www.eastbaytimes.com
Group: Digital First Media
Published: Mon, Tues, Wed, Thur, Fri, Sat, Sun
Weekday Frequency: m
Saturday Frequency: m
Circulation: 113,068; 102,592(sat); 135,131(sun)
Last Audit: AAM March 31, 2015
Advertising Rate (weekday/saturday): Open inch rate $127
Advertising Rate (sunday): Open inch rate $140
News services: AP, LAT-WP, NYT, States News Service, McClatchy. **Established:** 2005
Own Printing Facility?: Yes
Commercial Printers?: Yes
Syndicated Publications: Bloomberg Financial (S).
Digital Platform - Mobile: Apple
Digital Platform - Tablet: Apple iOS
Pres./Pub. .... Sharon Ryan
Exec. Ed. .... Neil Chase
Mng. Ed. .... Keith Randall
Exec. Asst. to the Ed. .... Theresa Martinez
Exec. Asst. .... Veronia Vargas
AME, Visual Journalism .... Sarah Dussault
Market Information: ADS; TMC; Zoned editions.
Mechanical Available: Offset; Black and 3 ROP colors; insert accepted - all; page cutoffs - 22 3/4.
Mechanical Specifications: Type page 13 x 21 1/2; E - 6 cols, 2 1/16, 1/8 between; A - 6 cols, 2 1/16, 1/8 between; C - 10 cols, 1 1/4, 1/16 between.
Areas Served: Eastern part of Contra Costa County: Antioch, Pittsburg, Brentwood, Oakley, Discovery Bay, Bay Point, Bryon, Rio Vista, Knightsen, and Bethel Island.
Delivery Method: Mail, Carrier, RacksEquipment & Software: CLASSIFIED EQUIPMENT: Hardware — SII.; DISPLAY SOFTWARELayout Software — SCS/Layout 8000. EDITORIAL EQUIPMENT: Hardware — AT/9000, 3-IBM/21-IBM/PC, 5-RSK/TRS 100.
Note: Contra Costa Newspapers daily group includes the Richmond West County Times (mS), Pleasanton Valley Times (mS) and Walnut Creek Contra Costa Times (mS). The group combination rates are $228.00(d) and $254.00(S). Individual newspaper rates not made availab

WATSONVILLE

REGISTER-PAJARONIAN

100 Westridge Dr, Watsonville, Calif., 95076-6602, Santa Cruz; gen tel (831) 761-7300; adv tel (831) 761-7351; ed tel (831) 761-7322; gen fax (831) 722-8386; adv fax (831) 722-8386; ed fax (831) 761-7338; gen/nat adv e-mail businessoffice@register-pajaronian.com; disp adv e-mail advertising@register-pajaronian.com; ed e-mail newsroom@register-pajaronian.com; web site www.register-pajaronian.com - 107,596(views) 34,558(visitors)
Group: News Media Corp.
Published: Tues, Wed, Thur, Fri, Sat
Weekday Frequency: e
Saturday Frequency: e
Circulation: 5,153; 5,603(sat)
Last Audit: Sworn/Estimate/Non-Audited September 30, 2017
Newspaper Reps: John Bartlett
Advertising Rate (weekday/saturday): Open inch rate $28.75
News services: AP, SHNS. **Established:** 1868
Own Printing Facility?: No
Commercial Printers?: No
Special Editions: Home Improvement (Monthly); Progress (Oct).
Special Weekly Sections: Real Estate (Fri); Education (Sat); Business (Thur); Best Food Day (Tues).
Syndicated Publications: TV Weekly (Sat).
Controller .... Michael Rand
Pub. .... John Bartlett
Ad. Sales .... Allison Stenberg
Mng. Ed. .... Erik Chaloub
General Manager .... Amy Bartlett
Pub. .... Jeanie Johnson
Mechanical Available: Offset; Black and 3 ROP colors; insert accepted; page cutoffs - 22 3/4.
Mechanical Specifications: Type page 13 x 21; E - 6 cols, 2 1/16, 1/8 between; A - 6 cols, 2 1/16, 1/8 between; C - 9 cols, 1 3/8, 1/16 between.
Areas Served: 95076
Delivery Method: Mail, Newsstand, RacksEquipment & Software: MAILROOM EQUIPMENT: Tying Machines — 1/MLN.; BUSINESS EQUIPMENT: INSI CLASSIFIED EQUIPMENT: Hardware — 4-SII.; DISPLAY SOFTWARELayout Software — 2-COM. EDITORIAL EQUIPMENT: Hardware — 26-SII/5-RSK/TRS 80 model 100 remote terminal. PRODUCTION EQUIPMENT: Hardware — 2-COM/Videosetter, 2-COM/Advantage; Cameras — 1-C/Spartan II. CIRCULATION EQUIPMENT: PC CIRCULATION SOFTWARInterlink

WOODLAND

THE DAILY DEMOCRAT

711 Main St, Woodland, Calif., 95695-3406, Yolo; gen tel (530) 662-5421; adv tel (707) 453-8138; ed tel (530) 406-6230; gen fax (530) 406-6260; adv fax (530) 406-6260; ed fax (530) 406-6262; gen/nat adv e-mail news@dailydemocrat.com; disp adv e-mail aperkes@dailydemocrat.com; class adv e-mailclassifieds@dailydemocrat.com; ed e-mail news@dailydemocrat.com; web site www.dailydemocrat.com
Group: Digital First Media
Published: Tues, Wed, Thur, Fri, Sat, Sun
Weekday Frequency: m
Saturday Frequency: m
Circulation: 6,904; 6,904(sat); 7,179(sun)
Last Audit: AAM June 30, 2015
Advertising Rate (weekday/saturday): Open inch rate $24.24
Advertising Rate (sunday): Open inch rate $24.24
News services: AP, NYT, TMS. **Established:** 1857
Special Editions: Home & Garden (Apr); Childcare Directory (Aug); Christmas Express (Dec); Bridal Tab (Feb); Ad Packages (Jan); Made in Woodland (Jul); Class (Graduation) (Jun); National Ag Tab Sun (Mar); National Police (May); Holiday Gift (Nov); National Cosmetology Mont
Special Weekly Sections: Best Food Day (Wed); Farm, Goodlife, Arts (Thur); Real Estate, Business, Finance, Entertainment, Auto (Fri); Religion (Sat)
Syndicated Publications: Relish (Monthly); USA WEEKEND Magazine (S); American Profile (Weekly).
Pub. .... Jim Gleim
Adv. Dir. .... Allison Perkes
Ed. .... Jim Smith
Sports Ed. .... Bruce Burton
Internet Mgr. .... James Price
Pre Press Mgr. .... Nancy Nusz
Market Information: TMC.
Mechanical Available: Offset; Black and 3 ROP colors; insert accepted; page cutoffs - 22 3/4.
Mechanical Specifications: Type page 13 x 21 1/2; E - 6 cols, 2 1/16, 1/8 between; A - 6 cols, 2 1/16, 1/8 between; C - 10 cols, 1 3/8, 1/16 between.Equipment & Software: PRESSROOM EQUIPMENT: Lines — 8-G/Community 1970; MAILROOM EQUIPMENT: Counter Stackers — 1/BG; Tying Machines — 1-/MLN.; BUSINESS EQUIPMENT: ALR/REVQ, 1-HP/3000-917LX CLASSIFIED EQUIPMENT: Printers — 1-TI/Omni 800; CLASSIFIED SOFTWARE: Baseview. DISPLAY EQUIPMENT: Hardware — 1-APP/Mac IIci, 1-APP/Mac IIcx, 1-APP/Power Mac 6100-66; Printers — 1-APP/Mac LaserWriter II, 1-HP/LaserJet; Other Hardware — 1-APP/Mac CD-Rom, 1-APP/Mac Scan DISPLAY SOFTWAREAd Make-up Applications — Multi-Ad; Layout Software — Baseview/ALS. EDITORIAL EQUIPMENT: Hardware — SII/APP/Mac IIcx; Printers — 1-TI/Omni 800, 1-APP/Mac LaserWriter NT. PRODUCTION EQUIPMENT: Hardware — 2-NewGen/Laser printers; Cameras — Acti/225.

WOODLAND HILLS

LOS ANGELES DAILY NEWS

21860 Burbank Blvd, Ste 200, Woodland Hills, Calif., 91367-7439, Los Angeles; gen tel (818) 713-3000; adv tel (818) 713-3000; ed tel (818) 713-3639; gen fax (818) 713-0058; adv fax (818) 713-0062; ed fax (818) 713-0058; gen/nat adv e-mail paul.ingegneri@langnews.com ; disp adv e-mail melene.alfonso@dailynews.com; class adv e-mailmelene.alfonso@dailynews.com ; ed e-mail dnmetro@dailynews.com; web site www.dailynews.com
Group: Southern California News Group
Digital First Media
Published: Mon, Tues, Wed, Thur, Fri, Sat, Sun
Weekday Frequency: m
Saturday Frequency: m
Circulation: 33,400; 35,792(sat); 58,530(sun)
Last Audit: AAM March 31, 2017
Advertising Rate (weekday/saturday): Mon-Wed: $45; Th, Fri: $64
Advertising Rate (sunday): $72
News services: AP, MCT, NYT, City News Service, McClatchy. **Established:** 1911
Special Weekly Sections: High School Football Special (in season) (Fri); So. Cal. Wheels (Mon); Real Estate (S); Real Estate (Sat); Best Food Day (Wed).
Syndicated Publications: Relish (Monthly); Access (S).
CFO .... Dan Scofield
Adv. Vice Pres. .... Melene Alfonso
Dir., Mktg./Pub. Rel. .... Bill Vanlaningham
Dir., Mktg. Research .... Liz Hamm
Exec. Ed. .... Frank Pine
Restaurant Critic .... Larry Lipson
Columnist .... Dennis McCarthy
Photo Dir. .... Dean Musgrove
Entertainment/Book Ed. .... Robert Lowman
Features Ed. .... Sharyn Betz
Pres. & Pub. .... Ron Hasse
Exec News Ed .... Brian Harr
Chief Rev. Officer .... Tom Kelly
Managing Ed., Digital Op. .... Toni Sciacqua
Opinion Ed. .... Jessica Keating
Exec. Sports Ed. .... Tom Moore
Asst. Managing Ed. .... Kimberly Guimarin
VP, HR .... Gloria Arango
Dig. News Dir. .... Jessica Davis
Market Information: ADS; Split run; TMC; Zoned editions.
Mechanical Available: Offset; Black and 4 ROP colors; insert accepted - product samples; page cutoffs - 22.
Mechanical Specifications: Type page 11 1/2 x 21; E - 6 cols, 1 13/16, 1/8 between; A - 6 cols, 1 13/16, 1/8 between; C - 10 cols, 1 1/16, 1/16 between.
Areas Served: 91367, 91364, 91306, 91311, 91316, 91324, 91344, 91352, 91360, 91361, 91407, 91411, 91601, 93063, 93536, 93551, 91355, 91201, 91501, 91401Equipment & Software: PRESSROOM EQUIPMENT: Lines — 11-G/Headliner Offset double width 1989; 11-G/Headliner Offset double width 1989; 11-G/Headliner Offset double width 1990; Folders — 6-G/3:2; Pasters —10-GH/DigitalReels & Stands — 30; MAILROOM EQUIPMENT: Counter Stackers — 14-HL/Monitor HT, 2-QWI/SJ400; Inserters & Stuffers — 2-HI/1472, 1-HI/1372, 1-GMA/SLS 1000; Tying Machines — 2-MLN/2A, 14/Power Strap/PSN, 2-OVL/Strapmaster, Si; Wrapping Singles — 13-HL/440 Bottom Wrap, 2-/Power Strap/Bottom; BUSINESS EQUIPMENT: HP/997 BUSINESS SOFTWARE: Geac CLASSIFIED EQUIPMENT: Hardware — Tandem/Server; CLASSIFIED SOFTWARE: SII. DISPLAY EQUIPMENT: Hardware — HP/997; Printers — HP/5SI; Other Hardware — 2-DEC/VAX 6610, 1-DEC/Alpha 1000 DISPLAY SOFTWAREAd Make-up Applications — Geac/Advertising 8.02; Layout Software — SCS/Layout 8000. EDITORIAL EQUIPMENT: Hardware — Tandem/Server/1-DEC/VAX 6620, 2-DEC/VAX 6610, 1-DEC/Alpha 1000

EDITORIAL SOFTWARE: SII. PRODUCTION EQUIPMENT: Hardware — 2-AU/APS-6-108, 1-KFM/Flat Express II, 4-AU/3850, 1-SCREEN/LD-281-Q, 2-Konica/K400, 2-Konica/K550, 20-LE/2120; Cameras — C/Spartan III; Scanners — 2-AU/3750, 2-AU/APS COM PRODUCTION SOFTWARE: DTI.
Note: The Los Angeles Newspaper Group includes the Long Beach Press-Telegram (mS), Los Angeles Daily News (mS), Ontario Inland Valley Daily Bulletin (mS), Pasadena Star-News (mS), Redlands Daily Facts (eS), San Bernardino County Sun (mS), San Gabriel Valley Tri

YREKA

SISKIYOU DAILY NEWS

309 S Broadway St, Yreka, Calif., 96097-2905, Siskiyou; gen tel (530) 842-5777; adv tel (530) 842-5777; ed tel (530) 842-5777; gen fax (530) 842-6787; adv fax (530) 842-6787; ed fax (530) 842-6787; gen/nat adv e-mail advertising@siskiyoudaily.com; disp adv e-mail advertising@siskiyoudaily.com; class adv e-mailcmurphy@siskiyoudaily.com; ed e-mail editor@siskiyoudaily.com; web site www.siskiyoudaily.com
Group: New Media Investment Group
Published: Mon, Tues, Wed, Thur, Fri
Weekday Frequency: e
Circulation: 5,554
Last Audit: Sworn/Estimate/Non-Audited September 30, 2017
Advertising Rate (weekday/saturday): Open inch rate $15.95
News services: AP. **Established:** 1859
Special Editions: Spring Car Care (Apr); Siskiyou Golden Fair (Aug); Year-End Review (Dec); Chamber Information Book (Jun); Progress (Mar); Holiday Gift Guide (Nov); Football Kick-off (Sept).
Special Weekly Sections: Best Food Day (Tue); TV (Wed)
Syndicated Publications: Siskiyou Spotlight Tab (Fri); Siskiyou County Properties (Real Estate) (Monthly); American Profile (Weekly).
Pub. .... Matt Guthrie
Bookkeeper/Purchasing Agent .... Pat Mills
Adv. Dir. .... David Nelmes
Circ. Mgr. .... Jean Smith
Mng. Ed. .... Mike Slizewski
Sports Ed. .... Dan Murphy
Managing Ed .... David Smith
Market Information: TMC.
Mechanical Available: Offset; Black and 3 ROP colors; insert accepted; page cutoffs - 22 3/4.
Mechanical Specifications: Type page 13 x 21 1/2; E - 6 cols, 2 1/16, 1/8 between; A - 6 cols, 2 1/16, 1/8 between; C - 8 cols, 1 1/2, 1/8 between.
Areas Served: Siskiyou County
Delivery Method: CarrierEquipment & Software: PRESSROOM EQUIPMENT: Lines — 6-G/Community single width 1980; Folders — 1-G/Community.; MAILROOM EQUIPMENT: Tying Machines — 1/Us; Address Machine — 1-/Wm.; BUSINESS EQUIPMENT: Pentium/PC BUSINESS SOFTWARE: Microsoft CLASSIFIED EQUIPMENT: Hardware — APP/Mac; Printers — APP/Mac LaserWriter, Dot Matrix; CLASSIFIED SOFTWARE: Baseview, QPS/QuarkXPress. DISPLAY EQUIPMENT: Hardware — APP/Mac; Printers — APP/Mac LaserWriter II, APP/Mac LaserWriter Pro 600; DISPLAY SOFTWAREAd Make-up Applications — APP/Mac, QPS/QuarkXPress; Layout Software — APP/Mac, QPS/QuarkXPress. EDITORIAL EQUIPMENT: Hardware — APP/Mac/HP/Scanner; Printers — APP/Mac LaserWriter Pro 600, APP/Mac LaserWriter Pro 630 EDITORIAL SOFTWARE: Baseview, QPS/QuarkXPress. PRODUCTION EQUIPMENT: Hardware — 2-APP/Mac LaserWriter II NTX, 1-COM/88, 1-COM/IV, APP/Mac LaserWriter Pro 600, APP/Mac LaserWriter Pro 630, PrePress/Panther Pro 46; Cameras — 1-SCREEN/Vertical PRODUCTION SOFTWARE: QPS/QuarkXPress 4.0.

COLORADO

ALAMOSA

VALLEY COURIER

2205 State Ave, Alamosa, Colo., 81101-3559, Alamosa; gen tel (719) 589-2553; adv tel (719) 589-6573; ed tel (719) 589-6573; gen fax (719) 589-6573; adv fax (719) 589-6573; ed fax (719) 589-6573; gen/nat adv e-mail ads@alamosanews.com; disp adv e-mail ads@alamosanews.com; class adv e-mailwantads@alamosanews.com; ed e-mail news@alamosanews.com; web site www.alamosanews.com
- 600,000(views) 50,000(visitors)
Group: News Media Corp.
Published: Tues, Wed, Thur, Fri, Sat
Weekday Frequency: m
Saturday Frequency: m
Circulation: 5,300; 5,500(sat)
Last Audit: Sworn/Estimate/Non-Audited October 1, 2017
Newspaper Reps: Colorado Press Association
Advertising Rate (weekday/saturday): Open inch rate $21 net
Advertising Rate (sunday): n/a
Online Advertising Rate: Flat rated- $89/week
News services: AP. **Established:** 1926
Own Printing Facility?: Yes
Commercial Printers?: Yes
Special Editions: Home Improvement (Apr) (Sept); Back-to-School (Aug); Christmas (Dec); Rodeo (Jul); Summer Lifestyle (May); Ski (Nov); Hunting (Sept); others too numerous to mention.
Special Weekly Sections: Western Living: Outdoors and Agriculture (Thur).
Digital Platform - Mobile: Apple, Android, Windows, Blackberry
Digital Platform - Tablet: Apple iOS, Android, Windows 7, Blackberry Tablet OS, Kindle, Nook, Kindle Fire
Publisher .... Keith R. Cerny
Circ. Mgr. .... Shasta Quintana
Editor .... Ruth Heide
Prodn. Foreman, Pressroom .... Vernon Trujillo
Sports Editor .... Stephen Jiron
Advertising Manager .... Debra Sowards-Cerny
advertising sales .... Steven Willis
Adv. sales .... Marco Garmendia
Market Information: San Luis Valley, CO
Mechanical Available: Offset; Black and 3 ROP colors; inserts accepted; page cutoffs - 21 1/2.
Mechanical Specifications: Type page 11 1/2 x 21 1/2; E - 6 cols, 1 13/16, 1/8 between; A - 6 cols, 1 13/16, 1/8 between; C - 8 cols, 1 1/3, 1/8 between.
Areas Served: 81101 81120 81123 81124 81125 81130 81131 81132 81133 81136 81140 81141 81144 81146 81148 81149 81151 81152 81154
Delivery Method: Mail, Newsstand, Carrier, RacksEquipment & Software: PRESSROOM EQUIPMENT: Lines — 6-G/Community.; Folders — 8-1988.; MAILROOM EQUIPMENT: Tying Machines — 1; BUSINESS EQUIPMENT: IBM/PC CLASSIFIED EQUIPMENT: Hardware — Mk, APP/Mac; Printers - APP/Mac; CLASSIFIED SOFTWARE: Mk. DISPLAY EQUIPMENT: Hardware — APP/Mac; Printers — APP/Mac LaserPrinter; Other Hardware — APP/Mac. DISPLAY SOFTWAREAd Make-up Applications — APP/Mac; EDITORIAL EQUIPMENT: Hardware — APP/Mac; Printers — 2-APP/Mac LaserPrinter EDITORIAL SOFTWARE: APP/Mac. PRODUCTION EQUIPMENT: Macintosh PRODUCTION SOFTWARE: Indesign, CS5.5 CIRCULATION EQUIPMENT: PC CIRCULATION SOFTWARInterlink

ASPEN

ASPEN DAILY NEWS

625 E Main St Unit 204, 2nd Floor, Aspen, Colo., 81611-2154, Pitkin; gen tel (970) 925-2220; adv tel (970) 925-2220; ed tel (970) 925-2220; gen fax (970) 925-6397; adv fax (970) 925-6397; ed fax (970) 925-6397; gen/nat adv e-mail david@aspendailynews.com; disp adv e-mail david@aspendailynews.com; class adv e-mailclassifieds@aspendailynews.com; ed e-mail letters@aspendailynews.com; web site www.aspendailynews.com
- 165,000(views) 18,000(visitors)
Group: Silver News, LLC
Published: Mon, Tues, Wed, Thur, Fri, Sat, Sun
Weekday Frequency: m
Saturday Frequency: m
Circulation: 12,500; 12,500(sat); 12,500(sun)
Last Audit: Sworn/Estimate/Non-Audited December 18, 2017
Advertising Rate (weekday/saturday): Open inch rate $8.50
News services: AP. **Established:** 1978
Own Printing Facility?: Yes
Commercial Printers?: Yes
Special Editions: Winter Guide (Dec); Winterskol (Jan); Summer Guide (Jun); Winternational (Mar); Spruce Up for Spring (May); 24 Hours of Aspen (Nov).
Special Weekly Sections: Time Out (A&E, Thur)
Digital Platform - Mobile: Apple, Android
Digital Platform - Tablet: Apple iOS, Android
Owner .... David N. Danforth
Bus. Mgr. .... Dawn Manges
Adv. Dir. .... Lynn Chaffier
Circ. Mgr. .... Rafael Perez
Mng. Ed. .... Curtis Wackerle
Ed. .... Carolyn Sackariason
Web/Assoc. Special Sections Ed. .... Damien Williamson
Mechanical Available: Offset Web; Black and 3 ROP colors; insert accepted - will contract to print inserts; page cutoffs - 14 1/2.
Mechanical Specifications: Type page 10 1/4 x 14; E - 4 cols, 2 7/16, 1/3 between; A - 6 cols, 1 1/2, 1/6 between; C - 6 cols, 1 1/2, 1/6 between.
Areas Served: Roaring Fork Valley (CO)
Delivery Method: RacksEquipment & Software: PRESSROOM EQUIPMENT: Lines — 5-G/Community; Folders — G/Community.; BUSINESS EQUIPMENT: APP/Mac SE30, APP/Mac Classic BUSINESS SOFTWARE: Proprietary CLASSIFIED EQUIPMENT: Hardware — 2-APP/Mac LC III; Printers — GCC/SelectPress 600; CLASSIFIED SOFTWARE: Baseview/Ad Manager Pro. DISPLAY EQUIPMENT: Hardware — 1-APP/Power Mac; Printers — APP/Mac LaserWriter 360; DISPLAY SOFTWAREAd Make-up Applications — QPS/QuarkXPress 3.3; Layout Software — QPS. EDITORIAL EQUIPMENT: Hardware — 4-APP/Mac Quadra 610/8-APP/Mac LC III; Printers — 2-APP/Mac LaserWriter, GCC/SelectPress 600 EDITORIAL SOFTWARE: QPS/QuarkXPress 3.3. PRODUCTION EQUIPMENT: Hardware — Adobe/Photoshop 3.0, 3-COM/Editwriter 7500, APP/Mac IIcx, APP/Mac LaserWriter II NTX; Cameras — AG/Repromaster 1100, SCREEN/Auto Companica; Scanners — 2-APP/Mac IIcx, Umax/Vista T630 PRODUCTION SOFTWARE: QPS/QuarkXPress 3.3.

THE ASPEN TIMES

314 E Hyman Ave, Aspen, Colo., 81611-1918, Pitkin; gen tel (970) 925-3414; adv tel (925) 925-9937; ed tel (970) 925-3414; gen fax (970) 925-6240; adv fax (970) 925-5647; ed fax (970) 925-6240; gen/nat adv e-mail gunilla@aspentimes.com; disp adv e-mail ahewitt@aspentimes.com; class adv e-mailclassifieds@cmnm.org; ed e-mail rcarroll@aspentimes.com; web site www.aspentimes.com
- 3,575,778(views) 1,651,360(visitors)
Group: Swift Communications, Inc.
Published: Mon, Tues, Wed, Thur, Fri, Sat, Sun
Weekday Frequency: m
Saturday Frequency: m
Circulation: 11,000; 11,000(sat)
Last Audit: Sworn/Estimate/Non-Audited September 30, 2017
Advertising Rate (weekday/saturday): Open inch rate $11.00
News services: AP, LAT-WP, NYT. **Established:** 1881
Special Editions: Restaurant Guide (Dec); Style (Jun).
Syndicated Publications: Weekend (Fri).
Pub. .... Jenna Weatherred
Bus. Mgr. .... Dottie Wolcott
Adv. Dir. .... Gunilla Asher
Circ. Mgr. .... Bob Lombardi
Mng. Ed. .... Rick Carroll
Arts Ed. .... Stewart Oksenhorn
Sports Ed. .... Dale Strode
Ad. Dir. .... David Laughren
Gen. Mgr. .... Samantha Johnston
Market Information: ADS; TMC.
Mechanical Available: Offset; Black and ROP colors; insert accepted; page cutoffs - 16.
Mechanical Specifications: Type page 11 1/2 x 17 1/4; E - 5 cols, 1 9/10, 1/6 between; A - 5 cols, 1 9/10, 1/6 between; C - 5 cols, 1 9/10, 1/6 between.
Areas Served: Pitkin County (CO)
Equipment & Software: PRESSROOM EQUIPMENT: Lines — 5-WPC/Web Leader; Reels & Stands — 5; MAILROOM EQUIPMENT: Counter Stackers — BG; Tying Machines — Bu.; BUSINESS EQUIPMENT: Osicom CLASSIFIED EQUIPMENT: Hardware — 2-APP/Mac vx, APP/Mac LC II; CLASSIFIED SOFTWARE: Baseview. DISPLAY EQUIPMENT: Hardware — APP/Mac; DISPLAY SOFTWAREAd Make-up Applications — Baseview; Layout Software — 2-APP/Mac ci. EDITORIAL EQUIPMENT: Hardware — 12-APP/Mac LC II, APP/Mac ci; Printers — LaserMaster/, AG EDITORIAL SOFTWARE: Baseview. PRODUCTION EQUIPMENT: Hardware — 3-APP/Mac LaserPrinter, Pre Press/Panther Imagesetter; Cameras — LE.

AVON

VAIL DAILY

40780 US Hwy 6 & 24, Avon, Colo., 81620, Eagle; gen tel (970) 949-0555; adv tel (970) 949-0555; ed tel (970) 949-0555; gen fax (970) 949-7096; adv fax (970) 949-7094; ed fax (970) 949-7096; gen/nat adv e-mail pconnolly@vaildaily.com; disp adv e-mail pconnolly@vaildaily.com; class adv e-mailclassifieds@cmnm.org; ed e-mail estoner@vaildaily.com; web site www.vaildaily.com
- 3,302,480(views) 2,209,634(visitors)
Group: Swift Communications, Inc.
Published: Mon, Tues, Wed, Thur, Fri, Sat, Sun
Weekday Frequency: m
Saturday Frequency: m
Circulation: 10,525; 10,525(sat); 9,332(sun)
Last Audit: Sworn/Estimate/Non-Audited September 30, 2017
Advertising Rate (weekday/saturday): Open inch rate $18.43
News services: AP. **Established:** 1981
Special Editions: Taste of Vail (Apr); Rocky Mtn. Wedding Guide (Feb); Best of the Vail Valley (Jan); Eagle County Rodeo Program (Jul); High Country Homestyle (Jun); Vail Valley Summertime (May); Vail Valley Holiday Guide (Nov).
Special Weekly Sections: Mountain Homes & Properties Real Estate (S); Religion (Sat); Education (Thur); The Marketplace (Tues); Food & Wine (Wed).
Mng. Ed. .... Edward Stoner
Mktg. Dir. .... Mark Bricklin
Bus. Ed. .... Scott Miller
Sports Ed. .... Chris Freud
Prod. Mgr., Press .... Jim Hemig
Prodn. Mgr., Pre Press .... Tommy Kubitsky
Nat'l Acct. Mgr. .... Sandy Sandberg
Adv. Dir. .... Patrick Connolly
Circ. Mgr. .... Wren Wertin
Mechanical Available: Offset; Black and 3 ROP colors; insert accepted; page cutoffs - 22 3/4.
Mechanical Specifications: Type page 10 2/3 x 16; E - 5 cols, 2, 1/6 between; A - 5 cols, 2, 1/6 between; C - 7 cols, 1 2/5, 1/6 between.
Areas Served: Vail, Lionshead, Beaver Creek, Arrowhead, Ski Cooper & surrounding communities
Equipment & Software: PRESSROOM EQUIPMENT: Lines — 10-KP/News King 1985; Folders — 1-KP/KJ-8.; MAILROOM EQUIPMENT: Counter Stackers — HL Monitors; Inserters & Stuffers — MM; Tying Machines — MLN.; BUSINESS EQUIPMENT: PBS CLASSIFIED EQUIPMENT:

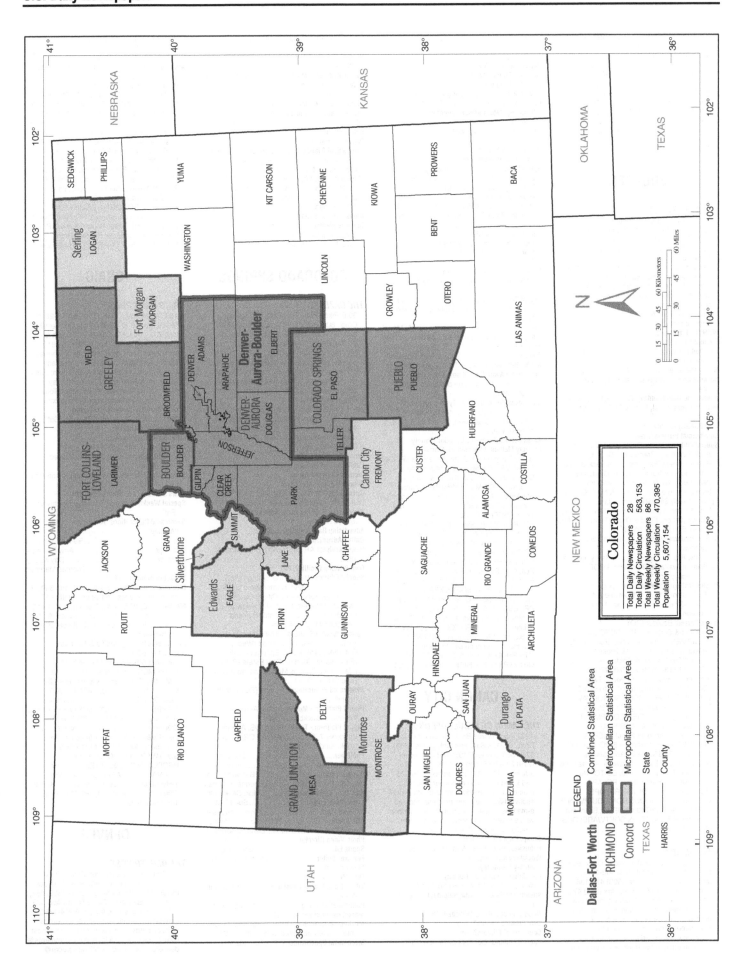

LEGEND

Dallas-Fort Worth Combined Statistical Area
RICHMOND Metropolitan Statistical Area
Concord Micropolitan Statistical Area
TEXAS State
HARRIS County

Colorado

Total Daily Newspapers	28
Total Daily Circulation	563,153
Total Weekly Newspapers	86
Total Weekly Circulation	470,395
Population	5,607,154

Hardware — PC, APP/Mac; Printers — HP; CLASSIFIED SOFTWARE: Baseview. DISPLAY EQUIPMENT: Hardware — APP/ Mac; Printers — APP/Mac LaserPrinter, HP; DISPLAY SOFTWAREAd Make-up Applications — QPS/QuarkXPress, Adobe.; EDITORIAL EQUIPMENT: Hardware — APP/ Mac; Printers — APP/Mac LaserWriter EDITORIAL SOFTWARE: Baseview. PRODUCTION EQUIPMENT: Hardware — Pre Press/Panther Plus; Cameras — AG; Scanners — HP PRODUCTION SOFTWARE: MEI/ALS 2.0.

BOULDER

COLORADO DAILY

2500 55th St, Ste. 210, Boulder, Colo., 80301, Boulder; gen tel (303) 473-1414; adv tel (303) 473-1414; ed tel (303) 473-1414; gen fax 3034447971; adv fax (303) 444-7971; ed fax (303) 444-7971; gen/nat adv e-mail johnsonk@dailycamera.com; disp adv e-mail johnsonk@dailycamera.com; class adv e-mailjohnsonk@dailycamera.com; ed e-mail johnsonk@dailycamera.com; web site www.coloradodaily.com

Group: Digital First Media
Published: Mon, Tues, Wed, Thur, Fri
Weekday Frequency: m
Circulation: 15,329
Last Audit: Sworn/Estimate/Non-Audited September 1, 2017
Newspaper Reps: johnsonk@dailycamera.com
Advertising Rate (weekday/saturday): Open inch rate $27.00
Advertising Rate (sunday): Open inch rate $35.00
News services: CSM, MCT, UPI. **Established:** 1892
Own Printing Facility?: Yes
Commercial Printers?: Yes
Special Editions: Menu Guide (Apr); Welcome Back Fall (Aug); Graduation (Dec); CU & Boulder's Best (Feb); Welcome Back Spring (Jan); Boulder Summer (Jun); Graduation (May); Boulder Winter (Oct); Stadium Stampede (6 editions in Oct & Nov) (Other).
Special Weekly Sections: Real Estate, Entertainment (Fri); Our Town (Mon); Visitors' Edition (Other); Food & Drink (Thur); The Arts (Tues); Body & Soul (Wed).
Digital Platform - Mobile: Apple, Android, Windows
Nat'l Adv. Rep. ....Kathy Johnson
Mechanical Available: Black and 3 ROP colors; insert accepted.
Mechanical Specifications: Type page 11 1/2 x 15; E - 6 cols, 1 1/2, 3/8 between; A - 6 cols, 1 1/2, 3/8 between; C - 8 cols, 1 1/4, 1/8 between.
Areas Served: Boulder (CO)
Equipment & Software: PRESSROOM EQUIPMENT: Lines — 8-G/Community 1972, 2-Dauphin/DGM 430 1998; Press Drive — Baldor/P36801410155; Folders — Rockwell/ SSC.; MAILROOM EQUIPMENT: Counter Stackers — BG/Count-O-Veyor; Tying Machines — Dynaric/RLM-1.; BUSINESS EQUIPMENT: PC BUSINESS SOFTWARE: Fake Brains-Advertising, Quick Books-Accounting CLASSIFIED EQUIPMENT: Hardware — 4-PC; CLASSIFIED SOFTWARE: Account Scout. DISPLAY EQUIPMENT: Hardware — 8-PC; DISPLAY SOFTWAREAd Make-up Applications — Account Scout; Layout Software — Baseview/ Managing Editor, Ad Force. EDITORIAL EQUIPMENT: Hardware — PC, APP/ Mac EDITORIAL SOFTWARE: QPS/ QuarkXPress. PRODUCTION EQUIPMENT: Hardware — Nu/FT40 V6 UPNS; Scanners — Scitex PRODUCTION SOFTWARE: QPS/ QuarkXPress.

DAILY CAMERA

2500 55th St, Ste 210, Boulder, Colo., 80301-5740, Boulder; gen tel (303) 442-1202; adv tel (303) 473-1400; ed tel (303) 473-1365; gen fax (303) 449-9358; adv fax (303) 473-1144; ed fax (303) 449-9358; gen/nat adv e-mail jstravolemos@prairiemountainmedia.com; disp adv e-mail stravolemosj@dailycamera.com; class adv e-mailjill@dailycamera.com; ed e-mail kaufmank@dailycamera.com; web site www.dailycamera.com
- 4,000,000(views) 1,478,939(visitors)

Group: Digital First Media
Published: Mon, Tues, Wed, Thur, Fri, Sat, Sun
Weekday Frequency: m
Saturday Frequency: m
Circulation: 20,043; 20,668(sat); 21,703(sun)
Last Audit: AAM September 30, 2016
Advertising Rate (weekday/saturday): Open inch rate $31.21
News services: AP, LAT-WP, NYT, SHNS. **Established:** 1890
Own Printing Facility?: No
Commercial Printers?: Yes
Special Editions: Summer Camping (Apr); Back-to-School (Aug); Holiday Guide (Dec); Wedding Guides (Feb); Home & Garden/ HGTV Mag. (Jul); Wedding Guides (Jun); Home & Gardens/HGTV Mag. (Mar); Bolder Boulder Race Guide (May); School Choice Guide (Nov); Voter's Guide (Oct).
Special Weekly Sections: Monday, Business Plus, Wednesday, Essentials, Friday, Friday Magazine and At Home, Sunday, Life and Style
Syndicated Publications: Parade (S).
Digital Platform - Mobile: Apple, Android, Blackberry
Digital Platform - Tablet: Apple iOS, Android, Windows 7, Blackberry Tablet OS, Kindle, Nook
Pub. ....Al Manzi
Mgr., Mktg./Promo./New Media.. Jill Stravolemos
Exec. Ed. .... Kevin Kaufman
City Ed. .... Matt Sebastian
Market Information: ADS; TMC; Zoned editions.
Mechanical Available: Offset; Black and 3 ROP colors; insert accepted - product samples; page cutoffs - 20.5 in
Mechanical Specifications: Type page 11 5/8 x 21 1/2; E - 6 cols, 1 5/6, 1/8 between; A - 6 cols, 1 5/6, 1/8 between; C - 9 cols, 1 1/16, 1/36 between.
Areas Served: Primarily Boulder County
Delivery Method: Newsstand, Carrier, RacksEquipment & Software: PRESSROOM EQUIPMENT: Lines — Outsourced to Denver MAN presses ; Reels & Stands — 5; MAILROOM EQUIPMENT: Counter Stackers — Outsourced to Denver production operation; BUSINESS EQUIPMENT: Sun/ Solaris BUSINESS SOFTWARE: PBS/ CM, PBS/AM, PeopleSoft AAP, AGL, PAY CLASSIFIED EQUIPMENT: Hardware — 2-Pentium/PC Servers, 18-Pentium/ PC Clients; HI/Ad Pag; CLASSIFIED SOFTWARE: HI/Ad Power. DISPLAY EQUIPMENT: Hardware — 2-Pentium/PC; Printers — HP/Laser 5si; Other Hardware — SCS. DISPLAY SOFTWAREAd Make-up Applications — Outsourced to Denver.. PPI; EDITORIAL EQUIPMENT: Hardware — Moving to Methode system/APP/Server; Printers — HP/5si EDITORIAL SOFTWARE: HI 3.5, HI. PRODUCTION EQUIPMENT: Hardware — Outsourced to Denver CTP PRODUCTION SOFTWARE: QPS/ QuarkXPress 6.5, HI/Newsmaker Pagination.

CANON CITY

THE CANON CITY DAILY RECORD

1202 Royal Gorge Blvd, Canon City, Colo., 81212-3836, Fremont; gen tel (719) 275-7565; adv tel (719) 275-5300; ed tel (719) 275-7565; gen fax (719) 275-1353; adv fax (719) 275-1353; ed fax (719) 275-1353; gen/nat adv e-mail kwurzbach@prairiemountainmedia.com; disp adv e-mail sschimpf@prairiemountainmedia.com; ed e-mail malcala@prairiemountainmedia.com; web site www.canoncitydailyrecord.com
- 500,000(views) 70,000(visitors)

Group: Digital First Media
Published: Mon, Tues, Wed, Thur, Fri, Sat
Weekday Frequency: m
Saturday Frequency: m
Circulation: 2,800; 2,800(sat)
Last Audit: AAM September 30, 2017
Advertising Rate (weekday/saturday): Open inch rate $15.00
News services: AP. **Established:** 1873
Own Printing Facility?: Yes
Commercial Printers?: Yes
Special Editions: Community Report (Progress Edition) (Apr); Bridal Guide (Feb); Real Estate Preview (Semi-monthly);
Special Weekly Sections: American Profile (Weekly).
Syndicated Publications: Relish (Monthly); USA WEEKEND Magazine (Sat); American Profile (Weekly).
Digital Platform - Mobile: Apple, Android
Digital Platform - Tablet: Apple iOS, Android
Ed. .... Michael Alcala
Pub./Gen. Mgr. .... Karl Wurzbach
Market Information: TMC.
Mechanical Available: Offset; Black and 3 ROP colors; insert accepted - single, broadsheet, tab; page cutoffs - 22 3/4.
Mechanical Specifications: Type page 10 1/2 x 21 1/2; E - 6 cols, 1 5/8, 1/8 between; A - 6 cols, 1 5/8, 1/8 between; C - 9 cols, 1 1/16, 1/8 between.
Areas Served: 81212
Delivery Method: Mail, Newsstand, CarrierEquipment & Software: DISPLAY EQUIPMENT: Printers — Sharp;

COLORADO SPRINGS

THE GAZETTE

30 E Pikes Peak Ave, Colorado Springs, Colo., 80903-1504, El Paso; gen tel (719) 632-5511; adv tel (719) 636-0306; ed tel (719) 636-0266; gen fax (719) 636-0118; adv fax (719) 476-4858; ed fax (719) 636-0202; gen/nat adv e-mail nicole.raphael@gazette.com; disp adv e-mail erik.carlson@gazette.com; class adv e-mailjulie.bland@gazette.com; ed e-mail opinion@gazette.com; web site www.gazette.com
- 4,700,000(views) 148,206(visitors); web site 2 www.coloradosprings.com - 430,000(views) 79,000(visitors); web site 3 www.outtherecolorado.com - 300,000(views) 25,000(visitors)

Group: Clarity Media
Published: Mon, Tues, Wed, Thur, Fri, Sat, Sun
Weekday Frequency: m
Saturday Frequency: m
Circulation: 42,934; 41,854(sat); 56,875(sun)
Last Audit: AAM September 30, 2017
Advertising Rate (weekday/saturday): Open inch rate $51.55
Advertising Rate (sunday): $62.88
Online Advertising Rate: $10
News services: AP, MCT/LAT-WP **Established:** 1872
Own Printing Facility?: No
Special Editions: Best of the Springs (Apr); Summer Fun (May), Homebuyers Guide, Prep Peak Performers, Dining Guide (Jun.), Parade of Homes, Football Preview (Aug); FYI Magazine (Sep.), WInter Fun and Celebrate Magazine (Nov.)
Special Weekly Sections: Family (Mon.), Health+Wellness (Tue.),Food (Wed.); Out There (Thu.); Go!, SpringsWheels (Fri.), Home+Garden, Real Estate (Sat.); Life+Travel, Springs Military Life, Your Career, Real Estate (Sun.)
Syndicated Publications: Parade (Sun.) Dash (monthly)
Digital Platform - Mobile: Apple, Android, Windows, Blackberry, Other
Digital Platform - Tablet: Apple iOS, Android, Windows 7, Blackberry Tablet OS, Kindle, Nook, Kindle Fire, Other
Publisher..Dan Steever
ManagingEditor .... Joanna Bean
Business Editor............................Barbara Cotter
Regional Director HR ....Katherine Florman
Adv. Dir., Sales Opns. .... Vicki Cederholm
Local News Editor .... Sue McMillin
Editorial Page Ed. ....Wayne Laugesen
A&E Editor.......................... Tracy Mobley-Martinez
Presentation Director .... Dena Rosenberry
Photo/Video Director.......................... Mark Reis
Sports Ed. .... Jim O'Connell
Features Editor .... Nathan Van Dyne
Michael Beach
Rich Williams
VP of IT and Digital Development......... Stephanie Weber
Political advertising .... Michael Greene
Market Information: ADS; TMC.
Mechanical Available: Offset; Black and 3 ROP colors; insert accepted; page cutoffs - 21"
Mechanical Specifications: 6 col broadsheet (Classified is 10) 1col: 1.72", 2 col: 3.6", 3 col: 5.5", 4 col: 7.36", 5 col: 9.24", 6 col: 11.12", Full: 6 col x 19.75", Dbltrk: 23.12" x 19.75"
Areas Served: El Paso, Pueblo, Fremont, Elbert, Teller, Douglas, Fremont counties.
Delivery Method: Carrier, RacksEquipment & Software: BUSINESS EQUIPMENT: HP-Compaq BUSINESS SOFTWARE: PBS-Circ. Hosted/Local PBS AdPlus CLASSIFIED EQUIPMENT: Hardware — HP-Compaq; Dell clients; Printers — Kyocera/Laser PrinterHP Laser printer; CLASSIFIED SOFTWARE: PBS AdPlus DISPLAY EQUIPMENT: Hardware — Sun/Servers; Printers — Kyocera/Laser Printer, Xerox, HP & Kyocera; Other Hardware — HP Plotters DISPLAY SOFTWAREAd Make-up Applications — DTI AdSpeed 7; Layout Software — PBS/ MediaPlus. EDITORIAL EQUIPMENT: Hardware — Sun/Servers, PCs/Dell Clients; Printers — HP/Laser Printer, Xerox/HP/ Kyocersa Color Laser Printer, Nikon/Digital EDITORIAL SOFTWARE: DTI NewsSpeed 7

CRAIG

CRAIG DAILY PRESS

466 Yampa Ave, Craig, Colo., 81625-2610, Moffat; gen tel (970) 824-7031; adv tel (970) 824-7031; ed tel (970) 824-7031; gen fax (970) 824-6810; adv fax (970) 824-6810; ed fax (970) 824-6810; gen/nat adv e-mail kbalfour@craigdailypress.com; disp adv e-mail kbalfour@craigdailypress.com; class adv e-mailveverard@SteamboatToday.com; ed e-mail lschlichtman@SteamboatToday.com; web site www.craigdailypress.com

Group: Swift Communications, Inc.
Published: Mon, Tues, Wed, Thur, Fri, Sat
Weekday Frequency: m
Saturday Frequency: m
Circulation: 3,400; 9,600(sat)
Last Audit: Sworn/Estimate/Non-Audited September 30, 2017
Advertising Rate (weekday/saturday): Open inch rate $10.19
News services: AP. **Established:** 1891
Special Weekly Sections: Saturday Northwest (Sat).
Syndicated Publications: American Profile (Weekly).
Pub...Renee Campbell
Circ. Mgr....................................... Amy Fontenot
Designer ....Day Kelsey
Ed... Thomas Martinez
Market Information: TMC.
Mechanical Available: Offset; Black and 3 ROP colors; insert accepted; page cutoffs - 17.
Mechanical Specifications: Type page 10 13/16 x 16; E - 5 cols, 2 1/16, 1/8 between; A - 5 cols, 2 1/16, 1/8 between; C - 5 cols, 2 1/16, 1/8 between.
Areas Served: Craig, Moffat & Rio Blanco Counties (CO)
Equipment & Software: MAILROOM EQUIPMENT: Tying Machines — 1/Bu, 1-MLN/ML2EE; Address Machine — 2-/ Wm.; BUSINESS EQUIPMENT: 1-ATT CLASSIFIED EQUIPMENT: Hardware — 1-APP/Mac II.; DISPLAY SOFTWARELayout Software — 2-APP/Mac II. EDITORIAL EQUIPMENT: Hardware — 6-APP/Mac II, 2-APP/Mac SE30, 1-APP/Mac IIci; Printers — Hyphen/600, HP/4MV EDITORIAL SOFTWARE: QPS/QuarkXPress. PRODUCTION EQUIPMENT: Hardware — 1-V/VT600, 1-APP/Mac LaserWriter, 1-Hyphen/Copal 600; Cameras — 1-K, Nat; Scanners — 1-Truvell, 1-APP/Mac Scanner, 1-HP/Scanner.

DENVER

THE DENVER POST

101 W Colfax Ave, Denver, Colo., 80202-5167, Denver; gen tel (303) 954-1010; adv tel (303) 892-2525 (class.); ed tel (303) 954-1201; gen fax (303) 954-1334; adv fax (303) 892-5243 (class.); ed fax (303) 954-1369; gen/nat adv e-mail jkittelson@denverpost.com; disp adv e-mail jkittelson@denverpost.com; class adv e-mailquestions-comments@denverpost.com; ed e-mail newsroom@

denverpost.com; web site www.denverpost.com
- 37,825,321(views) 7,167,139(visitors)
Group: Digital First Media
Published: Mon, Tues, Wed, Thur, Fri, Sat, Sun
Weekday Frequency: m
Saturday Frequency: m
Circulation: 285,027; 297,553(sat); 395,910(sun)
Last Audit: AAM March 31, 2015
Advertising Rate (weekday/saturday): Open inch rate $862.64 (M-F); $893.61 (Sat)
Advertising Rate (sunday): Open inch rate $1,055.07
News services: AP, NYT, LAT-WP, Bloomberg, McClatchy. **Established:** 1892
Own Printing Facility?: No
Commercial Printers?: Yes
Special Editions: The Deal
Going Green
National Western Stock Show
Home Show
Parade of Homes
Komen Race for the Cure
Denver Auto Show
Ski Expo
Syndicated Publications: Parade (S)
Color Comics (S)
TV (S)
USA Weekend (S)
Digital Platform - Mobile: Apple, Android
Digital Platform - Tablet: Apple iOS, Android, Blackberry Tablet OS, Kindle
Ed. .... Lee Ann Colacioppo
Editorial Librarian .... Vicki Makings
News Director .... Kevin Dale
Dir., News Ops .... Linda Shapley
ME, Presentation .... J. Damon Cain
AME-Photography .... Tim Rasmussen
Asst. Managing Ed. Sports .... Scott Monserud
Senior Ed. News .... Larry Ryckman
Dana Plewka
Geri Meireis
Jerry Grilly
Sr. VP. of Circ. .... William Reynolds
Pub. Chief Exec. Officer .... Mac Tully
Senior VP of Finance and Chief Financial Officer ... Michael Henry
VP of Adv. .... Christine Moser
Senior VP Pres, Cir. .... Bill Reynolds
Senior VP Pres., HR, Labor Relations Missy Miller
VP, Info. Tech. & Pre-Pub. .... Bob Kinney
VP Pres. of Dig. Sales .... Reid Wicoff
Senior Ed. for Photography & Multimedia .. Megan Lyden
Night Ed. .... Jim Bates
Editorial Ed. .... Chuck Plunkett
Market Information: TMC and Electronic Edition
Mechanical Available: Offset; Black and 3 ROP colors; insert accepted.
Mechanical Specifications: Type page 12 x 21; ROP 6 cols, 1.75, 1/8 between; Class: 10 cols, 1.06, 1/16 between.
Areas Served: Entire Colorado region
Delivery Method: Newsstand, CarrierEquipment & Software: PRESSROOM EQUIPMENT: Press Drive — 3, 2; Pasters —G/CT-45Reels & Stands — G/CT-45.; MAILROOM EQUIPMENT: Counter Stackers — 41/QWI; Inserters & Stuffers — Fg/Drum 5 Lines, 3-HI/13-72, 1-HI/14-72, 4-HI/630-23; Tying Machines — 23-/OVL, 23-/Power Strap, 15-/Sterling, 2-/Dynaric; Control System — Burt Technologies; Address Machine — Domi; CLASSIFIED EQUIPMENT: Hardware — Sun/450; CLASSIFIED SOFTWARE: AT, Enterprise 1.4. DISPLAY EQUIPMENT: Hardware — Compaq/NT Services, APP/Mac; Printers — HP/5SI, HP/4MV, HP/2500, Xante/8200, HP/1055, HP/855ON, Rainbow/2730; Other Hardware — AII/3850 Imagesetter, Crossfield/E Unit DISPLAY SOFTWAREAd Make-up Applications — QPS/QuarkXPress 4.1, INDesign, DPS, Ad Tracker; Layout Software — Unisys, AT, Enterprise EDITORIAL EQUIPMENT: Hardware — SII/61 Risc, APP/Mac G4; Printers — Centronics/351, DEC/LA 180, HP/2500, Cyclone/Savin Color EDITORIAL SOFTWARE: Eidos Methode PRODUCTION EQUIPMENT: Hardware — 2-AU/APS-6 1085, DIT/Line 303-820-1710, Glunz & Jensen/Online, AG/SelectSet 5000; Cameras — Konica/Newspager, C/Spartan III; Scanners — 3-AG/Horizon, 2-AII/3750, CD, Kk.
Note: For detailed business information see Denver Newspaper Agency listing.

DURANGO

DURANGO HERALD

1275 Main Ave, Durango, Colo., 81301-5137, La Plata; gen tel (970) 247-3504; adv tel (970) 247-3504; ed tel (970) 247-3504; gen fax (970) 259-5011; adv fax (970) 259-5011; ed fax (970) 259-5011; gen/nat adv e-mail sales@durangoherald.com; disp adv e-mail sales@durangoherald.com; class adv e-mailsales@durangoherald.com; ed e-mail dlindley@durangoherald.com; web site www.durangoherald.com
Group: Ballantine Communications
Published: Mon, Tues, Wed, Thur, Fri, Sat, Sun
Weekday Frequency: m
Saturday Frequency: m
Circulation: 6,198; 6,198(sat); 6,891(sun)
Last Audit: AAM September 30, 2015
Advertising Rate (weekday/saturday): Open inch rate $14.65
News services: AP, NYT, CNS. **Established:** 1881
Special Editions: Southwest Summer (Apr); Focus on Business (Feb); County Fair (Jul); Newcomers (Jun); Christmas Gift Guide (Nov); Southwest Winter (Oct).
Special Weekly Sections: Religion (Fri); Arts & Entertainment (Mon); Business (S); Arts & Entertainment (Thur); TV (Tues); Education (Wed).
Syndicated Publications: USA WEEKEND Magazine (Sat); Cross Currents (Semi-monthly).
Pub. .... Richard G. Ballantine
Mktg/Promos .... Sharon Hermes
Dir., Adv./Mktg. .... Mark Drudge
Circ. Mgr. .... John Ellis
IT Mgr. .... David Tabar
Market Information: TMC.
Mechanical Available: Offset; Black and 3 ROP colors; insert accepted; page cutoffs - 22 7/8.
Mechanical Specifications: Type page 13 x 21; E - 6 cols, 2, 1/8 between; A - 6 cols, 2, 1/8 between; C - 7 cols, 1 3/4, 1/8 between.
Areas Served: Southwest Colorado
Equipment & Software: PRESSROOM EQUIPMENT: Lines — 5-KP/News King single width 1979, 1-KP/News King 1994, 4-KP/News King single width 1998; Folders — KP/KJ8 1998.; MAILROOM EQUIPMENT: Tying Machines — MLN.; BUSINESS EQUIPMENT: PBS, SBS CLASSIFIED EQUIPMENT: Hardware — 4-Pentium/PC-90 486; Pre Press/Panther 34P Imagesetter; Printers — TI/500, NewGen; CLASSIFIED SOFTWARE: QPS/QuarkXPress, APT. DISPLAY EQUIPMENT: Hardware — PC 486; Printers — HP/4MV, HP/5000; Other Hardware — Microtek/Scanmaker III DISPLAY SOFTWAREAd Make-up Applications — Aldus/FreeHand, Aldus/PageMaker, QPS/QuarkXPress; Layout Software — ACT. EDITORIAL EQUIPMENT: Hardware — 28-Pentium/90 486 PC/Pre Press/Panther 34P Imagesetter, Lf/AP Leaf Picture Desk, Microtek/Scanmaker III; Printers — NewGen, HP/4MV, HP/5000, HP/MVP5 EDITORIAL SOFTWARE: QPS/QuarkXPress, APT. PRODUCTION EQUIPMENT: Hardware — TI/OmniPage, Prepress/Panther/34P; Scanners — Tecsa/Scanner, GEI PRODUCTION SOFTWARE: QPS/QuarkXPress, APT.

FORT COLLINS

THE COLORADOAN

1300 Riverside Ave, Fort Collins, Colo., 80524-4353, Larimer; gen tel (970) 493-6397; ed tel (970) 224-7730; gen fax (970) 224-7726; ed fax (970) 224-7899; gen/nat adv e-mail tylerkidd@coloradoan.com; disp adv e-mail tylerkidd@coloradoan.com; class adv e-mailclassifieds@colroadoan.com; ed e-mail lgustus@reno.gannett.com; web site www.coloradoan.com
Group: Gannett
Published: Mon, Tues, Wed, Thur, Fri, Sat, Sun
Weekday Frequency: m
Saturday Frequency: m
Circulation: 18,897; 18,897(sat); 23,781(sun)
Last Audit: AAM September 30, 2015
Advertising Rate (weekday/saturday): $34.20
Advertising Rate (sunday): $45.20
News services: AP, GNS, LAT-WP. **Established:** 1873
Own Printing Facility?: Yes
Commercial Printers?: No
Special Weekly Sections: Xplore; Ticket; Real Estate Guide; TV Week
Syndicated Publications: Mind & Body, FYI, NOCO Health Directory
Digital Platform - Mobile: Apple, Android
Digital Platform - Tablet: Apple iOS, Android, Kindle
Pres./Pub. .... Kathy Jack-Romero
Exec. Ed. .... Josh Awtry
Finance Dir., Controller .... Jared Bartels
Sr. Ed. for Platforms .... Rebecca Powell
Digital Sales Mgr. .... Joseph Harmon
Market Information: TMC.
Areas Served: 80512, 80521, 80523, 80524, 80525, 80526, 80528, 80534, 80535, 80536, 80537, 80538, 80539, 80545, 80546, 80547, 80549, 80550, 80610, 80615, 80631, 80634
Delivery Method: Mail, Newsstand, Carrier, Racks

FORT MORGAN

FORT MORGAN TIMES

329 Main St, Fort Morgan, Colo., 80701-2108, Morgan; gen tel (970) 867-5651; adv tel (970) 867-5651; ed tel (970) 867-5651; gen fax (970) 867-7448; adv fax (970) 867-7448; ed fax (970) 867-7448; gen/nat adv e-mail jtonsing@fmtimes.com ; disp adv e-mail jtonsing@fmtimes.com ; class adv e-mailecpcadvertising@dailycamera.com ; ed e-mail editor@fmtimes.com ; web site www.fortmorgantimes.com
Group: Digital First Media
Published: Mon, Tues, Wed, Thur, Fri, Sat
Weekday Frequency: e
Saturday Frequency: m
Circulation: 3,186; 3,186(sat)
Last Audit: Sworn/Estimate/Non-Audited September 30, 2017
Advertising Rate (weekday/saturday): Open inch rate $12.00
News services: AP. **Established:** 1884
Special Editions: Senior Living (Apr); Back to School (Aug); Christmas Greetings/Letters to Santa (Dec); Income Tax Preparation Guide (Feb); Soil Conservation District Annual Meeting (Jan); Morgan County Fair (Jul); July 4th/Rodeo (Jun); Progress (Mar); Graduation (May); C
Special Weekly Sections: TV Schedule (Sat).
Syndicated Publications: American Profile (Weekly).
Digital Platform - Mobile: Apple
Digital Platform - Tablet: Apple iOS
Circ. Mgr. .... Josephina Monsivais
Ed. .... Rachel Alexander
Bus. Ed. .... Dan Barker
Farm/Agriculture Ed. .... Jesse Chaney
Sports Ed. .... Rich Headley
Mng. Ed. .... Robert Leininger
Pub. .... Brian Porter
Market Information: TMC.
Mechanical Available: Offset; Black and 3 ROP colors; insert accepted - half-fold; page cutoffs - 22 3/4.
Mechanical Specifications: Type page 11 13/16 x 21 1/2; E - 4 cols, 2 13/16, 1/8 between; A - 6 cols, 1 13/16, 1/8 between; C - 6 cols, 1 13/16, 1/8 between.
Areas Served: Fort Morgan & Morgan County
Equipment & Software: PRESSROOM EQUIPMENT: Lines — 6-G/Community; Folders — 1-G/2:1, 1-G/Community.; MAILROOM EQUIPMENT: Tying Machines — 1-Marlow/Mc; Address Machine — AKI/Addressograph, AKI/Labeler, AKI/Electronic Labeler.; CLASSIFIED EQUIPMENT: Hardware — 1-APP/Mac Plus; Printers — APP/Mac LaserWriter II, Xante/Accel-a-Writer; CLASSIFIED SOFTWARE: Baseview. DISPLAY EQUIPMENT: Printers — APP/Mac LaserWriter II, Xante/Accel-a-Writer; DISPLAY SOFTWAREAd Make-up Applications — QPS/QuarkXPress; Layout Software — 2-APP/Mac Plus, 1-Murata/F-32 Fax, QPS/QuarkXPress. EDITORIAL EQUIPMENT: Hardware — 12-APP/Mac, Ethernet, APP/Mac Server; Printers — 2-APP/Mac LaserWriter II, Xante/Accel-a-Writer EDITORIAL SOFTWARE: Baseview, QPS/QuarkXPress, Adobe/Photoshop. PRODUCTION EQUIPMENT: Hardware — 1-Nu/Sink, Jobo/Processor; Cameras — 1-R, B/Horizontal PRODUCTION SOFTWARE: QPS/QuarkXPress.

FRISCO

SUMMIT DAILY NEWS

331 W Main St, Frisco, Colo., 80443, Summit; gen tel (970) 668-3998; adv tel (970) 668-3998; ed tel (970) 668-3998; gen fax (970) 668-0755; adv fax (970) 668-0755; ed fax (970) 668-0755; gen/nat adv e-mail jwoodside@summitdaily.com; disp adv e-mail mbutler@summitdaily.com; class adv e-mailclassifieds@cmnm.org; ed e-mail news@summitdaily.com; web site www.summitdaily.com
- 2,826,984(views) 1,388,572(visitors)
Group: Swift Communications, Inc.
Published: Mon, Tues, Wed, Thur, Fri, Sat, Sun
Weekday Frequency: All day
Saturday Frequency: All day
Last Audit: Sworn/Estimate/Non-Audited September 30, 2017
Advertising Rate (weekday/saturday): Open inch rate $14.35
News services: AP. **Established:** 1989
Special Weekly Sections: Summit Scene (Fri); Summit Homes & Properties (Sat).
Publisher .... Matt Sandberg
Mng. Ed. .... Ben Trollinger
Circ. Dir. .... Shawn Butler
Mechanical Available: Offset; Black and ROP colors; insert accepted; page cutoffs - 15 1/4.
Mechanical Specifications: Type page 10 5/8 x 16; E - 6 cols, 1 1/2, 1/6 between; A - 6 cols, 1 1/2, 1/6 between; C - 7 cols, 1 1/2, 1 3/8 between.
Areas Served: Summit County & the Rocky Mountain Region (CO)
Equipment & Software: PRESSROOM EQUIPMENT: Folders — DGM/Quarter.; MAILROOM EQUIPMENT: Counter Stackers — HL; Inserters & Stuffers — MM/227; Tying Machines — Signode.; BUSINESS EQUIPMENT: Unix, PBS CLASSIFIED EQUIPMENT: Hardware — APP/Mac; APP/Mac; Printers — APP/Mac LaserWriter IIg; CLASSIFIED SOFTWARE: Baseview. DISPLAY EQUIPMENT: Hardware — APP/Power Mac PC; DISPLAY SOFTWAREAd Make-up Applications — QPS, Adobe/Illustrator, Adobe/Photoshop; Layout Software — APP/Mac. EDITORIAL EQUIPMENT: Hardware — APP/Mac EDITORIAL SOFTWARE: QPS/QuarkXPress, Adobe/Photoshop. PRODUCTION EQUIPMENT: Hardware — Nu; Cameras — AG; Scanners — Kk, HP PRODUCTION SOFTWARE: MEI/ALS.
Note: The Summit Daily News is printed at the Colorado Mountain News Media plant. For detailed commodity consumption, advertising and production, see Vail Daily News listing.

GLENWOOD SPRINGS

GLENWOOD SPRINGS POST INDEPENDENT

824 Grand Ave, Glenwood Springs, Colo., 81601-3557, Garfield; gen tel (970) 945-8515; adv tel (970) 945-8515; ed tel (970) 945-8515; gen/nat adv e-mail glenwoodads@cmnm.org; disp adv e-mail glenwoodads@cmnm.org; class adv e-mailclassifieds@cmnm.org; ed e-mail ressex@postindependent.com ; web site www.postindependent.com
- 870,000(views) 150,000(visitors)
Group: Swift Communications, Inc.
Published: Mon, Tues, Wed, Thur, Fri, Sat, Sun
Weekday Frequency: All day
Saturday Frequency: All day
Last Audit: Sworn/Estimate/Non-Audited September 1, 2017
Advertising Rate (weekday/saturday): Open inch rate $19
Advertising Rate (sunday): Open inch rate $19
News services: AP. **Established:** 1889
Special Editions: Bicycling (March); Summer Recreation Guide (May); Locals' Choice

(May); Hunting (Aug); Adventures in Aging (Oct.); Holiday Kick-off (Thanksgiving)
Special Weekly Sections: Church (Sat); Business (Mon); Go! (outdoors/entertainment, Fridays starting in April 2017)
Digital Platform - Mobile: Apple, Android, Windows
Digital Platform - Tablet: Apple iOS, Android
Publisher and Editor....................... Randy Essex
Advertising Director........................Brad Howard
Outdoors and entertainment editor Will Grandbois
Reporter..John Stroud
Reporter.................................Ryan Summerlin
Advertising sales....................Amanda Cerveny
Advertising sales............................ Becky Levin
Advertising sales........................ Casey Weaver
Visual journalist............................Chelsea Self
Ariella Gintzler
Sports editor..................................Josh Carney
Market Information: TMC.
Mechanical Available: Offset; Black and 3 ROP colors; insert accepted; page cutoffs - 22 3/4.
Mechanical Specifications: Type page 13 x 21 1/2; E - 6 cols, 2 1/4, 1/6 between; A - 6 cols, 2 1/4, 1/6 between; C - 6 cols, 2 1/4, 1/6 between.
Areas Served: Glenwood Springs & Garfield County
Delivery Method: Newsstand, RacksEquipment & Software: PRESSROOM EQUIPMENT: Lines — 6-G/Community (upper former); Folders — G/2:1.; MAILROOM EQUIPMENT: Tying Machines — 1/OVL, 1-/MLN; Address Machine — Automecha/Accufast, Intermountain.; BUSINESS EQUIPMENT: Epson CLASSIFIED EQUIPMENT: Hardware — APP/Mac IIsi; Printers — APP/ Mac LaserWriter II NTX; CLASSIFIED SOFTWARE: Baseview, QPS/QuarkXPress. DISPLAY EQUIPMENT: Hardware — APP/ Mac IIsi; Printers — APP/Mac LaserWriter II GS; Other Hardware — 2-APP/Mac CD-Rom DISPLAY SOFTWAREAd Make-up Applications — Multi-Ad/Creator, QPS/ QuarkXPress; Layout Software — Ad Force by Ad Manager, Inc. EDITORIAL EQUIPMENT: Hardware — APP/Mac/ APP/Mac Scanner; Printers — APP/ Mac LaserWriter II NTXs EDITORIAL SOFTWARE: QPS/QuarkXPress, Baseview/ Extension. PRODUCTION EQUIPMENT: Hardware — MON/1270; Cameras — Acti.

GRAND JUNCTION

THE DAILY SENTINEL

734 S 7th St, Grand Junction, Colo., 81501-7737, Mesa; gen tel (970) 242-5050; adv tel (970) 242-5050; ed tel (970) 242-5050; gen fax (970) 241-6860; adv fax (970) 241-6860; ed fax (970) 244-8578; gen/nat adv e-mail robin.gavegan@gjsentinel.com; disp adv e-mail robin.gavegan@gjsentinel.com; class adv e-mailclassified@gjsentinel.com; web site www.gjsentinel.com
Group: Cox Media Group
Published: Mon, Tues, Wed, Thur, Fri, Sat, Sun
Weekday Frequency: m
Saturday Frequency: m
Circulation: 18,869; 19,991(sat); 22,508(sun)
Last Audit: AAM September 30, 2016
Advertising Rate (weekday/saturday): Open inch rate $48.21 (Mon-Thur); $50.89 (Fri-Sat)
Advertising Rate (sunday): Open inch rate $56.93
Online Advertising Rate: Starting from $7.00 to $10.00
News services: AP, NYT (Pony). **Established:** 1893
Own Printing Facility?: Yes
Commercial Printers?: Yes
Special Editions: Food and Fitness (Apr); Grand Valley Values (Aug); Late Shopper's Guide (Dec); Grand Valley Values (Feb); Coupon Book (Jan); Home Improvement Directory (Jul); Grand Valley Values (Jun); Baseball (Mar); Coupon Book (May); Coupon Book (Nov); Grand Valley Va
Special Weekly Sections: Health & Wellness (Tue); Best Food Day, TMC (Wed); Outdoors (Fri); Home, Garden, Religion (Sat); Business, Real Estate, Employment (Sun)
Syndicated Publications: Parade (S). Dash
Digital Platform - Mobile: Apple, Android
Digital Platform - Tablet: Apple iOS, Android
Adv. Dir......................................Dennis Mitchell
Production Mgr...............................Bud Winslow
Circ. Mgr.....................................Tracy Gettman
Mktg. Dir........................Laurena Mayne Davis
Sports Editor.......................................Tim Harty
Editorial Page Ed.......................Bob Silbernagel
Graphics Ed./Art Dir......................Robert Garcia
News Editor.................................Dave Haynes
Photo Editor............................Gretel Daugherty
Managing Editor...........................Mike Wiggins
Web Editor.................................Richie Ashcraft
Mgr., Mgmt. Info Servs......................Bob Eicher
Prodn. Foreman, Pressroom.........Lonnie Vincent
Prodn. Foreman, Pressroom......... Scott Crabtree
Human Resources......................Sandra Rogers
Chief Financial Officer................Sheryl Huffaker
Classified Manager................. Jennifer Campos
Pub....Jay Seaton
Nat'l Adv. Coord...........................Linda Wilson
Market Information: Split run; TMC.
Mechanical Available: Offset; Black and 3 ROP colors; insert accepted; page cutoffs - 22.
Mechanical Specifications: Type page 12 x 21; E - 6 cols, 1 7/8, 1/6 between; A - 6 cols, 1 7/8, 1/6 between; C - 9 cols, 1 3/16, 1/6 between.
Delivery Method: Mail, Newsstand, Carrier, RacksEquipment & Software: PRESSROOM EQUIPMENT: Lines — 5-G/Headliner; Folders — 2-G/2:1.; MAILROOM EQUIPMENT: Counter Stackers — 2-QWI/500; Inserters & Stuffers — 1-GMA/ SLS 1000; Tying Machines — 1-CYP/ RTV-7-600.; BUSINESS EQUIPMENT: HP/E3000 BUSINESS SOFTWARE: DTI. CLASSIFIED EQUIPMENT: Hardware — APP/Mac; CLASSIFIED SOFTWARE: DTI. DISPLAY EQUIPMENT: Hardware — APP/ Mac; DISPLAY SOFTWARELayout Software — APP/Mac. EDITORIAL EQUIPMENT: Hardware — APP/Mac EDITORIAL SOFTWARE: DTI. PRODUCTION EQUIPMENT: Hardware — 1-Nat/A250, DTI PRODUCTION SOFTWARE: DTI. IT EQUIPMENT: Hardware
Sun v440 (2)
Sun 3310 (3)
Sun 3320 (2)
HP Proliant DL380 (2)
Mac Servers (4)
PC Servers (1) IT SOFTWARE:Solaris
Red Hat Linux
Windows Server 2007
Windows XP
Mac OS X Server
DTI 5.5 CIRCULATION SOFTWARDTI.

GREELEY

GREELEY DAILY TRIBUNE

501 8th Ave, Greeley, Colo., 80631-3913, Weld; gen tel (970) 352-0211; adv tel (970) 352-0211; ed tel (970) 352-0211; gen fax (970) 352-7817; adv fax (970) 352-7817; ed fax (970) 352-7817; gen/nat adv e-mail advertising@greeleytribune.com; disp adv e-mail advertising@greeleytribune.com; class adv e-mailclassifieds@greeleytribune.com; ed e-mail editorial@greeleytribune.com; web site www.greeleytribune.com
Group: Swift Communications, Inc.
Published: Mon, Tues, Wed, Thur, Fri, Sat, Sun
Weekday Frequency: m
Saturday Frequency: m
Circulation: 11,799; 11,799(sat); 14,446(sun)
Last Audit: CAC December 31, 2016
Advertising Rate (weekday/saturday): Open inch rate $37.18
News services: LAT-WP, AP. **Established:** 1870
Special Editions: Stampede (Jul); Panorama (Mar); Homes On Parade (May); Holiday Magazine (Nov); Click (Oct); Homes On Parade (Sept).
Special Weekly Sections: Preview TV/ Entertainment (Fri); People/Senior (S); Education (Sat); Outdoors (Thur); Family/ Health (Wed).
Syndicated Publications: USA WEEKEND Magazine (S).
Pub....Bart Smith
Circ. Dir..................................Joe Luethmers
Ed....Randy Bangert
Mng. Ed...Kelly Tracer
Action Line Ed..................................Mike Peters
City Ed........................................Sharon Dunn
Entertainment Ed............... Donovan Henderson
Farm/Agriculture Ed.........................Bill Jackson
Sports Ed........................................Nate Miller
Mgmt. Info Servs. Mgr..........................Jeff Kelly
Prodn. Mgr., Mailroom...........................Ron Heil
Prodn. Foreman, Pressroom...........Robert Rodd
Prodn. Mgr., Pre Press......................Dustin Bell
Sports Rep....................................Kayla Cornett
Market Information: TMC; Zoned editions.
Mechanical Available: Offset; Black and 3 ROP colors; insert accepted; page cutoffs - 22 3/4.
Mechanical Specifications: Type page 13 x 21 1/2; E - 6 cols, 2 1/16, 1/8 between; A - 6 cols, 2 1/16, 1/8 between; C - 9 cols, 1 1/2, 1/8 between.
Areas Served: Northern Colorado
Equipment & Software: PRESSROOM EQUIPMENT: Lines — 13-G/Urbanite; G/Community; Reels & Stands — G.; MAILROOM EQUIPMENT: Counter Stackers — 2/BG; Inserters & Stuffers — S/1372 12:1; Tying Machines — MLN; Address Machine — 1-/Ch.; BUSINESS EQUIPMENT: Sun/Sparc Server 670 mp BUSINESS SOFTWARE: PBS CLASSIFIED EQUIPMENT: Hardware — APP/iMac; Printers — HP/LaserJet; CLASSIFIED SOFTWARE: Baseview/ AD Manager Pro. DISPLAY EQUIPMENT: Printers — HP/LaserJet; DISPLAY SOFTWAREAd Make-up Applications — QuarkXPress; Layout Software — APP/G4. EDITORIAL EQUIPMENT: Hardware — APP/ G4; Printers — HP/LaserJet EDITORIAL SOFTWARE: QuarkXPress 4.1, Baseview. PRODUCTION EQUIPMENT: Hardware — 2-Pre Press/Panther Pro G2, 1-DP PRODUCTION SOFTWARE: QuarkXPress.

LA JUNTA

LA JUNTA TRIBUNE-DEMOCRAT

422 Colorado Ave, La Junta, Colo., 81050-2336, Otero; gen tel (719) 384-1437; adv tel (719) 384-1437; ed tel (719) 384-1437; gen fax (719) 384-5999; adv fax (719) 384-5999; ed fax (719) 384-5999; gen/nat adv e-mail agsales@ljtdmail.com; disp adv e-mail tara@ ljtdmail.com; class adv e-mailclassifieds@ ljtdmail.com; ed e-mail publisher@ljtdmail. com; web site www.lajuntatribunedemocrat. com
Group: New Media Investment Group
Published: Mon, Tues, Wed, Thur, Fri
Weekday Frequency: e
Circulation: 3,721
Last Audit: Sworn/Estimate/Non-Audited September 30, 2017
Advertising Rate (weekday/saturday): Open inch rate $10.05(e-fri)
News services: AP.
Special Editions: Spring Fashion (Apr); Kids Rodeo (Aug); Progress (Jan); Christmas Shopping (Nov).
Special Weekly Sections: Agriculture (Fri); Best Food Day (Tues); Best Food Day (Wed).
Syndicated Publications: This Week in La Junta (Sat).
Ed....Candi Hill
Class. Adv....................................... Rita Ojeda
Asst. Ed.................................Jennifer Justice
Adv. Dir...................................Jason Gallegos
Market Information: TMC.
Mechanical Available: Offset; Black and 3 ROP colors; insert accepted; page cutoffs - 22 3/4.
Mechanical Specifications: Type page 10 13/16 x 14 1/4; E - 5 cols, 2 1/16, 1/8 between; A - 5 cols, 2 1/16, 1/8 between; C - 5 cols, 2 1/16, 1/8 between.
Areas Served: La Junta (CO)
Equipment & Software: PRESSROOM EQUIPMENT: Lines — 1-G/Community; Folders — 1-G/2:1.; MAILROOM EQUIPMENT: Tying Machines — 1/Bu; Address Machine — 1-/KR.; BUSINESS EQUIPMENT: 1-IMS/International CLASSIFIED EQUIPMENT: Hardware — 1-Mk/4001.; DISPLAY SOFTWARELayout Software — 2-COM/Powerview. EDITORIAL EQUIPMENT: Hardware — 5-Mk/4001. PRODUCTION EQUIPMENT: Hardware — 1-COM/2961, 1-COM/8400; Cameras — 1-Acti.

LONGMONT

LONGMONT TIMES-CALL

1860 Industrial Cir, Longmont, Colo., 80501-6559, Boulder; gen tel (303) 776-2244; adv tel (303) 776-2244; ed tel (303) 776-2244; gen fax (303) 678-8615; adv fax (303) 774-8088; ed fax (303) 678-8615; gen/nat adv e-mail labozanc@dailycamera.com; disp adv e-mail labozanc@dailycamera.com; class adv e-maillambertk@dailycamera.com; ed e-mail jvahlenkamp@times-call.com; web site www.timescall.com
Group: Digital First Media
Published: Mon, Tues, Wed, Thur, Fri, Sat, Sun
Weekday Frequency: m
Saturday Frequency: m
Circulation: 20,800; 20,800(sat); 34,029(sun)
Last Audit: AAM September 30, 2014
Advertising Rate (weekday/saturday): Open inch rate $21.78
Advertising Rate (sunday): Open inch rate $23.72
News services: AP, U.S. Suburban Press Inc., The Newspaper Network (TNN). **Established:** 1871
Special Editions: Inside & Out (Apr); Longmont Magazine (Aug); Holiday Gifts (Dec); Bridal (Feb); Health Magazine (Jan); Fair & Rodeo (Jul); Health Directory (Jun); Progress (Mar); Graduation (May); Coupon Book (Monthly); Longmont Magazine (Nov); A Taste of Home (Oct); Boo
Special Weekly Sections: Best Food Day, Education (Wed); Religion, Health, Entertainment (Fri); Home, Design, Religion, Outdoor, Real Estate (Sat); Business, Travel (Sun)
Syndicated Publications: Relish (Monthly); USA WEEKEND Magazine (S); American Profile (Sat).
Digital Platform - Mobile: Apple, Android, Blackberry
Adv. Dir..............................Christine Labozan
NIE Coord.......................................Cindy Piller
Circ. Dir., Cor............................Maurice Elhart
Mng. Ed..................................John Vahlenkamp
Bus. Ed......................................Tony Kindelspire
Day Ed.......................................Quentin Young
Chief Photographer..................Richard Hackett
Travis Pryor
Pub....Albert Manzi
Major/Nat'l Acct. Rep...................Kathy Johnson
Prod. Services Mgr...........................Lori Cooper
Market Information: Split run; TMC.
Mechanical Available: Offset; Black and 3 ROP colors; insert accepted; page cutoffs - 22 3/4.
Mechanical Specifications: Type page 11 1/4 x 21 1/4; E - 6 cols, 1 3/4, 1/8 between; A - 6 cols, 1 3/4, 1/8 between; C - 9 cols, 1 1/4, 1/8 between.
Areas Served: Northern Colorado
Equipment & Software: PRESSROOM EQUIPMENT: Lines — 9-G 1974 (4 units), 1975 (1 unit), 1976 (2 units), 1994 (1 unit); Folders — 1-G/Urbanite, 1.; MAILROOM EQUIPMENT: Counter Stackers — 2-QWI/400, QWI/350; Inserters & Stuffers — GMA/SLS 2000 12:1; Tying Machines — 2-Samuel/NT 30, Power Strap/200; Address Machine — VideoJet; BUSINESS EQUIPMENT: HP/3000 & 922LX BUSINESS SOFTWARE: Microsoft Office XP, Open Office 1.03 CLASSIFIED EQUIPMENT: Hardware — Dell/Linux Servers, Dell/ Windows 2000/XP; Printers — HP/ Laserjets; CLASSIFIED SOFTWARE: SCS/ Classified/Admax. DISPLAY EQUIPMENT: Hardware — Dell/Linux; Printers — HP/ LaserJets; DISPLAY SOFTWAREAd Make-up Applications — Dell/Windows 2000/ XP; Layout Software — SCS/Layout 8000. EDITORIAL EQUIPMENT: Hardware — Dell/Windows 2000, Dell/Workstations/AP/ AdSend; Printers — ECR/4550 Knockouts, HP/LaserJet EDITORIAL SOFTWARE: SCS/GN3, SCS/Tark Archive System. PRODUCTION EQUIPMENT: Hardware — 2-Burgess/Vacolux, Windows/2000; Cameras — C/Spartan III PRODUCTION SOFTWARE: SCS/GoodNews 3.

LOVELAND

LOVELAND REPORTER-HERALD

201 E 5th St, Loveland, Colo., 80537-5605, Larimer; gen tel (970) 669-5050; adv tel (970) 635-3650; ed tel (970) 669-5050; gen fax (970) 667-1111; adv fax (970) 663-6892; ed fax (970) 667-1111; gen/nat adv e-mail advertising@reporter-herald.com; disp adv e-mail advertising@reporter-herald.com; class adv e-mailadvertising@reporter-herald.com; ed e-mail news@reporter-herald.com; web site www.reporterherald.com

Group: Digital First Media
Published: Mon, Tues, Wed, Thur, Fri, Sat, Sun
Weekday Frequency: m
Saturday Frequency: m
Circulation: 10,051; 10,051(sat); 11,240(sun)
Last Audit: AAM September 30, 2016
Advertising Rate (weekday/saturday): Open inch rate $26.01
Advertising Rate (sunday): Open inch rate $27.31
News services: AP, LAT-WP, TMS. **Established:** 1880
Special Editions: Vacation Guide (Apr); Corn Roast (Aug); Community photo calendar (Dec); Making a Difference (Feb); Wedding (Jan); Loveland Snapshot (Jul); Tour of New Homes (Jun); Home and Garden How-To (Mar); Women in Business (May); Coupon Book (Monthly); Holiday Open
Special Weekly Sections: Food (Wed); Kids, Outdoors (Thur); Entertainment (Fri); Agriculture, Consumer, Home, Real Estate, Business (Sat); TV, Commentary, Stock, Travel (Sun)
Syndicated Publications: Health Line (Monthly); USA WEEKEND Magazine (S); American Profile (Sat).
Digital Platform - Mobile: Apple, Android, Blackberry
Digital Platform - Tablet: Apple iOS, Android
Pub. .... Edward Lehman
Adv. Dir. .... Linda Story
HR Coord. .... Marge Reiber
Mgr., Mktg./Promo. .... Linda Larsen
Circ. Mgr. .... John Ellis
Mng. Ed. .... Jeff Stahla
Gen. Mgr./Ed. .... Kenneth J Amundson
Pres. .... Dean G. Lehman
Librarian .... Linda Mitchell
Sports Ed. .... Mike Brohard
Online Mgr. .... Bill Schmich
Prodn. Creative Servs. Mgr. .... Dennis Book
Market Information: Split run; TMC.
Mechanical Available: Offset; Black and 3 ROP colors; insert accepted - rotos; page cutoffs - 22 3/4.
Mechanical Specifications: Type page 11 5/8 x 21 1/2; E - 6 cols, 1 5/6, 1/8 between; A - 6 cols, 1 5/6, 1/8 between; C - 9 cols, 1 3/16, 1/8 between.
Areas Served: 80537, 80513, 80534
Delivery Method: Carrier, RacksEquipment & Software: MAILROOM EQUIPMENT: Tying Machines — 1/Bu; Address Machine — 1-/El.; BUSINESS EQUIPMENT: 1-HP/3000 CLASSIFIED EQUIPMENT: Hardware — Dell; CLASSIFIED SOFTWARE: WebTerm X. DISPLAY EQUIPMENT: Hardware — SCS, Dell; DISPLAY SOFTWAREAd Make-up Applications — WebTerm X; Layout Software — SCS/Class Pag. EDITORIAL EQUIPMENT: Hardware — Dell/1-APP/Mac II, Lf/AP Leaf Picture Desk, APP/Mac Quadra EDITORIAL SOFTWARE: Good News. PRODUCTION EQUIPMENT: Cameras — AG.

MONTROSE

THE MONTROSE DAILY PRESS

3684 N Townsend Ave, Montrose, Colo., 81401-5949, Montrose; gen tel (970) 249-3444; adv tel (970) 249-3444; ed tel (970) 249-3444; gen fax (970) 249-3331; adv fax (970) 249-3331; ed fax (970) 249-2370; gen/nat adv e-mail ads@montrosepress.com; disp adv e-mail ads@montrosepress.com; class adv e-mailclassified@montrosepress.com; ed e-mail editor@montrosepress.com; web site www.montrosepress.com

Group: Wick Communications
Published: Tues, Wed, Thur, Fri, Sat, Sun
Weekday Frequency: m
Saturday Frequency: m
Circulation: 4,116; 4,116(sat); 4,778(sun)
Last Audit: VAC December 31, 2016
Advertising Rate (weekday/saturday): Open inch rate $13.25
Advertising Rate (sunday): Open inch rate $13.25
News services: AP. **Established:** 1882
Own Printing Facility?: Yes
Commercial Printers?: Yes
Special Editions: January ....
Sun .... Year in review
Sun .... Lifestyles

February ....
Thur .... Home, Garden, Business Expo
Sat .... Answer Book

March ....
Sat .... Spring Sports Preview
Sat .... Home & Garden w/Earth Day

April ....
Sun .... Destination Montrose
Sun .... Lifestyles

May ....
Sat .... Graduation Tab
Thur .... Montrose County Fair Book

June ....
Outlook editions ....
Tues .... Agriculture
Wed .... Community
Thurs .... Non-profits
Fri .... Health
Sat .... Industry
Sun .... Photo Expo

July ....
Thur .... M. County Fair and Rodeo
Sun .... Lifestyles

August ....
Thur .... Olathe Sweet Corn
Sat .... Back to School
Thur .... Fall Sports Preview

September ....
Sat .... Best of the Valley

October ....
Sat .... Energy Guide
Sun .... Destination Montrose
Sun .... Lifestyle

November ....
Thur .... Veterans Tab
Sat .... Winter Sports Tab
Sun .... Holiday Gift guide

Special Weekly Sections: Best Food Day (Wed); Scene, Entertainment, TV (Fri); Focus (Sun)
Syndicated Publications: .
Adv. Dir. .... Dennis Anderson
Circ. Dir. .... Tisha McCombs
Features Ed. .... Elaine Hale Jones
News Ed. .... Katharhynn Hydlberg
Sports Ed. .... Matt Lindberg
Prodn. Mgr., Mailroom .... Denny Haulman
Managing Editor .... Mike Easterling
Pub./Gen. Mgr. .... Stephen Woody
Adv. Dir./Nat'l Adv. Mgr. .... Tim Frates
Pub .... Francis Wick
Managing Ed. .... Justin Joiner
Managing Ed .... Paul Wahl
Market Information: ADS; TMC; Zoned editions.
Mechanical Available: Offset; Black and 3 ROP colors; insert accepted - full or part run, quarter folded; page cutoffs - 21 1/2.
Mechanical Specifications: Type page 10 x 21; E - 6 cols, 2 1/16, 1/8 between; A - 6 cols, 2 1/16, 1/8 between; C - 8 cols, 1 1/2, 1/8 between.
Areas Served: 81401, 81402, 81403, 81425, 81432
Delivery Method: Newsstand, Carrier, RacksEquipment & Software: PRESSROOM EQUIPMENT: Lines — 6-G/Community; Reels & Stands — 6; MAILROOM EQUIPMENT: Tying Machines — 2/Bu; Address Machine — 1-St/1200.; BUSINESS EQUIPMENT: 2-RSK/TRS 80, 2-RSK/1000 HD, 2-IBM CLASSIFIED EQUIPMENT: Hardware — 2-Mk, APP/Imacs; Printers — Xante; CLASSIFIED SOFTWARE: Baseview. DISPLAY SOFTWAREAd Make-up Applications — QPS/QuarkXPress; Layout Software — APP/Imacs. EDITORIAL EQUIPMENT: Hardware — APP/Imacs; Printers — Xante EDITORIAL SOFTWARE: QPS/QuarkXPress. PRODUCTION EQUIPMENT: Hardware — Linotype-Hell/LaserWriter; Cameras — 1-Nu/2024, 1-AG

PUEBLO

THE PUEBLO CHIEFTAIN

825 W 6th St, Pueblo, Colo., 81003-2313, Pueblo; gen tel (719) 544-3520; adv tel (719) 544-3520; ed tel (719) 544-3520; gen fax (719) 542-3329; adv fax (719) 546-3235; ed fax (719) 542-3329; gen/nat adv e-mail msweeney@chieftain.com; disp adv e-mail msweeney@chieftain.com; class adv e-mailclassads@chieftain.com; ed e-mail city@chieftain.com; web site www.chieftain.com

Group: Star-Journal Publishing Corp.
Published: Mon, Tues, Wed, Thur, Fri, Sat, Sun
Weekday Frequency: m
Saturday Frequency: m
Circulation: 33,234; 33,234(sat); 33,824(sun)
Last Audit: AAM September 30, 2016
Advertising Rate (weekday/saturday): Open inch rate $62.10
Advertising Rate (sunday): Open inch rate $66.30
News services: AP, MCT, TMS. **Established:** 1868
Own Printing Facility?: Yes
Commercial Printers?: Yes
Special Editions: Colorado State Fair (Aug); Holiday Greetings (Dec); Graduation (Jun); Spring Home & Garden (Mar); Classroom Chieftain (May); Active Years, 50 & Above (Monthly); Winterfest (Nov); Generation X-tra (Quarterly); Fall Home Improvement (Sept).
Special Weekly Sections: Real Estate (Fri); Real Estate (S); Best Food Day (Wed).
Syndicated Publications: Relish (Monthly); Parade (S); TV Magazine (Sat).
Digital Platform - Mobile: Apple, Android
Digital Platform - Tablet: Apple iOS, Android, Kindle Fire
Pub./Ed. .... Robert H. Rawlings
Gen. Mgr. .... Brad Slater
Mgr., Bus. Office/Purchasing Agent .. Diane Tafoya
Adv. Dir., Mktg./Online Publishing . Bernie Schutz
Adv. Mgr., Display .... Bob Hudson
Circ. Dir. .... Matt Butorac
Mng. Ed., News .... Steve Henson
Mng. Ed., Prodn. .... Chris Woodka
Bus. Ed. .... Dennis Darrow
City Ed. .... Larry Lopez
Editorial Page Ed. .... Charles Campbell
Lifestyle Ed. .... Peter Strescino
Photo Dir. .... Chris McLean
Sports Editor .... Joe Cervi
HR Dir. .... Maya Galeas
City Ed. .... Tom Purfield
Market Information: Split run; TMC.
Mechanical Available: Offset; Black and 3 ROP colors; insert accepted; page cutoffs - 22.
Mechanical Specifications: Type page 13 x 21 1/2; E - 6 cols, 2 1/16, 1/8 between; A - 6 cols, 2 1/16, 1/8 between; C - 9 cols, 1 3/8, 1/16 between.
Areas Served: Southern Colorado
Delivery Method: Mail, Newsstand, Carrier, RacksEquipment & Software: PRESSROOM EQUIPMENT: Lines — 6-MAN/Roland uniset (single width) 32 couples 1996; Folders — 2-MAN/Roland Jaw; Control System — MAN/Roland Pecom.; MAILROOM EQUIPMENT: Counter Stackers — 2-HL/Monitor, 3-HL/Dual Carrier; Inserters & Stuffers — 2-HI/1372R; Tying Machines — 5-Sterling/Tying Machine; Address Machine — VideoJet 4000; BUSINESS EQUIPMENT: 1-IBM/Sys 36, 1-IBM/5225, 1-Decision Data/6708, 4-IBM/PC, 1-IBM/RS6000, 19-Dell/PC CLASSIFIED EQUIPMENT: Hardware — HI 8300, 10-HI 8864; Printers — Dataproducts B600; CLASSIFIED SOFTWARE: HI/CPS software. DISPLAY EQUIPMENT: Hardware — 3-HI/8860, 1-HI/8900, IBM/PS2, IBM/RS 6000; Printers — ALPS/P2100; DISPLAY SOFTWAREAd Make-up Applications — HI/PLS-SCS, PBS/AM; Layout Software — SCS/Layout 8000, PBS/AM. EDITORIAL EQUIPMENT: Hardware — HI/PEN System, 23-HI, HI/PLS 8300, 5-HI/8860/IBM/PC; Printers — HP/LaserJet II EDITORIAL SOFTWARE: Crosstalk. PRODUCTION EQUIPMENT: Hardware — KFM, AG/Litex 26, Norscreen MS 250 PRODUCTION SOFTWARE: DTI.

ROCKY FORD

ROCKY FORD DAILY GAZETTE

912 Elm Ave, Rocky Ford, Colo., 81067-1249, Otero; gen tel (719) 254-3351; adv tel (719) 254-3351; ed tel (719) 254-3351; gen fax (719) 254-3354; adv fax (719) 254-3354; ed fax (719) 254-3354; gen/nat adv e-mail sales@rockyforddailygazette.com; disp adv e-mail sales@rockyforddailygazette.com; class adv e-mailsales@rockyforddailygazette.com; ed e-mail news@rockyforddailygazette.com; web site Doesn't have a website

Group: Rocky Ford Publishing Company Inc.
Published: Mon, Tues, Wed, Thur, Fri
Weekday Frequency: e
Circulation: 3,013
Last Audit: Sworn/Estimate/Non-Audited September 30, 2017
Advertising Rate (weekday/saturday): Open inch rate $6.35
News services: 1887
Special Weekly Sections: Best Food Days (Tue/Wed)
Syndicated Publications: Television (Fri).
Pub./Ed./Bus. Mgr. .... J.R. Thompson
Adv. Mgr. .... Laura Thompson
Circ. Dir. .... Jessica Tofoya
Mechanical Available: Offset; Black and 3 ROP colors; insert accepted; page cutoffs - 22 3/4.
Mechanical Specifications: Type page 13 x 21; E - 6 cols, 2 1/16, 1/8 between; A - 6 cols, 2 1/16, 1/8 between; C - 6 cols, 2 1/16, 1/8 between.
Areas Served: Otero & Crowley Counties (CO)
Equipment & Software: BUSINESS EQUIPMENT: APP/Mac BUSINESS SOFTWARE: Checkmark CLASSIFIED EQUIPMENT: Hardware — APP/Mac; CLASSIFIED SOFTWARE: Microsoft/Word. DISPLAY EQUIPMENT: Hardware — APP/Power Mac; DISPLAY SOFTWAREAd Make-up Applications — Aldus/PageMaker 6.0; Layout Software — APP/Mac. EDITORIAL EQUIPMENT: Hardware — APP/Mac, APP/Power Mac; Printers — APP/Mac LaserWriter II NT, APP/Mac LaserWriter Plus, HP/LaserJet IV M EDITORIAL SOFTWARE: Microsoft/Word, Aldus/SuperPaint, Aldus/PageMaker.

SALIDA

THE MOUNTAIN MAIL

125 E 2nd St, Salida, Colo., 81201-2114, Chaffee; gen tel (719) 539-6691; adv tel (719) 539-6691; ed tel (719) 539-6691; gen fax (719) 539-6630; adv fax (719) 539-6630; ed fax (719) 539-6630; gen/nat adv e-mail vickiesue@avpsalida.com; disp adv e-mail vickiesue@avpsalida.com; class adv e-mailclassifieds@themountainmail.com; ed e-mail pgoetz@themountainmail.com; web site www.themountainmail.com

Published: Mon, Tues, Wed, Thur, Fri
Weekday Frequency: m
Circulation: 3,465
Last Audit: Sworn/Estimate/Non-Audited October 20, 2017
Advertising Rate (weekday/saturday): Open inch rate $8.50
News services: Papert (Landon). **Established:** 1880
Own Printing Facility?: Yes
Commercial Printers?: Yes
Digital Platform - Mobile: Windows
Pub .... Merle Baranczyk
Adv. Mgr. .... Vicki Vigil
Circ. Mgr. .... Sandra Christensen
Mng. Ed. .... Paul Goetz
Online Contact .... Holly Russell
Online Mgr. .... Joerge Hasselbrink
Prodn. Mgr. .... Morris Christensen
Copy Ed .... Shelley Mayer
Market Information: TMC.
Mechanical Available: Offset; Black and 2 ROP colors; insert accepted; page cutoffs - 15 3/4.
Mechanical Specifications: Type page 10 1/2 x 15 3/4; E - 5 cols, 2, 1/8 between; A - 5 cols, 2,

1/8 between; C - 5 cols, 2, 1/8 between.
Areas Served: Salida & Upper Arkansas Valley
Delivery Method: Mail, Carrier, RacksEquipment & Software: PRESSROOM EQUIPMENT: Lines — 7-G/Community; MAILROOM EQUIPMENT: Address Machine — 2/Wm.; BUSINESS EQUIPMENT: EPS BUSINESS SOFTWARE: Synaptic CLASSIFIED EQUIPMENT: Hardware — 2-APP/Mac.; DISPLAY EQUIPMENT: Hardware — APP/Macs; DISPLAY SOFTWAREAd Make-up Applications — QPS/QuarkXPress; Layout Software — 2-APP/Mac. EDITORIAL EQUIPMENT: Hardware — APP/Mac; Printers — Xante/8100, Xante/8200 EDITORIAL SOFTWARE: QPS/QuarkXPress 3.33, Adobe/Photoshop 5.0, Adobe/Illustrator 5.0. PRODUCTION EQUIPMENT: Hardware — 2-APP/Mac; Cameras — 1-Acti/183; Scanners — LaCie/Silver Scanner II, Polaroid/SprintScan PRODUCTION SOFTWARE: QPS/QuarkXPress 3.31.

STEAMBOAT SPRINGS

STEAMBOAT TODAY

1901 Curve Plz, Steamboat Springs, Colo., 80487-4912, Routt; gen tel (970) 879-1502; adv tel (970) 879-1502; ed tel (970) 879-1502; gen fax (970) 879-2888; adv fax (970) 879-7541; ed fax (970) 879-2888; gen/nat adv e-mail advertising@steamboatToday.com; disp adv e-mail advertising@SteamboatToday.com; class adv e-mailqkaufhold@SteamboatToday.com; ed e-mail news@SteamboatToday.com; web site www.steamboattoday.com
Group: Swift Communications, Inc.
Published: Mon, Tues, Wed, Thur, Fri, Sat
Weekday Frequency: m
Saturday Frequency: m
Circulation: 9,830; 8,563(sat); 5,600(sun)
Last Audit: Sworn/Estimate/Non-Audited September 30, 2017
Advertising Rate (sunday): Open inch rate $13.95
News services: AP. **Established:** 1884
Own Printing Facility?: Yes
Commercial Printers?: Yes
Special Weekly Sections: 4 Points (Fri).
Syndicated Publications: At Home in Steamboat Springs
Colorado Hunter
Explore Steamboat
Digital Platform - Mobile: Apple, Android, Windows
Digital Platform - Tablet: Apple iOS, Android, Windows 7, Blackberry Tablet OS, Kindle, Kindle Fire
Pub. .... Suzanne Schlicht
Circ. Dir. .... Steve Balgenorth
General Manager .... Scott Stanford
Ed. .... Lisa Schlichtman
Online Devel. Mgr. .... Tyler Jacobs
Adv. Dir. .... Laura Tamucci
Mechanical Available: Offset; Black and 1 ROP colors; insert accepted.
Mechanical Specifications: Type page 14 x 21 1/2; E - 6 cols, 2 1/8, 1/4 between; A - 6 cols, 2 1/8, 1/4 between; C - 6 cols, 2 1/8, 1/4 between.
Areas Served: 80477-80488
Delivery Method: RacksEquipment & Software: PRESSROOM EQUIPMENT: Lines — 5-G/Community double width 1992; Press Drive — Fin/902.; MAILROOM EQUIPMENT: Tying Machines — Akebono.; CLASSIFIED EQUIPMENT: Hardware — IBM; CLASSIFIED SOFTWARE: DOS. DISPLAY EQUIPMENT: Hardware — APP/Power Mac; Printers — HP/LaserJet, Xante; DISPLAY SOFTWAREAd Make-up Applications — QPS/QuarkXPress, Adobe/Illustrator, Adobe/Photoshop; Layout Software — APP/Power Mac. EDITORIAL EQUIPMENT: Hardware — APP/Power Mac; Printers — HP/LaserJet EDITORIAL SOFTWARE: Claris/Works, QPS/QuarkXPress, APP/Mac Laserwriter II. PRODUCTION EQUIPMENT: Hardware — Ultra/Plus Flip Top, Polaroid/SprintScan; Cameras — Kk/50603 Image Maker PRODUCTION SOFTWARE: QPS/QuarkXPress 4.0.

STERLING

JOURNAL-ADVOCATE

504 N 3rd St, Sterling, Colo., 80751-3203, Logan; gen tel (970) 522-1990; adv tel (970) 526-9299; ed tel (970) 526-9310; gen fax (970) 522-2320; gen/nat adv e-mail dmcclain@journal-advocate.com; disp adv e-mail ecpcadvertising@dailycamera.com; ed e-mail swaite@journal-advocate.com; web site www.journal-advocate.com
Group: Digital First Media
Published: Mon, Tues, Wed, Thur, Fri, Sat
Weekday Frequency: e
Saturday Frequency: m
Last Audit: Sworn/Estimate/Non-Audited September 30, 2017
Advertising Rate (weekday/saturday): Open inch rate $14.00
Own Printing Facility?: Yes
Commercial Printers?: Yes
Special Weekly Sections: Lifestyles (Mon); Business, Food (Tue); Agriculture (Thur); Religion (Fri)
Pub. .... Julie Tonsing
Mng. Ed. .... Sara Waite
Pre-press Mgr. .... Duane Miles
Prodn. Dir. .... Michael Foster
Circ. .... Krista Kasten
Areas Served: 80751

TELLURIDE

TELLURIDE DAILY PLANET; THE WATCH; THE NORWOOD POST

307 E Colorado Ave, Telluride, Colo., 81435, San Miguel; gen tel (970) 728-9788; adv tel (970) 728-9788; ed tel (970) 728-9788; gen fax (970) 728-8061; adv fax (970) 728-8061; ed fax (970) 728-8061; gen/nat adv e-mail maureen@telluridedailyplanet.com; class adv e-mailclassifieds@telluridenews.com; ed e-mail editor@tellurideplanet.com; web site www.telluridenews.com
Group: Telluride Newspapers
Published: Wed, Thur, Fri, Sun
Weekday Frequency: m
Circulation: 3,841
Last Audit: Sworn/Estimate/Non-Audited October 1, 2017
News services: 1898
Special Editions: Publishers of Telluride Style, Adventure Guide and Shelter magazines in the summer and winter.
Pub. .... Andrew Mirrington
Assoc. Pub. .... Dusty Atherton
Adv. Mgr. .... Maureen Pelisson
Shelly Kennett
Areas Served: San Miguel, Ouray and Montrose Counties
Delivery Method: Mail, Newsstand, Racks
Note: Printed at Montrose, CO. For detailed production and mechanical specifications, refer to Montrose Daily Press listing.

TRINIDAD

THE CHRONICLE-NEWS

200 Church St, Trinidad, Colo., 81082-2603, Las Animas; gen tel (719) 846-3311; adv tel (719) 846-3311; ed tel (719) 846-3311; gen fax (719) 846-3612; adv fax (719) 846-3612; ed fax (719) 846-3612; gen/nat adv e-mail news@trinidadchroniclenews.com; disp adv e-mail tparker@trinidadchroniclenews.com; class adv e-mailtparker@trinidadchroniclenews.com; ed e-mail mhiesiger@trinidadchroniclenews.com; web site www.thechronicle-news.com
Group: Shearman Corporation
Published: Mon, Tues, Wed, Thur, Fri
Weekday Frequency: e
Circulation: 3,275
Last Audit: Sworn/Estimate/Non-Audited September 30, 2017
Advertising Rate (weekday/saturday): Open inch rate $11.58
News services: AP. **Established:** 1877
Special Editions: Rodeo (Other).
Special Weekly Sections: TV Entertainment (Thur).
Syndicated Publications: Parade (Weekly).
Pub. .... Aileen Hood
Prodn. Mgr. .... Sheila Hamlan
Editor .... Eric John Monson
Gen. Mgr. .... Allyson Sheumaker
Ed. .... Bruce Leonard
Ad .... Adam Sperandio
Market Information: Split run; TMC.
Mechanical Available: Offset; Black and 1 ROP colors; insert accepted; page cutoffs - 22 3/4.
Mechanical Specifications: Type page 13 x 22; E - 6 cols, 2 1/16, 1/8 between; A - 6 cols, 2 1/16, 1/8 between; C - 8 cols, 1 1/2, 1/8 between.
Areas Served: Southeastern Colorady & Northeastern New Mexico
Equipment & Software: PRESSROOM EQUIPMENT: Lines — 2-KP/Color King.; MAILROOM EQUIPMENT: Address Machine — 1/Am.; CLASSIFIED EQUIPMENT: Hardware — APP/Mac Quadra 630; Printers — Xante/Accel-a-Writer 8200; CLASSIFIED SOFTWARE: Baseview/Class Manager, FoxBase. DISPLAY EQUIPMENT: Hardware — APP/Power Mac 8100; Printers — Xante/Accel-a-Writer 8200; DISPLAY SOFTWAREAd Make-up Applications — QPS/QuarkXPress 3.32, Adobe/Photoshop 3.2, Adobe/Illustrator.; EDITORIAL EQUIPMENT: Hardware — APP/Power Mac 8500; Printers — Xante/Accel-a-Writer 8200 EDITORIAL SOFTWARE: QPS/QuarkXPress 3.32. PRODUCTION EQUIPMENT: Hardware — 1-Nu; Cameras — 1-R/500 PRODUCTION SOFTWARE: QPS/QuarkXPress 3.32.

CONNECTICUT

BRIDGEPORT

CONNECTICUT POST

410 State St, Bridgeport, Conn., 06604-4501, Fairfield; gen tel (203) 333-0161; adv tel (203) 330-6409; ed tel (203) 330-6233; gen fax (203) 367-8158; adv fax (203) 367-8158; ed fax (203) 367-8158; gen/nat adv e-mail ehuron@hearstmediact.com; disp adv e-mail gdoucette@hearstmediact.com; class adv e-mailclassifieds@ctpost.com; ed e-mail editorials@ctpost.com; web site www.ctpost.com
- 22,000,000(views) 885,891(visitors)
Group: Hearst Communications, Inc.
Published: Mon, Tues, Wed, Thur, Fri, Sat, Sun
Weekday Frequency: m
Saturday Frequency: m
Circulation: 31,086; 24,562(sat); 43,660(sun)
Last Audit: AAM September 30, 2015
Advertising Rate (weekday/saturday): Open inch rate $132.90
News services: AP, MCT, LAT-WP, CNS, NYT, SHNS, TMS. **Established:** 1883
Special Editions: Summer Education (Apr); Higher Education (Aug); Holiday Gift Guide 2 (Dec); Bact to School/College (Fall); President's Day Auto (Feb); Education (Jan); Retirement Options (Jul); Trumbull Day (Jun); New York Auto Show (Mar); Stratford Day (May); Christmas
Special Weekly Sections: Auto/Truck (Fri); Seniors (Mon); Arts/Theater (S); Religion (Sat); Preview (Thur).
Syndicated Publications: Preview/Entertainment Guide (Fri); Relish (Monthly); USA WEEKEND Magazine (S); Parade (Weekly).
Digital Platform - Mobile: Apple, Android
Digital Platform - Tablet: Apple iOS, Android
CFO .... Lance Deda
Adv. Dir. .... Eugene Jackson
Adv. Mgr., Classified .... Nancy Toth
Adv. Mgr., Nat'l .... Dorothy Cicerro
Circ. Dir. .... John Truitt
Assistant Managing Editor .... Debra West
Editorial Page Ed. .... Michael Daly
Features Ed. .... Sev Rinaldi
Metro Ed. .... John Schwing
Photo/Graphics Ed. .... Cathy Zuraw
Sports Ed. .... Gary Rogo
State News Ed. .... Anna Amato
Facility Mgr. .... James Shay
IT Dir. .... Robert Walsh
Co-Mng. Ed. .... John Alcott
Co-Mng. Ed. .... Ted Tompkins
Market Information: Split run; TMC; Zoned editions.
Mechanical Available: Offset; Black and 3 ROP colors; insert accepted; page cutoffs - 21 1/2.
Mechanical Specifications: Type page 11 5/8 x 20 1/4; E - 6 cols, 1 5/6, 1/8 between; A - 6 cols, 1 5/6, 1/8 between; C - 10 cols, 1 2/25, 1/16 between.
Areas Served: Greater Fairfield County
Equipment & Software: PRESSROOM EQUIPMENT: Lines — 9-G/Metro offset (5 half decks); Folders — 2-G/3:2; MAILROOM EQUIPMENT: Counter Stackers — 3-HL/Monitor HTs, 1-HL/Dual Carrier; Inserters & Stuffers — 2-GMA/SLS 1000 18:1; Tying Machines — 4-OVL/JP40, 1-OVL/415, 1-MLN/EE.; BUSINESS EQUIPMENT: 2-DEC/VAX, III/6310, III/4700A BUSINESS SOFTWARE: CJ CLASSIFIED EQUIPMENT: Hardware — Digital/3000 Alpha Chip; Printers — Epson; CLASSIFIED SOFTWARE: AT. DISPLAY EQUIPMENT: Hardware — DEC/VAX 6310, III/4700A; Printers — DEC/LP25, DEC/LP27, Genicom; DISPLAY SOFTWAREAd Make-up Applications — Multi-Ad; Layout Software — Managing Editor/ALS. EDITORIAL EQUIPMENT: Hardware — Digital/3000 Alpha Chip; Printers — HP/LaserJet IV M, AU/APS Broadsheet EDITORIAL SOFTWARE: Digital/3000 Alpha Chip, QPS/QuarkXPress 3.3, AT/Dewarview 2.1. PRODUCTION EQUIPMENT: Hardware — 4-LE, 2-Digital/RIP, III/3850; Cameras — 2-C/Spartan III; Scanners — Epson PRODUCTION SOFTWARE: Dewar/View 2.1, Computext/CompoClass.

BRISTOL

THE BRISTOL PRESS

188 Main St, Bristol, Conn., 06010-6308, Hartford; gen tel (860) 584-0501; adv tel (860) 583-2378; ed tel (860) 584-0501; gen fax (860) 584-2192; adv fax (860) 584-2192; ed fax (860) 584-2192; gen/nat adv e-mail gcurran@centralctcommunications.com; disp adv e-mail gcurran@centralctcommunications.com; class adv e-mailgcurran@centralctcommunications.com; ed e-mail letters@centralctcommunications.com; web site www.bristolpress.com
- 669,000(views) 78,000(visitors)
Group: Central Connecticut Communications LLC
Published: Mon, Tues, Wed, Thur, Fri, Sat
Weekday Frequency: m
Saturday Frequency: m
Circulation: 4,019; 4,019(sat)
Last Audit: AAM September 30, 2015
Branch Offices: New Britain, CT
Advertising Rate (weekday/saturday): Open inch rate $23.52
News services: AP. **Established:** 1871
Own Printing Facility?: No
Commercial Printers?: No
Special Editions: Bridal (Jan); Bristol Home Show (Feb); Business & Industry Review (Jan); Home Improvement (Apr); Bridal (Jun); Back-to-School (Aug); Home Improvement (Oct); Gift Guide (Nov); Holiday Gift Guides (Nov-Dec).
Special Weekly Sections: Prime Time (Mon); Religion (Sat); Healthy Living (Tues); Weekend (Thurs); Food (Wed); Home & Garden (Fri).
Digital Platform - Mobile: Apple, Android
Digital Platform - Tablet: Apple iOS, Android
Pub. .... Michael Schroeder
Adv. Mgr. .... Gary Curran
Chief Photographer .... Michael Orazzi
Sports Ed. .... Paul Angilly
Editor .... Michael Marciano
Associate editor .... James Drzewiecki
Market Information: TMC.
Mechanical Available: Offset; Black and 3 ROP colors; insert accepted; page cutoffs - 22 3/4.
Mechanical Specifications: Tabloid format. Image area 9.675" x 10.75" 5 column.
Areas Served: 06013, 06032, 06051, 06052, 06111, 06109, 06067, 06037, 06489,

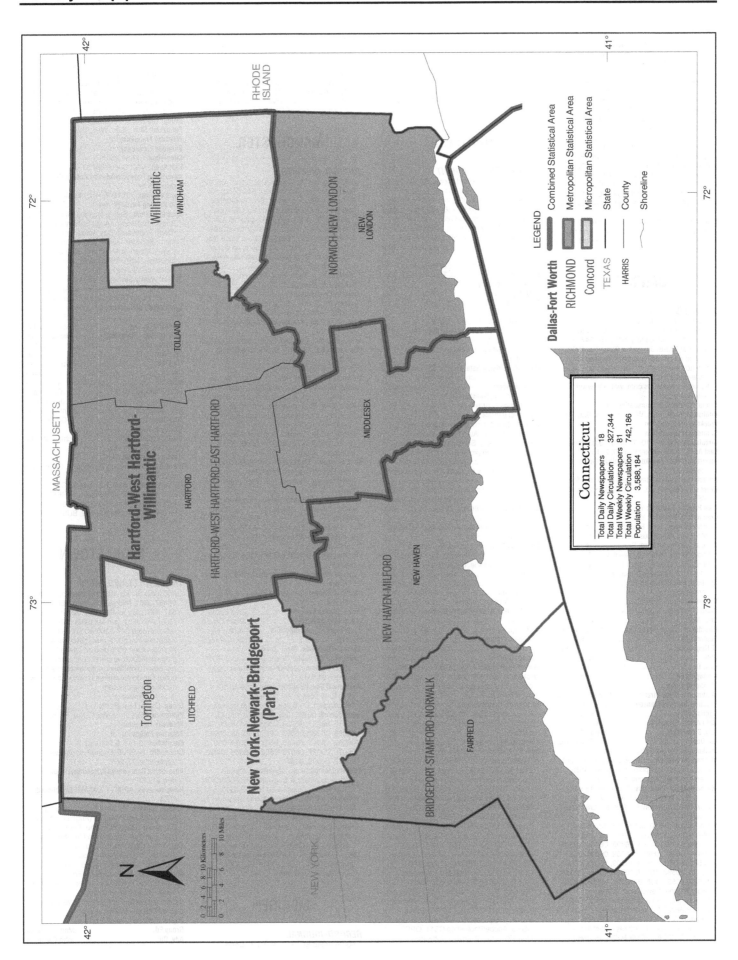

Connecticut

Total Daily Newspapers	18
Total Daily Circulation	327,344
Total Weekly Newspapers	81
Total Weekly Circulation	742,186
Population	3,588,184

LEGEND

Dallas-Fort Worth	Combined Statistical Area
RICHMOND	Metropolitan Statistical Area
Concord	Micropolitan Statistical Area
TEXAS	State
HARRIS	County
	Shoreline

Hartford-West Hartford-Willimantic

Willimantic

WINDHAM

NORWICH-NEW LONDON

NEW LONDON

TOLLAND

HARTFORD

HARTFORD-WEST HARTFORD-EAST HARTFORD

MIDDLESEX

New York-Newark-Bridgeport (Part)

Torrington

LITCHFIELD

NEW HAVEN-MILFORD

NEW HAVEN

BRIDGEPORT-STAMFORD-NORWALK

FAIRFIELD

MASSACHUSETTS

RHODE ISLAND

NEW YORK

0 2 4 6 8 10 Kilometers

0 2 4 6 8 10 Miles

42°

41°

72°

73°

06716, 06782, 06786, 06787Equipment & Software: BUSINESS SOFTWARE: Advanced Publishing Technology — Falcon Editorial, Web, Advertising, Circulation CLASSIFIED SOFTWARE: Advanced Publishing Technology — Falcon DISPLAY EQUIPMENT: PC/Windows DISPLAY SOFTWAREAdvanced Publishing Technology — Falcon; Adobe CC EDITORIAL EQUIPMENT: PC/Windows EDITORIAL SOFTWARE: Advanced Publishing Technology — Falcon; Adobe CC PRODUCTION EQUIPMENT: PC/ Windows PRODUCTION SOFTWARE: Advanced Publishing Technology — Falcon; Adobe CC IT EQUIPMENT: Dell Servers IT SOFTWARE:Windows server CIRCULATION EQUIPMENT: PC/Windows CIRCULATION SOFTWARAdvanced Publishing Technology — Falcon

Note: The Bristol Press shares a combined Sunday edition, The Herald Press, with the New Britain Herald (m). See the Herald listing for circulation.

DANBURY

THE NEWS-TIMES

333 Main St, Danbury, Conn., 06810-5818, Fairfield; gen tel (203) 744-5100; adv tel (203) 744-5100; ed tel (203) 731-3347; gen fax (203) 792-8730; ed fax (203) 792-8730; gen/nat adv e-mail ads@newstimes.com; disp adv e-mail ads@newstimes.com; class adv e-mailads@newstimes.com; ed e-mail editors@newstimes.com; web site www.newstimes.com

Group: Hearst Communications, Inc.
Published: Mon, Tues, Wed, Thur, Fri, Sat, Sun
Weekday Frequency: m
Saturday Frequency: m
Circulation: 14,084; 10,703(sat); 19,834(sun)
Last Audit: AAM September 30, 2015
Advertising Rate (weekday/saturday): Open inch rate $46.57
Advertising Rate (sunday): Open inch rate $52.40
News services: AP, DJ, MCT, ONS. **Established:** 1883
Own Printing Facility?: Yes
Commercial Printers?: Yes
Special Editions: Real Estate Showcase (Monthly); Inside Business (Quarterly).
Special Weekly Sections: Sports (Mon); Best Food (Wed); Business, Neighbors (Thur); Weekend, Entertainment (Fri); Religion (Sat); Travel, TV, Business, Stock (Sun)
Syndicated Publications: Relish (Monthly); Parade (S).
Digital Platform - Mobile: Apple, Android
Digital Platform - Tablet: Apple iOS
Circ. Mgr. .... David Parks
Director of Human Resources .... Karen Geffert
Features Ed. .... Linda Tuccio-Koonz
IT Help Desk .... Rich Joudy
Pub. .... Shawn Palmer
Ops. Dir. .... Ron Darr
Managing Ed. .... Jacqueline Smith
Managing Editor .... Jean Dubail
Multimedia Sales Director .... Stephen Spinosa
Creative Services Manager .... Nancy Mengler
Sports Editor .... Rich Gregory
Nat'l Accts. Sales Dir. .... Eugene Jackson
Adv. Sales Mgr. .... Loraine Marshall
Ed. Dept. .... Susan Tuz
Market Information: TMC.
Mechanical Available: Offset; Black and 4 ROP colors; insert accepted - mini tabs, cards, merchandise; page cutoffs - 22 3/4.
Mechanical Specifications: Type page 13 x 21; E - 6 cols, 2 1/16, 1/8 between; A - 6 cols, 2 1/16, 1/8 between; C - 9 cols, 1 3/8, 1/16 between.
Areas Served: 06810, 06811, 06812, 06784, 06776, 06755, 06785, 06757, 06754, 06777, 06794, 06793, 06783, 06798, 06804, 06801, 06470, 06482, 06488, 06752, 06896, 06877, 12564, 12531, 12563, 10509, 10541, 10560, 10536, 10590, 10518, 10526, 10597, 10578, 10589, 10505, 10598, 10527, 10501, 10536
Delivery Method: Newsstand, Carrier, RacksEquipment & Software: MAILROOM EQUIPMENT: Counter Stackers — QWI; Inserters & Stuffers — 14-SCS/2000; Tying Machines — 2/OVL; Address Machine — Prism.; DISPLAY EQUIPMENT: Hardware — PC; Printers — HP; Other Hardware — ECR/4050 DISPLAY SOFTWAREAd Make-up Applications — Adobe/Photoshop; Layout Software — MEI/ALS. EDITORIAL EQUIPMENT: Hardware — AT, Dewar/View. PRODUCTION EQUIPMENT: Hardware — 2-ECR/Knockout 4050, AG/Accuset 1000; Cameras — 1-C/Spartan II PRODUCTION SOFTWARE: AT.

HARTFORD

THE HARTFORD COURANT

285 Broad St, Hartford, Conn., 06105-3785, Hartford; gen tel (860) 241-6200; ed tel (860) 241-3698; gen fax (860) 241-3863; adv fax (860) 241-3864; ed fax (860) 520-6941; gen/nat adv e-mail llatusek@courant.com; disp adv e-mail ecom@tribune.com; class adv e-mailmtingley@courant.com; ed e-mail letters@courant.com.; web site www.courant.com
- 24,447,578(views) 2,652,406(visitors)

Published: Mon, Tues, Wed, Thur, Fri, Sat, Sun
Weekday Frequency: m
Saturday Frequency: m
Circulation: 107,410; 120,797(sat); 171,592(sun)
Last Audit: AAM March 31, 2016
Advertising Rate (weekday/saturday): Open inch rate $158 (Thur-Sat), $126 (Mon-Wed)
Advertising Rate (sunday): Open inch rate $203.00
Online Advertising Rate: start at $8, $10 and $12 depending on reach for base sizes.
News services: Reuters, WP-Bloomberg, MCT, RN Photo. **Established:** 1764
Own Printing Facility?: Yes
Commercial Printers?: Yes
Special Editions: Scholastic Sports (Jan); President's Day Auto I (Feb); Guide To Education (Apr); Scholastic Sports (Apr); Travelers Championship Golf Tournament (June); Scholastic Sports (Jul); UConn Football Preview (Aug); Guide to Education (Aug); Breast Cancer Awareness (Oct); UConn Basketball Preview (Nov); Ski, Sun and Travel (Nov); Guide To Education (Dec);
Special Weekly Sections: TV Week (Sun.), Flavor (Thur.), At Home (Fri.),
Proprietary Publications: Annual Manual (Aug) Top Workplaces (Sept)
Digital Platform - Mobile: Apple, Android
Digital Platform - Tablet: Apple iOS, Android, Windows 7, Kindle, Kindle Fire
VP Adv. .... Mary Lou Stoneburner
Circ. Dir. .... Susan Kerr
Circ. Ops. Dir. .... Brian McEnery
Publisher & Editor-in-Chief .... Andrew S. Julien
Dir. of Marketing and Communications . Jennifer T. Humes
Sr. VP Ops Admin. .... Thomas J. Anischik
VP/Digital Platform .... Christine W. Taylor
Adv. Dir. .... Michele Tingley
Finance Director .... Dana Bisconti
Market Information: ADS; TMC; Zoned editions.
Mechanical Available: Offset; Black and 3 ROP colors; insert accepted - product samples; page cutoffs - 22 3/4.
Mechanical Specifications: Type page 10 x 21; E - 6 cols, 1.525", 1/8 between; A - 6 cols, 1.525", 1/8 between; C -6 cols, 1.525", 1/8 between.
Areas Served: Entire state of Connecticut
Delivery Method: Mail, Newsstand, Carrier, RacksEquipment & Software: PRESSROOM EQUIPMENT: Lines — 8-G/Metro offset (4 half decks) 1976; 8-G/Metro offset (4 half decks) 1976; 8-G/Metro offset (4 half decks) 1985; 8-G/Metro offset (4 half decks) 1985; Folders - 6-G/3:2.; MAILROOM EQUIPMENT: Counter Stackers — 6-QWI/351, 3-NP/160; Inserters & Stuffers — 4-GMA/3000; Tying Machines — 6-/Dynaric, 3-Dynaric/Offline; BUSINESS EQUIPMENT: IBM/RS6000 BUSINESS SOFTWARE: PBS/MediaPlus, ADIT/AX Microsoft/Office, Peoplesoft CLASSIFIED EQUIPMENT: Hardware — 4-2-IBM/RS6000, Pentium/100NT CLASSIFIED SOFTWARE: ADIT DISPLAY EQUIPMENT: Hardware — 32-APP/MacPro; Xerox MFD; DISPLAY SOFTWAREAd Make-up Applications — Adobe/InDesign CS5.5, Adobe/Photoshop CS11, QPS/QuarkXPress 6.0; Layout Software — Layout/8000. EDITORIAL EQUIPMENT: Centralized EDITORIAL SOFTWARE: CCI/NewsGate PRODUCTION EQUIPMENT: Hardware — Agfa DL CTP imagers - 3; KFM/VIPB; Scanners — 1- PRODUCTION SOFTWARE: AT/R5 Classified Pagination, QPS/QuarkXPress, CCI/Editorial Pagination. CIRCULATION EQUIPMENT: Centralized CIRCULATION SOFTWARDSI

MANCHESTER

JOURNAL INQUIRER

306 Progress Dr, Manchester, Conn., 06042-9011, Hartford; gen tel (860) 646-0500; adv tel (860) 646-0500; ed tel (860) 646-0500; gen fax (860) 646-9867; adv fax (860) 643-1180; ed fax (860) 646-9867; gen/nat adv e-mail jiads@journalinquirer.com; disp adv e-mail jiads@journalinquirer.com; class adv e-mailjiads@journalinquirer.com; ed e-mail news@journalinquirer.com; web site www.journalinquirer.com

Published: Mon, Tues, Wed, Thur, Fri, Sat
Weekday Frequency: e
Saturday Frequency: m
Circulation: 25,904; 29,450(sat)
Last Audit: AAM March 31, 2016
Advertising Rate (weekday/saturday): Open inch rate $44.20
Advertising Rate (sunday): Open inch rate $44.20
News services: AP, NYT, SHNS. **Established:** 1968
Own Printing Facility?: No
Commercial Printers?: No
Special Editions: Spring Home & Garden (Apr); Back-to-School (Aug); Washington's Birthday Auto (Feb); Super Sunday (Feb); Discovery (Jul); Fall Brides (Jun); Business Profiles (June); Dining Out Guide (May); Sleighbell (Nov); Inside Football (Oct); Fall Sports (Sept). UCONN Football (August). Uconn Basketball (Oct).
Special Weekly Sections: Parade (Weekend); Time Out (Thursday); Food Day (Wednesday). Homes Plus (Sat). Autos Plus (Sat).
Syndicated Publications: Parade (Weekend), Relish (Monthly), American Profile (Weekly).
Publisher .... Elizabeth S. Ellis
Vice President for Finance .... Walter Rudewicz
Vice President for Advertising ... William K. Sybert
Circulation Director .... Gary Catania
Vice President for News and Managing Editor Chris Powell
Assistant Managing Editor for Production .... Lee Giguere
Assistant Managing Editor for News .... Ralph W. Williams
Living Section Editor .... Chip LeClerc
Executive Sports Editor .... Brian Coyne
Vice President for Production .... Timothy Noon
State Ed. .... Kimberly Philips
Market Information: TMC; Zoned editions.
Mechanical Available: Offset; Black and 3 ROP colors; insert accepted - single sheet; page cutoffs - 21 5/8.
Mechanical Specifications: Type page 10 1/2 x 11.5; E - 5 cols, 2, 1/6 between; A - 5 cols, 2, 1/6 between; C - 8 cols, 1 1/3, 1/6 between.
Areas Served: 06231, 06232, 06278, 06043, 06016, 06237, 06238, 06026, 06118, 06108, 06088, 06029, 06082, 06033, 06248, 06040, 06042, 06045, 06250, 06071, 06074, 06075, 06076, 06077, 06078, 06084, 06066, 06093, 06279, 06095, 06096
Delivery Method: Mail, Newsstand, Carrier, RacksEquipment & Software: PRESSROOM EQUIPMENT: Lines — 10-HI/845 2000; Pasters —6-MEG; Registration System — 1 MAILROOM EQUIPMENT: Counter Stackers — 2 Quipp; Inserters & Stuffers — HI/1472; Tying Machines — 1/Power Strap, 3-/Sterling; Address Machine — 1-Domino/Ink Jet.; DISPLAY SOFTWARELayout Software — MEI. EDITORIAL SOFTWARE: Microsoft/Windows NT 4.0, CNI. PRODUCTION EQUIPMENT: Cameras — 1-C

MERIDEN

RECORD-JOURNAL

500 S Broad St, Ste 1, Meriden, Conn., 06450-6643, New Haven; gen tel (203) 235-1661; adv tel (203) 317-2407; ed tel (203) 317-2385; gen fax (203) 639-0210; adv fax (203) 235-4048; ed fax (203) 639-0210; gen/nat adv e-mail dpare@record-journal.com; disp adv e-mail dpare@record-journal.com; class adv e-mailclassified@record-journal.com; ed e-mail newsroom@record-journal.com; web site www.myrecordjournal.com

Group: The Record-Journal Publishing Co.
Published: Mon, Tues, Wed, Thur, Fri, Sat, Sun
Weekday Frequency: m
Saturday Frequency: m
Circulation: ; 12,842(sun)
Last Audit: VAC December 31, 2015
Advertising Rate (weekday/saturday): Open inch rate $36.54
News services: AP, NYT, RNS. **Established:** 1867
Own Printing Facility?: Yes
Special Editions: Spring Home & Garden (Apr); Bus & Homeroom (Aug); Holiday Gift Pages (Dec); President's Day Auto (Feb); Weddings (Jan); Services Guide (Jul); Summertime (Jun); Design-An-Ad (Mar); Business & Industry (May); Holiday Shopping (Nov); Celebrate Wallingford (O
Special Weekly Sections: Health & Fitness (Fri); Front Porch (Mon); Neighbors (S); Enjoy! (Thur); Home (Tues); Great Taste (Wed).
Syndicated Publications: Parade (S)
Pub. .... Eliot C. White
VP/Assist. to Pub. .... Elizabeth White
Sr. Vice Pres., Sales/Mktg. .... Michael Killian
Sr. Vice Pres. .... Tim Ryan
Circ. Dir. .... David Pare
Mng. Ed. .... Ralph Tomaselli
City Ed. .... Eric Cotton
News Ed. .... Michael Misarski
Chief Photographer .... Chris Zajac
Sr. Writer .... Jeffery Kurz
Asst. Sports Ed. .... Bryant Carpenter
Copy Desk Chief .... Doug Bevins
Carolyn Wallach
Digital Content Editor .... Richie Rathsack
Alison W. Muschinsky
Market Information: TMC.
Areas Served: Meridan, Wallingford, Southington & Cheshire (CT)
Delivery Method: Mail, Newsstand, Carrier, RacksEquipment & Software: PRESSROOM EQUIPMENT: Lines — outsource; Folders — 2-WH/2:1; Pasters —5, 2. BUSINESS SOFTWARE: CJ

MIDDLETOWN

THE MIDDLETOWN PRESS

386 Main St, Ste 101, Middletown, Conn., 06457-3361, Middlesex; gen tel (860) 347-3331; adv tel (860) 347-3331; ed tel (860) 347-3331; gen fax (860) 347-3380; adv fax (860) 347-3380; ed fax (860) 347-3380; gen/nat adv e-mail jgallacher@registercitizen.com; disp adv e-mail jpage@middletownpress.com; class adv e-mailsam@middletownpress.com; ed e-mail editor@middletownpress.com; web site www.middletownpress.com
1,394,520(visitors)

Group: Digital First Media
Published: Mon, Tues, Wed, Thur, Fri, Sat
Weekday Frequency: m
Saturday Frequency: m
Circulation: 6,114; 6,114(sat)
Last Audit: Sworn/Estimate/Non-Audited September 30, 2017
Advertising Rate (weekday/saturday): Open inch rate $19.84
News services: AP, NYT, LAT-WP. **Established:** 1884
Special Editions: Summer Entertaining (Apr); College Student's Guide (Aug); Last Minute Gift Guide (Dec); Valentine (Feb); Super Bowl (Jan); Hartford Open (Jul); Middlesex Summer (Jun); March Madness (Mar); Summer Preview (May); Coupon Book (Monthly); Thanksgiving (Nov); M
Special Weekly Sections: Auto (Fri); Seniors (Mon); Real Estate (Sat); Entertainer (Thur); Health (Tues); Food (Wed)
Syndicated Publications: Parade (Weekly).
Digital Platform - Mobile: Apple
Digital Platform - Tablet: Apple iOS
Group Ed. .... Matt DeRienzo
Adv. Dir. .... John Gallacher

Class. ....Sam Spencer
Ed. ....John Berry
Circ. Dir. ....Phil Hudson
Pub. ....Kevin Corrado
Exec. Ed. ....Mark Brackenbury
Market Information: TMC.
Mechanical Available: Offset; Black and 3 ROP colors; insert accepted - pocket books, free-standing stuffers, etc.; page cutoffs - 21 3/8.
Mechanical Specifications: Type page 13 x 22 1/2; E - 6 cols, 1 7/8, 1/8 between; A - 6 cols, 1 7/8, 1/8 between; C - 9 cols, 1 3/8, 3/16 between.
Areas Served: Middlesex County (CT) Equipment & Software: MAILROOM EQUIPMENT: Tying Machines — 1-Sa/Ty.; CLASSIFIED EQUIPMENT: Printers — Xante; DISPLAY SOFTWAREAd Make-up Applications — Mk/Ad Builder, Multi-Ad, QPS/QuarkXPress.; EDITORIAL EQUIPMENT: Hardware — HP laptops, Netbooks EDITORIAL SOFTWARE: Prestige (remote) PRODUCTION EQUIPMENT: Hardware — 1-C.
Note: The Middletown Press shares a combined Sunday edition with The New Haven Register.

NEW BRITAIN

NEW BRITAIN HERALD

One Liberty Square, 3rd Floor, New Britain, Conn., 6050, Hartford; gen tel (860) 225-4601; adv tel (860) 229-8687; ed tel (860) 225-4601; gen fax (860) 225-2611; adv fax (860) 229-5718; ed fax (860) 223-8171; gen/nat adv e-mail lfletcher@newbritainherald.com; disp adv e-mail gcurran@newbritainherald.com; class adv e-mailgcurran@newbritainherald.com; ed e-mail mbatterson@newbritainherald.com; web site www.newbritainherald.com
- 419,000(views) 63,000(visitors)
Group: Central Connecticut Communications LLC
Published: Mon, Tues, Wed, Thur, Fri, Sat, Sun
Weekday Frequency: m
Saturday Frequency: m
Circulation: 4,054; 4,054(sat); 7,907(sun)
Last Audit: AAM March 31, 2015
Advertising Rate (weekday/saturday): Open inch rate $30.65
News services: AP. **Established:** 1880
Special Editions: Senior Citizens (Apr); Coupon Book (Aug); Christmas Song Book (Dec); Presidents' Sale (Feb); Health & Fitness (Jan); Crazy Days (Jul); Father's Day Co-op (Jun); Basketball (Mar); Mother's Day Dining (May); Homefinder (Monthly); Thanksgiving Dining (Nov);
Special Weekly Sections: Your Weekend (Fri); Property Transfers (Mon); Health and Tech (S); Rental Guide (Sat); Auto (Thur); Classroom (Tues); Best Food Day (Wed).
Syndicated Publications: USA WEEKEND Magazine (S).
Ed. & Pub. ....Michael E. Schroeder
Sports Ed. ....Matt Straub
Prepress Mgr. ....Wayne DePaolo
Adv. Mgr. ....Gary Curran
Mng. Ed. ....Brad Carroll
Market Information: Split run; TMC; Zoned editions.
Mechanical Available: Offset; Black and 3 ROP colors; insert accepted; page cutoffs - 21 3/4.
Mechanical Specifications: Type page 12 x 21 1/2; E - 6 cols, 1 5/6, 1/6 between; A - 6 cols, 1 5/6, 1/6 between; C - 10 cols, 1 1/4, 1/16 between.
Areas Served: New Britain, Berlin, Plainville, Newington, Wethersfield & Southington (CT) Equipment & Software: PRESSROOM EQUIPMENT: Lines — 6-G/Metro (2 half decks); Reels & Stands — 6; MAILROOM EQUIPMENT: Counter Stackers — 1-SH/Backup, 1-QWI/351; Inserters & Stuffers — 2-MM/227; Tying Machines — 1/CYP, 2-/Sa, 2-/Bu, 1-/MLN, 2-MLN/2A; Address Machine — 1-/Ch.; BUSINESS EQUIPMENT: Sun/Micro Systems BUSINESS SOFTWARE: Vision Data CLASSIFIED EQUIPMENT: Hardware — AT; 5-Pentium/ALR; Printers — Software AT.; DISPLAY EQUIPMENT: Hardware — 7-APP/Mac; Printers — 2-QMS/860; DISPLAY SOFTWAREAd Make-up Applications — Multi-Ad, QPS/

QuarkXPress.; EDITORIAL EQUIPMENT: Hardware — CNI, 25-Pentium/100-166/2-Ultre/4000 Imagesetters; Printers — 2-Xante/8200 EDITORIAL SOFTWARE: CNI, Microsoft/Word for Windows, QPS/QuarkXPress. PRODUCTION EQUIPMENT: Hardware — 2-Ultra/4000, 1-Nu/Flip Top; Cameras — 1-C/Marathon; Scanners — Lf/Leafax 35.
Note: The Herald Press is a combined Sunday edition of The Bristol Press (e), Middletown Press (m) and (New Britain) Herald (e).

NEW HAVEN

NEW HAVEN REGISTER

100 Gando Dr, New Haven, Conn., 06513-1049, New Haven; gen tel (203) 789-5200; adv tel (203) 789-5200; ed tel (203) 789-5708; gen fax (203) 789-5209; adv fax (203) 789-5770; ed fax (203) 789-5209; gen/nat adv e-mail pprovost@digitalfirstmedia.com; disp adv e-mail pprovost@digitalfirstmedia.com; class adv e-mailclassified@nhregister.com; ed e-mail letters@nhregister.com; web site www.nhregister.com
899,392(visitors)
Group: Hearst Communications, Inc.
Published: Mon, Tues, Wed, Thur, Fri, Sat, Sun
Weekday Frequency: m
Saturday Frequency: m
Circulation: 29,730; 23,421(sat); 47,748(sun)
Last Audit: AAM September 30, 2016
Advertising Rate (weekday/saturday): 1/60 Pg $298.50
Advertising Rate (sunday): 1/60 Pg $376.60
News services: AP, SHNS, LAT-WP, MCT, NYT, TMS. **Established:** 1812
Special Editions: NCAA Section (Apr); Courses & Careers (Aug); Holiday Gift Guides (Dec); Internet Guide (Feb); Walter Camp Football Foundation (Jan); Menu Guide (Jul); International Festival Arts/Ideas (Jun); Home Show (Mar); Zoomers (May); Business Expo (Nov); Luxury Liv
Special Weekly Sections: Spirit, Finance, Business (Mon); Health, Science, Zone (Tue); Best Food (Wed); Lifestyle, Zone (Thur); Weekend, Gardening, Overdrive Auto (Fri); Home Furnishing, Home, Real Estate, Cars (Sat); Arts, Travel, TV, Living (Sun)
Syndicated Publications: USA WEEKEND Magazine (S); Parade (Weekly).
Digital Platform - Mobile: Apple, Android
Digital Platform - Tablet: Apple iOS, Android
Credit Mgr. ....Helen Rogers
Display Adv. Dir. ....Kelly Tremaine
Promo. Mgr. ....Kristen Alves
Circ. Mgr. ....Tim Solt
Ed. ....Jack Kramer
Arts/Travel Ed. ....Donna Doherty
Bus. Ed. ....Cara Baruzzi
Editorial Page Ed. ....Charles P. Kochakian
Entertainment Ed. ....Patrick Ferrucci
Graphics Ed. ....Ann Dallas
Librarian ....Angel Diggs
Living Ed. ....Richard Sandella
Photo Ed. ....Vern Williams
Radio/Television Ed. ....Joseph Amarante
Sports Ed. ....Sean Barker
State/City Ed. ....Helen Bennett Harvey
Pres./Pub. ....Kevin Corrado
Market Information: Split run; TMC; Zoned editions.
Mechanical Available: Offset; Black and 3 ROP colors; insert accepted - die cut, straight edge one side; page cutoffs - 22 2/25.
Mechanical Specifications: Type page 12 x 21; E - 6 cols, 1 7/8, 1/8 between; A - 6 cols, 1 7/8, 1/8 between; C - 10 cols, 1 1/4, 1/16 between.
Areas Served: New Haven County
Delivery Method: Mail, Newsstand, Carrier, RacksEquipment & Software: PRESSROOM EQUIPMENT: Lines — 7-G/Metroliner-3272 double width (3 half decks); 7-G/Metroliner 3273 double width (3 half decks); Folders — 2-G/Imperial 3:2; Reels & Stands — 14-G/45 RTP 3-arm; Control System — G/EPCS-PAR.; MAILROOM EQUIPMENT: Counter Stackers — 4-GMA/CombiStack, 1-MM/310, 1-HL/Monitor, 1-HL/Dual Carrier, 2-QWI/501, 1-QWI/451; Inserters & Stuffers — 1-GMA/SLS 2000 22:1, 2-GMA/SLS 3000 16:2; Tying Machines — 4-Dynaric;

BUSINESS EQUIPMENT: IBM/AS-400 E50, DEC/4000 BUSINESS SOFTWARE: INSI, CJ CLASSIFIED EQUIPMENT: Hardware — AT/with 30 workstation; 8-APP/Mac; Printers — Epson/FX1050, Lintronic, HP/LaserPrinter; CLASSIFIED SOFTWARE: AT/Release 4.7.7. DISPLAY EQUIPMENT: Hardware — APP/Mac G3; Printers — APP/Mac, MON/600; Other Hardware — 2-X/765 Flatbed Scanner, APP/Mac G3 DISPLAY SOFTWAREAd Make-up Applications — Multi-Ad/Creator 4.0.1, QPS/QuarkXPress 4.04; Layout Software — MEI/ALS 25. EDITORIAL EQUIPMENT: Hardware — AT/9-APP/Mac, 40-RSK/100, 24-IBM/PS 2, Lf/AP Leaf Picture Desk; Printers — Panasonic/1124, NEC/P5300 EDITORIAL SOFTWARE: Prestige. PRODUCTION EQUIPMENT: Hardware — 2-MON/Express 1200, 2-PPRMSTR/600, 1-Lf/Leafscan 45, 2-Glunz & Jensen; Cameras — 2-C/Spartan III PRODUCTION SOFTWARE: Prestige.

NEW LONDON

THE DAY

47 Eugene Oneill Dr, New London, Conn., 06320-6306, New London; gen tel (860) 442-2200; adv tel (860) 701-4200; ed tel (860) 440-1000; gen fax (860) 437-1176; adv fax (860) 442-5443; ed fax (860) 437-1176; gen/nat adv e-mail b.briere@theday.com; disp adv e-mail advertising1@theday.com; class adv e-mailclass@theday.com; ed e-mail m.nadolny@theday.com; web site www.theday.com
- 3,500,000(views) 553,000(visitors)
Group: The Day Publishing Co.
Published: Mon, Tues, Wed, Thur, Fri, Sat, Sun
Weekday Frequency: m
Saturday Frequency: m
Circulation: 22,977; 22,564(sat); 24,042(sun)
Last Audit: AAM June 30, 2016
Advertising Rate (weekday/saturday): Open inch rate $52.35
Advertising Rate (sunday): Open inch rate $59.50
News services: AP, CQ, NYT, MCT, New England News Service, TMS. **Established:** 1881
Own Printing Facility?: Yes
Commercial Printers?: Yes
Special Editions: Education Guide (Bi-annually); DaySaver - Coupons (Monthly); Special Auto (Bi-annually); Dining (Annually); Song Book (Annually); Gift Guide (Annually)
Special Weekly Sections: Travel, Employment, Business, Marketplace, Daybreak (Sun); Education (Mon); Best Food, Recruitment (Wed); Night and Day (Thur); Real Estate, Home Court, Beliefs (Fri); Auto, Military, People (Sat)
Syndicated Publications: Mystic Country Magazine (Annually); Go Westerly Magazine (Annually), Grace Magazine (Bi-Monthly); Sound & Country Magazine (Quarterly)
Digital Platform - Mobile: Apple, Android
Digital Platform - Tablet: Apple iOS, Android
Pub./Ed. ....Lisa Miksis
Adv. Mgr. ....Bob Briere
Managing Editor ....Tim Cotter
Director of Operations ....William Langman
Director of Audience DevelopmentDaniel Williams
Director of Information Technology..............Chris Cleaveland
Commercial Print Sales Manager... Michael Flaig
Product Manager ....Colleen Proctor
Press Manager ....Timothy Tighe
Advertising Services Manager ....Christine Brown
Classified Advertising Manager Bence Strickland
Sales Development Manager ....David Gellar
Managing Editor/Multimedia........ Sally Stapleton
Deputy Managing Editor/News Operations ....Carol McCarthy
AME/Reporters.............................Lisa McGinley
Purchasing Agent.......................Mel Seeger
Adv. Mgr., Classified ....Richard Zesk
Adv. Mgr., Classified/Telephone Sales..... Roberta McLaughlin
Adv. Dir. ....Shawn E. Palmer
Adv. Mgr., Retail ....Diane Martin
Circ. Dir. ....Mark L. Barry
Circ. Mgr. ....Janet M. Ballestrini
Pub ....Gary Farrugia
Market Information: TMC; Zoned editions.
Mechanical Available: Offset; Black and 3 ROP

colors; insert accepted - product samples accepted with conditions; page cutoffs - 21.
Mechanical Specifications: Type page 12 1/4 x 21; E - 6 cols, 2 1/16, 1/8 between; A - 6 cols, 2 1/16, 1/8 between; C - 10 cols, 1 7/32, 1/16 between.
Areas Served: Southeastern Connecticut
Delivery Method: Newsstand, Carrier, RacksEquipment & Software: PRESSROOM EQUIPMENT: Lines — 7-G/Headliner Offset double width 1988; 1-HI/248 Sheet; Komori/GS228P Sheet 2003; 1-Ryobi/envelope; Press Drive — Allen Bradley; Folders — G/Imperial 3:2, 2; Pasters —G/RTP4SReels & Stands — 7; Control System — Press Control System; MAILROOM EQUIPMENT: Counter Stackers — 2-QWI/200, 3-QWI/350, 1-QWI/400; Inserters & Stuffers — S/NP630 22-stations; Tying Machines — 6/Power Strap, 3-/Power Strap/3/4 Wraps, 3-Matthews/Ink Jet System; Control System — QWI/Programmer, ICON/300; Address Machine — Addressing m; BUSINESS EQUIPMENT: IBM/Lenovo BUSINESS SOFTWARE: Microsoft (various) CLASSIFIED EQUIPMENT: Hardware — IBM; Printers — HP/Konica, CLASSIFIED SOFTWARE: Miles 33/Futureproof DISPLAY EQUIPMENT: Hardware — IBM/Apple; Printers — HP/Konica; Other Hardware — HP/Konica DISPLAY SOFTWAREAd Make-up Applications — Adobe CS3; EDITORIAL EQUIPMENT: Hardware — IBM/Lenovo; Printers — HP/Konica EDITORIAL SOFTWARE: MediaSpectrum/ContentWatch

NORWALK

THE HOUR

301 Merritt 7, 4th Floor, Norwalk, Conn., 6851, Fairfield; gen tel (203) 846-3281; adv tel (203) 354-1093; ed tel (203) 354-1062; gen fax (203) 846-9897; adv fax (203)846-9897; ed fax (203) 846-9897; gen/nat adv e-mail jbrosz@thehour.com; disp adv e-mail jreid@thehour.com; class adv e-mailclassified@thehour.com; ed e-mail news@thehour.com; web site www.thehour.com
- 1,500,000(views) 205,000(visitors)
Group: Hearst Communications, Inc.
Published: Mon, Tues, Wed, Thur, Fri, Sat, Sun
Weekday Frequency: m
Saturday Frequency: m
Circulation: 10,935; 10,935(sat); 12,965(sun)
Last Audit: AAM December 31, 2015
Advertising Rate (weekday/saturday): $34.15/col inch daily
Advertising Rate (sunday): $34.15/col inch daily
Online Advertising Rate: Leaderboard ROS $12 CPM
Medium ROS $14 CPM
Sliding Billboard ROS $15.50 CPM
News services: AP, MCT. **Established:** 1871
Own Printing Facility?: No
Commercial Printers?: No
Special Editions: The Stamford Times
Wilton Villager
Special Weekly Sections: Health (Tues); Entertainment (Thur); Fitness (Tues)
Syndicated Publications: USA WEEKEND Magazine (S); American Profile (Weekly). Relish (Monthly), Spry (Monthly)
Digital Platform - Mobile: Apple, Android, Windows
Digital Platform - Tablet: Apple iOS
Pub./COO ....Chet Valiante
Classified Advertising Supervisor Jocelyn Battista
Bus. Systems Mgr. ....Peter Kish
Co-Managing Editor, Bus. Ed. ....Chris Bosak
Editor Emeritus ....John P. Reilly
Asst. Sports Ed. ....George Albano
VP Sales & Marketing ....John Brosz
President...............................Brett Whitton
Asst. Circulation Director........Darlene Temple
News Editor ....Jeff Dale
Managing Sports Editor ....John Nash
Production Director...............Robert Marsala
Advertising Manager ....Jim Reid
Executive Assistant to the Publisher....Lorna Sura
Regional Editor - Wilton Villager, Stamford Times. Chase Wright
Advertising Director ....Debra Hanson
Ed. ....Jeannette Ross
Market Information: TMC.

Areas Served: Norwalk & Surrounding areas
Delivery Method: Mail, Newsstand, Carrier, RacksEquipment & Software: BUSINESS EQUIPMENT: 2-HP/3000 BUSINESS SOFTWARE: CJ CLASSIFIED EQUIPMENT: Hardware — 8-APP/Mac G3; Printers — 1-GCC/Elite XL; CLASSIFIED SOFTWARE: Baseview/Ad Manager Pro 2.06. DISPLAY EQUIPMENT: Hardware — 2-HP/3000; DISPLAY SOFTWAREAd Make-up Applications — CJ; Layout Software — CJ. EDITORIAL EQUIPMENT: Hardware — 4-APP/Mac 7200, 1-APP/Mac 9600, 1-APP/Mac 8600, 36-APP/Mac G3/1-Dell/ Pentium PC; Printers — 2-HP/LaserJet 8000 EDITORIAL SOFTWARE: Baseview/ NewsEdit Pro IQUE 3.2.3. PRODUCTION EQUIPMENT: Hardware — Caere/OmniPage Pro 7.0, AP/Picture Desk Server; Scanners — JK&A/1Z70 PRODUCTION SOFTWARE: QPS/QuarkXPress 4.1.

NORWICH

THE BULLETIN

10 Railroad Ave, Norwich, Conn., 06360-5829, New London; gen tel (860) 887-9211; adv tel (860) 887-9211; ed tel (860) 887-9211; gen fax (860) 887-1949; adv fax (860) 887-1949; ed fax (860) 887-1949; gen/nat adv e-mail ttergeoglou@norwichbulletin.com; disp adv e-mail ttergeoglou@norwichbulletin.com; class adv e-mailclassifieds@ norwichbulletin.com; ed e-mail news@ norwichbulletin.com; web site www. norwichbulletin.com
Group: New Media Investment Group
Published: Mon, Tues, Wed, Thur, Fri, Sat, Sun
Weekday Frequency: m
Saturday Frequency: m
Circulation: 11,352; 11,352(sat); 14,990(sun)
Last Audit: AAM June 30, 2016
Advertising Rate (weekday/saturday): Open inch rate $38.53
Advertising Rate (sunday): Open inch rate $43.14
News services: AP, GNS. **Established:** 1791
Own Printing Facility?: Yes
Commercial Printers?: No
Special Editions: Spring Home & Garden (Apr); Back-to-School (Aug); Holiday Gift Guides (Dec); Home Improvement (Feb); Job Fair (Jan); Back-to-School (Jul); Job Fair (Jun); Job Fair (Mar); Spring Home & Garden (May); Job Fair (Nov); Job Fair (Sept).
Special Weekly Sections: Best Food (Wed/Sun); Business (Mon); Healthy, Living, Technology (Tue); Entertainment, Home Improvement, Furnishing, Gardening (Thur); Auto (Sat); Society, Building, Business (Sun)
Syndicated Publications: USA WEEKEND Magazine (S).
Digital Platform - Mobile: Apple, Android, Blackberry
Pub. ....Chris Voccio
Controller/Director of Operations/Pub. ....Nadine McBride
Exec. Editor .... Jim Konrad
Editorial Page Ed. .... Ray Hackett
Advertising Director .... Dan Graziano
Circ. Mgr. .... Michele Marquis
Mktg. Dir. .... Sara Glynn
Market Information: Split run; TMC.
Mechanical Available: Offset; Black and 3 ROP colors; insert accepted - sample bags; page cutoffs - 22 3/4.
Mechanical Specifications: Type page 11 5/8 x 21 1/2; E - 6 cols, 1 5/6, 1/8 between; A - 6 cols, 1 5/6, 1/8 between; C - 10 cols, 1 1/25, 1/12 between.
Areas Served: Eastern Connecticut
Delivery Method: Mail, Newsstand, Carrier, RacksEquipment & Software: DISPLAY EQUIPMENT: Hardware — PC; EDITORIAL EQUIPMENT: Hardware — 5-MS/NT Server, 39-PC; Printers — Pre Press/Panther Pro EDITORIAL SOFTWARE: Microsoft/Word 97, QPS/QuarkXPress 3.32. PRODUCTION EQUIPMENT: Hardware — Pre Press/ Panther Plus, Adobe/Photoshop; Scanners — Kk/RFS 2035 Plus, Microtek PRODUCTION SOFTWARE: QPS/QuarkXPress 4.11.

OLD GREENWICH

GREENWICH TIME

1445 E Putnam Ave, Ste 6, Old Greenwich, Conn., 06870-1377, Fairfield; gen tel (203) 625-4400; adv tel (203) 964-2428; ed tel (203) 964-2293; gen fax (203) 625-4419; adv fax (203) 964-3773; ed fax (203) 964-2345; gen/nat adv e-mail ehuron@hearstmediact. com; disp adv e-mail twhite@hearstmediact. com; class adv e-mailclassified@scni.com; ed e-mail editorials@scni.com; web site www. greenwichtime.com
- 22,000,000(views) 376,537(visitors)
Group: Hearst Communications, Inc.
Published: Mon, Tues, Wed, Thur, Fri, Sat, Sun
Weekday Frequency: m
Saturday Frequency: m
Circulation: 5,221; 4,224(sat); 6,749(sun)
Last Audit: AAM September 30, 2015
News services: AP, LAT-WP, MCT. **Established:** 1877
Own Printing Facility?: No
Commercial Printers?: No
Special Editions: New York Auto Show (Apr); Survey of Education (Aug); Great Gift Ideas (Dec); Cruise/Guide (Feb); Weddings (Jan); Travel (Jul); Water, Water, Water (Jun); Home (Mar); New England Vacations (May); Holiday Countdown (Nov); Kitchen & Bath (Oct); Bahamas Trave
Special Weekly Sections: Weekend (Fri); Family Room (Mon); Travel (S); Life & Style (Thur); Health (Tues); Food (Wed).
Syndicated Publications: Parade (S).
Digital Platform - Mobile: Apple, Android
Digital Platform - Tablet: Apple iOS, Android
Pub. ....Michelle McAbee
Exec. Editor .... Barbara Roessner
Sports Editor ....Chris McNamee
Vice Pres. Operations ....Craig Allen
Prodn. Mgr., Pre Press ....Dennis Tidrick
Group Publisher and President .. Henry B. Haitz III
Business Editior ....Stephanie Borise
Mng. Ed. ....Thomas Mellana
Market Information: Split run; TMC; Zoned editions.
Mechanical Available: Offset; Black and 3 ROP colors; insert accepted; page cutoffs - 22 3/4.
Mechanical Specifications: Type page 12 x 21 1/2; E - 6 cols, 1 7/8, 1/6 between; A - 6 cols, 1 7/8, 1/6 between; C - 10 cols, 1 7/8, 1/6 between.
Areas Served: 06830, 06831, 06807, 06870, 06878
Delivery Method: Mail, Newsstand, Carrier, RacksEquipment & Software: PRESSROOM EQUIPMENT: Pasters —9-MEG/ Automatic; Reels & Stands — MEG.; MAILROOM EQUIPMENT: Counter Stackers — 1-QWI/3500, 1-QWI/3500, 1/ QWI; Inserters & Stuffers — 1-HI/1472; Tying Machines — 4-OVL/JP40; Address Machine — 2-KR/215, 1-Barstrom/In-Line; BUSINESS EQUIPMENT: 1-DEC/VAX 4100, CJ CLASSIFIED EQUIPMENT: Hardware — 3-APP/Mac G3, DTI/Enterprise 450; Printers — AII/3850, HP/4050; CLASSIFIED SOFTWARE: DTI/Class Speed, Baseview/ Ad Manager, Plan Builder. DISPLAY EQUIPMENT: Hardware — APP/Mac; Printers — APP/Mac LaserWriters, Graphic Enterprises/PS 3; DISPLAY SOFTWAREAd Make-up Applications — Multi-Ad/Creator, QPS/QuarkXPress; Layout Software — 13-APP/Mac, AII/SQL, Baseview. EDITORIAL EQUIPMENT: Hardware — 30-APP/Mac/ Lf/AP Leaf Picture Desk, APP/Mac, Kk/ Scanners; Printers — Graphic Enterprises/PS 3, III/3850 EDITORIAL SOFTWARE: QPS/ QuarkXPress, Adobe/Photoshop, Baseview/ Newsedit Pro IQUE, Adobe/Illustrator. PRODUCTION EQUIPMENT: Hardware — 2-Nu/Flip Top, 2-WL/38D; Scanners — Kk/ Scanner, 2-Linotype-Hell.
Note: Printed at the Connecticut Post Plant. For detailed mechanical equipment information, see the Stamford Advocate listing. Advertising is sold in combination with the Stamford Advocate (mS) for $80.80(d) and $89.70(S). Individual newspaper rates not made a

PAWCATUCK

THE WESTERLY SUN

99 Mechanic St, Pawcatuck, Conn., 06379-2187, New London; gen tel (401) 348-1000; gen fax (401) 348-5080; disp adv e-mail ktremaine@thewesterlysun.com; class adv e-mailclassified@thewesterlysun.com; ed e-mail editorial@thewesterlysun.com; web site www.thewesterlysun.com
- 2(views) 377,346(visitors)
Group: Sun Publishing Company
Published: Mon, Tues, Wed, Thur, Fri, Sat, Sun
Weekday Frequency: m
Saturday Frequency: m
Circulation: 6,003; 6,003(sat); 6,642(sun)
Last Audit: CAC September 30, 2015
Advertising Rate (weekday/saturday): Open inch rate $19.00
News services: AP. **Established:** 1856
Own Printing Facility?: No
Commercial Printers?: No
Special Editions: Christmas Gift Guide (Dec); Automobile (Feb); Year-in-Review (Jan); Schoolboy Football (Nov); Automobile (Oct); Home Improvement (Sept).
Special Weekly Sections: Places in the Sun (Fri); Business (S); Business (Sat); The Guide (Thur); Food (Wed).
Syndicated Publications: Relish (Monthly); USA WEEKEND Magazine (S); American Profile (Weekly).
VP & Editor ....David Tranchida
VP and Advertising director ....John Layton
Sr. Vice Pres. ....Shawn Palmer
Circ Dir ....Dave Pare
News & Digital Editor ....Corey Fyke
Digital Advertising Mgr ....Heather Caulkins
Classified Adv. Mgr ....Karen Davis
Assoc. Ed. ....Mike Souza
Sales Dir ....Mike Blais
Associate Publisher
Kelly Tremaine
Market Information: Split run; TMC.
Mechanical Available: Offset; Black and 3 ROP colors; insert accepted - all; page cutoffs - 22 3/4.
Mechanical Specifications: Type page 11 5/8 x 21 1/2; E - 6 cols, 1 13/16, 1/8 between; A - 6 cols, 1 13/16, 1/8 between; C - 8 cols, 1 3/8, 1/8 between.
Areas Served: Washington County & New London County (CT)
Delivery Method: Mail, Newsstand, Carrier, RacksEquipment & Software: PRESSROOM EQUIPMENT: Lines — 6-HI/V-15A single width.; MAILROOM EQUIPMENT: Counter Stackers — 1/QWI; Inserters & Stuffers — 1-/S; Tying Machines — 1-/Strapex, 1-/Power Strap.; BUSINESS EQUIPMENT: 1-DEC/BL 2 CLASSIFIED EQUIPMENT: Hardware — PC; CLASSIFIED SOFTWARE: Brainworks. DISPLAY EQUIPMENT: Printers — 2-HP/ LaserJet IV; Other Hardware — 1-HP/ ScanJet IIcx DISPLAY SOFTWAREAd Make-up Applications — Aldus/FreeHand 3.1, Adobe/Photoshop 2.5, Microsoft/ Word 5.1a, Multi-Ad/Creator 3.5; Layout Software — 3-APP/Mac Quadra 800. EDITORIAL EQUIPMENT: Hardware — PC. PRODUCTION EQUIPMENT: Hardware — 2-COM/Unisetter; Cameras — 1-Nu/18 x 24; Scanners — Lf/AP Scanner, AG/Flatbed.

STAMFORD

THE ADVOCATE

9A Riverbend Dr S, Stamford, Conn., 06907-2524, Fairfield; gen tel (203) 964-2200; adv tel (203) 964-2428; ed tel (203) 964-2293; gen fax (203) 964-2345; adv fax (203) 964-3773; ed fax (203) 964-2345; gen/nat adv e-mail scniads@scni.com; disp adv e-mail scniads@scni.com; class adv e-mailclassified@scni.com; ed e-mail editorials@scni.com; web site www. stamfordadvocate.com
- 22,000,000(views) 404,362(visitors)
Group: Hearst Communications, Inc.
Published: Mon, Tues, Wed, Thur, Fri, Sat, Sun
Weekday Frequency: m
Saturday Frequency: m
Circulation: 8,597; 6,620(sat); 12,267(sun)
Last Audit: AAM September 30, 2015

Advertising Rate (weekday/saturday): Open inch rate $80.80
Advertising Rate (sunday): Open inch rate $89.70
News services: AP, LAT-WP, MCT. **Established:** 1829
Special Editions: Garden (Apr); Educational Outlook (Aug); Steppin Out New Years (Dec); Business & Economic Review (Feb); Educational Outlook (Jan); Healthy Connections (Jul); Summer Party Guide (Jun); NY Auto Show (Mar); Health & Wellness (May); Stamford Business Outlook
Special Weekly Sections: Family, Technology (Mon); Health, Fitness (Tue; Best Food (Wed); Weekend (Thur); Life, Real Estate, Auto (Fri); Religion (Sat); Arts, Travel, TV Times, Neighbors, Community, Comics (Sun)
Syndicated Publications: Color Comics (S).
Digital Platform - Mobile: Apple, Android
Digital Platform - Tablet: Apple iOS, Android
Pub. ....Michelle McAbee
Vice Pres., Opns./Circ. Dir. ....Craig Allen
Gen. Mgr. ....Vincent Yade
Ed. ....Christine Hall
Bus. Ed. ....James Zebora
Editorial Page Ed. ....Tom Mellano
Sports Ed. ....Tom Renner
Prodn. Mgr., Pre Press ....Dennis Tidrick
Prodn. Mgr., Transportation .....Trevor Viechweg
Prodn. Supvr., Pagination-Night ....Robert Reed
Market Information: Split run; TMC; Zoned editions.
Mechanical Available: Offset; Black and 3 ROP colors; insert accepted; page cutoffs - 22 3/4.
Mechanical Specifications: Type page 11 5/8 x 21 1/2; E - 6 cols, 1 7/8, 1/6 between; A - 6 cols, 1 7/8, 1/6 between; C - 10 cols, 1 1/8, 1/6 between.
Areas Served: Stamford (IL)
Equipment & Software: PRESSROOM EQUIPMENT: Lines — 8-HI/1660 offset double width 1982, 2-HI/1660 double width 1991; Pasters —9-MEG/Automatic; Reels & Stands — MEG.; MAILROOM EQUIPMENT: Counter Stackers — 1-QWI/3500, 1-QWI/3500, 1-QWI/3500; Inserters & Stuffers — 1-HI/1472 online; Tying Machines — 4-OVL/JP40; Address Machine — 2-KR/215; BUSINESS EQUIPMENT: 1-DEC/ VAX 4100, CJ CLASSIFIED EQUIPMENT: Hardware — 1-DTI/Enterprise 450, 35-APP/ Mac G3; Printers — AII/3850, HP/4050; CLASSIFIED SOFTWARE: DTI/ClassSpeed. DISPLAY EQUIPMENT: Hardware — APP/ Mac; Printers — APP/Mac LaserWriters, Graphic Enterprises/PS 3, III/3850; DISPLAY SOFTWAREAd Make-up Applications — Multi-Ad/Creator, QPS/QuarkXPress 4.1; Layout Software — 13-APP/Mac, AII/SQL Admanager. EDITORIAL EQUIPMENT: Hardware — 75-APP/Mac/Lf/AP Leaf Picture Desk, Nikon/Scanners; Printers — Graphic Enterprises/PS 3, III/3850 EDITORIAL SOFTWARE: QPS/QuarkXPress 4.1, Adobe/Photoshop, Baseview/NewsEdit Pro IQUE, Adobe/Illustrator. PRODUCTION EQUIPMENT: Hardware — 3-III/3850, 1-KFM; Scanners — Kk/scanner, 1-Linotype-Hell, 1-Linotype-Hell PRODUCTION SOFTWARE: QPS/QuarkXPress 4.1.
Note: Advertising is sold in combination with the Greenwich Time (mS) for $80.80(d) and $89.70(S). Individual newspaper rates not made available.

TORRINGTON

THE REGISTER CITIZEN

59 Field St, Torrington, Conn., 06790-4942, Litchfield; gen tel (860) 489-3121; adv tel (860) 489-3121 ext. 312; ed tel (860) 489-3121; gen fax (860) 489-6790; adv fax (860) 626-7196; ed fax (860) 489-6790; gen/nat adv e-mail advertising@ registercitizen.com; disp adv e-mail advertising@registercitizen.com; class adv e-mailclassified@registercitizen.com; ed e-mail editor@registercitizen.com; web site www.registercitizen.com
1,394,520(visitors)
Group: Hearst Communications, Inc.
Published: Mon, Tues, Wed, Thur, Fri, Sat, Sun
Weekday Frequency: m
Saturday Frequency: m
Circulation: 2,069; 2,069(sat); 2,410(sun)

Last Audit: AAM September 30, 2015
Advertising Rate (weekday/saturday): Open inch rate $20.66
Advertising Rate (sunday): Open inch rate $20.66
News services: AP. **Established:** 1874
Special Editions: Home Improvement (Apr); Fall Festivals (Aug); First Night (Dec); Progress (Feb); Bridal (Jan); Torrington (Jul); Graduation (Jun); Car Care (Mar); Memorial Day Activities (May); Christmas Gift Guide (Nov); Fall Car Care (Oct); Fall Bridal (Sept).
Special Weekly Sections: Senior (Mon); Health, Science (Tue); Religion (Wed); Arts, Entertainment (Thur); Food (Fri); Auto, Real Estate (Sat); Help Wanted, Home, Garden, Local History, Business, Wedding, Engagements (Sun)
Syndicated Publications: Comics (S).
Pub. .... Matt DeRienzo
Adv. Dir. .... Donn Naparstek
Circ. Dir. .... Timothy Lee
Ed. .... John Berry
Mng. Ed. .... Liz Strillacci
Sports Ed. .... Garrett Dale
Adv. Mgr. .... John Gallacher
Market Information: ADS; Split run; TMC; Zoned editions.
Mechanical Available: Offset; Black and 3 ROP colors; insert accepted - single card; page cutoffs - 22 3/4.
Mechanical Specifications: Type page 13 x 21 1/4; E - 6 cols, 1 7/8, 1/8 between; A - 6 cols, 1 7/8, 1/8 between; C - 9 cols, 1 3/8, 1/16 between.
Areas Served: Northwestern Connecticut
Delivery Method: Mail, Newsstand, Carrier, Racks

WATERBURY

REPUBLICAN-AMERICAN

389 Meadow St, Waterbury, Conn., 06702-1808, New Haven; gen tel 203-574-3636; adv tel (203) 574-3636; ed tel (203) 574-3636; gen fax (203) 596-9277; adv fax (203) 754-0644; ed fax (203) 596-9277; gen/nat adv e-mail adres@rep-am.com; disp adv e-mail adres@rep-am.com; class adv e-mailclassads@rep-am.com; ed e-mail smacoy@rep-am.com; web site www.rep-am.com
Group: American-Republican, Incorporated
Published: Mon, Tues, Wed, Thur, Fri, Sat, Sun
Weekday Frequency: m
Saturday Frequency: m
Circulation: 33,228; 32,780(sat); 39,737(sun)
Last Audit: AAM September 30, 2016
Branch Offices: Naugatuck, Hartford, Southbury, Southington, Torrington.
Advertising Rate (weekday/saturday): Mon/Tues/Sat - $37.78 CPI; Wed/Fri. - $39.76 CPI; Thurs./Sun. - $46.93 CPI
Advertising Rate (sunday): Open inch rate $46.93
Online Advertising Rate: Digital (Online)
Open Rate is $12.00 CPM
Interstitials $14.00 CPM
News services: AP, MCT, **Established:** 1844
Own Printing Facility?: Yes
Commercial Printers?: Yes
Special Editions: Coupon Madness (Jan thru Dec). President's Day Auto (Feb); Brides Guides (Feb & Oct); Home & Energy (Feb & Oct..); Health Matters (March & Sept); Homestyle (Apr & Sept); Main St Wtby (June, Nov. & Dec); Summer Lifestyles (May); Table of Tides (May): Graduation (June); College Bound (July); Litchfield Jazz (Aug); Autumn Lifestyles (Aug); Kitchen & Bath (Oct) Holidays on Magical Mile (Nov); HS Football (Nov); Holiday Gift Guide (Nov. & Dec.); Annual Calendars (Dec).
Special Weekly Sections: Real Estate/Home, Commentary, Travel/Leisure, Comics (Sun); Technology (Sat); Best Food Day (Wed); Country Life (Thur); Connecticut Weekend (Fri): Wheels Page (Sat); Lifestyle; Business (Daily)
Syndicated Publications: Parade (S). Dash (Monthly - Wed); Athlon Sports (Monthly - Wed)
Proprietary Publications: Heritage Villager, Country Life, Southington Observer, Bristol Observer, Plainville Observer, Citizen's News, Weekend Extra
Digital Platform - Mobile: Apple, Android
Digital Platform - Tablet: Apple iOS, Android
Publisher .... William J. Pape II
Nat'l Adv. Mgr. .... Richard Welch
Advertising Director .... Susan Sprano
President .... William B. Pape
Controller .... Richard Stoll
Managing Editor .... Anne Karolyi
Human Resources Manager .... Robert Lee
Vice President/Circulation Director .... Edward Winters
Market Information: ADS; Split run; TMC; Zoned editions.
Mechanical Available: Offset; Black and 3 ROP colors; insert accepted - single sheets; page cutoffs - 22 3/4.
Mechanical Specifications: Full page 10 7/8 x 20, 6 cols
Double truck 22-5/8 x 20, 13 cols
Tabloid 9 x 10-1/2, 5 cols
Tabloid Double Truck 19-1/2 x 10-1/2, 11 cols
Column inch widths: 1col -15/8", 2col 3-1/2", 3col 5-11/32", 4col 7-3/16, 5 col 9", 6col 10-7/8".
Areas Served: 06010 to 06798
Delivery Method: Mail, Newsstand, Carrier, RacksEquipment & Software: PRESSROOM EQUIPMENT: Lines — 6-G/Metro double width (2 decks) 1969; Folders — G/2:1; Reels & Stands — 6; MAILROOM EQUIPMENT: Counter
Stackers — 6/QWI; Inserters & Stuffers — 1-HI/1472 online,
1-HI/1372; Tying Machines — 4-MLN/2A, 1-Ca/Tyers, 3-Dynaric/NP-3;
Wrapping Singles — 2-HL/Bottom Wrap, 1-QWI; Control System — MM;
Address Machine — 1-/Ch; BUSINESS EQUIPMENT: MicroSoft Hyper-V Virtualization
BUSINESS SOFTWARE: Great Plains 5.0, Circ. AR DSI/Newscycle;
Adv. AR Miles 33 CLASSIFIED SOFTWARE: Miles 33/FutureProof, Miles 33/Beacon. DISPLAY EQUIPMENT: Ad Creation outsourced DISPLAY SOFTWARELayout Software — Miles 33/Beacon. EDITORIAL EQUIPMENT: on location - Microsoft Hyper-V Virtualization EDITORIAL SOFTWARE: Saxo/Newscycle PRODUCTION EQUIPMENT: Hardware — 2 HPDL380; Scanners — 2-HP/4C PRODUCTION SOFTWARE: Polka Dots

WILLIMANTIC

THE CHRONICLE

1 Chronicle Rd, PO Box 148, Willimantic, Conn., 06226-1932, Windham; gen tel (860) 423-8466; ed tel (860) 423-8466; gen fax (860) 423-7641; ed fax (860) 423-6585; gen/nat adv e-mail advertising@thechronicle.com; disp adv e-mail advertising@thechronicle.com; class adv e-mailclassified@thechronicle.com; ed e-mail news@thechronicle.com; web site www.thechronicle.com
Group: Central Connecticut Communications LLC
Published: Mon, Tues, Wed, Thur, Fri, Sat
Weekday Frequency: e
Saturday Frequency: m
Circulation: 4,561; 5,859(sat)
Last Audit: CAC December 31, 2016
Advertising Rate (weekday/saturday): Open inch rate $27.95
News services: Reuters, McClatchy Tribune News Services **Established:** 1877
Own Printing Facility?: Yes
Commercial Printers?: Yes
Special Editions: Back-to-School (Aug); Gift Gallery (Dec); Bridal (Jan); Summer Guide (Jun); Spring Special (May); Christmas (Nov); Harvest Values (Oct); Sports (Sept).
Special Weekly Sections: Real Estate (Mon); Society/Wedding (Sat); Arts (Thur); Food (Wed).
Syndicated Publications: Album (Sat); American Profile (Weekly).
Pub. .... Patrice Crosbie
Ed. .... Charles Ryan
Adv. Dir. .... Thomas Nevers
Circ. Dir. .... Todd Charland
Prodn. Mgr. .... Lynn Coleman
Market Information: ADS; TMC.
Mechanical Available: Offset; Black and 3 ROP colors; insert accepted; page cutoffs - 21 1/2.
Mechanical Specifications: Type page 13 x 21 1/2; E - 6 cols, 2 1/16, 1/8 between; A - 6 cols, 2 1/16, 1/8 between; C - 9 cols, 1 9/16, 1/16 between.
Areas Served: 06226, 06257, 06242, 06278, 06279, 06269, 06268, 06238, 06232, 06248, 06237, 06249, 06254, 06264, 06247, 06235, 06250, 06256, 06280
Delivery Method: Mail, Newsstand, Carrier, RacksEquipment & Software: PRESSROOM EQUIPMENT: Lines — 5-WPC/Web Leader; 2-WPC/Web Leader.; MAILROOM EQUIPMENT: Tying Machines — MLN.; BUSINESS EQUIPMENT: DEC/Micro VAX II BUSINESS SOFTWARE: Vision Data CLASSIFIED EQUIPMENT: Hardware — 4-Vision Data; Printers — APP/Mac LaserWriter NT; CLASSIFIED SOFTWARE: Vision Data. DISPLAY EQUIPMENT: Hardware — 6-IBM; Printers — HP; DISPLAY SOFTWAREAd Make-up Applications — QPS/QuarkXPress.; EDITORIAL EQUIPMENT: Hardware — 20-CText, IBM; Printers — HP EDITORIAL SOFTWARE: CText. PRODUCTION EQUIPMENT: Hardware — Nat; Scanners — HP.

DELAWARE

DOVER

DELAWARE STATE NEWS

110 Galaxy Dr, Dover, Del., 19901-9262, Kent; gen tel (302) 674-3600; adv tel (302) 741-8200; ed tel (302) 741-8229; gen fax (302) 760-7459; adv fax (302) 760-7459; ed fax (302) 760-7459; gen/nat adv e-mail adsales@newszap.com; disp adv e-mail adsales@newszap.com; class adv e-mailclassads@newszap.com; ed e-mail newsroom@newszap.com; web site http://delawarestatenews.net
- 207,000(views) 72,000(visitors)
Group: Independent Newsmedia Inc. Usa
Published: Mon, Tues, Wed, Thur, Fri, Sat, Sun
Weekday Frequency: m
Saturday Frequency: m
Circulation: 8,871; 8,871(sat); 12,983(sun)
Last Audit: CAC December 31, 2016
Newspaper Reps: Tom Byrd, Publisher; Tonda Parks, Director of Advertising Development; Andrew West, Managing Editor; Heather Cregar, Promotions Manager
Advertising Rate (weekday/saturday): 1/16 Pg $176.00; 1/8 Pg $343.00; 1/6 Pg $518.00; 1/4 Pg $651.00; 1/3 Pg $915.00; 1/2 Pg $1,170.00; 3/4 Pg $1,670.00; Full page $1,988.00.
Advertising Rate (sunday): 1/16 Pg $264.00; 1/8 Pg $487.00; 1/6 Pg $620.00; 1/4 Pg $878.00; 1/3 Pg $1,098.00; 1/2 Pg $1,493.00; 3/4 Pg $2,005.00; Full page $2,386.00.
Online Advertising Rate: $30/M Leaderboard; $20/M Medium Rectangle
News services: AP **Established:** 1953
Own Printing Facility?: Yes
Commercial Printers?: Yes
Special Editions: Bridal (Feb/Oct); Black History (Feb); Holiday Gift Guide (Nov); NASCAR Race Tabs (May and Sept/Oct): Holiday Events & Celebrations (Nov/Dec); 100 Things to do this Summer (May); Summer Camp Guide (March)
Special Weekly Sections: Education (Tue); Best Food Day (Wed), Health & Wellness (Thurs); Entertainment (Fri); Religion (Sat); Real Estate, Auto (Sun); Business (Mon); NASCAR (Thurs)
Syndicated Publications: PARADE Magazine (Sunday); Select TV/Comics (Sunday)
Proprietary Publications: Kent County Profile; Sussex County Profile; Outside the Oval
Digital Platform - Mobile: Apple, Android, Windows, Blackberry
Digital Platform - Tablet: Apple iOS, Android, Windows 7, Blackberry Tablet OS, Kindle, Nook, Kindle Fire
Sr. VP New Media .... Darel LaPrade
Promo. Mgr. .... Heather Cregar
Mng. Ed. .... Andrew West
Sports Ed. .... Andy Walter
Circ. Dir. .... Rita Maier
VP, Adv. Develop. .... Tonda Parks
CEO/President .... Ed Dulin
Major Accounts Advertising Manager .... Tim Gary
Classified Manager .... Dianna Sellers
Publisher .... Tom Byrd
Printing Plant - Operations Manager Tom Bugbee
Market Information: TMC on Wednesday to greater Dover, Delaware market area.
Mechanical Available: Offset; Black and 3 ROP colors; insert accepted; 12" compact size.
Mechanical Specifications: Printed page size 10.75 x 12. 4 columns. Width of 1 column = 2.343. Width of column rule: 0.125.
Areas Served: 19709 Middletown 19711 Newark 19730 Odessa 19734 Townsend 19801 Wilmington 19901 Dover 19904 West Dover 19930 Bethany Beach 19933 Bridgeville 19934 Camden/Wyoming 19936 Cheswold 19938 Clayton 19939 Dagsboro 19940 Delmar 19941 Ellendale 19950 Farmington/ Greenwood 19943 Felton 19944 Fenwick Island 19945 Frankford 19946 Frederica 19947 Georgetown 19950 Greenwood 19951 Harbeson 19952 Harrington 19953 Hartly 19954 Houston 19955 Kenton 19956 Laurel 19958 Lewes 19960 Lincoln 19962 Magnolia 19963 Milford 19964 Marydel 19966 Millsboro/Long Neck/ Oak Orchard 19967 Millville 19968 Milton 19969 Nassau 19970 Ocean View/ Clarksville 19971 Rehoboth Beach 19973 Seaford 19975 Selbyville 19977 Smyrna 19979 Viola 19980 Woodside 21607 Barclay 21913 Cecilton 21617 Centreville 21620 Chestertown 21623 Church Hill 21628 Crumpton 21675 Delmar 21629 Denton 21632 Federalsburg 21635 Galena 21636 Goldsboro 21639 Greensboro 21640 Henderson 21645 Kennedyville 21649 Marydel 21651 Millington 21657 Queen Anne 21660 Ridgely 21661 Rock Hall 21667 Still Pond 21668 Sudlersville 21678 Worton
Delivery Method: Newsstand, Carrier, RacksEquipment & Software: PRESSROOM EQUIPMENT: Lines — Koenig & Bauer AG Colora Press; BUSINESS SOFTWARE: PBS DISPLAY EQUIPMENT: Hardware — PC; DISPLAY SOFTWAREAd Make-up Applications — In-Design, Adobe/Photoshop;
Note: Special Events - W3 What Women Want Fest (April); Best Friends Pet Expo (Oct)
Maryland-Delaware-DC Press Association Editorial and Advertising Awards

NEW CASTLE

THE NEWS JOURNAL

950 W Basin Rd, New Castle, Del., 19720-1008, New Castle; gen tel (302) 324-2500; adv tel (302) 324-2631; ed tel (302) 324-2990; gen fax (302) 324-5509; adv fax (302) 324-2620; ed fax (302) 324-2390; gen/nat adv e-mail wjames@delawareonline.com; ed e-mail jsweeny@delawareonline.com; web site www.delawareonline.com
- 8,493,535(views) 1,197,614(visitors)
Group: Gannett
Published: Mon, Tues, Wed, Thur, Fri, Sat, Sun
Weekday Frequency: m
Saturday Frequency: m
Circulation: 64,711; 63,674(sat); 78,607(sun)
Last Audit: AAM December 31, 2015
Advertising Rate (weekday/saturday): Modular Rate $300
News services: AP, GNS, LAT-WP, Baltimore Sun. **Established:** 1919
Own Printing Facility?: Yes
Special Editions: Football (Aug); Shopping Guide (Nov & Dec); Academic All Stars (Jun); Camp Guide (Mar); Beach Guide (May)
Special Weekly Sections: 55 Hours (Fri); Arts (Fri); Family (Mon); Food & Drink (Wed); Auto (Sat); Crossroads (Thurs); Family Life (Tues); Education (Sun)
Syndicated Publications: USA WEEKEND Magazine (S).
Digital Platform - Mobile: Apple, Android, Windows, Blackberry
Digital Platform - Tablet: Apple iOS, Android, Windows 7, Blackberry Tablet OS, Kindle, Nook, Kindle Fire
President & Publisher .... Susan D. Leath
Vice Pres., Adv. .... Dennis Wichterman

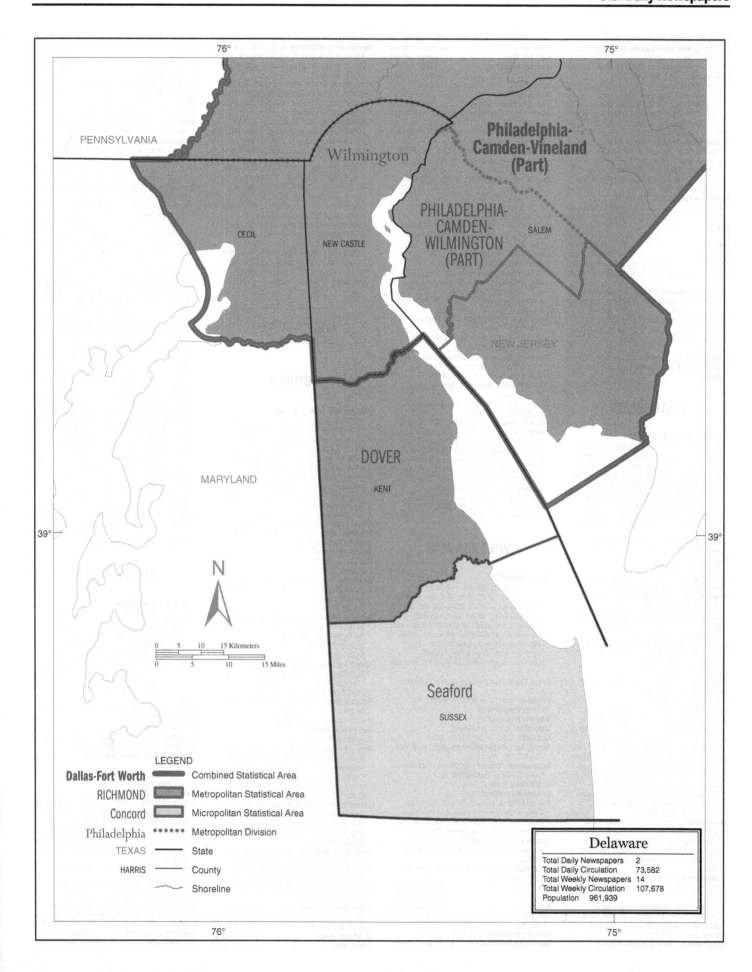

PENNSYLVANIA

Wilmington

Philadelphia-
Camden-Vineland
(Part)

CECIL

NEW CASTLE

PHILADELPHIA-
CAMDEN-
WILMINGTON
(PART)

SALEM

NEW JERSEY

MARYLAND

DOVER

KENT

39°

39°

N

| 0 | 5 | 10 | 15 Kilometers |
| 0 | 5 | 10 | 15 Miles |

Seaford

SUSSEX

LEGEND

Dallas-Fort Worth	Combined Statistical Area
RICHMOND	Metropolitan Statistical Area
Concord	Micropolitan Statistical Area
Philadelphia	•••••• Metropolitan Division
TEXAS	State
HARRIS	County
	Shoreline

Delaware

Total Daily Newspapers	2
Total Daily Circulation	73,582
Total Weekly Newspapers	14
Total Weekly Circulation	107,678
Population	961,939

76°

75°

Sales Operations Director........... Michael Walton
Marketing Director............................ Eileen Cox
Consumer Experience Director
Robert Long
Market Information: ADS; TMC; Zoned editions.
Mechanical Available: Offset; Black and 3 ROP colors; insert accepted - card inserts, custom-designed; page cutoffs - 21 1/8.
Mechanical Specifications: Type page 13 1/8 x 21 1/4; E - 6 cols, 2 1/16, 1/8 between; A - 6 cols, 2 1/16, 1/8 between; C - 10 cols, 1 1/4, 1/16 between.
Areas Served: New Castle County, Sussex County, Kent County
Delivery Method: Mail, NewsstandEquipment & Software: PRESSROOM EQUIPMENT: Lines — 8-G/Headliner Offset 1989, 1-G/ Metrocolor Tower 1994; 8-G/Headliner Offset 1989, 1-G/Metro color tower 1994; Pasters —16-G/RTP CT50; Reels & Stands — Press Registration System 2-G/ Quadtech.; MAILROOM EQUIPMENT: Counter Stackers — 3-HL/Monitor, 13/QWI; Inserters & Stuffers — 1-GE/1372, 2-HI/1472; Tying Machines — 8-/Power Strap; Wrapping Singles — 5-/Power Strap 3/4 wrap; Address Machine — 2-/Barstrom, 3-/Barstrom; BUSINESS EQUIPMENT: IBM/AS-400 BUSINESS SOFTWARE: Genesys :Circ, Adv, Lawson :Fin, Cyborg :Payroll CLASSIFIED EQUIPMENT: Hardware — IBM/Server, 35-PC; CLASSIFIED SOFTWARE: Unisys 3.0. DISPLAY EQUIPMENT: Hardware — IBM/AS-400; Printers — HP/LaserJet III, Spectraset; Other Hardware — AP AdSend, AdLink, Digiflex, Imagenet DISPLAY SOFTWAREAd Make-up Applications — Genesys; Layout Software — SCS/ Layout 8000, APP/Mac with QuarkXPress. EDITORIAL EQUIPMENT: Hardware — IBM/ Server, APP/Mac, PC/1-Colormaster/Plus, IBM, MS/NT Advanced Server, GMTI/Digital Archive; Printers — ECR/3850, ECR/Wildcat XL180 DTP EDITORIAL SOFTWARE: QPS 2.0.10. PRODUCTION EQUIPMENT: Hardware — W/Optical Plate Bender, KFM, ECR/Wildcat XL 180, Barco; Scanners — 2-Kk/2035 Pro, Umax/1200 PRODUCTION SOFTWARE: QPS 2.0.10.

DISTRICT OF COLUMBIA

WASHINGTON

THE WASHINGTON POST

1301 K St NW, Washington, D.C., 20071-0004, District Of Columbia; gen tel (202) 334-6000; adv tel (202) 334-5299; ed tel (202) 334-7410; adv fax (202) 334-7185; gen/ed fax (202) 334-5547 (Nat'l News); gen/nat adv e-mail @washpost.com; disp adv e-mail washingtonpostads@washpost.com; class adv e-mailpokusab@washpost.com; ed e-mail national@washpost.com; web site www.washingtonpost.com
- 959,000,000(views) 83,000,000(visitors)

Group: Nash Holdings
Published: Mon, Tues, Wed, Thur, Fri, Sat, Sun
Weekday Frequency: m
Saturday Frequency: m
Circulation: 349,586; 315,008(sat); 522,055(sun)
Last Audit: AAM September 30, 2016
Advertising Rate (weekday/saturday): Open inch rate
Advertising Rate (sunday): Open inch rate
News services: AFP, AP, CT, DJ, MCT, NEA, NNS, RN. **Established:** 1877
Own Printing Facility?: Yes
Commercial Printers?: Yes
Special Editions: Home & Design (Apr); Football Preview (Aug); Holiday Guide Feature (Dec); Cruise (Feb); Bridal Feature (Jan); Homes Showcase (Jul); Homes Showcase (Jun); Home Showcase (Mar); Outdoor Living Feature (May); Ski (Nov); Bermuda & the Bahamas (Oct); Fall Fashion
Special Weekly Sections: Health (Tue); Food (Wed); Local Living (Thur); Weekend (Fri); Real Estate (Sat); Travel, Outlook, Arts & Style (Sun)
Syndicated Publications: Washington Post Magazine
Digital Platform - Mobile: Apple, Android
Digital Platform - Tablet: Apple iOS, Android, Windows 7, Kindle, Nook, Kindle Fire
Vice Pres., Prodn................................Jim Coley
Director, Consumer Marketing........ Rich Handloff
Vice President........................ Gregg Fernandes
Dir. of Operations & Planning............Hugh Price
Division Manager Commercial Sales $ Deli Bryant Despeaux
Director of Advertising, MAU........... Ethan Selzer
Account Manager, National Retail...... Sheila Daw
Director of Digital Marketing............ Jared Farber
Director, Regional Sales............ Rebecca Haase
Chief Revenue Officer......................Jed Hartman
CFO/VP, Finance & Admin..........Stephen Gibson
VP, Audience Develop..........................Beth Diaz
VP, Communications....................Kristine Coratti
Partner Program Manager...............Molly Urciolo
Editor..Martin Baron
Publisher...Fred Ryan
Market Information: Split run; TMC; Zoned editions.
Mechanical Available: Letterpress and offset; Black and 3 ROP colors; insert accepted; page cutoffs - 22.
Mechanical Specifications: Type page 12 x 21; E - 6 cols, 1 15/16, 1/8 between; A - 6 cols, 1 15/16, 1/8 between; C - 10 cols, 1 1/8, 1/16 between.
Areas Served: Entire United States
Delivery Method: Mail, Newsstand, Carrier, RacksEquipment & Software: PRESSROOM EQUIPMENT: Lines — 42-G/Mark I (5:G); 18-G/Mark II (3:G); 31-G/Metro (2:G); 10-TKS/Offset (1-TKS); 46-G/MKI (6:G); Folders — 2-G/2:1, 14-G/3:2; Pasters —133, 10. MAILROOM EQUIPMENT: Counter Stackers — 28-HL/Monitor, 6-Id/330, 5-Id/440, 2-Id/220; Inserters & Stuffers — 2-S/72P, 3-HI/Collator, 6-GMA/SLS 1000, 1-GMA/ SLS 1000 16:1; Tying Machines — 6-GMA/ SLS 1000, 16-MLN/MLN2, 2-MLN/2AHS, 24-MLN/2A.; BUSINESS EQUIPMENT: IBM, Oracle, DSI BUSINESS SOFTWARE: Microsoft/Windows 98, Microsoft/Windows NT, Microsoft/Windows 95 CLASSIFIED EQUIPMENT: Hardware — SII/Synthesis 66.; DISPLAY EQUIPMENT: Printers — GE/ Proofer; DISPLAY SOFTWAREAd Make-up Applications — Multi-Ad/Creator; Layout Software — MEI, Mk/Ad Director. EDITORIAL EQUIPMENT: Hardware — SII/Synthesis 66. PRODUCTION EQUIPMENT: Hardware — Na, 6-Titan, 4-C/220, 1-WL/Lith 10, 1-WL/ Lith 3, KFM/Auto Benders; Cameras — 1-C/ Marathon, 1-C/Newspager PRODUCTION SOFTWARE: ECI.

THE WASHINGTON TIMES

3600 New York Ave NE, Washington, D.C., 20002-1947, District Of Columbia; gen tel (202) 636-3000; adv tel (202) 636-3000; ed tel (202) 636-3000; gen fax (202) 636-8906; adv fax (202) 526-9348; ed fax (202) 715-0037; gen/nat adv e-mail nationaladvertising@washingtontimes.com; disp adv e-mail acrofoot@washingtontimes.com; class adv e-mailjalmond@washingtontimes.com; ed e-mail yourletters@washingtontimes.com; web site www.washingtontimes.com
- 14,904,284(views) 5,650,000(visitors); web site 2 www.times247.com

Group: Community Newspaper Holdings, Inc.
The Washington Times
Published: Mon, Tues, Wed, Thur, Fri
Weekday Frequency: All day
Saturday Frequency: m
Circulation: 67,148; 8,768(sat); 45,427(sun)
Last Audit: Sworn/Estimate/Non-Audited September 30, 2017
Advertising Rate (weekday/saturday): 1/8 Pg H $625.00; 1/8 Pg S $625.00
Online Advertising Rate: Online Shares $125.00
News services: MCT, AP, RN, CNS, Bloomberg, AFP, SHNS, Cox News Service, UPI, CSM, London Daily Telegraph, Xinhua News Service, CN, NEA. **Established:** 1982
Own Printing Facility?: Yes
Commercial Printers?: No
Special Editions: Farm Review & Forecast (Apr); Back-to-School (Aug); Christmas (Dec); Customer Appreciation (Jan); Progress (Jul); Basketball (Mar); Basketball (Nov); Sidewalk Sale Days (Sept).
Special Weekly Sections: Classifieds, Opinions (Daily); Home, Weekend, Auto (Fri)
Syndicated Publications: American Profile (Sat).
Digital Platform - Mobile: Apple, Android, Windows, Blackberry
Digital Platform - Tablet: Apple iOS
Circ. Mgr., Systems............................ Lisa Gray
Asst. Mng. Ed, Universal Desk........ Maria Stainer
Politics Ed..................................Stephen Dinan
Denver Bureau Chief............ Valerie Richardson
Asst. Mng. Ed........................... John Bourantas
Mng. Ed............................... Christopher Dolan
Dir. Adv. & Sales................ Adam VerCamman
Pres. & CEO................................ Larry Beasley
Managing Ed. - Dig........................... Ian Bishop
Market Information: ADS; Split run.
Mechanical Available: Offset; Black and 3 ROP colors; insert accepted - polybag samples; magazines; page cutoffs - 22 3/4.
Mechanical Specifications: Type page 11 5/8 x 21 1/2; E - 6 cols, 1 5/6, 1/8 between; A - 6 cols, 1 5/6, 1/8 between; C - 10 cols, 1 3/50, 1/8 between.
Areas Served: Washington, DC
Delivery Method: Mail, Newsstand, Carrier, RacksEquipment & Software: PRESSROOM EQUIPMENT: Lines — 10-G/Urbanite; 10-G/ Urbanite; 14-G/Urbanite; 14-G/Urbanite; Pasters —32-Cary/FP4540; Reels & Stands — 32-Cary/CLFP; Control System — 10-Fin/ Drive.; MAILROOM EQUIPMENT: Counter Stackers — 4-Gammerler, 4-QWI/502; Inserters & Stuffers — 1-HI/1372P, 1-K&M/1372; Tying Machines — 2-MLN/2A, 6/Power Strap, 2-Mosca/Cross Strap; Wrapping Singles — 4-G/Bottom Wrap; Control System — HL; Address Machine — 1-Pr; BUSINESS EQUIPMENT: 2-DEC/ Alpha 4100, 300-APP/Mac, 90-IBM/ PC, 20-Dell/PowerEdge 2450, 5-Dell/ PowerEdge 2650 BUSINESS SOFTWARE: Microsoft/Word, Microsoft/Excel, Powerpoint CLASSIFIED EQUIPMENT: Printers — HP/ LaserJet; CLASSIFIED SOFTWARE: Atex/ Enterprise 1.7. DISPLAY EQUIPMENT: Hardware — 2-DEC/Alpha 4100, 22-APP/ Power Mac; Printers — 3-Xante/Accel-a-Writer 8200, 1-Epson/3000 Color Printer, 1-HP/1000 Color; Other Hardware — Black Magic System, 2-HP/1050 Plotter, DISPLAY SOFTWAREAd Make-up Applications — MEI/Roundhouse, QPS/QuarkXPress 6.5, Adobe/Illustrator; EDITORIAL EQUIPMENT: Hardware — 2-Sun/Enterprise 450, 8-Dell/ Pentium, 200-APP/iMac/40-APP/Mac Page Makeup Workstation; Printers — 3-HP/18150 EDITORIAL SOFTWARE: Managing Editor/ALS, Saxotech/Saxopress 5.5. PRODUCTION EQUIPMENT: Hardware — TI/OmniPage Pro 5.0, 2-WL/Lith-X-Pozer III PRODUCTION SOFTWARE: QPS/ QuarkXPress 6.5.

WASHINGTON POST EXPRESS

1150 15th St NW, Washington, D.C., 20071-0001, District Of Columbia; gen tel (202) 334-6000; adv tel (202) 334-7642; gen fax (202) 334-4613; gen/nat adv e-mail Ronald.Ulrich@washpost.com; disp adv e-mail Ronald.Ulrich@washpost.com; ed e-mail Inbox@readexpress.com; web site www.expressnightout.com

Group: The Washington Post
Published: Mon, Tues, Wed, Thur, Fri
Weekday Frequency: m
Circulation: 150,634; 151,019(sat)
Last Audit: CAC October 1, 2015
Advertising Rate (weekday/saturday): Open inch rate $108
Online Advertising Rate: Inserts $144.07
News services: 2003
Adv..Ronald Ulrich
Delivery Method: Mail, Newsstand, Racks

FLORIDA

BRADENTON

BRADENTON HERALD

1111 3rd Ave W, Bradenton, Fla., 34205-7834, Manatee; gen tel (941) 748-0411; gen fax (941) 745-7025; gen/nat adv e-mail dhaimer@bradenton.com; disp adv e-mail dhaimer@bradenton.com; class adv e-mailjpatterson@bradenton.com; ed e-mail cwille@bradenton.com; web site www.bradenton.com
- 4,341,445(views) 939,181(visitors)

Group: The McClatchy Company
Published: Mon, Tues, Wed, Thur, Fri, Sat, Sun
Weekday Frequency: m
Saturday Frequency: m
Circulation: 26,294; 27,308(sat); 36,492(sun)
Last Audit: AAM December 31, 2015
Advertising Rate (weekday/saturday): Open inch rate $45.99
Advertising Rate (sunday): Open inch rate $54.49
Online Advertising Rate: Ruler - 300x100 $15
Leaderboard - 728x90 $18
Med. Rectangle - 300x250 $20
News services: 1922
Own Printing Facility?: No
Commercial Printers?: No
Special Weekly Sections: Best Food (Wed); Travel, Arts, Entertainment (Sun); Health (Tue); Taste (Wed); Weekend (Thur); Neighbors (Fri); Religion, Real Estate (Sat)
Digital Platform - Mobile: Apple, Android, Windows
Digital Platform - Tablet: Apple iOS, Android, Windows 7
Pub.. Robert Turner
VP, Adv.......................................Darren Haimer
Display Advertising Manager........Jami Patterson
Market Information: Primary market - Manatee County
Mechanical Specifications: Page size 11" x 21", print area 10" x 20"
Areas Served: 34201, 34202, 34203, 34205, 34207, 34208, 34209, 34210, 34211, 34212, 34215, 34216, 34217, 34218, 34219, 34221, 34222, 34243
Delivery Method: Newsstand, CarrierEquipment & Software: BUSINESS EQUIPMENT: HP4000 & Dell servers BUSINESS SOFTWARE: AIM
Peoplesoft
Kronos CLASSIFIED EQUIPMENT: HP & Dell servers CLASSIFIED SOFTWARE: ATS Classified Systems DISPLAY EQUIPMENT: HP & Dell Servers DISPLAY SOFTWAREXpance EDITORIAL EQUIPMENT: HP & Dell EDITORIAL SOFTWARE: Saxotech PRODUCTION EQUIPMENT: Mac & PC workstations PRODUCTION SOFTWARE: Xpance, ALS, CLS
(Managing Editor) IT EQUIPMENT: HP & Dell IT SOFTWARE:Entersys, Cisco, MS Office, Adobe CIRCULATION EQUIPMENT: Offsite Enterprise Servers CIRCULATION SOFTWARNCS (DTI)

CAPE CORAL

CAPE CORAL BREEZE

2510 Del Prado Blvd S, Cape Coral, Fla., 33904-5750, Lee; gen tel (239) 574-1110; adv tel (239) 574-1110; ed tel (239) 574-1110; gen fax (239) 573-2318; adv fax (239) 574-3403; ed fax (239) 574-5693; disp adv e-mail sstruense@breezenewspapers.com; ed e-mail news@breezenewspapers.com; web site www.cape-coral-daily-breeze.com

Group: Ogden Newspapers Inc.
Published: Tues, Wed, Fri, Sat
Weekday Frequency: m
Saturday Frequency: m
Circulation: 1,097; 1,097(sat)
Last Audit: Sworn/Estimate/Non-Audited September 30, 2017
Advertising Rate (weekday/saturday): Modular Rate 1/8 page $1.25

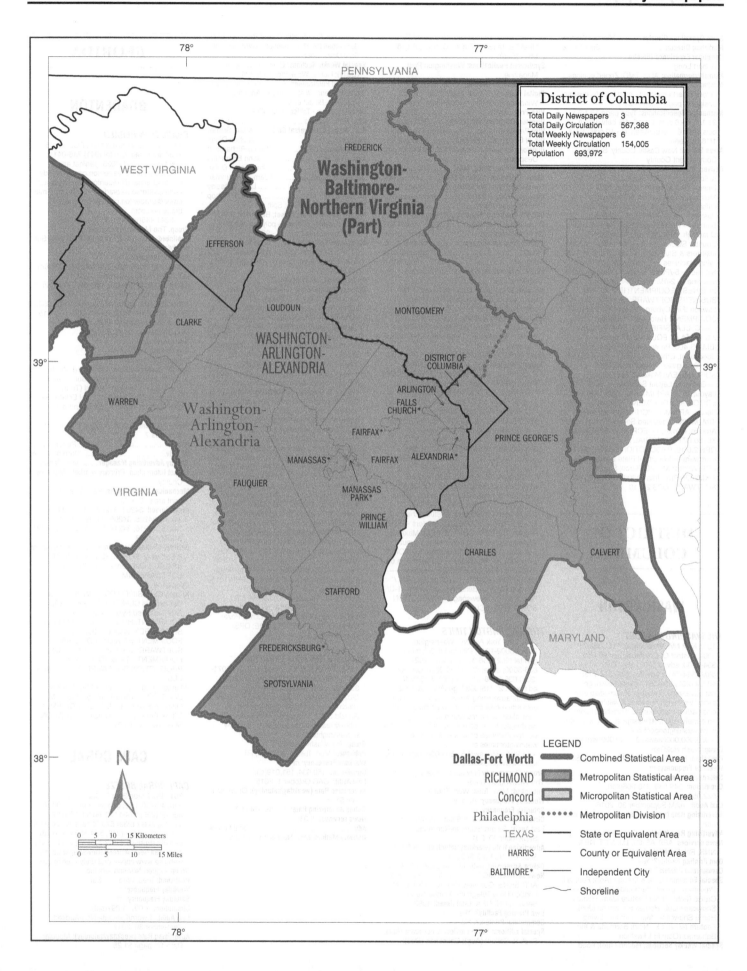

PENNSYLVANIA

WEST VIRGINIA

FREDERICK

**Washington-
Baltimore-
Northern Virginia
(Part)**

JEFFERSON

LOUDOUN

MONTGOMERY

CLARKE

WASHINGTON-
ARLINGTON-
ALEXANDRIA

DISTRICT OF
COLUMBIA

WARREN

ARLINGTON

FALLS
CHURCH*

*Washington-
Arlington-
Alexandria*

FAIRFAX*

PRINCE GEORGE'S

MANASSAS*

FAIRFAX

ALEXANDRIA*

FAUQUIER

MANASSAS
PARK*

VIRGINIA

PRINCE
WILLIAM

CHARLES

CALVERT

STAFFORD

MARYLAND

FREDERICKSBURG*

SPOTSYLVANIA

District of Columbia

Total Daily Newspapers	3
Total Daily Circulation	567,368
Total Weekly Newspapers	6
Total Weekly Circulation	154,005
Population	693,972

N

0   5   10   15 Kilometers

0   5   10   15 Miles

LEGEND

Dallas-Fort Worth   Combined Statistical Area

RICHMOND   Metropolitan Statistical Area

Concord   Micropolitan Statistical Area

Philadelphia   Metropolitan Division

TEXAS   State or Equivalent Area

HARRIS   County or Equivalent Area

BALTIMORE*   Independent City

Shoreline

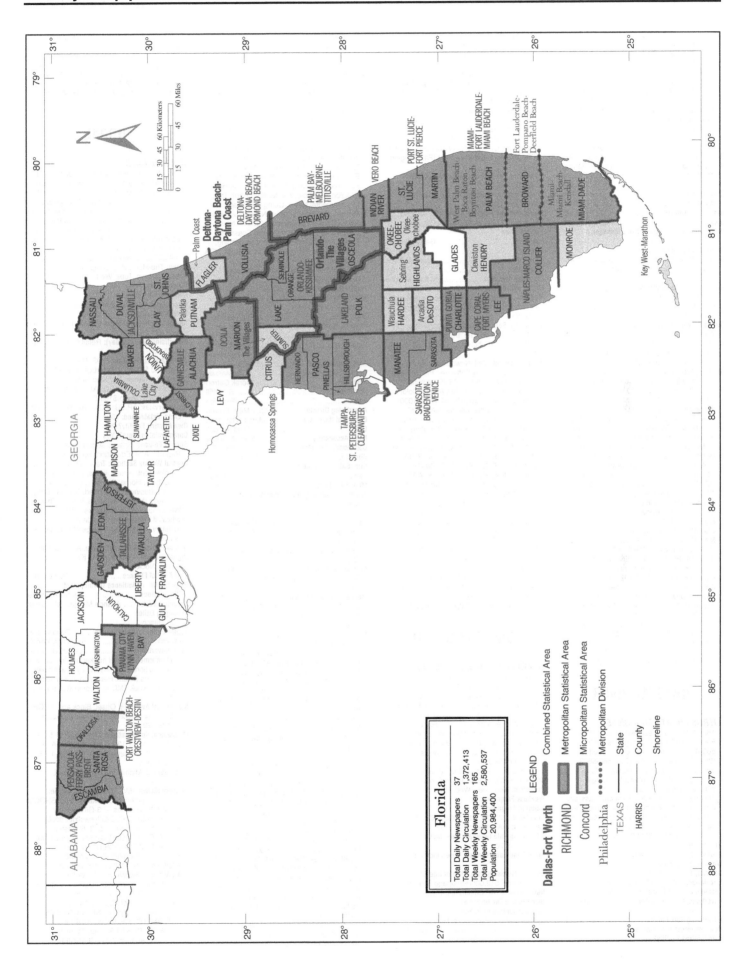

Florida

Total Daily Newspapers	37
Total Daily Circulation	1,372,413
Total Weekly Newspapers	165
Total Weekly Circulation	2,580,537
Population	20,984,400

LEGEND

Dallas-Fort Worth   Combined Statistical Area

RICHMOND   Metropolitan Statistical Area

Concord   Micropolitan Statistical Area

Philadelphia   Metropolitan Division

TEXAS   State

HARRIS   County

Shoreline

News services: AP. **Established:** 1961
Own Printing Facility?: No
Commercial Printers?: Yes
Special Editions: Progress Edition (Apr); Newcomers Guide (Aug); Caroling Book (Dec); Valentine's Day (Feb); Best of The Cape Ballot Ads Start (Jan); July 4th Page (Jul); Father's Day (Jun); Visitors Guide (Mar); Memorial Day Flag (May); Veterans Salute (Nov); Visitor's Gu
Special Weekly Sections: RPM (Sat).
Pub...Scott Blonde
Adv. Dir........................................Renee Brown
Mng. Ed........................................Chris Strine
Executive ed.............................Valarie Harring
Photo Dept. Mgr...................Michael Pistella
Sports Ed....................................Jim Linette
Prodn. Mgr., Press....................Henry Keim
Circulation Director.................Smith Barbara
Advertisng Director...................Jim Konig
Assoc. ed................................Tiffany Repecki
National & Major Account Sales Manager............
Stephanie Struense
Market Information: TMC.
Mechanical Available: Offset; Black and 3 ROP colors; insert accepted - single sheets; page cutoffs - 22.
Mechanical Specifications: Type page 11 3/4 x 21 1/2; E - 6 cols, 2 1/16, 1/4 between; A - 8 cols, 1 3/8, 3/16 between; C - 8 cols, 1 3/8, 3/16 between.
Areas Served: 33901,33903,33904,33905,33907,33908,33909,33912,33913,33914,33916,33917,33920,33921,33922,33924,33928,33931,33936,33957,33966,33971,33972,33973,33974,33990,33991,33993,34134
Delivery Method: Mail, Newsstand, Carrier, RacksEquipment & Software: PRESSROOM EQUIPMENT: Lines — 20 unit DGM 430 Single Wide. 4- 4 Color Towers Standard Ink and 1- 4 Color Tower UV ; Press Drive —4- Fincor 150 H.P. Drive Motors; Folders — 2-DGM 1035; Reels & Stands — 8-Jardis/Splicers. 5-jardis infeeds; Control System — Microcolor 2 Automatic Remote Inking; Registration System — Quad Tech Register Motorization System 2000 MAILROOM EQUIPMENT: Counter Stackers — 2-Rima/RS2510, ; Inserters & Stuffers — K & M 1472 Rotary Inserter; Tying Machines — Dynaric D2400, Samuel NT 440; Address Machine — Kirf Rudy Ink Jet Labeler; BUSINESS EQUIPMENT: NCR CLASSIFIED EQUIPMENT: Hardware — Daktech/52X Max; Printers — HP/LaserJet 2100TN; CLASSIFIED SOFTWARE: ONI/Class 0.5.4. DISPLAY EQUIPMENT: Hardware — Umax/C500; Printers — HP/LaserJet 4MV; DISPLAY SOFTWAREAd Make-up Applications — Multi-Ad/Creator 4.01; Layout Software — Metro/CDs. EDITORIAL EQUIPMENT: Hardware — APP/Power Mac G3; Printers — HP/LaserJet 4MV EDITORIAL SOFTWARE: QPS/QuarkXPress 3.32. PRODUCTION EQUIPMENT: Hardware — Kodak Prinergy Evo and Kodak Trendsetter computer-to-plate PRODUCTION SOFTWARE: QPS/QuarkXPress 3.32.

CRYSTAL RIVER

CITRUS COUNTY CHRONICLE
1624 N Meadowcrest Blvd, Crystal River, Fla., 34429-5760, Citrus; gen tel (352) 563-6363; adv tel (352) 563-5592; ed tel (352) 563-5660; gen fax (352) 563-5665; adv fax (352) 563-5665; ed fax (352) 563-3280; gen/nat adv e-mail advertising@chronicleonline.com; disp adv e-mail advertising@chronicleonline.com; class adv e-mailadvertising@chronicleonline.com; ed e-mail newsdesk@chronicleonline.com; web site www.chronicleonline.com
- 474,000(views) 99,000(visitors)
Group: Landmark Communications, Inc.
Published: Mon, Tues, Wed, Thur, Fri, Sat, Sun
Weekday Frequency: m
Saturday Frequency: m
Circulation: 17,553; 17,553(sat); 21,786(sun)
Last Audit: AAM December 31, 2016
Advertising Rate (weekday/saturday): Open inch rate $40.71
Advertising Rate (sunday): Open inch rate $48.19
News services: AP. **Established:** 1890
Own Printing Facility?: Yes

Commercial Printers?: Yes
Special Editions: Home Improvement (Apr); Football (Aug); Gift Guide (Dec); Business Almanac (Feb); Income Tax Guide (Jan); Snowbird (Jul); Nature Coast (Jun); Fair Guide (Mar); Hurricane Tab (May); Seniors Illustrated (Monthly); Crystal River Merchants (Nov); Festival of
Special Weekly Sections: Commentary, Sports, Business, Real Estate, Stocks, Comics, Community (Sun); Sports, Community (Mon); Stocks, Health, Fitness, Auto (Tue); Stocks, Education, Community (Wed); Food, Stocks (Thur); Stocks, Entertainment (Fri); Religion (Sat)
Syndicated Publications: USA WEEKEND Magazine (S).
Digital Platform - Mobile: Apple, Android, Windows, Blackberry
Digital Platform - Tablet: Apple iOS, Android, Windows 7, Blackberry Tablet OS, Nook, Kindle Fire
Pub........................................Gerry Mulligan
Mng. Ed................................... Mike Arnold
Photo Ed.................................Matthew Beck
Prodn. Mgr...............................Tom Feeney
Classified Adv. Mgr..................John Murphy
Market Information: TMC; Zoned editions.
Mechanical Available: Web Offset; Black and 3 ROP colors; insert accepted; page cutoffs - 22 3/4.
Mechanical Specifications: Type page 13 x 21 1/2; E - 6 cols, 2 1/16, 1/8 between; A - 6 cols, 2 1/16, 1/8 between; C - 10 cols, 1 1/8, 1/8 between.
Delivery Method: Mail, Newsstand, Carrier, RacksEquipment & Software: PRESSROOM EQUIPMENT: Lines — 7-G/Community SC (1 univ offset color), 1-DGM/4-high Color; Folders — G/Community SC, DGM/1030; Pasters —7-Jardis/Splicers. MAILROOM EQUIPMENT: Counter Stackers — 1-HL/Monitor, QWI/401; Inserters & Stuffers — 1-AM/Graphics NP 1372 w/icon, 1-MM/8:1; Tying Machines — 2-MLN/Strapper; Address Machine — KR; BUSINESS EQUIPMENT: IBM/Sys 36 BUSINESS SOFTWARE: Lotus CLASSIFIED SOFTWARE: APT. DISPLAY EQUIPMENT: Hardware — APP/Mac; Other Hardware — Epson/11x17 color paper proof printer, 4-Epson/Flat Bed Scanners DISPLAY SOFTWAREAd Make-up Applications — Multi-Ad/Creator, QPS/QuarkXPress; Layout Software — APP/Mac. EDITORIAL EQUIPMENT: Hardware — CText; Printers — ECR/11 X 17 proof printer EDITORIAL SOFTWARE: XYQUEST/XyWrite, QPS/QuarkXPress 3.3. PRODUCTION EQUIPMENT: Hardware — Caere/OmniPage, APP/Mac, AG/Online; Cameras — AG; Scanners — 3-Nikon, 2-AG PRODUCTION SOFTWARE: Layout 8000.

DAYTONA BEACH

DAYTONA BEACH NEWS-JOURNAL
901 6th St, Daytona Beach, Fla., 32117-3352, Volusia; gen tel (386) 252-1511; adv tel (386) 681-2750; ed tel (386) 681-2220; gen fax (386) 258-8469; adv fax (386) 253-6487; ed fax (386) 258-8465; gen/nat adv e-mail bill.offill@news-jrnl.com; disp adv e-mail adv@news-jrnl.com; class adv e-maildebbie.keesee@news-jrnl.com; ed e-mail njscoop@news-jrnl.com; web site www.news-journalonline.com
- 4,500,000(views) 469,000(visitors)
Group: New Media Investment Group
Published: Mon, Tues, Wed, Thur, Fri, Sat, Sun
Weekday Frequency: m
Saturday Frequency: m
Circulation: 50,470; 51,259(sat); 62,731(sun)
Last Audit: AAM March 31, 2017
Advertising Rate (weekday/saturday): Open inch rate $146.70
Advertising Rate (sunday): Open inch rate $196.10
Online Advertising Rate: Run of Site $10.00; Run of Channel $12.00; Homepage $15 .00
News services: AP. **Established:** 1883
Own Printing Facility?: Yes
Commercial Printers?: Yes
Special Editions: Palm Coast How to Guide (Apr); Football Preview (NFL) (Aug); Letters to Santa (Dec); Volusia County Schools

Newsletter (Every other month); Bridal Guide (Feb); Prospectus (Jan); Speed (Jul); Disaster Guide (Jun); Garden & Leisure Lifestyle Show (Mar); Par
Special Weekly Sections: Business, Parimutuel News, TV Listings/Comics (Daily); At Your Service, Cold Case, Fresh Talk, Snapshots, To Your Health (Mon); Pet Connection, Chasing Rainbows, Heyville, Words from War (Tue); School Daze, Taking up Space, Married to the Movies, Gen Zgen, Game On, Supper Club or Lunch Brunch, Footnote, Campus Page (Wed); Police Beat, Pets of the Week, The Beat Goes On, Fresh Talk, At Home (Thur); Fishing News, Go Entertainment Section, Market News, Movies, Footnote (Fri); Faith, Market News, Movies, Religion, Footnote, Ask Martha, Earth Talk, Environmental News, Going Wild (Sat); Movies, Arts/Books, Travel News, Business News, Comics, Chatterbox, Cultural News, Deeds & Building Permits, Fun Coast Real Estate, Innovations, National Auto Racing, Political News, Travel News, TV Journal, USA Weekend, Amusement Section (Sun)
Syndicated Publications: Homes & Property (Monthly); TV Journal (S).
Digital Platform - Mobile: Apple, Android
Digital Platform - Tablet: Apple iOS, Android, Kindle, Kindle Fire
Mgr., Mktg. Devel.....................Brad Gordner
Mng. Ed./Bureau Chief............Frank Fernandez
Mgr., Strategic Mktg..........................Lori Kopp
Circ. Mgr................................John K. Shaw
Mng. Ed..............................Cory Lancaster
Asst. Bureau Chief.....................Aaron London
Deputy Mng. Ed., News.............Cal Massey
Asst. Mng. Ed...........................Derek Catron
Publisher.................................... Bill Offill
Editor.. Pat Rice
Advertising Director...................Mike Baskin
Chrmn. of the Board................Marc L. Davidson
CFO......................................David Kendall
Mgr., Accounting....................Ellen Andrews
Community Rel. Mgr.....................Kathy Tiller
Circ. Dir.............................Douglas R. Davis
Circ. Sales/Mktg. Mgr..............Larry Saffer
Co-Ed................................. Marc Davidson
Mng. Ed., Online.........................Tony Briggs
Assistant Managing Editor/Team Leader........ Nick Klasne
David Woroinger
Ed... Rachael Smith
Retail Adv. Mgr...........................Cynthia Cross
Advert Director..............................Jane Katona
Market Information: ADS; Split run; TMC; Zoned editions.
Mechanical Available: Offset; Black and full color ROP colors; insert accepted - samples; page cutoffs - 22.
Mechanical Specifications: Type page 11 5/8 x 20 3/4; E - 6 cols, 1 13/16, 1/8 between; A - 6 cols, 1 13/16, 1/8 between; C - 9 cols, 1 1/4, 1/16 between.
Areas Served: All of Volusia and Flagler counties
Delivery Method: Mail, Newsstand, Carrier, RacksEquipment & Software: PRESSROOM EQUIPMENT: Lines — 14-G/Metroliner; Folders — 2-G/3:2, 2-G/2:1; MAILROOM EQUIPMENT: Counter Stackers — 1-QWI/100, 5-QWI/200, 2-QWI/310, 3-QWI/350, 2-MM/CS70-338; Inserters & Stuffers — HI/1472, HI/1372, HI/2299, NP/120 Gripper Conveyor; Tying Machines — 8-Dynaric/NP-2, 2-Dynaric/NP-1, 4-Malow/50-S String Typer; Wrapping Singles — Wrapping Singles; BUSINESS EQUIPMENT: 2-DEC/Alpha 4610 CLASSIFIED EQUIPMENT: Hardware — AST/Bravo MS 5166M, 37-IBM PS/1; Printers — 2-Digital/L030W Companion, Okipage/6e; CLASSIFIED SOFTWARE: Cx/Intertext, HI. DISPLAY EQUIPMENT: Hardware — DEC/Alpha-4610, SCS/Layout 8000, HP/200, APP/Mac G3 Server, Micronet/Array, APP/Mac 950, APP/Mac 840, APP/Mac 7100, APP/Mac 9600, APP/Mac 7300, APP/Mac G3; Printers — Dec/LA30, QMS/PS-860, QMS/2060, QMS/1660, Tektronix/Phaser 300, Tektronix/380; EDITORIAL EQUIPMENT: Hardware — 2-Sun/Ultra2, 3-Sun/Sparc 10 Server, 2-Sun/Sparc Storage Arrays, 50-Dell/Dimension XPS T450, 20-Dell/Dimension V350, 10-Dell/Optiplex; Printers — QMS/1660, MON/Proofer, HP/8100N EDITORIAL SOFTWARE: HI/Newsmaker 3.31, Microsoft/Windows NT, Microsoft/Wor PRODUCTION EQUIPMENT:

Hardware — 2-MON/ExpressMaster 25, 3-MON/RIP Express, 3-Sun/Ultra Sparc 2Xs, SCREEN/Doubletruck Imagesetter, Harlequin/RIP; Cameras — 2-C, 1-Payea, 1-C/Spartan; Scanners — 3-ECR/Autokon, 1-SCREEN/608 Scanner, HP/ScanJet Plus PRODUCTION SOFTWARE: HI/Newsmaker 2.0

DORAL

MIAMI HERALD
3511 NW 91st Ave, Doral, Fla., 33172-1216, Miami-Dade; gen tel (800)766-2820; adv tel (866) 860-6000; ed tel (305) 376-2317; adv fax (305) 376-2094; ed fax (305) 376-5287; gen/nat adv e-mail adinfo@miamiherald.com; disp adv e-mail adinfo@miamiherald.com; class adv e-mailadinfo@miamiherald.com; ed e-mail AMarques@MiamiHerald.com; web site www.miamiherald.com
- 45,360,278(views) 18,106,861(visitors)
Group: The McClatchy Company
Published: Mon, Tues, Wed, Thur, Fri, Sun
Weekday Frequency: m
Saturday Frequency: m
Circulation: 95,416; 129,096(sun)
Last Audit: AAM June 30, 2017
Advertising Rate (weekday/saturday): Retail Open inch rate $170.00
Advertising Rate (sunday): Retail Open inch rate $245.00
Online Advertising Rate: ROS: Rectangle 300x250 $14.70, Leaderboard 728X90 $10.50. Channel Targeted Rectangle 300x250 $16.25 to $18.00, Leaderboard 728X90 $11.75 to $13.25
News services: AP, DJ, MCT, LAT-WP, SOU, TV Data. **Established:** 1903
Own Printing Facility?: Yes
Commercial Printers?: Yes
Special Editions: Special sections: Health Reports, Arts, Education, Sports, Hispanic
Special Weekly Sections: Travel, Home, Design, Employment, Issues, ideas, Comics, TV, Neighbors, Home, Design (Sun); Local, Sports, Business, Classified, Tropical (Daily); Business (Mon); Neighbors, Values (Thur); Weekend (Fri); Auto, Homes (Sat)
Syndicated Publications: Parade (S).
Proprietary Publications: Indulge Magazine, 7x per year
Digital Platform - Mobile: Apple, Android, Other
Digital Platform - Tablet: Apple iOS, Android, Kindle, Nook
CFO & VP of Finance......................Greg Curling
Regional Dir. of Audience Development (Circulation)..........................Bernie Kosanke
Executive Editor.......Aminda Marques Gonzalez
Managing Editor
Rick Hirsch
Senior Editor / Administration..........Dave Wilson
Pres./Pub...............................Alexandra Villoch
VP of Advertising......................Lesley DeCanio
Market Information: total market distribution and zoned editions ROP, inserts by total market, zones, ZIPs (Miami Herald only) and non-subs mid week TMC and opt-in Yes! Sunday Select
Mechanical Available: Offset; Black and 3 ROP colors; insert accepted - single sheets; page cutoffs - 22.
Mechanical Specifications: Type page 11 5/8 x 21; E - 6 cols, 1 13/16, 1/6 between; A - 6 cols, 1 5/6, 1/8 between; C - 10 cols, 1 1/6, 1/8 between.
Areas Served: Miami-Dade and Broward Counties
Delivery Method: Mail, Newsstand, Carrier, RacksEquipment & Software: PRESSROOM EQUIPMENT: Lines — 3-G/Newsliner double width 1997, 2-G/Newsliner double width 1999; Folders — 5, 3, 5; Pasters —45-G/CT50Reels & Stands —45-CT/50.; MAILROOM EQUIPMENT: Counter Stackers — 2-QWI/300, 2-QWI/300, 2-QWI/300, 1-QWI/350, 10-QWI/350, 4-QWI/350, 3-QWI/350, 6-QWI/350, 4-QWI/400, 2-QWI/400; Inserters & Stuffers — 1-HI/1372P, 1-HI/1372P, 2-HI/1472P, 1-HI/1572, 2-GMA/SLS1000A; Tying Machines — 1-Dynaric/NP-; BUSINESS EQUIPMENT: 1-HP/3000, 1-HP/3000, 1-HP/9000 BUSINESS SOFTWARE: CJ 6.03K, Admarc 7.0.D CLASSIFIED

EQUIPMENT: Hardware — 180-HP/PC; Printers — HP/5000.; DISPLAY EQUIPMENT: Hardware — PC, Novell, Unix, APP/Mac; Printers — HP/5000; Other Hardware — All/3850 DISPLAY SOFTWAREAd Make-up Applications — SCS/Layout 8000, Managing Editor/ALS; Layout Software — SCS/ Layout 8000, Cascade, MEI. EDITORIAL EQUIPMENT: Hardware — SII/Tandem Servernet, 350-HP/PC; Printers — HP/5000, OMS/2060 EDITORIAL SOFTWARE: SII/ Coyote 3, SII/Layout. PRODUCTION EQUIPMENT: Hardware — 4-WL/38-G, 2-WL/OPB, 5-All/3850; Scanners — 2-Eskofot/2636, 2-Tecsa, 1-Howtek/ Scanmaster 2500, 1-Howtek/Scanmaster 6500 PRODUCTION SOFTWARE: QPS/ QuarkXPress 4.11, SII/Layout 1.94.

ENGLEWOOD

ENGLEWOOD SUN

120 W Dearborn St, Englewood, Fla., 34223-3237, Sarasota; gen tel (941) 681-3000; gen/ nat adv e-mail cymoore@sun-herald.com; web site www.yoursun.com/csp/mediapool/ sites/SunNews/Englewood/index.csp
Group: Sun Coast Media Group Inc
Published: Mon, Tues, Wed, Thur, Fri, Sat, Sun
Last Audit: Sworn/Estimate/Non-Audited December 11, 2017
Pub. .... Carol Moore

FORT LAUDERDALE

SOUTH FLORIDA SUN-SENTINEL

This Location Closed, Fort Lauderdale, Fla., 33394, Broward; gen tel (954) 356-4000; adv tel (954) 425-1817; ed tel 954.356.4500; gen fax (954) 425-1894; ed fax 954.356.4609; gen/nat adv e-mail dscroggin@sun-sentinel. com; disp adv e-mail dscroggin@sun-sentinel.com; class adv e-maildscroggin@ sun-sentinel.com; ed e-mail dbanker@ sunsentinel.com; web site www.sun-sentinel. com
- 18,000,000(views) 4,000,000(visitors)
Group: tronc
Published: Mon, Tues, Wed, Thur, Fri, Sat, Sun
Weekday Frequency: m
Saturday Frequency: m
Circulation: 97,653; 115,617(sat); 180,220(sun)
Last Audit: AAM June 30, 2017
Branch Offices: None
Online Advertising Rate: Saturday, Sunday & Holiday is $130/column inch
Color is +20%
Daily is $77 per column inch
color is +20%
News services: 1911
Own Printing Facility?: No
Commercial Printers?: No
Special Editions: PRIME
Special Weekly Sections: Seminar Notices (Mon); Food, Shalom (Wed); Jewish journal, Inside Auto, Society, (Thur); Temple, Community, Marketplace, Showtime (Fri); Inside Real Estate, Auto (Sat); Travel, Lifestyle, Home and Garden, Employment, Comics, Community, Real Estate, Outlook, Sports (Sun)
Dir., Major Adv. .... Doug Scroggin
Ed. .... Howard Saltz
Vice President Sales/Advertising ... Rob Cravaritis
Manufacturing Director .... Joel Meyer
Areas Served: Broward County
Palm Beach CountyEquipment & Software: PRESSROOM EQUIPMENT: Goss Color Liner PRESSROOM SOFTWARE: Rockwell MAILROOM EQUIPMENT: Mueller Martini MAILROOM SOFTWARE:Win Lics

FORT WALTON BEACH

NORTHWEST FLORIDA DAILY NEWS

2 Eglin Pkwy NE, Fort Walton Beach, Fla., 32548-4915, Okaloosa; gen tel (850) 863-1111; adv tel (850) 863-1111; ed tel (850) 863-1111; gen fax (850) 862-5230; adv fax (850) 863-9348; ed fax (850) 863-7834; gen/ nat adv e-mail scollins@pcnh.com; disp adv e-mail staylor@nwfdailynews.com; class adv e-mailJbranda@pcnh.com; ed e-mail news@nwfdailynews.com; web site www. nwfdailynews.com
- 2(views) 242,800(visitors)
Group: New Media Investment Group
Published: Mon, Tues, Wed, Thur, Fri, Sat, Sun
Weekday Frequency: m
Saturday Frequency: m
Circulation: 22,477; 22,477(sat); 26,250(sun)
Last Audit: CAC December 31, 2016
Advertising Rate (weekday/saturday): Call for rates
Advertising Rate (sunday): Call for rates
Online Advertising Rate: $10 Average CPM rate
News services: AP **Established:** 1946
Own Printing Facility?: No
Commercial Printers?: Yes
Special Editions: Football (Aug); Gift Guide (Dec); Home Improvement (Mar); Welcome Guide (May).
Special Weekly Sections: Showcase/ Entertainment (Fri); Food (Wed).
Syndicated Publications: Parade (S).
Digital Platform - Mobile: Apple, Android
Editorial Page Ed. .... Jim Shoffner
Ent. Ed. .... Brenda Shoffner
Online Ed. .... Del Stone
IT Dir. .... Noel Shauf
Donna Talla
Publisher .... Diane Winnemuller
Regional Business Development and Marketing Director .... Vickie Gainer
Regional Human Resource Dir ...... Eleanor Hypes
Shawna Laethem
RJ Driskill
Roger Underwood
Wendy Victora
Market Information: Okaloosa, Walton and part of Santa Rosa counties
Mechanical Available: Offset; Black and 3 ROP colors; insert accepted - all
Areas Served: 32531, 32536, 32539, 32541, 32542, 32547, 32548, 32549, 32564, 32544, 32567, 32569, 32578, 32588, 32579, 32580, 32563, 32583, 32566, 32433, 32435, 32439, 32550, 32434, 32538, 32455, 32459
Delivery Method: Mail, Newsstand, Carrier, RacksEquipment & Software: PRESSROOM EQUIPMENT: Goss Universal 45 with EAE control and Software MAILROOM EQUIPMENT: SOS 3000, MAILROOM SOFTWARE:Window Base Software Systems BUSINESS EQUIPMENT: PC BUSINESS SOFTWARE: Lawson CLASSIFIED EQUIPMENT: Hardware — PC; CLASSIFIED SOFTWARE: APT. DISPLAY EQUIPMENT: Hardware — PC; DISPLAY SOFTWAREInDesign and Photoshop. Xpance System. EDITORIAL EQUIPMENT: Hardware — PC EDITORIAL SOFTWARE: APT. PRODUCTION EQUIPMENT: See press description PRODUCTION SOFTWARE: Kodak Platemaker IT EQUIPMENT: PC CIRCULATION EQUIPMENT: PC

GAINESVILLE

THE GAINESVILLE SUN

2700 SW 13th St, Gainesville, Fla., 32608-2015, Alachua; gen tel (352) 378-1411; adv tel (352) 374-5012; ed tel (352) 374-5075; gen fax (352) 374-5099; adv fax (352) 338-3125; ed fax (352) 338-3128; gen/nat adv e-mail online@gvillesun.com; disp adv e-mail Lynda.strickland@gvillesun.com; class adv e-mailclassified@gvillesun.com; ed e-mail doug.ray@gvillesun.com; web site www. gainesville.com
618,591(visitors)
Group: New Media Investment Group
Published: Mon, Tues, Wed, Thur, Fri, Sat, Sun
Weekday Frequency: m
Saturday Frequency: m
Circulation: 24,849; 25,105(sat); 33,033(sun)
Last Audit: AAM March 31, 2016
Advertising Rate (weekday/saturday): Open inch rate $93.61
Advertising Rate (sunday): Open inch rate $101.00
News services: AP, NYT, LAT-WP, MCT, SHNS, TMS. **Established:** 1876
Special Editions: Gainesville Magazine (Apr); Gainesville Magazine (Aug); Gainesville Magazine (Dec); Gainesville Magazine (Feb); Wedding Book (Jan); Travel-Caribbean Value Season (Jul); Gainesville Magazine (Jun); Travel-Summer in Europe (Mar); Travel-USA & Canada (May);
Special Weekly Sections: BEst Food Day (Wed); Scene, House, Home, Wheels, Movies (Fri); Gardening, Church (Sat); Real Estate, Travel, Entertainment (Sun); Finance (Tue-Sun)
Syndicated Publications: Parade (S).
Pub. .... James E. Doughton
Controller .... Jeffrey Pole
Bus. Devel. Mgr. .... James Holmes
Online Sales Mgr. .... Craig Grant
Circ. Dir. .... Jim Miller
Exec. Ed. .... Jim Osteen
Mng. Ed. .... Jacki Levine
Bus. Ed. .... Anthony Clark
Amusements/Entertainment Ed. .. Dave Schlenker
Editorial Page Ed. .... Ron Cunningham
Editorial Page Ed.
Nathan Crabbe
Educ. Writer, Lower .... Cindy Swirko
Health Ed. .... Diane Chun
Metro Ed. .... Jon Rabiroff
Sr. Adv. Mgr. .... Lynda Strickland
Sports Ed. .... Arnold Feliciano
Gen Mgr .... Douglas K. Ray
Market Information: ADS; Split run; TMC.
Mechanical Available: Offset; Black and 3 ROP colors; insert accepted - all; page cutoffs - 22.
Mechanical Specifications: Type page 11 5/8 x 21; E - 6 cols, 2 1/16, 1/8 between; A - 6 cols, 2 1/16, 1/8 between; C - 10 cols, 1 3/16, 1/8 between.Equipment & Software: PRESSROOM EQUIPMENT: Lines — 7-G/ Headliner offset (5 half decks); Folders — 2-G/2:1 (with 1 motter stitch online stitching head); Reels & Stands — 7; MAILROOM EQUIPMENT: Counter Stackers — 2-Id/2200, 2-QWI/350, 1-QWI/610; Inserters & Stuffers — HI/1472P; Tying Machines — 1-MLN/2A, 2-Dynaric/NP2; Wrapping Singles — 2-QWI/ Viper w/Fox Ink Jet Printers; Address Machine — 1/Ch, 1-/KR, Domino/Online, InkJet; BUSINESS EQUIPMENT: 1-IBM/ AS 400 BUSINESS SOFTWARE: Microsoft/ Office 97 CLASSIFIED EQUIPMENT: Hardware — APP/Mac; CLASSIFIED SOFTWARE: DTI/ClassSpeed 4.23. DISPLAY EQUIPMENT: Hardware — 6-APP/ Mac Pagination, 2-APP/Mac Text Input; Printers — 2-HP/8000, 2-AU/APS-HS-3850, 1-ECR/4550; DISPLAY SOFTWAREAd Make-up Applications — DTI/AdSpeed, DTI/SpeedPlanner 4.23; Layout Software — DTI/AdSpeed, DTI/AdManager, DTI/ SpeedPlanner. EDITORIAL EQUIPMENT: Hardware — AT/9000, APP/Mac; Printers — 2-HP/8000, 2-AU/APS Ace 1 3N EDITORIAL SOFTWARE: DTI/SpeedWriter, DTI/SpeedPlanner, DTI/PageSpeed 4.2. PRODUCTION EQUIPMENT: Hardware — Caere/OmniPage, 2-AU/APS 3850 HS, 1-ECR/4550; Cameras — 1-C/Newspager; Scanners — CD/646IE Color Scanner, Kk/ Pro Rfs 2035, Umax/PowerLook, Umax/Ultra Vision PRODUCTION SOFTWARE: DTI/ PageSpeed 4.23.

THE INDEPENDENT FLORIDA ALLIGATOR

PO Box 14257, Gainesville, Fla., 32604-2257, Alachua; gen tel 352-376-4446; adv tel (352) 376-4482; ed tel (352) 376-4458; gen fax (352) 376-4556; adv fax (352) 376-4556; ed fax (352) 376-4467; gen/nat adv e-mail tcarey@alligator.org; disp adv e-mail advertising @alligator.org; class adv e-maillellight@alligator.org; ed e-mail editor@ alligator.org; web site www.alligator.org
Published: Mon, Tues, Wed, Thur, Fri
Weekday Frequency: m
Last Audit: Sworn/Estimate/Non-Audited September 30, 2017
Advertising Rate (weekday/saturday): Open inch rate $42.65
News services: 1906
Own Printing Facility?: Yes
Special Weekly Sections: Thursday Entertainment section
Ed. .... Kristan Wiggins
Mng. Ed. Print .... Colleen Wright
Mng. Ed. Online .... Bakr Saliq
University Ed. .... Beatrice Dupuy
Metro Ed. .... Rachel Crosby
Opinions Ed. .... Elliot Levy
Areas Served: uf campus, all og Gainesville
Delivery Method: Racks

JACKSONVILLE

THE FLORIDA TIMES-UNION

1 Riverside Ave, Jacksonville, Fla., 32202-4917, Duval; gen tel (904) 359-4111; ed tel (904) 359-4280; adv fax (904) 359-4452; gen/ nat adv e-mail dianne.knapp@jacksonville. com; disp adv e-mail lyn.sargent@ jacksonville.com; ed e-mail julie.kanner@ jacksonville.com; web site www.jacksonville. com
1,800,490(visitors); web site 2 www. floridatimesunion.com
Group: GateHouse Media, Inc.
Published: Mon, Tues, Wed, Thur, Fri, Sat, Sun
Weekday Frequency: m
Saturday Frequency: m
Circulation: 48,554; 53,283(sat); 78,045(sun)
Last Audit: AAM June 30, 2017
Advertising Rate (weekday/saturday): Open inch rate $283.00
News services: AP **Established:** 1864
Own Printing Facility?: Yes
Commercial Printers?: Yes
Special Editions: TPC (May), Fl/Ga (October) Football (August)
Special Weekly Sections: Home (Sat); Drive (Saturday) Religion (Saturday) Health (Wednesday) Taste (Thursday) Jack - weekly entertainment (Friday) Sholrelines (sat)
Syndicated Publications: Parade
Digital Platform - Mobile: Apple, Android, Windows
Digital Platform - Tablet: Apple iOS
Controller, Div. .... W. Mitchel Denning
VP Human Resources .... Carol Holmes
Mgr., Promo. .... Karen Brashear
Ed. .... Frank Denton
VP- Circulation/Marketing .... Amy McSwain
VP-Operations .... Mike Clemons
Pres. .... Mark Nusbaum
VP Audience Development .... Kurt Caywood
VP Sales .... Lana Champion
Managing Ed., Sports, Features and Specialty Publications .... Joe Desalvo
Editorial Page Ed. .... Mike Clark
Market Information: ADS; Split run; Zoned editions.
Mechanical Available: Offset; Black and 3 ROP colors; insert accepted; page cutoffs - 22 3/4.
Mechanical Specifications: Type page 11 5/8 x 21 1/2; E - 6 cols, 1 13/16, 1/8 between; A - 6 cols, 1 13/16, 1/16 between; C - 10 cols, 1 1/8, 1/16 between.
Areas Served: 32202, 32206, 32208, 32209, 32218, 32219, 32226, 32227, 32233, 32250, 32266, 32211, 32225, 32277, 32224, 32246, 32256, 32207, 32216, 32217, 32223, 32257, 32258, 32204, 32205, 32220, 32221, 32234, 32254, 32210, 32212, 32222, 32244, 32003, 32043, 32065, 32068, 32073, 32079, 32033, 32084, 32096, 32080, 32081, 32082, 32092, 32095, 32259, 32009, 32034, 32097, 32011,
Delivery Method: Mail, Newsstand, Carrier, RacksEquipment & Software: PRESSROOM EQUIPMENT: Lines — G/Metro 3213 8Units, 4 color decks 20 print couples; G/ Metro: 3076; 9 units, 5 color decks, 23 print couples; G/Metro 3019 9 units, 5 decks, 23 print couples; Folders — 6-G/3:2 4; Reels & Stands — 23; MAILROOM EQUIPMENT: Counter Stackers — 3-HI/HT, 4-QWI/501, 8-QWI/401; Inserters & Stuffers — 2-HI/ MP 632; Tying Machines — 6-Dynaric/3000; Wrapping Singles — Manual.; BUSINESS EQUIPMENT: SAP Accounting/Ad Order Entry PBS Circulation Management CLASSIFIED EQUIPMENT: Hardware — DTI, Sun/Server, 65-APP/Mac; Printers — Epson, HP; CLASSIFIED SOFTWARE: DTI 5.01. DISPLAY EQUIPMENT: Hardware — Sun/Sparc Server 450, Intel/NT; Printers — X, 2-HP 2500, Typhoon, 1-HP/1055 CM; DISPLAY SOFTWAREAd Make-up Applications — Archtype, Op, Adobe/ PS/3, Alpha; Layout Software — 12-APP/ Mac G3, All/AdManager 3.1. EDITORIAL EQUIPMENT: Hardware — Media cloud based/Kodak CTP; Printers — HP, Xante, XIT EDITORIAL SOFTWARE: Media Spectrum Content Watch PRODUCTION EQUIPMENT: Hardware — Lf/AP Leaf Picture Desk,

2 Kodak Trendsetter 200 CTP devices; Accutech Optical registration and Benders 10, 5-APP/Mac, 2-III/3850H, 2-III/3850H PRODUCTION SOFTWARE: Media Spectrum Ad Watch and Content Wacth; DTI Pagination
Note: Advertising is sold in combination with St. Augustine Record (mS) for $243.00(d), $259.00(m-sat) and $279.00(S).

KEY WEST

KEY WEST CITIZEN
3420 Northside Dr, Key West, Fla., 33040-4254, Monroe; gen tel (305) 292-7777; adv tel (305) 292-7777; ed tel (305) 292-7777; gen fax (305) 294-0768; adv fax (305) 295-8013; ed fax (305) 292-3008; class adv e-mail classifieds@keysnews.com; web site www.keysnews.com
- 223,869(views)
Group: Cooke Communications Florida, LLC
Published: Mon, Tues, Wed, Thur, Fri, Sat, Sun
Weekday Frequency: m
Saturday Frequency: m
Circulation: 7,597; 7,597(sat); 7,789(sun)
Last Audit: AAM March 31, 2016
Branch Offices: Key West
Tavernier
News services: AP. **Established:** 1876
Own Printing Facility?: Yes
Commercial Printers?: Yes
Special Editions: Bridal Magazine(Jan); Taste of Key West (Apr); Hurricane Tab (May); Summer Fun (Jun); Your Pet (Sept); Fantasy Fest (Oct); Gift Guide (Nov); Keys Style: A Locals Guide (Monthly); Healthfile (Quarterly); Home Improvement (Quarterly); Menu Guide (Quarterly)
Special Weekly Sections: Business, Finance (Daily); Best Food (Wed); Arts, Entertainment (Thur); Religion (Fri); Health, Auto (Sat); Auto, Health, Home, Living, Real Estate, Business, Arts, Entertainment (Sun)
Syndicated Publications: Comics (S).
Pub....Paul Clarin
Market Information: ADS; TMC.
Mechanical Available: Offset; Black and 3 ROP colors; insert accepted; page cutoffs - 21 1/2.
Mechanical Specifications: Type page 13 x 21 1/2; E - 6 cols, 2 1/16, 1/8 between; A - 6 cols, 2 1/16, 1/8 between; C - 9 cols, 1 5/16, 1/16 between.
Areas Served: Monroe County
Delivery Method: Mail, Newsstand, Carrier, RacksEquipment & Software: PRESSROOM EQUIPMENT: Lines — 9-G/1109SS; MAILROOM EQUIPMENT: Tying Machines — 1-/OVL; Address Machine — 1-/El.; BUSINESS EQUIPMENT: ATT CLASSIFIED EQUIPMENT: Hardware — APP/Mac iMac; Printers — HP/4050; CLASSIFIED SOFTWARE: AdManager/Pro. DISPLAY EQUIPMENT: Hardware — APP/Mac Quadra 8100, APP/Mac G3; Printers — Epson/3000c, HP/8000, Pre Press/Panther; DISPLAY SOFTWAREAd Make-up Applications — Adobe/Photoshop, Adobe/Illustrator, QPS, QPS/QuarkXPress; Layout Software — Baseview, APP/Mac. EDITORIAL EQUIPMENT: Hardware — APP/Mac, Mk, PC; Printers — HP/5000 EDITORIAL SOFTWARE: Baseview. PRODUCTION EQUIPMENT: Hardware — Panther/Pro 62, V/5300; Cameras — SCREEN/Companica 680C; Scanners — AG/Arcus Plus PRODUCTION SOFTWARE: Adobe/Illustrator, Adobe/Photoshop, QPS/QuarkXPress, QPS. CIRCULATION SOFTWARNewzware

LAKE CITY

LAKE CITY REPORTER
180 E Duval St, Lake City, Fla., 32055-4085, Columbia; gen tel (386) 752-1293; adv tel (386) 755-5440; ed tel (386) 754-0428; gen fax (386) 752-9400; adv fax (386) 752-9400; ed fax (386) 752-9400; gen/nat adv e-mail twilson@lakecityreporter.com; disp adv e-mail abutcher@lakecityreporter.com; ed e-mail rbridges@lakecityreporter.com; web

site www.lakecityreporter.com
Group: Community Newspapers, Inc.
Published: Tues, Wed, Thur, Fri, Sat, Sun
Weekday Frequency: m
Saturday Frequency: m
Circulation: 8,887; 8,887(sat); 8,887(sun)
Last Audit: Sworn/Estimate/Non-Audited September 30, 2017
Advertising Rate (weekday/saturday): Open inch rate $19.50
News services: AP, SHNS. **Established:** 1874
Own Printing Facility?: Yes
Commercial Printers?: Yes
Special Editions: Suwannee Valley Vacation Guide (Jan.); Rodeo magazine (March); North Florida Living (Apr); Football (Aug); Song Book (Dec); Physicians Directory (Jan); Columbia Style Biz (Jul); Best of the Best (May); Home for the Holidays (Nov); Guide to Columbia County (Oct); County Fair magazine (Oct.); Health & Nutrition (Sept).
Special Weekly Sections: Real Estate (Fri);
Syndicated Publications: Parade (S); American Profile (Weekly).
Publisher...Todd Wilson
Controller...Sue Brannon
Sports Ed....Tim Kirby
IT Mgr....Dave Kimler
Advertising Director.................Ashley Butcher
Editor...Robert Bridges
Circulation Director.................Mandy Brown
Adv. Dir....Lynda Strickland
Circ. Dir....Russell Waters
Ed....Tom Mayer
Mng. Ed....Jerry Spaeder
Market Information: TMC.
Mechanical Available: Offset; Black and 3 ROP colors; insert accepted - hand bill size; page cutoffs - 22 1/4.
Mechanical Specifications: Type page 13 x 21 1/2; E - 6 cols, 1 5/6, 1/8 between; A - 6 cols, 1 5/6, 1/8 between; C - 6 cols, 1 5/6, 1/8 between.
Delivery Method: Mail, Newsstand, Carrier, RacksEquipment & Software: BUSINESS EQUIPMENT: IBM/AS-400 CLASSIFIED EQUIPMENT: Hardware — APP/Macs; Printers — Xante/Accel-a-Writer, APP/Laserwriter; CLASSIFIED SOFTWARE: Baseview. DISPLAY EQUIPMENT: Hardware — APP/Macs; Printers — Xante/Accel-a-Writer, APP/Laserwriter; DISPLAY SOFTWAREAd Make-up Applications — QPS/QuarkXPress.; EDITORIAL EQUIPMENT: Hardware — APP/Macs; Printers — Panther/Imagesetter, Xante/Accel-a-Writer, APP/Laserwriter EDITORIAL SOFTWARE: Baseview, QPS, Adobe/Photoshop. PRODUCTION EQUIPMENT: Hardware — Panther PRODUCTION SOFTWARE: Baseview.

LAKELAND

THE LEDGER
300 W Lime St, 300 West Lime Street, Lakeland, Fla., 33815-4649, Polk; gen tel (863) 802-7323; adv tel (863) 802-7381; ed tel (863) 802-7504; gen fax (863) 802-7804; adv fax (863) 802-7813; ed fax (863) 802-7849; gen/nat adv e-mail ron.moates@theledger.com; disp adv e-mail ron.moates@theledger.com; class adv e-mailkim.edwards@ledgermediagroup.com; ed e-mail newstips@theledger.com; web site www.theledger.com
- 10,333,000(views) 907,423(visitors)
Group: New Media Investment Group
Published: Mon, Tues, Wed, Thur, Fri, Sat, Sun
Weekday Frequency: m
Saturday Frequency: m
Circulation: 33,603; 31,571(sat); 39,843(sun)
Last Audit: AAM December 31, 2016
Advertising Rate (weekday/saturday): 1.75 Inches $158.10
Advertising Rate (sunday): 1.75 Inches $189.04
News services: AP, NYT, MCT, LAT-WP. **Established:** 1924
Own Printing Facility?: Yes
Commercial Printers?: Yes
Special Editions: Back-to-School (Aug); Year In Review (Dec); Automotive (Jan); Football (Jul); Spring Health Care (Mar); Mayfaire-By-The-Lake (May); Today's Senior (Monthly); Reader's Choice (Nov); Parade of Homes

(Oct); Fall Health Care (Sept).
Special Weekly Sections: Health (Tue); The Arts (Wed); Best Food Day, Entertainment (Thur); Religion, Real Estate (Sat); Senior (Sun)
Syndicated Publications: Parade (S).
Digital Platform - Mobile: Apple
Digital Platform - Tablet: Apple iOS
Dig. Dir....Scott Girouard
Ed....Lenore Devore
Art Dir....Mark Williams
East Polk Ed....Jeff Kline
Agriculture Reporter
Kevin Bouffard
Asst. Editorial Page Ed..................Glenn Marston
Assistant Managing Editor, Metro
Lynn Maddox
Health/Medical Ed..................Robin Adams
Home/Garden Ed..................Lyle McBride
Online Ed....Barry Friedman
Outdoors Ed..................Delwin Milligan
Political/Gov't Ed..................Bill Rufty
Exec. Ed....Skip M. Perez
nat'l Adv. Mgr..................Ron Moates
Sales & Mktg. Mgr..................Maria Iannucci
Market Information: ADS; TMC; Zoned editions.
Mechanical Available: Offset; Black and 3 ROP colors; insert accepted - spadea comic wraps; page cutoffs - 22.
Mechanical Specifications: Type page 13 x 21 1/2; E - 6 cols, 2 1/16, 1/8 between; A - 6 cols, 2 1/16, 1/8 between; C - 9 cols, 1 3/8, between.
Areas Served: 33565, 33566, 33567, 33801, 33803, 33805, 33809, 33810, 33811, 33812, 33813, 33815, 33823, 33827, 33830, 33834, 33835, 33837, 33896, 33897, 33838, 33839, 33841, 33843, 33844, 33850, 33851, 33853, 33859, 33855, 33856, 33860
Delivery Method: Mail, Newsstand, Carrier, RacksEquipment & Software: PRESSROOM EQUIPMENT: Pasters —8-G/RIP (ea. press); Reels & Stands — 8; Control System — G/Control; Registration System — G/Pin Register. MAILROOM EQUIPMENT: Counter Stackers — 8-QWI/350; Inserters & Stuffers — 1-HI/RS25, 4-GMA/2000 14:1; Tying Machines — 8/Power Strap/News Tyers; Control System — Machine Design; Address Machine — 1-/Ch, 1-/St.; BUSINESS EQUIPMENT: IBM/AS-400 CLASSIFIED EQUIPMENT: Hardware — AT/SYSDECO-Classified Pagination; CLASSIFIED SOFTWARE: AT/SYSDECO Classified Pagination. DISPLAY EQUIPMENT: Hardware — AT/LAS; Printers — HP/8000 Laser Jet; DISPLAY SOFTWAREAd Make-up Applications — AT/Classpage FPO; Layout Software — SCS/Layout 8000, SCS/LYNX. EDITORIAL EQUIPMENT: Hardware — AT/SYSDECO, APP/Mac Press-to-Go/Lf/AP Leaf Picture Desk, AP/Leafax, APP/Laserphoto; Printers — AU/Laserprinter, Okidata EDITORIAL SOFTWARE: AT/SYSDECO. PRODUCTION EQUIPMENT: Hardware — Kk/RFS 2035, 2-Microtek/600, CD/5400; Cameras — 1-C/Spartan; Scanners — 1-Kk/RFS 2035, 2-PixelCraft/7650X, 1-Howtek/D4000 PRODUCTION SOFTWARE: AT/Classpage FPO, AT, Press 2go, QPS/QuarkXPress.

LEESBURG

THE DAILY COMMERCIAL
212 E Main St, Leesburg, Fla., 34748-5227, Lake; gen tel (352) 365-8200; adv tel (352) 365-8287; ed tel (357) 365-8266; gen fax (352) 365-1951; adv fax (352) 365-1951; ed fax (352) 365-1951; gen/nat adv e-mail news@dailycommercial.com; disp adv e-mail kevinaustin@dailycommercial.com; class adv e-mail linda@dailycommercial.com; ed e-mail news@dailycommercial.com; web site www.dailycommercial.com
Group: New Media Investment Group
Published: Mon, Tues, Wed, Thur, Fri, Sat, Sun
Weekday Frequency: m
Saturday Frequency: m
Circulation: 11,842; 11,842(sat); 13,943(sun)
Last Audit: AAM March 31, 2017
Advertising Rate (weekday/saturday): Open inch rate $26.58
Advertising Rate (sunday): Open inch rate $29.94
News services: AP, NYT. **Established:** 1875
Special Editions: Home Improvement (Apr);

Women's Quarterly (Aug); Holiday Gift Guide (Dec); Women's Quarterly (Feb); Super Bowl Preview (Jan); For Your Health (Mar); Women's Quarterly (May); Women's Quarterly (Nov); Welcome Back (Oct).
Special Weekly Sections: Medicine in the News (Mon); Best Food (Wed); Health (Thur); Church, Real Estate (Sat); TV, (Sun); Explore Leesburg, Golden Triangle (Monthly)
Syndicated Publications: TV Week (offset) (S); USA WEEKEND Magazine (Thur).
Prodn. Mgr., Pressroom.........James Bilderback
Circ. Dir....Tina Reader
News Ed....Bill Koch
Rich Pinder
Major/Nat'l Accts. Mgr..............Melanie Randall
Adv. Dir....Kevin Austin
Director of Sales and Marketing.................Mary Manning-Jacobs
Mechanical Available: Offset; Black and 3 ROP colors; insert accepted; page cutoffs - 22 3/4.Equipment & Software: PRESSROOM EQUIPMENT: Lines — 10-G/Urbanite; MAILROOM EQUIPMENT: Counter Stackers — 4/QWI, 2-Id; Inserters & Stuffers — 1-HI/848; Tying Machines — 2-/MLN, 1-MLN/Spirit; Address Machine — 1-/Ch.; BUSINESS EQUIPMENT: IBM/Sys 36 CLASSIFIED EQUIPMENT: Hardware — 9-StarMax/4000; Printers — APP/Mac 4/600; CLASSIFIED SOFTWARE: Baseview/Ad Manager Pro 1.0.4. DISPLAY EQUIPMENT: Hardware — 5-StarMax/4000; Printers — Xante/Accel-a-Writer 8200, GCC/Elite XL616, APP/Mac LaserWriter Pro; DISPLAY SOFTWAREAd Make-up Applications — QPS/QuarkXPress, Adobe/Photoshop, Adobe/Illustrator.; EDITORIAL EQUIPMENT: Hardware — 8-StarMax/4000, 12-StarMax/3000, 10-APP/Mac G4; Printers — Teletype/MOD 40, Xante/Accel-a-Writer 8200, GCC/Elite XL 616, APP/Mac LaserWriter Pro 16 EDITORIAL SOFTWARE: Baseview/NewsEdit Pro 3.0, Baseview/IQUE, QPS/QuarkXPress. PRODUCTION EQUIPMENT: Hardware — 2-Pre Press/Panther Pro 36, 1-C/80, 1-C/80RA, 1-Konica/K-550; Cameras — 1-C, 1-LE; Scanners — Kk/RFS 2035, 2-AG/StudioScan.

MARIANNA

JACKSON COUNTY FLORIDAN
4403 Constitution Ln, Marianna, Fla., 32448-4472, Jackson; gen tel (850) 526-3614; adv tel (850) 526-3614; ed tel (850) 526-3614; gen fax (850) 482-4478; adv fax (850) 482-4478; ed fax (850) 482-4478; gen/nat adv e-mail editorial@jcfloridan.com; disp adv e-mail sales@jcfloridan.com; class adv e-mail classifieds@jcfloridan.com; ed e-mail editorial@jcfloridan.com; web site www.jcfloridan.com
Group: BH Media Group
Published: Tues, Wed, Thur, Fri, Sun
Weekday Frequency: m
Circulation: 3,690; 3,690(sat); 3,733(sun)
Last Audit: AAM March 31, 2016
Advertising Rate (weekday/saturday): Open Inch Rate $23.00
Advertising Rate (sunday): Open Inch Rate $23.00
News services: Associated Press **Established:** 1928
Own Printing Facility?: No
Commercial Printers?: No
Special Editions: Senior Citizen (Apr); Football (Aug); Marianna Christmas Bucks (Dec); Visitor's Guide Supplement (Feb); Income Tax (Jan); Senior Citizen (Jul); Visitor's Guide Supplement (Jun); Home & Garden (Mar); Mother's Day (May); Farm City (Nov); Back To School (Sep
Special Weekly Sections: Business (Daily); Religion (Fri); Family, Real Estate (Sun)
Syndicated Publications: Relish, USA Weekend, American Profile, Spry.
Pub./Adv. Dir..................Valeria Roberts
Circ. Mgr....Dena Oberski
Photographer/Photo Ed..................Mark Skinner
Sports Editor.................Rolando Rosa
Reporter...Angie Cook
Reporter.................Deborah Buckhalter
Ed....Michael Becker
Market Information: TMC

Mechanical Available: Offset; Black and 3 ROP colors; insert accepted; page cutoffs - 22 3/4.
Mechanical Specifications: Type page 12 x 21 1/2; E - 6 cols, 1 3/4, 1/6 between; A - 6 cols, 1 3/4, 1/6 between; C - 6 cols, 1 3/4, 1/6 between.
Areas Served: 32420, 32423, 32426, 32431, 32432, 32440, 32442, 32443, 32431, 32445, 32446, 32447, 32448, 32460
Delivery Method: Mail, Newsstand, Carrier, Racks

MELBOURNE

FLORIDA TODAY

1 Gannett Plaza, Melbourne, Fla., 32940, Brevard; gen tel 1-877-424-0156; adv tel (321) 242-3765; ed tel (321) 242-3606; gen fax (321) 253-0071; adv fax (321) 242-6618; ed fax (321) 242-6620; gen/nat adv e-mail sshook@floridatoday.com; disp adv e-mail jprice@floridatoday.com; ed e-mail bstover@floridatoday.com; web site www.floridatoday.com
Group: Gannett
Published: Mon, Tues, Wed, Thur, Fri, Sat, Sun
Weekday Frequency: m
Saturday Frequency: m
Circulation: 40,150; 39,957(sat); 54,200(sun)
Last Audit: AAM March 31, 2016
Advertising Rate (weekday/saturday): Open inch rate: $116.08
Advertising Rate (sunday): Open inch rate $177.27
News services: AP, Gannett Content One **Established:** 1966
Own Printing Facility?: Yes
Commercial Printers?: Yes
Special Editions: HealthSource; Health & Medicine; Brevard County Moms; Fact Book;
Special Weekly Sections: Money (Mon); Health, Fitness (Tue); Community (Wed); Best Food, Health, Style (Thur); TGIF (Fri); Spaces (Sat); Style, Comics, TV (Sun)
Syndicated Publications: USA Weekend (Sun)
Controller................................. Robert Van Epp
Sales and Marketing Dir................. Greg Watson
Strategic Marketing Solutions Dir.......Gina Kaiser
Credit Mgr................................. Sharon Secord
Operations Dir................................ John Vizzini
Adv. Dir..Chris Wood
VP/South Region, HR Business Partner Team. Julie Lusk
Controller................................Landra Burgess
Systems Mgr.................................. Dan Patellis
Adv. Mgr., Classified........................ Kay Wartell
Ops.Production Mgr......................Bob Campbell
Distribution Ops. Mgr................. Cedric Johnson
Retail Sales Mgr.......................... Leween Jones
Editorial Page Ed.............................John Glisch
Packaging Center Mgr..................Marcus Greco
Editorial Writer..........................Annette Clifford
Multimedia Editor...........................Jeff Meesey
Features Ed................................Deidre Gordon
Public Interest Editor..........................Matt Reed
Lifestyles Ed................... Suzy Fleming Leonard
Delivery News Editor.....................Eric Garwood
Sports Editor................................Mike Parsons
Visuals Editor................................. Tim Walters
Custom Content Editor.................. Susy Leonard
Business Editor......................Adam Lowenstein
Enterprise Editor / space, family, education.. Mara Bellaby
Enterprise Editor/county, state, environment..John McCarthy
Enterprise Editor/breaking news, military, religion Lee Nessel
Adv. Dir...........................Stephanie McLoughlin
Pub....Jeff Kiel
Pub.... J. Pason Gaddis
Market Information: Electronic Edition; Sunday Select; TMC
Mechanical Available: Offset; Black and 3 ROP colors; preprinted inserts accepted
Mechanical Specifications: Type page 10"x21". 6 cols, 1 5/6", 1/8" between
Areas Served: Brevard County, FL
Delivery Method: Mail, Newsstand, Carrier, RacksEquipment & Software: PRESSROOM EQUIPMENT: Lines — 16-G/Headliner Offset double width; 8-G/C150 Community offset single width; Press Drive — Fin; Folders — r-G/3:2, 1-G/1:1, Twafolder; Pasters —16-G/45 RTP, 2-Enkel/Zero Speed Pasters; Reels & Stands — Static belt tension 3 arm Reels & Stands; Control System — Fin/Drive; Registration System — KFM MAILROOM EQUIPMENT: Counter Stackers — 1-MM, 2-HL/Dual Carrier, 2-QWI/Dual Carrier, 2-HL/Monitor, 2-QWI/401, 1-Gammerler/KL503, 1-Gammerler/STC-700; Inserters & Stuffers — 1-Mailstar, 2-HI/630, 1-HI/632; Tying Machines — 3-Dynaric/NP 1500, 3-Power Strap, Newstyer/2000; Wrapping Singles — 3-HL/Bottom Wrap, 3-HI/Bottomwrap, 2-QWI/Viper Bottomwrap; Control System — 2-Prima/Icon 300; Address Machine — 1-Ch, 1-Barstrom; BUSINESS EQUIPMENT: 1-IBM/AS-400 Model F45, IBM/AS-400 500-2141 BUSINESS SOFTWARE: Cyborg, Lawson, Gen ledger, Corporate 1997 : Adv, Circ CLASSIFIED EQUIPMENT: Hardware — Gateway; HI/Classified AdPag; Printers — Florida Data; CLASSIFIED SOFTWARE: HI/AdPower, HI/AdPower. DISPLAY EQUIPMENT: Hardware — APP/Mac; Printers — HP/Color Laser Jet, HP/Jaser Jet, Tektronix/Phaser 780; DISPLAY SOFTWAREAd Make-up Applications — Adobe/Creative Suite, QPS/QuarkXPress 4.11, Multi-Ad/Creator Pro 6.5, File Maker Pro, DPS/AdTracker, DPS/AdTracker 5.0.1, Aldus/FreeHand 9.0; EDITORIAL EQUIPMENT: Hardware — 2-Sun/Enterprise 450/HI/NewsMaker Pagination; Printers — Epson EDITORIAL SOFTWARE: HI/NewsMaker Editorial 4.5. PRODUCTION EQUIPMENT: Hardware — 2-CD/646IE, Anites/SN48 Processor, WL/Lithobender; Scanners — 2-Linotype-Hell/Topaz, 1-Kk/RFS 2035 Plus PRODUCTION SOFTWARE: HI/NewsMaker.

NAPLES

NAPLES DAILY NEWS

1100 Immokalee Rd, Naples, Fla., 34110-4810, Collier; gen tel (239) 262-3161; adv tel (239) 262-3161 (display); ed tel (239) 263-4863; gen fax (239) 263-4816; adv fax (239) 263-4703 (class); ed fax (239) 263-4816; gen/nat adv e-mail info@naplesnews.com; disp adv e-mail sales@naplesnews.com; class adv e-mailclassad@naplesnews.com; web site www.naplesnews.com 955,407(visitors)
Group: Journal Media Group
Published: Mon, Tues, Wed, Thur, Fri, Sat, Sun
Weekday Frequency: m
Saturday Frequency: m
Circulation: 45,197; 45,197(sat); 51,849(sun)
Last Audit: AAM June 30, 2017
Advertising Rate (weekday/saturday): Open inch rate $83.70 (Mon-Wed); $86.30 (Thur-Sat)
Advertising Rate (sunday): Open inch rate $99.24
News services: AP, SHNS, NYT.
Own Printing Facility?: Yes
Commercial Printers?: Yes
Special Editions: Newcomers (Apr); Back-to-School (Aug); Newcomers (Dec); Ambience (Feb); Newcomers (Jan); In Business (Jul); Parents & Kids (Jun); Newcomers (Mar); Parents & Kids (May); Real Estate Marketplace (Monthly); Homes for the Holidays (Nov); Portfolio of Homes (O
Special Weekly Sections: Business (Mon); Health (Tue); Food (Wed); Arts (Thur); Home (Fri); Gulf Life, Religion (Sat); Real Estate, Travel, Comics (Sun)
Syndicated Publications: Visitor's Guide (Other); Comics (S).
Digital Platform - Mobile: Apple, Android
Digital Platform - Tablet: Apple iOS, Android, Kindle Fire
Asst. Pub........................................Trish Priller
City Ed....Allen Bartlett
Homes/Ambience Ed.... Harriet Howard Heithaus
News Ed...Tim Aten
Sports Ed....................................Greg Hardwig
Mgr., IS/Pre Press.......................Cathy Rodrick
Mgr., Packaging..........................Glenn Williams
Prodn. Mgr., Pressroom.................Cassay Cote
Pres./Pub....Bill Barker
Nat'l Adv. Mgr................................. Len Egdish
Editor... Manny Garcia
Digital Content Director..................Jigsha Desai
Director of Marketing.................. Robin Lankton
Advertising Director....................Shawna Devlin
Market Information: Zoned editions.
Mechanical Available: Offset; Black and 3 ROP colors; insert accepted; page cutoffs - 23 9/16.
Mechanical Specifications: Type page 13 x 22 1/4; E - 6 cols, 2 1/16, 1/8 between; A - 6 cols, 2 1/16, 1/8 between; C - 10 cols, 1 1/5, 1/8 between.
Areas Served: South Lee County, Collier CountyEquipment & Software: PRESSROOM EQUIPMENT: Lines — 9-G/Metro double width (5 half decks) 1994; Press Drive — 10-HP/75; Folders — 3-G/3:2 double; Reels & Stands — G/Reels & Stands.; MAILROOM EQUIPMENT: Counter Stackers — 6-HL/Monitor; Inserters & Stuffers — 1-S/1472, 1-S/1272P; Tying Machines — 1/Power Strap/PSN-2, 2-/Power Strap/PSN-6, 3-Dynaric/NP 1500; Wrapping Singles — 4-/CH, 1-HL/Underwrap; Control System — 2-/PC, Image Packagi; BUSINESS EQUIPMENT: Sun/Sparc BUSINESS SOFTWARE: PBS: Microsoft/Office CLASSIFIED EQUIPMENT: Hardware — Dell/200; Printers — Epson/DFX 5000, Konica/Laser, HP; CLASSIFIED SOFTWARE: HI/AdPower. DISPLAY EQUIPMENT: Hardware — Sun/Sparc 20; Printers — HP/LaserJet III, C.Itoh/C1400, Data products/1550, Techtronic Phaser; DISPLAY SOFTWAREAd Make-up Applications — SCS; Layout Software — SCS/Layout 8000. EDITORIAL EQUIPMENT: Hardware — HI/Newsmaker; Printers — Epson, IBM, Konica, HP EDITORIAL SOFTWARE: HI/NME. PRODUCTION EQUIPMENT: Hardware — 2-AU/3850 Doublewidth, WL/Lith-X-Pozer III, WL/Lithobender SD 30, Automated/Optical Film Punch; Scanners — Scitex/System, Kk/2035, Graphic Enterprises/3050 Copy Dot PRODUCTION SOFTWARE: QPS/QuarkXPress 3.31, HI/XP-21-DASH, HI/XP-21 NMP, HI/XP-21 NME.

NORTH PORT

NORTH PORT SUN

13487 Tamiami Trl, North Port, Fla., 34287-1211, Sarasota; gen tel (941) 429-3000; gen fax (941) 423-2318; gen/nat adv e-mail cymoore@sun-herald.com; web site www.yoursun.com/csp/mediapool/sites/SunNews/NorthPort/index.csp
Group: Sun Coast Media Group Inc
Published: Mon, Tues, Wed, Thur, Fri, Sat, Sun
Last Audit: Sworn/Estimate/Non-Audited December 11, 2017
General Manager...........................Carol Moore

OCALA

OCALA STAR-BANNER

2121 SW 19th Avenue Rd, Ocala, Fla., 34471-7752, Marion; gen tel (352) 867-4010; adv tel (352) 867-4060; ed tel (352) 867-4013; gen fax (352) 867-4028; adv fax (352) 867-4028; ed fax (352) 867-4018; gen/nat adv e-mail online@starbanner.com; disp adv e-mail steve.martin@starbanner.com; class adv e-mailclassified@starbanner.com; ed e-mail doug.ray@gvillesun.com; web site www.ocala.com - 7,814,477(views) 605,052(visitors)
Group: New Media Investment Group
Published: Mon, Tues, Wed, Thur, Fri, Sat, Sun
Weekday Frequency: m
Saturday Frequency: m
Circulation: 22,998; 23,230(sat); 28,380(sun)
Last Audit: AAM March 31, 2017
Advertising Rate (weekday/saturday): Open inch rate $93.61
Advertising Rate (sunday): Open inch rate $101.00
News services: AP, NYT **Established:** 1866
Own Printing Facility?: Yes
Commercial Printers?: Yes
Special Editions: Hurricane Guide, Living Here (area guide)
Special Weekly Sections: TV, Business, Sports, Entertainment Weather (Daily); Stock (Tue-Sat); Life (Mon-Wed); Entertainment, Best Food (Thur); Auto, TMC (Fri); Home, Real Estate, Religion (Sat); Arts, Entertainment, business, Travel (Sun)
Syndicated Publications: Real Estate Review (Sat); Parade (S);
Adv. Mgr., Classified....................... Melody Day
Adv. Mgr., Retail............................ Steve Martin
Community Relations..................... Mary Baggs
Circ. Mgr.... Bill Hayter
Dir Edit.. Tom McNiff
Assistant Managing Editor....................Jim Ross
Photo Editor............................Alan Youngblood
Sports Ed... Andy Marks
Advertising Director....................Susan Pinder
Executive Editor.............................. Jim Osteen
Online Community Editor.........Richard Anguiano
Editorial Page Ed........................... Brad Rogers
Pub...Jim Doughton
Nat'l Adv. Acct. Exec....................Bryce Abshier
Adv. Dir...................................... Susan Leitgeb
Exec Ed/Gen Mgr.......................Douglas K. Ray
Market Information: TMC, Sunday Select
Mechanical Available: Offset; Black and 3 ROP colors; insert accepted.
Mechanical Specifications: Type page 13 x 21 1/3; E - 6 cols, 2 1/16, 1/8 between; A - 6 cols, 2 1/16, 1/8 between; C - 9 cols, 1 3/8, 1/16 between.
Delivery Method: Newsstand, Carrier, RacksEquipment & Software: PRESSROOM EQUIPMENT: Lines — 5-G/Headliner 1988; MAILROOM EQUIPMENT: Counter Stackers — 3/QWI; Inserters & Stuffers — 1-/HI; Tying Machines — 3-/MLN; BUSINESS EQUIPMENT: 1-IBM/AS-400 36 CLASSIFIED EQUIPMENT: Hardware — 15-PC, MS/NT Server; CLASSIFIED SOFTWARE: AT/Advantage. DISPLAY EQUIPMENT: Hardware — 1-IBM, 12-APP/Mac workstation; Printers — 2-QMS/860, 1-Phaser/300i; DISPLAY SOFTWAREAd Make-up Applications — DTI/SpeedPlanner, DTI/AdSpeed; Layout Software — DTI/SpeedPlanner. EDITORIAL EQUIPMENT: Hardware — 2-AT/Series 60, 15-PC Power pagination editing station/46-AT; Printers — 1-QMS/860 EDITORIAL SOFTWARE: DTI/Pagespeed, DTI/SpeedPlanner, DTI/SpeedDriver. PRODUCTION EQUIPMENT: Hardware — 1-AU/APS-6 5-8, 3-Pre Press/Panther Pro 46, 1-C/80RA, 2-P/Online; Cameras — 1-C/Spartan III 1270, 1-C/Newspager PRODUCTION SOFTWARE: DTI/SpeedPlanner, DTI/SpeedDriver, MEI/Page Director.

ORLANDO

ORLANDO SENTINEL

633 N Orange Ave, Lbby, Orlando, Fla., 32801-1300, Orange; gen tel (407) 420-5000; adv tel (407) 420-5100; ed tel (407) 420-5411; adv fax (407) 420-5768; ed fax (407) 420-5350; gen/nat adv e-mail ecom@tronc.com; class adv e-mailclassified_ad@orlandosentinel.com; ed e-mail insight@orlandosentinel.com; web site www.orlandosentinel.com 2,907,248(visitors); web site 2 www.elsentinel.com
Group: Tronc, Inc.
Published: Mon, Tues, Wed, Thur, Fri, Sat, Sun
Weekday Frequency: m
Saturday Frequency: m
Circulation: 121,799; 92,730(sat); 187,646(sun)
Last Audit: AAM March 31, 2017
Advertising Rate (weekday/saturday): 1/126 Pg $258.00; 1/63 Pg $518.00
Advertising Rate (sunday): 1/126 Pg $343.00; 1/63 Pg $691.00
News services: NYT, MCT, LAT-WP, AP, Cox News Service, CQ, TMS. **Established:** 1876
Own Printing Facility?: Yes
Commercial Printers?: Yes
Special Editions: Dealer's Choice (Apr); Football Preview (Aug); Holiday Dining (Dec); Lake County Spring Parade of Homes (Feb); Florida Forecast (Jan); Hot Cars (Jul); Career Builder Xtra (Jun); Bay Hill Invitational (Mar); Hurricane Survival Guide (May); Auto Show I (Nov
Special Weekly Sections: Business, Stock (Daily); Homes, Travel (Sun); Lifestyle, Entertainment (Mon-Sun); Business, Features (Mon); Good Eating (Wed); Drive (Thur); Calendar (Fri)
Syndicated Publications: Parade (S).
Digital Platform - Mobile: Apple, Android, Windows
Digital Platform - Tablet: Apple iOS, Android,

Windows 7, Blackberry Tablet OS, Kindle, Nook, Kindle Fire
Editor/SVP/Director of Content-Florida..........Avido Khahaifa
Compensation/Commun. Mgr...........Dyana Burke
Adv. Vice Pres./Dir...................John D'Orlando
Adv. Sr. Mgr., Delivery....................Jack Curtin
Adv. Mgr., Bus...................................Rich Miller
Vice Pres., Interactive..........Linda Schaible
Circ. Vice Pres...........................Bert Ortiz
Circ. Mgr., Subscriber Servs...........Dave Elder
Ed...Charlotte H. Hall
Vice President, Editor, Webmaster...Mark Russell
Assoc. Mng. Ed., Bus..................Gail Rayos
Assoc. Mng. Ed., Features.........Kim Marcum
Assoc. Mng. Ed., Photo/Design/Visuals......Bonita Burton
Ed., Recruitment/Staff Devel..........Dana Eagles
Arts/Entertainment Ed.....................Anne Dunlap
Bus. News Ed.......................Bill Zimmerman
City Ed...................................Lisa Cianci
Lifestyles Ed.............................Barry Glenn
Acct. Mgr...................Chance Schlesman
Nat'l Retail Dir.....................Dana Wardeh Amy Moon
Market Information: ADS; Split run; TMC; Zoned editions.
Mechanical Available: Offset; Black and 3 ROP colors; insert accepted - product samples; page cutoffs - 22 1/25.
Mechanical Specifications: Type page 12 x 20 7/8; E - 6 cols, 2 1/16, 1/8 between; A - 6 cols, 2 1/16, 1/8 between; C - 10 cols, 1 1/8, 1/8 between.
Areas Served: 32801 Equipment & Software: PRESSROOM EQUIPMENT: Lines — 27-G/Metro double width, 4-G/Imperial double width 1981; 18-G/Head double width, 3-G/Imperial double width 1985; 5-G/Newsliner 4 over 4 color towers, digital inking; Press Drive — Fin; Folders — 7-G/3:2; Pasters —45-G/RTPReels & Stands — Reel; MAILROOM EQUIPMENT: Counter Stackers — 13-QWI/351, 2-QWI/401, 6-QWI/501, 4-BG/Exactistack Count-o-veyor; Inserters & Stuffers — 2-HI/2299, 2-SLS/3000 30:22, 1-HI/1630; Tying Machines — 5-GMA/Combistack, 5-Dynaric/NP 2-3, 5-Dynaric/RLM-1, 1-Dynaric/DF-2400, 7-Signode; BUSINESS EQUIPMENT: IBM/PS-2 Pentium, Dell/6x100, Dell/CPI, Dell/LS BUSINESS SOFTWARE: WordPerfect, Microsoft/Word, Microsoft/Excel, Microsoft/Access, Microsoft/Office 97 CLASSIFIED EQUIPMENT: Hardware — 4-SII/Sys 77 S7002; Ad-Star, Fax Action, GDT/Gateway; CLASSIFIED SOFTWARE: Czar I, Coyote/3 1.4, SCS/Claspag 4.44. DISPLAY EQUIPMENT: Hardware — 2-Sun/Sparc 5, 6-Sun/Sparc 1000E, 6-Sun/Ultra 2, 2-Sun/Ultra 250; Other Hardware — GEI/Pagecheck E-Proofing, ZPS/Insert Order Entry DISPLAY SOFTWAREAd Make-up Applications — CCI/Addesk Production 5.5.3, Solaris 2.6; Layout Software — SCS/Layout 8000. EDITORIAL EQUIPMENT: Hardware — IBM/RS 6000/350-PC; Printers — HP, GEI, OSE EDITORIAL SOFTWARE: CCI/Newsdesk 5.5.5, Microsoft/Windows NT XP 4.0. PRODUCTION EQUIPMENT: Hardware — 4-3850 SST-Wide, 9-APP/Mac, 3-Sharp/2X-610; Cameras — 1-C/Newspager; Scanners — 2-Eskofot.

PALATKA

PALATKA DAILY NEWS
1825 Saint Johns Ave, Palatka, Fla., 32177-4442, Putnam; gen tel (386) 312-5200; adv tel (386) 312-5210; gen fax (386) 312-5209; gen/nat adv e-mail mwells@palatkadailynews.com; ed e-mail akrombach@palatkadailynews.com; web site www.palatkadailynews.com
Group: Community Newspapers, Inc.
Published: Tues, Wed, Thur, Fri, Sat
Weekday Frequency: m
Saturday Frequency: m
Circulation: 11,804; 13,309(sat)
Last Audit: Sworn/Estimate/Non-Audited September 30, 2017
Advertising Rate (weekday/saturday): Open inch rate $22.11
News services: AP. **Established:** 1885
Special Editions: Back-to-School (Aug); Fact

Book (Feb); Meet the Manager (Jan); Blue Crab Festival (May); Gift Guide (Nov); Create a Beautiful Home (Oct); Industry Appreciation (Sept).
Special Weekly Sections: Currents (Fri); Health and Fitness Page (Wed).
Adv. Dir...................................Mary Kaye Wells
Circ. Dir...............................John Allender
Sports Ed..................................Andy Hall
Pub...................................Wayne Knuckles
Ed...Scott Bryan
Market Information: TMC; Zoned editions.
Mechanical Available: Offset; Black and 3 ROP colors; insert accepted - small catalogs, cards; page cutoffs - 22 3/4.
Mechanical Specifications: Type page 13 x 21 1/2; E - 6 cols, 2 1/16, 1/8 between; A - 6 cols, 2 1/16, 1/8 between; C - 9 cols, 1 3/8, 1/16 between.Equipment & Software: MAILROOM EQUIPMENT: Address Machine — Ch/586.; BUSINESS EQUIPMENT: IBM/S-36, PC Network BUSINESS SOFTWARE: Microsoft/Excel, Microsoft/Word, INSI CLASSIFIED EQUIPMENT: Hardware — Computext/CompuClass; Printers — APP/Mac LaserWriter II; CLASSIFIED SOFTWARE: Computext/CompuClass. DISPLAY EQUIPMENT: Hardware — 1-APP/Mac II, 1-APP/Mac IIci, 1-APP/Mac Quadra 950; Printers — 1-DEC/VT 820 Plain Paper, 1-Pre Press/Panther Plus; DISPLAY SOFTWAREAd Make-up Applications — Multi-Ad/Creator, QPS/QuarkXPress, Adobe/Photoshop.; EDITORIAL EQUIPMENT: Hardware — 8-IBM/486, 5-PC Pagination Station/APP/Mac IIcx, APP/Mac 300, Shava/Telebridge, Microcom/9600 Modem, Lf/AP Leaf Picture Desk, APP/Mac vx; Printers — 1-APP/Mac LaserWriter II NTX EDITORIAL SOFTWARE: Computext. PRODUCTION EQUIPMENT: Hardware — TI/OmniPage, 1-Konica/K550; Scanners - 2-Microtek/II XE, 1-Kk/RFS 2035 PRODUCTION SOFTWARE: Computext/Comet.

PALM BEACH

PALM BEACH DAILY NEWS
400 Royal Palm Way, Ste 100, Palm Beach, Fla., 33480-4117, Palm Beach; gen tel (561) 820-3800; adv tel (561) 820-3815; ed tel (561) 820-3865; gen fax (561) 820-3802; adv fax (561) 655-4594; ed fax (561) 655-4594; gen/nat adv e-mail lgoings@pbdailynews.com; disp adv e-mail lgoings@pbdailynews.com; class adv e-maillgoings@pbdailynews.com; ed e-mail jreingold@pbdailynews.com; web site www.palmbeachdailynews.com
Group: New Media Investment Group
Published: Mon, Tues, Wed, Thur, Fri, Sat, Sun
Weekday Frequency: m
Saturday Frequency: m
Circulation: 2,913; 2,657(sat); 4,498(sun)
Last Audit: AAM June 30, 2015
Advertising Rate (weekday/saturday): 1/12 Pg $294.89; 1/10 Pg $353.86
Advertising Rate (sunday): 1/12 Pg $393.18; 1/10 Pg $471.82
News services: 1897
Special Weekly Sections: Insider Society Section (Wed); Home, Real Estate (Fri); Business, Finance, Fashion (Sun)
Syndicated Publications: Palm Beach Life
Digital Platform - Tablet: Apple iOS, Kindle
Pres...Tim Burke
Pub...Joyce Reingold
Nat'l Acct. Exec.....................Paula Hoekstra
Adv. Team Leader...........................Jill Staudt
Adv. Dir...Linda Goings
Managing Ed..................................Shelly Darby
Delivery Method: Mail, Racks

PANAMA CITY

THE NEWS HERALD
501 W 11th St, Panama City, Fla., 32401-2330, Bay; gen tel (850) 747-5000; adv tel (850) 747-5030; ed tel (850) 747-5070; gen fax (850) 747-5018; adv fax (850) 763-4636; ed fax (850) 747-5097; gen/nat adv e-mail news@pcnh.com; disp adv e-mail lcarver@pcnh.com; class adv e-mailjbullock@pcnh.

com; ed e-mail skent@pcnh.com; web site www.newsherald.com; web site 2 www.panamacity.com
Group: New Media Investment Group
Published: Mon, Tues, Wed, Thur, Fri, Sat, Sun
Weekday Frequency: m
Saturday Frequency: m
Circulation: 18,446; 18,446(sat); 21,923(sun)
Last Audit: CAC March 31, 2015
Advertising Rate (weekday/saturday): Open inch rate $50.00
News services: AP, MCT. **Established:** 1937
Own Printing Facility?: Yes
Commercial Printers?: Yes
Special Weekly Sections: Lifestyle & Viewpoint (S); Religion (Sat); Outdoors (Thur); Food (Wed).
Syndicated Publications: Parade Magazine (S).
Proprietary Publications: Gulf Defender PanamaCity.com
Digital Platform - Mobile: Apple, Android, Windows
Digital Platform - Tablet: Apple iOS, Android, Windows 7
Rgl.Controller..........................Robert Delaney
Rgl HR Dir...........................Lorraine Grimes
Circ. Customer Service Mgr.........Glenda Sullivan
Adv. Services Mgr...................Joye McCormick
Eastern Ed., Halifax NW Florida Group..........Mike Cazalas
Online Ed...........................Tony Simmons
Sports Ed.............................Pat McCann
Rgl. Ops. Dir...............................Ron Smith
Rgl. Circ. Dir........................Sharon Heckler
Managing Ed...........................Will Glover
Copy Desk Chief..........................Ray Glenn
Adv. Dir...............................Lori Ann Carver
Adv. Mgr. - Digital..........................Tonya Clay
Retail Adv. Mgr...........................Wayne Kight
Rgl. IT Dir..............................Ron Bennett
Rgl. Mktg. Dir.......................Vickie Gainer Roger Underwood
Pub...Lee Knapp
Publisher..................................Tim Thompson
Market Information: ADS.
Mechanical Available: Offset; Black and 3 ROP colors; insert accepted; page cutoffs - 21.
Mechanical Specifications: Type page 11 2/3 x 20; E - 6 cols, 1 13/16, 1/8 between; A - 6 cols, 1 13/16, 1/8 between; C - 9 cols, 1 1/4, 1/16 between.
Areas Served: Bay, Gulf, Franklin, Jackson, Washington, Holmes and Walton Counties in Florida
Delivery Method: Mail, Newsstand, Carrier, RacksEquipment & Software: PRESSROOM EQUIPMENT: Lines — 28 unit Goss Universal; Press Drive — Shaftless; Reels & Stands — 10; Control System — EAE; Registration System — Manual MAILROOM EQUIPMENT: Counter Stackers — 2-Gaemmeler; Inserters & Stuffers — SLS 3000 - 12 heads; Tying Machines — 3 Dynaric and 1 Sterling; Wrapping Singles — 2-/Bu; Address Machine — KAN; CLASSIFIED EQUIPMENT: Hardware — PC; Printers — HP/4000, HP/5SI; CLASSIFIED SOFTWARE: APT. DISPLAY EQUIPMENT: Hardware — PC; Printers — HP/750, HP/5MX; DISPLAY SOFTWAREAd Make-up Applications — APT; Layout Software — APT. EDITORIAL EQUIPMENT: Hardware — PC; Printers — HP/5MX EDITORIAL SOFTWARE: APT. PRODUCTION EQUIPMENT: Hardware — Kk/Newsway PRODUCTION SOFTWARE: APT.

PENSACOLA

PENSACOLA NEWS JOURNAL
2 N Palafox St, Pensacola, Fla., 32502-5626, Escambia; gen tel (850) 435-8500; adv tel (850) 435-8585; ed tel (850) 435-8542; gen fax (850) 435-8633; adv fax (850) 435-8570; ed fax (850) 435-8633; gen/nat adv e-mail jbell@pnj.com; disp adv e-mail rboles@pnj.com; class adv e-mail1889; ed e-mail news@pnj.com; web site www.pnj.com
505,065(visitors)
Group: Gannett
Published: Mon, Tues, Wed, Thur, Fri, Sat, Sun
Weekday Frequency: m
Saturday Frequency: m
Circulation: 27,295; 27,295(sat); 39,136(sun)
Last Audit: AAM December 31, 2016

Advertising Rate (weekday/saturday): Open inch rate $153.34
Advertising Rate (sunday): Open inch rate $190.11
News services: AP, GNS.
Special Editions: Football (Aug); Hurricane (May).
Special Weekly Sections: Business (Mon-Sat); Food & Wine, Moneysaver (Wed); Weekender (Fri); Coast Life, Homefinder, Cars, School (Sat); Business, Coast Life, Jobs, Health, Fitness, Travel, Military (Sun)
Syndicated Publications: USA WEEKEND Magazine (S).
Pub./Pres...................................Kevin Doyle
Dir., Finance...................................Tom Hartley
Dir., Adv. Sales...............................Bobby Rice
Adv. Mgr., Retail..........................Nadja Silvey
Adv. Mgr., Inside Sales................Debora Lefort
Dir., Market Devel.......................Becca Boles
Strategic Mktg. Mgr..................Gregory L. Clay
Circ. Dir.....................................Pat Daugherty
Exec. Ed...........................Richard Schneider
Mng. Ed...Gray Biel
Archives Mgr...............................Earl Melvin
Community Content Editor..............Julio Diaz
Editorial Page Ed.....................Carl Wernicke
Circ. Direc...................................Mark Everett
President & Publisher
Lisa Reese
Nat'l Sales Coord.................Carolyn Campbell
Content Coach/Watchdog
Rob Johnson
Director of Sales
Jodi Bell
Market Information: ADS; TMC; Zoned editions.
Mechanical Available: Offset; Black and 3 ROP colors; insert accepted - min 4 x 7-80 lbs stock; page cutoffs - 22.
Mechanical Specifications: Type page 11 5/8 x 20 3/4; E - 6 cols, 1 5/6, 1/8 between; A - 6 cols, 1 5/6, 1/8 between; C - 10 cols, 1, 1/8 between.Equipment & Software: PRESSROOM EQUIPMENT: Lines — 7-G/Headliner Offset double width 1997; Press Drive — 5-Fin/125 h.p. Digital; Folders — 2-G/3:2 160 PG; Control System — G/MPCS.; MAILROOM EQUIPMENT: Counter Stackers — 2-Id/2200, 1-HL/Monitor, 2/Quipp 400, 1-/Compass 180; Inserters & Stuffers — AM Graphics/630 21 hopper; Tying Machines — 2-Dynaric/NP-1, 2-Dynaric/NP-1, 2-Dynaric/NP 1500; Control System — Id/TCP Bundle Control Syste; BUSINESS EQUIPMENT: IBM/AS-400E 9406-620 BUSINESS SOFTWARE: Microsoft/Office 97 Desktop Suite CLASSIFIED EQUIPMENT: Hardware — Dell/Poweredge Server; Mobile Advertising Sales System; CLASSIFIED SOFTWARE: Mactive Adbase. DISPLAY EQUIPMENT: Hardware — 7-APP/Mac; Other Hardware — Mobile Advertising Sales System DISPLAY SOFTWAREAd Make-up Applications — Multi-Ad/Creator; Layout Software — MEI ALS. EDITORIAL EQUIPMENT: Hardware — IBM/XSeries Servers; Printers — Accel A Writer 45 EDITORIAL SOFTWARE: Harris Newsjaz 2.0. PRODUCTION EQUIPMENT: Hardware — KFM/Twin-Line Semi-auto, 2-AU/APS PIP II, 1-AU/3850; Scanners — Tecsa PRODUCTION SOFTWARE: Harris/NewsJaz 2.0, M Active PGL.

PORT SAINT LUCIE

ST. LUCIE NEWS TRIBUNE
760 NW Enterprise Dr, Port Saint Lucie, Fla., 34986-2228, Saint Lucie; gen tel (722) 337-5800; adv tel (772) 409-1361; gen fax (772) 469-2139; ed e-mail adam.neal@tcpalm.com; web site www.tcpalm.com
Group: Gannett
Published: Mon, Tues, Wed, Thur, Fri, Sat, Sun
Weekday Frequency: m
Circulation: 52,210; 51,039(sat); 66,322(sun)
Last Audit: AAM June 30, 2017
Editor..Adam Neal

PUNTA GORDA

CHARLOTTE SUN
23170 Harborview Rd, Punta Gorda, Fla.,

33980-2100, Charlotte; gen tel (941) 206-1000; adv tel (941) 206-1214; ed tel (941) 206-1100; gen fax (941) 629-2085; adv fax (941) 629-4499; ed fax (941) 629-2085; gen/nat adv e-mail sstevens@sun-herald.com; disp adv e-mail sstevens@sun-herald.com; class adv e-mailsstevens@sun-herald.com; web site www.yoursun.com
Group: Sun Coast Media Group Inc
Published: Mon, Tues, Wed, Thur, Fri, Sat, Sun
Weekday Frequency: m
Saturday Frequency: m
Circulation: 35,223; 29,608(sat); 48,004(sun)
Last Audit: AAM March 31, 2016
Advertising Rate (weekday/saturday): Open inch rate $71.90
Advertising Rate (sunday): Open inch rate $71.90
News services: MCT, AP Limited, AP Photo Feed, Bloomberg-Washington Post, News Service of Florida, St. Petersburg Times **Established:** 1977
Own Printing Facility?: Yes
Commercial Printers?: Yes
Special Editions: Charlotte Sun
Englewood Sun
North Port Sun
Venice Gondolier Sun
Special Weekly Sections: Best Food Day (Wed); Fishing, Boating, Best Food (Thur); Auto, Entertainment, Travel (Fri); Real Estate, Furniture (Sat); TV, Business, Style (Sun)
Syndicated Publications: USA Weekend, Harbor Style
Pres. .... David Dunn-Rankin
Exec. Ed. .... Chris Porter
Circ. Dir. .... Mark Yero
VP of Marketing .... Debbie Dunn-Rankin
Viewpoint Ed. .... Brian Gleason
Features Ed. .... Donna Davidson
Charlotte Sun Ed. .... Rusty Pray
Deputy Sports Ed. .... Mark Lawrence
Asst Sports Ed. .... Matthew Stevens
Systems Ed. .... Jim Merchant
Class/Telmktg Mgr. .... Geri Kotz
Systems Mgr. .... Ed McIntosh
Press Room Mgr. .... Chris Germann
Mgr., HR .... Mary Skaggs
Adv. Mgr., Classified .... Frank Ledo
Exec. Ed. .... Jim Gouvellis
Ed. .... Phil Fernandez
Exec. Sports Ed. .... Pat Obley
Data Processing Mgr. .... Joanne Hackney
Nat'l/Major Acct. Sales .... Cynthia Acevedo
Pub .... Robert Lee
Market Information: Split run; TMC; Zoned editions.
Mechanical Available: Offset; Black and ROP colors; insert accepted; page cutoffs - 22.
Mechanical Specifications: Type page 10 x 20.75; E - 6 cols, 21, 1/8 between; A - 6 cols, 21, 1/8 between; C 6 cols, 16, 1/8 between.
Areas Served: 33834, 33873, 33890, 33921, 33946, 33947, 33948, 33950, 33952, 33953, 33954, 33955, 33980, 33981, 33982, 33983, 34223, 34224, 34229, 34266, 34269, 34275, 34285, 34286, 34287, 34288, 34289, 34291, 34292, 34293
Delivery Method: Mail, Newsstand, Carrier, RacksEquipment & Software: PRESSROOM EQUIPMENT: Lines — 12-G/Urbanite U-5019 5 units DGM 850; Folders — 2 goss 5000 series Folders 2 goss quarter Folders; Pasters —7 JARDIS flying Pasters 1-MARTIN zero speed pasterReels & Stands — Press Control System 2-Fin/2193E-150-38D, 1-Fin/2193E-100-38D.; MAILROOM EQUIPMENT: Counter Stackers — 1-HI/251017, 1-HL/Monitor, 1-BG/105; Inserters & Stuffers — 1-HI/848; Tying Machines — 1-MLN/ML2EE, 1-MLN/A1672A, 1/Bu.; BUSINESS EQUIPMENT: Dell Workgroup Server BUSINESS SOFTWARE: Saxotech-Data Sciences Inc CLASSIFIED EQUIPMENT: Hardware — Dell Workgroup Server; Printers — Konica BizHub; CLASSIFIED SOFTWARE: Brainworks. DISPLAY EQUIPMENT: Hardware — Dell Workgroup Server; Printers — Konica BizHub; DISPLAY SOFTWAREAd Make-up Applications — Multiad Creator Pro 8.5; Layout Software — MEI. EDITORIAL EQUIPMENT: Hardware — Dell (Lattitude E6500 series and Inspiron 1500 series)/ FA/Compact, FP/230B; Printers — Konica BizHub EDITORIAL SOFTWARE: DTI Content Publisher/Adobe InDesign & InCopy PRODUCTION EQUIPMENT: Hardware — Kodak Trendsetter 150 CTP, Kodak PDF workflow, Newsmanager/Preps. Nela Vision Bender.; Scanners — Epson Scanner PRODUCTION SOFTWARE: MEI/ALS 2.0.2rl.

SAINT AUGUSTINE

THE ST. AUGUSTINE RECORD

1 News Pl, Saint Augustine, Fla., 32086-6520, Saint Johns; gen tel (904) 829-6562; adv tel (904) 819-3475; gen fax (904) 819-3538; adv fax (904) 819-3557; ed fax (904) 819-3558; gen/nat adv e-mail ads@staugustinerecord.com; ed e-mail editor@staugustinerecord.com; web site www.staugustine.com
Group: GateHouse Media, Inc.
Published: Mon, Tues, Wed, Thur, Fri, Sat, Sun
Weekday Frequency: m
Saturday Frequency: m
Circulation: 13,760; 14,465(sat); 17,311(sun)
Last Audit: AAM June 30, 2016
Advertising Rate (weekday/saturday): Open inch rate $23.00
Advertising Rate (sunday): Open inch rate $24.50
News services: AP, MCT, LAT-WP, Morris News Service.
Special Editions: Active Lifestyles (Apr); Back-to-School (Aug); Christmas Greetings (Dec); Bridal (Feb); Active Lifestyles (Jan); Active Lifestyles (Jul); Just Say No (Mar); Real Estate Today (May); Holiday Style & Fashion (Nov); Explore St. John's (Oct); Football (Sept).
Special Weekly Sections: Neighbors, Morning Brew, Club Life (Mon); Community (Tue); Coupons (Wed); Food, Health & Science (Thur); Arts, Entertainment, Religion, Driving, NASCAR, Neighbors (Fri); Seniors, Gardening, Business, Real Estate, Fashion (Sat); Lifestyles, TV, Travel, Youth, Education, Business, Job Finder (Sun);
Syndicated Publications: Relish (Monthly); USA WEEKEND Magazine (S).
Digital Platform - Mobile: Apple
Circ. Mgr. .... Paul Kennedy
Senior Writer .... Peter Guinta
Compass Ed. .... Renee Unsworth
Features Ed. .... Anne Heymen
Health Ed. .... Shaun Ryan
Prodn. Dir. .... Steve Everberg
Special Projects Dir. .... Gail Cumiskey
Publisher .... Delinda Fogel
Sports writer .... Austen Gregerson
Pub. .... Ron Davidson
Adv. Dir. .... Tonya Clay
Nat'l Coord. .... Tiffany Lowe
Market Information: TMC.
Mechanical Available: Offset; Black and 3 ROP colors; insert accepted - odd size; page cutoffs - 22 3/4.
Mechanical Specifications: Type page 11 5/8 x 21 1/12; E - 6 cols, 1 5/6, 1/6 between; A - 6 cols, 1 5/6, 1/6 between; C - 9 cols, 11/72 between.Equipment & Software: PRESSROOM EQUIPMENT: Lines — 10 1/2-G/Urbanite; Folders — G/Urbanite Half; Reels & Stands — HI/Roll Stands; Registration System — Carlson. MAILROOM EQUIPMENT: Counter Stackers — 1/MM; Inserters & Stuffers — 1-MM/227S; Tying Machines — 2-MLN/ML2EE; Address Machine — 1-Am/1900, KAN.; BUSINESS EQUIPMENT: IBM BUSINESS SOFTWARE: PBS CLASSIFIED EQUIPMENT: Hardware — IBM, DTI; Printers — Epson; CLASSIFIED SOFTWARE: DTI 5.2. DISPLAY EQUIPMENT: Hardware — APP/Mac; Printers — XIT/Navigator, HP; Other Hardware — AG/1500 Imagesetter DISPLAY SOFTWAREAd Make-up Applications — Adobe/InDesign, DTI 5.2; Layout Software — MEI/ALS. EDITORIAL EQUIPMENT: Hardware — IBM, 40-APP/Mac/AG/1500 Imagesetter; Printers — XIT/Navigator, HP EDITORIAL SOFTWARE: DTI 5.2. PRODUCTION EQUIPMENT: Hardware — XIT/Navigator, Ag/1500; Cameras — AG/Accuset 1500 PRODUCTION SOFTWARE: DTI 5.2.
Note: Advertising is sold in combination with Jacksonville Florida Times Union (mS) for $243.00(d), $259.00(m-sat) and $279.00(S).

SARASOTA

SARASOTA HERALD-TRIBUNE

1741 Main St, Sarasota, Fla., 34236-5812, Sarasota; gen tel (941) 953-7755; adv tel (941) 361-4000; ed tel (941) 361-4800; gen fax 941-361-4580; adv fax (941) 361-4095; ed fax (941) 361-4880; gen/nat adv e-mail carmen.cook@heraldtribune.com; disp adv e-mail shari.brickley@heraldtribune.com; class adv e-mailgreg.trippel@heraldtribune.com; ed e-mail advocate@heraldtribune.com; web site www.heraldtribune.com 1,344,419(visitors)
Group: New Media Investment Group
Published: Mon, Tues, Wed, Thur, Fri, Sat, Sun
Weekday Frequency: m
Saturday Frequency: m
Circulation: 55,109; 57,656(sat); 69,974(sun)
Last Audit: AAM December 31, 2016
Advertising Rate (weekday/saturday): Open inch rate - $108.00 (Mon-Wed); $116.64 (Thur-Sat)
Advertising Rate (sunday): Open inch rate - $131.76
News services: AP, LAT-WP, NYT. **Established:** 1925
Own Printing Facility?: Yes
Commercial Printers?: Yes
Special Editions: Golf Guide (Apr); Year-End Auto Clearance (Aug); Auto Showcase (Dec); Dining Guide (Feb); Jubilee (Jan); Dining Guide (Jul); Suncoast Off-shore Program (Jun); Wine Fest (Mar); Hurricane (May); Holiday Gift Guide (Nov); Season (Oct); Clubs (Sept).
Special Weekly Sections: Business (Mon); Health, Fitness (Tue); Food, Wine (Wed); Entertainment (Thur); Home (Fri); Real Estate (Sat); Comics, Real Estate, Arts (Sun)
Syndicated Publications: Style Magazine (Luxury Lifestyle), 1st Sunday Monthly; Better Living (Senior Lifestyle), quarterly
Digital Platform - Mobile: Apple, Android, Blackberry
Digital Platform - Tablet: Apple iOS, Android, Kindle, Nook, Kindle Fire
Adv. Dir. .... Shari Brickley
Circ. Mgr. .... Jennifer Eichorn
Asst. Mng. Ed. .... Deborah Winsor
Mng. Ed. .... Matt Sauer
Columnist .... David Grimes
Columnist .... Tom Lyons
Critic, Theater/Television .... Jay Handelman
Editorial Page Ed. .... Thomas Lee Tryon
Front Page Ed. .... Kyle Booth
Photo Dir. .... Mike Lang
Web Ed. .... Cindy Allegretto
Keisha Gray
Nat'l Adv. Sales .... Holly Ronnick
Pub. .... Patrick E. Dorsey
Robert Bolone
Market Information: Zoned editions.
Mechanical Available: Offset; Black and 4 ROP colors; insert accepted; page cutoffs - 22.
Mechanical Specifications: Type page 11 x 21; E - 6 cols, 1 4/5, 1/8 between; A - 6 cols, 1 4/5, 1/8 between
Areas Served: 34203, 34205, 34207, 34208, 34209, 34210, 34215, 34217, 34221, 34222, 34201, 34202, 34211, 34212, 34219, 34243, 34251, 34228, 34229, 34231, 34232, 34233, 34234, 34235, 34236, 34237, 34238, 34239, 34240, 34241, 34242, 34275, 34285, 34292, 34293, 34286, 34287, 34288, 34289, 34291, 33921, 33946, 33947, 33953, 33981, 34223, 34224
Delivery Method: Mail, Newsstand, Carrier, RacksEquipment & Software: PRESSROOM EQUIPMENT: Lines — G/(18 unit Lines with 1 4-color tower & 3 decks) 1994; Folders — Imperial/144-page; Pasters —G/RTP 45 DIA; Control System — G/MPCS III; Registration System — WPC/Web Control. MAILROOM EQUIPMENT: Counter Stackers — 6/QWI; Inserters & Stuffers — 3-HI/NP 1372; Tying Machines — 2-/Power Strap/PSN, 5-/Dynaric; Wrapping Singles — 8-HL/Monarch; Address Machine — 1-Ch/S42.; BUSINESS EQUIPMENT: 2-IBM/4381, III/TECS 2 BUSINESS SOFTWARE: Admarc CLASSIFIED EQUIPMENT: Hardware — AT; CLASSIFIED SOFTWARE: AT. DISPLAY EQUIPMENT: Hardware — Sun; Other Hardware — 4-APP/Mac DISPLAY SOFTWAREAd Make-up Applications — Cx, QPS/QuarkXPress, Multi-Ad/Creator; Layout Software — AT. EDITORIAL EQUIPMENT: Hardware — AT EDITORIAL SOFTWARE: AT. PRODUCTION EQUIPMENT: Hardware — KFM/Plate Express, 4-III/3850, WL/III; Scanners — ECR/1000, ECR/2045, ECR/8400, Nikon/Scanners.

SEBRING

HIGHLANDS NEWS-SUN

207 Circle Park Dr, Sebring, Fla., 33870-3312, Highlands; gen tel (863) 385-6155; adv tel (863) 386-5631; ed tel (863) 386-5800; gen fax (863) 385-1944; adv fax (863) 385-1954; ed fax (863) 385-2453; gen/nat adv e-mail vickie.jones@newssun.com; disp adv e-mail amarsella@newssun.com; ed e-mail romona.washington@newssun.com; web site www.newssun.com
Group: Sun Coast Media Group Inc
Published: Mon, Tues, Wed, Thur, Fri, Sat, Sun
Weekday Frequency: m
Saturday Frequency: m
Circulation: 7,190; 16,609(sat); 16,609(sun)
Last Audit: Sworn/Estimate/Non-Audited September 30, 2017
Advertising Rate (weekday/saturday): Open inch rate $12.08
News services: AP, TMS. **Established:** 1927
Own Printing Facility?: Yes
Commercial Printers?: Yes
Special Editions: 101 Things to do in the Heartland (Jan); 12 Hours of Sebring Race Tab (Mar).
Special Weekly Sections: Business (S); Religion (Sat).
Syndicated Publications: USA WEEKEND Magazine (Fri); American Profile (Mon).
Adv. Rep. .... Vickie Watson
Pub. .... Glen Nickerson
Exec. Ed. .... Romona Washington
Office Mgr. .... Mike Henry
Circ. Dir. .... Kevin Flores
Market Information: Zoned editions.
Mechanical Available: Black and 3 ROP colors; insert accepted; page cutoffs - 21.
Mechanical Specifications: Type page 13 x 21 1/2, 6 col. format
Areas Served: 33825, 33852, 33857, 33870, 33872, 33875, 33876
Delivery Method: Mail, Newsstand, Carrier, Racks
Note: For detailed press information, see the Tampa Tribune.

ST PETERSBURG

TAMPA BAY TIMES

490 1st Ave S, St Petersburg, Fla., 33701-4204, Pinellas; gen tel (727) 893-8289; adv tel (727) 894-1141; ed tel (727) 893-8215; gen fax (727) 893-8675; adv fax (727) 892-2209; ed fax (813) 259-8080; gen/nat adv e-mail mediakit@tampabay.com; disp adv e-mail tbtadvertise@tbt.com; class adv e-mailtbtadvertise@tbt.com; ed e-mail local@tampabay.com; web site www.tampabay.com - 9,296,000(views) 2,011,000(visitors); web site 2 www.weathercenter.com ; web site 3 www.tbo.com
Group: Times Publishing Co
Published: Mon, Tues, Wed, Thur, Fri, Sat, Sun
Weekday Frequency: m
Saturday Frequency: m
Circulation: 219,920; 199,702(sat); 370,983(sun)
Last Audit: AAM December 31, 2016
Advertising Rate (weekday/saturday): Open inch rate $640.00
Advertising Rate (sunday): Open inch rate $770.00
News services: AP, NYT, LAT-WP, SHNS, MCT. **Established:** 1884
Own Printing Facility?: Yes
Commercial Printers?: Yes
Special Editions: Clearwater Fun 'n Sun (Apr); Football (Aug); Personal Best (Every other month); Hernando Profiles (Feb); School Search (Jan); Wedding Guides (Jul); West Virginia (Jun); Chasco Fiesta (Mar); Hurricane (May); Home Search (Monthly); Holiday Gift Guide (Nov);

Special Weekly Sections: Health (Tue); Best Food (Wed); Entertainment (Thur); Auto (Sat); Travel, Arts, Literature, Homes, Real Estate (Sun)
Syndicated Publications: Bay (Every other month); Sunday Comics (S).
Chairman & CEO ....Paul Tash
VP / CFO ....Jana Jones
Vice Pres./Sec. ....Andrew P. Corty
VP / Tampa Pub., TampaBay.com Pub. Joe DeLuca
HR Dir. ....Sebastian Dortch
Dir., Cor. Giving ....Nancy Waclawek
Adv. Mgr. ....Mark Shurman
Adv. Mgr., Classified ....Michelle Mitchell
Marketing Dir. ....Kerry O'Reilly
Community/Events Mgr. ....Dave LaBell
Communications Dir. .... Jounice Nealy-Brown
Ed. & VP ....Neil Brown
Dir., Editorial/Creative, Times Targeted Media...... Gretchen Letterman
Sr. Ed. ....Jim Booth
Ed., North Suncoast ....Bill Stevens
Mng. Ed., Enterprise ....Mike Wilson
Mng. Ed., Tampa Bay ....Joe Childs
Deputy Managing Ed./Features, Lifestyles Jeanne Grinstead
Op. Dir. ....Ben Hayes
Jerry Haynes
Debbie Doane
VP / Sales & Marketing ....Bruce Faulmann
Nat'l Sales ....Kelly Spamer
Sr. Adv. Mgr. ....Monica Boyer
Digital General Mgr. .... John Schlander
Amber McDonald
Managing Ed. ....Jennifer Orsi
Deputy Managing Ed./Investigations ..Chris Davis
Deputy Managing Ed./tampabay.com, Presentation Ron Brackett
Deputy Managing Ed./Politics, Business .... Amy Hollyfield
Ed. of Editorials ....Tim Nickens
Chief Info. Officer ....Ed Nicholson
Market Information: Split run; TMC; Zoned editions.
Mechanical Available: Offset; Black and 4 ROP colors; insert accepted - pre-approved samples; page cutoffs - 22 3/4.
Mechanical Specifications: Type page 11 27/100 x 21 1/2; E - 6 cols, 2 1/16, 1/8 between; A - 6 cols, 2 1/16, 1/8 between; C - 10 cols, 1 5/16, 1/16 between. Equipment & Software: PRESSROOM EQUIPMENT: Lines — 21-G/Metroliner double width; 21-G/Metroliner double width; 21-G/Metroliner double width; Folders — 5-G/single, 4-G/double; MAILROOM EQUIPMENT: Counter Stackers — 5-QWI/350, 24-QWI/400; Inserters & Stuffers — 5-S/1472, 1-HI/In-Line 30 632; Tying Machines — 9-Dynaric/NP, 12-Dynaric/NP-2, 17-Dynaric/NP3, 2-Mosca/Z-5; Wrapping Singles — 10-QWI/Viper 30, 16-QWI/Viper 50; Control System — Mailroom control s; BUSINESS EQUIPMENT: 1-HP/900 BUSINESS SOFTWARE: Peoplesoft HRMS, Microsoft/Office2003, Microsoft/Windows XP XP, GEAC World Class Advertising System, WinStar CLASSIFIED EQUIPMENT: Hardware — 10-SII/K1000, SII/Tandem; 120-PCs with Coyote-3; Printers — ECR/4550 Imagesetters, 7-Ad Proof/Printers; CLASSIFIED SOFTWARE: Mactive/AdBase. DISPLAY EQUIPMENT: Printers — 2-APP/Mac LaserWriter; DISPLAY SOFTWAREAd Make-up Applications — In-house; Layout Software — III, In-house/Layout Sys. EDITORIAL EQUIPMENT: Printers — 5-HP/LaserJet. EDITORIAL SOFTWARE: CCI/News Gate, HI/NewsMaker Pagination. PRODUCTION EQUIPMENT: Hardware — 4-KPG/85, 2-Anitec/SN48, 4-Trendsetter 200. PRODUCTION SOFTWARE: CCI/New Desk.

STUART

THE STUART NEWS
1939 SE Federal Hwy, Stuart, Fla., 34994-3915, Martin; gen tel (772) 287-1550; gen fax (772) 221-4175; ed e-mail feedback@tcpalm.com; web site www.tcpalm.com
Group: Gannett
Published: Mon, Tues, Wed, Thur, Fri, Sat, Sun
Weekday Frequency: m
Circulation: 48,143; 47,102(sat); 65,452(sun)
Last Audit: AAM June 30, 2017
Mng. Ed. ....Adam Neal

TALLAHASSEE

TALLAHASSEE DEMOCRAT
277 N Magnolia Dr, Tallahassee, Fla., 32301-2664, Leon; gen tel (850) 599-2100; adv tel (850) 599-2189; ed tel (850) 599-2210; adv fax (850) 942-0185; ed fax (850) 599-2224; gen/nat adv e-mail clevans@tallahassee.com; disp adv e-mail clevans@tallahassee.com; class adv e-mailkhanselman @tallahassee.com; ed e-mail letters@tallahassee.com; web site www.tallahassee.com
Group: Gannett
Published: Mon, Tues, Wed, Thur, Fri, Sat, Sun
Weekday Frequency: m
Saturday Frequency: m
Circulation: 27,753; 27,753(sat); 32,893(sun)
Last Audit: AAM September 30, 2016
Advertising Rate (weekday/saturday): Open inch rate $103.25
Advertising Rate (sunday): Open inch rate $145.75
News services: MCT, AP, TMS, GNS. **Established:** 1905
Own Printing Facility?: Yes
Commercial Printers?: Yes
Special Editions: Living Here (Aug); Home & Design (Every other month); College Football Preview (Fall); Business Outlook (Feb); North Florida Home Show (Jan); Chamber of Commerce (Jul); Legislature 2008 (Mar); Money Clip (Monthly); Holiday Planner (Nov); Physicians & Health; Your Health (monthly); Moms like Me (Monthly);
Special Weekly Sections: Family (Sun); Volunteer (Mon); Schools, Education (Tue); Health (Wed); Taste (Thur); My Nest, Limelight (Fri); Faith (Sat)
Syndicated Publications: USA WEEKEND Magazine (S).
Adv. Dir. ....Cari Evans
Gen. Manager ....Bill Taylor
Controller ....Scott LaFuria
Distribution Director ....Richard Kay
Bus. Ed. ....Dave Hodges
State Editor ....Paul Flemming
Managing Ed. ....Rebeccah Cantley
Prepress, Postpress, IT Mgr ......Randy Fingeroot
Pres./Pub. ....Patrick E. Dorsey
Adv. Dir. ....Carrie Evans
Metro Ed. ....Byron Dobson
News Ass't ....Debra Galloway
Sports Editor ....Jim Henry
Exec Ed ....William Hatfield
Mechanical Available: Offset; Black and 3 ROP colors; insert accepted - product samples; page cutoffs - 22 3/4.
Mechanical Specifications: Type page 10 1/8 x 21 1/2; E - 6 cols, 1 9/16, 1/6 between; A - 6 cols, 1 9/16, 1/6 between; C - 9 cols, 1 3/8, 1/16 between.
Areas Served: 31792, 32301. 32302, 32303, 32304, 32305, 32306, 32308, 32309, 32310, 32311, 32312, 32317, 32320, 32321, 32322, 32323, 32324, 32327, 32328, 32330, 32331, 32332, 32333, 32334, 32337, 32340, 32343, 32344, 32346, 32347, 32348, 32351, 32352, 32355, 32358, 32361, 32399, 32421, 32424, 32425, 32428, 32446, 32447, 32448, 32456, 32460, 39817, 39819, 39827, 39828, 39897
Delivery Method: Mail, Newsstand, Carrier, RacksEquipment & Software: PRESSROOM EQUIPMENT: Lines — 7-G/Metro double width (4 decks) 1979; 6-G/Urbanite single width; Folders — 1-G/Metro, 1, 1-G/Urbanite, 2-G/Uniflow 2:1; Pasters —7-G/Automatic RTPReels & Stands — 4-G/Urbanite high roll stand.; MAILROOM EQUIPMENT: Counter Stackers — 1-MM/310-20, 2-Baldwin/108, 3-QWI/400; Inserters & Stuffers — 1-Titan G60 22 heads; Tying Machines — 2-Samuel/NT 440, 3-Samuel/Newstyer 2000; Wrapping Singles — 3-QWI/50 bottom wrap, 1-Samuel; BUSINESS SOFTWARE: Word Processing CLASSIFIED EQUIPMENT: Hardware — 2-Sun/Enterprise 450, 21-IBM/PC Workstation; Printers — Variety; CLASSIFIED SOFTWARE: DTI/Classified 5.3. DISPLAY EQUIPMENT: Hardware — 2x Sunfire V440; Printers — HP 5000; DISPLAY SOFTWAREAd Make-up Applications — DTI; Layout Software — DTI Speedplanner 7.3 EDITORIAL EQUIPMENT: Hardware — 2x sunfire v440; Printers — HP5000 EDITORIAL SOFTWARE: DTI 7.3 PRODUCTION

EQUIPMENT: Hardware — 2-Anacoil/LX45, Anacoil/Thermal PRODUCTION SOFTWARE: DTI 7.3.

THE VILLAGES

THE VILLAGES DAILY SUN
1100 Main St, The Villages, Fla., 32159-7719, Lake; gen tel (352) 753-1119; adv tel (352) 753-1119; ed tel (352) 753-1119; gen fax (352) 751-7995; adv fax (352) 751-7996; ed fax (352) 753-7787; gen/nat adv e-mail advertising@thevillagesmedia.com; disp adv e-mail advertising@thevillagesmedia.com; class adv e-mailclassifieds@thevillagesmedia.com; ed e-mail larry.croom@thevillagesmedia.com; web site www.thevillagesdailysun.com
- 143,000(views) 67,000(visitors); web site 2 www.searchthevillages.com - 9,000(views) 3,200(visitors); web site 3 www.thevillagesphonebok.com - 17,000(views) 1,000(visitors)
Published: Mon, Tues, Wed, Thur, Fri, Sat, Sun
Weekday Frequency: m
Saturday Frequency: m
Circulation: 45,857; 45,857(sat); 47,842(sun)
Last Audit: AAM March 31, 2017
Advertising Rate (weekday/saturday): Open inch rate $30.00
Advertising Rate (sunday): $31.50
Online Advertising Rate: NA
News services: AP. **Established:** 1997
Own Printing Facility?: Yes
Commercial Printers?: Yes
Special Editions: Salute to Business (Apr); Football Preview (Aug); Paradise in Pictures (Feb); Social Security (Mar); Hurricane Preparedness Guide (May); Newcomers (Sept).
Special Weekly Sections: Wheels (Fri), Home & Garden (Sat), Travel (Sun), Next Door News (Sat.)
Syndicated Publications: Parade Magazine (S): Athlon Sports (Monthly).
Proprietary Publications: The Villages Magazine (monthly)
The Villages Phone Book (annually - Oct)
Sound Clips (every other month)
Grandparents Magazine (every other month)
Digital Platform - Mobile: Apple, Android
Digital Platform - Tablet: Apple iOS, Android
Circ. Dir. ....John Gagnon
Customer Service Manager ....Wendy Crowther-Barnes
Ombudsman ....Larry Croom
Managing Editor ....Matt Fry
Managing Editor of Projects ....Curt Hills
Director of Operations ....Steven Infinger
Printing & Distribution Manager ....William McNair
Vice President for Editorial Operations .... Bonita Burton
Director, Marketing/Publishing ....Dan Sprung
General Manager ....James Sprung
Pub. ....Philip Markward
Market Information: Split run; Zoned editions. Saturday zoned editions
Mechanical Available: Offset; Black and 3 ROP colors; insert accepted; page cutoffs - 22 3/4 & 4 color UV
Mechanical Specifications: Type page 11 5/8 x 21 7/16; E - 6 cols, 1 11/16, 3/16 between; A - 6 cols, 1 11/16, 3/16 between; C - 6 cols, 1 13/16, 1/8 between.
Areas Served: 32162;32163;32159,32179;32195;32726;32757;32778;33513;33538;34420;34473;34481;34484;34491;34731;34748;34785;34788; 34471; 34472; 34474; 34476; 34480
Delivery Method: Newsstand, Carrier, RacksEquipment & Software: PRESSROOM EQUIPMENT: Lines — 7 - 8 DGM color towers/1 Goss Community color tower; 2 mono units; Press Drive — 2 Fincor 125HP drives, 4 Fincor 150 HP drives ; Folders — DGM 1035, DGM 1240; Reels & Stands — 13 Jardis Splicers; Registration System — QTI Multicam PRESSROOM SOFTWARE: Puzzle Flow MAILROOM EQUIPMENT: Counter Stackers — Quipp Packman, Gammerler, Inserters & Stuffers — KANSA, Muller Martini 3000; Tying Machines — Dynaric; Muller Martini Stitcher 335 MAILROOM SOFTWARE:Cintech
BCC Mailer BUSINESS EQUIPMENT:

Windows PCs AS400
Mac BUSINESS SOFTWARE: Oracle CLASSIFIED EQUIPMENT: Hardware — Apple Servers Apple PC's; iPads; Printers — HP; CLASSIFIED SOFTWARE: AdManager Pro DISPLAY EQUIPMENT: Hardware — Apple Servers Apple PCs; Printers — HP; DISPLAY SOFTWAREAd Make-up Applications — AdManagerPro InDesign; Layout Software — Adobe EDITORIAL EQUIPMENT: Hardware — Apple Servers Apple PCs; Printers — HP EDITORIAL SOFTWARE: WoodWing
Quickwire
Adobe PRODUCTION EQUIPMENT: Hardware — Pre Press/2- Kodak Trendsetter News CTP; Scanners — Nikon, Microtek.
2 Screen Platerite News 200S PRODUCTION SOFTWARE: PuzzleFlow Automator
Cintech IT EQUIPMENT: Windows Server
Apple Servers IT SOFTWARE:Web Help Desk
CIRCULATION EQUIPMENT: Apple Servers
Apple Pics CIRCULATION SOFTWARCirculation Pro

VERO BEACH

INDIAN RIVER PRESS JOURNAL
2066 14th Ave, Ste 200, Vero Beach, Fla., 32960-4420, Indian River; gen tel (772) 287-1550; gen fax (772) 221-4175; gen/nat adv e-mail feedback@tcpalm.com; web site www.tcpalm.com
Group: Gannett
Published: Mon, Tues, Wed, Thur, Fri, Sat, Sun
Weekday Frequency: m
Circulation: 52,210; 46,996(sat); 62,452(sun)
Last Audit: AAM June 30, 2017
Editor ....Adam Neal

WEST PALM BEACH

THE PALM BEACH POST
2751 S Dixie Hwy, West Palm Beach, Fla., 33405-1233, Palm Beach; gen tel (561) 820-4100; adv tel (561) 820-4300; ed tel (561) 820-4401; gen fax (561) 820-4136; adv fax (561) 837-8434; ed fax (561) 820-4445; gen/nat adv e-mail ablizzard@pbpost.com; disp adv e-mail ablizzard@pbpost.com; class adv e-mailtdiglio@pbpost.com; ed e-mail pb_metro@pbpost.com; pb_sports@pbpost.com; pb_business@pbpost.com; web site www.pbpost.com
1,244,742(visitors)
Group: New Media Investment Group
Published: Mon, Tues, Wed, Thur, Fri, Sat, Sun
Weekday Frequency: m
Saturday Frequency: m
Circulation: 73,037; 68,745(sat); 97,198(sun)
Last Audit: AAM June 30, 2017
Advertising Rate (weekday/saturday): 1 Col.x2" $372.06 (Mon-Tue); $360.62 (Wed); $457.89 (Thur-Sat)
Advertising Rate (sunday): 1 Col.x2" $601.00
News services: AP, Bloomberg, LAT-WP, NYT, PR Newswire, Cox. **Established:** 1908
Special Editions: SunFest (Apr); Football (Aug); Holiday Gift Guide (Dec); Treasure Coast Fairs & Festivals (Feb); Super Bowl (Jan); Back To School (Jul); Palm Beach Medical Society Directory (Jun); Home & Garden (Mar); Discover Florida (May); Palm Beach Post Financial Sho
Special Weekly Sections: Local Business (Mon); Health, Living (Tue); Food, Dining, (Wed); Neighborhood Post/Florida Pennysaver (zoned); Notables (in Accent May-September) (Thur); Religion/Church News, TGIF, Florida Home New Home (Fri); Neighborhoods (Sat); Book Reviews, Health, Accent, Comics, TV, Real Money (Sun)
Syndicated Publications: Color Comics (S).
Vice Pres./Gen. Mgr. ....Charles Gerardi
Vice Pres., HR ....Linda Murphy
Credit Mgr. ....Susan Meldonian
Adv. Dir., Opns. ....Gregg Harr
Adv. Mgr., Retail, Bureau Offices ....Steve Waxelbaum
Dir., Mktg. Servs. ....Laura Cunningham
Internet Mktg. Mgr. ....Michelle Ruzgar
Mgr., Research/Sales Presentations ...... Suzanne Willcox

Circ. Vice Pres................................... Barry Berg
Circ. Mgr., Admin. Servs........... Linda Campbell
Circ. Mgr., Opns............................ Rich Schnars
Editorial Page Ed............................ Rick Christie
Asst. Mng. Ed., Photo........................ Pete Cross
Asst. Mng. Ed., Projects........................ Bill Greer
Data interactive editor.............. Michelle Quigley
VP Operations
Christopher Caneles
VP, Revenue Develop.................... Andy Blizzard
Market Information: Split run; TMC; Zoned editions.
Mechanical Available: Offset; Black and 3 ROP colors; insert accepted; page cutoffs - 23 9/16.
Mechanical Specifications: Type page 11 5/8 x 22 1/2; E - 6 cols, 1 5/6, 1/8 between; A - 6 cols, 1 5/6, 1/8 between; C - 10 cols, 1 11/100, 1/16 between.Equipment & Software: PRESSROOM EQUIPMENT: Lines — 24-G/ Metro (12 color decks) double width; 8-G/ Suburban single width; 6-G/Colorliner double width; Reels & Stands — 32; MAILROOM EQUIPMENT: Counter Stackers — 1/HL, HI/ Rima, 7-/QWI; Inserters & Stuffers — 3-GMA/ SLS 1000, 1-/Stepper Solo; Tying Machines — 11-/Dynaric, 3-Dynaric/RLM-1; Wrapping Singles — 4-/Constellation, 2-/MLN; Control System — GMA; Address Machine — K; BUSINESS EQUIPMENT: Unisys/2200 BUSINESS SOFTWARE: Labrador CLASSIFIED EQUIPMENT: Hardware — Sun/OTI, 55-APP/Mac G4; Ricoh/77 Fax; Printers — HP/5000 N; CLASSIFIED SOFTWARE: AT/Do Fax, DTI/Class Speed 5.5. DISPLAY EQUIPMENT: Hardware — Sun/DTI, 6-APP/Mac G 4; Printers — APP/Mac Laser Writer 8500; DISPLAY SOFTWAREAd Make-up Applications — DTI/Adspeed 5.5; Layout Software — DTI/ AdInput, DTI/Planbuilder. EDITORIAL EQUIPMENT: Hardware — 8-Sun, 105-APP/Power Mac G4/6-Networks in Bureaus EDITORIAL SOFTWARE: DTI/Editorial 4.3. PRODUCTION EQUIPMENT: Hardware — Harlequin/Rips 5.12, Vision Bender, Scitex/ Eversmart Pro II, 2-AU/APS, 2-3850 SST, 2-AU/APS 3850 SST Wide PRODUCTION SOFTWARE: DTI 4.3, Pagespeed 4.3, Speedplanner 4.3, Adspeed 5.5, Classpeed 5.5, DTI/Planbuilder 3.8.

WINTER HAVEN

NEWS CHIEF

455 6th St NW, Winter Haven, Fla., 33881-4061, Polk; gen tel (863) 401-6900; adv tel (863) 401-6938; ed tel (863) 802-7504; gen fax (863) 401-6999; adv fax (863) 401-6999; ed fax (863) 401-6999; gen/nat adv e-mail jerome.ferson@theledger.com; disp adv e-mail susan.gossett@newschief.com; class adv e-mailleslie.colon@newschief.com; ed e-mail news@newschief.com; features@ newschief.com; web site www.newschief.com - 855,000(views) 83,000(visitors)
Group: New Media Investment Group
Published: Mon, Tues, Wed, Thur, Fri, Sat, Sun
Weekday Frequency: m
Saturday Frequency: m
Circulation: 1,417; 1,417(sat); 1,865(sun)
Last Audit: AAM June 30, 2017
Advertising Rate (weekday/saturday): 1 col. x1.75 $34.37; 2 col. x1.75 $68.74
News services: AP, SHNS, DF, LAT-WP. **Established:** 1911
Own Printing Facility?: No
Commercial Printers?: Yes
Special Editions: Citrus Exposition (Feb); Newcomer's Guide (Jan); Outlook (Mar).
Special Weekly Sections: Home Finder (Sat).
Syndicated Publications: Real Estate (Fri); Relish (Monthly); Retirement Living (Other); USA WEEKEND Magazine (S).
Digital Platform - Mobile: Apple
Bus. Mgr... Bruce Baker
Circ. Dir.... Jeff Amero
Exec. Ed... Roger Ballas
Prodn. Dir................................ Dennis Wilkinson
Publisher.. Kevin Drake
Nat'l Adv. Mgr................................. Ron Moates
Digital Adv. Mgr............................ Scott Girouard
Market Information: TMC.
Mechanical Available: Offset; Black and 3 ROP colors; insert accepted; page cutoffs - 22 3/4.
Mechanical Specifications: Type page 13 x 21 1/2; E - 6 cols, 2 1/16, 1/8 between; A - 6 cols, 2 1/16, 1/8 between; C - 6 cols, 2 1/16, 1/8 between.
Delivery Method: Newsstand, Carrier, RacksEquipment & Software: PRESSROOM EQUIPMENT: Lines — 6-G/Urbanite (1 3-color); 8-HI/V-15A (Color deck); Folders — 1, 1.; MAILROOM EQUIPMENT: Counter Stackers — 1-MM/1231, 1-QWI/928; Inserters & Stuffers — 1-S/NP524, 1-MM/227; Tying Machines — 2-MLN/MLN; Address Machine — 1/EI, 1-KAN/Labeler.; BUSINESS EQUIPMENT: ATT/6386 E-33 WGS CLASSIFIED EQUIPMENT: Hardware — APP/Mac G3 fileserver, 13-APP/Mac G3; Printers — HP/4100; CLASSIFIED SOFTWARE: BaseView/AJ Manager 3.X. DISPLAY EQUIPMENT: Printers — 1-HP/5000, 1-HP/8550; Other Hardware — CD-Rom/Scanners DISPLAY SOFTWAREAd Make-up Applications — QuarkPress 4.11, Photoshop SS; Layout Software — 1-APP/ Mac G4 Server, 8-APP/Mac G35 and G45. EDITORIAL EQUIPMENT: Hardware — 6-APP/G3 PowerMac fileserver, 1-APP/ Mac fx fileserver, 5-APP/iMac/APP/Mac Scanner EDITORIAL SOFTWARE: Caere/ OmniPage. PRODUCTION EQUIPMENT: Hardware — 2-V/4000 RIP/5500 Typesetter, Nikon; Cameras — 1-C/Spartan II; Scanners — Howtek PRODUCTION SOFTWARE: QuarkPress 4.11-.

GEORGIA

AMERICUS

AMERICUS TIMES-RECORDER

101 Hwy 27 E, Americus, Ga., 31709, Sumter; gen tel (229) 924-2751; adv tel (229) 924-2751 ext. 1518; ed tel (229) 924-2751 ext. 1529; gen fax (229) 928-6344; gen/nat adv e-mail tom.overton@gaflnews.com; disp adv e-mail joshua.burdick@gaflnews.com; ed e-mail beth.alston@gaflnews.com; web site www.americustimesrecorder.com
Group: Boone Newspapers, Inc.
Published: Tues, Wed, Thur, Fri
Weekday Frequency: m
Circulation: 6,962; 6,917(sun)
Last Audit: Sworn/Estimate/Non-Audited September 30, 2017
Advertising Rate (weekday/saturday): Open inch rate $17.55 (Wed); $33.85 (Sun)
Online Advertising Rate: $5/day
News services: AP, TNN. **Established:** 1879
Special Editions: Car Care (Apr); Football (Aug); Holiday Cookbook (Dec); Business & Service Directory (Feb); Insurance Week (Jan); Christmas in July (Jul); Summer Recreation (Jun); Lawn & Garden (Mar); Mother's Day (May); ValueTown-Thanksgiving (Nov); Home-Owned Business
Special Weekly Sections: Church Briefs (Wed); Area Beat (Sun, Wed).
Syndicated Publications: South Georgia Rural Living (Monthly); Parade (S).
Pub./Adv. Dir............................... Tom Overton
Circ. Dir............................. Rachel Wainwright
Executive Editor............................. Beth Alston
Sports Ed.................................. Scott Phillips
Ad Sales.................................. Joshua Greene
Ad Sales................................ Pamela Bledsoe
Major/Nat'l Adv. Mgr...................... Laura Rogers
Market Information: TMC.
Mechanical Available: Offset; Black and 3 ROP colors; insert accepted - single sheet; page cutoffs - 22 3/4.
Mechanical Specifications: Type page 13 x 21 1/2; E - 6 cols, 2 1/16, 1/8 between; A - 6 cols, 2 1/16, 1/8 between; C - 9 cols, 1 7/8, 1/16 between.
Areas Served: 31709
Delivery Method: Mail, Newsstand, Carrier, RacksEquipment & Software: PRESSROOM EQUIPMENT: Lines — G/Community (upper former); Folders — G/Half, G/ Quarter.; MAILROOM EQUIPMENT: Tying Machines — MLN/Auto Bundler.; BUSINESS EQUIPMENT: PBS CLASSIFIED EQUIPMENT: Hardware — 1-APP/Mac Centris 610; 4-ATT.; DISPLAY EQUIPMENT: Hardware — APP/Mac IIci, APP/Mac 610 Centris; Printers — 2-APP/Mac LaserPrinter, Tegra/Varityper/5060W, Tegra/ Varityper/600W; DISPLAY SOFTWAREAd Make-up Applications — Multi-Ad/Creator, Aldus/FreeHand, Adobe/Illustrator, QPS/ QuarkXPress; Layout Software — APP/ Mac IIci, APP/Mac Centris 610. EDITORIAL EQUIPMENT: Hardware — 7-APP/Mac LC III, 2-APP/Mac Centris 610/Pre Press/ Panther Pro 46; Printers — HP/LaserJet 4MV EDITORIAL SOFTWARE: QPS/QuarkXPress. PRODUCTION EQUIPMENT: Hardware — Caere/OmniPage Pro 2.12, APP/Mac 610 Centris; Cameras — B/Horizontal, SCREEN/ Vertical PRODUCTION SOFTWARE: QPS/ QuarkXPress 3.32.

ATHENS

ATHENS BANNER-HERALD

1 Press Pl, Athens, Ga., 30601-2605, Clarke; gen tel (706) 549-0123; adv tel (706) 208-2281; ed tel (706) 208-2227; gen fax (706) 208-2298; adv fax (706) 543-5234; ed fax (706) 208-2246; gen/nat adv e-mail tracy.traylor@onlineathens.com; disp adv e-mail tracy.traylor@onlineathens.com; class adv e-mailtracy.traylor@onlineathens.com; ed e-mail scot.morrissey@onlineathens.com; web site www.onlineathens.com - 8,000,000(views) 1,350,000(visitors)
Group: GateHouse Media, Inc.
Published: Mon, Tues, Wed, Thur, Fri, Sat, Sun
Weekday Frequency: m
Saturday Frequency: m
Circulation: 10,374; 10,374(sat); 13,192(sun)
Last Audit: AAM June 30, 2017
Advertising Rate (weekday/saturday): Open inch rate $23.00
Advertising Rate (sunday): Open inch rate $25.00
News services: AP, BPI, LAT-WP. **Established:** 1832
Special Editions: Golf Guide (Apr); College Football (Aug); Gift Guide (Dec); Spotlight 1 (Feb); Top Citizen (Jan); Locally Owned Business (Jun); Spotlight 2 (Mar); Twilight Criterium (May); New Car Intro (Nov); Gameday (Oct); Senior Living/Primetime (Quarterly); Gameday (
Special Weekly Sections: Health, Fitness (Tue); Best Food Day (Wed); Around Athens, Arts, Entertainment (Thur); Church, Auto (Sat); Business, Society, Family, Real Estate, Nat'l Coupons (Sun)
Syndicated Publications: Relish (Monthly); Homefront, USA Weekend (S); Marquee (Entertainment) (Thur).
Proprietary Publications: Athens Magazine, Thrive Magazine, Daily Deal
Digital Platform - Mobile: Apple
Controller, Division.................. Greg Williamson
VP of Ad Sales........................ Jordan Magness
Director of Mktg...................... Maeghan Pawley
Circ. Dir..................................... Linda Howard
Managing Ed................................ Donnie Fetter
Arts/Entertainment Ed.................. Andre Gallant
Bus./Finance Ed.............................. Don Nelson
Editorial Page Ed....................... Jim Thompson
Features Ed........................... Courtney Pomeroy
Metro Ed.................................. Roger Nielsen
Oconee Ed.................................... Wayne Ford
Photo Dir....................................... John Curry
Prodn. Dir............................ Dennis McCraven
Pub.... Scott Morrissey
Market Information: ADS; Split run; TMC; Zoned editions.
Mechanical Available: Offset; Black and 3 ROP colors; insert accepted; page cutoffs - 22 3/4.
Mechanical Specifications: Type page 11 5/8 x 21 1/4; E - 6 cols, 2 1/16, 1/8 between; A - 6 cols, 1 13/16, 1/8 between; C - 10 cols, 1 1/16, 5/64 between.Equipment & Software: PRESSROOM EQUIPMENT: Lines — 12-G/ Urbanite; Folders — G/2:1.; MAILROOM EQUIPMENT: Counter Stackers — 3-HL/ HT II, 1/Stackpack, 2-QWI/Soin, 2-TMSI; Inserters & Stuffers — 1-/AM Graphics/048P, NP/848; Tying Machines — G-3/Titan, 3-Dynamic; Wrapping Singles — 2-/ Samuels, 1-/QWI; Address Machine — 2-/Ch; BUSINESS EQUIPMENT: PBS, Bay Network Hub, IBM/RISC 6000, Raid Tower, Gateway, IBM, HP/5M BUSINESS SOFTWARE: WordPerfect 5.0, PC file, Lotus/1-2-3, Microsoft/Windows, MPS, Microsoft/Word, Microsoft/Excel CLASSIFIED EQUIPMENT: Hardware — 8-Gateway; Printers — HP/5000 Gn; CLASSIFIED SOFTWARE: DTI 5.42. DISPLAY EQUIPMENT: Hardware — 2-APP/Mac G4, 6-APP/Mac G3; Printers — Tektronix/Color Printer, 2-HP/5M, 2-HP/5000 GN; DISPLAY SOFTWAREAd Make-up Applications — Adobe/Creative Suite 2, QPS/QuarkXPress 6.5, 6-Outlook/ Express 4.5; Layout Software — MEI/ALS 4.2. EDITORIAL EQUIPMENT: Hardware — 21-Gateway/2000, 2-APP/Power Mac, 2-Gateway/2000, Umax/5900, APP/Mac G4; Printers — 1-HP/5M, 1-HP/5000 GN Printer EDITORIAL SOFTWARE: Baseview 3.5.6, Adobe/Illustrator 9.0, QPS/QuarkXPress 6.5, Adobe/Acrobat 3.0, Adobe/Creative Suite 2. PRODUCTION EQUIPMENT: Hardware — Ap Windows 2000 Photo Server, 2-AG/1500, 2-APP/Mac G3; Scanners — 1-Kk/2035 PRODUCTION SOFTWARE: QPS/ QuarkXPress 4.11, Adobe/Photoshop 7.0, Adobe/Creative Suite 2.

ATLANTA

ATLANTA JOURNAL-CONSTITUTION

223 Perimeter Center Pkwy NE, Atlanta, Ga., 30346-1301, Dekalb; gen tel (404) 526-7003; adv tel (404) 577-5775; ed tel (404) 526-2161; gen fax (404) 526-5746; ed fax (404) 526-5746; gen/nat adv e-mail allen.dunstan@coxinc.com; disp adv e-mail eric.myers@ajc.com; class adv e-mailajcclass@ ajc.com; ed e-mail newstips@ajc.com; web site www.ajc.com 4,808,000(visitors); web site 2 www.accessatlanta.com
Group: Cox Media Group
Published: Mon, Tues, Wed, Thur, Fri, Sat, Sun
Weekday Frequency: m
Saturday Frequency: m
Circulation: 139,864; 139,864(sat); 269,437(sun)
Last Audit: AAM September 30, 2016
Advertising Rate (weekday/saturday): Open inch rate $566.00 (Mon-Wed); $585.00 (Thur-Sat)
Advertising Rate (sunday): Open inch rate $755.00
News services: Cox News Service, AP, DJ, LAT-WP, NYT, MCT, CNS, CQ, NNS, PNS, SHNS, TMS. **Established:** 1868
Own Printing Facility?: Yes
Commercial Printers?: No
Special Editions: Breast Cancer Education (Annually); Golf/Masters (Apr); Back to School (Aug); Holiday Gift Guides (Dec); Brides (Feb); Safety Vehicles (Jan); Peachtree Road Race (Jul); Executive Homes (Jun); Braves Baseball Preview (Mar); Fun in the Sun (May); Pulse (Mon
Special Weekly Sections: Food & Drink (Thur); Go Guide, Cars (Fri); AJC Cars (Sat); Homefinder, Business, Jobs (Sun)
Syndicated Publications: Color Comics (S).
Digital Platform - Mobile: Apple, Android
Digital Platform - Tablet: Apple iOS, Kindle
VP, Marketing................................ Amy Chown
Dir., Mktg. Devel........................... Laura Inman
Mktg. Mgr., Classified/Territory.......... Chris Hood
Pub.... Amy Glennon
Ed... Kevin Riley
VP, Adv. Sales................................ Eric Myers
Sr. Dir., Nat'l Accts...................... Allen Dunstan
Sr. VP, Finance & Business Op......... Brian Cooper
Sr. VP, Audience & Group Lead for CMG Newspapers.............................. Mark Medici
VP, Fulfillment.......................... Joe McKinnon
Market Information: ADS; Split run; TMC; Zoned editions.
Mechanical Available: Offset; Black and 3 ROP colors; insert accepted - zoned areas; page cutoffs - 21 1/4.
Mechanical Specifications: Type page 12 5/8 x 21 1/4; E - 6 cols, 1 13/16, 1/8 between; A - 6 cols, 1 13/16, 1/8 between; C - 10 cols, 1 1/16, 1/8 between.
Areas Served: 30002 30004 30005 30008 30009 30011 30012 30013 30014 30016 30017 30018 30019 30021 30022 30024 30025 30028 30030 30032 30033 30034 30035

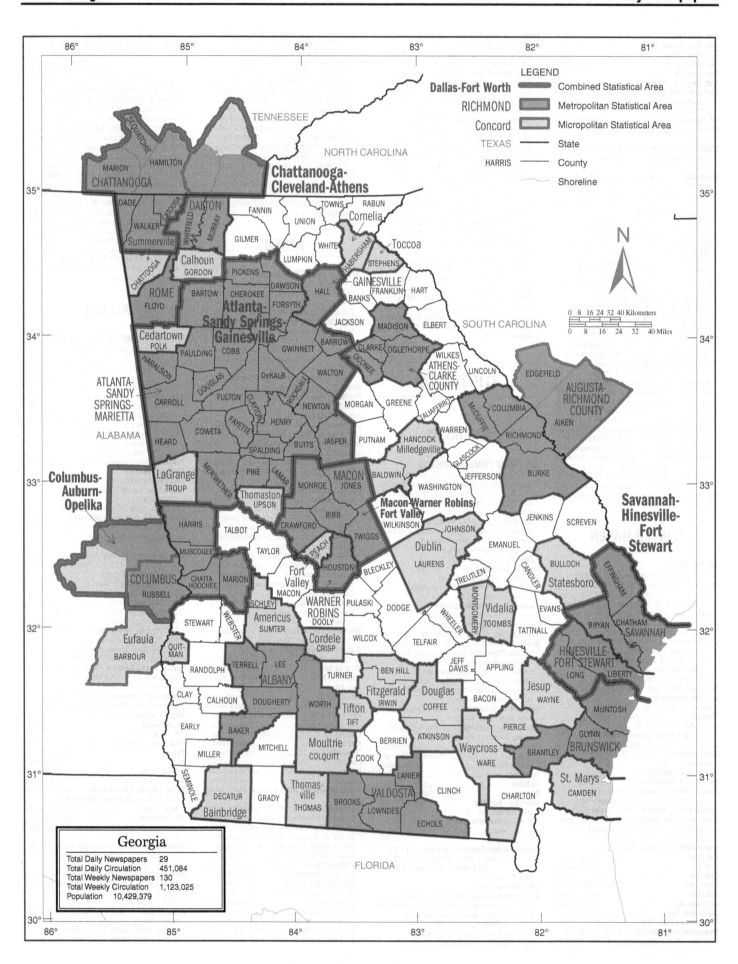

LEGEND

Dallas-Fort Worth — Combined Statistical Area

RICHMOND — Metropolitan Statistical Area

Concord — Micropolitan Statistical Area

TEXAS — State

HARRIS — County

Shoreline

Chattanooga-Cleveland-Athens

Atlanta-Sandy Springs-Gainesville

Columbus-Auburn-Opelika

Macon-Warner Robins-Fort Valley

Savannah-Hinesville-Fort Stewart

Georgia	
Total Daily Newspapers	29
Total Daily Circulation	451,084
Total Weekly Newspapers	130
Total Weekly Circulation	1,123,025
Population	10,429,379

30038 30039 30040 30041 30043 30044 30045 30046 30047 30052 30054 30055 30056 30058 30060 30062 30064 30066 30067 30068 30071 30075 30076 30078 30079 30080 30082 30083 30084 30087 30088 30092 30093 30094 30096 30097 30101 30102 30103 30104 30105 30106 30107 30108 30110 30113 30114 30115 30116 30117 30120 30121 30122 30124 30125 30126 30127 30132 30134 30135 30137 30141 30143 30144 30145 30147 30152 30153 30157 30161 30165 30168 30170 30171 30172 30173 30176 30178 30179 30180 30183 30184 30185 30187 30188 30189 30204 30213 30214 30215 30220 30223 30228 30229 30233 30236 30238 30248 30250 30252 30253 30259 30260 30263 30265 30268 30269 30272 30273 30274 30276 30277 30281 30288 30290 30291 30294 30295 30296 30297 30303 30305 30306 30307 30308 30309 30310 30311 30312 30313 30314 30315 30316 30317 30318 30319 30320 30322 30324 30326 30327 30328 30329 30331 30334 30336 30337 30338 30339 30340 30341 30342 30344 30345 30346 30349 30350 30354 30360 30361 30363 30501 30504 30506 30507 30510 30517 30518 30519 30523 30525 30527 30528 30529 30533 30534 30542 30548 30549 30554 30564 30566 30577 30601 30605 30606 30607 30620 30621 30622 30642 30655 30656 30666 30677 30680 30683 30701 30733 31024 31029 31030 31061 31088 31201

Delivery Method: Mail, Newsstand, Carrier, RacksEquipment & Software: PRESSROOM EQUIPMENT: Lines — 4-TKS/(20 half decks; 4 satellites) (Gwinnett); 2-TKS/7000CD tower units (Gwinnett); 4-TKS/(20 half decks; 4 satellites) (Fulton); Folders — 8-TKS/ (Fulton), 8-TKS/(Gwinnett); Reels & Stands — 40, 40.; MAILROOM EQUIPMENT: Counter Stackers — 13-SH/257 (Fulton), 16-QWI/300-350 (Gwinnett); Inserters & Stuffers — 1-NP/1472, 3-QWI/201, 4-QWI/200 (Reach), 2-GMA/SLS 2000 30:2 (Gwinnett), 1-GMA/SLS 2000 36:2 (Gwinnett), 1-QWI/400 (Reach); Tying Machines — 11-Si/Fulton, 14; BUSINESS EQUIPMENT: IBM/9672 RC4 BUSINESS SOFTWARE: CA, Global CLASSIFIED EQUIPMENT: Hardware — 145-IBM/3192, 2-Ad Star; CLASSIFIED SOFTWARE: In-house. DISPLAY EQUIPMENT: Hardware — IBM 9672; Other Hardware — IBM/7060H75 DISPLAY SOFTWAREAd Make-up Applications — NW/Admarc, NW/Discuss; Layout Software — DTI/Speed Planner. EDITORIAL EQUIPMENT: Hardware — 620-APP/Mac, 175-APP/Mac Powerbook/18-Sun/ Server, 2-Dell/Gu55 Server; Printers — HP, Xante, Canon EDITORIAL SOFTWARE: DTI. PRODUCTION EQUIPMENT: Hardware — 4-KFM/Bender single width, 2-Cx/Bidco, Glunz & Jensen/K2; Cameras — 4-C/Spartan; Scanners — 1-Howtek, 2-ECR/1800, 2-ECR/Autokon 1000, 2-Pixel Craft (tab size), 1-Scitex/Smartscan, 1-Tecsa/ TS2470, 1-Tecsa/TS2570 PRODUCTION SOFTWARE: DTI.

FULTON COUNTY DAILY REPORT

190 Pryor St SW, Atlanta, Ga., 30303-3607, Fulton; gen tel (404) 521-1227; adv tel (404) 419-2870; adv fax (404) 419 - 2819; gen/nat adv e-mail lsimcoe@alm.com; web site www.dailyreportonline.com

Group: ALM
Published: Mon, Tues, Wed, Thur, Fri, Sat, Sun
Weekday Frequency: m
Saturday Frequency: m
Circulation: 2,805; 3,095(sat); 3,095(sun)
Last Audit: VAC December 31, 2016
Own Printing Facility?: No
Commercial Printers?: Yes
Digital Platform - Mobile: Apple, Android, Windows, Blackberry
Editor....Ed Bean
Group Publisher....Wayne Curtis
Systems Director....Scott Pitman
Regional Editor-in-Chief....George Haj
Mng. Ed.....Jonathan Ringel
Delivery Method: Mail, Newsstand, Carrier, Racks

AUGUSTA

THE AUGUSTA CHRONICLE

725 Broad St, Augusta, Ga., 30901-1336, Richmond; gen tel (706) 724-0851; adv tel (706) 823-3283; ed tel (706) 823-3430; ed fax (706) 823-3345; gen/nat adv e-mail newsroom@augustachronicle.com; disp adv e-mail adsales@augustachronicle.com; class adv e-mailadvertising@augustachronicle.com; ed e-mail letters@augustachronicle.com; web site www.chronicle.augusta.com/ - 5,019,380(views) 622,408(visitors); web site 2 http://augusta.com - 962,936(views) 234,316(visitors)

Group: GateHouse Media, Inc.
Published: Mon, Tues, Wed, Thur, Fri, Sat, Sun
Weekday Frequency: m
Saturday Frequency: m
Circulation: 41,663; 42,831(sat); 47,814(sun)
Last Audit: AAM March 31, 2017
Advertising Rate (weekday/saturday): Open inch rate $54.41(m-thur) $62.97 (Fri and Sat)
Advertising Rate (sunday): $69.73
Online Advertising Rate: $10 cpm, geotargeting and other filters additional. 728x90, 160x600 or 300x250
News services: AP, MCT, Morris, SHNS, **Established:** 1785
Own Printing Facility?: Yes
Commercial Printers?: Yes
Special Editions: Masters Golf (Apr); Back-to-School (Aug); Gift Guides (Dec); Brides (Jan); Graduation (May); Eat (December and June), Food and Fun Guide (April),
Special Weekly Sections: Applause (Fri); Today's Home (S); Religion (Sat); Food (Wed).
Syndicated Publications: Relish (Monthly); USA WEEKEND Magazine (S).
Spry
Digital Platform - Mobile: Apple, Android, Windows
Digital Platform - Tablet: Apple iOS, Android, Windows 7, Blackberry Tablet OS, Kindle
Publisher....William S. Morris III
Publisher, AUGUSTA MAGAZINE....Ashlee Duren
VP of Circulation....David Enoch
Editorial Cartoonist....Rick McKee
Editorial Page Editor....Michael Ryan
Executive Editor....John Gogick
Sports Editor....John Boyette
HR Director....Cynthia Spencer
Production Director....Pat McCue
VP of Sales....James Holmes
Administrative Assistant to the President... Rachel Watson
Division Controller....Greg Williamson
Marketing Director....Ashlee Edelen
Pres.....Stephen Wade
Advertising Director, AUGUSTA Magazine Lisa Dorn
Business Editor....Tim Rausch
Digital Product Development Director.Kim Luciani
Market Information: ADS; Split run; SMC; Zoned editions.
Mechanical Available: Offset; Black and 3 ROP colors; insert accepted; page cutoffs - 22 3/4.
Mechanical Specifications: Type page 10.1667 x 21 1/4
Areas Served: 30802, 30809, 30813, 30814, 30815, 30901, 30904, 30906, 30907, 30909, 28941, 29860
Delivery Method: Mail, Newsstand, Carrier, RacksEquipment & Software: PRESSROOM EQUIPMENT: Lines — 1-G/Metro (6 color decks and 3 mono units) Folders — 2-G/3:2 Imperial folders 144 page, 8 reels & stands MAILROOM EQUIPMENT: Counter Stackers — 4/ StraPack 2/Quipp 351, 2 GMA SLS 2000 inserting machines, 4 StraPack strapping machines 2Dynaric NP-2 strapping machines; 2 StraPack bottom wrap machines and 3 Quipp bottom wrap machines BUSINESS EQUIPMENT: 2-IBM/RISC6000 BUSINESS SOFTWARE: PBS/Circ. 3.2, PBS/Adv. 2.8 CLASSIFIED EQUIPMENT: Hardware — DTI, APP/Mac; CLASSIFIED SOFTWARE: DTI, APP/Mac. DISPLAY EQUIPMENT: Hardware — APP/Mac, APP/ Mac NTX, APP/Power Mac; Printers — XIT/ Clipper, Tektronix/Phaser; Other Hardware — APP/Mac Kodak Prinergy Evo with 2 Creo CTP devices DISPLAY SOFTWAREAd Make-up Applications — Multi-Ad/Creator, QPS/ QuarkXPress, Adobe/Photoshop; EDITORIAL EQUIPMENT: Hardware — APP/Power Mac; Prinergy Evo with 2 Creo CTP devices EDITORIAL SOFTWARE: ContentWatch PRODUCTION EQUIPMENT: 1 9 unit metro press unit with 6 color decks with 2 144 page Imperial folders Goss Metro PRODUCTION SOFTWARE: QPS/Qu
Note: New Business Unit: Main Street Digital Provides full product set of digital services

BRUNSWICK

THE BRUNSWICK NEWS

3011 Altama Ave, Brunswick, Ga., 31520-4626, Glynn; gen tel (912) 265-8320; gen fax (912) 264-4973; gen/nat adv e-mail advertising@thebrunswicknews.com; ed e-mail editor@thebrunswicknews.com; newsroom@thebrunswicknews.com; web site www.thebrunswicknews.com - 580,000(views) 60,000(visitors)

Published: Mon, Tues, Wed, Thur, Fri, Sat
Weekday Frequency: m
Saturday Frequency: m
Circulation: 17,800; 17,800(sat)
Last Audit: USPS September 27, 2017
Advertising Rate (weekday/saturday): Open inch rate $12.99
Online Advertising Rate: Banner - $700; Leaderboard - $300; Skyscraper -$250; Buttons - $100
News services: AP, NEA. **Established:** 1902
Own Printing Facility?: Yes
Commercial Printers?: Yes
Special Editions: Newcomers Guide (Apr); Football (Aug); Christmas Greetings (Dec); Wedding Bells (Feb); Outlook Glynn (Jan); Back to School (Jul); Hurricane Survival (Jun); Tour of Homes (Mar); Graduation (May); Holiday Gift Guide (Nov); Celebration (Oct); Health and Fitn
Special Weekly Sections: Health Section (Tue); Real Estate & Homes (Fri); Weekend Driver (Fri).
Syndicated Publications: Relish (Monthly; Spry (monthly); American Profile (Weekly); News & Advertiser (Weekly).
President and Publisher....Buff Leavy
Vice President/General Manager.. Ron Maulden
Circulation Director....Frank Lane
Mng. Ed.....Hank Rowland
City Ed.....Buddy Hughes
Dir of Advert & Mktg....Amy Lee
Exec. Ed.....Tim O'Briant
Mechanical Available: Offset; Black and 3 ROP colors; insert accepted; page cutoffs - 22 3/4.
Mechanical Specifications: Type page 13 x 21; E - 6 cols, 2 1/16, 1/8 between; A - 6 cols, 2 1/16, 1/8 between; C - 8 cols, 1 1/2, 1/8 between.
Areas Served: 31520,31521,31522,31523,31525,31527,31561,31305,31331,31543,31565,31566,31569
Delivery Method: Newsstand, Carrier, RacksEquipment & Software: PRESSROOM EQUIPMENT: Lines — 8-G/Community 1974.; MAILROOM EQUIPMENT: Address Machine — Papertrack System.; BUSINESS EQUIPMENT: Papertrak/System CLASSIFIED SOFTWARE: Baseview, QPS/ QuarkXPress. DISPLAY EQUIPMENT: Hardware — Baseview.; EDITORIAL SOFTWARE: Baseview. PRODUCTION EQUIPMENT: Hardware — Nu/Flip Top, DP; Cameras — C/Spartan III PRODUCTION SOFTWARE: Baseview.

CANTON

CHEROKEE TRIBUNE

521 E Main St, Canton, Ga., 30114-2805, Cherokee; gen tel (770) 479-1441; adv tel (770) 479-1441; ed tel (770) 479-1441; gen fax (770) 479-3505; adv fax (770) 479-3505; ed fax (770) 479-3505; gen/nat adv e-mail wstephens@mdjonline.com; disp adv e-mail wstephens@mdjonline.com; ed e-mail kfowler@cherokeetribune.com; web site www.cherokeetribune.com

Group: McNaughton Newspapers
Neighbor Newspapers
Times-Journal, Inc.
Published: Wed, Thur, Fri, Sat, Sun
Weekday Frequency: m
Saturday Frequency: m
Circulation: 4,238; 4,238(sat); 4,449(sun)
Last Audit: AAM December 31, 2014
Advertising Rate (weekday/saturday): Open inch rate $22.80 (Wed); $15.60 (Thurs-Sat)
Advertising Rate (sunday): Open inch rate $16.70
News services: AP.
Special Weekly Sections: Real Estate (S).
Syndicated Publications: USA WEEKEND Magazine (S).
CEO/Pub.....Otis Brumby
Adv. Mgr.....Kim Fowler
Circ. Mgr.....Matt Heck
Ed.....Barbara Jacoby
VP, Sales/Mktg....Wade Stephens
Gen. Mgr.....Lee Garrett
Circ. Mgr.....Dave Gossett
VP, Productions....Joe Fernandez
Market Information: ADS; TMC.
Mechanical Available: Offset; Black and ROP colors; insert accepted.
Mechanical Specifications: Type page 11 5/8 x 21.

CARROLLTON

TIMES-GEORGIAN

901 Hays Mill Rd, Carrollton, Ga., 30117-9576, Carroll; gen tel (770) 834-6631; adv tel (770) 214-2285; ed tel (770) 214-2285; gen fax (770) 834-9991; adv fax (770) 834-9991; ed fax (770) 834-9991; gen/nat adv e-mail melissa@times-georgian.com; class adv e-mailclassifieds@times-georgian.com; ed e-mail circulation@times-georgian.com; web site www.times-georgian.com - 239,329(views) 13,595(visitors)

Group: Paxton Media Group, LLC
Published: Tues, Wed, Thur, Fri, Sun
Weekday Frequency: m
Circulation: 5,092; 5,092(sun)
Last Audit: USPS September 28, 2016
Advertising Rate (weekday/saturday): Open inch rate $20.00
Advertising Rate (sunday): Open inch rate $20.00
News services: AP. **Established:** 1871
Own Printing Facility?: Yes
Commercial Printers?: Yes
Managing Ed.....Bruce Browning
Sports Ed.....Corey Cusick
Reg. Adv. Dir.....Melissa Wilson
Pub.....Marvin Enderle
Cir. Dir.....Mark Golding
Press Mgr.....Branyon Michael
IT Mgr.....Ricky Stilley
Market Information: TMC.
Mechanical Available: Offset; Black and 3 ROP colors; insert accepted; page cutoffs - 11 X 22.
Mechanical Specifications: Type page 10 x 21; E - 6 cols, 1 9/16, 1/8 between; A - 6 cols, 1 9/16, 1/8 between; C - 1 9/16 1/8 between.
Areas Served: Carroll County, GA
Delivery Method: Mail, Newsstand, Carrier, RacksEquipment & Software: PRESSROOM EQUIPMENT: Lines — 9-G/Community.; MAILROOM EQUIPMENT: Counter Stackers — 1-BG/Count-O-Veyor; Inserters & Stuffers — 2/MM; Tying Machines — 2-/MLN; Address Machine — 1-/KR.; BUSINESS EQUIPMENT: 6-APP/Mac BUSINESS SOFTWARE: Baseview/Ap Manager Pro CLASSIFIED EQUIPMENT: Hardware — 5-APP/Mac; CLASSIFIED SOFTWARE: Baseview/ Ad Manager Pro. DISPLAY EQUIPMENT: Hardware — 9-APP/Mac; DISPLAY SOFTWAREAd Make-up Applications — Multi-Ad/Creator.; EDITORIAL EQUIPMENT: Hardware — 11-APP/Mac; Printers — 1-APP/ Mac LaserWriter II NTX, APP/Mac Printer EDITORIAL SOFTWARE: Baseview, Baseview/NewsEdit Pro, QPS/QuarkXPress. PRODUCTION EQUIPMENT: Hardware — Caere/Omnipage Pro 6.0; Cameras — 1-C/ Spartan III PRODUCTION SOFTWARE: QPS/QuarkXPress 3.32.

CARTERSVILLE

THE DAILY TRIBUNE NEWS

251 S Tennessee St, Cartersville, Ga., 30120-3605, Bartow; gen tel (770) 382-4545; gen fax (770) 382-2711; gen/nat adv e-mail advertising@daily-tribune.com; disp adv

e-mail jennifer.moates@daily-tribune.com; class adv e-mailclassifieds@daily-tribune.com; ed e-mail jason.greenberg@daily-tribune.com; web site www.daily-tribune.com
Group: Cleveland Newspapers, Inc.
Published: Tues, Wed, Thur, Fri, Sat, Sun
Weekday Frequency: m
Saturday Frequency: m
Circulation: 4,867; 4,867(sat); 5,369(sun)
Last Audit: AAM September 30, 2017
Advertising Rate (weekday/saturday): Open inch rate $11.44
News services: AP INAME, SNPA, SCAMA **Established:** 1946
Own Printing Facility?: Yes
Commercial Printers?: No
Special Editions: Earth Day Tab (Apr); Christmas Greetings (Dec); Medical Tab (Feb); Chamber Tab (Jan); Progress (Jul); Graduation (Jun); Holiday Cookbook (Nov).
Special Weekly Sections: Best Food Day (Sun); Legal (Thur); Real Estate, Auto (Fri); Wedding, Select TV, Business, Arts, Entertainment, Consumer (Sun)
Syndicated Publications: Relish (Monthly); TV Outlook (S); American Profile (Weekly).
Prod. Dir., Pressroom ....Byron Pezzarossi
Retail Adv. Dir. ....Jennifer Moates
Pub. .... Alan Davis
Office Mgr. ....Mindy Salaman
Market Information: TMC; Zoned editions.
Mechanical Available: Offset; Black and 3 ROP colors; insert accepted - any; page cutoffs - 22 3/4.
Mechanical Specifications: Type page 13 x 21 1/2; E - 6 cols, 2 1/16, 1/8 between; A - 6 cols, 2 1/16, 1/8 between; C - 6 cols, 2 1/16, 1/8 between.
Areas Served: Bartow County
Delivery Method: Mail, Carrier, RacksEquipment & Software: PRESSROOM EQUIPMENT: Lines — 7-WPC/Web Leader (2-Color quad); 4-WPC/Web Leader (1-Color quad); 3-WPC/Web leader (1-Color quad); MAILROOM EQUIPMENT: Counter Stackers — 1/Mid America Graphics; Inserters & Stuffers — MM/7:1; Tying Machines — 2-/Bu, 1-Strapex/Solomat; Address Machine — 3-/Dispensa-Matic/16.; BUSINESS EQUIPMENT: DEC/PC XL 466D2, 1-Mk/Digital CLASSIFIED EQUIPMENT: Hardware — 2-APP/Mac; Printers — APP/Mac LaserWriter Pro 630; CLASSIFIED SOFTWARE: Baseview. DISPLAY EQUIPMENT: Hardware — 4-APP/Mac, 4-Radius/81-110; Printers — APP/Mac LaserWriter Pro 630; DISPLAY SOFTWAREAd Make-up Applications — Multi-Ad/Creator, QPS/QuarkXPress 3.3, Aldus/FreeHand; Layout Software — APP/Mac. EDITORIAL EQUIPMENT: Hardware — APP/Mac/7-APP/Mac; Printers — APP/Mac LaserWriter Pro 630 EDITORIAL SOFTWARE: Baseview 3.3. PRODUCTION EQUIPMENT: Hardware — C/Powermatic-66F, Adobe/Photoshop, V/3990; Cameras — 1-C/Spartan III; Scanners — 1-AG/Arcus II, 1-AG/Arcus Plus, 1-Polaroid/SprintScan 35 PRODUCTION SOFTWARE: Baseview, QPS/QuarkXPress.

COLUMBUS

COLUMBUS LEDGER-ENQUIRER

945 Broadway Ste 102, Suite 102, Columbus, Ga., 31901-2772, Muscogee; gen tel (706) 324-5526; adv tel (706) 320-4407; ed tel (706) 571-8565; gen fax (706) 576-6236; adv fax (706) 576-6236; ed fax (706) 576-6290; gen/nat adv e-mail rmcduffie@ledger-enquirer.com; disp adv e-mail rmcduffie@ledger-enquirer.com; class adv e-mailrmcduffie@ledger-enquirer.com; ed e-mail dkholmes@ledger-enquirer.com; web site www.ledger-enquirer.com - 4,100,000(views) 622,000(visitors); web site 2 dealsaver.com

Group: The McClatchy Company
Published: Mon, Tues, Wed, Thur, Fri, Sat, Sun
Weekday Frequency: m
Saturday Frequency: m
Circulation: 19,742; 19,341(sat); 26,646(sun)
Last Audit: AAM March 31, 2016
News services: 1930
Special Weekly Sections: Best Food (Wed); Vacation, Travel, Living, Society, TV (Sun); Money, Business, Family (Mon); Health, Fitness (Tue); Community (Wed); Entertainment (Thur); Auto, Religion, Homes (Sat); Business (Tue-Sat)
Syndicated Publications: Parade (S).
Proprietary Publications: Her magazine, The Big To Do, The Bayonet & Saber, Sunday Select, Neighbors
Digital Platform - Mobile: Apple, Android
Digital Platform - Tablet: Apple iOS, Android
HR Manager .... Wanda Howell
Circ. Dir. .... Pat Chitwood
Exec. Ed. .... Dimon Kendrick-holmes
Assoc. Ed. ....Marcia McAllister
Columnist.................................... Tim Chitwood
Entertainment Writer...................... Brad Barnes
Features Ed....................................Dawn Minty
News Ed.... Larry Foley
Sports Ed. .... Kevin Price
Chief Technician .... Jimmy Mann
Prodn. Foreman, Platemaking .... David Crute
Circ. Mktg. .... Heather Williams
Pres./Pub....................................Valerie Canepa
Sr. Nat'l/Major Sales Rep....................... Bill Wall
VP of Ads. .... Ross McDuffie
Market Information: ADS; TMC; Zoned editions.
Mechanical Available: Offset; Black and 3 ROP colors; insert accepted - product samples; page cutoffs - 22.
Mechanical Specifications: Type page 9.89 x 21
Delivery Method: Newsstand, Carrier

DALTON

THE DAILY CITIZEN

308 S Thornton Ave, Dalton, Ga., 30720-8268, Whitfield; gen tel (706) 217-6397; adv tel (706) 272-7729; ed tel (706) 272-7714; gen fax (706) 275-6641; adv fax (706) 272-7743; ed fax (706) 275-6641; gen/nat adv e-mail internet@daltoncitizen.com; disp adv e-mail jeffmutter@daltoncitizen.com; ed e-mail internet@daltoncitizen.com; web site http://daltondailycitizen.com/; web site 2 DALTONnow.com
Group: Community Newspaper Holdings, Inc.
Published: Mon, Tues, Wed, Thur, Fri, Sat, Sun
Weekday Frequency: m
Saturday Frequency: m
Circulation: 11,040; 11,040(sat); 10,426(sun)
Last Audit: Sworn/Estimate/Non-Audited September 30, 2017
Advertising Rate (weekday/saturday): Open inch rate $19.50
News services: AP, SHNS.
Special Editions: Progress (Mar).
Special Weekly Sections: Entertainment (Sat).
Syndicated Publications: Relish (Monthly); USA WEEKEND Magazine (S).
Pub... William Bronson
Bus. Mgr. .... Laddie Tony
Adv. Dir... Gary Jones
Bus. Ed. .... Jamie Jones
News Ed........................................Wes Chance
Sports Ed. .... Larry Fleming
Online Mgr. ....Victor Miller
Prodn. Mgr., Post Press .... Norma Jackson
Market Information: TMC.
Mechanical Available: Offset; Black and 3 ROP colors; insert accepted; page cutoffs - 21 1/2.
Mechanical Specifications: Type page 11 1/2 x 21 1/2; E - 6 cols, 1 13/16, 5/32 between; A - 6 cols, 1 13/16, 5/32 between; C - 6 cols, 1 13/16, 5/32 between.Equipment & Software: PRESSROOM EQUIPMENT: Lines — 10-G/Community.; MAILROOM EQUIPMENT: Tying Machines — 1-Bu/String Tying Machine; Address Machine — 1/KR, 1-/KAN.; BUSINESS EQUIPMENT: ICanon (ATT) BUSINESS SOFTWARE: Microsoft/Office 97 CLASSIFIED EQUIPMENT: Hardware — APP/Mac; CLASSIFIED SOFTWARE: FSI. EDITORIAL EQUIPMENT: Hardware — APP/Mac/APP/Mac Graphics Network, APP/Mac. PRODUCTION EQUIPMENT: Hardware — Pre Press/Panther 2042; Scanners — Umax/Mirage PRODUCTION SOFTWARE: QPS/QuarkXPress, Multi-Ad/Creator, Macromedia/Freehand.

DUBLIN

THE COURIER HERALD

115 S Jefferson St, Dublin, Ga., 31021-5146, Laurens; gen tel (478) 272-5522; adv tel (478) 272-5522; gen fax (478) 272-2189; adv fax (478) 272-2189; gen/nat adv e-mail advertising@courier-herald.com; disp adv e-mail advertising@courier-herald.com; class adv e-mailclassifieds@courier-herald.com; ed e-mail news@courier-herald.com; web site www.courier-herald.com
Group: Herald Newspapers, Inc.
Published: Mon, Tues, Wed, Thur, Fri, Sat
Weekday Frequency: e
Saturday Frequency: e
Circulation: 8,728; 8,728(sat)
Last Audit: AAM December 31, 2014
Advertising Rate (weekday/saturday): Open inch rate $14.65
Online Advertising Rate: $100-$400
News services: AP. **Established:** 1876
Own Printing Facility?: Yes
Commercial Printers?: Yes
Special Editions: Medical Directory (Jan); Bridal Guide (Feb); St. Patrick's Preview (Feb); Porter's Guide to Hunting & Fishing (Mar, Aug, Nov); Worship Tab (Apr); Home & Garden Tab (Apr); Graduation Year Book (May) Senior Citizens Guide (Jun); Back To School (Aug); Football Preview (Aug); Go Green (Sept); Relish Cooking School (Oct); Holiday Gift Guide (Nov); Christmas Greetings (Dec)
Special Weekly Sections: Best Food Day, Lifestyle (Wed); Business (Thur); Legal, Religion, Entertainment (Sat)
Syndicated Publications: USA WEEKEND Magazine (Sat).
Adv. Dir.... Pam Burney
Classified ....Prudence Price
Circ. Mgr... Cheryl Gay
Managing Ed. ....Jason Halcombe
Photo Ed. .... Joey Wilson
Pub... Griffin Lovett
Online Mgr. .... Travis Ryan
Prodn. Mgr. .... Elizabeth Mimbs
CEO...DuBose Porter
Market Information: TMC.
Mechanical Available: Offset; Black and 3 ROP colors; insert accepted - max size 11 x 14; page cutoffs - 22 3/4.
Mechanical Specifications: Type page 13 x 21 1/2; E - 6 cols, 2 1/16, 1/8 between; A - 6 cols, 2 1/16, 1/8 between; C - 6 cols, 2 1/16, 1/8 between.
Delivery Method: Carrier, RacksEquipment & Software: PRESSROOM EQUIPMENT: 8-G/SC (with Gev-Flexicolor half deck); Folders — 1-G/SC. MAILROOM EQUIPMENT: Tying Machines — 2/AMP, 1-/MLN, 1-/Bu; Address Machine — 1-/Ch.; BUSINESS EQUIPMENT: MTI/Micro-Computer CLASSIFIED EQUIPMENT: Hardware — Mk.; DISPLAY EQUIPMENT: Hardware — APP/Mac Radius 19 color monitor; DISPLAY SOFTWARELayout Software — 2-APP/Mac IIcx. EDITORIAL EQUIPMENT: Hardware — Mk. PRODUCTION EQUIPMENT: Hardware — 1-APP/Mac LaserWriter NT, 1-Dataproducts/11 x 17; Cameras — 1-CL/Horizontal, 1-R/Vertical; Scanners — 1-APP/Mac, 1-Mirror/Color scanner.

GAINESVILLE

THE TIMES

345 Green St NW, Gainesville, Ga., 30501-3370, Hall; gen tel (770) 532-6338; gen fax (770) 532-7085; adv fax (770) 532-8187; ed fax (770) 532-0457; gen/nat adv e-mail lnelson@gainesvilletimes.com; disp adv e-mail lnelson@gainesvilletimes.com; ed e-mail news@gainesvilletimes.com; web site www.gainesvilletimes.com - 2,040,000(views) 241,000(visitors)
Group: Morris Multimedia, Inc.
Published: Mon, Tues, Wed, Thur, Fri, Sat, Sun
Weekday Frequency: m
Saturday Frequency: m
Circulation: 14,000; 14,000(sat); 16,000(sun)
Last Audit: Sworn/Estimate/Non-Audited September 1, 2017
Advertising Rate (weekday/saturday): Open inch rate $23.12
Advertising Rate (sunday): Open inch rate $29.89
Online Advertising Rate: $10 per thousand
News services: AP, AP Sportswire, AP Photo, AP Graphics,MCT **Established:** 1947
Own Printing Facility?: Yes
Commercial Printers?: Yes
Special Editions: Back to School (Aug); Newcomers Guide (July); Health Watch (quarterly); Progress (Mar); ; Business Link (Monthly);
Special Weekly Sections: Church Page (Sat); Get Out (Thur); Food (Wed).
Syndicated Publications: Relish (monthly)
Proprietary Publications: HOME Living in North Georgia (Monthly magazine)
Digital Platform - Mobile: Apple, Android
Digital Platform - Tablet: Apple iOS, Android
Gen. Mgr................................... Norman Baggs
Exec. Ed....................................Keith Albertson
Managing Editor ....Shannon Casas
New Media Ed. .... Michael Beard
Mgmt. Info Servs. Mgr. .... DeJuan Woodward
Prodn. Dir.... Mark Hall
Circ. Dir. .... Scott Whitworth
Ad. Director.................................. Leah Nelson
Market Information: TMC.
Mechanical Available: Offset; Black and 3 ROP colors; insert accepted - mini-tabs; page cutoffs - 22 3/4.
Mechanical Specifications: Type page 13 x 21 1/2; E - 6 cols, 2 1/16, 1/8 between; A - 6 cols, 2 1/16, 1/8 between; C - 10 cols, 1 3/16, 1/16 between.
Areas Served: 30501 30502 30503 30504 30506 30542
Delivery Method: Newsstand, Carrier, RacksEquipment & Software: PRESSROOM EQUIPMENT: Lines — 4-G/Urbanite 1970, 8-G/Urbanite 1982, 2-G/Urbanite 1984, 1-G/Urbanite 1985; Press Drive — 4-Fin/100 h.p. Drive Motors; Folders — G/Urbanite U775, G/Urbanite U1362; MAILROOM EQUIPMENT: Counter Stackers — 1-QWI/300, 1/PPK, 1-QWI/351; Inserters & Stuffers — 3-/MM; Tying Machines — 2-/Bu, 2-/MLN; Address Machine — 1-Barstrom/Labeler, 1-/Ch; CLASSIFIED EQUIPMENT: Hardware — 5-PC P166, 1-Pentium/Pro 200 PC; SyQuest/Disc Reader; Printers — 1-Lexmark/Optra; CLASSIFIED SOFTWARE: APT/V2. DISPLAY EQUIPMENT: Hardware — 1-PC/P200, 3-APP/Mac 8500, 3-APP/Mac 8100, 1-APP/Mac 7200, 1-APP/Mac 7100; Printers — 2-APP/Mac LaserWriter 630, 1-Xante/Accel-a-Writer; Other Hardware — SyQuest/Tape Drive DISPLAY SOFTWAREAd Make-up Applications — APT; Layout Software — APT. EDITORIAL EQUIPMENT: Hardware — 21-PC P166, 9-PC P200, 1-Pentium/PC Pro 2000; Printers — 1-Lexmark/Optra, 1-HP/LaserJet 4MV EDITORIAL SOFTWARE: Scoop PRODUCTION EQUIPMENT: Hardware — 2-ECR/4550 Imagesetter with PC RIP, 1-ECR/Autokon 1000 DE, Pre Press/Panther Plus, Epson/Stylus ProxI Proofer, Xante/Accel-a-Writer 8900 Plain Paper, 2-ECR/4500; Scanners — ECR/Autokon 1000 DE, AG/Arcus Plus, Umax/Flat

GRIFFIN

GRIFFIN DAILY NEWS

1403 N Expressway, Ste J, Griffin, Ga., 30223-9015, Spalding; gen tel (770) 227-3276; gen fax (770) 412-1678; gen/nat adv e-mail advertising@griffindailynews.com; disp adv e-mail advertising@griffindailynews.com; ed e-mail editor@griffindailynews.com; web site www.griffindailynews.com
Group: Paxton Media Group, LLC
Published: Tues, Wed, Thur, Fri, Sun
Weekday Frequency: m
Circulation: 6,936; 6,936(sat); 6,246(sun)
Last Audit: Sworn/Estimate/Non-Audited September 30, 2017
Advertising Rate (weekday/saturday): Open inch rate $24.80
Advertising Rate (sunday): $24.80
News services: AP.
Own Printing Facility?: No
Commercial Printers?: No
Special Editions: Progress (Apr); Football (Aug); Valentines (Feb); Super Bowl (Jan); Vacation (Jun); Spring Fashion (Mar); Youth Sports

(May); Newcomer's Guide (Sept).
Special Weekly Sections: TV Notes (S).
Syndicated Publications: USA WEEKEND Magazine (S).
Pub./Adv. Dir. .... Joy Gaddy
Circ. Dir. .... Mark Golding
Mng. Ed. .... Tim Daly
Asst. Mng. Ed. .... Anthony Rhoades
Market Information: ADS; TMC; Zoned editions.
Mechanical Available: Offset; Black and 3 ROP colors; insert accepted - single sheets; page cutoffs - 21 1/2.
Mechanical Specifications: Type page 13 x 21 1/2; E - 6 cols, 2, 1/6 between; A - 6 cols, 2, 1/6 between; C - 9 cols, 1 1/3, 1/6 between.
Delivery Method: Mail, Carrier, RacksEquipment & Software: PRESSROOM EQUIPMENT: Lines — 8-G 1968; Folders — SC/ Community.; MAILROOM EQUIPMENT: Counter Stackers — 1-BG/Count-O-Veyor; Inserters & Stuffers — 1-MM/5 pocket; Tying Machines — 1/Bu; Address Machine — KAN/Zip Code Separator, KAN/Label Applicator.; BUSINESS EQUIPMENT: 1-Cumulus/GLC 1220 W CLASSIFIED EQUIPMENT: Hardware — APP/Mac; TI/ Omni 800; Printers — QMS/2060.; DISPLAY EQUIPMENT: Hardware — APP/Mac; Printers — QMS/2060; Other Hardware — AG/T 1200, MK/Scanner 4 DISPLAY SOFTWAREAd Make-up Applications — Aldus/FreeHand, Adobe Illustrator 8.01, Photoshop 5.5, Acrobat Exchange 3.0, Multi-Ad/Creator 4.0.3, QPS/QuarkXPress 4.04; Layout Software — 2-APP/Power Mac 4400, APP/Mac EDITORIAL EQUIPMENT: Hardware — APP/Mac EDITORIAL SOFTWARE: Baseview/NewsEdit Pro IQue, QPS/QuarkXPress 4.04. PRODUCTION EQUIPMENT: Hardware — Caere/ OmniPage, QMS/2060; Cameras — 1-C/ Spartan II; Scanners — 2-APP/Mac One Scanner PRODUCTION SOFTWARE: QPS/ QuarkXPress 4.04.

JONESBORO

CLAYTON NEWS DAILY

138 Church St, Jonesboro, Ga., 30236-3514, Clayton; gen tel (770) 478-5753; gen fax (770) 473-9032; adv fax (770) 472-2121; ed fax (770) 472-2060; gen/nat adv e-mail ccollier@news-daily.com; disp adv e-mail ccollier@news-daily.com; class adv e-mailccollier@news-daily.com; ed e-mail info@news-daily.com; web site www.news-daily.com
Group: Southern Community Newspapers, Inc.
Published: Wed, Thur, Fri, Sat
Weekday Frequency: m
Saturday Frequency: m
Circulation: 1,600; 1,600(sat)
Last Audit: CAC September 30, 2012
Advertising Rate (weekday/saturday): Open inch rate $13.00
News services: AP. **Established:** 1970
Special Editions: Spring Tour of Homes (Apr); Football Kick-off (Aug); Christmas Gift Guide (Dec); Bride's Tour (Feb); Progress (Jan); Newcomer's Guide (Jul); Spring Car Care (Mar); Welcome Summer (May); Meet the Merchants (Oct); Introduction to New Cars (Sept).
Special Weekly Sections: Best Food Day (Wed); Real Estate (Last Fri/Month); Religion (Sat)
Syndicated Publications: Relish (Monthly); USA WEEKEND Magazine (Sat).
Bus. Mgr. .... Donna Goodson
Adv. Dir. .... Christy Collier
Ed .... Jim Zachary
Columnist/Entertainment Critic .... Joel Hall
Sports Ed. .... Luke Strickland
Prodn. Foreman, Pressroom .... Gary Toohey
Classified Adv. Mgr. .... Rita Camp
Circ. Mgr. .... Thom Bell
Market Information: Split run; TMC.
Mechanical Available: Offset; Black and 3 ROP colors; insert accepted; page cutoffs - 21 1/2.
Mechanical Specifications: Type page 13 x 21 1/2; E - 6 cols, 2 1/16, 1/8 between; A - 6 cols, 2 1/16, 1/8 between; C - 6 cols, 2 1/16, 1/8 between.Equipment & Software: PRESSROOM EQUIPMENT: Lines — 6-KP/ News King; 8-KP/News King; Reels & Stands — 6; MAILROOM EQUIPMENT: Counter Stackers — 1/BG; Tying Machines — 2-/Bu; Address Machine — 1-/Ch.; DISPLAY EQUIPMENT: Hardware — COM/ Power View.; EDITORIAL EQUIPMENT: Hardware — COM/One Sys. PRODUCTION EQUIPMENT: Hardware — 11-COM/8400; Cameras — 1-C/17 x 24, 1-K/Vertical 16 x 22.

LAGRANGE

LAGRANGE DAILY NEWS

105 Ashton St, Lagrange, Ga., 30240-3111, Troup; gen tel (706) 884-7311; adv tel (706) 884-7311 ext. 238; ed tel (706) 884-7311 x232; gen fax (706) 884-8712; gen/nat adv e-mail advertising@lagrangenews.com; disp adv e-mail advertising@lagrangenews.com; class adv e-mailadvertising@lagrangenews.com; ed e-mail editor@lagrangenews.com; web site www.lagrangenews.com - 500,000(views) 65,000(visitors); web site 2 www.myownlagrange.com - 45,000(views)
Group: Boone Newspapers, Inc.
Published: Mon, Tues, Wed, Thur, Fri, Sat
Weekday Frequency: e
Saturday Frequency: m
Circulation: 13,400; 13,400(sat); 13,400(sun)
Last Audit: Sworn/Estimate/Non-Audited September 30, 2017
Advertising Rate (weekday/saturday): Open inch rate $18.10
Advertising Rate (sunday): Open inch rate $18.10
News services: AP, NEA. **Established:** 1843
Own Printing Facility?: Yes
Commercial Printers?: Yes
Special Weekly Sections: Best Food Day (Wed); Auto (Thur); Real Estate (Fri); Religion, Arts, Entertainment, Living (Sat); Art, Entertainment, Living (Sun)
Syndicated Publications: USA WEEKEND Magazine (S); American Profile (Weekly).
Digital Platform - Mobile: Apple, Android
Pub. .... Jeff Parra
Adv. Dir .... Brian Moncrief
Ed .... Jennifer Shrader
Sports Ed. .... Kevin Eckleberry
Classified Ads .... Brandi Hockett
Circ. Mgr .... Ed Pugh
Graphic Designer .... Kim Pemberton
Market Information: TMC; Zoned editions.
Mechanical Available: Offset; Black and 3 ROP colors; insert accepted; page cutoffs - 22.
Mechanical Specifications: Type page 13 3/4 x 21 1/2; E - 6 cols, 1 5/6, 1/8 between; A - 6 cols, 1 5/6, 1/8 between; C - 9 cols, 1 3/16, 1/16 between.
Areas Served: 30240
Delivery Method: Mail, Newsstand, Carrier, RacksEquipment & Software: PRESSROOM EQUIPMENT: Lines — 7-G; BUSINESS EQUIPMENT: 1-Bs/90 DISPLAY SOFTWARELayout Software — 3-COM/On-line. EDITORIAL EQUIPMENT: Hardware — COM/One Sys. PRODUCTION EQUIPMENT: Hardware - COM/OS; Cameras — 1-B, 1-C.

MACON

THE TELEGRAPH

487 Cherry St, Ste 100, Macon, Ga., 31201-7992, Bibb; gen tel (478) 744-4200; adv tel (478) 744-4359; ed tel (478) 744-4342; gen fax (478) 744-4385; gen/nat adv e-mail rmcduffie@ledger-enquirer.com; disp adv e-mail rmcduffie@ledger-enquirer.com; class adv e-mailrmcduffie@ledger-enquirer.com; web site www.macon.com - 6,518,872(views) 844,458(visitors)
Group: The McClatchy Company
Published: Mon, Tues, Wed, Thur, Fri, Sat, Sun
Weekday Frequency: m
Saturday Frequency: m
Circulation: 25,399; 25,399(sat); 35,418(sun)
Last Audit: AAM June 30, 2016
Advertising Rate (weekday/saturday): Open inch rate $81.30; $86.50 (Fri/Sat)
Advertising Rate (sunday): Open inch rate $117.80
Online Advertising Rate: ROS - $10cpm
News services: AP, MCT, LAT-WP, HN, NYT, TMS. **Established:** 1826
Own Printing Facility?: No
Commercial Printers?: Yes
Special Weekly Sections: Best Food Day (Wed); Health, Fitness (Mon); Bibb County TMC (Tue); Home, Garden (Thur); Entertainment (Fri); Spiritual Living (Sat); Homes, Travel (Sun)
Digital Platform - Mobile: Apple, Android
Digital Platform - Tablet: Apple iOS, Android, Windows 7, Kindle, Kindle Fire
Exec. Ed. .... Sherrie Maxwell
Adv. Mgr., Classified .... Clero Wright
Exec. Ed. .... Sherrie Marshall
Editorial Columnist .... Charles Richardson
News Ed. .... Oby Brown
News Ed. .... Ben Yoder
Chief, Photography .... Woody Marshall
Sports Ed. .... Daniel Shirley
Sports Columnist .... Michael Lough
Adv. Mgr., Retail .... Lisa Berrian
Interactive Mgr. .... Ryan Gilchrest
Pres./Pub. .... Don Bailey
Vp of Advertising .... Travis Knight
Vp of Advertising .... Lisa Berian
Events and Engagement .... Wendy Martin
Market Information: ADS; Split run; TMC; Zoned editions.
Mechanical Available: Flexographic; Black and 3 ROP colors; insert accepted; page cutoffs - 22.
Mechanical Specifications: Type page 11 3/4 x 21 1/8; E - 6 cols, 1 7/8, 1/8 between; A - 6 cols, 1 7/8, 1/8 between; C - 10 cols, 1 7/100, 1/5 between.
Areas Served: 31201, 31204, 31206, 31210, 31211, 31216, 31217, 31220, 31052, , 31088, 31093 & 98, 31069, 31047, 31028, 31005, 31030, 31008, 31016, 31029, 31046, Part 31220, part 31210, 31044, 31017, 31020, Part 31217, 31032, 31033, Part 31217, part 31052, 31050, 31078, 31066, 31061, 31014, 31023, 31077, 31012, 31009, 31027, 31022, 31021, 31036, 31024, 31031, 31054, 31015, 31091, 31092, 31041, 31057, 31063, 31068, 31011, 31549, 31750, 31539, 31055, 31060, 31001, 31079, 31096, 31002, 30445, 30474, 30457, 30411, , 30642, 31038, 31064, 31087, 31089, 31082, 30204, 30286, 31006, 31016, 31029, 31046,31044, 31017, 31020,31032, 31033, 31052, 31050, 31078, 31066, 31217, 31061, 31014, 31023, 31077, 31012, 31009, 31027, 31022, 31021, 31036, 31024, 31031, 31054,31015, 30642, 31201, 31204, 31206, 31210, 31211, 31216, 31217, 31220, 31052, 31088, 31093, 31098, 31025, 31047, 31028, 31005, 31030, 31008
Delivery Method: Newsstand, Carrier, RacksEquipment & Software: BUSINESS EQUIPMENT: 1-HP/3000 Series 957 BUSINESS SOFTWARE: Microsoft/Excel, Microsoft/Word, Reflections, Monarc, CJ/AIM-CIS CLASSIFIED EQUIPMENT: Hardware — Sun/Ultra Enterprise Servers, APP/ Macs; MON/4550, MON/1270, 2-MON/News Express; Printers — HP/Lasers; CLASSIFIED SOFTWARE: DTI. DISPLAY EQUIPMENT: Hardware — Sun/Ultra Enterprise Servers, APP/Macs; Printers — APP/Mac LaserWriter, HP/Lasers; Other Hardware — MON, ECR/1270, ECR/4550, 2-MON/News Express DISPLAY SOFTWAREAd Make-up Applications — QPS/QuarkXPress, AdSpeed; Layout Software — MEI. EDITORIAL EQUIPMENT: Hardware — DTI, Sun/Ultra Enterprise Servers, APP/Macs/MON/4550, MON/1270, 2-MON/News Express; Printers — HP/Lasers EDITORIAL SOFTWARE: Saxotech PRODUCTION EQUIPMENT: Hardware — 2-MON/1200 News Express, 1-Na/FPII, 3-Glunz & Jensen PRODUCTION SOFTWARE: DTI.

MARIETTA

MARIETTA DAILY JOURNAL

580 S Fairground St SE, Marietta, Ga., 30060-2751, Cobb; gen tel (770) 428-9411; adv tel (770) 428-9411; ed tel (770) 428-9411 ext. 512; gen fax (770) 422-9533; adv fax (770) 428-7945; ed fax (770) 422-9533; gen/ nat adv e-mail mdjnews@mdjonline.com; disp adv e-mail advertising@mdjonline.com; ed e-mail letters@mdjonline.com; web site www.mdjonline.com
Group: Times-Journal, Inc.
Published: Mon, Tues, Wed, Thur, Fri, Sat, Sun
Weekday Frequency: m
Saturday Frequency: m
Circulation: 12,571; 12,571(sat); 13,410(sun)
Last Audit: AAM December 31, 2016
Advertising Rate (weekday/saturday): Open inch rate $26.45
Advertising Rate (sunday): Open inch rate $26.45
News services: AP, SHNS, CNS, LAT-WP, TMS. **Established:** 1866
Special Editions: Lawn & Garden (Apr); Football Preview (Aug); Gift Guide (Dec); Progress (Feb); Year-in-Review (Jan); Fact Book (Jul); Father's Day (Jun); Brides (Mar); Spring Car Care (May); Thanksgiving (Nov); Fall Home & Garden (Sept).
Special Weekly Sections: Lifestyle, TV, Comics, Real Estate, Business, Coupons (Sun); Business (Mon); Food (Thur); Auto, Public Notices, Entertainment (Fri); Religion (Sat)
Syndicated Publications: Going Out (local entertainment) (Fri); USA WEEKEND Magazine (S).
CEO/Pub. .... Otis A. Brumby
Assoc. Pub. .... Jay Whorton
Accounting Mgr. .... Joanne Shivley
Gen. Mgr. .... Lee Garrett
VP, Sales/Mktg. .... Wade Stephens
Mng. Ed. .... Billy Mitchell
Columnist .... Bill Kinney
Columnist .... Dick Yarbourgh
Photo Dept. Mgr. .... Damion Guarnieri
Online Mgr. .... Zuriel Reyes
Prodn. Mgr. .... David Tallmadge
Circ. Dir. .... Matt Heck
Prodn. Mgr., Mailroom .... Pat McClesky
Prodn. Mgr., Pre Press .... Leigh Braddy
Credit Mgr. .... Alice Davis
Mng. Ed. .... J. K. Murphy
Market Information: ADS; TMC.
Mechanical Available: Offset; Black and 3 ROP colors; insert accepted; page cutoffs - 21.
Mechanical Specifications: Type page 11 5/8 x 21; E - 6 cols, 1 5/6, 2/5 between; A - 6 cols, 2, 2/5 between; C - 10 cols, 2/5 between. Equipment & Software: PRESSROOM EQUIPMENT: Lines — 5-MAN/4 x 2 double width 1995; MAILROOM EQUIPMENT: Counter Stackers — 3-HL/Monitor; Inserters & Stuffers — 3/KR; Tying Machines — 4-/ Bu, 2-Si.; BUSINESS EQUIPMENT: 1-IBM/ RSC 6000, Compaq/5500 BUSINESS SOFTWARE: APT, PBS, Quark XPress, Microsoft Word, SBS CLASSIFIED EQUIPMENT: Hardware — Ik; Printers — Panasonic; CLASSIFIED SOFTWARE: Ik. DISPLAY EQUIPMENT: Hardware — 6-PC; Printers — Okidata, Xante; Other Hardware — ECR/Scriptsetter DISPLAY SOFTWAREAd Make-up Applications — QPS/QuarkXPress 4.11, Adobe/Photoshop 7.0, Adobe/Illustrator 10; Layout Software — QPS/QuarkXPress 4.11. EDITORIAL EQUIPMENT: Hardware — Ik/ECR/Scriptsetter; Printers — Okidata, Xante, QMS/6100, QMS/4032, HP/5000 EDITORIAL SOFTWARE: Ik. PRODUCTION EQUIPMENT: Hardware — 1-Konica, EV/ Jetsetter, ECR/Scriptsetter; Cameras — 1-C/ Spartan, 1-C/Spartan III PRODUCTION SOFTWARE: ACT.

MILLEDGEVILLE

THE UNION-RECORDER

165 Garrett Way NW, Milledgeville, Ga., 31061-2318, Baldwin; gen tel (478) 452-0567; adv tel (478) 453-1430; ed tel (478) 453-1450; gen fax (478) 453-1449; adv fax (478) 453-1439; ed fax (478) 453-1459; disp adv e-mail mhinton@unionrecorder.com; class adv e-mailclassifieds@unionrecorder.com; ed e-mail newsroom@unionrecorder.com; web site www.unionrecorder.com
Group: Community Newspaper Holdings, Inc.
Published: Tues, Wed, Thur, Fri, Sat
Weekday Frequency: m
Saturday Frequency: m
Circulation: 7,416; 7,416(sat)
Last Audit: Sworn/Estimate/Non-Audited September 30, 2017
Advertising Rate (weekday/saturday): Open inch rate $15.80
News services: AP.
Special Editions: Football (Aug); Gift Ideas (Dec); Black History (Feb); Focus on Milledgeville (Jul); Home Improvement & Gardening (Mar);

Graduation (May); Gift Guide (Nov); Historic Guide to Milledgeville (Oct).
Special Weekly Sections: Schools (Fri); Family (Sat); Health (Tues); Wedding Planner (Weekly).
Syndicated Publications: TV Magazine (Fri); Relish (Monthly); USA WEEKEND Magazine (Sat).
Pub...................................... Keith E. Barlow
Bus. Mgr. .... Lynda Jackson
Adv. Dir. .... Erin Simmons
Circ. Dir. .... Michael Evans
Mng. Ed. .... Natalie Davis
City Ed. .... Jonathan Jackson
Prodn. Dir. .... Keith Justice
Ed. .... Natalie Davis Linder
Market Information: ADS; TMC.
Mechanical Available: Offset; Black and 3 ROP colors; insert accepted; page cutoffs - 22 3/4.
Mechanical Specifications: Type page 11 3/4 x 21 1/2; E - 6 cols, 1 3/4, 1/8 between; A - 6 cols, 2 1/16, 1/8 between; C - 9 cols, 1, 1/16 between.Equipment & Software: PRESSROOM EQUIPMENT: Lines — 7-G/ Community.; MAILROOM EQUIPMENT: Tying Machines — Bu/Plastic and string.; BUSINESS EQUIPMENT: Canyon Lake Software, Navision, Baseview/Ad Manager-Pro BUSINESS SOFTWARE: Microsoft/ Office 4.0 CLASSIFIED EQUIPMENT: Hardware — APP/Macs; Printers — Xante/8200; CLASSIFIED SOFTWARE: Baseview/Ad Manage Pro. DISPLAY EQUIPMENT: Hardware — APP/Power Mac 9500; Printers — Xante/8200; Other Hardware — HP/IIcx Scanner. DISPLAY SOFTWAREAd Make-up Applications — QPS/QuarkXPress, Aldus/Illustrator, Aldus/ FreeHand, Adobe/Photoshop; EDITORIAL EQUIPMENT: Hardware — APP/Mac; Printers — Xante/8200, Unity/1800 PMR EDITORIAL SOFTWARE: Baseview/NewsEd. PRODUCTION EQUIPMENT: Hardware — Caere/OmniPage Pro 8.0, Pre Press/Panther Plus 46; Cameras — C/Spartan III; Scanners — Lf/Leafscan 35, Polaroid/Sprint ScanPlus, HP/2CX PRODUCTION SOFTWARE: QPS/ QuarkXPress 4.01.

MOULTRIE

THE MOULTRIE OBSERVER
25 N Main St, Moultrie, Ga., 31768-3861, Colquitt; gen tel (229) 985-4545; adv tel (229) 985-4545; ed tel (229) 985-4545; gen fax (229) 985-3569; adv fax (229) 985-3569; ed fax (229) 985-3569; gen/nat adv e-mail laura.rogers@gaflnews.com; disp adv e-mail chris.white@gaflnews.com; ed e-mail dwain. walden@gaflnews.com; web site www. moultrieobserver.com
Group: Community Newspaper Holdings, Inc.
Published: Tues, Wed, Thur, Fri, Sat, Sun
Weekday Frequency: m
Saturday Frequency: m
Circulation: 7,198; 7,198(sat); 7,198(sun)
Last Audit: Sworn/Estimate/Non-Audited September 30, 2017
Advertising Rate (weekday/saturday): Open inch rate $21.05
Advertising Rate (sunday): Open inch rate $29.05
News services: AP. **Established:** 1894
Special Editions: Brides (Apr); Back-to-School (Aug); Progress (Jul); Colquitt Pride (Jun); Home, Lawn & Garden (Mar); Super Mom (May); Agricultural Exposition (Oct); New Car (Sept).
Special Weekly Sections: Real Estate, Business, Comics, Money, TV (Daily); Best Food (Wed); Church (Fri); Comics, TV, Entertainment, Wedding, Engagements (Sun)
Syndicated Publications: Chamber of Commerce Guide (Annually); Relish (Monthly); Parade (S).
Adv. Mgr....................................Chris White
Adv. Mgr., Nat'l/Major Accts...........Laura Rogers
Circ. Dir. .... Andrew Wardle
Pub........................................Dwain Walden
Prodn. Foreman, Composing ... Glenda Apperson
Market Information: TMC.
Mechanical Available: Offset; Black and 3 ROP colors; insert accepted; page cutoffs - 22 3/4.
Mechanical Specifications: Type page 13 x 21 1/2; E - 6 cols, 2 1/16, 1/8 between; A - 6 cols, 2 1/16, 1/8 between; C - 9 cols,

1 1/4, 1/8 between.Equipment & Software: PRESSROOM EQUIPMENT: Lines — 8-G/ Community; Folders - 1-G/2:1.; MAILROOM EQUIPMENT: Tying Machines - 2/Bu; Address Machine — 2-/Wm.; BUSINESS EQUIPMENT: IBM/AS-400 CLASSIFIED EQUIPMENT: Hardware — APP/Mac; CLASSIFIED SOFTWARE: FSI. DISPLAY SOFTWARELayout Software — PBS. EDITORIAL EQUIPMENT: Hardware — APP/ Mac EDITORIAL SOFTWARE: FSI/Edit. PRODUCTION EQUIPMENT: Hardware — 2-Dy/Mark 4, 4-COM/4961, 1-COM/2961, 1-COM/7200; Cameras — 1-C/Spartan II, ECR/Autokon.

NEWNAN

THE NEWNAN TIMES-HERALD
16 Jefferson St, Newnan, Ga., 30263-1913, Coweta; gen tel (770) 253-1576; adv tel (770) 683-1707; ed tel 770-683-1723; gen fax (770) 253-2538; gen/nat adv e-mail colleen@ newnan.com; disp adv e-mail colleen@ newnan.com; class adv e-mailclassifieds@ newnan.com; ed e-mail winston@newnan. com; web site www.times-herald.com
- 400,000(views) 430,000(visitors)
Published: Wed, Thur, Fri, Sun
Weekday Frequency: m
Saturday Frequency: m
Circulation: 9,300; 9,300(sun)
Last Audit: USPS September 30, 2016
Advertising Rate (weekday/saturday): Open inch rate $15.00 p.c.i. net
Advertising Rate (sunday): $15.00 p.c.i. net
Online Advertising Rate: Leaderboard $15/M, Top Rectangle $12/M, Story Tower $9/M
News services: AP. **Established:** 1865
Own Printing Facility?: No
Commercial Printers?: No
Special Editions: Back to School, 50 Things to Do, Vision, Year in Review, Bridal Planner, Football, Chamber Annual Report, Coweta Living
Special Weekly Sections: Community, Education, Religion, Sports, Health, Senior Living, See & Do
Digital Platform - Mobile: Apple, Android
Digital Platform - Tablet: Apple iOS, Android
Pres............................William W. Thomasson
VP............................Marianne Thomasson
Controller...........................Diana Shellabarger
Sales & Marketing Dir. ....Colleen Mitchell
News Ed. ....Winston Skinner
Reporter................................... Kandice Bell
Sports Editor ....Doug Gorman
Reporter .... Neely Clay
Reporter ....Sarah Campbell
Sports Writer ....Jeff Armstrong
Market Information: Times-Herald Xtra/TMC
Mechanical Available: Offset; Black and 3 ROP colors; inserts accepted.
Mechanical Specifications: 6 columns x 20.75"
Areas Served: Newnan, Senoia, Moreland, Sharpsburg, Grantville, Palmetto
Delivery Method: Newsstand, Carrier, RacksEquipment & Software: MAILROOM EQUIPMENT: PC BUSINESS EQUIPMENT: PC CLASSIFIED EQUIPMENT: Hardware — APP/Mac; CLASSIFIED SOFTWARE: Baseview. DISPLAY EQUIPMENT: Mac EDITORIAL EQUIPMENT: Hardware — APP/Mac EDITORIAL SOFTWARE: InDesign PRODUCTION EQUIPMENT: Mac PRODUCTION SOFTWARE: InDesign IT EQUIPMENT: Mac CIRCULATION EQUIPMENT: PC

ROME

ROME NEWS-TRIBUNE
305 E 6th Ave, Rome, Ga., 30161-6007, Floyd; gen tel (706) 291-6397; adv tel (706) 290-5220; ed tel (706) 290-5252; gen fax (706) 290 - 5252; adv fax (706) 235 - 6478; ed fax (706) 234-6478; gen/nat adv e-mail romenewstribune@rn-t.com; web site www. romenews-tribune.com
- 2,266,978(views) 199,685(visitors)
Group: Rome News-Tribune
Published: Mon, Tues, Wed, Thur, Fri, Sat, Sun
Weekday Frequency: m

Saturday Frequency: m
Circulation: 14,921; 14,921(sat); 15,466(sun)
Last Audit: Sworn/Estimate/Non-Audited September 30, 2017
Advertising Rate (weekday/saturday): Open inch rate $26.26
Advertising Rate (sunday): $28.66
News services: NYT, AP, NEA, MCT. **Established:** 1843
Own Printing Facility?: Yes
Commercial Printers?: Yes
Special Editions: Administrative Professionals (Apr); Harmon Football Forecast (Aug); Santas Letters (Dec); Prime Time (Every other month); Review and Forecast (Feb); Bride's World I (Jan); Rome Symphony (Jul); Medical (Jun); Review and Forecast (Mar); Memorial Classified
Special Weekly Sections: Roman Record (Mon); Roman Life (S); Tribune Viewers Guide (Sat); Young Romans (Tues); Best Food Guide (Wed).
Syndicated Publications: Business Tab (Mon); Parade (S); TV/Cable Program Magazine (Sat); Youth Tab (Tues).
Proprietary Publications: Calhoun Times, The Cantoosa County News, The Cedartown Standard, Cherokee County Herald, Fort Oglethorpe Press, The Rockmart Journal, Walker County Messenger
Digital Platform - Mobile: Apple, Android, Windows
Digital Platform - Tablet: Apple iOS, Android, Windows 7
Adv. Dir. .... Cecilia Crow
Mng. Ed. .... Mike Colombo
Sports Ed. .... Jeremy Stewart
Prodn. Dir., Dispatch. ....Tona Deaton
Prodn. Mgr., Press.......................Rob Broadway
Pub........................................Burgett H. Mooney
Dan Mozley
Market Information: Split run; TMC.
Mechanical Available: Offset; Black and 3 ROP colors; insert accepted; page cutoffs - 22 3/4.
Mechanical Specifications: Type page 11 1/2 x 21 1/4; E - 6 cols, 1 5/6, 1/8 between; A - 6 cols, 1 5/6, 1/8 between; C - 9 cols, 1 9/50, 1/16 between.
Areas Served: Rome, Cedartown, Rockmart, Cartersville, Centre , Al, Sumerville
Delivery Method: Mail, Newsstand, Carrier, RacksEquipment & Software: PRESSROOM EQUIPMENT: Lines — 15 unit Dgm 430; MAILROOM EQUIPMENT: Counter Stackers — Stima/Poly Wrap Insert 12.1; Inserters & Stuffers — Newstec/SLS 1000 10:2; Tying Machines — 1-MLN/MLEE; Control System — Prism; Address Machine — KR/ Inkjet, 1-Prism/InkJet Labeling System.; BUSINESS EQUIPMENT: 1-IBM RS6000 BUSINESS SOFTWARE: PBS CM 2.7, PBS/AM 2.8, SBS-GL CLASSIFIED EQUIPMENT: Hardware — Intergraph/ IS 8000 Server, 7-Compaq/2000 DeskPro, Microsoft/NT Server; Printers — HP/5000; CLASSIFIED SOFTWARE: ACT. DISPLAY EQUIPMENT: Hardware — 3-Compaq/2000 DeskPro; Printers — HP/5000; DISPLAY SOFTWAREAd Make-up Applications — QPS/QuarkXPress.; EDITORIAL EQUIPMENT: Hardware - 1-Compaq/ Proliant Server, 27-Compaq/2000 DeskPro/ ACT; Printers — HP/5000 EDITORIAL SOFTWARE: Novell/Network 4.1, Microsoft/ NT 4.0. PRODUCTION EQUIPMENT: Hardware — LaserMaster/1200dpi, ECR/4550, ECR/VRL 36; Scanners — HP/ ScanJet 5P, Nikon/LS-2000, Microtech/ ScanMaker V6000, GEI/Tecsa 5000 Full Page PRODUCTION SOFTWARE: ACT.

SAVANNAH

SAVANNAH MORNING NEWS
1375 Chatham Pkwy, Fl 1, Savannah, Ga., 31405-0304, Chatham; gen tel (912) 236-9511; adv tel (912) 652-0241; ed tel (912) 652-0327; gen fax (912) 525-0796; adv fax (912) 652-0260; ed fax (912) 234-6522; web site www.savannahnow.com; web site 2 http://www.dosavannah.com/
Group: GateHouse Media, Inc.
Published: Mon, Tues, Wed, Thur, Fri, Sat, Sun
Weekday Frequency: m
Saturday Frequency: m

Circulation: 23,858; 23,858(sat); 34,018(sun)
Last Audit: AAM March 31, 2016
Advertising Rate (weekday/saturday): Open inch rate $95.00
Advertising Rate (sunday): Open inch rate $110.00
News services: AP, NEA, MCT, LAT.
Special Weekly Sections: Accent, Exchange, TV, Homes, Real Estate (Sun); Best Food (Wed); Entertainment (Thur); Homes, Real Estate (Sat)
Syndicated Publications: Relish (Monthly); USA WEEKEND Magazine (S).
Digital Platform - Mobile: Apple, Android
Digital Platform - Tablet: Apple iOS, Android
Pub............................Michael Traynor
HR Dir............................Frankie Fort
Adv. Dir............................Randy Mooney
Adv. Mgr., Classified ....Ken Boler
Adv. Mgr., Display ....Cynthia Barnes
Acct. Mgr............................Elena Mitchell
Dir., Mktg./Promo............................Stacy Jennings
Circ. Dir............................Todd Timmons
Circ. Mgr............................David Ellis
Exec. Ed............................Susan Catron
Community Ed............................Steve Corrigan
Editorial Page Ed............................Tom Barton
Editorial Writer...........................Edward Fulford
Educ. Reporter...........................Jenel Few
Environmental Reporter...............Mary Landers
Gov't/Bus. Ed............................Pamela E. Walck
News Planning Ed. ....Stephen Komives
Steve Yelvington
Josh Rayburn
VP, Adv............................Tim Anderson
Nat'l Acct. Rep. ....Kathy Harmon
Market Information: ADS; TMC; Zoned editions.
Mechanical Available: Offset; Black and 3 ROP colors; insert accepted - odd sizes subject to approval; page cutoffs - 22 3/4.
Mechanical Specifications: Type page 11 1/2 x 21 1/2; E - 6 cols, 1 3/4, 3/16 between; A - 6 cols, 1 3/4, 3/16 between; C - 9 cols, 1 1/16, 1/16 between.Equipment & Software: PRESSROOM EQUIPMENT: Lines — 7-G/3176; Folders — 2-G/2:1; Reels & Stands — 7; MAILROOM EQUIPMENT: Counter Stackers — 1-HL/HT-2, 3-TMSI/ Compass 180; Inserters & Stuffers — MM/227, 3-MM/6:1, Heidelberg/632 14:1; Tying Machines — 2-Dynaric/NP-2, 2-Dynaric/NP 1500; Address Machine — 2/ Ch, 1-/KR, Videojet/7000; BUSINESS EQUIPMENT: Gateway 2000 P5-90 BUSINESS SOFTWARE: Microsoft/Excel, WordPerfect, Microsoft/Word CLASSIFIED EQUIPMENT: Hardware — IBM/AT; Printers — IBM/2391; CLASSIFIED SOFTWARE: DTI/Classified 5.0. DISPLAY EQUIPMENT: Hardware — APP/Mac; Printers — APP/ Mac LaserWriter IIg, Tektronix/Phaser III, III/XIT, Clipper/Navigator, HP/1200C; Other Hardware — APP/Mac CD-Rom, Mi DISPLAY SOFTWAREAd Make-up Applications — Multi-Ad/Creator, Aldus/FreeHand, Adobe/ Illustrator, QPS/QuarkXPress, PBS, Adobe/ Photoshop; EDITORIAL EQUIPMENT: Hardware — IBM/AT, APP/Mac 8100-80, APP/Mac IIfx, APP/Mac SE, APP/Mac 8500-100/IBM/Selectric; Printers — HP/4, III/XIT, HP/5000 EDITORIAL SOFTWARE: DTI/Edit 5.2, QPS/QuarkXPress, Adobe/ Illustrator, Aldus/FreeHand. PRODUCTION EQUIPMENT: Hardware — 2-Nu/Flip Top FT40UPNS, AG/Accuset 1500, Nu/ Vacuum plate burner; Cameras — 1-C/ Spartan III; Scanners — Polaroid/SprintScan, Nikon/ScanTouch, Epson/G36, Ag/Studio Star PRODUCTION SOFTWARE: QPS/ QuarkXPress, Archetype/OPI, Adobe/ Illustrator, Adobe/In Des

STATESBORO

STATESBORO HERALD
1 Proctor St, Statesboro, Ga., 30458-1387, Bulloch; gen tel (912) 764-9031; adv tel (912) 764-9031; ed tel (912) 489-9400; gen fax (912) 489-8181; adv fax (912) 489-8181; ed fax (912) 489-9445; gen/nat adv e-mail jmelton@statesboroherald.com; disp adv e-mail jmelton@statesboroherald.com; class adv e-mailppollard@statesboroherald.com; ed e-mail jwermers@statesboroherald.com;

web site www.statesboroherald.com - 540,000(views) 85,000(visitors)
Group: Morris Multimedia, Inc.
Published: Tues, Wed, Thur, Fri, Sat, Sun
Weekday Frequency: m
Saturday Frequency: m
Circulation: 6,700; 6,700(sat); 7,100(sun)
Last Audit: USPS July 10, 2014
Advertising Rate (weekday/saturday): Open inch rate $13.04
News services: AP, The Newspaper Network, SHNS. **Established:** 1937
Own Printing Facility?: Yes
Commercial Printers?: Yes
Special Editions: Bridal (Apr); Community Pride (Feb); Newcomer's Guide (Jun); Home Improvement (Mar); Georgia Southern University New Student Guide (May); Healthy Living (Nov); Best
Special Weekly Sections: TV Tab (S); Community Voice (Thur); Business Tuesday (Tues).
Syndicated Publications: Parade (S); Relish; American Profile; Athlon Sports
Proprietary Publications: Moments Magazine; Connect Statesboro
Digital Platform - Mobile: Apple, Android, Windows, Blackberry
Digital Platform - Tablet: Apple iOS, Android, Windows 7, Blackberry Tablet OS, Kindle
Pub .... James Healy
Regl. Controller .... Jennifer Lewis
Adv. Dir. .... Jan Melton
Adv. Mgr., Classified .... Pamela Pollard
Print Adv. Mgr. .... Kelly Dailey
Circ. Mgr. .... Darrell Elliott
Asst. Ed. .... Eddie Ledbetter
Editor .... Jason Wermers
Operations Manager .... Jim Healy
Market Information: TMC.
Mechanical Available: Offset; Black and 3 ROP colors; insert accepted; page cutoffs - 22.
Mechanical Specifications: Type page 10 1/2 x 21; E - 6 cols, 1 16/25, 1/8 between; A - 6 cols, 1 16/25, 1/8 between; C - 6 cols, 1 16/25, 1/6 between.
Areas Served: 30458;30461
Delivery Method: Mail, Newsstand, Carrier, RacksEquipment & Software: PRESSROOM EQUIPMENT: Lines — 12-G/Community 1993; MAILROOM EQUIPMENT: Counter Stackers — Heidelberg-Harris; Inserters & Stuffers — Alphaliner, 1997; Tying Machines — Signode; BUSINESS EQUIPMENT: Dell CLASSIFIED EQUIPMENT: Hardware — Dell; Printers — HP laserjet 5000; CLASSIFIED SOFTWARE: DTI DISPLAY EQUIPMENT: Other Hardware — Scanners/ printers DISPLAY SOFTWAREAd Make-up Applications — InDesign; Layout Software — 3 Dell Servers EDITORIAL EQUIPMENT: Hardware — Dell/DTI; Printers — HP Laserjet5000 EDITORIAL SOFTWARE: InDesign
Adobe Photoshop PRODUCTION EQUIPMENT: Hardware — Kodak direct to plate PRODUCTION SOFTWARE: InDesign CIRCULATION SOFTWARDTI

THOMASVILLE

THOMASVILLE TIMES-ENTERPRISE

106 South St, Thomasville, Ga., 31792-6061, Thomas; gen tel (229) 226-2400; gen fax (229) 228-5863; gen/nat adv e-mail laura.rogers@gaflnews.com; disp adv e-mail andrew.wardle@gaflnews.com; ed e-mail mark.lastinger@gaflnews.com; web site www.timesenterprise.com - 400,000(views) 75,000(visitors); web site 2 http://m.timesenterprise.com - 90,000(views) 10,000(visitors)
Group: Community Newspaper Holdings, Inc.
Published: Tues, Wed, Thur, Fri, Sat, Sun
Weekday Frequency: m
Saturday Frequency: m
Circulation: 8,293; 8,293(sat); 8,291(sun)
Last Audit: Sworn/Estimate/Non-Audited September 30, 2017
Advertising Rate (weekday/saturday): Open inch rate $22.05
News services: AP.
Own Printing Facility?: No
Commercial Printers?: Yes
Special Editions: Rural Living (Monthly), Health Matters, Home Style, Bridal Scene, Rose City Run
Special Weekly Sections: Church Pages (Fri); Business (S); Weekend Page (Thur); Best Food Days (Tues); Best Food Days (Wed).
Syndicated Publications: Relish (Monthly); Color Comics (S).
Digital Platform - Mobile: Apple, Android, Windows, Blackberry
Digital Platform - Tablet: Apple iOS, Android, Windows 7, Blackberry Tablet OS, Kindle, Nook, Kindle Fire
Pub .... Norman Bankston
Adv. Dir. .... Chris White
Adv. Mgr., Major/Nat'l Accts .... Laura Rogers
Circ. Dir. .... Thomas H. Clements
Mng. Ed. .... Mark Lastinger
Prodn. Mgr. .... Monte Kilcrease
Prodn. Mgr., Composing .... Travis Ouzts
Circ. Dir. .... Andrew Wardle
Market Information: ADS; Split run; TMC; Zoned editions.
Mechanical Available: Offset; Black and 3 ROP colors; insert accepted - free standing; page cutoffs - 22 1/2.
Mechanical Specifications: Type page 13 x 21 1/2; E - 6 cols, 2 1/16, 1/8 between; A - 6 cols, 2 1/16, 1/8 between; C - 9 cols, 1 5/16, 1/8 between.
Delivery Method: Mail, Newsstand, Carrier, RacksEquipment & Software: PRESSROOM EQUIPMENT: Lines — 8-G, 7-G/Community (1 color unit).; MAILROOM EQUIPMENT: Tying Machines — 1-/OVL; Address Machine — 3-Wm/5.; BUSINESS EQUIPMENT: 6-ATT/Business Sys BUSINESS SOFTWARE: WordPerfect 6.0, Lotus 4.1 CLASSIFIED EQUIPMENT: Hardware — APP/Mac.; DISPLAY EQUIPMENT: Other Hardware — APP/Mac. EDITORIAL EQUIPMENT: Hardware — FSI EDITORIAL SOFTWARE: QPS/QuarkXPress, FSI. PRODUCTION EQUIPMENT: Hardware — 1-APP/Mac LaserWriter, Tegra/Varityper, 2-APP/Mac, 1-Mk/AdComp; Cameras — SCREEN/Vertical; Scanners — Lf/Leafscan.

TIFTON

THE TIFTON GAZETTE

211 Tift Ave N, Tifton, Ga., 31794-4463, Tift; gen tel (229) 382-4321; adv tel (229) 382-4321; ed tel (229) 382-4321; gen fax (229) 387-7322; adv fax (229) 387-7322; ed fax (229) 387-7322; gen/nat adv e-mail ttg.editorial@gaflnews.com; disp adv e-mail kitty.stone@gaflnews.com; class adv e-mailkitty.stone@gaflnews.com; ed e-mail ttg.editorial@gaflnews.com; web site www.tiftongazette.com
Group: Community Newspaper Holdings, Inc.
Published: Tues, Wed, Thur, Fri, Sun
Weekday Frequency: m
Circulation: 9,046; 9,046(sat); 9,046(sun)
Last Audit: Sworn/Estimate/Non-Audited September 30, 2017
Advertising Rate (weekday/saturday): Open inch rate $17.62
Advertising Rate (sunday): Open inch rate $17.62
Online Advertising Rate: Banner - $125
News services: AP. **Established:** 1888
Own Printing Facility?: No
Commercial Printers?: Yes
Special Editions: Love Affair Tab (Apr); Back-to-School (Aug); Christmas Greetings (Dec); Love Lines (Feb); Health & Fitness (Jan); Home-owned Business (Jul); Home and Garden (Mar); Mother's Day (May); Holiday Gift Guide (Nov); Shop Early (Oct); Oktoberfest (Sept).
Special Weekly Sections: Entertainment (Sun); Education (Thur); Best Food Day (Wed).
Pub/Adv. Dir .... Dan Sutton
Office Mgr. .... Jetty Tanner
Adv. Mgr. .... Laura Rogers
Adv. Mgr., Retail Sales .... Kitty Stone
Promo. Mgr. .... Melody Cowart
Circ. Mgr. .... Rachel Wainwright
Mng. Ed. .... Angye Morrison
Sports Ed. .... Becky Taylor
Market Information: TMC.
Mechanical Available: Offset; Black and 3 ROP colors; insert accepted - any; page cutoffs - 22 3/4.
Mechanical Specifications: Type page 13 x 21 1/2; E - 6 cols, 2 1/16, 1/8 between; A - 6 cols, 2 1/16, 1/8 between; C - 9 cols, 1 3/8, 1/16 between.
Delivery Method: Newsstand, Carrier, RacksEquipment & Software: PRESSROOM EQUIPMENT: Lines — 6-G/Community; MAILROOM EQUIPMENT: Counter Stackers — BG; Tying Machines — 1/Bu, 1-/Staplex; Address Machine — 2-/Wm.; BUSINESS EQUIPMENT: ATT CLASSIFIED EQUIPMENT: Hardware — Mk/1100.; EDITORIAL EQUIPMENT: Hardware — Mk/1100. PRODUCTION EQUIPMENT: Hardware — 2-Mk/Laserwriter; Cameras — 1-III/Newsprint.

VALDOSTA

VALDOSTA DAILY TIMES

201 N Troup St, Valdosta, Ga., 31601-5774, Lowndes; gen tel (229) 244-1880; gen fax (229) 244-2560; gen/nat adv e-mail vdt.advertising@gaflnews.com; class adv e-mailclassified.marketplace@gaflnews.com; ed e-mail vdt.newsroom@gaflnews.com; web site www.valdostadailytimes.com - 894,677(views) 253,017(visitors)
Group: Community Newspaper Holdings, Inc.
Published: Tues, Wed, Thur, Fri, Sat, Sun
Weekday Frequency: m
Saturday Frequency: m
Circulation: 10,796; 10,528(sat); 12,419(sun)
Last Audit: Sworn/Estimate/Non-Audited September 1, 2017
Advertising Rate (weekday/saturday): Open inch rate $27.30
News services: AP, SHNS. **Established:** 1867
Own Printing Facility?: Yes
Commercial Printers?: Yes
Special Editions: Football (Aug); Cookbook (Jun); Yearbook (Mar); Living Here (Nov).
Special Weekly Sections: Business Page (S); Church Page (Sat); Food Page (Tues).
Syndicated Publications: Relish (Monthly); Parade (S).
Digital Platform - Mobile: Apple, Android, Windows
Digital Platform - Tablet: Apple iOS, Android, Windows 7, Blackberry Tablet OS, Kindle, Nook, Kindle Fire
VP Circ. .... Andrew Wardle
VP Technology .... Hubby Brooks
VP Prodn. .... Vince Cribb
Adv. VP .... Jeff Masters
Controller .... Dan Friedman
Business Mgr. .... Shan Miller
Ed. .... Jim Zachary
Advertising Director .... Theresa Westberry
Market Information: ADS; TMC.
Mechanical Available: Offset; Black and 3 ROP colors; insert accepted; page cutoffs - 22 3/4.
Mechanical Specifications: Type page 11 1/2 x 21 1/2; E - 6 cols, 1 4/5, 1/6 between; A - 6 cols, 1 4/5, 1/6 between; C - 6 cols, 1 13/16, 1/6 between.
Areas Served: 31601, 31602, 31603, 31605, 31606, 31620, 31625, 31629, 31632, 31634, 31635, 31636, 31638, 31639, 31641, 31643, 31645, 31647, 31648, 31649, 31699
Delivery Method: Mail, Newsstand, Carrier, RacksEquipment & Software: PRESSROOM EQUIPMENT: Lines — 16-2000; Folders — 1, 1.; MAILROOM EQUIPMENT: Counter Stackers — 2-MM/(3 station automatic inserter), 2/Sheridan, 2-/Monitors HT, 2-/ Compass 100; Inserters & Stuffers — 2-GMA/ SLS-1000; Tying Machines — 2-Signode, 2-/ PowerStrap, 2-/Samuel; Address Machine — 1-/Kick Rudy; BUSINESS EQUIPMENT: PBS, Oracle CLASSIFIED EQUIPMENT: Hardware — Baseview, APP/Mac; Pre Press/Panther Pro 62; Printers — HP/5000; CLASSIFIED SOFTWARE: Baseview 2.1.1, QPS/QuarkXPress 3.32. DISPLAY SOFTWARELayout Software — QPS/ QuarkXPress, Multi-Ad/Creator. EDITORIAL EQUIPMENT: Hardware — FSI, APP/Mac; Printers — Xante/Accel-A-Writer 8300, Pre Press/Panther Pro 46, Pre Press/Panther Pro 62, Canon/360 PS EDITORIAL SOFTWARE: FSI, QPS/QuarkXPress 3.32, Multi-Ad/ Creator 4.03, Adobe/Illustrator 7, Adobe/ Photoshop 4.0. PRODUCTION EQUIPMENT: Hardware — Nu/FT40V6, Pre Press/ Panther Pro 46, Pre Press/Panther Pro 62; Cameras — 1-LE/121, C, SCREEN/C 680; Scanners — Umax/Mirage, Umax/Mirage II PRODUCTION SOFTWARE: FSI, Multi-Ad/ Creator, QPS/QuarkXPress.

WAYCROSS

WAYCROSS JOURNAL-HERALD

400 Isabella St, Waycross, Ga., 31501-3637, Ware; gen tel (912) 283-2244; gen fax (912) 283-2815; adv fax (912) 285-5255; gen/nat adv e-mail wjhnews@wjhnews.com; disp adv e-mail ads.production@wjhnews.com; ed e-mail newsroom@wjhnews.com; web site www.wjhnews.com
Published: Mon, Tues, Wed, Thur, Fri, Sat
Weekday Frequency: e
Saturday Frequency: e
Circulation: 6,475; 6,475(sat)
Last Audit: Sworn/Estimate/Non-Audited December 19, 2017
Advertising Rate (weekday/saturday): Open inch rate $15.00
News services: AP **Established:** 1875
Own Printing Facility?: Yes
Commercial Printers?: Yes
Special Editions: Football (Aug); Christmas (Dec); Bridal (Feb); Spring (Mar); Cookbook (Oct); Fair (Sept)
Pub .... Roger L. Williams
Adv. Mgr., Nat'l .... Van Carter
Adv. Mgr., Classified .... Debbie Rowell
Business/General Manager .... Donnie Carter
Amusements Ed. .... Scott Cooper
Film/Theater Ed. .... Gary Griffin
Food/Garden Ed. .... Myra Thrift
Photo Dept. Mgr. .... James Hooks
Vice President .... Jack Williams
Circ. Mgr. .... Donna Cox
Mechanical Available: Editorial:QuarkXPress,Photoshop, Adobe Illustrator;Advertising:MultiAd Creator and QuarkXPress;Circulation:IBM
Mechanical Specifications: type page: 12 x 20.25, display adv.: 6 cols.; classified adv. 9 cols.
Areas Served: 31501,31510,31516,31550,31551 ,31552,31564,31650
Delivery Method: Carrier, RacksEquipment & Software: PRESSROOM EQUIPMENT: Lines — 10-unit Goss Community offset press; MAILROOM EQUIPMENT: Address Machine — IBM/Sys 36.; BUSINESS EQUIPMENT: 1-IBM/Sys 54 CLASSIFIED EQUIPMENT: Hardware — 2-Mk/Touchwriter Plus; Printers — APP/Mac LaserPrinter.; DISPLAY EQUIPMENT: Hardware — APP/ Mac; Printers — APP/Mac LaserPrinter; Other Hardware — APP/Mac. DISPLAY SOFTWAREAd Make-up Applications — Multi-Ad/Creator 3.6.1; Layout Software — APP/Mac. EDITORIAL EQUIPMENT: Hardware — APP/Mac, Mk/1100 Plus/1-COM/7200H; Printers — APP/Mac LaserPrinter EDITORIAL SOFTWARE: QPS 3.31. PRODUCTION EQUIPMENT: Hardware — TI/OmniPage 3.1, 1-BKY; Cameras — 1-C/ Spartan III PRODUCTION SOFTWARE: QPS 3.31.

HAWAII

HILO

HAWAII TRIBUNE-HERALD

355 Kinoole St, Hilo, Hawaii, 96720-2945, Hawaii; gen tel (808) 935-6621; adv tel (808) 935-6622; gen fax (808) 935-3680; adv fax (808) 935-9100; disp adv e-mail displayads@hawaiitribune-herald.com; class adv e-mailclassifieds@hawaiitribune-herald.com; web site www.hawaiitribune-herald.com
Group: Oahu Publications Inc.
Published: Mon, Tues, Wed, Thur, Fri, Sun
Weekday Frequency: m
Saturday Frequency: m
Circulation: 13,264; 15,825(sun)
Last Audit: AAM March 31, 2016
Advertising Rate (weekday/saturday): Open inch

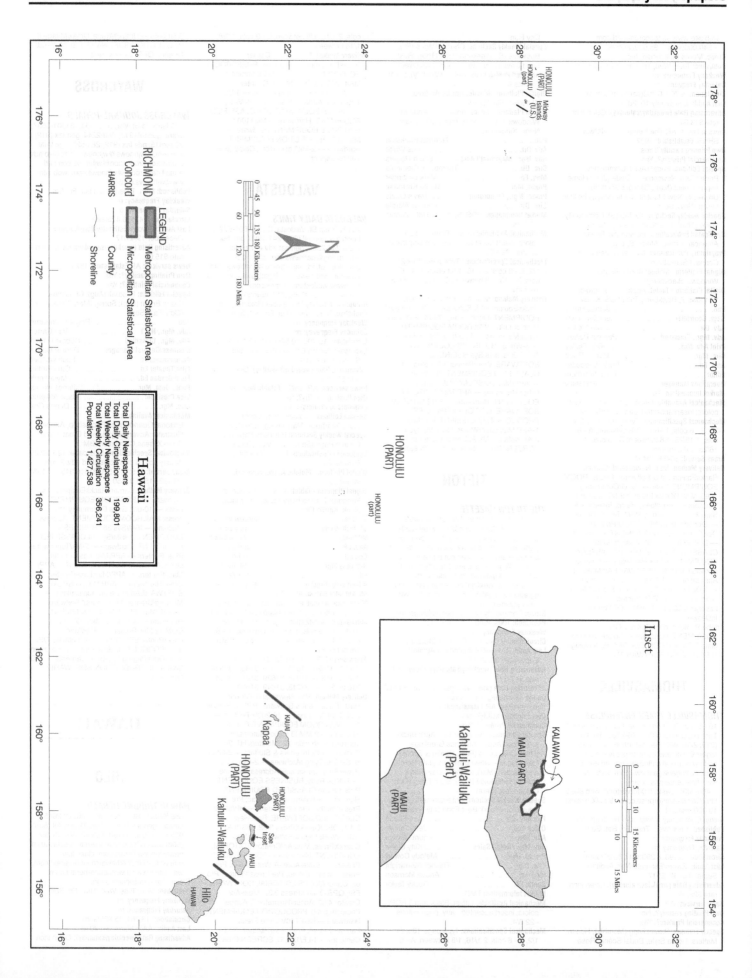

Hawaii

Total Daily Newspapers	6
Total Daily Circulation	199,801
Total Weekly Newspapers	7
Total Weekly Circulation	356,241
Population	1,427,538

LEGEND

RICHMOND — Metropolitan Statistical Area
Concord — Micropolitan Statistical Area

HARRIS — County
— Shoreline

0 45 90 135 180 Kilometers
0 60 120 180 Miles

Inset

Kahului-Wailuku (Part)

MAUI (PART)

KALAWAO

MAUI (PART)

0 5 10 15 Kilometers
0 5 10 15 Miles

HONOLULU (PART)
HONOLULU (part)

Midway Islands (U.S.)
HONOLULU (PART)
HONOLULU (part)

Kapaa
KAUAI
HONOLULU (PART)
HONOLULU (PART)
See Inset
Kahului-Wailuku
MAUI
Hilo
HAWAII

rate $34
Advertising Rate (sunday): Open inch rate $35
Publisher and Editor..........................David Bock
President............................Dennis Francis
Chief Revenue Officer................Dave Kennedy
VP Business Development & Regional Sales....Jay Higa
Systems Manager....................Arian Vierra
Sports Editor.................................Matt Gerhart
Police/Courts Reporter..............John Burnett
County/Government Reporter............Tom Callis
Sports Reporter............................Kevin Jakahi
General Assignment Reporter.....Kirsten Johnson
Health/General Assignment Reporter..Jeff Hansel
Photographer................................Hollyn Johnson
Mechanical Available: Offset; Black and 3 ROP colors; insert accepted; page cutoffs - 21 1/2.
Mechanical Specifications: Type page 12 x 21 1/2; E - 6 cols, 1 7/8, 1/6 between; A - 6 cols, 1 7/8, 1/6 between; C - 9 cols, 1 1/4, 2/15 between.
Delivery Method: Newsstand, Carrier, RacksEquipment & Software: MAILROOM EQUIPMENT: Inserters & Stuffers — MM/227; Tying Machines — Sig LB2330; Address Machine — Videojet 7300; BUSINESS SOFTWARE: MPA CLASSIFIED EQUIPMENT: APP/Mac; Printers — NewGen, HP/1300 CP, Epson/1520, ; CLASSIFIED SOFTWARE: Baseview/Ad Manager Pro. Adicio DISPLAY EQUIPMENT: APP/Mac G3; Printers — Xante/Accel-aWriter; DISPLAY SOFTWAREAdobe/InDesign, Baseview/Ad Manager Pro, Adobe/Photoshop, Adobe/Illustrator; Layout Software - Baseview. EDITORIAL EQUIPMENT: APP/Mac, QPS/QuarkXPress 4.11, Baseview/News Edit Pro 3.2.3/Nikon/LS 1000, Epson/1200 Scanners; Printers — LaserMaster/, APP/Mac, Epson/3000 EDITORIAL SOFTWARE: NewsEngin Adobe/InDesign. CIRCULATION SOFTWARCircPro

HONOLULU

HONOLULU STAR-ADVERTISER
500 Ala Moana Blvd Ste 7-500, Ste 7-500, Honolulu, Hawaii, 96813-4930, Honolulu; gen tel (808) 529-4700; ed tel (808) 529-4747; gen fax (808) 529-4898; ed fax (808) 529-4750; gen/nat adv e-mail displayads@staradvertiser.com; disp adv e-mail displayads@staradvertiser.com; class adv e-mailclassifieds@staradvertiser.com; ed e-mail citydesk@staradvertiser.com; web site www.staradvertiser.com
- 11,717,736(views) 1,437,816(visitors)
Group: Black Press Group Ltd.
Oahu Publications Inc.
Published: Mon, Tues, Wed, Thur, Fri, Sat, Sun
Weekday Frequency: m
Saturday Frequency: m
Circulation: 151,585; 146,366(sat); 165,538(sun)
Last Audit: AAM December 31, 2016
Advertising Rate (weekday/saturday): $193 pci (rates do not include Hawaii General Excise tax of 4.712%)
Advertising Rate (sunday): $243 pci (rate does not include Hawaii General Excise tax of 4.712%)
News services: 2010
Own Printing Facility?: Yes
Commercial Printers?: Yes
Special Editions: Ala Moana (Mar, Jun, Nov) Career Expo (March & Aug) Chamber of Commerce Annual Directory (Dec) Community Support Guide (Oct) Credit Union (Oct) Earth Day (Apr) Easter (Apr) Football Fever (Aug-Jan) Hawaii's Best (Jun) Hawaii Talks (June, Sep, Dec) Holiday Gift Guides (Nov-Dec) Honolulu Pulse Awards (Aug) Keiki Day (May) Military Appreciation (Apr) Nurses Week (May) School Sections (Mar, Jun) Top Restaurants (Oct) University of Hawaii Sports (Aug-May) Young at Heart (Mar & Sep)
Special Weekly Sections: tgif (Fri), Dining Out

(Sun), Hawaii Renovation (Sun), Crave (Wed)
Syndicated Publications: HILuxury, Waikiki Magazine, Go Kailua, Go Kapolei, Aulani (Disney Aulani Resort in-room magazine), Ko Olina, Trump Hookipa (Trump International Hotel in-room magazine), Kahala Life, Aloha Hilton Hawaiian Village, Aloha Waikoloa Village, Castle Resorts Hoonanea, 101 Things To Do, Drive
Digital Platform - Mobile: Apple, Android, Windows
Digital Platform - Tablet: Apple iOS, Android, Windows 7, Blackberry Tablet OS, Kindle, Nook, Kindle Fire
Pres. & Pub...........................Dennis Francis
Chief Revenue Officer................Dave Kennedy
VP/Ed..............................Frank Bridgewater
VP/Tech..............................Roger Forness
VP/Prod...............................Marty Black
VP/Digital Media...................Troy Fujimoto
VP/HR..............................Rebecca Stolar
VP/Controller.........................TC Gray
VP/Advertising......................Patrick Klein
National Adv........................Linda Woo
VP/Circ.............................Aaron Kotarek
VP/Bus. Dev. & Reg. Sales.............Jay Higa
Managing Ed...........................Ed Lynch
Managing Ed./Design..........Michael Rovner
Managing Ed./Prod..............Betty Shimabukuro
Mechanical Available: Offset Presses; Black + 3 ROP Colors; Inserts Accepted - Preprints, Post-it Notes; 70,000 CPM; 6 Sections; Page Cutoff 21".
Mechanical Specifications: Type page 11 x 21; E - 6 cols, 1 - 1/2", 1/8 between; A - 6 cols, 1 - 1/2, 1/8 between; C - 10 cols, 7/8", 3/32"between.
Areas Served: All
Delivery Method: Mail, Newsstand, Carrier, RacksEquipment & Software: PRESSROOM EQUIPMENT: Lines — 6 Towers Man Roland Regioman 2004; 6 Towers Man Roland Regioman 2004; Press Drive — VFD - Shaftless; Folders — KFZ 80 (2-3-3) Jaw Folder System; Pasters —CD-13Reels & Stands — CD-13; Control System — PECOM; Registration System — PECOM MAILROOM EQUIPMENT: Counter Stackers — 4 - Quipp 501 1 - Quipp 401 4 - Muller Martini Combi Stacks; Inserters & Stuffers — 2 - GMA/SLS 2000; Tying Machines — 4-Dynaric NP 3000 4-Dynaric NP 1500; Control System — SAM; News Grip Links; Address Machine — Videojet BX 6500 ink jet printer; BUSINESS EQUIPMENT: Dell/Windows CLASSIFIED EQUIPMENT: Hardware — Dell/Windows; Printers — HP; CLASSIFIED SOFTWARE: ATEX DISPLAY EQUIPMENT: Hardware — Dell/Windows; DISPLAY SOFTWAREAd Make-up Applications — ATEX; Layout Software — QuarkXPress EDITORIAL EQUIPMENT: Hardware — Mac OS X EDITORIAL SOFTWARE: Newsedit Pro PRODUCTION EQUIPMENT: Cameras — Canon

USA TODAY HAWAII EDITION
500 Ala Moana Blvd, Ste 7-500, Honolulu, Hawaii, 96813-4930, Honolulu; gen tel (808) 529-4700; gen fax (808) 529-4898; gen/nat adv e-mail lwoo@staradvertiser.com
Group: Oahu Publications Inc.
Published: Mon, Tues, Wed, Thur, Fri
Weekday Frequency: m
Circulation: 6,794
Last Audit: AAM December 31, 2016
Advertising Rate (weekday/saturday): National $8.00 PCI
News services: 2012
Own Printing Facility?: Yes
Pres. & Pub...........................Dennis Francis
CRO.............................Dave Kennedy
VP Business Development/Regional Sales Jay Higa
VP of Circulation....................Aaron Kotarek
VP of Advertising.....................Patrick Klein
Mechanical Specifications: Type Page 11 x 21; 6 cols 1-1/2", 1/8 between; 5 cols 1-7/8", 1/8 between
Areas Served: All
Delivery Method: Newsstand, Carrier, Racks

KAILUA KONA

WEST HAWAII TODAY
75-5580 Kuakini Hwy, Kailua Kona, Hawaii,

96740-1647, Hawaii; gen tel (808) 329-9311; adv tel (808) 329-2644; gen fax (808) 329-4860; adv fax (808)329-3659; gen/nat adv e-mail kbolyard@westhawaiitoday.com; disp adv e-mail displayads@westhawaiitoday.com; class adv e-mailclassifieds@westhawaiitoday.com; web site www.westhawaiitoday.com
- 448,350(views) 130,558(visitors)
Group: Oahu Publications Inc.
Published: Mon, Tues, Wed, Thur, Fri, Sun
Weekday Frequency: m
Saturday Frequency: m
Circulation: 8,024; 9,993(sun)
Last Audit: AAM March 31, 2016
Advertising Rate (weekday/saturday): Open inch rate $26.00
Advertising Rate (sunday): Open inch rate $29.00
News services: 1968
Own Printing Facility?: Yes
President............................Dennis Francis
Chief Revenue Officer................Dave Kennedy
Advertising Director................Kelly Bolyard
Ed..............................Tom Hasslinger
VP Regional Sales....................Jay Higa
Associate Editor...................Chelsea Jensen
Sports Editor........................J.R. De Groote
County/Gov. Reporter...........Nancy Cook-Lauer
Education Reporter..................Max Dible
Community Reporter............Cameron Miculka
Sports Reporter.....................Rick Winters
Police & Courts Reporter........Tiffany DeMasters
Photographer........................Laura Ruminski
Mechanical Available: Offset; Black and 3 ROP colors; insert accepted - card-70 lbs bound stock; page cutoffs - 22 3/4.
Mechanical Specifications: Type page 11 5/8 x 21 1/2; E - 6 cols, 1 3/4, 3/16 between; A - 6 cols, 1 3/4, 3/16 between; C - 9 cols, 1 3/16, 1/8 between.
Delivery Method: Newsstand, Carrier, RacksEquipment & Software: PRESSROOM EQUIPMENT: Lines — 8-G/Community; Press Drive — 2-Fin/60 h.p.; Folders — 1-G/SC.; MAILROOM EQUIPMENT: Counter Stackers — MM/310; Inserters & Stuffers — MM/227; Tying Machines — 2-MLN/Strapper; Address Machine — 3/Wm.; CLASSIFIED EQUIPMENT: Hardware — APP/Mac; Printers — HP; CLASSIFIED SOFTWARE: Baseview/AdManager Pro, QPS/QuarkXPress. DISPLAY EQUIPMENT: Printers — 2-Xante/Accel-a-Writer 3N; DISPLAY SOFTWAREAd Make-up Applications — Adobe/CS2; Layout Software — 5-APP/Mac G4. EDITORIAL EQUIPMENT: Hardware — APP/Mac; Printers — 1-Xante/Accel-a-Writer 3N EDITORIAL SOFTWARE: Adobe/Illustrator CS2, Adobe/InDesign CS2, Adobe/Photoshop CS2, Baseview. PRODUCTION EQUIPMENT: Hardware — 1-Pre Press/Panther Pro 36-HS, 1-Mon/Ultra 36; Cameras — 1-LE/490 vertical PRODUCTION SOFTWARE: Adobe/CS2.

LIHUE

THE GARDEN ISLAND, KAUAI
3-3137 Kuhio Hwy, Lihue, Hawaii, 96766-1141, Kauai; gen tel (808) 245-3681; gen fax (808) 245-5286; disp adv e-mail displayads@thegardenisland.com; class adv e-mailtgiclassifieds@thegardenisland.com; ed e-mail bbuley@thegardenisland.com; web site www.thegardenisland.com
- 1,654,666(views) 189,544(visitors)
Group: Oahu Publications Inc.
Published: Mon, Tues, Wed, Thur, Fri, Sun
Weekday Frequency: m
Circulation: 6,493; 6,867(sun)
Last Audit: AAM March 31, 2016
Advertising Rate (weekday/saturday): $46.50 pci (rates do not include Hawaii General Excise tax of 4.712%)
Advertising Rate (sunday): $50.50 pci (rates do not include Hawaii General Excise tax of 4.712%)
News services: 1902
Own Printing Facility?: Yes
Commercial Printers?: Yes
Digital Platform - Mobile: Apple, Android, Windows
Digital Platform - Tablet: Apple iOS, Android, Windows 7, Blackberry Tablet OS, Kindle, Nook, Kindle Fire
Pres...........................Dennis Francis

Adv. Dir.................................Jay Higa
Ed..................................Bill Mossman
CRO.............................Dave Kennedy
Circ.............................Christopher Harm
Sales Mgr............................Darwin Rogers
VP, Circ............................Aaron Kotarek
Mechanical Available: Offset Presses; Black + 3 ROP Colors; Inserts Accepted - Preprints; 70,000 CPM; 2 Sections; Page Cutoff 21"; FC capacity on every page.
Mechanical Specifications: Type page 11 x 21; E - 6 cols, 1 - 1/2", 1/8 between; A - 6 cols, 1 - 1/2, 1/8 between; C - 10 cols, 7/8", 3/32"between.
Areas Served: All
Delivery Method: Mail, Newsstand, Carrier, RacksEquipment & Software: PRESSROOM EQUIPMENT: Lines — 6 Towers Man Roland Regioman 2004; 6 Towers Man Roland Regioman 2004; Press Drive — VFD - Shaftless; Folders — KFZ 80 (2-3-3) Jaw Folder System; Pasters —CD-13Reels & Stands — CD-13; Control System — PECOM; Registration System — PECOM MAILROOM EQUIPMENT: Counter Stackers — 4 - Quipp 501 1 - Quipp 401 4 - Muller Martini Combi Stacks; Inserters & Stuffers — 2 - GMA/SLS 2000; Tying Machines — 4-Dynaric NP 3000 4-Dynaric NP 1500; Control System — SAM; News Grip Links; Address Machine — Videojet BX 6500 ink jet printer;

WAILUKU

THE MAUI NEWS
100 Mahalani St, Wailuku, Hawaii, 96793-2529, Maui; gen tel (808) 244-3981; adv tel (808) 242-6363; ed tel (808) 242-6343; gen fax (808) 242-6315; adv fax (808) 242-6390; ed fax (808) 242-9087; gen/nat adv e-mail advmgr@mauinews.com; disp adv e-mail adsales@mauinews.com; class adv e-mailclass@mauinews.com; ed e-mail letters@mauinews.com; web site www.mauinews.com
Group: Ogden Newspapers Inc.
Published: Mon, Tues, Wed, Thur, Fri, Sat, Sun
Weekday Frequency: m
Saturday Frequency: m
Circulation: 13,641, 13,641(sat), 15,565(sun)
Last Audit: AAM March 31, 2017
Advertising Rate (weekday/saturday): Open inch rate $40.25
News services: AP, **Established:** 1900
Own Printing Facility?: Yes
Commercial Printers?: Yes
Special Editions: Back-to-School (Aug);Best of Maui (Sept), Kahului Industrial Area, Christmas (Dec); Bridal Fair (Feb); Outlook (Economic Outlook Tab) (Jan); Maui Contractors Assoc.-Building & Materials Expo (Jun); Graduation (May); First Hawaiian Auto Show (Nov); Aloha Festivals (Oct); Maui Real Estate (Quarterly); Parade
Special Weekly Sections: Real Estate (Fri); Weekly TV Tab (S); Maui Scene (Thur); Super Market Ads (Tues)., Scene Magazine (Entertainment) Thurs.
Syndicated Publications: Parade (S).
Pub.................................Joe Bradley
Adv. Mgr., Retail..................Dawne Miguel
Circ. Mgr............................Chris Minford
City Ed.................................Brian Perry
News Ed.................................Lee Imada
Sports Ed..................................Brad Sherman
Lehia Apana
Market Information: TMC.
Mechanical Available: Offset; Black and 3 ROP colors; insert accepted; page cutoffs - 21"
Mechanical Specifications: Type page 10.25 x19.75"
Areas Served: 96793, 96732, 96753, 96761, 96708, 96714, 96790, 96748
Delivery Method: Mail, Newsstand, Carrier, RacksEquipment & Software: PRESSROOM EQUIPMENT: Lines — 12 DGM Advantage II units; MAILROOM EQUIPMENT: Counter Stackers — MM/TYP 267; Inserters & Stuffers — 1 K&M 14 into 1 inserter; Tying Machines — MLN/Wilton; Address Machine — St.; BUSINESS EQUIPMENT: IBM CLASSIFIED EQUIPMENT: Hardware — PC; CLASSIFIED SOFTWARE: FSI. DISPLAY EQUIPMENT: Hardware —

Macintosh; Printers — HP 5200; DISPLAY SOFTWAREAd Make-up Applications — Ad Force 4. Creator 8; Layout Software — Quark X-Press Macintosh EDITORIAL EQUIPMENT: Hardware — Macintosh/ IMACS for page layout EDITORIAL SOFTWARE: Quark X-Press PRODUCTION EQUIPMENT: Hardware — 2 Kodak Trendsetter CTP units

IDAHO

BLACKFOOT

MORNING NEWS

34 N Ash St, Blackfoot, Idaho, 83221-2101, Bingham; gen tel (208) 785-1100; adv tel (208) 785-1100; ed tel (208) 785-1100; gen fax (208) 785-4239; adv fax (208) 785-4239; ed fax (208) 785-4239; gen/nat adv e-mail jacquegraham@cableone.net; disp adv e-mail wingram@cableone.net; class adv e-mailclass@cableone.net; ed e-mail mnews@cableone.net; web site www.am-news.com
- 102,400(views) 32,000(visitors)

Group: Horizon Publications Inc.
Published: Mon, Tues, Wed, Thur, Fri, Sat
Weekday Frequency: m
Saturday Frequency: m
Circulation: 3,450; 3,450(sat)
Last Audit: Sworn/Estimate/Non-Audited September 30, 2017
Advertising Rate (weekday/saturday): Open inch rate $15.00
News services: AP. **Established:** 1903
Own Printing Facility?: Yes
Commercial Printers?: Yes
Special Editions: Progress (Mar); Outdoors (May/Aug); State Fair (Aug); Seniors (Jul/ Nov).
Special Weekly Sections: Religion News (Fri); Agriculture (Sat); Food Day (Wed).
Syndicated Publications: American Profile (Weekly).
Digital Platform - Mobile: Apple, Android
Digital Platform - Tablet: Apple iOS, Android
Pub. .... Leonard Martin
Adv. Mgr. .... Wayne Ingram
Circ. Mgr. .... Joe Kimbro
Ed. .... Robert Hudson
Sports Ed. .... Jason Ens
Prodn. Mgr. .... Kelly Koontz
Market Information: TMC.
Mechanical Available: Offset; Black and 3 ROP colors; insert accepted; page cutoffs - 22 3/4.
Mechanical Specifications: Image area - 10.12 x 21.5; 6 columns.
Areas Served: Blackfoot, Bingham County and Southeast Idaho
Delivery Method: Mail, Newsstand, Carrier, RacksEquipment & Software: PRESSROOM EQUIPMENT: Folders — KP/KJ-6.; MAILROOM EQUIPMENT: Counter Stackers — 1-BG/Count-O-Veyor; Inserters & Stuffers — MM/227E 2:1; Tying Machines — 2/Bu; Address Machine — 1-/Sp.; BUSINESS EQUIPMENT: PC's BUSINESS SOFTWARE: List Master Systems CLASSIFIED EQUIPMENT: Hardware — Mac Mini's; CLASSIFIED SOFTWARE: Baseview/Ad Pro, Baseview/Classflow. DISPLAY EQUIPMENT: Hardware — Mac Mini's; Printers — PrePress - Two Panter 46 Imagesetters; DISPLAY SOFTWAREAd Make-up Applications — InDesign, Adobe/Acrobat, Adobe/Photoshop, Adobe/Illustrator; EDITORIAL EQUIPMENT: Hardware — Mac Mini's; Printers — Pre Press - Two Panther 46 Imagesetters, HP/5000 Laser. EDITORIAL SOFTWARE: InDesign PRODUCTION EQUIPMENT: Hardware — Mac Mini's - PrePress - Two Panther 46 Imagesetters

BOISE

IDAHO STATESMAN

1200 N Curtis Rd, Boise, Idaho, 83706-1239, Ada; gen tel (208) 377-6200; adv tel (208) 377-6333; ed tel (208) 377-6400; ed fax (208) 377-6224; disp adv e-mail advertising@idahostatesman.com; ed e-mail newsroom@idahostatesman.com; web site www.idahostatesman.com
- 8,405,340(views) 978,726(visitors)

Group: The McClatchy Company
Published: Mon, Tues, Wed, Thur, Fri, Sat, Sun
Weekday Frequency: m
Saturday Frequency: m
Circulation: 38,224; 38,224(sat); 48,882(sun)
Last Audit: AAM June 30, 2017
News services: AP, GNS, LAT-WP, MCT. **Established:** 1864
Own Printing Facility?: No
Commercial Printers?: No
Special Editions: Idaho Private 100 (Oct); Best of Treasure Valley (Sept) Treasure (4x yr)
Special Weekly Sections: Parade (Fri); Scene/ Entertainment (Fri); Automotive (Sat)
Syndicated Publications: Business Insider (Monthly)
Digital Platform - Mobile: Apple, Android
Digital Platform - Tablet: Apple iOS, Android, Kindle, Nook, Kindle Fire, Other
Ed./VP .... Rhonda Prast
Adv. Dir. .... Logan Osterman
Market Information: ADS; TMC
Areas Served: Ada and Canyon County
Delivery Method: Mail, Carrier, RacksEquipment & Software: CLASSIFIED SOFTWARE: DTI. DISPLAY EQUIPMENT: Hardware — APP/ Mac; Printers — HP; Other Hardware — AU/ Oman DISPLAY SOFTWAREAd Make-up Applications — QPS/QuarkXPress 3.32; Layout Software — APP/Mac, QPS/ QuarkXPress. EDITORIAL SOFTWARE: QPS. PRODUCTION SOFTWARE: DTI (classified), QPS/(news).

COEUR D ALENE

COEUR D'ALENE PRESS

215 N 2nd St, Coeur D Alene, Idaho, 83814-2803, Kootenai; gen tel (208) 664-8176; adv tel (208) 664-8176 ext. 3049; ed tel (208) 664-8176 ext. 2000; gen fax (208) 765-4263; adv fax (208) 765-4263; ed fax (208) 664-0212; gen/nat adv e-mail amurdock@cdapress.com; disp adv e-mail kpacker@cdapress.com; class adv e-mailclassifieds@cdapress.com; ed e-mail mpatrick@cdapress.com; web site www.cdapress.com
- 1,005,279(views) 246,834(visitors); web site 2 www.cdapressextra.com

Group: Hagadone Corporation
Published: Mon, Tues, Wed, Thur, Fri, Sat, Sun
Weekday Frequency: m
Saturday Frequency: m
Circulation: ; 21,340(sat); 28,500(sun)
Last Audit: Sworn/Estimate/Non-Audited December 18, 2017
Advertising Rate (weekday/saturday): Open inch rate $24.43
Advertising Rate (sunday): Open inch rate $26.87
Online Advertising Rate: Leaderboard $24.00 CPM (10 to 45 impressions); Banners ROS $16.00 CPM. Will negotiate based on frequency plan
News services: AP, NEA. **Established:** 1887
Own Printing Facility?: Yes
Commercial Printers?: Yes
Special Editions: Real Estate Digest. Live Well Magazine. Big Deals and Values. Living 50 Plus. Inland NW Bridal
Special Weekly Sections: Real Estate (S); Auto Plus (Sat). Health and Food (Wed). Entertainment (F). Outdoors (Thurs)
Syndicated Publications: CDA Magazine (Semi-yearly); American Profile (bi-weekly).
Digital Platform - Mobile: Apple, Android, Windows
Digital Platform - Tablet: Apple iOS, Android, Windows 7, Kindle
Ed. .... Mike Patrick
National Ad. Director .... Aafke Murdock
Classified Adv. Dir. .... Kattie George
Sales Manager .... Kari Packer
Pub. .... Larry Riley
Market Information: TMC; Zoned editions.
Mechanical Available: Offset; Black and 3 ROP colors; inserts accepted.
No Display zoning
Mechanical Specifications: Type page 13 x 21 1/2; E - 6 cols, 2 1/16, 1/8 between; A - 6 cols, 2 1/16, 1/8 between; C - 8 cols, 1 3/8, 1/8 between.
Areas Served: 83814, 83858, 83854, 83835, 83869
Delivery Method: Mail, Newsstand, Carrier, RacksEquipment & Software: PRESSROOM EQUIPMENT: Lines — Goss Magnum ; MAILROOM EQUIPMENT: Counter Stackers — Quipp; Inserters & Stuffers — 2299; Tying Machines — 1-Bu/PP8-6; Control System — OMNICON; Address Machine — 1-Ch/500PM.; CLASSIFIED EQUIPMENT: Hardware — 1-Dy/Cps 300.; EDITORIAL EQUIPMENT: Hardware — 1-Dy/Cps 300. PRODUCTION EQUIPMENT: Hardware — 2-Dy/Cps 300; Cameras — 1-K/Vertical 24.
Note: The North Idaho Sunday serves the five northern counties in Idaho and is a combined effort of three dailies and three weeklies: Coeur d'Alene Press (m), Sandpoint Bonner County Daily Bee (m), Kellogg Shoshone News-Press (m), Priest River Times (w), Bonner

IDAHO FALLS

POST REGISTER

333 Northgate Mile, Idaho Falls, Idaho, 83401-2529, Bonneville; gen tel (208) 522-1800; adv tel (208) 542-6711; ed tel (208) 542-6795; gen fax (208) 522-5790; adv fax (208) 529-3142; ed fax (208) 529-9683; gen/nat adv e-mail dmills@postregister.com; disp adv e-mail bacor@postregister.com; class adv e-mailclassifieds@postregister.com; ed e-mail mlaorange@postregister.com; web site www.postregister.com
- 481,727(views) 72,031(visitors)

Group: Adams Publishing Group, LLC
Published: Tues, Wed, Thur, Fri, Sat, Sun
Weekday Frequency: m
Saturday Frequency: m
Circulation: 18,200; 18,200(sat); 19,000(sun)
Last Audit: Sworn/Estimate/Non-Audited September 30, 2017
Advertising Rate (weekday/saturday): Open inch rate $20.23 (Local); $25.59 (National)
Advertising Rate (sunday): Open inch rate $20.60 (Local); $27.29 (National)
Online Advertising Rate: Inquire.
News services: AP, SHNS, MCT. **Established:** 1880
Own Printing Facility?: Yes
Commercial Printers?: Yes
Special Editions: Progress (Jan); Restaurant Guide (Jan); Health & Fitness (Feb); Home Improvement (Apr); Block by Block (Jul); Mayhem on the Middle Folk (Jun); Upset (May); Perfect Ending (May); 10 Peaks in 10 Weeks (May); In the Woods (Apr); Twice as Nice (Mar).
Special Weekly Sections: Community; Food & Home; Sports; Farm & Ranch.
Syndicated Publications: Parade (S).
Digital Platform - Mobile: Apple, Android, Blackberry
Digital Platform - Tablet: Apple iOS, Android, Kindle, Nook, Kindle Fire
Pub./Ed. .... Roger Plothow
Sales Dir. .... Brett Acor
Asst. Mng. Ed. .... Monte LaOrange
Market Information: ADS; TMC; Zoned editions.
Mechanical Available: Offset; Black and 3 ROP colors; insert accepted - free-standing cards; page cutoffs - 21.
Mechanical Specifications: Contact us.
Areas Served: Eastern Idaho
Delivery Method: Mail, Newsstand, Carrier, RacksEquipment & Software: PRESSROOM EQUIPMENT: Lines — 16-unit Goss Magnum; Pasters —Yes MAILROOM EQUIPMENT: Control System — Goss Omnizone; Address Machine — Yes; BUSINESS SOFTWARE: PBS DISPLAY SOFTWARELayout Software — DTI PRODUCTION EQUIPMENT: Hardware — All CTP
Note: Also own and operate three weekly newspapers and one monthly b-to-b publication with associated web sites.

LEWISTON

LEWISTON MORNING TRIBUNE

505 Capital St, Lewiston, Idaho, 83501-1843, Nez Perce; gen tel (208) 746-8742; adv tel (208) 848-2251; ed tel (208) 848-2269; gen fax (208) 746-1185; adv fax (208) 746-7341; ed fax (208) 746-1185; gen/nat adv e-mail kburner@lmtribune.com; disp adv e-mail cmccollum@lmtribune.com; class adv e-mailhposey@lmtribune.com; ed e-mail dbauer@lmtribune.com; web site www.lmtribune.com

Group: Verstovia Corp.
Published: Mon, Tues, Wed, Thur, Fri, Sat, Sun
Weekday Frequency: m
Saturday Frequency: m
Circulation: 20,626; 20,626(sat); 21,599(sun)
Last Audit: Sworn/Estimate/Non-Audited September 30, 2017
Advertising Rate (weekday/saturday): Open inch rate $18.99
Advertising Rate (sunday): Open inch rate $20.14
Online Advertising Rate: Leaderboard/Skybox $13.00 CPM; In-Story $14.00 CPM
News services: AP, MCT. **Established:** 1892
Own Printing Facility?: Yes
Commercial Printers?: Yes
Special Editions: Balance (Jul); Golden Times (Jul); Highway 12 (Jul); LC Valley Homes (May); Auto Finder (Apr); Students (Apr); Nez Perce Fair (Aug); Christmas Greeters (Dec); Explorations (Feb); Getting Married (Jan); Coupons (Jul); Health Beat (Jun); Spring Car Care (Mar); Agriculture (May); Getting Ready (Nov); At Home (Oct); From House to Home (Quarterly).
Special Weekly Sections: Arts & Entertainment (Fri); Agriculture (Mon); Business (S); Outdoors (Thur); Food (Wed).
Syndicated Publications: Parade (S).
Digital Platform - Mobile: Apple, Android
Digital Platform - Tablet: Apple iOS, Android
Pub./Ed. .... Nathan Alford
Adv. Mgr. .... Kim Burner
Gen. Mgr. .... Fred Board
Mng. Ed. .... Doug Bauer
Controller .... Philip Charlo
Circ. Dir. .... Michael McBride
City Ed. .... Craig Clohessy
Editorial Page Ed. .... Marty Trillhause
Environmental Ed. .... Eric Barker
Garden Ed. .... Jeanne DePaul
Graphics Ed./Art Dir. .... Brian Beesley
Health/Medical Ed. .... Susan Engle
News Ed. .... Bill Furstenau
Pressroom Manager .... Jay Brown
Librarian .... Phyllis Collins
Market Information: TMC.
Mechanical Available: Offset; Black and 3 ROP colors; insert accepted - sample packets; page cutoffs - 22 3/4.
Mechanical Specifications: Type page 12 1/2 x 21 1/2; E - 6 cols, 1 13/16, 1/8 between; A - 6 cols, 1 13/16, 1/8 between; C - 9 cols, 1 1/4, 1/8 between.
Areas Served: 83501 83541 83524 83540 83545 83544 83520 83553 83546 83827 83539 53533 83554 83530 83522 82526 83549 83552 83525 83531 83832 83535 83843/844 83537 83871 83823 83855 83857 83834 83806 83872 83523 83543 83536 83555 99403 99401 99402 99347 99102 99111 99113 99130 66161 99163/164 99179
Delivery Method: Mail, Newsstand, CarrierEquipment & Software: PRESSROOM EQUIPMENT: Lines — Man Roland Uniset 75; Reels & Stands — 4-Roll/ Stand; Registration System — Stoesser/ Register Systems. MAILROOM EQUIPMENT: Counter Stackers — 2-BG/104; Inserters & Stuffers — 2-MM/227E; Tying Machines — 1-MLN/ML2EE; Address Machine — 1/ MG.; BUSINESS EQUIPMENT: Newzware CLASSIFIED EQUIPMENT: Hardware — Pentium I; Printers — HP/1200; CLASSIFIED SOFTWARE: Sybase 11.5, AT/Enterprise, Microsoft/Word 6.0, Microsoft/Word 6.0, AT/Press, Windows NT 4.0. DISPLAY EQUIPMENT: Printers — HP 8000N; Other Hardware — 2-APP/Power Mac DISPLAY SOFTWAREAd Make-up Applications — Microsoft/Windows 98, Aldus/PageMaker 6.5,

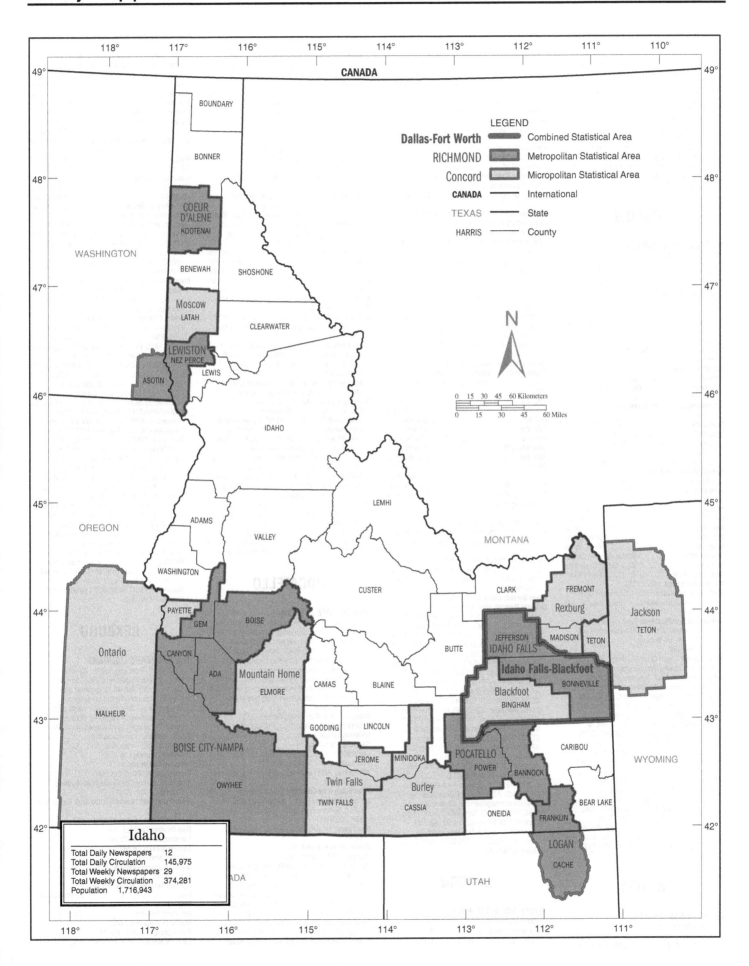

CANADA

49°

BOUNDARY

BONNER

48°

COEUR
D'ALENE
KOOTENAI

WASHINGTON

BENEWAH

SHOSHONE

47°

Moscow
LATAH

CLEARWATER

LEWISTON
NEZ PERCE

LEWIS

ASOTIN

46°

IDAHO

LEGEND

Dallas-Fort Worth — Combined Statistical Area
RICHMOND — Metropolitan Statistical Area
Concord — Micropolitan Statistical Area
CANADA — International
TEXAS — State
HARRIS — County

N

0 15 30 45 60 Kilometers
0 15 30 45 60 Miles

OREGON

ADAMS

LEMHI

VALLEY

MONTANA

WASHINGTON

CUSTER

CLARK

FREMONT

45°

PAYETTE

BOISE

Rexburg

Jackson
TETON

Ontario

GEM

CANYON

JEFFERSON
IDAHO FALLS

MADISON TETON

44°

ADA

Mountain Home

BUTTE

Idaho Falls-Blackfoot

BONNEVILLE

ELMORE

Blackfoot

MALHEUR

CAMAS

BLAINE

BINGHAM

43°

BOISE CITY-NAMPA

GOODING

LINCOLN

CARIBOU

WYOMING

POCATELLO

JEROME MINIDOKA

POWER

BANNOCK

OWYHEE

Twin Falls

Burley

BEAR LAKE

TWIN FALLS

CASSIA

ONEIDA

FRANKLIN

42°

LOGAN

CACHE

Idaho

Total Daily Newspapers   12
Total Daily Circulation   145,975
Total Weekly Newspapers 29
Total Weekly Circulation   374,281
Population   1,716,943

ADA

UTAH

Archetype/Corel Draw 3.0, Microsoft/Word 6.0, Adobe/Photoshop 5.0, Macromedia/ Freehand 7.0, Adobe/Illustrator; Layout Software — SCS/Layout 8000. EDITORIAL EQUIPMENT: Hardware — AT, Compaq/ Windows NT 4.0, Genic/P4 Pentium/ Pentium II, Linix; Printers — HP/5SIMX, HP/8000N EDITORIAL SOFTWARE: QPS 3.3, Microsoft/Windows 98, Dewar/ DewarView, Microsoft/Word 6.0, Sybase 11.5, Novell/Netware 4.11, Windows NT 4.0. PRODUCTION EQUIPMENT: Hardware — 1-B/5KW, 2-Harlequin/RIP, ECRM/VLR, ECRM/5100; Cameras — 1-C/Spartan III; Scanners — 2-HP/Scanner PRODUCTION SOFTWARE: Dewar/View 1.40, QPS/ QuarkXPress 3.31, Microsoft/Word 6.0.

MOSCOW

MOSCOW-PULLMAN DAILY NEWS

220 E 5th St Rm 218, Rm 218, Moscow, Idaho, 83843-2964, Latah; gen tel (208) 882-5561; adv tel (208) 882-5561; ed tel (208) 882-5561; gen fax (208) 883-8205; adv fax (208) 883-8205; ed fax (208) 883-8205; gen/nat adv e-mail ad@dnews.com; disp adv e-mail ad@dnews.com; class adv e-mailclass@dnews.com; ed e-mail editor@dnews.com; web site www.dnews.com
Group: Verstovia Corp.
Published: Mon, Tues, Wed, Thur, Fri, Sat
Weekday Frequency: m
Saturday Frequency: m
Circulation: 6,140; 6,500(sat)
Last Audit: Sworn/Estimate/Non-Audited September 30, 2017
Advertising Rate (weekday/saturday): Open inch rate $13.24
News services: AP, SHNS. **Established:** 1911
Special Editions: Tax Help (Apr); Fall Ag (Aug); Bridal (Feb); Brides (Jan); Agriculture (Mar); Mother's Day (May); Christmas Opening (Nov); Brides (Oct); Football (Sept).
Special Weekly Sections: Slice of Life (Sat); Arts & Entertainment (Thur); Business (Sat).
Syndicated Publications: USA Weekend (Weekly).
Pub./Ed. .... Nathan Alford
Gen. Mgr. .... Fred Board
Adv. Mgr. .... Craig Staszkow
Circ. Mgr. .... Mike McBride
News Ed. .... Alan Solan
Sports Editor .... Michael-Shawn Dugar
Photo Ed. .... Geoff Crimmins
Managing Editor .... Lee Rozen
Market Information: ADS; TMC.
Mechanical Available: Offset; Black and 3 ROP colors; insert accepted - all; page cutoffs - 22 3/4.
Mechanical Specifications: Type page 13 x 21 1/2; E - 6 cols, 2 1/16, 1/8 between; A - 6 cols, 2 1/16, 1/8 between; C - 9 cols, 1 3/8, 1/16 between.
Areas Served: Latah County, Idaho, and Whitman County, Washington
Delivery Method: Mail, Newsstand, Carrier, RacksEquipment & Software: PRESSROOM EQUIPMENT: Lines — 5-HI/Cotrell V-25; Reels & Stands — 4-HI/Cotrell.; MAILROOM EQUIPMENT: Counter Stackers — 7-KAN/480; Tying Machines — 1-MLN/ ML2EE.; BUSINESS EQUIPMENT: CDS CLASSIFIED EQUIPMENT: Hardware — APP/Macs; DISPLAY EQUIPMENT: Hardware — APP/Macs; Printers — QMS/ Laser Printers; DISPLAY SOFTWAREAd Make-up Applications — QPS; Layout Software — APP/Macs. EDITORIAL EQUIPMENT: Hardware — APP/Macs; Printers — QMS, HP, Xante EDITORIAL SOFTWARE: QPS. PRODUCTION EQUIPMENT: Hardware — QMS, Adobe/ Photoshop; Cameras — SCREEN; Scanners — Lf, Microtek PRODUCTION SOFTWARE: QPS.

NAMPA

IDAHO PRESS-TRIBUNE

1618 N Midland Blvd, Nampa, Idaho, 83651-1751, Canyon; gen tel (208) 467-9251; adv tel (208) 465-8149; ed tel (208) 465-8124; gen fax (208) 467-9562; adv fax (208) 467-1863; ed fax (208) 467-9562; gen/nat adv e-mail asammons@idahopress.com; disp adv e-mail svogel@idahopress.com; class adv e-mailclassifieds@idahopress.com; ed e-mail vholbrook@idahopress.com; web site www.idahopress.com
Group: Pioneer Newspapers Inc
Published: Mon, Tues, Wed, Thur, Fri, Sat, Sun
Weekday Frequency: m
Saturday Frequency: m
Circulation: 17,277; 17,277(sat); 21,457(sun)
Last Audit: CAC June 30, 2015
Advertising Rate (weekday/saturday): Open inch rate $19.95
Advertising Rate (sunday): Open inch rate $22.95
Online Advertising Rate: Leaderboard $18.00 CPM; Bottom Banner $15.00 CPM; Big Box $25.00 CPM
News services: AP, SHNS. **Established:** 1883
Own Printing Facility?: Yes
Commercial Printers?: Yes
Special Editions: Today's Woman (May); Snake River Stampede 2013 (Jul); Homemakers School (Apr); Caldwell Night Rodeo (Aug); Holiday Gift Guide (Dec); Cavalcade (Feb); Newcomer's Guide (Jul); Graduation (Jun); Mom of the Year (May); Holiday Delights (Nov); Get Ready for Winter (Oct); Healthy Living (Sept).
Special Weekly Sections: M.O.R.E. (Fri); Health Page (Mon); Family (S); Religion (Sat); Movie Review (Thur); People (Wed).
Syndicated Publications: Relish (Monthly); Parade (S).
Digital Platform - Mobile: Apple, Android
Digital Platform - Tablet: Apple iOS, Android, Windows 7, Kindle, Nook, Kindle Fire
Pub. .... Matt Davison
Mng. Ed. .... Scott McIntosh
Adv. Dir. .... Stacy Vogel
Adv. Mgr .... Michelle Robinson
Adv. Mgr. .... Angela Sammons
Bus. Mgr. .... Rhonda McMurtrie
Advertising Manager .... Erik Franks
Asst. Mng. Ed. .... David Woosley
Community Ed. .... Kaye Steffler
Sports Ed. .... Tom Fox
Prodn. Dir., Mailroom .... Joe Hansen
Prodn. Dir., Press .... Daniel Paris
Advertising Director
Sean Evans
Market Information: ADS; TMC.
Mechanical Available: Offset; Black and 3 ROP colors; insert accepted - almost all; page cutoffs - 21 1/2.
Mechanical Specifications: Type page 12 1/2 x 20 1/2; E - 6 cols, 2 1/16, 1/8 between; A - 6 cols, 2 1/16, 1/8 between; C - 9 cols, 1 3/8, 1/16 between.
Areas Served: Canyon County
Delivery Method: Mail, Newsstand, Carrier, RacksEquipment & Software: PRESSROOM EQUIPMENT: Lines — 16-DGM/440.; MAILROOM EQUIPMENT: Counter Stackers — Schur; Tying Machines — 1-MLN/ML2-EE, Si/LB-News 3000; BUSINESS EQUIPMENT: Sun/Ultrabox BUSINESS SOFTWARE: Media Plus, PBS, SBS CLASSIFIED EQUIPMENT: Hardware — APP/Mac Quadra 630; Printers — APP/Mac ImageWriter, Okidata/320; CLASSIFIED SOFTWARE: Baseview/ Class Manager 3.2. DISPLAY EQUIPMENT: Hardware — 4-APP/Mac IIci, 1-APP/Mac IIfx, 3-APP/Mac Classic, 1-Sun/Sparc ELC.; EDITORIAL EQUIPMENT: Hardware — APP/Power Mac 8100-80, APP/Mac G3, APP/Mac G4, APP/iMacPrinters — 2-AG/ Accuset 1100 EDITORIAL SOFTWARE: Baseview/NewsEdit Pro 2.0. PRODUCTION EQUIPMENT: Hardware — 1-Nu/Flip Top FT 40LNS, AG/P-3400, PS/Laserprinter, 2-Accuset/Imagesetters; Cameras — 2-SCREEN/680C, Sony/MVC-2000 Digital, Canon/RV301-Digital, QuickTake 150; Scanners — APP/Mac, Polaroid/Neg Scanner PRODUCTION SOFTWARE: QPS/ QuarkXPress 4.0.

OSBURN

SHOSHONE NEWS-PRESS

620 E Mullan, Osburn, Idaho, 83849, Shoshone; gen tel (208) 783-1107; adv tel (208) 783-1107; ed tel (208) 783-1107; gen fax (208) 784-6791; adv fax (208) 784-6791; ed fax (208) 784-6791; gen/nat adv e-mail kalexander@shoshonenewspress.com; disp adv e-mail kalexander@shoshonenewspress.com; class adv e-mailkalexander@shoshonenewspress.com; ed e-mail ddrewry@shoshonenewspress.com; web site www.shoshonenewspress.com
Group: Hagadone Corporation
Published: Tues, Wed, Thur, Fri, Sat, Sun
Weekday Frequency: m
Saturday Frequency: m
Circulation: ; 3,315(sat); 28,500(sun)
Last Audit: Sworn/Estimate/Non-Audited September 30, 2017
Advertising Rate (weekday/saturday): Open inch rate $14.66
News services: AP, NEA. **Established:** 1897
Special Editions: Progress (Other).
Special Weekly Sections: Best Food Days (Wed);
Syndicated Publications: Relish (Monthly); The North Idaho Advertiser (Other); Visitor's Guide Tab (Thur); American Profile (Weekly).
Adv. Specialist .... Linn Reese
Assistant Adv. Dir. .... Amber Kitt
Ed. .... Kelsey Saintz
Interim Ed. .... Zak Failla
Mgr./Adv. Dir. .... Keri Alexander
Marketing Consultant .... Jennifer Smith
Market Information: TMC.
Mechanical Available: Offset; Black and 3 ROP colors; insert accepted - any; page cutoffs - 22 3/4.
Mechanical Specifications: Type page 13 x 21 1/2; E - 6 cols, 2 1/16, 1/8 between; A - 6 cols, 2 1/16, 1/8 between; C - 8 cols, 1 1/2, 1/16 between.
Areas Served: Shoshone County and Cataldo/ Medimont areas in Kootenai County
Delivery Method: Mail, Newsstand, CarrierEquipment & Software: PRESSROOM EQUIPMENT: Lines — 4-G/ Community; Folders — 1-G/Community.; MAILROOM EQUIPMENT: Tying Machines — 1/It; Address Machine — 2-/Am.; BUSINESS EQUIPMENT: 2-DEC/UT220 B2 CLASSIFIED EQUIPMENT: Hardware — 1-APP/Mac SE30.; EDITORIAL EQUIPMENT: Hardware — APP/Mac SE30. PRODUCTION EQUIPMENT: Hardware — 1-Nu.
Note: The North Idaho Sunday serves the five northern counties in Idaho and is a combined effort of three dailies and three weeklies: Coeur d'Alene Press (m), Sandpoint Bonner County Daily Bee (m), Shoshone News-Press (m), Priest River Times (w), Bonners Ferry

POCATELLO

IDAHO STATE JOURNAL

305 S Arthur Ave, Pocatello, Idaho, 83204-3306, Bannock; gen tel (208) 232-4161; adv tel (208) 239-3151; ed tel (208) 239-3121; gen fax (208) 233-8007; adv fax (208) 233-1642; ed fax (208) 233-8007; gen/nat adv e-mail lshutes@journalnet.com; disp adv e-mail kclements@journalnet.com; class adv e-mailstubbs@journalnet.com; ed e-mail ifennell@journalnet.com; web site www.journalnet.com
Group: Adams Publishing Group, LLC
Published: Tues, Wed, Thur, Fri, Sat, Sun
Weekday Frequency: m
Saturday Frequency: m
Circulation: 13,337; 13,337(sat); 14,755(sun)
Last Audit: CAC June 30, 2015
Advertising Rate (weekday/saturday): Open inch rate $29.50
Advertising Rate (sunday): Open inch rate $30.85
Online Advertising Rate: Leaderboard $18.00 CPM; Bottom Banner $15.00 CPM; Big Box $25.00 CPM
News services: AP, MCT, SHNS. **Established:** 1890
Own Printing Facility?: Yes
Commercial Printers?: Yes
Special Editions: Summer Recreation (Jun); Yesteryear (Dec); Family Living (Monthly); Flourish (Monthly); Medical Guide (Apr); 101 Things to Do in Pocatello (Dec); Tis the Season (Nov); At Home (Apr); Bridal Guide 2013 (Jun); Park & Recreation (Apr).
Special Weekly Sections: Church (Fri); Youth Page (Mon); HomeLife (Sat); Escapes (Thur); Teen Page (Tues); Best Food Day (Wed).
Syndicated Publications: Parade (S); TV Journal (Sat).
Digital Platform - Mobile: Apple, Android
Digital Platform - Tablet: Apple iOS, Android, Windows 7, Kindle, Nook, Kindle Fire
Pub. .... Andy Pennington
Bus. Mgr. .... Henry Johnson
Adv. Dir. .... Michele True
Classified Adv. Mgr. .... Susie Tubbs
General Sales Mgr. .... Linda Shutes
Circ. Dir. .... Nathan Slater
Circ. Mgr., Newspapers in Educ./Sales .... Matthew Plooster
Mng. Ed. .... Ian Fennell
City Ed. .... John O'Connell
Community Editor .... Jodeane Albright
Photo Ed. .... Doug Lindley
Sports Ed. .... Tim Flagstad
Dir., Info Tech Servs. .... Justin Smith
Market Information: ADS; TMC.
Mechanical Available: Offset; Black and 3 ROP colors; insert accepted; page cutoffs - 22 3/4.
Mechanical Specifications: Type page 13 x 21 1/2; E - 6 cols, 2 1/16, 1/8 between; A - 6 cols, 2 1/16, 1/8 between; C - 9 cols, 1 3/8, 1/16 between.
Areas Served: Pocatello, American Falls, Blackfoot, Inkom, Chubbuck, Fort Hall, Lava Hot Springs, Downey, McCammon, Soda Springs, Malad, and Preston
Delivery Method: Mail, Newsstand, Carrier, RacksEquipment & Software: PRESSROOM EQUIPMENT: Lines — 7-G/Urbanite single width 1968; Folders — 1-G/5000; Registration System — Duarte/Punch System. MAILROOM EQUIPMENT: Counter Stackers — 1/BG; Inserters & Stuffers — 2-MM/217E; Tying Machines — 2-Si; BUSINESS EQUIPMENT: Sun/Sparc fileserver BUSINESS SOFTWARE: PBS CLASSIFIED EQUIPMENT: Hardware — APP/Mac; Printers — APP/Mac ImageWriter II, HP/ LaserJet 4M; CLASSIFIED SOFTWARE: Baseview. DISPLAY EQUIPMENT: Printers — APP/Mac Laser Writer IIg, HP/Color LaserJet 4500; Other Hardware — Nikon/ Coolscan, Microtek/Scanners, Epson/ Scanners DISPLAY SOFTWAREAd Make-up Applications — QPS/QuarkXPress 4.0, Adobe/Illustrator 6.0, Adobe/Photoshop 5.0; Layout Software — 1-APP/Power Mac 7200, 2-APP/Power Mac 750 EDITORIAL EQUIPMENT: Hardware — APP/Mac; Printers — HP/4M-2, HP/LaserJet 5000 EDITORIAL SOFTWARE: Baseview/ NewsEdit, QPS/QuarkXPress 3.32. PRODUCTION EQUIPMENT: Hardware — AG/Accuset 1000, Graham M28; Cameras — 1-K, 1-Argile/16 x 23; Scanners — Nikon PRODUCTION SOFTWARE: QPS/ QuarkXPress 4.0.

REXBURG

THE STANDARD-JOURNAL

23 S 1st E, Rexburg, Idaho, 83440-1901, Madison; gen tel (208) 356-5441; gen fax (208) 356-8312; gen/nat adv e-mail sanderson@uvsj.com; disp adv e-mail sjads@uvsj.com; class adv e-mailclassifieds@uvsj.com; ed e-mail editor@uvsj.com; web site www.uvsj.com
Group: Pioneer Newspapers Inc
Published: Tues, Thur, Sat, Sun
Weekday Frequency: e
Saturday Frequency: m
Circulation: 5,000; 5,000(sat)
Last Audit: Sworn/Estimate/Non-Audited September 30, 2017
Advertising Rate (weekday/saturday): Open inch rate $14.00
News services: AP **Established:** 1881
Own Printing Facility?: Yes
Commercial Printers?: Yes
Special Weekly Sections: Parade; Food; Entertainment.
Digital Platform - Mobile: Apple, Android, Windows
Digital Platform - Tablet: Apple iOS
Pub. .... Scott Anderson
Mng. Ed. .... Mike Henneke
Audience Dev. Dir. .... Jeremy Cooley
Market Information: TMC
Areas Served: 83440, 83445
Delivery Method: Mail, Newsstand, Carrier

SANDPOINT

BONNER COUNTY DAILY BEE

310 Church St, Sandpoint, Idaho, 83864-1345, Bonner; gen tel (208) 263-9534; gen fax (208) 263-9091; gen/nat adv e-mail jmckiernan@bonnercountydailybee.com; disp adv e-mail jmckiernan@bonnercountydailybee.com; class adv e-mailctraver@cdapress.com; ed e-mail clobsinger@bonnercountydailybee.com; web site www.bonnercountydailybee.com - 211,000(views) 42,600(visitors)
Group: Hagadone Corporation
Published: Tues, Wed, Thur, Fri, Sat, Sun
Weekday Frequency: m
Saturday Frequency: m
Circulation: 5,500; 5,537(sat); 28,500(sun)
Last Audit: USPS October 1, 2015
Advertising Rate (weekday/saturday): Open inch rate $13.76
Advertising Rate (sunday): Open inch rate $13.76
Online Advertising Rate: All ad positions $10/cpm
News services: AP. **Established:** 1966
Own Printing Facility?: Yes
Commercial Printers?: Yes
Special Editions: Progress (Apr); Neighbors (Monthly); Real Estate Guide (Monthly); Spring (Mar); Resource Guide (May); Chamber Directory (Sept) Winter Sports (Nov)
Syndicated Publications: Relish (Monthly); American Profile (Weekly).
Digital Platform - Mobile: Apple, Android, Windows
Digital Platform - Tablet: Apple iOS, Android, Windows 7, Kindle, Nook, Kindle Fire
News Ed. .... Keith Kinnaird
News Room Ed. .... Caroline Lobsinger
Sports Ed. .... Eric Plummer
Business Mgr. .... Sheri Jones
Publisher .... Jim McKiernan
Market Information: Local Deals - Reaches 9400 non subscribers
Mechanical Available: Offset; Black and 3 ROP colors; insert accepted; page cutoffs - 22 3/4.
Mechanical Specifications: Type page 13 x 21 1/2; E - 6 cols, 2 1/16, 1/8 between; A - 6 cols, 2 1/16, 1/8 between; C - 8 cols, 1 5/8, 1/8 between.
Areas Served: Bonner County, Boundary County and Northern Idaho and Western Montana.
Delivery Method: Newsstand, Carrier, RacksEquipment & Software: MAILROOM EQUIPMENT: Address Machine — 1/St.; BUSINESS EQUIPMENT: CIT CLASSIFIED EQUIPMENT: Hardware — APP/Mac SE.; EDITORIAL EQUIPMENT: Hardware — APP/Mac SE. PRODUCTION EQUIPMENT: Hardware — DP.
Note: The North Idaho Sunday serves the five northern counties in Idaho and is a combined effort of three dailies and three weeklies: Coeur d'Alene Press (m), Bonner County Daily Bee (m), Kellogg Shoshone News-Press (m), Priest River Times (w), Bonners Ferry He

TWIN FALLS

THE TIMES-NEWS

132 Fairfield St W, Twin Falls, Idaho, 83301-5492, Twin Falls; gen tel (208) 733-0931; gen fax (208) 734-5538; gen/nat adv e-mail clapp@magicvalley.com; disp adv e-mail debi.perkins@magicvalley.com; class adv e-mailapackham@magicvalley.com; ed e-mail mchristensen@magicvalley.com; web site www.magicvalley.com - 2,800,000(views) 575,000(visitors)
Group: Lee Enterprises, Inc.
Published: Mon, Tues, Wed, Thur, Fri, Sat, Sun
Weekday Frequency: m
Saturday Frequency: m
Circulation: 18,221; 18,221(sat); 16,361(sun)
Last Audit: AAM September 30, 2015
Branch Offices: 1510 Overland Ave. Burley, Id 83318
Advertising Rate (weekday/saturday): Open inch rate $28.35
News services: AP, WP-Bloomberg **Established:** 1904
Own Printing Facility?: Yes
Commercial Printers?: Yes
Special Editions: Football Tab (Aug) Readers Choice (Jun)
Special Weekly Sections: Entertainment (Fri); Business (Tues); Church Page (Sat); Outdoors (Thurs); Food (Wed); Ag (Mon)
Syndicated Publications: TV Magazine (Sun); Parade (Sun)
Proprietary Publications: The Voice Magic Valley Messenger
Digital Platform - Mobile: Apple, Android, Windows, Blackberry
Digital Platform - Tablet: Apple iOS, Android, Windows 7, Blackberry Tablet OS, Kindle, Nook, Kindle Fire
Pub. .... Travis Quast
Sports Ed. .... Matt Christensen
Market Information: ADS; Split run; TMC; Zoned editions.
Mechanical Available: Offset; Black and 3 ROP colors; insert accepted; page cutoffs - 21 1/2.
Mechanical Specifications: Type page 12 1/2 x 21 1/2; E - 6 cols, 2 1/16, 1/8 between; A - 6 cols, 2 1/16, 1/8 between; C - 9 cols, 1 3/8, 1/16 between.
Areas Served: Southern Idaho / Magic Valley 8-county region
Delivery Method: Mail, Newsstand, Carrier, RacksEquipment & Software: PRESSROOM EQUIPMENT: Lines — 7-G/Urbanite (Cole/3 Knife trimmer); 1-G/Urbanite color deck; Folders — 1, 1-G/quarter folder; Control System — 2-Fin/control, 2-DC Motors/100 h.p..; MAILROOM EQUIPMENT: Counter Stackers — 1-HL/Monitors; Inserters & Stuffers — MM/227; Tying Machines — MLN; Wrapping Singles — Id; BUSINESS EQUIPMENT: Sun/Sparc, Compaq CLASSIFIED EQUIPMENT: Hardware — Sun; PC 4-286DG; Printers — APP/Mac LaserPrinters; CLASSIFIED SOFTWARE: Lotus/Notes 4.6. DISPLAY EQUIPMENT: Hardware — APP/Mac G4; Printers — 1-Linotype-Hell/Linotronic 500, ECR/Pelbox, APP/Mac LaserWriters; DISPLAY SOFTWAREAd Make-up Applications — QPS/QuarkXPress; Layout Software — APP/Mac G4. EDITORIAL EQUIPMENT: Hardware — Sun, Mk; Printers — 1-Linotype-Hell/Linotronic 500, ECR/Pelbox, APP/Mac LaserPrinter EDITORIAL SOFTWARE: Lotus/Notes 4.6. PRODUCTION EQUIPMENT: Hardware — ECR/Pelbox, Linotype-Hell/Linotronic 500, APP/Mac LaserWriter; Cameras — Canon; Scanners — Truvell, Nikon.

ILLINOIS

ALTON

THE TELEGRAPH

111 E Broadway, Alton, Ill., 62002-6218, Madison; gen tel (618) 463-2500; adv tel (618) 463-2527; ed tel (618) 463-2551; gen fax (618) 463-9829; adv fax (618) 463-2544; ed fax (618) 463-2578; gen/nat adv e-mail bmarkham@civitasmedia.com; disp adv e-mail bmarkham@civitasmedia.com; class adv e-mailjuliejones@civitasmedia.com; ed e-mail ngrimm@civitasmedia.com; web site www.thetelegraph.com - 1,882,352(views) 308,536(visitors)
Group: Civitas Media, LLC-OOB
Published: Mon, Tues, Wed, Thur, Fri, Sat, Sun
Weekday Frequency: m
Saturday Frequency: m
Circulation: 12,003; 12,003(sat); 14,910(sun)
Last Audit: AAM September 30, 2015
Advertising Rate (weekday/saturday): Open inch rate $45.33
Advertising Rate (sunday): Open inch rate $48.45
News services: AP, NEA, SHNS. **Established:** 1836
Own Printing Facility?: Yes
Commercial Printers?: No
Special Editions: Senior Living (Apr); Back-to-School (Aug); Wrap it Up (Dec); Focus (Feb); Brides & Grooms (Jan); Bridal Guide (Jul); The Guide (Jun); Home Improvement (Mar); Heroes (May); Holiday Dining (Nov); Car Care (Oct); Fall Home Improvement (Sept).
Special Weekly Sections: Best Food Day (Wed); Entertainment (Thur); TV (Sun)
Syndicated Publications: Parade (S); American Profile (Weekly).
Digital Platform - Mobile: Apple, Android
Digital Platform - Tablet: Apple iOS, Android
Photo Dept. Mgr. .... John Badman
Pub. .... James E. Shrader
Asst. Sports Ed. .... Greg Shashack
Mng. Ed. .... Nathan Grimm
Advertising Director .... Bonnie Markham
Circ. Dir .... Jill Sinkclear
Market Information: Zoned editions.
Mechanical Available: Offset; Black and 3 ROP colors; insert accepted - spadeas, free-standing insert; page cutoffs - 21 3/8.
Mechanical Specifications: Type page 9 7/8 x 22 1/2; E - 6 cols, 1.54", .125" between; A - 6 cols, 1.54", .125" between; C - 1.54", .125" between.
Areas Served: Madison, Jersey, Calhoun, Macoupin & Greene Counties (IL)
Delivery Method: Mail, Newsstand, Carrier, RacksEquipment & Software: PRESSROOM EQUIPMENT: Lines — 7-MAN/Uniman 4 x 2 1986; Press Drive — 3-GE/DC 300 1986; Pasters —6-MEG 1986; Reels & Stands — 7-MEG 1986.; MAILROOM EQUIPMENT: Counter Stackers — 2-HL/Monitor; Inserters & Stuffers — 1-MM/4 bay, AM Graphics/NP 848; Tying Machines — 1-MLN/ML2EE, 1-MLN/ML2CC; Wrapping Singles — Manual; Address Machine — 1-Cheshire/525-E.; BUSINESS EQUIPMENT: IBM/AS-400 BUSINESS SOFTWARE: INSI, Transient Management Systems, Vision Data, AR 2000, Great Plains CLASSIFIED EQUIPMENT: Hardware — Compaq; Printers — 2-HP/8100.; DISPLAY EQUIPMENT: Printers — 3-APP/Mac Scanners; DISPLAY SOFTWAREAd Make-up Applications — QPS/QuarkXPress, Adobe/Freehand, Multi Ad Creator; Layout Software — APP/Mac. EDITORIAL EQUIPMENT: Hardware — Compaq/Lf/AP Leaf Picture Desk, APP/Mac, Nikon/Scanner; Printers — 1-Panasonic/KX P1624, 2-HP/8100 EDITORIAL SOFTWARE: QPS/QuarkXPress, Microsoft/Word. PRODUCTION EQUIPMENT: Hardware — 2-Tegra/XP-1000, 2-Tegra/Varityper/XP-1000, 1-Hyphen/Dash 72E; Cameras — 1-Commodore/2638 PRODUCTION SOFTWARE: QPS/QuarkXPress 6.0.

ARLINGTON HEIGHTS

DAILY HERALD

155 E Algonquin Rd, Arlington Heights, Ill., 60005-4617, Cook; gen tel (847) 427-4300; adv tel (847) 427-4624; ed tel (847) 427-4642; gen fax (847) 427-1550; adv fax (847) 427-1203; ed fax (847) 427-1301; gen/nat adv e-mail sales@dailyherald.com; disp adv e-mail sales@dailyherald.com; class adv e-mailsales@dailyherald.com; ed e-mail news@dailyherald.com; web site www.dailyherald.com - 5,012,756(views) 1,980,717(visitors)
Group: Paddock Publications
Published: Mon, Tues, Wed, Thur, Fri, Sat, Sun
Weekday Frequency: m
Saturday Frequency: m
Circulation: 72,106; 68,597(sat); 78,786(sun)
Last Audit: AAM March 31, 2017
Advertising Rate (weekday/saturday): Open inch rate $133.95 Daily; $136.30 Sunday
Advertising Rate (sunday): Open inch rate $136.30
News services: AP, CSM, RN, Bloomberg. **Established:** 1872
Own Printing Facility?: Yes
Commercial Printers?: Yes
Digital Platform - Mobile: Apple, Android
Digital Platform - Tablet: Apple iOS, Android, Kindle
Chairman Emeritus .... Daniel Baumann
Chairman/Publisher/CEO .... Douglas K. Ray
Vice Chairman/Exec. Vice Pres./Administration .... Robert Y. Paddock
Sr. Vice Pres., Director of Content and Strategic Planning .... Colin O'Donnell
Sr. Vice Pres./CFO/Treasurer/Secretary .... Kent Johnson
Vice Pres./Director Human Resources .... Heather Ritter
President/Chief Operating Officer .... Scott Stone
Vice Pres./Director Strategic Marketing and Innovation .... M. Eileen Brown
Audience Analytics/Digital Ad Operations Manager John Graham
Sr. Vice. Pres./Director of Circulation .... James J. Galetano
Circulation Manager .... John G. Janos
Circ. Mgr., New Bus. .... Wayne S. Gebis
Circulation Manager, Single Copy Sales Joseph M. Marek
Sr. Vice Pres./Director of Digital and Information Technologies .... Stuart Paddock
Sr. Vice Pres. / General Manager / Southern Illinois Local Media Group .... Stefanie Anderson
Sr. Vice Pres./Editor .... John Lampinen
Vice Pres./Managing Editor .... Jim Baumann
Vice Pres./Director of Advertising Peter Rosengren
Director of Display Advertising .... Ronald Salata
Major Retail Account Manager ... Robert W. Smith
Manager Digital Ops. .... Mark Stallings
Business Editor, Daily Herald Business Products ... Kim Mikus
Digital Editor for Engagement .... Kelly Void
Senior Deputy Managing Editor .... Diane Dungey
Director of Local Advertising .... Mike Evans
Advertising Operations Manager .... Alan Musial
Manager of Digital Technology .... Philippe Hall
Deputy Managing Editor/Opinion Page Jim Slusher
Exec Asst to Exec VP/Vice Chairman Angela Pindel
Build. Maint. Sup. .... John McCarty
Financial Ops Mgr. .... Greg Foster
Deputy Managing Editor / News .... Jim Davis
Deputy Managing Editor / News .... Pete Nenni
Group Editor / Southern Illinois Local Media Group Renee Trappe
Assistant Managing Editor / Sports ... Tom Quinlan
Digital Editor / Online Content .... Travis Siebrass
Assistant Managing Editor / Copy Desk .... Neil Holdway
Senior Director of Visual Journalism .... Jeff Knox
Assistant Corporate Secretary .... Kristine Wilson
Director of Production .... Don Stamper
Market Information: Split run; TMC; Zoned editions.
Mechanical Available: Offset; Black and 3 ROP colors; insert accepted; page cutoff - 21 1/2.
Mechanical Specifications: Type page 11 1/8 x 21; E - 6 cols, 1 5/7, 2/13 between; A - 6 cols, 1 5/7, 2/13 between; C - 10 cols, 1 1/12, 1/11 between.
Areas Served: McHenry, Lake, Kane, DuPage, Cook and Will Counties (IL)
Delivery Method: Mail, Newsstand, Carrier, RacksEquipment & Software: PRESSROOM EQUIPMENT: 2 Lines — MAN/Roland Regioman 48 pages double wide;
Reels & Stands - MAN CD13;
Control System — Pecom; MAILROOM EQUIPMENT: 3 Lines - 20:1/9:1 Single/Double Out Heidleberg NP630 MAILROOM SOFTWARE:Miracom, Omnizone BUSINESS EQUIPMENT: 2-DEC/VAX 4000-700 BUSINESS SOFTWARE: GEAC, Ledger, Payables CLASSIFIED EQUIPMENT: Hardware — Cisco, VMware; Printers — III/Postscript; CLASSIFIED SOFTWARE: At/Enterprise. DISPLAY EQUIPMENT: Hardware — DEC/VAX 1000; Printers — Hp/4000; DISPLAY SOFTWAREAd Make-up Applications — QPS/QuarkXPress, Adobe/Illustrator, Macromedia/Freehand, Adobe/InDesign, Adobe/Acrobat, Adobe/Photoshop, Asura, Soluero; Layout Software — PPI/Plan Page. EDITORIAL EQUIPMENT: Hardware — Cisco, VMware; Printers — III/Postscript EDITORIAL SOFTWARE: Newscycle Solutions/Saxotech PRODUCTION EQUIPMENT: Hardware — Agfa and PPI Media PRODUCTION SOFTWARE: InDesign CIRCULATION EQUIPMENT: Dec/Vax 1000; Printers CIRCULATION SOFTWARHardware: Newscycle Solutions/AIM Circulation
Note: Listing covers 28 editions of the Daily Herald serving markets in Cook, Du Page, Kane, Lake, McHenry and Will counties.

AURORA

DAILY SOUTHTOWN

495 N Commons Dr, Aurora, Ill., 60504-8187, Dupage; gen tel (708) 342-5646; adv tel (312) 283-7056; ed tel (708) 342-5646; gen/nat adv

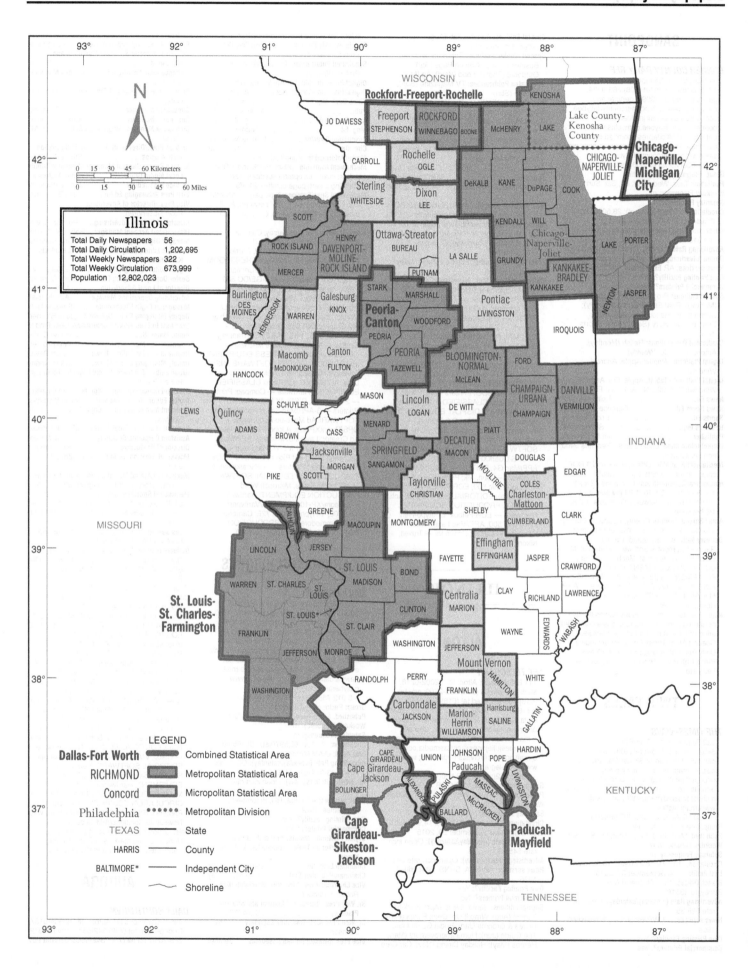

Illinois

Total Daily Newspapers	56
Total Daily Circulation	1,202,695
Total Weekly Newspapers	322
Total Weekly Circulation	673,999
Population	12,802,023

LEGEND

Dallas-Fort Worth	Combined Statistical Area
RICHMOND	Metropolitan Statistical Area
Concord	Micropolitan Statistical Area
Philadelphia	Metropolitan Division
TEXAS	State
HARRIS	County
BALTIMORE*	Independent City
	Shoreline

e-mail CTMGSuburbanAdvertising@ctmg.com; ed e-mail jbiesk@tribpub.com; web site www.dailysouthtown.com - 1,200,000(views)
Group: Tronc, Inc.
Published: Mon, Tues, Wed, Thur, Fri, Sun
Weekday Frequency: m
Saturday Frequency: m
Circulation: 10,545; 14,038(sun)
Last Audit: AAM March 31, 2015
Advertising Rate (weekday/saturday): Open inch rate $28
News services: AP **Established:** 1906
Own Printing Facility?: Yes
Commercial Printers?: Yes
Special Weekly Sections: Sunday Rides, Wednesday Living, Thursday Homes,Friday Auto Mart, Friday Weekend Section
Digital Platform - Mobile: Apple, Android
Digital Platform - Tablet: Apple iOS, Android
Gen. Mgr. .... Jim Rotche
Ed. .... Joe Biesk
News Ed. .... Paul Eisenberg
Sports Ed. .... Bill Scheibe
Mechanical Specifications: Broad sheet 10" x 21"
Areas Served: Chicago Southland
Delivery Method: Newsstand, Carrier, Racks

THE COURIER-NEWS

495 N Commons Dr, Aurora, Ill., 60504-8187, Dupage; gen tel (847) 696-6019; gen/nat adv e-mail ahalston@tribpub.com; disp adv e-mail jmcdermott@tribpub.com; web site chicagotribune.com/suburbs/elgin-courier-news
Group: Tronc, Inc.
Published: Mon, Tues, Wed, Thur, Fri, Sun
Weekday Frequency: m
Saturday Frequency: m
Circulation: 1,135; 1,218(sun)
Last Audit: AAM March 31, 2015
News services: 1875
Own Printing Facility?: No
Commercial Printers?: No
Special Editions: Destination Spring Travel (Apr); Windfall of Homes (Aug); Readers Choice (Dec); Auto Show (Feb); Health Extra (Jan); Education Outlook (Jul); Health Extra (Jun); Education Outlook (Mar); Health Extra (Nov); Home Improvement (Oct); Health Extra (Sept).
Special Weekly Sections: Auto (Daily); Entertainment (Friday); New Homes (Friday)
Syndicated Publications: TV Week (Fri); USA WEEKEND Magazine (S).
Digital Platform - Mobile: Apple, Android
Digital Platform - Tablet: Apple iOS, Android
Ed. .... Anne Halston
Metro Ed. .... Robert Oswald
Sports Ed. .... Bill Scheibe
Exec. Ed. .... Phil Jurik
VP of Adv. .... Jill McDermott
Areas Served: Fox Valley (IL)
Delivery Method: Mail, Newsstand, Carrier, RacksEquipment & Software: BUSINESS EQUIPMENT: CJ CLASSIFIED EQUIPMENT: Hardware — AST/386; Printers — Dataproducts; CLASSIFIED SOFTWARE: Dewar. DISPLAY EQUIPMENT: Hardware — Dewar; DISPLAY SOFTWAREAd Make-up Applications — CJ; Layout Software — CJ.

BELLEVILLE

BELLEVILLE NEWS-DEMOCRAT

120 S Illinois St, Belleville, Ill., 62220-2130, Saint Clair; gen tel (618) 234-1000; adv tel (618) 239-2541; ed tel (618) 239-2500; gen fax (618) 234-9597; adv fax (618) 235-0556; ed fax (618) 234-9597; gen/nat adv e-mail mmason@bnd.com; disp adv e-mail mmason@bnd.com; class adv e-mailclassified@bnd.com; ed e-mail newsroom@bnd.com; web site www.bnd.com - 7,750,000(views) 1,369,000(visitors)
Group: McClatchy
Published: Mon, Tues, Wed, Thur, Fri, Sat, Sun
Weekday Frequency: m
Saturday Frequency: m
Circulation: 31,737; 28,081(sat); 40,422(sun)
Last Audit: AAM December 31, 2016
Newspaper Reps: Melissa Mason, Advertising Jeffry Couch, News
Advertising Rate (weekday/saturday): Open inch rate $56.46
Advertising Rate (sunday): Open inch rate $72.45
Online Advertising Rate: Med Rec 300x250 $10 cpm Leaderboard 728x90 $8 cpm
News services: NYT, AP, McClatchy, Tribune Media Services **Established:** 1858
Own Printing Facility?: Yes
Commercial Printers?: Yes
Special Editions: Baseball (Apr); Home Builders' Show Tab (Feb); Auto Show Tab (Jan); MetroEast Living (Jul); Senior Citizens Tab (Jun); Home Improvement Tab (Mar);Auto Care Tab
Special Weekly Sections: Home/Fashion (Fri); Business (Mon); TV; Religion (Sat); Entertainment (Thur); Food (Tues); Shopping Guide (Fri)
Syndicated Publications: Parade (S).
Proprietary Publications: Catholic Schools Week; Heart 2 Heart; Belleville Chamber Awards; Valentine's Day dining; Madison County Progress' HBA Show Guide; St. Patrick's Day; Lawn and Tractor; Nat'l Agriculture Week; Assisted Living, Cahokia Dupo Welcome; Cardinal Preview (Premium) Easter Dining; Golf Guide; Lawn and Tractor'Camps for Kids-BND; Camps for kids-SSEL; Mother's Day Dining/gifts; Art on the Square; Summer fun (Premium); Horseradish Festival; Leadership Belleville; Social Security; Father's Day Dining;Metro-East Guide (Premium); Health and Wellness; Salute to the Arts; High School Preview; Swansea Welcome Guide; Religious Directory; Reader's Choice; Football preview (Premium); Italian Fest; St. Clair Co. Progress; Chili Cook-off; Kitchen & Bath; Women in Business; St. E's Breast Cancer pages; Hunting Guide; Metro East Gift Guide; Holiday song Book; Holiday Preview Pages;NYE Dining & Party Guide; Business Card Directory; Baby's First Christmas;
Digital Platform - Mobile: Apple, Android, Windows, Blackberry
Digital Platform - Tablet: Apple iOS, Android, Windows 7, Blackberry Tablet OS
VP Adv. .... Melissa Mason
VP Finance .... Stacy Richardson
Editor/VP .... Jeffrey Couch
Prod. Dir .... Don Bradley
Pres./Pub. .... Jay Tebbe
Online Ed. .... Joe Ostermeier
City Ed. .... Gary Dotson
Asst. City Ed. .... Michael Koziatek
Newsroom .... Brian Brueggermann
Newsroom .... Mike Fitzgerald
Newsroom .... Jamie Forsythe
Newsroom .... Beth Hundsdorfer
Newsroom .... George Pawlaczyk
Newsroom .... Carolyn Smith
Features .... Teri Maddox
Features .... Roger Schueter
Sports .... Dean Criddle
Sports .... Norm Sanders
Photo Ed. .... Brad Weisenstein
Photo .... Derik Holtmann
Photo .... Steve Nagy
Copy .... John Buese
Copy .... Mary Cooley
Adv. .... Julie Ambry
Adv. .... Sharon Peterson
Adv. .... Darla Reynolds
Adv. .... Erin Rinderer
Adv. .... Tim Tucker
Adv. .... Cathy White
Michelle O'Leary
Debbie Buese
Donna Buckley
Sylvia Hammitt
Brian Keller
Joann Wymer
Eric Freeman
Dan Sliment
Bart Tate
Mark Watts
Tara Webster
Colleen Kleinschmidt
Greg Purcell
Bil Harrison
Kerry Wendler
Jerry Wilson
Copy Editor .... Joseph Bustos
Garen Vartanian
Teresa Buelt
Pam Phelps
Ellen Gammill
Eschman Todd
David Wilhelm
Reporter .... Robyn Kirsch
Copy Desk .... Casey Bischel
Josh Connelly
Elizabeth O'Donnell
Stephanie Maher
Jarrod Beasley
Lucy Burton
Elizabeth Donald
Adam Evans
Jennifer Green
Hamner Robert
Jeff Hutchinson
Angie Hasamear
Jason Koch
Karen Latta
Becky Lemons
Jim Marks
Warren Mayes
Glenn McCoy
Dawn Peil
Jamie Phelps
Robin smith
Mike Strebel
Market Information: St. Louis MSA/Eastern IL portion
Mechanical Available: Offset; Black and 3 ROP colors; insert accepted; page cutoffs - 22 3/4.
Mechanical Specifications: Page image size: 10 x 20 3/4, all sections; 6 column format, all sections; column width 1.562"; gutters, 1.562"
Areas Served: St. Clair, Madison, Monroe, Clinton, Randolph & Washington Counties
Delivery Method: Mail, Newsstand, Carrier, RacksEquipment & Software: PRESSROOM EQUIPMENT: Lines — 14-G/Urbanite; 7-G/Community; Folders — G/Urbanite, 1-G/Folder w/balloon, 2-G/Community Folders, 1.;Kodak Trendsetter CTP 70 (2) MAILROOM EQUIPMENT: Counter Stackers -3 QUIPP/Sport, 2-Quipp 501; Inserters & Stuffers; Muller-Martini/SLS 2000; Tying Machines — 3 Dynaric/NP2, 2 Dynaric/1500, 1-Dynaric/NP4, Address Machine — Buskro/Inkjet; Muller Martini stitcher-trimmer; Accraply Post it machine -3. BUSINESS EQUIPMENT: PC, VAX,HP printers BUSINESS SOFTWARE: Microsoft/Office; People Soft CLASSIFIED EQUIPMENT: Hardware — PC; Printers, Kodak Work Flow to CTP; CLASSIFIED SOFTWARE: PPI. DISPLAY EQUIPMENT: Hardware — DEC/VAX; Printers — HP; DISPLAY SOFTWAREXPance, Indesign, Newsgate EDITORIAL EQUIPMENT: HP laptops and desktops; Newsgate/CCI front end system; printers; HP Laserjet 5000s EDITORIAL SOFTWARE: Newsgate/CCI PRODUCTION EQUIPMENT: Hardware — Pre Press/ Kodak Workflow to CTP; Scanners, Macs, PCs, Microsoft Office PRODUCTION SOFTWARE: Newsgate/CCI, Indesign IT EQUIPMENT: MACs, PCs IT SOFTWARE:BL CIRCULATION EQUIPMENT: PCs CIRCULATION SOFTWARNewscycle
Note: The BND has won numerous state and national awards for investigative reporting and other public service journalism, including the sweepstake awards in the Illinois Press Association and Illinois APME contests, National Headliner Grand award, IRE awards, the Casey Medal for Meritorious Journalism, the Robert F. Kennedy Journalism Award and the George Polk Award.

BENTON

BENTON EVENING NEWS

111 E Church St, Benton, Ill., 62812-2238, Franklin; gen tel (618) 438-5611; gen fax (618) 435-2413; gen/nat adv e-mail jvitek@bentoneveningnews.com; disp adv e-mail jarview@bentoneveningnews.com ; class adv e-mailmdarnell@bentoneveningnews.com; ed e-mail newsroom@bentoneveningnews.com ; web site www.bentoneveningnews.com
Group: New Media Investment Group
Published: Mon, Tues, Wed, Thur, Fri
Weekday Frequency: e
Circulation: 3,472; 3,472(sat)
Last Audit: Sworn/Estimate/Non-Audited September 30, 2017
Advertising Rate (weekday/saturday): Open inch rate $10.62
News services: AP.
Special Editions:
Syndicated Publications: American Profile (Fri); USA WEEKEND Magazine (Sat).
Pub. .... Lynne Campbell
Classified Mgr. .... Crystal Bullette
Circ. Dir. .... Sam Waters
Reporter .... Mona Sandefur
Sports Ed. .... Bruce Marsan
Sales Mgr. .... Jaime Reynolds
Multi-Media Acct. Exec. .... Joe Vitek
Digital Mktg. Specialist .... Kristen Reid
Ed. .... Geoffery Ritter
Mechanical Available: Laser; Black and 3 ROP colors; insert accepted - all; page cutoffs - 21 1/2.
Mechanical Specifications: Type page 12 x 21 1/2; E - 6 cols, 2, 1/6 between; A - 6 cols, 2, 1/6 between; C - 8 cols, 1 1/2, 1/6 between.
Areas Served: 62812, 62822Equipment & Software: MAILROOM EQUIPMENT: Tying Machines — 1/Bu.; BUSINESS EQUIPMENT: Club America BUSINESS SOFTWARE: Nomads/Listmaster CLASSIFIED EQUIPMENT: Hardware — APP/iMac; Printers — APP/Mac LaserWriter II.; DISPLAY EQUIPMENT: Hardware — APP/iMac.; EDITORIAL EQUIPMENT: Hardware — APP/iMac; Printers — APP/Mac LaserWriter II EDITORIAL SOFTWARE: Microsoft/Word. PRODUCTION EQUIPMENT: Hardware — Adobe/Photoshop 2.5; Cameras — SCREEN/Companica 680C; Scanners — Nikon/Coolscan, Scanmaker II XE PRODUCTION SOFTWARE: QPS/QuarkXPress 3.31.

BLOOMINGTON

THE PANTAGRAPH

301 W Washington St, Bloomington, Ill., 61701-3827, McLean; gen tel (309) 829-9000; adv tel (309) 829-9000; ed tel (309) 829-9000; adv fax (309) 829-9104; ed fax (309) 829-7000; gen/nat adv e-mail advertising@pantagraph.com; disp adv e-mail advertising@pantagraph.com; class adv e-mailadvertising@pantagraph.com; ed e-mail newsroom@pantagraph.com; web site www.pantagraph.com - 6,000,000(views) 500,000(visitors)
Group: Lee Enterprises, Inc.
Published: Mon, Tues, Wed, Thur, Fri, Sat, Sun
Weekday Frequency: m
Saturday Frequency: m
Circulation: 28,060; 27,318(sat); 33,525(sun)
Last Audit: AAM March 31, 2016
Advertising Rate (weekday/saturday): Open inch rate $73.88
Advertising Rate (sunday): Open inch rate $82.13
Online Advertising Rate: Run of Site, $25; Fixed position, $30; Home Page $35; BT $35; Video $35; Mobile $35.
News services: AP, McClatchey. **Established:** 1837
Own Printing Facility?: No
Commercial Printers?: No
Special Editions: Health and Fitness (Jan); Agribusiness (Feb); Home Show (March); Annual Report (March); Money Smart Week (April); Golf Guide (March); Spring Home and Garden (April); The Guide to Summer Fun and Entertainment (May); Campus Guide (August); Breast Cancer Awareness (Oct.); Calendar (Nov.) Hometown Holidays (Nov.) Readers Choice (July).
Special Weekly Sections: Business (Daily); Health, Fitness (Mon); Family (Tue); Food (Wed); Entertainment (Thur); Lifestyles, Real Estate (Fri); TV, Homes (Sat); Business, Viewpoint, Values (Sun)
Syndicated Publications: Relish (Monthly); Parade (S); American Profile (Wed).
Digital Platform - Mobile: Apple, Android, Windows
Digital Platform - Tablet: Apple iOS
Gen. Mgr. .... Barry L. Winterland
Adv. Mgr., Majors/Nat'l .... Steve Lahr
Mktg. Servs. Mgr. .... Jonell Kehias
Circ. Dir. .... Bob Scott
Ed. .... Mark Pickering
Enterprise Ed. .... Julie Gerke
Bus. Ed. .... Karen Hansen
Capitol Bureau Chief .... Kurt Erickson
Entertainment Ed. .... Dan Craft
Features Ed. .... Chuck Blystone
Regional Editor .... Gary Sawyer
Adv. Dir. .... Joel Fletcher

Staci Molony-Klimek
Adv. Dept. .... Lori Nelson
Market Information: TMC; Zoned editions.
Mechanical Available: Offset; Black and 3 ROP colors; insert accepted; page cutoffs - 20 1/2.
Mechanical Specifications: Full: 9.8889 x 20.5; Build: 9.8889 X 20.25; 6 col retail and classified, 1.556 = 1 Column
Areas Served: 61704, 61701, 61761Equipment & Software: BUSINESS EQUIPMENT: 1-IBM/AS-400E BUSINESS SOFTWARE: In-house CLASSIFIED EQUIPMENT: Hardware — Mactive/SOL 2000, Compaq/ML530 Server, 25-Dell/Pentium III; Printers — HP/4M Plus; CLASSIFIED SOFTWARE: Mactive 2.21. DISPLAY EQUIPMENT: Hardware — 12-APP/Mac, Compaq/Proiant ML370; Printers — HP/1050 Plotter, 1-HP/8150, 1-HP/5500 DN; DISPLAY SOFTWAREAd Make-up Applications — Multi-Ad/Creator 6.5; Layout Software — DPS/AD-Tracker. EDITORIAL EQUIPMENT: Hardware — 50-Compaq/2000 Desk Pro, Compaq/Proliant 1600, Novell 4.11/APP/Server; Printers — HP/8100 EDITORIAL SOFTWARE: QPS/QuarkXPress 4.11. PRODUCTION EQUIPMENT: Hardware — Nu/Flip Top, HP/1050, MON/RIP Express ImageMaster 1000, 2-MON/RIP Express Imagemaster 1500; Cameras — C/Marathon; Scanners — 1-AG/1236X 325, 1-AG/Duoscan T1200, Kk/RFS 2035, Epson/836 XL, Microtech/9800 XL, AG/Duoscan F40 PRODUCTION SOFTWARE: APP/Mac

CANTON

DAILY LEDGER

53 W Elm St, Canton, Ill., 61520-2511, Fulton; gen tel (309) 647-5100; gen fax (309) 647-4665; adv fax (309) 649-1047; ed fax (309) 647-4665; gen/nat adv e-mail mwhite@cantondalyledger.com; disp adv e-mail ads@cantondailyledger.com; class adv e-mailswelker@cantondailyledger.com; ed e-mail editor@cantondailyledger.com; web site www.cantondailyledger.com
Group: New Media Investment Group
Published: Mon, Tues, Wed, Thur, Fri, Sat
Weekday Frequency: e
Saturday Frequency: m
Circulation: 3,800; 3,900(sat)
Last Audit: Sworn/Estimate/Non-Audited September 30, 2017
Advertising Rate (weekday/saturday): Open inch rate $13.20
News services: AP. **Established:** 1849
Special Editions: Lawn & Garden (Apr); Agriculture (Aug); Christmas Wishbook (Dec); Agriculture (Feb); Income Tax (Jan); Bridal (Jul); Father's Day (Jun); Car Care (Mar); Home Improvement (May); Turkey Give-away (Nov); Home Improvement (Oct); Pre-Labor Day (Sept).
Syndicated Publications: Channel Guide (Fri); American Profile (Weekly).
Reporter .... Larry Eskridge
Sports Ed. .... Stephen Shank
Circ. Mgr. .... Rick Bybee
Class. .... Sandy Welker
Adv. Mgr. .... Mary White
Pub. .... David Adams
News Ed. .... John Froehling
Ed. .... Deb Robinson
Market Information: TMC.
Mechanical Available: Offset; Black and 3 ROP colors; insert accepted; page cutoffs - 22 3/4.
Mechanical Specifications: Type page 12 x 21 1/2; E - 6 cols, 1 3/4, 1/8 between; A - 6 cols, 1 3/4, 1/8 between; C - 8 cols, 1 3/16, 1/16 between.
Areas Served: Fulton County (IL)
Equipment & Software: PRESSROOM EQUIPMENT: Lines — 6-G/Community; Control System — G/Community 50DC (Suburban Control).; MAILROOM EQUIPMENT: Tying Machines — Bu/67590; Address Machine — Dispensa-Matic/16; BUSINESS EQUIPMENT: 2-IBM/PC CLASSIFIED EQUIPMENT: Hardware — APP/Mac G4.; EDITORIAL EQUIPMENT: Hardware — APP/Mac G4. PRODUCTION EQUIPMENT: Hardware — 3-APP/Mac G4, Pre Press/Panther ImageSetter; Cameras — 1-SCREEN; Scanners — SCREEN C/680, C.

CARBONDALE

THE SOUTHERN ILLINOISAN

710 N Illinois Ave, Carbondale, Ill., 62901-1283, Jackson; gen tel (618) 529-5454; adv tel (618) 351-5001; ed tel (618) 351-5090; gen fax (618) 457-2935; adv fax (618) 529-3774; gen/nat adv e-mail lisa.giampaolo@thesouthern.com; disp adv e-mail lyn.sargent@thesouthern.com; class adv e-mailangela.oliver@thesouthern.com; ed e-mail news@thesouthern.com; web site www.thesouthern.com
- 1,600,000(views) 325,000(visitors)
Group: Lee Enterprises, Inc.
Published: Tues, Wed, Thur, Fri, Sat, Sun
Weekday Frequency: m
Saturday Frequency: m
Circulation: 13,388; 14,066(sat); 21,598(sun)
Last Audit: AAM September 30, 2016
Newspaper Reps: Craig Rogers- Publisher
Tom English- Executive Editor
Terra Kerekemeyer- Circulation Director
Lyn Sargent- Advertising Director
Alee Quick- Digital Editor
Lisa Morgan- Accounting Manager
Dean Thompson- Press Room Manager
Kevin Morgan- Production Manager
Advertising Rate (weekday/saturday): Open inch rate $26.00
Advertising Rate (sunday): Open inch rate $28.00
Online Advertising Rate: $13.00 CPM
News services: AP, MCT, SHNS, TMS. **Established:** 1878
Own Printing Facility?: Yes
Commercial Printers?: Yes
Special Editions: Spring Lawn & Garden (Apr); Football Preview (Aug); Holiday Wishes (Dec); Auto Racing (Feb); Southern Illinois Tourism Guide (Jan); Jackson City Visitor's Guide (Jul); Locally Owned Business (Jun); Spring Home Improvement (Mar); Southern Illinois Guide (M
Special Weekly Sections: Best Food Day (Wed); Health, Environment (Tue); Entertainment (Thur); Outdoors (Fri); Family, Religion (Sat); Technology, Auto (Daily); Parenting, TV, Finance, Real Estate, Home, Business, Outdoors (Sun_
Syndicated Publications: Parade (S); American Profile (Weekly).
Proprietary Publications: Southern Business Journal (Monthly)
Life & Style Magazine (Quarterly)
Digital Platform - Mobile: Apple, Android, Blackberry
Digital Platform - Tablet: Apple iOS, Android
Pub. .... Craig Rogers
Exec. Ed. .... Tom English
Sports Ed. .... Les Winkeler
Digital Editor .... Alee Quick
Photo Ed. .... Byron Hetzler
Night Ed. .... Codell Rodriguez
Market Information: ADS; Split run; TMC; Zoned editions.
Mechanical Available: Offset; Black and 3 ROP colors; insert accepted - We-Prints; page cutoffs - 22 3/4.
Mechanical Specifications: Type page 12 x 21 1/2; E - 6 cols, 1 7/8, 5/32 between; A - 6 cols, 1 7/8, 5/32 between; C - 6 cols, 1 7/8, 5/32 between.
Areas Served: Southern Illinois
Delivery Method: Mail, Newsstand, Carrier, RacksEquipment & Software: PRESSROOM EQUIPMENT: Lines — 8-G/Urbanite (balloon former); Folders — 2-G/2:1, 1-G/1:4; Reels & Stands — 8-G/Stands.; MAILROOM EQUIPMENT: Counter Stackers — 1/HI; Inserters & Stuffers — 2-MM/270, 8-/HI; Tying Machines — 1-/Sa, 2-Si; Address Machine — Ch; BUSINESS EQUIPMENT: IBM/AS-400 CLASSIFIED EQUIPMENT: Hardware — HI; Printers — HP/8000; CLASSIFIED SOFTWARE: HI. DISPLAY EQUIPMENT: Hardware — HI/XP-21; Printers — HP/AU; Other Hardware — APP/Mac DISPLAY SOFTWAREAd Make-up Applications — HI; Layout Software — HI/PLS. EDITORIAL EQUIPMENT: Hardware — HI; Printers — HP EDITORIAL SOFTWARE: HI. PRODUCTION EQUIPMENT: Hardware — AU/Laser, Lf/AP Leaf Picture Desk, HI; Cameras — 1-C/Spartan III; Scanners — AU, Nikon/Scanner, Umax/Powerlook 2, Astra, HP/ScanJet 5P PRODUCTION SOFTWARE: HI/AU.

CARMI

THE CARMI TIMES

323 E Main St, Carmi, Ill., 62821-1810, White; gen tel (618) 382-4176; adv tel (618) 382-4176; ed tel (618) 382-4176; gen fax (618) 384-2163; adv fax (618) 384-2163; ed fax (618) 384-2163; gen/nat adv e-mail carmitimes@yourclearwave.com; disp adv e-mail carmitimes@yourclearwave.com; class adv e-mailcarmitimes@yourclearwave.com; ed e-mail editorial@carmitimes.com; web site www.carmitimes.com
Group: New Media Investment Group
Published: Mon, Tues, Thur, Fri
Weekday Frequency: e
Circulation: 2,718
Last Audit: Sworn/Estimate/Non-Audited September 30, 2017
Advertising Rate (weekday/saturday): Open inch rate $12.99
News services: AP. **Established:** 1950
Special Weekly Sections: Best Food Day (Tue)
Digital Platform - Mobile: Apple, Android, Windows
Digital Platform - Tablet: Apple iOS, Android, Windows 7
Pub. .... Kevin Haezebroeck
Circ. Mgr. .... Rhonda Beason
Gen. Mgr. .... Barry Cleveland
Adv. Mgr. .... Cherly Trout
Market Information: TMC.
Mechanical Available: Offset; Black and 3 ROP colors; insert accepted; page cutoffs - 21 1/2.
Mechanical Specifications: Type page 13 x 21 1/2; E - 6 cols, 2, 1/8 between; A - 6 cols, 2, 1/8 between; C - 8 cols, 1 1/2, 1/16 between.
Areas Served: Carmi and White County
Delivery Method: Mail, NewsstandEquipment & Software: PRESSROOM EQUIPMENT: Lines — 1-G; G.; MAILROOM EQUIPMENT: Address Machine — 1/Am, 1-Ap/Mac ImageWriter.; DISPLAY EQUIPMENT: Printers — 1-APP/Mac LaserWriter II NTX; DISPLAY SOFTWAREAd Make-up Applications — Aldus/PageMaker, Aldus/FreeHand; Layout Software — 2-APP/Mac SE, 1-APP/Mac IIsi. EDITORIAL EQUIPMENT: Hardware — 5-APP/Mac Plus, 1-APP/Mac Classic, 1-APP/Mac Classic II; Printers — APP/Mac LaserWriter II, APP/Mac ImageWriter EDITORIAL SOFTWARE: Microsoft/Word, Aldus/PageMaker. PRODUCTION EQUIPMENT: Hardware — X, 1-LU.

CENTRALIA

MORNING SENTINEL

232 E Broadway, Centralia, Ill., 62801-3251, Marion; gen tel (618) 532-5604; ed tel (618) 532-5601; gen fax (618) 532-1212; ed fax (618) 532-1212; gen/nat adv e-mail sentinelvip@charter.net; disp adv e-mail sentinelvip@charter.net; class adv e-mailclassifieds@morningsentinel.com; ed e-mail news@morningsentinel.com
Group: Centralia Press Ltd.
Published: Tues, Wed, Thur, Fri, Sat, Sun
Weekday Frequency: m
Saturday Frequency: m
Circulation: 11,416; 12,090(sat); 12,360(sun)
Last Audit: CVC March 31, 2016
Branch Offices: Morning Sentinel in Mt. Vernon
Advertising Rate (weekday/saturday): Open inch rate $10.78
Advertising Rate (sunday): Open inch rates $11.08
News services: AP. **Established:** 1863
Own Printing Facility?: Yes
Special Weekly Sections: Gardening (Tues.); Education (Thurs.); Religion (Fri); Food (Sat.); Farm,, Comics, Feature (Sun); Local News, Sports, Stocks, Lifestyles, State, World News (Daily)
Syndicated Publications: Telly Times (Sat.); Comics (S).
Office Mgr. .... Julie Copple
Pub. .... John Perrine
Adv. Mgr. .... Daniel Nichols
Farm Ed./Features Ed. .... Judith Joy
Sr. Ed. .... LuAnn Droege
Prodn. Supvr., Composing .... Terri Kelly
Market Information: Split run; TMC; Zoned editions.
Mechanical Available: Offset; Black and 3 ROP colors; insert accepted - 3 x 5 in size to 15 x 11 1/2; page cutoffs - 22 3/4.
Mechanical Specifications: Type page 13 x 21 1/4; E - 6 cols, 2 3/16, 1/16 between; A - 6 cols, 2 3/16, 1/16 between; C - 8 cols, 2 1/16, 1/16 between.
Areas Served: We Cover Marion, Clinton, Jefferson, Marion and Washington Counties
Delivery Method: Mail, Newsstand, Carrier, RacksEquipment & Software: PRESSROOM EQUIPMENT: Lines — 6-G/Urbanite Offset 1972; Reels & Stands — 6-G/Roll Stand.; MAILROOM EQUIPMENT: Tying Machines — 2-/Bu; Address Machine — Ultra Comp/PC (with Panasonic Printer for Labels).; CLASSIFIED EQUIPMENT: Hardware — Mk/1100 Plus, 2-Mk.; DISPLAY EQUIPMENT: Printers — QMS/860, APP/Mac LaserWriter II; DISPLAY SOFTWAREAd Make-up Applications — QPS/QuarkXPress, Adobe/Illustrator; Layout Software — 2-Mk/Ad Comp, APP/Mac Quadra 650, APP/Mac. EDITORIAL EQUIPMENT: Hardware — 13-Mk, 1-APP/Mac. PRODUCTION EQUIPMENT: Hardware — 2-M/202, APP/Mac LaserWriter, APP/Mac LaserWriter II, QMS/860, Hyphen/Spectraset 2400; Cameras — 1-R/481; Scanners — AG/Arcus, Kk/RFS Film Scanner.

CHAMPAIGN

THE NEWS-GAZETTE

15 E Main St, Champaign, Ill., 61820-3625, Champaign; gen tel (217) 351-5252; adv tel (217) 351-5281; ed tel (217) 351-5211; gen fax (217) 351-5291; ed fax (217) 351-5374; gen/nat adv e-mail advertising@news-gazette.com; disp adv e-mail advertising@news-gazette.com; class adv e-mailadvertising@news-gazette.com; ed e-mail news@news-gazette.com; web site www.news-gazette.com
Published: Mon, Tues, Wed, Thur, Fri, Sat, Sun
Weekday Frequency: m
Saturday Frequency: m
Circulation: 39,710; 39,565(sat); 44,012(sun)
Last Audit: AAM September 30, 2016
Advertising Rate (weekday/saturday): Open inch rate $47.53
Advertising Rate (sunday): Open inch rate $52.72
News services: AP, CNS, MCT, SHNS. **Established:** 1852
Own Printing Facility?: Yes
Commercial Printers?: Yes
Special Editions: Football (Aug); Holiday Shopping Guides (Nov-Dec.); Health Care Guide (Feb); Money Matters (Jan); Agri-Business (Mar); Summer Fun Guide (May); Home & Garden (Sept).
Special Weekly Sections: Business, Technology, Entertainment (Mon); Best Food Day (Wed); Living, Spin Off (Thur); Entertainment, Health, Fitness (Fri); Home, Real Estate (Sat); Farm, Travel, Entertainment, Business (Sun)
Syndicated Publications: e3 Magazine (Thur); Parade (Sun); TV This Week (Sat).
Pres. .... John Foreman
Columnist .... Tom Kacich
Librarian .... Carolyn Vance
Photo Ed. .... Darrell Hoemann
Ed. .... Jim Rossow
Circ. Dir. .... Pete Jones
CEO/Pub. .... John Reed
VP/Dir. HR .... Tracy Nally
VP/Gen. Mgr. Radio .... Mike Haile
Adv. Dir. .... Tom Zalabak
Adv. Sales Mgr. & National Sales ... Jackie Martin
Customer Care Center Manager . Denny Santarelli
Opinions Page Ed. .... Jim Dey
Features Ed. .... Tony Mancuso
Dir. of Market Dev. .... Amy George
Adv. Services Mgr. .... Alice Vaughan
Online Ed. .... Niko Dugan
Market Information: ADS; Split run; TMC; Zoned editions.
Mechanical Available: Offset; Black and 3 ROP colors; insert accepted; page cutoffs - 21 1/2.
Mechanical Specifications: Type page 11 3/4 x 21 1/2; E - 6 cols, 1 4/5, 1/8 between; A - 6 cols, 1 4/5, 1/8 between; C - 9 cols, 1 1/3, 1/8 between.

Areas Served: Counties served: Champaign (primary), DeWitt, Douglas, Edgar, Ford, Iroquois, McLean, Piatt, Vermilion, Coles
Delivery Method: Mail, Newsstand, Carrier, Racks

CHICAGO

CHICAGO SUN-TIMES

350 N Orleans St Ste 1000, Fl 10, Chicago, Ill., 60654-1700, Cook; gen tel (312) 321-3000; gen fax (312) 321-2299; adv fax (312) 321-9655; gen/nat adv e-mail nkirby@suntimes.com; disp adv e-mail advertisinginfo@suntimes.com; class adv e-mailgarroyo@suntimes.com; ed e-mail jkirk@suntimes.com; web site www.suntimes.com
- 14,317,000(views) 3,291,000(visitors)
Group: Sun-Times Media Group Inc.
Published: Mon, Tues, Wed, Thur, Fri, Sat, Sun
Weekday Frequency: m
Saturday Frequency: m
Circulation: 134,874; 115,699(sat); 141,549(sun)
Last Audit: AAM March 31, 2016
Advertising Rate (weekday/saturday): Open inch rate $608.00
News services: AP, UPI, DJ, LAT-WP, RN, Chicago City News Bureau. **Established:** 1844
Special Editions: Baseball Preview (Apr); Education Guide (Aug); 10 Days & Counting (Dec); Black History Month (Feb); Bride & Groom (Jan); Bride & Groom (Jul); Education Guide (Mar); Mother's Day Greeting Ads (May); Holiday Gift Guide (Nov); Bulls/NBA Preview (Oct); Energy
Special Weekly Sections: Autotimes (Fri); Autotimes (Mon); TV Preview (S); Autotimes (Wed).
Syndicated Publications: USA WEEKEND Magazine (S).
Digital Platform - Mobile: Apple, Android, Windows
Digital Platform - Tablet: Apple iOS, Android, Kindle Fire
CEO .... Tim Knight
Vice Pres., Labor Rel. (Chicago Sun-Times/Chicago Grp.) .... Ted Rilea
Adv. Vice Pres. .... Gladys Arroyo
Adv. Vice Pres., Classified .... Jim Dyer
Adv. Dir., Art/Entertainment/Local Markets David D. Ruiz
Adv. Vice Pres., Cor. Accts. .... Dean R. Spencer
Adv. Dir., Local .... Dave Sherman
Vice Pres., Mktg. .... Willie Wilkov
Circ. Dir., Distr. .... Michael Perrone
Circ. Dir., Opns .... Peter Belluomini
Circ. Dir., Sales .... Robert Edwards
Circ. Dir., Single Copy Sales .... Sandra Mather
Asst. to Ed. .... Toby Roberts
Bus. Ed. .... Polly Smith
Editorial Cartoonist .... Jack Higgins
Editorial Page Ed. .... Tom McNamee
Pub. / Ed. in Chief .... Jim Kirk
Sr. Mgr. Retail Relationship .... Adam Shibla
Deputy Managing Ed., News/Sports Chris De Luca
Dir of Dig. and Editorial Innovation Steve Warmbir
Mng. ed. .... Chris Fusko
Market Information: ADS; Split run; TMC; Zoned editions.
Mechanical Available: Offset; Black and 3 ROP colors; insert accepted - Polybags; page cutoffs - 23 9/16.
Mechanical Specifications: Type page 10 1/4 x 12; E - 6 cols, 1 9/16, 1/6 between; A - 6 cols, 1 9/16, 1/6 between; C - 8 cols, 1 3/16, 1/8 between.
Areas Served: 60654Equipment & Software: PRESSROOM EQUIPMENT: Lines — 21-G/Mark I Headliner; 21-G/Mark I Headliner; 24-G/Mark I Headliner; Reels & Stands — 8-W/C-SE-5B, 1-W/CFP, 12-G/Digital Pilot, 21-G/Amplidine, 12-G/Selsyn.; MAILROOM EQUIPMENT: Counter Stackers — 12-HL/Sta-Hi ZS7S, 2-HL/Dual Carrier; Inserters & Stuffers — 2-S/272P, 1/AM Graphics/2299; Tying Machines — 12-MLN/MLN2A, 9-/Power Strap/PSN6; Address Machine — PC Systems.; BUSINESS EQUIPMENT: 1-IBM/370 CLASSIFIED EQUIPMENT: Hardware — 4-AT/J-11, 60-IBM/486 DX-2; 2-AT, 2-IBM/RS 6000 pagination; CLASSIFIED SOFTWARE: AT 7.0. DISPLAY EQUIPMENT: Hardware — 12-APP/Mac; Printers — 3-AU/6600; DISPLAY SOFTWAREAd Make-up Applications — Multi-Ad/Creator.; EDITORIAL EQUIPMENT: Hardware — 8-AT/J-11, 200-IBM/486 DX-2/25-AT, IBM/RS 6000, 15-IBM/Power PC EDITORIAL SOFTWARE: AT 7.0. PRODUCTION EQUIPMENT: Hardware — 3-AU/APS-5, Na, 1-Kk/Kodamatic 24, 1-P/Lith; Cameras — 2-C/Newspager, 1-C/Marathon, 1-C/Spartan III; Scanners — 1-SCREEN/608G Color Scanner.

CHICAGO TRIBUNE

435 N Michigan Ave, Chicago, Ill., 60611-4066, Cook; gen tel (312) 222-3232; adv tel (800) 974-7520; ed tel (312) 222-3540; gen fax (312) 222-2595; ed fax (312) 222-4674; gen/nat adv e-mail ecom@tribune.com; disp adv e-mail ecom@tribune.com; class adv e-mailclassadinfo@tribune.com; ed e-mail metro@tribune.com; sports@tribune.com; sunday@tribune.com; business@tribune.com; web site www.chicagotribune.com
- 37,975,000(views) 5,097,000(visitors)
Group: Tronc, Inc.
Published: Mon, Tues, Wed, Thur, Fri, Sat, Sun
Weekday Frequency: m
Saturday Frequency: m
Circulation: 419,864; 355,742(sat); 720,669(sun)
Last Audit: AAM March 31, 2016
Advertising Rate (weekday/saturday): Open inch rate $667.00
News services: AP, RN, NYT, TMS, DJ, MCT. **Established:** 1847
Special Editions: Education Today-Summer (Apr); Fall Fashion (Aug); Year in Pictures (Dec); Cruise Planner (Feb); Winter Breaker (Jan); Golf (Jun); Education Today-Spring (Mar); Midwest Vacations (May); Ski Time (Nov); Follow the Sun (Oct); Fall/Winter Cruises (Sept).
Special Weekly Sections: Friday (Fri); Business Technology (Mon); Transportation (S); New Homes (Sat); Cars (Thur); Good Eating (Wed).
Syndicated Publications: Parade (S).
Digital Platform - Mobile: Apple, Android, Windows, Blackberry
Digital Platform - Tablet: Apple iOS, Android, Windows 7, Blackberry Tablet OS, Kindle, Nook, Kindle Fire
Pub. .... Tony Hunter
Vice Pres., Finance/CFO .... Phil Doherty
Vice Pres., HR .... Janice Jacobs
Dir., Technical Devel. .... Scott Tafelski
Dir., Technical Opns./Help Desk .... Sarp Uzkan
Dir., Client Servs. .... Deepak Agarwal
Adv. Sr. Vice Pres. .... Robert Fleck
Adv. Vice Pres., Interactive .... Joe Farrell
Adv. Dir., Classified .... Barbara Swanson
Adv. Dir., Devel. .... Kathy Manilla
Dir., Brand Mktg. .... Kelly Shannon
Gen. Mgr. of Suburban Weeklies .... Maggie Wartik
Stephen Rynkiewicz
Clarence Page
Assoc. Ed. .... Colin McMahon
Mark Barrons
Mng. Ed. .... Peter Kendall
Associate Manger, Editor of National News .... Joycelynn Winnecke
Director of Major Accounts .... John Gregorio
SVP Ed. .... Gerould Ken
Pub./Ed.-in-Chief .... R. Bruce Dold
Asst. Subj. Ed., Nat. .... Kester Alleyne-Morris
Ed. Designer .... Daniel Ellman
Market Information: Split run; TMC; Zoned editions.
Mechanical Available: Offset; Black and 3 ROP colors; insert accepted - product samples,cd's,shopping bags; page cutoffs - 22.
Mechanical Specifications: Type page 13 x 21; E - 6 cols, 2 1/16, 1/8 between; A - 6 cols, 2 1/16, 1/8 between; C - 9 cols, 1 3/8, 1/16 between.Equipment & Software: PRESSROOM EQUIPMENT: Lines — 90-G/Metroliner offset presses (2 color decks per press), 8-G/Metroliner Offset Units, 3, 1, 1; 10-RKW/Metrocolor Press Units(Added to end of existing presses), 9-G/Metroliner Offset Units, 2, 1; 9-G/Metroliner Offset Units, 2,; MAILROOM EQUIPMENT: Counter Stackers — 25-SH/257S, HL/HT, 17-Quipp/350, 9-Quipp/400, 12-Quipp/350 Stackers; Inserters & Stuffers — 5-S/72P, 1-HI/1372P, AM Graphics/NP 2299, AM Graphics/NP100, 4-Heidelberg/2299 with 22 hoppers, 2-Heidelberg/2299 with 21 hoppers, 3-Harris; BUSINESS EQUIPMENT: 4-DEC/KL 10, IBM/3083 JX3, IBM/3090-18 E, IBM/4381-R14 CLASSIFIED EQUIPMENT: Hardware — Dell/Optiplex GX100 Workstation; Printers — HP/Laserjet 5, HP/LJ 4000, HP LJ4050, HP/LJ 4100, HP/LJ 4500, HP/LJ 4600, Lexmark/4226; CLASSIFIED SOFTWARE: Coyote/3 Client 51136.vvvv.001. DISPLAY EQUIPMENT: Hardware — Mac/PC Workstations; Printers — Xerox/Phaser 4400N, HP/1050, HP/2000; Other Hardware — APP/Mac, SCS Layout 8000. DISPLAY SOFTWAREAd Make-up Applications — CCI Addesk 5.5.5adp38h; EDITORIAL EQUIPMENT: Hardware — PC Workstations/CCI Newsdesk; Printers — Xerox/Phaser 4400N EDITORIAL SOFTWARE: CCI Newsdesk 5.5.5.22t. PRODUCTION EQUIPMENT: Hardware — 3-Mk/Lasercompll, 3-Xenotron/UX 90, 2-L/300, 1-L/500, 1-Pixel, 1-Lynart; Cameras — 1-SCREEN/Rollmatic 475 PRODUCTION SOFTWARE: cci Newsdesk 5.5.5.22t.

THE BEACON NEWS

350 N Orleans St, Chicago, Ill., 60654-1975, Cook; adv tel (866) 399-0537; gen/nat adv e-mail ahalston@tribpub.com; disp adv e-mail CTMGSuburbanAdvertising@ctmg.com; web site www.chicagotribune.com/suburbs/aurora-beacon-news
Group: Tronc, Inc.
Published: Mon, Tues, Wed, Thur, Fri, Sat, Sun
Weekday Frequency: m
Saturday Frequency: m
Circulation: 4,901; 5,684(sun)
Last Audit: AAM March 31, 2015
News services: CNS, AP, NEA, NYT.
Special Editions: Destination Spring Travel (Apr); Windfall of Homes (Aug); Readers Choice Awards (Dec); Auto Show (Feb); Health Extra (Jan); Education Outlook (Jul); Wedding Planner (Jun); Education Outlook (Mar); Education Outlook (Nov); Home Improvement (Oct); Windfall
Special Weekly Sections: Religion (Fri); Real Estate Showcase (S); New Homes (Sat); Go (Thur); Food (Wed).
Syndicated Publications: TV Program Guide (S); USA WEEKEND Magazine (Sat).
Digital Platform - Mobile: Apple, Android
Digital Platform - Tablet: Apple iOS, Android
Ed. .... Anne Halston
Metro Ed. .... Dan Cassidy
Exec. Ed. .... Phil Jurik
VP of Adv. .... Jill McDermott
Market Information: ADS; Split run; TMC; Zoned editions.
Mechanical Available: Offset; Black and 3 ROP colors; insert accepted - single sheet, product samples; page cutoffs - 22 3/4.
Mechanical Specifications: Type page 13 x 21; E - 6 cols, 2 1/25, 1/6 between; A - 6 cols, 2 1/8, 1/6 between; C - 10 cols, 1 3/16, 1/16 between.
Areas Served: Fox Valley (IL)
Equipment & Software: BUSINESS EQUIPMENT: DEC/VAX CLASSIFIED EQUIPMENT: Hardware — Cybergraphics; Printers — HP; CLASSIFIED SOFTWARE: Centronics/Print Station 351. DISPLAY EQUIPMENT: Hardware — APP/Mac; Printers — APP/Mac LaserWriter; DISPLAY SOFTWAREAd Make-up Applications — DTI; Layout Software — DTI. EDITORIAL EQUIPMENT: Hardware — Cybergraphics/; Printers — HP EDITORIAL SOFTWARE: SII.
Note: Suburban Chicago Newspapers includes the Aurora Beacon News (mS), Elgin Courier News (mS), Joliet Herald News (mS), Naperville Sun (mS) and Waukegan Lake County News-Sun (e). The group combination rate is $170.50 (dS). Individual newspaper rates not made

THE HERALD NEWS

350 N Orleans St, Chicago, Ill., 60654-1975, Cook; gen tel (312) 321-2333; adv tel (312) 321-2333; ed tel (312) 321-2333; gen fax (815) 729-6059; adv fax (815) 729-6392; ed fax (815) 729-6059; gen/nat adv e-mail advertisinginfo@suntimes.com; disp adv e-mail advertisinginfo@suntimes.com; class adv e-mailclassifieds@stmedianetwork.com; ed e-mail HeraldNews@stmedianetwork.com; web site www.heraldnews.suntimes.com
Group: Paddock Publications
Published: Mon, Tues, Wed, Thur, Fri, Sun
Weekday Frequency: m
Saturday Frequency: m
Circulation: 17,561; 20,556(sun)
Last Audit: AAM March 31, 2015
Advertising Rate (weekday/saturday): 1/8 Pg $154.00; 1/6 Pg $242.00
Advertising Rate (sunday): 1/8 Pg $154.00; 1/6 Pg $242.00
News services: AP, CNS, NYT. **Established:** 1877
Special Editions: Destination Spring Travel (Apr); Windfall of Homes (Aug); Readers Choice Awards (Dec); New Homes Spring Buyers (Feb); Super Suburban Jobs (Jan); Education Outlook (Jul); Wedding Planner (Jun); Education Outlook (Mar); Education Outlook (Nov); Home Improve
Special Weekly Sections: Automotive (Fri); Community Calendar (Mon); Health (S); Church (Sat); Weekend (Thur); Consumer Page (Tues); Food Page (Wed).
Syndicated Publications: USA WEEKEND Magazine (S); TV Update (Sat).
Digital Platform - Mobile: Android
Digital Platform - Tablet: Android
Adv. Mgr., Retail Sales .... Steve Vanisko
Circ. Mgr., Regl. .... Ray Kartis
Ed. .... Joe Biesk
News Ed. .... Matt Cappelini
Sports Ed. .... Dick Goss
Online Mgr. .... Steve Sumner
Market Information: Split run; TMC; Zoned editions.
Mechanical Available: Offset; Black and 3 ROP colors; insert accepted - any; page cutoffs - 21.
Mechanical Specifications: Type page 13 x 21; E - 6 cols, 2 1/16, 3/16 between; A - 6 cols, 2 5/32, 1/16 between; C - 10 cols, 1 3/8, 1/16 between.
Areas Served: Joliet & Surrounding areas (IL)
Equipment & Software: PRESSROOM EQUIPMENT: Lines — 4-G/Colorliner 2065 double width 1992; 4-G/Colorliner 2066 double width 1992; Reels & Stands — 10-G/CT50.; MAILROOM EQUIPMENT: Counter Stackers — 6/QWI, 2-/HL; Inserters & Stuffers — 2-GMA/SLS 1000 14:1; Tying Machines — 8-/Power Strap; Address Machine — 2-/AVY, 1-/Ch.; BUSINESS EQUIPMENT: DEC BUSINESS SOFTWARE: Archetype/Corel Draw, MicroGraphics/Designer DISPLAY EQUIPMENT: Hardware — DEC; Printers — OMS/Laser Printer; DISPLAY SOFTWAREAd Make-up Applications — CJ.; EDITORIAL EQUIPMENT: Hardware — SII/Sys 55, 25-SII/Coyote, SII/Coyote 3, SII/MTX/1-APP/Mac II, 1-APP/Mac IIci, 1-APP/Mac SE; Printers — 1-TI/810, APP/Mac LaserWriter NTX EDITORIAL SOFTWARE: SII. PRODUCTION EQUIPMENT: Hardware — 2-AU/APS-108, 2-AU/APS-6000 Proofers, 4-Sierra/3850 Imagers, 2-HP/8000 b/w Proofers; Cameras — 2-B; Scanners — 1-ECR/Autokon 2030, 1-Howtek/4500 PRODUCTION SOFTWARE: QPS/QuarkXPress 6.0, AU/Grafix Rips 4, Apscom (send) 4, Apscom (receive) 4.
Note: Suburban Chicago Newspapers includes the Aurora Beacon News (mS), Elgin Courier News (mS), Joliet Herald News (mS), Naperville Sun (mS) and Waukegan Lake County News-Sun (e). The group combination rate is $170.50 (dS). Individual newspaper rates not made

CRYSTAL LAKE

NORTHWEST HERALD

7717 S Route 31, Crystal Lake, Ill., 60014, McHenry; gen tel (815) 459-4040; adv tel (815) 459-4040; ed tel (800) 589-8910; gen fax (815) 477-4960; adv fax (815) 477-4960; ed fax (815) 459-5640; gen/nat adv e-mail advertising@nwherald.com; disp adv e-mail advertising@nwherald.com; class adv e-mailclassified@nwherald.com; ed e-mail tips@nwherald.com; web site www.nwherald.com
- 3,700,000(views) 610,000(visitors); web site 2 www.ShawMedia.com
Group: Shaw Media
Published: Mon, Tues, Wed, Thur, Fri, Sat, Sun

Weekday Frequency: m
Saturday Frequency: m
Circulation: 20,617; 20,617(sat); 23,416(sun)
Last Audit: AAM March 31, 2016
Newspaper Reps: Kate Weber, Publisher
Jason Hegna, Group Advertising Director
Jason Schaumburg, Editor
LeeAnn Atwood, Group Marketing Director
Advertising Rate (weekday/saturday): Open inch rate $26.00
Advertising Rate (sunday): Open inch rate $26.00
Online Advertising Rate: ROS (big box) $15cpm; Rich Media $25cpm; Premium Reserved Position $20cpm
News services: AP, Gatehouse, Washington Post/Bloomberg News Service, Illinois Statehouse News, Tribune Content Agency, New York Times Syndicate **Established:** 1851
Own Printing Facility?: No
Commercial Printers?: Yes
Special Editions: Auto Show Preview (Feb), Everyday Heroes Progress Edition (Feb), Spring Home Improvement (Mar), Prep Football Guide (Aug), Best Under 40 (Oct), Hometown Holidays (Nov), Last Minute Gift (Dec)
Special Weekly Sections: Food (Wed), Real Estate (Thurs), Entertainment Pl@y (Thurs), Wheels (Fri), Business (Sun), Jobs (Sun)
Syndicated Publications: Relish; American Profile, Spry, Athlon Sports
Proprietary Publications: McHenry County Magazine
Digital Platform - Mobile: Apple, Android, Windows, Blackberry
Digital Platform - Tablet: Apple iOS, Android, Windows 7, Blackberry Tablet OS, Kindle, Nook, Kindle Fire
Executive Group Editor Dan McCaleb
VP/Production....Kevin Elder
I.T. Director....Steve Sulouff
Classified Mgr.....Shelly Bissell
Features Ed.....Scott Helmchen
Editor, Northwest Herald....Jason Schaumburg
Advertising Operations Director....Megan Hampton
Group Sales Dir.....Maureen Ringness
Major/Nat'l Sales Coord.....Rebecca Dienhart
Publisher....Kate Weber
Senior Circulation Director....Bob Edwards
Group H.R. Manager....Karla Ahr
Group Classified Director....Brad Hanahan
Gen. Mgr.....Jim Ringness
Managing Ed.....Kevin Lyons
Market Information: Greater McHenry County Area
Mechanical Specifications: 6 col wide (11.125 inches) x 20.5 inches high
Areas Served: McHenry County
Delivery Method: Newsstand, Carrier, RacksEquipment & Software: BUSINESS EQUIPMENT: Hardware — Mac BUSINESS SOFTWARE: VisionData CLASSIFIED EQUIPMENT: Hardware — Mac CLASSIFIED SOFTWARE: VisionData DISPLAY EQUIPMENT: Hardware — Mac; DISPLAY SOFTWAREAd Make-up Applications — InDesign; EDITORIAL EQUIPMENT: Hardware — Mac EDITORIAL SOFTWARE: Roxen CIRCULATION EQUIPMENT: Hardware — Mac CIRCULATION SOFTWARDTI Circulation

DANVILLE

COMMERCIAL NEWS

28 Logan Terrace Three, Danville, Ill., 61832-1651, Vermilion; gen tel (217) 446-1000; adv tel (217) 447-5115; ed tel (217) 447-5155; gen fax (217) 446-9825; ed fax (217) 446-6648; gen/nat adv e-mail info@dancomnews.com; ed e-mail newsroom@dancomnews.com; web site www.commercial-news.com
Group: Community Newspaper Holdings, Inc.
Published: Tues, Wed, Thur, Fri, Sat, Sun
Weekday Frequency: m
Saturday Frequency: m
Circulation: 8,681; 8,681(sat); 10,361(sun)
Last Audit: AAM September 30, 2012
Advertising Rate (weekday/saturday): Open inch rate $21.00
News services: AP, SHNS. **Established:** 1866
Own Printing Facility?: No
Commercial Printers?: No
Special Editions: Turn the Key (Monthly).
Special Weekly Sections: Farm Page (Fri); Home Place (Thur); Best Food Day (Wed).
Syndicated Publications: Teleview (Fri); USA WEEKEND Magazine (S).
Digital Platform - Mobile: Apple, Android, Windows, Blackberry
Ed.....Larry Smith
City Ed.....Mary Wicoff
Sports Ed.....Chad Dare
Circ. Dir.....Scott Mathis
Business Mgr.....Paula Campbell
Adv. Sales. Mgr.....Cindy Decker
Jennifer Bailey
Newsroom....Brian Huchel
Newsroom....Carol Roehm
Sports....Marvin Holman
Adv.....Dana Burress
Adv.....Mimi Saylor
Adv.....Diane Ross
Class.....Jennifer Kindle
Class.....Susan Winchester
Circ....Gail Costello
Circ....Sherrill Sherman
Pub....Amy Winter
Market Information: TMC; Zoned editions.
Mechanical Available: Offset; Black and 3 ROP colors; insert accepted - 6"x9" cards, single sheets 8 1/2" x 11"; max size 12.5" x 11.25"
Mechanical Specifications: Type page 10 x 20 1/2; Retail - 6 cols, 1 5/6, 1/8 between; Class - 9 cols, 1 3/8, 1/8 between.
Areas Served: Greater Danville, IL
Delivery Method: Mail, Newsstand, Carrier, Racks

DECATUR

HERALD & REVIEW, DECATUR

601 E William St, Decatur, Ill., 62523-1142, Macon; gen tel (217) 429-5151; adv tel (217) 421-6920; ed tel (217) 421-6979; gen fax (217) 421-6913; adv fax (217) 421-6942; ed fax (217) 421-7965; gen/nat adv e-mail jfletcher@herald-review.com; disp adv e-mail chittmeier@herald-review.com; class adv e-maillconnelly@herald-review.com; ed e-mail ddawson@herald-review.com; web site www.herald-review.com - 1,700,000(views) 240,000(visitors)
Group: Lee Enterprises, Inc.
Published: Mon, Tues, Wed, Thur, Fri, Sat, Sun
Weekday Frequency: m
Saturday Frequency: m
Circulation: 22,816; 22,816(sat); 28,391(sun)
Last Audit: AAM September 30, 2016
Advertising Rate (weekday/saturday): Open inch rate $55.85
News services: AP, Metro Surburbia Inc.. **Established:** 1873
Special Editions: Christmas Storybook (Other).
Special Weekly Sections: Entertainment (Fri); Business (S); Religion/Family (Sat); Teens (Thur); Food/Health (Wed).
Syndicated Publications: Parade (S).
Digital Platform - Mobile: Apple, Android
Digital Platform - Tablet: Apple iOS, Android, Kindle Fire
Managing. Ed./ Print....Scott Perry
Audience Engagement Ed.....Tim Cain
Sports Ed.....Mike Albright
Data Processing Supvr.....Karen Woare
Tech. Servs. Mgr.....Brad Marshall
Online Mgr.....Beth McCormick
Prodn. Mgr., Press....Chuck Rutherford
Circulation Operations Manager....Mark Hall
Ed.....Chris Coates
Managing Ed./Digital....Allison Petty
Adv. Dir.....Shawna Lawrence
Dig. Adv. Sales Mgr.....Cayla Hittmeier
Gen. Mgr.....Joel Fletcher
Deputy Managing Ed. / Print....Jeana Matherly
Deputy Managing Ed./Digital....John Reidy
Market Information: ADS; Split run; TMC; Zoned editions.
Mechanical Available: Flexography; Black and 3 ROP colors; insert accepted; page cutoffs - 21 5/8.
Mechanical Specifications: Type page 13 x 21 1/2; E - 6 cols, 2 1/16, 1/8 between; A - 6 cols, 2 1/16, 1/8 between; C - 9 cols, 1 3/8, 1/16 between.
Areas Served: Decatur & Macon County
Equipment & Software: PRESSROOM EQUIPMENT: Lines — KBA/Colormax 1994; Folders — H/Double 3:2.; MAILROOM EQUIPMENT: Counter Stackers — 1-HL/Monitor, 2-QWI/300, 1-QWI/351; Inserters & Stuffers — 1-MM/227 5:1, HI/1372, Phillipsburg/6:1; Tying Machines — 2/Power Strap/PSN6, 3-MLN/2A, 2-Bu/String Tyer; Wrapping Singles — 2-/Bu; Address Machine — 1-BH/Mg 1530,; BUSINESS EQUIPMENT: IBM/AS-400 CLASSIFIED EQUIPMENT: Hardware — CText/Advision ALPS; Printers — AG/Avantra 25.; DISPLAY EQUIPMENT: Hardware — Cascade Dataflow/Image Flow; Printers — AG/Avantra 25; Other Hardware — AP AdSend DISPLAY SOFTWAREAd Make-up Applications — QPS/QuarkXPress; Layout Software — MEI/ALS. EDITORIAL EQUIPMENT: Hardware — CText/Dateline-Expressline; Printers — AG/Avantra 25. PRODUCTION EQUIPMENT: Hardware — 2-AG/Avantra 25 Laser Drum Imager, 1-Na/Consolux; Cameras — C/Spartan III; Scanners — Kk/2035, Pixelcraft/8200.

DEKALB

DAILY CHRONICLE

1586 Barber Greene Rd, Dekalb, Ill., 60115-7900, Dekalb; gen tel (815) 756-4841; gen fax (815) 756-2079; ed fax (815) 758-5059; gen/nat adv e-mail kpletsch@shawmedia.com; disp adv e-mail kpletsch@shawmedia.com; class adv e-mailclassified@shawsuburban.com; ed e-mail news@daily-chronicle.com; web site www.daily-chronicle.com
Group: Shaw Media
Published: Mon, Tues, Wed, Thur, Fri, Sat, Sun
Weekday Frequency: m
Saturday Frequency: m
Circulation: 6,068; 6,068(sat); 6,500(sun)
Last Audit: AAM June 30, 2017
Advertising Rate (weekday/saturday): Open inch rate $14.81
News services: AP, TMS, Gatehouse News Service, Washington Post/Bloomberg **Established:** 1880
Own Printing Facility?: No
Commercial Printers?: No
Special Editions: Progress (Apr); Back-to-School (Aug); Gift Guide (Dec); Farm Forecast (Jan); Spring Fashion (Mar); Home Improvement-Lawn & Garden (May); Christmas (Nov); Fall Farm (Oct); Fall Home Improvement (Sept).
Syndicated Publications: USA WEEKEND Magazine (Weekly), Relish (Monthly), American Profile (Weekly), Spry (Monthly), Athlon Sports (Monthly)
Pub....Karen Pletsch
Ed.....Eric Olson
Features Ed.....Inger Koch
News Editor....Brett Rowland
Photo Ed.....Danielle Guerra
Web Ed.....Lawrence Synett
Sports Ed.....Eddie Carifio
Sports Reporter....Steve Nitz
Photographer....Monica Maschak
Reporter....Katie Dahlstrom
Reporter....Andrea Azzo
Reporter....Jessi Haish
Areas Served: 60111 60112 60115 60135 60145 60146 60530 60531 60150 60151 60536 60537 60541 60545 61068 60548 60549 60550 60551 60552 60178 60556
Delivery Method: Newsstand, Carrier, RacksEquipment & Software: BUSINESS EQUIPMENT: Sun/Mac BUSINESS SOFTWARE: VisionData CLASSIFIED EQUIPMENT: Hardware — Sun/Mac; CLASSIFIED SOFTWARE: VisionData DISPLAY EQUIPMENT: Hardware — Mac; DISPLAY SOFTWAREAd Make-up Applications — InDesign; EDITORIAL EQUIPMENT: Hardware — Mac EDITORIAL SOFTWARE: Roxen
Note: Production outsourced to commercial printer.

DIXON

THE TELEGRAPH

113 S Peoria Ave, Ste 1, Dixon, Ill., 61021-2905, Lee; gen tel (815) 284-2224; adv tel (815) 284-2224; ed tel (815) 284-2224; gen fax (815) 284-2078; adv fax (815) 284-2078; ed fax (815) 284-2078; gen/nat adv e-mail jbaratta@saukvalley.com; disp adv e-mail jbaratta@saukvalley.com; class adv e-mailjdiehl@saukvalley.com; ed e-mail llough@saukvalley.com; web site www.saukvalley.com
Group: Shaw Media
Published: Mon, Tues, Wed, Thur, Fri
Weekday Frequency: e
Saturday Frequency: e
Circulation: 4,977
Last Audit: AAM September 30, 2017
Advertising Rate (weekday/saturday): Open inch rate $14.05
Advertising Rate (sunday): Open inch rate $23.91
News services: AP, CNS, SHNS. **Established:** 1851
Special Editions: Career Guide (Apr); Whiteside County Fair (Aug); Last Minute Gift Guide (Dec); Internet Directory (Feb); Health & Fitness (Jan); Dixon Sidewalk Sale (Jul); Dixon Petunia Festival (Jun); Home & Garden (Mar); Today's Farm (May); Senior Echo (Monthly); Baske
Special Weekly Sections: Celebrations (Bi-Weekly); Food (Wed); Real Estate, Entertainment (Thur); Auto, Recreation, Travel (Sat)
Adv. Mgr.....Jennifer Baratta
Gen. Mgr.....Ed Bushman
Circ. Mgr.....Sheryl Gulbranson
Exec. Ed....Larry Lough
Sports Ed.....Will Larkin
Travel Ed.....Andrea Mills
Prodn. Mgr.....Ernie Appleyard
Pub.....Sam Fisher
Customer Service....Kim Weinstock
Mktg. Mgr.....Nicole Bollman
Finance Dir.....JoAnne Mills
Market Information: TMC.
Mechanical Available: Offset; Black and 3 ROP colors; insert accepted - all; page cutoffs - 22 3/4.
Mechanical Specifications: Type page 11 5/8 x 21 1/2; E - 6 cols, 1 5/6, 1/8 between; A - 6 cols, 1 5/6, 1/8 between; C - 9 cols, 1 1/4, 1/8 between.
Areas Served: 61021, 61081, 61071Equipment & Software: PRESSROOM EQUIPMENT: Lines — 8-G/Urbanite; 7-HI/V-15A w/Glue Line; MAILROOM EQUIPMENT: Counter Stackers — Exact/Stack, QWI/Sport II Stacker; Inserters & Stuffers — HI/1372; Tying Machines — 3-B/18, Dynaric/RLM-1, Sterling/GR45; Address Machine — 1/Dispensa-Matic, Ch/595.; BUSINESS EQUIPMENT: ATT, APP/Mac, Convergent/S480 CLASSIFIED EQUIPMENT: Hardware — 8-APP/Mac; Printers — 1-Okidata/Microline 320 dot matrix, 1-HP/8100 N; CLASSIFIED SOFTWARE: Baseview. DISPLAY EQUIPMENT: Hardware — 7-APP/Mac; Printers — 2-HP/LaserJet 8150N; DISPLAY SOFTWAREAd Make-up Applications — QPS/QuarkXPress 4.1, Adobe/Photoshop 6.0, Adobe/Illustrator 9.0.; EDITORIAL EQUIPMENT: Hardware — 28-APP/Mac; Printers — 2-HP/8150 N EDITORIAL SOFTWARE: Baseview 3.21. PRODUCTION EQUIPMENT: Hardware — 1-Nu/Flip Top FT40L, 1-ECR/5100, Konica K-28; Cameras — 1-B/4000-C, Nu/SSTE 2024SB; Scanners — 2-AG/Arcus II PRODUCTION SOFTWARE: Baseview 3.21.
Note: The Dixon Telegraph (e, wknd) has a combination rate of $30.27 with The Sterling Daily Gazette (e, wknd). Individual newspaper rates not made available.

DU QUOIN

DU QUOIN EVENING CALL

9 N Division St, Du Quoin, Ill., 62832-1405, Perry; gen tel (618) 542-2133; gen fax (618) 542-2726; gen/nat adv e-mail duquoin@frontier.com; disp adv e-mail csmith@duquoin.com; class adv e-mailamilam@duquoin.com; ed e-mail jcroessman@duquoin.com; web site www.duquoin.com
Group: New Media Investment Group
Published: Mon, Tues, Wed, Thur, Fri
Weekday Frequency: e
Circulation: 3,800
Last Audit: Sworn/Estimate/Non-Audited September 30, 2017

Advertising Rate (weekday/saturday): Open inch rate $9.75
News services: AP. **Established:** 1895
Own Printing Facility?: No
Commercial Printers?: No
Special Editions: Spring Home Improvements (Apr); Du Quoin State Fair (Aug); Tax Guide Tab (Feb); Bridal Show (Jan); Progress (Mar); Christmas Preview (Nov); Fall Home Improvements (Oct).
Special Weekly Sections: American Weekend (Fri); Business (Sat).
Syndicated Publications: USA WEEKEND Magazine (Sat); American Profile (Weekly).
Digital Platform - Mobile: Apple
Digital Platform - Tablet: Apple iOS
Pub. .... Lynne Campbell
Office Mgr. .... Debra Burns
Circ. Mgr. .... Patty Malinee
Sports Ed. .... Doug Daniels
News Ed. .... Kathy Kopshever
Adv. Mgr. .... Craig Smith
Market Information: TMC.
Mechanical Available: Offset; Black and 4 ROP colors; insert accepted; page cutoffs - 21 1/2.
Mechanical Specifications: Type page 13 4/5 x 23; E - 6 cols, 2 1/16, 1/8 between; A - 6 cols, 2 1/16, 1/8 between; C - 8 cols, 1 1/4, 1/8 between.
Areas Served: Perry, Franklin, Randolph and Jackson Counties in Southern Illinois
Delivery Method: Mail, Newsstand, Carrier, RacksEquipment & Software: PRESSROOM EQUIPMENT: Lines — G/Community; MAILROOM EQUIPMENT: Tying Machines — 1/Bu; Address Machine — IBM/Listmaster.; BUSINESS EQUIPMENT: HP CLASSIFIED EQUIPMENT: Apple I-Mac CLASSIFIED SOFTWARE: Multi-Ad/CAMS. DISPLAY EQUIPMENT: Apple I-Mac DISPLAY SOFTWAREAd Make-up Applications — Multi-Ad/Creator; EDITORIAL EQUIPMENT: Apple I-Mac EDITORIAL SOFTWARE: OS10.5 PRODUCTION EQUIPMENT: Apple I-Mac PRODUCTION SOFTWARE: QPS/QuarkXPress.

EDWARDSVILLE

EDWARDSVILLE INTELLIGENCER
117 N 2nd St, Edwardsville, Ill., 62025-1938, Madison; gen tel (618) 656-4700; gen fax (618) 656-7618; gen/nat adv e-mail aschaake@edwpub.net; disp adv e-mail aschaake@edwpub.net; class adv e-mailnewads@edwpub.net; ed e-mail news@edwpub.net; web site www.theintelligencer.com/ - 550,000(views)
Group: Hearst Communications, Inc.
Published: Mon, Tues, Wed, Thur, Fri, Sat
Weekday Frequency: e
Saturday Frequency: m
Circulation: 4,288; 4,288(sat)
Last Audit: Sworn/Estimate/Non-Audited September 30, 2017
Advertising Rate (weekday/saturday): Open inch rate $17.20
News services: AP, HN. **Established:** 1862
Special Editions: Good News (Apr); Fall Sports (Aug); Christmas Greetings (Dec); Draw-an-Ad (Feb); Auto Show (Jan); Customer Appreciation (Jun); Spring Sports (Mar); Travel & Leisure (May); Veterans Day (Nov); Harvest Homefest (Oct); Answer Book/Madison Co. (Sept).
Special Weekly Sections: Real Estate (Fri); Family (Mon); Best Food Day (Sat).
Syndicated Publications: Weekender (Entertainment) (Sat).
Pub. .... Denise Vonder Haar
Adv. Mgr. .... Schaake Amy
Editor .... Bill Tucker
Mgmt. Info Servs. Mgr. .... Ron Harris
Prodn. Supvr., Mailroom .... Nick Tennyson
Adv. Design Mgr. .... Jennifer Dyer
Prodn. Foreman, Press/Camera .... David White
Opns. Mgr. .... Rosemary Kebel
Sports Ed. .... Bill Roseberry
Market Information: TMC.
Mechanical Available: Offset; Black and 3 ROP colors; insert accepted; page cutoffs - 22 3/4.
Mechanical Specifications: Type page 12 7/8 x 21 1/2; E - 6 cols, 2 1/16, 1/8 between; A - 6 cols, 2 1/16, 1/8 between; C - 9 cols, 1 3/8,

1/16 between.
Areas Served: Edwardsville, Glen Carbon, Maryville, Collinsville, Troy, Worden, Alhambra & Hamel (IL)
Equipment & Software: PRESSROOM EQUIPMENT: Folders — 1-KP/KJ-6. MAILROOM EQUIPMENT: Counter Stackers — 1/BG; Inserters & Stuffers — 1-KAN/320, 4-KAN/Station inserter; Tying Machines — 2-Bu/String Tying Machine; Address Machine — 1-Automecha/Accufast PL-M; BUSINESS EQUIPMENT: 3-IBM/486 DX2, 2-ALR/Powerflex, 3-Packard Bell/486 DX2, Compaq/286, 1-IBM/AST 486 DX2 BUSINESS SOFTWARE: Infinum, MSExcel, MS/Word CLASSIFIED EQUIPMENT: Hardware — 2-APP/Mac Quadra 605; Printers — 1-TI; CLASSIFIED SOFTWARE: FSI/Classified. DISPLAY EQUIPMENT: Hardware — 2-APP/Power Mac 7200, 2-APP/Mac Quadra 650; Printers — APP/Mac LaserWriter IIg, Lynx/Imagesetter, Imager/Plus 12; DISPLAY SOFTWAREAd Make-up Applications — Multi-Ad/Creator, APP/Mac System 7.1, QPS/QuarkXPress 3.3; Layout Software — 2-Mk. EDITORIAL EQUIPMENT: Hardware — APP/Mac Quadras, APP/Mac LC IIIs/4-RSK/Tandy TRS 100 EDITORIAL SOFTWARE: QPS/QuarkXPress. PRODUCTION EQUIPMENT: Hardware — 4-APP/Mac LaserWriter, Dataproducts/LZR-1560, APP/Mac LaserWriter IIg, Lynx/Imagesetter; Cameras — 1-R; Scanners — 1-APP/Mac Scanner, Nikon PRODUCTION SOFTWARE: FSI.

EFFINGHAM

EFFINGHAM DAILY NEWS
201 N Banker St, Effingham, Ill., 62401-2304, Effingham; gen tel (217) 347-7151 x 112; gen fax (217) 342-9315; disp adv e-mail darrell. lewis@effinghamdailynews.com; class adv e-mailcarrie.wente@effinghamdailynews. com; ed e-mail editor@effinghamdailynews. com; web site www.effinghamdailynews.com - 290,000(views) 74,000(visitors)
Group: Community Newspaper Holdings, Inc.
Published: Mon, Tues, Wed, Thur, Fri, Sat
Weekday Frequency: m
Saturday Frequency: m
Circulation: 7,500; 8,000(sat)
Last Audit: Sworn/Estimate/Non-Audited September 11, 2017
Advertising Rate (weekday/saturday): 16.50
Advertising Rate (sunday): 17.30
Online Advertising Rate: 12.00 desktop 15.00 mobile
News services: AP. **Established:** 1935
Own Printing Facility?: No
Commercial Printers?: No
Special Weekly Sections: Homes (Tue); Health (Wed); Farm, NASCAR (Thur); Church, Entertainment (Fri); Food (Sat)
Pub./Adv. Dir. .... Darrell Lewis
Ed. .... Jeff Long
Mng. Ed. .... Cathy Griffith
Circ. Mgr. .... Todd Buenker
Bus. Mgr. .... Jane Herring
Composing Suprv. .... Linda Niebrugge
Market Information: ADS; TMC.
Mechanical Available: Offset; Black and 3 ROP colors; insert accepted; page cutoffs - 22 3/4.
Mechanical Specifications: Type page 13 x 21 1/2; E - 6 cols, 1 7/8, 1/8 between; A - 6 cols, 2 1/14, 1/8 between; C - 9 cols, 1 9/16, 1/8 between.
Areas Served: Effingham & Surrounding areas
Delivery Method: Mail, Newsstand, Carrier, Racks

FREEPORT

THE JOURNAL-STANDARD
50 W Douglas St, Fl 9th, Freeport, Ill., 61032-4129, Stephenson; gen tel (815) 232-1171; adv tel (815) 232-2171; ed tel (815) 232-0166; gen fax (815) 232-3601; adv fax (815) 232-0104; ed fax (815) 232-0105; gen/nat adv e-mail ann.young@journalstandard.com; disp adv e-mail ann. young@journalstandard.com; class adv e-mailclassifieds@journalstandard.com; ed

e-mail frontdoor@journalstandard.com; web site www.journalstandard.com
Group: New Media Investment Group
Published: Tues, Wed, Thur, Fri, Sat, Sun
Weekday Frequency: m
Saturday Frequency: m
Circulation: 5,547; 5,547(sat); 6,156(sun)
Last Audit: AAM June 30, 2017
Advertising Rate (weekday/saturday): Open inch rate $20.19
Advertising Rate (sunday): Open inch rate $22.71
News services: AP, CNS, MCT. **Established:** 1847
Special Editions: Dream Homes (Apr); Football Tab (Aug); Homefront (Every other month); Home & Garden (Mar); Summer Calendar (May); Christmas Gift Guide (Nov).
Special Weekly Sections: Hometown Connections (Tue); Food, Fashion (Wed); Auto, Education, Faith (Thur); Arts, Books, Movies (Fri); Get Up & Go, Home, Garden (Sat); Business, careers, Travel, TV, Celebrations, Comics (Sun)
Syndicated Publications: Parade (S); American Profile (Weekly).
Gen. Mgr. .... Michele Massoth
Circ. Mgr. .... Doris Schaible
Mng. Ed. .... Anna Derocher
Pub. .... Paul Gaier
Sales Adv. Mgr. .... Mike Cowan
Market Information: TMC; Zoned editions.
Mechanical Available: Offset; Black and 3 ROP colors; insert accepted - machine insertable; page cutoffs - 21 1/2.
Mechanical Specifications: Type page 11 5/8 x 21 1/4; E - 6 cols, 1 5/6, 1/8 between; A - 6 cols, 1 5/6, 1/8 between; C - 9 cols, 1 1/5, 1/8 between.
Areas Served: Northwest Illinois
Equipment & Software: PRESSROOM EQUIPMENT: 7-G/Urbanite 1994. MAILROOM EQUIPMENT: Counter Stackers — 2-HL/Monitor; Inserters & Stuffers — 1-MM/227; Tying Machines — OVL; Control System — HL.; BUSINESS EQUIPMENT: Sun/Micro, DEC/VT420s BUSINESS SOFTWARE: Vision Data CLASSIFIED EQUIPMENT: Hardware — Sun/Sparc II Server, Sun/Sparc Terminals; Printers — Dataproducts; CLASSIFIED SOFTWARE: Vision Data/Island Write. DISPLAY EQUIPMENT: Hardware — 5-APP/Mac II, 1-APP/Mac IIci, APP/Mac with Radius monitors; Printers — APP/Mac LaserWriter, Imager/1200L, Hyphen RIP; Other Hardware — APP/Mac Scanner, 2-APP/Mac CD-Rom, 1-NEC/CD-Rom, 2-Poweruser DISPLAY SOFTWAREAd Make-up Applications — QPS/QuarkXPress, Adobe/Illustrator; EDITORIAL EQUIPMENT: Hardware — 3-Compaq/386, 15-Amdek/VDT, APP/Power Mac 7100, 2-APP/Mac II, 6-APP/Mac IIci, 2-APP/Mac IIcx, Sun/Storage System 2gig/Editorial/NEC/CD-Rom; Printers — 1-APP/Mac LaserWriter, APP/Mac LaserWriter EDITORIAL SOFTWARE: QPS/QuarkXPress. PRODUCTION EQUIPMENT: Hardware — ECR/Pelbox, Sun/Storage System 4gig, OPI; Scanners — AG/7A Flatbed-Slide Scanner, APP/Mac Scanner, Kk/Slide-Negative Scanner.

GALESBURG

THE REGISTER-MAIL
140 S Prairie St, Galesburg, Ill., 61401-4605, Knox; gen tel (309) 343-7181; adv tel (309) 343-7181; ed tel (309) 343-7181; gen fax (309) 342-5171; adv fax (309) 342-5171; ed fax (309) 343-2382; gen/nat adv e-mail lcampbell@gatehousemedia.com; disp adv e-mail lcampbell@gatehousemedia.com; class adv e-mailcuhlmann@register-mail. com; ed e-mail tmartin@register-mail.com; web site www.galesburg.com
Group: New Media Investment Group
Published: Mon, Tues, Wed, Thur, Fri, Sat, Sun
Weekday Frequency: m
Saturday Frequency: m
Circulation: 9,194; 9,194(sat); 10,362(sun)
Last Audit: AAM September 30, 2014
Advertising Rate (weekday/saturday): Open inch rate $88.74
Advertising Rate (sunday): Open inch rate $100.22
News services: AP.

Special Editions: Lawn & Garden (Apr); Football (Aug); Gift Ads (Dec); Bridal Tab (Feb); Senior Citizens (Jan); Knox Co. Fair (Jul); Farmers' Forecast (Jun); Ag Day (Mar); Real Estate (May); Basketball (Nov); Farmers' Forecast (Oct); Senior Citizens (Sept).
Special Weekly Sections: Kids, Family (Mon); Business, Agriculture, Personal Income, Stargazers (tue); Food, Recipes, health, Fitness, Cook's Corner (Wed); Entertainment, Meeting Place, Trends (Thur); Auto, Parenting, Education (Fri); Home, Garden, Business (Sat); Travel, Arts (Sun)
Syndicated Publications: Parade (S).
Adv. Mgr. .... Nathan Clark
Ed. .... Tom Martin
Local News Ed. .... Robert Buck
Pub. .... David Adams
Sports Ed. .... Mike Trueblood
Prodn. Mgr. .... John Bown
Jan Blair
Pub. .... Tony Scott
Market Information: TMC.
Mechanical Available: Offset; Black and 3 ROP colors; insert accepted; page cutoffs - 22 5/8.
Mechanical Specifications: Type page 13 3/4 x 22 5/8; E - 6 cols, 2, 1/6 between; A - 6 cols, 2, 1/6 between; C - 9 cols, 1 2/5, between.
Areas Served: 61401, 61430, 61448, 61488, 61410, 61462Equipment & Software: PRESSROOM EQUIPMENT: Lines — 4-Wd/double width, Wd/Lithoflex; 3-G/Community; 10-WPC/Atlas (w/2-Quadra-color unit); MAILROOM EQUIPMENT: Tying Machines — Strapper; Address Machine — KAN/500.; BUSINESS EQUIPMENT: ATT, Vision Data BUSINESS SOFTWARE: Vision Data CLASSIFIED EQUIPMENT: Hardware — Dewar; CLASSIFIED SOFTWARE: Dewar. DISPLAY EQUIPMENT: Hardware — APP/Mac; Printers — APP/Mac; Other Hardware — Dewar/DiscNet DISPLAY SOFTWAREAd Make-up Applications — Multi-Ad/Creator; Layout Software — Multi-Ad/Creator. EDITORIAL EQUIPMENT: Hardware — Dewar/APP/Mac Photo System, Lf/AP Leaf Picture Desk; Printers — T/300, Okidata/182 EDITORIAL SOFTWARE: Dewar. PRODUCTION EQUIPMENT: Hardware — 2-Nu, 1-Nat; Cameras — 1-SCREEN.
Note: The Galesburg Register-Mail (eS) has a combination rate of $86.16(d) and $97.30(S) with the Peoria Journal Star (mS). Individual newspaper rates not made available.

GURNEE

LAKE COUNTY NEWS-SUN
1225 Tri State Pkwy Ste 570, Suite 570, Gurnee, Ill., 60031-9163, Lake; gen tel (312) 222-2425; adv tel (312) 283-7056; ed tel (312) 222-2350; gen/nat adv e-mail jbiesk@tribpub.com; disp adv e-mail CTMGSuburbanAdvertising@ctmg.com; ed e-mail jbiesk@tribpub.com; web site www.newssunonline.com; web site 2 www. chicagotribune.com/suburbs/lake-county-news-sun
Group: Tronc, Inc.
Published: Mon, Tues, Wed, Thur, Fri, Sat
Weekday Frequency: m
Last Audit: Sworn/Estimate/Non-Audited September 30, 2017
Advertising Rate (weekday/saturday): 1/8 Pg $590.00; 1/6 Pg $710.00; 1/4 Pg $950.00
News services: AP.
Special Weekly Sections: SEARCHchicagoautos (Fri).
Syndicated Publications: USA WEEKEND Magazine (Sat).
Mng. Ed. .... Jon Rabiroff
News Ed. .... Dan Moran
Ed. .... Joe Biesk
Exec. Ed. .... Phil Jurik
VP of Adv. .... Jill McDermott
Mechanical Available: Offset; Black and 4 ROP colors; insert accepted - single sheet flyers; page cutoffs - 11.
Mechanical Specifications: Type page 13 x 21; E - 6 cols, 2, between; A - 6 cols, 2 1/16, between; C - 10 cols, between.
Areas Served: 60085
Note: Suburban Chicago Newspapers includes the Aurora Beacon News (mS), Elgin Courier News (mS), Joliet Herald News

(mS), Naperville Sun (mS) and Waukegan Lake County News-Sun (m). The group combination rate is $170.50 (dS). Individual newspaper rates not made

HARRISBURG

ELDORADO DAILY JOURNAL

35 S Vine St, Harrisburg, Ill., 62946-1725, Saline; gen tel (618) 253-7146; gen fax (618) 252-0863; gen/nat adv e-mail crann@dailyregister.com; class adv e-mailnhawkins@dailyregister.com; ed e-mail bdeneal@dailyregsiter.com; web site www.dailyregister.com

Group: GateHouse Media, Inc.
Published: Mon, Tues, Wed, Thur, Fri
Weekday Frequency: e
Circulation: 650
Last Audit: Sworn/Estimate/Non-Audited September 30, 2017
Advertising Rate (weekday/saturday): Open inch rate $12-99
News services: AP **Established:** 1911
Own Printing Facility?: No
Commercial Printers?: No
Syndicated Publications: TV Guide (Fri); USA WEEKEND Magazine (Sat).
Prodn. Mgr. .... Brian DeNeal
Circ. Mgr. .... Norma Riley
Pub. .... David Adams
Ed. .... John Homan
Mechanical Available: Offset; Black and 4 ROP colors; insert accepted.
Mechanical Specifications: Type page 10.625 x 19.713; E - 6 cols, 1.667, .1667 between; A - 6 cols, 1.667, .1667 between; C - 10 cols, .982, .744 between.
Areas Served: 62930, 62946, 62935. 62984, 62977
Delivery Method: Mail, Newsstand, Carrier, RacksEquipment & Software: MAILROOM EQUIPMENT: Tying Machines — 1/Bu.; EDITORIAL EQUIPMENT: Hardware — 5-APP/Mac.

THE DAILY REGISTER

35 S Vine St, Harrisburg, Ill., 62946-1725, Saline; gen tel (618) 253-7146; adv tel (618) 253-7146; ed tel (618) 253-7146; gen fax (618) 252-0863; adv fax (618) 252-0863; ed fax (618) 252-0863; gen/nat adv e-mail crann@dailyregister.com; disp adv e-mail crann@dailyregister.com; class adv e-mailnhawkins@dailyregister.com; ed e-mail bdeneal@dailyregister.com; web site www.dailyregister.com

Group: New Media Investment Group
Published: Mon, Tues, Wed, Thur, Fri
Weekday Frequency: e
Saturday Frequency: m
Circulation: 3,700
Last Audit: Sworn/Estimate/Non-Audited September 30, 2017
Advertising Rate (weekday/saturday): Open inch rate $11.80
News services: AP. **Established:** 1869
Syndicated Publications: American Profile (Fri); USA WEEKEND Magazine (Sat).
Bus. Mgr. .... Kay Brandsasse
Prodn. Mgr. .... Gatha Moore
Managing Editor .... Brian DeNeal
Pres. Pub. .... Lynne Campbell
Circ Mgr .... Norma Riley
Sports Ed .... Michael Dann
Reporter .... Tom Kane
Mechanical Available: Offset; Black and 3 ROP colors; insert accepted; page cutoffs - 20.
Mechanical Specifications: Type page 10.625 x 19.713; E - 6 cols, 1.667, .1667 between; A - 6 cols, 1.667, .1667 between; C - 10 cols, .982, .744 between.
Areas Served: 62946, 62930, 62917, 62931, 62919, 62934, 62935, 62938, 62947, 62965, 62977, 62979, 62984, 62987
Delivery Method: Mail, Newsstand, Carrier, RacksEquipment & Software: MAILROOM EQUIPMENT: Tying Machines — 1/Bu; Address Machine — 2-/Wm.; BUSINESS EQUIPMENT: IBM CLASSIFIED EQUIPMENT: Hardware — APP/Mac; CLASSIFIED SOFTWARE: Multi-Ad. DISPLAY SOFTWARELayout Software — APP/Mac. EDITORIAL EQUIPMENT: Hardware — APP/Mac/2-APP/Mac PowerBook 140B.

JACKSONVILLE

JACKSONVILLE JOURNAL-COURIER

235 W State St, Jacksonville, Ill., 62650-2001, Morgan; gen tel (217) 245-6121; gen fax (217) 245-1226; adv fax (217) 245-4570; gen/nat adv e-mail vselby@myjournalcourier.com; disp adv e-mail vselby@myjournalcourier.com; class adv e-mailvselby@myjournalcourier.com; ed e-mail news@myjournalcourier.com; web site www.myjournalcourier.com - 800(views)

Group: Hearst Newspapers
Published: Mon, Tues, Wed, Thur, Fri, Sat, Sun
Weekday Frequency: m
Saturday Frequency: m
Circulation: 10,136; 10,136(sat); 10,859(sun)
Last Audit: Sworn/Estimate/Non-Audited November 30, 2017
Advertising Rate (weekday/saturday): Open inch rate $20.50
News services: AP, MCT **Established:** 1830
Own Printing Facility?: Yes
Commercial Printers?: Yes
Special Editions: Back-to-School (Aug); New Year's Eve (Dec); Fall Auto Care Tab (Fall); Valentine Idea (Feb); July $ Days (Jul); Father's Day (Jun); Tax Preparation (Mar); Graduation Tab (May); Modern Farmer (Other); Spring Auto Tab (Spring); Summer Bridal Tab (Summer).
Special Weekly Sections: Society (S); Fling (Thur); Food (Wed).
Syndicated Publications: Parade magazine (S); American Profile (Weekly); Relish (Weekly)
Digital Platform - Mobile: Apple, Android, Windows
Digital Platform - Tablet: Apple iOS, Android
Editor and publisher .... David C.L. Bauer
Sports Ed. .... Dennis Mathes
Prodn. Mgr. .... Jeff Lonergan
Advertising manager .... Vicki Selby
Circulation director .... Brian Pond
Market Information: TMC.
Mechanical Available: Offset; Black and 3 ROP colors; insert accepted; page cutoffs - 22 3/4.
Mechanical Specifications: Type page 12 1/2 x 21 1/2; E - 6 cols, 1 7/8, 1/8 between; A - 6 cols, 1 7/8, 1/8 between; C - 9 cols, 1 3/16, 1/8 between.
Areas Served: Morgan, Greene, Scott, Schuyler, Cass, Pike and Macoupin counties
Delivery Method: Mail, Newsstand, Carrier, RacksEquipment & Software: PRESSROOM EQUIPMENT: Lines — 8-G/Urbanite 1992.; EDITORIAL SOFTWARE: NewsEngin Creative Suite (InDesign)

JOLIET

THE HERALD-NEWS

2175 Oneida St, Joliet, Ill., 60435-6560, Will; gen tel (815) 280-4100; adv tel 815-280-4101; gen fax (815) 729-2019; gen/nat adv e-mail thnads@shawmedia.com; class adv e-mailclassified@shawsuburban.com; ed e-mail news@theherald-news.com; web site theherald-news.com

Group: Shaw Media
Published: Mon, Tues, Wed, Thur, Fri, Sun
Circulation: 17,066; 17,066(sat); 21,028(sun)
Last Audit: Sworn/Estimate/Non-Audited March 31, 2017
News services: 1839
Gen. Mgr. .... Steve Vanisko
Ed. .... Jon Styf

KANKAKEE

THE DAILY JOURNAL

8 Dearborn Sq, Kankakee, Ill., 60901-3909, Kankakee; gen tel (815) 937-3300; adv tel (815) 937-3376; ed tel (815) 802-5144; gen fax (815) 937-3301; adv fax 815-929-2128; ed fax (815) 937-3876; gen/nat adv e-mail advertise@daily-journal.com ; disp adv e-mail advertise@daily-journal.com ; class adv e-mailclassified@daily-journal.com; ed e-mail editors@daily-journal.com; web site www.daily-journal.com

Group: Small Newspaper Group
Published: Mon, Tues, Wed, Thur, Sat
Weekday Frequency: e
Saturday Frequency: m
Circulation: 17,874; 22,976(sat)
Last Audit: CAC March 31, 2016
Advertising Rate (weekday/saturday): Open inch rate $32.25 (M-F)
Advertising Rate (sunday): $38.70 (Sat)
Online Advertising Rate: $6.00 per thousand with minimum of 20,000 with year commitment
News services: AP; Washington Post; Bloomberg; Tribune News Service **Established:** 1853
Own Printing Facility?: Yes
Commercial Printers?: No
Special Editions: Farm (Mar); House & Garden (May); Medical Guide (June); Summertime Fun (May);Ask the Experts (June); Farmer's Market (Jul); Back To School (Aug); Breast Cancer Awareness (Sept); Sports (Aug/Nov); Veterans Day (Nov); All Wrapped Up In One (Dec); Weddings (Spring/Summer/Fall/Winter); Family First (Feb, May, July, Oct.); Health & Wellness (Jan); Chicago Bears Training Camp Program (Jul); Progress (Mar/Apr); Graduation (May); HomeFinder (Monthly); Homebuyers Guide (Aug); THRIVE (Sept); Home & Yard (Oct);Holiday Guides I & II (Nov/Dec)
Special Weekly Sections: TV Weekly (Sat)
Digital Platform - Mobile: Apple, Android, Windows
Digital Platform - Tablet: Apple iOS, Android, Windows 7, Kindle Fire
Editor & Publisher .... Len Robert Small
Bus. Mgr. .... Cindy Liptak
Dir., Network Operations .... Wade LeBeau
Gen. Mgr .... Kevin Norden
VP-Finance .... Sally Hendron
HR Asst.-Personnel Dev. .... Brenda Montgomery
HR Asst.-Benefits Coordinator .... Lori Baranowski
Sr. Sales Mgr .... Lyle Turro
Circulation & Audience Director .... Rebecca Meyer
Ed .... Mike Frey
Market Information: TMC - MoneySaver
Mechanical Available: Offset; Black and 3 ROP colors; insert accepted; page cutoffs - 22 3/4.
Mechanical Specifications: Type page 10 19/50 x 21 1/2 ; E - 6 cols, 1 16/25, 11/100 between; A - 6 cols, 1 16/25, 11/100 between; C - 6 cols, 1 16/25, 11/100 between.
Areas Served: 60910, 60913, 60914, 60915, 60917, 60935, 60940, 60941, 60901, 60950, 60954, 60956, 60958, 60961, 60964, 60969, 60911, 60912, 60922, 60924, 60927, 60928, 60930, 60931, 60938, 60945, 60951, 60953, 60955, 60966, 60968, 60970, 60920, 60929, 60420, 60401, 60408, 60418, 60442, 60449, 60468, 60481, 60918, 60919, 60946, 60959, 60416, 60424, 60474
Delivery Method: Mail, Newsstand, Carrier, RacksEquipment & Software: PRESSROOM EQUIPMENT: Lines — 7-G/Metro (3 Color Deck, 2 Tol); Reels & Stands — 6; MAILROOM EQUIPMENT: Counter Stackers — 4-IDAB 2000, 3/MM 310, 1-Quipp 351; Inserters & Stuffers — 1-MM/227, 1-MM/308, 1-GMA SLS 1000; Tying Machines — 7-Dynaric NP1. 2-Dynaric NP 1500 Address Machine — MCM Array, Kodak DS5120; Bottom Wrappers — 2- Quipp Viper, 1 - IDAB; Finishing Equipment — Muller Martini 221 Stitch/Trimmer BUSINESS EQUIPMENT: PC Workstations and Servers. BUSINESS SOFTWARE: Microsoft/Office DTI CLASSIFIED EQUIPMENT: Hardware — PC Workstations and servers.; Printers — HP Laser Printer; CLASSIFIED SOFTWARE: DTI DISPLAY EQUIPMENT: Hardware — Apple iMac; Windows 10 PC; Printers — HP/LaserJet 8000, Ricoh color; DISPLAY SOFTWAREAd Make-up Applications — Adobe CC, InDesign, Ilustrator, Acrobat, and Photoshop; Layout Software — DTI; Adobe CS3; DPS Adtracker EDITORIAL EQUIPMENT: Hardware — PC & Mac Workstations;PC Server; Printers — 2-HP/Laserjet 8150 EDITORIAL SOFTWARE: Ngage. PRODUCTION EQUIPMENT: Hardware — Dell Servers and RIPS; Scanners — Epson/10000 XL Epson/1688 PRODUCTION SOFTWARE: Polkadots Prepageit CIRCULATION EQUIPMENT: Dell PC CIRCULATION SOFTWARDTI Linux

KEWANEE

STAR-COURIER

105 E Central Blvd, Kewanee, Ill., 61443-2245, Henry; gen tel (309) 852-2181; adv tel (309) 852-2181; ed tel (309) 852-2181; gen fax (309) 852-0010; adv fax (309) 852-0010; ed fax (309) 852-0010; gen/nat adv e-mail diane@starcourier.com; disp adv e-mail diane@starcourier.com; class adv e-mailclassifieds@starcourier.com; ed e-mail editor@starcourier.com; web site www.starcourier.com

Group: New Media Investment Group
Published: Tues, Wed, Thur, Fri, Sat
Weekday Frequency: m
Saturday Frequency: m
Circulation: 4,739; 4,739(sat)
Last Audit: Sworn/Estimate/Non-Audited September 30, 2017
Advertising Rate (weekday/saturday): Open inch rate $14.25
News services: AP. **Established:** 1898
Special Editions: Home Improvement (Apr); Hogsmopolitan (Aug); Bridal (Jan); People Making a Difference (Jul); Fair Tab (Jun); 101 Things to do in Henry County (May); Farm Tab (Monthly).
Special Weekly Sections: Best Food Day (Wed); Farm (Tue/Thur); Outdoors (Tue); Business (Thur); TV, Everyday, Church (Fri)
Syndicated Publications: American Profile (Weekly).
Pub. .... Dietra Evans
Classified Adv. Mgr. .... Kathy Werderman
Ed. .... Mike Landis
Assoc. Ed. .... Mike Berry
Sales Mgr. .... Diane Mikenas
Market Information: ADS; TMC.
Mechanical Available: Offset; Black and 3 ROP colors; insert accepted; page cutoffs - 22 3/4.
Mechanical Specifications: Type page 13 x 21 1/2; E - 6 cols, 2 1/16, 1/8 between; A - 6 cols, 2 1/16, 1/8 between; C - 9 cols, 1 3/8, 1/16 between.
Areas Served: Kewanee (IL)
Equipment & Software: PRESSROOM EQUIPMENT: Lines — 4-G/Colorliner.; MAILROOM EQUIPMENT: Tying Machines — 2/Bu.; BUSINESS EQUIPMENT: 4-IBM/PC-KT, 2-Compaq/386-S BUSINESS SOFTWARE: Microsoft/Access, Microsoft/Excel, Microsoft/Word CLASSIFIED EQUIPMENT: Hardware — APP/Mac; Printers — APP/Mac; CLASSIFIED SOFTWARE: Baseview. DISPLAY EQUIPMENT: Hardware — APP/Mac; Printers — HP, APP/Mac; DISPLAY SOFTWAREAd Make-up Applications — QPS/QuarkXPress.; EDITORIAL EQUIPMENT: Hardware — APP/Mac/8-COM/Computype, 1-TC; Printers — HP, APP/Mac. PRODUCTION EQUIPMENT: Hardware — APP/Mac; Scanners — 1-GMS/E-Z-Scan II PRODUCTION SOFTWARE: QPS/QuarkXPress.

LA SALLE

NEWS-TRIBUNE

426 2nd St, La Salle, Ill., 61301-2334, La Salle; gen tel (815) 223-3200; adv tel (815) 220-6945; ed tel (815) 220-6940; gen fax (815) 223-2543; adv fax (815) 223-2543; gen/nat adv e-mail vpsales@newstrib.com; disp adv e-mail vpsales@newstrib.com; class adv e-mailsupport@newstrib.com; ed e-mail ntnews@newstrib.com; web site www.newstrib.com - 1,000,000(views) 100,000(visitors); web site 2 815Life.com - 35,000(views) 6,500(visitors)

Group: DAILY NEWS-TRIBUNE, INC
Published: Mon, Tues, Wed, Thur, Fri, Sat
Weekday Frequency: e
Saturday Frequency: m
Circulation: 21,510; 21,510(sat)
Last Audit: CAC September 30, 2016
Advertising Rate (weekday/saturday): Open inch rate $26.00
News services: AP. **Established:** 1946
Own Printing Facility?: Yes
Commercial Printers?: Yes
Special Editions: Monthly: engagements,

home improvement, health, financial, niche publications (magazines) focused: Boomers; Home/Garden/Life, Parent; Dream Wedding; annual: business/community review
Syndicated Publications: American Profile Magazine (Sat)
Digital Platform - Mobile: Apple, Android, Windows
Digital Platform - Tablet: Apple iOS, Android, Windows 7, Kindle
Pub. .... Joyce McCullough
Cor. Accounting Mgr. .... Craig Baker
Adv. Dir. .... Scott Stavrakas
Circ. Dir. .... Mike Miller
News Ed. .... Craig Sterrett
Online Ed. .... Linda Kleczewski
Online Mgr. .... Diane Seghers
Prodn. Mgr., Mailroom .... Fort Miller
Prodn. Mgr., Pre Press .... Joseph Zokal
Prodn. Mgr., Pressroom .... Jeff Hoos
Market Information: ADS; Split run; TMC.
Mechanical Available: Offset; Black and 3 ROP colors; insert accepted; page cutoffs - 21 3/4.
Mechanical Specifications: Type page 10 5/8 x 21 1/2; E - 6 cols, 1/8 between; A & C- 6 cols, 1 5/6, 1/8 between
Areas Served: LaSalle-Putnam-Bureau-Marshall counties, IL
Delivery Method: Mail, Carrier, RacksEquipment & Software: PRESSROOM EQUIPMENT: Lines — 10-G/Urbanite 1972.; MAILROOM EQUIPMENT: Tying Machines — ML2EE, MS Sterling/SSM 40, Si/LB-2000; Kansa inserter; CLASSIFIED EQUIPMENT: Hardware — PC CLASSIFIED SOFTWARE: Brainworks DISPLAY EQUIPMENT: Hardware — APP/Mac DISPLAY SOFTWAREAd Make-up Applications — APT 2001; Layout Software — QPS/QuarkXPress 4.1, Multi-Ad/Illustrator 8.0, Adobe/Photoshop 5.0, Adobe/Acrobat In-Design EDITORIAL EQUIPMENT: Hardware — APT; EDITORIAL SOFTWARE: APT PRODUCTION EQUIPMENT: Hardware — 2-COM, PC IT EQUIPMENT: VMWare IT SOFTWARE:VShare; Windows; Various CIRCULATION EQUIPMENT: PC CIRCULATION SOFTWARMSSI
Note: Taste oF Home Show (with common-owned radio stations)

LAWRENCEVILLE

DAILY RECORD

1209 State St, Lawrenceville, Ill., 62439-2332, Lawrence; gen tel (618) 943-2331; gen fax (618) 943-3976; gen/nat adv e-mail syoung@lawdailyrecord.com; disp adv e-mail mlewsader@lawdailyrecord.com ; class adv e-mailclassads@lawdailyrecord.com ; ed e-mail lawnews@lawdailyrecord.com; web site www.lawdailyrecord.com
Group: Lewis Newspapers
Published: Mon, Tues, Wed, Thur, Fri
Weekday Frequency: e
Circulation: 3,964
Last Audit: Sworn/Estimate/Non-Audited September 30, 2017
Advertising Rate (weekday/saturday): Open inch rate $7.50
News services: AP, CNS. **Established:** 1847
Special Editions: Kreative Kids (Apr); Back-to-School (Aug); Christmas Greetings (Dec); Tax Guide (Feb); Summer Savings (Jul); Senior Citizen Salute (Jun); Spring Ag Salute (Mar); American Home Week (May); Christmas Opening (Nov); Working Women (Oct); Fall Festival (Sept).
Special Weekly Sections: Business (1 & 3 Tue); Health & Fitness (2 & 4 Tue); Shop at Home (3 Tues); Kids (Tue); Entertainment (Wed); Restaurant (1 & 3 Thur); Farm (2 & 4 Fri); Church (Fri)
Syndicated Publications: TV Section (Fri).
Pub. .... Kathleen Lewis
Mng. Ed. .... Michael Van Dorn
Adv. Dir. .... Sandie Young
Circ. Mgr. .... Joyce Tredway
Sports Ed. .... Bill Richardson
Layout Mgr. .... Beverly Johnson
Market Information: ADS; TMC; Zoned editions.
Mechanical Available: Offset; Black and 4 ROP colors; insert accepted - all, quarter folded (max. size 7 x 11); page cutoffs - 22 3/4.
Mechanical Specifications: Type page 13 x 21; E - 6 cols, 1 5/8, 1/8 between; A - 6 cols, 1 5/8, 1/8 between; C - 9 cols, 1 3/8, 1/16 between.
Areas Served: Lawrence County (IL)
Delivery Method: Mail, Carrier, RacksEquipment & Software: MAILROOM EQUIPMENT: Tying Machines — 1/US; Address Machine — 1-/Am.; BUSINESS EQUIPMENT: APP/Mac BUSINESS SOFTWARE: Microsoft/Word 5.0, Microsoft/Excel 5.0 CLASSIFIED EQUIPMENT: Hardware — APP/Mac; Printers — Xante/Accel-a-Writer 8200; CLASSIFIED SOFTWARE: Hypercard. DISPLAY EQUIPMENT: Hardware — APP/Mac; Printers — Xante/Accel-a-Writer 8100A; Other Hardware — Mk/ScanMaker print scanner DISPLAY SOFTWAREAd Make-up Applications — Adobe/Illustrator, Multi-Ad/Creator; Layout Software — APP/Mac ci, Xante/Accel-a-Writer 8200. EDITORIAL EQUIPMENT: Hardware — APP/Mac; Printers — 2-Xante/Accel-a-Writer 8200 EDITORIAL SOFTWARE: Baseview/NewsEdit Pro 1.1. PRODUCTION EQUIPMENT: Hardware — 1-APP/Mac LaserWriter PRODUCTION SOFTWARE: QPS/QuarkXPress 3.3.

LINCOLN

LINCOLN COURIER

206 S Chicago St, Lincoln, Ill., 62656-2701, Logan; gen tel (217) 732-2101; adv tel (217) 732-2101; ed tel (217) 732-2101; gen fax (217) 732-7039; adv fax (217) 732-7039; ed fax (217) 732-7039; gen/nat adv e-mail ted.wolf@lincolncourier.com; disp adv e-mail advertise@lincolncourier.com; class adv e-mailadvertise@lincolncourier.com; ed e-mail news@lincolncourier.com; web site www.lincolncourier.com
Group: New Media Investment Group
Published: Mon, Tues, Wed, Thur, Fri, Sat
Weekday Frequency: m
Saturday Frequency: m
Circulation: 5,623; 5,813(sat)
Last Audit: Sworn/Estimate/Non-Audited October 4, 2017
Advertising Rate (weekday/saturday): Open inch rate $80.95
Advertising Rate (sunday): Open inch rate $89.05
News services: AP, CNS, SHNS. **Established:** 1856
Own Printing Facility?: Yes
Commercial Printers?: No
Special Editions: County Fair (Aug); Progress (Mar).
Special Weekly Sections: Finance, TV (Daily); Best Food, Agriculture (Wed); Agriculture (Thur); TV (Fri)
Syndicated Publications: American Profile (Weekly).
Digital Platform - Mobile: Windows
Mng. Ed. .... Jean Ann Miller
Pub. .... Todd Sears
Advertising Manager .... Ted Wolf
Market Information: TMC.
Mechanical Available: Offset; Black and 3 ROP colors; insert accepted; page cutoffs - 21 1/4.
Mechanical Specifications: Type page 13 x 21; E - 6 cols, 2 1/16, 1/8 between; A - 6 cols, 2 1/16, 1/8 between; C - 9 cols, 1 3/8, 1/16 between.
Areas Served: Lincoln and Logan County
Delivery Method: Mail, Newsstand, RacksEquipment & Software: PRESSROOM EQUIPMENT: Lines — 7-G/Community 1978.; MAILROOM EQUIPMENT: Tying Machines — MLN, 2-Si.; CLASSIFIED EQUIPMENT: Printers — XIT/Clipper; CLASSIFIED SOFTWARE: Dewar/Disc Net. DISPLAY EQUIPMENT: Hardware — 1-Dewar/Discovery; DISPLAY SOFTWAREAd Make-up Applications — Dewar/Disc Net, Dewar/Sys II, Dewar/Sys IV, Dewar/Discovery.; EDITORIAL EQUIPMENT: Hardware — Lf/AP Leaf Picture Desk; Printers — XIT/Clipper EDITORIAL SOFTWARE: Dewar/Disc Net, Dewar/Sys II, Dewar/Sys IV, Dewar/Discovery. PRODUCTION EQUIPMENT: Hardware — XIT/Clipper; Cameras — R/500, C/Marathon.
Note: The Lincoln Courier (e) has a combination rate of $74.13 with the Springfield State Journal-Register (mS). Individual newspaper rates not available.

LITCHFIELD

NEWS-HERALD

112 E Ryder St, Litchfield, Ill., 62056-2031, Montgomery; gen tel (217) 324-2121; gen fax (217) 324-2122; gen/nat adv e-mail lfdnews@litchfieldil.com; disp adv e-mail ads.lfdnews@yahoo.com; web site No website
Published: Mon, Tues, Wed, Thur, Fri
Weekday Frequency: e
Circulation: 5,880
Last Audit: Sworn/Estimate/Non-Audited February 1, 2018
Advertising Rate (weekday/saturday): Open inch rate $5.00
News services: AP. **Established:** 1856
Own Printing Facility?: Yes
Commercial Printers?: No
Special Editions: Dollar Day (Aug); Back-to-School (Fall); Dollar Day (Feb); Christmas (Nov); Great Outdoors (Spring).
Pub. .... John C. Hanafin
Admin. Exec. Asst. to Pub. .... Lisa Land
Wire Ed. .... Michelle Romanus
Prodn. Supt. .... James Keith
Mechanical Available: Offset; Black and 3 ROP colors; insert accepted; page cutoffs - 22 3/4.
Mechanical Specifications: Type page 14 x 21 1/2; E - 8 cols, 1 2/3, 1/8 between; A - 8 cols, 1 2/3, 1/8 between; C - 8 cols, 1 2/3, 1/8 between.
Areas Served: 62056, 62033, 62069, 62560, 62533, 62572, 62049 and across the United States
Delivery Method: Mail, Newsstand, Carrier, RacksEquipment & Software: PRESSROOM EQUIPMENT: Lines — 4-G/Community.; MAILROOM EQUIPMENT: Tying Machines — 1/B; Address Machine — 1-Am/1900.; EDITORIAL EQUIPMENT: Hardware — 4-COM/MDT 350. PRODUCTION EQUIPMENT: Hardware — 2-COM/2961HS, 1-COM/ACM9000; Cameras — 1-DSA/Companica-64OC.

MACOMB

THE MCDONOUGH COUNTY VOICE

26 W Side Sq, Macomb, Ill., 61455-2219, McDonough; gen tel (309) 833-2114; gen fax (309) 833-2346; gen/nat adv e-mail mringenberger@mcdonoughvoice.com; disp adv e-mail mringenberger@mcdonoughvoice.com; class adv e-mailahousewright@mcdonoughvoice.com; ed e-mail jsmith@mcdonoughvoice.com; web site www.mcdonoughvoice.com
Group: GateHouse Media, Inc.
Published: Tues, Wed, Thur, Fri, Sat
Weekday Frequency: m
Saturday Frequency: m
Circulation: 3,800; 5,000(sat)
Last Audit: Sworn/Estimate/Non-Audited September 30, 2017
Advertising Rate (weekday/saturday): Open inch rate $14.00
News services: AP, LAT-WP.
Own Printing Facility?: Yes
Commercial Printers?: Yes
Special Editions: Restaurant Directory
Business directory
Central Illinois Family Magazine (Monthly)
Western Illinois University Coupon book
Special Weekly Sections: Church (Fri); Seniors (Mon); Lifestyles (S); Entertainment (Happenings) (Thur); Agriculture (Tues);Health (Wed).Business (Sat)
Syndicated Publications: Parade (S); American Profile (Weekly).Relish (Tuesday) Spry (Tuesday) Central Illinois Family Magazine (First Wed. month)
Pub. .... Tony Scott
Ed. .... Jackie Smith
Adv. Mgr., Display .... Michelle Ringenberger
Circ. Mgr. .... Dusty Vaughn
Sports Ed. .... Scott Holland
Prodn. Mgr. .... Tabitha Palm
Market Information: TMC.
Mechanical Available: Offset; Black and 3 ROP colors; insert accepted; page cutoffs - 22 3/4.
Mechanical Specifications: Type page 13 x 21 1/2; E - 6 cols, 2 1/16, 1/8 between; A - 6 cols, 2 1/16, 1/8 between; C - 10 cols, 1 1/4, 1/16 between.
Areas Served: 61455, 61422, 62326,61420, 61438,61450,62367
Delivery Method: Mail, Newsstand, Carrier, RacksEquipment & Software: PRESSROOM EQUIPMENT: Lines — 7-G/Community 1970.; MAILROOM EQUIPMENT: Tying Machines — 2/Bu.; BUSINESS SOFTWARE: MSSI CLASSIFIED EQUIPMENT: Hardware — APP/Mac 7200-75; Printers — HP/LaserJet 5MP; CLASSIFIED SOFTWARE: CAMS. DISPLAY EQUIPMENT: Hardware — APP/Mac G4; Printers — APP/Mac LaserWriter NTX, APP/Mac Pro 810l ; Biz Hub; Other Hardware — HP/ScanJet II cx. DISPLAY SOFTWAREAd Make-up Applications — QPS/QuarkXPress, Multi-Ad/Creator; EDITORIAL EQUIPMENT: Hardware — APP/iMac, APP/Mac G4/Nikon/Super Coolscan LS1000; Printers — APP/Mac LaserWriter NTX, HP/LaserJet EDITORIAL SOFTWARE: QPS/QuarkXPress, Microsoft/Word. PRODUCTION EQUIPMENT: Hardware — Tl/OmniPage Professional, Tl/OmniPage Professional, APP/Mac Pro 810, Mk, APP/Mac LaserWriter NTX, APP/Mac Pro 810; Cameras — R, R; Scanners — HP/ScanJet IIcx, HP/ScanJet IIcx PRODUCTION SOFTWARE: QPS/QuarkXPress 5.0.

MARION

THE MARION DAILY REPUBLICAN

502 W Jackson St, Marion, Ill., 62959-2355, Williamson; gen tel (618) 993-2626; adv tel (618) 993-2626; ed tel (618) 993-2626; gen fax (618) 993-8326; adv fax (618) 993-8326; ed fax (618) 993-8326; gen/nat adv e-mail ad_manager@dailyrepublicannews.com; disp adv e-mail ad_manager@dailyrepublicannews.com; class adv e-mailclassified@dailyrepublicannews.com; ed e-mail editor@dailyrepublicannews.com; web site www.dailyrepublicannews.com
Group: New Media Investment Group
Published: Tues, Wed, Thur, Fri, Sat
Weekday Frequency: e
Saturday Frequency: m
Circulation: 3,600; 3,600(sat)
Last Audit: Sworn/Estimate/Non-Audited September 30, 2017
Advertising Rate (weekday/saturday): Open inch rate $11.38
News services: AP.
Special Weekly Sections: Best Food Day (Mon)
Syndicated Publications: USA WEEKEND Magazine (Sat); American Profile (Weekly).
News Ed. .... Bill Swinford
Sports Ed. .... Justin Walker
Prodn. Mgr., Composition .... Steve Triest
Group Pub. .... Lynne Campbell
Adv. Sales. .... Kathy Metcalf
Market Information: TMC.
Mechanical Available: Offset; Black and 4 ROP colors; insert accepted - min. 8 1/2 x 11; page cutoffs - 21 1/2.
Mechanical Specifications: Type page 13 x 21 1/2; E - 6 cols, 2 1/16, 1/8 between; A - 6 cols, 2 1/16, 1/8 between; C - 8 cols, 1 5/8, 1/16 between.Equipment & Software: MAILROOM EQUIPMENT: Tying Machines — 2/Bu.; BUSINESS EQUIPMENT: 2-Club America/486 BUSINESS SOFTWARE: Nomads/Listmaster CLASSIFIED EQUIPMENT: Hardware — APP/Mac; Printers — APP/Mac LaserWriter II; CLASSIFIED SOFTWARE: Baseview. DISPLAY EQUIPMENT: Hardware — 4-APP/Mac; Printers — APP/Mac LaserWriter IIg; Other Hardware — CD-Rom DISPLAY SOFTWAREAd Make-up Applications — Aldus/PageMaker; Layout Software — APP/Mac. EDITORIAL EQUIPMENT: Hardware — 1-APP/Mac II; Printers — APP/Mac LaserWriter II EDITORIAL SOFTWARE: Microsoft/Word. PRODUCTION EQUIPMENT: Hardware — Nu/FT40U3VP; Cameras — B.

MATTOON

JOURNAL GAZETTE & TIMES-COURIER

700 Broadway Ave E, Ste 9A, Mattoon, Ill., 61938-4617, Coles; gen tel (217) 235-

5656; adv tel (217) 235-5656; ed tel (217) 235-5656; gen fax (217) 238-6886; adv fax (217) 238-6886; ed fax (217) 238-6886; gen/nat adv e-mail steve.lahr@lee.net; disp adv e-mail steve.lahr@lee.net; class adv e-mailcanderson@jg-tc.com; ed e-mail cwalworth@jg-tc.com; web site www.jg-tc.com

Group: Lee Enterprises, Inc.
Published: Mon, Tues, Wed, Thur, Fri, Sat
Weekday Frequency: m
Saturday Frequency: m
Circulation: 10,761; 10,845(sat)
Last Audit: AAM September 30, 2014
Advertising Rate (weekday/saturday): Open inch rate $23.25
Advertising Rate (sunday): Open inch rate $25.25
News services: AP. **Established:** 1840
Special Editions: Farm (Jan); Bagelfest (Jul); Graduation (May); Thanksgiving Day (Nov); Automotive (Oct).
Special Weekly Sections: Best Food, Business, NIE, Kids (Mon); Community, Internet (Tue); Community (Wed); Farm Feature (Thur); Church, Outdoors (Fri); School, Sports, lifestyle, NASCAR (Sat); Wellness (1st Thur)
Syndicated Publications: USA WEEKEND Magazine (Sat).
Digital Platform - Mobile: Apple
Digital Platform - Tablet: Apple iOS
Adv. Dir. .... Tammy Jordan
Oper. Dir. .... Mark Hall
Nat'l Adv. Mgr. .... Steve Lahr
Editor .... Penny Weaver
Mechanical Available: Offset; Black and 3 ROP colors; insert accepted; page cutoffs - 22 3/4.
Mechanical Specifications: Type page 11 1/2 x 21 1/2; E - 6 cols, 1 3/4, 1/6 between; A - 6 cols, 1 3/4, 1/6 between; C - 6 cols, 1 3/4, 1/6 between.
Areas Served: Mattoon & Charleston (IL)
Equipment & Software: PRESSROOM EQUIPMENT: Lines — 12-G/Community; MAILROOM EQUIPMENT: Counter Stackers — 1-BG/Count-O-Veyor 106; Inserters & Stuffers — 2-MM/227E; Tying Machines — 1-Bu/BT16, 3-MLN/ML2EE; Address Machine — 2-Wm/5.; BUSINESS EQUIPMENT: 1-Compaq/386, Sun/4110 CLASSIFIED EQUIPMENT: Hardware — Sun/XWindows, Dell/GX 110; Printers — 1-HP/IIIP, HP/4050N; CLASSIFIED SOFTWARE: Sun/OS (with Vision Data 4GL). DISPLAY EQUIPMENT: Hardware — 7-APP/Mac II, 2-APP/Mac SE30, 1-APP/Mac ci, 1-APP/Power Mac 9500; Printers — ECR/1085; Other Hardware — 2-APP/Mac CD-Rom DISPLAY SOFTWAREAd Make-up Applications — QPS/QuarkXPress 3.32, Adobe/Photoshop 3.05, Adobe/Illustrator 6.0; Layout Software — SCS/Layout 8000. EDITORIAL EQUIPMENT: Hardware — 16-Sun/SLC, 6-Sun/Sparc II, Dell/Optiplex 6-1; Printers — Xante/Accel-a-Writer 8200, HP/LaserJet 4MV, ECR/1085 EDITORIAL SOFTWARE: Sun/Micro Sys, Unix/Arbotext, Lotus/Notes 4 6.4, Domino Server, Windows/NT. PRODUCTION EQUIPMENT: Hardware — Caere/OmniPro 5.0, Lf/Leafscan 35; Cameras — SCREEN/Companica 680C; Scanners — 2-HP/ScanJet Plus, AG/Horizon PRODUCTION SOFTWARE: QPS/QuarkXPress 3.32, SCS/Lynx 3.1.
Note: Advertising is sold in combination with the Charleston (IL) Times-Courier for $19.75 (m). Individual newspaper rates not made available.

MOLINE

THE DISPATCH-ARGUS

1720 5th Ave, Moline, Ill., 61265-7907, Rock Island; gen tel (309) 764-4344; adv tel (309) 757-5019; ed tel (309) 757-4990; gen fax (309) 797-0311; adv fax (309) 797-0321; ed fax (309) 757-4992; gen/nat adv e-mail info@qconline.com; disp adv e-mail advertising@qconline.com; class adv e-mailclassifieds@qconline.com; ed e-mail press@qconline.com; web site www.qconline.com - 1,583,872(views) 168,199(visitors)

Group: Lee Enterprises, Inc.
Published: Mon, Tues, Wed, Thur, Fri, Sat, Sun
Weekday Frequency: m
Saturday Frequency: m
Circulation: 19,378; 20,164(sat); 22,632(sun)
Last Audit: AAM March 31, 2017
Advertising Rate (weekday/saturday): Open inch rate $51.76
News services: MCT, NYT, AP, NEA, Bloomberg.
Own Printing Facility?: No
Commercial Printers?: No
Special Editions: QC Q & A (Aug); Holiday Gift Guide (Dec); Home Builders Show (Feb); Home Improvement (Jan); Back to School (Jul); Lawn & Garden (Mar); Summer Events (May); Holiday Cookbook (Nov); Fall Home Improvement (Oct); Bridal Guide (Sept).
Special Weekly Sections: TV Week (S); Religion (Sat); Entertainment (Thur); Best Food Day (Wed).
Syndicated Publications: PARADE Magazine (S).
Digital Platform - Mobile: Apple, Android, Windows, Blackberry
Digital Platform - Tablet: Apple iOS, Android, Windows 7, Blackberry Tablet OS, Kindle, Nook, Kindle Fire
Managing Editor .... Roger Ruthhart
Editorial Page Ed. .... Kenda Burrows
Columnist .... John Marx
News Data Administrator .... Laura Yeater
Associate Managing Editor .... Laura Fraembs
Consumer Service Manager .... Jill Henderson
Information Editor/Sports & Recreation .... Marc Nesseler
Data Processing Mgr. .... Sue Gramling
Multi-Media Advertising Director .... Kelly Johannes
Information Editor/Photography & Multimedia Todd Mizener
Media Sales Manager .... Kenda Weber
General Manager .... Tom Biermann
Ed./Pub. .... Gerald J. Taylor
Chief Revenue Officer .... Val Yazbec
Financial Analyst .... Scott Aswege
HR Mgr. .... Donna Herbig
Assoc. ME/Print & Online Production Mike Romkey
Post Press/Facilities Manager .... Jack Myers
Co-Director Circulation/Sales & Marketing .... Joe Schaechter
Production Director .... Dan Wahlheim
Classified Telesales Supervisor .... Jamie Belha
Market Information: Split run; TMC; Zoned editions.
Mechanical Available: Offset; Black and 3 ROP colors; insert accepted - self-adhesive notes.
Mechanical Specifications: Type page 11 5/8 x 21 1/2; E - 6 cols, 1 5/8, 1/8 between; A - 6 cols, 1 5/8, 1/8 between; C - 9 cols, 1 5/8, 1/8 between.
Areas Served: 61230, 61231, 61412, 61413, 61232, 61233, 61234, 61235, 61236, 61238, 61239, 61241, 61240, 61241, 61242, 61244, 61284, 61250, 61434, 61254, 61256, 61257, 61258, 61259, 61260, 61442, 61443, 61453, 61261, 61262, 61263, 61264, 61344, 61265, 61462, 61272, 61465, 61468, 61273, 61274, 61275, 61276, 61277, 61278, 61279, 61201, 61476, 61281, 61282, 61283, 61284, 61486, 61490, 52722, 52801, 52802, 52803, 52804, 52806, 52807
Delivery Method: Mail, Newsstand, Carrier, Racks

MONMOUTH

DAILY REVIEW ATLAS

400 S Main St, Monmouth, Ill., 61462-2164, Warren; gen tel (309) 734-3176; gen fax (309) 734-7649; gen/nat adv e-mail jbolitho@reviewatlas.com; disp adv e-mail jbolitho@reviewatlas.com; class adv e-mailjbolitho@reviewatlas.com; ed e-mail jbolitho@reviewatlas.com; web site www.reviewatlas.com

Group: New Media Investment Group
Published: Tues, Wed, Thur, Fri, Sat
Weekday Frequency: e
Saturday Frequency: m
Circulation: 3,159; 3,159(sat)
Last Audit: Sworn/Estimate/Non-Audited September 30, 2017
Advertising Rate (weekday/saturday): Open inch rate $10.90
News services: AP. **Established:** 1890
Syndicated Publications: Senior Citizens Magazine (Monthly); Weekend Update (Sat); Channel Guide-Television Guide Section (Weekly).
Gen. Mgr. .... Tony Scott
Circ. Mgr. .... Brian Elliott
Sports Ed. .... Marty Pouchette
Prodn. Mgr. .... Barb Simmons
Ed. .... Jake Bolitho
Market Information: TMC.
Mechanical Available: Offset; Black and 3 ROP colors; insert accepted; page cutoffs - 22 3/4.
Mechanical Specifications: Type page 13 x 21 1/2; E - 6 cols, 2 1/16, 1/8 between; A - 6 cols, 1 3/8, 1/8 between; C - 9 cols, 1 3/8, 1/16 between.
Areas Served: Monmouth (IL)
Equipment & Software: MAILROOM EQUIPMENT: Tying Machines — 2/Bu; Address Machine — 2-/Am.; BUSINESS EQUIPMENT: 2-IBM/PC, AT CLASSIFIED EQUIPMENT: Hardware — 4-APP/Mac.; DISPLAY SOFTWARELayout Software — APP/Mac Desktop, APP/Mac Plus. EDITORIAL EQUIPMENT: Hardware — 6-Mk. PRODUCTION EQUIPMENT: Hardware — LE; Cameras — 1-B PRODUCTION SOFTWARE: Baseview.

MOUNT CARMEL

MOUNT CARMEL REGISTER

115 E 4th St, Mount Carmel, Ill., 62863-2110, Wabash; gen tel (618) 262-5144; gen fax (618) 263-4437; gen/nat adv e-mail news@mtcarmelregister.com; disp adv e-mail creativeads@mtcarmelregister.com; class adv e-mailswiseman@mtcarmelregister.com; ed e-mail news@mtcarmelregister.com; web site www.mtcarmelregister.com - 964,165(views) 180,539(visitors)

Group: Paxton Media Group, LLC
Published: Mon, Wed, Fri, Sun
Weekday Frequency: All day
Circulation: 3,057
Last Audit: Sworn/Estimate/Non-Audited September 30, 2017
Advertising Rate (weekday/saturday): Open inch rate $12.50 Weekly & Annual contracts available.
News services: Associated Press **Established:** 1839
Own Printing Facility?: No
Commercial Printers?: Yes
Special Editions: Bridal Fair, Healthy Lifestyles, Progress, Prom Expo (Jan); Soil & Water, Financial/Tax, FFA, Valentines, Savvy Lifestyles (Feb); Home & Garden, Kids & Family, Spring (Mar); Spring Car Care, Prom, Bridal, Easter (Apr); Mother's Day, Graduation, Memorial Day, Home Show, Savvy Lifestyles (May); Little League, Summer Coupon Book, Meet Your Merchants, Father's Day, Outstanding Student (Jun); 4th of July, Bridal, Ag Days, Various County Fairs, Christmas In July (Jul); 4-H, Guide to Edwards County, Fall Sports, Savvy Lifestyles, Back To School (Aug); Ribberfest, Labor Day, Parent & Child, Fall Home Improvement, Guide to Wabash County (Sep); Fall Coupon Book, Homecoming, Bridal, Firefighters Salute, Chamber of Commerce Annual (Oct); Holiday Gift Guide #1, Holiday Gift Guide #2, Savvy Lifestyles (Nov); Holiday Gift Guide #3, Holiday Gift Guide #4, Holiday Gift Guide #5, Songbook, Winter Sports, and Wellness Guide
Syndicated Publications: American Profile (bi-monthly);
Real Estate Homes (monthly) and TSM Outdoor Magazine (quarterly).
Digital Platform - Mobile: Apple, Android, Windows
Digital Platform - Tablet: Apple iOS, Android, Windows 7
Publisher/President .... Phil Summers
Editor .... Andrea Howe
Accounting Clerk .... Bob Tanquary
Classifieds .... Susan Wiseman
Advertising Sales Manager .... Sandra Higgins
Advertising Consultant/Digital Director .... Joey Luecke
Advertising Consultant .... Laurie Snidle
News Editor .... Marcus Smith
Sports Editor/General Reporter .... T.J. Hug
Mechanical Available: Offset; Black and 3 ROP colors; insert accepted; page cutoffs - 22 3/4.
Mechanical Specifications: Type page 10 x 21; E - 6 cols, 1.56, 1/8 between; A - 6 cols, 1.56, 1/8 between; C - 6 cols, 1.56, 1/8 between.
Areas Served: 62863, 62811, 62852, 62855, 62818, 62815, 62806, 62844, 62410, 62476 and mixed zips.
Delivery Method: Mail, Newsstand, Carrier, RacksEquipment & Software: MAILROOM EQUIPMENT: Tying Machines — 1-Sa/50; Address Machine — Wing-mailed labels.; BUSINESS EQUIPMENT: 2-PC BUSINESS SOFTWARE: Comet CLASSIFIED EQUIPMENT: Hardware — 2-APP/Mac; Printers — APP/Mac LaserWriter; CLASSIFIED SOFTWARE: Pre 1 software DISPLAY EQUIPMENT: Hardware — 3-APP/Mac; Printers — APP/Mac LaserWriter; DISPLAY SOFTWAREAd Make-up Applications — Multi-Ad/Creator 6.; EDITORIAL EQUIPMENT: Hardware — 5-APP/Mac; Printers — 2-APP/Mac LaserWriter EDITORIAL SOFTWARE: InCopy PRODUCTION SOFTWARE: InCopy

OLNEY

OLNEY DAILY MAIL

206 S Whittle Ave, Olney, Ill., 62450-2251, Richland; gen tel (618) 393-2931; gen fax (618) 392-2953; gen/nat adv e-mail advertising@olneydailymail.com; disp adv e-mail advertising@olneydailymail.com; class adv e-mailclassifieds@olneydailymail.com; ed e-mail editor@olneydailymail.com; web site www.olneydailymail.com

Group: New Media Investment Group
Published: Mon, Tues, Wed, Thur, Fri
Weekday Frequency: e
Circulation: 2,650
Last Audit: Sworn/Estimate/Non-Audited October 13, 2017
Advertising Rate (weekday/saturday): Open inch rate $18.55
News services: AP. **Established:** 1898
Own Printing Facility?: Yes
Commercial Printers?: Yes
Special Editions: Its About Family; Richland County Shopper
Special Weekly Sections: Best Food Day (Mon); School Life (Tues).
Syndicated Publications: American Profile (Weekly); Spry (Monthly); USA Weekend (Weekly);
Pub. .... Kerry Kocher
Prodn. Supvr., Press .... Mark Roberson
Market Information: TMC.
Mechanical Available: Offset; Black and 3 ROP colors; insert accepted; page cutoffs - 21 1/2.
Mechanical Specifications: Type page 10.5 x 21 1/2; E - 6 cols, 1/6 between; A - 6 cols, 1/6 between; C - 8 cols, 1/6 between.
Areas Served: 62450, 62421, 62868, 62425, 62452, 62476
Delivery Method: CarrierEquipment & Software: PRESSROOM EQUIPMENT: Lines — 7-G/Community 1965.; BUSINESS EQUIPMENT: IBM CLASSIFIED EQUIPMENT: Hardware — Apple; Printers — HP; CLASSIFIED SOFTWARE: TC. DISPLAY SOFTWAREAd Make-up Applications — Adobe; EDITORIAL SOFTWARE: Adobe

OTTAWA

THE TIMES

110 W Jefferson St, Ottawa, Ill., 61350-5010, La Salle; gen tel (815) 433-2000; adv tel (815) 433-2002; ed tel (815) 433-2004; gen fax (815) 433-1639; adv fax (815) 433-1626; ed fax (815) 433-1639; gen/nat adv e-mail classad@mywebtimes.com; disp adv e-mail classad@mywebtimes.com; class adv e-mailclassad@mywebtimes.com; ed e-mail newsroom@MyWebTimes.com; web site www.mywebtimes.com

Group: Shaw Media
Published: Mon, Tues, Wed, Thur, Fri, Sat, Sun
Weekday Frequency: e
Saturday Frequency: m
Circulation: 9,879; 9,879(sat)
Last Audit: CAC March 31, 2016
Advertising Rate (weekday/saturday): Open inch rate $24.54
News services: NEA, AP, TMS.
Special Editions: Spring Lawn & Garden (Apr); Football Preview (Aug); Holiday Gift Guide

(Dec); Spring Farm (Feb); Bridal Guide (Jan); Summer Farm (Jul); Dining & Entertainment (Jun); Home Improvement (Mar); Graduation (May); Real Estate/Realtor Guide (Monthly); Basketball
Special Weekly Sections: Back-n-Forth (Wed); Pulse (Tue); Food (Wed); Spotlight (Thur); Inside-n-Out (Fri); Hometowns (Sat)
Syndicated Publications: Parade (Weekly).
Pub. ....John Newby
Bus. Mgr. ....Cindy Liptak
Adv. Mgr. ....Sherry Patterson
Adv. Supvr., Classified ....Mindy Crouch
Circ. Dir. ....Cynthia J. Liptak
Editorial Page Ed. ....Dan Hrabel
Online Ed. ....Lonny Cain
Photo Ed. ....Tom Sistak
Wire Ed. ....Paul Carpenter
Mgr., Electronics ....Jerry Battles
Prodn. Foreman, Press ....Richard Todd
Prodn. Mgr., Mailroom ....Art Dougherty
Majors/Nat'l Accts. Mgr. ....Lisa Gerding
Adv. Dir. ....Mike Bertok
Other ....Dan Churney
Managing Editor ....Tammy Sloup
News Editor ....Derek Barichello
Digital Editor ....Stephanie Jaquins
Night Editor ....Julie Stroebel-Barichellow
Mechanical Available: Offset; Black and 3 ROP colors; insert accepted - all; page cutoffs - 22 3/4.
Mechanical Specifications: Type page 13 x 21 1/2; E - 6 cols, 2 1/16, 1/8 between; A - 6 cols, 2 1/16, 1/8 between; C - 10 cols, 1 3/16, 1/16 between.
Areas Served: La Salle County (IL)
Equipment & Software: PRESSROOM EQUIPMENT: Lines — 7-G/Urbanite (balloon former) 1968; Folders — 1-G/2:1.; MAILROOM EQUIPMENT: Tying Machines — Bu/16, MLN/ML2, 2-Bu/Tying Machine, 1-MLN/MLE 22 Strapper; Address Machine — 2-Sp/2605.; BUSINESS EQUIPMENT: 1-Magitronic, PC 486, 7-Wyse/Model 50, Microsoft/Windows NT Server, 6-PC CLASSIFIED EQUIPMENT: Hardware — 3-DTK/PC; Printers — HP/MP3; CLASSIFIED SOFTWARE: FSI/Class, QPS/QuarkXPress 4.04. DISPLAY EQUIPMENT: Hardware — 1-APP/Mac IIsi, 1-APP/Mac Centris 610; Printers — 1-APP/Mac Pro 630, HP/Color Laserjet 4500 N; Other Hardware — CD-Rom, 1-APP/Mac 630 Scanner, Nikon/3510 Slide Film Scanner, Zip Drives, Umax/120 DISPLAY SOFTWAREAd Make-up Applications — Multi-Ad/Creator 2 3.7.1, Intermedia; EDITORIAL EQUIPMENT: Hardware — 13-APP/Mac, 8-APP/Mac G3, 1-APP/Power Mac G3 Server, 1-Sun/Sparc Station 5, 1-Microsoft/Windows NT Server; Printers — APP/Mac LaserWriter Pro 630 EDITORIAL SOFTWARE: Cascade/Imageflow, FSI/Edit, FSI/Pagination. PRODUCTION EQUIPMENT: Hardware — TI/OmniPage 3.0, APP/Mac Laser Pro 8800, 2-Pre Press/Panther Pro 36; Cameras — R/480; Scanners — 2-Umax/1200 Flatbed Scanner, 1-Nikon/3510 Slide Film Scanner, 1-Polaroid/CoolScan 2000 PRODUCTION SOFTWARE: QPS/QuarkXPress 4.04, FSI.

PEKIN

PEKIN DAILY TIMES

306 Court St, Pekin, Ill., 61554-3104, Tazewell; gen tel (309) 346-1111; adv tel (309) 346-1111; ed tel (309) 346-1111; gen fax (309) 346-9815; adv fax (309) 346-9815; ed fax (309) 346-9815; gen/nat adv e-mail advertise@pekintimes.com; disp adv e-mail advertise@pekintimes.com; class adv e-mailtmont@pekintimes.com; ed e-mail mteheux@pekintimes.com; web site www.pekintimes.com
Group: New Media Investment Group
Published: Mon, Tues, Wed, Thur, Fri, Sat
Weekday Frequency: m
Saturday Frequency: m
Circulation: 8,637; 8,637(sat)
Last Audit: Sworn/Estimate/Non-Audited September 30, 2017
Advertising Rate (weekday/saturday): Open inch rate $21.65
News services: AP, TMS. **Established:** 1873
Special Weekly Sections: Farm (Tue); Photo (Thur); Senior Citizen, School, Religion, Lifestyles (Sat); Business, Photo, Features (Daily)
Syndicated Publications: American Profile (Sat); Parade (Weekly).
Digital Platform - Mobile: Apple, Android
Ed. ....Amy Gehrt
Production Mgr. ....Barb Schisler
Sales Mgr. ....Mike Mehl
Mng. Ed. ....Drew Veskauf
Assoc. Ed. ....Nick McMillion
Market Information: TMC
Mechanical Available: Offset; Black and 3 ROP colors; insert accepted; page cutoffs - 22 3/4.
Mechanical Specifications: Type page 11 1/2 x 21 1/2; E - 6 cols, 1 39/50, 1/8 between; A - 6 cols, 1 39/50, 1/16 between; C - 9 cols, 1 13/100, 1/8 between.
Areas Served: 61534, 61546, 61550, 61554, 61564, 61567, 61568, 61607, 61610, 61611, 61734, 61747, 61755, 617,59, 62644, 62664, 62682
Delivery Method: Mail, CarrierEquipment & Software: BUSINESS EQUIPMENT: 2-ATT/3B1, 1-Sun/Sparc 402 CLASSIFIED EQUIPMENT: Hardware — 1-OS/40, Sun/Ultra; Printers — Hp/4MV.; DISPLAY SOFTWARELayout Software — APP/Mac G3. EDITORIAL EQUIPMENT: Hardware — Sun/Sparc Station, APP/Mac G3; Printers — HP/Laserjet 4 MV, HP/4050 EDITORIAL SOFTWARE: Sun/OS 413 UBI, Solaris 2.6, Linux 6.1. PRODUCTION EQUIPMENT: Hardware — 1-Nu, 2-APP/Mac LaserWriter, ECR/Autokon, ECR/Pelbox 1085; Cameras — 1-R/580; Scanners — Nikon/LS 1000, Epson/836X1 PRODUCTION SOFTWARE: QPS/QuarkXPress 4.1.

PEORIA

JOURNAL STAR

1 News Plz, Peoria, Ill., 61643-0001, Peoria; gen tel (309) 686-3000; adv tel (309) 686-3035; ed tel (309) 686-3114; ed fax (309) 686-3296; gen/nat adv e-mail Lsutton@pjstar.com; disp adv e-mail dmoore@pjstar.com; class adv e-mailtkelling@pjstar.com; ed e-mail news@pjstar.com; web site www.pjstar.com
Group: New Media Investment Group
Published: Mon, Tues, Wed, Thur, Fri, Sat, Sun
Weekday Frequency: m
Saturday Frequency: m
Circulation: 46,915; 45,628(sat); 51,973(sun)
Last Audit: AAM December 31, 2016
Advertising Rate (weekday/saturday): Open inch rate $69
News services: AP, LAT-WP, SNS, CNS, TMS. **Established:** 1855
Special Weekly Sections: Cue (Thurs), Real Estate Connection (Fri), Home & Garden (Sat)
Syndicated Publications: Parade (S); AThlon Sports;
Digital Platform - Mobile: Apple, Android
Digital Platform - Tablet: Apple iOS, Android
Pub. ....Ken Mauser
Controller ....Brian Kier
Asst. Gen. Mgr. ....Gene Clime
Credit Mgr. ....Joe Dunlap
Mgr., Mktg./Pub. Affairs ....Phil Jordan
Exec. Ed. ....Dennis Anderson
Asst. Mng. Ed., Sunday Features/Servs. ....Sally McKee
Bus. Ed. ....Steve Tarter
City Ed., Night ....Anthony Smith
Entertainment Ed. ....Danielle Hatch
Head Librarian ....Judy Hicks
Lifestyles Ed. ....Jennifer Davis
Metro Ed. ....Mike Cecil
Neighbors Ed. ....Jennifer Tower
Angie Lyons
Market Information: Split run; TMC; Zoned editions.
Mechanical Available: Offset; Black and 3 ROP colors; insert accepted; page cutoffs - 21 1/2.
Mechanical Specifications: Type page 11 5/8 x 20 53/100; E - 6 cols, 1 5/6, 3/16 between; A - 6 cols, 1 5/6, 3/16 between; C - 9 cols, 1 6/25, 3/32 between.
Areas Served: Peoria (IL) and Surrounding areas
Equipment & Software: PRESSROOM EQUIPMENT: Lines — 6-MAN/Geoman; Reels & Stands — MAN/CD13 Reel Splicer; Registration System — Grafikontrol. MAILROOM EQUIPMENT: Counter Stackers — 4-QWI/500, 3-QWI/300, 1-GMA/6 Station Buffer, 2-GMA/Unwinders; Inserters & Stuffers — 2-GMA/16:2; Tying Machines — 8-Dynaric; Wrapping Singles — 4-QWI/Bottom Wrap.; BUSINESS EQUIPMENT: IBM/AS-400 620 CLASSIFIED EQUIPMENT: Hardware — HI/AD Power; Printers — HP/8500; CLASSIFIED SOFTWARE: HI/AD Power 2.3, ADPAG. DISPLAY EQUIPMENT: Hardware — APP/Power Mac; DISPLAY SOFTWAREAd Make-up Applications — All/Ad Manager 5, Multi-Ad/Creator 6.5; Layout Software — SCS/Layout 8000 10. EDITORIAL SOFTWARE: ATS/Media Desk 3.4. PRODUCTION EQUIPMENT: Hardware — Glunz & Jensen/85V, Adobe/Photoshop; Cameras — 1-B/24, 1-C/Newspager II; Scanners — 5-Nikon, 1-Eskofot/2034 PRODUCTION SOFTWARE: HI/AdPag.
Note: The Peoria Journal Star(mS) has a combination rate of $86.16(d) and $97.30(S) with the Galesburg Register-Mail(eS). Individual newspaper rates not made available.

PONTIAC

THE DAILY LEADER

318 N Main St, Pontiac, Ill., 61764-1930, Livingston; gen tel 8158421153; adv tel (815) 842-1153; ed tel (815) 842-1153; gen fax (815) 842-4388; gen/nat adv e-mail lstiles@pontiacdailyleader.com; disp adv e-mail lstiles@pontiacdailyleader.com; class adv e-mailtmelvin@pontiacdailyleader.com; ed e-mail lstiles@pontiacdailyleader.com; web site www.pontiacdailyleader.com
Group: New Media Investment Group
Published: Tues, Wed, Thur, Fri, Sat
Weekday Frequency: m
Saturday Frequency: m
Circulation: 2,800; 2,800(sat)
Last Audit: Sworn/Estimate/Non-Audited October 10, 2017
Advertising Rate (weekday/saturday): Open inch rate $10.50
News services: AP. **Established:** 1880
Own Printing Facility?: No
Commercial Printers?: No
Special Weekly Sections: Business Page (Wed); Agriculture Page (Thur)
Syndicated Publications: Parade (Sat); American Profile (Weekly).
Digital Platform - Mobile: Apple
Gen Mgr/Adv Mgr ....Linda Stiles
Bus. Mgr. ....Linda Stiles
Mng. Ed. ....Erich Murphy
Pub ....David Adams
Market Information: TMC.
Mechanical Available: Offset; Black and 3 ROP colors; insert accepted; page cutoffs - 21.
Mechanical Specifications: Type page 10.11 x 20.25; E - 6 cols, 1.58 .
Areas Served: Pontiac/Livingston County
Delivery Method: Mail, Newsstand, Carrier, RacksEquipment & Software: MAILROOM EQUIPMENT: Counter Tying Machines — 2/Bu, 2-/Malow; Address Machine — 1-MG/1530.; CLASSIFIED SOFTWARE: 4-D DISPLAY SOFTWAREAd Make-up Applications — Multi-Ad/Creator, QPS/QuarkXPress.; EDITORIAL SOFTWARE: Baseview. PRODUCTION EQUIPMENT: Hardware — 2-B/2332; Cameras — 1-R/580, 1-VG/POS-1-CPS.

QUINCY

THE QUINCY HERALD-WHIG

130 S 5th St, Quincy, Ill., 62301-3916, Adams; gen tel (217) 223-5100; adv tel (217) 231-3464; ed tel (217) 221-3361; gen fax (217) 221-3397; adv fax (217) 221-3397; ed fax (217) 221-3395; gen/nat adv e-mail tkelling@whig.com; disp adv e-mail tkelling@whig.com; class adv e-mailsmcintee@whig.com; ed e-mail mhilfrink@whig.com; web site www.whig.com
Group: Quincy Media, Inc.
Published: Mon, Tues, Wed, Thur, Fri, Sat, Sun
Weekday Frequency: e
Saturday Frequency: m
Circulation: 15,637; 15,637(sat); 17,684(sun)
Last Audit: AAM June 30, 2016
Advertising Rate (weekday/saturday): Open inch rate $21.76
Advertising Rate (sunday): Open inch rate $24.81
News services: AP, Scripps-Howard. **Established:** 1926
Special Editions: Home Improvement (Apr); Progress (Mar); Basketball (Nov); Car Care (Oct); Fast Forward (Quarterly); Football (Sept).
Special Weekly Sections: Business, Finance (Daily); Work, Farm, Arts, Entertainment, Living, Travel, Parenting, Home Decor (Sun); Food, Health, Fitness (Wed); Entertainment (Thur); TV, Religion, Real Estate (Sat)
Syndicated Publications: Parade (S); TV Week Mini Book (Sat).
Digital Platform - Mobile: Apple, Android, Windows, Blackberry
Digital Platform - Tablet: Apple iOS, Android, Windows 7, Blackberry Tablet OS, Kindle, Nook, Kindle Fire
Pub. ....Thomas A. Oakley
Gen. Mgr./Exec. Ed ....Michael B. Hilfrink
Adv. Dir. ....Tom Kelling
Mng. Ed. ....Don Crim
Farm Ed. ....Debbie Gurtz Husar
Page 1 Ed. ....Kevin Murphy
Photo Ed. ....Phil Carlson
Sports Ed. ....Don O'Brien
Online Contact ....Holly Wagner
Prodn. Dir., Opns. ....Joe Genenbacher
Gen. Mgr. ....Ron Wallace
Classified Adv. Mgr. ....Sophie McIntee
Market Information: Split run; TMC.
Mechanical Available: Offset; Black and 3 ROP colors; insert accepted; page cutoffs - 22.
Mechanical Specifications: Type page 12 x 21; E - 6 cols, 2 1/16, 1/8 between; A - 6 cols, 2 1/16, 1/8 between; C - 9 cols, 1 3/8, 1/16 between.
Areas Served: Counties in West-Central Illinois & Northeast Missouri
Equipment & Software: PRESSROOM EQUIPMENT: Lines — 8-G/Urbanite 1989; MAILROOM EQUIPMENT: Counter Stackers — HL/Monitors; Inserters & Stuffers — HI/13/72; Tying Machines — MLN/330, MLN/LS 300, Dynaric; Control System — 1-MM/Stitcher-Trimmer 948125.; BUSINESS EQUIPMENT: IBM/AS-400 BUSINESS SOFTWARE: INSI: Bus, Circ CLASSIFIED EQUIPMENT: Hardware — APP/Mac; Printers — Okidata/192; CLASSIFIED SOFTWARE: Baseview. DISPLAY EQUIPMENT: Hardware — 5-APP/Mac 7300-120; Printers — 2-LaserMaster/1000, Compaq/20; DISPLAY SOFTWAREAd Make-up Applications — Multi-Ad/Creator, QPS/QuarkXPress; Layout Software — APP/Mac. EDITORIAL EQUIPMENT: Hardware — APP/Mac/APP/Mac; Printers — Page/Marq 20, Lexmark EDITORIAL SOFTWARE: Baseview 8.0. PRODUCTION EQUIPMENT: Hardware — Pre Press/Panther Pro 13.3, Pre Press/Panther Plus 46; Cameras — R; Scanners — Microtek, Microtek/600ZS Scanner, PixelCraft/8200, Nikon/Coolscan 1000 PRODUCTION SOFTWARE: Baseview 8.0, QPS/QuarkXPress.

ROBINSON

DAILY NEWS

302 S Cross St, Robinson, Ill., 62454-2137, Crawford; gen tel (618) 544-2101; gen fax (618) 544-9533; gen/nat adv e-mail wpiper@robdailynews.com; disp adv e-mail kjones@robdailynews.com; class adv e-maildcorder@robdailynews.com; ed e-mail news@robdailynews.com; web site www.robdailynews.com
Group: Lewis Newspapers
Published: Mon, Tues, Wed, Thur, Fri
Weekday Frequency: e
Saturday Frequency: m
Circulation: 5,933; 5,933(sat)
Last Audit: Sworn/Estimate/Non-Audited September 30, 2017
Advertising Rate (weekday/saturday): Open inch rate $9.50
News services: AP. **Established:** 1919
Special Editions: American Homes (Apr);

LTC (Aug); Tax Guide (Feb); 4-H Fair (Jul); Agriculture (Mar); Heath Toffee Festival (May); Veteran's Salute (Nov); Working Women (Oct); Robinson Fall Festival (Sept).
Pub./Bus. Mgr./Sec./Treasurer......... Kathy Lewis
Adv. Mgr...Winnie Piper
Circ...Michelle Knup
Managing Ed.................................Greg Bilbney
Sports Ed........................................Josh Brown
Prodn. Foreman, Press............ Gregg Cummins
Mechanical Available: Offset; Black and 4 ROP colors; insert accepted; page cutoffs - 21.
Mechanical Specifications: Type page 13 x 21; E - 6 cols, 1 5/6, 1/8 between; A - 6 cols, 1 5/6, 1/8 between; C - 9 cols, 1 1/6, 1/8 between.Equipment & Software: PRESSROOM EQUIPMENT: Lines — 6-G/ Community; Folders — 1-G/2:1.; MAILROOM EQUIPMENT: Counter Stackers — 1-BG/ Count-O-Veyor; Tying Machines — 2/Bu; Control System — Addressing machine 1-Am/Speed-umat 2600.; BUSINESS EQUIPMENT: Mk, APP/Mac BUSINESS SOFTWARE: Baseview CLASSIFIED EQUIPMENT: Hardware — APP/Mac, Sun; Printers — Xante, LaserMaster/Unity, QMS.; DISPLAY EQUIPMENT: Hardware — APP/ Mac; Printers — Xante, LaserMaster/ Unity; DISPLAY SOFTWAREAd Make-up Applications — Multi-Ad/Creator, QPS, Adobe/Photoshop, Adobe/Illustrator; Layout Software — APP/Mac. EDITORIAL EQUIPMENT: Hardware — 7-Mk, 7-APP/ Mac; Printers — Xante, LaserMaster/ Unity EDITORIAL SOFTWARE: Baseview, QPS/QuarkXPress, Adobe/Photoshop. PRODUCTION EQUIPMENT: Hardware — 2-COM/Unisetter, 1-COM/4961, 1-COM/7200; Cameras — 1-B/Caravel.

ROCKFORD

ROCKFORD REGISTER STAR

99 E State St, Rockford, Ill., 61104-1009, Winnebago; gen tel (815) 987-1200; adv tel (815) 987-1300; ed tel (815) 987-1350; gen fax (815) 964-2472; adv fax (815) 962-6578; ed fax (815) 987-1365; gen/ nat adv e-mail dlecher@rrstar.com; disp adv e-mail dlecher@rrstar.com; class adv e-mailclassified@rrstar.com; ed e-mail mbaldwin@rrstar.com; web site www.rrstar.com
- 3,433,757(views) 555,658(visitors)
Group: New Media Investment Group
Published: Mon, Tues, Wed, Thur, Fri, Sat, Sun
Weekday Frequency: m
Saturday Frequency: m
Circulation: 25,077; 25,644(sat); 34,061(sun)
Last Audit: AAM June 30, 2017
Advertising Rate (weekday/saturday): Open inch rate $82.51
Advertising Rate (sunday): $111.19
News services: AP, GNS, MCT, LAT-WP. **Established:** 1840
Own Printing Facility?: Yes
Commercial Printers?: Yes
Special Editions: Real Estate Marketplace (Monthly).
Special Weekly Sections: Go (Friday); Real Estate (S);Weekly TMC (Wednesday)
Syndicated Publications: USA WEEKEND Magazine (S); American Profile (Weekly).
Digital Platform - Mobile: Apple, Android, Windows, Blackberry
Publisher..Paul Gaier
Exec. Ed.....................................Mark Baldwin
Asst. Mng. Ed..........................Anna Derocher
Prodn. Dir.................................Mike Kreppert
Adv. Dir.....................................Denny Lecher
Market Information: TMC.
Mechanical Available: Offset; Black and 3 ROP colors; insert accepted.
Mechanical Specifications: Type page 11 1/8 x 19 1/4; E - 6 cols, 1 3/4, 1/8 between; A - 6 cols, 1 3/4, 1/8 between; C - 10 cols, 1 2/25, 1/25 between.
Areas Served: 61101, 61102, 61103, 61104, 61107, 61108, 61109, 61111, 61112, 61114, 61115, 61016, 61072, 61073, 61080, 61008, 61010, 61065
Delivery Method: Mail, Newsstand, Carrier, RacksEquipment & Software: PRESSROOM EQUIPMENT: Lines — KBA 2006; Folders — 2, 2-KBA; Reels & Stands — 8, 6-KBA/ EAE; Control System — 1991; Registration System — Microtrack/9500. MAILROOM EQUIPMENT: Counter Stackers — 2-HL/ Monitor HT, 4-QWI/401; Inserters & Stuffers — Hopper/632E 29; Tying Machines — 2/ Dynaric, 4-/Sterling; Wrapping Singles — Bu; Control System — Omnizone; Address Machine — KAN/600.; BUSINESS EQUIPMENT: 11-IBM/AS-400 BUSINESS SOFTWARE: Micosoft/Office 2000 CLASSIFIED EQUIPMENT: Hardware — Tandem/K1000, SII; CLASSIFIED SOFTWARE: SII/Release 6.0.1, ATS. DISPLAY EQUIPMENT: Hardware — 13-APP/Mac; Printers — HP/LaserJet 4MV, HP/8100, HP/755CM, HP/1055CM; Other Hardware — Microtek, CD Burner, Epson/836XL DISPLAY SOFTWAREAd Make-up Applications — QPS/QuarkXPress 4.11, Multi-Ad/Creator 2; Layout Software — Managing Editor/ALS, Adobe/InDesign. EDITORIAL EQUIPMENT: Hardware — SII/ Synthesis 66XR, Tandem/K1000; Printers — HP/LaserJet IV, HP/DesignJet 755CM EDITORIAL SOFTWARE: Saxotech. PRODUCTION EQUIPMENT: Hardware — 1-Pre Press/Panther, 1-AG/Avantra; Scanners — Microtek/Scanmaker III, Epson/836XL PRODUCTION SOFTWARE: MEI/ALS.

SPRINGFIELD

THE STATE JOURNAL-REGISTER

1 Copley Plz, Springfield, Ill., 62701-1927, Sangamon; gen tel (217) 788-1300; adv tel (217) 788-1353; ed tel (217) 788-1513; adv fax (217) 788-1352; ed fax (217) 788-1551; gen/nat adv e-mail advertise@sj-r.com; class adv e-mailangela.stewart@sj-r.com; ed e-mail sjr@sj-r.com; web site www.sj-r.com
Group: New Media Investment Group
Published: Mon, Tues, Wed, Thur, Fri, Sat, Sun
Weekday Frequency: m
Saturday Frequency: m
Circulation: 30,289; 31,681(sat); 38,791(sun)
Last Audit: AAM September 30, 2016
Advertising Rate (weekday/saturday): Open inch rate $80.95
Advertising Rate (sunday): Open inch rate $89.05
News services: AP, MCT, GateHouse News Service **Established:** 1831
Own Printing Facility?: No
Commercial Printers?: No
Special Editions: Fall Festival Guide (Aug); Mother's Day Gifts (May); Welcome to Your Health (Monthly); Holiday Events Calender (Nov); SO Magazine (Other); Fall Home Improvement (Sept)., Seniors (monthly), & Home & Garden (monthly)
Special Weekly Sections: Financial, TV (Daily); Health (Mon); Teen (Th); Food (Wed): Arts, Entertainment (Thur); Religion, TV (Sun)
Syndicated Publications: Parade (S)., Relish, Dash, & Athlon
Digital Platform - Mobile: Apple, Android, Windows, Blackberry
Digital Platform - Tablet: Apple iOS, Android, Kindle, Nook
Bus. Ed...Tim Landis
Digital Mang. Ed.
Jason Piscia
Photo Ed...Rich Saal
Asst. Photo Ed..............................Ted Schurter
Bart Bolton
Classified Adv. Mgr..................Angela Stewart
Pub....Todd Sears
Editorial Ed.....................................Kate Schott
Sports Ed....................................Todd Adams
VP of Adv..................................Eric Mayberry
Market Information: Split run; TMC.
Mechanical Available: Offset; Black and 3 ROP colors; insert accepted; page cutoffs - 22 3/4.
Areas Served: 62705
Delivery Method: Mail, Newsstand, Carrier, RacksEquipment & Software: CLASSIFIED EQUIPMENT: Hardware — Dell/Power Edge 2550; Printers — HP/LaserJet; CLASSIFIED SOFTWARE: ATS/Advisor. DISPLAY EQUIPMENT: Hardware — Dell; Printers — HP/Laser Jet, HP/2000, HP/1050, HP/2500; DISPLAY SOFTWAREAd Make-up Applications — QPS/QuarkXPress 5.0; Layout Software — MEI/ALS. EDITORIAL EQUIPMENT: Hardware — Dell; Printers — HP/LaserJet EDITORIAL SOFTWARE: ATS/ Media Desk. PRODUCTION SOFTWARE: Northwood Publishing/Class Page.
Note: The State Journal-Register (mS) has a combination rate of $80.95 with the Lincoln Courier (e). Individual newspaper rates not made available.

STERLING

DAILY GAZETTE

3200 E Lincolnway, Sterling, Ill., 61081-1773, Whiteside; gen tel (815) 625-3600; gen fax (815) 625-9390; gen/nat adv e-mail jbaratta@saukvalley.com; disp adv e-mail jbaratta@saukvalley.com; class adv e-mailjdiehl@saukvalley.com; ed e-mail llough@saukvalley.com; web site www.saukvalley.com
Group: Shaw Media
Published: Mon, Tues, Wed, Thur, Fri, Sat, Sun
Weekday Frequency: e
Saturday Frequency: m
Circulation: 8,320; 8,320(sat); 13,670(sun)
Last Audit: AAM September 30, 2015
Advertising Rate (weekday/saturday): Open inch rate $25.00
News services: AP, CNS, United Media Service, SHNS. **Established:** 1854
Own Printing Facility?: Yes
Commercial Printers?: Yes
Special Editions: Career Guide (Apr); Today's Farm (Aug); Sterling Sights & Sounds (Dec); Internet Directory (Feb); Health & Fitness (Jan); Dixon Sidewalk Sale (Jul); Dixon Petunia Festival (Jun); Extra Circulation Sunday (Mar); Mother's Day (May); Senior Echo (Monthly); F
Syndicated Publications: TV Week (Fri); USA WEEKEND Magazine (S); Big E (Entertainment Guide) (Thur).
Adv. Dir...................................Jennifer Baratta
Circ. Dir...............................Sheryl Gulbranson
Exec. Ed...Larry Lough
Chief Photographer........................Alex Paschal
Production Dir..........................Ernie Appleyard
Finance Dir................................Joanne Doherty
Pub....Sam Fisher
Market Information: TMC.
Mechanical Available: Offset; Black and 3 ROP colors; insert accepted - any; page cutoffs - 22 3/4.
Mechanical Specifications: Type page 11 3/5 x 21 1/2; E - 6 cols, 1 5/6, 1/8 between; A - 6 cols, 1 5/6, 1/8 between; C - 6 cols, 1 1/4, 1/8 between.
Areas Served: Sauk Valley (IL)
Equipment & Software: PRESSROOM EQUIPMENT: Lines — 8-G/Urbanite double width 1995; MAILROOM EQUIPMENT: Counter Stackers — Exact/Stack, QWI/ Sport II; Inserters & Stuffers — HI/1372; Tying Machines — Dynaric/RLM-1; Address Machine — Dispensamatic Ct/595.; BUSINESS EQUIPMENT: ATT/3B2500 BUSINESS SOFTWARE: Unix CLASSIFIED EQUIPMENT: Hardware — APP/ Mac; Printers — Okidata, 1-HP/8100N; CLASSIFIED SOFTWARE: Baseview/ Ad Manager Pro V 1.0.4.B. DISPLAY EQUIPMENT: Hardware — 7-APP/Power Mac 7100; Printers — 2-HP/LaserJet 8150N; DISPLAY SOFTWAREAd Make-up Applications — QPS/QuarkXPress 4.1, Adobe/Photoshop 6.0, Adobe/ Illustrator 9.0.; EDITORIAL EQUIPMENT: Hardware — 28-APP/Power Mac 7100; Printers — 2-HP/8150N EDITORIAL SOFTWARE: Baseview/NewsEdit Pro IQue 2.2.2. PRODUCTION EQUIPMENT: Hardware — 1-ECR/9100, Konica K-28; Scanners — Nikon/LS 1000, AG/Studio Star PRODUCTION SOFTWARE: Baseview 3.31.
Note: The Sterling Daily Gazette (e, wknd) has a combination rate of $30.27 with the Dixon Telegraph (e, wknd). Individual newspaper rates not made available.

TAYLORVILLE

BREEZE COURIER

212 S Main St, Taylorville, Ill., 62568-2219, Christian; gen tel (217) 824-2233; gen fax (217) 824-2026; gen/nat adv e-mail breezecourier@breezecourier.com; disp adv e-mail breezecourier@breezecourier.com; class adv e-mailbreezeclassifieds@breezecourier.com; ed e-mail breezenews@breezecourier.com; web site www.breezecourier.com
- 97,776(views) 54,294(visitors)
Published: Mon, Tues, Wed, Thur, Fri, Sun
Weekday Frequency: e
Circulation: 5,000; 5,157(sun)
Last Audit: Sworn/Estimate/Non-Audited September 30, 2017
Advertising Rate (weekday/saturday): Open inch rate $6.50
Advertising Rate (sunday): $6.50
Online Advertising Rate: we do not price CPM
News services: AP **Established:** 1864
Own Printing Facility?: Yes
Commercial Printers?: Yes
Special Editions: Home Improvement (Apr); Back-to-School (Aug); First Baby (Dec); Senior Citizens (Feb); Tax Tab (Jan); County Fair (Jul); Bridal (Jun); Agriculture (Mar); Winter Sports (Nov); Car Care (Oct); Fall Home Improvement (Sept).
Special Weekly Sections: TV Tab (T).
Syndicated Publications: American Profile (S).
Digital Platform - Mobile: Apple, Android, Blackberry
Digital Platform - Tablet: Apple iOS, Android, Blackberry Tablet OS
Exec. Vice Pres..................Wilda Quinn Cooper
Pub...Marylee Rasar
Prodn. Mgr.....................................Jeff Nation
Adv....Rhonda Wilson
Adv....Ron Verardi
Adv....Dee Carroll
Adv...Laurie Sparling
Class./Commercial Printing.........Tracy Marshall
News...Andy Lasswell
Sports Ed.......................................Derek Parris
News...Jacob Griffin
News...Jamie Painter
Business.......................................Barb Profeta
Business...................................Owen Lasswell
Production......................................Ryan Myles
Market Information: Split run; TMC; Zoned editions.
Mechanical Available: Offset; Black and 3 ROP colors; insert accepted - any size; page cutoffs - 21.
Mechanical Specifications: Type page 11.625" x 21; E - 6 cols, 1.833", 1/6 between; A - 6 cols, 2 1/12, 1/6 between; C - 9 cols, 1.187", 1/12 between.
Areas Served: 62568
Delivery Method: Mail, Newsstand, Carrier, RacksEquipment & Software: PRESSROOM EQUIPMENT: Lines — 4-G/Community; MAILROOM EQUIPMENT: Tying Machines — 1-Bu/7; Address Machine — 1/Am.; BUSINESS EQUIPMENT: APP/Mac BUSINESS SOFTWARE: QPS, Adobe/ Photoshop, TI/OmniPage, Baseview CLASSIFIED EQUIPMENT: Hardware — APP/Mac; Printers — HP; CLASSIFIED SOFTWARE: Baseview. DISPLAY EQUIPMENT: Hardware — APP/Mac; Printers — APP/Mac LaserWriter II NTX, HP/8100 N; Other Hardware — APP/Mac CD-Rom, APP/Mac Scanner DISPLAY SOFTWAREAd Make-up Applications — QPS/Quark 4.0; Layout Software — APP/ Mac. EDITORIAL EQUIPMENT: Hardware — APP/Mac/Microtek/Scanner, Nikon/Coolscan, Kk/DCS200 Digital camera; Printers — MON, APP/Mac LaserWriters, HP/LaserJet EDITORIAL SOFTWARE: Baseview, QPS, Adobe/Photoshop. PRODUCTION EQUIPMENT: Hardware — 1-B/1500, HP PRODUCTION SOFTWARE: QPS/ QuarkXPress 4.0.

WATSEKA

TIMES-REPUBLIC

1492 E Walnut St, Watseka, Ill., 60970-1806, Iroquois; gen tel (815) 432-5227; adv tel (815) 432-5227; ed tel (815) 432-5227; gen fax (815) 432-5159; adv fax (815) 432-5159; ed fax (815) 432-5159; gen/nat adv e-mail watsekasales@intranix.com; disp adv e-mail watsekasales@intranix.com; class adv e-mailclassifieds@intranix.com; ed e-mail cwaters@intranix.com; web site www.

watsekatimesrepublic.com
Group: Community Media Group
Published: Mon, Tues, Wed, Thur, Fri
Weekday Frequency: m
Circulation: 2,373
Last Audit: Sworn/Estimate/Non-Audited September 30, 2017
Advertising Rate (weekday/saturday): Open inch rate $10.95
News services: AP. **Established:** 1870
Special Editions: Twin State Farmer (Every other month); Bridal (Other); Twin State News & Views (Quarterly).
Prod. Dir. .... Kevin Armold
Pub. .... Don Hurd
Mng. Ed. .... Carla Waters
Adv. Dir. .... Roberta Kempen
Market Information: TMC.
Mechanical Available: Offset; Black and 1 ROP colors; insert accepted - single sheets; page cutoffs - 15.
Mechanical Specifications: Type page 10 1/4 x 14; E - 6 cols, 1 3/5, 1/6 between; A - 6 cols, 1 3/5, 1/6 between; C - 6 cols, 1 3/5, 1/6 between.
Areas Served: Iroquois County (IL)
Equipment & Software: PRESSROOM EQUIPMENT: Lines — 4-KP/News King 1976; MAILROOM EQUIPMENT: Counter Stackers — 1/CH; Tying Machines — 4-/Bu; Address Machine — 1-/Ch.; BUSINESS EQUIPMENT: 2-IBM/Sys 36 BUSINESS SOFTWARE: Microsoft/Windows 95, Microsoft/Word, Microsoft/Excel CLASSIFIED EQUIPMENT: Hardware — 1-APP/Mac, 4-APP/iMac; HP/laser Jet 2100TN; Printers — HP/Laser Jet 8100 Series, 1-Xante/Accel-a-Writer 8200; CLASSIFIED SOFTWARE: Baseview/Ad Manager Pro, QPS/QuarkXPress. DISPLAY EQUIPMENT: Printers — 1-Xante/Accel-a-Writer 8200, HP/Laser Jet 8100 Series; Other Hardware — CD-Rom, HP/Scanner, Bernouilli/External Hard Drive, Bernouilli/Zip Drive DISPLAY SOFTWAREAd Make-up Applications — 3-Multi-Ad/Creator 3.5, Microsoft/Word, QPS/QuarkXPress, Multi-Ad/Creator 4.0; EDITORIAL EQUIPMENT: Hardware — 5-APP/Mac; Printers — 1-Xante/Accel-a-Writer 8200, HP/LaserJet 8100 Series EDITORIAL SOFTWARE: Baseview/NewsEdit. PRODUCTION EQUIPMENT: Hardware — Tl/OmniPage 2.12, HP/Laser Jet 8100 Series; Cameras — 1-Nu, 1-R PRODUCTION SOFTWARE: QPS/QuarkXPress 4.0.

WEST FRANKFORT

THE DAILY AMERICAN

111 S Emma St, West Frankfort, Ill., 62896-2729, Franklin; gen tel (618) 932-2146; adv tel (814) 444-5900; ed tel (814) 444-5928; gen fax (618) 937-6006; adv fax (618) 937-6006; ed fax (618) 937-6006; gen/nat adv e-mail lashbrook@dailyamericannews.com; disp adv e-mail wfadvertising2@dailyamericannews.com; class adv e-mailwfclass@dailyamericannews.com; ed e-mail editor@dailyamericannews.com; web site www.dailyamericannews.com
Group: New Media Investment Group
Published: Mon, Tues, Wed, Thur, Fri
Weekday Frequency: e
Saturday Frequency: m
Circulation: 3,510; 3,510(sat)
Last Audit: Sworn/Estimate/Non-Audited September 30, 2017
Advertising Rate (weekday/saturday): Open inch rate $10.25
News services: AP, TMS. **Established:** 1920
Special Editions: Progress (Feb); Bridal (Jan); Fourth of July Celebration (Jun); Homes (Monthly); Home Improvement (Oct).
Syndicated Publications: USA WEEKEND Magazine (Fri); Sports Saturday (Sat); American Profile (Weekly).
Digital Platform - Mobile: Apple, Android
Digital Platform - Tablet: Apple iOS, Android
Reg. Pub. .... Kevin Haezebroek
Adv. Mgr., Classified .... Crystal Bullett
Office/Circ. Mgr. .... Heather Little
Market Information: ADS; TMC.
Mechanical Available: Offset; Black and 4 ROP colors; insert accepted; page cutoffs - 21 1/2.
Mechanical Specifications: Type page 13 3/4 x 21 1/2; E - 6 cols, 2 1/16, 1/8 between; A - 6 cols, 2 1/16, 1/8 between; C - 8 cols, 1 1/2, 1/8 between.
Areas Served: Somerset County (IL)
Equipment & Software: PRESSROOM EQUIPMENT: Lines — 11-G/Community; Folders — G/Suburban.; MAILROOM EQUIPMENT: Counter Stackers — St; Inserters & Stuffers — St; CLASSIFIED EQUIPMENT: Hardware — IBM.; DISPLAY EQUIPMENT: Printers — APP/Mac 630; Other Hardware — APP/Mac Scanner, V/Imagesetter DISPLAY SOFTWAREAd Make-up Applications — QPS, Multi-Ad/Creator, Adobe/Photoshop; Layout Software — APP/Mac 650, APP/Mac 800. EDITORIAL EQUIPMENT: Hardware — APP/Mac 610, APP/Mac 605; Printers — APP/Mac 630 EDITORIAL SOFTWARE: QPS, Multi-Ad/Creator, Microsoft, Adobe/Photoshop. PRODUCTION EQUIPMENT: Hardware — V PRODUCTION SOFTWARE: QPS 3.3.

INDIANA

ANDERSON

THE HERALD BULLETIN

1133 Jackson St, Anderson, Ind., 46016-1433, Madison; gen tel (765) 622-1212; adv tel (765) 640-2312; ed tel (765) 622-1212; gen fax (765) 640-4820; adv fax (765) 640-4820; ed fax (765) 640-4815; gen/nat adv e-mail annette.burcharts@indianamediagroup.com; disp adv e-mail annette.burcharts@indianamediagroup.com; class adv e-mailannette.burcharts@indianamediagroup.com; ed e-mail scott.underwood@heraldbulletin.com; web site www.theheraldbulletin.com
Group: Community Newspaper Holdings, Inc.
Published: Mon, Tues, Wed, Thur, Fri, Sat, Sun
Weekday Frequency: m
Saturday Frequency: m
Circulation: 18,691; 18,691(sat); 20,422(sun)
Last Audit: Sworn/Estimate/Non-Audited September 30, 2017
Advertising Rate (weekday/saturday): Open inch rate $31.00
Advertising Rate (sunday): Open inch rate $35.00
Online Advertising Rate: Leaderboard 17.50 CPM; Banner Ad $20.00 CPM; Floorboard, Sliding Billboard $25.00 CPM
News services: AP. **Established:** 1868
Own Printing Facility?: Yes
Commercial Printers?: Yes
Special Editions: Spring Auto Guide (Apr); Fall Football (Aug); Visitor's Guide (Dec); Winter Clearance (Feb); Active Times (Jan); USA Proud (Jul); Father's Day Pages (Jun); Visitor's Guide (Mar); Mother's Day Gift Guide (May); Gift Guide (Nov); Active Times (Oct).
Special Weekly Sections: Food (Mon); Homes (S).
Syndicated Publications: Parade (S).
Proprietary Publications: Photo News (Wed); Madison
Digital Platform - Mobile: Apple, Android
Digital Platform - Tablet: Apple iOS, Android, Kindle, Nook, Kindle Fire
Pub. .... Beverly Joyce
Adv. Dir. .... Mark Elliott
Classifieds .... Annette Burcharts
Ed .... Scott Underwood
Circ. Dir. .... Amy Winter
Accounting .... Peggy Crabtree
Adv. Graphics .... Peg Melton
Newsroom Coord. .... Janis Bowling
Editorial Asst. .... Tammy Everitt
Asst. Ed. .... Steve Dick
Photo Ed. .... John Cleary
Market Information: ADS; Split run; TMC.
Mechanical Available: Offset; Black and 3 ROP colors; insert accepted; page cutoffs - 22 3/4.
Mechanical Specifications: Type page 13 x 21 1/2; E - 6 cols, 2 1/16, 1/8 between; A - 6 cols, 2 1/16, 1/8 between; C - 9 cols, 1 3/8, 1/16 between.
Areas Served: Madison County
Delivery Method: Mail, Newsstand, Carrier, RacksEquipment & Software: PRESSROOM EQUIPMENT: Lines — 8-G/Urbanite single width; Reels & Stands — 6-G/Stands.; MAILROOM EQUIPMENT: Counter Stackers — 1/HL, 1-/HI; Inserters & Stuffers — 1-MM/SLS 2000; Tying Machines — 1-/MLN, 1-/Bu; Address Machine — KR, FMC; BUSINESS EQUIPMENT: 2-HP/9000 BUSINESS SOFTWARE: Oracle: Financials, PBS: Circ, Adv CLASSIFIED EQUIPMENT: Hardware — 2-DEC/433 ST; 10-DEC/333C; Printers — 1-C.Itoh; CLASSIFIED SOFTWARE: CText. DISPLAY EQUIPMENT: Hardware — 2-IBM/PS2; Printers — 1-C.Itoh; Other Hardware — 2-IBM/PS-2, 1-DEC/466 D2LP66, 6-Compaq/ProLiner P133, 1-Dec/420 DISPLAY SOFTWAREAd Make-up Applications — SCS/Layout 8000; Layout Software — Archetype/Designer. EDITORIAL EQUIPMENT: Hardware — CText, 2-DEC/433 ST/23-DEC/333C, 2-DEC/420SX, 1-DEC/466LP2, 5-Compaq/DeskPro 133; Printers — V/4000-5300E, 1-Pre Press/Panther Pro 46 EDITORIAL SOFTWARE: CText. PRODUCTION EQUIPMENT: Hardware — Nu/Ultra Violet burner, 1-V/Pan; Cameras — 2-SCREEN/6500C; Scanners — 1-Sharp/1200R, 1-Lf/AP Leaf 35mm, ECR/Autokon, 3-AG/Arcus PRODUCTION SOFTWARE: QPS 3.312.

ANGOLA

THE HERALD REPUBLICAN

45 S Public Sq, Angola, Ind., 46703-1926, Steuben; gen tel (260) 665-3117; adv tel (260) 665-3117 ext. 110; ed tel (260) 665-3117 ext. 140; gen fax (260) 665-2322; adv fax (260) 665-2322; ed fax (260) 665-2322; gen/nat adv e-mail lconley@kpcmedia.com; disp adv e-mail lconley@kpcmedia.com; class adv e-mailasaggars@kpcmedia.com; ed e-mail news@kpcmedia.com; web site www.kpcnews.com - 500,000(views) 100,000(visitors)
Group: KPC Media Group, Inc.
Published: Mon, Tues, Wed, Thur, Fri, Sat, Sun
Weekday Frequency: m
Saturday Frequency: m
Circulation: 4,070; 4,070(sat); 4,230(sun)
Last Audit: AAM December 31, 2014
Advertising Rate (weekday/saturday): Open inch rate $14.60
Advertising Rate (sunday): Open inch rate $14.60
Online Advertising Rate: Page Curl $150.00 per week; Top Banner $200.00 per week; Lower Leaderboard $60.00 per week
News services: AP, SHNS. **Established:** 1857
Own Printing Facility?: Yes
Commercial Printers?: Yes
Special Editions: Wedding Planner (Feb); Steuben County Answer Book (Jan); Big Bang 4th of July Sale (Jul); All In The Family Business (Jun); Angola Chamber Guide (Mar); Summer in Northeast Indiana (May).
Special Weekly Sections: Outdoor Life (Fri); Homes To Own (S).
Syndicated Publications: USA WEEKEND Magazine (S).
Digital Platform - Mobile: Other
Digital Platform - Tablet: Other
Pres./CEO/Pub. .... Terry Housholder
Ed. .... Michael Marturello
News Ed. .... Amy Oberlin
Sports Ed. .... Ken Fillmore
Adv. Dir. .... Lynette Donley
Acct. Exec. .... Marta Wysong
Acct. Exec. .... Machele Waid
IT Mgr. .... Brian Glick
Market Information: ADS; TMC; Zoned editions.
Mechanical Specifications: Type page 13 x 21 1/2; E - 6 cols, 2, 1/6 between; A - 6 cols, 2 1/16, 1/6 between; C - 9 cols, 1 3/8, 1/6 between.
Areas Served: 46703, 46705, 46737, 46742, 46747, 46776, 46779
Delivery Method: Mail, Newsstand, Carrier, RacksEquipment & Software: PRESSROOM EQUIPMENT: Lines — 6-G/Community.; DISPLAY EQUIPMENT: Hardware — PC, APP/Mac, ECR/ImageSetter Sun; DISPLAY SOFTWARELayout Software — Multi-Ad 4.0, QPS/QuarkXPress, Adobe/PageMaker 6.5. EDITORIAL SOFTWARE: ACT.
Note: All production of the Herald-Republican is done at the central plant in Kendallville.

AUBURN

THE STAR

102 N Main St, Auburn, Ind., 46706-1857, De Kalb; gen tel (260) 347-0400; adv tel (260) 347-0400; ed tel (260) 347-0400; gen fax (260) 925-2625; adv fax (260) 925-2625; ed fax (260) 925-2625; gen/nat adv e-mail jnewman@kpcmedia.com; disp adv e-mail jnewman@kpcmedia.com; class adv e-mailrandymitchell@kpcmedia.com; ed e-mail randymitchell@kpcmedia.com; web site kpcnews.com/news/latest/eveningstar - 608,581(views) 172,250(visitors)
Group: KPC Media Group, Inc.
Published: Mon, Tues, Wed, Thur, Fri, Sat, Sun
Weekday Frequency: m
Saturday Frequency: m
Circulation: 5,272; 5,272(sat); 4,963(sun)
Last Audit: AAM March 31, 2015
Advertising Rate (weekday/saturday): Open inch rate $14.60
Advertising Rate (sunday): Open inch rate $14.60
Online Advertising Rate: Page Curl $150.00 per week; Top Banner $200.00 per week; Lower Leaderboard $60.00 per week
News services: AP. **Established:** 1871
Own Printing Facility?: Yes
Commercial Printers?: Yes
Special Editions: Health & wellness (Jan); DeKalb Community Guide (Feb); Business Card Blowout (Mar); Go West (Jul); Parade of Homes (Aug); DeKalb Co. 4-H Scrapbook (Oct); Festival of Trees (Nov); Holiday Gift Guide (Dec).
How-To Guide Oct.
Senior Service Directory in April
Hunting Guide in Oct.
Special Weekly Sections: Outdoor Life (Fri); Business Page (Other); Homes To Own (S); Agri-Business (Sat); Entertainment Page (Thur); Best Food Day (Wed).
Digital Platform - Mobile: Apple, Android, Other
Digital Platform - Tablet: Apple iOS, Android, Other
Pres./Pub./CEO .... Terry Housholder
Exec. Ed. .... Dave Kurtz
District Mgr. .... Christy Day
Adv. Dir. .... Lynette Donley
Account Exec. .... Lisa Myers
Multimedia Sales Executive.. Jonathan Anderson
CEO .... Randy Mitchell
Market Information: ADS; TMC; Zoned editions.
Mechanical Available: Offset; Black and 3 ROP colors; insert accepted - product samples; page cutoffs - 22 3/4.
Mechanical Specifications: Type page 11 1/2 x 21 1/2; E - 6 cols, 1 13/16, 1/8 between; A - 6 cols, 1 13/16, 1/8 between; C - 9 cols, 1 1/6, 1/8 between.
Areas Served: 46706, 46705, 46721, 46730, 46738, 46710, 46763, 46785, 46788,46793
Delivery Method: Mail, Newsstand, Carrier, RacksEquipment & Software: PRESSROOM EQUIPMENT: Lines — 1-G/Floor SSC Units 1988, 1-Stalk/Pathfinder 1988; 2-G/4-High 1999; Folders — 2-G/SSC; Pasters — 2-KTI/SplicerControl System — 1-Ebway/Industries Pneumatic Master Control.; MAILROOM EQUIPMENT: Counter Stackers — 1/The Stacker Machine Co/S-N 316-19, 1-BG/Count-O-Veyor; Inserters & Stuffers — 1-KAN/5 pocket, KAN/Twin Stacker, MM/Saddlebinder 4 pocket, 1-Challenge/Single Knife; Tying Machines — 1-Akebono/Strapper, IT; BUSINESS EQUIPMENT: 1-Compaq/Proliant 5000 BUSINESS SOFTWARE: Baseview/Ad Manager Pro 2.02, Dynamic Great Plains, Baseview/Circulation Pro 1.8.0 CLASSIFIED EQUIPMENT: Hardware — 3-APP/Mac; Printers — 2-APP/Mac LaserWriter; CLASSIFIED SOFTWARE: Baseview, QPS/QuarkXPress. DISPLAY EQUIPMENT: Hardware — 9-APP/Mac; Printers — 2-APP/Mac LaserWriter; DISPLAY SOFTWAREAd Make-up Applications — QPS/QuarkXPress, Multi-Ad.; EDITORIAL EQUIPMENT: Hardware — 12-APP/Mac/6-RSK/TRS 80 Model 100; Printers — 2-APP/Mac LaserWriter EDITORIAL SOFTWARE: Baseview, QPS/QuarkXPress.

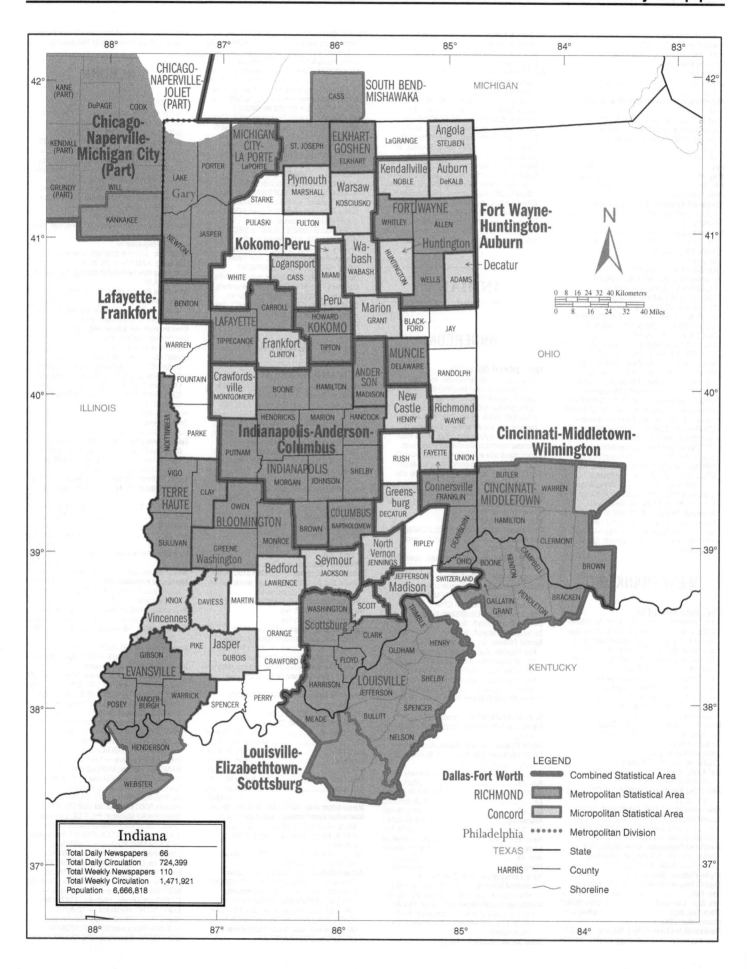

Indiana

Total Daily Newspapers	66
Total Daily Circulation	724,399
Total Weekly Newspapers	110
Total Weekly Circulation	1,471,921
Population	6,666,818

LEGEND

Dallas-Fort Worth	Combined Statistical Area
RICHMOND	Metropolitan Statistical Area
Concord	Micropolitan Statistical Area
Philadelphia	Metropolitan Division
TEXAS	State
HARRIS	County
	Shoreline

PRODUCTION EQUIPMENT: Hardware — 2-AG/Imagesetter 1200, Luntz & Jensen, 1-Tek Color/4C Printer; Cameras — 1-B, 1-Kk/Image Maker IM600; Scanners — APP/Mac, 1-AG/Arcus, 2-AG/Arcus Plus, 1-Kk/RFS 2035 PRODUCTION SOFTWARE: QPS/QuarkXPress 4.0.

Note: All production of the The Star is done at the central plant in Kendallville.

BEDFORD

THE TIMES-MAIL

813 16th St, Bedford, Ind., 47421-3822, Lawrence; gen tel (812) 275-3355; adv tel (812) 331-4292; ed tel (812) 277-7258; gen fax (812) 275-4191; adv fax (812) 275-4191; ed fax (812) 275-4191; gen/nat adv e-mail lragle@schurz.com; disp adv e-mail cgiddens@schurz.com; class adv e-maillleahy@hoosiertimes.com; ed e-mail mikel@tmnews.com; web site www.tmnews.com
- 600,000(views) 40,000(visitors)

Group: Schurz Communications Inc
Published: Mon, Tues, Wed, Thur, Fri, Sat, Sun
Weekday Frequency: m
Circulation: ; 11,218(sat); 40,171(sun)
Last Audit: Sworn/Estimate/Non-Audited September 30, 2017
Advertising Rate (weekday/saturday): Open inch rate $18.74
Advertising Rate (sunday): Open inch rate $40.21
Online Advertising Rate: Run of Site (Static) $10.00 CPM; Rich Media/Flash $10.00 CPM; 300x600 $14.00 CPM
News services: AP. **Established:** 1884
Special Editions: Business Expo (Apr); Back-to-School (Aug); Holiday Gift Guide (Dec); Area Dining Guide (Feb); Financial Focus (Jan); City-Wide Sidewalk Sale (Jul); Women in Business (Jun); Kitchen, Bath and Furniture (Mar); Summer Fun (May); Prime Advantage (Monthly).
Special Weekly Sections: TV Week (Fri).
Syndicated Publications: Parade (S).
Digital Platform - Mobile: Apple, Android
Digital Platform - Tablet: Apple iOS, Android
Prod. Mgr. .... Stacey Brown
Adv. Dir. .... Laurie Ragle
Circ. Dir. .... Tim D. Smith
Photo Ed. .... Rich Janzaruk
Digital Media Dir. .... Todd Davidson
Sales Mgr. .... Chad Giddens
Classified Ad. Mgr. .... Leah Leahy
Sports Ed. .... Sean Duncan
District Mgr. .... Steve Sallee
Managing Ed. .... Krystal Ragle
Market Information: Split run; TMC.
Mechanical Available: Offset; Black and 3 ROP colors; insert accepted - standing card; page cutoffs - 22 3/4.
Mechanical Specifications: Type page 13 x 21; E - 6 cols, 2 1/16, 1/8 between; A - 6 cols, 2 1/16, 1/8 between; C - 9 cols, 1 3/8, 1/16 between.
Areas Served: Lawrence County
Delivery Method: Mail, Newsstand, Carrier, RacksEquipment & Software: PRESSROOM EQUIPMENT: Lines — 15-G/Community single width (Color); Folders — 1-G/SC1045 Balloon Double Former, 1-G/SC1045.; MAILROOM EQUIPMENT: Counter Stackers — 1-BG/Stabb Brick, Rima/RS25; Inserters & Stuffers — 2-KAN/480; Tying Machines — 1-FMC/APM2A, 1-Sa/SR2A, 2/Dynaric, 2-/Bu, 1-/Interlake, Sterling; Address Machine — Ch, KR; BUSINESS EQUIPMENT: 1-DEC/VAX, 1-DEC/Rainbow, IBM CLASSIFIED EQUIPMENT: Hardware — Novell/Server; Printers — 1-Dataproducts/LZR 1580; CLASSIFIED SOFTWARE: Baseview/Ad Manager Pro. DISPLAY EQUIPMENT: Hardware — 6-APP/Power Mac; Printers — Dataproducts/LaserPrinter 1580, APP/Mac LaserWriter II NTX; DISPLAY SOFTWAREAd Make-up Applications - Adobe/Photoshop, Aldus/PageMaker, Multi-Ad/Creator, QPS/QuarkXPress, Aldus/FreeHand; Layout Software — 2-AU/APS5, APP/Mac. EDITORIAL EQUIPMENT: Hardware — APP/Mac 9150-120 Workgroup Server; Printers — 2-Dataproducts/LZR 1580 EDITORIAL SOFTWARE: Baseview/IQUE Server. PRODUCTION EQUIPMENT: Hardware — 2-Hardot/15.75 Imagesetter, Pre Press/Panther Pro 46, Pre Press/Panther Pro 46 HS, Adobe/PageMaker, Macromedia/Freehand, Multi-Ad; Cameras — 1-Screen/C-260-D; Scanners — 1-Lf/Leafscan 45, 3-Kk/RFE 2035, APP/Mac PRODUCTION SOFTWARE: QPS/QuarkXPress, Ba

Note: This publication shares a joint Sunday edition with the Bloomington (IN) Herald-Times (mS) and the Martinsville (IN) Reporter-Times (eS).

BLOOMINGTON

THE HERALD TIMES

1900 S Walnut St, Bloomington, Ind., 47401-7720, Monroe; gen tel (812) 332-4401; adv tel (812) 331-4281; ed tel (812) 331-4364; gen fax (812) 331-4285; adv fax (812) 331-4285; ed fax (812) 331-4385; gen/nat adv e-mail cgiddens@schurz.com; disp adv e-mail lragle@schurz.com; class adv e-maillleahy@heraldt.com; ed e-mail rzaltsberg@heraldt.com; web site www.heraldtimesonline.com
- 2,200,000(views) 175,000(visitors)

Group: Schurz Communications Inc
Published: Mon, Tues, Wed, Thur, Fri, Sat, Sun
Weekday Frequency: m
Saturday Frequency: m
Circulation: 25,732; 28,408(sat); 40,171(sun)
Last Audit: Sworn/Estimate/Non-Audited September 30, 2017
Advertising Rate (weekday/saturday): Open inch rate $33.03
Advertising Rate (sunday): Open inch Rate $40.21
Online Advertising Rate: Run of Site (Static) $10.00 CPM; Rich Media/Flash $10.00 CPM; 300x600 $14.00 CPM
News services: AP. **Established:** 1877
Special Editions: Reader's Choice (Apr); Westside Shopper (Dec); Home Lifestyles (Bi-Monthly); MCBA Home Show (Jan); Picnic with the Pops (Jun); Family (Mar); Parade of Homes (May); Buy It Now (Monthly); Eastside Shopper (Nov); Rental Guide (Quarterly).
Special Weekly Sections: Your Weekend (Fri); Neighbors (Mon-Fri); Outdoor (S); More Weekend (Sat); Experience (Thur); Youth Ink (Tues); Food Section (Wed).
Syndicated Publications: Relish (Monthly); Parade (S); American Profile (Wed).
Digital Platform - Mobile: Apple, Android
Digital Platform - Tablet: Apple iOS, Android
Pres. & Pub. .... Scott C. Schurz
Ed .... Robert Zaltsberg
Features/Lifestyle Ed. .... William Strother
Circ. Dir. .... Tim D. Smith
Photo Mgr. .... David Snodgress
Online Mgr. .... Todd Davidson
Prodn. Mgr., Pre Press .... Greg Davinport
Prodn. Dir. .... Brad Clarke
Adv. Dir. .... Laurie Ragle
Adv. Dir. .... Cory Bollinger
Sports Ed. .... Chris Korman
Bobbie Treadway
Marketing Mgr. .... Shaylan Owen
HR. Dir. .... Devon Perry
Asst. Managing Ed. .... Bill Strother
News Ed. .... Rod Spaw
Sarah Morin
Digital Content Mgr. .... Kat Carlton
Sports Ed. .... Pat Beane
News Ed. .... Janice Rickert
Arts Ed. .... Marcela Creps
Adv. Sales Mgr. .... Chad Giddens
Classified Sales Mgr. .... Leah Leahy
Managing Ed. .... Bob Zaltsberg
Bobbie Threadway
Market Information: TMC.
Mechanical Available: Offset; Black and 3 ROP colors; insert accepted; page cutoffs - 22.
Mechanical Specifications: Type page 11 5/8 x 21; E - 6 cols, 1 5/6, 1/6 between; A - 6 cols, 1 5/6, 1/6 between; C - 9 cols, 1 1/4, 1/10 between.
Areas Served: Monroe County, Greene County, Dunn County
Delivery Method: Mail, Newsstand, Carrier, RacksEquipment & Software: PRESSROOM EQUIPMENT: Lines — 5-KB/(3 color humps) double width 1985; Folders — 2-KB/3:2 KF 80 Jaw; Pasters —MEG; Reels & Stands — 5-MEG.; MAILROOM EQUIPMENT: Counter Stackers — 1-QWI/300, 1-Rima/RS30, 2-HL/Dual Carrier; Inserters & Stuffers — 1-KAN/480 6:1, 1/AM Graphics/NP 630 13:1; Tying Machines — 2-/Power Strap/PSN20; Address Machine — 1-/KR, 1-/Ch, 1-/Ink Jet.; BUSINESS EQUIPMENT: 2-DEC/VAX 3900, Microsoft/Windows NT CLASSIFIED EQUIPMENT: Hardware — DEC/Alphasaver 2000; CLASSIFIED SOFTWARE: APT. DISPLAY EQUIPMENT: Hardware — APP/Mac fileserver; DISPLAY SOFTWAREAd Make-up Applications — Adobe/InDesign, Multi-Ad, SCS/Layout 8000; Layout Software — APP/Mac. EDITORIAL EQUIPMENT: Hardware — 2-DEC/Micro VAX 3000/AU/OPI Server, 2-AU/3850; Printers — HP/4MV EDITORIAL SOFTWARE: Dewar/View, Microsoft/Windows, Microsoft/Word 2.0, QPS/QuarkXPress 3.2. PRODUCTION EQUIPMENT: Hardware — 2-AU/3850, 1-Nu/Flip Top FT40V6UPNS; Cameras — Nu/Horizontal; Scanners — 2-Linotype-Hell/Saphire, 1-Linotype-Hell/S3300 Drum PRODUCTION SOFTWARE: Dewar.

Note: This publication shares a joint Sunday edition with the Bedford (IN) Times-Mail (mS) and the Martinsville (IN) Reporter-Times (eS).

BLUFFTON

NEWS-BANNER

125 N Johnson St, Bluffton, Ind., 46714-1907, Wells; gen tel (260) 824-0224; adv tel (260) 824-0224; ed tel (260) 824-0224; gen fax (260) 824-0700; adv fax (260) 824-0700; ed fax (260) 824-0700; gen/nat adv e-mail jeanb@news-banner.com; disp adv e-mail jeanb@news-banner.com; class adv e-mailjeanb@news-banner.com; ed e-mail daves@news-banner.com; web site www.news-banner.com

Published: Mon, Tues, Wed, Thur, Fri, Sat
Weekday Frequency: e
Saturday Frequency: m
Circulation: 3,862; 3,862(sat)
Last Audit: Sworn/Estimate/Non-Audited January 29, 2018
Advertising Rate (weekday/saturday): Open inch rate $12.50 (Local); $15.20 (National)
Online Advertising Rate: Web-Blast $35.00; Boosted Posts $59.00
News services: AP. **Established:** 1892
Own Printing Facility?: Yes
Commercial Printers?: Yes
Special Editions: Christmas Greetings (Dec); Progress (Jun); Senior Lifestyle (Quarterly).
Special Weekly Sections: Agri-Business, All About Health, Spotlight on Business (Tue); House & Home (Wed); Best Food Day, Racing (Thur); Church (Fri); Church Directory, Finance/Local Business News, Ent./TV Weekly (Sat)
Syndicated Publications: Relish (Sat).
Digital Platform - Mobile: Apple, Android, Windows, Blackberry
Digital Platform - Tablet: Apple iOS, Android
Vice President, Opinion Page Editor Mark F. Miller
Bus. Mgr. .... Martha Poling
Adv. Sales Mgr. .... Jean Bordner
Dir., Mktg, Treasurer .... Dianne Witwer
Asst. Ed. .... David Schultz
Mng. Ed. .... Glen Werling
Sports Ed. .... Paul Beitler
Prodn. Supt. .... Howard Jones
Classified Mgr. .... Patty Elwell
President & Publisher .... Doug Brown
Market Information: TMC.
Mechanical Available: Offset; Black and 2 ROP colors; insert accepted; page cutoffs - 22 3/4.
Mechanical Specifications: Type page 10 1/2 x 21 1/2; E - 6 cols, 1 5/8, 3/20 between; A - 6 cols, 1 5/8, 3/20 between; C - 6 cols, 1 5/8, 3/20 between.
Areas Served: 46714, 46777, 46759, 46778, 46766, 46781, 46731, 46770, 46791, 46799, 46798, 46792, 47359
Delivery Method: Mail, Newsstand, Carrier, RacksEquipment & Software: PRESSROOM EQUIPMENT: Lines — 5-G/Community 1975.; MAILROOM EQUIPMENT: Tying Machines — 2/Bs.; BUSINESS SOFTWARE: Vision Data CLASSIFIED EQUIPMENT: Hardware — APP/Mac, APP/iMac; CLASSIFIED SOFTWARE: Baseview/ClassAct/FP 3. DISPLAY EQUIPMENT: Hardware — APP/Mac G3, APP/Mac G4; Printers — Xante; DISPLAY SOFTWAREAd Make-up Applications — 6-Multi-Ad/Creator, QPS/QuarkXPress 4.1, Adobe/Photoshop.; EDITORIAL EQUIPMENT: Hardware — APP/Mac G3, APP/Power Mac, 2-APP/Mac G4; Printers — APP/Mac 8500 EDITORIAL SOFTWARE: QPS/QuarkXPress 3.32, Baseview, Adobe/Photoshop 5.0. PRODUCTION EQUIPMENT: Hardware — 1-Nu; Cameras — 1-Nu PRODUCTION SOFTWARE: QPS/QuarkXPress 3.32.

BRAZIL

THE BRAZIL TIMES

531 E National Ave, Brazil, Ind., 47834-2633, Clay; gen tel (812) 446-2216; gen fax (812) 446-0938; gen/nat adv e-mail jeanneburris.braziltimes@gmail.com; disp adv e-mail brazilads@yahoo.com; class adv e-mailclassifiedcallcenter@yahoo.com; ed e-mail Frank.phillips@gmail.com; web site www.thebraziltimes.com
- 363,090(views) 88,830(visitors)

Group: Rust Communications
Published: Mon, Wed, Fri, Sat
Weekday Frequency: m
Saturday Frequency: m
Circulation: 4,133; 4,633(sat)
Last Audit: Sworn/Estimate/Non-Audited December 19, 2017
Advertising Rate (weekday/saturday): Open inch rate $14.70
News services: AP **Established:** 1888
Own Printing Facility?: Yes
Commercial Printers?: Yes
Special Editions: Christmas Greetings (Dec); Football (Fall); New Year's Baby (Jan); Graduation (May); Business & Industry (Other).
Special Weekly Sections: Best Food Day (Mon); School News Page (Sat); Agri-Business (Tues).
Syndicated Publications: Relish (Monthly); Weekender (Sat).
Digital Platform - Mobile: Apple, Android
Digital Platform - Tablet: Apple iOS, Android
Pub. .... Chris Pruett
Gen. Mgr. .... Jeanne Burris
Circ. Mgr. .... Karen Barnhart
Sports Ed. .... Carey Fox
Editor .... Pete Wilson
Frank Phillips
Ivy Jacobs
Ad. rep .... Christina Meyer
Market Information: ADS; TMC.
Mechanical Available: Offset; Black and 3 ROP colors; insert accepted; page cutoffs - 22 3/4.
Mechanical Specifications: Type page 11 5/8 x 21 1/2; E - 6 cols, 1 13/16, 1/8 between; A - 6 cols, 1 13/16, 1/8 between; C - 9 cols, 1 3/16, 1/16 between.
Areas Served: 47834 46171 47833 47837 47840 47841 47853 47857 47881
Delivery Method: Mail, Newsstand, RacksEquipment & Software: PRESSROOM EQUIPMENT: Lines — 6-G/Community single width.; MAILROOM EQUIPMENT: Counter Stackers — 1-BG/Count-O-Veyor; Tying Machines — 1/Malow.; CLASSIFIED SOFTWARE: Baseview. DISPLAY SOFTWAREAd Make-up Applications — Multi-Ad/Creator 3.7; Layout Software — Multi-Ad/Creator, QPS/QuarkXPress. EDITORIAL SOFTWARE: Baseview/NewsEdit 2.0, Adobe/Photoshop 4.0, QPS/QuarkXPress 3.31. PRODUCTION EQUIPMENT: Hardware — 1-LE/LD-18; Cameras — 1-R/480 PRODUCTION SOFTWARE: QPS/QuarkXPress 4.0.

CHESTERTON

CHESTERTON TRIBUNE

193 S Calumet Rd, Chesterton, Ind., 46304-2433, Porter; gen tel (219) 926-1131; adv tel (219) 926-1131; ed tel (219) 926-1131; gen fax (219) 926-6389; adv fax (219) 926-6389; ed fax (219) 926-6389; gen/nat adv e-mail ads@chestertontribune.com; disp adv e-mail ads@chestertontribune.com; class adv

e-mailads@chestertontribune.com; ed e-mail news@chestertontribune.com; web site www.chestertontribune.com
- 200,000(views) 40,000(visitors)
Group: Chesterton Tribune, Inc.
Published: Mon, Tues, Wed, Thur, Fri
Weekday Frequency: e
Circulation: 3,900
Last Audit: Sworn/Estimate/Non-Audited December 19, 2017
Advertising Rate (weekday/saturday): Open inch rate $7.40
Online Advertising Rate: Banner/Skyscraper $1.00 CPM; Leaderboard/Medium Rectangle $1.50 CPM.
News services: AP. **Established:** 1884
Own Printing Facility?: Yes
Commercial Printers?: Yes
Special Editions: Graduation (Jun); Pigskin Picks Football Contest (Autumn); Christmas Shopping Guide (Nov); Christmas Greeting (Dec).
Special Weekly Sections: Coupon Day (Mon); Professional Directory (Tues); Community (Wed, Thur) Church (Fri).
Managing Ed./Pub. ....David Canright
Sports Ed. ....TR Harlan
Co-Pub....................Margaret Willis
Market Information: TMC.
Mechanical Available: Offset; Black; insert accepted; page cutoffs - 22.
Mechanical Specifications: Type page 13 x 21; E - 6 cols, 2 1/16, 1/8 between; A - 6 cols, 2 1/16, 1/8 between; C - 6 cols, 2 1/16, 1/8 between.
Areas Served: 46304, 46383, 46385, 46301, 46391
Delivery Method: Mail, Carrier, RacksEquipment & Software: PRESSROOM EQUIPMENT: Lines — 3-G/Community CLASSIFIED EQUIPMENT: Hardware — APP/Mac Quadra; Printers — HP/LaserJet 4050N; CLASSIFIED SOFTWARE: Mediaspan/Classified. DISPLAY EQUIPMENT: Hardware — APP/Mac G4; Printers — HP/LaserJet 5000N; DISPLAY SOFTWAREAd Make-up Applications — Quark; Layout Software — Quark. EDITORIAL EQUIPMENT: Hardware — Baseview/NewsEdit Pro; Printers — HP/LaserJet 5000N, HP/LaserJet 4050N EDITORIAL SOFTWARE: Baseview. PRODUCTION EQUIPMENT: Hardware — HP/LaserJet 5000N; Cameras — R.

CLINTON

THE DAILY CLINTONIAN

422 S Main St, Clinton, Ind., 47842-2414, Vermillion; gen tel (765) 832-2443; adv tel (765) 832-2443; ed tel (765) 832-2443; gen fax (765) 832-2560; adv fax (765) 832-2560; ed fax (765) 832-2560; gen/nat adv e-mail cccc@mikes.com; disp adv e-mail cccc@mikes.com; class adv e-mailcccc@mikes.com; ed e-mail cccc@mikes.com; web site www.ccc-clintonian.com
Published: Mon, Tues, Wed, Thur, Fri
Weekday Frequency: e
Circulation: 5
Last Audit: USPS January 12, 2017
Newspaper Reps: Jinanne Carey, Editor
Advertising Rate (weekday/saturday): $8.00 per SAU col. in.
Advertising Rate (sunday): n/a
Online Advertising Rate: n/a
News services: AP **Established:** 1912 (Daily)r
Own Printing Facility?: Yes
Commercial Printers?: Yes
Special Editions: Il Bollettino, Labor Day Weekend
Christmas Edition
Proprietary Publications: Il Bollettino
Digital Platform - Mobile: Apple, Windows
Digital Platform - Tablet: Apple iOS, Other
Pres./Pub.....................George B. Carey
Mechanical Available: on request
Mechanical Specifications: on request
Areas Served: Vermillion and Parke Counties
Delivery Method: Mail, Newsstand, CarrierEquipment & Software: PRESSROOM EQUIPMENT: Offset, CTP platemaking, Color King
press. MAILROOM EQUIPMENT: Kirk-Rudy labeling BUSINESS EQUIPMENT: 3 computers BUSINESS SOFTWARE: Custom Cirdulation and Quick Books CLASSIFIED EQUIPMENT: 2 computers CLASSIFIED SOFTWARE: Windows, SunType programming DISPLAY EQUIPMENT: 5 computers DISPLAY SOFTWAREWindows, Corel Draw, Adobe CS6 EDITORIAL EQUIPMENT: 3 computers EDITORIAL SOFTWARE: Windows, Sprint PRODUCTION EQUIPMENT: 3 computers PRODUCTION SOFTWARE: Windows, Xerox, custom programming CIRCULATION EQUIPMENT: 1 computer CIRCULATION SOFTWARWindows 10 Pro

COLUMBIA CITY

THE POST & MAIL

927 W Connexion Way, Columbia City, Ind., 46725-1031, Whitley; gen tel (260) 244-5153; adv tel (260) 244-5153; ed tel (260) 244-5153 ext. 202; gen fax (260) 244-7598; adv fax (260) 244-7598; ed fax (260) 244-7598; gen/nat adv e-mail postandmailadvertising@gmail.com; disp adv e-mail postandmailadvertising@gmail.com; class adv e-mailpostandmailclassifieds@earthlink.com; ed e-mail editor@thepostandmail.com; web site www.thepostandmail.com
Group: Horizon Publications Inc.
Published: Mon, Tues, Wed, Thur, Fri, Sat
Weekday Frequency: e
Saturday Frequency: m
Circulation: 4,058; 4,058(sat)
Last Audit: Sworn/Estimate/Non-Audited September 30, 2017
Advertising Rate (weekday/saturday): Open inch rate $9.20
Online Advertising Rate: Top Banner $99.00/month; Skyscraper $99.00/month; Weather Box, Tile $99.00/month
News services: AP. **Established:** 2007
Special Editions: Day in the Life of Whitley County (Jul); Real Estate Guide (Jul); On the Lakes (Jun); Athletes of the Year (Jul); Home & Garden Tab (Apr); 4-H Tab (Aug); Progress (Feb); Taxes & Finances Tab (Jan); Old Settlers Day (Community Festival) Program (Jul); Car Care Tab (May); TV Monthly (Monthly); High School Sports Tab (Nov).
Syndicated Publications: USA WEEKEND Magazine (Sat); American Profile (Weekly).
Digital Platform - Mobile: Apple, Android
Digital Platform - Tablet: Apple iOS, Android
Pub.....................Rick Kreps
Circ. Mgr.....................Sally Ballard
Ed.....................Nicole Ott
Market Information: TMC.
Mechanical Available: Offset; Black and 3 ROP colors; insert accepted - max 29; page cutoffs - 21 1/2.
Mechanical Specifications: Type page 13 x 21 1/2; E - 6 cols, 1 3/4, 1/8 between; A - 6 cols, 1 3/4, 1/8 between; C - 9 cols, 1 1/8, 1/8 between.
Areas Served: Whitley County
Delivery Method: Mail, Newsstand, Carrier, RacksEquipment & Software: MAILROOM EQUIPMENT: Tying Machines — 2/Bu.; CLASSIFIED EQUIPMENT: Hardware — 1-Mk.; DISPLAY EQUIPMENT: Hardware — APP/Mac; Printers — APP/Mac LaserPrinter.; EDITORIAL EQUIPMENT: Hardware — Mk, APP/Mac/5-Mk; Printers — APP/Mac. PRODUCTION EQUIPMENT: Hardware — 1-Ic; Cameras — 1-SCREEN; Scanners — Microtek.

COLUMBUS

THE REPUBLIC

333 2nd St, Columbus, Ind., 47201-6709, Bartholomew; gen tel (812) 372-7811; adv tel (812) 379-5652; ed tel (812) 379-5665; gen fax (812) 372-1634; adv fax (812) 379-5776; ed fax (812) 379-5711; gen/nat adv e-mail shardin@therepublic.com; disp adv e-mail advertise@therepublic.com; class adv e-mailclassifieds@therepublic.com; ed e-mail editorial@therepublic.com; web site www.therepublic.com
Group: AIM Media Indiana
Published: Mon, Tues, Wed, Thur, Fri, Sat, Sun
Weekday Frequency: m
Saturday Frequency: m
Circulation: 14,067; 14,067(sat); 14,924(sun)
Last Audit: CAC March 31, 2016
Advertising Rate (weekday/saturday): Open inch rate $27.52
Advertising Rate (sunday): Open inch rate $28.89
Online Advertising Rate: All display ads are automatically placed online in the E-Edition for an additional $5 flat fee per insertion.
News services: AP, NEA, SHNS, MCT. **Established:** 1872
Special Editions: Business Profiles (Apr); Education (Aug); Year-in-Review (Dec); Tourism (Feb); 4-H (Jul); Answer Book (Jun); Fashion (Mar); Garden (May); Gift Guide (Nov); Cookbook (Oct); Home Improvement (Sept).
Special Weekly Sections: Health (Fri); School (Mon); Kids Page (S); Auto (Sat); Entertainment (Thur).
Syndicated Publications: Sunday Color Comics Continental (Other); USA WEEKEND Magazine (S).
Digital Platform - Mobile: Apple, Android
Digital Platform - Tablet: Apple iOS, Android
Circ. Mgr.....................Cheryl Spurgeon
Digital Media Dir.....................Scott Hardin
Ed.....................Tom Jekel
Newsroom Coord.....................Jane Peabody
Asst. Managing Ed.....................Kirk Johannesen
Asst. Managing Ed.....................Julie McClure
Chief Photographer....................Andrew Laker
Sports Ed.....................Jay Heater
Lifestyle Ed.....................Jenny Elig
Features Ed.....................Brian Blair
Adv. Dir.....................Mike Rossetti
Adv. Ops. Mgr.....................Kathy Burnett
Classified Adv. Mgr.....................Jaime Vemillion
Press Supvr.....................Randy Reeves
Adv. Dir., Sales/Mktg.....................Sharon Shumate
Prodn. Mgr., Post Press....................Wally Veluzat
Market Information: TMC.
Mechanical Available: Offset; Black and 3 ROP colors; insert accepted - product sampling bags; page cutoffs - 22 3/4.
Mechanical Specifications: Type page 13 x 21 1/2; E - 6 cols, 2 1/16, 1/8 between; A - 6 cols, 2 1/16, 1/8 between; C - 9 cols, 1 3/8, 1/16 between.
Areas Served: Bartholomew County
Delivery Method: Mail, Newsstand, CarrierEquipment & Software: PRESSROOM EQUIPMENT: Lines — 12-DGM/850 single width 1998; Press Drive — 3-Fin/150 HP Drive 1998; Folders — 1, 1-1998; Reels & Stands — 2-G/Stands 1998; Control System — Smith/Spray Bars, 1998.; MAILROOM EQUIPMENT: Counter Stackers — 2-HI/Olympian, HI/Rima; Inserters & Stuffers — 1-S/1472; Tying Machines — 2-Sterling/MR45, 1-OVL/410.; BUSINESS EQUIPMENT: MS/NT Server 4.0, ALR/Evolution, HP/LC2000 Exchange BUSINESS SOFTWARE: PBS/MediaPlus CLASSIFIED EQUIPMENT: Hardware — 9-HP/PC, 9-Gateway/Celeron 350; Printers — HP/4M Plus; CLASSIFIED SOFTWARE: PPI, ACT, Classified. DISPLAY EQUIPMENT: Hardware — 12-APP/Mac; Printers — 1-HP/4MV, 2-HP/LaserJet 5000, 2-AG/Selectset 5000/MON RIP, Pre Press/Panther Pro 62, Pre Press/Panther RIP; DISPLAY SOFTWAREAd Make-up Applications — QPS/QuarkXPress 3.332; Layout Software — Mk/Ad Director, APP/Mac. EDITORIAL EQUIPMENT: Hardware — 8-Gateway/P200, 22-IBM/486-33, 2-Novell/SFt3-ALR, 10-Gateway/PIII 500, 22-Gateway/Celerah 350, 2-HP/LC2000 NT/SQL/APP/Power Mac 7100, APP/Mac 8100-100, APP/Power Mac, 5-APP/Mac G3; Printers — 1-Panasonic/KX P1595, 1-APP/Mac LaserWr PRODUCTION EQUIPMENT: Hardware — Tl/OmniPage 5.0, APP/Mac, Pre Press/Panther Pro 62, Pre Press/Panther RIP, Pre Press/Panther Imposer; Cameras — 1-C/Spartan II; Scanners — 1-ECR/1030, 3-Umax, 1-Lf/AP Leafscan 45, 3-Kk/2035 PRODUCTION SOFTWARE: ACT/V2, ACT/V04, ACT/V003.

CONNERSVILLE

CONNERSVILLE NEWS-EXAMINER

406 N Central Ave, Connersville, Ind., 47331-1926, Fayette; gen tel (765) 825-0581; adv tel (765) 825-0581 ext. 247; ed tel (765) 825-0588 ext. 235; gen fax (765) 825-4599; adv fax (765) 825-4599; ed fax (765) 825-4599; gen/nat adv e-mail mspillers@newsexaminer.com; disp adv e-mail mspillers@newsexaminer.com; class adv e-mailmspillers@newsexaminer.com; ed e-mail newsexaminer@newsexaminer.com; web site www.newsexaminer.com
Group: Paxton Media Group, LLC
Published: Tues, Wed, Thur, Fri, Sun
Weekday Frequency: m
Saturday Frequency: m
Circulation: 4,390; 4,390(sun)
Last Audit: Sworn/Estimate/Non-Audited September 30, 2017
Advertising Rate (weekday/saturday): Open inch rate $18.85
Advertising Rate (sunday): Open inch rate $18.85
News services: AP. **Established:** 1887
Own Printing Facility?: No
Commercial Printers?: No
Special Editions: Progress (Mar); Home Improvement (Apr); County Fair (Aug); Christmas Greetings (Dec); Bridal (Jan); TV (Mar); Cookbook Magazine (Nov); Car Care (Oct).
Special Weekly Sections: Church (Fri); Best Food Day (Mon); Best Real Estate Days (Thur); School coverage (Wed)
Digital Platform - Mobile: Apple, Android
Digital Platform - Tablet: Apple iOS, Android
Adv. Dir.....................Melissa Spillers
Reporter....................Darrell Smith
Ed.....................James Sprague
Sports Ed.....................Grady Tate
District/Circ. Mgr.....................Neisah Wicker
Reporter....................Will Fehlinger
Adv. Rep....................Cheryl Hreno
Adv. Rep.....................Donna Moses
Ad account texecutive....................Dillon Burch
Market Information: TMC.
Mechanical Available: Offset; Black and 3 ROP colors; inserts accepted - free standing; page cutoffs - 22 3/4.
Mechanical Specifications: Type page 13 x 21; E - 6 cols, 2 1/16, 1/8 between; A - 6 cols, 2 1/16, 1/8 between; C - 9 cols, 1 5/16, 1/8 between.
Areas Served: Fayette, Franklin, Union and Western Wayne County in East Central Indiana
Delivery Method: Newsstand, Carrier, RacksEquipment & Software: PRESSROOM EQUIPMENT: Lines — none;

CRAWFORDSVILLE

JOURNAL REVIEW

119 N Green St, Crawfordsville, Ind., 47933-1708, Montgomery; gen tel (765) 362-1200; adv tel (765) 362-1200 ext. 109; ed tel (765) 362-1200 ext. 119; gen fax (765) 364-5427; adv fax (765) 364-5425; ed fax (765) 364-5425; gen/nat adv e-mail shawn.storie@jrpress.com; disp adv e-mail kmanlief@jrpress.com; class adv e-mailsuzanne@jrpress.com; ed e-mail tmcgrady@jrpress.com; web site www.journalreview.com
- 550,000(views)
Group: PTS, Inc.
Published: Mon, Tues, Wed, Thur, Fri, Sat
Weekday Frequency: m
Saturday Frequency: m
Circulation: 4,995; 4,995(sat)
Last Audit: CAC September 30, 2017
Advertising Rate (weekday/saturday): Open inch rate $13.80
News services: AP. **Established:** 1841
Own Printing Facility?: No
Commercial Printers?: Yes
Special Editions: Home Improvement (Apr); Fall Sports Preview (Aug); Caroling Song Book (Dec); Wedding Planner (Jul); Strawberry Festival (Jun); Area Golf Guide (Mar); Indy 500 (May); Basketball (Nov); Home Improvement (Oct); Fall Activity Guide (Sept).
Special Weekly Sections: Business Page: Wednesday
Health Page: Thursday
Chalk Board: Friday
Syndicated Publications: Montgomery County Directory (Annually); Montgomery County Realty (Monthly); USA WEEKEND Magazine (Sat).

Digital Platform - Mobile: Apple, Android
Digital Platform - Tablet: Apple iOS, Android
Group Mgr./Pub. ....Shawn Storie
Ed. ....Tina McGrady
Composing Mgr. ....Addie Cucore
Adv. Mgr. ....Kim Starnes
Cir. Mgr. ....Carla Walters
Mechanical Available: Offset; Black and 3 ROP colors; insert accepted; page cutoffs - 22 3/4.
Mechanical Specifications: Type page 13 x 21 1/2; E - 6 cols, 2 1/16, 1/8 between; A - 6 cols, 2 1/16, 1/8 between; C - 9 cols, 1 11/32, 1/8 between.
Areas Served: Montgomery County
Delivery Method: Mail, Newsstand, Carrier, RacksEquipment & Software: PRESSROOM EQUIPMENT: Lines — 9-HI/V-15D 1981; Press Drive — HI/Cutler Hammer; Reels & Stands — 7; MAILROOM EQUIPMENT: Tying Machines — MLN, Bu.; BUSINESS EQUIPMENT: 4-HP BUSINESS SOFTWARE: Great Plains, AR Works CLASSIFIED EQUIPMENT: Hardware — APP/ Mac; Printers — Epson; CLASSIFIED SOFTWARE: Baseview/Class Manager Plus. DISPLAY EQUIPMENT: Hardware — 1-APP/ Mac G3, 4-APP/Mac 7300; Printers — APP/ Mac LaserWriter, QMS/860; Other Hardware — APP/Mac Scanner, HP/ScanJet IIcx, 2-Umax/Powerlook DISPLAY SOFTWAREAd Make-up Applications — Multi-Ad 3.8, Multi-Ad/Creator 2.0; Layout Software — 4-APP/ Mac. EDITORIAL EQUIPMENT: Hardware — APP/Mac; Printers — GCC/SelectPress 600, Epson EDITORIAL SOFTWARE: Baseview 3.0. PRODUCTION EQUIPMENT: Hardware — APP/Mac, GCC/Select Press 600, QMS/860 Print System; Cameras — 1-B; Scanners — Umax/Powerlook II, Nikon/ Film PRODUCTION SOFTWARE: QPS/ QuarkXPress 3.32.

THE PAPER OF MONTGOMERY COUNTY

201 E Jefferson St, Crawfordsville, Ind., 47933-2804, Montgomery; gen tel (765) 361-0100; gen fax (765) 361-5901; gen/nat adv e-mail kvanmatre@thepaper24-7.com; disp adv e-mail kvanmatre@thepaper24-7.com; class adv e-mailkvanmatre@thepaper24-7.com; ed e-mail news@thepaper24-7.com; web site www.thepaper24-7.com - 90,000(views) 30,000(visitors)
Group: Sagamore News Media
Published: Mon, Tues, Wed, Thur, Fri, Sat
Weekday Frequency: m
Saturday Frequency: m
Circulation: 4,000
Last Audit: Sworn/Estimate/Non-Audited October 1, 2017
Advertising Rate (weekday/saturday): Open inch rate $8.00 per column inch
Online Advertising Rate: Tiles $149.00 per month; Banners $299.00 per month
News services: 2004
Own Printing Facility?: No
Commercial Printers?: No
Special Editions: Readers' Choice (Jan); Agriculture; Spring Home; Spring Car; 4-H Fair (Jul); How-To Guide; Christmas Gift Guide (Dec); Last-Minute Gift Guide (Dec). Soil & Water
Digital Platform - Mobile: Apple, Android, Blackberry
Digital Platform - Tablet: Apple iOS, Android, Other
Pub. ....Tim Timmons
Adv. Mgr. ....Kim VanMatre
Market Information: TMC.
Areas Served: 47933, 47916, 47940, 47954, 47955, 47965, 47967, 47968, 47989, 47990, 47994
Delivery Method: Mail, Newsstand, Racks

CROWN POINT

POST-TRIBUNE

2100 N Main St Ste 212, Suite 212, Crown Point, Ind., 46307-1877, Lake; gen tel (219) 663-4212; adv tel (219) 455-2349; gen fax (219) 663-2077; adv fax (219) 648-3003; ed fax (219) 648-3131; gen/ nat adv e-mail rcains@post-trib.com; disp adv e-mail rcains@post-trib.com; class adv e-mailclassifieds@post-trib.com; ed e-mail jbiesk@tribpub.com; web site chicagotribune.com/suburbs/post-tribune
Group: Tronc, Inc.
Published: Mon, Tues, Wed, Thur, Fri, Sat, Sun
Weekday Frequency: m
Saturday Frequency: m
Circulation: 16,000; 16,000(sat); 40,000(sun)
Last Audit: AAM October 16, 2013
Branch Offices: Crown Point, Indiana
Online Advertising Rate: Varied rates frequency based, Impression, Geo Fencing, Sliding billboards, Eblast, Wallpaper, Native, Video, Web design, SEM, SEO, Social, Reputation monitoring and more.
News services: AP, MCT, LAT-WP. **Established:** 1908
Own Printing Facility?: Yes
Commercial Printers?: Yes
Special Editions: Cancer, Lifetime of Health, Senior, Neonatal, New Health Developments, Heart, Progress, Innovations, Neighbors' Choice, TimeOut Sports
Special Weekly Sections: Weekend, Health, Business, Today's Homes
Syndicated Publications: USA WEEKEND Magazine (S).
Digital Platform - Mobile: Apple, Android
Digital Platform - Tablet: Apple iOS, Android
Ed. ....Joe Biesk
Web Content Ed. ....Joe Puchek
Advisor ....Jerry Davich
Jill McDermott
Exec. Ed. ....Phil Jurik
Market Information: Split run; TMC; Zoned editions.
Mechanical Available: Offset; Black and 3 ROP colors; insert accepted - other inserts on request; page cutoffs - 22.
Mechanical Specifications: Tab format 44" web Full page 6 x 10 (10" x 9.875")
Areas Served: Northwest Indiana
Delivery Method: Newsstand, CarrierEquipment & Software: DISPLAY EQUIPMENT: Hardware — APP/Mac; DISPLAY SOFTWAREAd Make-up Applications — QPS/QuarkXPress 3.3, Adobe/Photoshop 3.0, Adobe/Illustrator 5.5; Layout Software — CJ, HP. EDITORIAL EQUIPMENT: Hardware — APP/iMac workstations EDITORIAL SOFTWARE: QPS. PRODUCTION EQUIPMENT: Hardware — Caere Omni Page Pro 8.0, 1-MON/Laserpress, 1-MON/ News Express; Cameras — 1-C/Spartan III, 2-C/Marathon; Scanners — 1-ECR/Autokon, 2-Lf/Leafscan 35, Scanview/Scanmate 4000 PRODUCTION SOFTWARE: MEI/ALS 1.7.
Note: Chicago Tribune Freedom Center

DECATUR

DECATUR DAILY DEMOCRAT

141 S 2nd St, Decatur, Ind., 46733-1664, Adams; gen tel (260) 724-2121; adv tel (260) 724-2121; ed tel (260) 724-2121; gen fax (260) 724-7981; adv fax (260) 724-7981; ed fax (260) 724-7981; gen/nat adv e-mail businessmanager@decaturdailydemocrat.com; disp adv e-mail advertising@decaturdailydemocrat.com; class adv e-mailclassified@decaturdailydemocrat.com; ed e-mail circulation@decaturdailydemocrat.com; web site www.decaturdailydemocrat.com
Group: Horizon Publications Inc.
Published: Mon, Tues, Wed, Thur, Fri, Sat
Weekday Frequency: e
Saturday Frequency: m
Circulation: 4,300; 4,500(sat)
Last Audit: Sworn/Estimate/Non-Audited September 30, 2017
Advertising Rate (weekday/saturday): Open inch rate $14.40
Online Advertising Rate: Static Ads $20.00/month
News services: AP. **Established:** 1857
Own Printing Facility?: Yes
Commercial Printers?: No
Special Editions: Basketball (Feb); Christmas Opening (Nov); Callithumpian (Oct).
Special Weekly Sections: Business Working for You (Mon); Kids, (Tue); Health (Wed); Entertainment, Nascar (Thur); Church (Fri); Business (Sat)
Syndicated Publications: Weekly TV Section (Fri);
Digital Platform - Mobile: Apple, Android
Digital Platform - Tablet: Apple iOS, Android, Kindle, Nook, Kindle Fire
Pub. ....Ronald Storey
Office/Bus. Mgr. ....Jennifer Kaehr
Managing Ed. ....J. Swygart
Associate Ed./News Ed. ....Jannaya Andrews
Circ. Mgr. ....Pam Mohr
Graphics ....Karri Rice
Classified Mgr. ....Nichole Perry
Reporter ....Ashley Bailey
Reporter ....Mike Lamm
Market Information: TMC.
Mechanical Available: Offset; Black and 3 ROP colors; insert accepted - all inserts accepted; page cutoffs - 22 3/4.
Mechanical Specifications: Type page 10.5 x 21 1/2; E - 6 cols, 2 1/8, 1/8 between; A - 6 cols, 2 1/8, 1/8 between; C - 6 cols, 2 1/8, 1/8 between.
Areas Served: Adams County
Delivery Method: Newsstand, Carrier, RacksEquipment & Software: PRESSROOM EQUIPMENT: Lines — 8-G/Community (2 stacks); MAILROOM EQUIPMENT: Tying Machines — 1-Bu/162X; CLASSIFIED EQUIPMENT: Hardware — APP/Mac Quadra 610; CLASSIFIED SOFTWARE: Claris/ FileMaker Pro. EDITORIAL EQUIPMENT: Hardware — 4-APP/Mac Quadra 605, APP/ Mac Quadra 630, 2-APP/Mac Quadra 610, APP/Mac Quadra 650; Printers — APP/Mac LaserWriter 630 Pro, APP/Mac LaserWriter 16-1600 PS EDITORIAL SOFTWARE: Baseview/NewsEdit. PRODUCTION EQUIPMENT: Hardware — 2-APP/Power Mac, 1-APP/Mac Pro 630; Cameras — 1-R/400; Scanners — 3-Microtek PRODUCTION SOFTWARE: QPS/ QuarkXPress 3.31.

ELKHART

ELKHART TRUTH

421 S 2nd St, Ste 100, Elkhart, Ind., 46516-3230, Elkhart; gen tel (574) 294-1661; ed tel (574) 296-5805; gen fax (574) 294-4014; adv fax (574) 293-3302; ed fax (574) 294-3895; gen/nat adv e-mail proos@elkharttruth.com; disp adv e-mail proos@elkharttruth.com; ed e-mail newsroom@elkharttruth.com; web site www.elkharttruth.com - 2,383,978(views) 305,400(visitors)
Group: Paxton Media Group, LLC
Published: Mon, Tues, Wed, Thur, Fri, Sat, Sun
Weekday Frequency: m
Saturday Frequency: m
Circulation: 15,250; 15,250(sat); 18,550(sun)
Last Audit: Sworn/Estimate/Non-Audited December 18, 2017
Advertising Rate (weekday/saturday): Open inch rate $27.50
Advertising Rate (sunday): Open inch rate $27.50
Online Advertising Rate: $12 cpm
News services: AP, SHNS, MCT **Established:** 1889
Own Printing Facility?: No
Commercial Printers?: No
Special Editions: Spring Car Care (Apr); Healthy Living (May & October); Business & Industry (Feb); Brides (Jan); 4-H Fair (Jul); Best of Elkhart (March); Fall Home Improvement (Sept).
Special Weekly Sections: Weekend Projects (Fri); A&E (Thurs); Faith (Sat); Food (Mon.); Health & Fitness (Wed); TV (Fri)
Digital Platform - Mobile: Apple, Android
Digital Platform - Tablet: Apple iOS, Android
Pub. ....Pete Van Baalen
Market Information: ADS; Split run; TMC.
Mechanical Available: Web Offset; Black and 3 ROP colors; insert accepted - card stock, single sheets, quarter folded; page cutoffs - 22 3/4.
Mechanical Specifications: Type page 10 x 21 1/2; E - 5 cols, 1.9, 1/8 between; A - 5 cols, 1.9, 1/8 between; C - 6 cols, 1.5625, 1/8 between.
Areas Served: 46514, 46516, 46517, 46526, 46528, 46507, 46540, 46565, 46543, 46567, 46553, 46550, 46573, 46544, 46545, 46530, 49112, 49130, 49099
Delivery Method: Mail, Newsstand, Carrier, RacksEquipment & Software: BUSINESS EQUIPMENT: Dell BUSINESS SOFTWARE: G/Dynamics CLASSIFIED EQUIPMENT: Hardware — APP/Mac; Printers — APP/ Mac LaserWriter; CLASSIFIED SOFTWARE: DTI/Class Manager Pro, QPS/QuarkXPress. DISPLAY EQUIPMENT: Hardware — APP/ Mac; Printers — HP/Laserjet 8150N, HP/ Color Laserjet SM; Other Hardware — 8-APP/Mac color scanner 64 DISPLAY SOFTWAREAd Make-up Applications — DTI/ Ad Manager Pro; Layout Software — MEI/ ALS. EDITORIAL EQUIPMENT: Hardware — APP/Mac; Printers — HP/Laserjet 8100 N, NewGen EDITORIAL SOFTWARE: Saxotech/InDesign

ELWOOD

THE ELWOOD CALL-LEADER

317 S Anderson St, Elwood, Ind., 46036-2018, Madison; gen tel (765) 552-3355; adv tel (765) 552-3355; ed tel (765) 552-3355; gen fax (765) 552-3358; adv fax (765) 552-3358; ed fax (765) 552-3358; gen/nat adv e-mail elpub@elwoodpublishing.com; disp adv e-mail elpub@elwoodpublishing.com; class adv e-mailelpub@elwoodpublishing.com; ed e-mail elpub@elwoodpublishing.com; web site www.elwoodpublishing.com
Group: Ray Barnes Newspapers, Inc.
Published: Mon, Tues, Wed, Thur, Fri, Sat
Weekday Frequency: e
Saturday Frequency: m
Circulation: 2,100; 2,100(sat)
Last Audit: Sworn/Estimate/Non-Audited September 30, 2017
Advertising Rate (weekday/saturday): Open inch rate $7.50; Special Call-Leader: Open inch rate Saturday $8.50
Online Advertising Rate: Right Side Ads $10.00/ week; Top of Page Banner $20.00/week; Top right Corner $25.00/week
News services: AP. **Established:** 1891
Special Editions: Farm & Garden (Apr); Fair Wrap-up (Aug); Cookbook (Feb); Mature Years (Jan); Welcome to Elwood (Jun); Spring Opening (Mar); Spring Home Improvement (May); Christmas Opening (Nov); Fall Brides (Oct); Frankton Heritage Days Festival (Sept).
Special Weekly Sections: Best Food Day (Mon).
Syndicated Publications: What's On TV (Fri); The Mini-Page for Kids (Tues).
Digital Platform - Mobile: Apple, Android
Digital Platform - Tablet: Apple iOS, Android, Kindle, Nook, Kindle Fire
Pres. ....Jack Barnes
Pub. ....Robert L. Nash
Mng. Ed. ....Sandy Burton
Sports Ed. ....Ed Hamilton
Circ. Mgr. ....Chris Idlewine-Wesco
Prodn. Mgr. ....Randy Bayne
Market Information: TMC.
Mechanical Available: Web Offset; Black and 3 ROP colors; insert accepted; page cutoffs - 22 3/4.
Mechanical Specifications: Type page 13 x 21 1/2; E - 6 cols, 2 1/16, 1/8 between; A - 6 cols, 2 1/16, 1/8 between; C - 8 cols, 1 1/2, 3/20 between.
Areas Served: Madison and Tipton County
Delivery Method: Mail, Newsstand, Carrier, RacksEquipment & Software: PRESSROOM EQUIPMENT: Lines — 4-G/Community; MAILROOM EQUIPMENT: Tying Machines — 2/Malow; Address Machine — 2-/Am.; BUSINESS EQUIPMENT: 1-BS/B-20, 1-RSK/ TRS 80 model 4 CLASSIFIED EQUIPMENT: Hardware — Mk/1100; CLASSIFIED SOFTWARE: Mk/Mycro-Comp. EDITORIAL EQUIPMENT: Hardware — Mk/1100 EDITORIAL SOFTWARE: Mk/Mycro-Comp. PRODUCTION EQUIPMENT: Hardware — 2-APP/Mac LaserWriter II NT/NTX; Cameras — 1-R/Commodore.

EVANSVILLE

EVANSVILLE COURIER & PRESS

300 E Walnut St, Evansville, Ind., 47713-1938, Vanderburgh; gen tel (812) 424-7711; adv tel (812) 424-7711; ed tel (812) 464-7430; gen fax (812) 422-8196; adv fax (812) 422-8196; ed fax (812) 422-8196; gen/nat adv e-mail stephensonm@courierpress.com; disp adv e-mail haydent@courierpress.com; class adv e-mailstephensonm@courierpress.com; ed e-mail ethridget@courierpress.com;

web site www.courierpress.com 712,940(visitors)
Group: Gannett
Published: Mon, Tues, Wed, Thur, Fri, Sat, Sun
Weekday Frequency: m
Saturday Frequency: m
Circulation: 39,750; 39,396(sat); 55,867(sun)
Last Audit: AAM December 31, 2015
Advertising Rate (weekday/saturday): Open inch rate $111.00
News services: AP, SHNS. **Established:** 1846
Own Printing Facility?: Yes
Commercial Printers?: Yes
Special Editions: Education Guide (Fall 2013); Discover Evansville (Jun); Homes (Aug); Progress (Jul); Coupon Book (Mar); Visitor Guide "Discover" (Jun); Progress (Aug); Coupon Book (Monthly).
Special Weekly Sections: TV Book, West, Warrick
Syndicated Publications: Access (Fri); Parade (S).
Digital Platform - Mobile: Apple, Android
Digital Platform - Tablet: Apple iOS, Android, Kindle, Kindle Fire
Dir., Mktg. .... Kathryn Gieneart
I.T. Director .... Krista McDivitt
Dir./Circ. Sales .... Steve Traud
Adv. Mgr., Retail Sales .... Ron Obermeier
Mgr., Mktg. Servs. .... Carolyn Franklin
Editorial Page Ed. .... Chuck Leach
Librarian .... Roseann Derk
Exec. Ed. .... Tim Ethridge
VP of Sales .... Tim Hayden
Market Information: ADS; Split run; TMC; Zoned editions.
Mechanical Available: Flexo; Black and 3 ROP colors; insert accepted; page cutoffs - 22 1/32.
Mechanical Specifications: Type page 12 x 21 1/8; E - 6 cols, 2 1/16, 1/6 between; A - 6 cols, 2 1/16, 1/6 between; C - 10 cols, 1 1/4, 1/6 between.
Areas Served: 47711,42420, 47601
Delivery Method: Mail, Newsstand, Carrier, RacksEquipment & Software: PRESSROOM EQUIPMENT: Lines — MOT/Flexo double width 1989, 12; Folders — 2-MOT/2:1, 1-MOT/3:2; Pasters —MOT/AutoReels & Stands — 12; MAILROOM EQUIPMENT: Counter Stackers — 2-HL/Monitor HT, 2-HL/ Monitor HT II, 4/RIMA, QWI, 1-/QUIPP, TMSI; Inserters & Stuffers — 2-Heidelberg/2299, NP-2299; Tying Machines — Power Strap, Power Strap/PSN6E, 4-/Power Strap/ PSN6, 1-/Power Strap/PSN6E, 3-/Pow; BUSINESS EQUIPMENT: Wyse Thin Clients, Dell laptops BUSINESS SOFTWARE: Word, Excel, Access, Outlook, Mediaware, Brainworks CLASSIFIED EQUIPMENT: Hardware — Wyse Thin Clients, Dell laptops; Printers — HP/LaserJets, Ricoh MFP; CLASSIFIED SOFTWARE: Brainworks DISPLAY EQUIPMENT: Hardware - APP/ Mac G3, Dell 24 Widescreen; Printers — LaserJets; DISPLAY SOFTWAREAd Make-up Applications — Mediaware - Saxotech; Layout Software — APP/Mac, MEI. EDITORIAL EQUIPMENT: Hardware — Wyse Thin Clients, Dell laptops; Printers — LaserJets EDITORIAL SOFTWARE: Mediaware PRODUCTION EQUIPMENT: Hardware — Scitex/Dolev 800, Scitex/Dolev 450, Scitex/Dolev 4 Press, III/Laser; Cameras — Pager, Nu Arc SSTE-2024-C; Scanners — Scitex/Smart, Scitex/Smart 2, AG/Arcus II, 5-Kodak/RFS 2035, HP/ScanJet 40, AG Duoscan T1200 PRODUCTION SOFTWARE: QPS 1.12, AT/Class P

FORT WAYNE

THE NEWS-SENTINEL

600 W Main St, Fort Wayne, Ind., 46802-1408, Allen; gen tel (260) 461-8449; adv tel (260) 461-8243; ed tel (260) 461-8239; gen fax (260) 461-8817; adv fax (260) 461-8817; ed fax (260) 461-8817; gen/nat adv e-mail dcuddihy@fortwayne.com; disp adv e-mail dcuddihy@fortwayne.com; class adv e-maildcuddihy@fortwayne.com; ed e-mail bsaleik@news-sentinel.com; web site www.news-sentinel.com - 450,000(views) 220,000(visitors)
Group: Ogden Newspapers Inc.
Published: Mon, Tues, Wed, Thur, Fri, Sat, Sun
Weekday Frequency: e
Saturday Frequency: e
Circulation: 57,281; 80,879(sun)
Last Audit: AAM December 31, 2015
Advertising Rate (weekday/saturday): Open inch rate $19.00 (Mon-Thur); $26.00 (Fri-Sat)
Advertising Rate (sunday): Open inch rate $26.00
Online Advertising Rate: Homepage Leaderboard/Skyscraper $15.75 CPM; Homepage Cube $8.48 CPM; Corner Peel $22.00 CPM
News services: AP **Established:** 1833
Own Printing Facility?: Yes
Commercial Printers?: Yes
Special Editions: Home & Lawn (Apr); Health Career Expo (Feb); Big Boys Tech & Toys Show (Jan); Back-to-School (Jul); Town & Country (Mar); Indy 500 (May); Holiday Shopping Guide (Nov); Diner's Guide (Oct); Parade of Homes (Sept).
Special Weekly Sections: Business (Mon); Features/Food Section (Tues); Neighbors (Wed, Sat); Ticket!/Entertainment (Thurs); TV listings (Sat).
Syndicated Publications: Summit City Savings (Sat).
CEO/Pres./Pub. .... Michael J. Christman
Sr. Ed. .... Kerry Hubartt
Asst. Metro/Bus. Ed.
Lisa Esquivel Long
Multimedia Ed. .... Laura Weston-Elchert
Sports Ed. .... Tom Davis
Design Ed. .... Brad Saleik
Features Ed. .... Kevin Kilbane
Reporter/columnist .... Kevin Leininger
Multimedia Specialist .... Dan Vance
Multimedia Specialist .... Justin Kenny
Blake Sebring
Reggie Hayes
Market Information: ADS.
Mechanical Available: Flexo, Letterpress; Black and ROP colors; insert accepted; page cutoffs - 23 9/16.
Mechanical Specifications: Type page 13 x 22; E - 6 cols, 2 1/16, 1/8 between; A - 6 cols, 2 1/16, 1/8 between; C - 10 cols, 1 1/4, 1/16 between.
Delivery Method: Newsstand, Carrier, RacksEquipment & Software: CLASSIFIED EQUIPMENT: Hardware — Dell; Printers — Epson, HP/LaserJet; CLASSIFIED SOFTWARE: III/Tecs 2. EDITORIAL EQUIPMENT: Hardware — Dell; Printers — Epson, HP/LaserJet EDITORIAL SOFTWARE: III/Tecs 2.
Note: For detailed production and mechanical information, see Fort Wayne Newspapers Inc. listing.

FRANKFORT

THE TIMES

211 N Jackson St, Frankfort, Ind., 46041-1936, Clinton; gen tel (765) 659-4622; adv tel (765) 659-4622; ed tel (765) 659-4622; gen fax (765) 654-7031; adv fax (765) 654-7031; ed fax (765) 654-7031; gen/nat adv e-mail advertising@ftimes.com; disp adv e-mail advertising@ftimes.com; class adv e-mailclassified@ftimes.com; ed e-mail news@ftimes.com; web site www.ftimes.com
Group: Paxton Media Group, LLC
Published: Tues, Wed, Thur, Fri, Sun
Weekday Frequency: m
Saturday Frequency: m
Circulation: 4,694; 4,694(sat)
Last Audit: Sworn/Estimate/Non-Audited September 30, 2017
Advertising Rate (weekday/saturday): Open inch rate $18.90
Online Advertising Rate: Leaderboard $350.00 CPM
News services: AP. **Established:** 1877
Own Printing Facility?: Yes
Commercial Printers?: Yes
Special Editions: Back to School (Aug); Spring Home Improvement (Apr); Fall Home Improvement (Fall); Father's Day (Jun); Mother's Day (May); 4-H Tab (Other); Fall Farm (Sept); Fall Gridiron (Aug); Spring Farm (Spring).
Syndicated Publications: USA WEEKEND Magazine (Fri).
Digital Platform - Mobile: Apple, Android
Digital Platform - Tablet: Apple iOS, Android
Pub. .... Sharon Bardonner
Circ. Dir. .... Amanda Marcel
Circ. Mgr. .... Linda Clark
Classified/Retail Inside Sales .... Angie Hale
Accounting Clerk .... Joann Spaulding
Adv. Dir. .... Thaya Sterrett
Ed. .... Scott Cousins
Mng. Ed. .... Brian Peloza
Market Information: TMC.
Mechanical Available: Offset; Black and 3 ROP colors; insert accepted - single sheets, booklets; page cutoffs - 22 3/4.
Mechanical Specifications: Type page 10 x 21 1/2; E - 6 cols, 4.587, 1/8 between; A - 6 cols, 1.587, 1/8 between
Areas Served: 46041, 46065, 46035, 46050, 46039, 46057, 46067, 46058
Delivery Method: Mail, Newsstand, Carrier, RacksEquipment & Software: PRESSROOM EQUIPMENT: Lines — Print at Chronicle-Tribune, Marion, IN; MAILROOM EQUIPMENT: Counter Stackers — Insert at Chronicle-Tribune, Marion, IN; BUSINESS EQUIPMENT: PC BUSINESS SOFTWARE: MediaSpan CLASSIFIED EQUIPMENT: Hardware — PC; CLASSIFIED SOFTWARE: MediaSpan DISPLAY EQUIPMENT: Hardware — PC; DISPLAY SOFTWAREAd Make-up Applications — MediaSpan; EDITORIAL EQUIPMENT: Hardware — PC EDITORIAL SOFTWARE: Falcon; InDesign PRODUCTION SOFTWARE: InDesign

FRANKLIN

DAILY JOURNAL

30 S Water St, Ste A, Franklin, Ind., 46131-2316, Johnson; gen tel (317) 736-7101; adv tel (317) 736-2730; ed tel (317) 736-2712; gen fax (317) 736-2754; adv fax (317) 736-2754; ed fax (317) 736-2766; gen/nat adv e-mail nbingham@dailyjournal.net; disp adv e-mail nbingham@dailyjournal.net; class adv e-mailcwarren@dailyjournal.net; ed e-mail newstips@dailyjournal.net; web site www.dailyjournal.net
Group: AIM Media Indiana
Published: Mon, Tues, Wed, Thur, Fri, Sat
Weekday Frequency: m
Saturday Frequency: m
Circulation: 11,240; 12,904(sat)
Last Audit: CAC March 31, 2014
Advertising Rate (weekday/saturday): Mon-Fri: Open inch rate $15.49 (Local); $19.80 (National). Sat: Open inch rate $15.71 (Local); $20.20 (National)
Advertising Rate (sunday): Saturday is weekend Open $15.71 (local); $20.20 (National)
Online Advertising Rate: $22/M with contract
News services: AP, SHNS. **Established:** 1963
Own Printing Facility?: Yes
Commercial Printers?: Yes
Special Editions: Chronologies (Jan); Boomers (Mar); Business Exchange (Jun); American Home Week (Apr); Back to School (Aug); Worship Directory (Dec); Wedding Planner (Jan); Johnson County 4-H Fair (Jul); Junior Journal (Mar); Salute (May); Coupons Plus (Monthly); Holiday Gift Guide (Nov); Health Guide (Oct); Family (Quarterly).
Special Weekly Sections: School Page (Mon); Business Pages (Sat); Best Food Day (Thursday).
Syndicated Publications: Parade (Sat).
Proprietary Publications: Daily Journal
Edinburgh Courier
SOUTH Magazine
FARM INDUABA
Digital Platform - Mobile: Apple, Android
Digital Platform - Tablet: Apple iOS, Android, Kindle, Nook, Kindle Fire
Adv. Dir. .... Christina Cosner
IT mgr. .... Mike Brogdon
Group Ed. .... Scarlett Syse
Asst. Managing Ed., News .... Annie Goeller
Operations Coord. .... Nicole Bingham
Special Publications Ed. .... Paul Hoffman
Cindy Warren
Ed. .... Michele Holtkamp
Market Information: all of Johnson County and southern Marion County
Mechanical Available: Offset; Black and 3 ROP colors; insert accepted; page cutoffs - 21.50.
Mechanical Specifications: Type page 11 5/8 x 21;A 6 cols, 1.833"wide per column; Classifieds - 9 cols, 1.203" wide per
Areas Served: Franklin, Greenwood, Center Grove, Whiteland, New Whiteland, Bargersville, Trafalgar, Edinburgh, Morgantown and southern Marion County
Delivery Method: Mail, Newsstand, Carrier, RacksEquipment & Software: PRESSROOM EQUIPMENT: Reels & Stands — 9-G/ Roll Stand.; MAILROOM EQUIPMENT: Counter Stackers — BG/105, Rima/RS 2517; Inserters & Stuffers — 2-KAN/420; Tying Machines — 3/Bu, 1-/MLN; Wrapping Singles — Power Strap/Bottom Wrap.; CLASSIFIED EQUIPMENT: Hardware — 4-PC, 1-MS 2000 Server; Printers — Lexmark T520; CLASSIFIED SOFTWARE: QPS/QuarkXPress 4.11, ACT. DISPLAY EQUIPMENT: Hardware — 5-AP/Mac G4; Printers — ECR/VR 36, Laserwriter 16/600; DISPLAY SOFTWAREAd Make-up Applications — Multi-Ad/Creator 4.0, CNI/ Ad Database; Layout Software — Multi-Ad, CNI/Ad Database. EDITORIAL EQUIPMENT: Hardware — 10-PC, 2-APT/PC fileservers, 12-PC, MS 2000 Server/Umax/Power Look IV, AP/Mac G4; Printers — ECR/VR 36, ECR/4550 EDITORIAL SOFTWARE: QPS/ QuarkXPress 4.11, Microsoft/Word 2.0. PRODUCTION EQUIPMENT: Hardware — APP/Mac LaserWriter II NT, ECR/VR 36, Unity/1200 XLO, APP/Mac LaserWriter IIg, ECR/4550; Scanners — Umax/Power Look III PRODUCTION SOFTWARE: APT, QPS/ QuarkXPress 4.11.

GOSHEN

THE GOSHEN NEWS

114 S Main St, Goshen, Ind., 46526-3702, Elkhart; gen tel (574) 533-2151; adv tel (574) 533-2151; ed tel (574) 533-2151; gen fax (574) 533-0839; adv fax (574) 533-0839; ed fax (574) 534-8830; gen/nat adv e-mail angie.kulczar@goshennews.com; disp adv e-mail cara.norvell@goshennews.com; class adv e-mailclassifieds@goshennews.com; ed e-mail news@goshennews.com; web site www.goshennews.com - 460,000(views) 206,000(visitors)
Group: Community Newspaper Holdings, Inc.
Published: Mon, Tues, Wed, Thur, Fri, Sat
Weekday Frequency: m
Saturday Frequency: m
Circulation: 8,800; 8,900(sat)
Last Audit: Sworn/Estimate/Non-Audited December 18, 2017
Newspaper Reps: Cara Norvell
Melissa Troxel
Sharon Hite
Derreck Stahley
Brian Bloom
Advertising Rate (weekday/saturday): Open inch rate $22.00
Advertising Rate (sunday): Open inch rate $24.80
Online Advertising Rate: $15 cpm
News services: AP. **Established:** 1837
Own Printing Facility?: No
Commercial Printers?: No
Special Editions: Elkhart County Living - Six times annually - Magazine
Reader's Choice - January
Progress Magazine - February
Living Spaces - March
Lawn & Garden - April
Fifty-Plus - May
Graduation - June
Generations - June
Elkhart County Fair - July
How To guide - August
Hometown Heroes - September
Power of Pink - October
Holiday Gift Guide - November
Bridal Guide - December
Special Weekly Sections: Food/Recipe (Mon); Health (Wed); Religion (Sat); Senior Focus, TV Spotlight (Sat.); Business (Mon-Sat.); Entertainment (Daily)
Syndicated Publications: Parade (S).
Proprietary Publications: The hART
Digital Platform - Mobile: Android, Windows
Digital Platform - Tablet: Android
Pub. .... Brian Bloom
Ed. .... Julie Beer
IT Dir. .... Richard Leinbach
Accounting .... Kris Erb

Accounting .... Brenda Donat
Classified Mgr. .... Angie Kulczar
City Ed. .... Roger Schneider
Regl. Ed. .... Sheila Selman
Sales Manager .... Cara Norvell
Account Executive .... Derreck Stahley
Account Executive .... Melissa Troxel
Account Executive .... Sharon Hite
Out-bound Sales .... Valerie Kite
Reporter .... Geoff Lesar
Reporter .... John Kline
Reporter .... Leandra Beabout
Reporter .... Aimee Ambrose
Lifestyles .... Ann Showalter
Sports Editor .... Stephen Brooks
Sports reporter .... Greg Keim
Market Information: TMC.
Mechanical Available: Offset; Black and 3 ROP colors; insert accepted; page cutoffs - 22 3/4.
Mechanical Specifications: six column format - 10.125" x 19.75"
Areas Served: 46526,46528,46540, 46550, 46565, 46543, 46553
Delivery Method: Mail, Newsstand, RacksEquipment & Software: BUSINESS EQUIPMENT: DEC, PC BUSINESS SOFTWARE: Vision Data EDITORIAL EQUIPMENT: Hardware — PC EDITORIAL SOFTWARE: InCopy, InDesign

GREENCASTLE

BANNER-GRAPHIC

100 N Jackson St, Greencastle, Ind., 46135-1240, Putnam; gen tel (765) 653-5151; gen fax (765) 653-2063; gen/nat adv e-mail mpingleton@bannergraphic.com; disp adv e-mail mpingleton@bannergraphic.com; class adv e-mailclesko@bannergraphic.com; ed e-mail ebernsee@bannergraphic.com; web site www.bannergraphic.com - 648,660(views) 147,870(visitors)
Group: Rust Communications
Published: Mon, Wed, Fri, Sat
Weekday Frequency: m
Saturday Frequency: m
Circulation: 10,500; 5,403(sat)
Last Audit: Sworn/Estimate/Non-Audited October 1, 2017
Advertising Rate (weekday/saturday): Open inch rate $16.63 (Mon); Open inch rate $13.60 (Wed-Sat)
Online Advertising Rate: Landing Page $25.00 CPM; Dog Ear $50.00 CPM; Page-Specific $150.00 CPM; Leaderboard $260.00 CPM; Right Rectangular Ad $260.00 CPM;
News services: AP. **Established:** 1843
Own Printing Facility?: Yes
Commercial Printers?: Yes
Syndicated Publications: Relish (Monthly); USA WEEKEND Magazine (Sat); American Profile (Weekly).
Digital Platform - Mobile: Apple, Android
Digital Platform - Tablet: Apple iOS, Android, Kindle, Nook, Kindle Fire
Gen. Mgr. .... Daryl Taylor
Adv. Mgr. .... Merlin Maltsberger
Ed. .... Eric Bernsee
Asst. Ed. .... Jared Jernagan
Pub. .... Chris Pruett
Marketing Consultant .... Montica Pingleton
Marketing Consultant .... Kandi Collins
Office Mgr. .... Tina Coltharp
Accounting .... Kristin Judy
Receptionist/Typist .... Cathy Lesko
Circ./NIE Asst. .... June Leer
Nick Wilson
Sports Editor .... Bennett Joey
Reporter .... Modglin Chelsea
Market Information: TMC.
Mechanical Available: Offset; Black and 3 ROP colors; insert accepted; page cutoffs - 22 3/4.
Mechanical Specifications: Type page 13 x 21; E - 6 cols, 2 1/16, 1/8 between; A - 6 cols, 2 1/16, 1/8 between; C - 8 cols, 1 3/4, 1/8 between.
Areas Served: Greencastle, Bainbridge, Cloverdale, Coatesville, Fillmore, Reelsville, Roachdale, Russelville
Delivery Method: Mail, Newsstand, RacksEquipment & Software: PRESSROOM EQUIPMENT: Lines — 5-G/Community 1977; Folders — 1-G/2:1.; MAILROOM EQUIPMENT: Tying Machines — 2/BN; Address Machine — 1-/Wm.; CLASSIFIED SOFTWARE: Baseview. DISPLAY SOFTWAREAd Make-up Applications — Multi-Ad/Creator.; EDITORIAL SOFTWARE: Baseview. PRODUCTION EQUIPMENT: Hardware — Nu/Flip Top; Cameras — LE, R/500.

GREENFIELD

DAILY REPORTER

22 W New Rd, Greenfield, Ind., 46140-1090, Hancock; gen tel (317) 462-5528; adv tel (317) 467-6001; ed tel (317) 467-6022; gen fax (317) 467-6017; adv fax (317) 467-6009; ed fax (317) 467-6017; gen/nat adv e-mail advert@greenfieldreporter.com; disp adv e-mail advert@greenfieldreporter.com; class adv e-mailclass@greenfieldreporter.com; ed e-mail editorial@greenfieldreporter.com; web site www.greenfieldreporter.com - 40,000(views)
Group: AIM Media Indiana
Published: Tues, Wed, Thur, Fri, Sat
Weekday Frequency: m
Saturday Frequency: m
Circulation: 8,729; 8,729(sat)
Last Audit: Sworn/Estimate/Non-Audited September 30, 2017
Advertising Rate (weekday/saturday): Daily: Open inch rate $12.75; Wed: Open inch rate $19.00
Online Advertising Rate: Run of site Leaderboard/Square $18.00 CPM; Homepage Feature Position $20.00 CPM; Section Leaderboard/Square $22.00 CPM
News services: AP, NEA. **Established:** 1908
Own Printing Facility?: Yes
Commercial Printers?: Yes
Special Editions: Senior Living (Feb); Sports Posters (Mar); Spring Home/Garden (Apr); Meet Your Merchants (Apr); 4-H Fair (May); HS Grad. (May); Dining Guide (Jun); Discover (Aug); Riley Festival (Sept); Spirit to Survive (Oct); Church Directory (Nov); Letters to Santa (Dec); Year in Review (Dec).
Special Weekly Sections: Religion (Sat); Business (Fri); Arts/Ent. (Thur); Education, opinion (Tues);
Syndicated Publications: Pendleton Times-Post (Wed); New Palestine Press (Wed); Fortville/McCordsville Reporter (Thur); Parade (Sat).
Proprietary Publications: Hancock Home Magazine (Monthly)
Digital Platform - Mobile: Apple, Android
Digital Platform - Tablet: Apple iOS, Android
Pub. .... Chuck Wells
Noelle Steele
Admin. Mgr. .... Debby Brooks
Circ. Mgr. .... John Senger
Adv. Mgr., Clas. .... Tammy Clifton
Mng. Ed. .... Karen Crawford
Photo Ed. .... Tom Russo
Community Ed. .... Scott Slade
Copy Ed. .... Anne Smith
Ed. Asst. .... Jane Smith
Circ. Clerk .... Holly Lewis
Circ. District Mgr. .... Ron Richmond
Sales Mgr. .... Beverly Dillback
Sr. Adv. Rep. .... Erika Whittington
Sports Ed. .... Rich Torres
Adv. Rep., Clas .... Alana Lashaway
Circ. Dir. .... Paul Hart
Prodn. Dir. .... Larry Ham
Tech. Support .... Jason Corgman
Commercial Print Coord. .... Carrie Lacy
Production Pre-Press .... Jim Steele
Market Information: TMC; Zoned editions.
Mechanical Available: Offset; Black and 3 ROP colors; insert accepted - max. size 11 x 13; page cutoffs - 22 3/4.
Mechanical Specifications: Type page 11 1/2 x 21 1/2; E - 6 cols, 1 3/4, 1/8 between; A - 6 cols, 1 3/4, 1/8 between; C - 9 cols, 1 3/16, 1/16 between.
Areas Served: Hancock County
Delivery Method: Mail, Carrier, RacksEquipment & Software: PRESSROOM EQUIPMENT: Lines — 19-G/Community; 13-G/Community; Press Drive — 4-Fin/75 h.p., 2-Fin/125 hp; Folders — 3-G/Community SSC; Pasters —6-Enkel/Zero Speed Splicer 1990Control System — Fin/Control System 1994.; MAILROOM EQUIPMENT: Counter Stackers — Rima/25 105, GMA 2000; Inserters & Stuffers — GMA; Tying Machines — 1-MLN/Spirit, 2-Bu/BT-18, 1-Bu/BT-18.; BUSINESS EQUIPMENT: PC BUSINESS SOFTWARE: APT CLASSIFIED EQUIPMENT: Hardware - PC; CLASSIFIED SOFTWARE: APT DISPLAY EQUIPMENT: Hardware — Mac; EDITORIAL EQUIPMENT: Hardware — PC EDITORIAL SOFTWARE: APT PRODUCTION EQUIPMENT: Hardware — Kreo PRODUCTION SOFTWARE: APT

GREENSBURG

GREENSBURG DAILY NEWS

135 S Franklin St, Greensburg, Ind., 47240-2023, Decatur; gen tel (812) 663-3111; adv tel (812) 663-3111 ext. 7017; ed tel (812) 663-3111 ext. 7003; gen fax (812) 663-2985; adv fax (812) 663-2985; ed fax (812) 663-2985; gen/nat adv e-mail keith.wells@indianamediagroup.com; disp adv e-mail keith.wells@indianamediagroup.com; class adv e-maillinda.siefert@greensburgdailynews.com; ed e-mail news@greensburgdailynews.com; web site www.greensburgdailynews.com - 350,000(views) 60,000(visitors)
Group: Community Newspaper Holdings, Inc.
Published: Tues, Wed, Thur, Fri, Sat
Weekday Frequency: All day
Saturday Frequency: All day
Circulation: 4,200; 4,350(sat)
Last Audit: Sworn/Estimate/Non-Audited September 30, 2017
Advertising Rate (weekday/saturday): Open inch rate $16.65
Online Advertising Rate: $15.00 CPM
News services: AP. **Established:** 1894
Own Printing Facility?: No
Commercial Printers?: No
Special Editions: Health & Wellness (Feb); Graduation (May); Summer Fun (Jun).
Special Weekly Sections: School News (Tues); Business News (Tues); Agri-News (Wed); Pastimes (Thur); Church News (Fri).
Syndicated Publications: Relish (Monthly); American Profile (Weekly).
Proprietary Publications: Country Roads (Bi-Monthly)
Digital Platform - Mobile: Apple, Android, Windows, Blackberry
Digital Platform - Tablet: Apple iOS, Android, Windows 7, Blackberry Tablet OS, Kindle, Nook, Kindle Fire
Managing Ed. .... Melissa Conrad
News Ed. .... Brent Brown
Operations Mgr. .... Natalie Acra
Dir. Audience Dev. .... Lisa Huff
HR/Accounting .... Shelley Barton
IT Dir. .... Denver E. Sullivan
Rgl. Pub. .... Laura Welborn
Staff Writer .... Boris Ladwig
Staff Writer .... Amanda Browning
Sports .... Eric Wohlford
Acc. Exec. .... Jeanie York
Acc. Exec. .... Chrystal Bushorn
Expeditor .... Susan Peters
Market Information: TMC.
Mechanical Available: Offset; Black and 3 ROP colors; insert accepted - all; page cutoffs - 23.
Mechanical Specifications: Full page 10.15" x 21" - 6 cols, 1 col 1.6"' 2 col 3.31"; 3 col, 5.0"; 4 col 6.71"; 5 col 8.43"; 6 col. 10.15".
Areas Served: Decatur and surrounding counties
Delivery Method: Newsstand, Carrier, Racks

HARTFORD CITY

NEWS TIMES

100 N Jefferson St, Hartford City, Ind., 47348-2201, Blackford; gen tel (765) 348-0110; adv tel (765) 348-0110; ed tel (765) 348-0110; gen fax (765) 348-0112; adv fax (765) 348-0112; ed fax (765) 348-0112; gen/nat adv e-mail ntoffice@comcast.net; disp adv e-mail ntoffice@comcast.net; class adv e-mailntoffice@comcast.net; ed e-mail newstimes@comcast.net; web site www.hartfordcitynewstimes.com
Group: Community Media Group
Published: Mon, Wed, Thur, Fri, Sat
Weekday Frequency: m
Saturday Frequency: m
Circulation: 1,500
Last Audit: USPS September 30, 2011
Advertising Rate (weekday/saturday): Open inch rate $9.45
Online Advertising Rate: Contact Josh Goff for details
News services: AP. **Established:** 1885
Own Printing Facility?: Yes
Commercial Printers?: Yes
Special Editions: Spring Car Care (Apr); Progress (Feb); 4-H (Jul); Home & Garden (Mar); Graduation (May); Christmas Tab (Nov); Fall Home Yard Garden (Oct); Sizzlin' Summer Clearances (Aug), Big Boy Toys (Jun); Mother's Day (May); Spring Fling Specials (Apr); Black Friday (Nov); Give Thanks to Kids (Nov); Last Minute Gift Guide (Dec); Heartland (Quarterly); Seasons (Quarterly); Healthbeat (Quarterly).
Special Weekly Sections: Sports; Environment; Around Indiana.
Proprietary Publications: Red Ball Express
Digital Platform - Tablet: Kindle
Ed. .... Pat Hughes
Adv. Conslt. .... Valarie Ashley
Adv. Conslt. .... Teresa Hargis
Market Information: TMC.
Mechanical Available: Offset; Black and 3 ROP colors; inserts accepted; page cutoffs - 21 1/2.
Mechanical Specifications: Type page 13 x 21 1/2; E - 6 cols, 2, 1/6 between; A - 6 cols, 2, 1/6 between; C - 8 cols, 2, 1/6 between.
Areas Served: Blackford County
Delivery Method: Mail, Carrier, RacksEquipment & Software: MAILROOM EQUIPMENT: Tying Machines — Bu.; BUSINESS EQUIPMENT: PC DISPLAY EQUIPMENT: Hardware — Macs ; DISPLAY SOFTWAREAd Make-up Applications — InDesign; EDITORIAL EQUIPMENT: Hardware — Macs EDITORIAL SOFTWARE: InDesign

HUNTINGTON

HUNTINGTON HERALD-PRESS

7 N Jefferson St, Huntington, Ind., 46750-2839, Huntington; gen tel (260) 356-6700; adv tel (260) 356-6700; ed tel (260) 356-6700; gen fax (260) 356-9026; adv fax (260) 356-9026; ed fax (260) 356-9026; gen/nat adv e-mail ariggers@h-ponline.com; disp adv e-mail hpads@h-ponline.com; class adv e-mailhpclass@h-ponline.com; ed e-mail hpnews@h-ponline.com; web site http://www.chronicle-tribune.com/hp_online/ - 100,000(views) 60,000(visitors)
Group: Paxton Media Group, LLC
Published: Mon, Tues, Wed, Thur, Fri, Sat, Sun
Weekday Frequency: m
Saturday Frequency: m
Circulation: 4,576; 3,564(sun)
Last Audit: USPS October 12, 2012
Advertising Rate (weekday/saturday): Open inch rate $18.00
Advertising Rate (sunday): Open inch rate $20.70
Online Advertising Rate: $150.00/month; Package (includes 5 areas) $250.00/month
News services: AP. **Established:** 1848
Commercial Printers?: Yes
Special Editions: Spring Home & Garden II (Apr); Markle Wildcat Days (Aug); Gift Hang-Up (Dec); Huntington County Landmarks (Feb); Girl's Basketball Sectional (Jan); Andrews Summer Festival (Jul); Heritage Days (Jun); Farm (Mar); Golf Guide (May); Holiday Charm (Nov); Nati
Special Weekly Sections: Church Page (Fri); Best Food Days (S); Business (Thur); Business Page (Tues); Farm Page (Wed).
Syndicated Publications: Current Bargains (Mon); Comics (S).
Ed. .... Megan Greve
Pub. Gen. Mgr. .... Audra Riggers
Sports Ed. .... John Dempsey
Adv. Mgr., Classified .... Brenda Ross
Market Information: Split run; TMC; Zoned editions.
Mechanical Available: Offset; Black and 3 ROP colors; insert accepted; page cutoffs - 21.
Mechanical Specifications: Type page 13 x 21; E - 6 cols, 2 1/16, 1/8 between; A - 6 cols, 2 1/16, 1/8 between; C - 8 cols, 1 3/8, 1/16 between.
Areas Served: 46702, 46750, 46770, 46783, 46792
Delivery Method: Carrier, RacksEquipment &

Software: PRESSROOM EQUIPMENT: Lines — 2-G/Urbanite 1967, 1-G/Urbanite (3 color) 1967.; MAILROOM EQUIPMENT: Tying Machines — Dynaric.; BUSINESS EQUIPMENT: Dell PC BUSINESS SOFTWARE: Dynamics (Great Plains) CLASSIFIED EQUIPMENT: Hardware — APP/Power Mac; Printers — APP/Mac LaserWriter NTX; CLASSIFIED SOFTWARE: AMP DISPLAY EQUIPMENT: Hardware — 2-APP/Power Mac; Printers — APP/Mac LaserWriter II NTX; DISPLAY SOFTWAREAd Make-up Applications — QPS/QuarkXPress, Multi-Ad, Aldus/FreeHand, Adobe/Illustrator, Baseview/Display Manager.; EDITORIAL EQUIPMENT: Hardware — 3-APP/Power Mac; Printers — APP/Mac LaserWriter NT, 2-APP/Mac LaserWriter NTX EDITORIAL SOFTWARE: Baseview/NewsEdit, QPS/QuarkXPress, Adobe/Photoshop, Aldus/FreeHand, Multi-Ad. PRODUCTION EQUIPMENT: Hardware — TI/OmniPage 2.0, Mk/MSF 300, Kk/35mm Scanner; Cameras — 1-B/Caravelle; Scanners — 3-HP, HP/ScanJet, 2-Microtek/Flatbed, HP/ScanJet 5P PRODUCTION SOFTWARE: QPS/QuarkXPress 3.32.

INDIANAPOLIS

THE INDIANAPOLIS STAR

130 S Meridian St, Indianapolis, Ind., 46225-1046, Marion; gen tel (317) 444-4000; adv tel (317) 444-7000; ed tel (317) 444-6160; gen fax (317) 444-7100; adv fax (317) 444-7500; ed fax (317) 444-6600; gen/nat adv e-mail Kevin.Marshall@indystar.com; disp adv e-mail andrew.insley@indystar.com; ed e-mail jeff.taylor@indystar.com; web site www.indystar.com
- 28,500,000(views)
Group: Gannett
Published: Mon, Tues, Wed, Thur, Fri, Sat, Sun
Weekday Frequency: m
Saturday Frequency: m
Circulation: 109,121; 104,226(sat); 170,943(sun)
Last Audit: AAM December 31, 2016
Advertising Rate (weekday/saturday): Open inch rate $323.00
Advertising Rate (sunday): Open inch rate $406.00
News services: AP. **Established:** 1903
Own Printing Facility?: Yes
Commercial Printers?: Yes
Special Editions: Pro & College Football (Aug); Final Four (Mar); 500-Mile Auto Race Souvenir (May); Voter's Guide (Nov); Pro Basketball (Oct).
Special Weekly Sections: Arts, Entertainment, Health (Tue); Movies, Best Food Day (Fri); Garden, Home, Religion, Auto (Sat); Real Estate, Travel, Auto, Arts, Entertainment (Sun)
Syndicated Publications: USA WEEKEND Magazine (S).
Digital Platform - Mobile: Apple, Android
Digital Platform - Tablet: Apple iOS, Android, Kindle, Nook, Kindle Fire
President, Gannett Indiana .... Patricia Miller
Vice Pres./Ed. .... Jeff Taylor
Executive Editor .... Ronnie Ramos
Sports Director .... Jenny Green
News Director .... Amanda Kingsbury
Exec. Admin. Asst. .... Kim Mitchell
Opinion Director .... Tim Swarens
Senior Content Coach .... Steve Berta
News Director
Alvie Lindsay
Director of Key Accounts
David Hakanson
Client Services Director .... Ann Gelfius
Regional Finance Director .... Mitch Still
Market Information: TMC; Zoned editions.
Mechanical Available: Offset; Black and 4 ROP colors; insert accepted; page cutoffs - 21 1/2.
Mechanical Specifications: Type page 10 x 20 1/2; E - 6 cols, 1 1/2, 5/32 between; A - 6 cols, 1 1/2, 5/32 between; C - 10 cols, 29/32, 1/16 between.
Areas Served: Indiana
Delivery Method: Mail, Newsstand, Carrier, RacksEquipment & Software: PRESSROOM EQUIPMENT: Lines — 7-MAN/Geoman 75; 7-MAN/Geoman 75; 7-MAN/Geoman 75;

3-MAN/Geoman 75; Press Drive — MAN Roland; Folders — 1-MAN/Quarterfold, 7-MAN/2:5:5 Jaw; Reels & Stands — 24-MAN/CD13 RTP; Control System — MAN/PECOM; MAILROOM EQUIPMENT: Counter Stackers — 7-HPS/Dual carrier, 5-Prim/Hail Commmercial, 3/Gammerler, 14-/QWI 401, 2-/HT, 2-QWI/501C; Inserters & Stuffers — 2-HI/1472P, 1-Na/NP2299, 1-Na/NP 630; Tying Machines — 29-/Dynaric; Wrapping Singles — Addressing machine 2-/AVY, 4-QP/Vipers 97,; BUSINESS EQUIPMENT: IBM/ES9000-170, IBM/AS-400 BUSINESS SOFTWARE: ESA, DUS/VSE CLASSIFIED EQUIPMENT: Hardware — AT/Enterprise 205-seat, Compaq, 2-Sun/E4500; AT/Classified, AT/Pagination, IBM/RISC 6000; Printers — 8-HP/LaserJet; CLASSIFIED SOFTWARE: AT/Enterprise 1.7xml, AT/Classified 1.7xml, AT/Retail 1.7xml, AT/Preprints 1.7xml. DISPLAY EQUIPMENT: Hardware — iMac 27, 2-Sun/Ultra 3000; Printers — Canon ImageRunner C4080; Other Hardware — AP AdSend DISPLAY SOFTWAREAd Make-up Applications — DPS AdTracker/Adobe Creative Suite 4; Layout Software — MEI/ALS 4.2. EDITORIAL EQUIPMENT: Hardware — AT, Compaq; Printers — 25-Epson, TI, NEC, HP/LaserPrinter, HP/DeskJet EDITORIAL SOFTWARE: CCI 6.0. PRODUCTION EQUIPMENT: Hardware — 3-Creo/Trendsetter 200, 1-ICG/3601; Scanners — 2-Creo/IQSmart2 PRODUCTION SOFTWARE: CCI 6.0.

JASPER

THE HERALD

216 E 4th St, Jasper, Ind., 47546-3102, Dubois; gen tel (812) 482-2424; adv tel (812) 482-2424; ed tel (812) 482-2626; gen fax (812) 482-4104; adv fax (812) 482-4104; ed fax (812) 634-7142; gen/nat adv e-mail ads@dcherald.com; disp adv e-mail ads@dcherald.com; class adv e-mailclassads@dcherald.com; ed e-mail news@dcherald.com; web site www.duboiscountyherald.com
- 700,000(views)
Group: Jasper Herald Co.
Published: Mon, Tues, Wed, Thur, Fri, Sat
Weekday Frequency: e
Saturday Frequency: m
Circulation: 9,108; 9,108(sat)
Last Audit: Sworn/Estimate/Non-Audited October 19, 2017
Advertising Rate (weekday/saturday): Open inch rate $14.00 CPM
Online Advertising Rate: ROS $150.00/month (300x250 and 300x90)
News services: AP, CNS. **Established:** 1895
Own Printing Facility?: Yes
Commercial Printers?: Yes
Special Editions: Home, Lawn & Garden (Apr); Christmas Greetings (Dec); Boys Basketball Sectional (Feb); Brides & Weddings (Jan); 4-Fair Kick-off (Jul); Senior Citizen Salute (Jun); Boys Basketball Sectional (Mar); Graduation (May); Christmas Opening (Nov); Car Care (Winter 2012); Newspaper in Education (Dec).
Special Weekly Sections: Food (Tues); Religion (Fri); Science (Mon); Travel (Thur).
Digital Platform - Mobile: Apple, Android
Digital Platform - Tablet: Apple iOS, Android, Kindle, Nook, Kindle Fire
Co-president; co-publisher .... Dan E. Rumbach
Co-president; co-publisher; editor .... John A. Rumbach
Mng. Ed. .... Justin Rumbach
Controller/Treasurer .... Mark Fierst
Mgr., HR .... Mike Mazur
Subscriber Services manager .... Don Weisheit
Wire Ed. .... Dawn Mazur
Adv. Dir. .... Tom Stephens
Dist. Mgr. .... Dan Hoppenjans
Single Copy Sales & Print Distribution Manager .... Alan Baumeister
Market Information: Split run; Zoned editions.
Mechanical Available: Offset; Black and 3 ROP colors; insert accepted - subject to approval; page cutoffs - 17 1/2.
Mechanical Specifications: Type page 10 3/16 x 16; E - 5 cols, 1 7/8, 1/8 between; A - 5 cols, 1 7/8, 1/8 between; C - 6 cols, 1 1/2,

1/8 between.
Areas Served: 47546, 47542, 47527, 47521, 47532, 47513, 47541, 47575, 47580, 47523, 47531, 47536, 47537, 47550, 47552, 47556, 47577, 47579, 47611, 47564, 47585, 47590, 47598.
Delivery Method: Mail, Newsstand, Carrier, RacksEquipment & Software: PRESSROOM EQUIPMENT: Lines — 6-G/with hump single width 1974; 1-G/Color single width.; MAILROOM EQUIPMENT: Counter Stackers — 1/Gammerler STC70; Inserters & Stuffers — KAN/480, Kan/4-Bay/Multi-Feeder; Tying Machines — 3-Bu/60-71; Address Machine — 1-Am/57; BUSINESS EQUIPMENT: Novell/Network BUSINESS SOFTWARE: MSSI CLASSIFIED EQUIPMENT: Hardware — 2-APP/Mac; CLASSIFIED SOFTWARE: Baseview. DISPLAY EQUIPMENT: Hardware — 6-APP/Mac; Printers — Xerox Phaser 5500; DISPLAY SOFTWAREAd Make-up Applications — Multi-Ad/Creator, Baseview/PMP; Layout Software — Mk/Managing Editor AdForce. EDITORIAL EQUIPMENT: Hardware — 19-APP/Mac; Printers — Xerox Phaser 5500, APP/Mac HP Laserjet EDITORIAL SOFTWARE: QPS/QuarkXPress 6.5, Baseview/NewsEdit Pro IQUE, Adobe/Photoshop CS. PRODUCTION EQUIPMENT: Hardware — Kodak CTP; Cameras — DSA; Scanners — 1-AG/Arcus 2 PRODUCTION SOFTWARE: InDesign, MediaSpan.

JEFFERSONVILLE

NEWS AND TRIBUNE

221 Spring St, Jeffersonville, Ind., 47130-3353, Clark; gen tel (812) 283-6636; adv tel (812) 206-2143; ed tel (812) 206-2130; gen fax (812) 284-7081; adv fax (812) 284-7081; ed fax (812) 284-7081; gen/nat adv e-mail duke.freeman@newsandtribune.com; disp adv e-mail mary.tuttle@newsandtribune.com; class adv e-mailclassifieds@newsandtribune.com; ed e-mail shea.vanhoy@newsandtribune.com; web site www.newsandtribune.com
Group: Community Newspaper Holdings, Inc.
Published: Mon, Tues, Wed, Thur, Fri, Sat
Weekday Frequency: e
Saturday Frequency: m
Circulation: 7,152; 7,152(sat)
Last Audit: Sworn/Estimate/Non-Audited September 30, 2017
Branch Offices: Clark County, Floyd County
Advertising Rate (weekday/saturday): Open inch rate $13.25
Advertising Rate (sunday): Open inch rate $14.00
Online Advertising Rate: Business Marquee Link $10.00/day; Big Ads & Skyscraper inside $150.00 CPM; Homepage Skyscraper $159.00 CPM; Mobile Banner $200.00/share; Homepage Big Ad $209.00 CPM;
News services: AP, NEA, Scripps Howard. **Established:** 1851
Special Editions: Bridal Guide, Medical Directory, Worship Guide, Life Planning, Visitors/Relocation Guide (Jan, Feb, Mar); Southern Indiana Progress, Spring Home & Garden (Apr, May, Jun); Art Walk Guide, Back to School, HS Football Preview, Clark County Readers' Choice, Harvest Homecoming Guide, GCCS NAFC School Directory (Jul, Aug, Sept); Floyd County Readers' Choice, Boys and Girls Basketball, Letters to Santa, Power of Pink (Oct, Nov, Dec)
Special Weekly Sections: TV Weekly (Sat).
Syndicated Publications: TV News/Golden Opportunity (Monthly).
Digital Platform - Mobile: Apple, Android
Digital Platform - Tablet: Apple iOS, Android
Pub. .... Bill Hanson
Dir. of Aud. Dev. .... Mike Massek
Bus. Mgr. .... Janice Ashby
Sports Ed. .... Greg Mengelt
Adv. Mgr. .... Mary Tuttle
Asst. Ed. .... Chris Morris
Asst. Ed. .... Jason Thomas
Prod. Mgr. .... Stephen Allen
Pg. Designer .... Claire White
Market Information: TMC.
Mechanical Available: Offset; Black and 3 ROP colors; insert accepted; page cutoffs - 21 1/2.
Mechanical Specifications: Type page 13 x 21 1/2; E - 6 cols, 2, 1/12 between; A - 6 cols, 2,

1/8 between; C - 9 cols, 1 1/3, 1/12 between.
Areas Served: Clark, Floyd County
Delivery Method: Mail, Newsstand, Carrier, RacksEquipment & Software: PRESSROOM EQUIPMENT: Lines — 19-G/Urbanite IF 6507; 20-G/Urbanite IF 6507; 21-G/Urbanite IF 6507; 22-G/Urbanite IF 6507; 23-G/Urbanite IF 6507; Folders — G/U-1280-1D29054; Reels & Stands — 1-G/2 Tier, 1-G/3 Tier; Control System — 2; MAILROOM EQUIPMENT: Counter Stackers — BG; Inserters & Stuffers — Mc/60-40; Tying Machines — 2/Bu; Address Machine — Wm.; BUSINESS EQUIPMENT: DEC/VT320 BUSINESS SOFTWARE: Vision Data CLASSIFIED EQUIPMENT: Hardware — APP/Mac Quadra 800; Printers — LaserMaster/Unity 1200XL, APP/Mac LaserWriter IIg; CLASSIFIED SOFTWARE: QPS/QuarkXPress, Baseview/NewsEdit. EDITORIAL EQUIPMENT: Hardware — APP/Mac Quadra 800; Printers — LaserMaster/Unity 1200XL, APP/Mac LaserWriter IIg EDITORIAL SOFTWARE: QPS/QuarkXPress, Baseview/NewsEdit. PRODUCTION EQUIPMENT: Hardware — TI/OmniPage 2.1, LaserMaster/Unity 1200 XLO; Cameras — SCREEN/C-690-C; Scanners — Umax/840 PRODUCTION SOFTWARE: QPS/QuarkXPress 3.3.
Note: The Jeffersonville Evening News (e) has a combination rate of $23.62 with the New Albany Tribune (eS). Individual newspaper rates not made available.

KENDALLVILLE

THE NEWS SUN

102 N Main St, Kendallville, Ind., 46755-1714, Noble; gen tel (260) 347-0400; adv tel (260) 347-0400; ed tel (260) 347-0400; gen fax (260) 347-7282; adv fax (260) 347-7282; ed fax (260) 347-2693; gen/nat adv e-mail ldonley@kpcmedia.com; disp adv e-mail cmiller@kpcmedia.com; class adv e-mailasaggars@kpcmedia.com; ed e-mail dkurtz@kpcmedia.com; web site www.kpcnews.com
- 500,000(views) 100,000(visitors)
Group: KPC Media Group, Inc.
Published: Mon, Tues, Wed, Thur, Fri, Sat, Sun
Weekday Frequency: m
Saturday Frequency: m
Circulation: 7,731; 7,731(sat); 7,193(sun)
Last Audit: AAM December 31, 2014
Advertising Rate (weekday/saturday): Open inch rate $16.75
Advertising Rate (sunday): Open inch rate $16.75
Online Advertising Rate: Page Curl $150.00 per week; Top Banner $200.00 per week; Lower Leaderboard $60.00 per week
News services: AP. **Established:** 1911
Own Printing Facility?: Yes
Commercial Printers?: Yes
Special Editions: Look at Lagrange (Apr); Wedding Planner (Aug); Wedding Planner (Feb); Noble County Answer Book (Jan); Noble Co. 4-H Scrapbook (Jul); Sectional Basketball Preview (Mar); Graduation (May); Basketball Preview (Nov); Apple Festival (Oct); ACD Festival (Sept).
Special Weekly Sections: Church Page (Fri); Business Page (Other); Homes To Own (S); Agri-Business Page (Sat); Outdoor Life (Thur).
Syndicated Publications: USA WEEKEND Magazine (S); American Profile (Weekly).
Digital Platform - Mobile: Apple, Android
Digital Platform - Tablet: Apple iOS, Android
Pres./CEO/Pub. .... Terry Housholder
Circ. Dir. .... Bruce Hakala
Managing Ed. .... Barry Rochford
Night Ed. .... Mark Murdock
Presentation Ed. .... Erin Doucette
Life Ed. .... Jan Richardson
Desk Ed. .... Carol Ernsberger
Adv. Dir. .... Lynette Donley
Acct. Exec. .... Cynthia Miller
Acct. Exec. .... Terri Myers
Production Mgr. .... Gary Crager
Creative Mgr. .... Ann Saggers
Market Information: ADS; TMC; Zoned editions.
Mechanical Available: Offset; Black and 3 ROP colors; insert accepted - product samples; page cutoffs - 22 3/4.

Mechanical Specifications: Type page 11 1/2 x 21 1/2; E - 6 cols, 1 3/4, 1/8 between; A - 6 cols, 1 3/4, 1/8 between; C - 9 cols, 1 3/4, 1/8 between.
Areas Served: 46565; 46701; 46730; 46732; 46746; 46747; 46755; 46760; 46761; 46763; 46767; 46771; 46784; 46794; 46795
Delivery Method: Mail, Newsstand, Carrier, RacksEquipment & Software: PRESSROOM EQUIPMENT: Lines — 4-G/Floor SSC Units 1988, 1-Stalk/Pathfinder 1988; 2-G/4-High 1991; 1999; MAILROOM EQUIPMENT: Counter Stackers — 1/ The Stacker Machine Co/S-N 316-19; Inserters & Stuffers — 1-KAN/5 pocket, KAN/Twin Stacker, MM/Saddle Binds-5 Pocket, 1-Challenge/Single Knife; Tying Machines — It; BUSINESS EQUIPMENT: 1-Covicint/580 BUSINESS SOFTWARE: Baseview/Ad Manager Pro 2.02, Dynamics/ Great Plains, Baseview/Circulation Pro 1.8.0 CLASSIFIED EQUIPMENT: Hardware — 3-APP/Mac; Printers — 2-APP/Mac LaserWriter; CLASSIFIED SOFTWARE: Baseview, QPS/QuarkXPress. DISPLAY EQUIPMENT: Hardware — 9-APP/Mac; Printers — 2-APP/Mac LaserWriter; DISPLAY SOFTWAREAd Make-up Applications — QPS/QuarkXPress, Multi-Ad.; EDITORIAL EQUIPMENT: Hardware — 12-APP/ Mac/6-RSK/TRS 80 Model 100; Printers — 2-APP/Mac LaserWriter EDITORIAL SOFTWARE: Baseview, QPS/QuarkXPress. PRODUCTION EQUIPMENT: Hardware — Caere/OmniPage 6.0, AG/Imagesetter 1200; Cameras — 1-B; Scanners — 1-Kk, 4-AG PRODUCTION SOFTWARE: QPS/ QuarkXPress 4.0.

KOKOMO

KOKOMO TRIBUNE

300 N Union St, Kokomo, Ind., 46901-4612, Howard; gen tel (765) 459-3121; adv tel (765) 459-3121 ext. 6717; ed tel (765) 454-8584; gen fax (765) 456-3815; adv fax (765) 854-6734; ed fax (765) 854-6733; gen/nat adv e-mail susan.mccauley@kokomotribune.com; disp adv e-mail peggy.martino@kokomotribune.com; class adv e-mailkristin.johnson@kokomotribune.com; ed e-mail jeff.kovaleski@kokomotribune.com; web site www.kokomotribune.com
Group: Community Newspaper Holdings, Inc.
Published: Mon, Tues, Wed, Thur, Fri, Sat, Sun
Weekday Frequency: m
Saturday Frequency: m
Circulation: 20,100; 20,100(sat); 20,544(sun)
Last Audit: Sworn/Estimate/Non-Audited September 30, 2017
Advertising Rate (weekday/saturday): Open inch rate $45.90
Advertising Rate (sunday): Open inch rate $40.40
Online Advertising Rate: Homepage $15.00 CPM; Other pages $12.00 CPM
News services: AP. **Established:** 1850
Own Printing Facility?: Yes
Commercial Printers?: Yes
Special Editions: Howard County 4H Fair 2013 (Jul); Women Today (Jul); Brides 2013 (Jan); Best of Kokomo (Jan).
Special Weekly Sections: TV Weekly (Sat).
Syndicated Publications: Relish (Monthly); TV Update (Other); Parade (S).
Digital Platform - Mobile: Apple, Android
Digital Platform - Tablet: Apple iOS, Android
Photo Ed. .... Tim Bath
Ed./Op. Page Ed .... Jeff Kovaleski
Managing Ed. .... Jill Bond
City Ed. .... Robert Burgess
Reg. Circ. Dir. .... Robin Harper
Customer Service Mgr. .... Misty Whittaker
Customer Serice Rep./NIE Coord. Jessyka Betzner
Rgl. Adv. Dir. .... Beverly Sams
Reg. Digital Mgr. .... Kristin Johnson
Pub. .... Robyn McCloskey
Market Information: ADS; TMC; Zoned editions.
Mechanical Available: Offset; Black and 3 ROP colors; insert accepted - any; page cutoffs - 22 3/4.
Mechanical Specifications: Type page 13 x 21 1/2; E - 6 cols, 2 1/16, 1/8 between; A - 6 cols, 2 1/16, 1/8 between; C - 9 cols, 1 3/8, 1/16 between.
Areas Served: Howard County
Delivery Method: Mail, Carrier, RacksEquipment & Software: MAILROOM EQUIPMENT: Tying Machines — 2-Signode/MLN-2A Strapper; Address Machine — Nikor Mark-Model-20.; BUSINESS EQUIPMENT: 1-DEC/1170 CLASSIFIED EQUIPMENT: Hardware — APP/Mac G3; Umax, Epson/ Scanner; Printers — GCC; CLASSIFIED SOFTWARE: AT. DISPLAY EQUIPMENT: Hardware — APP/Mac G3; Printers — GCC, Tektronix; Other Hardware — Umax, Epson/ Scanners DISPLAY SOFTWAREAd Make-up Applications — QPS/QuarkXPress 4.x; Layout Software — Baseview. EDITORIAL EQUIPMENT: Hardware — APP/Mac 73/ APP/Mac; Printers — GCC EDITORIAL SOFTWARE: Baseview 3.1.8. PRODUCTION EQUIPMENT: Hardware — QPS/ QuarkXPress 4.x, Baseview/NewsEdit Pro-Que 3.1.x.

LA PORTE

HERALD-ARGUS

701 State St, La Porte, Ind., 46350-3328, La Porte; gen tel (219) 362-2161; adv tel (219) 326-3881; ed tel (219) 326-3858; gen fax (219) 362-2166; ed fax (219) 362-2166; gen/nat adv e-mail breisig@heraldargus.com; disp adv e-mail display@heraldargus.com; class adv e-mailclassified@heraldargus.com; web site www.heraldargus.com
Group: Paxton Media Group, LLC
Published: Mon, Tues, Wed, Thur, Fri, Sat
Weekday Frequency: e
Saturday Frequency: e
Circulation: 5,054; 5,054(sat)
Last Audit: AAM September 30, 2014
Advertising Rate (weekday/saturday): Open inch rate $15.46
News services: AP, SHNS. **Established:** 1880
Special Editions: Home Improvement/Gardening (Apr); Finance (Feb); Farm (Mar); Christmas (Nov); Car Care (Oct).
Special Weekly Sections: Senior (Fri); Best Food Day (Mon); Religion (Sat); Homes (Thur); Agriculture (Tues); Business/Industry (Wed).
Syndicated Publications: TV Viewer (Sat); American Profile (Weekly).
Digital Platform - Mobile: Apple, Android
Digital Platform - Tablet: Apple iOS, Android, Kindle, Nook, Kindle Fire
Pub. .... Bill Hackney
Mng. Ed. .... Kim King
Acct. Exec. .... Carolyn Smith
Acct. Exec. .... Patty Bryant
Lead News Ed. .... Amanda Haverstick
Managing Ed. .... Adam Parkhouse
News Ed. .... Matt Christy
Reporter .... Jessica Campbell
District Sales Mgr. .... Leslie Dean
Advertising Dir. .... Isis Cains
Acc. Exec. .... Cathie Doria
Market Information: TMC.
Mechanical Available: Offset; Black and 3 ROP colors; insert accepted; page cutoffs - 22 3/4.
Mechanical Specifications: Type page 13 x 21 1/2; E - 6 cols, 2 1/16, 1/8 between; A - 6 cols, 2 1/16, 1/8 between; C - 9 cols, 1 3/8, 1/16 between.
Areas Served: 46350
Delivery Method: Mail, Newsstand, Carrier, RacksEquipment & Software: PRESSROOM EQUIPMENT: Lines — 6-G/Urbanite, 1-G/3-Color single width; Folders — 1-G/Universal 1963; Control System — 1995; MAILROOM EQUIPMENT: Tying Machines — 1-Bu/String Tyer, 1-MLN/EE.; BUSINESS EQUIPMENT: DTK/Pentium-100 CLASSIFIED EQUIPMENT: Hardware — Dewar/Sys II; 5-Dewar/Discribe; CLASSIFIED SOFTWARE: Dewar/Disc Net. DISPLAY EQUIPMENT: Hardware — 2-Dewar/AST; DISPLAY SOFTWARELayout Software — 2-Dewar/ Sys IV. EDITORIAL EQUIPMENT: Hardware — Dewar/Sys II, DTK/16-Dewar/Discribe, 16-DTK EDITORIAL SOFTWARE: Dewar/ Disc Net, FSI. PRODUCTION EQUIPMENT: Hardware — 1-MON/PaperMaster 2, 1-MON/ ImageMaster 1000, 3-MON/Image Master 1500; Cameras — 1-Nu/2024-V, 1-R/580; Scanners — Nikon/ScanTouch 8 1/2 x 14 PRODUCTION SOFTWARE: FSI, QPS/ QuarkXPress 3.32.

LAFAYETTE

JOURNAL AND COURIER

823 Park East Blvd, Ste C, Lafayette, Ind., 47905-0811, Tippecanoe; gen tel (765) 423-5511; adv tel (765) 423-5272; ed tel (765) 420-5235; gen fax (765) 742-5633; adv fax (765) 742-5633; ed fax (765) 420-5246; gen/nat adv e-mail sdavis@journalandcourier.com; disp adv e-mail jholm@journalandcourier.com; class adv e-mailamecklenburg@journalandcourier.com; ed e-mail jstafford@journalandcourier.com; web site www.jconline.com
- 5,775,000(views) 415,500(visitors)
Group: Gannett
Published: Mon, Tues, Wed, Thur, Fri, Sat, Sun
Weekday Frequency: m
Saturday Frequency: m
Circulation: 20,717; 20,717(sat); 27,721(sun)
Last Audit: AAM March 31, 2016
Advertising Rate (weekday/saturday): Open inch rate $57.87
Advertising Rate (sunday): Sunday TV Journal: Open inch rate $20.35; Sunday Comics Page: Open inch rate $840.00 (Full Page)
Online Advertising Rate: In-Story Ads $6.00 CPM; In-Story Video Ads $13.00 CPM; Umbrella Page $720.00; News page $490.00; Business Page $230.00; Sports Page $310.00
News services: AP, GNS, LAT-WP. **Established:** 1920
Own Printing Facility?: Yes
Commercial Printers?: Yes
Special Editions: Schools of Greater Lafayette (May); Bragging Rights (Apr); Community Connections (Aug); Builders Showcase (Bi-Monthly); Football Saturday (Fall); Grading Our Schools (Jan); Spring Home Improvement (Mar); Coupon Express (Monthly); Profiles (Oct).
Special Weekly Sections: TGIF (Fri); Food & Drink (Mon); Life (S); Homes (Sat); Diversion (Thur); Health & Fitness (Tues); Relate (Wed).
Syndicated Publications: USA WEEKEND Magazine (Sat).
Digital Platform - Mobile: Apple, Android
Digital Platform - Tablet: Apple iOS, Android, Kindle, Nook, Kindle Fire
Controller .... Chris Deno
Adv. Mgr., Classified .... Becky Taylor
Dir., Market Devel. .... Nancy Jo Trafton
Cashier/Customer Service Rep. .... Brenda Rudd
Regl. Digital Dir. .... Bill Cannon
Planning Ed. .... Ken Thompson
Features Ed. .... Julie McClure
Content Strategist .... Carol Bangert
Engagement Ed .... Dave Bangert
Exec. Ed. .... George Spohr
Market Information: TMC.
Mechanical Available: Letterpress; Black and 3 ROP colors; insert accepted - Sample-packs and We-Prints; page cutoffs - 22 3/4.
Mechanical Specifications: Type page 13 x 21 1/2; E - 6 cols, 2 1/8, 1/8 between; A - 6 cols, 2 1/8, 1/8 between; C - 9 cols, 1 3/8, 1/8 between.
Areas Served: Tippecanoe, Benton, Carroll, Clinton, Fountain, Jasper, Newton, Warren, and White County
Delivery Method: Mail, Newsstand, Carrier, RacksEquipment & Software: PRESSROOM EQUIPMENT: Lines — 6-G/Mark (2 half decks; 1 hump) 1959; Folders — G/2:1; Registration System — K&F/Pin Registration. MAILROOM EQUIPMENT: Counter Stackers — HL, 1/QWI; Inserters & Stuffers — 1-HI/1472; Tying Machines — Dynaric; Address Machine — Ch.; BUSINESS EQUIPMENT: 1-IBM/AS-400 F35 CLASSIFIED EQUIPMENT: Hardware — IBM/Server, Dell/Workstations; Printers — HP/8150N; CLASSIFIED SOFTWARE: Mactive 2.16.50. DISPLAY EQUIPMENT: Hardware — APP/Mac, 9-APP/Mac; Printers — 1-Linotype-Hell/Linotronic 530, 2-Pre Press/Panther 46H5; DISPLAY SOFTWAREAd Make-up Applications — Multi-Ad; Layout Software — APP/Mac. EDITORIAL EQUIPMENT: Hardware — 47-APP/Mac, 32-APP/Mac Server/APP/Mac G4, APP/E-Mac; Printers — DEC/LA 180, OCE/ Proof Express EDITORIAL SOFTWARE: Baseview/NewsEdit Pro. PRODUCTION EQUIPMENT: Hardware — 1-Lf, 2-Panther/ PrePress; Scanners — Kk/CoolScan PRODUCTION SOFTWARE: Baseview.

LEBANON

THE REPORTER

117 E Washington St, Lebanon, Ind., 46052-2209, Boone; gen tel (765) 482-4650; adv tel (765) 482-4650; ed tel (765) 482-4650 ext. 4; gen fax (765) 482-4652; adv fax (765) 482-4652; ed fax (765) 482-4652; gen/nat adv e-mail rick.whiteman@reporter.net; disp adv e-mail mary.ball@reporter.net; class adv e-mailrick.whiteman@reporter.net; ed e-mail news@reporter.net; web site www.reporter.net
- 30,000(views) 22,000(visitors)
Group: Community Newspaper Holdings, Inc.
Published: Tues, Wed, Thur, Fri, Sat
Weekday Frequency: m
Saturday Frequency: m
Circulation: 5,264; 5,264(sat)
Last Audit: Sworn/Estimate/Non-Audited September 30, 2017
Advertising Rate (weekday/saturday): Open inch rate $11.00; $15.00 (Wednesday TMC)
Online Advertising Rate: Share of Voice $150.00 per month
News services: AP. **Established:** 1891
Own Printing Facility?: No
Special Editions: County 4-H Fair and Open Show (Jul); Home and Garden (April); Graduation sections (May)
Special Weekly Sections: Business Page (Fri); Farm Pages (Tues);
Syndicated Publications: TV Times (Sat); American Profile (Weekly).
Digital Platform - Mobile: Apple, Android
Digital Platform - Tablet: Apple iOS, Android, Kindle, Nook
Mng. Ed. .... Marda Johnson
Pub. .... Greta Sanderson
Farm Ed. .... Rod Rose
Copy Ed. .... Andrea Badger
Sports Ed. .... Will Willems
Adv. Rep. .... Mary Ball
Adv. Rep. .... Tim Peters
Classified Rep. .... Julie Benavides
Circ. and Prod. .... Diane Clemens
Office Mgr. .... Kerry Luchetta
Sales Dir. .... Jared Selch
Market Information: TMC.
Mechanical Available: Offset; Black and 3 ROP colors; insert accepted; page cutoffs - 22 3/4.
Mechanical Specifications: Type page 13 x 21; E - 6 cols, 2 1/16, 1/8 between; A - 6 cols, 2 1/16, 1/8 between; C - 6 cols, 2 1/16, 1/8 between.
Areas Served: Boone County, Advance, Jamestown, Sheridan, Thorntown, Whitestown and Zionsville
Delivery Method: Mail, RacksEquipment & Software: PRESSROOM EQUIPMENT: Lines — 7-G/Community; MAILROOM EQUIPMENT: Tying Machines — 1/Dynaric; Address Machine — Wm.; BUSINESS EQUIPMENT: IBM

LINTON

GREENE COUNTY DAILY WORLD

79 S Main St, Linton, Ind., 47441-1818, Greene; gen tel (812) 847-4487; adv tel (812) 847-4487; ed tel (812) 847-4487; gen fax (812) 847-9513; adv fax (812) 847-9513; ed fax (812) 847-9513; gen/nat adv e-mail greenecountyads@yahoo.com; disp adv e-mail christy_lehman@hotmail.com; class adv e-mailchristy_lehman@hotmail.com; ed e-mail westfallgcdw@gmail.com; web site www.gcdailyworld.com
- 1,102,170(views) 253,800(visitors)
Group: Rust Communications
Published: Tues, Wed, Fri, Sat
Weekday Frequency: m
Saturday Frequency: m
Circulation: 3,500; 3,500(sat)
Last Audit: Sworn/Estimate/Non-Audited December 18, 2017
Advertising Rate (weekday/saturday): Open inch rate $8.32
News services: AP. **Established:** 1905
Own Printing Facility?: Yes

Commercial Printers?: Yes
Digital Platform - Mobile: Apple, Android
Digital Platform - Tablet: Apple iOS, Android, Kindle, Nook, Kindle Fire
Publisher.. Chris Pruett
Sports Editor.................................. Travis David
Sports Writer................. Terry Schwinghammer
Pressman....................................... Mike Miller
Pressman................................... Cory Anweiler
Ad rep.. Heidi Puckett
Ad rep.. Tina Davis
Editor................................. Stockrahm Sabrina
Reporter............................. Andrew Christman
Reporter.. Patti Danner
Reporter
Kelly Slaven
Market Information: TMC.
Mechanical Available: Offset; Black and 3 ROP colors; inserts accepted; page cutoffs - 22 3/4.
Mechanical Specifications: Type page 13 x 21 1/2; E - 6 cols, 2 1/16, 1/8 between; A - 6 cols, 2 1/16, 1/8 between; C - 9 cols, 1 1/2, 1/8 between.
Areas Served: Linton, Jasonville, Sandborn, Lyons, Switz City, Worthington, Coalmont, Midland, Dugger, Newberry, Solsberry, Owensburg, Scotland, Elnora, Springville, Bloomfield
Delivery Method: Mail, Newsstand, RacksEquipment & Software: PRESSROOM EQUIPMENT: Lines — 7-G/Community; 1-ABD/360; Folders — G/C.; EDITORIAL EQUIPMENT: Hardware — APP/Macs PRODUCTION EQUIPMENT: Cameras — 1-R

LOGANSPORT

PHAROS-TRIBUNE

517 E Broadway, Logansport, Ind., 46947-3154, Cass; gen tel (574) 722-5000; adv tel (574) 732-5156; ed tel (574) 732-5155; gen fax (574) 732-5080; adv fax (574) 732-5050; ed fax (574) 732-5070; gen/nat adv e-mail becky.kesler@pharostribune.com; disp adv e-mail lori.thornton@pharostribune.com; class adv e-mailjody.taylor@pharostribune.com; ed e-mail kevin.burkett@pharostribune.com; web site www.pharostribune.com
- 377,903(views) 85,972(visitors)
Group: Community Newspaper Holdings, Inc.
Published: Mon, Tues, Wed, Thur, Fri, Sat
Weekday Frequency: m
Saturday Frequency: m
Circulation: 6,000; 7,200(sat)
Last Audit: Sworn/Estimate/Non-Audited October 1, 2017
Advertising Rate (weekday/saturday): Open inch rate $17.40
Advertising Rate (sunday): Open inch rate $18.40
News services: AP, MCT. **Established:** 1844
Own Printing Facility?: Yes
Commercial Printers?: Yes
Special Editions: Football (Aug); 4-H (Jul); Winter Sports (Nov).
Special Weekly Sections: Religion (S); TV Encore(F).
Syndicated Publications: Parade (S).
Digital Platform - Mobile: Apple, Android
Digital Platform - Tablet: Apple iOS, Android, Kindle, Nook, Kindle Fire
Sports Ed...................................... Beau Wicker
News Ed................................. Sarah Einselen
Regl. Adv. Dir.............................. Beverly Sams
Marketing Exec........................... Renee LoCoco
Regional Director Audience Developement.. Robin Harper
Circ. Supervisor......................... Theresia Kuritz
Customer Service Rep................ Kayanna Smith
Reg. Op. Mgr.............................. Amy Newcom
Editor.. Kevin Burkett
HR/Finance............................. Jessica Deitrich
Regional Publisher/ Senior VP Operations CNHI.... Robyn McCloskey
Classified / Expeditor........................ Jody Taylor
Market Information: TMC.
Mechanical Available: Offset; Black and 3 ROP colors; insert accepted; page cutoffs - 22 3/4.
Mechanical Specifications: Type page 13 x 21 1/2; E - 6 cols, 2 1/16, 1/8 between; A - 6 cols, 2 1/16, 1/8 between; C - 6 cols, 2 1/16, 1/8 between.
Areas Served: Cass County
Delivery Method: Mail, Newsstand, CarrierEquipment & Software: PRESSROOM EQUIPMENT: Lines — 19-G/SSC 1984.; MAILROOM EQUIPMENT: Tying Machines — 1-/MLN, OVL/415.; BUSINESS EQUIPMENT: 1-Sun/4-110, 1-Sun/SLC, 1-Compaq/Prolinca 3/25 BUSINESS SOFTWARE: Vision Data, ADP CLASSIFIED EQUIPMENT: Hardware — Sun, NCD; Printers — HP/LaserJet, Copal/Dash 600; CLASSIFIED SOFTWARE: Atex. DISPLAY EQUIPMENT: Hardware — APP/Mac II; Printers — 2-APP/Mac LaserWriter II NTX, 2-Copal/Dash 600; DISPLAY SOFTWAREAd Make-up Applications — Adobe/InDesign; Layout Software — ALS. EDITORIAL EQUIPMENT: Hardware — Sun/Lf/AP Leaf Picture Desk, Lf/Leafscan 35; Printers — 2-APP/Mac LaserWriter II NTX, 2-Copal/Dash 600 EDITORIAL SOFTWARE: Baseview. PRODUCTION EQUIPMENT: Hardware — Tl/OmniPage 2.12, 1-AG/Focus Color Plus; Scanners — Horizon PRODUCTION SOFTWARE: QPS/QuarkXPress 4.11.

MADISON

MADISON COURIER, INC.

310 West St, Madison, Ind., 47250-3711, Jefferson; gen tel (812) 265-3641; adv tel (812) 265-3641 ext. 228; ed tel (812) 265-3641 ext. 230; gen fax (812) 273-5903; adv fax (812) 273-6903; ed fax (812) 273-6903; gen/nat adv e-mail cjacobs@madisoncourier.com; disp adv e-mail addept@madisoncourier.com; class adv e-mailclassifieds@madisoncourier.com; ed e-mail etompkin@madisoncourier.com; web site www.madisoncourier.com
- 845,900(views) 324,000(visitors)
Published: Mon, Tues, Wed, Thur, Fri, Sat
Weekday Frequency: e
Saturday Frequency: m
Circulation: 5,400; 6,000(sat)
Last Audit: USPS October 14, 2017
Advertising Rate (weekday/saturday): Open inch rate $12.50
Online Advertising Rate: Button, Tile $50.00/month
News services: AP, NEA. **Established:** 1837
Own Printing Facility?: Yes
Commercial Printers?: No
Special Editions: Home and Car Improvement Tab (Apr); Year-End Tab (Dec); Tax Tab (Feb); Wedding Tab (Jan); 4-H Fair Tab (Jul); Lawn & Garden Tab (Mar); Graduation Tab (May); Health Mind & Body (quarterly); Chautauqua Tab (Sept).
Syndicated Publications: American Profile (Weekly).
Proprietary Publications: HMB-Health Mind & Body
Digital Platform - Mobile: Apple, Android
Digital Platform - Tablet: Apple iOS, Android
Nt'l. Acc. and Job Listings............. Mark McKee
Pub... Curt Jacobs
Sports Ed................................. Mark Campbell
Sports Ed............................... David Campbell
New Media Dir................................. Robin Cull
Ed... Elliot Tompkin
Inside Sales.............................. Dianne Colber
Carrier Mgr............................ Shawntale Tingle
Market Information: TMC.
Mechanical Available: Offset; Black and 3 ROP colors; insert accepted - single sheet, booklets, samples; page cutoffs - 22 3/4.
Mechanical Specifications: Type page 13 x 21 1/2; E - 6 cols, 2 1/16, 1/8 between; A - 6 cols, 2 1/16, 1/8 between; C - 8 cols, 1 1/2, 1/8 between.
Areas Served: Jefferson and Switzerland County, Indiana and Trimble and Carroll County, Kentucky.
Delivery Method: Mail, Newsstand, Carrier, RacksEquipment & Software: PRESSROOM EQUIPMENT: Lines — 6-KP/News King; Reels & Stands — 6; Control System — 1; MAILROOM EQUIPMENT: Tying Machines — 2/Bu.; BUSINESS EQUIPMENT: 4-TI/1505 CLASSIFIED EQUIPMENT: Hardware — 3-APP/Power Mac G3; Printers — 1-APP/Mac ImageWriter II NT; CLASSIFIED SOFTWARE: Baseview. DISPLAY EQUIPMENT: Hardware — 3-APP/Mac G3, 4-APP/iMac G3; Printers — APP/Mac LaserWriter II NT, 1-Dataproducts/Typhoon 8; DISPLAY SOFTWAREAd Make-up Applications — DTI, QPS/QuarkXPress 3.32, Multi-Ad/Creator; Layout Software — COM/One System, 1-APP/Mac 7600. EDITORIAL EQUIPMENT: Hardware — 9-APP/Power Mac 7200, 3-APP/Power Mac G3/1-RSK/Tandy portable Model 100, 3-APP/Power Mac 7200-120 for remote office; Printers — 1-APP/Mac LaserWriter II NT EDITORIAL SOFTWARE: Baseview, Ethernet. PRODUCTION EQUIPMENT: Hardware — 1-Nu, Pre Press/Panther, Pre Press/Panther 34P; Cameras — R/400; Scanners — 1-Nikon/LS 1000, Epson 1600 PRODUCTION SOFTWARE: QPS/QuarkXPress 4.0.

MARION

CHRONICLE-TRIBUNE

610 S Adams St, Marion, Ind., 46953-2041, Grant; gen tel (765) 664-5111; adv tel (765) 671-2230; ed tel (765) 671-2250; gen fax (765) 664-6292; adv fax (765) 664-0729; ed fax (765) 668-4256; gen/nat adv e-mail lkelsay@chronicle-tribune.com; disp adv e-mail showard@chronicle-tribune.com; class adv e-mailshoward@chronicle-tribune.com; ed e-mail dpenticuff@chronicle-tribune.com; web site www.chronicle-tribune.com
- 2,000,000(views) 87,000(visitors)
Group: Paxton Media Group, LLC
Published: Mon, Tues, Wed, Thur, Fri, Sat, Sun
Weekday Frequency: m
Saturday Frequency: m
Circulation: 12,536; 12,536(sat); 14,524(sun)
Last Audit: AAM March 31, 2014
Advertising Rate (weekday/saturday): Open inch rate $41.04
Online Advertising Rate: Bottom Button Ad, Smale Tile Ads $150.00 CPM; Large Tile Ads $175.00 CPM; In-story Ads, Top Button Ads $200.00 CPM
News services: AP, GNS. **Established:** 1867
Own Printing Facility?: Yes
Commercial Printers?: Yes
Special Editions: Football Preview (Aug); Medical Directory (Feb); Bridal Tab (Jan); Senior Citizens (Jul); Progress (Mar); Women's Expo (Oct); Crossword Puzzle (Semi-yearly).
Special Weekly Sections: Travel (Fri); Best Food Day (Mon); Business (S); Business (Sat); Home (Thur); Kids Zone (Tues); Relationships (Wed).
Syndicated Publications: Northern Neighbors (S).
Digital Platform - Mobile: Apple, Android
Digital Platform - Tablet: Apple iOS, Android
President & Pub............................. Linda Kelsay
Ed... David Penticuff
Adv. Dir....................................... Stan Howard
Circ. Mgr.............................. Heather Korporal
Pressroom Mgr............................. Time Stanley
Managing Ed........................... Tyler Juranovich
Distr. Mgr..................................... Neal Bartrum
Market Information: TMC.
Mechanical Available: Offset; Black and 3 ROP colors; insert accepted - 4x 5 cards to 11 3/8 x 13 3/4 products; page cutoffs - 22 3/4.
Mechanical Specifications: Type page 11 5/8 x 21 1/2; E - 7 cols, 1 2/3, between; A - 6 cols, 2 1/16, 1/8 between; C - 9 cols, 1 3/8, 1/16 between.
Areas Served: Frankfort, Huntington, Peru, and Wabash
Delivery Method: Mail, Newsstand, Carrier, RacksEquipment & Software: PRESSROOM EQUIPMENT: Lines — 12-G/Urbanite 845 single width 1970; 6-G/Urbanite 557 single width 1974; Control System — Fin/Drive Sys.; MAILROOM EQUIPMENT: Counter Stackers — 1-HL/Monitor HI II, 2-HI/RS30; Inserters & Stuffers — 1-Mc/660-20; Tying Machines — 1-MLN/2A, OVL/415, Bu/String; Wrapping Singles — Manual; Address Machine — Ch/596-985.; BUSINESS EQUIPMENT: Time Mgt Sys, IBM/AS-400 CLASSIFIED EQUIPMENT: Hardware — IBM; Accuset/1000 Imagesetters; Printers — HP/4MV, HP/8000; CLASSIFIED SOFTWARE: APT 2.006.004. DISPLAY EQUIPMENT: Hardware — APP/Mac; Printers — HP/4MV, HP/8000; Other Hardware — Accuset/1000 Imagesetters DISPLAY SOFTWAREAd Make-up Applications - Multi-Ad/Creator; Layout Software — APP/Mac. EDITORIAL EQUIPMENT: Hardware — IBM; Printers — HP/8550, HP/8000, HP/4MV EDITORIAL SOFTWARE: APT 2.006.004. PRODUCTION EQUIPMENT: Hardware — 2-MON/1000 Imagesetter, Nu/Flip Top FT40APRNS; Cameras — 1-C/Spartan III; Scanners — Howtek/D7500, Microtek PRODUCTION SOFTWARE: QPS/QuarkXPress 4.10.

MARTINSVILLE

THE REPORTER TIMES

60 S Jefferson St, Martinsville, Ind., 46151-1968, Morgan; gen tel (765) 342-3311; adv tel (800) 804-8420; ed tel (765) 342-3311; gen fax (765) 342-1446; adv fax (765) 342-1459; ed fax (765) 342-1446; gen/nat adv e-mail lragle@heraldt.com; disp adv e-mail cgiddens@schurz.com; class adv e-maillragle@heraldt.com; ed e-mail bculp@reporter-times.com; web site www.reporter-times.com

- 200,000(views) 35,000(visitors)
Group: Schurz Communications Inc
Published: Mon, Tues, Wed, Thur, Fri, Sat, Sun
Weekday Frequency: e
Saturday Frequency: m
Circulation: 4,714; 4,714(sat); 40,171(sun)
Last Audit: Sworn/Estimate/Non-Audited September 30, 2017
Advertising Rate (weekday/saturday): Open inch rate $14.89
Advertising Rate (sunday): Open inch rate $40.21
Online Advertising Rate: Run of Site (Static) $10.00 CPM; Rich Media/Flash $10.00 CPM; 300x600 $14.00 CPM
News services: AP. **Established:** 1889
Special Editions: Football Preview (Aug); Last Minute Gifts (Dec); Boy Scout Page (Feb); Father's Day (Jun); Girl Scout Page (Mar); Graduation (May); Christmas Kick-Off (Nov); Fall Festival Program (Oct); Customer Appreciation Days (Sept).
Special Weekly Sections: NASCAR (Fri); Church (Sat); Health (Tues).
Syndicated Publications: TV Times (Sat).
Digital Platform - Mobile: Apple, Android
Digital Platform - Tablet: Apple iOS, Android
Adv. Mgr..................................... Karen DeWitt
Circ. Dir... Tim D. Smith
Mng. Ed.... Brian Culp
Todd Davidson
Laurie Ragle
HR Dir... Devon Perry
Adv. Sales Mgr........................... Chad Giddens
Sports Ed....................................... Steve Page
District Mgr................................. Phillip Tucker
Finance Mgr................................. Jennifer Paul
Front Desk Coord......................... Angie Skaggs
Sr. Vice Pres., Newspaper Opns.......... Charles V. Pittman
Pub... Cory Publisher
News Ed., Reporter.............. Alexis Fitzpatrick
Market Information: TMC.
Mechanical Available: Offset; Black and 3 ROP colors; insert accepted - all; page cutoffs - 22 3/4.
Mechanical Specifications: Type page 13 x 21 1/2; E - 6 cols, 2, 1/8 between; A - 6 cols, 2, 1/8 between; C - 9 cols, 1 5/16, 1/16 between.
Areas Served: Martinsville and Morgan County
Delivery Method: Mail, Newsstand, Carrier, RacksEquipment & Software: PRESSROOM EQUIPMENT: Lines — 7-G/Community (color unit); Folders — 1-G/2:1.; MAILROOM EQUIPMENT: Tying Machines — 2/Bu.; BUSINESS SOFTWARE: Baseview EDITORIAL EQUIPMENT: Hardware — APP/Mac; Printers — APP/Mac LaserWriter.
Note: This publication shares a joint Sunday edition with the Bedford (IN) Times-Mail (mS) and the Bloomington (IN) Herald-Times (mS).

MICHIGAN CITY

NEWS DISPATCH

121 W Michigan Blvd, Michigan City, Ind., 46360-3274, La Porte; gen tel (219) 874-7211; adv tel (219) 874-7211 ext. 400; ed

tel (219) 874-7211 ext. 451; gen fax (219) 872-8511; adv fax (219) 878-4487; ed fax (219) 872-8511; gen/nat adv e-mail icains@thenewsdispatch.com; disp adv e-mail ads@thenewsdispatch.com; class adv e-mailclassifieds@thenewsdispatch.com; ed e-mail jmcclure@thenewsdispatch.com; web site www.thenewsdispatch.com
Group: Paxton Media Group, LLC
Published: Mon, Tues, Wed, Thur, Fri, Sat, Sun
Weekday Frequency: m
Saturday Frequency: m
Circulation: 11,004; 5,586(sat)
Last Audit: AAM September 30, 2014
Advertising Rate (weekday/saturday): Open inch rate $22.30
News services: AP. **Established:** 1938
Own Printing Facility?: Yes
Special Editions: Real Estate Guide (Monthly).
Special Weekly Sections: Book Review (Fri); Business (S); Real Estate (Sat); Best Food Day (Fri).
Syndicated Publications: USA WEEKEND Magazine (S); TV Listings (own, local newsprint) (Sat).
Digital Platform - Mobile: Apple, Android
Digital Platform - Tablet: Apple iOS, Android
Adv. Dir. .... Isis Cains
Publisher .... Bill Hackney
Managing Ed. .... Adam Parkhouse
News Ed. .... Andy Steinke
Asst. Sports Ed. .... Carron Phillips
Sports Ed. .... Aaron McKrell
Market Information: ADS; TMC; Zoned editions.
Mechanical Available: Offset; Black and 3 ROP colors; insert accepted; page cutoffs - 22 3/4.
Mechanical Specifications: Type page 11 5/8 x 21 1/2; E - 6 cols, 1 5/6, 1/8 between; A - 6 cols, 1 5/6, 1/8 between; C - 9 cols, 1 1/6, 1/8 between.
Areas Served: 46360
Delivery Method: Mail, Newsstand, Carrier, RacksEquipment & Software: PRESSROOM EQUIPMENT: Lines — 8-G/Urbanite (3 color) 1972; Folders — G/Half & Quarter; Reels & Stands — 8-G/Reel Stand.; MAILROOM EQUIPMENT: Counter Stackers — BG/110HB; Inserters & Stuffers — 3-KAN/320; Tying Machines — MLN.; BUSINESS EQUIPMENT: Baseview CLASSIFIED EQUIPMENT: Hardware — APP/Mac; Printers — 2-APP/Mac LaserWriter IINTX, HP/4MV, QMS/860, Tektronix/300X; CLASSIFIED SOFTWARE: Baseview/Class Manager Pro. DISPLAY EQUIPMENT: Hardware — APP/Mac; Printers — 2-APP/Mac LaserWriter II NTX, HP/4MV, QMS/860, Tektronix/300x; DISPLAY SOFTWAREAd Make-up Applications — Managing Editor/ALS, QPS/QuarkXPress; Layout Software — APP/Mac. EDITORIAL EQUIPMENT: Hardware — APP/Mac; Printers — 2-APP/Mac LaserWriter II NTX, HP/4MV, QMS/860, Tektronix/300X EDITORIAL SOFTWARE: Baseview, QPS/QuarkXPress 3.32, Baseview/NewsEdit. PRODUCTION EQUIPMENT: Hardware — Caere/OmniPage, AG/Rapline 17; Cameras — R; Scanners — Visioneer/Paperport, Nikon/Super Coolscan, Lf/AP Leafscan 35, AG/StudioScan II, Hp/ScanJet HC, AG/Studio Star PRODUCTION SOFTWARE: QPS/QuarkXPress 3.32.

MONTICELLO

HERALD JOURNAL

114 S Main St, Monticello, Ind., 47960-2328, White; gen tel (574) 583-5121; adv tel (574) 583-5121; ed tel (574) 583-5121; gen fax (574) 583-4241; adv fax (574) 583-4241; ed fax (574) 583-4241; gen/nat adv e-mail sales@thehj.com; disp adv e-mail dcarlson@thehj.com; class adv e-mailtspear@thehj.com; ed e-mail wriggs@thehj.com; web site www.thehj.com
Group: Community Newspaper Holdings, Inc.
Published: Mon, Tues, Wed, Thur, Fri, Sat
Weekday Frequency: m
Saturday Frequency: m
Circulation: 3,500; 3,500(sat)
Last Audit: Sworn/Estimate/Non-Audited September 30, 2017
Advertising Rate (weekday/saturday): Open inch rate $18.00
Online Advertising Rate: Website Chip $99.00/month
News services: AP. **Established:** 1862
Own Printing Facility?: Yes
Commercial Printers?: No
Special Editions: 2014 Where
Special Weekly Sections: TV (Fri); Best Food Day (Thurs); Business & Financial (Sat); Best Food Day (Thur); Senior Citizens (Tues); Self Help (Wed).
Digital Platform - Mobile: Apple, Android
Digital Platform - Tablet: Apple iOS, Android, Kindle, Nook, Kindle Fire
Circ. Dir. .... Greg Perrotto
Circ. Dir. .... Cyndi Grace
Adv. Mgr. .... Deb Carlson
Pub. .... Mark Hornung
Adv. Dir. .... Tom Tiernan
Sports Ed. .... Kris Mills
Adv. Mgr. .... Vicki Shore
Market Information: TMC.
Mechanical Available: Offset; Black and 3 ROP colors; insert accepted; page cutoffs - 22 3/4.
Mechanical Specifications: Type page 13 x 21 1/2; E - 6 cols, 1 5/6, 1/8 between; A - 6 cols, 1 5/6, 1/8 between; C - 9 cols, 1 5/16, 1/8 between.
Areas Served: White County
Delivery Method: Mail, Newsstand, RacksEquipment & Software: PRESSROOM EQUIPMENT: Lines — 5-G/Community 1963.; CLASSIFIED EQUIPMENT: Hardware — Dell/PC; Printers — APP/Mac LaserWriter II; CLASSIFIED SOFTWARE: APT 4.0. DISPLAY EQUIPMENT: Hardware — Quark, Ad Builder; Printers — APP/Mac LaserWriter II; DISPLAY SOFTWARELayout Software — APP/Mac. EDITORIAL EQUIPMENT: Hardware — Dell/PC; Printers — APP/Mac LaserWriter II EDITORIAL SOFTWARE: APT 4.0. PRODUCTION EQUIPMENT: Hardware — 1-Nu/Flip Top FT40UPNS, SCREEN; Cameras — LE, R.

MUNCIE

THE STAR PRESS

345 S High St, Muncie, Ind., 47305-2326, Delaware; gen tel (765) 213-5701; adv tel (765) 213-5732; ed tel (765) 213-5732; gen fax (765) 213-5703; adv fax (765) 213-5937; ed fax (765) 213-5858; gen/nat adv e-mail clindus@muncie.gannett.com; disp adv e-mail msheridan@muncie.gannett.com; class adv e-mailtreese@muncie.gannett.com; ed e-mail gfallon@muncie.gannett.com; web site www.thestarpress.com
Group: Gannett
Published: Mon, Tues, Wed, Thur, Fri, Sat, Sun
Weekday Frequency: m
Saturday Frequency: m
Circulation: 18,449; 18,449(sat); 23,096(sun)
Last Audit: AAM September 30, 2016
Advertising Rate (weekday/saturday): Open inch rate $21.50
Advertising Rate (sunday): Open inch rate $21.50
Online Advertising Rate: Run of Site $37.50 CPM
News services: AP, MCT, SHNS, GNS. **Established:** 1899
Own Printing Facility?: Yes
Commercial Printers?: Yes
Special Weekly Sections: Best Food (S).
Syndicated Publications: TV Week (S).
Digital Platform - Mobile: Apple, Android
Digital Platform - Tablet: Apple iOS, Android
Gen. Mgr./Adv. Dir. .... Cheryl Lindus
Classified Sales Rep. .... Danyel Decker
Legal Adv. Clerk .... Josie James
Classified Supervisor .... Tammy Reese
HR Coord./Exec. Asst. .... Jane Jakubiak
Marketing Coord. .... Heather Ault
Online Ed. .... Phil Beebe
Managing Ed. .... Greg Fallon
Copy Ed. .... Chris Simons
Account Mgr. .... Cortney Felton
Retail Adv. Mgr. .... Mark Sheridan
Adv. Sales Exec. .... Robin Webb
Key Acct. Exec. .... Mary Vannatta
Community Conversation Ed. .... Jeff Ward
Night News Ed. .... Kathy Scott
Market Information: ADS; Split run; TMC; Zoned editions.
Mechanical Available: Letterpress; Black and 3 ROP colors; insert accepted; page cutoffs - 22 3/4.
Mechanical Specifications: Type page 13 x 21 3/8; E - 6 cols, 2, 1/6 between; A - 6 cols, 2, 1/6 between; C - 9 cols, 1 3/8, 1/16 between.
Areas Served: Delaware County
Delivery Method: Mail, Newsstand, Carrier, RacksEquipment & Software: PRESSROOM EQUIPMENT: Lines — 6-G/double width 1964.; MAILROOM EQUIPMENT: Counter Stackers — 2/QWI; Tying Machines — 2-/Power Strap; Wrapping Singles — Manual; Address Machine — Manual, Topping.; BUSINESS EQUIPMENT: 2-Sun/Ultra 10, Sun/Sparc 20 BUSINESS SOFTWARE: PBS, SBS, Cyborg CLASSIFIED EQUIPMENT: Hardware — APP/Mac; Printers — HP/4050; CLASSIFIED SOFTWARE: Baseview. DISPLAY EQUIPMENT: Hardware — Sun/Servers, APP/Macs; Printers — APP/Mac LaserPrinter; Other Hardware — AG/Selectset, AG/Avantra DISPLAY SOFTWAREAd Make-up Applications — DTI/311 4.3; Layout Software — DTI 4.3. EDITORIAL EQUIPMENT: Hardware — APP/Mac, Sun/HP/1020 Platter; Printers — APP/Mac LaserPrinter, HPM, Lexmark EDITORIAL SOFTWARE: DTI 4.3. PRODUCTION EQUIPMENT: Hardware — 2-AG/Select 7000, 1-AG/Avantra 25; Cameras — KI PRODUCTION SOFTWARE: DTI/Speed Planner 3.1.

MUNSTER

THE TIMES OF NORTHWEST INDIANA

601 45th St, Munster, Ind., 46321-2875, Lake; gen tel (219) 933-3200; adv tel (219) 852-4338; ed tel (219) 933-3223; gen fax (219) 933-3249; adv fax (219) 933-3325; gen/nat adv e-mail eric.horon@nwi.com; disp adv e-mail eric.horon@nwi.com; class adv e-mailroxanne.olejnik@nwi.com; ed e-mail bob.heisse@nwi.com; web site www.nwi.com - 15,602,223(views) 1,411,129(visitors)
Group: Lee Enterprises, Inc.
The Times Media Company
Published: Mon, Tues, Wed, Thur, Fri, Sat, Sun
Weekday Frequency: m
Saturday Frequency: m
Circulation: 32,305; 32,305(sat); 44,660(sun)
Last Audit: AAM June 30, 2017
Branch Offices: Munster, Crown Point, Valparaiso
Advertising Rate (weekday/saturday): Open inch rate $69 black & white, $78 color (net)
Advertising Rate (sunday): Open inch rate $78 black & white, $90 color (net)
Online Advertising Rate: ROS Box (300 x 250) $12 CPM
(Targeting additional $2 CPM)
(content, geo, BT, Day-part, etc.)
In unit video (300 x 250) $12 CPM
Floating Bar (1170 x 50 and 480 x 50) $25 CPM
News services: AP, CNS **Established:** 1906
Own Printing Facility?: Yes
Commercial Printers?: Yes
Special Editions: Christmas Gift Guide (Nov/Dec); Best of the Region (May); NWI Now (February/March)
Special Weekly Sections: A & E (Thursday); Forum (Sunday); Food (Wednesday); Homes (Saturday)
Syndicated Publications: BusINess (Quarterly); Color Comics (Sunday); Get Healthy (6x/yr);
Medical Guide (September)
Proprietary Publications: BusINess; Get Healthy;
Digital Platform - Mobile: Apple, Android, Windows
Digital Platform - Tablet: Apple iOS, Android, Windows 7, Kindle, Kindle Fire
Publisher .... Chris White
Ed. .... Bob Heisse
Dir. Finance .... Judy Milne
VP of Sales .... Joe Battistoni
Adv. Ops. Mgr. .... Eric Horon
Bus. Ed. .... Larry Avila
Digital and Audience Engagement Editor Summer Moore
Page Ed., Investigative Reporter .... Marc Chase
Porter County Ed. .... Doug Ross
News Ed. .... Crista Zivanovic
Marketing Mgr .... Jim Pellegrini
Retail Adv. Mgr. .... Oostman Scott
Digital Operations Manager .... Chris Mallonee
Reg. HR. Generalist .... Lisa Vosburg
Reg. Circ. Dir. .... Scott Kitner
Market Information: Split run; TMC; Zoned editions
Mechanical Available: Offset; Black and 3 ROP colors; insert accepted - envelope, card; page cutoffs - 21.
Mechanical Specifications: Type page 10"x21"; E - 6 cols, 1/8 between; A - 6 cols, 1/8 between; C - 6 cols, 1/8 between
Areas Served: Lake and Porter County in Indiana, mainly; however, we also deliver to LaPorte, Newton, and Jasper counties
Delivery Method: Mail, Newsstand, Carrier, RacksEquipment & Software: PRESSROOM EQUIPMENT: MAGNUM SINGLE WIDTH HEADLINER OFFSET HT70 DOUBLE WIDE HEADLINER OFFSET DOUBLE WIDE MAILROOM EQUIPMENT: Counter Stackers — 3/MM, 1-MM/388, 3-MM/310, 1-/HL; Inserters & Stuffers — 4-MM/308, GMA/SLS 2000; Tying Machines — 3-/MLN, 2-/OVL, 1-/Sterling, Dynaric; Wrapping Singles — 2-KP/KJ; Control System — GMA/SAM; Address Machine — 2-/Bar; BUSINESS EQUIPMENT: Sun/4, COM, 10-PC CLASSIFIED EQUIPMENT: Hardware — 7-Sun/Sparc, 14-NCD, 6-Sun/Sparc, 2-NCD, 5-PC; Printers — APP/Mac Laser; CLASSIFIED SOFTWARE: Vision Data. DISPLAY EQUIPMENT: Hardware — 40-APP/Mac; Printers — Iptech/RIP; DISPLAY SOFTWAREAd Make-up Applications — QPS/QuarkXPress; Layout Software — SCS/Layout 8000, MIE. EDITORIAL EQUIPMENT: Hardware — 12-Sun/Sparc, 80-PC; Printers — HP/Laser, Iptech/RIP EDITORIAL SOFTWARE: Sun/Lotus Notes. PRODUCTION EQUIPMENT: Hardware — 2-ECR/Pelbox Full-page, 2-APP/Mac Laser, Hyphen/3100, Epson/836XL; Cameras — WL/Digital Camera, Nikon/D1; Scanners — 4-Epson/836XLT, Iptech/RIP PRODUCTION SOFTWARE: QPS/QuarkXPress 4.11.

NEW ALBANY

TRIBUNE

318 Pearl St, Ste 100, New Albany, Ind., 47150-3450, Floyd; gen tel (812) 944-6481; adv tel (812) 206-2133; ed tel (812) 206-2130; gen fax (812) 949-6587; adv fax (812) 949-6587; ed fax (812) 949-6587; gen/nat adv e-mail duke.freeman@newsandtribune.com; disp adv e-mail mary.tuttle@newsandtribune.com; class adv e-mailclassifieds@newsandtribune.com; ed e-mail shea.vanhoy@newsandtribune.com; web site www.newsandtribune.com
Group: Community Newspaper Holdings, Inc.
Published: Mon, Tues, Wed, Thur, Fri, Sat
Weekday Frequency: e
Circulation: 13,054; 9,854(sun)
Last Audit: Sworn/Estimate/Non-Audited September 30, 2017
Branch Offices: Clark County, Floyd County
Advertising Rate (weekday/saturday): Open inch rate $13.25
Advertising Rate (sunday): Open inch rate $14.00
Online Advertising Rate: Business Marquee Link $10.00/day; Big Ads & Skyscraper inside $150.00 CPM; Homepage Skyscraper $159.00 CPM; Mobile Banner $200.00/share; Homepage Big Ad $209.00 CPM;
News services: AP. **Established:** 1851
Special Editions: Bridal Guide, Medical Directory, Worship Guide, Life Planning, Visitors/Relocation Guide (Jan, Feb, Mar); Southern Indiana Progress, Spring Home & Garden (Apr, May, Jun); Art Walk Guide, Back to School, HS Football Preview, Clark County Readers' Choice, Harvest Homecoming Guide, GCCS NAFC School Directory (Jul, Aug, Sept); Floyd County Readers' Choice, Boys and Girls Basketball, Letters to Santa, Power of Pink (Oct, Nov, Dec)
Special Weekly Sections: TV Weekly (Sat).
Syndicated Publications: Color Comics (S).
Digital Platform - Mobile: Apple, Android
Digital Platform - Tablet: Apple iOS, Android
Asst. Ed. .... Chris Morris
Pub. .... Bill Hanson
Business Mgr. .... Janice Ashby
Circ. Mgr. .... Mike Massek
Sports Ed. .... Greg Mengelt
Adv. Mgr. .... Mary Tuttle
Asst. Ed. .... Jason Thomas

Prod. Mgr.....................................Stephen Allen
Ed..Susan Duncan
Market Information: TMC.
Mechanical Available: Offset; Black and 1 ROP colors; insert accepted; page cutoffs - 21 1/2.
Mechanical Specifications: Type page 13 x 21 1/2; E - 6 cols, 2 1/16, 1/8 between; A - 6 cols, 2 1/16, 1/8 between; C - 9 cols, 1 5/16, 1/8 between.
Areas Served: Clark, Floyd County
Equipment & Software: PRESSROOM EQUIPMENT: Lines — 8-G; Folders — 1-G/2:1.; MAILROOM EQUIPMENT: Tying Machines — 1/Bu; Address Machine — 1-/Am.; BUSINESS EQUIPMENT: 2-Auto Tape/9100 CLASSIFIED EQUIPMENT: Hardware — 1-COM/One.; EDITORIAL EQUIPMENT: Hardware — 1-COM/One. PRODUCTION EQUIPMENT: Hardware — 1-LE; Cameras — 1-LE.
Note: The New Albany Tribune (eS) has a combination rate of $23.62 with the Jeffersonville Evening News (e). Individual newspaper rates not made available.

NEW CASTLE

THE COURIER-TIMES

201 S 14th St, New Castle, Ind., 47362-3328, Henry; gen tel (765) 529-1111; adv tel (765) 575-4634; ed tel (765) 575-4651; gen fax (765) 529-1731; adv fax (765) 529-1731; ed fax (765) 529-1731; gen/nat adv e-mail information@thecouriertimes.com; disp adv e-mail information@thecouriertimes.com; class adv e-mailinformation@thecouriertimes.com; ed e-mail information@thecouriertimes.com; web site www.thecouriertimes.com
Group: Paxton Media Group, LLC
Published: Tues, Wed, Thur, Fri, Sun
Weekday Frequency: m
Circulation: 4,500; 4,500(sun)
Last Audit: Sworn/Estimate/Non-Audited September 30, 2017
Advertising Rate (weekday/saturday): Open inch rate $18.10
Advertising Rate (sunday): same
Online Advertising Rate: Leaderboard $275.00 CPM; Big Ad $225.00; Skyscraper $200.00; Middle Page Banner $150.00
News services: AP. **Established:** 1841
Own Printing Facility?: No
Commercial Printers?: Yes
Special Editions: Hope (good news) Edition, (Feb); Agriculture (March) Car Care (Mar); Graduation Tab (May); Football (Aug) Basketball (Nov); Her magazine (Quarterly March, June, Sept. Dec), Bargain Buddy coupon mag (monthly)
Special Weekly Sections: Neighbors (society) Sunday
Digital Platform - Mobile: Apple, Android, Blackberry
Digital Platform - Tablet: Apple iOS, Android
Neighbors Ed....................................Donna Cronk
Pub...Bob Hansen
Customer Service Specialist..........Hope Stevens
Home Delivery Mgr........................Shaun Adkins
Adv. Sales. Exec.............................Jayson Nunn
Editor..Katie Clontz
Adv. Sales Exec...............................Belinda Wise
Adv. Dir....................................Stacie Wrightsman
Market Information: TMC.
Mechanical Available: Web Offset; Black and 3 ROP colors; insert accepted; page cutoffs - 22 3/4.
Mechanical Specifications: Type page 13 x 21 1/2; E - 6 cols, 2 1/16, 1/8 between; A - 6 cols, 2 1/16, 1/8 between; C - 9 cols, 1 3/8, 1/16 between.
Areas Served: Henry County
Delivery Method: Mail, Newsstand, Carrier, RacksEquipment & Software: PRESSROOM EQUIPMENT: Lines — 5-G/Urbanite 1990; Press Drive — Fin/120hp; MAILROOM EQUIPMENT: Counter Stackers — 1-BG/Count-O-Veyor 108; Tying Machines — 1-Bu/20, 1-Bu/String Tyer, 1-Bu/Tape Wrapper; Address Machine — 1-Am/6341B.; BUSINESS EQUIPMENT: IBM/AS-400 CLASSIFIED EQUIPMENT: Hardware — 4-APP/iMAC, GCC/Elite 12/600; Printers — Okidata/3410; CLASSIFIED SOFTWARE: Baseview, Ad Manager Pro. DISPLAY EQUIPMENT: Hardware — 1-APP/Power Mac 7300, 2-APP/Power Mac G3, 1-APP/Mac IIci, 1-APP/Mac Color Classic; Printers — QMS/860, APP/Mac LaserPrinter II, APP/Mac Laser Writer 8500; DISPLAY SOFTWAREAd Make-up Applications — QPS/QuarkXPress 3.32.; EDITORIAL EQUIPMENT: Hardware — 1-APP/Power Mac 9500, 1-APP/Power Mac 8150, 1-APP/Power Mac 8100, 3-APP/Power Mac 7100, 4-APP/Power Mac 6100, 5-APP/Mac Quadra 630, 1-APP/Mac Quadra 605, 2-APP/Mac PowerBook 150, 2-APP/Mac PowerBook 190, 1-APP/Mac II; Printers — Xante/Accel-A-W PRODUCTION EQUIPMENT: Hardware — Caere/OmniPage 6.0; Cameras — 1-R/580; Scanners — AG/Studio STM, Microtek/ScanMaster IIXE, Minolta/Quick Scan 35, Nikon/Coolscan 2000 PRODUCTION SOFTWARE: QPS/QuarkXPress 3.32.

NOBLESVILLE

THE TIMES

920 Logan St, Noblesville, Ind., 46060-2261, Hamilton; gen tel (317) 773-9960; adv tel (317) 773-9960 ext. 117; ed tel (317) 773-9960 ext. 128; gen fax (317) 770-9376; gen/nat adv e-mail melissa@thetimes24-7.com; disp adv e-mail melissa@thetimes24-7.com; class adv e-mailmelissa@thetimes24-7.com; ed e-mail news@thetimes24-7.com; web site www.thetimes24-7.com
Group: Sagamore News Media
Published: Mon, Wed, Thur, Fri, Sat
Weekday Frequency: All day
Saturday Frequency: All day
Circulation: 5,000
Last Audit: Sworn/Estimate/Non-Audited October 1, 2017
Advertising Rate (weekday/saturday): Open inch rate $11 per column inch
News services: 1904
Own Printing Facility?: No
Commercial Printers?: No
Special Editions: Readers' Choice (Jan); Home Care (Spring); Car Care (Spring); Valentine's (Feb); Flag Day (Jul); 4-H Fair Preview and Results (Jul); Fall Festival Guide (Fall); Golf Guide; Christmas Gift Guide (Dec); Last-Minute Gift Guide (Dec).
Syndicated Publications: Hamilton County Sports Report
Advertising Director.....................Melissa Meme
Managing Editor........................Kevin Thompkins
Areas Served: 46030, 46031, 46032, 46033, 46034, 46037, 46038, 46060, 46061, 46062, 46069, 46074, 46082, 46085
Delivery Method: Mail, Newsstand, Racks

PERU

PERU TRIBUNE

26 W 3rd St, Peru, Ind., 46970-2155, Miami; gen tel (765) 473-6641; adv tel (765) 473-6641; ed tel (765) 473-6641; gen fax (765) 472-4438; adv fax (765) 472-4438; ed fax (765) 472-4438; gen/nat adv e-mail twest@perutribune.com; disp adv e-mail twest@perutribune.com; class adv e-mailclassifieds@perutribune.com; ed e-mail ptnews@perutribune.com; web site www.perutribune.com
Group: Paxton Media Group, LLC
Published: Tues, Wed, Thur, Fri, Sat, Sun
Weekday Frequency: m
Circulation: 3,600; 3,600(sat); 3,600(sun)
Last Audit: Sworn/Estimate/Non-Audited September 30, 2017
Advertising Rate (weekday/saturday): Open inch rate $20.70
Online Advertising Rate: Revamping Site: Call Tom Gray for more information
News services: AP. **Established:** 1921
Special Editions: Business Expo (Apr); This is Miami County (Aug); Christmas Gift Guides (Dec); Girls Basketball (Feb); Soil & Water (Jan); Circus (Jul); Softball Pages (Jun); Spring Farm (Mar); Mother's Day (May); Christmas Opening (Nov); Shopping with Santa (Oct).
Special Weekly Sections: Business Page (Mon); Milestones (Weddings, Engagements) (Sat); Food Page (Thur); School Page (Wed).
Syndicated Publications: Calendar (Annually); Channel Changer (Sat).
Bus. Mgr...................................Patricia Nelson
Adv. Dir...Misty Sharp
Circ. Supvr...Eric Steg
Mng. Ed.......................................Aaron Turner
News Ed....................................Laurie Kietaber
Sports Ed........................................Austan Kas
Pub....Tom Gray
Ed...Derek Beigh
Market Information: ADS; TMC.
Mechanical Available: Offset; Black and 3 ROP colors; insert accepted - single sheets, DOO sizes; page cutoffs - 22 3/4.
Mechanical Specifications: Type page 10 1/8 x 21 1/2; E - 6 cols, 1 5/8, 1/8 between; A - 6 cols, 1 5/8, 1/8 between; C - 9 cols, 1 1/16, 1/8 between.
Areas Served: Miami County
Delivery Method: Mail, Newsstand, Carrier, RacksEquipment & Software: PRESSROOM EQUIPMENT: Lines — 4-G/Urbanite; Folders — 1-G/2:1; MAILROOM EQUIPMENT: Tying Machines — 1/Bu, 1-/Plastic Strap; Address Machine — 1-/WM.; BUSINESS EQUIPMENT: IBM/AS-400 CLASSIFIED EQUIPMENT: Hardware — 2-HI/Micro-Store.; DISPLAY EQUIPMENT: Printers — APP/Mac LaserWriter, Xante; Other Hardware — AP AdScan, ALS AD Program, Claris/FileMaker Pro DISPLAY SOFTWAREAd Make-up Applications — Multi-Ad/Creator 3.5; Layout Software — APP/Mac. EDITORIAL EQUIPMENT: Hardware — APP/Mac; Printers — APP/Mac LaserWriters EDITORIAL SOFTWARE: Baseview/NewsEdit 3.1, QPS/QuarkXPress 3.3. PRODUCTION EQUIPMENT: Hardware — Multi-Ad/Creator 3.5, 2-APP/Mac PRODUCTION SOFTWARE: QPS/QuarkXPress.

PLYMOUTH

PILOT NEWS

214 N Michigan St, Plymouth, Ind., 46563-2135, Marshall; gen tel (574) 936-3101; adv tel (574) 936-3101; ed tel (574) 936-3101; gen fax (574) 936-7491; adv fax (574) 936-7491; ed fax (574) 936-3844; gen/nat adv e-mail cstockton@thepilotnews.com; disp adv e-mail cstockton@thepilotnews.com; class adv e-mailclass@thepilotnews.com; ed e-mail ghildebrand@thepilotnews.com; web site www.thepilotnews.com
Group: Heritage Publications (2003) Inc.
Published: Mon, Tues, Wed, Thur, Fri, Sat
Weekday Frequency: e
Saturday Frequency: m
Circulation: 4,100; 4,150(sat)
Last Audit: Sworn/Estimate/Non-Audited October 1, 2017
Advertising Rate (weekday/saturday): Open inch rate $11.75
News services: AP, SHNS. **Established:** 1851
Commercial Printers?: Yes
Special Weekly Sections: Entertainment; Sports; Pet ; Faces and Places
Syndicated Publications: Community Table-monthly
Proprietary Publications: The Bremen Enquirer, News-Mirror, The Culver Citizen, The Leader of Starke County, Advance News (Weekly)
Digital Platform - Mobile: Apple, Android
Digital Platform - Tablet: Apple iOS, Android
Managing Ed..............................Greg Hildebrand
Accounting Mgr.....................Michele Louderback
Adv. Mgr., Mktg...........................Cindy Stockton
Rusty Nixon
Market Information: TMC.
Mechanical Available: Offset; Black and 3 ROP colors; insert accepted; page cutoffs - 22 3/4.
Mechanical Specifications: Type page 13 x 21 1/2; E - 6 cols, 2 1/16, 1/8 between; A - 6 cols, 2 1/16, 1/8 between; C - 10 cols, 1 3/8, 1/16 between.
Areas Served: Marshall County
Delivery Method: Mail, Newsstand, Carrier, RacksEquipment & Software: MAILROOM EQUIPMENT: Tying Machines — 1/Bu; Address Machine — El/3101.; CLASSIFIED EQUIPMENT: Hardware — APP/Mac; CLASSIFIED SOFTWARE: Baseview. DISPLAY EQUIPMENT: Hardware — APP/Mac; DISPLAY SOFTWAREAd Make-up Applications — QPS/QuarkXPress.; EDITORIAL EQUIPMENT: Hardware — APP/Mac EDITORIAL SOFTWARE: Baseview. PRODUCTION EQUIPMENT: Hardware — HP/Laserjet 4, Xante/Accel-a-Writer; Cameras — 1-B/Caravel PRODUCTION SOFTWARE: QPS/QuarkXPress 3.3.

PORTLAND

THE COMMERCIAL REVIEW

309 W Main St, Portland, Ind., 47371-1803, Jay; gen tel (260) 726-8141; adv tel (260) 726-8144; gen fax (260) 726-8143; gen/nat adv e-mail cr.news@comcast.net; disp adv e-mail cr.ads@comcast.net; class adv e-mailcr.classifieds@comcast.net; ed e-mail cr.news@comcast.net; web site www.thecr.com
Group: Graphic Printing Co., Inc.
Published: Mon, Tues, Wed, Thur, Fri, Sat
Weekday Frequency: e
Saturday Frequency: m
Circulation: 4,000; 3,384(sat)
Last Audit: Sworn/Estimate/Non-Audited September 30, 2017
Advertising Rate (weekday/saturday): Open inch rate $11.45
Online Advertising Rate: Tiles on Rotation $25.00 CPM; w/ Copy Change Weekly $40.00 CPM; Banner/Homepage $50.00 CPM; w/ Copy Change Weekly $75.00 CPM
News services: AP. **Established:** 1871
Own Printing Facility?: Yes
Commercial Printers?: Yes
Special Editions: Spring Sports (Apr); Engine and Tractor Show (Aug); Christmas Greetings (Dec); New Cars (Feb); Brides (Jan); Swiss Days (Jul); Seniors (Jun); Spring Home Improvement (Mar); Graduation (May); Winter Sports (Nov); Harvest (Oct); Fall Home Improvement (Sept)
Special Weekly Sections: Best Food Days (Mon/Wed); Best Auto Day (Thur); Real Estate (Wed); Business (Sat); Church (Thur); TV Listings (Sat)
Syndicated Publications: American Profile (Sat).
Proprietary Publications: The News and Sun (Wed)
Digital Platform - Mobile: Apple, Android
Digital Platform - Tablet: Apple iOS, Android
Adv. Mgr., Promo............................Jeanne Lutz
Pub....Jack Ronald
Ed..Ray Cooney
Sports Ed......................................Chris Schanz
Reporter..................................Nathan Rubbelke
Reporter.......................................Caleb Bauer
Market Information: TMC.
Mechanical Available: Offset; Black and 3 ROP colors; insert accepted; page cutoffs - 22.
Mechanical Specifications: Type page 13 x 21 1/4; E - 6 cols, 2 1/16, 1/8 between; A - 6 cols, 2 1/16, 1/8 between; C - 8 cols, 1 1/2, 1/16 between.
Areas Served: 47371, 47373, 47326, 47336, 47369, 47381
Delivery Method: Mail, Newsstand, CarrierEquipment & Software: PRESSROOM EQUIPMENT: Lines — 5-G/Community (DEV Horizon Stack Unit); BUSINESS EQUIPMENT: IBM/PC-AT BUSINESS SOFTWARE: Great Plains CLASSIFIED EQUIPMENT: Hardware — APP/Mac; Printers — APP/Mac; CLASSIFIED SOFTWARE: Baseview. DISPLAY EQUIPMENT: Hardware — APP/Mac; Printers — APP/Mac LaserPrinter; DISPLAY SOFTWAREAd Make-up Applications — QPS/QuarkXPress.; EDITORIAL EQUIPMENT: Hardware — APP/Mac; Printers — APP/Mac EDITORIAL SOFTWARE: Baseview, QPS/QuarkXPress. PRODUCTION EQUIPMENT: Hardware — APP/Mac LaserPrinters, 1-B/30x40; Cameras — 1-R/20x24; Scanners — HP/ScanJet.

PRINCETON

PRINCETON DAILY CLARION

100 N Gibson St, Princeton, Ind., 47670-1855, Gibson; gen tel (812) 385-2525; adv tel (812) 385-2525; ed tel (812) 385-2525;

gen fax (812) 386-6199; adv fax (812) 386-6199; ed fax (812) 386-6199; gen/nat adv e-mail news@pdclarion.com; disp adv e-mail admail@pdclarion.com; class adv e-mailadmail@pdclarion.com; ed e-mail andrea@pdclarion.com; web site www.tristate-media.com
- 1,112,422(views) 173,974(visitors)
Group: Paxton Media Group, LLC
Published: Mon, Tues, Wed, Thur, Fri
Weekday Frequency: m
Circulation: 5,330
Last Audit: Sworn/Estimate/Non-Audited September 30, 2017
Advertising Rate (weekday/saturday): Open inch rate $14.50
Online Advertising Rate: Small leaderboard $125.00/month; Button $175.00/month; Pencil $200.00/month
News services: AP. **Established:** 1846
Own Printing Facility?: Yes
Commercial Printers?: Yes
Special Weekly Sections: Entertainment Page (Fri); Best Food Day (Mon); Business Page (Thur)
Syndicated Publications: Savvy lifestyle; Outdoor News (Hunting & Fishing).
Proprietary Publications: Today TMC (Mon).
Digital Platform - Mobile: Apple, Android
Digital Platform - Tablet: Apple iOS, Android, Kindle, Nook, Kindle Fire
Pub. .... Jeff Shumacher
Ed. .... Andrea Howe
Presentation Ed. .... Michael Caterina
Sports Ed. .... Pete Swanson
Bus. Mgr. .... Marietta Nelson
Accounting Mgr. .... Nancy Wilder
Admin. Asst, ... Lorri Rembe
Class. Adv. Mgr. .... Maggie Armstrong
Adv. Mgr. .... Lori Martin
Prod. Specialist .... Mark Short
Prod. Coord. .... Cindy Walton
Circl. Mgr. .... Rick Simmons
Distribution Mgr. .... Joe Vessels
Circ. Clerk .... Amanda Cooper
Creative Dept. Mgr. .... Jancey Smith
Graphic Designer .... Chad Phillips
Graphic Designer .... Madonna Smith
Graphic Designer .... Jason Hembree
Computer Specialist .... Ryan Spear
Market Information: ADS; TMC.
Mechanical Available: Offset; Black and 3 ROP colors; insert accepted; page cutoffs - 22 3/4.
Mechanical Specifications: Type page 12 x 21 1/2; E - 6 cols, 1 7/10, 1/6 between; A - 6 cols, 1 7/10, 1/6 between; C - 8 cols, 1 1/4, 1/6 between.
Areas Served: 47670, 47666, 47640,47648,47649,47665,47660,
Delivery Method: Mail, Newsstand, Carrier, RacksEquipment & Software: PRESSROOM EQUIPMENT: Lines — 8-G/Community.; BUSINESS EQUIPMENT: Qantel CLASSIFIED EQUIPMENT: Hardware — APP/Macs; CLASSIFIED SOFTWARE: Baseview. DISPLAY EQUIPMENT: Hardware — APP/Mac; DISPLAY SOFTWAREAd Make-up Applications — Multi-Ad/Creator.; EDITORIAL EQUIPMENT: Hardware — APP/Macs; Printers — Pre Press/Panther PRODUCTION EQUIPMENT: Hardware — APP/Mac LaserWriters, Pre Press/ Kodak CTP/Presteligence PRODUCTION SOFTWARE: QPS/QuarkXPress. CIRCULATION SOFTWARInterlink

RENSSELAER

RENSSELAER REPUBLICAN
117 N Van Rensselaer St, Rensselaer, Ind., 47978-2651, Jasper; gen tel (219) 866-5111; adv tel (219) 866-5111; ed tel (219) 866-5111; gen fax (219) 866-3775; adv fax (219) 866-3775; ed fax (219) 866-3775; gen/nat adv e-mail cindy@rensselaerrepublican.com; disp adv e-mail cindy@rensselaerrepublican.com; class adv e-mailclassifieds@rensselaerrepublican.com; ed e-mail editor@rensselaerrepublican.com; web site www.myrepublican.info
Group: Community Media Group
Published: Mon, Tues, Wed, Thur, Fri, Sat
Weekday Frequency: m
Saturday Frequency: m
Circulation: 2,049; 2,049(sat)
Last Audit: Sworn/Estimate/Non-Audited September 30, 2017
Advertising Rate (weekday/saturday): Open inch rate $15.90
Online Advertising Rate: Corner peel $100.00/ month; Popover $200.00/month; Window $300.00/month
News services: AP. **Established:** 1866
Special Editions: Football Preview (Aug); Spring Bridal (Feb); Business Established (Jan); Progress (Jun); Ag Day (Mar); Auto News (Monthly); Christmas Tab (Nov); Fall Home Improvement (Sept).
Special Weekly Sections: Church Page (Fri); Youth on the Move (Mon); Farm (Sat); Best Food Day (Thur); Business News (Tues); Farm (Wed).
Syndicated Publications: Final Score (Monthly); Farm Focus (Other).
Digital Platform - Mobile: Apple, Android
Digital Platform - Tablet: Apple iOS, Android, Kindle, Nook, Kindle Fire
Pub. .... Robert Blankenship
Graphics/Art .... Misty Longstreth
Sports Ed. .... Harley Tomlinson
Adv. Acct. Rep. .... Anita Padgett
Gen. Mgr. .... Greg Perrotto
Circ. .... Cyndi Grace
Front Desk/Class. .... Ashley Lawrence
Market Information: TMC; Zoned editions.
Mechanical Available: Offset; Black and 2 ROP colors; insert accepted; page cutoffs - 22 3/4.
Mechanical Specifications: Type page 13 x 21 1/2; E - 6 cols, 2, 1/4 between; A - 6 cols, 2, 1/4 between; C - 9 cols, 1/4 between.
Areas Served: Jasper County
Delivery Method: Mail, Newsstand, Carrier, RacksEquipment & Software: PRESSROOM EQUIPMENT: Lines — 5-HI/V-15D single width 1994; Folders — HI/JF-25; Reels & Stands — 5; MAILROOM EQUIPMENT: Counter Stackers — BG/Count-O-Veyor 08; Tying Machines — 1-EAM-Mosca/ Strapper, 1/Miller-Bevco/Strapper; Address Machine — 2-/Address-matic.; BUSINESS EQUIPMENT: 1-PC 386, 1-PC 486, APP/Mac LC III BUSINESS SOFTWARE: Lotus 1-2-3, Microsoft/Excel, Microsoft/Office, Listmaster CLASSIFIED EQUIPMENT: Hardware — 2-Ultra/486D-40; Printers — 2-Epson/ LQ 1170; CLASSIFIED SOFTWARE: Mk/Newscraft. DISPLAY EQUIPMENT: Hardware — 3-APP/Mac Quadra; Printers — APP/Mac LaserWriter 16 600 PS, APP/ Mac LaserWriter Pro 630; Other Hardware — 2-Quicktake/150 Camera, Microtek/ ScanMake DISPLAY SOFTWAREAd Make-up Applications — Multi-Ad 3.8, Adobe/ Photoshop 2.5.1, QPS/QuarkXPress 3.2, Broderbund/Typestyler 2.0; EDITORIAL EQUIPMENT: Hardware — 2-APP/Mac 610, 9-APP/Mac LC II; Printers — APP/ Mac LaserWriter Pro, APP/Mac LaserWriter IIg EDITORIAL SOFTWARE: Baseview/ NewsEdit 3.25, QPS/QuarkXPress 3.2. PRODUCTION EQUIPMENT: Hardware — Nu/FT40V2UP; Cameras — SCREEN/680-C; Scanners — Microtek/ScanMaker IIsp, Microtek/ScanMaker IIxe PRODUCTION SOFTWARE: QPS/QuarkXPress 3.2.

RICHMOND

PALLADIUM-ITEM
1175 N A St, Richmond, Ind., 47374-3226, Wayne; gen tel (765) 962-1575; adv tel (765) 973-4422; ed tel (765) 962-1575; gen fax (765) 973-4570; adv fax (765) 973-4420; ed fax (765) 973-4570; gen/nat adv e-mail sbrandle@richmond.gannett.com; disp adv e-mail dbutler@richmond.gannett.com; class adv e-mailbregister@pal-item.com; ed e-mail bguth@pal-item.com; web site www.pal-item.com
Group: Gannett
Published: Mon, Tues, Wed, Thur, Fri, Sat, Sun
Weekday Frequency: m
Saturday Frequency: m
Circulation: 7,943; 7,943(sat); 11,749(sun)
Last Audit: AAM June 30, 2017
Advertising Rate (weekday/saturday): Open inch rate $29.21
Advertising Rate (sunday): Open inch rate $38.71
Online Advertising Rate: Run of site: Leaderboard $7.00 CPM; Large Rectangle $8.00 CPM; Half-page $14.00 CPM
News services: AP, GNS. **Established:** 1831
Own Printing Facility?: Yes
Commercial Printers?: Yes
Special Editions: Progress (Apr); Newcomer's Community Guide (Aug); Bridal (Feb); Farm (Jan); Home Improvement (Jul); Home Improvement (Jun); Racing (May); Home Improvement (Sept).
Special Weekly Sections: Education (Mon); Automotive Sunday (S); Business (Sat); Entertainment (Thur); Farm (Wed).
Syndicated Publications: USA WEEKEND Magazine (S).
Digital Platform - Mobile: Apple, Android, Blackberry
Digital Platform - Tablet: Apple iOS, Android, Kindle, Nook, Kindle Fire
Sports Ed. .... Josh Chapin
Retail Adv. Mgr. .... Sharon Brandley
District Mgr. .... Ron Mason
District Mgr. .... Lori Shaver
Classified Sales Rep. .... Barb Register
Special Content Ed. .... Millie Martin
Online Ed. .... Jason Truitt
Circ. Dir. .... Cheryl Joyce
Market Information: TMC.
Mechanical Available: Offset; Black and 3 ROP colors; insert accepted - single sheets; page cutoffs - 22.
Mechanical Specifications: Type page 11 63/100 x 21; E - 6 cols, 2 1/16, 1/8 between; A - 6 cols, 1 5/6, 1/8 between; C - 9 cols, 1 6/25, 1/8 between.
Areas Served: Wayne County
Delivery Method: Mail, Newsstand, Carrier, RacksEquipment & Software: PRESSROOM EQUIPMENT: Lines — 18-G/Urbanite single width 1984; 4-HI/V15A-6%; Reels & Stands — G/2-Arm RTP.; MAILROOM EQUIPMENT: Counter Stackers — 1-PPK/Ministack, 2/ MM, 2-QWI/350, QWI/GC610; Inserters & Stuffers — 1-MM/EM 101, 1-GMA/SLS 1000; Tying Machines — 3-/MLN, 1-Sa/Twine, Power Strap, OVL; Wrapping Singles — 1-/ Sa; Address Machine — 1-/Barstrom, 1-/ Ch.; BUSINESS EQUIPMENT: IBM/AS-400 CLASSIFIED EQUIPMENT: Hardware — APT; Printers — HP; CLASSIFIED SOFTWARE: APT. DISPLAY EQUIPMENT: Hardware — CNI; Printers — GCC; DISPLAY SOFTWAREAd Make-up Applications — Multi-Ad/Creator 4.04, QPS/QuarkXPress 4.1, Adobe/Illustrator, Adobe/PhotoShop 5.0; Layout Software — CNI. EDITORIAL EQUIPMENT: Hardware — APT; Printers — HP EDITORIAL SOFTWARE: Microsoft/ Windows 95, Microsoft/Word, QPS/ QuarkXPress. PRODUCTION EQUIPMENT: Hardware — 3-Nu/Flip Top FT4OV6UPNS, 1-Anitec; Cameras — C/Spartan III; Scanners — 2-GEI/Copydot 1000, Lf/Leafscan 35, Umax/8 PRODUCTION SOFTWARE: QPS/ QuarkXPress.

ROCHESTER

THE ROCHESTER SENTINEL
118 E 8th St, Rochester, Ind., 46975-1508, Fulton; gen tel (574) 223-2111; adv tel (574) 224-5323; ed tel (574) 224-5327; gen fax (574) 223-5782; adv fax (574) 223-5782; ed fax (574) 223-5782; gen/nat adv e-mail advertising@rochsent.com; disp adv e-mail ads@rochsent.com; class adv e-mailclassads@rochsent.com; ed e-mail christinas@rochsent.com; web site www.rochsent.com
Group: The Sentinel Corp.
Published: Mon, Tues, Wed, Thur, Fri, Sat
Weekday Frequency: m
Saturday Frequency: m
Circulation: 3,800; 3,800(sat)
Last Audit: USPS October 1, 2015
Advertising Rate (weekday/saturday): Open inch rate $7.66; National ROP rate $10.18
Online Advertising Rate: Run of site $13.57 CPM
News services: AP, CNS, TMS. **Established:** 1858
Own Printing Facility?: No
Commercial Printers?: No
Special Editions: Agriculture (Jan); High School Football (Aug); Year-in-Review (Dec); Basketball (Feb); Taxes (Jan); 4-H Fair (Jul); Home, Lawn, Garden (Mar and Sept); Graduates (May); Christmas Shopping (Nov); Winter Car Care (Oct); Senior Lifestyle (Sept); Round Barn Festival (June); Chili Fest and Car Show (Oct).
Special Weekly Sections: TV Guide (Sat); Church Page.
Syndicated Publications: American Profile; Spry Living
Digital Platform - Mobile: Apple, Android
Digital Platform - Tablet: Apple iOS, Android
Pub. .... Sarah O. Wilson
Adv. Dir. .... Karen Vojtasek
Exec. Ed. .... William S. Wilson
Mng. Ed. .... Christina Seiler
Photo Dept. Mgr. .... Michael Kenny
Sports Ed. .... Val Tsoutsouris
Market Information: TMC.
Mechanical Available: Offset; Black and 3 ROP colors; insert accepted; page cutoffs - 22 1/2.
Mechanical Specifications: 22-inch web. 6 columns wide by 21.5 inches deep. 1 column: 1.58 inches wide or 9 picas 6 points. .. 6 columns: 10.126 inches wide or 60 picas 9 points.
Areas Served: 46975, 46939, 46910, 46912, 46931, 46945,46922
Delivery Method: Mail, Newsstand, RacksEquipment & Software: MAILROOM EQUIPMENT: Tying Machines — 1-Bu/169D.;

SEYMOUR

THE TRIBUNE
100 Saint Louis Ave, Seymour, Ind., 47274-2304, Jackson; gen tel (812) 522-4871; adv tel (812) 523-7052; ed tel (812) 523-7051; gen fax (812) 522-7691; adv fax (812) 522-7691; ed fax (812) 522-3371; gen/nat adv e-mail MBane@TribTown.com; disp adv e-mail BWalters@TribTown.com; class adv e-mailcotte@TribTown.com; ed e-mail awoods@hnenewspapers.com; web site www.tribtown.com
Published: Mon, Tues, Wed, Thur, Fri, Sat
Weekday Frequency: All day
Saturday Frequency: All day
Circulation: 8,951; 8,951(sat)
Last Audit: Sworn/Estimate/Non-Audited September 30, 2017
Advertising Rate (weekday/saturday): Open inch rate $13.84 (Local); $19.73 (National)
Online Advertising Rate: Run of Site $12.00 CPM; Run of Section $15.00 CPM; Run of Local $18.00 CPM
News services: AP, Freedom Wire, Knight Ridder **Established:** 1877
Own Printing Facility?: Yes
Commercial Printers?: No
Special Editions: Veteran's (Nov); Holidays (Dec)
Digital Platform - Mobile: Apple, Android
Digital Platform - Tablet: Apple iOS, Android
Pub. .... Chuck Wells
Bus. Mgr. .... Tammy Smith
Adv. Dir. .... Melissa Bane
Circ. Dir. .... Paul Hart
Ed. .... Dan Davis
Commun./Copy Ed. .... Joanne Persinger
Page Ed. .... Michael Brabley
Sports Ed. .... Zach Spicer
Sales Rep. .... Anita Emigh
Sales Rep. .... Jeremiah McCulley
Adv. Admin .... Barb Walters
Business Office .... Debbie Felix
Ops. Mgr. .... Gary McDonough
Ed. .... Aubrey Woods
Market Information: TMC.
Areas Served: Jackson County
Delivery Method: Mail, Newsstand, Carrier, RacksEquipment & Software: PRESSROOM EQUIPMENT: Lines — 4-G/Urbanite (retired);

SHELBYVILLE

THE SHELBYVILLE NEWS
123 E Washington St, Shelbyville, Ind., 46176-1463, Shelby; gen tel (317) 398-6631; adv tel (317) 398-1264; ed tel (317) 398-1270; gen fax (317) 398-0194; adv fax (317) 398-0194; ed fax (317) 398-0194; gen/nat adv e-mail rhonda@shelbynews.com; disp adv e-mail rhonda@shelbynews.com; class adv e-mailrhonda@shelbynews.com; ed e-mail pgable@shelbynews.com; web site

www.shelbynews.com
Group: Paxton Media Group, LLC
Published: Tues, Wed, Thur, Fri, Sun
Weekday Frequency: e
Saturday Frequency: m
Circulation: 8,315; 8,315(sat)
Last Audit: Sworn/Estimate/Non-Audited September 30, 2017
Advertising Rate (weekday/saturday): Open inch rate $18.40
Advertising Rate (sunday): Open inch rate $18.40
Online Advertising Rate: Weather Sponsor $3.00 CPM; Masthead $4.00 CPM; Stock Sponsor $6.00 CPM; Leaderboard $8.00 CPM
News services: AP Graphics, MCT, NEA, SHNS, AP. **Established:** 1947
Special Editions: Then & Now (Jul); Shelby County Fair (Jun); Class of 2013 (May); Home & Garden (Apr); Santa Letters and Coloring Book (Dec); Girls Sectional Preview (Feb); Health & Fitness (Jan); Back-to-School (Jul); Car Care (May); Holiday Gift Guide (Nov); Home Improvement (Oct); Shelby County Profiles (Sept).
Syndicated Publications: USA WEEKEND Magazine (Sat).
Digital Platform - Mobile: Apple, Android
Digital Platform - Tablet: Apple iOS, Android
Pub.. Rachael Raney
Sports Ed. .... Jeff Brown
Customer Service Rep.................. Kim Haggard
Ed... Paul Gable
Adv. Dir............................ Rhonda Schwegman
Adv. Acct. Exec........................... Melissa Smith
Adv. Acct. Exec........................... Ashly Spurlock
Circ. Dir. .... Jack Hutcheson
Single Copy Mgr. .... Anna Tungate
Market Information: TMC.
Mechanical Available: Offset; Black and 3 ROP colors; insert accepted; page cutoffs - 22 3/4.
Mechanical Specifications: Type page 10 1/8 x 21 1/2; E - 6 cols, 1 19/32, 1/8 between; A - 6 cols, 1 5/6, 1/8 between; C - 9 cols, 1 13/32, 1/8 between.
Areas Served: Shelby County
Delivery Method: Mail, Newsstand, Carrier, RacksEquipment & Software: PRESSROOM EQUIPMENT: Lines — 8-G/SSC, 1-G/SSC UOP single width; 2-G/SSC single width; 1-G/SSC UOP single width; Folders — 2-G/2:1; Pasters —2-Butler/Automatic. MAILROOM EQUIPMENT: Counter Stackers — 2-BG/105; Inserters & Stuffers — 6-KAN/320, 7-KAN/760; Tying Machines — 3/ Bu.; BUSINESS EQUIPMENT: APP/Mac, Baseview BUSINESS SOFTWARE: Great Plains, Baseview CLASSIFIED EQUIPMENT: Hardware — Baseview, APP/Mac; Printers — Lexmark/Optra; CLASSIFIED SOFTWARE: Baseview. DISPLAY EQUIPMENT: Hardware — APP/Power Macs; Printers — Lexmark/ Optra Rnt; Other Hardware — Iomega/ Jazz drive, Zip drive, JVC/CD-Rom recorder DISPLAY SOFTWAREAd Make-up Applications — QPS, Multi-Ad/Creator, Aldus/Freehand, Adobe/Photoshop, Adobe/ Illustrator; Layout Software — Multi-Ad/ALS 2.0.2. EDITORIAL EQUIPMENT: Hardware — Baseview, APP/Mac; Printers — Lexmark/ Optra RN Plus EDITORIAL SOFTWARE: Baseview. PRODUCTION EQUIPMENT: Hardware — Caere/OmniPage Pro 6, 2-Harlequin/RIP, Pre Press/Panther Pro 46 with Ap Power Mac 8500 PC RIP, Kk/RFS; Cameras — SCREEN/C680-C; Scanners — Kk/RFS 2035, AG/Arcus, Umax/PowerBook, Nikon/LS1000 PRODUCTION SOFTWARE: QPS/QuarkXPress 4.1.

SOUTH BEND

SOUTH BEND TRIBUNE

225 W Colfax Ave, South Bend, Ind., 46626-1000, St Joseph; gen tel (574) 235-6222; adv tel (574) 235-6221; ed tel (574) 235-6161; gen fax (574) 239-2648; adv fax (574) 239-2648; ed fax (574) 236-1765; gen/nat adv e-mail jherum@sbtinfo.com; disp adv e-mail jherum@sbtinfo.com; class adv e-mailclassifieds@sbtinfo.com; ed e-mail letters@sbtinfo.com; web site www.southbendtribune.com
Group: Schurz Communications Inc
Published: Mon, Tues, Wed, Thur, Fri, Sat, Sun
Weekday Frequency: m
Saturday Frequency: m
Circulation: 35,702; 40,098(sat); 48,595(sun)
Last Audit: AAM March 31, 2017
Advertising Rate (weekday/saturday): Open inch rate $56.00
Advertising Rate (sunday): Open inch rate $67.00
Online Advertising Rate: ROS $10.00; Homepage $15.00; Section Takeover $500/day; Homepage Takeover $860/day
News services: AP, SHNS, PR Newswire. **Established:** 1872
Special Editions: ND Insider (Fri)
Special Weekly Sections: Faith (Fri); Food Focus (Mon); Automotion (S); Farming (Sat); Family (Tues); Our Health (Wed).
Syndicated Publications: TV Magazine (S).
Digital Platform - Mobile: Apple, Android
Digital Platform - Tablet: Apple iOS, Android
VP, Operations................................ Kevin Shaw
Exec. Ed... Alan Achkar
Local Adv. Agr. .... Peggy Bassier
Classified, Adv. Mgr.......................... Mary Zenor
INTHEBEND.COM Ed. .... Jennifer Ellis
HR BUSINESS PARTNER
Ed Henry
Sr. VP., Gen. Mgr........................... Sally Brown
Controller .... Carol Shultz
VP, Adv... Shelley Chakan
Market Information: ADS; Split run; TMC; Zoned editions.
Mechanical Available: Anilox Keyless Offset; Black and 3 ROP colors; insert accepted; page cutoffs - 21 3/16.
Mechanical Specifications: Type page 13 x 22 1/4; E - 6 cols, 2 1/16, 1/8 between; A - 6 cols, 2 1/16, 1/8 between; C - 10 cols, 1 3/16, 1/16 between.
Areas Served: St. Joseph County, Cass, Lagrange, Elkhart, Marshall, Fulton, Pulaski, Starke, LaPorte, Berrien, Kosclusko
Delivery Method: Mail, Newsstand, CarrierEquipment & Software: PRESSROOM EQUIPMENT: Lines — 20-KBA/Anilox Keyless Offset double width 1994; Folders — 1-KBA/gear, 2-KBA/jaw; Control System — 1994; MAILROOM EQUIPMENT: Counter Stackers — 6-S; Inserters & Stuffers — 2-Fg/ Drum 6:1, HI 630 13:1; Tying Machines — 6-MVP/5000, 6-MVP/2000; BUSINESS EQUIPMENT: 1-DEC/VAX 4000-300, 1-DEC/ VAX 400-705 BUSINESS SOFTWARE: GEAC, CIS 7.05, AIM 8.02H CLASSIFIED EQUIPMENT: Hardware — Compaq/Alpha-NT; CLASSIFIED SOFTWARE: Compuclass. DISPLAY EQUIPMENT: Hardware — 8-APP/ Mac, 3-PC, Compaq/Alpha-NT; Printers — V/600dpi, X/VP300 Proofer, III/VP600 Proofer, Tektronix/Phaser 300, color proofer, HP/755; DISPLAY SOFTWAREAd Make-up Applications — AD-Tracker; Layout Software — AD-Tracker. EDITORIAL EQUIPMENT: Hardware — Compaq/Alpha-NT EDITORIAL SOFTWARE: Dewar. PRODUCTION EQUIPMENT: Hardware — 3-III/3850 Negative Output Devices, 2-Linotype-Hell/ Lino 530; Cameras — 2-C/Marathon, 1-K/ v241; Scanners — 1-III/Infoscan 3725, 1-ScanView/ScanMate 5000, Horizon/Flatbed PRODUCTION SOFTWARE: Dewar.

SPENCER

SPENCER EVENING WORLD

114 E Franklin St, Spencer, Ind., 47460-1818, Owen; gen tel (812) 829-2255; gen fax (812) 829-4666; gen/nat adv e-mail kim@spencereveningworld.com; disp adv e-mail editor@spencereveningworld.com; class adv e-maileditor@spencereveningworld.com; ed e-mail editor@spencereveningworld.com; web site www.spencereveningworld.com
Group: Spencer Evening World Publishing, Inc.
Published: Mon, Tues, Wed, Thur, Fri
Weekday Frequency: m
Circulation: 3,590
Last Audit: Sworn/Estimate/Non-Audited December 12, 2017
News services: 1927
Own Printing Facility?: Yes
Commercial Printers?: Yes
Digital Platform - Mobile: Apple, Android
Digital Platform - Tablet: Apple iOS, Android
Market Information: TMC.
Mechanical Available: Offset; Black and 2 ROP colors; insert accepted; page cutoffs - 22 3/4.
Mechanical Specifications: Type page 15 1/8 x 21; E - 7 cols, 2 1/16, 1/8 between; A - 7 cols, 2 1/16, 1/8 between; C - 7 cols, 2 1/16, 1/8 between.
Areas Served: Owen County
Delivery Method: Mail, Newsstand, Carrier, RacksEquipment & Software: PRESSROOM EQUIPMENT: Lines — 4-G/Community.; MAILROOM EQUIPMENT: Tying Machines — 1-Bu/29480; Address Machine — 1-El/300; PRODUCTION EQUIPMENT: Hardware — 2-APP/Mac Laser, 1-B/2500; Cameras — 1-K/240, 1-R; Scanners — Microtek.

SULLIVAN

THE SULLIVAN DAILY TIMES

115 W Jackson St, Sullivan, Ind., 47882-1505, Sullivan; gen tel (812) 268-6356; adv tel (812) 268-6356; ed tel (812) 268-6356; gen fax (812) 268-3110; adv fax (812) 268-3110; ed fax (812) 268-3110; gen/nat adv e-mail ads.sdt@gmail.com ; disp adv e-mail ads2.sdt@gmail.com; class adv e-mailsdt.classifieds@gmail.com; ed e-mail editor.sdt@gmail.com; web site www.sullivan-times.com
Group: Pierce Publishing, Inc.
Published: Mon, Tues, Wed, Thur, Fri
Weekday Frequency: e
Circulation: 4,115
Last Audit: Sworn/Estimate/Non-Audited September 30, 2017
Advertising Rate (weekday/saturday): Open inch rate $8.25
News services: AP. **Established:** 1854
Special Editions: Bridal (Jan); SWCD Report (Feb); Spring Home & Garden (Mar); Spring Car Care (Apr); Graduation (May); 4-H Fair Preview (Jul); Corn Festival Preview (Sept); Christmas Shopping (Nov); Letters to Santa (Dec)
Special Weekly Sections: Religion (Fri); Agriculture (Mon); Nostalgia (Thur); Business (Tues); Opinion (Wed).
Syndicated Publications: Senior (Citizen) Informant (Monthly); TV Times (Thur).
Digital Platform - Mobile: Apple, Android
Digital Platform - Tablet: Apple iOS, Android
Bus. Mgr. .... Patricia Morgan
Sports Ed. .... Aaron Kennedy
Classifieds..................................... Jamie Isbell
Adv. Rep. .... Sarah Smith
Adv. Rep.... Gillian Kelk
Graphic Artist/Composing................ Doug Smith
Circ., Local Happenings .... Darcy O'Dell
Ed.. Andrew Krull
Pub. .... Gillan Kelk
Market Information: TMC.
Mechanical Available: Offset; Black and 2 ROP colors; insert accepted; page cutoffs - 21.
Mechanical Specifications: Type page 13 3/8 x 21; E - 6 cols, 2 1/12, 1/6 between; A - 6 cols, 2 1/12, 1/6 between; C - 6 cols, 2 1/12, 1/6 between.
Areas Served: Sullivan County
Delivery Method: Newsstand, Carrier, RacksEquipment & Software: PRESSROOM EQUIPMENT: Lines — 4-HI/V-15A 1973; Folders — HI/J-7.; MAILROOM EQUIPMENT: Tying Machines — Sa.; BUSINESS EQUIPMENT: PC 386 DX, PC 286 BUSINESS SOFTWARE: Synaptic/ Micro Solutions CLASSIFIED EQUIPMENT: Hardware — 5-Pentium/PC; CLASSIFIED SOFTWARE: SunType, QPS/QuarkXPress, Adobe/PhotoShop. DISPLAY EQUIPMENT: Hardware — APP/Mac 8000, APP/Mac Scanner; Printers — Xante/11x17; DISPLAY SOFTWAREAd Make-up Applications — Advent/3B2, Archetype/Corel Draw, QPS/ QuarkXPress, Adobe/Photoshop; Layout Software — APP/Power Mac 7100, APP/ PowerMac 7100. EDITORIAL EQUIPMENT: Hardware — 4-APP/iMac, PC 486, PC 386 DX; Printers — Xante/11x17 EDITORIAL SOFTWARE: SunType, QPS/QuarkXPress, Adobe/Photoshop. PRODUCTION EQUIPMENT: Cameras — R/500; Scanners — APP/Mac PRODUCTION SOFTWARE: QPS/QuarkXPress, Adobe/PhotoShop.

TERRE HAUTE

THE TRIBUNE STAR

222 S 7th St, Terre Haute, Ind., 47807-3601, Vigo; gen tel (812) 231-4200; adv tel (812) 231-4226; ed tel (812) 231-4336; gen fax (812) 231-4347; adv fax (812) 231-4234; ed fax (812) 231-4321; gen/nat adv e-mail erin.powell@tribstar.com; disp adv e-mail erin.powell@tribstar.com; class adv e-mailamanda.davis@tribstar.com; ed e-mail max.jones@tribstar.com; web site www.tribstar.com
- 819,702(views) 183,276(visitors)
Group: Community Newspaper Holdings, Inc.
Published: Mon, Tues, Wed, Thur, Fri, Sat, Sun
Weekday Frequency: m
Saturday Frequency: m
Circulation: 13,827; 13,827(sat); 17,338(sun)
Last Audit: AAM March 31, 2016
Advertising Rate (weekday/saturday): Open inch rate $26.25
Advertising Rate (sunday): Open inch rate $26.25
Online Advertising Rate: Basic $375.00/month; Prominent $480.00/month; Dominant $645.00/month
News services: AP, MCT. **Established:** 1983
Own Printing Facility?: Yes
Commercial Printers?: Yes
Special Weekly Sections: Entertainment (Fri); Best Food Day (Mon); Religion (Sat); Education (Wed).
Syndicated Publications: Terre Haute Living (Bi-Monthly); Valley Homes Tab (Fri); Parade (S).
Digital Platform - Mobile: Apple, Android
Digital Platform - Tablet: Apple iOS, Android, Blackberry Tablet OS, Kindle
Pub... B.J. Riley
Adv. Dir... Robert Miller
Mktg. Dir................................. Courtney Zellars
Circ. Mgr., Single Copy .... Kyle Poorman
Ed... Max Jones
Columnist...................................... Mark Bennett
News Ed....................................... Susan Duncan
Online Ed. .... Sheila K. Ter Meer
Sports Ed. .... Todd Golden
Prod. Dir. .... Brian Lane
News/Digital Ed. .... Alicia Morgan
Chief Photographer...................... Joseph Garza
Adv. Dir... Erin Powell
Marketing Mgr................................. Amy Francis
Marketing Mgr............................ Dianne Hadley
Adv. Sales Exec. .... Nikki Robinson
Adv. Sales Exec............................... Lynn Smith
Adv. Sales Exec............................ Mike Sullivan
Adv. Sales Exec........................ Courtney Zellers
Customer Service Mgr............. Michelle Poorman
District Mgr. .... Tad Wesley
Credit Mgr. .... Vicki Woodcock
Prod. Mgr... Tony Sciotto
Controller .... Jerry Bringle
District Mgr. .... Mark McGranahan
Market Information: ADS; TMC.
Mechanical Available: Offset; Black and 3 ROP colors; insert accepted; page cutoffs - 22 3/4.
Mechanical Specifications: Type page 11 3/4 x 21 1/2; E - 6 cols, 1 5/6, 1/8 between; A - 6 cols, 1 5/6, 1/8 between; C - 9 cols, 1 5/6, 1/16 between.
Areas Served: Vigo, Clay, Sullivan, Greene, Parke, and Vermillion in Indiana and Edgar, Clark, and Crawford in Illinois.
Delivery Method: Mail, Newsstand, Carrier, RacksEquipment & Software: PRESSROOM EQUIPMENT: Lines — 10-G/Urbanite 1978; Reels & Stands — 4; MAILROOM EQUIPMENT: Counter Stackers — 2-Id/2000; Inserters & Stuffers — 1-GMA/SLS 1000, 1-GMA/SLS 2000 12:1; Tying Machines — 2-Dynaric/NP2; Address Machine — 1/ Ch.; BUSINESS EQUIPMENT: HP/9000 BUSINESS SOFTWARE: PBS CLASSIFIED EQUIPMENT: Hardware — DEC, APP/MAC; CLASSIFIED SOFTWARE: CText/Classified Advertising System, Baseview/Ad Manager Pro. DISPLAY EQUIPMENT: Hardware — APP/Mac; DISPLAY SOFTWAREAd Make-up Applications — Managing Editor/ALS, QPS/ QuarkXPress; Layout Software — APP/ Mac. EDITORIAL EQUIPMENT: Hardware — DEC, APP/Mac EDITORIAL SOFTWARE: CText/AFM, Baseview, Baseview/NewsEdit Pro I Que. PRODUCTION EQUIPMENT: Hardware — X, Pre Press/Panther Pro, Pre Press/Panther Pro 46; Cameras — 1-B/1822, 1-LC/21121; Scanners — 1-Lf/Leafscan 35,

1-Sharp/JX600, 2-Nikon/Super Coolscan, 2-Polaroid/SprintScan 35 PRODUCTION SOFTWARE: QPS/QuarkXPress.

TIPTON

TIPTON COUNTY TRIBUNE

116 S Main St, Ste A, Tipton, Ind., 46072-1864, Tipton; gen tel (765) 675-2115; adv tel (765) 675-2115; ed tel (765) 675-2115; gen fax (765) 675-4147; adv fax (765) 675-4147; ed fax (765) 675-4147; gen/nat adv e-mail tiptontribune@elwoodpublishing.com; disp adv e-mail tiptoneditor@elwoodpublishing.com; class adv e-mailtiptoneditor@elwoodpublishing.com; ed e-mail tiptoneditor@elwoodpublishing.com; web site www.elwoodpublishing.com
Group: Ray Barnes Newspapers, Inc.
Published: Mon, Tues, Wed, Thur, Fri, Sat
Weekday Frequency: e
Saturday Frequency: m
Circulation: 5,200; 2,816(sat)
Last Audit: Sworn/Estimate/Non-Audited September 30, 2017
Advertising Rate (weekday/saturday): Open inch rate $6.50
Online Advertising Rate: Position A $25.00 per week; Position B $20.00 per week; Position C $10.00 per week
News services: AP. **Established:** 1825
Special Editions: Farm & Garden (Apr); Football Preview (Aug); Mature Years (Jan); Mature Years (Jul); Spring Brides (Mar); Spring Home Improvement (May); Christmas Opening (Nov); Fall Home Improvement (Oct).
Syndicated Publications: Kid's Scoop (Other).
Pub... Robert L. Nash
Managing Ed. ....Jackie Henry
Sports Ed. .... Michelle Garmon
Prod. Mgr......................................Randy Bayne
Pres...Jack Barnes
Circ. Mgr......................................Tammy Boyer
Adv. Mgr. ....Lori Nash
Market Information: ADS; TMC.
Mechanical Available: Web Offset; Black and 3 ROP colors; insert accepted; page cutoffs - 22 3/4.
Mechanical Specifications: Type page 13 x 21 1/2; E - 6 cols, 2 1/16, 1/8 between; A - 6 cols, 2 1/16, 1/8 between; C - 8 cols, 1 1/2, 1/32 between.
Areas Served: 46072, 46076, 46036, 46047, 46068
Delivery Method: Mail, Newsstand, Carrier, RacksEquipment & Software: PRESSROOM EQUIPMENT: Lines — 4-G/Community; MAILROOM EQUIPMENT: Tying Machines — 1/Malow, 1-/Bu.; BUSINESS EQUIPMENT: 1-Bs/B-20, 1-RSK/TRS 80 model 4 CLASSIFIED EQUIPMENT: Hardware — Mk/1100; CLASSIFIED SOFTWARE: Mk/Mycro-Comp. DISPLAY SOFTWARELayout Software — 2-APP/Mac SE. EDITORIAL EQUIPMENT: Hardware — Mk/1100 EDITORIAL SOFTWARE: Mk/Mycro-Comp. PRODUCTION EQUIPMENT: Hardware — 2-APP/Mac LaserWriter II NT/NTX; Cameras — 1-R/Commodore.

VINCENNES

VINCENNES SUN-COMMERCIAL

702 Main St, Vincennes, Ind., 47591-2910, Knox; gen tel (812) 886-9955; gen fax (812) 885-2237; adv fax (812) 885-2237; gen/nat adv e-mail retail@suncommercial.com; disp adv e-mail retail@suncommercial.com; class adv e-mailclassified@suncommercial.com; ed e-mail grobbins@suncommercial.com; web site www.suncommercial.com
Group: Paxton Media Group, LLC
Published: Tues, Wed, Thur, Fri, Sat, Sun
Weekday Frequency: m
Saturday Frequency: m
Circulation: 4,867; 4,867(sat); 5,387(sun)
Last Audit: Sworn/Estimate/Non-Audited September 30, 2017
Advertising Rate (weekday/saturday): Open inch rate $17.75
Advertising Rate (sunday): 19.67
Online Advertising Rate: $350 Flat rate for one month (leaderboard)
News services: AP. **Established:** 1804
Own Printing Facility?: No
Commercial Printers?: Yes
Special Editions: Bridal Planner (Jan.) Farm Review (Feb) Spring Home & Garden (March) Dining Guide (April, August) Knox County Fair (July) Vincennes University Campus guide (Aug.) Readers Choice (Aug.) Progress (Oct.) Christmas Gift Guide (Nov.)
Special Weekly Sections: TV Guide (Sunday) Wabash Valley NOW (Wed)
Syndicated Publications: Spry, American Profile, USA Weekend, Antholon
Pub...Gayle Robbins
Adv. Dir... Kim Gordon
Acct. Exec. .... Veronica Gordon
Sports...Tom Graham
Sports...Rodney Lopez
Dis. Mgr...................................... David Adkins
Reporter ....Jess Cohen
Market Information: Wabash Valley NOW Wednesday delivery to nonsubscribers
Mechanical Available: Offset; Black and 3 ROP colors; insert accepted; page cutoffs - 22 3/4.
Mechanical Specifications: 6 col broadsheet format. 21.375 depth
1 col 1.6225, 2 col 3.375, 3 col 5.125, 4 col 6.875, 5 col 8.625, 6 col 10.375
Areas Served: Vincennes, IN/Knox County, IN/Lawrence County, IL
Delivery Method: Mail, Newsstand, Carrier, RacksEquipment & Software: PRESSROOM EQUIPMENT: Lines — 5-G/Urbanite (2 balloon formers) 1968; MAILROOM EQUIPMENT: Tying Machines — Bu.; BUSINESS EQUIPMENT: 1-IBM/Sys 36 BUSINESS SOFTWARE: In-house CLASSIFIED EQUIPMENT: Hardware — APP/Mac;PC CLASSIFIED SOFTWARE: Baseview/Clas
Indesign DISPLAY EQUIPMENT: Hardware — APP/Mac;PC DISPLAY SOFTWAREAd Make-up Applications — Multi-Ad/Creator, QPS/QuarkXPress 3.1.; EDITORIAL EQUIPMENT: Hardware — APP/Mac/SCS/Linx EDITORIAL SOFTWARE: Baseview/NewsEdit, Baseview/Wire Manager. PRODUCTION EQUIPMENT: Hardware — 1-Nat/330, Nikon, Adobe/Photoshop; Cameras — 1-R/500.

WABASH

WABASH PLAIN DEALER

123 W Canal St, Wabash, Ind., 46992-3042, Wabash; gen tel 260.563.2131; adv tel (260) 225-4949; ed tel (260) 225-4602; gen fax 260.563.0816; adv fax (260) 563-0816; ed fax (260) 563-0816; gen/nat adv e-mail kgretschmann@wabashplaindealer.com; disp adv e-mail kgretschmann@wabashplaindealer.com; class adv e-mailcsmith@wabashplaindealer.com; ed e-mail news@wabashplaindealer.com; web site www.wabashplaindealer.com - 99,660(views)
Group: Paxton Media Group, LLC
Published: Tues, Wed, Thur, Fri, Sun
Weekday Frequency: m
Saturday Frequency: m
Circulation: 3,000; 3,000(sun)
Last Audit: Sworn/Estimate/Non-Audited September 30, 2017
Advertising Rate (weekday/saturday): Both - varies
Advertising Rate (sunday): Both - varies
Online Advertising Rate: Weather Sponsor $175.00/month; Rail Top,Tile Top $200.00/month; Leaderboard Middle $300.00/month; Leaderboard Top $400.00/month
News services: AP **Established:** 1859
Own Printing Facility?: Yes
Commercial Printers?: Yes
Special Editions: Spring Home Improvement (Mar); Valentine's Day (Feb); Spring Working the Land (Mar); Wabash County 4-H Fair (Jul); Bridal Guide (Feb); Fall Home Improvement (Sept); Fall Working the Land (Sept); Reader's Choice (May)
Special Weekly Sections: Entertainment (Tue), North Manchester (Wed), Food (Thu), Worship (Fri), Business and Milestones (Sun)
General Sales Manager......... Kelly Gretschmann
Advertising Account Executive .... Cindy Brown
Managing Editor ....Eric Seaman
Customer Service Rep/Legals Clerk Christy Smith
Reporter.................................Makenzie Holland
Reporter...............................Mackenzi Klemann
Sports Editor.................................. Jacob Rude
Market Information: ADS; TMC.
Mechanical Available: Offset; Black and 3 ROP colors; insert accepted; page cutoffs - 22 3/4.
Areas Served: LaFontaine, Lagro, North Manchester, Roann, Urbana, Wabash, Somerset
Delivery Method: Mail, Newsstand, Carrier, RacksEquipment & Software: PRESSROOM EQUIPMENT: Lines — 4-G/Urbanite; Folders — 1, 1-G/Quarter.; MAILROOM EQUIPMENT: Counter Stackers — 1/BG; Tying Machines — 3-/Bu.; CLASSIFIED EQUIPMENT: Hardware — APP/Mac; Printers — APP/Mac; CLASSIFIED SOFTWARE: Baseview. DISPLAY EQUIPMENT: Hardware — APP/Mac; DISPLAY SOFTWAREAd Make-up Applications — QPS/QuarkXPress, Multi-Ad.; EDITORIAL EQUIPMENT: Hardware — APP/Mac EDITORIAL SOFTWARE: QPS/QuarkXPress. PRODUCTION EQUIPMENT: Hardware — 2-Nu, 1-ECR; Cameras — 1-R PRODUCTION SOFTWARE: QPS/QuarkXPress.

WARSAW

TIMES-UNION

123 E Market St, Corner Market and Indiana St, Warsaw, Ind., 46580-2807, Kosciusko; gen tel (574) 267-3111; adv tel (574) 267-3111; ed tel (574) 267-3111; gen fax (574) 267-7784; adv fax (574) 268-1300; ed fax (574) 267-7784; gen/nat adv e-mail advertising@timesuniononline.com; disp adv e-mail advertising@timesuniononline.com; class adv e-mailclassified@timesuniononline.com; ed e-mail news@timesuniononline.com; web site www.timesuniononline.com - 237,765(views) 58,786(visitors)
Published: Mon, Tues, Wed, Thur, Fri, Sat
Weekday Frequency: e
Saturday Frequency: m
Circulation: 7,116; 7,570(sat)
Last Audit: CAC June 30, 2017
Advertising Rate (weekday/saturday): Open inch rate $11.20(Local); $13.20 (National)
Online Advertising Rate: Bottom Banner $99.00/month; Sub section sponsor $109.00/month; Tile #3 $149.00/month; Search Sponsor $159.00/month
News services: AP, AP Laserphoto, MCT, NEA, SHNS. **Established:** 1854
Own Printing Facility?: Yes
Commercial Printers?: No
Special Editions: Home Improvement (Apr); Holiday Wrap-Up (Dec); Girls' Sectional Preview (Feb); Halftimes (Jan); Customer Appreciation Week (Jul); Holiday Gift Guide (Nov); Home Improvement (Sept).
Special Weekly Sections: Business (Sat); Home & Auto (Sat) Education Pages (Tue) Leisure (Thur); Farm Page (Wed).
Digital Platform - Mobile: Apple, Android, Windows
Digital Platform - Tablet: Apple iOS, Android, Windows 7
Gen. Mgr........................................ Gary Gerard
Classified Supervisor .... Laura Sowers
IT Dir./Circ. Mgr............................... David Hays
Prod. Dir. ....Gary Kunkle
Comptroller..........................Jessica Rodriguez
Advertising Manager......................... Paul Smith
Market Information: TMC.
Mechanical Available: Offset; Black and 3 ROP colors; insert accepted - all; page cutoffs - 21.
Mechanical Specifications: Type page 11 5/8 x 21; E - 6 cols, 1 5/6, 1/8 between; A - 6 cols, 1 5/6, 1/8 between; C - 9 cols, 1 1/6, 1/8 between.
Areas Served: 46502, 46508, 46510, 46524, 46538, 46539, 46542, 46555, 46562, 46566, 46567, 46580, 46581, 46582, 46590, 46982
Delivery Method: Mail, Newsstand, Carrier, RacksEquipment & Software: PRESSROOM EQUIPMENT: Lines — 6-G/Urbanite 1974; MAILROOM EQUIPMENT: Counter Stackers — 1-Rima-Harris/RS-2510; Inserters & Stuffers — MM/227E 5-into-1; Tying Machines — 2/Bu; Address Machine — 1-/Am, 1-/El.; BUSINESS EQUIPMENT: IBM CLASSIFIED EQUIPMENT: Hardware — 4-iMac; Printers — Xante ZM4 CTP Pre Press/Panther Pro Imagesetter 46; CLASSIFIED SOFTWARE: Baseview. DISPLAY EQUIPMENT: Hardware — 6-Mac; Printers — Xante 3E; DISPLAY SOFTWAREAd Make-up Applications — Multi-Ad/Creator, Aldus/FreeHand 8.0.; EDITORIAL EQUIPMENT: Hardware — 15-Mac, 2-Mac G4, 1-Mac G3/Pre Press/Panther Pro Imagesetter 46; Printers — APP/Mac LaserWriter II, Xante/G3 EDITORIAL SOFTWARE: QPS/QuarkXPress 4.1, Adobe/Photoshop. PRODUCTION EQUIPMENT: Hardware — 1-Nu/Ultra-Plus; Cameras — 1-Nu/2024SST PRODUCTION SOFTWARE: QPS/QuarkXPress 4.1, Adobe/Photoshop 5.5.

WINCHESTER

THE NEWS-GAZETTE

224 W Franklin St, Winchester, Ind., 47394-1808, Randolph; gen tel (765) 584-4501; adv tel (765) 584-4501; ed tel (765) 584-4501; gen fax (765) 584-3066; adv fax (765) 584-3066; ed fax (765) 584-3066; disp adv e-mail ngadvertising@comcast.net; class adv e-mailngadvertising@comcast.net; ed e-mail ngeditor@comcast.net; web site www.winchesternewsgazette.com
Group: Community Media Group
Published: Mon, Tues, Wed, Thur, Fri, Sat
Weekday Frequency: e
Saturday Frequency: m
Circulation: 3,700; 3,700(sat)
Last Audit: Sworn/Estimate/Non-Audited September 30, 2017
Advertising Rate (weekday/saturday): Open inch rate $12.00
News services: AP. **Established:** 1873
Own Printing Facility?: Yes
Commercial Printers?: Yes
Special Weekly Sections: Church (Fri); Farm (Sat); Business Salute (Tues).
Syndicated Publications: American Profile (Weekly).
Proprietary Publications: Red Ball Express
Digital Platform - Mobile: Apple, Android
Digital Platform - Tablet: Apple iOS, Android
Circ. Mgr..................................... Diane Jackson
Prod. Mgr..................................... Lesa Hawkins
Mng. Ed./Sports Ed. ....Rick Reed
City Ed. .... Bill Richmond
Press Room Mgr. ....Dale Byrd
Market Information: TMC; Zoned editions.
Mechanical Available: Offset; Black and 3 ROP colors; insert accepted; page cutoffs - 22 3/4.
Mechanical Specifications: Type page 13 x 21 1/2; E - 6 cols, 2 1/14, 1/8 between; A - 6 cols, 2 1/14, 1/8 between; C - 10 cols, 1 1/5, 1/6 between.
Areas Served: Randolph County
Delivery Method: Mail, Newsstand, Carrier, RacksEquipment & Software: PRESSROOM EQUIPMENT: Lines — 5-G/Community 1973; MAILROOM EQUIPMENT: Tying Machines — 2-Bu/String Tyer; Address Machine — 2/Am.; BUSINESS SOFTWARE: Microsoft/Office, Listmaster CLASSIFIED EQUIPMENT: Hardware — APP/Mac 605; Printers — APP/Mac LaserWriter Pro 630; CLASSIFIED SOFTWARE: Baseview. DISPLAY EQUIPMENT: Hardware — APP/Mac 610; Printers — APP/Mac LaserWriter Pro 630; DISPLAY SOFTWARELayout Software — Multi-Ad, QPS/QuarkXPress, Adobe/Photoshop. EDITORIAL EQUIPMENT: Hardware — APP/Mac 605, APP/Mac 610, APP/Power Mac 7200; Printers — APP/Mac LaserWriter Pro 630 EDITORIAL SOFTWARE: QPS/QuarkXPress, Baseview. PRODUCTION EQUIPMENT: Hardware — Nu/Flip Top; Cameras — R/500.

IOWA

AMES

AMES TRIBUNE

317 5th St, Ames, Iowa, 50010-6101, Story; gen tel (515) 232-2160; adv tel (515) 663-6947; ed tel (515) 663-6917; gen fax (515) 232-2364; gen/nat adv e-mail knelson@amestrib.com; disp adv e-mail jgreving@amestrib.com; class adv e-mailclassifieds@amestrib.com; ed e-mail mcrumb@amestrib.com; web site www.amestrib.com - 495,000(views) 93,938(visitors)
Group: New Media Investment Group
Published: Tues, Wed, Thur, Fri, Sat, Sun
Weekday Frequency: e
Saturday Frequency: m
Circulation: 5,665; 6,387(sat); 6,510(sun)
Last Audit: VAC September 30, 2016
Advertising Rate (weekday/saturday): Open inch rate $17.20
Advertising Rate (sunday): Open inch rate $27.15
Online Advertising Rate: Open Rate $20.00 CPM; Page Curl $100.00 per day
News services: AP, CNS, NYT, TMS, Washington Post Bloomberg **Established:** 1868
Own Printing Facility?: Yes
Commercial Printers?: No
Special Editions: Game Day; University (May and Aug); Facets (Monthly); Ames Business Monthly (Monthly); Green Together (Quarterly).
Special Weekly Sections: Art and Culture plus TV (Sunday); Ames Out Loud (Thur); Taste(Wed) Business (Sunday); Life and Leisure (Saturday);
Syndicated Publications: Art & Culture Plus TV (S); Ames Out Loud (Thur); Taste(Wed); Business (S); Life & Leisure (Sat).
Digital Platform - Mobile: Apple, Android
Digital Platform - Tablet: Apple iOS, Android
Adv. Dir. .... John Greving
Bus. Mgr. .... Patricia Snyder
Circ. Dir. .... Pat Cottril
Marketing Dir. .... Ashleigh Fischer
Managing Ed. .... Michael Crumb
Pub. .... Scott Anderson
Circulation Sales/Ops manager ..... Michael Lynch
Circulation Delivery Ops Manager .. Kathy Greiner
Market Information: ADS; Split run; TMC;
Mechanical Available: Offset; Black and 3 ROP colors; insert accepted; page cutoffs - 22 3/4.
Mechanical Specifications: Type page 6 cols x 21 1/2
Areas Served: 50010, 50011, 50014, 50105, 50075, 50130, 50230, 50231, 50236, 50248, 50278, 50056, 50154, 50161, 50201, 50036, 50124, 50134, 50244, 50046, 50055
Delivery Method: Mail, Newsstand, Carrier, RacksEquipment & Software: BUSINESS EQUIPMENT: 5-Dell BUSINESS SOFTWARE: PBS, APT CLASSIFIED EQUIPMENT: Hardware — 2-dells; Printers — HP; CLASSIFIED SOFTWARE: APT, DISPLAY EQUIPMENT: Hardware — 4-Dells 2-Mac; Printers — HP; Other Hardware — Scanner DISPLAY SOFTWAREAd Make-up Applications — Indesign, Illustrator, Photoshop; Layout Software — ALS EDITORIAL EQUIPMENT: Hardware — 20-Dells/Nikon cameras; Printers — HP EDITORIAL SOFTWARE: NewsEngine; Indesign

ATLANTIC

ATLANTIC NEWS TELEGRAPH

410 Walnut St, Atlantic, Iowa, 50022-1365, Cass; gen tel (712) 243-2624; adv tel (712) 243-2624; ed tel (712) 243-2624; gen fax (712) 243-4988; adv fax (712) 243-4988; ed fax (712) 243-4988; gen/nat adv e-mail ant@ant-news.com; disp adv e-mail ant@ant-news.com; class adv e-mailant@ant-news.com; ed e-mail jrlund@ant-news.com; web site www.atlanticnewstelegraph.com
Group: Community Media Group
Published: Mon, Tues, Wed, Thur, Fri, Sat, Sun
Weekday Frequency: e
Saturday Frequency: m
Circulation: 2,800; 2,800(sat)
Last Audit: Sworn/Estimate/Non-Audited September 30, 2017
Advertising Rate (weekday/saturday): Open inch rate $10.83
News services: AP. **Established:** 1871
Special Editions: Beauty/Cosmetology (Annually); Wedding (Jun); Wedding (Jan); Graduation (May); Real Estate (Monthly); Health (Quarterly).
Special Weekly Sections: Entertainment (Thur); Shopper (Tues)
Syndicated Publications: Atlantic Farm (Monthly); American Profile (Weekly).
Digital Platform - Mobile: Apple, Android
Digital Platform - Tablet: Apple iOS, Android
Pub./Gen Mgr. .... Jeff Lundquist
Circ. Dir. .... Deb Baker
Adv. Mgr. .... Mike Ruddy
Sports Ed. .... Nate Tenopir
Market Information: ADS; TMC.
Mechanical Available: Offset; Black and 4 ROP colors; insert accepted - free samples; page cutoffs - 22 3/4.
Mechanical Specifications: Type page 13 1/8 x 21 1/2; E - 6 cols, 2 1/16, 1/8 between; A - 6 cols, 2 1/16, 1/8 between; C - 6 cols, 2 1/16, 1/8 between.
Areas Served: Southwest Iowa
Delivery Method: Mail, CarrierEquipment & Software: PRESSROOM EQUIPMENT: Lines — 6-G; Folders — 1-G/2:1.; MAILROOM EQUIPMENT: Tying Machines — 3/Bu.; BUSINESS EQUIPMENT: IBM CLASSIFIED EQUIPMENT: Hardware — 1-APP/Mac.; EDITORIAL EQUIPMENT: Hardware — 1-APP/Mac. PRODUCTION EQUIPMENT: Hardware — 1-Ic; Cameras — 1-Nu; Scanners — APP/Mac One, 1-APP/Mac LaserPrinter Scanner.

BURLINGTON

THE HAWK EYE

800 S Main St, Burlington, Iowa, 52601-5870, Des Moines; gen tel (319) 754-8461; adv tel (319) 758-8130; ed tel (319) 754-8461; gen fax (319) 754-6824; adv fax (319) 754-6824; ed fax (319) 754-6824; gen/nat adv e-mail cconrad@thehawkeye.com; disp adv e-mail lengler@thehawkeye.com; class adv e-mailclassifieds@thehawkeye.com; ed e-mail dalison@thehawkeye.com; web site www.thehawkeye.com
Group: GateHouse Media, Inc.
Published: Mon, Tues, Wed, Thur, Fri, Sat, Sun
Weekday Frequency: m
Saturday Frequency: m
Circulation: 15,247; 15,247(sat); 16,105(sun)
Last Audit: VAC September 30, 2015
Advertising Rate (weekday/saturday): Open inch rate $21.98
News services: AP. **Established:** 1833
Own Printing Facility?: Yes
Commercial Printers?: Yes
Special Editions: Homeless Shelter Open House (Jul); The Downtowner (Jun); WasteWrap Summer 2013 (Jun); Progress (Feb); Progress (Mar); Guide to Hawk Eye Land (May).
Special Weekly Sections: Education (Mon); Mutual Funds & Stocks (S); Religion (Sat); Entertainment (Thur); Health (Tues); Best Food Day (Wed).
Syndicated Publications: Relish (Monthly); TV Section (S); Home Magazine (Sat); American Profile (Weekly).
Digital Platform - Mobile: Apple, Android
Digital Platform - Tablet: Apple iOS, Android
Pub./Ed. .... Steve Delaney
Mng. Ed. .... Dale Alison
Prodn. Mgr. .... Steve Deggendorf
Bus. Mgr. .... LeDonna Kitsch
Mgr., HR .... Jan Jaeger
Adv. Mgr., Classified .... Laurie Trautner
Adv. Coord., Major Accts. .... Cheryl Newell
News Ed. .... Randy Miller
Photo Dept. Mgr. .... John Gaines
Sports Editor .... John Bohenkamp
Prodn. Mgr., Systems .... Tony Miller
Prodn. Supt. .... Tom Lingenfelter
Digital Media Manager .... Christy Ayer
Market Information: TMC.
Mechanical Available: Offset; Black and 3 ROP colors; insert accepted; page cutoffs - 22 3/4.
Mechanical Specifications: Type page 11 63/100 x 21 1/2; E - 6 cols, 1 5/6, 1/8 between; A - 6 cols, 1 5/6, 1/8 between; C - 8 cols, 1 19/50, 4/50 between.
Areas Served: 52601, 52655, 52565, 52620, 52627, 61425, 62330, 52624, 52625, 52626, 52632, 52637, 61450, 61454, 52637, 52638, 52639, 52640, 52641, 52645, 52646, 52648, 52649, 52627, 52650, 52657, 61480, 52656, 52658, 52659, 52660
Delivery Method: Mail, Carrier, RacksEquipment & Software: PRESSROOM EQUIPMENT: Lines — 6-G/1008 single width (2 formers); Reels & Stands — Roll/Stands.; MAILROOM EQUIPMENT: Counter Stackers — Id/660, QWI/400; Inserters & Stuffers — MM (6 inserter, auto eject); Tying Machines — Sterling/MR50; BUSINESS EQUIPMENT: Data Sciences CLASSIFIED EQUIPMENT: Hardware — 4-APP/Mac G3, APP/Mac 7350 ASIP Server; Printers — HP/6 MP; CLASSIFIED SOFTWARE: Baseview. DISPLAY EQUIPMENT: Hardware — 3-APP/Mac 7500-100, 3-APP/Mac G3, 2-Umax/C500, 1-APP/Mac 8100, 2-APP/Mac Q 650; Printers — Epson/740; DISPLAY SOFTWAREAd Make-up Applications — Multi-Ad/Creator 4.0.1; Layout Software — MEI/ALS 2.0. EDITORIAL EQUIPMENT: Hardware — APP/Mac; Printers — HP/5000, 2-HP/4000, HP/750C Plus EDITORIAL SOFTWARE: Baseview/News Edit Pro IQue 3.1.8. PRODUCTION EQUIPMENT: Hardware — Nat/Subtractive 33-1, 1-Nu/Flip Top FT40URNS, 2-Carnfeldt/RA; Cameras — 1-R; Scanners — 1-Umax/Vista 58, 7-Umax/Flatbed PRODUCTION SOFTWARE: QPS/QuarkXPress 4.11.

CARROLL

CARROLL DAILY TIMES HERALD

508 N Court St, Carroll, Iowa, 51401-2747, Carroll; gen tel (712) 792-3573; adv tel (712) 792-3575 ext. 26; ed tel (712) 792-3573; gen fax (712) 792-5218; adv fax (712) 792-5218; ed fax (712) 792-5218; gen/nat adv e-mail m.jensen@carrollspaper.com; disp adv e-mail t.burns@carrollspaper.com; class adv e-mailj.rohe@carrollspaper.com; ed e-mail newspaper@carrollspaper.com; web site www.carrollspaper.com
Published: Mon, Tues, Wed, Thur, Fri
Weekday Frequency: e
Circulation: 6,321
Last Audit: Sworn/Estimate/Non-Audited September 30, 2017
Advertising Rate (weekday/saturday): Open inch rate $8.00
News services: AP. **Established:** 1868
Special Editions: Chamber (Other).
Syndicated Publications: TV Magazine (Fri); American Profile (Weekly).
Gen Mgr. .... Ann Wilson
Adv. Mgr., Retail .... Tom Burns
Circ. Mgr. .... Daniel Haberl
News Ed. .... Larry Devine
Co-owner/Online Ed. .... Douglas Burns
Sports Ed. .... Brett Christie
Prodn. Foreman, Press .... Tim Bohling
Asst. Sports Ed. .... Marty Ball
Market Information: TMC; Zoned editions.
Mechanical Available: Offset; Black and 3 ROP colors; insert accepted; page cutoffs - 21 1/2.
Mechanical Specifications: Type page 12 1/2 x 21; E - 6 cols, 1 5/6, 1/6 between; A - 6 cols, 1 5/6, 1/6 between; C - 8 cols, 1 1/3, 1/6 between.
Delivery Method: Mail, CarrierEquipment & Software: PRESSROOM EQUIPMENT: Lines — 6-HI/Cotrell V-15A; Folders — 1-G/2:1.; MAILROOM EQUIPMENT: Tying Machines — 1-MM/Strap-Tyer.; BUSINESS EQUIPMENT: Synaptic/Circulation Sys CLASSIFIED EQUIPMENT: Hardware — APP/Mac; Printers — APP/Mac LaserWriter.; DISPLAY EQUIPMENT: Printers — APP/Mac LaserWriter; Other Hardware — HP/ScanJet 4C DISPLAY SOFTWAREAd Make-up Applications — Adobe/PageMaker 6.0, Adobe/Photoshop 6.0, Microsoft/Word 6.0.1; Layout Software — APP/Mac. EDITORIAL EQUIPMENT: Hardware — APP/Mac; Printers — APP/Mac LaserWriter EDITORIAL SOFTWARE: Microsoft/Word 6.0.1. PRODUCTION EQUIPMENT: Hardware — APP/Mac LaserWriter; Cameras — 1-Nu/SST 1923.

CEDAR RAPIDS

THE GAZETTE

501 2nd Ave SE, Cedar Rapids, Iowa, 52401-1303, Linn; gen tel (319) 398-8333; adv tel (319) 398-8222; ed tel (319) 398-8313; gen fax (319) 398-5848; adv fax (319) 398-5848; ed fax (319) 398-5846; gen/nat adv e-mail advertise@gazcomm.com; disp adv e-mail advertise@sourcemedia.net; class adv e-mailclassifieds@sourcemedia.net; ed e-mail editorial@thegazette.com; web site www.thegazette.com - 1,071,630(views) 196,502(visitors)
Group: Iowa SourceMedia Group
Published: Mon, Tues, Wed, Thur, Fri, Sat, Sun
Weekday Frequency: m
Saturday Frequency: m
Circulation: 38,704; 44,699(sat); 47,060(sun)
Last Audit: AAM June 30, 2016
Advertising Rate (weekday/saturday): 1x1.5 mod $139.37 (Mon-Wed); $174.21 (Thur-Fri); $182.92 (Sat)
Advertising Rate (sunday): 1x1.5 mod $209.05
News services: AP, LAT-WP, MCT. **Established:** 1883
Own Printing Facility?: Yes
Commercial Printers?: Yes
Special Editions: College/Pro & Prep Football Guide (Aug); New Baby News (Feb); Stocks & Business Review (Jan); Freedom Festival Guide (Jun); Spring Car Care (Mar); Explore (May); College Guide (Sept).
Special Weekly Sections: Community (Mon-Wed); Hoopla, Arts, Entertainment, Food (Thur); House, Decorations, Living, Religion, People, Places (Fri); TV, Health (Sat); Home, Farm, Finance, Real Estate, Books, Wedding, Engagements (Sun)
Syndicated Publications: Dash(Monthly); Parade (S);
Digital Platform - Mobile: Apple, Android
Digital Platform - Tablet: Apple iOS, Android, Kindle, Nook, Kindle Fire
Chrmn. .... Joe Hladky
CEO/Pres. .... Chuck Peters
Vice Pres./Treasurer .... Ken Slaughter
Editor .... Lyle Muller
Columnist .... Dave Rasdal
Opinion Page Ed. .... Jeff Tecklenburg
Publisher .... Tim McDougall
Product Director .... Steve Lorenz
Managing Editor .... Annette Schulte
Columnist .... Todd Dorman
Columnist .... Jennifer Hemmingsen
Pub./Vice Pres./Gen. Mgr., Gazette Communications .... Dave Storey
Sec. .... Elizabeth T. Barry
Dir., Market Research/Adv. Servs. .... Jeff Wolff
Circ. Systems Admin. .... Ted Fries
Ed. .... Steve Buttry
Automotive Columnist .... Tim Banse
Columnist .... Mike Deupree
Community Ed. .... Diana Nolen
George Ford
Iowa Ed. .... Mary Sharp
Online Ed. .... Kathy Alter
Outdoors Writer .... Orlan Love
Picture Ed. .... Rollin Banderob
VP, Adv. .... Chris Edwards
Elizabeth Schott
Market Information: TMC
Mechanical Available: Offset; Black and 3 ROP colors; insert accepted - preprinted tab, booklets, single sheet; page cutoffs - 20.
Mechanical Specifications: Type page 11 5/8 x 20; E - 6 cols, 2, between; A - 6 cols, 2, between; C - 6 cols, 1 1/3, 2/3 between.
Areas Served: Eastern Iowa
Delivery Method: Mail, Newsstand, Carrier, RacksEquipment & Software: PRESSROOM EQUIPMENT: Lines — 9-G/Universal 70 single width (8-four towers)(1-5 high tower) 1999; Folders — 1-G/J233 double width 1999, 3-G/J233 single width 1999; Pasters —Enkel/Universal, 14-Enkel/Autoweb; Reels & Stands — Enkel/Megtec; Control System — Honeywell/P; MAILROOM EQUIPMENT: Counter Stackers — HI/

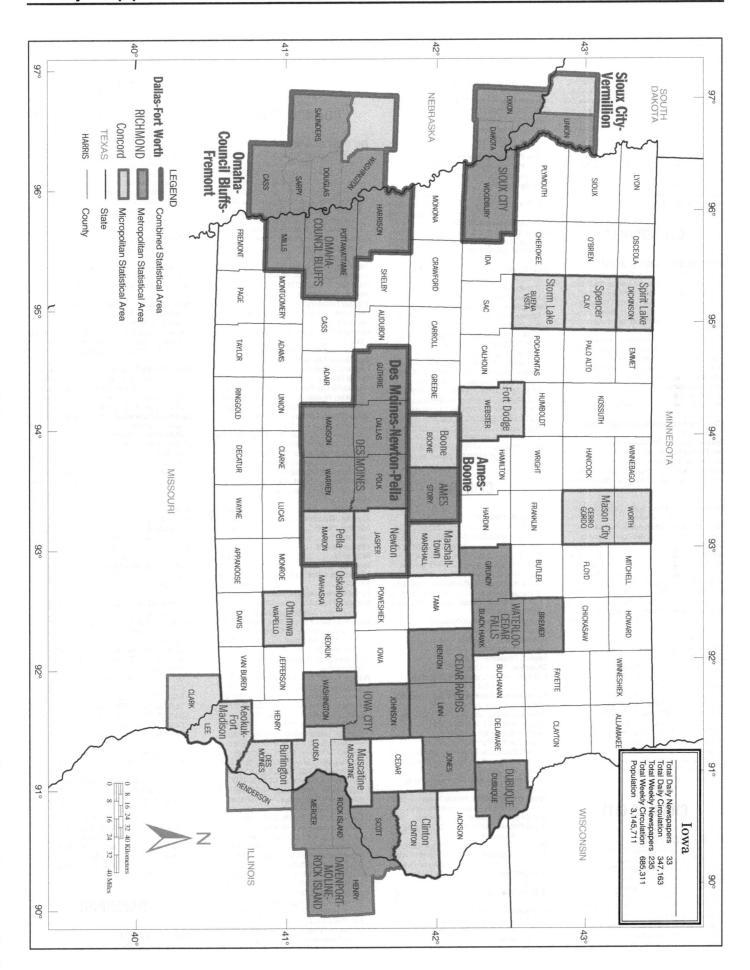

LEGEND

Combined Statistical Area

Metropolitan Statistical Area

Micropolitan Statistical Area

State

County

Iowa	
Total Daily Newspapers	33
Total Daily Circulation	347,163
Total Weekly Newspapers	235
Total Weekly Circulation	685,311
Population	3,145,711

Olympian, 2-QWI/350, 2-Rima/SN 2510, 3-Rima/SL 3010, 1-Rima/105; Inserters & Stuffers — 2-GMA/SLS2000; Tying Machines — GMA/Combi Stacks; Control System — GMA/SAM; Address Machine — 2/Dm, 2-/ Videojet Systems; BUSINESS EQUIPMENT: 4-Sun/Sparc 1000, Alpha/2000 BUSINESS SOFTWARE: Oracle, Microsoft/Windows, DSI CLASSIFIED EQUIPMENT: Hardware — HP; Quest/Page Pair, Mindset Live Pag; Printers — HP/LaserJet, ; CLASSIFIED SOFTWARE: Atex DISPLAY EQUIPMENT: Hardware — PC; Printers — HP; Other Hardware — MON/Print Express 2000, Engage/Ad Tracking DISPLAY SOFTWAREAd Make-up Applications — In Design; EDITORIAL EQUIPMENT: Hardware — HP/Saxotech and In Design; Printers — HP PRODUCTION EQUIPMENT: Hardware — Kodak CTP

CENTERVILLE

AD-EXPRESS & DAILY IOWEGIAN

201 N 13th St, Frnt Frnt, Centerville, Iowa, 52544-1748, Appanoose; gen tel (641) 856-6336; adv tel (641) 856-6336; ed tel (641) 856-6336; gen fax (641) 856-8118; adv fax (641) 856-8118; ed fax (641) 856-8118; gen/nat adv e-mail cmbriggs@dailyiowegian.com; disp adv e-mail bmaxwell@dailyiowegian.com; class adv e-mailsselix@dailyiowegian.com; ed e-mail kocker@dailyiowegian.com; web site www.dailyiowegian.com
Group: Community Newspaper Holdings, Inc.
Published: Mon, Tues, Wed, Thur, Fri
Weekday Frequency: m
Circulation: 2,806
Last Audit: Sworn/Estimate/Non-Audited December 19, 2017
Advertising Rate (weekday/saturday): Open inch rate $10.60
News services: AP. **Established:** 1864
Own Printing Facility?: No
Commercial Printers?: No
Special Editions: Farm (Apr); Progress (Feb); Outdoor Recreation (Jun); Fall-Winter Sports Tab (Nov); Farm (Oct); Fall-Winter Sports Tab (Sept).
Syndicated Publications: Relish (Monthly); American Profile (Weekly).
Digital Platform - Mobile: Apple, Android
Digital Platform - Tablet: Apple iOS, Android
Circ. Mgr. .... Becky Maxwell
Society Ed. .... Kristal Fowler
Bus. Mgr. .... Cindy Briggs
Editor .... Kyle Ocker
Market Information: ADS; TMC.
Mechanical Available: Offset; Black and 3 ROP colors; insert accepted; page cutoffs - 22 3/4.
Mechanical Specifications: Type page 12 x 21 1/2; E - 6 cols, 1 7/8, 1/8 between; A - 6 cols, 1 7/8, 1/8 between; C - 6 cols, 1 7/8, 1/8 between.
Areas Served: Appanoose and Wayne County
Delivery Method: Mail, Newsstand, CarrierEquipment & Software: PRESSROOM EQUIPMENT: Lines — G/Community; G/Community; G/Community; G/Community.; BUSINESS EQUIPMENT: HP/2000 CLASSIFIED EQUIPMENT: Hardware — APP/Mac; DISPLAY SOFTWARELayout Software — APP/Mac. EDITORIAL EQUIPMENT: Hardware — APP/Mac; Printers — APP/Mac LaserWriter, Xante/Accel-a-Writer EDITORIAL SOFTWARE: QPS, Baseview. PRODUCTION EQUIPMENT: Hardware — Nu; Cameras — Acti.

CHARLES CITY

CHARLES CITY PRESS

801 Riverside Dr, Charles City, Iowa, 50616-2248, Floyd; gen tel (641) 228-3211; adv tel (641) 228-3211; ed tel (641) 228-3211; gen fax (641) 228-2641; adv fax (641) 228-2641; ed fax (641) 228-2641; gen/nat adv e-mail joelg@charlescitypress.com ; disp adv e-mail chris@charlescitypress.com; class adv e-mailclassifiedads@charlescitypress.com; ed e-mail editor@charlescitypress.com; web site www.charlescitypress.com
Group: Enterprise Media Inc.
Published: Mon, Tues, Wed, Thur, Fri
Weekday Frequency: All day
Circulation: 2,970
Last Audit: Sworn/Estimate/Non-Audited September 30, 2017
Advertising Rate (weekday/saturday): Open inch rate $15.88
News services: INA, AP. **Established:** 1896
Own Printing Facility?: Yes
Commercial Printers?: Yes
Special Editions: Agriculture (Feb); Agriculture (Jan); Agriculture (Jul); Beef (May); Pork (Oct).
Digital Platform - Mobile: Apple, Android
Digital Platform - Tablet: Apple iOS, Android, Kindle, Nook, Kindle Fire
Gen. Mgr./Adv. Mgr. .... Joel Gray
Ed. .... Christopher Baldus
Adv. Rep. .... Chris Rimrod
Owner .... Christopher Hall
Market Information: ADS; TMC.
Mechanical Available: Offset; Black and 3 ROP colors; insert accepted; page cutoffs - 22 1/2.
Mechanical Specifications: Type page 11 1/2 x 21 1/2; E - 6 cols, 1 3/4, 1/6 between;
Areas Served: Osage, Riceville, Orchard, Elma, Alta Vista, Rudd, Floyd, Charles City, Rockford, New Hampton, Ionia, Marble Rock, Nashua, Greene, and Clarksville
Delivery Method: Mail, Newsstand, Carrier, RacksEquipment & Software: PRESSROOM EQUIPMENT: Lines — 13-G/Community 1984; Folders — 1-G/SC, 1-G/Community.; MAILROOM EQUIPMENT: Counter Stackers — BG/Count-O-Veyor; Tying Machines — Bu; Wrapping Singles — El.; Address Machine — VideoJet; CLASSIFIED EQUIPMENT: Hardware — APP/Mac ; CLASSIFIED SOFTWARE: Quark DISPLAY EQUIPMENT: Hardware — APP/Mac, APP/Mac ; Printers — APP/Mac LaserWriter; DISPLAY SOFTWAREAd Make-up Applications — Multi-Ad/Creator, QPS.; EDITORIAL EQUIPMENT: Hardware — APP/Mac ; Printers — APP/Mac LaserWriter Plus EDITORIAL SOFTWARE: Quark, Baseview

CLINTON

CLINTON HERALD

221 6th Ave S, Clinton, Iowa, 52732-4305, Clinton; gen tel (563) 242-7101; adv tel (563) 242-7142 ext. 141; ed tel (563) 242-7142 ext. 155; gen fax (563) 242-7147; adv fax (563) 242-7147; ed fax (563) 242-7147; gen/nat adv e-mail shanelle@clintonherald.com; disp adv e-mail rgutierrez@cnhi.com ; class adv e-mailsenright@clintonherald.com; ed e-mail cbielema@clintonherald.com; web site www.clintonherald.com
- 450,000(views) 95,000(visitors)
Group: Community Newspaper Holdings, Inc.
Published: Mon, Tues, Wed, Thur, Fri, Sat
Weekday Frequency: m
Saturday Frequency: m
Circulation: 6,350; 6,590(sat)
Last Audit: Sworn/Estimate/Non-Audited February 16, 2018
Advertising Rate (weekday/saturday): Open inch rate $16.26; National rate $19.16
Online Advertising Rate: 15 CPM
News services: AP. **Established:** 1855
Own Printing Facility?: No
Commercial Printers?: Yes
Special Editions: Car Care (Apr); Wedding (Jan); Progress (Mar); Beef (May); Pre-Christmas (Nov); Car Care (Oct).
Special Weekly Sections: Church Page (Sat); Best Food Day (Tue).
Syndicated Publications: Parade Magazine (Sat); TV Tab (Mon); American Profile (Weekly).
Digital Platform - Mobile: Apple, Android
Digital Platform - Tablet: Apple iOS, Android, Kindle, Nook, Kindle Fire
Pub. .... Ron Gutierrez
Adv. Mgr., Classified .... Sherri Enright
Ed. .... Charlene Bielema
Market Information: River View Marketplace - 14,400
Mechanical Available: Offset; Black and 3 ROP colors; insert accepted; page cutoffs - 22 3/4.
Mechanical Specifications: Type page 11 3/5 x 21 1/2; E - 6 cols, 1 4/5, 1/8 between; A - 6 cols, 1 4/5, 1/8 between; C - 9 cols, 1 1/5, 1/16 between.
Areas Served: Clinton and Camanche, Iowa Fulton,IL
Delivery Method: Mail, Newsstand, Carrier, RacksEquipment & Software: PRESSROOM EQUIPMENT: Lines — 4-G/Urbanite; Folders — 1-G/2:1; Pasters —Butler/Automatic.

COUNCIL BLUFFS

THE DAILY NONPAREIL

535 W Broadway, Ste 300, Council Bluffs, Iowa, 51503-0831, Pottawattamie; gen tel (712) 328-1811; adv tel (712) 325-5688; ed tel (712) 325-5728; gen fax (712) 325-5776; adv fax (712) 325-5813; ed fax (712) 325-5776; gen/nat adv e-mail dan.collin@nonpareilonline.com; disp adv e-mail advertising@nonpareilonline.com; class adv e-mailclassified@nonpareilonline.com; ed e-mail jon.leu@nonpareilonline.com; web site www.nonpareilonline.com
63,854(visitors)
Group: BH Media Group
Southwest Iowa Newspapers
Published: Tues, Wed, Thur, Fri, Sat, Sun
Weekday Frequency: e
Saturday Frequency: e
Circulation: 8,122; 8,122(sat); 9,074(sun)
Last Audit: CAC June 30, 2016
Advertising Rate (weekday/saturday): Open inch rate $27.50
News services: AP. **Established:** 1849
Own Printing Facility?: Yes
Commercial Printers?: Yes
Special Editions: Outdoor Living (Apr); Back-to-School (Aug); Presidents' Day Sale (Feb); Working Women (Jul); Spring Car Care (Mar); New Car Care (Oct); Golden Years (Sept).
Special Weekly Sections: Church News (Fri); Business and Farm (S); TV Preview Magazine (Sat); Diversions Magazine (Thur); Best Food Day (Tues).
Syndicated Publications: USA WEEKEND Magazine (S); American Profile (Weekly).
Digital Platform - Mobile: Apple, Android
Digital Platform - Tablet: Apple iOS, Android, Kindle, Nook, Kindle Fire
Pub. .... Tom Schmitt
Comptroller .... Amy McKay
Adv. Mgr., Classified .... Jaimi Miller
Adv. Mgr., Retail .... Cindy Bunten
Asst. Mng. Ed. .... Courtney Brummer
Editorial Page Ed. .... Jon Leu
Religion Ed. .... Kim Bousquet
Sports Ed. .... Kevin White
Internet Coord./New Media Ed. .. Marsha Hoffman
Adv. Dir. .... Andy Ryba
Market Information: ADS; TMC.
Mechanical Available: Offset; Black and 3 ROP colors; insert accepted; page cutoffs - 22 3/4.
Mechanical Specifications: Type page 12 1/2 x 21 1/2; E - 6 cols, 2 1/16, 1/8 between; A - 6 cols, 2 1/16, 1/8 between; C - 9 cols, 1 3/8, 1/16 between.
Areas Served: Southwestern Iowa and outlying communities
Delivery Method: Mail, CarrierEquipment & Software: PRESSROOM EQUIPMENT: Lines — 8-G/Community (3-Color Unit & 1-Stack Unit).; MAILROOM EQUIPMENT: Counter Stackers — 1-Toledo/Scale #1938; Inserters & Stuffers — 1-Mandelli/Star 100 (paper cutter); Tying Machines — 1-MLN/Spirit, 1-MLN/SP 300; Control System — MM/1511 Stitcher-Trimmer; Address Machine — 1-Ch/595.; BUSINESS EQUIPMENT: 1-NCR/I9020 BUSINESS SOFTWARE: Newzware CLASSIFIED EQUIPMENT: Hardware — 4-Cx.; DISPLAY EQUIPMENT: Hardware — 5-APP/Mac 7200; Printers — APP/Mac Pro 630, HP/LaserJet 4MV, 2-Pre Press/Panther Pro 36; Other Hardware — 2-APP/Mac Scanner, Bernoui DISPLAY SOFTWAREAd Make-up Applications — Aldus/FreeHand 3.1, Aldus/PageMaker 5.0, QPS/QuarkXPress 3.3, Broderbund/Typestyler 2.1, Ofoto 2.0; EDITORIAL EQUIPMENT: Hardware — 15-APP/Mac 2200, 4-APP/Mac 8500/Lf/AP Leaf Picture Desk, APP/Mac Quadra; Printers — 2-Pre Press/Panther Pro 36, HP/LaserJet 4MV EDITORIAL SOFTWARE: FSI. PRODUCTION EQUIPMENT: Hardware - Caere/OmniPage 3.0, HP/4MV, 2-Pre Press/Panther Pro 36; Cameras — 1-SCREEN; Scanners — APP/Mac Scanners PRODUCTION SOFTWARE: QPS/QuarkXPress 3.3, FSI.

CRESTON

CRESTON NEWS ADVERTISER

503 W Adams St, Creston, Iowa, 50801-3112, Union; gen tel (641) 782-2141; adv tel (641) 782-2141; ed tel (641) 782-2141; gen fax (641) 782-6628; adv fax (641) 782-6628; ed fax (641) 782-6628; gen/nat adv e-mail advertising@crestonnews.com; disp adv e-mail cmittag@crestonnews.com; class adv e-mailclassified@crestonnews.com; ed e-mail sfinley@crestonnews.com; web site www.crestonnewsadvertiser.com
- 200,000(views) 30,000(visitors)
Group: Shaw Media
Published: Mon, Tues, Wed, Thur, Fri
Weekday Frequency: e
Circulation: 4,677
Last Audit: Sworn/Estimate/Non-Audited September 30, 2017
Advertising Rate (weekday/saturday): Open inch rate $11.10
News services: AP. **Established:** 1879
Own Printing Facility?: Yes
Commercial Printers?: Yes
Special Editions: Car Care (Apr); Wedding (Jan); Progress (Mar); Beef (May); Pre-Christmas (Nov); Car Care (Oct). Ag Mag, Living Sections
Special Weekly Sections: People (Tues); Farm & Business (Wed); Community, The Entertainer Channel Guide (Fri); TV & Entertainment (Fri); Church Page (Thur); Best Food Day (Tues); Farm Page (Wed)
Syndicated Publications: American Profile (Fri); Relish (Monthly).
Digital Platform - Mobile: Apple, Android
Digital Platform - Tablet: Apple iOS, Android
Office Mgr. .... Rose Henry
Adv. Mgr. .... Craig Mittag
Prodn. Mgr. .... Kevin Lindley
Circ. Mgr. .... Sandy Allison
Pub. .... Mark Spensley
Mng., Ed. .... Scott Vicker
Associate Ed. .... Kelsey Haugen
Sports Ed. .... Ryan Kronberg
Sports Reporter .... Kaleb Carter
Market Information: TMC.
Mechanical Available: Offset; Black and 3 ROP colors; insert accepted; page cutoffs - 22 3/4.
Mechanical Specifications: Type page 13 x 21 1/2; E - 6 cols, 2, 1/6 between; A - 6 cols, 2, 1/6 between; C - 9 cols, 1 3/10, 3/20 between.
Areas Served: Adair, Madison, Adams, Union, Clarke, Taylor, and Ringgold
Delivery Method: Mail, Newsstand, Carrier, RacksEquipment & Software: PRESSROOM EQUIPMENT: Lines — G/Community single width 1965; G/Community single width 1965; G/Community single width 1965; G/Community single width 1976; G/Community single width 1976.; MAILROOM EQUIPMENT: Tying Machines — Bu.; BUSINESS EQUIPMENT: Digital/Prioris XL 6200 BUSINESS SOFTWARE: Vision Data CLASSIFIED EQUIPMENT: Hardware — APP/Mac; Printers — APP/Mac LaserWriter; CLASSIFIED SOFTWARE: Baseview/Class Manager Pro, Claris/Hypercard. DISPLAY EQUIPMENT: Hardware — APP/Mac G4; Printers — APP/Mac LaserWriter; DISPLAY SOFTWAREAd Make-up Applications — QPS/QuarkXPress 4.04.; EDITORIAL EQUIPMENT: Hardware — APP/Mac, APP/iMac/Polaroid/SprintScan, AG/Flatbed Scanner; Printers — APP/Mac LaserWriter EDITORIAL SOFTWARE: Baseview/NewsEdit, Baseview/QXEdit. PRODUCTION EQUIPMENT: Hardware — Text-Bridge; Cameras — B/Caravelle; Scanners — APP/Mac Scanner, APP/Mac, AG PRODUCTION SOFTWARE: Baseview 3.15.

DAVENPORT

QUAD-CITY TIMES

500 E 3rd St, Davenport, Iowa, 52801-

1708, Scott; gen tel (563) 383-2200; adv tel (563) 383-2483; ed tel (563) 383-2264; gen fax (563) 383-2433; adv fax (563) 322-6733; ed fax (563) 383-2370; gen/nat adv e-mail dmcallister@qctimes.com; disp adv e-mail dmcallister@qctimes.com; class adv e-mailqctimes@qctimes.com; ed e-mail newsroom@qctimes.com; web site www.qctimes.com
Group: Lee Enterprises, Inc.
Published: Mon, Tues, Wed, Thur, Fri, Sat, Sun
Weekday Frequency: m
Saturday Frequency: m
Circulation: 24,547; 23,967(sat); 37,341(sun)
Last Audit: AAM March 31, 2017
Advertising Rate (weekday/saturday): Open inch rate $79.59
Advertising Rate (sunday): Open inch rate $92.36
News services: AP, CNA, Associations, Inc.. **Established:** 1848
Own Printing Facility?: Yes
Commercial Printers?: Yes
Special Editions: Answer Book (Other); Spring Fashion (Spring); Summer Fun (Summer).
Special Weekly Sections: Home & Garden, Celebrate (Sun); Best Food (Wed);
Syndicated Publications: Relish (Monthly); Parade (S).
Digital Platform - Mobile: Apple, Android
Digital Platform - Tablet: Apple iOS, Android, Kindle, Nook, Kindle Fire
Pub. .... Deborah Anselm
Ed. .... Autumn Phillips
Asst. Managing Ed. .... Dan Bowerman
Dir. Audience Development .... Brett Riley
Reg. Dir. HR .... Andrew Wall
Controller .... David Zorich
Editorial Page Ed. .... Jon Alexander
Bus. Ed. .... Deborah Brasier
Sports Ed. .... Adam Soebbing
Adv. Sales Dir. .... Ann Boyd
Adv. Sales Mgr. .... Jennifer Carter
Adv. Sales Mgr .... Jessica Daack
Nat'l Adv. Coord .... Debbie McAllister
Exec. Admin. Asst. .... Jennifer Johnston
Ops. Mgr. .... Mark Mosbrucker
Market Information: TMC; Zoned editions.
Mechanical Available: Offset; Black and 3 ROP colors; insert accepted; page cutoffs - 22.
Mechanical Specifications: Type page 9 29/32 x 20 7/8; E - 6 cols, 1 9/16, 3/32 between; A - 6 cols, 1 9/16, 3/32 between; C - 6 cols, 1 9/16, 3/32 between.
Areas Served: Davenport, Bettendorf, Moline, Rock Island and the Quad Cities Area of Iowa and Illinois
Delivery Method: Mail, Newsstand, Carrier, RacksEquipment & Software: PRESSROOM EQUIPMENT: Lines — 26-G/Colorliner 1990; 10-G/Community 1976, 18-G/Community; 28-G/Colorliner; Folders — 6-G/3:2, 2-G/SSC 1995; Reels & Stands — 8; MAILROOM EQUIPMENT: Counter Stackers — 4-QWI/400; Inserters & Stuffers — 1-MM/227, 2-HI/1372 w/Icon System; Tying Machines — 1-MLN/MLN2A, 1-MLN/MLN2, 2-Dynaric/1500; Control System — HI; Address Machine — 2/CH; BUSINESS EQUIPMENT: IBM/AS-400 CLASSIFIED EQUIPMENT: Hardware — Gateway/P155; Printers — HP/LaserJet; CLASSIFIED SOFTWARE: CText/AdVision. DISPLAY EQUIPMENT: Hardware — APP/Mac; Printers — HP/LaserJet; DISPLAY SOFTWAREAd Make-up Applications — QPS/QuarkXPress 4.0, Adobe/Photoshop 4.0; Layout Software — SCS/Layout 8000. EDITORIAL EQUIPMENT: Hardware — Gateway/P155; Printers — HP/LaserJet EDITORIAL SOFTWARE: CText/Dateline, CText/Expressline. PRODUCTION EQUIPMENT: Hardware — 2-AU/APS-800, 2-AU/APS-108; Cameras — 1-C/19, 1-Nu/19; Scanners — Howtek/2500 PRODUCTION SOFTWARE: CText/ALPS. CIRCULATION SOFTWARFalcon (proprietary)

DENISON

DENISON BULLETIN & REVIEW

1410 Broadway, Denison, Iowa, 51442-2053, Crawford; gen tel (712) 263-2122; adv tel (712) 263-2122; ed tel (712) 263-2122; gen fax (712) 263-8484; adv fax (712) 263-8484; ed fax (712) 263-8484; gen/nat adv e-mail lori.wehle@bulletinreview.com; disp adv e-mail lori.wehle@bulletinreview.com; class adv e-maileileen.mullin@bulletinreview.com; ed e-mail gordon.wolf@bulletinreview.com; web site www.dbrnews.com
Group: Tampa Media Group
Published: Mon, Tues, Wed, Fri
Weekday Frequency: e
Circulation: 3,650
Last Audit: Sworn/Estimate/Non-Audited September 30, 2017
Advertising Rate (weekday/saturday): Open inch rate $9.75
Online Advertising Rate: Monthly web site ads starting at $20.00 per week
News services: 1867
Own Printing Facility?: Yes
Commercial Printers?: No
Digital Platform - Mobile: Apple, Android, Windows
Digital Platform - Tablet: Apple iOS, Android, Blackberry Tablet OS
Pub. .... Greg Wehle
Circ. Mgr. .... Jolene Stoelk
Ed. .... Gordon Wolf
Prodn. Mgr. .... Bonnie Hill
Sports Ed. .... Todd Banner
Adv. Sales Rep. .... Lori Wehle
Office Mgr. .... Cathy Jacoby
Bookkeeper .... Angele Boehm
Market Information: Zoned editions.
Mechanical Specifications: Type page 10.25x 21 1/2; E - 6 cols, 2 1/8, 1/10 between; A - 6 cols, 2 1/18, 1/10 between; C - 8 cols, 1 1/2, 1/10 between.
Areas Served: Woodbury, Ida, Sac, Calhoun, Mohona, Crawford, Carroll, Greene, Harrison, Shelby, Audubon, Guthrie, Pottawattamie, Cass, and Adair
Delivery Method: Mail, Carrier

DES MOINES

THE DES MOINES REGISTER

400 Locust St, Ste 500, Des Moines, Iowa, 50309-2355, Polk; gen tel (515) 284-8000; adv tel (515) 284-8043; ed tel (515) 284-8201; gen fax (515) 284-2540; adv fax (515) 284-8420; ed fax (515) 284-2540; gen/nat adv e-mail mwurzer@registermedia.com; disp adv e-mail mwurzer@registermedia.com; class adv e-mailclassifieds@dmreg.com; ed e-mail letters@news.dmreg.com; web site www.desmoinesregister.com - 6,957,000(views) 750,000(visitors); web site 2 www.registermedia.com
Group: Gannett
Published: Mon, Tues, Wed, Thur, Fri, Sat, Sun
Weekday Frequency: m
Saturday Frequency: m
Circulation: 74,573; 76,724(sat); 119,129(sun)
Last Audit: AAM June 30, 2017
Advertising Rate (weekday/saturday): Open inch rate $275.95
Advertising Rate (sunday): Open inch rate $341.25
Online Advertising Rate: Visit www.registermedia.com for rate cards
News services: AP, LAT-WP, MCT, NYT, GNS, Bloomberg. **Established:** 1915
Own Printing Facility?: Yes
Commercial Printers?: Yes
Special Editions: Fall Auto Preview (October), Spring Auto Preview (March), Vacation Iowa (May), Ultimate Guide to Des Moines (June), State Fair (August), College Guide (Sept), Top Workplaces Guide (Sept).
Special Weekly Sections: Business, Career (Mon); Community, Best Food (Tue); Young Reader (Wed); Datebook, Community (Thur); Marketplace, Real Estate, Community (Fri); Home, Garden, Auto (Sat); Main, Iowa Life, Business, Farm, TV, Travel, Opinion (Sun)
Syndicated Publications: USA WEEKEND Magazine (S).
Digital Platform - Mobile: Apple, Android
Digital Platform - Tablet: Apple iOS, Android
Gen. Mgr. .... Julie Shaw
VP, Finance .... Julie Harvey
GM, Production Ops. .... Kevin Johnson
VP, Info. Tech. .... Phil Legler
Sr. Distribution Dir. .... Orton Preikschat
VP, Adv. .... Mark Wurzer
Engagement/Opinion Ed. .... Lynn Hicks
Sr. News Dir. Digital .... Kelli Brown
Comm. Content Specialist- Juice Andrea Crowley
Int. Exec. Ed. .... Carol Hunter
Univ. of Iowa Reporter .... Chad Leistikow
Content Strategist Mike Trautmann
Pub. & Pres. .... David Chivers
Storytelling Coach .... Lisa Rossi
Chief Political Reporter .... Jason Noble
Market Information: Split run; TMC; Zoned editions.
Mechanical Available: Cold Web Offset; Black and 3 ROP colors; insert accepted; page cutoffs - 21 1/2.
Mechanical Specifications: Type page 11 1/2 x 20 1/2; E - 6 cols, 2 1/16, 1/8 between; A - 6 cols, 2 1/16, 1/8 between; C - 10 cols, 1 3/16, 1/8 between.
Areas Served: Des Moines and Central Iowa
Delivery Method: Newsstand, Carrier, RacksEquipment & Software: PRESSROOM EQUIPMENT: Folders — 3, 2; MAILROOM EQUIPMENT: Counter Stackers — 9-QWI/401, 4-QWI/351, 2-BG/STC70; Inserters & Stuffers — 2-HI/NP632-30; Tying Machines — 13-Sterling/NS50, 2-Sterling/NS45; Control System — 1-HI/PRIMA, 1-QWI/BDS; Address Machine — 1-AVY/Labeler 5209, 1-KAN/600.; BUSINESS EQUIPMENT: 1-IBM AS/-400, 1-IBM AS/-400 BUSINESS SOFTWARE: Microsoft/Office CLASSIFIED EQUIPMENT: Hardware — Sun/420; ROLM, ACD; Printers — QMS, HP/Laserjet; CLASSIFIED SOFTWARE: DTI/Classpeed 5.0.1. DISPLAY EQUIPMENT: Hardware — APP/Macs, Sun/630S, Sun/3000; Printers — 2-QMS, Epson/Stylus, HP/LaserJet; Other Hardware — DTI. DISPLAY SOFTWAREAd Make-up Applications — DTI/AdSpeed, DTI/Speedplanner; EDITORIAL EQUIPMENT: Hardware — Sun/3000/APP/Mac; Printers — APP/Mac LaserWriter, HP/LaserJet, QMS EDITORIAL SOFTWARE: DTI/Speedplanner, DTI/Pagespeed, DTI/Speedwriter. PRODUCTION EQUIPMENT: Hardware — 2-III/3850 Grafix Color Imager, 1-Aii 3850 Wide; Scanners — Horizon/Color, AGFA-T2000, PURUP-ESKOFOT 2024, Umax Mirage II, Umax Powerlook III, Kodak Pro 3570 PRODUCTION SOFTWARE: DTI 4.3.

DUBUQUE

TELEGRAPH HERALD

801 Bluff St, Dubuque, Iowa, 52001-4661, Dubuque; gen tel (563) 588-5611; adv tel (563) 588-5680; ed tel (563) 588-5663; gen fax (563) 588-5739; adv fax (563) 588-3834; ed fax (563) 588-5745; gen/nat adv e-mail mike.fortman@wcinet.com; disp adv e-mail Luke.rodham@thmedia.com; class adv e-mailcolson@wcinet.com; ed e-mail amy.gilligan@thmedia.com; web site www.thonline.com; web site 2 gofindmyhome.com; web site 3 gofindmycar.com; web site 4Biztimes.biz
Group: Woodward Communications, Inc.
Published: Mon, Tues, Wed, Thur, Fri, Sat, Sun
Weekday Frequency: m
Saturday Frequency: m
Circulation: 18,349; 18,349(sat); 22,491(sun)
Last Audit: AAM June 30, 2017
Advertising Rate (weekday/saturday): Open inch rate $33.54
Advertising Rate (sunday): Open inch rate $40.68
News services: AP, MCT. **Established:** 1836
Own Printing Facility?: No
Commercial Printers?: No
Special Editions: Her Magazine; Fair (Aug); Chronology (Jan); Last Minute Gift Guide (Dec); Baby of the Year (Feb); Biz.Times (Mar); Chronology (Jan); Senior Living (Quarterly); Home Builders Show (Mar); Those We Remember (May); Holiday Food & Entertaining (Nov); My Vacationland (May, Sept.), Real Estate Magazine (Monthly).
Special Weekly Sections: Health, Fitness (Mon); Around the House, Family, Nostalgia, Images, Fashion (Tue); Food, Auto (Wed); Arts, Entertainment, NASCAR, Alternative Teen (Thur); Arts, Entertainment, TV (Fri); Religion, Youth (Sat); Travel, Business, Technology, Agriculture, Home/Garden, Lifestyle, Family, Music (Sun)
Syndicated Publications: Spry (Monthly)
Digital Platform - Mobile: Apple, Android
Digital Platform - Tablet: Apple iOS, Android
Copy Ed. .... Gary Dura
Editorial Page Ed. .... Brian Cooper
Features Ed. .... Jim Swenson
News Ed. .... Monty Gilles
Photo Mgr. .... Dave Kettering
Sports Ed. .... Jim Leitner
Natl./Rgl. Acct. Rep. .... Jamie Bahl
Adv. Sales Suprv. .... Luke Rodham
Clas. Dir. .... Cindi Olson
Pub. .... Steve Fisher
Group Dir. of Adv. .... Mike Fortman
Mng. Dir. .... Amy Gilligan
Interactive Media/Database Director Matt Connolly
Market Information: TMC.
Mechanical Available: Mechanical (Print) - Offset; black and 3 ROP colors; insert accepted - single sheet, 60 lbs., min.; page cutoffs - 20.8"
Mechanical Specifications: Mechanical specs (Print) - type page 10 x 19.8; E - 6 cols, 1.562, 1/8 between; A - 6 cols, 1.562, 1/8 between; C-9 cols 1, 1/8 between
Delivery Method: Mail, Newsstand, Carrier, RacksEquipment & Software: MAILROOM EQUIPMENT: Counter Stackers — 2-QWI, HI/Olympian; Inserters & Stuffers — 1-SLS/1000 14:1; Tying Machines — 1-Samuel, 1/MLN, Si/LB-News 3000; Address Machine — 1-Ch/4-Up.; BUSINESS EQUIPMENT: HP Desktops/Laptops, HP File Servers (Microsoft 2008 Server), Dell Equalogic SAN
BUSINESS SOFTWARE: DTI, ATEX, Paycom, Netsuite, Microsoft Office CLASSIFIED EQUIPMENT: HP Desktops/Laptops, HP File Servers (Microsoft 2008 Server), Dell Equalogic SAN CLASSIFIED SOFTWARE: Atex, Microsoft SQL Server 2008, PGL Layout, Xpance
DISPLAY EQUIPMENT: HP Desktops/Laptops, HP File Servers (Microsoft 2008 Server), Dell Equalogic SAN
DISPLAY SOFTWAREAtex, Microsoft SQL Server 2008, Xpance, Adobe InDesign, Asura
EDITORIAL EQUIPMENT: TownNews server cluster, HP Desktops/Laptops, MAC Laptops HP File Servers (Microsoft 2008 Server), Dell Equalogic SAN
EDITORIAL SOFTWARE: TownNews, Amendo, Intellitune, Adobe InDesign and Photoshop, Managing Editor ALS
PRODUCTION EQUIPMENT: Third-party printing facility CIRCULATION SOFTWARDTI

FAIRFIELD

THE FAIRFIELD LEDGER

112 E Broadway Ave, Fairfield, Iowa, 52556-3202, Jefferson; gen tel (641) 472-4129; adv tel (641) 472-4130; ed tel (641) 472-2116; gen fax (641) 472-1916; adv fax (641) 472-1916; ed fax (641) 472-1916; gen/nat adv e-mail adv@fledger.com; disp adv e-mail adv@fledger.com; class adv e-mailclassifieds@fledger.com; ed e-mail news@fledger.com; web site www.fledger.com
Group: Cedar Rapids Press
Published: Mon, Tues, Wed, Thur, Fri
Weekday Frequency: e
Circulation: 2,530
Last Audit: Sworn/Estimate/Non-Audited September 30, 2017
Advertising Rate (weekday/saturday): Open inch rate $11.46
News services: AP. **Established:** 1849
Own Printing Facility?: Yes
Commercial Printers?: Yes
Special Editions: Senior Lifestyles (June); Home Improvement (Apr); Back-to-School (Aug); Bridal (Feb); Fairfield InfoGuide (Jan); Progress (Jul); Conservation (Mar); Beef Month (May); Pork Month (Oct); Women in Business (Oct); Draw an Ad (Feb); Health (Dec)
Special Weekly Sections: Religion (Fri); Business (Mon); Opinion (Thurs)
Syndicated Publications: Relish; Spry; American Profile (Weekly).
Digital Platform - Mobile: Apple, Android
Digital Platform - Tablet: Apple iOS, Android
Office Mgr. .... Melanie Imhoff

Circ. Mgr. .... Janice Shaw
News Ed. .... Vicki Tillis
Retail ad manager .... Sherry Jipp
ad sales .... Leann Nolte
Prodn. Mgr. .... Beth Ruckman
Publisher .... Amy Sparby
Editor .... Andy Hallman
Reporter .... Diane Vance
Market Information: TMC; Zoned editions.
Mechanical Available: Offset; Black and 3 ROP colors; insert accepted; page cutoffs - 22 3/4.
Mechanical Specifications: Type page 13 x 21 1/2; E - 6 cols, 2 1/16, 1/8 between; A - 6 cols, 2 1/16, 1/8 between; C - 8 cols, 1 1/2, 1/8 between.
Areas Served: Fairfield and Jefferson County
Delivery Method: Mail, Newsstand, Carrier, RacksEquipment & Software: PRESSROOM EQUIPMENT: Lines — 5-G/Community; Folders — 1-G/Community, 1-G/Gregg Plow.; MAILROOM EQUIPMENT: Tying Machines — 1/Sa; Address Machine — St/1600.; EDITORIAL EQUIPMENT: Hardware — Mk. PRODUCTION EQUIPMENT: Hardware — 1-Nu; Cameras — 1-K/241.

FORT DODGE

THE MESSENGER

713 Central Ave, Fort Dodge, Iowa, 50501-3813, Webster; gen tel (515) 573-2141; adv tel (515) 573-2141 ext. 416; ed tel (515) 573-2141 ext. 458; gen fax (515) 573-2148; adv fax (515) 573-2136; ed fax (515) 574-4529; gen/nat adv e-mail cbargfrede@messengernews.net; disp adv e-mail cbargfrede@messengernews.net; class adv e-mailjeanwarg@messengernews.net; ed e-mail bshea@messengernews.net; web site www.messengernews.net
- 815,134(views) 66,264(visitors)
Group: Ogden Newspapers Inc.
Published: Mon, Tues, Wed, Thur, Fri, Sat, Sun
Weekday Frequency: m
Saturday Frequency: m
Circulation: 9,835; 9,835(sat); 12,009(sun)
Last Audit: AAM June 30, 2017
Advertising Rate (weekday/saturday): Open inch rate $29.00
Advertising Rate (sunday): Open inch rate $29.00
Online Advertising Rate: Leaderboard/ Skyscraper $16.00 CPM; Half Banner $8.00 CPM; Middle Banner $11.00 CPM
News services: AP **Established:** 1856
Own Printing Facility?: Yes
Commercial Printers?: No
Special Editions: Bridal Guide (Jan); Progress Edition (Feb); Crime Prevention (Feb); Home & Garden Show (Mar); Golf Directory (Apr); Visitors Guide (May); Hometown Pride (June); Wedding Planner (July); Little League (July); Girls Sate Softball Tournament (July); Football Preview (Aug); All About Home (Sept); Winter Sports (Nov); Holiday Showcase (Dec); Sunday Value Pack (Monthly); Senior's Tab (Monthly); Business Review (Monthly); Real Estate Buyer's Guide (Monthly), Fort Dodge Today Magazine (monthly)
Special Weekly Sections: Education Page (Mon); Business (S); Religion (Sat); Best Food Day (Wed); Select TV (S)
Syndicated Publications: Parade (S)
Digital Platform - Mobile: Apple, Android
Digital Platform - Tablet: Apple iOS, Android
Publisher .... Terry Christensen
Adv. Mgr., Class. .... Jean Warg
Circ. Dir. .... Grant Gibbons
Editorial Page Ed. .... Terry Dwyer
Farm Ed. .... Krissan Nelson
Prodn Sup .... Michelle Colshan
Sports Ed. .... Eric Pratt
Data Processing Mgr. .... Rex Lee
Multi-Media Sales Manager .... Regina Suhrbier
Adv. Dir. .... Cory Bargfrede
City Editor .... Bill Shea
Office Manager .... Melissa Wendland
Editor .... Jane Curtis
Market Information: TMC
Mechanical Available: Offset; Black and 3 ROP colors; insert accepted; page cutoffs - 22 3/4.
Mechanical Specifications: Type page 11 1/106 x 21 1/2; E - 6 cols, 1 3/4, 1/16 between; A - 6 cols, 1 3/4, 1/16 between; C - 9 cols, 1 1/4, 1/16 between.
Areas Served: 50501-50599, 50246, 50249, 51449, 50132, 50040, 51453
Delivery Method: Mail, Newsstand, Carrier, RacksEquipment & Software: PRESSROOM EQUIPMENT: Lines — 14-G; Press Drive — 2-Fin/100 h.p.; Folders — 1-G/3:2, 1-G/SSC, 1-G/SSC/Quarter Folder; Pasters —8-Martin/ EC Splicer. MAILROOM EQUIPMENT: Counter Stackers — 2-BG/108, HI/HT II, 1-HI/RS25; Inserters & Stuffers — HI/1372, Muller 227 6/1; Tying Machines — 3/ Bu; Wrapping Singles — 1-Power Strap; Address Machine — KR/Inkjet; CLASSIFIED EQUIPMENT: Hardware — MS Windows 2003; Printers — 1-LaserJet 2035n DISPLAY EQUIPMENT: Printers — HP LaserJet 2035n DISPLAY SOFTWAREAd Make-up Applications — Multi-Ad/Creator 8; Quark Xpress 8; Layout Software — ALS/Page Director 4.1.7. EDITORIAL EQUIPMENT: Hardware — MS Windows 2003; IMAC G6; Printers — 1-HP LaserJet 5100 EDITORIAL SOFTWARE: QPS/QuarkXPress 8, Adobe/Photoshop CS6 PRODUCTION EQUIPMENT: Hardware — HP 5500n Printer; HP 5550n Printer; Scanners — Epson V330 Scanner PRODUCTION SOFTWARE: QPS/QuarkXPress 8; Multi-Ad/ Creator 8; Adobe
Note: National advertising is sold in combination with the Webster City Daily Freeman-Journal (e) for $53.15 individual newspaper rates not made available.

FORT MADISON

FORT MADISON DAILY DEMOCRAT

1226 Avenue H, Fort Madison, Iowa, 52627-4544, Lee; gen tel (319) 372-6421; adv tel (319) 372-6421 ext. 234; ed tel (319) 372-6421; gen fax (319) 372-3867; adv fax (319) 372-3867; ed fax (319) 372-3867; gen/nat adv e-mail advertising@dailydem.com; disp adv e-mail lvandenberg@dailydem.com; class adv e-mailclassified@dailydem.com; ed e-mail editor@dailydem.com; web site www.dailydem.com
- 334,485(views) 47,360(visitors)
Group: Community Media Group
Published: Mon, Tues, Wed, Thur, Fri
Weekday Frequency: e
Circulation: 4,847
Last Audit: Sworn/Estimate/Non-Audited September 30, 2017
Advertising Rate (weekday/saturday): Open inch rate $16.25 (National rate)
Online Advertising Rate: Additional charge of $12.00 per display ad to appear online; Open Preprint Rates $57.95 CPM (Card)
News services: AP. **Established:** 1868
Own Printing Facility?: Yes
Commercial Printers?: Yes
Special Editions: MV Living (Jan); Business Profiles (Feb); Dinner Theatre (Apr); Small Business Salute (May); Outdoor Adventures (Apr); Tri-State Rodeo (Aug); Bridal Planner (Jan); Fair Outdoor Adventures (Jul); Summer Outdoor Adventures (Jun); Dinner Guide (Sept); Healthy New You (Dec.); Last Minute Gift Guide (Dec).
Special Weekly Sections: Religion (Fri); Weekend Sports Wrap-Up (Mon); Entertainment (Thur); Farm Page (Tues); Business Page (Wed).
Syndicated Publications: American Profile (Mon).
Digital Platform - Mobile: Apple, Android
Digital Platform - Tablet: Apple iOS, Android
Bus. Mgr. .... Mary Older
Mng. Ed. .... Robin Delaney
Sports Ed. .... Chris Faulkner
Reporter .... Jeff Hunt
Ad. Dir. .... Lee Vandenberg
Pub. .... Chuck Vandenberg
Market Information: TMC.
Mechanical Available: Offset; Black and 3 ROP colors; insert accepted; page cutoffs - 22 3/4.
Mechanical Specifications: Type page 11 5/8 x 21 1/2; E - 6 cols, 1 5/6, 1/8 between; A - 6 cols, 1 5/6, 1/8 between; C - 6 cols, 1 5/6, 1/8 between.
Areas Served: Fort Madison, West Point, Donnellson, Montrose, Denmark, Wever, Farmington, Dallas City, Nauvoo, and Niota
Delivery Method: Mail, Newsstand, Carrier, RacksEquipment & Software: PRESSROOM EQUIPMENT: Lines — 10-G/Community; Pasters —BG/Acumeter. MAILROOM EQUIPMENT: Tying Machines — Bu, MLN/Strappers; Address Machine — Wm; BUSINESS EQUIPMENT: Qantel, SBS BUSINESS SOFTWARE: Quatro Pro 4.0, Word Perfect 5.1, Microsoft/Windows 3.1 CLASSIFIED EQUIPMENT: Hardware — APP/Mac Quadra 630; Okidata/320 Microline Printer; Printers — COM/8400; CLASSIFIED SOFTWARE: Baseview/Class Manager. DISPLAY EQUIPMENT: Hardware - APP/ Mac; Printers — COM/8400, Pre Press/ Panther Plus Imagesetter; DISPLAY SOFTWAREAd Make-up Applications — QPS/QuarkXPress, Baseview, Adobe/ Photoshop, Multi-Ad/Creator; Layout Software — 1-APP/Power Mac 7100. EDITORIAL EQUIPMENT: Hardware - 1-APP/Mac 7100, APP/Mac Quadra 630; Printers — 1-COM/8400, NewGen/Laser Printer, Pre Press/Panther Plus Imagesetter EDITORIAL SOFTWARE: DragX, QPS/ QuarkXPress, Baseview/Qtools, Baseview/ NewsEdit Pro. PRODUCTION EQUIPMENT: Hardware — 1-Nu, Pre Press/Panther Plus, Kodak CTP; Cameras — Acti; Scanners — Lf/Leafscan 35, Umax/PowerLook, Nikon/ LS1000 PRODUCTION SOFTWARE: QPS/ QuarkXPress, Baseview/Qtools, DragX.
Note: Democrat Co. is owned by Brehm Communications Inc. Through it's subsidiaries, Democrat Co., Gull Communications, Hi-Desert Publishing Co., Inc., News West Publishing Company Inc., Penny Power Publications Inc., Placer Community Newspapers, Inc. and Princ

IOWA CITY

IOWA CITY PRESS-CITIZEN

123 N Linn St, Ste 2E, Iowa City, Iowa, 52245-2147, Johnson; gen tel (319) 337-3181; adv tel (319) 337-3181; ed tel (319) 337-3181; gen fax (319) 339-7342; adv fax (319) 339-5953; ed fax (319) 339-7342; gen/nat adv e-mail advertising@press-citizen.com; disp adv e-mail advertising@press-citizen.com; class adv e-mailclassifieds@press-citizen.com; ed e-mail newsroom@press-citizen.com; web site www.press-citizen.com
Group: Gannett
Published: Mon, Tues, Wed, Thur, Fri, Sat
Weekday Frequency: All day
Saturday Frequency: All day
Circulation: 8,576; 9,668(sat); 552(sun)
Last Audit: AAM September 30, 2017
Advertising Rate (weekday/saturday): Open inch rate $41.64; $43.33 (Wed)
Advertising Rate (sunday): Open inch rate $42.50
News services: AP, GNS **Established:** 1920
Own Printing Facility?: No
Commercial Printers?: No
Special Editions: Key (Aug); Holiday Guide (Dec); Best of Area (Nov)
Special Weekly Sections: Taste (Wednesdays), Go - entertainment (Thursdays)
Digital Platform - Mobile: Apple, Android, Windows, Blackberry, Other
Digital Platform - Tablet: Apple iOS, Android, Kindle, Nook, Kindle Fire
News Dir. .... Katie Brumbeloe
Market Information: TMC.
Mechanical Available: Offset; Black and 3 ROP colors; insert accepted; page cutoffs - 22 3/4.
Mechanical Specifications: Type page 11 5/8 x 21 1/2; E - 6 cols, 1 5/16, 1/8 between; A - 6 cols, 1 5/16, 1/8 between; C - 9 cols, 1 1/6, 1/8 between.
Areas Served: Johnson County, Iowa
Delivery Method: Mail, Newsstand, Carrier, RacksEquipment & Software: PRESSROOM EQUIPMENT: Lines — 14-G/Urbanite 1000 Series; Control System — G.; MAILROOM EQUIPMENT: Counter Stackers — QWI/400, QWI/500, QWI/501; Inserters & Stuffers — HI/1372; Tying Machines — 1-Dynaric/1500, 1/MLN; Wrapping Singles — QWI/Underwrap; BUSINESS EQUIPMENT: IBM/AS-400 CLASSIFIED EQUIPMENT: Hardware — 1-APT.; DISPLAY EQUIPMENT: Printers — HP/LaserJet 4MV; Other Hardware — Kk/DC-50 Digital Camera, AG/Arcus Scanner, QMS/ Flatbed Scanner. DISPLAY SOFTWAREAd Make-up Applications — QPS/QuarkXPress, Adobe/Photoshop, Adobe/PageMaker, Adobe/Illustrator, Macromedia/Freehand; EDITORIAL EQUIPMENT: Hardware — 1-APT. PRODUCTION EQUIPMENT: Hardware — KPG; Scanners — Diadem/200S Direct Screen PRODUCTION SOFTWARE: ProImage/NewsWay.
Note: On Sundays, readers receive the Sunday state edition of the Des Moines Register wrapped in a full local news section provided by the Iowa City Press-Citizen. See the Des Moines Register listing for Sunday circulation and advertising rates.

KEOKUK

DAILY GATE CITY

1016 Main St, Keokuk, Iowa, 52632-4656, Lee; gen tel (319) 524-8300; adv tel (319) 524-8300; ed tel (319) 524-8300; gen fax (319) 524-4363; adv fax (319) 524-4363; ed fax (319) 524-4363; gen/nat adv e-mail admanager@dailygate.com; disp adv e-mail advertising@dailygate.com; class adv e-mailclassified@dailygate.com; ed e-mail dgceditor@dailygate.com; web site www.dailygate.com
Group: Community Media Group
Published: Mon, Tues, Wed, Thur, Fri
Weekday Frequency: e
Circulation: 5,500
Last Audit: Sworn/Estimate/Non-Audited February 16, 2018
Advertising Rate (weekday/saturday): Open inch rate $15.45
News services: AP. **Established:** 1847
Own Printing Facility?: Yes
Commercial Printers?: Yes
Special Editions: Clark County Pride 2013 (Jun); Senior Lifestyles 2013 (Apr); Lawn & Garden (Apr); Labor Day (Aug); Chronology (Dec); Progress (Feb); Bridal (Jan); Estate (Jun); Spring Car Care (Mar); Newcomers & Vacation (May); Winter Sports (Nov); Woman (Oct); Fall Home Improvement (Sept).
Syndicated Publications: TV Magazine (Fri); American Profile (Weekly).
Digital Platform - Mobile: Apple, Android
Digital Platform - Tablet: Apple iOS, Android, Kindle, Nook, Kindle Fire
Mng. Ed. .... Steve Dunn
Mng. Ed. .... Cindy Iutzi
Ad. Mgr. .... Amy Morgan
Circ. .... Deana Young
Pub. .... Chuck Vandenberg
Staff Writer .... Megan McNeill
Market Information: ADS; TMC.
Mechanical Available: Offset; Black and 3 ROP colors; insert accepted; page cutoffs - 22 3/4.
Mechanical Specifications: Type page 13 1/4 x 21 1/2; E - 6 cols, 2 1/16, 1/16 between; A - 8 cols, 1 1/2, 1/8 between; C - 8 cols, 1 1/2, 1/8 between.
Areas Served: Fort Madison, West Point, Donnellson, Montrose, Denmark, Wever, Farmington, Dallas City, Nauvoo, and Niota
Delivery Method: Mail, Newsstand, Carrier, RacksEquipment & Software: MAILROOM EQUIPMENT: Tying Machines — MLN/2EE.; BUSINESS EQUIPMENT: Qantel CLASSIFIED EQUIPMENT: Hardware — APP/Mac; CLASSIFIED SOFTWARE: Baseview. DISPLAY EQUIPMENT: Hardware — APP/Mac; Printers — Xante/8200; DISPLAY SOFTWARELayout Software — 3-APP/Power Mac 7100. EDITORIAL EQUIPMENT: Hardware — APP/Mac EDITORIAL SOFTWARE: Baseview. PRODUCTION EQUIPMENT: Hardware — Xante/8200, Adobe/Photoshop; Cameras — 1-R/24580 PRODUCTION SOFTWARE: Baseview.

LE MARS

LE MARS DAILY SENTINEL

41 1st Ave NE, Le Mars, Iowa, 51031-3535, Plymouth; gen tel (712) 546-7031; adv tel (712) 546-7031 ext. 21; ed tel (712) 546-7031 ext. 15; gen fax (712) 546-7035; adv fax (712) 546-7035; ed fax (712) 546-7035; gen/nat adv e-mail dcopenhaver@lemarssentinel.com; disp adv e-mail pgrant@lemarssentinel.

com; class adv e-mailmjost@lemarssentinel.com; ed e-mail dseditor@frontiernet.net; web site www.lemarssentinel.com
Group: Rust Communications
Published: Mon, Tues, Wed, Thur, Fri
Weekday Frequency: e
Circulation: 2,584
Last Audit: Sworn/Estimate/Non-Audited September 30, 2017
Advertising Rate (weekday/saturday): Open inch rate $12.85
News services: AP. **Established:** 1870
Own Printing Facility?: Yes
Commercial Printers?: Yes
Special Editions: Visitor's Guide (Apr); Back-to-School (Aug); Holiday (Dec); Pride in Plymouth Co. (Feb); Bridal (Jan); County Fair (Jul); Summer Sports (Jun); Homes n' Style (Mar); Grad Tab (May); Homes n' Style (Sept).
Special Weekly Sections: NASCAR (Fri); Agriculture (Thur); Cooking (Tues);
Syndicated Publications: Relish (Monthly); American Profile (Weekly). Athlon Sports (Monthly)
Digital Platform - Mobile: Apple, Android
Digital Platform - Tablet: Apple iOS, Android
Pub. .... Randy List
Editor .... Joanne Glamm
Mktg. Dir. .... Monte Jost
Lifestyles Ed. .... Beverly Van Buskirk
Data Processing Mgr. .... Judy Barnable
Account manager-Advertising .... Shannon Jost
Contributing Editor .... Magdalene Landegent
Staff Writer .... Amy Erickson
Sports Editor .... Jay Bell
Market Information: TMC.
Mechanical Available: Offset; Black and 3 ROP colors; insert accepted; page cutoffs - 21 1/2.
Mechanical Specifications: Type page 13 x 21 1/2; E - 6 cols, 2 1/16, 1/8 between; A - 6 cols, 2 1/16, 1/8 between; C - 6 cols, 2 1/16, 1/8 between.
Areas Served: 51031, 51001, 51024, 1028, 51038, 51045, 51050, 51101-51008
Delivery Method: Mail, Carrier, RacksEquipment & Software: PRESSROOM EQUIPMENT: Lines — 6-G/Community; Reels & Stands — 5-G/Community Stand.; MAILROOM EQUIPMENT: Tying Machines — Malow/50, Bu; Address Machine — Miller/Bevco 285.; BUSINESS EQUIPMENT: 4-Gateway/2000, Compaq, Compaq CLASSIFIED EQUIPMENT: Hardware — APP/Mac, CAMS; Printers — APP/Mac LaserWriters; CLASSIFIED SOFTWARE: QPS/QuarkXPress 6.0. DISPLAY EQUIPMENT: Hardware — APP/Mac; Printers — APP/Mac LaserWriter; DISPLAY SOFTWAREAd Make-up Applications — QPS/QuarkXPress 6.0.; EDITORIAL EQUIPMENT: Hardware — APP/Mac/Konica, Imagesetter; Printers — APP/Mac LaserWriters, QMS/860, NewGen/DesignXpress EDITORIAL SOFTWARE: APP/Mac, QPS/QuarkXPress 6.0. PRODUCTION EQUIPMENT: Hardware — SL/GNS-28; Cameras — 1-SCREEN/C-240-D, Kyoto/Japan; Scanners — Polaroid.

MARSHALLTOWN

TIMES-REPUBLICAN

135 W Main St, Marshalltown, Iowa, 50158-5843, Marshall; gen tel (641) 753-6611; gen fax (641) 753-8813; gen/nat adv e-mail tradv@timesrepublican.com; disp adv e-mail tradv@timesrepublican.com; class adv e-mailtrclass@timesrepublican.com ; ed e-mail news@timesrepublican.com; web site www.timesrepublican.com
Group: Ogden Newspapers Inc.
Published: Mon, Tues, Wed, Thur, Fri, Sat, Sun
Weekday Frequency: m
Saturday Frequency: m
Circulation: 6,523; 6,523(sat); 6,715(sun)
Last Audit: AAM June 30, 2017
Advertising Rate (weekday/saturday): Open inch rate $25.59
Advertising Rate (sunday): Open inch rate $25.59
News services: AP. **Established:** 1856
Own Printing Facility?: Yes
Commercial Printers?: Yes
Special Editions: Seniors Tab (Apr); Football Contest (Aug); Holiday Greetings (Dec); Agri-Business (Feb); Bridal Tab (Jan); Little League Review (Jul); Outdoors (Jun); Home Improvement (Mar); Health Tab (May); Business Magazine (Monthly); Christmas Countdown (Nov).
Special Weekly Sections: Business/Financial (Daily); Best Food Day (Wed); Auto, Entertainment (Thur); Real Estate, Religion (Sat)
Syndicated Publications: Parade (S).
Digital Platform - Mobile: Apple, Android
Digital Platform - Tablet: Apple iOS, Android
Ed. .... Jeff Hutton
Circ. Dir. .... Randy Cutright
Copy Ed. .... Wes Burns
Educ. Reporter .... Andrew Potter
Sports Ed. .... Ross Thede
IT Dir. .... Steve Plain
Prodn. Mgr., Press .... Clayton Steil
Adv. Dir. .... Linda R. Gould
Reporter .... Adam Sodders
Pub. .... Mike Schlesinger
Market Information: ADS; TMC.
Mechanical Available: Offset; Black and 3 ROP colors; insert accepted - all, no brokered group ads; page cutoffs - 22 3/4.
Mechanical Specifications: Type page 10 x 21 1/2; E - 6 cols, 1 1/2, 1/4 between; A - 6 cols, 1 1/2, 1/4 between; C - 9 cols, 1, 1/8 between.
Areas Served: 50005; 50051; 50056; 50078; 50106; 50112; 50120; 50122; 50141; 50142; 50148; 50158; 50163; 50173; 50234; 50239; 50247; 50258; 50269; 50278; 50609; 50621; 50627; 50632; 50635; 50637; 50638; 50680; 52339; 52342
Delivery Method: Mail, Newsstand, Carrier, RacksEquipment & Software: PRESSROOM EQUIPMENT: Lines — 8-G/Community (upper former) 1988; 8-G/Community (upper former) 1988; MAILROOM EQUIPMENT: Counter Stackers — Hl; Tying Machines — EAM-Mosca/Automatic, MLN; Wrapping Singles — QWI; Address Machine — Ch.; BUSINESS EQUIPMENT: Dell CLASSIFIED EQUIPMENT: Hardware — Dell; DISPLAY SOFTWAREAd Make-up Applications — Multi-Ad/Creator, QPS/QuarkXPress; Layout Software — G-5s EDITORIAL EQUIPMENT: Hardware — G-5s PRODUCTION EQUIPMENT: Hardware — ECRM - CTP

MASON CITY

GLOBE GAZETTE, MASON CITY

300 N Washington Ave, Mason City, Iowa, 50401-3222, Cerro Gordo; gen tel (641) 421-0500; adv tel (641) 421-0546; ed tel (641) 421-0524; gen fax (641) 421-7108; adv fax (641) 421-7108; ed fax (641) 421-7108; gen/nat adv e-mail rose.walker@globegazette.com; disp adv e-mail greg.wilderman@globegazette.com; class adv e-mailolivia.stalker@globegazette.com; ed e-mail howard.query@globegazette.com; web site www.globegazette.com
Group: Lee Enterprises, Inc.
Published: Mon, Tues, Wed, Thur, Fri, Sat, Sun
Weekday Frequency: m
Saturday Frequency: m
Circulation: 10,315; 10,315(sat); 12,840(sun)
Last Audit: AAM September 30, 2017
Advertising Rate (weekday/saturday): Open inch rate $32.45
Advertising Rate (sunday): Open inchr ate $38.95
Online Advertising Rate: 2 days in print and online for $18.00
News services: AP. **Established:** 1862
Own Printing Facility?: Yes
Commercial Printers?: Yes
Special Editions: Lawn & Garden (May); North Iowa Farmer (Monthly); High School Winter Sports (Nov); Builder's Tour (Apr); Fall Fashion Show (Aug); Gifts (Dec); All About Love (Feb); Health & Fitness (Jan); Economic Report (Jul); Grilling Made Easy (Jun); Do It Yourself (Mar).
Special Weekly Sections: Style, Business, Celebrations, TV (Sun); Taste (Tue); Health, Fitness (Wed); Entertainment (Thur); Home, Garden (Fri); Faith, Outdoor (Sat); Travel (1st Sunday)
Syndicated Publications: Relish (Monthly); Parade (S); American Profile (Weekly).
Digital Platform - Mobile: Apple, Android
Digital Platform - Tablet: Apple iOS, Android
Financial Mgr. .... Linda Halfman
Adv. Mgr., Classified .... Amy Stoeffler
Adv. Mgr., Display .... Greg Wilderman
Mktg. Mgr. .... Ruth Miller
Circ. Mgr. .... Jeff Binstock
Ed. .... Joe Buttweiler
City Ed. .... Jane Reynolds
Editorial Page Ed. .... Bob Steenson
Editorial Page Ed. .... Tom Thomas
Librarian .... Judy Delperdang
Lifestyle Ed. .... Karen Jacobs
Online Ed. .... Olivia Ostrander
Reporter .... Jan Horgen
Sports Ed. .... Kirk Hard Castle
Data Processing Mgr. .... Terry Balek
Prodn. Supvr., Pre Press .... Lisa Ahrens
Prodn. Supvr., Pressroom .... Rob Curly
Nat'l Adv. Rep. .... Rose Walker
Pub. .... Roy Biondi
Market Information: ADS; Split run; TMC.
Mechanical Available: Letterpress; Black and 3 ROP colors; insert accepted - self-adhesive notes, samples; page cutoffs - 22.
Mechanical Specifications: Type page 12 x 21; E - 6 cols, 2 1/16, 1/8 between; A - 6 cols, 2 1/16, 1/8 between; C - 9 cols, 1 3/8, 1/16 between.
Areas Served: 50421, 50423, 50424, 50616, 50428, 50436, 50438, 50441, 50446, 50447, 50448, 50452, 50401, 50457, 50458, 50459, 50461, 50464, 50467, 50470, 50472, 50475, 50477, 50479, 50511, 50605, 50625
Delivery Method: Mail, Newsstand, Carrier, RacksEquipment & Software: PRESSROOM EQUIPMENT: Lines — 8-KBA/Mot-Colormax 5W with CIC single width; Folders — 1-G/SSC, 1.; MAILROOM EQUIPMENT: Tying Machines — 2-MLN/ML2EE; Address Machine — 1-Ch/595-596.; BUSINESS EQUIPMENT: 1-IBM/AS-400 CLASSIFIED EQUIPMENT: Hardware — 2-IBM/RS 6000; Printers — HP.; DISPLAY EQUIPMENT: Hardware — APP/Mac; Printers — HP; DISPLAY SOFTWAREAd Make-up Applications — QPS/QuarkXPress 4.02; Layout Software — MEI/ALS. EDITORIAL EQUIPMENT: Hardware — 2-IBM/RS 6000, Compaq/Proliant Server 2500; Printers — HP EDITORIAL SOFTWARE: MS/NT 4.0. PRODUCTION EQUIPMENT: Hardware — 2-Pre Press/Panther Pro-46, APP/Mac Preserver; Cameras — 1-R/480, 1-C/Spartan II, ECR/Autokon 1000; Scanners — AG/Argus II PRODUCTION SOFTWARE: QPS/QuarkXPress 3.32.

MOUNT PLEASANT

MT. PLEASANT NEWS

215 W Monroe St, Mount Pleasant, Iowa, 52641-2110, Henry; gen tel 319-385-3131; adv tel (319) 385-3131; ed tel (319) 986-5186; gen fax (319) 385-8048; adv fax (319) 385-8048; ed fax (319) 385-8048; gen/nat adv e-mail adv@mpnews.net; disp adv e-mail adv@mpnews.net; class adv e-mailadv@mpnews.net; ed e-mail news@mpnews.net; web site www.mpnews.net; web site 2 goldentriangle.jobs
Group: Cedar Rapids Press
Published: Mon, Tues, Wed, Thur, Fri
Weekday Frequency: e
Circulation: 2,668
Last Audit: Sworn/Estimate/Non-Audited September 30, 2017
Advertising Rate (weekday/saturday): Open inch rate $13.72
News services: AP. **Established:** 1878
Own Printing Facility?: No
Commercial Printers?: No
Special Editions: Home Improvement (Apr); Senior Citizen (Aug); Basketball (Dec); Brides (Jan); Fair (Jul); Little League/Softball (Jun); Agriculture (Mar); Summer Fun (May); Christmas Showcase (Nov); Chamber of Commerce (Oct); Senior Lifestyle (Sept).
Special Weekly Sections: Entertainment (Fri); Business (Mon); Education (Thur); Agriculture (Tues); Editorial Page (Wed).
Syndicated Publications: American Profile (Mon).
Digital Platform - Mobile: Apple, Android
Digital Platform - Tablet: Apple iOS, Android
Publisher .... Matt Bryant
News Editor .... Brooks Taylor
Advertising Manager .... Kaci Lundsford
Editor & Publisher .... Bill Gray
Market Information: ADS; TMC.
Mechanical Available: Offset; Black and 3 ROP colors; insert accepted - any; page cutoffs - 22 5/8.
Mechanical Specifications: Type page 13 x 21 1/2; E - 6 cols, 2 1/16, 1/8 between; A - 6 cols, 2 1/16, 1/8 between; C - 8 cols, 1 7/16, 1/8 between.
Areas Served: Mt. Pleasant and Henry County
Delivery Method: Mail, Newsstand, Carrier, RacksEquipment & Software: MAILROOM EQUIPMENT: Tying Machines — 1/Bu; Address Machine — 2-/Wm.; BUSINESS EQUIPMENT: IBM CLASSIFIED EQUIPMENT: Hardware — 1-APP/Power Mac.; DISPLAY SOFTWARELayout Software — 2-APP/Mac G3, APP/Mac Quadra 650. EDITORIAL EQUIPMENT: Hardware — 1-APP/Power Mac, 1-APP/Mac G3, 1-APP/iMac. PRODUCTION EQUIPMENT: Hardware — 1-Nat/250; Cameras — 1-Nu; Scanners — APP/Mac PRODUCTION SOFTWARE: QPS/QuarkXPress 4.0.

MUSCATINE

MUSCATINE JOURNAL

301 E 3rd St, Muscatine, Iowa, 52761-4116, Muscatine; gen tel (563) 262-0550; adv tel (563) 262-0543; ed tel (563) 262-0532; gen fax (563) 262-8042; adv fax (563) 262-8042; ed fax (563) 262-8042; gen/nat adv e-mail jweikert@muscatinejournal.com; disp adv e-mail sales@muscatinejournal.com; class adv e-mailbecky.gray@muscatinejournal.com; ed e-mail rusty.schrader@muscatinejournal.com; web site www.muscatinejournal.com
- 1,076,000(views) 102,691(visitors)
Group: Lee Enterprises, Inc.
Published: Mon, Tues, Wed, Thur, Fri, Sat
Weekday Frequency: m
Saturday Frequency: m
Circulation: 2,097; 2,066(sat)
Last Audit: AAM March 31, 2016
Advertising Rate (weekday/saturday): Open inch rate $17.64
Advertising Rate (sunday): Open inch rate $18.06
Online Advertising Rate: $10.00
News services: AP, DF, TMS. **Established:** 1840
Own Printing Facility?: Yes
Commercial Printers?: No
Special Editions: Best of Muscatine 2012 (Nov); Muscatine Journal Graduation 2013 (May); Spring Car Care (Apr); Back-to-School (Aug); Gift Guide (Dec); Answer Book (Jul); Little League (Jun); Gift Guide (Nov); Car Care (Oct); Find it in Muscatine (Sept).
Special Weekly Sections: Sports (Mon); Best Food Day (Tue); Outdoor (Tue); Family, Friends, Real Estate (Wed); Health, Lifestyles (Thur); Faith (Fri); TV, Work, Money, Business, Agriculture (Sat)
Syndicated Publications: Primetime (Thur).
Digital Platform - Mobile: Apple
Digital Platform - Tablet: Apple iOS
News Ed. .... Rusty Schrader
Editor / Publisher .... Steve Jameson
Sports Editor .... Nick Cusick
Pub. .... Karla Pinner
Market Information: ADS; TMC.
Mechanical Available: Offset; Black and 3 ROP colors; insert accepted; page cutoffs - 20 1/2.
Mechanical Specifications: Type page 11 3/5 x 20 1/2; E - 6 cols, 1 4/5, 1/8 between; A - 6 cols, 1 4/5, 1/8 between; C - 9 cols, 1 3/8, 1/16 between.
Areas Served: 52761, 52653, 52720, 52738, 52747, 52749, 52752, 52754, 52760, 52766, 52776
Delivery Method: Mail, Newsstand, Carrier, RacksEquipment & Software: MAILROOM EQUIPMENT: Tying Machines — 1-MLN/Spirit-Strapper.; BUSINESS EQUIPMENT: IBM/AS-400, Remote access via T-1, PC Workstations BUSINESS SOFTWARE: IBM/AS-400, Lee Business System, Microsoft/Office 2000 CLASSIFIED EQUIPMENT: Hardware — APP/Mac; Printers — HP 8150; CLASSIFIED SOFTWARE: Baseview. DISPLAY EQUIPMENT: Hardware — APP/Mac; Printers — HP/5MV, HP/8000 DN, HP/8150 DN; Other Hardware — HP/Scanner, CD-Rom, Iomega/Jazz Drive IGB, Hammer/DE compact disk recorder DISPLAY

SOFTWAREAd Make-up Applications — QPS/QuarkXPress; Layout Software — APP/Mac, QPS/QuarkXPress. EDITORIAL EQUIPMENT: Hardware — APP/Mac/APP/Mac IIsi, AP/GraphicsNet, Lf/AP Leaf Picture Desk, Lf/Negative Scanner; Printers — HP 551 EDITORIAL SOFTWARE: Baseview. PRODUCTION EQUIPMENT: Hardware — Lf/AP Leaf Picture Desk, AG/Rapiline 17; Scanners — APP/Mac One Scanner, HP/ScanJet PRODUCTION SOFTWARE: Baseview.

NEWTON

NEWTON DAILY NEWS

200 1st Ave E, Newton, Iowa, 50208-3716, Jasper; gen tel (641) 792-3121; adv tel (641) 792-3121; ed tel (641) 792-3121; gen fax (641) 791-7104; adv fax (641) 791-7104; ed fax (641) 791-7104; gen/nat adv e-mail advertising@newtondailynews.com; disp adv e-mail advertising@newtondailynews.com; class adv e-mailjholschuh@newtondailynews.com; ed e-mail beschliman@newtondailynews.com; web site www.newtondailynews.com

Group: Shaw Media
Published: Mon, Tues, Wed, Thur, Fri
Weekday Frequency: e
Circulation: 5,476
Last Audit: Sworn/Estimate/Non-Audited September 30, 2017
Advertising Rate (weekday/saturday): Open inch rate $13.50
Online Advertising Rate: Online insertion $7.00 per day
News services: AP, CNS, MCT, NEA, TMS. **Established:** 1902
Special Editions: Jasper County Fair (Jul); Alumni Weekend (Jun); Health & Medical Directory 2013 (Apr); Recycling Guide (Apr); Progress Edition (Feb); Spring Bridal (Jan); Business Showcase (Nov); Local Business Women (Oct); Fall Football (Sept).
Special Weekly Sections: TV Digest (Fri).
Syndicated Publications: Relish (Monthly); American Profile (Thur).
Digital Platform - Mobile: Apple, Android
Digital Platform - Tablet: Apple iOS, Android, Kindle, Nook, Kindle Fire
Pub. .... Dan Goetz
Bus. Mgr. .... Brenda Lamb
Adv. Mgr. .... Jeff Holschuh
Ed. .... Bob Eschliman
Prodn. Mgr. .... Kelly Vest
Prodn. Mgr., Commercial Printing Chris Basinger
Prodn. Supvr., Composing Room Mari Jo DeGrado
Editor .... Abigail Pelzer
Market Information: TMC.
Mechanical Available: Offset; Black and 3 ROP colors; insert accepted; page cutoffs - 22 3/4.
Mechanical Specifications: Type page 12 1/2 x 21 1/2; E - 6 cols, 1 7/8, 1/8 between; A - 6 cols, 1 7/8, 1/8 between; C - 9 cols, 1 1/4, 1/16 between.
Delivery Method: Mail, Newsstand, Carrier, RacksEquipment & Software: PRESSROOM EQUIPMENT: Lines — 6-G/Suburban 1969.; MAILROOM EQUIPMENT: Counter Stackers — 1/BG; Tying Machines — 3-Bu, 3-Strapmatic; Address Machine — KR.; BUSINESS EQUIPMENT: 2-Bl, ATT CLASSIFIED EQUIPMENT: Hardware — APP/iMac; CLASSIFIED SOFTWARE: Baseview. DISPLAY EQUIPMENT: Hardware — iMac/G4; DISPLAY SOFTWARELayout Software — Adforce. EDITORIAL EQUIPMENT: Hardware — APP/Mac; Printers — APP/Mac LaserWriter Plus EDITORIAL SOFTWARE: QPS/QuarkXPress 4.1, Microsoft/Word. PRODUCTION EQUIPMENT: Hardware — 1-Nu, APP/Mac, Konica/5100T 5.3, Konica/3100S 5.1; Cameras — 1-Kk PRODUCTION SOFTWARE: QuarkXPress 4.1.

OELWEIN

THE OELWEIN DAILY REGISTER

25 1st St SE, Oelwein, Iowa, 50662-2306, Fayette; gen tel (319) 283-2144; adv tel (319) 283-2144; ed tel (319) 283-2144; gen fax (319) 283-3268; adv fax (319) 283-3268; ed fax (319) 283-3268; gen/nat adv e-mail tracy.cummings@oelweindailyregister.com; disp adv e-mail ads@oelweindailyregister.com; class adv e-mailclassifieds@oelweindailyregister.com; ed e-mail editor@oelweindailyregister.com; web site www.oelweindailyregister.com

Group: Community Media Group
Published: Mon, Tues, Wed, Thur, Fri, Sat
Weekday Frequency: All day
Saturday Frequency: All day
Circulation: 2,354; 2,354(sat)
Last Audit: Sworn/Estimate/Non-Audited September 30, 2017
Advertising Rate (weekday/saturday): Open inch rate $18.60
News services: AP. **Established:** 1882
Own Printing Facility?: Yes
Commercial Printers?: Yes
Special Editions: Husky (Apr); Pigskin Preview (Aug); Christmas Promotions (Dec); Soil Conservation (Feb); Bridal (Jan); Summer Sports (Jul); Father's Day (Jun); Update (Mar); Graduation (May); Christmas Open House (Nov); Fire Prevention (Oct); Fall-Tourism (Sept).
Special Weekly Sections: Weekly TV (Fri); Agriculture Edition (Wed).
Digital Platform - Mobile: Apple, Android
Digital Platform - Tablet: Apple iOS, Android, Kindle, Nook
Pub. .... Deb Weigel
Mng. Ed. .... Jack Swanson
City Ed. .... Deb Kunkle
Prodn. Mgr. .... David Gelhausen
Circ. Mgr. .... James Barbutes
Market Information: TMC.
Mechanical Available: Offset; Black and 3 ROP colors; insert accepted; page cutoffs - 22 3/4.
Mechanical Specifications: Type page 12 x 21 1/2; E - 6 cols, 1 7/8, 1/6 between; A - 6 cols, 1 7/8, 1/6 between; C - 9 cols, 1 1/2, 1/12 between.
Areas Served: Northeast Iowa
Delivery Method: Mail, Newsstand, RacksEquipment & Software: PRESSROOM EQUIPMENT: Lines — 7-G/C901; MAILROOM EQUIPMENT: Tying Machines — 1/Bu, 1-/Sa, 1-Malow/MC-50; Address Machine — 1-SC/labeler.; PRODUCTION EQUIPMENT: Hardware — 2-COM/Unisetter, 1-COM/Area Unified Composer.

OSKALOOSA

OSKALOOSA HERALD

1901 A Ave W, Oskaloosa, Iowa, 52577-1962, Mahaska; gen tel (641) 672-2581 ext. 427; adv tel (641) 672-2581 ext. 413; ed tel (641) 672-2581 ext. 425; gen fax ; adv fax (641) 673-8226; ed fax ; gen/nat adv e-mail debve@oskyherald.com; disp adv e-mail debve@oskyherald.com; class adv e-mailoskyclass@oskyherald.com; ed e-mail oskynews@oskyherald.com; web site www.oskaloosaherald.com

Group: Community Newspaper Holdings, Inc.
Published: Mon, Tues, Thur, Fri
Weekday Frequency: All day
Circulation: 2,174
Last Audit: Sworn/Estimate/Non-Audited October 1, 2017
Advertising Rate (weekday/saturday): Open inch rate $10.43
Online Advertising Rate: $15.00 cpm
News services: NEA, INA, AP. **Established:** 1850
Special Editions: Progress (Mar).
Special Weekly Sections: Health, Outdoors (Mon); Business (Wed); School (Thur); Church (Fri); TV (Daily)
Syndicated Publications: Relish (Monthly); American Profile (Weekly).
Digital Platform - Mobile: Apple, Android
Digital Platform - Tablet: Apple iOS, Android, Kindle, Nook, Kindle Fire
Pub./Adv. Sales./Classified Adv. Mgr./Display Adv. Deb Van Engelenhoven
Market Information: TMC.
Mechanical Available: Offset; Black and 3 ROP colors; insert accepted - all; page cutoffs - 22 3/4.
Mechanical Specifications: Type page 13 x 21 1/2; E - 6 cols, 2 1/16, 1/8 between; A - 6 cols, 2 1/16, 1/8 between; C - 6 cols, 2 1/16, 1/16 between.
Delivery Method: Mail, CarrierEquipment & Software: PRESSROOM EQUIPMENT: Lines — 6-WPC/Web Leader.; MAILROOM EQUIPMENT: Tying Machines — 1-Bu/182XE4, 1-Sa/SR2CTAN; Address Machine — 1-Am/1950B.; BUSINESS EQUIPMENT: IBM CLASSIFIED EQUIPMENT: Hardware — APP/Mac.; DISPLAY SOFTWARELayout Software — APP/Mac. EDITORIAL EQUIPMENT: Hardware — APP/Mac EDITORIAL SOFTWARE: QPS. PRODUCTION EQUIPMENT: Hardware — 1-Nu/Flip Top FT40L, LE/24AQ; Cameras — Acti/S 25; Scanners — APP/Mac.

OTTUMWA

THE OTTUMWA COURIER

213 E 2nd St, Ottumwa, Iowa, 52501-2902, Wapello; gen tel (641) 684-4611; adv tel (641) 683-5349; ed tel (641) 683-5365; gen fax (641) 684-7834; adv fax (641) 683-4118; ed fax (641) 684-7326; gen/nat adv e-mail dsylvester@ottumwacourier.com; disp adv e-mail dsylvester@ottumwacourier.com; class adv e-mailclassmgr@ottumwacourier.com; ed e-mail news@ottumwacourier.com; web site www.ottumwacourier.com - 400,000(views) 120,000(visitors)

Group: Community Newspaper Holdings, Inc.
Published: Tues, Wed, Thur, Fri, Sat
Weekday Frequency: m
Saturday Frequency: m
Circulation: 9,303; 9,168(sat)
Last Audit: Sworn/Estimate/Non-Audited September 30, 2017
Advertising Rate (weekday/saturday): Open inch rate $20.25
News services: AP. **Established:** 1848
Own Printing Facility?: Yes
Commercial Printers?: Yes
Special Editions: Spring Home Improvement (Apr); Bridal Tab (Feb); Home Expo (Mar); Salute to Graduates (May); Fall Sports Preview (Sept).
Special Weekly Sections: Lifestyle, Racing, Bowling (Tue); Learning, Health (Wed); Food, Entertainment, Remember When (Thur); TV, NASCAR (Fri); Religion, Outdoors (Sat)
Syndicated Publications: Relish (Monthly); American Profile (Weekly); Parade (Weekly)
Digital Platform - Mobile: Apple, Android
Digital Platform - Tablet: Apple iOS, Android
Pub./Ed. .... Wanda Moeller
Audience Development Director Traci Counterman
Adv. Mgr. .... Dan Sylvester
Reporter .... Danielle Lunsford
Classified Supervisor .... Erica Kenney
Business Manager .... Marcia Kamerick
Production Director .... Nick Workman
Market Information: ADS; Split run; TMC.
Mechanical Available: Offset; Black and 3 ROP colors; insert accepted; page cutoffs - 22 3/4.
Mechanical Specifications: Type page 13 x 21 1/2; E - 6 cols, 2 1/16, 1/6 between; A - 6 cols, 2 1/16, 1/6 between; C - 9 cols, 1 3/8, 1/16 between.
Areas Served: Wapello and Southeast Iowa
Delivery Method: Mail, Newsstand, CarrierEquipment & Software: PRESSROOM EQUIPMENT: Lines — 5-G/Urbanite 850 1971; Folders — 1-G/2:1; Reels & Stands — 1, 9.; MAILROOM EQUIPMENT: Counter Stackers — 1-HL/Monitor; Inserters & Stuffers — MM/227E 5:1; Tying Machines — 1/Cyclops, 1-/MLN, 1-Dynaric/NP1500; Wrapping Singles — 1-Id/Bottom Wrapper; Address Machine — 1-Ch/582N, 1-VideoJet/569 Labeler; BUSINESS EQUIPMENT: IBM/AS-400, 4-Gateway/166, Corporate WAN BUSINESS SOFTWARE: Microsoft/Excel, Microsoft/Word PC Support, WordPerfect, Microsoft/Access CLASSIFIED EQUIPMENT: Hardware — 1-APP/Mac 8550 Workgroup Server, 5-APP/Mac 7200-120; Printers — HP/5MP; CLASSIFIED SOFTWARE: Baseview/Class Manager Pro. DISPLAY EQUIPMENT: Hardware — 2-Motorola/StarMax 4000/200, Motorola/StarMax 3000-180, 3-APP/Power Mac 7600; Printers — QMS/PS-410, HP/LaserJet IIIsi, Unity/LaserMaster 1800, HP/455 Ca; DISPLAY SOFTWAREAd Make-up Applications — Multi-Ad/Creator 4.0, Aldus/Freehand 8.0, Aldus/PageMaker 6.5, QPS/QuarkXPress; EDITORIAL EQUIPMENT: Hardware — 2-APP/Mac 8550 Workgroup Server, 1-APP/Mac 7250 Workgroup Server, 11-Motorola/StarMax 3800-180, 6-Motorola/StarMax 4000-200/Microtek/ScanMaker, Polaroid/SprintScan, Lf/AP Leaf Picture Desk; Printers — HP/6MP EDITORIAL SOFTWARE: News edit pro PRODUCTION EQUIPMENT: Hardware — Digi-Colour, Caere/OmniPage Direct, Adobe/Photoshop 5.0; Cameras — 1-C/Spartan II, 1-SCREEN; Scanners — HP/ScanJet Plus, HP/ScanJet IIp, 2-Microtek III, Polaroid/SprintScan PRODUCTION SOFTWARE: QPS/QuarkXPress 3.32, Adobe/PageMaker 5.0.

SIOUX CITY

SIOUX CITY JOURNAL

515 Pavonia St, Sioux City, Iowa, 51101-2245, Woodbury; gen tel (712) 293-4250; adv tel (712) 293-4325; ed tel (712) 293-4224; gen fax (712) 279-5099; adv fax (712) 279-5099; ed fax (712) 279-5059; gen/nat adv e-mail adv@siouxcityjournal.com; disp adv e-mail adv@siouxcityjournal.com; class adv e-mailadv@siouxcityjournal.com; ed e-mail bhayworth@siouxcityjournal.com; web site www.siouxcityjournal.com - 320,730(views) 216,000(visitors)

Group: Lee Enterprises, Inc.
Published: Mon, Tues, Wed, Thur, Fri, Sat, Sun
Weekday Frequency: All day
Saturday Frequency: All day
Circulation: 20,781; 20,781(sat); 24,189(sun)
Last Audit: AAM September 30, 2016
Advertising Rate (weekday/saturday): Open inch rate $75.00
Advertising Rate (sunday): Open inch rate $82.75
News services: AP. **Established:** 1864
Own Printing Facility?: Yes
Commercial Printers?: No
Special Editions: Progress (Mar).
Special Weekly Sections: Best Food (Wed); Health (Fri); Auto, Expanded Sports (Sat); Business, Sports, Living, Entertainment
Syndicated Publications: Parade Magazine (S); American Profile (Weekly).
Digital Platform - Mobile: Apple, Android
Digital Platform - Tablet: Apple iOS, Android, Kindle, Nook, Kindle Fire
Pub. .... Ron Peterson
Controller .... Sue Stusse
Ed. .... Mitch Pugh
Mng. Ed., Sports .... Jeff Tobin
City Ed. .... Barbara Walker
Opinion Ed. .... Mike Gors
Librarian .... Janet Lubsen
Music Ed. .... Bruce Miller
News Ed., Night .... Jim Jenkins
Photo Dept. Mgr. .... Tim Hynds
Society/Women's Ed. .... Tim Gallagher
Sports Ed. .... Terry Hersom
Mgmt. Info Servs. Mgr. .... Mark Schmith
Online Mgr. .... Rob Kritzer
Prodn. Foreman, Mailroom Brad Christopherson
Nat'l Adv. Mgr. .... Beth Birdsell
Retail Adv. Dir. .... Tom Kuchera
Managing Editor/News .... Dave Dreeszen
Cir. Dir. .... Daniel Walock
Market Information: ADS; Split run; TMC; Zoned editions.
Mechanical Available: Offset; Black and 3 ROP colors; insert accepted; page cutoffs - 22 3/4.
Mechanical Specifications: Type page 11 1/2 x 21 1/2; E - 6 cols, 1 3/4, 1/8 between; A - 6 cols, 1 3/4, 1/8 between; C - 9 cols, 1 1/16, 1/8 between.
Delivery Method: Mail, Newsstand, Carrier, RacksEquipment & Software: PRESSROOM EQUIPMENT: Lines — 14-G/Urbanite (6 Stacked).; MAILROOM EQUIPMENT: Counter Stackers — 3-QWI; Inserters & Stuffers — GMA; Tying Machines — QWI; Address Machine — Kk.; BUSINESS EQUIPMENT: APP/Mac G3 BUSINESS SOFTWARE: Baseview CLASSIFIED EQUIPMENT: Hardware — COM/Intrepid 48, APP/Mac; Printers — NewGen; CLASSIFIED SOFTWARE: APT. DISPLAY EQUIPMENT: Hardware — APP/Mac G4; Printers — NewGen, Pre Press/Panther Pro Imagesetter 36; Other Hardware — 1-Max/

Vista DISPLAY SOFTWAREAd Make-up Applications — QPS/QuarkXPress 3.0, Multi-Ad/Creator; Layout Software — APP/Mac G4, MEI. EDITORIAL EQUIPMENT: Hardware — COM/Intrepid 48, APP/Mac; Printers — NewGen, HP, Pre Press/Panther Imagesetter 36 EDITORIAL SOFTWARE: Lotus/Notes, QPS/QuarkXPress, News Engine. PRODUCTION EQUIPMENT: Hardware — 2-NewGen, Pre Press/Panther Pro Imagesetter 36; Scanners — Panasonic/Image Scanner 16.

SPENCER

THE DAILY REPORTER

310 E Milwaukee St, Spencer, Iowa, 51301-4569, Clay; gen tel (712) 262-6610; adv tel (712) 262-6610; ed tel (712) 262-6610; gen fax (712) 262-3044; adv fax (712) 262-3044; ed fax (712) 262-3044; gen/nat adv e-mail tmorse@spencerdailyreporter.com; disp adv e-mail advertising@spencerdailyreporter.com; class adv e-mailtjmurphyr@spencerdailyreporter.com; ed e-mail news@spencerdailyreporter.com; web site www.spencerdailyreporter.com
Group: Rust Communications
Published: Tues, Thur, Fri, Sat
Weekday Frequency: m
Saturday Frequency: m
Circulation: 4,004; 3,852(sat)
Last Audit: Sworn/Estimate/Non-Audited September 30, 2017
Advertising Rate (weekday/saturday): Open inch rate $8.05
News services: AP, NEA. **Established:** 1959
Special Weekly Sections: Religion (Fri); TV (Thur)
Syndicated Publications: Relish (Monthly); TV Update (Thur); American Profile (Weekly).
Pub. .... Paula Buenger
Adv. Dir. .... Jason Lindsey
Ed. .... Randy Cauthron
Sports Ed. .... Zach Jevne
Staff Writer .... Seth Boyes
Market Information: Split run; TMC; Zoned editions.
Mechanical Available: Offset; Black and 3 ROP colors; insert accepted - any; page cutoffs - 22 5/8.
Mechanical Specifications: Type page 13 x 21 1/2; E - 6 cols, 2 1/16, 1/8 between; A - 6 cols, 2 1/16, 1/8 between; C - 6 cols, 2 1/16, 1/8 between.
Delivery Method: Mail, CarrierEquipment & Software: PRESSROOM EQUIPMENT: Lines — 5-G/Community.; MAILROOM EQUIPMENT: Tying Machines — Bu; Address Machine — Am.; BUSINESS EQUIPMENT: APP/Mac CLASSIFIED EQUIPMENT: Hardware — Mk.; DISPLAY SOFTWARELayout Software — 4-APP/Mac. EDITORIAL EQUIPMENT: Hardware — Mk. PRODUCTION EQUIPMENT: Hardware — Nat/A-250; Cameras — SCREEN/Companica; Scanners — Gam.

WASHINGTON

THE WASHINGTON EVENING JOURNAL

111 N Marion Ave, Washington, Iowa, 52353-1728, Washington; gen tel (319) 653-2191; adv tel (319) 653-2191; ed tel (319) 653-2191; gen fax (319) 653-7524; adv fax (319) 653-7524; ed fax (319) 653-7524; gen/nat adv e-mail sales@washjrnl.com; disp adv e-mail adv@washjrnl.com; class adv e-mailadv@washjrnl.com; ed e-mail news@washjrnl.com; web site www.washjrnl.com; web site 2 goldentriangle.jobs
Group: Cedar Rapids Press
Published: Mon, Tues, Wed, Thur, Fri
Weekday Frequency: e
Circulation: 3,462
Last Audit: Sworn/Estimate/Non-Audited September 30, 2017
Advertising Rate (weekday/saturday): Open inch rate $12.34
News services: AP.
Own Printing Facility?: Yes
Commercial Printers?: Yes
Special Editions: Christmas (Dec); Fall Opening (Fall); Beef Issue (May); Pork Production

(Oct); Spring Opening (Spring).
Special Weekly Sections: Week in Review (Fri); Business (Mon); Farm Page (Thur); Best Food Day (Tues).
Syndicated Publications: American Profile (Mon); Relish (Monthly).
Digital Platform - Mobile: Apple, Android
Digital Platform - Tablet: Apple iOS, Android
Circ. Dir. .... Kim Stout
President .... Darwin K. Sherman
Sports Ed. .... Aaron Viner
Prodn. Mgr. .... Steve Dunbar
Publisher .... Matt Bryant
Market Information: ADS; Split run; TMC.
Mechanical Available: Offset; Black and 3 ROP colors; insert accepted; page cutoffs - 22 3/4.
Mechanical Specifications: Type page 13 x 21 1/2; E - 6 cols, 2 1/16, 1/16 between; A - 6 cols, 2 1/16, 1/16 between; C - 8 cols, 1 9/16, 1/8 between.
Areas Served: Washington County
Delivery Method: Mail, Newsstand, Carrier, RacksEquipment & Software: PRESSROOM EQUIPMENT: Lines — HI/V-15A 1972.; BUSINESS EQUIPMENT: PC BUSINESS SOFTWARE: BMF CLASSIFIED EQUIPMENT: Hardware — APP/Mac; CLASSIFIED SOFTWARE: Microsoft/Word, Aldus/PageMaker. DISPLAY EQUIPMENT: Hardware — APP/Mac; Printers — APP/Mac LaserWriter II NT 630; DISPLAY SOFTWAREAd Make-up Applications — Aldus/PageMaker, Multi-Ad/Creator.; EDITORIAL EQUIPMENT: Hardware — APP/Mac; Printers — APP/Mac LaserWriter II NT 630 EDITORIAL SOFTWARE: Microsoft/Word. PRODUCTION EQUIPMENT: Hardware — APP/Mac NT.

WATERLOO

THE COURIER

100 E 4th St, PO Box 540, Waterloo, Iowa, 50703-4714, Black Hawk; gen tel (800) 798-1717; adv tel (319) 291-1497; ed tel (319) 291-1460; gen fax (319) 291-1569; adv fax (319) 234-3297; ed fax (319) 291-2069; gen/nat adv e-mail tara.seible@wcfcourier.com; disp adv e-mail angela.dark@wcfcourier.com; class adv e-mailclassads@wcfcourier.com; ed e-mail woo.newsroom@wcfcourier.com; web site www.wcfcourier.com
 - 3,500,000(views) 372,000(visitors)
Group: Lee Enterprises, Inc.
Published: Mon, Tues, Wed, Thur, Fri, Sun
Weekday Frequency: e
Saturday Frequency: m
Circulation: 27,433; 37,324(sun)
Last Audit: AAM March 31, 2016
Advertising Rate (weekday/saturday): Open inch rate $43.13
Advertising Rate (sunday): Open inch rate $59.69
Online Advertising Rate: Open rate $25.00/month; Pick-Up rate (with print ad purchase) $10.00/Month
News services: AP. **Established:** 1858
Own Printing Facility?: No
Commercial Printers?: Yes
Special Editions: Babies on Parade (Jan); Progress Editions (Feb); Spring Farm (Mar); Spring/Summer Activities Guide (Apr); Bid & Buy Auction (May); Boone Bash (Jun); Chamber Book (Jun); Our Hometown (Jul); Crazy Days (Jul); School Calendar (Aug); Faces In The Crowd (Sept); Ladies Night (Oct); Wacky Wednesday (Nov); Holiday Greetings (Dec).
Special Weekly Sections: Flavor (Tue); Best Food Day, Health (Wed); Entertainment (Thur); Arts, Auto, Business, Home, Living, Real Estate, Technology, Travel, Women (Sun)
Syndicated Publications: Cedar Valley Business (Monthly)
Proprietary Publications: Cedar Valley Home & Garden, Wheels, B-True, INCLUSION, Pulse
Digital Platform - Mobile: Apple, Android, Windows
Digital Platform - Tablet: Apple iOS, Android, Kindle, Kindle Fire
Pub. .... Roy Biondi
Controller .... Barbara Anderson
Mktg. Dir. .... Angela Dark
News Ed. .... Pat Kinney
Community Desk Ed. .... Catherine Kittrell
Sports Ed. .... Doug Newhoff

Lifestyles Ed. .... Melody Parker
Adv. Dir. .... Tara Seible
Circ. Mgr. .... Adam Bolander
Asst. News Ed. .... Doug Hines
IT Dir. .... Larry Orth
Circ. Mgr./Ops. Dir. .... Scott Kinter
Market Information: Split run; TMC; Zoned editions.
Mechanical Available: Offset; Black and 3 ROP colors; insert accepted; page cutoffs - 22 3/4.
Mechanical Specifications: Full page: 9.889" x 20". 6 column width: 1 col: 1.556"; 2 col: 3.222"; 3 col:4.889"; 4 col: 6.556"; 5 col: 8.222"; 6 col: 9.889".
Areas Served: 50613, 50614, 50701-06, 50705, 50667, 50703, 50626, 50613, 50643, 50651, 50648, 50644, 52326, 50612, 52224, 50675, 52229, 50669, 50638, 50642, 50642, 50600, 50665, 50770, 50602, 50649, 50658, 50630, 50659, 52154, 50666, 50676, 50674, 50677, 50647, 50622, 50668.
Delivery Method: Mail, Newsstand, Carrier, RacksEquipment & Software: PRESSROOM EQUIPMENT: Lines — Outsourced; BUSINESS EQUIPMENT: 1-Sun/Sparc BUSINESS SOFTWARE: Vision Data CLASSIFIED EQUIPMENT: Hardware — Sun; Printers — APP/Mac LaserWriters, ECR/Pelbox; CLASSIFIED SOFTWARE: Vision Data DISPLAY EQUIPMENT: Hardware — APP/Mac; Printers — APP/Mac LaserWriters, ECR/Pelbox; DISPLAY SOFTWAREAd Make-up Applications — InDesign; Layout Software — PageMaker

WEBSTER CITY

THE DAILY FREEMAN-JOURNAL

720 2nd St, Webster City, Iowa, 50595-1437, Hamilton; gen tel (515) 832-4350; adv tel (515) 832-4350; ed tel (515) 832-4350; gen fax (515) 832-2314; adv fax (515) 832-2314; ed fax (515) 832-2314; gen/nat adv e-mail cbargfrede@freemanjournal.net; disp adv e-mail jlovelace@freemanjournal.net; class adv e-mailadvertising@freemanjournal.net; ed e-mail editor@freemanjournal.net; web site www.freemanjournal.net
 - 150,000(views) 46,650(visitors)
Group: Ogden Newspapers Inc.
Published: Mon, Tues, Wed, Thur, Fri
Weekday Frequency: e
Circulation: 1,920
Last Audit: AAM June 30, 2017
Advertising Rate (weekday/saturday): Open inch rate $53.67
Advertising Rate (sunday): Open inch rate $53.67
Online Advertising Rate: Leaderboard $16.00 CPM; Half Banner $8.00 CPM; Middle Banner $11.00 CPM
News services: AP. **Established:** 1857
Own Printing Facility?: Yes
Commercial Printers?: Yes
Special Editions: Babies on Parade (Jan); Progress Editions (Feb); Spring Farm (Mar); Spring/Summer Activities Guide (Apr); Bid & Buy Auction (May); Boone Bash (Jun); Chamber Book (Jun); Our Hometown (Jul); Crazy Days (Jul); School Calendar (Aug); Faces In The Crowd (Sept); Ladies Night (Oct); Wacky Wednesday (Nov); Holiday Greetings (Dec).
Special Weekly Sections: Comics, Sports, Lifestyles, Entertainment (Daily); Education (Mon); Best Food (Wed); Business (Thur/Sun); Religion (Sat); TV, Comics, Entertainment, Farm (Sun)
Digital Platform - Mobile: Apple, Android
Digital Platform - Tablet: Apple iOS, Android
Gen. Mgr./Pub .... Terry Christensen
Circ. Dir. .... Grant Gibbon
Adv. Mgr. .... Cory Bargfrede
Mng. Ed. .... Anne Blankenship
Sports Ed. .... Troy Banning
Adv. Consultant .... Lance Draeger
Adv. Mgr. .... Josh Lovelace
Adv. Dir. .... Cory Bargfrede
Market Information: TMC.
Mechanical Available: Offset; Black and 3 ROP colors; insert accepted; page cutoffs - 22 3/4.
Mechanical Specifications: Type page 13 x 21 1/2; E - 6 cols, 2 1/16, 1/8 between; A - 6 cols, 2 1/16, 1/8 between; C - 9 cols, 1 5/16, 1/8 between.
Areas Served: Wright, Webster, Franklin, and

Hardin County
Delivery Method: Mail, Newsstand, Carrier, RacksEquipment & Software: PRESSROOM EQUIPMENT: Lines — 14-G/Suburban; Press Drive — 2-HP/100; Folders — 1-G/Urbanite, 1.; MAILROOM EQUIPMENT: Counter Stackers — 2-HI/RS 25; Inserters & Stuffers — HI; Tying Machines — 2/Bu; Address Machine — 2-/Ch; CLASSIFIED EQUIPMENT: Hardware — APP/Mac G3.; EDITORIAL EQUIPMENT: Hardware — 2-APP/Mac G3, APP/Power Mac, 2-APP/Mac G4; Printers — ECR/108, ECR/1500, Konica/Jetsetter. PRODUCTION EQUIPMENT: Hardware — 1-Nu, 2-Pako, APP/Mac, ECR/6200; Cameras — 1-Spartan II Flatbed Scanner PRODUCTION SOFTWARE: QPS.
Note: Advertising is sold in combination with the Fort Dodge Messenger (mS) for $43.22. Individual newspaper rates not made available.

KANSAS

ABILENE

ABILENE REFLECTOR-CHRONICLE

303 N Broadway St, Abilene, Kan., 67410-2616, Dickinson; gen tel (785) 263-1000; adv tel (785) 263-1000; ed tel (785) 263-1000; gen fax (785) 263-1645; adv fax (785) 263-1645; ed fax (785) 263-1645; gen/nat adv e-mail advertising@abilene-rc.com; disp adv e-mail advertising@abilene-rc.com; class adv e-mailadvertising@abilene-rc.com; ed e-mail arc.editor@abilene-rc.com; web site www.abilene-rc.com
 - 126,815(views) 13,733(visitors)
Group: The White Corporation
Published: Mon, Tues, Wed, Thur, Fri
Weekday Frequency: e
Saturday Frequency: m
Circulation: 3,935
Last Audit: Sworn/Estimate/Non-Audited September 30, 2017
Newspaper Reps: Mike Heronomus Editor Kim Maguire Sales Manager
Advertising Rate (weekday/saturday): 7.09 Per column inch
Online Advertising Rate: Background Ad $75.00/Daily; Peel Back $119.00/month; Homepage Top Banner $129.00/month
News services: AP. **Established:** 1942
Own Printing Facility?: No
Commercial Printers?: No
Special Editions: (Jan); DARE Coloring Contest (Jan); Outlook (Feb); Spring Sports (Mar); Flint Hills Guide (Jul); Fall Auto Care (Sept); Women in Business (Oct); Christmas (Dec); Fall Home Tour Tab (Fall); Graduation (May).
Special Weekly Sections: Church/Religion (Thur); Organization/Club (Thur); Home & Garden ; Arts/Books (Sat); Business TV Listings Thurs Weddings/Engagements daily; School Youth Thurs(t); Health/Fitness (.).
Syndicated Publications: American Profile (Fri).
Interim News Ed. .... Kathy Hageman
Sports .... Ron Preston
Adv. Asst. .... Susi Parker
Adv. Sales Rep. .... Kim Maguire
Editor .... Mike Heronumus
Reporter .... Gale Parsons
Market Information: TMC; Zoned editions.
Mechanical Available: Offset; Black and 3 ROP colors; insert accepted; page cutoffs - 21 1/2.
Mechanical Specifications: Type page 12 1/2 x 21 1/2; E - 6 cols, 1 7/8, 1/8 between; A - 6 cols, 1 7/8, 1/8 between; C - 6 cols, 1 7/8, 1/8 between.
Areas Served: Dickinson County
Delivery Method: Mail, Newsstand, Carrier, RacksEquipment & Software: PRESSROOM EQUIPMENT: Lines — 4-G; Folders — 1-G/2:1.; MAILROOM EQUIPMENT: Tying Machines — 1/Sa; Address Machine — 1-/Am.; CLASSIFIED EQUIPMENT: Hardware — 2-IBM/Typewriter; CLASSIFIED SOFTWARE: Microsoft/Word, QPS/QuarkXPress. DISPLAY SOFTWAREAd Make-up Applications — QPS/QuarkXPress;

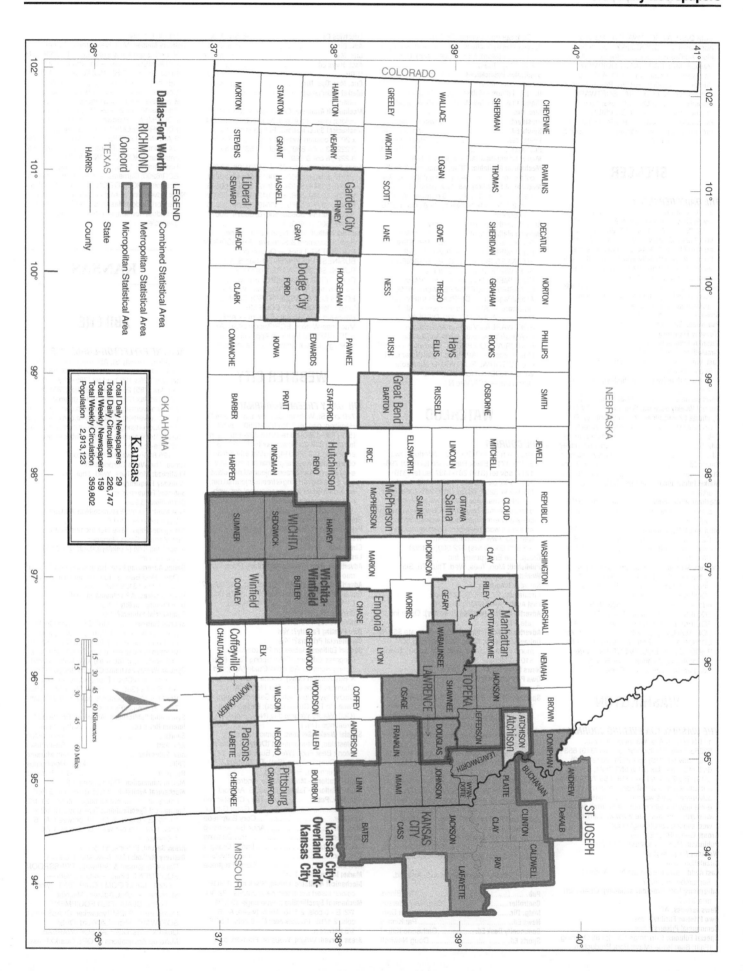

LEGEND

Dallas-Fort Worth — Combined Statistical Area
RICHMOND — Metropolitan Statistical Area
Concord — Micropolitan Statistical Area

TEXAS — State
HARRIS — County

Kansas

Total Daily Newspapers 29
Total Daily Circulation 226,747
Total Weekly Newspapers 159
Total Weekly Circulation 359,802
Population 2,913,123

0 15 30 45 60 Kilometers
0 15 30 45 60 Miles

N

Layout Software — QPS/QuarkXPress. EDITORIAL SOFTWARE: QPS/QuarkXPress. PRODUCTION EQUIPMENT: Hardware — 1-Nat/A-250; Cameras — 1-Acti.

ARKANSAS CITY

THE ARKANSAS CITY TRAVELER

200 E 5th Ave, Arkansas City, Kan., 67005-2606, Cowley; gen tel (620) 442-4200; adv tel (620) 442-4200; ed tel (620) 442-4200; gen fax (620) 442-7483; adv fax (620) 442-7483; ed fax (620) 442-7483; gen/nat adv e-mail ads@arkcity.net; disp adv e-mail adman@arkcity.net; class adv e-mailclassman@arkcity.net; ed e-mail arkcity@arkcity.net; web site www.arkcity.net
- 350,351(views) 127,195(visitors)
Group: Kansas Press Association
Seaton Group
Published: Tues, Wed, Thur, Fri, Sat
Weekday Frequency: e
Saturday Frequency: e
Circulation: 4,832; 4,832(sat)
Last Audit: Sworn/Estimate/Non-Audited September 30, 2017
Advertising Rate (weekday/saturday): Open inch rate $10.32
Online Advertising Rate: Prices start at $60.00 per month.
News services: AP. **Established:** 1870
Own Printing Facility?: Yes
Commercial Printers?: Yes
Special Editions: Senior (Bi-monthly)
Special Weekly Sections: Food & Health (Wed); Education (Mon); Weddings/Engagements (Sat); Nature (Thur); Faith (Fri); Business (Tues).
Syndicated Publications: USA WEEKEND Magazine (Sat).
Proprietary Publications: The Border
Digital Platform - Mobile: Apple, Android, Windows, Blackberry, Other
Digital Platform - Tablet: Apple iOS, Android, Windows 7, Blackberry Tablet OS, Nook, Kindle Fire, Other
Pub. .... Dave Seaton
Bus. Mgr. .... Susie Kincaid
Managing Ed. .... Andrew Lawson
Sports Ed. .... Joey Sprinkle
Photographer/Videographer .... Donita Clausen
Lifestyle/Action Ed. .... Grant Urban
Online Ed. .... Kayleigh Lawson
Ad Director .... Arty Hicks
Assistant Ad Director .... Suvanah Perdue
Adv. Consultant .... Tina Pride
Circulation Manager .... Marilyn Coury
Jennie Steelman
Head Pressman .... Lukas Young
Society Ed. .... Jean Crowley
Adv. Consultant .... Moody R. Alford
Adv. Asst. .... Janet Darnall
Classified Mgr. .... Amber Cook
Prodn. Mgr., Pre Press .... Kay Batdorf
Market Information: Split run; TMC; Zoned editions.
Mechanical Available: Offset; Black and 3 ROP colors; insert accepted - all.
Mechanical Specifications: Type page 13 x 21 1/2; E - 6 cols, 2, 3/16 between; A - 6 cols, 2, 3/16 between; C - 6 cols, 2, 3/16 between.
Areas Served: Arkansas City, Kansas; Cowley County, Kay County, Oklahoma
Delivery Method: Mail, Newsstand, RacksEquipment & Software: PRESSROOM EQUIPMENT: Lines — 7-G/Community; MAILROOM EQUIPMENT: Tying Machines — 1/Sa; Address Machine — 2-/Am.; BUSINESS EQUIPMENT: ATT CLASSIFIED EQUIPMENT: Hardware — 1-APP/Mac; Printers — APP/Mac LaserPrinter.; DISPLAY EQUIPMENT: Printers — APP/Mac LaserWriter II, APP/Mac LaserWriter II NTX.; EDITORIAL EQUIPMENT: Hardware — APP/Mac, 3-APP/Mac IIsi, 5-APP/Mac Classic, 6-APP/Mac SE, 1-APP/Mac IIci/SMS/Stauffer Gold, APP/Mac SE Super Drive. PRODUCTION EQUIPMENT: Hardware — APP/Mac LaserWriter II, APP/Mac LaserWriter II NTX; Cameras — 1-B, Acti.

CHANUTE

THE CHANUTE TRIBUNE

26 W Main St, Chanute, Kan., 66720-1701, Neosho; gen tel (620) 431-4100; gen fax (620) 431-2635; gen/nat adv e-mail shanna@chanute.com; disp adv e-mail brandi@chanute.com; class adv e-mailclassified@chanute.com; ed e-mail stu@chanute.com; web site www.chanute.com
Published: Tues, Wed, Thur, Fri, Sat
Weekday Frequency: m
Saturday Frequency: m
Circulation: 4,359; 4,359(sat)
Last Audit: Sworn/Estimate/Non-Audited December 18, 2017
Advertising Rate (weekday/saturday): Open inch rate $8
Online Advertising Rate: Price per word (10 word minimum) 2 Days $0.98 per word; 5 Days $1.35 per word; 10 Days $2.22 per word
News services: AP. **Established:** 1892
Own Printing Facility?: Yes
Commercial Printers?: Yes
Special Editions: Basketball (Apr); Back-to-School (Aug); Holiday Recipe (Dec); Tax Tab (Feb); Bridal Tab (Jan); Medical Tab (Jul); Summer Fun (Jun); Football (Sept).
Special Weekly Sections: Family (Fri); Social/Anniversaries (Sat); Education (Thur); Community News (Tues); Edit (Wed).
Digital Platform - Mobile: Apple, Android
Digital Platform - Tablet: Apple iOS, Android, Kindle, Nook, Kindle Fire
Pub./Bus. Mgr. .... Shanna Guiot
Circ. Mgr. .... Amy Jensen
Exec. Ed. .... Stu Butcher
Market Information: TMC.
Mechanical Available: Offset; Black and 3 ROP colors; insert accepted; page cutoffs - 22 3/4.
Mechanical Specifications: Type page 11 5/8 x 21 1/2; E - 6 cols, 1 5/6, 1/8 between; A - 6 cols, 1 5/6, 1/8 between; C - 8 cols, 1 3/8, 1/16 between.
Areas Served: Chanute and the four-county area
Delivery Method: Mail, Newsstand, Carrier, RacksEquipment & Software: BUSINESS EQUIPMENT: Icanon/Newzware CLASSIFIED EQUIPMENT: Hardware — AP/Mac CLASSIFIED SOFTWARE: Baseview 4.0. EDITORIAL EQUIPMENT: Hardware — AP/Mac; Printers — Xante EDITORIAL SOFTWARE: InDesign PRODUCTION EQUIPMENT: Hardware — Xante/8200, Xante/G3 PRODUCTION SOFTWARE: InDesign

CLAY CENTER

THE CLAY CENTER DISPATCH

805 5th St, Clay Center, Kan., 67432-2502, Clay; gen tel (785) 632-2127; adv tel (785) 632-2127; ed tel (785) 632-2127; gen fax (785) 632-6526; adv fax (785) 632-6526; ed fax (785) 632-6526; gen/nat adv e-mail dispatch@claycenter.com; disp adv e-mail addesk@claycenter.com; class adv e-mailaddesk@claycenter.com; ed e-mail news@claycenter.com; web site www.claycenter.com
- 110,000(views) 1,555(visitors)
Published: Mon, Tues, Wed, Thur, Fri
Weekday Frequency: e
Circulation: 1,500
Last Audit: Sworn/Estimate/Non-Audited December 12, 2017
Newspaper Reps: Kansas Press Association
Advertising Rate (weekday/saturday): Open inch rate $7.00
News services: AP. McClatchy **Established:** 1871
Own Printing Facility?: Yes
Commercial Printers?: No
Special Editions: Home & Garden (Apr); Back-to-School (Aug); F.F.A. (Feb); Social Security/Tax (Jan); Fair Preview Tab (Jul); Car Care (Mar); Graduation (May); Christmas (Nov); Car Care (Oct); Rodeo (Sept).
Special Weekly Sections: Clay Center Saver
Digital Platform - Mobile: Windows
Digital Platform - Tablet: Windows 7
Pres./Pub./Treasurer .... Harry E. Valentine
Sports Ed. .... Dave Berggren
Prodn. Supt./Foreman, Composing .... Aaron Bull
Circulation .... Lori Reardon
Ad Director .... Alicia Morgison
Market Information: TMC.
Mechanical Available: Offset; Black and 3 ROP colors; insert accepted; page cutoffs - 22 3/4.
Mechanical Specifications: Type page 13 x 21; E - 6 cols, 2 1/16, 1/8 between; A - 6 cols, 2 1/16, 1/8 between; C - 6 cols, 2 1/16, 1/8 between.
Areas Served: 67432, 67487, 67468, 67466, 66937, 66938, 66962, 66449, 66953, 67447, 66531, 67458, 67417
Delivery Method: Mail, Newsstand, CarrierEquipment & Software: PRESSROOM EQUIPMENT: Lines — G/Community; Folders — 1-G/3:1.; MAILROOM EQUIPMENT: Address Machine — 1/Ch.; BUSINESS EQUIPMENT: Epson/386, Acer/486, Nobilis-Pentium CLASSIFIED EQUIPMENT: Hardware — PC; Printers — HP/LaserJet.; DISPLAY EQUIPMENT: Hardware — PC; DISPLAY SOFTWARELayout Software — Archetype/Corel Draw. EDITORIAL EQUIPMENT: Hardware — PC; Printers — HP/LaserJet. PRODUCTION EQUIPMENT: Hardware — HP; Cameras — 1-K/240V.

COLBY

COLBY FREE PRESS

155 W 5th St, Colby, Kan., 67701-2312, Thomas; gen tel (785) 462-3963; gen fax (785) 462-7749; gen/nat adv e-mail sfriedlander@nwkansas.com; disp adv e-mail sfriedlander @nwkansas.com; class adv e-mailkhunter@nwkansas.com; ed e-mail colby.editor@nwkansas.com; web site www.nwkansas.com
Group: Haynes Publishing Co.
Published: Mon, Wed, Thur, Fri
Weekday Frequency: e
Circulation: 1,954
Last Audit: Sworn/Estimate/Non-Audited October 1, 2017
Advertising Rate (weekday/saturday): Open inch rate $8.25
Advertising Rate (sunday): NA
News services: AP. **Established:** 1888
Own Printing Facility?: Yes
Commercial Printers?: Yes
Special Weekly Sections: Business Directory
Pub .... Sharon Friedlander
Adv. Rep. .... Kathryn Ballard
Classified/ Adv. Graphic Designer .... Kylee Hunter
Office Mgr. .... Melissa Edmondson
sales .... Janene Woodall
Market Information: TMC. Open rate $13.95 ROP, $16.80 classified
Mechanical Available: Offset page cutoffs - 21
Mechanical Specifications: Type page 13 x 21 ; E - 6 cols, 1 column 1.892, 2 column 3.916, 3 column 5.9375, 4 column 7.958, 5 column 9.979, 6 column 12.0
Areas Served: Thomas County
Delivery Method: Mail, Newsstand, Carrier, RacksEquipment & Software: PRESSROOM EQUIPMENT: Lines — none; BUSINESS EQUIPMENT: IBM/AT, IBM/PC-2 CLASSIFIED EQUIPMENT: Hardware — 1-APP/Mac.; DISPLAY SOFTWARELayout Software — 1-APP/Mac. EDITORIAL EQUIPMENT: Hardware — Apple Mac EDITORIAL SOFTWARE: inDesign, neoOffice, PhotoShop

CONCORDIA

CONCORDIA BLADE-EMPIRE

510 Washington St, Concordia, Kan., 66901-2117, Cloud; gen tel (785) 243-2424; adv tel (785) 243-2424; ed tel (785) 243-2424; gen fax (785) 243-4407; gen/nat adv e-mail bladeempire@nckcn.com; disp adv e-mail dixiewinter@nckcn.com; class adv e-maildeniselah@nckcn.com; ed e-mail bladeempire@nckcn.com; web site www.bladeempire.com
- 1,821,200(views) 847,300(visitors)
Published: Mon, Tues, Wed, Thur, Fri
Weekday Frequency: e
Circulation: 2,357
Last Audit: Sworn/Estimate/Non-Audited September 30, 2017
Advertising Rate (weekday/saturday): Open inch rate $6.10 (National) $5.90 (Local)
Online Advertising Rate: Leaderboard $210.00/month; Others $150.00/month
News services: AP. **Established:** 1920
Bus. Mgr. .... John Hamel
Ed./Pub. .... Brad Lowell
Sports Ed./Managing Ed. .... Jim Lowell
Social Ed. .... Sharon Coy
Adv. Sales .... Dixie Winter
Adv. Sale/Photographer .... Jessica Leduc
Classified Adv. .... Denise Lahodny
Online Ed./Photographer/Adv. Sales .... Jay Lowell
Mechanical Available: Offset; Black and 3 ROP colors; insert accepted; page cutoffs - 22 1/2.
Areas Served: Cloud County and surrounding counties
Delivery Method: Mail, Newsstand, CarrierEquipment & Software: PRESSROOM EQUIPMENT: Lines — 4-1968.; MAILROOM EQUIPMENT: Tying Machines — Bu.; BUSINESS EQUIPMENT: RSK/Tandy CLASSIFIED EQUIPMENT: Hardware — Mk; CLASSIFIED SOFTWARE: Mk/Mycro-Comp AdWriter. EDITORIAL EQUIPMENT: Hardware — Mk EDITORIAL SOFTWARE: Mk/Mycro-Comp AdWriter. PRODUCTION EQUIPMENT: Hardware — 1-Nu; Cameras — DAI.

COUNCIL GROVE

COUNCIL GROVE REPUBLICAN

208 W Main St, Council Grove, Kan., 66846-1705, Morris; gen tel (620) 767-5123; adv tel (620) 767-5123; ed tel (620) 767-5123; gen fax (620) 767-5124; adv fax (620) 767-5124; ed fax (620) 767-5124; gen/nat adv e-mail cgnews@cgtelco.net; disp adv e-mail cgnews@cgtelco.net; class adv e-mailcgnews@cgtelco.net; ed e-mail cgnews@cgtelco.net; web site N/A
Group: Council Grove Publishing Company, Inc.
Published: Mon, Tues, Wed, Thur, Fri
Weekday Frequency: e
Circulation: 1,400
Last Audit: Sworn/Estimate/Non-Audited September 30, 2017
Advertising Rate (weekday/saturday): Open inch rate $6.30
News services: AP. **Established:** 1872
Own Printing Facility?: No
Commercial Printers?: No
Special Editions: Tourism (Apr); Bridal (Feb); Soil Conservation (Jan); County Fair (Jul); Historical Festival (June) (Jun).
Pub./Ed. .... Craig A. McNeal
Adv. Dir. .... Becky Evans
Circ. Mgr. .... Christy Jimerson
Kay Roberts
Market Information: TMC.
Mechanical Available: Offset; Black and 3 ROP colors; insert accepted; page cutoffs - 22 3/4.
Mechanical Specifications: Type page 15 3/16 x 21 1/2; E - 7 cols, 2 1/12, 1/6 between; A - 7 cols, 2 1/12, 1/6 between; C - 7 cols, 2 1/12, 1/6 between.
Areas Served: Morris County and adjacent counties
Delivery Method: Mail, Newsstand, CarrierEquipment & Software: MAILROOM EQUIPMENT: Address Machine — Ap/Mac ImageWriter II; CLASSIFIED EQUIPMENT: Hardware — 1-APP/Power Mac Performa; Printers — APP/Mac LaserWriter 16/600 PS; CLASSIFIED SOFTWARE: Microsoft/Word 6.0, Aldus/PageMaker 5.0. DISPLAY EQUIPMENT: Hardware — 1-APP/Power Mac Performa; Printers — APP/Mac LaserWriter 16/600 PS; DISPLAY SOFTWAREAd Make-up Applications — Aldus/PageMaker 5.0.; EDITORIAL EQUIPMENT: Hardware — 3-APP/Mac; Printers — APP/Mac LaserWriter II NT EDITORIAL SOFTWARE: Microsoft/Word 3.0. PRODUCTION EQUIPMENT: Hardware — 1-APP/Mac LaserWriter II NT, APP/Mac LaserWriter 16/600 PS.

DODGE CITY

DODGE CITY DAILY GLOBE

705 N 2nd Ave, Dodge City, Kan., 67801-

4410, Ford; gen tel (620) 225-4151; adv tel (620) 408-9919; ed tel (620) 408-9913; gen fax (620) 225-4154; adv fax (620) 225-4154; ed fax (620) 225-4154; gen/nat adv e-mail ceasterday@dodgeglobe.com; disp adv e-mail ndirks@dodgeglobe.com; class adv e-mailrmyers@dodgeglobe.com; ed e-mail emily.shultz@dodgeglobe.com; web site www.dodgeglobe.com
- 263,651(views) 187,263(visitors)
Group: New Media Investment Group
Published: Tues, Wed, Thur, Fri, Sat
Weekday Frequency: m
Saturday Frequency: m
Circulation: 9,700; 9,700(sat)
Last Audit: Sworn/Estimate/Non-Audited September 30, 2017
Advertising Rate (weekday/saturday): Open inch rate $9.40
Online Advertising Rate: Prices start at $20.00 per month.
News services: AP. **Established:** 1878
Special Editions: Progress (Feb); Bridal Tab (Jan); Bridal Tab (Jul); City Guide (Jun); Tourist Tab (Mar); Christmas Kick-Off (Thanksgiving Day) (Nov); Senior Citizens (Oct); Fall Fashion (Sept).
Special Weekly Sections: Youth (Fri); Seniors (Mon); Business (Sat); Health (Tues); Best Food Day (Wed).
Syndicated Publications: USA WEEKEND Magazine (Fri); Relish (Monthly).
Digital Platform - Mobile: Apple, Android
Digital Platform - Tablet: Apple iOS, Android, Kindle, Kindle Fire
Production Foreman.................... Edward O'Neil
Gen. Mgr............................... Conrad Easterday
Classified Adv. Mgr....................... Robbin Myers
Retail Adv. Mgr................................ Nicole Dirks
Sports Editor..................................... John Curtis
Business Office........................... Kathy Runquist
Market Information: TMC.
Mechanical Available: Offset; Black and 3 ROP colors; insert accepted; page cutoffs - 22 3/4.
Mechanical Specifications: Type page 11 1/4 x 21 1/2; E - 6 cols, 1 7/8, 1/16 between; A - 6 cols, 1 7/8, 1/16 between; C - 6 cols, 1 7/8, 1/16 between.
Areas Served: Ford County
Delivery Method: Mail, Newsstand, CarrierEquipment & Software: PRESSROOM EQUIPMENT: Lines — 7-G/Community 1976; MAILROOM EQUIPMENT: Address Machine — Ch/705.; BUSINESS EQUIPMENT: Epson/486, Unix, Wyse/terminals BUSINESS SOFTWARE: SMS/Business Software, Unix CLASSIFIED EQUIPMENT: Hardware — APP/Mac G3; Printers — APP/Mac LaserWriter NTX; CLASSIFIED SOFTWARE: Baseview. DISPLAY EQUIPMENT: Hardware — 4-APP/Mac G3, APP/Mac 7600, APP/Mac 4400; DISPLAY SOFTWAREAd Make-up Applications — Aldus/PageMaker, Aldus/FreeHand, QPS/QuarkXPress; Layout Software — APP/Mac. EDITORIAL EQUIPMENT: Hardware — 6-APP/iMac, 3-APP/Mac SE, 4-APP/Mac Classic, 2-APP/Mac Quadra 610, APP/Mac 4400, APP/Mac 7600; Printers — APP/Mac LaserWriter NTX, MON, HP/LaserJet EDITORIAL SOFTWARE: Baseview, QPS/QuarkXPress. PRODUCTION EQUIPMENT: Hardware — APP/Mac LaserWriter NTX, APP/Mac LaserWriter NT, MON, HP/LaserJet 4MV.

EMPORIA

THE EMPORIA GAZETTE

517 Merchant St, Frnt, Emporia, Kan., 66801-7215, Lyon; gen tel (620) 342-4800; adv tel (620) 342-4841 ext. 233; ed tel (620) 342-4805; gen fax (620) 342-8108; adv fax (620) 342-8108; ed fax (620) 342-8108; gen/nat adv e-mail sales13@emporiagazette.com; disp adv e-mail sales20@emporiagazette.com; class adv e-mailclassifieds@emporiagazette.com; ed e-mail news@emporia.com; web site www.emporiagazette.com
- 177,109(views) 6,291(visitors)
Group: Kansas Press Association
The White Corporation
Published: Mon, Tues, Wed, Thur, Fri, Sat
Weekday Frequency: e
Saturday Frequency: e
Circulation: 5,746; 5,746(sat)
Last Audit: AAM September 30, 2012
Advertising Rate (weekday/saturday): Open inch rate $9.39 (Local); $10.56 (National)
Online Advertising Rate: Top Ear Tile $189.00/month; Mobile $199.00/month; Mid Banner $219.00/month
News services: AP, NYT, Kansas Press Association **Established:** 1895
Own Printing Facility?: No
Special Editions: Healthy Living (Jan); Spring Home Improvement (Feb); Ads by Kids, Baseball/Softball (Mar); Reader's Choice, Mature Living (Apr); Discover (May); Summer Theatre, Bridal Tab (Jun); Back to School (Jul); Campus Life (Aug); Football, Mature Living (Sept); Breast Cancer Awareness (Oct); Veterans (Nov); Basketball (Dec);
Special Weekly Sections: Weekend Business (Sat).
Syndicated Publications: TV Week (Sat).
Digital Platform - Mobile: Apple, Android
Digital Platform - Tablet: Apple iOS, Android, Kindle, Nook, Kindle Fire
Pres...................................... Paul David Walker
Pub./Ed......................Christopher White Walker
Travel Ed..........................Barbara White Walker
Circ. Mgr................................ Brenda Armitage
Gen. Mgr........................................Ray J. Beals
Adv. Mgr., Display/Nat'l.................... Jay Wilson
Circ. Mgr................................... Melissa Heinitz
Mng. Ed....................................... Gwen Larson
Editorial Page Ed......................Patrick S. Kelley
Prodn. Mgr.............................. Dallas Sedgwick
Mgr., Distr..................................... Larry Leaver
Lori Hickey
Ronda Henery
Adv. Mgr.... Briana Julo
Mark Matthews
Market Information: TMC.
Mechanical Available: Offset; Black and 3 ROP colors; insert accepted - single sheets, 8 1/2 x 11 min.; page cutoffs - 22 3/4.
Mechanical Specifications: Type page 13 x 21; E - 6 cols, 2 1/16, 1/8 between; A - 6 cols, 2 1/16, 1/8 between; C - 6 cols, 2 1/16, 1/8 between.
Areas Served: Admire, Cottonwood Falls, Hamilton, Olpe, Allen, Council Grove, Hartford, Osage City, Americus, Dunlap, Lebo, Reading, Burlington, Emporia, Madison, Strong City, Bushong, Gridley, and Neosho Rapids.
Delivery Method: Mail, CarrierEquipment & Software: PRESSROOM EQUIPMENT: Lines — 7-G/Community single width 1974; MAILROOM EQUIPMENT: Tying Machines — 2-Bu/23; Address Machine — 1-KAN/Labeler.; BUSINESS EQUIPMENT: IBM/340 BUSINESS SOFTWARE: SMS CLASSIFIED EQUIPMENT: Hardware — APP/Power Mac 7200-120; Printers — HP/LaserJet 5P; CLASSIFIED SOFTWARE: FSI, Advance Sales. DISPLAY EQUIPMENT: Hardware — APP/Power Mac 7200-120; DISPLAY SOFTWAREAd Make-up Applications — FSI; Layout Software — FSI, ROP Layout, Advance Pro (for booking ads). EDITORIAL EQUIPMENT: Hardware — APP/Power Mac 7200-120; Printers — 2-Select Press/600 EDITORIAL SOFTWARE: QPS/QuarkXPress, FSI. PRODUCTION EQUIPMENT: Hardware — Text Bridge, Burgess/Light Source; Cameras - 1-Acti/183; Scanners — Umax/PowerBook 2000, 2-Umax/PowerBook II, Nikon/Coolscan II, APP/Color one 600-27, 2-Umax Mirage IIse PRODUCTION SOFTWARE: QPS/QuarkXPress/with FSI extensions.

FORT SCOTT

THE FORT SCOTT TRIBUNE

PO Box 150, 12 E Wall St, Fort Scott, Kan., 66701-0150, Bourbon; gen tel (620) 223-1460; adv tel (620) 223-1460; ed tel (620) 223-1462; gen fax (620) 223-0515; adv fax (620) 223-0515; ed fax (620) 223-1469; gen/nat adv e-mail advertising@fstribune.com; disp adv e-mail advertising@fstribune.com; class adv e-mailadvertising@fstribune.com; ed e-mail thelm@fstribune.com; web site www.fstribune.com
- 292,504(views) 65,923(visitors)
Group: Rust Communications
Published: Tues, Wed, Thur, Fri, Sat
Weekday Frequency: m
Saturday Frequency: m
Circulation: 3,289; 3,289(sat)
Last Audit: Sworn/Estimate/Non-Audited September 30, 2017
Advertising Rate (weekday/saturday): Open inch rate $6.50 (Wed/Fri); Open inch rate $8.25 (Sat); National rate $10.25
Online Advertising Rate: Leaderboard $155.00/month; Rectangle $155.00/month
News services: AP. **Established:** 1884
Own Printing Facility?: Yes
Commercial Printers?: No
Special Editions: Back-to-School (Aug); Basketball (Dec); Wedding (Jan); Fair (Jul); Good Ol' Days (Jun); Home Show (Mar); Graduation (May); Car Care (Oct); Football (Sept).
Special Weekly Sections: Church (Fri); Business (Thur); Senior Page (Tues)
Syndicated Publications: Fort Scott Countryside/The Nevada News (Wed)
Proprietary Publications: Fort Scott The Magazine (Bi-montly)
Digital Platform - Mobile: Apple, Android
Digital Platform - Tablet: Apple iOS, Android, Kindle, Nook, Kindle Fire
Pub..Floyd Jernigan
Adv. Mgr./Office Mgr. .... Teresa Klumpp
Composition Mgr. ....Sara Simonds
Mng. Ed. .... Tammy Helm
Sports Ed. ....Scott Nuzum
Pub./Dir. of Adv. .... Lorie Harter
Adv. Consultant..........................Andrew LaSota
Circ. Asst. .... Christi Allmond
Market Information: TMC.
Mechanical Available: Offset; Black and 1 ROP colors; insert accepted; page cutoffs - 22 3/4.
Mechanical Specifications: Type page 13 x 21; E - 6 cols, 2 1/16, 1/8 between; A - 6 cols, 2 1/16, 1/8 between; C - 8 cols, 1 1/2, 1/8 between.
Areas Served: 66056, 66075, 66701, 66716, 66738, 66754, 66767, 66769, 66779
Delivery Method: Mail, Carrier, RacksEquipment & Software: MAILROOM EQUIPMENT: Tying Machines — 1-Bu/BT-17; Address Machine — Compudyne/486SX-25.; BUSINESS EQUIPMENT: 1-Compudyne/386DN-25, 1-Compudyne/486DN BUSINESS SOFTWARE: Listmaster Systems (Omaha, NE) CLASSIFIED EQUIPMENT: Hardware — APP/Mac; 1-APP/Mac, 1-Radius/Monitor; Printers — APP/Mac LaserWriter II.; EDITORIAL EQUIPMENT: Hardware — APP/Mac/APP/Mac Scanner, 5-APP/Mac, 1-Radius; Printers — APP/Mac LaserWriter II. PRODUCTION EQUIPMENT: Hardware — B/Ultra-Lite 1500, LE/Line 17; Cameras — 1-Acti.

GARDEN CITY

THE GARDEN CITY TELEGRAM

310 N 7th St, Garden City, Kan., 67846-5521, Finney; gen tel (620) 275-8500; adv tel (620) 276-6862 ext. 225; ed tel (620) 275-8500 ext. 201; gen fax (866) 757-6842; adv fax (866) 757-6842; ed fax (866) 450-5936; gen/nat adv e-mail advertising@gctelegram.com; disp adv e-mail advertising@gctelegram.com; class adv e-mailclassifieds@gctelegram.com; ed e-mail newsroom@gctelegram.com; web site www.gctelegram.com
- 148,000(views) 51,000(visitors)
Group: GateHouse Media, Inc.
Published: Mon, Tues, Wed, Thur, Fri, Sat
Weekday Frequency: m
Saturday Frequency: m
Circulation: 7,432; 7,966(sat)
Last Audit: Sworn/Estimate/Non-Audited September 30, 2017
Advertising Rate (weekday/saturday): Open inch rate $11.10 (Local); $14.88 (National)
Online Advertising Rate: Homepage Bottom Banner, Small Square $7.00 CPM; Bottom Right Square $9.00 CPM; Middle Right Square $10.00 CPM; Top Banner $15.00 CPM
News services: AP, Harris News Service. **Established:** 1906
Own Printing Facility?: Yes
Commercial Printers?: Yes
Special Editions: Health & Wellness (Summer 2013); Discover Southwest Kansas (2013); Southwest Kansas Agriculture (May); Graduation Class of 2013 (May); Head Over Heels (Feb).
Special Weekly Sections: Weddings/Engagements (Sat); Church News (Fri); Real Estate Guide (Fri); Agricultural News (Thur); Classtime (Wed); Best Food Day (Tues).
Syndicated Publications: USA WEEKEND Magazine (Sat).
Digital Platform - Mobile: Apple, Android
Digital Platform - Tablet: Apple iOS, Android, Kindle, Nook, Kindle Fire
Pub./Ed... Dena Sattler
Circ. Mgr..................................Jeremy Banwell
Mng. Ed. ....Brett Riggs
Photo Dept. Mgr............................. Brad Nading
Classifieds Mgr.......................Sharynn Bowman
Market Information: TMC.
Mechanical Available: Offset; Black and 3 ROP colors; insert accepted - we prints-Telegram prints; page cutoffs - 22 3/4.
Mechanical Specifications: Type page 13 x 21 1/2; E - 6 cols, 2 1/8, 3/8 between; A - 6 cols, 2 1/8, 3/8 between; C - 8 cols, 1 1/2, 1/16 between.
Areas Served: Greeley, Wichita, Scott, Lane, Hamilton, Kearny, Finney, Stanton, Grant, Haskell, Gray, and Stevens County.
Delivery Method: Mail, Newsstand, Carrier, RacksEquipment & Software: PRESSROOM EQUIPMENT: Lines — 8-G/SC 578; MAILROOM EQUIPMENT: Tying Machines — 1-Bu/66858, 1-Bu/32133; Address Machine — 1-Am/1900, 1/Ch.; BUSINESS EQUIPMENT: 3-DEC/PC LPV 433 DX, 6-TI/DSI Digital Venturis BUSINESS SOFTWARE: Microsoft/Office, Microsoft/Windows, Informix/Smart II CLASSIFIED EQUIPMENT: Hardware — APP/Mac Centris 610s, APP/Mac Quadra 800, 2-COM; Printers — NewGen/1200B Laser Printer; CLASSIFIED SOFTWARE: Multi-Ad/Creator, QPS/QuarkXPress, Baseview. DISPLAY EQUIPMENT: Hardware — APP/Mac IIsx, APP/Mac Centris 610, APP/Mac Centris 650, APP/Mac Centris 800, APP/Mac Quadra 610, APP/Mac Quadra 650, APP/Mac Quadra 800, APP/Power Mac G3; Printers — NewGen/1200B Laser Printer; DISPLAY SOFTWAREAd Make-up Applications — Multi-Ad/Creator, QPS/QuarkXPress, Base; EDITORIAL EQUIPMENT: Hardware — APP/Mac Centris 610, APP/Mac Centris 650, APP/Mac Centris 660, APP/Mac Centris 800, APP/Mac Quadra 610, APP/Mac Quadra 650, APP/Mac Quadra 660, APP/Mac Quadra 800; Printers — NewGen/1200B, ECR/Pelbox VR 36 EDITORIAL SOFTWARE: Baseview/NewsEdit IQUE, QP PRODUCTION EQUIPMENT: Hardware — Caere/OmniPage Pro, Adobe/Photoshop, APP/Power Mac 7100; Cameras — 1-R/580 PRODUCTION SOFTWARE: QPS/QuarkXPress 3.3.

GREAT BEND

GREAT BEND TRIBUNE

2012 Forest Ave, Great Bend, Kan., 67530-4014, Barton; gen tel (620) 792-1211; adv tel (620) 792-1211; ed tel (620) 792-1211; gen fax (620) 792-3441; adv fax (620) 792-3441; ed fax (620) 792-8381; gen/nat adv e-mail tmason@gbtribune.com; disp adv e-mail tmason@gbtribune.com; class adv e-mailclassifieds@gbtribune.com; ed e-mail dhogg@gbtribune.com; web site www.gbtribune.com
Group: Morris Multimedia, Inc.
Published: Tues, Wed, Thur, Fri, Sun
Weekday Frequency: m
Circulation: 5,977; 5,977(sun)
Last Audit: USPS September 30, 2006
Advertising Rate (weekday/saturday): Open inch rate $12.06
Online Advertising Rate: Leaderboard $300.00 per month; Half Page Ad $500.00 per month; Medium Rectangle $300.00 per month
News services: AP. **Established:** 1876
Own Printing Facility?: Yes
Commercial Printers?: Yes

Special Editions: Area Source Magazines; Glossy Special Publications, Inspire Health
Special Weekly Sections: Church Page (Fri); Health (S); 50+ (Thur); Food Day (Wed).
Digital Platform - Mobile: Apple, Android, Windows
Digital Platform - Tablet: Apple iOS, Android, Windows 7
Pub .... Mary Hoisington
Mng. Ed. .... Dale Hogg
Prodn. Mgr., Pre Press .... Karma Byers
Press manager .... James Audus
Advertising Director .... Diane Lacy-Trostle
Marketing Consultant .... Tammy Mason
Circ. Dir. .... Shonita Swank
Graphic Designer .... Jeff LeRoy
Digital Media/Innovative Projects Coord. .... Hugo Gonzalez
Classifieds .... Gina Werth
Distributors Asst. .... LeeAnn Byers
Planning Editor Print & Digital Amie Thompson
Advertising Director Jennifer Sorenson
Market Information: TMC; Zoned editions.
Mechanical Available: Offset; Black and 3 ROP colors; insert accepted - all; page cutoffs - 22 1/2.
Mechanical Specifications: Type page 10.5 x 21 1/2; E - 6 cols, 2, 1/8 between; A - 6 cols, 2, 1/8 between; C - 8 cols, 1 3/8, 1/8 between.
Delivery Method: Mail, Newsstand, Carrier, RacksEquipment & Software: PRESSROOM EQUIPMENT: Lines — 8-G/Community.; MAILROOM EQUIPMENT: Counter Stackers — BG/Count-O-Veyor; Tying Machines — 2-Bu/Tyer; Address Machine — KR.; BUSINESS EQUIPMENT: PC BUSINESS SOFTWARE: MAS 90 CLASSIFIED EQUIPMENT: Hardware — mac Printers — HP; CLASSIFIED SOFTWARE: Fake Brains DISPLAY EQUIPMENT: Hardware-PC DISPLAY SOFTWAREAdobe EDITORIAL EQUIPMENT: Hardware — IBM/PC; Printers — hp EDITORIAL SOFTWARE: adobe creative suite PRODUCTION EQUIPMENT: Hardware — pc/ Pre Press/Ctp; Cameras — 1-Op; Scanners — APP/Mac LC III PRODUCTION SOFTWARE: Adobe Creative Suite CIRCULATION EQUIPMENT: PC CIRCULATION SOFTWARDTI

HAYS

THE HAYS DAILY NEWS

507 Main St, Hays, Kan., 67601-4228, Ellis; gen tel (785) 628-1081; adv tel (785) 628-1081 ext. 118; ed tel (785) 628-1081 ext. 164; gen fax (785) 628-8186; adv fax (785) 628-8186; ed fax (785) 628-8186; gen/nat adv e-mail maryk_ads@dailynews.net; disp adv e-mail maryk_ads@dailynews.net; class adv e-mailadvertising@dailynews.net; ed e-mail nschwien@dailynews.net; web site www.hdnews.net
- 380,109(views) 63,975(visitors)
Group: GateHouse Media, Inc.
Published: Mon, Tues, Wed, Thur, Fri, Sun
Weekday Frequency: e
Circulation: 6,000; 6,500(sun)
Last Audit: Sworn/Estimate/Non-Audited December 1, 2017
Advertising Rate (weekday/saturday): Open inch rate $14.00
Advertising Rate (sunday): Open inch rate $15.28
Online Advertising Rate: $8 CPM
News services: Harris News Service. **Established:** 1929
Own Printing Facility?: Yes
Commercial Printers?: No
Special Editions: College (Aug); Christmas & New Years Greetings (Dec); Bridal Fair (Feb); Sidewalk Bazaar (Jul); Wild West Festival (Jun); Travel & Tourism (May); Christmas (Nov); Area Football (Sept).
Special Weekly Sections: Community (Mon/Thur); Food, Arts (Tues); Generations (Wed); Faith, Outdoors (Fri); Business, Weddings, Births, Real Estate, Engagements, Comics (Sun)
Syndicated Publications: Das Haus (Bi-Monthly); TV Guide (Fri); USA WEEKEND Magazine (S); Sports Ink (Monthly).
Proprietary Publications: The Extra (Wed)
Digital Platform - Mobile: Apple, Android
Digital Platform - Tablet: Apple iOS, Android, Blackberry Tablet OS, Kindle, Kindle Fire
Pub. .... Olaf Frandsen
Bus. Mgr. .... Janice Tinkel
Adv. Dir. .... Mary Karst
Circ. Mgr. .... Robert Wiegel
Managing Editor .... Nick Schwien
Special Projects Coord. .... Mike Corn
Sports Ed. .... Nick McQueen
Sales Associate .... Joleen Fisher
Sales Associate .... Ashley Bergman
Sales Associate .... Eric Rathke
Customer Service Rep. .... Whitney Duscher
IT Dir. .... Jon Howard
Market Information: TMC.
Mechanical Available: Offset; Black and 3 ROP colors; insert accepted - all; page cutoffs - 22 3/4.
Mechanical Specifications: Type page 10.2917 x 21 1/2; E - 6 cols, 1.6111, 1/8 between; A - 6 cols, 1.6111, 1/8 between; C - 8 cols, 1.1892, 3/32 between.
Areas Served: 67601, 67737, 67738, 67748, 67701, 67740, 67736,67752,67751, 67631, 67672, 67656, 67637, 67548, 67667, 67553, 67575, 67516, 67660, 67560, 67556, 67572, 67584, 67521, 67520, 67661, 67646, 67669, 67663, 67651, 67654, 67639, 67622, 67645, 66967, 67675, 67657, 67632, 67625, 67642, 67623, 67473, 67650, 67659, 67640, 67665, 67671, 67627
Delivery Method: Mail, Newsstand, Carrier, RacksEquipment & Software: PRESSROOM EQUIPMENT: Lines — 8-G/SC 650 Single width 1974; Folders — 1-G/3:2.; MAILROOM EQUIPMENT: Tying Machines — Mc/40 String Tyer, Transpak/A-72 Strapper; Address Machine — Videojet/Excel inkjet printer.; BUSINESS EQUIPMENT: TI/941 BUSINESS SOFTWARE: Microsoft/Office, Newzware CLASSIFIED EQUIPMENT: Hardware — APP/Mac; Printers — Epson, Epson/LQ 1170; CLASSIFIED SOFTWARE: QPS/QuarkXPress 3.3, FSI/Advance Pro. Indesign 3 DISPLAY EQUIPMENT: Hardware — 1-APP/Mac Classic, 1-APP/Power Mac, 1-APP/Mac Quadra 650, 1-APP/Power Mac; Printers — Design Express/6, GCC/Elite XL600; Other Hardware — Microtek/II HR Scanner, Microtek/Scanmaker V6 DISPLAY SOFTWAREAd Make-up Applications — Microsoft/Word, QPS/QuarkXPress 3.3; Layout Software — Mu EDITORIAL EQUIPMENT: Hardware — APP/Mac EDITORIAL SOFTWARE: FSI/Edit, QPS/QuarkXPress 3.3. PRODUCTION EQUIPMENT: Hardware — Caere/OmniPage 5.0, ECR/VR36, Elite XL 20/60; Cameras — 1-R/580; Scanners — 2-Lf/Leafscan 35, Microtek/II HR PRODUCTION SOFTWARE: QPS/QuarkXPress 3.3. Indesign 3

HUTCHINSON

THE HUTCHINSON NEWS

300 W 2nd Ave, Hutchinson, Kan., 67501-5211, Reno; gen tel (620) 694-5700; gen fax (620) 694-5799; adv fax (620) 662-4186; ed fax (620) 662-4186; gen/nat adv e-mail astuckey@hutchnews.com; disp adv e-mail astuckey@hutchnews.com; class adv e-mailclassifieds@hutchnews.com; ed e-mail rsylvester@hutchnews.com; web site www.hutchnews.com
- 1,150,000(views) 220,000(visitors); web site 2 www.ksagland.com - 106,500(views) 40,300(visitors)
Group: GateHouse Media, Inc.
Published: Mon, Tues, Wed, Thur, Fri, Sat, Sun
Weekday Frequency: m
Saturday Frequency: m
Circulation: 17,605; 17,605(sat); 21,393(sun)
Last Audit: VAC October 1, 2015
Advertising Rate (weekday/saturday): Open inch rate $29.47
Advertising Rate (sunday): Open inch rate $33.85
News services: AP, SHNS, TMS **Established:** 1872
Own Printing Facility?: Yes
Commercial Printers?: Yes
Special Editions: Experience Pratt (Jul); Tech 2013 (Jul); Kansas Homes Guide (monthly); Progress (March); Dream Homes (Jun); Discover (May)
Special Weekly Sections: Business (S); Weddings & Engagements (S); Taste of Life (Wed); Entertainment (Thurs); Preview (Fri); Faith (Sat).
Syndicated Publications: Parade Magazine (S), Athlon Sports (Monthly), Spry (Monday), Relish (Monday).
Proprietary Publications: The Bee (Thurs), Kansas Agland (quarterly).
Digital Platform - Mobile: Apple, Android
Digital Platform - Tablet: Apple iOS, Android, Kindle, Kindle Fire
Ed./Pub. .... John Montgomery
Adv. Supvr., Sales .... Anita Stuckey
Circ. Mgr., Opns.; Marketing Director ... Sara Bass
Mng. Ed. .... Ron Sylvester
Opinion/Weekend Editor .... Jason Probst
Business Editor .... John Green
Production Director .... Gregg Beals
Press Manager .... Mike Heim
Packaging/Distribution Manager .... Jeremy Coen
Advertising Director .... Jeanny Sharp
Marketing Consultant .... Shelby Dryden
Inside Sales Mgr. .... Rachelle Fideldy
Marketing Consultant .... Kyle Flax
Graphic Designer .... DeRay Gamble
Graphic Designer .... Rachel Hixson
Sales Asst. .... Debbie Hoffman
Graphic Designer .... Kim Hoskinson
Graphic Designer .... Nate Weaver
Agland Ed. .... Amy Bickel
Online Ed. .... Ryan Buchanan
News Clerk .... Tina Carpenter
Page Designer .... Ryan Christer
Sports Ed. .... Brad Hallier
Photo Ed. .... Sandra Milburn
News Clerk .... Pat Peschka
Single Copy Mgr. .... Elizabeth Garwood
Business & HR Director .... Rex Christner
Market Information: Zoned editions.
Mechanical Available: Offset; Black and 3 ROP colors; inserts accepted - Tab-ons; page cutoffs - 21 1/2.
Mechanical Specifications: Type page 11 3/4 x 21 1/2; E - 6 cols, 1 4/5, 1/7 between; A - 6 cols, 1 4/5, 1/7 between; C - 9 cols, 1 1/5, 1/7 between.
Areas Served: Greeley, Wichita, Scott, Lane, Hamilton, Kearny, Finney, Stanton, Grant, Haskell, Gray, Stevens, Seward, Meade, Ness, Hodgeman, Ford, Clark, Rush, Pawnee, Edwards, Kiowa, Comanche, Barton, Stafford, Pratt, Barber, Ellsworth, Rice, Reno, Kingman, Harper, McPherson, Harvey and Marion County
Delivery Method: Mail, Newsstand, Carrier, RacksEquipment & Software: PRESSROOM EQUIPMENT: Lines — 8-G/1018-4-72; Press Drive — 2, 2-150 HP/Electic Motors; Folders — 1-G/1018 Folder w/upper Former; Reels & Stands — 8; MAILROOM EQUIPMENT: Counter Stackers — HL/DC, HL/Monitor; Inserters & Stuffers — 1-MM/227E, GMA/SLS 1000A; Tying Machines — 1-Sterling/MR45CH, 2-MLN/2EE; Address Machine — 1-KR/221 227.; BUSINESS EQUIPMENT: 1-Dell/Poweredge 2500 BUSINESS SOFTWARE: Microsoft/Office XP Pro, Newzware CLASSIFIED EQUIPMENT: Hardware — Dell/Pentium Server NT 4.0; Printers — HP/Laserjet 4v; CLASSIFIED SOFTWARE: APT/ACT 3.05. DISPLAY EQUIPMENT: Hardware — Pentium Dell Server NT, Umax/Scanners, Dell/PC's; Printers — HP/Laserjet 8000N; Other Hardware — HP/Laserjet Color 8550N DISPLAY SOFTWAREAd Make-up Applications — Adobe/Illustrator 9.0, QPS 4.0, Adobe/Photoshop 6.0; Layout Software — APT. EDITORIAL EQUIPMENT: Hardware — Dell/Pentium Server NT 40, 30-PC; Printers — HP/Laserjet 8000N 1999 EDITORIAL SOFTWARE: TownNews Blox PRODUCTION EQUIPMENT: Hardware — 1-Nu/FT40UPNS, Adobe/Photoshop, 2-3850 Sierra Imager, III/3850 15 Imager, HP/Laserjet 8000N PRODUCTION SOFTWARE: TownNews Blox, InDesign

INDEPENDENCE

INDEPENDENCE DAILY REPORTER

320 N 6th St, Independence, Kan., 67301-3129, Montgomery; gen tel (620) 331-3550; adv tel (620) 331-3550; ed tel (620) 331-3550; gen fax (620) 331-3550; gen/nat adv e-mail ads@dreporter.com; disp adv e-mail ads@dreporter.com; class adv e-mailads@dreporter.com; ed e-mail ads@dreporter.com; web site http://www.indydailyreporter.com
Published: Tues, Wed, Thur, Fri
Weekday Frequency: e
Circulation: 6,654; 6,654(sun)
Last Audit: Sworn/Estimate/Non-Audited September 30, 2017
Advertising Rate (weekday/saturday): Open inch rate $7.85
Advertising Rate (sunday): Open inch rate $7.85
News services: AP.
Own Printing Facility?: No
Commercial Printers?: No
Pub. .... Josh Umholtz
Scott Wood
Scott Wesner
Adv. Mgr. .... Steve McBride
Market Information: Split run.
Mechanical Available: Offset; Black and 3 ROP colors; insert accepted; page cutoffs - 22 3/4.
Mechanical Specifications: Type page 13 x 21; E - 6 cols, 2 1/16, 1/8 between; A - 6 cols, 2 1/16, 1/8 between; C - 6 cols, 2 1/16, 1/8 between.
Areas Served: Montgomery County
Delivery Method: Mail, NewsstandEquipment & Software: PRESSROOM EQUIPMENT: Lines — 6-G/SC 1973.; MAILROOM EQUIPMENT: Tying Machines — 1-Malow/51; Wrapping Singles — 2-St/510W.; BUSINESS EQUIPMENT: 5-Unix/U5000-30C BUSINESS SOFTWARE: Unix, R&D Systems CLASSIFIED EQUIPMENT: Hardware — Mk/1100, 3-APP/Mac Quadra 630; CLASSIFIED SOFTWARE: Mk/1100, FSI/Vanguard System. EDITORIAL EQUIPMENT: Hardware — Mk/1100, 7-APP/Mac Quadra 630 EDITORIAL SOFTWARE: Mk/1100, FSI/Vanguard System. PRODUCTION EQUIPMENT: Hardware — 2-APP/Mac LaserWriter II; Cameras — 1-Acti/183.

IOLA

THE IOLA REGISTER

302 S Washington Ave, Iola, Kan., 66749-3255, Allen; gen tel (620) 365-2111; adv tel (620) 365-2111; ed tel (620) 365-2111; gen fax (620) 365-6289; adv fax (620) 365-6289; ed fax (620) 365-6289; gen/nat adv e-mail registerdisplay@gmail.com; disp adv e-mail registerdisplay@gmail.com; class adv e-mailclassifieds@iolaregister.com; ed e-mail editorial@iolaregister.com; web site www.iolaregister.com
- 318,308(views)
Group: Kansas Press Association
Published: Mon, Tues, Wed, Thur, Sat
Weekday Frequency: e
Saturday Frequency: m
Circulation: 3,750; 3,750(sat)
Last Audit: Sworn/Estimate/Non-Audited September 30, 2017
Advertising Rate (weekday/saturday): Open inch rate $9.70
Online Advertising Rate: Web page standing ads $75 per month
News services: AP. **Established:** 1897
Own Printing Facility?: Yes
Commercial Printers?: Yes
Special Editions: Fair (Aug); Sports Tab (Dec); Fair (Jun); Spring (Mar); Business & Professional Tab (Oct); Sports Tab (Sept).
Special Weekly Sections: Humboldt News, Grocery Day, Farm Page (Tues); Colony News (Wed); TV Guide (Thur); NASCAR, Weddings, Court Report (Sat);
Digital Platform - Mobile: Apple, Android
Digital Platform - Tablet: Apple iOS, Android
Pub./Ed. .... Susan Lynn
Adv. Mgr. .... Mark L. Hastings
Adv. Mgr., Classified .... Pam Holland
Sports Ed. .... Richard Luken
Prod. Mgr. .... Sara Weide
Health/Medical Ed. .... Jenelle Johnson
City Ed. .... Bob Johnson
Online Ed. .... David Gilham
Photo Ed. .... Jocelyn Sheets
Adv. Rep. .... Sarah Stansbury
Adv. Rep./Graphic Designer .... Whitney Coblentz
Circ. Mgr. .... Susan Locke
Classified Adv. .... Sarah Gonzalez
Commercial Printing .... Kevin Swepton
Market Information: TMC.

Mechanical Available: Offset; Black and 1 ROP colors; insert accepted; page cutoffs - 21 1/2.
Mechanical Specifications: Type page 13 x 21 1/2; E - 6 cols, 2 1/16, 3/16 between; A - 6 cols, 2 1/16, 3/16 between; C - 8 cols, 2 1/16, 3/16 between.
Areas Served: Allen County
Delivery Method: Mail, Newsstand, RacksEquipment & Software: PRESSROOM EQUIPMENT: Lines — HI/Cotrell V-15A; Control System — 1972; BUSINESS EQUIPMENT: 3-SAMTRON/SM-460 BUSINESS SOFTWARE: Microsoft/Windows 95, Pachioli/Works DISPLAY EQUIPMENT: Hardware — APP/Mac G3, APP/Mac 7600; Printers — Xante; DISPLAY SOFTWAREAd Make-up Applications — APP/Mac Sys 8.0, APP/Mac Sys 7.5, Adobe/Photoshop, Multi-Ad/Creator.; EDITORIAL EQUIPMENT: Hardware — APP/Mac 7600, APP/Mac 9600, APP/Mac G3, APP/Mac G4; Printers — Xante, HP/4000 EDITORIAL SOFTWARE: Baseview, QPS/QuarkXPress, Microsoft/Word. PRODUCTION EQUIPMENT: Hardware — LE/LD18; Cameras — Acti/183.

JUNCTION CITY

THE DAILY UNION
222 W 6th St, Junction City, Kan., 66441-5500, Geary; gen tel (785) 762-5000; adv tel (785) 762-5000; ed tel (785) 762-5000; gen fax (785) 762-4584; adv fax (785) 762-4584; ed fax (785) 762-4584; gen/nat adv e-mail m.tyson@thedailyunion.net; disp adv e-mail du.adv@thedailyunion.net; class adv e-maildu.adv@thedailyunion.net; ed e-mail m.editor@thedailyunion.net; web site www.yourdu.net
- 106,800(views), 9,680(visitors)
Group: The White Corporation Willgratten Publications
Published: Tues, Wed, Thur, Fri, Sat
Weekday Frequency: m
Saturday Frequency: m
Circulation: 3,092; 3,092(sat)
Last Audit: Sworn/Estimate/Non-Audited September 30, 2017
Advertising Rate (weekday/saturday): Open inch rate $8.60
News services: AP, CNS, TMS. **Established:** 1861
Own Printing Facility?: Yes
Commercial Printers?: Yes
Special Editions: A-Z Page (Aug); Christmas Greetings (Dec); Outlook (Feb); Bridal (Jan); JC Guide (Jul); Spring Home & Garden (Mar); Gift Guide (Nov); Design an Ad (Oct); Football (Sept).
Special Weekly Sections: Faith (Fri); Wedding Page (S); Lifestyle (Thur); Food (Tues).
Syndicated Publications: TV Channel Cues (local, newsprint) (S).
Digital Platform - Mobile: Apple, Android, Windows, Blackberry
Digital Platform - Tablet: Apple iOS, Android, Windows 7, Blackberry Tablet OS
Publisher/Advertising Manager ...... Melissa Tyson
Managing Editor .... Alix Kunkel
Market Information: TMC.
Mechanical Available: Offset; Black and 3 ROP colors; insert accepted; page cutoffs - 22 3/4.
Mechanical Specifications: Type page 13 x 21 1/2; E - 6 cols, 2 1/16, 1/8 between; A - 6 cols, 2 1/16, 1/8 between; C - 6 cols, 2 1/16, 1/8 between.
Areas Served: 66441, 66442
Delivery Method: Mail, Newsstand, RacksEquipment & Software: PRESSROOM EQUIPMENT: Lines — 6-G/Community; Folders — 1-G/Suburban.; MAILROOM EQUIPMENT: Tying Machines — 1/Bu, 2-Malow/MC Straptyer.; BUSINESS EQUIPMENT: 6-APP/iMac G3, 1-Power Computing/180, 1-Power Computing/150 BUSINESS SOFTWARE: Baseview CLASSIFIED EQUIPMENT: Hardware — 1-Power Computing/180, APP/iMac G3; Printers — 2-Tally/T-6050; CLASSIFIED SOFTWARE: Baseview. DISPLAY EQUIPMENT: Hardware — 1-APP/Mac 8500, 2-APP/Mac 7100, 2-Power Computing/150, 2-APP/Mac G3, 1-APP/Mac G4; Printers — HP/4MV, 1-Epson 3000, 1-QMS/2060; DISPLAY SOFTWAREAd Make-up Applications — Multi-Ad/Creator

4.0, QPS/QuarkXPress 4.1, Adobe/Photoshop 6.0, Adobe/Illustrator 8.0, Adobe/Acrobat 5.0; EDITORIAL EQUIPMENT: Hardware — 14-Power Computing/180, 3-Power Computing/225, 1-APP/iMac G3 EDITORIAL SOFTWARE: Baseview. PRODUCTION EQUIPMENT: Hardware — 1-Nu, 1-QMS/2060 LaserWriter, 1-Pre Press/Panther Pro 46 Imagesetter; Cameras — 1-Acti; Scanners — 4-Microtek/Scanner, 1-Poloroid/Sprint Scan 35 PRODUCTION SOFTWARE: Baseview.

LAWRENCE

LAWRENCE JOURNAL-WORLD
PO Box 1597, 645 New Hampshire St, Lawrence, Kan., 66044-8597, Douglas; gen tel (785) 843-1000; adv tel (785) 832-6307; ed tel (785) 832-6361 ; gen fax (785) 843-1922; adv fax (785) 843-1922; ed fax (785) 843-4512; gen/nat adv e-mail sstanford@ljworld.com; disp adv e-mail ads@ljworld.com; class adv e-mailhstein@ljworld.com; ed e-mail clawhorn@ljworld.com; web site www.ljworld.com
- 1,000,000(views) 477,000(visitors); web site 2 www.kusports.com - 1,000,000(views) 475,000(visitors)
Group: Ogden Newspapers Inc.
Published: Mon, Tues, Wed, Thur, Fri, Sat, Sun
Weekday Frequency: m
Saturday Frequency: m
Circulation: 9,805; 9,805(sat); 11,215(sun)
Last Audit: AAM September 30, 2016
Advertising Rate (weekday/saturday): Modular: 1/32 $137.00; 1/16 $275.00; 1/8 $550.00
Online Advertising Rate: Bottom Leaderboard $500.00 CPM; Medium Rectangle $700.00 CPM; Top Leaderboard $1000.00 CPM
News services: AP **Established:** 1891
Own Printing Facility?: No
Commercial Printers?: No
Special Editions: Only in Lawrence (Apr); Kansas University (Aug); KU Basketball (Oct); Holiday Gift Guide (Nov).
Special Weekly Sections: Hometown Lawrence (Real Estate); Go!
Syndicated Publications: USA WEEKEND Magazine (S); Spry (Mon); Relish (Wed); American Profile (Sat)
Digital Platform - Mobile: Apple, Android
Digital Platform - Tablet: Apple iOS, Android, Kindle, Nook, Kindle Fire
Sports Ed. .... Tom Keegan
Publisher .... Scott Stanford
Editor .... Chad Lawhorn
Digital Ed. .... Nick Gerik
Advertising Manager .... Kathleen Johnson
Market Information: TMC; ADS.
Mechanical Available: Offset; Black and 3 ROP colors; inserts accepted; page cutoffs - 22.
Mechanical Specifications: Type page 10.25" x 20.833"; E - 6 cols, 1.6042, 1/8 between; A - 6 cols, 1.6042, 1/8 between; C - 8 cols, 1.222, .07" between.
Areas Served: 66025, 66044, 66045, 66046, 66047, 66049, 66050, 66066
Delivery Method: Mail, Newsstand, Carrier, RacksEquipment & Software: PRESSROOM EQUIPMENT: Lines — Goss Urbanite, 18 units; Goss Urbanite 12 units; Press Drive — Fincor; Folders — Goss; Pasters —Enkel Autoweb MAILROOM EQUIPMENT: Counter Stackers — Quipp; Inserters & Stuffers — Muller 227, 308, and GMA SLS100A; Tying Machines — Signode, Dynaric and Oval; Address Machine — Cheshire; BUSINESS EQUIPMENT: Dell, HP, IBM BUSINESS SOFTWARE: Great Plains CLASSIFIED EQUIPMENT: Hardware — Dell, HP, IBM; CLASSIFIED SOFTWARE: Advanced Publishing Technology DISPLAY EQUIPMENT: Hardware — MAC; DISPLAY SOFTWAREAd Make-up Applications — Mediaspan Production Manager Pro; EDITORIAL EQUIPMENT: Hardware — MAC; Printers — HP 1050C EDITORIAL SOFTWARE: Baseview/NewsEdit. PRODUCTION EQUIPMENT: Hardware — alfaQuest CTP, two lines; Cameras — 1-B PRODUCTION SOFTWARE: alphaQuest Print Xpress

LEAVENWORTH

THE LEAVENWORTH TIMES
422 Seneca St, Leavenworth, Kan., 66048-1910, Leavenworth; gen tel (913) 682-0305; adv tel (913) 682-0305; ed tel (913) 682-0305; gen fax (913) 682-1114; adv fax (913) 682-1114; ed fax (913) 682-1114; gen/nat adv e-mail kfrey@leavenworthtimes.com; disp adv e-mail kheptig@leavenworthtimes.com; class adv e-mailbdaniels@leavenworthtimes.com; ed e-mail jroberts@leavenworthtimes.com; web site www.leavenworthtimes.com
Group: New Media Investment Group
Published: Tues, Wed, Thur, Fri, Sat
Weekday Frequency: m
Saturday Frequency: m
Circulation: 4,020; 4,100(sat)
Last Audit: Sworn/Estimate/Non-Audited September 30, 2017
Advertising Rate (weekday/saturday): Open inch rate $16.75
Online Advertising Rate: 15 Words 1 day print and online $25.00; 6 days $30.00
News services: AP. GateHouse Media News **Established:** 1857
Own Printing Facility?: Yes
Commercial Printers?: No
Syndicated Publications: USA WEEKEND Magazine (S).
Digital Platform - Mobile: Apple, Android
Digital Platform - Tablet: Apple iOS, Android, Kindle, Nook, Kindle Fire
Classifieds/Circ. Dir. .... Barbara Daniels
Gen. Mgr./Adv. Dir. .... Sandy Hattock
Bus. Mgr. .... Beckie Mitchell
Sports Ed. .... Brent Lager
Reporter .... John Richemeier
Reporter .... Tim Linn
Classified Mgr. .... Kristi Vornholt
Adv. Acct. Exec. .... Kristen Frey
Av. Acct. Exec. .... Kathy Heptig
Adv. Acct. Exec. .... Tammy Lawson
Managing Editor .... Mark Rountree
News Ed. .... Rimsie McConiga
Gen. Mgr./Adv. Dir. .... Sandy Hattock
Market Information: TMC.
Mechanical Available: Offset; Black and 3 ROP colors; insert accepted - free-standing cards; page cutoffs - 22 3/4.
Mechanical Specifications: Type page 11 x 21 1/2; E - 6 cols, 1 13/16, 1/8 between; A - 6 cols, 1 13/16, 1/8 between; C - 9 cols, 1 3/16, 1/8 between.
Areas Served: 66048
Delivery Method: Mail, Newsstand, Carrier, RacksEquipment & Software: BUSINESS EQUIPMENT: PC BUSINESS SOFTWARE: Nomads/ListMaster CLASSIFIED EQUIPMENT: Hardware — APP/iMac; Printers — APP/Mac 12-640; CLASSIFIED SOFTWARE: CAMS. DISPLAY EQUIPMENT: Printers — HP/LaserJet 4MV; Other Hardware — Pre Press/Panther Pro 46 DISPLAY SOFTWAREAd Make-up Applications — Multi-Ad/Creator, APP/Mac System 9; Layout Software — APP/Mac. EDITORIAL EQUIPMENT: Hardware — APP/Mac/Pre Press/Panther Pro 36; Printers — HP/LaserJet 4MV EDITORIAL SOFTWARE: Baseview. PRODUCTION EQUIPMENT: Hardware — Caere/OmniPage 7.0, 1-COM/8400, 2-APP/Mac; Cameras — 1-Nu PRODUCTION SOFTWARE: QPS/QuarkXPress 4.1.
Note: Printing and mailroom outsourced

LIBERAL

THE LEADER & TIMES
16 S Kansas Ave, Liberal, Kan., 67901-3732, Seward; gen tel (620) 626-0840; adv tel (620) 626-0840; ed tel (620) 626-0840; gen fax (620) 626-9854; adv fax (620) 626-9854; ed fax (620) 626-9854; gen/nat adv e-mail earl@hpleader.com; disp adv e-mail ads@hpleader.com; class adv e-maildenasa@hpleader.com; ed e-mail news@hpleader.com; web site www.leaderandtimes.com
Group: Kansas Press Association
Published: Mon, Tues, Wed, Thur, Fri, Sun
Weekday Frequency: m
Circulation: 4,250; 4,500(sun)

Last Audit: Sworn/Estimate/Non-Audited September 30, 2017
Advertising Rate (weekday/saturday): Open inch rate $15.00
Advertising Rate (sunday): Open inch rate $15.00
Online Advertising Rate: Based on clicks: Call for pricing
News services: AP. **Established:** 1987
Special Editions: Life & Times (Mar); Life & Times (Sept).
Special Weekly Sections: Entertainment (Fri); Leisure Times (S); Farm & Ranch (Thur); Business Day (Tues); Best Food Day (Wed).
Syndicated Publications: FYI (S).
Digital Platform - Mobile: Apple, Android
Digital Platform - Tablet: Apple iOS, Android
Pub. .... Earl Watt
Classified Adv. Mgr. .... Denasa Rice
News. .... Jessica Crawford
Market Information: Split run; TMC; Zoned editions.
Mechanical Available: Offset; Black and 3 ROP colors; insert accepted - cards, catalogs; page cutoffs - 21 1/2.
Mechanical Specifications: Type page 12 1/2 x 20; E - 6 cols, 2, 1/8 between; A - 6 cols, 2, 1/8 between; C - 9 cols, 1 5/16, 1/16 between.
Areas Served: Seward County
Delivery Method: Mail, Newsstand, Carrier, RacksEquipment & Software: PRESSROOM EQUIPMENT: Lines — 5-WPC/Atlas (1-Quadra color;; MAILROOM EQUIPMENT: Counter Stackers — 1-KAN/4 station; Tying Machines — 2/Bu; BUSINESS EQUIPMENT: 7-HP/Pentium II CLASSIFIED EQUIPMENT: Hardware — 1-APP/Mac SE, 1-APP/Mac SE30, APP/Mac LC III; Printers — APP/Mac ImageWriter II; CLASSIFIED SOFTWARE: Baseview/Class Manager. DISPLAY EQUIPMENT: Hardware — 1-APP/Mac Classic, 2-APP/Mac II, 1-APP/Mac Classic, APP/Mac Centris 660AV; Printers — Pre Press/Panther ImageSetter; Other Hardware — Umax/Scan DISPLAY SOFTWAREAd Make-up Applications — Aldus/PageMaker, Broderbund/TypeStyler, QPS/QuarkXPress, Adobe/Photoshop 2.5, AP AdSend; EDITORIAL EQUIPMENT: Hardware — 7-APP/Power Mac/2-Flatbed Scanners, Lf/Leafscan Negative Scanner, Pre Press/Panther Imagesetter; Printers — 2-Elite/XL 608 600 DPI EDITORIAL SOFTWARE: Baseview/NewsEdit, QPS/QuarkXPress 3.31, Adobe/Photoshop 2.5.1. PRODUCTION EQUIPMENT: Hardware — Caere/OmniPage 2.1, 1-Pre-Press/ImageSetter, Konica/7200; Cameras — Acti/Horizontal Full Frame; Scanners — Relisys/Color Scan, 1-Lf/Leafscan 35mm Negative Scanner PRODUCTION SOFTWARE: QPS/QuarkXPress 3.31.

MANHATTAN

THE MANHATTAN MERCURY
318 N 5th St, Manhattan, Kan., 66502-5910, Riley; gen tel (785) 776-2200; adv tel (785) 776-2200; ed tel (785) 776-2300; gen fax (785) 776-8807; adv fax (785) 776-8807; ed fax (785) 776-8807; gen/nat adv e-mail advertising@themercury.com; disp adv e-mail advertising@themercury.com; class adv e-mailclassifieds@themercury.com; ed e-mail news@themercury.com; web site www.themercury.com
- 837,000(views) 386,000(visitors)
Group: Kansas Press Association Seaton Group
Published: Mon, Tues, Wed, Thur, Fri, Sun
Weekday Frequency: e
Circulation: 8,340; 9,136(sun)
Last Audit: CAC March 31, 2015
Advertising Rate (weekday/saturday): Open inch rate $10.06 (M-Tue) $11.18 (Wed-Fri)
Advertising Rate (sunday): Open inch rate $11.73
Online Advertising Rate: Starting from $15.00 CPM
News services: AP, NYT, LAT-WP, SHNS. **Established:** 1909
Special Editions: Spring Fix-Up (Apr); KSU (Aug); Weddings/Brides (Feb); Financial Planning (Jan); Senior Citizens (Monthly); Homes (Quarterly); Guide to Manhattan (Sept).

Special Weekly Sections: Food & Health (Tue); Plan-A-Weekend (Thur); Family & Youth, Church, Automotive (Fri); Entertainment, Travel, Business, Ag, Education, Weddings, Military, Home & Garden (Sun)
Syndicated Publications: TV Preview (Fri); Parade (Sun)
Digital Platform - Mobile: Apple, Android
Digital Platform - Tablet: Apple iOS, Android
Pub./Ed. in Chief .... Ned M. Seaton
Chairman .... Edward Seaton
Editorial Page Ed. .... Walter Braun
Sports Ed. .... Josh Kinder
Exec. Ed. .... Megan Moser
Wire Ed. .... Mike Dendurent
Photographer .... Sarah Midgorden
Adv./Prod. Dir. .... Steve Stallwitz
Office Mgr. .... Jemie Wataha
Adv. Rep. .... Tami Yeager
Circ. Mgr. .... Bonnie Raglin
Customer Service Supervisor .... Kari Wilson
Online Content Mgr. .... Jelani Yancey
Market Information: ADS; TMC.
Mechanical Available: Offset; Black and 3 ROP colors; insert accepted - all; page cutoffs - 22 3/4.
Mechanical Specifications: Type page 13 x 21 1/2; E - 6 cols, 2 1/16, 1/8 between; A - 6 cols, 2 1/16, 1/8 between; C - 6 cols, 2 1/16, 1/8 between.
Areas Served: Riley and Pottawatomie County
Delivery Method: Mail, CarrierEquipment & Software: PRESSROOM EQUIPMENT: Lines — 6-HI/845 1970; Folders — 1-HI/2:1; Reels & Stands — 1; Control System — Haley/Controller 1970.; MAILROOM EQUIPMENT: Counter Stackers — 1-BG/Count-O-Veyor 107; Inserters & Stuffers — 5-KAN/480; Tying Machines — 1-Bu/Constellation K101; Address Machine — 1/KAN.; BUSINESS EQUIPMENT: APP/Mac BUSINESS SOFTWARE: Quickbooks CLASSIFIED EQUIPMENT: Hardware — 5-APP/Mac; IBM; Printers — APP/Mac LaserWriter NTX, TI, HP/LaserJet; CLASSIFIED SOFTWARE: Baseview/Ad Manager Pro. DISPLAY EQUIPMENT: Hardware — 1-APP/Mac; Printers — HP/LaserJet; DISPLAY SOFTWAREAd Make-up Applications — QPS/QuarkXPress, Adobe/Acrobat; Layout Software — Baseview. EDITORIAL EQUIPMENT: Hardware — 1-Mk/1100 Plus, IBM, 14-RSK/TRS 80-100, 4-APP/Mac, 10-Mk; Printers — APP/Mac LaserWriter NTX, TI, HP/LaserJet, Xante/Accel-A-Writer EDITORIAL SOFTWARE: Mk/Page, QPS/QuarkXPress. PRODUCTION EQUIPMENT: Hardware — Caere/OmniPage Pro 5.0, HP/4MV; Cameras — 1-R/580; Scanners — Umax/UG80, 1-KK/RFS 2035, 1-Umax/Powerbook II, Umax/Mirage II PRODUCTION SOFTWARE: QPS/QuarkXPress 3.21.

MCPHERSON

MCPHERSON SENTINEL

116 S Main St, McPherson, Kan., 67460-4852, McPherson; gen tel (620) 241-2422; gen fax (620) 241-2425; class adv e-maillborn@mcphersonsentinel.com; ed e-mail news@mcphersonsentinel.com; web site www.mcphersonsentinel.com
Group: New Media Investment Group
Published: Tues, Wed, Thur, Fri, Sat
Weekday Frequency: e
Saturday Frequency: m
Circulation: 3,600; 3,600(sat)
Last Audit: Sworn/Estimate/Non-Audited October 1, 2017
Advertising Rate (weekday/saturday): Open inch rate $14.50
News services: AP. **Established:** 1887
Own Printing Facility?: Yes
Commercial Printers?: Yes
Special Editions: Football (Sept); Hunting (Oct); Back-to-School (Aug); Christmas (Dec); Soil Conservation (Jan); 4-H & County Fair (Jul)
Special Weekly Sections: This Week on TV (Fri); Space & Places (Real Estate)
Syndicated Publications: American Profile (Sat); Spry (Sat); Relish (Sat); McPherson County Guide (Yearly); Bridal (Jan)
Digital Platform - Mobile: Apple, Android
Digital Platform - Tablet: Apple iOS, Android
Adv. Dir., Classified .... Linda Born-Smith
Circ. Mgr. .... Barbara Herl
Managing Editor .... Cheyenne Schroeder
Market Information: TMC.
Mechanical Available: Offset; Black and 3 ROP colors; insert accepted; page cutoffs - 21 1/2.
Mechanical Specifications: Type page 11 x 21 1/2; E - 6 cols, 1 3/4, 1/6 between; A - 6 cols, 1 3/4, 1/6 between; C - 6 cols, 1 3/4, 1/6 between.
Areas Served: 67460
Delivery Method: Mail, Newsstand, Carrier, RacksEquipment & Software: PRESSROOM EQUIPMENT: Lines — 5-G/Community 1974; 1-G/Community 1995.; MAILROOM EQUIPMENT: Tying Machines — 1/Marlo, Miller-Bevco/Strapper.; CLASSIFIED EQUIPMENT: Hardware — APP/Mac; Printers — APP/Mac LaserWriter II; CLASSIFIED SOFTWARE: Baseview. DISPLAY EQUIPMENT: Hardware — APP/Mac G3, APP/Mac G4; Printers — Xante/Accel-A-Writer 3G; Other Hardware — Umax/Scanner. DISPLAY SOFTWAREAd Make-up Applications — QPS/QuarkXPress 7.5; EDITORIAL EQUIPMENT: Hardware — APP/Mac/Umax/S-6E Flatbed Scanner, Polaroid/Sprint Scan 35; Printers — Xante/Accel-A-Writer 3G EDITORIAL SOFTWARE: Adobe/Photoshop 3.0, QPS/QuarkXPress 7.53, Baseview. PRODUCTION EQUIPMENT: Hardware — Nu/Flip Top FT4OUPNS; Cameras — Acti.

NEWTON

THE NEWTON KANSAN

121 W 6th St, Newton, Kan., 67114-2117, Harvey; gen tel (316) 283-1500; adv tel (316) 283-1500 ext. 110; ed tel (316) 283-1500 ext. 105; gen fax (316) 283-2471; adv fax (316) 283-2471; ed fax (316) 283-2471; gen/nat adv e-mail cwallace@thekansan.com; disp adv e-mail jnewman@andoveramerican.com; class adv e-mailjgarnica@thekansan.com; ed e-mail cfrey@thekansan.com; web site www.thekansan.com
- 3,813(views) 260,665(visitors)
Group: New Media Investment Group
Published: Mon, Tues, Wed, Thur, Fri, Sat, Sun
Weekday Frequency: e
Saturday Frequency: m
Circulation: 7,513; 7,513(sat)
Last Audit: Sworn/Estimate/Non-Audited September 30, 2017
Advertising Rate (weekday/saturday): Open inch rate $14.50; $16.25 (National)
Advertising Rate (sunday): Open inch rate $14.50; $16.25 (National)
Online Advertising Rate: Top Banner, Block, Tile, Postage Stamp, Weather, Page Curl $99.00 (12 Months); $115.00 (6 Months); $125 (3 Months)
News services: AP. **Established:** 1872
Special Editions: Bridal Tab (Jan); Welcome to Harvey County (Jun); Home Improvement (Mar); Christmas Kick-Off (Nov); Holiday Creations-Including Cookbook (Oct); Living Well (Quarterly).
Special Weekly Sections: Religion (Fri); Business, Community Calendar (Sat); Farm (Thur).
Syndicated Publications: Relish (Monthly); USA WEEKEND Magazine (Sat).
Proprietary Publications: Harvey County Living (Monthly)
Digital Platform - Mobile: Apple, Android
Digital Platform - Tablet: Apple iOS, Android
Mng. Ed. .... Chad Frey
Controller/Business Dir. .... Shelly Drake
Sports Ed. .... Mark Schnabel
Multimedia Sales Exec. .... Connie Wallace
Classifieds Adv/ .... Jenna Garnica
Business Asst. .... Verna Rowe
Circ. Supervisor .... Jamie Seger
Creative Design .... Matt Janzen
Pub. .... Lee Bachlet
Recruitment .... Maria Lazcano
Market Information: ADS; TMC.
Mechanical Available: Offset; Black and 3 ROP colors; insert accepted; page cutoffs - 22 3/4.
Mechanical Specifications: Type page 13 x 21 1/2; E - 6 cols, 2 1/2, 1/6 between; A - 6 cols, 2 1/2, 1/6 between; C - 6 cols, 2 1/2, 1/6 between.
Areas Served: Newton and Harvey County
Delivery Method: Mail, Carrier, RacksEquipment & Software: PRESSROOM EQUIPMENT: Lines — 7-G/Single Width 1972; Folders — 1-G/SC.; MAILROOM EQUIPMENT: Tying Machines — 2/Bu; Address Machine — 1-/Ch.; BUSINESS EQUIPMENT: Gateway BUSINESS SOFTWARE: PBS CLASSIFIED EQUIPMENT: Hardware — 1-APP/iMac 333; Printers — APP/Mac Imagewriter, APP/Mac LaserWriter 16-600 PS; CLASSIFIED SOFTWARE: QPS/QuarkXPress, Baseview/Classified, Adobe/Photoshop 5.0, Adobe/Acrobat 5.0. DISPLAY EQUIPMENT: Hardware — 2-APP/Mac G3, 1-Power PC/7300-180, 1-Power PC/7200-120, APP/Mac G3; Printers — 1-MON/Imagesetter, HP/LaserWriter 4050; DISPLAY SOFTWAREAd Make-up Applications — QPS/QuarkXPress 4.0, Multi-Ad/Creator 4.0, Adobe/Photoshop 5.5, Adobe/Acrobat 4.0; Layout Software — Ad Force II. EDITORIAL EQUIPMENT: Hardware — 1-APP/Mac G3, APP/Mac G4, 2-APP/Mac Power PC 4400-200, 4-APP/Mac Power PC 7300-80/2-APP/Mac Quadra 650, Nikon/Film Scanner, Nikon/Scantouch Flatbed; Printers — MON/Imagesetter EDITORIAL SOFTWARE: Adobe/Photoshop 5.5, QPS/QuarkXPress 3.32, PRODUCTION EQUIPMENT: Hardware — OmniPage, APP/Mac G3, APP/Mac G4; Cameras — DAI/DS; Scanners — Umax/Astra 4000LS, Nikon/Color Film Scanner, Nikon/Scantouch Flatbed PRODUCTION SOFTWARE: QPS/QuarkXPress 4.1.

PARSONS

PARSONS SUN

220 S 18th St, Parsons, Kan., 67357-4218, Labette; gen tel (620) 421-2000; adv tel (620) 421-2000; ed tel (620) 421-2000; gen fax (620) 421-2217; adv fax (620) 421-2217; ed fax (620) 421-2217; gen/nat adv e-mail jstrait@parsonssun.com; disp adv e-mail hwiford@parsonssun.com; class adv e-mailkroot@parsonssun.com; ed e-mail rnolting@parsonssun.com; web site www.parsonssun.com
Published: Mon, Tues, Wed, Thur, Fri, Sat, Sun
Weekday Frequency: e
Saturday Frequency: m
Circulation: 5,420; 5,420(sat)
Last Audit: Sworn/Estimate/Non-Audited September 30, 2017
Advertising Rate (weekday/saturday): Open inch rate $10.00
Online Advertising Rate: Side Box $75.00 CPM; Top Banner $125.00 CPM; Call for Online/Print Bundle Pricing
News services: AP, Harris News Service. **Established:** 1871
Special Editions: Spring Home Improvement (Apr); Back-to-School (Aug); Basketball (Dec); Senior Lifestyles (Bi-monthy); Community (Feb); Tax & Financial Planning (Jan); Fair Tab (Jul); Why My Dad's the Greatest (Jun); Agriculture (Mar); Outdoor Living (May).
Special Weekly Sections: TV Scene (Fri); Business (Mon); Best Food Day (Wed).
Syndicated Publications: American Profile (Weekly).
Digital Platform - Mobile: Apple, Android
Digital Platform - Tablet: Apple iOS, Android, Kindle, Nook, Kindle Fire
Pub. .... Peter J. Cook
Circ. Mgr. .... Amy Jensen
Mng. Ed. .... Ray Nolting
Asst. Mng. Ed. .... Jamie Willey
Bus. Mgr. .... Shanna Guiot
Sports Ed. .... Jason Peake
Display Adv. Sales .... Jan Strait
Display Adv. Sales .... Haley Wiford
Classified Adv. Sales .... Kim Root
Graphic Designer .... Michele Cave
Graphic Desgner .... Emily Gudde
Circ. Clerk .... Tina Freeberg
Circ. Clerk .... Lori Luma
Production Mgr. .... James Jenson
Market Information: TMC.
Mechanical Available: Offset; Black and 3 ROP colors; insert accepted - any; page cutoffs - 22 3/4.
Mechanical Specifications: Type page 13 x 21; E - 6 cols, 2 1/16, 1/8 between; A - 6 cols, 2 1/16, 1/8 between; C - 6 cols, 2 1/16, 1/8 between.
Areas Served: Labette County
Delivery Method: Mail, Carrier, RacksEquipment & Software: PRESSROOM EQUIPMENT: Lines — 7-G; Folders — 1-G/2:1.; MAILROOM EQUIPMENT: Tying Machines — 2/Bu.; BUSINESS EQUIPMENT: DSI/PaperTrak BUSINESS SOFTWARE: Microsoft/Excel, Microsoft/Word CLASSIFIED EQUIPMENT: Hardware — APP/Mac; Printers — Okidata, Xante/3G, Xante/8200; CLASSIFIED SOFTWARE: Baseview. DISPLAY EQUIPMENT: Hardware — APP/Mac, 1998-APP/Mac; Printers — APP/Mac LaserWriter II, Xante/8200; DISPLAY SOFTWAREAd Make-up Applications — QPS, Baseview, Multi-Ad/Creator, Adobe/Photoshop; Layout Software — Baseview. EDITORIAL EQUIPMENT: Hardware — APP/Mac; Printers — Xante/3G, Xante/8200 EDITORIAL SOFTWARE: Aldus/FreeHand, QPS, Multi-Ad/Creator, Baseview, Adobe/Photoshop, QPS/QuarkXPress. PRODUCTION EQUIPMENT: Hardware — Nu, NuArc Nu; Cameras — 1-Acti; Scanners — APP/Mac One, APP/Mac, Umax/UC1260 PRODUCTION SOFTWARE: Baseview 2.05.

PITTSBURG

THE MORNING SUN

701 N Locust St, Pittsburg, Kan., 66762-4038, Crawford; gen tel (620) 231-2600; adv tel (620) 231-2600 ext. 105; ed tel (620) 231-2600 ext. 140; gen fax (620) 231-0645; adv fax (620) 231-0645; ed fax (620) 231-0645; gen/nat adv e-mail jryan@morningsun.net; disp adv e-mail jsimon@morningsun.net; class adv e-maillbush@morningsun.net; ed e-mail anash@morningsun.net; web site www.morningsun.net
Group: New Media Investment Group
Published: Tues, Wed, Thur, Fri, Sat, Sun
Weekday Frequency: m
Saturday Frequency: m
Circulation: 5,500; 5,900(sat); 6,000(sun)
Last Audit: Sworn/Estimate/Non-Audited September 30, 2017
Advertising Rate (weekday/saturday): Open inch rate $12.95
Advertising Rate (sunday): Open inch rate $13.67
Online Advertising Rate: Small Box $100.00/month; Small Banner $110.00/month; Banner $125.00/month
News services: AP. **Established:** 1887
Own Printing Facility?: Yes
Commercial Printers?: Yes
Special Weekly Sections: Business (Other); Bridal (S); Church (Sat); Best Food Day (Wed).
Syndicated Publications: Relish (Monthly); USA WEEKEND Magazine (S); American Profile (Sat).
Digital Platform - Mobile: Apple, Android
Digital Platform - Tablet: Apple iOS, Android, Kindle, Nook, Kindle Fire
Managing Ed. .... Andrew Nash
Classified Adv. Mgr. .... Linda Bush
Adv. Rep. .... Nancy Howell
Asst. Bookkeeper .... Amy Iori
Sports Editor .... Lucas Davis
Pub. .... Matt Guthrie
Market Information: TMC.
Mechanical Available: Offset; Black and 3 ROP colors; insert accepted; page cutoffs - 22 3/4.
Mechanical Specifications: Type page 10 x 21 1/2; E - 6 cols, 1.55", .1389" between; A - 6 cols, 1.55, .1389 between; C - 6 cols, 1.12, 1/8 between.
Areas Served: 66762, 66712, 66763, 66743, 66781, 66701, 66734, 66724, 66711, 66756, 64769, 66773, 64832, 64762, 66760, 66782
Delivery Method: Mail, Newsstand, Carrier, RacksEquipment & Software: PRESSROOM EQUIPMENT: Lines — 5-G/Urbanite; Folders — 1-G/2:1.; MAILROOM EQUIPMENT: Tying Machines — 1-MLN/ML2EE; Address Machine — 1/Ch; BUSINESS EQUIPMENT: MSSI CLASSIFIED EQUIPMENT: Hardware — MediaSpan Ad Pro; DISPLAY EQUIPMENT: Hardware — Mac; DISPLAY SOFTWAREAd Make-up Applications — CS 3; Layout Software — APP/Mac. EDITORIAL EQUIPMENT: Hardware — Mac EDITORIAL SOFTWARE: CS 3 PRODUCTION

EQUIPMENT: Hardware — 1-B/500-255; Cameras — 1-B/Commodore 241305.

SALINA

THE SALINA JOURNAL

333 S 4th St, Salina, Kan., 67401-3903, Saline; gen tel (785) 823-6363; adv tel (785) 822-1446; ed tel (785) 822-1411; gen fax (785) 827-6363; adv fax (785) 823-3207; ed fax (785) 827-6363; gen/nat adv e-mail dgilchrist@salina.com; disp adv e-mail kmalm@salina.com; class adv e-maildnelson@salina.com; ed e-mail smontague@salina.com; web site www.salina.com
Group: GateHouse Media, Inc.
Published: Mon, Tues, Wed, Thur, Fri, Sat, Sun
Weekday Frequency: m
Saturday Frequency: m
Circulation: 18,365; 18,365(sat); 19,317(sun)
Last Audit: VAC December 31, 2016
Advertising Rate (weekday/saturday): Open inch rate $31.00
Advertising Rate (sunday): Open inch rate $31.00
News services: AP, MCT, Tribune **Established:** 1871
Own Printing Facility?: Yes
Commercial Printers?: Yes
Special Editions: Guide to Salina (Aug); Christmas Gift Guide (Dec); Progress (Feb); Bridal (Jan); Back-to-School (Jul); Progress (Mar); Travel (May); Christmas Gift Guide (Nov); Football (Sept).
Special Weekly Sections: Scene/Entertainment (Fri); Neighbors (Mon); Church (Sat); Home/Garden (Thur); Best Food Day (Wed).
Syndicated Publications: Dream Homes (Quarterly); USA WEEKEND Magazine (S); TV Week (TV Listings) (Sat).
Digital Platform - Mobile: Apple, Android
Digital Platform - Tablet: Apple iOS, Android, Kindle, Nook, Kindle Fire
Pub. .... M. Olaf Frandsen
Adv. Mgr. .... Kathy Malm
Circ. Mgr. .... Mollie Purcell
Exec. Ed. .... Sharon Montague
Chief Photograher .... Tom Dorsey
Sports Ed. .... Bob Davidson
Rgl. Adv. Dir. .... Dave Gilchrist
Classified Consultant .... Debbie Nelson
Classified Consultant .... Sue Austin
Prod. Dir. .... Norbert Laue
Business Office Mgr. .... Roxy Belden
Market Information: Split run; TMC; Zoned editions.
Mechanical Available: Offset; Black and 3 ROP colors; insert accepted; page cutoffs - 22 3/4.
Mechanical Specifications: Type page 12 x 21 1/2; E - 6 cols, 1 7/8, 1/8 between; A - 6 cols, 1 7/8, 1/8 between; C - 9 cols, 1 1/4, 1/16 between.
Areas Served: North-central and northwest Kansas
Delivery Method: Mail, Newsstand, Carrier, RacksEquipment & Software: PRESSROOM EQUIPMENT: Lines — 3-G/Urbanite (color), 5-G/Urbanite (black); Folders — 1-G/2:1; Reels & Stands — 6, 2-G/Stands, 2-G/Rolls.; MAILROOM EQUIPMENT: Counter Stackers — QWI; Inserters & Stuffers — HI/1472-13 head; Tying Machines — MLN; Wrapping Singles — MLN; Address Machine — MM.; BUSINESS EQUIPMENT: Data Sciences, HP BUSINESS SOFTWARE: PaperTrack CLASSIFIED EQUIPMENT: Hardware — APP/Mac Servers IP; Printers — Okidata/393, HP/DeskJet; CLASSIFIED SOFTWARE: Baseview. DISPLAY EQUIPMENT: Hardware — APP/Mac Quadra 950, 8-APP/Mac G3; Printers — 2-Epson/Stylus 3000, HP/4000, HP/4MV; Other Hardware — 2-Zip Drive 100 DISPLAY SOFTWAREAd Make-up Applications — Multi-Ad/Creator, QPS/QuarkXPress 4.1.1, Adobe/Acrobat, Adobe/Illustrator, Adobe/Photoshop; Layout Software — Pentium/NT Serv EDITORIAL EQUIPMENT: Hardware — 12-APP/Mac G4, 3-Pentium/File Server, 3-Microsoft/Windows NT, 16-APP/iMac; Printers — HP/4MV, APP/Mac 12/640 PS EDITORIAL SOFTWARE: Citrix, 3-LiveWire. PRODUCTION EQUIPMENT: Hardware — 2-XIT, 1-Nu/Flip Top FT40APRNS; Scanners — 2-AG/Arcus Scanner

TOPEKA

THE TOPEKA CAPITAL-JOURNAL

616 SE Jefferson St, Topeka, Kan., 66607-1137, Shawnee; gen tel (785) 295-1111; adv tel (785) 295-1263; ed tel (785) 295-1212; gen fax (785) 295-1230; adv fax (785) 295-1261; ed fax (785) 295-1230; gen/nat adv e-mail susan.cantrell@cjonline.com; disp adv e-mail susan.cantrell@cjonline.com; class adv e-maillinda.girardin@cjonline.com; ed e-mail tomari.quinn@cjonline.com; web site www.cjonline.com
- 13,890,000(views) 1,459,500(visitors)
Group: GateHouse Media, Inc.
Published: Mon, Tues, Wed, Thur, Fri, Sat, Sun
Weekday Frequency: m
Saturday Frequency: m
Circulation: 20,273; 20,273(sat); 25,480(sun)
Last Audit: AAM June 30, 2017
News services: SHNS, AP, LAT-WP. **Established:** 1858
Own Printing Facility?: No
Commercial Printers?: No
Special Editions: Best of Topeka; Prime Time, Downtown Topeka, Momentum 2022
Special Weekly Sections: Real Estate (Sat); Religion (Sat); Food & Fun (Sun)
Syndicated Publications: Relish (Wednesday) Parade (Sunday)
Proprietary Publications: Northeast Kansas Weddings
Digital Platform - Mobile: Apple, Android
Digital Platform - Tablet: Apple iOS, Android, Kindle, Nook, Kindle Fire
President and Publisher .... Zach Ahrens
Ed. and VP audience .... Tomari Quinn
Dir., HR .... Heather Johanning
Prod. .... Ron Beavers
Dir. of Circ. .... Gary Warner
VP of Sales/Mktg. .... Susan Cantrell
Market Information: TMC (Wednesday)
Mechanical Available: Offset; Black and 3 ROP colors; insert accepted - cards; page cutoffs - 23 9/16.
Mechanical Specifications: Type page 11 5/8 x 22 3/4; E - 6 cols, 2 1/16, 1/8 between; A - 6 cols, 2 1/16, 1/8 between; C - 10 cols, 1 1/16, 3/32 between.
Areas Served: Shawnee County
Delivery Method: Mail, Newsstand, Carrier, RacksEquipment & Software: BUSINESS EQUIPMENT: 1-IBM/RS 6000 BUSINESS SOFTWARE: Unix, Claris Financials CLASSIFIED EQUIPMENT: Hardware — APP/Mac CLASSIFIED SOFTWARE: Ad Speed DISPLAY EQUIPMENT: Hardware — APP/Mac; Printers — HP; DISPLAY SOFTWAREAd Make-up Applications — Adobe/Illustrator, DTI; Layout Software — DTI. EDITORIAL EQUIPMENT: Hardware — APP/Mac; Printers — HP EDITORIAL SOFTWARE: Adobe/Photoshop, DTI 4.3. PRODUCTION EQUIPMENT: Hardware — 2-Nu/Flip Top; Scanners — HP/ScanJet IIcx PRODUCTION SOFTWARE: QPS/QuarkXPress 3.3, DT.

WICHITA

THE WICHITA EAGLE

825 E Douglas Ave, Wichita, Kan., 67202-3512, Sedgwick; gen tel (316) 268-6000; adv tel (316) 269-6709; ed tel (316) 268-6351; gen fax (316) 268-6395; adv fax (316) 268-6234; ed fax (316) 268-6627; gen/nat adv e-mail jgarcia@wichitaeagle.com; disp adv e-mail jgarcia@wichitaeagle.com; class adv e-mailclassified@wichitaeagle.com; ed e-mail schisenhall@wichitaeagle.com; web site www.kansas.com
- 1,100,000(views) 1,560,000(visitors); web site 2 www.varsitykansas.com
Group: The McClatchy Company
Published: Mon, Tues, Wed, Thur, Fri, Sat, Sun
Weekday Frequency: m
Saturday Frequency: m
Circulation: 45,557; 44,347(sat); 66,077(sun)
Last Audit: AAM June 30, 2016
Advertising Rate (weekday/saturday): Open inch rate $133.75
Advertising Rate (sunday): Open inch rate $185.90
News services: AP, MCT, WP/BLOOM
Established: 1872
Own Printing Facility?: Yes
Commercial Printers?: Yes
Special Editions: Voter's Guide (Apr); Wine Festival (Aug); Economic Outlook (Oct); Brides Guide (Jan); Reader' Choice (July); Summer Activities (May); Woofstock (Oct)
Special Weekly Sections: Business (Tue-Sun); Health (Tues); Go! (Fri)
Syndicated Publications: Parade (S)
Digital Platform - Mobile: Apple, Android, Windows
Digital Platform - Tablet: Apple iOS, Android, Kindle, Nook, Kindle Fire
Investigations Ed. .... Jean Hays
Deputy Ed./Print .... Tom Shine
Deputy Ed./Pub. .... Michael Roehrman
Metro Ed. .... Marcia Werts
Opinion editor .... Phillip Brownlee
Comm. Eng. Ed. .... Kirk Seminoff
Asst. Sports Ed. .... Tom Seals
Features Editor .... Ardua Harris
Visuals Editor .... Brian Corn
News Editor .... Jill Erickson
News Editor .... Julie Mah
News Editor .... Diane McCartney
News Editor .... Vicki Reynolds
Ed. in Chief .... Josh Wood
President and Publisher .... Roy Heatherly
Marketing Director .... Ben Jennings
Pub. & V.P. of Adv. .... Kelly Mirt
Market Information: ADS; Split run; TMC; Zoned editions.
Mechanical Available: Flexo; Black and 3 ROP colors; insert accepted; page cutoffs - 21.
Mechanical Specifications: Type page 12 x 21; E - 6 cols, 1 3/16, 1/6 between; A - 6 cols, 1 3/16, 1/6 between; C - 10 cols, 1 1/8, 1/12 between.
Areas Served: Sedgwick County
Delivery Method: Newsstand, Carrier, RacksEquipment & Software: PRESSROOM EQUIPMENT: Lines — 10-KBA/Colormax II 2002; MAILROOM EQUIPMENT: Counter Stackers — 4-QWI/300, 2-QWI/350, 3-QWI/400; Inserters & Stuffers — 3-S/72P; Tying Machines — 6-Dynaric/NP-2; Wrapping Singles — 2-OVL/415; Address Machine — 1/KAN; BUSINESS EQUIPMENT: HP/3000-KS/969 BUSINESS SOFTWARE: CIS 3.02:Payroll, CIS 6.05.A, GEAC/Payroll 3.02C, Mediastream/CIS 6.05B CLASSIFIED EQUIPMENT: Hardware — HP/Desktop PCs, Sun/Servers; Edgil/EdgCapture Credit Card Authorization Server; Printers — HP/LaserJet; CLASSIFIED SOFTWARE: AT/Enterprise. DISPLAY EQUIPMENT: Hardware — APP/Mac G4, APP/Mac G3; Printers — Canon, OCE, HP/750C, Xante/Color Laser; Other Hardware — Arcus II DISPLAY SOFTWAREAd Make-up Applications — Multi-Ad/Creator 4.0.3; Layout Software — AT/Architect. EDITORIAL EQUIPMENT: Hardware — HP/Desktop PCs, MS/Windows NT/Lf/AP Leaf Picture Desk; Printers — HP/LaserJet EDITORIAL SOFTWARE: Dewar/View. PRODUCTION EQUIPMENT: Hardware — 2-III/3850, Adobe/Photoshop 4.0; Cameras — 1-C/Marathon; Scanners — ECRM, Arcus II, Agfa/Duoscan PRODUCTION SOFTWARE: Ad Manager.

WINFIELD

WINFIELD DAILY COURIER

201 E 9th Ave, Winfield, Kan., 67156-2817, Cowley; gen tel (620) 221-1050; adv tel (620) 221-1050; ed tel (620) 221-1050; gen fax (620) 221-1101; adv fax (620) 221-1101; ed fax (620) 221-1101; gen/nat adv e-mail courier@winfieldcourier.com; disp adv e-mail advertising@winfieldcourier.com; class adv e-mailclassified@winfieldcourier.com; ed e-mail zaccaria@winfieldcourier.com; web site www.winfieldcourier.com
Group: Kansas Press Association
Published: Tues, Wed, Thur, Fri, Sat
Weekday Frequency: e
Saturday Frequency: m
Circulation: 4,522; 4,522(sat)
Last Audit: Sworn/Estimate/Non-Audited September 30, 2017
Advertising Rate (weekday/saturday): Open inch rate $10.32
Online Advertising Rate: Starting from $80.00/week
News services: AP, LAT-WP. **Established:** 1873
Own Printing Facility?: Yes
Commercial Printers?: Yes
Special Editions: Health Care (Apr); Cowley County Fair (Aug); Achievement (Feb); Spring Clean Up Tab (Mar); Cowley County Farmer-Rancher (Monthly); Getting Ready for Winter (Oct); Football Tab (Sept).
Special Weekly Sections: Recipes Tab; Kids Today.
Syndicated Publications: USA WEEKEND Magazine (Sat).
Digital Platform - Mobile: Apple, Android
Digital Platform - Tablet: Apple iOS, Android, Kindle, Nook, Kindle Fire
Pub. .... Lloyd Craig
Adv. Dir. .... Marsha Wesseler
Editorial Page Ed. .... Frederick D. Seaton
Managing Ed. .... Judy Zaccaria
Chairman .... Dave Seaton
Pub. .... David Allen Seaton
Adv. Sales .... Jennifer Harrison
Adv. Sales .... Diana Taylor
Circ. Mgr. .... Beth Glantz
Office Mgr. .... Janet Dolch
Webmaster .... Thomas Carver
Composition .... Stella Lankton
Classified .... Terri Snow
Market Information: TMC.
Mechanical Available: Offset; Black and 3 ROP colors; insert accepted - will consider any requests; page cutoffs - 22.
Mechanical Specifications: Type page 13 x 21; E - 6 cols, 2 1/16, 1/8 between; A - 6 cols, 2 1/16, 1/8 between; C - 8 cols, 1 1/2, 1/8 between.
Areas Served: Cowley, Sumner, Butler, Elk, and Chautauqua County
Delivery Method: Mail, Newsstand, RacksEquipment & Software: PRESSROOM EQUIPMENT: Lines — 8-G/Community.; MAILROOM EQUIPMENT: Tying Machines — 1/Miller-Bevco; Address Machine — 2-Am/1900.; BUSINESS EQUIPMENT: PC BUSINESS SOFTWARE: BMF CLASSIFIED EQUIPMENT: Hardware — Printers — Epson/DFX-5000, Epson/LQ-1070; CLASSIFIED SOFTWARE: BMF. DISPLAY EQUIPMENT: Hardware — APP/Power Mac; Printers — LaserMaster, APP/Mac PS; Other Hardware — APP/Mac One Scanner, CD-Rom DISPLAY SOFTWAREAd Make-up Applications — FSI; Layout Software — Multi-Ad/Creator, Aldus/PageMaker, Canvas, QPS/QuarkXPress. EDITORIAL EQUIPMENT: Hardware — 9-Mk/APP/Mac One Scanner, Nikon/Negative Scanner, 2-Umax/Flatbed Scanner; Printers — LaserMaster/, Xante/Accel-A-Writer, APP/Mac G3 Imagesetter, ECR EDITORIAL SOFTWARE: FSI, Multi-Ad/Creator, InDesigns. PRODUCTION EQUIPMENT: Hardware — 1-B, 1-Kk/Ektamatic; Cameras — 1-Acti; Scanners — Umax, Nikon PRODUCTION SOFTWARE: Multi-Ad Creator

KENTUCKY

ASHLAND

THE DAILY INDEPENDENT

226 17th St, Ashland, Ky., 41101-7606, Boyd; gen tel (606) 326-2600; adv tel (606) 326-2611; ed tel (606) 326-2648; gen fax (606) 326-2679; adv fax (606) 326-2680; ed fax (606) 326-2678; gen/nat adv e-mail mgelbman@dailyindependent.com; disp adv e-mail adservices@dailyindependent.com; class adv e-mailclassified@dailyindependent.com; ed e-mail mmaynard@dailyindependent.com; web site www.dailyindependent.com
- 998,000(views) 157,000(visitors)
Group: Community Newspaper Holdings, Inc.
Published: Mon, Tues, Wed, Thur, Fri, Sat, Sun
Weekday Frequency: m
Saturday Frequency: m
Circulation: 8,342; 8,342(sat); 9,172(sun)

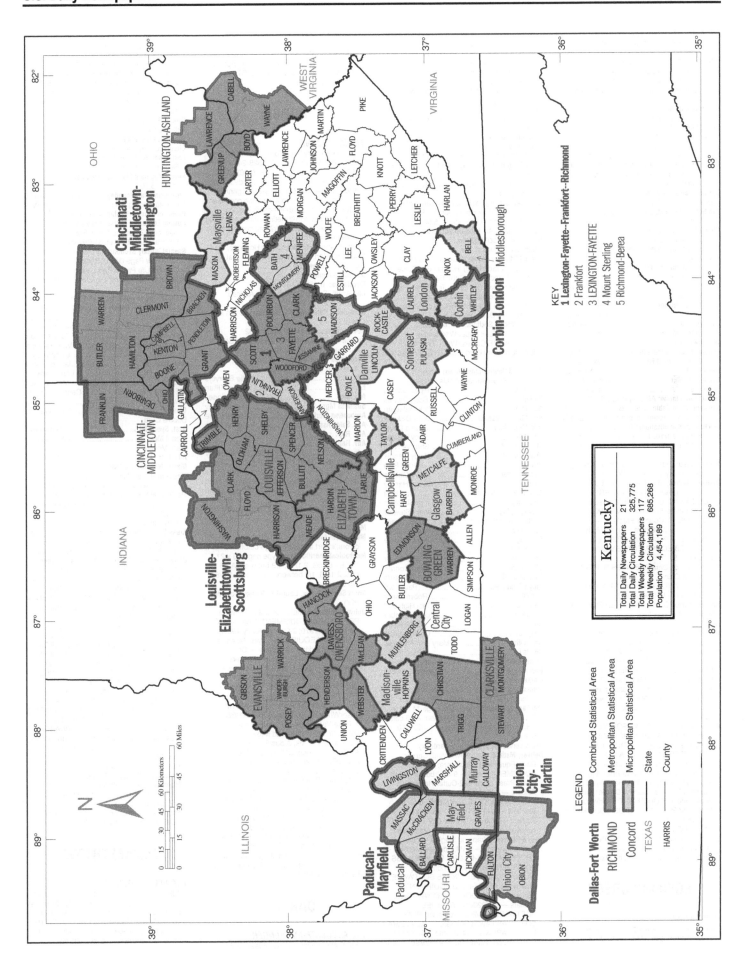

Cincinnati-
Middletown-
Wilmington

OHIO

WEST
VIRGINIA

VIRGINIA

HUNTINGTON-ASHLAND

Middlesborough

Corbin-London

KEY
1 Lexington--Fayette--Frankfort--Richmond
2 Frankfort
3 LEXINGTON-FAYETTE
4 Mount Sterling
5 Richmond-Berea

CINCINNATI-
MIDDLETOWN

INDIANA

Louisville-
Elizabethtown-
Scottsburg

TENNESSEE

Kentucky	
Total Daily Newspapers	21
Total Daily Circulation	325,775
Total Weekly Newspapers	117
Total Weekly Circulation	685,268
Population	4,454,189

ILLINOIS

Evansville

Owensboro

Madison-
ville

Central
City

Clarksville

Paducah-
Mayfield

Union
City-
Martin

MISSOURI

Paducah

Union City

60 Miles

60 Kilometers

N

LEGEND

Dallas-Fort Worth   Combined Statistical Area
RICHMOND   Metropolitan Statistical Area
Concord   Micropolitan Statistical Area
_____   State
TEXAS
HARRIS   County

Last Audit: AAM December 31, 2017
Advertising Rate (weekday/saturday): Open inch rate $33.50
Advertising Rate (sunday): Open inch rate $37.50
Online Advertising Rate: Homepage $300.00/month; Other Sections $150.00/month
News services: AP, CNHI, SHNS. **Established:** 1896
Own Printing Facility?: Yes
Commercial Printers?: No
Special Editions: Design-An-Ad (Apr); ACC Tab (Aug); Girls Basketball (Dec); Parents & Kids (Feb); Taxes & Investing (Jan); Primetime (Jul); Carter County Salute (Jun); Entertainment (Mar); Greenup County Salute (May); Boys Basketball (Nov); Insight (Oct); Entertainment (S
Special Weekly Sections: Best Food Day (S); Best Food Day (Wed).
Syndicated Publications: Relish (Monthly); Parade (S).
Proprietary Publications: The Independent Magazine (Quarterly)
Digital Platform - Mobile: Apple, Android, Windows
Digital Platform - Tablet: Apple iOS, Android, Kindle, Nook, Kindle Fire
Pub. .... Eddie Blakeley
Business Manager .... Lisa Callihan
Advertising Director .... Michael Gelbman
Editor .... Mark Maynard
Lifestyles Ed. .... Lee Ward
Prodn. Mgr., Mailroom .... Bengy Barrett
Website Creative/Adv. .... Mary Goldy
Audience Development Director .... David Rigas
Copy Desk Ed./Night Ed. .... Adam Vankirk
News Clerk .... Jami Kelley
Composing Mgr. .... Gene Hallahan
Sports Ed. .... Aaron Snyder
Market Information: ADS; Split run; TMC.
Mechanical Available: Offset; Black and 3 ROP colors; insert accepted; page cutoffs - 22 3/4.
Mechanical Specifications: Type page 13 x 21; E - 6 cols, 2 1/16, 1/8 between; A - 6 cols, 2 1/16, 1/8 between; C - 8 cols, 1 9/16, 1/16 between.
Areas Served: Greenup County, Boyd County, Carter County, Lawrence County
Delivery Method: Mail, Newsstand, Carrier, RacksEquipment & Software: PRESSROOM EQUIPMENT: Lines — 7-HI/Cotrell 845 1970; Folders — 1-HI/2:1.; MAILROOM EQUIPMENT: Counter Stackers — 2/HL; Inserters & Stuffers — 1-/GMA; Tying Machines — Power Strap/PSN-6E.; BUSINESS EQUIPMENT: IBM D80
Hardware - PC
Server - Vision Data BUSINESS SOFTWARE: Microsoft Office
VNC CLASSIFIED EQUIPMENT: Hardware - PC; Printers - HP LaserJet 3600
Server - Vision Data CLASSIFIED SOFTWARE: Vision Data Classified;
Open Office;
VNC DISPLAY EQUIPMENT: Hardware — Apple, Printer - HP LaserJet;
Servers - Vision Data and PuzzleFlow; Apple Servers DISPLAY SOFTWAREAdobe InDesign; Quark; Adobe Illustrator; Adobe Photoshop; ALS by MEI; Vision Data; Microsoft Office; Adobe Acrobat and Distiller EDITORIAL EQUIPMENT: Hardware - Apple; Printer - HP LaserJet M700;
Servers - Baseview,
Apple Servers EDITORIAL SOFTWARE: Baseview; Quark; Open Office; Adobe Acrobat and Distiller PRODUCTION EQUIPMENT: Hardware - Apple,
Printer - HP LaserJet M700; Servers - PuzzleFlow, Apple Servers PRODUCTION SOFTWARE: PuzzleFlow, Harelequin RIP; Quark; Adobe Acrobat and Distiller; Acrobat Photoshop. IT EQUIPMENT: Hardware - Apple and PC CIRCULATION EQUIPMENT: Hardware - PC;
Printers - HP LaserJet;
Server - Vision Data CIRCULATION SOFTWARVision Data Circulation applications, VNC, Microsoft Office

BOWLING GREEN

DAILY NEWS

813 College St, Bowling Green, Ky., 42101-2132, Warren; gen tel (270) 781-1700; adv tel (270) 783-3233; ed tel (270) 783-3269; gen fax (270) 781-0726; adv fax (270) 783-3221; ed fax (270) 783-3237; gen/nat adv e-mail mmahagan@bgdailynews.com; disp adv e-mail mmahagan@bgdailynews.com; class adv e-mailjdickens@bgdailynews.com; ed e-mail sgaines@bgdailynews.com; web site www.bgdailynews.com
Group: Bowling Green news Publishing Co.
Published: Mon, Tues, Wed, Thur, Fri, Sat, Sun
Weekday Frequency: e
Saturday Frequency: m
Circulation: 21,620; 21,620(sat); 22,785(sun)
Last Audit: AAM September 30, 2013
Advertising Rate (weekday/saturday): Open inch rate $32.30
Advertising Rate (sunday): Open inch rate $39.15 (Wed/Sun)
Online Advertising Rate: 12 month agreement $8.00 CPM; 6 month agreement $11.00 CPM; 3 month agreement $15.00 CPM
News services: AP. **Established:** 1854
Own Printing Facility?: Yes
Commercial Printers?: No
Special Editions: Home & Garden Tab (Apr); Pets on Parade (Aug); Holiday Gift Guide (Dec); Financial Tab (Feb); Back to School Tab (Jul); Soap Box Derby Tab (May); High School Basketball Tab (Nov); Industry Appreciation Tab (Oct); House to Home (Quarterly); Better Health &
Special Weekly Sections: Comics (Sun); Education (Tue); Super Wednesday, Business, NIE Copies (Wed); Time Out, Entertainment (Thur); Faith (Friday); Wellness (Sat);
Syndicated Publications: Relish (Monthly); Parade (S); American Profile (Weekly).
Pub./Pres. .... Pipes Gaines
Co-Pub. .... Scott Gaines
Adv. Mgr. .... Mark Mahagan
Adv. Mgr., Classified .... Julie Dickens
Adv. Mgr., Nat'l .... Joanie Davis
Circ. Mgr. .... Troy Warren
Mgr., Educ. Serv. .... Sharrye Noel
Managing Ed. .... Andy Dennis
City Ed. .... Daniel Pike
Editorial Page Ed. .... Steve Gaines
Features Ed. .... Alyssa Harvey
Asst. Mgr./Photo Editor .... Joe Imel
Prodn. Mgr. .... Larry Simpson
Packaging Mgr. .... George Stewart
Prodn. Mgr., Pressroom .... Glen Spear
Co-Owner .... Mary Gaines
Gen. Mgr. .... Kent O'Toole
Office Mgr. .... Melissa Miller
Accountant .... Glenda Spear
Office Asst. .... Shirleen Conrad
Asst. Circ. Dir. .... Tommy Richards
Single Copy Mgr. .... Paul Ford
City Ed. .... Robyn Minor
News Ed. .... Debi Highland
Weekend Ed. .... Eugene Embry
Copy Ed. .... Scotty Hyde
Copy Ed. .... Crystal Akers
Copy Editor .... Mary Ann Andrews
Sports Ed. .... Rob Herbst
Chief Photographer .... Miranda Pederson
Packaging Mgr. .... George Steward
Market Information: ADS; TMC.
Mechanical Available: Offset; Black and 3 ROP colors; insert accepted; page cutoffs - 22 3/4.
Mechanical Specifications: Type page 11 5/8 x 21; E - 6 cols, 1 4/5, 1/8 between; A - 6 cols, 1 4/5, 1/8 between; C - 9 cols, 1 1/5, 1/10 between.
Areas Served: South Central Kentucky
Delivery Method: Mail, Newsstand, Carrier, RacksEquipment & Software: PRESSROOM EQUIPMENT: Lines — 9-G/Urbanite single width; Press Drive — 2-Cutter Hammer; Folders — 1-G/Urbanite; Reels & Stands — 8-; MAILROOM EQUIPMENT: Counter Stackers — 3 QUIPP 400; Inserters & Stuffers — 1 Muller Tandem 227 10 into 1, 1 K&M Titan 12 into 1 ; Tying Machines — 3-Samuel; Wrapping Singles — N/A; Control System — K&M; Address Machine — PROFIT PKGING-P3 LABLER; BUSINESS EQUIPMENT: Microsoft/Windows 98, A-Open, Compaq BUSINESS SOFTWARE: Brainworks CLASSIFIED EQUIPMENT: Hardware — WINDOWS ; BRAINWORKS; Printers — HP/2200; CLASSIFIED SOFTWARE: FSI/Brainworks. DISPLAY SOFTWARELayout Software — Baseview/Ad Force, 1-APP/Mac G4, 2-Imac. EDITORIAL EQUIPMENT: Hardware — APP/Mac, 1-G/3, 10-IMAC, 13-G/4; Printers — 1-HP/5100 EDITORIAL SOFTWARE: MediaSpan PRODUCTION EQUIPMENT: Hardware — Mac/CTP-Screen; Cameras — 1-C/Spartan III PRODUCTION SOFTWARE: CTP-PRESTILIGENCE

CORBIN

TIMES-TRIBUNE

201 N Kentucky Ave, Corbin, Ky., 40701-1529, Whitley; gen tel (606) 528-2464; adv tel (606) 528-7898 ext. 27; ed tel (606) 528-7898 ext. 37; gen fax (606) 528-1335; adv fax (606) 528-1335; ed fax (606) 528-9850; gen/nat adv e-mail kjones@sentinel-echo.com; disp adv e-mail rconn@thetimestribune.com; class adv e-mailrlawson@thetimestribune.com; ed e-mail editor@thetimestribune.com; web site www.thetimestribune.com
Group: Community Newspaper Holdings, Inc.
Published: Mon, Tues, Wed, Thur, Fri, Sat
Weekday Frequency: e
Saturday Frequency: m
Circulation: 6,166; 6,166(sat)
Last Audit: Sworn/Estimate/Non-Audited September 30, 2017
Advertising Rate (weekday/saturday): Open inch rate $14.74
News services: AP. **Established:** 1882
Special Weekly Sections: Church Page (Sat); Business (Tues); Best Food Day (Wed).
Syndicated Publications: TV Guide (Sat); American Profile (Weekly).
Pub. .... Willie Sawyers
Ed. .... Becky Killian
Adv. Mgr. .... Kathy Jones
Business Mgr. .... Kristie Gray
Accounting Clerk .... Brenda House
Adv. Sales Asst. .... Rebecca Conn
Adv. Rep. .... Lisa Harrison
Adv. Rep. .... Ruth Rose
Adv. Clerk .... Patricia Humphrey
Adv. Classified Clerk .... Rhonda Lawson
Circ. Mgr. .... Cathy Farris
Circ. District Mgr. .... Yolanda Couch
Circ. Clerk .... Renee Smith
Sports Ed. .... Chris Parsons
Web/Special Pages Ed. .... Christina Bentley
Nighttime/Religion Page Ed. .... Brad Hall
Market Information: TMC.
Mechanical Available: Offset; Black and 3 ROP colors; insert accepted; page cutoffs - 22 3/4.
Mechanical Specifications: Type page 13 x 21 1/2; E - 6 cols, 2 1/16, 1/8 between; A - 6 cols, 2 1/16, 1/8 between; C - 9 cols, 1 3/8, 1/8 between.
Areas Served: Knox, Laurel & Whitley Counties (KY)
Delivery Method: MailEquipment & Software: PRESSROOM EQUIPMENT: Lines — 4-G/Community 1970; 2-G/Community 1980.; MAILROOM EQUIPMENT: Tying Machines — Strapex; Address Machine — Ch.; BUSINESS EQUIPMENT: ListMasters CLASSIFIED EQUIPMENT: Hardware — Mk; Printers — 2-APP/Mac LaserWriter; CLASSIFIED SOFTWARE: Mk. DISPLAY EQUIPMENT: Hardware — Mk, APP/Mac IIcx, APP/Mac IIci; Printers — 2-APP/Mac LaserWriter, 2-Tegra/Varityper VT600W, 1-Tegra/Varityper 4990T Imagesetter; DISPLAY SOFTWAREAd Make-up Applications — Mk, Aldus/FreeHand, Adobe/Photoshop, QPS/QuarkXPress, Aldus/PageMaker, Multi-Ad/Creator; Layout Software — Multi-A EDITORIAL EQUIPMENT: Hardware — Mk, APP/Mac IIci, APP/Mac IIcx; Printers — 2-APP/Mac LaserWriter, 2-Tegra/Varityper VT600W, 1-Tegra/Varityper 4990T Imagesetter EDITORIAL SOFTWARE: Mk, Aldus/FreeHand, Adobe/Photoshop, QPS/QuarkXPress, Aldus/PageMaker, Multi-Ad/Creator. PRODUCTION EQUIPMENT: Hardware — Caere/OmniPage; Cameras — 1-Nu, 1-SCREEN/680C; Scanners — Lf/Leafscan 35, AVR.

DANVILLE

THE ADVOCATE-MESSENGER

330 S 4th St, Danville, Ky., 40422-2033, Boyle; gen tel (859) 236-2551; adv tel (859) 236-2551; ed tel (859) 236-2551; gen fax (859) 236-9566; adv fax (859) 236-9566; ed fax (859) 236-9566; gen/nat adv e-mail gprice@amnews.com; disp adv e-mail gprice@amnews.com; class adv e-mailcwarren@amnews.com; ed e-mail johnn@amnews.com; web site www.amnews.com
Group: Boone Newspapers, Inc.
Published: Mon, Tues, Wed, Thur, Fri, Sun
Weekday Frequency: m
Circulation: 8,214; 9,913(sun)
Last Audit: Sworn/Estimate/Non-Audited September 30, 2017
Advertising Rate (weekday/saturday): Open inch rate $13.10
Advertising Rate (sunday): Open inch rate $16.55
Online Advertising Rate: Starting at $7.00 CPM
News services: AP. **Established:** 1940
Special Editions: Football Preview (Aug); Season's Greetings (Dec); Brass Band Festival (Jun); Basketball Preview (Nov).
Special Weekly Sections: Church Page (Fri); Tec Know Page (Mon); Business Page (S); Country Life Page (Tues); Seasonings (Wed).
Syndicated Publications: Parade (S); American Profile (Weekly).
Digital Platform - Mobile: Apple, Android
Digital Platform - Tablet: Apple iOS, Android
Controller .... Renita Cox
District Mgr. .... Brenda Townes
Exec. Ed. .... John Nelson
Asst. Managing Ed. .... Vicki Stevens
Sports Ed. .... Larry Vaught
Info. Tech. Dir. .... James Morris
Pres./Pub./Ed. .... Larry Hensley
Circ. Mgr. .... Mark Walker
NIE Coord. .... Candi Campbell
Adv. Mgr. .... Geri Ray
Classifieds Asst. .... Carol Warren
Bobbie Curd
Asst. Sports Ed. .... Hal Morris
Digital Mgr. .... John Preston
Gary Moyers
Adv. Mgr., Nat'l .... Jerry Dunn
Market Information: TMC.
Mechanical Available: Offset; Black and 3 ROP colors; insert accepted; page cutoffs - 22 3/4.
Mechanical Specifications: Type page 13 3/4 x 21 1/2; E - 6 cols, 2 1/16, 1/8 between; A - 6 cols, 2 1/16, 1/8 between; C - 9 cols, 1 3/8, 1/16 between.
Areas Served: South central Kentucky, south of Lexington, with distribution primarily in Boyle, Lincoln, Casey, Mercer and Garrard counties
Delivery Method: CarrierEquipment & Software: PRESSROOM EQUIPMENT: Lines — 5-MAN/Uniman 4x2 (half color decks) 1985; Press Drive — Reliance/Max Pac Plus; MAILROOM EQUIPMENT: Counter Stackers — 2-HI/Graphics Model 2512; Inserters & Stuffers — MM/227E; Tying Machines — 1-Bu/AS210A, 1-Akebono/515A; Control System — HL/Conveyor; Address Machine — KR/515 Base w/211 Head; BUSINESS EQUIPMENT: Great Plains Dynamic IBM/RISC Sys 6000 CIO, Microsoft/Windows NT Server BUSINESS SOFTWARE: PBS, Lotus/Release 5, Ad Management 3.0 CLASSIFIED EQUIPMENT: Hardware — APP/Mac; CLASSIFIED SOFTWARE: Baseview/Class Manager Pro 1.0.7. DISPLAY EQUIPMENT: Hardware — APP/Mac; Printers — Ultra; DISPLAY SOFTWAREAd Make-up Applications — QPS/QuarkXPress 4.0; Layout Software — ALS. EDITORIAL EQUIPMENT: Hardware — APP/Mac EDITORIAL SOFTWARE: Baseview/NewsEdit. PRODUCTION EQUIPMENT: Hardware — 2-APP/Mac LaserPrinters, 3-Ultra/94 Imagesetter; Cameras — 1-LE, 1-R; Scanners — Data Copy/730 GS, Microtek/Scanmaker E6 PRODUCTION SOFTWARE: QPS/QuarkXPress 4.11.

ELIZABETHTOWN

THE NEWS-ENTERPRISE

408 W Dixie Ave, Elizabethtown, Ky., 42701-2455, Hardin; gen tel (270) 769-1200; adv tel (270) 505-1409; ed tel (270) 505-1764; gen fax (270) 765-7318; adv fax (270) 765-7318; ed fax (270) 769-6965; gen/nat adv e-mail ehahn@thenewsenterprise.com; disp adv

e-mail ehahn@thenewsenterprise.com; class adv e-mailbchism@thenewsenterprise.com; ed e-mail bsheroan@thenewsenterprise.com; web site www.thenewsenterprise.com - 680,000(views) 110,000(visitors)
Group: Landmark Communications, Inc.
Published: Mon, Tues, Wed, Thur, Fri, Sun
Weekday Frequency: m
Circulation: 9,734; 12,483(sun)
Last Audit: AAM December 31, 2017
Advertising Rate (weekday/saturday): Open inch rate $22.98
Advertising Rate (sunday): Open inch rate $31.09
Online Advertising Rate: $10 per thousand pageviews
News services: AP. **Established:** 1974
Own Printing Facility?: Yes
Commercial Printers?: Yes
Special Weekly Sections: Entertainment (Thu); Senior Living (Mon); Business Pages (T, Th, S); Best Food Day (Tue); Real Estate (Fri); Features (fri).
Syndicated Publications: Relish (Monthly); Spry Living (Monthly); Parade (S).
Digital Platform - Mobile: Apple, Android, Windows
Digital Platform - Tablet: Apple iOS, Windows 7
Pub. .... Chris Ordway
Graphic Design/IT Mgr. .... Lydia Leasor
Sports Ed. .... Chuck Jones
Production Mgr. .... David Dickens
Prodn. Press Team Leader .... Charles Love
Ed. .... Ben Sheroan
Business Mgr. .... Lisa D'Alessio
Adv. Dir. .... Erin Hahn
Circ. Mgr. .... Tom Siemers
Market Information: TMC.
Mechanical Available: Offset; Black and 4 ROP colors; insert accepted - all; page cutoffs - 22 3/4.
Mechanical Specifications: Type page 11 5/8 x 21 1/2; E - 6 cols, 1 5/6, 1/8 between; A - 6 cols, 1 5/6, 1/8 between; C - 8 cols, 1 1/2, 1/8 between.
Areas Served: Elizabethtown (KY), Hardin County & Surrounding areas
Delivery Method: Newsstand, Carrier, RacksEquipment & Software: PRESSROOM EQUIPMENT: Lines — 11-G/Community single width; Folders — 1-KP/2:1.; MAILROOM EQUIPMENT: Counter Stackers — 2/BG, 1-MM/310-20, 1-MM/231; Inserters & Stuffers — 3-/MM; Tying Machines - 3-/Bu, 3-/MLN; Address Machine — 1-/Ch, 1-/KR.; BUSINESS EQUIPMENT: 8-IBM/5251 terminal, Papertrak BUSINESS SOFTWARE: Lotus, Microsoft/Works 3.1 CLASSIFIED EQUIPMENT: Hardware — CText; Printers — C.Itoh/CI 5000; CLASSIFIED SOFTWARE: CText, Novell 4.0. DISPLAY EQUIPMENT: Hardware — Dell/220; Printers — HP/LaserJet IVP; DISPLAY SOFTWAREAd Make-up Applications — SCS/Layout 8000 6.08; Layout Software — 11-APP/Mac II. EDITORIAL EQUIPMENT: Hardware — CText/1-Turbo/XT, 2-Dell/220, SCS/Layout 8000. PRODUCTION EQUIPMENT: Hardware — 2-VHreSetter/94E, PageScan/3, APP/Mac LaserWriter II NTX, Compaq/LaserWriter; Cameras — DST/240C; Scanners — Kk/2035RFS, Microtek/Scanmaker IIXE PRODUCTION SOFTWARE: QPS/QuarkXPress 3.31 R5.

FRANKFORT

THE STATE JOURNAL

1216 Wilkinson Blvd, Frankfort, Ky., 40601-1243, Franklin; gen tel (502) 227-4556; adv tel (502) 227-4556; ed tel (502) 227-4556; gen fax (502) 227-2831; adv fax (502) 227-2831; ed fax (502) 227-2831; gen/nat adv e-mail admaenza@state-journal.com; disp adv e-mail llynch@state-journal.com; class adv e-mailllynch@state-journal.com; ed e-mail pcase@state-journal.com; web site www.state-journal.com
Group: Boone Newspapers, Inc.
Published: Mon, Tues, Wed, Thur, Fri, Sun
Weekday Frequency: All day
Circulation: 6,397; 7,361(sun)
Last Audit: CAC March 31, 2015
Advertising Rate (weekday/saturday): Open inch rate $12.00
Advertising Rate (sunday): Open inch rate $12.00
Online Advertising Rate: Half Banner $6.00 CPM; Button Ad, Standard Banner, Skyscraper $7.00 CPM; Box Ad $7.50 CPM
News services: AP, NYT. **Established:** 1902
Own Printing Facility?: Yes
Syndicated Publications: Main Street (S); American Profile (Weekly).
Pub. .... Ann Dix Maenza
Adv. Dir. .... Lloyd Lynch
Ed. .... Carlton West
Circ. Mgr. .... Ben Briggs
News Ed. .... Katheron Wasson
Sports Ed. .... Phil Case
Composing Dir. .... Linda Roberts
Prodn. Foreman, Pressroom .... Steve Estes
Market Information: TMC.
Mechanical Available: Offset; Black and 3 ROP colors; insert accepted - all; page cutoffs - 21 1/2.
Mechanical Specifications: Type page 13 x 21 1/2; E - 6 cols, 2, 1/9 between; A - 6 cols, 2, 1/9 between; C - 8 cols, 1 1/2, 1/9 between.
Areas Served: Franklin County, Lawrence County
Delivery Method: Mail, Newsstand, Carrier, RacksEquipment & Software: PRESSROOM EQUIPMENT: Lines — 8-G/Community (color deck).; MAILROOM EQUIPMENT: Tying Machines — 2-/Bu; Address Machine — 1-/KR.; BUSINESS EQUIPMENT: APT CLASSIFIED EQUIPMENT: Hardware — 3-Mk; CLASSIFIED SOFTWARE: Mk. DISPLAY SOFTWAREAd Make-up Applications — Aldus/PageMaker, QPS/QuarkXPress; Layout Software — APP/Mac IIci, APP/Power Mac 6100. EDITORIAL EQUIPMENT: Hardware — APP/Mac Quadra 950, APP/Mac Quadra 840, 11-APP/Power Mac 6100, 1-APP/Power Mac 8100, 1-APP/Mac Quadra 700/Lf/AP Leaf Picture Desk, 2-Nikon/Scanner; Printers — 1-APP/Mac LaserPrinter IIg, 1-TI/810 EDITORIAL SOFTWARE: Microsoft/Word, PowerSh PRODUCTION EQUIPMENT: Hardware — 2-APP/Mac ci, 1-XIT/Clipper, 2-APP/Mac LaserPrinter, 3-QMax/Imagesetter, 4-APP/Power Mac 7100, 1-APP/Power Mac 8100; Cameras — 2-B/Vertical; Scanners — 2-Nikon/Scanner PRODUCTION SOFTWARE: QPS/QuarkXPress 3.31.

GLASGOW

GLASGOW DAILY TIMES

100 Commerce Dr, Glasgow, Ky., 42141-1153, Barren; gen tel (270) 678-5171; adv tel (270) 678-5171 ext. 235; ed tel (270) 678-5171 ext. 234; gen fax (270) 678-3372; adv fax (270) 678-3372; ed fax (270) 678-3372; gen/nat adv e-mail kponder@glasgowdailytimes.com; disp adv e-mail kponder@glasgowdailytimes.com; class adv e-mailclassified@glasgowdailytimes.com; ed e-mail mthomas@glasgowdailytimes.com; web site www.glasgowdailytimes.com
Group: Community Newspaper Holdings, Inc.
Published: Tues, Wed, Thur, Fri, Sat, Sun
Weekday Frequency: m
Saturday Frequency: m
Circulation: 5,218; 6,267(sat); 6,267(sun)
Last Audit: AAM September 30, 2014
Advertising Rate (weekday/saturday): Open inch rate $13.44
News services: AP. **Established:** 1865
Own Printing Facility?: No
Commercial Printers?: No
Special Weekly Sections: TV Screen (Sat); Church (S);
Syndicated Publications: Relish (Monthly); Parade (S).
Pub. .... Bill Hanson
Business Mgr. .... Cindy Green
Digital Ed. .... James Brown
Gen. Mgr. .... Daniel Pike
News Ed. .... Lisa Simpson Strange
Newsroom Clerk .... Martha J. Thomas
Sports Ed. .... Scott Wilson
Special Accounts Mgr. .... Michelle Copass
Acct. Exec. .... Lori Decker
Teresa Furlong
Teresa S. Nunn
Acct. Exec. .... Steven D. Wilson
Circ. Bookkeeper .... Janis Davis
Classified Sales Exec. .... Sherry Powell
Prodn. Dir. .... Chuck Roberts
Circ. Dir. .... Mary Pike
General Manager .... Scotty Maxwell
Adv. Dir. .... Amy Lee
Customer Service .... Katie Batey
Mechanical Available: Offset; Black and 3 ROP colors; insert accepted; page cutoffs - 21 1/2.
Mechanical Specifications: Type page 13 x 21 1/2; E - 6 cols, 2 1/16, 1/8 between; A - 6 cols, 2 1/16, 1/8 between; C - 8 cols, 1 5/16, 1/8 between.
Areas Served: 42717; 42722; 42127; 42129; 42133; 42141; 42746; 42152; 42749; 42759; 42765; 42160; 42171; 42166; 42167
Delivery Method: Mail, Newsstand, RacksEquipment & Software: DISPLAY SOFTWAREAd Make-up Applications — Ad Force 1.0, Adobe; Layout Software — 1-APP/Power Mac 7200-90 with Ad Force 1.0, Adobe. EDITORIAL EQUIPMENT: Hardware — APP/Power Mac/IBM/Selectric; Printers — 1-APP/Mac LaserWriter IIg, Xante/Accel-a-Writer 8200

HARLAN

THE HARLAN DAILY ENTERPRISE

1548 S US Highway 421, Harlan, Ky., 40831-2501, Harlan; gen tel (606) 573-4510; adv tel (606) 573-4510; ed tel (606) 573-4510; gen fax (606) 573-0042; adv fax (606) 573-0042; ed fax (606) 573-0042; gen/nat adv e-mail wminard@civitasmedia.com; disp adv e-mail wminiard@civitasmedia.com; class adv e-mailebell@civitasmesia.com; ed e-mail bmoore@civitasmedia.com; web site www.harlandaily.com
Group: Civitas Media, LLC-OOB
Published: Tues, Wed, Thur, Fri, Sat
Weekday Frequency: m
Saturday Frequency: m
Circulation: 5,000; 5,000(sat)
Last Audit: Sworn/Estimate/Non-Audited September 30, 2017
Advertising Rate (weekday/saturday): Open inch rate $18.10; $21.30 (National)
Online Advertising Rate: Below the Fold $11.70; Above the Fold $14.40; Wallpaper Ads $35.00
News services: Landon Media Group. **Established:** 1928
Own Printing Facility?: No
Commercial Printers?: No
Special Editions: Home Improvement (Apr); Christmas Greetings (Dec); Harlan County Heritage Tab (Feb); Christmas Shopping Guide (Nov); Fall Car Care Tab (Oct); Home Improvement (Sept).
Syndicated Publications: USA WEEKEND Magazine (Sat); American Profile (Weekly).
News Ed. .... Debbie Caldwell
Receptionist/Classifieds/Legals .... Eva Bell
Editorial Clerk .... Bethany Moore
Staff Writer .... Nola Sizemore
Publisher .... Cynthia Orr
Rgl. Admin. Coord. .... Pat Cheek
Inside Sales Rep .... Wylene Miniard
Business Development Specialist .... Bryan Key
Rgl. Delivery Mgr .... Kipper House
Sports Ed. .... John Henson
Mechanical Available: Offset; Black and 3 ROP colors; insert accepted - catalogs; page cutoffs - 21 1/2.
Mechanical Specifications: Type page 13 x 21 1/2; E - 6 cols, 2 1/16, 1/8 between; A - 6 cols, 2 1/16, 1/8 between; C - 8 cols, 1 3/4, 1/16 between.
Areas Served: Harlan County, Kentucky
Delivery Method: Mail, Newsstand, Carrier, RacksEquipment & Software: MAILROOM EQUIPMENT: Tying Machines — 2/Bu; Address Machine — KR.; BUSINESS EQUIPMENT: IBM/Sys 36, IBM/PC CLASSIFIED EQUIPMENT: Hardware — 1-APP/Mac; Printers — Okidata; CLASSIFIED SOFTWARE: Fox. DISPLAY EQUIPMENT: Hardware — 2-APP/Mac; DISPLAY SOFTWAREAd Make-up Applications — Multi-Ad/Creator.; EDITORIAL EQUIPMENT: Hardware — 6-APP/Mac/APP/Mac Scanner; Printers — 2-APP/Mac LaserWriter II EDITORIAL SOFTWARE: QPS/QuarkXPress, Baseview/NewsEdit. PRODUCTION EQUIPMENT: Hardware — 1-Nu; Cameras — 1-C/Spartan III; Scanners — Ca/Sharpshooter Densi-Probe.

HENDERSON

THE GLEANER

455 Klutey Park Plaza Dr, Ste A, Henderson, Ky., 42420-5213, Henderson; gen tel (270) 827-2000; adv tel (270) 827-2000; ed tel (270) 831-8333; gen fax (270) 827-2765; adv fax (270) 827-2765; ed fax (270) 827-2765; gen/nat adv e-mail PMaurice@TheGleaner.com; disp adv e-mail PMaurice@TheGleaner.com; class adv e-mailPMaurice@TheGleaner.com; ed e-mail DDixon@TheGleaner.com; web site www.thegleaner.com
712,940(visitors)
Group: Gannett
Published: Tues, Wed, Thur, Fri, Sat, Sun
Weekday Frequency: m
Saturday Frequency: m
Circulation: 6,324; 6,324(sat); 7,488(sun)
Last Audit: AAM December 31, 2015
Advertising Rate (weekday/saturday): Open inch rate $15.00
Advertising Rate (sunday): Open inch rate $17.58
Online Advertising Rate: Starting at $10.00 CPM
News services: AP. **Established:** 1885
Special Editions: Do-It-Yourself (Apr); Football Tab (Aug); Fair (Jul); Lawn & Garden (Mar); Holiday Entertaining (Nov).
Special Weekly Sections: NASCAR (Fri); Business (S); Farm (Sat); Health (Thur); Gleaner Jr. (Tues).
Syndicated Publications: Parade (S).
Digital Platform - Mobile: Apple, Android
Digital Platform - Tablet: Apple iOS, Android
Pub. .... Jack Pate
Circ. Mgr. .... Lori Bush
Ed. .... David Dixon
Graphics Ed./Art Dir. .... Mike Moore
Health/Medical Ed. .... Judy Jenkins
Lifestyle Ed. .... Donna Stinnett
News Ed. .... Doug White
Photo Ed. .... Mike Lawrence
Religion Ed. .... Frank Boyett
Science/Technology Ed. .... Chuck Stinnett
Sales Mgr. .... Caroline Sexton
Classified Sales .... Sharon Alvey
Customer Service Rep. .... Karen Cox
Market Information: Split run; TMC.
Mechanical Available: Offset; Black and 3 ROP colors; insert accepted - any; page cutoffs - 22 3/4.
Mechanical Specifications: Type page 13 x 21 1/2; E - 6 cols, 2 1/16, 1/8 between; A - 6 cols, 1 5/6, 1/8 between; C - 9 cols, 1 1/2, 1/16 between.
Areas Served: Henderson (KY)
Delivery Method: Mail, CarrierEquipment & Software: MAILROOM EQUIPMENT: Counter Stackers — Gammerler/KL 507; Inserters & Stuffers — 6-MM/227; Tying Machines — 2/Sterling; Address Machine — 2-/Wm, 1-/KAN; BUSINESS EQUIPMENT: TI/1500 CLASSIFIED EQUIPMENT: Hardware — 5-FSI.; DISPLAY SOFTWARELayout Software — 1-HI/8600. EDITORIAL EQUIPMENT: Hardware — 1-HI/Lf/AP Leaf Picture Desk, 20-HI. PRODUCTION EQUIPMENT: Hardware — 1-ECR, 1-ECR; Cameras — 1-SCREEN.

HOPKINSVILLE

KENTUCKY NEW ERA

1618 E 9th St, Hopkinsville, Ky., 42240-4430, Christian; gen tel (270) 886-4444; adv tel (270) 887-3278; ed tel (270) 887-3230; gen fax (270) 887-3222; adv fax (270) 887-3222; ed fax (270) 887-3222; gen/nat adv e-mail advertising@kentuckynewera.com; disp adv e-mail advertising@kentuckynewera.com; class adv e-mailclassified@kentuckynewera.com; ed e-mail editor@kentuckynewera.com; web site www.kentuckynewera.com
Published: Mon, Wed, Thur, Fri, Sat
Weekday Frequency: e
Saturday Frequency: e
Circulation: 6,779; 7,073(sat)
Last Audit: AAM September 30, 2015
Advertising Rate (weekday/saturday): Open inch rate $11.00; $13.00 (Sat)
Online Advertising Rate: Starting at $250.00/month
News services: AP, TMS. **Established:** 1869

Own Printing Facility?: Yes
Special Editions: Please call our advertising department for a full list of special sections published monthly and yearly.
Special Weekly Sections: University of Kentucky Sports Page (Fri); Tax Tips (weekly, Jan-Apr) (Other); Outdoor Page (Sat); Farm Page (Thur); Best Food Day (Wed); Homes and Building Tips (Apr.-Jan.) (Weekly).
Syndicated Publications: Relish (Monthly); USA WEEKEND Magazine (Sat); American Profile (Weekly), Spry (Monthly), Athlon Sports (Monthly)
Pub.....Taylor Wood Hayes
VP and Gen. Mgr.....Sheryl Ellis
Adv./Mktg. Mgr.....Ted Jatczak
Classified Manager....Nancy Reece
Circ. Dir.....Tony Henson
Ed.....Eli Pace
Prod. Mgr.....Chris Hollis
Sports Editor....Joe Wilson
Photographer / Copy Desk Chief....Dana Long
Opinion Ed.....Jennifer Brown
Sports Editor....Chris Jung
Features Ed.....Melissa Mollohan
Adv. Rep.....Richard Wimsatt
Adv. Rep.....Kristi Williams
Adv. Rep.....Jillian Weatherford
Adv. Rep.....Bernie Starr
Adv. Rep.....Traci Rodgers
Classified Adv. Sales....Cynthia Cunningham
Webmaster....John Godsey
Pres.....Chuck Henderson
Copy Ed.....Cole Davis
Market Information: TMC.
Mechanical Available: Offset; Black and 3 ROP colors; insert accepted; page cutoffs - 22 3/4.
Mechanical Specifications: Type page 11 5/8 x 21 1/2; E - 6 cols, 1/8 between; A - 6 cols, 1/8 between; C - 9 cols, 1/8 between.
Areas Served: 42240, 42262, 42234, 42286, 42223, 42211, 42220, 42221, 42236, 42241, 42254, 42266, 42445, 42280, 42220, 42204, 42216
Delivery Method: Newsstand, Carrier, RacksEquipment & Software: PRESSROOM EQUIPMENT: Lines — 7-G/Urbanite U864 (Upper former) 1971; MAILROOM EQUIPMENT: Tying Machines — 2/OVL, 1-/OVL; Wrapping Singles — 4-/Dri wrap; Address Machine — 1-St/mailing label, 6-/Wm.; BUSINESS EQUIPMENT: Dell BUSINESS SOFTWARE: Vision Data CLASSIFIED EQUIPMENT: Hardware — Dell; Printers — HP; CLASSIFIED SOFTWARE: Vision Data DISPLAY EQUIPMENT: Hardware — Dell; Printers — HP Laser; DISPLAY SOFTWAREAd Make-up Applications — QPS/QuarkXPress 4.0, Aldus/FreeHand 7.0, Adobe/Photoshop 4.0; Layout Software — QPS/QuarkXPress. Adobe Indesign EDITORIAL EQUIPMENT: Hardware — APT/1-Ultra/4000 Imagesetter, 1-Ultra/5400 Imagesetter, 1-Konica/Image Setter, Konica/EV Jetsetter; Printers — 6-HP, 4-HP/5000N EDITORIAL SOFTWARE: APT, ACT. PRODUCTION EQUIPMENT: Hardware — 1-Nu/Flip Top, 1-Nat/26, 1-Konica/ EV Jetsetter; Scanners — 1-HP/Scanner, 4-Microtek/ScanMaker II 5P PRODUCTION SOFTWARE: QPS/QuarkXPress 4.0.

LEXINGTON

LEXINGTON HERALD-LEADER

100 Midland Ave, Lexington, Ky., 40508-1943, Fayette; gen tel (859) 231-3100; adv tel (859) 231-3434; ed tel (859) 231-3446; gen fax (859) 231-3454; adv fax (859) 231-3454; ed fax (859) 231-3454; gen/nat adv e-mail kwoods@herald-leader.com; disp adv e-mail kwoods@herald-leader.com; class adv e-mailkwoods@herald-leader.com; ed e-mail pbaniak@herald-leader.com; web site www.kentucky.com
- 13,932,767(views) 2,063,045(visitors)
Group: McClatchy
Published: Mon, Tues, Wed, Thur, Fri, Sat, Sun
Weekday Frequency: m
Saturday Frequency: m
Circulation: 56,426; 56,426(sat); 76,877(sun)
Last Audit: AAM December 31, 2016
Branch Offices: Frankfort, Somerset
News services: AP, NYT, MCT, WP.
Own Printing Facility?: No
Commercial Printers?: Yes
Special Weekly Sections: Weekender (Fri); Business Monday (Mon);
Syndicated Publications: Parade (S).
Proprietary Publications: PISTON Auto! Magazine, YES, Sunday Select
Digital Platform - Mobile: Apple, Android, Windows
Digital Platform - Tablet: Apple iOS, Android, Windows 7, Nook, Kindle Fire
Pres. & Pub.....Rufus Friday
HR Dir.....Michael Wells
Ed.....Peter Baniak
Cartoonist....Joel Pett
Editorial Page Ed.....Vanessa Gallman
Visual Ed.....Ron Garrison
Online Ed.....Deedra Lawhead
VP, Adv.....Kim Woods
DESIGN DIRECTOR
Brian Simms
Features Ed.....Sally Scherer
Copy Ed.....Will Scott
Copy Ed.....Dennis Varney
Audience Operations Manager....Richard Morgan
Dig. & Class. Adv. Dir.....Heather McGinnis
Dig. Sales Mgr.....Kate Powers
Adv. Sales Mgr., Local Adv.....Fran Elsen
Adv. Sales Mgr., Auto. Adv.....Marty Davis
Market Information: ADS; Split run; TMC; Zoned editions.
Areas Served: Fayette, Bourbon, Clark, Montgomery, Powell, Estill, Madison, Garrard, Jessamine, Boyle, Mercer, Woodford, Anderson, Franklin, Scott, Harrison
Delivery Method: Mail, Newsstand, Carrier, RacksEquipment & Software: PRESSROOM EQUIPMENT: half decks); 7-G/Metro (3 half decks); Folders — 3-G/Imperial 3:2; Pasters —14-G/Digital; Reels & Stands — 14-G/ Reels & Stands; Control System — G/ PCS; Registration System — Standard/Pin Register. MAILROOM EQUIPMENT: 1/QWI, 2-/MM, 4-Id/2100, Gammerler; Inserters & Stuffers — 2-/Fg; Tying Machines — 5-MLN/ HS, 1-MLN/EE, 1-/Bu, 2-Dynaric/NPZ; Wrapping Singles — 4-/QWI; Address Machine — 2-KAN/AVY Labeler;
Note: Pulitzer Prizes: 2000 for Editorial Cartooning, Joel Pett; 1992 for Editorial Writing, Maria Henson; 1986 for Investigative Reporting, Mike York and Jeff Marx.

LOUISVILLE

THE COURIER-JOURNAL

525 W Broadway, Louisville, Ky., 40202-2206, Jefferson; gen tel (502) 582-4011; adv tel (502) 582-4711; ed tel (502) 582-4691; gen fax (502) 582-7111; adv fax (502) 582-7111; ed fax (502) 582-4200; gen/nat adv e-mail erhelton@gannett.com; disp adv e-mail erhelton@gannett.com; class adv e-mailclassifieds@courier-journal.com; ed e-mail nbudde@courier-journal.com; web site www.courier-journal.com
- 14,700,000(views) 1,537,329(visitors)
Group: Gannett
Published: Mon, Tues, Wed, Thur, Fri, Sat, Sun
Weekday Frequency: m
Saturday Frequency: m
Circulation: 108,363; 109,056(sat); 151,598(sun)
Last Audit: AAM September 30, 2015
Advertising Rate (weekday/saturday): Open inch rate $150.00
Advertising Rate (sunday): Open inch rate $185.00
Online Advertising Rate: Sponsorship $3.00 CPM; Leaderboard, Medium Rectangle $10.00 CPM; Halfpage $14.00 CPM
News services: AP, NYT, LAT-WP, GNS, Dow Jones. **Established:** 1868
Own Printing Facility?: Yes
Commercial Printers?: Yes
Special Editions: Thunder Preview (Apr); Used Car Guide (Aug); Be Heathly Kentuckiana (Feb); Parent's Survival Guide (Jul); Savvy Home Buyer (Mar); Be Healthy Kentuckiana (May); Be Healthy Kentuckiana (Nov); Tour of Homes-2nd Edition (Oct); On Course (Sept).
Special Weekly Sections: Food (Wed); Health & Fitness (Fri); Home & Garden (Sat); Arts, Sunday Scene (Sun)
Syndicated Publications: Her Scene (Quarterly); TV Week & Cable Guide (S); USA WEEKEND Magazine (Sat).
Proprietary Publications: Velocity (Thur);
Pres./Pub.....Arnold Garson
Food/Restaurants Editor....Jere Downs
Metro Ed.....Mike Trautman
Music Critic....Jeffrey Puckett
Op. News Mgr.....James Kirchner
Opinion Pages Ed.....Keith Runyon
Religion Writer....Peter Smith
Sports Ed.....Harry Bryan
News Dir.....Veda Morgan
Online Production Mgr.
Jeff Faughender
Pres./Pub.....Wesley Jackson
VP, IT....Peter Bateman
Exec. Ed./VP, News....Neil Budde
Exec. Producer....Dan Blake
Photo Dir.....David Harrison
Community Engagement Dir.....Kim Kolarik
Market Information: Split run; TMC; Zoned editions.
Mechanical Available: Offset; Black and 3 ROP colors; insert accepted - samples; page cutoffs - 21.
Mechanical Specifications: Type page 11 x 20; E - 6 cols, 1 13/16, 1/8 between; A - 6 cols, 1 13/16, 1/8 between; C - 10 cols, 1 1/20, 1/8 between.
Areas Served: Kentucky & Indiana
Delivery Method: Mail, Newsstand, Carrier, RacksEquipment & Software: PRESSROOM EQUIPMENT: Lines — 7-G/Mark I 1948, 2-KBA/MOT 5 color DW 1992; 7-G/Mark I 1948, 2-KBA/MOT 5 color DW 1992; 6-H/ Color Convertible 1953, 2-KBA/MOT 5 color DW 1992; 7-G/Mark II 1968, 2-KBA/MOT 5 color DW 1992; Folders — 3-G/3:2, 1-H/2:1.; MAILROOM EQUIPMENT: Counter Stackers — 3-QWI/SJ201, 4-QWI/301B, 3/QWI 401; Inserters & Stuffers — 3-HI/72P, 1-/HI 630; Tying Machines — 2-EAM-Mosca/RO-TA-500PA, 2-/Power Strap/PSN-5, 1-/Power Strap/PSN-6, 3-MLN/2A, 6-Samuel/NT30 Strappers, 3-Samuel/NT30; Address Machine — Addressing; CLASSIFIED EQUIPMENT: Hardware — 2-AT; Printers — HP/4MV Laserjet; CLASSIFIED SOFTWARE: AT 4.7.6. DISPLAY EQUIPMENT: Hardware — APP/ Mac, Sun/Ultra II; Printers — GE/Proofer, HP/755 CM; DISPLAY SOFTWAREAd Make-up Applications — III 9.3.3.35; Layout Software — Baseview, Ad Manager AII. EDITORIAL EQUIPMENT: Hardware — 6-AT/ JII; Printers — Florida Data/Line Printer, GE/ Proofer EDITORIAL SOFTWARE: AT 4.7.6. PRODUCTION EQUIPMENT: Hardware — 3-III/3810, 3-AII/3850; Cameras — 2-C/ Pager II PRODUCTION SOFTWARE: AT/ Press 2 GO.

MADISONVILLE

THE MESSENGER

221 S Main St, Madisonville, Ky., 42431-2557, Hopkins; gen tel (270) 824-3300; adv tel (270) 824-3300; ed tel (270) 824-3221; gen fax (270) 821-6855; adv fax (270) 821-6855; ed fax (270) 825-3733; gen/nat adv e-mail newsroom@the-messenger.com; disp adv e-mail rwelch@the-messenger.com; class adv e-mailcsr@messenger-inquirer.com; ed e-mail letters@the-messenger.com; web site www.the-messenger.com
- 2,200,000(views) 72,000(visitors)
Group: Paxton Media Group, LLC
Published: Tues, Wed, Thur, Fri, Sat, Sun
Weekday Frequency: m
Saturday Frequency: m
Circulation: 5,147; 5,147(sat); 5,147(sun)
Last Audit: USPS December 11, 2017
Advertising Rate (weekday/saturday): Open inch rate $17,75
Advertising Rate (sunday): $19.67
Online Advertising Rate: Flat rates available — Run of site
OPEN, 6 MO., BEST*....

Top Leaderboard....728 x 90
$550....$500
$450
Top Half Banner....235 x 90
$500....$450
$400
Weather....125 x 125
$475....$425
$375
Stock Sponsor....120 x 90
$425....$375
$325
Big Ad/In Story....300 x 250
$500....$450
$400
Tile Ad #2....160 x 160
$450....$400
$350
Tile Ad #3....160 x 160
$425....$375
$325
Lower Leader....728 x 90
$350....$300
$250
News services: AP. **Established:** 1917
Own Printing Facility?: No
Commercial Printers?: Yes
Special Editions: Football (Aug); Christmas Sections (Dec); Bridal Tour (Jan); Fair Tab (Jul); Christmas Sections (Nov); Women in Business (Oct); Progress (Sept).
Special Weekly Sections: Pennyrile Plus News & Review (Wed).
Syndicated Publications: Parade Magazine (S). Athlon Sports, Spry, Relish
American Profile (W)
Digital Platform - Mobile: Apple, Android, Windows, Blackberry
Digital Platform - Tablet: Apple iOS, Android, Windows 7, Blackberry Tablet OS, Kindle, Nook, Kindle Fire
Pub.....Rick Welch
Adv. Dir.....Deborah Littlepage
Ed.....Don Perryman
Bus. Office....Melanie Miller
Retail Acct. Exec.....Tina Dillingham
Retail Acct. Exec.....Melanie Duncan
Circ. Dir.....Barry Carden
Market Information: ADS; TMC.
Mechanical Available: Offset; Black and 3 ROP colors; insert accepted; page cutoffs - 22 3/4.
Mechanical Specifications: Type page ROP (6 COL)
1 COL.... 1.6225
2 COL.... 3.375
3 COL.... 5.125
4 COL.... 6.875
5 COL.... 8.625
6 COL.... 10.375
Bdsheet.... 10.375x21.375; CLASSIFIED (7 COL)
1 COL.... 1.375
2 COL.... 2.875
3 COL.... 4.375
4 COL.... 5.875
5 COL.... 7.375
6 COL.... 8.875
7 COL.... 10.375
Bdsheet.... 10.375x21.375
Areas Served: 42431
Delivery Method: Mail, Newsstand, Carrier, RacksEquipment & Software: PRESSROOM EQUIPMENT: Lines — 8-G/Community.; MAILROOM EQUIPMENT: Tying Machines — 1-Si/LB.; BUSINESS EQUIPMENT: Baseview BUSINESS SOFTWARE: Adinfinitum CLASSIFIED EQUIPMENT: Hardware — 4-AT/5000.; DISPLAY EQUIPMENT: Printers — APP/Mac LaserWriter 650, Dataproducts/ LZR1560, ECR/Imagesetter; Other Hardware — APP/Mac Color One Scanner, Microtek/ ScanMaker IIXE DISPLAY SOFTWAREAd Make-up Applications — Multi-Ad/Creator, Broderbund/TypeStyler, Claris/MacDraw Pro, Adobe/Photoshop, Adobe/Illustrator; Media Span; Adinfinitum EDITORIAL EQUIPMENT: Hardware — 14-AT/5000, APP/Power Mac/3-APP/Mac SE, Lf/AP Leaf Picture Desk EDITORIAL SOFTWARE: QPS/InDesign/ NewSys. PRODUCTION EQUIPMENT: Hardware — 2-COM/8400, ECR/Imagesetter; Cameras — 1-Nu. IT SOFTWARE:Townnews CIRCULATION SOFTWARCirc. PRO
Note: Winner KPA Excellence Award 2012 Chamber Small Business of the Year 2010

MAYSVILLE

THE LEDGER INDEPENDENT

120 Limestone St, Maysville, Ky., 41056-1284, Mason; gen tel (606) 564-9091; adv tel (606) 564-9091; ed tel (606) 564-9091; gen

fax (606) 564-6893; adv fax (606) 564-6893; ed fax (606) 564-6893; gen/nat adv e-mail patty.moore@lee.net; disp adv e-mail patty.moore@lee.net; class adv e-maillindsey.landsaw@lee.net; ed e-mail Mary.Kearns@lee.net; web site www.maysville-online.com
Group: Lee Enterprises, Inc.
Published: Mon, Wed, Thur, Fri, Sat
Weekday Frequency: m
Saturday Frequency: m
Circulation: 4,581; 5,139(sat)
Last Audit: AAM September 30, 2016
Advertising Rate (weekday/saturday): Open inch rate $17.89; 19.50 (National)
Online Advertising Rate: Starting at $12.00 CPM
News services: AP. **Established:** 1968
Own Printing Facility?: Yes
Commercial Printers?: Yes
Special Editions: Car Care (Apr); Back-to-School (Aug); Christmas Greetings (Dec); Cookbook (Feb); Income Tax Guide (Jan); Dairy Month (Jun); Basketball (Mar); Homemakers (May); Basketball (Nov); 4-H (Oct); Car Care (Sept).
Special Weekly Sections: Food (Mon); Lifestyles/TV (Sat); Home and Garden (Thur); Food (Tues); Food (Wed).
Syndicated Publications: Relish (Monthly); Parade (Weekly).
Pub .... Robert L. Hendrickson
Controller .... Kellie Cracraft
Adv. Mgr. .... Patricia Moore
Ed. .... Mary Ann Kerns
Cir. Mgr. .... Jennifer Marshall
Market Information: ADS; TMC.
Mechanical Available: Offset; Black and 3 ROP colors; insert accepted; page cutoffs - 22 3/4.
Mechanical Specifications: Type page 13 x 21 1/2; E - 6 cols, 2 1/16, 1/8 between; A - 6 cols, 2 1/16, 1/8 between; C - 8 cols, 1 1/2, 1/8 between.
Areas Served: Seven-countys from Northern Kentucky and Southern Ohio
Delivery Method: Mail, Carrier, RacksEquipment & Software: PRESSROOM EQUIPMENT: Lines — 10-G/Community; Folders — 1-HI/Cotrell.; MAILROOM EQUIPMENT: Counter Stackers — 1/BG; Inserters & Stuffers — MM; Tying Machines — MLN; Address Machine — 1-/Ch.; BUSINESS EQUIPMENT: 2-ATT, BI, ATT/7300 CLASSIFIED EQUIPMENT: Hardware — CText.; DISPLAY SOFTWARELayout Software — DEC/Layout 8000. EDITORIAL EQUIPMENT: Hardware — TCMS PRODUCTION EQUIPMENT: Kodak Trendsetter; ECRM violet imager

MIDDLESBORO

MIDDLESBORO DAILY NEWS

1275 N 25th St, Middlesboro, Ky., 40965-1964, Bell; gen tel (606) 248-1010; adv tel (606) 248-1010 ext. 1131; ed tel (606) 248-1010 ext. 1123; gen fax (606) 248-7614; adv fax (606) 248-7614; ed fax (606) 248-7614; gen/nat adv e-mail pcheek@heartlandpublications.com; disp adv e-mail wpaul@heartlandpublications.com; class adv e-mailkrhymer@heartlandpublications.com; ed e-mail dcaldwell@civitasmedia.com; web site www.middlesborodailynews.com
Published: Tues, Wed, Thur, Fri, Sat
Weekday Frequency: e
Saturday Frequency: m
Circulation: 5,873; 5,873(sat)
Last Audit: Sworn/Estimate/Non-Audited September 30, 2017
Advertising Rate (weekday/saturday): Open inch rate $17.70
Online Advertising Rate: Below the Fold $11.70; Above the Fold $14.40; Wallpaper Ads $35.00
News services: AP. **Established:** 1911
Special Editions: Chamber of Commerce Membership Directory (Apr); Football (Aug); Letters to Santa (Dec); Progress (Feb); I'm Proud to be an American (Jul); Like Father Like Son (Jun); Home Improvement (Mar); Graduation (May); Caroling Book (Nov); Fall Festival (Oct); Read
Special Weekly Sections: Religion Page (Fri); Business Page (Thur).
Syndicated Publications: USA WEEKEND Magazine (Sat); American Profile (Tues).
Adv. Dir. .... Pat Cheek
Reg. Ed. .... Debbie Caldwell
Pub. .... Cynthia Orr
Business Development Specialist .... Wanda Paul
Business Development Specialist .... Aimee Brock
Trading Post Clerk .... Angela Wright
Editorial Clerk .... Bethany Moore
Prod. mgr. .... Roger Kirk
Market Information: TMC.
Mechanical Available: Offset; Black and 3 ROP colors; insert accepted; page cutoffs - 22 3/4.
Mechanical Specifications: Type page 11 5/8 x 21 1/2; E - 6 cols, 1 13/16, 1/8 between; A - 6 cols, 1 13/16, 1/8 between; C - 9 cols, 1 13/16, 1/8 between.
Areas Served: Tri-state Area
Delivery Method: Mail, Newsstand, Carrier, RacksEquipment & Software: PRESSROOM EQUIPMENT: Lines — 6-G/Community 1971.; MAILROOM EQUIPMENT: Tying Machines — 3/Bu.; BUSINESS EQUIPMENT: IBM/Sys 36 CLASSIFIED EQUIPMENT: Hardware — APP/Mac; Printers — APP/Mac LaserPrinter; CLASSIFIED SOFTWARE: Baseview. DISPLAY EQUIPMENT: Hardware — 2-APP/Mac; Printers — APP/Mac LaserPrinter; Other Hardware — APP/Mac Scanner. DISPLAY SOFTWAREAd Make-up Applications — Baseview; EDITORIAL EQUIPMENT: Hardware — APP/Mac; Printers — APP/Mac LaserPrinter EDITORIAL SOFTWARE: Baseview. PRODUCTION EQUIPMENT: Hardware — APP/Mac; Cameras — Acti PRODUCTION SOFTWARE: QPS/QuarkXPress.

MURRAY

THE MURRAY LEDGER & TIMES

1001 Whitnell Ave, Murray, Ky., 42071-2975, Calloway; gen tel (270) 753-1916; adv tel (270) 753-1916; ed tel (270) 753-1916; gen fax (270) 753-1927; adv fax (270) 753-1927; ed fax (270) 753-1927; gen/nat adv e-mail mdavis@murrayledger.com; disp adv e-mail ads@murrayledger.com; class adv e-mailclassified@murrayledger.com; ed e-mail editor@murrayledger.com; web site www.murrayledger.com
Group: Lancaster Management, Inc.
Published: Mon, Tues, Wed, Thur, Fri, Sat
Weekday Frequency: m
Saturday Frequency: m
Circulation: 7,100; 7,100(sat)
Last Audit: Sworn/Estimate/Non-Audited September 30, 2017
Advertising Rate (weekday/saturday): $10.50 PCI
Advertising Rate (sunday): N/A
News services: AP, TMS. **Established:** 1879
Own Printing Facility?: Yes
Commercial Printers?: No
Special Editions: Home Improvement (Apr); Back-to-School (Aug); In Our Backyard Magazine (June & Dec); Brides (Jan); Brides (Jun); Car Care (May); Fall Home Improvement (Oct); Homecoming (Sept).
Special Weekly Sections: Church Page (Fri); Farm Page (Mon); Outdoor Page (Sat); Arts & Entertainment (Thur); Education Page (Tues); Best Food Day (Wed).
Syndicated Publications: In Our Backyard Published in June and December
Managing Ed. .... Greg Travis
Pub .... Mike Davis
Adv. Mgr .... Chris Woodall
Adv. Rep. .... Crystal Duvall
Sports Ed. .... Jeff Arenz
Classified Mgr. .... Nicki Peach
Ed .... John Wright
Mechanical Available: Offset; Black and 3 ROP colors; insert accepted - all; page cutoffs - 21.
Mechanical Specifications: Type page 12 1/2 x 21 1/2; E - 6 cols, 1 5/6, 1/8 between; A - 6 cols, 1 5/6, 1/8 between; C - 9 cols, 1 1/4, 1/16 between.
Areas Served: 42071; 42066; 42049; 42040; 42025; 42048; 42076; 38251; 38222; 38242
Delivery Method: Mail, Newsstand, Carrier, RacksEquipment & Software: PRESSROOM EQUIPMENT: Lines — 8-G/Community (upper former) 1981; MAILROOM EQUIPMENT: Counter Stackers — 1/KAN; Inserters & Stuffers — 2-/Bu; Wrapping Singles — 1-/Ch; Address Machine — Address Machine — 1; BUSINESS EQUIPMENT: AcerView 54E BUSINESS SOFTWARE: MSSI CLASSIFIED EQUIPMENT: Hardware — APP/Mac G3; Printers — Okidata, Xante/Accel-A-Writer; CLASSIFIED SOFTWARE: Baseview/Ad Manager Pro. DISPLAY EQUIPMENT: Hardware — APP/Mac; Printers — Xante/8200; Other Hardware — 4-Microtek/Flatbed Scanner DISPLAY SOFTWAREAd Make-up Applications — QPS/QuarkXPress 4.0, Adobe/Photoshop 4.0; Layout Software — APP/Mac. EDITORIAL EQUIPMENT: Hardware — APP/Mac; Printers — Xante/8200 EDITORIAL SOFTWARE: Baseview/NewsEdit Pro, QPS/QuarkXPress 4.0. PRODUCTION EQUIPMENT: Hardware — 13-APP/Mac G5, Xante/Accel-A-Writer 8200; Cameras — 1-DAI/Vertical PRODUCTION SOFTWARE: QPS/QuarkXPress 6.1.

OWENSBORO

MESSENGER-INQUIRER

1401 Frederica St, Owensboro, Ky., 42301-4804, Daviess; gen tel (270) 926-0123; adv tel (270) 691-7239; ed tel (270) 691-7292; gen fax (270) 691-7244; adv fax (270) 691-7244; ed fax (270) 686-7868; gen/nat adv e-mail amayes@messenger-inquirer.com; disp adv e-mail amayes@messenger-inquirer.com; class adv e-mailgaustin@messenger-inquirer.com; ed e-mail mfrancis@messenger-inquirer.com; web site www.messenger-inquirer.com
Group: Paxton Media Group, LLC
Published: Mon, Tues, Wed, Thur, Fri, Sat, Sun
Weekday Frequency: m
Saturday Frequency: m
Circulation: 20,613; 20,613(sat); 23,791(sun)
Last Audit: AAM February 16, 2018
Advertising Rate (weekday/saturday): Open inch rate $34.47
Advertising Rate (sunday): Open inch rate $37.57
Online Advertising Rate: Rail Bottom $100.00 CPM; Tile Middle $200.00 CPM; Page Curl $375.00 CPM
News services: AP, MCT. **Established:** 1875
Own Printing Facility?: Yes
Commercial Printers?: Yes
Special Editions: Spring Improvements (Apr); Holiday Greetings (Dec); Home & Garden Show (Feb); Coupon Quarterly (Jan); Made in our Backyard (Jul); Southern Living Cooking School (Jun); Prime (Mar); Bar-B-Q Festival (May); Holiday Entertainments & Gifts (Nov); Voter's Guid
Special Weekly Sections: Entertainment (Fri); Style (S); Sports Weekend (Sat); Health (Thur); Community (Tues); Education (Wed).
Syndicated Publications: USA WEEKEND Magazine (S).
Parade
Digital Platform - Mobile: Apple, Android
Digital Platform - Tablet: Apple iOS, Android, Windows 7
Circ. Dir. .... Barry Carden
Mng. Ed. .... Matthew Francis
Copy Ed .... Mary Kissel
Librarian .... Sherri Heckel
Photo Ed. .... Robert Bruck
Ops. Mgr. .... Mike Weafer
City Ed .... Bob Bruck
News Ed. .... Scott Hagerman
Asst. News Ed. .... Shawn Rumsey
Mailroom Mgr. .... Jay Wear
Market Information: Full run; TMC.
Mechanical Available: Offset; Black and 3 ROP colors; insert accepted - sizes up to 14 x 10 1/2 large; 5 x 7 small; page cutoffs - 22 3/4.
Mechanical Specifications: Type page 13 x 21; E - 5 cols, 2 1/16, 1/6 between; A - 6 cols, 2 1/16, 1/6 between; C - 10 cols, 1 1/4, 1/6 between.
Areas Served: Daviess, Hancock, McLean, Muhlenberg & Ohio Counties
Delivery Method: CarrierEquipment & Software: PRESSROOM EQUIPMENT: Lines — 4-G/Metro 3033 double width 1968; Folders — 1-G/2:1 double width; Pasters —3-G/AutoReels & Stands — 4; MAILROOM EQUIPMENT: Counter Stackers — 1-Quipp 450 1 Quip 350; Inserters & Stuffers —K&M Titan 24:1:2; Tying Machines — 2-/Power Strap/PSN6, 1-MLN/ML2EE; Control system: K&M Address Machine — Addressing; BUSINESS EQUIPMENT: HP/937LX BUSINESS SOFTWARE: CJ/AIM CLASSIFIED EQUIPMENT: Hardware — 11-APP/Power Mac G3 300, OS 8.5.1; CLASSIFIED SOFTWARE: Baseview/AppleShare IP 6.0, Baseview/Ad Manager Pro 2.0.6, AR Module, Baseview/Class Flow 2.2.1. DISPLAY SOFTWAREAd Make-up Applications — QPS/QuarkXPress, Adobe/Illustrator; Layout Software — Mk/Managing Editor, Mk/Ad Director. EDITORIAL EQUIPMENT: Hardware — 5-APP/Power Mac G3 400 Mhz, 32-APP/I-Mac, 9-APP/Power Mac G3 300 Mhz/1-Lf/AP Leaf Picture Desk, 5-Cascade/OPI Server, Sun/Sparc 20, Cascade/Dataflow Server; Printers — 1-Lf/AP Leaf Picture Desk, 1-Cascade/OPI Server, Ultra 2, Casca PRODUCTION EQUIPMENT: Hardware — 1-Douthitt, Hyphen/Imagesetter 3100, 2-Xante/Accel-a-Writer 8300; Cameras — 1-C/Spartan, 1-SCREEN/Vertical; Scanners — ECR/8400 Line & halftone camera, 1-Howtek/D-400 drum scanner, AG/Arcus II PRODUCTION SOFTWARE: QPS/QuarkXPress 4.0.4.

PADUCAH

THE PADUCAH SUN

408 Kentucky Ave, Paducah, Ky., 42003-1550, McCracken; gen tel (270) 575-8600; adv tel (270) 575-8750; ed tel (270) 575-8650; gen fax (270) 575-8780; adv fax (270) 575-8771; ed fax (270) 442-7859; gen/nat adv e-mail craney@paducahsun.com; disp adv e-mail craney@paducahsun.com; class adv e-mailclassifieds@paducahsun.com; ed e-mail news@paducahsun.com; web site www.paducahsun.com
Group: Paxton Media Group, LLC
Published: Mon, Tues, Wed, Thur, Fri, Sat, Sun
Weekday Frequency: m
Saturday Frequency: m
Circulation: 19,618; 19,618(sat); 22,473(sun)
Last Audit: AAM September 30, 2011
Advertising Rate (weekday/saturday): Open inch rate $35.50
Advertising Rate (sunday): Open inch rate $35.50
Online Advertising Rate: Starting from $175.00/month
News services: AP, MCT. **Established:** 1896
Special Editions: Quilt Show (Apr); Newspapers in Education Advertising Kick-Off (Aug); Holiday Greetings (Dec); NASCAR (Feb); Brides (Jan); Fall Fashion (Jul); The Crimestopping Handbook (Jun); Spring Outdoors (Mar); Lakeland (May); House Call (Monthly); Holiday Gift Guid
Special Weekly Sections: Church (Fri); Health (Mon); Books (S); Outdoor (Sat); Food Day (Tues); Outdoor (Wed).
Syndicated Publications: USA WEEKEND Magazine (S); Posh (Semi-monthly).
Controller .... Jamie Paxton
Gen. Mgr. .... Gary Adkisson
Adv. Dir. .... Carolyn Raney
Circ. Mgr. .... Judy Lynch
Mng. Ed. .... Duke Conover
Bus./Finance Ed. .... Joe Walker
Editorial Page Ed. .... Mac Thrower
Entertainment/Amusements Ed. .... C.D. Bradley
Farm/Agriculture Ed. .... Ron Clark
Home Furnishings Ed. .... Leigh Landini Wright
Nat'l Ed. .... Chris Ash
News Ed. .... Mark Hultman
Online Ed. .... Crystal Shackelford
Photo Ed. .... Barkley Thielman
Political/Gov't Ed. .... Bill Bartleman
Market Information: Split run; TMC; Zoned editions.
Mechanical Available: Offset; Black and 3 ROP colors; insert accepted; page cutoffs - 21 1/4.
Mechanical Specifications: Type page 13 1/8 x 21 1/4; E - 6 cols, 1 5/6, 1/8 between; A - 6 cols, 1 5/6, 1/8 between; C - 9 cols, 1 5/8, 1/8 between.
Areas Served: Western Kentucky
Delivery Method: CarrierEquipment & Software: PRESSROOM EQUIPMENT: Lines — 10-G/Urbanite; Folders — G/Urbanite.; MAILROOM EQUIPMENT: Counter Stackers — 2/Id, 1-/S; Inserters & Stuffers — 1-/HI; Tying Machines — 2-/Bu, 1-Id.; BUSINESS EQUIPMENT: APP/Mac LAN, Microsoft/Windows NT BUSINESS SOFTWARE: Great Plains, Baseview CLASSIFIED

EQUIPMENT: Hardware — 4-APP/Mac 4400; APP/Mac 9650-233 fileserver; Printers — APP/Mac Personal LaserWriter, APP/Mac Imagewriter; CLASSIFIED SOFTWARE: Multi-Ad, Baseview, Baseview/Ad Manager Pro. DISPLAY EQUIPMENT: Hardware — Sun/Sparc; Printers — APP/Mac LaserWriter; Other Hardware — 5-APP/Mac DISPLAY SOFTWARELayout Software — SII, MEI. EDITORIAL EQUIPMENT: Hardware — 2-Sun/Sparc 5, 1-Sun/Sparc Ultra/HP/1600CM Color Printer; Printers — QMS/1660, APP/Mac LaserWriter 16-600, 2-ECR/4550, MON/2000 EDITORIAL SOFTWARE: DTI, APP/Mac Sys 8.1. PRODUCTION EQUIPMENT: Hardware — Caere/OmniPage, Publish Pac, Adobe/Photoshop 4.0, ECR 1085, Textroix Phaser 740; Cameras — C/Spartan II, AG/20 x 24, Kk Ap Digital Camera; Scanners — 2-Polaroid/SprintScan 35, Microtek/IIXE, Dest, Nikon/3510AF, Microtek/IISP, 2-Microtek/Scanma

RICHMOND

THE RICHMOND REGISTER

380 Big Hill Ave, Richmond, Ky., 40475-2012, Madison; gen tel (859) 623-1669; adv tel (859) 624-6681; ed tel (859) 623-1669; gen fax (859) 623-2337; adv fax (859) 623-2337; ed fax (859) 623-7408; gen/nat adv e-mail pstocker@richmondregister.com; disp adv e-mail nwoodward@richmondregister.com; class adv e-mailclassifieds@richmondregister.com; ed e-mail editor@richmondregister.com; web site www.richmondregister.com

Group: Community Newspaper Holdings, Inc.
Published: Tues, Wed, Thur, Fri, Sat, Sun
Weekday Frequency: e
Saturday Frequency: e
Circulation: 4,060; 4,060(sat); 4,423(sun)
Last Audit: AAM March 31, 2014
Advertising Rate (weekday/saturday): Open inch rate $12.96
Advertising Rate (sunday): Open inch rate $12.96
Online Advertising Rate: Starting at $127.00/month
News services: AP. **Established:** 1917
Special Weekly Sections: Real Estate (Fri); Health & Fitness (Sun); TV Supplement (Sat); Outdoors (Thur); Food (Wed).
Ed./News Ed. .... Bill Robinson
Rgl. Sales Mgr. .... Sherrie Hawn
Circ. Mgr. .... Heather Petitjean
Sports Ed. .... Nathan Hutchison
Features Ed. .... Carrie Curry
Page Designer .... Liz Denny
Media Advisor .... Nancy Woodward
Media Consultant .... Perry Stocker
Joyce Rose
Office Mgr. .... Marilyn Stewart
Publisher .... Dave Eldridge
Editor .... Jonathan Greene
Market Information: TMC; Zoned editions.
Mechanical Available: Offset; Black and 3 ROP colors; insert accepted; page cutoffs - 23.
Mechanical Specifications: Type page 13 x 21 1/2; E - 6 cols, 2 1/16, 1/8 between; A - 6 cols, 2 1/16, 1/8 between; C - 9 cols, 1 3/8, 1/16 between.
Areas Served: Richmond, Berea & Madison Counties (KY)
Delivery Method: Carrier, RacksEquipment & Software: PRESSROOM EQUIPMENT: Lines — 6-G/Community; Folders — 2-G/2:1.; MAILROOM EQUIPMENT: Tying Machines — 1/MLN, 1-MLN/MLIEE; Address Machine — 1-Am/1900.; CLASSIFIED EQUIPMENT: Hardware — 2-Mk/4010.; DISPLAY SOFTWARELayout Software — Mk/Ad Comp. EDITORIAL EQUIPMENT: Hardware — 6-Mk/4003 EDITORIAL SOFTWARE: HI/Compuedit, HI/1420. PRODUCTION EQUIPMENT: Hardware — 2-COM/2961HS, 1-COM/Unisetter, 1-M/101; Cameras — 1-R/500.

SOMERSET

THE COMMONWEALTH-JOURNAL

110 E Mount Vernon St, Somerset, Ky., 42501-1411, Pulaski; gen tel (606) 678-8191; adv tel (606) 451-4904; ed tel (606) 451-4920; gen fax (606) 679-9225; adv fax (606) 679-4866; ed fax (606) 679-9225; gen/nat adv e-mail mhornback@somerset-kentucky.com; disp adv e-mail maflynn@somerset-kentucky.com; class adv e-mailclassifieds@somerset-kentucky.com; ed e-mail kshmidheiser@somerset-kentucky.com; web site www.somerset-kentucky.com

Group: Community Newspaper Holdings, Inc.
Published: Tues, Wed, Thur, Fri, Sat, Sun
Weekday Frequency: m
Saturday Frequency: m
Circulation: 4,200; 4,200(sat); 4,764(sun)
Last Audit: Sworn/Estimate/Non-Audited December 19, 2017
Advertising Rate (weekday/saturday): Open inch rate $14.77
News services: AP, NEA. **Established:** 1895
Special Editions: High School Football (Aug); Christmas Songbook (Dec); Winter Clearance (Feb); Chamber Annual Report (Jan); Back-to-School (Jul); Summer Clearance (Jun); Agriculture Week (Mar); Grads (May); Regional Basketball Preview (Nov); Professional
Special Weekly Sections: Business (S); Best Food Days (Wed).
Syndicated Publications: Relish (Monthly); Parade (S).
Digital Platform - Mobile: Apple, Android, Windows, Blackberry, Other
Digital Platform - Tablet: Apple iOS, Android, Blackberry Tablet OS, Kindle, Kindle Fire
Adv. Dir. .... Mike Hornback
Managing Ed. .... Ken Shmidheiser
News Ed. .... Jeff Neal
Sports Ed. .... Steve Cornelius
Pub. .... Rob McCollough
Adv. Rep. .... Mary Ann Flynn
Adv. Clerk & Political Spec. .... Kathy Lee
Classified Adv. Dir. .... Debra Gossett
Circ. Clerk .... Carol LaFavers
Accounting/HR Mgr. .... Paula Jones
Compositor .... Shirley Randall
Classified Mgr .... Jakaye Garth
Classified Clerk .... Kathleen Hall
Ad sales rep .... Acie Perercheif
Circulation Manager .... Mark Walker
Reporter .... Janie Slaven
Carla Slavey
Steve Cornelius
Market Information: ADS; TMC.
Mechanical Available: Offset; Black and 3 ROP colors; insert accepted - half-fold, quarter-fold; page cutoffs - 22 3/4.
Mechanical Specifications: Type page 13 x 21 1/2; E - 6 cols, 2 1/16, 1/8 between; A - 6 cols, 2 1/16, 1/8 between; C - 10 cols, 1 3/16, 1/12 between.
Areas Served: Pulaski County (KY)
Delivery Method: CarrierEquipment & Software: BUSINESS EQUIPMENT: Vision Data/486 CLASSIFIED EQUIPMENT: Hardware — Equipment 2-APP/Mac Quadra 605.; DISPLAY EQUIPMENT: Printers — 1-APP/Mac LaserWriter; DISPLAY SOFTWARELayout Software — 2-APP/Mac Quadra 650. EDITORIAL EQUIPMENT: Hardware — APP/Mac Quadra 650, APP/Mac Quadra 610, APP/Mac Quadra 605; Printers — HP/LaserJet EDITORIAL SOFTWARE: QPS/QuarkXPress. PRODUCTION EQUIPMENT: Hardware — 2-APP/Mac Quadra 650; Cameras — 1-BKY/Omega 20x24.

WINCHESTER

THE WINCHESTER SUN

20 Wall St, Winchester, Ky., 40391-1900, Clark; gen tel (859) 744-3123; adv tel (859) 355-1239; ed tel (859) 355-1218; gen fax (859) 745-0638; gen/nat adv e-mail Jfoley@winchestersun.com; disp adv e-mail Jfoley@winchestersun.com; class adv e-mailRbenton@winchestersun.com; ed e-mail Dstone@winchestersun.com; web site www.winchestersun.com

Group: Boone Newspapers, Inc.
Published: Mon, Tues, Wed, Thur, Fri, Sun
Weekday Frequency: e
Saturday Frequency: m
Circulation: 6,000; 6,000(sat)
Last Audit: USPS October 1, 2013
Advertising Rate (weekday/saturday): Open inch rate $11.70
News services: AP. **Established:** 1878
Own Printing Facility?: Yes
Commercial Printers?: Yes
Special Editions: Back-to-School (Aug); Holiday Greetings (Dec); Parade of Babies (Jan); Year In Review (Jul); Kids Today (Jun); Spring Home Improvement (Mar); Seniors Graduation (May); Holiday Gift Guide (Nov); Holiday Bazaars (Oct); Literacy (Sept).
Special Weekly Sections: Health & Fitness (Mon); Church (Sat); Business (Wed).
Syndicated Publications: Relish (Monthly); American Profile (Weekly).
Digital Platform - Mobile: Apple, Android
Digital Platform - Tablet: Apple iOS, Android
Pres./Pub./Ed. .... Larry Hensley
Member Services Rep./Adv. Rep. .... Lana Smith
Digital Media Consultant .... Jordan Toler
Editor .... David Stone
Sports Ed. .... Keith Taylor
Pre-Press Mgr. .... Terah Hatton
Circ. Dir. .... Tiffany Sokolowski
Exec. Ed. .... John Nelson
Digital Mgr./Audience Relations Mgr. John Preston
Web Developer .... Gary Moyers
Commercial Printing Mgr./Ops. Mgr. ... Bob Martin
Mechanical Available: Offset; Black and 3 ROP colors; insert accepted; page cutoffs - 22 3/4.
Mechanical Specifications: Type page 11 x 21 1/2; E - 6 cols, 1 11/16, 1/8 between; A - 6 cols, 1 11/16, 1/8 between; C - 8 cols, 1 3/16, 1/8 between.
Areas Served: Clark County (KY)
Delivery Method: Mail, Newsstand, Carrier, RacksEquipment & Software: PRESSROOM EQUIPMENT: Lines — 7, 2; MAILROOM EQUIPMENT: Counter Stackers — Stacker/652; Inserters & Stuffers — MM, KAN/480; Tying Machines — 2/Bu; Address Machine — 1-/KR, KR/1090 Inline Mailtable & Electric Head; EDITORIAL EQUIPMENT: Hardware — 9-APP/Mac EDITORIAL SOFTWARE: Baseview/NewsEdit/InDesign

LOUISIANA

ABBEVILLE

ABBEVILLE MERIDIONAL

318 N Main St, Abbeville, La., 70510-4608, Vermilion; gen tel (337) 893-4223; adv tel (337) 893-4223; ed tel (337) 893-4223; gen fax (337) 898-9022; adv fax (337) 898-9022; ed fax (337) 898-9022; gen/nat adv e-mail kathy.cormier@vermiliontoday.com; disp adv e-mail kathy.cormier@vermiliontoday.com; class adv e-mailashley.bossley@vermiliontoday.com; ed e-mail chris.rosa@vermiliontoday.com; web site www.vermiliontoday.com

Group: LSN Publishing Company LLC
Published: Tues, Wed, Thur, Fri
Weekday Frequency: m
Circulation: 5,379; 5,379(sun)
Last Audit: Sworn/Estimate/Non-Audited September 30, 2017
Advertising Rate (weekday/saturday): Open inch rate $9.50
Online Advertising Rate: Leaderboard, Large Rectangle $7.00 CPM; Half page, Marquee $10.00 CPM
News services: AP, NEA. **Established:** 1856
Special Editions: Progress (Apr); Football (Aug); Newcomer (Feb); Bridal (Jan); Back To School (Jul); Substance Abuse (Jun); Home Improvement (Mar); Graduation (May); Christmas Gift Guide (Nov); Giant Omelette Festival (Oct); Women's Tab (Sept).
Special Weekly Sections: Bridal (S).
Syndicated Publications: Parade (S).
Pub. .... Kathy Cormier
Managing Ed. .... Cynthia Nicholas
Managing Ed. .... Christopher Rosa
News Ed. .... Shaun Hearen
Lifestyles Ed. .... Nikki Vidos
Sports Ed. .... Joseph Cunningham
Adv. Sales Rep. .... Jessica Meaux
Adv. Sales Rep. .... Emeral Hebert
Classified Sales Rep. .... Ashley Bossley
Business Mgr. .... Theresa Milliman
Market Information: TMC.
Mechanical Available: Offset; Black and 3 ROP colors; insert accepted; page cutoffs - 22 7/8.
Mechanical Specifications: Type page 11 11/16 x 21 1/2; E - 6 cols, 1 4/5, 1/8 between; A - 6 cols, 1 4/5, 1/16 between; C - 9 cols, 1 3/20, 1/8 between.
Areas Served: Vermillion
Delivery Method: Mail, Newsstand, Carrier, RacksEquipment & Software: PRESSROOM EQUIPMENT: Lines — 6-KP/News King.; MAILROOM EQUIPMENT: Tying Machines — 1/Bu; Address Machine — IBM/Sys (with printer for labeling).; BUSINESS EQUIPMENT: PC CLASSIFIED EQUIPMENT: Hardware — Mk; 1-COM.; DISPLAY SOFTWARELayout Software — APP/Mac. EDITORIAL EQUIPMENT: Hardware — Mk/9-COM. PRODUCTION EQUIPMENT: Hardware — 2-APP/Mac LaserWriter; Cameras — SCREEN/Companica Horizontal.

ALEXANDRIA

THE TOWN TALK

1201 3rd St, Alexandria, La., 71301-8246, Rapides; gen tel (318) 487-6397; adv tel (318) 487-6388; ed tel (318) 487-6409; gen fax (318) 487-2950; adv fax (318) 487-2950; ed fax (318) 487-2950; gen/nat adv e-mail christina.pierce@thetowntalk.com; disp adv e-mail christina.pierce@thetowntalk.com; class adv e-maillegals@thetowntalk.com; ed e-mail news@thetowntalk.com; web site www.thetowntalk.com

Group: Gannett
Published: Mon, Tues, Wed, Thur, Fri, Sat, Sun
Weekday Frequency: m
Saturday Frequency: m
Circulation: 15,983; 15,983(sat); 21,384(sun)
Last Audit: AAM December 31, 2014
Advertising Rate (weekday/saturday): Open inch rate $30.70
Advertising Rate (sunday): Open inch rate $35.65
Online Advertising Rate: Leaderboard $4.00 CPM; Large Rectangle $5.00 CPM; Halfpage $9.00 CPM
News services: AP, SHNS, GNS. **Established:** 1883
Own Printing Facility?: Yes
Commercial Printers?: No
Special Editions: Football (Aug)
Special Weekly Sections: Weekend (Fri); Amusement Page (S); Church (Sat); Shopper's Marketplace (Wed).
Digital Platform - Mobile: Apple, Android, Windows
Digital Platform - Tablet: Apple iOS, Android, Windows 7, Kindle, Kindle Fire
Engagement & Community Content Editor .... Jim Smilie
Gen. Mgr./Adv. Dir. .... Christina Pierce
Distribution Mgr. .... Deborah Schulte
Market Information: TMC.
Mechanical Available: Offset; Black and 3 ROP colors; insert accepted; page cutoffs - 22.
Mechanical Specifications: Type page 11 5/8 x 21; E - 6 cols, 1 13/16, 1/8 between; A - 6 cols, 1 13/16, 1/8 between; C - 9 cols, 1 13/16, 1/16 between.
Areas Served: Rapides Parish
Delivery Method: Mail, Newsstand, Carrier, RacksEquipment & Software: PRESSROOM EQUIPMENT: Lines — Manroland Uniset 70; Folders — 2-manroland 3:2; Pasters —10 Enkel Reel Stands MAILROOM EQUIPMENT: Counter Stackers — 2-QWI/501; 1-QWI/400; Inserters & Stuffers — 2-SLS1000; Tying Machines — 4 oval strappers; BUSINESS EQUIPMENT: PCs BUSINESS SOFTWARE: MS Windows Genysis CLASSIFIED EQUIPMENT: Hardware — PCs; CLASSIFIED SOFTWARE: MS Windows; Mactive DISPLAY EQUIPMENT: Hardware — PCs; DISPLAY SOFTWAREAd Make-up Applications — MS Windows; Adobe InDesign; EDITORIAL EQUIPMENT: Hardware — PCs EDITORIAL SOFTWARE: MS Windows; Harris; Adobe InDesign PRODUCTION EQUIPMENT: Hardware — 2 Agfa 3850 ImageSetters

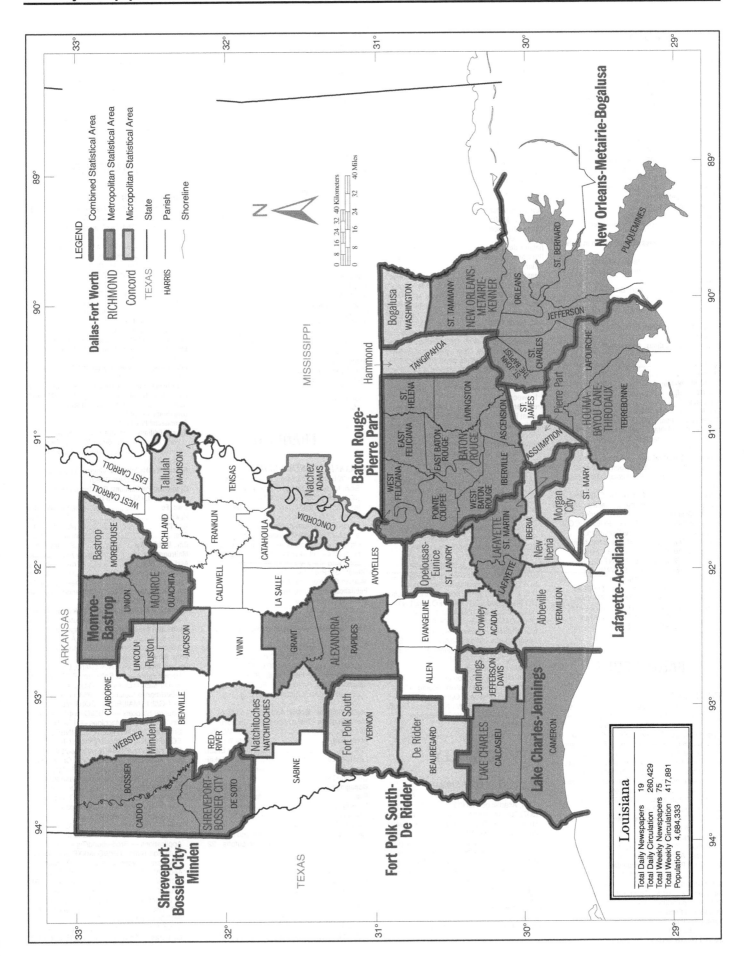

LEGEND

Dallas-Fort Worth — Combined Statistical Area
RICHMOND — Metropolitan Statistical Area
Concord — Micropolitan Statistical Area

TEXAS — State
HARRIS — Parish
— Shoreline

N

0 8 16 24 32 40 Kilometers
0 8 16 24 32 40 Miles

Louisiana

Total Daily Newspapers	19
Total Daily Circulation	260,429
Total Weekly Newspapers	75
Total Weekly Circulation	417,891
Population	4,684,333

BASTROP

BASTROP DAILY ENTERPRISE

119 W Hickory Ave, Bastrop, La., 71220-4549, Morehouse; gen tel (318) 281-4421; adv tel (318) 281-4421; ed tel (318) 281-2691; gen fax (318) 283-1699; adv fax (318) 283-1699; ed fax (318) 283-1699; gen/nat adv e-mail sharrell@gatehousemedia.com; disp adv e-mail advertising@bastropenterprise.com; class adv e-mailtturner@bastropenterprise.com; ed e-mail kstewart@bastropenterprise.com; web site www.bastropenterprise.com
Group: New Media Investment Group
Published: Tues, Wed, Thur, Fri, Sat
Weekday Frequency: m
Saturday Frequency: m
Circulation: 4,241; 4,241(sat)
Last Audit: Sworn/Estimate/Non-Audited September 30, 2017
Advertising Rate (weekday/saturday): Open inch rate $10.00
Online Advertising Rate: Banner Ad $75.00 CPM; Instory Ad $120.00; Weather $175.00 CPM
News services: 1898
Special Editions: Pride (Apr); Bridal (Feb); Newcomer Guide (Jul); Graduation (May); Gift Guide (Nov); Quarterly (Oct); Gin Whistle (Sept).
Special Weekly Sections: Farm (Thur); Food (Wed).
Syndicated Publications: American Profile (Weekly).
Rgl. Pub. ....Scott Harrell
Sports Ed. ....Marq Mitcham
Classified Adv. Mgr. ....Tanya Armfield
Circ. Mgr. ....Carmen Turner
Adv. Sales .... Pat Tullos
Gen. Mgr./Retail Adv. Sales ....Eddie Bayless
Market Information: TMC.
Mechanical Available: Offset; Black and 3 ROP colors; insert accepted - any; page cutoffs - 22 3/4.
Mechanical Specifications: Type page 13 x 21; E - 6 cols, 2 1/16, 1/8 between; A - 6 cols, 2 1/16, 1/8 between; C - 9 cols, 1 5/16, 1/8 between.
Areas Served: Bastrop, Oak Ridge, Collinston, Jones, Bonita, Mer Rouge, Crossett
Delivery Method: Mail, Newsstand, Carrier, RacksEquipment & Software: PRESSROOM EQUIPMENT: Lines — 5-G/Suburban.; MAILROOM EQUIPMENT: Tying Machines — 2-/Bu; Address Machine — 3-/Dispensa-Matic.; BUSINESS EQUIPMENT: 2-RSK/II-TRS-80 BUSINESS SOFTWARE: Word Processing CLASSIFIED EQUIPMENT: Hardware — Mk.; DISPLAY SOFTWARELayout Software — APP/Mac. EDITORIAL EQUIPMENT: Hardware — Mk. PRODUCTION EQUIPMENT: Hardware — APP/Mac LaserWriter, 1-B; Cameras — 1-C/Model T, 1-CL.

BATON ROUGE

THE ADVOCATE

10705 Reiger Rd, Baton Rouge, La., 70809-4520, East Baton Rouge; gen tel (225) 383-1111; adv tel (225) 388-0262; ed tel (225) 388-0283; gen fax (225) 388-0323; adv fax (225) 388-0348; ed fax (225) 388-0371; gen/nat adv e-mail csettle@theadvocate.com; disp adv e-mail srunnels@theadvocate.com; class adv e-mailadelatorre@theadvocate.com; ed e-mail fkalmbach@theadvocate.com; web site www.theadvocate.com
- 12,040,700(views) 1,772,500(visitors)
Group: Capital City Press
Published: Mon, Tues, Wed, Thur, Fri, Sat, Sun
Weekday Frequency: m
Saturday Frequency: m
Circulation: 79,123; 83,139(sat); 90,118(sun)
Last Audit: AAM September 30, 2017
Advertising Rate (weekday/saturday): Open inch rate $70.26 (Mon-Wed); $73.33 (Thur-Sat)
Advertising Rate (sunday): Open inch rate $81.10
News services: AP, MCT-LAT. **Established:** 1925
Own Printing Facility?: Yes
Commercial Printers?: Yes
Special Editions: The New Orleans Advocate The Acadiana Advocate
Special Weekly Sections: Wheels (Fri);

Entertainment RED (Fri); Business (Sun); Wheels (Sun); Homes (Sun)
Syndicated Publications: Parade (S)
Digital Platform - Mobile: Apple, Android
Digital Platform - Tablet: Apple iOS, Android
Night Metro Editor ....Vicki Ferstel
Photo Dir. ....John Ballance
VP of Production ....Sterling Rabalais
Pub./CEO ....John Georges
Features Ed. ....Karen Martin
Pres./COO .... Dan Shea
VP, Adv. ....Sheila Runnels
National Adv. Mgr. ....Connie Settle
Adv. Asst. ....Karen Marchand
Marketing Dir. ....Charlene Robert
Exec. News Ed. ....Jennifer Brown
Exec. Asst. .... Dianne Guidry
Editorial Page Ed. ....Danny Heitman
Exec. Sports Ed. ....Joseph Schiefelbein
New Orleans Managing Ed. ....Martha Carr
VP, Digital Media .... Michael Wilson
Online Adv. Coord.
Jason Gele
Retail Sales Dir. .... Lou Hudson
Director of Sales/Marketing ....Sara Barnard
Editor ....Peter Kovacs
Managing Ed. .... Fred Kalmbach
CNB Ed. ....Mark Ballard
Special Sections Editor ....Lori Tucker
Metro Editor ....Laura Maggi
Online News Editor ....Ken Duhe
Asst. Sports Editor ....Perryn Keys
Online Sports Editor ....Pierce Huff
Market Information: ADS; TMC; Zoned editions.
Mechanical Available: Offset; Black and 3 ROP colors; insert accepted; page cutoffs - 21.
Mechanical Specifications: Type page 11 1/8 x 20; E - 6 cols, 1 3/4, 1/8 between; A - 6 cols, 1 3/4, 1/8 between; C - 9 cols, 1 1/8, 1/8 between.
Areas Served: West Feliciana, Pointe Coupee, West Baton Rouge, East Baton Rouge, East Feliciana, St. Helena, Livingston, Tangipahoa, Ascension, St. James, Assumption
Delivery Method: Mail, Newsstand, Carrier, RacksEquipment & Software: PRESSROOM EQUIPMENT: Lines — 1-manroland Regioman; Folders — 2-G/3:2; Reels & Stands — 8; Control System — PECOM - 3 stations; MAILROOM EQUIPMENT: Counter Stackers — 6-Quipp 501, 3-Schur palletizers; Inserters & Stuffers — 2-GMA/SLS 3000; 1- GMA/SLS 2000; Tying Machines — 7-Dynaric/NP-2; Wrapping Singles — 1-Dynaric/DFII; BUSINESS EQUIPMENT: Cisco UCS VM Servers BUSINESS SOFTWARE: A/R: Atex-AIM, A/P-G/L:Epicor, P/R: ADP CLASSIFIED EQUIPMENT: VMware Servers CLASSIFIED SOFTWARE: Computext/CompuClass. DISPLAY SOFTWAREXpance, Adobe Suite, DTI Planspeed EDITORIAL EQUIPMENT: Hosted Cloud EDITORIAL SOFTWARE: DTI, InDesign, Merlin PRODUCTION EQUIPMENT: Hardware — 2-Agfa Advantage DL imagers, 2-Agfa VSP 85-S processors, 1-Nela plate punch & bender PRODUCTION SOFTWARE: DTI CMS Publishing, Newscycle Circulation IT EQUIPMENT: Cisco Routers and Switches; Cisco UCS Servers, NetApp Storage IT SOFTWARE:Microsoft Operating System CIRCULATION EQUIPMENT: Hosted Cloud CIRCULATION SOFTWARNewscycle Circulation

CROWLEY

THE CROWLEY POST-SIGNAL

602 N Parkerson Ave, Crowley, La., 70526-4354, Acadia; gen tel (337) 783-3450; adv tel (337) 783-3450; ed tel (337) 783-3450; gen fax (337) 788-0949; adv fax (337) 788-0949; ed fax (337) 788-0949; gen/nat adv e-mail harold.gonzales@crowleytoday.com; disp adv e-mail advertising@crowleytoday.com; class adv e-mailclassifieds@crowleytoday.com; ed e-mail steve.bandy@crowleytoday.com; web site www.crowleypostsignal.com
Group: LSN Publishing Company LLC
Published: Tues, Wed, Thur, Fri, Sun
Weekday Frequency: m
Circulation: 4,476; 4,476(sun)
Last Audit: Sworn/Estimate/Non-Audited September 30, 2017

Advertising Rate (weekday/saturday): Open inch rate $9.20 (Local); $10.77 (National)
Advertising Rate (sunday): Open inch rate $9.20 (Local); $10.77 (National)
Online Advertising Rate: Leaderboard, Large Rectangle $7.00 CPM; Half page, Marquee $10.00 CPM
News services: AP, NEA. **Established:** 1885
Special Editions: National DARE Day (Apr); Drive Safely Page (Aug); Acadia Parish First Baby (Dec); Vo-Tech Education Week (Feb); Honor Roll (Jan); Rice Field Day (Jul); Flag Day (Jun); Home Improvement (Mar); Iota Graduation Page (May); Pharmacy Week (Nov); National 4-H W
Special Weekly Sections: Business (Wed.); Agriculture (Thur); Devotional (Fri)
Syndicated Publications: Parade (S).
Gen. Mgr. ....Harold Gonzales
Production Mgr. ....Kathy Duncan
Managing Ed. .... Steve Bandy
Online Ed. ....Jeannine LeJeune
Lifestyles Ed. ....Saja Hoffpauir
Ed. .... Howie Dennis
Sports Ed. ....Chris Quebedeaux
Adv. Mgr. ....Janet Doucet
Classifieds Adv. .... Becky LaFleur
Bookkeeping .... Wendy Newman
Market Information: ADS; TMC.
Mechanical Available: Offset; Black and 4 ROP colors; insert accepted; page cutoffs - 21 1/2.
Mechanical Specifications: Type page 13 x 21 1/2; E - 6 cols, 1 3/4, 1/8 between; A - 6 cols, 1 3/4, 1/8 between; C - 6 cols, 1 3/4, 1/8 between.
Areas Served: Acadia
Delivery Method: Mail, Newsstand, Carrier, RacksEquipment & Software: MAILROOM EQUIPMENT: Tying Machines — 1-Wilton/Stra Pack; Address Machine — 2/Dispensa-Matic.;

FRANKLIN

FRANKLIN BANNER-TRIBUNE

115 Wilson St, Franklin, La., 70538-6149, Saint Mary; gen tel (337) 828-3706; adv tel (337) 828-3706; ed tel (337) 828-3706; gen fax (337) 828-2874; adv fax (337) 828-2874; ed fax (337) 828-2874; gen/nat adv e-mail admanager@banner-tribune.com; disp adv e-mail admanager@banner-tribune.com; class adv e-mailclassifieds@banner-tribune.com; ed e-mail webmaster@banner-tribune.com; web site www.stmarynow.com
Group: LSN Publishing Company LLC Morgan City Newspapers LLC
Published: Mon, Tues, Wed, Thur, Fri
Weekday Frequency: e
Circulation: 3,500
Last Audit: USPS September 28, 2012
Advertising Rate (weekday/saturday): Open inch rate $7.70
Online Advertising Rate: Marquee, Half Page open rate $10.00 CPM; 30 day $500 Leaderboard opoe rate $7.00 CPM
News services: AP. **Established:** 1885
Special Editions: Profile (Apr); Football (Aug); Christmas (Dec); Bridal (Jan); Drug Free (Oct).
Digital Platform - Mobile: Android, Windows
Digital Platform - Tablet: Apple iOS, Android
Adv. Mgr. ....Debbie Von Werder
Accounting .... Judy Touchet
Circ. Mgr. .... Debbie Billiot
Lifestyles Ed. ....Michelle Baker
Sports Ed. .... Anthony Mitchell
Christine Duhon
Managing Ed. .... Roger Stouff
Pub. ....Allan Von Werder
Classifieds Adv. Mgr. ....Tanya Sonnier
Adv. Rep. ....Angela Guckeen
Market Information: TMC.
Mechanical Available: Offset; Black and 3 ROP colors; insert accepted - all; page cutoffs - 22 3/4.
Mechanical Specifications: 11.75 w x 21 h
Areas Served: 70538;70514;70522;70540
Delivery Method: Mail, Newsstand, CarrierEquipment & Software: PRESSROOM EQUIPMENT: Lines — 2-G/Suburban; BUSINESS EQUIPMENT: 2-PC 386 BUSINESS SOFTWARE: In-house CLASSIFIED EQUIPMENT: Hardware — COM/One Sys; CLASSIFIED SOFTWARE:

COM/RTR Translator III. DISPLAY EQUIPMENT: Hardware — PC 486, PC 486 (with CD-Rom); Printers — 2-NewGen/Turbo Laser; DISPLAY SOFTWAREAd Make-up Applications — Archetype/Corel Draw.; EDITORIAL EQUIPMENT: Hardware — COM/One Sys/Panasonic; Printers — 2-NewGen/Turbo Laser EDITORIAL SOFTWARE: COM/RTR Edit. PRODUCTION EQUIPMENT: Hardware — 2-NewGen/600B Laser Printer.
Note: We are a daily.

HAMMOND

THE DAILY STAR

725 S Morrison Blvd, Hammond, La., 70403-5401, Tangipahoa; gen tel (985) 254-7827; adv tel (985) 254-7827; ed tel (985) 254-7827; gen fax (985) 542-5292; adv fax (985) 542-5292; ed fax (985) 542-5292; gen/nat adv e-mail kgingles@hammondstar.com; disp adv e-mail mgallo@hammondstar.com; class adv e-mailclassads@hammondstar.com; ed e-mail editor@hammondstar.com; web site www.hammondstar.com
Group: Paxton Media Group, LLC
Published: Tues, Wed, Thur, Fri, Sat, Sun
Weekday Frequency: m
Saturday Frequency: m
Circulation: 9,595; 9,595(sat); 11,186(sun)
Last Audit: Sworn/Estimate/Non-Audited September 30, 2017
Advertising Rate (weekday/saturday): Open inch rate $20.00 (Tue-Thur, Sat); $22.50 (Fri)
Advertising Rate (sunday): Open inch rate $25.00
Online Advertising Rate: Starting at $75.00 CPM
News services: AP. **Established:** 1959
Own Printing Facility?: Yes
Commercial Printers?: Yes
Special Editions: Strawberry Festival (Apr); Football (Aug); Basketball Tourney (Dec); Profile Progress (Feb); Medical (Jul); Kids Beat (Mar).
Special Weekly Sections: Church (Fri); Business (S); Best Food Days (Wed).
Syndicated Publications: Bon Temps (Fri); USA WEEKEND Magazine (S).
Exec. Ed. ....Lillian K. Mirando
News Ed. ...............................A.M. Sheehan
Adv. Dir. ....Michelle Gallo
Circ. Dir. ....William Calcutt
Circ. District Mgr. ....Stanley Davis
Mailroom Mgr. ....Mary Ann Giovingo
Asst. Bus. Mgr. .... Trudy Shockley
Pressroom Supervisor ....David Bordok
Sports Ed. ....James Summerlin
Circ. District Mgr. ....Catherine Massawe
Market Information: TMC.
Mechanical Available: Offset; Black and 3 ROP colors; insert accepted; page cutoffs - 22 3/4.
Mechanical Specifications: Type page 13 x 21 1/2; E - 6 cols, 2, 1/6 between; A - 6 cols, 2, 1/6 between; C - 9 cols, 1 2/5, 1/8 between.
Areas Served: Tangipahoa Parish
Delivery Method: Mail, Newsstand, Carrier, RacksEquipment & Software: PRESSROOM EQUIPMENT: Lines — 7-G/Urbanite, 1-G/Urbanite (color unit) 1983; Folders — 1-G/2:1.; MAILROOM EQUIPMENT: Counter Stackers — 1-BG/Count-O-Veyor, HH/3017S; Tying Machines — 1-MLN/Strapper, 1-MLN/Strapper; BUSINESS EQUIPMENT: Microsoft/Windows NT BUSINESS SOFTWARE: Microsoft/Windows, Microsoft/Excel, Microsoft/Word CLASSIFIED EQUIPMENT: Hardware — APP/Mac; Printers — Okidata, APP/Mac LaserWriter; CLASSIFIED SOFTWARE: Baseview/Class Manager. DISPLAY EQUIPMENT: Hardware — APP/Mac; Printers — 2-Compaq/Page Marq 20; Other Hardware — APP/Mac CD-Rom, Micronet/Optical 650 drive DISPLAY SOFTWAREAd Make-up Applications — Broderbund/Typestyler 2.0, Multi-Ad/Creator, QPS/QuarkXPress, Aldus/FreeHand; Layout Software — APP/Mac 4400, APP/Mac Quadra 650, APP/Powe EDITORIAL EQUIPMENT: Hardware — APP/Mac/HP/ScanJet 2C, CD-Rom; Printers — 2-Compaq/PageMarq 20 EDITORIAL SOFTWARE: Baseview, QPS/QuarkXPress. PRODUCTION EQUIPMENT: Hardware — MON/1270 Imagesetter, Douthitt/3040; Cameras — Acti/Horizontal, AG/Rapiline 17;

Scanners — HP/ScanJet 2C PRODUCTION SOFTWARE: QPS/QuarkXPress 3.31.

HOUMA

THE COURIER

3030 Barrow St, Houma, La., 70360-7641, Terrebonne; gen tel (985) 850-1100; adv tel (985) 857-2270; ed tel (985) 857-2201; gen fax (985) 857-2233; adv fax (985) 857-2273; ed fax (985) 857-2233; gen/nat adv e-mail alan.rini@houmatoday.com; disp adv e-mail robin.blanchard@houmatoday.com; class adv e-mailrobin.blanchard@houmatoday.com; ed e-mail keith.magill@houmatoday.com; web site www.houmatoday.com
- 5,500,000(views) 352,000(visitors)

Group: New Media Investment Group
Published: Mon, Tues, Wed, Thur, Fri, Sat, Sun
Weekday Frequency: e
Saturday Frequency: m
Circulation: 11,044; 18,166(sat); 13,850(sun)
Last Audit: AAM December 31, 2015
Advertising Rate (weekday/saturday): Open inch rate $23.49; $28.48 (Wed)
Advertising Rate (sunday): Open inch rate $26.38
News services: AP **Established:** 1878
Own Printing Facility?: Yes
Commercial Printers?: Yes
Special Editions: Bayou Gourmet Cookbook (Apr); Football Tab (Aug); Christmas Greetings (Dec); Mardi Gras Tab (Feb); Tax Guide (Jan); Graduation (May); Bridal (Oct); Oil & Industry (Sept).
Special Weekly Sections: Big Fun on the Bayou (Fri); Health & Fitness (Mon); Louisiana Style (S); Outdoors (Thur); Home & Family (Tues); Bon Appetit (Wed).
Syndicated Publications: Parade (S); Athlon Sports (TH)
Proprietary Publications: Big Fun on the BAYOU (Fri);
Digital Platform - Mobile: Apple, Android, Blackberry
Finance Dir. .... Darlene Rodrigue
Executive Editor .... Keith Magill
Circ. Mgr. .... Lawrence Knoblock
HR .... Karen Dauzat
Adv. Sales .... Alan Rini
Adv. Sales .... Pam Fahey
Adv. Sales .... Peyvand Maghsoud
Circ. Clerk .... Karen Robichaux
Accountant .... Mindy Thibodaux
District Mgr. .... Patricia Cheavis
Night City Ed .... Mike Hill
Sports Ed. .... Brent St. Germain
Adv. Dir. .... Marian Long
Pub .... Lee Bachlet
Market Information: ADS; TMC.
Mechanical Available: Offset; Black and 3 ROP colors; insert accepted - zoned inserts; page cutoffs - 22.75
Mechanical Specifications: Type page 11" x 22"; E - 6 cols, 1.708", 11 pts. between; A - 6 cols, 1.708", 11 pts. between; C - 9 cols, 1.126", 11 pts. between.
Areas Served: 70361, 70360, 70363, 70364, 70301, 70394, 70395, 70374, 70343, 70344, 70345, 70353, 70354, 70356, 70357, 70359, 70377, 70397
Delivery Method: Mail, Newsstand, Carrier, RacksEquipment & Software: PRESSROOM EQUIPMENT: Lines — DGM 440 44 page with 28 pages of Color (7 towers 4 mono units); Press Drive — Rex Roth; Folders — DGM 440 & Goss SSC; Pasters —Martin Reels & Stands — Martin; Control System — DGM with Perretta ink controls; Registration System — Quad Tec MAILROOM EQUIPMENT: Counter Stackers — 3-Id/660; Inserters & Stuffers — GMA/SLS 1000A; Tying Machines — 1/Bu, 2-MLN/2; Address Machine — 2-/El, KR/211; BUSINESS SOFTWARE: web apps CLASSIFIED EQUIPMENT: Hardware — IBM Compatable; PC's ATS; CLASSIFIED SOFTWARE: ATS DISPLAY EQUIPMENT: Hardware — 6-APP/Mac; Printers — Xerox 325 copier / printer; DISPLAY SOFTWAREAd Make-up Applications — Xpance; mICROSOFT; Layout Software — LAYOUT 8000 EDITORIAL EQUIPMENT: Hardware — PC/PC's; Printers — Xerox EDITORIAL SOFTWARE: ATS PRODUCTION EQUIPMENT: Hardware — 2 Agfa Advantage X PRODUCTION SOFTWARE: Presstelligence

JENNINGS

JENNINGS (LA) DAILY NEWS

238 N Market St, Jennings, La., 70546-5862, Jefferson Davis; gen tel (337) 824-3011; adv tel (337) 824-3011; ed tel (337) 824-3011; gen fax (337) 824-3019; adv fax (337) 824-3019; ed fax (337) 824-3019; gen/nat adv e-mail jdnpublisher@bellsouth.net; disp adv e-mail jdngm@jenningsdailynews.net; class adv e-mailjdngm@jenningsdailynews.net; ed e-mail jenningsnews@bellsouth.net; web site www.jenningsdailynews.net

Group: Fackelman Newspapers
Published: Tues, Wed, Thur, Fri, Sun
Weekday Frequency: e
Circulation: 4,816; 4,816(sun)
Last Audit: Sworn/Estimate/Non-Audited September 30, 2017
Advertising Rate (weekday/saturday): Open inch rate $11.00
Advertising Rate (sunday): Open inch rate $15.00
News services: AP. **Established:** 1896
Special Editions: Pride in Business (Apr); Football (Aug); Home Buyer's Guide (Every other month); Business Focus (Feb); Income Tax (Jan); Rice Harvest (Jul); Pride in Business (Jun); Spring Lawn & Garden (Mar); Pride in Business (May); Drug Awareness (Nov); Christmas Head
Syndicated Publications: Market Street Trader (Wed).
Pub .... Dona H. Smith
Circ. Mgr. .... Sandra Miller
News/Family/Living Ed .... Rebecca Chaisson
Gen. Mgr./Adv. Mgr. .... Paula Bonin
Prod. Mgr. .... Casey Smith
Asst. Ed. .... Sheila Smith
Bookkeeping .... Sandy Crochet
Composing Mgr. .... Brigette Boudreaux
Sports .... Kevin Bruchhaus
Market Information: TMC.
Mechanical Available: Offset; Black and 3 ROP colors; insert accepted - all; page cutoffs - 21 1/2.
Mechanical Specifications: Type page 13 x 21 1/2; E - 6 cols, 2 1/16, 1/8 between; A - 6 cols, 2 1/16, 1/8 between; C - 8 cols, 1 1/2, 1/8 between.
Areas Served: Jenninggs, Welsh, Roanoke, Lake Arthur, Elton, Evangeline & Iota, Fenton, Lacassine, Iowa, Mermentau
Delivery Method: Mail, Newsstand, Carrier, RacksEquipment & Software: PRESSROOM EQUIPMENT: Lines — 4-HI/Cotrell V-15A.; MAILROOM EQUIPMENT: Address Machine — IBM/486.; CLASSIFIED EQUIPMENT: Hardware — APP/Mac G4; Printers — HP/5100 Series, Okidata/Microline 320 Turbo; CLASSIFIED SOFTWARE: Baseview/Class Manager. DISPLAY EQUIPMENT: Printers — HP/5100 Series; Other Hardware — Mk DISPLAY SOFTWARELayout Software — APP/Mac G4. EDITORIAL EQUIPMENT: Hardware — APP/Mac G4/Minolta/Quick Scan Negative Scanner, Abaton/Flatbed Scanner; Printers — HP/5100 Series EDITORIAL SOFTWARE: QPS/QuarkXPress 4.0, Adobe/InDesign. PRODUCTION EQUIPMENT: Hardware — 1-Nu/Flip Top FT40, APP/Mac Pro Edit 600; Scanners — Minolta/Negative scanner.

LAFAYETTE

THE DAILY ADVERTISER

1100 Bertrand Dr, Lafayette, La., 70506-4110, Lafayette; gen tel (337) 289-6397; adv tel (337) 289-6397; ed tel (337) 289-6397; gen fax (337) 289-6443; adv fax (337) 289-6466; ed fax (337) 289-6443; gen/nat adv e-mail news@theadvertiser.com; disp adv e-mail arichards1@theadvertiser.com; class adv e-mailarichards1@theadvertiser.com; ed e-mail editorial@theadvertiser.com; web site www.theadvertiser.com

Group: Gannett
Published: Mon, Tues, Wed, Thur, Fri, Sat, Sun
Weekday Frequency: m
Saturday Frequency: m
Circulation: 22,460; 22,460(sat); 30,289(sun)
Last Audit: AAM March 31, 2015
Advertising Rate (weekday/saturday): Open inch rate $81.62
Advertising Rate (sunday): Open inch rate $92.56
Online Advertising Rate: Leaderboard $7.00 CPM; Large Rectangle $8.00 CPM; Half Page $14.00 CPM
News services: AP, NYT, GNS. **Established:** 1865
Special Editions: Homes by Design (Apr); Back-to-School/Fall Fashion (Aug); Launching a New Millenium (Dec); Mardi Gras Tab (Feb); Technology for the Millennium (Jul); 3rd Annual Cookbook (Jun); Bridal/Spring Fashion (Mar); Acadiana Yearbook (May); Holiday Giver's Guide (N
Special Weekly Sections: Wheels (S); TV Week (Sat); Church Page (Weekly).
Syndicated Publications: USA WEEKEND Magazine (S).Bill Decker
Digital Programming Ed. .... Caitlin Jacob
Exec. Ed./Rgl. Ed. .... Cindy McCurry-Ross
Copy Ed .... Diane Pantaleo
Asst. Sports Ed. .... Eric Narcisse
Online Ed. .... Heidi Venable
Opinion Page Ed. .... Judy Bastien
Metro Ed. .... Ken Stickney
Sports Ed. .... Kevin Foote
News Clerk .... Margurite Shipley
Regional Finance Director Jared Bartels
Pres./Pub. .... Judith Terzotis
News Dir./Content Strategist .... Kristin Askelson
Market Information: ADS; TMC; Zoned editions.
Mechanical Available: Offset; Black and 3 ROP colors; insert accepted - any; page cutoffs - 21 1/2.
Mechanical Specifications: Type page 11 1/2 x 20 1/2; E - 6 cols, 1 3/4, between; A - 6 cols, 1 5/6, between; C - 9 cols, 1 3/16, between.
Areas Served: Jefferson ParishEquipment & Software: PRESSROOM EQUIPMENT: Lines — MAN/Roland uriset 70 32 couples 1999; Folders — G/U 1320; Pasters —8-Cary/Pasters, 10Registration System — Duarte/Pin System. MAILROOM EQUIPMENT: Counter Stackers — 4/Compass 180; Inserters & Stuffers — GMA/SLS 1000; Tying Machines — 4-/Samuel; Wrapping Singles — Id; Control System — GMA; Address Machine — KAN; BUSINESS EQUIPMENT: PBS BUSINESS SOFTWARE: Unix CLASSIFIED EQUIPMENT: Hardware — APP/Mac; Printers — HP/Laser Jet 8100N; CLASSIFIED SOFTWARE: Baseview/Ad Manager Pro 2.0.6. DISPLAY EQUIPMENT: Hardware — APP/Mac G4; Printers — HP/LaserJet 5si/MX, Postscript; DISPLAY SOFTWAREAd Make-up Applications — QPS/QuarkXPress 4, Adobe/Photoshop 5.5, Adobe/Illustrator 8; Layout Software — APP/Mac. EDITORIAL EQUIPMENT: Hardware — APP/Mac; Printers — HP/LaserJet 5si/MX, Postscript, HP/DeskJet 750C Plus, V/3000-5300B, Pre Press/Panther Pro 46HS, 2-Konica/Jetsetter 6200 EDITORIAL SOFTWARE: QPS/QuarkXPress 3.32, Baseview/NewsEdit Pro IQUE. PRODUCTION EQUIPMENT: Hardware — Caere/OmniPage, LE/220-QT, 2-Colenta/Online Processors, 2-Glunz & Jensen; Cameras — COM/680C; Scanners — Kk/RFS 2035, 3-Nikon/Super Coolscan PRODUCTION SOFTWARE: QPS/QuarkXPress 4.11, Baseview/Drag X.

LAKE CHARLES

AMERICAN PRESS

4900 Highway 90 E, Lake Charles, La., 70615-4037, Calcasieu; gen tel (337) 433-3000; adv tel (337) 494-4097; ed tel (337) 494-4080; gen fax (337) 494-4013; adv fax (337) 494-4008; ed fax (337) 494-4070; gen/nat adv e-mail cstevenson@americanpress.com; disp adv e-mail ayellott@americanpress.com.; class adv e-mailayellott@americanpress.com.; ed e-mail news@americanpress.com; web site www.americanpress.com

Group: Shearman Corporation
Published: Mon, Tues, Wed, Thur, Fri, Sat, Sun
Weekday Frequency: m
Saturday Frequency: m
Circulation: 22,426; 22,426(sat); 26,269(sun)
Last Audit: AAM December 31, 2016
Advertising Rate (weekday/saturday): Open inch rate $26.25
Advertising Rate (sunday): Open inch rate $28.05
Online Advertising Rate: Button $4.00 CPM; Big Box $7.00 CPM
News services: AP. **Established:** 1895
Own Printing Facility?: Yes
Commercial Printers?: Yes
Special Editions: Home Improvement (Apr); Back-to-School (Aug); Brides (Feb); Mardi Gras (Jan); Contraband Days (May); Christmas Gift Guide (Nov); Football (Sept).
Special Weekly Sections: Marquee (Fri); Face to Face (Mon); Face to Face (Tues).
Syndicated Publications: Parade (S); Focus (Sat).
Digital Platform - Mobile: Apple, Android, Windows
Digital Platform - Tablet: Apple iOS, Android, Windows 7, Blackberry Tablet OS, Kindle, Nook, Kindle Fire
Sports Ed. .... Scooter Hobbs
Adv. Dir. .... Ava Yellott
National Desk/Sr. Acct. Exec. .... Karen Cole
Preprints/Acct. Exec. .... Jessika Sarver
Exec. Ed. .... Crystal Stevenson
Copy Ed. .... Andrew Perzo
Living Ed. .... Pamela Seal
Managing Ed. .... Jim Gazzolo
Market Information: TMC
Mechanical Available: Offset; Black and 3 ROP colors; insert accepted; page cutoffs - 22 3/4.
Mechanical Specifications: Type page 13 x 22; E - 6 cols, 2 1/16, 1/8 between; A - 6 cols, 2 1/16, 1/8 between; C - 10 cols, 1 1/6, 1/6 between.
Areas Served: 70601-70663, Allen-Beauregard-Calcasieu-Cameron-Jeff Davis
Delivery Method: Mail, Newsstand, Carrier, RacksEquipment & Software: PRESSROOM EQUIPMENT: Lines — 8-HI/1660 1982; Pasters —7-MEG/2-ARM 1982. MAILROOM EQUIPMENT: Counter Stackers — 3-QWI/300; Inserters & Stuffers — 2-S/72P; Tying Machines — 3/Dynaric; Address Machine — 1-/Ch; BUSINESS EQUIPMENT: Gateway, APP/Mac BUSINESS SOFTWARE: CJ, Baseview, Great Plains Dynamics CLASSIFIED EQUIPMENT: Hardware — APP/Mac; CLASSIFIED SOFTWARE: Baseview. DISPLAY EQUIPMENT: Hardware — APP/Mac; DISPLAY SOFTWARELayout Software — Baseview/Ad Manager Pro. EDITORIAL EQUIPMENT: Hardware — Tandem, APP/Mac EDITORIAL SOFTWARE: SII, QPS/QuarkXPress. PRODUCTION EQUIPMENT: Hardware — V, Sharp/600; Cameras — C/Spartan III; Scanners — HP, APP/Mac, Sharp, Lf/Leafscan 35 PRODUCTION SOFTWARE: QPS/QuarkXPress.

MINDEN

MINDEN PRESS HERALD

203 Gleason St, Minden, La., 71055-3455, Webster; gen tel (318) 377-1866; adv tel (318) 377-1866; ed tel (318) 377-1866; gen fax (318) 377-1895; adv fax (318) 377-1895; ed fax (318) 377-1895; gen/nat adv e-mail advertising@press-herald.com; disp adv e-mail advertising@press-herald.com; class adv e-mailclassifieds@press-herald.com; ed e-mail bruce@press-herald.com; web site www.press-herald.com
- 68,000(views) 31,000(visitors)

Group: Specht Newspapers, Inc.
Published: Mon, Tues, Wed, Thur, Fri
Weekday Frequency: e
Circulation: 5,150
Last Audit: Sworn/Estimate/Non-Audited December 19, 2017
Advertising Rate (weekday/saturday): Open inch rate $8.00
Online Advertising Rate: Button $300.00/month; Banner $400.00/month
News services: AP. **Established:** 1895
Own Printing Facility?: Yes
Commercial Printers?: Yes
Special Editions: Car Care (Fall); Car Care (Spring). Profile (February)
Ed. .... Bruce Franklin
Adv. Dir. .... Telina Worley
Adv. Exec. .... Curtis Mays
Sports Writer .... Blake Branch

Mechanical Available: Offset; 4-color process, black; insert accepted; page cutoffs - 21.
Mechanical Specifications: Type page 13 1/16 x 21; E - 6 cols, 2 1/16, 1/8 between; A - 6 cols, 2 1/16, 1/8 between; C - 9 cols, 1 3/8, 1/8 between.
Areas Served: Minden and Webster Parish
Delivery Method: Mail, Newsstand, Carrier, RacksEquipment & Software: PRESSROOM EQUIPMENT: Lines — 6-WPC/Leader; 2 WPC Quad Stack MAILROOM EQUIPMENT: Tying Machines — 1-Felins/Pack Tyer; Address Machine — Wm.; BUSINESS EQUIPMENT: IBM/Sys 36 PC LINV CLASSIFIED EQUIPMENT: Hardware — PC; CLASSIFIED SOFTWARE: BMF. DISPLAY EQUIPMENT: Hardware — APP/Mac.; EDITORIAL EQUIPMENT: Hardware — APP/Mac; Printers — HP/4MV EDITORIAL SOFTWARE: QPS 3.3. PRODUCTION EQUIPMENT: Hardware — 1-Nu/Flip Top; Cameras — 1-Argyle/23-G23.

MONROE

THE NEWS-STAR

411 N 4th St, Monroe, La., 71201-6743, Ouachita; gen tel (318) 322-5161; adv tel (318) 322-5161; ed tel (318) 322-5161; gen fax (318) 362-0225; adv fax (318) 362-0225; ed fax (318) 362-0225; gen/nat adv e-mail dpetty@monroe.gannett.com; disp adv e-mail christina.pierce@monroe.gannett.com; class adv e-mailchristina.pierce@monroe.gannett.com; ed e-mail kspurlock@monroe.gannett.com; web site www.thenewsstar.com
Group: Gannett
Published: Mon, Tues, Wed, Thur, Fri, Sat, Sun
Weekday Frequency: m
Saturday Frequency: m
Circulation: 16,256; 15,815(sat); 19,466(sun)
Last Audit: AAM December 31, 2016
Advertising Rate (weekday/saturday): Open inch rate $57.55 (Local); $81.48 (National)
Advertising Rate (sunday): Open inch rate $68.38 (Local); $97.39 (National)
Online Advertising Rate: Small Rectangle $7.00; Medium Rectangle $8.00
News services: AP, GNS, MCT, LAT-WP. **Established:** 1890
Special Weekly Sections: Auto (Fri); Travel (S); Best Food Edition (Wed).
Syndicated Publications: This Week (Fri); USA WEEKEND Magazine (S).
Pres./Pub. .... David B. Petty
Adv. Dir. .... Brad Lackey
Gen. Sales Mgr. .... Debbie Coplen
Mng. Ed. .... Ken Stickney
Asst. Mng. Ed., Local .... Eleanor Rushing
Asst. Mng. Ed., Online/Sports .... Nick Delso
Accent Ed. .... Hope Young
Multimedia Ed. .... Fred Phillips
News Ed. .... Mark Henderson
Photography Ed. .... Margaret Croft
Prodn. Dir. .... Doug Nobles
Exec. Ed. .... Kathy Spurlock
Adv. Sales Leader .... Mike Romaguera
Multi-media Acc. Exec. .... Chad Eymard
Classified Inside Sales .... Antoinette Holbrook
Market Information: ADS; TMC; Zoned editions.
Mechanical Available: Letterpress; Black and 3 ROP colors; insert accepted; page cutoffs - 22 1/2.
Mechanical Specifications: Type page 13 1/12 x 22 1/2; E - 6 cols, 2, 1/6 between; A - 6 cols, 2, 1/6 between; C - 9 cols, 1 7/18, 1/2 between.
Areas Served: Ouachita Parish
Delivery Method: Mail, Newsstand, Carrier, RacksEquipment & Software: PRESSROOM EQUIPMENT: Lines — 8-G/Mark I Letterpress 2138 Double Width (3 half-deck); Folders — 1-G/Double; Control System — 8-Fin/3122 60hp DC drives; Registration System — WL/Magnetic Saddles. MAILROOM EQUIPMENT: Counter Stackers — 2-HL/HT, 1-Id/NS440; Inserters & Stuffers — 1-HI/NP 624; Tying Machines — MLN; Wrapping Singles — Id.; BUSINESS EQUIPMENT: IBM/AS-400 F10 BUSINESS SOFTWARE: IBM/AS-400 F10 CLASSIFIED EQUIPMENT: Hardware — PC; 14-PC; Printers — HP/LaserJet 8000; CLASSIFIED SOFTWARE: APT. DISPLAY EQUIPMENT: Hardware — 2-APP/Mac Quadra 840 AV, 2-APP/Mac Quadra 610, 1-APP/Mac Quadra 950 fileserver; Printers — AU/APS-6-84-ACS, AU/APS-1560 LaserPrinter; DISPLAY SOFTWARELayout Software — COM. EDITORIAL EQUIPMENT: Hardware — PC/42-PC, 6-APP/Mac; Printers — 1-AU/LZR-1200 Laser Printer, 1-HP/LaserJet 8000 EDITORIAL SOFTWARE: APT. PRODUCTION EQUIPMENT: Hardware — AU/3850 Sierra with LE Processor, 2-LE/APS-36, 2-P/EL26, 1-C/P66F; Cameras — 1-C/Spartan III, 1-C/Newspager; Scanners — 1-ECR/Autokon PRODUCTION SOFTWARE: QPS/QuarkXPress 4.03, QPS/QuarkXPress 3.32.

MORGAN CITY

THE DAILY REVIEW

1014 Front St, Morgan City, La., 70380-3226, Saint Mary; gen tel (985) 384-8370; adv tel (985) 384-8370; ed tel (985) 384-8370; gen fax (985) 384-4255; adv fax (985) 384-4255; ed fax (985) 384-4255; gen/nat adv e-mail news@daily-review.com; disp adv e-mail advertising@daily-review.com; class adv e-mailclassified@daily-review.com; ed e-mail news@daily-review.com; web site http://www.banner-tribune.com; web site 2 stmarynow.com
Group: LSN Publishing Company LLC Morgan City Newspapers LLC
Published: Mon, Tues, Wed, Thur, Fri
Weekday Frequency: e
Circulation: 5,946
Last Audit: Sworn/Estimate/Non-Audited September 30, 2017
Advertising Rate (weekday/saturday): Open inch rate $8.98
Online Advertising Rate: Open Rate $10.00 CPM/30 Day $350/ 6 month $315 per month.
News services: AP. **Established:** 1872
Special Editions: Progress (Apr); Energy Coastal (Dec); Chamber of Commerce (Jan); Dixie Youth-Little League Baseball (Jul); Drug Free Tab (Oct); Shrimp & Petroleum Festival-Oil/Seafood (Sept).
Special Weekly Sections: Real Estate (Fri).
Pub. .... Allan Von Werder
Webmaster .... Tom Coleman
Managing Ed. .... Bill Decker
Market Information: TMC.
Mechanical Available: Offset; Black and 3 ROP colors; insert accepted - 8 1/2 x 11 card or single sheet; page cutoffs - 22 15/16.
Mechanical Specifications: Type page 13 x 21 1/2; E - 6 cols, 2 1/16, 1/8 between; A - 6 cols, 2 1/16, 1/8 between; C - 8 cols, 1 1/2, 1/8 between.
Areas Served: Morgan City/St. Mary/70380-70381Equipment & Software: PRESSROOM EQUIPMENT: Lines — 12-G; Folders — 1, 1-G/Urbanite.; BUSINESS EQUIPMENT: DEC CLASSIFIED EQUIPMENT: Hardware — Microsoft/Windows NT 4; Printers — NewGen/Laser PS-840E, Dupont, ECR/Knock Imagesetter; CLASSIFIED SOFTWARE: APT/ACT. DISPLAY EQUIPMENT: Other Hardware — 2-Gateway/Pentium 2, APT. EDITORIAL EQUIPMENT: Hardware — Microsoft/Windows NT 4/Xante; Printers — NewGen/Laser PS 840E, Dupont, ECR/Knock Out Imagesetter EDITORIAL SOFTWARE: APT/ACT. PRODUCTION EQUIPMENT: Hardware — 3-Nu, 2-NewGen/Turbo PS-840E; Cameras — Acti/Tech; Scanners — Panasonic, Microtek.

NEW IBERIA

THE DAILY IBERIAN

926 E Main St, New Iberia, La., 70560-3866, Iberia; gen tel (333) 365-6773; adv tel (337) 365-6773; ed tel (337) 365-6773; gen fax (337) 367-9640; adv fax (337) 367-9640; ed fax (337) 367-9640; gen/nat adv e-mail dailyiberian@cox.net; disp adv e-mail iberianads@cox.net; class adv e-maildiclass@cox.net; ed e-mail dailyiberian@cox.net; web site www.iberianet.com
Group: Wick Communications
Published: Mon, Tues, Wed, Thur, Fri, Sun
Weekday Frequency: e
Circulation: 7,184; 7,758(sun)
Last Audit: VAC June 30, 2017
Advertising Rate (weekday/saturday): Open inch rate $16.95 (Local); $19.94 (National)
Advertising Rate (sunday): Open inch rate $17.70 (Local); $20.69 (National)
Online Advertising Rate: Leaderboard, Button, Rectangle $230.00/month
News services: AP. **Established:** 1893
Special Editions: HS Graduation (Apr); Estate Planning (Aug); Gift Guide (Dec); Newcomer's Guide (Feb); Bridal (Jan); Focus on Women (Jul); Father's Day (Jun); Home & Garden (Mar); Mother's Day (May); Gift Guide (Nov); Farm (Oct); Cookbook (Sept).
Special Weekly Sections: Church Page (Fri); Business (S); Business News (Thur); Health News (Tues); Food (Wed).
Syndicated Publications: TV Listings (Fri); USA WEEKEND Magazine (S).
Admin. Secretary .... Beth Renard
Bus. Mgr. .... Mandy Seneca
Bus. Asst. .... Jackie Babineaux
Adv. Dir. .... Bill Heirtzler
Ed. .... Jeff Zeringue
Sports Ed. .... Chris Landry
Circ. Mgr. .... JP Poirier
District Mgr. .... Justin Bourque
Prodn. Mgr. .... Jerry Sexton
Pub. .... Christina Pierce
Sr. News. Ed./Outdoor Ed. .... Don Shoopman
Classified Adv. Supv. .... Delores Houston
Market Information: ADS; TMC; Zoned editions.
Mechanical Available: Offset; Black and 3 ROP colors; insert accepted; page cutoffs - 22 3/4.
Mechanical Specifications: Type page 11 5/8 x 21 1/2; E - 6 cols, 1 3/4, 3/16 between; A - 6 cols, 1 3/4, 3/16 between; C - 9 cols, 1 5/16, between.
Areas Served: Iberia Parish
Delivery Method: Mail, NewsstandEquipment & Software: PRESSROOM EQUIPMENT: Lines — 5-G/Urbanite; Folders — G/Urbanite U521.; MAILROOM EQUIPMENT: Counter Stackers — MRS; Tying Machines — MLN.; BUSINESS EQUIPMENT: Vision Data CLASSIFIED EQUIPMENT: Hardware — Baseview, 1-APP/Mac G3, 2-APP/Power Mac; APP/Mac LaserWriter NTF; Printers — Xante/Accel-A-Writer 8200, Okidata/Pacemark 3410; CLASSIFIED SOFTWARE: Baseview. DISPLAY EQUIPMENT: Hardware — APP/Mac G4, 3-APP/Mac G3 300, Motorola/3000-200; Printers — APP/Mac, Xante/8300; Other Hardware — Umax/Astra Scanner DISPLAY SOFTWAREAd Make-up Applications — Aldus/PageMaker 5.0, Multi-Ad/Creator 4.0, Lotus, QPS/QuarkXPress 4.04, Adobe/Photoshop 3.0, Adobe/Photoshop 4.0; EDITORIAL EQUIPMENT: Hardware — APP/Mac, APP/Mac G4/2-Nikon/Scanner, 2-AG/Flat Bed Scanner; Printers — Xante/8300-1200 DPI, ECR/8600 Imagesetter EDITORIAL SOFTWARE: AppleShare 6.3, QPS/QuarkXPress 4.01, Microsoft/Word 6.0. PRODUCTION EQUIPMENT: Hardware — Caere/OmniPage 2.1, APP/Mac LaserWriter NT, APP/Mac LaserWriter NTX, APP/Mac LaserWriter, WDS, APP/Mac Asante, 2-Xante/8300, 1-ECR/Imagesetter; Cameras — Acti/183; Scanners — APP/Mac Scanner PRODUCTION SOFTWARE: QPS/QuarkXPress 4.04.

OPELOUSAS

DAILY WORLD

5367 I 49 S Service Rd, Opelousas, La., 70570-0743, Saint Landry; gen tel (337) 942-4971; adv tel (337) 942-4971; ed tel (337) 942-4971; gen fax (337) 943-7067; adv fax (337) 943-7067; ed fax (337) 943-7067; gen/nat adv e-mail cmcross@gannett.com; disp adv e-mail scarr2@mediaacadien.com; class adv e-mailscarr2@mediaacadien.com; ed e-mail cmcross@gannett.com; web site www.dailyworld.com
Group: Gannett
Published: Mon, Tues, Wed, Thur, Fri, Sat, Sun
Weekday Frequency: m
Saturday Frequency: m
Circulation: 4,096; 57(sat); 5,119(sun)
Last Audit: AAM December 31, 2015
Advertising Rate (weekday/saturday): Open inch rate $49.00
Advertising Rate (sunday): Open inch rate $57.82
Online Advertising Rate: Leaderboard $7.00 CPM; Large Rectangle $8.00 CPM; Half Page $14.00 CPM
News services: AP. **Established:** 1939
Own Printing Facility?: Yes
Commercial Printers?: Yes
Special Editions: Brides (Apr); Football Round-up (Aug); Progress (Feb); Woman's World (Jul); Father's Day (Jun); Home Improvement (Mar); Real Estate Magazine (Monthly); Fall Car Care (Nov); Cooking (Oct).
Special Weekly Sections: Church Page (Fri); Farm Page (Mon); Business (S); Acadiana TV Listings (Thur); Medical Page (Tues); Food Page (Wed).
Syndicated Publications: USA WEEKEND Magazine (S).
Pres./Pub. .... Judi Terzotis
Adv. Sales Dir. .... Scott Carr
Circ. Distribution Dir. .... Jim Keeble
Home Delivery Mgr. .... Dean Taylor
City Ed. .... Cheryl Devall
Photographer .... Freddie Herpin
Exec. Ed. .... Cindy McCurry-Ross
Market Information: TMC; Zoned editions.
Mechanical Available: Offset; Black and 3 ROP colors; insert accepted; page cutoffs - 23 1/2.
Mechanical Specifications: Type page 13 x 21 1/2; E - 6 cols, 2 1/16, 3/16 between; A - 6 cols, 2 1/16, 3/16 between; C - 9 cols, 1 3/8, 1/8 between.
Areas Served: Lafayette
Delivery Method: Mail, Newsstand, Carrier, RacksEquipment & Software: PRESSROOM EQUIPMENT: Lines — 8-G/Community 1993; MAILROOM EQUIPMENT: Counter Stackers — BG/Count-O-Veyor; Inserters & Stuffers — KAN/4into1; Tying Machines — 1/Bu, 1-/Power Strap; Address Machine — 1-/Ch.; BUSINESS EQUIPMENT: DPT/8200, IBM/3600, IBM/PC-Model 50, IBM/PC-Model 25 CLASSIFIED EQUIPMENT: Hardware — 1-AT/5000; 4-AT, IBM.; DISPLAY EQUIPMENT: Other Hardware — 2-Softsetter/ATE GED3 DISPLAY SOFTWARELayout Software — 1-AT. EDITORIAL EQUIPMENT: Hardware — 2-AT/5000, IBM, APP/Power Mac/21-AT EDITORIAL SOFTWARE: Baseview 2.1. PRODUCTION EQUIPMENT: Hardware — Pre Press/Panther Pro, 2-Pre Press/Panther Plus, 1-Nu/52; Cameras — 1-C/Spartan II PRODUCTION SOFTWARE: Baseview 2.1, QPS/QuarkXPress.

RUSTON

RUSTON (LA) DAILY LEADER

212 W Park Ave, Ruston, La., 71270-4314, Lincoln; gen tel (318) 255-4353; adv tel (318) 255-4353; ed tel (318) 255-4353; gen fax (318) 255-4006; adv fax (318) 255-4006; ed fax (318) 255-4006; gen/nat adv e-mail rick@rustonleader.com; disp adv e-mail flint@rustonleader.com; class adv e-mailflint@rustonleader.com; ed e-mail buddy@rustonleader.com; web site www.rustonleader.com - 928,000(views) 573,460(visitors)
Group: Fackelman Newspapers
Published: Mon, Tues, Wed, Thur, Fri, Sun
Weekday Frequency: e
Circulation: 4,834; 5,268(sun)
Last Audit: Sworn/Estimate/Non-Audited September 30, 2017
Advertising Rate (weekday/saturday): Daily Open inch rate $11.00
Advertising Rate (sunday): Daily Open inch rate $11.75
Online Advertising Rate: Starts at $150.00/month
News services: AP. **Established:** 1894
Own Printing Facility?: Yes
Commercial Printers?: Yes
Special Editions: Chamber Connection, Home Guide, Living Well, Progress Edition, Ruston USA (Jan); Business Card Directory, Chamber Connection, Medical Directory, Spring Bride (Feb); Home Guide, Redi Reference (Mar); Pride Edition, Living Well (April); Graduation Edition (May); Peach Festival (June); Back to School Edition (Jul);

Gridiron Glory, Dawtown (Aug); North Louisiana Outdoors (Sept); Chicken Festival, Ducks Unlimited, Tech Homecoming (Oct); Veterans, Thanksgiging, Downtown Open House (Nov); Last Minute Santa, Seasons Greetings, Holiday Shopping (Dec.)
Syndicated Publications: Parade (S), Living Well (S) quarterly
Digital Platform - Mobile: Apple
Digital Platform - Tablet: Apple iOS
Adv. Mgr. .... Jeanie McCartney
Pub./Ed. .... Rick Hohlt
Sports Ed. .... O.K. Davis
Gen. Mgr. .... Cody Richard
Asst. Adv. Mgr. .... Adam Hohlt
Circ. Mgr. .... Caskey Schexnyder
News Ed. .... Elizabeth DeGrie
Composing Mgr. .... Will Avery
Adv. Sales Exec. .... Flint Boyce
Office Mgr. .... Tina Richard
Mechanical Available: Offset; Black and 3 ROP colors; insert accepted; page cutoffs - 21 1/2.
Mechanical Specifications: Type page 10.5 x 21 1/2; E - 6 cols, 1.792", 1/8 between.
Areas Served: 71270, 71222, 71241, 71260, 71201, 71277, 71280, 71225, 71235, Lincoln Parish Police Jury, Lincoln Parish School Board, Lincoln Parish Sherriff's office and the municipalities of Ruston, Choudrant, Grambling, Simsboro and Vienna.
Delivery Method: Mail, Newsstand, Carrier, RacksEquipment & Software: PRESSROOM EQUIPMENT: Lines — 7 Unit Goss Community; Registration System — CTP MAILROOM EQUIPMENT: Tying Machines — 2/Bu; Address Machine — 1-/Am.; BUSINESS EQUIPMENT: 1-RSK/80 CLASSIFIED EQUIPMENT: Hardware — APP/Mac; CLASSIFIED SOFTWARE: Baseview/Class Manager. DISPLAY EQUIPMENT: Hardware — APP/ Mac; DISPLAY SOFTWAREAd Make-up Applications — Aldus/PageMaker; Layout Software — APP/Mac SE, APP/Mac Plus. EDITORIAL EQUIPMENT: Hardware — APP/ Mac EDITORIAL SOFTWARE: InDesign PRODUCTION EQUIPMENT: Hardware — 1-Nat; Cameras — 1-AG; Scanners — Abaton/Scanner.

SHREVEPORT

THE TIMES

401 Market St, Ste 1600, Shreveport, La., 71101-6911, Caddo; gen tel (318) 459-3200; adv tel (318) 459-3200; ed tel (318) 459-3233; gen fax (318) 459-3301; adv fax (318) 459-3301; ed fax (318) 459-3301; gen/nat adv e-mail Richard.Rose@shreveporttimes.com; disp adv e-mail Richard.Rose@shreveporttimes.com; class adv e-mailRichard.Rose@shreveporttimes.com; ed e-mail aenglish@gannett.com; web site www.shreveporttimes.com
- 4,500,000(views) 350,000(visitors)
Group: Gannett
Published: Mon, Tues, Wed, Thur, Fri, Sat, Sun
Weekday Frequency: m
Saturday Frequency: m
Circulation: 27,186; 27,186(sat); 35,017(sun)
Last Audit: AAM December 31, 2016
Advertising Rate (weekday/saturday): Open inch rate $140.55
Online Advertising Rate: ROS Rectangle $8.00 CPM
News services: AP, GNS. **Established:** 1872
Own Printing Facility?: Yes
Commercial Printers?: Yes
Special Editions: Independence Bowl (Dec); Home Products Show (Feb); Outlook (Jan); Parade of Homes (Jun); Red River Revel (Sept).
Special Weekly Sections: Preview (Entertainment) (Fri); Voices (W); Automotive (Sat); Food (Wed).
Syndicated Publications: USA WEEKEND Magazine (S).
Adv. Dir. .... Anton Kaufer
Territory Sales Mgr. .... Rick Rose
Circ. Dir. .... Kevin Welsh
Features Content Strategist .... Michele Marcotte
Sports Planning Ed. .... Scott Ferrell
Pres./Pub. .... Alan English
Exec. Ed. .... Jeff Gauger
Digital Sales Mgr. .... Keyle Cavalier
News Planning Ed. .... Ricky Duke
Market Information: TMC; Zoned editions.
Mechanical Available: Offset; Black and 3 ROP colors; insert accepted; page cutoffs - 18.5".
Mechanical Specifications: Type page 10 x 17.25; E - 6 cols, 1.54", .17" between; A - 6 cols, 1.54", .17" between; C - 6 cols, 1.54", .16" between.
Areas Served: 71001, 71003, 71006, 71007, 71009, 71018, 71019, 71023, 71024, 71027, 71028, 71030, 71032, 71033, 71037, 71038, 71039, 71040, 71044, 71047, 71049, 71051, 71052, 71055, 71060, 71061, 71063, 71064, 71065, 71067, 71068, 71071, 71072, 71073, 71075, 71078, 71082, 71101, 71103, 71104, 71105, 71106, 71107, 71108, 71109, 71110, 71111, 71112, 71115, 71118, 71119, 71129, 71251, 71270, 71411, 71419, 71429, 71449, 71457, 75633, 75639, 75670, 75672, 75692
Delivery Method: Mail, Newsstand, Carrier, RacksEquipment & Software: PRESSROOM EQUIPMENT: Lines — 4 towers Wifag OF790 (double width) 1991; Folders — 2 Wifag 5:3.; Pasters —6 Wifag w-arm auto Pasters MAILROOM EQUIPMENT: Counter Stackers — 2/quipp packman; 2/Gammerler; 1/Quipp 400; Inserters & Stuffers — 1/G 2299; Tying Machines — 3/Dynaric.; Control System — 1/Miracom ; Address Machine — 1/ Videojet; BUSINESS SOFTWARE: Microsoft/ Office 2000 CLASSIFIED EQUIPMENT: Hardware — PC-based; Printers - PC Desktop; CLASSIFIED SOFTWARE: Mactive. DISPLAY EQUIPMENT: Hardware — PC; DISPLAY SOFTWARELayout Software — CS5. EDITORIAL EQUIPMENT: Hardware — SII/CLX 840; Printers — Tandem/5212, APP/Mac LaserWriter II NT EDITORIAL SOFTWARE: SII/Guardian 90. PRODUCTION EQUIPMENT: Hardware — AU/APS6-108S, P/OL260; Scanners — Lf/ Leafscan 35, AG, AG/Arcus PRODUCTION SOFTWARE: QPS/QuarkXPress 3.31.

THIBODAUX

DAILY COMET

104 Hickory St, Thibodaux, La., 70301-2008, Lafourche; gen tel (985) 448-7600; adv tel (985) 857-2291; ed tel (985) 448-7612; gen fax (985) 857-2233; adv fax (985) 857-2273; gen/nat adv e-mail marian.long@houmatoday.com; disp adv e-mail marian.long@dailycomet.com; class adv e-mailpeyvand.maghsoud@houmatoday.com; ed e-mail news@dailycomet.com; web site www.dailycomet.com
- 1,526,000(views) 176,000(visitors)
Group: New Media Investment Group
Published: Mon, Tues, Wed, Thur, Fri
Weekday Frequency: e
Saturday Frequency: e
Circulation: 6,734
Last Audit: AAM December 31, 2015
Advertising Rate (weekday/saturday): Daily Open inch rate $23.49; Wed $28.48
Advertising Rate (sunday): Sunday Rate $26.38
Online Advertising Rate: call for rates
News services: AP, NYT. **Established:** 1889
Own Printing Facility?: No
Commercial Printers?: Yes
Special Editions: Living Here (Jan); Graduation (May); Christmas Opening (Nov); Football (Aug);Oil & Gas Section
Special Weekly Sections: Religion Page (Fri); Bridal Announcements (Mon); Mes Amis (Thur); Health Page (Tues); Best Food Day (Wed).
Syndicated Publications: USA WEEKEND Magazine (Fri); Athlon Sports (Th)
Proprietary Publications: Big Fun on the Bayou (Fri)
Digital Platform - Mobile: Apple, Android, Blackberry
Finance Dir. .... Darlene Rodrigue
Exec. Ed. .... Keith Magill
City Ed. .... Mike Hill
Op. Ed. .... Mike Gorman
Pub. .... Lee Bachlet
Circ. Clerk .... Karen Robichaux
Adv. Dir. .... Marian Long
Circ. Mgr. .... Lawrence Knoblock
Sports Writer .... Teddy Renois
District Mgr. .... Gloria Lebouef
Digital Sales .... Alysa Hebert
Acct. .... Mindy Thibodaux
Market Information: TMC.
Mechanical Available: Offset; Black and 3 ROP colors; insert accepted; page cutoffs - 22.75"
Mechanical Specifications: Type page 11" x 22"; E - 6 cols, 1.708", 11 pts. between; A - 6 cols, 1.708", 11 pts. between; C - 9 cols, 1.126", 11 pts. between.
Areas Served: 70301, 70359, 70394, 70374, 70354, 70357, 70359, 70390, 70372, 70090, 70086,70372
Delivery Method: Mail, Newsstand, Carrier, RacksEquipment & Software: PRESSROOM EQUIPMENT: DGM 440 PRESSROOM SOFTWARE: Paretta Ink Controls, Quad-Tech Registration MAILROOM EQUIPMENT: SLS 2000 BUSINESS SOFTWARE: PBS CLASSIFIED SOFTWARE: ATS DISPLAY SOFTWAREAd Make-up Applications — Xpance EDITORIAL SOFTWARE: ATS PRODUCTION SOFTWARE: ATS, Prestiligence Workflow IT SOFTWARE:SQL CIRCULATION SOFTWARPBS
Note: The Thibodaux Daily Comet (e) has a combination rate of $45.05 with the Houma Courier (eS). Individual newspaper rates not made available.

MAINE

AUGUSTA

KENNEBEC JOURNAL

36 Anthony Ave Ste 101, Suite 101, Augusta, Maine, 04330-7891, Kennebec; gen tel (207) 623-3811; adv tel (207) 623-3811; ed tel (207) 623-3811; gen fax 207-623-2220; adv fax (207) 623-0614; ed fax (207) 623-2220; gen/nat adv e-mail kjcommunity@mainetoday.com; disp adv e-mail kjcommunity@mainetoday.com; class adv e-mailCMarcoux@mainetoday.com; ed e-mail smonroe@mainetoday.com; web site www.centralmaine.com
243,450(visitors)
Group: Maine Today Media Inc.
Published: Mon, Tues, Wed, Thur, Fri, Sat, Sun
Weekday Frequency: m
Saturday Frequency: m
Circulation: 7,293; 7,293(sat); 7,977(sun)
Last Audit: AAM March 31, 2017
Advertising Rate (weekday/saturday): Open inch rate $45.05
Advertising Rate (sunday): Open inch rate $47.78
Online Advertising Rate: Pencil with pushdown $675.00/day; Homepage Top Roadblock $1300.00/day; Homepage Takeovers $1650.00/day
News services: AP, NYT, LAT-WP, SHNS. **Established:** 1825
Own Printing Facility?: Yes
Commercial Printers?: Yes
Special Editions: Spring Scouting (Apr); College Bound (Aug); Winter Scouting (Dec); Baby Parade (Feb); Maine Manufacturing Housing (Jan); Old Hallowell Days (Jul); Winslow 4th of July (Jun); Medical Journal (Mar); Brides & Grooms (May); Winter in Maine (Nov); Old Hallowel
Special Weekly Sections: What's Happening (entertainment) (Fri); What's on TV (S).
Syndicated Publications: USA WEEKEND Magazine (S).
Digital Platform - Mobile: Apple, Android
Digital Platform - Tablet: Apple iOS, Android
Asst. Sports Ed. .... Scott Monroe
News Ed. .... Maureen Milliken
City Ed. .... Susan Cover
Editorial Page Ed. .... Ben Bragdon
Exec. Sports Ed. .... Bill Stewart
Community Ed. .... Tedda Henry
Sports/ Copy Ed. .... Travis Lazarczyk
Photographer .... Andy Molloy
Market Information: Split run; TMC.
Mechanical Available: Offset; Black and 3 ROP colors; insert accepted - product samples; page cutoffs - 22 3/4.
Mechanical Specifications: Type page 13 x 21 1/2; E - 6 cols, 2 1/16, 1/8 between; A - 6 cols, 2 1/16, 1/8 between; C - 9 cols, 1 3/8, 1/16 between.
Areas Served: Kennebec County
Delivery Method: Mail, Newsstand, Carrier, RacksEquipment & Software: PRESSROOM EQUIPMENT: Lines — 14-G/Urbanite; 2-D&R/(on Press Glue Sys); Press Drive — 4-HP/100; Folders — 2-G/Urbanite, 2-G/ Quarterfolder; Pasters —6-KTI/Splicers. MAILROOM EQUIPMENT: Counter Stackers — 1-Gammerler/STC 70, 1-HL/ Monitor, 1-HI/RS25, 2-Powerstrap/PSN-6C, 2-TMSI/Compass180; Inserters & Stuffers — 1-HI/1372; Tying Machines — 2-It/SX 500, 1-Dynarc/NP2; Control System — HI/ Stacker Program 009; Address Machine — Addressing mac; BUSINESS EQUIPMENT: IBM/4331 II, DEC/VAX 3100, Dell/Pentium BUSINESS SOFTWARE: Microsoft/ Excel, Microsoft/Word, CJ CLASSIFIED EQUIPMENT: Hardware — Dell/Pentium PCs; Printers — HP/LaserPrinter; CLASSIFIED SOFTWARE: SCS. DISPLAY EQUIPMENT: Hardware — SCS, APP/ Power Macs; Printers — Xante/8300; Other Hardware — APP/Mac PowerBook, Howtek, Scan/Master DISPLAY SOFTWAREAd Make-up Applications — Multi-Ad/Creator, QPS/ QuarkXPress 3.31; Layout Software — SCS/ Layout 8000. EDITORIAL EQUIPMENT: Hardware — SCS, Dell/Pentium PCs; Printers — HP/LaserPrinter, Xante/8300 EDITORIAL SOFTWARE: SCS. PRODUCTION EQUIPMENT: Hardware — 2-AG/Avantra 25, 2-Nu/FT40; Cameras — 1-C/Spartan II, 2-AG/RPS; Scanners — Howtek, Scan/ Master 2500 PRODUCTION SOFTWARE: QPS/QuarkXPress 3.31, SCS.
Note: The Augusta Kennebec Journal (mS) has a combination rate of $56.86 (m-mon to sat) and $59.65 (S) with the Waterville Morning Sentinel (mS). Individual newspaper rates not made available.

BANGOR

BANGOR DAILY NEWS

1 Merchants Plz Ste 1, Suite 1, Bangor, Maine, 04401-8302, Penobscot; gen tel (207) 990-8000; adv tel (207) 990-8020; ed tel (207) 990-8175; gen fax (207) 941-9476; adv fax (207) 941-0885; ed fax (207) 941-9476; gen/nat adv e-mail advertising@bangordailynews.net; disp adv e-mail aconstantine@bangordailynews.com; class adv e-mailtmcleod@bangordailynews.com; ed e-mail syoung@bangordailynews.com; web site www.bangordailynews.com
- 12,500,000(views) 2,094,593(visitors)
Published: Mon, Tues, Wed, Thur, Fri, Sat
Weekday Frequency: m
Saturday Frequency: m
Circulation: 27,996; 35,017(sat)
Last Audit: AAM September 30, 2016
Advertising Rate (weekday/saturday): Modular: (Mon-Wed) 1/30 $200.00; 1/16 $300.00; 1/8 $590.00; (Thur-Fri) 1/30 $250.00; 1/16 $400.00; 1/8 $785; (Sat) 1/30 $285.00; 1/16 $500.00; 1/8 $985.00
Online Advertising Rate: Home page: $15.00 per 1,000 impressions.
News services: AP, LAT-WP. **Established:** 1889
Own Printing Facility?: No
Commercial Printers?: No
Special Editions: Bangor Spring Home Show (Apr); Home Furnishings: Trends & Styles (Aug); High School Basketball (Dec); Eastern Agency On Aging-Life Times (Feb); Photographs of the Year: The Best From Our Pages (Jan); Planning Your Wedding (Jul); Experience Maine (Jun); Do
Special Weekly Sections: Maine Style (S).
Syndicated Publications: Color Comics (S); Food (Wed).
Digital Platform - Mobile: Apple, Android
Digital Platform - Tablet: Apple iOS, Android, Kindle
Vice President .... Jennifer Holmes
Pub. .... Richard J. Warren
Metro/Standards Ed. .... Micheal J. Dowd
Editorial Page Ed. .... Susan Young
V.P./C.O.O. .... Todd Benoit
Exec. Asst. .... Jeanne Luetjen
Finance Dir. .... Kimberly Gonzales
Events and Brand Coord. .... Kelly Donnelly
HR Asst. .... Michele Madden

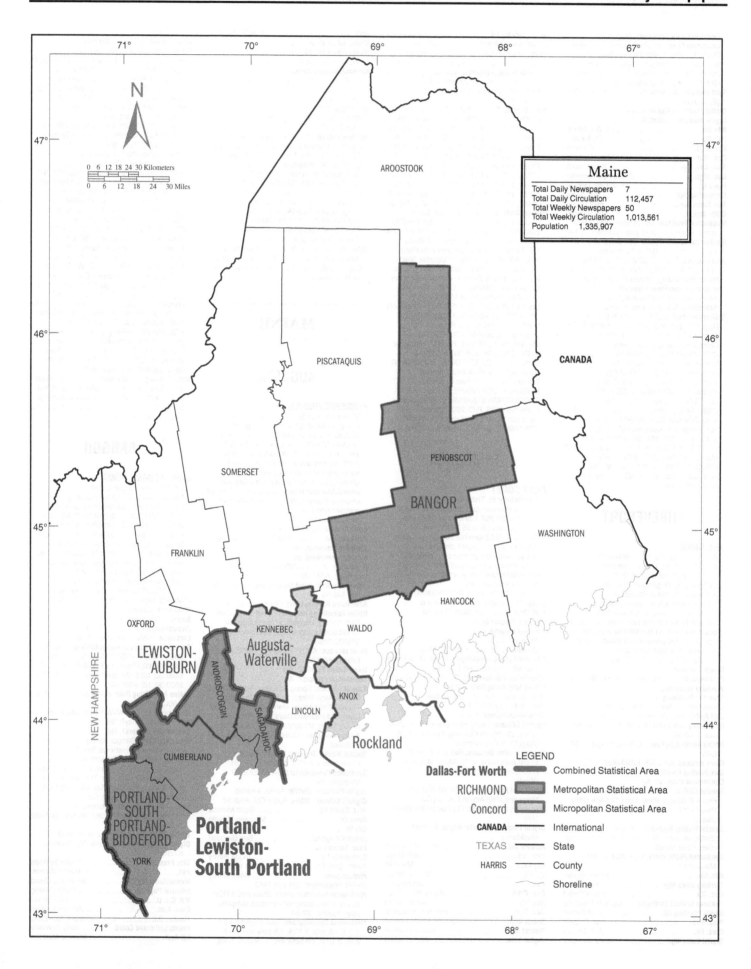

N

0 6 12 18 24 30 Kilometers
0 6   12   18   24   30 Miles

AROOSTOOK

CANADA

PISCATAQUIS

PENOBSCOT

SOMERSET

BANGOR

WASHINGTON

FRANKLIN

HANCOCK

OXFORD

KENNEBEC

WALDO

LEWISTON-
AUBURN

Augusta-
Waterville

ANDROSCOGGIN

KNOX

SAGADAHOC

LINCOLN

NEW HAMPSHIRE

CUMBERLAND

Rockland

PORTLAND-
SOUTH
PORTLAND-
BIDDEFORD

YORK

Portland-
Lewiston-
South Portland

Maine

Total Daily Newspapers	7
Total Daily Circulation	112,457
Total Weekly Newspapers	50
Total Weekly Circulation	1,013,561
Population	1,335,907

LEGEND

Dallas-Fort Worth	Combined Statistical Area
RICHMOND	Metropolitan Statistical Area
Concord	Micropolitan Statistical Area
CANADA	International
TEXAS	State
HARRIS	County
	Shoreline

Sales and Marketing Dir. .... Brian Cotlar
Client Advocate Mgr. .... Josh O'Donnell
Exec. Dir. .... Anthony Ronzio
Universal Desk Ed. .... Judy Long
State Ed. .... Rick Levasseur
Sports Ed. .... Joe McLaughlin
Audience Dev't Mgr. .... Jason Oliver
News/Features Ed. .... Sarah Walker Caron
Production Dir., Post Press .... Luis Azeredo
Kurt Parent
Dir., Mktg. Servs. .... Elizabeth Hansen
Graphics/Design Ed. .... Eric Zelz
Copy Ed. .... Christopher Burns
Copy Ed. .... Kaylie Reese
Project Coord. .... Jennifer Austin
Dir. of Circu. .... Michael Prazma
Circ. Customer Advocate Mgr. .... fred Stewart
Sr. Adv. Circ. .... James Hayes
Chair, Board of Dir. .... Carolyn Mowers
Features Reporter .... Lauren Abbate
Market Information: Split run; TMC; Zoned editions.
Mechanical Available: Flexography; Black and 3 ROP colors; insert accepted - free standing, single sheet, product samples; page cutoffs - 22.
Mechanical Specifications: Type page 11 5/8 x 21; E - 6 cols, 1 5/6, 1/8 between; A - 6 cols, 1 5/6, 1/8 between; C - 9 cols, 1 3/8, 3/32 between.
Areas Served: Penobscot County
Delivery Method: Mail, Newsstand, Carrier, RacksEquipment & Software: PRESSROOM EQUIPMENT: Lines — 8-H/PEC (double width flexo); Folders — 1-H/3:2.; MAILROOM EQUIPMENT: Counter Stackers — 4/HL, 1-Id/4400; Inserters & Stuffers — 1-HI/1472, 1-GMA/SLS 1000; Tying Machines — 1-/Power Strap/PSN5, 4-/Power Strap/PSN6, 1-Samuel/NT 40; Wrapping Singles — 6-Monarch/Bottom wrap; Address Machine — 1-KAN/Labeling System; BUSINESS EQUIPMENT: IBM/AS-400 BUSINESS SOFTWARE: In-house, Accts Receivable CLASSIFIED EQUIPMENT: Hardware — 2-Dell/Poweredge 4200, 18-IBM/Aptiva; Printers — 1-HP/Laserjet 4000, HP/Laserjet 6P, HP/Laserjet 4MV; CLASSIFIED SOFTWARE: Unisys/AD Center, Informatel/AdPlacer. DISPLAY EQUIPMENT: Hardware — 9-APP/MAC; Printers — 1-Canon/2100, 1-HP/Laserjet 4, 1-Docuprint N32; DISPLAY SOFTWAREAd Make-up Applications — Multi Ad/Creator, QPS/QuarkXPress; Layout Software — MEI/ALS, 6-APP/Mac. EDITORIAL EQUIPMENT: Hardware — 2-IBM/Netfinity 5500, IBM/PC/PC Bureau Dial-up Network; Printers — HP/Laserjet, X/Docuprint N32 EDITORIAL SOFTWARE: AT/Dewarview (2000). PRODUCTION EQUIPMENT: Hardware — 1-LaserMaster/1200, 2-SelectSet/5000, 2-Rapid, 1-Avantra/25; Scanners — 1-AG/Arcus II, 1-AG/Duoscan PRODUCTION SOFTWARE: AT/Pagemaker, QPS/QuarkXPress.

BIDDEFORD

JOURNAL-TRIBUNE

457 Alfred St, Biddeford, Maine, 04005-9447, York; gen tel (207) 282-1535; adv tel (207) 282-1535 ext. 341; ed tel (207) 282-1535 ext. 322; gen fax (207) 282-3138; adv fax (207) 282-3138; ed fax (207) 282-3138; gen/nat adv e-mail publisher@journaltribune.com; disp adv e-mail publisher@journaltribune.com; class adv e-mailClassifieds@journaltribune.com; ed e-mail Editor@journaltribune.com; web site www.journaltribune.com
Group: Sample News Group LLC
Published: Mon, Tues, Wed, Thur, Fri, Sat
Weekday Frequency: e
Saturday Frequency: m
Circulation: 6,676; 7,476(sat)
Last Audit: Sworn/Estimate/Non-Audited December 18, 2017
Advertising Rate (weekday/saturday): Open inch rate $14.25
Online Advertising Rate: Run of Site $15.50 CPM
News services: AP, SHNS. **Established:** 1884
Own Printing Facility?: Yes
Commercial Printers?: No
Special Weekly Sections: Business; Religion
Syndicated Publications: USA WEEKEND Magazine (Sat).
Digital Platform - Mobile: Apple, Android
Digital Platform - Tablet: Apple iOS, Android
Executive Editor .... Ed Pierce
Assoc. Sports Ed. .... Alex Sponseller
Pub. .... Bruce Hardina
Market Information: TMC.
Mechanical Available: Offset; Black and 3 ROP colors; insert accepted; page cutoffs - 22 3/4.
Mechanical Specifications: Type page 13 x 21 1/2; E - 6 cols, 2 1/16, 1/8 between; A - 6 cols, 2 1/16, 1/8 between; C - 9 cols, 1 3/8, 1/16 between.
Areas Served: 04005, 04072, 04073, 04083, 04054, 04063, 04027, 04074, 03907, 04087, 04030, 04005, 04042, 04093, 04004, 04038, 04048, 04095, 04076, 04001, 03906, 04002, 04046, 04094, 04046, 04090, 04043, 04002, 04064, 04014, 04042, 04061, 04006
Delivery Method: Newsstand, Carrier, RacksEquipment & Software: PRESSROOM EQUIPMENT: Lines — 6-G/U 553; MAILROOM EQUIPMENT: Tying Machines — 2/Sa, 1-/MLN; Address Machine — 1-Ch/525E.; BUSINESS EQUIPMENT: 1-TI/690 CLASSIFIED EQUIPMENT: Hardware — Ik/Minitek I; Printers — NewGen/Turbo 600, Design Express lo, 6-Micro Laser 600.; DISPLAY EQUIPMENT: Printers — 1-APP/Mac, Micro Laser 600; DISPLAY SOFTWARELayout Software — 5-APP/Mac IIcx, 3-APP/Mac SE, 1-NewGen/630, 1-NewGen/660, 2-APP/Power Mac 6100, 1-APP/Mac LC 520. EDITORIAL EQUIPMENT: Hardware — Ik/Minitek I, 1-APP/Mac SE, 1-APP/Mac IIcx, 2-APP/Mac G3, 2-APP/Mac 6100 EDITORIAL SOFTWARE: Baseview/NewsEdit Pro. PRODUCTION EQUIPMENT: Hardware — ECR/VRL 36, DAI/LD-260-L; Cameras — 1-R/5000; Scanners — Umax, APP/Mac PRODUCTION SOFTWARE: QPS/QuarkXPress 4.0.

BRUNSWICK

THE TIMES RECORD

3 Business Pkwy, Ste 1, Brunswick, Maine, 04011-7390, Cumberland; gen tel (207)729-3311; adv tel (207)504-8270; ed tel (207)729-3311; gen fax (207) 729-5728; adv fax (207) 725-8619; ed fax (207) 721-3151; gen/nat adv e-mail mlester@timesrecord.com; disp adv e-mail mlester@timesrecord.com; class adv e-mailmlester@timesrecord.com; ed e-mail mlester@timesrecord.com; web site www.timesrecord.com
- 207,345(views) 48,532(visitors)
Group: Sample News Group LLC
Published: Mon, Tues, Wed, Thur, Fri
Weekday Frequency: e
Circulation: 7,200; 8,500(sun)
Last Audit: Sworn/Estimate/Non-Audited August 30, 2017
Advertising Rate (weekday/saturday): Open inch rate $17.75 Mon-Thurs
Advertising Rate (sunday): $18.70 Friday
Online Advertising Rate: Rates based on position and rotations.
News services: AP, NYT. **Established:** 1967
Own Printing Facility?: No
Commercial Printers?: No
Special Editions: Spring Home Improvement (April), Summer Guide (May), Taste of the Midcoast (June), Summer Guide 2 (July), Best of the Midcoast (Aug), Fall Home Improvement (Sept), Veterans (Nov), Holiday Gift Guides (Nov/Dec). Monthly: Healthy Living
Special Weekly Sections: Ticket (Fri); Best Food Day (Fri); Sights & Sounds (Thur); Milestones (Weddings & Engagements) (Tues); Business (Wed).
Syndicated Publications: Real Estate Plus, biweekly on Fridays; Healthy Living, third Wednesday of each month
Digital Platform - Mobile: Apple, Android, Windows, Blackberry
Digital Platform - Tablet: Apple iOS, Android, Windows 7, Blackberry Tablet OS, Kindle, Nook, Kindle Fire
Subscriber Services Mgr. .... George Reichert
Business Mgr. .... Stacy Wight
Ed. .... John Swinconeck
Mechanical Available: Offset; Black and 2 ROP colors; insert accepted; page cutoffs - 22 3/4.
Mechanical Specifications: 10.5 X 21"
Areas Served: Cumberland and Mid-Coast Maine
Delivery Method: Newsstand, Carrier, RacksEquipment & Software: PRESSROOM EQUIPMENT: Lines — G/Community (2-4HI, 1-2HI) (single width) 1985; G/Community (6, 1 VOP) (single width) 1980; DGM/430 (1-4HI) (single width) 1999; Press Drive — Fin/Digital Drive; Folders — 2-G/SSC, 1; Pasters —3-Enkel/OSpud. MAILROOM EQUIPMENT: Counter Stackers — 3-Gammler/KL 503/1; Inserters & Stuffers — 1-MM/227E; Tying Machines — 4-EAM-Mosca/Rom, 1-Si/LB-2000; Address Machine — 1-Ch/539, KR/512; BUSINESS EQUIPMENT: Sun/4-110 BUSINESS SOFTWARE: Vision Data CLASSIFIED EQUIPMENT: Hardware — APP/Mac; Printers — HP/5000; CLASSIFIED SOFTWARE: Caere/OmniPage Plus, Baseview. DISPLAY EQUIPMENT: Hardware — APP/Mac; Printers — Compaq/PageMarq 20, HP/8000, 2-Linotype-Hell/L530 Imagesetter with RIP 4.5; Other Hardware — ECR/Autokon 1000, Desktop/Scanner DISPLAY SOFTWAREAd Make-up Applications — QPS/QuarkXPress 3.32; Layout Software — APP/Mac, QPS/QuarkXPress. EDITORIAL EQUIPMENT: Hardware — APP/Mac/2-Linotype-Hell/L530 Imagesetter with Ultra Rip 4.5; Printers — 1-MON, HP/5000 EDITORIAL SOFTWARE: Baseview/Server IQUE. PRODUCTION EQUIPMENT: Hardware — 2-L/530, LE/PC 1800, LE/Excel 26; Cameras — C/Spartan III; Scanners — AG/Arcus Scanner, 1-APP/Mac PRODUCTION SOFTWARE: QPS/QuarkXPress 4.10.

LEWISTON

SUN JOURNAL

104 Park St, Lewiston, Maine, 04240-7202, Androscoggin; gen tel (207) 784-5411; adv tel (207) 784-5411; ed tel (207) 784-5411; gen fax (207) 777-3436; adv fax (207) 784-5955; ed fax (207) 777-3436; gen/nat adv e-mail jjalbert@sunjournal.com; disp adv e-mail brioux@sunjournal.com; class adv e-mailscostello@sunjournal.com; ed e-mail editor@sunjournal.com; web site www.sunjournal.com
- 730,000(views) 240,000(visitors)
Group: Sun Media Group
Published: Mon, Tues, Wed, Thur, Fri, Sat, Sun
Weekday Frequency: m
Saturday Frequency: m
Circulation: 15,489; 15,489(sat); 16,774(sun)
Last Audit: CAC September 30, 2017
Branch Offices: Lewiston, Norway, Rumford, Farmington
Advertising Rate (weekday/saturday): Open inch rate $30.15; 2 times: $22.61; 3 times: $20.10;
Advertising Rate (sunday): Open inch rate $31.66; 2 times $23.75; 3 times $21.11;
Online Advertising Rate: Top Corner $30.00 CPM; Half page $35.00 CPM; Medium Rectangle $50.00 CPM;
News services: AP, CSM, MCT. **Established:** 1861
Own Printing Facility?: Yes
Commercial Printers?: Yes
Special Editions: HEALTHY LIVING, CHAMBERS AWARDS, CATHOLIC SCHOOLS WEEKLY (Jan); SPRING WEDDING GUIDE, PRESIDENTS DAY (Feb); SPRING HOME IMPROVEMENT, WESTERN ME BUILDERS, SPRING CAR CARE, LIVING WELL, LEWISTON AUBURN FILM FESTIVAL (Mar); LANDSCAPE & GARDEN, COLLEGE BOUND, PROFILE (Apr); GRADUATION, SUMMER IN MAINE, RIVER VALLEY RALLEY RELAY FOR LIFE (May); ANDROCSOGGIN RELAY FOR LIFE, BUSINESS TO BUSINESS TRADE SHOW (Jun); MOXIE FESTIVAL, TD BANK 250 (Jul); OUR TOWN, BALLOON FESTIVAL, FALL WEDDING GUIDE (Aug); FALL SPORTS, PROSPER, FALL HOME IMPROVEMENT, FALL CAR CARE, TASTE OF HOME, COOKING SCHOOL (Sept); FAMILY, CREDIT UNION DAY (Oct); VETERANS DAY, SHRINER'S FESTIVAL OF TREES, WESTERN ME HOLIDAY SERIES, HOLIDAY SERIES-ALL EDITIONS (Nov); WINTER SPORTS,WINTER IN MAINE, BUSINESS REVIEW (Dec);
Special Weekly Sections: Economy/Business, Weddings, Ent. (Sun); TV Preview (Sat).
Syndicated Publications: Relish (Monthly); USA WEEKEND Magazine, PARADE Magazine (Sun); American Profile (Weekly); Spry (Monthly); Decathalon Sports (Monthly).
Digital Platform - Mobile: Apple, Android
Digital Platform - Tablet: Apple iOS, Android
Vice Pres. Adv./Mktg. .... Stephen M. Costello
Adv. Mgr. .... Jody Jalbert
Circ. Dir. .... Mike Theriault
Exec. Ed. .... Rex Rhoades
Mng. Ed., Day .... Judith Meyer
Mng. Ed., Night .... Peter Phelan
Sr. Design .... Heather McCarthy
Chief Photographer .... Russell Dillingham
REGL. ED.
Scott Thistle
Vice Pres./Bus. Mgr. .... James A. Thornton
Major Acc. Mgr. .... Bruce Rioux
Acc. Exec. .... Larry Baril
Acc. Exec. .... Mike Blanchet
Acc. Exec. .... Brian Croteau
Acc. Exec. .... Dan McManus
Acc. Exec. .... Norman Moreau
Acc. Exec. .... Kelly Wade
Special Sections Ed. .... Denise Scammon
Web Ed. .... Carl Natale
Business, News Ed. .... Mark Mogensen
Web Content Ed./Regl. Ed. .... Steve Sherlock
Sports Ed. .... Justin Pelletier
Copy Desk Chief .... Karen Kerworuka
Copy Ed. .... Mary Delamater
VP, Technology .... David Costello
Vice Pres., HR .... Maureen Wedge
Adv. Sales .... Bill Anctil
Market Information: Zoned editions.
Mechanical Available: Offset; Black and 3 ROP colors; insert accepted; page cutoffs - 22 3/4.
Mechanical Specifications: Type page 11 3/5 x 21; E - 6 cols, 1 4/5, 1/8 between; A - 6 cols, 1 4/5, 1/8 between; C - 9 cols, 1 1/5, 1/16 between.
Areas Served: Androscoggin County and Western Maine
Delivery Method: Mail, Newsstand, Carrier, RacksEquipment & Software: PRESSROOM EQUIPMENT: Lines — 15-G/Urbanite 1283; Folders — 1-G/2:1; Control System — Fincore; MAILROOM EQUIPMENT: Counter Stackers — 3-QWI/SJ200; Inserters & Stuffers — 1-HI/1372 1-SLS 1000; Tying Machines — 1/MLN, 2-/AHS, 1-MLN/MLIEE, 1-MLN/Spirit.; Control System — Burt; Address Machine — Micro Ink-jet; CLASSIFIED EQUIPMENT: Hardware — PC; Printers — HP/11x17; CLASSIFIED SOFTWARE: PPI DISPLAY EQUIPMENT: Hardware — PC; Printers — HP/11x17; DISPLAY SOFTWAREAd Make-up Applications — In-design, Xpance, Photoshop; EDITORIAL EQUIPMENT: Hardware — 3-PC Server/APP/Mac Plus Agaton Scanner, CD, 3-HP/11x17; Printers — 2-AU/APS2000, 11x17, 3-AG/Accuset 1500 EDITORIAL SOFTWARE: MS/NT, QPS/QuarkXPress, Microsoft/Word 7.0. PRODUCTION EQUIPMENT: Hardware — AG/Accuset 1500, AG/660 Rapid Access, C/Rapid Access; Cameras — 1-R/481, 1-R/432; Scanners — ECR/Autokon 1000, AG/RPS 20 x 24, 1-CD/625E Scanner PRODUCTION SOFTWARE: ACI.

PORTLAND

PORTLAND PRESS HERALD / MAINE SUNDAY TELEGRAM

1 City Ctr Stop 7, 5th Floor, Portland, Maine, 04101-4009, Cumberland; gen tel (207) 791-6650; adv tel (207) 791-6200; ed tel (207) 791-6320; gen fax (207) 791-6920; adv fax (207) 791-6925; ed fax (207) 791-6920; gen/nat adv e-mail amuhs@mainetoday.com; disp adv e-mail sbryan@mainetoday.com; class adv e-mailcmnclass@centralmaine.com; ed e-mail cschechtman@mainetoday.com ; web site www.pressherald.com
- 4,600,000(views) 1,173,434(visitors)
Group: Maine Today Media Inc.
Published: Mon, Tues, Wed, Thur, Fri, Sat, Sun
Weekday Frequency: m

Saturday Frequency: m
Circulation: 38,560; 38,128(sat); 54,506(sun)
Last Audit: AAM September 30, 2017
Advertising Rate (weekday/saturday): Open inch rate $88.20
Advertising Rate (sunday): Open inch rate $130.78
Online Advertising Rate: Position 3: Med. Rectangle or Half Page $5.00 CPM; Leaderboard $9.00 CPM; Position 2: Med. Rectangle or Half Page $11.00 CPM
News services: AP, LAT-WP, Tribune Media, Universal Press, King Features, United Media, CSM, CQ. **Established:** 1862
Own Printing Facility?: Yes
Commercial Printers?: Yes
Special Editions: 50 Plus (Apr); Vacationland (Aug); National Engineers Week (Feb); Wedding Planner (Jan); People's Choice, Seniority (Jul); Vacationland (Jun); Death and Dying (Mar); Vacationland (May); Holiday Gift Guide (Nov); Home Furnishings (Oct); Home Improvement (Fall).
Special Weekly Sections: Business Friday (Fri); On Screen (S); Religion & Values (Sat); GO (Thur); Business (Tues); Food & Health (Wed).
Syndicated Publications: Parade (S); American Profile (Weekly).
Proprietary Publications: MaineToday Magazine (Thur)
Digital Platform - Mobile: Apple, Android
Digital Platform - Tablet: Apple iOS, Android, Kindle, Nook, Kindle Fire
Prodn. Mgr., Pressroom/Distr. ..... Keith Toothaker
Classified Adv. Mgr. .... Jennifer Sorenson
Deputy Mng. Ed., Opns./Sports .... Don Coulter
Deputy Managing Ed. .... Dieter Bradbury
Exec. Ed. .... Cliff Schechtman
Managing Ed. .... Steve Greenlee
City Ed. .... Katherine Lee
Features Ed. .... Chelsea Conaboy
CEO/Publisher .... Lisa DeSisto
VP/Adv. .... Barbara Bock
Dir. Digital Products .... John Moore
VP/Labor & Employee Relations ..... Maryann Kelly
VP/Circ. & Marketing .... Stefanie Manning
Chief Information Officer .... Stewart Wright
Market Information: ADS; Split run; TMC; Zoned editions.
Mechanical Available: Flexographic; Black and 3 ROP colors; insert accepted - all; page cutoffs - 22.
Mechanical Specifications: Type page 11 5/8 x 21; E - 6 cols, 1 5/6, 1/8 between; A - 6 cols, 1 5/6, 1/8 between; C - 10 cols, 1 1/16, 3/16 between.
Areas Served: Southern Maine
Delivery Method: Mail, Newsstand, Carrier, RacksEquipment & Software: PRESSROOM EQUIPMENT: Lines — 6-G/Flexoliner 1989; 6-G/Flexoliner 1989; Folders — 2-G/160 Page Sovereign, G/Double Delivery; Pasters —12-G/CT 50Reels & Stands — 12-G/Reels & Stands; Registration System — 4-Web/ Press Controls. MAILROOM EQUIPMENT: Counter Stackers — 6-HL/HT2, 1/ QWI; Inserters & Stuffers — 1-HI/2299, 1-HI/1372; Tying Machines — 10-OVL/ JP40, 2-/MLN, 1-/Dynaric; Wrapping Singles — Altek/Skid Stretch Wrap Machine; Control System — HL/Dock console; Address Machine — Addressing machine; BUSINESS EQUIPMENT: Digital Alpha Servers BUSINESS SOFTWARE: Microsoft/ Office 4.3, Great Plains Dynamics C/S CLASSIFIED EQUIPMENT: Hardware — 2-Sun/3000e, 54-APP/Mac PPC; Printers — 3-HP/4000, 1-AII/2500, 2-HP/2500; CLASSIFIED SOFTWARE: DTI 4.2.3. DISPLAY EQUIPMENT: Hardware — 2-Sun/3000e; Printers — 2-HP/XL 3000, 1-HP/755 CM, 2-HP/4000; Other Hardware — 1-ECR/1000 DISPLAY SOFTWAREAd Make-up Applications — QPS/QuarkXPress, Multi-Ad, Macromedia/Freehand, Adobe/ Photoshop, DTI; Layout Software — DTI. EDITORIAL EQUIPMENT: Hardware — 2-Sun/3000e, 160-APP/Mac PPC; Printers — 6-HP/4000, 2-AII/2500, 1-AII/1055, AII/APS 2000, 2-HP/1055 EDITORIAL SOFTWARE: DTI 4.2.3. PRODUCTION EQUIPMENT: Hardware — 2-MacDermit CTP, 2-NAPP/Flex Processor Unit; Scanners — ECR, 7-HP/3C, 2-Kk/2035, 1-Howtek PRODUCTION SOFTWARE: DTI/PlanBuilder 4.2.3.

WATERVILLE

MORNING SENTINEL

31 Front St, Waterville, Maine, 04901-6626, Kennebec; gen tel (207) 873-3341; adv tel (207) 873-3341; ed tel (207) 873-3341; gen fax (207) 861-9223; adv fax (207) 861-9222; ed fax (207) 861-9191; gen/nat adv e-mail sentinelnews@mainetoday.com; disp adv e-mail mscommunity@mainetoday.com; class adv e-mailcmnclass@centralmaine.com; ed e-mail smonroe@mainetoday.com; web site www.onlinesentinel.com
243,450(visitors); web site 2 www. centralmaine.com
Group: Maine Today Media Inc.
Published: Mon, Tues, Wed, Thur, Fri, Sat, Sun
Weekday Frequency: m
Saturday Frequency: m
Circulation: 9,243; 9,243(sat); 9,746(sun)
Last Audit: AAM March 31, 2017
Advertising Rate (weekday/saturday): Open inch rate $45.05
Advertising Rate (sunday): Open inch rate $47.78
Online Advertising Rate: Pencil with pushdown $675.00/day; Homepage Top Roadblock $1300.00/day; Homepage Takeovers $1650.00/day
News services: AP, LAT-WP, SHNS. **Established:** 1904
Own Printing Facility?: Yes
Commercial Printers?: Yes
Special Editions: Spring Scouting (Apr); Skowhegan Fair (Aug); Holiday Shopping Guide II (Dec); Family Expo (Feb); Bridal (Jan); Pre-Owned Autos/Trucks/SUVs (Jul); Graduation (Jun); Maine Paper Expo (Mar); Start Your Engines (May); Holiday Shopping Guide I (Nov); Fall Home
Special Weekly Sections: What's Happening (entertainment) (Fri); What's on TV (S).
Syndicated Publications: USA WEEKEND Magazine (S).
Digital Platform - Mobile: Apple, Android
Digital Platform - Tablet: Apple iOS, Android
Managing Ed. .... Scott Monroe
News Ed. .... Maureen Milliken
Community News Ed. .... Stacy Blanchet
Editorial Page Ed. .... Ben Bragdon
Exec. Sports Ed. .... Bill Stewart
Photographers .... Dave Leaming
Sports Writer .... Drew Bonifant
Reporter .... Amy Calder
Mechanical Available: Offset; Black and 3 ROP colors; insert accepted - product samples; page cutoffs - 22 3/4.
Mechanical Specifications: Type page 13 x 21 1/2; E - 6 cols, 2 1/32, 5/32 between; A - 6 cols, 2 1/32, 5/32 between; C - 9 cols, 1 5/16, 1/16 between.
Areas Served: Franklin, Kennebec, Penobscot, and Somerset County
Delivery Method: Mail, Newsstand, Carrier, RacksEquipment & Software: PRESSROOM EQUIPMENT: Lines — G/Urbanite; MAILROOM EQUIPMENT: Counter Stackers — 1-HI/R525, 3-H/4 Monitor, Gammerter/ STC 70; Inserters & Stuffers — 1-HI/1372; Tying Machines — 2-IT/SX 500, 2/Power Strap/PSN 65; Wrapping Singles — Mailroom Control System HI/Stacker Program 009; Address Machine — 1-Domino/Amjet Jerray; BUSINESS EQUIPMENT: Dell/486 BUSINESS SOFTWARE: Microsoft/ Word, Microsoft/Excel, CJ CLASSIFIED EQUIPMENT: Hardware — Dell/Pentium PCs; Printers — HP/LaserPrinter; CLASSIFIED SOFTWARE: SCS. DISPLAY EQUIPMENT: Hardware — 5-PC; Printers — HP, C.Itoh, Dataproducts/LZR1560; Other Hardware — APP/Mac PowerBooks DISPLAY SOFTWAREAd Make-up Applications — Multi-Ad/Creator 4.0.1; Layout Software — SCS/Layout 8000. EDITORIAL EQUIPMENT: Hardware — 3-Dell; Printers — HP/LaserPrinters EDITORIAL SOFTWARE: SCS. PRODUCTION EQUIPMENT: Hardware — Dataproducts/L2R2080 Laser printer, Graham; Cameras — 1-C/Spartan III; Scanners — HP, Howtek/Scan-Master 2500 PRODUCTION SOFTWARE: SCS, QPS/ QuarkXPress 3.31.
Note: The Waterville Morning Sentinel (mS) has a combination rate of $56.86 (m-mon to sat) and $59.65 (S) with the Augusta Kennebec Journal (mS). Individual newspaper rates not made available.

MARYLAND

ANNAPOLIS

THE CAPITAL

888 Bestgate Rd Ste 104, Suite 104, Annapolis, Md., 21401-2950, Anne Arundel; gen tel (410) 268-5000; adv tel (410) 268-7000; ed tel (410) 268-5000; gen fax (410) 268-4643; adv fax (410) 280-5974; ed fax (410) 280-5953; gen/nat adv e-mail mpadden@capgaznews.com; disp adv e-mail mpadden@capgaznews.com; class adv e-mailclassifieds@capgaznews.com; ed e-mail rhutzell@capgaznews.com; web site www.capitalgazette.com
- 3,500,000(views)
Published: Mon, Tues, Wed, Thur, Fri, Sat, Sun
Weekday Frequency: m
Saturday Frequency: m
Circulation: 22,535; 22,535(sat); 27,094(sun)
Last Audit: AAM December 31, 2016
Newspaper Reps: tronc
News services: AP, tronc **Established:** 1884
Own Printing Facility?: Yes
Commercial Printers?: Yes
Digital Platform - Mobile: Apple, Android
Digital Platform - Tablet: Apple iOS, Android, Windows 7
Editorial Page Ed. .... Gerald Fischman
Adv. Dir. .... Martin Padden
Editor .... Rick Hutzell
Publisher .... Tim Thomas
Managing Editor .... Rob Hiassen
Areas Served: Annapolis, Anne Arundel County and Kent Island, Maryland.
Delivery Method: Newsstand, Carrier, Racks

BALTIMORE

THE BALTIMORE SUN

501 N Calvert St, Baltimore, Md., 21278-1000, Baltimore City; gen tel (410) 332-6000; adv tel (410) 332-6300; ed tel (410) 332-6221; gen fax (410) 332-6670; adv fax (410) 332-6084; ed fax (410) 332-6100; gen/nat adv e-mail advertise@baltsun.com; disp adv e-mail advertise@baltsun.com; class adv e-mailadvertise@baltsun.com; ed e-mail trif.alatzas@baltsun.com; web site www. baltimoresun.com
5,029,173(visitors)
Group: Tronc, Inc.
Published: Mon, Tues, Wed, Thur, Fri, Sat, Sun
Weekday Frequency: m
Saturday Frequency: m
Circulation: 106,443; 179,740(sat); 230,588(sun)
Last Audit: AAM December 31, 2016
Advertising Rate (weekday/saturday): 1/32 H or SQ - $1,674.00; 1/64 H - $1,395.00
Advertising Rate (sunday): 1/32 H or SQ - $1,860.00; 1/64 H - $1,725.00
News services: Tribune Newspaper Network, RN, MCT, NYT, DJ, LAT-WP, AFP. **Established:** 1837
Own Printing Facility?: Yes
Commercial Printers?: Yes
Special Editions: Preakness Wrap-Up (Apr); Our Future/Carroll Schools (Aug); High Tech Education (Dec); Health Today (Every other month); College Goal Sunday Program (Feb); Career Builder XL II (Jan); Ravens Training Camp (Jul); A.A. Co. Residents Guide (Jun); Credit Union.
Special Weekly Sections: Business (Tue); Taste (Wed); Health & Style (Thur); Live! (Fri); At Home, Sports (Sat); Travel, Art, Entertainment, Real Estate, Sports (Sun);
Syndicated Publications: Parade (Sun); Sun Magazine (6 times annually); Howard Magazine (8 times annually); Harford Magazine (5 times annually); Maryland Family (10 times annually); Chesapeake Home (7 times annually)
Digital Platform - Mobile: Apple, Android
Digital Platform - Tablet: Apple iOS, Android
Pub./Ed. -in-Chief .... Triffon Alatzas
Managing Ed. .... Samuel Davis
Asst. Managing Ed. .... Laura Smitherman
Asst. Managing Ed. Digital .... Peter Sweigard
SVP - targeted Media .... Patricia Carroll
Adv. Dir. .... Susan Duchin
Enterprise Ed. .... Matthew Brown
Columnist .... Jacques Kelly
Sr. Ed. sports .... Ron Fritz
Deputy Sports Ed. .... Andrew Knobel
Features Content Ed. .... Ellen Fishel
Events Mgr. .... Lori Sears
Editorial Page Ed. .... Andrew Green
Dir. Audience/Dev. .... Matt Bracken
Sr. Ed. Interactive Design .... Adam Marton
Sr. Ed. visuals .... Jay Judge
News Ed. .... Steve Young
Market Information: ADS; TMC; Zoned editions.
Mechanical Available: Offset; Black and 3 ROP colors; insert accepted - all; page cutoffs - 22.
Mechanical Specifications: Type page 11 5/8 x 20 3/4; E - 6 cols, 1 13/16, 1/8 between; A - 6 cols, 1 13/16, 1/8 between; C - 10 cols, 1 1/16, 1/8 between.
Areas Served: All of Maryland
Delivery Method: Mail, Newsstand, CarrierEquipment & Software: PRESSROOM EQUIPMENT: Lines — 12-G/Colorliner double width; 12-G/Colorliner double width; 12-G/Colorliner double width; 12-G/Colorliner double width; Folders — 3-G/Double 3:2, 1-G/Single 3:2; Reels & Stands — 48-CT/50 Reels & Stands.; MAILROOM EQUIPMENT: Counter Stackers — 2/Stackpack, 2-/ Gammerler, 20-HL/HT II, 12-/QUI; Inserters & Stuffers — 1-GMA/SLS 2000 12:2, 2-GMA/ SLS 2000 20:2, 2-GMA/SLS 2000 26:2; Tying Machines — 32-/Power Strap (5,6,6E), 17-/Dynaric; Wrapping Singles — 3-HL/ Monarch, 20; BUSINESS EQUIPMENT: Dell 780's 390's Dell 6420,30 BUSINESS SOFTWARE: Admarc, DSI, CRM, Kronos, Peoplesoft CLASSIFIED EQUIPMENT: Hardware — SII/Tandem K2000, Sun/Ultra 3000; 1-TDD-TYY C-Phone 1-A; Printers — HP/2500, HP/1050, Xante/Accel-a-Writer 3G, Xante/Color Laser, HP/LaserJet 4050N, HP/5SI; CLASSIFIED SOFTWARE: SII/Czar II, Scoop, A151 Fax Action, SII/SCP 1.7n. DISPLAY EQUIPMENT: Hardware — 75-APP/Mac, 200- Dell 250's 280's; Printers — HP/2500, HP/1050, Xante/Accel-a-Writer 3G, Xante/Color Laser, HP/LaserJet 4050N, HP 5500 HP 8150 ; DISPLAY SOFTWAREAd Make-up Applications — Managing Editor/ ALS 3.0, SII/Coyote3, QPS/QuarkXPress 4.1, Adobe/Photoshop 5.5, A; Layout Software — Adobe Creative Suite, Newsgate EDITORIAL EQUIPMENT: Hardware — Dell 520, 280, 780's 390's/2-AP/Preserver; Printers — HP/2500, HP/1050, Xante/Accel-a-Writer 3G, Xante/Color Laser, HP/LaserJet 4050N, HP/5SI, OCE/Proofer EDITORIAL SOFTWARE: Merlin Newsgate, Adobe/Phot PRODUCTION EQUIPMENT: Hardware — 5-III/3850, 1-WL/3, Umax/D-16L Flat Bed, 1-ECR/Stingray, 9-Flat Bed Scanners, Nikon/Cool Scan; Scanners — 2-Eskofot PRODUCTION SOFTWARE: HI/NMP 4.7.

THE DAILY RECORD

11 E Saratoga St, Baltimore, Md., 21202-2115, Baltimore City; gen tel (443) 524-8100; adv tel (443) 524-8100; ed tel (443) 524-8150; gen fax (410) 752-2894; adv fax (410) 752-2894; ed fax (410) 752-2894; gen/nat adv e-mail suzanne.huettner@thedailyrecord.com; disp adv e-mail advertising@thedailyrecord.com; class adv e-mailjustin.carson@thedailyrecord.com; ed e-mail tbaden@thedailyrecord.com; web site www.thedailyrecord.com
Group: The Dolan Company
Published: Mon, Tues, Wed, Thur, Fri
Weekday Frequency: m
Circulation: 2,572
Last Audit: CVC March 31, 2014
Advertising Rate (weekday/saturday): Open inch rate $510.00/Day
Online Advertising Rate: 3:1 Rectangle $355.00/ month; Medium Rectangle $430.00/month; Leaderboard $850.00/month
News services: 1888
Publisher .... Suzanne Fischer-Huettner
Comptroller .... Maria Kelly

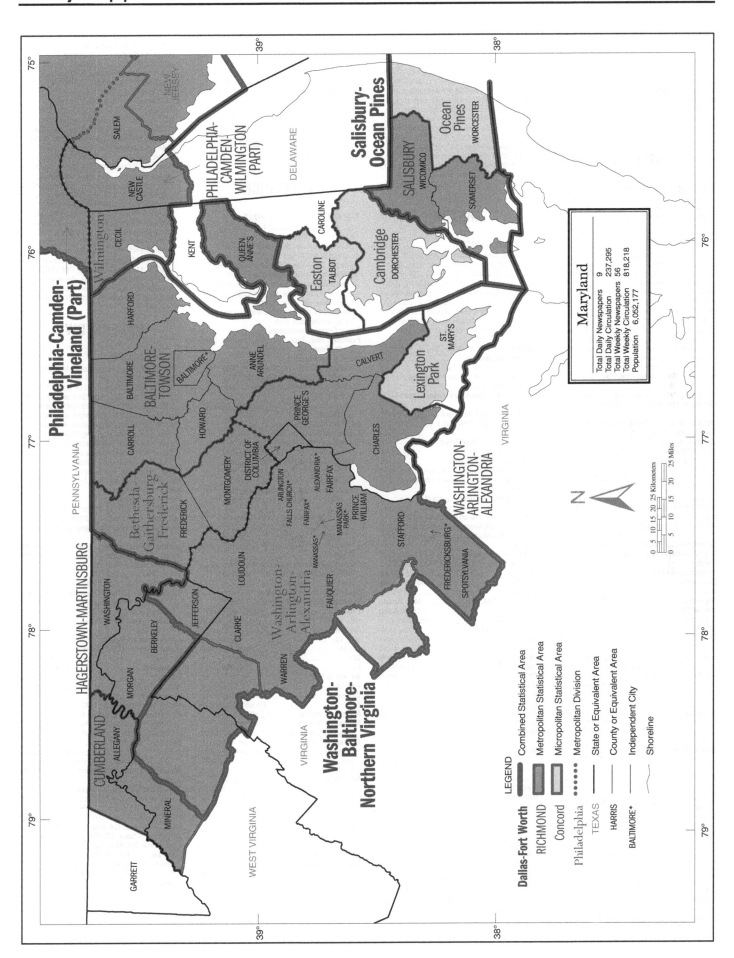

Maryland

Total Daily Newspapers	9
Total Daily Circulation	237,295
Total Weekly Newspapers	56
Total Weekly Circulation	818,218
Population	6,052,177

Philadelphia-Camden-Vineland (Part)

HAGERSTOWN-MARTINSBURG

Washington-Baltimore-Northern Virginia

Washington-Arlington-Alexandria

WASHINGTON-ARLINGTON-ALEXANDRIA

Salisbury-Ocean Pines

PHILADELPHIA-CAMDEN-WILMINGTON (PART)

Bethesda-Gaithersburg-Frederick

LEGEND

Dallas-Fort Worth	Combined Statistical Area
RICHMOND	Metropolitan Statistical Area
Concord	Micropolitan Statistical Area
•••••	Metropolitan Division
TEXAS	State or Equivalent Area
HARRIS	County or Equivalent Area
BALTIMORE*	Independent City
	Shoreline
Philadelphia	

N

0 5 10 15 20 25 Kilometers
0 5 10 15 20 25 Miles

Counties and places labeled on map:
SALEM, NEW CASTLE, Wilmington, CECIL, KENT, QUEEN ANNE'S, CAROLINE, Easton, TALBOT, Cambridge, DORCHESTER, SALISBURY, WICOMICO, Ocean Pines, WORCESTER, SOMERSET, DELAWARE, NEW JERSEY, HARFORD, BALTIMORE, BALTIMORE-TOWSON, Baltimore*, ANNE ARUNDEL, PRINCE GEORGE'S, ST. MARY'S, CALVERT, Lexington Park, CHARLES, CARROLL, HOWARD, FREDERICK, MONTGOMERY, DISTRICT OF COLUMBIA, ARLINGTON, ALEXANDRIA*, FAIRFAX, FALLS CHURCH*, FAIRFAX*, MANASSAS PARK*, PRINCE WILLIAM, MANASSAS*, LOUDOUN, CLARKE, WARREN, FAUQUIER, STAFFORD, FREDERICKSBURG*, SPOTSYLVANIA, WASHINGTON, BERKELEY, JEFFERSON, MORGAN, ALLEGANY, CUMBERLAND, MINERAL, GARRETT, WEST VIRGINIA, VIRGINIA, PENNSYLVANIA

Audience Dev. Dir. .... Tracy Bumba
Admin. Asst. .... Shelby Carter
Ed. .... Thomas Baden Jr.
Digital Ed. .... Jason Whong
Legal Ed. .... Danny Jacobs
Sr. Photographer .... Maximilian Franz
Special Products Ed. .... Jessica Gregg
Acc. Mgr. .... Darice Miller
Acc. Mgr. .... Terri Thompson
Mktg. and Event Coord. .... Haley Poling
Areas Served: 21202-2115

CUMBERLAND

THE CUMBERLAND TIMES-NEWS

19 Baltimore St, Cumberland, Md., 21502-3023, Allegany; gen tel (301) 722-4600; adv tel (301) 722-2504; ed tel (301) 784-2517; gen fax (301) 722-4870; adv fax (301) 722-4870; ed fax (301) 722-5270; gen/nat adv e-mail advertising@times-news.com; disp adv e-mail advertising@times-news.com; class adv e-mailclassified@times-news.com; ed e-mail ctn@times-news.com; web site www.times-news.com
Group: Community Newspaper Holdings, Inc.
Published: Mon, Tues, Wed, Thur, Fri, Sat, Sun
Weekday Frequency: m
Saturday Frequency: m
Circulation: 17,314; 17,314(sat); 18,735(sun)
Last Audit: AAM September 30, 2016
Newspaper Reps: Robin Quillon, publisher
Craig Springer, advertising director
Jeff Clark, circulation director
Advertising Rate (weekday/saturday): Open inch rate $21.38
Advertising Rate (sunday): Open inch rate $22.88
Online Advertising Rate: $15.00 CPM (requires 4,000 min)
News services: AP, CNHI **Established:** 1988
Own Printing Facility?: Yes
Commercial Printers?: Yes
Special Editions: Back-to-School (Aug); Bridal Tab (Feb); Tax Tips Tab (Jan); Regional Outlook (March); Home Improvement (May); Sports Magazine (Monthly); Car Care Tab (Oct); Home Improvement (Sept). Medical Journal (Monthly)
Special Weekly Sections: Real Estate (Sat); TV & Entertainment (Sat)
Syndicated Publications: Relish (Monthly); Parade (Sunday).
Digital Platform - Mobile: Apple, Android
Digital Platform - Tablet: Apple iOS, Android
Sports Ed. .... Mike Burke
Editorial page editor .... Jim Goldsworthy
Community Editor .... Debbie Haan
City Editor .... Mark Harris
Digital Ed. .... Teresa McMinn
Special Projects Editor .... Debbie Meyer
Outdoor Editor .... Mike Sawyers
Managing Editor .... John Smith
News Editor .... Marisa Hammond
Market Information: TMC.
Mechanical Available: Offset; Black and 3 ROP colors; insert accepted; page cutoffs - 22 3/4.
Mechanical Specifications: Type page 11 5/8 x 21 1/2; E - 6 cols, 1 5/6, 1/8 between; A - 6 cols, 1 5/6, 1/8 between; C - 9 cols, 1 1/4, 1/16 between.
Areas Served: Cumberland and the surrounding areas of Allegany and Garrett counties in Maryland, and Mineral County in West Virginia.
Delivery Method: Mail, Newsstand, Carrier, RacksEquipment & Software: PRESSROOM EQUIPMENT: Lines — 8-G/Cosmo, 1-G/Cosmo Press-5units-#3543 1979; Reels & Stands — 5, 10.; MAILROOM EQUIPMENT: Counter Stackers — 1-Id/2000; Inserters & Stuffers — GMA/8 pocket, GMA/SLS 1000; Tying Machines — 1-MLN/NPS 80, OVL/JP-40, MLN/2EE, Power Strap/PSNG, PS/5; Address Machine — KR; BUSINESS EQUIPMENT: IBM/Sys 36, M/8, K/9000 BUSINESS SOFTWARE: Newzware CLASSIFIED EQUIPMENT: Hardware — PC, APP/iMac, APP/Mac G3; 4-COM; Printers — Genicom, Tegra/4000, Pre Press/Panther Pro, V/5100, DEC/1152, Xante/36, Pre Press/Panther Pro 36, Pre Press/Panther Pro 46; CLASSIFIED SOFTWARE: COM/One Sys, CText, Baseview/Ad Manger Pro. DISPLAY EQUIPMENT: Hardware — PC, APP/iMac; Printers — DEC/Laser 1152, Pre Press/Panther Pro 46, Pre Press/Panther Pro 36, Xante/36; DISPLAY SOFTWAREAd Make-up Applications — CText, Multi-Ad/Creator 4.0.6; Layout Software — SCS/Layout 8000, ALS 2.5, MEI/ALS. EDITORIAL EQUIPMENT: Hardware — PC, APP/iMac, APP/Mac G3/14-COM, APP/Mac Quadra 950, X/1200 R Scanner, Lf/AP Leaf Picture Desk, Lf/Leafscan 35; Printers — Genicom, Tegra/4000, Pre Press/Panther Pro, V/5100, DEC/1152, Xante/36, Pre Press/Panther Pro 36, Pre Press/ PRODUCTION EQUIPMENT: Hardware — 1-Nu/Flip Top FT40V4UP, 2-V/5100, 1-V/4000, 1-V/5300E; Cameras — 1-C/Spartan II; Scanners — Sharp/Color, X/B-W PRODUCTION SOFTWARE: QPS/QuarkXPress 3.12, QPS/QuarkXPress 3.1.

EASTON

THE STAR-DEMOCRAT

29088 Airpark Dr, Easton, Md., 21601-7000, Talbot; gen tel (410) 822-1500; adv tel (410) 770-4040; ed tel (410) 770-4093; gen fax (410) 770-4011; adv fax (410) 770-4048; ed fax (410) 770-4019; gen/nat adv e-mail klaprade@chespub.com; disp adv e-mail klaprade@chespub.com; class adv e-mailsgarcia@chespub.com; ed e-mail bsauers@chespub.com; web site www.stardem.com
Published: Mon, Tues, Wed, Thur, Fri, Sun
Weekday Frequency: m
Circulation: 15,284; 16,326(sun)
Last Audit: Sworn/Estimate/Non-Audited September 30, 2017
Advertising Rate (weekday/saturday): Open inch rate $24.95
Online Advertising Rate: Rail 4 or 5 $8.00 CPM; In Story $10.00 CPM; Rail 1, 2, or 3 $12.00 CPM;
News services: AP. **Established:** 1896
Own Printing Facility?: Yes
Commercial Printers?: Yes
Special Editions: Healthy Living (Monthly); Chesapeake 360 (Quarterly); Business Ledger (Quarterly)
Special Weekly Sections: Church Page (Fri); Weekend (Fri); Family Page (Mon); Life on the Shore (S); Life on the Shore (Wed).
Syndicated Publications: Relish (Monthly); USA WEEKEND Magazine (S); American Profile (Weekly).
Digital Platform - Mobile: Apple, Android
Digital Platform - Tablet: Apple iOS, Android
Pres./Pub. .... David Fike
Circ. Dir. .... Kevin A. Fike
Exec. Ed. .... John Griep
Rgl. Plant & Prod. Dir. .... Mike Bowen
Rgl. IT Mgr. .... David Alltop
Rgl. Controller .... Melodie Haufe
Deputy/Weekend Ed. .... Greg Maki
News Ed. .... Josh Bollinger
Sports Ed. .... William Haufe
Business Ed. .... Richard Polk
Community Ed. .... Katie Willis
Staff Writer .... Ayman Alam
Staff Writer .... Chris Polk
Reporter .... Connie Connolly
Staff Writer .... David Insley
Reporter .... Sarah Drury
Adv. Dir. .... Brandon Silverstein
Mechanical Available: Offset; Black and 3 ROP colors; insert accepted; page cutoffs - 22 3/4.
Mechanical Specifications: Type page 12 x 21; E - 6 cols, 1 7/8, 1/10 between; A - 6 cols, 1 7/8, 1/10 between; C - 9 cols, 1 3/16, 1/10 between.
Areas Served: 21601
Delivery Method: Mail, Newsstand, Carrier, RacksEquipment & Software: PRESSROOM EQUIPMENT: Lines — 1-DGM/430; 14-G/Community; Folders — 2-G/SSC; Control System — Fin.; MAILROOM EQUIPMENT: Counter Stackers — QWI/400, Newstech, SLS/1000; Tying Machines — 4-Dynaric; Address Machine — 1-Ch/Labeler, 2-Videojet/4000.; BUSINESS EQUIPMENT: TI/990, AST/386, AST/286 BUSINESS SOFTWARE: ICIS, Lotus, Prologic/PR, Xenix, Aware CLASSIFIED EQUIPMENT: Hardware — APP/Mac, PC; Printers — APP/Mac Laser, Birmy/Page Scan 3, HP/551, HP/400; CLASSIFIED SOFTWARE: Brainworks/Classified. DISPLAY EQUIPMENT: Hardware — APP/Mac; Printers — APP/Mac Laser, HP/551; Other Hardware — Microtek/MSF-300G Image Scanner DISPLAY SOFTWAREAd Make-up Applications — QPS/QuarkXPress 4.04; Layout Software — MEI/ALS. EDITORIAL EQUIPMENT: Hardware — APP/Mac, APP/Mac G3, APP/Mac G4/APP/Mac Scanner, Sun/Sparc, Sun/Sparc Station, AP/Satellite Data Sys, Lf/AP Leaf Picture Desk; Printers — APP/Mac Laser, HP/551 EDITORIAL SOFTWARE: QPS/QuarkXPress 4.04, Microsoft/Windows. PRODUCTION EQUIPMENT: Hardware — Amerigraph/Magnum.

FREDERICK

THE FREDERICK NEWS-POST

351 Ballenger Center Dr, Frederick, Md., 21703-7095, Frederick; gen tel (301) 662-1177; adv tel (301) 662-1162; ed tel (301) 662-1178; gen fax (301) 682-7831; adv fax (301) 698-5206; ed fax (301) 662-8299; gen/nat adv e-mail chastings@newspost.com; disp adv e-mail wmillander@newspost.com; class adv e-mailclassifieds@fredericknewspost.com; ed e-mail theadlee@newspost.com; web site www.fredericknewspost.com
Group: Ogden Newspapers Inc.
Published: Mon, Tues, Wed, Thur, Fri, Sat, Sun
Weekday Frequency: m
Saturday Frequency: m
Circulation: 26,155; 26,155(sat); 28,056(sun)
Last Audit: AAM September 30, 2015
Advertising Rate (weekday/saturday): Open inch rate $25.50
News services: AP, SHNS, CNS, MCT, TMS. **Established:** 1883
Own Printing Facility?: Yes
Commercial Printers?: Yes
Special Editions: Frederick Keys Orioles Supplement (Pullout) (Apr); Fall Football Guide (Aug); Holiday Gift Guide (Dec); Wedding Planner (Jan); Hello Frederick County (Jul); Progress (Mar); Spring Automotive (May); Holiday Magazine (Nov); Fall Automotive (Oct); Healthy Frederick (Dec).
Special Weekly Sections: Lifestyle (Fri); Farm (Mon); Religion & Ethics (Sat); Business (Mon); Comics (S); Auto (Sat); Home & Family (Thur); Health & Fitness (Tues); Food (Wed).
Syndicated Publications: Relish (Monthly); USA WEEKEND Magazine (S); TV Week (Sat); American Profile (Wed).
Digital Platform - Mobile: Apple, Android
Digital Platform - Tablet: Apple iOS, Android
Pres .... Myron W. Randall
Pub .... Geordie Wilson
Adv. Mgr. .... Connie Hastings
Mng. Ed. .... Terry Headlee
City Ed. .... Peter McCarthy
CEO .... Will Randall
Ed. .... Patrick Pexton
Dir. Adv. & Mrktg. .... Brent Renken
Web Ed. .... Travis Pratt
Community News .... Karen James
Ed. ....Christopher Kinsler
Market Information: Split run; TMC.
Mechanical Available: Offset; Black and 3 ROP colors; insert accepted - all; page cutoffs - 21.
Mechanical Specifications: Type page 11 1/2 x 21; E - 6 cols, 1 13/16, 1/8 between; A - 6 cols, 1 13/16, 1/8 between; C - 9 cols, 1 1/8, 1/8 between.
Areas Served: 21701, 21704, 21702, 21703, 21710, 21717, 21754, 21765, 21770, 21771, 21774, 21797, 21727, 21757, 21778, 21780, 21787, 21788, 21791, 21157, 21158, 21762, 21776, 21793, 21798, 20180, 21195, 21713, 21716, 21755, 21756, 21758, 21777, 21779, 21782, 21714, 21718, 21740, 21741, 21742, 21746, 21769, 21773, 21783, 20837, 20841, 20842, 20850, 20855
Delivery Method: Mail, Newsstand, Carrier, RacksEquipment & Software: PRESSROOM EQUIPMENT: Lines — 6-TKS Colortop 4000; Press Drive — shaftless; Folders — 2- TKS 3:2:2 (1 with quarter fold); Pasters —9-MegtecControl System — TKS; Registration System — QTI MAILROOM EQUIPMENT: Counter Stackers — 3-QWI/501, 1-QWI/401; Inserters & Stuffers — GMA/SLS 2000 12:2, SLS3000 24:2; Tying Machines — 3-DynaricViper, 2-/PackMan; Wrapping Singles — 1-HL/Monarch; Address Machine — KirkRudy; BUSINESS EQUIPMENT: APP/iMac, APP/Mac G4, Baseview CLASSIFIED EQUIPMENT: Hardware — 8-APP/eMac, 3-APP/iBook, APP/PowerBook G4, IMac; 2-ECR/Autokon; Printers — Xerox; CLASSIFIED SOFTWARE: Baseview/Advertising Pro DISPLAY EQUIPMENT: Hardware — 7-APP/iBook, 3-APP/iMac, 2-APP/PowerBook G4, 2-APP/PowerMac G4; Printers — Xerox/ColorCube; Other Hardware — 2-AG/Horizon Scanners, 2 DISPLAY SOFTWAREAd Make-up Applications — Baseview/Advertising Pro 2.1.x, Baseview/ProductionManagerPro 1.9; EDITORIAL EQUIPMENT: Hardware — 12-APP/eMac, 24-APP/PowerMac G4, 6-APP/iBook, 5-APP/PowerBook G4; Printers — Xerox EDITORIAL SOFTWARE: Baseview/NewsEditPro IQue 3.5.3, QPS/QuarkXPress 4.1.1, DD. PRODUCTION EQUIPMENT: Hardware — 1-Nat/A-250, 4-Multi-Ad; Scanners — Epson/Expression 1640XL, Microtek/Artix 2020 PRODUCTION SOFTWARE: QuarkXPress, Baseview/NewsEditPro IQue, Baseview/Classflow, MEI/ALS 4.2, Baseview/ProductionManagerPro

HAGERSTOWN

THE HERALD-MAIL

100 Summit Ave, Hagerstown, Md., 21740-5509, Washington; gen tel (301) 733-5131; adv tel (301) 733-5131; ed tel (301) 733-5131; gen fax (301) 739-7518; adv fax (301) 739-7518; ed fax (301) 739-7518; gen/nat adv e-mail brittneyh@herald-mail.com; disp adv e-mail advertising@herald-mail.com; class adv e-mailadvertising@herald-mail.com; ed e-mail billk@herald-mail.com; web site www.heraldmailmedia.com
- 4,000,000(views) 330,000(visitors)
Group: Schurz Communications Inc
Published: Mon, Tues, Wed, Thur, Fri, Sat, Sun
Weekday Frequency: m
Saturday Frequency: m
Circulation: 23,637; 23,637(sat); 28,289(sun)
Last Audit: AAM March 31, 2014
Advertising Rate (weekday/saturday): Open inch rate $27.00
Advertising Rate (sunday): Open inch rate $28.00
Online Advertising Rate: Leaderboard $15 CPM
Wow (300x250 pixles) $15 CPM
Super Wow (300x600) $17 CPM
News services: AP. **Established:** 1873
Special Weekly Sections: Money (S); Weekend (Thur); Farm Page (Tues); Food Pages & Recipes (Wed).
Syndicated Publications: Relish (Monthly); Parade (S).
Digital Platform - Mobile: Apple, Android
Digital Platform - Tablet: Apple iOS, Android
Sports Ed. .... Andy Mason
Lifestyle Ed. .... Crystal Schelle
Exec. Ed. .... Jake Womer
Asst. Sports Ed. .... Dan Kauffman
Managing Ed. .... Terry Headlee
Market Information: ADS; TMC.
Mechanical Available: Offset; Black and 3 ROP colors; insert accepted - Product Samples/Donation Bags; page cutoffs - 21 1/2.
Mechanical Specifications: Type page 12 x 21 1/2; E - 6 cols, 1 5/6, 1/8 between; A - 6 cols, 1 5/6, 1/8 between; C - 9 cols, between.
Areas Served: Maryland, Pennsylvania and West Virginia
Delivery Method: Mail, Newsstand, Carrier, RacksEquipment & Software: PRESSROOM EQUIPMENT: Control System — 2, 2. EDITORIAL EQUIPMENT: Hardware — APP/iMac, APP/Mac G4, Mac Mini, MacBooks; Printers — Savin EDITORIAL SOFTWARE: Baseview. PRODUCTION EQUIPMENT: Hardware — Nat, Nu; Scanners — Epson Expression Umax Powerlook III PRODUCTION SOFTWARE: Baseview/NewsEdit Pro IQue 3+, InDesign CS2

SALISBURY

THE DAILY TIMES

618 Beam St, Salisbury, Md., 21801-7803, Wicomico; gen tel (410) 749-7171; adv tel (410) 749-7171; ed tel (410) 749-7171; gen fax (410) 543-8736; adv fax (410) 543-8736; ed fax (410) 749-7290; gen/nat adv e-mail cstubbs@dmg.gannett.com; disp adv e-mail cstubbs@dmg.gannett.com; class adv e-mailkrowan@dmg.gannett.com; ed e-mail mkilian@dmg.gannett.com; web site www.delmarvanow.com
Group: Gannett
Published: Mon, Tues, Wed, Thur, Fri, Sat, Sun
Weekday Frequency: m
Saturday Frequency: m
Circulation: 11,334; 11,334(sat); 14,799(sun)
Last Audit: AAM December 31, 2016
Branch Offices: Maryland, Virginia, Delaware
Advertising Rate (weekday/saturday): Open inch rate $24.00
News services: AP, NEA. **Established:** 1886
Own Printing Facility?: No
Commercial Printers?: No
Special Editions: Visitor's Guide (Apr); Health Guide (Feb); Eastern Shore Real Estate (Monthly); Visitor's Guide (Sept).
Special Weekly Sections: Go! (Fri); Best Food Days (S); TV (Sat); Best Food Days (Wed).
Digital Platform - Mobile: Apple, Android
Digital Platform - Tablet: Apple iOS, Android, Windows 7, Blackberry Tablet OS, Kindle, Nook, Kindle Fire
Adv. Dir. .... Robb Scott
Ops. Dir. .... Ron Smith
Classified Key Rep. .... Greg Ardis
Lou Haut
Sales Mgr. .... Latasha Cooper-Peters
Customer Service Rep .... Jennifer Stutzman
Exec. Asst. .... Nikki Iovacchini
Exec. Ed. .... Mike Kilian
Market Information: TMC.
Areas Served: Wicomico County
Delivery Method: Mail, Newsstand, Carrier, Racks

WESTMINSTER

CARROLL COUNTY TIMES

201 Railroad Ave, Westminster, Md., 21157-4823, Carroll; gen tel (410) 848-4400; adv tel (410) 848-4400; ed tel (410) 857-7878; gen fax (410) 857-1176; adv fax (410) 857-1176; ed fax (410) 857-1176; gen/nat adv e-mail marketing@carrollcountytimes.com; disp adv e-mail erin.hahn@carrollcountytimes.com; class adv e-mailclassified@lcniofmd.com; ed e-mail jim.lee@carrollcountytimes.com; web site www.carrollcountytimes.com
- 1,290,000(views) 100,000(visitors)
Group: Landmark Media Enterprises, LLC
Published: Mon, Tues, Wed, Thur, Fri, Sat, Sun
Weekday Frequency: m
Saturday Frequency: m
Circulation: 12,021; 12,021(sat); 14,957(sun)
Last Audit: AAM December 31, 2017
Advertising Rate (weekday/saturday): Open inch rate $20.45
Advertising Rate (sunday): Open inch rate $22.90
Online Advertising Rate: Top Leaderboard $25.65 CPM; Top Cube $20.25 CPM; Bottom Cube 16.20 CPM.
News services: AP, GNS, SHNS. **Established:** 1911
Own Printing Facility?: Yes
Commercial Printers?: Yes
Special Editions: Bridal Guide (Jan); Home & Garden (Mar); Pet Guide (June); Carroll Living (June); Fall Sports (Aug); Fall Home Improvement (Oct); Wine Festival (Sept); Holiday Guide (Nov).
Special Weekly Sections: Prep Sports (Fri); Religion (Sat); Entertainment/Encore (Thur); Best Food Day (Wed).
Syndicated Publications: Relish (Monthly); Parade Magazine (S); American Profile (Weekly); Spry (Monthly)
Digital Platform - Mobile: Apple, Android
Digital Platform - Tablet: Apple iOS, Android
News Ed. .... Bob Blubaugh
Prodn. Dir. .... Greg Linard
Post Press Mgr. .... Sandra Rosewag
Commercial Printing Consultant
Kevin Berrier
Online Ed.
Patrick Brannan
Creative Services Manager .... Amy Stem
Ed. .... Wayne Carter
Sr. V.P. .... Trish Carrol
Adv. Dir. .... Adam Malat
Sports Ed. .... Pat Stoetzer
Adv. Asst. .... Corrine Kauffman
Night Ed. .... Brian Compere
Online/Multimedia Prod. .... Max Simpson
Photo Ed. .... Jeff Bill
Market Information: TMC; Zoned editions.
Mechanical Available: Offset; Black and 3 ROP colors; insert accepted; page cutoffs - 22 3/4.
Mechanical Specifications: Type page 13 x 21 1/2; E - 6 cols, 2 1/16, 1/8 between; A - 6 cols, 2 1/16, 1/8 between; C - 6 cols, 2 1/16, 1/8 between.
Areas Served: 21048, 21074, 21102, 21104, 21117, 21136, 21155, 21157, 21158, 21757, 21765, 21771, 21776, 21784, 21787, 21791, 21797
Delivery Method: Newsstand, Carrier, RacksEquipment & Software: PRESSROOM EQUIPMENT: Lines — 9-G/Super Community; 5-G/Community; 10-G/Urbanite; Pasters —6, 1Reels & Stands — Mill/Stands.; MAILROOM EQUIPMENT: Counter Stackers — 2-HI/RS-3010, 1-HI/RS, LD, 1-BG/Count-O-Veyor 1055MM; Inserters & Stuffers — 1-MM/7:1, 1-HI/1372 (Dual Delivery Lines), 1-MM/Stacker, 2-Id/Stacker; Tying Machines — 2/Bu, 2-/OVL, 1-OVL/Semi-automatic, 1-Ty/Tech; Address Machine — Addressing ma; BUSINESS EQUIPMENT: IBM/Sys 36, 3-Convergent/AWS, PC 386, PC 486, PC 586 BUSINESS SOFTWARE: Microsoft/DOS 310, Microsoft/Works, Microsoft/Office, Lotus, Corel/Word Perfect 6.1, Microsoft/Windows 95 CLASSIFIED EQUIPMENT: Hardware — Compaq/Proliant, Dell/Pentium III, Microsoft/Windows NT 4.0; Printers — 2-AG, HP/LaserJet 4050 TN, Avantra/25xT Imagesetter; CLASSIFIED SOFTWARE: APT/Classified System. DISPLAY EQUIPMENT: Hardware — 13-APP/Mac, 2-APP/Power Mac 7100, APP/Power Mac 7300, APP/Mac G3; Printers — HP/LaserJet, ECR/Pelbox 3850, ECR/Pelbox 1245CX, AG, Avantra/25xT, HP/LaserJet 8000; Other Hardware — QuarkXPress, Adobe/Photoshop, DISPLAY SOFTWAREAd Make-up Applications — Multi-Ad/Creator 4.01; EDITORIAL EQUIPMENT: Hardware — Novell, Dell/Pentium II; Printers — HP/LaserJet IV, Avantra/25xT Imagesetter EDITORIAL SOFTWARE: BLOX Total CMS platform PRODUCTION EQUIPMENT: Hardware — WL, Teaneck, Konica/OL Conveyor System; Cameras — C/Spartan III, AG/2024; Scanners — AG/Arcus II, Umax/Astra 2400S, Scitex/Smart 342L, 2-Umax/Powerlook II, HP/ScanJet 4C PRODUCTION SOFTWARE: APT/Classified System with QuarkXPress 3.32.

MASSACHUSETTS

ATHOL

ATHOL DAILY NEWS

225 Exchange St, Athol, Mass., 01331-1843, Worcester; gen tel (978) 249-3535; adv tel (978) 249-3535 ext. 615; ed tel (978) 249-3535 ext. 658; gen fax (978) 249-9630; adv fax (978) 249-9630; ed fax (978) 249-9630; gen/nat adv e-mail advertising@atholdailynews.com; disp adv e-mail advertising@atholdailynews.com; class adv e-mailclassified@atholdailynews.com; ed e-mail newsroom@atholdailynews.com; web site www.atholdailynews.com
Group: Athol Press Inc.
Published: Mon, Tues, Wed, Thur, Fri, Sat
Weekday Frequency: e
Saturday Frequency: m
Circulation: 4,661; 4,661(sat)
Last Audit: Sworn/Estimate/Non-Audited September 30, 2017
Advertising Rate (weekday/saturday): Open inch rate $8.00
Advertising Rate (sunday): Open inch rate $9.20
Online Advertising Rate:
News services: AP. **Established:** 1934
Own Printing Facility?: Yes
Commercial Printers?: Yes
Special Editions: River Rat Review (Apr); First Baby Contest (Dec); Boy Scout Page (Feb); Bridal Supplement (Jan); Graduation Pages (Jun); Graduation Pages (May); Thanksgiving Greetings (Nov); Fire Prevention (Oct); Football Pages (Sept). Back to School supplement (Aug)
Special Weekly Sections: Quabbin Times (Tues).
Digital Platform - Mobile: Apple, Android, Blackberry
Digital Platform - Tablet: Apple iOS, Android, Blackberry Tablet OS
Pub. .... Richard J. Chase
Ed. .... Deborrah Porter
Adv. Mgr. .... Jacqueline Caron
Office Mgr. .... Lisa Arnot
Circ. Mgr. .... Brandy Nadeau
Sports Ed. .... Josh Talbot
Classified Adv. .... Dee Wheeler
Prod. Mgr. .... Theresa Cody
Webmaster .... Jared Robinson
Market Information: TMC.
Mechanical Available: Offset; Black and 3 ROP colors; insert accepted - single sheet 8 1/2 x 11 minimum; page cutoffs - 22 3/4.
Mechanical Specifications: Type page 13 x 21; E - 6 cols, 2 1/16, 1/4 between; A - 6 cols, 2 1/16, 1/4 between; C - 8 cols, 1 1/2, 1/8 between.
Areas Served: 01331, 01364, 01365, 01378, 01344, 01366, 01368, 01379, 01468
Delivery Method: Mail, Newsstand, CarrierEquipment & Software: PRESSROOM EQUIPMENT: Lines — 4-G.; MAILROOM EQUIPMENT: Tying Machines — 1/Strapex; Address Machine — 1-RSK/TRS 80, Vision Data/Circ Sys, 1-/Ch.; BUSINESS EQUIPMENT: RSK/TRS-80, Vision Data/Business Sys, APP/Mac Desktop Pub Sys CLASSIFIED EQUIPMENT: Hardware — APP/Mac; CLASSIFIED SOFTWARE: Baseview. DISPLAY EQUIPMENT: Hardware — Vision Data; DISPLAY SOFTWARELayout Software — APP/Mac. EDITORIAL EQUIPMENT: Hardware — APP/Mac; Printers - MON/PageScan, GCC EDITORIAL SOFTWARE: Baseview. PRODUCTION EQUIPMENT: Hardware — 1-Nu; Cameras — 1-Nu/20 x 24.

ATTLEBORO

THE SUN CHRONICLE

34 S Main St, Attleboro, Mass., 02703-2920, Bristol; gen tel (508) 222-7000; adv tel (508) 236-0309; ed tel (508) 236-0887; gen fax (508) 226-0456; adv fax (508) 236-0461; ed fax (508) 236-0462; gen/nat adv e-mail rlacaillade@thesunchronicle.com; disp adv e-mail jcambridge@thesunchronicle.com; class adv e-mailclass@thesunchronicle.com; ed e-mail cborges@thesunchronicle.com; web site www.thesunchronicle.com
- 1,568,000(views) 500,000(visitors)
Group: United Communications Corporation
Published: Mon, Tues, Wed, Thur, Fri, Sat, Sun
Weekday Frequency: m
Saturday Frequency: m
Circulation: 10,769; 10,769(sat); 11,752(sun)
Last Audit: AAM June 30, 2016
Advertising Rate (weekday/saturday): Open inch rate $19.47
Advertising Rate (sunday): Open inch rate $19.47
News services: AP **Established:** 1889
Own Printing Facility?: Yes
Commercial Printers?: Yes
Special Editions: Health & Fitness, Your Home, Super Bowl, Preschool, Kindergarten, Childcare (Jan); Valentines, Bridal, Auto (Feb); Coupons (Mar); Readers' Choice, Beautiful Homes & Gardens, Business Card (Apr); Mother's Day Dining, Summertime Golf (May); Parenting, Church Directory (June); Back-to-School, Bus Routes, Sales Tax, Wedding Expo (Aug); High School Football, Home Impreovement (Sept); Frequent Flyer, Pink October, Dining Guide (Oct); Holiday Gift Guide (Nov); Last Minute Gifts, Festive Foods, Holiday Viewers, Basketball, New Year's Dining (Dec)
Special Weekly Sections: Pets (Mon); Teens (Tues); Best Food Day (Wed), Entertainment (Thurs).
Syndicated Publications: Relish (Monthly); USA WEEKEND Magazine (S); American Profile (Weekly).
Digital Platform - Mobile: Apple, Android
Digital Platform - Tablet: Apple iOS, Android, Windows 7
Ed. .... Mike Kirby
Asst. Mng. Ed., Features .... Ken Ross
Business .... Craig Borges
Editorial Page Ed. .... Mark Flanagan
Sports Ed. .... Dale Ransom
Sunday Ed. .... Tom Reilly
Pub. .... Jeff Peterson
Emily O'Donnell
Circ. Sales Mgr. .... Kathy Powell
IT /Digital Media Mgr. .... David Kiely
Sports .... Ken Lechtanski
Market Information: Split run; TMC;
Mechanical Available: Offset; Black and 4 ROP colors; insert accepted; page cutoffs - 22 3/4.
Mechanical Specifications: Type page 13 x 21 1/2; E - 6 cols, 2 1/16, 1/8 between; A - 6 cols, 2 1/16, 1/8 between; C - 9 cols, 1 3/8, 1/16 between.
Areas Served: Attleboro and North Attleboro, Foxboro, Mansfield, Norfolk, Norton, Plainville, Rehoboth, Seekonk, and Wrentham
Delivery Method: Mail, Newsstand, Carrier, RacksEquipment & Software: PRESSROOM EQUIPMENT: Lines — 10-G/Urbanite; MAILROOM EQUIPMENT: Counter Stackers — 2-HL/Monitor II; Inserters & Stuffers — GMA/SLS 1000 (10 pockets); Tying Machines — 1/MLN, 2-MLN/ML2EE, Power Strap.; BUSINESS EQUIPMENT: HP/3000 Model 927 BUSINESS SOFTWARE: GEAC/Vision Shift CLASSIFIED EQUIPMENT: Hardware — Novell/Netserver; Printers — 2-Typhoon/800 dpi; CLASSIFIED SOFTWARE: CText/OS-2 Advision. DISPLAY EQUIPMENT: Hardware — PC fileserver; Printers — Hyphen/600 dpi, Typhoon/800 dpi, 2-AU/APS 6/84; Other Hardware — 3-Umax/840 scanners DISPLAY SOFTWAREAd Make-up Applications — QuarkXPress, Microsoft/Windows NT; Layout Software — 3-PC, Layout/8000. EDITORIAL EQUIPMENT: Hardware — Novell/Netserver/AU/APS 6-84 ACS, Imagesetters; Printers — Typhoon/800 dpi, Hyphen/600 dpi EDITORIAL SOFTWARE: CText/Dateline, Microsoft/Windows NT. PRODUCTION EQUIPMENT: Hardware — 2-AU/APS 6/84 ACS, 3-APP/Mac LaserWriter NTX, Hyphen/600 dpi, 2-Typhoon/800 dpi PRODUCTION SOFTWARE: QPS/QuarkXPress 3.1.

BEVERLY

THE SALEM NEWS

32 Dunham Rd, Beverly, Mass., 01915-1844, Essex; gen tel (978) 922-1234; adv tel (978) 338-2640; ed tel (978) 338-2531; gen fax (978) 927-4330; adv fax (978) 927-4330; ed fax (978) 927-4330; gen/nat adv e-mail btrefethen@salemnews.com; disp adv e-mail btrefethen@salemnews.com; class adv e-mailbtrefethen@salemnews.com; ed e-mail dolson@salemnews.com; web site www.salemnews.com
- 2,300,000(views)
Group: Community Newspaper Holdings, Inc.
Published: Mon, Tues, Wed, Thur, Fri, Sat
Weekday Frequency: e
Saturday Frequency: e
Circulation: 13,730; 13,730(sat)
Last Audit: AAM June 30, 2017
Advertising Rate (weekday/saturday): Open inch rate $40.95
Online Advertising Rate: Skyscrapper $150.00; Medium Rectangle $295.00; Homepage $350.00;
News services: AP **Established:** 1880
Own Printing Facility?: Yes
Commercial Printers?: Yes
Syndicated Publications: Marblehead Home & Style
Digital Platform - Mobile: Apple, Android,

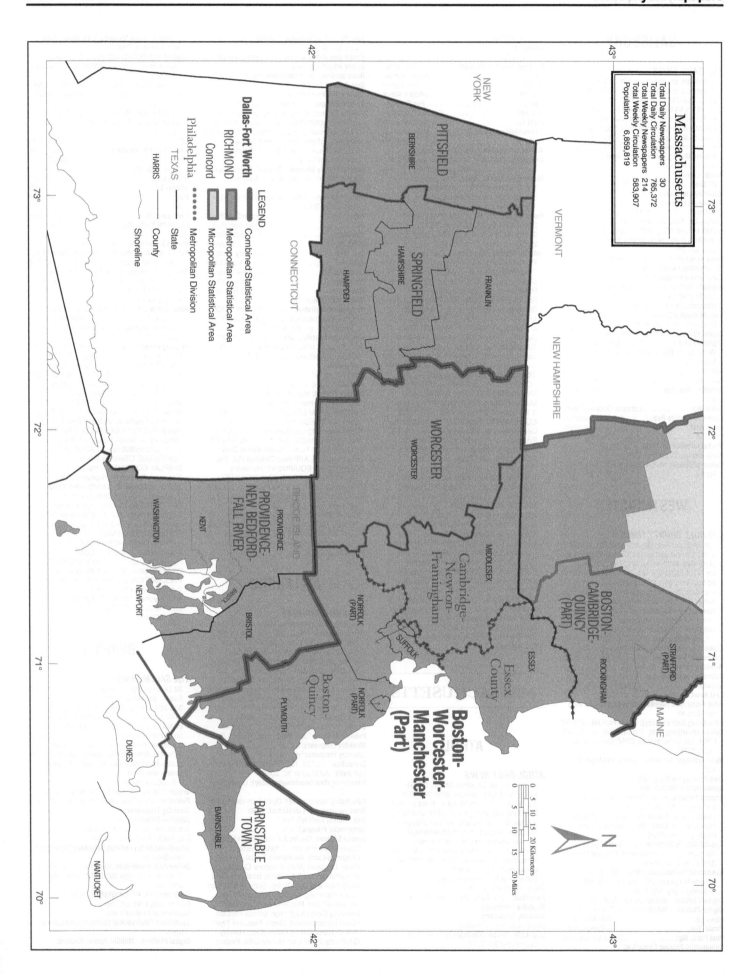

Massachusetts

Total Daily Newspapers	30
Total Daily Circulation	765,372
Total Weekly Newspapers	214
Total Weekly Circulation	583,907
Population	6,859,819

LEGEND

Combined Statistical Area
Metropolitan Statistical Area
Micropolitan Statistical Area
Metropolitan Division

Dallas-Fort Worth
RICHMOND
Concord
Philadelphia

TEXAS — State
HARRIS — County
—— Shoreline

Windows
Digital Platform - Tablet: Apple iOS, Android, Windows 7
Pub... Karen Andreas
Ed... David Olson
Retail Adv. Mgr............................. Bill Trefethen
Mng. Ed....................................... Helen Gifford
Sports Ed........................................ Phil Stacey
Night Ed................................. Dove Morissette
Community Ed.......................... Muriel Hoffacker
Market Information: TMC; Zoned editions.
Areas Served: Salem, Beverly, Danvers, Peabody, Ipswich, Hamilton, Wenham, Marblehead, Swampscott, Middleton, Topsfield, Boxford and Manchester
Delivery Method: Mail, Newsstand, Carrier, Racks

BOSTON

BOSTON HERALD

70 Fargo St Ste 600, Seaport Center, Boston, Mass., 02210-2131, Suffolk; gen tel (617) 426-3000; adv tel (617) 619-6185; ed tel (617) 619-6515; gen fax (617) 619-6450; adv fax (617) 619-6160; ed fax (617) 619-6450; gen/nat adv e-mail advertising@bostonherald.com; disp adv e-mail advertising@bostonherald.com; class adv e-mailclassifiedads@bostonherald.com; ed e-mail citydesk@bostonherald.com; web site www.bostonherald.com - 35,000,000(views) 4,879,000(visitors)
Group: Digital First Media
Published: Mon, Tues, Wed, Thur, Fri, Sat, Sun
Weekday Frequency: m
Saturday Frequency: m
Circulation: 86,567; 74,266(sat); 76,798(sun)
Last Audit: AAM March 31, 2016
Advertising Rate (weekday/saturday): Open rate $444.00 per modular unit
Advertising Rate (sunday): Open rate $444.00 per modular unit
News services: AP, RN, Business Wire, DJ, TMS. **Established:** 1846
Own Printing Facility?: No
Commercial Printers?: No
Special Editions: Careers Extra (Monthly); Health (Semi-Yearly).
Special Weekly Sections: Scene (Fri); Business Extra (Mon); Sports Pull-Out (Sun); Super Saturday Classifieds (Sat); Travel (Thur); Tuesday Business(Tues); Food (Wed).
Digital Platform - Mobile: Apple, Android
Digital Platform - Tablet: Apple iOS, Android, Kindle, Kindle Fire
Pres./Pub..................................... Patrick Purcell
VP, Finance................................ Jeffrey Magram
Circ. Mgr., Home Delivery................ Gerald Sher
Circ. Mgr., Single Copy Sales.......... John Palmer
Deputy Mgr. Ed., Features................ Sandra Kent
Exec. City Ed..................................... Jen Miller
Design/Prod. Ed.................................. Jim Potter
Editorial Page Ed............................ Shelly Cohen
Sr. Dir. Finance & Info Technology Joseph O'Neill
Ed. in Chief.................................. Joseph Sciacca
VP/Promotion.................................. Gwen Gage
Vice Pres./Display Advertising.............. Brian Cox
Vice Pres./Classified Advt........... Joseph LoPilato
Dir. of Display Adv....................John Nemerowski
Dir. of Information Systems.......... Steve Bowden
Dir. of Publishing Systems.............. Duncan Suss
Washington Ed............................. Kimberly Atkins
Editorial Page Ed......................... Rachelle Cohen
Managing Editor........................ John Strahinich
City Desk Ed.............................. Joseph Dwinell
Producer Herald Radio.................. Tom Shattuck
Sunday Editor................................ Fiona Molloy
City Ed...................................... Jules Crittenden
Photo Ed.................................... James Mahoney
Multimedia Ed..................................... Zuri Berry
Asst.t Photo Ed............................. Arthur Pollock
Art Dir... Gustavo Leon
Food Ed....................................... Scott Kearnan
Market Information: Split run.
Mechanical Available: Offset (direct); Black and 3 ROP colors; insert accepted; page cutoffs - 22 3/4.
Mechanical Specifications: Type page 10 1/2 x 10.875; E - 6 cols, 1.5625, 1/8 between; A - 6 cols, 1.5625, 1/8 between; C - 9 cols, 1 , 1/8 between.
Areas Served: 02210
Delivery Method: Mail, Newsstand, Carrier, RacksEquipment & Software: BUSINESS EQUIPMENT: 1-Microsoft/NT CS System, 2-Unix C/S Systems, 1-Unix/SCO, 1-Unisys Advtg. System BUSINESS SOFTWARE: Lawson, ADP CLASSIFIED EQUIPMENT: Hardware — Sun/E450; 40-PC Clients; Printers — Panasonic/1180, 1-C.Itoh/8000, 2-HP/DeskJet 520, 1-HP/LaserJet IIP, 1-PAN/KXP-1826, 1-PAN/KXP-1624, 1-PAN/KXP-2124; CLASSIFIED SOFTWARE: Unisys/Ad Manager 3.0. DISPLAY EQUIPMENT: Hardware — 15-APP/Mac; Other Hardware — 2-APP/Mac Classic, 2-PC 486 DISPLAY SOFTWAREAd Make-up Applications — NPSI/Classpag; Layout Software — MEI/ALS. Multi-Ad Creator, Adobe InDesign EDITORIAL EQUIPMENT: HP DL380, VMware, DTI PageSpeed, 60 Macintosh/40 Windows 7 EDITORIAL SOFTWARE: DTI PageSpeed 7.5.2 PRODUCTION EQUIPMENT: Dell PowerEdge 2950 PRODUCTION SOFTWARE: Agfa Arkitex IT EQUIPMENT: HP DL380, Sun/Oracle 7310 storage IT SOFTWARE:VMware VSphere 5.5 CIRCULATION EQUIPMENT: Dell , HP CIRCULATION SOFTWARDSI Home Delivery, NTI Single Copy
Note: herald radio

METRO BOSTON

101 Arch Street, 8th floor, Boston, Mass., 2110, Suffolk; gen tel (617) 210-7905; adv tel (617) 532-0100; ed fax (617) 357-4706; gen/nat adv e-mail adsboston@metro.us; disp adv e-mail adsboston@metro.us; class adv e-mailadsboston@metro.us; ed e-mail letters@metro.us; web site metro.us/boston - 2,971,029(views) 1,191,680(visitors); web site 2 boston.metro.us
Group: Metro US
Published: Mon, Tues, Wed, Thur, Fri
Weekday Frequency: m
Circulation: 57,804
Last Audit: CAC September 30, 2016
Newspaper Reps: Brian Cox - 617-532-0120
Advertising Rate (weekday/saturday): $13,380 Full Page
Advertising Rate (sunday): N/A
Online Advertising Rate: Leaderboard 728x90 $12 CPM
Big Box 300x250 $14 CPM
News services: 2001
Own Printing Facility?: No
Commercial Printers?: No
Digital Platform - Mobile: Apple, Android
Digital Platform - Tablet: Apple iOS, Android
Associate Publisher/ Executive Sales Director ...... Brian Cox
Mechanical Available: 10"x11" Full Page
6 Columns
1 column = 1.53"
2 columns = 3.22"
3 colum sns = 4.92"
4 columns = 6.61"
5 columns = N/A
6 columns = 10"
Areas Served: Great Boston: Suffolk, Middlesex, Norfolk, Essex
Delivery Method: Racks

THE BOSTON GLOBE

135 William T Morrissey Blvd, Boston, Mass., 02125-3310, Suffolk; gen tel (617) 929-2000; adv tel (617) 929-2100; ed tel (617) 929-3059; gen fax (617) 929-3318; adv fax (617) 929-3481; ed fax (617) 929-3186; gen/nat adv e-mail advertising@globe.com; disp adv e-mail p_andrews@globe.com; class adv e-mailclassified@globe.com; ed e-mail mcgrory@globe.com; web site www.bostonglobe.com - 200,000,000(views) 5,500,000(visitors); web site 2 www.boston.com - 41,600,000(views) 2,900,000(visitors)
Published: Mon, Tues, Wed, Thur, Fri, Sat, Sun
Weekday Frequency: m
Saturday Frequency: m
Circulation: 224,286; 222,522(sat); 323,524(sun)
Last Audit: AAM March 31, 2017
Advertising Rate (weekday/saturday): Open inch rate $577.00
Advertising Rate (sunday): Open inch rate $685.00
News services: AP, DJ, LAT-WP, MCT, RN. **Established:** 1872
Own Printing Facility?: Yes
Commercial Printers?: Yes
Special Editions: Mother's Day Restaurants (May); Cape Cod Distinctive Homes (Apr); College Football Preview (Aug); Continuing Education (Dec); Florida (Feb); Valentine's Day Restaurants (Jan); NHIS NASCAR (Jul); Cape Cod Distinctive Shopping (Jun); Health and Hospitals (Mar).
Special Weekly Sections: Real Estate (S); Life At Home (Thur); Health/Science (Tues); Food (Wed).
Syndicated Publications: Parade (S).
Digital Platform - Mobile: Apple, Android
Digital Platform - Tablet: Apple iOS, Android, Kindle, Nook, Kindle Fire
Ed.... Brian McGrory
Vice Pres., HR.......................... Christopher Hall
Mng. Dir., Pdct. Innovation...... Lucy Bartholomay
Adv. Dir., Opns......................... Richard Masotta
Adv. Div. Mgr., Amusement...... Elizabeth Sucher
Deputy Managing Ed., Features........ Janice Page
Sr. Deputy Managing Ed................ Mark Morrow
Deputy Managing Ed..................... Dante Ramos
Asst. Managing Ed........................... David Dahl
Production Ed............................. Michael Bailey
Copy Ed................................... Kenneth Cafarell
Asst. Night Ed............................... Mary Creane
Layout Ed................................. John Harrington
Sports Ed....................................... Matt Pepin
Features Ed................................. Katie McLeod
Prod.... Andrew Mahoney
Travel Ed..................................... Chris Morris
Dir. Adv. Sales.................................. Mary Kelly
Ed. Business............................. Larry Edelman
Dir. Event Mktg......................... Scott Halstead
Asst. Managing Ed....................... Mark Pothier
Prod. Ed................................... Daniel Coleman
Sr. Ed./Video........................... Anush Elbakyan
Managing Ed......................... Christine Chinlund
Managing Ed./Digital........... Kathleen Kingsbury
Market Information: ADS; Split run; TMC; Zoned editions.
Mechanical Available: Offset; Black and 3 ROP colors; insert accepted - product samples; page cutoffs - 22.
Mechanical Specifications: Type page 12 1/2 x 22; E - 6 cols, 1 5/6, 1/8 between; A - 6 cols, 1 5/6, 1/8 between; C - 10 cols, 1, 1/16 between.
Areas Served: Metropolitan Statistical Areas surrounding Boston (MSAs include Boston, Barnstable-Hyannis, Brockton, Fitchburg-Leominster, Lawrence, Lowell, New Bedford, Worcester, MA: Providence-Warwick, RI: Manchester, Nashua, Portsmouth-Rochester, NH)
Delivery Method: Mail, Newsstand, Carrier, RacksEquipment & Software: PRESSROOM EQUIPMENT: Lines — 10-G/Metroliner, 2-G/Metro Color (4/4-color tower); 10-G/Metroliner, 2-G/Metro Color (4/4-color tower); 10-G/Metroliner, 2-G/Metro Color (4/4 color tower); 10-G/Metroliner, 2-G/Metro Color (4/4 color tower); MAILROOM EQUIPMENT: Counter Stackers — 21-QWI/301, 6-HL/Dual Carriers, 16/QWI; Inserters & Stuffers — 15-MM/6:1, 3-GMA/Alphaliner 14:1, 1-GMA/Alphaliner 6:1, 3-GMA/SLS 1000 28:2, 15-GMA/SLS 1000 6:1, 2-GMA/SLS 2000 8:1; Tying Machines — Dynaric/30, Power Strap/13; BUSINESS EQUIPMENT: 1-DEC/VAX 7840, 1-DEC/VAX 7740, 2-DEC/VAX 6620, 1-DEC/VAX 6420, 3-DEC/Alpha 2000, 3-DEC/VAX 4000, 2-DEC/Alpha 4000 CLASSIFIED EQUIPMENT: Hardware — PDP 11; Edgil/credit card processing, MCT/AdFax, MCT/AdFast, Ad Express, AP/AdSend, Cascade/DataFlow; Printers — HP; CLASSIFIED SOFTWARE: ATEX IAS. DISPLAY EQUIPMENT: Hardware — ATEX PDP 11; Printers — AII, AU/Oman direct to plate; Other Hardware — AT/RS6000 (Makeup) DISPLAY SOFTWAREAd Make-up Applications — Cx, AT; Layout Software — 6-IBM/RS 6000-320 at class page, 5-Cx/360, 3-Cx/380, 3-Cx/Sparc IFC, APP/Mac, Cascade/Image, Data Flow. EDITORIAL EQUIPMENT: Hardware — SUN 6800/Reporter System News Engin; Printers — HP EDITORIAL SOFTWARE: CCI. PRODUCTION EQUIPMENT: Hardware — TextBridge, 5-Jensen PRODUCTION SOFTWARE: AT/Ed Page 1.7, Press To Go, AT/Architect.

BROCKTON

THE ENTERPRISE

1324 Belmont St Ste 102, Unit 102, Brockton, Mass., 02301-4435, Plymouth; gen tel (508) 586-6200; adv tel (508) 638-5580; ed tel (508) 427-4054; gen fax (508) 427-4949; adv fax (508) 638-5570; ed fax (508) 427-4027; gen/nat adv e-mail salesteam@wickedlocal.com; disp adv e-mail salesteam@wickedlocal.com; class adv e-mailsalesteam@wickedlocal.com; ed e-mail newsroom@enterprisenews.com; web site www.enterprisenews.com
Group: New Media Investment Group
Published: Mon, Tues, Wed, Thur, Fri, Sat, Sun
Weekday Frequency: e
Saturday Frequency: m
Circulation: 12,135; 12,709(sat); 17,501(sun)
Last Audit: AAM September 30, 2015
Advertising Rate (weekday/saturday): Open inch rate $50.35
Advertising Rate (sunday): Open inch rate $54.13
Online Advertising Rate: Leaderboard $13.00 CPM; Other positions $17.00 CPM
News services: AP, LAT-WP, SHNS. **Established:** 1880
Own Printing Facility?: Yes
Commercial Printers?: Yes
Special Editions: Education (Apr); Coupon Book (Aug); Chronology Pages/Year in Review (Dec); Living Well (Every other month); Coupon Book (Feb); Golfers Corner (Jul); How to Guide (Jun); Progress (Mar); Professional Profiles (May); Gift Guide (Nov); Coupon Book (Oct); Foot
Special Weekly Sections: Style (Fri); Next (Mon); Travel (S); Family Life (Sat); Mind & Body (Thur); Mind & Body (Tues); Good Taste (Wed).
Syndicated Publications: USA WEEKEND Magazine (S).
Digital Platform - Mobile: Apple, Android
Digital Platform - Tablet: Apple iOS, Android
Sports Ed...................................... Mark Torpey
Ed... Chazy Dowaliby
Managing Ed............................. Steven Damish
Evening News Ed.......................... Joe Brosseau
Online Ed...................................... Ken Johnson
Features Ed................................. Dana Barbuto
Visuals Ed...................................... Jen Wagner
Exec. Ed... Lisa Strattan
Market Information: Split run; TMC; Zoned editions.
Mechanical Available: Letterpress and Flexo combined; Black and 3 ROP colors; insert accepted - samples; page cutoffs - 22 3/4.
Mechanical Specifications: Type page 13 x 21; E - 6 cols, 2 1/16, 1/8 between; A - 6 cols, 2 1/16, 1/8 between; C - 9 cols, 1 3/8, 1/16 between.
Areas Served: 02048, 02072, 02301, 02302, 02322, 02324, 02330, 02333, 02338, 02339, 02341, 02343, 02346, 02347, 02351, 02356, 02359, 02360, 02364, 02367, 02368, 02370, 02375, 02379, 02382, 02571, 02718, 02766, 02767, 02779, 02780, 99999
Delivery Method: Mail, CarrierEquipment & Software: PRESSROOM EQUIPMENT: Lines — G/Mark I (double width) 1960; MAN/Flexoman (double width) 1989; MAN/Flexoman (w/hump) (double width) 1989; G/Mark I (double width) 1960; G/Mark I (double width) 1960; MAN/Flexoman (double width) 1989; MAILROOM EQUIPMENT: Counter Stackers — 2-QWI/Sport; Inserters & Stuffers — 1-GMA/SLS 1000; Tying Machines — 1-OVL/JP-80, 1-OVL/JP-80, 2-OVL/Strapmaster; Wrapping Singles — Addressing machine ;2-VideoJet/Series 270.; BUSINESS EQUIPMENT: DEC/VAX 4100, Microsoft/Windows NT, CI/1000 Sge Printer, HP/4050, Dell/GX1 workstation, Mac/O/S, SCO/Unix BUSINESS SOFTWARE: CJ, Southware/Accounting Systems, Geac/Circulation Systems, SCS/ADMAX-Billing CLASSIFIED EQUIPMENT: Hardware — 1-Dell/6300 Application Server, AT/SYSDECO-Classified Pagination Server, 11-Dell/GX1 Workstation; HP/Flatbed Scanner; Printers — 1-HP/8000, HP/4050; CLASSIFIED SOFTWARE: SCS/Admax-Classified, Microsoft/Office 2000, Adobe/Photoshop. DISPLAY EQUIPMENT: Hardware — 1-Dell/6300 Application Server, 1-Dell/4300 Application

Server, 1-Dell/2300 Application Server, 7-APP/Mac G3 workstation, 10-Dell/GX1 Workstation, Umax/Page Scanner; Printers — 1-HP/8000, HP/4050, 1-HP/LaserJet 4MV, 1-Epson/3000; DISPLAY SOFTWAREAd Make-up Applications — SCS; EDITORIAL EQUIPMENT: Hardware — 2-Dell/6400 Application Server, 1-Dell/4400 Library Server, 2-Dell/GX1 AP Wire Service, 2-Dell/GX1 Primary & Secondary Domain Name Controllers, 1-Dell/GX110 Terminal Server, 45-Dell/Optiplex/GX1 workstation, 6-APP/Mac workstation, 3-APP/iMac, 3 PRODUCTION EQUIPMENT: Hardware — Na/Systems Flexo Processor, 2-MON/RipExpress RIP, 2-ECR/PelBox 108C, 1-III/3850, Konica/RIP; Cameras — 1-C/Spartan III, 1-P/Pager; Scanners — 1-ECR/Autokon 1000, X/7650, Umax PRODUCTION SOFTWARE: Tera/GN3-Fred.

FALL RIVER

THE HERALD NEWS

207 Pocasset St, Fall River, Mass., 02721-1532, Bristol; gen tel (508) 676-8211; adv tel (508) 676-2560; ed tel (508) 676-2534; gen fax (508) 676-2588; adv fax (508) 676-2588; ed fax (508) 676-2566; gen/nat adv e-mail ads@heraldnews.com; disp adv e-mail lrufener@heraldnews.com; class adv e-maillrufener@heraldnews.com; ed e-mail lsullivan@heraldnews.com; web site www.heraldnews.com
- 292,685(views) 55,947(visitors)
Group: New Media Investment Group
Published: Mon, Tues, Wed, Thur, Fri, Sat, Sun
Weekday Frequency: m
Saturday Frequency: m
Circulation: 9,199; 9,199(sat); 10,661(sun)
Last Audit: AAM June 30, 2017
Advertising Rate (weekday/saturday): Open inch rate $37.33
Advertising Rate (sunday): Open inch rate $39.57
Online Advertising Rate: Page Peel, Sliding Billboard $30.00 CPM; Bottom Bar $36.00 CPM
News services: AP. **Established:** 1892
Own Printing Facility?: Yes
Commercial Printers?: Yes
Special Editions: Progress (Mar); Home & Garden (Apr); Home & Garden (May); Fall River Celebrates America (Aug); Hockey & Basketball Preview (Dec); Auto (Feb); Super Bowl (Jan); Business Review (Jul); Bridal (Jun); County Kids (Monthly); Christmas in Fall River (Nov).
Special Weekly Sections: Entertainment Guide (Fri); Lifestyle (S); Real Estate Guide (Sat); Wheels (Tues); Best Food Day (Wed).
Syndicated Publications: Comics (S).
Digital Platform - Mobile: Apple, Android
Digital Platform - Tablet: Apple iOS, Android
Pub...Lisa Strattan
Circ. Dir. ....Thomas Amato
Editor-in-Chief ....Lynne Sullivan
Sales Mgr. ....Chris Avis
Lifestyles Ed.......................Linda Murphy
Content/Interactive Dir. ....Jon Root
City Ed. ....Will Richmond
Sports Ed. ....Mike Thomas
Editorial Page Ed. ....Aaron Frechette
Pub.................................Mark Olivieri
Market Information: TMC.
Mechanical Available: Offset; Black and 3 ROP colors; insert accepted; page cutoffs - 22 3/4.
Mechanical Specifications: Type page 12 x 21 1/2; E - 6 cols, 2, 1/8 between; A - 6 cols, 2, 1/8 between; C - 9 cols, 2 3/4, 1/12 between.
Delivery Method: Mail, CarrierEquipment & Software: PRESSROOM EQUIPMENT: Lines — 9-G/Urbanite single width; Folders — G/Urbanite 2:1; Pasters —8-Jardis/Automatic 4540. MAILROOM EQUIPMENT: Counter Stackers — 2-HL/Monitor, 1-MM/CN70 (388); Inserters & Stuffers — GMA/SLS 1000A 10:1; Tying Machines — 4-MLN/EE, 1-MLN/2A; Address Machine — 1-Ch/515010.; BUSINESS EQUIPMENT: 1-Bs/92, IBM/AS-400 BUSINESS SOFTWARE: INSI CLASSIFIED EQUIPMENT: Hardware — Dewar/Information System, PC Network; CLASSIFIED SOFTWARE: Dewar/Sys IV. DISPLAY EQUIPMENT: Hardware — APP/Mac Centris 650; Printers — MON; DISPLAY

SOFTWAREAd Make-up Applications — Multi-Ad/Creator; Layout Software — Dewar. EDITORIAL EQUIPMENT: Hardware — Dewar/Information System, PC Network; Printers — MON EDITORIAL SOFTWARE: Dewar/View. PRODUCTION EQUIPMENT: Hardware — 2-MON/ExpressMaster 1200, 1-MON/PaperMaster 600; Cameras — 1-C/Spartan III; Scanners — Lf/Leafscan 35 PRODUCTION SOFTWARE: Dewar/View, QPS.
Note: The Herald News also prints the Taunton Daily Gazette.

FITCHBURG

SENTINEL & ENTERPRISE

808 Main St, Fitchburg, Mass., 01420-3153, Worcester; gen tel (978) 343-6911; adv tel (978) 343-6911; ed tel (978) 343-6911; gen fax (978) 342-1158; adv fax (978) 345-8421; ed fax (978) 342-1158; gen/nat adv e-mail hconry@MediaOneNe.com; disp adv e-mail hconry@MediaOneNe.com; class adv e-mailhconry@MediaOneNe.com; ed e-mail cstamand@sentinelandenterprise.com; web site www.sentinelandenterprise.com
Group: Digital First Media
Published: Mon, Tues, Wed, Thur, Fri, Sat, Sun
Weekday Frequency: m
Saturday Frequency: m
Circulation: 8,186; 8,186(sat); 9,415(sun)
Last Audit: AAM June 30, 2015
Advertising Rate (weekday/saturday): Open inch rate $28.00
Advertising Rate (sunday): Open inch rate $28.00
Online Advertising Rate: Banner Ad $10.00 CPM (Homepage); $8.00 CPM (Others)
News services: AP, SHNS, TMS. **Established:** 1838
Special Editions: Back-to-School (Aug); Holiday Gift Guides (Dec); Washington's Birthday (Feb); Bride & Groom (Jan); Longso Bike Race (Jul); Spring Home Improvement (Mar); Graduation (May); Thanksgiving Sports (Nov); Fall Car Care (Oct); Fall Home Improvement (Sept).
Special Weekly Sections: Auto (Thur); Gallery of Homes (Wed); TV Week (Weekly).
Syndicated Publications: USA WEEKEND Magazine (S).
Digital Platform - Mobile: Apple, Android, Windows
Digital Platform - Tablet: Apple iOS, Android, Windows 7, Blackberry Tablet OS
Ed...........................Charles St. Amand
Sports Ed. ....Ross Edwards
Circ. Mgr. ....Dennis West
Emerging Media Dir. ....Andrea Mendes
Adv. Mgr. ....David Florence
Adv. Admin. ....Holly Conry
City Ed. ....Cliff Clark
Market Information: ADS; Split run; TMC.
Mechanical Available: Offset; Black and 3 ROP colors; insert accepted - single sheet; page cutoffs - 20 1/2.
Mechanical Specifications: Type page 13 x 21 1/2; E - 6 cols, 2 1/16, 1/8 between; A - 6 cols, 2 1/16, 1/8 between; C - 9 cols, 1 3/8, 1/16 between.
Areas Served: 01430, 01431, 01420, 01444, 01523, 01453, 01412, 01364, 01464, 01469, 01473, 01475
Delivery Method: Mail, CarrierEquipment & Software: PRESSROOM EQUIPMENT: Lines — 8-G/Urbanite; 6-MAN; Folders — 1-G/2:1, MR/2:1; Control System — Thin Core; Registration System — Duarte. MAILROOM EQUIPMENT: Counter Stackers — S/J4109-2200-2, QWI/300-4; Inserters & Stuffers — K&M/1372-2; Tying Machines — OVL, Dynaric; Address Machine — KR; BUSINESS EQUIPMENT: PBS BUSINESS SOFTWARE: PBS/MediaPlus CLASSIFIED EQUIPMENT: Hardware — CText, Microsoft/Windows NT; Printers — Pre Press/Panther; CLASSIFIED SOFTWARE: PPI. DISPLAY EQUIPMENT: Hardware — APP/Power Mac; Printers — Pre Press/Panther, HP/LaserJet 4VMV, HP/LaserJet 4Plus; DISPLAY SOFTWAREAd Make-up Applications — QPS/QuarkXPress, Adobe/Photoshop; Layout Software — Layout/8000. EDITORIAL EQUIPMENT: Hardware — CText, APP/Mac/HP/Laser Printer; Printers — Pre Press/

Panther EDITORIAL SOFTWARE: CText, Baseview/NewsEdit Pro. PRODUCTION EQUIPMENT: Hardware — Pre Press/Panther, HP/LaserJet 4Plus, HP/LaserJet 4VMV; Cameras — LE/121; Scanners — Nikon, Polaroid PRODUCTION SOFTWARE: QPS/QuarkXPress.

FRAMINGHAM

METROWEST DAILY NEWS

33 New York Ave, Framingham, Mass., 01701-8857, Middlesex; gen tel 508-626-4412; adv tel (508) 626-3984; ed tel (508) 626-3871; gen fax 508-626-4400 ; gen/nat adv e-mail metrowest@wickedlocal.com; disp adv e-mail salesteam@wickedlocal.com; ed e-mail rlodge@wickedlocal.com; web site www.metrowestdailynews.com
Group: New Media Investment Group
Published: Mon, Tues, Wed, Thur, Fri, Sat, Sun
Weekday Frequency: m
Saturday Frequency: m
Circulation: 10,121; 9,156(sat); 13,473(sun)
Last Audit: AAM June 30, 2017
Advertising Rate (weekday/saturday): Open inch rate $41.25
Advertising Rate (sunday): Open inch rate $46.50
Online Advertising Rate: Leaderboard $13.00 CPM; Other positions $17.00 CPM
News services: AP, GateHouse News Service, State House News Service **Established:** 1897
Own Printing Facility?: Yes
Commercial Printers?: Yes
Special Editions: Spring Home & Garden (Apr); Back-to-School/College (Aug); Last Minute Gift Guide (Dec); Presidents' Day (Feb); Weddings (Jan); Community Guides (Jul); MetroWest Community Guide (Jun); Business (Mar); Health & Lifestyles (May); Holiday Gift Guide (Nov).
Special Weekly Sections: Autoweekly (Fri); MetroWest Business Journal (Mon); Expanded Entertainment (S); Mutual Fund Listing (Sat); MetroWest Weekend (Thur); Health and Environment (Tues); Best Food Day (Wed).
Syndicated Publications: USA WEEKEND Magazine (S).
Digital Platform - Mobile: Apple, Android, Blackberry
Digital Platform - Tablet: Apple iOS, Android, Blackberry Tablet OS
Features Ed. ....Nancy Olesin
Photo Dept. Mgr. ....Art Illman
Metro/Sun. Ed. ....Rob Heneisen
Dig. Ed. ....Meghan Kelly
Bus. Ed. ....Bob Tremblay
Art Davidson
Market Information: ADS; Split run; TMC; Zoned editions.
Mechanical Available: Offset; Black and 3 ROP colors; insert accepted; page cutoffs - 21 1/2.
Mechanical Specifications: Type page 11 3/4 x 21; E - 6 cols, 2 1/16, 1/8 between; A - 6 cols, 2 1/16, 1/8 between; C - 9 cols, 1 3/8, 1/16 between.
Areas Served: 01701
Delivery Method: Mail, Newsstand, Carrier, RacksEquipment & Software: PRESSROOM EQUIPMENT: Lines — 12-G/Urbanite single width 1979; 12-G/Urbanite single width 1979; 1-G/HV single width 1979; Folders — 2-G/Urbanite 1000 Series w 1/4 Folders, 1-G/HV Signature Folder; Pasters —20-G/Automatic 2 armReels & Stands — Reels & Stands and St; MAILROOM EQUIPMENT: Counter Stackers — 4-HL/Monitor, 2/Compass, 1-/RIMA; Inserters & Stuffers — 1-GMA/Alpaliner, 1-GMA/SLS 1000; Tying Machines — 6-/MLN; Address Machine — 3-Domino/Ink Jet Printer.; BUSINESS EQUIPMENT: Sun/Sparc Station 20-Unix, 2-Axiom/Netware 4.11 BUSINESS SOFTWARE: Microsoft/Windows 95 CLASSIFIED EQUIPMENT: Hardware — PC 486; Microcom/Modems; Printers — HP/LaserJet 4MV; CLASSIFIED SOFTWARE: III/Classified Software. DISPLAY SOFTWARELayout Software — 2-HI/2002, 2-HI/2220, 2-HI/1420, 1-COM/MDT 350, 2-HI/1250, 2-Vecra. EDITORIAL EQUIPMENT: Hardware — Pentium/PC 586, PC 486/Microcom/Modems, US Robotics/Modems; Printers — HP/LaserJet 4MV EDITORIAL SOFTWARE: III/

Editorial System, Microsoft/Windows 95. PRODUCTION EQUIPMENT: Hardware — 3-Graham, 2-CK Optical/5%; Cameras — 2-Image Maker/506A, 2-C/Newspager; Scanners — 3-Kk/2035 Film Scanner, 1-AG/Arcus Plus Color Scanner, 1-Autokon/Flatbed Scanner PRODUCTION SOFTWARE: QPS/QuarkXPress 3.3.

GARDNER

THE GARDNER NEWS

309 Central St, Gardner, Mass., 01440-3839, Worcester; gen tel (978) 632-8000; adv tel (978) 632-8000 ext. 33; ed tel (978) 632-8000 ext. 20; gen fax (978) 630- 1346; adv fax (978) 630-2231; ed fax (978) 630-5410; gen/nat adv e-mail ablake@thegardnernews.com; disp adv e-mail cholden@thegardnernews.com; class adv e-maillineclassified@thegardnernews.com; ed e-mail editorial@thegardnernews.com; web site www.thegardnernews.com
Group: The Gardner News, Inc.
Published: Mon, Tues, Wed, Thur, Fri, Sat
Weekday Frequency: e
Saturday Frequency: m
Circulation: 4,099; 4,099(sat)
Last Audit: AAM June 30, 2016
Advertising Rate (weekday/saturday): Open inch rate $8.78
Online Advertising Rate: Homepage Banner $140.00/month
News services: AP. **Established:** 1869
Own Printing Facility?: Yes
Commercial Printers?: No
Special Weekly Sections: Lifestyle (Mon); Serial Stories (Mon); Business (Tues); Voice (Tues); Food (Wed); Interactive Kids Page (Sat).
Digital Platform - Mobile: Apple, Android, Windows
Digital Platform - Tablet: Apple iOS, Android, Blackberry Tablet OS, Kindle
Pres./Pub..........................Alberta S. Bell
Asst. Managing Ed. ....John Vincent
Sports Ed. ....Tom Trainque
Adv. Rep. ....Marc Barrieault
Managing Ed. ....Matt Garay
NIE Coord./Asst. Ed. ....Matthew Roy
Adv. Rep. ....Anne Blake
Market Information: TMC.
Mechanical Available: Offset; Black and 2 ROP colors; insert accepted; page cutoffs - 22 1/4.
Mechanical Specifications: Type page 12 5/8 x 21 1/4; E - 7 cols, 1 5/8, 1/6 between; A - 7 cols, 1 5/8, 1/6 between; C - 7 cols, 1 5/8, 1/6 between.
Areas Served: 01440, 01430, 01452, 01468, 01473, 01475
Delivery Method: Mail, Newsstand, Carrier, RacksEquipment & Software: PRESSROOM EQUIPMENT: Lines — Web press; MAILROOM EQUIPMENT: Counter Stackers — 6; Tying Machines — 1-Akebono/Oval Strapping.; BUSINESS EQUIPMENT: Dell pc BUSINESS SOFTWARE: Peachtree CLASSIFIED EQUIPMENT: Hardware — Dell PC; Macs; Printers — 1-APP/Mac ImageWriter II, 1-Okidata/293, 1-NEC/90 LaserPrinter; CLASSIFIED SOFTWARE: Accountscout DISPLAY EQUIPMENT: Hardware — 3-APP/Mac ci 8-160; Printers — 2-NEC/90 LaserPrinter; DISPLAY SOFTWAREAd Make-up Applications — APP/Mac with Multi-Ad.; EDITORIAL EQUIPMENT: Hardware — 4-COM/Intrepid 4, COM/Power Editors-28A EDITORIAL SOFTWARE: COM/One System. PRODUCTION EQUIPMENT: Hardware — Nu/Flip Top FT40UNS; Cameras — Acti/Process; Scanners — Typist/3.0, Konica, ECR/Autokon 1040.

GLOUCESTER

GLOUCESTER DAILY TIMES

36 Whittemore St, Gloucester, Mass., 01930-2553, Essex; gen tel (978) 283-7000; adv tel (978) 283-7000 ext. 3446; ed tel (978) 283-7000 ext. 3438; gen fax (978) 282-4397; adv fax (978) 282-4397; ed fax (978) 282-4397; gen/nat adv e-mail mzappala@gloucestertimes.com; disp adv e-mail

mzappala@gloucestertimes.com; class adv e-mailmbcallahan@gloucestertimes.com; ed e-mail rlamont@gloucestertimes.com; web site www.gloucestertimes.com
- 1,055,319(views) 146,207(visitors)
Group: Community Newspaper Holdings, Inc.
Published: Mon, Tues, Wed, Thur, Fri, Sat
Weekday Frequency: e
Saturday Frequency: e
Circulation: 5,270; 5,270(sat)
Last Audit: AAM June 30, 2017
Advertising Rate (weekday/saturday): Open inch rate $21.95
Online Advertising Rate: Skyscrapper $150.00; Medium Rectangle $295.00; Homepage $350.00;
News services: AP, ONS. **Established:** 1888
Own Printing Facility?: Yes
Commercial Printers?: No
Special Editions: Spring Home Improvement (Apr); Washington's Birthday Auto (Feb); Business Update (Jan); Guide to the North Shore (Jun); Spring Bride (Mar); Spring Real Estate Review (May); Fall Home & Garden (Oct); Fall Fashions (Sept).
Special Weekly Sections: Food (Wed).
Syndicated Publications: USA WEEKEND Magazine (Fri); Relish (Monthly).
Digital Platform - Mobile: Apple, Android, Windows
Digital Platform - Tablet: Apple iOS, Android, Windows 7
Pub. .... Karen Andreas
City Issues Reporter .... Ray Lamont
Managing Ed. .... Andrea Holbrook
Sports Ed. .... Nick Curcuru
Community News Ed. .... Christina Parisi
VP, Adv. .... Mark Zappala
Adv. Mgr. .... Marybeth Callahan
Ed. .... David Olson
Market Information: TMC.
Mechanical Available: Offset; Black and 3 ROP colors; insert accepted - any; page cutoffs - 21.
Mechanical Specifications: Type page 11 x 21.5; E - 6 cols
Areas Served: 01929, 01930, 01944, 01966
Delivery Method: Mail, Newsstand, Carrier, RacksEquipment & Software: PRESSROOM EQUIPMENT: Lines — 8-G/Metro (3 color decks); Folders — 1-G/Double 2:1; MAILROOM EQUIPMENT: Counter Stackers — Goss Olympian; Inserters & Stuffers — 4 wo Goss 630 inserters; Control System — Omnizone; Address Machine — Domino; BUSINESS EQUIPMENT: IBM/AS-400 CLASSIFIED EQUIPMENT: Hardware — APT; CLASSIFIED SOFTWARE: APT DISPLAY EQUIPMENT: Hardware — APP/ Mac, PC; Printers — HP/ Laser Jet 4 Plus; DISPLAY SOFTWAREAd Make-up Applications — InDesign; Layout Software — MEI/ALS 7.0 EDITORIAL EQUIPMENT: Hardware — Mediaspan; Printers — QMS/860 EDITORIAL SOFTWARE: Mediaspan PRODUCTION EQUIPMENT: Hardware — Agfa Advantage Imagesetters; Cameras — Kodak Cannon; Scanners — ECR/100 Epson/636 Polaroid/Sprint S PRODUCTION SOFTWARE: Adobe InDesign

GREENFIELD

THE RECORDER

115 Conz Street, Greenfield, Mass., 1342, Franklin; gen tel (413) 772-0261; adv tel (413) 772-0261; ed tel (413) 772-0261; gen fax (413) 772-2906; adv fax (413) 774-5511; ed fax (413) 774-5020; gen/nat adv e-mail sales@recorder.com; disp adv e-mail sales@recorder.com; class adv e-mailclasinfo@recorder.com; ed e-mail news@recorder.com; web site www.recorder.com
- 650,000(views) 190,000(visitors)
Group: Newspapers of New England
Published: Mon, Tues, Wed, Thur, Fri, Sat
Weekday Frequency: m
Saturday Frequency: m
Circulation: 10,272; 10,272(sat)
Last Audit: Sworn/Estimate/Non-Audited September 30, 2017
Advertising Rate (weekday/saturday): Open inch rate $18.26
Online Advertising Rate: $15/m
News services: AP, LAT-WP. **Established:** 1792
Own Printing Facility?: Yes
Commercial Printers?: Yes
Special Editions: Business (Apr); Back-to-School (Aug); Holiday Recipes (Dec); Finance (Feb); Bridal (Jan); Summer Tourism (Jun); First Snow (Nov); Winter Tourism (Oct); Fall Tourism (Sept).
Special Weekly Sections: Rental Property Page (Fri); Child Services (Mon); Home & Garden (Sat); Arts/Entertainment (Thur); Classes, Courses & Workshops (Tues).
Syndicated Publications: Relish (Monthly); USA WEEKEND Magazine (Sat); American Profile (Weekly).
Digital Platform - Mobile: Apple, Android
Digital Platform - Tablet: Apple iOS, Android
Pub. .... Michael Rifanburg
Adv. Mgr. .... Sharon Cross
Classified Adv. Coord. .... Suzanne Hunter
Circ. Dir. .... Kevin Lamagdelaine
Ed. in chief .... George Forcier
Market Information: ADS; TMC.
Mechanical Available: Offset; Black and 3 ROP colors; insert accepted - all; page cutoffs - 22 3/4.
Mechanical Specifications: Type page 13 x 21 3/8; E - 6 cols, 2 1/2, 1/6 between; A - 6 cols, 2 1/2, 1/6 between; C - 9 cols, 1 5/16, 3/32 between.
Areas Served: 01301, 01302
Delivery Method: Newsstand, CarrierEquipment & Software: PRESSROOM EQUIPMENT: 2008 Cerrutti Flexo MAILROOM EQUIPMENT: SLS1000 12/1 BUSINESS EQUIPMENT: HP/3000 CLASSIFIED EQUIPMENT: Hardware — 5-APP/ Mac; Printers — APP/Laser Writer; CLASSIFIED SOFTWARE: Baseview. DISPLAY EQUIPMENT: Hardware — Macintosh; Printers — Xante/Accel-a-Writer 3G; DISPLAY SOFTWAREAd Make-up Applications — Multi/Ad Creator; Layout Software — MEI/ALS. EDITORIAL EQUIPMENT: Hardware — Pentium/Pre Press/Panther Pro 36; Printers — Epson, HP EDITORIAL SOFTWARE: Atex/Prestige. PRODUCTION EQUIPMENT: Hardware — 2-Pre Press/Panther Pro 36, Nu; Cameras — C/Spartan I; Scanners — Nikon/LS 1000, PixelCraft/8200 PRODUCTION SOFTWARE: Atex Prestige.

HYANNIS

CAPE COD TIMES

319 Main St, Hyannis, Mass., 02601-4037, Barnstable; gen tel (508) 775-1200; adv tel (508) 775-6201; ed tel (508) 862-1166; gen fax (508) 771-3292; adv fax (508) 778-0330; ed fax (508) 771-3292; gen/nat adv e-mail advertising@capecodonline.com; disp adv e-mail advertising@capecodonline.com; class adv e-mailclassified@capecodonline.com; ed e-mail news@capecodonline.com; web site www.capecodtimes.com
- 4,500,000(views) 1,000,000(visitors)
Group: New Media Investment Group
Published: Mon, Tues, Wed, Thur, Fri, Sat, Sun
Weekday Frequency: m
Saturday Frequency: m
Circulation: 25,428; 25,428(sat); 29,417(sun)
Last Audit: AAM December 31, 2016
Advertising Rate (weekday/saturday): Open Rate: Mon-Thur $41.38; Fri-Sat $44.59
Advertising Rate (sunday): Open Rate; Sun $49.77
Online Advertising Rate: OL CPM $10.00
News services: AP, DJ, ONS, NYT, LAT-WP. **Established:** 1936
Own Printing Facility?: No
Commercial Printers?: Yes
Special Editions: Classroom Times, Spring Times, Beyond 50, Rising Stars, Summer Destination, Cape House, Holiday Guide
Special Weekly Sections: Outdoors (Fri); Golf (Mon); At Home (S); Arts & Entertainment (Sat); Health & Fitness (Thur); Health & Science (Tues); Food (Wed).
Syndicated Publications: CapeWeek Magazine (Fri); Prime Time (Quarterly); Parade (S).
Digital Platform - Mobile: Apple, Android
Digital Platform - Tablet: Apple iOS, Android, Kindle Fire
President & Publisher .... Peter D. Meyer
Ed. .... Paul Pronovost
Controller .... David Hundt
Mgr., HR .... Stacia Plumb
Adv. Dir. .... Molly Evans
Circ. Dir. .... Chad Campbell
Digital Sales Mgr. .... Angela Bucar
Market Information: TMC.
Mechanical Available: Offset; Black and 3 ROP colors; insert accepted; page cutoffs - 22 3/4.
Mechanical Specifications: Type page 13 x 21 1/2; E - 6 cols, 2, 1/3 between; A - 6 cols, 2 1/16, 1/3 between; C - 9 cols, 1 2/5, 1/6 between.
Areas Served: 02360, 02532, 02534, 02536, 02537, 02538, 02540, 02540, 02543, 02553, 02556, 02558, 02559, 02561, 02562, 02563, 02565, 02571, 02574, 02576, 02601, 02630, 02631, 02632, 02633, 02635, 02637, 02638, 02639, 02641, 02642, 02643, 02644, 02645, 02646, 02647, 02648, 02649, 02650, 02651, 02652, 02653, 02655, 02657, 02659, 02660, 02661, 02662, 02663, 02664, 02666, 02667, 02668, 02669, 02670, 02671, 02672, 02673, 02675
Delivery Method: Mail, Newsstand, Carrier, RacksEquipment & Software: BUSINESS EQUIPMENT: HP 8000 desktops
HP 7900 desktops
HP 8440p laptops
HP 6930 laptops
BUSINESS SOFTWARE: Atex Adbase & ATOL (Advertising)
DTI (Circulation)
SAP & Lawson (Finance)
Newscycle Solutions Mediaware & Saxotech
Adobe Creative Suite
Citrix
CLASSIFIED EQUIPMENT: HP 8000 desktops
HP 7900 desktops
HP 8440p laptops CLASSIFIED SOFTWARE: Atex AdBase EDITORIAL EQUIPMENT: HP 8000 desktops
HP 7900 desktops
HP 8440p laptops
HP 6930 laptops EDITORIAL SOFTWARE: Newscycle Solutions Mediaware & Saxotech
Adobe Creative Suite
Citrix IT EQUIPMENT: HP ProLiant DL360 servers
Dell PowerEdge 750 servers
Cisco routers & switches IT SOFTWARE:Automate 6
Cisco AMP Connector
CIRCULATION EQUIPMENT: HP 8000 desktops
HP 7900 desktops
HP 6930p laptops CIRCULATION SOFTWARDTI

LOWELL

THE SUN

491 Dutton St Ste 2, Suite 2, Lowell, Mass., 01854-4292, Middlesex; gen tel (978) 458-7100; adv tel (978) 458-7100; ed tel (978) 970-4621; gen fax (978) 970-4800; adv fax (978) 970-4723; ed fax (978) 970-4600; gen/nat adv e-mail advertising@lowellsun.com; disp adv e-mail enajeeullah@mediaonene.com; class adv e-mailrrudeen@mediaonene.com; ed e-mail jcampanini@lowellsun.com; web site www.lowellsun.com
- 4,220,212(views) 629,630(visitors)
Group: Digital First Media
Published: Mon, Tues, Wed, Thur, Fri, Sat, Sun
Weekday Frequency: e
Saturday Frequency: m
Circulation: 37,379; 30,944(sat); 41,624(sun)
Last Audit: AAM June 30, 2015
Advertising Rate (weekday/saturday): Open inch rate $43.00
Advertising Rate (sunday): Open inch rate $43.00
Online Advertising Rate: Drop Down Banner Ad $395.00 per day (Homepage); Skyscraper $10.00 CPM (Homepage); $8.00 CPM (Any pages)
News services: AP, SHNS, NEA, MCT. **Established:** 1878
Own Printing Facility?: Yes
Commercial Printers?: Yes
Special Editions: Bridal (Feb); Local Heroes (Jan); Home & Garden/Home Improvement (Apr); Summer Auto (Aug); Christmas Gift Guide (Dec); Folk Festival (Jul); Summer Living (Jun); Spring Auto (Mar); Women in Business (May); Holiday Happenings (Nov); Fall Auto (Oct).
Special Weekly Sections: Color Comics (S); Restaurant Guide (Sat); Stepping Out (Thur); Food (Wed).
Syndicated Publications: USA WEEKEND Magazine (S).
Digital Platform - Mobile: Apple, Android
Digital Platform - Tablet: Apple iOS, Android
Pres./Pub. .... Mark O'Neil
CFO .... John Habbe
Dir. Emerging Media .... Andrea Mendes
Circ. Mgr., Alternate Delivery Maureen Sylvester
Circ. Mgr., Home Delivery .... Gary Wright
Circ. Mgr., Systems .... Tom Gauthier
Circ. Mgr., Telemktg./Promo. .... Shelley Laurencio
Ed. .... James Campanini
Mng. Ed. .... Charles St. Amand
Asst. Mng. Ed., Local News .... Kris Pisarik
Asst. Mng. Ed., Local News-Weekend Tom Zuppa
Bus. Ed. .... Dan O'Brien
City Ed. .... Chris Scott
Columnist/Copy Ed. .... Dan Phelps
Copy Ed. .... Bruce Phillips
Lifestyle Copy Ed. .... Joanne Deegan
VP Circulation .... Mike Sheehan
Director Of Operations .... Bill Walker
Chrmn. .... Kendall M. Wallace
Copy Ed. .... Emily Reily
Digital Sales Mgr. .... Brandin Power
Multimedia Retail Adv. Mgr. .... Katelyn McNamara
Sports Ed. .... Dennis Whitton
Market Information: ADS; Split run; TMC; Zoned editions.
Mechanical Available: DiLitho; Black and 3 ROP colors; insert accepted - spadea; page cutoffs - 21 1/2.
Mechanical Specifications: Type page 12 x 21 1/2; E - 6 cols, 1 9/10, 1/8 between; A - 6 cols, 1 9/10, 1/16 between; C - 9 cols, 1 1/5, 1/8 between.
Delivery Method: Mail, Newsstand, Carrier, RacksEquipment & Software: PRESSROOM EQUIPMENT: Lines — 6-MAN, H/double width; 8-G/Urbanite single width; Press Drive — GE/Tenetrol; Folders — H/2:1 1967; Control System — GE/SCR.; MAILROOM EQUIPMENT: Counter Stackers — 4-QWI/300; Tying Machines — 2-Dynaric; Address Machine — 2-KR.; BUSINESS EQUIPMENT: IBM/AS-400 Advanced 36 CLASSIFIED EQUIPMENT: Hardware — PPI/System; Printers — V/5100 Typesetter; DISPLAY EQUIPMENT: Hardware — 8-APP/Mac; Printers — HP 5000/N; Other Hardware — 3-Microtek/Scanner, 2-AG/ Arcus Scanner DISPLAY SOFTWAREAd Make-up Applications — Multi-Ad/Creator, QPS/QuarkXPress 4.1; Layout Software — 8-APP/Mac. EDITORIAL EQUIPMENT: Hardware — 1-APP/Mac LAN and WAN; Printers — HP/4MV, HP/5000N EDITORIAL SOFTWARE: QPS/QuarkXPress, Baseview/ Qtools, Baseview/QXedit, Baseview/ NewsEdit, APP/Appleshare & Windows NT Network. PRODUCTION EQUIPMENT: Hardware — Mk, Caere/OmniPage Professional, Adobe/Photoshop; Cameras — AG PRODUCTION SOFTWARE: QPS/ QuarkXPress 4.1, Baseview/Qtools, Baseview/QXedit.

LYNN

THE DAILY ITEM

38 Exchange St, Ste 5, Lynn, Mass., 01901-1425, Essex; gen tel (781) 593-7700; adv tel (781) 593-7700 ext. 1251; ed tel (781) 593-7700 ext. 1349; gen fax (781) 581-3178; adv fax (781) 581-3178; ed fax (781) 598-2891; gen/nat adv e-mail advertising@itemlive.com; disp adv e-mail lquigley@itemlive.com; class adv e-mailclassified@itemlive.com; ed e-mail vderubeis@itemlive.com; web site itemlive.com
- 1,950,000(views) 420,000(visitors)
Group: Hastings & Sons Publishing Co.
Published: Mon, Tues, Wed, Thur, Fri, Sat, Sun
Weekday Frequency: m
Saturday Frequency: m
Circulation: 20,434; 6,469(sat)
Last Audit: CAC June 30, 2017
Advertising Rate (weekday/saturday): Open inch rate $27.00
Advertising Rate (sunday): Open inch rate $30.00

Online Advertising Rate: $12 CPM with a 12 month contract
News services: AP, SHNS. **Established:** 1877
Own Printing Facility?: Yes
Commercial Printers?: No
Special Editions: Spring Home Improvement (Apr); Back-to-School (Aug); Holiday Songbook (Dec); Washington's Birthday Auto (Feb); Brides Tab (Jan); House-To-Home; Senior Living (Jun); Progress (Mar); Spring Car Care (May); New Car Preview (Nov); Business & Professional Womem (
Special Weekly Sections: Health (Mon); Religion (Sat); On-The-Town (Fri); Business (Tues); Lynn Neighbors (Wed); Saugus Neighbors (Thurs.).
Digital Platform - Mobile: Apple, Android, Blackberry
Digital Platform - Tablet: Apple iOS, Android, Kindle, Kindle Fire
Pub.....Gary Grossman
Controller, HR....Len Machesic
Circ. Dir.....Fred Scheller
Adv. Dir.....Patty Bennett
Managing Ed.....David R. Hilliard
Features Ed.....Joanne Arbogast
Sports Ed.....Todd Stanford
Adv. Services Mgr.....Lori Seebold
Classifieds....Carla Treon
Market Information: TMC.
Mechanical Available: Black and 3 ROP colors; insert accepted - any; page cutoffs - 21 1/4.
Mechanical Specifications: Type page 11 x 21; E - 6 cols, 2 1/16, 1/8 between; A - 6 cols, 2 1/16, 1/8 between; C - 9 cols, 1 5/16, 1/8 between.
Areas Served: 01901, 01902, 01904, 01905, 01906, 01945, 01960, 01970
Delivery Method: Mail, Newsstand, Carrier, RacksEquipment & Software: BUSINESS EQUIPMENT: Newzware BUSINESS SOFTWARE: Newzware CLASSIFIED EQUIPMENT: Hardware — AST/Bravo MS 4.66d Terminals; Icanon; CLASSIFIED SOFTWARE: Newzware/Pongras DISPLAY EQUIPMENT: Hardware — Power Mac, MS/NT Server, Gateway; Printers — 1-APP/Mac LaserWriter; Other Hardware — 2-APP/Mac One Scanner, 2-A DISPLAY SOFTWAREAd Make-up Applications — Adobe/Illustrator, Adobe/Streamline, Adobe/Photoshop, Macromedia/Freehand, AP AdSend, Multi-Ad/Creator, QPS/QuarkXPress; EDITORIAL EQUIPMENT: Hardware — Gateway/Desktop/Laptops; Printers — Lexmark/Optra LXI Plus Printer EDITORIAL SOFTWARE: Microsoft/Windows 98, Microsoft/Office 2000, QPS/QuarkXPress 4.1. PRODUCTION EQUIPMENT: Hardware — 1-Gateway/P6 NT Server on Xytron/RIP, 1-Gateway/P5, 1-ScanJet/Scanner; Cameras — Canon PRODUCTION SOFTWARE: InDesign 4.0, MEI/ALS 3.0.
Note: Printed, inserted offsite

MILFORD

MILFORD DAILY NEWS

197 Main St, Milford, Mass., 01757-2635, Worcester; gen tel (508) 634-7522; adv tel (508) 626-3984; ed tel (508) 626-3871; gen fax (508) 634-7514; adv fax (508) 634-7514; ed fax (508) 634-7514; gen/nat adv e-mail salesteam@wickedlocal.com; disp adv e-mail salesteam@wickedlocal.com; class adv e-mailcrobinson@wickedlocal.com; ed e-mail rlodge@wickedlocal.com; web site www.milforddailynews.com
- 1,100,000(views) 145,000(visitors)
Group: New Media Investment Group
Published: Mon, Tues, Wed, Thur, Fri, Sat, Sun
Weekday Frequency: m
Saturday Frequency: m
Circulation: 3,533; 3,533(sat); 4,155(sun)
Last Audit: AAM June 30, 2017
Advertising Rate (weekday/saturday): Open inch rate $21.70
Advertising Rate (sunday): Open inch rate $21.70
Online Advertising Rate: Leaderboard $13.00 CPM; Other positions $17.00 CPM
News services: NYT, AP. **Established:** 1887
Own Printing Facility?: Yes
Commercial Printers?: Yes
Special Editions: Summer Fun Tab (May); Secretaries' Week Pages (Apr); Pawtucket Red Sox Night (Aug); Christmas Cards (Dec); Spring Bridal Tab (Feb); Tax Column (Jan); Sidewalk Sale Days (Jul); Father's Day Page (Jun); Physical Fitness Page (Mar); Gift Spotter (Nov).
Special Weekly Sections: Bridal Registry (Mon).
Syndicated Publications: Sports Extra (Fri); USA Weekender (Sat).
Digital Platform - Mobile: Apple, Android
Digital Platform - Tablet: Apple iOS, Android
Sports Ed.....Art Davidson
Managing Ed.....Elizabeth Banks
Opinion Ed.....Rick Holmes
Metro/Sun. Ed.....Rob Heneisen
Digital Ed.....Meghan Kelly
Bus. Ed.....Bob Tremblay
Chief Photographer....Art Illman
Market Information: ADS; Split run; TMC; Zoned editions.
Mechanical Available: Offset; Black and 3 ROP colors; insert accepted - min size 5 x 8; page cutoffs - 21 1/2.
Mechanical Specifications: Type page 13 x 21 1/2; E - 6 cols, 2 1/16, 1/8 between; A - 6 cols, 2 1/16, 1/8 between; C - 9 cols, 1 3/8, 1/16 between.
Delivery Method: Mail, CarrierEquipment & Software: BUSINESS EQUIPMENT: TI/990-12R BUSINESS SOFTWARE: DSI CLASSIFIED EQUIPMENT: Hardware — 4-PC; Printers — Toshiba/P351 SX; CLASSIFIED SOFTWARE: III 3.9. DISPLAY EQUIPMENT: Hardware — 10-APP/Mac; Printers — 2-APP/Mac LaserWriter, 2-QMS/860, HP/4MV, HP6; DISPLAY SOFTWAREAd Make-up Applications — DTI/AdSpeed, QPS/QuarkXPress.; EDITORIAL EQUIPMENT: Hardware — 25-PC/18-RSK/TRS 80 Model 100, RSK/TRS 80 Model 200, Lf/Leafscan 35; Printers — Toshiba/P351 SQ, APP/Mac LaserWriter, 2-QMS/860, HP/4M Plus EDITORIAL SOFTWARE: III 3.9. PRODUCTION EQUIPMENT: Hardware — 2-QMS/860, AG, ECR/VL 36 Imagesetter; Cameras — 1-R, 1-LE/R, AG/RPS 6100S; Scanners — Lf/Leafscan 35, Microtek, HP/Scanner PRODUCTION SOFTWARE: QPS/QuarkXPress 3.3, Microsoft/Windows, APP/Mac.

NEW BEDFORD

THE STANDARD-TIMES

25 Elm St, New Bedford, Mass., 02740-6228, Bristol; gen tel (508) 997-7411; adv tel (508) 997-0011; ed tel (508) 979-4450; gen fax (508) 862-1132; adv fax (508) 977-4585; ed fax (508) 997-7491; gen/nat adv e-mail advertising@s-t.com; disp adv e-mail ekedzierski@s-t.com; class adv e-mailksilvia@s-t.com; ed e-mail bperdue@s-t.com; web site www.southcoasttoday.com
- 2,600,000(views) 579,000(visitors)
Group: New Media Investment Group
Published: Mon, Tues, Wed, Thur, Fri, Sat, Sun
Weekday Frequency: m
Saturday Frequency: m
Circulation: 15,374; 15,374(sat); 16,262(sun)
Last Audit: AAM December 31, 2016
Advertising Rate (weekday/saturday): Open inch rate $47.50
Advertising Rate (sunday): Open inch rate $52.50
Online Advertising Rate: Medium Box $10 cpm ROS and $20 cpm for home page ; Leaderboard $10 cpm ROS and $20 cpm home page; Double Display $10 cpm ROS and $20 cpm home page.
News services: AP, NYT, DJ, ONS. **Established:** 1850
Own Printing Facility?: No
Commercial Printers?: Yes
Special Editions: Spring Auto Service (Apr); Health & Medicine (Aug); Last Minute Gift Guide (Dec); Washington's Birthday Auto (Feb); Parenting (Jan); Parenting (Jul); Seniors (Jun); Spring Home & Garden (Mar); Seaside Summer Recreation (May); Holiday Planner (Nov); Fall A
Special Weekly Sections: Sports Monday (Mon); At Home (S); Real Estate Today (Sat); Coastin' Entertainment (Th); Auto Today (W)
Digital Platform - Mobile: Apple, Android, Blackberry
Digital Platform - Tablet: Apple iOS, Android, Blackberry Tablet OS
Pres./Pub.....Peter Meyer
HR....Stacia Plumb
Controller....David Hundt
Regional Circ. Dir.....Chad Campbell
Editor....Beth Perdue
Adv. Dir.....Molly Evans
Market Information: Split run; TMC
Mechanical Available: Offset; Black and 3 ROP colors; insert accepted - single sheets, catabooks; page cutoffs - 22.
Mechanical Specifications: Type page 13 x 21 1/2; E - 6 cols, 2 1/16, 1/8 between; A - 6 cols, 2 1/16, 1/8 between; C - 9 cols, 1 3/8, 1/16 between.
Areas Served: 02743, 02719, 02745, 02746, 02740, 02744, 02747, 02748, 02790, 02739, 02738, 02770, 02717, 02702, 02558, 02571, 02576, 02538, 02532, 02346, 02347
Delivery Method: Newsstand, CarrierEquipment & Software: BUSINESS EQUIPMENT: IBM/AS-400 BUSINESS SOFTWARE: INSI, Software Plus, Computer Associates, Lawson, ATEX CLASSIFIED EQUIPMENT: Hardware - Desktops
CLASSIFIED SOFTWARE: AdBase
ATOL
DISPLAY EQUIPMENT: Hardware — PC's
DISPLAY SOFTWAREAdBase
ATOL
EDITORIAL EQUIPMENT: Hardware — 45-Dell/486 66mhz; Printers — 2-HP/4M, 1-HP/44 Color Plotter, 1-NewGen/11x17 Laser Printer EDITORIAL SOFTWARE: Dewar/Unixaix Network. PRODUCTION EQUIPMENT: Hardware — 1-Wing Lynch/Color, 1-Lf/Leafscan 45; Cameras — 1-C/Spartan III, 1-C/Marathon; Scanners — 1-ECR/Autokon 1000DE PRODUCTION SOFTWARE: QPS/QuarkXPress 3.3. CIRCULATION EQUIPMENT: HP Desktops CIRCULATION SOFTWARDTI

NEWBURYPORT

THE DAILY NEWS

23 Liberty St, Newburyport, Mass., 01950-2750, Essex; gen tel (978) 462-6666; adv tel (978) 462-6666 ext. 3242; ed tel (978) 462-6666 ext. 3255; gen fax (978) 465-8505; adv fax (978) 463-9612; ed fax (978) 462-8505; gen/nat adv e-mail bmacdonald@newburyportnews.com; disp adv e-mail btrefethen@newburyportnews.com; class adv e-mailbmacdonald@newburyportnews.com; ed e-mail jmacone@newburyportnews.com; web site www.newburyportnews.com
Group: Community Newspaper Holdings, Inc.
Published: Mon, Tues, Wed, Thur, Fri, Sat
Weekday Frequency: e
Saturday Frequency: e
Circulation: 7,131; 7,131(sat)
Last Audit: AAM June 30, 2017
Advertising Rate (weekday/saturday): Open inch rate $23.95
Online Advertising Rate: Skyscrapper $150.00; Medium Rectangle $295.00; Homepage $350.00;
News services: AP, ONS. **Established:** 1887
Special Editions: Amesbury Guide (May); Yankee Homecoming (Jul); Auto Showcase (Apr); Back-to-School (Aug); Christmas Gift Guide (Dec); Presidents' Day (Feb); Pulse (Jan); Guides to The North Shore (May); Traditions (Nov); Year End Clearance (Oct); Fall Home Improvement (Sept).
Special Weekly Sections: Food (Wed).
Syndicated Publications: USA WEEKEND Magazine (Fri).
Digital Platform - Mobile: Apple, Android
Digital Platform - Tablet: Apple iOS, Android
Pub.....Karen Andreas
Night Ed.....Merrily Buchs
Sports Ed.....Dan Guttenplan
Features Ed.....Ann Reily
Photo Ed.....Bryan Eaton
VP, Adv.....Mark Zappala
Adv. Mgr.....Bill Trefethen
Managing Ed.....Richard Lodge
Home Delivery Mgr.....christine Greco
Market Information: TMC.
Mechanical Available: Offset; Black and 3 ROP colors; insert accepted; page cutoffs - 22 3/4.
Mechanical Specifications: Type page 11 1/2 x 21; E - 6 cols, 1 13/16, 5/16 between; A - 6 cols, 1 13/16, 5/16 between; C - 9 cols, 1 7/32, 3/32 between.
Areas Served: Seabrook, Merrimac, Amesbury, Salisbury, West Newbury, Newburyport, Byfield, Newbury, and Rowley.
Delivery Method: Mail, CarrierEquipment & Software: BUSINESS EQUIPMENT: IBM/AS400 CLASSIFIED EQUIPMENT: Hardware — AT.; DISPLAY EQUIPMENT: Hardware — PC Network; DISPLAY SOFTWAREAd Make-up Applications — QPS/QuarkXPress, Archetype/Designer; Layout Software - PC. EDITORIAL EQUIPMENT: Hardware — PC EDITORIAL SOFTWARE: QPS/QuarkXPress. PRODUCTION EQUIPMENT: Hardware — Nu-Arc; Scanners — Epson PRODUCTION SOFTWARE: QuarkXpress 4.0.

NORTH ANDOVER

THE EAGLE-TRIBUNE

100 Turnpike St, North Andover, Mass., 01845-5033, Essex; gen tel (978) 946-2000; adv tel (978) 946-2000; ed tel (978) 946-2000; gen fax (978) 687-6045; adv fax (978) 687-6045; ed fax (978) 687-6045; gen/nat adv e-mail mzappala@eagletribune.com; disp adv e-mail mzappala@eagletribune.com; class adv e-mailmzappala@eagletribune.com; ed e-mail awhite@eagletribune.com; web site www.eagletribune.com
- 3,304,000(views) 1,400,000(visitors)
Group: Community Newspaper Holdings, Inc.
Published: Mon, Tues, Wed, Thur, Fri, Sat, Sun
Weekday Frequency: e
Saturday Frequency: e
Circulation: 22,241; 22,241(sat); 23,310(sun)
Last Audit: AAM June 30, 2017
Advertising Rate (weekday/saturday): Open inch rate $41.25
Advertising Rate (sunday): Open inch rate $43.65
Online Advertising Rate: Leaderboard $350.00; Medium Rectangle $295.00; Skyscraper $150.00
News services: AP, SHNS. **Established:** 1868
Own Printing Facility?: Yes
Commercial Printers?: Yes
Special Editions: Auto Weekend (Oct); Where we Live (Jun); Easter Church Pages (Apr); Health & Fitness (Aug); Parent! (Feb); Accent on Finance (Jan); Parent! (Jun); Real Estate Review (Mar); Real Estate Review (Nov); Columbus Day (Oct).
Special Weekly Sections: Entertainment
Syndicated Publications: USA WEEKEND Magazine (S).
Digital Platform - Mobile: Apple, Android
Digital Platform - Tablet: Apple iOS, Android
Pub.....Karen Andreas
VP of Adv.....Mark Zappala
Circ. Dir.....Steve Milone
Mng. Ed.....Tracey Rauh
Retail Adv. Dir.....Sean McKenna
Metro Ed.....Ken Johnson
Exec. Sports Ed.....Bill Burt
Photo Dir.....Amy Sweeney
Community News Ed.....Betsy Curry
City Ed.....Warren Talbot
Packaging Ctr. Mgr.....David Lavigne
Market Information: TMC; Zoned editions.
Mechanical Available: Offset; Black and 3 ROP colors; insert accepted; page cutoffs - 22 3/4.
Mechanical Specifications: Type page 11 1/16 x 21 1/2; E - 6 cols, 1 5/6, 1/8 between; A - 6 cols, 1 5/6, 1/8 between; C - 10 cols, 1 1/16, 1/16 between.
Areas Served: 01810,01825,01830,01832,01833,01834,01835,01840,01841,01843,01844,01845,01850,01860,01864,01876,01887,01913,01921,01949,01950,01952,01985,03036,03038,03053,03076,03079,03087,03811,03819,03826,03827,03841,03842,03848,03858,03865,03873,03874,
Delivery Method: Mail, Newsstand, Carrier, RacksEquipment & Software: PRESSROOM EQUIPMENT: Lines — 8-G/Metro (3 color decks); Folders — 1-G/Double 2:1.; MAILROOM EQUIPMENT: Counter Stackers — Goss Olympian; Inserters & Stuffers — 7wo, Goss 630 inserters; Tying Machines — 4/Power Strap; Control System — Omnizone; Address Machine — Domino; BUSINESS EQUIPMENT: IBM/AS-400 BUSINESS SOFTWARE: INSI CLASSIFIED EQUIPMENT: Hardware

— APT; Printers — Epson/LaserWriter; CLASSIFIED SOFTWARE: APT DISPLAY EQUIPMENT: Hardware — APP/Mac, PC; Printers — HP/LaserJet 4 Plus; DISPLAY SOFTWAREAd Make-up Applications — APT; Layout Software — MEI/ALS 7.0. EDITORIAL EQUIPMENT: Hardware — Mediaspan; Printers — QMS/860 EDITORIAL SOFTWARE: Mediaspan PRODUCTION EQUIPMENT: Hardware — Agfa Advantage Imagesetters; Cameras — Kodak, Cannon; Scanners — ECR/1000, Epson/636, Polaroid/ SprintScan PRODUCTION SOFTWARE: Adobe, InDesign

NORTHAMPTON

DAILY HAMPSHIRE GAZETTE

115 Conz St, Ste 1, Northampton, Mass., 01060-4445, Hampshire; gen tel (413) 584-5000; adv tel (413) 586-1700; ed tel (413) 585-5250; gen fax (413) 585-5297; adv fax (413) 585-5293; ed fax (413) 586-1700; gen/nat adv e-mail sales@gazettenet.com; disp adv e-mail sales@gazettenet.com; class adv e-mailclassifieds@gazettenet.com; ed e-mail editor@gazettenet.com; web site www.gazettenet.com
- 1,000,699(views) 227,000(visitors)

Group: Newspapers of New England Inc.
Published: Mon, Tues, Wed, Thur, Fri, Sat
Weekday Frequency: m
Saturday Frequency: m
Circulation: 13,089; 14,249(sat)
Last Audit: AAM December 31, 2016
Advertising Rate (weekday/saturday): Open inch rate $22.97
Online Advertising Rate: Halfpage, Medium Rectangle $150.00; Leaderboard $170.00
News services: AP, LAT-WP. **Established:** 1786
Own Printing Facility?: Yes
Commercial Printers?: Yes
Special Editions: Spring Home & Garden (Apr); Back-to-School (Aug); Wine (Dec); Business & Industry (Feb); Summer Guide (Jun); Spring Fashion (Mar); Create-An-Ad (May); Christmas Shopping Bag (Nov); Auto (Oct); Valley Almanac (Sept).
Special Weekly Sections: Real Estate (Fri); Automotive (Sat); Home & Garden (Thur); Health (Tues); Lifestyle Features (Wed).
Syndicated Publications: Television Log (Sat).
Digital Platform - Mobile: Apple, Android
Digital Platform - Tablet: Apple iOS, Android
Adv. Prodn. Mgr. .... Rita Turcotte
Mng. Ed., Features .... Debra Scherban
Religion Ed. .... Deb Oakley
Prodn. Mgr., Distr. Ctr. .... Chris Kostek
Prodn. Mgr., Pressroom .... John Raymer
Adv. Sales .... John Stafford
Pub. .... Michael Rifanburg
Adv. Dir. .... Jon Stafford
Night Managing Ed. .... Chad Cain
Photographer .... Sarah Crosby
Managing Ed. .... Dan Crowley
Reporter/Sunday Ed. .... Amanda Drane
Sports Ed. .... Mike Moran
Commercial Printing Mgr. .... Jordan Prickett
Market Information: Split run; TMC.
Mechanical Available: Offset; Black and 3 ROP colors; insert accepted - product samples; page cutoffs - 22 3/4.
Mechanical Specifications: Type page 11 5/8 x 21 1/2; E - 6 cols, 1 5/6, 1/8 between; A - 6 cols, 1 5/6, 1/8 between; C - 9 cols, 1 1/4, 1/8 between.
Areas Served: 01002, 01059, 01330, 01007, 01011, 01012, 01084, 01020, 01026, 01342, 01027, 01062, 01032, 01033, 01301, 01035, 01038, 01039, 01040, 01050, 01053, 01054, 01060, 01070, 01072, 01073, 01373, 01075, 01375, 01093, 01096, 01098, 01351
Delivery Method: Mail, CarrierEquipment & Software: PRESSROOM EQUIPMENT: Lines — 11-G/Urbanite single width (3-color satellite unit); Press Drive — 2, 100-HP/ Westinghouse, 100-HP/GE; Folders — 1-G/ Urbanite; Reels & Stands — 2-G/3-High Stands; Registration System — Duarte/Pin Register System. MAILROOM EQUIPMENT: Counter Stackers — 3/QWI; Inserters & Stuffers — 1-GMA/SLS 1000 12:2; Tying Machines — 2-Dynaric/SSB 70; Control System — Linc/Packaging Line Control System, Address/Linc, Stack/Line, Key/ Line; Address Machine — 2-/Ch, Address/ Linc I; BUSINESS EQUIPMENT: 1-DEC/ Prioris HX 590 System, Papertrack/2000 BUSINESS SOFTWARE: Newzware CLASSIFIED EQUIPMENT: Hardware — 6-PC Workstation, Compaq/Proliant 1600; Printers — HP, X; CLASSIFIED SOFTWARE: APT/ACT 2.06, QPS/QuarkXPress 3.32. DISPLAY EQUIPMENT: Hardware — 20-PC Workstation; Printers — HP, X; DISPLAY SOFTWAREAd Make-up Applications — Ad Tracking, APT/ACT, Adobe/Photoshop, QPS/QuarkXPress 4.0, Adobe/Illustrator; Layout Software — Compaq/Proliant 1600. EDITORIAL EQUIPMENT: Hardware — Dell/Poweredge 1300, 60-PC Workstation, 2-Compaq/Proliant 1600; Printers — X, 1-Xerox/NP32 EDITORIAL SOFTWARE: APT/ACT 2.06, Microsoft/Word 6.0. PRODUCTION EQUIPMENT: Hardware — AP Server; Scanners — Microtek/ Scanmaker 3 PRODUCTION SOFTWARE: QPS/QuarkXPress 3.32, APT/ACT 2.06. CIRCULATION SOFTWARNewzware

PITTSFIELD

THE BERKSHIRE EAGLE

75 S Church St, Ste L1, Pittsfield, Mass., 01201-6140, Berkshire; gen tel (413) 447-7311; gen fax (413) 499-3419; gen/nat adv e-mail kteutsch@berkshireeagle.com ; disp adv e-mail kteutsch@berkshireeagle.com; class adv e-mailclassifieds@berkshireeagle.com; ed e-mail news@berkshireeagle.com; web site www.berkshireeagle.com

Group: Birdland Acquisition LLC.
Published: Mon, Tues, Wed, Thur, Fri, Sat, Sun
Weekday Frequency: All day
Saturday Frequency: All day
Circulation: 21,328; 21,328(sat); 23,466(sun)
Last Audit: AAM June 30, 2016
Newspaper Reps: President Fredric D. Rutberg
Branch Offices: Great Barrington, Mass.
North Adams, Mass.
News services: AP, New York Times, Washington Post **Established:** 1891
Own Printing Facility?: Yes
Commercial Printers?: Yes
Digital Platform - Mobile: Apple, Android, Windows, Blackberry, Other
Digital Platform - Tablet: Apple iOS, Android, Windows 7, Blackberry Tablet OS, Kindle, Nook, Kindle Fire, Other
Systems Director .... Bill Macfarlane
VP, Ops .... Andy Swanton
HR .... Catherine Wandrei
Editorial Page Ed. .... Bill Everhart
Bus. Ed. .... Tony Dobrowolski
Ent. Ed. .... Jeffrey Borak
Online Ed. .... Jennifer Huberdeau
Digital News Ed. .... Erik Sokolowski
Rgl. Pub .... Kevin Moran
Managing Ed. .... Tom Tripicco
VP, Audience Development, Sales, Mktg Warren C. Dews Jr.
Circ. Office. Mgr. .... Holly Hartman
Publisher .... Alan English
Managing Editor for News .... Samantha Wood
Investigations Editor .... Larry Parnass
Market Information: TMC.
Areas Served: 01220, 01247, 01267, 01343, 01367, 05352, 01225, 01237, 01256, 01270, 01011, 01223, 01226, 01235, 01243, 01201, 01254, 01262, 01266, 01029, 01238, 01240, 01242, 01253, 01260, 01264, 01222, 01229, 01230, 01236, 01244, 01245, 01252, 01255, 01257, 01258, 01259, 12017, 12166, 12029, 12060, 12125, 12168
Delivery Method: Mail, Newsstand, Carrier, RacksEquipment & Software: MAILROOM EQUIPMENT: Counter Stackers — 3-TMST/ Compass; Inserters & Stuffers — GMA/SLS 1000 8:1; Tying Machines — 3-Samuel/Power Strap, Bu; Wrapping Singles — Mailroom Control System ;Prism; Address Machine — Ch;

QUINCY

THE PATRIOT LEDGER

400 Crown Colony Dr, Ste 1, Quincy, Mass., 02169-0930, Norfolk; gen tel (508) 676-2524; ed tel (617) 768-7026; gen fax (617) 786-7025; adv fax (617) 786-7193; ed fax (617) 786-7025; gen/nat adv e-mail pub@wickedlocal.com; web site www.patriotledger.com

Group: New Media Investment Group
Published: Mon, Tues, Wed, Thur, Fri, Sat
Weekday Frequency: e
Saturday Frequency: m
Circulation: 24,326; 34,153(sat)
Last Audit: AAM December 31, 2015
Advertising Rate (weekday/saturday): Open inch rate $72.21
Advertising Rate (sunday): $73.27
News services: NYT, AP, SHNS, TMS. **Established:** 1837
Own Printing Facility?: No
Commercial Printers?: No
Special Editions: Jobs & Education (Apr); Your Community (Aug); Jobs & Education (Dec); Coupon Book (Feb); Superbowl (Jan); Jobs & Education II (Jul); Advice for the Experts (Jun); South Shore Women II (Mar); Career Connection I (May)
Special Weekly Sections: Housing Extra (Real Estate Section) (Fri); Lifestyle (Mon); Home (Sat); Get Out (Thur); Health/Science (Tues); Food (Wed).
Syndicated Publications: USA WEEKEND Magazine (Sat).
Digital Platform - Mobile: Apple, Android
Digital Platform - Tablet: Apple iOS, Android
Vice Pres., Finance .... James Piasecki
Exec. Office Mgr. .... Gayle Sheehan
Features Ed. .... Dana Barbuto
City Editor .... Linda Shepherd
Online Ed. .... Ken Johnson
Photo/Graphics Ed./Copy Desk Chief .... Jennifer Wagner
Regional Publisher .... Mark Olivieri
Executive Editor .... Lisa Strattan
President & COO Gatehouse Media, Inc Kirk Davis
Managing editor .... Ken Johnson
Market Information: TMC; Zoned editions.
Mechanical Available: Letterpress (direct); Black and 3 ROP colors; insert accepted; page cutoffs - 23 9/16.
Mechanical Specifications: Type page 13 x 22; E - 6 cols, 2, 1/8 between; A - 6 cols, 2, 1/8 between; C - 9 cols, 1 3/8, 3/4 between.
Areas Served: 02021, 02025, 02026, 02035, 02043, 02045, 02047, 02050, 02061, 02062, 02066, 02067, 02072, 02081, 02090, 02111, 02122, 02124, 02125, 02127, 02136, 02169, 02170, 02171, 02184, 02186, 02188, 02189, 02190, 02191, 02301, 02302, 02322, 02324, 02330, 02332, 02333, 02338, 02339, 02341, 02343, 02346, 02351, 02359, 02360, 02364, 02367, 02368, 02370, 02379, 02382, 02563, 99999
Delivery Method: Mail, CarrierEquipment & Software: MAILROOM EQUIPMENT: Counter Stackers — 2-HL/HT-2, 3-HL/ Monitor; Inserters & Stuffers — 2-GMA/ SLS 1000 8:1; Tying Machines — 4-OVL/ JP-80, 1-OVL/Constellation, 1-MLN/ WorldNews; Wrapping Singles — 2-HL/ Bottom Wrap; Address Machine — 1-IBM/ AS 400.; BUSINESS EQUIPMENT: 1-IBM/AS-400 Model 9402, SCS/AdMax CLASSIFIED EQUIPMENT: Hardware — 1-Dell/6300 PowerEdge, 2-Dell/2300 PowerEdge, 27-Dell/Optiplex PC; Printers — 1-HP/4050, 1-HP/8000, 1-Citoh/SQE; CLASSIFIED SOFTWARE: SCS/AdMax, SCS/ClassPag. DISPLAY EQUIPMENT: Hardware — 1-Dell/6300 PowerEdge, 2-Dell/4300 PowerEdge, 17-Optiplex PC, 10-APP/Mac G3/G4, 1-Dell/Inspiron; Printers — 3-HP/4050, 2-QMS/2560, 1-QMS-Minolta/6100; DISPLAY SOFTWAREAd Make-up Applications — SCS/AdMax, SCS/ AdTrack, SCS/Layout, Multi-Ad/Creator, Adobe/Photoshop, Adobe/Illus; EDITORIAL EQUIPMENT: Hardware — 2-Dell/6300 PowerEdge, 1-Dell/4300, 3-Dell/6400GX1, 1-AP/IBM Photo Server, 74-Dell/Optiplex PC, 16-Dell/Inspiron, 6-APP/Mac G3/G4/1-HP/Scanjet 6300C, 1-Epson/Expression 836XL, 2-Nikon/CoolScan; Printers — 1-HP/4050, 3-HP/5000, 1-HP PRODUCTION EQUIPMENT: Hardware — 2-Na/Starlite, Konica/4550 Imagesetter, Konica/6200 Imagesetter; Cameras — 1-C/Pager, 1-R/432 Mic II, 1-AG/RPS 2024 Automatic PRODUCTION SOFTWARE: Tera/Good News 3.

SOUTHBRIDGE

SOUTHBRIDGE EVENING NEWS

PO Box 90, 25 Elm St, Southbridge, Mass., 01550-0090, Worcester; gen tel (508) 764-4325; adv tel (508) 909-4104; ed tel (508) 764-4325; gen fax (508) 764-8102; adv fax (508) 764-8102; ed fax (508) 764-8015; gen/nat adv e-mail jashton@stonebridgepress.com; disp adv e-mail jashton@stonebridgepress.com; class adv e-mailclassifieds@stonebridgepress.com; ed e-mail aminor@stonebridgepress.com; web site www.stonebridgepress.com
50,000(visitors)

Group: Stonebridge Press, Inc.
Published: Mon, Tues, Wed, Thur, Fri
Weekday Frequency: All day
Circulation: 4,500
Last Audit: Sworn/Estimate/Non-Audited September 30, 2017
Advertising Rate (weekday/saturday): Open inch rate $15.00
News services: AP. **Established:** 1923
Own Printing Facility?: Yes
Commercial Printers?: No
Digital Platform - Mobile: Apple, Android
Digital Platform - Tablet: Apple iOS, Android
President & Publisher .... Frank Chilinski
Display Adv. .... Jean Ashton
Ed. .... Adam Minor
Circc. .... Kerri Peterson
Sports Ed. .... Nick Ethier
Market Information: TMC.
Mechanical Available: Offset; Black and 3 ROP colors; insert accepted; page cutoffs - 17.
Mechanical Specifications: Type page 9 5/8 x 16; E - 6 cols, 1 1/2, 3/16 between; A - 6 cols, 1 1/2, 1/10 between; C - 7 cols, 1 3/8, 1/10 between.
Areas Served: 01550
Delivery Method: Mail, Carrier

SPRINGFIELD

THE REPUBLICAN

1860 Main St, Springfield, Mass., 01103-1000, Hampden; gen tel (413) 788-1000; adv tel (413) 788-1250; ed tel (413) 788-1200; gen fax (413) 788-1199; adv fax (413) 788-1199; ed fax (413) 788-1301; gen/nat adv e-mail mfrench@repub.com; disp adv e-mail fsmith@repub.com; class adv e-mailmmooney@repub.com; ed e-mail wphaneuf@repub.com; web site www.masslive.com/republican
- 13,000,000(views) 709,000(visitors)

Group: Advance Publications, Inc.
Published: Mon, Tues, Wed, Thur, Fri, Sat, Sun
Weekday Frequency: m
Saturday Frequency: m
Circulation: 50,244; 31,208(sat); 74,226(sun)
Last Audit: AAM March 31, 2017
Advertising Rate (weekday/saturday): Open inch rate $92.00 (Mon-Wed, Fri, Sat); $109.00 (Thur)
Advertising Rate (sunday): Open inch rate $126.00
Online Advertising Rate: Starting at $7.00 CPM
News services: AP, NYT, LAT-WP, NNS. **Established:** 1824
Own Printing Facility?: Yes
Commercial Printers?: Yes
Special Editions: Back-to-School (Aug); Presidents' Day Auto (Feb); Outlook (Jan); Home Show (Mar); Fall Home Improvement (Sept).
Special Weekly Sections: Movies (Fri); Parenting (Mon); TV Time (S); Weekend (Thur); Unlisted for Teens (Tues); Best Food Day (Wed).
Syndicated Publications: Leisure Time (S).
Digital Platform - Mobile: Apple, Android
Digital Platform - Tablet: Apple iOS, Android
Adv. Dir. .... Mark French
Adv. Mgr., Classified .... Marysue Mooney
Asst. Managing Ed., Ent. .... Ray Kelly
Managing Ed. .... Cynthia Simison
Bus. Ed. .... James Kinney
City Ed., Night .... Lu R. Feorino
Online .... Joe Deburro
Exec. Ed. .... Wayne E. Phaneuf
Asst. Online Ed. .... Robert Rizzuto
Asst. Managing Ed., Sports .... Vernon Hill
Asst. Managing Ed., Lifestyles Anne Gerard-Flynn

City Ed, Days ....Stephen D. Smith
Chief Photographer ....Mark Murray
Editorial Page Ed..............Carolyn Robbins
Major Accts. Mgr. ....John Mazzulli
Digital Adv. Sales Mgr...................Dave Kotfila
Adv. Sales Mgr.........................Fran Smith
Sales/Retention Mgr. ....Aileen Casey
NIE ....Denise Browne
Dir., HR ....Judith C. Fraser
Ops. Dir...................................Tom Sewall
Pres...................................Allison Werder
Marketing Mgr. ....Sally Azar
HR Mgr. ....Natalia Collins
Sales Mgr., Worcester.................Mike Curtin
Ed. in Chief............................Ed. Kubosiak
Dir. of Dig. Ops...........................John Beattie
Sales Mgr. ....Michael Burnham
Market Information: ADS; Split run; TMC; Zoned editions.
Mechanical Available: Offset; Black and 3 ROP colors; insert accepted - BFD inserts; page cutoffs - 21.
Mechanical Specifications: Type page 11 5/8 x 20 1/4; E - 6 cols, 1 5/6, 1/8 between; A - 6 cols, 1 5/6, 1/8 between; C - 10 cols, 1 7/100, 1/16 between.
Areas Served: Western Massachusetts
Delivery Method: Mail, Newsstand, Carrier, RacksEquipment & Software: PRESSROOM EQUIPMENT: Lines — 5-MAN/Regioman (8 couples); Press Drive — Bammueller; Reels & Stands — 6-MAN/CD 13.; MAILROOM EQUIPMENT: Counter Stackers — 5-QWI/400, 2-QWI/300, 1-Gammerler/KL 503; Inserters & Stuffers — 1-SLS/3000 28:2, 2-SLS/3000 14:2; Tying Machines — 3/Strapex, 6-/Dynaric; Wrapping Singles — 6-/QWI; Address Machine — 3-Ch/525E Labeler; BUSINESS EQUIPMENT: 2-Dell, IBM/AS-400, Power Edge/4200 BUSINESS SOFTWARE: AP, GL, Platinum, Ultipro Payroll System CLASSIFIED EQUIPMENT: Hardware — Dell; Printers — Dataproducts; CLASSIFIED SOFTWARE: Mactive 2.24. DISPLAY EQUIPMENT: Hardware — Mactive; Other Hardware — 1-HI/8900 Pixel Editing, 5-APP/Mac G3, 4-Microtek, 6-Umax, Flatbed/Scanner DISPLAY SOFTWAREAd Make-up Applications — QPS/QuarkXPress; Layout Software — Mactive/PGL. EDITORIAL EQUIPMENT: Hardware — Dell; Printers — 2-HP/Designjet 2500 EDITORIAL SOFTWARE: HI/Newsmaker Editorial. PRODUCTION EQUIPMENT: Hardware — Adobe/Photoshop, APP/Mac Desktop PRODUCTION SOFTWARE: HI/Newsmaker, Mactive/PGL, Proimage/Newsway.

TAUNTON

TAUNTON DAILY GAZETTE
5 Cohannet St, Taunton, Mass., 02780-3903, Bristol; gen tel (508) 880-9000; adv tel (508) 967-3120; ed tel (508) 967-3141; gen fax (508) 967-3109; adv fax (508) 967-3101; ed fax (508) 967-3101; gen/nat adv e-mail ttalbot@tauntongazette.com; disp adv e-mail ttalbot@tauntongazette.com; class adv e-mailclassified@tauntongazette.com; ed e-mail lsullivan@heraldnews.com; web site www.tauntongazette.com
- 1,154,957(views) 244,866(visitors)
Group: New Media Investment Group
Published: Mon, Tues, Wed, Thur, Fri, Sat, Sun
Weekday Frequency: m
Saturday Frequency: m
Circulation: 4,939; 4,939(sat); 5,452(sun)
Last Audit: AAM December 31, 2015
Advertising Rate (weekday/saturday): Open inch rate $24.58
Advertising Rate (sunday): Open inch rate $24.81
Online Advertising Rate: Leaderboard $13.00 CPM; Other positions $17.00 CPM
News services: AP. **Established:** 1848
Own Printing Facility?: Yes
Commercial Printers?: Yes
Special Editions: Springs Looking Good (Apr); Back-to-School (Aug); Procrastinator's Guide (Dec); Presidents' Day (Feb); Bridal Guide (Jan); Best of Best (Jul); Cape Road (Jun); Winter Wipe Out (Mar); Design an Ad (May); Coupons (Monthly); Christmas Gift (Nov); Trick or Tr
Special Weekly Sections: Look at Area Business (Fri); Professional Directory (Mon); Real Estate (Sat); Look at Area Business (Tues); Food Page (Wed).
Syndicated Publications: Coupons Tab (Monthly); USA WEEKEND Magazine (S).
Digital Platform - Mobile: Apple, Android
Digital Platform - Tablet: Apple iOS, Android
Pub....................................Lisa Stratton
Circ. Dir. ....Tom Amato
Editor-in-Chief ....Lynne Sullivan
Exec. City. Ed. ....Rory Schuler
Content Dir. ....Jon Root
Adv. Dir. ....Paige Webster
Market Information: ADS; TMC.
Mechanical Available: Offset; Black and 3 ROP colors; insert accepted - all; page cutoffs - 22 3/4.
Mechanical Specifications: Type page 12 x 21 1/2; E - 6 cols, 1 7/8, 3/16 between; A - 6 cols, 1 7/8, 3/16 between; C - 9 cols, 1 1/4, 1/8 between.
Areas Served: Taunton, Raynham, Dighton, Berkley, Rehoboth, Lakeville, Freetown, and Norton
Delivery Method: Mail, CarrierEquipment & Software: PRESSROOM EQUIPMENT: Lines — 9-G/Urbanite single width; Pasters —8-Jardis/EbwayRegistration System — Duarte/Pin Registration System. MAILROOM EQUIPMENT: Counter Stackers — 3/Hall; Inserters & Stuffers — GMA/SLS 1000; Tying Machines — MLN/ML2E, Signode/MLN 2A; Wrapping Singles — 3-Hall/Monarch; Address Machine — CH/525.; BUSINESS EQUIPMENT: CCPS BUSINESS SOFTWARE: Microsoft/Excel 7, Lotus 5.0, Newzware CLASSIFIED EQUIPMENT: Hardware — Mk, APP/Mac; Printers — HP; CLASSIFIED SOFTWARE: AT. DISPLAY EQUIPMENT: Hardware — HP; Printers — HP; DISPLAY SOFTWAREAd Make-up Applications — NewzWare; Layout Software — Mk/MasterPlanner. EDITORIAL EQUIPMENT: Hardware — Mk, APP/Mac; Printers — Okidata, HP/HMV EDITORIAL SOFTWARE: Mk, APP/Mac, Baseview. PRODUCTION EQUIPMENT: Hardware — Nu; Cameras — SCREEN, R, C/Spartan 3; Scanners — Epson, Nikon/Super Coolscan PRODUCTION SOFTWARE: QPS/QuarkXPress 4.0.

WAKEFIELD

WAKEFIELD DAILY ITEM
26 Albion St, Wakefield, Mass., 01880-2803, Middlesex; gen tel (781) 245-0080; adv tel (781) 245-0080; ed tel (781) 245-0080; gen fax (781) 246-0061; adv fax (781) 246-0061; ed fax (781) 246-0061; gen/nat adv e-mail ads@wakefielditem.com; disp adv e-mail ads@wakefielditem.com; class adv e-mailads@wakefielditem.com; ed e-mail news@wakefielditem.com; web site wp.localheadlinenews.com
Group: The Wakefield Item Co.
Published: Mon, Tues, Wed, Thur, Fri
Weekday Frequency: e
Circulation: 4,556
Last Audit: Sworn/Estimate/Non-Audited September 30, 2017
Advertising Rate (weekday/saturday): Open inch rate $9.50
News services: AP. **Established:** 1894
Special Editions: Mother's Day Page (Apr); Back-to-School (Aug); New Baby (Dec); Valentine's Page (Feb); Bridal Supplement (Jan); 4th of July (Jul); Father's Day Page (Jun); Easter Page (Mar); Graduation Pages (May); Thanksgiving Day (Nov); Columbus Day (Sept).
Pub./Gen. Mgr. ....Glenn Dolbeare
Adv. Mgr. ....Phil Simonson
Adv. Mgr., Classified ....Marcia Perry
Circ. Mgr. ....Thomas Tine
Ed. ....Peter Rossi
Asst. Ed. ....Robert Burgess
School Ed. ....Gail Lowe
Sports Ed. ....Jim Southmayd
Market Information: TMC.
Mechanical Available: Offset; Black.
Mechanical Specifications: Type page 13 x 21; E - 6 cols, 2 1/16, 1/8 between; A - 9 cols, 1 1/4, 1/8 between; C - 9 cols, 1 1/4, 1/8 between.
Areas Served: 01880

Delivery Method: Mail, Newsstand, Carrier, RacksEquipment & Software: EDITORIAL SOFTWARE: Baseview/NewsEdit.

WESTFIELD

THE WESTFIELD NEWS
62 School St, Westfield, Mass., 01085-2835, Hampden; gen tel (413) 562-4181; adv tel (413) 562-4181 ext. 101; ed tel (413) 562-4181 ext. 116; gen fax (413) 562-4185; adv fax (413) 562-4185; ed fax (413) 562-4185; gen/nat adv e-mail sales@thewestfieldnewsgroup.com; disp adv e-mail martybaillargeon@thewestfieldnewsgroup.com; class adv e-mailclassifieds@thewestfieldnews.com; ed e-mail danmoriarty@thewestfieldnews.com; web site www.thewestfieldnews.com
Group: The Westfield News Group LLC
Published: Mon, Tues, Wed, Thur, Fri, Sat
Weekday Frequency: m
Saturday Frequency: m
Circulation: 4,600; 4,600(sat)
Last Audit: Sworn/Estimate/Non-Audited September 30, 2017
Advertising Rate (weekday/saturday): Open inch rate $14.00
Online Advertising Rate: Cube $100.00/wk; Skyscraper $90.00/wk; Box $60.00/wk
News services: AP. **Established:** 1971
Special Weekly Sections: Around Town; Business; Health; Entertainment.
Digital Platform - Mobile: Apple, Android
Digital Platform - Tablet: Apple iOS, Android
Pres...................................Patrick Berry
Bus. Mgr. ....Marie Brazee
Ed.....................................Dan Moriarty
Longmeadow Ed. ....Hope Tremblay
Sports Ed. ....Chris Putz
Circ. Mgr. ....Melissa Hartman
Content Dir. ....Jim McKeever
Classifieds Sales Mgr..............Flora Masciadrelli
Art Room Dir................................Lorie Perry
Chief Photographer ....Fred Gore
Market Information: TMC.
Areas Served: Westfield, Southwick, and the surrounding Hilltowns
Delivery Method: Mail, Newsstand, CarrierEquipment & Software: MAILROOM EQUIPMENT: Tying Machines — 2/Bu; PRODUCTION EQUIPMENT: Hardware — APP/Mac; Cameras — AG/1600

WOBURN

DAILY TIMES CHRONICLE
1 Arrow Dr, Ste 1, Woburn, Mass., 01801-2090, Middlesex; gen tel (781) 933-3700; adv tel (781) 933-3700; ed tel (781) 933-3700; gen fax (781) 932-3321; adv fax (781) 932-3321; ed fax (781) 932-3321; gen/nat adv e-mail news@dailytimesinc.com; disp adv e-mail advertising@dailytimesinc.com; class adv e-mailwoburnclass@rcn.com; ed e-mail news@woburnonline.com; web site www.homenewshere.com
- 100,378(views) 59,300(visitors)
Group: Woburn Daily Times, Inc.
Published: Mon, Tues, Wed, Thur, Fri
Weekday Frequency: e
Circulation: 10,872
Last Audit: Sworn/Estimate/Non-Audited September 30, 2017
Advertising Rate (weekday/saturday): Open inch rate $23.75
Online Advertising Rate: Small Banner $165.00; Medium Banner $210.00
News services: AP, NEA. **Established:** 1901
Special Editions: Spring Home Improvement (Apr); Pre-Season Football (Aug); Christmas (Dec); Your Health (Feb); Graduation (Jun); Social Security (Mar); Spring Home Improvement (May); Fall Home Improvement (Nov); Fall Home Improvement (Oct); Bridal (Sept).
Special Weekly Sections: Bridal Directory (Fri); Medical Directory (Mon); Business Guide (Thur); Business Guide (Tues); Medical Directory (Wed).
Syndicated Publications: Middlesex East (Wed).
Digital Platform - Mobile: Apple, Android
Digital Platform - Tablet: Apple iOS, Android

Pres./Pub./Treasurer/Personnel Mgr......... Peter M. Haggerty
Office Mgr./Purchasing Agent.........Joel Haggerty
Controller ....Christopher Campbell
Adv. Dir. ....Thomas Kirk
Mgr., Promo. ....Mark Haggerty
Circ. Mgr. ....Peter Curran
City Ed.............................Gordon Vincent
Film/Theater Ed. ....Michael Haggerty
Nat'l Ed. ....James Haggerty
News Ed. ....James D. Haggerty
News Ed., Burlington ....John White
News Ed., Winchester ....Chris Connelly
Social Ed. ....Melissa Finn
Sports Ed. ....Steve Algeri
Prodn. Mgr. ....Jay M. Haggerty
Prodn. Mgr., Pressroom ....Lance Jonsson
Market Information: ADS; Split run; TMC; Zoned editions.
Mechanical Available: Offset; Black and 3 ROP colors; insert accepted; page cutoffs - 21.
Mechanical Specifications: Type page 11 5/8 x 21; E - 6 cols, 1 4/5, 1/8 between; A - 6 cols, 1 4/5, 1/16 between; C - 9 cols, 1 3/20, 1/8 between.
Areas Served: 01801, 01890, 01803, 01867
Delivery Method: Mail, CarrierEquipment & Software: PRESSROOM EQUIPMENT: Lines — 8-G/Community 1975.; MAILROOM EQUIPMENT: Tying Machines — 1/CYP, 2-/Sa; Wrapping Singles — Am; Address Machine — 2-Am/1800.; BUSINESS EQUIPMENT: 6-Vision Data CLASSIFIED EQUIPMENT: Hardware — 6-APP/iMac; CLASSIFIED SOFTWARE: Baseview. DISPLAY EQUIPMENT: Hardware — Konica/2100 Turbo EV-Jetsetter; Printers — HP/LaserJet 5000N; Other Hardware — Umax/5-12 DISPLAY SOFTWAREAd Make-up Applications — Baseview; Layout Software — 2-APP/Power Mac 7100-80, 4-APP/iMac G4. EDITORIAL EQUIPMENT: Hardware — 5-APP/iMac/Okidata/Doc-IT 4000 Scanner; Printers — 2-HP/LaserJet 4 EDITORIAL SOFTWARE: Baseview. PRODUCTION EQUIPMENT: Hardware — 1-BKY, 1-Ca; Cameras — 2-DSA.

WORCESTER

TELEGRAM & GAZETTE
100 Front St Ste 500, PO Box 15012, Worcester, Mass., 01608-1440, Worcester; gen tel (508) 793-9100; adv tel (508) 793-9200; ed tel (508) 793-9245; gen fax (508) 793-9313; adv fax (508) 793-9308; ed fax (508) 793-9281; gen/nat adv e-mail advertise@telegram.com; disp adv e-mail advertise@telegram.com; class adv e-mailadvertise@telegram.com; ed e-mail newstips@telegram.com; web site www.telegram.com
- 5,800,000(views) 1,100,000(visitors)
Group: New Media Investment Group
Published: Mon, Tues, Wed, Thur, Fri, Sat, Sun
Weekday Frequency: m
Saturday Frequency: m
Circulation: 38,299; 36,380(sat); 41,504(sun)
Last Audit: AAM December 31, 2016
News services: AP, NYT, Bloomberg. **Established:** 1866
Own Printing Facility?: No
Commercial Printers?: No
Special Editions: President's Auto, Summer Book, Worcester Living quarterly magazine, Hometeam, Winter Book, Community Profiles
Special Weekly Sections: Business Matters, Sunday Living, Go! entertainment guide
Syndicated Publications: Parade magazine, Relish magazine, Spry magazine
Proprietary Publications: Telegram & Gazette, Sunday Telegram, The Item
Digital Platform - Mobile: Apple, Android, Blackberry
Digital Platform - Tablet: Apple iOS, Android
Exec. Ed. ....Karen Webber
Editorial Page Editor ....Tony Simollardes
Pub.....................................Paul Provost
Finance Director ....Christine Ortoleva
Chief Revenue Officer.........Michele Marquis
Digital Solutions Director ....Gregory Richards
Advertising Director ....Joseph Valencourt
Mechanical Specifications: Full broad sheet 11.625 inches x 21 inches Double truck 24.125 x 21

1 column 1.833 inches
2 column 3.792
3 column 5.750
4 column 7.708
5 Column 9.667
6 Column 11.625
Areas Served: Worcester County
Delivery Method: Mail, Newsstand, Carrier, Racks
Note: In 2013, The Telegram & Gazette won 56 awards from the New England Newspaper & Press Association.

MICHIGAN

ADRIAN

THE DAILY TELEGRAM

133 N Winter St, Adrian, Mich., 49221-2042, Lenawee; gen tel (517) 265-5111; adv tel (517) 265-5111 ext. 226; ed tel (517) 265-5111 ext. 230; gen fax (517) 263-4152; adv fax (517) 265-3030; ed fax (517) 263-4152; gen/nat adv e-mail dwerner@telegramadvertising.com; disp adv e-mail dwerner@telegramadvertising.com; class adv e-mailcgoodlockproctor@lenconnect.com; ed e-mail editor@lenconnect.com; web site www.lenconnect.com - 1,230,000(views) 7,950(visitors)
Group: New Media Investment Group
Published: Mon, Tues, Wed, Thur, Fri, Sat, Sun
Weekday Frequency: e
Saturday Frequency: m
Circulation: 10,207; 10,207(sat); 11,762(sun)
Last Audit: AAM March 31, 2016
Advertising Rate (weekday/saturday): Open inch rate $31.25
Advertising Rate (sunday): Open inch rate $32.25
Online Advertising Rate: Starting from $8.00 CPM
News services: GateHouse Media, Inc. **Established:** 1892
Own Printing Facility?: Yes
Commercial Printers?: Yes
Special Weekly Sections: Entertainment TV Log (Fri); Outdoor Page (S); Church Page (Sat). Life & Style (Sun)
Syndicated Publications: Parade (S).
Proprietary Publications: Lenawee Magazine, Lenawee Pulse Magazine
Digital Platform - Mobile: Apple, Android, Windows
Digital Platform - Tablet: Apple iOS, Android, Windows 7
Ed.....Mark Lenz
Prepress Mgr.....Bruce Banks
Circ. Dir.....Jeff Stahl
District Mgr.....Al Seabolt
Controller....Christine Nader
Classified Mgr.....Carol Perez
VP Adv.....Jackie Park
Dir. Adv. Operations....Brenda Lenoard
Market Information: ADS; TMC.
Mechanical Available: Offset; Black and 3 ROP colors; insert accepted - front page self-adhesive notes; page cutoffs - 22 3/4.
Mechanical Specifications: Type page 13 1/16 x 21 1/2; E - 6 cols, 1 7/8, 1/8 between; A - 6 cols, 1 7/8, 1/8 between; C - 9 cols, 1/8 between.
Areas Served: 49220, 49221, 49228, 49229, 49230, 49233, 49235, 49236, 49238, 49247, 49248, 49253, 49256, 49265, 49268, 49276, 49279, 49282, 49286, 49287, 49288, 43533
Delivery Method: Mail, Newsstand, Carrier, RacksEquipment & Software: PRESSROOM EQUIPMENT: Lines — 1Tensor Four High 9-G/Community (3 color decks; 2 formers); Folders — 1-G/55C.; MAILROOM EQUIPMENT: Counter Stackers — 2-HL/Monitor; Inserters & Stuffers — Titan/12:1; Tying Machines — Sa; Address Machine — Prism.; BUSINESS EQUIPMENT: PC CLASSIFIED EQUIPMENT: Hardware — APP/Mac; App/Mac; CLASSIFIED SOFTWARE: Media Span. DISPLAY SOFTWAREAd Make-up Applications — QPS/QuarkXPress, Adobe/Photoshop, Multi-Ad/Creator, Media Span; Layout Software — APP/Mac. EDITORIAL EQUIPMENT: Hardware — APP/Mac EDITORIAL SOFTWARE: QPS/QuarkXPress, Media Span IQ/NewsEdit. PRODUCTION EQUIPMENT: Hardware — ECRM/CTP

ALMA

MORNING SUN

311 E Superior St Ste A, Suite P, Alma, Mich., 48801-1832, Gratiot; gen tel (989) 779-6000; adv tel (989) 779-6110; ed tel (989) 779-6003; gen fax (989) 776-6012; adv fax (989) 779-6101; ed fax (989) 779-6051; gen/nat adv e-mail cturner@michigannewspapers.com; disp adv e-mail cturner@michigannewspapers.com; class adv e-mailclassifieds@michigannewspapers.com; ed e-mail rmills@michigannewspapers.com; web site www.themorningsun.com - 21,000,000(views) 1,860,000(visitors)
Group: Digital First Media
Published: Mon, Tues, Wed, Thur, Fri, Sat, Sun
Weekday Frequency: m
Saturday Frequency: m
Circulation: 6,715; 6,685(sat); 7,736(sun)
Last Audit: AAM September 30, 2014
Advertising Rate (weekday/saturday): Open inch rate $17.36
Advertising Rate (sunday): Open inch rate $18.25
Online Advertising Rate: Starting at $55.00 CPM
News services: AP. **Established:** 1977
Own Printing Facility?: Yes
Commercial Printers?: Yes
Special Editions: Yard & Garden (Apr); Football Preview (Aug); Basketball Tab (Dec); Progress (Feb); Bridal Tab (Jan); Bridal Tab (Jul); Home Show (Mar); Highland Festival (May); Thanksgiving Day (Nov); Car Care (Oct); Fall Yard and Garden (Sept).
Special Weekly Sections: Dining (Fri); Health Lifestyles (Thur); Golf (Tues).
Syndicated Publications: Parade (S).
Digital Platform - Mobile: Apple, Android
Digital Platform - Tablet: Apple iOS, Android
Ed.....Rick Mills
Sports Ed.....Jim Lahde
Community Ed.....Kullen Logsdon
Recruitment Specialist....Cindy Terwilliger
Market Information: ADS; TMC; Zoned editions.
Mechanical Available: Offset; Black and 3 ROP colors; insert accepted; page cutoffs - 22.
Mechanical Specifications: Type page 13 x 21; E - 6 cols, 2 1/16, 1/8 between; A - 8 cols, 3 1/5, 1/8 between; C - 8 cols, 1 1/2, 1/8 between.
Areas Served: 48615, 48617, 48618, 48622, 48625, 48632, 48801, 48832, 48847, 48858, 48877, 48878, 78880, 48883, 48893, 49310, 49340
Delivery Method: Carrier, RacksEquipment & Software: PRESSROOM EQUIPMENT: Lines — 14-G/Community (2 Path finder color decks); 10-G/Community.; MAILROOM EQUIPMENT: Counter Stackers — 2/BG; Inserters & Stuffers — 1-K&M/1472, 3-MM; Tying Machines — 6-/Bu; BUSINESS EQUIPMENT: Compaq/PL 1500 CLASSIFIED EQUIPMENT: Hardware — Compaq/PL 1500; Printers — 1-Epson/DFX-8000; CLASSIFIED SOFTWARE: PBS/AdPlus. DISPLAY EQUIPMENT: Hardware — 13-APP/Mac; Printers — 2-HP/5000, 1-NewGen/Imager Plus 12, 1-HP/4V, 1-AG/Accuset 1000, 1-Scitex/Dolev 400; DISPLAY SOFTWAREAd Make-up Applications — QPS/QuarkXPress 4.0, Adobe/Photoshop 5.0, Adobe/Illustrator 7.0; Layout Software — PBS/AdPlus, PBS/AdPlacer. EDITORIAL EQUIPMENT: Printers — HP/4P, HP/5P EDITORIAL SOFTWARE: Alfa PRODUCTION EQUIPMENT: Cameras — 1-B/4000, 1-Nu/VIC-1418, 1-TogeeMD/480, 1-Acti/253; Scanners — 1-AG/Arcus Plus, AG/Horizon Flatbed PRODUCTION SOFTWARE: PBS/AdPlacer.

ALPENA

THE ALPENA NEWS

130 Park Pl, Alpena, Mich., 49707-2828, Alpena; gen tel (989) 354-3111; gen fax (989) 354-2096; gen/nat adv e-mail cwerda@thealpenanews.com; disp adv e-mail alpenaads@thealpenanews.com; class adv e-mail alpenaclassifieds@thealpenanews.com; ed e-mail newsroom@thealpenanews.com; web site www.thealpenanews.com - 375,000(views)
Group: Ogden Newspapers Inc.
Published: Mon, Tues, Wed, Thur, Fri, Sat
Weekday Frequency: m
Saturday Frequency: m
Circulation: 6,866; 7,830(sat)
Last Audit: AAM September 30, 2017
Advertising Rate (weekday/saturday): Open inch rate $25.46
News services: AP, NEA. **Established:** 1899
Own Printing Facility?: Yes
Commercial Printers?: Yes
Special Editions: Graduation (May); Young At Heart (Jun); Bridal Tab (Feb); Proud to Be an American (Jul); Sunrise Side's Best of the Best (Apr); Back-to-School (Aug); Home Improvement (Mar); Deer Hunting (Oct)
Special Weekly Sections: Entertainment (Thur); Entertainment (Fri); Entertainment (Sat); Real Estate Section (Thur).
Digital Platform - Mobile: Apple, Android
Digital Platform - Tablet: Apple iOS, Android
Pub./Ed.....Bill Speer
Adv. Mgr.....Christie Werda
Lifestyles Ed.....Diane Speer
Managing Ed.....Steve Murch
Sports Ed.....James Andersen
Business Office Mgr.....Kathryn Burton
Circ. Mgr.....Ken Pokorzynski
Market Information: ADS; TMC; Zoned editions.
Mechanical Available: Offset; Black and 3 ROP colors; insert accepted; page cutoffs - 22 3/4.
Mechanical Specifications: Type page 10 x 21 1/2; E - 6 cols, 1.583, .16 between; A - 6 cols, 1.583, .16 between; C - 8 cols, 1.163, .16 between.
Areas Served: 49743, 49759, 49765, 49776, 49779, 49707, 49744, 49747, 49753, 49766, 49777, 49709, 49746, 48705, 48721, 48740, 48742, 48745, 48750, 48762
Delivery Method: Mail, Newsstand, Carrier, RacksEquipment & Software: PRESSROOM EQUIPMENT: Lines — 6-G/U 911; MAILROOM EQUIPMENT: Tying Machines — 1/Sa, 2-/MLN; Address Machine — 1-/St.; DISPLAY SOFTWAREAd Make-up Applications — Aldus, QPS, Multi-Ad, Aldus/FreeHand, Adobe/Photoshop; Layout Software — APP/Power Mac.

BAD AXE

HURON DAILY TRIBUNE

211 N Heisterman St, Bad Axe, Mich., 48413-1239, Huron; gen tel 9892696461; adv tel (989) 269-6461; ed tel (989) 269-6461; gen fax (989) 269-9435; adv fax (989) 269-2691; ed fax (989) 269-9435; gen/nat adv e-mail rwatson@hearstnp.com; disp adv e-mail rwatson@hearstnp.com; class adv e-mailrwatson@hearstnp.com; ed e-mail khessling@hearstnp.com; web site www.michigansthumb.com
Group: Hearst Communications, Inc.
Published: Tues, Wed, Thur, Fri, Sat
Weekday Frequency: e
Saturday Frequency: e
Circulation: 3,800; 4,000(sat)
Last Audit: Sworn/Estimate/Non-Audited August 31, 2017
News services: AP. **Established:** 1876
Own Printing Facility?: Yes
Commercial Printers?: Yes
Special Editions: Golf (Apr); Real Estate Guides (Aug); Holiday Gift Guide (Dec); Real Estate Guides (Feb); Progress (Jan); Real Estate Guides (Jul); Real Estate Guides (Jun); Traveler (May); Holiday Gift Guide (Nov); Home Improvement (Sept).
Digital Platform - Mobile: Apple, Android
Digital Platform - Tablet: Apple iOS, Android
Ed.....Kate Hessling
Circ. Dir.....Gary Wamsley
Sports Ed.....Paul Adams
General Manager....Rebecca Watson
Market Information: TMC.
Mechanical Available: Offset; Black and 3 ROP colors; insert accepted - subject to approval; page cutoffs - 22 3/4.
Mechanical Specifications: Type page 13 x 21 1/2; E - 6 cols, 2 1/16, 1/8 between; A - 6 cols, 2 1/16, 1/8 between; C - 9 cols, 1 3/8, 1/16 between.
Areas Served: 48413, 48720, 48723, 48725, 48726, 48427, 48731, 48432, 48434, 48735, 48441, 48445, 48453, 48456, 48754, 48465, 48755, 48467, 48468, 48470, 48759, 48472, 48475, 48767
Delivery Method: Mail, CarrierEquipment & Software: PRESSROOM EQUIPMENT: Lines — 9-KP/News King; Pasters —BG/Acumeter. MAILROOM EQUIPMENT: Tying Machines — 2/Bu; Address Machine — Ch.; BUSINESS EQUIPMENT: AdMark BUSINESS SOFTWARE: Discus CLASSIFIED EQUIPMENT: Hardware — APP/Mac; APP/Mac Scanner; Printers — APP/Mac LaserWriter II; CLASSIFIED SOFTWARE: Baseview, Mk/Class Manager 3.2. DISPLAY EQUIPMENT: Hardware — APP/Power Mac, APP/Power Mac PC 7100; Printers — APP/Mac LaserWriter II, APP/Mac LaserWriter 810; Other Hardware — NEC, CD-Rom DISPLAY SOFTWAREAd Make-up Applications — QPS/QuarkXPress 3.3; Layout Software — Ad Director. EDITORIAL EQUIPMENT: Hardware — APP/Mac/APP/Mac Scanner, Lf/AP Leaf Picture Desk, APP/Power Mac, APP/Power Mac/7100 Photo Desk; Printers — APP/Mac LaserWriter II, APP/Mac LaserWriter 810, AG/Imagesetter 800 EDITORIAL SOFTWARE: Baseview/NewsEdit 3.3, Baseview. PRODUCTION EQUIPMENT: Hardware — AG/800 Imagesetter, Power PC/8100; Cameras — C/Spartan III, C/Marathon; Scanners — Umax, Nikon PRODUCTION SOFTWARE: AG, QPS/QuarkXPress 4.0.

BATTLE CREEK

BATTLE CREEK ENQUIRER

77 Michigan Ave E Ste 101, Suite 101, Battle Creek, Mich., 49017-7033, Calhoun; gen tel (269) 964-7161; adv tel (269) 966-0570; ed tel (269) 966-0672; gen fax (269) 964-0299; adv fax (269) 964-8242; ed fax (269) 964-0299; gen/nat adv e-mail bsours@battlecreekenquirer.com; disp adv e-mail bsours@battlecreekenquirer.com; class adv e-mailalyon@battlecreekenquirer.com; ed e-mail mmccullo@battlecreekenquirer.com; web site battlecreekenquirer.com - 1,058,062(views) 203,605(visitors)
Group: Gannett
Published: Mon, Tues, Wed, Thur, Fri, Sat, Sun
Weekday Frequency: m
Saturday Frequency: m
Circulation: 10,114; 10,114(sat); 15,048(sun)
Last Audit: AAM June 30, 2016
Advertising Rate (weekday/saturday): Open inch rate $53.28 (National); Open inch rate $35.64 (Annual Contract)
Advertising Rate (sunday): Open inch rate $64.36; Open inch rate $50.13 (Annual Contract)
Online Advertising Rate: Template Landing Page $25.00 per month; Email Blasts (Targeted) $80.00 CPM
News services: AP, GNS. **Established:** 1900
Own Printing Facility?: No
Special Editions: Wedding Planner (Jan); Senior Connections (Jan, Mar, May, Jul, Nov) Progress (Feb); Homezone (Mar); Homebuyer Guide (Mar); Golf (April); Outdoors (Apr, Sep); Travel (May); Airshow (June); Big Summer Deals (June); Grad section (June); Resident Resource (Jul); Back to School (Jul); Football (Aug); Kidvertising (Oct); Holiday (Nov); Basketball (Dec).
Special Weekly Sections: WOW (Fri).
Syndicated Publications: USA WEEKEND Magazine (Fri).
Digital Platform - Mobile: Apple, Android, Windows
Digital Platform - Tablet: Apple iOS, Android, Windows 7
Op. Mgr.....Merrie Shina
Gen. Mgr. and Exec. Ed.....Michael McCullough
News Ed.....Bob Warner
Photo Ed.....John Grap
Sports Ed.....Bill Broderick
ASSISTANT MNG. ED.
Charles Carlson
Features Ed.....Annie Kelley

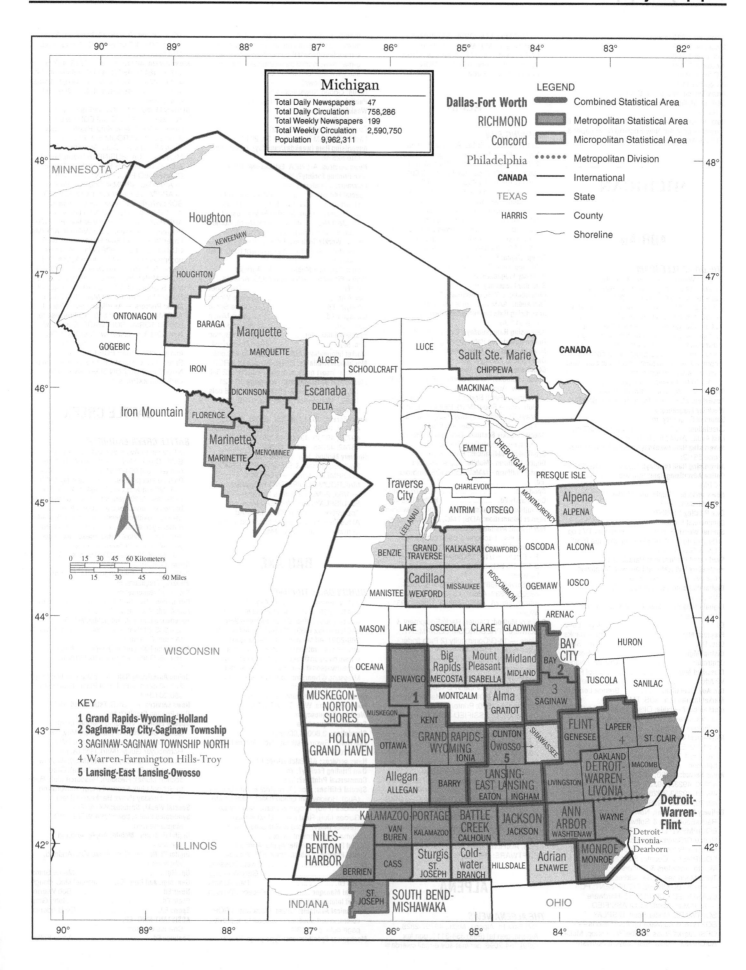

Michigan
Total Daily Newspapers	47
Total Daily Circulation	758,286
Total Weekly Newspapers	199
Total Weekly Circulation	2,590,750
Population	9,962,311

LEGEND
Dallas-Fort Worth — Combined Statistical Area
RICHMOND — Metropolitan Statistical Area
Concord — Micropolitan Statistical Area
Philadelphia ••••• Metropolitan Division
CANADA — International
TEXAS — State
HARRIS — County
— Shoreline

KEY
1 Grand Rapids-Wyoming-Holland
2 Saginaw-Bay City-Saginaw Township
3 SAGINAW-SAGINAW TOWNSHIP NORTH
4 Warren-Farmington Hills-Troy
5 Lansing-East Lansing-Owosso

Opinion Page Ed. .... Steve Smith
Mechanical Available: Offset; Black and 3 ROP colors; insert accepted - zoned;
Areas Served: 49017; 49015; 49037; 49014; 49020; 49021; 49046; 49050; 49058; 49060; 49073;49076; 49096; 49033; 49068; 49224; 49245; 49092; 49011; 49028; 49029; 49036; 49040; 49051; 49082; 49089; 49094; 49012; 49034; 49053;
Delivery Method: Mail, Newsstand, Carrier, RacksEquipment & Software: PRODUCTION SOFTWARE: Newsgate/CCI

BAY CITY

THE BAY CITY TIMES

311 5th St, Bay City, Mich., 48708-5802, Bay; gen tel (989) 895-8551; adv tel (800) 446-5588; gen fax (989) 895-5910; gen/nat adv e-mail msharp@mlive.com; disp adv e-mail cplaxton@mlive.com; class adv e-mailmcovingt@mlive.com; ed e-mail rclark2@mlive.com; web site http://www.mlive.com/bay-city
- 18,000,000(views) 1,500,000(visitors)

Group: Advance Publications, Inc.
Published: Tues, Thur, Fri, Sun
Weekday Frequency: m
Circulation: 13,213; 21,266(sun)
Last Audit: AAM December 31, 2016
Advertising Rate (weekday/saturday): Open inch rate $22.55
Advertising Rate (sunday): Open inch rate 33.82
News services: AP, LAT-WP, NNS. **Established:** 1873
Own Printing Facility?: Yes
Commercial Printers?: No
Special Editions: Catching ZZZ's (Apr); Football Tab (Aug); Last Minute Gifts (Dec); Everyday Money (Feb); Weddings (Jan); Salute to Bay Area Business (Jul); For Your Wedding (Jun); Women's Expo (Mar); Health Care (May); Five Star Favorites (Nov); Fall Care Care (Sept).
Special Weekly Sections: Outdoor Pages (Fri); Food (Mon); Farm Pages (S); Anniversaries (Sat); Weekend Scene Magazine (Thur); Kids Pages (Tues); Homestyle (Wed).
Syndicated Publications: Parade (S).
Digital Platform - Mobile: Apple, Android
Digital Platform - Tablet: Apple iOS, Android, Windows 7
Pres. .... Dan Gaydou
Sr. Dir. for National Accounts .... Steve Westphal
Dir. of Adv. Operations .... Bob White
Chief Revenue Officer .... Charity Plaxton
VP of Sales .... Michael Assink
Dir. of Real Estate & Careers Sales Andy Boldryeff
VP of Content .... John Hiner
Dir. of Sports News .... Bill Emkow
Sr. Dir. for Journalism and Engagement Kelly Frick
Sr. Dir. for Digital Culture and Innovation . Colleen Stone
Exec. Ed. of Print .... Paul Keep
Automotive Dir. .... Khalida Cook
Small Business Dir. .... Andrea Sipka
Sr. Strategy Dir. .... Nick Dionne
Sr. Retail Dir. .... Brett Christie
Regional Sales Dir. of Detroit & Ann Arbor. Christy Keizer
Regional Sales Dir. of Flint, Saginaw and Bay City Robert Graham
Regional Sales Dir. of Grand Rapids & Muskegon . Jamie Dionne
General Mgr. .... Laurel Champion
Agency Relations Dir. .... Jeff Leitch
Advertising Support Dir. .... Andrea Miller
Dir. of News .... Marjory Raymer
Dir. of Community Engagement .... Jen Eyer
Rgl. Sales Dir. .... Angel Offredi
Rgl. Sales Mgr. .... Colleen Huff
Chief Digital Officer .... Mark Hauptschein
VP, Sales and Marketing .... Matt Sharp
Market Information: Split run; TMC; Zoned editions.
Mechanical Available: Offset; Black and full color ROP colors; insert accepted; page cutoffs - 20.
Mechanical Specifications: Type page 13 x 22 1/4; E - 6 cols, 2 1/16, 1/8 between; A - 6 cols, 2 1/16, 1/8 between; C - 10 cols, 1 1/4, 1/16 between.
Areas Served: 48706 48708 48732 48611 48650 48631 48634 48661 48658 48759 48624 48750 48703 48763 48747 48659 48730 48767 48642 48755 48739 48653 48733 48610 48701
Delivery Method: Mail, Newsstand, Carrier, RacksEquipment & Software: MAILROOM EQUIPMENT: Counter Stackers — Flexi Roll Buffer; Inserters & Stuffers — 2/SLS 3000, 5-/AU PP 500; Tying Machines — Dyneric.; BUSINESS EQUIPMENT: 1-Sun/Ultra Sparc 140, 1-Sun/Sparc 20, 1-Sun/Ultra 200 E BUSINESS SOFTWARE: PBS, Solaris/OS, SBS CLASSIFIED EQUIPMENT: Hardware — AT/9000; CLASSIFIED SOFTWARE: AT 4.4.10. DISPLAY EQUIPMENT: Hardware — APP/Mac, Dell/486 PC, Dell/NT 2400, Harlequin 5.x, Sun/Sparc 20 RIP Express 3000; Printers — HP/4 MV, HP/5000N; DISPLAY SOFTWAREAd Make-up Applications — QPS/QuarkXPress 4.11, Multi-Ad/Creator 6.5, Adobe/Photoshop 7.0, Baseview/PMP.; EDITORIAL EQUIPMENT: Hardware — Apple/APP/Mac; Printers — HP/LaserJet II EDITORIAL SOFTWARE: Baseview. PRODUCTION EQUIPMENT: Hardware — AP; Scanners — 2-AG/ Duoscan T1200 PRODUCTION SOFTWARE: Baseview.

BIG RAPIDS

THE PIONEER - BIG RAPIDS

115 N Michigan Ave, Big Rapids, Mich., 49307-1401, Mecosta; gen tel (231) 796-4831; adv tel (231) 592-8359; ed tel (231) 592-8360; gen fax (231) 796-1152; adv fax (231) 796-1152; ed fax (231) 796-1152; gen/nat adv e-mail advertising@pioneergroup.com; disp adv e-mail advertising@pioneergroup.com; class adv e-mailclassified@pioneergroup.com ; ed e-mail editor@pioneergroup.com; web site www.bigrapidsnews.com
- 130,000(views) 16,000(visitors)

Group: The Pioneer Group
Published: Mon, Tues, Wed, Thur, Fri, Sat
Weekday Frequency: m
Saturday Frequency: m
Circulation: 5,221; 5,221(sat)
Last Audit: Sworn/Estimate/Non-Audited September 30, 2017
Advertising Rate (weekday/saturday): Open inch rate $10.00 (Local); $13.00 (National)
Online Advertising Rate: Homepage Button $125.00/month; Bottom Banner $150.00 CPM; Inside Story Box $195.00 CPM
News services: AP. **Established:** 1862
Special Editions: Recreation (Apr); Ferris State University Orientation Welcome (Aug); Songbook (Dec); Car Care Tab (Fall); Bridal Issue (Jan); Sidewalk Sales (Jul); Progress (Jun); Graduation (May); Christmas Gift Guide (Nov); Soil Conservation (Sept); Car Care Tab (Sprin
Special Weekly Sections: Eye on Entertainment (Sat).
Syndicated Publications: USA WEEKEND Magazine (Sat); American Profile (Tues).
Digital Platform - Mobile: Apple, Android
Digital Platform - Tablet: Apple iOS, Android, Kindle, Nook, Kindle Fire
CFO .... Sharon Doxee
Pub. .... John Norton
HR Mgr. .... Patti Wilson
Adv. Mgr. .... Sharon Frederick
Sports Ed. .... Zeke Jennings
Press. Mgr. .... Robert Kaminski
Ed. .... Jim Crees
Adv. .... Danette Doyle
News Ed. .... Jonathan Eppley
Market Information: ADS; TMC; Zoned editions.
Mechanical Available: Offset; Black and 3 ROP colors; insert accepted - all; page cutoffs - 21.
Mechanical Specifications: Type page 12 x 21 1/2; E - 6 cols, 2, 1/6 between; A - 6 cols, 1 3/8, 7/16 between; C - 6 cols, 1 3/8, 7/16 between.
Areas Served: Big Rapids, Mecosta, Osceola, and parts of Lake and Newaygo Counties.
Delivery Method: Mail, CarrierEquipment & Software: PRESSROOM EQUIPMENT: Lines — 2-4/HI, 2-2/HI, 2, 2-HI/JF-35 Folders; 1-4/HI, 2-2/HI, 2, HI/JF-35 Folder single width; Press Drive — 30, 100, GE/ Motor Drive; Folders — 1-HI/JF7, 1-HI/ JF-35; Pasters —4-Martin/EC Plus zero speedReels & Stands — 5; MAILROOM EQUIPMENT: Counter Stackers — Rima, RS/25; Inserters & Stuffers — KAN/480 6:1; Tying Machines — 2-Bu/String Tyers, 1-Mosca/Strapper; Address Machine — Wm.; BUSINESS EQUIPMENT: Microsoft/ Windows NT 4.0, APP/Power Mac Work Group 8550 BUSINESS SOFTWARE: Great Plains, Baseview CLASSIFIED EQUIPMENT: Hardware — APP/Mac, Poweruser/ fileserver; 2-APP/Mac, Xante, ECR/ Imagesetter; Printers — ECR/Imagesetter; CLASSIFIED SOFTWARE: APP/Power Mac, Baseview/Ad Manager Pro. DISPLAY EQUIPMENT: Hardware — APP/Power Mac, Baseview/Ad Manager Pro; Printers — Xante/Accel-a-Writer 8100; DISPLAY SOFTWARELayout Software — APP/Power Macs. EDITORIAL EQUIPMENT: Hardware — APP/Mac, Poweruser/fileserver/9-APP/ Mac, 1-APP/Mac II; Printers — Xante, ECR/ Imagesetter, X/Color Laser EDITORIAL SOFTWARE: Baseview/NewsEdit Pro 2.2.2. PRODUCTION EQUIPMENT: Hardware — 2-APP/Mac LaserWriter II, 1-Nu/ FT40LNS; Cameras — 1-AG/RPS 2024S, 1-LE/480; Scanners — 1-AG/Studio Star, 1-Polaroid/SprintScan Plus PRODUCTION SOFTWARE: QPS/QuarkXPress 3.2.

CADILLAC

CADILLAC NEWS

130 N Mitchell St, Cadillac, Mich., 49601-1856, Wexford; gen tel (231) 775-6565; adv tel (231) 779-4138; ed tel (231) 779-4126; gen fax (231) 775-8790; adv fax (231) 775-8790; ed fax (231) 775-8790; gen/nat adv e-mail jbailey@cadillacnews.com; disp adv e-mail jbailey@cadillacnews.com; class adv e-mailcustomerservice@cadillacnews.com; ed e-mail mseward@cadillacnews.com; web site www.cadillacnews.com
- 330,000(views) 52,500(visitors)

Published: Mon, Tues, Wed, Thur, Fri, Sat
Weekday Frequency: m
Saturday Frequency: m
Circulation: 7,200; 7,200(sat)
Last Audit: USPS October 1, 2017
Advertising Rate (weekday/saturday): Open inch rate $18.25
Online Advertising Rate: Run of Site $8.00 CPM
News services: AP. **Established:** 1872
Own Printing Facility?: Yes
Commercial Printers?: Yes
Special Editions: Spring Home Improvement (Apr); Brides & Weddings (Aug); Christmas Gift Guide (Dec); Home Show (Feb); Generations (50+) (Jan); Summer Recreation II (Jun); Progress (Mar); Summer Recreation I (May); Hunting Guide (Nov); Generations (50+) (Oct); Fall Home Im
Special Weekly Sections: Church (Fri); Outdoors (Sat); Entertainment (Thur); Seniors (Tues); Family (Wed).
Syndicated Publications: USA WEEKEND Magazine (Sat); American Profile (Weekly).
Digital Platform - Mobile: Apple, Android, Windows
Digital Platform - Tablet: Apple iOS, Android, Windows 7
Pub. .... Christopher Huckle
Ed. .... Matthew Seward
Prod. Mgr. .... Ken Koch
Circ./Marketing Dir. .... Josh Bailey
Market Information: TMC; Zoned editions.
Mechanical Available: Offset; Black and 3 ROP colors; insert accepted; page cutoffs - 22 3/4.
Mechanical Specifications: Type page 10 3/8 x 21 1/2; E - 6 cols, 2 1/16, 1/8 between; A - 6 cols, 2 1/16, 1/8 between; C - 6 cols, 2 1/16, 1/8 between.
Areas Served: 49601, 49618, 49638, 49657, 49665, 49656, 49688, 49655, 49631, 49677, 49623, 49639, 49679, 79663, 49651, 49667, 49632, 49668, 49620, 49689, 49633, 49644, 49625, 49684, 49686
Delivery Method: Mail, CarrierEquipment & Software: PRESSROOM EQUIPMENT: Lines — 6-HI/V-15A (Upper Former) 1969.; MAILROOM EQUIPMENT: Tying Machines — Bu; Address Machine — Domino/ Ink Jet.; BUSINESS EQUIPMENT: APP/ Mac BUSINESS SOFTWARE: Baseview CLASSIFIED EQUIPMENT: Hardware — Mac; Printers — Xerox; CLASSIFIED SOFTWARE: Baseview/Classified, Baseview/ Ad Manager Pro. DISPLAY EQUIPMENT: Hardware — Mac; DISPLAY SOFTWAREAd Make-up Applications — Multi-Ad/Creator; Layout Software — MEI/ALS. EDITORIAL SOFTWARE: Woodwing/InDesign

CHEBOYGAN

CHEBOYGAN DAILY TRIBUNE

308 N Main St, Cheboygan, Mich., 49721-1545, Cheboygan; gen tel (231) 627-7144; adv tel (231) 627-7144; ed tel (231) 627-7144; gen fax (231) 627-5331; adv fax (231) 627-5331; ed fax (231) 627-5331; gen/nat adv e-mail nkidder@cheboygantribune.com; disp adv e-mail cheryl.mercer@cheboygantribune.com; class adv e-maildeedra@cheboygantribune.com; ed e-mail richard@cheboygantribune.com; web site www.cheboygannews.com

Group: New Media Investment Group
Published: Mon, Tues, Wed, Thur, Fri, Sat
Weekday Frequency: m
Saturday Frequency: m
Circulation: 4,864
Last Audit: Sworn/Estimate/Non-Audited September 30, 2017
Advertising Rate (weekday/saturday): Open inch rate $11.85 (Local); $15.90 (National)
Online Advertising Rate: Top Banner $120.00/ month; Half Banner $60.00/month
News services: AP. **Established:** 1876
Special Editions: Home Improvement (Apr); Design an Ad (Feb); Home Improvement (Mar).
Special Weekly Sections: Real Estate (Fri); Schools (Mon); Food (Thur); Business (Tues); Weddings (Wed).
Syndicated Publications: American Profile (Weekly).
Digital Platform - Mobile: Apple, Android, Windows
Digital Platform - Tablet: Apple iOS, Android, Windows 7
Pub. .... Gary Lamberg
Adv. Mgr. .... Nancy Kidder
Circ. Mgr. .... Mary Whaley
Pub. .... Richard Crofton
Prod. Mgr., Pressroom .... Jerry Pond
Business Mgr. .... Janis Coryell
Composition Mgr. .... Patty Niester
Market Information: ADS; TMC.
Mechanical Available: Offset; Black and 2 ROP colors; insert accepted; page cutoffs - 21 1/2.
Mechanical Specifications: Type page 12 1/2 x 21; E - 6 cols, 2 1/16, 1/8 between; A - 6 cols, 2 1/16, 1/8 between; C - 6 cols, 2 1/16, 1/8 between.
Areas Served: 49701, 49705, 49718, 49721, 49749, 49755, 49759, 49761, 49765, 49769, 49791, 49792, 49799
Delivery Method: Mail, Carrier, RacksEquipment & Software: PRESSROOM EQUIPMENT: Lines — 5-G/Community single width; MAILROOM EQUIPMENT: Tying Machines — Bu, Malow; Address Machine — Am.; BUSINESS EQUIPMENT: PC CLASSIFIED EQUIPMENT: Hardware — APP/ Mac; Printers — Xante 3G.; DISPLAY EQUIPMENT: Printers — Laserwriter 16/6000 PS; DISPLAY SOFTWAREAd Make-up Applications — Aldus/Freehand 5.5, QPS/QuarkXPress; Layout Software — 3-APP/Power Mac 7200-120. EDITORIAL EQUIPMENT: Hardware — APP/Mac; Printers — LaserWriter 16/600 EDITORIAL SOFTWARE: QPS/QuarkXPress 3.3, Macromedia/Freehand, Baseview/NewsEdit. PRODUCTION EQUIPMENT: Hardware — 1-Nu; Cameras — 2-K.

CLINTON TOWNSHIP

THE DAILY TRIBUNE

19176 Hall Rd, Ste 200, Clinton Township, Mich., 48038-6914, Macomb; gen tel (586) 469-4510; adv tel (586) 783-0315; ed tel (248) 745-4587; gen fax (586) 469-2892; adv fax (586) 469-2892; ed fax (586) 469-2892; gen/nat adv e-mail dave.swantek@gdnn.com; disp adv e-mail nklomp@21st-centurymedia.com; class adv e-mailnklomp@21st-

centurymedia.com; ed e-mail Ggilbert@21st-centurymedia.com; web site www.dailytribune.com
424,924(visitors)
Group: 21st Century Media
Published: Wed, Thur, Fri, Sun
Weekday Frequency: m
Circulation: 4,182; 5,455(sun)
Last Audit: AAM September 30, 2014
Newspaper Reps: Michigan Newspapers, Inc., USSPI Media.
Advertising Rate (weekday/saturday): Open inch rate $72.03
Advertising Rate (sunday): Open inch rate $78.17
Online Advertising Rate: Starting at $51.00 CPM
News services: 1902
Special Weekly Sections: Best Food Day (Wed.); Entertainment (Thur); Real Estate (Fri); Real Estate, TV Time, Travel, Automotive (Sun)
Rgl. VP, Sales.......................... Teresa Goodrich
VP, News.. Don Wyatt
Sports Ed. .... George Pohly
Classifieds Dir. .... Noelle Klomp
Pub. .... Jeanine Parent

THE MACOMB DAILY

19176 Hall Rd Ste 200, 2nd Floor, Clinton Township, Mich., 48038-6914, Macomb; gen tel (586) 469-4510; adv tel (586) 783-0293; ed tel (586) 469-4510; gen fax (586) 469-4512; adv fax (586) 469-4711; ed fax (586) 469-2892; gen/nat adv e-mail onlineads@21stcenturynewspapers.com; disp adv e-mail roger.hages@macombdaily.com; class adv e-mailnklomp@21st-centurymedia.com; ed e-mail ken.kish@macombdaily.com; web site www.macombdaily.com
513,650(visitors)
Group: Digital First Media
Published: Mon, Tues, Wed, Thur, Fri, Sat, Sun
Weekday Frequency: m
Saturday Frequency: m
Circulation: 29,864; 28,192(sat); 45,248(sun)
Last Audit: AAM March 31, 2016
Advertising Rate (weekday/saturday): Open inch rate $55.84
Advertising Rate (sunday): Open inch rate $68.15
Online Advertising Rate: Starting at $51.00 CPM
News services: AP **Established:** 1841
Own Printing Facility?: No
Commercial Printers?: Yes
Special Editions: Brides & Grooms (Jan); Social Security (Jan); North American (Jan); Auto Show (Jan); WaterWays/Detroit Boat Show (Feb); Choices in Education (Mar); Macomb on the Move/Quality of Life (Mar); Macomb on the Move/Made in Michigan (Mar); Macomb on the Move/Education (Apr); Spring Golf (Apr); Macomb on the Move/Business & Industry (May); Travels (May); Best of the Best (Jun); Brides & Grooms (Jun); Macomb Preps (Aug); Waterways (Sept); Travels (Sept); Choices in Education (Oct); Holiday Ideas (Nov); Last Minute Gift Guide (Dec); Holiday Wrap (Dec); Holiday Greetings to the Troops (Dec)
Special Weekly Sections: Homes (S); Marquee/Entertainment (Fri); Health (Tues); Lifelines (S) Homefront (S) Wheels (Thur & S)
Syndicated Publications: Parade (S).
Digital Platform - Mobile: Apple, Android
Digital Platform - Tablet: Apple iOS, Android
Sports Ed. .... George Pohly
Pub... Jim O'Rourke
Rgl. VP, Sales.......................... Teresa Goodrich
Classifieds.................................... Noelle Klomp
VP, News.. Don Wyatt
Managing Ed. .... Jeff Payne
Market Information: TMC; Zoned editions.
Mechanical Available: Offset; Black and 3 ROP colors; insert accepted - card stock, books; page cutoffs - 20".
Mechanical Specifications: Broadsheet page - 6 columns (9.89") x 20"; column gutter 8 pts.; page gutter 80 pts.; page margins 40 pts.
Areas Served: 48065, 48005, 48062, 48095, 48094, 48096, 48050, 48048, 48316, 48317, 48314, 48315, 48313, 48312, 48310, 48089, 48088, 48091, 48092, 48093, 48015, 48026, 48021, 48080, 48081, 48082, 48035, 48036, 48038, 48043, 48045, 48042, 48044, 48051, 48047
Delivery Method: Newsstand, Carrier, RacksEquipment & Software: MAILROOM EQUIPMENT: Control System — Burt Technologies; DISPLAY SOFTWAREAd Make-up Applications — Adobe InDesign; Layout Software — SCS/Layout 8000, PC Workstations.

COLDWATER

THE DAILY REPORTER

15 W Pearl St, Coldwater, Mich., 49036-1912, Branch; gen tel (517) 278-2318; adv tel (517) 278-2318 ext. 15; ed tel (517) 278-2318 ext. 27; gen fax (517) 278-6041; adv fax (517) 278-6041; ed fax (517) 278-6041; gen/nat adv e-mail dferro@thedailyreporter.com; disp adv e-mail dferro@thedailyreporter.com; class adv e-maildferro@thedailyreporter.com; ed e-mail jbarrand@thedailyreporter.com; web site www.thedailyreporter.com
Group: New Media Investment Group
Published: Mon, Tues, Wed, Thur, Fri, Sat
Weekday Frequency: m
Saturday Frequency: m
Circulation: 5,316; 5,316(sat)
Last Audit: Sworn/Estimate/Non-Audited September 30, 2017
Advertising Rate (weekday/saturday): Open inch rate $10.75
Online Advertising Rate: Big box $149.00/month
News services: AP, LAT-WP. **Established:** 1895
Special Weekly Sections: TV Listing (Sat); NASCAR (Thur).
Syndicated Publications: American Profile (Weekly).
Digital Platform - Mobile: Apple, Android
Digital Platform - Tablet: Apple iOS, Android
Interim Ed. .... Amanda VanAuker
Sports Ed. .... Troy Tennyson
Circ. Mgr....................................... Karen Allard
Adv. Dir.... Lisa Vickers
Market Information: TMC.
Mechanical Available: Offset; Black and 3 ROP colors; insert accepted - 8 x 11 1/2 & over; page cutoffs - 21 1/2.
Mechanical Specifications: Type page 11 3/4 x 21 5/8; E - 6 cols, 1/6 between; A - 6 cols, 1/6 between; C - 9 cols, 1/6 between.
Areas Served: 49036, 49028, 49082, 49094, 49092, 49089, 49274, 49011, 49245, 49029
Delivery Method: Mail, CarrierEquipment & Software: BUSINESS EQUIPMENT: Vision Data CLASSIFIED EQUIPMENT: Hardware — APP/Mac; Printers — Okidata; CLASSIFIED SOFTWARE: Baseview. DISPLAY EQUIPMENT: Hardware — APP/Power Mac; Printers — APP/Mac Laser, Xante/Accel-a-Writer 8300, Epson/5200 Color; DISPLAY SOFTWAREAd Make-up Applications — Multi-Ad/Creator 4.0, QPS/QuarkXPress 4.04; Layout Software — Baseview. EDITORIAL EQUIPMENT: Hardware — APP/Mac; Printers — APP/Mac LaserWriter, Xante/Accel-a-Writer 8300, Epson/5200 Color EDITORIAL SOFTWARE: Adobe/Photoshop 4.0, Macromedia/Freehand 7.0, QPS/QuarkXPress 4.04, Baseview. PRODUCTION EQUIPMENT: Hardware — Caere/OmniPage, Nikon/Scan; Scanners — Umax PRODUCTION SOFTWARE: QPS/QuarkXPress 4.04.

DETROIT

DETROIT FREE PRESS

615 W Lafayette Blvd, Detroit, Mich., 48226-3124, Wayne; gen tel (313) 222-6400; adv tel (313) 222-2700; ed tel (313) 222-6600; gen fax (313) 222-5981; adv fax (313) 496-4886; ed fax (313) 222-6774; gen/nat adv e-mail lrudy@dnps.com; disp adv e-mail jtaylor@dnps.com; class adv e-maillanteigne@dnps.com; ed e-mail letters@freepress.com ; web site www.freep.com
- 1,100,000(views) 6,022,082(visitors)
Group: Gannett
Published: Mon, Tues, Wed, Thur, Fri, Sun
Weekday Frequency: m
Saturday Frequency: m
Circulation: 156,321; 273,141(sun)
Last Audit: AAM March 31, 2017
Advertising Rate (weekday/saturday): $411.00 (2 col.x2")
Advertising Rate (sunday): $2,779 (2 col.x2")
Online Advertising Rate: Starting at $14.00 CPM
News services: AP, NYT, RN, DJ, GNS. **Established:** 1831
Own Printing Facility?: Yes
Commercial Printers?: Yes
Special Editions: Tiger Baseball (Apr); Michiganians of the Year (May) ; Auto Show (Jan); Rosa Parks Scholars (Jun); NBA/Pistons (Nov); NHL/Red Wings (Oct); Prep Football (Aug); College football (Aug); NFL (Sept).
Special Weekly Sections: Life, Working, Your Money, Sports (Mon); Life, Arts & Style, Sports (Tues); Life, Business, Sports (Wed); Motor City, Drive, Food (Thur); Homestyle, Sports (Fri); Life, Business, Weekend, Sports (Sat); Main, Business, Entertainment, Life, Auto, Real Estate, Travel, News & Views, Sports, Jobs, Sports (Sun)
Syndicated Publications: USA WEEKEND Magazine (S).
Digital Platform - Mobile: Apple, Android, Windows, Blackberry
Digital Platform - Tablet: Apple iOS, Android, Windows 7, Blackberry Tablet OS, Kindle, Nook, Kindle Fire
Admin. Mgr. .... Grace Bennett
Editor and Publisher................ Jonathan Wolman
Asst. Managing Editor................. Michael Brown
Deputy Mng. Ed. .... Dale Parry
Online Content Dir................... Pam Shermeyer
Deputy Mng. Ed. .... Jeff Taylor
Deputy Mng. Ed. .... Julie Topping
City Ed., Night .... Chris Rizk
Business Editor...................... Joanna Firestone
Presentation Editor .... Richard Epps
Asst. Mng. Ed., Web .... Nancy Laughlin
Auto Editor .... Alan Derringer
Editorial Page Ed. .... Ron Dzwonkowski
Bus. Ed. .... Randy Essex
Asst. Managing Editor.......... Felecia Henderson
Copy Desk Chief.............................. Alex Cruden
Asst. Managing Editor.......... Walter Middlebrook
Editorial Page Editor .... Nolan Finley
Library Dir..................................... Alice Pepper
Deputy Managing Editor .... Gary Miles
Metro Ed. .... Jim Wilhelm
Sports Editor.................................. Phil Laciura
Deputy Metro Ed. .... Todd Spangler
Copy Ed........................................ Carl Feusse
Dir. of Business and Local Enterprise .Christopher Kirkpatrick
VP. of Marketing .... Aaron Velthoven
Asst. Ed., Opinion
Jewel Gopwani
TECHNICAL SERVICES DIR. .... Joseph Amormino
Facilities Mgr. .... Dawn Buckner
Director, Retail Sales
Shawn Fox
Sales Dir.
David Kiehle
Sr. VP of Sales & Marketing
Rebecca Steckler
Pub. .... Joyce Jenereaux
Market Information: Zoned editions.
Mechanical Specifications: Broadsheet Page: 11.625" x 20"
Tab Page: 9.667" x 11.375"
Areas Served: Service to +650 zip codes in Metro and State
Delivery Method: Mail, Newsstand, Carrier, RacksEquipment & Software: PRESSROOM EQUIPMENT: Lines — ManRoland Geoman 75 with 50 printing couples; ManRoland Geoman 75 with 50 printing couples; ManRoland Geoman 75 with 50 printing couples; ManRoland Geoman 75 with 50 printing couples; ManRoland Geoman 75 with 50 printing couples; ManRoland Geoman 75 with 50 printing couples; Folders — 6 ManRoland 2:5:5; Reels & Stands — 60 ManRoland ; Control System — PPM/Pecom; MAILROOM EQUIPMENT: Counter Stackers — 10 TMSI 3 Gammler 21 Quipp 300 23 Quipp 500 ; Inserters & Stuffers — 4 Goss Heidelberg 630's 1 Goss Heidelberg 632; Tying Machines — 24 Dynaric NP 3000 28 Dynaric NP 5000 3 D 2400's; Control System — GMA Enternet BURT Cannon; CLASSIFIED EQUIPMENT: Hardware — Dell R710 running VMWare; Dell ; CLASSIFIED SOFTWARE: Mactive DISPLAY EQUIPMENT: Hardware — CCI; DISPLAY SOFTWAREAd Make-up Applications — DPS AdTracker; Layout Software — Layout 8000 EDITORIAL EQUIPMENT: Hardware — Dell 270 Optiplex PCs Macintosh Pro /Dell; Printers — HP DesignJet 1050C broadsheet proofer HP 9000 11x17 B&W proofer HP 4250 network printers EDITORIAL SOFTWARE: CCI Newsline, Adobe, Apple PRODUCTION EQUIPMENT: Hardware — PRINTERS EPSON 9880 COLORBURST 44 HP T770 DESIGNJET HP 1050C DESIGNJET 13 MACS NEWSWAY; Scanners — EPSON EXPRESSION 1680 EPSON GT 20000 PRODUCTION SOFTWARE: NEWSWAY MGS CCI MACTIVE FOR CLASS ADS & PAGINATION GENESYS & FOR RETAIL ADS ADTRACKER FOR AD DATABASE ADOBE SOFTWARE: CS5 ACROBAT INDESIGN ILLUSTRATOR PHOTOSHOP OTHER: QUARK EXPRESS 8.0 PITSTOP 10 GMG INK OPTIMIZER ASSURA FILE PROCESSING SOFTWARE HARLEQUIN RIPS
Note: Effective March 30, 2009, the Detroit Fee Press will cease daily print publication, and will publish Thursdays, Fridays and Sundays. For detailed mechanical specifications, advertising, circulation, production and other business office personnel, see Detr

THE DETROIT NEWS

160 W Fort St, Ste 300, Detroit, Mich., 48226-3700, Wayne; gen tel (313) 222-2300; adv tel (313) 222-2700; ed tel (313) 222-2292; gen fax (313) 222-2335; adv fax (586) 826-7019; ed fax (313) 496-5253; gen/nat adv e-mail tdgruber@michigan.com ; disp adv e-mail tdgruber@michigan.com ; class adv e-mailtdgruber@michigan.com ; ed e-mail newsroom@detroitnews.com - letters@detroitnews.com ; web site www.detroitnews.com
- 33,000,000(views) 3,030,000(visitors)
Group: Digital First Media
Published: Mon, Tues, Wed, Thur, Fri, Sat
Weekday Frequency: m
Saturday Frequency: m
Circulation: 80,145; 80,145(sat)
Last Audit: AAM March 31, 2017
Branch Offices: Wash. DC, Nat. Press Building - Lansing, Michigan -
Detroit City/County Building
Advertising Rate (weekday/saturday): Net full-page rates (118.5 col inches) -............ Th/Fr: $17,626.88 -........................ MTWSa: $7,554
Online Advertising Rate: -......320x50 & 300x250: $12.50
- 320x50 & 300x250 & 728x90: $10.75
- 320x50 & 300x250 & 300x600: $13.00
- 320x50 & 300x250 & 300x600 & 728x90: $11.50
- Pre-roll: 920x508 & 1024x576: $30.00

News services: Associated Press, Bloomberg, MCT **Established:** 1873
Own Printing Facility?: Yes
Commercial Printers?: Yes
Special Weekly Sections: Monday - Arts & Style
Tuesday- Arts & Style
Wednesday-Business and Auto
Thursday –Think, Go, Eats and Drinks, Drive
Friday - On Screen, Homestyle
Saturday - Weekend
Digital Platform - Mobile: Apple, Android
Digital Platform - Tablet: Apple iOS, Android
Ed and Pub .... Jonathan Wolman
Managing Ed. .... Gary Miles
Editorial Pg. Ed.............................. Nolan Finley
Asst. Managing Ed., Features Felecia Henderson
Asst. Managing Ed., I-Team ..Walter Middlebrook
Digital News Ed........................ Dawn Needham
News Ed. .... Andreas Supanich
Multi Media Editor..................... Pam Shermeyer
Areas Served: 48001, 48002, 48003, 48005, 48006, 48009, 48014, 48015, 48017, 48021, 48022, 48023, 48025, 48026, 48027, 48028, 48030, 48032, 48033, 48034, 48035, 48036, 48038, 48039, 48040, 48041, 48042, 48043, 48044, 48045, 48046, 48047, 48048, 48049, 48050, 48051, 48054, 48059, 48060, 48062, 48063, 48064, 48065, 48066, 48067, 48069, 48070, 48071, 48072, 48073, 48074, 48075, 48076, 48079, 48080, 48081, 48082, 48083, 48084, 48085, 48088, 48089, 48091, 48092, 48093, 48094, 48095, 48096, 48097, 48098, 48101, 48103, 48104, 48105, 48108, 48109, 48111, 48114, 48116, 48117, 48118, 48120, 48122, 48124, 48125, 48126, 48127, 48128, 48130, 48131, 48133, 48134, 48135, 48137, 48138, 48139, 48140, 48141, 48143, 48144, 48145, 48146, 48150, 48152, 48154, 48157, 48158, 48159, 48160, 48161, 48162, 48164, 48165, 48166, 48167, 48168, 48169, 48170, 48173, 48174, 48176, 48178, 48179, 48180,

48182, 48183, 48184, 48185, 48186, 48187, 48188, 48189, 48190, 48191, 48192, 48193, 48195, 48197, 48198, 48201, 48202, 48203, 48204, 48205, 48206, 48207, 48208, 48209, 48210, 48211, 48212, 48213, 48214, 48215, 48216, 48217, 48218, 48219, 48220, 48221, 48223, 48224, 48225, 48226, 48227, 48228, 48229, 48230, 48234, 48235, 48236, 48237, 48238, 48239, 48240, 48242, 48243, 48301, 48302, 48304, 48306, 48307, 48309, 48310, 48312, 48313, 48314, 48315, 48316, 48317, 48320, 48322, 48323, 48324, 48326, 48327, 48328, 48329, 48331, 48334, 48335, 48336, 48340, 48341, 48342, 48343, 48346, 48348, 48350, 48353, 48356, 48357, 48359, 48360, 48362, 48363, 48367, 48370, 48371, 48374, 48375, 48377, 48380, 48381, 48382, 48383, 48386, 48390, 48393, 48401, 48412, 48413, 48415, 48416, 48418, 48419, 48420, 48421, 48422, 48423, 48426, 48427, 48428, 48429, 48430, 48433, 48437, 48438, 48439, 48441, 48442, 48444, 48445, 48446, 48449, 48450, 48451, 48453, 48454, 48455, 48456, 48457, 48458, 48460, 48461, 48462, 48463, 48465, 48466, 48467, 48469, 48471, 48473, 48502, 48503, 48504, 48505, 48506, 48507, 48509, 48519, 48529, 48532, 48551, 48601, 48602, 48603, 48604, 48607, 48609, 48610, 48611, 48612, 48615, 48616, 48617, 48618, 48619, 48621, 48622, 48623, 48624, 48625, 48626, 48627, 48628, 48629, 48630, 48631, 48632, 48635, 48636, 48638, 48640, 48642, 48647, 48649, 48650, 48651, 48653, 48654, 48656, 48657, 48658, 48659, 48661, 48703, 48706, 48708, 48720, 48721, 48722, 48723, 48725, 48726, 48729, 48730, 48731, 48732, 48734, 48737, 48738, 48739, 48740, 48741, 48742, 48745, 48746, 48748, 48750, 48755, 48756, 48759, 48761, 48762, 48763, 48768, 48770, 48801, 48808, 48811, 48813, 48817, 48818, 48819, 48820, 48821, 48822, 48823, 48824, 48827, 48831, 48832, 48835, 48836, 48837, 48838, 48840, 48842, 48843, 48846, 48847, 48848, 48849, 48854, 48855, 48856, 48858, 48864, 48866, 48867, 48871, 48872, 48873, 48875, 48876, 48878, 48879, 48880, 48881, 48883, 48892, 48884, 48886, 48888, 48890, 48893, 48894, 48895, 48906, 48909, 48910, 48911, 48912, 48915, 48917, 48919, 48924, 48933, 49001, 49002, 49004, 49005, 49006, 49007, 49008, 49009, 49010, 49011, 49012, 49013, 49014, 49015, 49017, 49020, 49021, 49022, 49024, 49028, 49029, 49032, 49036, 49037, 49038, 49040, 49041, 49045, 49046, 49047, 49048, 49053, 49055, 49057, 49058, 49060, 49065, 49068, 49071, 49072, 49073, 49076, 49078, 49079, 49080, 49082, 49083, 49085, 49087, 49090, 49091, 49092, 49093, 49094, 49096, 49097, 49098, 49099, 49127, 49130, 49201, 49202, 49203, 49220, 49221, 49224, 49228, 49229, 49230, 49233, 49234, 49235, 49236, 49237, 49240, 49242, 49245, 49246, 49247, 49249, 49250, 49251, 49252, 49253, 49254, 49261, 49262, 49264, 49265, 49266, 49267, 49269, 49270, 49271, 49274, 49282, 49283, 49285, 49286, 49287, 49301, 49304, 49305, 49307, 49311, 49315, 49316, 49317, 49319, 49321, 49327, 49329, 49331, 49332, 49333, 49336, 49337, 49338, 49340, 49341, 49346, 49348, 49401, 49404, 49406, 49408, 49409, 49410, 49411, 49412, 49415, 49416, 49417, 49418, 49420, 49423, 49424, 49431, 49426, 49428, 49436, 49437, 49440, 49441, 49442, 49444, 49445, 49448, 49449, 49453, 49454, 49456, 49457, 49460, 49461, 49464, 49503, 49504, 49505, 49506, 49507, 49508, 49509, 49512, 49519, 49525, 49534, 49544, 49546, 49548, 49601, 49610, 49612, 49614, 49615, 49616, 49617, 49619, 49621, 49622, 49623, 49625, 49627, 49628, 49629, 49630, 49631, 49632, 49633, 49635, 49636, 49637, 49638, 49639, 49640, 49643, 49644, 49645, 49646, 49648, 49649, 49650, 49651, 49653, 49654, 49655, 49657, 49659, 49660, 49664, 49665, 49668, 49670, 49674, 49675, 49676, 49677, 49679, 49682, 49683, 49684, 49685, 49686, 49688, 49689, 49690, 49696, 49701, 49706, 49707, 49709, 49711, 49712, 49713, 49715, 49716, 49718, 49719, 49720, 49721, 49722, 49723, 49725, 49726, 49727, 49730, 49733, 49735, 49736, 49738, 49740, 49743, 49745, 49746, 49747, 49749, 49751, 49752, 49753, 49755, 49756, 49757, 49759, 49761, 49765, 49766, 49769, 49770, 49774, 49776, 49777, 49779, 49780, 49781, 49782, 49783, 49788, 49791, 49795, 49796, 49797, 49820, 49855, 49864, 49908, 49971

Delivery Method: Newsstand, Carrier, RacksEquipment & Software: PRESSROOM EQUIPMENT: Plateroom - AGFA Polaris CTP (6)
Pressroom - MANRoland GeoMAN 75 presses (6)
Siemens Demantic ASRS storage system
PRESSROOM SOFTWARE: ProImage workflow and Man Production Management control software MAILROOM EQUIPMENT: Goss 29:1 inserter lines (5)
Cannon Cart System MAILROOM SOFTWARE:Burt Technologies
Enternet Technology CLASSIFIED SOFTWARE: Mactive Classified EDITORIAL SOFTWARE: CCI Enterprise Newsgate System PRODUCTION SOFTWARE: ProImage NewsWay
IT SOFTWARE:Microsoft Office 365 Subscription Based Service CIRCULATION EQUIPMENT: ISeries CIRCULATION SOFTWARGenesys

ESCANABA

DAILY PRESS

600 Ludington St, Escanaba, Mich., 49829-3830, Delta; gen tel (906) 786-2021; adv tel (906) 786-2021; ed tel (906) 786-2021; gen fax (906) 786-3752; adv fax (906) 786-3752; ed fax (906) 786-9006; gen/nat adv e-mail cderoeck@dailypress.net; disp adv e-mail tbelongie@dailypress.net; class adv e-mailclassified@dailypress.net; ed e-mail news@dailypress.net; web site www.dailypress.net
- 850,000(views) 125,000(visitors)

Group: Ogden Newspapers Inc.
Published: Mon, Tues, Wed, Thur, Fri, Sat
Weekday Frequency: e
Saturday Frequency: m
Circulation: 5,932; 6,571(sat)
Last Audit: AAM March 31, 2016
Advertising Rate (weekday/saturday): Open inch rate $25.26
Online Advertising Rate: Weather $4.00; Half Banners $9.00; Top Leaderboard $17.00
News services: AP. **Established:** 1909
Own Printing Facility?: Yes
Commercial Printers?: Yes
Special Editions: Spring Fashion (Apr); Fall Back-to-School (Aug); Bride & Groom (Jan); Fashion (Sept).
Syndicated Publications: USA WEEKEND Magazine (Sat).
Digital Platform - Mobile: Apple, Android, Windows
Digital Platform - Tablet: Apple iOS, Android, Windows 7
Political/Gov't Ed. .... Brian Rowell
Prodn. Foreman, Pressroom .... Jessica Koth
Publisher .... corky deroeck
Market Information: TMC.
Mechanical Available: Offset; Black and 3 ROP colors; insert accepted - small booklets; page cutoffs - 22 3/4.
Mechanical Specifications: Type page 11 3/4 x 21 1/2; E - 6 cols, 1 3/4, 1/6 between; A - 6 cols, 1 3/4, 1/6 between; C - 9 cols, 1 3/8, 1/8 between.
Areas Served: 49812, 49874, 49886, 49847, 49896, 49845, 49807, 49894, 49837, 49818, 49872, 49880, 49829, 49878, 49835, 49817, 49854, 49840
Delivery Method: Mail, Newsstand, Carrier, RacksEquipment & Software: PRESSROOM EQUIPMENT: Lines — 9-G/Community (Color head); MAILROOM EQUIPMENT: Tying Machines — 2-Bu/Strapper, MLN/Spirit-Strapper; Address Machine — SAC/JR.; BUSINESS EQUIPMENT: ATT CLASSIFIED EQUIPMENT: Hardware — Mk; Printers — 2-V.; DISPLAY SOFTWARELayout Software — Mk. EDITORIAL EQUIPMENT: Hardware — Mk/4-Panasonic; Printers — TI/KSR Omni Printer. PRODUCTION EQUIPMENT: Hardware — 1-LE; Cameras — 1-Nu/SST 20 x 24.

FLINT

THE FLINT JOURNAL

540 S Saginaw St Ste 101, Suite 101, Flint, Mich., 48502-1813, Genesee; gen tel (810) 766-6100; adv tel (800) 446-5588; adv fax (810) 767-9480; gen/nat adv e-mail advertise@mlive.com; disp adv e-mail advertise@mlive.com; class adv e-mailadvertise@mlive.com; ed e-mail flnews@mlive.com; web site www.mlive.com/flint

Group: Advance Publications, Inc.
Published: Tues, Thur, Fri, Sun
Weekday Frequency: e
Saturday Frequency: m
Circulation: 31,731; 192(sat); 39,415(sun)
Last Audit: AAM December 31, 2016
Advertising Rate (weekday/saturday): Open inch rate $28.34
Advertising Rate (sunday): Open inch rate $42.51
News services: AP, NYT, LAT-WP, NNS. **Established:** 1876
Special Editions: Golf (Apr); HS Football Preview (Aug); Wrap (Dec); Black History Month (Feb); Weddings (Jan); Business Profiles (Jun); The Answer Book (Mar); Home & Yard (May); Wrap (Nov); Senior Health Expo (Oct); Life & Legacy (Sept).
Special Weekly Sections: The Entertainer (Fri); Technology-Tempo (Mon); Viewpoint (S); Religion (Sat); Wheels (Thur); Food-Tempo (Tues); Education (Wed).
Syndicated Publications: Color Comics (S); Coupon Books (Wed).
Digital Platform - Mobile: Apple, Android, Windows, Blackberry
Digital Platform - Tablet: Apple iOS, Android
Pub .... Dan Gaydou
Sr. Dir. for National Accounts .... Steve Westphal
Dir. of Adv. Operations .... Bob White
Chief Revenue Officer .... Charity Plaxton
VP of Sales .... Michael Assink
Sr. Platform Director .... Colleen Huff
Dir. of Real Estate & Careers Sales Andy Boldryeff
VP of Content .... John Hiner
Dir. of Sports News .... Bill Emkow
Sr. Dir. for Journalism and Engagement Kelly Frick
Sr. Dir. for Digital Culture and Innovation . Colleen Stone
Exec. Editor of Print .... Paul Keep
Small Business Dir. .... Andrea Sipka
Automotive Dir. .... Khalida Cook
Sr. Strategy Dir. .... Nick Dionne
Sr. Retail Dir. .... Brett Christie
Regional Sales Dir. of Detroit & Ann Arbor. Christy Keizer
Regional Sales Dir. of Flint, Saginaw and Bay City Robert Graham
Regional Sales Dir. of Grand Rapids & Muskegon Jamie Dionne
Gen. Mgr. .... Laurel Champion
Agency Relations Dir. .... Andrea Miller
Dir. of News .... Marjory Raymer
Dir. of Community Engagement .... Jen Eyer
Market Information: Split run; TMC.
Mechanical Available: Offset; Black and 3 ROP colors; insert accepted - zoned pre-prints, minis; page cutoffs - 21.
Mechanical Specifications: Type page 11 5/8 x 20; E - 6 cols, 1 5/6, 1/8 between; A - 6 cols, 1 5/6, 1/8 between; C - 10 cols, 1 1/8, 1/8 between.
Areas Served: 48412-48867
Delivery Method: Mail, Newsstand, Carrier, RacksEquipment & Software: PRESSROOM EQUIPMENT: Lines — MAN/Roland Regioman; MAN/Roland Regioman; Press Drive — Baumuller; Folders — 1-MAN/ Double-out 64 pg.; Reels & Stands — 4-MAN/CD13; Control System — PECOM.; MAILROOM EQUIPMENT: Counter Stackers — 4-QWI/501, 1-QWI/400, 2-HL/Dual Carrier; Inserters & Stuffers — 2-GMA/SLS3000; Tying Machines — 5-Dynaric/4.; BUSINESS EQUIPMENT: Apple Xserve Dell HP Hitachi BUSINESS SOFTWARE: DTI CircView RouteSmart VMware 4-5 CLASSIFIED EQUIPMENT: Hardware — Dell & HP PCss; Printers — HP, Canon, IKON; CLASSIFIED SOFTWARE: Atex Mactive 3.0 Encompass Office 2010 DISPLAY EQUIPMENT: Hardware — LCDs; Printers — Canon, IKON; Other Hardware — Baseview DISPLAY SOFTWAREAd Make-up Applications — InDesign Xpance; Layout Software — InDesign PPI ATEX PageLayout Xpance EDITORIAL EQUIPMENT: Hardware — Dell PCs/Dell & HP PCs; Printers — HP, Ikon, Canon EDITORIAL SOFTWARE: Media Span Baseview, Adobe InDesign/InCopy PRODUCTION EQUIPMENT: Hardware — Dell & HP PC Apple Macs; Scanners — Epson Canon PRODUCTION SOFTWARE: PPI AGFA IntelliTune Adobe Illustrator Adobe InDesign Adobe Flash Adobe Photoshop Xpance ATEX Mactive PageLayout ZenDesk

GRAND HAVEN

GRAND HAVEN TRIBUNE

101 N 3rd St, Grand Haven, Mich., 49417-1209, Ottawa; gen tel (616) 842-6400; adv tel (616) 842-6400 ext. 241; ed tel (616) 842-6400 ext. 232; gen fax (616) 842-9584; adv fax (616) 842-9584; ed fax (616) 842-9584; gen/nat adv e-mail ads@grandhaventribune.com; disp adv e-mail rfrancis@grandhaventribune.com; class adv e-mailclassifieds@grandhaventribune.com; ed e-mail cwelch@grandhaventribune.com; web site www.grandhaventribune.com

Group: Sandusky Newspapers, Inc.
Published: Mon, Tues, Wed, Thur, Fri, Sat
Weekday Frequency: e
Saturday Frequency: e
Circulation: 8,813; 8,813(sat)
Last Audit: AAM September 30, 2011
Advertising Rate (weekday/saturday): Open inch rate $15.30
Online Advertising Rate: Starting at $99.00 CPM
News services: 1885
Own Printing Facility?: Yes
Commercial Printers?: Yes
Special Weekly Sections: Living Local (Sat); Church (Sat); Business (Thur)
Syndicated Publications: USA WEEKEND Magazine (Sat); Athlon Sports; American Profile; Spry; Relish
Digital Platform - Mobile: Apple, Android
Digital Platform - Tablet: Apple iOS, Android, Blackberry Tablet OS, Kindle
Pub./VP .... Kevin Hook
Dir. of Rev. Dev. .... Rob Francis
Content Dir. & Audience Dev't. .... Matt DeYoung
Press Foreman/Supvr. .... Jerry Grimminck
Dir. of Op. Support .... Don Rogers
Business Services Supervisor .... Jen Hosman
Market Information: TMC.
Mechanical Available: Offset; Black and 3 ROP colors; insert accepted; page cutoffs - 22 1/2.
Mechanical Specifications: Type page 13 x 21 1/2; E - 6 cols, 2 1/16, 1/8 between; A - 6 cols, 2 1/16, 1/8 between; C - 8 cols, 1 7/8, 1/8 between.
Areas Served: 49417, 49456, 49460, 49415, 49404, 40448, 49409
Delivery Method: Mail, Newsstand, Carrier, RacksEquipment & Software: PRESSROOM EQUIPMENT: Lines — 5-G/Urbanite; MAILROOM EQUIPMENT: Tying Machines — 1-Sa/BM1A.; BUSINESS EQUIPMENT: 1-Unisys/5000 CLASSIFIED EQUIPMENT: Hardware — 3-Sun; Printers — HP/LaserJet; CLASSIFIED SOFTWARE: Vision Data. DISPLAY EQUIPMENT: Hardware — APP/Mac G4; Printers — Xante; DISPLAY SOFTWAREAd Make-up Applications — Adobe/PageMaker, QPS/QuarkXPress, Adobe/Photoshop.; EDITORIAL EQUIPMENT: Hardware — 2-CD/2330, 15-APP/Mac; Printers — HP/ LaserJet EDITORIAL SOFTWARE: Baseview. PRODUCTION EQUIPMENT: Hardware — 1-Nat/Super A-250; Cameras — 1-SCREEN/650C.

GRAND RAPIDS

THE GRAND RAPIDS PRESS

169 Monroe Ave NW Ste 100, Suite 100, Grand Rapids, Mich., 49503-2632, Kent; gen tel (616) 222-5400; adv tel (800) 446-5588; gen/nat adv e-mail advertise@mlive.com; disp adv e-mail advertise@mlive.com; class adv e-mailadvertise@mlive.com; ed e-mail grnews@mlive.com; web site www.mlive.com/grand-rapids
4,584,000(visitors)

Group: Advance Publications, Inc.
Published: Mon, Tues, Wed, Thur, Fri, Sat, Sun
Weekday Frequency: e
Saturday Frequency: m
Circulation: 70,120; 4,456(sat); 111,963(sun)
Last Audit: AAM September 30, 2014
Advertising Rate (weekday/saturday): Open inch

rate $31.11
Advertising Rate (sunday): Open inch rate $59.10
News services: AP, NYT, SHNS, NNS, TMS.
Established: 1892
Special Editions: Golf (Apr); High School Football (Aug); Home Expo (Feb); International Auto Show (Jan); Lakeshore Living (Jun); Home & Garden (Mar); Parade of Homes (May); Lakeshore Holidays (Nov); Grand Rapids Griffins-IHL Hockey (Oct); On Stage-Entertainment/Arts (Sept
Special Weekly Sections: Home and Garden (S); Outdoors (Sat); Weekend (Thur).
Syndicated Publications: Parade (S).
Digital Platform - Mobile: Apple, Android, Windows, Blackberry
Digital Platform - Tablet: Apple iOS, Android
Pres. .... Dan Gaydou
Chief Revenue Officer .... Charity Plaxton
Chief Digital Officer: .... Matt Sharp
VP of Content .... John Hiner
Sr. Strategy Dir. .... Nick Dionne
VP of Sales .... Michael Assink
Regional Sales Dir. of Grand Rapids & Muskegon . Jamie Dionne
Dir. of Automotive Sales .... Khalida Cook
Dir of Mktg .... Eric Hultgren
Dir of Creative .... Anne Drummond
Sr. Dir. of Culture and Innovation ... Colleen Stone
Agency Relations Dir. .... Jeff Leitch
Dir. of Real Estate and Career Sales .... Andy Boldryeff
Regional Sales Dir. of Flint, Saginaw and Bay City Robert Graham
Regional Sales Dir. of Detroit & Ann Arbor. Christy Keizer
Gen. Mgr. .... Laurel Champion
Small Business Dir. .... Andrea Sipka
Dir. of Ad Operations .... Bob White
Adv. Support Dir. .... Andrea Miller
Sr. Dir. of Journalism & Engagement ... Kelly Frick
Dir. of News .... Marjory Raymer
Dir. of Sports News .... Bill Emkow
Dir. of Community Engagement .... Jen Eyer
Market Information: TMC; Zoned editions.
Mechanical Available: Offset; Black and 3 ROP colors; insert accepted - spadea; page cutoffs - 21.
Mechanical Specifications: Type page 10 7/8 x 19 1/2; E - 6 cols, 1 23/32, 3/32 between; A - 6 cols, 1 23/32, 3/32 between; C - 10 cols, 1 1/16, 1/32 between.
Areas Served: 48809 through 49770
Delivery Method: Mail, Newsstand, Carrier, RacksEquipment & Software: PRESSROOM EQUIPMENT: Lines — MAN/Geoman (64 couples); Press Drive — Baumueller; Folders — 2-MAN; Pasters —12-MAN; Reels & Stands — 12-MAN; Control System — MAN; Registration System — Graphic Control. MAILROOM EQUIPMENT: Counter Stackers — 10-QWI/500; Inserters & Stuffers — 3-GMA/SLS 3000 (30:2); Tying Machines — 13/Dynaric; Wrapping Singles — 5-Dynaric/Single tyer; Control System — GMA/SAM; Address Machine — 2-Ch/Labeler; BUSINESS EQUIPMENT: Apple Xserve Dell servers HP servers Hitachi HDS BUSINESS SOFTWARE: DTI CircView RouteSmart VMware 4-5 CLASSIFIED EQUIPMENT: Hardware — Dell & HP PCs; Dell & HP PCs; Printers — HP, Canon, IKON; CLASSIFIED SOFTWARE: Atex Mactive 3.0 Encompass Office 2010 DISPLAY EQUIPMENT: Hardware — LCDs, Macs, PCs; Printers — Canon, IKON; DISPLAY SOFTWAREAd Make-up Applications — InDesign Xpance; Layout Software — InDesign PPI ATEX PageLayout Xpance EDITORIAL EQUIPMENT: Hardware — Dell & HP PCs; Printers — HP, Ikon, Canon EDITORIAL SOFTWARE: Media Span Baseview, Adobe InDesign/InCopy PRODUCTION EQUIPMENT: Hardware — Epson Canon; Scanners — Epson Canon PRODUCTION SOFTWARE: PPI AGFA IntelliTune Adobe Illustrator Adobe InDesign Adobe Flash Adobe Photoshop Xpance ATEX Mactive PageLayout ZenDesk.

GREENVILLE

THE DAILY NEWS

109 N Lafayette St, Greenville, Mich., 48838-1853, Montcalm; gen tel (616) 754-9301; adv

tel (616) 754-9301; ed tel (616) 754-9301; gen fax (616) 754-8559; adv fax (616) 754-8559; ed fax (616) 754-8559; gen/nat adv e-mail info@staffordgroup.com; disp adv e-mail info@staffordgroup.com; class adv e-mailclassifieds@staffordgroup.com; ed e-mail dclark@staffordgroup.com; web site www.thedailynews.cc
Group: Stafford Media Solutions Incorporated
Published: Mon, Tues, Wed, Thur, Fri, Sat
Weekday Frequency: e
Saturday Frequency: m
Circulation: 7,754; 8,406(sat)
Last Audit: Sworn/Estimate/Non-Audited September 30, 2017
Advertising Rate (weekday/saturday): Open inch rate $13.50
News services: AP. **Established:** 1855
Special Weekly Sections: TV Guide (Fri); Business Page (Mon); Home (Sat); Leisure Page (Thur); Food Page (Tues); Agriculture Page (Wed).
Syndicated Publications: USA WEEKEND Magazine (Sat).
Digital Platform - Mobile: Apple, Android
Digital Platform - Tablet: Apple iOS, Android, Kindle, Nook, Kindle Fire
Pres./Gen. Mgr., Publications .... Rob Stafford
Circ. Dir .... Carol Pettengill
News Ed. .... Darrin Clark
Prodn. Mgr. .... Jeff Morris
Market Information: ADS; TMC.
Mechanical Available: Offset; Black and 3 ROP colors; insert accepted; page cutoffs - 22 3/4.
Mechanical Specifications: Type page 13 3/4 x 21; E - 6 cols, 2 1/18, between; A - 6 cols, 2 1/18, between; C - 6 cols, 2 1/18, between.
Delivery Method: Mail, CarrierEquipment & Software: PRESSROOM EQUIPMENT: Lines — 8-G/Community SSC (1-4-high) 1986; Folders — 1-G/SSC; Reels & Stands — 1-FBWAY/HS-35000.; MAILROOM EQUIPMENT: Tying Machines — 1/MLN, 1-/Bu; Address Machine — 1-/KR; BUSINESS EQUIPMENT: Microsoft/Windows NT, HP/133 DL Server BUSINESS SOFTWARE: Great Plains CLASSIFIED EQUIPMENT: Hardware — 1-APP/Mac 8150 Workgroup Server; Printers — APP/Mac LaserWriter IIg, Okidata/Line Printer; CLASSIFIED SOFTWARE: Baseview/Class Flow 2.2.5, QPS/QuarkXPress 3.32, Baseview/Class Manager Pro. DISPLAY EQUIPMENT: Hardware — APP/Mac 8550-200 Workgroup Server, 2-APP/Mac 7500, 1-APP/Mac 7100, 1-APP/Mac4400, 2-APP/Mac 6100, 1-APP/Mac Centris 650, 1-Power Computing/Pro 210, 1-APP/Mac IIsi, 1-APP/Mac IIcx, 1-APP/Mac LCII; Printers — 1-QMS/860, 1-GCC/Elite XL 1208, APP/M; EDITORIAL EQUIPMENT: Hardware — 1-APP/Mac 8150 Workgroup Server, 4-APP/Power Mac 7100-80, 1-Power Computing/210, 7-APP/Mac Performa 638CD, APP/Mac LC III/Minolta/RP605Z microfilm reader, Kk/35 mm Film Scanner, Nikon/LS 1000 Film Scanner; Printers — APP/Mac LaserW PRODUCTION EQUIPMENT: Hardware — Caere/OmniPage Pro 7.0, 1-APP/Mac 9600-200, Tektronix/Phaser 300X Color Printer; Cameras — COM/6700; Scanners — HSD/Scan-X Pro, Kk/35mm rapid film scanner.

HILLSDALE

HILLSDALE DAILY NEWS

2764 W Carleton Rd, Hillsdale, Mich., 49242-9191, Hillsdale; gen tel (517) 437-7351; adv tel (517) 437-7351; ed tel (517) 278-2318 ext. 27; gen fax (517) 437-3963; adv fax (517) 437-3963; ed fax (517) 437-3963; gen/nat adv e-mail david.ferro@hillsdale.net; disp adv e-mail david.ferro@hillsdale.net; class adv e-maildavid.ferro@hillsdale.net; ed e-mail editor@thedailyreporter.com; web site www.hillsdale.net
Group: New Media Investment Group
Published: Mon, Tues, Wed, Thur, Fri, Sat
Weekday Frequency: e
Saturday Frequency: m
Circulation: 7,285; 7,285(sat)
Last Audit: Sworn/Estimate/Non-Audited September 30, 2017
Advertising Rate (weekday/saturday): Open inch rate $8.65

Online Advertising Rate: Slider $99.00/month; Half-Banner $129.00/month; Leaderboard $149.00/month
News services: AP. **Established:** 1846
Special Editions: Classified Promotion (Apr); Jonesville Sidewalk Sales (Aug); New Year's Baby Promotion (Dec); Valentine's Promotion (Feb); Progress (Jan); Hillsdale Sidewalk Days (Jul); Silver Salute Tab (Jun); Health & Fitness Tab (Mar); Memoriams (May); Pre-Christmas (
Special Weekly Sections: TV Key (Fri).
Syndicated Publications: Relish (Monthly); USA WEEKEND Magazine (Sat); American Profile (Weekly).
Digital Platform - Mobile: Apple, Android, Windows
Digital Platform - Tablet: Apple iOS, Android, Windows 7
Pub./ Gen. Mgr. .... David Ferro
Circ. Mgr. .... RoxAnne Morgret
Exec. Ed. .... Jamie Barrand
News Ed. .... Amanda VanAuker
Sports Ed. .... Ed Patino
Night Desk Ed. .... Matthew Thompson
Managing Ed. .... Andy Barrand
Market Information: ADS; TMC.
Mechanical Available: Offset; Black and 3 ROP colors; insert accepted; page cutoffs - 22 3/4.
Mechanical Specifications: Type page 13 1/16 x 21 1/2; E - 6 cols, 2 1/16, 1/8 between; A - 6 cols, 2 1/16, 1/8 between; C - 8 cols, 1 7/8, 1/8 between.
Delivery Method: Mail, CarrierEquipment & Software: PRESSROOM EQUIPMENT: Lines — 5-G/Community; MAILROOM EQUIPMENT: Tying Machines — MLN/1100, 1/MLN, 1-/Strapex; Address Machine — Ch/705, Automecha/AccuFast PL.; BUSINESS EQUIPMENT: HP, 4-ATT/610 BUSINESS SOFTWARE: Unix/SCO U-386, SMS CLASSIFIED EQUIPMENT: Hardware — APP/Mac; Printers — APP/Mac LaserWriter NTX; CLASSIFIED SOFTWARE: Baseview/Classified. DISPLAY EQUIPMENT: Hardware — APP/Mac; Printers — APP/Mac LaserWriter 630; Other Hardware — Panasonic/CD-Rom. DISPLAY SOFTWAREAd Make-up Applications — QPS/QuarkXPress, Multi-Ad/Creator; EDITORIAL EQUIPMENT: Hardware — APP/Mac; Printers — APP/Mac LaserWriter NTX EDITORIAL SOFTWARE: Baseview/NewsEdit. PRODUCTION EQUIPMENT: Hardware — APP/Mac LaserWriter 600, Adobe/Photoshop; Cameras — SCREEN/250; Scanners — APP/Mac Scanner, Nikon/Photo, Microtek/Scanmaker II.

HOLLAND

THE HOLLAND SENTINEL

54 W 8th St, Holland, Mich., 49423-3104, Ottawa; gen tel (616) 546-4200; adv tel (616) 546-4227; ed tel (616) 392-2314; gen fax (616) 392-3526; disp adv e-mail james. briggs@hollandsentinel.com; class adv e-mailHaley.Kelley@hollandsentinel.com; ed e-mail newsroom@hollandsentinel.com; web site www.hollandsentinel.com
- 3,000,000(views) 350,000(visitors)
Group: New Media Investment Group
Published: Tues, Wed, Thur, Fri, Sat, Sun
Weekday Frequency: m
Saturday Frequency: m
Circulation: 8,210; 8,210(sat); 10,795(sun)
Last Audit: AAM September 30, 2017
Advertising Rate (weekday/saturday): Open inch rate $15.23
News services: AP, MCT. **Established:** 1896
Own Printing Facility?: Yes
Commercial Printers?: Yes
Digital Platform - Mobile: Apple, Android
Digital Platform - Tablet: Apple iOS, Android
Prodn. Mgr., Pre Press .... Jerry Raab
Circ. Dir. .... Steve Kenemer
Asst. Mng. Ed. .... Sarah Leach
Pres. and Pub. .... Brent Morris
Market Information: ADS; TMC.
Mechanical Available: Offset; Black and 3 ROP colors; insert accepted; page cutoffs - 21.5".
Mechanical Specifications: Type page 10 x 21; E - 6 cols, 1 5/6, 1/8 between; A - 6 cols, 1 5/6, 1/8 between; C - 9 cols, 1 3/16, 1/8 between.

Areas Served: Ottawa and Allegan Counties
Delivery Method: Mail, Newsstand, Carrier, RacksEquipment & Software: PRESSROOM EQUIPMENT: Lines — 24 - Dev MAILROOM EQUIPMENT: Counter Stackers — 2/HL; Inserters & Stuffers — 1-HI/NP 848; Tying Machines — 1-Signode, 1-Sterling/MR45CH; Address Machine — 1-/Ch.; BUSINESS EQUIPMENT: Pc BUSINESS SOFTWARE: Media Span CLASSIFIED EQUIPMENT: Hardware — APP/Power Mac 233; Printers — APP/Mac LaserWriter II NTX; CLASSIFIED SOFTWARE: Media Span DISPLAY EQUIPMENT: Macs and PCs DISPLAY SOFTWAREMedia Span EDITORIAL EQUIPMENT: Macs and PCs EDITORIAL SOFTWARE: Saxotech PRODUCTION EQUIPMENT: Hardware — Nat, 2-MON/1270; Cameras — R; Scanners — Epson, Microtek, HP.

HOUGHTON

THE DAILY MINING GAZETTE

206 Shelden Ave, Houghton, Mich., 49931-2134, Houghton; gen tel (906) 482-1500; adv tel (906) 483-2220; ed tel (906) 482-1500; gen fax (906) 482-2726; adv fax (906) 483-2219; ed fax (906) 483-2726; gen/nat adv e-mail yrobillard@mininggazette.com; disp adv e-mail yrobillard@mininggazette.com; class adv e-mailgazetteadv@mininggazette.com; ed e-mail cpeterson@mininggazette.com; web site www.mininggazette.com - 512,000(views) 240,000(visitors)
Group: Ogden Newspapers Inc.
Published: Mon, Tues, Wed, Thur, Fri, Sat
Weekday Frequency: e
Saturday Frequency: m
Circulation: 6,047; 6,292(sat)
Last Audit: AAM March 31, 2016
Advertising Rate (weekday/saturday): Print Ad $303.00 (3 per week); $432 (5 per week)
Online Advertising Rate: Internet Ad Large Button $50.00 per month
News services: AP, Nutting Newspapers Inc.
Established: 1859
Own Printing Facility?: Yes
Commercial Printers?: Yes
Syndicated Publications: Happenings/TV Book (Thur).
Digital Platform - Mobile: Apple, Android
Digital Platform - Tablet: Apple iOS, Android, Kindle, Kindle Fire
Pub. .... Michael Scott
Adv. Dir. .... Yvonne Robillard
Circ. Mgr. .... Carolyn Brown
Mng. Ed. .... Craig Peterson
Market Information: ADS; TMC.
Mechanical Available: Offset; Black and 3 ROP colors; insert accepted - up to 11 x 13; page cutoffs - 21.
Mechanical Specifications: Type page 13 x 21 1/2; E - 6 cols, 2, 1/6 between; A - 6 cols, 2, 1/6 between; C - 9 cols, 1 1/3, 1/6 between.
Areas Served: 49931; Michigan's Upper Peninsula: Baraga, Houghton, Keweenaw and Ontonagon.
Delivery Method: Mail, Newsstand, Carrier, RacksEquipment & Software: PRESSROOM EQUIPMENT: Lines — 8-G/Offset 1980.; MAILROOM EQUIPMENT: Tying Machines — 4/Bu; Address Machine — PC.; BUSINESS EQUIPMENT: 6-IBM/PC network BUSINESS SOFTWARE: Q&A, Lotus, Microsoft/Windows CLASSIFIED EQUIPMENT: Hardware — Mk/1100 Plus; Printers — TI/810; CLASSIFIED SOFTWARE: Mk. DISPLAY EQUIPMENT: Hardware — APP/Mac IIsi; Printers — APP/Mac LaserWriter II; DISPLAY SOFTWAREAd Make-up Applications — QPS/QuarkXPress, Multi-Ad/Creator 3.5; Layout Software — APP/Mac. EDITORIAL EQUIPMENT: Hardware — Mk/1100 Plus; Printers — TI/810 EDITORIAL SOFTWARE: Mk. PRODUCTION EQUIPMENT: Hardware — Lf, Lf; Cameras — COM/680C.

HOWELL

THE LIVINGSTON COUNTY DAILY PRESS & ARGUS

323 E Grand River Ave, Howell, Mich.,

48843-2322, Livingston; gen tel (517) 548-2000; adv tel (517) 548-2000; ed tel (517) 548-2000; gen fax (517) 548-3005; adv fax (517) 548-3005; ed fax (517) 548-3005; gen/nat adv e-mail lvernon@hometownlife.com; disp adv e-mail lvernon@hometownlife.com; class adv e-maillvernon@hometownlife.com; ed e-mail mmalott@gannett.com; web site www.livingstondaily.com
- 1,400,000(views) 475,900(visitors)
Group: Gannett
Published: Mon, Tues, Wed, Thur, Fri, Sun
Weekday Frequency: m
Circulation: 7,499; 122(sat); 10,237(sun)
Last Audit: AAM September 30, 2017
Advertising Rate (weekday/saturday): Open inch rate $14.82
Advertising Rate (sunday): Open inch rate $18.52
Online Advertising Rate: Call for online rates
News services: AP. **Established:** 1843
Own Printing Facility?: Yes
Commercial Printers?: Yes
Syndicated Publications: USA WEEKEND Magazine (S); American Profile (Weekly).
Digital Platform - Mobile: Apple, Android
Digital Platform - Tablet: Apple iOS, Android
Sports Ed. .... Tim Robinson
Managing Ed. .... Mike Malott
Multimedia Sales Mgr. ....Lisa Vernon
Pub./Gen. Mgr. .... Susan Rosiek
Copy Desk Chief .... Matt Smith
Niche Products Ed. ....Chris Nagy
Multimedia Ed. ....Al Ward
Web Ed. .... Amanda Whitesell
Digital Specialist
Brett Maynard
Market Information: Zoned editions.
Areas Served: Livingston
Delivery Method: Mail, Carrier

IONIA

IONIA SENTINEL-STANDARD
114 N Depot St, Ionia, Mich., 48846-1602, Ionia; gen tel (616) 527-2100; adv tel (616) 527-2100; ed tel (616) 527-2100 ext. 104; gen fax (616) 527-6860; adv fax (616) 527-6860; ed fax (616) 527-6860; gen/nat adv e-mail lori.kilchermann@sentinel-standard.com; disp adv e-mail lori.kilchermann@sentinel-standard.com; class adv e-mailclassads@sentinel-standard.com; ed e-mail lori.kilchermann@sentinel-standard.com; web site www.sentinel-standard.com
Group: New Media Investment Group
Published: Tues, Wed, Thur, Fri, Sat
Weekday Frequency: m
Saturday Frequency: m
Circulation: 2,001; 2,001(sat)
Last Audit: Sworn/Estimate/Non-Audited September 30, 2017
Advertising Rate (weekday/saturday): Open inch rate $9.50 (Tue-Fri); $12.75 (Sat);
Online Advertising Rate: Starting at $150.00 CPM
News services: AP/More Content Now **Established:** 1866
Special Editions: Senior Life
Ionia Free Fair
In the Locker Room
Medical Guide
Syndicated Publications: American Profile (Weekly).
Digital Platform - Mobile: Apple, Android, Windows
Digital Platform - Tablet: Apple iOS, Android, Windows 7
General Manager .... Lori Kilchermann
Business Office Mgr. .... Kim Mathewson
Sports Editor .... Connor Ryan
News Editor .... Darcy Meade
Market Information: Split run; TMC; Zoned editions.
Mechanical Available: Offset; Black and 4 ROP colors; insert accepted; page cutoffs - 22.
Mechanical Specifications: Type page 12 x 22; E - 6 cols, 1 5/16, 1/8 between; A - 6 cols, 1 5/16, 1/8 between; C - 8 cols, 1 7/8, 1/8 between.
Areas Served: 48809, 48851, 48845, 48846, 48849, 48851, 48860, 48865, 48870, 48873, 48875, 48881, 48897, 49331
Delivery Method: Mail, Newsstand, Carrier, RacksEquipment & Software: PRESSROOM EQUIPMENT: Lines — 4-HI/V-15A;

MAILROOM EQUIPMENT: Tying Machines — 1/Sa, 1-/Bu.; BUSINESS EQUIPMENT: 2-Dell, 2-Packard Bell/Legend 401CD CLASSIFIED EQUIPMENT: Hardware — APP/Mac G3; Printers — APP/Mac LaserWriter; CLASSIFIED SOFTWARE: Baseview. DISPLAY EQUIPMENT: Hardware — APP/Mac IIvx; Printers — HP/Laser; DISPLAY SOFTWARELayout Software — Multi-Ad/Creator. EDITORIAL EQUIPMENT: Hardware — 1-APP/Mac Quadra 630, 2-APP/Power Mac 6100-60, APP/iMac, 2-APP/Mac G3; Printers — 1-APP/Mac LaserWriter 16-600 PS EDITORIAL SOFTWARE: QPS/QuarkXPress, Baseview/NewsEdit Pro. PRODUCTION EQUIPMENT: Hardware — 1-Nat, 1-C; Cameras — 1-B PRODUCTION SOFTWARE: QPS/QuarkXPress 3.3.

IRON MOUNTAIN

THE DAILY NEWS
215 E Ludington St, Iron Mountain, Mich., 49801-2917, Dickinson; gen tel (906) 774-2772; adv tel (906) 774-2772 ext. 35; ed tel (906) 774-2772 ext. 40; gen fax (906) 774-7660; adv fax (906) 774-9545; ed fax (906) 774-1285; gen/nat adv e-mail advertising@ironmountaindailynews.com; disp adv e-mail advertising@ironmountaindailynews.com; class adv e-mailclassified@ironmountaindailynews.com; ed e-mail news@ironmountaindailynews.com; web site www.ironmountaindailynews.com
- 732,354(views) 70,523(visitors)
Group: Ogden Newspapers Inc
Published: Mon, Tues, Wed, Thur, Fri, Sat
Weekday Frequency: e
Saturday Frequency: m
Circulation: 6,344; 7,243(sat)
Last Audit: Sworn/Estimate/Non-Audited September 30, 2017
Advertising Rate (weekday/saturday): Open inch rate $31.89
Advertising Rate (sunday): $31.89
Online Advertising Rate: Many options, call for pricing
News services: AP, TMS. **Established:** 1921
Own Printing Facility?: Yes
Commercial Printers?: Yes
Special Editions: Book Reviews (Jul); Progress 2014 Education (Jun); Logging Today (Apr); Vacation Guide (Aug); Christmas (Dec); Ski Jumping (Feb); Bride (Jan); Rodeo (Jul); Vacation Guide (Jun); Baby (Mar); Graduation (May); Cookbook (Nov); Hunting (Oct); Drug Coloring Book (Other); Logging Today (Sept).
Special Weekly Sections: TV Preview (Fri); Food (Mon); Business (Sat); Health (Thur); Business (Tues).
Syndicated Publications: Weekly entertainment guide
Digital Platform - Mobile: Apple, Android, Windows
Digital Platform - Tablet: Apple iOS, Android
Adv. Mgr. .... Ray King
Ent. Ed. .... Marguerite Lanthier
Lifestyles Ed. .... Terri Castelaz
News Ed. .... Jim Anderson
Online Mgr. .... Maggie Lanthier
Prodn. Mgr., Mailroom .... Sally Johnson
Prodn. Mgr., Pressroom .... Jeff Schwaller
Prod. Supv., Graphics .... Joe Edlebeck
Photo Ed. ....Theresa Prpudfit
Accounting Mgr. .... Kristen Erickson
Business Ed. .... Linda Lobeck
Photo Ed. ....Theresa Proudfit
Cir. Dir. .... Jennifer Flynn
NIE Coord. ....Diane Adams
Ed. .... Betsy Bloom
Publisher .... Corky DeRoeck
Market Information: TMC.
Mechanical Available: Offset; Black and 3 ROP colors; insert accepted - all; page cutoffs - 22 3/4.
Mechanical Specifications: Type page 10 x 21 1/2; E - 6 cols, 1 1/2, 1/8 between; A - 6 cols, 1 1/2, 1/8 between; C - 9 cols, 1, between.
Areas Served: 49801 49802 49807 49815 49831 49834 49847 49852 49870 49874 49876 49881 49892 49902 49903 49915 49920 49935 54103 54119 54120 54121 54125 54151 54156
Delivery Method: Mail, Newsstand, Carrier, RacksEquipment & Software: PRESSROOM

EQUIPMENT: Lines — 11-G/Community single width; Folders — 2, 1-G/Community SSC, 1-SC/Community.; MAILROOM EQUIPMENT: Counter Stackers — 1-Baldwin/Coun-O-Stacker; Inserters & Stuffers — 1-MM/6 pocket & head; Tying Machines — 2-Mosca/Rom-P2, 1/Bu; BUSINESS EQUIPMENT: APP/Mac, IBM CLASSIFIED EQUIPMENT: Hardware — iMac, Dell, HP; Printers — HP; CLASSIFIED SOFTWARE: Microsoft Office DISPLAY EQUIPMENT: Hardware — iMac, HP; Printers — HP Laserjet; Other Hardware — Canon Scanner DISPLAY SOFTWAREAd Make-up Applications — Multi-Ad/Creator 8, Adobe/Illustrator; Layout Software — iMac EDITORIAL EQUIPMENT: Hardware — iMac/iMac; Printers — HP EDITORIAL SOFTWARE: QuarkXpress, Adobe Creative Suite

IRONWOOD

THE DAILY GLOBE
118 E McLeod Ave, Ironwood, Mich., 49938-2120, Gogebic; gen tel (906) 932-2211; adv tel (906) 932-2211 ext. 129; ed tel (906) 932-4211; gen fax (906) 932-5358; adv fax (906) 932-5358; ed fax (906) 932-4211; gen/nat adv e-mail gpennington@yourdailyglobe.com; disp adv e-mail gpennington@yourdailyglobe.com; class adv e-mailclassifieds@yourdailyglobe.com; ed e-mail lholcombe@yourdailyglobe.com; web site www.yourdailyglobe.com
Group: Stevenson Newspapers
Published: Mon, Tues, Wed, Thur, Fri, Sat
Weekday Frequency: m
Saturday Frequency: m
Circulation: 4,500; 6,498(sat)
Last Audit: Sworn/Estimate/Non-Audited September 30, 2017
Advertising Rate (weekday/saturday): Open inch rate $12.00
Online Advertising Rate: Banner $79.00/month; Weather Sponsor $99.00/month
News services: AP, LAT-WP. **Established:** 1919
Own Printing Facility?: Yes
Commercial Printers?: Yes
Special Editions: Business Card Directory (Jul); Forget No Soldier (Jun); Home Improvement (Apr & Oct); County Fair (Jul); Christmas Gift Guide (Dec); Progress (Feb); Winter Fun Guide (Jan); Home Builders (Mar); Summer Fun Guide (May); Senior Sentinel (Monthly); Deer Hunting (Nov); Summer Fun (May) Winter Fun Guide (Oct); Resource Guide (Aug).
Special Weekly Sections: Health (Tues), Home & Garden (Fri), Dining Guide (Thurs), Education (Mon)
Syndicated Publications: TV Entertainment (Fri); American Profile (Mon);
Digital Platform - Mobile: Apple, Android
Digital Platform - Tablet: Apple iOS, Android
Mng. Ed. .... Larry Holcombe
Pub. .... Sue Mizell
Exec. Asst. ....Jenna Martilla
Circulation Supervisor .... Marissa Casari
Adv. Dir. ....Heidi Ofstad
Market Information: ADS; TMC.
Mechanical Available: Offset; Black and 4 ROP colors; insert accepted; page cutoffs - 22 3/4.
Mechanical Specifications: Type page 13 x 21 1/2; E - 6 cols, 2 1/16, 1/8 between; A - 6 cols, 2 1/16, 1/8 between; C - 9 cols, 1 3/8, 1/16 between.
Areas Served: Michigan: Ironwood, Bessemer, Wakefield, Ontonagon, Watersmeet, Ewen, Bergland, Marenisco; Wisconsin: Hurley, Mercer, Montreal, Gile, Boulder Jct., Mellen, Manitowish Waters, Land O'Lakes.
Delivery Method: Mail, CarrierEquipment & Software: PRESSROOM EQUIPMENT: Lines — 8-G/Community; Folders — 1-G/2.1.; MAILROOM EQUIPMENT: Tying Machines — 3/Bu; Address Machine — 1-Miller/Bevco 285.; CLASSIFIED EQUIPMENT: Hardware — APP/Mac; Printers — 1-QMS/Nx17; CLASSIFIED SOFTWARE: 2-Baseview. DISPLAY EQUIPMENT: Hardware — APP/Mac; Printers — 1-QMC/11x17; Other Hardware — Pre Press/Panther Varityper. DISPLAY SOFTWAREAd Make-up Applications — QPS/QuarkXPress, Adobe/

Photoshop; EDITORIAL EQUIPMENT: Hardware — 9-APP/Mac/Pre Press/Panther Vorityper; Printers — 2-QMS/11x17 EDITORIAL SOFTWARE: Adobe/Photoshop, QPS/QuarkXPress. PRODUCTION EQUIPMENT: Hardware — 1-Nu; Cameras — 1-Co/Horizontal 25 CS; Scanners — Epson, Umax, Polariod/Sprintscan PRODUCTION SOFTWARE: QPS/QuarkXPress 5.0, Macromedia/Freehand, Adobe/Photoshop 6.

JACKSON

THE JACKSON CITIZEN PATRIOT
100 E Michigan Ave, Ste 100, Jackson, Mich., 49201-1403, Jackson; gen tel (517) 787-2300; adv tel (800) 446-5588; gen/nat adv e-mail advertise@mlive.com; disp adv e-mail advertise@mlive.com; class adv e-mailadvertise@mlive.com; ed e-mail janews@mlive.com; web site www.mlive.com/jackson
Group: Advance Publications, Inc.
Published: Mon, Tues, Wed, Thur, Fri, Sat, Sun
Weekday Frequency: e
Saturday Frequency: m
Circulation: 16,040; 2,067(sat); 20,338(sun)
Last Audit: AAM December 31, 2015
Advertising Rate (weekday/saturday): Open inch rate $16.88
Advertising Rate (sunday): Open inch rate $21.95
News services: AP, MCT **Established:** 1865
Own Printing Facility?: Yes
Commercial Printers?: No
Special Weekly Sections: In Town & Around Entertainment guide, Thursdays; TV magazine, Friday
Syndicated Publications: Parade (S); TV Mag (Fri).
Digital Platform - Mobile: Apple, Android, Windows, Blackberry
Digital Platform - Tablet: Apple iOS, Android, Kindle
Pres. .... Dan Gaydou
Chief Revenue Officer ....Charity Plaxton
Sr. Dir. for National Accounts ....Steve Westphal
Dir.of Adv. Operations .... Bob White
VP of Sales .... Michael Assink
Sr. Platform Dir. ....Colleen Huff
Dir. of Real Estate & Careers Sales Andy Boldryeff
VP of Content ....John Hiner
Dir. of Sports News .... Bill Emkow
Sr. Dir. for Journalism and Engagement Kelly Frick
Sr. Dir. for Digital Culture and Innovation . Colleen Stone
Exec. Ed. of Print .... Paul Keep
Dir. of Automotive Sales .... Khalida Cook
Small Business Dir. ....Andrea Sipka
Sr. Strategy Dir. .... Nick Dionne
Sr. Retail Dir. .... Brett Christie
Regional Sales Dir. of Detroit & Ann Arbor. Christy Keizer
Regional Sales Dir. of Flint, Saginaw and Bay City Robert Graham
Regional Sales Dir. of Grand Rapids & Muskegon . Jamie Dionne
Gen. Mgr. .... Laurel Champion
Adv. Support Dir. .... Andrea Miller
Dir. of News ....Marjory Raymer
Dir. of Community Engagement .... Jen Eyer
Market Information: ADS; TMC; Zoned editions.
Mechanical Available: Offset; Black and 3 ROP colors; insert accepted - any; page cutoffs - 22 3/4.
Mechanical Specifications: Type page 13 x 21 3/4; E - 6 cols, 2 1/16, 1/8 between; A - 6 cols, 2 1/16, 1/8 between; C - 10 cols, 1 1/4, 1/16 between.
Areas Served: 49201, 49202, 49203, 49234, 49230
Delivery Method: Mail, Newsstand, Carrier, RacksEquipment & Software: PRESSROOM EQUIPMENT: Lines — Goss; Goss; BUSINESS EQUIPMENT: Apple Xserve Dell servers HP servers Hitachi HDS BUSINESS SOFTWARE: DTI CircView RouteSmart VMware 4-5 CLASSIFIED EQUIPMENT: Hardware — Dell & HP PCs; Printers — HP, Canon, IKON; CLASSIFIED SOFTWARE: Atex Mactive 3.0 Encompass Office 2010 DISPLAY EQUIPMENT: Hardware — PC/Mac LCDs ; Printers — Canon, IKON; DISPLAY SOFTWAREAd Make-up Applications — InDesign Xpance; Layout

Software — InDesign PPI ATEX PageLayout Xpance EDITORIAL EQUIPMENT: Hardware — Dell & HP PCs; Printers — HP, Ikon, Canon EDITORIAL SOFTWARE: Media Span Baseview, Adobe InDesign/InCopy PRODUCTION EQUIPMENT: Hardware — Dell & HP PC Apple Macs; Scanners — Epson Canon PRODUCTION SOFTWARE: PPI AGFA IntelliTune Adobe Illustrator Adobe InDesign Adobe Flash Adobe Photoshop Xpance ATEX Mactive PageLayout ZenDesk

KALAMAZOO

THE KALAMAZOO GAZETTE

306 S Kalamazoo Mall, Kalamazoo, Mich., 49007-4807, Kalamazoo; gen tel (269) 345-3511; adv tel (800) 446-5588; gen/nat adv e-mail advertise@mlive.com; disp adv e-mail advertise@mlive.com; class adv e-mailadvertise@mlive.com; web site www.mlive.com/kalamazoo

Group: Advance Publications, Inc.
Published: Mon, Tues, Wed, Thur, Fri, Sat, Sun
Weekday Frequency: e
Saturday Frequency: m
Circulation: 31,493; 3,553(sat); 38,946(sun)
Last Audit: AAM December 31, 2015
Advertising Rate (weekday/saturday): Open inch rate $20.44
Advertising Rate (sunday): Open inch rate $30.66
News services: 1834
Digital Platform - Mobile: Apple, Android, Windows, Blackberry
Digital Platform - Tablet: Apple iOS, Android, Kindle, Kindle Fire
Pres. .... Dan Gaydou
Chief Revenue Officer .... Charity Plaxton
Sr. Dir. for National Accounts .... Steve Westphal
Dir. of Adv. Operations .... Bob White
VP of Sales .... Michael Assink
Sr. Platform Dir. .... Colleen Huff
Dir. of Real Estate & Careers Sales Andy Boldyreff
VP of Content .... John Hiner
Dir. of Sports News .... Bill Emkow
Sr. Dir. of Journalism and Engagement. Kelly Frick
Sr. Dir. for Digital Culture and Innovation . Colleen Stone
Dir. of Automotive Sales .... Khalida Cook
Small Business Dir. .... Andrea Sipka
Sr. Retail Dir. .... Brett Christie
Regional Sales Dir. of Detroit & Ann Arbor. Christy Keizer
Regional Sales Dir. of Flint, Saginaw and Bay City Robert Graham
Regional Sales Dir. of Grand Rapids & Muskegon . Jamie Dionne
Gen. Mgr. .... Laurel Champion
Agency Relations Dir. .... Jeff Leitch
Adv. Support Dir. .... Andrea Miller
Dir. of News .... Marjory Raymer
Dir. of Community Engagement .... Jen Eyer
Exec. Ed. of Print .... Paul Keep
Areas Served: 49001 through 49450
Delivery Method: Mail, Newsstand, Carrier, RacksEquipment & Software: PRESSROOM EQUIPMENT: Lines — MAN/Roland Geoioman; MAN/Roland Geoioman; Press Drive — Baumuller; Folders — 1-MAN/ Double-out 64 pg.; Reels & Stands — MAN/ CD13; MAILROOM EQUIPMENT: Counter Stackers — 4-QWI/501, 1-QWI/400, 2-HL/ Dual Carrier; Inserters & Stuffers — 2-GMA/ SLS3000; Tying Machines — 5-Dynaric/4; BUSINESS EQUIPMENT: Apple Xserve Dell servers HP servers Hitachi HDS BUSINESS SOFTWARE: DTI CircView RouteSmart VMware 4-5 CLASSIFIED EQUIPMENT: Hardware — Dell & HP PCs; Printers — HP, Canon, IKON; CLASSIFIED SOFTWARE: Atex Mactive 3.0 Encompass Office 2010 DISPLAY EQUIPMENT: Hardware — LCDs Apple Macs Dell & HP PCs; Printers — Canon, IKON; DISPLAY SOFTWAREAd Make-up Applications — InDesign Xpance; Layout Software — InDesign PPI ATEX PageLayout Xpance EDITORIAL EQUIPMENT: Hardware — Dell & HP PCs; Printers — HP, Ikon, Canon EDITORIAL SOFTWARE: Media Span Baseview, Adobe InDesign/InCopy PRODUCTION EQUIPMENT: Hardware — Dell & HP PC Apple Macs; Scanners — Epson Canon PRODUCTION SOFTWARE: PPI AGFA IntelliTune Adobe Illustrator Adobe InDesign Adobe Flash Adobe Photoshop Xpance ATEX Mactive PageLayout ZenDesk

LANSING

LANSING STATE JOURNAL

300 S Washington Sq, Ste 300, Lansing, Mich., 48933-2102, Ingham; gen tel 517-377-1001; adv tel 517-377-1001; ed tel (517) 377-1001; gen fax (517) 377-1059; adv fax (517) 482-5476; ed fax (517) 377-1298; gen/nat adv e-mail cschnepf@michigan.com; disp adv e-mail sholmes@michigan.com; class adv e-maillkeiser@michigan.com; ed e-mail sangel@lsj.com; web site http://www.lsj.com

Group: Gannett
Published: Mon, Tues, Wed, Thur, Fri, Sat, Sun
Weekday Frequency: m
Saturday Frequency: m
Circulation: 32,571; 34,080(sat); 44,261(sun)
Last Audit: AAM June 30, 2016
News services: AP, GNS. **Established:** 1855
Own Printing Facility?: No
Commercial Printers?: Yes
Special Weekly Sections: Business Monday (Mon); Sunday Real Estate Advertising (S); What's On (Thur); Greater Lansing Real Estate Weekly (Wed).
Syndicated Publications: Parade
Digital Platform - Mobile: Apple, Android, Windows
Digital Platform - Tablet: Apple iOS, Android, Windows 7
Controller .... David Davies
Accts. Mgr. .... Kathi Waters
Dir., HR .... Melissa Alford
Dir., Market Devel. .... Kevin McFatridge
Mktg. Mgr. .... Ramon Brown
Circ. Dir. .... Linda Argue
Mng. Ed. .... Stephanie Angel
Asst. City Ed. .... Jason Cody
Asst. City Ed., Night .... David McClendum
Editorial Page Ed .... Derek Melot
Entertainment Ed. .... Mike Hughes
Features Ed. .... Robin Swartz
News Ed. .... Cindy Hudson
Online News Ed. .... Suzanne Salay
Political/Gov't Ed. .... Chris Andrews
Sports Ed. .... Mark Meyer
Prodn. Dir. .... Rick Wagoner
Content Strategist Elaine Kulhanek
President .... Rebecca Poynter
Market Information: Split run; TMC.
Mechanical Available: Offset; Black and 3 ROP colors; insert accepted; page cutoffs - 23 9/16.
Mechanical Specifications: Type page 11 5/8 x 22; E - 6 cols, 1 5/6, 1/8 between; A - 6 cols, 1 5/6, 1/8 between; C - 10 cols, 1 1/8, 1/16 between.
Areas Served: 48801, 48806, 48807, 48808, 48811, 48813, 48817, 48818, 48819, 48820, 48821, 48822, 48823, 48824, 48827, 48831, 48835, 48837, 48838, 48840, 48842, 48845, 48846, 48847, 48848, 48849, 48851, 48854, 48857, 48858, 48860, 48861, 48864, 48866, 48867, 48871, 48872, 48873, 48875, 48876, 48879, 48880, 48883, 48884, 48888, 48892, 48893, 48894, 48895, 48897, 48906, 48908, 48910, 48911, 48912, 48915, 48917, 48933, 49021, 49050, 49058, 49073, 49076, 49096, 49251, 49264, 49284, 49285
Delivery Method: Mail, Carrier, RacksEquipment & Software: PRESSROOM EQUIPMENT: Lines — TKS/Offset (9 units; 5 half decks); Press Drive — SCR/DC-55-KW; Folders — 1-TKS/3:2 Double Delivery; Pasters —3-ARM/RTP. MAILROOM EQUIPMENT: Counter Stackers — 3-QWI/300, 2-Id/660; Inserters & Stuffers — 1-HI/WP 630 (27 Head); Tying Machines — 2/Power Strap/ PSN 6, 3-/Power Strap/PSN 6-E; Wrapping Singles — Hand; Address Machine — Ch/525E.; BUSINESS EQUIPMENT: IBM/Sys 38 CLASSIFIED EQUIPMENT: Hardware — 34-AT; 16-DEC.; DISPLAY EQUIPMENT: Hardware — APP/Macs, AT; Printers — Linotype-Hell/Linotronic Imagesetter; Other Hardware — Sun/ Workstation DISPLAY SOFTWAREAd Make-up Applications — APP/Mac, Multi-Ad/Creator, QPS/QuarkXPress, Adobe/ Photoshop; Layout Software — AT/Architect. EDITORIAL EQUIPMENT: Hardware — AT. PRODUCTION EQUIPMENT: Hardware — 1-He/200, 1-LE/LD18; Cameras — 1-C/ Newspager II, 1-C/Spartan II.

LUDINGTON

LUDINGTON DAILY NEWS

202 N Rath Ave, Ludington, Mich., 49431-1663, Mason; gen tel (231) 845-5181; adv tel (231) 845-5181 ext. 320; ed tel (231) 845-5182 ext. 326; gen fax (231) 843-4011; adv fax (231) 843-4011; ed fax (231) 843-4011; gen/nat adv e-mail Ray McGrew <rmcgrew@cmgms.com>; disp adv e-mail Ray McGrew <rmcgrew@cmgms.com>; class adv e-mailJeriann Steiger <jsteiger@ludingtondailynews.com>; ed e-mail sbegnoche@ludingtondailynews.com; web site www.ludingtondailynews.com

Group: Community Media Group
Published: Mon, Tues, Wed, Thur, Fri, Sat
Weekday Frequency: e
Saturday Frequency: e
Circulation: 6,489; 6,489(sat)
Last Audit: Sworn/Estimate/Non-Audited September 30, 2017
Advertising Rate (weekday/saturday): Open inch rate $15.79
Online Advertising Rate: Banner $175.00/month; Right Square Ads $150.00/month
News services: AP. **Established:** 1867
Own Printing Facility?: Yes
Commercial Printers?: Yes
Special Editions: Local Sports (Apr); Back-to-School (Aug); Christmas Catalogue (Dec); Bridal (Feb); Graduation (Jun); Progress (Mar); Lake Winds (May); Christmas Opener (Nov); Home Care/Car Care (Oct); Local Sports (Sept).
Special Weekly Sections: TV Week (Fri); Best Food Day (Mon); Youth (Sat); Outdoor (Thur); Bridal (Tues); Business (Wed).
Syndicated Publications: American Profile (Weekly). Relish (weekly)
Digital Platform - Mobile: Apple, Android, Windows, Blackberry
Digital Platform - Tablet: Apple iOS, Android, Windows 7, Blackberry Tablet OS, Kindle, Nook, Kindle Fire
Circ. Mgr. .... Julie Payment
Sports Ed. .... David Bossick
Gen. Mgr. .... Ray McGrew
Managing Ed. .... Patti Klevorn
Market Information: ADS; TMC.
Mechanical Available: Offset; Black and 3 ROP colors; insert accepted; page cutoffs - 22 3/4.
Mechanical Specifications: Type page 13 x 21 1/2; E - 6 cols, 2 1/12, 1/6 between; A - 6 cols, 2 1/12, 1/6 between; C - 6 cols, 2 1/12, 1/6 between.
Areas Served: 49431, 49454, 49405, 49410, 49458, 49411
Delivery Method: Mail, Newsstand, CarrierEquipment & Software: PRESSROOM EQUIPMENT: Lines — 12-G/Community 1972; Folders — G/Community.; MAILROOM EQUIPMENT: Tying Machines — MLN, Bu, Malow.; BUSINESS EQUIPMENT: IBM/Sys 36, IBM/PC BUSINESS SOFTWARE: INSI, Lotus, WordPerfect, Query CLASSIFIED EQUIPMENT: Hardware — APP/Mac; Printers — APP/Mac, NewGen/Imager, HP/ LaserJet 4MV; CLASSIFIED SOFTWARE: Baseview. DISPLAY EQUIPMENT: Hardware — APP/Mac; Printers — APP/Mac, HP/ LaserJet 4MV; Other Hardware — Pioneer/ CD-Rom 600. DISPLAY SOFTWAREAd Make-up Applications — Aldus/PageMaker, Multi-Ad, QPS/QuarkXPress, Adobe/ Illustrator, Adobe/Photoshop, Macromedia/ Freehand, Streamline; EDITORIAL EQUIPMENT: Hardware — 12-APP/Mac; Printers — 2-APP/Mac, NewGen/Imager Plus 12 EDITORIAL SOFTWARE: Adobe Suite: InCopy, InDesign, Photoshop PRODUCTION EQUIPMENT: Hardware — ECR/ ScriptWriter; Scanners — Umax/Mirage, HP/ ScanJet PRODUCTION SOFTWARE: QPS/ QuarkXPress 3.31, Adobe/PageMaker 6.0.
Note: Seven time winner of Michigan Press Association, Newspaper of the Year, Dailies 10,000 circ or under.

MANISTEE

MANISTEE NEWS ADVOCATE

75 Maple St, Manistee, Mich., 49660-1554, Manistee; gen tel (231) 723-3592; adv tel (231) 398-3115; ed tel (231) 398-3106; gen fax (231) 723-4733; adv fax (231) 723-4733; ed fax (231) 723-4733; gen/nat adv e-mail mnainfo@pioneergroup.com; disp adv e-mail advertisingmna@pioneergroup.com; class adv e-mailclassmna@pioneergroup.com; ed e-mail editormna@pioneergroup.com; web site www.manisteenews.com

Group: Pioneer Group
The Pioneer Group
Published: Mon, Tues, Wed, Thur, Fri, Sat
Weekday Frequency: m
Saturday Frequency: m
Circulation: 4,928; 4,928(sat)
Last Audit: Sworn/Estimate/Non-Audited September 30, 2017
Advertising Rate (weekday/saturday): Open inch rate $11.50
News services: AP. **Established:** 1898
Special Editions: Spring Sports (Apr); Christmas Opening (Dec); Forest Festival (Jun); Bridal (Mar); Hunting (Oct); Fall Sports (Sept).
Special Weekly Sections: Religion (Fri); Business (Mon); Seniors (Sat); Outdoors (Thur); Lifestyles (Tues).
Syndicated Publications: USA WEEKEND Magazine (Sat); American Profile (Weekly).
Digital Platform - Mobile: Apple, Android
Digital Platform - Tablet: Apple iOS, Android, Kindle, Kindle Fire
Pub. .... Marilyn Barker
Circ. Mgr. .... Aaron Dekuiper
Religion Ed. .... David Barber
Prodn. Mgr., Pressroom .... Sheryl Rossen
Sports Ed. .... Dylan Savela
Managing Ed. .... Michelle Graves
Market Information: ADS; Split run; TMC.
Mechanical Available: Offset; Black and 3 ROP colors; insert accepted - all; page cutoffs - 22 1/2.
Mechanical Specifications: Type page 13 1/2 x 21 3/4; E - 6 cols, 2 1/16, 1/8 between; A - 6 cols, 2 1/16, 1/8 between; C - 9 cols, 1 3/8, 1/8 between.
Areas Served: 49660
Delivery Method: Mail, CarrierEquipment & Software: PRESSROOM EQUIPMENT: Lines — 7-HI/Cotrell 15A; Folders — 1-HI/2:1.; MAILROOM EQUIPMENT: Tying Machines — Sa; Address Machine — Wm.; BUSINESS EQUIPMENT: 3-IBM CLASSIFIED EQUIPMENT: Hardware — 3-APP/Mac; 2-APP/Mac; Printers — QMS; CLASSIFIED SOFTWARE: Baseview. DISPLAY EQUIPMENT: Printers — QMS; DISPLAY SOFTWAREAd Make-up Applications — Baseview/Ad Manager; Layout Software — 3-APP/Mac. EDITORIAL EQUIPMENT: Hardware — 9-APP/ Mac; Printers — HP, QMS EDITORIAL SOFTWARE: Aldus/PageMaker, QPS/ QuarkXPress, Baseview/NewsEdit Pro. PRODUCTION EQUIPMENT: Hardware — 1-Nu, ECR/Scriptsetter; Scanners — AG, Polaroid PRODUCTION SOFTWARE: Adobe/ Pagemaker 6.5, Adobe/Photoshop 4.0.

MARQUETTE

THE MINING JOURNAL

249 W Washington St, Marquette, Mich., 49855-4321, Marquette; gen tel (906) 228-2500; adv tel (906) 228-2500 ext. 258; ed tel (906) 228-2500 ext. 244; gen fax (906) 228-5556; adv fax (906) 228-3273; ed fax (906) 228-2617; gen/nat adv e-mail ldoyle@miningjournal.net; disp adv e-mail ldoyle@miningjournal.net; class adv e-mailsjohnson@miningjournal.net; ed e-mail bsargent@miningjournal.net; web site www.miningjournal.net
110,000(visitors)

Group: Ogden Newspapers Inc.
Published: Mon, Tues, Wed, Thur, Fri, Sat, Sun
Weekday Frequency: e
Saturday Frequency: m
Circulation: 10,377; 10,377(sat); 11,210(sun)
Last Audit: AAM March 31, 2017
Newspaper Reps: Michigan Press Association

Advertising Rate (weekday/saturday): Open inch rate $25.84 (Local); $37.29 (National)
Advertising Rate (sunday): Open inch rate $25.84 (Local); $37.29 (National)
Online Advertising Rate: Leaderboard $16.00 CPM; Center Banner $16.00 CPM
News services: AP, **Established:** 1846
Own Printing Facility?: Yes
Commercial Printers?: Yes
Special Editions: Superiorland (Sept); Menu Guide (May); Progress (Mar); Readers' Choice Winners (Jun); Bridal (Feb); Spring Home Improvement (Mar); Lawn & Garden (May); Cookbook (Nov); Fall Car Care (Oct).
Special Weekly Sections: Your Money (Mon); Health (Tues); Learning (Wed); Boomers & Beyond (Thur); Outdoors (Fri); Weekend (Sat); Our Youth (Sun); Scene Magazine (Mon); House To Home (Thur); TV Guide (Sat); Church Page (Sat); Automotive (Sun).
Syndicated Publications: TV Week (Sat); Parade (S).
Digital Platform - Mobile: Apple, Android
Digital Platform - Tablet: Apple iOS, Android, Windows 7
Pub. .... James A. Reevs
Circ. Mgr. .... Jerry Newhouse
Mng. Ed. .... Bud Sargent
Retail Sales Dir. .... Larry Doyle
Classified Mgr. .... Sharon Johnson
Accountant .... Emily Xu
Graphics Mgr. .... David Bond
Sports Editor .... Steve Brownlee
Justin Marietta
Press room manager .... Glen Fisk
Market Information: TMC.
Mechanical Available: Offset; Black and 3 ROP colors; insert accepted; page cutoffs - 22 3/4.
Mechanical Specifications: Type page 11 x 21 1/2; E - 6 cols, 1.583
Areas Served: 49855, 49908, 49946, 49970, 49919, 49884, 49862, 49806, 49883, 49853, 49868, 49866, 49861, 49871, 49833, 49808, 49891, 49820, 49853
Delivery Method: Mail, Newsstand, Carrier, RacksEquipment & Software: MAILROOM EQUIPMENT: Tying Machines — 2-MLN/ML1EE, 1-MLN/Spirit; Address Machine — 1/Wm.; BUSINESS EQUIPMENT: Anzio CLASSIFIED EQUIPMENT: Hardware — Mac's; DISPLAY SOFTWARELayout Software - COM/MCS 100, 3-APP/Mac Centris 650, 1-APP/Mac IIcx. EDITORIAL EQUIPMENT: Hardware — Mac's; Printers — V/4990 LaserPrinter, Konica/2100 EV Jetsetter EDITORIAL SOFTWARE: Mk/Mycro-Comp Touchwriter. PRODUCTION EQUIPMENT: Hardware — 1-Nu/Flip Top FT40UPNS, APP/Mac Scanner- DTP; Cameras — 1-SCREEN/Auto Companica 690C.

MIDLAND

MIDLAND DAILY NEWS

124 S McDonald St, Midland, Mich., 48640-5161, Midland; gen tel (989) 835-7171; adv tel (989) 839-4222; ed tel (989) 839-4254; gen fax (989) 835-9151; adv fax (989) 835-8591; ed fax (989) 835-6991; gen/nat adv e-mail mmellstead@mdn.net; disp adv e-mail cbott@mdn.net; class adv e-mailclassified@mdn.net; ed e-mail mdnletters@mdn.net; web site www.ourmidland.com
- 120,000(views) 857,841(visitors)
Group: Hearst Communications, Inc.
Published: Mon, Tues, Wed, Thur, Fri, Sat, Sun
Weekday Frequency: e
Saturday Frequency: e
Circulation: 7,408; 8,192(sat); 8,192(sun)
Last Audit: AAM September 30, 2017
Advertising Rate (weekday/saturday): Open inch rate $28.00
Advertising Rate (sunday): Open inch rate $29.50
Online Advertising Rate: Coupon Queen Package $286.99/month; Special Package $595.00/month; Homepage Package $708.00/month
News services: AP, NYT, HN. **Established:** 1937
Own Printing Facility?: Yes
Commercial Printers?: Yes
Special Editions: Envision (Feb); Envision (Mar).
Special Weekly Sections: Midland Living & Entertainment (Fri); Best Food Day (Mon); Science Page (S); Church Page (Sat); Agriculture (Thur); Arts Page (Wed).
Syndicated Publications: Color Comics (S); USA WEEKEND Magazine (Sat).
Digital Platform - Mobile: Apple, Android
Digital Platform - Tablet: Apple iOS, Android
Circ. Dir. .... Gary Wamsley
Editorial Page Ed. .... Ralph E. Wirtz
Accent Ed. .... Lori Qualls
Sports Ed. .... Chris Stevens
Gen. Mgr. .... Tim Newman
Adv. Mgr., Online Sales .... Erik Barnard
Photo Ed. .... Ryan Wood
Ed. .... Jack Telfer
Group Adv. Dir. .... Peter Ricker
Market Information: ADS; Split run; TMC.
Mechanical Available: Offset; Black and 3 ROP colors; insert accepted; page cutoffs - 22 3/4.
Mechanical Specifications: Type page 13 x 21 1/2; E - 6 cols, 2 1/16, 1/8 between; A - 6 cols, 2 1/16, 1/8 between; C - 9 cols, 1 1/2, 1/16 between.
Areas Served: 48624, 48652, 48620, 48612, 48618, 48628, 48657, 48883, 48640, 48642, 48611, 48706, 48615, 48637, 48623, 48626, 48617
Delivery Method: Mail, CarrierEquipment & Software: PRESSROOM EQUIPMENT: Lines — 8-G/Urbanite single width 1984; Reels & Stands — 2; MAILROOM EQUIPMENT: Counter Stackers — HL/Monitor; Inserters & Stuffers — S/P48; Tying Machines — OVL; BUSINESS EQUIPMENT: IBM/AS-400 CLASSIFIED EQUIPMENT: Hardware — 5-APP/Mac Quadra 105, 2-APP/Power Mac 7300; Printers — 1-APP/LaserJet 2100M; CLASSIFIED SOFTWARE: Baseview/Class Manager 3.3.4. DISPLAY EQUIPMENT: Hardware — 2-APP/Mac 7300, 2-Umax 5900, APP/Power Mac 5100, 1-APP/Mac, 2-APP/iMac G3; Printers — 2-HP/LaserJet 4M; Other Hardware — CD-Rom Burner DISPLAY SOFTWAREAd Make-up Applications — QPS/QuarkXPress 4.04, Adobe/Photoshop 5.5; Layout Software — ALS (version 2.1.1). EDITORIAL EQUIPMENT: Hardware — 4-APP/Mac Quadra 650, 10-APP/Mac Quadra 605, 2-Umax/5900/2-Accuset/1500 Imagesetter; Printers — 1-APP/LaserJet 2100M, 1-APP/Mac LaserWriter Pro 630 EDITORIAL SOFTWARE: Baseview/NewsEdit 1.12, QPS/QuarkXPress 3.31. PRODUCTION EQUIPMENT: Hardware — 1-Neg, 1-APP/Mac 8500-132; Cameras — 1-C/Spartan III, AG/RPS6100S; Scanners — 1-Nikon/35mm, Epson/800C Flatbed, 1-Nikon/1000 35mm, 1-AG/Arcus II Flatbed PRODUCTION SOFTWARE: QPS/QuarkXPress 3.3.2, QPS/QuarkXPress 4.04.

MONROE

THE MONROE NEWS

20 W 1st St, Monroe, Mich., 48161-2333, Monroe; gen tel (734) 242-1100; adv tel (734) 240-5025; ed tel (734) 240-5748; gen fax (734) 242-3175; adv fax (734) 242-3175; ed fax (734) 242-0937; gen/nat adv e-mail jbragg@monroenews.com; disp adv e-mail jbragg@monroenews.com; class adv e-mailkprater@monroenews.com; ed e-mail jnevels-haun@monroenews.com; web site www.monroenews.com
Group: New Media Investment Group
Published: Mon, Tues, Wed, Thur, Fri, Sat, Sun
Weekday Frequency: e
Saturday Frequency: e
Circulation: 12,246; 12,246(sat); 15,328(sun)
Last Audit: AAM December 31, 2016
Advertising Rate (weekday/saturday): Open inch rate $24.68
Advertising Rate (sunday): Open inch rate $26.75
Online Advertising Rate: Homepage Rectangle $12.00 CPM; Half page $10.00 CPM; Medium Rectangle $6.00 CPM
News services: AP **Established:** 1825
Own Printing Facility?: Yes
Commercial Printers?: Yes
Special Editions: Fair Premium Guide (Apr); Fall Sports (Aug); High School Basketball (Dec); Auto Showcase (Jan); Monroe County Fair (Jul); Business Profiles (Jun); Bedford Business Association (Mar); Medical Directory (May).
Special Weekly Sections: Farm (Fri); Best Food Day (Mon); Business (S); Living (Thur); Health (Tues).
Syndicated Publications: Relish (Monthly); Parade (S).
Digital Platform - Mobile: Apple, Android
Digital Platform - Tablet: Apple iOS, Android
Publisher .... Lonnie Peppler-Moyer
CFO .... Jay Hollon
Adv. Dir., Sales .... Jeanine Bragg
Circ. Mgr. .... David Zewicky
Opns. Dir., Systems .... Trent Langton
District Mgr. .... John Rankin
Classifieds .... Kristi Prater
City Ed. .... Barbara Krolak
Editor .... Jill Nevels-Haun
Market Information: TMC.
Mechanical Available: Offset; Black and 3 ROP colors; insert accepted - self-adhesive notes, product samples
Mechanical Specifications: Type page 10x19.75
Areas Served: 48161, 48162, 48117, 48159, 48131, 48160, 49267, 49276, 48144, 48182, 48140, 49270, 48134, 48173, 48164, 48183, 48133, 48157, 48179, 48166, 48145
Delivery Method: Mail, Newsstand, Carrier, RacksEquipment & Software: BUSINESS EQUIPMENT: PC Based BUSINESS SOFTWARE: Microsoft Dynamics DTI CLASSIFIED EQUIPMENT: Hardware — PC Based; CLASSIFIED SOFTWARE: Vision Data DISPLAY EQUIPMENT: Hardware — Macintosh Based; Printers — Xante/Accel-a-Writer, X/Phaser 1235; DISPLAY SOFTWAREAd Make-up Applications — Adobe Indesign; EDITORIAL EQUIPMENT: Hardware — PC Based; Printers — Newscycle Solutions PRODUCTION EQUIPMENT: Hardware — PC Based; Cameras — LE; Scanners — Kk, Microtek/ScanMaker II, PRODUCTION SOFTWARE: Adobe Indesign

MUSKEGON

THE MUSKEGON CHRONICLE

379 W Western Ave Ste 100, Suite 100, Muskegon, Mich., 49440-1265, Muskegon; gen tel (231) 722-3161; adv tel (800) 446-5588; gen/nat adv e-mail advertise@mlive.com; disp adv e-mail advertise@Mlive.com; class adv e-mailadvertise@mlive.com; ed e-mail munews@mlive.com; web site www.mlive.com/muskegon
Group: Advance Publications, Inc.
Published: Mon, Tues, Wed, Thur, Fri, Sat, Sun
Weekday Frequency: e
Saturday Frequency: m
Circulation: 19,654; 1,895(sat); 23,663(sun)
Last Audit: AAM December 31, 2016
Advertising Rate (weekday/saturday): Open inch rate $19.09
Advertising Rate (sunday): Open inch rate $24.82
News services: AP, NYT, SHNS, NNS, TMS. **Established:** 1857
Special Editions: Spring Sports (Apr); Football (Aug); Winter Sports (Dec); Home Show (Feb); Living Here (Jan); Personal Safety (Jul); Senior Lifestyles (Jun); Today's Living (Mar); Pet Care (May); Home for the Holidays (Nov); Full Cruisin' (Oct); Parade of Homes (Sept).
Special Weekly Sections: Church Pages (Fri); Best Food Day (Mon); Stock Market (S); Kids Pages (Sat); Venture Outdoors (Thur); Wheels (Wed).
Syndicated Publications: Parade (S).
Digital Platform - Mobile: Apple, Android, Windows, Blackberry
Digital Platform - Tablet: Apple iOS, Android, Kindle
Pres. .... Dan Gaydou
Sr. Dir. for National Accounts .... Steve Westphal
Dir. of Adv. Operations .... Bob White
Chief Revenue Officer .... Charity Plaxton
VP of Sales .... Michael Assink
Sr. Platform Dir. .... Colleen Huff
Dir. of Real Estate & Careers Sales Andy Boldryeff
VP of Content .... John Hiner
Dir. of Sports News .... Bill Emkow
Sr. Dir. for Journalism and Engagement Kelly Frick
Sr. Dir. for Digital Culture and Innovation . Colleen Stone
Exec. Ed. of Print .... Paul Keep
Dir. of Automotive Sales .... Khalida Cook
Small Business Dir. .... Andrea Sipka
Sr. Strategy Dir. .... Nick Dionne
Sr. Retail Dir. .... Brett Christie
Regional Sales Director of Detroit & Ann Arbor ..... Christy Keizer
Regional Sales Dir. of Flint, Saginaw and Bay City Robert Graham
Regional Sales Dir. of Grand Rapids & Muskegon . Jamie Dionne
Gen. Mgr. .... Laurel Champion
Agency Relations Dir. .... Jeff Leitch
Adv. Support Dir. .... Andrea Miller
Dir. of News .... Marjory Raymer
Dir. of Community Engagement .... Jen Eyer
Market Information: TMC; Zoned editions.
Mechanical Available: Offset; Black and 3 ROP colors; insert accepted - spadea; page cutoffs - 21.
Mechanical Specifications: Type page 10 7/8 x 19 1/2; E - 6 cols, 1 23/32, 3/32 between; A - 6 cols, 1 23/32, 3/32 between; C - 10 cols, 1 1/16, 1/32 between.
Areas Served: 49441 49442 49445 49444 49461 49456 49457 49417 49437 49415 49412 49451 49421 49455 49425 49420 49446 49448 49440 49452 49431 49436 49327 49449
Delivery Method: Mail, Newsstand, Carrier, RacksEquipment & Software: PRESSROOM EQUIPMENT: Lines — MAN/Geoman (64 couples); Press Drive — Baumueller; Folders — 2-MAN; Pasters —12-MAN; Reels & Stands — 12-MAN; Control System — MAN; Registration System — Graphic Control. MAILROOM EQUIPMENT: Counter Stackers — 10-QWI/500; Inserters & Stuffers — 3-GMA/SLS 3000 (30:2); Tying Machines — 13/Dynaric; Wrapping Singles — 5-Dynaric/Single tyer; Control System — GMA/SAM; Address Machine — 2-Ch/Labeler; BUSINESS EQUIPMENT: Apple Xserve Dell servers HP servers Hitachi HDS BUSINESS SOFTWARE: DTI CircView RouteSmart VMware 4-5 CLASSIFIED EQUIPMENT: Hardware — Dell & HP PCs; Dell & HP PCs; Printers — HP, Canon, IKON; CLASSIFIED SOFTWARE: Atex Mactive 3.0 Encompass Office 2010 DISPLAY EQUIPMENT: Hardware — LCDs, Macs, PCs; Printers — Canon, IKON; DISPLAY SOFTWAREAd Make-up Applications — InDesign Xpance; Layout Software — InDesign PPI ATEX PageLayout Xpance EDITORIAL EQUIPMENT: Hardware — Dell & HP PCs; Printers — HP, Ikon, Canon EDITORIAL SOFTWARE: Media Span Baseview, Adobe InDesign/InCopy PRODUCTION EQUIPMENT: Hardware — Epson Canon; Scanners — Epson Canon PRODUCTION SOFTWARE: PPI AGFA IntelliTune Adobe Illustrator Adobe InDesign Adobe Flash Adobe Photoshop Xpance ATEX Mactive PageLayout ZenDesk.

NILES

DOWAGIAC DAILY NEWS

217 N 4th St, Niles, Mich., 49120-2301, Berrien; gen tel 269-683-2100; ed tel (269) 687-7706; gen fax (269) 687-2175; ed fax (269) 683-2175; gen/nat adv e-mail ambrosia.neldon@leaderpub.com; disp adv e-mail phil.langer@leaderpub.com; class adv e-maildonna.knight@leaderpub.com; ed e-mail ambrosia.neldon@leaderpub.com; web site www.leaderpub.com
- 450,000(views) 48,000(visitors)
Group: Boone Newspapers, Inc.
Published: Mon, Tues, Wed, Thur, Fri
Weekday Frequency: m
Circulation: 1,386
Last Audit: Sworn/Estimate/Non-Audited September 30, 2017
News services: **Established:** 1886
Own Printing Facility?: Yes
Commercial Printers?: Yes
Digital Platform - Mobile: Apple, Android
Digital Platform - Tablet: Apple iOS, Android, Blackberry Tablet OS, Kindle
Community Ed. .... Ted Yoakum
Market Information: Home delivered saturation shopper; Zoned editions.
Mechanical Available: Offset; Black and 3 ROP colors; insert accepted - all; page cutoffs - 14".
Mechanical Specifications: Type page 9.75 x 14; E - 6 cols

Areas Served: 49120-49121-49047
Delivery Method: Mail, Newsstand, RacksEquipment & Software: PRESSROOM EQUIPMENT: Lines — 10-KP/News King single width.; CLASSIFIED EQUIPMENT: Hardware — APP/Mac; Printers — HP/4MV; CLASSIFIED SOFTWARE: Baseview. DISPLAY EQUIPMENT: Hardware — APP/Mac; DISPLAY SOFTWAREAd Make-up Applications — DTI/AdSpeed; Layout Software — InDesign EDITORIAL EQUIPMENT: Hardware — APP/Mac; Printers — HP/4MV EDITORIAL SOFTWARE: InDesign PRODUCTION EQUIPMENT: Hardware — QPS/QuarkXPress. CIRCULATION SOFTWARPBS
Note: For detailed production information, see the Niles Daily Star listing.

NILES DAILY STAR

217 N 4th St, Niles, Mich., 49120-2301, Berrien; gen tel (269) 683-2100; adv tel (269) 687-7700; ed tel (269) 687-7720; gen fax (269) 683-2175; adv fax (269) 683-2175; ed fax (269) 683-2175; gen/nat adv e-mail mike.caldwell@leaderpub.com; disp adv e-mail mike.caldwell@leaderpub.com; class adv e-maildonna.knight@leaderpub.com; ed e-mail ambrosia.neldon@leaderpub.com; web site www.leaderpub.com
- 450,000(views) 48,000(visitors)
Group: Boone Newspapers, Inc.
Published: Mon, Tues, Wed, Thur, Fri
Weekday Frequency: m
Circulation: 1,531
Last Audit: Sworn/Estimate/Non-Audited September 30, 2017
Newspaper Reps:
Advertising Rate (weekday/saturday): Open inch rate $5.00
Online Advertising Rate: Starting at $8.00 CPM
News services: 1867
Own Printing Facility?: Yes
Commercial Printers?: Yes
Special Editions: College Choices (Jan); Progress (Feb); Summer Fun (May); Home Improvement (Mar & Sep); Best of the Best (Apr); Answer Book (June)
Special Weekly Sections: Off The Water (A&E)
Syndicated Publications:
Digital Platform - Mobile: Apple, Android
Digital Platform - Tablet: Apple iOS, Android, Windows 7, Blackberry Tablet OS, Kindle, Nook, Kindle Fire
Pub........................................Michael Bennett
Sports Ed. .... Scott Novak
Community Editor ....Craig Haupert
Market Information: Home Delivered saturation shopper; Zoned editions.
Mechanical Available: Offset; Black and 3 ROP colors; insert accepted - all; page cutoffs - 14".
Mechanical Specifications: Tab page 9.75 x 14; E - 6 cols
Areas Served: 49120-49121
Delivery Method: Mail, Newsstand, RacksEquipment & Software: PRESSROOM EQUIPMENT: Lines — 10-KP/News King single width; MAILROOM EQUIPMENT: Counter Stackers — 1-BG/Count-O-Veyor 108; Inserters & Stuffers — MM/3 Station; Tying Machines — 3/Bu, 1-/Sa, 1-/MLN; Address Machine — Dispensa-Matic.; BUSINESS EQUIPMENT: 1-IBM/5364-PC Sys 36, 2-IBM/5150, 2-RSK/1000TL2 CLASSIFIED EQUIPMENT: Hardware — APP/Mac; CLASSIFIED SOFTWARE: Baseview. DISPLAY EQUIPMENT: Apple DISPLAY SOFTWAREPBS EDITORIAL EQUIPMENT: Apple EDITORIAL SOFTWARE: InDesign PRODUCTION EQUIPMENT: Apple PRODUCTION SOFTWARE: InDesign CIRCULATION EQUIPMENT: Apple CIRCULATION SOFTWARPBS

OWOSSO

THE ARGUS-PRESS

201 E Exchange St, Owosso, Mich., 48867-3009, Shiawassee; gen tel (989) 725-5136; adv tel (989) 725-5136; ed tel (989) 725-5136; gen fax (989) 725-6376; adv fax (989) 725-6376; ed fax (989) 725-6376; gen/nat adv e-mail ccampbell@argus-press.com; disp adv e-mail ccampbell@argus-press.com; class adv e-mailbwotring@argus-press.com; ed e-mail drbasso@argus-press.com; web site www.argus-press.com
- 399,100(views) 229,806(visitors)
Published: Mon, Tues, Wed, Thur, Fri, Sat, Sun
Weekday Frequency: e
Saturday Frequency: m
Circulation: 7,150; 7,150(sat); 7,150(sun)
Last Audit: Sworn/Estimate/Non-Audited September 30, 2017
Advertising Rate (weekday/saturday): Open inch rate $17.00
Advertising Rate (sunday): Open inch rate $17.00
News services: AP **Established:** 1854
Own Printing Facility?: Yes
Commercial Printers?: Yes
Special Editions: Baby Faces (Jan.); Agriculture (Mar.); Social Security (Spring / Fall); Car Care (Fall); Football Preview (August); Best of Shiawassee (Annually); Christmas Gift Guide (Nov).
Syndicated Publications: Color Comics (S)
Proprietary Publications: Home Buyers' Guide
Digital Platform - Mobile: Apple, Android
Digital Platform - Tablet: Apple iOS, Android
Pub....................................Thomas E. Campbell
Adv. Dir............................. Catherine Campbell
Circ. Mgr...Kirk Tobey
Managing Ed. ....Dan Basso
Sports Ed. ....Ryan Weiss
Weekend Ed. ....Tim Rath
Market Information: TMC.
Mechanical Available: Offset; Black and 3 ROP colors; insert accepted - subject to approval; page cutoffs - 21 1/2.
Mechanical Specifications: Type page 13 x 21 1/2; E - 6 cols, 2 1/16, 1/8 between; A - 6 cols, 2 1/16, 1/8 between; C - 9 cols, 1 3/8, 1/16 between.
Areas Served: 48414, 48418, 48817, 48429, 48841, 48848, 48449, 48857, 48460, 48867, 48872, 48882, 48476, 48616, 48649, 48831, 48866, 48879, 48436, 48473, 48807
Delivery Method: Mail, Newsstand, Carrier, RacksEquipment & Software: PRESSROOM EQUIPMENT: Lines — 5-G/Urbanite 1964.; PRESSROOM SOFTWARE: NewsXtreme MAILROOM EQUIPMENT: Tying Machines — EAM-Mosca; Inserting Machines — Kansa BUSINESS EQUIPMENT: Acer/PC BUSINESS SOFTWARE: Quickbooks CLASSIFIED EQUIPMENT: Hardware — APP/iMac; CLASSIFIED SOFTWARE: Baseview/Ad Manager Pro. EDITORIAL EQUIPMENT: Hardware — APP/iMac/Mac Pro/; Printers — HP/701 EDITORIAL SOFTWARE: InDesign Creative Cloud PRODUCTION EQUIPMENT: Hardware — ECRM/Mako News; Inca 70

PETOSKEY

PETOSKEY NEWS-REVIEW

319 State St, Petoskey, Mich., 49770-2746, Emmet; gen tel (231) 347-2544; adv tel (231) 439-9329; ed tel (231) 439-9302; gen fax (231) 347-6833; adv fax (231) 347-0669; ed fax (231) 347-5461; gen/nat adv e-mail clyons@petoskeynews.com; disp adv e-mail clyons@petoskeynews.com; class adv e-mailhaugust@petoskeynews.com; ed e-mail petoskeynews@petoskeynews.com; web site www.petoskeynews.com
Group: Schurz Communications Inc
Published: Mon, Tues, Wed, Thur, Fri
Weekday Frequency: e
Circulation: 8,994
Last Audit: Sworn/Estimate/Non-Audited September 30, 2017
Advertising Rate (weekday/saturday): Open inch rate $20.50
Online Advertising Rate: 5 lines 1-2 days for $25.00; 5 lines 3 days for $30.00
News services: AP, U.S. Suburban Press Inc. **Established:** 1875
Special Editions: Summer Guide (Apr); Football Preview (Aug); Christmas Time Memories (Dec); Parenting Awareness (Feb); East Jordan Snow Blast (Jan); Petoskey Sidewalk Sales (Jul); Welcome Back Resorters (Jun); Your Home (Mar); Dining Guide (May); Homes (Monthly); Winter Guide
Special Weekly Sections: Real Estate (Fri); Food (Mon); NASCAR (Thur); Health (Tues); Outdoor (Wed).
Syndicated Publications: Parade (Fri).
Digital Platform - Mobile: Apple, Android
Digital Platform - Tablet: Apple iOS, Android
Adv. Dir........................................Christy Lyons
Goodlife Ed. ....Debbie McGuiness
CFO..Larry Hensley
Classifieds....................................Hilary August
Pres./Pub......................................Doug Caldwell
Asst. Ed. ....Craig Currier
Exec. Sports Ed. ....Jeremy Speer
Exec. Ed. ....Jeremy McBain
Market Information: ADS; TMC.
Mechanical Available: Offset; Black and 3 ROP colors; insert accepted - one page flyers, catalog size; page cutoffs - 22 3/4.
Mechanical Specifications: Type page 11 5/8 x 21 1/2; E - 6 cols, 1 5/6, 1/8 between; A - 6 cols, 1 5/6, 1/8 between; C - 6 cols, 1 5/6, 1/8 between.
Areas Served: 49770
Delivery Method: Mail, CarrierEquipment & Software: PRESSROOM EQUIPMENT: Lines — 8-G/Community single width, 2-DGM/4 Highs 2000; G 2000; Folders — 1-G/SSC.; MAILROOM EQUIPMENT: Counter Stackers — BG/205; Tying Machines — 1/Bu, 2-Mosca/Strapper.; BUSINESS EQUIPMENT: DEC/1000A 4-233 Alpha Server BUSINESS SOFTWARE: PBS CLASSIFIED EQUIPMENT: Hardware — APP/Mac; Printers — ECR/VRL 36HS; CLASSIFIED SOFTWARE: Baseview/Ad Manager Pro. DISPLAY EQUIPMENT: Hardware — APP/Mac; Printers — APP/Mac LaserWriter 8500, ECR/VRL 36HS Scriptsetter; DISPLAY SOFTWAREAd Make-up Applications — QPS/QuarkXPress; Layout Software — Adobe/InDesign CSI. EDITORIAL EQUIPMENT: Hardware — APP/Mac; Printers — APP/Mac 8500, ECR/VRL 36HS EDITORIAL SOFTWARE: Adobe/InDesign CSI, Baseview/NewsEdit Pro. PRODUCTION EQUIPMENT: Hardware — ECR/VRL 36HS Scriptsetter, Panther/Pro 62; Scanners — Mycro-Tek/9900XL PRODUCTION SOFTWARE: Adobe/InDesign CSI.

PONTIAC

THE OAKLAND PRESS

48 W Huron St, Pontiac, Mich., 48342-2101, Oakland; gen tel (248) 332-8181; adv tel (248) 745-4595; ed tel (248) 745-4587; gen fax (248) 332-8885; adv fax (248) 332-1657; ed fax (248) 332-8885; gen/nat adv e-mail tgoodrich@digitalfirstmedia.com; disp adv e-mail lrao-cheney@digitalfirstmedia.com; class adv e-mailnoelle.klomp@oakpress.com; ed e-mail glenn.gilbert@oakpress.com; web site www.theoaklandpress.com
- 2,000,000(views) 157,467(visitors)
Group: Digital First Media
Published: Mon, Tues, Wed, Thur, Fri, Sat, Sun
Weekday Frequency: m
Saturday Frequency: m
Circulation: 20,903; 21,865(sat); 29,910(sun)
Last Audit: AAM September 30, 2014
Advertising Rate (weekday/saturday): Open inch rate $80.00; $82.00 (Thur)
Advertising Rate (sunday): Open inch rate $90.00
Online Advertising Rate: Broadsheet sizes $52.00 full page; $38.00 1/4 to full page; $22.00 up to 1/4 page
News services: AP, LAT-WP, SHNS, NYT, TMS. **Established:** 1844
Own Printing Facility?: Yes
Commercial Printers?: Yes
Special Editions: Religious Directory (Apr); Salute to Business (Aug); Tis the Season (Dec); Senior Living (Feb); No Ordinary Sale (Jan); Concours d'Elegance (Jul); Senior Living (Jun); Spring Home & Garden/Cobo (Mar); MI Vacation Guide (May); Lagniappe (Nov); College Guid
Special Weekly Sections: Marquee Entertainment Tab (Fri); Food (Mon); Real Estate (S); Building (Sat); Health (Thur); Youth & Teen (Tues); Real Estate (Wed).
Syndicated Publications: Parade (S).
Digital Platform - Mobile: Apple, Android
Digital Platform - Tablet: Apple iOS, Android, Windows 7
Pub...Jeannie Parent
Rgl VP, Sales..........................Teresa Goodrich
Circ. Mgr. .... Dwight Major
Local News Ed................. Julie Jacobson-Hines
Digital Dir. ....Angel Offredi
Metro Ed. ....Lee Dryden
Classifieds Dir.................................Noelle Klomp
Promotions Mgr. .... Joe Hildebrand
VP, News...Don Wyatt
Ent. Ed..................................Nicole Robertson
News Ed...Matt Myftiu
Business Ed................................... Kathy Blake
Online Ed. ....Stephen Frye
Community Engagement Ed........... Monica Drake
Photo Ed. ....Tim Thompson
Sports Ed. .... Jeff Keuhn
Market Information: ADS; Split run; TMC; Zoned editions.
Mechanical Available: Headliner Offset; Black and 3 ROP colors; insert accepted - 7 hm books; page cutoffs - 22 1/4.
Mechanical Specifications: Type page 13 1/4 x 21; E - 6 cols, 1 3/4, 1/8 between; A - 6 cols, 1 3/4, between; C - 10 cols, 1 3/16, 1/8 between.
Areas Served: 48430, 48442, 48350, 48462, 48348, 48346, 48371, 48362, 48360, 48359, 48370, 48267, 48366, 48363, 48306, 48307, 48309, 48326, 48346, 48342, 48341, 48328, 48329, 48327, 48386, 48383, 48356, 48357, 48380, 48381, 48382, 48390, 48326, 48324, 48323, 48322, 48302, 48304, 48301, 48009, 48098, 48084, 48083, 48017, 48071, 48067, 48030, 48229, 48237, 48070, 48072, 48076, 48075, 48025, 48034, 48336, 48334, 48331, 48335, 48375, 48377, 48393, 48165, 48178, 48374, 48167
Delivery Method: Mail, CarrierEquipment & Software: PRESSROOM EQUIPMENT: Lines — 10-G/Headliner Offset double width; Folders — 1-G/3:2; Reels & Stands — 10-Reels & Stands/Stands; Control System — G/MPCS.; MAILROOM EQUIPMENT: Counter Stackers — 3-QWI/300, 1-Id/2000; Inserters & Stuffers — 1/AM Graphics/NP 630, 24-/Hopper; Tying Machines — 6-/NP2, Dynarics; Control System — Burt Technologies.; BUSINESS EQUIPMENT: IBM/J50 RISC 6000, 1-IBM/590 RISC 6000 BUSINESS SOFTWARE: PBS/MediaPlus 3.0, Word Processing, PBS 3.0, SBS 3.0 CLASSIFIED EQUIPMENT: Hardware — Pentium/PC-100, Pentium/II, Gateway, Compaq, Microsoft/Windows NT; CLASSIFIED SOFTWARE: CompuClass/Computext. DISPLAY EQUIPMENT: Hardware — IBM/J50-RISC6000, APP/Mac G3, Radius/ZOE Monitor; Printers — 1-APP/Mac II NTX; DISPLAY SOFTWAREAd Make-up Applications — Managing Editor/ALS 2.0; Layout Software — Mk/Managing Editor. EDITORIAL EQUIPMENT: Hardware — 2-APP/Mac 9500, Main/Back-up Server/1-APP/Mac 950 with Wire Manager, 1-APP/Mac 6100; Printers — 10-HP/DeskWriters EDITORIAL SOFTWARE: Baseview/Client Server 2.2. PRODUCTION EQUIPMENT: Hardware — 2-ECR/3850, 3-XIT/Clipper Plain Paper 11 x 17, Aii/3850 Imagesetter; Cameras — C/Spartan III; Scanners — AG/Flatbed Scanner, Kk/Transparency Film Scanner PRODUCTION SOFTWARE: QPS/QuarkXPress, AU, AU/OMAN OPI.

PORT HURON

TIMES HERALD

911 Military St, Fl 2, Port Huron, Mich., 48060-5414, Saint Clair; gen tel (810) 985-7171; adv tel (810) 985-7171; ed tel (810) 989-6257; gen fax (810) 989-6262; adv fax (810) 989-6262; ed fax (810) 989-6294; gen/nat adv e-mail lgougeon@michigan.com; web site www.thetimesherald.com
- 2,844,001(views) 311,620(visitors)
Group: Gannett
Published: Mon, Tues, Wed, Thur, Fri, Sat, Sun
Weekday Frequency: m
Saturday Frequency: m
Circulation: 12,685; 14,460(sat); 20,136(sun)
Last Audit: AAM September 30, 2016
Advertising Rate (weekday/saturday): Open inch rate $43.30
Advertising Rate (sunday): Open inch rate $67.20
Online Advertising Rate: Starting from $21.00

CPM
News services: AP, GNS and Thinkstock
Established: 1869
Own Printing Facility?: No
Commercial Printers?: No
Special Editions: Savvy (Bi-Monthly); Bridal (January); Cars.com (Qtrly); Woman's Day Expo (February); In Bloom (March); Golf (April); Blue Water Summer Guide (May); Menu Guide (May); Graduation (May); Mackinac (July); Football (August); Season s End (September); Election Guide (October); Blue Water Winter Guide (October); Business Expo (November).
Special Weekly Sections: Manufacturers' Coupons (M-S) Spin Magazine (Thur); Outdoors Column (Fri); Religion (Sat); Real Estate/Classified Section (S); Full Color Comics (S); TV listings(S); Wedding Announcements (S); Engagements/ Anniversaries (S); The Mix (S); Automotive Listings (S).
Digital Platform - Mobile: Apple, Android, Windows
Digital Platform - Tablet: Apple iOS, Android
Ed. .... Michael Eckert
Office Mgr. .... Michelle Brown
HR Dir. .... Cheryl Richardson
Adv. Mgr. .... Lori Gougeon
Reg. Controller .... David Davies
Local Content Ed. .... Liz Shepard
Pres. .... Rebecca Poynter
Distribution Manager .... Mike Doucette
Market Information: ADS; Split run; TMC.
Mechanical Available: Offset; Black and 3 ROP colors; insert accepted; page cutoffs - 22 3/4.
Mechanical Specifications: Type page 10 x 21.5; E - 6 cols, 1.583, 0.069 between; A - 6 cols, 1.583, 0.069 between; C - 9 cols, 1.063, 0.069 between.
Areas Served: St. Clair County
Delivery Method: Mail, Newsstand, CarrierEquipment & Software: CLASSIFIED SOFTWARE: APT. EDITORIAL SOFTWARE: APT.

SAGINAW

THE SAGINAW NEWS

100 S Michigan Ave Ste 3, Suite 3, Saginaw, Mich., 48602-2054, Saginaw; gen tel (989) 752-7171; adv tel (800) 446-5588; gen/nat adv e-mail advertise@mlive.com; disp adv e-mail advertise@mlive.com; class adv e-mailadvertise@mlive.com; ed e-mail sanews@mlive.com; web site www.mlive.com/saginaw
Group: Advance Publications, Inc.
Published: Mon, Tues, Wed, Thur, Fri, Sat, Sun
Weekday Frequency: m
Circulation: 14,368; 22,640(sun)
Last Audit: AAM December 31, 2016
Advertising Rate (weekday/saturday): Open inch rate $27.99
Advertising Rate (sunday): Open inch rate $36.38
News services: Metro Suburbia Inc./Newhouse Newspapers, NNA, AP. **Established:** 1859
Special Editions: Garden Pages (Apr); Frankenmuth Music Fest (Aug); NASCAR Tab (Feb); Shiver on the River (Jan); Golf Pages (Jul); Garden Pages (Jun); HBA (Mar); Garden Pages (May); Holiday Gift Catalogue (Nov); Fall Parade of Homes (Oct); Frankenmuth Octoberfest (Sept).
Special Weekly Sections: Dining & Entertainment Guide (Fri); Agriculture (Mon); Color Comics (S); Religion (Sat); Venture Outdoors (Thur); Family/Living (Tues); At Home/Living (Wed).
Syndicated Publications: Parade (S).
Digital Platform - Mobile: Apple, Android, Windows, Blackberry
Pres. .... Dan Gaydou
Dir. of Adv. Operations .... Bob White
VP of Sales .... Charity Plaxton
VP of Sales .... Michael Assink
Sr. Platform Dir. .... Colleen Huff
VP of Content .... John Hiner
Dir. of Sports News .... Bill Emkow
Sr. Dir. for Journalism and Engagement Kelly Frick
Sr. Dir. for Digital Culture and Innovation . Colleen Stone
Exec. Ed. of Print .... Paul Keep
Automotive Dir. .... Khalida Cook
Sr. Strategy Dir. .... Nick Dionne
Sr. Retail Dir. .... Brett Christie
Senior Dir. for National Accounts . Steve Westphal
Dir. of Real Estate & Careers Sales Andy Boldryeff
Regional Sales Dir. of Detroit & Ann Arbor. Christy Keizer
Regional Sales Dir. of Flint, Saginaw and Bay City Robert Graham
Regional Sales Dir. of Grand Rapids & Muskegon Jamie Dionne
Gen. Mgr. .... Laurel Champion
Adv. Support Dir. .... Andrea Sipka
Dir. of News .... Marjory Raymer
Dir. of Community Engagement .... Jen Eyer
Market Information: TMC.
Mechanical Available: Letterpress (direct), other; Black and 3 ROP colors; insert accepted; page cutoffs - 23 9/16.
Mechanical Specifications: Type page 13 x 22 1/4; E - 6 cols, 2 1/16, 1/8 between; A - 6 cols, 2 1/16, 1/8 between; C - 10 cols, 1 1/4, 1/16 between.
Areas Served: 48655 through 48880
Delivery Method: Mail, Newsstand, Carrier, RacksEquipment & Software: PRESSROOM EQUIPMENT: Lines — 8-G/Mark I double width; MAILROOM EQUIPMENT: Counter Stackers — 4/QWI; Inserters & Stuffers — 2-S/9-48P single, 1-GMA/SLS 2000; Tying Machines — 2-/Sterling; Address Machine — 4-/Wm.; BUSINESS EQUIPMENT: 1-PBS/ Media Plus, 1-SBS/Xponet CLASSIFIED EQUIPMENT: Hardware — AT; 13-AT.; DISPLAY EQUIPMENT: Hardware — Power Computing 200; Printers — HP/4M, ColorPASS C700; Other Hardware — 3-AT DISPLAY SOFTWAREAd Make-up Applications — QPS/QuarkXPress 4.11, Multi-Ad/Creator 4.02; Layout Software — APP/Mac G4 400, APP/Mac G3 233, MEI/ALS 4.0. EDITORIAL EQUIPMENT: Hardware — 50-APP/Mac G4 400/39-AT; Printers — HP/4000, HP/5000, Xante/Accel-a-Writer 3G, ColorPass C700 EDITORIAL SOFTWARE: Baseview/NewsEdit Pro IQue 3.23, QPS/QuarkXPress 4.11. PRODUCTION EQUIPMENT: Hardware — 2-Cx/Bitsetter, 1-AU/APS-PSP2 with A156, 1-AU/APS Grafix RIP with 3850; Cameras — 1-C/NewsPager I; Scanners — AG/Desk Top PRODUCTION SOFTWARE: QPS/ QuarkXPress 4.11.

SAINT JOSEPH

THE HERALD-PALLADIUM

3450 Hollywood Rd, Saint Joseph, Mich., 49085-9155, Berrien; gen tel (269) 429-2400; adv tel (269) 429-2400; ed tel (269) 429-4298; gen fax (269) 429-7661; adv fax (269) 429-7661; ed fax (269) 429-4398; gen/nat adv e-mail advertising@theh-p.com; disp adv e-mail advertising@theh-p.com; class adv e-mailclassifieds@theh-p.com; ed e-mail dbrown@theh-p.com; web site www.theh-p.com; web site 2 www.heraldpalladium.com
Group: Paxton Media Group, LLC
Published: Mon, Tues, Wed, Thur, Fri, Sat, Sun
Weekday Frequency: m
Saturday Frequency: m
Circulation: 11,659; 11,659(sat); 14,391(sun)
Last Audit: AAM March 31, 2014
Advertising Rate (weekday/saturday): Open inch rate $31.50
Advertising Rate (sunday): Open inch rate $33.00
News services: AP, NEA, SHNS, LAT-WP. **Established:** 1868
Own Printing Facility?: Yes
Commercial Printers?: Yes
Special Editions: Tour Guide (Apr); Berrien County Youth Fair (Aug); Basketball Preview (Dec); Spring Brides (Feb); Glad-Peach Festival (Jul); Golden Years (Jun); Spring Car Care (Mar); Graduation Tab (May); Living in the Southwest (Monthly); Holiday Recipe/ Craft Guide (No
Special Weekly Sections: Weekend Entertainment (Thur).
Syndicated Publications: USA WEEKEND Magazine (Sat).
Digital Platform - Mobile: Apple, Android
Digital Platform - Tablet: Apple iOS, Android
Pub. .... David Holgate
Controller .... Robert Estes
Managing Ed. .... Dave Brown
News Ed. .... Steve Jewell
Editorial Page Ed. .... Dale Brewer
Features Ed. .... Katie Krawczak
Sports Ed. .... Jason Mitchell
Photo Ed. .... Don Campbell
Asst. Local News Ed. .... Jim Dalgleish
Circ. Dir. .... Julie Simpleman
Market Information: TMC.
Mechanical Available: Offset; Black and 3 ROP colors; insert accepted; page cutoffs - 22 3/4.
Mechanical Specifications: Type page 13 x 21 1/2; E - 6 cols, 2 1/16, 1/8 between; A - 6 cols, 2 1/16, 1/8 between; C - 9 cols, 1 15/16, 1/8 between.
Areas Served: Southwest Michigan: Berrien, Cass, Van Buren, and Allegan
Delivery Method: Mail, Newsstand, Carrier, RacksEquipment & Software: PRESSROOM EQUIPMENT: Lines — 4-G/Cosmo double width 1978, 2-1990; Pasters —4-G/Automatic. MAILROOM EQUIPMENT: Counter Stackers — 1-Id/NS440, 2-Id/Marathoner; Inserters & Stuffers — 2-Mc/660; Tying Machines — 2-Dynaric/NP2.; BUSINESS EQUIPMENT: 2-HP/9000 BUSINESS SOFTWARE: Baseview CLASSIFIED EQUIPMENT: Hardware — APP/Mac; CLASSIFIED SOFTWARE: Baseview/ClassFlow 2.0. DISPLAY EQUIPMENT: Hardware — APP/ Mac; DISPLAY SOFTWAREAd Make-up Applications — Multi-Ad/Creator 3.8, QPS/QuarkXPress 3.32; EDITORIAL EQUIPMENT: Hardware — APP/Mac/1-APP/ Mac IIci, 4-TM, 9-RSK, 5-Falcon, APP/Mac Quadra 800 EDITORIAL SOFTWARE: QPS/ QuarkXPress, Baseview/NewsEdit IQUE 3.02. PRODUCTION EQUIPMENT: Hardware — 1-Nu/Flip Top FT40, 1-SCREEN/LD281Q, 1-V/1200; Cameras — 1-C/Spartan II.

SAULT SAINTE MARIE

SAULT STE. MARIE EVENING NEWS

109 Arlington St, Sault Sainte Marie, Mich., 49783-1901, Chippewa; gen tel (906) 632-2235; adv tel (906) 632-2235; ed tel (906) 632-2235; gen fax (906) 632-1222; adv fax (906) 632-1222; ed fax (906) 632-1222; gen/nat adv e-mail kmills@sooeveningnews.com; disp adv e-mail kmills@sooeveningnews.com; class adv e-mailcfritz@sooeveningnews.com; ed e-mail brigotti@sooeveningnews.com; web site www.sooeveningnews.com
Group: New Media Investment Group
Published: Mon, Tues, Wed, Thur, Fri, Sat
Weekday Frequency: m
Saturday Frequency: m
Circulation: 3,772; 3,772(sat)
Last Audit: Sworn/Estimate/Non-Audited September 30, 2017
Advertising Rate (weekday/saturday): Open inch rate $17.92
Advertising Rate (sunday): Open inch rate $19.23
News services: AP. **Established:** 1903
Own Printing Facility?: Yes
Commercial Printers?: Yes
Special Editions: Fall Sports (Aug); Christmas (Dec); Graduation (Jun); Vacation Guide (May); Christmas (Nov).
Special Weekly Sections: TV Listing (Fri); Health (Mon); People (Tue); Arts/Entertainment (Thur); Education (Fri); Business, Religion (Sun)
Syndicated Publications: American Profile (Weekly).
Digital Platform - Mobile: Apple, Android
Digital Platform - Tablet: Apple iOS, Android
Ed. .... Richard Crofton
Composing Mgr. .... Dave Brey
Sports Ed. .... Rob Roos
Sunday Ed. .... Brenda Rigotti
Sales Manager .... Karlene Mills
Circulation Manager .... Melissa Mansfield
Market Information: TMC.
Mechanical Available: Offset; Black and 3 ROP colors; insert accepted; page cutoffs - 22 3/4.
Mechanical Specifications: Type page 13 x 21; E - 6 cols, 2 1/16, 1/8 between; A - 6 cols, 2 1/16, 1/8 between; C - 9 cols, 1 3/8, 1/16 between.
Areas Served: 49710, 49715, 49717, 49724, 49725, 49726, 49728, 49827, 49780, 49736, 49838, 49748, 49788, 49752, 49757, 49853, 49762, 49868, 49774, 49715, 49785, 49783, 49730, 49790, 49781, 49793
Delivery Method: Mail, Newsstand, CarrierEquipment & Software: PRESSROOM EQUIPMENT: Lines — 7-HI/V-15A; Folders — HI/JF-7.; MAILROOM EQUIPMENT: Tying Machines — 2/MLN; Address Machine — 1-/ Am.; BUSINESS EQUIPMENT: PC Designs CLASSIFIED EQUIPMENT: Hardware - PC Designs.; DISPLAY SOFTWAREAd Make-up Applications — APP/Mac IIsi; Layout Software — PC Designs. EDITORIAL EQUIPMENT: Hardware — APP/Mac. PRODUCTION EQUIPMENT: Hardware — 5-COM; Scanners — 2-COM.

STURGIS

STURGIS JOURNAL

205 E Chicago Rd, Sturgis, Mich., 49091-1753, Saint Joseph; gen tel (269) 651-5407; adv tel (269) 651-5407; ed tel (269) 651-5407; gen fax (269) 651-2296; adv fax (269) 651-2296; ed fax (269) 651-2296; gen/nat adv e-mail lvickers@thedailyreporter.com; disp adv e-mail lvickers@thedailyreporter.com; class adv e-mailclassifieds@sturgisjournal.com; ed e-mail phelps@sturgisjournal.com; web site www.sturgisjournal.com - 379,000(views) 58,000(visitors)
Group: New Media Investment Group
Published: Mon, Tues, Wed, Thur, Fri, Sat
Weekday Frequency: m
Saturday Frequency: m
Circulation: 5,000; 5,500(sat)
Last Audit: Sworn/Estimate/Non-Audited October 1, 2017
Advertising Rate (weekday/saturday): Open inch rate $12.50
Online Advertising Rate: 20 words, five days print and online $30.00
News services: AP. **Established:** 1859
Own Printing Facility?: No
Commercial Printers?: Yes
Special Weekly Sections: Best Food Day (Mon); Church Page (Sat); Dining & Entertainment (Thur).
Syndicated Publications: Shoreline Magazine, TV Times (Saturday); American Profile (Weekly).
Digital Platform - Mobile: Apple, Android, Windows
Digital Platform - Tablet: Apple iOS, Android, Windows 7, Blackberry Tablet OS, Kindle
Bus. Mgr. .... Gwen Donmyer
Ed./Website Mgr. .... Candice Phelps
Feat. Ed. .... Dennis Volkert
Sports Ed. .... Corky Emrick
Prepress Mgr. .... Sandy Mielcarek
Market Information: TMC.
Mechanical Available: Offset; Black and 3 ROP colors; insert accepted; page cutoffs - 21.5"
Mechanical Specifications: Type page 10.25 x 21 1/2; E - 6 column, 1 column=1.593"
Areas Served: 49091, 49028, 49030, 49032, 49040, 49042, 49066, 49072, 49075, 49093, 49089, 49099, 46746
Delivery Method: Mail, Newsstand, Carrier, RacksEquipment & Software: DISPLAY SOFTWARELayout Software — APP/Mac. EDITORIAL EQUIPMENT: Hardware — APP/ Mac.

THREE RIVERS

THREE RIVERS COMMERCIAL-NEWS

124 N Main St, Three Rivers, Mich., 49093-1522, Saint Joseph; gen tel (269) 279-7488; adv tel (269) 279-7488 ext. 20; ed tel (269) 279-7488 ext. 26; gen fax (269) 279-6007; adv fax (269) 279-6007; ed fax (269) 279-6007; gen/nat adv e-mail marnie@threeriversnews.com; disp adv e-mail christina@threeriversnews.com; class adv e-mailclassified@threeriversnews.com; ed e-mail publisher@threeriversnews.com; web site www.threeriversnews.com
Group: Surf New Media
Published: Mon, Tues, Wed, Thur, Fri, Sat
Weekday Frequency: e
Saturday Frequency: m
Circulation: 3,043; 3,043(sat)
Last Audit: Sworn/Estimate/Non-Audited September 30, 2017
Advertising Rate (weekday/saturday): Open inch rate $13.35

News services: AP. **Established:** 1895
Special Editions: 2013 Graduation Keepsake (May); 2013 Bridal Guide (Jan); Spring Car Care (Apr); Football Preview (Aug); Gift Certificate Page (Dec); White Sale (Feb); The Way We Were (Jan); Michigan Medical Society (Jul); The Way We Were (Jun); NCAA Basketball (grid) (Mar); Graduation (May); Gift Guide (Nov).
Special Weekly Sections: Best Food Day, Lifestyles (Mon); Business (Tue); Entertainment (Thur); Seniors (Fri); Real Estate, Church, Farm News (Sat);
Syndicated Publications: American Profile (Weekly).
Digital Platform - Mobile: Apple, Android
Digital Platform - Tablet: Apple iOS, Android
Pub. ....Dirk Milliman
Gen. Mgr. ....Barb England
Managing Ed. ....Elena Hines
Adv. Sales ....Marnie Apa
Sports Ed. ....Scott Hassinger
Classifieds ....Ashley Ware
Circ. ....Kricket Arevalo
Market Information: TMC.
Mechanical Available: Offset; Black and 3 ROP colors; insert accepted - any; page cutoffs - 22 3/4.
Mechanical Specifications: Type page 12 3/4 x 21 1/2; E - 6 cols, 2, 1/6 between; A - 8 cols, 1 1/2, 1/9 between; C - 8 cols, 1 1/2, 1/9 between.
Areas Served: 49032, 49040, 49042, 49061, 49066, 49067, 49072, 49075, 49093, 49087, 49091, 49097, 49099
Delivery Method: Mail, Carrier, RacksEquipment & Software: PRESSROOM EQUIPMENT: Lines — 5-HI/Cotrell V-15A; MAILROOM EQUIPMENT: Tying Machines — 2/Bu; Address Machine — 1-/Am.; BUSINESS EQUIPMENT: Compaq/Deskpro CLASSIFIED EQUIPMENT: Hardware — 1-Mk/1100 Plus.; EDITORIAL EQUIPMENT: Hardware — 3-Mk/1100 Plus, 2-COM EDITORIAL SOFTWARE: Mk/1100. PRODUCTION EQUIPMENT: Hardware — 1-COM/8400, 1-COM/Trendsetter; Cameras — 1-B/Caravelle, 1-Cl.

TRAVERSE CITY

TRAVERSE CITY RECORD-EAGLE

120 W Front St, Traverse City, Mich., 49684-2202, Grand Traverse; gen tel (231) 946-2000; adv tel (231) 933-1465; ed tel (231) 933-1472; gen fax (231) 946-8273; adv fax (231) 946-0340; ed fax (231) 946-8632; gen/nat adv e-mail mzucco@record-eagle.com; disp adv e-mail mzucco@record-eagle.com; class adv e-mailclassifieds@record-eagle.com; ed e-mail mtyree@record-eagle.com; web site www.record-eagle.com - 1,200,000(views) 283,000(visitors)
Group: Community Newspaper Holdings, Inc.
Published: Mon, Tues, Wed, Thur, Fri, Sat, Sun
Weekday Frequency: m
Saturday Frequency: m
Circulation: 16,325; 17,099(sat); 21,737(sun)
Last Audit: AAM December 31, 2015
Advertising Rate (weekday/saturday): Open inch rate $33.10
Advertising Rate (sunday): Open inch rate $41.80
Online Advertising Rate: Homepage Section $350.00 per month (Annual Contract); Other Sections $200.00 per month (Annual Contract)
News services: AP, DJ, ONS, MCT, LAT-WP. **Established:** 1858
Own Printing Facility?: Yes
Commercial Printers?: Yes
Special Editions: Spring Guide (Apr); Autumn Guide (Aug); Holiday Gift Guide (Dec); Winter Home (Jan); Mid Summer Home (Jul); Summer Guide (Jun); Bridal (Mar); Lawn & Garden (May); Coupon Savings (Monthly); Ski Directory (Nov); Autumn Guide (Oct); Wine (Other); Summer Guide (Jun).
Special Weekly Sections: Arts & Entertainment (Fri); Food (Mon); Business (S); Faith (Sat); Our Town (Thur); Education (Tues); Business (Wed).
Syndicated Publications: Parade (S).
Digital Platform - Mobile: Apple, Android, Windows
Digital Platform - Tablet: Apple iOS, Android, Windows 7
Pub. ....Paul Heidbreder
Circ. Dir. ....Rich Roxbury
Advertising Department ....Dan Roach
Mktg. Dir. ....Maia Conway
Editorial Page Ed. ....Dave Miller
Regl. Ed. ....Loraine Anderson
Prodn. Dir. ....Michelle Mulliner
Prodn. Mgr., Mailroom ....Monica Stanley
Single Copy Mgr. ....Jan Burda
Sports Ed. ....Denny Chase
Home Delivery Sales Mgr. ....Chuck Staske
Business Ed ....Dan Nielsen
Features Ed. ....Nathan Payne
Ed. in Chief ....Brian Steele
Associate Ed ....Andy Taylor
Adv. Dir. ....Shawn Winter
Market Information: ADS; TMC.
Mechanical Available: Offset; Black and 3 ROP colors; insert accepted - sample bags, envelopes; page cutoffs - 21.
Mechanical Specifications: Type page 11 3/4 x 21 1/2; E - 6 cols, 1 7/8, 1/8 between; A - 6 cols, 1 7/8, 1/8 between; C - 9 cols, 1 1/5, 1/5 between.
Areas Served: Northern Michigan
Delivery Method: Mail, CarrierEquipment & Software: PRESSROOM EQUIPMENT: Lines — 5-1992.; MAILROOM EQUIPMENT: Counter Stackers — 3/QWI; Inserters & Stuffers — 14-GMA/SLS 1000; Tying Machines — 3-/Power Strap; BUSINESS EQUIPMENT: IBM/AS-400, APP/Mac CLASSIFIED EQUIPMENT: Hardware — Dewar/Sys II; Printers — Okidata/320; CLASSIFIED SOFTWARE: Dewar/Sys II. DISPLAY EQUIPMENT: Hardware — 7-PC P166; Printers — 2-Okidata/320, 3-HP/4MV, 1-HP/5SI MX; DISPLAY SOFTWAREAd Make-up Applications — QPS/QuarkXPress; Layout Software — PCs, QPS/QuarkXPress. EDITORIAL EQUIPMENT: Hardware — 41-PC P133, 2-IBM/RS 6000 Server; Printers — 2-Okidata/320, 3-HP/4MV, 1-HP/5SI MX EDITORIAL SOFTWARE: Microsoft/Windows 95, Microsoft/Word 7.0, Dewar/View, Adobe/Photoshop, QPS/QuarkXPress. PRODUCTION EQUIPMENT: Hardware — Caere/OmniPage Pro, 1-Tegra/Varityper 5510, 2-MON/Imagesetter; Scanners — HP/ScanJet PRODUCTION SOFTWARE: Dewar/View.

MINNESOTA

ALBERT LEA

ALBERT LEA TRIBUNE

808 W Front St, Albert Lea, Minn., 56007-1947, Freeborn; gen tel (507) 373-1411; adv tel (507) 379-3428; ed tel (507) 379-3433; gen fax (507) 373-0333; adv fax (507) 373-0333; ed fax (507) 373-1411; gen/nat adv e-mail catherine.buboltz@albertleatribune.com; disp adv e-mail catherine.buboltz@albertleatribune.com; class adv e-mailmichelle.daveiga@albertleatribune.com; ed e-mail tim.engstrom@albertleatribune.com; web site www.albertleatribune.com
Group: Boone Newspapers, Inc.
Published: Mon, Tues, Wed, Thur, Fri, Sun
Weekday Frequency: e
Circulation: 5,456; 6,415(sun)
Last Audit: Sworn/Estimate/Non-Audited September 30, 2017
Advertising Rate (weekday/saturday): Open inch rate $19.25
Advertising Rate (sunday): Open inch rate $19.25
Online Advertising Rate: 1 day for $7.00; $15.00 CPM (Masthead Sponsor); $12.00 CPM (Leaderboard Banner)
News services: AP. **Established:** 1897
Own Printing Facility?: Yes
Commercial Printers?: Yes
Special Editions: Sports (Apr); Fair (Aug); Progress (Feb); Pork (Jan); Albert Lea Guide (Jun); Health/Wellness (Mar); Wedding (May); Sports (Nov); Car Care (Oct); Seniors (Quarterly).
Special Weekly Sections: Religion (Fri); Lifestyles (S); Entertainment (Wed).
Syndicated Publications: Parade (S); Southern Minnesota Magazine (Quarterly).
Digital Platform - Mobile: Apple, Android, Windows, Blackberry
Digital Platform - Tablet: Apple iOS, Android, Windows 7, Blackberry Tablet OS, Kindle, Nook, Kindle Fire
Pub. ....Crystal Miller
Ed. ....Tim Engstrom
Asst. Ed. ....Sarah Stultz
Adv. Dir. ....Catherine Buboltz
Circ. Rep. ....Melissa Goodwin
Creative Dir. ....Kathy Johnson
Production Dir. ....Terry Thissen
Acct. Mgr. ....Lisa Foley
Mailroom Mgr. ....Rich Mirelli
Sports Ed. ....Micah Bader
Community Ed. ....Colleen Harrison
Special Sections Ed. ....Hannah Dillon
Market Information: ADS; TMC.
Mechanical Available: Offset; Black and 3 ROP colors; insert accepted; page cutoffs - 22 3/4.
Mechanical Specifications: Type page 6 x 21 1/2; E - 6 cols, 2 1/16, 1/8 between; A - 6 cols, 2 1/16, 1/8 between; C - 10 cols, 1 3/8, 1/8 between.
Areas Served: 56007
Delivery Method: Mail, Newsstand, Carrier, RacksEquipment & Software: BUSINESS EQUIPMENT: Macs, Dell BUSINESS SOFTWARE: Quicken, PBS CLASSIFIED EQUIPMENT: Hardware — Mac; Printers — HP; CLASSIFIED SOFTWARE: In Design, Baseview. DISPLAY EQUIPMENT: Hardware — Mac; DISPLAY SOFTWAREAd Make-up Applications — In Design; Layout Software — In Design EDITORIAL EQUIPMENT: Hardware — Mac; Printers — HP Laser EDITORIAL SOFTWARE: In Design PRODUCTION EQUIPMENT: Hardware — Mac, Dell; Cameras — All Cannon; Scanners — DTI

AUSTIN

AUSTIN DAILY HERALD

310 2nd St NE, Austin, Minn., 55912-3436, Mower; gen tel (507) 433-8851; adv tel (507) 434-2220; ed tel (507) 434-2231; gen fax (507) 437-8644; adv fax (507) 437-8644; ed fax (507) 437-8644; gen/nat adv e-mail ben.ankeny@austindailyherald.com; disp adv e-mail ben.ankeny@austindailyherald.com; class adv e-mailclassifieds@austindailyherald.com; ed e-mail newsroom@austindailyherald.com; web site www.austindailyherald.com
Group: Boone Newspapers, Inc.
Published: Mon, Tues, Wed, Thur, Fri, Sun
Weekday Frequency: e
Circulation: 4,200; 5,280(sun)
Last Audit: Sworn/Estimate/Non-Audited September 30, 2017
Advertising Rate (weekday/saturday): Open inch rate $18.50
Advertising Rate (sunday): Open inch rate $18.50
Online Advertising Rate: Starting at $10.00 CPM
News services: AP. **Established:** 1891
Own Printing Facility?: Yes
Commercial Printers?: Yes
Special Editions: Freedom Fest (Jul); Picnic Patrol; Jump Start (2012-2013); Austin Living Magazine (Summer 2013); The Best of Mower County; Wedding Showcase; Discover Summer; Progress 2013; Southern Exposure
Special Weekly Sections: Lifestyles (S).
Syndicated Publications: Relish (Monthly); Parade (S); Southern MN Magazine (Quarterly).
Digital Platform - Mobile: Apple, Android
Digital Platform - Tablet: Apple iOS, Android
Pub. ....Jana Gray
Managing Ed. ....Jason Schoonover
Mktg. Consultant ....Ben Ankeny
Sports Ed. ....Rocky Hulne
Classifieds Sales Consultant ....Sherri Thissen
Home Delivery Mgr. ....Trina Miller
Market Information: Split run; TMC.
Mechanical Available: Offset; Black and 3 ROP colors; insert accepted; page cutoffs - 22 3/4.
Mechanical Specifications: Type page 6 x 21 1/2; E - 6 cols, 2, 1/8 between; A - 6 cols, 2, 1/8 between; C - 9 cols, 2, 1/8 between.
Areas Served: 55912, 55918, 55909, 55917, 55926, 55933, 56007
Delivery Method: Mail, CarrierEquipment & Software: PRESSROOM EQUIPMENT: Lines — 8-G/Community 1976.; MAILROOM EQUIPMENT: Tying Machines — 2-Bu/Tyer.; CLASSIFIED EQUIPMENT: Hardware — 1-APP/Mac; Printers — HP; CLASSIFIED SOFTWARE: Baseview/News Edit Pro. DISPLAY EQUIPMENT: Hardware — APP/Mac; Printers — HP/Imagesetter; DISPLAY SOFTWAREAd Make-up Applications — QPS/QuarkXPress, Adobe/Illustrator, Adobe/PhotoShop.; EDITORIAL EQUIPMENT: Hardware — APP/Power Mac; Printers — PrePress/Panther Pro Imagesetter EDITORIAL SOFTWARE: QPS/QuarkXPress, Adobe/Photshop, Baseview/News Edit Pro. PRODUCTION EQUIPMENT: Hardware — Digi-Colour; Cameras — R, LE PRODUCTION SOFTWARE: QPS/QuarkXPress 4.0.

BEMIDJI

THE BEMIDJI PIONEER

1320 Neilson Ave SE, Bemidji, Minn., 56601-5406, Beltrami; gen tel (218) 333-9200; adv tel (218) 333-9778; ed tel (218) 333-9200; gen fax (218) 333-9819; adv fax (218) 333-9819; ed fax (218) 333-9819; gen/nat adv e-mail tkeute@bemidjipioneer.com; disp adv e-mail tkeute@bemidjipioneer.com; class adv e-mailclassifieds@bemidjipioneer.com; ed e-mail mcory@bemidjipioneer.com; web site www.bemidjipioneer.com - 500,000(views) 100,000(visitors)
Group: Forum Communications Co.
Published: Tues, Wed, Thur, Fri, Sat, Sun
Weekday Frequency: m
Saturday Frequency: m
Circulation: 5,690; 5,119(sat); 6,089(sun)
Last Audit: VAC September 30, 2016
Newspaper Reps: Matt Cory, Editor
Todd Keute, Advertising Director
Advertising Rate (weekday/saturday): Open inch rate $22.00
Advertising Rate (sunday): Open inch rate $22.00
News services: NEA. **Established:** 1896
Own Printing Facility?: No
Commercial Printers?: No
Special Editions: FYI Bemidji Magazine, InMagazine, Meet Your Bemidji Business People
Special Weekly Sections: Living, Entertainment, Comics (Sun); Downtown Weekly (Tue); Outdoors (Fri.), Faith (Thur);
Syndicated Publications: Relish (Monthly); Parade (S).
Digital Platform - Mobile: Apple, Android
Digital Platform - Tablet: Apple iOS, Android
Pub. ....Dennis Doeden
Distribution Mgr. ....Miles Kastella
Ed. ....Matt Cory
Controller ....Tammie Brooks
Home Delivery Mgr. ....Tim Webb
Advertising Director ....Todd Keute
Market Information: TMC.
Mechanical Available: Offset; Black and 3 ROP colors; insert accepted - free-standing cards & envelopes; page cutoffs - 22 3/4.
Mechanical Specifications: Type page 6 x 21; E - 6 cols, 1 5/6, 1/8 between; A - 6 cols, 1 5/6, 1/8 between; C - 10 cols, 1 1/4, 1/16 between.
Areas Served: 56601, 56630, 56650, 56667, 56621, 56676, 56678, 56663, 56633, 56647, 56683, 56661
Delivery Method: Mail, Carrier, RacksEquipment & Software: BUSINESS EQUIPMENT: Dell, Microsoft/Windows XP BUSINESS SOFTWARE: Microsoft/Windows XP, Citrix, Microsoft/Excel CLASSIFIED EQUIPMENT: Hardware — Microsoft/Windows XP, Dell; Printers — HP/LaserJet 4000; CLASSIFIED SOFTWARE: APT/ACT. DISPLAY EQUIPMENT: Hardware — Microsoft/Windows XP, Dell, APP/Mac; Printers — Dataproducts/Typhoon 16; Other Hardware — Umax/Flatbed Scanner, APP/Mac Flatbed Scanner. DISPLAY SOFTWAREAd Make-up Applications — QPS/QuarkXPress 4.1; EDITORIAL EQUIPMENT: Hardware — Microsoft/Windows XP, Dell/Polaroid/Slide Scanner; Printers — Dataproducts/

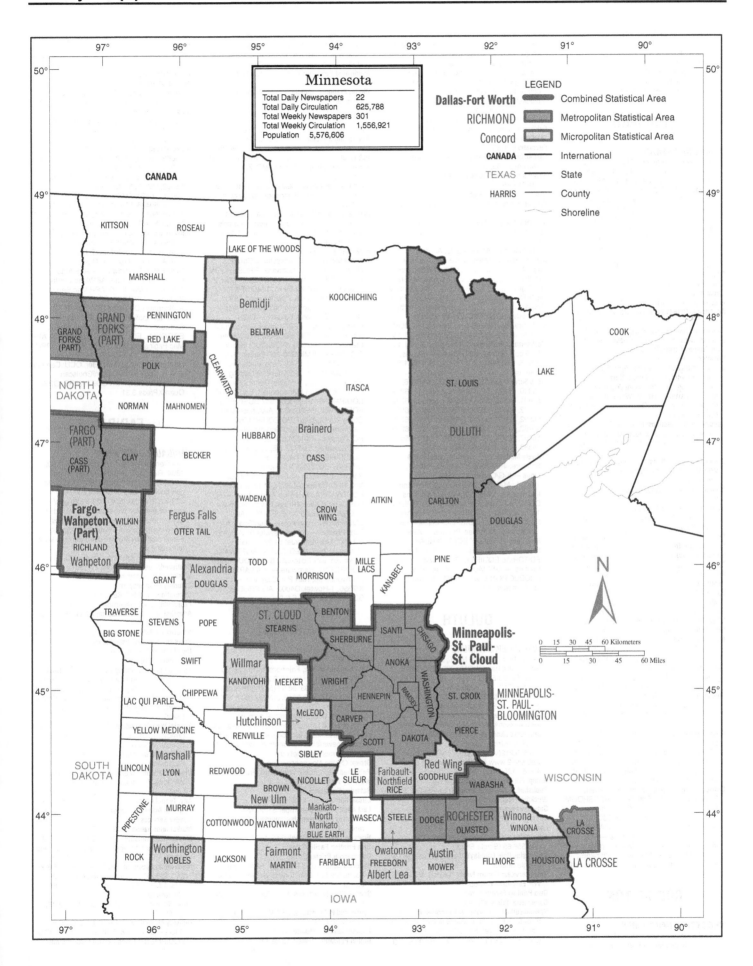

Minnesota

Total Daily Newspapers	22
Total Daily Circulation	625,788
Total Weekly Newspapers	301
Total Weekly Circulation	1,556,921
Population	5,576,606

LEGEND

Dallas-Fort Worth	Combined Statistical Area
RICHMOND	Metropolitan Statistical Area
Concord	Micropolitan Statistical Area
CANADA	International
TEXAS	State
HARRIS	County
	Shoreline

Typhoon 16 EDITORIAL SOFTWARE: APT/ ACT. PRODUCTION EQUIPMENT: Hardware — 1-Nat/340; Cameras — 1-B/1822, Epson; Scanners — 2-Umax/Powerlook II, Microtek/Scanners, Polaroid/Slide Scanner PRODUCTION SOFTWARE: Adobe/ Photoshop 5.5, QPS/QuarkXPress 4.1.

BRAINERD

BRAINERD DISPATCH

506 James St, Brainerd, Minn., 56401-2942, Crow Wing; gen tel (218) 829-4705; adv tel (218) 855-5835; ed tel (218) 855-5860; gen fax (218) 829-7735; adv fax (218) 829-7735; ed fax (218) 829-0211; gen/nat adv e-mail susie.alters@brainerddispatch.com; disp adv e-mail susie.alters@brainerddispatch.com; class adv e-mailsusie.alters@brainerddispatch.com; ed e-mail Matt.Erickson@brainerddispatch.com; web site www.brainerddispatch.com

Group: Forum Communications Co.
Published: Mon, Tues, Wed, Thur, Fri, Sun
Weekday Frequency: m
Circulation: 7,592; 10,827(sun)
Last Audit: AAM September 30, 2017
Advertising Rate (weekday/saturday): Open inch rate $13.90
Advertising Rate (sunday): Open inch rate $17.00
News services: AP, LAT-WP. **Established:** 1881
Own Printing Facility?: Yes
Commercial Printers?: Yes
Special Editions: Golf Guide (Apr); Senior Class (Monthly); Weddings North (Feb); Up North Autos; Christmas Catalog (Nov); Her Voice (Quarterly); Health Watch (Quarterly); Outdoors Traditions (Quarterly); We are 181 (Spring & Fall)
Special Weekly Sections: Housing Page (Fri); TV Week, Outdoors, Business, Money (Sun); Auto, Dining, Food, Entertainment (Thur); Neighbors (Wed).
Syndicated Publications: Relish (Monthly); USA WEEKEND; Parade Magazine (S); American Profile (Weekly).
Digital Platform - Mobile: Apple, Android, Windows
Digital Platform - Tablet: Apple iOS, Android, Windows 7, Blackberry Tablet OS, Kindle, Nook, Kindle Fire
Pub. .... Tim Bogenschutz
Controller/HR Dir. .... Kari Lake
Sales Dir./Classified .... Susie Alters
Circ. Dir. .... John Gagliano
Assoc. Ed. .... Mike O'Rourke
Photographer .... Steve Kohls
Sports Ed. .... Mike Bialka
IT Mgr. .... Jason Walkowiak
Prodn. Coord. .... Dianna Kiehlbauch
VP of Revenue Development .... Sam Swanson
Distribution Manager .... Jamie Olson
Marketing Coord. .... Nikki Lyter
Online Ed. .... Denton Newman
Ed. .... Matt Erickson
Market Information: TMC.
Mechanical Available: Offset; Black and 3 ROP colors; insert accepted; page cutoffs - 22 3/4.
Mechanical Specifications: Type page 6 x 21 1/2; E - 6 cols, 1 3/4, 1/4 between; A - 6 cols, 1 3/4, 1/4 between; C - 6 cols, 1 3/4, 1/4 between.
Areas Served: 56338, 56345, 56364, 56401, 56431, 56435, 56441, 56442, 56443, 56444, 56447, 56448, 56449, 56450, 56452, 56456, 56459, 56465, 56466, 56468, 56472, 56473, 56474, 56479, 56481, 56482, 56484, 56662, 56438, 56359, 56469, 56475
Delivery Method: Mail, Newsstand, Carrier, RacksEquipment & Software: PRESSROOM EQUIPMENT: Lines — 8-G/Community (balloon) 1978; Folders — 1-G/SSC; Registration System — Duarte. MAILROOM EQUIPMENT: Counter Stackers — BG; Inserters & Stuffers — MM/4; Tying Machines — 2/MLN; Address Machine — Ch/525E.; PRODUCTION EQUIPMENT: Cameras — D

CROOKSTON

CROOKSTON DAILY TIMES

124 S Broadway, Crookston, Minn., 56716-1955, Polk; gen tel (218) 281-2730; adv tel (218) 281-2730; ed tel (218) 281-2730; gen fax (218) 281-7234; adv fax (218) 281-7234; ed fax (218) 281-7234; gen/nat adv e-mail canderson@crookstontimes.com ; disp adv e-mail canderson@crookstontimes.com ; class adv e-mailsherberg@crookstontimes.com; ed e-mail mchristopherson@crookstontimes.com ; web site www.crookstontimes.com

Group: New Media Investment Group
Published: Mon, Tues, Wed, Thur, Fri
Weekday Frequency: e
Circulation: 1,367
Last Audit: Sworn/Estimate/Non-Audited September 30, 2017
Advertising Rate (weekday/saturday): Open inch rate $13.85
News services: AP. **Established:** 1885
Special Editions: Religion Directory (Jul); Super Service Directory (Jul).
Special Weekly Sections: Best Foods (Tue)
Syndicated Publications: American Profile (Weekly).
Digital Platform - Mobile: Apple, Android
Digital Platform - Tablet: Apple iOS, Android
Mng. Ed. .... Mike Christopherson
Adv. Mgr. .... Calvin Anderson
Circ. Mgr .... Carl Melbye
Sports Ed. .... Derek Martin
Classifieds .... Samantha Herberg
Market Information: TMC; Zoned editions.
Mechanical Available: Offset; Black and 4 ROP colors; insert accepted; page cutoffs - 21 1/2.
Mechanical Specifications: Type page 6 x 21 1/2; E - 6 cols, 2 1/16, 1/8 between; A - 6 cols, 2 1/16, 1/8 between; C - 6 cols, 2 1/16, 1/8 between.
Areas Served: 55101, 55102, 55108, 55126, 55330, 55371, 55415, 55424, 55811, 56379, 56401, 56510, 56517, 56523, 56535, 56540, 56542, 56548, 56556, 56560, 56562, 56581, 56592, 56601, 56716, 56722, 56723, 56750, 56762, 57201, 58078, 58201, 58203, 58208, 60197, 62914, 63501, 66601, 77479, 85021, 94583, 95822, 97070, 99326
Delivery Method: Mail, CarrierEquipment & Software: PRESSROOM EQUIPMENT: Lines — 5-G/Community 1980; Folders — 1-G/2:1.; MAILROOM EQUIPMENT: Tying Machines — 1/Marlow; Address Machine — DEC/Line Printer.; BUSINESS EQUIPMENT: 1-Corsair/120 mp BUSINESS SOFTWARE: Nomads/Listmaster DISPLAY EQUIPMENT: Hardware — APP/Mac; Printers — APP/ Mac Laser; DISPLAY SOFTWAREAd Make-up Applications — Aldus/PageMaker.; EDITORIAL EQUIPMENT: Hardware — Mk; Printers — APP/Mac LaserWriter Plus. PRODUCTION EQUIPMENT: Hardware — LE; Cameras — B.

DULUTH

DULUTH NEWS TRIBUNE

424 W 1st St, Duluth, Minn., 55802-1596, Saint Louis; gen tel (218) 723-5281; adv tel (218) 723-5225; ed tel (218) 723-5300; gen fax (218) 723-5295; adv fax (218) 723-5295; ed fax (218) 720-4120; gen/nat adv e-mail mwedel@duluthnews.com; disp adv e-mail mwedel@duluthnews.com; class adv e-maileolson@duluthnews.com; ed e-mail letters@duluthnews.com; web site www.duluthnewstribune.com - 4,805,212(views) 565,175(visitors); web site 2 www.duluthnews.com - 4,805,212(views) 565,175(visitors)

Group: Forum Communications Co.
Published: Mon, Tues, Wed, Thur, Fri, Sat, Sun
Weekday Frequency: m
Saturday Frequency: m
Circulation: 22,342; 22,342(sat); 31,533(sun)
Last Audit: VAC September 30, 2016
Advertising Rate (weekday/saturday): Open inch rate $56.65 (Single Sheet)
Advertising Rate (sunday): Open inch rate $61.80 (Single Sheet)
News services: Forum News Service, MCT, LAT-WP. **Established:** 1869
Own Printing Facility?: Yes
Commercial Printers?: Yes
Special Editions: Builders & Remodelers (Apr); Back to School (Aug); Gift Guide (Dec); Boat, Sports and Travel (Feb); Wedding Planner (Jan); Outlook Progress (Mar); Spring Living (May); Healthy Living (Nov); Northland Winter Visitor (Oct); Northern Hunter (Sept).
Special Weekly Sections: WAVE (Fri); Travel (S); Home & Garden (Sat); Taste (Thur).
Syndicated Publications: Parade (S); Dash (Monthly)
Digital Platform - Mobile: Apple, Android, Windows
Digital Platform - Tablet: Apple iOS, Android, Windows 7, Kindle
Editor .... Rick Lubbers
Advertising Director .... Megan Wedel
Circulation Director .... Rich Roxbury
Publisher .... Neal Ronquist
Market Information: Split run; TMC; Zoned editions.
Mechanical Available: Flexographic; Black and 3 ROP colors; insert accepted; page cutoffs - 22 3/4.
Mechanical Specifications: Type page 6 x 21; E - 6 cols, 1 13/16, 1/8 between; A - 6 cols, 1 13/16, 1/16 between; C - 10 cols, 1 13/16, 1/8 between.
Areas Served: 55802
Delivery Method: Mail, Newsstand, Carrier, RacksEquipment & Software: PRESSROOM EQUIPMENT: Lines — 1-MOT/Color Max (Flexo); 1-MOT/FX4 Flexo; 1-MOT/FX4 Flexo (w/half deck & 2 color tower) 1990; 2-MOT/FX4 Flexo (with half deck); Press Drive — PEC/Bond; Folders — G/2:1; Control System — PEC/James Bond, PEC/Bond.; MAILROOM EQUIPMENT: Counter Stackers — 1-Id/660, 5-QWI/200; Inserters & Stuffers — 1-MM/308-208 Biliner, 1-HI/Stuffing Machine 1372; Tying Machines — 2/Power Strap, 1-/Dynaric; Wrapping Singles — 1-/Ca, 1-/Maylo; Control System — 1-Prism/Insert Management; BUSINESS EQUIPMENT: 1-HP/3000-947 BUSINESS SOFTWARE: GEAC, CIS, AIM, Microsoft/Office Pro CLASSIFIED EQUIPMENT: Hardware — 2-Pentium/Servers, 20-Pentium/PC; Printers — 1-HP/LaserJet 5si/MX, 1-HP/LaserJet 5si/MX, 1-Epson/Dot Matrix; CLASSIFIED SOFTWARE: HI/CASH. DISPLAY EQUIPMENT: Hardware — 2-Sun/Sparc 51; Printers — 1-HP/LaserJet 5si/MX, 1-HP/DesignJet 755 CM; DISPLAY SOFTWAREAd Make-up Applications — HI/Dash, QPS/QuarkXPress; Layout Software — GEAC/Layout 5.0.1 E. EDITORIAL EQUIPMENT: Hardware — Sun/Sparc 51, PCs; Printers — 1-HP/LaserJet IV, 2-Epson/LQ 550, 1-HP/LaserJet 5si/MX, 1-HP/DesignJet 755CM EDITORIAL SOFTWARE: HI/Newsmaker Editorial 2.6. PRODUCTION EQUIPMENT: Hardware — 3-AII/APS6-108c, AG/Avontra 30, Na/FP II; Scanners — Lf, X/7650, 1-Howtek/D4000, AG PRODUCTION SOFTWARE: HI/PLS 2.0.

FAIRMONT

SENTINEL

64 Downtown Plz, Fairmont, Minn., 56031-1732, Martin; gen tel (507) 235-3303; adv tel (507) 235-3303; ed tel (507) 235-3303; gen fax (507) 235-3718; adv fax (507) 235-3718; ed fax (507) 235-3718; gen/nat adv e-mail ads@fairmontsentinel.com; disp adv e-mail ads@fairmontsentinel.com; class adv e-mailclassified@fairmontsentinel.com; ed e-mail news@fairmontsentinel.com; web site www.fairmontsentinel.com

Group: Ogden Newspapers Inc.
Published: Mon, Tues, Wed, Thur, Fri, Sat
Weekday Frequency: m
Saturday Frequency: m
Circulation: 4,750; 4,881(sat)
Last Audit: AAM December 31, 2015
Advertising Rate (weekday/saturday): Open inch rate $26.55
News services: AP. **Established:** 1874
Own Printing Facility?: Yes
Commercial Printers?: Yes
Special Editions: Golf Directory; Hometown Youth; Medical Directory; Bridal Tab; Visitor Guide.
Special Weekly Sections: Best Food (Mon); TV Book (Fri).
Syndicated Publications: USA WEEKEND Magazine (Sat).
Digital Platform - Mobile: Apple
Digital Platform - Tablet: Apple iOS
Pub. .... Gary Andersen
Adv. Dir. .... Kathy Ratcliff
Office Mgr. .... Amy Miller
Ed. .... Lee Smith
Composition Supvr. .... Lisa Thate
Market Information: ADS; TMC.
Mechanical Available: Offset; Black and 3 ROP colors; insert accepted; page cutoffs - 18 1/2.
Mechanical Specifications: Type page 13 x 21 1/2; E - 6 cols, 1 43/50, 1/8 between; A - 6 cols, 1 43/50, 1/8 between; C - 9 cols, 1 19/100, 1/16 between.
Areas Served: 56031, 56075, 56039, 56060, 56062, 56088, 56181, 50514, 50517, 50522, 50581, 51334, 50539, 50559, 50578, 50590, 56010, 56013, 56023, 56025, 56047, 56001, 56002, 56003, 56006, 56097, 560898, 56014, 50424, 56027, 56033, 56051, 50451, 50556, 50465, 50480, 56121, 56127, 56171, 56176, 56111, 56118, 56120, 56143, 56159, 56160, 56162, 56081, 56101
Delivery Method: Mail, CarrierEquipment & Software: BUSINESS EQUIPMENT: NCR CLASSIFIED EQUIPMENT: Hardware — 2-APP/PPC 7100/80.; DISPLAY EQUIPMENT: Hardware — APP/Mac LC, APP/Mac Quadra, APP/Mac Centris, APP/Power Mac 6100, APP/Mac Server; Printers — QMS/860; Other Hardware — Scanners DISPLAY SOFTWAREAd Make-up Applications — QPS; Layout Software — APP/Mac, Multi-Ad/Creator. EDITORIAL EQUIPMENT: Hardware — APP/Mac Pagination Network, 10-APP/Mac PPC 7100-80. PRODUCTION EQUIPMENT: Hardware — APP/Mac Laser, OCU; Cameras — 1-B; Scanners — Nikon/Coolscan 35mm PRODUCTION SOFTWARE: QPS/QuarkXPress 3.31.

FARIBAULT

FARIBAULT DAILY NEWS

514 Central Ave N, Faribault, Minn., 55021-4304, Rice; gen tel (507) 333-3111; adv tel (507) 333-3108; ed tel (507) 333-3134; gen fax (507) 333-3102; adv fax (507) 333-3102; ed fax (507) 333-3103; gen/nat adv e-mail kfavro@faribault.com; disp adv e-mail suzyrook@gmail.com; class adv e-mailbnguyen@owatonna.com; ed e-mail suzyrook@gmail.com; web site www.faribault.com

Group: Adams Publishing Group, LLC
Published: Tues, Wed, Thur, Fri, Sat
Weekday Frequency: m
Saturday Frequency: m
Circulation: 4,065; 6,687(sat)
Last Audit: CAC December 12, 2017
Advertising Rate (weekday/saturday): Open inch rate $20.10
Advertising Rate (sunday): Open inch rate $23.15
News services: AP. **Established:** 1914
Own Printing Facility?: Yes
Commercial Printers?: Yes
Special Editions: Spring Sports (Apr); Christmas Song Book (Dec); Brides (Jan); Rice County Fair (Jul); Heritage Festival (Jun); Community Profile (Mar); Senior Lifestyles (May); Winter Sports Preview (Nov); Home & Garden (Sept).
Special Weekly Sections: Business (Tue); Seniors (Wed); Entertainment (Thur); Religion (Fri); Education (Sat)
Digital Platform - Mobile: Apple, Android, Blackberry
Digital Platform - Tablet: Apple iOS, Android, Windows 7, Blackberry Tablet OS
Ed./Pub. .... Sam Gett
Adv. Team Leader .... Mark Nelson
Regional Managing Editor .... Suzanne Rook
Reader Services .... Stacy Murphy
Market Information: ADS; TMC.
Mechanical Available: Offset; Black and 4 ROP colors; insert accepted - free standing; page cutoffs - 22 3/4.
Mechanical Specifications: Type page 11 5/8 x 21 1/2; E - 6 cols, 1 5/6, 1/8 between; A - 6 cols, 1 5/6, 1/8 between; C - 6 cols, 1 5/6, 1/8 between.
Areas Served: 55021, 55018, 55019, 55946, 56069, 55052.
Delivery Method: Mail, Newsstand, Carrier, RacksEquipment & Software: PRESSROOM EQUIPMENT: Lines — 16-G/Community

Single Width; Folders — DGM/1030; Control System — Fin.; MAILROOM EQUIPMENT: Counter Stackers — 1-KAN/Newstac; Inserters & Stuffers — 1-KAN/480 Station Inserter 12:1; Tying Machines — 3-Si/LB2000, 1-Si/LB2330 Auto Strapper; Address Machine — 1-Domino/Jet-A-Ray; BUSINESS EQUIPMENT: pc's BUSINESS SOFTWARE: DTI SBS CLASSIFIED EQUIPMENT: Hardware — macs; CLASSIFIED SOFTWARE: Baseview/Ad Manager Pro DISPLAY SOFTWARELayout Software — Powerplan EDITORIAL EQUIPMENT: Hardware — PC's EDITORIAL SOFTWARE: TCMS PRODUCTION EQUIPMENT: Hardware — 1-Kk/Trendsetter 50, 1-Kk/Trendsetter 100.

FERGUS FALLS

THE FERGUS FALLS DAILY JOURNAL

914 E Channing Ave, Fergus Falls, Minn., 56537-3738, Otter Tail; gen tel (218) 736-7511; adv tel (218) 205-8435; ed tel (218) 739-7023; gen fax (218) 736-5919; adv fax (218) 736-5919; ed fax (218) 736-5919; gen/nat adv e-mail adassist@fergusfallsjournal.com; disp adv e-mail dave.churchill@austindailyherald.com; class adv e-maillinda.reese@fergusfallsjournal.com; ed e-mail joel.myhre@fergusfallsjournal.com; web site www.fergusfallsjournal.com

Group: Boone Newspapers, Inc.
Published: Mon, Tues, Wed, Thur, Fri, Sun
Weekday Frequency: e
Saturday Frequency: m
Circulation: 5,943; 8,414(sun)
Last Audit: Sworn/Estimate/Non-Audited September 30, 2017
Advertising Rate (weekday/saturday): Open inch rate $17.80
Advertising Rate (sunday): Open inch rate $17.80
Online Advertising Rate: Open rate $10.00 cpm (Annual commitment $5.00 cpm; 6 month $7.00 cpm)
News services: AP. **Established:** 1873
Special Editions: Resorter (Aug); Christmas Gift Guide 3 (Dec); Profile (Feb); Chamber Tab (Jan); Crazy Days (Jul); Summer Fun Guide (Jun); Home & Health (Mar); Resorter (May); Christmas Gift Guide 1 (Nov); BPW (Oct); F.Y.I. (Sept).
Special Weekly Sections: Best Food (Wed); Business (Mon); Education, Outdoors (Tue); Real Estate (Wed); Church, Entertainment (Thur); Farm, Auto, Real Estate (Fri); Lifestyles, Home (Sun);
Syndicated Publications: USA WEEKEND Magazine (Sat); TV Journal (Thur).
Digital Platform - Mobile: Apple, Android
Digital Platform - Tablet: Apple iOS, Android
Pub.....David D. Churchill
Ed.....Joel Myhre
Assistant Ed.....Debbie Irmen
Prodn. Foreman, Pressroom....Jeff Schreiber
Prodn. Mgr., Distr./Mailroom....Connie Knapp
Prodn. Mgr., Pre Press....Deb Erikson
Market Information: Split run; TMC; Zoned editions.
Mechanical Available: Web-Offset; Black and 3 ROP colors; insert accepted; page cutoffs - 22 3/4.
Mechanical Specifications: Type page 6 x 21; E - 6 cols, 2 1/16, 1/8 between; A - 6 cols, 2 1/16, 1/8 between; C - 9 cols, 1 1/3, 1/8 between.
Delivery Method: Mail, CarrierEquipment & Software: PRESSROOM EQUIPMENT: Lines — 7-G/Community, 1-G/Colorliner.; MAILROOM EQUIPMENT: Tying Machines — 1/Bu, 1-/Gd; Address Machine — 1-/Ch.; BUSINESS EQUIPMENT: 3-IBM/VP 486-33 SX BUSINESS SOFTWARE: RPG/II CLASSIFIED EQUIPMENT: Hardware — 3-APP/Mac, APP/Power Mac; Printers — APP/LaserWriter 630; CLASSIFIED SOFTWARE: Baseview. DISPLAY EQUIPMENT: Hardware — 1-PC, 1-APP/Mac; DISPLAY SOFTWAREAd Make-up Applications — PBS 3.0.; EDITORIAL EQUIPMENT: Hardware — APP/Power Mac, APP/Mac G4, APP/iMac; Printers — HP/4MV EDITORIAL SOFTWARE: QPS/QuarkXPress 4.1. PRODUCTION EQUIPMENT: Hardware — Nat/A-250; Cameras — SCREEN/Vertical, SCREEN/Horizontal PRODUCTION SOFTWARE: QPS/QuarkXPress.

HIBBING

HIBBING DAILY TRIBUNE

2142 1st Ave, Hibbing, Minn., 55746-3759, Saint Louis; gen tel (218) 262-1011; ed tel (218) 262-1014; gen fax (218) 262-4318; gen/nat adv e-mail taune@hibbingdailytribune.net; disp adv e-mail jodegaard@hibbingdailytribune.net; class adv e-mailmferris@hibbingdailytribune.net; ed e-mail kgrinsteinner@hibbingdailytribune.net; web site www.hibbingmn.com

Group: Adams Publishing Group, LLC
Published: Tues, Wed, Thur, Fri, Sat, Sun
Weekday Frequency: m
Saturday Frequency: m
Circulation: 5,523; 4,519(sat); 4,973(sun)
Last Audit: Sworn/Estimate/Non-Audited September 30, 2017
Advertising Rate (weekday/saturday): Open inch rate $15.90
Advertising Rate (sunday): Open inch rate $15.90
Online Advertising Rate: Online Display Flat Rate $10.00
News services: AP. **Established:** 1893
Own Printing Facility?: No
Commercial Printers?: No
Special Editions: Home Improvement (Apr); Back-to-School (Aug); Progress (Feb); Bridal (Jan); Christmas (Nov); Car Fix-up (Sept).
Special Weekly Sections: TV Week (S); Churches (Sat).
Syndicated Publications: Relish (Monthly); American Profile (S).
Digital Platform - Mobile: Apple, Android, Windows
Digital Platform - Tablet: Apple iOS, Android, Windows 7
Pub.....Kelly Grinsteinner
Family Ed.....Sue Hancock
Sports Ed.....Gary Giombetti
Market Information: TMC.
Mechanical Available: Offset; Black and 3 ROP colors; insert accepted; page cutoffs - 21 1/2.
Delivery Method: Mail, CarrierEquipment & Software: MAILROOM EQUIPMENT: Tying Machines — 2/Bu; Wrapping Singles — 1-/Bu; Address Machine — 1-/Am.; BUSINESS EQUIPMENT: Packard Bell BUSINESS SOFTWARE: Vision Data CLASSIFIED EQUIPMENT: Hardware — APP/Mac G3; Printers — HP/Laserjet 5000N, HP/LaserJet 8100N; CLASSIFIED SOFTWARE: Baseview. DISPLAY EQUIPMENT: Hardware — 3-APP/Mac G3; Printers — HP/Laserjet 5000N, HP/LaserJet 8100N; DISPLAY SOFTWAREAd Make-up Applications — QPS/QuarkXPress; Layout Software — Multi-Ad/Creator, QPS/QuarkXPress. EDITORIAL EQUIPMENT: Hardware — APP/Power Mac G3/Lf/AP Leaf Picture Desk, AP/Graphics; Printers — HP/Laserjet 5000N, HP/LaserJet 8100N EDITORIAL SOFTWARE: Baseview. PRODUCTION EQUIPMENT: Hardware — HP/Laserjet 5000N; Cameras — B/30x 40; Scanners — Nikon/LS-2000 PRODUCTION SOFTWARE: Baseview/NewsEdit Pro.
Note: The Hibbing Daily Tribune is a sister paper to the Mesabi Daily News in Virginia, Minn., the Chisholm Tribune Press in Chisholm, Minn., the Grand Rapids-Herald Review in Grand Rapids, Minn., and the Walker Independent Pilot in Walker, Minn.

MANKATO

THE FREE PRESS

418 S 2nd St, Mankato, Minn., 56001-3727, Blue Earth; gen tel (507) 625-4451; adv tel (507) 344-6364; ed tel (507) 344-6397; gen fax (507) 625-1149; adv fax (507) 625-1149; ed fax (507) 388-4355; gen/nat adv e-mail advertising@mankatofreepress.com ; disp adv e-mail mfpads@mankatofreepress.com ; class adv e-mailclassified@mankatofreepress.com; ed e-mail editor@mankatofreepress.com; web site www.mankatofrThe Free Press

Group: Community Newspaper Holdings, Inc.
Published: Mon, Tues, Wed, Thur, Fri, Sat, Sun
Weekday Frequency: m
Saturday Frequency: m
Circulation: 20,481; 20,481(sat); 20,512(sun)
Last Audit: Sworn/Estimate/Non-Audited September 30, 2017
Advertising Rate (weekday/saturday): Open inch rate $28.38
Advertising Rate (sunday): Open inch rate $29.67
Online Advertising Rate: Starting at $28.50 CPM
News services: AP. **Established:** 1887
Special Editions: Spring Spectator (Apr); Financial Planning (Feb); Senior Citizens (Jan); Senior Citizens (Jul); Meet Your Area Business People (Jun); Mother's Day (May); Holiday Gift Guide (Nov); Senior Citizens (Oct); Fall Improvement (Sept).
Special Weekly Sections: Religion (Fri); Business & Financial (Mon); Wedding/Engagement (S); Home & Garden (Sat); Arts & Entertainment (Thur); Food (Tues).
Syndicated Publications: Parade (Fri).
Digital Platform - Mobile: Apple, Android
Digital Platform - Tablet: Apple iOS, Android
Circ. Dir.....Denise Zernechel
Mng. Ed.....Joe Spear
Features Editor....Robb Murray
News Ed., Day....Kathy Vos
Sports Ed.....Jim Rueda
Prodn. Dir.....Glen Asleson
Prodn. Foreman, Pressroom....Lon Youngerberg
Bus. Mgr.....Brooke High
Adv. Dir.....Ginny Bergerson
Market Information: TMC.
Mechanical Available: Offset; Black and 3 ROP colors; insert accepted - half-tab, free-standing cards; page cutoffs - 22 3/4.
Mechanical Specifications: Type page 6 x 21 1/4; E - 6 cols, 1 7/8, 1/8 between; A - 6 cols, 1 7/8, 1/8 between; C - 9 cols, 1 3/16, 1/8 between.
Delivery Method: Mail, CarrierEquipment & Software: PRESSROOM EQUIPMENT: Lines — 6-G/Urbanite 1969; 2-G/Urbanite 1999; MAILROOM EQUIPMENT: Counter Stackers — Id/2200, Id/Olympian, TMS I; Inserters & Stuffers — GMA/SLS 1000R; Tying Machines — 3-MLN/MLNEE, 1-MLN/2EE, 2-MLN/IEE, 1/Power Strap/Newstyer 2000, Power Strap/P-250 A; Address Machine — 1-/Ch, 1-/KR.; BUSINESS EQUIPMENT: 1-IBM/AS-400 CLASSIFIED EQUIPMENT: Hardware — 8-IBM/300 PL; Printers — HP/4MV; CLASSIFIED SOFTWARE: AT/Enterprise. DISPLAY EQUIPMENT: Hardware — Dewar, 1-APP/Power Mac 8500, APP/Mac G3, APP/Power Mac 6100; Printers — HP/5Si; DISPLAY SOFTWAREAd Make-up Applications — Managing Editor/Ad Dummy, Multi-Ad/Creator, QPS/QuarkXPress, Adobe/Photoshop, Adobe/Illustrator; Layout Software — 7-IBM/350. EDITORIAL EQUIPMENT: Hardware — 29-IBM/350/1-Lf/AP Leaf Picture Desk, 1-APP/Power Mac 7100; Printers — HP/4 MV, HP/5Si, HP/2500CP EDITORIAL SOFTWARE: Dewar/View, QPS/QuarkXPress, Adobe/Photoshop. PRODUCTION EQUIPMENT: Hardware — 2-AG/Accuset 1500, 1-ECR/4550 JetSetter; Cameras — C/Spartan III; Scanners — 1-ECR/Autokon 1030N PRODUCTION SOFTWARE: Dewar/View, QPS/QuarkXPress.

MARSHALL

INDEPENDENT

PO Box 411, 508 W Main St, Marshall, Minn., 56258-0411, Lyon; gen tel (507) 537-1551; adv tel (507) 537-1551 ext. 116; ed tel (507) 537-1551 ext. 126; gen fax (507) 537-1557; gen/nat adv e-mail tbrandl@marshallindependent.com; disp adv e-mail adcomp@marshallindependent.com; class adv e-mailrstaeffler@marshallindependent.com; ed e-mail phpeterson@marshallindependent.com; web site www.marshallindependent.com - 116,821(views) 36,079(visitors)

Group: Ogden Newspapers Inc.
Published: Mon, Tues, Wed, Thur, Fri, Sat
Weekday Frequency: m
Saturday Frequency: m
Circulation: 5,077; 5,120(sat)
Last Audit: AAM December 31, 2016
Advertising Rate (weekday/saturday): Open inch rate $16.90 per column inch (local rates); $16.90 (national net rate)
News services: AP. **Established:** 1874
Own Printing Facility?: No
Commercial Printers?: Yes
Special Editions: Lawn & Garden (Apr); Back-to-School (Aug); Spring Bridal (Feb); Pork Products Tab (Jan); Crazy Days (Jul); Graduation (May); Cookbook (Nov); Fall Car Care (Oct).
Special Weekly Sections: Church News (Fri); Business (Mon); Weddings (Sat); Farm Focus (Thur); Best Food Day (Wed).
Digital Platform - Mobile: Apple, Android
Digital Platform - Tablet: Apple iOS, Android, Windows 7, Kindle, Kindle Fire
Pub.....Russell D. Labat
Bus. Mgr.....Jane Sovell
Adv. Mgr.....Tara Brandl
News Ed.....Per Peterson
Creative Services Mgr....Deb Johnson
Circulation Manager....Rob Purington
Market Information: TMC; Zoned editions.
Mechanical Available: Offset; Black and 3 ROP colors; insert accepted; page cutoffs - 22 3/4.
Mechanical Specifications: Type page 6 x 21 1/2; E - 6 cols, 1 col = 1.583" ; A - 6 cols, 1 col = 1.583"; C - 9 cols, 1 col = 1.022"
Areas Served: 56258,56115,56229,56130,56132,56239,56157,56264,56169,56291,56175,56113,56136,56142,56149,56178,56139,56170,56123,56214,56255,56263,56218,56292,56293,56180,56220,56223,56237,56241,56245,56280,56232,56297,56172.56152,56283,56151,56183,56164
Delivery Method: Mail, Newsstand, Carrier, RacksEquipment & Software: BUSINESS EQUIPMENT: 1-NCR CLASSIFIED EQUIPMENT: Hardware — Power IMacs's; Printers — Canon, HP; CLASSIFIED SOFTWARE: Quark EDITORIAL EQUIPMENT: Printers — Canon, HP EDITORIAL SOFTWARE: Quark PRODUCTION EQUIPMENT: Hardware — CTP; Cameras — CTP PRODUCTION SOFTWARE: QuarkXPress

MINNEAPOLIS

STAR TRIBUNE

425 Portland Ave, Minneapolis, Minn., 55488-1511, Hennepin; gen tel (612) 673-4000; adv tel (612) 673-7777; ed tel (612) 673-7937; gen fax (612) 673-7701; adv fax (612) 673-7701; ed fax (612) 673-4359; gen/nat adv e-mail advertisinginformation@startribune.com; disp adv e-mail paul.kasbohm@startribune.com; class adv e-mailLinda.Thies@startribune.com; ed e-mail nancyb@startribune.com; web site www.startribune.com - 80,800,000(views) 7,300,000(visitors)

Group: Star Tribune
Published: Mon, Tues, Wed, Thur, Fri, Sat, Sun
Weekday Frequency: m
Saturday Frequency: m
Circulation: 278,013; 246,984(sat); 452,362(sun)
Last Audit: AAM March 31, 2017
Advertising Rate (weekday/saturday): Open inch rate $163.00
Advertising Rate (sunday): Open inch rate $276.00
Online Advertising Rate: Leader POS 2+ $14.00 CPM; MedRec POS 1 $16.00 CPM; SuperLeader $24.00 CPM; DoubleBill $36.00 CPM
News services: Associated Press, New York Times Service, McClatchy Tribune Information Service, Washington Post/Bloomberg Service, Scripps Howard News Service, Bloomberg, Dow Jones Information Service **Established:** 1867
Own Printing Facility?: Yes
Commercial Printers?: Yes
Special Editions: Balance (Jan); MN Explorer (Mar, Aug, Nov); Golden Gavel (Mar, Sep); The Good Life (Mar, Apr, Aug, Sep); Drive (Spring/Fall); Top Workplaces (Jun); State Fair Preview (Aug); College Fair Guide (Oct); Charitable Giving Guide (Nov); Holiday Gift Guide (Nov); Homes Magazine (Monthly).
Special Weekly Sections: Business + Money (Sun); Travel, Opinion Exchange, Sunday Comics, Twin Cities + Life (Sun); Dakota

County (Sun); StribExpress (Sun); Business Insider (Mon); Variety H+G, West Extra, South Extra (Wed); Vita.mn: Entertainment, Taste (Thur); Twin Cities Values (Sat).
Syndicated Publications: Parade (Sun.); TV Week Lite (Fri. Single Copy); DASH (Monthly)
Digital Platform - Mobile: Apple, Android, Windows, Blackberry
Digital Platform - Tablet: Apple iOS, Android, Windows 7, Blackberry Tablet OS, Kindle, Nook, Kindle Fire
Pub./CEO .... Michael Klingensmith
Sr. VP, Op. .... Kevin Desmond
Sr. VP, Circ. .... Steven H. Alexander
Sr. VP, CFO .... Chuck Brown
CFO .... Paul Kasbohm
Creative Director .... Jane Messenger
Dir., Sales Mktg./Research .... Dave Gundersen
Circ. Vice Pres. .... Cindy Doege
Ed./Sr. Vice Pres. .... Nancy Barnes
Ed. Editorial Pages .... Scott Gillespie
Ed. & Sr. VP .... Rene Sanchez
Mng. Ed., Presentation/Innovation .... Cory Powell
Asst. Mng. Ed., Admin. .... Bob Schafer
Asst. Mng. Ed., Continuous News ...... Terry Sauer
VP and Chief Marketing Officer
Steve Yaeger
Chief Revenue Officer .... Jeff Griffing
VP, Consumer Marketing .... Rob Gursha
Managing Editor, Operations .... Duchesne Drew
Sr. VP, Digital .... Jim Bernard
Sr. V.P. & Gen. Counsel .... Randy Lebedoff
VP, National & Emerging Media
Ray Faust
Sr. VP, HR .... Adrienne Sirany
Joe Allen
Asst. Managing Ed., Visuals ...... Derek Simmons
Drew Duchesne
Associate VP, Digital Sales .... John Hoeft
Director, Digital Yield
James Byrd
Services Sales Supervisor
Jason Cole
Retail Marketing Analyst
Nicholas Gusmano
Retail Marketing Manager
Jeff Sebesta
Retail Marketing Specialist
Andrew Reinhardt
Sales Supervisor
Jennifer Beckman
Sr. VP, Cir. .... Arden Dickey
Exec. Dir., Digital .... Jason Erdahl
Brad Larson
Preprint Sales Mgr. .... Katherine Kohls
Nicole Shannon
Director, Sales Development
Sean Haley
Todd Molldrem
Ed .... Patricia Lopez
Market Information: Split run; TMC; Zoned editions.
Mechanical Available: Offset; Black and 3 ROP colors; insert accepted - free standing, bags; page cutoffs - 22 1/16.
Mechanical Specifications: Type page 6 x 21; E - 6 cols, 1 3/4, 1/6 between; A - 6 cols, 1 3/4, 1/6 between; C - 10 cols, 1 1/16, 1/12 between.
Areas Served: 612, 651, 763, 952 (MN), 715, 534 (WI)
Delivery Method: Mail, Newsstand, Carrier, RacksEquipment & Software: PRESSROOM EQUIPMENT: Lines — 11-G/Headliner Offset (6 half decks) 1987; 11-G/Headliner Offset (6 half decks) 1987; 11-G/Headliner Offset (6 half decks) 1987; 11-G/Headliner Offset (6 half decks) 1987; MAILROOM EQUIPMENT: Counter Stackers — 14 Quipp Model 400; 1 Quipp Model 500; 9 Ferag stackers ; Inserters & Stuffers — 3 Ferag 16:1 Rollstream/Drums; 1 Ferag 6-unit disk pool; 1 Ferag 8-unit disk pool; 2 Heidelberg NP-632s ; Wrapping Singles — 2 Schur palletizer; 1 Windab shrinkwrapper; 7 Dynaric Model 3000 strappers; 18 Dynaric Model 4000 strappers ;

NEW ULM

THE JOURNAL

PO Box 487, 303 N Minnesota St # 487, New Ulm, Minn., 56073-0487, Brown; gen tel (507) 359-2911; adv tel (507) 359-2911; ed tel (507) 359-2911; gen fax (507) 359-7362; adv fax (507) 359-7362; ed fax (507) 359-7362; gen/nat adv e-mail ads@nujournal.com; disp adv e-mail tbabel@nujournal.com; class adv e-mailclassads@nujournal.com; ed e-mail ksweeney@nujournal.com; web site www.nujournal.com
Group: Ogden Newspapers Inc.
Published: Mon, Tues, Wed, Thur, Fri, Sat, Sun
Weekday Frequency: m
Saturday Frequency: m
Circulation: 6,063; 6,063(sat); 6,455(sun)
Last Audit: AAM December 31, 2015
Advertising Rate (weekday/saturday): Open inch rate $28.76
Advertising Rate (sunday): Open inch rate $28.76
Online Advertising Rate: Leaderboard $16.00 CPM; Banner $11.00 CPM; Skyscraper $16.00 CPM
News services: AP. **Established:** 1898
Own Printing Facility?: No
Commercial Printers?: No
Special Editions: Tax Guide (Jan); Bridal Booklet (Jan); Visitor Guide (Jan); Progress (Feb); Health (Feb); Home Improvement (Mar); Spring Real Estate Guide (Apr); Medical Directory (Annually); Fall Car Care (Fall); Presidents' Day Coupon (Feb); January Thaw (Jan); Shamrock Days (Mar); Graduation Tab (May); Christmas Kick-Off (Nov); Spring Car Care (Spring); Winter Sports (Winter).
Special Weekly Sections: Best Food (Tue); Agribusiness (Fri); Church (Sat); Lifestyle, TV Time, Comics (Sun)
Syndicated Publications: Parade (S).
Digital Platform - Mobile: Apple, Android, Windows
Digital Platform - Tablet: Apple iOS, Android, Windows 7
Pub .... Bruce Fenske
Circ. Mgr. .... Steve Grosam
Ed .... Kevin Sweeney
Adv. Dir. .... Tim Babel
Market Information: TMC.
Mechanical Available: Offset; Black and 3 ROP colors; insert accepted; page cutoffs - 21 1/2.
Mechanical Specifications: Type page 10 x 21 1/2; E - 6 cols, 1/8 between; A - 6 cols, 1/8 between; C - 9 cols, 1/16 between.
Areas Served: 56073
Delivery Method: Mail, Newsstand, Carrier, RacksEquipment & Software: BUSINESS EQUIPMENT: NCR/Tower CLASSIFIED EQUIPMENT: Hardware — Apple iMac; Printers — HP.; DISPLAY EQUIPMENT: Hardware — Apple iMac; DISPLAY SOFTWAREAd Make-up Applications — Multi-Ad/Creator II; Layout Software — 1-APP/Power Mac G3, 3-APP/Mac G4. EDITORIAL EQUIPMENT: Hardware — Apple IMac & G4/Polaroid/Film Scanner, 2-APP/Mac PC 6100, 1-APP/Mac PC 7100; Printers — HP EDITORIAL SOFTWARE: QPS/QuarkXPress 4.0. PRODUCTION EQUIPMENT: Hardware — 2-HP/LaserPrinter PRODUCTION SOFTWARE: QPS/QuarkXPress 4.0.

OWATONNA

OWATONNA PEOPLE'S PRESS

135 W Pearl St, Owatonna, Minn., 55060-2316, Steele; gen tel (507) 451-2840; adv tel (507) 444-2389; ed tel (507) 444-2370; gen fax (507) 444-2382; adv fax (507) 444-2382; ed fax (507) 451-6020; gen/nat adv e-mail gbergerson@owatonna.com; disp adv e-mail gbergerson@owatonna.com; class adv e-mailclassified@owatonna.com; ed e-mail jjackson@owatonna.com; web site www.owatonna.com
- 370,000(views)
Group: Adams Publishing Group, LLC
Published: Tues, Wed, Thur, Fri, Sat
Weekday Frequency: m
Saturday Frequency: m
Circulation: 4,608; 5,104(sat)
Last Audit: CAC December 31, 2015
Advertising Rate (weekday/saturday): Open inch rate $20.10; $23.10(Tue/Sat)
News services: AP. **Established:** 1874
Own Printing Facility?: Yes
Commercial Printers?: Yes
Special Editions: Spring Sports (Apr); Steele County Fair (Aug); Park & Rec (Feb); Bridal (Jan); Park & Rec (Jul); Bridal (Jun); Portraits (Mar); Graduation (May); Christmas Kick-Off (Nov); Welcome Guide (May, Oct); Home & Garden (Sept).
Special Weekly Sections: Seniors (Wed); Entertainment (Thur); Trends (Fri); Religion, Real Estate (Sat)
Syndicated Publications: American Profile (Weekly);
Digital Platform - Mobile: Apple, Android, Windows
Digital Platform - Tablet: Apple iOS, Android, Windows 7
Circ. Mgr. .... Carol Harvey
Mng. Ed. .... Jeffrey Jackson
Prodn. Mgr. .... Roger Stolley
Advertising Director .... Ginny Bergerson
Publisher .... Julie Frazier
Pub./Ed. .... Ronald Ensley
Adv. Dir. .... Debbie Ensley
Market Information: TMC
Mechanical Available: Offset; Black and 4 ROP colors; insert accepted - free standing; page cutoffs - 22 3/4.
Mechanical Specifications: Type page 6 x 21 1/2; E - 6 cols, 1 16/25, 1/8 between; A - 6 cols, 1 16/25, 1/8 between; C - 6 cols, 1 16/25, 1/8 between.
Areas Served: 55060, 55049, 55924, 55917,56026, 55927
Delivery Method: Mail, Newsstand, Carrier, RacksEquipment & Software: PRESSROOM EQUIPMENT: Lines — 16-G/Community single width; Folders — DGM/1030; Pasters —Jardis; Control System — Fin.; MAILROOM EQUIPMENT: Counter Stackers — KAN/Newstac; Inserters & Stuffers — KAN/480 Station Inserter12:1; Tying Machines — 3-Si/LB2000, 1-Si/LB2330 Auto Strapper; Address Machine — 1-Domino/Jet-A-Ray; BUSINESS EQUIPMENT: PC's BUSINESS SOFTWARE: Windows 7 DISPLAY EQUIPMENT: Hardware — PC's; Printers — HP/Color Laserjet Printer, QMS/2060 Printer; DISPLAY SOFTWAREAd Make-up Applications — Adobe/InDesign CS 5.5.; EDITORIAL EQUIPMENT: Hardware — PC's EDITORIAL SOFTWARE: TownNews TCMS, Adobe/InDesign 5.5. PRODUCTION EQUIPMENT: Hardware — 1-ECR/36 HS, 1-Kk/Trendsetter 100, 2-APP/Mac G3 PRODUCTION SOFTWARE: Prinergy, Integis, Pit Stop, QPS/QuarkXPress 6.1.

ROCHESTER

POST-BULLETIN

18 1st Ave SE, Rochester, Minn., 55904-3722, Olmsted; gen tel (507) 285-7600; adv tel (507) 285-7783; ed tel (507) 285-7700; gen fax (507) 285-7666; ed fax (507) 285-7772; gen/nat adv e-mail mbarebo@postbulletin.com; disp adv e-mail advertising@postbulletin.com; class adv e-mailslovejoy@postbulletin.com; ed e-mail letters@postbulletin.com; web site www.postbulletin.com
- 558,280(views) 326,420(visitors); web site 2 www.agrinews.com; web site 3 www.pb507.com; web site 4www.rochestermagazine.com
Group: Small Newspaper Group
Published: Mon, Tues, Wed, Thur, Fri, Sat
Weekday Frequency: e
Saturday Frequency: e
Circulation: 28,294; 31,895(sat)
Last Audit: CAC March 31, 2017
Advertising Rate (weekday/saturday): Weekday - $59
Advertising Rate (sunday): Weekend edition (Saturday) - $65.80
News services: AP, NYT, MCT. **Established:** 1916
Own Printing Facility?: Yes
Commercial Printers?: Yes
Special Editions: Pets (May); Dairy 2013 (Jun); Boomer (Apr); Education (Aug); Last Minute Gift Catalog (Dec); Rochester Area Builders Home Show (Feb); Weddings (Jan); Honor Roll (Jul); Rochesterfest (Jun); Employment (Mar); Spring Home & Garden (May); Home for the Holidays (Nov); Drive Magazine (Oct).
Special Weekly Sections: Real Estate Marketplace (Fri); Seniors (Mon); Travel (Sat); Prevue (Thur); Teen Beat (Tues); Food (Wed).
Syndicated Publications: Homefinder (Monthly); USA WEEKEND Magazine (Sat); American Profile (Weekly).
Digital Platform - Mobile: Apple, Android, Windows
Digital Platform - Tablet: Apple iOS, Android, Windows 7
Pub. .... Randy Chapman
Dir., HR .... Carmen Kyllo
Bus. Mgr. .... Chris Blade
Adv. Mgr., Classified .... Sue Lovejoy
Adv. Dir. .... Mark Barebo
Circ. Mgr. .... Todd Heroff
Circ. Mgr., Customer Serv. .... Carla Severson
Ed. .... Robert Hill
Mng. Ed. .... Jay Furst
City Ed. .... Randi Kallas
Editorial Page Ed. .... Greg Sellnow
Environmental/Ecology Ed. .... John Weiss
Lifestyle Ed. .... Janice McFarland
Sports Ed. .... Craig Swalboski
Dir., Tech. Servs. .... Victor Denny
Dir., Internet Servs. .... G. Mark Kelm
Prodn. Dir., Opns. .... Jeffrey Lansing
Market Information: Split run; TMC; Zoned editions.
Mechanical Available: Offset; Black and 3 ROP colors; insert accepted; page cutoffs - 22.
Mechanical Specifications: Type page 13 x 21; E - 6 cols, 2 1/16, 1/8 between; A - 6 cols, 2 1/16, 1/8 between; C - 8 cols, 1 9/16, 1/16 between.
Areas Served: southeastern Minnesota
Delivery Method: Mail, CarrierEquipment & Software: PRESSROOM EQUIPMENT: Lines — 5-G/Headliner Offset (3 decks) double width 1988; Folders — G/2:1.; MAILROOM EQUIPMENT: Counter Stackers — 3-QWI/500, 1-QWI/401; Inserters & Stuffers — GMA/3000 20:2, GMA/10 Heads; Tying Machines — Ovalstrapping; Wrapping Singles — Mosca; Control System — GMA/SAM; Address Machine — KR, Prism; BUSINESS EQUIPMENT: IBM/AS-400 720-2062, PCs, Sun/Enterprise BUSINESS SOFTWARE: IBM/AS-400, Microsoft/Office, Abra Suite, PBS CLASSIFIED EQUIPMENT: Hardware — APP/Mac; Printers — HP; CLASSIFIED SOFTWARE: Baseview. DISPLAY EQUIPMENT: Hardware — APP/Mac; Printers — 2-AG/SelectSet 5000, 1-AG/9400PS; Other Hardware — 1-Epson/636 Scanner, 2-OPI/Print Desk, 2-Polaroid/SprintScan 35 Plus DISPLAY SOFTWAREAd Make-up Applications — QPS/QuarkXPress, Adobe/Illustrator, Adobe/Photoshop; Layout Software — Mk/Ad Director. EDITORIAL EQUIPMENT: Hardware — APP/Mac; Printers — HP EDITORIAL SOFTWARE: Baseview. PRODUCTION EQUIPMENT: Hardware — 2-Polaroid/Sprintscant, 1-Devotec/DE; Scanners — Polaroid/Sprintscant, Umax, Nikon, AG PRODUCTION SOFTWARE: QPS 3.11, QPS 4.0.

SAINT CLOUD

ST. CLOUD TIMES

3000 7th St N, Saint Cloud, Minn., 56303-3108, Stearns; gen tel (320) 255-8700; adv tel (320) 255-8793; ed tel (320) 255-8776; gen fax (320) 255-8775; adv fax (320) 255-8773; gen/nat adv e-mail mbirkland@stcloud.gannett.com; disp adv e-mail jschlaghec@stcloud.gannett.com; class adv e-mailclassifieds@stcloudtimes.com; ed e-mail rkrebs@stcloud.gannett.com; web site www.sctimes.com
- 4,695,000(views) 489,000(visitors)
Group: Gannett
Published: Mon, Tues, Wed, Thur, Fri, Sat, Sun
Weekday Frequency: m
Saturday Frequency: m
Circulation: 18,892; 22,059(sat); 23,882(sun)
Last Audit: AAM September 30, 2015
Advertising Rate (weekday/saturday): Open inch rate $34.30
Advertising Rate (sunday): Open inch rate $47.55
Online Advertising Rate: Leaderboard $8.00; Half Page Poster $14.00; Large Rectangle $9.00
News services: AP, GNS, Forum, **Established:** 1861
Own Printing Facility?: Yes
Commercial Printers?: No
Special Editions: Christmas Gift Guide (Dec); Bridal (Jan); Bridal (Jul); Home Times (Semi-

monthly); Football (Sept), Extra Helpings (Thanksgiving), Rocori Times (10x/year), Festival Guide (May), Progress Edition (Sept.), Quarterly Business Report, Whitney Times (4x/year), Prep Football (August), Auto Preview (Jan).
Special Weekly Sections: Travel Page (S); Weddings/Engagements (Sat); Up Next (Thur), Auto (Friday), Homes (Saturday); D'Lish (Wed), Business (7 days/week), Citizen Times (Monday)
Syndicated Publications: USA WEEKEND Magazine (Fri)
Proprietary Publications: Style Magazine
Digital Platform - Mobile: Apple, Android, Windows
Digital Platform - Tablet: Apple iOS, Android, Windows 7
Exec. Ed. ....John L. Bodette
Adv. Mgr., Online Devel. ....Julie Schlagheck
Adv. Mgr., Territory Retail Sales .Marilyn Birkland
Circ. Sales Mgr. ....Tom Steve
Asst. Mng. Ed. ....Mike Knaak
Ed. Page Ed. ....Randy Krebs
Photo Dept. Mgr. ....David Schwarz
President/Publisher ....Melinda Vonderahe
Market Information: Split run; TMC.
Mechanical Available: Offset; Black and 3 ROP colors; insert accepted Tuesday - Sunday; page cutoffs - 21 1/2.
Mechanical Specifications: Type page 6 x 20; E - 6 cols, 1.562, 1/8 between; A - 6 cols, 1.562, 1/8 between; C - 10 cols, 1", .02 between.
Delivery Method: Mail, Newsstand, Carrier, RacksEquipment & Software: PRESSROOM EQUIPMENT: MAN Uniset 70 - 6 towers; Baumueller Drives MAILROOM EQUIPMENT: 10 head GMA SLS2000
14 head GMA SLS2000
4- Dynaric in-line strappers
Quipp 350 and 400 stackers
In-line ink jet capabilities BUSINESS EQUIPMENT: IBM/AS-400 (located in Phoenix) CLASSIFIED EQUIPMENT: 2 Mactive Servers. Both IBM 3650's; 6 classified PC's strictly classified; Another 8 PC's with Mactive in Advertising for keying DISPLAY EQUIPMENT: 5 Power Mac's DISPLAY SOFTWAREAd Make-up Applications — Multi-Ad/Creator 4.0; Layout Software — MEI/ALS. EDITORIAL EQUIPMENT: ENG; Nothing local EDITORIAL SOFTWARE: Newsgate

SAINT PAUL

ST. PAUL PIONEER PRESS
10 River Park Plz, Ste 700, Saint Paul, Minn., 55107-1223, Ramsey; gen tel (651) 222-1111; adv tel (651) 228-5365; ed tel (651) 228-5490; gen fax (651) 225-5500; adv fax (651) 228-5308; ed fax (651) 228-5500; gen/nat adv e-mail gmazanec@pioneerpress.com; disp adv e-mail gmazanec@pioneerpress.com; class adv e-maildmccants@pioneerpress.com; ed e-mail letters@pioneerpress.com; web site www.twincities.com
- 20,000,000(views) 1,995,608(visitors)
Group: Digital First Media
Published: Mon, Tues, Wed, Thur, Fri, Sat, Sun
Weekday Frequency: m
Saturday Frequency: m
Circulation: 165,768; 111,889(sat); 244,742(sun)
Last Audit: AAM December 31, 2016
Advertising Rate (weekday/saturday): Open inch rate $242.00
Advertising Rate (sunday): Open inch rate $262.00
Online Advertising Rate: Weekday: 3 lines for $13.00 (local) and $15.29 (national); Sunday: 3 lines for $14.00 (local) and $16.47 (national)
News services: AP, MCT, LAT-WP, The Newspaper Network (TNN). **Established:** 1849
Own Printing Facility?: Yes
Commercial Printers?: Yes
Special Editions: Fall Gardening (Sep, Oct); Travel Guides (Mar, Aug); Live to Age Well (Mar, Aug, Nov); Worship Directory (Apr, Dec); Higher Education (Jul, Dec); State Fair (Aug); Vikings Season Preview (Sep); Arts previews (Mar, Sep, Nov); Breast Cancer Awareness (Oct); Non Profit Giving Guide

(Nov); Golf Guide (Apr); Home & Lifestyle (Aug); Ski (Dec); Winter Carnival (Jan); Home & Lifestyle (Jul); Summer Fun Guide (Jun); Summer Camp for Kids (Mar); Home & Lifestyle (Oct).
Special Weekly Sections: Eat (Thur); Wheels (Fri/Sat); TV Weekly, Real Estate, Business (Sun)
Syndicated Publications: Parade (S).
Digital Platform - Mobile: Apple, Android, Windows, Blackberry
Digital Platform - Tablet: Apple iOS, Android, Windows 7, Blackberry Tablet OS, Kindle, Nook, Kindle Fire
Publisher ....Guy Gilmore
Ed. ....Mike Burbach
Commun. Mgr. ....Pat Effenberger
Vice Pres., Adv. ....Greg Mazanec
Adv. Dir., Classified ....Dee Mccants
Vice Pres., Circ. ....Andrew Mok
Dir., Mktg. ....Lori Swanson
Dir., Market Research/Info. ......Jean Pearson
VP, Production ....Kevin Garris
CFO ....Neil Mullen
Michael Garyantes
Hal Davis
Market Information: Split run; TMC; Zoned editions.
Mechanical Available: Offset; Black and 3 ROP colors; insert accepted - self-adhesive notes, paper bags, product samples; page cutoffs - 22.
Mechanical Specifications: Type page 6 x 21; E - 5 cols, 1 11/16, 3/16 between; A - 6 cols, 2 1/16, 3/16 between; C - 10 cols, 1 1/8, between.
Areas Served: 55001 to 56750
Delivery Method: Mail, Newsstand, Carrier, RacksEquipment & Software: PRESSROOM EQUIPMENT: Lines — 6-G/Metroliner Double Width; 6-G/Metroliner Double Width; 6-G/Metroliner Double Width; Folders — 3-G/3:2 single.; MAILROOM EQUIPMENT: Counter Stackers — 7-Quipp, 5-HL/Monitor; Inserters & Stuffers — 2-Dynaric/NP;

VIRGINIA

MESABI DAILY NEWS
704 S 7th Ave, Virginia, Minn., 55792-3086, Saint Louis; gen tel (218) 741-5544; adv tel (218) 741-5544; ed tel (218) 741-5544; gen fax (218) 741-1005; adv fax (218) 749-1836; ed fax (218) 741-1005; gen/nat adv e-mail cknight@mesabidailynews.net; disp adv e-mail cknight@mesabidailynews.net; class adv e-mailklaugen@mesabidailynews.net; ed e-mail bhanna@mesabidailynews.net; web site www.virginiamn.com
Group: Adams Publishing Group, LLC
Published: Tues, Wed, Thur, Fri, Sat, Sun
Weekday Frequency: m
Saturday Frequency: m
Circulation: 9,143; 9,143(sat); 10,488(sun)
Last Audit: Sworn/Estimate/Non-Audited September 30, 2017
Advertising Rate (weekday/saturday): Open inch rate $14.15
Advertising Rate (sunday): Open inch rate $14.15
Online Advertising Rate: 1 week for $7.00
News services: AP, NEA, TMS. **Established:** 1893
Special Editions: Our Schools (May); Business & Industry (Mar); Business & Industry (Feb).
Special Weekly Sections: Food (Wed); Business, Teen (Sat); Church, Outdoor, TV News (Sun)
Syndicated Publications: Relish (Monthly); USA WEEKEND Magazine (S); American Profile (Weekly).
Digital Platform - Mobile: Apple, Android
Digital Platform - Tablet: Apple iOS, Android
Gen. Mgr./Adv. Dir. ....Christopher Knight
Exec. Ed. ....Bill Hanna
Circ. Mgr. ....Tom Siemers
Market Information: Split run; TMC; Zoned editions.
Mechanical Available: Offset; Black and 3 ROP colors; insert accepted; page cutoffs - 20.
Mechanical Specifications: Type page 6 x 20; E - 6 cols, 1 5/6, 5/16 between; A - 6 cols, 1 5/6, 5/16 between; C - 9 cols, 1 1/6, 5/16 between.
Delivery Method: Mail, CarrierEquipment & Software: PRESSROOM EQUIPMENT: Lines — 8-G/Urbanite; Folders — 1-G/2:1.; MAILROOM EQUIPMENT: Counter Stackers — 1/HL; Inserters & Stuffers —

6-KAN/660; Tying Machines — 1-Sterling/MR40, 1-Sterling/SSM-Mini; Wrapping Singles — 2-/Bu; Address Machine — 1-/KAN.; BUSINESS EQUIPMENT: 1-IBM/Risc 6000 CLASSIFIED EQUIPMENT: Printers — 1-APP/Mac LaserWriter NTX, 2-HP/8000N, 1-Ag/Accuset 1000, 1-AG/25SX; CLASSIFIED SOFTWARE: Baseview. DISPLAY EQUIPMENT: Printers — 2-HP/8000N, 1-MON/1000, 1-AG/255X; DISPLAY SOFTWAREAd Make-up Applications — Multi-Ad, QPS/QuarkXPress, Aldus/FreeHand; Layout Software — 4-APP/Power Mac G-3, 1-APP/Power Mac 9500. EDITORIAL EQUIPMENT: Hardware — 18-APP/Mac; Printers — 1-APP/Mac LaserWriter NTX, 2-HP/8000N, 1-AG/25SX, 1-AG/Accuset 1000 EDITORIAL SOFTWARE: APP/Mac, Baseview. PRODUCTION EQUIPMENT: Hardware — Caere/OmniPage, MON/1000; Cameras — 1-B; Scanners — AG/Arcus, 2-Umax 1200S PRODUCTION SOFTWARE: QPS/QuarkXPress, Baseview.

WILLMAR

WEST CENTRAL TRIBUNE
2208 Trott Ave SW, Willmar, Minn., 56201-2723, Kandiyohi; gen tel (320) 235-1150; adv tel (320) 235-1150; ed tel (320) 235-1150; gen fax (320) 235-6769; adv fax (320) 235-6769; ed fax (320) 235-6769; gen/nat adv e-mail news@wctrib.com; disp adv e-mail wctads@wctrib.com; class adv e-mailwctads@wctrib.com; ed e-mail SLunneborg@wctrib.com; web site www.wctrib.com
Group: Forum Communications Co.
Published: Mon, Tues, Wed, Thur, Fri, Sat
Weekday Frequency: m
Saturday Frequency: m
Circulation: 9,827; 9,827(sat)
Last Audit: VAC September 30, 2017
Advertising Rate (weekday/saturday): Open inch rate $22.01
Online Advertising Rate: Starting at $11.64 CPM
News services: Forum News Service **Established:** 1895
Own Printing Facility?: Yes
Commercial Printers?: Yes
Special Editions: Earth Day (Apr); Fall Football Preview (Aug); Holiday (Dec); Bridal I (Feb); Willmar Mid Summer (Jul); City Festival (Jun); Agriculture (Mar); Mother's Day (May); Holiday Greetings (Nov); Health Services Directory (Oct); Fall Home Improvement (Sept).
Special Weekly Sections: Best Food Days, Health (Mon); Business (Tue); Arts/Entertainment, Auto (Thur); Church, Real Estate, TV (Fri); Farm, Outdoors, Travel, Technology (Sat)
Syndicated Publications: Parade (S).
Digital Platform - Mobile: Apple, Android
Digital Platform - Tablet: Apple iOS, Android
Publisher ....Steve Ammerman
Editor ....Kelly Boldan
Features Ed. ....Sharon Bomstad
News Ed. ....Susan Lunneborg
Circulation Manager ....Nate Schueller
Advert. Mgr. ....Christie Steffel
Market Information: TMC.
Mechanical Available: Offset; Black and 3 ROP colors; insert accepted - print & deliver program; page cutoffs - 22 3/4.
Mechanical Specifications: Type page 6 x 20.75; E - 6 cols, 1 13/16, 1/8 between; A - 6 cols, 1 13/16, 1/8 between; C - 8 cols, 1 13/16, 1/8 between.
Delivery Method: Mail, CarrierEquipment & Software: PRESSROOM EQUIPMENT: Lines — BG/Dampening System, 8-G/Community; Folders — 1-G/SCI, G/SSC.; MAILROOM EQUIPMENT: Tying Machines — OVL; Address Machine — Ch/596.; BUSINESS EQUIPMENT: DEC/VAX 6410, DEC/2100A Alpha BUSINESS SOFTWARE: Collier-Jackson Inc CLASSIFIED EQUIPMENT: Hardware — Dell, Micron/Workstation, Compaq; Printers — AU/APS2000, Au/Imagesetter, HP/4m; CLASSIFIED SOFTWARE: APT. DISPLAY EQUIPMENT: Hardware — Micron/Workstations, Dell, Compaq; Printers — APD/2000; DISPLAY SOFTWAREAd

Make-up Applications — APT; Layout Software — APT. EDITORIAL EQUIPMENT: Hardware — Micron/workstation, Dell, Compaq/Server/APP/Mac G4; Printers — AU/APS2000, AU/Imagesetter, Epson/Color Proofer, HP EDITORIAL SOFTWARE: APT. PRODUCTION EQUIPMENT: Hardware — Wordlinx 2.1, AU/108C; Cameras — 2-C/Spartan III; Scanners — 3-Umax/PowerLook PRODUCTION SOFTWARE: APT.

WINONA

WINONA DAILY NEWS
902 E 2nd St, Ste 110, Winona, Minn., 55987-6512, Winona; gen tel (507) 453-3500; adv tel (507) 453-3561; ed tel (507) 453-3510; gen fax (507) 454-1440; adv fax (507) 454-1440; ed fax (507) 453-3517; gen/nat adv e-mail sales@winonadailynews.com; disp adv e-mail stacia.king@lee.net; class adv e-mailclassifieds@winonadailynews.com; ed e-mail letters@winonadailynews.com; web site www.winonadailynews.com
- 987,168(views) 159,968(visitors)
Group: Lee Enterprises, Inc.
Published: Mon, Tues, Wed, Thur, Fri, Sat, Sun
Weekday Frequency: m
Saturday Frequency: m
Circulation: 6,864; 7,929(sat); 7,993(sun)
Last Audit: AAM March 31, 2016
Advertising Rate (weekday/saturday): Open inch rate $23.88
Advertising Rate (sunday): Open inch rate $26.32
Online Advertising Rate: 14 days for $10.00
News services: AP, Lee National Sales Group. **Established:** 1855
Own Printing Facility?: No
Commercial Printers?: Yes
Special Editions: Kid's Korner (Jul); Home Buyers Guide (Jun); Real Estate Resource (Jun); Business Report (May); River Valley (May); Bike Trail (Apr); Bridal Showcase (Jan); Home Improvement (Mar, May, Aug, Oct); Farm Outlook (Mar, Sept) Golf Guide; Bike Guide (Apr); Back-to-School/Campus (Aug); Christmas (Dec).
Special Weekly Sections: Connections, Outdoors, Comics (Sun); Business (Mon); Best Food, Business Card (Wed); Preps, Live! (Thur); NASCAR, NFL, Real Estate (Fri); Neighbors (Sat)
Syndicated Publications: Parade (S); American Profile (Weekly).
Digital Platform - Mobile: Apple, Android, Windows
Digital Platform - Tablet: Apple iOS, Android, Windows 7, Blackberry Tablet OS, Kindle, Nook, Kindle Fire
Group Publisher ....Mike Burns
Ret'l Adv. Mgr. ....Thomas Kelley
Ed ....Brian Voerding
City Ed. ....Matt Christensen
Online Ed. ....Jerome Christenson
Market Information: TMC.
Mechanical Available: Offset; Black and 3 ROP colors; insert accepted - self-adhesive notes, poly bags; page cutoffs - 22 3/4.
Mechanical Specifications: Type page 6 x 21 1/2; E - 6 cols, 1 5/6, 1/8 between; A - 6 cols, 1 5/6, 1/8 between; C - 9 cols, 1 1/5, 1/16 between.
Areas Served: 55987; 55981; 55979; 55974; 55972; 55971; 55969; 55962; 55959; 55952; 55947; 55943; 55925; 55921; 55910; 54773; 54756; 54747; 54661; 54630; 54629; 54625; 54622; 54612; 54610
Delivery Method: Mail, Newsstand, CarrierEquipment & Software: PRESSROOM EQUIPMENT: Lines — 13 - Goss Urbanite & DGM 850; 5 - Goss Urbanite; Press Drive — 2 digital drives; Folders — 1-Goss Urbanite 2:1 1 DGM 2:1; Pasters —5 - Hurst; Reels & Stands — 1 Goss Urbanite roll stand; Registration System — Jardis MAILROOM EQUIPMENT: Counter Stackers — 1 - Hall Monitor 2 - Quipp 1 - Gammerler; Inserters & Stuffers — 1 Harris 1372 1 K&M 1372; Tying Machines — 2 - Dynaric NP-2 strappers; Address Machine — 1 - Videojet inkjet labeler ; BUSINESS EQUIPMENT: IBM/AS-400 BUSINESS SOFTWARE: Custom Software CLASSIFIED EQUIPMENT: Hardware — 3-Gateway/2000 P5-90; CLASSIFIED SOFTWARE: CText/Advision

OS-2 3.00. DISPLAY EQUIPMENT: Printers — 1-HP/4MV, 1-HP/4M Plus; Other Hardware — 2-Nikon/ScanTouch Scanners DISPLAY SOFTWAREAd Make-up Applications — Multi-Ad/Creator, Aldus/FreeHand, Adobe/Photoshop, Adobe/TypeStyler, Kwick Query, Watch It; Layout Software — 4-APP/Power Mac, 1-APP/Mac Quadra 950. EDITORIAL EQUIPMENT: Hardware — 14-Gateway/2000 P5-90, 2-Gateway/2000 P5-100/1-APP/Power Mac 8500-180, 1-Nikon/Scanner, 1-APP/Mac IIci, 1-APP/Mac Classic; Printers — 2-HP/5Si, 1-HP/4Si, 1-APP/Mac LaserWriter IIf EDITORIAL SOFTWARE: CText/Dateline OS-2 3.00. PRODUCTION EQUIPMENT: Hardware — 2-HP/5Si; Cameras — 1-B.

WORTHINGTON

WORTHINGTON DAILY GLOBE

300 11th St, Worthington, Minn., 56187-2451, Nobles; gen tel (507) 376-9711; adv tel (507) 376-9711; ed tel (507) 376-9711; gen fax (507) 376-5202; adv fax (507) 376-5202; ed fax (507) 376-5202; gen/nat adv e-mail dellerbroek@dglobe.com; disp adv e-mail ccarlson@dglobe.com; class adv e-maildgclassified@dglobe.com; ed e-mail rmcgaughey@dglobe.com; web site www.dglobe.com
Group: Forum Communications Co.
Published: Mon, Tues, Wed, Thur, Fri, Sat
Weekday Frequency: m
Saturday Frequency: m
Circulation: 5,830; 5,830(sat)
Last Audit: VAC September 30, 2016
Advertising Rate (weekday/saturday): Open inch rate $25.65
Online Advertising Rate: 19 words or less for $23.45; 20-26 words for $25.75
News services: AP. **Established:** 1872
Own Printing Facility?: Yes
Special Editions: Home Improvement (Apr); Real Estate Guide (Every other month); Builders (Fall); Bridal Tab (Jan); Bridal Tab (Jun); Progress Annual Report (Mar); Active Life (Quarterly); Builders (Spring).
Special Weekly Sections: Best Food Days, Business (Mon); Agriculture, Home (Tue); Health (Wed); Religion (Thur); Dining, Entertainment, Outdoors (Fri); People, Education (Sat)
Syndicated Publications: TV Pre-Vu (Fri); Relish (Monthly); Parade (S); American Profile (Sat).
Digital Platform - Mobile: Apple, Android
Digital Platform - Tablet: Apple iOS, Android
Pub. .... Joni Harms
Sports Ed. .... Aaron Hagen
Features Ed .... Beth Rickers
Prodn. Mgr. .... Rob Muck
Mng. Ed. .... Ryan McGaughey
Business Mgr. .... Anita J Holmes
Market Information: TMC.
Mechanical Available: Offset; Black and 3 ROP colors; insert accepted; page cutoffs - 21.
Mechanical Specifications: Type page 11 5/8 x 21; E - 6 cols, 1 7/8, 1/8 between; A - 6 cols, 1 7/8, 1/8 between; C - 9 cols, 1 1/4, 1/8 between.
Areas Served: 56170, 56139, 56164, 56186, 56135, 56140, 56177, 56128, 56123, 56125, 56151, 56133, 56172, 56114, 56122, 56141, 56131, 56183, 56174, 56145, 56101, 56159, 56118, 56144, 56134, 56156, 56116, 56158, 56138, 56173, 56147, 56153, 56126, 56155, 56185, 56165, 56119, 56110, 56168, 56187, 56129, 56117, 56167, 56184, 56137, 56161, 56150, 56143, 51242, 51246, 51243, 51230, 51237, 51235, 51249, 51394, 51345, 51232, 51350, 51347, 51360, 51363, 51355, 51331, 51351, 51364, 51247, 51239, 51234, 51201, 51248, 51346, 51340, 51301
Delivery Method: Mail, CarrierEquipment & Software: PRESSROOM EQUIPMENT: Lines — 11-HI/V15 SingleWidth 1999; Folders — 2, HI/JF-7, HI/JF-25.; MAILROOM EQUIPMENT: Counter Stackers — Tiger; Inserters & Stuffers — Manual; Tying Machines — 2/Akebono; Address Machine — KR; BUSINESS EQUIPMENT: 10-Micron PC, 1-Dell PC BUSINESS SOFTWARE: Microsoft/Office, Microsoft/Windows 95, Microsoft/Windows 98, Microsoft/Excell 2000, Citrix/Great Plains Postaboft Geac CLASSIFIED EQUIPMENT: Printers — Dataproducts/Typhoon 16, HP; CLASSIFIED SOFTWARE: ACT 2.06.004. DISPLAY EQUIPMENT: Hardware — 3-APP/Mac IIci; Printers — Data Products/Typhoon 16, Epson/1270; Other Hardware — AVR/GS3000 scanner, NEC/CD-Rom DISPLAY SOFTWAREAd Make-up Applications — QPS/QuarkXPress 4.0; Layout Software — APP/Mac. EDITORIAL EQUIPMENT: Hardware — 4-APP/Mac; Printers — Data Products/Typhoon 16, Epson/1270 EDITORIAL SOFTWARE: ACT 2.06.004. PRODUCTION EQUIPMENT: Hardware — Nu/Flip Top FT40V6UPNS, 2-Glunz & Jensen/Online Processor; Cameras — SCREEN; Scanners — 3-Umax/Powerlook 2 PRODUCTION SOFTWARE: QPS/QuarkXpress 4.0.

MISSISSIPPI

BROOKHAVEN

DAILY LEADER

128 N Railroad Ave, Brookhaven, Miss., 39601-3043, Lincoln; gen tel (601) 833-6961; adv tel (601) 833-6961; ed tel (601) 833-6961; gen fax (601) 833-6714; adv fax (601) 823-5853; ed fax (601) 833-6714; gen/nat adv e-mail carol.teasley@dailyleader.com; disp adv e-mail zane.brown@dailyleader.com; class adv e-mailanna.montgomery@dailyleader.com; ed e-mail rachel.eide@dailyleader.com; web site www.dailyleader.com
Group: Boone Newspapers, Inc.
Published: Tues, Wed, Thur, Fri, Sun
Weekday Frequency: e
Saturday Frequency: m
Circulation: 5,130; 5,384(sun)
Last Audit: AAM September 30, 2012
Advertising Rate (weekday/saturday): Open inch rate $10.77
Advertising Rate (sunday): Open inch rate $11.22
Online Advertising Rate: 3 lines 2 days $13.00
News services: AP. **Established:** 1883
Own Printing Facility?: Yes
Commercial Printers?: Yes
Special Editions: FOCUS Magazine - quarterly
Brides Magazine - annually
Gridiron Magazine - annually
Special Weekly Sections: Business, Agriculture, Health (Tue); Food, Community, School (Wed); Faith (Fri); Business, Outdoor (Sun)
Syndicated Publications: Parade (S). Relish (m)
Digital Platform - Mobile: Apple, Android
Digital Platform - Tablet: Apple iOS, Android
Exec. Vice Pres./Sec./Treasurer .... Amy A. Jacobs
Pub. .... Rick Reynolds
Ed. / Gen. Mgr. .... Rachel Eide
Sports Ed. .... Tom Goetz
Prodn. Mgr., Pressroom .... Malcom Stewart
Market Information: TMC.
Mechanical Available: Offset; Black and 3 ROP colors; insert accepted; page cutoffs - 21 1/2.
Mechanical Specifications: Type page 13 x 21 1/2; E - 6 cols, 2 1/16, 1/8 between; A - 6 cols, 2 1/16, 1/8 between; C - 6 cols, 2 1/16, 1/8 between.
Areas Served: 39601,39629,39662,39191,39654,39665,39641,39647,39668,39644,39666
Delivery Method: Mail, Carrier, RacksEquipment & Software: PRESSROOM EQUIPMENT: Lines — KP/News King 1988; KP/News King 1988; KP/News King 1988; KP/News King 1988; KP/News King 1988; KP/News King 1996; KP/News King 1994; Folders — KP/KJ-8.; MAILROOM EQUIPMENT: Tying Machines — Sivaron; Address Machine — Cheshire; BUSINESS EQUIPMENT: PC BUSINESS SOFTWARE: Vision Data CLASSIFIED EQUIPMENT: Hardware — Imac; CLASSIFIED SOFTWARE: Mk, Baseview. DISPLAY EQUIPMENT: Hardware — iMac; Printers — APP/Mac LaserWriter II; DISPLAY SOFTWAREAd Make-up Applications — InDesign; Layout Software — APP/Mac. EDITORIAL EQUIPMENT: Hardware — Imac EDITORIAL SOFTWARE: MS Word, InDesign PRODUCTION EQUIPMENT: Hardware — BaysPrint; Scanners — APP/Mac Scanner PRODUCTION SOFTWARE: InDesign

CLEVELAND

THE BOLIVAR COMMERCIAL

821 N Chrisman Ave, Cleveland, Miss., 38732-2110, Bolivar; gen tel (662) 843-4241; adv tel (662) 843-4241 ext. 25; ed tel (662) 843-4241 ext. 34; gen fax (662) 843-1830; adv fax (662) 843-1830; ed fax (662) 843-1830; gen/nat adv e-mail advertising@bolivarcommercial.com; disp adv e-mail advertising@bolivarcommercial.com; class adv e-mailclassifieds@bolivarcommercial.com; ed e-mail news@bolivarcommercial.com; web site www.bolivarcom.com
Group: Cleveland Newspapers, Inc.
Published: Tues, Wed, Thur, Fri, Sun
Weekday Frequency: e
Saturday Frequency: m
Circulation: 6,205
Last Audit: Sworn/Estimate/Non-Audited September 30, 2017
Advertising Rate (weekday/saturday): Open inch rate $10.75
Advertising Rate (sunday): Open inch rate $10.75
News services: AP. **Established:** 1969
Special Editions: Crosstie Arts Festival (Apr); Football (Aug); Christmas Gift Guide (Dec); Valentine (Feb); Delta Agriculture Expo (Jan); Back-to-School (Jul); Summer/Outdoor (Jun); Italian Festival of Mississippi (Mar); Nurses' Week (May); Light Up Your Holidays (Nov); B
Special Weekly Sections: Food (Wed); Business, Religion (Fri); Sports, Mini-page (Sun)
Syndicated Publications: American Profile (Weekly).
Digital Platform - Mobile: Apple, Android, Windows
Digital Platform - Tablet: Apple iOS, Android, Windows 7
Pub. .... Mark Williams
Adv. Mgr. .... David Laster
Mng. Ed. .... Denise Strub
Sports Ed. .... Andy Collier
Prodn. Mgr. .... Sharon Clinton
Head Pressman .... Spencer Haywood
Market Information: Split run; TMC; Zoned editions.
Mechanical Available: Offset; Black and 1 ROP colors; insert accepted; page cutoffs - 22 3/4.
Mechanical Specifications: Type page 13 x 21 1/2; E - 6 cols, 2 1/16, 1/8 between; A - 6 cols, 2 1/16, 1/8 between; C - 8 cols, 1 1/2, 1/8 between.
Delivery Method: Mail, CarrierEquipment & Software: PRESSROOM EQUIPMENT: Lines — 5-G/Community; MAILROOM EQUIPMENT: Counter Stackers — Systems Technology Inc.; Tying Machines — 1/MLN; Control System — RSK/4025 LX; Address Machine — 2-/Dispensa-Matic/16.; BUSINESS EQUIPMENT: DEC/XL-466, 2-Genicom/3840P Printer BUSINESS SOFTWARE: PBS CLASSIFIED EQUIPMENT: Hardware — 1-APP/Mac Quadra; CLASSIFIED SOFTWARE: Baseview. DISPLAY EQUIPMENT: Hardware — 3-APP/Mac Quadra 650; DISPLAY SOFTWAREAd Make-up Applications — QPS/QuarkXPress, Adobe/Photoshop.; EDITORIAL EQUIPMENT: Hardware — 8-APP/Mac Quadra 605; Printers — NewGen/1200 Turbo Laser EDITORIAL SOFTWARE: Baseview. PRODUCTION EQUIPMENT: Hardware — 1-Amerigraph, Polaroid; Cameras — 1-B; Scanners — 1-HP, Polaroid PRODUCTION SOFTWARE: Baseview.

COLUMBUS

THE COMMERCIAL DISPATCH

516 Main St, Columbus, Miss., 39701-5734, Lowndes; gen tel (662) 328-2424; adv tel (662) 328-2424; ed tel (662) 328-2471; gen fax (662) 329-1521; adv fax (662) 329-1521; ed fax (662) 329-8937; gen/nat adv e-mail lmassey@cdispatch.com; disp adv e-mail bproffitt@cdispatch.com; class adv e-mailclassifieds@cdispatch.com; ed e-mail letters@cdispatch.com; web site www.cdispatch.com
Published: Mon, Tues, Wed, Thur, Fri, Sun
Weekday Frequency: e
Saturday Frequency: m
Circulation: 13,338; 13,997(sun)
Last Audit: Sworn/Estimate/Non-Audited September 30, 2017
Advertising Rate (weekday/saturday): Open inch rate $13.10
Advertising Rate (sunday): Open inch rate $13.10
Online Advertising Rate: 300x250 Box $8.00 CPM
News services: AP, LAT-WP. **Established:** 1879
Own Printing Facility?: Yes
Commercial Printers?: Yes
Special Editions: Catfish Alley magazine (quarterly); Football Preview (Aug); Health & Fitness (Feb); Money & Taxes (Jan); FYI (Jun); Home & Garden (Mar); Salute to Family Owned Business (May); Back to School (Sept).
Special Weekly Sections: Food (Wed); Business (Thur); Religion (Fri); TV Week (Sun); Church (Fri/Sun)
Syndicated Publications: Parade (S).
Digital Platform - Mobile: Apple, Android, Windows
Digital Platform - Tablet: Apple iOS, Android, Windows 7
Pub. .... Birney Imes
Gen. Mgr. .... Peter Imes
Adv. Dir. .... Beth Proffitt
Reporter & Columnist .... Slim Smith
Prepress Mgr. .... Tina Perry
Circ. & Production Mgr. .... Mike Floyd
Acct. Clerk .... Debbie Foster
Catfish Alley Ed. .... Stacy Clark
Sports Ed. .... Adam Minichino
Mechanical Available: Offset; Black and 3 ROP colors; insert accepted - pocket-book or single card; page cutoffs - 21 1/2.
Mechanical Specifications: Type page 13 x 21 1/2; E - 6 cols, 2 1/16, 1/8 between; A - 6 cols, 2 1/16, 1/8 between; C - 9 cols, 1 3/8, 1/8 between.
Areas Served: Lowndes County, Oktibbeha County, Clay County, Noxubee County, Monroe County
Delivery Method: Mail, CarrierEquipment & Software: PRESSROOM EQUIPMENT: Lines — 7-G/501(1), G/Urbanite.; MAILROOM EQUIPMENT: Counter Stackers — HL/Monitor; Inserters & Stuffers — MM/227S 6:1; Tying Machines — 1-Sterling/GR40.;

CORINTH

THE DAILY CORINTHIAN

1607 S Harper Rd, Corinth, Miss., 38834-6653, Alcorn; gen tel (662) 287-6111; adv tel (662) 287-6111 ext. 339; gen fax (662) 287-3525; gen/nat adv e-mail advertising@dailycorinthian.com; disp adv e-mail advertising@dailycorinthian.com; class adv e-mailclassad@dailycorinthian.com; ed e-mail news@dailycorinthian.com; web site www.dailycorinthian.com
Group: Paxton Media Group, LLC
Published: Tues, Wed, Thur, Fri, Sat, Sun
Weekday Frequency: m
Saturday Frequency: m
Circulation: 6,113; 6,113(sat); 6,186(sun)
Last Audit: Sworn/Estimate/Non-Audited September 30, 2017
Advertising Rate (weekday/saturday): Open inch rate $16.95
Advertising Rate (sunday): 16.95
News services: AP. **Established:** 1895
Own Printing Facility?: Yes
Commercial Printers?: Yes
Special Editions: Crossroads Magazine monthly
Special Weekly Sections: Church Page (Fri).
Syndicated Publications: USA WEEKEND Magazine (S).
Digital Platform - Mobile: Apple, Android
Digital Platform - Tablet: Apple iOS, Android
Pub. .... Reese Terry
Circ. Dir. .... Wille Walker
Ed. .... Mark Boehler
Adv. Mgr. .... Fallon Hunt
Market Information: TMC.
Mechanical Available: Offset; Black and 3 ROP colors; insert accepted; page cutoffs - 21.

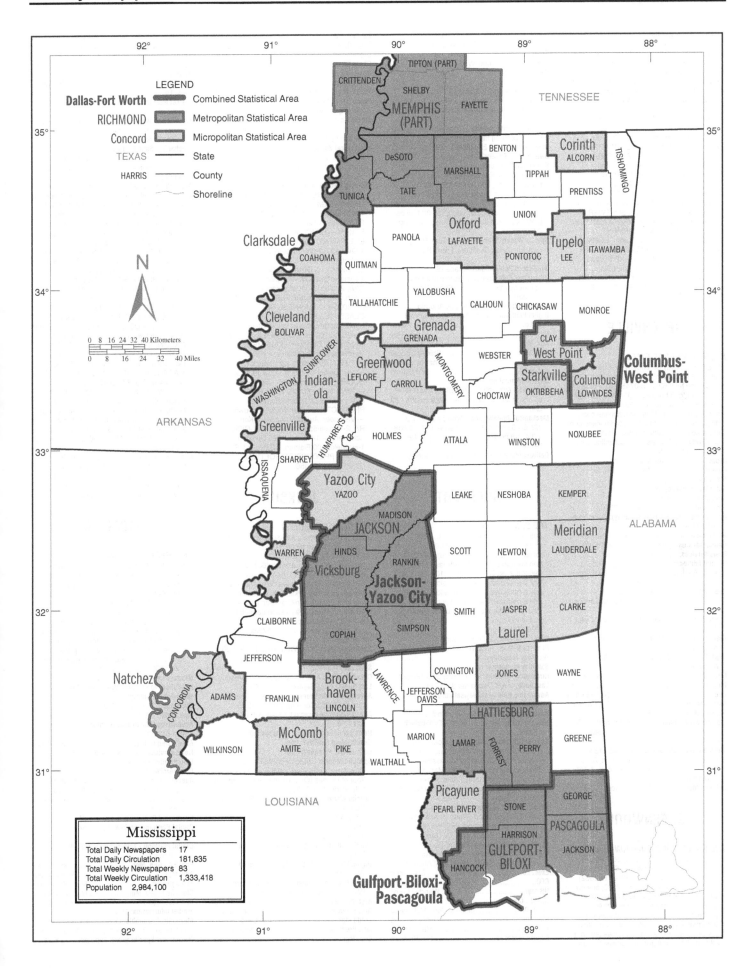

LEGEND

Dallas-Fort Worth   Combined Statistical Area
RICHMOND   Metropolitan Statistical Area
Concord   Micropolitan Statistical Area
TEXAS   State
HARRIS   County
    Shoreline

N

0 8 16 24 32 40 Kilometers
0 8   16   24   32   40 Miles

Mississippi

Total Daily Newspapers   17
Total Daily Circulation   181,835
Total Weekly Newspapers 83
Total Weekly Circulation 1,333,418
Population   2,984,100

Mechanical Specifications: Type page 10.125 x 21; E - 6 cols, A - 6 cols, C - 9 cols.
Areas Served: 38236,38339,38357,38367,38375 ,38683,38833,38834,38846,38865,38852
Delivery Method: Newsstand, Carrier, RacksEquipment & Software: PRESSROOM EQUIPMENT: Lines — 9-G/Community 1982.; MAILROOM EQUIPMENT: Tying Machines — MLN/Strapper.; BUSINESS EQUIPMENT: APP/Mac BUSINESS SOFTWARE: INSI CLASSIFIED EQUIPMENT: Hardware — APP/Mac; APP/Mac; CLASSIFIED SOFTWARE: Ad Manager Pro 5. DISPLAY EQUIPMENT: Hardware — 4-APP/Mac G5; Printers — Xante/8200, HP 5520; DISPLAY SOFTWAREAd Make-up Applications — Multi-Ad/Creator, QPS/QuarkXPress 3.32.; EDITORIAL EQUIPMENT: Hardware — APP/Mac/IQueWeb EDITORIAL SOFTWARE: Baseview/NewsEdit Pro, QPS/QuarkXPress 3.32. PRODUCTION EQUIPMENT: Hardware — 1-Nu/Plate Burner, ECRM 6200; Cameras — 1-B/Caravel; Scanners — 2-Microtek/ScanMaker II XE Flatbed, Nikon/Coolscan-Polaroid/Sprint Scan, Microtek 9600 XL Flatbed PRODUCTION SOFTWARE: InDesign CIRCULATION SOFTWARMediaSpan

GREENVILLE

DELTA DEMOCRAT TIMES

988 N Broadway St, Greenville, Miss., 38701-2349, Washington; gen tel (662) 335-1155; adv tel (662) 378-0745; ed tel (662) 378-0711; gen fax (662) 335-2860; adv fax (662) 335-2860; ed fax (662) 378-0777; gen/nat adv e-mail suetriplett@ddtonline.com; disp adv e-mail keithwilliams@ddtonline.com; class adv e-mailcathybramuchi@ddtonline.com; ed e-mail lauarsmith@ddtonline.com; web site www.ddtonline.com
Group: Emmerich Newspapers, Inc.
Published: Mon, Tues, Wed, Thur, Fri, Sun
Weekday Frequency: e
Saturday Frequency: m
Circulation: 4,864; 5,458(sun)
Last Audit: AAM September 30, 2016
Advertising Rate (weekday/saturday): Open inch rate $17.47
Advertising Rate (sunday): Open inch rate $17.47
Online Advertising Rate: 1-2 lines for $10.80
News services: AP. **Established:** 1938
Special Editions: Fall Football (Aug); Bridal (Feb); Back-to-School (Jul); Our Town (Mar); Holiday Shopping Guide (Nov).
Special Weekly Sections: Food (Wed); Entertainment (Thur); Church (Fri); Comics, TV (Sun)
Syndicated Publications: USA Weekend, Color Comics (S)
Digital Platform - Mobile: Apple, Android, Windows
Digital Platform - Tablet: Apple iOS, Android, Windows 7
Circ. Mgr. .... Curtis Peeples
Mng. Ed. .... Laura Smith
Pub. .... Matt Guthrie
Asst. Adv. Dir. .... Lisa Edwards
Market Information: ADS; TMC.
Mechanical Available: Offset; Black and 3 ROP colors; insert accepted - booklets; page cutoffs - 22 3/4.
Mechanical Specifications: Type page 13 x 21 1/2; E - 6 cols, 2 1/16, 1/8 between; A - 6 cols, 2 1/16, 1/8 between; C - 8 cols, 1 1/2, 1/16 between.
Delivery Method: Mail, Carrier, Racks

GREENWOOD

THE GREENWOOD COMMONWEALTH

329 Highway 82 W, Greenwood, Miss., 38930-6538, Leflore; gen tel (662) 453-5312; adv tel (662) 581-7230; ed tel (662) 581-7243; gen fax (662) 453-2908; adv fax (662) 453-2908; ed fax (662) 453-2908; gen/nat adv e-mail commonwealth@gwcommonwealth.com; disp adv e-mail lalderman@gwcommonwealth.com; class adv e-mailkturner@gwcommonwealth.com; ed e-mail tkalich@gwcommonwealth.com; web site www.gwcommonwealth.com - 295,194(views) 36,743(visitors)
Group: Emmerich Newspapers, Inc.
Published: Mon, Tues, Wed, Thur, Fri, Sun
Weekday Frequency: e
Saturday Frequency: m
Circulation: 4,918; 5,229(sun)
Last Audit: AAM March 31, 2017
Advertising Rate (weekday/saturday): Open inch rate $15.60
Advertising Rate (sunday): Open inch rate $15.60
Online Advertising Rate: $9.40 ROS
News services: AP. **Established:** 1896
Own Printing Facility?: Yes
Commercial Printers?: Yes
Special Editions: Football (Aug); Health and Fitness (Sept); People's Choice (Oct); Christmas Gift Guide (Nov); Christmas Greetings (Dec); Profile (Feb); Top 30 Under 40 (March every other year); Top 30 Places to Work (March every other year); Farming (May)
Special Weekly Sections: Food (Tue); Religion (Fri); Lifestyles, Outdoors, Farm, Business (Sun)
Syndicated Publications: Parade (S)
Proprietary Publications: Leflore Illustrated (quarterly magazine); The Phone Book (annual)
Digital Platform - Mobile: Apple, Android
Digital Platform - Tablet: Apple iOS, Android
Pub./Ed .... Tim Kalich
Bus. Mgr. .... Eddie Ray
Adv. Mgr. .... Larry Alderman
Circ. Mgr. .... Shirley Cooper
Mng. Ed. .... Charles Corder
Sports Ed. .... Bill Burrus
Market Information: TMC.
Mechanical Available: Offset; Black and 3 ROP colors; insert accepted - all; page cutoffs - 22 3/4.
Mechanical Specifications: Type page 11 x 21 1/2; E - 6 cols, 1 3/4, 1/8 between; A - 6 cols, 1 3/4, 1/8 between; C - 8 cols, 1 1/4, 1/8 between.
Delivery Method: Mail, Newsstand, Carrier, Racks

GULFPORT

THE SUN HERALD

205 Debuys Rd, Gulfport, Miss., 39507-2838, Harrison; gen tel (228) 896-2100; adv tel (228) 896-2490; ed tel (228) 896-2301; gen fax (228) 896-2362; adv fax (228) 896-2362; ed fax (228) 896-2104; gen/nat adv e-mail dladnerl@sunherald.com; disp adv e-mail dladnerl@sunherald.com; class adv e-mailsellit@sunherald.com; ed e-mail letters@sunherald.com; web site www.sunherald.com
526,614(visitors)
Group: The McClatchy Company
Published: Mon, Tues, Wed, Thur, Fri, Sat, Sun
Weekday Frequency: m
Saturday Frequency: m
Circulation: 24,004; 23,762(sat); 29,218(sun)
Last Audit: AAM December 31, 2014
Advertising Rate (weekday/saturday): Open inch rate $59.98
Advertising Rate (sunday): Open inch rate $71.38
News services: AP, MCT, SHNS. **Established:** 1884
Special Editions: Guide to Gulf Coast Living (Apr); Football (Aug); Attractions (Feb); Annual Progress (Jan); Wellness/Healthcare Directory (Jul); Nike Classic (Mar); Home & Products Show (May); Auto Showroom (Nov); Annual Salute to the Military (Oct); NIE Literacy (Sept).
Special Weekly Sections: Soundoff (Mon); Casinos (Tue); Food (Wed); Health, Marquee (Thur); Faith, Neighbors (Fri); Home & Garden (Sat); Arts, Travel, TV (Sun)
Syndicated Publications: Parade (S).
Digital Platform - Mobile: Apple, Android
Digital Platform - Tablet: Apple iOS, Android
Exec. Ed. .... Stan Tiner
CFO .... Flora Point
HR Mgr. .... Wanda Howell
Coord., Credit .... Faye Taylor
Mktg. Dir. .... John McFarland
Circ. Dir. .... Gary Raskett
Editorial Dir. .... Marie Harris
Entertainment Ed. .... Jean Prescott
Features Ed. .... Scott Hawkins
Local News Ed. .... Kate Magandy
Outdoors Ed .... Al Jones
Photo Ed. .... Drew Tarter
Sports Ed. .... Doug Barber
Data Processing Mgr. .... Carole Brown
Prodn. Mgr., Composing .... Gary Rachuba
Prodn. Mgr., Distr. .... Randy Seib
Prodn. Mgr., Pressroom .... Dean Cook
Mechanical Available: Offset; Black and 3 ROP colors; insert accepted - product samples; page cutoffs - 21.
Mechanical Specifications: Type page 13 x 21; E - 6 cols, 2 1/16, 1/8 between; A - 6 cols, 2 1/16, 1/8 between; C - 10 cols, 1 3/8, 1/16 between.
Delivery Method: Mail, CarrierEquipment & Software: PRESSROOM EQUIPMENT: Lines — 6-G/Headliner Offset double width 1987; Folders — 1-G/3:2 1987; Pasters —6/RTP; Reels & Stands — CT/50; Control System — G/MCC-MPCS.; MAILROOM EQUIPMENT: Counter Stackers — 1-QWI/400, 2-QWI/350; Inserters & Stuffers — 1-Harris 8/48, 1-HI/1572, 1-HI 8/48; Tying Machines — 3-Dynaric/1500, 1-OVL/JP-80, 1/Dynaric Q52000; Wrapping Singles — 2-/QWI, 2-Id/6113, Viper; Address Machine — 1-/Ch, 1-Ch/5; BUSINESS EQUIPMENT: HP/3000-937 BUSINESS SOFTWARE: CJ CLASSIFIED EQUIPMENT: Hardware — Cybergraphics, Cybersell; Printers — HP/LaserJet 2100TN; CLASSIFIED SOFTWARE: Genera 4.6. DISPLAY EQUIPMENT: Hardware — HP; Printers — HP; DISPLAY SOFTWAREAd Make-up Applications — CJ 8.02H; Layout Software — CJ. EDITORIAL EQUIPMENT: Hardware — Sun; Printers — HP/LaserJet 8000N EDITORIAL SOFTWARE: DTI/Client Software. PRODUCTION EQUIPMENT: Hardware — Visioneer, Au/3850 Imager, 1-Konica/66 RA, 2-Konica/550; Cameras — 1-C/Pager; Scanners — 1-Howtek/4000 Desktop, 1-Howtek/2500 Flatbed, AG/Arcus II Flatbed, Aii/3750 PRODUCTION SOFTWARE: DTI Ultra Enterprise 450.

JACKSON

THE CLARION-LEDGER

201 S Congress St, Jackson, Miss., 39201-4202, Hinds; gen tel (601) 961-7000; adv tel (601) 961-7143; ed tel (601) 961-7101; gen fax (601) 961-7211; adv fax (601) 961-7155; ed fax (601) 961-7211; gen/nat adv e-mail rweeks@jackson.gannett.com; disp adv e-mail rcaputo@jackson.gannett.com; class adv e-mailkparkman@jackson.gannett.com; ed e-mail dskipper@jackson.gannett.com; web site www.clarionledger.com - 8,134,213(views) 1,132,687(visitors)
Group: Gannett
Published: Mon, Tues, Wed, Thur, Fri, Sat, Sun
Weekday Frequency: m
Saturday Frequency: m
Circulation: 35,482; 35,169(sat); 41,194(sun)
Last Audit: AAM September 30, 2017
Advertising Rate (weekday/saturday): Open inch rate $180.35 (Mon-Fri); $180.35 (Sat)
Advertising Rate (sunday): Open inch rate $217.66
News services: AP, GNS, **Established:** 1837
Own Printing Facility?: Yes
Commercial Printers?: Yes
Special Editions: College Football (Aug); Discovery (Jun); Week on the Water (May); Tour of Homes (Oct); Tis the Season Holiday Gift Guide (Nov & Dec.)
Special Weekly Sections: Business, Real Estate, Sports, Outdoors, Arts (Sun); Health (Tue); Food (Wed); Community, Entertainment (Thur); Autos, Homes, Home & Garden (Fri); Religion (Sat);
Syndicated Publications: USA WEEKEND Magazine (S)
Digital Platform - Mobile: Apple, Android, Windows
Digital Platform - Tablet: Apple iOS, Android, Windows 7, Kindle, Kindle Fire
Asst. Managing Ed. .... Debbie Skipper
Dir., Finance .... Joe Williams
Credit Mgr. .... Carolyn Allen
Adv. Pre Prints .... Beverly Bennett
Circ. Mgr. .... Vera Bridges
Circ. Mgr., Single Copy .... Chris Hutchinson
Editorial Cartoonist .... Marshall Ramsey
Advertising Sales Manager .... Katie Parkman
Publisher .... Jason Taylor
Sales Dir. .... Stacia King
Adv. Dir. .... Judi Terzotis
Exec. Ed. .... Sam Hall
Market Information: Split run; TMC; Zoned editions.
Mechanical Available: Offset; Black and 4 ROP colors; insert accepted - print & deliver, samples; page cutoffs - 22.
Mechanical Specifications: Type page 11 1/8 x 21; E - 6 cols, 1 3/4, 1/8 between; A - 6 cols, 1 3/4, 1/8 between; C - 10 cols, 1.063, .0556 between.
Areas Served: 39201; 39157; 39110; 39046
Delivery Method: Mail, Carrier, RacksEquipment & Software: PRESSROOM EQUIPMENT: Lines — 8-G/Metroliner (double width) 1982; 8-G/Metroliner (double width) 1995; Folders — 2-1982, 2-1995; Pasters —G/3-arm RTP. MAILROOM EQUIPMENT: Counter Stackers — 3-Id, 6/QWI; Inserters & Stuffers — 2-S/1372P, 1-NP/630; Tying Machines — 2-MLN/News 90, 4-/Sterlings, 2-/OVL; BUSINESS EQUIPMENT: IBM AS/400 CLASSIFIED EQUIPMENT: Hardware — DELL PC; Printers — HP, CANON; CLASSIFIED SOFTWARE: DTI/ClassSpeed 4.2.2. DISPLAY EQUIPMENT: Hardware — DELL PC; Printers — QMS/860, AU/Broadsheet, HP/650C, Tektronix/780, CANON, XANTE; DISPLAY SOFTWAREAd Make-up Applications — AD TEACHER/INDESIGN; Layout Software — MEI/ALS. MACTIVE PGL EDITORIAL EQUIPMENT: Hardware - Dell PC EDITORIAL SOFTWARE: Newsgate PRODUCTION EQUIPMENT: Hardware — APP/Server, Graham, 1-K/550; Cameras — 1-C/Spartan; Scanners — 6-Umax/UC-1260 Flatbed, 2-Tecsa/TS2470, 2-AG/Argus 2, 1-Linotype-Hell/Opal Ultra PRODUCTION SOFTWARE: Newsgate
Note: The Jackson Clarion-Ledger (mS) has a combination rate of $180.35(mon to fri), $180.35(sat) and $217.66(S) with the Hattiesburg American (eS). Individual newspaper rates not made available.

MCCOMB

ENTERPRISE-JOURNAL

112 Oliver Emmerich Dr, McComb, Miss., 39648-6330, Pike; gen tel (601) 684-2421; adv tel (601) 684-2421 ext. 229; ed tel (601) 684-2421 ext. 217; gen fax (601) 684-0836; adv fax (601) 684-0836; ed fax (601) 684-0836; gen/nat adv e-mail advertising@enterprise-journal.com; disp adv e-mail advertising@enterprise-journal.com; class adv e-mailclassifieds@enterprise-journal.com; ed e-mail publisher@enterprise-journal.com; web site www.enterprise-journal.com - 200,000(views) 10,000(visitors)
Group: Emmerich Newspapers, Inc.
Published: Mon, Tues, Wed, Thur, Fri, Sun
Weekday Frequency: e
Circulation: 7,128; 7,523(sun)
Last Audit: AAM June 30, 2017
Advertising Rate (weekday/saturday): Open inch rate $17.80
Advertising Rate (sunday): Open inch rate $18.60
News services: AP. **Established:** 1889
Own Printing Facility?: Yes
Commercial Printers?: Yes
Special Editions: Graduation (Apr); Football (Aug); Christmas Greetings (Dec); Back-to-School (Jul); Perspective (Mar); Recipe (Sept); Adventure (Oct).
Syndicated Publications: Parade (S).
Digital Platform - Mobile: Apple, Android, Windows
Digital Platform - Tablet: Apple iOS, Android, Windows 7
Pub./Ed./ Gen. Mgr. .... Jack Ryan
Adv. Mgr. .... Vicky Deere
Managing Ed. .... Matt Williamson
Classifieds Adv. Mgr. .... Margie Williams
Business Mgr. .... Kim Golden
Market Information: TMC.
Mechanical Available: Offset; Black and 3 ROP colors; insert accepted; page cutoffs - 22 3/4.
Mechanical Specifications: Type page 13 x 21

1/2; E - 6 cols, 2, 1/8 between; A - 6 cols, 2, 1/8 between; C - 8 cols, 1 1/2, 1/8 between.
Areas Served: McComb/Pike/39648
Delivery Method: Mail, Carrier, RacksEquipment & Software: PRESSROOM EQUIPMENT: Folders — 1, 1-KP/JK8.

MERIDIAN

THE MERIDIAN STAR

814 22nd Ave, Meridian, Miss., 39301-5023, Lauderdale; gen tel (601) 693-1551; adv tel (601) 693-1551 ext. 3257; ed tel (601) 693-1551 ext. 3213; gen fax (601) 485-1275; adv fax (601) 485-1229; ed fax (601) 485-1275; gen/nat adv e-mail advertising@themeridianstar.com; disp adv e-mail advertising@themeridianstar.com; class adv e-mailjwilliams@themeidianstar.com; ed e-mail editor@themeridianstar.com; web site www.meridianstar.com
Group: Community Newspaper Holdings, Inc.
Published: Tues, Wed, Thur, Fri, Sat, Sun
Weekday Frequency: m
Saturday Frequency: m
Circulation: 7,295; 7,295(sat); 8,615(sun)
Last Audit: AAM September 30, 2014
Advertising Rate (weekday/saturday): Open inch rate $29.45
Advertising Rate (sunday): Open inch rate $31.13
News services: AP. **Established:** 1898
Own Printing Facility?: Yes
Commercial Printers?: No
Special Editions: EMCC Salute (Apr); Bands & Cheerleaders (Aug); Christmas Greetings (Dec); Profile (Feb); Tanning Page (Jan); FYI (Jul); State Games Tab (Jun); Spring Lawn & Garden (Mar); Jimmie Rogers Days (May); Christmas Early Bird Buys (Nov); Who's The Best (Oct); Fal
Special Weekly Sections: Food (Wed); Religion (Sat); Business, Finance (Sun)
Syndicated Publications: Relish (Monthly); Parade (S); American Profile (Weekly).
Photo Dept. Mgr. .... Paula Merritt
Staff Writer .... Ida Brown
Church Pages & Bus. Review .... Elizabeth Ryan
Pub. .... Alexander Gould
Ed. .... Dave Bohrer
Market Information: ADS; TMC.
Mechanical Available: Offset; Black and 3 ROP colors; insert accepted; page cutoffs - 22 3/4.
Mechanical Specifications: Type page 11 x 21; E - 6 cols, 2, 1/6 between; A - 6 cols, 2, 1/6 between; C - 8 cols, 1 1/2, 1/6 between.
Areas Served: 30301, 30305
Delivery Method: CarrierEquipment & Software: MAILROOM EQUIPMENT: Counter Stackers — 2/HL; Inserters & Stuffers — 1-/MM 4:1, 1-/KAN (6:1); Tying Machines — 4-/MLN; Address Machine — El.; BUSINESS SOFTWARE: Vision Data CLASSIFIED EQUIPMENT: Hardware — Vision Data; Printers — APP/Mac LaserWriter II NTX; CLASSIFIED SOFTWARE: Vision Data, Baseview. DISPLAY EQUIPMENT: Hardware — APP/Mac, APP/Mac II NTX; DISPLAY SOFTWAREAd Make-up Applications — Aldus/PageMaker; Layout Software — APP/Mac. EDITORIAL EQUIPMENT: Hardware — APP/Mac; Printers — APP/Mac LaserWriter II NTX, V EDITORIAL SOFTWARE: APP/Mac. PRODUCTION EQUIPMENT: Cameras — C/Spartan III.

NATCHEZ

THE NATCHEZ DEMOCRAT

503 N Canal St, Natchez, Miss., 39120-2902, Adams; gen tel (601) 442-9101; adv tel (601) 445-3634; ed tel (601) 445-3539; gen fax (601) 442-7315; adv fax (601) 442-7315; ed fax (601) 442-7315; gen/nat adv e-mail newsroom@natchezdemocrat.com; disp adv e-mail sue.hicks@natchezdemocrat.com; class adv e-mailsue.hicks@natchezdemocrat.com; ed e-mail julie.cooper@natchezdemocrat.com; web site www.natchezdemocrat.com
Group: Boone Newspapers, Inc.
Published: Mon, Tues, Wed, Thur, Fri, Sat, Sun
Weekday Frequency: m
Saturday Frequency: m
Circulation: 8,428; 8,428(sat); 8,536(sun)
Last Audit: Sworn/Estimate/Non-Audited September 30, 2017
Advertising Rate (weekday/saturday): Open inch rate $22.50
Advertising Rate (sunday): Open inch rate $24.00
News services: AP. **Established:** 1865
Own Printing Facility?: Yes
Commercial Printers?: Yes
Special Editions: Profile (Feb); Natchez & Its Neighbors (Jul); Spring Pilgrimage (Mar); Fall Pilgrimage (Oct).
Special Weekly Sections: People (Wed/Sun); Religion (Sat); Business, Finance (Sun);
Syndicated Publications: USA WEEKEND Magazine (S).
Natchez the Magazine (bi-monthly)
Digital Platform - Mobile: Apple, Android, Windows
Digital Platform - Tablet: Apple iOS, Android, Windows 7, Blackberry Tablet OS, Kindle, Nook, Kindle Fire
Pub. .... Kevin Cooper
Marketing Coord. .... Ryan Richardson
Managing Ed. .... Julie Cooper
Circ. Mgr. .... Sam King
Market Information: ADS; TMC; Zoned editions.
Mechanical Available: Offset; Black and 3 ROP colors; insert accepted; page cutoffs - 22 3/4.
Mechanical Specifications: Type page 11 x 21 1/2; E - 6 cols, 2 1/16, 1/8 between; A - 6 cols, 2 1/16, 1/8 between; C - 9 cols, 1 3/8, 1/16 between.
Areas Served: 39120, 39669, 39661, 39069, 71326, 71334, 71343, 71354, 71373, 71375
Delivery Method: Newsstand, Carrier, RacksEquipment & Software: PRESSROOM EQUIPMENT: Lines — 10-KP/News King; Folders — 1-KP/Balloon former; Reels & Stands — 8; MAILROOM EQUIPMENT: Counter Stackers — 1-BG/Count-O-Veyor; Tying Machines — 1/Md; Address Machine — 2-/El, 2-/Am.;

OXFORD

THE OXFORD EAGLE

4 Private Road 2050, Oxford, Miss., 38655-8887, Lafayette; gen tel (662) 234-4331; adv tel (662) 234-4331; ed tel (662) 234-4331; gen fax (662) 234-4351; adv fax (662) 234-4351; ed fax (662) 234-4351; gen/nat adv e-mail addirector@oxfordeagle.com; disp adv e-mail addirector@oxfordeagle.com; class adv e-mailclassifieds@oxfordeagle.com; ed e-mail news@oxfordeagle.com; web site www.oxfordeagle.com
Group: Boone Newspapers, Inc.
Published: Mon, Tues, Wed, Thur, Fri
Weekday Frequency: e
Circulation: 5,016
Last Audit: Sworn/Estimate/Non-Audited September 30, 2017
Advertising Rate (weekday/saturday): Open inch rate $9.55
News services: AP. **Established:** 1867
Special Editions: Brides 2013 (Jan); Best of Oxford 2013 (Feb); Home Market Guide; Lease on Living (Mar); Senior Living Magazine (Apr); Graduation (May); Spring 2013; Welcome Back Rebels (Aug).
Special Weekly Sections: Business, Finance (Mon); Education (Tue); Lifestyle, Best Food Day (Wed); Health (Thur); Living, Weekend, Church (Fri)
Syndicated Publications: American Profile (Weekly).
Digital Platform - Mobile: Apple, Android
Digital Platform - Tablet: Apple iOS, Android
Circ. Mgr. .... Belinda Jones
Photo Ed. .... Bruce Newman
Head Pressman .... Eddie Lance
Adv. Dir. .... Delia Childers
Sports Ed. .... Davis Potter
Ed. .... Alex McDaniel
Market Information: TMC.
Mechanical Available: Offset; Black and 3 ROP colors; insert accepted; page cutoffs - 22 3/4.
Mechanical Specifications: Type page 13 1/8 x 21; E - 6 cols, 2 1/16, 1/8 between; A - 6 cols, 2 1/16, 1/8 between; C - 8 cols, 1 1/2, 1/8 between.
Delivery Method: Mail, CarrierEquipment & Software: PRESSROOM EQUIPMENT: Lines — 6-G/Community (upper folder).; MAILROOM EQUIPMENT: Tying Machines — 2/Felins; Address Machine — 1-/Am.; BUSINESS EQUIPMENT: 1-RSK/16B, 1-RSK/DT 100, 2-RSK/100 BUSINESS SOFTWARE: Word processing CLASSIFIED EQUIPMENT: Hardware — COM; CLASSIFIED SOFTWARE: Baseview/Class Manager. DISPLAY SOFTWARELayout Software — COM. EDITORIAL EQUIPMENT: Hardware — COM EDITORIAL SOFTWARE: Baseview/NewsEdit. PRODUCTION EQUIPMENT: Hardware — 1-COM/CRT; Cameras — 1-R.

PICAYUNE

PICAYUNE ITEM

17 Richardson Ozona Rd, Picayune, Miss., 39466-7865, Pearl River; gen tel (601) 798-4766; adv tel (601) 798-4766; ed tel (601) 798-4766; gen fax (601) 798-8602; adv fax (601) 798-8602; ed fax (601) 798-8602; gen/nat adv e-mail vstockstill@bellsouth.net; disp adv e-mail ksmyth@picayuneitem.com; class adv e-mailitemreaderads@picayuneitem.com; ed e-mail editor@picayuneitem.com; web site www.picayuneitem.com
Group: Boone Newspapers, Inc.
Published: Tues, Wed, Thur, Fri, Sun
Weekday Frequency: m
Circulation: 6,136; 5,369(sun)
Last Audit: Sworn/Estimate/Non-Audited September 30, 2017
Advertising Rate (weekday/saturday): Open inch rate $12.00
Online Advertising Rate: 3 lines 5 days print and 7 days online $15.00
News services: AP, NEA. **Established:** 1904
Special Editions: Pearl River County Today (Other).
Special Weekly Sections: Sports, Lifestyles, Business, Comics, Entertainment (Sun); Local Sports, Food (Tue); Lifestyles, Agriculture, Food, Farm (Wed); Education, Entertainment (Thur); Religion (Fri)
Syndicated Publications: Relish (Monthly); Profile Sunday Magazine (S); River County Football (Th).
Digital Platform - Mobile: Apple, Android
Digital Platform - Tablet: Apple iOS, Android
Bus. Mgr. .... Cindy Woods
Circ. Dir. .... Annett Webber
Prodn. Foreman, Pressroom .... Steven Ellis
Pub. .... Linda Gilmore
Sports/News Writer .... Taylor Welsh
Assoc. Pub./Ed. .... Jeremy Pittari
Market Information: TMC.
Mechanical Available: Offset; Black and 3 ROP colors; insert accepted; page cutoffs - 22 3/4.
Delivery Method: Mail, CarrierEquipment & Software: MAILROOM EQUIPMENT: Counter Stackers — 1/BG; Tying Machines — 1-/Bu; Address Machine — Automecha/Accufast.; BUSINESS EQUIPMENT: Unisys CLASSIFIED EQUIPMENT: Hardware — 2-Mk.; DISPLAY EQUIPMENT: Printers — 1-APP/Mac LaserWriter II NTX, Dataproducts/LZR 1560; DISPLAY SOFTWAREAd Make-up Applications — QPS/QuarkXPress 4.0; Layout Software — 3-APP/Mac. EDITORIAL EQUIPMENT: Hardware — 5-Mk; Printers — 2-APP/Mac LaserWriter. PRODUCTION EQUIPMENT: Hardware — 2-APP/Mac LaserWriter II NTX; Cameras — Goerz/J72; Scanners — APP/Mac Scanner PRODUCTION SOFTWARE: Baseview.

STARKVILLE

STARKVILLE DAILY NEWS

304 E Lampkin St, Starkville, Miss., 39759-2910, Oktibbeha; gen tel (662) 323-1642; adv tel (662) 323-1642; ed tel (662) 324-8092; gen fax (662) 323-6586; adv fax (662) 323-6586; ed fax (662) 323-6586; gen/nat adv e-mail ads@starkvilledailynews.com; disp adv e-mail ads@starkvilledailynews.com; class adv e-mailclassified@starkvilledailynews.com; ed e-mail news@starkvilledailynews.com; web site www.starkvilledailynews.com
Group: Horizon Publications Inc.
Published: Mon, Tues, Wed, Thur, Fri, Sat, Sun
Weekday Frequency: m
Saturday Frequency: m
Circulation: 7,071; 7,071(sat); 7,071(sun)
Last Audit: Sworn/Estimate/Non-Audited September 30, 2017
Advertising Rate (weekday/saturday): Open inch rate $11.65
Advertising Rate (sunday): Open inch rate $13.72
News services: AP. **Established:** 1875
Special Editions: Bulldog Weekend (Apr); Welcome Back Miss. State (Aug); Progress (Feb); Christmas Gift Guide (Nov).
Special Weekly Sections: Education (Mon); Local Roundup (Tue); Best Food, Entertainment (Wed); Weekend Roundup (Fri); Religion (Sat); Lifestyle, Wedding (Sun)
Syndicated Publications: American Profile (S).
Digital Platform - Mobile: Apple, Android, Windows
Digital Platform - Tablet: Apple iOS, Android, Windows 7
Pub. .... Don Norman
Bus. Mgr. .... Mona Howell
Circ. Mgr. .... Byron Norman
Creative Dir. .... Larry Bost
Educ. Ed. .... Shea Staskowski
Ed. .... Brian Hawkins
Market Information: TMC.
Mechanical Available: Offset; Black and 3 ROP colors; insert accepted; page cutoffs - 22 3/4.
Mechanical Specifications: Type page 10 x 21 1/2; E - 6 cols, 1 9/16, 1/8 between; A - 6 cols, 1 9/16, 1/8 between; C - 9 cols, 1 1/32, 1/8 between.
Delivery Method: Mail, CarrierEquipment & Software: BUSINESS EQUIPMENT: PC CLASSIFIED EQUIPMENT: Hardware — APP/Mac Quadra 605; CLASSIFIED SOFTWARE: Baseview. DISPLAY EQUIPMENT: Hardware — APP/Mac Quadra 660, APP/Mac Quadra 650, Umax, APP/Power Mac, APP/Mac G3, APP/Mac G4; Printers — GCC/Elite XL; Other Hardware — Canon/Scanner, Microtek/Scanner, Polaroid/Scanner. DISPLAY SOFTWAREAd Make-up Applications — QPS/QuarkXPress 4.2; EDITORIAL EQUIPMENT: Hardware — APP/Power Mac, APP/Mac Quadra 605, APP/Mac G3, APP/Mac G4; Printers — APP/Mac LaserWriter II, GCC/Elite XL EDITORIAL SOFTWARE: Baseview. PRODUCTION EQUIPMENT: Hardware — QPS/QuarkXPress 4.2.
Note: For detailed production information, see West Point Daily Times Leader.

TUPELO

NORTHEAST MISSISSIPPI DAILY JOURNAL

1242 S Green St, Tupelo, Miss., 38804-6301, Lee; gen tel (662) 842-2611; adv tel (662) 842-2614; ed tel (662) 842-2612; gen fax (662) 842-2233; adv fax (662) 620-8301; ed fax (662) 842-2233; gen/nat adv e-mail ads@journalinc.com; disp adv e-mail ads@journalinc.com; class adv e-mailclassifieds@journalinc.com; ed e-mail editor@journalinc.com; web site www.djournal.com
Group: Journal Publishing Company
Published: Mon, Tues, Wed, Thur, Fri, Sat, Sun
Weekday Frequency: m
Saturday Frequency: m
Circulation: 28,138; 27,766(sat); 30,681(sun)
Last Audit: AAM December 31, 2015
Advertising Rate (weekday/saturday): Open inch rate $26.16
Advertising Rate (sunday): Open inch rate $26.94
Online Advertising Rate: PP Pushdown Ad $25.00 CPM; Top of Site $15.00 CPM
News services: AP, MCT. **Established:** 1872
Own Printing Facility?: Yes
Commercial Printers?: Yes
Special Editions: Business Journal (Monthly); Healthly Living (Jan); North MS Health Journal Magazine (Mar & Aug); Spring Fashion (Mar); Blue Suede Cruise (May); Gum Tree Writing (May); The Source Magazine (May); Memorial Day (May); Graduation (May); Young at Heart (June); How To Guide (June); Election tab (July); Back to School (July); Traveler Magazine (Aug); High School Football (Aug); Fall Brides (Aug); College Football (Aug); Fall Home Improvement

(Sept); Fall Fashion (Sept); Marching Band Festival (Oct); Breast Cancer Awareness (Oct); Women at Work (Oct); Taste of the Season Cookbook (Nov); Holiday Gift Guide (Nov)
Special Weekly Sections: Education (Mon); NASCAR, Food (Wed); Neighbors (Thur); Health & Fitness, Auto, Home & Garden (Fri); Faith, Auto (Sat); Comics, Real Estate, Employment, Coupons (Sun)
Syndicated Publications: Relish (Monthly); Parade (S)
Digital Platform - Mobile: Apple, Android, Windows
Digital Platform - Tablet: Apple iOS, Android, Windows 7
Pub./CEO........Clay Foster
Assc. Pub.........Charlotte Wolfe
Exec. Ed.........Lloyd Gray
Finance Dir.........Rosemary Jarrell
Adv. & Marketing Dir.........Richard Crenshaw
Classified Adv. Mgr.........Cindy Carr
Editorial Ed.........Joe Rutherford
Lifestyles Ed.........Leslie Criss
Radio/Television Ed.........Judy Putt
Circ. Mgr.
Michael King
Nat'l Agency Coord.........Amy Speck
Market Information: TMC; Zoned editions.
Mechanical Available: Offset; Black and 3 ROP colors; insert accepted - all; page cutoffs - 22 3/4.
Mechanical Specifications: Type page 13 x 21 1/2; E - 6 cols, 2 1/16, 1/8 between; A - 6 cols, 2 1/16, 1/8 between; C - 8 cols, 1 1/2, 1/8 between.
Areas Served: 38603 to 38915
Delivery Method: Mail, Newsstand, Carrier, RacksEquipment & Software: PRESSROOM EQUIPMENT: Lines — 12-G/Urbanite U1366 1990; Folders — 1-G/U-1366 1990, 1-G/SU-1708 1990; MAILROOM EQUIPMENT: Counter Stackers — 1 HL/ Monitor; 3 TMSI-Compass; 1 TMSI4500; Inserters & Stuffers — 2 - SLS3000; Tying Machines — 4 - Dynaric NP3000; Address Machine — Scitex 120; BUSINESS EQUIPMENT: Dell BUSINESS SOFTWARE: Brainworks (AR) Navision (GL,PR,AP) Windows XP CLASSIFIED EQUIPMENT: Hardware — Dell; Printers — HP4250 Laserjet; CLASSIFIED SOFTWARE: Brainworks, AdPerks, Windows XP DISPLAY EQUIPMENT: Hardware — APPLE/MAC; Printers — HP8150, HP4700 Color; DISPLAY SOFTWAREAd Make-up Applications — Multi-Ad/Creator; Layout Software — SCS/ Layout 8000 EDITORIAL EQUIPMENT: Hardware — 35-APP/Mac; Printers — HP EDITORIAL SOFTWARE: NewsEdit; IQweb PRODUCTION EQUIPMENT: Hardware — 2 - Kodak NewsSetter TH100; Scanners — 1 - Epson 1640XL; 1 - Scanmaker 9800XL PRODUCTION SOFTWARE: NewsExtremes; QPS/QuarkXpress 6.50; Photoshop

VICKSBURG

THE VICKSBURG POST

1601F N Frontage Rd, Vicksburg, Miss., 39180-5149, Warren; gen tel (601) 636-4545; adv tel (601) 636-4545; ed tel (601) 636-4545; gen fax (601) 634-0897; adv fax (601) 634-0897; ed fax (601) 634-0897; gen/nat adv e-mail ads@vicksburgpost.com; disp adv e-mail bpartridge@vicksburgpost.com; class adv e-mailclassifieds@vicksburgpost.com; ed e-mail kgamble@vicksburgpost.com; web site www.vicksburgpost.com
Group: Boone Newspapers, Inc.
Published: Mon, Tues, Wed, Thur, Fri, Sat, Sun
Weekday Frequency: e
Saturday Frequency: e
Circulation: 9,811; 9,811(sat); 10,300(sun)
Last Audit: VAC March 31, 2013
Advertising Rate (weekday/saturday): Open inch rate $21.22
Advertising Rate (sunday): Open inch rate $22.31
News services: AP. **Established:** 1883
Special Editions: Home Improvement (Apr); High School Football (Aug); Last Minute Gift Guide (Dec); African American History (Feb); Brides (Jan); Family-Owned Business (Jun); Industry (Mar); Car Care (May); Health Services Directory (Nov); Home Improvement (Oct); College F
Special Weekly Sections: Best Food Day (Wed); Business (Mon-Sun); Comics (Sun);
Syndicated Publications: Parade (S).
Digital Platform - Mobile: Apple, Android
Digital Platform - Tablet: Apple iOS, Android
Gen. Mgr.........Jimmy Clark
Adv. Dir.........Barney Partridge
Prod. Mgr........Jimmy Mullen
President/Publisher........Tim Reeves
Exec. Ed.........Charles D. Mitchell
Asst. Mng. Ed., News........Misty McDermitt
Asst. Mng. Ed., Photo........Brian Loden
Asst. Mng. Ed., Sports........Steve Wilson
Presentation Ed.........Mary Kittrell
Publisher........Timothy Reeves
Mng. Ed.........Paul Barry
Ed........Jan Griffey
Market Information: TMC.
Mechanical Available: Offset; Black and 3 ROP colors; insert accepted; page cutoffs - 22 3/4.
Mechanical Specifications: Type page 13 x 21; E - 6 cols, 2 1/16, 1/8 between; A - 6 cols, 2 1/16, 1/8 between; C - 8 cols, 1 3/8, 1/16 between.
Delivery Method: Mail, CarrierEquipment & Software: PRESSROOM EQUIPMENT: Lines — 8-G/Urbanite; MAILROOM EQUIPMENT: Tying Machines — 2/MLN.; BUSINESS EQUIPMENT: 1-DEC/11-21, 5-DEC/101 CLASSIFIED EQUIPMENT: Hardware — 2-APP/Mac; Printers — 2-Xante; CLASSIFIED SOFTWARE: FSI, QPS. DISPLAY EQUIPMENT: Hardware — 6-APP/ Mac, 6-APP/Mac; Printers — 2-Xante, HP; DISPLAY SOFTWARELayout Software — FSI, QPS. EDITORIAL EQUIPMENT: Hardware — 30-APP/Mac; Printers — 3-Xante EDITORIAL SOFTWARE: FSI, QPS. PRODUCTION EQUIPMENT: Hardware — 2-Nu; Cameras — 1-R; Scanners — 2-Nikon/ Coolscan PRODUCTION SOFTWARE: FSI.

WEST POINT

DAILY TIMES LEADER

26463 E Main St, West Point, Miss., 39773-7995, Clay; gen tel (662) 494-1422; adv tel (662) 494-1422; ed tel (662) 494-1353; gen fax (662) 494-1414; adv fax (662) 494-1414; ed fax (662) 494-1414; gen/nat adv e-mail ads@dailytimesleader.com; disp adv e-mail ads@dailytimesleader.com; class adv e-mailclass@dailytimesleader.com; ed e-mail editor@dailytimesleader.com ; web site www.dailytimesleader.com
Group: Horizon Publications Inc.
Published: Tues, Wed, Thur, Fri, Sun
Weekday Frequency: m
Circulation: 2,758; 2,758(sun)
Last Audit: Sworn/Estimate/Non-Audited September 30, 2017
Advertising Rate (weekday/saturday): Open inch rate $8.70
Advertising Rate (sunday): Open inch rate $9.90
Online Advertising Rate: 3 days for $21.00
News services: AP. **Established:** 1867
Special Editions: Progress (Feb); Gift Guide (Nov); Prairie Arts Festival (Sept); Best of West Point (2013); Community Profile; Graduation 2013
Special Weekly Sections: Business (Tue); Food (Wed); School (Thur); Home, Health (Fri); People (Sun)
Syndicated Publications: TeleVisions; Tuned In (S); American Profile (Weekly).
Digital Platform - Mobile: Apple, Android, Windows
Digital Platform - Tablet: Apple iOS, Android, Windows 7
Pub........Don Norman
Circ. Clerk........Natasha Watson
Circ. Mgr.........Byron Norman
Gen. Mgr./Adv. Dir.........Mandy Stewart
Managing Ed.........Brandon Walker
Market Information: TMC.
Mechanical Available: Offset; Black and 3 ROP colors; insert accepted - Post It's; page cutoffs - 22 3/4.
Mechanical Specifications: Type page 11 5/8 x 21 1/2; E - 6 cols, 3 3/4, 1/8 between; A - 6 cols, 3 3/4, 1/8 between; C - 9 cols, 1 3/8, 1/8 between.
Delivery Method: Mail, CarrierEquipment & Software: PRESSROOM EQUIPMENT: Lines — 6-G/Community.; MAILROOM EQUIPMENT: Counter Stackers — BG; Tying Machines — Strapping.; BUSINESS EQUIPMENT: PC CLASSIFIED EQUIPMENT: Hardware — IMACS; CLASSIFIED SOFTWARE: Baseview. DISPLAY EQUIPMENT: Hardware — APP/Mac Radius; Printers — APP/Mac Laser Writer, GCC/Elite XL; DISPLAY SOFTWARELayout Software — APP/Power Mac G3, IMACS. EDITORIAL EQUIPMENT: Hardware — IMACS; Printers — APP/ Mac LaserWriter EDITORIAL SOFTWARE: Baseview. PRODUCTION EQUIPMENT: Hardware — APP/Mac LaserWriter II; Cameras — Konica PRODUCTION SOFTWARE: QPS/QuarkXPress 4.24.

MISSOURI

CAMDENTON

LAKE SUN LEADER

918 N Business Route 5, Camdenton, Mo., 65020-2648, Camden; gen tel (573) 346-2132; adv tel (573) 346-2132; ed tel (573) 346-2132; gen fax (573) 346-4508; adv fax (573) 346-4508; ed fax (573) 346-4045; gen/nat adv e-mail business@lakesunleader.com; disp adv e-mail michele.harris@lakesunonline.com; class adv e-mailclassifieds@lakesunonline.com; ed e-mail newsroom@lakesunonline.com; web site www.lakesunleader.com; web site 2 www.lakenewsonline.com
Group: New Media Investment Group
Published: Mon, Tues, Wed, Thur, Fri
Weekday Frequency: m
Circulation: 10,757
Last Audit: Sworn/Estimate/Non-Audited September 30, 2017
Advertising Rate (weekday/saturday): Open inch rate $9.10 (Mon-Thur); $9.60 (Fri)
News services: AP. **Established:** 1879
Special Weekly Sections: Travel, Sports (Mon); Business, School (Tue); Food (Wed); Upcoming Events (Thur); Real Estate, Entertainment (Fri)
Syndicated Publications: American Profile (Weekly).
Pub........John Tucker
Bus. Mgr.........Debbie Franklin
Ed. Dir.........Joyce Miller
Circ. /Dist./Subscriptions........Mike Valko
Market Information: Split run; TMC; Zoned editions.
Mechanical Available: Offset; Black and 2 ROP colors; insert accepted.
Mechanical Specifications: Type page 13 x 21 1/2; E - 6 cols, 2 1/16, 1/8 between; A - 6 cols, 2 1/16, 1/8 between; C - 6 cols, 2 1/16, 1/8 between.Equipment & Software: MAILROOM EQUIPMENT: Counter Stackers — KAN/320; Tying Machines — Bu; Address Machine — Ch.; BUSINESS EQUIPMENT: IBM/Sys 36, AmDek/Sys 286A CLASSIFIED EQUIPMENT: Hardware — COM/MCS.; DISPLAY EQUIPMENT: Hardware — APP/ Mac.; EDITORIAL EQUIPMENT: Hardware — APP/Mac/IBM, HP. PRODUCTION EQUIPMENT: Hardware — HP/LaserJet; Scanners — DSA.

CAPE GIRARDEAU

SOUTHEAST MISSOURIAN

301 Broadway St, Cape Girardeau, Mo., 63701-7330, Cape Girardeau; gen tel (573) 335-6611; adv tel (573) 338-2751; ed tel (573) 388-3625; gen fax (573) 339-0815; adv fax (573) 339-0815; ed fax (573) 334-7288; gen/nat adv e-mail advertising@semissourian.com; disp adv e-mail ddenson@semissourian.com; class adv e-mailddenson@semissourian.com; ed e-mail bmiller@semissourian.com; web site www.semissourian.com
Group: Rust Communications
Published: Mon, Tues, Wed, Thur, Fri, Sun
Weekday Frequency: m
Saturday Frequency: m
Circulation: 10,376; 12,416(sun)
Last Audit: CAC March 31, 2015
Advertising Rate (weekday/saturday): Open inch rate $23.40
Advertising Rate (sunday): Open inch rate $29.50
News services: AP. **Established:** 1904
Special Editions: University Tab (Apr); Back-to-School (Aug); Traditional Christmas (Dec); Progress (Feb); Bridal (Jan); Vacations (Jun); Lawn & Garden (Mar); Vacations (May); Best of the Season (Nov); Newcomer's Guide (Oct); Fall Home Improvement & Decorating (Sept).
Special Weekly Sections: Business (Mon); Learning (Tue); Food (Wed); Health (Thur); Arts (Fri); Lifestyle, Travel, Real Estate (Sun);
Syndicated Publications: 1st Sunday (Monthly); Parade (S).
Pub.........Jon K. Rust
Gen. Mgr.........Mark Kneer
Ed.........Bob Miller
Mng. Ed.........Matt Sanders
Prodn. Coord.........John Renaud
National Account Coord.........Danielle Smith
David Guay
Market Information: ADS; TMC; Zoned editions.
Mechanical Available: Offset; Black and 3 ROP colors; insert accepted - card 80 lb. stock; page cutoffs - 21 1/2.
Mechanical Specifications: Type page 11 5/8 x 20 3/4; E - 6 cols, 1 5/6, 1/8 between; A - 6 cols, 1 5/6, 1/8 between; C - 9 cols, 1 5/6, 1/8 between.Equipment & Software: PRESSROOM EQUIPMENT: Lines — 5-WPC/Leader (1-Quad color); 6-WPC/ Leader; Folders — 2-WPC/2:1.; MAILROOM EQUIPMENT: Tying Machines — 1-Sa/ EM9142, 1-Sa/ML2EE, 1/MLN; Wrapping Singles — 4-/Bu; Address Machine — Ch/ labeler.; BUSINESS EQUIPMENT: 12-IBM Clone BUSINESS SOFTWARE: Synaptic, Macola, Synaptic/AR CLASSIFIED EQUIPMENT: Hardware — 5-APP/ Mac; Printers — HP/5si; CLASSIFIED SOFTWARE: Baseview/Ad Manager. DISPLAY EQUIPMENT: Hardware — 16-APP/Mac, 1-IBM; Printers — HP/8000; Other Hardware — HP/DesignJet 2500 DISPLAY SOFTWAREAd Make-up Applications — Multi-Ad/Creator 6, Adobe/Photoshop CS, Adobe/Illustrator CS, QPS/QuarkXPress 4.1; Layout Software — MEI/AdForce. EDITORIAL EQUIPMENT: Hardware — 30-APP/Mac; Printers — 2-HP/8000 EDITORIAL SOFTWARE: Baseview, QPS/QuarkXPress 4.1, Adobe/Photoshop 6.0, Aldus/FreeHand 7. PRODUCTION EQUIPMENT: Hardware — Caere/OmniPage, HP/8000(G), HP/ DesignJet 2500; Cameras — R; Scanners — 2-Polaroid/SprintScan, 3-Epson/1200C.

CHILLICOTHE

CONSTITUTION-TRIBUNE

818 Washington St, Chillicothe, Mo., 64601-2232, Livingston; gen tel (660) 646-2411; adv tel (660) 646-2411; ed tel (660) 646-2411; gen fax (660) 646-2028; adv fax (660) 646-2028; ed fax (660) 646-2028; gen/nat adv e-mail advertising@chillicothenews.com; disp adv e-mail andrea@chillicothe.townnews.com; class adv e-mailadvertising@chillicothenews.com; ed e-mail ctnews@chillicothenews.com; web site www.chillicothenews.com
Group: New Media Investment Group
Published: Mon, Tues, Wed, Thur, Fri
Weekday Frequency: e
Circulation: 2,535
Last Audit: Sworn/Estimate/Non-Audited September 30, 2017
Advertising Rate (weekday/saturday): Open inch rate $7.90
News services: AP. **Established:** 1860
Special Weekly Sections: Agriculture (Tue); Best Food Day (Wed);
Digital Platform - Mobile: Apple, Android
Digital Platform - Tablet: Apple iOS, Android
Pub./Purchasing Agent........Rod Dixon
Adv. Dir.........Andrea Graves

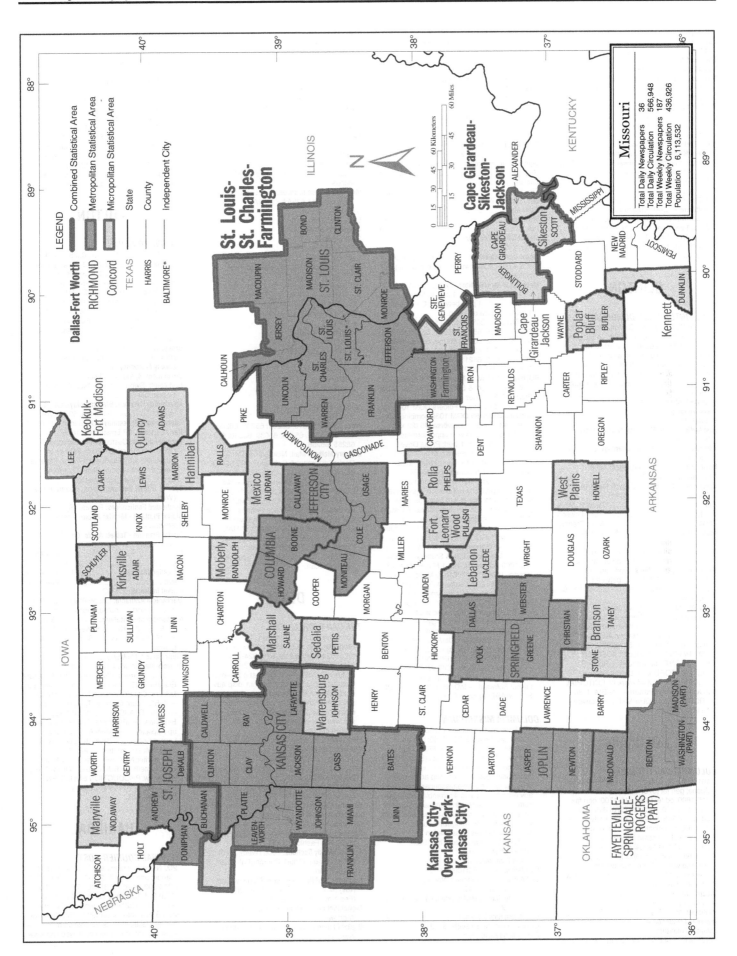

LEGEND

Combined Statistical Area — **Dallas-Fort Worth**
Metropolitan Statistical Area — **RICHMOND**
Micropolitan Statistical Area — Concord

State — **TEXAS**
County — HARRIS
Independent City — BALTIMORE*

Circ. Mgr. ....Jenetta Cramner
Political/Gov't Ed. ....Catherine Ripley
Sports Ed. ....Paul Sturm
Classified Ads Mgr. ....Connie Jones
Market Information: ADS; TMC; Zoned editions.
Mechanical Available: Offset; Black and 2 ROP colors; insert accepted - 1-page flyers; page cutoffs - 21 1/2.
Mechanical Specifications: Type page 13 1/2 x 21 1/2; E - 6 cols, 2 1/16, 1/8 between; A - 6 cols, 2 1/16, 1/8 between; C - 6 cols, 2 1/16, 1/8 between.
Areas Served: Livingston County
Delivery Method: Mail, Newsstand, Carrier, RacksEquipment & Software: PRESSROOM EQUIPMENT: Lines — 4-G/Community.; MAILROOM EQUIPMENT: Tying Machines — 1/Malow, 1-/Bu; Address Machine — 3-/Rp.; DISPLAY SOFTWARELayout Software — 3-APP/Mac Plus. EDITORIAL EQUIPMENT: Hardware — 6-CText/ CText/Fileserver, CText/AP Wire receiver. PRODUCTION EQUIPMENT: Hardware — 2-APP/Mac LaserWriter, 1-COM; Cameras — 1-Nu.

CLINTON

THE CLINTON DAILY DEMOCRAT

212 S Washington St, Clinton, Mo., 64735-2073, Henry; gen tel (660) 885-2281; gen fax (660) 885-2265; gen/nat adv e-mail dailydemocrat@embarqmail.com; disp adv e-mail democrat.ads@embarqmail.com; class adv e-maildem.subscription@embarqmail.com; ed e-mail dailydemocrat@embarqmail.com
Published: Mon, Tues, Wed, Thur, Fri
Weekday Frequency: e
Circulation: 3,595
Last Audit: Sworn/Estimate/Non-Audited September 30, 2017
Advertising Rate (weekday/saturday): Open inch rate $6.05 net.
News services: NEA. **Established:** 1868
Own Printing Facility?: Yes
Special Weekly Sections: Church News (Fri); Conservation/Outdoors (Thur).
Pub. ....Daniel B. Miles
Sports Ed. .... Jim Lawson
Prodn. Mgr. ....Mike Gregory
Associate Ed. ....Denise Smith
Market Information: TMC.
Mechanical Available: Offset; Black and1 ROP colors; insert accepted; page cutoffs - 21 1/2.
Mechanical Specifications: Type page 13 x 21 1/2; E - 6 cols, 2 1/16, 1/8 between; A - 6 cols, 2 1/16, 1/8 between; C - 6 cols, 2 1/16, 1/8 between.
Areas Served: Henry County Missouri
Delivery Method: Mail, CarrierEquipment & Software: MAILROOM EQUIPMENT: Tying Machines — 1/Malow; Address Machine — 1-Am/Mail 5.; BUSINESS EQUIPMENT: APP/Mac CLASSIFIED EQUIPMENT: Hardware — 1-Ro, 1-IBM.; DISPLAY SOFTWARELayout Software — 1-COM/7200, 1-COM/Mark IV. EDITORIAL EQUIPMENT: Hardware — 1-IBM, 1-Ro. PRODUCTION EQUIPMENT: Hardware — 1-HA, 1-EK.

COLUMBIA

COLUMBIA DAILY TRIBUNE

101 N 4th St, Columbia, Mo., 65201-4416, Boone; gen tel (573) 815-1600; adv tel (573) 815-1800; ed tel (573) 815-1700; gen fax (573) 815-1701; adv fax (573) 815-1801; ed fax (573) 815-1701; gen/nat adv e-mail display@columbiatribune.com; disp adv e-mail display@columbiatribune.com; class adv e-mailclassifieds@columbiatribune.com; ed e-mail editor@columbiatribune.com; web site www.columbiatribune.com; web site 2 www.tigerextra.com; web site 3 www.tribunepublishing.com
Group: GateHouse Media, Inc.
New Media Investment Group
Published: Mon, Tues, Wed, Thur, Fri, Sat, Sun
Weekday Frequency: e
Saturday Frequency: m
Circulation: 114,672; 14,672(sat); 17,705(sun)
Last Audit: AAM December 31, 2015
Advertising Rate (weekday/saturday): Open inch rate $20.50 (Mon-Tue/Thur-Sat); $25.00 (Wed)
Advertising Rate (sunday): Open inch rate $24.50
News services: AP, TMS, ABC, MPA, NAA **Established:** 1901
Own Printing Facility?: Yes
Commercial Printers?: Yes
Special Weekly Sections: Food (Wed); Business (Mon-Fri); Entertainment, TV (Thur); Church, (Sat); Home, Travel, Weddings (Sun);
Digital Platform - Mobile: Apple, Android, Windows, Blackberry
Digital Platform - Tablet: Apple iOS, Windows 7
Mng. Ed. ....Jim Robertson
Circ. Dir. ....Dirk Dunkle
Circ. Mgr. ....Michael Bousquet
Circ. Services Mgr. .... Laurel Killgore
Sales Mgr. ....Nick Henson
VP, Sales ....Les Borgmeyer
Pub ....Rustan Burton
Market Information: TMC distribution available Sun. / Wed.
Mechanical Available: Cold web offset; Black and 4 ROP colors; inserts accepted; page cutoffs - 22".
Mechanical Specifications: Type page 11 3/8 x 21; E - 6 cols, 1.75", 1 pica between; A - 6 cols, 1.75", 1 pica between; C - 7 cols, 1.5625", .5 pica between.
Areas Served: 65203, 65202, 65201, 65010, 65240, 65255, 65233, 65251, 65270, 65279, 65248, 65265, 65284, 65256, 65039, 65254, 65243, 65274, 65231, 65230, 65259, 65287, 65262, 65043, 65211, 65278, 65216, 65250, 65285, 65109, 65101, 65063
Delivery Method: Mail, Newsstand, Carrier, RacksEquipment & Software: PRESSROOM EQUIPMENT: Lines — 20 unit DGM 430 (22 3/4 x 35) with two Folders DGM 1030 combination folder DGM 1035 combination folder ; 48 unit Goss Universal 45 (22 x 35) 2- 1:3:3 jaw Folders with upper formers, q-fold and crosshead perf; Press Drive — Allen Bradley drives with drive shaft; Folders — DGM 1030 combination folder with q-fold and crosshead perf DGM 1035 combination folder with q-fold and crosshead perf Universal 2 1:3:3 jaw folder with uppper former; q-fold and crosshead perf; Pasters —Universal press has AMAL AR60C splicersRegistration System — Universal is equipped with I-Tech Registration System MAILROOM EQUIPMENT: Counter Stackers — Gammerler STC70 stackers on all press lines; Inserters & Stuffers — GMA SLS1000 inserter-12 into 1 Muller Martini 227 inserter-16 into 1 with CS-10 Muller stacker Muller Martini 227 inserter-4 into 1 with Rima RS counter stacker; Tying Machines — Signode LB-2330 strapper Signode LB-2000 tying machine Signode LBX-2000 tying machine; Wrapping Singles — Arpac 55G1-200 bundle shrinkwrapper; Address Machine — 3 - Domino JetArray in-line and off-line with Rima (Harris) RS12 Counter Stackers; DISPLAY EQUIPMENT: Printers — HP 1050; DISPLAY SOFTWAREAd Make-up Applications — Adobe Creative Suite; Layout Software — InDesign PRODUCTION SOFTWARE: Apogee Portal

COLUMBIA MISSOURIAN

221 S 8th St, Columbia, Mo., 65201-4868, Boone; gen tel (573) 882-5700; adv tel (573) 882-5748; ed tel (573) 882-5720; gen fax (573) 884-5293; ed fax (573) 882-5702; gen/nat adv e-mail advertising@columbiamissourian.com; disp adv e-mail advertising@columbiamissourian.com; class adv e-mailadvertising@columbiamissourian.com; ed e-mail editor@columbiamissourian.com; web site www.columbiamissourian.com; web site 2 www.voxmagazine.com
Group: Missouri Press Association
Published: Mon, Tues, Wed, Thur, Sun
Weekday Frequency: m
Saturday Frequency: m
Circulation: 6,202; 6,010(sun)
Last Audit: Sworn/Estimate/Non-Audited September 30, 2017
Advertising Rate (weekday/saturday): Open inch rate $8.50
Advertising Rate (sunday): Open inch rate $8.50
News services: AP **Established:** 1908
Own Printing Facility?: No
Special Editions: Progress (Growth of Columbia); Tourism (State of MO); Collegetown; Welcome Back; Tiger Kickoffs (Mizzou Football); Homecoming (Mizzou Tigers); Tiger Tipoffs (Mizzou Basketball)
Special Weekly Sections: Vox (Thur.)
Syndicated Publications: Parade (S)
Digital Platform - Mobile: Apple, Android
Digital Platform - Tablet: Apple iOS, Android
Gen. Mgr. .... Dan Potter
Managing Ed. .... Jeanne Abbott
Photo Dir. .... Brian Kratzer
Adv. Dir. .... Bryan Chester
Market Information: Zoned editions
Mechanical Available: Offset; Black and 4 ROP colors; insert accepted; page cutoffs - 20.5 inches
Mechanical Specifications: Broadsheet (ROP) Page Size: 11.625AA x 20.5AA
6 col = 11.625AA
5 col = 9.25AA
4 col = 7.375AA
3 col = 5.5AA
2 col = 3.625AA
1 col = 1.75AA
Tab Page Size (VOX, Special Sections):
Full Page = 9.75AA
x 11AA
1/2 pg Hor = 9.75AA
x 5.417AA
1/2 pg Ver = 4.79AA
x 11AA
1/4 pg Hor = 4.79AA
x 5.417AA
1/4 pg Ver = 2.3125AA
x 11AA
1/8 pg Hor = 4.79AA
x 2.625AA
1/8 pg Ver = 2.3125AA
x 5.417AA
1/16 pg = 2.3125AA
x 2.625AA
Areas Served: 65010, 65201, 65202, 65203, 65211, 65212, 65215, 65039, 65240, 65251, 65255, 65256
Delivery Method: Mail, Newsstand, Carrier, RacksEquipment & Software: PRESSROOM EQUIPMENT: Lines — N/A; MAILROOM EQUIPMENT: Counter Stackers — N/A; CLASSIFIED EQUIPMENT: Hardware — 2-HAS/Edit 8.; DISPLAY EQUIPMENT: Hardware — 5-APP/Mac.; Printers — Ricoh; EDITORIAL EQUIPMENT: Hardware — 2-HAS/HS-55, IBM/26-IBM/PC, 7-HAS/ Edit 3, 3-HAS/Edit 8, 2-HAS/Magician Layout, 2-HAS/NewsPro.; Printers — Ricoh PRODUCTION EQUIPMENT: Scanners — Dest/PC Scan.

DEXTER

THE DAILY STATESMAN

133 S Walnut St, Dexter, Mo., 63841-2141, Stoddard; gen tel (573) 624-4545; adv tel (573) 624-4545; ed tel (573) 624-4545; gen fax (573) 624-7449; adv fax (573) 624-7449; ed fax (573) 624-7449; gen/nat adv e-mail mharmon@dailystatesman.com; disp adv e-mail dglenn@dailystatesman.com; class adv e-maildlovins@dailystatesman.com; ed e-mail nhyslop@dailystatesman.com; web site www.dailystatesman.com
Group: Rust Communications
Published: Tues, Wed, Thur, Fri, Sun
Weekday Frequency: e
Circulation: 2,522; 3,150(sun)
Last Audit: Sworn/Estimate/Non-Audited September 30, 2017
Advertising Rate (weekday/saturday): Open inch rate $13.56 (Tue, Thur, Fri); $16.22 (Wed);
Advertising Rate (sunday): Open inch rate $13.56
News services: AP, NEA. **Established:** 1879
Own Printing Facility?: Yes
Special Editions: Spring Fashion (Apr); Progress (Feb); Fall Fashion (Sept).
Special Weekly Sections: Food (Wed); Farm, Entertainment (Thur); Church (Fri); Real Estate (Sun)
Syndicated Publications: Farm Monthly (Feb-Nov) (Monthly); Southeast Missouri Farmer (Feb-Nov) (Other); Parade (S).
Digital Platform - Mobile: Apple, Android, Windows
Digital Platform - Tablet: Apple iOS, Android, Windows 7
Gen/Manag Ed ....Noreen Hyslop
Market Information: Split run; TMC; Zoned editions.
Mechanical Available: Offset; Black and 3 ROP colors; insert accepted.
Mechanical Specifications: Type page 13 x 22 1/2; E - 6 cols, 2 1/16, 1/8 between; A - 6 cols, 2 1/16, 1/8 between; C - 8 cols, 1 1/2, 1/8 between.
Delivery Method: Mail, Carrier, RacksEquipment & Software: MAILROOM EQUIPMENT: Tying Machines — 1/Strap Tyer; CLASSIFIED EQUIPMENT: Hardware — 1-COM/MDT 350.; EDITORIAL EQUIPMENT: Hardware — 1-COM/MDT 350. PRODUCTION EQUIPMENT: Hardware — 1-COM/4961, 1-COM/2961; Cameras — 1-Acti/140.

FULTON

THE FULTON SUN

115 E 5th St, Fulton, Mo., 65251-1714, Callaway; gen tel (573) 642-7272; adv tel (573) 826-2415; ed tel (573) 826-2417; gen fax (573) 642-0656; adv fax (573) 642-0656; ed fax (573) 642-0656; gen/nat adv e-mail pmcdonald@fultonsun.com; disp adv e-mail display@fultonsun.com; class adv e-mailclass@fultonsun.com; ed e-mail news@fultonsun.com; web site www.fultonsun.com
Group: WEHCO Media, Inc.
Published: Tues, Wed, Thur, Fri, Sun
Weekday Frequency: m
Circulation: 4,300; 4,300(sun)
Last Audit: Sworn/Estimate/Non-Audited September 30, 2017
Advertising Rate (weekday/saturday): Open inch rate $8.60 (Tues, Thurs, Fri); $9.65 (Wed)
Advertising Rate (sunday): Open inch rate $9.65
News services: AP. **Established:** 1875
Special Editions: Customer Appreciation (Apr); Christmas Greetings (Dec); Women in Business (Jun); Graduation (May); Favorite Recipes (Oct); Senior Style (Quarterly); Sports Preview (Semi-yearly).
Special Weekly Sections: Farm, Health, Food (Wed); TV, Arts, Church (Fri)
Syndicated Publications: Parade (S).
Digital Platform - Mobile: Apple, Android, Windows
Digital Platform - Tablet: Apple iOS, Android, Windows 7
Ed ....Karen Atkins
Sports Ed. ....Ryan Boland
Marketing Manager ....Pati McDonald
Coord. .... Dean Asher
Market Information: TMC.
Mechanical Available: Offset; Black and 3 ROP colors; insert accepted; page cutoffs - 21 1/2.
Mechanical Specifications: Type page 13 x 21; E - 6 cols, 2 1/16, 1/8 between; A - 6 cols, 2 1/16, 1/8 between; C - 9 cols, 1 3/8, 1/16 between.
Areas Served: Callaway County
Delivery Method: Mail, Newsstand, Carrier, RacksEquipment & Software: PRESSROOM EQUIPMENT: Lines — 4-G/Community 1991; MAILROOM EQUIPMENT: Counter Stackers — 1-BG/Count-O-Veyor; Tying Machines — 1/Bu.; CLASSIFIED SOFTWARE: Baseview. DISPLAY SOFTWAREAd Make-up Applications — Multi-Ad, Baseview; Layout Software — Multi-Ad. EDITORIAL EQUIPMENT: Printers — APP/Mac LaserWriter NTX, APP/Mac LaserWriter Pro, Xante/8300 EDITORIAL SOFTWARE: Baseview. PRODUCTION EQUIPMENT: Hardware — APP/Mac LaserWriter Pro; Cameras — R.

HANNIBAL

HANNIBAL COURIER-POST

200 N 3rd St, Hannibal, Mo., 63401-3504, Marion; gen tel (573) 221-2800; adv tel (573) 221-2800; ed tel (573) 248-2757; gen fax (573) 221-1568; adv fax (573) 221-1568; ed fax (573) 221-5800; gen/nat adv e-mail jreynolds@gatehousemedia.com; class adv e-mailclassifieds@courierpost.com; ed e-mail newsroom@courierpost.com; web site www.

hannibal.net
Group: New Media Investment Group
Published: Tues, Wed, Thur, Fri, Sat
Weekday Frequency: m
Saturday Frequency: m
Circulation: 4,060; 4,432(sat)
Last Audit: Sworn/Estimate/Non-Audited August 30, 2017
Advertising Rate (weekday/saturday): 15.40
News services: AP **Established:** 1838
Own Printing Facility?: No
Commercial Printers?: Yes
Special Weekly Sections: Business (Tue); Health, Community (Wed); Education, Auctions (Thur); Religion, Weddings, Community Clubs (Sat)
Syndicated Publications: Relish (Monthly); USA WEEKEND Magazine (Sat); American Profile (Tues).
Digital Platform - Mobile: Apple, Android, Windows
Digital Platform - Tablet: Apple iOS, Android, Windows 7, Blackberry Tablet OS, Kindle, Kindle Fire
Market Information: TMC.
Mechanical Available: Offset; Black and 3 ROP colors; insert accepted - bags; page cutoffs - 22 3/4.
Mechanical Specifications: Type page 10.625 x 21.5, 6 cols
Areas Served: 63401
Delivery Method: Mail, Newsstand, CarrierEquipment & Software: PRESSROOM EQUIPMENT: Lines — 9-G/Community single width 1968; Folders — G/Quarter.; MAILROOM EQUIPMENT: Tying Machines — MLN; Address Machine — 1/Ch.; BUSINESS SOFTWARE: Unix/SCO 4.2 CLASSIFIED EQUIPMENT: Hardware — 2-APP/G-4; Printers — HP/4000, APP/Mac LaserWriter 630 Pro, HP/4MV, HP/Laser Jet 4050; CLASSIFIED SOFTWARE: AdManager Pro DISPLAY EQUIPMENT: Hardware — 4-APP/Mac ViewSonic 2-page displays; Printers — HP/4MV, HP/LaserJet 4000, HP/8550N Color Printer; DISPLAY SOFTWAREAd Make-up Applications — InDesign CS2; Layout Software — InDesign CS4 EDITORIAL EQUIPMENT: Hardware — 6-APP/G-4, 2-PC/Power/2-APP/Mac Flatbed scanners, 1-Nikon/LS-1000 Scanner, 1-Photootherm/Automatic Film Processor; Printers — APP/Mac 16/600 EDITORIAL SOFTWARE: NewsEdit Pro PRODUCTION EQUIPMENT: Hardware — Nu/Flip Top FT40VGUPNS, Pre Press/Panther RIP, Pre Press/Set 1000/Harlequin Navigator, AG/Accuset 1000; Scanners — Epson PRODUCTION SOFTWARE: InDesign CS4

INDEPENDENCE

THE EXAMINER / EXAMINER WEEKEND

410 S Liberty St, Independence, Mo., 64050-3805, Jackson; gen tel (816) 254-8600; adv tel (816) 350-6383; ed tel (816) 350-6365; gen fax (816) 836-3805; adv fax (816) 836-3805; ed fax (816) 254-0211; gen/nat adv e-mail displayads@examiner.net; disp adv e-mail displayads@examiner.net; class adv e-mailchris.goff@examiner.net; ed e-mail sheila.davis@examiner.net; web site www.examiner.net
Group: New Media Investment Group
Published: Mon, Tues, Wed, Fri, Sat
Weekday Frequency: m
Saturday Frequency: m
Circulation: 5,641; 6,210(sat)
Last Audit: VAC September 30, 2017
Advertising Rate (weekday/saturday): Open inch rate $27.03
News services: AP, SHNS. **Established:** 1898
Special Editions: Spring Car Care (Apr); Senior Citizens (Aug); Holiday Gift Guide (Dec); Review & Forecast (Feb); Tourist Guide (Jan); Guide to Independence (Jun); Health & Fitness (Mar); Spring Parade of Homes (May); Christmas Opening (Nov); Car Care (Oct); Fall Parade o
Special Weekly Sections: Best Food Day (Wed); Home Life, Family (Tue); Arts, Outdoors (Thur); Education (Fri); Religion, Lifestyles (Sat)
Syndicated Publications: Relish (Monthly); USA WEEKEND Magazine (Sat).
Digital Platform - Mobile: Apple, Android, Windows
Digital Platform - Tablet: Apple iOS, Android, Windows 7
Bus. Mgr. .... Deneane Hyde
Exec. Ed. .... Sheila Davis
Mng. Ed. .... Karl Zinke
Pub. .... Ryan Kedzierski
Adv. Dir. .... Tonya Maddox
Pub. .... Julie Moreno
Market Information: TMC.
Mechanical Available: Offset; Black and 3 ROP colors; insert accepted - all; page cutoffs - 22 3/4.
Mechanical Specifications: Type page 13 x 21 1/2; E - 6 cols, 2 1/16, 1/8 between; A - 6 cols, 2 1/16, 1/8 between; C - 8 cols, 1 1/2, 1/8 between.
Delivery Method: Mail, CarrierEquipment & Software: PRESSROOM EQUIPMENT: Lines — 7-G/Urbanite; Folders — 1-G/Urbanite, 1-G/Suburban.; MAILROOM EQUIPMENT: Counter Stackers — 1-Id; Inserters & Stuffers — 1-HI/NP 848; Tying Machines — 1/MLN; Address Machine - 1-/KR.; BUSINESS EQUIPMENT: 1-ATT/6386E-WGS CLASSIFIED EQUIPMENT: Hardware — 8-APP/Mac Performa 630; Printers — MON/Express Master 1270; CLASSIFIED SOFTWARE: Baseview. DISPLAY EQUIPMENT: Hardware — APP/Mac; Printers — APP/Mac, APP/Mac LaserWriter Pro; DISPLAY SOFTWAREAd Make-up Applications — Adobe/Photoshop, QPS/QuarkXPress 3.32, Adobe/Illustrator; Layout Software — 1-APP/Power Mac with Ad Director. EDITORIAL EQUIPMENT: Hardware — 26-APP/Mac/SMS/Library System; Printers — MON/270, Pre Press/Panther 46 EDITORIAL SOFTWARE: Baseview/Editorial System. PRODUCTION EQUIPMENT: Hardware — MON/Imagesetter, Nu/40V6U, Panther 46; Cameras — 1-B PRODUCTION SOFTWARE: QPS/QuarkXPress 4.0, Baseview/Editorial Systems.
Note: Advertising is sold in combination with the Blue Springs Examiner (e) for $30.55 (d). Individual newspaper rates not made available.

JEFFERSON CITY

NEWS TRIBUNE

210 Monroe St, Jefferson City, Mo., 65101-3210, Cole; gen tel (573) 636-3131; adv tel (573) 761-0228; ed tel (573) 761-0240; gen fax (573) 636-7035; ed fax (573) 636-0235; gen/nat adv e-mail display@newstribune.com; disp adv e-mail display@newstribune.com; class adv e-mailclass@newstribune.com; ed e-mail editor@newstribune.com; web site www.newstribune.com
- 1,000,000(views)
Group: WEHCO Media, Inc.
Published: Mon, Tues, Wed, Thur, Fri, Sat, Sun
Weekday Frequency: m
Saturday Frequency: m
Circulation: 11,446; 11,446(sat); 14,675(sun)
Last Audit: AAM September 30, 2017
Advertising Rate (weekday/saturday): Open inch rate $17.95
Advertising Rate (sunday): Open inch rate $19.80
News services: AP. **Established:** 1865
Own Printing Facility?: Yes
Commercial Printers?: Yes
Special Editions: Active Times (monthly); Escape (Thursday); Styles (Sunday); Health (Tuesday); Flavors (Wednesday); TV Week (Friday); Church Page (Friday); Real Estate (Friday); Home Living (semi-annual); HER Magazine (bi-monthly)
Special Weekly Sections: Health, Minipage (Tue); Flavor (Wed); Escape (Thur); Church, TV (Fri); Garden (Sun)
Syndicated Publications: Parade (S); HER Magazine (bi-monthly); Home Living (quarterly)
Proprietary Publications: California Democrat; Fulton Sun
Digital Platform - Mobile: Apple, Android, Windows
Digital Platform - Tablet: Apple iOS, Android, Windows 7
Pub. .... Walter E. Hussman
Adv. Mgr. .... Jane Haslag
Mng. Ed. .... Gary Castor
Sports Ed. .... Tom Rackers
Circ. Mgr. .... Michael Johns
Gen. Mgr. .... Terri Leifeste
Circ. Mgr. .... Mike Johns
Mechanical Available: Offset; Black and 3 ROP colors; insert accepted; page cutoffs - 20.25.
Mechanical Specifications: Type page 11 5/8 x 20 1/4; E - 6 cols, 2 1/16, 1/8 between; A - 6 cols, 2 1/16, 1/8 between; C - 6 cols, 2 1/16, 1/8 between.
Areas Served: 65001, 65010, 65013, 65014, 65016, 65018, 65023, 65024, 65026, 65032, 65035, 65039, 65043, 65046, 65048, 65049, 65051, 65053, 65054, 65058, 65059, 65061, 65063, 65066, 65074, 65075, 65076, 65080, 65081, 65082, 65084, 65085, 65101, 65109, 65251, 65086, 65582
Delivery Method: Mail, Newsstand, CarrierEquipment & Software: PRESSROOM EQUIPMENT: Lines — Man Roland Uniset 70; Reels & Stands — Megtec 70; MAILROOM EQUIPMENT: Counter Stackers — Quipp 440; Inserters & Stuffers — HI, GMA/1000; Tying Machines — Quipp; Address Machine — 1/Ch.; BUSINESS EQUIPMENT: PBS-Sun BUSINESS SOFTWARE: PBS CLASSIFIED EQUIPMENT: Hardware — PBS-DTI; Printers — Copiers; CLASSIFIED SOFTWARE: PBS-DTI DISPLAY EQUIPMENT: Hardware — APP/Mac; DISPLAY SOFTWARELayout Software — Multi-Ad, QPS/QuarkXPress. EDITORIAL EQUIPMENT: Hardware — APP/Mac; Printers — Copiers EDITORIAL SOFTWARE: Baseview. PRODUCTION EQUIPMENT: Hardware — Trendsetter 100 Trendsetter 50; Cameras — 1-R PRODUCTION SOFTWARE: InDesign

JOPLIN

THE JOPLIN GLOBE

117 E 4th St, Joplin, Mo., 64801-2302, Jasper; gen tel (417) 623-3480; adv tel (417) 627-7214; ed tel (417) 623-3480; gen fax (417) 623-8450; adv fax (417) 623-8598; ed fax (417) 623-8598; gen/nat adv e-mail bpowers@joplinglobe.com; disp adv e-mail bpowers@joplinglobe.com; class adv e-mailtholder@joplinglobe.com; ed e-mail cstark@joplinglobe.com; web site www.joplinglobe.com
Group: Community Newspaper Holdings, Inc.
Published: Mon, Tues, Wed, Thur, Fri, Sat, Sun
Weekday Frequency: m
Saturday Frequency: m
Circulation: 16,152; 16,152(sat); 22,170(sun)
Last Audit: AAM December 31, 2015
Advertising Rate (weekday/saturday): Open inch rate $38.75
Advertising Rate (sunday): Open inch rate $47.75
News services: AP. **Established:** 1896
Special Editions: Silver Enquirer (Monthly); Grace Magazine (Quarterly).
Special Weekly Sections: Sports (Mon); Business, Finance (Tue); Best Food Day (Wed); Health & Family (Thur); Entertainment (Fri); Religion (Sat); Real Estate, Comics (Sun)
Syndicated Publications: Parade (S).
Digital Platform - Mobile: Apple, Android, Windows, Blackberry
Digital Platform - Tablet: Apple iOS, Android, Windows 7, Blackberry Tablet OS, Kindle, Nook, Kindle Fire
Pres. .... Daniel P. Chiodo
Credit Mgr. .... Amber Severns
Adv. Supvr., Classified .... Sharon Fitzjohn
Ed. .... Carol Stark
Editorial Page Ed. .... Clair Goodwin
Metro Ed. .... Andy Ostemeyer
Sports Ed. .... Jim Henry
Online Mgr. .... John Cruzan
Prodn. Dir. .... David Starchman
Pub. .... Mike Beatty
Adv. Dir. .... Brent Powers
Nat'l Coord. .... Dee Baker
Ret'l Adv. Mgr. .... Janett Copper
Market Information: ADS; TMC.
Mechanical Available: Offset; Black and 3 ROP colors; insert accepted; page cutoffs - 22 3/4.
Mechanical Specifications: Type page 13 x 21 3/4; E - 6 cols, 2 1/16, 1/8 between; A - 6 cols, 2 1/16, 1/8 between; C - 6 cols, 2 1/16, 1/8 between.
Areas Served: Jasper County
Delivery Method: Mail, Newsstand, Carrier, RacksEquipment & Software: PRESSROOM EQUIPMENT: Lines — 5-G/Headliner Unit (2 color decks) 1986; Folders — 2-G/2:1; Pasters —G/Automatic 1986; Control System — PEC/Bond Drive 1985.; MAILROOM EQUIPMENT: Counter Stackers — 2/QWI, 1-/QWI; Inserters & Stuffers — MM/227 2:1; Tying Machines — 2-Si/Snl; Wrapping Singles — Bann/Tyer; Address Machine — 1-/Ch; BUSINESS EQUIPMENT: IBM/AS-400 CLASSIFIED EQUIPMENT: Hardware — IBM/RS 6000; Printers — HP/4; CLASSIFIED SOFTWARE: AT, Enterprise. DISPLAY SOFTWARELayout Software — IBM/PC. EDITORIAL EQUIPMENT: Hardware — IBM/RS 6000; Printers — HP/5, HP/4 EDITORIAL SOFTWARE: AT. PRODUCTION EQUIPMENT: Hardware — AmeriGraph/Magnum 453 Seds, Southern Litho/GNS 39, W/30 D; Cameras — 1-C, 1-R; Scanners — ECR/1000DE, ECR/1030C.

KANSAS CITY

THE KANSAS CITY STAR

1729 Grand Blvd, Kansas City, Mo., 64108-1413, Jackson; gen tel (816) 234-4636; adv tel (816) 234-4636; ed tel (816) 234-4900; adv fax (816) 234-4101; ed fax (816) 234-4876; gen/nat adv e-mail mjolles@kcstar.com; disp adv e-mail mjolles@kcstar.com; class adv e-mailclassfeedback@kcstar.com; ed e-mail tberg@kcstar.com; web site www.kansascity.com
- 30,000,000(views) 4,000,000(visitors)
Group: The McClatchy Company
Published: Mon, Tues, Wed, Thur, Fri, Sat, Sun
Weekday Frequency: m
Saturday Frequency: m
Circulation: 143,237; 130,511(sat); 225,460(sun)
Last Audit: AAM June 30, 2016
Advertising Rate (weekday/saturday): Open inch rate $530.00 (Mon-Thur); $538.00 (Fri-Sat)
Advertising Rate (sunday): Open inch rate $583.00
News services: AP, MCT, NYT. **Established:** 1880
Own Printing Facility?: Yes
Commercial Printers?: Yes
Special Editions: Lawn, Garden & Home (Apr); Diaper Days II (Aug); Holiday Religion (Dec); Remodeling & Decorating Expo (Feb); American Heart Association (Jan); Active Times (Jul); Progress (Jun); Recycling (Mar); Lawn, Garden & Home (May); The Star Gift Guide I (Nov); The
Special Weekly Sections: Sports (Mon); Business (Tue); Auto, Food, Neighborhood News (Wed); Entertainment (Thur); FYI (Fri); Auto, Faith, Neighborhood News (Sat); Travel, Home, Arts, Outdoor, Comics, Real Estate (Sun)
Syndicated Publications: Parade (S).
Digital Platform - Mobile: Apple, Android, Windows
Digital Platform - Tablet: Apple iOS, Android, Windows 7
Vice President, Finance .... Bryan Harbison
Ed. .... Mike Fannin
Cartoonist .... Lee Judge
Prod. Dev. Dir. .... Joe Coleman
Marketing Analyst .... Isaac Hindle
Pres./Pub. .... Tony Berg
Market Information: ADS; Split run; TMC; Zoned editions.
Mechanical Available: Converted Letterpress to Offset; Black and 3 ROP colors; insert accepted; page cutoffs - 23 9/16.
Mechanical Specifications: Type page 13 x 22 1/4; E - 6 cols, 2 1/16, 1/8 between; A - 6 cols, 2 1/16, 1/8 between; C - 10 cols, 1 3/16, 1/16 between.
Delivery Method: Mail, Newsstand, Carrier, RacksEquipment & Software: PRESSROOM EQUIPMENT: Lines — 10-H/Colormatic converted offset 1966; 10-H/Colormatic converted offset 1967; 10-H/Colormatic converted offset 1968; 15-H/Colormatic converted offset 1969; Folders — 9-H; Reels & Stands — 45-MAN.; MAILROOM EQUIPMENT: Counter Stackers — 11-HL/Monitor II; Inserters & Stuffers — 5-HI/1372;

Tying Machines — 11-Dynamic/Tying Machines NT-2; Address Machine — 2-Ch.; BUSINESS EQUIPMENT: PCs, DEC/VAX CLASSIFIED EQUIPMENT: Hardware — DEC/VAX; HDS, Northern Telephones.; DISPLAY EQUIPMENT: Hardware — 1-APP/Mac IIx, 8-APP/Mac IIcx, 8-APP/Mac ci, 1-APP/Mac IIfx, 2-APP/Mac Quadra 700, 1-APP/Mac Quadra 650, 4-APP/Mac Quadra 800, APP/Mac Centris 650, 1-APP/Mac SE, 2-APP/Mac Power PC 7100, 2-APP/Mac Quadra 900, 5-APP/Mac Plus, 2-PC 486, 1-PC 386; EDITORIAL EQUIPMENT: Hardware — 240-Novell/PC, 25-APP/Mac, APP/Power Mac/Lf/AP Leaf Picture Desk, APP/Mac; Printers — Epson/LaserPrinter, HP/LaserPrinter, QMS/Laser Printers EDITORIAL SOFTWARE: Dewar/Disc System IV, QPS/QuarkXPress 3.3. PRODUCTION EQUIPMENT: Hardware — 2-WL/Lith-X-Pozer III, 2-AU/7000 Imagesetters, 2-AU/APS-108 FC Imagesetters, 1-AU/APS-3850 SST; Cameras — 2-C/Newspager; Scanners — 1-ECR/2045C, 1-Scitex/Smart 2045C, 1-Scitex/Smart 342, 2-AG/Horizon Plus, 3-Umax/PowerLook II, 2-Kk/3570, 2-Kk/

KENNETT

THE DAILY DUNKLIN DEMOCRAT

203 1st St, Kennett, Mo., 63857-2052, Dunklin; gen tel (573) 888-4505; adv tel (573) 888-4505; ed tel (573) 888-4505; gen fax (573) 888-5114; adv fax (573) 888-5114; ed fax (573) 888-5114; gen/nat adv e-mail awright@dddnews.com; disp adv e-mail tcoleman@dddnews.com; class adv e-mailcfolkes@dddnews.com; ed e-mail mrasberry@dddnews.com; web site www.dddnews.com

Group: Rust Communications
Published: Tues, Wed, Thur, Fri, Sun
Weekday Frequency: e
Circulation: 2,500; 3,600(sun)
Last Audit: Sworn/Estimate/Non-Audited September 30, 2017
Advertising Rate (weekday/saturday): Open inch rate $14.55 (Tue/Thur/Fri); $17.28 (Wed)
Advertising Rate (sunday): Open inch rate $14.55
News services: AP. **Established:** 1888
Special Editions: Progress (Mar). Newcomer's (Jul)
Special Weekly Sections: Food (Wed); School (Tue/Thur); Religion, Real Estate (Fri); Seniors (Thur)
Syndicated Publications: Relish (Monthly); Parade (S); American Profile (Weekly).
Office Mgr. .... Debbie Wright
Interim Ed. .... Michelle Rasberry
Adv. Mgr. .... Terri Coleman
Sports Ed. .... Dustin Ward
Pub. .... Ron Kemp
Managing Ed. .... George Anderson
Circ. Mgr. .... Regina Lee
Office Mgr. .... Cody Tucker
Market Information: Split run; TMC; Zoned editions.
Mechanical Available: Offset; Black and 3 ROP colors; insert accepted; page cutoffs - 23.
Mechanical Specifications: Type page 11 5/8 x 21; E - 6 cols, 1 5/6, 1/8 between; A - 6 cols, 1 5/6, 1/8 between; C - 9 cols, 1 1/6, 1/8 between.
Delivery Method: Mail, Newsstand, Carrier, RacksEquipment & Software: PRESSROOM EQUIPMENT: Lines — 8-G/Community.; BUSINESS EQUIPMENT: 1-IBM EDITORIAL EQUIPMENT: Hardware — APP/iMac; Printers — HP/8000 EDITORIAL SOFTWARE: Baseview/NewsEdit Pro. PRODUCTION EQUIPMENT: Hardware — 3M.

KIRKSVILLE

KIRKSVILLE DAILY EXPRESS

110 E McPherson St, Kirksville, Mo., 63501-3506, Adair; gen tel (660) 665-2808; adv tel (660) 665-2808; ed tel (660) 665-2808; gen fax (660) 665-2608; adv fax (660) 665-2608; ed fax (660) 665-2608; gen/nat adv e-mail gwriedt@kirksvilledailyexpress.com; disp adv e-mail ads@kirksvilledailyexpress.com; class adv e-mailads@kirksvilledailyexpress.com; ed e-mail dailyexpresseditor@gmail.com; web site www.kirksvilledailyexpress.com

Group: New Media Investment Group
Published: Mon, Tues, Wed, Thur, Fri, Sun
Weekday Frequency: e
Circulation: 3,035; 4,263(sun)
Last Audit: Sworn/Estimate/Non-Audited September 30, 2017
Advertising Rate (weekday/saturday): Open inch rate $10.15
Advertising Rate (sunday): Open inch rate $10.15
Online Advertising Rate: 5 lines 1 day print and online $20
News services: AP. **Established:** 1901
Special Editions: Progress (Jul).
Special Weekly Sections: Entertainment (Thur); Religion (Fri); Business, Finance, Real Estate, Home, Living, Food (Sun)
Syndicated Publications: American Profile (S).
Digital Platform - Mobile: Apple, Android, Windows
Digital Platform - Tablet: Apple iOS, Android, Windows 7
Pub./Bus. Mgr. .... Larry W. Freels
Adv. Mgr. .... George Wriedt
Classified Ads. Mgr. .... Carole Murphy
Ed. .... Jason Hunsicker
Market Information: Split run; TMC.
Mechanical Available: Offset; Black and 3 ROP colors; insert accepted; page cutoffs - 22 3/4.
Mechanical Specifications: Type page 11 2/3 x 21; E - 6 cols, 1 15/16, 5/32 between; A - 6 cols, 1 15/16, 5/32 between; C - 6 cols, 1 15/16, 5/32 between.
Areas Served: Adair County
Delivery Method: Mail, Newsstand, CarrierEquipment & Software: PRESSROOM EQUIPMENT: Lines — 6-G/Community 1970; MAILROOM EQUIPMENT: Tying Machines — 2/Bu; Address Machine — 1-Miller/Bevco/LS-385.; BUSINESS EQUIPMENT: RSK/12, 1-IBM/AT CLASSIFIED EQUIPMENT: Hardware — 6-APP/Mac; CD-Rom; Printers — 3-APP/Mac LaserPrinter; CLASSIFIED SOFTWARE: Baseview. DISPLAY SOFTWAREAd Make-up Applications — QPS/QuarkXPress 6.1; Layout Software — QPS/QuarkXPress 6.1. EDITORIAL EQUIPMENT: Hardware — APP/Mac EDITORIAL SOFTWARE: APP/Mac. PRODUCTION EQUIPMENT: Hardware — 1-Nu/Double Flip Top; Cameras — 1-R/400; Scanners — 4-Scanmaker/X6EL.

LEBANON

THE LEBANON DAILY RECORD

100 E Commercial St, Lebanon, Mo., 65536-3257, Laclede; gen tel (417) 532-9131; adv tel (417) 532-9131; ed tel (417) 532-9131; gen fax (417) 532-8140; adv fax (417) 532-8140; ed fax (417) 532-8140; gen/nat adv e-mail jennifer@lebanondailyrecord.com; disp adv e-mail jennifer@lebanondailyrecord.com; class adv e-mailjennifer@lebanondailyrecord.com; ed e-mail fmassey@lebanondailyrecord.com; web site www.lebanondailyrecord.com - 151,170(views) 46,000(visitors)

Group: Lebanon Publishing Co.
Published: Mon, Tues, Wed, Thur, Fri, Sat
Weekday Frequency: e
Circulation: 4,300; 4,300(sat)
Last Audit: Sworn/Estimate/Non-Audited October 1, 2017
Advertising Rate (weekday/saturday): Open inch rate $8.95
Advertising Rate (sunday): Open inch rate $9.95
News services: AP. **Established:** 1934
Own Printing Facility?: No
Commercial Printers?: Yes
Special Editions: Back-to-School (Aug); Progress (Feb); Fair Tab (Jul); Welcome to Lebanon (Jul); Welcome to Bennett Sring (Dec); Senior Living (Monthly); Winter Sports (Nov).
Special Weekly Sections: Agriculture (Tue); Food (Wed); Religion (Fri)
Syndicated Publications: Senior Living (Monthly); American Profile (Weekly); Relish (Monthly).
Digital Platform - Mobile: Apple, Android, Windows
Digital Platform - Tablet: Apple iOS, Android, Windows 7
Pres./Pub. .... Dalton C. Wright
Ed. .... Julie Turner
Adv. Mgr. .... Rene Barker
Market Information: ADS;
Mechanical Available: Offset; Black and 3 ROP colors; insert accepted; page cutoffs - 22 3/4.
Mechanical Specifications: Type page 13 x 21 1/2; E - 6 cols, 2, 1/6 between; A - 6 cols, 2, 1/6 between; C - 6 cols, 2, 1/6 between.
Areas Served: 65536, 65622, 65632, 65667, 65662, 65590, 65722, 65556, 65567
Delivery Method: Mail, Newsstand, Carrier, RacksEquipment & Software: PRESSROOM EQUIPMENT: Lines — 4-G/Community 1964; 4-G/Community 1992.; MAILROOM EQUIPMENT: Counter Stackers — BG; Tying Machines — 2/Bu; Address Machine — KR/215.; BUSINESS EQUIPMENT: 3-PC 386 BUSINESS SOFTWARE: DAC/Easy, Lotus 1-2-3, Quattro/Pro CLASSIFIED EQUIPMENT: Hardware — APP/Mac; CLASSIFIED SOFTWARE: Multi-Ad/CAMS. DISPLAY EQUIPMENT: Hardware — APP/Mac; Printers — APP/Mac LaserWriter 16-600, New-Gen/Imager Plus 12xf; Other Hardware — APP/Mac. DISPLAY SOFTWAREAd Make-up Applications — Adobe/PageMaker 6.5, Multi-Ad/Creator 4.0, Adobe/Photoshop 3.05, QPS/QuarkXPress; Layout Software — APP/Mac. EDITORIAL EQUIPMENT: Hardware — APP/Power Mac/G4/TMac, APP/Mac; Printers — HP/5000 EDITORIAL SOFTWARE: Adobe/PageMaker 6.5, Adobe/Photoshop 3.0. PRODUCTION EQUIPMENT: Hardware — APP/Mac LaserWriter 4-600, APP/Mac LaserWriter 161600, NewGen/Imager Pro; Cameras — Nu/Horizontal SSTE2024; Scanners — Umax/5-8, Polaroid/SprintScan Neg Scanners PRODUCTION SOFTWARE: Adobe/PageMaker 6.5, Multi-Ad/Creator, Adobe/Photoshop, QPS/QuarkXPr

MARSHALL

THE MARSHALL DEMOCRAT-NEWS

121 N Lafayette Ave, Marshall, Mo., 65340-1747, Saline; gen tel (660) 886-2233; adv tel (660) 886-2233; ed tel (660) 815-0258; gen fax (660) 886-8544; adv fax (660) 886-8544; ed fax (660) 886-8544 ; gen/nat adv e-mail mdavis@marshallnews.com; disp adv e-mail mdavis@marshallnews.com; class adv e-mailstevis@marshallnews.com; ed e-mail ecrump@marshallnews.com; web site www.marshallnews.com

Group: Rust Communications
Published: Mon, Tues, Wed, Thur, Fri
Weekday Frequency: e
Circulation: 3,007
Last Audit: Sworn/Estimate/Non-Audited September 30, 2017
Advertising Rate (weekday/saturday): Open inch rate $8.84
News services: AP. **Established:** 1879
Special Weekly Sections: Agriculture, Health, Food (Tue); Business, NIE (Thur); Weddings, Church (Fri)
Syndicated Publications: TV Preview (Fri); Relish (Monthly).
Digital Platform - Mobile: Apple, Android, Windows
Digital Platform - Tablet: Apple iOS, Android, Windows 7
Pub. .... Dave Phillips
Adv. Mgr. .... Mike Davis
Circ. Mgr. .... Pat Morrow
Ed. .... Eric Crump
Sports Ed. .... Chris Allen
Market Information: TMC.
Mechanical Available: Offset; Black and 3 ROP colors; insert accepted; page cutoffs - 21 1/2.
Mechanical Specifications: Type page 13 x 21 1/2; E - 6 cols, 2 1/16, 1/8 between; A - 6 cols, 2 1/16, 1/8 between; C - 6 cols, 2 1/16, 1/8 between.
Delivery Method: Mail, RacksEquipment & Software: PRESSROOM EQUIPMENT: Lines — 5-KP/News King 1976.; MAILROOM EQUIPMENT: Tying Machines — 1/Bu; Wrapping Singles — Addressing machine 1-/Ch.; BUSINESS EQUIPMENT: 1-Packard Bell, 2-Acros CLASSIFIED EQUIPMENT: Hardware — 1-APP/Mac.; DISPLAY EQUIPMENT: Hardware — 2-APP/Mac; Printers — 1-APP/Mac.; EDITORIAL EQUIPMENT: Hardware — 8-APP/Mac; Printers — 1-APP/Mac. PRODUCTION EQUIPMENT: Hardware — 1-Nu; Cameras — 1-R/500, LE; Scanners — Gam/Digital Densitometer.

MARYVILLE

THE MARYVILLE DAILY FORUM

111 E Jenkins St, Maryville, Mo., 64468-2318, Nodaway; gen tel (660) 562-2424; adv tel (660) 562-2424; ed tel (660) 562-2424; gen fax (660) 562-2823; adv fax (660) 562-2823; ed fax (660) 562-2823; gen/nat adv e-mail kholtman@maryvilledailyforum.com; disp adv e-mail kholtman@maryvilledailyforum.com; class adv e-mailrpiveral@maryvilledailyforum.com; ed e-mail skyep@maryvilledailyforum.com; web site www.maryvilledailyforum.com - 270,000(views) 75,000(visitors)

Group: Cobb Publishing, LLC
Published: Mon, Tues, Wed, Thur, Fri
Weekday Frequency: m
Circulation: 2,000
Last Audit: Sworn/Estimate/Non-Audited September 16, 2017
Advertising Rate (weekday/saturday): Open inch rate $6.00
Online Advertising Rate: cost per thousand
News services: AP. **Established:** 1869
Own Printing Facility?: No
Commercial Printers?: No
Special Editions: Real Estate (Aug); Holiday Gift Guide (Dec); Progress (Jan); Newcomers (Jul); Fair (Jun); Spring Home Improvement (Mar); Real Estate (May); Fall Sports (Football) (Sept).
Special Weekly Sections: Agriculture, high school, community life
Syndicated Publications: American Profile (S); TV Forum (Thur).
Digital Platform - Mobile: Apple, Android, Windows
Digital Platform - Tablet: Apple iOS, Android, Windows 7
Pub. .... Phil Cobb
Business Mgr. .... Lana Cobb
Market Information: shopper
Mechanical Available: Offset; Black and process colors; insert accepted; page cutoffs - 21
Mechanical Specifications: Type page 10.25 x 20; E - 6 cols, 1.55", .1667 between;
Areas Served: 64468
Delivery Method: Mail, Newsstand, RacksEquipment & Software: CLASSIFIED SOFTWARE: Baseview.

MEXICO

MEXICO LEDGER

300 N Washington St, Mexico, Mo., 65265-2756, Audrain; gen tel (573) 581-1111; adv tel (573) 581-1111; ed tel (573) 581-1111; gen fax (573) 581-2029; adv fax (573) 581-2029; ed fax (573) 581-2029; gen/nat adv e-mail mkeller@mexicoledger.com; disp adv e-mail display@mexicoledger.com; class adv e-mailbfike@socket.net; ed e-mail news@mexicoledger.com; web site www.mexicoledger.com

Group: New Media Investment Group
Published: Mon, Tues, Wed, Thur, Fri, Sat
Weekday Frequency: e
Saturday Frequency: m
Circulation: 4,500
Last Audit: Sworn/Estimate/Non-Audited September 30, 2017
Advertising Rate (weekday/saturday): Open inch rate $13.25
News services: AP, SHNS. **Established:** 1855
Special Editions: Home Improvement (Apr); Football (Aug); Progress (Feb); Hometown (Jun); Car Care (Mar); Christmas Kick-Off (Nov); Back-to-School (Oct).
Special Weekly Sections: Food (Tue/Wed); Entertainment, Amusement, Business, Finance (Daily); Church (Fri);
Syndicated Publications: Relish (Monthly); American Profile (Sat).
Digital Platform - Mobile: Apple, Android, Windows
Digital Platform - Tablet: Apple iOS, Android,

Windows 7
Ed.....Janeen Sims
News Ed.....Brenda Fike
Sports Ed.....Jim Stanley
Adv. Mgr.....Martin Keller
Pub.....Joe May
Market Information: Split run; TMC.
Mechanical Available: Offset; Black and 3 ROP colors; insert accepted; page cutoffs - 21 1/2.
Mechanical Specifications: Type page 13 x 21 1/2; E - 6 cols, 2, 1/12 between; A - 6 cols, 2, 1/12 between; C - 7 cols, 2, 1/12 between.
Areas Served: Audrain County
Delivery Method: Mail, Carrier, RacksEquipment & Software: PRESSROOM EQUIPMENT: Lines — 7-G/Community; MAILROOM EQUIPMENT: Tying Machines — 1/Bu; Wrapping Singles — 1-Sa/SM; Address Machine — 1-/Ch.; BUSINESS EQUIPMENT: Maxtech/ChipTex BUSINESS SOFTWARE: Microsoft/Windows 98, QuickBooks, Excel Microsoft/Excel, Lotus 1-2-3, Microsoft/Word CLASSIFIED EQUIPMENT: Hardware — 1-APP/Mac Performa 6300; Printers — Ap; CLASSIFIED SOFTWARE: Cx. DISPLAY EQUIPMENT: Printers — HP/5000; Other Hardware — APP/Mac G3 DISPLAY SOFTWAREAd Make-up Applications — Multi-Ad/Creator, Aldus/PageMaker; Layout Software — 2-APP/Power Mac 7200-90. EDITORIAL EQUIPMENT: Hardware — 11-APP/Mac/APP/Mac; Printers — HP/4V, HP/5000 EDITORIAL SOFTWARE: QPS/QuarkXPress, Multi-Ad/Creator, Adobe/Photoshop, Adobe/PageMaker. PRODUCTION EQUIPMENT: Hardware — 1-Nu; Cameras — 1-R/580, 1-SCREEN/680C; Scanners — Lf/Leafscan, APP/Mac Scanner PRODUCTION SOFTWARE: QPS/QuarkXPress.

MOBERLY

THE MOBERLY MONITOR-INDEX

218 N Williams St, Moberly, Mo., 65270-1534, Randolph; gen tel (660) 263-4123; adv tel (660) 263-4123; ed tel (660) 263-4123; gen fax (660) 263-3626; adv fax (660) 263-3626; ed fax (660) 263-3626; gen/nat adv e-mail advertising@moberlymonitor.com; disp adv e-mail advertising@moberlymonitor.com; class adv e-mailnbartolacci@moberlymonitor.com; ed e-mail alindley@moberlymonitor.com; web site www.moberlymonitor.com
Group: New Media Investment Group
Published: Mon, Tues, Wed, Thur, Fri
Weekday Frequency: e
Circulation: 3,360; 5,342(sun)
Last Audit: Sworn/Estimate/Non-Audited September 30, 2017
Advertising Rate (weekday/saturday): Open inch rate $18.83
Online Advertising Rate: 5 lines 1 day print and online $20
News services: AP, NEA, TMS. **Established:** 1869
Special Editions: Chamber Tab (Apr); Back-to-School (Aug); Christmas Greetings (Dec); Valentine Hearts (Feb); Bridal (Jan); County Fairs (Jul); Spring Bridal (Jun); Progress (Mar); Graduation (May); Cookbook (Nov); Fall Fashion (Sept).
Special Weekly Sections: Food, Coupon (Tue); Dining (Wed); Business, Church (Thur); TV Spotlight (Fri)
Syndicated Publications: Business Review (Fri); 50 Something (Monthly); American Profile (S); Youth Today (Tues).
Digital Platform - Mobile: Apple, Android, Windows
Digital Platform - Tablet: Apple iOS, Android, Windows 7
Pub.....Rod Dixon
General Mgr./Adv. Dir.....Marsha Hargus
Bus. Mgr.....Debbie Lowery
Office Mgr.....Debbie Fitzpatrick
Jessie Embree
Classified Ads....Nancy Bartollacci
Ed.....Alecia Lassing
Market Information: Split run; TMC; Zoned editions.
Mechanical Available: Offset; Black and 3 ROP colors; insert accepted; page cutoffs - 22 3/4.
Mechanical Specifications: Type page 13 x 21 1/2; E - 6 cols, 2 1/16, 1/5 between; A - 6 cols, 2 1/16, 1/5 between; C - 8 cols, 1 1/2, 1/5 between.Equipment & Software: PRESSROOM EQUIPMENT: Lines — 6-Unit/Community; Folders — G/Suburban.; MAILROOM EQUIPMENT: Tying Machines — Strap-Matic 202A; Address Machine — Wm, MB-45/Labeling Machine.; BUSINESS EQUIPMENT: Mk, APP/Mac BUSINESS SOFTWARE: QuarkXPress 7.0, Baseview, Brainworks, SSPS System CLASSIFIED EQUIPMENT: Hardware — APP/Mac; APP/Mac Scanner; Printers - NewGen/DesignXpress 17; CLASSIFIED SOFTWARE: Baseview, Fox, Aldus, QPS/QuarkXPress. DISPLAY EQUIPMENT: Hardware — APP/Mac; Printers — APP/Mac LaserWriter Pro, NewGen/DesignXpress 17; Other Hardware — APP/Mac Scanner, CD-Rom, Jazz/Drive, Epson/Film Scanner DISPLAY SOFTWAREAd Make-up Applications — Multi-Ad/Creator, Aldus/FreeHand, QPS/QuarkXPress, Baseview, Brainworks; Layout Software — Baseview EDITORIAL EQUIPMENT: Hardware — Mk, APP/Mac/Epson/Film Scanner, APP/Mac Scanner; Printers — NewGen/Oversize, APP/Mac, APP/Mac LaserWriter Pro, NewGen/DesignXpress, Xante/Accel-A-Writer EDITORIAL SOFTWARE: Mk, QPS/QuarkXPress, Baseview, Brainworks. PRODUCTION EQUIPMENT: Hardware — 1-Nu, APP/Power Mac 64; Cameras — Acti; Scanners — APP/Mac, Epson/Film Scanner PRODUCTION SOFTWARE: Baseview.

MONETT

THE MONETT TIMES

505 E Broadway St, Monett, Mo., 65708-2333, Barry; gen tel (417) 235-3135; gen fax (417) 235-8852; gen/nat adv e-mail community@monett-times.com; disp adv e-mail community@monett-times.com; class adv e-mailclassifieds@monett-times.com; ed e-mail editor@monett-times.com; web site www.monett-times.com
Group: Rust Communications
Published: Tues, Wed, Fri, Sat
Weekday Frequency: e
Saturday Frequency: e
Circulation: 2,400
Last Audit: Sworn/Estimate/Non-Audited September 30, 2017
Advertising Rate (weekday/saturday): Open inch rate $7.40
Advertising Rate (sunday): Open inch rate $7.40
News services: AP **Established:** 1908
Special Editions: Christmas (Dec); Progress (Feb); Football (Oct); Basketball (Other).
Special Weekly Sections: Auctions (Wed)
Syndicated Publications: American Profile (Weekly).
Digital Platform - Mobile: Apple, Android, Windows
Digital Platform - Tablet: Apple iOS, Android, Windows 7
Pub.....Jacob Brower
Mng. Ed.....Murray Bishoff
Ed.....Kyle Troutman
Market Information: TMC.
Mechanical Available: Offset; Black and 3 ROP colors; insert accepted; page cutoffs - 22 3/4.
Mechanical Specifications: Type page 13 x 21 1/2; E - 6 cols, 2, 1/4 between; A - 6 cols, 2, 1/4 between; C - 6 cols, 2, 1/4 between.
Delivery Method: Mail, RacksEquipment & Software: PRESSROOM EQUIPMENT: Lines — 4-WPC/Quadra Color 1995; MAILROOM EQUIPMENT: Tying Machines — 2/Bu.; BUSINESS EQUIPMENT: DEC/PC XL 466D2 CLASSIFIED EQUIPMENT: Hardware — APP/Power Mac SE; Printers — APP/Mac LaserWriter; CLASSIFIED SOFTWARE: Microsoft/Word, Aldus/PageMaker, Microsoft/Windows. DISPLAY EQUIPMENT: Printers — APP/Mac LaserWriter, LaserMaster/1200 dpi; DISPLAY SOFTWAREAd Make-up Applications — Aldus/PageMaker; Layout Software — APP/Power Mac. EDITORIAL EQUIPMENT: Hardware — APP/Power Mac; Printers — APP/Mac LaserWriter EDITORIAL SOFTWARE: Microsoft/Word, Aldus/PageMaker, Microsoft/Windows. PRODUCTION EQUIPMENT: Hardware — APP/Power Mac, Adobe/Photoshop; Cameras — CL; Scanners — 1-LaCie, Minolta.

NEOSHO

NEOSHO DAILY NEWS

1000 W Harmony St, Neosho, Mo., 64850-1631, Newton; gen tel (417) 451-1520; adv tel (417) 451-1520; ed tel (417) 451-1520; gen fax (417) 451-6408; adv fax (417) 451-6408; ed fax (417) 451-6408; gen/nat adv e-mail rburtis@gatehousemedia.com; disp adv e-mail rburtis@gatehousemedia.com; class adv e-mailndnclassifieds@sbcglobal.net; ed e-mail editor@neoshodailynews.com; web site www.neoshodailynews.com
Group: New Media Investment Group
Published: Tues, Wed, Thur, Fri, Sun
Weekday Frequency: m
Last Audit: Sworn/Estimate/Non-Audited September 30, 2017
Advertising Rate (weekday/saturday): Open inch rate $9.75
Advertising Rate (sunday): Open inch rate $9.75
Online Advertising Rate: 5 lines 1 day print and online $20
News services: AP **Established:** 1905
Own Printing Facility?: Yes
Commercial Printers?: Yes
Special Editions: City-Wide Garage Sale (Apr); Back-to-School (Aug); Christmas Greetings (Dec); Year of Progress (Feb); Babies of Last Year (Jan); Fair Tabs (Jul); Lawn & Garden (Mar); Graduation (May); Holiday Gift Guide (Nov); Our Town (Oct).
Special Weekly Sections: Education (Wed); Religion (Fri); Seniors (Sun); Business (Sun)
Syndicated Publications: American Profile (Weekly).
Digital Platform - Mobile: Apple, Android, Windows
Digital Platform - Tablet: Apple iOS, Android, Windows 7
Gen. Mgr.....Robin Burtis
Prod. Mgr.....Mike Reese
Pub.....Matt Guthrie
Editor....Todd Nighswonger
Online Mgr/Mgmt Info Servs....John Ford
Market Information: TMC.
Mechanical Available: Offset; Black and 3 ROP colors; insert accepted; page cutoffs - 22 3/4.
Mechanical Specifications: Type page 11 5/8 x 21 1/2; E - 6 cols, 2 1/16, 1/8 between; A - 6 cols, 2 1/16, 1/8 between; C - 6 cols, 2 1/16, 1/8 between.
Delivery Method: Mail, Newsstand, Carrier, RacksEquipment & Software: PRESSROOM EQUIPMENT: Lines — 9-G/Community 1971; Folders — 1-G/Community, 1-G/SC 1971; Registration System — 2 MAILROOM EQUIPMENT: Counter Stackers — 1/BG; Tying Machines — 2-/Miller-Bevco.; BUSINESS EQUIPMENT: PC BUSINESS SOFTWARE: Nomads, QuickBooks CLASSIFIED EQUIPMENT: Hardware — APP/Mac; Printers — APP/Mac ImageWriter; CLASSIFIED SOFTWARE: CAMS. EDITORIAL EQUIPMENT: Hardware — APP/Mac/Pre Press/Panther Pro Imagesetter EDITORIAL SOFTWARE: Baseview. PRODUCTION EQUIPMENT: Hardware — APP/Mac LaserWriter Select, APP/Mac, HP/LaserJet 4MV, 2-Pre Press Panther Pro Imagesetter; Cameras — R; Scanners — 2-Microtek/EM6 PRODUCTION SOFTWARE: QPS/QuarkXPress, Pre Press/Imagesetter.

NEVADA

THE NEVADA DAILY MAIL

131 S Cedar St, Nevada, Mo., 64772-3309, Vernon; gen tel (417) 667-3344; adv tel (417) 667-3344; ed tel (417) 667-3344; gen fax (417) 667-8384; adv fax (417) 667-7475; ed fax (417) 667-1469; gen/nat adv e-mail advertising@nevadadailymail.com; disp adv e-mail advertising@nevadadailymail.com; class adv e-mailadvertising@nevadadailymail.com; ed e-mail editorial@nevadadailymail.com; web site www.nevadadailymail.com
Group: Rust Communications
Published: Tues, Wed, Thur, Fri
Weekday Frequency: m
Circulation: 1,400
Last Audit: Sworn/Estimate/Non-Audited September 30, 2017
Advertising Rate (weekday/saturday): Open inch rate $10.25
News services: AP, NEA. **Established:** 1883
Own Printing Facility?: Yes
Commercial Printers?: Yes
Special Editions: Back-to-School (Aug); Christmas Shoppers (Dec); Brides (Jan); Home Improvement (Mar); Graduation (May); Puzzle Pages (Monthly); Home Improvement (Oct).
Special Weekly Sections: Menus (Wed); Church, Senior (Fri)
Syndicated Publications: SHE; AGELESS
Digital Platform - Mobile: Apple, Android, Windows
Digital Platform - Tablet: Apple iOS, Android, Windows 7
Pub.....Sharon Knight
Adv. Dir.....Lorie Harter
Ed.....Lynn Wade
Lifestyles Ed.....Sharyon Duke
Prodn. Mgr.....Chris Jones
Circ. Supvr.....Shirley Johnson
Market Information: TMC.
Mechanical Available: Offset; Black and 3 ROP colors; insert accepted; page cutoffs - 21.
Mechanical Specifications: Type page 13 x 21; E - 6 cols, 2 1/16, 1/8 between; A - 6 cols, 2 1/16, 1/8 between; C - 6 cols, 2 1/16, 1/8 between.
Delivery Method: Mail, Newsstand, RacksEquipment & Software: PRESSROOM EQUIPMENT: Lines — 5-G/Community; MAILROOM EQUIPMENT: Tying Machines — 1/Bu, 1-/St; Wrapping Singles — 2-/Sa; DISPLAY SOFTWAREAd Make-up Applications — QPS/QuarkXPress 4.1.; EDITORIAL EQUIPMENT: Hardware — COM/UTS, APP/Mac. PRODUCTION EQUIPMENT: Hardware — CTP

PARK HILLS

DAILY JOURNAL, PARK HILLS

1513 S Saint Joe Dr, Park Hills, Mo., 63601-2402, Saint Francois; gen tel (573) 431-2010; adv tel (573) 431-2010; ed tel (573) 518-3615; gen fax (573) 431-7640; adv fax (573) 518-0765; ed fax (573) 431-7640; gen/nat adv e-mail lstarkey@dailyjournalonline.com; disp adv e-mail advertising@dailyjournalonline.com; class adv e-maillmaize@dailyjournalonline.com; ed e-mail editorial@dailyjournalonline.com; web site www.dailyjournalonline.com - 2,242,184(views) 240,169(visitors)
Group: Lee Enterprises, Inc.
Published: Mon, Tues, Wed, Thur, Fri, Sat
Weekday Frequency: m
Saturday Frequency: m
Circulation: 4,491; 4,978(sat)
Last Audit: AAM September 30, 2014
Branch Offices: Farmington, MO
Advertising Rate (weekday/saturday): Open inch rate $12.56
News services: NEA, AP, TMS. **Established:** 1935
Own Printing Facility?: No
Commercial Printers?: No
Special Editions: Family Disaster Preparedness; Family Owned Business; Memorial Day, Camping Guide, Spring Body and More; Automotive Service Guide; New Year New You; Info Guide, Life Planning Guide, Business Card Directory
Special Weekly Sections: Daily Journal Weekly Real Estate
Digital Platform - Mobile: Apple, Android, Windows, Blackberry, Other
Digital Platform - Tablet: Android, Windows 7
Pub.....Gary Berblinger
Managing Ed.....Doug Smith
Sports Ed.....Donn Adamson
Circulation Manager
Angel King
Advertising Director....Jamila Khalil
Market Information: TMC.
Mechanical Available: Offset; Black and 3 ROP colors; insert accepted; page cutoffs - 22 3/4.
Areas Served: St. Francois County, MO and portions of adjacent counties
Delivery Method: Mail, Newsstand, Carrier, Racks

POPLAR BLUFF

DAILY AMERICAN REPUBLIC

PO Box 7, Poplar Bluff, Mo., 63902-0007, Butler; gen tel (573) 785-1414; adv tel (573) 785-1414; ed tel (573) 785-1414; gen fax (573) 785-2706; adv fax (573) 785-2706; ed fax (573) 785-0476; gen/nat adv e-mail ads@darnews.com; disp adv e-mail cpierce@darnews.com; class adv e-mailcpierce@darnews.com; ed e-mail sberry@darnews.com; web site www.darnews.com
Group: Rust Communications
Published: Mon, Tues, Wed, Thur, Fri, Sun
Weekday Frequency: e
Circulation: 7,653; 7,653(sat); 8,824(sun)
Last Audit: CAC March 31, 2014
Advertising Rate (weekday/saturday): Open inch rate $18.04 (Mon-Tue/Thur-Fri); $18.65 (Wed)
Advertising Rate (sunday): Open inch rate $18.65
News services: AP, NYT. **Established:** 1869
Own Printing Facility?: Yes
Commercial Printers?: Yes
Special Weekly Sections: Regional (Mon); Education (Tue); Food, Business (Wed); Outdoors (Thur); TV, Religion (Fri); Lifestyles (Sun)
Syndicated Publications: USA Weekend, Parade (Sun).
Digital Platform - Mobile: Apple, Android
Digital Platform - Tablet: Apple iOS, Android, Kindle, Nook, Kindle Fire
Publisher.................................... Don Schrieber
Bus. Mgr./Controller................. Rachel Coleman
Editor.. Stan Berry
News Ed.................................... Barbara Horton
Sports Ed. .... Brian Rosener
Prodn. Foreman, Pressroom.......... Randy Graves
Advertising Director..................... Christy Pierce
Adv. Dir.... Joe Jordan
Circ. Dir. .... Gary Richard
Lifestyle Ed.............................. Michele Friedrich
Religion Ed. .... Dorothy Carlson
Market Information: TMC; Zoned editions.
Mechanical Available: Offset; Black and 2 ROP colors; insert accepted - product samples; page cutoffs - 22 3/4.
Mechanical Specifications: Type page 13 x 21 1/2; E - 6 cols, 2 1/16, 1/8 between; A - 6 cols, 2 1/16, 1/8 between; C - 6 cols, 2 1/16, 1/8 between.
Areas Served: Butler County
Delivery Method: Mail, Newsstand, Carrier, RacksEquipment & Software: PRESSROOM EQUIPMENT: Lines — 5-G/Urbanite; Folders — 1-G/2:1.; MAILROOM EQUIPMENT: Tying Machines — 1/Malow; Address Machine — RSK/TRS 80.; BUSINESS EQUIPMENT: 1-RSK/TRS 80-16B CLASSIFIED EQUIPMENT: Hardware — 1-COM/UC.; DISPLAY SOFTWARELayout Software — 2-COM/Advantage I. EDITORIAL EQUIPMENT: Hardware — 1-COM/UTS, 1-RSK/TRS 80-100. PRODUCTION EQUIPMENT: Hardware — 1-COM/8600, 1-COM/Unisetter, 2-COM/7200; Cameras — 1-B/4000.

ROLLA

ROLLA DAILY NEWS

101 W 7th St, Rolla, Mo., 65401-3243, Phelps; gen tel (573) 364-2468; adv tel (573) 364-2468; ed tel (573) 364-2468; gen fax (573) 341-5847; adv fax (573) 364-6107; ed fax (573) 341-5847; gen/nat adv e-mail mburns@therolladailynews.com; disp adv e-mail mpence@gatehousemedia.com; class adv e-mailmpence@gatehousemedia.com; ed e-mail LynnBrennan@therolladailynews.com; web site www.therolladailynews.com
Group: New Media Investment Group
Published: Mon, Tues, Wed, Thur, Fri, Sat
Weekday Frequency: m
Saturday Frequency: m
Circulation: 3,725; 4,875(sat)
Last Audit: Sworn/Estimate/Non-Audited September 30, 2017
Advertising Rate (weekday/saturday): Open inch rate $14.90 (Mon-Fri); $17.30 (Sat)
Online Advertising Rate: 15 words 6 days $33.00
News services: AP. **Established:** 1880
Special Editions: Fashion (Apr); Back-to-School (Aug); Car Care (Dec); Newcomers (Feb); Bridal (Jan); Progress (Jul); Lawn & Garden (Mar); Christmas (Nov); Car Care (Oct); Welcome Back Students (College) (Sept).
Syndicated Publications: Best Food Days (Tue/Thur); Health, TV (Fri); Comics (Daily)
Ed... Lynn Brennan
Managing Ed. .... Paul Hackbarth
Adv. Dir... Marcia Burns
Sports Ed. .... Dave Roberts
Nat'l Adv. Rep. .... Melissa Pence
Market Information: ADS; TMC.
Mechanical Available: Offset; Black and 4 ROP colors; insert accepted; page cutoffs - 21.
Mechanical Specifications: Type page 13 3/4 x 21; E - 6 cols, 2, 1/8 between; A - 6 cols, 2, 1/8 between; C - 6 cols, 2, 1/8 between.
Areas Served: Rolla, St. James Newburg, Doolittle, Edgar Springs, Phelps CountyEquipment & Software: MAILROOM EQUIPMENT: Tying Machines — 1-Strapper/Transpak, S/323; Address Machine — 1/Ch.; BUSINESS EQUIPMENT: 2-Amdek/268A, Nomad CLASSIFIED EQUIPMENT: Printers — Epson; CLASSIFIED SOFTWARE: TC. DISPLAY EQUIPMENT: Hardware — 3-APP/Mac SE; Printers — APP/Mac LaserWriter II; Other Hardware — APP/Mac Scanner. DISPLAY SOFTWAREAd Make-up Applications — QPS/QuarkXPress; EDITORIAL EQUIPMENT: Hardware — Rem; Printers — APP/Mac LaserWriter II EDITORIAL SOFTWARE: TC. PRODUCTION EQUIPMENT: Hardware — 1-Nat/A-250; Cameras — 1-Acti/183.
Note: This publication is printed at the Waynesville Daily Guide, St. Robert.

SAINT CHARLES

ST. CHARLES COUNTY BUSINESS RECORD

125 N Main St, Saint Charles, Mo., 63301-2800, Saint Charles; gen tel (636) 949-6928; adv tel (314) 558-3257; ed tel (314) 558-3221; gen fax (636) 949-6973; adv fax (314) 421-7080; ed fax (314) 621-1913; gen/nat adv e-mail johnny.aguirre@molawyersmedia.com; disp adv e-mail johnny.aguirre@molawyersmedia.com; ed e-mail fred.ehrlich@molawyersmedia.com
Group: GateHouse Media, Inc.
Published: Mon, Tues, Wed, Thur, Fri, Sat, Sun
Circulation: 600
Last Audit: Sworn/Estimate/Non-Audited September 30, 2017
Advertising Rate (weekday/saturday): Classified rate $115 an inch
Commercial Printers?: Yes
Pub.. Liz Irwin
Ed.. Fred Ehrlich
Produ Mgr.. John Reno
Advt Dir...................................... Johnny Aguirre
Bus Mgr................................ Amanda Passmore
Public Notice Mgr.......................... Karie Clark
Mechanical Specifications: Type page 10 x 16; E - 5 cols, 2, between; A - 5 cols, 2, between; C - 5 cols, 2, between.
Areas Served: 63301
Delivery Method: Mail, Newsstand

SAINT JOSEPH

ST. JOSEPH NEWS-PRESS

825 Edmond St, Saint Joseph, Mo., 64501-2737, Buchanan; gen tel (816) 271-8500; adv tel (816) 271-8666; ed tel (816) 271-8550; gen fax (816) 271-8692; adv fax (816) 271-8696; ed fax (816) 271-8692; gen/nat adv e-mail susan.white@newspressnow.com; disp adv e-mail tim.weddle@newspressnow.com; class adv e-mailclassified@newspressnow.com; ed e-mail dennis.ellsworth@newspressnow.com; web site www.newspressnow.com; web site 2 www.stjoenews-press.com
Group: Missouri Press Service, Inc.
News-Press & Gazette Co.
Published: Mon, Tues, Wed, Thur, Fri, Sat, Sun
Weekday Frequency: m
Saturday Frequency: m
Circulation: 20,965; 20,965(sat); 24,305(sun)
Last Audit: AAM September 30, 2014
Advertising Rate (weekday/saturday): Open inch rate $57.19
Advertising Rate (sunday): Open inch rate $63.20
News services: AP, MCT. **Established:** 1845
Own Printing Facility?: Yes
Commercial Printers?: Yes
Special Editions: Bridal (Jan); Progress Edition (Mar); Foodball (Aug/Sept); Gift Guide (Nov/Dec)
Special Weekly Sections: Health (Tue); Business, Finance (Tue-Sun); Best Food Day, Employment (Wed); Entertainment (Fri); Auto (Sat); Employment (Sun)
Syndicated Publications: Parade (S).
Digital Platform - Mobile: Apple, Android, Windows, Blackberry
Digital Platform - Tablet: Apple iOS, Android, Windows 7, Blackberry Tablet OS, Kindle, Nook, Kindle Fire
Exec. Ed.................................. Dennis Ellsworth
Adv. Dir.... Tim Weddle
Sports Ed. .... Ross Martin
News Dir. .... Dan Dozar
Dir of Adv/Sales.............................. Stacey Hill
Gen. Mgr................................. Lee M. Sawyer
Pub.. David Bradley
Nat'l Adv. Mgr................................ Susan White
Retail Adv. Mgr.................................. Tony Luke
Market Information: TMC.
Mechanical Available: Offset; Black and 3 ROP colors; insert accepted; page cutoffs - 21.
Mechanical Specifications: Type page 13 x 20; E - 6 cols, 2 1/16, 1/8 between; A - 6 cols, 2 1/16, 1/8 between; C - 9 cols, 1 3/8, 1/16 between.
Delivery Method: Mail, Newsstand, Carrier, RacksEquipment & Software: PRESSROOM EQUIPMENT: Lines — 28-G/SSC Magnum single width 1999; Folders — 1-G/Universal 45; Reels & Stands — Enkel; Registration System — QTI. MAILROOM EQUIPMENT: Counter Stackers — 2-QWI/400; Inserters & Stuffers — MM/319 Print Roll, GMA/SLS 2000, GMA/12 Into 2; Tying Machines — 2-Dynaric/NP-3; Wrapping Singles — 2-Id/Plastic; Address Machine — 1/Videojet 4000/7000; BUSINESS EQUIPMENT: Sun/Sparc Station 20, Dell/E250 Power Edge Dual 450 Mhz Processor BUSINESS SOFTWARE: SBS/Graphical 5.3.1, PBS/AM 3.2, PBS/CM 3.2 CLASSIFIED EQUIPMENT: Hardware — 13-Dell/Dimension 260 1.8GH2; Printers — HP/Deskjet 950; CLASSIFIED SOFTWARE: Brainworks. DISPLAY EQUIPMENT: Hardware — APP/Mac G3, APP/Mac G4, APP/Mac G5; Printers — HP/Deskjet 1050cer 16 600, X/882T; Other Hardware — Howtek/Scanmaster 2500, 1-Xerox/Proofer 8825, 1-HP/Proofer 10 DISPLAY SOFTWAREAd Make-up Applications — AG, Adobe/Photoshop, QPS/QuarkXPress, Aldus/FreeHand, Binuscan, Scitex; EDITORIAL EQUIPMENT: Hardware — 47-Nobilis/450; Printers — MON EDITORIAL SOFTWARE: Quark, METS, Binuscan, Scitex. PRODUCTION EQUIPMENT: Hardware — Caere/OmniPage, MON/MGS, APP/Mac 8100, APP/Mac 9500 FS; Scanners — 1-ECR/Autokon 2000, PixelCraft, X/7650, Microtek/600 ZS PRODUCTION SOFTWARE: FSI, Preps 3.61.

SAINT LOUIS

ST. LOUIS POST-DISPATCH

900 N Tucker Blvd, Saint Louis, Mo., 63101-1069, Saint Louis City; gen tel (314) 340-8000; adv tel (314) 340-8500; ed tel (314) 340-8387; gen fax (314) 569-9942; adv fax (314) 340-8665; ed fax (314) 340-3139; gen/nat adv e-mail dbischoff@post-dispatch.com; disp adv e-mail dbischoff@post-dispatch.com; class adv e-maildbischoff@post-dispatch.com; ed e-mail gbailon@post-dispatch.com; web site www.stltoday.com - 63,671,939(views) 7,744,856(visitors)
Group: Lee Enterprises, Inc.
Published: Mon, Tues, Wed, Thur, Fri, Sat, Sun
Weekday Frequency: m
Saturday Frequency: m
Circulation: 135,705; 135,652(sat); 197,933(sun)
Last Audit: AAM September 30, 2016
Advertising Rate (weekday/saturday): Full Page $21,854
Advertising Rate (sunday): Full Page $32,435
Online Advertising Rate: $8.00 ROS Banners
News services: AP, MCT, LAT-WP, NYT, RN, SHNS. **Established:** 1878
Own Printing Facility?: Yes
Commercial Printers?: Yes
Special Editions: Top 100 Restaurants, Baseball Preview, Golf Preview, GO! List, Summer Fun, Hockey Preview, Holiday Gift Guide
Special Weekly Sections: Lifestyle, A&E, Let's Eat, GO!
Syndicated Publications: Parade
Proprietary Publications: Feast Magazine
Ladue News
Suburban Journals of Southern IL
Suburban Journals of St. Charles County
Digital Platform - Mobile: Apple, Android, Windows
Digital Platform - Tablet: Apple iOS, Android, Windows 7, Blackberry Tablet OS, Kindle, Nook, Kindle Fire
Ed... Gilbert Bailon
Deputy Managing Ed................. Adam Goodman
Deputy Managing Ed......................... Bob Rose
Roland Klose
Dan Caesar
Digital Sales Dir.
Teresa Griffin
Director of Major & National Adv.
Susan Eckert
VP, Adv.
Donna Bischoff
Dir. of Photography..................... Lynden Steele
Multimedia Dir. .... Gary Hairlson
Dir. of News Admin......................... Mike Meiners
Market Information: Advertising: full distribution, 3 zones, zip level targeting for inserts
Mechanical Available: Offset; Black and 3 ROP colors; insert accepted; page cutoffs - 23 9/16.
Mechanical Specifications: Type page 9.8889" x 22";
column width: 1.5556"
Modular ad sizes
Areas Served: 62001, 62002, 62010, 62012, 62014, 62018, 62020, 62021, 62022, 62024, 62025, 62026, 62028, 62034, 62035, 62037, 62040, 62046, 62048, 62052, 62058, 62060, 62061, 62062, 62067, 62074, 62084, 62087, 62088, 62090, 62093, 62095, 62097, 62201, 62203, 62204, 62205, 62206, 62207, 62208, 62215, 62216, 62218, 62219, 62220, 62221, 62223, 62225, 62226, 62230, 62231, 62232, 62234, 62236, 62239, 62240, 62243, 62244, 62245, 62248, 62249, 62250, 62253, 62254, 62255, 62257, 62258, 62260, 62264, 62265, 62269, 62278, 62281, 62282, 62285, 62289, 62293, 62294, 62295, 62298, 63005, 63010, 63011, 63012, 63013, 63015, 63016, 63017, 63019, 63020, 63021, 63023, 63025, 63026, 63028, 63030, 63031, 63033, 63034, 63037, 63038, 63039, 63040, 63041, 63042, 63043, 63044, 63045, 63048, 63049, 63050, 63051, 63052, 63055, 63056, 63068, 63069, 63070, 63072, 63073, 63074, 63077, 63080, 63084, 63088, 63089, 63090, 63101, 63102, 63103, 63104, 63105, 63106, 63107, 63108, 63109, 63110, 63111, 63112, 63113, 63114, 63115, 63116, 63117, 63118, 63119, 63120, 63121, 63122, 63123, 63124, 63125, 63126, 63127, 63128, 63129, 63130, 63131, 63132, 63133, 63134, 63135, 63136, 63137, 63138, 63139, 63140, 63141, 63143, 63144, 63145, 63146, 63147, 63301, 63303, 63304, 63332, 63338, 63341, 63343, 63346, 63347, 63348, 63349, 63357, 63362, 63365, 63366, 63367, 63368, 63369, 63373, 63376, 63379, 63380, 63383, 63385, 63386, 63389, 63390
Delivery Method: Mail, Newsstand, Carrier, RacksEquipment & Software: PRESSROOM EQUIPMENT: Lines — 8-G/Metro 3113 Double Width 1972; 8-G/Metro 3115 Double Width 1972; 8-G/Metro 3114 Double Width 1972; 8-G/Metro 3117 Double Width 1972; 8-G/Metro 3049 Double Width 1968; 8-G/Metro 3116 Double Width 197; MAILROOM EQUIPMENT: Counter Stackers — 2/Sh, 20-/QWI, 3-/Boss; Inserters & Stuffers — 3-HI/1372P, 1-HI/1472P, 1-GMA/SLS 28-2; Tying Machines — 3-/Power Strap/PSN-6, 18-Sterling/MRCH40; Wrapping Singles — 4-/Wrappers-Stretchwrap; BUSINESS EQUIPMENT: 16-AT CLASSIFIED EQUIPMENT: Hardware — 2-Sun/Enterprise 4000, 79-HI/AD-Power Client Station; CLASSIFIED SOFTWARE: HI/REL 2.1. DISPLAY EQUIPMENT: Hardware — 1-APP/Mac Quadra 950, 4-Sun/Sparc 20, 1-Sun/

Sparc 5, 2-Sun/Enterprise 4000, 2-Sun/Ultra 2, 5-APP/Mac G3, 3-APP/Mac 8100, 2-APP/Mac 6300; Printers — All/4-6600, 3-Typhoon, 1-HP/8000, 3-HP/2500C; DISPLAY SOFTWAREAd Make-up Applications — HI/Page Layout Architecture; EDITORIAL EQUIPMENT: Hardware — HI/NMP (3.5.62), HI/NME 3.5, 26-HI/NewsMaker Pagination, 185-HI/NewsMaker Editorial, 4-Sun/Enterprise 4000/100-IBM/PC EDITORIAL SOFTWARE: 20-HI/Mac Browser. PRODUCTION EQUIPMENT: Hardware — TextBridge Pro 9.0, 3-WL/Lith-X-Pozer, 2-Eskofot/26365; Scanners — Epson/636 Scanner, ECR/Autokon 2045, 1-ECR/Autokon 1000 Scanner, 2-X, Scitex/Smartscanner, 2-X/1750, Ik/Digital PRODUCTION SOFTWARE: HI, NMP (3.5.62), 3-AdPag 3.5.

Note: Other St. Louis publications include:
Suburban Journals
Ladue News
Feast Magazine
St. Louis Best Bridal

SEDALIA

THE SEDALIA DEMOCRAT

700 S Massachusetts Ave, Sedalia, Mo., 65301-4548, Pettis; gen tel (660) 826-1000; adv tel (660) 826-1000; ed tel (660) 826-1000; gen fax (660) 826-2413; adv fax (660) 826-2413; ed fax (660) 826-2413; gen/nat adv e-mail news@sedaliademocrat.com; disp adv e-mail advertising@sedaliademocrat.com; class adv e-mailtheclassifieds@sedaliademocrat.com; ed e-mail editor@sedaliademocrat.com; web site www.sedaliademocrat.com
Group: Phillips Media Group LLC
Published: Mon, Tues, Wed, Thur, Fri, Sat
Weekday Frequency: m
Saturday Frequency: m
Circulation: 5,471; 5,786(sat)
Last Audit: CAC September 30, 2014
Advertising Rate (weekday/saturday): Open inch rate $16.00; $17.00 (Sat)
News services: AP. **Established:** 1868
Special Editions: Back-to-School (Aug); Progress (Feb); Tax Guide (Jan); Newcomers (Jun); Farm (Mar).
Special Weekly Sections: Education (Mon); Editorial (Wed); Religion (Thur); Entertainment, Arts (Fri); High School Sport, Rural life, Weddings, Seniors, Editorial, Engagements (Sat)
Syndicated Publications: Relish (Monthly); TV Week Magazine (S); American Profile (Weekly).
Digital Platform - Mobile: Apple, Android, Windows
Digital Platform - Tablet: Apple iOS, Android, Windows 7
Publisher....Denny Koenders
Ed....Bob Satnan
Sports Ed.....Kyle Smith
Webmaster/Data Processing Mgr. Richard Desort
Prodn., Commercial Sales....Dave Mullies
Prodn. Mgr., Mailroom....Henry Holtzclaw
Pub....Will Weibert
Ed....Nicole Cooke
Market Information: ADS; TMC.
Mechanical Available: Offset; Black and 3 ROP colors; insert accepted; page cutoffs - 22 3/4.
Mechanical Specifications: Type page 11 1/2 x 21 1/2; E - 6 cols, 1 39/50, 1/6 between; A - 6 cols, 1 39/50, 1/6 between; C - 8 cols, 1 29/100, 1/6 between.
Delivery Method: Mail, Newsstand, Carrier, RacksEquipment & Software: PRESSROOM EQUIPMENT: Lines — 10-G/Urbanite single width; 12-G/Urbanite single width 1999; Folders — G/Urbanite.; MAILROOM EQUIPMENT: Counter Stackers — 1/HL; Inserters & Stuffers — 1-/MM; Tying Machines — 2-/Ovid; Address Machine — 1-/Ch.; BUSINESS EQUIPMENT: Ram/486 DX66-16mb BUSINESS SOFTWARE: Southware, Brainworks, Vision Data CLASSIFIED EQUIPMENT: Hardware — APP/Mac; Printers — C.Itoh/On-Line, Genico/4110, Lexmark, APP/Mac II, NewGen/Imager Plus 6, GCC/Elite XL 808, Okidata/Line Printer, Pre Press/Panther Pro 46 Imagesetter; CLASSIFIED SOFTWARE: Baseview, QPS/QuarkXPress. DISPLAY EQUIPMENT: Hardware — APP/Mac, APP/Mac 8100-100, APP/Mac 7200-90; Printers — APP/Mac LaserWriter II, NewGen/Imager Plus 6, GCC/Elite XL 808, Pre Press Panther/Pro 46; Other Hardware — APP/Mac One Scanner, APP/M DISPLAY SOFTWAREAd Make-up Applications — APP/Mac, Managing Editor/ALS Page Director; EDITORIAL EQUIPMENT: Hardware — APP/Mac 7200-75 PPC, APP/Mac 7200-90 PPC/Lf/AP Leaf Picture Desk; Printers — GCC/Elite XL808, New Gen/Imager Plus 6, Pre Press/Panther Pro 46 EDITORIAL SOFTWARE: Baseview. PRODUCTION EQUIPMENT: Hardware — 1-Nu, Polaroid/SprintScan, Umax/Flatbed, Epson/Flatbed; Cameras — R PRODUCTION SOFTWARE: QPS/QuarkXPress 3.32.2.

SIKESTON

STANDARD DEMOCRAT

205 S New Madrid St, Sikeston, Mo., 63801-2953, Scott; gen tel (573) 471-1137; adv tel (573) 471-4141; ed tel (800) 675-6980; gen fax (573) 471-6277; adv fax (573) 471-6277; ed fax (573) 471-6277; gen/nat adv e-mail donc@standard-democrat.com; disp adv e-mail dnelson@standard-democrat.com; class adv e-mailclass@standard-democrat.com; ed e-mail news@standard-democrat.com; web site www.standard-democrat.com
Group: Rust Communications
Published: Mon, Tues, Wed, Thur, Fri, Sun
Weekday Frequency: e
Circulation: 4,387; 4,748(sun)
Last Audit: CAC September 30, 2014
Advertising Rate (weekday/saturday): Open inch rate $14.07 (Mon/Thur/Fri); $16.67 (Wed)
Advertising Rate (sunday): Open inch rate $19.24
News services: AP. **Established:** 1913
Special Editions: Real Estate Guide (Jun); YMCA (Spring 2013); Bright Holiday Wishes (2012); Veterans Day; About Us (2012)
Special Weekly Sections: Best Food Day (Wed); Real Estate, Church (Fri); Business, Finance, Dining, Wedding, Engagements (Sun)
Syndicated Publications: Parade (S).
Digital Platform - Mobile: Apple, Android, Windows
Digital Platform - Tablet: Apple iOS, Android, Windows 7
CEO....Don Culbertson
Pub....Michael L. Jensen
Co-Owner....Gary Rust
Gen. Mgr.....DeAnna Nelson
Circ. Mgr.....Merlin Hagy
News Ed....Jill Bock
Classified Mgr.....Shawn Crawford
Market Information: Split run; TMC.
Mechanical Available: Offset; Black and 3 ROP colors; insert accepted - card inserts; page cutoffs - 22 3/4.
Mechanical Specifications: Type page 13 x 21 1/2; E - 6 cols, 2 1/16, 1/8 between; A - 6 cols, 2 1/16, 1/8 between; C - 9 cols, 1 3/8, 1/16 between.
Areas Served: Scott County
Delivery Method: Mail, Newsstand, Carrier, RacksEquipment & Software: PRESSROOM EQUIPMENT: Lines — 8-G/Suburban (4 + 4 side by side).; MAILROOM EQUIPMENT: Tying Machines — 2-Bu/Packaging Machine; Wrapping Singles — 7-Sa/EM; Address Machine — 1-Am/1900.; CLASSIFIED EQUIPMENT: Hardware — COM/UTS.; EDITORIAL EQUIPMENT: Hardware — 2-COM/UTS, Mk. PRODUCTION EQUIPMENT: Hardware — 2-COM/Universal Videosetter; Cameras — 1-R/400.

SPRINGFIELD

SPRINGFIELD NEWS-LEADER

651 N Boonville Ave, Springfield, Mo., 65806-1005, Greene; gen tel (417) 836-1100; adv tel (417) 836-1108; ed tel (417) 836-1199; gen fax (417) 831-0891; adv fax (417) 836-1147; ed fax (417) 837-1381; gen/nat adv e-mail NationalAdManager@news-leader.com; disp adv e-mail AdDirector@news-leader.com; class adv e-mailClassifiedManager@news-leader.com; ed e-mail Letters@news-leader.com; web site www.news-leader.com
Group: Gannett
Published: Mon, Tues, Wed, Thur, Fri, Sat, Sun
Weekday Frequency: m
Saturday Frequency: m
Circulation: 9,938; 9,938(sat); 12,051(sun)
Last Audit: AAM September 30, 2017
Advertising Rate (weekday/saturday): Open inch rate $100.33
Advertising Rate (sunday): Open inch rate $157.35
News services: AP, GNS, NYT, TMS, LAT-WP. **Established:** 1867
Own Printing Facility?: Yes
Commercial Printers?: Yes
Special Editions: Garden (Apr); Progress (Feb); New Contruction (Jan); New Construction (Jul); Destinations (May); Coupon Clippers (Monthly); Holiday Gift Guide (Nov); New Construction (Oct); Progress (Sept).
Special Weekly Sections: E-Commerce (Mon); Health (Tue); Best Food Day, Auto (Wed); Outdoors (Thur); Weekend, Auto (Fri); Church, Real Estate (Sat); Travel, TV, Home (Sun)
Syndicated Publications: USA WEEKEND Magazine (S).
Digital Platform - Mobile: Apple, Android
Digital Platform - Tablet: Apple iOS, Android
Mng. Ed.....Cheryl Whitsitt
Exec. Ed.....Paul Berry
Consumer Exper. Dir....Allen Vaughan
Bus. Watchdog Rep.....Thomas Gounley
HR Dir.....Debbie Payne
Dir., Market Devel.....Cindy Butner
Circ. Dir.....David Brown
Circ. Mgr., Single Copy....Rudy Rinker
Graphics Ed.....John Dengler
Online Ed.....Gregory Mathews
Photo Ed.....Dean Curtis
Engagement Ed....Sony Hocklander
Prodn. Mgr., Distr. Ctr.....Mary Miller
Prodn. Mgr., Pressroom....Steve Smith
Prodn. Supvr., Composing (Day)....Jo Ann Sneed
Adv. Sales....Amanda Thompson
Pres./Pub.....Daniel Norselli
Pres....Allen Jones
Market Information: ADS; TMC.
Mechanical Available: Letterpress Direct; Black and 3 ROP colors; insert accepted - flexie single sheets; page cutoffs - 22 3/4.
Mechanical Specifications: Type page 13 x 21 1/2; E - 6 cols, 2 1/16, 1/8 between; A - 6 cols, 2 1/16, 1/8 between; C - 9 cols, 1 3/8, 1/16 between.
Delivery Method: Mail, Newsstand, Carrier, RacksEquipment & Software: PRESSROOM EQUIPMENT: Lines — 8-G/Mark II Headliner; Registration System — G/Web Control Auto Color. MAILROOM EQUIPMENT: Counter Stackers — 3-HL/Monitor, 2-HI/Dual Carrier Stackers, 2-HI/Olympian Stackers; Inserters & Stuffers — HI/72P, HI/NP 630 (26 Base/22 Head); Tying Machines — 3-MLN/News 90, 2-MLN/1-EE; Wrapping Singles — Kraft/Paper, 3-HI/Eclipse Bottomwraps; BUSINESS EQUIPMENT: 1-IBM/AS-400 BUSINESS SOFTWARE: Lotus R:5, WordPerfect, Microsoft/Windows CLASSIFIED EQUIPMENT: Hardware — SII/Synthesis 66; QPS, App/Mac System; Printers — Hyphen/Spectraset 2200, Hyphen/Spectraset 2400; CLASSIFIED SOFTWARE: SII/Pongrass Czar. DISPLAY EQUIPMENT: Hardware — IBM/4500, APP/Mac G4; Printers — 4-HP/Plotters, 2-AG/2400, Tektronix/Phaser III, HP/4MV; Other Hardware — SII/Terminals, AU/Oman, All DISPLAY SOFTWAREAd Make-up Applications — Multi-Ad/Creator, Broderbund/TypeStyler, Adobe/Photoshop, Type/Manager; Layout Software — MEI/ALS, Multi-Ad EDITORIAL EQUIPMENT: Hardware — QPS/70-APP/Power Mac 8500-7200; Printers — 2-Hyphen/Spectraset 2200, 2-Hyphen/Spectraset 2400 EDITORIAL SOFTWARE: AT, QPS/QuarkXPress. PRODUCTION EQUIPMENT: Hardware — AG/2200, Hyphen/Spectraset 2200, Hyphen/Spectraset 2400; Cameras — R/Comet 500; Scanners — 1-Microtek/MRS-600zs, 1-Pro Imager/8000 PixelCraft, 1-Pro Imager/8100 PixelCraft PRODUCTION SOFTWARE: SII/Pongrass Czar.

TRENTON

TRENTON REPUBLICAN-TIMES

122 E 8th St, Trenton, Mo., 64683-2183, Grundy; gen tel (660) 359-2212; adv tel (660) 359-2212; ed tel (660) 359-2212; gen fax (660) 359-4414; adv fax (660) 359-4414; ed fax (660) 359-4414; gen/nat adv e-mail rtimes@lyn.net; disp adv e-mail rtimes@lyn.net; class adv e-mailrtimes@lyn.net; ed e-mail rtimes@lyn.net; web site www.republican-times.com - 81,690(views)
Group: W.B. Rogers Printing Co., Inc.
Published: Mon, Tues, Wed, Thur, Fri
Weekday Frequency: e
Circulation: 2,321
Last Audit: Sworn/Estimate/Non-Audited September 30, 2017
Newspaper Reps: Missouri Press Association
Advertising Rate (weekday/saturday): Open inch rate $5.70
Advertising Rate (sunday): NA
Online Advertising Rate: Box Ad $270 per month
News services: AP. **Established:** 1864
Own Printing Facility?: No
Commercial Printers?: No
Special Editions: Home Improvement (Apr); Fall Sports (Aug); Graduation (May); Missouri Day Festival (Oct).
Fall Outdoors (Nov.)
Special Weekly Sections: TV Guide (Thur).
Pub.....Wendell Lenhart
Ed.....Diane Lowrey
Adv. Mgr.....Angela Dugan
Market Information: ADS; TMC.
Mechanical Available: Offset; Black and 3 ROP colors; insert accepted; page cutoffs - 21.
Mechanical Specifications: Type page 13 x 21; E - 6 cols, 1.833 PASS, 1/8 between; A - 6 cols, 1.833 PASS, 1/8 between; C - 6 cols, 2 1/16, 1/8 between.
Areas Served: 64683, 64641, 64652, 64679, 64673, 64661, 64648, 64642
Delivery Method: Mail, Newsstand, CarrierEquipment & Software: MAILROOM EQUIPMENT: Tying Machines — Bu, Miller-Bevco/Strapper.; BUSINESS EQUIPMENT: Pentium/PC CLASSIFIED EQUIPMENT: Hardware — APP/Power Mac; Printers — APP/Power Mac LaserWriter II NTX; CLASSIFIED SOFTWARE: QPS/QuarkXPress. DISPLAY EQUIPMENT: Hardware — iMac Printers — APP/Mac LaserWriter II NTX, HP/LaserJet 4MV; DISPLAY SOFTWAREApplic — QPS/QuarkXPress.; EDITORIAL EQUIPMENT: Hardware — APP/Power iMac; Printers — APP/Mac LaserWriter II NTX, HP/LaserJet 4MV EDITORIAL SOFTWARE: QPS/QuarkXPress. PRODUCTION EQUIPMENT: Hardware — APP/Mac LaserWriter II NTX, HP/LaserJet 4MR; Cameras — R/Vertical; Scanners — HP/ScanJet 3P, Polaroid/SprintScan 35, Polaroid/SprintScan 35ES PRODUCTION SOFTWARE: Baseview.

WARRENSBURG

THE DAILY STAR-JOURNAL

135 E Market St, Warrensburg, Mo., 64093-1817, Johnson; gen tel (660) 747-8123; adv tel (660) 747-8123 ext. 105; ed tel (660) 747-8123 ext. 110; gen fax (660) 747-8741; adv fax (660) 747-8741; ed fax (660) 747-8741; gen/nat adv e-mail Joani.Dittrich@npgco.com; disp adv e-mail Joani.Dittrich@npgco.com; class adv e-maildsjclassifieds@npgco.com; ed e-mail jack.miles@npgco.com; web site www.dailystarjournal.com - 298,000(views) 115,000(visitors)
Group: NPG Newspapers
Published: Tues, Wed, Thur, Sat
Weekday Frequency: m
Saturday Frequency: m
Circulation: 3,300
Last Audit: Sworn/Estimate/Non-Audited December 12, 2017
Newspaper Reps: Luke Lochiano
Mendy Kenny
Rebecca Bell
Advertising Rate (weekday/saturday): Open inch rate $14.00
Online Advertising Rate: Flat charge per month

News services: AP. **Established:** 1865
Own Printing Facility?: Yes
Commercial Printers?: No
Special Editions: Best of the Berg
Living 50 Plus
DRIVE
Dining Guide
Resource Guide
Sports Previews
Veterans Tribute
Digital Platform - Mobile: Apple, Android, Windows
Digital Platform - Tablet: Apple iOS, Android, Windows 7
Pub. .... Joe Warren
Ed. .... Jack Miles
Advertising Director .... Brian Burton
Market Information: TMC.
Mechanical Available: Offset; Black and 4 ROP colors; insert accepted; page cutoffs - 20".
Mechanical Specifications: Full Page 10.25" x 20"
Areas Served: Johnson County, MO
Delivery Method: Mail, RacksEquipment & Software: PRESSROOM EQUIPMENT: Lines — 1-HI/Cotrell V-15D; 1-Ryobi/11x17; 1-HI/L125C(0).; MAILROOM EQUIPMENT: Tying Machines — 1-Strap Tie/50; Address Machine — Ch/582N.; BUSINESS EQUIPMENT: 2-IBM/3151 BUSINESS SOFTWARE: PBS/MediaPlus CLASSIFIED EQUIPMENT: Hardware — 1-Acer; Printers — HP/2100; CLASSIFIED SOFTWARE: FSI. EDITORIAL EQUIPMENT: Hardware — 5-APP/iMac; Printers — 1-APP/Mac LaserWriter EDITORIAL SOFTWARE: FSI. PRODUCTION EQUIPMENT: Hardware — 1-Nat, 1-APP/Mac G4, 1-APP/Mac; Cameras — 1-DAI PRODUCTION SOFTWARE: QPS/QuarkXPress 4.1.
Note: First-place awards this year...
2017 - Missouri Press Association Gold Cup Sweepstakes award, General Excellence, Best Editorial, Serious Column, Breaking News, Headline Writing, Feature Writing, Obituary Story, Website, Religion Story, News Photo, Sports Photo, Outdoors Story
2017 -- Associated Press Managing Editors, Feature Writing, Photo Page, Opinion, Headline
2017 - Missouri State Teachers Association, Feature Writing and Photography.

WAYNESVILLE

DAILY GUIDE

108 Hull Dr, Waynesville, Mo., 65583-2364, Pulaski; gen tel (573) 336-3711; adv tel (573) 336-3711; ed tel (573) 336-3711; gen fax (573) 336-4640; adv fax (573) 336-4640; ed fax (573) 336-4640; gen/nat adv e-mail advertising@waynesvilledailyguide.com; disp adv e-mail advertising@waynesvilledailyguide.com; class adv e-mailclassified@waynesvilledailyguide.com; ed e-mail editor@waynesvilledailyguide.com; web site www.waynesvilledailyguide.com
Group: New Media Investment Group
Published: Tues, Wed, Thur, Fri, Sat
Weekday Frequency: m
Saturday Frequency: m
Circulation: 1,320; 892(sat)
Last Audit: Sworn/Estimate/Non-Audited September 30, 2017
Advertising Rate (weekday/saturday): Open inch rate $9.59
News services: AP. **Established:** 1967
Own Printing Facility?: Yes
Commercial Printers?: Yes
Special Editions: Profiles (Jul).
Special Weekly Sections: Best Food Day (Wed); Church (Fri)
Syndicated Publications: Own Newsprint Mag (Fri).
Digital Platform - Mobile: Apple, Android, Windows, Blackberry
Digital Platform - Tablet: Apple iOS, Android, Windows 7, Blackberry Tablet OS
Pub. .... Floyd Jernigan
Circ. Mgr. .... Mike Valko
Sports Ed. .... Dave Roberts
Ads Rep. .... Katy Quigley
Market Information: TMC; Zoned editions.
Mechanical Available: Offset; Black and 3 ROP colors; insert accepted; page cutoffs - 22 3/4.
Mechanical Specifications: Type page 13 x 21 1/2; E - 6 cols, 2 1/16, 1/8 between; A - 6 cols, 2 1/16, 1/8 between; C - 6 cols, 2 1/16, 1/8 between.
Areas Served: Crocker, Dixon, Laquey, Fort Leonard Wood, Richland, St. Robert and Waynesville
Delivery Method: Mail, Newsstand, Carrier, RacksEquipment & Software: PRESSROOM EQUIPMENT: Lines — 7-G/Community (balloon former) 1989; Folders — 1-G/SC, 1-G/Community.; MAILROOM EQUIPMENT: Counter Stackers — BG; Inserters & Stuffers — Mueller Martini inserter; Address Machine — 1/Am.; BUSINESS EQUIPMENT: Dell DISPLAY EQUIPMENT: Hardware — Imac; Printers — HP; DISPLAY SOFTWAREAd Make-up Applications — Adobe CS/Quark; EDITORIAL EQUIPMENT: Hardware — APP/Mac; Printers — APP/Mac LaserWriter 12-640 EDITORIAL SOFTWARE: Adobe/PageMaker. PRODUCTION EQUIPMENT: Hardware — 1-Nu, 1-AG/Rapid; Cameras — 1-Nu; Scanners — APP/Mac One.

WEST PLAINS

WEST PLAINS DAILY QUILL

205 Washington Ave, West Plains, Mo., 65775-3439, Howell; gen tel (417) 256-9191; adv tel (417) 256-9191; ed tel (417) 256-9191; gen fax (417) 256-9196; adv fax (417) 256-9196; ed fax (417) 256-9196; gen/nat adv e-mail ads@wpdailyquill.net; disp adv e-mail ads@wpdailyquill.net; class adv e-mailclassifieds@wpdailyquill.net; ed e-mail editor@wpdailyquill.net; web site www.westplainsdailyquill.net
- 246,582(views) 84,072(visitors)
Group: Phillips Media Group LLC
Published: Tues, Wed, Thur, Fri, Sat
Weekday Frequency: m
Saturday Frequency: m
Circulation: 5,075; 5,520(sat)
Last Audit: USPS October 1, 2016
Advertising Rate (weekday/saturday): Open inch rate $12.30
News services: AP. **Established:** 1903
Own Printing Facility?: Yes
Commercial Printers?: Yes
Special Editions: Tax Tips; Bridal (Jan.) Spring Church Directory;Spring Sports; Home Improvement;Doctor's Day (Mar): Valentine's Day;FFA Insert (Feb): Graduation Insert;Mother's Day;Older American Month;Memorial Day (May):Old Time Music Festival;Father's Day(June): Fair insert (July): Back-To-School;Fall Sports (Aug.): Grandparents Day;Fall Sports (Sept.): Breast Cancer Awareness(Oct.):Christmas Open House/Shop Locally;Black Friday (Nov.): Christmas Shopping Guide; Christmas Songbook; Christmas Greetings (Dec.)
Special Weekly Sections: People, Sports, Amusement (Daily); Outdoors (Fri); Food, Dining (Wed); Farm & Garden (Thu); Business, Finance (Thu); Auto, TV, Religion, Auctions, Real Estate (Fri); Color Comics (Sat); National Coupons (Sat)
Syndicated Publications: TV Week (Television Listings and Local Events Guide) (Sat); Smart Source (Sat); Parade (Sat); American Profile (Sat).
Digital Platform - Mobile: Apple, Android, Windows, Blackberry, Other
Digital Platform - Tablet: Apple iOS, Android, Windows 7, Blackberry Tablet OS, Kindle, Nook, Kindle Fire, Other
Publisher .... Jim Perry
Production Manager / Digital Services .... Mary Frazier
Managing Editor .... Allison Wilson
Sports Editor .... Cody Sanders
Advertising Manager .... Vicki Johnson
Web Services, Pagination, Digital Print .... Katie Dudden
Customer Service Representative .... Darla Evins
General Assignment Reporter .... Mary Ewers
Editorial Assistant, Senior Reporter Abby R Hess
Customer Service Representative .... Lisa Lonon
Commercial Printing .... Monty C Reynolds
Customer Service Representative .... Vicky Rutter
Customer Service Representative .... Cheryl Thompson
Police/Courts Reporter .... Ron Woolman
News Editor .... Regina Mozingo
Market Information: Only daily paper in the region 5,300 daily circ
Mechanical Available: Offset; Black and 3 ROP colors; insert accepted; page cutoffs - 21.
Mechanical Specifications: Type page 10" x 21"
Areas Served: 65775, 65793,65548, 65688, 65777, 65626, 65788, 65789, 65790, 65606, 65791, 65692, 65690, 65778, 65466, 65588, 65438, 65483, 65689, 65571, 65711, 65768, 65608, 65638, 65637, 65655, 65609, 65760, 65766, 65784, 72576, 72583, 72538, 72653, 72554
Delivery Method: Mail, RacksEquipment & Software: PRESSROOM EQUIPMENT: Goss, 8-unit; folders, pasters, inserters, labelers (inkjet), direct to plate. MAILROOM EQUIPMENT: full service including standard solo mailing BUSINESS EQUIPMENT: offsite fiber optic back ups; fully integrated business system with multiple billable options. CLASSIFIED EQUIPMENT: Hardware — APP/Mac networked G6 computers with full load; APP/Mac Scanners; Digital Color Printers — APP/Mac DISPLAY EQUIPMENT: Hardware — APP/Apple Macintosh computers with full back up and offsite storage. Assorted MacHardware — APP/Mac Scanners and color proofing. EDITORIAL EQUIPMENT: Hardware — APP/iMac and G6 computers, MacBook Air and remote transmission. PRODUCTION EQUIPMENT: Full color proofing with direct to plate technology

MONTANA

BILLINGS

BILLINGS GAZETTE

401 N 28th St, Billings, Mont., 59101-1243, Yellowstone; gen tel (406) 657-1200; adv tel (406) 657-1370; ed tel (406) 657-1241; gen fax (406) 657-1208; adv fax (406) 657-1278; ed fax (406) 657-1208; gen/nat adv e-mail citynews@billingsgazette.com; disp adv e-mail dworstell@billingsgazette.com; class adv e-mailrbrosseau@billingsgazette.com; ed e-mail citynews@billingsgazette.com; web site www.billingsgazette.com
- 10,000,000(views) 940,000(visitors)
Group: Lee Enterprises, Inc.
Published: Mon, Tues, Wed, Thur, Fri, Sat, Sun
Weekday Frequency: m
Saturday Frequency: m
Circulation: 31,369; 31,369(sat); 34,926(sun)
Last Audit: AAM September 30, 2016
Advertising Rate (weekday/saturday): Open inch rate $58.09 daily, $61.01 Sat
Advertising Rate (sunday): Open inch rate $$65.08
Online Advertising Rate: Big Ad $20/Run of Site Big Ads $16/Leaderboard $15/Run of Site Leaderboard $12/Tile Ad $12
News services: AP, CNS, MCT, TMS. **Established:** 1885
Special Editions: Readers' Choice Awards (Oct); Regional Medical Directory (Nov); Holiday Food and Gift Festival (Nov); Brawl of the Wild (Nov); Community of Giving (Dec); Winter Hoops (Dec); MT Economic Report (Dec); Season's Greetings (Dec); Still Growing Strong (Dec); Babies (Jan); 40 under Forty (Feb); Wrestling Tournament (Feb); Spring Home Improvement (Mar); MT Dream Homes (Mar); Yellowstone Park (May); Big Sky State Games (Jul); Back to School (Aug); Fall Home Improvement (Sept); Innovation & Quality in Health Care (Sept); Women in Business (Sept); Parade of Homes (September); Chamber Report (Sept); All Around Billings (May)
Special Weekly Sections: Auto Plus (Fri); Your Home (S); Outdoors (Thur); Business Sections (S); Wall Street Journal (S); Employment (S); Good Life (S); Health (Wed); Your Faith (Sat).
Syndicated Publications: Entertainment Tab (Fri); Relish (Monthly); Parade (S); TV Book (Sat); American Profile (Weekly).
Digital Platform - Mobile: Apple, Android
Digital Platform - Tablet: Apple iOS, Android, Kindle Fire
Controller .... Scott Patrick
Ed. .... Darrell Ehrlick
Adv. Dir., Sales/Mktg. .... Dave Worstell
Adv. Mgr., Classified .... Ryan Brosseau
Circ. Dir. .... Allen Wilson
Mng. Ed. .... Kristi Angel
Editorial Page Ed. .... Pat Bellinghausen
Entertainment/Amusements Ed. .... Jaci Webb
News Ed. .... Vic Bracht
Photo Chief .... Larry Mayer
Religion Reporter .... Sue Olp
Digital Dir. .... Kyle Rickhoff
Retail Advertising Manager .... Shelli Scott
Michael Gulledge
Market Information: ADS; TMC; Zoned editions.
Mechanical Available: Offset; Black and 3 ROP colors; insert accepted - Adhesive labels; page cutoffs - 22 3/4.
Mechanical Specifications: Type page 11 5/8 x 21 1/2; E - 6 cols, 1 53/64, 3/16 between; A - 6 cols, 1 53/64, 3/16 between; C - 9 cols, 1 11/64, 3/16 between.
Delivery Method: Mail, Newsstand, CarrierEquipment & Software: PRESSROOM EQUIPMENT: Lines — 6-G/Metro offset double width 1967; Control System — Press Drive Harland Simon, 7-MOT; Registration System — KFM. MAILROOM EQUIPMENT: Counter Stackers — 1-QWI/350, 1-QWI/400, 1-QWI/500; Inserters & Stuffers — 1-HI/1372; Tying Machines — 2/Power Strap, Dynaric; BUSINESS EQUIPMENT: IBM/Sys 38 BUSINESS SOFTWARE: Proprietary CLASSIFIED EQUIPMENT: Hardware — PC 5-166-OS-2; Printers — HP/5Simx; CLASSIFIED SOFTWARE: CText/AdVision. DISPLAY EQUIPMENT: Hardware — APP/Mac; Printers — HP/750C, HP/5Simx; Other Hardware — PC DISPLAY SOFTWAREAd Make-up Applications — Adobe/Illustrator, APP/Mac OSX, QPS 5.0; Layout Software — Layout/8000. EDITORIAL EQUIPMENT: Hardware — Microsoft/Windows NT PS-166; Printers — Epson/DFX 5000, HP/75 DC, HP/5Simx EDITORIAL SOFTWARE: APT, NT, Microsoft/Word, QPS/QuarkXPress. PRODUCTION EQUIPMENT: Hardware — AU/3850 Laser Imagers, 1-Graham, APP/Mac PRODUCTION SOFTWARE: APT, QPS/QuarkXPress.

BOZEMAN

BOZEMAN DAILY CHRONICLE

2820 W College St, Bozeman, Mont., 59718-3925, Gallatin; gen tel (406) 587-4491; gen fax (406) 587-7995; adv fax (406) 582-2658; ed fax (406) 582-2656; gen/nat adv e-mail national@dailychronicle.com; class adv e-mailclassifieds@dailychronicle.com; ed e-mail citydesk@dailychronicle.com; web site www.bozemandailychronicle.com
- 1,159,000(views) 231,000(visitors)
Group: Adams Publishing Group, LLC
Published: Tues, Wed, Thur, Fri, Sat, Sun
Weekday Frequency: m
Saturday Frequency: m
Circulation: 86,567; 74,266(sat); 76,798(sun)
Last Audit: AAM March 31, 2016
Advertising Rate (weekday/saturday): Open inch rate $19.17
Advertising Rate (sunday): Open inch rate $20.07
Online Advertising Rate: Billboard $250/Leaderboard $18/Big Box $20/Large Square $16
News services: AP, LAT-WP. **Established:** 1883
Own Printing Facility?: Yes
Commercial Printers?: Yes
Special Editions: Football (Aug); Christmas Cheer (Dec); Spring Home Improvement (Feb); Montana Winter Fair (Jan); Gallatin County Summer Fair (Jul); The Hatch is On (Jun); VISTA (Mar); Explore Yellowstone (May); Christmas Gift Catalog (Nov); Hunting (Oct); Home Improvemen
Special Weekly Sections: Health (Mon); Economy (S); Outdoors (Thur); Lifestyle (Wed).
Syndicated Publications: This Week (newsprint) (Fri); Parade (S).
Digital Platform - Mobile: Apple, Android, Windows, Blackberry
Digital Platform - Tablet: Apple iOS, Android, Windows 7, Blackberry Tablet OS

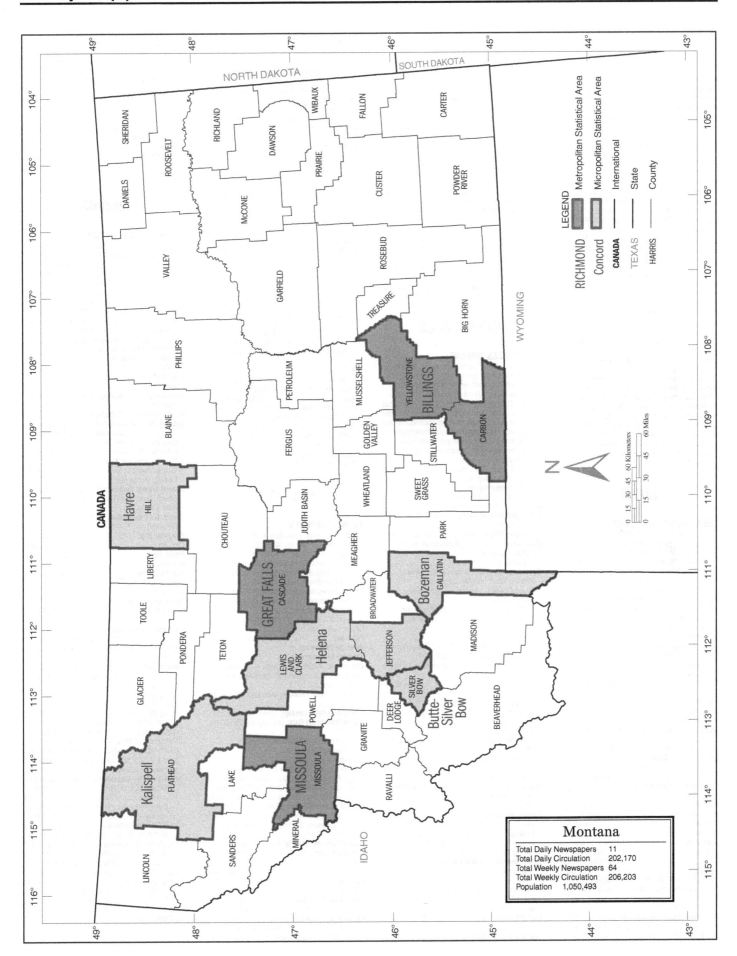

NORTH DAKOTA

SOUTH DAKOTA

SHERIDAN

RICHLAND

WIBAUX

FALLON

CARTER

DANIELS

ROOSEVELT

DAWSON

PRAIRIE

CUSTER

POWDER RIVER

McCONE

VALLEY

GARFIELD

ROSEBUD

TREASURE

BIG HORN

WYOMING

PHILLIPS

PETROLEUM

MUSSELSHELL

YELLOWSTONE

BILLINGS

BLAINE

FERGUS

GOLDEN VALLEY

STILLWATER

CARBON

SWEET GRASS

CANADA

Havre

HILL

CHOUTEAU

JUDITH BASIN

WHEATLAND

MEAGHER

PARK

LIBERTY

GREAT FALLS

CASCADE

Bozeman

GALLATIN

BROADWATER

TOOLE

Helena

LEWIS AND CLARK

JEFFERSON

MADISON

PONDERA

TETON

SILVER BOW

GLACIER

POWELL

DEER LODGE

Butte-Silver Bow

BEAVERHEAD

Kalispell

FLATHEAD

LAKE

GRANITE

MISSOULA

MISSOULA

RAVALLI

LINCOLN

SANDERS

MINERAL

IDAHO

LEGEND

RICHMOND Metropolitan Statistical Area
Concord Micropolitan Statistical Area
CANADA International
TEXAS State
HARRIS County

N

0 15 30 45 60 Kilometers
0 15 30 45 60 Miles

Montana	
Total Daily Newspapers	11
Total Daily Circulation	202,170
Total Weekly Newspapers	64
Total Weekly Circulation	206,203
Population	1,050,493

Pub./Pres. .... Stephanie Pressly
Bus. Mgr. .... Bob Eichenberger
Adv. Dir. .... Cindy Sease
Circ. Dir. .... Bill Frederick
Mng. Ed. .... Nick Ehli
Asst. Mng. Ed. .... Ted Sullivan
City Ed. .... Michael Becker
Prodn. Mgr., Mailroom .... Ed Renaud
Market Information: ADS; TMC.
Mechanical Available: Offset; Black and 3 ROP colors; insert accepted - most; page cutoffs - 21 1/2.
Mechanical Specifications: Type page 12 1/2 x 21 1/2; E - 6 cols, 2 1/16, 1/8 between; A - 6 cols, 2 1/16, 1/8 between; C - 9 cols, 1 3/8, 1/16 between.
Areas Served: City/county
Delivery Method: Mail, Newsstand, Carrier, RacksEquipment & Software: PRESSROOM EQUIPMENT: Lines — 16-2002, 2-G/Community 1976; MAILROOM EQUIPMENT: Counter Stackers — HI; Inserters & Stuffers — 1-MM/227; Tying Machines — MLN; BUSINESS EQUIPMENT: VisionData & SBS CLASSIFIED EQUIPMENT: Hardware — 5-APP/iMac; Printers — Typhoon/20, HP/5simx, Epson/Stylus Pro XL; CLASSIFIED SOFTWARE: Vision Data DISPLAY EQUIPMENT: Hardware — 7-APP/Power Mac; Printers — Accuset 1000, Typhoon/20, HP/5sinx, Epson/Stylus Pro XL, HP/1200 C; DISPLAY SOFTWAREAd Make-up Applications — QPS/QuarkXPress 4.0; Layout Software — Ad Layout System. EDITORIAL EQUIPMENT: Hardware — 7-APP/iMac, 2-APP/Mac, 3-APP/Power Mac, 3-APP/Power Mac, 4-APP/Power Mac; Printers — Hyphen/RIPs, 2-AG/9800 EDITORIAL SOFTWARE: Baseview/NewsEdit, QPS/QuarkXPress 4.0. PRODUCTION EQUIPMENT: Hardware — Caere/OmniPage, AG/Studio Scan IIsi; Cameras — 1-K/240, 1-SCREEN; Scanners — 2-Nikon/LS-3510AF, 2-Microtek/ScanMaker E6, AG/Studio Scan IIsi PRODUCTION SOFTWARE: QPS/QuarkXPress 4.0.

BUTTE

THE MONTANA STANDARD

25 W Granite St, Butte, Mont., 59701-9213, Silver Bow; gen tel (406) 496-5500; adv tel (406) 496-5583; ed tel (406) 496-5510; gen fax (406) 496-5551; adv fax (406) 496-5578; ed fax (406) 496-5551; gen/nat adv e-mail sales@mtstandard.com; disp adv e-mail sales@mtstandard.com; class adv e-mailclassified@mtstandard.com; ed e-mail editors@mtstandard.com; web site www.mtstandard.com
Group: Lee Enterprises, Inc.
Published: Mon, Tues, Wed, Thur, Fri, Sat, Sun
Weekday Frequency: m
Saturday Frequency: m
Circulation: 8,462; 8,462(sat); 8,648(sun)
Last Audit: AAM September 30, 2017
Advertising Rate (weekday/saturday): Open inch rate $33.00
Advertising Rate (sunday): Open inch rate $33.55
News services: AP, SHNS, MCT, TMS. **Established:** 1876
Special Editions: Fall Sports (Aug); Bridal Tab (Jan); Travel Guide (May); In Business (Quarterly); Hunting Tab (Sept).
Special Weekly Sections: Best Food Days (Wed); Religion, Entertainment, Tabloid (Sat); Business, Women's Section, Lifestyle (Sun)
Syndicated Publications: Big Sky View (S); Time Out (Sat).
Gen. Mgr. .... Lynn Lloyd
Retail Adv. Mgr. .... Jenean Salle
Circ. Mgr. .... Steve Biere
Mng. Ed. .... Carmen Winslow
Lead Copy Ed. .... Kristie Constantine
Photo Ed. .... Walter Hinick
Ed. .... David McCumber
Publisher .... Tyler Miller
Market Information: TMC; Zoned editions.
Mechanical Available: Offset; Black and 3 ROP colors; insert accepted - single sheet; page cutoffs - 21 1/2.
Mechanical Specifications: Type page 12 x 21 1/2; E - 6 cols, 2 1/16, 1/8 between; A - 6 cols, 2 1/16, 1/8 between; C - 9 cols, 1 3/8, 1/16 between.
Areas Served: Southwest Montana Equipment & Software: PRESSROOM EQUIPMENT: Lines — 5-G/Urbanite U849; 6-G/Community; MAILROOM EQUIPMENT: Tying Machines — 1-Malow/50-S, 1-Malow/50, 1/MLN; BUSINESS EQUIPMENT: Gateway/P5 166, IBM/AS-400 CLASSIFIED EQUIPMENT: Hardware — RSK/600, Compaq, Novell/Net; Printers — HP/5Si; CLASSIFIED SOFTWARE: CText/Advision. DISPLAY EQUIPMENT: Hardware — 1-APP/Mac; Printers — Pre Press/Panther Plus, Pre Press/VT1200; DISPLAY SOFTWAREAd Make-up Applications — Adobe/Photoshop, QPS/QuarkXPress; Layout Software — QPS/QuarkXPress. EDITORIAL EQUIPMENT: Hardware — RSK/600, Novell/Net, Novell/5/Pre Press/Panther Pro Imagesetter; Printers — Pre Press/Panther Pro 46 EDITORIAL SOFTWARE: CText/Dateline, CText/Expressline. PRODUCTION EQUIPMENT: Hardware — Caere/OmniPage, 1-Pre Press/VT 1200, 1-Pre Press/Panther Pro 46 Postscript; Cameras — 1-C/Spartan II, 1-Nu/2024V, 1-POS/I Daylight Camera, 1-Nu/Horizontal; Scanners — Lf/Leafscan 35, 1-HP, APP/Mac Quadra, 6-Epson/ES-1200C PRODUCTION SOFTWARE: QPS/Quar

GREAT FALLS

GREAT FALLS TRIBUNE

205 River Dr S, Great Falls, Mont., 59405-1854, Cascade; gen tel (406) 791-1444; adv tel (406) 791-1440; ed tel (406) 791-1460; gen fax (406) 791-1431; adv fax (406) 791-1436 (Class); ed fax (406) 791-1431; gen/nat adv e-mail advertising@greatfallstribune.com; disp adv e-mail msmith@greatfalltribune.com; class adv e-mailgbebee@greatfallstribune.com; ed e-mail tribcity@greatfallstribune.com; web site www.greatfallstribune.com
Group: Gannett
Published: Mon, Tues, Wed, Thur, Fri, Sat, Sun
Weekday Frequency: m
Saturday Frequency: m
Circulation: 20,845; 20,845(sat); 22,426(sun)
Last Audit: AAM September 30, 2016
Advertising Rate (weekday/saturday): Open inch rate $48.20
Advertising Rate (sunday): Open inch rate $64.85
News services: AP, GNS. **Established:** 1884
Own Printing Facility?: Yes
Commercial Printers?: Yes
Special Editions: Jan: Bridal Guide, What Women Want (WWW)magazine.
Feb: Ag Outlook, Healthy MT magazine, Outlook 20xx.
Mar: Western Art Roundup, What Women Want, College 101, Guide to Great Falls, Home and Garden Show.
Apr:Newcomers Guide
May:Draw Your Mom, Visit Great Falls,Glacier Gateway, WWW mag., Healthy MT.
June:101 Things to Do in Montana, Draw Your Dad
July: Visit Great Falls, State Fair Preview, WWW mag.,Back to School.
Aug:Healthy MT, Pet Idol, Ag Outlook, Football Preview.
Sept: College 101, Visit Great Falls, Fall Home Guide, WWW mag.
Oct:WWW Expo Guide, Your Health Medical Directory.
Nov:Visit Great Falls, WWW mag., Ag Outlook, Holiday Gift Guides, Healthy MT.
Dec:Visit Great Falls.
also Great Falls Business 6X/yr, fusion 12X/yr, Your Health 12X/yr,Military Retirees Appreciation 2X/yr,
Special Weekly Sections: Best Food Day (Wed); Health, Technology (Tue); Outdoors (Thur); Entertainment, Auto (Fri); Home, Living, Religion (Sat); Business/Agriculture, Travel, Family, Real Estate (Sun)
Syndicated Publications: USA WEEKEND Magazine (S).,relish (T), Spry (T).
Glossy:
What Women Want Magazine
Healthy MT
College 101
Digital Platform - Mobile: Apple, Android, Windows
Digital Platform - Tablet: Apple iOS, Android
Pres./Pub./Ed. .... James Strauss
Acct. Mgr. .... Viv Hunter
Production Operations Dir. .... Mike Grafe
Production Mgr., Mailroom .... Gene Hieb
Dir. of Business Development & Marketing Terry Oyhamburu
Specialty Publication Editor .... Amie Thompson
Business Editor .... Jo Dee Black
Sports Editor .... Scott Mansch
Circ. Sales and Retention Mgr. .... Lou Dewaele
Literacy Outreach Coordinator .... Lolly Hader
Adv. Mgr., Classified .... Grant Bebee
Market Information: ADS; Split run; Zoned editions.
Mechanical Available: Offset; Black and 3 ROP colors; insert accepted; page cutoffs - 22 3/4.
Mechanical Specifications: Type page 11 5/8 x 21 1/2; E - 6 cols, 1 5/6, 1/8 between; A - 6 cols, 1 5/6, 1/8 between; C - 9 cols, 1 1/4, 1/16 between.
Delivery Method: Mail, Newsstand, Carrier, RacksEquipment & Software: PRESSROOM EQUIPMENT: Lines — 6-G/Metro (2 color decks) doublewidth 6; 10-Goss Community 5 roll stand; Heidelberg MO 19x25 sheet fed; Folders — 2-G/2:1; Pasters —6-G/3-Arm RTP.Registration System — N/A MAILROOM EQUIPMENT: Counter Stackers — 3-Id/440, 2-QWI/350; Inserters & Stuffers — 1472 Harris; Tying Machines — 1/OVL, 1-/MLN; Wrapping Singles — Manual; Control System — K&M; Address Machine — 3-/Wm.; BUSINESS EQUIPMENT: 1-IBM/i5 BUSINESS SOFTWARE: IBM, Gannett CLASSIFIED EQUIPMENT: Hardware — Mactive; CLASSIFIED SOFTWARE: APT. DISPLAY EQUIPMENT: Hardware — Mactive, G3; Printers — Screen CTP; DISPLAY SOFTWAREAd Make-up Applications — CS-5; Layout Software — APT. EDITORIAL EQUIPMENT: Hardware — APT/Lf/AP Leaf Picture Desk; Printers — 2 Screen CTP EDITORIAL SOFTWARE: APT. PRODUCTION EQUIPMENT: Hardware — 2 Screen CTP; Cameras — Nikon; Scanners — Nikon/LS 1000, Nikon/LS 2000 PRODUCTION SOFTWARE: APT.

HAMILTON

RAVALLI REPUBLIC

232 W Main St, Hamilton, Mont., 59840-2552, Ravalli; gen tel (406) 363-3300; adv tel (406) 363-3300; ed tel (406) 363-3300; gen fax (406) 363-3569; adv fax (406) 363-3569; ed fax (406) 363-1767; gen/nat adv e-mail jodi.lopez@ravallirepublic.com ; class adv e-maillacey.davis@ravallirepublic.com; ed e-mail editor@ravallirepublic.com; web site www.ravallirepublic.com
- 400,000(views) 70,000(visitors)
Group: Lee Enterprises, Inc.
Published: Wed, Thur, Fri, Sat, Sun
Weekday Frequency: m
Saturday Frequency: m
Circulation: 4,236; 4,236(sat); 4,236(sun)
Last Audit: Sworn/Estimate/Non-Audited December 18, 2017
Advertising Rate (weekday/saturday): Open inch rate $11.25
Advertising Rate (sunday): Open inch rate $11.25
Online Advertising Rate: Starting from $100.00 CPM
News services: AP. **Established:** 1897
Own Printing Facility?: No
Commercial Printers?: No
Special Editions: Uncover Bitterroot (Sept); Agri-Business (Mar, Jun, Sept); Valley Vista (Tourism Publication) (March); Christmas Editions (Nov); Hunting and Outdoors (Oct).
Special Weekly Sections: Food, Health (Wed); Opinion, Business (Thur); TV, Entertainment (Fri); Outdoors (Sat); Opinion, Life in the Bitterroot (Sun)
Digital Platform - Mobile: Apple, Android
Digital Platform - Tablet: Apple iOS, Android
Pub. .... Mike Gulledge
Ed. .... Kathy Best
Bus. Mgr. .... Linda Pollard
Sales Mgr. .... Jodi Lopez
Mechanical Available: Offset; Black and 3 ROP colors; insert accepted; page cutoffs - 22 3/4.
Mechanical Specifications: Type page 13 x 21 1/2; E - 6 cols, 2 1/16, 1/8 between; A - 6 cols, 2 1/16, 1/8 between; C - 9 cols, 2 1/16, 1/8 between.
Areas Served: Ravalli County, Montana
Delivery Method: Carrier, RacksEquipment & Software: PRESSROOM EQUIPMENT: Lines — Folders 1 BUSINESS EQUIPMENT: 2-PC CLASSIFIED SOFTWARE: CText. DISPLAY EQUIPMENT: Hardware — 1-IBM/386, 1-Gateway/486, 2-Gateway/Pentium with CD-Rom; Printers — 1-QMS/LaserPrinter; DISPLAY SOFTWAREAd Make-up Applications — Aldus/PageMaker, Ventura, Signature.; EDITORIAL EQUIPMENT: Printers — 1-QMS/LaserPrinter. PRODUCTION EQUIPMENT: Hardware — HP/ScanJet IIc; Cameras — 1-K/241

HAVRE

THE HAVRE DAILY NEWS

119 2nd St, Havre, Mont., 59501-3507, Hill; gen tel (406) 265-6795; adv tel (406) 265-6795; ed tel (406) 265-6795; gen fax (406) 265-6798; adv fax (406) 265-6798; ed fax (406) 265-6798; gen/nat adv e-mail mgilman@havredailynews.com; disp adv e-mail adsales1@havredailynews.com; class adv e-mailadsales2@havredailynews.com; ed e-mail news@havredailynews.com; web site www.havredailynews.com
Group: Stevenson Newspapers
Published: Mon, Tues, Wed, Thur, Fri
Weekday Frequency: e
Circulation: 3,800
Last Audit: Sworn/Estimate/Non-Audited September 30, 2017
Advertising Rate (weekday/saturday): Open inch rate $13.00
News services: AP. **Established:** 1914
Special Editions: Home & Car Care (Apr); Fair (Aug); Christmas Greetings (Dec); Senior Citizens (Feb); Tax Guide (Jan); Senior Citizens (Jul); Senior Citizens (Jun); Who's Who in Northern Montana (Mar); Tourist Guide (May); Thanksgiving (Nov); Hunting & Fishing Guide (Oct)
Special Weekly Sections: Food (Tue); Agriculture (Wed); Business (Thur); Church, Society, Real Estate (Fri)
Syndicated Publications: American Profile (Weekly).
Pub./Adv. Mgr. .... Stacy Mantle
Circ. Dir. .... Craig Otterstrom
Prodn. Mgr. .... Scott Anderson
Adv. Dir. .... Jenn Thompson
Adv. Consultant .... Hannah Somers
Classified Adv. Mgr. .... Crystal Faldalen
Tim Leeds
Market Information: TMC.
Mechanical Available: Offset; Black and 3 ROP colors; insert accepted; page cutoffs - 22 3/4.
Mechanical Specifications: Type page 13 x 21 1/2; E - 6 cols, 2 1/16, 1/8 between; A - 6 cols, 2 1/16, 1/8 between; C - 9 cols, 1 3/8, 1/16 between.
Areas Served: 59501, 59520, 59521, 59523, 59525, 59528, 59532, 59540Equipment & Software: PRESSROOM EQUIPMENT: Lines — 4-G/Community; Folders — 1-G/2:1.; MAILROOM EQUIPMENT: Tying Machines — 2-Bu/16.; BUSINESS EQUIPMENT: 1-IBM/386 Compatible, 2-Wyse/370, 1-IBM/486-66 MHz, 1-IBM/Pentium-133 MHz, APP/Mac Performa 6400-180 BUSINESS SOFTWARE: PBS/Media Plus 2.5B CLASSIFIED EQUIPMENT: Hardware — 1-APP/Mac LC II; CLASSIFIED SOFTWARE: Baseview/Fox Base Plus 2.01. DISPLAY EQUIPMENT: Hardware — APP/Power Mac 7200-120, APP/Mac II ci; Printers — Dataproducts/LZR 1560, Typhoon/8; Other Hardware — 2-Iomega/Zip Drive. DISPLAY SOFTWAREAd Make-up Applications — APP/Mac System 7.5; EDITORIAL EQUIPMENT: Hardware — 3-APP/Mac IIci, 4-APP/Mac LC II, 2-APP/Mac 7200; Printers — Dataproducts/LZR 1560, Typhoon/8 EDITORIAL SOFTWARE: APP/Mac Sys 7.1, QPS/QuarkXPress 3.31, Baseview/NewsEdit 6.0. PRODUCTION EQUIPMENT: Hardware — Polaroid/SprintScan 35, 1-Typhoon/8; Cameras — 1-K/24; Scanners — Umax/UC630 Color Scanner.

HELENA

HELENA INDEPENDENT RECORD

317 N Cruse Ave, Helena, Mont., 59601-5003, Lewis And Clark; gen tel (406) 447-4000; adv tel (406) 447-4011; ed tel (406) 444-5120; gen fax (406) 447-4008; adv fax (406) 447-4052; ed fax (406) 447-4052; gen/nat adv e-mail tonda.meyer@helenair.com; disp adv e-mail tonda.meyer@helenair.com; class adv e-mailrebecca.bruno@helenair.com; ed e-mail irstaff@helenair.com; web site www.helenair.com
- 2,000,000(views) 240,000(visitors)
Group: Lee Enterprises, Inc.
Published: Mon, Tues, Wed, Thur, Fri, Sat, Sun
Weekday Frequency: m
Saturday Frequency: m
Circulation: 10,558; 10,558(sat); 11,132(sun)
Last Audit: AAM September 30, 2016
Advertising Rate (weekday/saturday): Open inch rate $21.44; Open Inch rate $24.16 (Fri)
Advertising Rate (sunday): Open Inch rate $24.16 (Sun)
News services: AP, NYT, States News Service, Cox News Service. **Established:** 1867
Own Printing Facility?: Yes
Commercial Printers?: Yes
Special Weekly Sections: Health, Fitness, Food (Wed); Entertainment, TV, Outdoors (Thur); Religion (Sat); Business, Travel (Sun)
Syndicated Publications: TV Guide (Fri); Parade (S); American Profile (Weekly).
Digital Platform - Mobile: Apple, Android, Windows, Blackberry
Digital Platform - Tablet: Apple iOS, Android, Windows 7
Pub. .... Tyler Miller
National Adv. Coord. .... Karen Rickman
Adv. Mgr. .... Jim Rickman
Reporter .... James DeHaven
Ed. .... Jesse Chaney
Market Information: ADS; Split run; TMC.
Mechanical Available: Offset; Black and ROP colors; insert accepted; page cutoffs - 22 3/4.
Mechanical Specifications: Type page 11 5/8 x 21 1/2; E - 6 cols, 2 1/14, 1/6 between; A - 6 cols, 2 1/14, 1/6 between; C - 9 cols, 1 4/11, 1/6 between.
Delivery Method: Mail, Carrier, RacksEquipment & Software: PRESSROOM EQUIPMENT: Lines — 8-G/Suburban (balloon former) 1978; Folders — G/Community SC.; MAILROOM EQUIPMENT: Counter Stackers — 1-WPC/Quarter folder; Inserters & Stuffers — 1/MM; Tying Machines - 1-/MLN, 1-/Malow; Address Machine — 1-/Ch; BUSINESS EQUIPMENT: Gateway BUSINESS SOFTWARE: Microsoft/Windows NT, Microsoft/Office CLASSIFIED EQUIPMENT: Hardware — 6-Gateway/PIII 1 GH; Printers — Pre Press/Panther Pro, Pre Press/PantherPro 46; CLASSIFIED SOFTWARE: CText/Advision. DISPLAY EQUIPMENT: Hardware — 8-APP/Power Mac 7600-120; Printers — HP 5000, Epson 2000, HP 4500; Other Hardware — APP/Mac Scanner DISPLAY SOFTWAREAd Make-up Applications — 2-Multi-Ad/Creator, Macromedia/FreeHand, QPS/QuarkXPress 4.0; Layout Software — MEI/ALS. EDITORIAL EQUIPMENT: Hardware — 12-Gateway/P5-166, 6-Gateway/P7-450/APP/Photo Server, IBM; Printers — 1-Pre Press/Panther Pro, 1-Pre Press/Panther Pro 46 EDITORIAL SOFTWARE: CText/Dateline, QPS/QuarkXPress 3.32. PRODUCTION EQUIPMENT: Hardware — Nu/FT40UPNS; Cameras — 3-Nikon/F2, 1-Nikon/F3; Scanners — APP/Mac Scanner, APP/Mac IIci.

KALISPELL

DAILY INTER LAKE

727 E Idaho St, Kalispell, Mont., 59901-3202, Flathead; gen tel (406) 755-7000; adv tel (406) 755-7000; ed tel (406) 755-7000; gen fax (406) 752-6114; ed fax (406) 758-4481; gen/nat adv e-mail wspencer@dailyinterlake.com; disp adv e-mail wspencer@dailyinterlake.com; class adv e-mailsmiller@dailyinterlake.com; ed e-mail edit@dailyinterlake.com; web site www.dailyinterlake.com
- 825,000(views) 278,302(visitors); web site 2 pages.dailyinterlake.com/hagadonedigitalmontana
Group: Hagadone Corporation
Published: Mon, Tues, Wed, Thur, Fri, Sat, Sun
Weekday Frequency: m
Saturday Frequency: m
Circulation: 14,570; 14,570(sat); 15,390(sun)
Last Audit: CAC March 31, 2016
Branch Offices: Hungry Horse News, Whitefish Pilot, Libby Western News, Lake County Leader, Clark Fork Valley Press, Mineral Independent.
Advertising Rate (weekday/saturday): Open inch rate $18.80
Advertising Rate (sunday): Open inch rate $20.80 cpi.
Online Advertising Rate: $10.00 cpm
News services: AP, LAT-WP. **Established:** 1888
Own Printing Facility?: Yes
Commercial Printers?: Yes
Special Editions: Homes & Real Estate (Monthly); 101 Things To Do (Spring). Flathead Business Journal, Parade of Homes
Special Weekly Sections: Montana Life (S); Outdoors (Thur); Active Seniors (Tues); Food (Wed). This Week in the Flathead (Thurs)
Syndicated Publications: TV Listings Magazine (Fri); Parade (S); American Profile (Weekly).
Digital Platform - Mobile: Apple, Android, Windows, Blackberry
Digital Platform - Tablet: Apple iOS, Android, Windows 7, Blackberry Tablet OS, Kindle, Nook, Kindle Fire
Bus. Mgr. ....Dorothy Glencross
Features Ed. ....Lynnette Hintze
Managing Ed. ....Frank Miele
Sports Ed. ....Dave Lesnick
Circulation Director ....Ken Varga
Publisher .... Rick Weaver
Collections ....Lisa Fleming
Regional Ed. ....Matt Baldwin
Market Information: ADS; TMC.
Mechanical Available: Offset; Black and 3 ROP colors; insert accepted - singles sheet, booklets; page cutoffs - 21.
Mechanical Specifications: Type page 11 7/8 x 21; E - 6 cols, 1 7/8, 1/8 between; A - 6 cols, 1 7/8, 1/8 between; C - 9 cols, 1 1/5, 1/8 between.
Areas Served: Flathead County, Lake County, Lincoln County
Delivery Method: Mail, Newsstand, Carrier, RacksEquipment & Software: PRESSROOM EQUIPMENT: Lines — 8-G/Community 1995.; MAILROOM EQUIPMENT: Tying Machines — MLN/2EE; Address Machine — Ch.; BUSINESS EQUIPMENT: NCS, DEC/Micro VAX, APP/Mac
HP 4515 BUSINESS SOFTWARE: Microsoft/Word, Microsoft/Excel CLASSIFIED EQUIPMENT: Hardware — APP/Mac; Printers — Brother HL2170W CLASSIFIED SOFTWARE: NCS, Ethernet. DISPLAY EQUIPMENT: Hardware — APP/Mac;
Ricoh 6330
Ricoh C831 DISPLAY SOFTWAREAd Make-up Applications — NCS, Adobe/Illustrator, Microsoft/Excel, Adobe/Photoshop.; EDITORIAL EQUIPMENT: Hardware — APP/Mac; Printers —
Ricoh 6330 EDITORIAL SOFTWARE: NCS, Adobe/Photoshop, Caere/OmniPage. PRODUCTION EQUIPMENT: Hardware — Apple iMac, ECRM NewsMatic HS, Newsmatic
2 Glunz Jensen processors, Burgess bender and punch PRODUCTION SOFTWARE: NCS, Indesign CS6, Adobe/Photoshop CC, Adobe/Acrobat Pro, Adobe/Illustrator CC, CIRCULATION EQUIPMENT: App/Mac
HP 9050
HP P3015 CIRCULATION SOFTWARNCS

LIVINGSTON

THE LIVINGSTON ENTERPRISE

401 S Main St, Livingston, Mont., 59047-3418, Park; gen tel (406) 222-2000; adv tel (800) 345-8412; ed tel (406) 222-2000; gen fax (406) 222-8580; adv fax (406) 222-8580; ed fax (406) 222-8580; gen/nat adv e-mail jdurfey@livent.net; disp adv e-mail jdurfey@livent.net; class adv e-mailclassifieds@livent.net; ed e-mail news@livent.net; web site www.livingstonenterprise.com
Group: Yellowstone Communications
Published: Mon, Tues, Wed, Thur, Fri
Weekday Frequency: e
Circulation: 2,606
Last Audit: Sworn/Estimate/Non-Audited September 30, 2017
Advertising Rate (weekday/saturday): Open inch rate $8.25
News services: AP. **Established:** 1883
Own Printing Facility?: Yes
Commercial Printers?: Yes
Special Editions: Home & Garden (Apr); Back-to-School (Aug); Christmas Eve (Dec); Fall Sports (Fall); Presidential History Tab (Feb); Bridal Tab (Other); Car Care (Spring); Winter Sport (Winter).
Special Weekly Sections: Best Food Day (Wed)
Syndicated Publications: American Profile (Weekly).
Pub. .... John Sullivan
Controller ....Scott Squillace
Adv. Dir. .... James Durfey
Circ. Dir ....David Campbell
Managing Editor ....Justin Post
News Ed. ....Dwight Harriman
Sports Editor .... Thomas Watson
Press Foreman .... Luke Miller
Production Mgr. .... Alan Bublitz
Market Information: ADS; TMC; Zoned editions.
Mechanical Available: Offset, Web; Black and 3 ROP colors; insert accepted; page cutoffs - 22 3/4.
Mechanical Specifications: Type page 13 x 21 1/4; E - 6 cols, 2 1/16, 1/8 between; A - 6 cols, 2 1/16, 1/8 between; C - 8 cols, 1 1/2, 1/8 between.
Areas Served: 59047,59018,59030,59027, 59065, 59082,59086
Delivery Method: Mail, Newsstand, Carrier, RacksEquipment & Software: PRESSROOM EQUIPMENT: Lines — 4-G/Community, 1-DEV/Color unit, 4-G/High Community; Folders — G/SSC, 1-G/Quarter Folder.; MAILROOM EQUIPMENT: Counter Stackers — BG/Count-O-Veyor; Tying Machines — 1/Bu, 2-Polychem/PC 500, Plastic Strap; Address Machine — 1-/Ch; BUSINESS EQUIPMENT: IBM BUSINESS SOFTWARE: SBS, BMF CLASSIFIED EQUIPMENT: Hardware — APP/Mac; CLASSIFIED SOFTWARE: Fake Brains, InDesign DISPLAY EQUIPMENT: Hardware — APP/Mac; Printers — APP/Mac LaserWriter, Pre Press/Panther Pro Imagesetter; DISPLAY SOFTWAREAd Make-up Applications — QPS, InDesign; EDITORIAL EQUIPMENT: Hardware — APP/Mac; Printers — APP/Mac, Pre Press/Panther Pro Imagesetter EDITORIAL SOFTWARE: Baseview. PRODUCTION EQUIPMENT: Hardware — APP/Mac LaserWriter, APP/Mac II, APP/Mac IIx, APP/Mac SE, Pre Press/Panther Pro; Cameras — CTP AlphaQuest; Scanners — APP/Mac.

MILES CITY

MILES CITY STAR

818 Main St, Miles City, Mont., 59301-3221, Custer; gen tel (406) 234-0450; adv tel (406) 234-0450; ed tel (406) 234-0450; gen fax (406) 234-6687; adv fax (406) 234-6687; ed fax (406) 234-6687; gen/nat adv e-mail advsales@midrivers.com; disp adv e-mail advsales@midrivers.com; class adv e-mailmcclassads@midrivers.com; ed e-mail mceditor@midrivers.com; web site www.milescitystar.com
Group: Yellowstone Communications
Published: Mon, Tues, Wed, Thur, Fri
Weekday Frequency: e
Circulation: 4,000
Last Audit: Sworn/Estimate/Non-Audited September 30, 2017
Advertising Rate (weekday/saturday): Open inch rate $7.45
News services: AP. **Established:** 1911
Commercial Printers?: Yes
Special Weekly Sections: Best Food Day (Tue); Livestock, Agriculture (Thur); Society, Entertainment (Wed); Society, Weekend (Fri)
Syndicated Publications: American Profile (Weekly).
Pub. .... Dan Killoy
Adv. Mgr. ....Alan Hauge
Ed. .... Marla Prell
News Ed. ....Elaine Forman
Sports Ed. ....Josh Samuelson
Data Processing Mgr. ....Sharon Cline
Mgr., Commercial Printing ...... Karen Hawkinson
Market Information: TMC. $535 insert rate
Mechanical Available: Offset; Black and 3 ROP colors; insert accepted; page cutoffs - 22 3/4.
Mechanical Specifications: Type page 12 x 21 1/2; E - 6 cols, 2 1/16, 1/8 between; A - 6 cols, 2 1/16, 1/8 between; C - 8 cols, 1 1/2, 1/8 between.
Areas Served: Custer County (MT)
Delivery Method: Mail, Newsstand, CarrierEquipment & Software: PRESSROOM EQUIPMENT: Lines — 6-G/Community.; MAILROOM EQUIPMENT: Tying Machines — 1/Bu String tie 2 Signod strappers; Address Machine — 1-/Am.; BUSINESS EQUIPMENT: BFM CLASSIFIED EQUIPMENT: Hardware — APP/Mac; Printers — LaserMaster/XLO, Okidata; CLASSIFIED SOFTWARE: Baseview/Class Manager Plus. DISPLAY EQUIPMENT: Hardware — APP/Mac; Printers — APP/Mac LaserPrinter, LaserMaster; DISPLAY SOFTWAREAd Make-up Applications — QPS, Metro Laser/CD-Rom; Layout Software — APP/Mac. EDITORIAL EQUIPMENT: Hardware — APP/Mac; Printers — APP/Mac LaserPrinter, LaserMaster/XLO, PrePress/Panther Pro Imagesetter EDITORIAL SOFTWARE: QPS, Baseview/NewsEdit. PRODUCTION EQUIPMENT: Hardware — APP/Mac, LaserMaster, Adobe/Photosho Indesign; Cameras — 1-K PRODUCTION SOFTWARE: Baseview/NewsEdit.

MISSOULA

MISSOULIAN

500 S Higgins Ave, Missoula, Mont., 59801-2736, Missoula; gen tel (406) 523-5200; adv tel (406) 523-5223; ed tel (406) 523-5240; gen fax (406) 523-5221; adv fax (406) 523-5221; ed fax (406) 523-5294; gen/nat adv e-mail advertising@missoulian.com; class adv e-mailclassified@missoulian.com; ed e-mail oped@missoulian.com; web site www.missoulian.com
- 4,351,563(views) 536,904(visitors)
Group: Lee Enterprises, Inc.
Published: Mon, Tues, Wed, Thur, Fri, Sat, Sun
Weekday Frequency: m
Saturday Frequency: m
Circulation: 15,157; 15,157(sat); 17,914(sun)
Last Audit: AAM September 30, 2016
Advertising Rate (weekday/saturday): Open inch rate $65.70
Advertising Rate (sunday): Open inch rate $76.20
Online Advertising Rate: Mobile $85.00 CPM; Homepage Takeover $1000.00
News services: AP, NYT. **Established:** 1905
Special Editions: Health Fair Tab (January), Missoula's Choice (January), Living Well (Bi-Monthly), Newspapers in Education (March), Montana's Cultural Treasures (March), Uncover Missoula (March), Spring Fasion (April), Montana Designs (April), International Wildlife Film Festival Program/Tab (April/May), Lawn & Garden (April), Graduation (June), Explore the Bitterroot (June), Hot Spots (June), HomeStyle (July), Montana Lyric Opera (July), Chamber of Commerce Directory (July), Missoula Relocation Guide (July), Western Montana Fair (August), MCPS Calendar (August), River City Roots Festival (August), Bear Necessities (August), Grizzly Game Day (Weekly beginning August through College football season), Montana Designs II (September),Fall Fashion (September), Hunting Journal (October), MT CINE International Film Festival (October), Health Resource Guide (October), Brawl of the Wild (November), Holiday Gift Guide (November), Faith Tab (December), Beer & Wine Journal (December), Montana Economic Report (December), Brides & Grooms (December)
Special Weekly Sections: Health (Tue); Food (Wed); Outdoors (Thur); Entertainment (Fri); Engagements, Business (Sun);
Syndicated Publications: Parade (Sunday),

Missoula Magazine (Quarterly), Athlon Sports (Third Tuesday of the Month), Corridor (Monthly),
Pub. .... Mike Gulledge
Marketing Mgr. .... Annalisa Martin
Co-op Adv. Coord. .... Debbie Larson
Ed. .... Kathy Best
City Ed. .... Gwen Florio
Market Information: TMC; Zoned editions.
Mechanical Available: Offset; Black and 3 ROP colors; insert accepted; page cutoffs - 22 3/4.
Mechanical Specifications: Type page 13 x 21 1/2; E - 6 cols, 2 1/16, 1/8 between; A - 6 cols, 2 1/16, 1/8 between; C - 9 cols, 1 5/16, 1/8 between.
Areas Served: Western Montana
Delivery Method: Mail, Newsstand, Carrier, RacksEquipment & Software: PRESSROOM EQUIPMENT: Lines — 9-G; 9-G/Urbanite; Folders — 2, 1-G/Quarter, 2-G/Urbanite 707; Reels & Stands — G/2 stands 3 high.; MAILROOM EQUIPMENT: Counter Stackers — 1-Id/Counter Stacker 660, 1-Id/Counter Stacker 2100; Inserters & Stuffers — 1-MM/227-0500 E, HI/1372; Tying Machines — 2-MLN/Automatic Power Strapping Machines; Address Machine — 1/AVY, Ch/582 M Base 721 Head; BUSINESS EQUIPMENT: 2-IBM/Sys 38 CLASSIFIED EQUIPMENT: Hardware — 12-Gateway/P166 Advision; 1-HP/Scanner; Printers — HP/6MP Postscript Printer; CLASSIFIED SOFTWARE: CText/Advision, CText/Alps pagination system. DISPLAY EQUIPMENT: Other Hardware — 4-APP/Mac Color One Scanner, 9-APP/Mac B&W One Scanner DISPLAY SOFTWAREAd Make-up Applications — QPS/QuarkXPress 4.0, Aldus/FreeHand 8.0, Adobe/Photoshop 5.0; Layout Software — APP/Mac, QPS/QuarkXPress. EDITORIAL EQUIPMENT: Hardware — Gateway/P166 Expressline Paginator, 24-Gateway/P166 Dateline Machine, 2-APP/Mac G3, 1-APP/Mac 8500, 1-APP/Mac 7100, 11-CText, 1-DEC/VT-220, 1-APP/Mac fx, 1-APP/Mac Dash, 1-APP/Mac ci, 1-APP/Power Mac 7100/1-APP/Mac Color One Scanne PRODUCTION EQUIPMENT: Hardware — APP/iMac, 7-Umax/Astra 12200 Scanner, 1-Pre Press/Panther Pro 46, 1-Pre Press/Panther Pro Imagesetter; Cameras — 1-C/Spartan II, 1-Nu; Scanners — 1-PC 386 PRODUCTION SOFTWARE: CText, QPS/QuarkXPress 3.3.

NEBRASKA

ALLIANCE

ALLIANCE TIMES-HERALD
114 E 4th St, P O Box G, Alliance, Neb., 69301-3402, Box Butte; gen tel (308) 762-3060; adv tel (308) 762-3060; ed tel (308) 762-3060; gen fax (308) 762-3063; adv fax (308) 762-3063; ed fax (308) 762-3063; gen/nat adv e-mail cassie@alliancetimes.com; disp adv e-mail erica@alliancetimes.com; class adv e-mailclassified@alliancetimes.com; ed e-mail athnews@alliancetimes.com; web site www.alliancetimes.com
 - 90,000(views) 75,000(visitors)
Group: Seaton Group
Published: Mon, Tues, Wed, Thur, Fri, Sat
Weekday Frequency: e
Saturday Frequency: m
Circulation: 3,025; 3,025(sat)
Last Audit: Sworn/Estimate/Non-Audited September 30, 2017
Advertising Rate (weekday/saturday): Open inch rate $9.95
Online Advertising Rate: $0.01/click
News services: AP. **Established:** 1887
Own Printing Facility?: Yes
Commercial Printers?: No
Special Editions: Spring Home & Garden (Recycling) (Apr); Fair Section-Results (Aug); Letters to Santa and Christmas Greetings (Dec); Business & Industry (Feb); Tax (Jan); Heritage Days Festival (Jul); Spring Ag & Ranch (Mar); Beef (May); Winter Sports

(Nov); Fall Ag (Oct)
Special Weekly Sections: Business Page (Other); Farm & Ranch (Thur); Food (Wed).
Pres. .... Donald R. Seaton
Pub. .... Tom Shaal
Vice Pres. .... Edward L. Seaton
Distr. Mgr. .... Chris Nowak
Mng. Ed. .... John Weare
Lifestyles Ed. .... Luayne Weisgerber
Pressroom Mgr. .... Mark Sherlock
Dir. of Op. .... Aaron Wade
Class. & Legals .... Sally Yeager
Asst. Mng. Ed. .... Mark Dykes
Lifestyles Ed. .... Luayne Weisberger
Market Information: Split run; TMC.
Mechanical Available: Offset; Black and 3 ROP colors; insert accepted; page cutoffs - 21 1/2.
Mechanical Specifications: Type page 14 x 24; E - 6 cols, 1 4/5, 1/8 between; A - 6 cols, 1 4/5, 1/8 between; C - 7 cols, 1 1/2, 1/8 between.
Areas Served: 69301
Delivery Method: Mail, Newsstand, Carrier, RacksEquipment & Software: PRESSROOM EQUIPMENT: Lines — 5-G/Community; MAILROOM EQUIPMENT: Tying Machines — 1-/Bu.; BUSINESS EQUIPMENT: PC BUSINESS SOFTWARE: QuickBooks Pro. 2011 CLASSIFIED EQUIPMENT: Hardware — 1-APP Mac G5; Printers — HP 5000; CLASSIFIED SOFTWARE: Baseview. DISPLAY EQUIPMENT: Hardware — APP/ Mac G5; Printers — Xante/Accel-a-Writer; DISPLAY SOFTWAREAd Make-up Applications — Adobe/Photoshop, Microsoft/Word, QPS/QuarkXPress; Layout Software — APP/ Mac G5. EDITORIAL EQUIPMENT: Hardware — 7-APP/Mac G5; Printers — Xante/Accel-a-Writer, HP/LaserJet EDITORIAL SOFTWARE: QPS/QuarkXPress, Microsoft/Word. PRODUCTION EQUIPMENT: Hardware — Xante/Accel-a-Writer; Cameras — R

BEATRICE

BEATRICE DAILY SUN
110 S 6th St, Beatrice, Neb., 68310-3912, Gage; gen tel (402) 223-5233; adv tel (402) 223-5233; ed tel (402) 223-5233; gen fax (402) 228-3571; adv fax (402) 228-3571; ed fax (402) 228-3571; gen/nat adv e-mail astokebrand@beatricedailysun.com; disp adv e-mail astokebrand@beatricedailysun.com; ed e-mail news@beatricedailysun.com ; web site www.beatricedailysun.com
 - 1,300,000(views) 40,000(visitors)
Group: Lee Enterprises, Inc.
Published: Tues, Wed, Thur, Fri, Sat
Weekday Frequency: m
Saturday Frequency: m
Circulation: 4,255; 4,239(sat)
Last Audit: Sworn/Estimate/Non-Audited February 3, 2018
Advertising Rate (weekday/saturday): Daily $15.66; Wed $18; Sat $17.41
Online Advertising Rate: $595.00/mo.
News services: AP, NEA. **Established:** 1902
Own Printing Facility?: Yes
Commercial Printers?: Yes
Special Editions: Clean-up (Apr); Back-to-School (Aug); Senior Citizens (Feb); County Fair (Jul); Homestead Days (Jun); Family Business (Mar); Graduation (May); Sports (Nov); 4-H (Oct); Hunting (Sept).
Special Weekly Sections: Farm Page (Fri); Youth (Sat); Religion (Thur); Cooking (Wed).
Syndicated Publications: Relish (Monthly); USA WEEKEND Magazine (Sat); American Profile (Weekly).
Digital Platform - Mobile: Apple, Android, Windows
Digital Platform - Tablet: Apple iOS, Android, Windows 7, Kindle, Kindle Fire
Regl. Pub. .... Patrick Ethridge
Composing Mgr. .... Becky Reedy
Sales TL .... Amy Stokebrand
Market Information: TMC.
Mechanical Available: Offset; Black and 3 ROP colors; insert accepted; page cutoffs - 22 3/4.
Mechanical Specifications: Type page 13 x 21 1/2; E - 6 cols, 2, 1/6 between; A - 6 cols, 2, 1/6 between; C - 6 cols, 2, 1/6 between.
Areas Served: Southeast Nebraska
Delivery Method: Mail, Newsstand, Carrier, RacksEquipment & Software: PRESSROOM

EQUIPMENT: Lines — 7-G/Community.; MAILROOM EQUIPMENT: Tying Machines — 2/Malow.; CLASSIFIED EQUIPMENT: Hardware — 3-APP/Mac LC III; CLASSIFIED SOFTWARE: Multi-Ad/CAMS. DISPLAY EQUIPMENT: Hardware — 3-APP/Mac G3, 1-APP/Mac Quadra 950, 1-APP/Power Mac 7200; Printers — 2-APP/Mac LaserWriter IIg, 2-HP/4MV; DISPLAY SOFTWAREAd Make-up Applications — Multi-Ad/Creator 5.1.; EDITORIAL EQUIPMENT: Hardware — 13-APP/Mac Classic II EDITORIAL SOFTWARE: Baseview/NewsEdit. PRODUCTION EQUIPMENT: Hardware — 1-APP/Mac 6100/66, ECR; Cameras — 1-Nippon/C24DLA; Scanners — Umax/840 PowerLook II, AG/Studio Scan IISI.

COLUMBUS

THE COLUMBUS TELEGRAM
1254 27th Ave, Columbus, Neb., 68601-5656, Platte; gen tel (402) 564-2741; adv tel (402) 564-2741; ed tel (402) 564-2741; gen fax (402) 563-7500; adv fax (402) 563-7500; ed fax (402) 563-7500; gen/nat adv e-mail amy.bell@lee.net; disp adv e-mail amy.bell@lee.net; ed e-mail jdean@columbustelegram.com; web site www.columbustelegram.com
 - 700,000(views)
Group: Lee Enterprises, Inc.
Published: Mon, Tues, Wed, Thur, Fri, Sun
Weekday Frequency: e
Circulation: 5,865; 6,910(sun)
Last Audit: AAM September 30, 2014
Advertising Rate (weekday/saturday): Open inch rate $23.00
Advertising Rate (sunday): Open inch rate $24.96
News services: AP, MCT, NEA. **Established:** 1879
Special Editions: Senior Salute (Apr); Columbus Day (Aug); Last Minute Gift Idea (Dec); Columbus Home Show (Feb); Bridal (Jan); Farm & Fair (Jul); Father's Day (Jun); Chamber of Commerce (Mar); Ag/Almanac/Beef (May); Christmas Opening (Nov); Power and Progress (Oct); Colle
Special Weekly Sections: Sports, Lifestyles, Business, Precious Memories (Sun); Sports, Farm (Mon); Sports, Food, Health (Tue); Sports, Youth, Business (Wed); Sports, Dining, Entertainment, Home, Garden (Thur); Sports, Religion, Senior (Fri)
Syndicated Publications: Relish (Monthly); USA WEEKEND Magazine (S); American Profile (Wed).
Interim Pub. .... John DiMambro
Controller .... Amy Bell
Adv. Dir. .... Ann Blunt
Circ. Dir. .... Greg Pehrson
Copy Desk Chief .... Patrick Murphy
Educ. Reporter. .... Julie Blum
Prodn. Mgr. .... Jerry Gaver
Interim Ed. .... Tyler Ellyson
Sales Exec. .... Kelly Muchmore
Market Information: ADS; TMC.
Mechanical Available: Offset; Black and 3 ROP colors; insert accepted; page cutoffs - 21 1/2.
Mechanical Specifications: Type page 12 x 21 1/2; E - 6 cols, 1 7/8, 1/6 between; A - 6 cols, 1 7/8, 1/6 between; C - 9 cols, 1 3/8, 1/6 between.
Areas Served: Boone, Butler, Colfax, Merrick, Nance, Platte & Polk Counties (NE)
Equipment & Software: PRESSROOM EQUIPMENT: Lines — 9-HI/V-15A 1997; Folders — HI/JF 15.; MAILROOM EQUIPMENT: Counter Stackers — BG; Inserters & Stuffers — 6-KAN/480; Tying Machines — MLN/Spirit, Miller-Bevco/SS 901; Address Machine — KAN/600.; BUSINESS EQUIPMENT: DEC/VT 320, DEC/PC, Unix/Platform BUSINESS SOFTWARE: Vision Data CLASSIFIED EQUIPMENT: Hardware — APP/Mac, CText/fileserver; Printers — APP/Mac LaserPrinter, C.Itoh/Line Printer; CLASSIFIED SOFTWARE: Baseview. DISPLAY SOFTWARELayout Software — APP/Mac. EDITORIAL EQUIPMENT: Hardware — APP/Mac, Baseview/APP/Mac, Lf/AP Leaf Picture Desk; Printers — APP/Mac EDITORIAL SOFTWARE: Baseview. PRODUCTION EQUIPMENT: Hardware — Caere/OmniPage 5.0, AG/Accuset 1000, HP/LaserJet 4MV, Pre Press/Panther Pro Imagesetter 46 H/S;

Cameras — Photo Ace/250D, D, C/250; Scanners — AG/Arcus II PRODUCTION SOFTWARE: QPS/QuarkXPress 4.1.

FREMONT

FREMONT TRIBUNE
135 N Main St, Fremont, Neb., 68025-5673, Dodge; gen tel (402) 721-5000; adv tel (402) 941-1446; ed tel (402) 941-1433; gen fax (402) 721-8047; adv fax (402) 721-8047; ed fax (402) 721-8047; gen/nat adv e-mail julie.veskerna@lee.net; disp adv e-mail julie.veskerna@lee.net; ed e-mail fremont.newsroom@lee.net; web site www.fremonttribune.com
 - 1,000,000(views)
Group: Lee Enterprises, Inc.
Published: Mon, Tues, Wed, Thur, Fri, Sat
Weekday Frequency: e
Saturday Frequency: m
Circulation: 5,187; 5,373(sat)
Last Audit: AAM September 30, 2014
Advertising Rate (weekday/saturday): Open inch rate $16.75
Online Advertising Rate: Open rate $17.55
News services: AP, Lee National Sales Group. **Established:** 1868
Special Editions: Bridal Tab (Other).
Special Weekly Sections: Fremont Living (Fri); Church Page (Sat); Agricultural Day (Thur); Business Day (Tues).
Syndicated Publications: Relish (Monthly); USA WEEKEND Magazine (Sat); TV Week (Weekly).
Controller .... Amy Bill
Credit Mgr. .... Jessica Noel
Adv. Mgr. .... Vincent Laboy
Circ. Dir. .... Greg Pehrson
Exec. Ed. .... Tracy Buffington
News Ed. .... Tammy McKeighan
Sports Ed. .... Brent Wasenius
Prodn. Mgr. .... Janelle Prehal
Prodn. Mgr., Press .... Joe Gaver
News Ed. .... Tony Gray
Market Information: TMC.
Mechanical Available: Offset; Black and 3 ROP colors; insert accepted - coupon envelopes; page cutoffs - 22 3/4.
Mechanical Specifications: Type page 12 1/4 x 21 3/4; E - 6 cols, 1 7/8, 1/8 between; A - 6 cols, 1 7/8, 1/8 between; C - 9 cols, 1 1/4, 1/16 between.
Areas Served: Burt, Colfax, Cuming, Dodge, Douglas, Saunders and Washington countiesEquipment & Software: PRESSROOM EQUIPMENT: Lines — 4-HI/V-22-25; 6-HI/V22-25; Folders — 2-HI/2:1.; MAILROOM EQUIPMENT: Counter Stackers — 1/PPK; Tying Machines — 1-MLN/ML2EES; Address Machine — 2-Wm/3.; BUSINESS EQUIPMENT: 1-DEC/1144 CLASSIFIED EQUIPMENT: Hardware — APP/Mac; CLASSIFIED SOFTWARE: Baseview. DISPLAY SOFTWARELayout Software — APP/Mac. EDITORIAL EQUIPMENT: Hardware — Baseview, APP/Mac EDITORIAL SOFTWARE: Baseview. PRODUCTION EQUIPMENT: Hardware — Panther Pro/46, 1-LE/24BQ; Cameras — 1-C/Spartan III; Scanners — 2-Cp/Alpha.

GRAND ISLAND

THE GRAND ISLAND INDEPENDENT
422 W 1st St, Grand Island, Neb., 68801-5802, Hall; gen tel (308) 382-1000; adv tel (308) 382-1000; ed tel (308) 382-1000; gen fax (308) 381-9431; adv fax (308) 384-9362; ed fax (308) 381-9431; gen/nat adv e-mail patricia.bell@theindependent.com; disp adv e-mail kimberly.sweetser@theindependent.com; class adv e-mailpatricia.bell@theindependent.com ; ed e-mail newsdesk@theindependent.com; web site www.theindependent.com
Group: BH Media Group
Published: Mon, Tues, Wed, Thur, Fri, Sat, Sun
Weekday Frequency: m
Saturday Frequency: m
Circulation: 69,003; 6,117(sat); 91,321(sun)
Last Audit: AAM December 31, 2016
Advertising Rate (weekday/saturday): Open inch

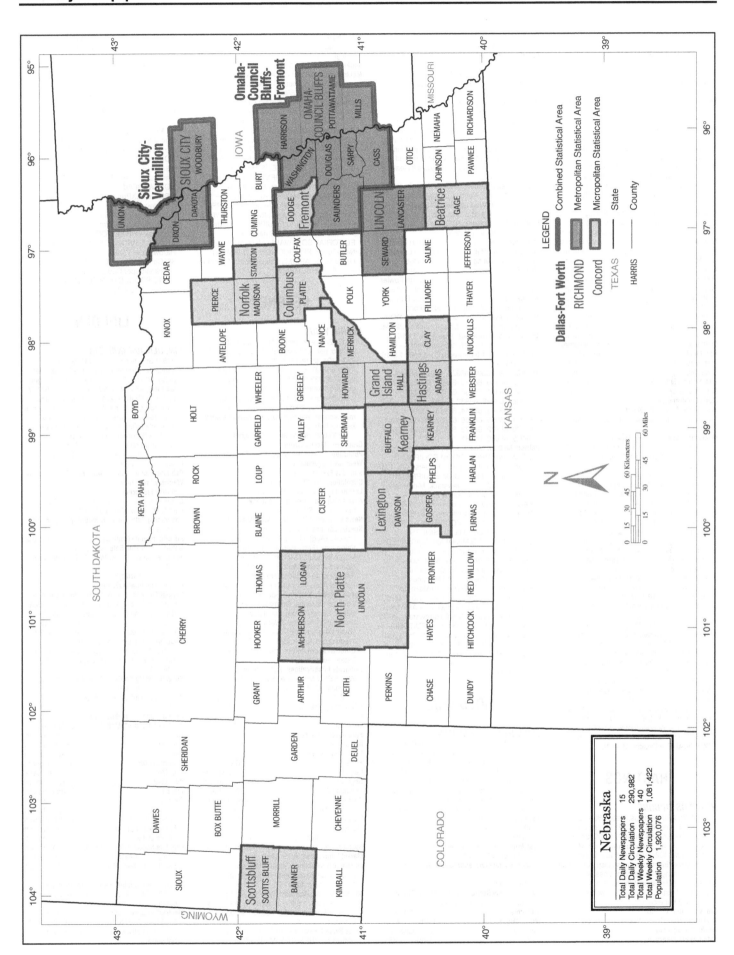

Nebraska

Total Daily Newspapers	15
Total Daily Circulation	290,982
Total Weekly Newspapers	140
Total Weekly Circulation	1,081,422
Population	1,920,076

LEGEND

Dallas-Fort Worth	Combined Statistical Area
RICHMOND	Metropolitan Statistical Area
Concord	Micropolitan Statistical Area
TEXAS	State
HARRIS	County

rate $26.50
Advertising Rate (sunday): Open inch rate $28.30
Online Advertising Rate: $120.00/per 10,000 impressions
News services: AP, SHNS.
Own Printing Facility?: Yes
Commercial Printers?: Yes
Special Editions: Back-to-School (Aug); Progress and Bridal (Jan); Cooking Show (March) Farm (Mar); Graduation (May); Home Improvement (Monthly); Nebraska State Fair (Aug.); Senior EXPO (Sept); Salute to Women (Oct); Farm (Sept).Christmas Opening (Nov);
Special Weekly Sections: Entertainment (Fri); Building Page (Mon); Weddings/ Engagements (S); Weekend Sports (Sat); Club Calendar (Thur); City Council (Tues); Lifelines (Wed).
Syndicated Publications: Relish (Monthly); TV Week (S); American Profile (Weekly).
Pub./Pres. ....Donald S. Smith
HR Mgr. ....Molly Holcher
Adv. Dir. ....Pat Bell
Adv. Mgr., Retail ....Kim Sweetser
Assoc. Ed. ....Pete Letheby
Mng. Ed. ....Jim Faddis
Prepress Prod. Supervisor ....Lora Ruzicka
Photo Ed. ....Barrett Stinson
Sports Ed. ....Bob Hamar
Women's Ed. ....Terri Hahn
Prodn. Dir., Opns. ....John Lilly
Circ. Dir. ....Pat Brown
Controller ....Jack Schiefelbein
New Media Dir. ....Carrie Colburn
Asst. Mng. Ed. ....RJ Post
Class. Mgr. ....Bill Parten
Web/Social Media Ed. ....Stephanie Romanski
Gen. Mgr. ....Terrie Baker
Market Information: TMC.
Mechanical Available: Offset; Black and 3 ROP colors; insert accepted - all; page cutoffs - 22 3/4.
Mechanical Specifications: Type page 10 1/2 x 21 1/2; E - 6 cols, 1 5/8, 1/8 between; A - 6 cols, 1 5/8, 1/8 between; C - 8 cols, 1 3/16, 1/8 between.
Areas Served: Central Nebraska
Delivery Method: Mail, Newsstand, Carrier, RacksEquipment & Software: PRESSROOM EQUIPMENT: Lines — 10-G/Urbanite double width; Press Drive — 2-Fin/100 h.p.; Folders — 1-G/2:1.; MAILROOM EQUIPMENT: Counter Stackers — 1-Id/440, 1-Id/Marathoner; Inserters & Stuffers — KM Rotary 14/Pocket; Tying Machines — 2-MLN/2A; Address Machine — 1-KAN/550.; BUSINESS EQUIPMENT: HP BUSINESS SOFTWARE: APT CLASSIFIED EQUIPMENT: Hardware — APP/Power HP; Printers — APP/Mac LaserWriter; CLASSIFIED SOFTWARE: APT DISPLAY EQUIPMENT: Hardware — 2-APP/Mac G3, 6-APP/Mac G4; Other Hardware — 3-APP/Mac Scanner, 3-Microtek DISPLAY SOFTWAREAd Make-up Applications — APT/ALS, Multi-Ad/Creator, QPS/ QuarkXPress, Adobe/Photoshop; Layout Software — Quadra 880, MEI/ALS. EDITORIAL EQUIPMENT: Hardware — APP/ Macs; Printers — APP/Mac LaserPrinters, V/Imagesetters, 2-Pre Press/Panther Pro EDITORIAL SOFTWARE: Baseview, QPS/ QuarkXPress. PRODUCTION EQUIPMENT: Hardware — Adobe/Photoshop 2.51, 1-Pre Press/Panther 36 PRODUCTION SOFTWARE: InDesign, Multi AD

HASTINGS

HASTINGS TRIBUNE

908 W 2nd St, Hastings, Neb., 68901-5063, Adams; gen tel (402) 462-2131; adv tel (402) 461-1242; ed tel (402) 462-2131; gen fax 402-461-4657; adv fax (402) 461-4657; ed fax (402) 462-2184; gen/nat adv e-mail legals@hastingstribune.com; disp adv e-mail class@hastingstribune.com; class adv e-mailclass@hastingstribune.com; ed e-mail apalser@hastingstribune.com; web site www.hastingstribune.com
Group: Seaton Group
Published: Mon, Tues, Wed, Thur, Fri, Sat
Weekday Frequency: e
Saturday Frequency: m
Circulation: 7,923; 7,923(sat)
Last Audit: CAC March 31, 2015
Advertising Rate (weekday/saturday): Open inch rate $14.30
Online Advertising Rate: Call to inquire
News services: AP, NEA, SHNS, TMS. **Established:** 1905
Own Printing Facility?: Yes
Commercial Printers?: No
Special Editions: Business Outlook (Feb.); Tax & Financial Planning (Feb.); Ag Outlook (March); Home & Garden (March); Parenting (March); Medical News (May); Bridal (June); Back To School (August); College Bound (September); Auto Guide (October); Health & Wellness (Dec.)
Special Weekly Sections: Reader Scrapbook Page (Monday); Food (Tuesday); Senior/ Health Page (Wednesday); NASCAR (Thursday); Agri/Biz (Saturday)
Syndicated Publications: Happenings (Sat); American Profile (Weekly).
Owner/President ....Donald R. Seaton
Bus. Mgr./Credit Mgr. ....Donald L. Kissler
Director of Marketing ....Deb Bunde
Mktg. Dir. ....Carla Carda
Pub ....Darran Fowler
Produ. Mgr. ....Scott Carstens
Webmaster ....Doug Edwards
Market Information: TMC; Zoned editions.
Mechanical Available: Offset; Black and 3 ROP colors; insert accepted; page cutoffs - 22 3/4.
Mechanical Specifications: Type page 11 1/2 x 21; E - 6 cols, 1 13/16, 1/8 between; A - 6 cols, 1 13/16, 1/8 between; C - 8 cols, 1 5/16, 1/8 between.
Areas Served: 68901, 68925, 68933, 68935, 68938, 68939, 68370, 68930, 68322, 68335, 68340, 68361, 68436, 68452, 68832, 688883, 68928, 68932, 68933, 68934, 68941, 68942, 68944, 68945, 68950, 68952, 68954, 68955, 68956, 68957, 68959, 68961, 68970, 68972, 68973, 68974, 68975, 68978, 68979, 68980, 68981
Delivery Method: Mail, Carrier, RacksEquipment & Software: PRESSROOM EQUIPMENT: Lines — 6-G/Urbanite 917; Folders — 1, 1-G/ Cole Quarter.; MAILROOM EQUIPMENT: Counter Stackers — Newstack, Mid America Graphics, KAN; Inserters & Stuffers — KAN/480; Tying Machines — MLN/MLEE, MLN/2A; Address Machine — Kan/600 Labeler.; BUSINESS EQUIPMENT: 9-IBM/ RISC 6000 (9 terminals) BUSINESS SOFTWARE: PBS/MediaPlus CLASSIFIED EQUIPMENT: Hardware — APP/Mac; Printers — APP/Mac LaserWriter 600, ECR/Scriptsetter II VR36; CLASSIFIED SOFTWARE: Baseview/Ad Manager Pro. DISPLAY SOFTWAREAd Make-up Applications — Multi-Ad/Creator 7.0.1, QPS/ QuarkXPress; Layout Software — APP/Mac. EDITORIAL EQUIPMENT: Hardware — APP/ Mac/APP/Mac, Epson/Scanner EDITORIAL SOFTWARE: Baseview/NewsEdit Pro 3.5.4, QPS/QuarkXPress 6.1. PRODUCTION EQUIPMENT: Scanners — Nikon/Coolscan PRODUCTION SOFTWARE: QPS/ QuarkXPress.

HOLDREGE

HOLDREGE DAILY CITIZEN

418 Garfield St, Holdrege, Neb., 68949-2219, Phelps; gen tel (308) 995-4441; adv tel (308) 995-4441; ed tel (308) 995-4441; gen fax (308) 995-5992; adv fax (308) 995-5992; ed fax (308) 995-5992; gen/nat adv e-mail holdregecitizenads@yahoo.com; disp adv e-mail holdregecitizenads@yahoo.com; class adv e-mailholdregecitizenads@yahoo.com
Published: Mon, Tues, Wed, Thur, Fri
Weekday Frequency: e
Circulation: 2,904
Last Audit: Sworn/Estimate/Non-Audited September 30, 2017
Advertising Rate (weekday/saturday): Open inch rate $8.25
News services: AP.
Special Weekly Sections: Farm (Mon); Church (Thur); Best Food Day (Wed).
Vice Pres. ....Ruth E. King
Mgr., Mktg./Promo. ....Barbara Penrod
Circ. Mgr. ....Julie Horn
Pub ....Robert D. King
Science Ed. ....Tunney Price
Prodn. Mgr. ....Daniel Jordan
Adv. Mgr. ....Linda Boyll
Market Information: TMC.
Mechanical Available: Offset; Black and 3 ROP colors; insert accepted - free-standing inserts; page cutoffs - 22 3/4.
Mechanical Specifications: Type page 13 1/4 x 21; E - 6 cols, 2, 1/6 between; A - 6 cols, 2, 1/6 between; C - 8 cols, 1 1/2, 1/6 between. Equipment & Software: PRESSROOM EQUIPMENT: Lines — 4-G/Community 1973.; MAILROOM EQUIPMENT: Tying Machines — Bu; Address Machine — Am.; CLASSIFIED EQUIPMENT: Hardware — Mk.; DISPLAY EQUIPMENT: Printers — APP/Mac LaserWriter IIf; DISPLAY SOFTWAREAd Make-up Applications — APP/Mac Scanner, Multi-Ad/Creator, APP/ Mac AppleTalk; Layout Software — APP/Mac Radius. EDITORIAL EQUIPMENT: Hardware — 5-Mk/Mk/1100 Plus (2 hard drives) EDITORIAL SOFTWARE: Mk/1100 Plus, Mk/ NewsTouch. PRODUCTION EQUIPMENT: Hardware — APP/Mac LaserWriter; Cameras — D, C/260, SCREEN.

KEARNEY

KEARNEY HUB

13 E 22nd St, Kearney, Neb., 68847-5404, Buffalo; gen tel (308) 237-2152; adv tel (308) 233-9701; ed tel (308) 237-2152; gen fax (308) 233-9736; adv fax (308) 233-9736; ed fax (308) 233-9745; gen/nat adv e-mail lori.guthard@kearneyhub.com; disp adv e-mail lori.guthard@kearneyhub.com; class adv e-mailjill.green@kearneyhub.com; ed e-mail mike.konz@kearneyhub.com; web site www.kearneyhub.com
- 1,500,000(views) 300,000(visitors)
Group: BH Media Group
Published: Mon, Tues, Wed, Thur, Fri, Sat
Weekday Frequency: e
Saturday Frequency: m
Circulation: 9,007; 9,928(sat)
Last Audit: CAC June 30, 2016
Advertising Rate (weekday/saturday): Open inch rate $20.80; $22.85 (Sat)
News services: AP, SHNS. **Established:** 1888
Special Editions: Home & Decor (Apr); Fair Results (Aug); Home & Decor (Dec); Valentines (Feb); Bridal (Jan); Prime Magazine (Jul); Discover Kearney (Jun); Home & Decor (Mar); Rodeo Nebraska (May); Home & Decor (Nov); Business Profiles (Oct); A Home of Your Own (Sept).
Special Weekly Sections: Sports, Public Record, Editorial Opinions, Comics, Markets (Daily); Senior Citizen (Mon); Lifestyles, Best Food Day (Tue); Lifestyles (Wed); Entertainment, Youth (Thur); Health, Cooking, Engagements, Weddings, Church, Business, Farm, Entertainment, Home Improvement, Real Estate, Auto (Sat)
Syndicated Publications: Relish (Monthly); USA WEEKEND Magazine (Sat); TV Plus (Thur); American Profile (Weekly).
Pres./Pub. ....Julie Speirs
Adv. Mgr., Sales ....Lori Guthard
Ed ....Stephen Chatelain
Educ. Ed ....Vicki Rice
Farm/Agriculture Ed. ....Lori Potter
Managing Ed. ....Michael Konz
Food/Women's Ed. ....Rick Brown
News Ed ....Dan Speirs
Regl. Ed. ....Amy Schweitzer
Regl. Ed. ....Tammy Skrdlant
Religion Ed. ....Carol Fettin
Sports Ed. ....Buck Mahoney
Audiotex Mgr. ....Dean Buse
Prodn. Mgr. ....Jerry Schmitz
Cathy Headlee
Prodn. Mgr., Distr. ....Ed Szymanski
Business Mgr. ....Robert Moncrief
Market Information: ADS; TMC.
Mechanical Available: Offset; Black and 3 ROP colors; insert accepted - min 5 x 7, max 11 x 12 1/2; page cutoffs - 22.
Mechanical Specifications: Type page 11 5/8 x 21; E - 6 cols, 1 5/6, 1/8 between; A - 6 cols, 1 5/6, 1/8 between; C - 9 cols, 1 9/50, 1/8 between.
Areas Served: Kearney (NB)Equipment & Software: PRESSROOM EQUIPMENT: Lines — 13-G/SSC single width (formers) 1990; Folders — 1-G/SSC; Registration System — Carlson/Ternis. MAILROOM EQUIPMENT: Counter Stackers — QWI/400W; Inserters & Stuffers — 1-KAN/480 7:1; Tying Machines — 1-MLN/ MLN2, 1-Dynamic/D2300; Address Machine — 1-KAN/600PS labeler.; BUSINESS EQUIPMENT: DEC/VAX II BUSINESS SOFTWARE: Microsoft/Office CLASSIFIED EQUIPMENT: Hardware — Dell, Intergraph; Printers — Pre Press/ Panther Pro Imagesetter; CLASSIFIED SOFTWARE: APT. DISPLAY EQUIPMENT: Hardware — PC; Printers — HP; Other Hardware — APP/Mac Scanner DISPLAY SOFTWAREAd Make-up Applications — QPS/QuarkXPress 4.0, Adobe/Photoshop 4.0; Layout Software — PC. EDITORIAL EQUIPMENT: Hardware — Dell, Intergraph/ Pre Press/Panther Pro Imagesetter; Printers — HP EDITORIAL SOFTWARE: APT 2.6.3. PRODUCTION EQUIPMENT: Hardware — V 4.03, Pre Press/Panther Pro 36; Cameras — 1-SCREEN/C 240; Scanners — Nikon/Super Coolscan, AG/Arcus II, HP/4C PRODUCTION SOFTWARE: QPS/ QuarkXPress 4.03.

LINCOLN

LINCOLN JOURNAL STAR

926 P St, Lincoln, Neb., 68508-3615, Lancaster; gen tel (402) 475-4200; adv tel (402) 473-7450; ed tel (402) 473-7306; gen fax (402) 473-7414; adv fax (402) 473-7177; ed fax (402) 473-7291; gen/nat adv e-mail advertising@journalstar.com; disp adv e-mail advertising@journalstar.com; class adv e-mailclassified@journalstar.com; ed e-mail citydesk@journalstar.com; web site www.journalstar.com
- 9,091,065(views) 1,204,163(visitors)
Group: Lee Enterprises, Inc.
Published: Mon, Tues, Wed, Thur, Fri, Sat, Sun
Weekday Frequency: m
Saturday Frequency: m
Circulation: 44,143; 41,405(sat); 51,405(sun)
Last Audit: AAM March 31, 2017
Advertising Rate (weekday/saturday): Open inch rate $69.51
Advertising Rate (sunday): Open inch rate $78.22
Online Advertising Rate: $10 CPM
News services: AP, LAT-WP, MCT. **Established:** 1867
Own Printing Facility?: Yes
Commercial Printers?: Yes
Special Editions: Lincoln Living (Apr); Ultimate Campus Guide (Aug); Last Minute Gift Ideas (Dec); Weddings (Jan); Salute to Lincoln Business (Jul); Lincoln Living (Jun); Girls Basketball (Mar); Lincoln Living (May); Gift Guide (Nov); Lincoln Living (Oct); Inside Football; Bridal Guide (Jan), Seniors/Prime Time (Feb, March, July, Sept); Medical Guide (March)
Special Weekly Sections: Entertainment Pages (Fri); Garden/Home (S);
Syndicated Publications: L Magazine; Star City Sports
Digital Platform - Mobile: Apple, Android
Digital Platform - Tablet: Apple iOS, Android
Ed ....Dave Bundy
Controller ....Linda Sackshewsky
Pub ....Ava Thomas
Operations Dir. ....Brady Svendgard
Pkg. Mgr. ....Matt Kasik
Bus. Editor ....Dick Piersol
City Ed. ....Todd Henrichs
Focus Ed. ....Patty Beutler
Asst. City Ed. ....Shelly Kulhanek
Editorial Page Ed. ....Gordon Winters
Entertainment Reporter ....L. Kent Wolgamott
Features Editor ....Jeff Korbelik
Families/Schools/Kids Reporter ....Erin Andersen
Farm/Agribus. Reporter ....Art Hovey
Market Information: ADS; Split run; TMC; Zoned editions.
Mechanical Available: Flexo (direct); Black and 3 ROP colors; insert accepted; page cutoffs - 22.
Mechanical Specifications: Type page 12 x 21; E - 6 cols, 2 1/16, 1/8 between; A - 6 cols, 2 1/16, 1/8 between; C - 9 cols, 1 5/16, 1/16 between.

Areas Served: Lancaster
Delivery Method: Mail, RacksEquipment & Software: PRESSROOM EQUIPMENT: Lines — 1-MAN/Roland Flexoman-S 2000; Folders — 2-MAN/Roland.; MAILROOM EQUIPMENT: Counter Stackers — 6/QWI; Inserters & Stuffers — 2-GMA/SLS 2000; Tying Machines — 4-Dynaric/NP-2; Control System — GMA/SAM; Address Machine — 2-Scitex/Ink Jet.; BUSINESS EQUIPMENT: 1-IBM/AS-400 BUSINESS SOFTWARE: Microsoft/Windows NT CLASSIFIED EQUIPMENT: Hardware — CText, 20-APP/ Mac Workstation; CLASSIFIED SOFTWARE: HI. DISPLAY SOFTWAREAd Make-up Applications — QPS/QuarkXPress.; EDITORIAL EQUIPMENT: Hardware — 12-PC 486, HI/Newsmaker EDITORIAL SOFTWARE: Microsoft/Excel, HI. PRODUCTION EQUIPMENT: Hardware — 2-AU/APS-6, 2-LE/LD2600A; Cameras — 2-C/Spartan II; Scanners — Howtek, Nikon PRODUCTION SOFTWARE: HI, QPS/ QuarkXPress.

MC COOK

MCCOOK DAILY GAZETTE

W First & E Sts, Mc Cook, Neb., 69001, Red Willow; gen tel (308) 345-4500; adv tel (308) 345-4500 ext. 101; ed tel (308) 345-4500 ext. 120; gen fax (308) 345-7881; adv fax (308) 345-7881; ed fax (308) 345-7881 ; gen/nat adv e-mail adsales5@mccookgazette.com; disp adv e-mail adsales5@mccokgazette.com; class adv e-mailclassifieds@mccookgazette.com; ed e-mail editor@mccookgazette.com; web site www.mccookgazette.com - 363,000(views) 49,000(visitors)
Group: Rust Communications
Published: Mon, Tues, Wed, Thur, Fri
Weekday Frequency: e
Circulation: 5,100
Last Audit: Sworn/Estimate/Non-Audited September 30, 2017
Advertising Rate (weekday/saturday): Open inch rate $10.75
Online Advertising Rate: $260.00/mo. (for 2000 impressions)
News services: AP. **Established:** 1911
Own Printing Facility?: Yes
Special Weekly Sections: TV Week (Fri); Farm (Thur); Grocery (Tues).
Syndicated Publications: Relish (Monthly); American Profile (Weekly).
Pub. .... Sharyn Skiles
Circ. Mgr. .... Marybeth Roschewski
Regional Ed .... Connie Jo Discoe
Sports Ed. .... Steve Kodov
Ed. .... Bruce Crosby
Press Foreman .... Dave Mefford
Prodn. Mgr., Pre Press .... Lloyd Shields
Bus. Mgr. .... Brenda Gillen
Assoc. Ed. .... Jeremy Blomstedt
Market Information: ADS.
Mechanical Available: Offset; Black and 3 ROP colors; insert accepted; page cutoffs - 22 3/4.
Mechanical Specifications: Type page 13 x 21 1/2; E - 6 cols, 2, 1/8 between; A - 6 cols, 2, 1/8 between; C - 6 cols, 2, 1/8 between.
Areas Served: 69001
Delivery Method: Mail, Newsstand, Carrier, RacksEquipment & Software: PRESSROOM EQUIPMENT: Lines — 6-G/Suburban (2 Stacked units).; MAILROOM EQUIPMENT: Tying Machines — 2/Bu; Wrapping Singles — 8-/Sa; Address Machine — 1-LN/25 Auto Mecha.; BUSINESS EQUIPMENT: 3-IBM/PC, AT BUSINESS SOFTWARE: PBS CLASSIFIED EQUIPMENT: Hardware — 1-HI, 1-APP/Mac; 2-IBM; CLASSIFIED SOFTWARE: PBS EDITORIAL EQUIPMENT: Mac EDITORIAL SOFTWARE: QPS/QuarkXPress,

NORFOLK

NORFOLK DAILY NEWS

525 W Norfolk Ave, Norfolk, Neb., 68701-5236, Madison; gen tel (402) 371-1020; adv tel (402) 371-1020; ed tel (402) 371-1020; gen fax (402) 371-5802; adv fax (402) 371-5802; ed fax (402) 371-5802; gen/nat adv e-mail ads@norfolkdailynews.com; disp adv e-mail ads@norfolkdailynews.com; class adv e-maillmcgill@norfolkdailynews.com; ed e-mail editor@norfolkdailynews.com; web site www.norfolkdailynews.com - 1,400,000(views) 210,000(visitors)
Published: Mon, Tues, Wed, Thur, Fri, Sat
Weekday Frequency: e
Saturday Frequency: e
Circulation: 12,396; 12,396(sat)
Last Audit: AAM March 31, 2016
Advertising Rate (weekday/saturday): Open inch rate $21.00
Online Advertising Rate: $19.75 PCI
News services: AP, SHNS. **Established:** 1887
Special Editions: Agriculture (Apr); Back-to-School (Aug); Christmas Greetings (Dec); Insight (Progress) (Feb); All About Norfolk (Jul); Spring Car Care (Mar); Car Care (Nov); Restaurant (Oct).
Special Weekly Sections: TV Tab (Fri); Farm Pages (Thur); Youth Pages (Tues); Food Pages (Wed).
Syndicated Publications: USA WEEKEND Magazine (Sat).
Pres./Pub. .... Jerry Huse
Gen. Mgr. .... Les Mann
Bus. Mgr. .... Deb Warneke
Circ. Mgr. .... Cristina Anderson
Ed. .... Kent Warneke
City Ed. .... Grace Petersen
Farm Ed. .... Mary Pat Finn-Hoag
Regl. Ed. .... Greg Wees
Sports Ed. .... Jay Prauner
Prodn. Mgr. .... Mike Jones
Prodn. Foreman, Pressroom .... Jeff Jones
Prodn. Foreman, Mailroom .... Jason Feddern
Adv. Dir. .... Vickie Hrabanek
Retail Mgr. .... Pam Zoucha
E-Media Sales Mgr. .... Sarah Noel
Reg. Ed. .... Jerry Guenther
News Ed. .... Tim Pearson
Asst. Sports Ed. .... Tom Behmer
Asst. Sports Ed. .... Nick Benes
Agriculture/Youth Ed. .... Mary Hoag
Ed. Asst. .... Ashley Fortkamp
Living Page Ed. .... Sheryl Schmeckpeper
Photo Mgr./Online Ed. .... Dennis Meyer
Photo Chief .... Darin Epperly
News Ed. .... Isaiah May
Gatekeeper/News Ed. .... Chris Avery
Prod. Mgr. .... Tyler Eisenbraun
Systems Mgr. .... Matt Petersen
Online News Ed. .... Kathryn Harris
Market Information: TMC.
Mechanical Available: Offset; Black and 3 ROP colors; insert accepted; page cutoffs - 22 3/4.
Mechanical Specifications: Type page 11 3/4 x 21 1/2; E - 6 cols, 1 13/16, 1/8 between; A - 6 cols, 1 13/16, 1/8 between; C - 8 cols, 1 5/16, 1/8 between.
Areas Served: Madison CountyEquipment & Software: PRESSROOM EQUIPMENT: Lines — 8-G/Urbanite 1972; Control System — 1972; MAILROOM EQUIPMENT: Counter Stackers — 1-Id, 1/Quipp; Inserters & Stuffers — KAN/5:1, MM/4:1; Tying Machines — 2-/Bu, 1-MLN/2A, 1-/Strapack; Address Machine — 1-/KAN.; BUSINESS EQUIPMENT: IBM/AS400, Gateway/Pentium, HP/Pentium CLASSIFIED EQUIPMENT: Hardware — 5-Baseview; Xante/8300 11x17; Printers — Okidata/Pacemark 3410, APP/ Mac LaserWriter Pro 630; CLASSIFIED SOFTWARE: Baseview/Ad Manager Pro. DISPLAY EQUIPMENT: Hardware — PC, 2-APP/Power Mac 7100, 2-APP/Mac Quadra; Printers — Printware/1217, APP/ Mac LaserWriter Pro 630, Pre Press/Panther Imagesetter; Other Hardware — Microtek/ MSII fl DISPLAY SOFTWAREAd Make-up Applications — Dewar, Adobe/Photoshop, Aldus/PageMaker, QPS/QuarkXPress, Multi-Ad; EDITORIAL EQUIPMENT: Hardware — Dewar/Sys IV, APP/Mac II C, 8-Baseview; Printers — Panasonic/1093, Xante/8300 11x17 EDITORIAL SOFTWARE: Dewar, Novell 3.11, Baseview/NewsEdit Pro IQUE, QPS/QuarkXPress 3.32. PRODUCTION EQUIPMENT: Hardware — Caere/ OmniPage, Pre Press/7220, Prepress/ Panther Plus 46; Cameras — 1-DAI/Vertical, 1-DAI/Horizontal; Scanners — AG/Argus II Scanner PRODUCTION SOFTWARE: Baseview/NewsEdit Pro IQ, QPS/ QuarkXPress 3.32.

NORTH PLATTE

THE NORTH PLATTE TELEGRAPH

621 N Chestnut St, North Platte, Neb., 69101-4131, Lincoln; gen tel (308) 532-6000; adv tel (308) 532-6000; ed tel (308) 532-6000; gen fax (308) 532-9268; adv fax (308) 532-9268; ed fax (308) 532-9268; gen/nat adv e-mail cal.petersen@nptelegraph.com; disp adv e-mail advertising@nptelegraph.com; class adv e-mailadvertising@nptelegraph.com; ed e-mail editor@nptelegraph.com; web site www.nptelegraph.com
Group: BH Media Group
Published: Tues, Wed, Thur, Fri, Sat, Sun
Weekday Frequency: m
Saturday Frequency: m
Circulation: 7,880; 7,880(sat); 7,976(sun)
Last Audit: CAC June 30, 2016
Advertising Rate (weekday/saturday): Open inch rate $14.93
Advertising Rate (sunday): Open inch rate $14.68
Online Advertising Rate: Call to inquire.
News services: AP. **Established:** 1881
Special Editions: Real Estate Guide (Monthly).
Special Weekly Sections: TV Week (S).
Syndicated Publications: Relish (Monthly); Parade (S); American Profile (Weekly).
Bus. Mgr. .... Holli Synder
Dir., Sales (NPC) .... Dee Klein
Circ. Dir. .... Joe Volcek
News Ed. .... Sage Merritt
Prodn. Mgr. .... John Bates
Sports Ed. .... Andrew Bottrell
Asst. Mng. Ed. .... Deb Egenberger
Copy Ed. .... Aly Rinehart
Copy Ed. .... Mikayla Wiseman
Dist. Mgr., Circ. .... Claudia Cable
Dist. Mgr., Circ. .... Peg Kruger
Prod. Mgr. .... Rob Hampton
Pub. .... Terrie Baker
Managing Ed. .... Joan Von Kampen
Market Information: ADS; TMC.
Mechanical Available: Offset; Black and 3 ROP colors; insert accepted - others, contact for specs; page cutoffs - 22 3/4.
Mechanical Specifications: Type page 11 63/100 x 21 3/4; E - 6 cols, 1 5/6, 1/8 between; A - 6 cols, 1 5/6, 1/8 between; C - 9 cols, 1 5/6, 1/16 between.
Areas Served: North Platte (NE) Equipment & Software: PRESSROOM EQUIPMENT: Lines — 9-HI/V-22 1965.; MAILROOM EQUIPMENT: Counter Stackers — TMSI; Inserters & Stuffers — 24-HI/6; Tying Machines — MLN/MLEE; Address Machine — Miller/Bevco/1 up Labeler.; BUSINESS EQUIPMENT: Gateway, 8-Gateway/PS-100, 6-E/3200 CLASSIFIED EQUIPMENT: Hardware — 2-Gateway/GP6-350, 1-Gateway/GP6-333; 1-Epson/Perfection 1200u Flatbed Scanner; Printers — 6-HP; CLASSIFIED SOFTWARE: ACT. DISPLAY EQUIPMENT: Hardware — 1-Gateway/ GP6-400 with 21 monitor, 2-Gateway/P-500 with 21 monitor, 2-Dell/800; Printers — HP/Si Mx; Other Hardware — 4-Epson/ Perfection 1200u, Flatbed/Scanner DISPLAY SOFTWAREAd Make-up Applications — DPS/AdTracker, QPS/QuarkXPress 4.11; Layout Software — DPS/AdTracker. EDITORIAL EQUIPMENT: Hardware — 4-Gateway/GP6-400, 2-Gateway/GP6-500/ Umax/Mirage IIse, Microsoft/Windows NT Server, 1-Kk/RFS 2035 Plus Film Scanner, 1-Epson/Perfection 1200u; Printers — HP/ SI Mx EDITORIAL SOFTWARE: Dewar/ View 2.0, Dewar, QPS/QuarkXPress 4.04. PRODUCTION EQUIPMENT: Hardware — Text Bridge/Pro98; Cameras — Acti/225; Scanners — Umax/Mirage IIse.

OMAHA

OMAHA WORLD-HERALD

1314 Douglas St, Ste 1500, Omaha, Neb., 68102-1848, Douglas; gen tel (402) 444-1000; adv tel (402) 444-1420; ed tel (402) 444-1304; gen fax (402) 444-1231; adv fax (402) 444-1299; ed fax (402) 444-1231; gen/nat adv e-mail phil.taylor@owh.com; disp adv e-mail brett.snead@owh.com; class adv e-maildebbie.mcchesney@owh.com; ed e-mail news@owh.com; web site www.omaha.com - 17,000,000(views) 2,417,167(visitors)
Group: BH Media Group
Published: Mon, Tues, Wed, Thur, Fri, Sat, Sun
Weekday Frequency: m
Saturday Frequency: m
Circulation: 101,287; 98,564(sat); 123,805(sun)
Last Audit: AAM December 31, 2016
Advertising Rate (weekday/saturday): Open inch rate $177.00
Advertising Rate (sunday): Open inch rate $222.00
News services: AP, Washington Post News Service with Bloomberg, Tribune News Service (formerly MCT) **Established:** 1885
Own Printing Facility?: Yes
Commercial Printers?: Yes
Special Editions: Auto Show
Outlook
Kids Camp
ACEC Engineers
Colon Cancer
Auction Block
Omaha's Choice Awards (ballot)
NCAA Basketball Preview + Sports wraps
Better Business Bureau
Worship – Easter
Lawn, Garden & Home (Saturday Living)
Omaha Chamber – Business Hall of Fame
Golf Wrap (Sports)
Spring Outdoors (Sports)
Small Business Week (pop-out)
Spring & Summer Travel/RV Lifestyle
Berkshire Hathaway
Best Places to Work
World-Herald Scholars
Parenting by Momaha
Super Go! Summer Events & Attractions
Go! Taste of Omaha
College World Series + Sports wraps
Omaha's Choice Awards (winners)
Football Preview – High School
Football Preview – College
Metro Guide
Septemberfest (pop-out)
Arts Preview
Fall Hunting (Sports)
Aksarben Coronation
We Don't Coast – Omaha Chamber
Automotive Year Review
Architecture
Basketball Preview – College
Smart Energy Talks
The Holiday Book
Small Business Saturday (pop-out)
Worship – Holiday
Welcome Visitors (quarterly)
College & Careers (spring & fall)
Parade of Homes
Special Weekly Sections: Food Express (Wednesday), GO! Entertainment (Thursday), Home Guide (Friday), Autos (Saturday), HOMES (Sunday)
Syndicated Publications: Parade (Sunday)
Proprietary Publications: Inspired Living (every other month), Wedding Essentials (quarterly), Momaha (monthly), Live Well (monthly)
Digital Platform - Mobile: Apple, Android, Windows
Digital Platform - Tablet: Apple iOS, Android, Kindle, Kindle Fire
Pres. & CEO, Pub. .... Terry J. Kroeger
Dir., Digital Development .... Jeff Carney
Dir., Production .... Kristy Gerry
CFO/Sr. Vice Pres. .... Duane Polodna
Sr. VP/Gen. Counsel .... Scott Searl
Exec VP .... Doug Hiemstra
Finance Dir./Controller .... Mike Kirk
Chief Revenue Officer .... Thom Kastrup
Director of Local Sales .... Brett Snead
Adv. Mgr., Custom Publishing/Events .. Tam Webb
Classified Employment Manager .. Aaron Consalvi
Director of Classified Advertising Deb McChesney
Mgr., Suburban Newspapers .... Paul Swanson
VP of Advertising .... Keely Byars
Dir Community Relations .... Susan Violi
Executive Editor .... Melissa Matczak
General Manager .... Phil Taylor
Market Information: ADS; Split run; TMC.
Mechanical Available: Offset; Black and 3 ROP colors; inserts accepted - product samples, single sheet fliers; page cutoffs - 22.047".
Mechanical Specifications: Type page 10.0833" x 21.075";
E - 6 cols, 1.54", .1667" between;
A - 6 cols, 1.54", .1667" between;
C - 6 cols, 1.54", .1667" between.

Areas Served: 50020, 50022, 50025, 50076, 50801, 50833, 50841, 50848, 50849, 50851, 50853, 50864, 51034, 51040, 51063, 51104, 51105, 5110651401, 51430, 51442, 51445, 51446, 51454, 51455, 51461, 51463, 51465, 51467, 51501, 51503, 51510, 51521, 51525, 51526, 51527, 51528, 51529, 51530, 51531, 51532, 51533, 51534, 51535, 51536, 51537, 51540, 51541, 51542, 51544, 51545, 51546, 51548, 51549, 51551, 51553, 51555, 51556, 51557, 51559, 51560, 51561, 51562, 51563, 51564,51565, 51566, 51570, 51571, 51573, 51575, 51576, 51577, 51579, 51601, 51631, 51632, 51638, 51639, 51640, 51646, 51649, 51650, 51652, 51653, 51654, 64446, 64482, 68002, 68003, 68004, 68005, 68007, 68008, 68010, 68015, 68016, 68017, 68018, 68019, 68020, 68022, 68023, 68025,68028, 68029, 68031, 68033, 68034, 68036, 68037, 68038, 68041, 68044, 68045, 68046, 68047, 68048, 68050, 68055, 68057, 68058, 68059, 68061, 68063, 68064, 68065, 68066, 68067, 68068, 68069, 68070, 68071, 68072, 68073,68102, 68104, 68105, 68106, 68107, 68108, 68110, 68111, 68112, 68113, 68114, 68116, 68117, 68118, 68122, 68123, 68124, 68127, 68128, 68130, 68131, 68132, 68133, 68134, 68135, 68136, 68137, 68138, 68142, 68144, 68147, 68154, 68157, 68164, 68183, 69198, 68305, 68310, 68320, 68333, 68337, 68347, 68349, 68352, 68355, 68359, 68361, 68366, 68370, 68371, 68376, 68378, 68405, 68407, 68409, 68410, 68413, 68420, 68421, 68434, 68442, 68446, 68447, 68448, 68450, 68455, 68456, 68463, 68465, 68466, 68467, 68501, 68502, 68503, 68504, 68505, 68506, 68507, 68508, 68509, 68510, 68512, 68516, 68520, 68521, 68522, 68524, 68526, 68528, 68542, 68601, 68620, 68621, 68624, 68626, 68627, 68629, 68632, 68633, 68634, 68636, 68638, 68640, 68641, 68642, 68643, 68644, 68647, 68648, 68649, 68651, 68652, 68653, 68654, 68658, 68660, 68661, 68662, 68663, 68664, 68665, 68666, 68669, 68701, 68714, 68715, 68716, 68720, 68726, 68731, 68733, 68739, 68745, 68748, 68756, 68757, 68758, 68764, 68765, 68767, 68768, 68769, 68770, 68771, 68774, 68776, 68779, 68780, 68781, 68784, 68787, 68788, 68790, 68791, 68801, 68803, 68818, 68824, 68826, 68836, 68840, 68845, 68847, 68866, 68869, 68873, 68876, 68883, 68901, 68924, 68927, 68933, 68944, 68949, 68955, 68956, 68959, 68961, 68978, 68982, 69101

Delivery Method: Mail, Newsstand, Carrier, RacksEquipment & Software: PRESSROOM EQUIPMENT: Lines — Man/Geoman 3/8 Shaftless; 1-Line/18 Towers; 15 4/1 Towers; 3 4/4 Towers; Folders — 3, 1; Pasters —Man/ AuroPrep; Reels & Stands — 18; Control System — Man/PPM-PECOM; MAILROOM EQUIPMENT: Counter Stackers — 16-Quipp; Inserters & Stuffers — 2-HI/632, 1-HI/632; Wrapping Singles — 14-Quipp/3/4 Viper; Control System — Burt, GE; Address Machine — 2-Barstrom/In-Line Labeler; BUSINESS EQUIPMENT: Dell PE710. VMware BUSINESS SOFTWARE: Circ 2000, Mactive, Oracle Financials CLASSIFIED EQUIPMENT: Hardware — Dell PE710. VMware; CLASSIFIED SOFTWARE: AdbaseE, Mactive, OPI, Xpance DISPLAY EQUIPMENT: Printers — 2-MON/ ProofExpress; DISPLAY SOFTWARELayout Software — PPI/Planfag. EDITORIAL EQUIPMENT: Hardware — Dell PE710. VMware/Saxotech CMS / Online PRODUCTION EQUIPMENT: Hardware — 2-Agfa/Advantage CLS, 2-K&F VIPB-27 Vision Benders,2-G&J VSP-85S Plate Processors PRODUCTION SOFTWARE: AGFA Newsdrive, PPI PlanPag, PPI Pilot

SCOTTSBLUFF

STAR-HERALD

1405 Broadway, Scottsbluff, Neb., 69361-3151, Scotts Bluff; gen tel (308) 632-9000; adv tel (308) 632-9020; ed tel (308) 632-9040; gen fax (308) 632-9001; adv fax (308) 632-9001; ed fax (308) 632-9003; gen/nat adv e-mail starherald@starherald.com; disp adv e-mail doug.southard@starherald.com; class adv e-mailclass@starherald.com; ed e-mail news@starherald.com; web site www.

starherald.com
Group: BH Media Group
Published: Tues, Wed, Thur, Fri, Sat, Sun
Weekday Frequency: m
Saturday Frequency: m
Circulation: 9,418; 9,418(sat); 9,824(sun)
Last Audit: CAC June 30, 2016
Advertising Rate (weekday/saturday): Open inch rate $20.10
Advertising Rate (sunday): Open inch rate $16.50
Online Advertising Rate: $10.00/pci
News services: AP. **Established:** 1912
Special Weekly Sections: Farm & Ranch (S); TV Week (Sat); Motor News (Wed).
Syndicated Publications: Entertainment (Fri); Parade (S); Church & Religious (Sat); Health & Science (Thur); Business News (Tues); Best Food Day (Wed); American Profile (Weekly).
Dir., Bus./Personnel Servs. .... Debbie Flowers
Adv. Dir. .... Doug Southard
Ed. ....Steve Frederick
Sports Ed. ....Jeff Fielder
Online Mgr. .... Jim Mortimore
Gen. Mgr. ....Roger Tollefson
Prodn. Mgr., Distr. ....Richard Knott
Mktg. & Dig. Med. Mgr. .... Kelly Zwetzig
New Med. Dir. .... Maunette Loeks
Market Information: ADS; TMC.
Mechanical Available: Offset; Black and 3 ROP colors; insert accepted - quarter fold, coupon books, alternate delivery; page cutoffs - 21 3/4.
Mechanical Specifications: Type page 10 1/4 x 21 1/2; E - 6 cols, 1 1/2, 1/12 between; A - 6 cols, 1 1/2, 1/12 between; C - 8 cols, 1 3/8, 1/12 between.Equipment & Software: PRESSROOM EQUIPMENT: Lines — 6-HI/845 1972; 4-G/Community 1968 1997; Press Drive — Haley/Control PCL; Folders — HI/Cotrell; Control System — MHI/PLC.; MAILROOM EQUIPMENT: Counter Stackers — 1-BG/107, 1-HL/Monitor, 1-BG/108; Inserters & Stuffers — 1-HI/624P; Tying Machines — 2-MLN/ML2EE, 1/MLN Sorter-Tyer; Address Machine — 1-KR/215.; BUSINESS EQUIPMENT: Gateways BUSINESS SOFTWARE: Archetype/ Corel Draw, Microsoft/Works, Microsoft/ Windows CLASSIFIED EQUIPMENT: Hardware — GraphX; Printers — Okidata; CLASSIFIED SOFTWARE: GraphX/1.6 Ad taker. DISPLAY EQUIPMENT: Hardware — IBM/Windows base; Printers — Okidata, HP/Laser Color; DISPLAY SOFTWAREAd Make-up Applications — Archetype/Corel Draw, Adobe/Photoshop, QPS/QuarkXPress; Layout Software — CNI/Ad-tracker, QPS/ QuarkXPress. EDITORIAL EQUIPMENT: Hardware — Dewar/Disc Net, Nar/(Windows base)/Lf/AP Leaf Picture Desk (receiver only); Printers — Okidata, HP/5S1 EDITORIAL SOFTWARE: Dewar/Disc Net, Adobe/ Photoshop. PRODUCTION EQUIPMENT: Hardware — Text/Bridge, LaserMaster/ Type, Nat, XIT/HP5 XITron; Cameras — Kk/ Image Maker, 1-Acti/SSII; Scanners — Nikon/ Neg, Microtek/Flatbed, Umax, HP, Kk/RFS PRODUCTION SOFTWARE: Dewar/View.

YORK

YORK NEWS-TIMES

327 N Platte Ave, York, Neb., 68467-3547, York; gen tel (402) 362-4478; adv tel (402) 362-4478; ed tel (402) 362-4478; gen fax (402) 362-6748; adv fax (402) 362-6748; ed fax (402) 362-6748; gen/nat adv e-mail kathy. larson@yorknewstimes.com; disp adv e-mail garrett.schwarz@yorknewstimes.com; class adv e-mailcheri.knoell@yorknewstimes.com; ed e-mail steve.moseley@ yorknewstimes. com; web site www.yorknewstimes.com
Group: BH Media Group
Published: Tues, Wed, Thur, Fri, Sat
Weekday Frequency: m
Saturday Frequency: m
Circulation: 3,589; 3,589(sat)
Last Audit: Sworn/Estimate/Non-Audited September 30, 2017
Advertising Rate (weekday/saturday): Open inch rate $13.90
Online Advertising Rate: Banner: $199/mo.
News services: AP. **Established:** 1867
Own Printing Facility?: Yes

Commercial Printers?: No
Special Weekly Sections: Church Directory/ Religion Page (Fri); Regional News (Mon); Prime Time TV Tab (Thur); Best Food Day (Tues); Senior Citizens (Wed).
Syndicated Publications: Relish (Monthly); USA WEEKEND Magazine (Sat).
Digital Platform - Mobile: Android, Windows
Digital Platform - Tablet: Android, Windows 7, Blackberry Tablet OS, Kindle Fire
Adv. Sales Mgr. .... Kathy Larson
Ed. .... Steve Moseley
Online Ed. ....Eric Eckert
Sports Ed. ....Ken Kush
Copy Ed./Layout/Obits. .... Kerri Pankratz
Copy Ed./Layout .... Caitlyn Parker
Pub. .... Carrie Colburn
Market Information: TMC.
Mechanical Available: Offset; Black and 3 ROP colors; insert accepted; page cutoffs - 22 3/4.
Mechanical Specifications: Type page 13 x 21; E - 6 cols, 2 1/12, 1/8 between; A - 6 cols, 2 1/12, 1/8 between; C - 6 cols, 2 1/12, 1/8 between.
Areas Served: 68467, 68460,48456,68666,6843 4,68436,68654,68651,68406,68401,68371,6 8843,68367,68365,68361,68359,68354,6835 1,68330,68319,68316,68313,
Delivery Method: Mail, Newsstand, Carrier, RacksEquipment & Software: BUSINESS SOFTWARE: SMS CLASSIFIED SOFTWARE: APT DISPLAY EQUIPMENT: Hardware — APP/Power Mac 7200, APP/ Power Mac 7300; Printers — APP/Mac LaserWriter Pro 630, HP/LaserJet 5M; DISPLAY SOFTWARELayout Software — Quark, INDesign

---

NEVADA

CARSON CITY

NEVADA APPEAL

580 Mallory Way, Carson City, Nev., 89701-5360, Carson City; gen tel (775) 882-2111; adv tel (775) 881-7653; ed tel (775) 882-2111; gen fax (775) 887-2420; adv fax (775) 887-2420; ed fax (775) 887-2420; gen/nat adv e-mail mraher@sierranevadamedia.com; disp adv e-mail jtreece@sierranevadamedia. com; class adv e-mailclassifieds@ sierranevadamedia.com; ed e-mail editor@ nevadaappeal.com; web site www. nevadaappeal.com
- 343,840(views) 169,592(visitors)
Group: Swift Communications, Inc.
Published: Tues, Wed, Thur, Fri, Sat, Sun
Weekday Frequency: m
Saturday Frequency: m
Circulation: 8,079; 8,079(sat); 8,924(sun)
Last Audit: CAC December 31, 2015
Advertising Rate (weekday/saturday): Open inch rate 1/32 page: $79; Business Card: $93; 1/16 page: $145
Advertising Rate (sunday): Open inch rate 1/32 page: $92; Business Card: $108; 1/16 page: $170
Online Advertising Rate: $12 cpm, $14.40 cpm, $16.80 cpm
News services: AP. **Established:** 1865
Own Printing Facility?: Yes
Commercial Printers?: Yes
Special Editions: Deadline Home Improvement (Apr); Deadline Primary Election (Aug); Last Minute Appeal Bonus (Dec); Deadline Customer Appreciation Appeal (Jul); Deadline Father's Day Bonus (Jun); Carson Country (Mar); Deadline Mother's Day Bonus (May); Thanksgiving Gift (N
Special Weekly Sections: Real Estate (Fri); TV Log (S); On the Road (Sat); Food (Wed).
Syndicated Publications: Sierra Magazine/ Seniors (Monthly); TV Mag (S); American Profile (Weekly).
Pub. .... Mark Raymond
Cir. Dir. .... Keith Sampson
Class. Adv. Mgr. .... Alsy Brinkmeyer
Ed. .... Adam Trumble
Bus. Dev. Mgr. .... Jenny Treece
Gen. Mgr. .... Brooke Warner

Dir. of Sales .... Michael Raher
Market Information: TMC; Zoned editions.
Mechanical Available: Offset; Black and 3 ROP colors; insert accepted - single sheets; page cutoffs - 22 3/4.
Mechanical Specifications: Type page 12 4/5 x 21 1/2; E - 6 cols, 2, 1/6 between; A - 6 cols, 2, 1/6 between; C - 9 cols, 1 1/3, 1/6 between.
Areas Served: 89403, 89410, 89423, 89429, 89447, 89701, 89703, 89704, 89705, 89706
Delivery Method: Mail, Newsstand, Carrier, RacksEquipment & Software: PRESSROOM EQUIPMENT: Lines — 16-G/Community single width 1996; Folders — 2-G/2:1.; MAILROOM EQUIPMENT: Counter Stackers — 2/QWI 200; Inserters & Stuffers — 1372-/ Valley Remanufacturing; Tying Machines — 2-Dynaric/NP3; Control System — Prism System.; BUSINESS EQUIPMENT: 2-IBM/PC, Link/MC5 Business ET960 CLASSIFIED EQUIPMENT: Hardware — 8-APP/Mac.; DISPLAY EQUIPMENT: Hardware — APP/Mac; Printers — APP/ Mac LaserWriter II NTX, APP/Mac Color Printer; DISPLAY SOFTWAREAd Make-up Applications — QPS/QuarkXPress 4.0, Freehand, Adobe/Illustrator, Adobe/ Acrobat, Adobe/Photoshop; Layout Software — 6-APP/Mac. EDITORIAL EQUIPMENT: Hardware — 20-APP/Mac. PRODUCTION EQUIPMENT: Hardware — 1-Amerigraph/ Magnum, 2-Graham/Subtractive; Cameras — 1-Hx/150B; Scanners — 1-Hx/150B, 1-CK Optical PRODUCTION SOFTWARE: QPS/ QuarkXPress 4.0.

ELKO

ELKO DAILY FREE PRESS

3720 E Idaho St, Elko, Nev., 89801-4611, Elko; gen tel (775) 738-3118; gen fax (775) 738-3131; adv fax (775) 738-2215; ed fax (775) 778-3131; gen/nat adv e-mail advertising@elkodaily.com; disp adv e-mail advertising@elkodaily.com; class adv e-mailclassified@elkodaily.com; ed e-mail editor@elkodaily.com; web site www. elkodaily.com
- 1,000,000(views) 7,900(visitors)
Group: Lee Enterprises, Inc.
Published: Mon, Tues, Wed, Thur, Fri, Sat
Weekday Frequency: m
Saturday Frequency: m
Circulation: 4,983; 4,983(sat); 5,122(sun)
Last Audit: CAC September 30, 2014
Advertising Rate (weekday/saturday): Open inch rate $15.30
News services: AP, TMS. **Established:** 1883
Own Printing Facility?: No
Commercial Printers?: Yes
Special Editions: Mining Quarterly (March, June, September, December); Fall Sports Preview (Aug); Christmas Gift Guide (Dec); Cowboy Poetry Gathering (Jan) Mining Expo (Jun); Newspapers in Education (Mar);
Special Weekly Sections: Entertainment (Fri); Society/Events/Business (Sat); Best Food Day (Tues).
Syndicated Publications: PARADE Magazine (Sat).
Digital Platform - Mobile: Apple
Pub. ....Travis Quast
Ed. .... Jeff Mullens
Adv. Dir. .... Nancy Streets
Cir. ....Robert Cooper
Market Information: TMC.
Mechanical Available: Offset; Black and 3 ROP colors; insert accepted; page cutoffs - 22 3/4.
Mechanical Specifications: Type page 10 x 21 1/2; E - 6 cols, 1.574", 1/8 between; A - 6 cols, 1.574, 1/8 between; C - 6 cols, 1.574", 1/8 between.
Areas Served: all of Elko countyEquipment & Software: PRESSROOM EQUIPMENT: Lines — 7-KP/News King (single); Folders — 1-KP/2:1.; MAILROOM EQUIPMENT: Tying Machines — CyKlop.; BUSINESS EQUIPMENT: IBM/PC, APP/Mac CLASSIFIED EQUIPMENT: Hardware — APP/Mac; CLASSIFIED SOFTWARE: Baseview. DISPLAY EQUIPMENT: Other Hardware — 3-M/MUP, 1-Mk DISPLAY SOFTWAREAd Make-up Applications — Multi-Ad, QPS/QuarkXPress; Layout Software — APP/Mac. EDITORIAL EQUIPMENT:

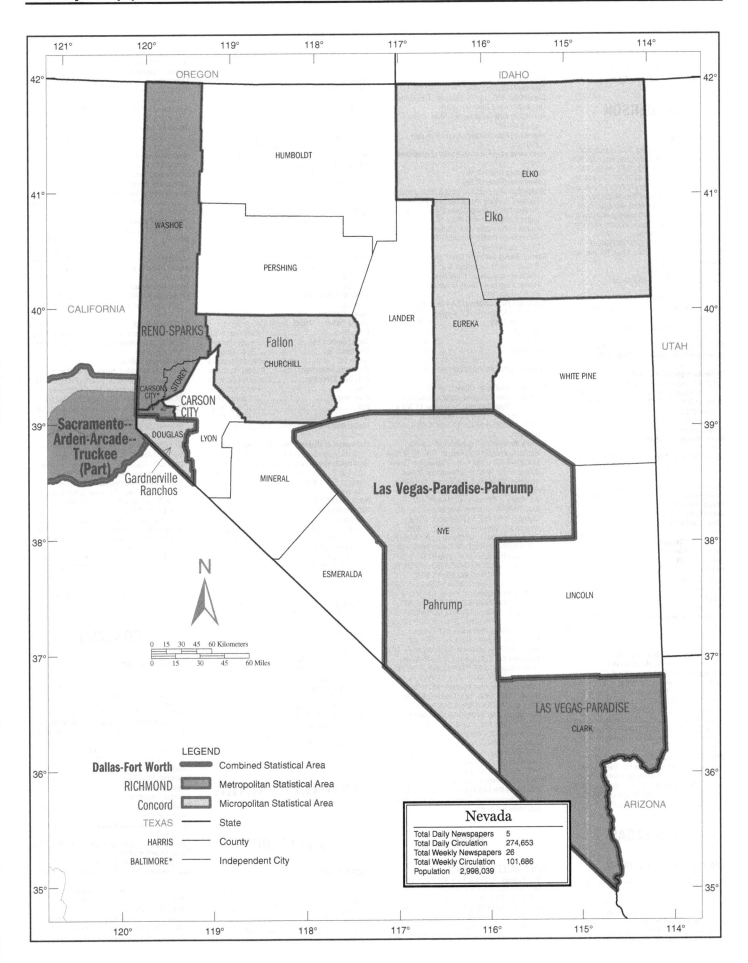

OREGON

IDAHO

42°

HUMBOLDT

ELKO

41°

WASHOE

Elko

PERSHING

40°

CALIFORNIA

RENO-SPARKS

Fallon

LANDER

EUREKA

UTAH

CHURCHILL

STOREY

WHITE PINE

CARSON
CITY*

**CARSON
CITY**

**Sacramento--
Arden-Arcade--
Truckee
(Part)**

DOUGLAS

LYON

39°

Gardnerville
Ranchos

Las Vegas-Paradise-Pahrump

MINERAL

NYE

38°

ESMERALDA

LINCOLN

Pahrump

N

37°

LAS VEGAS-PARADISE

ARIZONA

CLARK

36°

35°

0 15 30 45 60 Kilometers

0 15 30 45 60 Miles

LEGEND

Dallas-Fort Worth	Combined Statistical Area
RICHMOND	Metropolitan Statistical Area
Concord	Micropolitan Statistical Area
TEXAS	State
HARRIS	County
BALTIMORE*	Independent City

Nevada

Total Daily Newspapers	5
Total Daily Circulation	274,653
Total Weekly Newspapers	26
Total Weekly Circulation	101,686
Population	2,998,039

Hardware — 1-APP/Mac EDITORIAL SOFTWARE: Baseview/NewsEdit Pro 3.2.2. PRODUCTION EQUIPMENT: Hardware — Pre Press/Panther, Pre Press/Panther Plus; Cameras — 1-B/2000, 1-Acti PRODUCTION SOFTWARE: QPS/QuarkXPress 4.1.

HENDERSON

LAS VEGAS SUN

2275 Corporate Cir, Ste 300, Henderson, Nev., 89074-7745, Clark; gen tel (702) 385-3111; adv tel (702) 383-0388; ed tel (702) 385-3111; gen fax (702) 383-7264; adv fax (702) 383-0389; ed fax (702) 383-7264; gen/nat adv e-mail rebecca@lasvegassun.com; disp adv e-mail brian@lasvegassun.com; class adv e-mailbrian@lasvegassun.com; ed e-mail letters@lasvegassun.com; web site www.lasvegassun.com
 - 8,200,000(views) 1,500,000(visitors)
Published: Mon, Tues, Wed, Thur, Fri, Sat, Sun
Weekday Frequency: m
Saturday Frequency: m
Circulation: 127,648; 120,573(sat); 138,209(sun)
Last Audit: AAM March 31, 2014
Newspaper Reps: Brian Greenspun, Editor and Publisher
Tom Gorman, Executive Editor
Ric Anderson, Managing Editor
Donn Jersey, Director of On-line Media
Advertising Rate (weekday/saturday): Open inch rate $198.00
Online Advertising Rate: Mobile Banner Ads:$17.50 cpm; Geo-targeted Banner Ads: $17.50 cpm; Geo-targeted Half-Page Ad: $25
News services: AP, NYT, SHNS, DJ, GNS.
Established: 1950
Own Printing Facility?: No
Commercial Printers?: No
Digital Platform - Mobile: Apple, Android, Windows, Blackberry
Digital Platform - Tablet: Apple iOS, Android, Windows 7, Blackberry Tablet OS, Kindle, Nook, Kindle Fire
CEO/Pub./Ed. .... Brian Greenspun
Managing Ed. .... Ric Anderson
Deputy Managing Editor/Digital ....John Frtiz
Senior Editor/Sports ....Ray Brewer
Office Coordinator .... Nadine Guy
COO ....Robert Cauthorn
The Sunday Managing Ed. .... Dave Mondt
Carson City Bureau Chief ....Cy Ryan
Special Pub. Ed. ....Craig Peterson
Web Ed. .... Wade McAferty
Assoc. Creative Dir. .... Elizabeth Brown
Designer .... LeAnn Elias
Copy Ed. ....Jamie Genter
Designer .... Marvin Lucas
Mechanical Specifications: Type page 11 1/2 x 21; E - 6 cols, 1 5/6, 5/36 between; A - 6 cols, 1 5/6, 1/9 between; C - 10 cols, 1 1/24, 1/9 between.
Areas Served: Las Vegas, Henderson, North Las Vegas, Boulder City/Clark County
Delivery Method: Mail, Newsstand, Carrier, RacksEquipment & Software: EDITORIAL EQUIPMENT: Digital Hardware — (2) HP DL385P GEN8 6376 8-SFF US SVR/S-BUY (1) HP P2000 G3 SAS MSA DC W/12 1TB 6G SAS 10K SFF HDD 12TB BUNDLE storage unit EDITORIAL SOFTWARE: Digital Software — KVM with Customized LAMP Stack
Note: The Las Vegas Sun is distributed as a section of the Las Vegas Review-Journal. See the Review-Journal for information on circulation, advertising rates and production. The Sun remains editorially separate and publishes online content as well.

LAS VEGAS

LAS VEGAS REVIEW-JOURNAL

1111 W Bonanza Rd, Las Vegas, Nev., 89106-3545, Clark; gen tel (702) 383-0211; adv tel (702) 383-0388; ed tel (702) 383-0264; gen fax (702) 383-4676; adv fax (702) 383-0389; ed fax (702) 383-4676; gen/nat adv e-mail kparker@reviewjournal.com; disp adv e-mail adhelp@reviewjournal.com; class adv e-mailkdavis@reviewjournal.com; ed

e-mail gcook@reviewjournal.com; web site www.reviewjournal.com
 - 12,000,000(views) 1,626,961(visitors)
Group: Las Vegas Review-Journal, Inc.
Published: Mon, Tues, Wed, Thur, Fri, Sat, Sun
Weekday Frequency: m
Saturday Frequency: m
Circulation: 106,702; 98,696(sat); 128,403(sun)
Last Audit: AAM June 30, 2016
Advertising Rate (weekday/saturday): Open inch rate $466.00
Advertising Rate (sunday): Open inch rate $507.00
News services: AP, LAT-WP, MCT. **Established:** 1905
Own Printing Facility?: Yes
Commercial Printers?: Yes
Special Editions: Guide to Pool & Patio (Apr); Football Preview (Aug); National Finals Rodeo (Dec); Dining Guide (Feb); Super Bowl (Jan); Guide to Pool & Patio (Jul); Dining Guide (Jun); Home and Garden (Mar); Home Furnishings (May); National Family Week (Nov); Las Vegas I
Special Weekly Sections: Travel, Living, Entertainment, Business, Sun Opinions (Sun); Neighborhood (Tue); Taste (Wed); Home, Furniture (Thur); Entertainment (Fri); Real Estate (Sat)
Syndicated Publications: USA Weekend, PARADE Magazine, TV Magazine (S).
Asst. Dir. of Photo ..........................K.M. Cannon
Office Mgr. .... Patricia Rice
Pub. .... Craig Moon
Ed. in Chief.................................J. Keith Moyer
Mng. Ed. .... Glenn Cook
Market Information: ADS; Split run; TMC; Zoned editions.
Mechanical Available: Offset; Black and 3 ROP colors; insert accepted; page cutoffs - 22.
Mechanical Specifications: Type page 11 3/4 x 21; E - 6 cols, 1 7/8, 1/8 between; A - 6 cols, 1 7/8, 1/8 between; C - 10 cols, 1 1/16, 3/32 between.
Delivery Method: Mail, Newsstand, Carrier, RacksEquipment & Software: PRESSROOM EQUIPMENT: Lines — 8-G/Newsliner Tower double width 1999; 8-G/Newsliner Tower double width 2000; 8-G/Community 1981; Folders — 2, Sovereign/160-Double Folder 3:2; Reels & Stands - 20; MAILROOM EQUIPMENT: Counter Stackers — 12-HI/Olympic, 3-HL/HT, 1-QWI/Sport, 1/MM; Inserters & Stuffers — 4-HI/632, 1-/MM; Tying Machines — 14-/Dynaric.; BUSINESS EQUIPMENT: HP/3000-KS 959, HP/9000-KZ 210 BUSINESS SOFTWARE: CJ 8.02H, Progress 8.2B CLASSIFIED EQUIPMENT: Hardware — AT/Sysdecoaix RS 6000, Clarion Raid/System; MON, MON/MGS OPI System, AT/Pagination; Printers — MON/EM 3850; CLASSIFIED SOFTWARE: AT/Enterprise 1.4.8. DISPLAY EQUIPMENT: Hardware — APP/Mac, DTI, HP 959KS200, HP/959KS200; Printers — XIT/Clippers, MON/3850 Express Masters; DISPLAY SOFTWAREAd Make-up Applications — DTI/AdSpeed 8.2, CJ/Layout; Layout Software — APP/Mac, CJ. EDITORIAL EQUIPMENT: Hardware — DTI/APP/Mac, Lf; Printers — MON/3850 Express Masters, MON/Paper Master EDITORIAL SOFTWARE: ESP/2, DTI 4.2. PRODUCTION EQUIPMENT: Hardware — MON/3850 Express Masters, MON, Futuro, Sharp/Jx-610, Lf/Leafscan 45, Lf/Leafscan 35; Cameras — C/Marathon, B; Scanners — 2-Lf/Leafscan 35, 3-Kk/2035, 1-ECR/Autokon 2045c, 1-Sharp/JX-610, 1-Lf/Leafscan 45, 1-Autokon-1000 PRODUCTION SOFTWARE: DTI/Page S
Note: The Las Vegas Review-Journal prints and distributes the Las Vegas Sun as a section of the Review-Journal. The two newspapers are editorially separate.

RENO

RENO GAZETTE-JOURNAL

955 Kuenzli St, Reno, Nev., 89502-1160, Washoe; gen tel (775) 788-6397; adv tel (775) 788-7355; ed tel (775) 788-6397; gen fax (775) 788-6458; adv fax (775) 788-6458; ed fax (775) 788-6458; gen/nat adv e-mail ngladys@rgj.com; disp adv e-mail ngladys@rgj.com; class adv e-mailngladys@rgj.com;

ed e-mail letters@rgj.com; web site www.rgj.com
 - 11,000,000(views) 1,000,000(visitors)
Group: Gannett
Published: Mon, Tues, Wed, Thur, Fri, Sat, Sun
Weekday Frequency: m
Saturday Frequency: m
Circulation: 27,241; 26,652(sat); 32,561(sun)
Last Audit: AAM September 30, 2017
Branch Offices: 12 S. Main St. Yerington, NV 89447
Advertising Rate (weekday/saturday): Open inch rate $55 (Mon.-Wed.); $60 (Thurs-Sat)
Advertising Rate (sunday): Open inch rate $70
Online Advertising Rate: $9 cpm
News services: AP, GNS, LAT-WP, Knight Ridder. **Established:** 1870
Own Printing Facility?: Yes
Commercial Printers?: Yes
Special Editions: Nevada Living (Apr); Football (Aug); Super Bowl (Jan); Hot August Nights (Jul); Reno Rodeo (Jun); Dining Guide (May); Dining Guide (Nov); Health Source (Oct); National Air Races (Sept).
Special Weekly Sections: Sierra Living (seasonal) (Fri); Technology (Mon); TV Week (S); Homefinder (Sat); Best Bets (Thur); Auto Finder (Wed).
Syndicated Publications: USA WEEKEND Magazine (S).
Digital Platform - Mobile: Apple, Android
Digital Platform - Tablet: Apple iOS, Android
Exec. Ed. .... Kelly Ann Scott
Senior Content Ed. ....Peggy Santoro
Key Topics Ed. .... Brian Duggan
Sports Ed. .... Johanna Huybers
Key Accnt. Sales Mgr. .... Robert Galloway
Bus. Dev. Sales Mgr.............Danielle Lacombe
Pres. ....Ryan Kedzierski
Controller .... Conrad Velin
Pub. ....Craig Moon
Ed. ....Keith Moyer
Market Information: Split run; TMC; Zoned editions.
Mechanical Available: Offset; Black and 3 ROP colors; insert accepted; page cutoffs - 22 3/4.
Mechanical Specifications: Type page 11 5/8 x 21 1/2; E - 6 cols, 1 5/6, 1/8 between; A - 6 cols, 1 5/6, 1/8 between; C - 10 cols, 1, 1/8 between.
Areas Served: Metro area
Delivery Method: Mail, RacksEquipment & Software: PRESSROOM EQUIPMENT: Lines — 7-G/Metro double width (4 Half decks) 1981; Folders — Imperial/3:2; Pasters —G/AutomaticReels & Stands — G/Automatic, 7-G/3-arm.; MAILROOM EQUIPMENT: Counter Stackers — 2/HL, HI; Inserters & Stuffers — HI/630; Tying Machines — 2-/Dynaric; Control System — Heidelberg/Prima; Address Machine — Marconi/InkJet.; BUSINESS EQUIPMENT: IBM/AS/400 BUSINESS SOFTWARE: Lawson, Cyborg, Genesys CLASSIFIED EQUIPMENT: Hardware — AT, Compaq; CLASSIFIED SOFTWARE: CText. DISPLAY EQUIPMENT: Hardware — APP/Mac; Printers — AU; Other Hardware — PageScan/III DISPLAY SOFTWAREAd Make-up Applications — Multi-Ad; Layout Software — Layout/8000. EDITORIAL EQUIPMENT: Hardware — Compaq; Printers — Autologic EDITORIAL SOFTWARE: CText. PRODUCTION EQUIPMENT: Hardware — 1-LE, Lf/AP Leaf Picture Desk; Scanners — AG/Horizon, Kk, Nikon PRODUCTION SOFTWARE: Ctext.

NEW HAMPSHIRE

CLAREMONT

EAGLE TIMES

45 Crescent St, Claremont, N.H., 03743-2220, Sullivan; gen tel (603) 543-3100; gen fax (603) 542-9705; adv fax (603) 504-3199; gen/nat adv e-mail cheri@eagletimes.com; disp adv e-mail cheri@eagletimes.com; class adv e-mailclassi@eagletimes.com; ed e-mail news@eagletimes.com; web site www.

eagletimes.com
Group: Eagle Printing & Publishing LLC
Published: Mon, Tues, Wed, Thur, Fri, Sat
Weekday Frequency: m
Saturday Frequency: m
Circulation: 7,737; 8,016(sun)
Last Audit: Sworn/Estimate/Non-Audited September 30, 2017
Advertising Rate (weekday/saturday): Open inch rate $15.85
Online Advertising Rate: Mid-Banner 3: $100/mo.; Mid-Banner 2: $125/mo.; Mid-Banner 1: $150/mo.
News services: AP, TMS, Washington Post. **Established:** 1970
Own Printing Facility?: Yes
Commercial Printers?: Yes
Special Weekly Sections: Religion Page (Fri); Sports (S); Entertainment (Thur); Best Food Day (Wed).
Syndicated Publications: Color Comics (S); American Profile (Weekly).
Adv. Rep. .... Cheri Parkhurst
Ed........................... Cameron Paquette
Social Med. Ed. ....Amy Cotton
Argus Champion Ed................... Archie Mountain
Pub................................ Devin Hamilton
Market Information: ADS; Split run; TMC.
Mechanical Available: Offset; Black and full color ROP colors; insert accepted; page cutoffs - 22 3/4.
Mechanical Specifications: Type page 12 3/4 x 21 1/2; E - 6 cols, 2 1/16, 1/8 between; A - 6 cols, 2 1/16, 1/8 between; C - 8 cols, 1 9/16, 1/16 between.
Areas Served: Sullivan
Delivery Method: Mail, Newsstand, Carrier, RacksEquipment & Software: PRESSROOM EQUIPMENT: Lines — 8-G/Community SC468 1991.; MAILROOM EQUIPMENT: Counter Stackers — Mid America Graphics/News stacker; Tying Machines — 2/Sa, 1-/Sterling.; BUSINESS EQUIPMENT: Sun BUSINESS SOFTWARE: Vision Data CLASSIFIED EQUIPMENT: Hardware — 3-HP; CLASSIFIED SOFTWARE: APT. DISPLAY EQUIPMENT: Hardware — 3-APP/Mac; Printers — Xante/8300; DISPLAY SOFTWAREAd Make-up Applications — Adobe/PageMaker 6.5; Layout Software — Ad Force, MEI/ALS. EDITORIAL EQUIPMENT: Hardware — 6-APP/Mac G3, 11-APP/Mac; Printers — MON, Pre Press/Panther Pro Imagesetter, X/N32 EDITORIAL SOFTWARE: Baseview. PRODUCTION EQUIPMENT: Hardware — Pre Press/Panther Pro Imagesetter, 2-APP/Mac G3; Cameras — NU/SSTE2024S-19LT, Nu/VVE-14-18; Scanners — Lf/Leafscan 35, Sharp/JX-450 Color, Sony/UY-S77, Umax/Mirage II PRODUCTION SOFTWARE: QPS/QuarkXPress 4.0.

CONCORD

CONCORD MONITOR

1 Monitor Dr, Concord, N.H., 03301-1834, Merrimack; gen tel (603) 224-5301; adv tel (603) 224-5301; ed tel (603) 224-5301; gen fax (603) 228-8238; adv fax (603) 228-8238; ed fax (603) 224-8120; gen/nat adv e-mail ads@cmonitor.com; disp adv e-mail ads@cmonitor.com; class adv e-mailclassifieds@cmonitor.com; ed e-mail news@cmonitor.com; web site www.concordmonitor.com
 - 1,500,000(views) 320,000(visitors)
Group: Newspapers of New England
Published: Mon, Tues, Wed, Thur, Fri, Sat, Sun
Weekday Frequency: m
Saturday Frequency: m
Circulation: 11,818; 11,818(sat); 13,771(sun)
Last Audit: CAC March 31, 2015
Advertising Rate (weekday/saturday): Open inch rate $19.41
Advertising Rate (sunday): Open inch rate $20.75
Online Advertising Rate: Badge: $4.50; Half page: $6; leader board: $8
News services: AP, CSM, LAT-WP. **Established:** 1809
Special Editions: Speedway Parade (Apr); Belknap County Fair (Aug); Gift Guide (Dec); Auto (Feb); Wedding (Jan); Market Days (Jul); Summer Directory (Jun); Town Meeting (Mar); Gift Guide (Nov); Fall Recreation (Oct); Business Profiles (Sept).

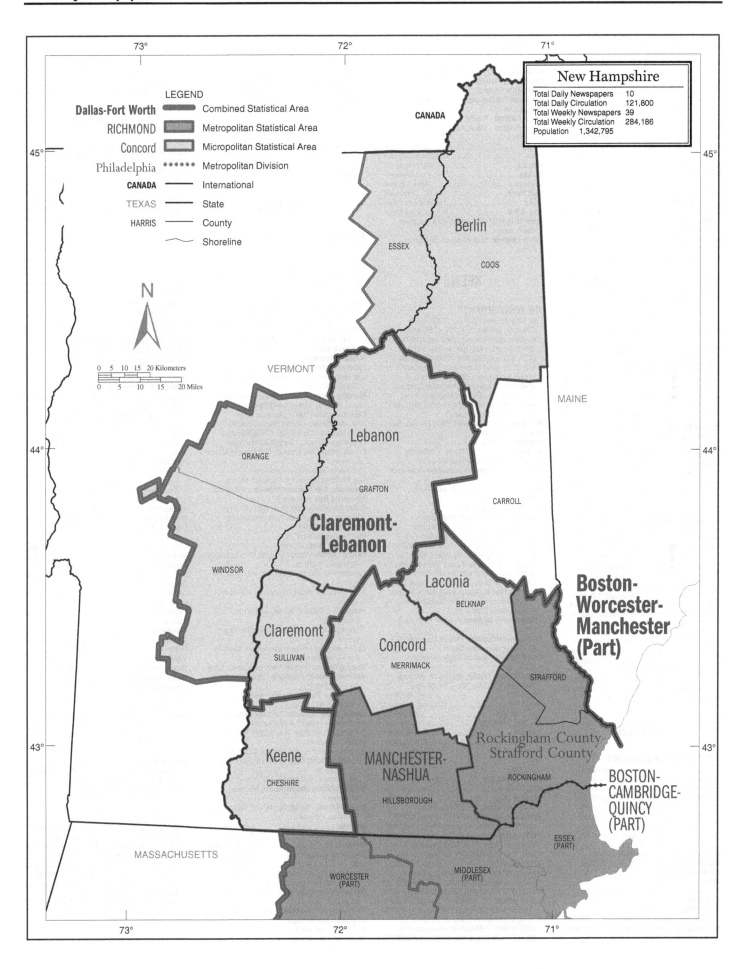

LEGEND

Dallas-Fort Worth Combined Statistical Area

RICHMOND Metropolitan Statistical Area

Concord Micropolitan Statistical Area

Philadelphia ••••• Metropolitan Division

CANADA International

TEXAS State

HARRIS County

Shoreline

N

0 5 10 15 20 Kilometers
0 5 10 15 20 Miles

New Hampshire	
Total Daily Newspapers	10
Total Daily Circulation	121,800
Total Weekly Newspapers	39
Total Weekly Circulation	284,186
Population	1,342,795

CANADA

VERMONT

MAINE

Berlin

ESSEX

COOS

Lebanon

ORANGE

GRAFTON

CARROLL

**Claremont-
Lebanon**

WINDSOR

Laconia

BELKNAP

**Boston-
Worcester-
Manchester
(Part)**

Claremont

SULLIVAN

Concord

MERRIMACK

STRAFFORD

Rockingham County-
Strafford County

Keene

CHESHIRE

**MANCHESTER-
NASHUA**

HILLSBOROUGH

ROCKINGHAM

**BOSTON-
CAMBRIDGE-
QUINCY
(PART)**

ESSEX
(PART)

MASSACHUSETTS

WORCESTER
(PART)

MIDDLESEX
(PART)

Special Weekly Sections: Entertainment (S); Auctions (Sat); Auctions (Thur); Business (Tues); Food (Wed).
Syndicated Publications: USA WEEKEND Magazine (S).
Controller ....Sandy Bourque
Pub. ....David Sangiorgio
Opinion Ed. ....Ralph Jimenez
Tech. Servs. Mgr. ....Ben Allen
Adv. Dir. ....Sean McKenna
Sales Dir. ....Deb Sanborn
Dist. Mgr. ....Thomas Ahearn
Ed., The Concord Insider ....Keith Testa
Copy Ed. ....Jon Bodell
Copy Ed. ....Julie Byrd-Jenkins
Comm. Ed. ....Susan Doucett
Day Ed. ....Jana Ford
Night Ed. ....Khela McGann
Asst. Sports Ed. ....Jeff Novotny
Sports Ed. ....Sandra Smith
LiveWell Ed. ....Jennifer VanPelt
Features Ed. ....Clay Wirestone
Ideas & Opinion Ed. ....Dana Wormald
Press/Camera Mgr. ....Harry Green Jr.
Market Information: ADS; Split run; TMC; Zoned editions.
Mechanical Available: Flexo; Black and 3 ROP colors; insert accepted; page cutoffs - 22.
Mechanical Specifications: Type page 13 x 21; E - 6 cols, 2 1/16, 1/8 between; A - 6 cols, 2 1/16, 1/8 between; C - 9 cols, 1 3/8, 3/32 between.
Areas Served: 03301, 03304, 03303, 03275, 03268, 03224, 03046, 03045, 03307, 03237, 03837, 03229, 03281, 03216, 03230, 03235, 03276, 03269, 03244, 03440, 03280, 03242, 03106, 03101, 03281, 03244, 03278, 03257, 03260, 03273, 03287, 03221, 03255, 03773, 03272, 03218, 03225, 03037, 03234, 03261, 03884, 03263, 03258, 03246, 03249, 03256, 03217, 03220, 03253, 03222, 03243, 03223, 03245, 03894, 03809, 03254, 03801
Delivery Method: Mail, Newsstand, RacksEquipment & Software: PRESSROOM EQUIPMENT: Lines — 6-PEC/double width (17 printing couples); Folders — 2-H/3:2.; MAILROOM EQUIPMENT: Counter Stackers — HL/Monitor HT II; Inserters & Stuffers — GMA/SLS 1000; Tying Machines — Dynaric; Wrapping Singles — HL/Monarch; Address Machine — 2-KR/211; BUSINESS EQUIPMENT: HP/Micro 3000XE BUSINESS SOFTWARE: CJ CLASSIFIED EQUIPMENT: Hardware — IBM, 8-AZZ/P4 1.8; Printers — 2-Pre Press/Panther Pro 36; CLASSIFIED SOFTWARE: PBS/AdPlacer 7.0. DISPLAY EQUIPMENT: Hardware — 4-APP/Power Mac 7500, 8-APP/G4; Printers — Xante/Accel-a-Writer 8200; DISPLAY SOFTWAREAd Make-up Applications — Multi-Ad/Creator 1.6; Layout Software — PBS, Adplacer 7.0. EDITORIAL EQUIPMENT: Hardware — NEC/Powermate Pro 2200x18 seats, NEC/Powermate V100x25 seats/Kante G3; Printers — Dataproducts/Typhoon 16 EDITORIAL SOFTWARE: CNI/Agile Teambase Special Edition, QPS/QuarkXPress, Microsoft/Word. PRODUCTION EQUIPMENT: Hardware — Na, 2-Pre Press/7225 DB, Epson; Cameras — C/Spartan II; Scanners — ECR/Autokon PRODUCTION SOFTWARE: AGL.

DOVER

FOSTER'S DAILY DEMOCRAT
150 Venture Dr, Dover, N.H., 03820-5913, Strafford; gen tel (603) 742-4455; adv tel (603) 516-2969; gen fax (888) 810-8988; adv fax (603) 740-3461; gen/nat adv e-mail news@fosters.com; disp adv e-mail dispatch@fosters.com; class adv e-mailfddads@fosters.com; ed e-mail news@fosters.com; web site www.fosters.com
 - 42,846(views) 35,000(visitors)
Group: New Media Investment Group
Published: Mon, Tues, Wed, Thur, Fri, Sat
Weekday Frequency: m
Saturday Frequency: m
Circulation: 10,559; 10,559(sat); 11,066(sun)
Last Audit: CAC September 30, 2014
Branch Offices: 835 Main St.
Sanford, ME 04073
Advertising Rate (weekday/saturday): Open inch rate $21.30

Advertising Rate (sunday): Open inch rate $21.30
Online Advertising Rate: $100/week (homepage position D) and up varying on position and week.
News services: AP, NYT. Established: 1873
Own Printing Facility?: Yes
Commercial Printers?: No
Syndicated Publications: USA WEEKEND Magazine (S)
Digital Platform - Mobile: Apple, Android
Digital Platform - Tablet: Apple iOS, Android, Windows 7
Cir. Dir. ....James Russell
IT Dir. ....Simeon Broughton
Mng. Ed. ....Mary Rowland
Ed. Rep. ....Paul Dietterle
Sports Ed. ....Mike Whaley
Chief Photo. ....John Huff
Ex. Ed. ....Howard Altschiller
Pres. & Pub. ....John Tabor
Areas Served: Tri-City, Seacoast & Southern Maine region
Delivery Method: Mail, Newsstand, Carrier, Racks

KEENE

THE KEENE SENTINEL
60 West St, Keene, N.H., 03431-3373, Cheshire; gen tel (603) 352-1234; adv tel (603) 352-1234 ext 1220; ed tel (603) 352-1234 ext. 1400; gen fax (603) 352-0437; adv fax (603) 352-9733; ed fax (603) 352-9700; gen/nat adv e-mail adassist@keenesentinel.com; disp adv e-mail advertising@keenesentinel.com; class adv e-mailclassified@keenesentinel.com; ed e-mail news@keenesentinel.com; web site www.sentinelsource.com
Published: Mon, Tues, Wed, Thur, Fri, Sat, Sun
Weekday Frequency: e
Saturday Frequency: m
Circulation: 7,081; 7,081(sat); 7,785(sun)
Last Audit: AAM September 30, 2017
Advertising Rate (weekday/saturday): Open inch rate $13.60
News services: AP, CNS, LAT-WP, TMS.
Established: 1799
Own Printing Facility?: Yes
Special Editions: Business Monadnock/Economic Outlook (Jan.); Brides (Feb.); Business Monadnock/Trendsetters (Mar.); Answer Book (Mar.); Home & Garden (Apr.); Reader's Choice Awards (May); Vows (Jun.); Monadnock Summer (Jun.); Extraordinary Women (Jul.); Monadnock Mid-Summer (Jul.); Keene State College City Guide (Aug.); Home & Hearth (Sep.); Monadnock Autumn (Oct.) Holiday Ideas (Nov.); Last Minute Holiday Ideas (Dec.)
Special Weekly Sections: Religion (Sat); ELF (Thur).
Syndicated Publications: Parade Magazine (S); Dash (1st Wed. Each Month)
Digital Platform - Mobile: Apple, Android, Windows
Digital Platform - Tablet: Apple iOS, Android, Windows 7, Kindle, Nook, Kindle Fire
Pres./COO ....Terry Williams
Own & Pub. ....Thomas M. Ewing
Bus. & HR Mgr. ....Linda Flagg
Adv. Mgr., Classified ....Lorraine Ellis
Exec. Ed. ....Paul A. Miller
Sports Ed. ....David Lanier
Dig. Content Ed. ....Cecily Weisburgh
IT Dir. ....Chris Carreira
Press Frmn ....Gregory Walker
Graph. & Prod. Mgr. ....Robert Farnsworth
Inter. Media Dir. ....Jessica Garcia
Executive Editor ....Paul Miller
Market Information: Zoned editions.
Mechanical Available: Offset; Black and 3 ROP colors; insert accepted; page cutoffs - 21 1/2.
Mechanical Specifications: Type page 11 3/5 x 21 1/2; E - 6 cols, 1 4/5, 1/8 between; A - 6 cols, 1 4/5, 1/8 between; C - 9 cols, 1 1/5, 1/8 between.
Delivery Method: Mail, Newsstand, Carrier, RacksEquipment & Software: PRESSROOM EQUIPMENT: Lines — 8-G/Community 1986; MAILROOM EQUIPMENT: Counter Stackers — HL/Monitor; Inserters & Stuffers — HI/848; Tying Machines — Dynaric.; BUSINESS SOFTWARE: PBS/SBS/Brainworks/SCS CLASSIFIED EQUIPMENT: PC CLASSIFIED

SOFTWARE: Layout 8000, Photoshop CS 5.5 DISPLAY EQUIPMENT: Hardware — 4-APP/Mac; Printers — HP/8100N; Other Hardware — 2-APP/Mac CD-Rom DISPLAY SOFTWAREAd Make-up Applications — QPS/QuarkXPress; Layout Software — SCS/Layout 8000. EDITORIAL EQUIPMENT: Printers — Kodak CTP EDITORIAL SOFTWARE: TownNews PRODUCTION EQUIPMENT: Hardware — Caere/OmniPage, ECR/VRL 36, Konica/9200; Cameras — R/24-580; Scanners — 1-Microtek PRODUCTION SOFTWARE: QPS/QuarkXPress. IT EQUIPMENT: HP Servers, Exchange CIRCULATION SOFTWARDTI

LACONIA

THE LACONIA DAILY SUN
1127 Union Ave, Ste 1, Laconia, N.H., 03246-2126, Belknap; gen tel (603) 737-2030; adv tel (603) 737-2020; ed tel (603) 737-2026; gen fax (603) 527-0056; adv fax (603) 527-0056; ed fax (603) 527-0056; gen/nat adv e-mail ads@laconiadailysun.com; disp adv e-mail ads@laconiadailysun.com; class adv e-mailads@laconiadailysun.com; ed e-mail news@laconiadailysun.com; web site www.laconiadailysun.com
 - 300,000(views) 150,000(visitors)
Published: Tues, Wed, Thur, Fri, Sat
Weekday Frequency: m
Saturday Frequency: m
Last Audit: Sworn/Estimate/Non-Audited October 19, 2017
Newspaper Reps: Adam Hirshan - Publisher
Elaine Hirshan - Advertising Manager
Crystal Furnee - Sales Representative
Jeanette Stewart - Sales Representative
Karin Nelson - Classifieds, Office Manager
Rosemary Nedeau - Classified Manager
Branch Offices: The Conway Daily Sun in North Conway, NH
The Berlin Daily Sun in Berlin, NH
The Portland Phoenix in Portland, Maine
Advertising Rate (weekday/saturday): $7.75 pci
Advertising Rate (sunday): $7.75 pci
Online Advertising Rate: Pricing available at http://laconiadailysun.flywheelsites.com/
News services: 2000
Own Printing Facility?: No
Commercial Printers?: Yes
Special Editions: Wedding Guide 25,000 copies Publishes in March
Summer Fun Guide 50,000 copies Publishes in May
Fall Fun Guide 40,000 copies Publishes in August
Holiday Gift Guide 8 weeks, November-December
Thanksgiving pull-out section Wednesday before Thanksgiving
Spring and Fall Home Improvement sections April-May; Sept-Oct
Boating Special Section - end of June-October
Saturday Weekend editions - Special features July-October
NH Pumpkin Festival Special Section - second weekend in October
Special Weekly Sections: Tuesday - Business Wednesday - Health & Wellness
Thursday - Lakestyle: Arts & Entertainment
Friday - Outdoors
Saturday - History and Feature Cover Stories
Proprietary Publications: Summer Fun Guide
Fall Fun Guide
Lakes Region Wedding Guide
Digital Platform - Mobile: Apple, Android, Windows
Digital Platform - Tablet: Apple iOS, Android, Windows 7, Nook
Publisher ....Adam Hirshan
Pub. ....Adam Hirshan
Managing Ed. ....Ginger Kozlowski
Advertising Manager ....Elaine Hirshan
Pres ....Edward Engler
Market Information: Serves 18 cities and towns in the Lakes Region of New Hampshire
Mechanical Available: 1/8th page, 1/4 page, 1/2 page, full page
Mechanical Specifications: 3.25" x 5" eighth page
5" x 6.65" quarter page
6.75" x 10" half page
10.25" x 13.5" full page

Areas Served: Laconia, Gilford, Meredith, Weirs Beach, Center Harbor, Belmont, Moultonborough, Winnisquam, Sanbornton, Tilton, Gilmanton, Alton, New Hampton, Plymouth, Bristol, Ashland, Holderness, Northfield, Franklin, Loudon, Wolfeboro
Delivery Method: Newsstand, Carrier, Racks

MANCHESTER

NEW HAMPSHIRE UNION LEADER/NEW HAMPSHIRE SUNDAY NEWS
100 William Loeb Dr, Manchester, N.H., 03109-5309, Hillsborough; gen tel (603) 668-4321; gen fax (603) 668-0382; adv fax (603) 624-0727; gen/nat adv e-mail jnormandin@unionleader.com; disp adv e-mail classified@unionleader.com; class adv e-mailclassified@unionleader.com; ed e-mail letters@unionleader.com; web site www.unionleader.com
 - 3,400,000(views) 703,000(visitors); web site 2 www.newhampshire.com - 353,000(views) 82,000(visitors)
Group: Union Leader Corporation
Published: Mon, Tues, Wed, Thur, Fri, Sat, Sun
Weekday Frequency: m
Saturday Frequency: m
Circulation: 33,231; 20,768(sat); 43,754(sun)
Last Audit: AAM March 31, 2016
Advertising Rate (weekday/saturday): $36.70
Advertising Rate (sunday): $38.95
News services: Reuters, WPNS, TMS
Established: 1863
Own Printing Facility?: No
Commercial Printers?: No
Special Editions: Health & Fitness (Apr); Working Woman (Aug); Holiday Planner (Dec); Washington's Birthday Auto (Feb); Baby Review (Jan); NASCAR Winston Cup (Jul); NH Home Show (Mar); Summer Vacation (May); Home for Holidays (Nov); Dining & Lodging (Oct); Fall House & Home
Special Weekly Sections: Religion (Thu); Monday's Business (Mon); Get Out! (S); Avenues (Fri); WheelsNH (Fri); NH Weekend (Thu); Veterans (Thur); Senior Page (Tues); At Home (Tue); Flavors (Wed).
Syndicated Publications: Parade (S).
Digital Platform - Mobile: Apple, Android
Digital Platform - Tablet: Apple iOS, Android, Kindle, Kindle Fire
Exec. Vice Pres. ....Dirk F. Ruemenapp
VP Finance ....Joyce M. Levesque
President. ....Brendan McQuaid
Adv. Servs. Mgr. ....Robin Wilson
Circ. Dir., Opns. ....Lucien G. Trahan
Deputy Mng. Ed., Bus. ....Mike Cote
Editorial Page Ed. ....Grant Boss
Publisher ....Joseph McQuaid
Exec. Ed. ....Trent Spiner
Community Relations Mgr. ......Shannon Sullivan
Chief Operating Officer ....James Normandin
IT Manager ....Andrew Loranger
Night Editor ....Sherry Wood
Managing Editor ....Matt Sartwell
Market Information: TMC; Zoned editions.
Mechanical Available: Offset; Black and 3 ROP colors; inserts accepted - samples, post-its; page cutoffs - 22.
Mechanical Specifications: Type page 10 1/4 x 21 1/4; E - 6 cols, 1 5/6, 1/8 between; A - 6 cols, 1 5/6, 1/8 between; C - 9 cols, 1 3/16, 1/8 between.
Areas Served: All New Hampshire
Delivery Method: Mail, Newsstand, Carrier, RacksEquipment & Software: PRESSROOM EQUIPMENT: Printing is outsourced MAILROOM EQUIPMENT: Mailroom operation outsourced BUSINESS SOFTWARE: AltiPro CLASSIFIED EQUIPMENT: Hardware — Dell/PowerEdge 4600, 20-Dell/Optiplex GX605; CLASSIFIED SOFTWARE: SCS/AdMAX-ClassPag DISPLAY EQUIPMENT: Hardware — Dell/PG 266-GXA; DISPLAY SOFTWAREAd Make-up Applications — SCS/AdBoss, AdMAX; Layout Software — SCS/Layout-8000 EDITORIAL EQUIPMENT: Hardware — 52-HP & Dell desktops EDITORIAL SOFTWARE: DTI-Saxotech CIRCULATION SOFTWARDTI

NASHUA

THE TELEGRAPH
110 Main St, Ste 1, Nashua, N.H., 03060-2723, Hillsborough; gen tel (603) 882-2741; adv tel (603) 594-6555; ed tel (603) 594-6467; gen fax (603) 882-5138; adv fax (603) 882-5138; ed fax (603) 882-2681; gen/nat adv e-mail mgorman@nashuatelegraph.com; disp adv e-mail adsales@nashuatelegraph.com; class adv e-mailgetclassifieds@nashuatelegraph.com; ed e-mail news@nashuatelegraph.com; web site www.nashuatelegraph.com
 - 1,600,000(views) 450,000(visitors); web site 2 www.nh.com - 200,000(views) 70,000(visitors); web site 3 www.cabinet.com - 60,000(views) 20,000(visitors)
Published: Mon, Tues, Wed, Thur, Fri, Sat, Sun
Weekday Frequency: m
Saturday Frequency: m
Circulation: 11,815; 11,815(sat); 16,105(sun)
Last Audit: AAM June 30, 2016
Advertising Rate (weekday/saturday): Open inch rate $30.60
Advertising Rate (sunday): Open inch rate $32.65
Online Advertising Rate: Leaderboard $20.00/Medium Rectangle $20.00/Vertical Banner $6.00/Wide Skyscraper $20.00/Bottom Banner $3.51
News services: AP, LAT-WP. **Established:** 1832
Own Printing Facility?: No
Commercial Printers?: Yes
Special Editions: Colossal Classified (Apr); Progress (March); Spring Home & Garden (April); Mothers Day (May); Summer Guide (May); Graduation (June); Community Guide (July); Back to Class (August); Fall Home & Garden (September); Holiday Gift Guide (November); Celebrate New Year's Eve (Dec); Valentine's Day (Feb); Celebrating Women (Oct).
Special Weekly Sections: Faith Pages (Sat); Encore — Arts - Entertainment - Food (Thur); Food (Wed).
Syndicated Publications: USA WEEKEND Magazine (S).
Digital Platform - Mobile: Apple, Android
Digital Platform - Tablet: Apple iOS
Sports Ed. ....Alan Greenwood
Aud. Dev. Mgr. ....David Jordan
Class. - Real Est. & Rec. Mgr. ....Laurie Blais
Pub. ....Jim Konig
Wk Ed. & Comm. Ed. ....Sandy Bucknam
Sr. Des. ....Beth Eisenberg
Photo Ed. / Staff Wtr. ....Don Himsel
NH.com Ed. ....Jessica Jordan
Encore Ed., Sunday Feat. ....Kathleen Palmer
Asst. Sports Reporter ....George Scione
Ed. Asst. ....Jo Arnold
Senior Online Adv. Exec. ....Debra Sutphen
IT Mgr. ....Dave Warren
Events Prod. ....Tracy Dionne
Retail adv. - S. Nashua.................Mary Gorman
Market Information: ADS; TMC.
Mechanical Available: Offset; Black and 3 ROP colors; insert accepted - Samples; page cutoffs - 22.
Mechanical Specifications: Type page 13 x 21; E - 6 cols, 2, 1/8 between; A - 6 cols, 2, 1/8 between; C - 9 cols, 1 2/5, 1/12 between.
Areas Served: In NH: Nashua, Hudson, Merrimack, Hollis, Brookline, Milford, Amherst, Litchfield, Londonderry Lyndeborough, Wilton, Mason, Greenville. In MA: Dunstable; Tyngsborough.
Delivery Method: Mail, Newsstand, Carrier, RacksEquipment & Software: BUSINESS EQUIPMENT: 1-Micron/Server P266, Compaq/Server Pro P90, 5-Micron/Server P450, 10-Compaq/P233 Clients BUSINESS SOFTWARE: Brainworks, Solomon, Ultipro CLASSIFIED EQUIPMENT: Hardware — 18-Novell/P233 4.1; Printers — HP/IV; CLASSIFIED SOFTWARE: ATS. DISPLAY EQUIPMENT: Hardware — 30-Novell/P200 Server 4.1; Printers — HP/IV, HP/850; Other Hardware — Digital Cameras DISPLAY SOFTWAREAd Make-up Applications — DPS/AdTracker, QPS/QuarkXPress 4.0; Layout Software — Informatel/Pagination. EDITORIAL EQUIPMENT: Hardware — 40-Pentium/PC 133, 6-Micron/P400; Printers — HP/4000, HP/5si, HP/IV EDITORIAL SOFTWARE: ATS, DTI PRODUCTION EQUIPMENT: Hardware — 2-P/33-43,

Caere/OmniPage Pro, 1-Kk/660; Scanners — AG/Arcus II, Mircotek PRODUCTION SOFTWARE: DTI CIRCULATION SOFTWARDSI

NORTH CONWAY

THE CONWAY DAILY SUN
64 Seavey St, North Conway, N.H., 03860-5355, Carroll; gen tel (603) 356-3456; adv tel (603) 733-5808; ed tel (603) 356-8360; gen fax (603) 356-8774; adv fax (603) 356-8774; ed fax (603) 356-8360; gen/nat adv e-mail joyce@conwaydailysun.com; disp adv e-mail Rick@conwaydailysun.com; class adv e-mailClassifieds@conwaydailysun.com; web site www.conwaydailysun.com
Published: Tues, Wed, Thur, Fri, Sat
Weekday Frequency: m
Saturday Frequency: m
Circulation: 16,100; 16,100(sat)
Last Audit: Sworn/Estimate/Non-Audited September 30, 2017
Advertising Rate (weekday/saturday): Open inch rate $9.00
Advertising Rate (sunday): Open inch rate $9.00
Online Advertising Rate: $300.00/mo. Country News Club
News services: AP, RN. **Established:** 1989
Own Printing Facility?: Yes
Commercial Printers?: Yes
Special Editions: Sports Preview (Apr); Dining Guide (Dec); Economic Review (Feb); Dining Guide (Jul); Sports Preview (May).
Special Weekly Sections: Education (Mon); Real Estate (Sat); Sports (Tues); Business (Wed).
Syndicated Publications: Cool News (Fri).
Pres. ....David N. Danforth
Pub. ....Mark Guerringue
Office Mgr. ....Joyce Brothers
Comm. Ed. ....Bart Bachman
Photography Ed. ....Jamie Gemmiti
Sports Ed. ....Lloyd Jones
Wire/Entertainment Ed. ....Alec Kerr
Sen. Press. ....Frank Haddy
Op-Ed. Ed ....Terry Leavitt
Graphics Mgr. ....Darcy Gautreau
Mng. Ed. ....Margaret McKenzie
Op. Mgr. / Adv. Sls Mgr. ....Joyce Brothers
Mechanical Available: Offset Web; Black and 1 ROP colors; insert accepted; page cutoffs - 15.
Mechanical Specifications: Type page 10 1/4 x 13 1/2; E - 4 cols, 2 3/4, 1/3 between; A - 6 cols, 1 3/5, 1/6 between; C - 6 cols, 1 3/5, 1/6 between.
Areas Served: 03818, 03812, 03813 (Ctr. Conway), 03813 (Chatham), 03817, 03818, 03832, 03836, 03838, 03845, 03846, 03847, 04051, 03849, 03860, 03875, 03886, 03864, 04037, 03894, 03254
Delivery Method: Mail, Newsstand, Carrier, RacksEquipment & Software: PRESSROOM EQUIPMENT: Lines — 5-G/Community Single-width.; BUSINESS EQUIPMENT: APP/Mac Plus CLASSIFIED EQUIPMENT: Hardware — 2-APP/Mac Quadra; CLASSIFIED SOFTWARE: Baseview. DISPLAY SOFTWARELayout Software — Aldus/PageMaker, QPS, Adobe/Photoshop, Aldus/FreeHand. EDITORIAL EQUIPMENT: Hardware — 10-APP/Mac/APP/Mac Scanner; Printers — 2-APP/Mac LaserWriter, 2-HP. PRODUCTION EQUIPMENT: Hardware — Kk/42A.

PORTSMOUTH

PORTSMOUTH HERALD
111 NH Ave, Portsmouth, N.H., 03801-2864, Rockingham; gen tel (800) 439-0303; adv tel (603) 436-1800; ed tel (603) 570-2129; gen fax (603) 433-5760; adv fax (603) 427-0550; ed fax (603) 433-5760; gen/nat adv e-mail sales@seacoastonline.com; disp adv e-mail scnadvertising@seacoastonline.com; class adv e-mailclassads@seacoastonline.com; ed e-mail news@seacoastonline.com; web site www.seacoastonline.com
Group: New Media Investment Group
Published: Mon, Tues, Wed, Thur, Fri, Sat, Sun
Weekday Frequency: m
Saturday Frequency: m

Circulation: 9,420; 9,420(sat); 10,976(sun)
Last Audit: AAM December 31, 2016
Advertising Rate (weekday/saturday): Open inch rate $24.19
Advertising Rate (sunday): Open inch rate $24.19
Online Advertising Rate: Top Tile Ad $4.20; Medium Rectangle $16.65; Half-page tower $21.20
News services: AP. **Established:** 1884
Special Editions: Spring Lawn/Garden (Apr); Healthy Living (Aug); Last Minute Gift (Dec); Pres. Auto (Feb); Bridal (Jan); Summer Ports of Call (Jun); St. Pat's Auto (Mar); Mother's Day (May); N.E. Holidays (Nov); Harvest (Oct); Menu Guide (Sept).
Special Weekly Sections: Spotlight Weekly Magazine (Thur); Best Food Day (Wed).
Syndicated Publications: R.E. Guide (Monthly); Commercial Real Estate Guide (Quarterly); TV Times (S); Value Zone (Sat); Spotlight Magazine (Thur).
Pub. ....John Tabor
Adv. Mgr., Classified/Sales ....Sandra Titus
Circ. Dir. ....Dennis Thompson
Exec. Ed. ....Howard Altschiller
Mng. Ed. ....Rick Fabrizio
Ad. Dir. ....Andrew Chernoff
Graphics Sup. ....Therese SanSoucie
Market Information: ADS; TMC.
Mechanical Available: Offset; Black and 3 ROP colors; insert accepted; page cutoffs - 22 3/4.
Mechanical Specifications: Type page 13 x 21 1/2; E - 6 cols, 2 1/16, 1/8 between; A - 6 cols, 2 1/16, 1/8 between; C - 9 cols, 1 3/8, 1/16 between.
Areas Served: Seacoast RegionEquipment & Software: PRESSROOM EQUIPMENT: Lines — 14-G/Community; Folders — Dauphin/1040, G/55C.; MAILROOM EQUIPMENT: Counter Stackers — Remor; Inserters & Stuffers — Valley Remanufacturing; Tying Machines — 1-OVL/Constellation, 1/CYP.; BUSINESS EQUIPMENT: 1-IBM-AS/400 BUSINESS SOFTWARE: Microsoft/Excel, Microsoft/Word CLASSIFIED EQUIPMENT: Hardware — PC; CLASSIFIED SOFTWARE: AT/Enterprise, QPS/QuarkXPress. DISPLAY EQUIPMENT: Hardware — QuarkXPress; Printers — Konica/JetSetter; DISPLAY SOFTWARELayout Software — PC. EDITORIAL EQUIPMENT: Hardware — PC; Printers — Konica/JetSetter EDITORIAL SOFTWARE: Dewar/View, QPS/QuarkXPress. PRODUCTION EQUIPMENT: Hardware — 1-Graham; Cameras — SCREEN PRODUCTION SOFTWARE: Classified Pagination 5.4.2.

WEST LEBANON

VALLEY NEWS
24 Interchange Dr, West Lebanon, N.H., 03784-2003, Grafton; gen tel (603) 298-8711; adv tel (603) 298-6082; ed tel (603) 727-3217; gen fax (603) 298-0212; adv fax (603) 298-0212; ed fax (603) 298-0212; gen/nat adv e-mail advertising@vnews.com; disp adv e-mail advertising@vnews.com; class adv e-mailclassified@vnews.com; ed e-mail newseditor@vnews.com; web site www.vnews.com
 - 1,008,520(views) 229,865(visitors)
Group: Newspapers of New England
Published: Mon, Tues, Wed, Thur, Fri, Sat, Sun
Weekday Frequency: m
Saturday Frequency: m
Circulation: 14,039; 14,039(sat); 14,346(sun)
Last Audit: CAC September 30, 2016
Advertising Rate (weekday/saturday): Open inch rate $18.79
Advertising Rate (sunday): Open inch rate $18.79
Online Advertising Rate: Leaderboard $140.00/Rectangle $140.00/Half Page $140.00
News services: AP, LAT-WP, New England Wire Service. **Established:** 1952
Own Printing Facility?: Yes
Commercial Printers?: Yes
Special Editions: Valley Guide (June); Dining Guide (June); Readers Choice (October); Valley Parents (Quarterly); Enterprise (Monthly Business); Upper Valley Holidays (November); Letters to Santa (Dec)
Special Weekly Sections: Books (Fri); Science & Technology (Mon); Life & Leisure (S); Movies

(Sat); Arts (Thur); Education (Tues); Food & Garden (Wed); Real Estate (Sat)
Syndicated Publications: Valley Television (S);
Digital Platform - Mobile: Apple, Android
Pub. ....Daniel D. McClory
Adv. Dir. ....Richard Wallace
Circ. Dir. ....James Carey
Editor ....Martin Frank
Sunday and Bus. News Ed. ....Ernie Kohlsaat
Operations ....Bob Mathewson
Feat., Ed. ....Alex Hanson
Photo Ed. ....Geoff Hansen
Editorial Page Ed. ....Dan Mackie
Sports Ed. ....Greg Fennell
News Editor ....John Gregg
Web Editor ....Maggie Cassidy
Market Information: ADS; Split run; TMC.
Mechanical Available: Flexography; Black and 3 ROP colors; insert accepted; page cutoffs - 22.
Mechanical Specifications: Type page 13 x 21; E - 6 cols, 2 1/16, 1/8 between; A - 6 cols, 2 1/16, 1/8 between; C - 9 cols, 1 5/16, 1/8 between.
Areas Served: Grafton
Delivery Method: Newsstand, Carrier, RacksEquipment & Software: PRESSROOM EQUIPMENT: Lines — 5-H/PEC (Colormatic Flexo Conversion) 1988; 5-H/PEC (Colormatic Flexo Conversion) 1988; Folders — 2-H/3:2; Registration System — 4 MAILROOM EQUIPMENT: Counter Stackers — 3-HL/Monitor HT; Inserters & Stuffers — HI/848 W/Icon System; Tying Machines — 1-EAM-Mosca, 2/MVP; Control System — Ic; BUSINESS EQUIPMENT: 2-Windows NT BUSINESS SOFTWARE: DSI, Circ, Solomon, ABRA, DSI CLASSIFIED EQUIPMENT: Hardware — PC Clones; Printers — QMS/860; CLASSIFIED SOFTWARE: Graph-X. DISPLAY EQUIPMENT: Hardware — 3-APP/Mac Quadra 650, 1-PC; Printers — QMS/860; Other Hardware — Microtek/Flatbed Scanner DISPLAY SOFTWAREAd Make-up Applications — Multi-Ad/Creator 4.X; Layout Software — 1-Mk/Managing Editor. EDITORIAL EQUIPMENT: Hardware — 40-PC, Compaq/fileserver; Printers — QMS/860, HP/LaserJet 4 EDITORIAL SOFTWARE: Novell/Network 3.12, QPS/QuarkXPress 3.31, Microsoft/Word 6.0, Azimuth Wire Capture. PRODUCTION EQUIPMENT: Hardware — Na, AG/Imagesetter 1500, PixelCraft/Quickscan 8000, Kk/RSS-2035 Plus; Cameras — R; Scanners — Lf/Leafscan 35, Howtech/4500, PixelCraft/Quickscan 8000, Kk/RSS-2035 Plus.

NEW JERSEY

CHERRY HILL

THE COURIER-POST
301 Cuthbert Blvd, Cherry Hill, N.J., 08002-2905, Camden; gen tel (856) 663-6000; adv tel (856) 486-2503; ed tel (856) 486-2402; gen fax (856) 663-2831; adv fax (856) 665-5788; ed fax (856) 663-2831; gen/nat adv e-mail info@courierpostonline.com; disp adv e-mail mbettner@gannett.com; class adv e-mailclassifiedads@courierpostonline.com; ed e-mail cpedit@courierpostonline.com; web site www.courierpostonline.com
Group: Gannett
Published: Mon, Tues, Wed, Thur, Fri, Sat, Sun
Weekday Frequency: m
Saturday Frequency: m
Circulation: 34,471; 37,969(sat); 46,953(sun)
Last Audit: AAM September 30, 2014
Advertising Rate (weekday/saturday): Open inch rate $185.00
Advertising Rate (sunday): Open inch rate $192.00
News services: AP, GNS. **Established:** 1875
Special Editions: Pic-a-Home Real Estate Magazine (); Cookbook (Apr); Labor Day Recipe Pages (Aug); End of Month Values (Dec); South Jersey Unlimited (Feb); Luxury Living (Jan); End of Month Values (Jul);

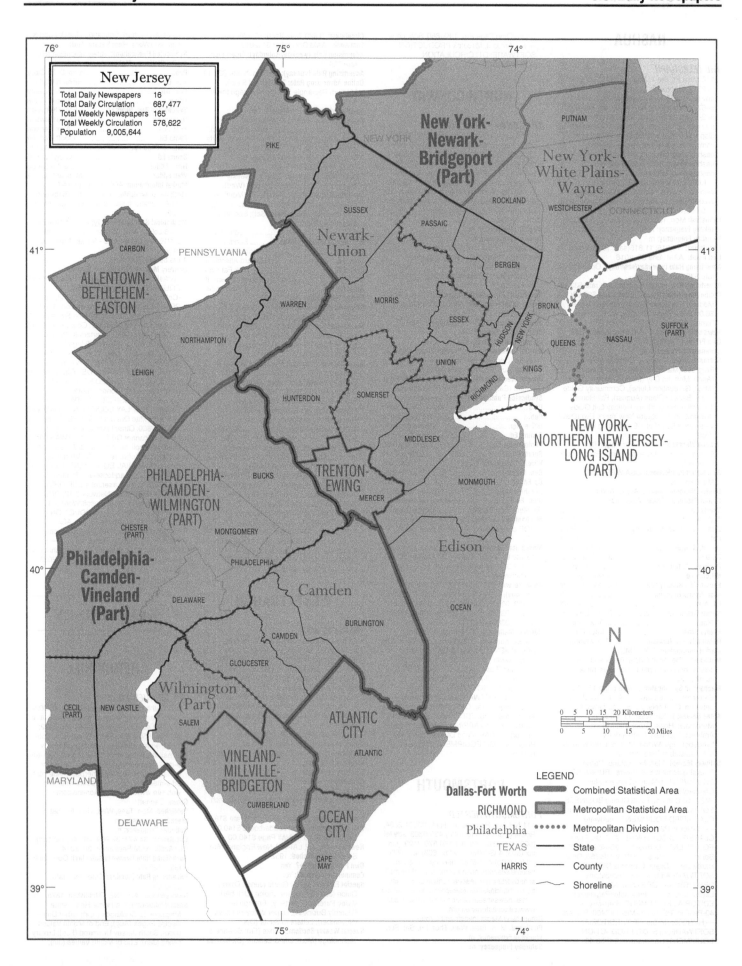

New Jersey

Total Daily Newspapers	16
Total Daily Circulation	687,477
Total Weekly Newspapers	165
Total Weekly Circulation	578,622
Population	9,005,644

New York-
Newark-
Bridgeport
(Part)

New York-
White Plains-
Wayne

PUTNAM

ROCKLAND

WESTCHESTER

CONNECTICUT

PIKE

NEW YORK

SUSSEX

PASSAIC

CARBON

PENNSYLVANIA

BERGEN

Newark-
Union

ALLENTOWN-
BETHLEHEM-
EASTON

NORTHAMPTON

WARREN

MORRIS

ESSEX

BRONX

LEHIGH

UNION

HUDSON

NEW YORK

QUEENS

NASSAU

SUFFOLK
(PART)

NEW YORK-
NORTHERN NEW JERSEY-
LONG ISLAND
(PART)

KINGS

RICHMOND

HUNTERDON

SOMERSET

MIDDLESEX

PHILADELPHIA-
CAMDEN-
WILMINGTON
(PART)

BUCKS

TRENTON-
EWING

MERCER

MONMOUTH

Edison

CHESTER
(PART)

MONTGOMERY

Philadelphia-
Camden-
Vineland
(Part)

PHILADELPHIA

Camden

OCEAN

DELAWARE

BURLINGTON

CECIL
(PART)

NEW CASTLE

Wilmington
(Part)

SALEM

CAMDEN

GLOUCESTER

ATLANTIC
CITY

MARYLAND

VINELAND-
MILLVILLE-
BRIDGETON

ATLANTIC

DELAWARE

CUMBERLAND

OCEAN
CITY

CAPE
MAY

N

0 5 10 15 20 Kilometers	
0 5 10 15 20 Miles	

LEGEND

Dallas-Fort Worth	Combined Statistical Area
RICHMOND	Metropolitan Statistical Area
Philadelphia	Metropolitan Division
TEXAS	State
HARRIS	County
	Shoreline

Luxury Living (Jun); Luxury Living (Mar); UMD (May); End of Month Va
Special Weekly Sections: Business (Daily); Living, Family, Sports, (Mon); Our Towns (Tue); Taste, Living, Sports (Wed); Sports (Thur); Arts, Entertainment, Living, Real Estate Sports (Fri); Business, Family Fun, Home, Gardens, High School Sports (Sat); Books, Health, Food, Travel, Business, Real Estate, TV, Comics, Sports (Sun);
Syndicated Publications: USA WEEKEND Magazine (S).
Controller.................................... Jean Wysocki
Regional Comm. Ed............................. M.J. Fine
Reg. Prod.................................... Sheri Berkery
Regional Prod.............................. Karen Morgan
Reg. Engagement Ed................... Tammy Paolino
Admin Assist........................... Janice Linneman
Cont. Strategist.................. Jerry Staas Haught
Photo/Video.................................. Chris LaChall
Reg. Sports Strategist/Editor .... Tom McGurk
Regional Ed.. Jason Alt
Dir., Info Servs........................... Craig Connolly
Reg. Plan..................................... Chris Silvestri
Pres. & Pub................................. Joseph Calchi
Asst. Cont. .... Leslie Emma
HR Mgr... Bonnie Still
Market Information: ADS; Split run; TMC; Zoned editions.
Mechanical Available: Offset; Black and 3 ROP colors; insert accepted - quarter fold; page cutoffs - 22.
Mechanical Specifications: Type page 12 1/2 x 21 7/16; E - 6 cols, 1 7/8, 1/8 between; A - 6 cols, 1 7/8, 1/8 between; C - 10 cols, 1 3/32, 1/16 between.Equipment & Software: PRESSROOM EQUIPMENT: Lines — 24-G/Headliner (12 half decks); Folders — 2-G/160-page double delivery; Reels & Stands — G/20 Reels & Stands.; MAILROOM EQUIPMENT: Counter Stackers — 4/Quipp 401, 1-/Quipp 501; Inserters & Stuffers — 2-/AM Graphics, HP/630; Tying Machines — 1-/MLN, 3-/Power Strap/Model 5; Control System — Id; Address Machine — 2-Barstrom/on-line; BUSINESS EQUIPMENT: 1-IBM/AS-400, 10-Windows NT, 4-Linux, 1-Tandem BUSINESS SOFTWARE: Lawson, Gensys, Brio IC Verify, Microsoft/Word, Microsoft/Excel, Cyborg, Edywyse, Digicol, Ad Tracker CLASSIFIED EQUIPMENT: Hardware — Mactive; Printers — HP; CLASSIFIED SOFTWARE: Ad Base 2.20. DISPLAY EQUIPMENT: Hardware — Mac; Printers — HP; DISPLAY SOFTWAREAd Make-up Applications — DPS; Layout Software — Mactive. EDITORIAL EQUIPMENT: Hardware — SII/Sys 55/1-Lf/ AP Leaf Picture Desk, 10-APP/Mac; Printers — HP, Ibon EDITORIAL SOFTWARE: SII/ Sys 55, Coyote Layout. PRODUCTION EQUIPMENT: Hardware — 2-KNF, GMTI/ Digicol, 2-AU/APS 108C, AU/APS 5000, 1-AU/3850, 2-AU/3850; Scanners — 1-Tesca, 1-Eshofot PRODUCTION SOFTWARE: SII/ Coyote Layout.

MULLICA HILL

SOUTH JERSEY TIMES

161 Bridgeton Pike, Ste E, Mullica Hill, N.J., 08062-2669, Gloucester; gen tel 856-754-7100; adv tel (856) 754-7152; ed tel (856) 754-7151; gen fax 856-754-7198; adv fax (856) 754-7198; ed fax (856) 754-7198; gen/nat adv e-mail sjadvertising@njadvancemedia.com; disp adv e-mail tdrummond@njadvancemedia.com; class adv e-mailsjtclassifieds@njadvancemedia.com; ed e-mail sjnews@njadvancemedia.com; web site www.nj.com/southjerseytimes
- 71,000,000(views) 14,200,000(visitors)
Group: Advance Publications, Inc.
Published: Mon, Tues, Wed, Thur, Fri, Sat, Sun
Weekday Frequency: m
Saturday Frequency: m
Circulation: 17,857; 21,451(sun)
Last Audit: AAM June 30, 2015
Advertising Rate (weekday/saturday): Open inch rate $27.66
Advertising Rate (sunday): $37.55
Online Advertising Rate: $13.65
News services: AP, U.S. Suburban Press Inc..
Own Printing Facility?: No
Commercial Printers?: No
Special Weekly Sections: Washington Township Times (Fridays)
Indulge (Fridays)
Syndicated Publications: Parade (S).
Digital Platform - Mobile: Apple, Android
Digital Platform - Tablet: Apple iOS, Android
VP Sales & Pub. .... Rhonda Barlow
Community Editor .... Jessica Beym
Market Information: TMC.
Mechanical Available: Offset; Black and 3 ROP colors; insert accepted; page cutoffs - 22 3/4.
Mechanical Specifications: Type page 13 x 21 1/2; E - 6 cols, 2 1/16, 1/8 between; A - 6 cols, 2 1/16, 1/8 between; C - 9 cols, 1 1/3, 1/8 between.
Areas Served: Cumberland, Gloucester and Salem Counties, NJ
Delivery Method: Mail, Newsstand, Carrier, RacksEquipment & Software: BUSINESS SOFTWARE: CJ CLASSIFIED SOFTWARE: CText. EDITORIAL SOFTWARE: CText.

NEPTUNE

ASBURY PARK PRESS

3600 State Route 66, Neptune, N.J., 07753-2605, Monmouth; gen tel (800) 822-9770; adv tel (732) 643-3703; ed tel (732) 922-6000 ; gen fax (732) 643-4013; ed fax (732) 643-4013; gen/nat adv e-mail applegals@gannett.com; disp adv e-mail bditty@njpressmedia.com; class adv e-mailappclass@gannett.com; ed e-mail yourviews@app.com; web site www.app.com
1,743,605(visitors)
Group: Gannett
Published: Mon, Tues, Wed, Thur, Fri, Sat, Sun
Weekday Frequency: m
Saturday Frequency: m
Circulation: 59,174; 63,694(sat); 91,925(sun)
Last Audit: AAM September 30, 2017
Advertising Rate (weekday/saturday): Open inch rate $226.00
News services: 1879
Digital Platform - Mobile: Apple, Android
Digital Platform - Tablet: Apple iOS, Android, Windows 7
Exec. Ed. & Vice Pres./News .... Hollis Towns
Pres. & Pub............................ Thomas Donavan
Regional VP/Adv.......................... Karen Guarasi
VP/Prod... Jack Roth
VP, Information Systems........... Wayne Peragallo
VP/Circ........................................ Jane Pettigrew
VP/Fin.... Erik Statler
News & Invest. Dir.
Paul D'Ambrosio
Areas Served: Monmouth & Ocean Counties (NJ)
Delivery Method: Mail, Newsstand, Carrier, Racks

NEWARK

THE STAR-LEDGER

55 Court St, Newark, N.J., 07102-1243, Essex; gen tel (888) 782-7533; adv tel (973) 392-5894; ed tel (973) 392-4040; gen fax (973) 643-4641; adv fax (973) 642-6764; ed fax (973) 392-5845; gen/nat adv e-mail imest@njadvancemedia.com; disp adv e-mail mhays@njadvancemedia.com; ed e-mail metro@starledger.com; web site www.nj.com/starledger
6,088,000(visitors)
Group: Advance Publications, Inc.
Published: Mon, Tues, Wed, Thur, Fri, Sat, Sun
Weekday Frequency: m
Saturday Frequency: m
Circulation: 161,963; 127,998(sat); 244,884(sun)
Last Audit: AAM June 30, 2016
Advertising Rate (weekday/saturday): Open inch rate $554.32(m-thur)
News services: Metro Suburbia Inc./Newhouse Newspapers, NNS, LAT-WP, DJ, RN, PR Newswire, MCT.
Own Printing Facility?: Yes
Commercial Printers?: Yes
Special Weekly Sections: Real Estate Marketplace (Fri); Education (S); Home & Garden (Thur); Body Shop (Tues); Savor (Wed).
Syndicated Publications: Parade (S).
Inside Jersey (mthly)
Pub.... Richard Vezza
Gen. Mgr................................... John F. Dennan
National Advertising Manager........... Brian Pfeifer
Director of Marketing. .... Robert C. Provost
Circ. Dir. .... Dennis Carletta
Mng. Ed. .... David Tucker
Assoc. Ed....................................... Tom Curran
Editorial Page Ed. .... Tom Moran
Deputy Editorial Page Ed............. Daniel Murphy
Advertising Director........... Louis Stancampiano
Dir. Adv. .... Bob Gray
Robert Jarrach
Patricia Wells
Frances Eiss
Director... Randi Ungar
VP of Advertising .... Steve Alessi
Market Information: Split run; TMC; Zoned editions.
Mechanical Available: Offset; Black and 3 ROP colors; insert accepted - print and deliver program available; page cutoffs - 22.
Mechanical Specifications: Type page 11 5/8 x 21 1/4; E - 6 cols, 1 5/6, 1/8 between; A - 6 cols, 1 5/6, 1/8 between; C - 10 cols, 1 3/16, 1/8 between.
Delivery Method: Mail, Newsstand, Carrier, RacksEquipment & Software: PRESSROOM EQUIPMENT: Lines — 9-TKS double width; 9-TKS double width; 10-TKS double width; 10-TKS double width; 10-TKS double width; 10-TKS double width; 10-TKS double width; Press Drive — 69-Tokyo Dinki; Folders — 11-TKS; Pasters —TKS/Automatic.Reels & Stands — TKS; Control System — TKS; Registration System — WPC MAILROOM EQUIPMENT: Counter Stackers — 28/HL, 14-/HL; Inserters & Stuffers — 2-LS/3000; Tying Machines — 22-/Dynaric, 6-/MLN.; BUSINESS EQUIPMENT: HP/Micro XE, HP/927, HP/947, HP/967, HP/969, HP/3000 BUSINESS SOFTWARE: CJ, Microsoft/Office CLASSIFIED EQUIPMENT: Hardware — CSI; 2-HI/8900; CLASSIFIED SOFTWARE: Mactive 2.20. DISPLAY SOFTWARELayout Software - SCS. EDITORIAL EQUIPMENT: Hardware — Sun/Sparc/10-HI/8900, 15-APP/Mac, 22-HI/2100; Printers — 3-MON/ Print Express EDITORIAL SOFTWARE: HI/XP21, HI/Newsmaker, MON/Postscript RIPS. PRODUCTION EQUIPMENT: Hardware — 1-AGFA/3850, 1-WL/Lith-X-Pozer 3; Scanners — Scitex, 2-AG/Eskofot PRODUCTION SOFTWARE: HI/XP-21 2.6.
Note: Combination rate for the Star-Ledger/ Times of Trenton are valid for select categories of advertising.

NEWTON

NEW JERSEY HERALD

2 Spring St, Newton, N.J., 07860-2077, Sussex; gen tel (973) 383-1500; adv tel (973) 383-1500 option 2; ed tel (973) 383-1500 ext. 31899; gen fax 973-383-8477; adv fax (973) 383-9284; ed fax (973) 383-8477; gen/nat adv e-mail advertising@njherald.com; disp adv e-mail kflinn@njherald.com; class adv e-mailclassified@njherald.com; ed e-mail newsroom@njherald.com; web site www.njherald.com
Group: Quincy Media, Inc.
Published: Mon, Tues, Wed, Thur, Fri, Sun
Weekday Frequency: All day
Circulation: 10,471; 15,304(sun)
Last Audit: AAM December 31, 2015
Advertising Rate (weekday/saturday): Open inch rate $31.20
Advertising Rate (sunday): Open inch rate $24.76
News services: AP, TMS. **Established:** 1829
Own Printing Facility?: Yes
Commercial Printers?: Yes
Special Editions: Home and Garden (Apr); Back-to-School (Aug); Christmas Gift Guides (Dec); Progress (Feb); White Sale (Jan); Newton Sidewalk Sale (Jul); New Jersey Cardinals (Jun); Expo (Mar); Home & Garden (May); Human Resources (Nov); New Car (Oct); Fall Home Improvemen
Special Weekly Sections: Entertainment (Fri); Business (Mon); Food (S); Best Food Day (Wed).
Syndicated Publications: TV Week (S); American Profile (Weekly).
Promo./Special Projects Mgr. .... Lee Williams
Exec. Ed.................................. Bruce Tomlinson
News Ed....................................... Kathy Stevens
Tech Mgr. .... Jaime Kerr
Pub.... Keith Flinn
Auto. Category Mgr. .... John Kopec
Class. Mgr........................... Mara Clingingsmith
Int. Dir. .... Amy Paterson
Copy Ed....................................... Jesse Kryscio
Senior Photo. .... Daniel Freel
Sports Ed. .... Carl Barbati
HR & Admin. Ass.......................... Robin Fichter
Cir. Dir. .... Jay Gillispie
Market Information: TMC.
Mechanical Available: Offset; Black and 3 ROP colors; insert accepted; page cutoffs - 22 3/4.
Mechanical Specifications: Type page 13 x 21 1/2; E - 6 cols, 2 1/16, 1/8 between; A - 6 cols, 2 1/16, 1/8 between; C - 9 cols, 1 3/8, 1/16 between.
Areas Served: 07860 07422
Delivery Method: Mail, Newsstand, Carrier, RacksEquipment & Software: BUSINESS SOFTWARE: INSI CLASSIFIED EQUIPMENT: Hardware — 1-APP/Power Mac G4, 6-APP/iMac G3; 7-AST/286; Printers — HP/4050 TN; CLASSIFIED SOFTWARE: Baseview/AdManager Pro 2.0.6. DISPLAY EQUIPMENT: Hardware — APP/Power Mac G4, 2-APP/Power Mac G3; Printers — 1-APP/Mac LaserWriter 16-600; Other Hardware — 1-Umax/Powerlook III Scanner DISPLAY SOFTWAREAd Make-up Applications — Baseview Production Manager Pro 1.6; Layout Software — Multi-Ad/Creator II. EDITORIAL EQUIPMENT: Hardware — 2-APP/Power Mac G4, 25-APP/Mac G3/16-AST/286; Printers — 1-QMS/2425 Ex EDITORIAL SOFTWARE: Baseview/NewsEdit Pro IQUE 3.2.3. PRODUCTION EQUIPMENT: Hardware — Adobe/Photoshop, 2-Pre Press/Panther Catara 46 Imagesetter; Cameras — 1-C/ Spartan III; Scanners — 2-AG.Duoscan T2000 XL PRODUCTION SOFTWARE: Baseview/NewsEdit Pro IQUE 3.2.3, QPS/ QuarkXPress 4.1.

PARSIPPANY

DAILY RECORD

6 Century Dr, Ste 3, Parsippany, N.J., 07054-4611, Morris; gen tel (973) 428-6200; adv tel (973) 428-6551; ed tel (973) 428-6610; gen fax (973) 428-6666; adv fax (973) 428-6529; ed fax (973) 428-6666; gen/nat adv e-mail jungaro@gannettnj.com; disp adv e-mail kguarasi@gannettnj.com; class adv e-maildrclass@gannett.com; ed e-mail jungaro@gannettnj.com; web site www.dailyrecord.com
- 2,300,000(views) 325,000(visitors)
Group: Gannett
Published: Mon, Tues, Wed, Thur, Fri, Sat, Sun
Weekday Frequency: m
Saturday Frequency: m
Circulation: 11,120; 11,120(sat); 13,917(sun)
Last Audit: AAM December 31, 2016
Advertising Rate (weekday/saturday): Open inch rate $98.00
News services: AP, GNS, Bloomberg, CNS, TMS. **Established:** 1900
Special Editions: Creative Homes (Apr); Family (Aug); Last Minute Gifts (Dec); Bridal (Feb); Coupon Clippers (Jan); Seniors (Jun); Fashion (Mar); Home Improvement (May); Going Shopping (Nov); Coupon Clippers (Oct); High School Football (Sept).
Special Weekly Sections: Real Estate (Fri); Technology (Mon); Real Estate (S); On The Row (Sat); Parisppany Plus (Thur); Business (Tues); Denville/Rockaway Plus (Wed).
Syndicated Publications: USA Weekend (S).
Reg. VP Adv. .... Karen Guarasi
General Manager/Editor .... Joe Ungaro
Market Information: TMC; Zoned editions.
Mechanical Available: Offset; Black and 3 ROP colors; insert accepted; page cutoffs - 22.
Mechanical Specifications: Type page 11 5/8 x 21; E - 6 cols, 1 5/6, 1/8 between; A - 6 cols, 1 5/6, 1/8 between; C - 10 cols, between.
Areas Served: Morris County (NJ)
Equipment & Software: PRESSROOM EQUIPMENT: Pasters —MEGReels & Stands — MEG.; MAILROOM EQUIPMENT: Counter Stackers — HL/Monitors, 3-HL/

Dual Carrier; Inserters & Stuffers — HI/1472; Tying Machines — 2-Dynaric/N-1, 2-Samuel/ NT 30; Address Machine — Domino/Ink Jet.; BUSINESS EQUIPMENT: AS400 BUSINESS SOFTWARE: Agile Editorial, Microsoft/ Office : Company, Gannett Genesys System CLASSIFIED EQUIPMENT: Hardware — PC Network; APP/Mac Workstation; Printers — Okidata/3410, NewGen/Postscript Printer; CLASSIFIED SOFTWARE: Intertext/ Classified Rev II. DISPLAY EQUIPMENT: Hardware — PC; Printers — APP/Mac LaserWriter; DISPLAY SOFTWAREAd Make-up Applications — SCS; Layout Software — SCS/Layout 8000. EDITORIAL EQUIPMENT: Hardware — PCs, APP/Macs/APP/Mac Workstation; Printers — 2-Postscript/ Page-proofer, 3-LaserWriter/ EDITORIAL SOFTWARE: CNI/Agile. PRODUCTION EQUIPMENT: Hardware — Caere/ OmniPage Pro, 2-C/APS6-108; Scanners — Kk/RFS-2035, HP/3C, 2-Scangraphics/ Dot4Dot PRODUCTION SOFTWARE: QPS/ QuarkXPress 4.1, MEI/ALS.

PLEASANTVILLE

THE PRESS OF ATLANTIC CITY

1000 W Washington Ave, Pleasantville, N.J., 08232-3861, Atlantic; gen tel (609) 272-7000; adv tel (609) 272-7000; ed tel (609) 272-7267; gen fax (609) 272-7224; adv fax (609) 272-7059; ed fax (609) 272-7224; gen/nat adv e-mail MRice@pressofac.com; class adv e-mailJCompton@pressofac.com; ed e-mail letters@pressofac.com; web site www.pressofatlanticcity.com
- 4,000,000(views) 500,000(visitors); web site 2 atlanticcityinsiders.com; web site 3 www.blissbridalexpo.com; web site 4MissAmericaNews.com

Group: BH Media Group
Published: Mon, Tues, Wed, Thur, Fri, Sat, Sun
Weekday Frequency: m
Saturday Frequency: m
Circulation: 29,041; 31,034(sat); 36,215(sun)
Last Audit: AAM September 30, 2017
Branch Offices: Cape May County
1 Enterprise Drive
Cape May Court House, NJ 08210
Advertising Rate (weekday/saturday): Open inch rate $81
Advertising Rate (sunday): Open inch rate $103
Online Advertising Rate: $18-$23/cpm
News services: AP, MCT, TMS **Established:** 1872
Own Printing Facility?: No
Commercial Printers?: No
Special Editions: Clips Monthly Coupon Digest, Health Quarterly Magazine, Bliss Bridal Magazine, Jersey Strong, Fore Golf Digest, Atlantic County Living, Cape May County Living, Indulge Dining Magazine, Summer Family Fun Guide, Fall Fun Guide, Best of Press Readers Choice Awards, Brendan Borek, (Sept); NACAC Education Guide, Big Book Holiday Guide, High School Sports Best of Fall
Special Weekly Sections: Wellness (Mon); Life (M, T, W, F, Sa); At The Shore (Th) Entertainment Guide; Movies (Fri); Travel, E-Life, Pets, Taste, Real Estate, Marketplace, Auto (Sun), Business (T-Sat)
Syndicated Publications: Parade (S).
Dash (monthly)
Proprietary Publications: Real Estate Monthly
Digital Platform - Mobile: Apple, Android, Windows
Digital Platform - Tablet: Apple iOS, Android, Windows 7, Blackberry Tablet OS
VP, News..Kris Worrell
Local Content Producer/Business.........Kevin Post
VP. of Sales / Mktg...................Michelle Rice
At The Shore Ed. / AC Weekly.......... Scott Cronick
Local Content Producer/Features .....Steve Cronin
Sports.. Mark Melhorn
Pub.. Blum Mark
Digital Mgr. ....Mike Dellavecchia
Adv. Sys. Mgr. .... Alison Leonard
Multi. Media Ed....................... Vernon Ogrodnek
Market Information: Split run; TMC; Zoned editions.
Areas Served: Atlantic, Cape May, Cumberland & South Ocean Counties (NJ)
Delivery Method: Mail, Newsstand, Carrier, RacksEquipment & Software: BUSINESS EQUIPMENT: Dell desktops and notebooks, asst models BUSINESS SOFTWARE: Finance Epicore, Circulation Atex WC, Adv Billing/credit Brainworks CLASSIFIED EQUIPMENT: Hardware — 2-Dell/ PowerEdge R610, twin E5640 2.66Ghz processors, 12GB mem, (2) 3TB external RAIDs running ATS AdvisorFlex; 3-AU/Grafix rips, 1-Anygraaf OPI system, 2-AU/3850 Sierra Wide; Printers — HP/LaserJe; DISPLAY EQUIPMENT: Hardware — 2-Dell/ PowerEdge 2600 2.8 GHz Zeon, 2-Dell/ PowerVault 221s w/MS Cluster, MAC/G4/Dell Optiplex; Printers — QMS/860, HP/LaserJet 8000N, HP/LaserJet 8100N, QMS/Magicolor 6100, HP/2500C, Xante/CL30 Color Laser; DISPLAY SOFTWAREAd Make-up Applications — QPS/QuarkXPress, Microsoft, Anygraaf; EDITORIAL EQUIPMENT: Hardware — Dell Virtual Server 3-2-1 setup/4-AU/Softpip, 2-Sierra/3850 Wide; Printers — QMS/860, HP DJ800PS EDITORIAL SOFTWARE: Anygraaf/Planner, QPS/QuarkXPress 4.1, Microsoft/Word 6.0 - 10.0. PRODUCTION EQUIPMENT: Hardware — Calera/M-Pro, Au/Sierra 3850 Wide PRODUCTION SOFTWARE: QPS/ QuarkXPress 4.1, Anygraaf Doris & Planner

ROCKAWAY

HERALD NEWS

100 Commons Way, Rockaway, N.J., 07866-2038, Morris; gen tel (973) 569-7000; adv tel (973) 905-4023; ed tel (973) 569-7100; gen fax (973) 569-7268; adv fax (973) 569-7834; ed fax (201) 457-2520; gen/nat adv e-mail bartholomew@northjersey.com; disp adv e-mail advertising@northjersey.com; class adv e-mailclassified@northjersey.com; ed e-mail newsroom@northjersey.com; web site www.northjersey.com; web site 2 www.bergencounty.com; web site 3 www.bergen.com

Group: North Jersey Media Group Inc.
Published: Mon, Tues, Wed, Thur, Fri, Sat, Sun
Weekday Frequency: m
Saturday Frequency: m
Circulation: 138,904; 143,087(sat); 146,759(sun)
Last Audit: AAM December 31, 2013
Advertising Rate (weekday/saturday): Open inch rate $244.15
Advertising Rate (sunday): Open inch rate $272.27
News services: AP, McClatchy, Washington Post, Bloomberg, Christian Science Monitor, Religion News Service, Scripps **Established:** 1872
Own Printing Facility?: Yes
Commercial Printers?: Yes
Special Editions: Health Quarterly (Feb., May., Aug., Sep.); Education (Mar., Oct.); Consumer Guide (Mar., Apr.); Holiday Dining (Monthly); High School Sports (Sept.); Breast Cancer Awareness (Oct.); Dine Out Guide (Nov.); Holiday Gift Guide (Dec.)
Syndicated Publications: TV Book (S).
Digital Platform - Mobile: Apple, Android, Windows
Digital Platform - Tablet: Apple iOS, Android, Kindle, Kindle Fire
Sr. Dir. ....Deirdre Sykes
Exec. Ed...Doug Clancy
Editorial Ed. ....Alfred Doblin
Dir. Sports.....................................John Balkun
Dir. News & Production .... Elizabeth Houlton
Dir. Photography............................... Jon Naso
VP Internet Technology.................. Yuri Demidov
VP Operations..................................Bob Konig
VP/Corp Secretary & General Counsel .Jennifer A. Borg
Web Ed. .... Sean Oates
CEO..Thomas Heffernan
VP Ed........................................Martin Gottlieb
Dir. Marketing ....Maggie Grande
Dir. Information Technology.........Greg Hoffmann
Classified Mgr. ....Mara Clingingsmith
Dir. Corporate & National Adv. Richard Colandrea
Director of Internet Sales........... Marc McGuigan
Dig. Ad. Ops. Mgr........................ Nick Maltezos
HR Man....................................Kathy Batemarco
Market Information: TMC.
Mechanical Available: Black and ROP colors; insert accepted.
Mechanical Specifications: Type page 11 x 20 1/50; E - 6 cols, 1 3/4, 3/32 between; A - 6 cols, 1 3/4, 3/32 between; C - 6 cols, 1 3/4, 3/32 between.
Areas Served: 07603, 07601, 07606, 07010, 07410, 07407, 07663, 07026, 07057, 07604, 07644, 07607, 07662, 07075, 07020, 07024, 07452, 07605, 07643, 07624, 07627, 07640, 07641, 07647, 07648, 07675, 0720, 07626, 07631, 07632, 07670, 07630, 07642, 07645, 07656, 07675, 07676, 07677, 07660, 07072, 07073, 07071, 07032, 07070, 07450, 07417, 07436, 07432, 07481, 07430, 07446, 07463, 07666, 07410, 07423, 07458, 07649, 07652, 07661, 07621, 07628, 07646, 07450, 07403, 07011, 07012, 07013, 07014, 07508, 07420, 07506, 07421, 07424, 07508, 07055, 07501, 07502, 07503, 07504, 07505, 07509, 07510, 07513, 07514, 07522, 07524, 07442, 07456, 07512, 07465, 07470, 07435 & 07480
Delivery Method: Mail, Newsstand, CarrierEquipment & Software: PRESSROOM EQUIPMENT: Lines — MHI-1991 ; MHI-1991; Wifag-2005; Press Drive — Fincor-MHI AMK-Wifag; Folders — MHI/3:2, 2 Wifag/2:5:5 Jaw,2; Pasters —MHI- 3 arm core tension Wifag-Autopaster- split armReels & Stands — 9- MHI per press 4-Wifag per press; Control System — Goss-MHI ABB-MHI ABB-Wifag,2; MAILROOM EQUIPMENT: Counter Stackers — Quipp Olympian; Inserters & Stuffers — SLS2000,2 Ferag MSD,2 630 Goss 2299 Goss; Tying Machines — Dynaric, Sterling Oval; Wrapping Singles — Lan Wrapper, 4; Control System — LineMaster/ Ferag Winlincs-SLS Omnicon/Omnizone-Goss ; Address Machine — Barstrom Scitex Accuply Miracom; BUSINESS EQUIPMENT: Dell BUSINESS SOFTWARE: Windows, RH Linux, SUSI Linux CLASSIFIED EQUIPMENT: Hardware — EMC VNX 5500 SAN, Dell R620 Servers CLASSIFIED SOFTWARE: DEC/61, Pongrass, News Cycle Adbase DISPLAY EQUIPMENT: Hardware — Dell/R620, EMC VNX 5500, APP/Mac; Printers — HP/ Laserjet 4000, HP/Laserjet 4050, HP/Laserjet 5000; DISPLAY SOFTWAREAd Make-up Applications — News Cycle Medialink, QPS/ QuarkXPress, Adobe/Photoshop, Adobe/ Illustrator, Macromedia/Freehand, News Cycle/Ad Base; Layout Software — ASLPPI, VM Ware EDITORIAL EQUIPMENT: Hardware — Dell/R620, EMC VNX 5500; Printers — Xante/8200, Xante/Accel-a-Writer EDITORIAL SOFTWARE: Agile/Teambase, Microsoft/Word, Microsoft/Windows Server 2012. PRODUCTION EQUIPMENT: Hardware — AFT/Photoeditor (4.2); Scanners — Nikon/LS 1000 (35 mm), Epson/ ES-800C PRODUCTION SOFTWARE: Agile/Teambase, QPS/QuarkXPress IT EQUIPMENT: Cisco, Apple
Dell, EMC
Sharp, HP IT SOFTWARE:Windows XP7, Windows Server, 2003-2012, Eset, Symantec, Mac OS, Acronis, Adobe, Open Office, RH Linux, AGFA, ABB, FERAG, Microsoft Office 2010, Exchange Server 2003, CIRCULATION SOFTWARNews Cycle Hosted
Note: The Herald News is a branded edition of The Record (Bergen County, NJ). Its circulation numbers are reported in the Branded Edition Circ sections of this survey. All other circulation numbers reported in this survey are for The Record.

SECAUCUS

THE JERSEY JOURNAL

1 Harmon Plz, Ste 1010, Secaucus, N.J., 07094-2804, Hudson; gen tel (201) 653-1000; adv tel (201) 217-2537; ed tel (201) 217-2500; gen fax (201) 653-6615; adv fax (201) 653-6615; ed fax (201) 653-1414; gen/nat adv e-mail pmagnani@jjournal.com; disp adv e-mail bbartholomew@jjournal.com; class adv e-mailclassifieds@jjournal.com; ed e-mail jjletters@jjournal.com; web site www.nj.com/jjournal

Group: Advance Publications, Inc.
Published: Mon, Tues, Wed, Thur, Fri, Sat
Weekday Frequency: m
Saturday Frequency: m
Circulation: 11,933; 15,410(sat)
Last Audit: AAM September 30, 2015
Advertising Rate (weekday/saturday): Open inch rate $50.40
News services: AP, MCT, NNS. **Established:** 1867
Special Editions: Home Sweet Homes Tab (Apr); Women in Business (Aug); Letters to Santa (Dec); President's Pages I & II (Feb); School Guide Pages (Jan); Kids Tab (Jun); Women in Business (Mar); Mother's Day Tab (May); Thanksgiving Day Dine-Out I & II (Nov); Home Improvemen
Special Weekly Sections: Friday Entertainment Guide (Fri); Senior (Thur); Health (Wed).
Syndicated Publications: Parade (Sat).
Pub... Kenneth Whitfield
Exec. Asst. to Pub. ....Fran Donovan
Oper. Dir. ....Denise Copeland
Mktg. Dir.....................................Sharon Ambis
Gen. Mgr..................................... S.I. Newhouse
Acct. Dept. Mgr................. John O'Shaughnessy
Adv. Mgr., Retail.......................... Tom Pritchard
Ed. in Chief.......................... Steven Newhouse
Ed....Judith Locorriere
VP & Ed.................................. Margaret Schmidt
News Ed....................................Agustin Torres
Sports Ed. .... Ron Zeitlinger
Mgmt. Info Servs. Mgr. .... Andy Savva
Prodn. Mgr., Pre Press................Gwen Ramsey
PUBLISHER .... Kendrick Ross
Market Information: ADS; Split run; TMC; Zoned editions.
Mechanical Available: Offset; Black and 3 ROP colors; insert accepted - sample pouches; page cutoffs - 20 1/2.
Mechanical Specifications: Type page 13 1/4 x 21; E - 6 cols, 2 1/16, 1/8 between; A - 6 cols, 2 1/16, 1/8 between; C - 10 cols, 1 1/4, 1/2 between.
Areas Served: Hudson County (NJ)Equipment & Software: MAILROOM EQUIPMENT: Counter Stackers — 1/St; Tying Machines — 1-/MLN.; BUSINESS EQUIPMENT: Icamon/Newzware, 2-Dell/Poweredge CLASSIFIED EQUIPMENT: Hardware — 2-UNIX/PC Servers; Printers — Equipment 20-PC; CLASSIFIED SOFTWARE: HI/ CASH. DISPLAY EQUIPMENT: Hardware — 2-PC P100; DISPLAY SOFTWAREAd Make-up Applications — HI/NewsMaker 3.4; Layout Software — 5-APP/Mac. EDITORIAL EQUIPMENT: Hardware — 45-HI/NewsMaker/HI/XP-21, 15-HI/2100 EDITORIAL SOFTWARE: HI/Newsmaker 3.4. PRODUCTION EQUIPMENT: Hardware — 1-AU/3850, 3-AU/APS Soft Pip, 5-HI/ Mac Browser, Adobe/Photoshop; Scanners — 3-Umax/Flatbed, 3-Kk/NegScanner PRODUCTION SOFTWARE: HI/XP-21 3.5.

SOMERVILLE

COURIER NEWS

92 E Main St, Ste 202, Somerville, N.J., 08876-2319, Somerset; gen tel 908-243-6600; adv tel (732) 643-3926; ed tel (908) 243-6600; gen fax 732-565-7207; adv fax (732) 565-7207; ed fax 732-565-7207; gen/nat adv e-mail www.gannettnj.com; disp adv e-mail www.gannettnj.com; class adv e-mailCNclass@gannett.com; ed e-mail cnmetro@mycentraljersey.com; web site mycentraljersey.com

Group: Gannett
Published: Mon, Tues, Wed, Thur, Fri, Sat, Sun
Weekday Frequency: m
Saturday Frequency: m
Circulation: 6,586; 6,586(sat); 8,406(sun)
Last Audit: AAM September 30, 2017
Advertising Rate (weekday/saturday): Open inch rate $61.09
Advertising Rate (sunday): Open inch rate $64.93
News services: USA TODAY NETWORK, AP **Established:** 1883
Own Printing Facility?: No
Commercial Printers?: No
Special Weekly Sections: Kicks (Friday entertainment section)
Digital Platform - Mobile: Apple, Android
Gen. Mgr./Ed.................................. Paul Grzella
Sen. Rep..........................Jay Jefferson Cooke
Comm. Ed. .... Keith Ryzewicz
President/Publisher............ Thomas M. Donovan
Mechanical Available: Offset; Black and 3 ROP colors; insert accepted - samples; page

cutoffs - 22 3/4.
Mechanical Specifications: Type page 11 5/8 x 21 1/2; E - 6 cols, 2 1/16, 1/8 between; A - 6 cols, 2 1/16, 1/8 between; C - 10 cols, 1 1/4, 1/16 between.
Areas Served: Somerset County
Delivery Method: Mail, Newsstand, RacksEquipment & Software: PRESSROOM EQUIPMENT: Lines — 9-H/Lithomatic 60 double width (plus 6 color decks); Press Drive — 9-HP/60, GE/Motors; Folders — 2-H/3:2; Pasters —9-H/Lithomatic 1972; Reels & Stands — 9-H/Lithomatic 60 1972; Control System — EDS/Control Master.; MAILROOM EQUIPMENT: Counter Stackers — 1-QWI/300, 2-QWI/20, 1/HL; Inserters & Stuffers — 1-HI/1472P; Tying Machines — 3-/Power Strap, 1-/Power Strap/Manual; Wrapping Singles — 2-/QWI; Address Machine — 2-Ch/539, 2-/Spegram.; BUSINESS EQUIPMENT: IBM/AS-400, Dell/PC, IBM/Netfinity BUSINESS SOFTWARE: Microsoft/Office 97, Microsoft/Access, SQL CLASSIFIED EQUIPMENT: Hardware — 17-Tandem/K200; Printers — HP/4000N; CLASSIFIED SOFTWARE: SII/Coyote 3002 (OOOA), Pongrass (Classified). DISPLAY EQUIPMENT: Hardware — APP/Mac; Printers — HP/4050; DISPLAY SOFTWAREAd Make-up Applications — Managing Editor/ALS; Layout Software — Managing Editor/ALS 2.5. EDITORIAL EQUIPMENT: Hardware — Tandem/Himalaya K200; Printers — HP/8100N EDITORIAL SOFTWARE: SII/Coyote 3002 (000A). PRODUCTION EQUIPMENT: Hardware — 2-Anacoil/XPD-32, Epson/Smart Panel; Cameras — 2-C/Marathon; Scanners — Tecsa/TS2470, 2-Epson/836 XL PRODUCTION SOFTWARE: QPS/QuarkXPress 4.11, Pongrass 3.1.16.
Note: Printed at consolidated Gannett site at Rockaway, NJ

HOME NEWS TRIBUNE

92 E Main St, Somerville, N.J., 08876-2319, Somerset; gen tel 908-243-6600; adv tel 732-643-3926; ed tel 908-243-6600; gen fax 732-565-7207; adv fax 732-565-7207; ed fax 732-565-7207; gen/nat adv e-mail www.gannettnj.com; disp adv e-mail www.gannettnj.com; class adv e-mailHNTclass@gannett.com; ed e-mail hntletters@mycentraljersey.com; web site www.mycentraljersey.com
Group: Gannett
Published: Mon, Tues, Wed, Thur, Fri, Sat, Sun
Weekday Frequency: m
Saturday Frequency: m
Circulation: 17,103; 17,103(sat); 20,464(sun)
Last Audit: AAM September 30, 2016
Advertising Rate (weekday/saturday): Open inch rate $76.39
Advertising Rate (sunday): Open inch rate $74.15
News services: USA TODAY, AP, Bloomberg. **Established:** 1879
Own Printing Facility?: No
Commercial Printers?: No
Special Weekly Sections: Pulse Weekend Preview(Fri)
Digital Platform - Mobile: Apple, Android
General Manager/Editor .... Paul Grzella
President/Publisher........... Thomas M. Donovan
Exec Ed. & VP News........................Hollis Towns
Sports Ed. ....Steve Feitl
Reg. Feat. Coord. ....Bill Canacci
Sr. Dir. IT ....Wayne L. Peragallo
Mechanical Available: Offset; Black and 3 ROP colors; insert accepted - Post-it note application on A1; page cutoffs - 22 1/25.
Mechanical Specifications: Type page 11 5/8 x 21; E - 6 cols, 1 5/6, 1/8 between; A - 6 cols, 1 5/6, 1/8 between; C - 10 cols, 1 1/10, 5/72 between.
Areas Served: Middlesex County
Delivery Method: MailEquipment & Software: PRESSROOM EQUIPMENT: Lines — 10-G/Metroliner offset double width 1996; 10-G/Metroliner offset double width 1996; 10-G/Metroliner offset double width 1997; Press Drive — Fin/Digital; Folders — 5-G/3:2; Reels & Stands — 30; MAILROOM EQUIPMENT: Counter Stackers — 1-MM/CS310, 11-QWI/SJ530, 2-Boss/Stacker, 2-QWI/SJ100; Inserters & Stuffers — 1-S/2299, 4-S/NP630, 1/Philipsburg/4 Station Inserter; Tying Machines — 1-Dynaric/SSB79, 6-/Power Strap/PSN-5, 1-/Power Strap/PSN-250, 7-/Power Stra; BUSINESS EQUIPMENT: 2-IBM/AS-400 BUSINESS SOFTWARE: GN/Genesys, Lawson, Cyborg CLASSIFIED EQUIPMENT: Hardware — SII/Sys 66; Printers — Equipment SII/Coyote 3; CLASSIFIED SOFTWARE: SII/Czar II. DISPLAY EQUIPMENT: Hardware — APP/Mac, AG/Scanner; Printers — QMS, HP/5000N; Other Hardware — 1-BBS, First Class, AP AdSend DISPLAY SOFTWAREAd Make-up Applications — Adobe/Illustrator 8.0, Multi-Ad/Creator 4.03, Adobe/Photoshop 5.0; Layout Software — SCS/Layout 8000, AU/Ad Manager. EDITORIAL EQUIPMENT: Hardware — SII/S4566/9-HI/NMP, 3-HI/Photo Browser, 96-SII/Coyote 3, 10-APP/Mac Powerbook; Printers — HP/755C, 2-HP/5000N EDITORIAL SOFTWARE: SII. PRODUCTION EQUIPMENT: Hardware — X, 1-Nu/Flip Top, 3-WL/Lith-X-Pozer III, 1-PrePress/Panther Pro62 Double Truck Imager, 1-AU/SST 3850; Cameras — 1-C/Newspager I; Scanners — 1-Eskofot/2636S, 2-AG/Horizon, 3-AG/Arcus, 3-Kk/2035 Plus, 2-Nikon/Film Scanner, 1-Scitex/Smartscan
Note: Printed at a consolidated Gannett site in Rockaway, NJ

TRENTON

THE TIMES

413 River View Plz, Trenton, N.J., 08611-3420, Mercer; gen tel (609) 989-5454; adv tel (609) 989-5452; ed tel (609) 989-5679; gen fax (609) 989-5739; adv fax (609) 989-5435; gen/nat adv e-mail jmason@njtimes.com; disp adv e-mail retail@njtimes.com; class adv e-mailclassify@njtimes.com; ed e-mail letters@njtimes.com; web site www.nj.com/times/
Group: Advance Publications, Inc.
Published: Mon, Tues, Wed, Thur, Fri, Sat, Sun
Weekday Frequency: m
Saturday Frequency: m
Circulation: 20,554; 21,904(sat); 23,922(sun)
Last Audit: AAM March 31, 2016
Advertising Rate (weekday/saturday): Open inch rate $79.39
Advertising Rate (sunday): Open inch rate $100.48
News services: AP, LAT-WP, NYT, NNS.
Special Editions: Spring Dining Guide (Apr); Fall Special Occasion Planner (Aug); Holiday Dining (Dec); Spring Wedding (Feb); Outlook (Jan); Summer Dining Guide (Jul); Parenting (Jun); Retirement Planning/Nature Living (Mar); Spring Auto (May); Benchmarks (Monthly); Race f
Special Weekly Sections: Best Food Day (Wed); Home (Thur); Entertainment (Fri); Travel, Business, Entertainment, TV (Sun); Business (Daily)
Syndicated Publications: Parade (S).
News Ed...Matt Dowling
Pub...Joan Mason
Mng. Prod / Comm. Ed. .... Kevin Shea
Adv. Mgr........................................ Nick Santise
Market Information: ADS; Split run; TMC; Zoned editions.
Mechanical Available: Offset; Black and 3 ROP colors; insert accepted - product sample-custom bags; page cutoffs - 22 3/4.
Mechanical Specifications: Type page 11 5/8 x 21 1/4; E - 6 cols, 1 13/16, 1/8 between; A - 6 cols, 1 13/16, 1/8 between; C - 10 cols, 1 1/8, 5/64 between.Equipment & Software: PRESSROOM EQUIPMENT: Lines — 10-G/Metro; Folders — 2-G/3:2; MAILROOM EQUIPMENT: Counter Stackers — 3-HL/HT, 1-HL/HT II; Inserters & Stuffers — 2-S/72P; Tying Machines — 2/MLN, 4-/Dynaric; Address Machine — 3-/Wm.; BUSINESS EQUIPMENT: 1-TS/SII, 1-HP/3000 CLASSIFIED EQUIPMENT: Hardware — AT.; DISPLAY EQUIPMENT: Hardware — 5-HI/2100.; EDITORIAL EQUIPMENT: Hardware — AT. PRODUCTION EQUIPMENT: Hardware — 2-AU/APS-6, 2-AU/3850, 1-WL/Lith III; Cameras — 1-C/Marathon, 1-C/NewsPager; Scanners — 1-Eskofot PRODUCTION SOFTWARE: HI/XP-21.

THE TRENTONIAN

600 Perry St, Trenton, N.J., 08618-3934, Mercer; gen tel (609) 989-7800; adv tel (609) 345-1706; ed tel (609) 349-7442; adv fax (609) 989-8758; ed fax (609) 393-6072; gen/nat adv e-mail paadvertising@digitalfirstmedia.com; disp adv e-mail bmurray@trentonian.com; class adv e-mailclassified@trentonian.com; ed e-mail letters@trentonian.com; web site www.trentonian.com
467,742(visitors)
Group: Digital First Media
Published: Mon, Tues, Wed, Thur, Fri, Sat, Sun
Weekday Frequency: m
Saturday Frequency: m
Circulation: 15,964; 14,615(sat); 15,173(sun)
Last Audit: AAM March 31, 2016
Advertising Rate (weekday/saturday): Open inch rate $94.71
News services: AP, SNS, MCT. **Established:** 1946
Special Editions: Trenton Thunder (Apr); NFL Preview (Aug); Gift Guides I, II & III (Dec); Today's Health Care (Feb); Progress (Jan); Family Living (Jul); The Entrepreneurs (Jun); Spring Fashion (Mar); Mother's Day (May); Election Tab (Nov); Women's Health (Oct); Bucks Cou
Special Weekly Sections: Entertainment (Fri); Entertainment (S); Auto (Sat); Best Food Days (Wed).
Syndicated Publications: USA WEEKEND Magazine (S).
Ed. ....John Berry
Adv. Dir......................................Maggie Ashley
Photo Ed. ....Gregg Slaboda
Cir. Dir...Philip Metz
Adv. Mgr....Bill Murray
Edward Condra
Mechanical Available: Letterpress (direct)/Flexo; Black and 3 ROP colors; insert accepted - in-house printing; page cutoffs - 14 3/4.
Mechanical Specifications: Type page 10 7/8 x 14 1/4; E - 5 cols, 2 1/16, 1/8 between; A - 5 cols, 2 1/16, 1/8 between; C - 7 cols, 1 3/8, 1/8 between.Equipment & Software: PRESSROOM EQUIPMENT: Lines — 6-H/6 letter mono unit (2 decks), 2-H/Flexo mono unit (2 decks); Folders — G/3:2, G/2:1; Control System — PEC/Supervisors.; MAILROOM EQUIPMENT: Counter Stackers — 2-HL/HT Monitor; Inserters & Stuffers — HI; Tying Machines — 1/MSB, 1-MLN/2AHS, 2-MLN/2EE; Wrapping Singles — Power Strap/PSN250; Control System — HI.; BUSINESS EQUIPMENT: IBM/AS-400 BUSINESS SOFTWARE: INSI CLASSIFIED EQUIPMENT: Hardware — PC Network; Printers — APP/Mac Laser Writer; CLASSIFIED SOFTWARE: PPI. DISPLAY EQUIPMENT: Hardware — Epson/Scanner; Printers — HP/5000; DISPLAY SOFTWAREAd Make-up Applications — Multi-Ad/Creator 4.0, Adobe/Illustrator 5.5, Adobe/Photoshop 4.0, QPS/QuarkXpress 4.0; Layout Software — ALS. EDITORIAL EQUIPMENT: Hardware — Dewar/Information System, PC Network; Printers — HP/5000, APP/Mac Laser Writers EDITORIAL SOFTWARE: Dewar/View, QPS/QuarkXPress 3.32. PRODUCTION EQUIPMENT: Hardware — Atm, Harlequin Rips, Burgess; Scanners — Epson PRODUCTION SOFTWARE: AT/Dewarview.

VINELAND

THE DAILY JOURNAL

891 E Oak Rd, Unit A, Vineland, N.J., 08360-2311, Cumberland; gen tel (856) 691-5000; adv tel (732) 643-3703; ed tel (856) 691-5000; gen fax (856) 563-5282; ed fax (856) 563-5308; gen/nat adv e-mail jcalchi@gannett.com; disp adv e-mail jcalchi@gannett.com; class adv e-mailclassified@thedailyjournal.com; ed e-mail djopinon@thedailyjournal.com; web site www.thedailyjournal.com
Group: Gannett
Published: Mon, Tues, Wed, Thur, Fri, Sat
Weekday Frequency: m
Saturday Frequency: m
Circulation: 9,664; 11,942(sat)
Last Audit: AAM December 31, 2015
Advertising Rate (weekday/saturday): Open inch rate $54.74
News services: AP, GNS. **Established:** 1875
Special Weekly Sections: Best Food Day (Wed); Real Estate (Fri); TV, School, Teen (Sat)
Syndicated Publications: TV Journal (Sat).
Pres. & Pub..................................Joseph Calchi
Circ. Ops. Mgr. .... Les Olson
Plan. Ed. .... John Garrahan
Reg. Ed....Jason Alt
Reg. Cont. Strategist........... Jerry Staas-Haught
Market Information: ADS; TMC.
Mechanical Available: Offset; Black and 3 ROP colors; insert accepted; page cutoffs - 21.
Mechanical Specifications: Type page 10 x 21; E - 6 cols, 1 1/4, 1/8 between; A - 6 cols, 1 1/4, 1/8 between; C - 10 cols, 7/8, 1/8 between.
Areas Served: Vineland, Millville & Greater Cumberland Counties (NJ)
Equipment & Software: PRESSROOM EQUIPMENT: Lines — 5-G/Metro double width 1971; Press Drive — Fin/60 HP West; Folders — G/2:1 double.; MAILROOM EQUIPMENT: Counter Stackers — QWI/100; Inserters & Stuffers — 2-MM/227 5:1; Tying Machines — 2/MLN, 2-/Power Strap/Newstyer 2000; Address Machine — 1-Domino/Ink Jet.; BUSINESS EQUIPMENT: 1-IBM/AS-400 B30 CLASSIFIED EQUIPMENT: Hardware — APT; HP/ScanJet 5s, Eskofot/EskoScan 2636, Teca/EU3000 Scanner; Printers — HP/4MV, HP/5000gn; CLASSIFIED SOFTWARE: APT/ACT, QPS/QuarkXPress 3.32, Microsoft/Word 97. DISPLAY EQUIPMENT: Hardware — APP/Mac Server, APP/MAC G3; Printers — HP/5000; Other Hardware — 2-AG/Studio Scanner DISPLAY SOFTWAREAd Make-up Applications — QPS/QuarkXPress, Adobe/Photoshop, Aldus/FreeHand; Layout Software — 1-APP/Power Mac 7100, 1-APP/Power Mac 8500, 3-APP/Mac G3, 1-APP/Power Mac 7200, 1-APP/Po EDITORIAL EQUIPMENT: Hardware — APT/Lf/AP Leaf Picture Desk, 2-AG/Studio Scanner, Nikon/LS1000 Coolscan; Printers — HP, HP/5000 EDITORIAL SOFTWARE: APT/ACT, QPS/QuarkXPress 3.32, Microsoft/Word 97. PRODUCTION EQUIPMENT: Hardware — HP/ScanJet 5s, ECR/4550, LE/LD800A, LE/R660; Cameras — C/Marathon, C/Spartan II; Scanners — ECR/Autokon 1000, Scanmate/3000, Eskofot/TecaPage Scanner PRODUCTION SOFTWARE: APT, QPS/QuarkXPress 3.32.

WILLINGBORO

BURLINGTON COUNTY TIMES

4284 Route 130, Willingboro, N.J., 08046-2027, Burlington; gen tel (609) 871-8000; adv tel (215) 949-4825; ed tel (609) 871-8143; gen fax (609) 871-0490; adv fax (609) 871-8145; ed fax (609) 871-0490; gen/nat adv e-mail feedback@thebct.com; disp adv e-mail epursley@thebct.com; class adv e-mailclassifieds@thebct.com; ed e-mail sfitzgerald@thebct.com; web site www.burlingtoncountytimes.com
800,000(visitors); web site 2 www.phillyburbs.com/bct
Group: GateHouse Media, Inc.
Published: Mon, Tues, Wed, Thur, Fri, Sun
Weekday Frequency: m
Saturday Frequency: m
Circulation: 17,634; 23,614(sun)
Last Audit: AAM June 30, 2016
Advertising Rate (weekday/saturday): $23.00 per column inch.
Advertising Rate (sunday): $25.00 per column inch.
Online Advertising Rate: Various sizes locations on the site and prices.
News services: AP, NEA. **Established:** 1958
Own Printing Facility?: Yes
Commercial Printers?: Yes
Special Editions: Discover Burlington (May); Best of Burlington (Sep); HS Fall Sports (Sep); Holiday Gift Guide (Dec).
Special Weekly Sections: To Do (Fri);
Digital Platform - Mobile: Apple, Android
Digital Platform - Tablet: Apple iOS, Android
Feat. Ed. .... Martha Esposito
Managing Editor ....Audrey Harvin
Executive Editor...................... Shane Fitzgerald
Market Information: Split run;
Mechanical Available: Offset; Black and 3 ROP colors; insert accepted - product samples;

page cutoffs - 21 1/2.
Mechanical Specifications: Type page 10.125" x 20"; E - 6 cols, 1.56", .153" between; A - 6 cols, 1.56", .153" between; C - 6 cols, 1.56", .153" between.
Areas Served: All of Burlington County, New Jersey
Delivery Method: Newsstand, Carrier, RacksEquipment & Software: PRESSROOM EQUIPMENT: Lines — 4-Man Roland Geoman 1994; Folders — 2-G/2:1; Reels & Stands — 5-G; Control System — PComm.; MAILROOM EQUIPMENT: 2 - SLS 3000 12 into 1 with combination stackers and strappers. BUSINESS SOFTWARE: Software Business Systems Inc., ADP Payroll Systems; CLASSIFIED SOFTWARE: ATEX. DISPLAY SOFTWAREATEX EDITORIAL SOFTWARE: Town News BLOX. Indesign. Presteligence. PRODUCTION EQUIPMENT: Hardware — CREO platemakers; Harlequin RIPS; PRODUCTION SOFTWARE: Indesign. CIRCULATION EQUIPMENT: Innovative Design Systems IVR CIRCULATION SOFTWARNewzware; RouteSmart
Note: There is a Greater Philadelphia Newspapers Group combination rate of $239.00(d) & $251.00(S) among the Levittown Bucks County (PA) Courier Times (mS), Doylestown (PA) Intelligencer (mS) & Willingboro Burlington County Times (mS). Individual newspaper rate

WOODLAND PARK

THE RECORD

1 Garret Mountain Plz, Ste 201, Woodland Park, N.J., 07424-3318, Passaic; gen tel (973) 569-7000; adv tel (973) 569-7434; ed tel (973) 569-7100; gen fax (973) 569-7268; adv fax (973) 905-4023; ed fax (201) 457-2520; gen/nat adv e-mail bartholomew@northjersey.com; disp adv e-mail szollar@northjersey.com; class adv e-mailclassifieds@northjersey.com; ed e-mail letterstotheeditor@northjersey.com; web site www.northjersey.com
6,795,911(visitors)
Group: Gannett
Published: Mon, Tues, Wed, Thur, Fri, Sat, Sun
Weekday Frequency: m
Saturday Frequency: m
Circulation: 125,038; 135,029(sat); 158,818(sun)
Last Audit: AAM December 31, 2016
News services: 1930
Chairman .... Malcom Borg
VP / HR .... Susan Beard
VP / Cir. & Mfg. .... Robert Konig
Dir. of Marketing .... Maggie Grande
Pres. .... Nancy Meyer
Adv. Dir. .... Mark Szollar
Deirdre Sykes
HR. Mgr. .... Kathy Batemarco

NEW MEXICO

ALAMOGORDO

ALAMOGORDO DAILY NEWS

518 24th St, Alamogordo, N.M., 88310-6104, Otero; gen tel (877) 301-0013; adv tel (575) 437-7120 ext. 7134; ed tel (575) 437-7120 ext. 7134; gen fax (575) 437-7795; gen/nat adv e-mail leudy@alamogordonews.com; disp adv e-mail eduran@alamogordonews.com; class adv e-mailbnajar@alamogordonews.com; ed e-mail dbarbati@alamogordonews.com; web site www.alamogordonews.com
- 413,000(views) 120,000(visitors)
Group: Gannett
Published: Tues, Wed, Thur, Fri, Sat, Sun
Weekday Frequency: m
Saturday Frequency: m
Circulation: 3,520; 3,520(sat); 3,910(sun)
Last Audit: AAM June 30, 2016
Advertising Rate (weekday/saturday): Open inch rate $14.62
Advertising Rate (sunday): Open inch rate $15.44
Online Advertising Rate: $10.00 per thousand
News services: AP, CNS. **Established:** 1898
Own Printing Facility?: No
Commercial Printers?: No
Special Editions: Back-to-School (Jul);Women of Merit (Mar); Holiday Gift Guide (Nov); Graduation (May)
Syndicated Publications: Relish (Monthly); USA WEEKEND Magazine (S);
Proprietary Publications: Hollogram
GM .... Carol Burgess
Lead Dist.Mgr. .... Rick Gwaltney
Dist. Mgr. .... Anthony Davis
Mng. Ed. .... Duane Barbati
Hollogram Ed .... Jacqueline Devine
Market Information: TMC.
Mechanical Available: Offset; Black and 3 ROP colors; insert accepted; page cutoffs - 22 3/4.
Mechanical Specifications: Type page 12 1/2 x 21 1/2; E - 6 cols, 2 1/16, 1/8 between; A - 6 cols, 2 1/16, 1/8 between; C - 8 cols, 1 3/8, 1/16 between.
Areas Served: Otero County
Delivery Method: Mail, Newsstand, Racks

ALBUQUERQUE

ALBUQUERQUE JOURNAL

7777 Jefferson St NE, Albuquerque, N.M., 87109-4343, Bernalillo; gen tel 505-823-7777; adv tel (505) 823-3300; ed tel (505) 823-3800; gen fax (505) 823-3369; adv fax (505) 823-3369; ed fax (505) 823-3994; gen/nat adv e-mail sfriedes@abqpubco.com; disp adv e-mail advertising@abqpubco.com; class adv e-mailsgutierrez@abqpubco.com; ed e-mail journal@abqjournal.com; web site www.abqjournal.com
679,091(visitors)
Group: Albuquerque Publishing Company
Published: Mon, Tues, Wed, Thur, Fri, Sat, Sun
Weekday Frequency: m
Saturday Frequency: m
Circulation: 83,795; 89,602(sat); 106,803(sun)
Last Audit: AAM December 31, 2016
Advertising Rate (weekday/saturday): Open inch rate
Advertising Rate (sunday): Open inch rate
Online Advertising Rate: Call Sharon Friedes for industry specific rates.
(505) 823-3301
News services: AP, LAT-WP, CSM, MCT, RN. **Established:** 1880
Own Printing Facility?: Yes
Commercial Printers?: Yes
Special Editions: At Home & Garden (Mar); American Home Week (Apr); Summer Guide (May); Green NM (Jun); Back to School, Native American Art NM (Aug); State Fair (Sept); Balloon Fiesta (Oct); Winter Guide (Nov); Holiday Gift Guide (Nov); Holiday Gift Ideas, Last Minute Gift Guide (Dec)
Special Weekly Sections: Business (Mon); Food (Wed); Venue (Fri); Entertainment (Sat); Travel, Leisure, Real Estate (Sun)
Syndicated Publications: Relish (Monthly); Parade (Sun); American Profile (Tue);Athlon Sports (Monthly)
Digital Platform - Mobile: Apple, Android
Digital Platform - Tablet: Apple iOS, Android, Kindle, Kindle Fire
Pres./CEO .... William P. Lang
VP/CFO .... Lowell A. Hare
Ed-in-Chief .... Kent Walz
Mng. Ed. .... Karen Moses
Bus. Ed. .... Charlie Moore
Asst. Mng. Ed., Online .... Donn Friedman
Journal Arts & Entertain. Editor ..... Adrian Gomez
Asst. Mng. Ed. .... Joe Kirby
Office Mgr. .... Sandy O'Dell
Asst. City Ed. .... Isabel Sanchez
City Ed. .... Nick Pappas
Asst. Bus. Ed. .... Ellen Marks
Bus. Edit. Asst. .... Terry Feld
Ed. Pg. Ed. .... Dan Herrera
Asst. Poli. Ed .... Stephen Williams
Special Sec./Feat. Ed. .... Helen Taylor
Journal Asst. Sports Ed. .... Ed Johnson
Journal Sports Ed. .... Randy Harrison
Journal Asst. Sports Ed. .... Mark Smith
Crime & Breaking News Ed., Onl. .... Robert Browman
Web Devel., Prod. .... Greg Peretti
Photo Ed. .... Morgan Petroski
Asst. Photo Ed. .... Greg Sorber
Copy Ed .... Robyn Smith
ABQJournal.com .... Nancy Tipton
Journal Wash. Bureau .... Michael Coleman
Market Information: Split run; Zoned editions
Mechanical Available: Offset; Black and 4 ROP colors; inserts accepted; page cutoffs - 21 1/2.
Areas Served: New Mexico
Delivery Method: Mail, Newsstand, Carrier, RacksEquipment & Software: CLASSIFIED SOFTWARE: C-Text.
Note: For current advertising rates and detailed production and printing information please contact Albuquerque Publishing Co. at 505-823-7777

ARTESIA

ARTESIA DAILY PRESS

503 W Main St, Artesia, N.M., 88210-2067, Eddy; gen tel (575) 746-3524; gen fax (575) 746-8795; gen/nat adv e-mail display@artesianews.com; class adv e-mailclassifieds@artesianews.com; ed e-mail editor@artesianews.com; web site www.artesianews.com
- 11,000(views) 11,000(visitors)
Published: Tues, Wed, Thur, Fri, Sun
Weekday Frequency: e
Circulation: 2,900; 3,500(sun)
Last Audit: USPS September 27, 2012
Newspaper Reps: Danny Scott
Walt Green
Advertising Rate (weekday/saturday): Open inch rate $7.35
Advertising Rate (sunday): $7.35
News services: ap **Established:** 1954
Own Printing Facility?: Yes
Commercial Printers?: No
Special Editions: Business Review- January
Tax Edition-February
Spring Edition- March
Health & Fitness- April
Graduation- May
County Fair- July
Football Preview- August
Oil & Soil Edition- September
Best of Artesia- October
Christmas Greetings- December
Digital Platform - Mobile: Windows
Digital Platform - Tablet: Windows 7
Pub. .... Danny Scott
Admin. .... Latisha Romine
Delivery Method: Mail, Newsstand, Carrier, Racks

CARLSBAD

CURRENT-ARGUS

620 S Main St, Carlsbad, N.M., 88220-6243, Eddy; gen tel (575) 887-5501; ed tel (575) 628-5531; gen fax (575) 885-1066; gen/nat adv e-mail lanaya@currentargus.com; disp adv e-mail carredondo@currentargus.com; class adv e-maildaortiz@currentargus.com; ed e-mail jonsurez@currentargus.com; web site www.currentargus.com
- 750,000(views) 90,000(visitors)
Group: Gannett
Published: Tues, Wed, Thur, Fri, Sat, Sun
Weekday Frequency: m
Saturday Frequency: m
Circulation: 3,302; 3,302(sat); 3,593(sun)
Last Audit: AAM September 30, 2015
Advertising Rate (weekday/saturday): Open inch rate $18.37
Advertising Rate (sunday): Open inch rate $16.02
News services: AP. **Established:** 1889
Special Editions: The Spring (Apr); Back-to-School (Aug); Christmas Greetings (Dec); Valentine's Love Photos (Feb); Chronology (Jan); Western Days (Jul); Our Town (Mar); Newspapers in Schools/Design-An-Ad (May); Christmas Gift Guide (Nov); Retirement (Oct); Football (Sept)
Special Weekly Sections: Best Real Estate Days (Fri); Best Real Estate Days (S); Best Food Day (Wed).
Syndicated Publications: TV Spotlight (Fri); USA WEEKEND Magazine (S); American Profile (Weekly).
Digital Platform - Mobile: Apple
Digital Platform - Tablet: Apple iOS
Multi. Med. Cons. .... Cynthia Arredondo
Sports Editor .... Matt Hollinshead
Acct. Crk. .... Shirley Maxwell
Gen. Mgr. .... Danny Fletcher
Cir. Dist. Mgr. .... Judi Freisinger
Class. Rep. .... Anthony Ortiz
Mng. Ed. .... Jessica Onsurez
Pub. .... David R. Stringer
Market Information: TMC.
Mechanical Available: Offset; Black and 3 ROP colors; insert accepted; page cutoffs - 22 1/2.
Mechanical Specifications: Type page 13 x 21 1/2; E - 6 cols, 2 1/16, 1/8 between; A - 6 cols, 2 1/16, 1/8 between; C - 6 cols, 2 1/16, 1/8 between.
Areas Served: Carlsbad, Artesia, Loving & Eddy Counties (NM)Equipment & Software: PRESSROOM EQUIPMENT: Lines — 6-G/Community 1975; Folders — G/Community Quarter.; MAILROOM EQUIPMENT: Tying Machines — Bu/Tyer.; BUSINESS EQUIPMENT: IBM/5363 CLASSIFIED EQUIPMENT: Hardware — CText; ECR/Imagesetter; Printers — APP/Mac LaserPrinters; CLASSIFIED SOFTWARE: XYQUEST/XyWrite, CText. DISPLAY EQUIPMENT: Hardware — CText/Adept; Printers — APP/Mac LaserPrinters; Other Hardware — ECR/Imagesetter DISPLAY SOFTWAREAd Make-up Applications — Microsoft/Windows; Layout Software — CText. EDITORIAL EQUIPMENT: Hardware — CText/ECR/Imagesetter; Printers — APP/Mac LaserPrinters EDITORIAL SOFTWARE: XYQUEST/XyWrite, CText. PRODUCTION EQUIPMENT: Hardware — ECR/Imagesetter; Cameras — Nu/2024 M2 Camera.

CLOVIS

EASTERN NEW MEXICO NEWS

521 Pile St, Clovis, N.M., 88101-6637, Curry; gen tel 15757633431; adv tel (575) 763-3431; ed tel (575) 763-3431; gen fax (575) 762-3879; adv fax (575) 762-3879; ed fax (575) 742-1349; gen/nat adv e-mail cnjadvertising@thenews.email; disp adv e-mail cnjadvertising@thenews.email; class adv e-mailclassified@thenews.email; ed e-mail dstevens@thenews.email; web site http://www.easternnewmexiconews.com/
- 565,596(views) 84,751(visitors)
Group: Stevenson Newspapers
Published: Tues, Wed, Thur, Fri, Sat, Sun
Weekday Frequency: m
Saturday Frequency: m
Circulation: 4,817; 4,817(sat); 5,717(sun)
Last Audit: VAC October 10, 2017
Advertising Rate (weekday/saturday): Open inch rate $20.00
Advertising Rate (sunday): Open inch rate $25.00
Online Advertising Rate: Daily - $25 (3-day minimum); Weekly - $125; Monthly - $450.
News services: AP, McClatchy **Established:** 1929
Own Printing Facility?: No
Commercial Printers?: No
Special Weekly Sections: Just TV (S)
Syndicated Publications: Parade - Sunday
PUBLISHER .... ROB LANGRELL
Ed. .... David Stevens
Circ. Dir. .... Cindy Cole
Hum. Res. Dir. .... Joyce Cruce
Creative Services Director .... Shawn Luscombe
Managing Editor .... Kevin Wilson
Business Manager .... Annie Stout
Market Information: TMC.
Mechanical Available: Offset; Black and 3 ROP colors; insert accepted; page cutoffs - 22.
Mechanical Specifications: Type page 11 x 21; E - 6 cols, 1 13/16, 1/8 between; A - 6 cols, 2 13/16, 1/8 between; C - 9 cols, 1 3/16, 1/8 between.
Areas Served: Clovis County, Portales County, Tucumari County, Cannon Air Force Base.
Delivery Method: Mail, Newsstand, Carrier, RacksEquipment & Software: PRESSROOM EQUIPMENT: Lines — 8-HI/V-15A 1974. Quad Stack Color Press; MAILROOM EQUIPMENT: Tying Machines — 2-/Bu.; BUSINESS EQUIPMENT: Dell/HP BUSINESS SOFTWARE: Vision Data AR2000, Quickbooks Pro CLASSIFIED

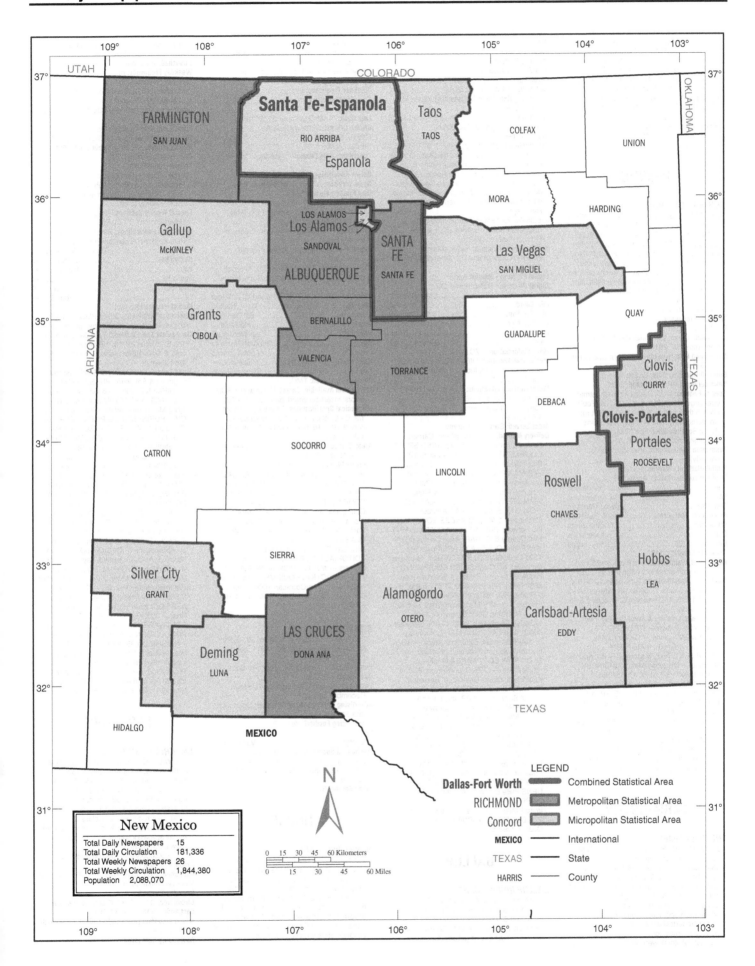

UTAH

109°   108°   107°   106°   105°   104°   103°

COLORADO

37°

FARMINGTON

SAN JUAN

Santa Fe-Espanola

RIO ARRIBA

Espanola

Taos

TAOS

COLFAX

UNION

OKLAHOMA

36°

Gallup

McKINLEY

LOS ALAMOS

Los Alamos

SANDOVAL

ALBUQUERQUE

SANTA
FE

SANTA FE

MORA

HARDING

Las Vegas

SAN MIGUEL

ARIZONA

Grants

CIBOLA

BERNALILLO

VALENCIA

TORRANCE

GUADALUPE

QUAY

35°

DEBACA

Clovis-Portales

Clovis

CURRY

TEXAS

CATRON

SOCORRO

LINCOLN

Portales

ROOSEVELT

34°

Roswell

CHAVES

SIERRA

Hobbs

LEA

33°

Silver City

GRANT

Alamogordo

OTERO

Carlsbad-Artesia

EDDY

32°

Deming

LUNA

LAS CRUCES

DONA ANA

HIDALGO

MEXICO

TEXAS

31°

N

New Mexico

Total Daily Newspapers   15
Total Daily Circulation   181,336
Total Weekly Newspapers   26
Total Weekly Circulation   1,844,380
Population   2,088,070

0   15   30   45   60 Kilometers

0   15   30   45   60 Miles

LEGEND

Dallas-Fort Worth ▬ Combined Statistical Area

RICHMOND ▮ Metropolitan Statistical Area

Concord ▯ Micropolitan Statistical Area

MEXICO ─── International

TEXAS ─── State

HARRIS ─── County

109°   108°   107°   106°   105°   104°   103°

EQUIPMENT: Hardware — APP/Mac; CLASSIFIED SOFTWARE: Baseview. DISPLAY EQUIPMENT: Hardware — APP/Mac; Printers — HP, Ricoh; DISPLAY SOFTWAREAd Make-up Applications — AdManager Pro 4; EDITORIAL EQUIPMENT: Hardware — APP/Mac; Printers — HP EDITORIAL SOFTWARE: Baseview. PRODUCTION EQUIPMENT: Hardware — App/MAC, Trendsetters; Cameras — R/580; Scanners — Umax Astra 1220U, Canon PRODUCTION SOFTWARE: QPS/QuarkXPress 6.5

DEMING

DEMING HEADLIGHT

219 E Maple St, Deming, N.M., 88030-4267, Luna; gen tel (575) 546-2611; adv tel (915) 541-5433; ed tel (575) 546-2611 ext. 2626; gen fax (575) 546-8116; adv fax (915) 546-6404; ed fax (915) 546-6284; gen/nat adv e-mail jngutierre@lcsun-news.com; class adv e-mailgwebb@deminghheadlight.com; ed e-mail barmendariz@demingheadlight.com; web site www.demingheadlight.com

Group: Gannett
Published: Mon, Tues, Wed, Thur, Fri
Weekday Frequency: m
Circulation: 3,541
Last Audit: Sworn/Estimate/Non-Audited September 30, 2017
Advertising Rate (weekday/saturday): Open inch rate $11.85
Online Advertising Rate: Call to inquire.
News services: AP. **Established:** 1881
Special Editions: Duck Race (Aug); Christmas Greetings (Dec); Community Guide (Feb); Life Off the Land (Jul); Medical Tab (Jun); Horizons (Mar); Senior (May); Christmas (Nov); Southwestern Fair (Oct); Mimbres Paguime Connection (Sept).
Syndicated Publications: American Profile (Weekly).
Digital Platform - Mobile: Apple
Digital Platform - Tablet: Apple iOS
Pres.....................Rynni Henderson
Ed.....................Bill Armendariz
Gen. Mgr.....................Jared Hamilton
Multi. Med. Acct. Exec.....................Joseph Gutierrez
Off. Admin.....................Debbie Seats
Rep.....................Jesse Moya
Circ. Mgr.....................Larry Higgs
Market Information: TMC.
Mechanical Available: Offset; Black and 3 ROP colors; insert accepted; page cutoffs - 16.
Mechanical Specifications: Type page 10 3/16 x 15 3/4; E - 5 cols, 1 15/16, 1/8 between; A - 5 cols, 1 15/16, 1/8 between; C - 7 cols, 1 5/16, 1/8 between.
Areas Served: Deming & Luna County (NM)
Equipment & Software: PRESSROOM EQUIPMENT: Lines — G/Community; Folders — 1-G/4:1.; MAILROOM EQUIPMENT: Tying Machines — Bu; Address Machine — Dispensa-Matic.; BUSINESS EQUIPMENT: 3-IBM/PC CLASSIFIED EQUIPMENT: Hardware — GraphX; 2-COM; Printers — HP/LaserJet IVsi.; DISPLAY EQUIPMENT: Hardware — APP/Mac; Other Hardware — APP/Mac, Umax/Vista 12 Scanner, Elite/XL1208 printer, APP/Power Mac. EDITORIAL EQUIPMENT: Hardware — APP/Mac/5-COM EDITORIAL SOFTWARE: Claris/Works, QPS/QuarkXPress. PRODUCTION EQUIPMENT: Hardware — 1-COM/Hd, 2-COM/2-Laser; Cameras — R/Horizontal.

FARMINGTON

THE DAILY TIMES

203 W Main St, Ste 101, Farmington, N.M., 87401-6209, San Juan; gen tel (505) 325-4545; adv tel (505) 325-4540; ed tel (505) 325-4545; gen fax (505) 564-4630; adv fax (505) 564-4630; ed fax (505) 564-4630; gen/nat adv e-mail chill@daily-times.com; disp adv e-mail gjohnson@daily-times.com; class adv e-mailmegonzalez@daily-times.com; ed e-mail croberts@daily-times.com; web site www.daily-times.com
121,725(visitors); web site 2 http://static.daily-times.com/customerservice/

Group: Gannett
Published: Mon, Tues, Wed, Thur, Fri, Sat, Sun
Weekday Frequency: m
Saturday Frequency: m
Circulation: 7,166; 7,166(sat); 7,940(sun)
Last Audit: AAM June 30, 2017
Advertising Rate (weekday/saturday): Open inch rate $25.30
Advertising Rate (sunday): Open inch rate $19.15
Online Advertising Rate: $10.00/pci
News services: AP, NYT.
Own Printing Facility?: Yes
Special Editions: Reader's Choice (Apr); Connie Mack (Aug); Christmas (Dec); Home Expo (Feb); National High School Rodeo (Jul); Freedom Days (Jun); San Juan County Fair (May); Travel Guide (Nov); Parade of Homes (Oct); Health Living (Quarterly); Shiprock Fair (Sept).
Special Weekly Sections: Automotive (Fri); Business (Mon); Lifestyles (S); Explore (Thur); Lifestyles (Wed).
Syndicated Publications: Relish (Monthly); USA WEEKEND Magazine (S); American Profile (Weekly).
Digital Platform - Mobile: Apple
Digital Platform - Tablet: Apple iOS
Ed.....................Chris Roberts
Adv. Coord.....................Chris Hill
Dist. Cir. Sup.....................Julie Gambell
Cir. Dist. Mgr.....................Rueben Acosta
Admin. Asst.....................Penni Curtis
Pres.....................Sammy Lopez
Market Information: TMC.
Mechanical Available: Offset; Black and 3 ROP colors; insert accepted - job shop; page cutoffs - 22 3/4.
Mechanical Specifications: Type page 11 3/4 x 21 1/2; E - 6 cols, 1 5/6, 1/6 between; A - 6 cols, 1 5/6, 1/6 between; C - 9 cols, 1 1/12, 1/6 between.
Areas Served: San Juan County
Delivery Method: Mail, Newsstand, Carrier, RacksEquipment & Software: PRESSROOM EQUIPMENT: Lines — 6-G/Urbanite 1979; Press Drive — 2-HP/100; Reels & Stands — 2; MAILROOM EQUIPMENT: Counter Stackers — 1-HL/Monitor HT II, 1/MM, 1-HL/Monitor, 1-/BG; Inserters & Stuffers — 2-MM/227; Tying Machines — 2-OVL/41E, 1-OVL/515, Samuel/NT440; Address Machine — 1-/KR; BUSINESS EQUIPMENT: PC Network, 2-AT, 1-Epson/LQ2550, 2-APP/Mac Quadra 610, 1-APP/Mac Centris 660AV, 1-APP/Mac Quadra 630, APP/Power Mac 7200-75 BUSINESS SOFTWARE: Baseview, Dynamics 4.0 CLASSIFIED EQUIPMENT: Hardware — 5-APP/iMac; 1-Toshiba/Copier 2532 Turbo, 1-Toshiba/Fax TF651 Turbo, 1-Brother/Fax 1850mc, 2-Nikon/Digital; Printers — 1-APP/Mac LaserWriter 12-640 PS, 1-APP/Mac Color Stylewriter 4100, 1-Okidata/Pacemark 3410, 1-HP/Deskwriter 560C,; DISPLAY EQUIPMENT: Hardware — 5-APP/Mac G4; Other Hardware — AG/Horizon Scanner, Polaroid/SprintScan 35 DISPLAY SOFTWAREAd Make-up Applications — QPS/QuarkXPress, Adobe/Photoshop, Caere/OmniPage, Baseview, Xante/Accel-a-Writer 8200, Adobe/Acrobat; Layout Software — APP/Mac network. EDITORIAL EQUIPMENT: Hardware — 1-APP/Mac PowerBook 520c, 5-APP/Mac Centris 650, 1-APP/Mac Quadra 605, 2-APP/Mac Quadra 610, 4-APP/Mac Quadra 630, 1-APP/Mac Quadra 700, 1-APP/Mac Quadra 900, 2-APP/Mac PowerBook 150, 1-APP/Mac PowerBook 1400CS, 1-APP/Mac PowerBook 3400C, 1-APP PRODUCTION EQUIPMENT: Hardware — 1-Nu/FT40V6 UPNS Plate Burner, 2-APP/Mac G3, 2-APP/Mac 7300, Pre Press/Panther Pro Imagesetter; Scanners — Scitex/Eversmart PRODUCTION SOFTWARE: QPS/QuarkXPress 5.0.

GALLUP

GALLUP INDEPENDENT

500 N Ninth St, Gallup, N.M., 87301-5379, McKinley; gen tel (505) 863-6811; adv tel (505) 863-6811 ext. 233; ed tel (505) 863-6811 ext. 213; gen fax (505) 722-5750; gen/nat adv e-mail ads1@gallupindependent.com; class adv e-mailgaindep.class@gmail.com; ed e-mail letters@gallupindependent.com; web site www.gallupindependent.com - 4,500(views)

Group: New Mexico Press Association
Published: Mon, Tues, Wed, Thur, Fri, Sat
Weekday Frequency: e
Saturday Frequency: m
Circulation: 12,370; 12,370(sat)
Last Audit: AAM December 31, 2015
Branch Offices: Window Rock, Ariz.
Grants, N.M.
Ramah, N.M.
Advertising Rate (weekday/saturday): Open inch rate $23.00
Online Advertising Rate: $200/mo.
News services: AP, NYT. **Established:** 1904
Own Printing Facility?: Yes
Commercial Printers?: Yes
Special Editions: Off the Beaten Path (May, Sept.) Ceremonial (Aug.)
Syndicated Publications: American Profile (bi-weekly Sat.).
Digital Platform - Mobile: Apple, Android, Blackberry
Digital Platform - Tablet: Apple iOS, Android, Blackberry Tablet OS, Kindle, Nook, Kindle Fire
Vice Pres./Pub.....................Robert C. Zollinger
Mng. Ed.....................Barry Heifner
Cops/courts....................Bill Donavan
Sports Ed.....................Alan Authur
Prod. Ed.....................Cecil Rodriguez
Adv.....................Deborah Ramirez
Circ.....................Leona Torrivio
Chief Photo.....................Cable Hoover
City Ed.....................Richard Reyes
Market Information: TMC;
Mechanical Available: Offset; Black and 3 ROP colors; insert accepted; page cutoffs - 22.
Mechanical Specifications: Type page 13 x 21 1/2; E - 6 cols, 2 1/16, 1/8 between; A - 6 cols, 2 1/16, 1/8 between; C - 7 cols, 1 3/4, 1/8 between.
Areas Served: Northwestern NM, Northeastern AZ & Navajo Nation
Delivery Method: Newsstand, Carrier, RacksEquipment & Software: PRESSROOM EQUIPMENT: Lines — 24-G/Magnum (6 towers); Folders — Universal.; MAILROOM EQUIPMENT: Counter Stackers — 1/Exact Count; Inserters & Stuffers — 10-MM/Alphaliner; Tying Machines — 2-Wilton/Stra Pack.; BUSINESS EQUIPMENT: 1-IBM/36 CLASSIFIED SOFTWARE: Baseview. DISPLAY EQUIPMENT: Hardware — HI.; EDITORIAL EQUIPMENT: Hardware — HI; Printers — MON EDITORIAL SOFTWARE: HI. PRODUCTION EQUIPMENT: Hardware — 2-Nu, 1-Nikon/Coolscan 1000, 1-Nikon/Coolscan 2000; Cameras — R/Lens, OH, LE/500

MESSENGER

500 N Ninth St, Gallup, N.M., 87301-5379, McKinley; gen tel (505) 863-6811; gen fax (505) 722-5750

Published: Mon, Tues, Wed, Thur, Fri, Sat
Circulation: 12,838
Last Audit: Sworn/Estimate/Non-Audited December 18, 2017
Advertising Rate (weekday/saturday): Open inch rate $4.38
Own Printing Facility?: Yes
Pub.....................Robert C. Zollinger
Circ. Mgr.....................Valda Brown
Mechanical Specifications: Type page 7 x 21 1/2; E - 7 cols, 2 1/16, 1/8 between; A - 7 cols, 2 1/16, 1/8 between; C - 7 cols, 2 1/16, 1/8 between.
Areas Served: 87305

HOBBS

HOBBS NEWS-SUN

201 N Thorp St, Hobbs, N.M., 88240-6058, Lea; gen tel (575) 393-2123; adv tel (575) 391-5404; ed tel (575) 393-2123; gen fax (575) 397-0610; adv fax (575) 397-0610; ed fax (575) 393-5724; gen/nat adv e-mail hnsads@hobbsnews.com; disp adv e-mail advertise@hobbsnews.com; class adv e-mailclassifieds@hobbsnews.com; ed e-mail editor@hobbsnews.com; web site www.hobbsnews.com

Group: New Mexico Press Association
Shearman Corporation
Published: Tues, Wed, Thur, Fri, Sat, Sun
Weekday Frequency: m
Saturday Frequency: m
Circulation: 5,512; 5,512(sat); 5,945(sun)
Last Audit: AAM December 31, 2016
Advertising Rate (weekday/saturday): Open inch rate $13.60
Advertising Rate (sunday): Open inch rate $9.75
Online Advertising Rate: (365x600): $50.00
News services: AP, MCT **Established:** 1928
Own Printing Facility?: Yes
Commercial Printers?: No
Special Editions: Back-to-School (Aug); Progress Issue (Mar); High School & College Graduation (May); Christmas Gift Guide (Nov); Energy (Oct)
Special Weekly Sections: Religion (Sat); Entertainment (Thur). Education (Fri)
Syndicated Publications: Relish (Monthly); Parade (Sun); American Profile (Sat).
Vice Pres.....................Thomas B. Shearman
Design Ed.....................Scott Jones
Pub.....................Daniel Russell
Sports Ed.....................Clayton Jones
Mng. Ed.....................Levi Hill
Ed.....................Todd Bailey
Market Information: TMC.
Mechanical Available: Offset; Black and 3 ROP colors; insert accepted; page cutoffs - 21 1/2.
Mechanical Specifications: Type page 13 x 21 1/2; E - 6 cols, 2 1/16, 1/8 between; A - 6 cols, 2 1/16, 1/8 between; C - 9 cols, 1 5/16, 1/8 between.
Areas Served: Lea County & Southeast NM
Equipment & Software: PRESSROOM EQUIPMENT: Lines — 6-G/Urbanite; Folders — G/1000.; MAILROOM EQUIPMENT: Tying Machines — Wilton/Stra Pack, 1-/OVL.; BUSINESS EQUIPMENT: BFR, GAT, Standard, IBM BUSINESS SOFTWARE: ADP, Lotus, Zen Write & Calc, WordPerfect 5.1, BMF, Great Plains, MediaSpan CLASSIFIED EQUIPMENT: Hardware — APP/Mac; 2-OS; Printers — Okidata, Imagesetter/II, APP/Mac LaserPrinter, HP/LaserJet; CLASSIFIED SOFTWARE: Baseview/Ad Manager Pro 2.06. DISPLAY EQUIPMENT: Hardware - APP/Mac; Printers — APP/Mac LaserPrinter; Other Hardware — Microtek/ScanMaker, 4-CD-Rom, Umax/Color Scanner, Pinnacle/CD Recorder DISPLAY SOFTWAREAd Make-up Applications — QPS/QuarkXPress 4.1, Multi-Ad, Aldus/FreeHand; Layout Software — APP/Mac. EDITORIAL EQUIPMENT: Hardware — APP/Mac/2-Pre Press/Panther Pro Imagesetter; Printers — Tektronix/380, V/5300B, Pre Press/Panther Imagesetter, APP/Mac LaserPrinter Color, Tektronix/Phaser 300, Kk/Full Color EDITORIAL SOFTWARE: Baseview/NewsEdit Pro 3.1.7. PRODUCTION EQUIPMENT: Hardware — Lf/Leafscan 35, APP/Mac LaserWriter, Imagesetter II, V/5300B, APP/Mac Color LaserWriter, Pre Press/Panther, Tektronix/Phaser 300, APP/Mac Color LaserWriter 12/600 PS; Cameras — 2-AG/NC 2000e, Nikon/D1, Nikon/Coolpix 880, 3-Olympus

LAS CRUCES

LAS CRUCES SUN-NEWS

256 W Las Cruces Ave, Las Cruces, N.M., 88005-1804, Dona Ana; gen tel (575) 541-5400; adv tel (575) 541-6200; ed tel (575) 541-5438; gen fax (575) 541-5498; ed fax (575) 541-5498; gen/nat adv e-mail bmills@lcsun-news.com; disp adv e-mail agoins@lcsun-news.com; class adv e-maillcclassgeneral@lcsun-news.com; ed e-mail sulloa@lcsun-news.com; web site www.lcsun-news.com - 14,000,000(views) 300,000(visitors)

Group: Gannett
Published: Mon, Tues, Wed, Thur, Fri, Sat, Sun
Weekday Frequency: m
Saturday Frequency: m
Circulation: 11,755; 9,498(sat); 12,893(sun)
Last Audit: AAM June 30, 2017
Advertising Rate (weekday/saturday): Open inch rate $29.40
Advertising Rate (sunday): 34.65

Online Advertising Rate: $10 cpm
News services: AP, LAT-WP. **Established:** 1881
Special Editions: Back to School (July); Football (Aug); Tough Enough to Wear Pink (Oct.); Holiday Preview (Dec); Basketball (Jan); Reader Choices (Jun); Business & Industry (Mar); Discover Greater Las Cruces (May); Mariachi Conference Publication (Oct); Game Day (Sept).
Special Weekly Sections: Business Weekly (Mon); Pulse (Thurs); My Las Cruces (Sun);
Syndicated Publications: USA WEEKEND Magazine (S); American Profile (Weekly).
Digital Platform - Mobile: Apple, Android
Digital Platform - Tablet: Apple iOS, Other
Pub. .... Rynni Henderson
Feat. Ed. .... Brenda Masengill
Bus Ed. .... Jason Gibbs
News Dir. .... Lucas Peerman
Sports Ed. .... Jason Groves
Mng. Ed. .... Sylvia Uloa
Reg. Opinion Pg. Ed. .... Walter Rubel
Adv. Mgr. .... Anita Goins
Cust. Serv. Sup. .... Sylvia Soto
Off. Admin. .... Jennifer Kozlowski
Market Information: TMC; Zoned editions.
Mechanical Available: Offset; Black and 3 ROP colors; insert accepted - any; page cutoffs - 22 3/4.
Mechanical Specifications: Type page 9.89"x21.0" 6 col x 21.0"; E - 6 cols, 1 7/8, 1/5 between; A - 6 cols, 1 7/8, 1/5 between; C - 9 cols, 1 1/5, 1/5 between.
Areas Served: Southeast New Mexico
Delivery Method: Mail, Newsstand, Carrier, RacksEquipment & Software: PRESSROOM EQUIPMENT: Lines — 10-G/U 1187 single width; Reels & Stands — 6; Control System — 2; MAILROOM EQUIPMENT: Tying Machines — 1/Bu, 1-Ace/50, Strapack/D-52; Address Machine — 1-El/Communications.; BUSINESS EQUIPMENT: PC Network, PC Wintell BUSINESS SOFTWARE: Geac Vision Shift CLASSIFIED EQUIPMENT: Hardware — APP/Mac; Printers — HP/LaserJet IVsi, HP/LaserJet 4MV; CLASSIFIED SOFTWARE: Baseview/AdManager Pro 2.0.5. DISPLAY EQUIPMENT: Hardware — APP/Mac; Printers — HP/LaserJet IVsi, HP/LaserJet 4MV; DISPLAY SOFTWAREAd Make-up Applications — Multi-Ad/Creator 3.8, QPS/QuarkXPress 3.32; Layout Software — 2.02-APP/Mac Page Director ALS. EDITORIAL EQUIPMENT: Hardware — APP/Mac; Printers — LaserMaster/1200 XL, HP/LaserJet IVsi, HP/LaserJet 4MV, ECR/Scriptsetter VRL 36/HS EDITORIAL SOFTWARE: Baseview/NewsEdit Pro IQUE 2.1.3. PRODUCTION EQUIPMENT: Hardware — Caere/OmniPage 3.0, 1-Nu/Flip Top FT40; Cameras — 3-C/Spartan; Scanners — 3-AG/Arcus II, 3-Nikon/LS1000 Film Scanners PRODUCTION SOFTWARE: QPS/QuarkXPress 3.32.

LOS ALAMOS

LOS ALAMOS MONITOR

256 Dp Rd, Los Alamos, N.M., 87544-3233, Los Alamos; gen tel (505) 662-4185; gen fax (505) 662-4334; gen/nat adv e-mail laads@lamonitor.com; disp adv e-mail info@lamonitor.com; class adv e-maillaclassifieds@lamonitor.com; ed e-mail laeditor@lamonitor.com; web site www.lamonitor.com
- 190,000(views) 35,000(visitors)

Group: Landmark Communications, Inc.
Published: Tues, Wed, Thur, Fri, Sun
Weekday Frequency: e
Circulation: 4,000; 4,200(sun)
Last Audit: Sworn/Estimate/Non-Audited September 30, 2017
Advertising Rate (weekday/saturday): Open inch rate $13.29
News services: AP. **Established:** 1963
Own Printing Facility?: Yes
Commercial Printers?: Yes
Special Editions: Call for details on special sections throughout the year.
Special Weekly Sections: Religion (Fri); Business (S); Diversions (Thur).
Syndicated Publications: Relish (Monthly); American Profile (S).
Ed. .... Jill McLaughlin
Adv. Dir. .... Jan Montoya
Market Information: TMC edition monthly
Mechanical Available: Offset; Black and 3 ROP colors; insert accepted - we-prints; page cutoffs - 22 3/4.
Mechanical Specifications: Type page 13 x 21 1/2; E - 6 cols, 1 3/4, 1/8 between; A - 6 cols, 1 3/4, 1/8 between; C - 8 cols, 1 5/16, 1/8 between.
Areas Served: 87544
Delivery Method: Newsstand, Carrier, RacksEquipment & Software: PRESSROOM EQUIPMENT: Lines — 5-G/Community; MAILROOM EQUIPMENT: Counter Stackers — BG/104A; BUSINESS EQUIPMENT: VGA PC, Dell/Hard Disc 3165X BUSINESS SOFTWARE: Dell/Hard Disc 3165X CLASSIFIED EQUIPMENT: Hardware — AST/Bravo 4-33; DISPLAY EQUIPMENT: Hardware — APP/Mac; Printers — 3-APP/Mac LaserPrinter; DISPLAY SOFTWAREAd Make-up Applications — Adobe/Illustrator, Adobe/Photoshop, Multi-Ad/Creator; Layout Software — 1-APP/Mac IIsi, 1-APP/Mac SE, 2-Mk/Ad Comp, 1-Mk/TouchWriter Plus, APP/Mac G-3. EDITORIAL EQUIPMENT: Hardware — APP/Mac, APP/Power Mac 7100-66; Printers — Xante/Accel-a-Writer EDITORIAL SOFTWARE: QPS/QuarkXPress. PRODUCTION EQUIPMENT: Hardware — 1-Nu/Flip Top; Cameras — Nu/2024; Scanners — Nikon PRODUCTION SOFTWARE: QPS/QuarkXPress, Multi-Ad/CAMS, Multi-Ad/Class Force.

ROSWELL

ROSWELL DAILY RECORD

2301 N Main St, Roswell, N.M., 88201-6452, Chaves; gen tel (575) 622-7710; adv tel (575) 622-7710; ed tel (575) 622-7710; gen fax (575) 625-0421; adv fax (575) 625-0421; ed fax (575) 625-0421; gen/nat adv e-mail hr@rdrnews.com; disp adv e-mail addirector@rdrnews.com; class adv e-mailclassifieds@rdnews.com; ed e-mail editor@rdrnews.com; web site www.rdrnews.com

Group: New Mexico Press Association
Published: Tues, Wed, Thur, Fri, Sat, Sun
Weekday Frequency: m
Saturday Frequency: m
Circulation: 9,000; 9,000(sat); 10,200(sun)
Last Audit: Sworn/Estimate/Non-Audited October 1, 2017
Advertising Rate (weekday/saturday): Open inch rate $15.20
News services: AP. **Established:** 1891
Own Printing Facility?: Yes
Commercial Printers?: No
Special Editions: Sports Tab (Aug); Christmas Time Page (Dec); Valentine's Specials (Feb);(Jan); Pet Tab (Jul); Summer Specials (Jun); Mother's Day (May); Pre-Christmas Coupon Book (Nov); Fair Days (Oct); Car Care Tab (Sept).
Special Weekly Sections: Screens (Fri).
Syndicated Publications: Vision Magazine (Monthly); USA WEEKEND Magazine (S); American Profile (Weekly).
Digital Platform - Mobile: Apple, Android
Digital Platform - Tablet: Apple iOS, Android
Pres. .... Robert H. Beck
Ed. .... Andrew Poertner
Pub. .... Dana Beck
General Manager .... Sara Fajardo
Cir. Dir. .... Jim Dish
Adv. Dir. .... Kim Gordon
Publisher .... Barbara Beck
Mechanical Available: Offset; Black and 3 ROP colors; insert accepted; page cutoffs - 22 3/4.
Mechanical Specifications: Type page 13 1/16 x 21 1/2; E - 6 cols, 2 1/16, 1/6 between; A - 6 cols, 2 1/16, 1/6 between; C - 8 cols, 1 1/2, 1/6 between.
Areas Served: Roswell, Chaves County
Dexter, Chaves County
Hagerman, Chaves County
Artesia, Eddy County
Capitan, Lincoln County
Delivery Method: Mail, Newsstand, Carrier, RacksEquipment & Software: PRESSROOM EQUIPMENT: Lines — 6-G/Urbanite (1 balloon former) single width; MAILROOM EQUIPMENT: Counter Stackers — 1/MM; Inserters & Stuffers — 1-MM/6 Pocket, 1-MM/227 6 Pocket; Tying Machines — 1-EAM-Mosca/Rom, 1-ACE/50; Address Machine — 1-Xenix/System; BUSINESS EQUIPMENT: Mk/Acer-View, Epson/Printer, BMF/Newspaper System BUSINESS SOFTWARE: Microsoft Dynamics GP CLASSIFIED EQUIPMENT: Hardware — APP/iMacs; Printers — APP/Mac Laser Writer 16/600 PS; CLASSIFIED SOFTWARE: Newscycle/AdManager Pro. DISPLAY EQUIPMENT: Hardware — NewsCycle, APP/Mac G3; Printers — HP/LaserJet 6MP; DISPLAY SOFTWAREAd Make-up Applications — Newscycle; Layout Software — Ad Force. EDITORIAL EQUIPMENT: Hardware — APP/Mac Performa 6116 CD-Roms, Polaroid/Sprintscan, AG/Arcus II Scanners/Lf/AP Leaf Picture Desk, Lf/Leafscan, Lf/AP Laserphoto, AG/Arcus II Scanners, Epson/Photo PC 600 Digital Camera; Printers — APP/Mac LaserPrinters PRODUCTION EQUIPMENT: Hardware — Caere/OmniPage 2.12, Konica EV Jetsetter 3100S, Xante/Laserprinters; Cameras — 1-C/Spartan II; Scanners — 2-APP/Mac Scanner, 2-AG/Arcus IIs PRODUCTION SOFTWARE: QPS/QuarkXPress 4.00.

SANTA FE

THE SANTA FE NEW MEXICAN

202 E Marcy St, Santa Fe, N.M., 87501-2021, Santa Fe; gen tel (505) 983-3303; adv tel (505) 986-3007; ed tel (505) 986-3035; gen fax (505) 995-3875; adv fax (505) 984-1785; ed fax (505) 986-9147; gen/nat adv e-mail advertising@sfnewmexican.com; disp adv e-mail wortega@sfnewmexican.com; class adv e-mailclassad@sfnewmexican.com; ed e-mail letters@sfnewmexican.com; web site www.santafenewmexican.com
- 1,700,000(views) 332,000(visitors)

Published: Mon, Tues, Wed, Thur, Fri, Sat, Sun
Weekday Frequency: m
Saturday Frequency: m
Circulation: 16,820; 16,820(sat); 18,638(sun)
Last Audit: AAM December 31, 2015
Advertising Rate (weekday/saturday): Open inch rate $31.60(Mon-Thurs), $33.30(Fr-Sat)
Advertising Rate (sunday): Open inch rate $33.65
Online Advertising Rate: ROS Medium Rectangle (300x250): $14.00/cpm
Skyscraper - (300x600) $14.00/cpm
News services: AP, NYT, LAT-WP, MCT. **Established:** 1849
Own Printing Facility?: Yes
Commercial Printers?: Yes
Special Editions: SF Winter Fiesta (Jan), Health Directory (Feb), NM Restaurant Week (Feb), Basketball State Tourney (Mar), Kids Summer (Apr), Golf (Apr), Bienvenidos (May), Native Treasures (May), North Stars (Jun), Buckaroo Ball (Jun), International Folk Art (Jun), Spanish Market (Jul), SOFA (Jul), Indian Market (Aug), Fiesta (Aug), Winterlife (Oct), Feliz Navidad (Nov)
Special Weekly Sections: Teen Page (Fri); Health & Science (Mon); Comics (S); Religion (Sat); Outdoors (Thur); Business (Tues);
Syndicated Publications: Pasatiempo-Weekend Art & Entertainment Magazine (Fri); Parade (S); TV Book (Sat).
Digital Platform - Mobile: Apple, Android, Blackberry
Digital Platform - Tablet: Apple iOS, Android, Blackberry Tablet OS, Kindle, Kindle Fire
Cir. Dir. .... Mike Reichard
City Ed. .... Howard Houghton
Pub. .... Tom Cross
Owner .... Robin Martin
News Ed./Copy Chief .... Cynthia Miller
Sports Ed. .... James Barron
Asst. Ed. .... Madeleine Nicklin
Director of Production .... Tim Cramer
Editor .... Phill Casaus
HR Director .... Susan Cahoon
Market Information: ADS
Mechanical Available: Offset; Black and 3 ROP colors; insert accepted - pre-sorted A/B; page cutoffs - 22 3/4.
Mechanical Specifications: Type page 11 5/8 x 21 1/3; E - 6 cols, 1 5/6, 1/8 between; A - 6 cols, 1 1/8, 1/8 between; C - 9 cols, 1 3/8, 1/16 between.
Areas Served: Santa Fe County (NM)
Delivery Method: Mail, Newsstand, Carrier, RacksEquipment & Software: PRESSROOM EQUIPMENT: Lines — 9-G/U 870A; Press Drive — 2, 2-HP/200 Baldor Motors; Reels & Stands — 7-G w/Jardis/Tension Control; Control System — Ry/Spray Bar System.; MAILROOM EQUIPMENT: Counter Stackers — 1-Id, QWI/300, QWI/350; Inserters & Stuffers — 1-GMA/SLS 1000 8:1; Tying Machines — 1-MLN/Spirit, 1/Power Strap/PSN-6E, 1-Dy/NP3; Control System — GMA; Address Machine — 1-GMA/Triton; BUSINESS EQUIPMENT: Supermicro BUSINESS SOFTWARE: SBS, Newscycle Adbase CLASSIFIED EQUIPMENT: iMacs, HP MFP CLASSIFIED SOFTWARE: Newscycle Adbase DISPLAY EQUIPMENT: Printers — 1-HP T1200 proofer, Konica Minolta e654e, 2008 Mac Pro DISPLAY SOFTWAREAd Make-up Applications — Creative Suite CS5, DPS Adtracker ad production software EDITORIAL EQUIPMENT: Hardware — 10-27" iMac; 10 - mac minis- 3- 13" mac book pro Printers — Konica Minolta 454e EDITORIAL SOFTWARE: NewsEngin GPS/Newsycycle NewsEditPro 6.2.9 PRODUCTION EQUIPMENT: Hardware — Agfa Platesetters, mac mini, mac pro, 2 Win7 desktops PRODUCTION SOFTWARE: CS5/CS6, Proimage Newsway v. 5, Arkitex for NYT IT EQUIPMENT: Supermicro Servers, Cisco ASA 5510 Firewall IT SOFTWARE:Vmware 6.0 virtual environment, Symantec anti virus, Barracuda email spam protection, Kerio Connect Mail Server, Windows Server 2008 and 2012, Acronis ExtremeZ-IP for mac file sharing, Onevision Asura PDF processing, CrushFTP FTP server, 3cx phone system

SILVER CITY

SILVER CITY SUN-NEWS

208 W Broadway St, Silver City, N.M., 88061-5353, Grant; gen tel (575) 538-5893; adv tel (538) 5893 ext. 5808; ed tel (538) 5893 ext. 5802; gen fax (575) 538-5844; adv fax (575) 538-5844; ed fax (575) 538-5844 ; gen/nat adv e-mail dborde@scsun-news.com; disp adv e-mail bmills@lcsun-news.com; ed e-mail editor@scsun-news.com; web site www.scsun-news.com

Group: Gannett
Published: Mon, Tues, Wed, Thur, Fri, Sat, Sun
Weekday Frequency: m
Saturday Frequency: m
Last Audit: Sworn/Estimate/Non-Audited September 30, 2017
Advertising Rate (weekday/saturday): Open inch rate $17.25
Pub. .... Rynni Henderson
Gen. Mgr. .... Jared Hamilton
Sports Ed. .... Danny Udero
Off. Admin. .... Hallie Richwine
Multi. Med. Acct. Exec. .... Desaree Borde
Cir. Mgr. .... Larry Higgs
Areas Served: Silver City, Grant County, Gila Region, Mimbres Valley & Mining District
Delivery Method: Mail, Racks

NEW YORK

ALBANY

TIMES UNION

645 Albany Shaker Rd, Albany, N.Y., 12211-1158, Albany; gen tel (518) 454-5694; adv tel (518) 454-5588; ed tel (518) 454-5323; gen fax (518) 454-5628; adv fax (518) 454-5417; ed fax (518) 454-5628; ed e-mail tuletters@timesunion.com; web site www.timesunion.com
- 35,000,000(views) 2,200,000(visitors)

Group: Hearst Communications, Inc.
Published: Mon, Tues, Wed, Thur, Fri, Sat, Sun
Weekday Frequency: m
Saturday Frequency: m

New York

Total Daily Newspapers	55
Total Daily Circulation	3,680,903
Total Weekly Newspapers	329
Total Weekly Circulation	1,054,672
Population	1,9849,399

LEGEND

Combined Statistical Area
Metropolitan Statistical Area
Micropolitan Statistical Area
Metropolitan Division

International
State
County
Shoreline

Dallas-Fort Worth
RICHMOND
Concord
Philadelphia
CANADA
TEXAS
HARRIS

Circulation: 42,336; 37,173(sat); 91,814(sun)
Last Audit: AAM September 30, 2017
Advertising Rate (weekday/saturday): $96.34 per colume Inch
Advertising Rate (sunday): $114.23 per colume Inch
News services: AP, Hearst Newspapers, NYT, MCT **Established:** 1856
Own Printing Facility?: Yes
Commercial Printers?: Yes
Special Weekly Sections: Preview (Thur)
Syndicated Publications: 518 Life; Woman @ Work
Digital Platform - Mobile: Apple, Android, Blackberry
Digital Platform - Tablet: Apple iOS
Pub./CEO .... George R. Hearst
Ed. .... Rex Smith
Vice President Circulation .... Todd Peterson
Vice President Advertising .... Tom Eason
Market Information: Split run; Zoned editions.
Mechanical Available: Offset Press 32/64 page, full color; variable web width - 21"" cutoff
Mechanical Specifications: Type page 11 x 21 1/2; Editorial - 6 cols, 1 7/8, 1/8 between; Advertising - 6 cols, 1 7/8, 1/8 between; Classified - 6 cols, 1 7/8, 1/8 between.
Delivery Method: Mail, Newsstand, Carrier, RacksEquipment & Software: PRESSROOM EQUIPMENT: Ferag conveyors 2 lines; KBA Commander GL 4 Tower - 32 couple - full color; Schur Palletizer PRESSROOM SOFTWARE: KBA Controls MAILROOM EQUIPMENT: Counter Stackers — 8/QWI; Inserters & Stuffers — 2-HI/2299 on-line, 1-HI/632, 1 Schur Palitizer; Tying Machines — 8-/Dynaric ; Control System — SAM, 2299; Address Machine — 1-/Ch, 2-/LSI; MAILROOM SOFTWARE:SAM planning Win Lines CLASSIFIED EQUIPMENT: Hardware — Sun Cluster; CLASSIFIED SOFTWARE: Mactive DISPLAY EQUIPMENT: Hardware — Sun Cluster; DISPLAY SOFTWAREAd Make-up Applications — Mactive; Layout Software — DTI, SCS Class Pag. EDITORIAL EQUIPMENT: Hardware — Sun EDITORIAL SOFTWARE: DTI PRODUCTION EQUIPMENT: AGFA Advantage NDL Platesetters - 1; VCF Chemfree Processors -2; Nela VCP Vision Benders PRODUCTION SOFTWARE: Newsway Integration; Afgar Arkitek IT EQUIPMENT: HP Blade Servers; Netap Filers; UPS Battery System; Diesel Generator IT SOFTWARE:Discuss

AMSTERDAM

THE RECORDER

1 Venner Rd, Amsterdam, N.Y., 12010-5617, Montgomery; gen tel (518) 843-1100; adv tel (518) 843-1100; ed tel (518) 843-1100; gen fax (518) 843-1338; adv fax (518) 843-1338; ed fax (518) 843-6580; gen/nat adv e-mail sales@recordernews.com; disp adv e-mail sales@recordernews.com; class adv e-mailsales2@recordernews.com; ed e-mail news@recordernews.com; web site www.recordernews.com
Published: Mon, Tues, Wed, Thur, Fri, Sat
Weekday Frequency: m
Saturday Frequency: m
Circulation: 8,116; 8,116(sat); 8,305(sun)
Last Audit: Sworn/Estimate/Non-Audited September 30, 2017
Advertising Rate (weekday/saturday): Open inch rate $21.00
News services: LAT-WP, AP, MCT.
Special Editions: Pro Baseball Preview (Apr); Summer Projects (Aug); Christmas Gift Guide II (Dec); Year Outlook (Feb); Bridal Book I (Jan); Saratoga Horse Racing (Jul); Bridal Book II (Jun); Cooking Contest (Mar); Christmas Gift Guide I (Nov); Fall Car Care (Oct); Autumn
Special Weekly Sections: Business (Mon); Senior Citizens (S); Best Food Days (Wed).
Syndicated Publications: Silver Lining (Monthly); Currents-Arts (S).
Digital Platform - Mobile: Apple, Android
Digital Platform - Tablet: Apple iOS, Android
Pub .... Kevin McClary
Gen. Mgr. .... Brian Krohn
Assoc. Pub. .... Geoff Dylong
Sports Ed. .... Paul Antonelli
Circ. .... Rich Kretser
Market Information: TMC.
Mechanical Available: Offset; Black and 3 ROP colors; insert accepted - samples, cards; page cutoffs - 22 3/4.
Mechanical Specifications: Type page 13 x 21 1/2; E - 6 cols, 2 1/16, 1/8 between; A - 6 cols, 2 1/16, 1/8 between; C - 8 cols, 1 9/16, 1/16 between.
Areas Served: Amsterdam & Montgomery Counties (NY)
Equipment & Software: PRESSROOM EQUIPMENT: Lines — 6-G/Urbanite (3-N3 in Line); Folders — G/2:1; Control System — 2-Fin/Console.; MAILROOM EQUIPMENT: Tying Machines — Bu/SA 505; Address Machine — Ch/596.; BUSINESS EQUIPMENT: 1-TI/1505 BUSINESS SOFTWARE: Papertrak CLASSIFIED EQUIPMENT: Hardware — 1-AT/7000.; DISPLAY EQUIPMENT: Printers — 2-Compaq/Pagemarq 20 Tabloid; DISPLAY SOFTWARELayout Software — 4-APP/Mac II. EDITORIAL EQUIPMENT: Hardware — 1-AT/7000/1-LE/PC 13 Dry Film Processor. PRODUCTION EQUIPMENT: Hardware — 2-AU/APS U5, 1-B/MP2, 1-Amerigraph/437S-S; Cameras — 1-B/24, 1-AG/2024; Scanners — HP/Scanner PRODUCTION SOFTWARE: QPS/QuarkXPress 3.3.

AUBURN

THE CITIZEN, AUBURN

25 Dill St, Auburn, N.Y., 13021-3605, Cayuga; gen tel (315) 253-5311; adv tel (315) 255-2241; ed tel (315) 282-2231; gen fax (315) 253-6031; adv fax (315) 253-6031; ed fax (315) 253-6031; gen/nat adv e-mail jeffrey.weigand@lee.net; disp adv e-mail jeffrey.weigand@lee.net; class adv e-mailjeffrey.weigand@lee.net; ed e-mail jeremy.boyer@lee.net; web site www.auburnpub.com - 1,800,000(views) 300,000(visitors)
Group: Lee Enterprises, Inc.
Published: Tues, Wed, Thur, Fri, Sat, Sun
Weekday Frequency: m
Saturday Frequency: m
Circulation: 5,391; 5,794(sat); 7,166(sun)
Last Audit: AAM June 30, 2016
Advertising Rate (weekday/saturday): Open inch rate $23.33
Online Advertising Rate: $15 ROS
News services: AP. **Established:** 1816
Own Printing Facility?: Yes
Commercial Printers?: Yes
Special Editions: Golf (Apr); Brides (Feb); Health (Jan); (Mar); Finger Lake Summer Travel Guide (May); Holiday Gift Guide (Nov); Tomato Fest (Sept).
Special Weekly Sections: Family Matters (Fri); Food (Mon); Community and Family Features (S); Arts & Entertainment (Thur); Price Busters Tab (Tues); Home (Wed).
Syndicated Publications: Color Comics (S).
Digital Platform - Mobile: Apple, Android, Windows
Digital Platform - Tablet: Apple iOS, Android, Windows 7, Kindle, Nook, Kindle Fire
Exec. Ed. .... Jeremy Boyer
Mng. Ed. .... Michael Dowd
Pres./Pub. .... Robert Forcey
Market Information: ADS; Split run; TMC; Zoned editions.
Mechanical Available: Offset; Black and 3 ROP colors; insert accepted - spadea; page cutoffs - 22 3/4.
Mechanical Specifications: Type page 11 x 21 1/2; E - 6 cols, 1.56, .167 between; A - 6 cols, 1.56, .167 between; C - 6 cols, 1.56, .167 between.
Areas Served: 13021 plus
Delivery Method: Mail, Newsstand, Carrier, RacksEquipment & Software: PRESSROOM EQUIPMENT: Lines — 14 G/comm, single width 2011; Folders — 1-G/2:1 1-G/4:1; Control System — Aug. 2011; Registration System — Stoesser/Register Systems. MAILROOM EQUIPMENT: Counter Stackers — 2-Id; Inserters & Stuffers — 8/MM; Tying Machines — 1-/OVL, 1-/MLN.; BUSINESS EQUIPMENT: 1-Sun/Sparc Station 2, 1-Compaq/386sx BUSINESS SOFTWARE: Vision Data, Ciridian CLASSIFIED EQUIPMENT: Hardware — 7-Sun/Sparc IPC; Printers — 1-HP/LaserJet 4ML; CLASSIFIED SOFTWARE: Vision Data/Island Write 4.0. DISPLAY EQUIPMENT: Hardware — 10-APP/Mac II, 2-APP/Mac SE, 2-APP/Mac Quadra 605, 1-APP/Mac LC III; Printers — Copal/Dash 600, APP/Mac LaserWriter II NTX; Other Hardware — 1-AG/Focus Color Plus Scan DISPLAY SOFTWAREAd Make-up Applications — QPS/QuarkXPress 3.3, Adobe/Illustrator 5.0, Adobe/Photoshop 3.0; EDITORIAL EQUIPMENT: Hardware — 17-Sun/3-50, 2-Sun/Sparc, 6-APP/Mac II, 2-APP/Power Mac 7100-80 CD/1-Telebit/Qblazer 9600 modem; Printers — 2-APP/Mac LaserWriter NTX EDITORIAL SOFTWARE: Unix, Arbortext, APP/Mac OS, QPS/QuarkXPress 3.3. PRODUCTION EQUIPMENT: Hardware — 1-Graham/M-28, 1-P, 1-APP/Mac LaserWriter II NTX; Cameras — 2-SCREEN/Companion 640C; Scanners — 1-Lf/Leafscan 35, 1-Nikon/LS 3500, AG/Horizon, 1-AG PRODUCTION SOFTWARE: SCS/Layout 8000, Lynx 4.0.

BATAVIA

THE DAILY NEWS

2 Apollo Dr, Batavia, N.Y., 14020-3002, Genesee; gen tel (585) 343-8000; adv tel (585) 343-8000; ed tel (585) 343-8000; gen fax (585) 343-2623; adv fax (585) 343-2623; ed fax (585) 345-1632; gen/nat adv e-mail adsales@batavianews.com ; disp adv e-mail adsales@batavianews.com; class adv e-mailclassified@batavianews.com; ed e-mail news@batavianews.com; web site www.thedailynewsonline.com - 1,269,931(views) 179,998(visitors)
Group: Johnson Newspaper Corp.
Published: Mon, Tues, Wed, Thur, Fri, Sat
Weekday Frequency: All day
Saturday Frequency: All day
Circulation: 9,937; 12,036(sat)
Last Audit: CVC December 19, 2017
Advertising Rate (weekday/saturday): Open inch rate $22.94
News services: AP, TMS. **Established:** 1831
Own Printing Facility?: Yes
Commercial Printers?: No
Special Editions: Spring Sports (Apr); Back To School (Aug); Christmas Greetings (Dec); Business Outlook (Feb); Bridal Guide (Jan); Genesee County Fair (Jul); Dairy Month (Jun); Jaycees Home Show (Mar); Mother's Day (May); Christmas Gift Guide (Nov); Fall Car Care (Oct); F
Special Weekly Sections: Entertainment (Thurs.-Fri); Business (Mon); Religion (Sat); Entertainment (Thur); Agriculture (Tues); Recreation (summer) (Wed).
Syndicated Publications: USA WEEKEND Magazine (Sat); American Profile (Wed).
Digital Platform - Mobile: Apple, Android, Windows, Blackberry
Digital Platform - Tablet: Apple iOS, Android, Windows 7, Blackberry Tablet OS, Kindle, Nook, Kindle Fire
BNC Pub. / JNC Dig. Dir. .... Michael Messerly
Managing Editor .... John Anderson
CEO / Co-Pub. .... John Johnson
Pres. .... Harold B. Johnson
Circulation Director .... Gary Durawa
HR VP .... Jeanette Hardy
Advert. Dir. .... Jennifer Zambito
Market Information: TMC; Zoned editions.
Mechanical Available: Offset; Black and 3 ROP colors; insert accepted - single sheets; page cutoffs - 22 3/4.
Mechanical Specifications: Type page 10.87 x 20. 6 cols.
Areas Served: 14005, 14011, 14013, 14020, 14036, 14040, 14054, 14058, 14103, 14125, 14143, 14167, 14411, 14416, 14422, 14427, 14470, 14482, 14525, 14530, 14550, 14569, 14591
Delivery Method: Newsstand, Carrier, RacksEquipment & Software: BUSINESS EQUIPMENT: IBM, IBM/AS-400 BUSINESS SOFTWARE: Micosoft/Windows 95, PBS CLASSIFIED EQUIPMENT: Hardware — 3-APP/Mac; Printers — APP/Mac LaserWriter; CLASSIFIED SOFTWARE: Baseview. DISPLAY EQUIPMENT: Hardware — 1-APP/Power Mac 8100 fileserver; Printers — Compaq/Page Marq 15; Other Hardware — HP/LaserJet 4MV, Graphic Enterprise/Pro Setter 1000 DISPLAY SOFTWAREAd Make-up Applications — Multi-Ad/Creator 3.71, QPS/QuarkXPress 3.31; Layout Software — 5-APP/Power Mac 8100. EDITORIAL EQUIPMENT: Hardware — 4-APP/Mac fileserver/2-HP/LaserJet 4MV; Printers — 1-Graphic Enterprise/Pro Setter, Graphic Enterprise/Pro Setter 1000 EDITORIAL SOFTWARE: Baseview. PRODUCTION EQUIPMENT: Hardware — Caere/OmniPage 8.0, Nu/Flip Top FT40APRNS 631, 1-Nu/FT40APRNS; Cameras — 1-R/480, 1-Eskofot/6006; Scanners — 1-AG/V20 x 24 PRODUCTION SOFTWARE: QPS/QuarkXPress 3.31.

BINGHAMTON

PRESS & SUN-BULLETIN

33 Lewis Rd, Ste 9, Binghamton, N.Y., 13905-1040, Broome; gen tel (607) 798-1234; adv tel (607) 798-1131; ed tel (607) 798-1151; gen fax 607-798-1238; adv fax (607) 798-1237; ed fax (607) 798-1113; gen/nat adv e-mail rscott@pressconnects.com; disp adv e-mail swinelan@binghamt.gannett.com; class adv e-mailjgilmore@binghamt.gannett.com; ed e-mail bgm-letters@gannett.com; web site www.pressconnects.com
Group: Gannett
Published: Mon, Tues, Wed, Thur, Fri, Sat, Sun
Weekday Frequency: m
Saturday Frequency: m
Circulation: 21,947; 21,947(sat); 31,496(sun)
Last Audit: AAM September 30, 2016
Advertising Rate (weekday/saturday): Open inch rate $108.50
News services: 1904
Own Printing Facility?: Yes
Commercial Printers?: Yes
Syndicated Publications: Good Times (Thur); Home Marketplace (Sat.)
Pub .... Thomas Claybaugh
Exec. Ed. .... Neill Borowski
Adv. Dir. .... Robb Scott
Gen. Mgr. / Gannett Pub. Serv. .... Kevin Crane
Pres. .... George Troyano
Areas Served: Broome, Tioga, Chenango, Delaware & Otsego Counties (NY); Susquehanna County (PA)
Equipment & Software: PRESSROOM EQUIPMENT: Lines — KBA Colora; Press Drive — KBA; Control System — EAE; MAILROOM EQUIPMENT: Counter Stackers — 7; Inserters & Stuffers — 2; Tying Machines — 7; Control System — Omnizone; Address Machine — 2 Kodak;

BROOKLYN

EL DIARIO LA PRENSA

1 Metrotech Ctr, Fl 18, Brooklyn, N.Y., 11201-3948, Kings; gen tel (212) 807-4785; adv tel (212) 807-4600; ed tel (212) 807-4725; gen fax (212) 807-4705; adv fax (212) 807-4617; ed fax (212) 807-4705; gen/nat adv e-mail jorge.ayala@eldiariony.com; disp adv e-mail mack.hood@eldiariony.com; class adv e-mailmack.hood@eldiariony.com; web site www.eldiariony.com
Group: impreMedia LLC
Published: Mon, Tues, Wed, Thur, Fri, Sat, Sun
Circulation: 25,223; 19,762(sat); 16,818(sun)
Last Audit: Sworn/Estimate/Non-Audited February 16, 2018
Advertising Rate (weekday/saturday): Open Rate $9,98/line
Advertising Rate (sunday): same
Online Advertising Rate: Open Rate $9cpm digital; $10 cpm mobile
News services: AP. **Established:** 1913
Own Printing Facility?: No
Special Editions: Dominican Independence, Charter Schools, Health, Education, Cinco de Mayo, Puerto Rican Heritage,World Cup,Colombian Independence, Peruvian Independence, Dominican Restoration, Mexican Independence, Hispanic Heritage, Holiday Gift Guide, El Awards, Mujeres Descatadas
Special Weekly Sections: Education, Health; Legal, Immigration, Food; Entertainment

Syndicated Publications: ESPN Deportes
Digital Platform - Mobile: Apple, Android
Digital Platform - Tablet: Apple iOS, Android
VP, Adv...Jorge Ayala
Retail Dir...Mack Hood
Market Information: 156,000 Readers per Scarborough 2017 R1
Mechanical Available: 6 column ROPI 7 column classified, page size 9.81 x 11
Areas Served: NYDMA
Delivery Method: NewsstandEquipment & Software: PRESSROOM EQUIPMENT: Folders — 1-G/Urbanite, 1-G/Community SSC. BUSINESS EQUIPMENT: PBS, IBM/RISC-600 340 BUSINESS SOFTWARE: PBS, Progress CLASSIFIED EQUIPMENT: Hardware — Dell/Power Edge 4300, Dell/PC; Printers — HP/LaserJet 4000N; CLASSIFIED SOFTWARE: Admax 5.38. DISPLAY EQUIPMENT: Hardware — APP/Mac 7200; Printers — Xante/Accel-a-Writer 8200; Other Hardware — Layout System DISPLAY SOFTWAREAd Make-up Applications — Adobe/Photoshop 4.0, QPS/QuarkXPress 3.11; Layout Software — DEC/Layout 8000, Dell/Power Edge 2300. EDITORIAL EQUIPMENT: Hardware — Dell/PC; Printers — HP/LaserJet 4000N EDITORIAL SOFTWARE: SCS/Editorial 8000, Good News 3.0. PRODUCTION EQUIPMENT: Hardware — Ofoto, 2-V/VT 5300-4000; Scanners — 4-LaCie/Silver Scan II PRODUCTION SOFTWARE: QPS/QuarkXPress 3.31, Adobe/Photoshop 3.5, Adobe/Illustrator 6.0.

NEW YORK DAILY CHALLENGE

1195 Atlantic Ave, Fl 2, Brooklyn, N.Y., 11216-2709, Kings; gen tel (718) 636-9500; adv tel (718) 636-9500; ed tel (718) 636-9500; adv fax (718) 636-8421; ed fax (718) 857-9115; gen/nat adv e-mail challengegroup@yahoo.com; disp adv e-mail challengegroup@gmail.com; class adv e-mailchallengegroup@yahoo.com; ed e-mail challengegroup@yahoo.com; web site facebook.com/Daily-Challenge-151449094871154
Published: Mon, Tues, Wed, Thur, Fri, Sat, Sun
Weekday Frequency: m
Saturday Frequency: m
Circulation: 56,544
Last Audit: Sworn/Estimate/Non-Audited September 30, 2017
Advertising Rate (weekday/saturday): Open inch rate $67.98
News services: 1972
Pub...Thomas H. Watkins
Assoc. Pub...T.J. Watkins
Marketing Director..Dale Watkins
Ed...Gary Brown
Areas Served: 11216
Delivery Method: Mail, Newsstand, Racks

BUFFALO

THE BUFFALO NEWS

1 News Plz, P.O. Box 100, Buffalo, N.Y., 14203-2905, Erie; gen tel (716) 849-4444; adv tel (716) 856-5555; ed tel (716) 849-4444; gen fax (716) 856-5150; adv fax (716) 849-3409; ed fax (716) 856-5150; gen/nat adv e-mail adops@buffnews.com; disp adv e-mail adops@buffnews.com; class adv e-mailsdeaton-callahan@buffnews.com; ed e-mail editor@buffnews.com; web site www.buffalonews.com
Group: BH Media Group
Published: Mon, Tues, Wed, Thur, Fri, Sat, Sun
Weekday Frequency: All day
Saturday Frequency: m
Circulation: 119,226; 125,169(sat); 180,776(sun)
Last Audit: AAM June 30, 2016
Advertising Rate (weekday/saturday): Open inch rate $286.19
Advertising Rate (sunday): Open inch rate $375.57
News services: AP, MCT, LAT-WP, RN. **Established:** 1880
Special Editions: First Sunday (Apr); Today's Education (Aug); Menus (Dec); Auto Show (Feb); Weddings (Jan); First Sunday (Jul); Horizons (Jun); Buffalo Home Show (Mar); WNY Nurses Assoc. (May); First Sunday (Nov); Bridal Planner (Oct); NFL Preview (Sept).
Special Weekly Sections: MoneySmart (Mon); Health, Sports (Tue); Best Food Day (Wed); Home, Garden, Entertainment (Fri); Real Estate (Sat); TV, Comics, Travel (Sun)
Syndicated Publications: Gusto (entertainment tab) (Fri); Monday Sports (tab) (Mon); Metro Comics (S); Home Finder (Sat); NEXT (young teens' tab) (Tues).
Pres./Pub...Warren T. Colville
Chairman..Warren E. Buffett
Ed...Mike Connelly
Mng. Ed...Brian Connolly
Deputy Mng. Ed...Stan Evans
Asst. Mng. Ed...Margaret Kenny
Editorial Page Ed...John Neville
Design Dir...Vince Chiaramonte
Market Information: Split run; TMC; Zoned editions.
Mechanical Available: Offset; Black and 3 ROP colors; insert accepted - preprinted tabs, card stock; page cutoffs - 21 1/4.
Mechanical Specifications: Type page 11 5/8 x 20; E - 6 cols, 1 5/6, 1/8 between; A - 6 cols, 1 3/32, 1/8 between; C - 10 cols, 1 1/4, 1/16 between.Equipment & Software: PRESSROOM EQUIPMENT: Lines — 7-KBA/Color A Offset double width; 7-KBA/Color A Offset double width; 6-Wd/Metropolitan (4-color deck) double width 1958; 6-Wd/Metropolitan (4-color deck) double width 1958; 6-Wd/Metropolitan (4-color deck) dou; MAILROOM EQUIPMENT: Counter Stackers — 8-HPS/Dual Carrier, 3-HPS/Dual Carrier, 3-QWI/501; Inserters & Stuffers — 1-AM Graphics/25-head dual delivery inserter, 1-AM Graphics/29-head dual delivery inserter; Tying Machines — 9-Dynaric/NP-1, 14-Dynaric/NP-2; Wrapping Singles — Wrapping si; BUSINESS EQUIPMENT: 1-HP/3000-928, 1-HP/3000-918LX, 1-HP/3000-928 BUSINESS SOFTWARE: CJ CLASSIFIED EQUIPMENT: Hardware — SII/Servernet (2000); 80-Coyote 3; Printers — HP/LaserJet 4MV; CLASSIFIED SOFTWARE: Guardian, OS/C30.9. DISPLAY EQUIPMENT: Hardware — APP/Mac; Printers — HP/LaserJet 4MV, GEI/Colorproof XL, GEI/Newsproof; DISPLAY SOFTWAREAd Make-up Applications — DPS/AdTracker, Adobe/InDesign 2.0; Layout Software — SII/Sys 77, SII/Sails. EDITORIAL EQUIPMENT: Hardware — SII/Servernet (2000)/Lf/AP Leaf Merlin Picture System, 125-Coyote/3 PC Emulation; Printers — HP/LaserJet 4MV EDITORIAL SOFTWARE: Guardian, OS/C30.9. PRODUCTION EQUIPMENT: Hardware — 2-AGFA/3850 CTP, 1-Horizon/Ultra, 1-Lf/Leafscan, 1-Kk/2035; Scanners — 1-AG/Horizon Plus, 1-AG/Horizon Ultra, PixelCraft 2x8100 Scanner, 1-Tecsa/TS2470 PRODUCTION SOFTWARE: SII/Coyote Layout.

CANANDAIGUA

DAILY MESSENGER

73 Buffalo St, Canandaigua, N.Y., 14424-1001, Ontario; gen tel (585) 394-0770; adv tel (585) 394-0770; ed tel (585) 394-0770; gen fax (585) 394-6837; adv fax (585) 394-1675; ed fax (585) 394-4160; gen/nat adv e-mail bkesel@messengerpostmedia.com; disp adv e-mail bkesel@messengerpostmedia.com; class adv e-mailclassifieds@messengerpostmedia.com; ed e-mail bkesel@messengerpostmedia.com; web site www.mpnnow.com
Group: New Media Investment Group
Published: Mon, Tues, Wed, Thur, Fri, Sun
Weekday Frequency: e
Circulation: 6,700; 9,325(sun)
Last Audit: Sworn/Estimate/Non-Audited September 30, 2017
Advertising Rate (weekday/saturday): Open inch rate $17.85
News services: AP, SHNS, LAT-WP. **Established:** 1776
Special Editions: Homes & Landscapes (Apr); Rx For Good Health (Aug); Holiday Gift Guide (Dec); Interiors (Feb); Wedding Guide (Jan); Summer Homes (Jul); Summer Dining Guide (Jun); Salute to Seniors (Mar); Vacation Guide (May); Holiday Gift Guide (Nov); Rx for Good Health
Special Weekly Sections: Real Estate (Fri); Weddings and Engagements (Mon); Business/Consumer Page (Mon-fri); Stock Page (S); Farm Page (Thur); Seniors Page (Tues); Religion (Wed).
Syndicated Publications: Accent on Homes (Fri); TV Viewer (S); Steppin' Out (Thur).
Gen. Mng./Adv. Dir...Beth Kesel
Exec. Ed...Sean McCrory
Local Ed...Mike Murphy
Digital Pub. Ed...Jennifer Reed
Cir. Mgr...Cathy Busker
Pres. / Pub...Brian Doane
Market Information: ADS; TMC.
Mechanical Available: Offset; Black and 3 ROP colors; insert accepted - pocket book style, approved product samples; page cutoffs - 20 1/2.
Mechanical Specifications: Type page 13 x 20 1/2; E - 6 cols, 1 13/16, 1/8 between; A - 6 cols, 1 13/16, 1/8 between; C - 8 cols, 1 3/8, 1/8 between.
Areas Served: Ontario, Wayne & Northern Yates Counties (NY)
Equipment & Software: PRESSROOM EQUIPMENT: Lines — 10-G/Community 1994; Folders — 1-G/SSC-8384.; MAILROOM EQUIPMENT: Counter Stackers — Id/440; Inserters & Stuffers — Am/Sheridan I372P; Tying Machines — MLN/Spirit Auto, Bu/Semi-Auto; Address Machine — Ch/Videojet; BUSINESS EQUIPMENT: 11-Intel/Pentium 188 BUSINESS SOFTWARE: MSSI CLASSIFIED EQUIPMENT: Hardware — HP/NetServers; CLASSIFIED SOFTWARE: Baseview/Ad Manager Pro. DISPLAY EQUIPMENT: Hardware — 10-APP/Mac G3/450; Printers - 1-QMS/1660, 1-APP/Mac Lasermaster Unity 1200XL, HP 5000 N; Other Hardware — 1-VMAX/Powerlook DISPLAY SOFTWAREAd Make-up Applications — QPS/QuarkXPress, Aldus/FreeHand, Adobe/Photoshop; Layout Software — MEI/ALS. EDITORIAL EQUIPMENT: Hardware — APP/Mac G3, HP/NetServers; Printers — HP/5000 N EDITORIAL SOFTWARE: APP/Appleworks, QPS/QuarkXPress, Adobe/Photoshop. PRODUCTION EQUIPMENT: Hardware — Textbridge, GRHAM, Wing-Lynch/Model 5, Glunz & Jensen/66; Cameras — Vertical; Scanners - 2-Umax/PowerLook 2000, 3-Kk/Professional 2035 PRODUCTION SOFTWARE: QPS/QuarkXPress 4.04.
Note: Messenger Post Newspapers also publishes the Daily Messenger in Canadaigua, New York and one monthly regional guide to arts and antiques.

CORNING

THE LEADER

34 W Pulteney St, Corning, N.Y., 14830-2211, Steuben; gen tel (607) 936-4651; adv tel (607) 936-4651; ed tel (607) 936-4651; gen fax (607) 936-9939; adv fax (607) 962-0782; ed fax (607) 936-9939; gen/nat adv e-mail amingos@the-leader.com; disp adv e-mail amingos@the-leader.com; class adv e-mailamingos@the-leader.com; ed e-mail sdupree@the-leader.com; web site www.the-leader.com
- 801,000(views) 200,500(visitors)
Group: New Media Investment Group
Published: Mon, Tues, Wed, Thur, Fri, Sat, Sun
Weekday Frequency: m
Saturday Frequency: m
Circulation: 9,500; 9,500(sat); 10,200(sun)
Last Audit: Sworn/Estimate/Non-Audited September 30, 2017
Advertising Rate (weekday/saturday): Open inch rate $20.00
Advertising Rate (sunday): Open inch rate $22.00
Online Advertising Rate: $12.00 CPM
News services: AP. **Established:** 1854
Own Printing Facility?: No
Commercial Printers?: Yes
Special Editions: Home Improvement (Apr); September Finger Lakes Fun Book (Aug); Gift Certificates (Dec); Valentine's Day Gifts (Feb); At Home (Jan); August Finger Lakes Fun Book (Jul); July Finger Lakes Fun Book (Jun); People Who Make a Difference (Mar); Corning Classic S
Special Weekly Sections: Flag to Flag Motorsports (Fri); Food (S); Entertainment (Thur).
Syndicated Publications: Parade (S); Weekend (Thur).
Digital Platform - Mobile: Apple, Android, Windows, Blackberry
Digital Platform - Tablet: Apple iOS, Android, Windows 7, Blackberry Tablet OS
Pub...Phil Husick
Circ. Dir...Elmer Kuehner
Features Ed...Derek Ek
Online Ed...Stella DuPree
Sports Ed...Shawn Vargo
Prodn. Foreman, Pressroom..Jim Jones
Adv. Mgr...Adam Mingos
Market Information: ADS.
Mechanical Available: Offset; Black and 3 ROP colors; insert accepted - spadea; page cutoffs - 22 3/4.
Mechanical Specifications: Type page 11 5/8 x 21 1/2; E - 6 cols, 1 5/6, 1/8 between; A - 6 cols, 1 5/6, 1/8 between; C - 9 cols, 1 3/16, 1/8 between.
Delivery Method: Newsstand, Carrier, RacksEquipment & Software: PRESSROOM EQUIPMENT: Lines — 1-G/Community.; MAILROOM EQUIPMENT: Counter Stackers — 1-BG/Count-O-Veyor, 1-Id, Compass/180; Inserters & Stuffers — 1-MM/Tandem heads; Tying Machines — 2-MLN/Plastic; Wrapping Singles — 1-Id; Address Machine — 1-Automecha/Accufast; BUSINESS EQUIPMENT: Sun/Micro 4-110, 3-Sun/Sparc SLC BUSINESS SOFTWARE: Vision Data, WordPerfect, Access Tech/20-20 CLASSIFIED EQUIPMENT: Hardware — 2-Sun/Microsys, Sun/Sparc, 1-Sun/Sparc Station II, 3-Sun/Sparc Station, 1-APP/MacG4; Printers — Lexmark, 2-HP/5000; CLASSIFIED SOFTWARE: Vision Data/Classified. DISPLAY EQUIPMENT: Hardware — Sun/Microsys 4-110, 6-APP/Mac II, 1-APP/Mac IIci, 1-APP/Power Mac, 1-APP/MacG4, 3-APP/MacG3; Printers — LaserMaster/Unity Turbo XLO, ECR/Pelbox 108, APP/Mac LaserWriter; DISPLAY SOFTWAREAd Make-up Applications — QPS/QuarkXPress 4.0, Adobe/Illustrator 8.0, Adobe/Photoshop 4.0; EDITORIAL EQUIPMENT: Hardware — 1-APP/Mac Quadra, 9-APP/MacG3/Kodak/Film Scanner, 2-APP/Mac IIci, Lf/AP Leaf Picture Desk; Printers — 1-ECR/Pelbox 108, 1-APP/Mac LaserWriter, LaserMaster/Unity Turbo XLO, 1-APP/Mac LaserWriter EDITORIAL SOFTWARE: Unix, Microsoft/WindowsNT PRODUCTION EQUIPMENT: Hardware — Offset, Nu/FT40V 3UPNS; Cameras — 1-K; Scanners — AG/Horizon, AG/Horizon Ultra, APP/Mac Scanner, Kk/Film Scanner PRODUCTION SOFTWARE: SCS/Linx 3.5.

CORTLAND

CORTLAND STANDARD

110 Main St, Cortland, N.Y., 13045-6600, Cortland; gen tel (607) 756-5665; adv tel (607) 756-5665; gen fax (607) 756-4758; adv fax (607) 756-4758; gen/nat adv e-mail manderson@cortlandstandard.net; disp adv e-mail manderson@cortlandstandard.net; class adv e-mailclassified@cortlandstandard.net; ed e-mail news@cortlandstandard.net; web site www.cortlandstandard.net
Group: New York Newspaper Advertising Service, Inc.
Published: Mon, Tues, Wed, Thur, Fri, Sat
Weekday Frequency: e
Saturday Frequency: m
Circulation: 8,240; 8,240(sat)
Last Audit: Sworn/Estimate/Non-Audited September 30, 2017
Advertising Rate (weekday/saturday): Open inch rate $17.34
News services: AP **Established:** 1867
Own Printing Facility?: Yes
Commercial Printers?: No
Special Editions: Bridal (Jan); Outlook/Progess (Feb); Business Showcase (Mar); 50 Plus (Apr/May); Summer Guide (May); Dairy Edition (May/Jun); Graduation (Jun); NY Jets Training Camp (Jul); College (Aug); Autumn Guide (Sept); Driver's Guide (Oct); Gift

Guides (Nov/Dec); Healthwise (Quarterly)
Special Weekly Sections: Best Food (Sat); Money/Financial (Sat); Business Pages (Mon-Fri); Home & Garden (Wed); Consumer News (Mon); Real Estate (Bi-Weekly Thurs)
President .... Kevin R. Howe
Adv. Mgr., Classified .... Thomas Shattuck
Adv. Mgr., Retail .... Michael J. Anderson
Circ. Dir. .... Guy C. Ussery
Exec. Ed. .... Sherwood W. Chapman
Mng. Ed. .... Kevin Conlon
News Ed. .... Michael Wells
Society/Women's Ed. .... Katie Hall
Sports Ed. .... Al Butler
Prodn. Foreman, Composing . Stanley Carruthers
Prodn. Foreman, Pressroom ...... Raymond Marsh
Publisher .... Evan Geibel
Business Manager .... Stephen Clark
Market Information: TMC.
Mechanical Available: Offset; Black and 2 ROP colors; insert accepted; page cutoffs - 22 3/4.
Mechanical Specifications: Type page 11 5/8 x 21 1/2; E - 6 cols, 1 3/4, 1/8 between; A - 6 cols, 1 3/4, 1/8 between; C - 6 cols, 1 3/4, 1/8 between.
Areas Served: 13077, 13087, 13141, 13159, 13052, 13158, 13045, 13118, 13092, 13073, 13068, 13101, 13053, 13040, 13863, 13803, 13738
Delivery Method: Mail, Newsstand, Carrier, Racks Equipment & Software: PRESSROOM EQUIPMENT: Lines — 4-G/Urbanite 1968; 1 DGM MAILROOM EQUIPMENT: Tying Machines — 1/MLN.; BUSINESS EQUIPMENT: Axil/311 BUSINESS SOFTWARE: Vision Data CLASSIFIED EQUIPMENT: Hardware — Mk/3000; Printers — TI/810; CLASSIFIED SOFTWARE: Mk/NewsTouch, AT/Classified. DISPLAY EQUIPMENT: Hardware — APP/Mac IIcx, APP/Mac IIci; Printers — APP/Mac LaserWriter II NT; DISPLAY SOFTWARE Ad Make-up Applications — Claris/MacDraw Pro, Aldus/FreeHand 4.0, QPS/QuarkXPress 3.3; Layout Software — APP/Mac Local Talk Network. EDITORIAL EQUIPMENT: Hardware — Mk/3000 System; Printers — Epson/LQ1010 EDITORIAL SOFTWARE: SCS SCOOPEdit PRODUCTION EQUIPMENT: Hardware — Read-it/Pro 3.0A, 2-LaserMaster/Unity 1800-XL Plus; Cameras — 1-Eskofot/6006, 1-B/Commodore 24; Scanners — Applescan.

DUNKIRK

THE OBSERVER
10 E 2nd St, Dunkirk, N.Y., 14048-1602, Chautauqua; gen tel (716) 366-3000; adv tel (716) 366-3000; ed tel (716) 366-3000; gen fax (716) 366-3005; adv fax (716) 679-1372; ed fax (716) 366-2389; gen/nat adv e-mail advertising@observertoday.com; disp adv e-mail advertising@observertoday.com; class adv e-mail classified@observertoday.com; ed e-mail editorial@observertoday.com; web site www.observertoday.com
Group: Ogden Newspapers Inc.
Published: Mon, Tues, Wed, Thur, Fri, Sat, Sun
Weekday Frequency: m
Saturday Frequency: m
Circulation: 6,824; 6,824(sat); 7,221(sun)
Last Audit: Sworn/Estimate/Non-Audited October 20, 2017
Advertising Rate (weekday/saturday): Open inch rate $13.78
News services: Associated Press **Established:** 1882
Own Printing Facility?: Yes
Syndicated Publications: TV Magazine (Fri); Senior Scene Tab (Monthly); USA WEEKEND Magazine (S).
Digital Platform - Mobile: Apple, Android, Windows, Blackberry
Digital Platform - Tablet: Apple iOS, Android, Windows 7, Blackberry Tablet OS, Kindle, Nook, Kindle Fire
Pub. .... John D'Agostino
Adv. Dir. .... Meredith V. Patton
Managing Editor .... Gregory Bacon
Circ. Mgr. .... Shawn Paulus
Bus. Mgr. .... Jamie Ribbing
Lifestyles coordinator .... Gib Snyder
News editor .... Craig Harvey
Classified coordinator .... Sheila Mcwillson

City editor .... Nicole Gugino
Market Information: ADS; TMC.
Mechanical Available: Offset; Black and 3 ROP colors; insert accepted - all; page cutoffs - 22 1/2.
Mechanical Specifications: Type page 11 3/4 x 21 1/2; E - 6 cols, 1 9/10, 1/8 between; A - 6 cols, 1 9/10, 1/8 between; C - 9 cols, 1 9/10, 1/12 between.
Areas Served: 14048, 14063, 14062, 14081, 14006, 14027, 14716. 14718, 14723, 14034, 14035, 14041, 14061, 14070, 14047, 14750, 14091. 14752, 14757, 14129, 14769, 14135, 14136, 14782, 14138, 14784, 14166, 14787 Equipment & Software: PRESSROOM EQUIPMENT: Lines - 5-G/Urbanite 1966.; MAILROOM EQUIPMENT: Counter Stackers — HL/Monitor; Tying Machines — 2/Bu, 1-/Sa.; BUSINESS EQUIPMENT: 5-Bs/25 BUSINESS SOFTWARE: Western Computer CLASSIFIED EQUIPMENT: Hardware — 4-APP/Mac Centris 610; Printers — APP/Mac LaserPrinter, 2-HP/2000; CLASSIFIED SOFTWARE: ONI/Class System. DISPLAY EQUIPMENT: Hardware — 4-APP/Mac G3 266; Printers — HP/4MV; DISPLAY SOFTWARE Ad Make-up Applications — QPS/QuarkXPress, Multi-Ad/Creator, Aldus/FreeHand, Adobe/Photoshop.; EDITORIAL EQUIPMENT: Hardware — 13-APP/Mac Centris 610; Printers — NewGen/PS480 Laser Printer, HP/4MV EDITORIAL SOFTWARE: WriteNow. PRODUCTION EQUIPMENT: Hardware — ECR/VRL36, BKY/Ascor; Cameras — B, Cannon Pro 70, Nikon/Coolpix 950; Scanners — HP IIcx, Nikon/3510 Scanner, Nikon/LS 1000, 2-Umax/Astra 1200S PRODUCTION SOFTWARE: QPS/QuarkXPress 3.32.
Note: The Dunkirk Observer (mS) has a combination rate of $92.08 with the Jamestown Post-Journal (mS). Individual newspaper rates not made available.

ELMIRA

STAR-GAZETTE
310 E Church St, Elmira, N.Y., 14901-2704, Chemung; gen tel (607) 734-5151; adv tel (607) 271-8474; ed tel (607) 734-5158; gen fax (607) 733-4408; adv fax (607) 733-4408; ed fax (607) 733-4408; gen/nat adv e-mail jzych@binghamt.gannett.com; disp adv e-mail jzych@binghamt.gannett.com; class adv e-mailCNY-classified@gannett.com; ed e-mail sgletters@gannett.com; web site www.stargazette.com
Group: Gannett
Published: Mon, Tues, Wed, Thur, Fri, Sat, Sun
Weekday Frequency: m
Saturday Frequency: m
Circulation: 11,915; 11,915(sat); 18,622(sun)
Last Audit: AAM March 30, 2016
Advertising Rate (weekday/saturday): Open inch rate $62.00
Advertising Rate (sunday): Open inch rate $65.56
News services: AP, GNS **Established:** 1828
Special Editions: Outlook (Feb); Home & Garden (spring/fall) Bridal tab (spring); Guide to the Twin Tiers (fall)
Special Weekly Sections: Twin Tiers Homes (Sat); Entertainment (Thurs.)
Syndicated Publications: Full-Color Comics (S); Time Out (Thur).
Adv. Mgr. .... Joe Darrow
Adv. Dir. .... Robb Scott
Pres. .... George Troyano
Gen. Mgr. / Gannett Pub. Serv. .... Kevin Crane
Exec. Ed. .... Neill Borowski
Market Information: ADS; Split run; TMC; Zoned editions.
Mechanical Specifications: Type page 12 1/2 x 21 1/2; E - 6 cols, 2, 1/8 between; A - 6 cols, 2, 1/8 between; C - 9 cols, 1 7/16, 1/16 between.
Areas Served: Chemung, Steuben & Schuyler Counties (NY); Bradford County (PA)
Equipment & Software: PRESSROOM EQUIPMENT: Lines — KBA Colora 8 towers with 6 (44) & 2 (42), Two Folders, online quarter folder & stitch ; Press Drive — KBA; Folders — 2-KBA; Pasters —10 KBA; Control System — EAE; Registration System — KBA EAE MAILROOM EQUIPMENT: Counter Stackers — 6 Quipp, 2 Gamblers;

Inserters & Stuffers — 2 NP630; Tying Machines — 6 Dynaric; Wrapping Singles — 2 Samual shrink Wrap; Control System — Goss; Address Machine — 2 Kodak; BUSINESS EQUIPMENT: 1-IBM/AS-400 CLASSIFIED EQUIPMENT: Hardware — Mac; CLASSIFIED SOFTWARE: Mactive DISPLAY EQUIPMENT: Printers — Clipper/3850; DISPLAY SOFTWARE Ad Make-up Applications — Multi-Ad/Creator, XIT/Clipper; Layout Software — MEI/ALS. EDITORIAL EQUIPMENT: Hardware — APP/Mac, SII/Tandem EDITORIAL SOFTWARE: SII. PRODUCTION EQUIPMENT: Hardware — 3 -Kodak Thermal plate processors PRODUCTION SOFTWARE: Newsway
Note: Newspapers are printed at the CNY plant located in Johnson City, NY

GENEVA

FINGER LAKES TIMES
218 Genesee St, Geneva, N.Y., 14456-2323, Ontario; gen tel (315) 789-3333; adv tel (315) 789-3333 ext. 263; ed tel (315) 789-3333; gen fax (315) 789-4077; adv fax (315) 789-3376; ed fax (315) 789-4077; gen/nat adv e-mail nneabel@fltimes.com; disp adv e-mail dduval@fltimes.com; class adv e-mailclassads@fltimes.com; ed e-mail opinion@fltimes.com; web site www.fltimes.com
Group: Community Media Group
Published: Mon, Tues, Wed, Thur, Fri, Sun
Weekday Frequency: e
Circulation: 9,062; 11,832(sun)
Last Audit: CAC September 30, 2016
Advertising Rate (weekday/saturday): Open inch rate $26.05
Advertising Rate (sunday): Open inch rate $28.50
News services: SHNS, AP, LAT-WP. **Established:** 1895
Own Printing Facility?: Yes
Commercial Printers?: Yes
Special Editions: Business Directory (Jan) ; Tax Guide & Money Management (Feb); Bridal Magazine (Feb); Vacation Guide (May); Graduation (Jun); Car Care/Home Improvement (Oct); High School Football (Aug); Empire Farm Days (Aug); Indulge (Sept); Bridal Magazine (Oct); Christmas Gift Guide (Nov); Last Minute Gift Guide (Dec); Year in Review (Dec)
Special Weekly Sections: Best Food Day, Inserts, Business, Stocks, health, Travel, Taste, Seniors, Entertainment (Sun); Farm (Mon); School (Tue); Pets (Wed); Finance, Business (Thur); Home, Garden, NASCAR, Religion, Real Estate (Fri)
Syndicated Publications: Automotion (Every other Wednesday); Jumpstart Entertainment (Thur); TV Times (Sun)
Digital Platform - Mobile: Apple, Android, Windows, Blackberry
Digital Platform - Tablet: Apple iOS, Android, Windows 7, Blackberry Tablet OS, Kindle, Nook, Kindle Fire, Other
Pub. .... Paul M Barrett
Business Mgr. .... Diane Lahr-Smith
Circ. Dir. .... Maurice Barcomb
Managing Ed. .... Chuck Schading
Production Mgr. .... Jesse P. Bond
Exec. Ed. .... Michael J. Cutillo
Adv. Dir. .... R. Nicholas Neabel
Circ. Mktg. Dir. .... Ethan Fogg
Market Information: TMC.
Mechanical Available: Offset; Black and 3 colors; inserts accepted; page cutoffs - 22 3/4.
Mechanical Specifications: Type page 12 x 21; E - 6 cols, 1 8/9, 1/8 between; A - 6 cols, 1 2/9, 1/8 between; C - 9 cols, 1 2/9, 1/16 between.
Areas Served: Ontario, Seneca, Wayne & Yates Counties (NY)
Delivery Method: Mail, Newsstand, Carrier, Racks Equipment & Software: PRESSROOM EQUIPMENT: Lines — 5-G/Urbanite. MAILROOM EQUIPMENT: Counter Stackers — 1/KAN; Inserters & Stuffers — 1-KAN/480; Tying Machines — 2-/MLN; Address Machine — 1-/El.; CLASSIFIED SOFTWARE: Media Span DISPLAY SOFTWARE Ad Make-up Applications — Managing Editor.; EDITORIAL SOFTWARE: MediaSpan, QPS/QuarkXPress 4.04. PRODUCTION EQUIPMENT: Hardware

— 2-Ultra Imagesetter; Cameras — 1-AG/RPS204 Vertical; Scanners — Epson/836 XL PRODUCTION SOFTWARE: QPS/QuarkXPress 4.04.

GLENS FALLS

THE POST-STAR
76 Lawrence St, Glens Falls, N.Y., 12801-3741, Warren ; gen tel (518) 792-3131; adv tel (518) 742-3304; ed tel (518) 792-3131; gen fax (518) 792-5902; adv fax (518) 798-5679; ed fax (518) 761-1255; gen/nat adv e-mail ads@poststar.com; disp adv e-mail mrice@poststar.com; class adv e-mailmorehouse@poststar.com; ed e-mail emanuel@poststar.com; web site www.poststar.com
- 4,700,000(views) 341,000(visitors)
Group: Lee Enterprises, Inc.
Published: Mon, Tues, Wed, Thur, Fri, Sat, Sun
Weekday Frequency: m
Saturday Frequency: m
Circulation: 21,027; 21,349(sat); 25,177(sun)
Last Audit: AAM June 30, 2016
Advertising Rate (weekday/saturday): Open inch rate $50.90
Advertising Rate (sunday): Open inch rate $54.95
News services: AP, MCT, TMS. **Established:** 1895
Own Printing Facility?: Yes
Commercial Printers?: Yes
Special Editions: Hockey (Oct); Football (Sept); Business Outlook (Feb.)
Syndicated Publications: Relish (Monthly); USA WEEKEND Magazine (S).
Pub. .... Robert Forcey
Controller .... Brian Corcoran
Circ. Dir. .... Michelle Giorgianni
Production Dir. .... Caren Kuhle
Ed. .... Ken Tingley
City Ed. .... Bob Condon
Projects Dir. .... Will Doolittle
Online Ed. .... Adam Colver
Market Information: Split run; Zoned editions.
Mechanical Available: Offset; Black and 3 ROP colors; insert accepted; page cutoffs - 22 3/4.
Mechanical Specifications: Type page 11 5/8 x 21 1/2; E - 6 cols, 1 5/6, 1/8 between; A - 6 cols, 1 5/6, 1/8 between; C - 9 cols, 1 9/50, 1/8 between.
Areas Served: Upstate New York
Equipment & Software: PRESSROOM EQUIPMENT: Lines — 10-G/Urbanite single width; Reels & Stands — 8; MAILROOM EQUIPMENT: Counter Stackers — 1-MM/338, 1-Id/Marathon, 1-Compass/180; Inserters & Stuffers — 1-SLS/1000R; Tying Machines — 1-MLN/MLN2HS, 1/OVL, 1-/Dynaric; Wrapping Singles — 1-HL/Monarch; BUSINESS EQUIPMENT: 10-Compaq/486, 1-Sun/Ultra BUSINESS SOFTWARE: Vision Data CLASSIFIED EQUIPMENT: Hardware — 3-APP/Mac G4, 1-Sun/Ultra, 10-Dell/Optiplex; Printers — HP/5000; CLASSIFIED SOFTWARE: Vision Data/Island Write. DISPLAY EQUIPMENT: Hardware — 17-APP/Mac G4, 2-Sun/Sparc 20; Printers — 1-HP/5000; Other Hardware — 2-Compaq/486, 1-Dell/Optiplex DISPLAY SOFTWARE Ad Make-up Applications — QPS/QuarkXPress 4.04, Adobe/Illustrator; Layout Software — SCS/Layout 8000. EDITORIAL EQUIPMENT: Hardware — 2-Micron/5200, 3-IBM/327, 2-Sun/Sparc 20, 28-Dell/Optiplex G1, 15-APP/Mac G4, 2-APP/MAC G5; Printers — HP/8000 EDITORIAL SOFTWARE: QPS/QuarkXPress 4.04, NewsEngin. PRODUCTION EQUIPMENT: Hardware — 1-Nu/Flip Top FT40V6UPNS, Nu/Flip Top FT32V3UP-KR, 1-AU/3850; Scanners — Nikon/Coolscan IV, 2-Epson/164XL PRODUCTION SOFTWARE: QPS/QuarkXPress 4.04.

GLOVERSVILLE

THE LEADER-HERALD
8 E Fulton St, Gloversville, N.Y., 12078-3227, Fulton; gen tel (518) 725-8616; adv tel (518) 725-8616; ed tel (518) 725-8616; gen fax (518) 773-3384; adv fax (518) 773-3384; ed fax (518) 725-7407; gen/nat adv e-mail advertising@leaderherald.com; disp adv

e-mail advertising@leaderherald.com; class adv e-mailclassifieds@leaderherald.com; ed e-mail tfonda@leaderherald.com; web site www.leaderherald.com
- 1,100,000(views)
Group: Ogden Newspapers Inc.
Published: Mon, Tues, Wed, Thur, Fri, Sat, Sun
Weekday Frequency: e
Saturday Frequency: e
Circulation: 6,490; 6,490(sat); 8,936(sun)
Last Audit: AAM December 31, 2015
Advertising Rate (weekday/saturday): Open inch rate $18.15
Advertising Rate (sunday): Open inch rate $18.55
News services: AP. **Established:** 1887
Own Printing Facility?: Yes
Commercial Printers?: Yes
Special Editions: Spring Home Improvement & Garden Time (Apr); Lake Country (Aug); Portraits (Feb); Lake Country (Jul); Lake Country (Jun); Spring Car Care (Mar); Spring & Summer Vacation Guide (May); Real Estate (Monthly); Christmas Gift Guide (Nov); Fall Car Care (Oct);
Special Weekly Sections: Business-Stocks (S); Church News (Sat); Best Food (Wed).
Syndicated Publications: Parade (S).
Circ. Dir. .... Toni Mosconi
Editorial Page Ed. .... Tim Fonda
Photo Ed. .... Bill Trojan
Mgmt. Info Servs. Mgr. .... Chad Fleck
Prodn. Mgr., Mailroom.............Tim VanAernam
Pub... Steve Herron
Accounting .... Jim Cornell
Market Information: The Leader Extra (TMC)
Mechanical Available: Offset; Black and 3 ROP colors; insert accepted - cards and booklets; page cutoffs - 22 3/4.
Mechanical Specifications: Type page 13 x 21 1/4; E - 6 cols, 2 1/16, 1/8 between; A - 6 cols, 2 1/16, 1/8 between; C - 8 cols, 1 1/2, 1/8 between.
Areas Served: Fulton, Hamilton & Montgomery Counties (NY)
Delivery Method: Mail, Newsstand, Carrier, RacksEquipment & Software: PRESSROOM EQUIPMENT: Lines — 6-G/Urbanite; 6-HI/V-15A; Folders — 1-G/2, 1-HI/ Combination; MAILROOM EQUIPMENT: Counter Stackers — 2-BG/Count-O-Veyor; Tying Machines — 2/MLN, 1-/Sa; Address Machine — Ch.; BUSINESS EQUIPMENT: NCR/386, Unix/486 System CLASSIFIED EQUIPMENT: Hardware — 3-COM/One Sys 140.; DISPLAY EQUIPMENT: Hardware — 4-APP/Mac; Printers — NewGen/660B, ECR/VRL 36, MON/ExpressMaster 1270; DISPLAY SOFTWAREAd Make-up Applications — Multi-Ad/Creator, Adobe/ Photoshop.; EDITORIAL EQUIPMENT: Hardware — COM/One 140, 5-APP/ Mac/18-COM; Printers — APP/Mac LaserWriter, MON/ExpressMaster 1270, ECR/URL 36 EDITORIAL SOFTWARE: QPS/ QuarkXPress, Aldus/FreeHand, Adobe/ Photoshop. PRODUCTION EQUIPMENT: Hardware — 1-WL/30C, 1-Imperial/Top Coater; Cameras — 1-R/5000H, 1-Acti; Scanners — 2-HP/ScanJet IIcx, 1-Kk/RS-2035 PRODUCTION SOFTWARE: QPS/ QuarkXPress 3.11.
Note: The Gloversville Leader-Herald (eS) has a combination rate of $43.00 with the Saranac Lake Adirondack Enterprise (e). Individual newspaper rates not made available.

HERKIMER

THE HERKIMER TELEGRAM

111 Green St, Herkimer, N.Y., 13350-1914, Herkimer; gen tel (315) 866-2220; adv tel (315) 866-2220; ed tel (315) 866-2220; gen fax (315) 866-5913; adv fax (315) 866-7613; ed fax (315) 866-5913; gen/nat adv e-mail bethadv@herkimertelegram.com; disp adv e-mail jshaffer@timestelegram.com; class adv e-mailbethadv@herkimertelegram.com; ed e-mail tdewan@littlefallstimes.com; web site www.herkimertelegram.com
Group: New Media Investment Group
Published: Mon, Tues, Wed, Thur, Fri, Sat
Weekday Frequency: e
Circulation: 6,657; 6,657(sat)
Last Audit: Sworn/Estimate/Non-Audited September 30, 2017
Advertising Rate (weekday/saturday): Open inch rate $17.81
News services: AP. **Established:** 1898
Special Editions: Our Children (Apr); NASCAR (Feb); Who, What, Where (Jul); Spring Preview (May); Winter Sports Preview (Nov); Senior Life (Sept).
Special Weekly Sections: Food, Bride (Sat); Entertainment (Thur); Senior Lifestyle (Tues); Senior Lifestyle (Wed)
Syndicated Publications: TV Guide Weekly (Sat); American Profile (Weekly).
Pub./Adv. Mgr. ....Beth Brewer
Trends Ed. ....Donna Thompson
Sports Ed. ....Jon Rathbun
Cir. Dir. ....Robert Gall
Mng. Ed. ....Rob Juteau
Market Information: TMC; Zoned editions.
Mechanical Available: Offset; Black and 3 ROP colors; insert accepted; page cutoffs - 22 1/4.
Mechanical Specifications: Type page 13 1/4 x 21 1/2; E - 6 cols, 2 1/16, 1/8 between; A - 6 cols, 2 1/16, 1/8 between; C - 8 cols, 1 3/4, 1/8 between.Equipment & Software: PRESSROOM EQUIPMENT: Lines — 6-G/ Community.; MAILROOM EQUIPMENT: Tying Machines — 1/Sa; Address Machine — 1-/ El.; BUSINESS EQUIPMENT: Packard Bell BUSINESS SOFTWARE: Microsoft/Excel CLASSIFIED EQUIPMENT: Hardware — APP/Mac; Printers — TI; CLASSIFIED SOFTWARE: Baseview/AdManager Pro. EDITORIAL EQUIPMENT: Hardware — APP/Mac; Printers — APP/Mac AdWriter EDITORIAL SOFTWARE: Baseview/News Edit. PRODUCTION EQUIPMENT: Hardware — 1-COM/4961, SCREEN; Cameras — 1-B, Olympus/Digital PRODUCTION SOFTWARE: Adobe/Pagemaker, QPS/QuarkXPress.

HORNELL

THE EVENING TRIBUNE

32 Broadway Mall, Hornell, N.Y., 14843-1920, Steuben; gen tel (607) 324-1425; adv tel (607) 324-1425; ed tel (607) 324-1425 ext. 205; gen fax (607) 324-2317; adv fax (607) 324-1753; ed fax (607) 324-2317; gen/nat adv e-mail advertising@ eveningtribune.com; disp adv e-mail kellyschecter@eveningtribune.com; class adv e-mailbethhults@eveningtribune.com; ed e-mail news@eveningtribune.com ; web site www.eveningtribune.com
Group: New Media Investment Group
Published: Mon, Tues, Wed, Thur, Fri, Sun
Weekday Frequency: e
Circulation: 5,400; 7,800(sun)
Last Audit: Sworn/Estimate/Non-Audited September 30, 2017
Advertising Rate (weekday/saturday): Open inch rate $9.65
Advertising Rate (sunday): Open inch rate $11.25
News services: AP. **Established:** 1872
Own Printing Facility?: Yes
Commercial Printers?: Yes
Special Editions: Chistmas (Dec); Interstate 86 Travel Guide (Fall); Interstate 86 Travel Guide (Spring).
Special Weekly Sections: Food, Travel, Real Estate (Sun)
Syndicated Publications: Parade (S).
Rgl. Ed.......................................John Anderson
Sports Ed. ....Derrick Balinsky
Reg. Pub....................................Rick Emanuel
Class. Adv. ....Beth Hults
Market Information: ADS; TMC.
Mechanical Available: Offset; Black and 3 ROP colors; insert accepted; page cutoffs - 22 3/4.
Mechanical Specifications: Type page 13 x 21 1/2; E - 6 cols, 2 1/16, 1/8 between; A - 6 cols, 2 1/16, 1/8 between; C - 6 cols, 2 1/16, 1/8 between.
Areas Served: 14843
Delivery Method: Mail, Newsstand, Carrier, RacksEquipment & Software: BUSINESS EQUIPMENT: 3-IBM/Nomad CLASSIFIED EQUIPMENT: Hardware — APP/Macs; Printers — APP/Mac Pro 630, HP/LaserJet 4MV; CLASSIFIED SOFTWARE: Baseview. DISPLAY EQUIPMENT: Hardware — 2-APP/Mac; Printers — HP/LaserJet 4MV.; EDITORIAL EQUIPMENT: Hardware — APP/ Macs; Printers — APP/Mac 630 Pro, HP/ LaserJet 4MV, Xante/8300 EDITORIAL SOFTWARE: Baseview. PRODUCTION EQUIPMENT: Hardware — APP/Mac Pro 630, HP/LaserJet 4MV, Xante/8300; Cameras — 1-C/Spartan III; Scanners — HP/ScanJet PRODUCTION SOFTWARE: Baseview.
Note: The Hornell Evening Tribune (e) and the Wellsville Daily Reporter (e) share a Sunday edition.

HUDSON

REGISTER-STAR

1 Hudson City Ctr, Ste 202, Hudson, N.Y., 12534-2355, Columbia; gen tel (518) 828-1616; adv tel (518) 828-1616 ext. 2463; ed tel (518) 828-1616 ext. 2490; gen fax 518-671-6043; adv fax (518) 671-6043; ed fax (518) 828-3870; gen/nat adv e-mail advertising@registerstar.com; disp adv e-mail advertising@registerstar.com; class adv e-mailclassifieds@registerstar.com; ed e-mail editorial@registerstar.com; web site www.hudsonvalley360.com
- 1,048,368(views) 162,011(visitors)
Group: Johnson Newspaper Corp.
Published: Tues, Wed, Thur, Fri, Sat, Sun
Weekday Frequency: m
Saturday Frequency: m
Circulation: 3,201; 3,847(sat)
Last Audit: AAM September 30, 2016
Newspaper Reps: Mark Vinciguerra, ext. 2401
Tammi Ullrich, ext. 2402
Mary Dempsey, ext. 2533
Gregory Appel, ext. 2463
Patti McKenna ext. 2413
Advertising Rate (weekday/saturday): Open inch rate $12.95
News services: AP. **Established:** 1785
Own Printing Facility?: No
Commercial Printers?: No
Special Editions: Car Care (Apr/Oct); Holiday (Nov./Dec); Progress Edition (April); Bridal (Jan/June); Holiday (Nov/Dec); Home Improvement (Sept./May)
We'll create special editions for your special events
Special Weekly Sections: Best Food Days (S); Best Food Days (Wed).
Syndicated Publications: USA Weekend, Parade Magazine, every week. Relish, Spry monthly.
Digital Platform - Mobile: Apple, Android, Windows, Blackberry
Digital Platform - Tablet: Apple iOS, Android, Windows 7, Blackberry Tablet OS, Kindle, Kindle Fire
Pub.................................. Mark Vinciguerra
HR/Business Mgr. ....Tammi Ullrich
Exec. Ed. ....Gregory Appel
Ed...Susan Chasney
Advertising Director....................Gregory Appel
Market Information: ADS; TMC.
Mechanical Specifications: Type page 10.25 x 21 1/2; E - 6 cols, 2 3/100, 1/6 between; A - 6 cols, 2 3/100, 1/6 between; C - 10 cols, 1 11/50, 1/12 between.
Areas Served: All Columbia County, Greene County.
Delivery Method: Mail, Newsstand, Carrier, RacksEquipment & Software: PRESSROOM EQUIPMENT: Lines — 13-G/Community 518-943-6953; Folders — G/SC.; MAILROOM EQUIPMENT: Tying Machines — Bu/ Strapper.; CLASSIFIED EQUIPMENT: Hardware — APP/Mac G3; APP/Power Mac, APP/Mac G3, AG/1500; Printers — HP/4MV; CLASSIFIED SOFTWARE: QPS/ QuarkXPress. DISPLAY EQUIPMENT: Hardware — APP/Mac 7100, APP/Power Mac, APP/Mac G3; Printers — HP/4MV; Other Hardware — Umax/Scanner, AG/1500 DISPLAY SOFTWAREAd Make-up Applications — Multi-Ad; Layout Software — APP/Mac. EDITORIAL EQUIPMENT: Hardware — APP/Power Mac, APP/ Mac G3/APP/Power Mac, APP/Mac G3, AG/1500; Printers — HP/4MV EDITORIAL SOFTWARE: Baseview/NewsEdit Pro, QPS/ QuarkXPress. PRODUCTION EQUIPMENT: Hardware — Caere/OmniPro, AG/1500 Imagesetter; Cameras — Ret PRODUCTION SOFTWARE: QPS/QuarkXPress.

THE DAILY MAIL

1 Hudson City Ctr, Ste 202, Hudson, N.Y., 12534-2355, Columbia; gen tel 5188281616; adv tel (518) 828-1616; ed tel (518) 828-1616; gen fax (518) 943-2063; adv fax (518) 671-6043; ed fax (518) 671-6043; gen/nat adv e-mail Tammiullrich@gmail.com; disp adv e-mail Tammiullrich@gmail.com; class adv e-mailTammiullrich@gmail.com; ed e-mail Tammiullrich@gmail.com; web site www.hudsonvalley360.com
- 1,048,368(views) 162,011(visitors)
Group: Johnson Newspaper Corp.
Published: Tues, Wed, Thur, Fri, Sat
Weekday Frequency: m
Saturday Frequency: m
Circulation: 1,858; 2,259(sat)
Last Audit: AAM September 30, 2016
Advertising Rate (weekday/saturday): Open inch rate $11.85
Advertising Rate (sunday): (weekend) $11.85
Online Advertising Rate: $10-$12
News services: AP. **Established:** 1792
Own Printing Facility?: No
Commercial Printers?: No
Special Editions: Car Care (Apr); Christmas Gift Guide (Dec); Progress Report (April); Bridal (Jan); Home Improvement (Mar); Christmas Gift Guide (Nov); Car Care (Oct); Home Improvement (Sept). destinations (May)
Special Weekly Sections: TV (Sat).On The Scene /entertainment guide (Fridays) Living Today (Saturday)
Syndicated Publications: Parade magazine (weekly);American Profile (Weekly); Spry (monthly); Relish (monthly)
Digital Platform - Mobile: Apple, Android, Windows, Blackberry, Other
Digital Platform - Tablet: Apple iOS, Android, Windows 7, Blackberry Tablet OS, Kindle, Nook, Kindle Fire
Ed...Ray Pignone
Admin./Asst.to the Pub. ....Tammi Ullrich
Pub./Gen. Mgr..........................Mark Vinciguerra
Advertising Director.....................Gregory Appel
Executive Editor.........................Mary Dempsey
Mechanical Available: Offset; Black and 3 ROP colors; insert accepted; page cutoffs - 22 3/4.
Mechanical Specifications: Type page 13 x 21 1/2; E - 6 cols, 2, 1/6 between; A - 6 cols, 2, 1/6 between; C - 10 cols, 1 1/5, 1/12 between.
Areas Served: Columbia and Greene Counties in NYS
Delivery Method: Mail, Newsstand, CarrierEquipment & Software: PRESSROOM EQUIPMENT: Lines — 13-G/Community; Folders — G/SC.; MAILROOM EQUIPMENT: Tying Machines — 2; Address Machine — 1/ Wm, 1-/X.; BUSINESS EQUIPMENT: 2-IBM BUSINESS SOFTWARE: PBS CLASSIFIED EQUIPMENT: Hardware — APP/Mac pro
IMAC
6100, APP/Power Mac 7100, APP/Mac G3; Umax/Scanner; Printers — HP; CLASSIFIED SOFTWARE: Baseview. DISPLAY EQUIPMENT: Hardware — APP/Mac 7100, APP/IMAC/MAC PRO
Printers — APP/Mac LaserPrinter II NT, Compaq/PageMarq 15; Other Hardware — Umax/Scanner DISPLAY SOFTWAREAd Make-up Applications — Multi-Ad/Creator; Layout Software — APP/Mac. EDITORIAL EQUIPMENT: Hardware — APP/Mac, APP/ Power Mac, APP/Mac G3/AG/1500; Printers — 3-HP EDITORIAL SOFTWARE: Baseview/ NewsEdit Pro. PRODUCTION EQUIPMENT: Hardware — 3-Laser, HP, 2-AG/ Imagesetters; Cameras — Repromaster/2001 PRODUCTION SOFTWARE: QPS/ QuarkXPress. IT EQUIPMENT: MAC PROS IT SOFTWARE:apple server CIRCULATION SOFTWARDTI

ITHACA

THE ITHACA JOURNAL

123 W State St, Ithaca, N.Y., 14850-5427, Tompkins; gen tel (607) 272-2321; adv tel (607) 798-1131; ed tel (607) 272-2321; gen/ nat adv e-mail jriesbec@ithacajournal.com; disp adv e-mail jriesbec@ithacajournal.com; ed e-mail nborowski@gannett.com; web site www.ithacajournal.com
Group: Gannett
Published: Mon, Tues, Wed, Thur, Fri, Sat
Weekday Frequency: m
Saturday Frequency: m

Circulation: 8,025; 10,979(sat)
Last Audit: AAM June 30, 2016
Advertising Rate (weekday/saturday): 1/4 Pg $1646.00, 1/2 Pg $2954.00, Full $5932.00
News services: AP, GNS,
Own Printing Facility?: Yes
Commercial Printers?: Yes
Syndicated Publications: The Real Estate Journal (Wed.)
Ticket (Thurs.)
Pres./Pub............................ Thomas Claybaugh
HR...Donna Bell
Exec. Ed....................................Neill A. Borowski
Gen. Mgr........................................Kevin Crane
Equipment & Software: PRESSROOM EQUIPMENT: Lines — KBA Colora; Press Drive — KBA; MAILROOM EQUIPMENT: Counter Stackers — 7; Inserters & Stuffers — 2; Tying Machines — 7; Control System — Omnizone; Address Machine — 2 Kodak;

JAMESTOWN

THE POST-JOURNAL

15 W 2nd St, Jamestown, N.Y., 14701-5215, Chautauqua; gen tel (716) 487-1111; adv tel (716) 487-1111; ed tel (716) 487-1111; gen fax (716) 664-3119; adv fax (716) 664-3119; ed fax (716) 664-5305; gen/nat adv e-mail advertising@post-journal.com; disp adv e-mail advertising@post-journal.com; class adv e-mailadsales@post-journal.com; ed e-mail editorial@post-journal.com; web site www.post-journal.com
- 318,888(views) 109,198(visitors)
Group: Ogden Newspapers Inc.
Published: Mon, Tues, Wed, Thur, Fri, Sat, Sun
Weekday Frequency: m
Saturday Frequency: m
Circulation: 12,335; 12,335(sat); 13,989(sun)
Last Audit: AAM June 30, 2016
Advertising Rate (weekday/saturday): Open inch rate $86.14
Advertising Rate (sunday): Open inch rate $86.14
Online Advertising Rate: Top Leaderboard: $16 (ROS), $20 (Targeted); Half Banner: $8 (ROS), $12 (Targeted); Skyscraper $16 (ROS), $20 (Targeted); Center Full Banner $11 (ROS), $15 (Targeted); Large Rectangle $15 (ROS), $19 (Targeted)
News services: AP. **Established:** 1826
Special Editions: Community Directory (Jan); Medical Directory & Weddings (Feb); Chataugua Profiles (Mar); Golf Guide, Spring Car Care, Camping Guide (Apr); Vacation Guide, Lawn & Garden Care, Discover Erie (May); Chautauqua Book (Jun); Cautauqua Lake, Wine Time, Chautauqua Fair, Readers Choice, 101 Things to Do (Jul); Youth Soccer, NFL Preview, Gridiron (Aug); Chautauqua Chamber Tab, Buffalo Bills & Sabres Schedules, Back to School, Fall sports (Sept); Survivors, Fall Brides, Gas Giveaway (Oct); Experience Winter, Best Gifts (Nov); Holidy Gift Guide, Wrapping Paper, Song Book (Dec)
Special Weekly Sections: Best Food Day (Sat)
Syndicated Publications: TV Book (Fri); Community Marketplace
Digital Platform - Mobile: Apple
Digital Platform - Tablet: Apple iOS
Pub...Micheal Bird
Adv. Dir......................................Debra Brunner
Mktg./Promo. ....Kirsten Johnson
Circ. Dir. .... Andy Gee
Bus./Finance Ed..........................Dennis Phillips
Ed...John Whittaker
Features Ed.............................. Aimee Frederick
Librarian..................................... Linda Carlson
Magazine Ed...........................Brigetta Overcash
News Ed..................................... Matt Spielman
Regl. Ed....Chris Kinsler
Sports Ed. ....Scott Kindberg
Prodn. Mgr., Pre Press..............Peter C. Elofson
Andrew Cavaretta
Market Information: ADS; Split run; TMC.
Mechanical Available: Offset; Black and 3 ROP colors; insert accepted; page cutoffs - 22 3/4.
Mechanical Specifications: Type page 11 3/4 x 21 3/4; E - 6 cols, 1 7/8, 1/8 between; A - 6 cols, 1 7/8, 1/8 between; C - 8 cols, 1 3/8, 1/16 between.
Areas Served: Southern Chautauqua County (NY)
Equipment & Software: PRESSROOM EQUIPMENT: Lines — 10-G/Urbanite single width; Press Drive — 2-Fin/150 h.p.; Folders — 1-G/Urbanite, 1-G/Suburban; Pasters —6-Martin/Splicer. MAILROOM EQUIPMENT: Counter Stackers — 1-RS/25, 3-HL/Monitor, 1/FDAB; Inserters & Stuffers — HI/NP 1372; Tying Machines — 2-Mosca/P2, 1-/Power Strap/5; Address Machine — 4-Typac/Label Dispenser; BUSINESS EQUIPMENT: NCR/Unix CLASSIFIED EQUIPMENT: Hardware — Pentium/III Server, 5-CEL/366; AG/Arcus II, 5-APP/Mac C500; Printers — 2-APP/Mac LaserWriter II, 1-MON/EM 1270, 2-HP/4MV, 2-HP/LJ 2100 TN; CLASSIFIED SOFTWARE: Microsoft/Windows NT, Microsoft/Windows 98. DISPLAY EQUIPMENT: Printers — 2-APP/Mac LaserWriter II, 1-MON/EM 1270, 2-HP/4MV; Other Hardware — Nikon/Coolscan, HP/ScanJet 4C, AG/Arcus II DISPLAY SOFTWAREAd Make-up Applications — Multi-Ad/Creator 4.05; Layout Software — 5-APP/Mac C500. EDITORIAL EQUIPMENT: Hardware — 2-Pentium/III Server, 22-CEL/366/3-RSK/TRS 100, 2-RSK/TRS 102, 2-RSK/TRS 200, 1-Lf/AP Leaf Picture Desk, Lf/Leafscan 35, HP/ScanJet 4C, 4-APP/Mac G3, 1-APP/Mac C500, 1-Nikon/Coolscan; Printers — 2-APP/Mac LaserWriter II, 1-MON/EM 1 PRODUCTION EQUIPMENT: Hardware — Nu/Flip Top FT40UPNS, 1-Trek/25, 1-MON/EM 1270, 1-APP/Mac C500, 1-APP/Mac AWS-60 Server, 2-HP/4MV, 1-APP/Mac AWS-7250 Server, 2-HP/LT 2100 TN; Cameras — 1-C/Spartan II, 1-C/Pager; Scanners — 1-Lf/Leafscan 35, 1-Nikon/Coolscan, 1-HP/ScanJet 4C,
Note: The Jamestown Post-Journal (mS) has a combination rate of $92.08 with the Dunkirk Observer (mS). Individual newspaper rates not made available.

KINGSTON

DAILY FREEMAN

79 Hurley Ave, Kingston, N.Y., 12401-2832, Ulster; gen tel (845) 331-5000; adv tel (845) 331-5000 Ext. 01099; ed tel (845) 331-5000; gen fax (845) 338-0672; adv fax (845) 338-0672; ed fax (845) 331-3557; gen/nat adv e-mail ttergeoglou@freemanonline.com; disp adv e-mail ttergeoglou@freemanonline.com; class adv e-mailclassified@freemanonline.com; ed e-mail letters@freemanonline.com; web site www.dailyfreeman.com
- 3,500,000(views) 519,977(visitors)
Group: Digital First Media
Published: Mon, Tues, Wed, Thur, Fri, Sat, Sun
Weekday Frequency: m
Saturday Frequency: m
Circulation: 9,984; 9,585(sat); 13,451(sun)
Last Audit: AAM September 30, 2015
Advertising Rate (weekday/saturday): 29.50daily/35.96 Sunday
News services: AP, TMS. **Established:** 1871
Own Printing Facility?: No
Commercial Printers?: No
Special Editions: Kingston Classic (Apr); Spotlight on the Arts (Aug); Last Minute Gift Guide (Dec); Internet Directory (Feb); Brides (Jan); Parenting (Jul); Graduation (Jun); Housing Solutions (Mar); Summer Car Care (May); Winter Lifestyles (Nov); Women's View
Special Weekly Sections: Entertainment (Fri); Financial (S); Best Food Edition (Wed).
Syndicated Publications: Preview Tab (Fri); People & Events Magazine (S).
Digital Platform - Mobile: Apple, Android
Digital Platform - Tablet: Apple iOS, Android
Mng. Ed.......................................Tony Adamis
City Ed....................................Jeremy Schiffres
Life. Ed. ....Ivan Lajara
Sports Ed. .... Ron Rosner
Controller.............................. Tony Sakellariou
Adv. Dir....................................Tim Tergeoglou
Pub. Emeritus ....Ira Fusfeld
Areas Served: Ulster County/NY
Delivery Method: Mail, Newsstand, Carrier, RacksEquipment & Software: BUSINESS EQUIPMENT: 4 HP DC5800 CLASSIFIED EQUIPMENT: Hardware — Atex, 2-RS6000 Pagination Terminal; Printers — HP/5000 GN; CLASSIFIED SOFTWARE: Enterprise/17. DISPLAY EQUIPMENT: Hardware - 4 G5 Mac 2 Lenova A4U; Printers — HP/5000 GN; Other Hardware — HP/II Cx Scanner DISPLAY SOFTWAREAd Make-up Applications — Multi-Ad/Creator 3.6; Layout Software — APP/Mac. EDITORIAL EQUIPMENT: Hardware — HP 6000 (14)/6 HP 6710; Printers — HP/5000 GN EDITORIAL SOFTWARE: Atex/Prestige Via Citrix (Cloud), Photoshop, 1 NDesign, 1N Copy PRODUCTION EQUIPMENT: Scanners — 3-HP/4c PRODUCTION SOFTWARE: QPS/QuarkXPress 3.32.

LOCKPORT

LOCKPORT UNION-SUN & JOURNAL

135 Main St, Ste 1, Lockport, N.Y., 14094-3728, Niagara; gen tel (716) 439-9222; adv tel (716) 439-1234; ed tel (716) 439-9222; gen fax (716) 439-9249; adv fax (716) 439-9249; ed fax (716) 439-9249; gen/nat adv e-mail ann.fisherbale@lockportjournal.com; disp adv e-mail dan.tronolone@lockportjournal.com; class adv e-mailleann.belfield@lockportjournal.com; ed e-mail joyce.miles@lockportjournal.com; web site www.lockportjournal.com
Group: Community Newspaper Holdings, Inc.
Published: Mon, Wed, Thur, Fri, Sat, Sun
Weekday Frequency: e
Saturday Frequency: m
Circulation: 5,130; 5,130(sat); 4,819(sun)
Last Audit: AAM December 31, 2016
Advertising Rate (weekday/saturday): Open inch rate $21.10
Advertising Rate (sunday): Open inch rate $53.96
News services: AP. **Established:** 1821
Special Editions: Spring Fashion (Apr); Farm Home (Aug); Car Care (Jun); Impact (Mar); Gift Guide (Nov); Better Homes (Oct); Women's World (Sept).
Special Weekly Sections: Best Food Day (Mon)
Sports Ed. .... John D'Onofrio
Mng. Ed....Joyce Miles
Pub....Chris Voccio
Exec. Ed....Rob Kaiser
Cir. ....Ken Skryp
Market Information: TMC.
Mechanical Available: Offset; Black and 3 ROP colors; insert accepted - free-standing inserts; page cutoffs - 21 1/2.
Mechanical Specifications: Type page 12 1/2 x 21 1/2; E - 6 cols, 1 3/4, 1/10 between; A - 6 cols, 1 3/4, 1/10 between; C - 10 cols, 1 1/5, 1/15 between.
Areas Served: Niagara County (NY)
Equipment & Software: PRESSROOM EQUIPMENT: Lines — 10-G/Community; 10-Unit/Community; Press Drive — 2-HP/60; Registration System — Duarte/Pin Registration. MAILROOM EQUIPMENT: Tying Machines — 2/Bu, 2-/Power Strappers; Wrapping Singles — 2-/Bottom Wrappers.; BUSINESS EQUIPMENT: Unix/E450, PBS BUSINESS SOFTWARE: PBS CLASSIFIED EQUIPMENT: Hardware — APP/Mac, APP/Mac; Printers — APP/Mac LaserWriter; CLASSIFIED SOFTWARE: QPS/QuarkXPress, DTI. DISPLAY EQUIPMENT: Hardware — APP/Mac, APP/Mac; Printers — APP/Mac LaserWriter; DISPLAY SOFTWAREAd Make-up Applications — QPS/QuarkXPress, DTI; Layout Software — APP/Mac. EDITORIAL EQUIPMENT: Hardware — APP/Mac, APP/Mac/2-HP; Printers — APP/Mac Laser EDITORIAL SOFTWARE: QPS/QuarkXPress, Baseview/NewsEdit, DTI. PRODUCTION EQUIPMENT: Hardware — Panther Pro, APP/Mac PRODUCTION SOFTWARE: DTI 4.3.
Note: This publication shares a joint Sunday edition with the Niagara Falls (NY) Niagara Gazette and the North Tonawanda (NY) Tonawanda News.

MALONE

THE MALONE TELEGRAM

469 E Main St, Ste 4, Malone, N.Y., 12953-2128, Franklin; gen tel (518) 483-4700; adv tel (518) 483-4720; ed tel (518) 483-2000; gen fax (518) 483-8579; adv fax (518) 483-8579; ed fax (518) 483-8579; gen/nat adv e-mail ads@mtelegram.com; disp adv e-mail kcarre@mtelegram.com; class adv e-mailclassified@mtelegram.com; ed e-mail news@mtelegram.com; web site www.mymalonetelegram.com
Group: Johnson Newspaper Corp.
Published: Mon, Tues, Wed, Thur, Fri, Sat
Weekday Frequency: m
Saturday Frequency: m
Circulation: 4,721; 4,721(sat)
Last Audit: Sworn/Estimate/Non-Audited December 14, 2017
Advertising Rate (weekday/saturday): Open inch rate $9.54
News services: AP. **Established:** 1905
Own Printing Facility?: No
Commercial Printers?: Yes
Special Editions: Fair Tab (Aug); Bridal Tab (Feb); Winter Carnival (Jan); Meet the Merchants (Jun); Spring Tab (Mar); Summer Visitor (May); Christmas Gift Guide (Nov).
Special Weekly Sections: Home (Mon); Arts, Entertainment, Real Estate (Tue); Religion (Fri); Best Food Day, Business (Sat);
Bus. Mgr. .... Betsy McGivney
Adv. Mgr....Karen Carre
Ed....Ej Conzola
Market Information: TMC.
Mechanical Available: Offset; Black and 2 ROP colors; insert accepted; page cutoffs - 22 5/8.
Mechanical Specifications: Type page 13 x 21 1/2; E - 6 cols, 2 1/16, 1/8 between; A - 6 cols, 2 1/16, 1/8 between; C - 8 cols, 1 1/2, 1/8 between.
Areas Served: Northern Franklin County, NY
Delivery Method: Mail, Newsstand, Carrier, RacksEquipment & Software: CLASSIFIED EQUIPMENT: Printers — HP/LaserJet; EDITORIAL EQUIPMENT: Printers — HP/LaserJet EDITORIAL SOFTWARE: Saxotech - InDesign, InCopy PRODUCTION SOFTWARE: QPS/QuarkXPress 3.31.

MASSENA

DAILY COURIER-OBSERVER/ADVANCE NEWS

1 Harrowgate Cmns, Massena, N.Y., 13662-2201, Saint Lawrence; gen tel (315) 769-2451; adv tel (315) 661-2512; ed tel (315) 661-2532; gen fax (315) 764-0337; adv fax (315) 764-0337; ed fax (315) 764-0337; gen/nat adv e-mail nbellinger@ogd.com; disp adv e-mail tmackin@ogd.com; class adv e-mailclass@ogd.com; ed e-mail rmartin@ogd.com; web site www.mpcourier.com/
Published: Tues, Wed, Thur, Fri, Sat
Weekday Frequency: m
Saturday Frequency: m
Circulation: 5,900; 5,900(sat)
Last Audit: Sworn/Estimate/Non-Audited September 30, 2017
Advertising Rate (weekday/saturday): Open inch rate $11.90
Digital Platform - Mobile: Apple, Android, Windows, Blackberry
Digital Platform - Tablet: Apple iOS, Android, Windows 7, Blackberry Tablet OS, Kindle
Ed....Pery White
Chief Exec. Off. / Co-Pub...............John Johnson
Pres. / Co-Pub...........................Harold Johnson
HR VP......................................Jeanette Hardy
Sales / Mktg. VP................................Gary Valik
Cir. CSR.....................................Amber Bogart
Adv. Acct. Exec. ....Nathan Bellinger
Delivery Method: Mail, Racks

MELVILLE

NEWSDAY

235 Pinelawn Rd, Melville, N.Y., 11747-4226, Suffolk; gen tel (800) 639-7329; adv tel (631) 843-7653; ed tel (631) 843-7653; gen fax (631) 843-4174; adv fax (631) 843-4174; ed fax (631) 843-4174; gen/nat adv e-mail advertising@newsday.com; disp adv e-mail advertising@newsday.com; class adv e-mailads.classified@newsday.com; ed e-mail letters@newsday.com; web site www.newsday.com
- 31,500,000(views) 2,463,000(visitors)
Group: Cablevision Systems Corporation
Published: Mon, Tues, Wed, Thur, Fri, Sat, Sun

Weekday Frequency: m
Saturday Frequency: m
Circulation: 309,047; 292,673(sat); 345,925(sun)
Last Audit: AAM September 30, 2016
Advertising Rate (weekday/saturday): 1/8 Pg $5,862.00
Advertising Rate (sunday): 1/8 Pg $6,685.00
News services: AP, CSM, DJ, LAT-WP, NNS, RN, SHNS. **Established:** 1940
Own Printing Facility?: Yes
Commercial Printers?: No
Special Editions: Caribbean American Chamber (Apr); Back-to-School (Aug); Holiday Gift Guide (Dec); President's Forum (Feb); Bridal (Jan); Auto Leasing (Jul); Dads & Grads (Jun); Tax Advice-Your Financial Checklist (Mar); Home, Lawn & Garden II (May); Holiday Almanac (Nov)
Special Weekly Sections: Business (Mon-Fri); Technology, Style (Mon); Health (Tue); Style, Kids (Wed); Food (Thur); Arts, Movies (Fri); Travel, Life (Sun)
Syndicated Publications: USA WEEKEND Magazine (Sat).
Digital Platform - Mobile: Apple, Android
Digital Platform - Tablet: Apple iOS, Android, Kindle Fire
Co-Pub.....Debby Krenek
Asst. Mng. Ed., Admin.....Mary Ann Skinner
Adv. Administrator, Newsday.com Bus.....Chris Gennario
Vice Pres./Mng. Ed.....Robert Keane
Mng. Ed., News....Richard Galant
Dir., Publishing Devel.....Peter Bengelsdorf
MGR Information Systems....Michael Gatta
James Rosenfeld
Director, Major Retail Sales....Chris Tobia
Lauren Andrich
Pub.....Gordon McLeod
Senior Director National Sales
Stefani Angeli
Co-Pub.....Edward Bushey
Ed.....Deborah Henley
Market Information: ADS; Split run; TMC; Zoned editions.
Mechanical Available: Offset; Black and 3 ROP colors; insert accepted - subscription blanks; page cutoffs - 21 1/2.
Mechanical Specifications: Type page 9 25/64 x 13; E - 6 cols, 1 1/2, 1/16 between; A - 6 cols, 1 1/2, 5/64 between; C - 8 cols, 1 3/16, 1/16 between.Equipment & Software: PRESSROOM EQUIPMENT: Lines — 2-G/Metro 144 pg., 4-G/Metro BB with half decks 1979, 4-G/Metro BB, 2-TKS/M-72; 1-G/Metro 144 pg., 4-G/Metro BB with half decks 1979, 4-G/Metro, 2-TKS/M-72; 1-G/Metro 144 pg., 4-G/Metro BB with half decks 1979, 4-G/Metro, 2-TKS/; MAILROOM EQUIPMENT: Counter Stackers — 15-QWI/350, 23-QWI/400; Inserters & Stuffers — 8/AM Graphics/NP 630, 2-HI/1472, 4-HI/2299; Tying Machines — 6-Dynaric/NP1, 54-Dynaric/NP2; Wrapping Singles — 6-Overhead/Spiral Wrapper; Control System — Burt/NT.; BUSINESS EQUIPMENT: Dell/Laptop, Dell/PC, 1-IBM/S-390 Parallel Enterprise Server 9672-R52, IBM/Netfinity Server, IBM/Laptop, IBM/PC, Sun/Enterprise Server BUSINESS SOFTWARE: ATEX/Enterprise, IBM/Lotus Notes, Unisys/Hermes CLASSIFIED EQUIPMENT: Hardware — AT/IAS System 10 Series 6; CLASSIFIED SOFTWARE: AT/Sysdeco 4.37. DISPLAY EQUIPMENT: Hardware — 67-APP/Power Mac; Printers — HP/LaserJet; DISPLAY SOFTWAREAd Make-up Applications — QPS/QuarkXPress, Adobe/Photoshop; Layout Software — 4-Cascade/Image Flow-Data Flow, Sun/20-70. EDITORIAL EQUIPMENT: Hardware — Dell/PC; Printers — HP/LaserJets EDITORIAL SOFTWARE: Unisys/Hermes 4.x. PRODUCTION EQUIPMENT: Hardware — WL, 2-Dolev/800, 2-III/3850 Sierra, 2-MON/RIP Server, NEC, Scitex; Scanners — 1-AG/XY, 2-Eskofot, 1-Scitex/EverSmart Pro PRODUCTION SOFTWARE: Cascade.
Note: Circulation is combined for Nasssau, Suffolk & Long Island editions.

MIDDLETOWN

THE TIMES HERALD-RECORD

40 Mulberry St, Middletown, N.Y., 10940-6302, Orange; gen tel 1-866-620-1700; adv tel (845) 341-1100 ext. 2094; ed tel (845) 346-3170; gen fax (845) 343-2050; adv fax (845) 343-2934; ed fax (845) 343-2170; gen/nat adv e-mail amcfarlane@recordonline.com; disp adv e-mail amcfarlane@recordonline.com; class adv e-mailkwalsh@th-record.com; ed e-mail letters@th-record.com; web site www.recordonline.com - 5,200,000(views) 38,500(visitors)
Group: New Media Investment Group
Published: Mon, Tues, Wed, Thur, Fri, Sat, Sun
Weekday Frequency: m
Saturday Frequency: m
Circulation: 32,437; 33,213(sat); 42,572(sun)
Last Audit: AAM December 31, 2016
Advertising Rate (weekday/saturday): Open inch rate $88.00
Advertising Rate (sunday): Open inch rate $106.00
Online Advertising Rate: Medium Rectangle $16; Leaderboard $16, Half Page $20
News services: AP, NewsCore **Established:** 1960
Own Printing Facility?: Yes
Commercial Printers?: Yes
Special Editions: NY Auto Show (Apr); Back-to-School (Aug); Wish Book (Dec); Bridal (Feb); Progress (Jan); Star Spangled (Jul); Family Focus (Mar); Summer Guide (May); Inside Health (Monthly); Gift Guide (Nov); New Car (Oct); Family Focus (Sept).
Special Weekly Sections: Auto (Tue); Best Food Day (Wed); Entertainment (Fri); Home, Real Estate (Sun)
Syndicated Publications: Go Plus (Fri); Relish (Monthly); Sunday Magazine (S); Auto Plus (Tues).
Digital Platform - Mobile: Windows
Digital Platform - Tablet: Windows 7
Pres./Pub.....Joe Vanderhoof
Commercial Printing....Stanton Frederick
Ed.....Barry Lewis
regional Ad Direcor....Anthony Mcfarlane
Market Information: Split run; TMC; Zoned editions.
Mechanical Available: Offset; Black and 3 ROP colors; insert accepted - print & deliver single sheets & tab inserts; page cutoffs - 12.
Mechanical Specifications: Type page 10 1/4 x 11; E - 4 cols, 3 1/6, 1/6 between; A - 6 cols, 1 1/2, 1/6 between; C - 8 cols, 1 1/4, 1/16 between.
Areas Served: Orange, Sullivan & Ulster Counties (NY), Pike County (PA), Sussex County (NJ)
Delivery Method: Newsstand, Carrier, RacksEquipment & Software: PRESSROOM EQUIPMENT: Lines — 7-Goss.; MAILROOM EQUIPMENT: Counter Stackers — 5-QWI/N200, 7-QWI; Inserters & Stuffers — 3-GMA/SLS 1000 8:1, 4-Newstec; Tying Machines — 5/OVL, 7-Dynaric; Control System — Newscom; Address Machine — 4-Mirajet.; BUSINESS EQUIPMENT: IBM/AS-400 BUSINESS SOFTWARE: Microsoft/Office, Lawson CLASSIFIED EQUIPMENT: Hardware — AT/Enterpriise, Dewar/View; Printers — 1-AU/APS 3850.; DISPLAY EQUIPMENT: Hardware — PC's, APP/Power Mac 7100; Printers — HP/4MV LaserJet, HP/5MV LaserJet; DISPLAY SOFTWAREAd Make-up Applications — Adobe InDesign; Layout Software — ALS Pagination. EDITORIAL EQUIPMENT: Hardware — Dell Optiplex/21-Dell/Alpha; Printers — 1-DEC/LA 120, 1-DEC/LA 75, HP/LaserJet 4V, HP/LaserJet 4MV, HP/LaserJet 5si, HP/LaserJet 5si EDITORIAL SOFTWARE: Jazbox PRODUCTION EQUIPMENT: Hardware — Arkitex; Scanners — Agfa PRODUCTION SOFTWARE: InDesign

NEW YORK

AMNEW YORK

240 W 35th St, Fl 9th, New York, N.Y., 10001-2506, New York; gen tel (646) 293-9499; adv tel (646) 293-9499; gen fax (212) 239-2828; adv fax (917) 591-6122; gen/nat adv e-mail amnyMarketing@am-ny.com; disp adv e-mail amnyMarketing@am-ny.com; class adv e-mailJneknez@newsday.com; ed e-mail thoughts@amny.com; web site www.amny.com
Published: Mon, Tues, Wed, Thur, Fri
Weekday Frequency: m
Circulation: 184,583
Last Audit: CAC September 30, 2017
Advertising Rate (weekday/saturday): $329.00
News services: 2003
Special Weekly Sections: Education, Careers (Mon); Style (Tue); Travel (Tue); Dining, Health (Wed); City Living, Real Estate (Thur); Weekend (Fri)
Digital Platform - Mobile: Apple, Android
Bus. Mgr.....Donna Chibaro
Cir. Dir....Bill Praz
National Sales Mktg Dir.
Nannette Fevola
Co-Pub.....Debby Krenek
Co-Pub.....Edward Bushey
Class.....Jason Neknez
Ed. in Chief....Polly Higgins
Equipment & Software: PRESSROOM EQUIPMENT: Lines — 212-239-5555;

METRO NEW YORK

120 Broadway, 6th Floor, New York, N.Y., 10271-0002, New York; gen tel (212) 457-7790; adv tel (212) 457-7735; gen fax (212) 952-1246; adv fax (212) 202-1505; gen/nat adv e-mail advertising@metro.us; disp adv e-mail advertising@metro.us; class adv e-mailnewyorkclassifieds@metro.us; ed e-mail letters@metro.us; web site metro.us - 4,987,057(views) 2,001,409(visitors)
Group: SB New York
Published: Mon, Tues, Wed, Thur, Fri
Weekday Frequency: m
Last Audit: AAM September 30, 2016
Branch Offices: New York – 120 Broadway, 6th Floor I 120 Broadway I NY, NY 10271
Boston – 234 Congress St, 4th Fl, Boston, MA 02110
Philadelphia - 30 South 15th StreetI 14th Floor I Philadelphia, PA 19102
Advertising Rate (weekday/saturday): 1/1 Full Page: $11,260 I 1/2 Half Page: $5,910 I 1/4 Quarter Page: $3,240
Advertising Rate (sunday): N/A
Online Advertising Rate: Desktop Leaderboard (728x90) & Big Box (300x250): $10 CPM
Mobile Leaderboard (320x50) & Big Box (300x250): $10 CPM
Billboard: $15 CPM
Page Grabber: $ 20 CPM
Site skin, wall paper, takeover, native, programmatic: costs available on request
News services: 2004
Own Printing Facility?: No
Commercial Printers?: No
Special Weekly Sections: Education & Job (Mon), Health & Wellbeing (Mon-Fri), Travel & Finance (Tue), Style, home, real estate (Wed), Going out & weekend (Thu & Fri)
Digital Platform - Mobile: Apple, Android
Digital Platform - Tablet: Apple iOS, Android
Metro US Exec./National Sales Dir.
& Associate Publisher Metro New York Ed Abrams
CEO & Publisher....Yggers Mortenson
US Mktg. Dir.....Wilf Maunoir
US Circ. Dir.....Joe Lauletta
Areas Served: New York DMA, Boston DMA, Philadelphia DMA
Delivery Method: Racks

NEW YORK DAILY NEWS

4 New York Plz Fl 6, Floor 6, New York, N.Y., 10004-2473, New York; gen tel (212) 210-2100; adv tel (212) 210-2004; ed tel (212) 210-6397; gen/nat adv e-mail LBrancato@nydailynews.com; class adv e-mailclassifiedads@nydailynews.com; ed e-mail voicers@nydailynews.com; web site www.nydailynews.com 42,832,510(visitors)
Published: Mon, Tues, Wed, Thur, Fri, Sat, Sun
Weekday Frequency: m
Saturday Frequency: m
Circulation: 271,163; 244,169(sat); 336,367(sun)
Last Audit: AAM September 30, 2016
Advertising Rate (weekday/saturday): Open inch rate $1,041.07
News services: AP, MCT, TMS. **Established:** 1919
Special Weekly Sections: Friday (Weekend Entertainment Guide) (Fri); City Lights (S); Style (Thur); Food (Wed).
Syndicated Publications: Relish (Monthly); Sunday Gravure (S).
Digital Platform - Mobile: Apple, Android, Windows, Blackberry
Digital Platform - Tablet: Apple iOS, Kindle, Nook
Chrmn./Pub.....Mortimer B. Zuckerman
CFO....Thomas H. Peck
Sr. Vice Pres., Circ./Distr.....James Brill
VP, Adv.....Rudy Zaccagno
VP Pres. Adv.....Linda Brancato
Retail Adv. Dir.....Joann Dinapoli
Circ. Vice Pres.....Rich Harknett
Sr. VP, Adv Dir.....John Polizano
Dir. Class. Adv. Sales
Lenny Brown
Sales Mgr, Natl. Retail & Preprints....Sindy Speelman
Pres., Editor-in-chief....Colin Myler
Dir., Digital Development....Kristen Lee
Deputy Managing Ed., Digital....Zach Haberman
Deputy Managing Ed., Digital Ent. Cristina Everett
Ed., Mobile....Christine Roberts
VP, Mktg.....Colleen Noonan
Pressroom....Tom Grosso
Mgr., Classified Tel. Sales....Kathy O'Dea
Dir., Nat. Adv.....Kevin O'Brien
Dir. of Multi-Cultural Retail Sales Mgr.....Joe Anzalone
Sales Mgr.....Bianka Ratzmann
Adv. Dir., Ed., Health & Hosp.....Lisa Netcher
Sales Mgr., Real Estate & Travel....Gina Rebelo
Acct. Mgr. Sup.....Douglas Fletcher
Account Exec., Financial....Dana Wynkoop
Mgr., Motion Pic.....Marc Horowitz
Mng. Ed.....Alex Jones
Market Information: Split run; Zoned editions.
Mechanical Available: Offset; Black and 3 ROP colors; insert accepted; page cutoffs - 22.
Mechanical Specifications: Type page 9 3/8 x 14; E - 5 cols, 1 3/4, 3/8 between; A - 6 cols, 1 1/2, 1/8 between; C - 7 cols, 1 1/4, 1/8 between.
Areas Served: Tri-State Area
Delivery Method: Mail, Newsstand, CarrierEquipment & Software: PRESSROOM EQUIPMENT: Lines — 17-G/Newsliner Units double width (3-4 over 4 units) 1996; 17-G/Newsliner Units double width (3-4 over 4 units) 1996; 17-G/Newsliner Units double width (3-4 over 4 units) 1996; Folders — 9-G/Metro 3:2 Imperial Folder; MAILROOM EQUIPMENT: Counter Stackers — 30-Id/550, 12-HL/Monitor, 9-Fg/SCC, 18-S/Olympian, 9-Fg/SCC Conveyor; Tying Machines — 40-MVP/Ultra 5000 Strappers; Control System — Fg/Integrated Bundle Management System, 2-AT/Ferag PKT Plate Conveyor; BUSINESS EQUIPMENT: 1-IBM/MVS BUSINESS SOFTWARE: DB/Millenium CLASSIFIED EQUIPMENT: Hardware — 5-AT/9000; 25-IBM/Selectric II, 25-TM/2277, APP/Mac.; DISPLAY EQUIPMENT: Printers — HP, Canon; Other Hardware — AG/Scanner DISPLAY SOFTWAREAd Make-up Applications — Adobe/Photoshop, QPS/QuarkXPress; Layout Software — 4-Cx/135, 8-Cx/2351. EDITORIAL EQUIPMENT: Hardware — AT/Series 6, IBM/RS 6000/4-APP/Mac, 2-APP/Mac Plus; Printers — HP, Canon, AG EDITORIAL SOFTWARE: AT/J-11, AT/Ed. PRODUCTION EQUIPMENT: Hardware — 4-M/606, 3-Cx/Supersetter.

NEW YORK POST

1211 Avenue of the Americas, Ste 900A, New York, N.Y., 10036-8790, New York; gen tel (212) 930-8000; adv tel (212) 930-5753; ed tel (212) 930-8288; gen fax (212) 930-8540; gen/nat adv e-mail slareau@nypost.com; class adv e-mailclloyd@nypost.com; ed e-mail letters@nypost.com; web site www.nypost.com
Group: News Corporation
Published: Mon, Tues, Wed, Thur, Fri, Sat, Sun
Weekday Frequency: m
Saturday Frequency: m
Circulation: 425,365; 391,882(sat); 399,569(sun)
Last Audit: AAM September 30, 2017
Advertising Rate (weekday/saturday): Open inch rate $641.88
News services: AP, LAT-WP. **Established:** 1801
Special Editions: Mexico (Apr); Ski Vacations (Dec); Alaska (Jan); Summer Get-Aways (Jun); Spring & Summer Cruises (Mar); Catskills (May); Mexico (Nov); Follow the Sun

(Oct); Autumn Travel (Sept).
Special Weekly Sections: Travel (Tues).
Syndicated Publications: Page Six (Quarterly); Parade (S).
Digital Platform - Mobile: Apple, Android
Digital Platform - Tablet: Apple iOS, Android
Adv. Mgr., Nat'l .... Ken Kiczales
Advertising .... Caitlin Lloyd
Ed. Dept./Photo .... David Rentas
Ed. Dept./Page Six .... Emily Smith
Ed. Dept./Sports .... Chris Shaw
Ed. Dept./Business .... Richard Wilner
Post Studios & Creative Services ... Brad Feldman
Pub. / CEO .... Jesse Angelo
Ed. .... Neil Nagraj
Market Information: Split run.
Mechanical Available: Letterpress (direct); Black and 1 ROP colors; insert accepted.
Mechanical Specifications: Type page 9 3/4 x 12 1/2; E - 6 cols, 1 1/2, 1/8 between; A - 6 cols, 1 1/2, 1/8 between; C - 7 cols, 1 5/16, 1/8 between.Equipment & Software: PRESSROOM EQUIPMENT: Lines — 8-G/Headliner Mark II; 8-G/Headliner Mark II; 8-G/Headliner Mark II; 8-G/Headliner Mark II; Folders — 4-G/3:2, 4-G/2:1.; MAILROOM EQUIPMENT: Counter Stackers — 9/St, 1-/HL; Tying Machines — 9-/MLN; Address Machine — 1-/Am.; DISPLAY SOFTWARELayout Software — 6-HI/2200 (on-line). EDITORIAL EQUIPMENT: Hardware — 4-HI, 36-HI/1720, 29-HI/1740, 36-HI/1780, 55-AST. PRODUCTION EQUIPMENT: Hardware — 2-AU/APS 5, 1-Kk; Cameras — 2-C, 3-SCREEN/240; Scanners — 1-ECR/Autokon.

THE NEW YORK TIMES

620 8th Ave, New York, N.Y., 10018-1618, New York; gen tel (212) 556-1234; adv tel (212) 556-7777; ed tel (800) 698-4637; gen fax (212) 556-3622; adv fax (212) 556-7088; ed fax (212) 556-3622; gen/nat adv e-mail advertising@nytimes.com; disp adv e-mail advertising@nytimes.com; class adv e-mailclassifiedadtrans.help@nytimes.com; ed e-mail editorial@nytimes.com; letters@nytimes.com; web site www.nytimes.com 29,817,000(visitors)
Group: The New York Times Co.
Published: Mon, Tues, Wed, Thur, Fri, Sat, Sun
Weekday Frequency: m
Saturday Frequency: m
Circulation: 513,776; 595,073(sat); 1,075,837(sun)
Last Audit: AAM September 30, 2017
Advertising Rate (weekday/saturday): Open inch rate $563.00 (ROP)
Advertising Rate (sunday): Open inch rate $861.00 (ROP)
News services: AP, RN, PR Newswire, DJ, Tass. **Established:** 1851
Special Editions: Business Travel (Apr); PGA Tour (Aug); Circuits (Dec); Business of Green (Feb); Deal Book (Mar); Wealth/Personal Finance (May); Giving (Nov); Retirement (Oct); Well (Children's Health) (Sept).
Special Weekly Sections: Weekend Arts (Fri); Arts & Leisure (S); ThursdayStyles (Thur); Science Times (Tues); Dining In/Dining Out (Wed).
Syndicated Publications: T (Other); The New York Times Magazine (S); Real Estate (S); Key (Semi-yearly).
Digital Platform - Mobile: Apple, Android, Windows, Blackberry
Digital Platform - Tablet: Apple iOS, Android
Pres./Gen. Mgr. .... Scott H. Heekin-Canedy
Pres., News Servs. .... Cristian L. Edwards
CIO .... Joseph Seibert
Sr. Vice Pres./Deputy Gen. Mgr. ... Dennis L. Stern
Sr. Vice Pres., Planning .... Thomas K. Carley
Sr. Vice Pres./Chief Adv. Officer Denise F. Warren
Sr. Vice Pres./CFO .... Roland A. Caputo
Vice Pres., HR .... Michael Valentine
Vice Pres., Labor Rel. .... Terry L. Hayes
Grp. Vice Pres. .... Virginia French
Adv. Sr. Vice Pres. .... Alexis Buryk
Adv. Vice Pres. .... Thomas Helling
Adv. Vice Pres. .... Mark W. Herlyn
Adv. Vice Pres. .... Paul Smurl
Adv. Vice Pres., Sales .... Guy D. Holliday
Adv. Vice Pres., Sales .... Seth Rogin
Senior VP, Adv. & Pub. .... Andy Wright
Sr. Vice Pres., Mktg./Circ. .... Yasmin Namini
Dir., Community Affairs .... Diane McNulty
Carol D'Andrea
Nick D'Andrea
Josh Williams
Todd Socia
VP, Circulation & Reader Applications ... Raymond Pearce
James Dao
Aidan McNulty
VP, Ad Product & Plan. Senior VP, Adv. Sebastian Tomich
Anthony Benten
Vice Chairman .... Michael Golden
Audience Expansion and Engagement Editor ... Alex MacCallum
CEO .... Mark Thompson
Ed., Innovation & Strategy .... Kinsey Wilson
Mat Yurow
Piper Rosenshein
Public Ed. .... Margaret Sullivan
Chairman & Pub. .... Arthur Sulzberger Jr.
Senior VP, Product .... David Perpich
Senior VP, Ad Products & Research & Dev. Michael Zimbalist
VP, Adv. & Sales Op. .... Kerrie Gillis
VP, Sales Dev. .... Daphne Schwab
VP, Adv. .... Laura Sonnenfeld
Chief Rev. Officer .... Meredith Kopit Levien
Editorial Ed. .... James Bennet
Mng. Ed. .... Joseph Kahn
Market Information: Split run; Zoned editions.
Mechanical Available: Offset; Black and 3 ROP colors; insert accepted; page cutoffs - 22 1/4.
Mechanical Specifications: Type page 13 x 21 3/8; E - 6 cols, 2, 1/8 between; A - 6 cols, 2, 1/8 between; C - 10 cols, 1 3/16, 1/16 between.Equipment & Software: PRESSROOM EQUIPMENT: Lines — 72-PEC/Converted offset (NY) 1978; 60-G/Colorliner (Edison NJ) 1989; Press Drive — 7, 7, 1; Folders — 9, 6-G/Sovereign; MAILROOM EQUIPMENT: Counter Stackers — 20-QWI/1000, 20-Id/2000, 6-Id/3000; Inserters & Stuffers — 8-HI/1472; Tying Machines — MLN/News 90, 12-Dynaric/Strap, 29-Metaveppa/Tyer; Address Machine — KR, St.; BUSINESS EQUIPMENT: 2-IBM/9121-621 CLASSIFIED EQUIPMENT: Hardware — 300-IBM/327, PC Custom Front End; AU/APS Imagesetter; Printers — 1-HP/LaserJet, 3-C.Itoh; CLASSIFIED SOFTWARE: IBM/CICS Custom Application. DISPLAY EQUIPMENT: Hardware — IBM/9121-732, SUN/Enterprise 3000-128GB; Printers — MON/Output Manager, AT/Edpage News, AT/Ad Pagination; DISPLAY SOFTWAREAd Make-up Applications — NWI/Admarc 7.0, All/Ad Manager; Layout Software — AT/Architect RS-6000, Computerease Page Finishing. EDITORIAL EQUIPMENT: Hardware — 42-AT/J-11, Pentium/PC 850, APP/Mac 300/150-Think Pad, 100-RSK/Tandy 1500, 40-Panasonic; Printers — HP/LaserJet 60, HP/4M Plus EDITORIAL SOFTWARE: AT 4.7. PRODUCTION EQUIPMENT: Hardware — 2-LE/2600 online, 3-LE/24-18-25A, 3-APP/Mac, 2-Fuji/603, 4-AU/PSPIP2, 3-AU/APS-6, 1-MON/Express Master; Cameras — Kk/Model 5068 vertical camera; Scanners — 3-ECR/Autokon 1000, 4-ECR/Autokon 2000, Scitex/Smart Scanner, AU/Information INtt3, Mon
Note: The New York Times prints a national satellite edition at eight locations around the U.S.: Chicago; Warren, OH; Austin, TX; Torrance, CA; Walnut Creek, CA; Tacoma, WA; Atlanta; Ft. Lauderdale, FL.

THE WALL STREET JOURNAL

1211 Avenue of the Americas, Lowr C3, New York, N.Y., 10036-8701, New York; gen tel (800) 568-7625; adv tel (312) 750-4235; ed tel (800) 568-7625; gen fax (212) 416-2755; gen/nat adv e-mail gloria.hauter@wsj.com; disp adv e-mail meri.westcott@wsj.com; class adv e-mailluke.bahrenburg@wsj.com; ed e-mail wsj.ltrs@wsj.com; web site www.wsj.com - 133,370,000(views) 13,971,000(visitors); web site 2 www.dj.com; web site 3 www.dowjones.com
Group: Dow Jones & Company
Published: Mon, Tues, Wed, Thur, Fri, Sat, Sun
Weekday Frequency: m
Saturday Frequency: m
Circulation: 1,111,167; 1,145,230(sat); 1,145,230(sun)
Last Audit: AAM September 30, 2017
Advertising Rate (weekday/saturday): Open inch rate $2,033.05
Online Advertising Rate: Full Page $25.71, 1/2 Page $16.22, 1/4 Page $8.14
News services: AP, DJ. **Established:** 1889
Special Editions: Golf (Apr); Business Insight (Aug); Business Insight (Dec); Encore/Retirement Guide (Feb); Trend Report (Jan); Your Money Matters-Guide to Personal Finance (Jul); 401K (Jun); NCAA Men's Basketball (Mar); Best On The Street Analysts (May); Monthly Mutual F
Special Weekly Sections: Weekend Journal (Fri); Personal Journal (Thur); Personal Journal (Tues); Personal Journal (Wed).
Digital Platform - Mobile: Apple
Digital Platform - Tablet: Apple iOS
Sr. Vice Pres./COO .... Todd H. Larsen
Exec. Chairman .... Rupert Murdoch
CEO, News Group .... Robert Thomson
Editor in Chief .... Gerard Baker
CEO & Publisher .... William Lewis
Deputy Editor in Chief .... Rebecca Blumenstein
Exec. Ed. .... Matthew Murray
Senior Deputy .... Michael W. Miller
Chief Revenue Officer .... Michael F. Rooney
Vice Pres., News Projects .... F. James Pensiero
Gen. Mgr., WSJ.com .... Daniel Bernard
Adv. Sr. Vice Pres. .... Judy Barry
Adv. Vice Pres., Bus. Grp. .... David Forgione
District Sales Mgr. .... Walter Hodge
Vice Pres., Mktg. Strategy .... Imtiaz Patel
Vice Pres., Circ. Mktg. .... Lynne K. Brennen
Deputy Mng. Ed. .... Deborah Brewster
Deputy Mng. Ed. .... Alix M. Freedman
Asst. Mng. Ed./Exec. Washington Ed. ...... Gerald F. Seib
VP. President of Communications .... Colleen Schwartz
Bureau Chief, Atlanta .... Robert Rose
Bureau Chief, Chicago .... Kevin Helliker
Head of Corp. Comm. .... Paula Keve
Head of Corporate Communication Ashley Huston
Director .... David Biderman
VP President, Customer Service Thom San Filippo
Gen. Adv., Sales Dir. .... Jennifer Budig
Gen. Adv., Sales Dir. .... Nancy McDonald
Lux. Adv., Sales Dir. .... Alberto Apodaca
Greater N.Y. Sec., Sales Dir. .... Paul V. Carlucci
Class. Adv., VP Vertical Markets .... Marti Gallardo
Market Information: ADS; Split run; TMC; Zoned editions.
Mechanical Available: Offset; Black and 3 ROP colors; insert accepted; page cutoffs - 22 3/4.
Mechanical Specifications: Type page 10 3/4 x 21 1/2.
Note: The Wall Street Journal is published in three regional editions: Eastern, Central, and Western. News content is the same in all editions, but advertising can be purchased in one or all editions or a combination thereof. Eastern Edition printed in White Oa

NIAGARA FALLS

NIAGARA GAZETTE

473 3rd St, Ste 201, Niagara Falls, N.Y., 14301-1500, Niagara; gen tel (716) 282-2311; gen fax (716) 286-3895; adv fax (716) 286-3811; gen/nat adv e-mail John Celestino <john.celestino@niagara-gazette.com>; disp adv e-mail classads@gnnewspapers.com; class adv e-mailKevin Krisnosky <kevin.krisnosky@niagara-gazette.com>; ed e-mail matt.winterhalter@niagara-gazette.com; web site www.niagara-gazette.com - 405,250(views) 287,936(visitors)
Group: Community Newspaper Holdings, Inc.
Published: Mon, Wed, Thur, Fri, Sat, Sun
Weekday Frequency: m
Saturday Frequency: m
Circulation: 9,158; 9,158(sat); 9,304(sun)
Last Audit: AAM December 31, 2016
Advertising Rate (weekday/saturday): Open inch rate $52.67
News services: AP, GNS. **Established:** 1854
Own Printing Facility?: Yes
Commercial Printers?: Yes
Special Editions: Senior Guide (Apr); Back-to-School (Aug); Holiday Greetings (Dec); Progress (Feb); Health & Wellness (Jan); Added Value Certificates (Jul); Dining Guide (Jun); Home Improvement (Mar); Summer Events (May); Holiday Gift Guide (Nov); Fall Dining Guide (Oct);
Special Weekly Sections: Home & Garden (Fri); Food (Mon); Comics (S); Religion (Sat).
Digital Platform - Mobile: Apple
Circ. Mgr. .... Paul Glaeser
Mng. Ed. .... Dick Lucinski
Copy Desk Chief .... Linda Noworyta
Graphics Ed. .... David Marra
Web Ed. .... James Neiss
Sports Ed., Sabres .... Tim Schmitt
Pub. .... Chris Voccio
Exec Ed. .... Rob Kaiser
Mechanical Available: Letterpress Offset; Black and 3 ROP colors; insert accepted - single sheet; page cutoffs - 22 3/4.
Mechanical Specifications: Type page 11 5/8 x 21 1/2; E - 6 cols, 1 13/16, 1/6 between; A - 6 cols, 1 13/16, 1/6 between; C - 8 cols, 1 7/16, 1/16 between.Equipment & Software: MAILROOM EQUIPMENT: Counter Stackers — 2-QWI/350, 2/Rockbuilt, 1-/Count-o-Veyor; Inserters & Stuffers — 2-GMA/SLS 1000 ID:1; Tying Machines — 2-/Power Strap; Wrapping Singles — 2-QWI/Bottom Wrap.; BUSINESS EQUIPMENT: IBM/AS-400 CLASSIFIED EQUIPMENT: Hardware — 6-APP/iMac; Printers — APP/Mac LaserWriter Pro; CLASSIFIED SOFTWARE: DTI 4.2. DISPLAY EQUIPMENT: Hardware — 1-APP/iMac, 7-APP/Mac G3; Printers — 1-NewGen/Turbo P.S., 1-APP/Mac LaserWriter Pro 630; Other Hardware — APP/PowerMac 8100, 2-APP/Mac Quadra 950, APP/Mac G3, Umax/J700 604e/180, ECR/1000. DISPLAY SOFTWAREAd Make-up Applications — DTI/AdSpeed 4.2; EDITORIAL EQUIPMENT: Hardware — Sun/Enterprise 450/12-APP/Mac Centris 610, 10-APP/Mac G4, 7-APP/Mac G4 Graphics Server, 2-APP/iMac, 8-APP/Mac G4 EDITORIAL SOFTWARE: DTI 4.2. PRODUCTION EQUIPMENT: Hardware — 2-Nu/Flip Top, ECR/Scriptsetter VRL36, 1-3.5gig hard drive; Cameras — Acti/125 24x36; Scanners — 2-Umax/Astra 1200, UMAX/Powerlook 2100XL, Umax/Astra 24005, Epson/Perfection 1240u PRODUCTION SOFTWARE: DTI/Speedwriter 4.2, DTI/SpeedDriver, DTI/AdSpeed
Note: This publication shares a joint Sunday edition with the Lockport (NY) Union-Sun & Journal and the North Tonawanda (NY) Tonawanda News.

NORWICH

THE EVENING SUN

29 Lackawanna Ave, Norwich, N.Y., 13815-1404, Chenango; gen tel (607) 334-3276; adv tel (607) 334-3276; ed tel (607) 334-3276; gen fax (607) 334-8273; adv fax (607) 334-8273; ed fax (607) 334-8273; gen/nat adv e-mail rfoote@pennysaveronline.com; disp adv e-mail bcarpenter@evesun.com; ed e-mail news@evesun.com; web site www.evesun.com
Group: Snyder Communications
Published: Mon, Tues, Wed, Thur, Fri
Weekday Frequency: e
Circulation: 4,000
Last Audit: Sworn/Estimate/Non-Audited September 30, 2017
Advertising Rate (weekday/saturday): Open inch rate $12.00
News services: AP. **Established:** 1891
Own Printing Facility?: Yes
Commercial Printers?: Yes
Special Weekly Sections: The Weekend Sun (Fri); Sports (Mon); Lifestyle (Thur); Health (Tues); Farm (Wed).
Digital Platform - Mobile: Apple
Digital Platform - Tablet: Apple iOS
Pres. .... Richard Snyder
Adv. Mgr. .... Russ Foote
General Manager Print Facility .... Marty Conklin
Managing Editor .... Alshey Babbitt
Market Information: Split run; TMC; Zoned editions.
Mechanical Available: Offset; Black and 4 ROP colors; insert accepted; page cutoffs - 22 3/4.
Mechanical Specifications: Type page 13 x 21 1/2; E - 7 cols, 1 2/3, 1/8 between; A - 7 cols, 1 2/3, 1/8 between; C - 7 cols, 1 2/3, 1/16 between.
Areas Served: Norwich Chenango Count NY

13815
Delivery Method: Newsstand, Carrier, RacksEquipment & Software: PRESSROOM EQUIPMENT: G/Community single width 1970; G/Community single width 1970; G/ Community single width 1974; Press Drive — Fin/100 HP; Folders — 1-G/SC, 1-G/ Community SC.; MAILROOM EQUIPMENT: Counter Stackers — Baldwin/Count-O-Veyor 109; Tying Machines — MA, Bu.; BUSINESS EQUIPMENT: PC, Unix CLASSIFIED EQUIPMENT: Hardware — Mk, APP/Mac; CLASSIFIED SOFTWARE: Baseview/Class Pro. DISPLAY EQUIPMENT: Hardware — APP/Mac; DISPLAY SOFTWAREAd Make-up Applications — Multi-Ad/Creator; Layout Software — APP/Mac. EDITORIAL EQUIPMENT: Hardware — Mk, APP/ Mac EDITORIAL SOFTWARE: Baseview/ NewsEdit Pro. PRODUCTION EQUIPMENT: Hardware — Caere/OmniPage Direct; Cameras — 1-AG PRODUCTION SOFTWARE: QPS/QuarkXPress 3.31.
Note: We also publish 7 Free Community Publications

OGDENSBURG

OGDENSBURG JOURNAL/ADVANCE NEWS

230 Caroline St, Ste 1, Ogdensburg, N.Y., 13669-1629, Saint Lawrence; gen tel 315-393-1003; adv tel (315) 661-2512; ed tel (315) 393-1003; gen fax 315-393-5108; gen/nat adv e-mail bward@ogd.com; disp adv e-mail arivera@ogd.com; class adv e-mailpeters@ogd.com; ed e-mail egraham@wdt.net; web site www.ogd.com
Group: Johnson Newspaper Corp.
Published: Mon, Tues, Wed, Thur, Fri, Sun
Weekday Frequency: m
Circulation: 4,000; 4,000(sat); 8,500(sun)
Last Audit: Sworn/Estimate/Non-Audited September 30, 2017
Advertising Rate (weekday/saturday): Open inch rate $11.50
News services: 1830
Digital Platform - Mobile: Apple, Android, Windows, Blackberry
Digital Platform - Tablet: Apple iOS, Android, Blackberry Tablet OS, Kindle
Corp VP Sales & Mktg. .... Gary Valik
Cir. CSR .... Amber Bogart
HR/Purch. .... Eileen Kast
Ed. .... Tom Graser
Adv. Mgr. .... Barbara Ward
Class. .... Debra Petersen
CEO / Co-Pub. .... John Johnson
Pres. / Co-Pub. .... Harold Johnson
Areas Served: St. Lawrence County (NY)
Delivery Method: Mail, Racks

OLEAN

OLEAN TIMES HERALD

639 W Norton Dr, Olean, N.Y., 14760-1402, Cattaraugus; gen tel (716) 372-3121; adv tel (716) 372-3121 ext. 208; ed tel (716) 372-3121 ext. 231; gen fax (716) 372-0740; gen/nat adv e-mail adcomp@oleantimesherald.com; disp adv e-mail jkeim@oleantimesherald.com; class adv e-mailcpowley@oleantimesherald.com; ed e-mail news@oleantimesherald.com; web site www.oleantimesherald.com
Group: New York Newspaper Advertising Service, Inc.
Community Media Group
Bradford Publishing Co.
Published: Mon, Tues, Wed, Thur, Fri, Sat, Sun
Weekday Frequency: e
Saturday Frequency: e
Circulation: 9,193; 9,193(sat); 10,056(sun)
Last Audit: AAM June 30, 2016
Advertising Rate (weekday/saturday): Open inch rate $29.65
Advertising Rate (sunday): Open inch rate $29.65
News services: AP, NEA, SHNS, CNS. **Established:** 2000
Special Editions: Golf Tab (Apr); Christmas Stories (Dec); Tax Tab (Feb); Bridal (Jan); Frozen Food (Mar); Christmas (Nov); Hunting (Oct); Consumer Electronics (Sept); Spring Buyer Tab (Spring).
Special Weekly Sections: Best Food Days (Mon); TV (Sun);
Syndicated Publications: Olean Review (Other); USA WEEKEND Magazine (S).
Proprietary Publications: Seniority (Quarterly); Real Estate (Monthly)
Pub .... Jim Bonn
Mng. Ed. .... Jim Eckstrom
Sports Ed. .... Chuck Pollock
Asst. Mng. Ed. .... Adam Vosler
Cir. Mgr. .... Nichole Finnerty
Market Information: ADS; TMC.
Mechanical Available: Offset; Black and 3 ROP colors; insert accepted - self-adhesive notes; page cutoffs - 21 1/2.
Mechanical Specifications: Type page 13 x 21 1/2; E - 6 cols, 2 1/16, 1/8 between; A - 6 cols, 2 1/16, 1/8 between; C - 9 cols, 1 3/8, 1/16 between.Equipment & Software: PRESSROOM EQUIPMENT: Lines — 7-G/U 791 (1 balloon former).; MAILROOM EQUIPMENT: Tying Machines — 2-MLN/ ML2-EE.; BUSINESS EQUIPMENT: Vision Data CLASSIFIED EQUIPMENT: Hardware — 3-APP/Power Mac; Printers — Okidata/193 Line Printer, HP/LaserJet 5000N; CLASSIFIED SOFTWARE: Baseview. DISPLAY EQUIPMENT: Hardware — APP/ Power Mac; Printers —HP/LaserJet 5000N; DISPLAY SOFTWAREAd Make-up Applications — Multi-Ad/Creator; Layout Software — Multi-Ad/Creator, Adobe/ Photoshop. EDITORIAL EQUIPMENT: Hardware — APP/Power Mac; Printers — HP/LaserJet 5000N, Pre Press/Panther Plus 36, Pre Press/Panther Plus EDITORIAL SOFTWARE: QPS/QuarkXPress. PRODUCTION EQUIPMENT: Hardware — 1-COM/7200, 2-COM/ACM9000, 2-COM/8600, 2-Unified/Composer; Cameras — 1-B/Commodore, 1-K/187; Scanners — 3-Dewar/Disc Net 55 Terminal, 3-Dewar/Discovery Display Ad Terminal PRODUCTION SOFTWARE: Baseview.
Note: This newspaper is published in tabloid format on Saturday.

ONEONTA

THE DAILY STAR

102 Chestnut St, Oneonta, N.Y., 13820-2584, Otsego; gen tel (607) 432-1000; ed tel (607) 432-1000; gen fax (607) 432-5847; ed fax (607) 432-5707; gen/nat adv e-mail mneighbour@thedailystar.com; disp adv e-mail mneighbour@thedailystar.com; class adv e-mailcbenson@thedailystar.com; ed e-mail letters@thedailystar.com; web site www.thedailystar.com
- 800,000(views) 125,000(visitors)
Group: Community Newspaper Holdings, Inc.
Published: Mon, Tues, Wed, Thur, Fri, Sat
Weekday Frequency: m
Saturday Frequency: m
Circulation: 9,145; 9,145(sat)
Last Audit: AAM December 31, 2015
Advertising Rate (weekday/saturday): Open inch rate $13.10
News services: AP, DJ, ONS, LAT-WP, TMS. **Established:** 1890
Own Printing Facility?: Yes
Commercial Printers?: Yes
Syndicated Publications: Relish (Monthly); Parade (Weekly).
Digital Platform - Mobile: Apple, Android, Windows, Blackberry
Digital Platform - Tablet: Apple iOS, Android, Windows 7, Blackberry Tablet OS, Kindle, Nook, Kindle Fire
Ed .... Sam Pollak
News Ed. .... Denise Richardson
Photo Dept. Mgr. .... Julie Lewis
Sports Ed. .... Dean Russin
Pub. .... Fred Scheller
Market Information: TMC; Zoned editions.
Mechanical Available: Offset; Black and 3 ROP colors; insert accepted; page cutoffs - 22 3/4.
Mechanical Specifications: Type page 11 13/16 x 21 1/2; E - 6 cols, 1 13/16, 1/8 between; A - 6 cols, 1 13/16, 1/8 between; C - 9 cols, 1 1/4, 1/16 between.
Delivery Method: Mail, Newsstand, Carrier, RacksEquipment & Software: PRESSROOM EQUIPMENT: Lines — 5-G/Urbanite single width 1974, 1-G/Urbanite 3-color single width 1999; Folders — 1-G/(with balloon); Reels & Stands — 5; Control System — 2; MAILROOM EQUIPMENT: Counter Stackers — QWI; Inserters & Stuffers — MM/227E; Tying Machines — 2-Sa/SR1A, 3-Si/LB 2000; Address Machine — Ch/Quarter folder Labeler.; BUSINESS EQUIPMENT: IBM/AS-400 BUSINESS SOFTWARE: 7-Microsoft/ Office XP CLASSIFIED EQUIPMENT: Hardware — 8-Dell; Printers — 1-HP; CLASSIFIED SOFTWARE: Atex/Enterprise. DISPLAY EQUIPMENT: Hardware — 5-Dell; Printers — HP; DISPLAY SOFTWAREAd Make-up Applications — QPS/QuarkXPress 5.0, 7-Archetype/Corel Draw; Layout Software — MEI/ALS. EDITORIAL EQUIPMENT: Hardware — 17-Dell; Printers — 2-HP EDITORIAL SOFTWARE: AT/Dewarview. PRODUCTION EQUIPMENT: Hardware — 2-Konica/E-V Jetsetter, Konica/K-550; Cameras — 1-C/Spartan III PRODUCTION SOFTWARE: QPS/QuarkXPress 3.0.

OSWEGO

THE PALLADIUM-TIMES

140 W 1st St, Oswego, N.Y., 13126-1514, Oswego; gen tel (315) 343-3800; adv tel (315) 343-3800; ed tel (315) 343-3800; gen fax (315) 343-0273; adv fax (315) 343-0273; ed fax (315) 343-0273; gen/nat adv e-mail kpercival@palltimes.com; disp adv e-mail kpercival@palltimes.com; class adv e-mailclassifieds@palltimes.com; ed e-mail smccrobie@palltimes.com; web site www.palltimes.com
Group: Sample News Group LLC
Published: Mon, Tues, Wed, Thur, Fri, Sat
Weekday Frequency: e
Saturday Frequency: m
Circulation: 8,507; 8,507(sat)
Last Audit: Sworn/Estimate/Non-Audited September 30, 2017
Advertising Rate (weekday/saturday): Open inch rate $15.00
News services: AP, SHNS. **Established:** 1845
Special Editions: Newcomer's Guide (Aug); Christmas Shopping (Dec); Welcome Back SUNY Tab (Feb); Weather (Jan); Auto Racing (Jul); Father's Day (Jun); Progress (Mar); Mother's Day (May); Historic (Monthly); Fall Sports (Oct); Bridal (Sept).
Special Weekly Sections: Health (Fri); Food (Mon); Entertainment (Thur); Business Pages (Tues).
Syndicated Publications: USA WEEKEND Magazine (Sat).
Pub. .... Jon Spaulding
Accountant .... Virginia DeCare
Mng. Ed. .... Debra Robillard
Sports Ed. .... Michael LeBoeuf
Circ. Mgr. .... Chrissy Mitchelson
Market Information: TMC.
Mechanical Available: Offset; Black and 3 ROP colors; insert accepted - free-standing cards; page cutoffs - 22 1/2.
Mechanical Specifications: Type page 13 x 21 1/2; E - 6 cols, 2 1/16, 1/8 between; A - 6 cols, 2 1/16, 1/8 between; C - 8 cols, 1 9/16, 1/16 between.Equipment & Software: PRESSROOM EQUIPMENT: Lines — 8-G/ Community (2 Forms) 1971.; MAILROOM EQUIPMENT: Tying Machines — Aldebo/ Bundler.; BUSINESS EQUIPMENT: APP/ Mac, NEC/386 BUSINESS SOFTWARE: Multi-Ad/Creator, Microsoft/Works, Lotus 2.4, Claris/MacDraw CLASSIFIED EQUIPMENT: Hardware — Mk; Printers — APP/Mac LaserPrinter.; EDITORIAL EQUIPMENT: Hardware — Mk/APP/Mac Classic II; Printers — APP/Mac LaserPrinters. PRODUCTION EQUIPMENT: Hardware — APP/Mac LaserPrinter; Cameras — LE/Horizontal.

PLATTSBURGH

PRESS-REPUBLICAN

170 Margaret St, Plattsburgh, N.Y., 12901-1838, Clinton; gen tel (518) 561-2300; adv tel (518) 561-2300; ed tel (518) 565-4131; gen fax (518) 561-3362; adv fax (518) 562-3361; ed fax (518) 561-3362; gen/nat adv e-mail grock@pressrepublican.com; disp adv e-mail grock@pressrepublican.com; class adv e-mailclassifieds@pressrepublican.com; ed e-mail news@pressrepublican.com; web site www.pressrepublican.com
- 2,000,000(views)
Group: Community Newspaper Holdings, Inc.
Published: Mon, Tues, Wed, Thur, Fri, Sat, Sun
Weekday Frequency: m
Saturday Frequency: m
Circulation: 11,623; 11,623(sat); 12,531(sun)
Last Audit: AAM June 30, 2017
Advertising Rate (weekday/saturday): Open inch rate $29.00
Advertising Rate (sunday): $31.00
News services: AP, SHNS. **Established:** 1942
Own Printing Facility?: Yes
Commercial Printers?: Yes
Special Editions: Senior Sentinel, (monthly); Jill Magazine for Women, (monthly); Newcomer News, (monthly); Clinton County Fair, (July); Holiday Bears, (November and December); Celebrations, (November); Gift Guide, (November).
Special Weekly Sections: Best Food Day (Saturday).
Syndicated Publications: Relish (monthly); Parade (Sundays); American Profile (weekly); Althon Sports, (monthly); Grandparenting Today (monthly).
Digital Platform - Mobile: Apple, Windows
Editor .... Lois Clermont
Feat. Ed. .... Nathan Ovalle
News Editor .... Suzanne Moore
Press Room Supervisor .... Kevin Hidook
Publisher .... Brad Bailey
Night Editor .... Ben Rowe
Sports Editor .... Ricky St. Clair
Market Information: TMC.
Mechanical Available: Offset; Black and 3 ROP colors; insert accepted; page cutoffs - 22 3/4.
Mechanical Specifications: Type page 10 1/4 x 21 1/2; E - 6 cols, 1 5/8, 1/16 between; A - 6 cols, 1 5/8, 1/16 between; C - 9 cols, 1 1/32, 1/16 between.
Areas Served: 12836, 12855, 12870, 12883, 12901, 12903, 12910, 12911, 12912, 12913, 12914, 12915, 12916, 12917, 12918, 12919, 12920, 12921, 12923, 12924, 12926, 12928, 12929, 12930, 12930, 12932, 12933, 12934, 12935, 12936, 12937, 12939, 12941, 12942, 12943, 12944, 12945, 12946, 12950, 12952, 12953, 12955, 12956, 12957, 12958, 12959, 12960, 12961, 12962, 12964, 12966, 12969, 12970, 12972, 12974, 12975, 12977, 12978, 12979, 12980, 12981, 12983, 12985, 12986, 12987, 12989, 12992, 12993, 12994, 12995, 12996, 12997, 12998, 13655
Delivery Method: Mail, Newsstand, Carrier, RacksEquipment & Software: PRESSROOM EQUIPMENT: Lines — 8-G/Urbanite; Press Drive — Fincor; MAILROOM EQUIPMENT: Counter Stackers — 2/Compass 1 Canon; Inserters & Stuffers — GMA/SLS 1000; Tying Machines — 2-MLN/2EE, 1-/Power Strap; Control System — Newscom; CLASSIFIED EQUIPMENT: Hardware — Dell/HP; IBM Server Microsoft Windows 2003 Server; Printers — HP 5200; CLASSIFIED SOFTWARE: VD Class Pag. and Total Ads DISPLAY EQUIPMENT: Hardware — Dell 733 Mhz; Printers — HP 5200; DISPLAY SOFTWAREAd Make-up Applications — Adobe/InDesign, CS5; Layout Software — MEI RLS EDITORIAL EQUIPMENT: Hardware — COM/ONE, IBM/300PL/AP/ Photo Server, IBM/RS6000; Printers — HP 5200 PRODUCTION EQUIPMENT: Hardware — 2 - ECRM CTP Violet Imagers.

POUGHKEEPSIE

POUGHKEEPSIE JOURNAL

85 Civic Center Plz, Poughkeepsie, N.Y., 12601-2498, Dutchess; gen tel (845) 454-2000; adv tel (845) 437-4789; ed tel (845) 437-4800; adv fax (845) 437-4908; ed fax (845) 437-4921; gen/nat adv e-mail jdewey@poughkeepsiejournal.com; disp adv e-mail jdewey@poughkeepsiejournal.com; class adv e-mailjdewey@poughkeepsiejournal.com; ed e-mail newsroom@poughkeepsiejournal.com; web site www.poughkeepsiejournal.com
Group: Gannett
Published: Mon, Tues, Wed, Thur, Fri, Sat, Sun

Weekday Frequency: m
Saturday Frequency: m
Circulation: 18,844; 18,844(sat); 24,956(sun)
Last Audit: AAM March 31, 2017
News services: AP, GNS **Established:** 1785
Own Printing Facility?: No
Commercial Printers?: No
Special Editions: Spring Home & Gardens (Apr); Luxury Auto (Aug); Songbook (Dec); Menus (Feb); Bridal (Jan);
Special Weekly Sections: Business (Daily); Food (Wed); Entertainment, Auto (Fri); Business, Senior Citizens, Baby Boomers, Auto (Sun)
Digital Platform - Mobile: Apple, Android
Digital Platform - Tablet: Apple iOS, Android, Kindle, Kindle Fire
HR partner.................................Nora Pietrafesa
Adv. Dir...Jan Dewey
Adv. Mgr., Retail..............................Peter Nylin
Circ. Mgr...Bill Farrell
Exec. Ed......................................Stuart Shinske
City Ed.......................................Kevin Lenihan
Editorial Page Ed...........................John Penney
Asst. Features Ed........... Barbara Gallo Farrell
Sports Reporter ....Stephen Haynes
Market Information: ADS; Split run;
Mechanical Available: color on every page
Mechanical Specifications: Type page 11 5/8 x 21; E - 6 cols, 1 5/6, 1/8 between; A - 6 cols, 1 5/6, 1/8 between; C - 10 cols, 1, 1/16 between.
Areas Served: Dutchess County Equipment & Software: BUSINESS EQUIPMENT: IBM/AS-400 BUSINESS SOFTWARE: Microsoft/Office, Microsoft/Outlook, AdSpeed 3.0, Adobe/Photoshop, Adobe/Illustrator, Aldus/FreeHand 4.0
Note: New York State Associated Press "Newspaper of Distinction," for best print and digital report in our circulation category, in four of the last six years (including 2015)

ROCHESTER

DEMOCRAT AND CHRONICLE

245 E Main St, Rochester, N.Y., 14604-2103, Monroe; gen tel (585) 232-7100; adv tel (585) 258-2552; ed tel (585) 258-2214; gen fax (585) 258-2265; adv fax (585) 258-2733; ed fax (585) 258-2237; gen/nat adv e-mail solutions@democratandchronicle.com; disp adv e-mail solutions@democratandchronicle.com; class adv e-mailclassified@democrat&chronicle.com; ed e-mail editor@democratandchronicle.com ; web site www.democratandchronicle.com
1,294,228(visitors)
Group: Gannett
Published: Mon, Tues, Wed, Thur, Fri, Sat, Sun
Weekday Frequency: m
Saturday Frequency: m
Circulation: 71,630; 92,223(sat); 103,112(sun)
Last Audit: AAM September 30, 2017
Advertising Rate (weekday/saturday): Open inch rate $480.75
Advertising Rate (sunday): Open inch rate $530.99
News services: AP, GNS, MCT, Bloomberg, National Weather Service, TMS. **Established:** 1833
Special Editions: Living Here (Apr); HOME: Design for Rochester (Every other month); Auto Show (Feb); College Guide (Jan); Rochester Music Fest (Jul); Jazz Fest (Jun); March Madness (Mar); NACAC College Fair (May); Day In The Life (Monthly); Rochester's Choice Winners (Nov
Special Weekly Sections: Inserts, Garden, Travel (Sun); Business (Mon); Editorial, Best Food Days (Tue); Health (Wed); Entertainment (Thur); Our Towns (Fri); Real Estate, Auto (Sat)
Syndicated Publications: Comics (S); Weekend Magazine (Thur).
Digital Platform - Mobile: Apple, Android
Digital Platform - Tablet: Apple iOS
VP Fin...Bill Hart
HR Dir. Gannett East Group............ Linda B. Baird
VP/Ed................................... Karen M. Magnuson
East Group VP, Mktg/Strategy...... Steve Simpson
GM/Ops Gannett Pub. Serv.......Travis Komidar
Vice Pres., Mktg./Commun......... James J. Fogler
Circ. Vice Pres............................... Bryn Amber
Gen. Mgr., Specialty Publications ....Dennis Floss
Pres........................................Daniel Norselli

VP, Digital Strategy & Development ... Traci Bauer
Bus. Ed....Steve Sink
Exec Admin Assist........................Dottie Savage
Planning Editor...............................Ben Jacobs
Features Ed....................................Cathy Robert
News Ed...Dick Moss
Community Content Ed. ....Cynthia Benjamin
Pop Music/Nite Scene Reporter.........Jeff Spevak
Content Strategist ....Steve Bradley
Sr. HR Business Partner ....Donna Bell
Don Lemire
Mktg. Mgr. ....April Synyard
Market Information: Split run; TMC; Zoned editions.
Mechanical Available: Offset; Black and 3 ROP colors; insert accepted; page cutoffs - 22 1/32.
Mechanical Specifications: Type page 11 5/8 x 21; E - 6 cols, 1 5/6, 1/8 between; A - 6 cols, 1 5/6, 1/8 between; C - 10 cols, 1 5/6, 1/16 between.
Areas Served: Rochester-area (NY)
Equipment & Software: PRESSROOM EQUIPMENT: Lines — MAN/Geoman 80 couples in 16 Footprints (2/3 presses) 1997; Folders — 3-MAN/3.2, 3-MAN/2:3:3; MAILROOM EQUIPMENT: Counter Stackers — 5-QWI/300, 5-QWI/350; Inserters & Stuffers — 2-HI/630 Inserters (28:1 or 13:2); Tying Machines — 9/Power Strap/PSN-6, 9-Dynaric/1500, 1-Samuel/NT30; Control System — Prima, GSN, QWI/Cart Loading System; Address Machine — Addressing m; BUSINESS EQUIPMENT: IBM/AS-400 BUSINESS SOFTWARE: Microsoft/Office 97, Microsoft/Office 2000, Microsoft/Windows 95, Microsoft/Windows 98, Microsoft/Windows 2000, Microsoft/Windows NT CLASSIFIED EQUIPMENT: Hardware — SII/45 XA, SII/71 Coyote 3, 4-Tandem/K-1000 CPUS; IBM/Netfinity 5500; Printers — Lexmark/Optra LXI; CLASSIFIED SOFTWARE: Mactive. DISPLAY EQUIPMENT: Hardware — Dell/2100 fileserver, 20-APP/Mac, 5-Dell/5133, MS/NT Server LH3; Printers — 8-HP; DISPLAY SOFTWAREAd Make-up Applications — QPS/QuarkXPress, Macromedia/Freehand, Adobe/PageMaker, Roudhouse/Ad Tracking 2.5.7, Adobe/Creative Suite 2, Adobe/Illustrator, Adobe/Photoshop, Adobe/A; EDITORIAL EQUIPMENT: Hardware — AT/114/60-APP/Mac, ESE, Kk/2035 Plus Negative Scanner, HP/Server, 19-APP/Mac PowerBook, 6-Wintel, 22-NC/2000, AP/Digital Cameras, MS/NT Server; Printers — 1-Okidata, Pagescan, 7-HP, 3-HP, TI/Monoprint, HP/11x17, MON/Express EDITORIAL SOFTWARE: Softwa PRODUCTION EQUIPMENT: Hardware — AG/Advantage 3350 DL; Scanners — 2-Scitex/320, AG/Duoscan 1200T, Umax/Powerlook 2100 XL PRODUCTION SOFTWARE: QPS/QuarkXPress 4.1, CCI 6.7.0.2AT, Adobe/Creative Suite 2, SCS/Linx 4.13, SCS/Layout 8000 9.1, SCS/Inlay-In Design, Mactive.

THE DAILY RECORD

16 W Main St Ste 341, Suite 341, Rochester, N.Y., 14614-1604, Monroe; gen tel (585) 232-6920 ; adv tel (585) 232-6920; ed tel (585) 232-6922; gen fax (585) 232-2740; gen/nat adv e-mail karla.thomas@nydailyrecord.com; class adv e-mailkarla.esley@nydailyrecord.com; ed e-mail bjacobs@nydailyrecord.com; web site http://nydailyrecord.com
Published: Mon, Tues, Wed, Thur, Fri
Weekday Frequency: m
Last Audit: Sworn/Estimate/Non-Audited September 30, 2017
Advertising Rate (weekday/saturday): 1/4 P $350, 1/2 P $475, Full $650
Online Advertising Rate: Leaderboard $450; Medium Rectangle $300; Half Banner $220; Square Pop-Up $300 (All prices are per 1 month)
News services: 1908
Acct. Mgr. ....Shappelle Thompson
Ed....Ben Jacobs
Pub. ....Suzanne Fischer-Huettner
Admin. / Class.................................Karla Esley

ROME

DAILY SENTINEL

333 W Dominick St, Rome, N.Y., 13440-5701, Oneida; gen tel (315) 337-4000; adv tel (315) 337-4000; gen fax (315) 337-4704; adv fax (315) 337-4704; ed fax (315) 339-6281; gen/nat adv e-mail bwaters@rny.com; disp adv e-mail bwaters@rny.com; class adv e-mailclassad@rny.com; ed e-mail camred@rny.com; web site www.romesentinel.com
Published: Mon, Tues, Wed, Thur, Fri, Sat
Weekday Frequency: e
Saturday Frequency: m
Circulation: 8,648; 8,648(sat)
Last Audit: AAM December 31, 2015
Advertising Rate (weekday/saturday): Open inch rate $21.42
News services: AP, TMS. **Established:** 1821
Own Printing Facility?: Yes
Commercial Printers?: No
Special Editions: Spring Fashion (Easter) (Apr); Back-to-School (Aug); Christmas Coupon (Dec); Know Your Retailer (Jan); Graduation (Jun); Bridal Planner (May); Senior Citizens Tab (Primetime) (Monthly); Santa's Tour (Nov); Fall Fashion (Oct); Recipe (Sept).
Special Weekly Sections: Best Food (Sun); Arts, Auto, Business, Finance, Entertainment, Family, Fashion, Health, Home, Living, Real Estate, Religion, Technology, Travel, Women (Daily)
Syndicated Publications: TV Guide (S).
Digital Platform - Mobile: Apple
Digital Platform - Tablet: Apple iOS
Pub.................................Stephen B. Waters
Sports Ed. ....Joseph Silkowski
Community Ed. ....Richard Miller
IT Mgr. ....Daniel P. Bronson
Production Mgr. ....Linda Karsten
Adv. Dir. ....Bradley Waters
Market Information: ADS; TMC.
Mechanical Available: Offset; Black and 3 ROP colors; insert accepted; page cutoffs - 21 1/2.
Mechanical Specifications: Type page 12 x 21 1/2; E - 6 cols, 1-11/16, 1/8 between; A - 6 cols, 1-11/16, 1/8 between; C - 8 cols, 1 1/4, 1/8 between.
Areas Served: 13440, 13316, 13309, 13471, 13363, 13478, 13308, 13354, 13424, 13303, 13490, 13486, 13489, 13162, 13438, 13323, 13476, 13502, 13442, 13421, 13492, 13304, 13461, 13401, 13338, 13042, 13054, 13469, 13157, 13368, 13403, 13501
Delivery Method: Mail, Newsstand, Carrier, RacksEquipment & Software: PRESSROOM EQUIPMENT: Lines — 6-G/Urbanite, 1-G/Urbanite (3 color); Press Drive — 1-100 HP; 1-75 HP; Folders — 1-G/Urbanite.; MAILROOM EQUIPMENT: Tying Machines — 2/Sa, 2-MLN/ML2EE, MLN.; BUSINESS EQUIPMENT: Cloud BUSINESS SOFTWARE: Newzware CLASSIFIED EQUIPMENT: Hardware — APP/Mac ; Printers — Lexmark; CLASSIFIED SOFTWARE: SCATS 1.0, Claris/Filemaker Pro 3.0. DISPLAY EQUIPMENT: Hardware — APP/Mac; DISPLAY SOFTWAREAd Make-up Applications — Adobe inDesign; EDITORIAL EQUIPMENT: Hardware — APP/Mac G3, 1999-APP/iMac; Printers — Lexmark, Epson EDITORIAL SOFTWARE: Saxotech PRODUCTION EQUIPMENT: Hardware — Adobe/Photoshop, APP/Power Mac G3; Scanners — Epson/Scanner PRODUCTION SOFTWARE: Mk/Page Director, Saxotech, Adobe inDesign

SARANAC LAKE

ADIRONDACK DAILY ENTERPRISE

54 Broadway, Saranac Lake, N.Y., 12983-1704, Franklin; gen tel (518) 891-2600; adv tel (518) 891-2600; ed tel (518) 891-2600; gen fax (518) 891-2756; adv fax (518) 891-2756; ed fax (518) 891-2756; gen/nat adv e-mail ads@adirondackdailyenterprise.com; disp adv e-mail ads@adirondackdailyenterprise.com; class adv e-mailclassifieds@adirondackdailyenterprise.com; ed e-mail adenews@adirondackdailyenterprise.com; web site www.adirondackdailyenterprise.com - 578,778(views) 95,473(visitors); web site

2 LakePlacidNews.com - 111,786(views) 49,158(visitors)
Group: Ogden Newspapers Inc.
Published: Mon, Tues, Wed, Thur, Fri, Sat
Weekday Frequency: e
Saturday Frequency: m
Circulation: 3,600; 3,600(sat)
Last Audit: USPS October 1, 2016
Advertising Rate (weekday/saturday): Open inch rate $15.00
Advertising Rate (sunday): n/a
Online Advertising Rate: Varies $10 to $5 CPM
News services: AP. **Established:** 1894
Own Printing Facility?: Yes
Commercial Printers?: Yes
Special Editions: Back-to-School (Aug); Seasons Greetings (Dec); Bridal (Feb); July 4th Blast (Jul); Adirondack Summer Guide (Jun); Human Services (Mar); Adirondack Living Real Estate Guide (Monthly); Christmas Gift Guide (Nov); North Country Dining Guide (Other); Bridal (
Special Weekly Sections: Weekender
Digital Platform - Mobile: Apple, Android
Digital Platform - Tablet: Apple iOS, Android, Windows 7, Nook
Pub....................................Catherine Moore
Mng. Ed. ....Peter Crowley
Prodn. Mgr. ....Steve Bradley
Pressroom Foreman ....Rick Burman
Sports Ed. ....Morgan Ryan
Circ. Mgr. ....Alec Bieber
City editor ....Brittany Proulx
Market Information: Adirondack Park, Essex & Franklin Counties, New York
Mechanical Available: Offset; Black and 3 ROP colors; insert accepted - all; page cutoffs - 21.
Mechanical Specifications: Type page 10 x 21; E - 6 cols, 1 1/2", 1/8 between; A - 6 cols, 1 1/2", 1/8 between; C - 8 cols, 1.125", 1/8 between.
Areas Served: Saranac Lake, Tupper Lake, Lake Placid, New York, Essex and Franklin County
Delivery Method: Mail, Newsstand, Carrier, RacksEquipment & Software: PRESSROOM EQUIPMENT: Lines — 6-G/Community.; BUSINESS EQUIPMENT: NCR DISPLAY EQUIPMENT: Hardware — APP/Mac SE; DISPLAY SOFTWAREAd Make-up Applications — QPS, Multi-Ad/Creator; Layout Software — APP/Mac. EDITORIAL EQUIPMENT: Hardware — COM, APP/Mac Classic EDITORIAL SOFTWARE: WriteNow, QPS/QuarkXPress. PRODUCTION EQUIPMENT: Hardware — X; Scanners — 4-APP/Mac PRODUCTION SOFTWARE: QPS/QuarkXPress.
Note: The Saranac Lake Adirondack Daily Enterprise (e) has a combination rate of $49.25 with the Gloversville Leader-Herald (eS). Individual newspaper rates not made available.

SARATOGA SPRINGS

THE SARATOGIAN

20 Lake Ave, Saratoga Springs, N.Y., 12866-2314, Saratoga; gen tel (518) 584-4242; adv tel (518) 584-4242; ed tel (518) 584-2101; gen fax (518) 583-8014; adv fax (518) 584-2645; ed fax (518) 584-7750; gen/nat adv e-mail bfignar@21st-centurymedia.com; disp adv e-mail lkilbara@saratogian.com; class adv e-mailclassified@saratogian.com; ed e-mail news@saratogian.com; web site www.saratogian.com
437,065(visitors)
Group: Digital First Media
Published: Mon, Tues, Wed, Thur, Fri, Sat, Sun
Weekday Frequency: m
Saturday Frequency: m
Circulation: 3,493; 3,493(sat); 4,025(sun)
Last Audit: AAM June 30, 2015
Advertising Rate (weekday/saturday): Open inch rate $42.94
Advertising Rate (sunday): Open inch rate $49.79
Online Advertising Rate: Leaderboard ATF $15; LREC ATF $15; Pencil Billboard $250 Daily 100% SOV; Vibrant Tool Bar/LREC $350 100% SOV; In Banner Video $18
News services: AP, MCT.
Special Editions: Thoroughbred Racing-Daily (Aug); Business Review (Jan); Summer Magazines (Jul); Summer Magazines (Jun); New Car Preview (Oct).

Special Weekly Sections: Property Transaction, Health, Business (Mon); Society, Athletes of the Week, Horse Racing (Tue); Popular Columnist (Wed); Local Entertainment (Thur); High School Sports, Entertainment (Fri); Auto, Real Estate (Sat); Music, Education, Travel, Real Estate, Business (Sun)
Syndicated Publications: USA WEEKEND Magazine (S).
Pub. .... Bob O'Leary
Circulation District Mgr. .... Joe Anderson
Reg. Adv. Dir. .... Timothy Tergeoglou
Asst. Digital First Sales Mgr ....Louise Kilbara
Multi Media Account Exec. .... Jaclyn Grady
Regional Digital Dir ....Jake Loeb
Multi-Media Account Exec. ....Jordyn Moulton
Classified Adv. Inside Sales/Customer Service......
Ashley Schaal
Managing Ed. ....Charlie Kraebel
Sports Ed. ....David Johnson
Controller .... Tom Cleary
Market Information: TMC; Zoned editions.
Mechanical Available: Offset; Black and 4 ROP colors; insert accepted; page cutoffs - 22.
Mechanical Specifications: Type page 12 3/8 x 21; E - 6 cols, 1 7/8, 5/16 between; A - 6 cols, 1 7/8, 5/16 between; C - 9 cols, 1 1/4, 5/16 between.Equipment & Software: BUSINESS EQUIPMENT: IBM/AS-400 BUSINESS SOFTWARE: Lotus 5.0 CLASSIFIED EQUIPMENT: Hardware — Novell/Network; CLASSIFIED SOFTWARE: Dewar. DISPLAY EQUIPMENT: Hardware — Sun/Ultra Enterprise 2; DISPLAY SOFTWAREAd Make-up Applications — Solaris/Unix 2.5; Layout Software — LinoPress/Ad Manager. EDITORIAL EQUIPMENT: Hardware — Sun/Ultra Enterprise 2 EDITORIAL SOFTWARE: Solaris/Unix 2.5, LinoPress. PRODUCTION EQUIPMENT: Hardware — Nikon/Coolscan, APP/Mac 7200 PRODUCTION SOFTWARE: LinoPress/Pagination 4.0.

SCHENECTADY

THE DAILY GAZETTE
2345 Maxon Rd Ext, Schenectady, N.Y., 12308-1105, Schenectady; gen tel (518) 374-4141; adv tel (518) 395-3020; ed tel (518) 395-3140; gen fax (518) 395-3089; adv fax (518) 372-5986; ed fax (518) 395-3089; gen/nat adv e-mail gazette@dailygazette.com; disp adv e-mail afennicks@dailygazette.net; class adv e-mailclassified@dailygazette.net; ed e-mail news@dailygazette.net; web site www.dailygazette.com
251,260(visitors)
Published: Mon, Tues, Wed, Thur, Fri, Sat, Sun
Weekday Frequency: m
Saturday Frequency: m
Circulation: 52,202; 51,853(sat); 56,136(sun)
Last Audit: AAM December 31, 2016
Advertising Rate (weekday/saturday): Open inch rate $49.20
Advertising Rate (sunday): Open inch rate $49.20
News services: AP, LAT-WP, CSM. **Established:** 1894
Own Printing Facility?: Yes
Special Editions: Football (Aug-Jan); Ski (Nov-Apr); Golf (Apr-Sept)
Special Weekly Sections: Best Food Day (Wed); Outdoors (Thur); Arts, Entertainment (Thur/Fri); Business, Travel, Lifestyle, Education, Regional (Sun);
Syndicated Publications: Relish (Monthly); USA WEEKEND Magazine (S).
VP....Elizabeth L. Lind
Sec. .... William S. Hume
Treasurer .... Ernest R. Grandy
Bus. Mgr. ....Paula Opel
Gen. Mgr. ....Daniel Beck
Credit Mgr. .... Andrea Goldy
Pres./Pub./Ed. .... John E.N. Hume
Ed....Judy Patrick
City Ed. ....Irving Dean
Editorial Page Ed. ....Arthur J. Clayman
Online Ed. ....Jeff Haff
Prodn. Mgr. ....James Grandy
Circulation Mgr/Mailroom.......Dennis Donoghue
Prodn. Foreman, Mailroom ... Gerald Shoemaker
Adv. Mgr., Classified .... Christine Palmer
Adv. Mgr., Retail ....Scott Osswald
City Ed. ....George Walsh
Production Dir. ....Ken Kanniard
Adv. Suprv. ....Annmarie Fennicks

Mng. Ed. .... Miles Reed
Vice President ....Jim Murphy
Market Information: Split run; Zoned editions.
Mechanical Available: Flexo; Black and 3 ROP colors; insert accepted; page cutoffs - 22 1/2.
Mechanical Specifications: Type page 12 x 21 1/8; E - 6 cols, 1 7/8, 1/6 between; A - 6 cols, 1 7/8, 1/6 between; C - 9 cols, 1 1/4, 1/8 between.
Areas Served: 12008, 12009, 12010, 12019, 12020, 12025, 12027, 12032, 12035, 12043, 12047, 12053, 12056, 12065, 12066, 12068, 12070, 12072, 12074, 12078, 12084, 12086, 12092, 12095, 12110, 12117, 12118, 12122, 12134, 12137, 12148, 12149, 12150, 12151, 12157, 12158, 12159, 12160, 12166, 12170, 12177, 12180, 12186, 12187, 12188, 12203, 12205, 12208, 12301, 12302, 12303, 12304, 12305, 12306, 12307, 12308, 12309, 12803, 12822, 12831, 12833, 12835, 12850, 12859, 12863, 12866, 13317, 13339, 13428, 13452, 13459
Delivery Method: Newsstand, Carrier, RacksEquipment & Software: PRESSROOM EQUIPMENT: Lines — 4-G/PEC (1-color hump; 2-color decks); Folders — 1-G/PEC; Pasters —G/PEC Auto; Reels & Stands — 8-G/PEC.; MAILROOM EQUIPMENT: Counter Stackers — 5/QWI; Inserters & Stuffers — 2-S/NP630; Tying Machines — Power Strap, NTP 40; Wrapping Singles — 1-/QWI; Address Machine — 1-/Ch.; BUSINESS EQUIPMENT: 1-IBM/AS-400, PC BUSINESS SOFTWARE: Brainworks CLASSIFIED EQUIPMENT: Hardware — 35-PC; LaCie/Scanner; CLASSIFIED SOFTWARE: HI/Adpower-Adpag. DISPLAY EQUIPMENT: Hardware — APP/Mac G3, APP/Mac G4; Printers — 1-HP/5000, HP/Design Jet 1050C (Full page color proofer); DISPLAY SOFTWAREAd Make-up Applications — Adobe/Photoshop 5.5, Adobe/InDesign CS; Layout Software — Brainworks. EDITORIAL EQUIPMENT: Hardware — 100-PC EDITORIAL SOFTWARE: CD/2400, HI/XP-21, Multi-Edit/Lantastic. PRODUCTION EQUIPMENT: Hardware — ISSI/Scanning System, 2-HP/Printer, 2-ECR/3850, Konica/Jetsetter; Scanners — 2-ECR PRODUCTION SOFTWARE: HI/NT 3.5.15.1.

STATEN ISLAND

STATEN ISLAND ADVANCE
950 W Fingerboard Rd, Staten Island, N.Y., 10305-1453, Richmond; gen tel (718) 981-1234; adv tel (718) 816-2804; ed tel (718) 981-1594; gen fax (718) 981-1456; adv fax (718) 981-1456; ed fax (718) 981-1456; gen/nat adv e-mail danryan@siadvance.com; disp adv e-mail danryan@siadvance.com; class adv e-mailvalenti@siadvance.com; ed e-mail tips@siadvance.com; web site www.silive.com
869,000(visitors)
Group: Advance Publications, Inc.
Published: Mon, Tues, Wed, Thur, Fri, Sat, Sun
Weekday Frequency: e
Saturday Frequency: m
Circulation: 26,216; 24,497(sat); 34,962(sun)
Last Audit: Sworn/Estimate/Non-Audited September 30, 2017
Advertising Rate (weekday/saturday): Open inch rate $68.00
Advertising Rate (sunday): Open inch rate $75.00
Online Advertising Rate: Custom
News services: AP, TNS, LAT-WP. **Established:** 1886
Own Printing Facility?: Yes
Commercial Printers?: Yes
Special Editions: Readers Choice - Jan
Bride & Groom - Feb
Cookbook Preview - March
Home - April
Cookbook - April
Women of Achievement - April
SI Guide - June
Bride & Groom - Aug
SI Foodie - Sept
Harvest Guide - Weekly pub Sept - Nov
Holiday Guide - Nov
Top Doc's/ Health - Dec
Building Awards - Dec
Special Weekly Sections: Health (Mon); Food

(Wed); AWE Entertainment (Thurs); Home (Thurs); Real Estate (Fri); Arts & Ideas (Sun)
Digital Platform - Mobile: Apple, Android
Digital Platform - Tablet: Apple iOS, Android
Pub. ....Caroline D Harrison
Controller ....Arthur Silverstein
Ed. ....Brian Laline
Production Director ....John Giustiniani
Robert Walters
Market Information: Split run; TMC; Zoned editions.
Mechanical Available: Offset; Black and 3 ROP colors; insert accepted; page cutoffs - 21 1/4.
Mechanical Specifications: Type page 11 5/8 x 21 1/4; E - 6 cols, 1 5/6, 1/8 between; A - 6 cols, 1 5/6, 1/8 between; C - 10 cols, 1 1/12, 1/12 between.
Areas Served: Staten Island
Delivery Method: Newsstand, CarrierEquipment & Software: PRESSROOM EQUIPMENT: Lines — MAN/Geoman 70 2002; Folders — 2-MAN; Pasters —6-MAN/AutoReels & Stands — 6-MAN; Control System — MAN/PECOM 2000 2002.;
GOSS/Compact Magnum 6 unit, Single wide, 32 page broadsheet, 64 tabloid capacity, Qtr fold, in-line stitch & Trim. PRESSROOM SOFTWARE: Goss Compact MAILROOM EQUIPMENT: 2-18 into 1 SLS3000 Inserters, 1- 10- into 1 SLS2000, Muller Martini news-grip and buffer system.
5 Quip 500, 3 Gamuller stackers.
2 offline Muller Martini 5 signature offline stitch & trim lines. BUSINESS SOFTWARE: Concur CLASSIFIED SOFTWARE: AdBase, AdBase-E, PGL DISPLAY EQUIPMENT: MacBook DISPLAY SOFTWAREAdBase, SalesForce, SalesPoint, ATOL EDITORIAL EQUIPMENT: MacBook EDITORIAL SOFTWARE: Moveable Type, Merlin, HSSN, Newscycle Content PRODUCTION EQUIPMENT: 3 Krause lines CTP, NELA benders PRODUCTION SOFTWARE: Proimage Newsway, PGL, Newscycle Content IT EQUIPMENT: Dell OptiPlex 7010, MacBook IT SOFTWARE:ManageEngine ServiceDeskPlus CIRCULATION SOFTWARNewscycle WorldClass Circulation

SYRACUSE

THE POST-STANDARD
220 S Warren St, Syracuse, N.Y., 13202-1676, Onondaga; gen tel (315) 470-0011; adv tel (315) 470-0032; ed tel (315) 470-0011; gen fax (315) 470-3081; adv fax (315) 470-3081; ed fax (315) 470-3081; gen/nat adv e-mail kbrill@advancemediany.com; disp adv e-mail kbrill@advancemediany.com; class adv e-mailgcarroll@advancemediany.com; ed e-mail letters@syracuse.com; web site www.syracuse.com
 - 49,400,000(views) 4,700,000(visitors); web site 2 newyorkupstate.com - 9,700,000(views) 1,700,000(visitors)
Group: Advance Publications, Inc.
Published: Mon, Tues, Wed, Thur, Fri, Sat, Sun
Weekday Frequency: m
Saturday Frequency: m
Circulation: 69,951; 32,227(sat); 113,704(sun)
Last Audit: AAM June 30, 2016
Advertising Rate (weekday/saturday): Open inch rate including 4 color $238.4
Advertising Rate (sunday): Open inch rate including 4 color $333.30
News services: NNS, NYT, LAT-WP, AP, MCT, CSM. **Established:** 1829
Own Printing Facility?: Yes
Commercial Printers?: Yes
Special Editions: Spotlight on Auto (Feb); Home & Garden (Mar) Holiday Shopper (Dec);Parade of Homes (Jun); NCAA Hoops (Mar); Holiday Guide (Nov)
Special Weekly Sections: Neighbors, Weekend Entertainment (Thur); Travel, Entertainment, Real Estate, Employment, Auto, Comics (Sun)
Syndicated Publications: Parade (Sun)
Proprietary Publications: The Good Life Magazine (6x /yr), Visitor's Guide (2x / yr)
President .... Tim Kennedy
Executive Assistant ....Kellie Caimano
Chairman ....Stephen Rogers
VP, Sales ....Bill Allison

VP Digital Solutions ....Michele Sardinia
Sales Director....................................Ken Brill
VP Marketing..............................Annette Peters
Market Information: Split run; Zoned editions.
Mechanical Available: Letterpress; Black and 3 ROP colors; insert accepted - some samples; page cutoffs - 21 1/2.
Mechanical Specifications: Type page 12 x 21 1/2; E - 6 cols, 1 7/8, 1/8 between; A - 6 cols, 1 7/8, 1/6 between; C - 10 cols, 1 5/16, 1/32 between.
Areas Served: Central New York
Delivery Method: Newsstand, Carrier

TROY

THE RECORD
270 River Triangle Suite 202B, Troy, N.Y., 12180, Rensselaer; gen tel (518) 270-1200; adv tel (518) 272-2255; ed tel (518) 270-1276; gen fax (518) 270-1251; adv fax (518) 270-1204 (display); ed fax (518) 270-1202; gen/nat adv e-mail retailmgr@troyrecord.com; disp adv e-mail retailmgr@troyrecord.com; class adv e-mailclass@troyrecord.com; ed e-mail newsroom@troyrecord.com; web site www.troyrecord.com
 - 1,677,636(views) 360,846(visitors)
Group: Digital First Media
Published: Mon, Tues, Wed, Thur, Fri, Sat, Sun
Weekday Frequency: m
Saturday Frequency: m
Circulation: 4,120; 4,120(sat); 4,565(sun)
Last Audit: AAM June 30, 2015
Advertising Rate (weekday/saturday): Open inch rate $28.30
Advertising Rate (sunday): Open inch rate $28.30
Online Advertising Rate: Leaderboard ATF $15; LREC ATF $15; Pencil Billboard $250 Daily 100% SOV; Vibrant Tool Bar/LREC $350 100% SOV; In Banner Video $18
News services: AP, MCT. **Established:** 1896
Special Editions: Spring Car Care (Apr); Truck Tab (Aug); Last Minute Gift Ideas (Dec); Baby Album (Feb); New Car Preview (Jan); Saratoga Life (Jul); Father's Day (Jun); Medical Physicians Guide (Mar); Mature Living (May); Christmas Gift Guide (Nov); Apple Fest (Oct); Heal
Special Weekly Sections: Health, Computers, Science (Mon); Money (Tue); Food, Stocks (Wed); Entertainment, Stocks (Thur); Education (Fri); Religion (Sat); TV (Sun); Real Estate (Monthly)
Syndicated Publications: Home Front (Monthly); Health Notes (Quarterly); TV & Cable quarter-fold magazine (S); Steppin' Out (Thur).
Ed....Charlie Krabel
Chief Photographer ....Mike McMahon
Managing Ed. ....Charlie Krabel
Reg. Adv. Dir. ....Timothy Tergeoglou
Market Information: Split run; TMC; Zoned editions.
Mechanical Available: Offset; Black and 3 ROP colors; insert accepted; page cutoffs - 22 1/12.
Mechanical Specifications: Type page 12 x 21; E - 6 cols, 1 7/8, 1/8 between; A - 6 cols, 1 7/8, 1/8 between; C - 9 cols, 1 5/16, 3/16 between.
Areas Served: Rensselaer, Albany & Saratoga Counties (NY)
Equipment & Software: PRESSROOM EQUIPMENT: Lines — 6-G/Headliner Offset w/gluer 1984; Folders — 1-G/quarter 2:1; Pasters —6-G/DigitalReels & Stands — 6; MAILROOM EQUIPMENT: Counter Stackers — 1/QWI, 1-HT/Monitor; Inserters & Stuffers — 3-MM/227 EM; Tying Machines — 4-/MLN, MLN/2HS, 3-MLN/2HS; CLASSIFIED EQUIPMENT: Hardware — Dewar/Information System; CLASSIFIED SOFTWARE: Dewar/Sys IV. DISPLAY EQUIPMENT: Hardware — APP/Mac Network; DISPLAY SOFTWAREAd Make-up Applications — Multi-Ad/Creator; Layout Software — Dewar/Sys. EDITORIAL EQUIPMENT: Hardware — Dewar/System EDITORIAL SOFTWARE: Dewar/View 2.1. PRODUCTION EQUIPMENT: Hardware — 2-MON/Imagesetter 1000, 1-Kk/66S; Cameras — 2-C/Spartan III; Scanners — Lf/Leafscan 35, Kk/Negative Scanner PRODUCTION SOFTWARE: QPS/

QuarkXPress 3.32.

UTICA

THE OBSERVER-DISPATCH

221 Oriskany St E, Utica, N.Y., 13501-1201, Oneida; gen tel (315) 792-5000; adv tel (315) 792-5107; ed tel (315) 792-5005; gen fax (315) 792-5033; adv fax (315) 792-5085; ed fax (315) 792-5033; gen/nat adv e-mail srosenburgh@uticaod.com; disp adv e-mail srosenburgh@uticaod.com; class adv e-mailpzehr@uticaod.com; ed e-mail news@uticaod.com; web site www.uticaod.com
- 2,640,000(views) 382,023(visitors)

Group: New Media Investment Group
Published: Mon, Tues, Wed, Thur, Fri, Sat, Sun
Weekday Frequency: m
Saturday Frequency: m
Circulation: 21,152; 21,152(sat); 29,017(sun)
Last Audit: AAM September 30, 2016
Advertising Rate (weekday/saturday):
Advertising Rate (sunday):
News services: AP, Tribune, GateHouse, Washington Post **Established:** 1817
Own Printing Facility?: No
Commercial Printers?: Yes
Special Editions: Gift Guide (Dec); Business Review (Feb); Bridal (Jan); Teen All-Stars (May); Boilermaker Sections (Jul); Football Preview (Sept.); Comets Preview (Oct.) Coupons (Monthly); Thanksgiving Day (Nov); Basketball Preview (Dec.)
Special Weekly Sections: Scene Entertainment (Thursdays); TV Guide (Sundays)
Proprietary Publications: Mid York Weekly; Your Valley
Digital Platform - Mobile: Apple, Android
Digital Platform - Tablet: Apple iOS, Android
Controller.................................Theresa Swider
Opinion Page Ed...........................Dave Dudajek
Sports Ed.....................................Fran Perritano
Pub...Terry Cascioli
Managing Ed...................................Ron Johns
Circ. Dir....Robert Gall
Scott Rosenburgh
Market Information: Split run; TMC; Zoned editions.
Mechanical Specifications: Image Area: 10" x 20.812"
Areas Served: Oneida County, Herkimer County, Madison County
Delivery Method: Mail, Newsstand, Carrier, RacksEquipment & Software: CLASSIFIED EQUIPMENT: Hardware — SII/Sys 55, 11-SII/Coyote, APP/Macs; 11-SII/Coyote; Printers — Software SII/Ad Director, Pongrass/Classified Pagemaker.; DISPLAY EQUIPMENT: Hardware — IBM/PC; Printers — QMS/860; Other Hardware — APP/Mac Interface, AP AdSend DISPLAY SOFTWAREAd Make-up Applications — Pongrass, Mk/Ad Director, Multi-Ad/Creator, QPS; Layout Software — SCS/Layout 8000, SII/Ad Director. PRODUCTION EQUIPMENT: Hardware — Caere/OmniPage 2.1, Lf/AP Leaf Picture Desk, LS/2800R; Cameras — C/Marathon; Scanners — APP/Mac Pac Interface, 3-Umax PRODUCTION SOFTWARE: QPS/QuarkXPress.

WATERTOWN

WATERTOWN DAILY TIMES

260 Washington St, Watertown, N.Y., 13601-4669, Jefferson; gen tel (315) 782-1000; adv tel (315) 661-2422; ed tel (315) 661-2359; gen fax (315) 661-2520; adv fax (315) 661-2522; ed fax (315) 661-2523; gen/nat adv e-mail relias@wdt; disp adv e-mail mbowers@wdt.net; class adv e-mailgvalik@wdt.net; ed e-mail news@wdt.net; web site www.watertowndailytimes.com
- 1,750,000(views) 350,000(visitors)

Group: Johnson Newspaper Corp.
Published: Mon, Tues, Wed, Thur, Fri, Sat, Sun
Weekday Frequency: m
Saturday Frequency: m
Circulation: 16,333; 16,333(sat); 20,299(sun)
Last Audit: AAM December 31, 2015
Advertising Rate (weekday/saturday): Open inch rate 20.80
Advertising Rate (sunday): Open inch rate 23.20
Online Advertising Rate: 15/M
News services: NYT, LAT-WP, MCT, Bloomberg, WAPO **Established:** 1861
Own Printing Facility?: Yes
Commercial Printers?: Yes
Special Weekly Sections: Best Food Day (Tues).
Syndicated Publications: Relish (Monthly); Parade (S); Farm & Garden Tab (newsprint) (Sat); American Profile (Weekly).
Digital Platform - Mobile: Apple, Android
Digital Platform - Tablet: Apple iOS, Android
CEO & Co-Pub...............................John Johnson
Asst. Feat. Ed.................................Cathie Egan
VP Finance......................................Ray Weston
Sports Ed......................................Gregory Gay
Sunday Ed....................................Mary Kaskan
CIO...Jill VanHoesen
Prod. Mgr...Dale Cronk
Editorial Page Ed..........................Gerald Moore
Pres. & Co-publisher.................Harold Johnson
VP News Ops.....................................Tim Farkas
Managing Ed...................................Perry White
Market Information: ADS; Split run; Zoned editions.
Mechanical Available: Offset; Black and 3 ROP colors; insert accepted; page cutoffs - 20 1/2.
Mechanical Specifications: Type page 13 x 21; E - 6 cols, 2 1/16, 1/8 between; A - 6 cols, 2 1/16, 1/8 between; C - 9 cols, 1 3/8, 1/16 between.
Areas Served: Three County Region
Delivery Method: Mail, Newsstand, Carrier, RacksEquipment & Software: PRESSROOM EQUIPMENT: Lines — 7-MAN/Uniman 4 x 2; Pasters —7-MEG; Reels & Stands — 7-MEG.; MAILROOM EQUIPMENT: Counter Stackers — 3/HL, 1-/KAN; Inserters & Stuffers — 2-GMA/SLS 1000; Tying Machines — 1-MLN/ML2EE, 2-/Dynaric; Address Machine — 1-Ch/582N.; CLASSIFIED SOFTWARE: AD PLUS DISPLAY EQUIPMENT: Hardware — MAC; DISPLAY SOFTWAREAd Make-up Applications — Multi-Ad; Layout Software — ALS EDITORIAL EQUIPMENT: Hardware — HP/DELL/MAC EDITORIAL SOFTWARE: Saxotech Cloud

WELLSVILLE

WELLSVILLE DAILY REPORTER

159 N Main St, Wellsville, N.Y., 14895-1149, Allegany; gen tel (585) 593-5300; adv tel (585) 593-5300; ed tel (585) 593-5300; gen fax (585) 593-5303; adv fax (585) 593-5303; ed fax (585) 593-5303; gen/nat adv e-mail wellsvillereader@aol.com; disp adv e-mail wellsvillereader@aol.com; class adv e-mailwellsvillereader@aol.com; ed e-mail editor@wellsvilledaily.com; web site www.wellsvilledaily.com

Group: New Media Investment Group
Published: Mon, Tues, Wed, Thur, Fri, Sun
Weekday Frequency: m
Circulation: 4,500; 10,390(sun)
Last Audit: Sworn/Estimate/Non-Audited September 30, 2017
Advertising Rate (weekday/saturday): Open inch rate $8.50
News services: AP. **Established:** 1880
Special Editions: Medical-Health Guide (Aug); Bride's Guide (Jan); Balloon Rally Guide (Jul); Graduation (Jun); Spring Outdoor (Mar); Christmas (Nov); Annual Fall Outdoor Guide (Sept).
Adv. Dir....Oak Duke
Circ. Mgr.......................................Robert Polley
Regional Ed................................John Anderson
Adv. Dir.................................Melissa VanSkiver
Market Information: TMC.
Mechanical Available: Offset; Black and 3 ROP colors; insert accepted; page cutoffs - 22 3/4.
Mechanical Specifications: Type page 13 x 21 1/2; E - 6 cols, 2 1/16, 1/8 between; A - 6 cols, 2 1/16, 1/8 between; C - 6 cols, 2 1/16, 1/8 between.Equipment & Software: BUSINESS EQUIPMENT: 1-DEC/Rainbow 100 CLASSIFIED EQUIPMENT: Hardware — Mk/1100.; EDITORIAL EQUIPMENT: Hardware — Mk/1100/2-IBM/Selectric II.
Note: The Wellsville Daily Reporter (e) and the Hornell Evening Tribune (e) share a Sunday edition.

WHITE PLAINS

THE JOURNAL NEWS

1133 Westchester Ave, Ste N-110, White Plains, N.Y., 10604-3511, Westchester; gen tel (914) 694-9300; adv tel (914) 694-5158; ed tel (914) 694-5077; gen fax (914) 696-8396; adv fax (914) 696-8173; ed fax (914) 696-8396; gen/nat adv e-mail ezaccagn@lohud.com; disp adv e-mail sbaker@lohud.com; ed e-mail letters@lohud.com; web site www.lohud.com
- 10,311,784(views) 1,448,635(visitors)

Group: Gannett
Published: Mon, Tues, Wed, Thur, Fri, Sat, Sun
Weekday Frequency: m
Saturday Frequency: m
Circulation: 45,361; 52,413(sat); 59,085(sun)
Last Audit: AAM March 31, 2017
Advertising Rate (weekday/saturday): Open inch rate $438.00
News services: AP, GNS, LAT-WP. **Established:** 1829
Special Editions: Suburban Golf (Apr); Back-to-School (Aug); Holiday Food (Dec); Spring Bridal (Feb); Suburban Golf (Jul); Summer Dine Out Guide (Jun); Spring Home Design (Mar); Suburban Golf (May); Holiday Gift Guide (Nov); Fall Home Design (Oct); In the City (Quarterly);
Special Weekly Sections: Wheels (Fri); Tech E (Mon); Real Estate (S); The Line (Thur).
Syndicated Publications: USA WEEKEND Magazine (S).
Pres./Pub...Mike Fisch
Vice Pres., Circ....................Anthony Simmons
Circ. Mgr., Single Copy...............Mauro Ferrotta
Vice Pres./Exec. News Ed...........Henry Freeman
Sr. Mng. Ed...................Cynthia Royle Lambert
Design Dir............................Robert Rodriguez
Editorial Page Ed............................Herb Pinder
Lifestyles Ed....................................Mary Dolan
Photo Ed...Hai Do
Sports Ed., Days..............................Mark Faller
Asst. Sports Ed.......................Mary Susan Arth
Travel Ed.................................Kathy McClusky
Prodn. Dir...Nat Hogan
Digital Team Leader..........................Ed Forbes
Liz Johnson
Market Information: ADS; Split run; TMC; Zoned editions.
Mechanical Available: Offset; Black and 4 ROP colors; insert accepted; page cutoffs - 22 3/4.
Mechanical Specifications: Type page 13 x 21 1/2; E - 6 cols, 1 5/6, 1/8 between; A - 6 cols, 1 5/6, 1/8 between; C - 10 cols, 1 1/10, 3/50 between.
Areas Served: Lower Hudson Valley
Equipment & Software: MAILROOM EQUIPMENT: Tying Machines — 2-MLN/MLM 2EE; Address Machine — 4-Barstrom/Labeler.; BUSINESS EQUIPMENT: 1-IBM/AS-400 320 BUSINESS SOFTWARE: Admarc EDITORIAL EQUIPMENT: Hardware — DEC/VAX Output Graphic Database; Printers — Okidata. PRODUCTION EQUIPMENT: Hardware — LE, AII/3850; Cameras — C/Spartan; Scanners — ImagiTex/940.

NORTH CAROLINA

ASHEBORO

THE COURIER-TRIBUNE

500 Sunset Ave, Asheboro, N.C., 27203-5330, Randolph; gen tel (336) 625-2101; adv tel (336) 626-6114; ed tel (336) 626-6140; gen fax (336) 626-7074; adv fax (336) 626-7074; ed fax (336) 626-7074; gen/nat adv e-mail ads@courier-tribune.com; disp adv e-mail ads@courier-tribune.com; class adv e-mailclassifieds@courier-tribune.com; ed e-mail news@courier-tribune.com; web site www.courier-tribune.com
- 425,000(views)

Group: New Media Investment Group
Published: Tues, Wed, Thur, Fri, Sat, Sun
Weekday Frequency: m
Saturday Frequency: m
Circulation: 8,392; 8,392(sat); 10,018(sun)
Last Audit: CAC March 31, 2015
Advertising Rate (weekday/saturday): Open inch rate $15.64
Advertising Rate (sunday): Open inch rate $16.72
Online Advertising Rate: Sliding Billboard $600; Leaderboard $300; Tower $225; Above the Fold $300; Mid-page $200; Below the fold $100
News services: AP, MCT, SHNS. **Established:** 1876
Special Editions: Back-to-School (Aug); Progress (Jan); Lawn & Garden (Mar); Graduation (May); Textile (Oct).
Special Weekly Sections: Church (Fri); Children's Page (S); Business (Wed).
Syndicated Publications: USA WEEKEND Magazine (S); Food (Wed).
Circ. Dir.......................................Gary Lockhart
Ed....Annette Jordan
Sports Ed....................................Dennis Garcia
Prodn. Mgr.................................Hazel Saunders
Prodn. Mgr., Pressroom......................Ben Kane
Digital Ed./News Ed........................Leslie Green
Market Information: TMC.
Mechanical Available: Offset; Black and 3 ROP colors; insert accepted; page cutoffs - 22 5/8.
Mechanical Specifications: Type page 13 x 21 1/2; E - 6 cols, 2 1/16, 1/8 between; A - 6 cols, 2 1/16, 1/8 between; C - 9 cols, 1 3/8, 1/16 between.
Areas Served: Asheboro & Randolph counties
Equipment & Software: PRESSROOM EQUIPMENT: Lines — 9-G/Urbanite 1990; MAILROOM EQUIPMENT: Counter Stackers — HL; Inserters & Stuffers — MM/4:1, MM/6:1; Tying Machines — 1/MLN.; BUSINESS EQUIPMENT: 1-CJ, 1-HP/3000 BUSINESS SOFTWARE: CJ CLASSIFIED EQUIPMENT: Hardware — 5-APP/Mac; CLASSIFIED SOFTWARE: Baseview. DISPLAY EQUIPMENT: Hardware — 4-APP/Mac; Printers — APP/Mac LaserWriter; DISPLAY SOFTWAREAd Make-up Applications — Multi-Ad/Creator.; EDITORIAL EQUIPMENT: Hardware — 16-APP/Mac/2-APP/Mac, Lf/Leafscan 35, Lf/AP Leaf Picture Desk; Printers — 2-Pre Press/Panther Pro EDITORIAL SOFTWARE: Baseview. PRODUCTION EQUIPMENT: Hardware — Pre Press/Panther Pro; Cameras — C/Spartan III.

ASHEVILLE

THE ASHEVILLE CITIZEN-TIMES

14 Ohenry Ave, Asheville, N.C., 28801-2604, Buncombe; gen tel (828) 252-5610; adv tel (828) 232-5989; ed tel (828) 252-5611; ed fax (828) 251-0585; gen/nat adv e-mail scoghlin@citizen-times.com; disp adv e-mail ehdugas@citizen-times.com; class adv e-mailtcalloway1@citizen-times.com; ed e-mail cterrell@citizen-times.com ; web site www.citizen-times.com
- 3,500,000(views) 575,000(visitors)

Group: Gannett
Published: Mon, Tues, Wed, Thur, Fri, Sat, Sun
Weekday Frequency: m
Saturday Frequency: m
Circulation: 26,347; 26,347(sat); 36,208(sun)
Last Audit: AAM December 31, 2016
Advertising Rate (weekday/saturday): Modular rates:: Please call for details
Advertising Rate (sunday): Modular rates: Please call for details
Online Advertising Rate: Call for information details
News services: AP, GNS, NNS. **Established:** 1870
Own Printing Facility?: No
Commercial Printers?: No
Special Editions: Mountain Travel Guide (Apr); Football (Aug); Agenda (Feb); Best of (Jun); Campus Connection (Oct); West Asheville (Quarterly); Mountain Travel Guide (Sept).
Special Weekly Sections: Take Five (Fri); Health & Fitness (Mon); Travel (S); Family (Thur); Computers & Technology (Tues); Food (Wed).
Syndicated Publications: USA WEEKEND Magazine (S).
Digital Platform - Mobile: Apple, Android
Digital Platform - Tablet: Apple iOS, Android, Kindle, Nook, Kindle Fire

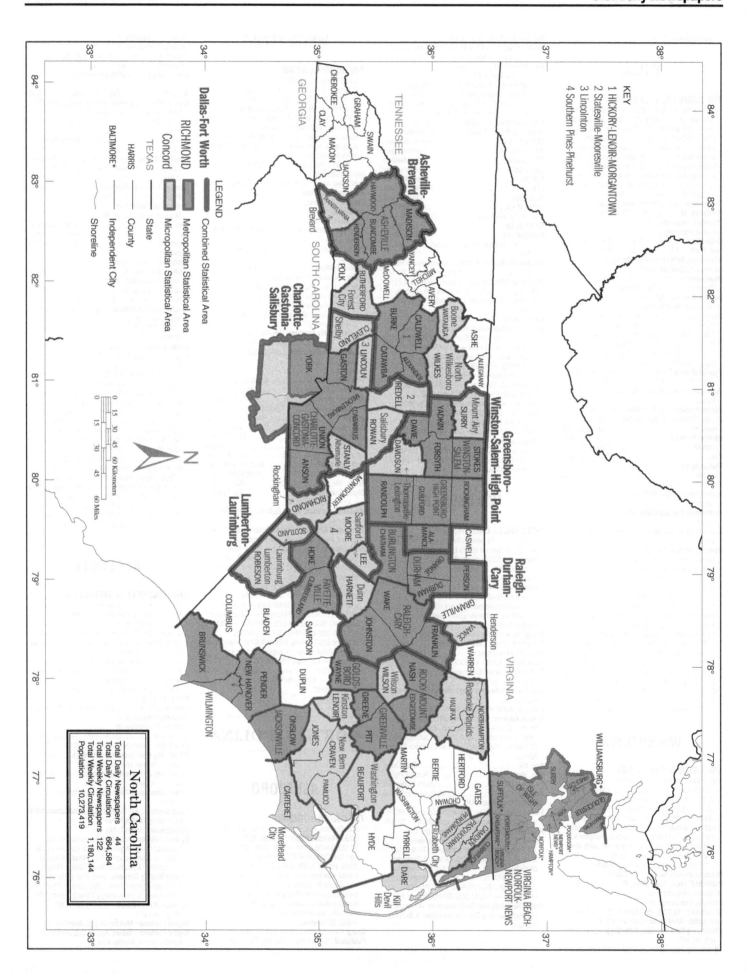

KEY
1 HICKORY-LENOIR-MORGANTOWN
2 Statesville-Mooresville
3 Lincolnton
4 Southern Pines-Pinehurst

LEGEND

Combined Statistical Area
Metropolitan Statistical Area
Micropolitan Statistical Area

Dallas-Fort Worth
RICHMOND
Concord
TEXAS
HARRIS
BALTIMORE*

State
County
Independent City
Shoreline

North Carolina

Total Daily Newspapers	44
Total Daily Circulation	664,584
Total Weekly Newspapers	122
Total Weekly Circulation	1,180,144
Population	10,273,419

Digital Producer ....Casey Swaney
News Dir. .... Katie Wadington
Planning Ed....................................Bruce Steele
Writing Coach................................Brian Ponder
Digital Prod...................................... Joe Castle
Operations Mgr............................. Vicki Harrison
Strategist/Analyst.......................... Todd Runkle
Ed.... Paul Clark
Dir. Adv. .... Vivian Murciano
Pres. .... Tom Claybaugh
Mechanical Available: Offset; Black and 3 ROP colors; insert accepted; page cutoffs - 22.
Mechanical Specifications: Type page 10 x 20; E - 6 cols, 1/6 between; A - 6 cols, 1/6 between; C - 10 cols, 1/12 between.
Delivery Method: Carrier, RacksEquipment & Software: MAILROOM EQUIPMENT: SLS 2000 MAILROOM SOFTWARE:Newscom BUSINESS EQUIPMENT: DELL; Canon BUSINESS SOFTWARE: Microsoft CLASSIFIED EQUIPMENT: Enterprise Classified Solutions CLASSIFIED SOFTWARE: Adbooker DISPLAY EQUIPMENT: OrderHub DISPLAY SOFTWAREGannett EDITORIAL EQUIPMENT: CCI Europe EDITORIAL SOFTWARE: NewsGate PRODUCTION EQUIPMENT: PressTeligence PRODUCTION SOFTWARE: NewsXtreme IT EQUIPMENT: DELL; Canon; CIRCULATION EQUIPMENT: POET; Halcyon

BOONE

HIGH COUNTRY PRESS

1600 Highway 105, Boone, N.C., 28607-8731, Watauga; gen tel (828) 264-2262; adv tel (828) 264-2262; ed tel (828) 264-2262; gen fax (828) 264-2254; adv fax (828) 264-2254; ed fax (828) 264-2254; gen/nat adv e-mail ads@highcountrypress.com; disp adv e-mail ads@highcountrypress.com; class adv e-mailads@highcountrypress.com; ed e-mail ken@highcountrypress.com; web site www.hcpress.com
Published: Mon, Tues, Wed, Thur, Fri, Sat, Sun
Weekday Frequency: m
Saturday Frequency: m
Last Audit: Sworn/Estimate/Non-Audited September 30, 2017
Advertising Rate (weekday/saturday): Open inch rate $17.63
News services: 2005
Digital Platform - Mobile: Apple, Android
Digital Platform - Tablet: Apple iOS, Android
Ad. Director................................Debbie Carter
Pub./Ed.... Ken Ketchie
News. Ed.....................................Jesse Wood
Office Mgr. ....Amanda Giles
Delivery Method: Mail, Newsstand

BURLINGTON

TIMES-NEWS

707 S Main St, Burlington, N.C., 27215-5844, Alamance; gen tel (336) 227-0131; adv tel (336) 227-0131; ed tel (336) 506-3040; gen fax (336) 229-2462; adv fax (336) 229-2462; ed fax (336) 229-2463; gen/nat adv e-mail sbowman@thetimesnews.com; disp adv e-mail Burl-ADV@thetimesnews.com; class adv e-maildshue@thetimesnews.com; ed e-mail mtaylor@thetimesnews.com; web site www.thetimesnews.com - 3,300,000(views) 250,000(visitors)
Group: New Media Investment Group
Published: Mon, Tues, Wed, Thur, Fri, Sat, Sun
Weekday Frequency: m
Saturday Frequency: m
Circulation: 17,044; 17,044(sat); 19,619(sun)
Last Audit: Sworn/Estimate/Non-Audited September 30, 2017
Advertising Rate (weekday/saturday): Open inch rate $26
Advertising Rate (sunday): Open inch rate $26
Online Advertising Rate: ROS $15; Section Targeted $20; Home page $20; Sliding billboard $750/day; Static billboard $500/day; Home page takeover $950/day
News services: AP, McClatchy Tribune **Established:** 1887
Own Printing Facility?: Yes
Commercial Printers?: Yes
Special Editions: Lawn & Garden/Home Improvement (Apr & Sept); Prep Ball Preview (Aug); Gift Guide (Dec); Racing Tab (Feb); Awards of Excellence(Apr))Holiday Lifestyles (Nov); Medical Reference Guide (June); Builders Parade(Oct); Living Here (Aug)Bridal Expo (Feb) Taste of Home (Oct) Alamance Health (quarterly)Business card directory (Jan) Super Bowl (Feb)Behind the Scenes (March)How-To Guide (May) Breast Cancer Awareness (Oct) Design an Ad (Nov) Back to School (July) Monster Job Fair (Apr)
Special Weekly Sections: Scene (Entertainment) (Thurs); Teens & Twenties (Mon); Homes Front (Sat); Mini Page (Fri). TV Guide (Sat) Food (Wed.) Accent (Sun.)
Syndicated Publications: Parade Magazine (S); American Profile (Tues). Athlon Sports, Relish (Food)
Digital Platform - Mobile: Apple, Android, Windows, Blackberry
Digital Platform - Tablet: Apple iOS, Android, Windows 7, Blackberry Tablet OS, Kindle, Nook, Kindle Fire
Sales Mgr.................................Serena Bowman
Mgr., Mktg./Promo. .... Michele Terry
Features Ed.................................Charity Apple
City Ed. ....Tom Jones
Sports Ed. ....Bob Sutton
HR Dir. .... Joyce Thompson
Production Director.................. Sherwood Bland
Chief Photog................................ Sam Roberts
Publisher...................................... Paul Mauney
Audience Development Director............... Regina Howard-Glaspie
Digital Director........................... Michael Russo
Market Information: ADS; TMC.
Mechanical Available: Offset; Black and 3 ROP colors; insert accepted; page cutoffs - 22 3/4.
Mechanical Specifications: Type page 11 5/8 x 21 1/2; E - 6 cols, 1 5/6, 1/8 between; A - 6 cols, 1 5/6, 1/8 between; C - 9 cols, 1 3/16, 1/8 between.
Areas Served: 27215, 27217, 27244, 27249, 27253, 27258, 27302
Delivery Method: Mail, Newsstand, Carrier, RacksEquipment & Software: PRESSROOM EQUIPMENT: Lines — 6-MAN/double width (2-half color deck) 1980; Press Drive — GE/Varitrol; Folders — 1-H/double 2:1; Reels & Stands — 5;
CTP 1 MAILROOM EQUIPMENT: Counter Stackers — QWI/351 QWI/501; Inserters & Stuffers — 1-GMA/SLS 2000 9:2;
1- GMA/SLS 2000 12:2 2-/Dynaric; BUSINESS EQUIPMENT: Microsoft/Office, Great Plains, AR/Works, PC Netware CLASSIFIED EQUIPMENT: Hardware — PC; Printers — HP; CLASSIFIED SOFTWARE: APT. DISPLAY EQUIPMENT: Hardware — PC, ; Printers — Okidata/2410, HP/ LaserJet III; DISPLAY SOFTWAREAd Make-up Applications — InDesign; Layout Software — APT. EDITORIAL EQUIPMENT: Hardware — PC/Desk/Scanner, ; Printers — Sharp & Camera Probe 9000 EDITORIAL SOFTWARE: APT. IT EQUIPMENT: PC, Mac, Printer IT SOFTWARE:Windows 7, Microsoft office, Windows Server 2003 & 2008 CIRCULATION EQUIPMENT: PC CIRCULATION SOFTWARNewscycle

CHARLOTTE

THE CHARLOTTE OBSERVER

550 S Caldwell St Ste 760, 10th Floor, Charlotte, N.C., 28202-2636, Mecklenburg; gen tel (704) 358-5000; adv tel (704) 358-5400; ed tel (704) 358-5040; gen fax (704) 358-5840; adv fax (704) 358-5542; ed fax (704) 358-5036; gen/nat adv e-mail drgordon@charlotteobserver.com; disp adv e-mail pweber@charlotteobserver.com; class adv e-mailchadmartin@charlotteobserver.com; ed e-mail opinion@charlotteobserver.com; web site www.charlotteobserver.com - 45,008,400(views) 6,335,602(visitors); web site 2 momscharlotte.com - 39,376(views) 17,877(visitors); web site 3 CharlotteFive.com - 343,654(views) 157,682(visitors); web site 4thatsracin.com - 285,438(views) 109,827(visitors)
Group: The McClatchy Company
Published: Mon, Tues, Wed, Thur, Fri, Sat, Sun
Weekday Frequency: m
Saturday Frequency: m
Circulation: 97,755; 102,605(sat); 137,639(sun)
Last Audit: AAM December 31, 2016
Newspaper Reps: Ann Caulkins, Jennifer Matts-Sprague, Jim Puryear, Sherry Chisenhall, Rick Thames, Risa McGrew, Kelly Mirt
Branch Offices: Research Drive
Advertising Rate (weekday/saturday): Open inch rate $353.00
Advertising Rate (sunday): Open inch rate $384.00
Online Advertising Rate: Native Advertising - 25,000 to 50,000 $42
News services: AP, Washington Post, Bloomberg News, NYT, Getty **Established:** 1886
Own Printing Facility?: Yes
Commercial Printers?: Yes
Special Editions: Road Trips (Spring&Fall); Living Here Lake Norman (May); Living Here (Sept); Panthers/NFL Preview (Sept); Arts Preview (Sept)
Special Weekly Sections: CLT (Fri); Carolina Living (Arts, Style, Travel) (S); Your Weekend (Faith, Garden Home)(Sat); Food&Drink (Wed), Wheels(Fri); HomelDesign(Sat)
Syndicated Publications: Parade (S), Dash
Proprietary Publications: Lake Norman, SouthPark, Carolina Brides
Digital Platform - Mobile: Apple, Android, Windows, Blackberry
Digital Platform - Tablet: Apple iOS, Android, Windows 7, Blackberry Tablet OS, Kindle, Nook, Kindle Fire
Pres./Pub..................................... Ann Caulkins
Dir. of National Adv..................... Donna Gordon
Editor/VP, News ....Rick Thames
VP, Adv....Kelly Mirt
Rick Thames
Managing Ed. .... Sherry Chisenhall
VP of Finance .... Jennifer Matts-Sprague
Market Information: ADS; Split run; TMC; Zoned editions.
Mechanical Available: Offset printing, Black and 3 ROP colors; page cutoffs is 22 3/4.
Mechanical Specifications: Type page 10 x 21 9/16; 6 columns, 1 1/2, 1/8 to 3/16 between.
Areas Served: North and South Carolina's
Delivery Method: Mail, Newsstand, Carrier, RacksEquipment & Software: PRESSROOM EQUIPMENT: 1 press line with 2 folders. 9 unit TKS/ OFFSET press, the 1 press line consists of 3 mono units 1982 these units are black only. 2, 2001 color towers, full color on ever page. And 4 2011 color towers full color on every page. 72 page capacity straight 48 pages of full color. 144 pages collect 96 pages of full color. Reels & Stands TKS as well. MAILROOM EQUIPMENT: Counter Stackers - 3 Quipp 301 stackers, 2 Quipp 400 stackers. 3 Quipp viper bottom wrap machines and 1 power strapp bottom wrap machine. 7 oval strap strapmasters single strap. 2 Dynaric single strappers and 1 Mosca single strap. 2 CCL labelers. Heidelberg Gripper, 3 ties lines, 4 boom loaders and a Harland Simon Totalizer. BUSINESS EQUIPMENT: Dell OptiPlex GX270 - Windows XP Operating System
Dell Optiplex GX280 - Windows XP Operating System
Dell Optiplex GX620 - Windows 7 Operating System
Dell Optiplex GX620 - Windows XP Operating System
Dell Optiplex GX740 - Windows XP Operating System
Dell Optiplex 745 - Windows 7 Operating System
Dell OptiPlex 755 - Windows XP Operating System
Dell Optiplex 780 - Windows 7 Operating System
Dell Optiplex 790 - Windows 7 Operating System
Dell Optiplex 9020 - Windows 7 Operating System
HP Compaq 8000 Elite – Windows 7 Operating System
HP Compaq 8200 Elite – Windows 7 Operating System
HP Compaq 8300 Elite – Windows 7 Operating System
BUSINESS SOFTWARE: Microsoft Office Professional 2003
Microsoft Office Standard 2008
Microsoft Office Standard 2011
Microsoft Office Standard 2013
Microsoft Office Professional 2013
CLASSIFIED EQUIPMENT: Hardware — SII/ Server Net; SII/ICP Pagination; Printers — Okidata, HP/Laser; CLASSIFIED SOFTWARE: SII/Server Net.,
Microsoft Office Professional 2003
Microsoft Office Standard 2008
Microsoft Office Standard 2011
Microsoft Office Standard 2013
Microsoft Office Professional 2013
DISPLAY EQUIPMENT: Hardware — APP/ Mac 266, HP/LNZ, Sun/Enterprise 3500, APP/Mac G3; Printers — 3-III/3850, Plain Paper Clipper/11 x 17 1200 dpi, HP/1050; DISPLAY SOFTWAREAd Make-up Applications — Multi-Ad/Creator, AII/Ad Assistant, QPS/QuarkXPress 5.0, Adobe/ Photoshop 5.0, Adobe/Illustrator 9.0; EDITORIAL EQUIPMENT: Hardware — IBM/S-70; Printers — Okidata, HP/Laser EDITORIAL SOFTWARE: CCI., Microsoft Office Professional 2003
Microsoft Office Standard 2008
Microsoft Office Standard 2011
Microsoft Office Standard 2013
Microsoft Office Professional 2013
PRODUCTION EQUIPMENT: Hardware — Mac OS & OS X, Cannon 755 HP2025; Cameras — GoPro4; Cannon Power Shot; Scanners — Kk/RFS 3570 Scanner, Umax/ PowerLook flatbed scanner, 8-LaCie/Silver Scan, 3-Topaz, Eskofot/1 PRODUCTION SOFTWARE: Adobe Creative Suite, Microsoft Pro, Acrobat Pro IT EQUIPMENT: Dell OptiPlex GX270 - Windows XP Operating System
Dell Optiplex GX280 - Windows XP Operating System
Dell Optiplex GX620 - Windows 7 Operating System
Dell Optiplex GX620 - Windows XP Operating System
Dell Optiplex GX740 - Windows XP Operating System
Dell Optiplex 745 - Windows 7 Operating System
Dell OptiPlex 755 - Windows XP Operating System
Dell Optiplex 780 - Windows 7 Operating System
Dell Optiplex 790 - Windows 7 Operating System
Dell Optiplex 9020 - Windows 7 Operating System
HP Compaq 8000 Elite – Windows 7 Operating System
HP Compaq 8200 Elite – Windows 7 Operating System
HP Compaq 8300 Elite – Windows 7 Operating System
IT SOFTWARE:Microsoft Office Professional 2003
Microsoft Office Standard 2008
Microsoft Office Standard 2011
Microsoft Office Standard 2013
Microsoft Office Professional 2013
CIRCULATION EQUIPMENT: PC Desktops:
Dell OptiPlex GX270 - Windows XP Operating System
Dell Optiplex GX280 - Windows XP Operating System
Dell Optiplex GX620 - Windows 7 Operating System
Dell Optiplex GX620 - Windows XP Operating System
Dell Optiplex GX740 - Windows XP Operating System
Dell Optiplex 745 - Windows 7 Operating System
Dell OptiPlex 755 - Windows XP Operating System
Dell Optiplex 780 - Windows 7 Operating System
Dell Optiplex 790 - Windows 7 Operating System
Dell Optiplex 9020 - Windows 7 Operating System
HP Compaq 8000 Elite – Windows 7 Operating System
HP Compaq 8200 Elite – Windows 7 Operating System
HP Compaq 8300 Elite – Windows 7 Operating System
PC Laptops:
HP EliteBook Folio 9470M – Windows 7 Operating System
HP ProBook 6570B - Windows 7 Operating System
Dell Latitude E5520 - Windows 7 Operating

System
Dell Latitude E6410 - Windows 7 Operating System
Dell Latitude E7440 - Windows 7 Operating System
Toshiba Portege R930 - Windows 7 Operating System
Xerox :
2100
5325
5638
Versant 80
D95
DC432AS
DC440AS
DC480ST
DT6100
DCOL6060
CIRCULATION SOFTWARNCS; Microsoft Office Professional 2003
Microsoft Office Standard 2008
Microsoft Office Standard 2011
Microsoft Office Standard 2013
Microsoft Office Professional 2013
Note: Southern Shows (4 yearly), Charlotte Observer Spelling Bee

CLINTON

THE SAMPSON INDEPENDENT

109 W Main St, Clinton, N.C., 28328-4046, Sampson; gen tel (910) 592-8137; adv tel (910) 592-8137; ed tel (910) 592-8137; gen fax (910) 592-8756; adv fax (910) 592-1419; ed fax (910) 592-8756; gen/nat adv e-mail smatthews@heartlandpublications.com; disp adv e-mail gpate@heartlandpublications.com; class adv e-mailgpate@heartlandpublications.com; ed e-mail smatthews@heartlandpublications.com; web site www.clintonnc.com
Group: Champion Media
Published: Tues, Wed, Thur, Fri, Sat, Sun
Weekday Frequency: e
Saturday Frequency: m
Circulation: 7,962; 7,962(sat); 8,100(sun)
Last Audit: Sworn/Estimate/Non-Audited September 30, 2017
Advertising Rate (weekday/saturday): Open inch rate $15.75
News services: AP. **Established:** 1924
Special Editions: Spring Fashion (Apr); Back-to-School (Aug); Xmas Gift Guide (Dec); Insight (Feb); Tobacco (Jul); Bridal (May); Cookbook (Nov); Fall Car Care (Oct); Fall Fashion (Sept).
Syndicated Publications: Parade (S).
Publisher/Editor .... Sherry Matthews
Adv. Dir., Classified .... Brenda McCullen
Adv. Dir., Retail .... Aothey Sampson
Circ. Dir. .... Alissa Bradford
Asst. Ed. .... Doug Clark
Media Dir. .... Shannon Best
Market Information: TMC.
Mechanical Available: Offset; Black and 4 ROP colors; insert accepted - products, bags; page cutoffs - 22 3/4.
Areas Served: Sampson County (NC)
Equipment & Software: PRESSROOM EQUIPMENT: Lines — 4-G/Community (1 folder), 8-G; MAILROOM EQUIPMENT: Tying Machines — 1/Malow, 2-/Malow.; BUSINESS SOFTWARE: Baseview, Baseview, Navision CLASSIFIED EQUIPMENT: Hardware — APP/Mac; Printers — APP/Mac; CLASSIFIED SOFTWARE: Baseview. DISPLAY EQUIPMENT: Hardware — APP/Mac; Printers — APP/Mac; DISPLAY SOFTWAREAd Make-up Applications — Multi-Ad, QPS/QuarkXPress; Layout Software — Multi-Ad, QPS/QuarkXPress. EDITORIAL EQUIPMENT: Hardware — 1-Mk/1100, 12-Mk/4100, APP/Mac; Printers — APP/Mac EDITORIAL SOFTWARE: Baseview. PRODUCTION EQUIPMENT: Hardware — Pre Press/Panther Pro, 1-COM/7200, 2-COM/Videosetter; Cameras — 1-CL/J-76CC; Scanners — 5-Astra, Umax, Nikon/Scanner PRODUCTION SOFTWARE: Pre Press/Panther Pro, QPS/QuarkXPress.

DUNN

THE DAILY RECORD

99 W Broad St, Dunn, N.C., 28334-6031, Harnett; gen tel (910) 891-1234; gen/nat adv e-mail traffic.io@mydailyrecord.com; disp adv e-mail retailads@mydailyrecord.com; class adv e-mailclassifieds@mydailyrecord.com; ed e-mail news@mydailyrecord.com; web site www.mydailyrecord.com
- 400,000(views) 18,000(visitors)
Group: Record Publishing
Published: Mon, Tues, Wed, Thur, Fri
Weekday Frequency: m
Circulation: 9,056
Last Audit: CAC October 17, 2016
Advertising Rate (weekday/saturday): Open inch rate $9.99
Online Advertising Rate: call for more info
News services: 1950
Own Printing Facility?: Yes
Commercial Printers?: Yes
Special Editions: Bridal Edition(Apr); Advertiser Appreciation (Aug); Christmas Greetings (Dec); Community Yearbook (Feb); January Clearance (Jan); Best of Harnett County (Jul); Business Card Directory (May); Secret Santa (Nov-Dec); Physicians Directory (Oct); Crepe Myrtle (Sept).
Special Weekly Sections: Weekend (Fri); Best Food Day (Wed).
Digital Platform - Mobile: Android, Windows, Other
Ed./Pub. .... Bart Adams
VP/Sec./Treas. .... Mellicent Adams
Online Ed. .... Lisa Farmer
Prodn. Mgr., Post Press .... Wendy Gregory
Mechanical Available: Offset; Black and 264 ROP colors; insert accepted - any; page cutoffs - 22 3/4.
Mechanical Specifications: Type page 11.625" x 21"; E - 6 cols, 1 5/6, 1/8 between; A - 6 cols, 1 5/6, 1/8 between; C - 6 cols, 1 5/6, 1/8 between.
Areas Served: 28334, 28339, 28342, 27524, 27526, 28344, 27543, 27546, 28356, 27552, 28366, 28368, 28382, 28390, 28395
Delivery Method: Mail, RacksEquipment & Software: PRESSROOM EQUIPMENT: Lines — 6-G/Community single width 1983, 1-stacked G/community 1999; Folders — 1-G/SE.; MAILROOM EQUIPMENT: Counter Stackers — BG/Count-O-Veyor; Inserters & Stuffers — KAN/480; Tying Machines — 2/Bu; Address Machine — X.; BUSINESS EQUIPMENT: Vision Data BUSINESS SOFTWARE: Windows CLASSIFIED EQUIPMENT: Hardware — Unix/Server; Printers — APP/HP 2300 N; CLASSIFIED SOFTWARE: News Memory,Vision Data, QuarkXPress 4.04. DISPLAY EQUIPMENT: Hardware — Unix/Server; Printers — APP/Mac LaserWriter NTX; DISPLAY SOFTWAREAd Make-up Applications — Vision Data; Layout Software — APP/Mac, Multi-Ad/Creator, Adobe/Photoshop, QPS/QuarkXPress, Adobe/Illustrator. EDITORIAL EQUIPMENT: Hardware — APP/Mac; Printers — HP/LaserJet 5M EDITORIAL SOFTWARE: Baseview/NewsEdit, QPS/QuarkXPress. PRODUCTION EQUIPMENT: Hardware — Caere/OmniPage Pro 8.0, ECR/EV Jetsetter 2100, APP/Mac G3; Cameras — C/Spartan III; Scanners — Polaroid/Sprint Scan 4000, Polaroid/Sprint Scan 35, Umax/PowerLook III, HP/Scan Jet III PRODUCTION SOFTWARE: QPS/QuarkXPress with Vision Data Interface.

DURHAM

THE HERALD-SUN

1530 N Gregson St, Ste 2A, Durham, N.C., 27701-1164, Durham; gen tel (919) 419-6500; adv tel (919) 419-6700; ed tel (919) 419-6684; gen fax (919) 419-6888; adv fax (919) 419-6878; disp adv e-mail drogers@newsobserver.com; class adv e-mailclassifieds@heraldsun.com; ed e-mail news@heraldsun.com; web site www.heraldsun.com
- 860,690(views) 337,685(visitors)
Group: The McClatchy Company
Published: Mon, Tues, Wed, Thur, Fri, Sat, Sun
Weekday Frequency: m
Saturday Frequency: m
Circulation: 9,385; 8,116(sat); 9,928(sun)
Last Audit: Sworn/Estimate/Non-Audited January 30, 2018
News services: AP **Established:** 1889
Own Printing Facility?: No
Commercial Printers?: No
Special Editions: Reader's Choice, Senior Times, ACC Basketball Preview,ACC Basketball tournament review, ACC Football Preview, Everything Durham, Everything Orange
Syndicated Publications: WE ARE DURHAM Magazine (Other); USA WEEKEND Magazine (S).
Digital Platform - Mobile: Apple, Android, Windows
Digital Platform - Tablet: Apple iOS, Android, Windows 7
Circ. Dir. .... Brent Agurs
Mng. Ed. .... Mark Schultz
Gen Mgr./ Adv. Dir. .... Doug Robers
Metro Ed. .... Mark Donovan
Market Information: TMC; Zoned editions.
Delivery Method: Mail, Newsstand, Carrier, Racks

ELIZABETH CITY

THE DAILY ADVANCE

215 S Water St, Elizabeth City, N.C., 27909-4844, Pasquotank; gen tel (252) 335-8076; adv tel (252) 335-8082; ed tel (252) 335-8110; gen fax (252) 335-4415; gen/nat adv e-mail sobrien@dailyadvance.com; disp adv e-mail sobrien@dailyadvance.com; class adv e-mailsharris@dailyadvance.com; ed e-mail elizabethcity@dailyadvance.com; web site www.dailyadvance.com
Group: Cooke Communications North Carolina, LLC
Cox Media Group
Published: Mon, Tues, Wed, Thur, Fri, Sat, Sun
Weekday Frequency: m
Saturday Frequency: m
Circulation: 7,840; 7,840(sat); 8,182(sun)
Last Audit: AAM September 30, 2014
Advertising Rate (weekday/saturday): Open inch rate $16.50 (Oct. 2011).65
News services: AP. **Established:** 1911
Own Printing Facility?: Yes
Commercial Printers?: Yes
Special Editions: Medical Directory (Jan.), Albemarle Magazine (quarterly), Coast Guard Anniversary Tab (July), Senior Living (April.), Holiday Recipe/Songbook (Dec.)
Special Weekly Sections: Albemarle Life (Wed.-Sun.), Shelter pets (Mon.), School Page (Tues); Business Page (Sun.).
Syndicated Publications: Parade (S).
Digital Platform - Mobile: Apple, Android
Digital Platform - Tablet: Apple iOS, Android
Circ. Mgr. .... Chuck Edwards
Albemarle Life Ed. .... Robert Kelly-Goss
Editor/Editorial Page Editor .... Mike Goodman
News Ed. .... Julian Eure
Asst. News Ed. .... Chris Day
Creative Services Manager .... Brian Gray
Customer Service/Classified Mgr. ....Susan Harris
Financial/Accounting Manager..Maureen Brinson
IS Manager .... Lynne Watkins
Director of Advertising Sales and Marketing . Sean O'Brien
Market Information: TMC; Zoned editions.
Mechanical Available: Offset; Black and 3 ROP colors; insert accepted; page cutoffs - 22"
Mechanical Specifications: Type page 13 1/4 x 21 1/2; E - 6 cols, 2 1/16, 1/8 between; A - 6 cols, 2 1/16, 1/8 between; C - 9 cols, 1 5/16, 1/8 between.
Delivery Method: Mail, Newsstand, Carrier, RacksEquipment & Software: PRESSROOM EQUIPMENT: Lines — 1-G/Urbanite; 4-G/Urbanite; Folders — 1-G/2:1, 1-G/Half, 1-G/Quarter; Registration System — Duarte/Pin Registration. MAILROOM EQUIPMENT: Counter Stackers — 1/BG; Inserters & Stuffers — 1-/MM; Tying Machines — 2-/Bu; Address Machine — Digital Label, KAN/Label; BUSINESS EQUIPMENT: HP BUSINESS SOFTWARE: WordPerfect 6.0, Lotus 1-2-3 5.0, Microsoft/Windows 95, Microsoft/Office 97, Microsoft/Excel CLASSIFIED EQUIPMENT: Hardware — 3-APP/Mac Quadra 605; Printers — 2-ECR/VRL 36; CLASSIFIED SOFTWARE: SII. DISPLAY EQUIPMENT: Hardware — APP/Mac Quadra 650 fileserver; Printers — 2-ECR/VRL 36; Other Hardware — Microtek/Scanmaker, AG/Arcus Scanner, AG/Scanner DISPLAY SOFTWAREAd Make-up Applications — Multi-Ad/Creator 3.70; Layout Software — 3-APP/Power Mac 7300, 1-APP/Power Mac 7600. EDITORIAL EQUIPMENT: Hardware — APP/Mac/1-APP/Power Mac 8600 Image Desk, Lf/AP Leaf Picture Desk; Printers — 2-ECR/VRL 36 EDITORIAL SOFTWARE: DTI. PRODUCTION EQUIPMENT: Hardware — Caere/OmniPage Pro 5.0, Mk, Jobo/Processor; Cameras — 1-R/500; Scanners — AG/Plus PRODUCTION SOFTWARE: QPS/QuarkXPress 3.3.

FAYETTEVILLE

THE FAYETTEVILLE OBSERVER

458 Whitfield St, Fayetteville, N.C., 28306-1614, Cumberland; gen tel (910) 323-4848; adv tel (910) 486-2786; ed tel (910) 486-3500; gen fax (910) 486-3545; adv fax (910) 486-3531; ed fax (910) 486-3545; gen/nat adv e-mail advertise@fayobserver.com; disp adv e-mail advertise@fayobserver.com; class adv e-mailpeikerb@fayobserver.com; ed e-mail eletters@fayobserver.com; web site www.fayobserver.com
- 5,861,074(views) 515,671(visitors)
Group: GateHouse Media, Inc.
Published: Mon, Tues, Wed, Thur, Fri, Sat, Sun
Weekday Frequency: m
Saturday Frequency: m
Circulation: 29,953; 31,823(sat); 38,846(sun)
Last Audit: AAM December 31, 2016
Advertising Rate (weekday/saturday): Open inch rate (Mon-Fri) $59.85 / (Sat) $70.75
Advertising Rate (sunday): Open inch rate (Sun) $70.75
Online Advertising Rate: Bottom Leaderboard $10; Dogear (Top) $12; Top Leaderboard $14
News services: AP, LAT-WP. **Established:** 1816
Special Editions: Wildcats (Apr); Discover Fayetteville (Aug); Holiday Gift Guide (Dec); Honor Roll (Feb); Cumberland Parent (Jan); Back-to-School (Jul); Storm Watch (Jun); Military Appreciation (May); Cumberland Parent (Nov); Motor Sports (Oct); Reader's Choice (Sept).
Special Weekly Sections: Faith (Fri); Health (Mon); Business (S); Real Estate Marketplace (Sat); Business (Thur); Business (Tues); Business (Wed).
Syndicated Publications: Relish (Monthly); Parade (S); TV Week (Sat).
Publisher .... Robert Gruber
Exec. Ed. .... Mike Adams
Exec. Ed. .... Matt Leclercq
Adv. Dir. .... Lynnie Guzman
Credit Mgr. .... Jill Koonce
Editorial Page Ed. .... Timothy White
Columnist .... Rodger Mullen
Circ. Dir. .... Alissa Melvin
Market Information: Split run; TMC; Zoned editions.
Mechanical Available: Offset; Black and 3 ROP colors; insert accepted - all; page cutoffs - 22.
Mechanical Specifications: Type page 12 1/2 x 21; E - 6 cols, 1 17/20, 1/8 between; A - 6 cols, 1 17/20, 1/8 between; C - 10 cols, 1 3/16, 1/16 between.Equipment & Software: PRESSROOM EQUIPMENT: Lines — 10-KB/Colora double width 1999; Pasters —7-1999, 2-1999. MAILROOM EQUIPMENT: Counter Stackers — 5-QWI/400W, 1-QWI/350, 1-Gammerler/Pathfinder 7.0; Inserters & Stuffers — HI/1372, HI/630; Tying Machines — 2-Dynaric/NP2, 3-Dynaric/1500; Wrapping Singles — 3-Id/Bottom Wrapper, 2-QWI/Cobra 3/4 Wrap w/inkjet, 2-QWI/Viper; BUSINESS EQUIPMENT: IBM/AS-400 F35 BUSINESS SOFTWARE: PBS, Microsoft/Excel, AdMarc CLASSIFIED EQUIPMENT: Hardware — 2-Dell/6300; 30-Dell/PC; Printers — HP/5000 GN; CLASSIFIED SOFTWARE: Mactive/Adbooker 2.8.18. DISPLAY EQUIPMENT: Hardware — APP/Mac, IBM/AS-400; Printers — HP/LaserPrinter; Other Hardware — Dell/PC DISPLAY SOFTWAREAd Make-up Applications — Multi-Ad/Creator, SCS

Track, Admarc; Layout Software — SCS/Layout 8000. EDITORIAL EQUIPMENT: Hardware — DEC, Intel, 2-Dell/4300/APP/Mac G4, HP/ScanJet IIcx, Kk/RFS 2035 Scanner, Nikon/Coolscan, 102-Dell/PC; Printers — 12-HP/5000GN EDITORIAL SOFTWARE: Tera, 3-Good News. PRODUCTION EQUIPMENT: Hardware — WL/7AW-DW-OPB, 3-AU/Soft Pips (Window NT), 1-Au/3850 Doublewide; Scanners — 1-PixelCraft, 1-Nikon, Data/Oy-Plate Scanner PRODUCTION SOFTWARE: Good News III.

FOREST CITY

THE DAILY COURIER
601 Oak St, Forest City, N.C., 28043-3471, Rutherford; gen tel (828) 245-6431; adv tel (828) 202-2908; ed tel (828) 202-2926; gen fax (828) 248-2790; adv fax (828) 248-2790; ed fax (828) 248-2790; gen/nat adv e-mail lspurling@thedigitalcourier.com; disp adv e-mail pdavis@thedigitalcourier.com; class adv e-mailemeyer@thedigitalcourier.com; ed e-mail mclark@thedigitalcourier.com; web site www.thedigitalcourier.com
Group: Paxton Media Group, LLC
Published: Tues, Wed, Thur, Fri, Sat, Sun
Weekday Frequency: m
Saturday Frequency: m
Circulation: 7,200; 7,200(sat); 7,200(sun)
Last Audit: Sworn/Estimate/Non-Audited September 30, 2017
Advertising Rate (weekday/saturday): Open inch rate $11.72
News services: AP. **Established:** 1969
Own Printing Facility?: Yes
Commercial Printers?: No
Special Editions: Home Improvement (Apr); Christmas Gift Guide (Dec); Income Tax (Jan); Back-to-School (Aug); Fall Sports (Aug); Health-Fitness (Jun); Everything Rutherford (Apr); Graduation (May); Outdoors (Sept).
Special Weekly Sections: Television (S).
Syndicated Publications: USA WEEKEND Magazine (S); Spry (S); American Profile (S)
Pub....Lori Spurling
Ed....Jean Gordon
Adv. Mgr...Erica Meyer
Circ. Dir....Pam Dixon
Photographer...................................Garrett Byer
Market Information: TMC.
Areas Served: 28018, 28020, 28040, 28043, 28114, 28139, 28160, 28167, 28746, 28752, 28756, 28761
Delivery Method: Mail, Newsstand, Carrier, Racks

GASTONIA

THE GASTON GAZETTE
1893 Remount Rd, Gastonia, N.C., 28054-7413, Gaston; gen tel (704) 869-1700; adv tel (704) 869-1735; ed tel (704) 869-1812; gen fax (704) 867-6988; adv fax (704) 867-6988; ed fax (704) 867-5751; gen/nat adv e-mail scherry@gastongazette.com; disp adv e-mail nsaunders@gastongazette.com; ed e-mail gastongazette@gastongazette.com; web site www.gastongazette.com
- 3,000,000(views) 600,000(visitors)
Group: New Media Investment Group
Published: Mon, Tues, Wed, Thur, Fri, Sat, Sun
Weekday Frequency: m
Saturday Frequency: m
Circulation: 19,757; 16,846(sat); 19,923(sun)
Last Audit: AAM December 31, 2015
Advertising Rate (weekday/saturday): Open inch rate $21.70
Advertising Rate (sunday): Open inch rate $23.60
Online Advertising Rate: 15
News services: AP, SHNS, NYT, NEA. **Established:** 1880
Own Printing Facility?: Yes
Commercial Printers?: Yes
Special Editions: Stress (Apr); Senior Living (Aug); Church Directory (Dec); Senior Living (Feb); Bridal Tab (Jan); Christmas in July (Jul); Legal Guide (Jun); Home & Garden (Mar); Senior Living (May); Senior Living (Nov); New Car Show (Oct); Travel (Sept).
Special Weekly Sections: Business Spotlight (Tues).
Syndicated Publications: Home Magazine (Fri); Gaston Seasons (Quarterly); USA WEEKEND Magazine (S); Lake Novman Gazette (Weekly).
Digital Platform - Mobile: Apple, Android, Windows, Blackberry, Other
Digital Platform - Tablet: Apple iOS, Android, Windows 7, Blackberry Tablet OS
Pub...Lucy Talley
Adv. Dir...............................Konrad LaPrade
Health/Medical Ed..................Will MacDonald
Gen. Mgr./Finance Dir..................Keith Raffone
Ad manager.....................Natasha Alexander
Classified manager...............Nancy Hogshead
Major accounts...................Stephany Cherry
Managing Editor.............................Kevin Ellis
Market Information: ADS; TMC.
Mechanical Available: Offset; Black and 3 ROP colors; insert accepted - product samples (prior approval required); page cutoffs - 22.
Mechanical Specifications: Type page 11 5/8 x 21 1/2; E - 6 cols, 1 5/6, 1/8 between; A - 6 cols, 1 5/6, 1/8 between; C - 9 cols, 1 3/16, 1/16 between.
Delivery Method: Mail, Newsstand, Carrier, RacksEquipment & Software: PRESSROOM EQUIPMENT: Lines — 42-G/Magnum single width units 2001; Folders — 1-G/Universal w/ 4 formers, 1-G/Universal w/ 2 formers; Reels & Stands — 18; Control System — G/GMI.; MAILROOM EQUIPMENT: Counter Stackers — 2-QWI/401; Inserters & Stuffers — GMA/SLS 2000 12:2; Tying Machines — 2/Samuels, 2-/Dynaric; Wrapping Singles — 1-/NJP; Address Machine — 1-X/542-090.; BUSINESS EQUIPMENT: MS/NT Network BUSINESS SOFTWARE: Vision Data, Great Plains, APT, Brainworks, Ceridian CLASSIFIED EQUIPMENT: Hardware — Compaq/Servers 300 mhz; Printers — Autologic; CLASSIFIED SOFTWARE: APT. DISPLAY EQUIPMENT: Hardware — PC; Printers — Autologic; DISPLAY SOFTWAREAd Make-up Applications — APT; EDITORIAL EQUIPMENT: Hardware — APT/Paginaters (700 mhz), APT/Reporter (500 mhz); Printers — HP/Plotter, Pre Press/Panther 36, Autologic EDITORIAL SOFTWARE: APT. PRODUCTION EQUIPMENT: Hardware — Scanview Drum Scanner, Nikon/Super Coolscan, Zip Disk Readers PRODUCTION SOFTWARE: APT.

GOLDSBORO

GOLDSBORO NEWS-ARGUS
310 N Berkeley Blvd, Goldsboro, N.C., 27534-4326, Wayne; gen tel (919) 778-2211; adv tel (919) 778-2000; ed tel (919) 739-7791; gen fax (919) 778-9891; adv fax (919) 778-9891; ed fax (919) 778-5408; gen/nat adv e-mail retailads@newsargus.com; disp adv e-mail displayads@newsargus.com; class adv e-mailclassads@newsargus.com; ed e-mail news@newsargus.com; web site www.newsargus.com
- 906,600(views) 70,100(visitors)
Group: Buchheit News Management, Inc.
Published: Mon, Tues, Wed, Thur, Fri, Sun
Weekday Frequency: e
Circulation: 11,888; 14,054(sun)
Last Audit: AAM December 31, 2016
Advertising Rate (weekday/saturday): Open inch rate $23.75
Advertising Rate (sunday): Open inch rate $25.75
Online Advertising Rate: Leaderboard $7.50 (CPM); Medium Rectangle $7.50 (CPM); Skyscraper $7.50 (CPM)
News services: AP. **Established:** 1885
Own Printing Facility?: Yes
Commercial Printers?: Yes
Special Editions: Wedding Guide (Jan); Progress (Feb); Batter Up & Home & Garden (Mar); Pickle Festival (Apr); Destination Summer (May); Business Card Directory & Healthy Living (Jun); Back to School and Football (Aug); Readers Choice (Sept); Health Care Directory (Oct); Holiday Planner (Nov); Last Minute Gift Guide & Spirit of the Season (Dec).
Special Weekly Sections: Food (Wed); Farm (Wed); Health (Thur); Church (Fri); Travel (Sun); Military (Sun); Features (Sun); Real Estate (Sun); Auto Review (Sun); Business (Daily); Entertainment (Daily).
Syndicated Publications: Parade (S).
Publisher...................................Hal H. Tanner
Mgr., HR..........................Debbie M. Pennell
Adv. Mgr., Nat'l.....................Georgia Gurley
Mng. Ed......................................Dennis Hill
Amusements Ed./Books Ed..............Matt Whittle
Editor...Renee Carey
Educ./Health Ed.......................Phyllis Moore
Online Ed....................................Keith Taylor
Society/Women's Ed................Becky Barclay
Sports Ed................................Rudy Coggins
Mgmt. Info Servs. Mgr..............David Rouse
Reporter..............................Rochelle Moore
Mechanical Available: Offset; Black and 3 ROP colors; insert accepted; page cutoffs - 22 3/4.
Mechanical Specifications: Type page 10 5/8 x 21 1/2; E - 6 cols, 1 4/5, 1/8 between; A - 6 cols, 1 4/5, 1/8 between; C - 8 cols, 1 1/5, 11/100 between.
Areas Served: Wayne, Johnston, Lenoir, Greene, Duplin & Sampson counties
Delivery Method: Mail, Newsstand, Carrier, RacksEquipment & Software: PRESSROOM EQUIPMENT: Lines — 9-G/Urbanite (color deck) single width 1970; Reels & Stands — 5; MAILROOM EQUIPMENT: Counter Stackers — Quipp 500 (3); Gammerler KL-5000; Inserters & Stuffers — 1 MM SLS2000 12:1; Tying Machines — 2 - Dynaric NP3000 - Quipp Viper bottomwrap; Wrapping Singles — Mailroom Control System 1-MM/1509 Minuteman Saddle Stitcher; Address Machine — 1-Cheshire/569; 1-Barstrom Labeler (inline); BUSINESS EQUIPMENT: Dell PowerEdge R410, Sun Sunfire v240 BUSINESS SOFTWARE: DTI, BSI, Microsoft/Office CLASSIFIED EQUIPMENT: Hardware — 7-APP/iMac; Printers — HP 4250; CLASSIFIED SOFTWARE: MediaSpan AMP4 DISPLAY EQUIPMENT: Hardware — 7-Apple eMacs, 1-Apple iMac; Printers — HP 8150; DISPLAY SOFTWAREAd Make-up Applications — MediaSpan AMP4, Quark Express 6, ; EDITORIAL EQUIPMENT: Hardware — 8-Apple iMacs, 7-Apple G5, 1-Apple MacPro; Printers — HP Laserjet 5200, HP Laserjet 2200 EDITORIAL SOFTWARE: MediaSpan 3.54 PRODUCTION EQUIPMENT: Hardware — 1-Nu, 7-APP/Mac, 1-PC, ECRM/Bluefin 62, 1-Xerox Phaser 7400, ECR/Scriptsetter VRL 36HS, Xante 3G laser printer; Scanners — 6-Umax PRODUCTION SOFTWARE: Baseview 3.5.4.

GREENSBORO

NEWS & RECORD
200 E Market St, Greensboro, N.C., 27401-2910, Guilford; gen tel (336) 373-7000; adv tel (336) 373-7360; ed tel (336) 373-7010; gen fax (336) 373-7183; adv fax (336) 412-5911; ed fax (336) 412-5920; gen/nat adv e-mail damon.crone@News-Record.com; disp adv e-mail kduckworth@News-Record.com; class adv e-mailsheryl.southern@News-Record.com; ed e-mail edpage@news-record.com; web site www.news-record.com
- 4,100,000(views) 403,710(visitors)
Group: BH Media Group
Published: Mon, Tues, Wed, Thur, Fri, Sat, Sun
Weekday Frequency: m
Saturday Frequency: m
Circulation: 39,941; 39,637(sat); 55,878(sun)
Last Audit: AAM December 31, 2016
Advertising Rate (weekday/saturday): Open inch rate $89.73 (M-Tue); $102.56 (W-F)
Advertising Rate (sunday): Open inch rate $128.20
Online Advertising Rate: (RON) Leaderboard: $12/Big box $13.20/ Magazine $15.60; (ROC) Leaderboard $16.65/Big box $18.32/ Magazine $21.65
News services: 1890
Own Printing Facility?: Yes
Commercial Printers?: Yes
Special Editions: Discover the Triad (Aug); NASCAR Preview (Feb); ACC Men's Basketball Tournament (Mar); Holiday Countdown-Wrapping-Up (Nov); Sports Extra-Greater Greensboro Chrysler Classic (Oct); Southern Ideal Home Show (Sept).
Special Weekly Sections: Careers (S); Food (Wed).
Digital Platform - Mobile: Android, Other
Executive Editor and Publisher..........Jeff Gauger
Editorial Page Ed......................Allen Johnson
Columnist.....................................Susan Ladd
Librarian......................................Diane Lamb
Local content editor...................Teresa Prout
Assistant Sports Editor.................Joe Sirera
Teresa Ridge
Managing Ed...............................Steve Doyle
Production manager................Dennis Creamer
Human Resources Generalist Sheby Luck Newton
Advertising Department Manager..............Keeley Duckworth
National Adv. Dir......................Bill Buschmann
Bus. Ed........................................John Nagy
Prodn. Dir.............................Dawn Swanson
New media director.....................Chris Brewer
Tommy McLeod
Areas Served: Guilford, Rockingham & Randolph counties (NC)
Delivery Method: Newsstand, Carrier, RacksEquipment & Software: PRESSROOM EQUIPMENT: Lines — 13-G/Metro double width 1974;

GREENVILLE

THE DAILY REFLECTOR
1150 Sugg Pkwy, Greenville, N.C., 27834-9077, Pitt; gen tel (252) 329-9500; adv tel (252) 329-9503; ed tel (252) 329-9560; gen fax (252) 752-9583; adv fax (252) 752-9583; ed fax (252) 754-8140; gen/nat adv e-mail dsingleton@reflector.com; disp adv e-mail dsingleton@reflector.com; ed e-mail baburns@reflector.com; web site www.reflector.com
- 5,000,000(views) 200,000(visitors)
Group: Cooke Communications North Carolina, LLC
Published: Mon, Tues, Wed, Thur, Fri, Sat, Sun
Weekday Frequency: m
Saturday Frequency: m
Circulation: 14,839; 14,939(sat); 16,160(sun)
Last Audit: AAM December 12, 2017
Advertising Rate (weekday/saturday): Open inch rate $22.00
Advertising Rate (sunday): Open inch rate $24.00
Online Advertising Rate: Home page: Big box $15.00/Leaderboard $15.00; Channel front/ Story level: Big box $12.00/ Leaderboard $12.00
News services: AP, NYT, LAT-WP. **Established:** 1882
Own Printing Facility?: Yes
Commercial Printers?: Yes
Special Editions: Parade of Homes (Apr); Back to School (Aug); College Football Bowl Preview (Dec); Home Expo (Feb); Bridal Planner (Jan); Design an Ad (Mar); Graduation (May); Holiday Show (Nov); Medical Directory (Oct); Community Business (Sept); Greenville Magazine
Special Weekly Sections: Workweek (Mon); Best Food Day (Wed); Real Estate, Church (Sat); Travel (Sun); Business, AP Stock, Lifestyles (Daily)
Syndicated Publications: Pirate Gameday (during football season) (Sat); Her Magazine (monthly), Mixer Magazine (monthly).
Digital Platform - Mobile: Apple, Android
Digital Platform - Tablet: Apple iOS, Android, Kindle
Pub....John Cooke
Chief Operating Officer.......................J. Tim Holt
CFO....................................Mariann McQueen
Circ. Dir..................................David Adams
HR Dir....................................Donna Allen
Display Adv. Dir........................Betty Williams
Dir., Mktg./Bus. Devel./Customer Care...Elizabeth Semple
Asst. Mng. Ed..........................Cherie Speller
Bus. Ed...................................Mike Grizzard
Features Ed................................Steve Cagle
Exec. Ed....................................Bobby Burns
Photo Ed...................................Rhett Butler
Sports Ed...................................Jim Gentry
Dir., Ops....................................Dan Mastin
Creative Servs. Mgr..................Dawn Newton
Facilities Mgr..............................James Webb
Pre-Press Mgr.............................Regina Lytle
Circulation Dir...........................David Adams
Market Information: TMC.
Mechanical Available: Offset; Black and 3 ROP colors; insert accepted; page cutoffs - 22.

Mechanical Specifications: Type page 11 5/8 x 21; E - 6 cols, 2 1/2, 1/6 between; A - 6 cols, 2 1/2, 1/6 between; C - 9 cols, 1 1/3, 1/8 between.
Areas Served: 28530, 28513, 28590, 27858, 27837, 27834, 27828, 27829, 27834, 27871, 27892, 28580
Delivery Method: Mail, Newsstand, Carrier, RacksEquipment & Software: PRESSROOM EQUIPMENT: ColdSet —
DGM 850 - 16 units/ 8 Jardis Flying Pasters
DGM 1050 Folder 1
DGM 1030 Folder 1
1 Inline Quipp 9910 Stacker
Coldset —
DGM 430 - 18 Units / 9 Jardis 0 Speed Splicers
DGM 1030 FOlder 2
1 Inline Gammerler Stacker
Heatset —
Harris M-110 - 4 Units / 1 Butler Splicer
Goss Folder 1
2 Inline Gammerler Stackers
PRESSROOM SOFTWARE: DTI MAILROOM EQUIPMENT: 2 SLS 1000 - 12/2 machines
4 Quipp 500 Stackers
4 Inline Dynaric Strappers
4 Moveable Dynaric Strappers
1 Inline Quipp 400 on the 850 Press
1 inline Accraply Labeler on 850 Press
1 Inline Accraply Labeler on SLS 1000 BUSINESS EQUIPMENT: HP/9000 BUSINESS SOFTWARE: CJ, Geac/World Class CLASSIFIED EQUIPMENT: Hardware — APP/Macs, Unix/Server; Printers — HP, Xante; CLASSIFIED SOFTWARE: DTI/ ClassSpeed. DISPLAY EQUIPMENT: Hardware — APP/Mac; Printers — 2-APP/ Mac LaserWriter, HP, Xante; DISPLAY SOFTWAREAd Make-up Applications — DTI; Layout Software — DTI/Speed Planner, APP/Macs, Unix/Server. EDITORIAL EQUIPMENT: Hardware — APP/Macs, Unix/ Server; Printers — HP, Xante EDITORIAL SOFTWARE: DTI. PRODUCTION EQUIPMENT: 4 Mac based ECRM Harlequin Rips v. 8.3.0 on Mac Pros w/ Snow Leopard 10.6.8
4 Mac Pros w/ Leopard 10.6.8.
2 Kodak Trendsetter News 100s CTP Devices
2 Glunz & Jensens Plate Processors
K&F Sorta Stacker 8 Bins
2 K&F Vision Benders PRODUCTION SOFTWARE: Adobe CS5, Pro PitStop 9
Arkitek Page Pairing System CIRCULATION SOFTWARCircSmart

HENDERSON

DAILY DISPATCH

304 S Chestnut St, Henderson, N.C., 27536-4225, Vance; gen tel (252) 436-2800; adv tel (252) 436-2812; ed tel (252) 436-2831; gen fax (252) 430-0125; adv fax (252) 430-0125; ed fax (252) 430-0125; gen/nat adv e-mail dtuck@hendersondispatch.com; disp adv e-mail dtuck@hendersondispatch.com; class adv e-maildtuck@hendersondispatch.com; ed e-mail news@hendersondispatch.com; web site www.hendersondispatch.com
Group: Paxton Media Group, LLC
Published: Tues, Wed, Thur, Fri, Sat, Sun
Weekday Frequency: m
Saturday Frequency: m
Circulation: 6,250; 6,000(sat); 6,500(sun)
Last Audit: Sworn/Estimate/Non-Audited September 30, 2017
Advertising Rate (weekday/saturday): Open inch rate $19.02
Advertising Rate (sunday): Open inch rate $19.02
News services: AP. **Established:** 1914
Own Printing Facility?: Yes
Commercial Printers?: Yes
Special Editions: Spring Home & Garden (Apr); Fall Sports (Aug); Christmas Greetings (Dec); Best of Vance County (Feb); Bridal (Jan); Funeral & Estate Planning (Jul); Graduation (Jun); Spring Fashion (Mar); Trade Show (May); Christmas Gift Guide (Nov); Football Contest (Se
Special Weekly Sections: Best Food Day (Wed). Faith (Sat). Showcase (Sun).
Syndicated Publications: USA WEEKEND Magazine (S). Spry. American Profile. Relish. Athlon Sports.
Digital Platform - Mobile: Apple, Android, Windows
Digital Platform - Tablet: Apple iOS, Android, Windows 7, Blackberry Tablet OS, Kindle, Nook, Kindle Fire
Adv. Dir. .... Deborah Tuck
Circulation Manager .... A.J. Woodell
Photographer .... Mark Dolejs
Features Ed. .... Dylan Wilson
Sports Editor .... John Holt
Pub./Ed. .... Nancy Wykle
Market Information: TMC
Mechanical Available: Offset; Black and 3 ROP colors; insert accepted - any; page cutoffs - 22.
Mechanical Specifications: Type page 10 x 21 1/2; E - 6 cols, 1 5/6, 1/6 between; A - 6 cols, 1 5/6, 1/6 between; C - 8 cols, 1 1/3, 1/6 between.
Areas Served: 23927, 27507, 27536, 27537, 27544, 27549, 27551, 27553, 27556, 27563, 27565, 27582, 27589
Delivery Method: Mail, Newsstand, Carrier, RacksEquipment & Software: BUSINESS SOFTWARE: Mediaspan CLASSIFIED SOFTWARE: Mediaspan DISPLAY SOFTWARELayout Software — Mediaspan EDITORIAL SOFTWARE: Mediaspan

HENDERSONVILLE

TIMES-NEWS

106 Henderson Crossing Plz, Hendersonville, N.C., 28792-2879, Henderson; gen tel (828) 692-0505; gen fax (828) 692-2319; ed fax (828) 693-5581; gen/nat adv e-mail Wanda.Edney@blueridgenow.com; disp adv e-mail tnads@blueridgenow.com; class adv e-maildebbie.owen@blueridgenow.com; ed e-mail tnletters@blueridgenow.com; web site www.blueridgenow.com
- 2,000,000(views) 200,000(visitors)
Group: New Media Investment Group
Published: Mon, Tues, Wed, Thur, Fri, Sat, Sun
Weekday Frequency: m
Saturday Frequency: m
Circulation: 10,937; 10,937(sat); 11,778(sun)
Last Audit: AAM September 30, 2014
Advertising Rate (weekday/saturday): Open inch rate $25.73
News services: AP, NYT. **Established:** 1881
Own Printing Facility?: Yes
Special Editions: Football (Aug); Apple Festival (Sep); Last Minute Gift Guide (Dec); Almanac (Feb); Medical Directory (Mar); Holiday Gift Guide (Nov); Motorama (Oct).
Special Weekly Sections: Weekend (Fri); Blue Ridge Living (S); Church Directory (Sat); Best Food Day (Wed).
Executive Editor .... Diane Norman
Adv. Mgr. .... Wanda Edney
Chief Photographer .... Michael Dirks
Sports Ed. .... Dean Hensley
Market Information: ADS; TMC.
Mechanical Available: Offset; Black and 3 ROP colors; insert accepted - tabs,broadsheets,singlesheets; page cutoffs - 22 3/4.
Mechanical Specifications: Type page 11 5/8 x 21 1/2; E - 6 cols, 1 13/16, 1/8 between; A - 6 cols, 1 13/16, 1/8 between; C - 9 cols, 1 3/16, 1/16 between.
Areas Served: Henderson, Polk & Transylvania Counties (NC)
Delivery Method: Carrier, RacksEquipment & Software: MAILROOM EQUIPMENT: Tying Machines — MLN; Address Machine — Am.; BUSINESS EQUIPMENT: IBM/Sys 3600 CLASSIFIED EQUIPMENT: Hardware — 5-Mac/G3; Printers — HP/1600; CLASSIFIED SOFTWARE: Baseview, Quark, Photoshop. DISPLAY EQUIPMENT: Hardware — G3; Other Hardware — 6-Quark/Photoshop G4 DISPLAY SOFTWAREAd Make-up Applications — Quark; Layout Software — Baseview. EDITORIAL EQUIPMENT: Hardware — 23-Mac/G4; Printers — Dataproducts/8500. PRODUCTION EQUIPMENT: Hardware — 2-Nu.

HICKORY

THE HICKORY DAILY RECORD

1100 11th Ave. Blvd. SE, Hickory, N.C., 28602, Catawba; gen tel (828) 322-4510; adv tel (828) 322-4510; ed tel (828) 322-4510; gen fax (828) 322-8439; adv fax (828) 267-0294; ed fax (828) 324-8179; gen/nat adv e-mail advertising@hickoryrecord.com; disp adv e-mail advertising@hickoryrecord.com; class adv e-mailclassified@carolinaclassifiedmarketplace.com; ed e-mail news@hickoryrecord.com; web site www.hickoryrecord.com
- 176,307(views) 8,709(visitors)
Group: BH Media Group
Published: Mon, Tues, Wed, Thur, Fri, Sat, Sun
Weekday Frequency: m
Saturday Frequency: m
Circulation: 12,035; 12,035(sat); 15,325(sun)
Last Audit: CAC December 31, 2016
Advertising Rate (weekday/saturday): Open inch rate $18.86 (Mon-Tue); $21.27 (Wed-Thur); $22.66 (Fri-Sat)
Advertising Rate (sunday): Open inch rate $23.72
News services: AP.
Special Editions: Hickory Hops (Apr); Hickory Heritage (Aug); Christmas (Dec); Health & Fitness (Feb); Visitor Guide (Jun); Taste of Hickory (Mar); Hickory Smoke (May); Christmas (Nov); Cultural Arts (Oct); Active Seniors (Quarterly); Best of Catawba (Sept).
Special Weekly Sections: Business, Best Food (Wed); Pastimes, Arts, Entertainment (Thur); Business, Learning (Fri); Building, Home, Garden, Living, Real Estate, Religion (Sat); Family (Sun)
Syndicated Publications: USA WEEKEND Magazine (S).
Digital Platform - Mobile: Apple, Android, Windows, Blackberry
Digital Platform - Tablet: Apple iOS, Android, Windows 7, Blackberry Tablet OS
Reg. Pub. .... Tim Dearman
Mng. Ed. .... John Miller
Circ. Dir. .... David Eggers
Prodn. Mgr. .... Jim Lillagore
Bus. Ed. .... John Dayberry
City Ed. .... Patrick Jean
Editor .... Josh LaFontaine
News Ed. .... Michelle L. Bloomfield
Interim Editor .... Larry Clark
Sports Ed. .... Chris Hobbs
Major Accounts Mgr. .... Vicki Hayes
Melanie Armino
Editor .... Scott Bryan
Market Information: ADS; TMC.
Mechanical Available: Offset; Black and 3 ROP colors; insert accepted; page cutoffs - 22.
Mechanical Specifications: Type page 13 x 21; E - 6 cols, 2 1/16, 1/8 between; A - 6 cols, 2 1/16, 1/8 between; C - 8 cols, 1 3/4, 1/16 between.
Areas Served: Catawba County
Delivery Method: Mail, Newsstand, RacksEquipment & Software: PRESSROOM EQUIPMENT: Lines — 7-MAN/Uniman; Pasters —MEGReels & Stands — MEG.; MAILROOM EQUIPMENT: Counter Stackers — 2/MM; Inserters & Stuffers — 2-/MM; Tying Machines — 2-/OVL.; BUSINESS EQUIPMENT: IBM/Sys 36 CLASSIFIED EQUIPMENT: Hardware — 5-HP; CLASSIFIED SOFTWARE: SII/Coyote XA. DISPLAY EQUIPMENT: Hardware — HP; DISPLAY SOFTWARELayout Software — ALS (version 2.5). EDITORIAL EQUIPMENT: Hardware — Tandem/Server, 22-HP; Printers - Konica EDITORIAL SOFTWARE: SII/Sys 77XR 5702A Coyote XE. PRODUCTION EQUIPMENT: Hardware — 1-Nu, 1-AU/ APS-6 PRODUCTION SOFTWARE: Coyote/ Layout.

HIGH POINT

HIGH POINT ENTERPRISE

213 Woodbine St, High Point, N.C., 27260-8339, Guilford; gen tel (336) 888-3500; adv tel (336) 885-3555 (class); ed tel (336) 888-3500; gen fax (336) 888-3642; adv fax (336) 888-3637; ed fax (336) 888-3644; gen/nat adv e-mail jmcclure@hpenews.com; disp adv e-mail jmcclure@hpenews.com; class adv e-mailclassified@hpenews.com; ed e-mail news@hpenews.com; web site www.hpenews.com/
- 436,000(views) 168,500(visitors)
Group: Paxton Media Group, LLC
Published: Mon, Tues, Wed, Thur, Fri, Sat, Sun
Weekday Frequency: m
Saturday Frequency: m
Circulation: 10,200; 10,200(sat); 12,200(sun)
Last Audit: Sworn/Estimate/Non-Audited December 18, 2017
Advertising Rate (weekday/saturday): Open inch rate $31.24
Advertising Rate (sunday): Open inch rate $32.31
News services: AP, MCT, CNS, SHNS, TMS. **Established:** 1883
Own Printing Facility?: Yes
Commercial Printers?: Yes
Special Editions: Everything High Point
Special Weekly Sections: Food (Wed); Dining, Entertainment (Thur); Travel, Real Estate (Sun); Business (Daily)
Syndicated Publications: American Profile (weekly); Athlon, Spry (1 a month)
Digital Platform - Mobile: Apple, Android
Digital Platform - Tablet: Apple iOS, Android
Pub. .... Rick Bean
Controller .... Nancy Baker
Adv. Dir. .... John McClure
Market Information: ADS; Split run; TMC.
Mechanical Available: Offset G/Metro; Black and 3 ROP colors; insert accepted; page cutoffs - 21.
Mechanical Specifications: Type page 11 x 21; E - 6 cols, 1.4792
Image area: 9.5" X 20.0"
Areas Served: Guilford, Davidson, Randolph, Forsyth counties (NC)
Delivery Method: Mail, Newsstand, Carrier, RacksEquipment & Software: PRESSROOM EQUIPMENT: Manugraph 360; 20 units; 4 color towers MAILROOM EQUIPMENT: Goss inserter (29/1. 28/2); 4 stackers; 4 strappers BUSINESS EQUIPMENT: mac/ pc BUSINESS SOFTWARE: mediaspan CLASSIFIED EQUIPMENT: mac, pc CLASSIFIED SOFTWARE: mediaspan EDITORIAL EQUIPMENT: mac, pc EDITORIAL SOFTWARE: mediaspan CIRCULATION EQUIPMENT: mac, pc CIRCULATION SOFTWARmediaspan

JACKSONVILLE

THE DAILY NEWS

724 Bell Fork Rd, Jacksonville, N.C., 28540-6311, Onslow; gen tel (910) 353-1171; adv tel (910) 353-1171; ed tel (910) 353-1171; gen fax (910) 353-7316; adv fax (910) 353-7316; ed fax (910) 353-7316; gen/nat adv e-mail matt.holbrook@kinston.com; disp adv e-mail Rachelle.Trout@JDNews.com; class adv e-mailLynnell.Burch@JDNews.com; ed e-mail editor@jdnews.com; web site www.jdnews.com
- 1,400,000(views)
Group: New Media Investment Group
Published: Mon, Tues, Wed, Thur, Fri, Sat, Sun
Weekday Frequency: m
Saturday Frequency: m
Circulation: 11,795; 11,795(sat); 13,479(sun)
Last Audit: CAC March 31, 2015
Advertising Rate (weekday/saturday): Open inch rate $32.00
Advertising Rate (sunday): Open inch rate $30.45
News services: AP.
Special Editions: Spring Car Care (Apr); Answer Book (Aug); Christmas Color Book (Dec); NASCAR Preview (Feb); Super Bowl (Jan); Celebrate the Fourth (Jul); June Bride (Jun); Spring Gardening (Mar); Graduation (May); Coupon Book (Monthly); Cookbook (Nov); Swansboros Mullet
Special Weekly Sections: Business Page (Mon); Visions (S); Business Spotlights (Tues); Food (Wed).
Syndicated Publications: American Profile (Every other week); USA WEEKEND Magazine (S); Max Magazine (Thur).
Adv. Dir. .... John Hettlzer
Circ. Mgr. .... Don Wilson
Graphics Ed./Art Dir. .... Paul Woodward
Photo Ed. .... Don Bryan
Travel Ed. .... J.T. Oliver
Prodn. Mgr., Pre Press .... Jeff Ashe
Prodn. Mgr., Pressroom .... George Farrior
Classifieds Adv. Mgr. .... Lynnell Burch
Mike Distelhorst
Market Information: ADS; Split run; TMC; Zoned editions.

Mechanical Available: Offset; Black and 3 ROP colors; insert accepted; page cutoffs - 22 3/4.
Mechanical Specifications: Type page 13 x 21 1/2; E - 6 cols, 2 1/16, 1/8 between; A - 6 cols, 2 1/16, 1/8 between; C - 8 cols, 1 1/2, 1/8 between.
Areas Served: Jacksonville, Camp Lejeune, Onslow County and surrounding areasEquipment & Software: PRESSROOM EQUIPMENT: Lines — 8-HI/1660 1986; 6-G/ Community; MAILROOM EQUIPMENT: Counter Stackers — HL; Tying Machines — 2/MLN.; BUSINESS EQUIPMENT: PC Network BUSINESS SOFTWARE: Great Plains/AR2000 CLASSIFIED EQUIPMENT: Hardware — PC Network; Printers — HP/5000; CLASSIFIED SOFTWARE: APT. DISPLAY EQUIPMENT: Hardware — PC Network; Printers — HP/8000; DISPLAY SOFTWAREAd Make-up Applications — APT; Layout Software — APT. EDITORIAL EQUIPMENT: Hardware — PC Network/ APP/Mac; Printers — HP/5000 EDITORIAL SOFTWARE: APT. PRODUCTION EQUIPMENT: Hardware — 2-Nu, PrePress/ Panther 46; Cameras — Spartan III; Scanners — Polaroid/Sprintscan, APP/ ScanJet PRODUCTION SOFTWARE: APT.

KINSTON

THE KINSTON FREE PRESS
2103 N Queen St, Kinston, N.C., 28501-1622, Lenoir; gen tel (252) 527-3191; adv tel (252) 527-3191; ed tel (252) 527-3191; gen fax (252) 527-1813; adv fax (252) 527-1813; ed fax (252) 527-9407; gen/nat adv e-mail matt.holbrook@kinston.com; disp adv e-mail matt.holbrook@kinston.com; class adv e-mailbilly_moore@link.freedom.com; web site www.kinston.com
Group: New Media Investment Group
Published: Mon, Tues, Wed, Thur, Fri, Sat, Sun
Weekday Frequency: m
Saturday Frequency: m
Circulation: 5,247; 5,247(sat); 5,894(sun)
Last Audit: CAC December 31, 2017
Advertising Rate (weekday/saturday): Open inch rate $22.00
Advertising Rate (sunday): Open inch rate $24.00
News services: AP. **Established:** 1882
Special Weekly Sections: School (Tue); Food (Wed); Auto (Fri); Real Estate (Sat);
Syndicated Publications: Homes Magazine (Every other month); USA WEEKEND Magazine (S); American Profile (Weekly).
Circ. Dir. .... Jim Register
Circ. Coord., NIE .... Molly Taylor
Exec. Ed. .... Patrick Holmes
Dir. of Sales,Marketing .... Judy Avery
Adv. Dir .... Matt Holbrook
Pub .... Mike Distelhorst
Online Ed. .... Jennifer Cannon
Market Information: ADS; TMC.
Mechanical Available: Offset; Black and 3 ROP colors; insert accepted; page cutoffs - 22 4/5.
Mechanical Specifications: Type page 13 x 21 1/2; E - 6 cols, 2 1/16, 1/8 between; A - 6 cols, 2 1/16, 1/8 between; C - 8 cols, 1 15/32, 5/32 between.Equipment & Software: PRESSROOM EQUIPMENT: Lines — 3-G/ Urbanite, 1-G/Urbanite (3 color).; MAILROOM EQUIPMENT: Tying Machines — 2/MLN.; BUSINESS EQUIPMENT: 2-Compaq/Pro Linea 486, Great Plains, Ceridian, Microsoft/ Office 97, Intel/Pentium II Fileserver, 4-Generic/Pentium PC, 1-Epson/DFX 8000 Printer, 1-Epson/DFX 5000 Printer, 2-Compaq/386 PC, 1-Compaq/486 DX PC, 1-Generic/486 PC, 1-Genicom Printer CLASSIFIED EQUIPMENT: Hardware — APP/Mac; Printers — 2-Okidata/320; CLASSIFIED SOFTWARE: Baseview. DISPLAY EQUIPMENT: Hardware — APP/ Mac; Printers — APP/Mac LaserWriter II g; Other Hardware — 3-IBM/8X. DISPLAY SOFTWAREAd Make-up Applications — Managing Editor/ALS Page Director, Baseview/Managing Editor; EDITORIAL EQUIPMENT: Hardware — APP/Mac/APP/ Mac Scanner; Printers — APP/Mac Accel-a-Writer 8200 EDITORIAL SOFTWARE: QPS/ QuarkXPress, Baseview. PRODUCTION EQUIPMENT: Hardware — 2-Nu, 2-Xante/8200, Pre Press/Panther Pro 36, Pre Press/Panther Plus 46; Cameras — C/ Spartan III; Scanners — AG, Kk/2035 plus, Linotype-Hell PRODUCTION SOFTWARE: Baseview, QPS/QuarkXPress/with FSI Extensions.

LAURINBURG

THE LAURINBURG EXCHANGE
211 W Cronly St, Laurinburg, N.C., 28352-3637, Scotland; gen tel (910) 276-2311; adv tel (910) 276-2311; ed tel (910) 276-2311; gen fax (910) 276-3815; adv fax (910) 276-3815; ed fax (910) 276-3815; gen/nat adv e-mail dperkins@civitasmedia.com; disp adv e-mail asimpson@civitasmedia.com; class adv e-maillexclassifieds@heartlandpublications.com; ed e-mail dperkins@civitasmedia.com; web site www.laurinburgexchange.com
30,000(visitors)
Group: Champion Media
Published: Tues, Wed, Thur, Fri, Sat
Weekday Frequency: m
Saturday Frequency: m
Circulation: 8,200; 8,200(sat)
Last Audit: Sworn/Estimate/Non-Audited September 30, 2017
Advertising Rate (weekday/saturday): Open inch rate $13.00
News services: AP. **Established:** 1882
Special Weekly Sections: Food (Wed); TV, Real Estate, Religion (Fri)
Syndicated Publications: American Profile (Weekly).
Ed. .... Scott Witten
Circ. Mgr. .... Sharon Burke
Bus. Off. Mgr. .... Susie Smith
Bus. Devp. Mgr. .... Althea Simpson
Classified .... Amy McNeill
Mechanical Specifications: Type page 13 x 21 1/2; E - 6 cols, 2 1/16, between; A - 6 cols, 2 1/16, between.

LENOIR

NEWS-TOPIC
123 Pennton Ave NW, Lenoir, N.C., 28645-4313, Caldwell; gen tel (828) 758-7381; adv tel (828) 610-8718; ed tel (828) 610-8737; class adv e-mailclassads@newstopicnews.com; ed e-mail news@newstopicnews.com; web site www.newstopicnews.com
- 214,000(views) 29,000(visitors)
Group: Paxton Media Group, LLC
Published: Tues, Wed, Thur, Fri, Sun
Weekday Frequency: m
Circulation: 5,135; 5,335(sun)
Last Audit: Sworn/Estimate/Non-Audited October 1, 2017
Advertising Rate (weekday/saturday): Open inch rate $25.8
News services: AP. **Established:** 1875
Own Printing Facility?: No
Commercial Printers?: No
Special Editions: Sports Tab (Aug.,Nov and March).Caldwell Book, May; Everything Caldwell, Feb
Special Weekly Sections: Church News (Fri).
Syndicated Publications: TV/Sunday Relish/Spry/Athlon Sports Thursday
Circ. Mgr. .... Mike Lambert
Ed. .... Guy Lucas
District Mgr. .... Melissa Haire
Sports Ed. .... Bryant Lilley
Market Information: TMC;
Mechanical Available: Offset; Black and 3 ROP colors; insert accepted; page cutoffs - 21
Mechanical Specifications: Type page 11 5/8 x 21 1/2; E - 6 cols, 1 5/6, 1/8 between; A - 6 cols, 1 5/6, 1/8 between; C - 9 cols, 1 19/100, 13/100 between.
Areas Served: 28645, 28630, 28638,
Delivery Method: Mail, Newsstand, Carrier, RacksEquipment & Software: PRESSROOM EQUIPMENT: Lines — 9-G/SSC Community 1997; MAILROOM EQUIPMENT: Counter Stackers — Mid America/Exact Stack; Inserters & Stuffers — KAN/480 5:1; Tying Machines — 1/MLN; BUSINESS EQUIPMENT: DPT/1800, APP/Mac BUSINESS SOFTWARE: Great Plains, Citrix CLASSIFIED EQUIPMENT: Hardware — 4-APP/Mac G3; APP/Laser Printer; Printers — Okidata/3410; CLASSIFIED SOFTWARE: Baseview. DISPLAY EQUIPMENT: Hardware — APP/Mac; Other Hardware — Panther/Imagesetter, Konica/EV-Jetsetter Imagesetter. DISPLAY SOFTWAREAd Make-up Applications — Baseview; EDITORIAL EQUIPMENT: Hardware — 12-APP/Mac G3/1-Microtek/Scanner; Printers — Laser Master/Unity 1200, Xante EDITORIAL SOFTWARE: Baseview. PRODUCTION EQUIPMENT: Hardware — PRO, Konica; Cameras — 1-C; Scanners — Microtek, Kk, Microtek PRODUCTION SOFTWARE: QPS/ QuarkXPress 4.0.

LEXINGTON

THE DISPATCH
30 E 1st Ave, Lexington, N.C., 27292-3302, Davidson; gen tel (336) 249-3981; adv tel (336) 249-1637; ed tel (336) 249-3981; gen fax (336) 249-0712; adv fax (336) 249-2944; ed fax (336) 249-0712; gen/nat adv e-mail tammie.wright@the-dispatch.com; disp adv e-mail tammie.wright@the-dispatch.com; class adv e-mailtammie.wright@the-dispatch.com; ed e-mail news@the-dispatch.com; web site www.the-dispatch.com
Group: New Media Investment Group
Published: Tues, Wed, Thur, Fri, Sat
Weekday Frequency: e
Saturday Frequency: m
Circulation: 6,343; 6,343(sat)
Last Audit: AAM December 31, 2015
Advertising Rate (weekday/saturday): Open inch rate $23.00
News services: AP, NYT. **Established:** 1882
Own Printing Facility?: Yes
Commercial Printers?: No
Special Weekly Sections: Business, Food (Wed); Religion (Sat)
Syndicated Publications: USA WEEKEND Magazine (Sat).
Pub .... Steve Skaggs
Asst. Controller .... Stephanie Sprayberry
Adv. Mgr .... Tammie Wright
Bus. Ed. .... Vikki Hodges
Chief Photographer .... Donnie Roberts
Sports Ed. .... Mike Duprez
IT Mgr. .... Lindsay Hedrick
Julia Hudgins
Market Information: Split run; TMC; Zoned editions.
Mechanical Available: Offset; Black and 3 ROP colors; insert accepted - coupon book, packages soap, etc..
Mechanical Specifications: Type page 13 x 21 1/2; E - 6 cols, 1 7/8, 1/8 between; A - 6 cols, 1 7/8, 1/8 between; C - 9 cols, 1 3/16, 1/16 between.
Delivery Method: Mail, Newsstand, Carrier, RacksEquipment & Software: PRESSROOM EQUIPMENT: Lines — G/Urbanite 1995; Folders — 1-HI.; CLASSIFIED EQUIPMENT: Hardware — AT.; EDITORIAL EQUIPMENT: Hardware — AT. PRODUCTION EQUIPMENT: Hardware — V.

LUMBERTON

THE ROBESONIAN
2175 N Roberts Ave, Lumberton, N.C., 28358-2867, Robeson; gen tel (910) 739-4322; adv tel (910) 416-5668; ed tel (910) 416-5649; gen fax (910) 739-6553; gen/nat adv e-mail rwalker@heartlandpublications.com; disp adv e-mail dmckenzie@heartlandpublications.com; class adv e-mailobesonianclass@robesonian.com; ed e-mail ddouglas@civitasmedia.com; web site www.robesonian.com
Group: Champion Media
Published: Tues, Wed, Thur, Fri, Sat, Sun
Weekday Frequency: e
Saturday Frequency: m
Circulation: 12,562; 12,562(sat); 15,108(sun)
Last Audit: Sworn/Estimate/Non-Audited September 30, 2017
Advertising Rate (weekday/saturday): Open inch rate $24.50
Advertising Rate (sunday): Open inch rate $28.10
News services: AP, CN, CNS, NYT, SHNS, LAT-WP. **Established:** 1870
Special Editions: Tobacco Market (Other).
Special Weekly Sections: Health, Entertainment (Tue); Food, Education, Lifestyles, Entertainment (Wed); Agriculture, Entertainment (Thur); Auto, Religion, TV Spotlight (Fri); Education, Brides, Stock, Business, Lifestyles, Comics (Sun)
Syndicated Publications: Parade (S).
Managing Ed. .... Sarah Willets
Bus. Ed. .... Scott Witten
Ed. .... Donnie Douglas
Educ. Ed. .... Knight Chamberlain
Lifestyle Ed. .... Michael Jaenicke
Online Ed. .... T.C. Hunter
Photo Dept. Mgr. .... Steve Humbert
Features Ed. .... Jaymie Baxley
Pub. .... Rick Thomason
Circ. Dir. .... Tammy Britt
Market Information: Split run; TMC.
Mechanical Available: Offset; Black and 3 ROP colors; insert accepted; page cutoffs - 21 1/2.
Mechanical Specifications: Type page 11 9/16 x 21 1/2; E - 6 cols, 1 7/8, 1/8 between; A - 6 cols, 1 7/8, 1/8 between; C - 9 cols, 1 3/16, 1/16 between.
Areas Served: Robeson County (NC)
Equipment & Software: PRESSROOM EQUIPMENT: Lines — 9-HI/V-15; Folders — 2-HI/2:1.; MAILROOM EQUIPMENT: Tying Machines — 1-Sa/1 Strapping Machine.; BUSINESS SOFTWARE: Vision Data CLASSIFIED EQUIPMENT: Hardware — APP/Mac, APP/Mac II, 3-APP/Mac LC III; Printers — 1-Okidata/320 Billing Printer; CLASSIFIED SOFTWARE: Baseview/Class Manager Plus. DISPLAY EQUIPMENT: Hardware — 3-APP/Mac Centris 650; Printers — 2-APP/Mac LaserWriter 11 x 17; Other Hardware — CD-Rom/Scanner DISPLAY SOFTWAREAd Make-up Applications — QPS/QuarkXPress, Caere/ OmniPage, Baseview/NewsEdit; Layout Software — 3-Mk/Ad Setter. EDITORIAL EQUIPMENT: Hardware — 4-APP/Mac Centris 650, APP/Mac LC III; Printers — 1-APP/Mac LaserPrinter IIg EDITORIAL SOFTWARE: QPS/QuarkXPress, Baseview/ Qtools, Baseview/NewsEdit. PRODUCTION EQUIPMENT: Hardware — APP/Mac; Cameras — AG; Scanners — CD-Rom/ Scanner, APP/Mac.

MARION

THE MCDOWELL NEWS
136 N Logan St, Marion, N.C., 28752-3754, McDowell; gen tel (828) 652-3313; adv tel (828) 559-4045; ed tel (828) 559-4051; gen fax (828) 655-1246; adv fax (828) 655-1246; ed fax (828) 655-1246; gen/nat adv e-mail ehorn@bhmginc.com; disp adv e-mail jlinens@morganton.com; class adv e-mailclassified@mcdowellnews.com; ed e-mail news@mcdowellnews.com; web site www.mcdowellnews.com
- 438,886(views) 79,640(visitors)
Group: BH Media Group
Published: Tues, Wed, Thur, Fri, Sun
Weekday Frequency: m
Circulation: 3,414; 3,444(sun)
Last Audit: CAC December 31, 2016
Advertising Rate (weekday/saturday): Open inch rate $9.02 (Tue/Thur); $9.75 (Wed/Fri)
Advertising Rate (sunday): Open inch rate $9.75
News services: AP.
Own Printing Facility?: No
Commercial Printers?: No
Special Weekly Sections: Business (Tue); Entertainment (Wed); Promotions, Specials (Monthly); Comics, Religion (Fri)
Syndicated Publications: American Profile (Weekly); USA WEEKEND Magazine (Weekly).
Pub. .... Lamar Smitherman
Ed. .... Scott Hollifield
Adv. Dir. .... Nina Linens
Adv. Asst./Circ. .... Linda Early
Market Information: TMC.
Mechanical Available: Offset; Black and 4 ROP colors; insert accepted; page cutoffs - 23.
Areas Served: McDowell County (NC)Equipment & Software: CLASSIFIED EQUIPMENT: Hardware — COM.; EDITORIAL EQUIPMENT: Hardware — COM.

MORGANTON

THE NEWS HERALD

301 Collett St, Morganton, N.C., 28655-3322, Burke; gen tel (828) 437-2161; adv tel (828) 437-2161; ed tel (828) 437-2161; gen fax (828) 437-5372; adv fax (828) 437-5372; ed fax (828) 437-5372; gen/nat adv e-mail advertising@morganton.com; disp adv e-mail advertising@morganton.com; class adv e-mailclassified@morganton.com; ed e-mail news@morganton.com; web site www.morganton.com
- 1,404,518(views) 123,564(visitors)
Group: BH Media Group
Published: Mon, Tues, Wed, Thur, Fri, Sun
Weekday Frequency: m
Circulation: 5,235; 5,684(sun)
Last Audit: Sworn/Estimate/Non-Audited January 17, 2018
Advertising Rate (weekday/saturday): Open inch rate $13.58
Advertising Rate (sunday): Open inch rate $15.20
News services: AP.
Own Printing Facility?: No
Commercial Printers?: No
Special Editions: Home & Garden (Apr); Football (Aug); Last Minute Gift Ideas (Dec); Valentine's Gift Ideas (Feb); % Off Sale (Jan); % Off Sale (Jul); Father's Day Gift Guide (Jun); Review & Forecast (Mar); Mother's Day Gift Guide (May); Christmas Around Burke (Nov); Hallo
Special Weekly Sections: Food (Wed); Entertainment, TV, Outdoor, Paw Prints (Thur); Church, Real Estate (Fri); Business, Social, Living, Women (Sun)
Syndicated Publications: TV Herald (Fri); American Profile (Weekly).
Pub. .... Lamar Smitherman
Bus. Mgr. .... Rhonda Hargenrader
Editor .... Lisa Wall
Jason Propst
Sales Leader .... Janina Linens
Market Information: ADS;
Mechanical Available: Offset; Black and 3 ROP colors; insert accepted - all; page cutoffs - 22 3/4.
Mechanical Specifications: Type page 13 1/4 x 21 1/2; E - 6 cols, 2, 1/8 between; A - 6 cols, 2, 1/8 between; C - 10 cols, 1 3/16, 1/16 between.Equipment & Software: PRESSROOM EQUIPMENT: Lines — 9-G 1994; MAILROOM EQUIPMENT: Tying Machines — 1/Dynaric; Address Machine — 1-X/730.; BUSINESS EQUIPMENT: 3-HP/ Vision Data CLASSIFIED EQUIPMENT: Hardware — 3-APP/Mac; CLASSIFIED SOFTWARE: Baseview. DISPLAY EQUIPMENT: Hardware — APP/Mac; Printers — 2-APP/Mac LaserPrinter; Other Hardware — ECR. DISPLAY SOFTWAREAd Make-up Applications — QPS/QuarkXPress; Layout Software — APP/Mac G3. EDITORIAL EQUIPMENT: Hardware — APP/Mac; Printers — ECR EDITORIAL SOFTWARE: Baseview. PRODUCTION EQUIPMENT: Hardware — 1-3M, Adobe/Photoshop; Cameras — 1-Nu; Scanners — APP/Mac.

MOUNT AIRY

MOUNT AIRY NEWS

319 N Renfro St, Mount Airy, N.C., 27030-3838, Surry; gen tel (336) 786-4141; gen fax (336) 789-2816; gen/nat adv e-mail shurley@civitasmedia.com; disp adv e-mail shurley@heartlandpublications.com; class adv e-mailmtaclassifieds@mtairynews.com; ed e-mail jpeters@civitasmedia.com; web site www.mtairynews.com
- 600,000(views) 78,000(visitors)
Group: Champion Media
Published: Tues, Wed, Thur, Fri, Sat, Sun
Weekday Frequency: m
Saturday Frequency: m
Circulation: 12,000; 11,221(sun)
Last Audit: Sworn/Estimate/Non-Audited September 30, 2017
Advertising Rate (weekday/saturday): Open inch rate $17.25
Advertising Rate (sunday): Open inch rate $17.25
Online Advertising Rate: Ranging per location: $300-725
News services: AP. **Established:** 1880
Own Printing Facility?: Yes
Special Editions: Simple Pleasures (Apr); Simple Pleasures (Aug); Simple Pleasures (Jul); Simple Pleasures (Jun); Progress (Mar); Simple Pleasures (May); Foothill Farmer (Monthly); Simple Pleasures (Oct); Simple Pleasures (Sept).
Special Weekly Sections: Best Food Day (Wed); Religion, Auto (Fri); Entertainment, TV, Real Estate (Sun)
Syndicated Publications: USA WEEKEND Magazine (S); American Profile (Weekly).
Adv. Mgr. .... Nikki Hawks
Ed .... John Peters
Nat'l Acct. Mgr. .... David Perkins
Rgl. Local Bus. Develop. Mgr. .... Nathan DiBagno
Bus./Circ Mgr. .... Ferris Simpson
Sports Ed. .... Thomas Smith
Regional Publisher .... Sandra Hurley
Assistant Editor .... Jeff Linville
Pub. .... Ron Clausen
Market Information: ADS; TMC; Zoned editions.
Mechanical Available: Offset; Black and 3 ROP colors; insert accepted; page cutoffs - 21 1/2.
Mechanical Specifications: Type page 10 5/16 x 13; E - 4 cols, 2 1/2, 1/8 between; A - 4 cols, 2 1/2, 1/8 between; C - 4 cols, 2 1/2, 1/8 between.
Areas Served: Surry County (NC)Equipment & Software: PRESSROOM EQUIPMENT: Lines — 6-G/Community 1975.; MAILROOM EQUIPMENT: Tying Machines — 2-MLN/ Spirit; Wrapping Singles — KR/Quarterfolder 324; Address Machine — KR.; BUSINESS EQUIPMENT: PC (IBM compatible) BUSINESS SOFTWARE: Business/Software CLASSIFIED EQUIPMENT: Hardware — 2-APP/Mac, 2-APP/Mac G3; Printers — Okidata; CLASSIFIED SOFTWARE: Baseview. DISPLAY EQUIPMENT: Hardware — APP/Mac, 5-APP/Mac 7200-120; Printers — APP/Mac LaserWriter IIg, HP/ LaserJet 4mv; Other Hardware — APP/ Mac G3 DISPLAY SOFTWAREAd Make-up Applications — Multi-Ad/Creator, Mk/ Touchwriter Plus, Mk/Ad Touch, Baseview; Layout Software — APP/Mac, Multi-Ad/ Creator, QPS/QuarkXPress, APP/Mac EDITORIAL EQUIPMENT: Hardware — 7-APP/Mac 7200-120, 6-APP/Mac 7200-90, 4-APP/iMac, 3-APP/Mac G3, 3-APP/Mac 7200-120, APP/Mac 8500-120, 1-APP/Mac G4/APP/Mac LC, Lf/AP Leaf Picture Desk, APP/Mac 8500-120, Polaroid/SprintScan, AG/Scanner, San/Disk, LF/AP Leaf Pictur PRODUCTION EQUIPMENT: Hardware — APP/Mac LaserWriter Plus, APP/Mac LaserWriter IIg, 2-APP/Mac G3, 2-APP/ Mac 7200-120, 1-APP/Mac G4; Cameras — SCREEN/C-260-D; Scanners — Polaroid/ SprintScan, AG/Argus II PRODUCTION SOFTWARE: QPS/QuarkXPress, Multi-Ad/ Creator.

NEW BERN

THE SUN JOURNAL

3200 Wellons Blvd, New Bern, N.C., 28562-5234, Craven; gen tel (252) 638-8101; adv tel (252) 638-8101; ed tel (252) 638-8101; gen fax 252-638-4580; adv fax (252) 638-4664; ed fax (252) 638-4580; gen/nat adv e-mail Scott.Embry@NewBernSJ.com; disp adv e-mail nbsjads@freedomenc.com; class adv e-mailencclassifieds@jdnews.com; ed e-mail sjnewsroom@newbernsj.com; web site www.newbernsj.com
- 1,400,000(views)
Group: New Media Investment Group
Published: Mon, Tues, Wed, Thur, Fri, Sat, Sun
Weekday Frequency: m
Saturday Frequency: m
Circulation: 8,801; 8,801(sat); 10,075(sun)
Last Audit: CAC December 31, 2017
Advertising Rate (weekday/saturday): Open inch rate $24.00
Advertising Rate (sunday): Open inch rate $25.00
News services: AP, NEA. **Established:** 1783
Special Editions: Back-to-School (Aug); Brides (Feb); Shriners (Jan); Hurricane Awareness (Jul); Home and Garden (Mar); Christmas Catalog (Nov); Fall Home Improvement (Sept).
Special Weekly Sections: Health; Food (Wed); Farm (Thur); Entertainment (Fri); Church (Sat); TV, Business (Sun);
Syndicated Publications: Real Estate (Monthly); Healthy Living (Quarterly); USA WEEKEND Magazine (S); American Profile (Weekly).
Ed. .... Randy Foster
Circ. Dir. .... Sheila Meadows
Adv. Dir. .... Terry Tokie
Sports Ed. .... Adam Thompson
Pub. .... Mike Distelhorst
Market Information: Split run; TMC; Zoned editions.
Mechanical Available: Offset; Black and 3 ROP colors; insert accepted - single sheet; page cutoffs - .
Mechanical Specifications: Type page 13 x 21 1/2; E - 6 cols, 2 1/16, 1/8 between; A - 6 cols, 2 1/16, 1/8 between; C - 8 cols, 1 1/2, 1/8 between.
Delivery Method: Mail, Newsstand, Carrier, RacksEquipment & Software: MAILROOM EQUIPMENT: Tying Machines — Dynaric.; BUSINESS EQUIPMENT: PC BUSINESS SOFTWARE: Vision Data, Southware

NEWTON

THE OBSERVER NEWS ENTERPRISE

309 N College Ave, Newton, N.C., 28658-3255, Catawba; gen tel (828) 464-0221; gen fax (828) 464-1267; gen/nat adv e-mail admanager@observernewsonline.com; disp adv e-mail admanager@observernewsonline.com; class adv e-mailoneclassifieds@observernewsonline.com; ed e-mail onenews@observernewsonline.com; web site www.observernewsonline.com
Group: Horizon Publications Inc.
Published: Tues, Wed, Thur, Fri, Sat
Weekday Frequency: m
Saturday Frequency: m
Circulation: 2,303; 2,303(sat)
Last Audit: Sworn/Estimate/Non-Audited September 30, 2017
Advertising Rate (weekday/saturday): Open inch rate $9.50
News services: AP. **Established:** 1879
Special Editions: Friday Magazine (Monthly).
Special Weekly Sections: Education (Tue); Business (Wed); Education, Health, Arts, Entertainment, Food, Family, Travel (Thur); Lifestyles, Religion (Sat); Real Estate (Upon Request)
Syndicated Publications: American Profile (Fri).
Mng. Ed. .... Yerby Ray
Circ. Dir. .... Cindy Hull
Sports Ed. .... Adams Houston
Prodn. Mgr. .... Philip Rogers
Prodn. Foreman, Pressroom .... Richard Patton
Pub./Ed. .... Seth Mabry
Bus. Office .... Greg Bailes
Market Information: TMC.
Mechanical Available: Offset; Black and 3 ROP colors; insert accepted; page cutoffs - 21 1/4.
Mechanical Specifications: Type page 13 x 21; E - 6 cols, 2 1/16, 1/8 between; A - 6 cols, 2 1/16, 1/8 between; C - 10 cols, 1 3/16, 3/32 between.
Areas Served: Catawba County (NC)Equipment & Software: PRESSROOM EQUIPMENT: Lines — 7-KP/Offset web 1976; 1-Stubbs/ Stacker; Control System — TF&E/Press Room Devices.; MAILROOM EQUIPMENT: Address Machine — Am.; BUSINESS EQUIPMENT: L/9000 CLASSIFIED EQUIPMENT: Hardware — COM.; DISPLAY EQUIPMENT: Printers — APP/Mac LaserPrinter; DISPLAY SOFTWARELayout Software — COM. EDITORIAL EQUIPMENT: Hardware — COM; Printers — COM. PRODUCTION EQUIPMENT: Hardware — COM; Cameras — LE.

RALEIGH

THE NEWS & OBSERVER

215 S McDowell St, Raleigh, N.C., 27601-1331, Wake; gen tel (919) 829-4500; adv tel (919) 836-5600; ed tel (919) 829-4564; gen fax (919) 829-4872; adv fax (919) 836-5689; ed fax (919) 829-4529; gen/nat adv e-mail placeads@newsobserver.com.; disp adv e-mail placeads@newsobserver.com.; class adv e-mailplaceads@newsobserver.com; ed e-mail forum@newsobserver.com; web site www.newsobserver.com
- 15,000,000(views) 2,224,619(visitors)
Group: The McClatchy Company
Published: Mon, Tues, Wed, Thur, Fri, Sat, Sun
Weekday Frequency: m
Saturday Frequency: m
Circulation: 100,395; 101,295(sat); 139,034(sun)
Last Audit: AAM June 30, 2016
Advertising Rate (weekday/saturday): Open inch rate $290.86
Advertising Rate (sunday): Open inch rate $322.33
News services: AP, Bloomberg, CT, MCT, LAT-WP, NYT. **Established:** 1894
Special Editions: Business Expo (Apr); Fall Style (Aug); What's Up/1st Night (Dec); Taxes Work & Money (Feb); Economic Outlook (Jan); The N&O 100 (State's Public Companies) (Jun); Spring Style (Mar); Nurses Association (May); Expanded What's Up for the Holidays (Nov); Scho
Special Weekly Sections: Sports, Entertainment, Money, Travel, Comics (Sun); Sports, Life (Mon); Business, Stocks (Tue); Food (Wed); (Faith, What's Up (Fri); Home, Channels (Sat)
Syndicated Publications: Parade (S).
Adv. Mgr. .... Doug Rogers
Adv. Prod. Mgr. .... Matt Long
Adv. Mgr., Group Adv. .... Cathy Wallace
Vice Pres., Circ. .... James Puryear
Managing Ed. .... John Drescher
Deputy Managing Ed. .... Dan Barkin
Deputy Mng. Ed. .... Steve Riley
VP, Classified Advertising .... Gary Smith
Major Acct. Mgr. .... Patti Vargas
Digital Acct. Mgr. .... Chris Trares
VP, HR .... Liz Mark
Market Information: ADS; Split run; TMC; Zoned editions.
Mechanical Available: Flexo (direct); Black and 3 ROP colors; insert accepted; page cutoffs - 22.
Mechanical Specifications: Type page 11 1/2 x 21; E - 6 cols, 1 13/16, 1/8 between; A - 6 cols, 1 13/16, 1/8 between; C - 10 cols, 1 1/12, 1/8 between.
Areas Served: Raleigh (NC)Equipment & Software: PRESSROOM EQUIPMENT: Lines — 9-KBA/MOT double width (CIC Fullcolor) 1995; 9-KBA/MOT double width (CIC Fullcolor) 1995; Folders — 3-KBA/ MOT 3:2 160 page capacity; Pasters —18-G/with AGS upgrader 1994; Registration System — 4 MAILROOM EQUIPMENT: Counter Stackers — 5-HL/Monitor, 4-HL/Dual Carriers, 2-QWI/400, 4-QWI/401; Inserters & Stuffers — 3-HI/1472 online; Tying Machines — 1-GMA/SLS-3000, 3-Newstyer/2000, 1/ Power Strap/PSN 4, 6-Dynaric/NP3, 3-GMA/ Combistacks; Address Machine — 1-C; BUSINESS EQUIPMENT: 1-HP/3000-979 BUSINESS SOFTWARE: Microsoft/Office, GEAC/Financial & Circulation CLASSIFIED EQUIPMENT: Hardware — Tandem/ Sys 77-ServerNet, 30-APP/Power Mac, 110-Intel/PCs; 1-Sun/Enterprise 5000; Printers — HP/DesignJet 1050C, 3-HP/ Dot Matrix; CLASSIFIED SOFTWARE: SII, 110-SII/Coyote 3, Morcor/Xpance. DISPLAY EQUIPMENT: Hardware — 1-HP/3000/979; Printers — 1-HP/LaserWriter Pro RB 121 30-N, 1-HP/LaserJet, 4-HP/LaserJet 4, 3-HP/ LaserJet 4L, 1-HP/Resolution Enhance, 2-LaserWriter 1600, 2-HP/2000C, X/Phaser 1235, HP/DesignJet 1050C, 2-Docuprint N2025; DISPLAY SOFTWAREAd Make-up Applications — Geac/AIM 7.0; EDITORIAL EQUIPMENT: Hardware — 1-Sun/Enterprise 5000, 1-APP/Mac GPSserver G3, 240-APP/ Power Mac, 2-Quickwire/Servers; Printers — Laser, HP/DesignJet 1050C EDITORIAL SOFTWARE: Quark/Copy Desk, QPS, QuickWire. PRODUCTION EQUIPMENT: Hardware — 3-Na/Flex, 2-HP, 2-Sun/5000S OPI, MON/RIPs, 7-Sun/Ultra 167 RIP, Alphaquest/Print Express PRODUCTION SOFTWARE: QPS, QPS/QuarkXPress.

REIDSVILLE

THE EDEN DAILY NEWS

1921 Vance St, Reidsville, N.C., 27320-3254,

Rockingham; gen tel 336-349-4331; adv tel (434) 385-5505; ed tel (336) 349-4331; gen fax (336) 342-2513; gen/nat adv e-mail pdurham@reidsvillereview.com; disp adv e-mail legalads@registerbee.com; class adv e-mailpdurham@reidsvillereview.com; ed e-mail alehmert@reidsvillereview.com; web site http://www.newsadvance.com/rockingham_now/
Group: North Carolina Press Service, Inc.
BH Media Group
Media General, Inc. (OOB)
Published: Tues, Wed, Thur, Fri, Sun
Weekday Frequency: m
Circulation: 3,961; 3,961(sun)
Last Audit: Sworn/Estimate/Non-Audited September 30, 2017
Advertising Rate (weekday/saturday): Open inch rate $18.00
Advertising Rate (sunday): Open inch rate $18.00
News services: AP, Universal Press Syndicate, NEA.
Special Weekly Sections: Food (Wed); Entertainment, Auto (Fri); Health (Thur); Home (Sat)
Syndicated Publications: USA WEEKEND Magazine (S).
Pub. ... Alton Brown
Office Mgr. ... Dreama Armstrong
Retail Adv. Dir. ... Pam Durham
Grp. Ed. ... Amanda K Lehmert
Circ. Mgr. ... Mary Thurman Terry Goad
Ed. ... Amanda Lehmert
Market Information: TMC.
Mechanical Available: Offset; Black and 3 ROP colors; insert accepted; page cutoffs - 22 3/4.
Mechanical Specifications: Type page 13 x 21 1/2; E - 6 cols, 2 1/16, 1/8 between; A - 6 cols, 2 1/16, 1/8 between; C - 9 cols, 1 1/3, 1/8 between.Equipment & Software: BUSINESS EQUIPMENT: IBM BUSINESS SOFTWARE: Vision Data CLASSIFIED EQUIPMENT: Hardware — 10-Mk, APP/Mac; Printers — HP/5000; CLASSIFIED SOFTWARE: Baseview. EDITORIAL EQUIPMENT: Hardware — APP/Mac, 10-MkPrinters — APP/Mac, HP/5000, APP/Mac LaserPrinter NT EDITORIAL SOFTWARE: QPS 3.3, Baseview/NewsEdit. PRODUCTION EQUIPMENT: Hardware — P PRODUCTION SOFTWARE: QPS 3.3.

ROANOKE RAPIDS

DAILY HERALD

916 Roanoke Ave, Roanoke Rapids, N.C., 27870-2720, Halifax; gen tel (252) 537-2505; adv tel (252) 537-2505; ed tel (252) 537-2505; gen fax (252) 537-2314; adv fax (252) 537-2314; ed fax (252) 537-2314; gen/nat adv e-mail pwhite@rrdailyherald.com; disp adv e-mail sconger@rrdailyherald.com; class adv e-maillindafoster@rrdailyherald.com; ed e-mail shemelt@rrdailyherald.com; web site www.rrdailyherald.com
Group: Paxton Media Group, LLC
Published: Tues, Wed, Thur, Fri, Sun
Weekday Frequency: e
Saturday Frequency: m
Circulation: 6,156; 6,793(sun)
Last Audit: VAC June 30, 2015
Advertising Rate (weekday/saturday): Open inch rate $13.50
Advertising Rate (sunday): Open inch rate $14.05
News services: AP. **Established:** 1914
Special Editions: Football Kick-off Tab (Aug); Christmas Greetings (Dec); Bride & Groom (Feb); Honor Roll of Business (Jan); July 4th Sales (Jul); Home & Garden (Mar); Progress Tab (May); Christmas Gift Guide (Nov); Businesswomen's Week (Oct); Fall Opening (Sept).
Special Weekly Sections: NIE (Tue); Food (Wed); Religion (Fri); Comics, Outdoor, Family, Senior (Sun)
Syndicated Publications: USA WEEKEND Magazine (S).
Pub. ... Titus Workman
Office Mgr. ... Linda Smith
Adv. Mgr., Classified ... Linda Foster
News Editor ... Tia Bedwell
News Ed. ... Kris Smith
Reporter ... Lance Martin
Prodn. Mgr., Distr. ... Carol Moseley
Prodn. Mgr., Mailroom ... Louise Harvey
Prodn. Mgr., Pre Press ... David Hager
Sports Ed. ... Travis Durkee
Market Information: Split run; TMC.
Mechanical Available: Offset; Black and 3 ROP colors; insert accepted - single sheets; page cutoffs - 22 3/4.
Mechanical Specifications: Type page 13 x 21 1/2; E - 6 cols, 2 1/16, 1/8 between; A - 6 cols, 2 1/16, 1/8 between; C - 9 cols, 1 5/16, 1/8 between.
Areas Served: Halifax & Northampton Counties (NC), Brunswick & Greensville Counties (VA)
Equipment & Software: PRESSROOM EQUIPMENT: Lines — 7-WPC/Web Atlas-Leader single width 1993; Reels & Stands — 6; MAILROOM EQUIPMENT: Tying Machines — 1/Bu; Address Machine — Vision Data.; BUSINESS SOFTWARE: Vision Data CLASSIFIED EQUIPMENT: Hardware — APP/Mac G3; CLASSIFIED SOFTWARE: Baseview 3.16. DISPLAY EQUIPMENT: Hardware — 4-APP/Mac G3; Printers — 1-Xante/8200, 1-APP/Mac G3; Other Hardware — Nikon/Coolscan DISPLAY SOFTWAREAd Make-up Applications — Multi-Ad/Creator 3.8; Layout Software — APP/Mac. EDITORIAL EQUIPMENT: Hardware — Mk/3000/Nikon/Coolscan; Printers — 1-Xante/8200, 1-APP/Mac G3. PRODUCTION EQUIPMENT: Hardware — Nat; Cameras — 1-B, Acti/Prod Camera; Scanners — Konica/Scanner PRODUCTION SOFTWARE: Baseview 3.16.

ROCKINGHAM

RICHMOND COUNTY DAILY JOURNAL

105 E Washington St, Rockingham, N.C., 28379-3639, Richmond; gen tel (910) 997-3111; adv tel (910) 997-3111; ed tel (910) 997-3111; gen fax (910) 997-4321; adv fax (910) 997-4880; ed fax (910) 997-4321; gen/nat adv e-mail rbacon@heartlandpublications.com; disp adv e-mail Rbacon@heartlandpublications.com; class adv e-mailrdjclassifieds@civitasmedia.com; ed e-mail Jrobbins@heartlandpublications.com; web site www.yourdailyjournal.com - 500,000(views) 150,000(visitors)
Group: Champion Media
Published: Tues, Wed, Thur, Fri, Sat, Sun
Weekday Frequency: m
Saturday Frequency: m
Circulation: 6,575; 7,000(sat)
Last Audit: Sworn/Estimate/Non-Audited September 30, 2017
Advertising Rate (weekday/saturday): Open inch rate $18.00
Advertising Rate (sunday): Open inch rate $18.00
News services: AP. **Established:** 1931
Own Printing Facility?: Yes
Commercial Printers?: No
Special Editions: Raider Football Review (Aug);
Special Weekly Sections: Food (Wed); Entertainment, Auto (Fri); Health (Thur); Home (Sat)
Syndicated Publications: Relish (Monthly); American Profile (S).
Digital Platform - Mobile: Apple, Android
Digital Platform - Tablet: Apple iOS, Kindle
Circ. Mgr. ... Jimmy Herring
Managing Editor/Sports Editor ... Shawn Stinson
Prodn. Supvr. ... Amanda Vaness
Ed./Content Manager ... Corey Friedman
Business Dev. Manager ... David Spencer
Ed ... Corey Friedman
Advertising Director and General Manager ... Scott Ricardi
Market Information: TMC.
Mechanical Available: Offset; Black and 3 ROP colors; insert accepted; page cutoffs - 21.
Mechanical Specifications: Type page 11x 21; E - 6 cols, 1 5/6, 1/8 between; A - 6 cols, 1 5/6, 1/8 between; C - 10 cols, 1 5/6, 1/8 between.
Areas Served: Richmond County (NC)
Delivery Method: Newsstand, Carrier, RacksEquipment & Software: MAILROOM EQUIPMENT: Address Machine — 2-/El.; BUSINESS EQUIPMENT: Vision Data CLASSIFIED EQUIPMENT: Hardware — Baseview.; DISPLAY EQUIPMENT: Hardware — APP/Mac; Printers — Rip Mac; DISPLAY SOFTWAREAd Make-up Applications — Multi-Ad/Creator 4.0; Layout Software — APP/Mac. EDITORIAL EQUIPMENT: Hardware — APP/Mac/Rip Mac; Printers — APP/Mac LaserWriter Pro EDITORIAL SOFTWARE: Newsengine

ROCKY MOUNT

ROCKY MOUNT TELEGRAM

1000 Hunter Hill Rd, Rocky Mount, N.C., 27804-1727, Nash; gen tel (252) 446-5161; adv tel (252)407-9927; ed tel (252)407-9943; gen fax (252) 446-7068; adv fax ; ed fax ; gen/nat adv e-mail jmbrown@rmtelegram.com; disp adv e-mail jmbrown@rmtelegram.com; class adv e-mailqmcneal@rmtelegram.com; ed e-mail jherrin@rmtelegram.com; web site www.rockymounttelegram.com - 3,200,000(views) 120,000(visitors)
Group: Cooke Communications North Carolina, LLC
Published: Mon, Tues, Wed, Thur, Fri, Sat, Sun
Weekday Frequency: m
Saturday Frequency: m
Circulation: 9,193; 9,193(sat); 11,094(sun)
Last Audit: AAM October 10, 2017
Advertising Rate (weekday/saturday): Open inch rate $17.95
Advertising Rate (sunday): Open inch rate $17.95
Online Advertising Rate: Big Box $14/m
Leaderboard $14/m
Sliding Billboard $14/m
News services: AP. **Established:** 1910
Own Printing Facility?: No
Commercial Printers?: Yes
Special Editions: Super Sunday (Jan), Brides (Feb), Carolina Charm (Mar), Home & Garden, Brew Scene (May), Medical Directory (June), Shop Local (July), Carolina Charm, Forever Young, Football Preview (Aug), Readers Choice, Welcome Home, Fall Car (Sep), United Way (Oct), Holiday Gift Guide, Brew Scene; Forever Young (Nov) Letters to Santa, Last Minute Gift Guide (Dec)
Special Weekly Sections: Religion (Fri); School (Mon); Technology (S); TV Magazine (Sun); Entertainment (Thur); Church Fri. News (Fri); Best Food Day (Wed).
Syndicated Publications: Local Color Comics (S).
Proprietary Publications: ;Brew Scene (May, Oct)
Digital Platform - Mobile: Apple, Android
Digital Platform - Tablet: Apple iOS, Android
Editor ... Jeff Herrin
Mgr., HR ... Gwen Davis
Pub. ... Mark Wilson
Classified Adv. Mgr. ... Quasha McNeal
Online/Print Ed. ... Gene Metrick
Features Ed. ... Ross Chandler
Online Ed. ... Jenny White
Cir. Mgr. ... Heidi Hibbert
Market Information: TMC 13,500 circ
Mechanical Available: Offset; Black and 3 ROP colors; insert accepted - single sheets, cards, coupons; page cutoffs - 21.
Mechanical Specifications: Type page 13 x 21; E - 6 cols, 2, 1/8 between; A - 6 cols, 2, 1/8 between; C - 6 cols, 1 1/8, 1/16 between.
Areas Served: 27801, 27802; 27803, 27804, 27809, 27816, 27822, 27823, 27844, 27852, 27856, 27864, 27868, 27874, 27878, 27882, 27886, 27891
Delivery Method: Mail, Newsstand, Carrier, RacksEquipment & Software: PRESSROOM SOFTWARE: Libercus effective 9/1/15 MAILROOM EQUIPMENT: Tying Machines — 2/OVL.; BUSINESS EQUIPMENT: PC BUSINESS SOFTWARE: Brainworks CLASSIFIED EQUIPMENT: Hardware — APP/Power Mac; CLASSIFIED SOFTWARE: Brainworks DISPLAY EQUIPMENT: Hardware — APP/Power Mac; PC DISPLAY SOFTWAREAd Make-up Applications — Brainworks CRM EDITORIAL EQUIPMENT: Hardware — APP/Power Mac/APP/Mac; Printers — HP/5MP, Xante/8300 EDITORIAL SOFTWARE: DTI 4.2.
Libercus PRODUCTION EQUIPMENT: Hardware/Mac — DTI. PRODUCTION SOFTWARE: DTI/Libercus IT EQUIPMENT: Mac/PC IT SOFTWARE:Brainworks
DTI
Libercus CIRCULATION EQUIPMENT: PC CIRCULATION SOFTWARBrainworks

SALISBURY

SALISBURY POST

131 W Innes St, Salisbury, N.C., 28144-4338, Rowan; gen tel (704) 633-8950; adv tel (704) 797-4241; ed tel (704)797-4250; gen fax (704) 639-0003; adv fax (704) 639-0003; ed fax (704) 639-0003; gen/nat adv e-mail displayads@Salisburypost.com; disp adv e-mail displayads@Salisburypost.com; class adv e-mailclassads@Salisburypost.com; ed e-mail letters@Salisburypost.com; web site www.salisburypost.com
Group: Boone Newspapers, Inc.
Published: Mon, Tues, Wed, Thur, Fri, Sat, Sun
Weekday Frequency: m
Saturday Frequency: m
Circulation: 15,086; 15,086(sat); 15,902(sun)
Last Audit: AAM September 30, 2014
Advertising Rate (weekday/saturday): Open inch rate $31.80
Advertising Rate (sunday): Open inch rate $32.94
News services: Papert (Landon), AP, NEA, SHNS, LAT-WP. **Established:** 1905
Special Editions: Nat'l Sportscasters & Sportswriters Association (Apr); Explorer (Aug); Christmas Carol Book (Dec); Bridal (Feb); Tax (Jan); A Day in the Life (Jul); Graduation (Jun); Explorer (Mar); Summer Fun (May); Hometown Heroes (Nov); October Tour (Oct); Fall Home I
Special Weekly Sections: Food (Wed); Time Out, TV (Thur); Youth, Senior (Fri); Real Estate, Church, Stocks (Sat); Business, Travel, Insight (Sun)
Syndicated Publications: Relish (Monthly); USA WEEKEND Magazine (S); American Profile (Weekly).
Digital Platform - Mobile: Apple, Android
Digital Platform - Tablet: Apple iOS, Android
Pub ... Greg Anderson
Dir., Sales/Mktg. ... Chris Ratliff
Circ. Dir. ... Ron Brooks
Ed. ... Elizabeth G. Cook
Books Ed. ... Deirdre Parker Smith
Editorial Page Ed. ... Chris Verner
Educ. Ed. ... Holly Lee
Photo Dept. Mgr. ... Wayne Hinshaw
Political Ed. ... Mark Wineka
Religion Ed. ... Katie Olson
Prodn. Vice Pres., Opns. ... Michael J. Bella
Sports Ed. ... Ronnie Gallagher
Teen-Age/Youth Ed. ... Katie Scarvey
Prodn. Mgr., Post Press ... Sharon Jackson
Jon Lakey
New City and Business Reporter ... David Putrell
Market Information: TMC.
Mechanical Available: Offset; Black and 3 ROP colors; insert accepted - all; page cutoffs - 22.
Mechanical Specifications: Type page 11 1/2 x 21; E - 6 cols, 2 1/16, 1/8 between; A - 6 cols, 2 1/16, 1/8 between; C - 9 cols, 1 3/8, 1/16 between.
Areas Served: Rowan, Davie & Cabaruss counties (NC)Equipment & Software: PRESSROOM EQUIPMENT: Lines — 7-G/Metroliner 3 decks double width 1982; Folders — 4-G/2:1, Regent/2:1.; MAILROOM EQUIPMENT: Counter Stackers — 1/HL, 1-/MM, 2-QWI/SJ300, 1-QWI/J400, 2-/HL; Inserters & Stuffers — 1-/MM, 1-/1372P; Tying Machines — 1-/Dynaric, 1-/Dynaric, 1-/QWI; Address Machine — 2-/Dispensa-Matic/U-45.; BUSINESS EQUIPMENT: 2-Convergent/Mighty Frame, 8-Wyse BUSINESS SOFTWARE: Vision Data CLASSIFIED EQUIPMENT: Hardware — Ik, Baseview, APP/Power Mac, 5-APP/Mac G3; Printers — 1-Centronics; CLASSIFIED SOFTWARE: ECS 4, Ad Manager Pro, Classflow, QPS/QuarkXPress, Ad Force II. DISPLAY EQUIPMENT: Hardware — 10-APP/Mac; DISPLAY SOFTWAREAd Make-up Applications — QPS/QuarkXPress 3.25, Adobe/Photoshop, Adobe/Illustrator, Adobe/Acrobat, Macromedia/Freehand; Layout Software — 3-APP/Mac G3, 3-APP/Mac G4. EDITORIAL EQUIPMENT: Hardware — Ik, QPS/QuarkXPress, APP/Mac Server, APP/iMac, APP/Mac G3, APP/Mac G4/1-APP/Mac, DTI/PageSpeed, Kk/2035 Scanner; Printers — 2-Epson, 2-C.Itoh, 1-Centronics, AU/APS 6600, APP/Mac LaserWriter, Phases/440 Color EDITORIAL SOFTWARE: ECS 4, QPS/ PRODUCTION EQUIPMENT: Hardware — Caere/OmniPage 6.0, 1-APP/

Super Mac, Adobe/Photoshop, Kk/Scanner, Adobe/Acrobat, Macromedia/Freehand, 36-Laser Imagers, 1-Xante/Color Proofer; Cameras — 1-C/Spartan II, 1-C/Spartan III; Scanners — 1-ECR/Autokon 1000, 2-Umax/1200 dpi color scan

SANFORD

HERALD-SANFORD

208 Saint Clair Ct, Sanford, N.C., 27330-3916, Lee; gen tel (919) 708-9000; adv tel (919) 718-1203; ed tel (919) 718-1226; gen fax (919) 774-4269; adv fax (919) 708-9001; ed fax (919) 708-9001; gen/nat adv e-mail adsales@sanfordherald.com; disp adv e-mail adsales@sanfordherald.com; class adv e-mailclassified@sanfordherald.com; ed e-mail news@sanfordherald.com; web site www.sanfordherald.com

Group: Paxton Media Group, LLC
Published: Tues, Wed, Thur, Fri, Sat, Sun
Weekday Frequency: m
Saturday Frequency: m
Circulation: 7,978; 7,978(sat); 7,901(sun)
Last Audit: Sworn/Estimate/Non-Audited September 30, 2017
Advertising Rate (weekday/saturday): Open inch rate $18.21 (Tue, Thur-Sat); $21.21 (Wed)
Advertising Rate (sunday): Open inch rate $18.21
News services: AP. **Established:** 1930
Special Editions: Car Care (Apr); Football (Aug); Christmas Gift Guide (Dec); IRS (Feb); Summer Lifestyle (Jun); Small Business Expo (May); Fair (Sept).
Special Weekly Sections: Food (Wed); Entertainment, Farm (Thur); Real Estate, Religion (Fri); Auto (Sat); Business, Free Time, Health, Travel, Women (Sun)
Syndicated Publications: TV Preview (Fri); USA WEEKEND Magazine (S).
Mgr., Mktg./Promo., Pub....Bill Horner
Circ. Dir.....Jeff Ayers
Advertising Dir.....Dave Shabaz
News Ed.....Jennifer Gentile
News Clerk....Judy McNeil
Market Information: Split run; TMC; Zoned editions.
Mechanical Available: Offset; Black and 3 ROP colors; insert accepted - up to 10 3/4 x 13; page cutoffs - 21 1/2.
Mechanical Specifications: Type page 13 x 21 1/2; E - 6 cols, 2, 1/6 between; A - 6 cols, 2 1/6, 1/8 between; C - 8 cols, 1 1/3, 1/8 between.Equipment & Software: PRESSROOM EQUIPMENT: Folders — 1-G/2:1. MAILROOM EQUIPMENT: Tying Machines — 1/Bu, 1-/MLN.; BUSINESS EQUIPMENT: Apple BUSINESS SOFTWARE: Baseview CLASSIFIED EQUIPMENT: Hardware — Apple; Baseview; DISPLAY EQUIPMENT: Hardware — Apple; DISPLAY SOFTWAREAd Make-up Applications — Baseview; EDITORIAL EQUIPMENT: Hardware — Apple EDITORIAL SOFTWARE: Baseview

SHELBY

THE STAR

315 E Graham St, Shelby, N.C., 28150-5452, Cleveland; gen tel (704) 669-3300; adv tel (704) 669-3366; ed tel (704) 669-3333; gen fax (704) 484-0805; adv fax (704) 482-2631; ed fax (704) 482-2631; gen/nat adv e-mail klaprade@gastongazette.com; disp adv e-mail klaprade@gastongazette.com; class adv e-mailclassifieds@gastongazette.com; ed e-mail kellis@gastongazette.com; web site www.shelbystar.com
- 1,800,000(views) 155,000(visitors)

Group: New Media Investment Group
Published: Mon, Tues, Wed, Thur, Fri, Sat, Sun
Weekday Frequency: m
Saturday Frequency: m
Circulation: 14,164; 14,164(sat); 14,389(sun)
Last Audit: Sworn/Estimate/Non-Audited December 18, 2017
Advertising Rate (weekday/saturday): Open inch rate $22.75 (Mon-Tue/Thur-Sat); $25.60 (Wed)
Advertising Rate (sunday): Open inch rate $23.40
News services: AP, SHNS. **Established:** 1894
Commercial Printers?: Yes
Special Editions: Your Health (Apr); Senior Living (Aug); Christmas Gift Guide (Dec); Senior Living (Feb); Your Health (Jan); Your Health (Jul); Cleveland Now (Mar); Senior Living (May); Real Estate (Lincoln & Cleveland counties) (Monthly); Senior Living (Nov); Your Health
Special Weekly Sections: Health (Tue); Food (Wed); Entertainment (Thur); Faith (Fri); Wedding, Real Estate, TV, Comics (Sun)
Syndicated Publications: USA WEEKEND Magazine (S).
Digital Platform - Mobile: Apple, Android, Windows
Digital Platform - Tablet: Apple iOS, Android, Windows 7
lifestyles reporter....Wade Allen
Prodn. Dir., Mailroom....Frankie Rice
Prodn. Mgr., Pressroom....Barry Croucher
Adv. Dir.....Konrad LaPrade
Gen. Mgr./Finance Dir.....Keith Raffone
Pub....Lucy Talley
Newsroom Clerk....Michelle Owens
managing editor....Diane Turbyfill
reporter....Joyce Orlando
photographer....Brittany Randolph
Market Information: TMC.
Mechanical Available: Offset; Black and 3 ROP colors; insert accepted - product samples; page cutoffs - 27 1/2.
Mechanical Specifications: Type page 11 1/3 x 21 1/2; E - 6 cols, 1 4/5, 1/8 between; A - 6 cols, 1 4/5, 1/8 between; C - 9 cols, 1 1/5, 1/8 between.
Areas Served: Cleveland County (NC)
Delivery Method: CarrierEquipment & Software: PRESSROOM EQUIPMENT: Lines — 6-G/Urbanite; Folders — G/2:1; Reels & Stands — 6; MAILROOM EQUIPMENT: Counter Stackers — 1/QWI; Tying Machines — 2-/Strapex; Wrapping Singles — 1-/QWI; Address Machine — 1-/KR; BUSINESS EQUIPMENT: 1-IBM/Newzware BUSINESS SOFTWARE: Great Plains Dynamics, Newzware, APT, Ceridian CLASSIFIED EQUIPMENT: Hardware — 3-PC, 2-PC P166, 1-PC P100; Printers — HP/4MV; CLASSIFIED SOFTWARE: APT/ACT 2.06.03. DISPLAY EQUIPMENT: Printers — HP/8150; Other Hardware — 1-Microtex Scanner, 1-AgFa/Ducscan, 2-Acer Scanners DISPLAY SOFTWAREAd Make-up Applications — APT/ACT 2.06.03; Layout Software — APT, QPS/QuarkXPress 4.04. EDITORIAL EQUIPMENT: Hardware — 3-Compaq/Proliant Server 600/19-PC, 1-APP/Mac, 1-MS/NT Workstation, 1-SII/Workstation, 3-Compaq/Servers, 1-IBM Server, 1-Compaq/UniX Server; Printers — 1-HP/4000, 1-HP/4MV, 1-Epson/Stylus, 1-Pre Press/Panther 46, 2-HP/8150, 1-HP/5 PRODUCTION EQUIPMENT: Hardware — 2-Pre Press/Panther Pro 46, AG/Duoscan, Pentium/PC II, Microtek; Cameras — 1-B, 1-SCREEN; Scanners — 1-AG/Duoscan, 1-Acer/Microtech PRODUCTION SOFTWARE: APT/ACT 2.06.03, Microsoft/NT 4.0.

STATESVILLE

STATESVILLE RECORD & LANDMARK

222 E Broad St, Statesville, N.C., 28677-5325, Iredell; gen tel (704) 873-1451; adv tel (704) 761-2927; ed tel (704) 873-1451; gen fax (704) 872-3150; gen/nat adv e-mail advertising@statesville.com; disp adv e-mail advertising@statesville.com; class adv e-mailclassified@statesville.com; ed e-mail dibach@statesville.com; web site www.statesville.com

Group: BH Media Group
Published: Mon, Tues, Wed, Thur, Fri, Sat, Sun
Weekday Frequency: m
Saturday Frequency: m
Circulation: 7,533; 7,533(sat); 9,787(sun)
Last Audit: CAC June 30, 2015
Advertising Rate (weekday/saturday): Open inch rate $12.67 (Mon, Tue, Sat); $13.70 (Wed, Thur, Fri)
Advertising Rate (sunday): Open inch rate $14.56
News services: 1874
Own Printing Facility?: Yes
Commercial Printers?: Yes
Special Weekly Sections: Education (Tue); Food (Wed); TV, Entertainment (Sun); Business (Daily)
Digital Platform - Mobile: Apple, Android, Windows, Blackberry
Digital Platform - Tablet: Apple iOS, Android, Kindle
Pub....Tim Dearman
Ed....Dave Ibach
Adv. Dir.....LeAnna Dunlap
Circ. Mgr.....Bud Welch
Business Mgr.....Lisa Guy
Eric Millsaps
Areas Served: 28677, 28625, 28115, 28117, 28634, 28689, 28678, 28166
Delivery Method: Mail, Newsstand, Carrier, RacksEquipment & Software: MAILROOM EQUIPMENT: Tying Machines — Alles.;

TRYON

TRYON DAILY BULLETIN

16 N Trade St, Tryon, N.C., 28782-6656, Polk; gen tel (828) 859-9151; gen fax (828) 859-5575; gen/nat adv e-mail news@tryondailybulletin.com; disp adv e-mail advertising@tryondailybulletin.com; class adv e-mailclassifieds@tryondailybulletin.com; ed e-mail news@tryondailybulletin.com; web site www.tryondailybulletin.com
30,000(visitors)

Group: Boone Newspapers, Inc.
Published: Tues, Wed, Thur, Fri, Sun
Weekday Frequency: m
Circulation: 4,250
Last Audit: Sworn/Estimate/Non-Audited December 18, 2017
Advertising Rate (weekday/saturday): Open inch rate $11.47
Advertising Rate (sunday): Open inch rate $11.47
News services: 1928
Own Printing Facility?: Yes
Special Editions: Progress (Feb); Steeplechase (Apr), Graduation (May), Fall Sports (Aug); Business Card Directory (Oct); Holiday Gift Guide (Nov)
Syndicated Publications: Foothills Magazine, Visitors Bulletin
Digital Platform - Mobile: Apple, Android
Managing Ed.....Claire Sachse
Press Room Mgr.....Jeff Allison
Gen. Mgr.....Kevin Powell
Mechanical Available: Offset; Black; insert accepted; page cutoffs - 11.
Areas Served: 28782, 28773, 28756, 28750, 29356, 28722, 29322
Delivery Method: Mail, Newsstand, RacksEquipment & Software: PRESSROOM EQUIPMENT: Lines — 2-KP/News King.; MAILROOM EQUIPMENT: Address Machine — 1-Automecha/Accufast PL.; BUSINESS EQUIPMENT: MAC CLASSIFIED EQUIPMENT: Hardware — PC; CLASSIFIED SOFTWARE: Aldus/PageMaker, Alpha 4. DISPLAY EQUIPMENT: Hardware — InDesign; DISPLAY SOFTWARELayout Software — PC. EDITORIAL EQUIPMENT: Hardware — MAC; Printers — APP/Mac LaserPrinter, Canon/LBP4 EDITORIAL SOFTWARE: Aldus/PageMaker. PRODUCTION EQUIPMENT: Hardware — Nu/Plate Maker PRODUCTION SOFTWARE: Aldus/PageMaker.

WASHINGTON

WASHINGTON DAILY NEWS

217 N Market St, Washington, N.C., 27889-4949, Beaufort; gen tel (252) 946-2144; adv tel (252) 946-2144; ed tel (252) 946-2144; gen fax (252) 946-9797; adv fax (252) 946-9797; ed fax (252) 946-9797; gen/nat adv e-mail kathryn.powell@thewashingtondailynews.com; disp adv e-mail kathryn.powell@thewashingtondailynews.com; class adv e-mailronnie.daw@thewashingtondailynews.com; ed e-mail news@thewashingtondailynews.com; web site www.wdnweb.com

Group: Boone Newspapers, Inc.
Published: Mon, Tues, Wed, Thur, Fri, Sat, Sun
Weekday Frequency: m
Saturday Frequency: m
Circulation: 8,644; 8,644(sat); 8,829(sun)
Last Audit: Sworn/Estimate/Non-Audited September 30, 2017
Advertising Rate (weekday/saturday): Open inch rate $20.00
Advertising Rate (sunday): Open inch rate $20.00
News services: AP. **Established:** 1909
Special Editions: Visitor's Tourist Guide Tab (Apr); Football Tab (Aug); Basketball Tab (Dec); Tax Tab (Jan); Summer Festival (Jul); Lawn and Garden Tab (Mar); Graduation Tab (May).
Special Weekly Sections: Society (Tue); Food (Wed); Farm (Thur); Channel, Church (Fri); Food, Society (Sun)
Syndicated Publications: Parade (S).
Pres./Pub.....Ashley B. Futrell
Vice Pres.....Susan B. Futrell
Treasurer....Rachel F. Futrell
Controller....Addie B. Laney
Adv. Dir.....Ray McKeithen
Adv. Mgr., Classified....Brenda Foster
Ed.....Mike Voss
Society Ed.....Brenda Watters
Sports Ed.....Kevin Travis
Prodn. Foreman, Mailroom....Jerry Cox
Prodn. Foreman, Pressroom....Vance Bell
Publisher....Ashley Vansant
Market Information: TMC; Zoned editions.
Mechanical Available: Offset; Black and 3 ROP colors; insert accepted; page cutoffs - 22 3/4.
Mechanical Specifications: Type page 13 x 21 1/2; E - 6 cols, 2 1/16, 1/8 between; A - 6 cols, 2 1/16, 1/8 between; C - 6 cols, 2 1/16, 1/8 between.Equipment & Software: PRESSROOM EQUIPMENT: Lines — 1-Zenith/Jobber 22, G/Community SC; 5-G/SC 210; Folders — 1, 1.; MAILROOM EQUIPMENT: Tying Machines — 1/Strap Tyer; Address Machine — 4-/Wm.; BUSINESS EQUIPMENT: 1-Bs, 1-TI/300A, DSI/Papertrak BUSINESS SOFTWARE: Business/Software CLASSIFIED EQUIPMENT: Hardware — Mk.; DISPLAY SOFTWARELayout Software — 1-Mk. EDITORIAL EQUIPMENT: Hardware — 9-Mk. PRODUCTION EQUIPMENT: Hardware — 1-Nu, 1-M; Cameras — 1-Nu, C.

WILMINGTON

STARNEWS

1003 S 17th St, Wilmington, N.C., 28401-8023, New Hanover; gen tel (910) 343-2000; gen fax (910) 343-2210; gen/nat adv e-mail cheryl.whitaker@starnewsonline.com; disp adv e-mail dave.cuddihy@starnewsonline.com; web site starnewsonline.com

Group: GateHouse Media, Inc.
Published: Mon, Tues, Wed, Thur, Fri, Sat, Sun
Last Audit: Sworn/Estimate/Non-Audited September 30, 2017
Pub.....Mike Distelhorst
Adv. Dir.....Dave Cuddihy
Office Mgr.....Cheryl Whitaker
Circ. Dir.....Sheila Meadows
Ed.....Randy Foster

WILSON

THE WILSON TIMES

126 Nash St NE, Wilson, N.C., 27893-4013, Wilson; gen tel (252) 243-5151; adv tel (252) 243-5151; ed tel (252) 243-5151; gen fax (252) 243-2999; adv fax (252) 243-2999; ed fax (252) 243-7501; gen/nat adv e-mail ads@wilsontimes.com; disp adv e-mail ads@wilsontimes.com; class adv e-mailclassads@wilsontimes.com; ed e-mail editor@wilsontimes.com; web site www.wilsontimes.com
- 1,000,000(views) 180,000(visitors)

Published: Mon, Tues, Wed, Thur, Fri, Sat
Weekday Frequency: m
Saturday Frequency: m
Circulation: 10,762; 10,762(sat)
Last Audit: CAC December 31, 2016
Advertising Rate (weekday/saturday): Open inch rate $22.00
News services: AP, **Established:** 1896
Own Printing Facility?: No
Commercial Printers?: Yes
Special Editions: Wilson Woman; Medical

Directory; Wilson Wellness; Readers Choice; Eyes on Main St.; Southern Parent; Graduation; My Wilson; United Way; Dining Guide; Football Preview; Veteran's Day; Letters to Santa; Whirligig Park
Special Weekly Sections: Weddings; Tabletop; Mind & Body; At Home; Schools; Real Estate; Wide Awake Wilson; Milestones; Family Life
Syndicated Publications: Relish (Monthly); Parade (Weekly)
Digital Platform - Mobile: Apple, Android, Windows, Blackberry
Digital Platform - Tablet: Apple iOS, Android, Windows 7, Blackberry Tablet OS, Kindle, Nook, Kindle Fire
Mng. Ed. .... Lisa Batts
Sports Ed. .... Paul Durham
Dir. Mktg & Adv .... Shana Hoover
Staff Writer .... Brie Handgraaf
Paginator .... Kelsey Padgett
Gen Mngr .... Keven Zepezauer
Circ Mngr .... Chris Coley
Pub .... Morgan Dickerman
Controller .... Debbie Boykin
Ad Rep .... Cynthia Collins
Ad Rep .... Beth Robbins
Ad Rep .... Lisa Pearson
Ad Sales Asst. .... Petina Garcia
Mechanical Available: Offset; Black and 3 ROP colors; insert accepted; page cutoffs - 22.
Mechanical Specifications: Type page 12 1/2 x 21; E - 6 cols, 1 13/16, 1/8 between; A - 6 cols, 1 13/16, 1/8 between; C - 9 cols, 1 13/16, 1/16 between.
Areas Served: Wilson, Nash, Edgecombe, pitt, Greene, Wayne & Johnston Counties (NC)
Delivery Method: Mail, Newsstand, Carrier, RacksEquipment & Software: BUSINESS EQUIPMENT: Mac BUSINESS SOFTWARE: Quickbooks CLASSIFIED EQUIPMENT: Mac CLASSIFIED SOFTWARE: Ad Manager Pro; Indesign; Creative Cloud DISPLAY EQUIPMENT: Mac DISPLAY SOFTWAREAd Manager Pro; Indesign; Creative Cloud EDITORIAL EQUIPMENT: Mac EDITORIAL SOFTWARE: Folderflow; Creative Cloud PRODUCTION EQUIPMENT: Mac PRODUCTION SOFTWARE: Indesign; Creative Cloud CIRCULATION EQUIPMENT: Mac CIRCULATION SOFTWARNewscycle

WINSTON SALEM

WINSTON-SALEM JOURNAL

418 N Marshall St, Winston Salem, N.C., 27101-2815, Forsyth; gen tel (336) 727-7211; adv tel (336) 727-7492; ed tel (336) 727-7359; gen fax N/A; adv fax N/A; ed fax N/A; gen/nat adv e-mail wbuschmann@wsjournal.com; disp adv e-mail gwhiting@wsjournal.com; class adv e-mailmyclassifiedad@wsjournal.com; ed e-mail letters@wsjournal.com; web site www.journalnow.com 710,000(visitors)
Group: BH Media Group
Published: Mon, Tues, Wed, Thur, Fri, Sat, Sun
Weekday Frequency: m
Saturday Frequency: m
Circulation: 42,071; 43,199(sat); 52,982(sun)
Last Audit: AAM September 30, 2016
Advertising Rate (weekday/saturday): Open inch rates $109.00
Advertising Rate (sunday): Open inch rate $119.00
Online Advertising Rate: $10.00
News services: AP, NYT, LAT-WP., TNS, **Established:** 1897
Own Printing Facility?: Yes
Commercial Printers?: Yes
Special Editions: Winston-Salem Monthly Magazine, SPARK Magazine, Carolina Weddings Magazine, City Guide, WSWorks Magazine, Physicians Directory, Calendar,
Special Weekly Sections: Business(daily); Food (Wed); Journal West (Wed); Relish (Thurs);
Syndicated Publications: Parade (S).
Digital Platform - Mobile: Apple, Android, Other
Digital Platform - Tablet: Apple iOS, Android, Other
Pub .... Alton Brown
Regional Controller .... David Stanfield
Food Ed. .... Michael Hastings
VP Advertiisng Sales .... Gail Whiting
Custom Publishing Manager .... Tammy Holoman
Managing Editor .... Andy Morrissey
Day Meto Editor .... Jeri Young
Features Editor, Travel .... Alan Cronk
Night Editor .... Jennifer Young
Photo Editor .... Walter Unks
Weekend Editor .... Jimison Jon
Sports Editor .... Jewell Watson
Digital Platform Director .... John O"Neal
Editoral .... John Railey
Digital Editor .... Ragan Robinson
Marketing Director .... Justin Gomez
IT Systems Manager .... Gary Eanes
Production Plant Manager .... Frank Clayton
Winston-Salem Monthly Magazine Editor.. Michael Breedlove
Winston-Salem Monthly Magazine Sales Manager Angie Tedder
Digital Sales Manager .... Kelly Martin
Circulation Manager .... Tommie McLeod
Circulation Retention Sales, Marketing & (N.I.E.) News In Education .... Letty Acosta
Major & National Manager .... Bill Buschmann
Advertising Sales Manager .... Lori Reese
Market Information: ADS; Split run; TMC; Zoned editions.
Mechanical Available: Offset; Black and 3 ROP colors; insert accepted; page cutoffs - 22.
Mechanical Specifications: Type page 12 x 21; E - 6 cols, 1 7/8, 1/8 between; A - 6 cols, 1 7/8, 1/8 between; C - 9 cols, 1 3/16, 1/16 between.
Areas Served: Winston-Salem, Forsyth Counties (NC)
Delivery Method: Newsstand, Carrier, RacksEquipment & Software: PRESSROOM EQUIPMENT: Reels & Stands — 10; MAILROOM EQUIPMENT: Counter Stackers — 3-HL/Monitor, 6-QWI/300; Inserters & Stuffers — 2-GMA/SLS 1000 20:2; Tying Machines — 3/OVL, 6-/Dynaric; Address Machine — 2-/Ch, 1-/KR.; BUSINESS EQUIPMENT: HP/3000 918LX CLASSIFIED EQUIPMENT: Hardware — 2-IBM/RS 6000-F40; IBM/RS6000, IBM/43P, HI/Classified Pagination; Printers — HP/LaserJet 4000; CLASSIFIED SOFTWARE: AT/Enterprise. DISPLAY EQUIPMENT: Hardware — HP/Vectra-2; Printers — 2-HP/LaserJet 6P; DISPLAY SOFTWARELayout Software — SCS/Layout 8000. EDITORIAL EQUIPMENT: Hardware — 6-AT/9000/AT/Ed Page, 9-IBM/RS6000 EDITORIAL SOFTWARE: AT/Editorial 4.7.7. PRODUCTION EQUIPMENT: Hardware — 3-III/3810, 1-III/3850, 1-ECR; Scanners — 1-III/3750, 1-III/3725 PRODUCTION SOFTWARE: AT.
Note: Carolina Wedding Show, Scripps National Spelling Bee

NORTH DAKOTA

BISMARCK

THE BISMARCK TRIBUNE

707 E Front Ave, Bismarck, N.D., 58504-5646, Burleigh; gen tel (701) 223-2500; adv tel (701) 250-8205; ed tel (701) 250-8247; gen fax (701) 223-4240; adv fax (701) 224-1412; ed fax (701) 223-2063; gen/nat adv e-mail brad.peltz@bismarcktribune.com; disp adv e-mail brad.peltz@bismarcktribune.com; class adv e-maillisa.weisz@bismarcktribune.com; ed e-mail news@bismarktribune.com; web site www.bismarcktribune.com - 5,000,000(views)
Group: Lee Enterprises, Inc.
Published: Mon, Tues, Wed, Thur, Fri, Sat, Sun
Weekday Frequency: m
Saturday Frequency: m
Circulation: 22,176; 21,224(sat); 24,904(sun)
Last Audit: AAM September 30, 2016
Advertising Rate (weekday/saturday): Open inch rate 1/60: $56.82; 1/30B: $113.64; 1/30A: $113.64
Advertising Rate (sunday): Open inch rate 1/60: $63.62; 1/30B: $127.24; 1/30A: $127.24
Online Advertising Rate: 728x90: $9 (35,000+ Impressions/mo.); 728x90: $14 (20,000-34,999 Impressions/mo.); 728x90: $18 (10,000-19,999 Impressions/mo.)
News services: AP, LAT-WP, NEA. **Established:** 1873
Own Printing Facility?: Yes
Commercial Printers?: Yes
Special Editions: Solutions (Quarterly).
Special Weekly Sections: Voices (Mon); Business Page (S); Religion Page (Thur); Business Page (Tues); Best Food Day (Wed).
Syndicated Publications: Parade Magazine (S).
Pub .... Libby Simes
Mktg. Mgr. .... Stacey Lang
HR Mgr. .... Chad Kourajian
Circ. Dir. .... Ken Bohl
Librarian .... Vicky Weiss
News Ed. .... Steve Wallick
Photographer .... Mike McCleary
Religion Reporter .... Karen Herzog
Terry Alveshere
Retail Ad. Mgr., Sales Mgr., The Finder ..... Duane Crabbe
Online Mgr. .... Keith Darnay
Systems Admin .... Stace Gooding
Sports Reporter .... Robert Reidell
Pub .... David Braton
Market Information: ADS; Split run; TMC; Zoned editions.
Mechanical Available: Offset; Black and 4 ROP colors; insert accepted; page cutoffs - 22 3/4.
Mechanical Specifications: Type page 13 x 21 1/2; E - 6 cols, 2 1/16, 1/8 between; A - 6 cols, 2 1/16, 1/8 between; C - 9 cols, 1 3/8, 1/16 between.
Areas Served: Burleigh County
Delivery Method: Mail, Newsstand, Carrier, RacksEquipment & Software: PRESSROOM EQUIPMENT: Lines — 10-G/Urbanite single width; Folders — 1-G/2:1, 1-G/1200 Quarter Folder.; MAILROOM EQUIPMENT: Tying Machines — 1-MLN/MLN2A, 2-MLN/Spirit; Address Machine — 1-Ch/528-010, 1-Ch/542-093, 1-Ch/542-090; BUSINESS EQUIPMENT: IBM/AS-400 CLASSIFIED EQUIPMENT: Hardware — HI, Unix; CLASSIFIED SOFTWARE: HI/CASH. DISPLAY SOFTWAREAd Make-up Applications — Multi-Ad/Creator, QPS/QuarkXPress; Layout Software — APP/Mac. EDITORIAL EQUIPMENT: Hardware — 1-HI/8306, 4-HI/8903/ISYS/Library System EDITORIAL SOFTWARE: HI/PLS-PEN. PRODUCTION EQUIPMENT: Hardware — 2-COM/8600, 1-Pre Press/Panther Pro 36, 1-Pre Press/Panther Pro 46; Cameras — 1-C/Spartan III, 2-Ik/530; Scanners — 2-Nikon/Coolscan, 2-Polaroid/SprintScan 35, 10-Microtek/Flatbed Scanmakers PRODUCTION SOFTWARE: HI/PLS 6.5.

DEVILS LAKE

DEVILS LAKE JOURNAL

516 4th St NE, Devils Lake, N.D., 58301-2502, Ramsey; gen tel (701) 662-2127; adv tel (701) 662-2127; ed tel (701) 662-2127; gen fax (701) 662-3115; adv fax (701) 662-3115; ed fax (701) 662-3115; gen/nat adv e-mail advertising@devilslakejournal.com; disp adv e-mail advertising@devilslakejournal.com; class adv e-mailclassifieds@devilslakejournal.com; ed e-mail news@devilslakejournal.com; web site www.devilslakejournal.com - 4,727,202(views)
Group: New Media Investment Group
Published: Mon, Tues, Wed, Thur, Fri
Weekday Frequency: e
Circulation: 2,400
Last Audit: Sworn/Estimate/Non-Audited October 1, 2017
Advertising Rate (weekday/saturday): Open inch rate $13.35
Online Advertising Rate: Slider: $120; Swirl: $125; Page Curl: $150
News services: AP. **Established:** 1906
Own Printing Facility?: Yes
Syndicated Publications: TV Preview (Fri); Golden Opportunities (Monthly); American Profile (Weekly).
Mng. Ed. .... Louise Oleson
Class. Ad. Mgr. .... Patty Schwab
Circ. Mgr. .... Melinda Bennes
G.M. .... J. Reed Anderson
Market Information: TMC.
Mechanical Available: Offset; Black and 4 ROP colors; insert accepted; page cutoffs - 21.
Mechanical Specifications: Type page 13 x 21; E - 6 cols, 2, 1/6 between; A - 6 cols, 2, 1/6 between; C - 10 cols, 1 1/4, 1/12 between.
Areas Served: Devils Lake (ND) Equipment & Software: PRESSROOM EQUIPMENT: Lines — 4-HI/Cotrell V-15A; MAILROOM EQUIPMENT: Tying Machines — 1-Felins/16; Address Machine — 1-Am/2600.; BUSINESS EQUIPMENT: IBM/Sys 34 CLASSIFIED EQUIPMENT: Hardware — 2-Mk, AT; Printers — 2-APP/Mac LaserPrinter II.; DISPLAY EQUIPMENT: Printers — APP/Mac LaserWriter II NTX; DISPLAY SOFTWARELayout Software — APP/Mac IIci. EDITORIAL EQUIPMENT: Hardware — Mk/1100 Plus; Printers — 2-APP/Mac LaserPrinter II EDITORIAL SOFTWARE: Mk/NewsTouch. PRODUCTION EQUIPMENT: Hardware — Mk, 1-Amerigraph/457 SEDS; Cameras — 1-B/Caravel.

DICKINSON

THE DICKINSON PRESS

1815 1st St W, Dickinson, N.D., 58601-2463, Stark; gen tel 701-225-8111; adv tel (701) 456-1220; ed tel (701) 456-1205; gen fax 701-225-4205; gen/nat adv e-mail bcarruth@thedickinsonpress.com; disp adv e-mail bcarruth@thedickinsonpress.com; ed e-mail DMonke@thedickinsonpress.com; web site www.thedickinsonpress.com
Published: Tues, Wed, Thur, Fri, Sat, Sun
Circulation: 5,599; 5,599(sun)
Last Audit: VAC September 30, 2016
Publisher .... Harvey Brock
Adv. Dir .... Bob Carruth
Bus. Mgr. .... Joy Schoch
Cir. Mgr .... John Hodges
Mng. Ed. .... Dustin Monke
Lifestyles Ed. .... Linda Sailer
Prod. Mgr .... Jeremy Kadrmas
Sports Ed. .... Colton Pool

FARGO

INFORUM

101 5th St N, Fargo, N.D., 58102-4826, Cass; gen tel (701) 235-7311; adv tel (701) 241-5431; ed tel (701) 235-7311; gen fax (701) 241-5406; adv fax (701) 241-5597; ed fax (701) 241-5487; gen/nat adv e-mail advsales@forumcomm.com; disp adv e-mail natladv@forumcomm.com; class adv e-mailclassifieds@forumcomm.com; ed e-mail letters@forumcomm.com; web site www.inforum.com; web site 2 www.inforumtv.com
Group: Forum Communications Co.
Published: Mon, Tues, Wed, Thur, Fri, Sat, Sun
Weekday Frequency: m
Saturday Frequency: m
Circulation: 34,976; 36,520(sat); 37,799(sun)
Last Audit: AAM March 31, 2017
Advertising Rate (weekday/saturday): Open inch rate $43.81 (Local Open); $51.53 (National Open); $25.77 (Civic Rate)
Advertising Rate (sunday): Open inch rate $44.95 (Local Open); $52.86 (National Open); $26.43 (Civic Rate)
Online Advertising Rate: Non-Employment Online Rates (When purchased with a print ad): $5 (7 days); $9.95 (8-30 days)
News services: AP, LAT-WP. **Established:** 1891
Own Printing Facility?: Yes
Special Editions: Auto Care (Apr); Generations (+55) (Aug); Celebrate Christmas (Dec); Generations (+55) (Jan); Father's Day (Jun); Generations (+55) (May); Generations (+55) (Nov); Auto Care (Oct).
Special Weekly Sections: Farmers Forum (Fri); Sports (Mon); Travel (S); TV Forum (Sat); Financial (Tues); Food (Wed).
Syndicated Publications: Relish (Monthly); Parade (S).
Digital Platform - Mobile: Apple, Android, Windows, Blackberry
Digital Platform - Tablet: Apple iOS, Android, Windows 7, Blackberry Tablet OS, Kindle, Nook
Publisher/COO/Executive Vice President William C. Marcil
Ed. .... Matthew Von Pinnon
Adv. Dir. .... Amy Fredrickson

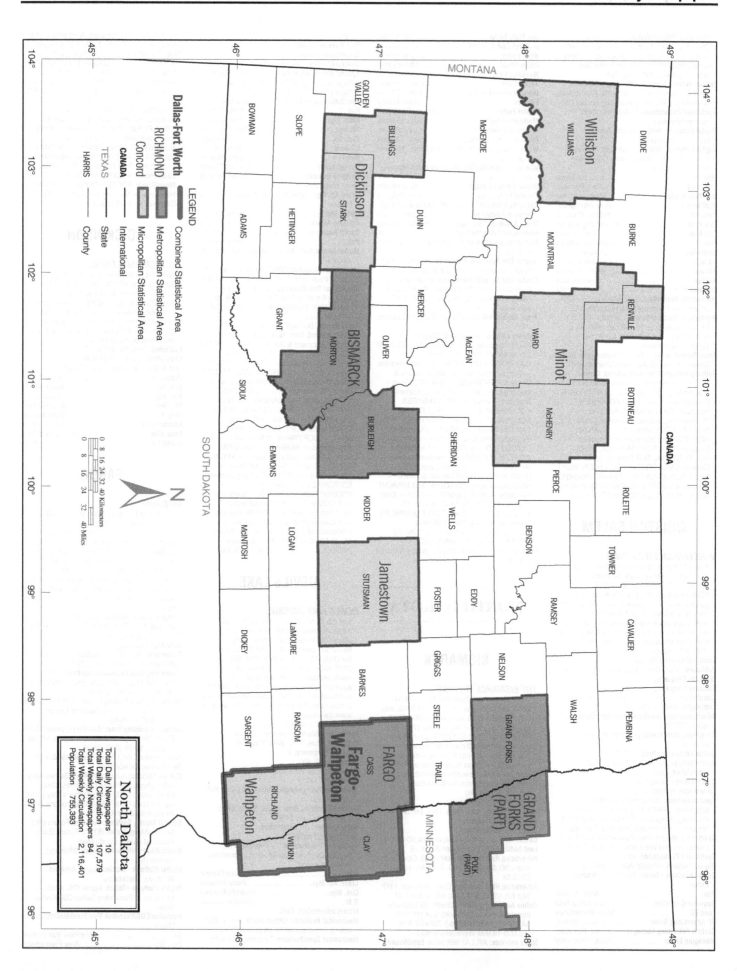

MONTANA

CANADA

SOUTH DAKOTA

MINNESOTA

LEGEND

Dallas-Fort Worth — Combined Statistical Area

RICHMOND — Metropolitan Statistical Area

Concord — Micropolitan Statistical Area

CANADA — International

TEXAS — State

HARRIS — County

0 8 16 24 32 40 Kilometers

0 8 16 24 32 40 Miles

N

North Dakota

Total Daily Newspapers	10
Total Daily Circulation	107,579
Total Weekly Newspapers	84
Total Weekly Circulation	2,116,401
Population	755,393

Counties and statistical areas labeled on map: DIVIDE, BURKE, RENVILLE, BOTTINEAU, ROLETTE, TOWNER, CAVALIER, PEMBINA, WILLIAMS (Williston), McKENZIE, MOUNTRAIL, WARD (Minot), McHENRY, PIERCE, BENSON, RAMSEY, WALSH, GOLDEN VALLEY, BILLINGS, DUNN, MERCER, McLEAN, SHERIDAN, WELLS, EDDY, FOSTER, NELSON, GRAND FORKS (PART), BOWMAN, SLOPE, STARK (Dickinson), OLIVER, MORTON (Bismarck), BURLEIGH, KIDDER, GRIGGS, STEELE, TRAIL, POLK (PART), ADAMS, HETTINGER, GRANT, SIOUX, EMMONS, LOGAN, STUTSMAN (Jamestown), BARNES, McINTOSH, DICKEY, LaMOURE, RANSOM, SARGENT, RICHLAND (Wahpeton), WILKIN, CASS (Fargo-Wahpeton), CLAY

Pres./COO .... Lloyd Case
CFO...John Hajostek
HR Dir. .... Kate Freimanis
Circ. Coord., Newspapers in Educ.........Kerri Kava
Editorial Page Ed. ....Jack Zaleski
Features Ed........................................John Lamb
Page Des. ....Mark Merck
Photo Ed. ....Mike Vosburg
News Ed., Bus......................................Jay Ulku
Online Ed. .... Rob Beer
Multi-Media Sales Mgr............... Jaclyn Hollands
Dir. of Adv. .... Scott Schmeltzer
Asst. Ed., W.F. Pioneer .... Wendy Reuer
Features/Business Editor............Sherri Richards
News Dir. ....Dave Roepke
Sports Ed. .... Kevin Schnepf
Asst. Feautures Ed........................Heidi Tetzman
Deputy Editor.................................Heidi Shaffer
Mechanical Available: Offset; Black and 3 ROP colors; insert accepted - Poly bags, samples; page cutoffs - 22.
Mechanical Specifications: Type page 11 5/8 x 20 3/4; E - 6 cols, 1 7/8, 1/6 between; A - 6 cols, 1 7/8, 1/6 between; C - 9 cols, 1 3/16, 1/8 between.Equipment & Software: PRESSROOM EQUIPMENT: Lines — 8-MAN/Roland MediaMan (Offset, 4 wide) 1993; Press DriveSiemens; Folders — MAN/Roland; Pasters —MEG 1993Reels & Stands — MEG/45 inch 1993; Control System — 1993; MAILROOM EQUIPMENT: Counter Stackers — 4-QWI/400; Inserters & Stuffers — SLS/2000; Tying Machines — 3-Samual/NT30; Control System — Winlines; Address Machine — 2-Scitex/5120.; BUSINESS EQUIPMENT: 1-DEC/Alpha 2100 BUSINESS SOFTWARE: GEAC/CIS 7.03, AIM 8.02 CLASSIFIED EQUIPMENT: Hardware — MS/NT Server; Printers — HP/4000; CLASSIFIED SOFTWARE: PBS/Media Plus 8.3. DISPLAY EQUIPMENT: Hardware — APP/Power Mac 7600; Other Hardware — 1-Flatbed Scanner, 4-Umax/PowerLook flatbed scanner DISPLAY SOFTWAREAd Make-up Applications — PBS, Multi-Ad/Creator 2; Layout Software — Multi-Ad/ALS. EDITORIAL EQUIPMENT: Hardware — MS/NT Server/APP/Mac Quadra 800, Pentium/PC 233MMX; Printers — Okidata/Microline 320, HP/LaserJet EDITORIAL SOFTWARE: Advanced Pub. Technology/Automated Complete Typesetting 2.06.4. PRODUCTION EQUIPMENT: Hardware — 2-AU/APS 6-108C, Caere/OmniPage 5.0, 2-Digital/1000 Alpha; Scanners — Kk, Nikon, Polaroid/SprintScan Plus, Epson/4996, Epson/10000XL, Polaroid/Sprintscan 4000 PRODUCTION SOFTWARE: APT, QPS/QuarkXPress 3.3.

GRAND FORKS

GRAND FORKS HERALD

375 2nd Ave N, Grand Forks, N.D., 58203-3707, Grand Forks; gen tel (701) 780-1160; adv tel (701) 780-1156; ed tel (701) 780-1100; gen fax (701) 780-1123; adv fax (701) 780-1185; ed fax (701) 780-1123; gen/nat adv e-mail slord@gfherald.com; disp adv e-mail slord@gfherald.com; class adv e-mailmsorensen@gfherald.com; ed e-mail kstromsodt@gfherald.com; web site www.grandforksherald.com
- 4,199,638(views) 549,687(visitors)
Group: Forum Communications Co.
Published: Mon, Tues, Wed, Thur, Fri, Sat, Sun
Weekday Frequency: m
Saturday Frequency: m
Circulation: 18,290; 20,992(sun)
Last Audit: VAC September 30, 2016
Branch Offices: We are a division of Forum Communications Company. Headquarters in Fargo, ND
Advertising Rate (weekday/saturday): $51.20 daily national, $53.95 Sunday national, M-Th local $33.04, F-Sun local $34.77
Advertising Rate (sunday): $34.77 local
Online Advertising Rate: Rates quoted per package and platform purchased. We offer ads on our network and also off of our network. View/uniques above are based on google analytics Oct. 22, 2017-Nov. 20, 2017.
News services: Forum News Service **Established:** 1879
Own Printing Facility?: Yes
Commercial Printers?: Yes
Special Editions: Home and Garden (April); Bride & Groom (Dec); Progress (Jan); East Grand Forks Pride (Jul); Senior Lifestyles (Jun); Coupon Book (Mar); Chamber of Commerce (May); Senior Lifestyles (Nov); Fall Home Improvement (Oct); College (Sept).
Special Weekly Sections: Expanded Sports (Mon);Business (Sat); Outdoors (Sunday)
Syndicated Publications: Relish (Monthly); Parade (S).
Proprietary Publications: Prairie Business magazine
Cont.... Anita Geffre
Assigning Ed. ....Kirsten Stromsodt
Editorial Page Ed. .... Tom Dennis
Sports Ed. .... Wayne Nelson
IT Dir....Mark Young
Prodn. Mgr., Pressroom ....Keith Haus
Pub... Korrie Wenzel
Adv. Dir... Staci Lord
circulation director........................Beth Bohlman
Mechanical Available: Offset; Black and 3 ROP colors; insert accepted; page cutoffs - 22.
Mechanical Specifications: Type page 10 9/16 x 20 3/4; E - 6 cols, 1 5/8, 1/8 between; A - 6 cols, 1 5/8, 1/8 between; C - 9 cols, 1, 1/16 between.
Areas Served: 582 and 567 inclusive
Delivery Method: Mail, Newsstand, Carrier, RacksEquipment & Software: PRESSROOM EQUIPMENT: Lines — 8-G/Urbanite 1973; Folders — G/2:1; Reels & Stands — 6-Kohler/Reels & Stands, 2-Roll/Stands.; MAILROOM EQUIPMENT: Counter Stackers — 1-Id/2000, 1-Id/660, 1-Id/440, 1-BG/108; Inserters & Stuffers — 2-MM/227E; Tying Machines — 2-MLN/MLN2A; Wrapping Singles — 1-Bu/BT16, 1-Bu/BT18; Address Machine — 2/AVY.; BUSINESS EQUIPMENT: 1-HP/Spectrum 922RX BUSINESS SOFTWARE: Cyborg CLASSIFIED EQUIPMENT: Hardware — DTI; Printers — 1-Dataproducts; CLASSIFIED SOFTWARE: DTI DISPLAY EQUIPMENT: Hardware — HI, APP/Mac 8500; Other Hardware — MON/Graphics System DISPLAY SOFTWARELayout Software — 2-HI/8300, APP/Mac. DTI EDITORIAL EQUIPMENT: Hardware — 4-AT/9000, 3-HI/8900; Printers — 2-Dataproducts/ EDITORIAL SOFTWARE: AT, HI. PRODUCTION EQUIPMENT: Hardware — 2-AU/APS Micro 5, 2-MON/Express, 1-III/3850 Imagesetter; Cameras — C/Spartan III; Scanners — 2-ECR/Autokon 1000 DE PRODUCTION SOFTWARE: HI/8900, HI/2100 CPAG 2.0.

JAMESTOWN

THE JAMESTOWN SUN

121 3rd St NW, Jamestown, N.D., 58401-3127, Stutsman; gen tel (701) 252-3120; adv tel (701) 252-3120; ed tel (701) 252-3120; gen fax (701) 251-2873; adv fax (701) 952-0025; ed fax (701) 952-8477; gen/nat adv e-mail rkeller@jamestownsun.com; disp adv e-mail jsadvertising@daktel.com; class adv e-mailrmcdonald@jamestownsun.com; ed e-mail ksteiner@jamestownsun.com; web site www.jamestownsun.com
Group: Forum Communications Co.
Published: Mon, Tues, Wed, Thur, Fri, Sat
Weekday Frequency: m
Saturday Frequency: m
Circulation: 4,168; 4,168(sat)
Last Audit: VAC September 30, 2017
Advertising Rate (weekday/saturday): Open inch rate $16.59
Online Advertising Rate: $12.00/cpm
News services: AP.
Own Printing Facility?: No
Commercial Printers?: No
Special Editions: Auto Show (Apr); Sport and Home (Feb); Progress (Mar); Fire Prevention (Oct).
Special Weekly Sections: Outdoors (Fri); Food (Sat); TV & Entertainment (Thur); Bridal (Wed).
Syndicated Publications: Relish (Monthly); Parade (S).
Picture Ed. .... John M. Steiner
Mng. Ed. ....Kathy Steiner
Press Foreman ....Boyd Anderson
Asst. Ed. .... Masaki Ova
Chief Photo. .... John Steiner
Sports Ed. .... Dave Selvig
Assignment Reporter.................. Tom LaVenture
Office manager..........................Kathy Hilgeman
Market Information: Split run; TMC; Zoned editions.
Mechanical Available: Offset; Black and 3 ROP colors; insert accepted; page cutoffs - 22 3/4.
Mechanical Specifications: Type page 12 3/4 x 21 1/2; E - 6 cols, 2, 1/6 between; A - 6 cols, 2, 1/6 between; C - 7 cols, 1 5/8, 1/6 between.
Areas Served: Jamestown & Stutsman Counties (ND)
Delivery Method: Mail, Newsstand, Carrier, RacksEquipment & Software: PRESSROOM EQUIPMENT: Lines — 2-G/Community 1974, 2-G/Community 1991; 4-G/Community 1970; Press Drive — 75-1991; Folders — 1-G/Upper Former 1993.; MAILROOM EQUIPMENT: Tying Machines — OVL/415, Bu; Address Machine — 2/Dispensa-Matic/16.; BUSINESS EQUIPMENT: IBM/Mega 4000, IBM/LEAT BUSINESS SOFTWARE: Nomads/Listmaster CLASSIFIED EQUIPMENT: Hardware — IBM; Printers — APP/Mac LaserWriter II; CLASSIFIED SOFTWARE: SunType. DISPLAY EQUIPMENT: Hardware — 2-APP/Power Mac 7200, 1-APP/Power Mac 7600; Printers — 2-APP/Mac LaserWriter Pro 810, 1-APP/Mac LaserWriter Pro 630; DISPLAY SOFTWAREAd Make-up Applications — Multi-Ad 4.0, Adobe/Photoshop 4.0, QPS/QuarkXPress 3.32.; EDITORIAL EQUIPMENT: Hardware — 11-M/2800/1-RSK/TRS 80, 1-RSK/TRS 100; Printers — 2-APP/Mac LaserWriter. PRODUCTION EQUIPMENT: Hardware — Multi-Ad, Aldus/FreeHand, QuarkXPress, Adobe/Photoshop; Cameras — DAI/Screen G-24-D-LA; Scanners — Microtek/Scanmaster E6.

MINOT

MINOT DAILY NEWS

301 4th St SE, Minot, N.D., 58701-4066, Ward; gen tel (701) 857-1900; adv tel (701) 857-1963; ed tel (701) 857-1950; gen fax (701) 857-1907; adv fax (701) 857-1907; ed fax (701) 857-1961; gen/nat adv e-mail jhart@minotdailynews.com; disp adv e-mail jhart@minotdailynews.com; class adv e-mailclassads@minotdailynews.com; ed e-mail editor@minotdailynews.com; web site www.minotdailynews.com
- 655,138(views) 158,755(visitors)
Group: Ogden Newspapers Inc.
Published: Mon, Tues, Wed, Thur, Fri, Sat, Sun
Weekday Frequency: m
Saturday Frequency: m
Circulation: 12,532; 12,532(sat); 13,631(sun)
Last Audit: AAM March 31, 2016
Advertising Rate (weekday/saturday): $32.35(net) / Natl $40.45 (net)
Advertising Rate (sunday): $32.35 (net) / Natl $40.45 (net)
Online Advertising Rate: Leaderboard - $16 CPM
Rectangle - $16 CPM
Skyscraper - $16 CPM
Half Banner - $8 CPM
Center Banner - $11 CPM
News services: AP.
Own Printing Facility?: Yes
Commercial Printers?: Yes
Special Editions: Year in Review (Jan);; Senior Scene (Qterly), Inside Ag (Qrterly), Coupon Book (Jan) (Mar); Progress (Apr); Destination Minot (May); Inside Energy (June/Dec), Booming Basin (Monthly, Graduation (May); State Fair (Jun); Football Preview(Aug); Hometown (Sept); Norsk Fest (Oct); Pulse (Nov); Readers' Choice (December)
Special Weekly Sections: Agriculture (Mon); Outdoor (S); Agriculture (Sat); Best Automotive Day (Thur); Best Food Day (Wed). Machinery Row (Sat)
Syndicated Publications: Parade (S).
Digital Platform - Mobile: Apple, Android
Digital Platform - Tablet: Apple iOS, AndroidJim Hart
Editor..Mike Sasser
Kolby Jensen
Garrick Hodge
Publisher....................................Dan McDonald
Market Information: ADS; Split run; TMC; Zoned editions.
Mechanical Available: Offset; Black and 3 ROP colors; insert accepted - sample packs and pouches; page cutoffs - 22 3/4.
Mechanical Specifications: Type page 12 x 21 1/2; E - 6 cols, 2 1/16, 1/6 between; A - 6 cols, 1 13/16, 1/6 between; C - 9 cols, 1 9/32, 1/12 between.
Areas Served: 58701
Delivery Method: Mail, Newsstand, Carrier, RacksEquipment & Software: PRESSROOM EQUIPMENT: Lines — G/Urbanite 1990.; MAILROOM EQUIPMENT: Counter Stackers — Id/440, Id/660, QWI/400; Inserters & Stuffers — HI; Tying Machines — Bu, MLN; Address Machine — Ch; BUSINESS EQUIPMENT: NCR CLASSIFIED EQUIPMENT: Hardware — MS/NT; Printers — APP/Mac LaserWriter II, MON/Imagemaster 1270, HP/2100; CLASSIFIED SOFTWARE: MS/NT. DISPLAY EQUIPMENT: Hardware — APP/Mac; Printers — APP/Mac LaserWriter II, MON/Imagemaster 1270, HP/2100, EPSON/1520; DISPLAY SOFTWAREAd Make-up Applications — NTI; Layout Software — APP/Mac. EDITORIAL EQUIPMENT: Hardware — MS/NT/APP/Mac; Printers — APP/Mac LaserWriter II, MON/Imagemaster 1270, HP/2100 EDITORIAL SOFTWARE: MS/NT. PRODUCTION EQUIPMENT: Hardware — Magnum; Cameras — SCREEN; Scanners — VG, Epson PRODUCTION SOFTWARE: QPS/QuarkXPress 4.01. IT EQUIPMENT: Windows Servers
Wired/WiFi Network IT SOFTWARE:Windows Mac OS X
iOS CIRCULATION EQUIPMENT: Hardware Printers
CIRCULATION SOFTWARAnzio System

VALLEY CITY

VALLEY CITY TIMES-RECORD

146 3rd St NE, Valley City, N.D., 58072-3047, Barnes; gen tel (701) 845-0463; adv tel (701) 845-0463; ed tel (701) 845-0463; gen fax (701) 845-0175; adv fax (701) 845-0175; ed fax (701) 845-0175; gen/nat adv e-mail trads.dave@gmail.com; disp adv e-mail trads.pam@gmail.com; class adv e-mailtrclass@times-online.com; ed e-mail treditor@times-online.com; web site http://www.times-online.com
Group: Horizon Publications Inc.
Published: Mon, Tues, Wed, Thur, Fri
Weekday Frequency: e
Circulation: 2,610
Last Audit: Sworn/Estimate/Non-Audited September 30, 2017
Advertising Rate (weekday/saturday): Varies. Call to inquire.
Advertising Rate (sunday): Varies. Call to inquire.
Online Advertising Rate: Varies. Call to inquire.
News services: AP, NEA. **Established:** 1879
Own Printing Facility?: Yes
Commercial Printers?: Yes
Special Editions: Car Care Tab (Apr); Back-to-School (Aug); Last Minute Gift Guide (Dec); Valentines (Feb); First Baby of the Year Tab (Jan); Progress (Jul); Senior Scene Tab (Jun); Girl Scouts (Mar); Graduation Tab (May); Holiday Preview (Nov); Fire Prevention Tab (Oct);
Special Weekly Sections: Church Directory (Fri); Business Page (Mon-fri); TV (Thur); Ag Page (Wed); Super Service Directory (Weekly).
Syndicated Publications: T-R Shopper (Other); American Profile (Weekly).
Office Mgr. .... Brenda Tompt
Sales ....Pam Stark
Ed...Paul Riemerman
Prod. Mgr...Tina Olson
Publisher..Bill Parsons
Market Information: TMC; Zoned editions.
Mechanical Available: Offset; Black and 1 ROP colors; insert accepted - self-adhesive notes, single sheet fliers; page cutoffs - 22 3/4.
Mechanical Specifications: Type page 11 3/4 x 21; E - 6 cols, 2, 1/8 between; A - 6 cols, 2, 1/8 between; C - 6 cols, 2, 1/8 between.
Areas Served: Barnes County (ND)
Delivery Method: Mail, RacksEquipment & Software: MAILROOM EQUIPMENT: Tying Machines — 1/Bu; Address Machine

— 1-/Am.; BUSINESS EQUIPMENT: APP/Mac CLASSIFIED EQUIPMENT: Hardware — APP/Mac; Printers — APP/Mac LaserWriter.; DISPLAY EQUIPMENT: Hardware — APP/Mac; Printers — GCC/Elite XL 20/600; DISPLAY SOFTWAREAd Make-up Applications — Multi-Ad, Adobe/PageMaker; Layout Software — PC. EDITORIAL EQUIPMENT: Hardware — APP/Mac; Printers — GCC/Elite XL 20/600. PRODUCTION EQUIPMENT: Hardware — APP/Mac; Cameras — 1-B/Commander; Scanners — Microtek/E-3.

WAHPETON

THE DAILY NEWS

601 Dakota Ave, Wahpeton, N.D., 58075-4325, Richland; gen tel (701) 642-8585; adv tel (701) 642-8585; ed tel (701) 642-8585; gen fax 701-642-6068; adv fax (701) 642-6068; ed fax (701) 642-6068; gen/nat adv e-mail ads@wahpetondailynews.com; disp adv e-mail ads@wahpetondailynews.com; class adv e-mailads@wahpetondailynews.com; ed e-mail editor@wahpetondailynews.com; web site www.wahpetondailynews.com

Group: Wick Communications
Published: Tues, Wed, Thur, Fri, Sun
Weekday Frequency: e
Circulation: 1,994; 2,216(sun)
Last Audit: Sworn/Estimate/Non-Audited September 30, 2017
Advertising Rate (weekday/saturday): Open inch rate $13.04
Advertising Rate (sunday): Open inch rate $13.04
Online Advertising Rate: Included with newspaper ad.
News services: AP.
Own Printing Facility?: Yes
Commercial Printers?: Yes
Special Editions: Progress Issue (Annually); School Activities Issue (Fall); News in Review (Jan); Voter's Guide (election years) (Nov); Bridal Issue (Other).
Syndicated Publications: Channeling (TV Section) (Fri); American Profile (Weekly).
Pub. .... Tara Klostreich
Mng. Ed. .... Kathy Leinen
Sports Ed. .... Turner Blaufuss
Prod. Mgr. .... Candace Engstrom
Circ. Clerk .... Janine Berg
Asst. Mng. Ed. .... Carrie McDermott
Reporter .... Frank Stanko
Multi-Media Sales Rep. .... Diana Hermes
Business Office Manager .... Patty Fugleberg
Market Information: TMC.
Mechanical Available: Offset; Black and 3 ROP colors; insert accepted; page cutoffs - 21 3/4.
Mechanical Specifications: Type page 11 7/8 x 21; E - 6 cols, 1 7/8, 1/8 between; A - 6 cols, 1 7/8, 1/8 between; C - 8 cols, 1 3/8, 1/16 between.
Areas Served: Richland & Wahpeton Counties (ND) and Wilkin County (MN), Breckenridge (MN)
Delivery Method: Mail, Newsstand, Carrier, RacksEquipment & Software: PRESSROOM EQUIPMENT: Lines — 6-G/Community single width; Folders — 1-G/Community.; MAILROOM EQUIPMENT: Tying Machines — 2-Felin/Pak-Tyer; Address Machine — 1-Am/R500.; BUSINESS EQUIPMENT: DEC BUSINESS SOFTWARE: Vision Data CLASSIFIED EQUIPMENT: Hardware — APP/Mac G3; Printers — HP/LaserJet 5000N; CLASSIFIED SOFTWARE: QPS/QuarkXPress 4.0, Baseview/News Edit Pro 3.1. DISPLAY EQUIPMENT: Hardware — APP/Mac G3; Printers — HP/Laser Jet 5000N; DISPLAY SOFTWAREAd Make-up Applications — QPS/QuarkXPress 4.04.; EDITORIAL EQUIPMENT: Hardware — Mk/1100 Plus, APP/Mac G3/Xante/Accel-a-Writer 36, HP/ScanJet 5300C; Printers — HP/LaserJet 5000N EDITORIAL SOFTWARE: QPS/QuarkXPress 4.04. PRODUCTION EQUIPMENT: Hardware — HP/LaserJet 5000N; Cameras — 1-B; Scanners — Umax/Astra 1200S PRODUCTION SOFTWARE: QPS/QuarkXPress 4.04.

WILLISTON

WILLISTON DAILY HERALD

PO Box 1447, Williston, N.D., 58802-1447, Williams; gen tel (701) 572-2165; adv tel (701) 572-2165; ed tel (701) 572-2165; gen fax 701-572-9563; adv fax (701) 572-9563; ed fax (701) 572-9563; gen/nat adv e-mail advertising@willistonherald.com; disp adv e-mail advertising@willistonherald.com; class adv e-mailclassified@willistonherald.com; ed e-mail editor@willistonherald.com; web site www.willistonherald.com
- 58,000(views) 56,264(visitors)

Group: Wick Communications
Published: Mon, Tues, Wed, Thur, Fri, Sat, Sun
Weekday Frequency: m
Saturday Frequency: m
Circulation: 2,834; 2,834(sat); 2,834(sun)
Last Audit: VAC September 30, 2016
Advertising Rate (weekday/saturday): Open inch rate $14.30 (retail), $10.10 (classified)
Advertising Rate (sunday): $14.30 (retail advertising), $10.10 (classified)
Online Advertising Rate: $205/mo.
News services: AP, Forum **Established:** 1911
Own Printing Facility?: Yes
Commercial Printers?: Yes
Special Weekly Sections: TV Guide
Proprietary Publications: Plains Reporter - Ag Publication (Mid-Week)
MonDak Savings Guide - Shopper (Mid-Week)
Comp. Dir. .... Aaron Hanson
Ret. Sales Mgr. .... Leah-Ann Kleber
Pub. .... Tara Klostreich
Managing Ed. .... Jamie Kelly
Circ. Mgr. .... Kathy Evenson
Market Information: Split run; TMC; Zoned editions.
Mechanical Available: Offset; Black and 3 ROP colors; insert accepted; page cutoffs - 21 1/2.
Mechanical Specifications: Type page 13 x 21; E - 6 cols, 2 1/14, 1/8 between; A - 6 cols, 2 1/14, 1/8 between; C - 9 cols, 1 3/8, 1/12 between.
Areas Served: Northwest ND & Northeast MT
Delivery Method: Mail, Newsstand, Carrier, RacksEquipment & Software: PRESSROOM EQUIPMENT: Lines — 5-HI/V-15A 1985; Folders — 2-HI/F-7 (with 1 balloon).; MAILROOM EQUIPMENT: Tying Machines — EAM-Mosca/RO-M.; BUSINESS EQUIPMENT: Ethernet, APP/Mac CLASSIFIED EQUIPMENT: Hardware — APP/Mac 7200-120; Printers — HP/Laser Writer 5000N, Unity/1800XL Plus; CLASSIFIED SOFTWARE: QPS/QuarkXPress, Adobe/Photoshop, Baseview/NewsEdit, Baseview/Class Pro. DISPLAY EQUIPMENT: Hardware — APP/Mac IIci, APP/Mac 7200-120; Printers — APP/Mac LaserWriter II, Unity/1800XL Plus, HP/LaserWriter 5000N; Other Hardware — APP/Mac CD-Rom, APP/Mac One Scanner, Microtek Scanner. DISPLAY SOFTWAREAd Make-up Applications — Multi-Ad/Creator, Caere/OmniPage, Caere/OmniPhoto; EDITORIAL EQUIPMENT: Hardware — APP/Mac 7200-120, APP/Mac 7300-180, APP/Mac 7600-120; Printers — HP/LaserWriter 5000N, Unity/1800XL Plus EDITORIAL SOFTWARE: QPS/QuarkXPress, Adobe/Photoshop, Baseview/Newsedit Pro. PRODUCTION EQUIPMENT: Hardware — 1-Nu, Unity/1800 XL Plus, HP/5000 N; Cameras — B; Scanners — Epson, Nikon/LS 1000 PRODUCTION SOFTWARE: QPS/QuarkXPress 3.32c, Baseview/NewsEdit Pro 2.2.2.

OHIO

AKRON

AKRON BEACON JOURNAL

44 E Exchange St, Akron, Ohio, 44308-1510, Summit; gen tel (330) 996-3000; adv tel (330) 996-3410; ed tel (330) 996-3512; gen fax (330) 996-3033; adv fax (330) 996-3299; ed fax (330) 996-3520; gen/nat adv e-mail lcarver@thebeaconjournal.com; disp adv e-mail lcarver@thebeaconjournal.com; class adv e-maillcarver@thebeaconjournal.com; ed e-mail bjnews@thebeaconjournal.com; web site www.ohio.com
- 7,718,024(views) 1,469,315(visitors)

Group: New Media Investment Group
Published: Mon, Tues, Wed, Thur, Fri, Sat, Sun
Weekday Frequency: m
Saturday Frequency: m
Circulation: 62,974; 74,355(sat); 80,634(sun)
Last Audit: AAM March 31, 2017
News services: AP, MCT, RN. **Established:** 1839
Own Printing Facility?: No
Commercial Printers?: No
Special Editions: New Year, New Career (Jan), Super Bowl; Summer Camp Guide; Beacon's Best; Envision; Auto Show; Home & Flower Show (Feb), New Baby News; Greater Akron Chamber (Mar), Great Places to Work; Beacon's Best Results(April), Star Students; Nurses Week; Summer Fun Guide; Green Chamber (May), Bridgestone Fan Guide; Boston Mills Artfest; Cavs Finals; Cavs Championship (June), High School Preview (Aug), Autumn Adventures (Sep), Halloween Happenings (Oct), Holiday Gift Guide; Veteran's Day; Beacon Savings Book (Nov), Holiday Gift Guide (Dec)
Special Weekly Sections: American Profile (Mon); Your Health (Tue); Food (Wed); Auto, Entertainment (Thur); Real Estate (Fri); Home, Saturday Lifestyle, Savvy Shopper, Relish, Spry (Sat); Life, Job Source (Sun)
Digital Platform - Mobile: Apple, Android, Blackberry
Digital Platform - Tablet: Apple iOS, Android, Blackberry Tablet OS, Kindle, Nook, Kindle Fire
Mng. Ed. .... Doug Oplinger
Controller .... Tim Betz
Publisher .... Mark Cohen
Night Mng. Ed. .... Bruce Winges
VP/Circulation .... Shaun Schweitzer
IT Director .... Dawn Bonfiglio
VP/Advertising .... Lori Carver
HR and Labor Relations Director .... Jay Hunter
Mechanical Specifications: Type page 11 x 22; E - 6 cols, 1 1/2, 1/8 between; A - 6 cols, 1 1/2, 1/8 between; C - 8 cols, 1 1/8, 1/8 between.
Areas Served: Summit, Medina, Stark, Portage, Wayne and parts of Cuyahoga Counties (OH)

ALLIANCE

THE REVIEW

40 S Linden Ave, Alliance, Ohio, 44601-2447, Stark; gen tel (330) 821-1200; adv tel (330) 821-1200; ed tel (330) 821-1300; gen fax (330) 821-8258; adv fax (330) 821-8258; ed fax (330) 821-8258; gen/nat adv e-mail reviewads@the-review.com ; disp adv e-mail reviewads@the-review.com ; class adv e-mailclassifieds@the-review.com; ed e-mail reviewedit@the-review.com; web site www.the-review.com

Published: Mon, Tues, Wed, Thur, Fri, Sat
Weekday Frequency: m
Saturday Frequency: m
Circulation: 8,069; 9,409(sat)
Last Audit: CAC June 30, 2017
Advertising Rate (weekday/saturday): Open inch rate $14.95
Online Advertising Rate: 3:1 Rectangle $6; Standard Banner $7; Wide Skyscraper $7; Button $7; Box $7.50; Leaderboard $8.50; Half Page $10; Text ads $15/week
News services: AP, CNS, DF, DJ, NYT, SHNS, TMS. **Established:** 1888
Special Editions: Year in Review (Jan).
Special Weekly Sections: Real Estate (Fri); Church Page (Sat); Entertainment-Let's Go (Thur); Business Page (Wed).
Syndicated Publications: TV Magazine (Fri); American Profile (Weekly).
Pub. .... G. Charles Dix
Gen. Mgr. .... Robert Waite
Accent Ed. .... Shannon Harsh
Sports Ed. .... Mike Brown
Market Information: ADS; Split run; TMC; Zoned editions.
Mechanical Available: Offset; Black and 3 ROP colors; insert accepted; page cutoffs - 21 1/2.
Mechanical Specifications: Type page 13 x 21 1/2; E - 6 cols, 2 1/16, 1/8 between; A - 6 cols, 2 1/16, 1/8 between; C - 6 cols, 2 1/16, 1/8 between.
Areas Served: Alliance (OH) and Surrounding areas
Equipment & Software: PRESSROOM EQUIPMENT: Lines — 6-G/Urbanite 1967; MAILROOM EQUIPMENT: Counter Stackers — BG/Count-O-Veyor; Inserters & Stuffers — MM; Tying Machines — Bu.; BUSINESS EQUIPMENT: DSI CLASSIFIED EQUIPMENT: Hardware — APP/Mac; Printers — HP; CLASSIFIED SOFTWARE: Vision Data. DISPLAY EQUIPMENT: Hardware — Wyse/Terminal, Dec/Processor; Printers — Okidata, Tally; DISPLAY SOFTWAREAd Make-up Applications — Data Sciences; Layout Software — Baseview. EDITORIAL EQUIPMENT: Hardware — APP/Mac; Printers — 6-New Gen/DesignXpress EDITORIAL SOFTWARE: Baseview. PRODUCTION EQUIPMENT: Hardware — 1-Nu, Ultre/94E, Konica/K-550; Cameras — Kk/PMT; Scanners — Umax, AG PRODUCTION SOFTWARE: Baseview.

ASHLAND

ASHLAND TIMES-GAZETTE

40 E 2nd St, Ashland, Ohio, 44805-2304, Ashland; gen tel (419) 281-0581; adv tel (419) 281-0581; ed tel (419) 281-0581 ext. 211; gen fax (419) 281-5591; adv fax (419) 281-8692; ed fax (419) 281-5591; gen/nat adv e-mail mkraker@times-gazette.com; disp adv e-mail internetadvertising@dixcom.com; class adv e-mailclassified@times-gazette.com; ed e-mail letters@times-gazette.com; web site www.times-gazette.com; web site 2 www.dixcom.com

Group: GateHouse Media, Inc.
Published: Mon, Tues, Wed, Thur, Fri, Sat
Weekday Frequency: m
Saturday Frequency: m
Circulation: 9,626; 9,626(sat)
Last Audit: CAC March 31, 2016
Advertising Rate (weekday/saturday): Open inch rate $12.15
News services: AP. **Established:** 1850
Own Printing Facility?: Yes
Commercial Printers?: No
Special Editions: Auto Tab (Apr); Football Preview (Aug); Christmas Songbook (Dec); Senior Citizens (Feb); Bridal Tab (Jan); Senior Citizens (Jul); Balloon Fest (Jun); Spring Home Improvement (Mar); Hospital Nursing (May); Holiday Cookbook (Nov); Health Focus (Oct); Fair (
Special Weekly Sections: Clip2Save (Mon); Health, Teen (Tue); Business (Wed/Fri); Food (Wed); Real Estate, Religion (Fri); Agricultural (Sat)
Syndicated Publications: TV Weekly (Sat).
Digital Platform - Mobile: Apple, Android, Blackberry
Digital Platform - Tablet: Apple iOS, Android, Blackberry Tablet OS
Publisher .... Andrew S. Dix
Cir. Mgr. .... Deb Boreman
Chief Photo. .... Tom Puskar
Sp. Proj. Ed. .... Jarred Opatz
Ed. / Gen. Mgr. .... Lance White
Adv. Mgr. .... Mark Kraker
Bus. Mgr. .... Angie Meade
Manager of Mergers & Acquisitions .... Troy Dix
Market Information: TMC.
Mechanical Available: Offset; Black and 3 ROP colors; insert accepted - single sheet; page cutoffs - 22 3/4.
Mechanical Specifications: Type page 12 1/2 x 21 1/2; E - 6 cols, 1 5/6, 1/8 between; A - 6 cols, 1 1/4, 1/8 between; C - 9 cols, 1 1/4, 1/8 between.
Areas Served: Ashland County
Delivery Method: Mail, Newsstand, Carrier, RacksEquipment & Software: PRESSROOM EQUIPMENT: Lines — 8-G/Community 1972, 1-G/Community 1992.; MAILROOM EQUIPMENT: Counter Stackers — BG/Count-O-Veyor; Tying Machines — Tri-Star/210, Mosca.; BUSINESS EQUIPMENT: DSI CLASSIFIED EQUIPMENT: Hardware — APP/iMac; Printers — Okidata; CLASSIFIED SOFTWARE: Baseview.

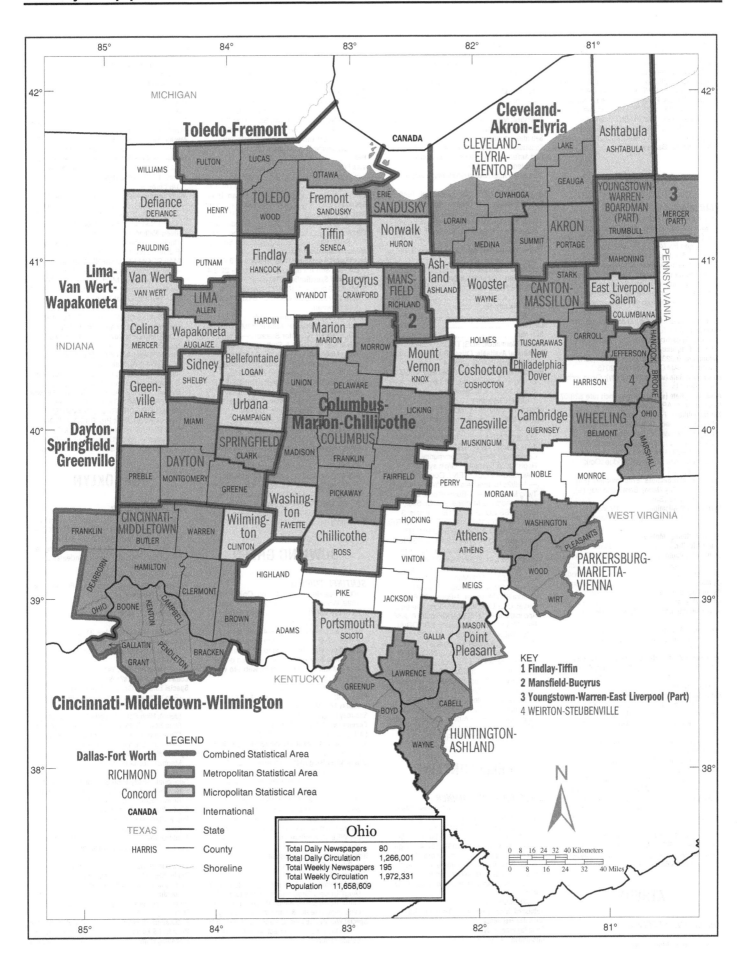

KEY
1 **Findlay-Tiffin**
2 **Mansfield-Bucyrus**
3 **Youngstown-Warren-East Liverpool (Part)**
4 WEIRTON-STEUBENVILLE

LEGEND

Dallas-Fort Worth	Combined Statistical Area
RICHMOND	Metropolitan Statistical Area
Concord	Micropolitan Statistical Area
CANADA	International
TEXAS	State
HARRIS	County
	Shoreline

Ohio

Total Daily Newspapers	80
Total Daily Circulation	1,266,001
Total Weekly Newspapers	195
Total Weekly Circulation	1,972,331
Population	11,658,609

DISPLAY EQUIPMENT: Hardware — APP/Mac; Printers — APP/Mac LaserWriter NTX, 2-ECR/VR 36 Imagesetter; DISPLAY SOFTWAREAd Make-up Applications — DSI.; EDITORIAL EQUIPMENT: Hardware — 2-Data General/Unix Server, 1-Data General/AV Disk Array, APP/Power Mac G3, APP/Power Mac G4; Printers — HP/Rip, Konica/Rip EDITORIAL SOFTWARE: Baseview. PRODUCTION EQUIPMENT: Hardware — 1-Nu, Adobe/Photoshop, QuarkXPress; Scanners — Epson PRODUCTION SOFTWARE: Baseview.

ASHTABULA

STAR BEACON

4626 Park Ave, Ashtabula, Ohio, 44004-6933, Ashtabula; gen tel (440) 998-2323 ; adv tel (440) 998-2323 Ext. 102; ed tel (440) 994-2323; gen fax (440) 998-7938; adv fax (440) 992-9655; ed fax (440) 998-7938; gen/nat adv e-mail marketplace@starbeacon.com; disp adv e-mail marketplace@starbeacon.com; class adv e-mailmarketplace@starbeacon.com; ed e-mail mhutton@starbeacon.com; web site www.starbeacon.com

Group: Community Newspaper Holdings, Inc.
Published: Mon, Tues, Wed, Thur, Fri, Sat, Sun
Weekday Frequency: m
Saturday Frequency: m
Circulation: 9,623; 9,623(sat); 11,134(sun)
Last Audit: AAM December 31, 2015
Advertising Rate (weekday/saturday): Open inch rate $25.71
Advertising Rate (sunday): Open inch rate $28.07
News services: AP. **Established:** 1888
Special Editions: Football Features (Aug); Christmas (Dec); Bridal (Jan); Dog Days (Jul); Ashtabula County Almanac (Jun); Washington's Birthday (Mar); Health Care (May); Family Life (Monthly); Women in Business (Nov); Covered Bridge (Oct); Progress (Sept).
Special Weekly Sections: Entertainment (Fri); Best Food Day (Mon); Best Food Day (S); Church News (Sat).
Syndicated Publications: Relish (Monthly); TV Scene Magazine (S); American Profile (Weekly).
Digital Platform - Mobile: Apple
Pub. / Adv. Dir. .... Jamie Beacom
Staff Writ. / Photo. .... Warren Dillaway
Ed. .... Matt Hutton
Bus. Mgr. .... Lisa Kondik
CS Mgr. .... Pam Harper
Dir. of Aud. Dev. (Cir.) .... Steve Traud
Adv. Acct. Exec. .... Shelley Lipps
Market Information: ADS; Split run; TMC; Zoned editions.
Mechanical Available: Offset; Black and 3 ROP colors; insert accepted - any; page cutoffs - 21 1/4.
Mechanical Specifications: Type page 13 x 21 1/2; E - 6 cols, 2 1/16, 1/8 between; A - 6 cols, 2 1/16, 1/8 between; C - 9 cols, 1 1/2, 1/16 between.
Areas Served: Ashtabula, Lake, Geauga, Trumbull, Crawford, Erie Counties (OH)
Equipment & Software: PRESSROOM EQUIPMENT: Lines — 6-G/Urbanite (1 color deck); MAILROOM EQUIPMENT: Counter Stackers — BG/108; Inserters & Stuffers — MM/227; Tying Machines — Sa/S1100.; BUSINESS EQUIPMENT: 6-ATT/3B2-500, 1-DEC/1173, 1-DEC CLASSIFIED EQUIPMENT: Hardware — 1-Mk; IBM; Printers — 1-TI; CLASSIFIED SOFTWARE: Mk. DISPLAY EQUIPMENT: Hardware — ATT; DISPLAY SOFTWAREAd Make-up Applications — ATT; Layout Software — ATT. EDITORIAL EQUIPMENT: Hardware — Mk, APP/Mac, IBM/1-Lf, 1-Lf; Printers — 1-II EDITORIAL SOFTWARE: Mk. PRODUCTION EQUIPMENT: Hardware — Tegra/Varityper 5300, 17-AG/660; Cameras — 1-Nu.

ATHENS

THE ATHENS MESSENGER

9300 Johnson Hollow Rd, Athens, Ohio, 45701-9028, Athens; gen tel (740) 592-6612; adv tel (740) 592-6612 ext. 209; ed tel (740) 592-6612 Ext. 224; gen fax (740) 592-4647; adv fax (740) 592-4647; ed fax (740) 592-4647; gen/nat adv e-mail jbunch@athensmessenger.com; disp adv e-mail gchristensen@athensmessenger.com; class adv e-mailpdennis@athensmessenger.com; ed e-mail jhiggins@athensmessenger.com; web site www.athensohiotoday.com

Published: Mon, Tues, Wed, Thur, Fri, Sat, Sun
Weekday Frequency: m
Saturday Frequency: m
Circulation: 11,272; 11,272(sat); 11,375(sun)
Last Audit: Sworn/Estimate/Non-Audited September 30, 2017
Advertising Rate (weekday/saturday): Open inch rate $23.94
News services: AP, SHNS. **Established:** 1848
Special Editions: New Babies (Apr); Football Tab (Aug); Wedding Guide (Feb); County Fair (Jul); Fashion (Mar); Spring/Summer Car Care (May); Basketball Tab (Nov); Fall Car Care (Oct).
Special Weekly Sections: Church Page (Fri); Home & Garden (S).
Syndicated Publications: Color Comics (S); American Profile (Weekly).
Pub. / APG Media Pres. .... Monica Nieporte
Ed. .... Joe Higgins
APG Media Adv. Dir. .... Pete Dennis
Adv. Dir. .... Jeff Bunch
Cir. Dir. .... Paul Brown
Bus. Mgr. .... Craig Dickelman
Market Information: ADS; TMC.
Mechanical Available: Offset; Black and 3 ROP colors; page cutoffs - 22 3/4.
Mechanical Specifications: Type page 11 5/8 x 21 1/4; E - 5 cols, 2 3/8, 3/16 between; A - 6 cols, 1 13/16, 3/16 between; C - 8 cols, 1 7/16, 3/16 between.
Areas Served: Athens County (OH)
Delivery Method: Newsstand, Carrier, RacksEquipment & Software: PRESSROOM EQUIPMENT: Lines — 5-G/Urbanite 1972, 1-G/Urbanite 1980, 1-G/Urbanite 1992; 4-G/Community 1983, 2-G/Community 1986; Registration System — G/pin system. MAILROOM EQUIPMENT: Counter Stackers — 1-HI/2510; Inserters & Stuffers — 1/MM; Tying Machines — 1-Bu/Akebone, 2-Dynaric/RLM-1; Address Machine — 1-Ch/596.; BUSINESS EQUIPMENT: 8 terminals, 3 PC's-Sun Ultra 10 BUSINESS SOFTWARE: Vision Data CLASSIFIED EQUIPMENT: Hardware — 3-APP/Mac G3; CLASSIFIED SOFTWARE: Baseview/Ad Manager Pro 2.0.5. DISPLAY EQUIPMENT: Hardware — 2-APP/Mac Quadra 800, 2-APP/Mac Quadra 650, 1-APP/Mac IIci, 1-Global/Dos-486; Other Hardware — 1-APP/Mac Quadra 800 fileserver, 1-Power/PC 6100 print server. DISPLAY SOFTWAREAd Make-up Applications — QPS/QuarkXPress, Aldus/PageMaker, Multi-Ad/Creator; EDITORIAL EQUIPMENT: Hardware — 18-APP/Mac G3; Printers — Okidata/Pacemark 3410, Okidata/MicroLine 320 EDITORIAL SOFTWARE: Baseview/News Edit Pro I QUE 3.1.8. PRODUCTION EQUIPMENT: Hardware — 2-NewGen/Turbo PS-660B, 2-NewGen/Design Express 1200 dpi, ECR/VRL 45HS Imagesetter, Xante/Accel-a-Writer 8200; Cameras — 1-C/Spartan III, 1-C/Vertical; Scanners — 1-ECR/Autokon 1030N, Umax/UC-1260, Agfa/Accas II, Nikon/LS 2000 PRODUCTION SOFTWARE: QPS

BELLEFONTAINE

BELLEFONTAINE EXAMINER

127 E Chillicothe Ave, Bellefontaine, Ohio, 43311-1957, Logan; gen tel (937) 592-3060; adv tel (937) 651-2125; ed tel (937) 651-1124; gen fax (937) 592-4463; adv fax (937) 592-4463; ed fax (937) 592-4463; gen/nat adv e-mail ads@examiner.org; disp adv e-mail bchampman@examiner.org; class adv e-mailclassifieds@examiner.org; ed e-mail news@examiner.org; web site www.examiner.org
- 175,000(views)

Published: Mon, Tues, Wed, Thur, Fri, Sat
Weekday Frequency: e
Saturday Frequency: m
Circulation: 9,130; 9,130(sat)
Last Audit: Sworn/Estimate/Non-Audited September 30, 2017
Advertising Rate (weekday/saturday): Open inch rate $11.75
News services: AP. **Established:** 1891
Own Printing Facility?: Yes
Commercial Printers?: No
Special Editions: Real Estate Tab (Apr); Sale Days (Aug); Christmas Greetings (Dec); Home Maintenance (Fall); Sale Days (Feb); Real Estate Tab (Jul); Bridal (Jun); Indian Lake Resort Tab (May); Real Estate Tab (Sept); Home Maintenance (Spring).
Pub. .... Janet K. Hubbard
Vice Pres. .... Jon B. Hubbard
Adv. Mgr. .... Bob Chapman
Circ. Mgr. .... Jill Thomas
Ed. .... Miriam Baier
Sports Ed. .... Matt Hammond
Asst. Gen. Mgr. .... TJ Hubbarb
Staff Writ. .... Mandy Loehr
Class. .... Diane Lewis
Adv. Sales. Rep. .... Jim Strzalka
Market Information: TMC.
Mechanical Available: Offset; Black and 3 ROP colors; insert accepted; page cutoffs - 22 3/4.
Mechanical Specifications: Type page 13 x 21 1/2; E - 6 cols, 2 1/16, 1/8 between; A - 6 cols, 2 1/16, 1/8 between; C - 8 cols, 1 3/8, 1/16 between.
Areas Served: Logan County (OH)
Equipment & Software: MAILROOM EQUIPMENT: Counter Stackers — 1-BG/106; Inserters & Stuffers — 5/KAN; Tying Machines — 1-/Bu, 1-EAM-Mosca; Address Machine — 1-Ch/515.; BUSINESS EQUIPMENT: 2-Laser/486 BUSINESS SOFTWARE: MSSI, Synaptic CLASSIFIED EQUIPMENT: Hardware — Dewar/Disc Net IV, 1-AST/286; Printers — Okidata/393; CLASSIFIED SOFTWARE: Dewar/Disc Net IV. DISPLAY EQUIPMENT: Hardware — Dewar/Discovery; DISPLAY SOFTWAREAd Make-up Applications — Dewar/Discovery; Layout Software - Dewar, 2-SIA/386. EDITORIAL EQUIPMENT: Hardware — Dewar/Disc Net IV, 16-AST/286, 5-SIA/386/dBase/IV, XYQUEST/XyWrite III, Novell/Netware; Printers — Okidata/320 EDITORIAL SOFTWARE: Dewar/Disc Net IV. PRODUCTION EQUIPMENT: Hardware — 1-Nu/Flip Top FT40APRNS; Cameras — 1-R/500.

BOWLING GREEN

SENTINEL-TRIBUNE

300 E Poe Rd, Bowling Green, Ohio, 43402-1329, Wood; gen tel (419) 352-4611; adv tel (419) 352-4611; ed tel (419) 352-4611; gen fax (419) 354-0314; adv fax (419) 354-0314; ed fax (419) 354-0314; gen/nat adv e-mail ads@sentinel-tribune.com; disp adv e-mail ads@sentinel-tribune.com; class adv e-mailads@sentinel-tribune.com; ed e-mail letters@sentinel-tribune.com; web site www.sent-trib.com

Group: AIM Media Indiana
Published: Mon, Tues, Wed, Thur, Fri, Sat
Weekday Frequency: e
Saturday Frequency: m
Circulation: 7,752; 7,752(sat)
Last Audit: AAM March 31, 2015
Advertising Rate (weekday/saturday): Open inch rate $12.25
Online Advertising Rate: Leaderboard $160; Business Card Rotator $42; Business Bulletin Board $77; Homepage Tile $42; Secondary Page Tile $27; Medium Rectangle Homepage $78; Medium Rectangle Secondary page $52; Skyscraper Homepage $135; Skyscraper Secondary page $62; Full Banner Homepage $115. (All previous rates per WEEK). Weather Tile Home page $400/Month
News services: AP. **Established:** 1867
Own Printing Facility?: Yes
Commercial Printers?: Yes
Special Editions: Art Walk (Apr); Back-to-College (Aug); Bride & Groom (Sep); Baby (Jan); Fair (Jun); Travel & Recreation (May); Christmas Gifts (Nov); Health & Fitness (Semi-yearly).
Special Weekly Sections: Church Page (Fri); Best Food Day (Thur); Auto Section (Mon); Real Estate (Thur)
Syndicated Publications: USA WEEKEND Magazine (Fri).
Digital Platform - Mobile: Apple
Digital Platform - Tablet: Apple iOS
President .... T.M. Haswell
Sec./Treasurer .... Kathryn A. Haswell
Cir. Mgr. .... Randy Machan
Pub. / V.P. .... Karmen Concannon
Adv. Dir. .... Banks Dishmon
Ed. .... Victoria Dugger
Market Information: Wood County
Mechanical Available: Offset; Black and 3 ROP colors; insert accepted; page cutoffs - 22 3/4.
Mechanical Specifications: Type page 10 29/32 x 21; E - 6 cols, 1 9/16, 1/8 between; A - 6 cols, 1 9/16, 1/8 between; C - 7 cols, 1 11/32, 1/8 between.
Areas Served: 43402, 43403, 43551, 44817, 43406, 43511, 43413, 43525, 43437, 43443, 43447, 45872, 43619, 43450, 43451, 43457, 43460, 43462, 43565, 43465, 43466, 43569
Delivery Method: Mail, Newsstand, Carrier, RacksEquipment & Software: PRESSROOM EQUIPMENT: Lines — 5-G/Urbanite; MAILROOM EQUIPMENT: Counter Stackers — HL/Monitor; Inserters & Stuffers — 1-KAN/760; Tying Machines — 1-Sa/SR2A; Address Machine — 2-Wm/No 2.; BUSINESS SOFTWARE: Great Plains/VisionData CLASSIFIED EQUIPMENT: Hardware — APP/Mac; CLASSIFIED SOFTWARE: VisionData/Ad Manager Pro. DISPLAY EQUIPMENT: Hardware — APP/Power Mac G3; Printers — APP/Mac LaserWriter Pro, HP/LaserJet 4V, HP/5000N; DISPLAY SOFTWAREAd Make-up Applications — InDesign / Multi-Ad Creator 4.0, QPS; Layout Software — Baseview/Advertising Layout System. EDITORIAL EQUIPMENT: Hardware — APP/Mac/APP/Server NT; Printers — Various HP EDITORIAL SOFTWARE: Baseview/NewsEdit Pro. PRODUCTION EQUIPMENT: Hardware — Kodak CTP; Scanners — Nikon/Coolscan III, HP/ScanJet 4C PRODUCTION SOFTWARE: InDesign

BROOKLYN

THE PLAIN DEALER

4800 Tiedeman Rd, Brooklyn, Ohio, 44144-2336, Cuyahoga; gen tel (216) 999-5000; ed tel (216) 999-4825; gen fax (216) 999-6209; ed fax (216) 325-1900; ed e-mail grodrigue@plaind.com; web site www.plaindealer.com
3,168,000(visitors)

Group: Advance Publications, Inc.
Published: Mon, Tues, Wed, Thur, Fri, Sat, Sun
Weekday Frequency: m
Saturday Frequency: m
Circulation: 179,224; 152,943(sat); 248,273(sun)
Last Audit: AAM December 31, 2016
News services: AP, NYT, Washington Post, Tribune News Service, Bloomberg
Established: 1842
Own Printing Facility?: Yes
Commercial Printers?: Yes
Special Editions: Greater Cleveland Auto Show (Feb.); Cleveland Indians preview (April); A-List Dining Guide (April); Top Workplaces (June); High School Football preview (Aug.); Ohio State/College Football preview (Aug.); Cleveland Browns/NFL preview (Sept.); Cleveland Cavaliers/NBA preview (Oct.)
Special Weekly Sections: Taste (Wed); Friday Magazine (Entertainment) (Fri). Arts & Life (Sun), Travel (Sun)
Seasonal: Varsity-High School football (Sat), Buckeye Extra-OSU/college football (Sun), Browns Extra-Pro football (Mon)
Digital Platform - Mobile: Apple, Android
Digital Platform - Tablet: Apple iOS, Android, Kindle, Kindle Fire
Facilities Mgr. .... Terry Stineman
Dir. Circ Distribution & Transportation .... Bryan Schneider
VP of Operations .... Joseph Bowman
Prodn. Mgr., Machinists/Engineers Damon Borom
Prod. Qual Assurance & Commercial Printing Coordinator .... Bob Dagostino
Prodn. Tech. Service Mgr. .... Nick Vangelos
IT Prod System Mgr .... Brian Ritchie
Publications Director .... Daryl Kannberg
President & Editor .... George Rodrigue
Managing Editor .... Tim Warsinskey

Dir Labor & Empl Relations......... Paul Cavanagh
Bus. Sol. Mgr., IT........................Jennifer Szucs
Market Information: Split run; Zoned editions.
Mechanical Available: Offset; Black and 4 ROP colors; insert accepted; page cutoffs - 22.
Mechanical Specifications: Type page 9.88 x 21; E - 6 cols, 1 3/4, 1/8 between; A - 6 cols, 1 13/16, 1/8 between; C - 10 cols, 1 1/8, 1/16 between.
Delivery Method: Mail, Newsstand, Carrier, RacksEquipment & Software: PRESSROOM EQUIPMENT: Lines — 4-GossColorliner 44" double width 1993; Control System — Rockwell; 4-Ad-A-Note Machines
MAILROOM EQUIPMENT: Counter Stackers — 8-HL/Monitor, 14-QWI, 2-QWI/Packman; Inserters & Stuffers — 4-GMA/SLS 1000, 1-GMA/SLS 2000, 2-GMA/SLS 3000; Tying Machines — 22-Dynaric. 8-Quipp; Control System — SAM Plans; Address Machine —1-KAN. 2-Accraply labelers. 3-Miracom.; CLASSIFIED SOFTWARE: News Cycle Advertising
News Cycle PGL DISPLAY SOFTWARELayout Software — News Cycle PGL. EDITORIAL SOFTWARE: News Cycle Content PRODUCTION EQUIPMENT: Hardware — 3-Kk/Trendsetter 150; 1 Trendsetter 200; PRODUCTION SOFTWARE: HI/Data Center.

BRYAN

THE BRYAN TIMES

127 S Walnut St, Bryan, Ohio, 43506-1718, Williams; gen tel (419) 636-1111; adv tel (419) 636-1111; ed tel (419) 636-1111; gen fax (419) 636-8937; adv fax (419) 636-8937; ed fax (419) 636-8937; gen/nat adv e-mail ads@bryantimes.com; disp adv e-mail ads@bryantimes.com; class adv e-mailclassifieds@bryantimes.com; ed e-mail editor@bryantimes.com; web site www. bryantimes.com
Group: Bryan Publishing Co.
Published: Mon, Tues, Wed, Thur, Sat
Weekday Frequency: e
Saturday Frequency: e
Circulation: 7,382; 7,995(sat)
Last Audit: AAM September 30, 2014
Advertising Rate (weekday/saturday): Open (rate $10.90
News services: AP, CT, CNS, CSM, TMS. **Established:** 1949
Special Editions: Car Care (Apr); Back to School (Aug); Gift Guide Tab (Dec); Personal Tax & Finance Guide (Feb); News Review (Jan); Fair Tab (Jul); Eye Care/Vision (Mar); Summer Guide (May); Christmas Opening (Nov); Your Health Tab (Oct); Fall Home Improvement Tab (Sept).
Special Weekly Sections: Business (Wed); Farm (Wed); Church (Fri); Football (In Season); Real Estate (Fri)
Syndicated Publications: Relish (Monthly); USA WEEKEND Magazine (Sat); American Profile (Weekly).
Chrmn./Pres./Pub...................Christopher Cullis
Adv....Shelley Davis
Gen. Mgr..................................Sally Heaston
Cir. Mgr........................................Mark J. Keller
Soc. Ed.......................................Sharon Patten
Asst. Ed.......................................Max Reinhart
Class. Adv. Mgr.........................Amy Thompson
Ed...Don Koralewski
Market Information: ADS; TMC.
Mechanical Available: Offset; Black and 4 ROP colors; insert accepted; page cutoffs - 22 3/4.
Mechanical Specifications: Type page 11 5/8 x 21; E - 6 cols, 1 5/6, 1/8 between; A - 6 cols, 1 5/6, 1/8 between; C - 9 cols, 1 5/16, 1/8 between.
Areas Served: 43501, 43505, 43506, 43517, 43518, 43531, 43543, 43554, 43557, 43570, 43502, 43521, 43553
Equipment & Software: PRESSROOM EQUIPMENT: Lines — 5-G/Community 1968, 1-G/3-Color Unit; 4-G/Community 1992; Folders — 1-G/Community, 1-G/ SC.; MAILROOM EQUIPMENT: Tying Machines — 3-EAM-Mosca, 1/Ty-Tech, 1-EAM-Mosca/Strapper; Address Machine — Epson/DF-5000, Epson/Equity 2.; BUSINESS EQUIPMENT: MSSI BUSINESS SOFTWARE: MSSI, Microsoft/Windows 95, Execubanc, ACH CLASSIFIED EQUIPMENT: Hardware — APP/Power Mac G4, APP/ Power Mac 7300/200; Printers — Pre Press/ Panther Pro 36; CLASSIFIED SOFTWARE: Baseview/Ad Manager Pro 2.2. DISPLAY EQUIPMENT: Hardware — 3-APP/Mac IIsi, APP/Mac G3, APP/Mac G4; Printers — 1-APP/Mac LaserWriter II NTX, Pre Press/ Panther Pro 36; DISPLAY SOFTWAREAd Make-up Applications — Multi-Ad/Creator, QPS/QuarkXPress; Layout Software — APP/Mac. EDITORIAL EQUIPMENT: Hardware — APP/Power Mac 7300-20, Pre Press/Panther Pro; Printers — APP/Mac LaserWriter Plus EDITORIAL SOFTWARE: Baseview/News Edit Pro 3.4, APP/Power Mac G4. PRODUCTION EQUIPMENT: Hardware — Pre Press/Panther Pro 36, Adobe/Photoshop; Cameras — 1-B/Caravel, 1-DSA/Vertical Camera; Scanners — APP/ Mac PRODUCTION SOFTWARE: QPS/ QuarkXPress 4.1.

CAMBRIDGE

THE DAILY JEFFERSONIAN

831 Wheeling Ave, Cambridge, Ohio, 43725-2316, Guernsey; gen tel (740) 439-3531; adv tel (740) 439-3532; ed tel (740) 439-3531; gen fax (740) 439-3533; adv fax (740) 439-3533; ed fax (740) 432-6219; gen/nat adv e-mail ads@daily-jeff.com; disp adv e-mail ads@daily-jeff.com; class adv e-mailkim@ daily-jeff.com; ed e-mail newsroom@daily-jeff.com; web site www.daily-jeff.com
Group: GateHouse Media, Inc.
Published: Mon, Tues, Wed, Thur, Fri, Sun
Weekday Frequency: m
Circulation: 7,647; 8,684(sun)
Last Audit: AAM June 30, 2017
Advertising Rate (weekday/saturday): Open inch rate $16.25
Advertising Rate (sunday): Open inch rate $16.25
News services: AP, Dixewire. **Established:** 1824
Special Editions: Babies (Apr); Back-to-School (Aug); Elected Officials Greetings (Dec); Health & Fitness (Feb); Tax Guide (Jan); Ohio Hills Folk Fest (Jul); Father's Day (Jun); Lawn & Garden (Mar); In Memoriam (May); Yuletide Gift Guide & Cash Give-away (Nov); Auto Care (
Special Weekly Sections: Best Food (Mon); Business, Engagements (Wed); Farm, Garden (Thur); Entertainment (Fri); Real Estate, Best Food Day, Stock, Market, Comics, Wedding, TV (Sun)
Syndicated Publications: Parade (S).
Pub...Andrew S. Dix
Controller..Joyce Yontz
Cir. Dir....Chris Cryder
Exec. Ed........................................Ray H. Booth
Sports Ed......................................Jeff Harrison
Prodn. Mgr........................................Ray Booth
Adv. Dir........................................Kim Brenning
Market Information: ADS; TMC; Zoned editions.
Mechanical Available: Offset; Black and 3 ROP colors; insert accepted - min 6 x 9, max 11 1/2 x 15; page cutoffs - 21 1/2.
Mechanical Specifications: Type page 13 x 21 1/2; E - 6 cols, 2 1/16, 1/8 between; A - 6 cols, 2 1/16, 1/8 between; C - 9 cols, 1 3/8, 1/16 between.Equipment & Software: PRESSROOM EQUIPMENT: Lines — 9-G/Community 1976; Press Drive — 2-HP/75; Folders — SC/folder.; MAILROOM EQUIPMENT: Tying Machines — 1-EAM-Mosca/13992, EAM-MOSCA/ ROM-P 60/50; Wrapping Singles — 1-Sa/ Table Top Spring Tyer; Address Machine — Ch/995150-06.; BUSINESS EQUIPMENT: DSI BUSINESS SOFTWARE: Papertrak 2000 CLASSIFIED EQUIPMENT: Hardware — Baseview, APP/Mac; Printers — 1-HP/ LaserJet 6MP; CLASSIFIED SOFTWARE: Baseview/Ad Manager Pro 2.0. DISPLAY EQUIPMENT: Hardware — APP/Mac G3; Printers — HP/LaserJet 4MV; DISPLAY SOFTWAREAd Make-up Applications — Mk, QPS/QuarkXPress 4.0, Multi-Ad/Creator 4.0; Layout Software — MEI/ALS 2.5. EDITORIAL EQUIPMENT: Hardware — APP/Mac G3, APP/G4, Imacs, APP/G5/2-Konica K-550; Printers — 1-HP/4MV LaserJet EDITORIAL SOFTWARE: Baseview/NewsEdit Pro IQUE 3.1.3. PRODUCTION EQUIPMENT: Hardware — Adobe/Photoshop 3.0.4, 2-Konica/6100 EV Jetsetter, 2-Konica/6100 EV Jetsetter; Cameras — DAI/Screen-6500C; Scanners — 1-Umax/Mirage 11x17, 2-Umax/8 1/2 x 14 Scanner, 1-Polaroid/ SprintScan PRODUCTION SOFTWARE: QPS/QuarkXPress 4.11.

CANTON

THE REPOSITORY

500 Market Ave S, Canton, Ohio, 44702-2112, Stark; gen tel (330) 580-8500; adv tel (330) 580-8401; ed tel (330) 580-8300; gen fax (330) 454-5610; adv fax (330) 580-2117; ed fax (330) 454-5610; gen/nat adv e-mail joey.barlow@cantonrep.com; disp adv e-mail sheila.casler@cantonrep.com; class adv e-mailclassconnect@cantonrep.com; ed e-mail scott.brown@cantonrep.com; web site www.cantonrep.com
Group: New Media Investment Group
Published: Mon, Tues, Wed, Thur, Fri, Sat, Sun
Weekday Frequency: m
Saturday Frequency: m
Circulation: 35,675; 35,675(sat); 46,398(sun)
Last Audit: AAM December 31, 2016
Advertising Rate (weekday/saturday): Open inch rate $70.95
Advertising Rate (sunday): Open inch rate $83.66
News services: AP, CNS, LAT-WP.
Special Editions: Home and Garden (Apr); HS Football (Aug); Christmas Gift Guide (Dec); Weddings by Design (Jan); Professional Football Hall of Fame Tab (Jul); Senior Living (Jun); Spring Truck & Van (Mar); Summer Fun (May); Pizzazz (Monthly); Christmas Gift Guide (Nov); W
Special Weekly Sections: Best Food Day (Wed); Weekend Entertainment, Garden (Fri); Real Estate (Sat); Travel, Wheels, Medicine, Books, Education, Finance (Sun)
Syndicated Publications: Comics (S).
Digital Platform - Mobile: Apple, Android
Digital Platform - Tablet: Apple iOS, Android
Class. Adv. Mgr....................................Gail Valli
Pub....Jim Porter
Cir. Dir...Anita Dunn
Exec. Ed....................................Rich Desrosiers
Ops. Dir....................................Kevin Ackerman
Controller....................................Linda Andrews
HR Dir......................................Greg Carpenter
Gen. Mgr......................................Maureen Ater
Mng. Ed........................................Scott Brown
Market Information: TMC.
Mechanical Available: Offset; Black and 3 ROP colors; insert accepted - envelopes, cards; page cutoffs - 22 3/4.
Mechanical Specifications: Type page 13 x 21 1/2; E - 6 cols, 2, 1/6 between; A - 6 cols, 2 1/16, 1/16 between; C - 10 cols, 1 1/4, 1/16 between.
Areas Served: 44702 and surrounding areasEquipment & Software: PRESSROOM EQUIPMENT: Lines — G/Colorliner (10 stands; 40 couples) 2001, G/ColorLiner (10 stands; 40 couples) 2001; Folders — G/3:2 Sovereign; Pasters —G/RTP-50Reels & Stands — G/RTP-50; Control System — G/ APCS 2001, G/APCS 2001.; MAILROOM EQUIPMENT: Counter Stackers — 2-Id, 1/ Compass, 3-/QWI; Inserters & Stuffers — 2-GMA/SLS 1000 16:1, GMA/20:1; Tying Machines — 6-Dynaric/MP-3; Wrapping Singles — 3-QWI/Viper Bottom Wrap; Control System — Newstec-NewsCom; Address Machine — Ch; BUSINESS EQUIPMENT: NewzWare 6.0, Dell/ Poweredge 6400, Linux CLASSIFIED EQUIPMENT: Hardware — 16-APP/Mac; IBM/Selectric II; Printers — 2-HP/4000N; CLASSIFIED SOFTWARE: Baseview/Class Ad Manager Pro. DISPLAY EQUIPMENT: Hardware — 1-APP/Mac; Printers — DEC/ VT-800 Plain Paper, Pagescan, HP; DISPLAY SOFTWAREAd Make-up Applications — CD, QPS/QuarkXPress 3.31R; Layout Software — MEI/ALS. EDITORIAL EQUIPMENT: Hardware — 68-APP/Mac/1-Lf, 2-APP/ Power Mac PC 8100, 1-APP/Mac Quadra 950; Printers — 1-Okidata/393, Graphic Enterprises/PageScan 18 x 24, 2-HP/4000N EDITORIAL SOFTWARE: QPS/QuarkXPress 3.31R, Baseview/NewsEdit Pro IQUE. PRODUCTION EQUIPMENT: Hardware — DAI, LE, 1-Konica/4550, Black Magic Newsprint Proofer/V24 Therman Printer; Cameras — DAI/Screen 475; Scanners — Tecsa/3050-double track PRODUCTION SOFTWARE: Baseview/NewsEdit Pro IQue, QPS/QuarkXPress 4.1, 10-G4, 2-Imac.

CELINA

THE DAILY STANDARD

123 E Market St, Celina, Ohio, 45822-1730, Mercer; gen tel (419) 586-2371; adv tel (419) 584-1961; gen fax (419) 586-6271; gen/nat adv e-mail rmorris@dailystandard.com ; disp adv e-mail missy@dailystandard.com ; class adv e-mailclassad@dailystandard.com; ed e-mail newsroom@dailystandard.com; web site www.dailystandard.com
Published: Mon, Tues, Wed, Thur, Fri, Sat
Weekday Frequency: e
Saturday Frequency: m
Circulation: 10,000; 10,000(sat)
Last Audit: Sworn/Estimate/Non-Audited September 30, 2017
Advertising Rate (weekday/saturday): Open inch rate $9.45
News services: AP, NYT, TMS. **Established:** 1848
Special Editions: Fall Sports (Aug); Christmas Greetings (Dec); Christmas Opening (Nov); Fall Opening (Sept).
Special Weekly Sections: Weekender (Fri); State Line Farmer (Tues).
Bus. Mgr...Dave Hoying
Adv. Mgr.....................................Richard Morris
Circ. Mgr.......................................Diane Buening
Mng. Ed...Pat Royse
Editorial Page Ed...........................Frank Snyder
Society/Women's Ed...................Betty Lawrence
Sports Ed...Ryan Hines
Wire Ed...Kelly Braun
Prodn. Supt..................................Larry Smelser
Market Information: Split run; TMC.
Mechanical Available: Web Offset; Black and 3 ROP colors; insert accepted - free standing; page cutoffs - 22 3/4.
Mechanical Specifications: Type page 15 x 21; E - 6 cols, 2, 1/8 between; A - 6 cols, 2, 1/8 between; C - 6 cols, 2, 1/8 between.
Areas Served: Mercer & Auglaize Counties (OH)
Equipment & Software: PRESSROOM EQUIPMENT: Lines — G/Suburban 1990.; MAILROOM EQUIPMENT: Tying Machines — Bu.; BUSINESS EQUIPMENT: PC CLASSIFIED EQUIPMENT: Hardware — APP/Mac, APP/Mac G4.; DISPLAY EQUIPMENT: Hardware — APP/Mac; DISPLAY SOFTWAREAd Make-up Applications — APP/Mac.; EDITORIAL EQUIPMENT: Hardware — APP/Mac. PRODUCTION EQUIPMENT: Hardware — 1-Nu; Scanners — HP, AP PRODUCTION SOFTWARE: QPS, Baseview.

CHILLICOTHE

CHILLICOTHE GAZETTE

50 W Main St, Chillicothe, Ohio, 45601-3103, Ross; gen tel (740) 773-2111; adv tel (740) 775-7355; ed tel (740) 772-9368; gen fax (740) 772-9502; adv fax (740) 772-9501; ed fax (740) 772-9505; gen/nat adv e-mail cgoadv@nncogannett.com; disp adv e-mail mrager@chillicothegazette.com; class adv e-mailksargent@mncogannett.com; ed e-mail gaznews@nncogannett.com; web site www. chillicothegazette.com
Group: Gannett
Published: Mon, Tues, Wed, Thur, Fri, Sat, Sun
Weekday Frequency: e
Saturday Frequency: m
Circulation: 6,462; 7,140(sat); 7,762(sun)
Last Audit: AAM March 31, 2017
Advertising Rate (weekday/saturday): 1/4 P $742, 1/2 P $1484, Full $2969
News services: AP, LAT-WP. **Established:** 1800
Own Printing Facility?: No
Commercial Printers?: No
Special Editions: Bridal/Weddings (Jan); Medical Directory (Feb) Ross County Fair (Aug); My Scioto Valley (Feb); Baby (Jun); Graduation (May); Holiday Gift Guide (Nov); Football Preview (August).
Special Weekly Sections: Transportation (Thur); Homes

Digital Platform - Mobile: Apple, Android, Windows, Blackberry
Digital Platform - Tablet: Apple iOS
Adv. Dir. .... Mark Rager
Ed. .... Michael W. Throne
Ops. Mgr. .... Phyllis Barnes
Class. Mgr. .... Karie Sargent
Market Information: TMC.
Areas Served: Ross and Pike counties
Delivery Method: Newsstand, Carrier, RacksEquipment & Software: MAILROOM EQUIPMENT: .; BUSINESS EQUIPMENT: PC CLASSIFIED EQUIPMENT: Hardware — APP/Mac; CLASSIFIED SOFTWARE: Ad Vision. DISPLAY EQUIPMENT: Hardware — APP/Mac; DISPLAY SOFTWAREAd Make-up Applications — QPS/QuarkXPress; Layout Software — APP/Mac. EDITORIAL EQUIPMENT: Hardware — APP/Mac EDITORIAL SOFTWARE: Baseview. PRODUCTION EQUIPMENT: Hardware — 2-MON/1000; Cameras — 1-C/Spartan II, 1-AG/3500; Scanners — Lf/Leafscan 35, Nikon/1000 PRODUCTION SOFTWARE: QPS/QuarkXPress 4.0.

CINCINNATI

THE CINCINNATI ENQUIRER

312 Elm St, Cincinnati, Ohio, 45202-2739, Hamilton; gen tel (513) 721-2700; adv tel (513) 768-8404; ed tel (513) 768-8600; adv fax (513) 242-4366; ed fax (513) 768-8340; gen/nat adv e-mail abaston@enquirer.com; disp adv e-mail abaston@enquirer.com; class adv e-mailabaston@enquirer.com; ed e-mail ltrujillo@cincinnati.com; web site www.cincinnati.com; www.enquirermedia.com - 5,200,000(views) 3,300,000(visitors)
Group: Gannett
Published: Mon, Tues, Wed, Thur, Fri, Sat, Sun
Weekday Frequency: m
Saturday Frequency: m
Circulation: 98,890; 97,016(sat); 150,603(sun)
Last Audit: AAM March 31, 2017
Advertising Rate (weekday/saturday): Awareness C $817.00; Awareness D $1633.00; 1/12 Pg V $3,901.00
Advertising Rate (sunday): Awareness C $851.00; Awareness D $1703.00; 1/12 Pg V $4,068.00
News services: AP, NYT, MCT, GNS. **Established:** 1841
Special Editions: Summer Vacations-Travel (Apr); Tennis Championships (Aug); Holiday Home Gift Guides (Dec); National Cruise Month Celebration (Feb); Warm Weather Travel Destinations (Jan); Regional Adventures (Jul); Homearama (Jun); Family Vacations (May); Holiday Gift Gu
Special Weekly Sections: Weather, Sports (Daily); Business, Sunday Forum, Good News, (Sun); Food, Classifieds (Wed); Healthy Living, Hometown (Thur); Weekend, Business (Fri); Home, Style, Hometown (Sat)
Syndicated Publications: USA WEEKEND Magazine (S).
Interim Editor .... Michael McCarter
Group Dir/Home Delivery . Denette Pfaffenberger
Dir of News Content .... Kate McGinty
Dir. of Print Prod .... Joe Powell
VP of Sales .... Chris Strong
Ed. & VP of Audience Engagement .... Peter Bhatia
Market Sales & Distribution Director. Jeff Lawson
Client Strategy Director .... Libby Korosec
Major Sales & Marketing Manager ...... John Berry
Market Information: Split run; Zoned editions.
Mechanical Available: Offset; Black and 3 ROP colors; insert accepted - based on sample submitted; page cutoffs - 22 3/4.
Mechanical Specifications: Type page 11 5/8 x 21 1/2; E - 7 cols, 1 1/2, 1/8 between; A - 6 cols, 1 13/16, 1/8 between; C - 10 cols, 1 3/32, 1/8 between.Equipment & Software: PRESSROOM EQUIPMENT: Lines — 10-G/Metro (6 half decks) 1978; 10-G/Metro (6 half decks) 1978; 10-G/Metro (6 half decks) 1980; 10-G/Metro (6 half decks) 1988; Folders — 4-G/double.; MAILROOM EQUIPMENT: Counter Stackers — 4-QWI/200, 5-QWI/400; Inserters & Stuffers — 1-HI/1472, 1-HI/1372, AM Graphics/NP 630, 1/Magnapack; Tying Machines — 8-/Dynaric; Address Machine — 1-/Ch, X; BUSINESS EQUIPMENT: IBM/AS-400 520, PC Micro, HP/9000 BUSINESS SOFTWARE: Genesys CLASSIFIED EQUIPMENT: Hardware — SII/Server Net; SII/Coyote QB, SII/Coyote 22, SII/Coyote 3; Printers — Centronics/351, Dataproducts/LZR-2600, Tetromix/Phaser 780, HP/8500, HP/4050; CLASSIFIED SOFTWARE: SII/Sys 55, C Text/ALPS Classified Pagination. DISPLAY EQUIPMENT: Hardware — 16-APP/Mac 7500, 1-APP/Mac WGS 80, 1763-350; Printers — APP/Mac LaserWriter NTX, Textronix/Phaser 780 I, GEI Color Proofer; DISPLAY SOFTWAREAd Make-up Applications — APP/Mac Appleshare 4.0, First class/BBS software; Layout Software — Multi-Ad/Creator II. EDITORIAL EQUIPMENT: Hardware — Tandem/CLX/SII/Coyote QB, SII/Dakota, APP/Mac, SII/CAT-ST, SII/Coyote 22, SII/Coyote 3; Printers — Centronics/351, Dataproducts/LZR 2600, APP/Mac LaserWriter NTX, Xante/8200, Textronix/Phaser 300 I EDITORIAL SOFTWARE: SII/Sys 55, SII/Sys 7 PRODUCTION EQUIPMENT: Hardware — Nova Publishing/Faxaction, 2-AU/APS 6108, 2-AU/APS 3850, 1-HQ-110PM; Cameras — 2-C/Newspager; Scanners — 1-ECR/Autokon 1000, Tecsa/3050.

CIRCLEVILLE

THE CIRCLEVILLE HERALD

401 E Main St, Circleville, Ohio, 43113-1843, Pickaway; gen tel (740) 474-3131; adv tel (740) 474-3131; ed tel (740) 474-3131; gen fax (740) 474-9525; adv fax (740) 474-9525; ed fax (740) 474-9525; gen/nat adv e-mail mklinebriel@circlevilleherald.com; disp adv e-mail tmaynard@circlevilleherald.com; class adv e-maillhedrick@circlevilleherald.com; ed e-mail news@circlevilleherald.com; web site www.circlevilleherald.com
Group: Adams Publishing Group, LLC
Published: Tues, Wed, Thur, Fri, Sat
Weekday Frequency: m
Saturday Frequency: m
Circulation: 3,837; 3,837(sat)
Last Audit: Sworn/Estimate/Non-Audited October 1, 2017
Advertising Rate (weekday/saturday): Open inch rate $12.18
News services: AP, U.S. Suburban Press Inc.. **Established:** 1817
Commercial Printers?: Yes
Special Editions: Real Estate (Apr); Football Review (Aug); Christmas Greetings (Dec); Progress (Feb); Graduation (Jun); 4-H (Mar); Basketball Preview (Nov); Pumpkin Show (Oct).
Special Weekly Sections: Best Food Days (Wed);
Syndicated Publications: USA WEEKEND Magazine (Sat); American Profile (Weekly).
Photographer .... Nancy Radcliff
Asst. Ed. .... Jennifer Bahney
Sports Ed. .... Brad Morris
Pub .... Teresa Maynard
Acct. Exec. .... Michelle Klinebriel
Cir. Mgr. .... Jeramiah Faulkner
Reporter .... Steven Collins
Advertising Executive .... Pennie McCain
Market Information: TMC.
Mechanical Available: Offset; Black and 3 ROP colors; insert accepted; page cutoffs - 22 3/4.
Mechanical Specifications: Type page 11 5/8 x 21 1/2; E - 6 cols, 1 13/16, 1/8 between; A - 6 cols, 1 13/16, 1/8 between; C - 8 cols, 1 5/16, 1/8 between.
Areas Served: Pickaway County (OH)
Delivery Method: Mail, Newsstand, Carrier, RacksEquipment & Software: PRODUCTION EQUIPMENT:

COLUMBUS

THE COLUMBUS DISPATCH

62 E Broad St, Columbus, Ohio, 43215-3500, Franklin; gen tel (614) 461-5000; adv tel (614) 888-8888; ed tel (614) 461-5200; gen fax (614) 461-8793; adv fax (614) 461-8793; ed fax (614) 461-8793; gen/nat adv e-mail cpettograsso@dispatch.com; class adv e-maillhammett@dispatch.com; ed e-mail letters@dispatch.com; web site www.dispatch.com 306,000(visitors)
Group: GateHouse Media, Inc.
Published: Mon, Tues, Wed, Thur, Fri, Sat, Sun
Weekday Frequency: m
Saturday Frequency: m
Circulation: 105,055; 121,506(sat); 183,341(sun)
Last Audit: AAM March 31, 2017
Advertising Rate (weekday/saturday): Open inch rate $52.00
Advertising Rate (sunday): Open inch rate $58.00
Online Advertising Rate: Skybox $900.00; Banner $1,620.00
News services: AP, MCT, LAT-WP, NYT, RN. **Established:** 1871
Special Editions: Showcase of Remodelers (Apr); High School Sports (Aug); Last-Minute Gift Guide (Dec); Valentine's Greetings (Feb); From House to Home (Jan); Employment (Jul); Parade of Homes Program (Jun); Delicious Deals (Mar); Memorial Daily 2 (May); Bonus Package (Nov
Special Weekly Sections: Life & Arts (Mon, Tue); Food & Life (Wed); Weekender (Thur); Faith (Fri); Auto (Sat); Travel, Arts, Home, Real Estate, Health (Sun)
Syndicated Publications: USA WEEKEND Magazine (Sat).
Digital Platform - Mobile: Apple, Android, Windows
Digital Platform - Tablet: Apple iOS, Android, Windows 7, Blackberry Tablet OS, Kindle, Nook, Kindle Fire
Vice Pres./New Media .... Phil Pikelny
Managing Ed. / Features .... Mary Plageman
Ed. .... Alan Miller
Gen. Mgr. .... Bob LeBoeuf
Class. Sales Mgr. .... Laura Hammett
Mktg. Dir. .... Nikhil Hunshikatti
Market Information: ADS; Split run; TMC; Zoned editions.
Mechanical Available: Offset; Black and 3 ROP colors; insert accepted; page cutoffs - 22.
Mechanical Specifications: Type page 13 x 21; E - 6 cols, 2 1/16, 1/8 between; A - 6 cols, 2 1/16, 1/8 between; C - 10 cols, 1 5/16, 1/16 between.
Areas Served: Central Ohio
Equipment & Software: PRESSROOM EQUIPMENT: Lines — 10-TKS/M-72 double width 1990, 1-TKS/6000 Press Tower 1999; 10-TKS/M-72 double width 1989, 1-TKS/6000 Press Tower 1999; 10-TKS/M-72 double width 1989, 1-TKS/6000 Press Tower 1999; 10-TKS/M-72 1989, 1-TKS/6000 Press Towe; MAILROOM EQUIPMENT: Counter Stackers — 9-Id/2000, 4/HI, 2-/Remor, 4-/QWI; Inserters & Stuffers — 4-Fg/Drums (2/5:1); Tying Machines — 13-/Power Strap; Control System — Id/Newssort.; BUSINESS EQUIPMENT: DEC/PDP 1183, Dell/PC Server BUSINESS SOFTWARE: Microsoft/NT 4.X, Microsoft/SQL 7.0 CLASSIFIED EQUIPMENT: Hardware — AT, 2-Sun, 3-IBM/RS6000-J40, 4-IBM/RS6000-25T; 114-Pentium/PC; Printers — HP/5si, HP/4MV; CLASSIFIED SOFTWARE: AT, Unix, AT/Enterprise Advertising, AT/Classified Pagination R5. DISPLAY EQUIPMENT: Hardware — 20-APP/Mac G3, APP/Mac G4, APP/Mac 9500; Printers — APP/Mac LaserWriters, QMS/Color, MON/Proof Express; Other Hardware — MON/Powerlink Ad Management & Tracking DISPLAY SOFTWAREAd Make-up Applications — QPS/QuarkXPress, Macromedia/Freehand, Adobe/Illustrator; Layout Software — SCS/La EDITORIAL EQUIPMENT: Hardware — AT, 220-IBM/PS2, 40-APP/Mac, 60-APP/Mac G4, 40-APP/Mac G3, 2-IBM/RS6000-25T/Kk, AG/Scanners, Purup-Eskofot/; Printers — APP/Mac LaserWriter, NEC, DEC, HP, MON/Proof Express EDITORIAL SOFTWARE: QPS/QuarkXPress, AT, Cx, Sun/Unix, 14-AT/Press PRODUCTION EQUIPMENT: Hardware — WL/347 Diamondsetter CTP, 1-WL/610 Diamondsetter CTP, 1-Scitex/Brisque, 3-MON/RIP Express, 2-Scitex/Dolev 4 News, 4-Mon/News Express; Scanners — 2-Purup-Eskofot 2047.

COSHOCTON

THE COSHOCTON TRIBUNE

550 Main St, Coshocton, Ohio, 43812-1612, Coshocton; gen tel (740) 622-1122; adv tel (740) 295-3450; ed tel (740) 295-3417; gen fax (740) 295-3460; adv fax (740) 295-3459; ed fax (740) 295-3460; gen/nat adv e-mail atrabitz@gannett.com; disp adv e-mail mwilson3@mncogannett.com; class adv e-mailksargent@gannett.com; ed e-mail psjames@gannett.com; web site www.coshoctontribune.com
Group: Gannett
Published: Mon, Tues, Wed, Thur, Fri, Sat, Sun
Weekday Frequency: m
Saturday Frequency: m
Circulation: 2,731; 2,694(sat); 3,312(sun)
Last Audit: AAM June 30, 2017
Advertising Rate (weekday/saturday): Open inch rate $17.50
Advertising Rate (sunday): Open inch rate $17.50
News services: AP, GNS. **Established:** 1909
Special Editions: Showcase of Homes (Other).
Special Weekly Sections: Best Food Days (Mon/Sun); TV Today (Weekly); Health, Science (Thur); Farm News (Sat); Entertainment, Comics, Lifestyles, Business (Sun); Homes (Monthly)
Syndicated Publications: USA WEEKEND Magazine (S).
Digital Platform - Mobile: Apple, Android
Digital Platform - Tablet: Apple iOS, Android
Ops. Dir. .... John Merriweather
Ed. .... Pam James
Sales Dir. .... Adam Trabitz
Class. Sales Ctr. Mgr. .... Karie Sargent
Market Information: ADS; TMC.
Mechanical Available: Offset; Black and 3 ROP colors; insert accepted - any; page cutoffs - 22 3/4.
Mechanical Specifications: Type page 12 1/2 x 21 1/4; E - 6 cols, 2 1/16, 1/8 between; A - 6 cols, 2 1/16, 1/8 between; C - 9 cols, 1 3/8, 1/16 between.
Areas Served: Coshocton County (OH)
Equipment & Software: BUSINESS EQUIPMENT: IBM/PC Clones, HP, Dell, Gateway, Toshiba, HP BUSINESS SOFTWARE: Microsoft/Office Professional CLASSIFIED EQUIPMENT: Hardware — IBM/PC; Printers — Xante/8200; CLASSIFIED SOFTWARE: ALPS. DISPLAY EQUIPMENT: Hardware — APP/Mac; Printers — Xante/8200; DISPLAY SOFTWAREAd Make-up Applications — QPS/QuarkXPress 4.04; Layout Software — MEI/ALS. EDITORIAL EQUIPMENT: Hardware — APP/Mac, APP/iMac; Printers — Xante/8200, Pre Press/Panther Pro 46 EDITORIAL SOFTWARE: Baseview/NewsEdit. PRODUCTION EQUIPMENT: Hardware — Caere/OmniPage, Adobe/Photoshop 5.5, APP/Mac LaserWriter, QuarkXPress 4.04; Cameras — NON; Scanners — Umax/UL 1200 SE, Umax/Power Look II PRODUCTION SOFTWARE: QPS/QuarkXPress 3.31, Baseview/Q-Tools.

DEFIANCE

THE CRESCENT-NEWS

624 W 2nd St, Defiance, Ohio, 43512-2105, Defiance; gen tel (419) 784-5441; gen fax (419) 784-1492; adv fax (419) 784-1492; ed fax (419) 782-2944; gen/nat adv e-mail advertising@crescent-news.com; disp adv e-mail advertising@crescent-news.com; class adv e-mailclassifieds@crescent-news.com; ed e-mail crescent@crescent-news.com; web site www.crescent-news.com - 745,000(views) 69,000(visitors)
Group: Adams Publishing Group, LLC
Published: Tues, Wed, Thur, Fri, Sun
Weekday Frequency: e
Saturday Frequency: e
Circulation: 12,940; 13,966(sun)
Last Audit: AAM June 30, 2017
Advertising Rate (weekday/saturday): Open inch rate $12.75
Advertising Rate (sunday): Open inch rate $13.30
Online Advertising Rate: Half Page (300x600) $10.00; Skyscraper (160x600) $7.00; Medium Rectangle (300x250) $7.50;

Leaderboard (728x90) $8.50; Banner (486x60) $7.00; 3:1 Rectangle (300x100) $6.00; Mobile Banner (320x50) $7.00
News services: AP, SHNS. **Established:** 1888
Own Printing Facility?: No
Commercial Printers?: No
Special Editions: Tax & Finance (Feb); Bridal (Feb, Jun); Farm Review (Feb, Sept); Brag Book (Mar); Lawn & Garden (Apr, May, Jun); Car Care (Apr, Oct); Health & Fitness (Apr); Graduation (May); Summer Entertainment (Jun); Defiance County Fair (Jul); Senior Lifestyle (Jul); Back To School (Aug); Reader's Choice (Aug); Football Preview (Aug); Home Improvement (Sept, Oct); Business & Industry (Sept); Family Health (Oct); Recipes (Nov); Veteran's (Nov); Basketball Preview (Nov); Holiday Gift Guide (Nov, Dec); Christmas Greetings (Dec); Year End Review (Dec)
Special Weekly Sections: NASCAR, Outdoor (Thur); Farm, Church (Fri); Business, TV, Home, Garden, Health (Sun)
Syndicated Publications: American Profile (Weekly), Parade (Sun)
Proprietary Publications: Northwest Ohio Homes Magazine
Digital Platform - Mobile: Apple, Android, Windows, Blackberry
Digital Platform - Tablet: Apple iOS, Android, Windows 7, Blackberry Tablet OS, Kindle, Kindle Fire
Educ. Ed.....Jenny Derringer
Features Ed.....Mark Froelich
Health/Med. Ed.....Darlene Prince
Political/Gov. Ed.....Todd Helberg
Lynn Groll
Adv. Mgr.....Chris Van Scoder
Circ. Mgr....Greg Meyers
Market Information: TMC to 43512 and 43545 zip codes;
Mechanical Specifications: Page size: 6 columns (10.625") x 19.75"; 1.66" columns with .13" gutter; 1 col=1.66", 2 col= 3.45", 3 col=5.25", 4 col=7.04", 5 col=8.83", 6 col=10.625". Preprints: 11.5" x 13" max., 4" x 6" min.
Areas Served: All of Defiance, Paulding, and Henry Counties and portions of Putnam, Fulton and Williams Counties
Delivery Method: Mail, Newsstand, Carrier, RacksEquipment & Software: BUSINESS EQUIPMENT: PC BUSINESS SOFTWARE: SBS CLASSIFIED EQUIPMENT: Mac CLASSIFIED SOFTWARE: Brainworks DISPLAY EQUIPMENT: Mac DISPLAY SOFTWAREBrainworks EDITORIAL EQUIPMENT: Mac EDITORIAL SOFTWARE: TownNews PRODUCTION EQUIPMENT: Mac PRODUCTION SOFTWARE: InDesign; Adobe Photoshop, Illustrator IT EQUIPMENT: Mac, Cisco CIRCULATION EQUIPMENT: Mac CIRCULATION SOFTWARMediaSpan CircPro

DELAWARE

THE DELAWARE GAZETTE

40 N Sandusky St, Ste 202, Delaware, Ohio, 43015-1973, Delaware; gen tel (740) 363-1161; adv tel (740) 413-0893; ed tel (740) 413-0900; gen fax (740) 363-6262; adv fax (740) 363-6262; ed fax (740) 363-6262; gen/nat adv e-mail addept@delgazette.com; disp adv e-mail addept@delgazette.com; class adv e-mailclassifieds@delgazette.com; ed e-mail newsroom@delgazette.com; web site www.delgazette.com
- 160,000(views) 22,000(visitors)
Group: Civitas Media, LLC-OOB
Published: Mon, Tues, Wed, Thur, Fri, Sat
Weekday Frequency: m
Saturday Frequency: m
Circulation: 6,000; 6,000(sat)
Last Audit: Sworn/Estimate/Non-Audited September 30, 2017
Advertising Rate (weekday/saturday): Open inch rate $12.65
News services: AP, U.S. Suburban Press Inc.. **Established:** 1818
Own Printing Facility?: No
Commercial Printers?: Yes
Special Editions: Baby Bulletin (Jan); 4-H Focus, Progress Edition (Feb); Home & Garden (Mar); Lawn, Feature (Apr); Graduation (May); Council, Summer Festival (June); Summer (Jul); Back to School, Fall (Aug); Sunday Fair, Fall Home Improvement (Sept); Fair in Review, Voters (Oct); Winter, Holiday (Nov); Holiday Gift Guide (Dec)
Special Weekly Sections: Best Food, Home (Mon); Auto (Tue); Business (Wed); NASCAR, Health (Thur); Church (Fri); Youth, Farm (Sat);
Gen. Mgr. / Adv. Mgr.....Sherry Fisher
Ed....Anthony Conchel
Off. Mgr.....Jeanne DeWeese
Cir. Mgr.....John Briggs
Med. Sales Cons.....Jean Cassan
Market Information: Zoned editions.
Mechanical Available: Offset; Black and 3 ROP colors; insert accepted; page cutoffs - 22 3/4.
Mechanical Specifications: Type page 13 x 21 1/2; E - 6 cols, 2 1/16, 1/8 between; A - 6 cols, 2 1/16, 1/8 between; C - 8 cols, 1 1/2, 1/8 between.
Areas Served: Delaware County (OH)
Delivery Method: Mail, Newsstand, Carrier, RacksEquipment & Software: CLASSIFIED EQUIPMENT: Hardware — WG/Server 8150, 3-APP/Mac G3; Printers — APP/Mac NTX, 2-APP/Mac ImageWriter II, 1-APP/Mac LaserWriter 12-640; CLASSIFIED SOFTWARE: Baseview. DISPLAY EQUIPMENT: Hardware — APP/Mac 7300, APP/Mac 7300, APP/Mac NTX, APP/Mac 7300 (with CD); Printers — HP/LaserJet 4MV/600dpi; DISPLAY SOFTWAREAd Make-up Applications — Synaptic, Multi-Ad/Creator 4.0, Aldus/FreeHand 3.1; Layout Software — MEI/ALS. EDITORIAL EQUIPMENT: Hardware — 8-PC 6100, 2-APP/Mac 610, 1-APP/Mac 7200-20, 3-APP/Power Mac 7300, 7-APP/iMac; Printers — APP/Mac 12/640 NT, APP/Mac LaserWriter NTX EDITORIAL SOFTWARE: QPS/QuarkXPress, 33-Claris/Macdraw Pro, Aldus/FreeHand, Baseview/NewsEdit 3.2. PRODUCTION EQUIPMENT: Hardware — Caere/OmniPage Pro 4.1.0, Caere/OmniPage Direct, APP/NT Server, 1-HP 4MV/600, 5-APP/Mac G3, 1-Accel-a-Writer 3N/1200; Cameras — 4-Canon/EOS, 3-Nikon/Cool Pix 950; Scanners — 1-HP, 1-AP, 1-AG PRODUCTION SOFTWARE: Baseview/ALS 3.1.

DELPHOS

DELPHOS DAILY HERALD

405 N Main St, Delphos, Ohio, 45833-1577, Allen; gen tel (419) 695-0015; adv tel (419) 695-0015 ext. 138; ed tel (419) 695-0015 ext. 134; gen fax (419) 692-7704; adv fax (419) 692-7116; ed fax (419) 692-7704; gen/nat adv e-mail dthornberry@delphosherald.com; disp adv e-mail mhoffman@delphosherald.com; class adv e-mailclassifieds@delphosherald.com; ed e-mail nspencer@delphosherald.com; web site www.delphosherald.com
Group: Delphos Herald, Inc.
Published: Mon, Wed, Thur, Fri, Sat
Weekday Frequency: m
Saturday Frequency: m
Circulation: 2,883
Last Audit: Sworn/Estimate/Non-Audited September 30, 2017
Advertising Rate (weekday/saturday): Open inch rate $14.60 (Mon); $11.30 (Wed-Sat)
Online Advertising Rate: Leaderboard: 3 mo. $85; 6 mo. $75; 12 mo. $45; ...Medium Rectangle: 3 mo. $75; 6 mo. $65; 12 mo. $55; ¦Rectangle: 3 mo. $55; 6 mo. $50; 12 mo. $45
News services: AP. **Established:** 1869
Own Printing Facility?: Yes
Commercial Printers?: No
Special Editions: National Secretaries Week (Apr); Football Tab (Aug); New Year Baby (Dec); Cooking School (Feb); 2 Dollar Days (Jan); 2 Dollar Days (Jul); 4-H Tab (Mar); Bride Tab (May); Senior Scenes (Monthly); Christmas Opening (Nov); Get Ready for Winter Tab (Oct); Old
Special Weekly Sections: Engagements, Weddings (Mon); Business (Wed); Farm (Thur); Church (Fri); Business Journal (Monthly)
Syndicated Publications: American Profile (Weekly).
Pub.....Murray Cohen
Gen. Mgr.....Ray Geary
Ed.....Nancy Spencer
Sports Ed.....Jim Metcalfe
Prod. Mgr.....Denny Klausing
Adv.....David Thornberry
Cir. / Class.....Lori Silette
Market Information: Split run; TMC.
Mechanical Available: Offset; Black and 3 ROP colors; insert accepted - cards, envelopes; page cutoffs - 22 3/4.
Mechanical Specifications: Type page 13 1/8 x 21 1/2; E - 6 cols, 2 1/16, 1/8 between; A - 6 cols, 2 1/16, 1/8 between; C - 8 cols, 1 5/8, 1/8 between.
Areas Served: 45833, 45887, 45893, 45863, 45809, 45844, 45876, 45807, 45853, 45894, 45827, 45891, 45830Equipment & Software: PRESSROOM EQUIPMENT: Folders — 2-HI/2:1, 1-HI/1:1 MAILROOM EQUIPMENT: Counter Stackers — 3/BG; Tying Machines — 3-/Bu, 4-MLN/Strapper; Address Machine — 1-/KR.; BUSINESS EQUIPMENT: 1-RSK/TRS 80 III, 1-IBM/PC CLASSIFIED EQUIPMENT: Hardware — 2-APP/Mac Plus Laser; CLASSIFIED SOFTWARE: Baseview. DISPLAY SOFTWAREAd Make-up Applications — Baseview.; EDITORIAL EQUIPMENT: Hardware — MediaSpan PRODUCTION EQUIPMENT: Hardware — 2-Nu, 1-Nat; Cameras — 1-R, 1-lk.

EAST LIVERPOOL

THE REVIEW

210 E 4th St, East Liverpool, Ohio, 43920-3144, Columbiana; gen tel (330) 385-4545; adv tel (330) 385-4545; ed tel (330) 385-4545; gen fax (330) 385-7114; adv fax (330) 385-7114; ed fax (330) 385-8142; gen/nat adv e-mail lludovici@reviewonline.com; disp adv e-mail retailadv@reviewonline.com; class adv e-mailclassified@reviewonline.com; ed e-mail newsroom@reviewonline.com; web site www.reviewonline.com
- 1,020,000(views) 62,500(visitors)
Group: Ogden Newspapers Inc.
Published: Mon, Tues, Wed, Thur, Fri, Sat, Sun
Weekday Frequency: m
Saturday Frequency: m
Circulation: 5,787; 5,787(sat); 5,834(sun)
Last Audit: AAM September 30, 2014
Advertising Rate (weekday/saturday): Open inch rate $26.92
Advertising Rate (sunday): Open inch rate $26.92
News services: AP. **Established:** 1879
Own Printing Facility?: Yes
Commercial Printers?: No
Special Editions: Business Profile Edition (Apr); Football (Aug); Basketball (Dec); Thanksgiving Day (Nov); Home Improvement (Apr/Oct)
Special Weekly Sections: Health, Travel, Arts, Entertainment (Sun); Entertainment (Fri); Religion (Sat)
Syndicated Publications: Parade (S); TV Review (Entertainment TV) (S)
Digital Platform - Mobile: Apple, Android
Pub....Tammie McIntosh
Adv. Dir.....Lisa Ludovici
Cir. Mgr.....Kevin Fenton
Ed.....Jim Mackey
Market Information: TMC.
Mechanical Available: Offset; Black and 3 ROP colors; insert accepted; page cutoffs - 20 1/2. 22" web
Mechanical Specifications: Type page 10 x 20 1/2; E - 6 cols, 1.58, 1/8 between; A - 6 cols, 2 1/16, 1/8 between; C - 9 cols, 1.02, 1/8 between.
Areas Served: 43920, 43932,43945,43961,43964,43968,44432,44441,44445,44492,26034,26050,26047,15059,15050,15043
Delivery Method: Mail, Newsstand, Carrier, RacksEquipment & Software: CLASSIFIED EQUIPMENT: Hardware — APP/Mac; Printers — V/8500; CLASSIFIED SOFTWARE: APP/Mac. DISPLAY EQUIPMENT: Hardware — APP/Mac G3; Printers — V/8500; DISPLAY SOFTWAREAd Make-up Applications — QPS/QuarkXPress; Layout Software — QPS/QuarkXPress 4.0, PC. EDITORIAL EQUIPMENT: Hardware — APP/Mac/APP/Mac, V/5300; Printers — V/8500 EDITORIAL SOFTWARE: APP/Mac. PRODUCTION EQUIPMENT: Hardware — V; Cameras — SCREEN/Companica 680E PRODUCTION SOFTWARE: APP/Mac.

ELYRIA

CHRONICLE-TELEGRAM

225 East Ave, Elyria, Ohio, 44035-5634, Lorain; gen tel (440) 329-7000; adv tel (440) 329-7216; ed tel (440) 329-7111; gen fax (440) 329-7282; adv fax (440) 329-7272; ed fax (440) 329-7282; gen/nat adv e-mail jpfeiffer@chroniclet.com; disp adv e-mail chama@chroniclet.com; class adv e-mailclassified@chroniclet.com; ed e-mail letters@chroniclet.com; web site www.chroniclet.com
Group: Lorain County Printing & Publishing Co.
Published: Mon, Tues, Wed, Thur, Fri, Sat, Sun
Weekday Frequency: m
Saturday Frequency: m
Circulation: 18,924; 18,924(sat); 19,867(sun)
Last Audit: AAM March 31, 2017
Advertising Rate (weekday/saturday): Open inch rate $33.65
News services: Papert (Landon), MCT, SHNS. **Established:** 1829
Special Editions: Earth Day (Apr); Melon Festival (Aug); Letters to Santa (Dec); Health & Fitness (Feb); Midway Mall Auto Show (Jan); Medical Society (Jul); International Festival Guide (Jun); Car Care (Mar); Ohio Edison Parade of Homes (May); Holiday Planning Guide (Nov);
Special Weekly Sections: Best Food (Sun/Mon); Entertainment, TV Book (Fri); Homes, Real Estate (Sun)
Syndicated Publications: TV Weekly Booklet (Fri); Parade (S); American Profile (Weekly).
Pres.....Paul Martin
Ed....Andy Young
Adv. Sales Mgr.....Carla Hama
Adv. Mgr. /Nt'l Sales....Jeff Pfeiffer
Mng. Ed.....Julie Wallace
Market Information: ADS; TMC; Zoned editions.
Mechanical Available: Offset; Black and 3 ROP colors; insert accepted; page cutoffs - 23 9/16.
Mechanical Specifications: Type page 13 x 22 1/2; E - 6 cols, 2, 1/6 between; A - 6 cols, 2, 1/6 between; C - 9 cols, 1 5/12, 1/12 between.
Areas Served: Lorain County (OH)
Equipment & Software: PRESSROOM EQUIPMENT: Lines — 5-G/Metro 1969; MAILROOM EQUIPMENT: Counter Stackers — 2/HL; Inserters & Stuffers — HI; Tying Machines — MLN.; BUSINESS EQUIPMENT: HP BUSINESS SOFTWARE: CJ CLASSIFIED EQUIPMENT: Hardware — CText; CLASSIFIED SOFTWARE: CText. DISPLAY EQUIPMENT: Hardware — HP; Printers — HP/2564B; DISPLAY SOFTWAREAd Make-up Applications — CJ; Layout Software — CJ/Layout. EDITORIAL EQUIPMENT: Hardware — CText; Printers — Panasonic EDITORIAL SOFTWARE: CText. PRODUCTION EQUIPMENT: Hardware — XIT/Clipper, Douthitt; Cameras — 1-C, 1-B.

FINDLAY

THE COURIER

701 W Sandusky St, Findlay, Ohio, 45840-2325, Hancock; gen tel (419) 422-5151; gen fax (419) 422-2937; ed fax (419) 422-8480; gen/nat adv e-mail karifaulkner@thecourier.com; disp adv e-mail karifaulkner@thecourier.com; class adv e-mailkarizellner@thecourier.com; ed e-mail news@thecourier.com; web site www.thecourier.com
- 950,000(views) 50,732(visitors); web site 2 SocialFindlay.com - 36,215(views) 4,414(visitors); web site 3 SportsBuzz.com - 6,842(views) 1,426(visitors); web site 4CourierBridal.com - 100(views) 30(visitors)
Group: Findlay Publishing Co.
Published: Mon, Tues, Wed, Thur, Fri, Sat
Weekday Frequency: m
Saturday Frequency: m
Circulation: 18,900; 18,900(sat)
Last Audit: CAC December 31, 2016
Advertising Rate (weekday/saturday): Open inch rate $18.00 (Weekday); $19.00 (Saturday)
News services: AP, WP, TMS **Established:** 1836

Own Printing Facility?: Yes
Commercial Printers?: Yes
Special Editions: Progress (Feb); , Agriculture (Mar); Golf, Home Improvement, Bride (Apr); Seniors, Mother's Day, Downtown Findlay (May); Fathers Day (Jun); Pets (Jul); Balloon Fest, Back to School, High School/College Football (Aug); Spirit, Home Improvement, Susan Komen, Downtown Findlay (Sept); Brides, Halloween (Oct); Pets, Veterans Day, Basketball (Nov); Holiday Greetings (Dec)
Special Weekly Sections: Weekend (Sat); Celebrations (Tues).
Syndicated Publications: Parade (Fri), American Profile (Mon.) Dash, Athalon Sports, Relish
Digital Platform - Mobile: Apple, Android, Windows, Blackberry
Digital Platform - Tablet: Apple iOS, Android, Windows 7, Blackberry Tablet OS, Kindle, Nook, Kindle Fire
Pres./Pub. .... Karl L. Heminger
VP/Broadcast Commun. .... David P. Glass
VP, CIO .... Kurt F. Heminger
Adv. Mgr. .... Kari Faulkner
Readership and Audience Dev. Dir. ... Kim Wilhelm
Circ. Mgr. .... Rob Jenney
City Ed. .... Kurt Leonard
Family Ed. .... Brenna Grietman
News Ed. .... James Harrold
Photo Ed. .... Randy Roberts
Digital Design Manager .... Charles Lightner
Market Information: TMC.
Mechanical Available: Offset; Black and 3 ROP colors; insert accepted; page cutoffs - 22 3/4.
Mechanical Specifications: Type page 11 5/8 x 21; E - 6 cols, 1 13/16, 1/8 between; A - 6 cols, 1 13/16, 1/8 between; C - 8 cols, 1 3/8, 1/8 between.
Areas Served: Findlay & Northwest Ohio
Delivery Method: Mail, Newsstand, Carrier, RacksEquipment & Software: PRESSROOM EQUIPMENT: Lines — 7-HI/845; Pasters —6-MEG. MAILROOM EQUIPMENT: Counter Stackers — 1-TMSI/Compass, 1 TMSI 4500; Quipp 501; Inserters & Stuffers — 1/AM Graphics/630; Tying Machines — 2-Dynaric; Address Machine — 1-Prism/ Jetmail.; MAILROOM SOFTWARE:Miarcom BUSINESS EQUIPMENT: 1-Sun/Sparc 20 BUSINESS SOFTWARE: Microsoft/Office Vision Data CLASSIFIED EQUIPMENT: SunSparc CLASSIFIED SOFTWARE: Vision Data Total Ad DISPLAY EQUIPMENT: Linux DISPLAY SOFTWARESCS Track
Layout 8000
InDesign EDITORIAL EQUIPMENT: Windows Server 2012 EDITORIAL SOFTWARE: JazBox Newscycle Solutions PRODUCTION EQUIPMENT: Windows Server 2008 PRODUCTION SOFTWARE: Trendsetter News
RipExpress IT EQUIPMENT: Dell IT SOFTWARE:Microsoft Active Directory
SQL CIRCULATION EQUIPMENT: Sun Sparc CIRCULATION SOFTWARVision Data Circulation

FOSTORIA

THE REVIEW TIMES

113 E Center St, Fostoria, Ohio, 44830-2905, Seneca; gen tel (419) 435-6641; adv tel (419) 435-6641; gen fax (419) 435-9073; adv fax (419) 435-9073; ed fax (419) 435-9073; gen/nat adv e-mail advertising@reviewtimes.com; disp adv e-mail advertising@reviewtimes.com; ed e-mail rtnews@reviewtimes.com; web site www.reviewtimes.com
Group: Findlay Publishing Co.
Published: Mon, Tues, Wed, Thur, Fri, Sat
Weekday Frequency: e
Saturday Frequency: e
Circulation: 2,500; 3,000(sat)
Last Audit: USPS October 1, 2017
Advertising Rate (weekday/saturday): Open inch rate $10.50
Online Advertising Rate: Home Page Adv $60/ Month; In-Content Adv $40/Month; Sky Scraper Adv $40/Month
News services: AP, LAT-WP.
Own Printing Facility?: No
Commercial Printers?: No
Special Editions: Super Bowl (Jan); Community (Feb); Healthy Living (Mar); Home Improvement, Bridal (Apr); Graduation, Police Week (May); Fostorian, Relay for Life (Jun); Flag (Jul); High School Football, School (Aug); Shape Up, Health and Safety (Sept); Election, Bridal (Oct); Christmas Gift Guide (Nov); Basketball & Christmas Gift Guide (Dec)
Special Weekly Sections: Best Food Days (Sat); Church (Fri); Weekend, Education (Sat)
Syndicated Publications: Parade
Athalon Sports
American Profile
Digital Platform - Mobile: Apple, Android
Digital Platform - Tablet: Apple iOS, Android, Kindle, Kindle Fire
Pres. .... Karl L. Heminger
News Ed. .... Linda Woodland
Gen. Mgr. .... Scott Scherf
Circ. Dir. .... Rob Jenney
Market Information: TMC
Mechanical Available: Offset; Black and 3 ROP colors; insert accepted; page cutoffs - 22 3/4.
Mechanical Specifications: Type page 11 5/8 x 21; E - 6 cols, 1 13/16, 1/8 between; A - 6 cols, 1 13/16, 1/8 between; C - 8 cols, 1 3/8, 1/8 between.
Areas Served: Seneca County (OH)
Delivery Method: Mail, Newsstand, Carrier, RacksEquipment & Software: BUSINESS SOFTWARE: Microsoft/Office Vision Data CLASSIFIED SOFTWARE: Vision Data. DISPLAY SOFTWARELayout Software — Layout/8000.
EDITORIAL SOFTWARE: HI/Jazbox. PRODUCTION SOFTWARE: HI/Jazbox.

FRANKLIN

DAYTON DAILY NEWS

5000 Commerce Center Dr, Franklin, Ohio, 45005-7200, Warren; gen tel (937) 225-2000; ed tel (937) 222-5700; gen fax (937) 225-2054; ed fax (937) 225-2489; gen/nat adv e-mail bruce.karlson@coxinc.com; disp adv e-mail bruce.karlson@coxinc.com; class adv e-mailbruce.karlson@coxinc.com; ed e-mail newsdesk@cmgohio.com; web site www.daytondailynews.com
- 15,800,000(views) 157,000(visitors)
Group: Cox Media Group
Published: Mon, Tues, Wed, Thur, Fri, Sat, Sun
Weekday Frequency: m
Saturday Frequency: m
Circulation: 65,835; 64,979(sat); 99,859(sun)
Last Audit: AAM June 30, 2017
Advertising Rate (weekday/saturday): Open Inch Rate $201.00
Advertising Rate (sunday): Open Inch Rate $227.00
News services: Cox News Service, SHNS, AP, NYT, MCT, TV Data. **Established:** 1898
Own Printing Facility?: Yes
Commercial Printers?: Yes
Special Editions: Pink Paper; Insight Section; various marketing milestones
Special Weekly Sections: Arts, Family, Food, Health, Home, Living, Real Estate (Mon)
Syndicated Publications: Parade (S).
Digital Platform - Mobile: Apple, Android, Blackberry
Digital Platform - Tablet: Apple iOS, Kindle, Other
Sr. Director, Sales .... Terry Bouquot
Sr. Director, Product Delivery .... Phonda Gamble
Market Vice President .... Julia Wallace
Senior Vice President & General Manager ...... Rob Rohr
Editor in Chief .... Jana Collier
Associate Editor .... Ron Rollins
Director, Copy Desks .... Mike Goheen
Senior Editor .... John Erickson
Sales Manager - National/Major .... Bruce Karlson
Senior Director, Local & Major Accounts Suzanne Klopfenstein
Director of Organizational Development & Editorial Support .... Connie Post
Sports Editor .... John Boyle
Shared Content Editor .... Jim Bebbington
Senior Director, Digital .... Quindelda McElroy
VP of Sales .... James Cosby
VP of Marketing .... Nick Roberts
Director of Human Resources .... Toni Mithcell
Senior Director, Production & Operations ..... Larry Powell
Senior Director, Technology & Operations ..... Dave Thomas
Vice President & CFO .... Robert Zikias
General Sales Manager - Radio .... Kathy Eagle
General Sales Manager - TV .... John Condit
General Sales Manager - Digital .... Chip Beale
Market Information: ADS; Split run; TMC; Zoned editions.
Mechanical Available: Offset; Black and 3 ROP colors; insert accepted - samples and other by arrangement; page cutoffs - 22.
Mechanical Specifications: Type page 11 5/8 x 21; E - 6 cols, 1 5/6, 1/8 between; A - 6 cols, 1 5/6, 1/8 between; C - 10 cols, 1 1/4, 1/16 between.
Areas Served: 43072, 43078, 43128, 43160, 43215, 43228, 43311, 43318, 43324, 43331, 43343, 43348, 43357, 45004, 45032, 45036, 45044, 45050, 45054, 45056, 55066, 45067, 45068, 45113, 45169, 45177, 45302, 45303, 45304, 45305, 45306, 45308, 45309, 45310, 45311, 45312, 45314, 45315, 45317, 45318, 45320, 45321, 45322, 45323, 45324, 45325, 45326, 45327, 45328, 45330, 45331, 45333, 45334, 45335, 45337, 45338, 45339, 45341, 45342, 45344, 45345, 45346, 45347, 45358, 45350, 45351, 45354, 45356, 45358, 45359, 45361, 45362, 45363, 45365, 45370, 45371, 45373, 45377, 45378, 45380, 45381, 45382, 45383, 45384, 45385, 45387, 45388, 45389, 45390, 45401, 45402, 45403, 45404, 45405, 45406, 45408, 45409, 45410, 45414, 45415, 45416, 45417, 45418, 45420, 45422, 45424, 45426, 45427, 45428, 45429, 45430, 45431, 45432, 45433. 45434. 45435. 45439, 45440, 45449, 45458, 45459, 45469. 45502, 45503, 45504, 45505, 45822, 45826, 45828, 45845, 45846, 45860, 45865, 45869, 45871, 45883, 45885, 45895
Delivery Method: Mail, Newsstand, Carrier, RacksEquipment & Software: PRESSROOM EQUIPMENT: Lines — 33-KBA/Colora couples double width 1999; 27-KBA/Colora couples double width 1999; 27-KBA/Colora couples double width 1999; Heidleberg 8-color single sheet ; Press Drive — EAE/ KBA Drive Tronic Shaftless System; Folders — 3-KFM/96 Jaw; Reels & Stands — 18-KBA/Pa; PRESSROOM SOFTWARE: EAE Print and Press Control Systems; Harland Simons Imposition Software; HK Roll Handling Systems MAILROOM EQUIPMENT: Counter Stackers — 5-HL/Monitor, 6-HL/ DC, 1-HL/Monitor HT, 12/Quipp; Inserters & Stuffers — 4-HI/632 26:2; Tying Machines — 10-MLN/MLN 2A, 3-Dynaric/NP 2, 12-/ Dynaric; Wrapping Singles — 12-HI/Eclipse Bottomwrap; Control System — Omnizone; MAILROOM SOFTWARE:Fast Technologies Enews Software; Fast Technologies Kart Software; Ephraim Controls Preprint Storage Software BUSINESS EQUIPMENT: Dell PC's BUSINESS SOFTWARE: Peoplesoft Great Plains Hyperion CLASSIFIED EQUIPMENT: Hardware — Sun Dell; PCs; Printers — Konica-Minolta; HP laserjets HP1050 proofers; CLASSIFIED SOFTWARE: DTI 5.5 DISPLAY EQUIPMENT: Hardware — PCs; Printers — Konica Minolta; HP Laserjet; HP1050 Proofers; Other Hardware — AdSend, Edgil Ads-to-Go DISPLAY SOFTWAREAd Make-up Applications — DTI 5.5; EDITORIAL EQUIPMENT: Hardware — PCs/Macs; Printers — Konica Minolta; HP Laserjets; HP1050 proofers EDITORIAL SOFTWARE: DTI 5.5 PRODUCTION EQUIPMENT: Hardware — Caere/OmniPro, Harlequin/RIP, 2-AU/3850 Wide, Kk/RFS 2035 plus film scanner, PixelCraft/Pro Imager 8000, Nikon/Coolscan; Scanners — Scitex, Graphic Enterprises/PageScan, Tecsa PRODUCTION SOFTWARE: DTI 5.5; Alfaquest PrintExpress CTP Output Systems (Adobe Rips); Agfa NewsDrive; Nela Systems IT EQUIPMENT: Dell PCs and Servers
Sun Servers
HP UX
Netapp
IT SOFTWARE:Windows, Solaris, VMWare, SQL, Linux
SCCM, SCOM, CIRCULATION SOFTWARNewsCycle
Syncronex
RouteSmart

FREMONT

NEWS HERALD

1800 E State St, Ste B, Fremont, Ohio, 43420-4083, Sandusky; gen tel (419) 332-5511; adv tel 419-332-1069; ed tel (419) 734-1059; gen fax (419) 332-9750; adv fax 419 332 9750; ed fax (419) 332-9750; gen/nat adv e-mail JCoppler@nncogannett.com; disp adv e-mail mcruz@fremont.gannett.com; class adv e-mailksargent@nncogannett.com; ed e-mail dyonke@gannett.com; web site www.portclintonnewsherald.com
Group: Gannett
Published: Mon, Tues, Wed, Thur, Fri, Sat, Sun
Weekday Frequency: e
Saturday Frequency: m
Circulation: 1,910; 2,430(sat); 76(sun)
Last Audit: Sworn/Estimate/Non-Audited September 30, 2017
Advertising Rate (weekday/saturday): Open inch rate $19.20
News services: AP.
Own Printing Facility?: No
Special Editions: Football (Aug); County Fair (Jul); Basketball (Nov).
Special Weekly Sections: Real Estate, Business (Wed); Entertainment (Thur); Religion (Sat)
Digital Platform - Mobile: Apple, Android
Digital Platform - Tablet: Apple iOS, Android
Ed. .... David Yonke
Dist. Mgr. .... Doug Hillis
Market Information: TMC.
Mechanical Available: Offset; Black and 3 ROP colors; insert accepted; page cutoffs - 22 3/4.
Mechanical Specifications: Type page 11 5/8 x 21 1/2; E - 6 cols, 1 13/16, 1/8 between; A - 6 cols, 1 13/16, 1/8 between; C - 9 cols, 1 3/8, 1/16 between.
Areas Served: Sandusky County (OH); Ottawa County (OH)
Delivery Method: Newsstand, Carrier, RacksEquipment & Software: BUSINESS EQUIPMENT: IBM/PC II CLASSIFIED EQUIPMENT: Hardware — APP/Mac; CLASSIFIED SOFTWARE: Baseview/ Class Manager. EDITORIAL EQUIPMENT: Hardware — APP/Mac EDITORIAL SOFTWARE: Baseview, QPS/QuarkXPress.
Note: Printed under contract by the Fremont News-Messenger. For production information, see Fremont listing.

THE NEWS-MESSENGER

1800 E State St, Ste B, Fremont, Ohio, 43420-4083, Sandusky; gen tel (419) 332-5511; adv tel (419) 334-1069; ed tel (419) 334-1059; gen fax (419) 332-9750; ed fax (419) 332-9750; gen/nat adv e-mail scourson@gannett.com; disp adv e-mail JCoppler@nncogannett.com; ed e-mail dyonke@gannett.com; web site www.thenews-messenger.com
Group: Gannett
Published: Mon, Tues, Wed, Thur, Fri, Sat, Sun
Weekday Frequency: e
Saturday Frequency: e
Circulation: 4,259; 4,803(sat); 143(sun)
Last Audit: AAM September 30, 2017
Advertising Rate (weekday/saturday): Open inch rate $29.20
News services: AP, GNS.
Own Printing Facility?: No
Special Editions: Home Week (Apr); Fair (Aug); Gift Guide (Dec); Progress (Feb); Bridal (Jan); Wellness (Jun); Accent on Agriculture (Mar); Graduation (May); Winter Sports (Nov); Fall Home Improvement (Oct); Business Showcase (Sept).
Special Weekly Sections: Neighbor (Mon); Real Estate (Wed); Weekly (Thur); Religion (Sat)
Digital Platform - Mobile: Apple, Android
Digital Platform - Tablet: Apple iOS, Android
Sales Mgr. .... Jeff Coppler
Cir. Dist. Mgr. .... Doug Hillis
Ed. .... David Yonke
Market Information: TMC.
Mechanical Available: Offset; Black and 3 ROP colors; insert accepted; page cutoffs - 22 3/4.
Mechanical Specifications: Type page 11 5/8 x 21 1/2; E - 6 cols, 1 13/16, 1/8 between; A - 6 cols, 1 13/16, 1/8 between; C - 9 cols, 1 3/16, 1/16 between.
Areas Served: Sandusky County (OH); Ottawa County (OH)
Delivery Method: Newsstand, Carrier,

RacksEquipment & Software: PRESSROOM EQUIPMENT: Lines — 6-G/Urbanite; Folders — 1-G/Quarter, 1-G/2:1 Half; Reels & Stands — 3; MAILROOM EQUIPMENT: Counter Stackers — 1-BG/107, 1-BG/109; Inserters & Stuffers — K&M/Titan 1372; Tying Machines — 3-MLN/ML2-EE, 1-Dynaric/NPZ; Address Machine — Ch/539.; BUSINESS EQUIPMENT: IBM/ AS-400 CLASSIFIED EQUIPMENT: Hardware — APP/Mac; Printers — HP/ LaserJet 4000 N; CLASSIFIED SOFTWARE: QPS/QuarkXPress, Advision. DISPLAY EQUIPMENT: Hardware — APP/Mac; Printers — AU/APS 6-82 ACS, QMS 2060; Other Hardware — HP/Designjet 800 ps DISPLAY SOFTWAREAd Make-up Applications — QPS/QuarkXPress 4.11; Layout Software — IBM/AS-400, SCS/ Layout 8000. EDITORIAL EQUIPMENT: Hardware — APP/Mac/APP/Server; Printers — AU/APS 6-82 ACS, All/3850, QMS/2060 EDITORIAL SOFTWARE: Baseview/IQ Pro, QPS/QuarkXPress 4.11. PRODUCTION EQUIPMENT: Hardware — AU/APS 6-82 ACS, All/3850, Umax; Scanners — Umax/ Powerlook III, Epson/Perfection 1670, AG/ Arcus II, Duoscan/TI200, AG/Duoscan PRODUCTION SOFTWARE: QPS/ QuarkXPress, Advision/ALPS 4.11.

GALLIPOLIS

GALLIPOLIS DAILY TRIBUNE

825 3rd Ave, Gallipolis, Ohio, 45631-1624, Gallia; gen tel (740) 446-2342; adv tel (740) 446-2342 ext. 11. or ext. 29; ed tel (740) 446-2342 ext 18; gen fax (740) 446-3008; gen/ nat adv e-mail jschultz@civitasmedia.com; disp adv e-mail jschultz@civitasmedia.com; class adv e-mailkcade@civitasmedia.com; ed e-mail michaeljohnson@civitasmedia.com; web site www.mydailytribune.com

Group: AIM Media Indiana
Published: Tues, Wed, Thur, Fri, Sat
Weekday Frequency: m
Saturday Frequency: m
Circulation: 4,466; 9,068(sun)
Last Audit: Sworn/Estimate/Non-Audited September 30, 2017
Advertising Rate (weekday/saturday): Open inch rate $10.15
News services: AP.
Own Printing Facility?: Yes
Commercial Printers?: Yes
Special Weekly Sections: TV Times (Fri); Best Food Day (S); Best Food Day (Wed).
Syndicated Publications: USA WEEKEND Magazine (S).
Pub. .... Bud Hunt
Ed. .... Michael Johnson
Adv. Dir. .... Julia Schulz
CSR .... Patricia Wamsley
Sports. Ed. .... Bryan Walters
Market Information: TMC.
Mechanical Available: Offset; Black and 3 ROP colors; insert accepted; page cutoffs - 21 1/4.
Mechanical Specifications: Type page 11 5/8 x 21 1/4; E - 6 cols, 1 7/8, 1/8 between; A - 6 cols, 1 7/8, 1/8 between; C - 9 cols, 1 3/16, 1/16 between.
Areas Served: Gallipolis, Gallia County
Delivery Method: Mail, Newsstand, Carrier, RacksEquipment & Software: PRESSROOM EQUIPMENT: Lines — 3-G/Urbanite 1967; 1-G/Urbanite 1970; 1-G/Urbanite 1973; G/Upper Former 1976; Folders — 1-G/ Suburban, 1-G/Urbanite; Control System — 1-Fin/Console.; MAILROOM EQUIPMENT: Counter Stackers — 1/BG; Inserters & Stuffers — 6-MM/Main Feeder; Tying Machines — 3-/Bu, 1-MLN/Strapper; Address Machine — 3-/Wm; BUSINESS EQUIPMENT: 1-IBM/AS-400 BUSINESS SOFTWARE: PBS CLASSIFIED EQUIPMENT: Hardware — APP/Mac; Printers — APP/Mac LaserWriter; CLASSIFIED SOFTWARE: Baseview 3.4. DISPLAY EQUIPMENT: Hardware — APP/Mac; DISPLAY SOFTWAREAd Make-up Applications — Baseview 3.4; Layout Software — Baseview. EDITORIAL EQUIPMENT: Hardware — APP/Mac/ HP/ScanJet Plus; Printers — APP/Mac LaserWriter EDITORIAL SOFTWARE: Baseview 3.4. PRODUCTION EQUIPMENT: Hardware — APP/Mac LaserWriter IIg, Panther Plus 46; Cameras — B/Caravel, ECR/Autokon 8400; Scanners — HP/ScanJet Plus PRODUCTION SOFTWARE: Baseview 3.4.
Note: The Gallipolis Daily Tribune and the Pomeroy Daily Sentinel share their Sunday edition, the Sunday Times-Sentinel. The combination rate is $14.20.

GREENVILLE

DAILY ADVOCATE

428 S Broadway St, Greenville, Ohio, 45331-1926, Darke; gen tel (937) 548-3151; adv tel (937) 548-3151; ed tel (937) 548-3151; gen fax (937) 548-3913; adv fax (937) 548-3913; ed fax (937) 548-3913; gen/nat adv e-mail advertising@dailyadvocate.com; disp adv e-mail mbevins@dailyadvocate.com; class adv e-mailcrandall@dailyadvocate.com; ed e-mail cchalmers@dailyadvocate.com; web site www.dailyadvocate.com

Group: AIM Media Indiana
Published: Mon, Tues, Wed, Thur, Fri
Weekday Frequency: m
Circulation: 6,468; 6,468(sat)
Last Audit: Sworn/Estimate/Non-Audited September 30, 2017
Advertising Rate (weekday/saturday): Open inch rate $17.50
News services: AP, NEA. **Established:** 1883
Special Weekly Sections: Next Generation (Mon); Religion Page, Senior (Fri); Prime Time (Wed).
Syndicated Publications: Cooks Corner (Mon); USA WEEKEND Magazine (Sat); Darke County Farmer Page (Tues); American Profile (Weekly).
Digital Platform - Mobile: Apple, Android, Windows, Blackberry
Digital Platform - Tablet: Apple iOS, Android, Windows 7, Blackberry Tablet OS
Adv. Mgr. .... Christie Randall
Rep .... Linda Moody
Sports Ed. .... Kyle Shaner
Ed .... Christina Chalmers
Cust. Sales / Serv. Rep. .... Teresa Ketring
Cust. Sales / Serv. Rep. .... Diana Sleppy
Market Information: TMC; Zoned editions.
Mechanical Available: Offset; Black and 3 ROP colors; insert accepted - catabook and mini-tab size; page cutoffs - 22 3/4.
Mechanical Specifications: Type page 13 3/4 x 21 1/2; E - 6 cols, 1 3/4, 1/8 between; A - 6 cols, 1 3/4, 1/8 between; C - 8 cols, 1 5/16, 1/8 between.
Areas Served: Darke County
Delivery Method: Mail, Newsstand, RacksEquipment & Software: CLASSIFIED EQUIPMENT: Hardware — APP/Power Mac; CLASSIFIED SOFTWARE: Baseview. DISPLAY SOFTWARELayout Software — MEI/ALS. EDITORIAL EQUIPMENT: Hardware — APP/Power Mac EDITORIAL SOFTWARE: Baseview/NewsEdit Pro IQUE. PRODUCTION EQUIPMENT: Hardware — 1-Nu, V/ImageSetter Plus; Cameras — R PRODUCTION SOFTWARE: QPS/ QuarkXPress 3.32.

HAMILTON

JOURNALNEWS

228 Court St, Hamilton, Ohio, 45011-2820, Butler; gen tel (513) 863-8200; ed tel (513) 705-2506; gen fax (937) 225-0588; adv fax (513) 863-0011; ed fax (513) 896-9489; web site www.journal-news.com

Group: Cox Media Group
Published: Mon, Tues, Wed, Thur, Fri, Sat, Sun
Weekday Frequency: m
Saturday Frequency: m
Circulation: 18,447; 22,638(sat); 26,246(sun)
Last Audit: AAM June 30, 2015
Advertising Rate (weekday/saturday): Open inch rate $22.50
News services: AP. **Established:** 1818
Special Editions: Perfect Wedding (Apr); Back to School (Aug); Progress (Feb); Perfect Wedding (Jan); Butler County Fair (Jul); NCAA (Mar); Explore Summer (May); Basketball Tip-Off (Nov); Fall Home Improvement (Sept).
Special Weekly Sections: Journal News (Mon); Test Drive (Sat).
Syndicated Publications: TV Update (S).
Controller .... Karen Lehman
Sr. Vice President Slaes .... Rob Rohr
Circ. Mgr. .... Mike Stephens
Ed. .... Kira Lisa Warren
Deputy Mng. Ed. .... Mike Wallace
City Ed. .... Rich Gillette
Editorial Page Ed. .... Mike Williams
Lifestyle Ed. .... Mandy Gambrell
Photo Ed. .... Greg Lynch
Religion Ed. .... Peggy McCracken
Sports Ed. .... John Boyle
Mgmt. Info Servs. Mgr. .... Carl Borsani
Market Information: TMC.
Mechanical Available: Offset; Black and 3 ROP colors; insert accepted - all; page cutoffs - 22 1/2.
Mechanical Specifications: Type page 13 x 21 1/2; E - 6 cols, 2 1/16, 1/8 between; A - 6 cols, 2 1/16, 1/8 between; C - 10 cols, 1 5/16, 1/16 between.Equipment & Software: BUSINESS EQUIPMENT: 1-HP/9000 K class server CLASSIFIED EQUIPMENT: Hardware — CText, PC 486 66Mhz; APP/Mac LaserWriter II NTX, HP/ ScanJet Plus; Printers — Pre Press/Panther Plus; CLASSIFIED SOFTWARE: CText/ Classified, CText/ALPS Pagination. DISPLAY EQUIPMENT: Hardware — 3-CText/486-66, APP/WGS 8100-110; Printers — 2-NewGen/ Imager Plus 12, Pre Press/Panther Plus; Other Hardware — 2-HP/ScanJet IIcx, Umax/1200 Color Scanner, 2-HP/ScanJet 3C DISPLAY SOFTWAREAd Make-up Applications — CText/Adept 3.2, QPS/ QuarkXPress 3.31; Layout Software — 3-APP/Mac, 3- EDITORIAL EQUIPMENT: Hardware — CText/486-66/Lf/AP Leaf Picture Desk, APP/Mac Laserphoto, SMS/ Stauffer Library; Printers — Pre Press/ Panther Plus EDITORIAL SOFTWARE: CText/AFM V6X, Expressline Pagination. PRODUCTION EQUIPMENT: Hardware — Pre Press/Panther Plus, 2-NewGen/Imager Plus, SCREEN/LD-281-Q; Cameras — 1-C/ Spartan III, 1-ECR/Autokon 8400; Scanners — Polaroid/SprintScan PRODUCTION SOFTWARE: QPS/QuarkXPress 3.31.
Note: Advertising is sold in combination with the Middletown Journal (mS) for $52.00(d) and $52.00(S). Individual newspaper rates not made available.

HILLSBORO

HILLSBORO TIMES-GAZETTE

108 Governor Trimble Pl, Hillsboro, Ohio, 45133-1145, Highland; gen tel (937) 393-3456; adv tel (937) 393-3456 ext. 1673; ed tel (937) 393-3456 ext. 1677; gen fax (937) 393-2059; adv fax (937) 393-2059; ed fax (937) 393-2059; gen/nat adv e-mail shughes@civitasmedia.com; disp adv e-mail cmiller@civitasmedia.com; class adv e-mailclassifieds@civitasmedia.com; ed e-mail jgilliland@civitasmedia.com; web site www.timesgazette.com

Group: AIM Media Indiana
Published: Tues, Wed, Thur, Fri, Sat
Weekday Frequency: m
Saturday Frequency: m
Circulation: 4,500; 4,500(sat)
Last Audit: Sworn/Estimate/Non-Audited September 30, 2017
Advertising Rate (weekday/saturday): Open inch rate $14.70
News services: AP. **Established:** 1818
Special Editions: Christmas Tab (Dec); Fall Festival of Leaves Tab (Fall); Basketball Tab (Other); Spring Tab (Spring); Summer Tab (Summer).
Special Weekly Sections: Church Page (Fri); Farm Page (Mon).
Syndicated Publications: USA WEEKEND Magazine (Sat); American Profile (Weekly).
Circ. Mgr. .... Brenda Earley
Pub. / Ed. .... Gary Abernathy
Asst. Ed. .... Jeff Gilliland
Med. Sales Mgr. .... Sharon Hughes
Med. Sales Cons. .... Chuck Miller
Med. Sales Cons. .... Tracie Guisinger
Mechanical Available: Offset; Black and 2 ROP colors; insert accepted; page cutoffs - 21 1/2.
Mechanical Specifications: Type page 13 x 21; E - 6 cols, 2 1/16, 1/8 between; A - 6 cols, 2 1/16, 1/8 between; C - 6 cols, 2 1/16, 1/8 between.
Areas Served: Highland County (OH)
Equipment & Software: PRESSROOM EQUIPMENT: Lines — G.; MAILROOM EQUIPMENT: Tying Machines — Bu; Address Machine — 1/Am, 1-/El.; EDITORIAL EQUIPMENT: Hardware — COM. PRODUCTION EQUIPMENT: Hardware — 3-COM; Cameras — 1-B, 1-Nu.

IRONTON

THE IRONTON TRIBUNE

2903 S 5th St, Ironton, Ohio, 45638-2866, Lawrence; gen tel (740) 532-1441; adv tel (740) 532-1445; ed tel (740) 532-1445; gen fax (740) 532-1506; adv fax (740) 532-1506; ed fax (740) 532-1506; gen/nat adv e-mail shawn.randolph@irontontribune.com; disp adv e-mail advertising@irontontribune.com; class adv e-mailbonita.creger@irontontribune.com; ed e-mail mike.caldwell@irontontribune.com; web site www.irontontribune.com

Group: Boone Newspapers, Inc.
Published: Mon, Tues, Wed, Thur, Fri, Sun
Weekday Frequency: e
Circulation: 5,228; 7,228(sun)
Last Audit: Sworn/Estimate/Non-Audited September 30, 2017
Advertising Rate (weekday/saturday): Open inch rate $13.50
Advertising Rate (sunday): 15.50
News services: AP, MCT. **Established:** 1928
Special Editions: Football Tab (Aug); Christmas (Dec); Profile (Feb); Bridal (Jan); Newcomer's Guide (Jul); Thanksgiving Day (Nov); Senior Citizen Guide (Sept).
Special Weekly Sections: Religion (Fri); Neighbors (S); Best Food Day (Wed).
Syndicated Publications: Parade (S).
Pres./Pub. .... Michael Caldwell
Mktg. / Adv. Dir. .... Shawn Randolph
Gen. Mgr. / Circ. Dir. .... Josh Morrison
Sports Ed. .... James Walker
Prod. Mgr. / Pres. Fore. .... Bo Elliott
Class. Mktg. Rep. .... Bonita Creger
Cir. Clerk / CSR .... Cindy Staton
Market Information: ADS; TMC; Zoned editions.
Mechanical Available: Offset; Black and 3 ROP colors; insert accepted; page cutoffs - 22 1/4.
Mechanical Specifications: Type page 11 5/8 x 21 1/4; E - 6 cols, 1/8 between; A - 6 cols, 1/8 between; C - 10 cols, between.
Areas Served: 45638Equipment & Software: PRESSROOM EQUIPMENT: Lines — 8-unit/ Community 1974.; MAILROOM EQUIPMENT: Tying Machines — It.; BUSINESS EQUIPMENT: Gateway BUSINESS SOFTWARE: PBS, Excel, Quicken CLASSIFIED EQUIPMENT: Hardware — APP/Mac; CLASSIFIED SOFTWARE: Baseview/NewsEdit, Baseview/Classified. DISPLAY EQUIPMENT: Printers — Xante/ Accel-A-Writer; DISPLAY SOFTWAREAd Make-up Applications — QPS/QuarkXPress 4.0; Layout Software — APP/Mac. EDITORIAL EQUIPMENT: Hardware — APP/Mac EDITORIAL SOFTWARE: Baseview/NewsEdit, Baseview/Classified. PRODUCTION EQUIPMENT: Hardware — Milart, Adobe/Photoshop; Cameras — C.

KENT

RECORD-COURIER

1050 W Main St, Kent, Ohio, 44240-2006, Portage; gen tel (330) 541-9400; adv tel (330) 298-2012; ed tel (330) 298-1124; gen fax (330) 296-2698; adv fax (330) 296-2698; ed fax (330) 296-2698; gen/nat adv e-mail kcontini@recordpub.com; disp adv e-mail advertising@recordpub.com; class adv e-mailclass@recordpub.com; ed e-mail editor@recordpub.com; web site www.recordpub.com
- 1,000,000(views) 150,000(visitors)

Group: GateHouse Media, Inc.
Published: Mon, Tues, Wed, Thur, Fri, Sat, Sun

Weekday Frequency: m
Saturday Frequency: m
Circulation: 12,071; 12,071(sat); 13,413(sun)
Last Audit: AAM March 31, 2016
Advertising Rate (weekday/saturday): Open inch rate $18.36
Online Advertising Rate: 3:1 Rectangle $6 CPM; Standard Banner $7 CPM; Box $7.50 CPM; Wide Skyscraper $7 CPM; Button $7 CPM; Leaderboard $8.50 CPM; Half Page $10 CPM
News services: AP, SHNS. **Established:** 1830
Special Editions: Home Improvement (Apr); Football & Fall Sports (Aug); Gift Guide (Dec); Progress (Feb); Bridal Tab (Jan); Bridal Tab (Jun); Car Care (Mar); Summer Lifestyles (May); Gift Guide (Nov); Car Care (Sept).
Special Weekly Sections: Entertainment (Thur); Best Food Day (Tues).
Syndicated Publications: USA WEEKEND Magazine (S).
Pub .... David E. Dix
Class. Adv. Dir. .... Nancy Whitehead
Mng. Ed. .... Heather Rainone
Ed. .... Roger DiPaolo
Cir. Mgr. .... Gary Hurst
Market Information: Split run; TMC; Zoned editions.
Mechanical Available: Offset; Black and 3 ROP colors; insert accepted; page cutoffs - 22 3/4.
Mechanical Specifications: Type page 12 7/8 x 21 1/2; E - 6 cols, 2 1/16, 1/8 between; A - 6 cols, 2 1/16, 1/8 between; C - 6 cols, 2 1/16, 1/8 between.
Areas Served: Portage County (OH)
Equipment & Software: PRESSROOM EQUIPMENT: Lines — 9-G/Urbanite; 13-G/Community; Folders — 1-G/1:1, 1-G/2:1.; MAILROOM EQUIPMENT: Counter Stackers — 1/BG; Inserters & Stuffers — 6-/MM; Tying Machines — 1-/MLN, 2-/Sa; Wrapping Singles — 1-/Sa; Address Machine — 1-/Ch.; BUSINESS EQUIPMENT: 1-DSI CLASSIFIED EQUIPMENT: Hardware — 11-APP/Mac; Printers — 2-APP/Mac LaserWriter NT XII, Okidata/5460; CLASSIFIED SOFTWARE: Baseview. DISPLAY EQUIPMENT: Hardware — APP/Mac; Printers — 2-HP/LaserJet 4MV; DISPLAY SOFTWAREAd Make-up Applications — Multi-Ad/Creator II 1.5; Layout Software — 8-APP/Mac. EDITORIAL EQUIPMENT: Hardware — 25-APP/Mac; Printers — 3-HP/LaserJet 4MV EDITORIAL SOFTWARE: Baseview. PRODUCTION EQUIPMENT: Hardware — 1-APP/Mac, 1-AG/Imagesetter, 1-Konica; Cameras — SCREEN; Scanners — Nikon/1000 PRODUCTION SOFTWARE: QPS, Baseview.

KENTON

THE KENTON TIMES

201 E Columbus St, Kenton, Ohio, 43326-1583, Hardin; gen tel (419) 674-4066; adv tel (419) 674-4066 ext. 221; ed tel (419) 674-4066 ext. 232; gen fax (419) 673-1125; adv fax (419) 673-1125; ed fax (419) 673-1125; gen/nat adv e-mail dvanbuskirk@kentontimes.com; disp adv e-mail lheacock@kentontimes.com; class adv e-maildvanbuskirk@kentontimes.com; ed e-mail kteditor@kentontimes.com; web site www.kentontimes.com
Group: Ray Barnes Newspapers, Inc.
Published: Mon, Tues, Wed, Thur, Fri, Sat, Sun
Weekday Frequency: e
Saturday Frequency: m
Circulation: 7,200; 7,200(sat)
Last Audit: Sworn/Estimate/Non-Audited September 30, 2017
Advertising Rate (weekday/saturday): Open inch rate $8.50
News services: AP.
Special Editions: Car Care (Apr); Pre-Fair (Aug); First Baby Sections (Dec); Presidents' Day Promotion (Feb); Baby Times (Jan); Fair Premium (Jul); Moonlight Madness Promotion (Jun); 4-H (Mar); Graduation (May); Christmas Shopping Kick-off (Nov); Moonlight Madness Promotio
Syndicated Publications: American Profile (Weekly).
Pub .... Jeff Barnes
Adv. Sales Mgr. .... Lesa Heacock
Staff Writ. .... Kendrick Jesionowski
News Ed. .... Timothy Thomas
Prod. Mgr. / Web. Admin. .... Curt Mullholland
Market Information: TMC.
Mechanical Available: Offset; Black and 3 ROP colors; insert accepted; page cutoffs - 21 1/2.
Mechanical Specifications: Type page 13 x 21 1/2; E - 6 cols, 2 1/16, 1/8 between; A - 6 cols, 2 1/16, 1/8 between; C - 6 cols, 2 1/16, 1/8 between.
Areas Served: Hardin County (OH)
Equipment & Software: PRESSROOM EQUIPMENT: Lines — 1-G/Community; Folders — 1-G/2:1.; MAILROOM EQUIPMENT: Tying Machines — 1/Bu; Address Machine — 1-/Kr, 1-/St.; BUSINESS EQUIPMENT: 3-B/25 DISPLAY SOFTWARELayout Software — 2-APP/Mac SE. EDITORIAL EQUIPMENT: Hardware — Mk. PRODUCTION EQUIPMENT: Hardware — 2-APP/Mac LaserWriter Plus, 1-APP/Mac LaserWriter NTX; Cameras — 1-B.

LANCASTER

EAGLE-GAZETTE MEDIA

138 W Chestnut St, Lancaster, Ohio, 43130-4308, Fairfield; gen tel (740) 654-1321; adv tel (877) 513-7355; ed tel (740) 681-4344; gen fax (740) 681-4505; adv fax (740) 681-4505; ed fax (740) 681-4456; gen/nat adv e-mail dnase@gannett.com; disp adv e-mail mrager@gannett.com; class adv e-mailksargent@nncogannett.com; ed e-mail jsabin@nncogannett.com; web site www.lancastereaglegazette.com
Group: Gannett
Published: Mon, Tues, Wed, Thur, Fri, Sat, Sun
Weekday Frequency: e
Saturday Frequency: e
Circulation: 6,906; 6,795(sat); 8,313(sun)
Last Audit: AAM September 30, 2015
Advertising Rate (weekday/saturday): Open inch rate $27.38
News services: AP, GNS. **Established:** 1807
Special Editions: Spring Car Care (Apr); Fall Sports Preview (Aug); Chamber Tab (Jan); Lancaster Festival (Jul); Pictorial Review (Jun); Home & Garden (Mar);
Special Weekly Sections: Color Comics (Sun); Entertainment (Thur); Best Food Day (Wed); Life Styles (Sun)
Syndicated Publications: USA WEEKEND Magazine (S).
Group Publisher .... Rick Szabrak
Ops. Mgr. .... Heather Bright
Editorial Page Ed. .... Jim Sabin
Sales. Mgr. .... Mark Rager
Class. Mgr. .... Karie Sargent
Market Information: ADS; TMC.
Mechanical Available: Offset; Black and 3 ROP colors; insert accepted - free-standing card; page cutoffs - 22 3/4.
Mechanical Specifications: Type page 11 3/4 x 21; E - 6 cols, 1 5/6, 1/8 between; A - 6 cols, 1 5/6, 1/8 between; C - 9 cols, 1 1/4, 1/8 between.
Areas Served: Fairfield County (OH)
Equipment & Software: MAILROOM EQUIPMENT: Tying Machines — 1-MLN/Strapper, 1/Akibono.; BUSINESS EQUIPMENT: IBM BUSINESS SOFTWARE: PBS, Oracle CLASSIFIED EQUIPMENT: Hardware — IBM; Printers — Xante; CLASSIFIED SOFTWARE: Advision. DISPLAY EQUIPMENT: Hardware — APP/Mac; Printers — Xante; DISPLAY SOFTWAREAd Make-up Applications — QPS/QuarkXPress; Layout Software — MEI/ALS. EDITORIAL EQUIPMENT: Hardware — APP/Mac; Printers — Xante EDITORIAL SOFTWARE: Baseview/NewsEdit Pro. PRODUCTION EQUIPMENT: Hardware — Wordlinx 20; Scanners — Umax/PowerLook PRODUCTION SOFTWARE: Mk, QPS/QuarkXPress.

LIBERTY TOWNSHIP

MIDDLETOWN JOURNAL

7320 Yankee Rd, Liberty Township, Ohio, 45044-9168, Butler; gen tel (877) 267-0018; adv tel (513) 705-2860; ed tel (513) 705-2525; gen fax (513) 422-2734; adv fax (513) 422-2794; ed fax (513) 423-6940; gen/nat adv e-mail bruce.karlson@coxinc.com; disp adv e-mail bruce.karlson@coxinc.com; class adv e-mailbruce.karlson@coxinc.com; ed e-mail news@coxohio.com; web site www.middletownjournal.com
Group: Cox Media Group
Published: Mon, Tues, Wed, Thur, Fri, Sat, Sun
Weekday Frequency: m
Saturday Frequency: m
Circulation: 11,208; 12,429(sat); 13,534(sun)
Last Audit: AAM September 30, 2013
Advertising Rate (weekday/saturday): Open inch rate $201.00
Advertising Rate (sunday): Open inch rate $227.00
News services: AP. **Established:** 1857
Special Editions: Home Improvement (Apr); Football (Aug); Progress (Feb); Bridal (Jan); Health & Fitness (Jul); Tax Guide (Mar); Outdoor Living (May); Christmas Gift Guide (Nov); Fall Car Care (Oct); Home Improvement (Sept).
Special Weekly Sections: Arts, Family, Food, Health, Home, Living, Real Estate (Monthly)
Syndicated Publications: TV Journal (S).
Adv. Mgr. .... Joan Hyland
Classified Dir. .... Terry Bouquot
Circ. Dir. .... J. Michael Stevens
City Ed. .... Kevin Aldridge
Editorial Page Ed. .... Michael Williams
Entertainment Ed. .... Eric Robinette
Features Ed. .... Rick McCrabb
Prodn. Mgr., Pre Press .... Jenny McClanahan
COO .... Brian Cooper
Sr. VP, Adv. .... Rob Rohr
Nat'l Dir. .... Bruce Karlson
Market Information: TMC.
Mechanical Available: Offset; Black and 3 ROP colors; insert accepted; page cutoffs - 22 3/4.
Mechanical Specifications: Type page 13 x 21 1/2; E - 6 cols, 2 1/16, 1/8 between; A - 6 cols, 2 1/16, 1/8 between; C - 10 cols, 1 3/16, 1/8 between.Equipment & Software: BUSINESS EQUIPMENT: HP/9000 Model G30 BUSINESS SOFTWARE: Oracle, PBS CLASSIFIED EQUIPMENT: Hardware — APP/Mac; Printers — Pre Press/Imagesetter; CLASSIFIED SOFTWARE: Baseview. DISPLAY EQUIPMENT: Hardware — APP/Mac; Other Hardware — APP/Mac Quadra 660AV, ZYQUEST/Drives DISPLAY SOFTWARELayout Software — QPS/QuarkXPress. EDITORIAL EQUIPMENT: Hardware — APP/Mac, Baseview; Printers — Pre Press/Panther Imagesetter EDITORIAL SOFTWARE: Baseview, QPS/QuarkXPress. PRODUCTION EQUIPMENT: Hardware — Caere/OmniPage; Cameras — 1-B/500LB; Scanners — AG/Arcus Plus PRODUCTION SOFTWARE: QPS/QuarkXPress.
Note: Advertising is sold in combination with the Hamilton JournalNews (mS) for $50.00(m) and $52.00(S). Individual newspaper rates not made available.

LIMA

THE LIMA NEWS

3515 Elida Rd, Lima, Ohio, 45807-1538, Allen; gen tel (419) 223-1010; adv tel (419) 993-2040; ed tel (419) 222-6397; gen fax (419) 229-2926; adv fax (419) 229-0426; ed fax (419) 229-2926; gen/nat adv e-mail bstaples@civitasmedia.com; disp adv e-mail jholtsberry@limanews.com; class adv e-mailclassifieds@limanews.com; ed e-mail info@limanews.com; web site www.limanews.com
- 1,560,000(views) 133,000(visitors)
Group: AIM Media Indiana
Published: Mon, Tues, Wed, Thur, Fri, Sat, Sun
Weekday Frequency: m
Saturday Frequency: m
Circulation: 20,602; 20,305(sat); 25,120(sun)
Last Audit: AAM September 30, 2016
Advertising Rate (weekday/saturday): Open inch rate $53.80
Advertising Rate (sunday): Open inch rate $70.05
News services: AP, CT, Freedom Wire, MCT, TMS. **Established:** 1885
Special Editions: Spring Car Care (Apr); Regional Football Preview (Aug); Christmas Gift Sections (Dec); Regional Prep Basketball Tournament Preview (Feb); Health & Fitness (Jan); Best of the Lima Region (Jul); Regional Salute to Graduates (Jun); Celebrating Our Spirit (Ma
Special Weekly Sections: 360 Entertainment Tab & Drivers Seat (Fri); Best Food Day (Mon); Agri-Business, Family, Consumer (S); Lifestyle Feature , Religion & High School Sports (Sat); Home & Fashion (Thur); Health (Tues); Lifestyle Feature, Reminisce & Antiques (Wed).
Syndicated Publications: 360 Entertainment Tab TV listings (Fri); Color Comics (S).
Pub./Gen. Mgr. .... James Shine
Dir., HR .... Leila Osting
Cir. Dir. .... John Quaintance
Ed. .... Jim Krumel
Mng. Ed. .... David Trinko
Pub .... Doug Olsson
Adv. Mgr. .... Barbara Staples
CS Mgr. .... Mary Van Schoyck
Market Information: TMC; Zoned editions.
Mechanical Available: Offset; Black and 3 ROP colors; insert accepted; page cutoffs - 22 3/4.
Mechanical Specifications: Type page 13 x 21 1/2; E - 6 cols, 1/8 between; A - 6 cols, 1/8 between; C - 9 cols, 1/16 between.
Areas Served: Allen, Auglaize, Hancock, Hardin, Logan, Mercer, Putnam, Shelby, Van Wert Counties (OH)
Equipment & Software: PRESSROOM EQUIPMENT: Lines — 6-MAN/Lithoflex double width; MAILROOM EQUIPMENT: Counter Stackers — 3-Hall/Monitor, TMSI/Dual Carrier; Inserters & Stuffers — GMA/SLS 1000; Tying Machines — 2-Dynaric; Wrapping Singles — 2-St/720.; Address Machine — 1-Am/1906, 1-Gr/6331.; BUSINESS EQUIPMENT: PC Pentium II 350 Mhz, Gateway BUSINESS SOFTWARE: IBM/PS2, Vision Data, Southware, Great Plains CLASSIFIED EQUIPMENT: Hardware — 2-Compaq/Proliant 3000; 8-APP/Mac; Printers — HP/DeskJet 870CSE, HP/LaserJet 4; CLASSIFIED SOFTWARE: Baseview. DISPLAY EQUIPMENT: Hardware — Compaq/Prosignia; Printers — HP/LaserJet 6Lxi, HP/LaserJet 4, Epson/Stylus Color 3000, HP/DesignJet 1050 C; Other Hardware — 8-APP/Power Mac DISPLAY SOFTWAREAd Make-up Applications — MK/Managing Editor Layout; Layout Software — 9-Multi-Ad/Creator. EDITORIAL EQUIPMENT: Hardware — 2-Compaq/Proliant 3000/35-Gateway/Pentium PC; Printers — 2-Pre-Press/Panther Pro 36 Imagesetters, HP/8000, HP/750C Color Proofer, 2-HP/5000 EDITORIAL SOFTWARE: APT/ACT Editorial System. PRODUCTION EQUIPMENT: Hardware — Nat/A-340, 2-Pre Press/Panther Pro 36 Imagesetters, APP/Mac Quadra 900, Polaroid/SprintScan 35; Cameras — Capanica #6500C; Scanners — 2-HP/Scan Jet II, 5-Umax/Powerlook II PRODUCTION SOFTWARE: APT/ACT Pagination 3.0, Baseview/Classified, Managing Edit

LISBON

MORNING JOURNAL

308 Maple St, Lisbon, Ohio, 44432-1205, Columbiana; gen tel (330) 424-9541; adv tel (330) 424-9541 ext. 257; ed tel (330) 424-9541 ext. 297; gen fax (330) 424-0048; adv fax (330) 424-0048; ed fax (330) 424-0048; gen/nat adv e-mail lmcintosh@mojonews.com; disp adv e-mail mspencer@mojonews.com; class adv e-maillmcintosh@mojonews.com; ed e-mail news@mojonews.com; web site www.morningjournalnews.com
Group: Ogden Newspapers Inc.
Published: Mon, Tues, Wed, Thur, Fri, Sat, Sun
Weekday Frequency: m
Saturday Frequency: m
Circulation: 8,119; 8,119(sat); 7,791(sun)
Last Audit: AAM September 30, 2016
Advertising Rate (weekday/saturday): Open inch rate $22.65
News services: AP.
Special Editions: Lawn & Garden (Apr); Fall Home Improvement (Aug); Songbook (Dec); Fact Book (Feb); Christmas in July (Jul); Car Care (Mar); Fun in the Sun (May); Christmas Gift Catalog (Nov); Car Care (Oct).

Special Weekly Sections: Dining Guide (Fri); TV Journal (S); Football (Sat); Entertainment (Thur); Roasts & Toasts (Tues); Farm (Wed).
Syndicated Publications: USA WEEKEND Magazine (S).
Pub. .... Larry Dorschner
Circ. Dir. .... Heidi Grimm
Ed. .... Dorma Tolson
Asst. Ed. .... Dennis Spalvieri
Mgmt. Info Servs. Mgr. .... Ron Flaviano
Prodn. Mgr., Press .... Mike Sweeney
Market Information: ADS; Split run; TMC.
Mechanical Available: Offset; Black and 3 ROP colors; insert accepted - samples; page cutoffs - 21.
Mechanical Specifications: Type page 13 x 20; E - 6 cols, 2 1/16, 1/8 between; A - 6 cols, 2 1/16, 1/8 between; C - 9 cols, 1 15/16, 1/8 between.
Areas Served: Columbiana & Southern Mahoning County
Delivery Method: Mail, Newsstand, Carrier, RacksEquipment & Software: PRESSROOM EQUIPMENT: Lines — 8-HI/NC 400; MAILROOM EQUIPMENT: Counter Stackers — 2/PPK; Tying Machines — 1-/Bu, 1-/Gs, 1-/Sa; Address Machine — 2-/Am, 1-/Ch; BUSINESS EQUIPMENT: Compaq BUSINESS SOFTWARE: Brainworks CLASSIFIED EQUIPMENT: Hardware — APP/Power Mac; Printers — XIT/Imagesetter, ECR/Imagesetter, HP/LaserJet 5000N; CLASSIFIED SOFTWARE: Baseview. DISPLAY EQUIPMENT: Hardware — APP/Mac; Printers — XIT/Imagesetter, ECR/Imagesetter, APP/Mac LaswerWriter 300, HP/LaserJet 5000N, Epson/Color Stylist 3000; DISPLAY SOFTWAREAd Make-up Applications — Multi-Ad/Creator, QPS; Layout Software — 4-APP/Mac. EDITORIAL EQUIPMENT: Hardware — APP/Power Mac/5-APP/Power Mac G3; Printers — XIT/Imagesetter, ECR/Imagesetter EDITORIAL SOFTWARE: Baseview. PRODUCTION EQUIPMENT: Hardware — OmniPro 8.0, ECR/Imagesetter; Scanners — Epson, Microtek, HP

LOGAN

LOGAN DAILY NEWS

72 E Main St, Logan, Ohio, 43138-1221, Hocking; gen tel (740) 385-2107; gen fax (740) 385-4514; gen/nat adv e-mail tmaynard@logandaily.com; disp adv e-mail tmaynard@logandaily.com; class adv e-mailburcham@logandaily.com; ed e-mail dtobin@logandaily.com; web site www.logandaily.com
Group: Adams Publishing Group, LLC
Published: Tues, Wed, Thur, Fri, Sat
Weekday Frequency: m
Saturday Frequency: m
Circulation: 3,000; 3,000(sat)
Last Audit: Sworn/Estimate/Non-Audited December 19, 2017
News services: Tribune News Service **Established:** 1842
Syndicated Publications: American Profile (Weekly).
Digital Platform - Mobile: Apple, Android, Windows, Blackberry
Digital Platform - Tablet: Apple iOS, Android, Blackberry Tablet OS, Kindle, Kindle Fire
Bus. Mgr. .... Lucy Burcham
Mechanical Available: Offset; Black and 3 ROP colors; insert accepted; page cutoffs - 22 3/4.
Mechanical Specifications: Type page 10.25" x 21"; E - 6 cols, 2 3/16, 3/16 between; A - 6 cols, 2 3/16, 3/16 between; C - 8 cols, 1 1/16, 1/8 between.
Areas Served: Buchtel, Carbon Hill, Laurelville, Logan, Nelsonville, New Straitsville, Rockbridge, Shawnee, South Bloomingville, Union Furnace (OH)
Delivery Method: Mail, Newsstand, Carrier, RacksEquipment & Software: MAILROOM EQUIPMENT: Tying Machines — 1/Bu; Address Machine — 2-/Wm.; CLASSIFIED EQUIPMENT: Hardware — APP/Mac IIsi; EDITORIAL EQUIPMENT: Hardware — APP/iMac

LONDON

THE MADISON PRESS

55 W High St, London, Ohio, 43140-1074, Madison; gen tel (740) 852-1616; adv tel (740) 852-1616 ext. 1623; ed tel (740) 852-1616 ext. 1619; gen fax (740) 852-1620; adv fax (740) 852-1620; ed fax (740) 852-1620; gen/nat adv e-mail jhenry@civitasmedia.com; disp adv e-mail jhenry@civitasmedia.com; class adv e-mailclassifieds@civitasmedia.com; ed e-mail LMPnews@civitasmedia.com; web site www.madison-press.com
Group: Civitas Media, LLC-OOB
Published: Tues, Wed, Thur, Fri, Sat
Weekday Frequency: m
Saturday Frequency: m
Circulation: 4,259; 4,259(sat)
Last Audit: Sworn/Estimate/Non-Audited September 30, 2017
Advertising Rate (weekday/saturday): Open inch rate $9.10
News services: AP. **Established:** 1842
Commercial Printers?: Yes
Special Editions: Antique (Apr); Summer Tab (Jun); Farm & Garden Tab (Mar); Home Improvement Tab (May); Car Tab (Oct); Variety (Sept).
Special Weekly Sections: Farm Page (Fri); Food Page (Mon); Outdoor Page (Thur); Kids Page (Wed).
Syndicated Publications: American Profile (Weekly).
Digital Platform - Mobile: Apple, Android, Windows
Ed. .... Andrea Chaffin
Cir. Mgr. .... Sandra Oiler
Ed. Asst. .... Diana Shaw
Pub. .... Lane Moon
Adv. Mgr. .... Jessica Henry
Class. .... Sandi Powers
Acct. Exec. .... Tara Renner
Market Information: TMC.
Mechanical Available: Offset; Black and 3 ROP colors; insert accepted; page cutoffs - 22 3/4.
Mechanical Specifications: Type page 13 x 21 1/2; E - 6 cols, 2 1/16, 1/8 between; A - 6 cols, 2 1/16, 1/8 between; C - 8 cols, 1 1/2, 1/8 between.
Areas Served: 43140, 43162, 43064, 43143
Delivery Method: Mail, Newsstand, Carrier, RacksEquipment & Software: PRESSROOM EQUIPMENT: Lines — 6-G/S1075.; MAILROOM EQUIPMENT: Counter Stackers — BG/104; Inserters & Stuffers — Bundle Tying Machines Bu; Address Machine — KR.; CLASSIFIED SOFTWARE: Mk. DISPLAY SOFTWAREAd Make-up Applications — Multi-Ad/Creator with CD-Rom; Layout Software — APP/Mac. EDITORIAL SOFTWARE: Mk. PRODUCTION EQUIPMENT: Hardware — APP/Mac; Cameras — Acti/204; Scanners — APP/Mac.

LORAIN

THE MORNING JOURNAL

1657 Broadway, Lorain, Ohio, 44052-3439, Lorain; gen tel (440) 245-6901; adv tel (440) 245-6901; ed tel (440) 245-6901 Ext. 90723; gen fax (440) 245-6922; adv fax (440) 245-5637; ed fax (440) 245-6922; gen/nat adv e-mail rbeal@morningjournal.com; disp adv e-mail lbarker@morningjournal.com; class adv e-maillegals@morningjournal.com; ed e-mail letters@morningjournal.com; web site www.morningjournal.com
479,756(visitors)
Group: Digital First Media
Published: Mon, Tues, Wed, Thur, Fri, Sat, Sun
Weekday Frequency: m
Saturday Frequency: m
Circulation: 18,745; 18,745(sat); 20,777(sun)
Last Audit: AAM March 30, 2015
Advertising Rate (weekday/saturday): $24.20 (Education); $28.65 (Political)
Advertising Rate (sunday): $26.50 (Education); $31.30 (Political)
News services: AP, NYT, MCT.
Special Editions: Golf I (Apr); Tour of Homes (Aug); Truck I & II Tab (Dec); Finance/Tax (Feb); Town Crier (Jan); Truck I Tab (Jul); International Festival (Jun); BIA Home Craft Show (Mar); Lorain Pride (May); Early Holiday Gift Guide (Nov); BIA Home Tab (Oct); Country Liv
Special Weekly Sections: Arcade/Entertaiment (Fri); Real Estate (S); Real Estate (Sat).
Syndicated Publications: The Edge (sports edition) (Fri); Today's Woman (Mon); Job Digest (Other); TV Journal (S); Color Comics (6 pages) (Sat).
Adv. Dir. / Gen. Mgr. .... Ron Beal
Ed. .... Tom Skoch
Pub. .... Jeff Schell
Cir. Dir. .... Douglas Fuller
Sales Mgr. .... Darlene Smith
Leg. Adv. .... Paula Velazquez
CFO .... Ron Adams
Market Information: ADS; TMC; Zoned editions.
Mechanical Available: Offset; Black and 3 ROP colors; insert accepted; page cutoffs - 22 3/4.
Mechanical Specifications: Type page 12 x 21 1/2; E - 6 cols, 1 7/8, 1/8 between; A - 6 cols, 1 7/8, 1/8 between; C - 9 cols, 1 3/16, 1/16 between.Equipment & Software: PRESSROOM EQUIPMENT: Lines — 12-G/Urbanite single width 1990; Folders — 2-G/2:1; MAILROOM EQUIPMENT: Counter Stackers — 3-HL/Monitor, 1-HL/Monitor HT; Inserters & Stuffers — 3-MM/227 7:1; Tying Machines — 3/Power Strap, 1-/MLN, 2-MLN/2E; Address Machine — 1-/BH.; BUSINESS EQUIPMENT: 1-IBM/AS-400 CLASSIFIED EQUIPMENT: Hardware — APP/Mac; Printers — 1-Printronix/300, 1-Star/10, CG/8600; CLASSIFIED SOFTWARE: Baseview. DISPLAY EQUIPMENT: Hardware — APP/Mac; Printers — APP/Mac LaserWriter 630, APP/Mac LaserWriter 16-600, GCC/Elite 12085, 2-Linotype-Hell/Linotronic 500, 1-Bidco/Imager; DISPLAY SOFTWAREAd Make-up Applications — QPS/QuarkXPress 4.03; Layout Software — Baseview. EDITORIAL EQUIPMENT: Hardware — APP/Mac; Printers — 2-Linotype-Hell/Linotronic 500, Bidco/Imager, APP/Mac Laserwriter 8500, APP/Mac LaserWriter 630, APP/Mac LaserWriter 16-600, GCC/Elite 12085 EDITORIAL SOFTWARE: Baseview. PRODUCTION EQUIPMENT: Hardware — CG/8600, 2-Linotype-Hell/L-500 Imagesetter, 1-Bidco/Imager, 1-P/24ML, 1-Konica/K720; Cameras — ECR/Spartan II, C/Newspager; Scanners — Lf/Leafscan 35, 2-Nikon/LS1000, 1-Kk, Umax/FlatBed Scanners PRODUCTION SOFTWARE: Baseview/Ad Manager Pro.

MANSFIELD

NEWS JOURNAL

70 W 4th St, Mansfield, Ohio, 44903-1676, Richland; gen tel (419) 522-3311; adv tel (419) 521-7343; ed tel (419) 521-7213; gen fax (419) 521-7414; adv fax (419) 521-7413; ed fax (419) 521-7415; gen/nat adv e-mail atrabitz@gannett.com; disp adv e-mail dordiway@gannett.com; class adv e-mailksargent@nncogannett.com; ed e-mail tbrennan@gannett.com; web site www.mansfieldnewsjournal.com
- 3,789,695(views) 381,796(visitors)
Group: Gannett
Published: Mon, Tues, Wed, Thur, Fri, Sat, Sun
Weekday Frequency: m
Saturday Frequency: m
Circulation: 14,906; 15,370(sat); 21,311(sun)
Last Audit: AAM December 31, 2015
Advertising Rate (weekday/saturday): Open inch rate $38.70
Advertising Rate (sunday): Open inch rate $44.90
News services: AP, GNS. **Established:** 1930
Own Printing Facility?: No
Commercial Printers?: No
Special Editions: He Is Risen (Apr); OSU Football (Aug); Share the Faith (Dec); Progress (Feb); Bridal Guide (Jan); Real Estate Today (Monthly); High School Football (Aug); Living Here
Special Weekly Sections: Health, Fitness (Mon); Best Food (Wed); Entertainment (Thur); Education, TV (Fri); Religion (Sat); Neighbors (Sun)
Syndicated Publications: USA WEEKEND Magazine (Sat).
Digital Platform - Mobile: Apple, Android, Windows, Blackberry
Digital Platform - Tablet: Apple iOS, Android, Windows 7, Blackberry Tablet OS, Kindle, Nook, Kindle Fire
Class. Sales Ctr. Mgr. .... Karie Sargent
Ed. .... Tom Brennan
Exec. Ed. .... Michael Shearer
Watchdog Rep. .... Linda Martz
Cons. Expert. Dir. .... Ryan Cook
Sales Dir .... Adam Trabitz
Cir. Mgr. .... Ida Hanning
Sales Mgr. .... Daniell Ordiway
Market Information: Split run; TMC.
Mechanical Available: Offset; Black and 3 ROP colors; insert accepted - free-standing cards; page cutoffs - 22.75
Mechanical Specifications: Type page - 10 x 21; Edit - 6 Cols, 1.5", 1.9" between; Class - 10 cols, 0.95", 0.07" between
Areas Served: Richland County & Surrounding areas (OH)
Equipment & Software: PRESSROOM EQUIPMENT: Goss Urbanite 1400: # of Printing Couples 32; # of Reels - 7 w/Jardis pasters; Cut-off - 22.75; web width............ 34 and
Goss Urbanite 1401: # of Printing Couples 36; # of Reels - 11 w/Jardis pasters; Cut-off - 22.75; web width 27 MAILROOM EQUIPMENT: Counter Stackers — 1-Quipp 400, 3-Quipp/500, 1 Rima RS2512, 1 Rima RS2510
Inserters — 2-GMA/SLS 1000, 1 with 10 inserts heads and 1 with 14 insert heads; Operating System - LINCS
Strappers — 3-BUNN Dynaric, 1-Sterling/NFT50, 1 -Oval Strapmaster CLASSIFIED EQUIPMENT: Hardware — Dell; Atex Adbase; Printers — HP/4200N, HP/5M; CLASSIFIED SOFTWARE: Atex/Adbase 3.1 DISPLAY EQUIPMENT: Hardware — 27" Mac; Printers — HP/2500CP, 2-HP/8150N; DISPLAY SOFTWARELayout Software — Adobe/InDesign CS. EDITORIAL EQUIPMENT: Hardware — remote servers; Printers — HP/8000N EDITORIAL SOFTWARE: CCI Newsgate PRODUCTION EQUIPMENT: Hardware — 1-AG/3850 Advantage DL PRODUCTION SOFTWARE: Agfa

TELEGRAPH-FORUM

PO Box 25, Mansfield, Ohio, 44901-0025, Richland; gen tel (419) 562-3333; adv tel (419) 562-3333; ed tel (419) 563-9227; gen fax (419) 562-9162; adv fax (419) 562-9162; ed fax (419) 562-9162; gen/nat adv e-mail atrabitz@gannett.com; disp adv e-mail abass@gannett.com; class adv e-mailclassified@nncogannett.com; ed e-mail jcoble@nncogannett.com; web site www.bucyrustelegraphforum.com
Group: Gannett
Published: Mon, Tues, Wed, Thur, Fri, Sat
Weekday Frequency: m
Saturday Frequency: m
Circulation: 2,854; 3,416(sat); 99(sun)
Last Audit: AAM September 30, 2017
Branch Offices: no office
Advertising Rate (weekday/saturday): Open inch rate $15.50
News services: AP, GNS, UPI.
Special Weekly Sections: Best Food (Mon, Tue, Sat); Home (Tue); Religion (Fri); Travel (Sat)
Digital Platform - Mobile: Apple, Android
Digital Platform - Tablet: Apple iOS, Android
Cir. Mgr. .... Ida Hanning
Adv. Sales Dir. .... Adam Trabitz
Market Information: TMC.
Mechanical Available: Offset; Black and 4 ROP colors; insert accepted - anything mailable, some bag samples; page cutoffs - 21 1/4.
Mechanical Specifications: Type page 11 5/8 x 21; E - 6 cols, 1 5/6, 1/8 between; A - 6 cols, 1 5/6, 1/8 between; C - 6 cols, 1 5/6, 1/8 between.
Areas Served: Crawford County (OH)
Delivery Method: Mail, Newsstand, CarrierEquipment & Software: BUSINESS EQUIPMENT: PBS, Oracle, Unix CLASSIFIED SOFTWARE: Ctext/Advision. DISPLAY EQUIPMENT: Printers — HP; DISPLAY SOFTWAREAd Make-up Applications — QPS/QuarkXPress, Multi-Ad/Creator; Layout Software — APP/Mac. EDITORIAL EQUIPMENT: Hardware — APP/Mac EDITORIAL SOFTWARE: Baseview/News Edit.

MARIETTA

THE MARIETTA TIMES

700 Channel Ln, Marietta, Ohio, 45750-2342, Washington; gen tel (740) 373-2121; adv tel (740) 373-2121 ext. 508; ed tel (740) 373-2121 ext. 536; gen fax (740) 373-6251; adv fax (740) 373-6251; ed fax (740) 376-5475; gen/nat adv e-mail advertising@mariettatimes.com; disp adv e-mail lnorthcraft@mariettatimes.com; class adv e-mailclassifieds@mariettatimes.com; ed e-mail letters@mariettatimes.com; web site www.mariettatimes.com
- 850,000(views) 85,000(visitors)
Group: Ogden Newspapers Inc.
Published: Mon, Tues, Wed, Thur, Fri, Sat
Weekday Frequency: e
Saturday Frequency: m
Circulation: 7,326; 8,821(sat)
Last Audit: AAM March 30, 2016
Advertising Rate (weekday/saturday): Open inch rate $29.32
News services: AP, GNS, GNS. **Established:** 1864
Own Printing Facility?: Yes
Commercial Printers?: Yes
Special Weekly Sections: Life Pages (Daily); World of Wonder, NIE (Tue); Youth Sports (Thur); Sport (Fri); Comics, Lifestyle (Sat);Home (Monthly); Value Shopper (Bi-Monthly); Health, Travel (Quarterly); Live Green (Bi-Yearly)
Syndicated Publications: TV Weekly, USA WEEKEND Magazine (Sat).
Digital Platform - Mobile: Apple, Android
Digital Platform - Tablet: Apple iOS, Android
Office Mgr. .... Patti Patton
Cir. Dir. .... Joseph Tranquill
Sr. Copy Ed. .... Jim Bartholow
Copy Ed. .... Claire Hogue-Heiby
Online Mgr. .... Art Smith
Info. Systems Mgr. .... Russ Ryan
Pub. .... Jenny Houtman
Class. .... Lisa Kehl
Ed. .... Kate York
Market Information: ADS; TMC; Zoned editions.
Mechanical Available: Offset; Black and 3 ROP colors; insert accepted; page cutoffs - 22 3/4.
Mechanical Specifications: Type page 13 x 21 1/2; E - 6 cols, 2 1/16, 1/6 between; A - 6 cols, 2 1/16, 1/6 between; C - 9 cols, 1 3/8, 1/16 between.
Areas Served: Marietta (OH)
Delivery Method: Mail, Newsstand, Carrier, RacksEquipment & Software: MAILROOM EQUIPMENT: Counter Stackers — HI/ Rima RS-2517; Tying Machines — 1/ Ty-Tech; Control System — MM/Saddle Stitcher.; BUSINESS EQUIPMENT: IBM/ PC CLASSIFIED SOFTWARE: ONI/Class. DISPLAY EQUIPMENT: Hardware — APP/ Mac.; EDITORIAL EQUIPMENT: Hardware — Dewar/Disc Net, APP/Mac EDITORIAL SOFTWARE: Baseview. PRODUCTION EQUIPMENT: Hardware — 1-LE/LD 1800; Cameras — 1-B/Commodore.

MARION

THE MARION STAR

163 E Center St, Ste 100, Marion, Ohio, 43302-3813, Marion; gen tel (740) 387-0400; adv tel (740) 375-5133; ed tel (740) 375-5107; gen fax (740) 375-5199; adv fax (740) 375-5199; ed fax (740) 375-5199; gen/nat adv e-mail scourson@gannett.com; disp adv e-mail atrabitz@gannett.com; class adv e-mailksargent@nncogannett.com; ed e-mail twilliams7@gannett.com; web site www.marionstar.com
Group: Gannett
Published: Mon, Tues, Wed, Thur, Fri, Sat, Sun
Weekday Frequency: m
Saturday Frequency: m
Circulation: 4,728; 4,728(sat); 5,858(sun)
Last Audit: AAM March 31, 2017
Advertising Rate (weekday/saturday): Open inch rate $26.80
Advertising Rate (sunday): Open inch rate $26.80
News services: AP. **Established:** 1877
Special Editions: Drum Corps Championships (Aug); Christmas Greetings (Dec); Bride (Jan); Progress (Mar); Christmas Gifts (Nov); Popcorn Festival (Sept).
Special Weekly Sections: Best Food, Business, Farm (Sun); Real Estate (Sat)
Syndicated Publications: Golden Opportunities (Senior Citizen) (Monthly); USA WEEKEND Magazine (S); Reflections (Wed).
Digital Platform - Mobile: Apple, Android
Digital Platform - Tablet: Apple iOS, Android
Pub. .... Tom Brennan
Adv. Dir. .... Jeff Coppler
Dis. Mgr. .... Ida Hanning
Sports Ed. .... Henry Conte
Cons. Exp. Dir. .... Ryan Cook
Enterprise Ed. .... Benjamin Lanka
Adv. Sales Dir. .... Adam Trabitz
Nat'l Sales Coord. .... Sharon Courson
Sales Mgr. .... Aaron Bass
Class. Sales Ctr. Mgr. .... Karie Sargent
Ed. .... Tom Williams
Market Information: ADS; Split run; TMC; Zoned editions.
Mechanical Available: Offset; Black and 3 ROP colors; insert accepted; page cutoffs - 22 3/4.
Mechanical Specifications: Type page 13 x 21 1/2; E - 6 cols, 2 1/16, 1/8 between; A - 6 cols, 2 1/16, 1/8 between; C - 9 cols, 1 3/8, 1/16 between.
Areas Served: Maroin County & Surrounding areas
Equipment & Software: PRESSROOM EQUIPMENT: Lines — 8-G/Community (2 half decks); Folders — 1-G/SSC.; MAILROOM EQUIPMENT: Tying Machines — 1-Bu/Straping; Address Machine — 2-Am/2000.; BUSINESS EQUIPMENT: ATT CLASSIFIED EQUIPMENT: Hardware — 4-RSK/Tandy, CText.; DISPLAY SOFTWARELayout Software — CText/Adept. EDITORIAL EQUIPMENT: Hardware — CText, 20-RSK/Tandy, CText. PRODUCTION EQUIPMENT: Hardware — Nat/A-250, 2-Tegra/Varityper/5100A, 3-APP/Mac Laser 486 SX; Cameras — 1-R/500-LB, SCREEN/C-680; Scanners — Nu.

MARTINS FERRY

THE TIMES LEADER

200 S 4th St, Martins Ferry, Ohio, 43935-1312, Belmont; gen tel (740) 633-1131; adv tel (740) 633-1131; ed tel (740) 633-1131; gen fax (740) 633-1122; adv fax (740) 633-1122; ed fax (740) 633-1122; gen/nat adv e-mail hclark@timesleaderonline.com; disp adv e-mail jlovell@timesleaderonline.com; class adv e-mailkcollette@timesleaderonline.com; ed e-mail jcompston@timesleaderonline.com; web site www.timesleaderonline.com
1,700(visitors)
Group: Ogden Newspapers Inc.
Published: Mon, Tues, Wed, Thur, Fri, Sat, Sun
Weekday Frequency: m
Saturday Frequency: m
Circulation: 8,836; 8,836(sat); 11,573(sun)
Last Audit: AAM March 31, 2017
Advertising Rate (weekday/saturday): Open inch rate $64.92
Advertising Rate (sunday): Open inch rate $99.56
News services: AP. **Established:** 1891
Own Printing Facility?: Yes
Special Editions: Home Improvement (Apr); Auto Racing Quarterly (Aug); Drunk Driving Page (Dec); National Children's Health Month (Feb); Tax & Investment Guide (Jan); Jamboree In The Hills (Jul); Vacation Guide (Jun); National Poison Prevention (Mar); Auto Racing Quarterly; Indulge magazine quarterly; Prime Times (seniors) monthly;
Special Weekly Sections: Entertainment, Business, Finance, Arts, Living, Auto (Daily); Style, Local, Sports, Real Estate, Help Wanted (Daily/Sun); Best Food (Sun/ Wed); Consumer, Money (Mon); Health (Tue); Health (Wed); Family/Kids (Thur); Entertainment, Weekend (Fri); Religion, Travel (Sat); Travel, People (Sun)
Syndicated Publications: TV Times/TV Magazine (S); USA WEEKEND Magazine (Sat).
Digital Platform - Mobile: Apple, Android
Digital Platform - Tablet: Apple iOS, Android
Exec. Sports Ed. .... Robert Kapral
Sports Ed. .... Seth R. Staskey
Adv Dir. .... Heidi Clark
Mng. Ed. .... Jennifer Compston-Strough
Class. / Ins. Sales Mgr. .... Kim Collette
Adv. Rep. .... Joe Lovell
Staff Writer/Lifestyles .... Shelley Hanson
Market Information: ADS; TMC; Zoned editions.
Mechanical Available: Offset; Black and 3 ROP colors; insert accepted; page cutoffs - 23 9/16.
Mechanical Specifications: Type page 13 x 22; E - 6 cols, 2 1/16, 1/8 between; A - 6 cols, 2 1/16, 1/8 between; C - 8 cols, 1 9/16, 1/16 between.
Areas Served: Belmont County (OH)
Monroe County (OH)
Harrison County (OH)
Parts of Jefferson County (OH)
Delivery Method: Mail, Newsstand, Carrier, RacksEquipment & Software: PRESSROOM EQUIPMENT: Lines — 4-G/Mark (Offset) 1984; 2-PEC/Eagle (3 Color Ink) 1984; Press Drive — PEC/Bond; Pasters —PEC/ Bond. MAILROOM EQUIPMENT: Counter Stackers — 2-HL/Monitor, 1-HL/HI II; Inserters & Stuffers — 5-HI/1372; Tying Machines — MLN/2EE, MLN/2, MLN/2A.; BUSINESS EQUIPMENT: NCR CLASSIFIED EQUIPMENT: Hardware — APP/Mac Fileserver; 3-COM.; DISPLAY EQUIPMENT: Hardware — APP/Mac Quadra 700, 2-APP/ Mac Centris, APP/Mac G4; Printers — Dataproducts/LZR 1560, NewGen/Turbo 360; Other Hardware — 2-Microtek/Scanmaker II DISPLAY SOFTWAREAd Make-up Applications — QPS/QuarkXPress, Adobe/ Photoshop, Aldus/FreeHand, Multi-Ad/ Creator; Layout Software — APP/Mac. EDITORIAL EQUIPMENT: Hardware — APP/ Mac
PC
Fileserver EDITORIAL SOFTWARE: QPS/ QuarkXPress, Writenow, Teachtext, TXWord, Photoshop PRODUCTION EQUIPMENT: Hardware — Nat/A-250, MON/1270 Imagesetter; Cameras — 1-AG/2024; Scanners — RZ/Scanner, HP/IIC Nikon/35, 2-Microtek.

MARYSVILLE

MARYSVILLE JOURNAL-TRIBUNE

207 N Main St, Marysville, Ohio, 43040-1161, Union; gen tel (937) 644-9111; adv tel (937) 642-5656; ed tel (937) 642-6397; gen fax (937) 644-9211; disp adv e-mail jtads@marysvillejt.com; web site www.marysvillejt.com
- 6,000,000(views) 1,000,000(visitors); web site 2 www.allohioballoonfest.com; web site 3 www.my2centsworth.biz; web site 4Www.rgnews.biz
Published: Mon, Tues, Wed, Thur, Fri, Sat
Weekday Frequency: e
Saturday Frequency: m
Circulation: 6,656; 7,000(sat)
Last Audit: USPS October 1, 2017
Advertising Rate (weekday/saturday): Open inch rate $10.90
Online Advertising Rate: $300/month
News services: AP **Established:** 1849
Own Printing Facility?: No
Commercial Printers?: Yes
Special Editions: Football Opener (Aug); Christmas Greetings (Dec); 4-H Clubs (Mar); Christmas Shopping Guide (Nov); Home Improvement (Spring);
Special Weekly Sections: TV
Syndicated Publications: TV (Tue); American Profile (Tues).
Digital Platform - Mobile: Apple, Android
Digital Platform - Tablet: Apple iOS, Android
Managing Ed. .... Chad Williamson
Adv. Dir. .... Marie Woodford
Pub. .... Daniel E. Behrens
Gen. Mgr. .... Kevin Behrens
Mechanical Available: Offset; Black and 3 ROP colors; insert accepted; page cutoffs - 21.
Mechanical Specifications: Type page 13 x 21; E - 6 cols, 2 1/16, 1/8 between; A - 6 cols, 2 1/16, 1/8 between; C - 8 cols, 1 1/2, 1/8 between.
Areas Served: 43040, 43344, 43045, 43060, 43067
Delivery Method: Mail, Newsstand, Carrier, RacksEquipment & Software: MAILROOM EQUIPMENT: Address Machine — Add-Tac.; BUSINESS EQUIPMENT: mac os BUSINESS SOFTWARE: Quickbooks Pro CLASSIFIED EQUIPMENT: Hardware — APP/iMac,emac,powermac Printers — Xerox 425 CLASSIFIED SOFTWARE: Baseview/ AdManager Pro. DISPLAY EQUIPMENT: Hardware — APP/PowerMac G5's, External hard drive's DISPLAY SOFTWAREAd Make-up Applications — Adobe/Creative Suite 3 EDITORIAL EQUIPMENT: Hardware — APP/iMac Intel, Mac Mini EDITORIAL SOFTWARE: Baseview/News Edit Pro, Adobe/Creative Suite 5.5
QPS/QuarkXPress 4.04., Microsoft Office CIRCULATION EQUIPMENT: Apple iMac G4, Windows 7 CIRCULATION SOFTWARMediaSpan CirculationPro 3

MASSILLON

THE INDEPENDENT

729 Lincoln Way E, Massillon, Ohio, 44646-6829, Stark; gen tel (330) 833-2631; adv tel (330) 833-2631; ed tel (330) 775-1125; gen fax (330) 833-2635; adv fax (330) 833-2635; ed fax (330) 834-3373; gen/nat adv e-mail jim.williams@cantonrep.com; disp adv e-mail stan.sidaway@indeonline.com; class adv e-mailgail.valli@cantonrep.com; ed e-mail veronica.vandress@indeonline.com; web site www.indeonline.com; web site 2 fnohio.com
Group: New Media Investment Group
Published: Mon, Tues, Wed, Thur, Fri, Sat
Weekday Frequency: m
Saturday Frequency: m
Circulation: 7,010; 7,010(sat)
Last Audit: AAM December 31, 2015
Advertising Rate (weekday/saturday): Open inch rate $25.00
News services: AP, CNS, DF, SHNS, TMS. **Established:** 1863
Special Editions: Home & Garden (Apr); Football Contest (Aug); Gift Ideas (Dec); Valentine (Feb); Hall of Fame (Jul); Fun In The sun (Jun); Holy Week & Easter Church Guide (Mar); College Guide (May); Christmas Countdown (Nov); How To (Oct); Community Guide (Sept).
Special Weekly Sections: Business, Industry, Senior (Tue); Cuisine, Food, Restaurant (Wed); Community (Tue, Bi-monthly)
Syndicated Publications: TV Times (entertainment tab) (S).
Pub. .... Jim Porter
Cir. Dir. .... Sheila Casler
Reporter .... Amy Knapp
Sports Ed. .... Chris Easterling
Gen. Mgr. .... Maureen Ater
Adv. Dir. .... Sharon Ackerman
Editor .... Veronica Van Dress
Reporter .... Christina McCune
Sports Writer .... Joe Mitchin
Reporter .... Steven Grazier
Photographer .... Kevin Whitlock
Mechanical Available: Offset; Black and 3 ROP colors; insert accepted - broadsheet, less than 13 x 22; page cutoffs - 23 1/2.
Mechanical Specifications: Type page 12 x 22; E - 6 cols, 1 7/8, 1/8 between; A - 6 cols, 1 7/8, 1/8 between; C - 10 cols, 1 1/8, 1/8 between.
Areas Served: Western Stark County (OH)
Delivery Method: Newsstand, Carrier, RacksEquipment & Software: MAILROOM EQUIPMENT: Tying Machines — 1/ Bu, 1-Polychem/PC500, 2-MLN/MLN24; Address Machine — Cheshire.; BUSINESS EQUIPMENT: 2-Dell/Dimension V350, 4-Gateway GP6-4000 BUSINESS SOFTWARE: PBS/Media Plus, INSI CLASSIFIED EQUIPMENT: Hardware — Imac; Printers — HP/2200; CLASSIFIED SOFTWARE: AdManager Pro, Admanager. EDITORIAL EQUIPMENT: Hardware — Mac/G-4, Compaq/6000/APP/Mac G3, APP/ Mac 8500; Printers — HP/9000, Xante/3n, Xante/3g EDITORIAL SOFTWARE: Baseview 3.5.7, QPS/QuarkXPress 6.5. PRODUCTION EQUIPMENT: Scanners — Umax/2100, 1-Epson/4870, 1-Microtek/ i700, 1-Microtek/4800 PRODUCTION SOFTWARE: QPS/QuarkXPress 6.5, Baseview 3.5.7.

MEDINA

THE MEDINA COUNTY GAZETTE

885 W Liberty St, Medina, Ohio, 44256-1312, Medina; gen tel (800) 633-4623; adv tel (330) 721-4002; ed tel (440) 329-7152; gen fax (330) 725-4299; adv fax (440) 329-7177; ed fax (440) 329-7282; gen/nat adv e-mail jgwinnup@medina-gazette.com; disp adv e-mail abarnes@medina-gazette.com; class adv e-mailkfraley@medina-gazette.com; ed e-mail letters@medina-gazette.com; web site www.medina-gazette.com
Group: Lorain County Printing & Publishing Co.
Published: Mon, Tues, Wed, Thur, Fri, Sat
Weekday Frequency: m
Saturday Frequency: m
Circulation: 9,496; 9,496(sat)
Last Audit: AAM March 31, 2017
Advertising Rate (weekday/saturday): Open inch rate $23.40; $40.l94 (Tue TMC)
News services: AP. **Established:** 1832
Special Editions: Spring Time Showcase (Apr); Back-to-School (Aug); Last Minute Holiday Shopping Guide (Dec); Your Heart's Desire (Feb); Health & Fitness (Jan); Wheels II (Jul); Academic Excellence (Jun); Spring Home & Flower Tab (Mar); Wheels (May); Golden Guide (Monthly)
Special Weekly Sections: Best Food (Mon/Tue); Accent, Auto (Tue); Business, Cover Story (Wed); Auto, Entertainment (Thur); Real Estate, TV (Fri); Accent, Auto, Church (Sat); Farm, Garden (Weekly)
Syndicated Publications: Miscellaneous (Sat); American Profile (Weekly).
Pub. .... George D. Hudnutt
Sports Ed. .... Betty Szudlo
Cir. Mgr. .... Gary Cozart
Mng. Ed. .... Lawrence Pantages
Ret. Adv. Mgr. .... Jason Gwinnup
Acct. Exec. .... Amy Barnes
Market Information: ADS; Split run; TMC; Zoned editions.
Mechanical Available: Offset; Black and 3 ROP colors; insert accepted - any; page cutoffs - 22 3/4.
Mechanical Specifications: Type page 13 x 21 1/2; E - 6 cols, 2 1/16, 1/8 between; A - 6 cols, 2 1/16, 1/8 between; C - 9 cols, 1 3/8, 1/16 between.
Areas Served: Medina County
Equipment & Software: PRESSROOM EQUIPMENT: Lines — 8-G/Community; MAILROOM EQUIPMENT: Counter Stackers — HL/Stackpack, HL/Monitor; Inserters & Stuffers — HI/NP 848; Tying Machines — 1/Bu, 1-/Sa, MLN; Address Machine — 1-Am/6341, 1-/Ch; BUSINESS EQUIPMENT: 1-HP CLASSIFIED EQUIPMENT: Hardware — PCs.; DISPLAY SOFTWARELayout Software — 2-CText/ Adept. EDITORIAL EQUIPMENT: Hardware — PCs/PCs EDITORIAL SOFTWARE: CText. PRODUCTION EQUIPMENT: Hardware — XIT/Clipper, XIT/Page Scan; Cameras — 1-LE/R500; Scanners — 1-Microtek/MS-300A Image Scanner.

MOUNT VERNON

MOUNT VERNON NEWS

18 E Vine St, Mount Vernon, Ohio, 43050-3226, Knox; gen tel (740) 397-5333; adv tel (740) 397-5333 ext. 240; ed tel (740) 397-5333 ext. 248; gen fax (740) 397-1321; adv fax (740) 397-1321; ed fax (740) 397-1321; gen/nat adv e-mail cwise@mountvernonnews.com; disp adv e-mail emily.butler@mountvernonnews.com; class adv e-mailkim@mountvernonnews.com; ed e-mail samantha.scoles@mountvernonnews.com; web site www.mountvernonnews.com - 480,000(views)
Group: Ohio Newspaper Services, Inc.
Published: Mon, Tues, Wed, Thur, Fri, Sat
Weekday Frequency: e
Saturday Frequency: m
Circulation: 9,099; 9,099(sat)
Last Audit: Sworn/Estimate/Non-Audited December 18, 2017
Newspaper Reps: Kay Culbertson, Pubisher
Advertising Rate (weekday/saturday): Open inch rate $13.95
News services: AP.
Own Printing Facility?: Yes
Commercial Printers?: Yes
Special Weekly Sections: Best Food Day (Wed); Farm (Sat);
Pub. .... Kay H. Culbertson
Asst. Pub. .... Elizabeth Lutwick
Mng. Ed. .... Samantha Scoles
Adv. Mgr. .... Corby Wise
Class. Mgr. .... Kim Schwarz
Coor. .... Michelle Hartman
City Ed. .... Fred Main
Sports Ed. .... Bill Davis
Rec. .... Sheryl Shannon
Market Information: ADS; TMC.
Mechanical Available: Offset; Black and 3 ROP colors; insert accepted; page cutoffs - 22 3/4.
Mechanical Specifications: Type page 13 x 21 1/2; E - 6 cols, 2 1/16, 1/8 between; A - 6 cols, 2 1/16, 1/8 between; C - 8 cols, 1 9/16, 1/16 between.
Areas Served: Knox County (OH)
Equipment & Software: PRESSROOM EQUIPMENT: Lines — 5-G/Urbanite; MAILROOM EQUIPMENT: Counter Stackers — 1-HI/RS-25; Inserters & Stuffers — 4-KAN/480; Tying Machines — 2/Bu, 1-/Ca; Address Machine — 1-/Ch, 2-/Am.; BUSINESS EQUIPMENT: Basic IV/MHI CLASSIFIED EQUIPMENT: Hardware — 4-APP/Mac Quadra 605; Printers — 1-APP/Mac LaserWriter.; DISPLAY EQUIPMENT: Printers — 3-APP/Mac LaserWriter; DISPLAY SOFTWARELayout Software — 7-APP/Mac. EDITORIAL EQUIPMENT: Hardware — 11-APP/Mac Quadra 605; Printers — 1-XIT/Clipper EDITORIAL SOFTWARE: QPS/QuarkXPress 3.3. PRODUCTION EQUIPMENT: Hardware — Caere/OmniPage Direct, 1-Nu/Flip Top FT4OLNS; Cameras — 1-B, 1-R; Scanners — Umax/UC 1200 SE, Nikon/Coolscan.

NAPOLEON

NORTHWEST SIGNAL

595 E Riverview Ave, Napoleon, Ohio, 43545-1865, Henry; gen tel (419) 592-5055; adv tel (419) 592-5055; ed tel (419) 592-5055; gen fax (419) 592-9778; adv fax (419) 592-9778; ed fax (419) 592-9778; gen/nat adv e-mail ads@northwestsignal.net; disp adv e-mail ads@northwestsignal.net; class adv e-mailclassifieds@northwestsignal.net; ed e-mail briank@northwestsignal.net; web site www.northwestsignal.net
Group: Bryan Publishing Co.
Published: Mon, Tues, Wed, Thur, Sat
Weekday Frequency: m
Saturday Frequency: m
Circulation: 4,454; 4,454(sat)
Last Audit: Sworn/Estimate/Non-Audited September 30, 2017
Advertising Rate (weekday/saturday): Open inch rate $12.05
Online Advertising Rate: Rates vary.
News services: AP. **Established:** 1852
Special Editions: Pigskin Preview (Aug); Greetings (Dec); Bride/Groom (Feb); First Baby (Jan); Community Salute (Jul); Automotive (Mar); Christmas (Nov).
Special Weekly Sections: Education (Mon); Health, Business (Tue); Business, Food (Wed); Farm (Thur); Church, Food (Sat)
Syndicated Publications: Relish (Monthly); American Profile (Weekly).
Pres./Pub. .... Christopher Cullis
VP, Adv./Mktg. Dir./Gen. Mgr. .... Sally Heaston
Web Bill. / Acct. .... Peggy Woods
Ed .... Brian Koeller
Sports Ed. .... Jeffrey Ratliff
Asst. Pub. / Asst. Gen. Mgr. .... Kim Imm
Adv. .... Heather Marr
Adv. .... Kim Cordes
Market Information: TMC.
Mechanical Available: Offset; Black and 3 ROP colors; insert accepted - card; page cutoffs - 21 1/2.
Mechanical Specifications: Type page 13 x 21; E - 6 cols, 2 1/16, 1/8 between; A - 6 cols, 2 1/16, 1/8 between; C - 6 cols, 2 1/16, 1/8 between.
Areas Served: Henry County (OH)
Equipment & Software: MAILROOM EQUIPMENT: Tying Machines — 1/MLN, 1-/Brainard; Address Machine — 1-/Am.; BUSINESS EQUIPMENT: 1-CDS/PC-XT CLASSIFIED EQUIPMENT: Hardware — APP/Mac; CLASSIFIED SOFTWARE: Baseview/Class Manager, QPS/QuarkXPress. DISPLAY SOFTWARELayout Software — Mk. EDITORIAL EQUIPMENT: Hardware — APP/Mac/1-APP/Mac LaserWriter; Printers — APP/Mac llg EDITORIAL SOFTWARE: Microsoft/Word, Baseview/NewsEdit. PRODUCTION EQUIPMENT: Hardware — Caere/OmniPage; Cameras — 1-Nu; Scanners — Epson/800 PRODUCTION SOFTWARE: Aldus/PageMaker 5.0.

NEW PHILADELPHIA

THE TIMES-REPORTER

629 Wabash Ave NW, New Philadelphia, Ohio, 44663-4145, Tuscarawas; gen tel (330) 364-5577; adv tel (330) 364-8321; ed tel (330) 364-8407; gen fax (330) 364-8449; adv fax (330) 364-8449; ed fax (330) 364-8416; gen/nat adv e-mail advertising@TimesReporter.com; disp adv e-mail advertising@timesreporter.com; class adv e-mailclassified@TimesReporter.com; ed e-mail news@timesreporter.com; web site www.timesreporter.com
Group: New Media Investment Group
Published: Mon, Tues, Wed, Thur, Fri, Sat, Sun
Weekday Frequency: m
Saturday Frequency: m
Circulation: 12,591; 12,591(sat); 13,005(sun)
Last Audit: AAM December 31, 2016
Advertising Rate (weekday/saturday): Tues - Sat Open inch rate $25.95
Advertising Rate (sunday): Sun/Mon Open inch rate $28.29
News services: AP, MCT, SHNS.
Special Editions: Medical Booklet (Apr); Italian Festival (Aug); Gift Guide (Dec); Bridal (Feb); Progress (Jan); Christmas in July (Jul); Father's Day (Jun); Home & Garden (Mar); Lawn & Garden (May); Home Digest (Nov); Interior Design (Oct); Swiss Festival (Sept).
Special Weekly Sections: Arts & Leisure (Fri); Best Food Day, Health (Mon); Automotive Showcase (Sun/Thu); Religion, Engagement/Bridal, Real Estate (Sat); Senior Citizen (Wed)
Syndicated Publications: Parade (S).
Digital Platform - Mobile: Apple
Digital Platform - Tablet: Apple iOS
Gen. Mgr. .... Paul Reynolds
Adv. Dir. .... Ann Blunt
Local News Ed. .... Hank Keathley
Ed. .... Melissa Griffy Seeton
Adv. Mgr. .... Robert Miller
Cir. Dir. .... Denise Milhoan
Ops. VP .... Kevin Ackerman
Market Information: TMC.
Mechanical Available: Offset; Black and 3 ROP colors; insert accepted - any; page cutoffs - 23 9/16.
Mechanical Specifications: Type page 12 x 22 1/4; E - 6 cols, 1 7/8, 3/16 between; A - 6 cols, 1 7/8, 3/16 between; C - 9 cols, 1 3/8, 1/16 between.Equipment & Software: PRESSROOM EQUIPMENT: Lines — 4-G/Metro (3 color decks) 1970; 11-G/Community 1999; 8-Ha/Mark 10 1986; Press Drive — Fin/Metro; Folders — 2, 2; Pasters —2-Cary/Auto, 2-Enkel/Auto (Heat Set; Commercial). MAILROOM EQUIPMENT: Counter Stackers — HL/Monitor, BG/107, 4/HI; Inserters & Stuffers — 2-Mc/4-Packet; Tying Machines — 1-/Bu, 1-EAM-Mosca, 3-/MLN, 1-EAM-Mosca/Wrapper.; BUSINESS EQUIPMENT: IBM/AS-400 BUSINESS SOFTWARE: Commercial printing bidding analysts, INSI CLASSIFIED EQUIPMENT: Hardware — HI/Composition System 8300, ATS/Network; CLASSIFIED SOFTWARE: HI/Composition. DISPLAY EQUIPMENT: Hardware — APP/Mac, HI, ALS/Managing Editor; DISPLAY SOFTWAREAd Make-up Applications — HI.; EDITORIAL EQUIPMENT: Hardware — HI/Composition Sys 8300, ATS/Network EDITORIAL SOFTWARE: HI/Composition. PRODUCTION EQUIPMENT: Hardware — 2-MON/Express, 2-Konica/EV Jetsetter; Cameras — SCREEN/458; Scanners — ECR PRODUCTION SOFTWARE: ALS/Managing Editor.

NEWARK

THE ADVOCATE

22 N 1st St, Newark, Ohio, 43055-5608, Licking; gen tel (740) 345-4053; adv tel (740) 328-8533; ed tel (740) 328-8821; gen fax (740) 328-8581; adv fax (740) 328-8581; ed fax (740) 328-8581; gen/nat adv e-mail scourson@gannett.com; disp adv e-mail atrabitz@gannett.com; class adv e-mailksargent@nncogannett.com; ed e-mail advocate@newarkadvocate.com; web site www.newarkadvocate.com
Group: Gannett
Published: Mon, Tues, Wed, Thur, Fri, Sat, Sun
Weekday Frequency: m
Saturday Frequency: m
Circulation: 9,475; 9,475(sat); 11,319(sun)
Last Audit: AAM March 31, 2017
Advertising Rate (weekday/saturday): Open inch rate $35.50
Advertising Rate (sunday): Open inch rate $35.50
News services: AP. **Established:** 1820
Own Printing Facility?: Yes
Commercial Printers?: No
Special Editions: Football (Aug); Various Christmas Sections (Dec); Bridal Guide (Jan); Annual Progress (Mar); Crossroads (Monthly);
Special Weekly Sections: Best Food Days (Mon/Wed); Society (Mon); Business (Tue); Farm (Wed); Real Estate (Sat); Stocks (Sun); Senior, Auto, Business, Health, Fitness, Home (Monthly)
Syndicated Publications: Color Comics (S); Real Estate Magazine (Sat).
Digital Platform - Mobile: Apple, Android
Digital Platform - Tablet: Apple iOS, Android
Sales Leader .... Adam Trabitz
Nat'l Sales Coord .... Sharon Courson
Ops. Mgr. .... John Merriweather
Class. Sales Ctr. Mgr. .... Karie Sargent
Mechanical Available: Offset; Black and 3 ROP colors; insert accepted; page cutoffs - 22 3/4.
Mechanical Specifications: Type page 13 x 21; E - 6 cols, 2 1/16, 1/8 between; A - 6 cols, 2 1/16, 1/8 between; C - 6 cols, 2 1/16, 1/8 between.
Areas Served: Licking County (OH)
Delivery Method: Carrier, RacksEquipment & Software: PRESSROOM EQUIPMENT: Lines — 8-G/Urbanite, 8-G/Urbanite (stacked); 8-G/Urbanite, 8-G/Urbanite (stacked); Folders — G/2:1; Reels & Stands — 8-G/Urbanite.; MAILROOM EQUIPMENT: Counter Stackers — 3-Id/2000; Inserters & Stuffers — 2-GMA/SLS 1000; Tying Machines — 2/Dynaric, 2-/Bu; Control System — 1-Id, 2-GMA/PMS1; Address Machine — 2-Ch/596; BUSINESS EQUIPMENT: PBS, Oracle BUSINESS SOFTWARE: Oracle, PBS CLASSIFIED EQUIPMENT: Hardware — 4-Cx.; DISPLAY EQUIPMENT: Hardware — HP; DISPLAY SOFTWAREAd Make-up Applications — PBS.; EDITORIAL EQUIPMENT: Hardware — 1-APP/Mac EDITORIAL SOFTWARE: Baseview. PRODUCTION EQUIPMENT: Hardware — 2-Pre Press/Panther Pro 46, SCREEN/281Q; Cameras — SCREEN/260 Horizontal; Scanners — Lf/Leafscan 35, Nikon/Coolscan, AG/Duoscan PRODUCTION SOFTWARE: Baseview, QPS/QuarkXPress 3.0.

NORWALK

NORWALK REFLECTOR

61 E Monroe St, Norwalk, Ohio, 44857-1532, Huron; gen tel (419) 668-3771; adv tel (419) 625-5500; ed tel (419) 668-3771 ext. 3; gen fax (419) 668-2424; adv fax (419) 668-2424; ed fax (419) 668-2424; gen/nat adv e-mail ashleypitts@norwalkreflector.com; disp adv e-mail crystalmatter@norwalkreflector.com; class adv e-mailmarkyocum@tandemnetwork.com; ed e-mail news@norwalkreflector.com; web site www.norwalkreflector.com
Group: Sandusky Newspapers, Inc.
Published: Mon, Tues, Wed, Thur, Fri, Sat
Weekday Frequency: e

Saturday Frequency: m
Circulation: 6,494; 6,494(sat)
Last Audit: AAM March 31, 2016
Advertising Rate (weekday/saturday): Open inch rate $15.59
News services: AP. **Established:** 1830
Special Editions: Home and Garden (Apr); Firelands Factbook (Mar); Christmas Gift Guide (Nov); Car Care (Apr/Oct).
Special Weekly Sections: Best Food Days (Mon/Wed)
Syndicated Publications: USA WEEKEND Magazine (Fri); American Profile (Weekly).
Pub. .... Andy Prutsok
Adv. Traffic Coor. .... Ashley Pitts
News Ed. .... Matt Roche
Dir. of Dig. Mktg .... Emily Andrews
Asst. Cir. Mgr. .... Ron Simpson
Mng. Ed. .... Joe Centers
Market Information: TMC.
Mechanical Available: Offset; Black and 2 ROP colors; insert accepted; page cutoffs - 21 3/4.
Mechanical Specifications: Type page 13 x 21 1/2; E - 6 cols, 2 1/16, 1/8 between; A - 6 cols, 2 1/16, 1/8 between; C - 9 cols, 1 3/8, 1/16 between.
Areas Served: 44807, 44811, 44814, 44826, 44837, 44846, 44847, 44851, 44855, 44857, 44850, 44865, 44889, 44890
Equipment & Software: PRESSROOM EQUIPMENT: Lines — 4-G/Community single width 1964; 1-G/Community single width 1967; Press Drive — Emerson/DC; Folders — 1-G/941 Community.; MAILROOM EQUIPMENT: Tying Machines — Bu/TS-21, Akebono/TS 250 APP.; BUSINESS EQUIPMENT: Unisys/S280 BUSINESS SOFTWARE: Vision Data CLASSIFIED EQUIPMENT: Hardware — APP/Mac SE30; Printers — APP/Mac LaserWriter II NTX, Xante/8200; CLASSIFIED SOFTWARE: Baseview/Class Manager. DISPLAY EQUIPMENT: Hardware — APP/Power Mac PC 8100, CD, APP/Mac IIfx; Printers — APP/Mac LaserWriter II NTX, Xante/8200; Other Hardware — Microtek/Scanner, Scan Maker II, AG/Arcus II, AG/Studio Sun IIsi. DISPLAY SOFTWAREAd Make-up Applications — Multi-Ad/Creator; EDITORIAL EQUIPMENT: Hardware — APP/Mac/Lf/AP Leaf Picture Desk, Lf/Leafscan 35, Kk/2035 Negative Scanner; Printers — APP/Mac LaserWriter II NTX, Xante/8200 EDITORIAL SOFTWARE: Baseview/NewsEdit, QPS/QuarkXPress 3.3. PRODUCTION EQUIPMENT: Hardware — Caere/OmniPage Pro, 2-Xante/8200, 1-APP/Mac LaserWriter IINTX; Cameras — 1-DAI PRODUCTION SOFTWARE: QPS/QuarkXPress 3.3.

PIQUA

PIQUA DAILY CALL

101 E High St, Piqua, Ohio, 45356-2307, Miami; gen tel (937) 773-2721; adv tel (937) 440-5252; ed tel (937) 773-2721 ; gen fax (937) 773-2782; adv fax (937) 335-9321; ed fax (937) 773-4225; gen/nat adv e-mail bsmith@civitasmedia.com; disp adv e-mail sblack@civitasmedia.com; class adv e-mailadillow@civitasmedia.com; ed e-mail pdceditorial@civitasmedia.com; web site www.dailycall.com
Group: Civitas Media, LLC-OOB
Published: Mon, Wed, Thur, Fri, Sat
Weekday Frequency: e
Saturday Frequency: m
Circulation: 6,789; 7,100(sat)
Last Audit: Sworn/Estimate/Non-Audited September 30, 2017
Advertising Rate (weekday/saturday): Open inch rate $18.00
News services: AP. **Established:** 1883
Own Printing Facility?: Yes
Commercial Printers?: Yes
Special Weekly Sections: Neighbors, Local (Mon); Health, School News (Tue); Seniors, Food (Wed); Church, Sports (Thur); Business, Parenting, NASCAR, TV (Fri); Lifestyles, Neighbors, Transactions (Sat)
Syndicated Publications: USA WEEKEND Magazine (Sat); American Profile (Weekly); Relish (Monthly); Spry (Monthly); Athlon Sports (Monthly); SCORE (Quarterly).
Ed. .... Melody Vallieu
Cir. Dir. .... Jami Young
Karen Brown
Adv. Mgr. .... Becky Smith
Dist. Mgr. .... Tammy Patrick
Market Information: TMC.
Mechanical Available: Web Offset; Black and 3 ROP colors; insert accepted; page cutoffs - 22 3/4.
Mechanical Specifications: Type page 12 1/2 x 21 1/4; E - 6 cols, 1 5/6, 1/8 between; A - 6 cols, 1 5/6, 1/16 between; C - 8 cols, 1 3/8, 1/8 between.
Areas Served: 45356, 45365, 45333, 45380, 45318, 45308, 45326, 45317, 43072, 45373, 45359.
Delivery Method: Mail, Newsstand, Carrier, RacksEquipment & Software: PRESSROOM EQUIPMENT: Lines — 5-G/Urbanite single width 1969; MAILROOM EQUIPMENT: Counter Stackers — Heidelberg; Inserters & Stuffers — KAN/5:1 480; Tying Machines — OVL/415A; Address Machine — SC/100.; BUSINESS EQUIPMENT: PC BUSINESS SOFTWARE: PBS 3.0 CLASSIFIED EQUIPMENT: Hardware — 2-APP/Mac G4; Printers — 1-HP/LaserJet 5; CLASSIFIED SOFTWARE: PBS, Baseveiw. DISPLAY EQUIPMENT: Hardware — 4-APP/Mac G4, 4-APP/PowerMac; Printers — HP/LaserJet 5000; Other Hardware — APP/Mac One Scanner, CD/SC Plus, 2-Umax/Scanner DISPLAY SOFTWAREAd Make-up Applications — QPS/QuarkXPress, Adobe/Photoshop, Aldus/FreeHand, PBS; Layout Software — APP/Mac G3, APP/Mac G4. EDITORIAL EQUIPMENT: Hardware — 10-APP/Mac G4/APP/Mac, APP/Super Mac, Lf/Color Photo; Printers — HP/LaserJet 5000 EDITORIAL SOFTWARE: Story Tracker PRODUCTION EQUIPMENT: Hardware — Pre Press/Panther Pro 46, 1-LE/LD 220, Jobo/ATL 1500; Cameras — 1-DAI/Screen C/680-C.

POMEROY

THE DAILY SENTINEL

109 W 2nd St, Pomeroy, Ohio, 45769-1035, Meigs; gen tel (740) 992-2156; adv tel (740) 992-2155; ed tel (740) 992-2342 ext. 2102; gen fax (740) 992-2157; adv fax (740) 992-2157; ed fax (740) 992-2157; gen/nat adv e-mail bdavis@civitasmedia.com; disp adv e-mail sthompson@civitasmedia.com; class adv e-mailsthompson@civitasmedia.com; ed e-mail sfilson@civitasmedia.com; web site www.mydailysentinel.com
Group: Civitas Media, LLC-OOB
Published: Tues, Wed, Thur, Fri
Weekday Frequency: m
Circulation: 3,471; 9,068(sun)
Last Audit: Sworn/Estimate/Non-Audited September 30, 2017
Advertising Rate (weekday/saturday): Open inch rate $13.50
Advertising Rate (sunday): Open inch rate $18.75
News services: AP.
Special Editions: Senior Quarterly (Quarterly); Spring Home (Spring); Health Mind & Body (Quarterly)
Special Weekly Sections: TV Times (Fri); Farm Page (S); Best Food Day (Wed).
Pub. .... Bud Hunt
Adv. Rep. .... Sarah Thompson
Adv. Dir. .... Julia Schultz
Ed. .... Michael Johnson
Mng. Ed. .... Sarah Hawley
Market Information: TMC.
Mechanical Available: Offset; Black and 3 ROP colors; insert accepted; page cutoffs - 21 1/4.
Mechanical Specifications: Type page 13 x 21 1/4; E - 6 cols, 2 1/16, 1/8 between; A - 6 cols, 2 1/16, 1/8 between; C - 8 cols, 1 1/2, 1/8 between.
Areas Served: Meigs County
Equipment & Software: CLASSIFIED EQUIPMENT: Hardware — APP/Mac; CLASSIFIED SOFTWARE: Baseview. EDITORIAL EQUIPMENT: Hardware — APP/Mac; Printers — APP/Mac LaserWriter EDITORIAL SOFTWARE: Baseview. PRODUCTION EQUIPMENT: Hardware — Mk/Ad Typesetting.
Note: The Pomeroy Daily Sentinel and Gallipolis Daily Tribune share their Sunday edition, the Sunday Times-Sentinel. The combination rate is $14.20.

PORTSMOUTH

THE PORTSMOUTH DAILY TIMES

637 6th St, Portsmouth, Ohio, 45662-3924, Scioto; gen tel (740) 353-3101; adv tel (740) 353-3101 ext. 4181; ed tel (740) 353-3101 ext. 4182; gen fax (740) 353-7280; adv fax (740) 353-7280; ed fax (740) 353-4676; gen/nat adv e-mail tison@civitasmedia.com; disp adv e-mail hadkins@civitasmedia.com; class adv e-mailpdtclassifieds@civitasmedia.com; ed e-mail pdtnews@civitasmedia.com; web site www.portsmouth-dailytimes.com; web site 2 www.myownportsmouth.com
Group: AIM Media Indiana
Published: Tues, Wed, Thur, Fri, Sat, Sun
Weekday Frequency: m
Saturday Frequency: m
Circulation: 12,447; 12,447(sat); 11,631(sun)
Last Audit: Sworn/Estimate/Non-Audited September 30, 2017
Advertising Rate (weekday/saturday): Open inch rate $22.20
Advertising Rate (sunday): Open inch rate $22.20
News services: AP. **Established:** 1852
Own Printing Facility?: No
Commercial Printers?: No
Special Editions: Back-to-School (Aug); Bridal (Jan); Home & Garden (Jun); Car Care (Mar); Christmas Preview (Nov); Car Care (Oct).
Special Weekly Sections: Education (Wed); Entertainment (Thur); Religion (Sat); Business, Agriculture, Food (Sun)
Cir. Mgr. .... Ed Litteral
Pub .... Hope Comer
Ed. .... Chris Slone
Market Information: ADS; TMC.
Mechanical Available: Offset; Black and 3 ROP colors; insert accepted - single sheet; page cutoffs - 23 9/16.
Mechanical Specifications: Type page 11 5/8 x 21 1/2; E - 6 cols, 2 1/16, 1/8 between; A - 6 cols, 2 1/16, 1/8 between; C - 9 cols, 1 3/8, 1/16 between.
Areas Served: Scioto, Pike, Adams, Jackson & Lawrence Counties (OH); Greenup & Lewis Counties (KY)
Delivery Method: Mail, Newsstand, Carrier, RacksEquipment & Software: PRESSROOM EQUIPMENT: Lines — 10-G/Community; Pasters —Web/Cement. MAILROOM EQUIPMENT: Tying Machines — 1-MLN/ML2EE; Address Machine — 1-Am/1900, FBM/90 Labeler.; BUSINESS EQUIPMENT: 1-NCR CLASSIFIED EQUIPMENT: Hardware — APP/Mac; CLASSIFIED SOFTWARE: Baseview. DISPLAY EQUIPMENT: Printers — APP/Mac LaserPrinter; DISPLAY SOFTWARELayout Software — APP/Mac, 2-PE/10. EDITORIAL EQUIPMENT: Hardware — APP/Mac EDITORIAL SOFTWARE: Baseview. PRODUCTION EQUIPMENT: Hardware — Laser; Cameras — 1-R/500 PRODUCTION SOFTWARE: QPS/QuarkXPress.

SAINT MARYS

THE EVENING LEADER

102 E Spring St, Saint Marys, Ohio, 45885-2310, Auglaize; gen tel (419) 394-7414; adv tel (419) 394-7414; ed tel (419) 394-7414; gen fax (419) 394-7202; adv fax (419) 394-7202; ed fax (419) 394-7202; gen/nat adv e-mail retailadv@wapakwdn.com; disp adv e-mail ads@theeveningleader.com; class adv e-mailclassifieds@theeveningleader.com; ed e-mail editor@theeveningleader.com; web site www.theeveningleader.com
Group: Horizon Publications Inc.
Published: Mon, Tues, Wed, Thur, Fri, Sat
Weekday Frequency: e
Saturday Frequency: m
Circulation: 4,470; 4,470(sat)
Last Audit: Sworn/Estimate/Non-Audited September 30, 2017
Advertising Rate (weekday/saturday): Open inch rate $15.53
News services: AP. **Established:** 1905
Own Printing Facility?: Yes
Commercial Printers?: No
Special Weekly Sections: Best Foods, Agriculture (Mon); Minipage, Life (Tue); County Life (Wed); Arts, TV (Thur); Faith, NASCAR (Fri); Business, Celebrations, Weddings, Engagements (Sat)
Syndicated Publications: The Source, TV Listing (Thur); American Profile (Tues).
Mng. Ed. .... Mike Burkholder
Pub./Mktg. Mgr. .... Gayle Masonbrink
Bus. Mgr. .... Amy Godinho
Cir. Mgr. .... Amy Zwez
Market Information: TMC.
Mechanical Available: Offset; Black and 4 ROP colors; insert accepted - all; page cutoffs - 21.
Mechanical Specifications: Type page 13 x 21 1/2; E - 6 cols, 2 1/16, 1/8 between; A - 9 cols, 1 3/8, 3/16 between; C - 9 cols, 1 3/8, 3/16 between.
Areas Served: Greater St. Mary's Ohio area
Delivery Method: Mail, Newsstand, Carrier, RacksEquipment & Software: MAILROOM EQUIPMENT: Address Machine — 1/MLN.; BUSINESS EQUIPMENT: 2-IBM BUSINESS SOFTWARE: Great Plains DISPLAY EQUIPMENT: Hardware — 7-APP/Mac; Printers — 3-APP/Mac LaserPrinter; DISPLAY SOFTWARELayout Software — APP/Mac. EDITORIAL EQUIPMENT: Hardware — APP/Mac; Printers — 3-APP/Mac Laser EDITORIAL SOFTWARE: Baseview, QPS, Adobe/Photoshop. PRODUCTION EQUIPMENT: Hardware — 2-IBM; Cameras — Nikon; Scanners — 1-Nu, DEC.

SALEM

SALEM NEWS

161 N Lincoln Ave, Salem, Ohio, 44460-2903, Columbiana; gen tel (330) 332-4601; adv tel (330) 332-4601; ed tel (330) 322-4601; gen fax (330) 332-1441; adv fax (330) 332-1441; ed fax (330) 332-1441; gen/nat adv e-mail advertising@salemnews.net; disp adv e-mail kpope@salemnews.net; class adv e-maillflowers@salemnews.net; ed e-mail salemnews@salemnews.net; web site www.salemnews.net
Group: Ogden Newspapers Inc.
Published: Mon, Tues, Wed, Thur, Fri, Sat, Sun
Weekday Frequency: m
Saturday Frequency: m
Circulation: 3,892; 3,892(sat); 3,968(sun)
Last Audit: AAM September 30, 2014
Advertising Rate (weekday/saturday): National Display $23.10
Advertising Rate (sunday): National Display $23.10
News services: AP. **Established:** 1889
Own Printing Facility?: Yes
Commercial Printers?: No
Special Editions: Spring Home Improvement (Apr); Fair (Aug); Christmas Gift Savings (Dec); Progress (Feb); Bridal (Jan); Jubilee (Jul); Family Business (Jun); Car Care (Mar); Health (Monthly); Thanksgiving (Nov); Cookbook (Oct); Football (Sept).
Special Weekly Sections: Arts, Food, Health, Travel, Entertainment (Sun); Arts, Entertainment (Tue); Religion (Sat)
Syndicated Publications: Parade (S);
Pub .... Beth Volosin
Mng. Ed. .... J.D. Creer
Cir. Mgr. .... Kevin Smith
Class. .... Laurie Flowers
Market Information: TMC.
Mechanical Available: Offset; Black and 3 ROP colors; insert accepted
Mechanical Specifications: Type page 10 x 20; A - 6 cols, 1.583, 1/8 between; A - 6 cols, C - 9 cols, 1.022, 1/16 between.
Areas Served: Columbiana County (OH)
Delivery Method: Mail, Newsstand, Carrier, RacksEquipment & Software: BUSINESS EQUIPMENT: 1-ATT/3B2 500 CLASSIFIED EQUIPMENT: Hardware — Mk.; EDITORIAL EQUIPMENT: Hardware — Mk. PRODUCTION EQUIPMENT: Hardware — APP/Mac LaserWriters; Cameras — 1-R/500, 1-LE.

SANDUSKY

SANDUSKY REGISTER

314 W Market St, Sandusky, Ohio, 44870-2410, Erie; gen tel (419) 625-5500; adv tel (419) 502-2121; ed tel (419) 502-2160; gen fax (419) 625-7211; adv fax (419) 625-1137; ed fax (419) 625-3007; gen/nat adv e-mail advertising@sanduskyregister.com; class adv e-mailclassified@sanduskyregister.com; ed e-mail mattwesterhold@sanduskyregister.com; web site www.sanduskyregister.com - 13,000,000(views) 598,135(visitors)
Group: Sandusky Newspapers, Inc.
Published: Mon, Tues, Wed, Thur, Fri, Sat, Sun
Weekday Frequency: e
Saturday Frequency: e
Circulation: 18,762; 18,762(sat); 22,215(sun)
Last Audit: AAM March 31, 2017
Advertising Rate (weekday/saturday): Open inch rate $23.06
Advertising Rate (sunday): Open inch rate $25.41
Online Advertising Rate: Call for rates
News services: AP, SHNS, Capitol Wire.
Established: 1822
Own Printing Facility?: Yes
Commercial Printers?: Yes
Special Editions: Progress (Apr); Football (Aug); Home Improvement (Mar); Thanksgiving Day Gift Guide (Nov); Fall Car Care (Oct).
Special Weekly Sections: At Home (Wed); Religion (Sat)
Syndicated Publications: USA WEEKEND Magazine (Sat); American Profile (Weekly).
Digital Platform - Mobile: Apple, Android, Windows, Blackberry, Other
Digital Platform - Tablet: Apple iOS, Android, Windows 7, Blackberry Tablet OS, Kindle, Nook, Kindle Fire, Other
Pub. .... Ron Waite
Mng. Ed. .... Matt Westerhold
Circ. Dir. .... William Ney
Ntnl Sales Mgr .... Bob Rapp
Foreman. .... Ric Miller
Staff Acct. .... Denise Martinez
Market Information: TMC.
Mechanical Available: Offset; Black and 3 ROP colors; insert accepted; page cutoffs - 22 3/4.
Mechanical Specifications: Type page 13 x 21 1/2; E - 6 cols, 2, 1/6 between; A - 6 cols, 2, 1/6 between; C - 9 cols, 1 5/16, 1/6 between.
Areas Served: 44870, 44824, 44846, 44839
Equipment & Software: PRESSROOM EQUIPMENT: Lines — 8-G/Urbanite 1968; Folders — 1-G/Urbanite; Control System — 1998; MAILROOM EQUIPMENT: Counter Stackers — 1/QWI, 1-TMSI/Monitor, HT/16 Monitor; Inserters & Stuffers — HI/Sheridan 13/72 12/1; Tying Machines — 1-/MR-45CH Sterling, SSN/40 Sterling; Address Machine — MM/Pressure Sensitive.; BUSINESS EQUIPMENT: Dell/Poweredge Server BUSINESS SOFTWARE: Lotus, DSI CLASSIFIED EQUIPMENT: Hardware — 1-Panasonic/Plain Paper Fax, Okidata, MM; Printers — 1-APP/Mac LaserWriter; CLASSIFIED SOFTWARE: CD, Baseview/Ad Manager Pro, Baseview/ClassFlow. DISPLAY EQUIPMENT: Hardware — 1-APP/Mac 8100, 4-APP/Mac G3, APP/Mac G4; Printers — 2-XIT/Clipper, 1-HP/8100N; DISPLAY SOFTWAREAd Make-up Applications — Multi-Ad/Creator 2, QPS/QuarkXPress.; EDITORIAL EQUIPMENT: Hardware — APP/Mac/APP/Mac Apple Share, Remote Access, APP/Mac Stocks, E-mail; Printers — ECR/4550, Ultre/94E Imagesetter EDITORIAL SOFTWARE: CD, Baseview/NewsEdit Pro, Baseview/IQUE, QPS/QuarkXPress. PRODUCTION EQUIPMENT: Hardware — 1-Graham, Xante, ECR, Ultre; Cameras — SCREEN/Liberator; Scanners — Microtek/600ZS, Microtek/Scanmaker II HR, Umax/PowerLook, AG/11 x 18, Polaroid/35mm PRODUCTION SOFTWARE: QPS/QuarkXPress.

SHELBY

DAILY GLOBE

37 W Main St, Shelby, Ohio, 44875-1238, Richland; gen tel (419) 342-4276; adv tel (419) 342-4276; ed tel (419) 342-3261; gen fax (419) 342-4246; adv fax (419) 342-4246; ed fax (419) 342-4246; gen/nat adv e-mail globe@sdgnewsgroup.com; disp adv e-mail globe@sdgnewsgroup.com; class adv e-mailglobe@sdgnewsgroup.com; ed e-mail globe@sdgnewsgroup.com; web site www.sdgnewsgroup.com
Published: Mon, Tues, Wed, Thur, Fri, Sat
Weekday Frequency: e
Saturday Frequency: m
Circulation: 3,400; 3,400(sat)
Last Audit: Sworn/Estimate/Non-Audited September 30, 2017
Advertising Rate (weekday/saturday): Open inch rate $12.76
News services: AP. **Established:** 1900
Own Printing Facility?: Yes
Special Editions: Home Improvement (Apr); Progress (Feb); Health & Fitness (Mar); Christmas Gift Guide (Nov); Car Care (Oct); City Directory (Sept).
Special Weekly Sections: Best Food Day (Mon); Farm Page (Thur).
Digital Platform - Mobile: Apple, Android, Windows
Pres./Pub. .... Scott M. Gove
Sports Ed. .... Chuck Ridenour
Assoc. Pub. .... Trent Gove
Market Information: ADS; TMC.
Mechanical Available: Offset; Black and 3 ROP colors; insert accepted; page cutoffs - 22 3/4.
Mechanical Specifications: Type page 13 x 21 1/2; E - 6 cols, 2 1/16, 1/8 between; A - 6 cols, 2 1/16, 1/8 between; C - 6 cols, 2 1/16, 1/8 between.
Delivery Method: Mail, Newsstand, Carrier, RacksEquipment & Software: PRESSROOM EQUIPMENT: Lines — 4-G/Community.; MAILROOM EQUIPMENT: Tying Machines — 1/Kogyo, 1-/Ty-Tech; Address Machine — 1-/SC.; BUSINESS EQUIPMENT: 1-RSK/Tandy 3100, 1-Club CLASSIFIED EQUIPMENT: Hardware — APP/Mac; CLASSIFIED SOFTWARE: Baseview. DISPLAY SOFTWAREAd Make-up Applications — QPS/QuarkXPress; Layout Software — APP/Mac. EDITORIAL EQUIPMENT: Hardware — APP/Mac EDITORIAL SOFTWARE: Baseview. PRODUCTION EQUIPMENT: Hardware — 1-B, Xante/LaserWriter; Cameras — 1-SCREEN/Companica; Scanners — Ag/Arcus II.

SIDNEY

THE SIDNEY DAILY NEWS

1451 N Vandemark Rd, Sidney, Ohio, 45365-3547, Shelby; gen tel (937) 498-8088; adv tel (937) 498-5915; ed tel (937) 538-4822; gen fax (937) 498-5990; adv fax (937) 498-5990; ed fax (937) 498-5990; gen/nat adv e-mail dbailey@civitasmedia.com; disp adv e-mail cpierce@civitasmedia.com; class adv e-maildbailey@civitasmedia.com; ed e-mail mspeicher@sidneydailynews.com; web site www.sidneydailynews.com
Published: Mon, Tues, Wed, Thur, Sat
Weekday Frequency: e
Saturday Frequency: m
Circulation: 10,519; 11,500(sat)
Last Audit: Sworn/Estimate/Non-Audited September 30, 2017
Advertising Rate (weekday/saturday): Open inch rate $21.00
News services: AP. **Established:** 1891
Own Printing Facility?: Yes
Commercial Printers?: Yes
Special Editions: Home Improvement (Apr); Fall Sports (Aug); Gifts & Greeting (Dec); Bride (Feb); Progress (Jan); Fair (Jul); Spring Sports (Mar); Graduation (May); Cookbook (Nov); Home Improvement (Sept).
Special Weekly Sections: Farm, Agriculture (Mon); Youth, Senior (Wed); Religion, NASCAR (Thur); Business (Sat)
Syndicated Publications: USA WEEKEND Magazine (Sat); American Profile (Weekly). Relish (Monthly); Athlon Sports (monthly); Spry (monthly);
Digital Platform - Mobile: Blackberry
Digital Platform - Tablet: Kindle
News Ed. .... Melanie Speicher
Gen. Mgr. / Med. Dir. .... Natalie Buzzard
Reg. Cir. Mgr. .... T. Mark Shorts
Dist. Cir. Mgr. .... Breonna Lindsey

Class. Adv. Sales Mgr. .... Donna Bailey
Sports Ed. .... Ken Barhorst
Med. Sales Cons. .... Carol Pierce
CSR .... Wesley Stratton
Market Information: ADS.
Mechanical Available: Offset; Black and 3 ROP colors; insert accepted; page cutoffs - 22 1/4.
Mechanical Specifications: Type page 11 5/8 x 21 1/4; E - 6 cols, 1 5/6, 1/8 between; A - 6 cols, 1 5/6, 1/8 between; C - 9 cols, 1 1/3, 1/16 between.
Areas Served: 45365, 45356, 45333, 45383, 45768, 45845, 45388, 45351, 45865, 45869, 45885, 45871, 45337, 45306, 45334, 45360, 45302, 45340, 45353, 43318, 43343, 43070.
Delivery Method: Mail, Newsstand, Carrier, RacksEquipment & Software: CLASSIFIED EQUIPMENT: Hardware — PPI, 5-PC; APP/Mac G4.; DISPLAY EQUIPMENT: Hardware — APP/Mac, 5-PC; DISPLAY SOFTWARELayout Software — PPI. EDITORIAL EQUIPMENT: Hardware — APP/Mac, PC/40-IBM/Selectric. PRODUCTION EQUIPMENT: Hardware — 2-AU/Micro 5, 2-Hyphen/Dash 600; Cameras — 1-C/Spartan III; Scanners — ECR/Autokon, Lf/Leafscan, 1-Cp/Super-Alpha.

SPRINGFIELD

SPRINGFIELD NEWS-SUN

202 N Limestone St, Springfield, Ohio, 45503-4246, Clark; gen tel (937) 328-0300; adv tel (937) 328-0241; ed tel (937) 328-0342; gen fax (937) 328-0227; adv fax (937) 328-0321; ed fax (937) 328-0328; gen/nat adv e-mail bruce.karlson@coxinc.com; disp adv e-mail bruce.karlson@coxinc.com; class adv e-mailbruce.karlson@coxinc.com; ed e-mail newssuneditor@coxohio.com; web site www.springfieldnewssun.com
Group: Cox Media Group
Published: Mon, Tues, Wed, Thur, Fri, Sat, Sun
Weekday Frequency: m
Saturday Frequency: m
Circulation: 12,864; 15,252(sat); 20,794(sun)
Last Audit: AAM June 30, 2015
Advertising Rate (weekday/saturday): Open inch rate $201.00
Advertising Rate (sunday): Open inch rate $227.00
News services: AP, MCT, LAT-WP, NYT, Cox News Service. **Established:** 1817
Special Editions: Arts, Family, Food, Health, Home, Living, Real Estate (Monthly)
Special Weekly Sections: Sports (Fri); Financial (S); Entertainment (Sat); Entertainment (Thur); Finances (Tues); Best Food Day (Wed).
Syndicated Publications: Channels-TV Book (S).
Pub. .... Steve Sidlo
Dir., HR .... Emily Chambers
Adv. Dir. .... Robert Mercer
Circ. Dir. .... Don Jordan
Ed. .... Jim Bebbington
Bus. Ed. .... Tim Bucey
Editorial Page Ed. .... Keith Streitenberger
Film/Theater Ed. .... Steve Cooper
Graphics Ed./Art Dir. .... Tom Hawkins
Photo Ed. .... Marshall Gorby
Sports Ed. .... Kermit Rowe
Women's Ed. .... Tom Stafford
Prodn. Supvr., Bldg. .... Jerry Maurer
COO .... Brian Cooper
Sr. VP, Adv. / Gen. Mgr. .... Rob Rohr
Market Information: ADS; Split run; TMC.
Mechanical Available: Offset; Black and 3 ROP colors; insert accepted; page cutoffs - 22 3/4.
Mechanical Specifications: Type page 11 5/8 x 21; E - 6 cols, 2 1/16, 1/8 between; A - 6 cols, 2 1/16, 1/8 between; C - 9 cols, 1 3/8, 1/16 between.Equipment & Software: PRESSROOM EQUIPMENT: Lines — 5-G/Metro double width 1975; Pasters — 5-G/RTP; Reels & Stands — 5-G/Reel.; MAILROOM EQUIPMENT: Counter Stackers — 4/QWI; Inserters & Stuffers — 1-GMA/SLS 1000; Tying Machines — 1-MLN/News 90, Ty-Tech, 3-/Sterling; Address Machine — 2-/KR; BUSINESS EQUIPMENT: 1-HP/9000-817S BUSINESS SOFTWARE: HP/UX 8.02, CJ CLASSIFIED EQUIPMENT: Printers — 1-HP/LaserPrinter; CLASSIFIED SOFTWARE: DTI 5.4.1. DISPLAY EQUIPMENT: Hardware — APP/Mac; Printers — HP/LaserPrinter; DISPLAY SOFTWAREAd Make-up Applications — DTI 4.3; Layout Software — APP/Power Mac G3/G4. EDITORIAL EQUIPMENT: Hardware — APP/Mac, SunPrinters — APP/Mac LaserWriter Plus, 1-TI/800, HP/LaserPrinter EDITORIAL SOFTWARE: DTI 4.3. PRODUCTION EQUIPMENT: Hardware — 2-AU/APS 6-82ACS, 1-AU/APS08FC, PixelCraft/Pro Imager 8000; Cameras — 1-C/Marathon, 1-C/Spartan PRODUCTION SOFTWARE: DTI 4.3.

STEUBENVILLE

HERALD-STAR

401 Herald Sq, Steubenville, Ohio, 43952-2059, Jefferson; gen tel (740) 283-4711; adv tel (740) 283-4711; ed tel (740) 283-4711; gen fax (740) 284-7355; adv fax (740) 282-4261; ed fax (740) 284-7355; gen/nat adv e-mail csteineman@heraldstaronline.com; disp adv e-mail ddelatore@heraldstaronline.com; class adv e-mailpscheel@heraldstaronline.com; ed e-mail frossano@heraldstaronline.com; web site www.heraldstaronline.com
Group: Ogden Newspapers Inc.
Published: Mon, Tues, Wed, Thur, Fri, Sat, Sun
Weekday Frequency: e
Saturday Frequency: m
Circulation: 8,363; 8,363(sat); 10,122(sun)
Last Audit: AAM December 31, 2016
Advertising Rate (weekday/saturday): Open inch rate $51.39
Advertising Rate (sunday): Open inch rate $51.39
News services: AP.
Own Printing Facility?: Yes
Commercial Printers?: Yes
Special Editions: Bridal (Apr); Football (Aug); Basketball (Dec); Progress (Feb); Fort Festival (Jun); Home & Garden (Mar); Car Care (May); Christmas Opening and Gift Guide (Nov); Car Care (Oct); Home Improvement (Sept).
Special Weekly Sections: Best Food Days (Wed/Sun); Building (Sun)
Syndicated Publications: USA WEEKEND Magazine (S).
Pub. .... Alex Marshall
Mng. Ed. .... Ross Gallabrese
Metro Ed. .... Jody Wisbith
News Ed. .... Fred Rossano
Sports. Ed. .... Mike Mathison
Press. Mgr. .... Pete Vitale
Adv. Dir. .... Denise Delatore
Lifestyles Ed. .... Janice Kiaski
Sales Mgr. .... Maggie McGinnis
Circ. Dir. .... John Hale
Nat'l Adv. Coord. .... Cindy Steineman
Adv. Sales Coord. .... Julie Howell
Market Information: ADS; TMC; Zoned editions.
Mechanical Available: Offset; Black and 3 ROP colors; insert accepted - catabook, card, envelope; page cutoffs - 22.
Mechanical Specifications: Type page 13 x 21 1/2; E - 6 cols, 1/8 between; A - 6 cols, 1/8 between; C - 9 cols, 1/16 between.
Areas Served: 43950
Delivery Method: Mail, Newsstand, Carrier, RacksEquipment & Software: PRESSROOM EQUIPMENT: Lines — 7-G/Urbanite 1990; Folders — G/Urbanite.; MAILROOM EQUIPMENT: Counter Stackers — 1-Id; Tying Machines — 1-MLN/Strapper, 1/Dynaric; Address Machine — Packard Bell.; BUSINESS EQUIPMENT: NCR, Packard Bell, HP BUSINESS SOFTWARE: Lotus 4.0 CLASSIFIED EQUIPMENT: Hardware — Mk; Printers — Tegra/Varityper 5000, Tegra/Varityper 5300; CLASSIFIED SOFTWARE: Mk/ACE II. DISPLAY EQUIPMENT: Hardware — APP/Mac; Printers — Tegra/Varityper 5000, Tegra/Varityper 5300; DISPLAY SOFTWAREAd Make-up Applications — Multi-Ad/Creator 3.54; Layout Software — APP/Mac. EDITORIAL EQUIPMENT: Hardware — Mk/6000, APP/Mac; Printers — Tegra/Varityper 5000, 2-Tegra/Varityper 5300, Tegra/Varityper 5300 E EDITORIAL SOFTWARE: Mk/ACE II, QPS/QuarkXPress 3.3. PRODUCTION EQUIPMENT: Hardware — 2-V, 3-Mk/VDT, Nikon/Color Access; Cameras — 2-DSA/680C, LE/121 PRODUCTION SOFTWARE: Scanners

Mirror/1200, Imax.

WEIRTON DAILY TIMES

401 Herald Sq, Steubenville, Ohio, 43952-2059, Jefferson; gen tel (740) 283-4711; adv tel (740) 283-4711; ed tel (740) 283-4711; gen fax (740) 282-4261; adv fax (740) 282-4261; ed fax (740) 284-7355; gen/nat adv e-mail csteineman@heraldstaronline.com; disp adv e-mail ddelatore@heraldstaronline.com; class adv e-mailddelatore@heraldstaronline.com; ed e-mail csteineman@heraldstaronline.com; web site www.weirtondailytimes.com/

Group: Ogden Newspapers Inc.
Published: Mon, Tues, Wed, Thur, Fri, Sat, Sun
Weekday Frequency: e
Saturday Frequency: e
Circulation: 3,351; 3,351(sat); 3,535(sun)
Last Audit: AAM December 31, 2016
Advertising Rate (weekday/saturday): Open inch rate $51.39
Advertising Rate (sunday): Open inch rate $51.39
Own Printing Facility?: Yes
Commercial Printers?: Yes
Special Weekly Sections: Best Food Days (Wed/Sun); Building (Sun)
Syndicated Publications: Kanawha Valley Neighbors
Pub. .... Alex Marshall
Adv. Dir. .... Denise Delatore
Nat'l Adv. Coord. .... Cindy Steineman
Areas Served: 26062
Delivery Method: Mail, Newsstand, Carrier, Racks

TIFFIN

THE ADVERTISER-TRIBUNE

320 Nelson St, Tiffin, Ohio, 44883-8956, Seneca; gen tel (419) 448-3200; adv tel (419) 448-3238; ed tel (419) 448-3240; gen fax (419) 447-3274; adv fax (419) 447-3274; ed fax (419) 447-3274; gen/nat adv e-mail advertising@advertiser-tribune.com; disp adv e-mail jsigler@advertiser-tribune.com; class adv e-mailclassified@advertiser-tribune.com; ed e-mail newsroom@advertiser-tribune.com; web site www.advertiser-tribune.com - 222,000(views) 75,000(visitors)

Group: Ogden Newspapers Inc.
Published: Mon, Tues, Wed, Thur, Fri, Sat, Sun
Weekday Frequency: m
Saturday Frequency: m
Circulation: 7,743; 7,743(sat); 8,736(sun)
Last Audit: AAM September 30, 2016
Advertising Rate (weekday/saturday): Open inch rate $24.50
Advertising Rate (sunday): Open inch rate $24.50
Online Advertising Rate: Rates vary.
News services: AP.
Special Editions: Fall Sports Tab (Aug); Winter Sports Tab (Dec); Fair Tab (Jul); Home Improvement (Mar); Spring Car Care Tab (May); Cooking Contest (Nov); Home Improvement (Oct); Heritage Festival Tab (Sept).
Special Weekly Sections: Auto (Mon); Home Front (Wed); Auto, Real Estate (Thur); Auto (Sat); Real Estate, Business (Sun); Food (Sun/Mon)
Syndicated Publications: USA WEEKEND Magazine (S).
Pub. .... Chris Dixon
Ed. .... Rob Weaver
Bus. Mgr. .... Mary Huss
Ed. .... MJ McVay
Nat'l Adv. Mgr. .... Kathy Sussang
Cir. Ops. Mgr. .... Rick Smith
Cir. CS .... Mary Martin
Market Information: ADS; TMC.
Mechanical Available: Offset; Black and 3 ROP colors; insert accepted - all; page cutoffs - 22 3/4.
Mechanical Specifications: Type page 13 x 21 1/2; E - 6 cols, 1 7/8, 1/8 between; A - 6 cols, 1 7/8, 1/8 between; C - 8 cols, 1 7/16, 1/8 between.
Areas Served: Seneca County (OH)
Equipment & Software: PRESSROOM EQUIPMENT: Lines — 8-G/Community 1974; Reels & Stands — 8; MAILROOM EQUIPMENT: Counter Stackers — 1-BG/Count-O-Veyor; Tying Machines — 2-MLN/Strapper.; BUSINESS EQUIPMENT: NCR BUSINESS SOFTWARE: Custom Software CLASSIFIED EQUIPMENT: Hardware — 1-APP/Mac.; EDITORIAL EQUIPMENT: Hardware — APP/Macs; Printers — 2-APP/Mac LaserWriter II NTX, 3-HP/LaserJet 4MV, 1-ECR/Scriptsetter VRL 36 EDITORIAL SOFTWARE: In-House Customized. PRODUCTION EQUIPMENT: Hardware — 3-HP/LaserJet 4MV, 1-ECR/Scriptsetter VRL 36; Scanners — Lf/AP Leaf Picture Desk 35, Polaroid/SprintScan 35, Umax/Vista-S6 PRODUCTION SOFTWARE: QPS/QuarkXPress.

TOLEDO

THE BLADE

541 N Superior St, Toledo, Ohio, 43660-1000, Lucas; gen tel (419) 724-6000; adv tel (419) 724-6350; ed tel (419) 724-6050; gen fax (419) 724-6471; adv fax (419) 724-6391; ed fax (419) 724-6439; gen/nat adv e-mail info@toledoblade.com; disp adv e-mail natadv@toledoblade.com; ed e-mail webeditor@toledoblade.com; web site www.toledoblade.com
1,525,714(visitors)

Group: Block Communications, Inc.
Published: Mon, Tues, Wed, Thur, Fri, Sat, Sun
Weekday Frequency: m
Saturday Frequency: m
Circulation: 69,118; 65,870(sat); 102,637(sun)
Last Audit: AAM September 30, 2016
Advertising Rate (weekday/saturday): Open inch rate $141.62
Advertising Rate (sunday): $188.10
Online Advertising Rate: 300x250 and 7258x90 - $20.00 cpm
News services: AP, RN, LAT-WP, MCT, CSM, NYT, SHNS, Bloomberg, TMS. **Established:** 1835
Own Printing Facility?: No
Special Editions: Campus Connections (qtrly); TADA Auto Show, Golf Tab, Engineer's Week, HBA House & Home Show (Feb); Toledo PRO Home Show, Special Interest Camps, Pet Idol (Mar); Earth Day, Recreational Camping, Celebration of Artchitecture (Apr); Nurse's Week, National Teacher's Day, Senior Expo, BCSN Rewind, Credit Union (May); Top Honors, Family Owned Business (Jun); African American, Marathon LPGA, Exclaim! (Jul); German-American Festival, High School Football (Aug); Labor on Parade, HBA Parade of Homes, Season of the Arts, Little Darlings, Education 2014 (Sep); Walleye Opener, Credit Union, Caregivers Awards, Business Profiles (Oct); Social Security, Hot Holiday gifts (Nov); Winter Sports (Dec)
Special Weekly Sections: Real Estate (S); Peach Weekender (Th).
Syndicated Publications: Comics (S).
Digital Platform - Mobile: Apple, Android, Windows
Digital Platform - Tablet: Apple iOS, Android, Windows 7, Blackberry Tablet OS, Kindle, Nook, Kindle Fire
Gen. Mgr. .... Joseph H. Zerbey
Dir. of HR. .... William Nolan
Sales Dir. .... Michael Mori
Circ. Dir. .... Richard Fuller
Circ. Mgr., Distr. .... Brad Schwanbeck
Ed. in Chief .... John Robinson Block
VP of New Media .... John Crisp
Director of Finance and IT .... William Southern
Executive Editor .... Kurt Franck
New Media Director .... Brad Vriezelaar
Managing Ed. .... Dave Murray
Asst. Managing Ed. .... Luann Sharp
Web News Ed. .... Greg Braknis
City Ed. .... Kim Bates
Sports Ed. .... Frank Corsoe
Audience Development and Customer Service Mgr. Tom Zeller
Circulation Manager, Operations .... Joe Bialorucki
Sr. IT Manager .... Bettyann Cole
Advertising Dir. .... Heather Foor
Asst. to Pres. .... Kim Johns
Exec. Asst. .... Isabel Sloan
Newspaper In Education Coordinator . Dr. Christine Smallman
News Ed. .... Tony Durham
News Editor - Sunday/Projects .... Doug Koerner
Columbus Bureau Chief .... Jim Provance
Controller .... Steve Dolley
IT Support Mgr .... Angie Fredericksen
Dir. of Mktg. .... John Fedderke
PrePress Mgr. .... Ken Burkett
Advert. Sales Mgr/PrePress Sup . Tom Sutherland
Market Information: ADS; Split run; TMC; Zoned editions.
Mechanical Available: Offset - cold set. Black and 4 color process. Stright run 80 pgs / 40 multi / 7 setions in broad sheet format. Physical page size 12" x 21" cutoff. 1270 DPI image setter resolution with 100 line screen.
Mechanical Specifications: Broad sheet image 6 column 11.04" x 19.75"
DT - 13 column 23.05" x 19.75"
Tab 4 or 5 column formats 9.175" x 10.75"
Areas Served: 75 zip codes served
Delivery Method: Mail, Newsstand, Carrier, RacksEquipment & Software: BUSINESS EQUIPMENT: Windows 2008 Servers in Virtual Environment BUSINESS SOFTWARE: AIM; Solomon, CLASSIFIED EQUIPMENT: Windows 2005 servers in a Virtual farm CLASSIFIED SOFTWARE: ATS Advisor, SCS Class Pag DISPLAY EQUIPMENT: Hardware — Macs; Printers — Various HP units DISPLAY SOFTWARECNI Tracking using InDesign EDITORIAL EQUIPMENT: Hosted solution from EVA EDITORIAL SOFTWARE: Libercus PRODUCTION EQUIPMENT: Hardware — Na/Nappflex, 3-AU/3850, 1-LE/PC 18, 3-Konica/3850 OL; Cameras — 1-C/NewsPager, 1-SCREEN/690D; Scanners — 2-ECR/Autokon 1000DE, 1-HP/ScanJet 4C, 1-Screen/1030 AI PRODUCTION SOFTWARE: Layout 8000 IT EQUIPMENT: Various solutions both hosted and in house using Microsoft Windows Products IT SOFTWARE:Microsoft Office 2010; Google email and apps CIRCULATION EQUIPMENT: Windows 2008 server; XP workstation CIRCULATION SOFTWARCIS, Bellatrix

TROY

TROY DAILY NEWS

224 S Market St, Troy, Ohio, 45373-3327, Miami; gen tel (937) 335-5634; adv tel (937) 552-2291 ext. 1639; ed tel (937) 552-2131; gen fax (937) 440-5286; adv fax (937) 335-9321; ed fax (937) 440-5286; gen/nat adv e-mail lstewart@civitasmedia.com; disp adv e-mail lstewart@civitasmedia.com; class adv e-mailmkaiser@civitasmedia.com; ed e-mail dfong@civitasmedia.com; web site www.troydailynews.com

Group: Civitas Media, LLC-OOB
Published: Mon, Wed, Thur, Fri, Sat, Sun
Weekday Frequency: e
Saturday Frequency: m
Circulation: 7,792; 7,918(sat); 9,827(sun)
Last Audit: Sworn/Estimate/Non-Audited September 30, 2017
Advertising Rate (weekday/saturday): Open inch rate $21.00
Advertising Rate (sunday): Open inch rate $24.50
News services: AP, **Established:** 1909
Own Printing Facility?: Yes
Commercial Printers?: Yes
Special Editions: Car Care (Fall); Bridal (Jan); Miami County Community Guide (May); Thanksgiving (Nov); Car Care (Spring).
Special Weekly Sections: Health, Fitness, NIE (Mon); Money, iN-75 (Wed); Food (Thur); Arts, Entertainment (Fri); Church, NASCAR (Sat); TV, Business, Community, Stock, Comics, Home, Garden, Real Estate, Travel, Senior Citizen, Parenting, Coupons (Sun)
Syndicated Publications: Color Comics (Other); USA WEEKEND Magazine (S); American Profile (Weekly)
Spry (Monthly); Relish (Monthly); Athlon Sports (Monthly); SCORE Magazine (quarterly).
Digital Platform - Mobile: Apple, Blackberry
Digital Platform - Tablet: Apple iOS, Kindle
Cir. Mgr. .... Tammy Patrick
Ed. .... Melody Vallieu
Pub. .... Joshua Byers
Adv. Dir. .... Becky Smith
Market Information: ADS; TMC.
Mechanical Available: Offset; Black and 3 ROP colors; insert accepted - all; page cutoffs - 22 3/4.
Mechanical Specifications: Type page 13 x 21 1/2; E - 6 cols, 1 5/6, 1/8 between; A - 6 cols, 1 5/6, 1/8 between; C - 8 cols, 1 1/3, 1/16 between.
Areas Served: 45373, 45371, 45383, 45337, 45339, 45359, 45312, 45389, 45356, 45318, 45326, 45317, 43072, 45326.
Delivery Method: Mail, Newsstand, Carrier, RacksEquipment & Software: PRESSROOM EQUIPMENT: Lines — 10-G/Urbanite single sheet 1990; Pasters —2-Butler/Splicer. MAILROOM EQUIPMENT: Counter Stackers — 2-H/RS 2512; Inserters & Stuffers — 1-KAN/760; Tying Machines — 2-EAM-Mosca/4044; Address Machine — 1/KR, PBS.; BUSINESS EQUIPMENT: Solomon, PBS, APP/Mac, APP/Power Mac 7500, 2-APP/Power Mac 7200, Lotus, Microsoft/Word, Microsoft/Excel, ADP, Sun/Suntype BUSINESS SOFTWARE: Microsoft/Excel, Microsoft/Office CLASSIFIED EQUIPMENT: Hardware — Dell/NT Server, 5-Compaq; Printers — 1-Xante/Accel-a-Writer 8200; CLASSIFIED SOFTWARE: Sun/Suntype. DISPLAY EQUIPMENT: Hardware — 7-APP/Power Mac G3, 2-APP/Power Mac 7500; Printers — 1-QMS/2060, Dell/Power Edge 1300 RIP; Other Hardware — CD-Rom, Zip Drive, Jazz/Drive, SyQuest/Drive, APP/Power Mac 7500 180 DISPLAY SOFTWAREAd Make-up Applications — Multi-Ad/Creator, QPS/QuarkXPress, Mk/Managing Editor; EDITORIAL EQUIPMENT: Hardware — APP/Mac/1-APP/Mac IIci, 1-Lf/AP Leaf Picture Desk, 5-APP/Power Mac G3, 5-CD-Rom, Kk/2035 Plus Scanner, 1-APP/Mac II, 2-Iomega/Jazz IGB, 2-Iomega/Zip Drive 100MB, Power Computing/Power Center Pro 240 Web Server, Quantum/5 Cort DLT A PRODUCTION EQUIPMENT: Hardware — Xante/Accel-a-Writer 8200 Laserprinter, Pre-Press/System, Pre Press/Panther Pro 36 with Ap Power Mac RIP, 1-APP/Power Mac 8100, 2-Power Computing/Power Center Pro 210, 1-APP/Power Mac 7500 180 mhz Apple Share IP server, 2-AU/3850 Imagers, Comp

UPPER SANDUSKY

THE DAILY CHIEF-UNION

111 W Wyandot Ave, Upper Sandusky, Ohio, 43351-1348, Wyandot; gen tel (419) 294-2332; adv tel (419) 294-2332 ext. 27; ed tel (419) 294-2331; gen fax (419) 294-5608; adv fax (419) 294-5608; ed fax (419) 294-5608; gen/nat adv e-mail dcuads@dailychiefunion.com; disp adv e-mail dcuads@dailychiefunion.com; class adv e-maildcuads@dailychiefunion.com; ed e-mail dcueditor@dailychiefunion.com; web site www.dailychiefunion.com

Group: Ray Barnes Newspapers, Inc.
Published: Mon, Tues, Wed, Thur, Fri, Sat
Weekday Frequency: e
Saturday Frequency: m
Circulation: 3,822; 3,822(sat)
Last Audit: Sworn/Estimate/Non-Audited September 30, 2017
Advertising Rate (weekday/saturday): Open inch rate $7.00
News services: AP.
Special Editions: Christmas Greeting (Dec); Football (Fall); Presidents' Sale (Feb); January Sale (Jan); June Dairy (Jun); Memorial Day (May); Christmas Kick-Off (Nov); Boy and Girl Scouts (Other).
Special Weekly Sections: Best Food (Mon); Farm (Tue); Business (Wed); Entertainment (Thur)
Syndicated Publications: Business Cards (Other); American Profile (Weekly).
Pub. .... Jeff Barnes
Sports Ed. .... Lonnie McMillan
Adv. Mgr. .... David Barnes
Cir. Mgr. .... Kelli Paugh
City Ed. .... Alissa Paolella
Market Information: ADS.
Mechanical Available: Offset; Black and 3 ROP colors; insert accepted; page cutoffs - 21.
Mechanical Specifications: Type page 12 15/16 x 21 1/2; E - 6 cols, 2, 1/8 between; A - 6 cols, 2, 1/8 between; C - 6 cols, 2, 1/8 between.
Equipment & Software: MAILROOM EQUIPMENT: Tying Machines — Ty-Tech; Address Machine — Am.; CLASSIFIED EQUIPMENT: Hardware — APP/Mac; Printers — TI.; DISPLAY EQUIPMENT: Hardware — APP/Mac IIsi; Printers — APP/Mac LaserWriter Plus; DISPLAY

SOFTWAREAd Make-up Applications — Multi-Ad/Creator.; EDITORIAL EQUIPMENT: Hardware — APP/Mac; Printers — TI. PRODUCTION EQUIPMENT: Hardware — 2-APP/Mac LaserWriter Plus; Cameras — Nu/UV-1418 PRODUCTION SOFTWARE: APP/Mac, Baseview.
Note: Printed by Kenton (OH) Times.

URBANA

URBANA DAILY CITIZEN

1637 E US Highway 36, Ste 10, Urbana, Ohio, 43078-9156, Champaign; gen tel (937) 652-1331; adv tel (937) 652-1331 ext. 1779; ed tel (937) 508-2301; gen fax (937) 652-1336; adv fax (937) 652-1336; ed fax (937) 652-1336; gen/nat adv e-mail jhenry@civitasmedia.com; disp adv e-mail jhenry@civitasmedia.com; class adv e-mailcherring@civitasmedia.com; ed e-mail UDCeditor@civitasmedia.com; web site www.urbanacitizen.com
- 230,000(views) 26,500(visitors)
Group: Civitas Media, LLC-OOB
Published: Mon, Tues, Wed, Thur, Fri, Sat
Weekday Frequency: m
Saturday Frequency: m
Circulation: 4,600; 4,600(sat)
Last Audit: Sworn/Estimate/Non-Audited September 30, 2017
Advertising Rate (weekday/saturday): Open inch rate $12.50
News services: AP. **Established:** 1838
Own Printing Facility?: Yes
Commercial Printers?: Yes
Special Editions: Football Preview (Aug); Christmas Greetings (Dec); Bride (Feb); County Fair (Aug); Health & Fitness (Jun); House and Home (Mar); Progress (May); Winter Sports (Nov); Crafts (Oct).
Special Weekly Sections: Best Food Days (Mon/Wed); Education, Farm (Tue); Business (Wed); Religion, Real Estate (Sat); Farm (Fri)
Syndicated Publications: USA WEEKEND Magazine (Sat).
Bus. Mgr. .... Brenda Amlin
Pub./Adv. Dir. .... Lane Moon
Ed. .... Brenda Burns
Sports Ed. .... Steve Stout
Market Information: ADS; TMC.
Mechanical Available: Offset; Black and 3 ROP colors; insert accepted - poly bags; page cutoffs - 22 3/4.
Mechanical Specifications: 9.889 x 21
Areas Served: City/County
Delivery Method: Mail, Newsstand, Carrier, Racks

VAN WERT

THE TIMES BULLETIN

700 Fox Rd, Van Wert, Ohio, 45891-2441, Van Wert; gen tel (419) 238-2285; adv tel (419) 238-2285; ed tel (419) 238-2285; gen fax (419) 238-0447; adv fax (419) 238-0447; ed fax (419) 238-0447; gen/nat adv e-mail tbyrd@timesbulletin.com; disp adv e-mail tbyrd@timesbulletin.com; class adv e-mailnswaney@timesbulletin.com; ed e-mail ecox@timesbulletin.com; web site www.timesbulletin.com
- 425,000(views)
Group: Delphos Herald, Inc.
Published: Mon, Wed, Thur, Fri, Sat
Weekday Frequency: m
Saturday Frequency: m
Circulation: 5,500; 5,500(sat)
Last Audit: Sworn/Estimate/Non-Audited September 30, 2017
Advertising Rate (weekday/saturday): Open inch rate $13.50
Online Advertising Rate: Home Page Leaderboard $250; Home Page Large Rectangle $200; Home Page Wide Skyscraper $200; Home Page Title $195; Section Banner $150; In-Story Large Rectangle $150; Mobile Site Sponsor $100 (All Monthly)
News services: AP. **Established:** 1844
Own Printing Facility?: Yes
Commercial Printers?: Yes
Special Editions: Spring Sports Magazine (Apr); Fall Sports Magazine (Aug); Christmas Greetings (Dec); Progress (Jan); Weddings II (Jun); Agriculture Almanac (Mar); Graduation (May); Holiday Traditions (Nov); Weddings III (Oct); PrimeTime (Quarterly); Home Improvement (Sep
Special Weekly Sections: Van Wert Country (Mon); Arts & Entertainment, Health, Business update (Wed); New Generation, Sports (Thu); Opinion, TV Times (Fri); Church Services, Church Page, Building your Dreams, Yesterday (Sat)
Syndicated Publications: USA WEEKEND Magazine (Sat); American Profile (Weekly).
Mkt. Dev. Dir. .... Tina Byrd
Cir. Mgr. .... Mike Marchek
Pub. .... Kirk Dougal
Obit. .... Sherry Missler
Bus. Off. .... Loretta Markward
Sports Ed. .... John Parent
News Ed. .... Erin Cox
Market Information: ADS; TMC.
Mechanical Available: Offset; Black and 4 ROP colors; insert accepted; page cutoffs - 22 3/4.
Mechanical Specifications: Type page 11 1/8 x 21 1/2; E - 6 cols, 1 3/4, 1/8 between; A - 6 cols, 1 3/4, 1/8 between; C - 8 cols, 1 5/16, 1/8 between.
Areas Served: 45874, 45891, 45894, 45898, 45899, 45832, 45863, 45833, 45838, 45886, 45882, 45862, 45822, 45828, 45879, 45851, 45849, 45880, 45855, 45844, 45827
Delivery Method: Mail, Newsstand, Carrier, RacksEquipment & Software: PRESSROOM EQUIPMENT: Folders — 1-G/2:1.; MAILROOM EQUIPMENT: Tying Machines — 1/Bu; Address Machine — Kirk Rudy.; BUSINESS EQUIPMENT: PC, Applications: MSSI CLASSIFIED EQUIPMENT: Hardware — APP/Mac; CLASSIFIED SOFTWARE: Baseview. DISPLAY SOFTWAREAd Make-up Applications — PBS.; EDITORIAL EQUIPMENT: Hardware — APP/Mac EDITORIAL SOFTWARE: QPS/QuarkXPress. PRODUCTION EQUIPMENT: Hardware — 1-Reconex; Cameras — 1-R/500; Scanners — AG/Arcus PRODUCTION SOFTWARE: Baseview, QPS/QuarkXPress 4.0.

WAPAKONETA

WAPAKONETA DAILY NEWS

520 Industrial Dr, Wapakoneta, Ohio, 45895-9200, Auglaize; gen tel (419) 738-2128; adv tel (419) 300-1076; ed tel (419) 739-3515; gen fax (419) 738-5352; gen/nat adv e-mail marketingetc@wapakwdn.com; disp adv e-mail marketingetc@wapakwdn.com; class adv e-mailclassified@wapakwdn.com; ed e-mail editor@wapakwdn.com; web site www.wapakdailynews.com
Group: Horizon Publications Inc.
Published: Mon, Tues, Wed, Thur, Fri, Sat, Sun
Weekday Frequency: e
Saturday Frequency: m
Circulation: 3,000; 3,000(sat)
Last Audit: Sworn/Estimate/Non-Audited October 1, 2017
Newspaper Reps: Deborah A. Zwez, publisher
Gayle Masonbrink, advertising manager
Tom Wehrhahn, managing editor
Advertising Rate (weekday/saturday): Open inch rate $29.00
Online Advertising Rate: bundled with rop rate; 1M-10M is $10/cpm
News services: AP. **Established:** 1905
Own Printing Facility?: Yes
Commercial Printers?: Yes
Special Editions: Home Improvement (Apr); Personal Image (Aug); Gift Guide (Dec); Progress (Feb); Bridal (Jan); Fair (Jul); Newspapers in Education (Mar); Graduation (May); Christmas Kick-Off (Nov); Car Care (Oct); Indian Summerfest (Sept).
Special Weekly Sections: Best Food Day (Mon); Farm News (Sat); Entertainment (Thur); Business (Tues).
Syndicated Publications: Homes/Real Estate (Monthly); American Profile (Weekly).
Pub. .... Deborah Zwez
Adv. Mgr. .... Gayle Masonbrink
Tom Wehrhahn
Market Information: TMC.
Mechanical Available: Offset; Black and 3 ROP colors; insert accepted; page cutoffs - 22 3/4.
Mechanical Specifications: Type page 13 x 21 1/2; E - 6 cols, 2 1/16, 1/8 between; A - 6 cols, 2 1/16, 1/8 between; C - 9 cols, 1 5/16, 1/8 between.
Areas Served: Wapakoneta, OH; 45895; Auglaize County
Delivery Method: Mail, Newsstand, Carrier, RacksEquipment & Software: MAILROOM EQUIPMENT: Tying Machines — 1/Sa; Address Machine — 3-/Wm.; BUSINESS EQUIPMENT: 1-Samsung/S550 CLASSIFIED EQUIPMENT: Hardware — APP/Power Mac; Printers — APP/Mac LaserWriter 16-600 PS; CLASSIFIED SOFTWARE: QPS/QuarkXPress, Claris/FileMaker Pro, QPS. DISPLAY EQUIPMENT: Hardware — APP/G4; Printers — APP/Mac LaserWriter 16-600 PS; DISPLAY SOFTWAREAd Make-up Applications — Adobe/PageMaker 5.0, Multi-Ad/Creator 3.63, QPS/QuarkXPress 4.0.; EDITORIAL EQUIPMENT: Hardware — APP/Mac G4; Printers — APP/Mac LaserWriter 16-600 PS, APP/Mac EDITORIAL SOFTWARE: QPS/QuarkXPress 4.0. PRODUCTION EQUIPMENT: Hardware — APP/Mac 7200-90, APP/Mac 7200-75, Adobe/Photoshop, APP/Mac LaserWriter 16-600 PS; Cameras — 1-Nu, 1-LE, Nu/SST 923; Scanners — LE/Sprint Scan 35, AG/SnapScan 600 PRODUCTION SOFTWARE: QPS/QuarkXPress 4.0.

WARREN

THE TRIBUNE CHRONICLE

240 Franklin St SE, Warren, Ohio, 44483-5711, Trumbull; gen tel (330) 841-1600; adv tel (330) 841-1621; ed tel (330) 841-1600; gen fax (330) 841-1721; adv fax (330) 841-1639; ed fax (330) 841-1717; gen/nat adv e-mail hnewman@tribtoday.com; disp adv e-mail hnewman@tribtoday.com; class adv e-mailclassified@tribtoday.com; ed e-mail blinert@tribtoday.com; web site www.tribtoday.com
- 412,000(views) 133,000(visitors)
Group: Ogden Newspapers Inc.
Published: Mon, Tues, Wed, Thur, Fri, Sat, Sun
Weekday Frequency: m
Saturday Frequency: m
Circulation: 19,939; 19,939(sat); 23,311(sun)
Last Audit: AAM December 31, 2016
Advertising Rate (weekday/saturday): Open inch rate $69.43
Advertising Rate (sunday): Open inch rate $69.43
News services: AP. **Established:** 1812
Own Printing Facility?: Yes
Commercial Printers?: Yes
Special Weekly Sections: Health (Tue); Best Food Day (Wed); Entertainment, Auto (Thur); Senior Citizen (Fri); Real Estate (Sat); Comics, TV (Sun)
Digital Platform - Mobile: Apple, Android
Pub. .... Charles Jarvis
Gen. Mgr. .... F. Len Blose
Ent. /Amusements Reporter .... Andy Gray
Prod. Mgr., Mailroom .... Scott Gee
Ed. .... Brenda Linert
Cir. Dir. .... Bill Waugaman
Ad Prod. Mgr. .... Mandy Miles
Market Information: Sunday Select
Mechanical Available: Offset; Black and 3 ROP colors; insert accepted; page cutoffs - 22 3/4.
Mechanical Specifications: Type page 11 x 21 1/2; E - 6 cols, 2 1/16, 1/8 between; A - 6 cols, 2 1/16, 1/8 between; C - 9 cols, 1 3/8, 1/16 between.
Areas Served: Trumbull County, Ohio
Delivery Method: Mail, Newsstand, Carrier, RacksEquipment & Software: PRESSROOM EQUIPMENT: Lines — 8-H/mono double width (6 half decks) 1992; Reels & Stands — 8; MAILROOM EQUIPMENT: Counter Stackers — 3-HL/Monitor, 1-Id; Inserters & Stuffers — HI/848, HI/1148; Tying Machines — 2/MLN, 2-/Dynaric; Address Machine — 1-/Ohio mailing machine.; CLASSIFIED EQUIPMENT: Printers — TI/Postscript.; DISPLAY SOFTWARELayout Software — Adept. PRODUCTION EQUIPMENT: Hardware — 1-V/5000, 1-V, 1-Pre Press/Panther Pro 45, 1-Xante; Cameras — 2-C.
Note: This newspaper is published in tabloid format on Saturday.

WASHINGTON COURT HOUSE

RECORD HERALD

757 W Elm St, Washington Court House, Ohio, 43160-2428, Fayette; gen tel (740) 335-3611; adv tel (740) 313-0347; ed tel (740) 335-0352; gen fax (740) 335-5728; adv fax (740) 335-5728; ed fax (740) 335-5728; gen/nat adv e-mail admanager@recordherald.com; disp adv e-mail ssattler@recordherald.com; class adv e-mailclassifieds@recordherald.com; ed e-mail ryancarter@civitasmedia.com; web site www.recordherald.com
Published: Mon, Tues, Wed, Thur, Fri, Sat
Weekday Frequency: e
Saturday Frequency: m
Circulation: 5,235; 5,235(sat)
Last Audit: Sworn/Estimate/Non-Audited September 30, 2017
Advertising Rate (weekday/saturday): Open inch rate $14.15
News services: AP. **Established:** 1941
Special Editions: In Your Prime (Quarterly); Acres (Monthly)
Special Weekly Sections: Best Food (Wed); Local (Mon); Health (Tue); Business (Wed); Food, Outdoors, Generations (Thur); Religion (Fri); Entertainment (Sat)
Ed. .... Ryan Carter
Med. Sales Cons. .... Kim Penwell
Cont. Prod. .... Martin Graham
Adv. Sales Coor. .... Julie Howell
Market Information: ADS; TMC.
Mechanical Available: Offset; Black and 3 ROP colors; insert accepted; page cutoffs - 22 3/4.
Mechanical Specifications: Type page 13 x 21 1/2; E - 6 cols, 2 1/16, 1/8 between; A - 6 cols, 2 1/16, 1/8 between; C - 8 cols, 1 3/4, 1/16 between.
Areas Served: South Central Ohio
Equipment & Software: MAILROOM EQUIPMENT: Tying Machines — 1/Bu.; BUSINESS EQUIPMENT: 1-IBM/AT, 4-AST/Bravo LC 4-33 BUSINESS SOFTWARE: MSSI/Ad Manager CLASSIFIED EQUIPMENT: Hardware — 1-APP/Mac.; DISPLAY EQUIPMENT: Printers — 1-APP/Mac; Other Hardware — CD-Rom. DISPLAY SOFTWAREAd Make-up Applications — QPS/QuarkXPress, Multi-Ad/Creator, Mk/Ad Builder; EDITORIAL EQUIPMENT: Hardware — 6-APP/Mac/2-APP/Mac Scanner; Printers — 1-APP/Mac EDITORIAL SOFTWARE: QPS/QuarkXPress 7.11. PRODUCTION EQUIPMENT: Hardware — Cameras ; 1-B/Caravel.

WILLOUGHBY

THE NEWS-HERALD

7085 Mentor Ave, Willoughby, Ohio, 44094-7948, Lake; gen tel (440) 951-0000; adv tel (440) 951-0000; ed tel (440) 951-0000; gen fax (440) 951-0080; adv fax (440) 951-0917; ed fax (440) 975-2293; gen/nat adv e-mail vlinhart@news-herald.com; disp adv e-mail advertising@news-herald.com; class adv e-mailclassifieds@news-herald.com; ed e-mail editor@news-herald.com; web site www.news-herald.com
736,918(visitors)
Group: Digital First Media
Published: Mon, Tues, Wed, Thur, Fri, Sat, Sun
Weekday Frequency: m
Saturday Frequency: m
Circulation: 25,462; 25,462(sat); 28,752(sun)
Last Audit: AAM September 30, 2014
Advertising Rate (weekday/saturday): Open inch rate $81.70
Advertising Rate (sunday): Open inch rate $92.85
News services: AP, MCT, CNS, SHNS. **Established:** 1879
Own Printing Facility?: Yes
Commercial Printers?: Yes
Special Editions: Golf (Apr); Most Beautiful Babies (Aug); Last Minute Gifts (Dec); Income Tax Guide (Feb); Chronology (Jan); Careers and Education (Jul); Graduation (Jun); Spring Lawn & Garden (Mar); Home Improvement (May); Elections (Nov); Fall Car Care (Oct); Fall Fashi

Special Weekly Sections: Technology, Video Games (Tue); Best Food Day (Wed); Entertainment (Fri); Religion (Sat); TV, Community, Real Estate, Travel (Sun)
Syndicated Publications: Coupon Book (Monthly); USA WEEKEND Magazine (Sat); Homes Alamanac (Semi-monthly); LIFE Magazine (Fri)
Controller .... Ron Adams
Adv. Dir. .... Jeff Schell
Exec. Ed. .... Tricia Ambrose
Mng. Ed. .... John Bertosa
Asst. Mng. Ed. / Feat. .... Mark Meszoros
Mobile/Digit. Ed. .... Cheryl Sadler
Cir. Dir. .... Douglas Fuller
Market Information: ADS; Split run; TMC; Zoned editions.
Mechanical Available: Offset; Black and 3 ROP colors; insert accepted - poly bag, samples; page cutoffs - 22 1/12.
Mechanical Specifications: Type page 13 x 21; E - 6 cols, 2 1/16, 1/8 between; A - 6 cols, 2 1/16, 1/8 between; C - 8 cols, 1 5/8, 1/16 between.
Areas Served: Lake & Geauga Counties (OH)
Delivery Method: Mail, Newsstand, Carrier, RacksEquipment & Software: PRESSROOM EQUIPMENT: Lines — 7-G/Metroliner (3 decks); Folders — 2-G/3:2; MAILROOM EQUIPMENT: Counter Stackers — 5/ Quipp-501; Inserters & Stuffers — GMA/ SLS 1000 (20:1) 2-GMA SLS 3000; Tying Machines — 1-Sterling/MR50 3-Dynaric NP-4000; Address Machine — 1-/KR, Ch/596-552 Quarter folder 1- Cheshire 595; BUSINESS EQUIPMENT: 2-IBM/AS-400 BUSINESS SOFTWARE: INSI CLASSIFIED EQUIPMENT: Hardware — HP/Compaq; Printers — APP/Mac Laser Writer 8500; CLASSIFIED SOFTWARE: Baseview/ Ad Manager Pro. DISPLAY EQUIPMENT: Hardware — APP/Mac Network; Printers — Canon; DISPLAY SOFTWARELayout Software — DTI/Make-up Sys. EDITORIAL EQUIPMENT: Hardware — HP/Compaq; Printers — APP/Mac LaserWriter 8500 EDITORIAL SOFTWARE: Baseview, Baseview/IQUE 313. PRODUCTION EQUIPMENT: Hardware — 2-ECRM Newsmatic HS PRODUCTION SOFTWARE: QPS/QuarkXPress 4.0.4. Indesign

WILMINGTON

WILMINGTON NEWS JOURNAL

761 S Nelson Ave, Wilmington, Ohio, 45177-2517, Clinton; gen tel (937) 382-2574; adv tel (937) 382-2574; ed tel (937) 382-2574 ext. 4119; gen fax (937) 226-9912; adv fax (937) 382-4392; ed fax (937) 382-4392; gen/nat adv e-mail emattingly@civitasmedia.com; disp adv e-mail akwiatkowski@civitasmedia.com; class adv e-mailbsullender@civitasmedia.com; ed e-mail tbarr@civitasmedia.com; web site www.wnewsj.com - 125,000(views) 40,000(visitors)
Group: Gannett
Published: Tues, Wed, Thur, Fri, Sat
Weekday Frequency: m
Saturday Frequency: m
Circulation: 5,800; 6,400(sat)
Last Audit: Sworn/Estimate/Non-Audited September 30, 2017
Advertising Rate (weekday/saturday): Open inch rate $17.00
News services: AP. **Established:** 1838
Own Printing Facility?: Yes
Commercial Printers?: Yes
Special Editions: Salt Magazine (Quarterly), Prep Sports (Fall); In Your Prime (Quarterly); Trip Travel Ohio (Semi-yearly); Prep Sports (Spring); Prep Sports (Winter). Clinton County Proud (yearly)
Special Weekly Sections: Books (Tue); Food (Wed); Business (Thur/Tue); Education (Thur); Religion, Arts, Leisure (Fri); Agriculture (Sat)
Syndicated Publications: USA WEEKEND Magazine (Fri). American Profile, Spry, Relish
Pub. .... Randy Graf
Cir. Mgr .... Dawn Gunkel
Editor .... Tom Barr
Admin. Asst. .... Denim Arrasmith
Adv. Mgr. .... Elizabeth Mattingly
Market Information: ADS; TMC.
Mechanical Available: Offset; Black and 3 ROP colors; insert accepted - we-prints, samples; page cutoffs - 21.
Mechanical Specifications: Type page 13 x 21; E - 6 cols, 2 1/16, 1/8 between; A - 6 cols, 2 1/16, 1/8 between; C - 8 cols, 1 3/16, 1/16 between.
Areas Served: 45177 WILMINGTON 45107 BLANCHESTER 45169 SABINA 45113 CLARKSVILLE 45114 CUBA 45135 LEESBURG 45138 LEES CREEK 45142 LYNCHBURG 45146 MARTINSVILLE 45148 MIDLAND 45159 NEW VIENNA 45164 PORT WILLIAM 45166 REESVILLE 45335 JAMESTOWN
Delivery Method: Mail, Newsstand, Carrier, RacksEquipment & Software: CLASSIFIED SOFTWARE: PBS, QPS/QuarkXPress, EDITORIAL SOFTWARE: Baseview/ NewsEdit, QPS/QuarkXPress, Adobe/ Photoshop. PRODUCTION EQUIPMENT: Hardware — Caere/OmniPage 610, Xante/ Accel-a-Writer 8200; Cameras — 1-B; Scanners — 2-AG/Arcus II PRODUCTION SOFTWARE: QPS/QuarkXPress.

WOOSTER

THE DAILY RECORD

212 E Liberty St, Wooster, Ohio, 44691-4348, Wayne; gen tel (330) 264-1125; adv tel (330) 264-1125; ed tel (330) 264-1125; gen fax (330) 264-3756; adv fax (330) 264-3756; ed fax (330) 264-1132; gen/nat adv e-mail adv@the-daily-record.com; disp adv e-mail kgearhart@the-daily-record.com; class adv e-mailclassified@the-daily-record.com; ed e-mail letters@the-daily-record.com; web site www.the-daily-record.com
Group: GateHouse Media, Inc.
Published: Mon, Tues, Wed, Thur, Fri, Sat, Sun
Weekday Frequency: m
Saturday Frequency: m
Circulation: 17,871; 17,871(sat); 19,180(sun)
Last Audit: AAM March 31, 2016
Advertising Rate (weekday/saturday): Open inch rate $29.85
Advertising Rate (sunday): Open inch rate $29.85
News services: AP.
Own Printing Facility?: Yes
Commercial Printers?: Yes
Special Editions: Home & Garden (Apr); Wayne County Fair (Aug); Holiday Greetings (Dec); Bridal Showcase (Feb); Bridal Showcase (Jun); Builders (Mar); Senior Memories (May); Cost Cutter (Monthly); Christmas Kick-Off (Nov); At Home (Oct); Football Preview (Sept).
Special Weekly Sections: Farm (Tue); Religion, Health (Fri); Youth, Education, Business (Sun);
Syndicated Publications: TV News (printed in plant) (S); American Profile (Weekly).
Nat'l Adv. Sales .... Randy Wilson
Mng. Ed. .... Lance White
Sports Ed. .... Aaron Dorksen
Off. Mgr. .... Elizabeth Miles
Pub .... Bill Albrecht
Market Information: TMC.
Mechanical Available: Offset; Black and 3 ROP colors; insert accepted - slip sheets, samples.
Mechanical Specifications: Type page 12 x 21 1/2; E - 6 cols, 1 5/6, 1/8 between; A - 6 cols, 1 5/6, 1/8 between; C - 9 cols, 1 3/16, 1/8 between.
Areas Served: Wayne & Holmes Counties (OH)
Delivery Method: CarrierEquipment & Software: PRESSROOM EQUIPMENT: Lines — KBA/Comet; Press Drive — EAE; Folders — 2-KBA/Half, 1-KBA/Quarter; Pasters —5-Amal; Control System — EAE; Registration System — Digital. MAILROOM EQUIPMENT: Counter Stackers — 3/QWI 3 Gammeler; Inserters & Stuffers — 1-GMA/ SLS 2000 1-GMA/SLS 3000; Tying Machines — 4 Dynaric; Control System — Quipp; Address Machine — 1-/Ch; BUSINESS EQUIPMENT: IBM BUSINESS SOFTWARE: APT CLASSIFIED EQUIPMENT: Hardware — 5-APP/iMac; Printers — HP/Laser 4MV; CLASSIFIED SOFTWARE: APT. DISPLAY EQUIPMENT: Hardware — 6 - Dual G4s; Printers — HP/Laser 9000; DISPLAY SOFTWAREAd Make-up Applications — In Design; EDITORIAL EQUIPMENT: Hardware — 35-Mac Mini and Mac Books; Printers — HP/Laser 9040 EDITORIAL SOFTWARE: Baseview. PRODUCTION EQUIPMENT: Hardware — 1-W, APP/Mac Electronic Darkroom-PowerBook; Scanners — 1-Nikon/ Coolscan, 4-Microtek/Flatbed, 2-U-Max, 1-Epson, 1-Microtek PRODUCTION SOFTWARE: Baseview.

XENIA

FAIRBORN DAILY HERALD

1836 W Park Sq, Xenia, Ohio, 45385-2668, Greene; gen tel (937) 372-3993; adv tel (937) 372-4444 ext 200; ed tel (937) 878-3993 ext. 134; gen fax (937) 372-1951; adv fax (937) 372-3385; ed fax (937) 372-1951; gen/nat adv e-mail bvandeventer@civitasmedia.com; disp adv e-mail cchambliss@civitasmedia.com; class adv e-mailttootle@civitasmedia.com; ed e-mail editor@xeniagazette.com; web site www.fairborndailyherald.com
Group: AIM Media Indiana
Published: Tues, Wed, Thur, Fri, Sat
Weekday Frequency: m
Saturday Frequency: m
Circulation: 3,999; 3,999(sat)
Last Audit: Sworn/Estimate/Non-Audited September 30, 2017
Advertising Rate (weekday/saturday): Open inch rate $7.25
Online Advertising Rate: Leaderboard $100/Ad rotation; Medium Rectangle $100/Ad rotation; Skyscraper $100/ad rotation. (All 3-Mnth Minimum contract)
News services: AP, U.S. Suburban Press Inc..
Special Editions: Private Property (Apr); Sidewalk Days (Jul); Business Directory (Mar); Car Care (May); Christmas Kick-Off (Nov); Home Improvement (Oct).
Syndicated Publications: USA WEEKEND Magazine (Sat).
Pub. .... Randy Graf
Gen. Mgr. .... Barb Vandeventer
Managing Ed. .... MerriLee Embs
Adv. .... Cathy Chambliss
Cir. Bus. Mgr. .... Linda Skinner
Market Information: Split run; TMC.
Mechanical Available: Offset; Black and 3 ROP colors; insert accepted; page cutoffs - 21 3/4.
Mechanical Specifications: Type page 13 x 21 1/2; E - 6 cols, 2 1/16, 1/8 between; A - 6 cols, 2 1/16, 1/8 between; C - 9 cols, 2 1/16, 1/8 between.
Areas Served: Fairborn, Enon & Yellow Springs (OH)
Equipment & Software: PRESSROOM EQUIPMENT: Lines — 9-G/Suburban; 9-G/Suburban; MAILROOM EQUIPMENT: Counter Stackers — 1-MM/5 Station; Tying Machines — 2/Bu.; BUSINESS EQUIPMENT: IBM/PC CLASSIFIED EQUIPMENT: Hardware — APP/Mac.; DISPLAY SOFTWARELayout Software — APP/Mac. EDITORIAL EQUIPMENT: Hardware — APP/ Mac EDITORIAL SOFTWARE: Microsoft/ Word, QPS. PRODUCTION EQUIPMENT: Hardware — COM/MCS 8400, Linotype-Hell/ Linotronic 101; Cameras — 1-B, 1-K/Vertical.

XENIA DAILY GAZETTE

1836 W Park Sq, Xenia, Ohio, 45385-2668, Greene; gen tel (937) 372-4444; adv tel (937) 372-4444 ext. 200; ed tel (937) 372-4444; gen fax (937) 372-3385; adv fax (937) 372-1951; ed fax (937) 372-1951; gen/nat adv e-mail nlebeau@civitasmedia.com; disp adv e-mail nlebeau@civitasmedia.com; class adv e-mailnlebeau@civitasmedia.com; ed e-mail editor@xeniagazette.com; web site www.xeniagazette.com
Group: Civitas Media, LLC-OOB
Published: Tues, Wed, Thur, Fri, Sat
Weekday Frequency: m
Saturday Frequency: m
Circulation: 5,858; 6,000(sat)
Last Audit: Sworn/Estimate/Non-Audited September 30, 2017
Advertising Rate (weekday/saturday): Open inch rate $10.80
News services: AP **Established:** 1868
Own Printing Facility?: No
Commercial Printers?: Yes
Pub. .... Diane Chiddister
Gen. Mgr. .... Barbara Vandevanter
Mng. Ed. .... Merrilee Embs
Adv. Mgr. .... Nancy LeBeau
Cir. .... Linda Skinner
Areas Served: Xenia (OH)
Delivery Method: Mail, Newsstand, Carrier

YOUNGSTOWN

THE VINDICATOR

107 Vindicator Sq, Youngstown, Ohio, 44503-1136, Mahoning; gen tel (330) 747-1471; adv tel (330) 740-2955; ed tel (330) 747-1471; gen fax (330) 747-4009; adv fax (330) 747-0399; ed fax (330) 747-6712; gen/nat adv e-mail jsovik@vindy.com; disp adv e-mail bstaples@vindy.com; class adv e-mailclassifieds@vindy.com; ed e-mail letters@vindy.com; web site www.vindy.com - 3,500,000(views) 300,000(visitors)
Group: Vindicator Printing Company
Published: Mon, Tues, Wed, Thur, Fri, Sat, Sun
Weekday Frequency: m
Saturday Frequency: m
Circulation: 33,210; 40,015(sat); 43,469(sun)
Last Audit: AAM December 31, 2016
Advertising Rate (weekday/saturday): $74.83 daily
Advertising Rate (sunday): $104.13 Sun
News services: AP, MCT **Established:** 1869
Own Printing Facility?: Yes
Commercial Printers?: Yes
Special Editions: How-to Section (Apr); Blitz High School Football Preview (Aug); Winter Destinations (Dec); Business Outlook (Feb); Bridal Planner (Jan); YSU Festival of the Arts (Jul); Destinations (Jun); Youngstown Jewish Community Center (Mar); Destinations (May); Holiday Gift Guide
Special Weekly Sections: Vibe entertainment
Syndicated Publications: Parade (S); TV Week (Sat).
Digital Platform - Mobile: Apple, Android
Digital Platform - Tablet: Apple iOS
Pub. .... Betty H. Brown Jagnow
Gen. Mgr. .... Mark A. Brown
Asst. Gen. Mgr. .... Ted E. Suffolk
HR Dir. .... Robert Wiseman
Mng. Ed. .... Mark Sweetwood
Graphics Ed./Art Dir. .... Robert McFerren
Ed. .... Todd Franko
Adv. Mgr. .... Barbara Staples
Market Information: Split run.
Mechanical Available: Offset Press; Black and 3 ROP colors; insert accepted; page cutoffs - 22 3/4.
Mechanical Specifications: Type page 10 7/8 x 21 1/2; E - 6 cols, 1 23/32, 1/8 between; A - 6 cols, 1 23/32, 1/8 between; C - 9 cols, 1 3/32, 1/8 between.
Areas Served: Mahoning & Shenango Valley
Delivery Method: Mail, Newsstand, Carrier, RacksEquipment & Software: PRESSROOM EQUIPMENT: Lines — 14-G/Metroliner Double Width 1984 1-G/Metro Color Tower Double Width 1995 1-G/Metro Double Width 1982; Press Drive — Parker Hannifin SSD Shaftless; Folders — 1- Double G/Imperial 3:2 1- Double out G/Sovereign; Pasters —14 G/PastersReels & Stands — 9 - G/Static Belt Reels & Stands 5 - G/CT45 Box Column Reels & Stands; Control System — Parker Hannefin SSD ; MAILROOM EQUIPMENT: Counter Stackers — 2/QWI Sport, 2-/QWI 401; Inserters & Stuffers — 1-G/630; Tying Machines — 8-/Sterling; Control System — 1-/MiraCom Insert 1-Burt Packaging/ Line Manager; BUSINESS EQUIPMENT: 1-HP/3000 928LX BUSINESS SOFTWARE: Cort, CJ/Geac CLASSIFIED EQUIPMENT: Hardware — 10 Mac/G4-400; Printers — Sharp MX 283 N.; CLASSIFIED SOFTWARE: MediaSpan: AMP2, Classflow XT DISPLAY EQUIPMENT: Hardware — iMac 20/Intel; Printers — Sharp 3610; Other Hardware — X/5042 copier, ECR/1000 DISPLAY SOFTWAREAd Make-up Applications — Mediaspan: PMP; Layout Software — Adobe Indesign, AdobePhotoshop, Adobe Illustrator, Adobe Acrobat, Adobe Distiller MultiAD Creator, Managing Editor Inc: ALS EDITORIAL EQUIPMENT: Hardware — 16-iMac 24-inch; 28 Macbook / Intel/80-APP/Mac G3; Printers — 2 Sharp 4110 EDITORIAL SOFTWARE: MediaSpan: IQue/ NewsEdit/Adobe: InDesign, Adobe InCopy PRODUCTION EQUIPMENT: Hardware

— 1 - AlfaQuest FasTRAK w/auto loader 1 - AlfaQuest NewsXpress w/auto loader 2 - Kodak Rapter 68 plate processors 1 - G/J Alliance Vision Punch/Bender 1 - G/J Alliance Edge Punch/Bender; Cameras — Canon: 7D; Scanners — Epson: GT-15000 Microtek Scanmaker 800 PRODUCTION SOFTWARE: alfaQuest: RIPs: Print Express, Adobe: InDesign, InCopy, Photoshop, Illustrator, Acrobat, Distiller, Multi-Ad Creator

ZANESVILLE

TIMES RECORDER

3871 Gorsky Dr, Ste G1, Zanesville, Ohio, 43701-3449, Muskingum; gen tel (740) 450-6700; adv tel (740) 452-4561; ed tel (740) 450-6750; gen fax (740) 450-6780; adv fax (740) 450-6780; ed fax (740) 450-6780; gen/nat adv e-mail scourson@gannett.com; disp adv e-mail atrabitz@gannett.com; class adv e-mailksargent@nncogannett.com; ed e-mail psjames@nncogannett.com; web site www.zanesvilletimesrecorder.com

Group: Gannett
Published: Mon, Tues, Wed, Thur, Fri, Sat, Sun
Weekday Frequency: m
Saturday Frequency: m
Circulation: 8,293; 8,293(sat); 9,695(sun)
Last Audit: AAM March 31, 2017
Advertising Rate (weekday/saturday): Open inch rate $35.50
Advertising Rate (sunday): Open inch rate $35.50
News services: Landon Media Group, Newspapers Now, Gannett, NEA, TMS, GNS. **Established:** 1852
Special Editions: Car Care (Apr); County Fair (Aug); Progress (Feb); Bridal (Jan); Bridal (Jun); Spring Sports (Mar); Graduation (May); Reader's Choice (Nov); Fall Sports (Sept).
Special Weekly Sections: Best Food Day, Arts (Wed); Technology (Tue); Entertainment, Health (Thur); Religion (Fri); Home, Real Estate (Sat); Best Food Day, Real Estate, Auto, Travel, Business (Sun)
Syndicated Publications: USA WEEKEND Magazine (S).
Digital Platform - Mobile: Apple, Android
Digital Platform - Tablet: Apple iOS, Android
Ed. .... Pam James
Adv. Sales Dir. .... Adam Trabitz
Nat'l Adv. Coord. .... Sharon Courson
Class. Sales Ctr. Mgr. .... Karie Sargent
Cir. Ops. Mgr. .... John Merriweather
Market Information: ADS; TMC.
Mechanical Available: Offset; Black and 3 ROP colors; insert accepted - catabooks, coupon envelopes; page cutoffs - 22 3/4.
Mechanical Specifications: Type page 11 1/16 x 21; E - 6 cols, 1 5/6, 1/8 between; A - 6 cols, 1 4/5, 1/8 between; C - 6 cols, 1 4/5, 1/8 between.
Areas Served: Muskingum County & Surrounding areas
Equipment & Software: BUSINESS EQUIPMENT: Windows 95, Gateway/PC BUSINESS SOFTWARE: PBS CLASSIFIED EQUIPMENT: Hardware — PCs; Printers — Xante; CLASSIFIED SOFTWARE: CText/Alps, Baseview/Alps. DISPLAY EQUIPMENT: Hardware — APP/Mac; Printers — Xante; DISPLAY SOFTWAREAd Make-up Applications — QPS/QuarkXPress, Adobe/Photoshop 4.0; Layout Software — APP/Mac. EDITORIAL EQUIPMENT: Hardware — Mk; Printers — Xante EDITORIAL SOFTWARE: Mk. PRODUCTION EQUIPMENT: Hardware — V/5160; Scanners — Polaroid/SprintScan 35, AG PRODUCTION SOFTWARE: QPS/QuarkXPress, Adobe/Acrobat 3.1.

OKLAHOMA

ADA

THE ADA NEWS

116 N Broadway Ave, Ada, Okla., 74820-5004, Pontotoc; gen tel (580) 332-4433; adv tel (580) 310-7502; ed tel (580) 310-7550; gen fax (580) 332-8734; adv fax (580) 332-8490; ed fax (580) 332-8841; gen/nat adv e-mail adanewsadvertising@cableone.net; disp adv e-mail adanewsadvertising@cableone.net; class adv e-mailmwise@theadanews.com; ed e-mail adanewseditor@cableone.net; web site www.theadanews.com

Group: Community Newspaper Holdings, Inc.
Published: Tues, Wed, Thur, Fri, Sun
Weekday Frequency: m
Circulation: 7,879; 7,879(sun)
Last Audit: Sworn/Estimate/Non-Audited September 30, 2017
Advertising Rate (weekday/saturday): Open inch rate $17.10
Advertising Rate (sunday): Open inch rate $17.10
News services: AP.
Special Editions: Christmas (Dec); Football (Fall); Newcomer's Guide (Other).
Special Weekly Sections: Business, Services (Daily); NIE (Tue); Restaurant, Stocks, Commodities (Wed); Religion, Church (Fri); Sports, Lifestyle, Wedding, Engagements, Finance, Stocks, Real Estate (Sun)
Syndicated Publications: Sunday Comics (S).
Cir. Mgr. .... Dawn Keathley
Sports Ed. .... Jeff Cali
Adv. Mgr. .... Maurisa Nelson
Pub. .... Amy Johns
Class. .... Monica Wise
Exec. Ed. .... Glenn Puit
Mng. Ed. .... Randy Mitchell
Market Information: ADS; TMC.
Mechanical Available: Offset; Black and 3 ROP colors; insert accepted; page cutoffs - 22 7/8.
Mechanical Specifications: Type page 13 x 21 1/2; E - 6 cols, 2 1/16, 1/8 between; A - 6 cols, 2 1/16, 1/8 between; C - 9 cols, 1 3/8, 1/16 between.Equipment & Software: PRESSROOM EQUIPMENT: Lines — 6-KP/News King.; MAILROOM EQUIPMENT: Tying Machines — Akebono.; BUSINESS EQUIPMENT: Compaq, WYSE, Unix/SCO Server BUSINESS SOFTWARE: Vision Data/6.0, Microsoft/Office 97 CLASSIFIED EQUIPMENT: Hardware — APP/Mac Quadra 660AV, APP/Power Mac 7200; Printers — APP/Mac LaserWriter NTX, Okidata/Pro 300LP; CLASSIFIED SOFTWARE: Baseview/Class Manager Pro 3.0. DISPLAY EQUIPMENT: Hardware — APP/Power Mac 7200, APP/Mac Centris 650, APP/Mac Quadra 650AV, APP/Mac Performa 6200; Printers — HP/LaserJet 4MV; Other Hardware — Umax/UC 300 Color Scanner, Asta/2400 Col DISPLAY SOFTWAREAd Make-up Applications — Multi-Ad/Creator, QPS/QuarkXPress 3.32, Adobe/Photoshop 5.0; EDITORIAL EQUIPMENT: Hardware — Ofoto, Ethernet, Nikon/Coolscan 35-mm, APP/Mac G3 266/3-APP/Power Mac 7200 Layout Station; Printers — APP/Mac LaserWriter 16-600, HP/LaserJet 4MV, Xante/3N, ECR/Scriptsetter VRL 36 EDITORIAL SOFTWARE: QPS/QuarkXPress 3.32, Aldus/PageMaker PRODUCTION EQUIPMENT: Hardware — 2-APP/Mac LaserWriter NTX, APP/Mac LaserWriter IIg, APP/Mac LaserWriter 600-16, HP/LaserJet 4MV, ECR/VRL 36; Cameras — Acti; Scanners — APP/Mac OneScan PRODUCTION SOFTWARE: QPS 3.3.

ALTUS

ALTUS TIMES

218 W Commerce St, Altus, Okla., 73521-3810, Jackson; gen tel (580) 482-1221; adv tel (580) 482-1221 ext. 2080; ed tel (580) 482-1221 ext. 2072; gen fax (580) 482-5709; adv fax (580) 482-5709; ed fax (580) 482-5709; gen/nat adv e-mail advertising@altustimes.com; disp adv e-mail advertising@altustimes.com; class adv e-mailadvertising@altustimes.com; ed e-mail esteinkopff@civitasmedia.com; web site www.altustimes.com; web site 2 myownaltus.com

Published: Tues, Wed, Thur, Fri, Sun
Weekday Frequency: e
Circulation: 4,591; 4,591(sun)
Last Audit: Sworn/Estimate/Non-Audited September 30, 2017
Advertising Rate (weekday/saturday): Open inch rate $13.00
Advertising Rate (sunday): Open inch rate $13.00
News services: AP. **Established:** 1900
Own Printing Facility?: Yes
Commercial Printers?: Yes
Special Weekly Sections: Best Food Day (Wed); Church (Fri); TV (Sun)
Syndicated Publications: USA WEEKEND Magazine (Fri); American Profile (Weekly).
Cir. Mgr. .... Sandy Graham
Pub. .... Matt Moran
Mng. Ed. .... Eric Steinkopff
Cir. Dir. .... Jared Lene
Adv. Sales Rep. .... Stephanie Bogart
Class. .... Lesley Baker
Market Information: TMC; Zoned editions.
Mechanical Available: Offset; Black and 3 ROP colors; insert accepted; page cutoffs - 22 3/4.
Mechanical Specifications: Type page 13 x 21 1/2; E - 6 cols, 2 1/14, 1/6 between; A - 6 cols, 2 1/14, 1/6 between; C - 8 cols, 1 2/3, 1/6 between.
Delivery Method: Mail, Newsstand, Carrier, RacksEquipment & Software: PRESSROOM EQUIPMENT: Lines — 5-G/Community 1969.; MAILROOM EQUIPMENT: Tying Machines — MLN/MCD-700; Address Machine — Label/4 Across.; CLASSIFIED EQUIPMENT: Hardware — APP/Mac; Printers - APP/Mac.; DISPLAY EQUIPMENT: Printers — APP/Mac NTX 360 Pro, HP/Laser; DISPLAY SOFTWAREAd Make-up Applications — Aldus/PageMaker 4.2, Multi-Ad/Creator 3.8; Layout Software — APP/Mac, PC. EDITORIAL EQUIPMENT: Hardware — APP/Mac; Printers — APP/Mac EDITORIAL SOFTWARE: Aldus/PageMaker 4.2. PRODUCTION EQUIPMENT: Hardware — 1-Nu; Cameras — R.

ANADARKO

THE ANADARKO DAILY NEWS

117 E Broadway St, Anadarko, Okla., 73005-2823, Caddo; gen tel (405) 247-3331; adv tel (405) 247-3331; ed tel (405) 247-3331; gen fax (405) 247-5571; adv fax (405) 247-5571; ed fax (405) 247-5571; gen/nat adv e-mail news@anadarko-news.com; disp adv e-mail news@anadarko-news.com; class adv e-mailnews@anadarko-news.com; ed e-mail news@anadarko-news.com

Published: Mon, Tues, Wed, Thur, Fri, Sat
Weekday Frequency: e
Saturday Frequency: m
Circulation: 3,000; 3,000(sat)
Last Audit: Sworn/Estimate/Non-Audited September 30, 2017
Advertising Rate (weekday/saturday): Open inch rate $7.50
News services: AP **Established:** 1901
Own Printing Facility?: Yes
Commercial Printers?: Yes
Special Weekly Sections: Best Food (Wed); TV (Fri)
Ed. .... Joe W. McBride
Mktg./Promo. .... Carla McBride-Alexander
Circ. Mgr. .... Philip Gomez
Pub. .... Carolyn N. McBride
Mechanical Available: Offset; Black and 3 ROP colors; insert accepted; page cutoffs - 22 3/4.
Mechanical Specifications: Type page 12.5" x 21"; col = 2"
Areas Served: 73005
Delivery Method: Mail, Newsstand, Carrier, RacksEquipment & Software: PRESSROOM EQUIPMENT: G/Community 1965, 1-G/Community 1984; Folders — G/Community.; BUSINESS EQUIPMENT: Apple BUSINESS SOFTWARE: Quark XPress, Acclivity, PhotoShop CLASSIFIED EQUIPMENT: Hardware — Apple; Printers — HP5200; CLASSIFIED SOFTWARE: Quark XPress DISPLAY EQUIPMENT: Hardware — Apple; Printers — HP5200; DISPLAY SOFTWAREAd Make-up Applications — Quark XPress; EDITORIAL EQUIPMENT: Hardware — Apple; Printers — HP5200 EDITORIAL SOFTWARE: Quark XPress PRODUCTION EQUIPMENT: Hardware — Apple; Scanners — Cannon PRODUCTION SOFTWARE: PhotoShop

ARDMORE

THE ARDMOREITE

117 W Broadway St, Ardmore, Okla., 73401-6226, Carter; gen tel (580) 223-2200; adv tel (580) 221-6501; ed tel (580) 221-6593; gen fax (580) 226-2363; adv fax (580) 223-3604; ed fax (580) 226-0050; gen/nat adv e-mail katherine.smith@ardmoreite.com; disp adv e-mail katherine.smith@ardmoreite.com; class adv e-mailclassmanager@ardmoreite.com; ed e-mail yournews@ardmoreite.com; web site www.ardmoreite.com - 500,000(views)

Group: New Media Investment Group
Published: Mon, Tues, Wed, Thur, Fri, Sat, Sun
Weekday Frequency: e
Saturday Frequency: m
Circulation: 4,703; 5,648(sun)
Last Audit: VAC June 30, 2017
Advertising Rate (weekday/saturday): Open inch rate $10.65
Advertising Rate (sunday): Open inch rate $11.15
Online Advertising Rate: 18.50 cpm
News services: AP. **Established:** 1893
Own Printing Facility?: Yes
Commercial Printers?: Yes
Special Editions: Best of the Best Q1 - Fashion (Spring). Football tab (Fall), Gift Guide (Christmas), Home Improvemet (Spring and Fall), Restaurant Guide (spring) Blue Ribbon Scholars (June)
Special Weekly Sections: Children, Best Food (Wed); Spotlight (Thur); Religion, Entertainment (Fri); TV, Business, Education, Weddings, Engagements, Agriculture (Sun); Real Estate (Daily)
Syndicated Publications: Relish (Monthly); Carousel (local, newsprint) (S); American Profile (Weekly). Athlon sports, Relish (monthly)
Digital Platform - Mobile: Apple, Android, Windows
Digital Platform - Tablet: Apple iOS, Kindle
Pub. .... Kim Benedict
News Ed. .... Marsha Miller
Business Manager .... Kathy Worley
Adv. Dir. .... Eddie Hunter
Class. Sales .... Catherine Norvell
Cir. Dist. Mgr. .... Mary Butler
Mng. Ed. .... Robbie Short
Market Information: ADS; TMC.
Mechanical Available: Offset; Black and 3 ROP colors; insert accepted - post cards, placards, etc.; page cutoffs - 22 3/4.
Mechanical Specifications: Type page 11 5/8 x 21 1/2; E - 6 cols, 1 5/6, 1/8 between; A - 6 cols, 1 5/6, 1/8 between; C - 8 cols, 1 1/2, 1/8 between.
Areas Served: 73401, 73443, 73456, 73463, 73438, 73030,73086,73460,73446
Delivery Method: Mail, Newsstand, Carrier, RacksEquipment & Software: PRESSROOM EQUIPMENT: Lines — 9-G; G/Community; Registration System — Duarte/Pin. MAILROOM EQUIPMENT: Tying Machines — 1-/Sa, 1-/Strapack; Address Machine — Ch.; BUSINESS EQUIPMENT: PC BUSINESS SOFTWARE: DTI, Datrose, ADP CLASSIFIED EQUIPMENT: Hardware — APP/Mac; Printers — APP/Mac LaserWriter NTX, Mon/Express Master 1270; CLASSIFIED SOFTWARE: Baseview, Class Manager/Plus, Adobe/Creator 4.03, Quark/Xpress 4.1. DISPLAY EQUIPMENT: Hardware — APP/Mac, CD, APP/Power Mac, Mk/Scanmaker II, APP/Mac; Printers — MON/Express Master 1270; Other Hardware — APP/Mac LaserWriter IIg DISPLAY SOFTWAREAd Make-up Applications — Multi-Ad/Creator 4.0.3, Adobe/Photoshop 5.0, QPS/QuarkXPress 4.1; Layout Software — ALS. EDITORIAL EQUIPMENT: Hardware — APP/Mac/1-APP/Mac; Printers — APP/Mac LaserWriter, MON/ExpressMaster 1270 EDITORIAL SOFTWARE: Baseview, NewsEdit/Pro, QPS/QuarkXPress 4.1, Adobe/Photoshop 5.0. PRODUCTION EQUIPMENT: Hardware — APP/Power Mac G3, 1-Richmond, P/26ML, Devotech 28 RA; Cameras — 1-LE/500, R; Scanners — APP/Mac Scanner Flat Top, Nikon/Scantouch PRODUCTION SOFTWARE: QPS/QuarkXPress 3.32.

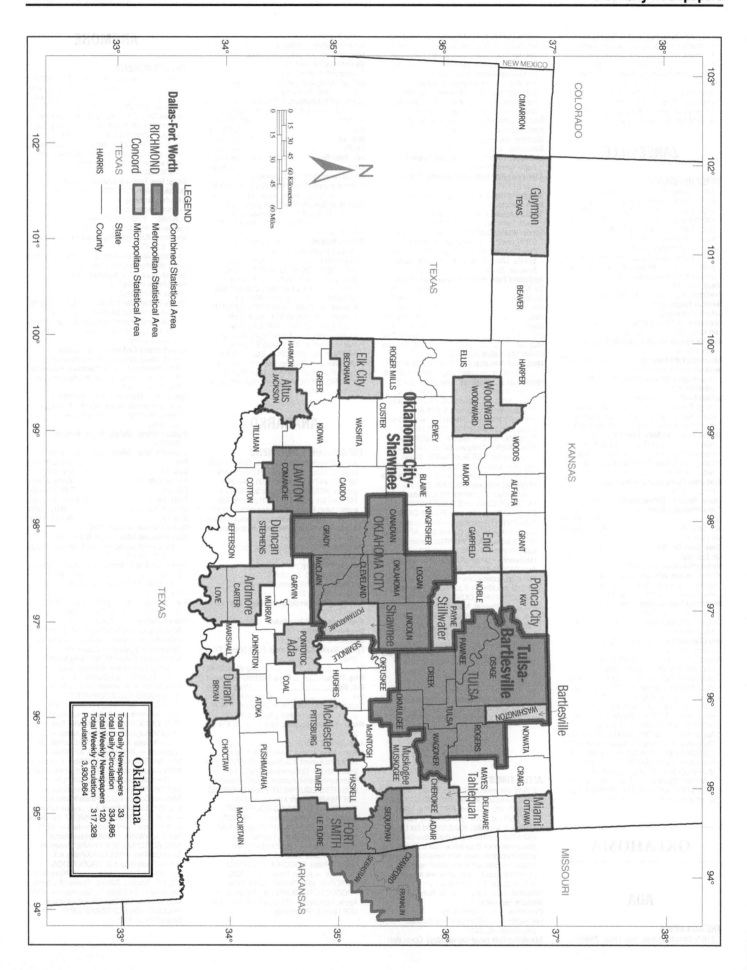

LEGEND

Combined Statistical Area — Dallas-Fort Worth

Metropolitan Statistical Area — RICHMOND

Micropolitan Statistical Area — Concord

State — TEXAS

County — HARRIS

Oklahoma

Total Daily Newspapers	33
Total Daily Circulation	334,895
Total Weekly Newspapers	120
Total Weekly Circulation	317,328
Population	3,930,864

BARTLESVILLE

EXAMINER-ENTERPRISE

4125 Nowata Rd, Bartlesville, Okla., 74006-5120, Washington; gen tel (918) 335-8200; adv tel (918) 335-8231; ed tel (918) 335-8246; gen fax (918) 335-3111; adv fax (918) 335-3111; ed fax (918) 335-0601; gen/nat adv e-mail ads@examiner-enterprise.com; disp adv e-mail ads@examiner-enterprise.com; class adv e-mailclassads@examiner-enterprise.com; ed e-mail cday@examiner-enterprise.com; web site www.examiner-enterprise.com
- 300,000(views) 50,000(visitors)

Group: New Media Investment Group
Published: Mon, Tues, Wed, Thur, Fri, Sun
Weekday Frequency: e
Circulation: 5,756; 6,519(sun)
Last Audit: AAM March 31, 2016
Advertising Rate (weekday/saturday): Open inch rate $17.70
Advertising Rate (sunday): Open inch rate $18.75
News services: AP.
Own Printing Facility?: Yes
Commercial Printers?: Yes
Special Editions: Tourism Guide (Apr); Christmas (Dec); Customer Appreciation (Jan); OK Mozart (Jun); Progress (Mar); Christmas (Nov); Our Hometown (Oct).
Special Weekly Sections: Community, Computer, Real Estate, Travel, TV (Sun); Business (Sun/Wed); Food, Health (Wed); Golf, NASCAR (Thur); Agriculture, Church, InterUrbal (Fri)
Syndicated Publications: USA WEEKEND Magazine (S); American Profile (Weekly).
Digital Platform - Mobile: Apple, Android
Digital Platform - Tablet: Apple iOS, Android, Windows 7, Kindle Fire
Cust. Rep. .... Janet Robinson
Sports Ed. .... Mike Tupa
Cir. Mgr. .... Robert Dye
Off. Mgr. .... Tammy Green
Pub. .... Matthew Tranquill
Market Information: Split run; TMC.
Mechanical Available: Offset; Black and 3 ROP colors; insert accepted - single sheets; page cutoffs - 22 3/4.
Mechanical Specifications: Type page 13 x 21 1/2; E - 6 cols, 2 1/16, 1/8 between; A - 6 cols, 2 1/16, 1/8 between; C - 9 cols, 1 3/8, 1/8 between.
Areas Served: Bartesville (OK)
Delivery Method: CarrierEquipment & Software: PRESSROOM EQUIPMENT: Lines — 8-G/Urbanite single width 1962; Press Drive — 2-Fin/75 h.p.; Reels & Stands — 16, 2.; MAILROOM EQUIPMENT: Counter Stackers — HL/Monitor; Inserters & Stuffers — KAN; Tying Machines - MLN; Control System — BG/Count-O-Veyor, 2-MLN/Strapping Machines.; BUSINESS EQUIPMENT: SCS BUSINESS SOFTWARE: Lotus 1-2-3, Orchestrator CLASSIFIED EQUIPMENT: Hardware — APP/Mac; Printers — 2-HP/4V 4MV, 2-Pre Press/Panther Plus Imagesetters; CLASSIFIED SOFTWARE: Baseview. DISPLAY EQUIPMENT: Hardware — APP/Mac; Printers — 2-HP/4V 4MV; DISPLAY SOFTWAREAd Make-up Applications — Baseview.; EDITORIAL EQUIPMENT: Hardware — APP/Mac; Printers — HP/4 MV, HP/4V, Pre Press/Panther Plus Imagesetter EDITORIAL SOFTWARE: Baseview. PRODUCTION EQUIPMENT: Hardware — Nu/Plate Maker, Lf/AP Leaf Picture Desk; Cameras — C/Spartan III; Scanners — AG/Studio Stars PRODUCTION SOFTWARE: Baseview.

CHICKASHA

THE EXPRESS-STAR

411 W Chickasha Ave, Ste 100, Chickasha, Okla., 73018-2472, Grady; gen tel (405) 224-2600; adv tel (405) 224-2600; ed tel (405) 224-2600; gen fax (405) 224-2604; adv fax (405) 224-2604; ed fax (405) 224-2604; gen/nat adv e-mail advertising@chickashanews.com; disp adv e-mail advertising@chickashanews.com; class adv e-mailclassifieds@chickashanews.com; ed e-mail editor@chickashanews.com; web site www.chickashanews.com

Group: Community Newspaper Holdings, Inc.
Published: Tues, Wed, Thur, Fri, Sun
Weekday Frequency: m
Circulation: 6,100; 6,300(sun)
Last Audit: Sworn/Estimate/Non-Audited September 30, 2017
Advertising Rate (weekday/saturday): Open inch rate $9.45
Advertising Rate (sunday): Open inch rate $9.45
News services: AP. **Established:** 1892
Special Editions: Fall Fashion (Aug); Progress (Feb); Christmas Gift Guides (Nov).
Special Weekly Sections: Best Food Day (wed); TV, Entertainment, Health (Sun); Business, Church (Fri)
Syndicated Publications: Relish (Monthly); TV Marquee (S).
Circ. Mgr. .... Vonnie Clark
Mailroom Supvr. .... Robin Rogers
Business Mgr. .... Kathy Black
Managing Ed. .... Debi DeSilver
Pub. .... James Bright
Mechanical Available: Offset; Black and 3 ROP colors; insert accepted; page cutoffs - 22 3/4.
Mechanical Specifications: Type page 13 x 21 1/2; E - 6 cols, 2 1/16, 1/8 between; A - 6 cols, 2 1/16, 1/8 between; C - 8 cols, 1 5/8, 1/8 between.
Areas Served: Grady County (OK)

CLAREMORE

THE CLAREMORE DAILY PROGRESS

315 W Will Rogers Blvd, Claremore, Okla., 74017-7021, Rogers; gen tel (918) 341-1101; adv tel (918) 341-1101 ext. 224; ed tel (918) 341-1101; gen fax (918) 341-1131; adv fax (918) 341-1131; ed fax (918) 341-1131; gen/nat adv e-mail ads@claremoreprogress.com; disp adv e-mail ads@claremoreprogress.com; class adv e-mailclassifieds@claremoreprogress.com; ed e-mail jdilmore@claremoreprogress.com; web site www.claremoreprogress.com

Group: Community Newspaper Holdings, Inc.
Published: Tues, Wed, Thur, Fri, Sun
Weekday Frequency: e
Circulation: 5,500; 6,500(sun)
Last Audit: Sworn/Estimate/Non-Audited September 30, 2017
Advertising Rate (weekday/saturday): Open inch rate $10.48
Advertising Rate (sunday): Open inch rate $10.48
News services: AP, NEA, TMS. **Established:** 1893
Own Printing Facility?: Yes
Commercial Printers?: Yes
Special Weekly Sections: Best Food (Wed); Family (Thur); Church (Fri); Health, Entertainment (Sun)
Syndicated Publications: Relish (Monthly); American Profile (S).
Ed. / Pub. .... John Dillmore
Staff Writer .... Tom Fink
Bus. Mgr. .... Amy Walsh
HR Mgr. .... Sheila Knight
Market Information: TMC.
Mechanical Available: Offset; Black and 3 ROP colors; insert accepted - hi-fi, spectacolor, speed 12; page cutoffs - 22 1/2.
Mechanical Specifications: Type page 13 x 21 1/2; E - 6 cols, 2 1/16, 1/8 between; A - 6 cols, 2 1/16, 1/8 between; C - 6 cols, 2 1/16, 1/8 between.
Areas Served: 74015-74019, 74031, 74036, 74053, 74055, 74080
Delivery Method: Mail, Newsstand, Carrier, RacksEquipment & Software: PRESSROOM EQUIPMENT: Lines — 8-G/Community; MAILROOM EQUIPMENT: Tying Machines — 2/Bu; Address Machine — 1-/Am.; BUSINESS EQUIPMENT: 1-DPT/8200 CLASSIFIED EQUIPMENT: Hardware — Mk; 1-DEC/LA 80.; DISPLAY EQUIPMENT: Hardware — Mk/Ad Builder; DISPLAY SOFTWARELayout Software — APP/Mac II. EDITORIAL EQUIPMENT: Hardware — Mk EDITORIAL SOFTWARE: Mk. PRODUCTION EQUIPMENT: Hardware — 1-Mk/AdWriter; Cameras — 1-R; Scanners — 2-COM.

CLINTON

THE CLINTON DAILY NEWS

522 Avant Ave, Clinton, Okla., 73601-3436, Custer; gen tel (580) 323-5151; gen fax (580) 323-5154; gen/nat adv e-mail cdnads@swbell.net; disp adv e-mail cdnads@swbell.net; class adv e-mailcdnclass@swbell.net; ed e-mail cdnews@swbell.net; web site www.clintondailynews.com
- 7,696(views) 4,789(visitors)

Published: Tues, Wed, Thur, Fri, Sat
Weekday Frequency: m
Saturday Frequency: m
Circulation: 3,613; 3,212(sat)
Last Audit: Sworn/Estimate/Non-Audited September 30, 2017
Advertising Rate (weekday/saturday): Open inch rate $11.10
Advertising Rate (sunday): Open inch rate $11.10
News services: 1903
Own Printing Facility?: Yes
Commercial Printers?: No
Special Editions: Health Care in February
Rt 66 Magazine in May
Saluting our Veterans in July
Senior Lifestyles in September
Saluting our Local Heroes in October
Holiday Magazine the first week of November
Special Weekly Sections: House of the Week (Tue); Oil, Gas (Wed); Entertainment, Legal, Farm, Food (Thur); Religion (Fri)
Digital Platform - Mobile: Apple, Android, Windows, Blackberry
Digital Platform - Tablet: Apple iOS, Android, Windows 7, Blackberry Tablet OS, Kindle, Nook, Kindle Fire
Vice Pres. .... Carol Sander
Circ. Mgr. .... Cindy Gagne
Pub./Ed. .... Rod Serfoss
Pho. .... Robert Bryan
Nat. Adv. Mgr. .... Sean Stephens
Prodn. Supv. .... Eric Hunter
Mechanical Available: Offset; Black and ROP full color. Insert accepted; page cutoffs - 22 3/4.
Mechanical Specifications: Page 11.66 x 21 1/2; E - 6 cols, 1.75", .16" between
Areas Served: 73601, 73620, 73622, 73624, 73625, 73632, 73639, 73647, 73669, 73096
Delivery Method: Mail, Newsstand, RacksEquipment & Software: PRESSROOM EQUIPMENT: Lines — 6-G/Community;

DUNCAN

THE DUNCAN BANNER

1001 W Elm Ave, Duncan, Okla., 73533-4746, Stephens; gen tel (580) 255-5354; adv tel (580) 255-5354; ed tel (580) 255-5354; gen fax (580) 255-8889; adv fax (580) 255-8889; ed fax (580) 255-8889; gen/nat adv e-mail dana.boyles@duncanbanner.com; disp adv e-mail dana.boyles@duncanbanner.com; class adv e-mailclassifieds@duncanbanner.com; ed e-mail editor@duncanbanner.com; web site www.duncanbanner.com

Group: Community Newspaper Holdings, Inc.
Published: Tues, Wed, Thur, Fri, Sat
Weekday Frequency: e
Circulation: 5,500; 6,000(sun)
Last Audit: Sworn/Estimate/Non-Audited October 1, 2017
Advertising Rate (weekday/saturday): Open inch rate $14.45
Advertising Rate (sunday): Open inch rate $14.45
Online Advertising Rate: $15
News services: AP, NEA. **Established:** 1892
Own Printing Facility?: No
Commercial Printers?: No
Special Weekly Sections: Best Food Day (Wed); Entertainment (Thur); Religion (Fri); TV (Sun)
Syndicated Publications: Relish (Monthly); American Profile (S).
Adv. Mgr. .... Dana Boyles
Adv. Mgr., Classified .... Paula Blair
Prodn. Mgr., Mailroom .... Mike McCormack
Business Mgr. .... Linda Rice
Publisher .... James Bright
Market Information: Split run; TMC; Zoned editions.
Mechanical Available: Offset; Black and 3 ROP colors; insert accepted; page cutoffs - 21.
Mechanical Specifications: Type page 9.961x 21; E - 6 cols, 1.556, 1/8 between; A - 6 cols, 1.556, 1/8 between; C - 8 cols, 1.136, 1/8 between.
Areas Served: Stephens County (OK)
Delivery Method: Mail, RacksEquipment & Software: PRESSROOM EQUIPMENT: Lines — 8-HI/Cotrell V-25; Reels & Stands — HI/Cotrell; Control System — HI/Cotrell.; MAILROOM EQUIPMENT: Tying Machines — 1-MLN/ML2-EE; Address Machine — 2/Wm; BUSINESS EQUIPMENT: 7-Sun/Ultra 5 BUSINESS SOFTWARE: PBS CLASSIFIED EQUIPMENT: Hardware — 2-APP/Power Mac; Iomega/Zip Drive; Printers — APP/Mac LaserWriter Plus; CLASSIFIED SOFTWARE: Baseview/Ad Manager Pro. DISPLAY EQUIPMENT: Hardware — APP/Power Mac 7600-120, APP/Power Mac 7300-200, APP/Power Mac 8500-120; Printers — APP/Mac LaserWriter 8500; Other Hardware — 2-APP/Mac Scanner. DISPLAY SOFTWAREAd Make-up Applications — Aldus/Freehand, Adobe/InDesign, Adobe/Photoshop, Adobe/Illustrator; EDITORIAL EQUIPMENT: Hardware — 15-APP/Power Mac/2-IBM/PC Notebook EDITORIAL SOFTWARE: Baseview/NewsEdit Pro. PRODUCTION EQUIPMENT: Hardware — Caere/OmniPage; Cameras — C/Spartan III; Scanners — Epson/Perf. 3170 PRODUCTION SOFTWARE: QPS/QuarkXPress 4.0.3, Baseview/Qtools 2.2.3, DragX (Inst. 1997) 2.2.2.

DURANT

DURANT DAILY DEMOCRAT

200 W Beech St, Durant, Okla., 74701-4316, Bryan; gen tel (580) 924-4388; adv tel (580) 634-2157; ed tel (580) 634-2161; gen fax (580) 924-0962; adv fax (580) 924-0962; ed fax (580) 924-6026; gen/nat adv e-mail esmith@civitasmedia.com; disp adv e-mail esmith@civitasmedia.com; class adv e-mailbpollard@civitasmedia.com; ed e-mail mswearengin@civitasmedia.com; web site www.durantdemocrat.com
28,000(visitors)

Published: Tues, Wed, Thur, Fri, Sun
Weekday Frequency: e
Saturday Frequency: m
Circulation: 5,123; 5,647(sun)
Last Audit: Sworn/Estimate/Non-Audited September 30, 2017
Advertising Rate (weekday/saturday): Open inch rate $12.55
Advertising Rate (sunday): Open inch rate $14.65
News services: AP, NEA. **Established:** 1901
Own Printing Facility?: Yes
Commercial Printers?: Yes
Special Editions: Christmas Greetings (Dec); Chamber of Commerce (Feb); Space Clearance (Jan); Graduation (May); Christmas Promotion (Nov); Basketball Opening (Oct); Football Opening (Sept).
Special Weekly Sections: County Style (Tue); Best Food, Dining, Entertainment (Wed); Church (Fri); Home, Real Estate (Sun); Weather (Daily)
Syndicated Publications: USA WEEKEND Magazine (Fri); Entertainment Showcase (local entertainment & TV listings) (S); American Profile (Weekly).
Mng. Ed. .... Matt Swearengin
Pub. .... Denny Koenders
Adv. .... Emily Smith
Class. .... Becky Pollard
Cir. Mgr. .... Kay Allen
Market Information: TMC.
Mechanical Available: Offset; Black and 3 ROP colors; insert accepted; page cutoffs - 22 3/4.
Mechanical Specifications: Type page 13 x 21 1/2; E - 6 cols, 2 1/16, 1/8 between; A - 6 cols, 2 1/16, 1/8 between; C - 8 cols, 1 1/2, 1/16 between.
Delivery Method: Mail, Newsstand, Carrier, RacksEquipment & Software: PRESSROOM EQUIPMENT: 8-Unit Goss MAILROOM EQUIPMENT: Tying Machines — 1/MLN; Wrapping Singles — 4-/Sa.; BUSINESS EQUIPMENT: Starlit/386-DX-40, CTX/Monitor, 3-Acer/Open, 3-Acer/View 34T Monitor, Scout Classic 144C Modem BUSINESS SOFTWARE: Progress/4GC Base System, Smart/One modem, Brainworks, Window 3.1 CLASSIFIED

EQUIPMENT: Hardware — 2-APP/Mac G3; CLASSIFIED SOFTWARE: Baseview. DISPLAY EQUIPMENT: Hardware — APP/Mac G3; DISPLAY SOFTWAREAd Make-up Applications — ALS; Layout Software — Baseview/AdForce. EDITORIAL EQUIPMENT: Hardware — 7-APP/Mac G3/MON/Imagesetter; Printers — 2-NewGen Design XP 12 EDITORIAL SOFTWARE: Microsoft/Word, QPS/QuarkXPress, SNews-Wire 3.15, Baseview. PRODUCTION EQUIPMENT: Hardware — Caere/OmniPage 3.0; Cameras — 1-Walzberg/26-10; Scanners — 2-APP/Mac Scanner PRODUCTION SOFTWARE: QPS/QuarkXPress 4.0, Baseview.

ELK CITY

ELK CITY DAILY NEWS
206 W Broadway Ave, Elk City, Okla., 73644-4742, Beckham; gen tel (580) 225-3000; adv tel (580) 225-3000; ed tel (580) 225-3000; gen fax (580) 243-2414; adv fax (580) 243-2414; ed fax (580) 243-2414; gen/nat adv e-mail ads@ecdailynews.com; disp adv e-mail ads@ecdailynews.com; class adv e-mailclassifieds@ecdailynews.com; ed e-mail news@ecdailynews.com; web site www.ecdailynews.com
Group: The Elk City Daily News, Inc.
Published: Tues, Wed, Thur, Fri, Sun
Weekday Frequency: e
Circulation: 3,700; 4,200(sun)
Last Audit: Sworn/Estimate/Non-Audited September 30, 2017
Advertising Rate (weekday/saturday): Open inch rate $11.75
Advertising Rate (sunday): Open inch rate $11.75
News services: AP. **Established:** 1901
Special Editions: Graduation, Football Preview, Outdoor & Hunting, Basketball Preview, Last Minute Christmas Gift Guide, Back to School, Health Awareness, Spring Sports Preview
Special Weekly Sections: Best Food Days (Wed/Sun); Church (Thur); Living, Religion (Fri); Fashion, Health, Home, Women, TV (Sun)
Mng. Ed. .... Robert Fisher
Circ. Mgr. .... Kathy James
Sports Ed. .... Blake Colston
News reporter .... Lorissa Graham
Community Ed. .... Cheryl Overstreet
Owner/Pres./Pub .... Elizabeth Perkinson Jim Nicholas
Sales .... Nancy McFarlin
Market Information: TMC; Zoned editions.
Mechanical Available: Offset; Black and 2 ROP colors; insert accepted; page cutoffs - 21.
Mechanical Specifications: Type page 13 x 20 1/2; E - 6 cols, 2 1/16, 1/8 between; A - 6 cols, 2 1/16, 1/8 between; C - 6 cols, 2 1/16, 1/8 between.
Areas Served: Elk City (OK)
Delivery Method: Mail, Newsstand, Carrier, RacksEquipment & Software: PRESSROOM EQUIPMENT: Lines — 4-G/Community; Folders — 1-G/2:1.; MAILROOM EQUIPMENT: Tying Machines — 1-/Cr; Address Machine — Am/Farrington, Innovative Technology/PC.; BUSINESS SOFTWARE: Microsoft, Indesign DISPLAY SOFTWAREAd Make-up Applications — Indesign; Layout Software — Indesign EDITORIAL SOFTWARE: Indesign PRODUCTION EQUIPMENT: Hardware — 1-WL, 1-Nat/A-250; Cameras — 1-B, 1-Acti/125 PRODUCTION SOFTWARE: Adobe/Pagemaker.

ENID

ENID NEWS & EAGLE
227 W Broadway Ave, Enid, Okla., 73701-4017, Garfield; gen tel (580) 233-6600; adv tel (580) 548-8136; ed tel (580) 548-8140; gen fax (580) 233-7645; adv fax (580) 233-7645; ed fax (580) 548-8147; gen/nat adv e-mail sales@enidnews.com; disp adv e-mail sales@enidnews.com; class adv e-mailclassified@enidnews.com; ed e-mail editor@enidnews.com; web site EnidNews.

com
- 995,508(views) 209,563(visitors)
Group: Community Newspaper Holdings, Inc. Raycom Media
Published: Mon, Tues, Wed, Thur, Fri, Sat, Sun
Weekday Frequency: m
Saturday Frequency: m
Circulation: 10,014; 10,014(sat); 10,851(sun)
Last Audit: AAM June 30, 2016
Newspaper Reps: Oklahoma Press Service
Advertising Rate (weekday/saturday): Open inch rate $23.00
Advertising Rate (sunday): Open inch rate $23.00
Online Advertising Rate: $15.00 cpm. Rate varies by platform and position
News services: Associated Press, CNHI News Service Established: 1893
Own Printing Facility?: Yes
Commercial Printers?: Yes
Special Weekly Sections: Amusement, Weekend, Entertainment (Daily); Best Food Day (Wed/Sun); Entertainment (Fri); Farm, Business, Homes, Lifestyle (Weekly); Home Improvement, Progress, Cookbook, Back to School, Christmas Gift Guide (Annually)
Proprietary Publications: Vance Airscoop (Fri) weekly newspaper for Vance Air Force Base
Digital Platform - Mobile: Apple, Android, Windows, Blackberry
Digital Platform - Tablet: Apple iOS, Android, Windows 7, Blackberry Tablet OS
Pres./Pub. .... Jeff Funk
Major Acct. Rep. .... Margie Campbell
Adv. Dir. .... Dee McCants
Director of Audience Development (circulation) .... Brad Nulph
Executive Editor .... Rob Collins
Business manager .... Kellan Hohmann
Marketing Director .... Frank Baker
Digital Director .... Violet Hassler
Prepress Mgr .... Mr. Kary Randles
Pressroom Mgr .... Tony Tolle
Market Information: Same-day delivery to 36 cities in NW Oklahoma
Mechanical Available: Web offset
Mechanical Specifications: 22 inch web width
Areas Served: Northwest Oklahoma
All or parts of these counties:
Delivery Method: Mail, Carrier, RacksEquipment & Software: PRESSROOM EQUIPMENT: Goss Urbanite press PRESSROOM SOFTWARE: Fincor MAILROOM EQUIPMENT: Meuller mechanical inserter BUSINESS EQUIPMENT: PC BUSINESS SOFTWARE: Vision Data CLASSIFIED EQUIPMENT: Mac CLASSIFIED SOFTWARE: Vision Data Total Ad DISPLAY EQUIPMENT: PC DISPLAY SOFTWAREVision Data Total Ad EDITORIAL EQUIPMENT: Mac EDITORIAL SOFTWARE: InDesign, NewsCycle NewsEdit Pro PRODUCTION EQUIPMENT: CTP PRODUCTION SOFTWARE: PuzzleFlow CIRCULATION EQUIPMENT: PC CIRCULATION SOFTWARVision Data
Note: Eagle Marketing (in-house marketing agency)

GUYMON

GUYMON DAILY HERALD
515 N Ellison St, Guymon, Okla., 73942-4311, Texas; gen tel (580) 338-3355; adv tel (580) 338-3355; ed tel (580) 338-3355; gen fax (580) 338-5000; adv fax (580) 338-5000; ed fax (580) 338-5000; gen/nat adv e-mail dailyheraldads@gmail.com; disp adv e-mail dailyheraldads@gmail.com; class adv e-mailadmanager@guymondailyherald.com; ed e-mail guymondailyeditor@gmail.com; web site www.guymondailyherald.com
Group: Horizon Publications Inc.
Published: Mon, Tues, Wed, Thur, Fri, Sat
Weekday Frequency: e
Saturday Frequency: m
Circulation: 2,332; 2,332(sat)
Last Audit: Sworn/Estimate/Non-Audited September 30, 2017
Advertising Rate (weekday/saturday): Open inch rate $8.72
News services: AP. **Established:** 1886
Special Editions: Pioneer Days (Apr); Christmas Greetings (Dec); Progress (Feb); Graduation (May); Christmas Gift Guide (Nov); Texas County Fair (Sept).

Special Weekly Sections: Best Food (Wed); Agriculture, Business (Thur); Real Estate, Religion (Fri); Entertainment, Health (Sat)
Syndicated Publications: TV Guide Tab (Fri); American Profile (Sat).
Off. Mgr. .... Myrna Campbell
Adv. Dir. / Gen. Mgr. .... Alison Gipe
Cir. Mgr. .... Peggy Martinez
Mng. Ed. .... Kitie Matire
Sports Ed. .... Shawn Yorks
Market Information: TMC; Zoned editions.
Mechanical Available: Offset; Black and 3 ROP colors; insert accepted - card; page cutoffs - 21 1/2.
Mechanical Specifications: Type page 13 x 21 1/2; E - 6 cols, 2 1/16, 1/8 between; A - 6 cols, 2 1/16, 1/8 between; C - 8 cols, 1 3/8, 1/16 between.
Areas Served: Entire Oklahoma region
Equipment & Software: PRESSROOM EQUIPMENT: Lines — 4-G/Community; Folders — 1-G/2:1.; MAILROOM EQUIPMENT: Tying Machines — 1-Malow/Mc Heavy Duty.; BUSINESS EQUIPMENT: Vision Data CLASSIFIED EQUIPMENT: Hardware — Mk/4003; Printers — APP/Mac LaserWriter.; DISPLAY EQUIPMENT: Printers — APP/Mac LaserWriter; DISPLAY SOFTWARELayout Software — APP/Mac. EDITORIAL EQUIPMENT: Hardware — Mk/4003; Printers — 2-APP/Mac LaserWriter EDITORIAL SOFTWARE: Mk. PRODUCTION EQUIPMENT: Hardware — C/T-45; Cameras — Acti/214.

IDABEL

MCCURTAIN DAILY GAZETTE
107 S Central Ave, Idabel, Okla., 74745-4847, McCurtain; gen tel (580) 286-3321; adv tel (580) 286-3321; ed tel (580) 286-3321; gen fax (580) 286-2208; adv fax (580) 286-2208; ed fax (580) 286-2208; gen/nat adv e-mail ads@mccurtain.com; disp adv e-mail ads@mccurtain.com; class adv e-mailads@mccurtain.com; ed e-mail paper@mccurtain.com
Published: Tues, Wed, Thur, Fri, Sun
Weekday Frequency: e
Circulation: 5,850; 7,800(sun)
Last Audit: Sworn/Estimate/Non-Audited September 30, 2017
Advertising Rate (weekday/saturday): Open inch rate $8.10
Advertising Rate (sunday): Open inch rate $9.60
News services: AP. **Established:** 1905
Special Editions: Health (Jan); Home,Garden (Feb); Readers' Choice (Mar); Progress (Apr); Owa-Chito Celebration (Jun); back to School, Football (Aug); County Fair (Sept); Community, Hunter's (Oct); Holiday (Nov); Christmas (Dec)
Special Weekly Sections: TV, Comic, Society, Sports, farm, Wildlife (Sun); Comic, Society, Sports (Daily)
Syndicated Publications: Sunday Showcase Entertainment Tab (S); American Profile (Weekly).
Vice Pres. / Off. Mgr. .... Gwen Willingham
Adv. Dir. .... Shelly Davis
Pub. Ed. .... Bruce Willingham
Reporter. .... Chris Willingham
Adv. Dir. .... Hallee Deramus
Market Information: TMC.
Mechanical Available: Offset; Black and 2 ROP colors; insert accepted; page cutoffs - 22 3/4.
Mechanical Specifications: Type page 13 x 21; E - 6 cols, 2 1/16, 1/8 between; A - 6 cols, 2 1/16, 1/8 between; C - 8 cols, 1 3/8, 1/16 between.
Areas Served: McCurtain County (OK)
Equipment & Software: PRESSROOM EQUIPMENT: Lines — 3-HI/V-15.; MAILROOM EQUIPMENT: Tying Machines — 2/WT; Address Machine — 1-RSK/TRS 80 Computer Printer.; BUSINESS EQUIPMENT: 2-RSK/TRS 80 II CLASSIFIED EQUIPMENT: Hardware — APP/Mac.; DISPLAY EQUIPMENT: Printers — APP/Mac LaserWriter; DISPLAY SOFTWARELayout Software — 3-APP/Mac. EDITORIAL EQUIPMENT: Hardware — TC EDITORIAL SOFTWARE: TC. PRODUCTION EQUIPMENT: Hardware — TC/Laserwriter; Cameras — 1-B.

LAWTON

THE LAWTON CONSTITUTION
102 SW 3rd St, Lawton, Okla., 73501-4031, Comanche; gen tel (580) 353-0620; adv tel (580) 585-5044; ed tel (580) 353-0620; gen fax (580) 585-5058; adv fax (580) 585-5103; ed fax (580) 585-5140; gen/nat adv e-mail pentler@lawton-constitution.com; disp adv e-mail ads@lawton-constitution.com; class adv e-mailjrobinson@swoknews.com; ed e-mail letters@swoknews.com; web site www.swoknews.com
Group: Southern Newspapers Inc.
Published: Mon, Tues, Wed, Thur, Fri, Sat, Sun
Weekday Frequency: m
Saturday Frequency: m
Circulation: 15,391; 15,391(sat); 16,510(sun)
Last Audit: AAM December 31, 2017
Advertising Rate (weekday/saturday): Open inch rate $19.45
Advertising Rate (sunday): Open inch rate $21.50
News services: AP, CNS. **Established:** 1910
Own Printing Facility?: Yes
Commercial Printers?: No
Special Weekly Sections: High Tech, Health (Mon); Best Food (Wed); Home, Garden, NASCAR (Thur); Entertainment (Fri); Religion (Sat); Religion (Sat); TV, Business, Real Estate, Auto (Sun)
Syndicated Publications: USA WEEKEND Magazine (S).
Digital Platform - Mobile: Apple, Android, Other
Digital Platform - Tablet: Apple iOS, Android, Blackberry Tablet OS, Kindle, Kindle Fire
Gen. Mgr. .... Mike Owensby
Cir. Dir. .... Larry Toth
City Ed. .... Steve Metzer
Managing Ed. .... David Hale
News Ed. .... Dee Ann Patterson
Adv. Dir. .... Kim Dodds
Nat'l Adv. Mgr. .... Patty Entler
Class. .... JoAnn Robinson
Mechanical Available: Offset; Black and 3 ROP colors; insert accepted.
Mechanical Specifications: Type page 10 1/2 x 21 1/2; E - 6 cols, 1 5/8, 1/8 between; A - 6 cols, 1 5/8, 1/8 between; C - 9 cols, 1 1/8, 1/8 between.
Areas Served: Southwest Oklahoma
Delivery Method: Mail, Newsstand, Carrier, RacksEquipment & Software: PRESSROOM EQUIPMENT: Lines — 6-HI/1650 offset double width 1978; Folders — HI/2:1 RBF; Pasters —5-MEG. MAILROOM EQUIPMENT: Counter Stackers — Id/440, Id/550, 2-MM/310; Inserters & Stuffers — 2-MM/227S 0-6; Tying Machines — 2/Dynaric; Address Machine — KR; BUSINESS EQUIPMENT: Digital/6200 BUSINESS SOFTWARE: DSI CLASSIFIED EQUIPMENT: Hardware — Pentium/PC; Printers — TI/8920, HP/4MV; CLASSIFIED SOFTWARE: FSI. DISPLAY EQUIPMENT: Hardware — APP/Mac; DISPLAY SOFTWAREAd Make-up Applications — Multi-Ad/Creator; Layout Software — Mk, FSI. EDITORIAL EQUIPMENT: Hardware — APP/Mac, Pentium/PC; Printers — TI/8920, HP/4MV EDITORIAL SOFTWARE: QPS/QuarkXPress, FSI. PRODUCTION EQUIPMENT: Hardware — 2-ECR/3850, Lf/Leafscan-Umax; Cameras — 2-C; Scanners — Hel PRODUCTION SOFTWARE: QPS/QuarkXPress 3.2.

MCALESTER

MCALESTER NEWS-CAPITAL
500 S 2nd St, McAlester, Okla., 74501-5812, Pittsburg; gen tel (918) 423-1700; adv tel (918) 421-2006; ed tel (918) 421-2023; gen fax (918) 426-3081; adv fax (918) 426-3082; ed fax (918) 426-3082; gen/nat adv e-mail advertising@mcalesternews.com; disp adv e-mail advertising@mcalesternews.com; class adv e-mailclass@mcalesternews.com; ed e-mail jbeaty@mcalesternews.com; web site www.mcalesternews.com
Group: Community Newspaper Holdings, Inc.
Published: Mon, Tues, Wed, Thur, Fri, Sun
Weekday Frequency: e
Circulation: 9,577; 10,046(sun)
Last Audit: Sworn/Estimate/Non-Audited

September 30, 2017
Advertising Rate (weekday/saturday): Open inch rate $17.25
Advertising Rate (sunday): Open inch rate $17.25
News services: AP, NEA. **Established:** 1896
Special Weekly Sections: Local, National News (Mon); Family (Tue); Best Food (Wed); Business (Thur); Religion (Fri); Real Estate, business, Milestone, Education, Health (Sun); Sports, Classifieds (Daily)
Syndicated Publications: Relish (Monthly); USA WEEKEND Magazine (S).
Pub. .... Amy Johns
Mng. Ed. .... James Beaty
Prod. Mgr. .... Debra Durbin
Adv. Dir. .... Reina Owens
Exec. Ed. .... Glenn Puit
Bus. Mgr. .... Pat Hessdorfer
Market Information: Split run; TMC; Zoned editions.
Mechanical Available: Offset; Black and 3 ROP colors; insert accepted - standing cards, samples, stick-ons; page cutoffs - 21 1/2.
Mechanical Specifications: Type page 12 x 21 1/2; E - 6 cols, 1 5/6, 1/8 between; A - 6 cols, 1 7/8, 1/8 between; C - 9 cols, 1 1/4, 1/12 between.
Areas Served: Southeast Oklahoma
Equipment & Software: PRESSROOM EQUIPMENT: Lines — 9-G/Community; Folders — 1-G/SC.; MAILROOM EQUIPMENT: Tying Machines — 1-Dynaric/SM-50, 1-Malow/Mc Heavy Duty Tyer.; BUSINESS SOFTWARE: Vision Data CLASSIFIED EQUIPMENT: Hardware — 2-APP/Mac; Printers — APP/Mac LaserWriter II; CLASSIFIED SOFTWARE: Mk, Baseview. DISPLAY EQUIPMENT: Hardware — Mk, APP/Mac; Printers — APP/Mac LaserWriter II; DISPLAY SOFTWAREAd Make-up Applications — Multi-Ad, Baseview; Layout Software — CD-Rom/Electronic Art. EDITORIAL EQUIPMENT: Hardware — 9-APP/Mac G3, 3-APP/Mac G4/APP/Mac One Scanner, Imagesetter; Printers — APP/Mac LaserWriter II EDITORIAL SOFTWARE: Baseview. PRODUCTION EQUIPMENT: Hardware — LF/AP Leaf Desk; Cameras — 1-C PRODUCTION SOFTWARE: Baseview, QPS/QuarkXPress 4.0.

MIAMI

MIAMI NEWS-RECORD
14 1st Ave NW, Miami, Okla., 74354-6224, Ottawa; gen tel (918) 542-5533; adv tel (918) 542-5533; ed tel (918) 542-5533; gen fax (918) 542-1903; adv fax (918) 542-1903; ed fax (918) 542-1903; gen/nat adv e-mail advertising@miaminewsrecord.com; disp adv e-mail advertising@miaminewsrecord.com; class adv e-mailclassifieds@miaminewsrecord.com; ed e-mail news@miaminewsrecord.com; web site www.miaminewsrecord.com
Group: New Media Investment Group
Published: Tues, Wed, Thur, Fri, Sun
Weekday Frequency: m
Circulation: 4,000; 4,000(sun)
Last Audit: Sworn/Estimate/Non-Audited September 30, 2017
Advertising Rate (weekday/saturday): Open inch rate $9.94
Advertising Rate (sunday): Open inch rate $10.46
News services: AP. **Established:** 1890
Own Printing Facility?: Yes
Commercial Printers?: No
Special Editions: Football (Aug); Christmas Greetings (Dec); Tax Tips (Feb); NEO Tournament (Jan); Sidewalk (Jul); Brides (Jun); Health (Mar); Graduation (May); Car Care (Nov); Community Visitor's Guide (Oct); Active Times (Quarterly); Hello Fall (Sept).
Special Weekly Sections: Best Food Day (Wed)
Syndicated Publications: TV Record (S).
Digital Platform - Mobile: Apple, Android, Windows
Digital Platform - Tablet: Apple iOS, Android, Windows 7, Kindle
Sports Ed. .... Jim Ellis
Prodn. Mgr. .... Darrel Rector
Market Information: Split run; TMC; Zoned editions.
Mechanical Available: Offset; Black and 3 ROP colors; insert accepted - standing cards; page

cutoffs - 21 1/2.
Mechanical Specifications: Type page 13 x 21; E - 6 cols, 2 1/16, 1/8 between; A - 6 cols, 2 1/16, 1/8 between; C - 10 cols, 1 1/5, 1/16 between.
Areas Served: Ottawa County (OK)
Delivery Method: Mail, Newsstand, Carrier, RacksEquipment & Software: PRESSROOM EQUIPMENT: Lines — G/Offset.; MAILROOM EQUIPMENT: Tying Machines — MLN; Wrapping Singles — Sa/E; Address Machine — 1-Am/1957E.; BUSINESS EQUIPMENT: 1-Gateway/2000 BUSINESS SOFTWARE: Microsoft/Windows 95, Microsoft/Office 98 CLASSIFIED EQUIPMENT: Hardware — APP/Mac.; DISPLAY SOFTWAREAd Make-up Applications — QPS/QuarkXPress, Adobe/Photoshop; Layout Software — APP/Mac. EDITORIAL EQUIPMENT: Hardware — 7-APP/Mac EDITORIAL SOFTWARE: QPS/QuarkXPress 3.3, Baseview/NewsEdit Pro. PRODUCTION EQUIPMENT: Hardware — 2-APP/Mac II, 2-APP/Mac LaserWriter II; Cameras — 1-C/1244; Scanners — Lacie, Kk PRODUCTION SOFTWARE: QPS/QuarkXPress 3.3.

MUSKOGEE

MUSKOGEE PHOENIX
214 Wall St, Muskogee, Okla., 74401-6644, Muskogee; gen tel (918) 684-2828; adv tel (918) 684-2804; ed tel (918) 684-2933; gen fax (918) 687-6270; adv fax (918) 687-6270; ed fax (918) 684-2865; gen/nat adv e-mail phxads@muskogeephoenix.com; disp adv e-mail troachell@muskogeephoenix.com/; class adv e-mailkhight@muskogeephoenix.com; ed e-mail news@muskogeephoenix.com; web site www.muskogeephoenix.com
Group: Community Newspaper Holdings, Inc.
Published: Mon, Tues, Wed, Thur, Fri, Sat, Sun
Weekday Frequency: m
Saturday Frequency: m
Circulation: 9,195; 9,195(sat); 10,500(sun)
Last Audit: AAM September 30, 2014
Advertising Rate (weekday/saturday): Open inch rate $34.67
Advertising Rate (sunday): Open inch rate $37.45
News services: AP, GNS. **Established:** 1888
Special Editions: Christmas Gift Guide (Annually); Visitors Guide (Semi-yearly).
Special Weekly Sections: Education, Parenting (Mon); Business, Health (Tue); Best Food (Wed); At Home (Thur); Entertainment (Fri); Auto, Religion (Sat); TV, Generations (Sun)
Syndicated Publications: USA WEEKEND Magazine (S).
Exec. Ed. .... Ed Choate
Sports Ed. .... Mike Kays
Pub. .... John Newby
News / Photo Ed. .... Jerry Willis
Dis. Mgr. .... Kevin Kizzia
Market Information: TMC.
Mechanical Available: Offset; Black and 3 ROP colors; insert accepted - Product Samples; page cutoffs - 22 3/4.
Mechanical Specifications: Type page 11 5/8 x 21 1/2; E - 6 cols, 2 1/16, 1/8 between; A - 6 cols, 2 1/16, 1/8 between; C - 9 cols, 1 3/8, 1/16 between.
Areas Served: Northeast Oklahoma
Equipment & Software: PRESSROOM EQUIPMENT: Lines — 8-G/Urbanite 1972; MAILROOM EQUIPMENT: Counter Stackers — HI/RS 2510, MM/310; Inserters & Stuffers — MM/227; Tying Machines — MLN/ML2EE, Si; Address Machine — Ch; BUSINESS EQUIPMENT: IBM/AS-400 BUSINESS SOFTWARE: Microsoft/Office 2000 CLASSIFIED EQUIPMENT: Hardware — APP/Mac; Printers — Okidata; CLASSIFIED SOFTWARE: Baseview. DISPLAY EQUIPMENT: Hardware — APP/Mac IIci, APP/Mac fx; Printers — APP/Mac LaserWriter, Phaser/300i Color Proofer, MON/1500, HP/LaserJet 5000 11x17, HP/DesignJet 1055CM Proofer; Other Hardware — CD-Rom, Nikon/Coolscan, Umax/Mir DISPLAY SOFTWAREAd Make-up Applications — Multi-Ad/Creator, QPS/QuarkXPress; EDITORIAL EQUIPMENT: Hardware — APP/Mac/APP/Mac, AP/Photos; Printers — MON/1500 EDITORIAL

SOFTWARE: Baseview/NewsEdit Pro, Baseview/IQUE 1.0. PRODUCTION EQUIPMENT: Hardware — Nat/A-250, Konica, ECR; Scanners — Lf/Leafscan 35, Nikon/Coolscan, Umax/Mirage II Scanner, Copy Dot Scanner PRODUCTION SOFTWARE: QPS/QuarkXPress 4.0.

NORMAN

NORMAN TRANSCRIPT
215 E Comanche St, Norman, Okla., 73069-6007, Cleveland; gen tel (405) 321-1800; adv tel (405) 366-3587; ed tel (405) 366-3542; gen fax (405) 366-3516; adv fax (405) 366-3516; ed fax (405) 366-3516; gen/nat adv e-mail rebekah@normantranscript.com; disp adv e-mail ads@normantranscript.com; class adv e-mailjan@normantranscript.com; ed e-mail editor@normantranscript.com; web site www.normantranscript.com
Group: Community Newspaper Holdings, Inc.
Published: Mon, Tues, Wed, Thur, Fri, Sat, Sun
Weekday Frequency: m
Saturday Frequency: m
Circulation: 7,688; 7,688(sat); 8,204(sun)
Last Audit: AAM September 30, 2016
Advertising Rate (weekday/saturday): Open inch rate $18.85
Advertising Rate (sunday): Open inch rate $22.50
News services: AP, MCT, NEA. **Established:** 1889
Special Editions: Garden Guide (Apr); Greetings (Dec); Salute to Business (Feb); Tax Guide (Jan); Gift Guide (Nov); Home Improvement (Oct); Football (Sept).
Special Weekly Sections: Senior (Tue); Food, Family (Wed); Church, Entertainment (Fri); Real Estate (Sat); Business, Society, TV (Sun)
Syndicated Publications: USA WEEKEND Magazine (S).
Adv. Mgr. .... Rebekah Collins
Class. Sales Exec. .... Jan Giza
Pub. .... Mark Millsap
Ed. .... Caleb Slinkard
Reg. Cir. Dir. .... Vonnie Clark
Bus. Mgr. .... Tammy Griffis
Market Information: TMC.
Mechanical Available: Offset; Black and 3 ROP colors; insert accepted; page cutoffs - 22 3/4.
Mechanical Specifications: Type page 13 x 21 1/2; E - 6 cols, 2 3/8, 1/8 between; A - 6 cols, 2, 1/8 between; C - 6 cols, 2, 1/8 between.
Areas Served: Norman, Cleveland & McClain Counties (OK)
Equipment & Software: PRESSROOM EQUIPMENT: Lines — 8-G 1975, G/Urbanite single width; Registration System — 1 MAILROOM EQUIPMENT: Tying Machines — Interlake/P 100, Interlake/P 940; CLASSIFIED EQUIPMENT: Hardware — APP/Mac; CLASSIFIED SOFTWARE: Baseview/Ad Manager Pro 1.0.7. DISPLAY EQUIPMENT: Hardware — APP/Mac; Printers — NEC/Imagerplus 12xf; DISPLAY SOFTWAREAd Make-up Applications — Multi-Ad/Creator 4.0; Layout Software — MEI/ALS. EDITORIAL EQUIPMENT: Hardware — APP/Mac; Printers — 2-Pre Press/Panther Imagesetter, 1-Pre Press/Panther Plus, 1-Pre Press/Panther Pro 36 EDITORIAL SOFTWARE: Baseview/NewsEdit Pro IQUE 3.0.3. PRODUCTION EQUIPMENT: Hardware — Caere/OmniPage 6, 1-Pre Press/Panther Pro 36; Cameras — 1-C/Spartan III; Scanners — Epson/Flatbed, Lf/Leafscan 35, Nikon/LS 1000 PRODUCTION SOFTWARE: Baseview 30, QPS/QuarkXPress 4.0.

OKLAHOMA CITY

THE OKLAHOMAN
100 W Main St Ste 100, Suite 100, Oklahoma City, Okla., 73102-9007, Oklahoma; gen tel (405) 475-3380; adv tel (405) 475-3380; ed tel (405) 475-3920; adv fax (405) 475-3444; ed fax (405) 475-3183; gen/nat adv e-mail dvillanueva@oklahoman.com; disp adv e-mail dvillanueva@oklahoman.com; class adv e-maildvillanueva@oklahoman.com; ed e-mail kfry@oklahoman.com; web site www.

newsok.com
- 18,050,225(views) 2,795,788(visitors)
Group: The Oklahoman Media Company
Published: Mon, Tues, Wed, Thur, Fri, Sat, Sun
Weekday Frequency: m
Saturday Frequency: m
Circulation: 102,742; 82,722(sat); 127,247(sun)
Last Audit: AAM September 30, 2017
Advertising Rate (weekday/saturday): Open inch rate $384.95
Advertising Rate (sunday): Open inch rate $450.39
Online Advertising Rate: Call 405-475-3380 for information
News services: Newspapers First, CT, DJ, CNS, MCT, SHNS, TMS. **Established:** 1903
Own Printing Facility?: No
Commercial Printers?: Yes
Special Editions: Call 405-475-3380 for information
Special Weekly Sections: Business, Sports (daily); Culture , Fashion, Pop, Lifestyles, People, Society (Sun); Life, Health, Science, Technology (Tue); Life, Food (Wed); Life, Style (Thur); Weekend Life, Entertainment (Fri); Religion, Ethics, Values (Sat); Sunday Life, Spiritual, Travel, Society, Entertainment (Sun)
Syndicated Publications: Parade (S).
Digital Platform - Mobile: Apple, Android
Digital Platform - Tablet: Apple iOS, Android
Pres. & Pub. .... Christopher Reen
VP, Admin. .... Scott Briggs
Financial Mgr. .... Kent Treadwell
Adv. Mgr., Classified .... Tom Hite
Mng. Ed. .... Mike Shannon
Asst. Mng. Ed. .... Robby Trammell
Bus. Ed. .... Clytie Bunyan
Dir. Multimedia .... Kelly Dyer Fry
National and Majors Sales Manager .... Derek Villanueva
Market Information: ADS; Split run; TMC; Zoned editions.
Mechanical Available: Offset; Black and 3 ROP colors; insert accepted; page cutoffs - 22 3/4.
Mechanical Specifications: Type page 12 1/2 x 21 1/2; E - 5 cols, 2 3/16, 5/16 between; A - 6 cols, 1 3/4, 5/32 between; C - 10 cols, 1, 1/8 between.
Areas Served: Entire Oklahoma region
Delivery Method: Mail, Newsstand, Carrier, RacksEquipment & Software: PRESSROOM EQUIPMENT: Lines — 10-G/Metroliner 1984; 10-G/Metroliner 1984; 10-G/Metroliner 1989; 2-G/Global Newslingers 2000; Folders — 3-G/3:2 Double Imperial, 1-G/2:3:3 Double Jaw 2000; Reels & Stands — 32; Control System — EAE; MAILROOM EQUIPMENT: Counter Stackers — 11-QWI/351, 2-QWI/350, 3-HL/Monitor, 2-QWI/400, 2-Gammerler/STC 70; Inserters & Stuffers — 1-HI/1372P, 3-HI/1472P, 1-HI/NP 630; Tying Machines — 11-Sterling/MR45CH, 2-Sterling/MR50CH; Control System — Burt; Address Machine — Addressin; BUSINESS EQUIPMENT: Hitachi/Pilot Series/P4, Model 15 BUSINESS SOFTWARE: SAP CLASSIFIED EQUIPMENT: Hardware — 2-Sun/Enterprise 4000 (ad entry), 80-PC (ad entry), 2-PC (pagination); Printers — HP/LaserJet 5si; CLASSIFIED SOFTWARE: HI/AdPower, Hi/Pagination. DISPLAY EQUIPMENT: Hardware — Sun/Enterprise 3000, 25-APP/Mac; Printers — 3-HP/2500 CP, Canon/Fiery, HP/5si; Other Hardware — 1-X/7650 scanner, 3-X/8000 Color Scanner, 1-AG/DuoScan, 1-Scanmate/scanview F8 DISPLAY SOFTWAREAd Make-up Applications — All/Ad Manager, Multi-Ad/Creator; Layout Software — 2-APP/Mac 9500 EDITORIAL EQUIPMENT: Hardware — 2-Sun/Enterprise 4000, 113-PC (editorial), 20-PC (pagination); Printers — HP/2500 CD, HP/5Si EDITORIAL SOFTWARE: HI/Newsmaker Editorial, Hi/NMP (pagination). PRODUCTION EQUIPMENT: Hardware — 3-Glunz & Jensen, AG/Due Scan, ScanView/F8; Scanners — 3-Epson/1640 PRODUCTION SOFTWARE: PPI.

OKMULGEE

OKMULGEE DAILY TIMES
320 W 6th St, Okmulgee, Okla., 74447-5018, Okmulgee; gen tel (918) 756-3600; adv

tel (918) 756-3691; ed tel (918) 756-3693; gen fax (918) 756-8197; adv fax (918) 756-8197; ed fax (918) 756-8197; gen/nat adv e-mail carrie@bigbasinllc.com; disp adv e-mail carrie@bigbasinllc.com; class adv e-mailkatina@bigbasinllc.com; ed e-mail herman@bigbasinllc.com; web site http://www.okmulgeecountynewssource.com
Published: Tues, Wed, Thur, Fri, Sun
Weekday Frequency: m
Circulation: 4,483; 6,547(sun)
Last Audit: Sworn/Estimate/Non-Audited September 30, 2017
Advertising Rate (weekday/saturday): Open inch rate $12.75
Advertising Rate (sunday): Open inch rate $12.75
News services: AP.
Special Editions: Okmulgee Trade Show (Other).
Special Weekly Sections: Best Food Day (Wed); TV, Real Estate (Sun)
Syndicated Publications: Entertainment Times (television section) (S); American Profile (Weekly).
Ed...Herman L. Brown
Sports Ed. ....Larry Owen
Pub...Jeff Mayo
Adv. Mgr....................................Carry Carberry
Class. ....Katrina Holland
Market Information: TMC; Zoned editions.
Mechanical Available: Offset; Black and 3 ROP colors; insert accepted; page cutoffs - 23.
Mechanical Specifications: Type page 13 x 21 1/2; E - 6 cols, 2 1/16, 1/8 between; A - 6 cols, 2 1/16, 1/8 between; C - 8 cols, 1 1/2, 1/8 between.Equipment & Software: PRESSROOM EQUIPMENT: Lines — 6-G/Community 1972.; MAILROOM EQUIPMENT: Tying Machines — Ca/Bond Tyer; Address Machine — Wm.; BUSINESS EQUIPMENT: PC BUSINESS SOFTWARE: Ar/Works: Bus CLASSIFIED EQUIPMENT: Hardware — APP/Mac 630, APP/Mac G4; Printers — APP/Mac LaserWriter NTX; CLASSIFIED SOFTWARE: Baseview. DISPLAY EQUIPMENT: Hardware — APP/Mac; Printers — APP/Mac LaserWriter NTX; DISPLAY SOFTWAREAd Make-up Applications — QPS/QuarkXPress 4.1, Baseview; Layout Software — APP/Mac G4, Baseview/Ad Force. EDITORIAL EQUIPMENT: Hardware — APP/Mac G4/APP/Mac Classic; Printers — APP/Mac LaserWriter II NTX EDITORIAL SOFTWARE: Baseview/NewsEdit Pro, QPS/QuarkXPress 4.1. PRODUCTION EQUIPMENT: Hardware — NewGen/DesignXpress 12; Cameras — 1-Acti/225 PRODUCTION SOFTWARE: Baseview/NewsEdit Pro, QPS/QuarkXPress 4.1.

PERRY

THE PERRY DAILY JOURNAL

714 Delaware St, Perry, Okla., 73077-6425, Noble; gen tel (580) 336-2222; adv tel (580) 336-2222; ed tel (580) 336-2222; gen fax (580) 336-3222; adv fax (580) 336-3222; ed fax (580) 336-3222; gen/nat adv e-mail mariapdj@yahoo.com; disp adv e-mail mcvaypdj@yahoo.com; class adv e-mailcircclasspdjnews@yahoo.com; ed e-mail pdjnews@yahoo.com; web site www.pdjnews.com
Published: Tues, Wed, Thur, Fri, Sat
Weekday Frequency: m
Saturday Frequency: m
Circulation: 3,250; 3,250(sat)
Last Audit: Sworn/Estimate/Non-Audited September 30, 2017
Advertising Rate (weekday/saturday): Open inch rate $13.68
News services: 1893
Own Printing Facility?: Yes
Special Editions: High School Graduation and Speical Edition in conjunction with Cherokee Strip Celebratioin
Special Weekly Sections: Best Food (Wed)
Owner/Pub. ....Phillip Reid
Legal / Bill. ....Lori Battles
Cir. Mgr....................................Bruce Atkinson
Managing Ed. ....Gloria G. Brown
Class. / Cir. ....Stefani Nichols
Market Information: TMC.
Mechanical Available: Offset; Black and 3 ROP colors; insert accepted - we-prints; page cutoffs - 21 1/2.
Mechanical Specifications: Type page 11 5/8 x 21 1/2; E - 6 cols, 1 5/6, 1/8 between; A - 6 cols, 1 5/6, 1/8 between; C - 6 cols, 1 5/6, 1/8 between.
Delivery Method: Mail, RacksEquipment & Software: PRESSROOM EQUIPMENT: Lines — 3-HI/Cotrell V-15A; Folders — 1, HI/JF-7. MAILROOM EQUIPMENT: Tying Machines — 1/Malow; Address Machine — 1-/Am.; BUSINESS EQUIPMENT: MaxTech BUSINESS SOFTWARE: Micro, Casecom CLASSIFIED EQUIPMENT: Hardware — APP/Mac; Printers — NewGen; CLASSIFIED SOFTWARE: SNews, QPS/QuarkXPress. DISPLAY EQUIPMENT: Hardware — 4-APP/Mac Centris 650; Printers — 2-NewGen/Turbo PS 660B; Other Hardware — 1-SyQuest/88MR DISPLAY SOFTWAREAd Make-up Applications — APP/Mac System 7.1; Layout Software — QPS/QuarkXPress, Adobe/PageMaker, Multi-Ad/Creator. EDITORIAL EQUIPMENT: Hardware — APP/Mac; Printers — NewGen EDITORIAL SOFTWARE: QPS/QuarkXPress. PRODUCTION EQUIPMENT: Hardware — Caere/OmniPage Direct 2.0; Cameras — 1-Ik, SCREEN/DS; Scanners — Umax/VC840 PRODUCTION SOFTWARE: QPS/QuarkXPress 3.11.

PONCA CITY

THE PONCA CITY NEWS

300 N 3rd St, Ponca City, Okla., 74601-4336, Kay; gen tel (580) 765-3311; adv tel (580) 765-3311; ed tel (580) 765-3311; gen fax (580) 762-6397; adv fax (580) 762-6397; ed fax (580) 765-7800; gen/nat adv e-mail ads@poncacitynews.com; disp adv e-mail ads@poncacitynews.com; class adv e-mailclassified@poncacitynews.com; ed e-mail letters@poncacitynews.com; web site www.poncacitynews.com
Published: Mon, Tues, Wed, Thur, Fri, Sun
Weekday Frequency: e
Circulation: 7,706; 8,838(sun)
Last Audit: AAM September 30, 2011
Advertising Rate (weekday/saturday): Open inch rate $13.00
Advertising Rate (sunday): Open inch rate $13.00
News services: AP. **Established:** 1893
Own Printing Facility?: Yes
Commercial Printers?: No
Special Editions: Spring Home Improvement (Mar); Oklahoma Football (Aug); Christmas Greetings (Dec); Brides (Feb); Income Tax Guide (Jan);Welcome Neighbors (May); Medical Guide (Jul); Spring Car Care (Mar); Back to School (Jul); Holiday Gift Guide (Nov);
Special Weekly Sections: Garden (Mon); Business, Finance, Cooking (Tue); Best Food, Women (Wed); Entertainment (Thur); Religion, Education (Fri); TV, Family, Real Estate (Sun)
Syndicated Publications: TV Week (S).
Controller.....................................Michael Ellis
Adv. Mgr...Pat Jordan
Ed. / Pub. ....Tom Muchmore
Mng. Ed ....Kristie Hayes
Sports reporter ....David Miller
Sports Ed. ....Fred Hilton
Prodn. Mgr. ....Jerry Helems
Retail Adv. Mgr...............................Robyn Ryan
Market Information: TMC.
Mechanical Available: Offset; Black and 3 ROP colors; insert accepted - odd sizes upon approval; page cutoffs - 22 3/4.
Mechanical Specifications: Type page 13 x 21 1/2; E - 6 cols, 2 1/16, 1/8 between; A - 6 cols, 2 1/16, 1/8 between; C - 9 cols, 1 3/8, 1/16 between.
Areas Served: 74604
Delivery Method: Mail, Newsstand, Carrier, RacksEquipment & Software: PRESSROOM EQUIPMENT: Lines — 8-G/Community 1975, 2-1992.; BUSINESS EQUIPMENT: PCs CLASSIFIED EQUIPMENT: Hardware — APP/Mac; CLASSIFIED SOFTWARE: Baseview. DISPLAY EQUIPMENT: Hardware — APP/Mac Quadra, APP/Mac Centris, DLI/CD-Roms, Sony, APP/Super Mac Monitors; Printers — APP/LW Pro 630, NewGen/1200B, ECR/VR 36 Imagesetter; DISPLAY SOFTWAREAd Make-up Applications — InDesign 4, Aldus/FreeHand 4.0, Adobe/Illustrator 5.5, Microsoft/Word 5.1a,; EDITORIAL EQUIPMENT: Hardware — APP/Mac/Lf/AP Leaf Picture Desk, Lf/Leafscan 35, Umax/Flatbed Scanner; Printers — APP/Mac LaserWriter 630, NewGen/1200B, ECR/VR 36 EDITORIAL SOFTWARE: Baseview. PRODUCTION EQUIPMENT: Hardware — Caere/OmniScan Pro; Cameras — C.

POTEAU

POTEAU DAILY NEWS

804 N Broadway St, Ste A, Poteau, Okla., 74953-3503, Le Flore; gen tel (918) 647-3188; adv tel (918) 647-3188; ed tel (918) 647-3188; gen fax (918) 647-8198; adv fax (918) 647-8198; ed fax (918) 647-8198; gen/nat adv e-mail publisher@poteaudailynews.com; disp adv e-mail nmckimmey.pdn@gmail.com; class adv e-mailclassifieds.pdn@gmail.com; ed e-mail editor@poteaudailynews.com; web site www.poteaudailynews.com
Group: Horizon Publications Inc.
Published: Tues, Wed, Thur, Fri, Sat
Weekday Frequency: m
Saturday Frequency: m
Circulation: 2,850; 3,100(sat)
Last Audit: Sworn/Estimate/Non-Audited December 12, 2017
Advertising Rate (weekday/saturday): Open inch rate $8.25 Weekday (M-F)
Advertising Rate (sunday): Open inch rate $9.75 Saturday only
News services: AP. **Established:** 1895
Own Printing Facility?: No
Commercial Printers?: No
Special Editions: Progress (Feb); Fact Book (Jul).
Special Weekly Sections: History (Tue); Agriculture (Wed); Education (Thur); Area Events (Fri); Celebrations (Sat)
Syndicated Publications: American Profile (Weekly).
General Manager/Circulation Director .... David McKimmey
Mechanical Available: Offset; Black and 3 ROP colors.
Areas Served: LeFlore County
Delivery Method: Mail, Newsstand, Carrier, RacksEquipment & Software: DISPLAY SOFTWARELayout Software — APP/Mac, APP/Mac SE30. EDITORIAL EQUIPMENT: Hardware — APP/Mac. PRODUCTION EQUIPMENT: Hardware — LE.

SAPULPA

SAPULPA DAILY HERALD

16 S Park St, Sapulpa, Okla., 74066-4220, Creek; gen tel (918) 224-5185; adv tel (918) 224-5185 ext. 103; ed tel (918) 224-5185; gen fax (918) 224-5196; adv fax (918) 224-5196; ed fax (918) 224-5196; gen/nat adv e-mail admanager@sapulpadailyherald.com; disp adv e-mail advertising1@sapulpadailyherald.com; class adv e-mailclassifieds@sapulpaheraldonline.com; ed e-mail editor@sapulpaheraldonline.com
Group: Community Newspaper Holdings, Inc.
Published: Mon, Tues, Wed, Thur, Fri, Sun
Weekday Frequency: e
Circulation: 4,501; 4,501(sun)
Last Audit: Sworn/Estimate/Non-Audited September 30, 2017
Advertising Rate (weekday/saturday): Open inch rate $10.00
Advertising Rate (sunday): Open inch rate $10.00
News services: AP. **Established:** 1914
Special Weekly Sections: Sports, Lifestyles (Daily); Best Food (Wed); Church (Fri); Business, TV (Sun)
Syndicated Publications: Relish (Monthly); TV Today (entertainment tab) (S); American Profile (Weekly).
Pub.......................................Darren D. Sumner
Prodn. Mgr. ....Teresa Cooper
Adv. Mgr....................................Chris Swafford
Cir. Mgr........................................Connie Jones
Ed. ....John Brock
Market Information: Split run; TMC.
Mechanical Available: Offset; Black and 3 ROP colors; insert accepted; page cutoffs - 22 3/4.
Mechanical Specifications: Type page 13 x 21 1/2; E - 6 cols, 2 1/14, 1/8 between; A - 6 cols, 2 1/14, 1/8 between; C - 8 cols, 1 1/2, 1/8 between.
Areas Served: Sapulpa and surrounding communities (OK)
Equipment & Software: PRESSROOM EQUIPMENT: Lines — 5-G/Community double width 1967; Folders — 1-G/Suburban.; MAILROOM EQUIPMENT: Counter Stackers — BG/Count-O-Veyor; Tying Machines — Marlow.; BUSINESS SOFTWARE: Vision Data CLASSIFIED EQUIPMENT: Hardware — APP/Mac.; EDITORIAL EQUIPMENT: Hardware — APP/Mac; Printers — APP/Mac Laser. PRODUCTION EQUIPMENT: Hardware — 2-APP/Mac LaserPrinter, Image Plus/12; Cameras — Uves/2024 MZ PRODUCTION SOFTWARE: QPS/QuarkXPress.

SEMINOLE

THE SEMINOLE PRODUCER

121 N Main St, Seminole, Okla., 74868-4627, Seminole; gen tel (405) 382-1100; adv tel (405) 382-1100; ed tel (405) 382-1100; gen fax (405) 382-1104; adv fax (405) 382-1104; ed fax (405) 382-1104; gen/nat adv e-mail ads@seminoleproducer.com; disp adv e-mail ads@seminoleproducer.com; class adv e-mailads@seminoleproducer.com; ed e-mail news@seminoleproducer.com; web site www.seminoleproducer.com; web site 2 www.seminoleoklahoma.com
Published: Tues, Wed, Thur, Fri, Sun
Weekday Frequency: m
Circulation: 5,600; 5,600(sun)
Last Audit: Sworn/Estimate/Non-Audited February 13, 2018
Newspaper Reps: Mike Gifford/General Manager
Advertising Rate (weekday/saturday): Open inch rate $6.30
Advertising Rate (sunday): Open inch rate $6.30
News services: CNS, NEA, Capitol Press Report. **Established:** 1927
Own Printing Facility?: Yes
Commercial Printers?: No
Special Weekly Sections: Best Foods (Wed)
Adv. Dir. ....Mike Gifford
Entertainment/Amusements Ed. .... Cheryl Phillips
Ed. / Pub. ....Stu Phillips
Teen-Age/Youth Ed.........................Cody Phillips
Prod. / Cir. Dir. ....John Lewis
Ken Childers
Market Information: TMC.
Mechanical Available: Offset; Black and 2 ROP colors; insert accepted; page cutoffs - 22 3/4.
Mechanical Specifications: Type page 13 x 21; E - 6 cols, 2 1/16, 1/8 between; A - 6 cols, 2 1/16, 1/8 between; C - 9 cols, 1 3/8, 1/16 between.
Areas Served: Seminole County (OK)
Delivery Method: Mail, Carrier, RacksEquipment & Software: PRESSROOM EQUIPMENT: Lines — 3-G/Community MAILROOM EQUIPMENT: Address Machine — RSK/Model II-LP V, Wm.; BUSINESS EQUIPMENT: 2-RAM/486, 1-HP/386 CLASSIFIED EQUIPMENT: Hardware — PC; Printers — HP/LaserWriter 4; CLASSIFIED SOFTWARE: ListMaster. DISPLAY EQUIPMENT: Hardware — PC; Printers — HP/LaserWriter 4; DISPLAY SOFTWAREAd Make-up Applications — Microsoft/Windows; Layout Software — PC 486-50. EDITORIAL EQUIPMENT: Hardware — PC; Printers — HP/IV EDITORIAL SOFTWARE: Microsoft/Windows. PRODUCTION EQUIPMENT: Hardware — APP/Mac NT; Cameras — 1-CL/24.

SHAWNEE

SHAWNEE NEWS-STAR

215 N Bell Ave, Shawnee, Okla., 74801-6913, Pottawatomie; gen tel (405) 273-4200; adv tel (405) 214-3941; ed tel (405) 214-3922; gen fax (405) 273-4207; adv fax (405) 273-4207; ed fax (405) 273-4207; gen/nat adv e-mail orvena.gregory@news-star.com;

disp adv e-mail maria.flanagan@news-star.com; class adv e-mailwanda.westerman@news-star.com; ed e-mail kimberly.morava@news-star.com; web site www.news-star.com
Group: New Media Investment Group
Published: Tues, Wed, Thur, Fri, Sat, Sun
Weekday Frequency: m
Saturday Frequency: m
Circulation: 7,175; 7,175(sat); 8,334(sun)
Last Audit: Sworn/Estimate/Non-Audited September 30, 2017
Advertising Rate (weekday/saturday): Open inch rate $10.00
Advertising Rate (sunday): Open inch rate $10.00
News services: AP. **Established:** 1894
Special Editions: School (Aug); Christmas (Dec); Bridal (Jan); Lawn and Garden (Mar); Gift Guide (Nov); Home Improvement (Sept).
Special Weekly Sections: Education (Tue); Best Food, Gardening (Wed); Pets (Thur); Weekend, Entertainment (Fri); Religion, Agriculture (Sat); TV, Business, Weddings, Health (Sun)
Syndicated Publications: Relish (Monthly); Color Comics (Other); USA WEEKEND Magazine (S).
Pub. .... Kent Bush
Multi-Med. Exec. .... Orvena Gregory
Adv. Sales Asst. .... Maria Flanagan
Class. Adv. Exec. .... Wanda Westerman
Asst. Cir. Mgr. .... Danielle Shoopman
CSR / Rec. .... Brittany Owen
Ed. .... Kim Morava
Mechanical Available: Offset; Black and 3 ROP colors; insert accepted; page cutoffs - 21 1/2.
Mechanical Specifications: Type page 11 x 21 1/2; E - 6 cols, 1 5/6, 1/8 between; A - 6 cols, 1 5/6, 1/8 between; C - 9 cols, 1/6 between.Equipment & Software: PRESSROOM EQUIPMENT: Lines — 7-G/U 1083; MAILROOM EQUIPMENT: Counter Stackers — 1-BG/Count-O-Veyor; Inserters & Stuffers — 1-MM/227; Tying Machines — 1-MLN/ML2EE; Address Machine — KAN/550, KAN-Quarter Folder.; BUSINESS EQUIPMENT: ATT/Unix PC BUSINESS SOFTWARE: APP/Mac Share CLASSIFIED EQUIPMENT: Hardware — APP/Mac, 5-APP/Mac G4; Printers — HP/5M; CLASSIFIED SOFTWARE: Baseview/Ad Manager Pro. DISPLAY EQUIPMENT: Printers — QMS/860 Plus, 2-Panther/RIP, HP/5000; DISPLAY SOFTWARELayout Software — APP/Mac G3/G4, APP/Mac 8500-180, APP/Mac Quadra 800. EDITORIAL EQUIPMENT: Hardware — APP/Mac, 6-APP/Mac G3, 6-APP/Mac 7300-180; Printers — APP/Mac LaserWriter 16-600, MON/1270 EDITORIAL SOFTWARE: Baseview. PRODUCTION EQUIPMENT: Hardware — APP/Mac LaserWriter, Caere/OmniPage Pro 2.1, Adobe/Photoshop, APP/Mac G4; Cameras — 1-R/500; Scanners — APP/Mac, Microtek/IIx, HP/9850A, HP/6100C PRODUCTION SOFTWARE: Quark.

STILLWATER

STILLWATER NEWS PRESS

211 W 9th Ave, Stillwater, Okla., 74074-4406, Payne; gen tel (405) 372-5000; gen fax (405) 372-3112; adv fax (405) 780-9993; ed fax (405) 372-3112; gen/nat adv e-mail advmgr@stwnewspress.com; disp adv e-mail advmgr@stwnewspress.com; class adv e-mailclassifieds@stwnewspress.com; ed e-mail editor@stwnewspress.com; web site www.stwnewspress.com - 130,000(views) 85,000(visitors)
Group: Community Newspaper Holdings, Inc.
Published: Tues, Wed, Thur, Fri, Sat, Sun
Weekday Frequency: m
Saturday Frequency: m
Circulation: 5,200; 5,200(sat); 5,800(sun)
Last Audit: Sworn/Estimate/Non-Audited September 30, 2017
Advertising Rate (weekday/saturday): Open inch rate $11.75 net
Advertising Rate (sunday): Open inch rate $12.75 net
Online Advertising Rate: $15
News services: Associated Press, CNHINS **Established:** 1900
Own Printing Facility?: No
Commercial Printers?: No
Special Editions: Medical Directory (Feb and Aug); Oklahoma State University Game Days (Fridays during Fall football season); Last Minute Gift Guide (Dec); Bridal (Jan); Payne County Fair (Jul); Progress (Jun); Apartment Guide (Sept. & Feb.); Graduation (May); Christmas Gift Guide (Nov); Dining Guide (Aug); Home Improvement (Sept, April).
Special Weekly Sections: Real Estate Weekly (Fri); Agriculture (S); TV Spotlight (Sun); Food (Wed).
Syndicated Publications: Parade (Fri.); Athlon Sports (monthly); Spry (Monthly); Comics (S).
Proprietary Publications: Stillwater Style community magazines
Digital Platform - Mobile: Apple, Android, Windows
Digital Platform - Tablet: Apple iOS, Android, Windows 7
Adv. Mgr. .... Jill Hunt
Pub. .... Dale Brendel
Dir. of Audience Dev. .... Joe Toth
Ed. .... Beau Simmons
Market Information: 16,000 circulation Wednesday TMC.
Mechanical Available: Offset; Black and 3 ROP colors; inserts accepted up to 11x11 inches
Mechanical Specifications: Type page 11 1/8 x 21 1/2; E - 6 cols, 1 3/4, 1/8 between; A - 6 cols, 3 5/8, between; C - 8 cols, between.
Areas Served: Payne County and parts of surrounding counties in Oklahoma
Delivery Method: Mail, Newsstand, Carrier, RacksEquipment & Software: BUSINESS SOFTWARE: Vision Data CLASSIFIED EQUIPMENT: Hardware — APP/Mac G4, APP/eMac; Printers — Okidata/Microline 320, APP/Mac LaserJet III; CLASSIFIED SOFTWARE: FSI. DISPLAY EQUIPMENT: Hardware — APP/iMac, 2-APP/Mac G4 400 mhz, 3-APP/Mac G4 466 mhz; Printers — HP/Color LaserJet 5M, APP/Mac LaserJet 8000DN, Pre Press/Panther Plus 46, ECR/Imagesetter; DISPLAY SOFTWAREAd Make-up Applications — Multi-Ad/Creator 4.02, Adobe/Photoshop 5.5, Adobe/Typesetter, QPS/QuarkXPres; EDITORIAL EQUIPMENT: Hardware — 7-APP/Power Mac, 4-APP/Mac Quadra, APP/Mac G4, 7-APP/eMac, 4-APP/iMac; Printers — HP/Color Laser 5M, HP/8000 DN, HP/Laser Jet 6MP, Pre Press/Panther Plus 46 Imagesetter EDITORIAL SOFTWARE: Media Span NewsEdit Pro/Quark CIRCULATION SOFTWARVision Data
Note: Bridal show each January

TAHLEQUAH

TAHLEQUAH DAILY PRESS

106 W 2nd St, Tahlequah, Okla., 74464-4724, Cherokee; gen tel 9184568833; adv tel (918) 456-8833; ed tel (918) 456-8833; gen fax (918) 456-2019; adv fax (918) 456-2019; ed fax (918) 456-2019; gen/nat adv e-mail s.elswick@muskogeephoenix.com; disp adv e-mail hruotolo@tahlequahdailypress.com; class adv e-mailhruotolo@tahlequahdailypress.com; ed e-mail kpoindexter@cnhi.com; web site www.tahlequahdailypress.com - 30,000(views)
Group: Community Newspaper Holdings, Inc.
Published: Tues, Wed, Thur, Fri, Sun
Weekday Frequency: m
Circulation: 3,100; 3,500(sun)
Last Audit: Sworn/Estimate/Non-Audited September 7, 2017
Newspaper Reps: no publisher at the moment
Advertising Rate (weekday/saturday): Open inch rate $12.50
Advertising Rate (sunday): $14.50
Online Advertising Rate: $12 - $30 (position dependent).
News services: AP. **Established:** 1844
Own Printing Facility?: No
Commercial Printers?: No
Special Editions: Tahlequah - Green Country Tourism (Jan.); Progress (Feb.); HealthWatch (Mar., June, Sept., Dec.); Football Preview (Aug.), Lakes & River (May, June, July, Aug., Sept., Dec.)
Special Weekly Sections: Arts & Entertainment (Fri.); Church (Wed); Business & Farm (Sun).
Syndicated Publications: Relish (Monthly); USA WEEKEND Magazine (S); American Profile (Weekly). 911 @Play (S)
Digital Platform - Mobile: Apple, Android
Digital Platform - Tablet: Apple iOS, Android
Exec. Ed. .... Kim Poindexter
Mult. Media Ed. .... Sheri Gourd
sports editor .... Byron Beers
courts & crime reporter .... Tes Jackson
news editor .... Sean Rowley
general assignment reporter .... Grant Crawford
Market Information: TMC. (Wednesdays - 16,600 circ.)
Mechanical Available: Offset; Black and 3 ROP colors; insert accepted; page cutoffs - 21 1/2.
Mechanical Specifications: Type page 13 1/4 x 21 1/2; E - 6 cols, 2 1/16, 1/8 between; A - 6 cols, 2 1/16, 1/8 between; C - 9 cols, 1 1/2, 1/8 between.
Areas Served: Tahlequah & Cherokee County (OK)
Delivery Method: Mail, Newsstand, RacksEquipment & Software: MAILROOM EQUIPMENT: Tying Machines — 1/Bu; Address Machine — 2-Am/1900.; CLASSIFIED EQUIPMENT: Hardware — 2-COM/Junior.; EDITORIAL EQUIPMENT: Hardware — 9-APP/Mac/2-COM/II, 2-COM/7200. PRODUCTION EQUIPMENT: Hardware — 1-Nu; Cameras — 1-K/Vertical 240.

TULSA

TULSA WORLD

315 S Boulder Ave, Tulsa, Okla., 74103-3401, Tulsa; gen tel (918) 583-2161; adv tel (918) 581-8510; ed tel (918) 581-8330; gen fax (918) 581-8353; adv fax (918) 583-3550; gen/nat adv e-mail advertising@tulsaworld.com; disp adv e-mail advertising@tulsaworld.com; class adv e-mailclassad@tulsaworld.com; ed e-mail letters@tulsaworld.com; web site www.tulsaworld.com 2,490,557(visitors)
Group: BH Media Group
Published: Mon, Tues, Wed, Thur, Fri, Sat, Sun
Weekday Frequency: m
Saturday Frequency: m
Circulation: 56,381; 59,631(sat); 75,040(sun)
Last Audit: AAM March 31, 2017
Advertising Rate (weekday/saturday): M-W $76.59; Th-Sat $94.13
Advertising Rate (sunday): $116.55
News services: AP, LAT-WP, MCT, GNS. **Established:** 1905
Own Printing Facility?: Yes
Commercial Printers?: Yes
Special Editions: Football Preview (Aug); Christmas Gift Guide (Dec).
Special Weekly Sections: Entertainment (Thu); World of Homes (Sat); Fashion (Thur); Best Food Day (Wed).
Syndicated Publications: USA WEEKEND Magazine (S).
Digital Platform - Mobile: Apple, Android, Windows, Blackberry
Digital Platform - Tablet: Apple iOS, Android, Windows 7, Kindle
Exec. Ed. .... Susan Ellerbach
Senior writer .... Wayne Greene
Mng. Ed. .... Mike Strain
Presentation editor .... Tim Chamberlin
City editor .... Paul Tyrrell
Sports editor .... Michael Peters
Chief designer .... James Royal
Chief photographer .... Tom Gilbert
Market Information: ADS; Split run;
Mechanical Available: Offset; Black and 3 ROP colors; insert accepted; page cutoffs - 21.
Mechanical Specifications: Type page 12 1/4 x 21; E - 6 cols, 1 15/16, 1/8 between; A - 6 cols, 1 15/16, 1/8 between; C - 10 cols, 1 1/8, 1/16 between.
Areas Served: 74103 - plus
Delivery Method: Mail, Carrier, RacksEquipment & Software: PRESSROOM EQUIPMENT: Lines — Wifag/OF 370 GTD double width 1998; Wifag/OF 370 GTD double width 2000; Folders — Wifag/Jaw Folder (one per line).; MAILROOM EQUIPMENT: Counter Stackers — 6-QWI/350, 2-HL/HT; Inserters & Stuffers — 1-HI/NP 630; Tying Machines — 5-MLN/MLN2, 7/Power Strap; Wrapping Singles — 4-/Power Strap 3/4; Control System — HI/Prima; Address Machine — 1-/BH.; CLASSIFIED EQUIPMENT: Hardware — 2-Tandem/CLX-RISC fileserver; Printers — Dataproducts, DEC, Tandem; CLASSIFIED SOFTWARE: SII. EDITORIAL EQUIPMENT: Hardware — 2-Tandem/CLX RISC-File Server; Printers — DEC, Tandem EDITORIAL SOFTWARE: SII. PRODUCTION EQUIPMENT: Hardware — 3-AU/3850; Scanners — Data/Oy-Plate Scanner PRODUCTION SOFTWARE: SII/ICP (Classified).

VINITA

THE VINITA DAILY JOURNAL

140 S Wilson St, Vinita, Okla., 74301-3730, Craig; gen tel (918) 256-6422; adv tel (918) 639-8921; ed tel (918) 256-6422; gen fax (918) 256-7100; adv fax (918) 256-7100; ed fax (918) 256-7100; gen/nat adv e-mail vdj@cableone.net; disp adv e-mail vdjproduction@cableone.net; class adv e-mailclassifieds@vinitanews.com; ed e-mail vdj@cableone.net; web site www.vdjonline.com
Published: Tues, Wed, Thur, Fri, Sat
Weekday Frequency: m
Saturday Frequency: m
Circulation: 4,331
Last Audit: Sworn/Estimate/Non-Audited September 30, 2017
Advertising Rate (weekday/saturday): Open inch rate $18.23
News services: AP, NEA. **Established:** 1907
Special Editions: Home Improvement (Apr); Rodeo Pioneer (Aug); Christmas (Dec); Business Profiles (Jul); Christmas (Nov); Almanac (Oct); Calf Fry (Sept).
Special Weekly Sections: Best Food Days (Wed)
Syndicated Publications: Vinita Viewer (Fri).
Pub. .... Phillip R. Reid
Mng. Ed. .... David Burgess
Adv. .... Michelle Milner
Market Information: Split run; TMC.
Mechanical Available: Offset; Black and 2 ROP colors; insert accepted - cards; page cutoffs - 22 3/4.
Mechanical Specifications: Type page 13 x 21 1/2; E - 6 cols, 2 1/16, 1/8 between; A - 6 cols, 2 1/16, 1/8 between; C - 8 cols, 1 1/2, 1/16 between.
Areas Served: Vinita, Craig County, Grand Lake & Northeast Oklahoma
Equipment & Software: PRESSROOM EQUIPMENT: Lines — 3-KP/News King; MAILROOM EQUIPMENT: Address Machine — 1/St.; BUSINESS EQUIPMENT: PC DISPLAY EQUIPMENT: Hardware — APP/Mac; DISPLAY SOFTWAREAd Make-up Applications — Aldus/PageMaker 3.0; Layout Software — APP/Mac. EDITORIAL EQUIPMENT: Hardware — APP/Mac. PRODUCTION EQUIPMENT: Hardware — 1-Nu; Cameras — 1-R/HOR12.

WEATHERFORD

WEATHERFORD DAILY NEWS

118 S Broadway St, Weatherford, Okla., 73096-4924, Custer; gen tel (580) 772-3301; adv tel (580) 772-3301; ed tel (580) 772-3301; gen fax (580) 772-7329; adv fax (580) 772-7329; ed fax (580) 772-7329; gen/nat adv e-mail wdn@wdnonline.com; disp adv e-mail wdn@wdnonline.com; class adv e-mailwdn@wdnonline.com; ed e-mail wdn@wdnonline.com; web site www.wdnonline.com
Published: Tues, Wed, Thur, Fri, Sat
Weekday Frequency: m
Saturday Frequency: m
Circulation: 4,464; 4,464(sat)
Last Audit: Sworn/Estimate/Non-Audited September 30, 2017
Advertising Rate (weekday/saturday): Open inch rate $18.04
Advertising Rate (sunday): Open inch rate $18.04
News services: AP, CNS, NYT, TMS. **Established:** 1898
Special Editions: Parade of Homes (Apr); Koupon Kraze (Aug); Christmas Greetings (Dec); Valentine's Promo (Feb); Health Quarterly (Jan); Summer Clearance (Jul); Father's Day Gift Guide (Jun); Spring Home Improvement Tab (Mar); Sidewalk Sales (May); Gift Guide (Nov);

Special Weekly Sections: Best Food (Wed/Sun); Church, Real Estate (Fri); Fashion, Entertainment, Health, Real Estate (Sun);
Syndicated Publications: TV Entertainment Tab (S).
Pub...Phillip R. Reid
Mktg. Rep..................................Robyn England
Class. Adv. Mgr. ....Sarah Ryan
Market Information: ADS; TMC.
Mechanical Available: Offset; Black and 3 ROP colors; insert accepted - any; page cutoffs - 18 1/2.
Mechanical Specifications: Type page 11 5/8 x 21 1/2; E - 6 cols, 1 7/8, 1/8 between; A - 6 cols, 1 7/8, 1/8 between; C - 6 cols, 1 7/8, 1/8 between.
Areas Served: Weatherford (OK)
Equipment & Software: PRESSROOM EQUIPMENT: Lines — 4-G/0-1047; MAILROOM EQUIPMENT: Address Machine — Bundle Tying Machines 1/Ca.; BUSINESS EQUIPMENT: 2-RSK, IBM CLASSIFIED EQUIPMENT: Hardware — IBM; Printers — HP/LaserPrinter; CLASSIFIED SOFTWARE: IBM, Microsoft/Word. DISPLAY SOFTWAREAd Make-up Applications — Aldus/PageMaker, Adobe/Typestyler, APP/Mac Scan; Layout Software — IBM. EDITORIAL EQUIPMENT: Hardware — IBM; Printers — HP/LaserWriter EDITORIAL SOFTWARE: IBM. PRODUCTION EQUIPMENT: Hardware — P/24SQ, IBM/PC; Cameras — 1-Nu/SST 1822x2024; Scanners — HP/Scan.

WOODWARD

WOODWARD NEWS

904 Oklahoma Ave, Woodward, Okla., 73801-4660, Woodward; gen tel (580) 256-2200; adv tel (580) 256-2200; ed tel (580) 256-2200; gen fax (580) 254-2159; adv fax (580) 254-2159; ed fax (580) 254-2159; gen/nat adv e-mail cthornton@woodwardnews.net; disp adv e-mail mray@woodwardnews.net; class adv e-mailclassified@woodwardnews.net; ed e-mail editor@woodwardnews.net; web site www.woodwardnews.net
Group: Community Newspaper Holdings, Inc.
Published: Tues, Wed, Thur, Fri, Sat, Sun
Weekday Frequency: m
Saturday Frequency: m
Circulation: 3,600; 3,600(sat); 3,700(sun)
Last Audit: Sworn/Estimate/Non-Audited September 30, 2017
Advertising Rate (weekday/saturday): Open inch rate $10.35 (Tue/Wed); $6.95 (Thur-Sat)
Advertising Rate (sunday): Open inch rate $6.95
News services: AP.
Own Printing Facility?: Yes
Commercial Printers?: No
Special Editions: Fall Sports (Aug); Spring Sports (Jan); Back-to-School (Jul); Progress (Mar).
Special Weekly Sections: Farm & Ranch (Tue); Best Food Day (Tue/Wed); Church, TV, Lap by Lap (Sat); Senior Scene (Sun)
Syndicated Publications: Relish (Monthly); American Profile (Weekly).
Digital Platform - Mobile: Apple
Digital Platform - Tablet: Apple iOS
Pub. / Ad Mgr. ....Sheila Gay
Ed. / Sports Ed. ....Johnny McMahan
Cir. ....Anita Roach
Adv........................................Carlinda Thornton
Market Information: TMC
Mechanical Available: Offset; Black and 3 ROP colors; insert accepted; page cutoffs - 16 1/2.
Mechanical Specifications: Type page 10 3/4 x 16 1/2; E - 5 cols, 2 1/16, 1/8 between; A - 5 cols, 2 1/16, 1/8 between; C - 5 cols, 2 1/16, 1/8 between.
Areas Served: Ellis, Harper, Dewey, Woodward & parts of Woods & Major Counties (OK)
Delivery Method: Mail, RacksEquipment & Software: CLASSIFIED EQUIPMENT: Hardware — APP/Mac; Printers — APP/Mac LaserWriter IIg; CLASSIFIED SOFTWARE: Baseview. DISPLAY EQUIPMENT: Hardware — APP/Mac; Printers — APP/Mac LaserWriter IIg; DISPLAY SOFTWAREAd Make-up Applications — QPS/QuarkXPress, Claris/MacWrite, Microsoft/Excel.; EDITORIAL EQUIPMENT: Hardware — APP/Mac; Printers — APP/Mac LaserWriter IIf EDITORIAL SOFTWARE: Baseview/NewsEdit, QPS/QuarkXPress. PRODUCTION EQUIPMENT: Hardware — P, Adobe/Photoshops.

OREGON

ALBANY

ALBANY DEMOCRAT-HERALD

600 Lyon St S, Albany, Ore., 97321-2919, Linn; gen tel (541) 926-2211; adv tel (541) 812-6073; ed tel (541) 812-6095; gen fax (541) 926-7209; adv fax (541) 926-5298; ed fax (541) 926-4799; gen/nat adv e-mail ads@dhonline.com; disp adv e-mail ads@dhonline.com; class adv e-mailads@dhonline.com; ed e-mail news@dhonline.com; web site www.democratherald.com - 1,300,000(views) 234,000(visitors)
Group: Lee Enterprises, Inc.
Published: Mon, Tues, Wed, Thur, Fri, Sat, Sun
Weekday Frequency: e
Saturday Frequency: m
Circulation: 9,516; 9,516(sat); 9,876(sun)
Last Audit: AAM December 31, 2016
Advertising Rate (weekday/saturday): Open inch rate $74.60
Advertising Rate (sunday): Open inch rate $74.60
Online Advertising Rate: Static Banner $11/ Interactive Video $21
News services: AP **Established:** 1865
Own Printing Facility?: Yes
Commercial Printers?: Yes
Special Weekly Sections: Business (Mon); People (Tue); Best Food, This Week, People (Wed); People, Young Voices (Thur); Religion, Entertainer, TV, Movies, Events, Arts, Dining (Fri); Home, Garden, Lifestyles (Sun);
Syndicated Publications: Relish (Monthly); Parade Magazine (S).
Digital Platform - Mobile: Apple, Android
Rgl. Pub..Rick Parrish
Pub./Ed. ....Mike McInally
Online Ed. ....Graham Kislingbury
Bus. Ed. ....Bennett Hall
Editorial Page Ed. ....Hasso Hering
News Ed...Kim Jackson
Sunday Ed. ....Steve Lundeberg
Photo Ed. ....Mark Ylen
Dir., Mgmt. Info Servs........................Bill Draper
Director of Audience....................Cody Castellano
Market Information: ADS; Split run; TMC.
Mechanical Available: Offset; Black and 3 ROP colors; insert accepted - free-standing inserts; page cutoffs - 22 3/4.
Mechanical Specifications: Type page 11 5/8 x 21; E - 6 cols, 1 4/5, between; A - 6 cols, 1 4/5, between; C - 9 cols, 1 1/5, between.
Areas Served: Albany & Linn County (OR)
Delivery Method: Mail, Newsstand, Carrier, RacksEquipment & Software: PRESSROOM EQUIPMENT: Lines — 6-G/Urbanite single width; Control System — 2; Registration System — Duarte/Pin Registration System. MAILROOM EQUIPMENT: Counter Stackers — 1/BG; Inserters & Stuffers — 2-KAN/480 6:1; Tying Machines — 1-/Strapex, 2-EAM-Mosca; Address Machine — 1-KAN/650, KR/label head.;

ASTORIA

THE DAILY ASTORIAN

949 Exchange St, Astoria, Ore., 97103-4605, Clatsop; gen tel (503) 325-3211; adv tel (503) 325-3211; ed tel (503) 325-3211; gen fax (503) 325-6573; adv fax (503) 325-6573; ed fax (503) 325-6573; gen/nat adv e-mail ads@dailyastorian.com; disp adv e-mail ads@dailyastorian.com; class adv e-mailclassifieds@dailyastorian.com; ed e-mail news@dailyastorian.com; web site www.dailyastorian.com - 330,000(views) 110,000(visitors); web site 2 www.discoverourcoast.com - 6,000(views) 2,500(visitors); web site 3 coastmarketplace.com - 50,000(views) 4,500(visitors); web site 4coast weekend.com - 44,000(views) 9,500(visitors)
Group: EO Media Group
Published: Mon, Tues, Wed, Thur, Fri
Weekday Frequency: e
Circulation: 5,479
Last Audit: AAM June 30, 2017
Advertising Rate (weekday/saturday): Open inch rate $16.43
Online Advertising Rate: Sponsor ad – $19.80 Leaderboard – $32
Cube – $32
Banner – $15
Newsletter Sponsor – $9.79
Anchorboacd – $10
Mobile Ad – $19.80
Sliding Billboard – $36.79
Homepage Takeover – Available on request
News services: AP, NYT. **Established:** 1873
Own Printing Facility?: Yes
Commercial Printers?: Yes
Special Editions: Bridal Planner (Feb); Our Coast magazine (Feb.); Good Health Directory (Mar); Spring Sports Tab (Mar); Crab, Seafood & Wine Festival (Apr.), Coastal Menu Guide (Jun); Scandinavian Festival (Jun); Car Care (Jun); Clatsop County Fair (July); At Home (July); Astoria Regatta (Aug); Who's Who in Clatsop Cty (Aug); Fall Sports Tab (Sept); Women In Business (Sept); Liberty Theater Presents (sept); Astor Street Opry (Oct); Home For the Holidays (Nov); Winter Sports Tab (Nov) & Property Lines (Jan, Mar, May, July, Sept., & Nov)
Special Weekly Sections: Marketplace (Tue); Observer, TV (Wed); Local Business, Entertainment (Thur); Religion, Community, Real Estate (Fri)
Syndicated Publications: Coast Weekend (Thur). Our Coast (February)
Digital Platform - Mobile: Apple
Digital Platform - Tablet: Apple iOS
Adv. Mgr...Betty Smith
Digital Development Director.......Cridalyn Lyster
Prodn. Mgr., Systems......................John Bruijin
Pressroom Supervisor..................Jim Stanovich
Managing Editor..........................Laura Sellers
Circulation Manager...............Heather Ramsdell
Corporate Systems Manager...............Carl Earl
Debby Bloom
Publisher and Editor..........................David Pero
Market Information: TMC.
Mechanical Available: Web Offset; Black and 3 ROP colors; insert accepted; page cutoffs - 22 3/4.
Mechanical Specifications: Type page 10.5 x 21.5; E - 6 cols, 2, 1/6 between; A - 6 cols, 2, 1/6 between; C - 8 cols, 1 1/2, 1/8 between.
Areas Served: 97102, 97103, 97110, 98614, 97016, 97138, 97121, 98624, 98631, 97130, 98637, 98638, 97131, 98640, 98641, 97138, 98644, 97145, 97146, 97016, 97147
Delivery Method: Mail, Newsstand, Carrier, RacksEquipment & Software: PRESSROOM EQUIPMENT: Lines — 2 Tensor 4-hgihs and 3 Community units (installed 2010); Folders — Goss SSC; BUSINESS EQUIPMENT: Vision Data BUSINESS SOFTWARE: Excel 5 CLASSIFIED EQUIPMENT: Hardware — APP/Mac; CLASSIFIED SOFTWARE: QPS/QuarkXPress, Baseview, Multi-Ad. DISPLAY EQUIPMENT: Hardware — APP/Mac; Printers — APP/Mac LaserWriter NTX, APP/Mac LaserWriter IIg, APP/Mac LaserWriter Pro 630; DISPLAY SOFTWAREAd Make-up Applications — Multi-Ad/Creator.; EDITORIAL EQUIPMENT: Hardware — APP/Mac; Printers — APP/Mac LaserWriter NTX, APP/Mac LaserWriter IIg, APP/Mac LaserWriter Pro 630, Au/APS 6-84 Imagesetter EDITORIAL SOFTWARE: NewsCycle Solutions, Photoshop, InCopy, InDesign PRODUCTION EQUIPMENT: Hardware — Au/APS-6-84-ACS; Cameras — K/V-241; Scanners — LaCie/Silver Scan II, Nikon/LS52000 PRODUCTION SOFTWARE: QPS/QuarkXPress 3.3.

BEND

THE BULLETIN

1777 SW Chandler Ave, Bend, Ore., 97702-3200, Deschutes; gen tel (541) 382-1811; adv tel (541) 385-5809; ed tel (541) 383-0367; gen fax (541) 385-5802; adv fax (541) 385-5802; ed fax (541) 385-5804; gen/nat adv e-mail addrop@bendbulletin.com; disp adv e-mail dderose@bendbulletin.com; class adv e-maildderose@bendbulletin.com; ed e-mail elukens@bendbulletin.com; web site www.bendbulletin.com
Group: Western Communications, Inc.
Published: Mon, Tues, Wed, Thur, Fri, Sat, Sun
Weekday Frequency: m
Saturday Frequency: m
Circulation: 25,193; 25,163(sat); 25,729(sun)
Last Audit: AAM December 31, 2015
Advertising Rate (weekday/saturday): Open inch rate $84.50
Advertising Rate (sunday): Open inch rate $93.00
News services: AP, LAT-WP, MCT, NYT. **Established:** 1903
Own Printing Facility?: Yes
Commercial Printers?: Yes
Special Editions: PULSE Health Magazine (4x annually); Public School Directory (Aug); Sisters Magazine (Every other month); Sportsman's Show Guide (Feb); Baby Book (Jan); Deschutes County Fair (Jul); Graduation (Jun); Tee to Green: Golf Guide (May); Tour of Homes (July) PRCA Rodeo Guide (Nov); Fall Home Show Guide (Oct); Central Ore. U Magazine: Women's Mag. 4x annually). New Home Living (4x annually) Picture Your Home: Monthly Real Estate Magazine. Bid N Buy Advertiser Auctions 2x annually. Ageless (Senior Magazine) 4x annually.
Special Weekly Sections: GO! Magazine, Family (Fri); Green, Community, Life, Comics (Mon); At Home, Best Food Day, Comics (Tue); Outdoors (Wed); Health, Fitness (Thur); Entertainment, TV (Sat); Weddings, Engagements, Travel, Business (Sun); Community, Life (Daily)
Syndicated Publications: U Magazine (Every other month); Picture Your Home (Monthly); Pulse (Quarterly); Parade (S).
Digital Platform - Mobile: Apple, Android, Windows
Digital Platform - Tablet: Apple iOS, Kindle
Publisher...John Costa
Associate editor.............................Denise Costa
Photo Ed. ....Dean Guernsey
Sports Ed. ....Bill Bigelow
IT Director..................................Steve Hoffmann
Prodn. Supvr. ....Alan Nelson
Editor..Erik Lukens
advertising director.........................dena derose
circulation director...............................mike hryko
Market Information: TMC.
Mechanical Available: Offset; Black and 3 ROP colors; insert accepted; page cutoffs - 21 1/2.
Mechanical Specifications: Type page: Broadsheet 10.71"w x 20.25"h; Editorial and Advertising: 6 columns are 1.65"w (with .17" gutter); Classified 9 columns are 1.12"w (with .08" gutter).
Areas Served: 20
Delivery Method: Mail, Newsstand, Carrier, RacksEquipment & Software: PRESSROOM EQUIPMENT: Lines — 1-KBA Comet 3 1/2 Tower (14 printing couples); Press Drive — 2-KBA/Shaftless; Folders — KBA/64; Reels & Stands — 5-AMAL/AR60; Control System — KBA/Ergotronic; Registration System — KBA/Ergotronic. MAILROOM EQUIPMENT: Counter Stackers — 1-MM/388, 1-BG/105, 1/MM, 2-QWI/400, 1-Gammerler/KL 50 7/1; Inserters & Stuffers — 16-MM/375, 12-MM/375, 4-MM/227; Tying Machines — 1-/MLN, 1-Dynaric/NPI, 1-Dynaric/NPI; BUSINESS EQUIPMENT: PCs BUSINESS SOFTWARE: DTI 5.5 CLASSIFIED EQUIPMENT: Hardware — PCs; Printers — HP, Canon; CLASSIFIED SOFTWARE: DTI 5.5 DISPLAY EQUIPMENT: Hardware — Mac G5; Printers — HP, Canon; DISPLAY SOFTWAREAd Make-up Applications — Adobe/InDesign, Adobe/Illustrator, Adobe/Photoshop; Layout Software — DTI 6.5 EDITORIAL EQUIPMENT: Hardware — PCs; Printers — Canon, HP EDITORIAL SOFTWARE: DTI 6.5 PRODUCTION EQUIPMENT: Hardware — Kodak EVO PRODUCTION SOFTWARE: Adobe/InDesign.

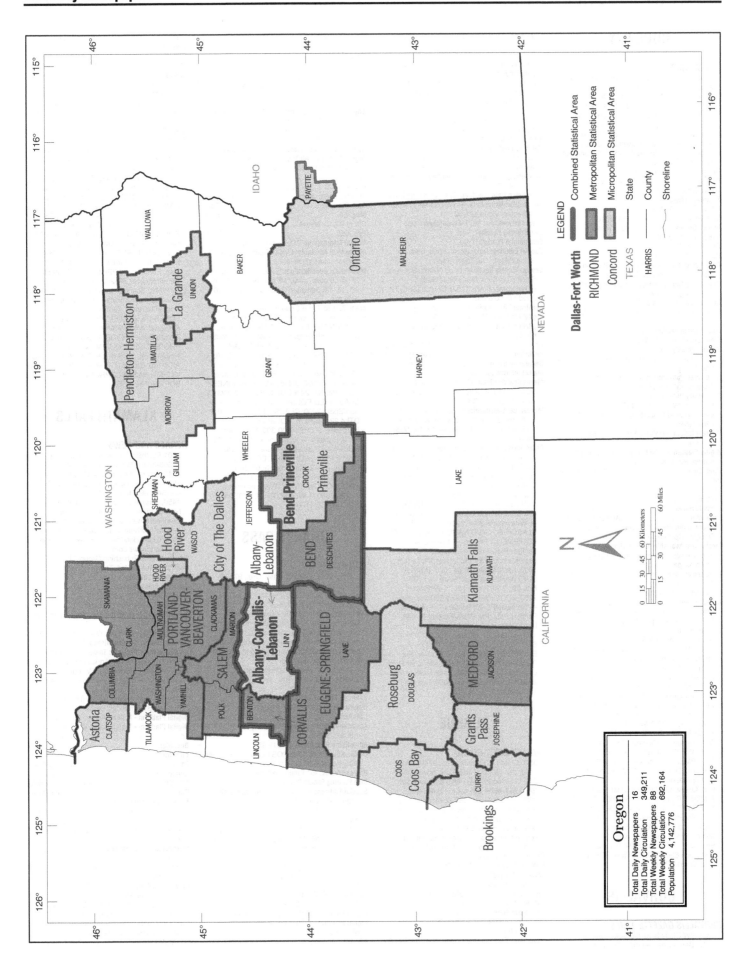

LEGEND

Dallas-Fort Worth — Combined Statistical Area
RICHMOND — Metropolitan Statistical Area
Concord — Micropolitan Statistical Area

TEXAS — State
HARRIS — County
— Shoreline

0 15 30 45 60 Kilometers
0 15 30 45 60 Miles

Oregon

Total Daily Newspapers	16
Total Daily Circulation	349,211
Total Weekly Newspapers	88
Total Weekly Circulation	692,164
Population	4,142,776

COOS BAY

THE WORLD

350 Commercial Ave, Coos Bay, Ore., 97420-2269, Coos; gen tel (541) 269-1222; adv tel (541) 269-1222; ed tel (541) 269-1222; gen fax (541) 267-0294; adv fax (541) 267-0294; ed fax (541) 269-5071; gen/nat adv e-mail chris.rush@theworldlink.com; disp adv e-mail dieter.kuhn@theworldlink.com; class adv e-mailmike.hrycko@theworldlink.com; ed e-mail larry.campbell@theworldlink.com; web site theworldlink.com

Group: Lee Enterprises, Inc.
Published: Mon, Tues, Wed, Thur, Sat
Weekday Frequency: e
Saturday Frequency: m
Circulation: 5,910; 6,202(sat)
Last Audit: AAM December 31, 2016
Branch Offices: Bandon Western World
1185 Baltimore SE
PO Box 248
Bandon, OR 97411
Advertising Rate (weekday/saturday): Open inch rate $21.49 weekday/$24.56 Sat.
Advertising Rate (sunday): No Sunday publication - Saturday is weekend
Online Advertising Rate: $15 CPM
News services: Associated Press **Established:** 1878
Own Printing Facility?: Yes
Commercial Printers?: Yes
Special Weekly Sections: Auto (Fri); Outdoor (Sat); Best Food Day (Tues); Gardening (Wed).
Syndicated Publications: Color Comics (Sat); American Profile (Sat).
Proprietary Publications: The World (Coos Bay); The World Link (EMC); Bandon Western World (Bandon); The Umpqua Post (Reedsport)
Digital Platform - Mobile: Apple, Android, Windows
Digital Platform - Tablet: Apple iOS, Android, Kindle, Nook, Kindle Fire
Prod. Supv. ....Dan Gordon
Pub. ....Chris Rush
Cir. Dir. ....Mike Hrycko
Exec. Ed. ....Larry Campbell
Press Foreman ....Dan Gordon
Prod. Mgr. ....Andris Jaunzems
Market Information: Coos County & western Douglas Co. Oregon
Mechanical Available: Offset; Black and 3 ROP colors; insert accepted - flyers, newspouch, samples; page cutoffs - 22 3/4.
Mechanical Specifications: 6 cols. Column width 1.556 inches.
Page depth 21.5 inches
Areas Served: Coos Bay, North Bend, Charleston, Coquille, Myrtle Point, Powers, Bandon & Reedstport (OR)
Delivery Method: Mail, Newsstand, Carrier, RacksEquipment & Software: PRESSROOM EQUIPMENT: Lines — 8-Goss/Community 1974, 1-G/Community 1994, 2-G/Community 2001; MAILROOM EQUIPMENT: Counter Stackers — MM; Inserters & Stuffers — 1/MM, 1-MM/EM 10, MM; Tying Machines — 2-/MLN; Wrapping Singles — Monarch/Bottom Wrap; Address Machine — 2-/Ch; BUSINESS EQUIPMENT: Suntype/Classified System BUSINESS SOFTWARE: Microsoft/Office XP CLASSIFIED EQUIPMENT: Hardware — Dell; Printers — Okidata/393; CLASSIFIED SOFTWARE: Synaptic, Suntype. DISPLAY EQUIPMENT: Printers — QMS/2060, AU/3850; DISPLAY SOFTWAREAd Make-up Applications — Multi-Ad/Creator 6.; EDITORIAL EQUIPMENT: Hardware — AU/3850; Printers — QMS/2060 EDITORIAL SOFTWARE: Baseview. PRODUCTION EQUIPMENT: Hardware — HP, Adobe/Photoshop 7, Mac/W/AP Server, Flatbed 35mm Film Scanner; Cameras — K; Scanners — Trecsa/TS-2470, Epson/Perfection 636 PRODUCTION SOFTWARE: QPS/QuarkXPress.

CORVALLIS

CORVALLIS GAZETTE-TIMES

1835 NW Circle Blvd, Corvallis, Ore., 97330-1310, Benton; gen tel (541) 753-2641; adv tel (541) 812-6073; ed tel (541) 753-2641; gen fax (541) 758-9505; adv fax (541) 758-9570; ed fax (541) 758-9505; gen/nat adv e-mail cyndi.sprinkel-hart@lee.net; disp adv e-mail cyndi.sprinkel-hart@lee.net; class adv e-mailcyndi.sprinkel-hart@lee.net; ed e-mail mike.mcinally@lee.net; web site www.gazettetimes.com
- 1,250,000(views) 182,655(visitors)

Group: Lee Enterprises, Inc.
Published: Mon, Tues, Wed, Thur, Fri, Sat, Sun
Weekday Frequency: m
Saturday Frequency: m
Circulation: 8,027; 7,583(sat); 7,744(sun)
Last Audit: AAM December 31, 2016
Advertising Rate (weekday/saturday): Open inch rate $74.60
Advertising Rate (sunday): Open inch rate $74.60
Online Advertising Rate: Static Banner $11.00; Interactive Video $21.00
News services: AP, MCT. **Established:** 1862
Own Printing Facility?: Yes
Commercial Printers?: Yes
Special Editions: Baby Book (April); Summer Guide (May); Our Town (Sept).
Special Weekly Sections: Food (Wed); Business, Stock (Tue-Sun); Best Food (Wed); Entertainment, Arts (Thu); Church (Sat); TV (Wed); People (Sat)
Syndicated Publications: Relish (Monthly);
Digital Platform - Mobile: Apple, Android
Digital Platform - Tablet: Apple iOS, Android, Kindle
Ed. ....Mike McInally
Publisher ....Jeff Precourt
General manager ....Doug Byers
Market Information: TMC.
Mechanical Available: Offset; Black and 3 ROP colors; insert accepted - standing card stock; page cutoffs - 22 3/4.
Mechanical Specifications: Type page 13 x 21; E - 6 cols, 2 1/16, 1/8 between; A - 6 cols, 2 1/16, 1/8 between; C - 9 cols, 1 5/16, 1/16 between.
Areas Served: Corvallis & Benton County (OR)
Equipment & Software: PRESSROOM EQUIPMENT: Lines — 5-G/Urbanite 1970; Control System — 2-Fin/Console.; MAILROOM EQUIPMENT: Address Machine — Bundle Tying Machines 2-/MLN.; BUSINESS EQUIPMENT: IBM/AS-400 CLASSIFIED EQUIPMENT: Hardware — Gateway/P5-90; Printers — HP/5P; CLASSIFIED SOFTWARE: CText. DISPLAY EQUIPMENT: Printers — Pre Press/Panther Plus, Pre Press/Panther Pro 46, LaserMaster/Unity 1800, LaserMaster/Unity 1200, LaserMaster/Unity 1000; DISPLAY SOFTWARELayout Software — 1-APP/Mac IIfx, 3-APP/Mac IIci, 10-APP/Mac 7200. EDITORIAL EQUIPMENT: Hardware — Gateway/P5-90; Printers — Pre Press/Panther Plus, Pre Press/Panther Pro 46, LaserMaster/Unity 1800, LaserMaster/Unity 1200, LaserMaster/Unity 1000 EDITORIAL SOFTWARE: CText. PRODUCTION EQUIPMENT: Hardware — 3-Laser, Pre Press/Panther Plus, Pre Press/Panther Pro, LaserMaster/Unity 1800, LaserMaster/Unity 1200, LaserMaster/Unity 1000; Cameras — 1-C/Spartan II, 1-Nu/2024.

EUGENE

THE REGISTER-GUARD

3500 Chad Dr, Eugene, Ore., 97408-7426, Lane; gen tel (541) 485-1234; adv tel (541) 342-1212; ed tel (541) 485-1234; gen fax (541) 984-4699; adv fax (541) 687-6668 (class.); ed fax (541) 687-6674; gen/nat adv e-mail kelly.grant@registerguard.com; disp adv e-mail bob.saltz@registerguard.com; class adv e-mailbob.saltz@registerguard.com; ed e-mail dave.baker@registerguard.com; web site www.registerguard.com

Group: GateHouse Media, Inc.
Published: Mon, Tues, Wed, Thur, Fri, Sat, Sun
Weekday Frequency: m
Saturday Frequency: m
Circulation: 46,247; 46,752(sat); 48,402(sun)
Last Audit: AAM March 31, 2017
Advertising Rate (weekday/saturday): Open inch rate $39.40 (Mon-Tue); $46.36 (Wed-Thur); $49.84 (Fri)
Advertising Rate (sunday): Open inch rate $49.84
News services: AP, NYT, LAT-WP, TMS. **Established:** 1867
Special Editions: College Football (Aug); Cycle Life (Jun); Fishing (Mar); Discovery Magazine (May); Home & Garden (Monthly); Holiday Gift Guide (Nov); Tastings (Quarterly); The Wedding Guide (Semi-yearly); Golf (Summer).
Special Weekly Sections: Health, Fitness (Mon); Outdoors (Tue); Food (Wed); Arts (Thur); Entertainment (Fri); Real Estate (Sat); Books, Travel, Wedding (Sun)
Syndicated Publications: blue chip (business)
Digital Platform - Mobile: Apple, Android
Digital Platform - Tablet: Apple iOS, Android
Mktg. Dir. ....Sally Wickes
Pub. Rel. Dir. ....Bridget Baker
Creative Servs. Mgr. ....Dan Villani
Circ. Dir. ....Mark Ogle
Mng. Ed. ....Dave Baker
Dir. of Dig. Solutions ....Tyler Mack
Pub./CEO ....Logan Molen
Market Information: ADS; Split run; TMC.
Mechanical Available: Offset; Black and 3 ROP colors; insert accepted; page cutoffs - 22.
Mechanical Specifications: Type page 11 5/8 x 21; E - 6 cols, 1 5/6, 1/8 between; A - 6 cols, 2 1/16, 1/8 between; C - 9 cols, 1 1/4, 1/16 between.
Areas Served: Lane County (OR)
Equipment & Software: PRESSROOM EQUIPMENT: Lines — 10-Mitsubishi/Lithopia double width; Folders — 1-Mitsubishi/Double 3:2; Reels & Stands — 8; MAILROOM EQUIPMENT: Counter Stackers — 5/QWI; Inserters & Stuffers — 3-/AM Graphics/NP 630; Tying Machines — 5-/Dynaric; Control System — AM/Graphics/AMCS.; BUSINESS EQUIPMENT: 2-DEC/4000-300, 1-DEC/3100 CLASSIFIED EQUIPMENT: Hardware — Sun/Sparc 3000; CLASSIFIED SOFTWARE: DTI 4.23. DISPLAY EQUIPMENT: Hardware — DEC/4000-300, Sun/Sparc 3000; Printers — X/Docuprint 75; DISPLAY SOFTWARELayout Software — DTI/Plan Builder (5.01). EDITORIAL EQUIPMENT: Hardware — 2-Sun/Sparc 3000, APP/Mac EDITORIAL SOFTWARE: DTI 4.23. PRODUCTION EQUIPMENT: Hardware — 2-III/3850, 1-WL/38G PRODUCTION SOFTWARE: DTI 4.2.

GRANTS PASS

DAILY COURIER

409 SE 7th St, Grants Pass, Ore., 97526-3003, Josephine; gen tel (541) 474-3700; adv tel (541) 474-3807; ed tel (541) 474-3823; gen fax (541) 474-3814; ed fax (541) 474-3824; gen/nat adv e-mail display@thedailycourier.com; disp adv e-mail display@thedailycourier.com; class adv e-mailclassified@thedailycourier.com; ed e-mail news@thedailycourier.com; web site www.thedailycourier.com
- 1,000,000(views) 80,000(visitors)

Published: Tues, Wed, Thur, Fri, Sun
Weekday Frequency: e
Saturday Frequency: e
Circulation: 10,912; 11,952(sun)
Last Audit: AAM December 31, 2016
Advertising Rate (weekday/saturday): Open inch rate $11.95
Advertising Rate (sunday): $12.95
Online Advertising Rate: ROS Leaderboard $199/ROS Box $159/ROS 1/2 Box $89
News services: AP. **Established:** 1885
Own Printing Facility?: Yes
Special Editions: A-Z in Josephine (Jan.); All About Pets (Feb.); Business Pulse (Feb.); Home & Garden (March-July); The Good Life (March); Health & Wellness (April, July, Oct.); Wheels (June, Oct.) Back to the 50s (July); Home & Family (Aug.-Sept.); Back to School (Aug.); Beer, Wine & Dine (Sept.); Home for the Holidays (Nov. - Dec.); Josephine County Fair Program (Aug); Holiday Gift Guide (Dec); Prime Time (Sept.); Charitable Giving Guide (Dec.)
Special Weekly Sections: Churches (Fri); Color Gardening (Sun); Best Food Day (Tues)
Digital Platform - Mobile: Apple, Android
Digital Platform - Tablet: Apple iOS, Android, Windows 7, Kindle
Adv. Dir. ....Debbie Thomas
Editor ....Scott Stoddard
Purchasing Agent ....Bill Parker
Circ. Mgr. ....Eileen Widdison
Market Information: ADS; TMC; Zoned editions.
Mechanical Available: Offset; Black and 3 ROP colors; insert accepted; page cutoffs - 22 3/4.
Mechanical Specifications: Type page 13 x 21 1/2; E - 6 cols, 2 1/16, 1/8 between; A - 6 cols, 2 1/16, 1/8 between; C - 6 cols, 2 1/16, 1/8 between.
Areas Served: Josephine County
Delivery Method: Mail, Newsstand, Carrier, RacksEquipment & Software: PRESSROOM EQUIPMENT: Lines — 5-G/Urbanite 1240; 6-G/Community; Folders — 2, 1-G/Quarter.; MAILROOM EQUIPMENT: Counter Stackers — 2-BG/Count-O-Veyor 108; Inserters & Stuffers — 2-MM/227E; Tying Machines — 2-MLN/Strapper, 2-Bu/Tyer; Address Machine — 3-Wm/Dick Gum labeler.; BUSINESS EQUIPMENT: IBM/RISC/6000 BUSINESS SOFTWARE: CJ CLASSIFIED EQUIPMENT: Hardware — 6-APP/Mac, IBM/RS6000; CLASSIFIED SOFTWARE: DTI. DISPLAY EQUIPMENT: Hardware — 16-APP/Mac; Printers — APP/Mac LaserWriter II, Dataproducts/LZR-2600; Other Hardware — APP/Mac Scanner. DISPLAY SOFTWAREAd Make-up Applications — Multi-Ad/Creator, Adobe/Illustrator, QPS/QuarkXPress; EDITORIAL EQUIPMENT: Hardware - 27-AT/Series 4/6-APP/Mac, 1-Lf/AP Leaf Picture Desk EDITORIAL SOFTWARE: AT. PRODUCTION EQUIPMENT: Hardware — Nat/24, 2-AU/APS-6-108, 6-APP/Mac, 2-AU/APS-100; Cameras — R, AG/6100; Scanners — 2-Nikon/LS-3500 PRODUCTION SOFTWARE: QPS.

KLAMATH FALLS

HERALD AND NEWS

2701 Foothills Blvd, Klamath Falls, Ore., 97603-3785, Klamath; gen tel (541) 885-4410; adv tel (541) 885-4410; ed tel (541) 885-4410; gen fax (541) 885-4456; adv fax (541) 883-4007; ed fax (541) 885-4456; gen/nat adv e-mail bkenfield@heraldandnews.com; disp adv e-mail bkenfield@heraldandnews.com; class adv e-mailsfry@heraldandnews.com; ed e-mail news@heraldandnews.com; web site www.heraldandnews.com

Group: Adams Publishing Group, LLC
Published: Tues, Wed, Thur, Fri, Sat, Sun
Weekday Frequency: m
Saturday Frequency: m
Circulation: 9,746; 9,463(sun)
Last Audit: AAM March 31, 2017
Advertising Rate (weekday/saturday): Open inch rate $23.84
Advertising Rate (sunday): Open inch rate $25.01
News services: AP. **Established:** 1906
Special Weekly Sections: Taste (Tue); Home, Garden, Kids (Wed); Agriculture, Diversions, Limelighter (Thur); Faith, TV (Fri); Connections (Sat); Living Well, Business, Focus (Sun); Sports (Daily)
Syndicated Publications: Relish (Monthly); Parade (S); American Profile (Weekly).
Digital Platform - Mobile: Apple, Android
Digital Platform - Tablet: Apple iOS, Android
Ed. ....Gerro O'Brien
Bus. Mgr. ....Jeanine Day
Circ. Dir. ....Dusty Metsker
Editor ....Gerry O'Brien
Opinion Ed. ....Pat Bushey
Adv. Dir. ....Benjamin Kenfield
Pres./Pub. ....Mark Dobie
Market Information: TMC.
Mechanical Available: Offset; Black and 3 ROP colors; insert accepted - envelopes, cards, sacks, self-adhesive notes; page cutoffs - 22 3/4.
Mechanical Specifications: Type page 12 3/8 x 21 1/2; E - 6 cols, 1 5/6, 1/6 between; A - 6 cols, 1 5/6, 1/6 between; C - 9 cols, 1 1/6, 1/8 between.
Areas Served: Klamath Falls (OR)
Delivery Method: Mail, RacksEquipment & Software: PRESSROOM EQUIPMENT: Lines — 7-G/U 650; MAILROOM EQUIPMENT: Counter Stackers — 1-BG/Count-O-Veyor; Inserters & Stuffers — 2-MM/Stitcher-Trimmer; Tying Machines

— MLN; Wrapping Singles — 1-Typak/#40.; CLASSIFIED EQUIPMENT: Hardware — APP/Mac; CLASSIFIED SOFTWARE: Baseview/Ad Manager Pro 2.0.6. DISPLAY EQUIPMENT: Hardware — APP/Mac; DISPLAY SOFTWARELayout Software — QPS/QuarkXPress, MEI/ALS. EDITORIAL EQUIPMENT: Hardware — APP/Mac; Printers — 2-AG, COM/Accuset EDITORIAL SOFTWARE: QPS/QuarkXPress, Adobe/Photoshop, Baseview/NewsEdit. PRODUCTION EQUIPMENT: Hardware — 1-Nu/Flip Top; Cameras — 1-MG/Photomaster; Scanners — 4-HP/ScanJet Plus, 2-Nikon.

MEDFORD

MAIL TRIBUNE
P.O. Box 1108, Medford, Ore., 97501, Jackson; gen tel (541) 776-4426; adv tel (541) 776-4422; ed tel (541) 776-4477; gen fax (541) 776-4369; adv fax (541) 776-4369; ed fax (541) 776-4376; gen/nat adv e-mail nsmith@mailtribune.com; disp adv e-mail nsmith@mailtribune.com; class adv e-mailclass@mailtribune.com; ed e-mail news@mailtribune.com; web site www.mailtribune.com
Group: New Media Investment Group
Published: Mon, Tues, Wed, Thur, Fri, Sat, Sun
Weekday Frequency: m
Saturday Frequency: m
Circulation: 14,572; 14,523(sat); 17,154(sun)
Last Audit: AAM December 31, 2016
Advertising Rate (weekday/saturday): Open inch rate $52.66 (Mon-Thur/Sat); $57.42 (Fri)
Advertising Rate (sunday): Open inch rate $57.42
News services: AP, DJ, LAT-WP. **Established:** 1906
Special Editions: Real Estate Review (Apr); Football (Aug); Classroom Tribune (Dec); Tax & Financial Planning (Jan); Regional Recreation Guide (Jul); Our Valley (Mar); Pets (May); Ashland Festival of Lights (Nov); Fall Real Estate (Oct); Hunting (Sept).
Special Weekly Sections: Healthy (Tue); Best Food (Wed); Outdoors (Thur); TV, Religion, Out There (Fri); Home, Religion (Sat); Business, Music, Arts, Local, Seniors, Comics (Sun)
Syndicated Publications: Tempo (Fri); Relish (Monthly); Parade (S); American Profile (Weekly).
Pub. ....James Grady Singletary
Adv. Mgr., Classified/Phone Sales .. Angela Fraley
Circ. Dir. ....John Mahalyo
Ed. ....Robert Hunter
Bus. Ed. ....Greg Stiles
Columnist ....Paul Fattig
Editorial Page Ed. ....Gary Nelson
Features Ed. ....Cathy Noah
Food/Garden Ed. ....Sarah Lemon
Librarian ....Pam Sieg
Music Ed. ....Bill Varble
News Ed. ....Rob Galvin
Online Ed. ....Julie Worth
Outdoors Ed. ....Mark Freeman
Photo Ed. ....Bob Pennell
Radio/Television Ed. ....Richard Moeschel
Sports Ed. ....Tim Trower
Nicholas Morgan
Adv. Dir. ....Dena DeRose
Market Information: TMC.
Mechanical Available: Offset; Black and 3 ROP colors; insert accepted - cards; page cutoffs - 22 3/4.
Mechanical Specifications: Type page 13 x 21 1/2; E - 6 cols, 2 1/16, 1/8 between; A - 6 cols, 2 1/16, 1/8 between; C - 9 cols, 1 3/8, 1/16 between.
Areas Served: Southern Oregon
Equipment & Software: PRESSROOM EQUIPMENT: Lines — 6-G/Metroliner double width (two half decks) 1995; Folders — 2-G/3:2; Pasters —6-G/Reel-Tension PasterReels & Stands — 6-G/Triple Reels & Stands.; MAILROOM EQUIPMENT: Counter Stackers — 2-HL/Monitor, 1-QWI/300, 1-QWI/351; Inserters & Stuffers — GMA/SLS 1000 16 pocket; Tying Machines — 2/MLN, 1-/Power Strap/PSN-6, 1-/Power Strap/PSN-6E; Wrapping Singles — 2-QWI/30; Address Machine — KR; BUSINESS EQUIPMENT: IBM/AS-400, DEC/VAX-4300 CLASSIFIED

EQUIPMENT: Hardware — IBM/PS2, DEC/VAX 4000-200, DEC/VAX 4000-300; 12-IBM/Sys 70; Printers — DEC/LA 210, DEC/LA 75; CLASSIFIED SOFTWARE: Cybergraphics 7.5. DISPLAY EQUIPMENT: Hardware — 6-IBM/PC, 3-APP/Power Mac; Printers — 2-HP/LaserJet 4MV, 1-HP/Color LaserJet; Other Hardware — 2-ECR/Knockout 4550 L Scriptsetter DISPLAY SOFTWAREAd Make-up Applications — QPS/QuarkXPress 3.32, Adobe/Illustrator 7.0, Adobe/Photoshop 4.0; Layout Software — APP/Mac 6100, MEI/ALS 2.0. EDITORIAL EQUIPMENT: Hardware — DEC/VAX 4000-200, DEC/VAX 4000-300, 33-IBM/70, IBM/PS2/2-RSK/TRS 80-100, 4-RSK/TRS 80-200; Printers — DEC/LA 210, Compaq/LA-75, Printronix/LPM 600 Band Printer EDITORIAL SOFTWARE: Cybergraphics 7.5. PRODUCTION EQUIPMENT: Hardware — 2-ECR/Autokon 12 max, 1-Anitec/D32; Cameras — 1-Spartan/III, 1-LE/17, 1-AP; Scanners — 2-Epson/ES-1200C.

THE ASHLAND DAILY TIDINGS
111 N Fir St, Medford, Ore., 97501-2772, Jackson; gen tel (541)776-4411; adv tel (541) 776-4422; ed tel (541) 776-4477; gen fax (541) 776-4369; adv fax (541) 776-4369; ed fax (541) 776-4376; gen/nat adv e-mail nsmith@mailtribune.com; disp adv e-mail nsmith@mailtribune.com; class adv e-mailclass@mailtribune.com; ed e-mail news@mailtribune.com; web site www.dailytidings.com
Group: New Media Investment Group
Published: Mon, Tues, Wed, Thur, Fri, Sat
Weekday Frequency: m
Saturday Frequency: m
Circulation: 1,297; 1,323(sat)
Last Audit: AAM March 31, 2015
Advertising Rate (weekday/saturday): Open inch rate $9.42
News services: AP. **Established:** 1876
Own Printing Facility?: Yes
Commercial Printers?: Yes
Special Weekly Sections: Healthy Living (Tue); Food, Entertainment (Wed); Medford Nickel (Thur); TV, Entertainment (Fri)
Syndicated Publications: Revels/On Television (Entertainment) (Thur).
Digital Platform - Mobile: Apple, Android, Windows, Blackberry
Digital Platform - Tablet: Apple iOS
Pub. ....James Grady Singletary
Adv. Dir. ....Dena DeRose
City Ed. ....Myles Murphy
Operations Director ....Ed Rose
Ed. ....Bert Etling
Market Information: ADS; TMC.
Mechanical Available: Offset; Black and 3 ROP colors; insert accepted - any; page cutoffs - 22 3/4.
Mechanical Specifications: Type page 13 x 21 1/2; E - 6 cols, 1 7/8, 1/8 between; A - 6 cols, 1 7/8, 1/8 between; C - 9 cols, 1 3/4, 1/16 between.
Areas Served: Ashland
Delivery Method: Newsstand, Carrier, RacksEquipment & Software: PRESSROOM EQUIPMENT: Lines — 6-G/Community; Folders — 1-G/2:1.; MAILROOM EQUIPMENT: Tying Machines — MLN; Address Machine — Pressure Sensitive/Labeling.; BUSINESS EQUIPMENT: NCR CLASSIFIED EQUIPMENT: Hardware — 3-APP/Mac; CLASSIFIED SOFTWARE: Baseview. EDITORIAL EQUIPMENT: Hardware — 10-APP/Mac EDITORIAL SOFTWARE: Baseview/NewsEdit Pro IQ 3.1. PRODUCTION EQUIPMENT: Hardware — 4-APP/Mac, 2-APP/Mac LaserPrinter, Konica/EV Jetsetter 5100S; Cameras — 1-SCREEN/650-D.

ONTARIO

ARGUS OBSERVER
1160 SW 4th St, Ontario, Ore., 97914-4365, Malheur; gen tel (541) 889-5387; adv tel (541) 889-5387; ed tel (541) 889-5387; gen fax (541) 889-3347; adv fax (541) 889-3347; ed fax (541) 889-3347; gen/nat adv e-mail kellyj@argusobserver.com; disp adv e-mail kellyj@argusobserver.com; class adv

e-mailtonyaw@argusobserver.com; ed e-mail editor@argusobserver.com; web site www.argusobserver.com
- 265,000(views) 75,000(visitors)
Group: Wick Communications
Published: Tues, Wed, Thur, Fri
Weekday Frequency: e
Circulation: 4,508
Last Audit: VAC June 30, 2016
Advertising Rate (weekday/saturday): Open inch rate $11.05
Advertising Rate (sunday): Open inch rate $11.35
Online Advertising Rate: $10 per thousand page view
News services: AP. **Established:** 1896
Own Printing Facility?: Yes
Commercial Printers?: Yes
Special Weekly Sections: Best Food Day (Tue); Church (Fri); Outdoor, Amusement, TV, (Sun); Farm (Mon)
Syndicated Publications: Parade (S).
Digital Platform - Mobile: Apple, Android, Windows, Blackberry
Digital Platform - Tablet: Apple iOS, Android, Windows 7, Blackberry Tablet OS, Kindle, Kindle Fire
Pub./Adv. Dir. ....John Dillon
Ed. ....Scott McIntosh
Adv. Mgr., Retail ....Andy Shimojima
Prodn. Mgr. ....Wade Cordes
Bus Mgr. ....Dee Lee
Market Information: ADS; TMC.
Mechanical Available: Offset; Black and 3 ROP colors; insert accepted - all sizes from 3 x 5 cards up; page cutoffs - 22 3/4.
Mechanical Specifications: Type page 13 x 21 1/2; E - 6 cols, 2 1/16, 1/8 between; A - 6 cols, 2 1/16, 1/8 between; C - 9 cols, 1 1/4, 1/8 between.
Areas Served: 97914, 97913, 97918, 97901, 97907, 83661, 83619, 83655, 83672, 83612, 83660
Delivery Method: Mail, Newsstand, Carrier, RacksEquipment & Software: PRESSROOM EQUIPMENT: Lines — 6-G; BUSINESS EQUIPMENT: DEC/Micro-VAX/3100 BUSINESS SOFTWARE: Vision Data CLASSIFIED EQUIPMENT: Hardware — APP/Mac; CtP; Printers — 2-HP/LaserJet; CLASSIFIED SOFTWARE: Baseview. DISPLAY EQUIPMENT: Hardware — APP/Mac; Printers — 2-HP/LaserJet; Other Hardware — APP/Mac with Baseview. DISPLAY SOFTWARELayout Software — APP/Mac with Baseview. EDITORIAL EQUIPMENT: Hardware — APP/Mac/CtP; Printers — HP/LaserJet PRODUCTION EQUIPMENT: Hardware — Nu/Ultra Plus; Cameras — SCREEN; Scanners — Umax, Polaroid/SprintScan PRODUCTION SOFTWARE: Baseview.

PENDLETON

EAST OREGONIAN
211 SE Byers Ave, Pendleton, Ore., 97801-2346, Umatilla; gen tel (541) 276-2211; adv tel (541) 278-2669; ed tel (541) 966-0835; gen fax (541) 276-8314; gen/nat adv e-mail sales@eastoregonian.com; disp adv e-mail addirector@eastoregonian.com; class adv e-mailclassifieds@eastoregonian.com; ed e-mail news@eastoregonian.com; web site www.eastoregonian.com
- 490,650(views) 120,083(visitors); web site 2 www.eastoregonrealestate.com - 13,252(views) 1,235(visitors); web site 3 www.eastoregonmarketplace.com/ - 17,167(views) 3,252(visitors)
Group: EO Media Group
Published: Tues, Wed, Thur, Fri, Sat
Weekday Frequency: m
Saturday Frequency: m
Circulation: 5,869; 5,869(sat)
Last Audit: CAC June 30, 2017
Branch Offices: Hermiston Bureau
333 E. Main St.
Hermiston, OR 97838
(541) 567-6211
Advertising Rate (weekday/saturday): $20.88 per inch, retail
Advertising Rate (sunday): N/A
Online Advertising Rate: Cube Ad 300x250 pixels, $12.00 (minimum 20,000 impressions per month)

News services: AP **Established:** 1875
Own Printing Facility?: Yes
Commercial Printers?: Yes
Special Editions: Umatilla County Fair
Farm-City Pro Rodeo
Pendleton Round-Up
Health & Wellness Guide
Cattle Barons Weekend
Graduation
Discover Eastern Oregon
Fall Sports
Winter Sports
Spring Sports
Home Improvement & Car Care
Kids & Christmas
Who's Who in Eastern Oregon
Progress Edition
Salute to Police
Firefighters Salute
Spring Home & Garden
Wedding Planner
Giving Guide
Special Weekly Sections: Lifestyles (Saturdays), includes:
Eat, Drink & Explore
Business
Outside
Proprietary Publications: Eastern Oregon Parent
Eastern Oregon Real Estate Guide
Eastern Oregon Marketplace
Digital Platform - Mobile: Apple, Android, Windows, Blackberry, Other
Digital Platform - Tablet: Apple iOS, Android, Windows 7, Blackberry Tablet OS, Kindle, Nook, Kindle Fire, Other
Pub ....Kathryn B. Brown
Managing Editor ....Daniel Wattenburger
Business Office Manager ......Janna Heimgartner
Opinion Page Editor ....Tim Trainor
Circulation Manager ....Marcy Rosenberg
Production Manager ....Mike Jensen
Regional Advertising Director ... Marissa Williams
Areas Served: Northeastern Oregon
Umatilla County includes Pendleton, Hermiston, Umatilla, Stanfield, Echo, Pilot Rock, Helix, Adams, Athena, Weston and Milton-Freewater
Morrow County includes Boardman, Irrigon, Heppner, Ione and Lexington
Delivery Method: Mail, Newsstand, Carrier, RacksEquipment & Software: PRESSROOM EQUIPMENT: 2 Tensor T-1400 color towers
1 Goss Community color tower
1 Re-aliner to add page count. A combination ribbon deck for all three towers in one assembly.
1 Goss Community half folder
1 DGM quarter folder
3 Jardis splicers
MAILROOM EQUIPMENT: 1 STI stacker
1 12:2 SLS 1000 inserter with inline ink jet print labeler
1 10:1 Mueller -Martini 227 E Inserter
2 Quipp 400 Stackers
1 Goval Strapmaster strapper
1 Dynaric ST1strapper
1 Cowart- Gagnon offline inkjet print labeler
1 Rosback Stitcher Trimmer
BUSINESS EQUIPMENT: Macs
BUSINESS SOFTWARE: Brainworks
CLASSIFIED EQUIPMENT: Macs
CLASSIFIED SOFTWARE: Brainworks
DISPLAY EQUIPMENT: Macs DISPLAY SOFTWAREBrainworks EDITORIAL EQUIPMENT: Macs EDITORIAL SOFTWARE: Newscycle PRODUCTION EQUIPMENT: 2 Kodak Trendsetter 800 platesetters CtP units PRODUCTION SOFTWARE: InDesign CIRCULATION SOFTWARBrainworks
Note: First Place Winner of the Oregon Newspaper Publishers Association General Excellence award, 2011-13 and 2015-17

PORTLAND

THE OREGONIAN
1500 SW 1st Ave, Ste 500, Portland, Ore., 97201-5870, Multnomah; gen tel (503) 221-8000; adv tel (503) 221-8000; ed tel (503) 221-8100; gen/nat adv e-mail dwalery@oregonian.com; disp adv e-mail gthompson@oregonian.com; class adv e-mailgthompson@oregonian.com; ed e-mail newsroom@oregonian.com; web site www.

oregonlive.com
- 64,815,324(views) 9,011,076(visitors)
Group: Advance Publications, Inc.
Published: Mon, Tues, Wed, Thur, Fri, Sat, Sun
Weekday Frequency: All day
Saturday Frequency: All day
Circulation: 143,220; 116,812(sat); 173,736(sun)
Last Audit: AAM June 30, 2016
Advertising Rate (weekday/saturday): Open Rate starts at $200 (1/36 page) Sun or Wed, $140 (1/36 page) Fri or Sat. Modular ad sizes ranging from 1/36 to full page and frequency discounts.
Advertising Rate (sunday): Open Rate starts at $200 (1/36 page) Sun or Wed. Modular ad sizes ranging from 1/36 to full page and frequency discounts.
News services: AP, NYT, MCT, WP-Bloomberg. **Established:** 1850
Special Weekly Sections: Living, Sports, FOODday, Metro, Arts & Entertainment, Business
Digital Platform - Mobile: Apple, Android, Windows, Blackberry
Digital Platform - Tablet: Apple iOS, Android, Windows 7, Blackberry Tablet OS, Kindle, Nook, Kindle Fire
Adv. Dir. .... Debi Walery
VP and General Manager .... Kevin Denny
Circ. Mgr., Opns. .... Jodie Krueger
Circ. Mgr., Single Copy .... Neal Burke
Mng. Ed., News .... Therese Bottomly
Ed., VP of Content .... Mark Katches
Chief Revenue Officer .... Mike Burns
Pres. .... John Maher
Dir. Local Retail .... Greg Thompson
Dir. Categories .... Jim Doyle
Dir. Cir. Audience .... Ed Rose
Market Information: Split run; TMC; Zoned editions; Full Run; Friday Living Zone
Mechanical Available: Offset; Black and 3 ROP colors; insert accepted; page cutoffs - 22 3/4.
Mechanical Specifications: Type page 11 7/8 x 21 1/2; E - 6 cols, 1 7/8, 1/8 between; A - 6 cols, 1 7/8, 1/8 between; C - 10 cols, 1 1/8, 1/16 between.
Areas Served: Entire state of Oregon
Delivery Method: CarrierEquipment & Software: BUSINESS SOFTWARE: Peoplesoft Analytics-Qlikview

ROSEBURG

THE NEWS-REVIEW

345 NE Winchester St, Roseburg, Ore., 97470-3328, Douglas; gen tel (541) 672-3321; adv tel (541) 957-4250; ed tel (541) 957-4203; gen fax (541) 957-4270; adv fax (541) 957-4270; ed fax (541) 957-4270; gen/nat adv e-mail tsmith@nrtoday.com; disp adv e-mail tsmith@nrtoday.com; class adv e-mailclassifieds@nrtoday.com; ed e-mail creed@nrtoday.com; web site www.nrtoday.com
- 340,000(views) 38,530(visitors)
Group: Swift Communications, Inc.
Published: Mon, Tues, Wed, Thur, Fri, Sun
Weekday Frequency: e
Circulation: 22,130; 23,045(sun)
Last Audit: CAC December 31, 2015
Advertising Rate (weekday/saturday): Open inch rate $35.59
Advertising Rate (sunday): Open inch rate $40.16
News services: AP. **Established:** 1867
Own Printing Facility?: Yes
Commercial Printers?: Yes
Special Editions: Recreational Vehicles (Apr); Blackberry Festival (Aug); Seasons Greetings (Dec); Readers Choice (Jan); Graffiti (Jul); All in the Family (Jun); How To Tab (Mar); Home & Garden (May); Encore (Monthly); Holiday Guide (Nov); DC Cou
Special Weekly Sections: Money (Mon); Tasty Tuesday (Tue); Health (Wed); Arts, Entertainment (Thur); Auto (Fri); Real Estate (Sun)
Syndicated Publications: Relish (Monthly); Parade (S); American Profile (Weekly).
Digital Platform - Mobile: Apple, Android, Windows
Digital Platform - Tablet: Apple iOS, Android, Windows 7, Kindle
Circ. Dir. .... Bob Franks
Features Ed. .... Craig Reed
Sports Ed. .... Tom Eggers
Prodn. Mgr. .... Rod Carlson
Human resources .... Gina Roberts
Pub. .... Mark Raymond
Nat'l/Major Accts. Mgr. .... Amber Hayman
Adv. Dir. .... Pat Bridges
Adv. Dir. .... Shannon Smith
Market Information: TMC.
Mechanical Available: Offset; Black and 3 ROP colors; insert accepted; page cutoffs - 21 1/2.
Mechanical Specifications: Type page 13 x 21 1/2; E - 6 cols, 2 1/16, 1/8 between; A - 6 cols, 2 1/16, 1/8 between; C - 9 cols, 1 3/8, 1/16 between.
Areas Served: 97417, 97429, 97432, 97435, 97436, 97443, 97447, 97457, 97462, 97469, 97470, 97471, 97473, 97479, 97484, 97486, 97495, 97496, 97499, 97481, 97416
Delivery Method: Mail, Newsstand, Carrier, RacksEquipment & Software: PRESSROOM EQUIPMENT: Lines — 6-G/Urbanite; Folders — 1-G/quarter folder.; MAILROOM EQUIPMENT: Counter Stackers — 1-Quipp/500; Inserters & Stuffers — 1-MM/227E, 1-KAN/480; Tying Machines - 2-MLN/ML2EE.; BUSINESS EQUIPMENT: 1-PBS/Convergent CLASSIFIED EQUIPMENT: Hardware — 4-APP/Mac SE 30.; DISPLAY EQUIPMENT: Hardware — 5-APP/Mac IIci, 4-APP/Mac Power PC 8100; DISPLAY SOFTWAREAd Make-up Applications — DTI/Adobe; EDITORIAL EQUIPMENT: Hardware — Apple Mac Minis and MacBook Airs EDITORIAL SOFTWARE: DTI PRODUCTION EQUIPMENT: Cameras — Cannon PRODUCTION SOFTWARE: DTI/Adobe

SALEM

STATESMAN JOURNAL

280 Church St NE, Salem, Ore., 97301-3734, Marion; gen tel (503) 399-6611; adv tel (503) 399-6648; ed tel (503) 399-6611; gen fax (503) 399-6706; adv fax (503) 399-6808; ed fax (503) 399-6706; gen/nat adv e-mail golocal@statesmanjournal.com; disp adv e-mail golocal@statesmanjournal.com; class adv e-mailads@statesmanjournal.com; ed e-mail letters@statesmanjournal.com; web site www.statesmanjournal.com
Group: Gannett
Published: Mon, Tues, Wed, Thur, Fri, Sat, Sun
Weekday Frequency: m
Saturday Frequency: m
Circulation: 31,518; 26,141(sat); 32,991(sun)
Last Audit: AAM March 31, 2017
Advertising Rate (weekday/saturday): Open inch rate $92.09
Advertising Rate (sunday): Open inch rate $106.17
News services: AP, GNS. **Established:** 1851
Special Editions: State Fair (Aug); Gift Guides (Nov); Home Show (Feb); Tour of Homes (Jun);
Special Weekly Sections: Life (Mon, Tue); Best Food Day (Wed); Recreation, Weekend (Thur); Real Living, Home, Life (Fri); Auto, Life (Sat); Arts, Travel, Business, Career (Sun)
Syndicated Publications: Comics (S).
Digital Platform - Mobile: Apple, Android
Digital Platform - Tablet: Apple iOS, Android
Exec. Ed. .... Michael Davis
Adv. Dir. .... Ryan Kedzierski
Class. Mgr. .... Valerie Thorne
CFO .... Jerry Scobie
Bus./Finance Ed. .... Don Currie
Digital Ed. .... Amy Read
Editorial Page Ed. .... Dick Hughes
Metro Ed. .... Dan Bender
Photo Ed. .... Diane Stevenson
Senior Ed. .... Michelle Maxwell
Senior Ed. .... Victor Panichkul
Sports Ed. .... James Day
Theater/Music Ed. .... Kelly Williams Brown
IT Mgr. .... Kristina Salaz
Prodn. Mgr., Distr. .... John Witherspoon
Pub. .... Lisa Reese
Acct. Mgr. .... Neil Potter
Auto Mgr. .... Patrick Bruce
Pub. .... Terry Horne
Market Information: ADS; Split run; TMC.
Mechanical Available: Offset; Black and 4 ROP colors; insert accepted; page cutoffs - 22 3/4.
Mechanical Specifications: Type page 10 x 21 1/2; E - 6 cols, 1 1/2, 1/6 between; A - 6 cols, 2, 1/6 between; C - 10 cols, 1, 1/12 between.
Areas Served: Salem & Keizer area (OR)
Delivery Method: Mail, Newsstand, Carrier, RacksEquipment & Software: PRESSROOM EQUIPMENT: Lines — 7-G/Metro double width 1975; Pasters —G/Digital Pilot & surface sensingReels & Stands — Spyder/arms.; MAILROOM EQUIPMENT: Counter Stackers — 4/Olympian; Inserters & Stuffers — HI/NP 632; Tying Machines — 4-/Dynaric; Control System — HI w/Icon System; Address Machine — Domino/InkJet.; CLASSIFIED EQUIPMENT: Hardware — IBM/Servers, Ethernet/100MB-Dell/Workstation; 2-Harlequin/Software RIP (for V/5500), 1-V/5300 Pixelburst Software RIP; Printers — V/5300 B, V/5500, HP/4000, HP/5SI, HP/8100, HP/8500; CLASSIFIED SOFTWARE: APT, MEI/CLS. DISPLAY EQUIPMENT: Hardware — IBM, APP/Mac G3; Printers — V/5300 B, HP/8100, HP/8500, HP/2500, HP/715; Other Hardware — X/Scanner, PixelCraft/7650C flatbed scanner, 2-Tecsa DISPLAY SOFTWAREAd Make-up Applications — Multi-Ad/Creator, QPS, Archetype/Corel Draw, Managing Editor/ALS, Roundhouse/Ad Tracking; EDITORIAL EQUIPMENT: Hardware — IBM, APP/Mac G3 Workstation, Ethernet/100MP; Printers — V/5500, V/5300 B, HP/5si, HP/8100, HP/8500, HP/2500, HP/715 EDITORIAL SOFTWARE: QPS. PRODUCTION EQUIPMENT: Hardware — V/5100, V/5500, V/5300 B, QMS; Cameras — Spartan/II Page; Scanners — CD, Lf/Leafscan 35, Sharp/Flatbed, Lf/Leafscan 45, 2-Tecsa/18 x 24, 2-Tecsa/14x24 PRODUCTION SOFTWARE: MEI/CLS, QPS.

THE DALLES

THE DALLES DAILY CHRONICLE

315 Federal St, The Dalles, Ore., 97058-2115, Wasco; gen tel (541) 296-2141; adv tel (541) 296-2141; ed tel (541) 296-2141; gen fax (541) 298-1365; adv fax (541) 298-1365; ed fax (541) 298-1365; gen/nat adv e-mail cmarr@thedalleschronicle.com; disp adv e-mail cmarr@thedalleschronicle.com; class adv e-mailcmarr@thedalleschronicle.com; ed e-mail mgibson@thedalleschronicle.com; web site www.thedalleschronicle.com
Group: Eagle Newspapers, Inc.
Published: Tues, Wed, Thur, Fri, Sun
Weekday Frequency: e
Circulation: 5,067; 5,468(sun)
Last Audit: Sworn/Estimate/Non-Audited September 30, 2017
Advertising Rate (weekday/saturday): Open inch rate $11.25
Advertising Rate (sunday): Open inch rate $11.25
News services: AP. **Established:** 1890
Special Editions: Progress (Feb); Visit the Gorge (May).
Special Weekly Sections: Best Food Day (Tue)
Syndicated Publications: American Profile (Weekly).
Pub. .... Marilyn Roth
Adv. Dir. .... Tonya Flory
Exec. Ed. .... Kathy Ursprung
Class. Mgr. .... Nick Deleon
Managing Ed. .... Kathy Gray
Office Mgr./Bookkeeper .... Cece Fix
Market Information: TMC; Zoned editions.
Mechanical Available: Offset; Black and 3 ROP colors; insert accepted - zoning available; page cutoffs - 21.
Mechanical Specifications: Type page 13 x 21; E - 6 cols, 2, 1/8 between; A - 6 cols, 2, 1/8 between; C - 6 cols, 2, 1/8 between. Equipment & Software: BUSINESS EQUIPMENT: 19-Magitonic BUSINESS SOFTWARE: QuarkXPress, Synaptic, Microsoft/Office, Adobe/Photoshop, Adobe/Illustratoe, Archetype/Corel Draw (PC Software/Bus. Applications) CLASSIFIED EQUIPMENT: Hardware — 2-ScrippSat; Printers — QMS/810 Turbo, Okidata/Microline 393 P14S; CLASSIFIED SOFTWARE: Synaptic. DISPLAY EQUIPMENT: Printers — QMS/810 Turbo, 2-PS, Elite, IBM; DISPLAY SOFTWARELayout Software — QPS/QuarkXPress, Archetype/Corel Draw, Adobe/Illustrator. EDITORIAL EQUIPMENT: Hardware — Sun; Printers — QMS/810 T, 2-PS, Elite, IBM EDITORIAL SOFTWARE: Sun. PRODUCTION EQUIPMENT: Hardware — 2-QMS/810 Turbo, PostScript/Printer; Cameras — Nikon, Kk/Digital.

PENNSYLVANIA

ALLENTOWN

THE MORNING CALL

101 N 6th St, PO Box 1260, Allentown, Pa., 18101-1403, Lehigh; gen tel (610) 820-6500; adv tel (610) 820-6633; ed tel (610) 820-6500; gen fax (610)820-6513; adv fax (610) 820-6513; ed fax (610) 820-6693; gen/nat adv e-mail ccampbell@mcall.com; disp adv e-mail ccampbell@mcall.com; class adv e-mailclassified@mcall.com; ed e-mail news@mcall.com; web site www.mcall.com
- 15,200,000(views) 1,074,410(visitors)
Group: Tronc, Inc.
Published: Mon, Tues, Wed, Thur, Fri, Sat, Sun
Weekday Frequency: m
Saturday Frequency: m
Circulation: 66,288; 85,378(sat); 115,938(sun)
Last Audit: AAM December 31, 2015
Advertising Rate (weekday/saturday): Open inch rate $102.36 (Mon-Tue); $110.77 (Wed-Fri); $117.78 (Sat)
Advertising Rate (sunday): Open inch rate $136.01
Online Advertising Rate: ROS Pricing: Leaderboard-$8.40 CPM; Cube-$8.40 CPM; Interchangeable-$5.25 CPM; Half Banner-$6.00 CPM
News services: 1883
Special Weekly Sections: Best Food Day, Golf (Wed/Sun); Health, Fitness (Mon); Business, Family (Tue); Entertainment (Thur); Entertainment, Home, Fashion, Trends, Pets, Movies (Fri); Travel, Home, Real Estate, Business (Sun);
Digital Platform - Mobile: Apple, Android
Publisher, President and CEO .... Timothy Ryan
Vice President /Editor .... David Erdman
VP, Adv. .... Jim Feher
Circ. Dir. .... Linda McDonald
Digital/Interactive Manager .... Daniel Sarko
Digital/ Interactive Manager .... Elizabeth Bartolai Veronica Walter
Nat'l Adv. Mgr. .... Adrienne Tunke
Dir. Major Accts./Nat'l Adv. .... Omar Zucco
Pub./Ed.-in-chief .... Robert York
Market Information: Lehigh County, Northampton county, Carbon CountiesEquipment & Software: CLASSIFIED SOFTWARE: SII. DISPLAY EQUIPMENT: Printers — HP;
Note: I'm only updating and verifying the Publisher's contact information.

ALTOONA

ALTOONA MIRROR

301 Cayuga Ave, Altoona, Pa., 16602-4323, Blair; gen tel (814) 946-7411; adv tel (814) 946-7411; ed tel (814) 946-7441; gen fax (814) 946-7547; adv fax (814) 946-7547; ed fax (814) 946-7540; gen/nat adv e-mail jhancock@altoonamirror.com; disp adv e-mail displayads@altoonamirror.com; class adv e-mailclassifieds@altoonamirror.com; ed e-mail news@altoonamirror.com; web site www.altoonamirror.com
- 1,500,000(views) 250,000(visitors)
Group: Ogden Newspapers Inc.
Published: Mon, Tues, Wed, Thur, Fri, Sat, Sun
Weekday Frequency: m
Saturday Frequency: m
Circulation: 21,904; 21,904(sat); 30,127(sun)
Last Audit: AAM December 31, 2016
Advertising Rate (weekday/saturday): Open inch rate $52.45
Advertising Rate (sunday): Open inch rate $59.23
News services: AP. **Established:** 1876
Own Printing Facility?: Yes
Commercial Printers?: Yes

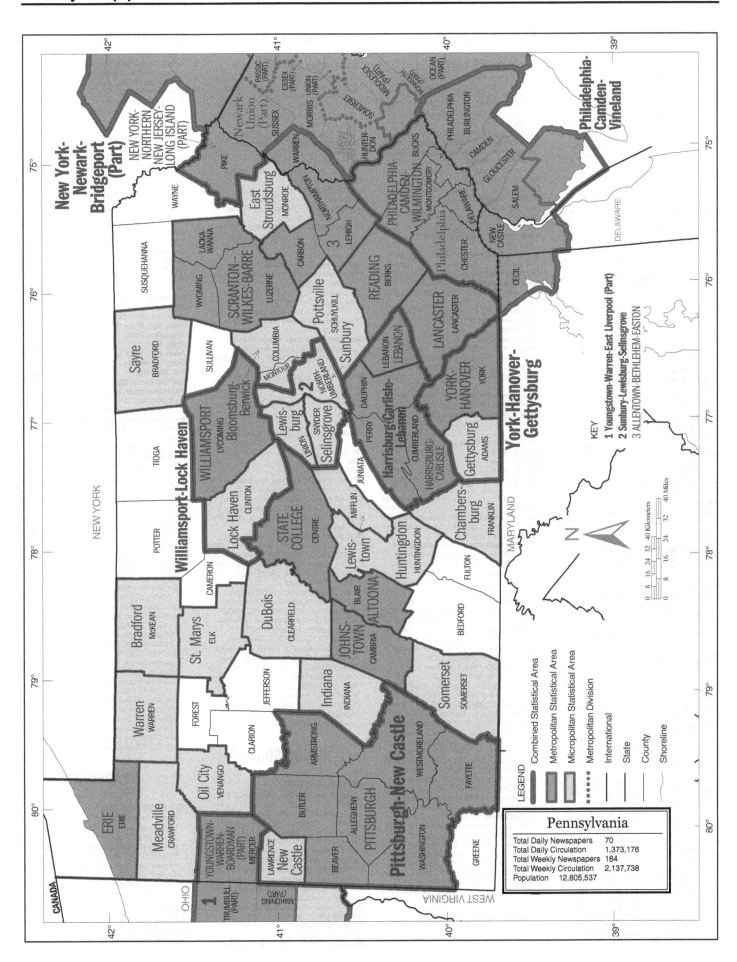

New York-Newark-Bridgeport (Part)

NEW YORK-NORTHERN NEW JERSEY-LONG ISLAND (PART)

Philadelphia-Camden-Vineland

East Stroudsburg

Scranton-Wilkes-Barre

Pottsville

Reading

Sunbury

Sayre

Bloomsburg-Berwick

Lewisburg

Williamsport-Lock Haven

WILLIAMSPORT

Selinsgrove

Harrisburg-Carlisle-Lebanon

York-Hanover

Gettysburg

York-Hanover-Gettysburg

Lock Haven

STATE COLLEGE

Lewistown

Huntingdon

Chambersburg

Bradford

St. Marys

DuBois

JOHNSTOWN

ALTOONA

Indiana

Somerset

Warren

Oil City

Meadville

YOUNGSTOWN-WARREN-BOARDMAN (PART)

New Castle

ERIE

Pittsburgh-New Castle

PITTSBURGH

KEY
1 Youngstown-Warren-East Liverpool (Part)
2 Sunbury-Lewisburg-Selinsgrove
3 ALLENTOWN-BETHLEHEM-EASTON

CANADA

OHIO

NEW YORK

MARYLAND

WEST VIRGINIA

DELAWARE

LEGEND

Combined Statistical Area
Metropolitan Statistical Area
Micropolitan Statistical Area
Metropolitan Division
International
State
County
Shoreline

Pennsylvania

Total Daily Newspapers	70
Total Daily Circulation	1,373,176
Total Weekly Newspapers	184
Total Weekly Circulation	2,137,738
Population	12,805,537

0 8 16 24 32 40 Kilometers
0 8 16 24 32 40 Miles

Special Editions: Alleghenies Adventure glossy, Bridal glossy, Health & Wellness newsprint (Jan); Mirror Moms glossy (Feb); Blair Living glossy (finance focus), People & Progress newsprint (largest edition of the year) (Mar); Central PA Pets glossy, Inside Pitch newsprint baseball preview, Tee It Up gold guide newsprint (Apr); Mirror Moms glossy, Born to Ride motorcycle glossy, On the Go special travel section newsprint (May); Blair Living glossy (summer bridal focus), Graduation community section newsprint (Jun); Alleghenies Adventure glossy, Here's My Card glossy booklet, Blitz high school football glossy (Jul); Mirror Moms glossy, Football preview (hs/college/NFL) newsprint (Aug); Blair Living glossy (medical focus), Health & Wellness newsprint, Penn State Gameday weekly newsprint (Sept); Central PA Pets glossy, Fall Home Improvement newsprint (Oct); Mirror Moms glossy, Thanksgiving Day newsprint wraps, Thanksgiving Day poly bag sponsorship (Nov); Blair Living (Hometown Favorites focus), Shop Local newsprint section/contest, Winter Heat sports preview newsprint. (Dec)
Special Weekly Sections: Kids (Mon); Jobs (Tue); Food (Wed); Entertainment, Religion (Fri); TV (Sat); Business, Travel (Sun)
Syndicated Publications: Blair Living (quarterly glossy); Mirror Moms (quarterly glossy); Alleghenies Adventure (quarterly glossy); Born to Ride (annual glossy); Taste of the Alleghenies (annual glossy); Central PA Pets (annual glossy). Bridal Bliss
(annual Glossy)
Digital Platform - Mobile: Apple, Android
Digital Platform - Tablet: Apple iOS, Android
Pub. .... Ed Kruger
Gen. Mgr. Adv. .... Ray Eckenrode
Circ. Dir. .... Dan Slep
Circ. Mgr., Office .... Beth Claar
Assist. Managing Ed. .... Steve Carpenter
Photo Ed. .... J.D. Cavrich
Sports Ed. .... Buck Frank
Women's Ed. .... Barbara Cowan
Prodn. Mgr. .... Rick Bacza
Managing Ed. .... Neil Rudel
Nat'l/Classifieds Adv. Mgr. .... Luann Ulicne
Marketing Mgr. .... Amy Hanna
Market Information: TMC.
Mechanical Available: Offset; Black and 3 ROP colors; insert accepted - others upon request- with publisher's approval; page cutoffs - 22 3/4.
Mechanical Specifications: Type page 13 x 21.5; E - 6 cols, 2 1/16, 1/8 between; A - 6 cols, 2 1/16, 1/8 between; C - 6 cols, 2 1/16, 1/8 between.
Areas Served: 16601, 16602, 16648, 16635, 16625, 16637, 16673, 16662, 16693, 16686, 16617, 16655, 15521, 16627, 15522, 16664, 16659, 16695, 16650, 16679, 16678, 16657, 16647, 16652, 16611, 16683, 16680, 16616, 16627, 16639, 16636, 16640, 16668, 16646, 15722, 16643, 15940, 16641, 16630, 15931, 15938, 15946, 15955, 15963,
Delivery Method: Mail, Newsstand, Carrier, RacksEquipment & Software: PRESSROOM EQUIPMENT: Lines — 6-G/Headliner Offset double width, 4-G/half decks double width; Reels & Stands — 5-G/Stands, 5-G/3-Arm Reels & Stands.; MAILROOM EQUIPMENT: Counter Stackers — 2/PPK, 2-Id/2200; Inserters & Stuffers — 6-/KAN, MC/660-20, GMA/SLS 1000; Tying Machines — 5-/Sa, 2-/MLN, Id; Control System — GMA; Address Machine — PBS/CIS; BUSINESS SOFTWARE: Excel, MS Word, Microsoft/Excel, Microsoft/Word CLASSIFIED EQUIPMENT: Printers — IBM, Konica/Marlins; CLASSIFIED SOFTWARE: Unix, CText. DISPLAY EQUIPMENT: Hardware — HP, APP/Mac; Printers — Konica/Marlin 2500; Other Hardware — Microtek/Scanners, Flatbed, Pro Imager/8200 DISPLAY SOFTWAREAd Make-up Applications — APP/Mac NLM 3.12, Novell/Netware 386 3.12, Microsoft/Windows, PBS, ReCas/4; Layout Software — SCS/Layout 8000, APP/Mac G3, APP/Mac G4, A EDITORIAL SOFTWARE: QPS/QuarkXPress. PRODUCTION EQUIPMENT: Hardware — KFM; Cameras — SCREEN, LD/281-Q; Scanners — ECR/Autokon, Sharp/35mm PRODUCTION SOFTWARE: APP/Mac NLM 3.12, Novell/Netware 386 3.12, Microsoft/Windows, Cheyenne/Arcserve.

BEAVER

BEAVER COUNTY TIMES

400 Fair Ave, Beaver, Pa., 15009-1958, Beaver; gen tel (724) 775-3200; adv tel (724) 774-1151; ed tel (724) 775-3200; gen fax (724) 775-7212; adv fax (724) 775-7212; ed fax (724) 775-4180; gen/nat adv e-mail llewis@timesonline.com; disp adv e-mail crager@timesonline.com; class adv e-mailtimesclassifieds@timesonline.com.; ed e-mail timesnews@timesonline.com; web site www.timesonline.com
- 1,918,236(views)
Group: GateHouse Media, Inc.
Published: Mon, Tues, Wed, Thur, Fri, Sun
Weekday Frequency: m
Saturday Frequency: m
Circulation: 21,323; 27,153(sun)
Last Audit: AAM June 30, 2017
Branch Offices: Ellwood City Ledger, Ellwood City, PA
Advertising Rate (weekday/saturday): Open inch rate $63.06
Advertising Rate (sunday): Open inch rate $67.49
Online Advertising Rate: $59.00/Month for Enhanced Listing; $79.00/Month for Storefront
News services: AP, GateHouse, More Content Now, Washington Post, Bloomberg News **Established:** 1851
Own Printing Facility?: No
Special Editions: Progress (Feb.); Big Knob Fair (July); Hookstown Fair (Aug.); Football Preview (Aug.); Basketball (Dec); Best of the Valley (May); Gift Guide (Nov); Car Care (Sept).
Special Weekly Sections: Time & Money (Wed.)
Digital Platform - Mobile: Apple, Android
Digital Platform - Tablet: Apple iOS, Android
Controller .... Tina Bequeath
Credit Mgr. .... Debbie Hays
Circ. Mgr., Home Delivery .... Mark Zuchelli
Circ. Mgr., Mktg. .... Vaughn Vacar
Mng. Ed., Content .... Tom Bickert
Dir., Adv. Sales .... Jody Schwartz
Classifieds Adv. Dir. .... Deborah Bianco
Mng. Ed. .... Patrick O'Shea
Asst. Mng. Ed. .... Kristen Doerschner
Controller .... Lori Holtz
Mechanical Available: Other; Black and 3 ROP colors; insert accepted - most sizes accepted; page cutoffs - 22 3/4.
Mechanical Specifications: Type page 13 x 21 1/2; E - 6 cols, 2 1/16, 1/8 between; A - 6 cols, 2 1/16, 1/8 between; C - 9 cols, 1 3/8, 1/16 between.
Areas Served: Beaver County, Allegheny and Lawrence counties
Delivery Method: Mail, Newsstand, Carrier, RacksEquipment & Software: PRESSROOM EQUIPMENT: Lines — 6-G/Mark I Headliner 2362 double width 1964; Folders — 1-G/2:1; Pasters —G/RTP; Control System — Ch/SCR.; MAILROOM EQUIPMENT: Counter Stackers — 1-HL/Stacker, 1-TMSI/Compass 360, 1-TMSI/Compass 180; Inserters & Stuffers — GMA/2000; Tying Machines — 2/Dynaric; Address Machine — 1-IBM/3031.; BUSINESS EQUIPMENT: IBM BUSINESS SOFTWARE: Microsoft/Office 97, Mactive, Open Pages CLASSIFIED EQUIPMENT: Hardware — 7-Dell/PC, 2-Dell/Server; HP/LaserJet Printer; Printers — MON/Expressmaster 1016; CLASSIFIED SOFTWARE: Mactive. DISPLAY EQUIPMENT: Hardware — 7-Dell/PC, 2-APP/Mac, 2-IBM/PC, 2-Compaq/Server; Printers — MON/PaperMaster II, 2-MON/Expressmaster 1016; Other Hardware — 2-HP/Scanners, AP Adsend, Quick Mail DISPLAY SOFTWAREAd Make-up Applications — QPS/QuarkXPress 4.1, Adobe/Photoshop, Adobe/Illustrator, AdTracker; EDITORIAL EQUIPMENT: Hardware — 31-Dell/PC, 14-Compaq, 5-APP/Mac, 2-Compaq/Servers/MON/SUN OPS System; Printers — MON/Proof Express, 2-MON/Expressmaster 1016, 3-HP/LaserJet Printer EDITORIAL SOFTWARE: ACI/Open Pages. PRODUCTION EQUIPMENT: Hardware — OCR, Caere/OmniPage, 2-Sun; Cameras — 1-C/Spartan III; Scanners — 4-HP/Scanner PRODUCTION SOFTWARE: QPS/QuarkXPress 3.2.

BEDFORD

THE BEDFORD GAZETTE

424 W Penn St, Bedford, Pa., 15522-1230, Bedford; gen tel (814) 623-1151; ed tel (800) 242-4250; gen fax (814) 623-5055; gen/nat adv e-mail sgrowden@bedfordgazette.com; disp adv e-mail advertise@bedfordgazette.com; class adv e-mailclassifieds@bedfordgazette.com; ed e-mail acarr@bedfordgazette.com; web site www.bedfordgazette.com
Group: Sample News Group LLC
Published: Mon, Tues, Wed, Thur, Fri, Sat
Weekday Frequency: m
Saturday Frequency: m
Circulation: 10,000; 9,837(sat)
Last Audit: Sworn/Estimate/Non-Audited September 30, 2017
Advertising Rate (weekday/saturday): Open inch rate $13.08 (Local); $16.47 (National)
Advertising Rate (sunday): $17.63 (Local); $22.48 (National)
News services: AP. **Established:** 1805
Special Editions: Home & Garden (Apr); Back-to-School (Aug); Christmas 3 (Dec); Boy Scout Week Pages (Feb); Jaycee Week Pages (Jan); Bedford County Fair (Jul); Dairy Farm (Jun); Bridal & Spring Fashion (Mar); Graduation & Careers (May); Golden Years (Monthly); Christmas Ed
Special Weekly Sections: Village Crier (Fri); Lifestyles (Mon); Church Page (Sat); Lifestyles (Thur); Lifestyles (Tues); Best Food Day (Wed).
Syndicated Publications: American Profile (Weekly).
Pres. .... George Sample
Pub. .... Joseph Beegle
Mng. Ed. .... Elizabeth Coyle
Ass. Ed. .... Andrew Carr
Bus. Mgr. .... Rebecca Smith
Cir. .... Susan Maybury
Adv. Dir. .... Sherri Growden
Class. .... Stacy Bollman
Market Information: TMC.
Mechanical Available: Offset; Black and 4 ROP colors; insert accepted; page cutoffs - 22 3/4.
Mechanical Specifications: Type page 13 x 21 1/2; E - 6 cols, 2 1/16, 1/8 between; A - 6 cols, 2 1/16, 1/8 between; C - 6 cols, 2 1/16, 1/8 between.
Areas Served: 15521, 17211, 15522, 15533, 15534, 16625, 15535, 16631, 15536, 16633, 16637, 15537, 15539, 16650, 15545, 16655, 16659, 15550, 16662, 15553, 16664, 15554, 16667, 16670, 16672, 16673, 16678, 15559, 16679, 16691, 16695
Equipment & Software: PRESSROOM EQUIPMENT: Lines — 5-G/Community 1983; Folders — 1-G/S-C.; MAILROOM EQUIPMENT: Tying Machines — Nichiro Kogyo; Address Machine — Ch/515.; BUSINESS EQUIPMENT: Real World, PC CLASSIFIED EQUIPMENT: Hardware — APP/Mac; Printers — APP/Mac Laser; CLASSIFIED SOFTWARE: Baseview. DISPLAY EQUIPMENT: Hardware — APP/Mac; EDITORIAL EQUIPMENT: Hardware — APP/Mac; Printers — APP/Mac Laser EDITORIAL SOFTWARE: Baseview/NewsEdit. PRODUCTION EQUIPMENT: Hardware — APP/Mac Laser; Cameras — K.

BLOOMSBURG

PRESS ENTERPRISE

3185 Lackawanna Ave, Bloomsburg, Pa., 17815-3329, Columbia; gen tel (570) 784-2121; adv tel (570) 387-1234 ext. 1210; ed tel (570) 784-2121 ext. 1305; gen fax (570) 784-9226; adv fax (570) 416-0220; ed fax (570) 784-9226; gen/nat adv e-mail adv@pressenterprise.net; disp adv e-mail adv@pressenterprise.net; class adv e-mailclass@pressenterprise.net; ed e-mail news@pressenterprise.net; web site www.pressenterpriseonline.com; web site 2 http://www.pressenterprise.net/
Group: Freedom Communications, Inc.
Published: Mon, Tues, Wed, Thur, Fri, Sat, Sun
Weekday Frequency: m
Saturday Frequency: m
Circulation: 17,572; 17,572(sat); 18,472(sun)
Last Audit: AAM December 31, 2017
Advertising Rate (weekday/saturday): Open inch rate $34.39
Advertising Rate (sunday): Open inch rate $34.39
News services: AP. **Established:** 1902
Own Printing Facility?: Yes
Commercial Printers?: Yes
Special Editions: Your Home (Apr); Back-to-School (Aug); Gift Guide (Dec); Progress (Feb); Bridal (Jan); FYI (Jul); Recreation (Jun); MenuTabs (Mar); Senior Citizen (May); Gift Guide (Nov); New Autos (Oct); Fair (Sept).
Special Weekly Sections: Business (Mon); Health (Tue); Best Food Day (Wed); Auto, Business, School (Thur); American Profile (Sat); Stock (Sun)
Syndicated Publications: Color Comics (S); American Profile (Weekly); USA Weekend (Sun)
Pres. .... Paul R. Eyerly
Treasurer .... James T. Micklow
Pub. .... Brandon R. Eyerly
Bus. Office Mgr. .... Dennis Ashenfelder
Adv. Dir. .... Sandra Sterner
Circ. Mgr. .... Pam Taylor
Mng. Ed., News .... Dean Kashner
Ed. .... James Sachetti
Graphics Ed./Art Dir. .... Lori Getty
Photo Ed. .... Bill Hughes
Mgmt. Info Servs. Mgr. .... Jeff Cragle
Prodn. Mgr., Bindery/Post Press .... Julie Neitz
Prodn. Mgr., Opns. .... Bill Bason
Prodn. Mgr., PM .... Robert Temple
Prodn. Mgr., Press .... Brad Conklin
Classifieds Adv. Mg. .... Carin Wharton
Bus. Office Mgr. .... Bill Pitcavage
Customer Service Mgr. .... Paula Ream
Market Information: ADS; TMC.
Mechanical Available: Offset; Black and 4 ROP colors; insert accepted; page cutoffs - 22 3/4.
Mechanical Specifications: Type page 12 x 21 1/2; E - 6 cols, 1 11/16', 1/10 between; A - 6 cols, 1 11/16, 1/10 between; C - 9 cols, 1 1/16, 1/10 between.
Areas Served: Columbia, Montour, and Luzerne Counties; including Bloomsburg, Danville, Berwick, Benton, Millville, Catawissa and Elysburg.
Equipment & Software: PRESSROOM EQUIPMENT: Lines — 8-G/Urbanite (3 color) single width 1972; 8-HI/NC 400 single width 1985; Tensor/1400 single width 1995; Tensor/1400 single width 1999; Reels & Stands — Roll/Stands.; MAILROOM EQUIPMENT: Counter Stackers — 1-BG/108, 1-BG/107, 1/PPK, 2-HI/RS25; Inserters & Stuffers — 1-/MM, GMA/SLS 1000; Tying Machines — 2-MLN/ML2EE, 1-/Sa, 3-/BU; Address Machine — 1-KR/Communications, 1-/KAN; BUSINESS EQUIPMENT: Dell 2950 BUSINESS SOFTWARE: DSI Software, Logic, Abra Suite, Great Plains CLASSIFIED EQUIPMENT: Hardware — Dell 2850; Printers — HP/Laserjet 4000; CLASSIFIED SOFTWARE: Brainworks DISPLAY EQUIPMENT: Printers — HP LaserJet 5si/MX; DISPLAY SOFTWAREAd Make-up Applications — Multi-Ad/Creator 3.7; Layout Software — APP/Mac. EDITORIAL EQUIPMENT: Hardware — Mac mini iMac, Xserve; Printers — Laser jet 8150 EDITORIAL SOFTWARE: Woodwing/InDesign PRODUCTION EQUIPMENT: Hardware — Nexus, Creo transetter news; Scanners — Epson PRODUCTION SOFTWARE: Baseview.

BRADFORD

THE BRADFORD ERA

43 Main St, Bradford, Pa., 16701-2019, McKean; gen tel (814) 368-3173; adv tel (814) 369-3173; ed tel (814) 362-6531; gen fax (814) 362-6510; adv fax (814) 362-6510; ed fax (814) 362-6510; gen/nat adv e-mail news@bradfordera.com; disp adv e-mail display@bradfordera.com; class adv e-maila.hayden@bradfordera.com; ed e-mail news@bradfordera.com; web site www.bradfordera.com
Group: Bradford Publishing Co.
Published: Mon, Tues, Wed, Thur, Fri, Sat
Weekday Frequency: m
Saturday Frequency: m

Circulation: 7,942; 7,942(sat)
Last Audit: VAC September 30, 2015
Advertising Rate (weekday/saturday): Open inch rate $17.68
News services: AP. **Established:** 1824
Own Printing Facility?: Yes
Commercial Printers?: Yes
Special Editions: Univ. of Pittsburgh at Bradford (Aug); Progress (Jan); Zippo Days (Jul); Summer Guide, Sun 'n Fun (Jun); Brides (Mar); Design-an-Ad (May); Christmas Guide (Nov); Hunting Guide (Oct).
Syndicated Publications: USA WEEKEND Magazine (Sat).
Grp Ed. .... Jim Eckstrom
Purchasing Agent .... Gretchen Gallagher
Adv. Mgr. .... Jill Henry
Pub. Ed. .... John H. Satterwhite
Mng. Ed. .... Marty Robacker Wilder
Prodn. Mgr., Mailroom/Post Press ...... Rick Kautz
Commercial Printing .... Linda Cardamone
Cir. Mng. .... Don Watts
Mark Brahaney
Market Information: TMC.
Mechanical Available: Offset; Black and 3 ROP colors; insert accepted - all; page cutoffs - 22 3/4.
Mechanical Specifications: Type page 12 x 21 1/2; E - 6 cols, 1 13/16, 1/6 between; A - 6 cols, 1 13/16, 1/6 between; C - 9 cols, 1 3/16, 1/12 between.
Areas Served: Mckean, Elk, Potter, Cameron Counties
Delivery Method: Mail, Newsstand, Carrier, RacksEquipment & Software: PRESSROOM EQUIPMENT: Lines — 8-HI/V-15D; Reels & Stands — 8; Control System — 2-CH/ Responder 210.; MAILROOM EQUIPMENT: Counter Stackers — 1/BG; Tying Machines — 2-/MLN; Address Machine - 1-/St, 1-/ KR.; BUSINESS EQUIPMENT: 1-Compaq/ Unix Box, 5-PC BUSINESS SOFTWARE: Vision Data CLASSIFIED EQUIPMENT: Hardware — APP/Mac; Printers — Okidata/ Microline 321 Turbo, Pre Press/Panther Pro Imagesetter; CLASSIFIED SOFTWARE: Baseview. DISPLAY EQUIPMENT: Hardware — 2-APP/Mac G3, 1-APP/Mac Quadra; Printers — 1-APP/Mac LaserWriter, 2-Pre Press/Panther Plus 46 Imagesetter, PrePress/Panther Pro; Other Hardware — 2-APP/Mac CD-Rom, Lf/45 Scanner, 2-Umax/As DISPLAY SOFTWAREAd Make-up Applications — Multi-Ad/Creator 4.0, Multi-Ad/Creator 2.0; EDITORIAL EQUIPMENT: Hardware — APP/Power Mac/1-APP/Mac IIsi, APP/GraphicsNet, 1-Lf/ AP Leaf Picture Desk (with Laser Photo); Printers — LaserWriter/Pro, Pre Press/ Panther Pro Imagesetter, Pre Press/Panther Plus Imagesetter EDITORIAL SOFTWARE: Baseview. PRODUCTION EQUIPMENT: Hardware — Visioneer 2.0, 1-Pre Press/ Panther Pro 46 (18 wide Imagesetter), 1-Pre Press/Panther Plus (13 1/3 wide Imagesetter); Cameras — R/500 Overhead; Scanners — 1-Lf/Leafscan 45, 3-Umax/Astra 12005 PRODUCTION SOFTWARE: QPS/ QuarkXPress 4.0.

BUTLER

BUTLER EAGLE

114 W Diamond St, Butler, Pa., 16001-5747, Butler; gen tel (724) 282-8000; gen fax (724) 282-1280; ed fax (724) 282-4180; gen/nat adv e-mail kgraham@butlereagle.com; disp adv e-mail kgraham@butlereagle.com; class adv e-mailclassified@butlereagle.com; ed e-mail letters@butlereagle.com; web site www.butlereagle.com
Group: Eagle Media
Published: Mon, Tues, Wed, Thur, Fri, Sun
Weekday Frequency: e
Circulation: 22,080; 24,116(sun)
Last Audit: AAM June 30, 2016
Advertising Rate (weekday/saturday): Open inch rate $30.00
Advertising Rate (sunday): Open inch rate $30.00
Online Advertising Rate: ROS Net Rate (CPM) Open Inch Rate:Big Box-$5.00; Leaderboard-$4.00; Skyscraper-$3.00; Rectangle-$2.00; Vertical Banner-$2.00
News services: AP. **Established:** 1895
Special Editions: Summer Car Care (Apr); Football (Aug); Christmas Photos of Children (Dec); Funeral Directors (Feb); Family Health Guide (Jan); Farm Show (Jul); Father's Day (Jun); Progress (Mar); Christmas (Nov); Diner's Guide (Oct); Ethnic Festival (Sept).
Special Weekly Sections: Best Food, TV, Weekend (Fri)
Syndicated Publications: USA WEEKEND Magazine (S).
Retail Sales Manager .... Keith Graham
Adv. Mgr., Classified .... Nedra Sutch
Cir. Dir. .... Alice Lunn
Ed. .... John Laing Wise
Editorial Writer. .... Joseph Kaspryzk
News Ed. .... David Heastings
Photo Ed. .... Justin Guido
Sports Ed. .... John Enrietto
Mng. Ed. .... Chris Morelli
Market Information: ADS; Split run; TMC.
Mechanical Available: Offset; Black and 4 ROP colors; insert accepted - any; page cutoffs - 21.
Mechanical Specifications: Type page 11 5/8 x 20; E - 6 cols, 1 5/6, 1/8 between; A - 6 cols, 1 5/6, 1/8 between; C - 9 cols, 1 1/6, 1/12 between.
Delivery Method: Mail, Newsstand, CarrierEquipment & Software: PRESSROOM EQUIPMENT: Lines — 7-G/Cosmo double width; MAILROOM EQUIPMENT: Counter Stackers — Galnmeler; Inserters & Stuffers — MM 3270; Tying Machines — Dynaric, Si, MLN.; CLASSIFIED EQUIPMENT: Hardware — 7-APP/Mac IIci, PC; 1-Microtek/Scanner; Printers — CTP; CLASSIFIED SOFTWARE: Brainworks. DISPLAY EQUIPMENT: Hardware — Mac/G-4; Other Hardware — CTP DISPLAY SOFTWAREAd Make-up Applications — Multi-Ad, Adobe/Photoshop, QPS/QuarkXPress; Layout Software — MEI/ ALS. EDITORIAL EQUIPMENT: Hardware — PC; Printers — CTP EDITORIAL SOFTWARE: Microsoft/Word, CNI Open. PRODUCTION EQUIPMENT: Hardware — Douthitt, GMTI; Cameras — 1-C, 1-B; Scanners — Graphic Enterprises/ PageScan 800, AG/Arcus, CD/Scanner 645 IM, CD/Scanview 600, 1-Howtek/7500 PRODUCTION SOFTWARE: QPS/ QuarkXPress.

CARLISLE

THE SENTINEL

457 E North St, Carlisle, Pa., 17013-2655, Cumberland; gen tel (717) 243-2611; ed tel (717) 240-7125; gen fax (717) 243-3754; ed fax (717) 243-3121; gen/nat adv e-mail ads@cumberlink.com; web site www.cumberlink.com
- 1,300,000(views) 270,000(visitors)
Group: Lee Enterprises, Inc.
Published: Mon, Tues, Wed, Thur, Fri, Sat
Weekday Frequency: m
Saturday Frequency: m
Circulation: 8,000; 9,000(sat)
Last Audit: Sworn/Estimate/Non-Audited September 30, 2017
Advertising Rate (weekday/saturday): Open inch rate $30.10
Advertising Rate (sunday): Open inch rate $33.05
News services: AP. **Established:** 1860
Own Printing Facility?: No
Commercial Printers?: No
Special Editions: Welcome (Aug); Football This Week (Dec); Annual (Feb); Brides (Jan); Racing This Week (Jul); Graduation (Jun); Home Improvement (Mar); Car Care (May); Holiday Gift Guide (Nov); Car Care (Oct); Football This Week (Sept).
Special Weekly Sections: History (Mon); Thrive (Tue); Cuisine (Wed); Scene (Thur); Family (Fri); Business, Homes (Sat); Autos, TV Week, Explore (Sun)
Syndicated Publications: Parade Magazine (S)
Proprietary Publications: Cumberland Valley Business Journal
Digital Platform - Mobile: Apple, Android
Digital Platform - Tablet: Apple iOS, Android
Cont .... Stephen Peterson
Ed. .... Jeff Pratt
Prodn. Mgr. .... Patrick Doane
Mktg. Dir. .... Kim Kamowski
Circ. Mgr. .... Kevin Woodward
Market Information: Split run; TMC.
Mechanical Available: Offset; Black and 3 ROP colors; insert accepted; page cutoffs - 22 3/4.
Mechanical Specifications: Type page 11 5/8 x 21 1/2; E - 6 cols, 2 1/16, 1/8 between; A - 6 cols, 2 1/16, 1/8 between; C - 9 cols, 1 1/4, 1/4 between.
Areas Served: Central and western Cumberland County from Mechanicsburg to slightly beyond Newville; Gardners and Idaville in Adams County; York Springs in York County; and central and western Perry County.
Delivery Method: Mail, Newsstand, CarrierEquipment & Software: BUSINESS EQUIPMENT: Sun/Ultra 2 BUSINESS SOFTWARE: Vision Data CLASSIFIED EQUIPMENT: Hardware — 7-Sun/Sparc II; CLASSIFIED SOFTWARE: Vision Data/Classified. DISPLAY EQUIPMENT: Hardware — 9-APP/Mac G3; DISPLAY SOFTWAREAd Make-up Applications — QPS/QuarkXPress 4.0, Adobe/Illustrator, Streamline.; EDITORIAL EQUIPMENT: Hardware — 4-PC-NT Servers, 18-MS/NT Notes Clients/8-APP/Mac G3; Printers — 1-PT/RIP, 1-ECR/108S Pelbox EDITORIAL SOFTWARE: Lotus/Domino Notes.

CHAMBERSBURG

PUBLIC OPINION

77 N 3rd St, Chambersburg, Pa., 17201-1812, Franklin; gen tel (717) 264-6161; adv tel (717) 262-4720; ed tel (717) 262-4764; adv fax (717) 264-2009; ed fax (717) 264-0377; gen/nat adv e-mail gharriger@mediaonespa.com; disp adv e-mail gharriger@mediaonespa.com; class adv e-mailgharriger@mediaonespa.com; ed e-mail bebennett@publicopinion.com; web site www.publicopiniononline.com
- 8,137,364(views) 1,603,024(visitors)
Group: Gannett
Published: Mon, Tues, Wed, Thur, Fri, Sat, Sun
Weekday Frequency: m
Saturday Frequency: m
Circulation: 8,629; 8,629(sat); 12,598(sun)
Last Audit: AAM June 30, 2016
Advertising Rate (weekday/saturday): Open inch rate $37.00
Advertising Rate (sunday): Open inch rate $37.00
News services: AP **Established:** 1869
Own Printing Facility?: Yes
Commercial Printers?: No
Special Editions: Baby Book (Feb), Builders Show (Mar), Golf Preview (Apr), Living in the Valley (Jul), Football Preview (Aug), Holiday Songbook (Dec)
Special Weekly Sections: Food (Wed); Religion, Auto, Weekender (thur); Real Estate (Fri); Business, Religion (Sat); Food, Outdoor, TV (Sun)
Syndicated Publications: USA WEEKEND Magazine (Sun).
Controller .... Caron Decker
Adv. Dir. .... Ginny Harriger
Ed. .... Becky Bennett
Circ. Dir. .... George Fuller
Production Dir. .... Dave Myers
City Ed. .... Andrea Wretch
Sports Ed. .... Ed Gotwals
Prodn. Mgr., Composing/Camera .. Patty Clugston
Circ. Asst. Mgr. .... Nancy Ramer
Pub .... Sara Glines
Market Information: via MediaOne PA
Mechanical Available: Offset - Black and 3 ROP colors;
Mechanical Specifications: Typed page 11 x 21 1/4
Areas Served: 17201 and surrounding in Franklin county, PA
Delivery Method: Mail, Newsstand, Carrier, RacksEquipment & Software: PRESSROOM EQUIPMENT: Lines — 6 units-Goss Urbanite installed 2007.; MAILROOM EQUIPMENT: Counter Stackers — 2/QWI, 1-/SH; Inserters & Stuffers — SH/1472; Tying Machines — MLN; BUSINESS EQUIPMENT: PC BUSINESS SOFTWARE: MS Office 2003, JDE for business, Mactive for Adv, PBS for Circ CLASSIFIED EQUIPMENT: Hardware — PC; Dell; CLASSIFIED SOFTWARE: Mactive DISPLAY EQUIPMENT: Hardware — Mac G4; DISPLAY SOFTWAREAd Make-up Applications — Multi-Ad, Mactive/ QuarkXPress; EDITORIAL EQUIPMENT: Hardware — APP/Mac/Dell and Mac EDITORIAL SOFTWARE: Baseview/ NewsEdit Pro 3.2.3. PRODUCTION SOFTWARE: Baseview/NewsEdit Pro 3.2.3.

CLEARFIELD

THE PROGRESS

PO Box 952, PO Box 291, Clearfield, Pa., 16830-0952, Clearfield; gen tel (814) 765-5581; adv tel (814) 765-9495; ed tel (814) 765-7813; gen fax (814) 765-5165; gen/nat adv e-mail display@theprogressnews.com; disp adv e-mail display@theprogressnews.com; class adv e-mailclassified@theprogressnews.com; ed e-mail news@theprogressnews.com; web site www.theprogressnews.com
- 925,235(views) 32,973(visitors)
Group: Community Media Group
Published: Mon, Tues, Wed, Thur, Fri, Sat
Weekday Frequency: e
Saturday Frequency: m
Circulation: 8,649; 8,649(sat)
Last Audit: CAC March 31, 2014
Newspaper Reps: Mid Atlantic Newspaper Services, Inc.
Advertising Rate (weekday/saturday): Open inch rate $18.73
Advertising Rate (sunday): N/A
News services: AP, **Established:** 1913
Own Printing Facility?: Yes
Commercial Printers?: No
Special Editions: Home & Garden (Apr); Football Tab (Aug); Bridal (Feb); Health & Fitness (Jan); County Fair (Jul); Summer Activities (May); Senior Lifestyles (Monthly); Hunting (Nov); Business (Oct); Holiday (Nov)
Special Weekly Sections: Postscript TV (Fri); Food (Fri).
Syndicated Publications: USA WEEKEND Magazine (Fri).
Pres. .... Margaret Krebs
Treasurer/Controller .... Linda Schultz
Credit Mgr./Purchasing Agent .... Ann K. Law
Asst. Pub./Bus. Mgr. .... Rebecca Johnson
Adv. Mgr., Display .... Jeannine Barger
Circ. Mgr. .... Cindy Aughenbaugh
Ed. .... Jill Golden
Sports Ed. .... Jaclyn Yingling
Prodn. Supt., Plant .... Steve Heichel
Assistant Editor .... Liza Miller
Classified Advertising Manager ..... Shirley Rowles
Market Information: Clearfield County
Mechanical Available: Offset; Black and 3 ROP colors; insert accepted; page cutoffs - 22 3/4.
Mechanical Specifications: Type page 13 x 21 1/2; E - 6 cols, 2 1/16, 1/8 between; A - 6 cols, 2 1/16, 1/8 between; C - 8 cols, 1 5/8, 1/16 between.
Areas Served: Clearfield, Curwensville, Philipsburg, and Moshannon Valley
Delivery Method: Mail, Newsstand, Carrier, RacksEquipment & Software: PRESSROOM EQUIPMENT: Lines — 9-G/Community; MAILROOM EQUIPMENT: Counter Stackers — 1-BG/Count-O-Veyor; Inserters & Stuffers — KAN/320; Tying Machines — Sa.; BUSINESS EQUIPMENT: IBM CLASSIFIED EQUIPMENT: Hardware — OS; Printers — MON; CLASSIFIED SOFTWARE: QPS/Q-Sales. EDITORIAL EQUIPMENT: Hardware — COM/One System; Printers — 4-NewGen EDITORIAL SOFTWARE: QPS/QuarkXpress 4.1. PRODUCTION EQUIPMENT: Hardware — NewGen, Ultra 4000, Ultra/Plus; Cameras — Nipon/Screen; Scanners — HP/Scan Jet 6300C PRODUCTION SOFTWARE: Quark 4.1.

CLINTON

PITTSBURGH POST-GAZETTE

2201 Sweeney Dr, Clinton, Pa., 15026-1818, Beaver; gen tel (412) 263-1100; adv tel (412) 263-1201 (class); ed tel (412) 263-1601; adv fax (412) 263-1263 (class); ed fax (412) 391-8452; gen/nat adv e-mail advertising@post-gazette.com; web site www.post-gazette.com
- 20,965,374(views) 4,400,000(visitors)
Group: Block Communications, Inc.
Published: Mon, Tues, Wed, Thur, Fri, Sat, Sun
Weekday Frequency: m

Saturday Frequency: m
Circulation: 153,738; 147,983(sat); 230,164(sun)
Last Audit: AAM March 31, 2016
Advertising Rate (weekday/saturday): Open inch rate $190.75
Advertising Rate (sunday): Open inch rate $286.25
Online Advertising Rate: CPM 30 days
Daily-26 days $7.63/inch
Sunday (4 days) $1.59/inch
News services: AP, NYT, NEA, WP, TCA, Bloomberg **Established:** 1786
Own Printing Facility?: Yes
Commercial Printers?: Yes
Special Editions: See PG Media Kit: http://pgmediakit.com/
Special Weekly Sections: Food; PowerSource; Local Xtra News, Sports Varsity Xtra; Weekend, Home and Garden; Forum; Travel; Comics; Real Estate
Syndicated Publications: Parade (S).
Proprietary Publications: Distinction Magazine
Digital Platform - Mobile: Apple, Android, Windows
Digital Platform - Tablet: Apple iOS, Kindle, Nook
Chairman, BCI .... Allan Block
Chairman, Publisher & Editor-in-Chief .... John Robinson Block
Human Resources .... Stephen Spolar
Director of Marketing and Audience .... Tracey DeAngelo
Home Delivery Distribution Opns. Mgr. .... Jeffrey Malone
Exec. Ed. & VP .... David Shribman
Asst. Mng. Ed., Content .... Matt Kennedy
Sr. Managing Editor/NewsSlide .... Jerry Micco
Arts Critic .... Mary Thomas
Director of Finance .... Bill Southern
Special Projects & Senior IT Manager . Joe Cronin
General Manager .... Lisa Hurm
Director of Operations .... Rob Weber
Director of Advertising & Digital Initiatives .. Adam Bush
Retail Advertising Manager .... Robert Morgan
Advertising Operation/System Manager. Tim Wirth
Research Mgr. .... Steve Posti
Manager Revenue Development, Classified .... Troy Piekarski
Classified Real Estate Mgr. .... Deb Hansen
Customer Service Supervisor Benjamin Eisenhardt
Managing Editor .... Sally Stapleton
Deputy Managing Editor .... Jim Iovino
Market Information: ADS; Split run; TMC; Zoned editions.
Mechanical Available: Letterpress, Flexo; Black and 3 ROP colors; insert accepted; page cutoffs - 23 9/16.
Mechanical Specifications: Type page 11 1/2 x 22; E - 6 cols, 1 13/16, 1/8 between; A - 6 cols, 1 13/16, 1/8 between; C - 10 cols, 1 2/25, 2/25 between.
Areas Served: Greater Pittsburgh Metropolitan Area
Delivery Method: Mail, Newsstand, Carrier, RacksEquipment & Software: PRESSROOM EQUIPMENT: 2014 Goss Uniliner 6x2 Coldset Printing Press. 48 broadsheet pages, straight, all color. 96 broadsheet pages, collect, all color. Press speed 80,000 CPH straight. Two 255 jaw folders. Four Megtec Reels. Ferag Gripper Conveyor. PRESSROOM SOFTWARE: HarlandSimon MAILROOM EQUIPMENT: Counter Stackers — 6 Quipp 500, 4 Ferag HPS, 2-Heidelberg Olympian; Inserters & Stuffers — Goss Magnapak w/Omnizone; Heidelberg 632 w/ Omnizone; Tying Machines — 4 Dynaric / NP3, 8-Dynaric/NP1500, 4 Samuel; 8-Power Strap under wrap; 3 Schur Palletizer MAILROOM SOFTWARE:OmniZone BUSINESS SOFTWARE: Microsoft/ Office CLASSIFIED SOFTWARE: DTI ClassSpeed DISPLAY EQUIPMENT: Hardware — Engage/DataFlow, 2-Sun/ Ultra, 30-APP/Mac; Printers — X/Docuprint 390; DISPLAY SOFTWAREAd Make-up Applications — Sun/Solaris; Layout Software — MEI/ALS. EDITORIAL EQUIPMENT: Hardware — 2-Sun/Enterprise 2000, 2-Sun/ V880's/265-PC; Printers — Toshiba, HP/ LaserJet EDITORIAL SOFTWARE: Libercus/ DTI/Indesign/InCopy. PRODUCTION EQUIPMENT: Hardware — Na, 1-Na/Starlite, 2-NA/C220 PRODUCTION SOFTWARE: DTI/Edit. CIRCULATION EQUIPMENT: Cloud CIRCULATION SOFTWARNewscycle, PBS

CONNELLSVILLE

DAILY COURIER

127 W Apple St, Connellsville, Pa., 15425-3132, Fayette; gen tel (724) 628-2000; adv tel (724) 628-2000; ed tel (724) 628-2000; gen fax (724) 626-3568; adv fax (724) 626-3568; ed fax (724) 626-3567; gen/nat adv e-mail cwhipley@dailycourier.com; disp adv e-mail cwhipley@dailycourier.com; class adv e-mailrfurman@dailycourier.com; ed e-mail newsroom@dailycourier.com; web site www.dailycourier.com
Group: Sample Media Group
Published: Mon, Tues, Wed, Thur, Fri, Sat, Sun
Weekday Frequency: e
Saturday Frequency: m
Circulation: 5,541; 4,958(sat); 901(sun)
Last Audit: AAM September 30, 2014
Advertising Rate (weekday/saturday): Open inch rate $219.39
Advertising Rate (sunday): Open inch rate $273.98
Online Advertising Rate: PNG ROP Rates per Edition: $194.20 Daily Courier: $15.78
News services: AP. **Established:** 1879
Special Editions: Football Preview (Aug); Year in Review (Dec); Bridal (Jan); Fayette County Fair (Jul); Bridal (Jun); Progress (Mar).
Special Weekly Sections: Society (Mon); Best Food Day (Wed/Sun); Entertainment, Neighborhood (Thur); Home, Garden (Sat); Travel, Real Estate (Sun)
Cir. Mgr. .... Karen Strickland
Mng. Ed. .... Roxanne Abramowitz
Sports Ed. .... Jason Black
Pub. .... Dave Boden
Rec. / Class. .... Marsha Shaffer
Market Information: TMC.
Mechanical Available: Offset; Black and 2 ROP colors; insert accepted; page cutoffs - 22 3/4.
Mechanical Specifications: Type page 13 x 21 1/2; E - 6 cols, 2 1/16, 1/8 between; A - 6 cols, 2 1/16, 1/8 between; C - 9 cols, 1 3/8, 1/16 between.Equipment & Software: MAILROOM EQUIPMENT: Tying Machines — OVL.; BUSINESS SOFTWARE: NCR/Software CLASSIFIED EQUIPMENT: Hardware — 3-Mk.; DISPLAY EQUIPMENT: Printers — 1-APP/Mac LaserPrinter, 2-LaserPrinter/11x17; DISPLAY SOFTWAREAd Make-up Applications — QPS/QuarkXPress, Multi-Ad/Creator; Layout Software — 3-APP/Mac fileserver. EDITORIAL EQUIPMENT: Hardware — APP/Mac EDITORIAL SOFTWARE: QPS/ QuarkXPress, Baseview, Adobe/Photoshop. PRODUCTION EQUIPMENT: Hardware — 2-XIT/Clipper; Cameras — 1-B, 2-Nu, 1-SCREEN.

CORRY

CORRY JOURNAL

28 W South St, Corry, Pa., 16407-1810, Erie; gen tel (814) 665-8291 ; adv tel (814) 665-8291 ext. 21, ext. 22; ed tel (814) 665-8291 ext. 31; gen fax (814) 664-2288; gen/nat adv e-mail tim@thecorryjournal.com; disp adv e-mail corryjournal@tbscc.com; class adv e-mailcorryjournal@tbscc.com; ed e-mail bwilliams@thecorryjournal.com; web site www.thecorryjournal.com
Group: Sample Media Group LLC
Published: Mon, Tues, Wed, Thur, Fri, Sat
Weekday Frequency: e
Saturday Frequency: e
Circulation: 4,300; 3,512(sat)
Last Audit: Sworn/Estimate/Non-Audited September 30, 2017
Advertising Rate (weekday/saturday): Open inch rate $8.50 (Mon-Fri) $9.50 (Sat)
News services: AP.
Special Weekly Sections: Best Food Day (Sat)
Syndicated Publications: American Profile (Weekly).
Pub. .... Bob Williams
Mng. Ed. .... Erin Passinger
Adv. Sales Mgr. .... Tim Joncas
Cir. Mgr. .... Terri Malek
Angie Burlew
Market Information: TMC.
Mechanical Available: Offset; Black and 3 ROP colors; insert accepted; page cutoffs - 22 1/4.
Mechanical Specifications: Type page 13 3/4 x 21 1/2; E - 6 cols, 2 1/16, 1/8 between; A - 6 cols, 2 1/16, 1/8 between; C - 6 cols, 2 1/16, 1/8 between.Equipment & Software: PRESSROOM EQUIPMENT: Lines — G/ Community.; MAILROOM EQUIPMENT: Counter Stackers — Count-o-Veyor; Tying Machines — 1/Sa; Address Machine — 1-/ Am; BUSINESS SOFTWARE: ListMaster 10.26 CLASSIFIED EQUIPMENT: Hardware — APP/Mac G3; Printers — HP/8150N; CLASSIFIED SOFTWARE: Class Act 1.0. EDITORIAL EQUIPMENT: Hardware — APP/iMac; Printers — Xante/Accel-a-Writer 3G, HP/8150N EDITORIAL SOFTWARE: Baseview/NewsEdit Pro 3.3. PRODUCTION EQUIPMENT: Hardware — APP/Mac Laser; Cameras — SCREEN; Scanners — 1-L/32 PRODUCTION SOFTWARE: QPS/ QuarkXPress 4.0.

DOYLESTOWN

THE INTELLIGENCER

333 N Broad St, Doylestown, Pa., 18901-3407, Bucks; gen tel (215) 345-3000; adv tel (215) 345-3080; ed tel (215) 345-3050; gen fax (215)345-3150; adv fax (215)345-3150; ed fax (215)345-3150; gen/nat adv e-mail komalley@calkins.com; disp adv e-mail komalley@calkins.com; class adv e-mailclassifieds@calkins.com; ed e-mail news@calkins.com; web site www.theintell.com
Group: Calkins Media
Published: Mon, Tues, Wed, Thur, Fri, Sun
Weekday Frequency: m
Circulation: 18,325; 26,337(sun)
Last Audit: AAM June 30, 2016
Advertising Rate (weekday/saturday): Open inch rate $23.00
Advertising Rate (sunday): Open inch rate $25.50
News services: AP. **Established:** 1804
Special Editions: Newspapers in Education (Apr); Savings (Jan); Auto (Oct).
Special Weekly Sections: At Home (Sat).
Syndicated Publications: Parade (S).
Pub. .... Mike Scobey
Controller .... Timothy J. Weaver
Adv. Dir. .... Kim Noble
Adv. Mgr., Classified/Retail .... Dale Machesic
Circ. Dir. .... William B. Lobecker
Mktg. Dir. .... Eric P. Eberhardt
Exec. Ed. .... Lanny Morgnanesi
Editorial Page Ed. .... Alan Kerr
Features Ed. .... Stacy Briggs
Sports Ed. .... Jeff Beideman
Systems Mgr. .... Paul Rohrman
Prodn. Dir. .... Bob Braun
Prodn. Foreman, Pressroom .... Tom Newman
Adv.Mng. Retail .... Kevin O'Malley
Dir. of Adv. .... Deanna Fox
Executive Ed. .... Patricia S. Meagher Walker
David Gilmartin
Exec. Ed .... Pat Walker
Market Information: Split run; TMC.
Mechanical Available: Offset; Black and 3 ROP colors; insert accepted - odd sizes accepted; page cutoffs - 22 1/2.
Mechanical Specifications: Type page 13 x 21 1/2; E - 6 cols, 2 1/16, 1/8 between; A - 6 cols, 2 1/16, 1/8 between; C - 9 cols, 1 3/8, 1/16 between.
Areas Served: Central Bucks County, Upper Bucks County and Eastern Montgomery County
Equipment & Software: PRESSROOM EQUIPMENT: Lines — 10-G/Urbanite 1973; Pasters —Enkel/Splicer; Reels & Stands — Press Registration System Duarte/Pin.; MAILROOM EQUIPMENT: Counter Stackers — 1/QWI, QWI/350B; Inserters & Stuffers — GMA/SLS 1000 8:1; Tying Machines — 1-/Power Strap, 1-/ MLN; Wrapping Singles — 1-/Sa; Address Machine — 1-/KR.; BUSINESS EQUIPMENT: IBM/9672 CLASSIFIED EQUIPMENT: Hardware — Mac/True; CLASSIFIED SOFTWARE: Cras. DISPLAY EQUIPMENT: Hardware — 8-APP/Mac, 3-PC 486; Printers — HP/Laser; DISPLAY SOFTWAREAd Make-up Applications — Adobe/PageMaker; Layout Software — IBM, SCS/Layout 8000. EDITORIAL EQUIPMENT: Hardware — 20-Dell/Novell/File Server, 60-PC; Printers — 1-IBM/3287, 2-EM/Imagesetter 3850 EDITORIAL SOFTWARE: ACI/Open Pages. PRODUCTION EQUIPMENT: Hardware — 1-NewGen/Laser, EM/Imagesetter 3850; Cameras — 1-C/Spartan II, 1-AG/6000; Scanners — 2-HP/Scanner PRODUCTION SOFTWARE: QPS/QuarkXPress.
Note: There is a Greater Philadelphia Newspaper group combination of $239.00 (d) & $251.00 (S) among Levittown Bucks County Courier (mS), Doylestown Intelligencer (mS) & Willingboro (NJ) Burlington County Times (mS). Individual newspaper rates not made availabl

DU BOIS

THE COURIER EXPRESS

500 Jeffers St, Du Bois, Pa., 15801-2430, Clearfield; gen tel (814) 371-4200; adv tel (814)503-8877; ed tel (814)503-8863; gen fax (814) 371-3241; adv fax (814)371-3241; ed fax (814)371-3241; gen/nat adv e-mail ads@thecourierexpress.com; disp adv e-mail ads@thecourierexpress.com; class adv e-mailclassified@thecourierexpress.com; ed e-mail letters@thecourierexpress.com; web site www.thecourierexpress.com
Group: Community Media Group
Published: Mon, Tues, Wed, Thur, Fri, Sun
Weekday Frequency: e
Circulation: 8,420; 14,002(sun)
Last Audit: AAM September 30, 2012
Advertising Rate (weekday/saturday): Open inch rate $12.70
Advertising Rate (sunday): Open inch rate $15.30
News services: AP, SHNS. **Established:** 1872
Own Printing Facility?: Yes
Commercial Printers?: Yes
Special Editions: Homes and Gardens (Apr); Fall Sports (Aug); Christmas Greetings (Dec); Cooking (Feb); Bridal (Jan); Little League All-Star (Jul); Vacation Close to Home (Jun); Easter Dining (Mar); Graduation and Careers (May); Christmas Kick-Off (Nov); Hunting (Oct); Fal
Special Weekly Sections: Snapshots Photo Page (Fri); Business Pages (S); Business Pages (Thur); Outdoors (Wed).
Syndicated Publications: Comics (S). TV (S)
Controller .... S.W. Kronenwetter
Adv. Dir., Nat'l .... Linda L. Smith
Adv. Mgr., Classified .... Dory Ferra
Circ. Mgr. .... Jim Nestlerode
Mng. Ed. .... Nick Hoffman
Copy Ed. .... Dena Bosak
News Ed. .... Alice Bish Sylvis
Sports Ed. .... Scott Shindledecker
Sunday Ed. .... Joy Norwood
Pub. .... Pat Patterson
Market Information: TMC; Zoned editions.
Mechanical Available: Offset; Black and 3 ROP colors; insert accepted; page cutoffs - 22 3/4.
Mechanical Specifications: Type page 13 x 21 1/2; E - 6 cols, 2 1/16, 1/6 between; A - 6 cols, 2 1/16, 1/6 between; C - 8 cols, 1 1/2, 1/6 between.
Areas Served: 15801, 15825, 15851, 15711, 15860, 15829, 15840, 15767, 15860, 15715, 15824, 168938, 15828, 16830, 15829, 16833, 15860, 15848, 15849, 15847, 15860, 15863
Delivery Method: Mail, Newsstand, Carrier, RacksEquipment & Software: PRESSROOM EQUIPMENT: Lines — 8-WPC/Atlas (with 2-Quadra-Color Unit); 8-KP/News King.; MAILROOM EQUIPMENT: Counter Stackers — 2-BG/Count-O-Veyor; Inserters & Stuffers — 1-MM/227E; Tying Machines — 2/Sa, Power Strap/250.; BUSINESS EQUIPMENT: IBM/RISC 6000 BUSINESS SOFTWARE: Solomon CLASSIFIED EQUIPMENT: Hardware — Mac; CLASSIFIED SOFTWARE: MediaSpan DISPLAY EQUIPMENT: Hardware — Mac; DISPLAY SOFTWAREAd Make-up Applications — MediaSpan; Layout Software — InDesign, Illustrator EDITORIAL EQUIPMENT: Hardware — Mac OSX 10.7; Printers — HP/4MV, QMS/2060 EDITORIAL SOFTWARE: MediaSpan PRODUCTION EQUIPMENT: Hardware — Kodak Trendsetter; Cameras — SCREEN/20 x 24 Horizontal Low Bed; Scanners — Umax

EASTON

THE EXPRESS-TIMES

30 N 4th St, Easton, Pa., 18042-3528, Northampton; gen tel (610)258-7171; adv tel (610)258-7171; ed tel (610)258-7171; gen fax (610)258-7130; adv fax (610) 559-7240; ed fax (610)258-7130; gen/nat adv e-mail advertising@express-times.com; disp adv e-mail expresstimesads@lehighvalleytimes.com; class adv e-mailexpresstimeads@lehighvalleytimes.com; ed e-mail news@express-times.com; web site www.lehighvalleylive.com
Group: Advance Publications, Inc.
Published: Mon, Tues, Wed, Thur, Fri, Sat, Sun
Weekday Frequency: m
Saturday Frequency: m
Circulation: 25,424; 16,810(sat); 32,853(sun)
Last Audit: AAM June 30, 2016
Advertising Rate (weekday/saturday): Open inch rate $56.00
Advertising Rate (sunday): $64.40
Online Advertising Rate: $10 CPM
News services: AP, Metro Suburbia Inc., LAT-WP, NNS.
Special Weekly Sections: Exposed, Entertainment Guide (Fri); Building & Real Estate Guide (Sun);
Syndicated Publications: Relish (Monthly); TV Update (quarterfold) (S).
Digital Platform - Mobile: Apple, Android, Windows, Blackberry
Digital Platform - Tablet: Apple iOS, Android, Windows 7, Blackberry Tablet OS, Kindle, Nook, Kindle Fire
President and Publisher .... Lou Stancampiano
Credit Mgr. .... Rebecca Weaver
HR ....Sherry Ferrello
Editor... Jim Deegan
Asst. Mng. Ed. .... Tony Rhodin
Lehigh Valley Editor.......................... Rudy Miller
Editorial Page Ed. ....James Flagg
Prodn. Mgr., Pre Press........................Sue Tyson
Mng. Ed ....Nick Falsone
Online Dir...............................Alyssa Passeggio
Advertising Sales Manager.............Rob Rindock
Adv Sales Manager.................Camille Lo Sapio
Market Information: Split run; TMC; Zoned editions.
Mechanical Available: Offset; Black and 3 ROP colors; insert accepted; page cutoffs - 22.
Mechanical Specifications: Type page 13 x 21; E - 6 cols, 2 1/16, 1/8 between; A - 6 cols, 1 5/6, 1/8 between; C - 10 cols, 1 3/16, 1/16 between.
Areas Served: 08865, 07823,07825, 07844, 07829, 07832, 07833, 07838, 07863, 07882, 08808, 07840, 07865, 08826, 08827, 07830, 08829, 08809, 0886, 08822, 08833, 08888, 08825, 08802, 08801, 08804, 08867, 08848, 18360, 18014, 18045, 18040, 18020, 18055, 18063, 18013, 18343, 1835, 18072, 18091, 18353, 18042, 18077, 18972, 18109, 18067, 18064, 18083, 18085, 18015, 18017, 18018
Delivery Method: Newsstand, Carrier, RacksEquipment & Software: BUSINESS EQUIPMENT: Dec/VAX 4000, Dec/Alpha, Addrox/50 VT 420, 20-PC WS BUSINESS SOFTWARE: Geac CJ/AIM, CIS, Lotus 1-2-3, WordPerfect 5.0, CJ CLASSIFIED EQUIPMENT: Hardware — 20-PPI/ Advertising Management System Classified; Novell/Netware 4.11; Printers — HP/3, APP/ Mac 8500; CLASSIFIED SOFTWARE: PPI/ Advertising Management System Classified, Class/Act Pagination. DISPLAY EQUIPMENT: Hardware — Compaq/3000, Compaq/WS, APP/Mac; Printers — APP/Mac 8500; Other Hardware — CNI/Ad Database DISPLAY SOFTWAREAd Make-up Applications — QPS/QuarkXPress, CNI/Btrieve; Layout Software — MEI/ALS, Novell, Compaq/3000. EDITORIAL EQUIPMENT: Hardware — Compaq/3000, Compaq/PC WS/Novell/ Netware 4.11; Printers — AST/8200 EDITORIAL SOFTWARE: CNI/Database, Microsoft/Word, QPS/QuarkXPress 3.32. PRODUCTION EQUIPMENT: Hardware — Nu/Flip Top, RIP NT, 1-ECR/4500 RIP NT, G/ OPI; Cameras — 1-C/Spartan II; Scanners — ECR/Autokon 1000, Umax/Mirage PRODUCTION SOFTWARE: Adobe Creative Suite, CNI/Btrieve Data, MEI/CLS, ALS.

ELLWOOD CITY

ELLWOOD CITY LEDGER

501 Lawrence Ave, Ellwood City, Pa., 16117-1927, Lawrence; gen tel (724) 758-5573; adv tel (724)846-6300; ed tel (724) 758-5573; gen fax (724) 758-2410; adv fax (724)758-2410; ed fax (724)758-2410; gen/nat adv e-mail ads@ellwoodcityledger.com; disp adv e-mail ads@ellwoodcityledger.com; class adv e-mailads@ellwoodcityledger.com; ed e-mail eclnews@ellwoodcityledger.com; web site www.ellwoodcityledger.com
Group: Calkins Media
Published: Mon, Tues, Wed, Thur, Fri, Sat
Weekday Frequency: m
Saturday Frequency: m
Circulation: 3,425; 3,425(sat)
Last Audit: Sworn/Estimate/Non-Audited September 30, 2017
Advertising Rate (weekday/saturday): Open inch rate $15.23
News services: AP, U.S. Suburban Press Inc.. **Established:** 1920
Special Editions: Annual Progress (Apr); Fall Bridal (Aug); Arts, Crafts & Food Festival (Jul); Visitor's Guide (Jun); Lawn & Garden (Mar); Car Care (May); Homefinders (Monthly); Health Care (Oct); Home Improvement (Sept).
Special Weekly Sections: Food Day (Mon); Food Day (Sat); Food Day (Wed).
Exec. Ed... Lisa Micco
Ed.......................................Steve Gugliociello
Market Information: ADS; TMC; Zoned editions.
Mechanical Available: Offset; Black and 3 ROP colors; insert accepted - single sheet; page cutoffs - 22 3/4.
Mechanical Specifications: Type page 13 x 21 1/2; E - 6 cols, 2 1/14, 1/6 between; A - 6 cols, 2 1/14, 1/6 between; C - 6 cols, 2 1/14, 1/6 between.Equipment & Software: PRESSROOM EQUIPMENT: Lines — 5-G/Community; Folders — 1-G/SSC.; MAILROOM EQUIPMENT: Tying Machines — 2-EAM-Mosca; Address Machine — 2/ Ch.; BUSINESS EQUIPMENT: 3-APP/ iMac BUSINESS SOFTWARE: Baseview CLASSIFIED EQUIPMENT: Hardware — 4-APP/iMac; Printers — HP/8000, AG/ Accuset; CLASSIFIED SOFTWARE: Baseview, QPS/QuarkXPress 4.0. DISPLAY EQUIPMENT: Hardware — APP/iMac; Printers — HP/8000, AG/Accuset; Other Hardware — Epson/Scanner, Microtec, AG DISPLAY SOFTWAREAd Make-up Applications — Aldus/PageMaker, QPS/ QuarkXPress, Multi-Ad/Creator 2.6; Layout Software — 3-APP/Power Mac, 2-APP/ Mac G3. EDITORIAL EQUIPMENT: Hardware — 7-PC/Lf/AP Leaf Picture Desk; Printers — HP/8000, AG/Accuset EDITORIAL SOFTWARE: Microsoft/Word, QPS/QuarkXPress 4.0. PRODUCTION EQUIPMENT: Hardware — 1-K, HP/8000 Plain Paper; Cameras — 1-B PRODUCTION SOFTWARE: QPS/QuarkXPress 4.0, Microsoft/Windows, APP/Mac.

ERIE

ERIE TIMES-NEWS

205 W 12th St, Erie, Pa., 16534-0002, Erie; gen tel (814) 870-1600; adv tel (814) 878-1642; ed tel (814) 870-1715; gen fax (814) 870-1615; adv fax (814) 870-1632; ed fax (814) 870-1808; gen/nat adv e-mail susan.schreiner@timesnews.com; disp adv e-mail kate.weber@timesnews.com; class adv e-mailclassify@timesnews.com ; ed e-mail letters@timesnews.com; web site www.goerie.com
Group: New Media Investment Group
Published: Mon, Tues, Wed, Thur, Fri, Sat, Sun
Weekday Frequency: m
Saturday Frequency: m
Circulation: 36,007; 35,770(sat); 49,603(sun)
Last Audit: AAM September 30, 2016
News services: AP, LAT-WP, MCT. **Established:** 1888
Own Printing Facility?: No
Commercial Printers?: No
Special Editions: Spring Car Care (Apr); New Year's Dining Guide (Dec); Home Remodeling (Feb); Bridal (Jan); Senior Lifestyle (Jul); Graduation (Jun); Easter Dining (Mar); Golf (May); Thanksgiving Dining Guide (Nov); Fall Car Care (Oct); Progress (Quarterly); Bridal (Sept)
Special Weekly Sections: Health, Learning (Mon); Home, Garden, Business (Tue); Food, Business (Wed); Entertainment, Family (Thur); Business, Weekend (Fri); Home (Sat); Business, Comics, Religion, Sunday Living (Sun)
Syndicated Publications: Parade, TV Schedule (Sun); Her Times; Lake Erie Lifestyle
Digital Platform - Mobile: Apple, Android, Windows
Digital Platform - Tablet: Apple iOS
Mng. Ed. .... Pat Howard
Online News Ed. .... Matt Martin
CTO..Rich Frosgren
Opns. Dir........................................David Stolar
Pub...Kenneth Nelson
Market Information: ADS; Split run; TMC; Zoned editions.
Mechanical Available: Offset; Black and 3 ROP colors; insert accepted; page cutoffs - 22 3/4.
Mechanical Specifications: Type page 11 1/16 x 21 1/2; E - 6 cols, 1 13/16, 1/64 between; A - 6 cols, 1 5/6, 1/8 between; C - 10 cols, 1 1/8, 7/16 between.
Delivery Method: Mail, Newsstand, Carrier, RacksEquipment & Software: PRESSROOM EQUIPMENT: Lines — 7-G/Metro (3 half decks) 1969; Folders — 1-G/double 2:1.; MAILROOM EQUIPMENT: Counter Stackers — 1-Id/NS550, 2-Id/NS2000, 1-Id/2100; Inserters & Stuffers — 1-GMA/ SLS 1000 (17 head), 1-GMA/SLS 1000 (9 head); Tying Machines — 3-MLN/2A, 2/Sa, 3-/Power Strap.; BUSINESS EQUIPMENT: 2-DEC/VAX 6510 BUSINESS SOFTWARE: Compushare, In-house CLASSIFIED EQUIPMENT: Hardware — DEC/PDP 11-84; 12-NSSE/400, 2-Sun/Sparc II; CLASSIFIED SOFTWARE: Atex. DISPLAY EQUIPMENT: Hardware — 2-Cx, APP/Mac Quadras, 5-Cx, Sun/Sparc 5 Breeze, APP/Power Mac 8100-80, 2-Sun/Sparc 20 Server, 2-Sun/ Sparc II Gateway; DISPLAY SOFTWAREAd Make-up Applications — Multi-Ad/Creator 3.6.1; Layout Software — SCS/Layout 8000, Xpance/Multi-Ad, 2-Sun/Sparc II. EDITORIAL EQUIPMENT: Hardware — DEC/PDP 11-84/30-NSSE/400, 4-APP/Mac Quadra EDITORIAL SOFTWARE: DEC/TMS, Agile/ Teambase. PRODUCTION EQUIPMENT: Hardware — Futura, Alfa-Quest, Pantera/32; Scanners — 2-AG/T-5000 Plus.

GETTYSBURG

GETTYSBURG TIMES

1570 Fairfield Rd, Gettysburg, Pa., 17325-7252, Adams; gen tel (717) 334-1131; adv tel (717) 253-9403; ed tel (717) 253-9413; gen fax (717) 334-4243; adv fax (717)334-4243; ed fax (717) 334-7408; gen/nat adv e-mail npritt@gettysburgtimes.com; disp adv e-mail npritt@gettysburgtimes.com; class adv e-mailclass@gettysburgtimes.com; ed e-mail ahayes@gettysburgtimes.com; web site www.gettysburgtimes.com - 1,654,701(views) 109,628(visitors)
Group: Sample News Group LLC
Published: Mon, Tues, Wed, Thur, Fri, Sat
Weekday Frequency: m
Saturday Frequency: m
Circulation: 10,520; 11,605(sat)
Last Audit: USPS March 31, 2013
Advertising Rate (weekday/saturday): Open inch rate $16.75
Online Advertising Rate: Leaderboard $14.00; Big Box #1 (video avail. for an addt'l. $50) $13.00; Big Box #2 (video avail. for an addt'l. $50) $12.00; Small Box $7.00; Anchor Banner $10.00
News services: AP, DF, MCT, SHNS, TMS, Washington Post News Group. **Established:** 1802
Own Printing Facility?: Yes
Commercial Printers?: No
Special Editions: Spring Lawn & Garden (Apr); Football Preview (Fall); Bridal Faire (Feb); Medical/Wellness Guide (Jul); Community Fact Book (Jun); Spring Automotive (Mar); Holiday Songbook (Nov); Bridal Tab (Quarterly); Spring Home Improvement (Spring); Winter Sports Prev
Special Weekly Sections: LifeStyles Feature (Wed); Arts & Leisure Feature (Thurs); Food For Thought Feature (Thurs); HomeStyle Section (Fri); Religion Feature (Sat)
Syndicated Publications: Parade (Sat).
Digital Platform - Mobile: Apple, Android, Windows, Blackberry
Digital Platform - Tablet: Apple iOS, Android, Windows 7, Blackberry Tablet OS, Kindle, Nook, Kindle Fire
Pub....Harry Hartman
Mng. Ed. .... Alex Hayes
Sports Ed. ....Josh Martin
Webmaster...................................... Kristy Allen
Sales Mgr........................................Nancy Pritt
Class. ....Debi Orndoff
Mechanical Available: Offset; Black and 3 ROP colors; insert accepted; page cutoffs - 21.
Mechanical Specifications: Type page 12 1/8 x 21; E - 6 cols, 1 5/6, 1/8 between; A - 6 cols, 1 5/6, 1/16 between; C - 9 cols, 1 5/24, 1/8 between.
Areas Served: 17325, 17307, 17320, 17353, 17310, 17306, 17331, 17340, 17372, 17344, 17350, 17304
Delivery Method: Mail, Newsstand, Carrier, RacksEquipment & Software: PRESSROOM EQUIPMENT: Lines — 8-G/Community Offset 1982; 4-G 1982; Folders — 1, 2-G/2:1.; MAILROOM EQUIPMENT: Tying Machines — 2/Sa; BUSINESS EQUIPMENT: Dell PC BUSINESS SOFTWARE: Microsoft Office CLASSIFIED EQUIPMENT: Hardware — Dell PC; CLASSIFIED SOFTWARE: Newzware DISPLAY EQUIPMENT: Hardware — Dell PC; Printers — HP/Color Laserjet BizHub; DISPLAY SOFTWAREAd Make-up Applications — Adobe/Illustrator, Adobe InAdobe InDesign CS5 Adobe/Photoshop; EDITORIAL EQUIPMENT: Hardware — Dell PC/Various Scanners; Printers — BizHub EDITORIAL SOFTWARE: Newzware PRODUCTION EQUIPMENT: Hardware — Panther Pro 62 Imagesetter, ; Cameras — Nikon still Canon video; Scanners — Umax/600s, Umax/1200s, Coolscan III, Nikon PRODUCTION SOFTWARE: FSI.

GREENSBURG

TRIBUNE-REVIEW

622 Cabin Hill Dr, Greensburg, Pa., 15601-1657, Westmoreland; gen tel (724) 838-5124; adv tel (724) 779-6959; ed tel (412) 321-6460; gen fax (412) 871-2351; adv fax (412) 871-2351; ed fax (412) 871-2351; gen/nat adv e-mail info@tribweb.com; disp adv e-mail golvido@tribweb.com; class adv e-mailgolvido@tribweb.com; ed e-mail tribcity@tribweb.com; web site www.triblive.com
4,737,075(visitors)
Group: Trib Total Media, Inc.
Published: Mon, Tues, Wed, Thur, , Sat, Sun
Weekday Frequency: m
Saturday Frequency: m
Circulation: 108,810; 90,160(sat); 200,592(sun)
Last Audit: AAM September 30, 2014
Advertising Rate (weekday/saturday): Open inch rate $219.39
Advertising Rate (sunday): Open Inch Rate $273.98
Online Advertising Rate: Open Rate $96.37 (Weekly); $141.37 (Sunday)
News services: AP, CNS, MCT, LAT-WP.
Special Editions: College Football (Aug); RV Show (Dec); Enterprise (Feb); Bridal (Jan); Steeler Training Camp (Jul); Medical Directory (Mar); Summer Fun (May); Gift Guide (Nov); Quest for the Best (Oct); Pro Football (Sept).
Special Weekly Sections: Society (Mon); Best Food Day (Wed, Sun); Entertainment, Neighborhood (Thur); Home, Garden (Sat); Travel, Real Estate (Sun)
Syndicated Publications: Ticket (Fri); Relish (Monthly); USA WEEKEND Magazine (S); American Profile (Weekly).
Chrmn./Pub............................ Richard M. Scaife
Pres...Ralph Martin
COO ....Jennifer Bertetto
Gen. Mgr., Westmoreland .... Arthur McMullen
Exec. Asst. to Pres.........................Martha Smith

Adv. Mgr., Major Accts. .... Nick Monico
Adv. Mgr., Nat'l .... Michele Vergenes
Vice Pres., Mktg. .... Kraig Cawley
Ed. .... Frank Craig
Ed. .... Sue McFarland
Deputy Mng. Ed., Features .... Sally Quinn
Bus. Ed. .... John Oravecz
City Ed., Westmoreland .... Frank Myers
Editorial Page Ed. .... Colin McNickle
Graphics Dir. .... Robert Newell
News Ed., Pittsburgh .... Sue Jones
Metro Ed. .... Gloria Ruane
Major/Nat'l Sales Exec. .... Gloria Olvido
Exec. Dir., Sales .... William M. Cotter
Managing Ed. .... Jim Cuddy Jr.
Deputy Managing Ed. .... Jim Kubus
Deputy Managing Ed. .... Sandra Tolliver
Systems Ed. .... Dirk Kaufman
Ops. Mgr. .... Carol Shrefler
Chief of Photography, Opinion .... Barry Reeger
Market Information: Split run; Zoned editions.
Mechanical Available: Offset; Black and 3 ROP colors; insert accepted; page cutoffs - 22 3/4.
Mechanical Specifications: Type page 13 x 21 1/2; E - 6 cols, 2 1/16, 1/8 between; A - 6 cols, 2 1/16, 1/8 between; C - 10 cols, 1 1/4, 1/16 between.
Areas Served: Westmoreland, Armstrong, Fayette and Indiana CountiesEquipment & Software: PRESSROOM EQUIPMENT: Lines — 5-G/Metro (2 color) 1978; 1-G/ Metro (Color Tower) 1994; 5-G/Newsliner (31 couples) 1997; 8-G/Universal 70 1999; Folders — G/double 2:1, G/double 3:2; Reels & Stands — 7, 6, 8.; MAILROOM EQUIPMENT: Counter Stackers — 2/HL, 2-/QWI, 6-/QWI; Inserters & Stuffers — HI, GMA, 72-P/Double Out, 2-GMA/SLS 2000, 1-GMA/SLS 1000; Tying Machines — 2-/ MLN, 5-/QWI; Control System — GMA/ SAM; Address Machine — KR.; BUSINESS EQUIPMENT: IBM BUSINESS SOFTWARE: Brainworks, PBS CLASSIFIED EQUIPMENT: Hardware — Intel; CLASSIFIED SOFTWARE: PPI/Informatel. DISPLAY EQUIPMENT: Hardware — APP/Mac; Printers — MON, HP; DISPLAY SOFTWAREAd Make-up Applications — Multi-Ad/Creator; Layout Software — APP/Mac. EDITORIAL EQUIPMENT: Hardware — IBM/APP/ Mac Pagination EDITORIAL SOFTWARE: Newsengin. PRODUCTION EQUIPMENT: Hardware — 3-MON/Express Master, 3-MON/Paper Express, 3-AG/Advantra 25, NewsWorks; Cameras — C, Spartan/ II, Spartan/III PRODUCTION SOFTWARE: QPS/QuarkXPress.

HAZLETON

HAZLETON STANDARD-SPEAKER

21 N Wyoming St, Hazleton, Pa., 18201-6068, Luzerne; gen tel (570) 455-3636; adv tel (570) 455-3636; ed tel (570) 455-3636 ext. 3615; gen fax (570) 455-4244; adv fax (570) 455-4244; ed fax (570) 455-4408; gen/nat adv e-mail sales@standardspeaker.com; disp adv e-mail sales@standardspeaker.com; class adv e-mailsales@standardspeaker.com; ed e-mail editorial@standardspeaker.com; web site www.standardspeaker.com - 1,000,000(views) 140,000(visitors)
Group: Times-Shamrock Communications
Published: Mon, Tues, Wed, Thur, Fri, Sun
Weekday Frequency: m
Saturday Frequency: m
Circulation: 10,540; 11,763(sun)
Last Audit: AAM December 31, 2017
Advertising Rate (weekday/saturday): Open inch rate $36.73
Advertising Rate (sunday): Open inch rate $36.73
News services: AP. **Established:** 1866
Own Printing Facility?: Yes
Special Editions: Home Improvement (Apr); Football Preview (Aug); Christmas Greetings (Dec); Bridal (Feb); Bridal II (Jul); Progress (Jun); Create An Ad (Mar); Senior Citizen (May); Holiday Gift Guide (Nov); Dining Guides (Oct); FunFest (Sept).
Special Weekly Sections: Best Food Day (Wed); Business (Mon); Health, Science, School (Tue); Food (Wed); Business, Golf (Thur); Sports, NASCAR (Fri); Real Estate, Travel (Sat); TV, Home, Arts, Outdoors, Travel, Business (Sun)
Syndicated Publications: TV Showtime (S); Best Food Days (Sat); Best Food Days (Wed); American Profile (Weekly).
Pres./Pub./CEO .... Scott Lynett
Adv. Dir. .... Paul Ross
Ops. Mgr. .... John Patton
Circ. Mgr., Distr. .... Gary Klinger
Lifestyle Ed. .... Mildred Rubinote
News Ed. .... Carl Christopher
Sports Ed. .... Babe Conroy
Prodn. Mgr. .... James R. Seybert
Prodn. Supt., Composing .... David Steiner
Pub. .... Matthew Haggerty
Gen. Mgr. .... Don Farley
Ed. .... Mark Katchur
Market Information: Southern Luzerne County and parts of Schuylkill and Carbon counties
Mechanical Available: Offset; Black and 3 ROP colors; insert accepted; page cutoffs - 21 1/2.
Mechanical Specifications: Type page 13 x 21 1/2; E - 6 cols, 2 1/16, 1/8 between; A - 6 cols, 2 1/16, 1/8 between; C - 9 cols, 1 3/8, 5/64 between.
Delivery Method: Newsstand, Carrier, RacksEquipment & Software: PRESSROOM EQUIPMENT: Lines — 5-G/Cosmo double width 1975; Press Drive — Fin w/2 GE 150 h.p. DC Motor; Control System — Fin/ Cabinet 2.; MAILROOM EQUIPMENT: Tying Machines — 1-MLN/ML2EE, 1-EAM-Mosca.; BUSINESS EQUIPMENT: IBM/C320 Power Station BUSINESS SOFTWARE: Vision Data 7.0, APT CLASSIFIED EQUIPMENT: Hardware — 8-HP/Vectra VE 8; APP/Mac Quadra 605, APP/Super Mac; Printers — ECR/Scriptsetter, 2-HP/LaserJet; CLASSIFIED SOFTWARE: APT/Classified. DISPLAY EQUIPMENT: Hardware — 8-HP/ Vectra VL6/450, 2-APP/Mac G3; Printers — HP/8000 N; Other Hardware — Image Scanner DISPLAY SOFTWAREAd Make-up Applications — QPS/QuarkXPress 4.04; Layout Software — APT/Ad Master. EDITORIAL EQUIPMENT: Hardware — 18-HP/Vectra VL6/450, 3-HP/Net Server 3/2-ECR/Imagesetter; Printers — 2-HP/8000 N EDITORIAL SOFTWARE: APT/Editorial. PRODUCTION EQUIPMENT: Hardware — LE/Maxim 26, 2-RIP with ECRM Pelbox; Cameras — C/Spartan III; Scanners — HP/ Scan Jet IIC, AG/T2000XL PRODUCTION SOFTWARE: QPS/QuarkXPress 4.04.

HONESDALE

THE WAYNE INDEPENDENT

220 8th St, Honesdale, Pa., 18431-1854, Wayne; gen tel (570) 253-3055 ext 301; adv tel (570) 253-3055 ext. 301; ed tel (570) 253-3055 ext. 329; gen fax (570) 253-5387; adv fax (570) 253-5387; ed fax (570) 253-5387; gen/nat adv e-mail mfleece@wayneindependent.com; disp adv e-mail mfleece@wayneindependent.com; class adv e-mailpjordan@wayneindependent.com; ed e-mail mleet@wayneindependent.com; web site www.wayneindependent.com - 148,912(views) 32,177(visitors)
Group: GateHouse Media, Inc.
Published: Tues, Wed, Thur, Fri, Sat
Weekday Frequency: m
Saturday Frequency: m
Circulation: 2,618; 2,618(sat)
Last Audit: USPS October 1, 2016
Newspaper Reps: Kevin Bernitt, Ashley Starnes, Peter Bocchieri and Carmon Flynn
Branch Offices: Honesdale, Hawley, Carbondale, Moscow and Milford
Advertising Rate (weekday/saturday): Open inch rate $17.21
Advertising Rate (sunday): N/A
Online Advertising Rate: 25% SOV $225/Month
News services: AP. **Established:** 1878
Own Printing Facility?: No
Commercial Printers?: No
Special Editions: Bridal Guide; Progress Edition; Home Improvement; Wayne County Fair/Jr Livestock Edition; Health; Family Magazine; Real Estate Guide; Restaurant/Dining
Special Weekly Sections: Business (Daily); Health, Home, Entertainment (Sat)
Syndicated Publications: American Profile (Weekly), Spry, Relish and Athlon (Monthly), Parade, TV Week
Group Sports Editor .... Kevin Edwards
Pub./Adv. Dir. .... Michelle Fleece
Managing Editor .... Melissa Lee
Market Information: TMC.
Mechanical Available: Offset; Black and Full color; inserts accepted - all; page cutoffs - 22 1/2.
Mechanical Specifications: Type page 13 x 21; E - 6 cols, 2 1/6, 1/4 between; A - 6 cols, 2 1/16, 1/4 between; C - 10 cols, 1 5/16, 13/100 between.
Areas Served: 18431, 18473, 18428, 18464, 18426, 18445, 18427, 18444, 18436, 18438, 18459, 18472, 18407, 18456, 18421, 18462, 18405, 18469, 18445, 18415, 18847, 18455, 18461, 18439, 18453, 18437, 18417, 13783, 12723, 12764, 18460, 18451, 18462, 18458, 18407, 18465
Delivery Method: Mail, Newsstand, RacksEquipment & Software: BUSINESS SOFTWARE: AMP5 CLASSIFIED EQUIPMENT: Hardware — Mac; Printers — APP/Mac LaserWriter II; CLASSIFIED SOFTWARE: AMP5 DISPLAY EQUIPMENT: Hardware — Mac; Printers — APP/Mac LaserWriter; EDITORIAL EQUIPMENT: Hardware — Mac; Printers — APP/Mac LaserWriter II EDITORIAL SOFTWARE: News Edit Pro/Pagemaker/Quark CIRCULATION SOFTWARCirc Pro

HUNTINGDON

THE HUNTINGDON DAILY NEWS

325 Penn St, Ste 1, Huntingdon, Pa., 16652-1470, Huntingdon; gen tel (814) 643-4040; adv tel (814)643-4040; ed tel (814)643-4040; gen fax (814) 641-9628; adv fax (814) 641-9628; ed fax (814) 643-0376; gen/nat adv e-mail dnewsads@huntingdailynews.com; disp adv e-mail dnewsads@huntingdondailynews.com; class adv e-mailclassifieds@huntingdondailynews.com; ed e-mail dnews@huntingdondailynews.com; web site www.huntingdondailynews.com
Group: Sample News Group LLC
Published: Mon, Tues, Wed, Thur, Fri, Sat
Weekday Frequency: e
Saturday Frequency: m
Circulation: 9,258; 9,258(sat)
Last Audit: Sworn/Estimate/Non-Audited September 30, 2017
Advertising Rate (weekday/saturday): Open inch rate $15.75
News services: AP. **Established:** 1922
Special Editions: Bridal (Feb); Spring Sports, Home and Garden (Mar); Hunting (Apr); Leisure (Summer); Firemen's Booklet (July); Back to School, Medical Directory (Aug); Football, Fall Home, Energy (Sept); Business Directory (Oct); Christmas Greeting (Dec)
Special Weekly Sections: Editorial, TV (Mon-Fri); Healthy Living (Tue); Best Food Days (Wed/ Sat); Farm (Thur); Real Estate (Fri, Monthly); Minipage (Sat);
Syndicated Publications: American Profile (Weekly).
Purchasing Agent .... Kenneth J. Smith
Adv. Dir. .... Carol A. Cutshall
Circ. Mgr. .... Heather Lohr
Editorial Page Ed. .... George Germann
News Ed. .... Polly McMullen
Sports Ed. .... Terry Bowser
Prodn. Mgr. .... Robert Dietz
Bus. Mng. .... Lori Stevens
Pub .... John Cook
Michelle Carolus
Assoc. Pub. .... Joseph F. Biddle II
Circ. Mgr. .... Brenda Hoover
Market Information: Split run; TMC.
Mechanical Available: Offset; Black and 3 ROP colors; insert accepted; page cutoffs - 22 1/2.
Mechanical Specifications: Type page 13 x 21 1/2; E - 6 cols, 2 1/16, 1/8 between; A - 6 cols, 2 1/16, 1/8 between; C - 9 cols, 1 3/8, 1/16 between.Equipment & Software: MAILROOM EQUIPMENT: Tying Machines — Sa, WeldLoc; Address Machine — Wm, KR.; BUSINESS EQUIPMENT: DEC/486, 6-DEC BUSINESS SOFTWARE: Vision Data, AR 6.2, APGL 5.0 CLASSIFIED EQUIPMENT: Hardware — APP/Mac; Printers — HP; CLASSIFIED SOFTWARE: Baseview/Ad Manager Pro. DISPLAY EQUIPMENT: Hardware — APP/Mac; Printers — HP/LaserJet 5si/MX; DISPLAY SOFTWAREAd Make-up Applications — QPS/QuarkXPress, Adobe/Illustrator, Adobe/ Photoshop; Layout Software — Baseview/Ad Manager, Baseview/Ad Force. EDITORIAL EQUIPMENT: Hardware — APP; Printers — APP, HP EDITORIAL SOFTWARE: Baseview/ NewsEdit. PRODUCTION EQUIPMENT: Hardware — Caere/OmniPage; Cameras — C; Scanners — HP PRODUCTION SOFTWARE: QPS/QuarkXPress 4.0.

INDIANA

THE INDIANA GAZETTE

899 Water St, Indiana, Pa., 15701-1705, Indiana; gen tel (724) 465-5555; adv tel (724) 465-5555; ed tel (724) 465-5555; gen fax (724) 465-0402; adv fax (724) 349-4550; ed fax (724) 465-8267; gen/nat adv e-mail jlash@indianagazette.net; disp adv e-mail awilliams@indianagazette.net; class adv e-mailbnichol@indianagazette.net; ed e-mail eebeling@indianagazette.net; web site www.indianagazette.com
Published: Mon, Tues, Wed, Thur, Fri, Sat, Sun
Weekday Frequency: e
Saturday Frequency: e
Circulation: 9,979; 9,979(sat); 10,569(sun)
Last Audit: AAM June 30, 2017
Advertising Rate (weekday/saturday): Open inch rate $22.75
Advertising Rate (sunday): Open inch rate $22.75
News services: AP, NEA, NYT. Scripps-Howard **Established:** 1890
Own Printing Facility?: Yes
Commercial Printers?: Yes
Special Editions: Lawn & Garden (Apr); Football (Aug); Winter Sports (Dec); Financial Fitness (Feb); Bridal (Jan); Arts Festival (Jul); Car Care (Jun); Homebuilders Real Estate (Mar); Summer Recreation (May); Holiday Gift Guide (Nov); Car Care (Oct); Resource Directory (Sept).
Special Weekly Sections: Health (Tue); Best Food (Wed/Sun); Religion (Sat); Business, Stock, TV (Sun)
Syndicated Publications: USA WEEKEND Magazine (S).
Digital Platform - Mobile: Blackberry
Digital Platform - Tablet: Kindle, Other
Pres./Pub. .... Michael J. Donnelly
News In Edu. Coordinator .... Hastie D. Kinter
Gen. Mgr. .... Joseph L. Geary
Controller .... Robert W. Kanick
Adv. Dir. .... Cathy Reed
Exec. Ed. .... Eric Ebeling
Editorial Page Ed. .... Michael Peterson
Chief Photo. .... Tom Peel
Sports Ed. .... Tony Coccagna
Prodn. Mgr. .... Donna Rethi
News Ed. .... Jason Levan
Chauncey Ross
Adv. / Mrkt. Dir. .... Jarrod Lash
Market Information: TMC.
Mechanical Available: Offset; Black and 3 ROP colors; insert accepted - odd sizes accepted, zoned; page cutoffs - 22 3/4.
Mechanical Specifications: Type page 13 x 21 1/2; E - 6 cols, 2 1/16, 1/8 between; A - 6 cols, 2 1/16, 1/8 between; C - 8 cols, 1 1/2, 1/8 between.
Areas Served: 15701, 15748, 15717, 15681, 15714, 15742, 15759
Delivery Method: Mail, Carrier, RacksEquipment & Software: PRESSROOM EQUIPMENT: Lines — 6-G/Urbanite (1 color unit), 1-G/ Urbanite 788; 10-HI/V-15D 1990; Folders — G/2:1; Reels & Stands — 2-G/Rollstands, 4-Martin/Splicer.; MAILROOM EQUIPMENT: Counter Stackers — MM/338, Gammerler/KL 503/1; Inserters & Stuffers — MM/310; Tying Machines — MM; Address Machine — 2/Ch; BUSINESS EQUIPMENT: Compaq/Proliant 3000 BUSINESS SOFTWARE: Platinum CLASSIFIED EQUIPMENT: Hardware — Compaq/Proliant 3000; Printers - HP/4000, AU/1000; CLASSIFIED SOFTWARE: APT. DISPLAY EQUIPMENT: Hardware — Compaq/Proliant 3000; Printers — HP/4000, AU/1000; DISPLAY SOFTWAREAd Make-up Applications — APT, QPS/QuarkXPress.; EDITORIAL EQUIPMENT: Hardware — Compaq/Proliant 3000; Printers — HP/4000, HP/4000C EDITORIAL SOFTWARE: APT. PRODUCTION EQUIPMENT: Hardware

— AU/APS-6-82 ACS, AU/1000; Cameras — 1-C/Marathon; Scanners — AG/Horizon Scanner PRODUCTION SOFTWARE: APT, QPS/QuarkXPress 4.0.

JOHNSTOWN

THE TRIBUNE-DEMOCRAT

425 Locust St, Johnstown, Pa., 15901-1817, Cambria; gen tel (814) 532-5199; adv tel (814) 532-5150; ed tel (814) 532-5050; gen fax (814) 539-1538; adv fax (814) 539-2292; ed fax (814) 539-1409; gen/nat adv e-mail tpritt@tribdem.com; disp adv e-mail marizzo@tribdem.com; class adv e-mailtribads@lenzlink.net; web site www.tribune-democrat.com

Group: Community Newspaper Holdings, Inc.
Published: Mon, Tues, Wed, Thur, Fri, Sat, Sun
Weekday Frequency: m
Saturday Frequency: m
Circulation: 24,162; 23,423(sat); 26,135(sun)
Last Audit: AAM March 31, 2017
Advertising Rate (weekday/saturday): Open inch rate $52.25
Advertising Rate (sunday): Open inch rate $57.45
News services: AP, NNS, GNS. **Established:** 1853
Special Editions: Spring Outdoor Guide (Apr); Simply the Best (Aug); Holiday Gift Guides (Dec); Progress (Feb); Bridal Guide (Jan); Bridal Guide (Jul); Real Estate (Mar); Summer Lifestyle (May); Holiday Gift Guides (Nov); Kitchen & Bath (Oct); Simply the Best (Sept).
Special Weekly Sections: Weekend, Entertainment (Fri); Best Food Days, Travel, Home, Auto, TV (Sun)
Syndicated Publications: Relish (Monthly); Parade (S).
Pub.....Robin Quillon
Controller....Louis Gjurich
Personnel Mgr.....Joan Hunter
Circ. Dir.....Julie Fox-Arnott
Editorial Page Ed.....Bruce Wissinger
Sports Ed.....Eric Knopsnyder
Style Ed.....Renee Carthew
Prodn. Dir.....Steve Sindleri
Major/Nat'l. Sales....Tina Pritt
Director Adv.....Mary Anne Rizzo
Market Information: Split run; TMC; Zoned editions.
Mechanical Available: Offset; Black and 3 ROP colors; insert accepted; page cutoffs - 22 3/4.
Mechanical Specifications: Type page 13 x 21 1/2; E - 6 cols, 2 1/16, 1/8 between; A - 6 cols, 2 1/16, 1/8 between; C - 9 cols, 1 5/16, 1/8 between.Equipment & Software: PRESSROOM EQUIPMENT: Lines — 5-G/Metro (2 decks) 1969; Reels & Stands — 5-G/RTP.; MAILROOM EQUIPMENT: Counter Stackers — 2-QWI/SJ100A, CH/Mk II; Inserters & Stuffers — S/848; Tying Machines — 2-MVP/P-53, Sterling/MR45CH, Sterling/MR40CH; Address Machine — 1-MG/50.; BUSINESS EQUIPMENT: Sun/Sparc BUSINESS SOFTWARE: Vision Data CLASSIFIED EQUIPMENT: Hardware — APP/Mac; 10-APP/Mac 4400; Printers — HP/6MP; CLASSIFIED SOFTWARE: Baseview/Ad Manager Pro. DISPLAY EQUIPMENT: Hardware — Sun/Sparc; Printers — 6-DEC/LG04 Plus; Other Hardware — 5-PC DISPLAY SOFTWAREAd Make-up Applications — Vision Data; Layout Software — MEI/ALS. EDITORIAL EQUIPMENT: Hardware — APP/Mac/APP/Mac 4400, APP/Mac 7300, APP/Mac 7200, APP/Mac G4; Printers — HP/Laser, APP/Mac EDITORIAL SOFTWARE: Baseview. PRODUCTION EQUIPMENT: Hardware — 2-APP/Power Mac 7300 with Adobe Photoshop 4.0, Pre Press/Panther Pro 46, Konica/9449-163, Microtek/2SPX, Microtek/E6, Microtek/35T; Cameras — 1-K/Vertical 18, C/Marathon; Scanners — Microtek/2SPX, Mictrotek/E6, 1-Microtek/35T, Polaroid/SprintS

KANE

THE KANE REPUBLICAN

200 N Fraley St, Kane, Pa., 16735-1177, McKean; gen tel (814) 837-6000; gen fax (814) 837-2227; gen/nat adv e-mail kradvertising@zitomedia.net; disp adv e-mail kradvertising@zitomedia.net; class adv e-mailkaneclassifieds@zitomedia.net; ed e-mail editor3@zitomedia.net; web site www.kanerepublican.com

Group: Horizon Publications Inc.
Published: Mon, Tues, Wed, Thur, Fri, Sat, Sun
Weekday Frequency: e
Saturday Frequency: m
Circulation: 1,996; 1,996(sat)
Last Audit: Sworn/Estimate/Non-Audited September 30, 2017
Advertising Rate (weekday/saturday): Open inch rate $8.65
News services: AP. **Established:** 1894
Special Editions: Football Preview (Aug); Christmas (Dec); Design-An-Ad (Jun); Timber/Progress (Oct).
Special Weekly Sections: Best Food Days (Mon/Sat); Dining Out, Entertainment (Fri)
Syndicated Publications: American Profile (Weekly).
Pub.....Christie Gardner
Ed.....Joseph Bell
Circulation/Business Manager....Cindy Hulings
Adv.Dir.....Julie Barrett
Mechanical Available: Offset; Black and 1 ROP colors; insert accepted; page cutoffs - 22 3/4.
Mechanical Specifications: Type page 13 x 21 1/2; E - 6 cols, 2 1/16, 1/8 between; A - 6 cols, 2 1/16, 1/8 between; C - 8 cols, 1 1/2, 1/8 between.Equipment & Software: MAILROOM EQUIPMENT: Tying Machines — 1/Sa; Address Machine — 1-/Am.; BUSINESS EQUIPMENT: Mk/550, APP/Mac EDITORIAL EQUIPMENT: Hardware — Mk/550 Sys EDITORIAL SOFTWARE: Mk/Newswriter.

KITTANNING

LEADER TIMES

1270 N Water St, Ste E, Kittanning, Pa., 16201-1055, Armstrong; gen tel (724) 543-1303; adv tel (724) 779-6959; ed tel (724) 543-1303; gen fax (724) 545-6768; adv fax (724)545-6768; ed fax (724)545-6768; gen/nat adv e-mail tbish@leadertimes.com; disp adv e-mail tbish@leadertimes.com; class adv e-mailclassified@leadertimes.com; ed e-mail newsroom@leadertimes; web site www.leadertimes.com

Group: Sample Media Group
Published: Mon, Tues, Wed, Thur, Fri, Sat, Sun
Weekday Frequency: e
Saturday Frequency: m
Circulation: 6,441; 5,968(sat); 704(sun)
Last Audit: AAM September 30, 2014
Advertising Rate (weekday/saturday): Open inch rate $219.39
Advertising Rate (sunday): Open inch rate $273.98
News services: AP.
Special Weekly Sections: Society (Mon); Best Food Day (Wed/Sun); Entertainment, Neighborhood (Thur); Home and Garden (Sat); Travel, Real Estate (Sun)
Digital Platform - Mobile: Apple
Digital Platform - Tablet: Apple iOS
Major/Nat'l Sales Asst.....Krista Reott
Exec. Dir., Sales....William M. Cotter
Mechanical Available: Offset; Black and 3 ROP colors; insert accepted; page cutoffs - 21 1/4.
Mechanical Specifications: Type page 13 x 21 1/4; E - 6 cols, 2 1/16, 1/8 between; A - 6 cols, 2 1/16, 1/8 between; C - 10 cols, 1 3/8, 1/8 between.
Areas Served: Armstrong CountyEquipment & Software: MAILROOM EQUIPMENT: Tying Machines — 1/Sterling.; CLASSIFIED EQUIPMENT: Hardware — PPI.; EDITORIAL EQUIPMENT: Hardware — APP/Mac, SII. PRODUCTION EQUIPMENT: Hardware — 2-COM/Trendsetter, 2-Mk, APP/Mac, 3-Laser PRODUCTION SOFTWARE: Multi-Ad/Creator.

LANCASTER

LNP

8 W King St, Lancaster, Pa., 17603-3824, Lancaster; gen tel (717) 291-8811; adv tel (717) 291-8711; ed tel (717) 291-8622; adv fax (717) 399-4968; ed fax (717) 399-6507; gen/nat adv e-mail lnp@lnpnews.com; disp adv e-mail advertising@lnpnews.com; class adv e-mailclass@lnpnews.com; ed e-mail editorialdepartment@LNPnews.com; web site www.lancasteronline.com - 5,952,214(views); web site 2 www.lancjobs.com - 94,547(views); web site 3 www.lancmoms.com - 1,218(views); web site 4www.realtywizard.com - 1,995(views)

Group: LNP Media Group
Published: Mon, Tues, Wed, Thur, Fri, Sat, Sun
Weekday Frequency: m
Saturday Frequency: m
Circulation: 49,547; 49,637(sat); 68,057(sun)
Last Audit: AAM December 31, 2016
Advertising Rate (weekday/saturday): Open inch rate $58.00 (Mon-Wed) $ 65.00 (Thur-Sat)
Advertising Rate (sunday): $72.00
Online Advertising Rate: $12/CPM for Medium rectangle and leaderboard.
News services: AP, NYT, MCT, LAT-WP, States News Service, NEA. **Established:** 1764
Own Printing Facility?: No
Commercial Printers?: No
Special Editions: (Feb) Always Lancaster; Summer Kids;I Do Bridal
(Mar) NIE Week Design an Ad;
(Apr) Visiting Lancaster;
(May) Mother's Day; Senior Living
(Aug) Readers Choice Awards;High School Football Preview
(Sep) Fall Home Pages; Grandparent's Day
Lancaster Chamber Business Expo
(Nov)College Night Guide Book;Holiday Gifts and Livestyle Holiday Showcase; Small Business Saturday
(Dec)Dear Santa;last Minute Gifts
Special Weekly Sections: Church (Sat); Entertainment (Thur);
Food (Wed)
Food (Sun)
Syndicated Publications: Parade (S)
Digital Platform - Mobile: Apple, Android, Windows, Blackberry
Digital Platform - Tablet: Apple iOS, Android, Windows 7, Blackberry Tablet OS, Kindle, Nook, Kindle Fire
Community Liaison....Barbara Hough Roda
Publisher and Chairman....Robert Krasne
Client Solutions Operations Manager....Michelle Fisher
Managing Editor....Tom Murse
IT Manager....Vic Nigro
Sr. Client Solutions Manager....Amanda Janaszek
Production Manager....Connie Solon
VP of Client Solutions....John Derr
Sr. Vice President of Administration....Shane Zimmerman
Chief Information Officer....Caroline Muraro
Managing Editor....Ted Sickler
Executive Vice President....Ralph Martin
Market Information: Zoned editions.
Mechanical Available: No Mechanical available on sight.
Mechanical Specifications: As per Advanced Central Services, Mechanicsburg
Areas Served: 17501,19501,19310,17502,19310,17502,17503,17504,17505,17506,17507,17508,17566,17509,19330,17512,17516,17517,17518,17519,17520,17022,17522,17521,17527,17528,17529,17532,19344,17533,17534,17535,17536,17537,17601,17602,17603,17604,17605,17606,17607,17608,17538,17540,17543,
17545,17547,17549,17550,17551,17552,17554,17555,17557,17560,19362,19363,17562,19365,17563,17564,17565,17566,17567,17568,17569,17572,17575,17576,17577,17578,17579,17580,17581,17582,17583,17584,17585
Delivery Method: Mail, Newsstand, Carrier, RacksEquipment & Software: PRESSROOM EQUIPMENT: None PRESSROOM SOFTWARE: None MAILROOM EQUIPMENT: None MAILROOM SOFTWARE:None BUSINESS EQUIPMENT: 1-Intell BUSINESS SOFTWARE: DTI, TMC, Avaya, Document express CLASSIFIED EQUIPMENT: Hardware — Dell Server; Dell Workstations; Printers — KM300i; CLASSIFIED SOFTWARE: Brainworks, Quark Xpress 8.5, Layout 8000 DISPLAY EQUIPMENT: Hardware — APP/Mac Mini, Dell Workstations; Printers — KM4035; DISPLAY SOFTWAREAd Make-up Applications — Xpancex, Adobe Creative Suite 5.5, QuarkXPress 8.5, Brainworks; Layout Software — SCS/Layout 8000 EDITORIAL EQUIPMENT: Hardware — Dell Virtual servers,NetApp
VMWare/ Printers — Kyocera 9520, 9130 EDITORIAL SOFTWARE: SCS/Scoop
Fotoware, Photoshop, Photo mechanic PRODUCTION EQUIPMENT: Hardware — Mac Mini Scanners — Epson/a640XL, Epson/836XL, 1-X/7650C PRODUCTION SOFTWARE: InDesign CS5.5,QuarkXPress 8.5, Adobe Creative Suite 5.5 IT EQUIPMENT: Dell Virtual Servers, Dell Physical Servers IT SOFTWARE:VMware 5.0
Microsoft Exchange
Quantum net backup
Cisco 4510
CIRCULATION EQUIPMENT: Dell 6600 Server CIRCULATION SOFTWARDTI
Note: No new titles

LANSDALE

THE REPORTER

307 Derstine Ave, Lansdale, Pa., 19446-3532, Montgomery; gen tel (215) 855-8440; adv tel (215) 855-8440; ed tel (215) 361-8820; gen fax 215-855-3432; ed fax (215) 855-3432; gen/nat adv e-mail advertising@thereporteronline.com; disp adv e-mail econdra@journalregister.com; class adv e-mailclassifieds@thereporteronline.com; ed e-mail citydesk@thereporteronline.com; web site www.thereporteronline.com - 1,050,922(views) 271,009(visitors)

Group: Digital First Media
Published: Mon, Tues, Wed, Thur, Fri, Sat
Weekday Frequency: m
Saturday Frequency: m
Circulation: 5,027; 4,939(sat)
Last Audit: AAM March 31, 2016
Newspaper Reps: Mid-Atlantic Newspaper Services; Robert Hitchings & Co., Inc.
Advertising Rate (weekday/saturday): Open inch rate $43.15
Advertising Rate (sunday): Open inch rate $77.60
Online Advertising Rate: Banner-LREC #1 ATF $15.00; LEADERBOARD ATF $15.00; LREC #2 & #3 $10.00; LREC w/Video + $100 set-up for new creative $18.00; LEADERBOARD BTF $7.00; LREC #4 BTF $10.00; Sliding Billboards-HOME PAGE $250 Daily; NEWS & SPORTS $350 Daily;
News services: AP, U.S. Suburban Press Inc., Robert Hitchings & Co.. **Established:** 1870
Special Editions: Garden (Apr); Fall Sports (Aug); Gift Guide (Dec); Business Outlook (Feb); Community Guide Book (Jul); Health & Fitness (Mar); Gift Guide (Nov); New Cars (Oct); Bridal (Quarterly).
Special Weekly Sections: Celebrations, Stocks, Business Coverage, Region News, State News, World News, Daily Movie, Cable Listings (Daily); Sports, Employment, Kids, Business (Mon); Kids, Athletes of the Week, High School Sports (Tue); Food, Features, Recipes (Wed); Weekend Entertainment (Thur); Teen, high School Sports (Fri); Religions, Real Estate, high School Sports (Sat); Comics, Engagements, Stock Summary, Jobs (Sun)
Syndicated Publications: Parade Magazine (Sun)
Controller/Purchasing Agent....Bernard DeAngelis
Lifestyles Ed.....Aixa Torregrosa
Night Ed.....Evelyn Short
Online Ed.....Geoff Patton
Ed.....Ann Cornell
Nat'l. Adv. Coord.....Holly Hill
Adv. Dir.....Edward Condra
Market Information: TMC.
Mechanical Available: Offset; Black and 3 ROP colors; insert accepted; page cutoffs - 20 1/2.
Mechanical Specifications: Type page 11 5/8 x 20 1/2; E - 6 (& 7 columns front page) cols, 1 4/5, 1/8 between; A - 6 cols, 1 4/5, 1/8 between; C - 10 cols, 1 2/25, 1/16 between. Equipment & Software: PRESSROOM EQUIPMENT: Lines — Man Roland Offset; Pasters —8-Cary/AutomaticControl System — G/PA.; MAILROOM EQUIPMENT: Counter Stackers — HL/HT, 1/PRK, HI/RS 25, Gammerler, QWI/Sports Stacker; Inserters & Stuffers — AlphaLine; Tying Machines — 2-/MLN, 2-/Dynaric; Wrapping Singles — 1-/Power Strap, 1-/Dynaric; Control System

— Linc; Address Machine — Addressing machine; BUSINESS EQUIPMENT: IBM/AS-400, IBM/RISC Model 170 BUSINESS SOFTWARE: Microsoft/Excel, Microsoft/Word 6.1 CLASSIFIED EQUIPMENT: Hardware — Sun/Ultra 2, APP/Power Mac; Printers — LaserJet/5000; CLASSIFIED SOFTWARE: Atex. DISPLAY EQUIPMENT: Hardware — Sun/Ultra 2, APP/Power Mac; Printers — HP/LaserJet 4MV; Other Hardware — SCS/Layout 8000 DISPLAY SOFTWAREAd Make-up Applications — QPS/QuarkXPress, Adobe/Illustrator, Adobe/Photoshop; Layout Software — Lino Press. EDITORIAL EQUIPMENT: Hardware — Sun/Ultra 2, APP/Power Mac/APP/Mac Quadra, AP/AdSend; Printers — HP/LaserJet 4MV EDITORIAL SOFTWARE: Lino Press. PRODUCTION EQUIPMENT: Hardware — 2-Ultre/5400, D, Anitec/SN32; Cameras — C/Spartan II; Scanners — Hel/Sapphire, Tecsa/Copy Dot Scanner PRODUCTION SOFTWARE: Lino Press 4.2.02.39, Lino Press 4.1.14.17A.

THE TIMES HERALD

307 Derstine Ave, Lansdale, Pa., 19446-3532, Montgomery; gen tel (610) 272-2500; adv tel (610) 272-3830; ed tel (610) 272-2501; gen fax (610) 272-4003; adv fax (610) 272-9515; ed fax (610) 272-4003; gen/nat adv e-mail advertising@timesherald.com; disp adv e-mail advertising@timesherald.com; class adv e-mailadvertising@timesherald.com; ed e-mail editors@timesherald.com; web site www.timesherald.com
- 1,000,000(views) 250,000(visitors)

Group: Digital First Media
Published: Mon, Tues, Wed, Thur, Fri, Sat, Sun
Weekday Frequency: m
Saturday Frequency: m
Circulation: 5,380; 5,380(sat); 12,964(sun)
Last Audit: AAM March 31, 2016
Advertising Rate (weekday/saturday): 1/40 Pg $68.90
Advertising Rate (sunday): 1/40 Pg $84.00
Online Advertising Rate: Leaderboard-$12 cpm; LREC (above fold)-$12 cpm; LREC (below fold)-$10 cpm; Skybox (right)-$12
News services: AP, SHNS. **Established:** 1799
Own Printing Facility?: Yes
Commercial Printers?: Yes
Special Editions: Senior Lifestyles (Apr); Football (Aug); Song Book (Dec); Parenting (Feb); Super Sale (Jan); Fall Education (Jul); Children's Guide (Jun); Coupon Book (Mar); Coupon Book (May); Holiday Season Preview (Nov); Car Care (Oct); Fall Bridal (Sept).
Special Weekly Sections: TV Showcase, Travel, Comics, Auto, Real Estate, Recruitment, Coupons, Jobs (Sun); Best Food (Wed); Auto, Church (Thur); Welcome Home, Real Estate (Fri)
Syndicated Publications: USA WEEKEND Magazine (S).
Digital Platform - Mobile: Apple, Android
Digital Platform - Tablet: Apple iOS, Android
Pub. .... Shelley Meenan
Asst. to Pub. .... Amy Bernstiel
Ed. .... Stan Huskey
City Ed. .... Cheryl Kehoe Rodgers
Market Information: Split run; TMC.
Mechanical Available: Offset; Black and ROP colors; insert accepted; page cutoffs - 21 1/2.
Mechanical Specifications: Type page 12 x 21 1/2; E - 6 cols, 1 7/8, 1/8 between; A - 6 cols, 1 7/8, 1/8 between; C - 10 cols, 1 3/16, 1/12 between.
Areas Served: Montgomery County, PA
Delivery Method: Mail, Newsstand, Carrier, RacksEquipment & Software: PRESSROOM EQUIPMENT: Lines — 5-HI/1650 1993; Press Drive — GE/200 h.p. Twin; Folders — 1-HI/double 2:1; Reels & Stands — 5-G/Manual Reel.; MAILROOM EQUIPMENT: Counter Stackers — KAN, QWI/SJ101; Inserters & Stuffers — 1-KAN/480, 1-KAN/480; Tying Machines — MLN/ML2CC, 1-MLN/ML2EE; Wrapping Singles — 1-HL/Monarch, 2/Si.; BUSINESS EQUIPMENT: IBM/AS-400 BUSINESS SOFTWARE: INSI CLASSIFIED EQUIPMENT: Hardware — Dewar; Printers — Dataproducts/LB 325; CLASSIFIED SOFTWARE: Dewar/Sys IV. DISPLAY EQUIPMENT: Hardware — Dewar/Discovery; Printers — HP/882; DISPLAY SOFTWAREAd Make-up Applications — Dewar; Layout Software — MEI. EDITORIAL EQUIPMENT: Hardware — ATS; Printers — HP/5000 EDITORIAL SOFTWARE: Dewar. PRODUCTION EQUIPMENT: Hardware — LE, APP/Mac, 1-Ultra 4000, 1-Bibco; Cameras — C/Spartan III, R/Vertical; Scanners — ECR/Autokon, Ultra/4000 Full Page Imagesetter, Umax PRODUCTION SOFTWARE: ATS/managing editor, Windows 2.7.

LATROBE

THE LATROBE BULLETIN

1211 Ligonier St, Latrobe, Pa., 15650-1921, Westmoreland; gen tel (724)537-3351; adv tel (724)537-3551 ext. 24; ed tel (724) 537-3351 ext. 27; gen fax (724)537-2689; adv fax (724)537-2689; ed fax (724)537-2689; gen/nat adv e-mail latbull@gmail.com; disp adv e-mail latbull@gmail.com; class adv e-maillb.class@verizon.net; ed e-mail lb.editor@verizon.net; web site www.latrobebulletin.com

Group: Sample News Group LLC
Published: Mon, Tues, Wed, Thur, Fri, Sat, Sun
Weekday Frequency: e
Saturday Frequency: m
Circulation: 7,767; 7,767(sat)
Last Audit: Sworn/Estimate/Non-Audited December 6, 2017
Advertising Rate (weekday/saturday): Open inch rate $16.50
News services: AP, SHNS, TMS.
Own Printing Facility?: Yes
Commercial Printers?: Yes
Special Editions: Spring Car Care (Apr); Fall Bridal (Aug); Ligonier Greetings (Dec); Spring Bridal (Feb); Ligonier's Art About Town-Sidewalk Days (Jul); Spring Home Improvement (Mar); Mother's Day (May); Senior Citizen (Nov); Fort Ligonier Days (Oct); Fall Home Improvemen
Syndicated Publications: American Profile (Weekly).Parade
Digital Platform - Mobile: Apple
Office Mgr. .... Jamie Knechtel
Pub., Adv. Dir. .... Gary Siegel
Ed. .... Steve Kittey
Sports Ed. .... Randy Skubek
Women's Ed. .... Louise F. Fritz
Prodn. Mgr., Pressroom .... Mike Feltes
Cir. Dir. .... Brittany Keeton
Mechanical Available: Offset; Black and 3 ROP colors; insert accepted; page cutoffs - 22 3/4.
Mechanical Specifications: Type page 12 x 21 1/2; E - 6 cols, 2 1/16, 1/8 between; A - 6 cols, 2 1/16, 1/8 between; C - 8 cols, 1 1/4, 3/16 between.
Delivery Method: Newsstand, Carrier, RacksEquipment & Software: PRESSROOM EQUIPMENT: Lines — 7-G/Community; Folders — 1-G/SC; Control System — FIN/3120.; MAILROOM EQUIPMENT: Counter Stackers — BG/108; Tying Machines — 1-Sa/SRIA 2460, 1-Sa/S1000 4991.; BUSINESS EQUIPMENT: APP/Mac BUSINESS SOFTWARE: Baseview CLASSIFIED EQUIPMENT: Hardware — APP/Mac; CLASSIFIED SOFTWARE: Baseview. DISPLAY EQUIPMENT: Hardware — APP/Mac; Printers — HP/8000; DISPLAY SOFTWAREAd Make-up Applications — QPS/QuarkXPress.; EDITORIAL EQUIPMENT: Hardware — Baseview. PRODUCTION EQUIPMENT: Hardware — LE/LD-24-AQ, ECRM Stingray 63; Cameras — 24-B/Commodore, B.

LEBANON

THE LEBANON DAILY NEWS

718 Poplar St, Lebanon, Pa., 17042-6755, Lebanon; gen tel (717) 272-5611; adv tel (717) 272-5611; ed tel (717) 272-5611; gen fax (717) 274-1608; adv fax (717) 274-1608; ed fax (717) 274-1608; gen/nat adv e-mail cbrewer@mediaonepa.com; disp adv e-mail cbrewer@mediaonepa.com; class adv e-mailadvertising@mediaonemarketplace.com; ed e-mail andrearich@ldnews.com; web site www.ldnews.com
- 1,000,000(views) 200,000(visitors)

Group: Gannett
Published: Mon, Tues, Wed, Thur, Fri, Sat, Sun
Weekday Frequency: e
Saturday Frequency: e
Circulation: 8,160; 8,160(sat); 10,216(sun)
Last Audit: AAM June 30, 2017
Advertising Rate (weekday/saturday): Open inch rate $38.75
Advertising Rate (sunday): Open inch rate $38.75
News services: AP, NYT, TMS. **Established:** 1872
Own Printing Facility?: No
Commercial Printers?: No
Special Editions: Valley Profiles (Progress)
Special Weekly Sections: Best Food Day (Wed); Church (Sat); Business (Sun)
Syndicated Publications: USA WEEKEND Magazine (S).
Digital Platform - Mobile: Apple, Android
Digital Platform - Tablet: Apple iOS
City Ed. .... Karol Gress
Photo Ed. .... Earl Brightbill
Managing Ed .... Andrea Rich
Editorial Page Ed. .... Rahn Forney
Weekend Ed. .... Jeff Clouser
Pub. .... Scott Downs
Controller .... Kevin Madden
HR
Jean Taylor
Circ. Mgr. .... Joe Clark
Adv. Mgr. .... Rich Canazaro
Community Engagement Team Leader .... Andrea Gillhoolley
Exec. Ed. .... Pat Bywater
Michelle Brown
Features Ed. .... Michael Waterloo
Market Information: TMC
Mechanical Available: Offset; Black and 3 ROP colors; insert accepted; page cutoffs - 22 3/4.
Mechanical Specifications: Broadsheet, Retail - 6 columns x 21.5 inches, 1 column = 1.556", Classified - 10 columns x 21.5 inches, 1 column = 0.889"Equipment & Software: BUSINESS EQUIPMENT: Oracle, PBS CLASSIFIED EQUIPMENT: Hardware — PC, Microsoft/Windows NT, APP/iMac; DISPLAY EQUIPMENT: Hardware — APP/Mac G3; Printers — Xante; Other Hardware — Microsoft/Windows NT DISPLAY SOFTWAREAd Make-up Applications — Multi-Ad/Creator; Layout Software — APP/Mac. EDITORIAL EQUIPMENT: Hardware — APP/Mac; Printers — 1-TI EDITORIAL SOFTWARE: Baseview. PRODUCTION EQUIPMENT: Scanners — Polaroid PRODUCTION SOFTWARE: QPS/QuarkXPress.

LEHIGHTON

TIMES NEWS

594 Blakeslee Boulevard Dr W, Lehighton, Pa., 18235-9818, Carbon; gen tel (610) 377-2051; adv tel (610) 377-2051; ed tel (610) 377-2051; gen fax (610) 826-9607; adv fax (610) 826-9607; gen/nat adv e-mail tnonline@postoffice.ptd.net; disp adv e-mail khardy@tnonline.com; class adv e-mailkhardy@tnonline.com; ed e-mail tneditor@tnonline.com; web site www.tnonline.com

Group: Pencor Services Inc.
Published: Mon, Tues, Wed, Thur, Fri, Sat
Weekday Frequency: e
Saturday Frequency: m
Circulation: 11,240; 11,240(sat)
Last Audit: AAM September 30, 2014
Newspaper Reps: Mid-Atlantic Newspaper Services; TIMES NEWS & The PRESS;
Advertising Rate (weekday/saturday): Open inch rate $18.85
Online Advertising Rate: National On-Line $8.90 CPM*
News services: AP, Papert (Landon). **Established:** 1883
Special Editions: Home Improvement (Apr); Spring Bridal (Jan); Pocono 500 (Jun); Spring Car Care (May); Christmas Shopping (Nov); Fall Car Care (Oct); Football (Sept).
Special Weekly Sections: Best Food Day (Mon?Sat); Entertainment (Fri/Sat/Tue);
Syndicated Publications: USA WEEKEND Magazine (Sat); American Profile (Weekly).
Pub. .... Fred L. Masenheimer
VP, Ops. .... Scott A. Masenheimer
Adv. Dir., Mktg. .... Donald Reese
Circ. Mgr. .... Kathy Carpenter
Entertainment Ed. .... Ron Gower
Lifestyle Ed. .... Karen Cimms
New Media Ed. .... George Taylor
Sports Ed. .... Ed Hedes
Wire Ed. .... Jim Zbick
Digital/Interactive Manager .... Will Schawb
Prodn. Dir. .... David Helmer
Prodn. Mgr., Pressroom .... Leonard Alabovitz
Dir. of Pre-Press Operations .... Bob Miller
Marketing Assistant .... Tanya Pecha
Mktg. .... Rebecca Wraight
Adv. Nat'l. Rep. .... Donna Hall
Rgl. Adv. Mgr. .... Kevin Hardy
Market Information: Split run; Zoned editions.
Mechanical Available: Offset; Black and 3 ROP colors; insert accepted - all; page cutoffs - 22 3/4.
Mechanical Specifications: Type page 13 x 21; E - 6 cols, 2 1/16, 1/8 between; A - 6 cols, 2 1/16, 1/8 between; C - 9 cols, 1 3/8, 1/16 between.
Areas Served: Carbon County, Schuylkill County, part of Monroe County, Part of North Hampton County, Part of Lehigh County
Equipment & Software: PRESSROOM EQUIPMENT: Lines — W/Colorflex; MAN/Uniman.; MAILROOM EQUIPMENT: Counter Stackers — 1-BG/108, 1-HL/Monitor; Inserters & Stuffers — 1-MM/227E; Tying Machines — 2-MLN/MLOAE.; BUSINESS EQUIPMENT: 2-IBM/AS-400 CLASSIFIED EQUIPMENT: Hardware — Mk/Mycro-Comp 1100, 2-Mk/MC4001.; DISPLAY SOFTWARELayout Software — 1-COM/AdVantage, Mk/Mycro-Comp Ad Touch, 1-COM/Dawn. EDITORIAL EQUIPMENT: Hardware — Mk, 3-COM/MDT 350, 22-Mk/MC4003/10-APP/Mac. PRODUCTION EQUIPMENT: Hardware — 2-Nat/250, 1-COM/Videosetter, 1-COM/7200, 1-COM/8600; Cameras — 1-R/20 x 24, 1-AG/Repromaster, 1-Eskofot, 2-Kk.

LEVITTOWN

BUCKS COUNTY COURIER TIMES

8400 Bristol Pike, Levittown, Pa., 19057-5117, Bucks; gen tel (215) 949-4000; adv tel (215) 949-4125; ed tel (215) 949-4162; gen fax (215) 949-4114; adv fax (215) 269-6030; ed fax (215) 949-4177; gen/nat adv e-mail bgropper@calkins.com; disp adv e-mail nstuski@calkins.com; class adv e-mailclassifieds@calkins.com; ed e-mail newstips@calkins.com; web site http://www.buckscountycouriertimes.com/

Group: Calkins Media
Published: Mon, Tues, Wed, Thur, Fri, Sun
Weekday Frequency: m
Saturday Frequency: m
Circulation: 24,218; 33,731(sun)
Last Audit: AAM June 30, 2017
Advertising Rate (weekday/saturday): Open inch rate $40.05(3 lines for 3 days)no column inch rate
News services: AP, NEA, SHNS, TMS. **Established:** 1954
Own Printing Facility?: Yes
Commercial Printers?: Yes
Special Editions: Investment Fair (Apr); Back-to-School (Aug); Bucks County Holiday (Dec); Job Fair (Feb); Mature Lifestyles (Jan); Mature Lifestyles (Jul); Internet Fair (Jun); Spring Home & Garden (Mar); Voter's Guide (May); Coupon Booklets (Monthly); Holiday Gift Guide
Special Weekly Sections: Focus On Newtown (Thur).
Syndicated Publications: Enjoy (entertainment magazine) (Fri); Parade (S).
Mng. Ed. .... Rose McIver
Editorial Ed. .... Guy Petroziello
Life Ed. .... Tom Haines
Exec. Ed. .... Pat Walker
Market Information: ADS; Split run; TMC; Zoned editions.
Mechanical Available: Letterpress; Black and 3 ROP colors; insert accepted - all; page cutoffs - 22 3/4.
Mechanical Specifications: Type page 13 x 21 1/2; E - 6 cols, 2, 1/6 between; A - 6 cols, 2, 1/6 between; C - 9 cols, 1 1/3, 1/12 between.
Equipment & Software: PRESSROOM EQUIPMENT: Lines — 6-G 1960, 2-G

1972; MAILROOM EQUIPMENT: Counter Stackers — QWI; Tying Machines - 2/ Power Strap.; BUSINESS EQUIPMENT: IBM/9672 BUSINESS SOFTWARE: Calkins CLASSIFIED EQUIPMENT: Hardware — IBM/9672; 17-IBM/3179; Printers — 1-IBM/3287; CLASSIFIED SOFTWARE: Calkins/Adv & Acct System. DISPLAY EQUIPMENT: Hardware — 15-PC; Printers — 1-QMS/2060; Other Hardware — SCS/ Layout 8000. DISPLAY SOFTWAREAd Make-up Applications — SCS/Layout 8000, QPS/ QuarkXPress 3.32, CNI/Display Ad Tracking; EDITORIAL EQUIPMENT: Hardware — PCs EDITORIAL SOFTWARE: ACI/Open Pages. PRODUCTION EQUIPMENT: Hardware — 2-Na/Starlite, 1-MON/ExpressMaster 3850 PRODUCTION SOFTWARE: Northwood Publishing/Class Page, QPS/QuarkXPress 3.32.

Note: There is a Greater Philadelphia Newspaper group combination of $239.00 (d) & $251.00 (S) among Levittown Bucks County Courier (mS), Doylestown Intelligencer (mS) & Willingboro (NJ) Burlington County Times (mS). Individual newspaper rates not made availabl

LEWISTOWN

THE SENTINEL

352 6th St, Lewistown, Pa., 17044-1213, Mifflin; gen tel (717) 248-6741; gen fax (717) 248-3481; gen/nat adv e-mail ads@lewistownsentinel.com; disp adv e-mail mbolich@lewistownsentinel.com; class adv e-mailmjordan@lewistownsentinel.com; web site www.lewistownsentinel.com

Group: Ogden Newspapers Inc.
Published: Mon, Tues, Wed, Thur, Fri, Sat
Weekday Frequency: m
Saturday Frequency: m
Circulation: 8,907; 10,533(sat)
Last Audit: AAM March 31, 2016
Advertising Rate (weekday/saturday): Open inch rate $19.00
News services: AP. **Established:** 1903
Special Editions: Home & Garden (Apr); Hall of Fame (Aug); Happy Holidays (Dec); Juniata Valley (Feb); Brides (Jan); Get to Know Us (Jul); Brides (Jun); Agriculture (Mar); Low-Fat Cookbook (May); Holiday Gift Guide (Nov); Winter Car Care (Oct); Goose Day (Sept).
Special Weekly Sections: Agriculture, Lifestyle (Mon); Senior (Tue); BEst Food (Wed); Entertainment, Outdoors (Thur); Schools, Health, Real Estate, TV (Fri); Cars, Religion, Business, Connections (Sat)
Syndicated Publications: USA WEEKEND Magazine (Sat).
Pub. ....Ruth Eddy
Adv. Dir. ....Matt Bolich
Circ. Mgr. ....Ed Williams
Food Ed. ....Jean Mort
Mng. Ed. ....Frank Jost
Photo Dept. Ed. ....Buffy Boyer
Online Mgr. ....Brad Siddons
Prodn. Foreman, Pressroom ....Jay McCaulley
Market Information: TMC.
Mechanical Available: Offset; Black and 3 ROP colors; insert accepted.
Mechanical Specifications: Type page 13 x 21 1/2; E - 6 cols, 2 1/16, 1/8 between; A - 6 cols, 2 1/16, 1/8 between; C - 6 cols, 2 1/16, 1/8 between.Equipment & Software: PRESSROOM EQUIPMENT: Lines — 9-G/Community 1973.; MAILROOM EQUIPMENT: Tying Machines — Bu/ Strapper; Address Machine — KAN.; BUSINESS EQUIPMENT: NCR BUSINESS SOFTWARE: In-house, Microsoft/Windows 3.1 CLASSIFIED EQUIPMENT: Hardware — APP/Mac; Printers — Okidata/210; CLASSIFIED SOFTWARE: Baseview. DISPLAY EQUIPMENT: Hardware — NCR; Printers - Talley; Other Hardware — NCR. EDITORIAL EQUIPMENT: Hardware — APP/ Mac EDITORIAL SOFTWARE: In-house. PRODUCTION EQUIPMENT: Hardware — APP/Mac Laser; Cameras — K/Vertical; Scanners — Polaroid.

MEADVILLE

THE MEADVILLE TRIBUNE

947 Federal Ct, Meadville, Pa., 16335-3234, Crawford; gen tel (814) 724-6370; adv tel (814)724-6370 ext. 258; ed tel (814) 724-6370 ext. 267; gen fax (814)337-2502; adv fax (814)337-2502; ed fax (814)337-2502; gen/nat adv e-mail hgebhardt@meadvilletribune.com; disp adv e-mail hgebhardt@meadvilletribune.com; class adv e-mailwendieb@meadvilletribune.com; ed e-mail rgreen@meadvilletribune.com; web site www.meadvilletribune.com

Group: Community Newspaper Holdings, Inc.
Published: Mon, Tues, Wed, Thur, Fri, Sat, Sun
Weekday Frequency: m
Saturday Frequency: m
Circulation: 8,954; 8,954(sat); 9,078(sun)
Last Audit: AAM June 30, 2016
Advertising Rate (weekday/saturday): Open inch rate $25.40
Advertising Rate (sunday): Open inch rate $25.40
News services: AP.
Special Editions: Home Improvement (Apr); Back-to-School (Aug); Winter Sports (Dec); Report to People (Feb); Bridal (Jan); Heritage Days (Jul); Hot Air Balloons (Jun); AG Day (Mar); Country Living (Monthly); Christmas Opening (Nov); Cookbook (Oct); Outdoor (Sept).
Special Weekly Sections: Faith, Values (Sat); Bridal (Wed); Entertainment (Thur); TV, Bridal (Sun)
Syndicated Publications: Relish (Monthly); USA WEEKEND Magazine (S).
Controller ....Michelle Brown
Circ. Dir. ....Devon Stout
Exec. Ed. ....Pat Bywater
Bus. Ed. ....Keith Gushard
Editorial Page Ed. ....Ed Maillard
IT Mgr. ....Matt Digiacomo
Prodn. Mgr., Mailroom ....Allen Lyon
Adv. Dir. ....Heidi Gebhardt
Pub. ....James Galantis
Classifieds Adv. Mgr. ....Wendie Bergendahl
Market Information: ADS; TMC; Zoned editions.
Mechanical Available: Offset; Black and 3 ROP colors; insert accepted; page cutoffs - 22 3/4.
Mechanical Specifications: Type page 13 x 21 1/2; E - 6 cols, 2 1/16, 1/8 between; A - 6 cols, 2 1/16, 1/8 between; C - 9 cols, 1 5/16, 1/8 between.
Areas Served: 16335
Delivery Method: Mail, Newsstand, Carrier, RacksEquipment & Software: PRESSROOM EQUIPMENT: Lines — 10-G/Community (color deck) 1989; Registration System — Duarte/Pin System. MAILROOM EQUIPMENT: Counter Stackers — 1/ Hall Monitor; Inserters & Stuffers — GMA/ Alphaliner Gintol; Tying Machines — EAM-Mosca, ROM; CLASSIFIED EQUIPMENT: Hardware — 3-APP/Mac; Printers — 1-HP/4MV; CLASSIFIED SOFTWARE: Baseview/Class Manager Pro 1.7. DISPLAY EQUIPMENT: Hardware — 2-APP/Mac 7600, 1-APP/Mac 7300; Printers — 1-HP/4MV; Other Hardware — Risograph/Duplicator, AP AdSend DISPLAY SOFTWAREAd Make-up Applications — Multi-Ad/Creator 4.1, Adobe/ Illustrator 6.0, QPS/QuarkXPress 3.32; Layout Software — MEI/ALS, MEI/ALS 2.1. EDITORIAL EQUIPMENT: Hardware — APP/ Mac/APP/Mac LD; Printers — 2-HP/4MV, Pre Press/Panther Pro 36 EDITORIAL SOFTWARE: Baseview/NewsEdit Pro IQUE 1.0. PRODUCTION EQUIPMENT: Hardware — 1-SCREEN/220, 1-SCREEN/LD281Q; Cameras — 1-C/Spartan, 1-SCREEN/680C; Scanners — 2-Polaroid/SprintScan, 1-AG/ Duo scan, 1-Pixelcraft PRODUCTION SOFTWARE: QPS/QuarkXPress 3.32.

MILTON

THE STANDARD-JOURNAL

21 N Arch St, Milton, Pa., 17847-1211, Northumberland; gen tel (570) 742-9671; adv tel (570) 742-9671; ed tel (570) 742-9671; gen fax (570) 742-9876; adv fax (570) 742-9876; ed fax (570) 742-9876; gen/nat adv e-mail amym@standard-journal.com; disp adv e-mail amym@standard-journal.com; class adv e-mailamym@standard-journal.com; ed e-mail newsroom@standard-journal.com; web site www.standard-journal.com

Group: Sample News Group LLC
Published: Mon, Tues, Wed, Thur, Fri, Sat, Sun
Weekday Frequency: e
Saturday Frequency: m
Circulation: 1,418; 1,418(sat)
Last Audit: Sworn/Estimate/Non-Audited September 30, 2017
Advertising Rate (weekday/saturday): Open inch rate $17.85
News services: AP.
Special Editions: Progress (Feb).
Special Weekly Sections: Best Food (Wed); Entertainment (Thur); Bridal (Sat)
Syndicated Publications: Relocation (Oct) (Annually).
Bus. Mgr. ....Karen Hendricks
Adv. Mgr. ....Amy Moyer
Circ. Dir. ....Kevin Mertz
Prodn. Mgr. ....Kevin Koch
Market Information: TMC.
Mechanical Available: Offset; Black and 3 ROP colors; insert accepted - post card up to SAU size; page cutoffs - 22 3/4.
Mechanical Specifications: Type page 13 x 21 1/2; E - 6 cols, 2 1/14, 1/6 between; A - 6 cols, 2 1/14, 1/6 between; C - 9 cols, 1 1/5, 1/12 between.Equipment & Software: PRESSROOM EQUIPMENT: Lines — 6-G/Community 1973; Folders — 1-G/SC.; MAILROOM EQUIPMENT: Counter Stackers — 1-BG/Count-O-Veyor; Inserters & Stuffers — DG/320 2:1; Tying Machines — 1-Bu/SP 505, 1-MLN/MS-T; Address Machine — Dispensa-Matic/U 45.; BUSINESS EQUIPMENT: 4-ATT/Unix PC 7300-3B1 BUSINESS SOFTWARE: Vision Data CLASSIFIED EQUIPMENT: Hardware — Mk/3000, 1-Mk/NewsTouch II; Printers — APP/Mac LaserWriter Plus, Okidata/ Microline 293 line printer; CLASSIFIED SOFTWARE: Mk. DISPLAY EQUIPMENT: Hardware — Mk; Printers — APP/Mac LaserWriter Plus; DISPLAY SOFTWAREAd Make-up Applications — Mk/NewsTouch II, Mk/Ad Touch.; EDITORIAL EQUIPMENT: Hardware — Mk/550, 3-Mk/NewsTouch; Printers — APP/Mac LaserWriter Plus EDITORIAL SOFTWARE: Mk. PRODUCTION EQUIPMENT: Hardware — 2-APP/Mac LaserWriter Plus; Cameras — LE/Horizontal.

MONESSEN

THE MON VALLEY INDEPENDENT

996 Donner Ave, Monessen, Pa., 15062-1001, Westmoreland; gen tel (714) 314-0030; gen fax (724) 314-0025; gen/nat adv e-mail Lbyron@yourmvi.com; web site monvalleyindependent.com

Published: Mon, Tues, Wed, Thur, Fri, Sat
Last Audit: Sworn/Estimate/Non-Audited September 30, 2017
Adv. Mgr. ....Laurie Byron

NEW CASTLE

NEW CASTLE NEWS

27 N Mercer St, New Castle, Pa., 16101-3806, Lawrence; gen tel (724) 654-6651; adv tel (724) 654-6651 ext. 657; ed tel (724)654-6651 ext. 614; gen fax (724) 654-9593; adv fax (724) 654-9593; ed fax (724)654-9593; gen/nat adv e-mail r_work@ncnewsonline.com; disp adv e-mail display@ncnewsonline.com; class adv e-mailr_work@ncnewsonline.com; ed e-mail nceditor@ncnewsonline.com; web site www.ncnewsonline.com

Group: Pennsylvania NewsMedia Association Community Newspaper Holdings, Inc.
Published: Mon, Tues, Wed, Thur, Fri, Sat
Weekday Frequency: m
Saturday Frequency: e
Circulation: 11,273; 11,273(sat)
Last Audit: AAM June 30, 2016
Advertising Rate (weekday/saturday): Open inch rate $35.75
News services: AP, SHNS.
Special Editions: Car Care (Apr); Football (Aug); First Baby (Dec); Business-Industrial Review (Feb); Brides (Jan); Senior Citizens (Jul); Summer Fun (Jun); Home Improvement (Mar); Mother's Day (May); Car Care (Oct); Home Improvement (Sept).
Special Weekly Sections: Best Food Day (Wed/ Sat); Family, parenting (Mon); Business (Tue); Education (Wed); Entertainment (Thur); religion, TV (Fri)
Syndicated Publications: Children's Mini Page (Fri); Relish (Monthly); USA WEEKEND Magazine (Sat).
Mgr., Computer Serv. ....Tom Covert
Mgr., Educ. Serv. ....Matt Kingman
Adv. Mgr., Retail ....Rick Work
Circ. Mgr. ....DuWayne Nelson
Mng. Ed. ....Mitch Olszak
Educ. Rep. ....Lugene Hudson
News Ed. ....Patrick Litowitz
Political Ed. ....John K. Manna
Religion Ed. ....Dan Irwin
Reporter ....Debbie Wachter Morris
Sports Ed. ....Kayleen Cubbal
Television/Film Ed. ....Tim Kolodziej
Larry Corvi
Pub. ....Sharon Sorg
Market Information: Split run; TMC.
Mechanical Available: Offset; Black and 3 ROP colors; insert accepted; page cutoffs - 22 3/4.
Mechanical Specifications: Type page 13 x 21 1/2; E - 6 cols, 2 1/16, 1/8 between; A - 6 cols, 2 1/16, 1/8 between; C - 9 cols, 1 3/8, 1/8 between.Equipment & Software: PRESSROOM EQUIPMENT: Lines — 4-G/ Metro (color deck); Pasters —G/Metro AutomaticReels & Stands — G/Reels & Stands.; MAILROOM EQUIPMENT: Tying Machines — 1-Sa/59SR1A, 1-MLN/ML2EE.; BUSINESS EQUIPMENT: PBS BUSINESS SOFTWARE: Microsoft/Excel CLASSIFIED EQUIPMENT: Hardware — 4-PC; Printers — PAN/KXP-180; CLASSIFIED SOFTWARE: III/Tecs 2. DISPLAY EQUIPMENT: Hardware — 7-APP/Mac; DISPLAY SOFTWAREAd Make-up Applications — Multi-Ad/ Creator; Layout Software — Baseview/ ALS. EDITORIAL EQUIPMENT: Hardware — APP/Mac G3, APP/Macs EDITORIAL SOFTWARE: Baseview. PRODUCTION EQUIPMENT: Hardware — 1-LE/24AQ, 1-LE/ PC13; Cameras — 1-C/Marathon, 1-B/2000, 1-K/240 Vertical PRODUCTION SOFTWARE: QPS/QuarkXPress.

OIL CITY

THE NEWS-HERALD/THE DERRICK

1510 W 1st St, Oil City, Pa., 16301-3211, Venango; gen tel (814) 676-7444; adv tel (814)677-8300; ed tel (814)677-8367; gen fax (814) 677-8347; adv fax (814)677-8351; ed fax (814)677-8347; gen/nat adv e-mail info.thederrick@gmail.com; disp adv e-mail info.thederrick@gmail.com; class adv e-mailclassifieds.thederrick@gmail.com; ed e-mail lukakrneta.thederrick@gmail.com; web site www.thederrick.com

Published: Mon, Tues, Wed, Thur, Fri, Sat, Sun
Weekday Frequency: m
Saturday Frequency: m
Circulation: 7,373; 7,373(sat)
Last Audit: Sworn/Estimate/Non-Audited September 30, 2017
Advertising Rate (weekday/saturday): Open inch rate $69.34
News services: AP.
Special Editions: Spring Car Care (Apr); Football (Aug); First Baby (Dec); Insurance (Feb); Senior Living (Jul); Today's Bride (Mar); Outdoor Living (May); Basketball (Nov); Cookbook I (Oct); Fall Car Care (Sept).
Special Weekly Sections: Best Food Day (Mon/ Wed); Entertainment (Thur)
Syndicated Publications: American Profile (Weekly).
Exec. Vice Pres./Treasurer ....E. Michael Boyle
Vice Pres./Controller ....W.R. Lutz
Sec. ....Peter T. Boyle
Adv. Dir. ....Edward B. Cowart
Ed. ....Glen Mohnkern
City Ed. ....Mark Oliver
Sports Ed. ....Edward Brannon
Prodn. Mgr., Pre Press ....Melvin J. Basham
Pres. ....Patrick C. Boyle
Pub. ....Ned Cowart
Market Information: TMC.
Mechanical Available: Black and 3 ROP colors;

insert accepted - offset; page cutoffs - 22 3/4.Equipment & Software: PRESSROOM EQUIPMENT: Lines — G/Community.; MAILROOM EQUIPMENT: Tying Machines — 2-MLN/SP 330; Address Machine — 2-KR/211.; CLASSIFIED EQUIPMENT: Hardware — CText; Printers — Graphic Enterprises/Pro Setter 1000; CLASSIFIED SOFTWARE: CText/Adept. DISPLAY EQUIPMENT: Hardware — APP/Mac, PCs; Printers — Graphic Enterprise/Pro Setter 1000; DISPLAY SOFTWAREAd Make-up Applications — CText/Adept, Multi-Ad/ Creator; Layout Software — 1-SCS/Layout 8000. EDITORIAL EQUIPMENT: Hardware — CText; Printers — Graphic Enterprises/Pro Setter 1000. PRODUCTION EQUIPMENT: Hardware — Glensen.

Note: Advertising is sold in combination with the Oil City Derrick (m) for $62.23(d). Individual newspaper rates not made available. All business and production are handled by Venango Newspapers Inc.

PHILADELPHIA

METRO PHILADELPHIA

2401 Walnut Street, Suite 102, Philadelphia, Pa., 19103, Philadelphia; gen tel (215) 717-2600; adv tel (215) 717-2695; gen fax (215) 717-2627; gen/nat adv e-mail adsphilly@metro.us; disp adv e-mail susan.peiffer@metro.us; class adv e-mailphillyclassifieds@metro.us; ed e-mail letters@metro.us; web site www.metro.us/philadelphia - 2,971,029(views) 1,191,680(visitors); web site 2 philadelphiia.metro.us

Group: Metro US
Published: Mon, Tues, Wed, Thur, Fri
Weekday Frequency: m
Last Audit: CAC September 30, 2016
Advertising Rate (weekday/saturday): $11,520 Full page
Advertising Rate (sunday): n/a
Online Advertising Rate: Leaderboard $10 CPM
Big Box $10 CPM
Half Page: $15 CPM
News services: 2000
Own Printing Facility?: No
Commercial Printers?: No
Special Weekly Sections: News, Entertainment, Sports, Gossip, Games (Daily); Careers, Education (Mon); Well Being, Health (Tue); Home (Wed); Going out, Travel (Thur); Weekend (Fri)
Digital Platform - Mobile: Apple, Android
Digital Platform - Tablet: Apple iOS, Android
Assoc. Pub. .... Susan Peiffer
Circ. Dir. .... Joseph Lauletta
Marketing Dir. .... Wilf Maunoir
Areas Served: Greater Philadelphia
Delivery Method: Newsstand, Racks

PHILADELPHIA INQUIRER, DAILY NEWS & PHILLY.COM

801 Market Street, Ste. 300, Philadelphia, Pa., 19107-3126, Philadelphia; gen tel 215 854 2000; adv tel (215) 854-5450; ed tel (215) 854-4531; gen fax 215-854-5884; adv fax (215) 854-4788; ed fax (215) 854-5099; gen/nat adv e-mail advertisingrequests@phillynews.com; disp adv e-mail advertisingrequests@phillynews.com; class adv e-mailadvertisingrequests@phillynews.com; web site www.philly.com 7,963,604(visitors)

Group: Philadelphia Media Network
Published: Mon, Tues, Wed, Thur, Fri, Sat, Sun
Weekday Frequency: m
Saturday Frequency: m
Circulation: 203,986; 178,933(sat); 363,700(sun)
Last Audit: AAM March 31, 2016
Branch Offices: Cherry Hill, NJ
Bristol, PA
Conshohocken, PA
News services: AP, DJ, MCT, LAT-WP, RN. **Established:** 1829
Own Printing Facility?: Yes
Commercial Printers?: No
Digital Platform - Mobile: Apple, Android, Windows
Digital Platform - Tablet: Apple iOS, Android
Staff Photographer .... Elizabeth Robertson
Executive Editor .... Stan Wischnowski
Editorial Page Editor .... Harold Jackson
Donna Yannessa
Pat McElwee
Advertising Director .... Barbara Sadler
Fred Lehman
Managing Ed., Features/Operations/Digital Gabriel Escobar
Publisher and CEO .... Terrance C.Z. Egger
Market Information: Split run; Zoned editions.
Mechanical Available: Offset; Black and 3 ROP colors; insert accepted - all; page cutoffs - 22.
Mechanical Specifications: Type page 13 x 21; E - 6 cols, 2 1/16, 1/8 between; A - 6 cols, 2 1/16, 1/8 between; C - 10 cols, 1 3/16, 1/16 between.
Areas Served: Philadelphia, PA
Delivery Method: Newsstand, Carrier, RacksEquipment & Software: PRESSROOM EQUIPMENT: Lines — 10-G/Colorliner double width (9 Lines); Folders — 9-Sovereign/160 Page 3:2; Pasters —90-G/CT-50Reels & Stands — 90-G/CT-50; Control System — G/APCS.; MAILROOM EQUIPMENT: Counter Stackers — 22-HL/HTZ, 10-QWI/400; Inserters & Stuffers — 3-GMA/SLS 1000A (23:1), 7-GMA/SLS 100 (12:1); Tying Machines — 12-Dynaric/NPI, 28-Dynaric/NP2, 4/NP3; Control System — GMA/IPCs, Map Con, Carnegie Mellon/Machine Design; BUSINESS EQUIPMENT: 1-IBM/390, 2-HP/937, 2-HP/957 Processor BUSINESS SOFTWARE: Microsoft/Suite CLASSIFIED EQUIPMENT: Hardware — AT/IAS, 150-AT, RSK/6000; 2-Konica, 2-Bs/DEX; CLASSIFIED SOFTWARE: AT 4.7.2, AT/ClassPage. DISPLAY EQUIPMENT: Hardware — 13-IBM/RS 6000, 10-APP/Mac; Printers — 2-Graphic Enterprises, 3-AU/108CS, 3-ACL/3850, 3-Au/3810; Other Hardware — 3-DEC/Alpha RIP, 3-Eskofot/Scanners, 2-AU/Oman 97, AU/APS Com Send/Receive DISPLAY SOFTWAREAd Make-up Applications — QPS/QuarkXPress 4.02, Camex; Layout Software — AT/Ar EDITORIAL EQUIPMENT: Hardware — AT/30, 14-AT/J-11, Unisys/Hermes/AT, 27-APP/Mac EDITORIAL SOFTWARE: AT 4.7.4, Hermes. PRODUCTION EQUIPMENT: Hardware — 3-AU/APS-6, 6-WL/Bender, 3-AU/3810; Cameras — 1-C/Pager II; Scanners — 3-AU/Page Scanners, 3-ECR/Autokon, Eskofot, 5-Kk/RS 2035, 5-Nikon/LS 2000 PRODUCTION SOFTWARE: Unisys/Hermes, AT/IAS.

POTTSTOWN

THE MERCURY

24 N Hanover St, Pottstown, Pa., 19464-5410, Montgomery; gen tel (610) 323-3000; adv tel (610) 323-3000; ed tel (610) 970-4455; gen fax (610) 327-3308; adv fax (610) 970-4492; ed fax (610) 323-0682; gen/nat adv e-mail paadvertising@digitalfirstmedia.com; disp adv e-mail paadvertising@digitalfirstmedia.com; class adv e-mailpaadvertising@digitalfirstmedia.com; ed e-mail shuskey@21-centurymedia.com; web site www.pottsmerc.com 477,882(visitors)

Group: Digital First Media
Published: Mon, Tues, Wed, Thur, Fri, Sat, Sun
Weekday Frequency: m
Saturday Frequency: m
Circulation: 17,497; 17,225(sat); 20,983(sun)
Last Audit: AAM September 30, 2014
Advertising Rate (weekday/saturday): 1/8 Pg $196.53
News services: AP, Robert Hitchings & Co.. **Established:** 1931
Special Editions: Lawn & Garden (Apr); Back-to-School (Aug); Last Minute Gift Guide (Dec); Washington's Birthday Auto (Feb); Education Outlook (Jan); Financial (Jul); Senior Lifestyles (Jun); Home Improvement (Mar); Racer's Edge (May); Automotive Today (Monthly); Pre-Holid
Special Weekly Sections: Health (Mon); Generations, Business (Tue); Best Food Days (Wed); Time Out, Auto (Thur); Schools, Auctions (Fri); Church, Auto (Sat); Real Estate, Recruitment, Jobs, Food, Auto, Wedding, Engagements, Travel, TV (Sun); Business (Daily)
Syndicated Publications: USA WEEKEND Magazine (S); US Express (Sat); Market Place (Wed).
Pub. .... Thomas Abbot
Controller .... Patricia McKelvey
Adv. Dir. .... Steve Batten
Adv. Mgr., Classified .... Mary Ann Matalavage
Mgr., Penny Pincher .... Cindy Eisenhauer
Ed. .... Nancy March
ity Editor/Opinion Page Editor/Columnist/Blogger .. Tony Phyrillas
Features Ed. .... Pat Sommers
Sports Ed. .... Don Seeley
Online Ed. .... Eileen Faust
Retail Adv. Mgr. .... Jerry Fuhrmeister
Circ. Dir. .... Joe Frost
Market Information: ADS; TMC; Zoned editions.
Mechanical Available: Offset; Black and 3 ROP colors; insert accepted; page cutoffs - 21.
Mechanical Specifications: Type page 11 5/8 x 20 1/2; E - 6 cols, 1 5/6, 1/8 between; A - 6 cols, 1 5/6, 1/8 between; C - 10 cols, between. Equipment & Software: PRESSROOM EQUIPMENT: Lines — 3-MAN/double width; 3-MAN/double width; Reels & Stands — 8-MAN/CD 13; Control System — PECOM.; MAILROOM EQUIPMENT: Counter Stackers — 2/HL; Inserters & Stuffers — 1-HI/Injector 1372 w/ARS; Tying Machines — 2-Sa/Auto, 1-Sa/Man; Wrapping Singles — 1-Sa/810; Address Machine — 2-Am/1900, 1-Am/5000.; BUSINESS EQUIPMENT: AS 400 CLASSIFIED EQUIPMENT: Hardware — AST/Bravo LC 5133, Dell/Gx150; MEI/CLS 2.6.6; Printers — NewGen/660B; CLASSIFIED SOFTWARE: Intertext/REV 12G, AT/5.7. DISPLAY EQUIPMENT: Hardware — 10-APP/Mac 8500, 3-APP/Mac G3, 1-APP/IMac, 2-APP/Mac G4; Printers — 2-NewGen 660B; Other Hardware — 1-ECR/Autokon 1030C DISPLAY SOFTWAREAd Make-up Applications — QPS/QuarkXPress 4.0, Multi-Ad Creator 2 Adobe/Acrobat, 3.02; Layout Software — APP/Mac, 3-APP/Mac G3. EDITORIAL EQUIPMENT: Hardware — 4-Compaq/ProLiant, Microsoft/Windows NT 4.0; Printers — 1-Xante/3G EDITORIAL SOFTWARE: CNI. PRODUCTION EQUIPMENT: Hardware — Omnipage Pro 7.0, Na, 1-R/Vertical; Cameras — 1-C/Spartan III, 1-R/Vertical; Scanners — ECR/Autokon 1030, Nikon/Scanner, HP/Scanjet 6100C PRODUCTION SOFTWARE: MEI/ALS 2.5.1, MEI/CLS 2.6.6.

POTTSVILLE

THE REPUBLICAN-HERALD

111 Mahantongo St, Pottsville, Pa., 17901-3071, Schuylkill; gen tel (570) 622-3456; adv tel (570) 628-6060; ed tel (570) 622-3456; gen fax (570) 628-6092; adv fax (570) 628-6077; ed fax (570) 628-6092; gen/nat adv e-mail mjoyce@republicanherald.com; disp adv e-mail mjoyce@republicanherald.com; class adv e-mailclassifieds@republicanherald.com; ed e-mail editorial@republicanherald.com; web site www.republicanherald.com - 1,415,000(views) 251,000(visitors)

Group: Times-Shamrock Communications
Published: Mon, Tues, Wed, Thur, Fri, Sat, Sun
Weekday Frequency: m
Saturday Frequency: m
Circulation: 19,486; 20,472(sat); 24,120(sun)
Last Audit: AAM December 11, 2017
Newspaper Reps: MANSI, Harrisburg, PA
Advertising Rate (weekday/saturday): $40.00 pci
Advertising Rate (sunday): $48.16 pci
Online Advertising Rate: $15/m
News services: AP **Established:** 1884
Own Printing Facility?: No
Commercial Printers?: Yes
Special Editions: Wedding Guides - January, April, June
Business Review - February
Home Improvement / Lawn & Garden - March, April, August, October
Senior Living - <arch, May, July, September, November
Business Card Directory - March
Reader's Choice - May
Graduation - May
Football - August
Church Directory - September
Education Guide - November
Christmas Gifts - November, December
Special Weekly Sections: Best Food Day (Wed); Business Extra (Mon); Health (Tues)
Entertainment (Fri)
Syndicated Publications: Relish (Monthly); Parade Magazine (S); American Profile (Sat); Mini-Page (Tues).
Digital Platform - Mobile: Apple, Android, Windows, Blackberry
Digital Platform - Tablet: Apple iOS, Android, Blackberry Tablet OS
Pub. .... Henry H. Nyce
Dir., Circ. .... David Sickle
Adv. Dir. .... Michael A. Joyce
Dir., Mktg./Community Serv. .... Janet Joyce
Home Delivery Mgr. .... Neal O'Brien
Ed. .... Pete Banko
Features Ed. .... Tina Tym
Sports Ed. .... Leroy Boyer
News Ed. .... Kathryn Campomizzi-Clews
Market Information: Sunday Select, an AAM audited opt-tin distribution program for inserts
Mechanical Available: Offset; Black and 3 ROP colors; insert accepted - product samples.
Mechanical Specifications: 1 column 1.6 inches, 9p4 picas
2 column 3.222 inches, 19p4 picas
3 column 4.889 inches, 29p4 picas
4 column 6.556 inches, 39p4 picas
5 column 8.222 inches, 49p4 picas
6 column 9.889 inches, 59p4 picas
Double truck 13 column, 20.889 inches, 125p4 picas
Full page broad sheet depth is 20.5 inches
Areas Served: Schuylkill County, Pa
Delivery Method: Mail, Newsstand, Carrier, RacksEquipment & Software: EDITORIAL EQUIPMENT: Hardware — Sun/Ultra 2, Dell/PII 350; Printers — AU/APS Broadsheeter, 2-AU/APS 6-84ACS 14 Imager, HP/LaserJet 5500 EDITORIAL SOFTWARE: HI/XP-21, HI/NewsMaker Pagination 3.5.15.1. PRODUCTION EQUIPMENT: Hardware — Calera/WordScan Plus, Graham/5327; Scanners — HP/Text Scanner, 1-ECR/Autokon 2045, 2-Umax/2400 PRODUCTION SOFTWARE: HI/NewsMaker Pagination 3.5.15.

PUNXSUTAWNEY

THE PUNXSUTAWNEY SPIRIT

510 Pine St, Punxsutawney, Pa., 15767-1404, Jefferson; gen tel (814) 938-8740; adv tel (814) 938-8740; ed tel (814) 938-8740; gen fax (814) 938-3794; adv fax (814) 938-3794; ed fax (814) 938-3794; gen/nat adv e-mail tlsmith@punxsutawneyspirit.com; disp adv e-mail tlsmith@punxsutawneyspirit.com; class adv e-mailtlsmith@punxsutawneyspirit.com; ed e-mail tchapin@punxsutawneyspirit.com; web site www.punxsutawneyspirit.com

Group: Horizon Publications Inc.
Published: Mon, Tues, Wed, Thur, Fri, Sat
Weekday Frequency: m
Saturday Frequency: m
Circulation: 5,545; 5,545(sat)
Last Audit: Sworn/Estimate/Non-Audited September 30, 2017
Advertising Rate (weekday/saturday): Open inch rate $12.50
Advertising Rate (sunday): Open inch rate 18.50
News services: AP. **Established:** 1873
Own Printing Facility?: Yes
Commercial Printers?: Yes
Special Editions: Home & Garden (Apr); Fall Sports (Aug); Senior Citizen (Feb); Spring Home Improvement (Mar); Home & Garden (May); Outdoors (Nov); Senior Citizen (Sept).
Special Weekly Sections: Best Food Day (Wed);
Syndicated Publications: American Profile (Tues).
Adv. Mgr., Classified .... Candice Shirley
Editor .... Zak Lantz
Sports Ed. .... Dan Walk
Prodn. Supvr., Composing .... Karen Petroff
Pub./Adv. Dir. .... Tracy Smith
Business Mgr. .... Susan Humble
Circ. Mgr. .... Cindy Covatch
Market Information: TMC; Zoned editions.
Mechanical Available: Offset; Black and 3 ROP colors; page cutoffs - 22 3/4.
Mechanical Specifications: Type page 11 1/16 x 21 1/2; E - 6 cols, 1 11/16, 3/8 between; A - 6 cols, 1 11/16, 3/8 between; C - 9 cols, 1 1/8, 1/8 between.

Delivery Method: Mail, Newsstand, Carrier, RacksEquipment & Software: PRESSROOM EQUIPMENT: Lines — 5-G/Community single width; Folders — 1, 1.; MAILROOM EQUIPMENT: Tying Machines — Semi Ace Sk 707, Strapmatic 202A; Address Machine — Ch.; CLASSIFIED EQUIPMENT: Hardware — 9-APP/Mac; CLASSIFIED SOFTWARE: Baseview. DISPLAY SOFTWARELayout Software — APP/Mac SE. EDITORIAL EQUIPMENT: Hardware — 6-APP/Mac EDITORIAL SOFTWARE: Baseview. PRODUCTION EQUIPMENT: Hardware — Graham/5-1-27.

READING

READING EAGLE

345 Penn St, Reading, Pa., 19601-4029, Berks; gen tel (610) 371-5000; adv tel (610) 371-5100; ed tel (610) 371-5010; adv fax (610) 371-5193; ed fax (610) 371-5098; gen/nat adv e-mail sflank@readingeagle.com; disp adv e-mail advertising@readingeagle.com; class adv e-mailClassified@readingeagle.com; ed e-mail news@readingeagle.com; web site www.readingeagle.com
- 3,269,780(views) 287,449(visitors)

Published: Mon, Tues, Wed, Thur, Fri, Sat, Sun
Weekday Frequency: m
Saturday Frequency: m
Circulation: 40,906; 40,609(sat); 57,034(sun)
Last Audit: AAM December 31, 2016
Advertising Rate (weekday/saturday): Modular rate 1% daily open $50; color addl. $11
Advertising Rate (sunday): Modular rate 1% Sunday open $66; color addl. $11
Online Advertising Rate: Banner ads $15 cpm-$17 cpm
Block ads (site or mobile) $15
Daily Site Splash ad $700/day
News services: AP, LAT-WP, SHNS. **Established:** 1868
Own Printing Facility?: Yes
Commercial Printers?: Yes
Special Editions: Clip-it Coupons (monthly); Health & Wellness (monthly, except December); Home & Garden (Feb., Apr, Sept.); Mature Living (Feb., Apr, June, Aug, Oct, Dec.); Bridal (Feb., July); Berks Jazz Fest Guide (March); Holiday Gift guides (Nov., Dec.); Craft Beer (June); Shop Local (June); Antiques (May); Voters Guide (April, Oct)
Special Weekly Sections: Garden Pages (Apr-Sept) (Mon); Home & Building/Real Estate (Sunday); Church (Sat); Restaurant & Entertainment (Thur); Voices (Tues); Best Food Day (Wed); Berks Country (Wed); Business Weekly (Tues) Classified Jobs (Sunday)
Syndicated Publications: Parade Magazine
Proprietary Publications: Reading Eagle (daily)
South Schuylkill News (weekly)
Digital Platform - Mobile: Apple, Android
Digital Platform - Tablet: Apple iOS, Android
Pres.CEO....................Peter Barbey
Chairman, Publisher....................William S. Flippin
Associate Pub/Ed.....................Harry J. Deitz
COO....................Anne T. Chubb
Exec. Dir of Circ & Promotions....................Dave Kline
Mng. Ed.....................David Mowery
Editorial Page Ed.....................Mark Nemirow
Asst. News Ed....................Keith Mayer
Asst. New Ed.....................Joe Hainthaler
Classified Mgr....................Sherry Jacobs
Senior Information Technology Director.......... Eric Schaeffer
Information Technology Director. Kevin Lawrence
Web Designer....................Brandi Swenson
Circulation Sales Director....................William J. Lobb
Senior Dir of Mktg....................Connie Andrews
Packaging/Distr. Dir.....................Albert A. Stallone
General Sales Director....................Steve Flank
Multimedia Sales Manager....................Denice Schaeffer
Sr. Director of Production....................Chris D'Angelo
CFO....................Shawn Moliatu
Market Information: Berks County; Tri-County area; South Schuylkill County
Mechanical Available: Offset, 4 color process, insert accepted - plastic bags; page cutoffs - 18 1/2.
Mechanical Specifications: 46" Web.
PRINTING PROCESS: Offset.
Broadsheet Paper Dimension: 11.5" wide x 18.5" high.
Full Page Image Area: 10.5" wide x 17" high.
BROADSHEET MODULAR AD SIZES

% of Page	Ad Dimension
100%	10.5" x 17"
75%	10.5" x 12.75"
70%	8.729" x 14.28"
67%	6.958" x 17"
65%	10.5" x 11.05"
50% V	5.187" x 17"
50% H	10.5" x 8.5"
39%	5.187" x 13.26"
33%	10.5" x 5.61"
30%	6.958" x 7.65"
25%	5.187" x 8.5"
23%	8.729" x 4.692"
20%	6.958" x 5.1"
15%	3.417" x 7.65"
14%	10.5" x 2.38"
13%	3.417" x 6.63"
12%	5.187" x 4.08"
10%	3.417" x 5.1"
9%	5.187" x 3.06"
8%	3.417" x 4.08"
6%	3.417" x 3.05"
4%	3.417" x 2.04"
3%	1.646" x 3.06"
2%	1.646" x 2.04"
1%	1.646" x 1.02"

Tabloid Paper Dimension: 9.25" wide x 11.5" high.
Full Page Image Area: 7.708" wide x 10.5" high.
WEEKEND TABLOID COLUMN-INCH AD SIZES

1 col.	1.833"
2 col.	3.792"
3 col.	5.75"
4 col.	7.708"

Areas Served: Reading-Berks County
Pottstown-Montgomery County
South Schuylkill County
Delivery Method: Mail, Newsstand, Carrier, RacksEquipment & Software: PRESSROOM EQUIPMENT: 1 KBA Colora, 2-KF3 KBA folders, 4-KBA 4x4 printing towers, 5-KBA reel stands, inline stitcher and quarter folder, Tecnotrans dampening system, Eletta balanket wask. MAILROOM EQUIPMENT: 5-Hi/Olympia NP502 , inserter - 1-Hi/NP632, Miracom control system, 2-NP-125gripper delivery, 1-NP200 online gripper conveyor, 1-NS300 belt conveyor,12-OVL/EX311, 2-OVL/415, 3-Profit packaging lable applicators. BUSINESS EQUIPMENT: 2-DEC/Alpha BUSINESS SOFTWARE: PBS CLASSIFIED EQUIPMENT: Hardware — Dell/Poweredge 4400-NT Cluster; Printers — HP/4000; CLASSIFIED SOFTWARE: Atex AdBase 3.0 DISPLAY EQUIPMENT: Apple iMac, Cannon 5500 proofing DISPLAY SOFTWAREAd Make-up Applications — Adobe InDesign 5.5; Adobe Design suite, Layout Software — Doris/Planner
NEO EDITORIAL EQUIPMENT: Hardware — PC Client Server/12-APP/Mac, Nikon/3510 scanners; Printers — 2-Panasonic, HP/LaserJet, APP/Mac LaserWriter EDITORIAL SOFTWARE: Anygraaf/Doris Pagination System.
NEO pagination system PRODUCTION EQUIPMENT: 2-Screen Platerite2000, 2-Protech105
processor, 1-Burgess punch bender CIRCULATION SOFTWARDTI
Note: Pretzel City Productions, LLC is a division of Reading Eagle Company created to produce and/or co-host events in the community.
WEEU 830AM - news/talk

RIDGWAY

THE RIDGWAY RECORD

325 Main St, Ste A, Ridgway, Pa., 15853-8019, Elk; gen tel (814) 773-3161; ed tel (814) 773-3151; gen fax (814) 776-1086; gen/nat adv e-mail sales@ridgwayrecord.com; disp adv e-mail sales@ridgwayrecord.com; class adv e-mailsales@ridgwayrecord.com; ed e-mail ridgwayrecord@shop-right.com; web site www.ridgwayrecord.com

Group: Horizon Publications Inc.
Published: Mon, Tues, Wed, Thur, Fri, Sat
Weekday Frequency: e
Saturday Frequency: m
Circulation: 2,656; 2,656(sat)
Last Audit: Sworn/Estimate/Non-Audited September 30, 2017
Advertising Rate (weekday/saturday): Open inch rate $9.50
News services: AP.
Own Printing Facility?: Yes
Commercial Printers?: Yes
Special Weekly Sections: Best Food Days (Sat);
Syndicated Publications: TV Section (Sat); American Profile (Weekly).
Pub.....................Christie Gardner
Ed.....................Joseph Bell
Bus. Mgr.....................Karen Kilhoffer
Circ. Mgr.....................Brandon Laiphner
Production Mgr.....................Mike Tucker
Harlan Beagley
Market Information: TMC.
Mechanical Available: Offset; Black and 3 ROP colors; insert accepted - any; page cutoffs - 22 3/4.
Mechanical Specifications: Type page 11 31/50 x 21 1/2; E - 6 cols, 1 3/4, 1/8 between; A - 6 cols, 1 3/4, 1/8 between; C - 8 cols, 1 9/25, 1/8 between.
Delivery Method: Mail, Newsstand, Carrier, RacksEquipment & Software: PRESSROOM EQUIPMENT: Lines — 8-G/Community; Folders — 1-G/SE.; MAILROOM EQUIPMENT: Tying Machines — 2/Sa, 2-Gd/808.; CLASSIFIED EQUIPMENT: Hardware — APP/Power Mac; Printers — APP/Mac LaserWriter; CLASSIFIED SOFTWARE: Baseview. DISPLAY EQUIPMENT: Hardware — APP/Mac.; EDITORIAL EQUIPMENT: Hardware — APP/Mac; Printers — APP/Mac LaserWriter, HP/LaserPrinter EDITORIAL SOFTWARE: Baseview. PRODUCTION EQUIPMENT: Hardware — Kk/65A; Cameras — Kk PRODUCTION SOFTWARE: Baseview.

SAINT MARYS

THE DAILY PRESS

245 Brusselles St, Saint Marys, Pa., 15857-1501, Elk; gen tel (814) 781-1596; adv tel (814)781-1596; ed tel (814) 781-1539; gen fax (814) 834-7473; adv fax (814)834-7473; ed fax (814)834-7473; gen/nat adv e-mail sales@zitomedia.net; disp adv e-mail sales@zitomedia.net; class adv e-mailclassifieds@smdailypress.com; ed e-mail editor3@zitomedia.net; web site www.smdailypress.com
- 62,000(views)

Group: Horizon Publications Inc.
Published: Mon, Tues, Wed, Thur, Fri, Sat
Weekday Frequency: m
Saturday Frequency: m
Circulation: 4,891; 4,891(sat)
Last Audit: Sworn/Estimate/Non-Audited September 30, 2017
Advertising Rate (weekday/saturday): Open inch rate $10.40
News services: AP.
Own Printing Facility?: No
Special Editions: Progress (Apr); Football (Aug); Elk Haven Greetings (Dec); Boy Scouts (Feb); Pet Parade (Jul); Spring Home Improvement (May); Holiday Gift Guide (Nov); Octoberfest (Oct); Hometown Festival (Sept).
Special Weekly Sections: Best Food Days (Mon/Tue); Senior (Other); Weekender TV (Sat).
Syndicated Publications: American Profile (Weekly).
Pub.....................Christie Gardner
Adv. Mgr.....................Krista Zameroski
Group Ed.....................Grace Kriegisch
Bus. Mgr.....................James R. Bauer
Adv. Mgr., Classified....................Billie Kunes
Sports Ed.....................James Mulcahy
Market Information: Split run; TMC.
Mechanical Available: Offset; Black and 3 ROP colors; insert accepted; page cutoffs - 21 1/2.
Mechanical Specifications: Type page 13 x 21 1/2; E - 6 cols, 1 13/16, 1/6 between; A - 6 cols, 1 13/16, 1/6 between; C - 8 cols, 1 3/8, 1/8 between.
Delivery Method: Mail, Newsstand, Carrier, RacksEquipment & Software: MAILROOM EQUIPMENT: Tying Machines — 1-JIA-IN/Industries Brand.; BUSINESS EQUIPMENT: Dell BUSINESS SOFTWARE: Tallgrass CLASSIFIED EQUIPMENT: Hardware — APP/Mac; Printers — Okidata/320; CLASSIFIED SOFTWARE: Mk, Baseview. DISPLAY EQUIPMENT: Hardware — APP/Mac; Printers — APP/Mac LaserJet, HP/LaserJet 4MV; DISPLAY SOFTWAREAd Make-up Applications — Aldus/PageMaker; Layout Software — APP/Mac. EDITORIAL EQUIPMENT: Hardware — APP/Mac; Printers — APP/Mac LaserJet, HP/Laser Jet 4MV EDITORIAL SOFTWARE: Baseview. PRODUCTION EQUIPMENT: Hardware — Kk/Kodamatic 65A; Cameras — Kk/Image Maker PRODUCTION SOFTWARE: QPS/QuarkXPress.

SAYRE

MORNING TIMES

201 N Lehigh Ave, Sayre, Pa., 18840-2246, Bradford; gen tel (570) 888-9643; gen fax (570) 888-6463; gen/nat adv e-mail ads@morning-times.com; disp adv e-mail ads@morning-times.com; class adv e-mailclassifieds@morning-times.com; ed e-mail whoweler@morning-times.com; web site www.morning-times.com
- 258,180(views) 90,450(visitors)

Group: Sample News Group LLC
Published: Mon, Tues, Wed, Thur, Fri, Sat
Weekday Frequency: m
Saturday Frequency: m
Circulation: 5,200; 5,400(sat)
Last Audit: Sworn/Estimate/Non-Audited October 16, 2017
Advertising Rate (weekday/saturday): Open inch rate $12.54
News services: AP. **Established:** 1890
Own Printing Facility?: No
Commercial Printers?: Yes
Special Editions: Multiple
Special Weekly Sections: Times Extra TMC
Digital Platform - Mobile: Apple, Android
Digital Platform - Tablet: Apple iOS, Android
Pub., Purchasing Agent....................Kelly Luvison
Mng. Ed.....................Warren Howeler
Sports Ed.....................Dave Post
Adv. Dir.....................Ashley Moore
Circulation Director....................Bill Kurtz
Production manager....................Kirk Luvison
Market Information: TMC.
Mechanical Available: Offset; Black and ROP colors; insert accepted; page cutoffs - 22 3/4.
Mechanical Specifications: Type page 11 3/4 x 21 1/2; E - 6 cols, 1 3/4, 1/6 between; A - 9 cols, 1 3/16, 1/6 between; C - 9 cols, 1 3/16, 1/6 between.
Areas Served: 18840, 18810, 14892, 18850, 18848, 18837, 18831, 18817, 14889, 14833, 14895, 14825, 13827, 13812, 13734
Delivery Method: Mail, Newsstand, Carrier, RacksEquipment & Software: BUSINESS EQUIPMENT: Dell/PCs BUSINESS SOFTWARE: MSSI/Quickbooks CLASSIFIED EQUIPMENT: APP/Mac CLASSIFIED SOFTWARE: Newscycle DISPLAY EQUIPMENT: Hardware — APP/Mac; Printers — Xante; DISPLAY SOFTWAREAdobe/Newscycle EDITORIAL EQUIPMENT: Hardware — APP/Mac; Printers — Xante EDITORIAL SOFTWARE: Newscycle CIRCULATION EQUIPMENT: Dell/PCs CIRCULATION SOFTWARMSSI

SCRANTON

THE TIMES-TRIBUNE

149 Penn Ave, Ofc, Scranton, Pa., 18503-2056, Lackawanna; gen tel (570) 348-9100; adv tel (570) 348-9100 ext. 5202; gen fax (570) 348-9109; adv fax (570) 348-9178; ed fax (570) 348-9135; gen/nat adv e-mail cdemas@timesshamrock.com; disp adv e-mail ads@timesshamrock.com; class adv e-mailads@timesshamrock.com; ed e-mail newsroom@timesshamrock.com; web site www.thetimes-tribune.com
- 4,000,000(views) 660,000(visitors)

Group: Times-Shamrock Communications
Published: Mon, Tues, Wed, Thur, Fri, Sat, Sun
Weekday Frequency: m
Saturday Frequency: m
Circulation: 38,202; 38,664(sat); 46,947(sun)

Last Audit: AAM December 31, 2016
Advertising Rate (weekday/saturday): Open inch rate $136.36
Advertising Rate (sunday): Open inch rate $137.69
News services: AP, NYT, MCT. **Established:** 1895
Special Editions: Easter Dining Guide (Apr); Football Tab (Aug); Christmas Songbook (Dec); Home Builders Expo (Feb); Good Times (Jan); Good Times (Jul); Bridal Tab (Jun); Good Times (Mar); Good Times (May); Good Times (Nov); United Way Tab (Oct); Fall Home Improvement Tab
Special Weekly Sections: Amusements, Comics, Finance, Stocks, Neighbors, TV (Daily); Best Food (Wed); Business, Real Estate, Weekend, Entertainment (Thur); Travel, Entertainment, Business, Finance, Comics, Real Estate, Stocks, Veterans, People, Arts (Sun)
Syndicated Publications: Relish (Monthly); USA WEEKEND Magazine (Sat); Electric City (Thur); American Profile (Weekly).
Pub. .... Mathew E. Haggerty
Pub. .... Robert J. Lynett
Ed./Pub. .... William R. Lynett
Credit Mgr. .... Carolyn Timlin
Controller/Purchasing Agent .... Alan Buntz
Dir., HR .... William P. Nish
Adv. Mgr. .... Amy Lutheran
Adv. Mgr., Nat'l .... Renee Puchalski
Dir., Mktg./Promo. .... Cathy Labori
Circ. Dir. .... Jim Phillips
Mng. Ed. .... Larry Beaupre
Mng. Ed. .... Larry Holeva
Asst. Mng. Ed. .... John Murphy
Automotive Ed. .... Ted Geltner
Bus./Finance Ed. .... Jessica Mathews
Cartoonist .... John Cole
Editorial Page Ed. .... Patrick J. McKenna
Features Ed. .... Terry Bonifanti
Stephanie Toffey
Adv. Mgr. .... Jason Jones
Production Director .... John McAndrew
Gen. Mgr. .... James E. Towner
Nat'l. Adv. Mgr. .... Carol Demas
Market Information: ADS; Split run; TMC; Zoned editions.
Mechanical Available: Offset; Black and 3 ROP colors; insert accepted - cards, envelopes; page cutoffs - 21 1/2.
Mechanical Specifications: Type page 13 x 21 1/2; E - 6 cols, 2 1/16, 1/8 between; A - 6 cols, 2 1/16, 1/8 between; C - 9 cols, 1 3/8, 1/8 between.
Delivery Method: CarrierEquipment & Software: PRESSROOM EQUIPMENT: 6-G/ho double width; Folders — 1-G/3:2, 1-G/ Page Jaw Folder; Control System — 1-G/ MPCS. MAILROOM EQUIPMENT: Counter Stackers — 3-Id/2000, 2-QWI/350; Inserters & Stuffers — 1-GMA/SLS 1000, 10/Pocket, 2-/Main Feeders; Tying Machines — 3-/ Dynaric; Address Machine — 3-/WM, 1-/ Ch, 1-/KR; BUSINESS EQUIPMENT: IBM/AS-400 CLASSIFIED EQUIPMENT: Hardware — PPI, 14-PC; Printers — HP; CLASSIFIED SOFTWARE: PPI. DISPLAY EQUIPMENT: Hardware — 20-APP/Mac; Printers — NewGen/600 dpi; DISPLAY SOFTWAREAd Make-up Applications — Multi-Ad/Creator 3.7; Layout Software — SCS/Layout 8000. EDITORIAL EQUIPMENT: Hardware — 48-PC, 2-Sun/Server; Printers — HP EDITORIAL SOFTWARE: HI/ NewsMaker. PRODUCTION EQUIPMENT: Hardware — 1-AU/APS-108C, MON/3850, Adobe/RIPs, 1-ECR/4550; Cameras — 1-C/ Spartan III; Scanners — Scitex/340, VMAX PRODUCTION SOFTWARE: HI/NewsMaker Pagination.
Note: The Scranton Times-Tribune (mS) has a combination rate of $132.39 (m) and $133.68 (S) with the Wilkes-Barre Citizens' Voice (mS). Individual newspaper rates not made available.

SHAMOKIN

THE NEWS-ITEM

707 N Rock St, Shamokin, Pa., 17872-4930, Northumberland; gen tel (570) 644-6397; adv tel (570)644-6397 ext 4; ed tel (570) 644-6397 ext. 1341; gen fax (570) 644-0892; adv fax (570) 644-0892; ed fax (570) 648-7581; gen/nat adv e-mail jessica_w@newsitem.com; disp adv e-mail jessica_w@newsitem.com; class adv e-mailclassifieds@newsitem.com; ed e-mail editorial@newsitem.com; web site www.newsitem.com
Group: Sample Media
Published: Mon, Tues, Wed, Thur, Fri, Sat, Sun
Weekday Frequency: m
Saturday Frequency: m
Circulation: 6,862; 6,798(sat); 6,959(sun)
Last Audit: Sworn/Estimate/Non-Audited October 15, 2017
Advertising Rate (weekday/saturday): Open inch rate $16.66
Advertising Rate (sunday): Open inch rate $16.16
News services: AP. **Established:** 1891
Own Printing Facility?: No
Commercial Printers?: Yes
Special Editions: Car Care (Apr); Back-to-School (Aug); Xmas Gift Guide (Dec); Progress/ Economic Review (Feb); Bridal (Jan); Christmas Gift Guide (Nov); Christmas Lay-Away (Oct); Fall Football Preview (Sept).
Special Weekly Sections: Area Schools Page (Fri); Church Pages (Sat); Outdoors Sports Page (Thur); Wedding and Engagement Pages (Tues); Business World Page (Wed); food and drink page.
Syndicated Publications: American Profile (Weekly). Parade magazine. Spry
General manager .... Amy Moyer
Dir., Circ. .... David Sickle
Exec. Ed. .... Andrew Heintzelman
Sports Ed. .... Charlie Rotch
Systems Mgr. .... Glenn Knarr
Prodn. Foreman, Composing .... Glenn A. Knarr
Rgl. Adv. Dir. .... David Barry
Mechanical Available: Offset; Black and 3 ROP colors; insert accepted; page cutoffs - 22 3/4.
Mechanical Specifications: Type page 13 x 21 1/2; E - 6 cols, 2 1/16, 1/8 between; A - 6 cols, 2 1/16, 1/8 between; C - 10 cols, 1 3/8, 1/16 between.
Areas Served: Northumberland, Columbia and Schuylkill counties
Delivery Method: Mail, Newsstand, Carrier, RacksEquipment & Software: MAILROOM EQUIPMENT: Tying Machines — 1-/ Sa; Address Machine — 1-RSK/Printer.; BUSINESS EQUIPMENT: IBM/AS-400 CLASSIFIED EQUIPMENT: Hardware — APP/Mac G3/233; Printers — HP, Xante; CLASSIFIED SOFTWARE: Baseview/ Ad Manager Pro. DISPLAY EQUIPMENT: Hardware — APP/Mac G3; Printers — Xante/Accel-a-Writer 3G 1200 dpi, 2-ECR/ Imagesetter; Other Hardware — Epson/ Expression 836 XL Scanner, Nikon/Coolscan III, Nikon/LS DISPLAY SOFTWAREAd Make-up Applications — Multi-Ad/Creator, Aldus/FreeHand, Adobe/Photoshop 5.5, QPS/QuarkXPress 4.04; EDITORIAL EQUIPMENT: Hardware — APP/Mac G3, APP/iMac; Printers — Xante EDITORIAL SOFTWARE: APP/Mac System 8.6, Baseview/NewsEdit 3.32, QPS/QuarkXPress 4.04. PRODUCTION EQUIPMENT: Hardware — 2-ECR/Imagesetter, HP/4MV, Xante/Accel-A-Writer 3G; Cameras — 1-C; Scanners — Epson/Expression 836 XL, Nikon LS, Nikon Coolscan III PRODUCTION SOFTWARE: Baseview/News Edit 3.2.2, QPS/QuarkXPress 4.04.

SHARON

THE HERALD

52 S Dock St, Sharon, Pa., 16146-1808, Mercer; gen tel (724) 981-6100; adv tel (724)981-6100; ed tel (724)981-6100; gen fax (724) 981-5116; adv fax (724) 981-7844; ed fax (724)981-6100; gen/nat adv e-mail rwork@sharonherald.com; disp adv e-mail rwork@sharonherald.com; class adv e-mailrwork@sharonherald.com; ed e-mail rcarey@sharonherald.com; web site www.sharonherald.com
Group: Community Newspaper Holdings, Inc.
Published: Mon, Tues, Wed, Thur, Fri, Sat, Sun
Weekday Frequency: m
Saturday Frequency: m
Circulation: 11,393; 11,393(sat); 12,133(sun)
Last Audit: AAM December 31, 2017
Advertising Rate (weekday/saturday): Open inch rate $39.32
Advertising Rate (sunday): Open inch rate $39.32
News services: AP, ONS. **Established:** 1864
Special Editions: Lawn & Garden (Apr); Football Magazine (Aug); Outlook (Feb); Summer Fun (Jun); Car Care (Mar); Golf Guide (May); Holiday Gift Guide (Nov); Women's World (Oct); National Fuel (Sept).
Special Weekly Sections: Best Food Day (Wed); Entertainment (Thur); Real Estate (Fri); Religion (Sat); Business, Health, Living Travel (Sun);
Syndicated Publications: Parade (S).
Digital Platform - Mobile: Apple, Android
Digital Platform - Tablet: Apple iOS, Kindle Fire
Controller .... Kelly Cummings
Pub. .... Sharon Sorg
Ed. .... Renee Carey
Adv. Sales Dir. .... Richard Work
Dir of Audience Development .... Devon Stout
Bus. Ed. .... Michael Roknick
Living/Lifestyle Ed. .... Nancy Ash
News Ed. .... Sarah Adams
Online Ed. .... John Zavinski
Religion Ed. .... Jeff Turk
Sports Ed. .... Lynn Saternow
Travel Ed. .... Richard Young
Adv. Mgr. .... Laurie Doyle
Market Information: TMC.
Mechanical Available: Offset; Black and 3 ROP colors; insert accepted; page cutoffs - 22 3/4.
Mechanical Specifications: Type page 13 x 21 1/2; E - 6 cols, 1 31/36, 1/6 between; A - 6 cols, 1 31/36, 1/6 between; C - 9 cols, 1 13/36, 1/12 between.
Areas Served: 16146, 16148, 16150, 16125, 44403, 44425, 16121, 16143, 16159Equipment & Software: PRESSROOM EQUIPMENT: Lines — 10-TKS/Offset; Folders — 2-TKS/3:2; Reels & Stands — TKS/30 Reels & Stands on 10 Stands.; MAILROOM EQUIPMENT: Counter Stackers — 2/SH; Inserters & Stuffers — 1-Mc/4 Jacket; Tying Machines — 4-OVL/ J80; Wrapping Singles — 2-AR/DAC; Address Machine — 2-/AVY.; BUSINESS EQUIPMENT: 2-IBM/Sys 38, IBM/AS-400 CLASSIFIED EQUIPMENT: Hardware — 4-AT.; DISPLAY EQUIPMENT: Printers — GCC/Elite Laser, HP/5500; DISPLAY SOFTWAREAd Make-up Applications — Archetype/Corel Draw; Layout Software — 3-IBM/Aptiva, 6-IBM/300 PL, Managing Editor/ALS. EDITORIAL EQUIPMENT: Hardware — AT/Pagination, 6-AT, 8-Dewar, AT/Remote Series 3. PRODUCTION EQUIPMENT: Hardware — Caere/OmniPage; Cameras — 1-C/Spartan I, 1-C/Spartan III, 1-RZ; Scanners — 6-Umax PRODUCTION SOFTWARE: QPS/QuarkXPress.
Note: The Herald is printed at West Penn Facility, New Castle.

SOMERSET

DAILY AMERICAN

334 W Main St, Somerset, Pa., 15501-1508, Somerset; gen tel (814) 444-5900; adv tel (814) 444-5922; ed tel (814) 444-5928; gen fax (814) 444-5966; adv fax (814) 445-2935; ed fax (814) 444-5966; gen/nat adv e-mail adcopy@dailyamerican.com; disp adv e-mail adcopy@dailyamerican.com; class adv e-mailpatf@dailyamerican.com; ed e-mail news@dailyamerican.com; web site www.dailyamerican.com
- 700,000(views) 160,000(visitors)
Group: Schurz Communications Inc
Published: Mon, Tues, Wed, Thur, Fri, Sat, Sun
Weekday Frequency: m
Saturday Frequency: m
Circulation: 11,412; 11,412(sat)
Last Audit: AAM September 30, 2014
Advertising Rate (weekday/saturday): Open inch rate $22.90
Advertising Rate (sunday): Open inch rate $22.90
Online Advertising Rate: 728X90, 300X250 and 234X60 $10.00
News services: AP. **Established:** 1929
Own Printing Facility?: No
Commercial Printers?: Yes
Special Editions: Outdoor ().
Special Weekly Sections: Best Food (Wed/Sat); Auto (Thur); Entertainment (Fri); Business, Finance, Real Estate, Religion (Sat)
Syndicated Publications: USA WEEKEND Magazine (Sat).
Digital Platform - Mobile: Apple, Android, Windows, Blackberry
Digital Platform - Tablet: Apple iOS, Android, Windows 7, Blackberry Tablet OS, Kindle, Nook, Kindle Fire
Pub. .... Andy Bruns
Office Mgr. .... Karen Thomas
Adv. Mgr. .... Tom Koppenhofer
Adv. Mgr., Classified .... Pat Foley
Editorial Page Ed. .... Brian Whipkey
Lifestyles Ed. .... Madolin Edwards
Sports Ed. .... Ronald Pritts
Gen. Mgr. .... Rebecca Flyte
Market Information: ADS; Split run; TMC.
Mechanical Available: Offset; Black and 3 ROP colors; insert accepted; page cutoffs - 22 3/4.
Mechanical Specifications: Type page 12 x 21 1/2; E - 6 cols, 1 3/4, 3/16 between; A - 6 cols, 1 3/4, 3/16 between; C - 9 cols, 1 3/16, 1/8 between.
Areas Served: Somerset and Cambria Counties, PA.
Delivery Method: Mail, Newsstand, Carrier, RacksEquipment & Software: PRESSROOM EQUIPMENT: Lines — 6-G/ Community 1980, 2-G/Community single width 1995; MAILROOM EQUIPMENT: Counter Stackers — 1-BG/105; Tying Machines — 2-Mosca/Rom 50-55; Address Machine — 1-KR w/Accufast.; BUSINESS EQUIPMENT: Compaq/Proliant, 13-Dell/ PC BUSINESS SOFTWARE: Brainworks, Visual Accountmate, Lotus, Microsoft/Office CLASSIFIED EQUIPMENT: Hardware — APP/Power Mac G3; Printers — HP/LaserJet 4V; CLASSIFIED SOFTWARE: Baseview/ Ad Manager Pro. DISPLAY EQUIPMENT: Hardware — APP/Mac G3; Printers — APP/ Mac LaserWriter II, HP/DeskJet 1600, HP/ LaserWriter 4MV, NP/LaserWriter 8500, APP/LaserWriter Pro; Other Hardware — Brainworks. DISPLAY SOFTWAREAd Make-up Applications — QPS/QuarkXPress, Multi-Ad/Creator 4.2, Adobe/Photoshop, Adobe/Illustrator, AP AdSend; EDITORIAL EQUIPMENT: Hardware — APP/Power Mac G3; Printers — HP/LaserJet 4V, Xante/ Accel-a-Writer 3G EDITORIAL SOFTWARE: Baseview. PRODUCTION EQUIPMENT: Hardware — PrePress/Panther Pro 46, 1-Nu/ Flip Top FT40L; Cameras — 1-Ik/430, 1-Nu/ Horizontal SST2024; Scanners — Microtek/ Scanmaker IIXC, AG/Arcus 2 PRODUCTION SOFTWARE: QPS/QuarkXPress 4.0.
Note: The Daily American publishes a Sunday edition in partnership with the Greensburg (PA) Tribune-Review, with original content wrapped around the Tribune-Review's Sunday edition. See the Tribune-Review for more information.

SOUTH WILLIAMSPORT

WILLIAMSPORT SUN-GAZETTE/LOCK HAVEN EXPRESS

216 E Mountain Ave, South Williamsport, Pa., 17702-7778, Lycoming; gen tel (570) 326-1551; adv tel (570) 326-1551; ed tel (570) 326-1551; gen fax (570) 323-0948; adv fax (570) 323-0948; ed fax (570) 326-0314; gen/nat adv e-mail news@sungazette.com; disp adv e-mail advertising@sungazette.com; ed e-mail news@sungazette.com; web site www.sungazette.com
Group: Ogden Newspapers Inc.
Published: Mon, Tues, Wed, Thur, Fri, Sat, Sun
Weekday Frequency: m
Saturday Frequency: m
Circulation: 17,793; 17,793(sat); 22,965(sun)
Last Audit: AAM December 31, 2016
Advertising Rate (weekday/saturday): Open inch rate $49.00
Advertising Rate (sunday): Open inch rate $52.00
News services: AP. **Established:** 1801
Own Printing Facility?: Yes
Commercial Printers?: Yes
Special Editions: Insurance (Apr); Back-to-School (Aug); Year in Review (Dec); Winter Bridal (Feb); Winter Furniture (Jan); Summer Furniture (Jul); Graduation (Jun); Women in Business (Mar); Outdoor Lifestyle (May); Christmas Opener (Nov); Fall Car Care (Oct); Fall Home Im
Special Weekly Sections: TV Magazine (S);

Religion (Sat); Entertainment (Thur); Best Food Day (Wed). Education (Mon); Health (Tues); Best Food Day (Wed); Religion (Sat); Business, Travel, Technology, Outdoors, Lifestyles (Sun)
Syndicated Publications: TV Week (S).
Publisher.................................. Bernard Oravec
Adv. Dir... John Leeser
Exec. News Ed................................. David Troisi
City Ed...................................... L. Lee Janssen
Environmental Ed.......................... Mike Reuther
News Ed..................................... Laura Janssen
Regl. Ed................................. James Carpenter
Other.. Ben Brigandi
Prodn. Supt., Composing .... Charles Smith
Nat'l Adv. Mgr. .... Diane Fedder
Market Information: TMC.
Mechanical Available: Offset; Black and 3 ROP colors; insert accepted - sample packs; page cutoffs - 22 3/4.
Mechanical Specifications: Type page 13 x 21 1/4; E - 6 cols, 2 1/16, 1/8 between; A - 6 cols, 2 1/16, 1/8 between; C - 8 cols, 1 9/16, 1/8 between.
Delivery Method: Mail, Newsstand, Carrier, RacksEquipment & Software: PRESSROOM EQUIPMENT: Lines — 6-G/Metro 3007; MAILROOM EQUIPMENT: Counter Stackers — HL/Monitor; Inserters & Stuffers — HI/72P; BUSINESS EQUIPMENT: Motorola CLASSIFIED EQUIPMENT: Hardware - Microsoft/Winmdows NT.; EDITORIAL EQUIPMENT: Hardware — Microsoft/ Windows NT. PRODUCTION EQUIPMENT: Hardware — Nu/Flip Top FT40UP; Cameras — C/Spartan III
Note: Advertising is sold in combination with The Lock Haven Express (e) for $76.12 (d) and $82.11 (S). Individual newspaper rates not made available.

STATE COLLEGE

CENTRE DAILY TIMES

3400 E College Ave, State College, Pa., 16801-7528, Centre; gen tel (814) 238-5000; adv tel (814) 231-4651; ed tel (814) 238-5000; gen fax (814) 238-1814; adv fax (814) 238-1814; ed fax (814) 238-1811; gen/nat adv e-mail adtransfer@centredaily.com; disp adv e-mail dbrown@centredaily.com; class adv e-maildbrown2@centredaily.com; ed e-mail cdtnewstips@centredaily.com; web site www.centredaily.com
- 4,464,091(views) 750,000(visitors)
Group: The McClatchy Company
Published: Mon, Tues, Wed, Thur, Fri, Sat, Sun
Weekday Frequency: m
Saturday Frequency: m
Circulation: 13,753; 14,318(sat); 18,824(sun)
Last Audit: AAM June 30, 2016
Advertising Rate (weekday/saturday): Open inch rate $58.21 (Mon-Thur); $58.01 (Fri-Sat)
Advertising Rate (sunday): Open inch rate $73.19
News services: AP, MCT. **Established:** 1898
Own Printing Facility?: Yes
Commercial Printers?: Yes
Special Editions: Active Life (Apr); This is Penn State (Aug); Gift Guide Two (Dec); The Wedding Album (Feb); Business Outlook (Jan); Art Festival Magazine (Jul); Newspapers in Education (Mar); Home Improvement (May); Real Estate Buyers Guide (Monthly); Gift Guide One (Nov
Special Weekly Sections: Health, Science (Mon); Local (Tue); Best Food (Wed); Outdoors, Teen, Auto (Thur); Entertainment, Penn State Campus (Fri); Religion (Sat); Travel, Books, Business, Careers, Homes, Real Estate (Sun)
Syndicated Publications: Parade (S).
Digital Platform - Mobile: Apple, Android
Digital Platform - Tablet: Apple iOS, Other
Controller... Erik Brown
Cir. Ops. Mgr. .... Candy Butterworth
Market Information: ADS; TMC.
Mechanical Available: Offset; Black and 3 ROP colors; insert accepted; page cutoffs - 22 3/4.
Mechanical Specifications: Type page 12 3/4 x 21 1/2; E - 6 cols, 2 1/16, 1/8 between; A - 6 cols, 2 1/16, 1/8 between; C - 10 cols, 1 1/4, 1/16 between.Equipment & Software: PRESSROOM EQUIPMENT: Lines — G/ Urbanite single width 1973; Folders — 7-G/2:1.; MAILROOM EQUIPMENT: Counter Stackers — 1-Rima/RS 2517S N Compensating Stacker; Inserters & Stuffers — 2-HI/Sheridan 1372; Tying Machines — M1255, Dynaric/NP2; Control System — Prism; Address Machine — 1/ Ch; BUSINESS EQUIPMENT: 1-HP/3000, 8-ATT/6300, 10-PCs, 5-HP/Vectra 386 BUSINESS SOFTWARE: Microsoft/Office 97, Reflections, Netscape CLASSIFIED EQUIPMENT: Hardware — APP/Power Mac, APP/Mac G3.; DISPLAY EQUIPMENT: Hardware — APP/Mac G3, APP/Mac 7100-66S; Printers — Lazerpronters & typesetters; Other Hardware — AP AdSend. DISPLAY SOFTWAREAd Make-up Applications — QPS 4.04, Adobe/Illustrator 8.0, Adobe/ Photoshop 5.0, Adode/Pagemaker 5.0; EDITORIAL EQUIPMENT: Hardware — APP/ Power Mac 7100-66S, APP/Mac G3/Lf/AP Leaf Picture Desk; Printers — LaserMaster/ Unity 1800 XLO, MON/1000 EDITORIAL SOFTWARE: Baseview, QPS, Baseview/ NewsEdit, Adobe/Photoshop. PRODUCTION EQUIPMENT: Hardware — Caere/Omnipage Pro, AG/1500, MON/ImageMaster 1200; Cameras — 1-SCREEN/260D, 1-R/432 Mk II; Scanners — Kk/RFS-2035+, Sharp/JX-610, AG/Arcus+, RZ/4050 PRODUCTION SOFTWARE: QPS/QuarkXPress.

STROUDSBURG

POCONO RECORD

511 Lenox St, Stroudsburg, Pa., 18360-1516, Monroe; gen tel (570) 421-3000; adv tel (570) 421-3000 (Display); ed tel (570) 421-3000; gen fax (570) 424-2625; adv fax (570) 424-2056 (Display); ed fax (570) 421-6284; gen/nat adv e-mail advertising@poconorecord.com; disp adv e-mail advertising@poconorecord.com; class adv e-mailkmcfall@poconorecord.com; ed e-mail newsroom@poconorecord.com; web site www.poconorecord.com
- 2,450,000(views) 28,900(visitors)
Group: New Media Investment Group
Published: Mon, Tues, Wed, Thur, Fri, Sat, Sun
Weekday Frequency: m
Saturday Frequency: m
Circulation: 7,885; 8,309(sat); 12,058(sun)
Last Audit: AAM December 31, 2016
Advertising Rate (weekday/saturday): 1/64 Pg $48.90
Advertising Rate (sunday): 1/64 Pg $60.60
News services: AP. **Established:** 1894
Own Printing Facility?: No
Commercial Printers?: No
Special Editions: Spring Home & Garden (Apr); Medical Directory (Aug); Gift Guide (Dec); Medical Directory (Feb); Pocono Summer (Jul); Pocono Raceway (Jun); Pocono Summer (May); Gift Guide (Nov);
Special Weekly Sections: Best Food Days (Sun/ Wed); Entertainment (Fri); Real Estate, Religion (Sat); Auto, Arts (Sun)
Syndicated Publications: Pocono Property Showcase (Monthly); Pocono Summer (May, July, Aug) (Other); TV Week (S); American Profile (Weekly).
Digital Platform - Mobile: Apple, Android, Windows
Digital Platform - Tablet: Apple iOS, Android
Pub.... Joe Vanderhoof
Executive Editor...................... Michael D. Kuhns
Adv. Sales Operation Manager........... Kelli McFall
Print and Digital ad Manager............... Stephanie Fairbanks
Market Information: TMC.
Mechanical Available: Offset; Black and 4 ROP colors; insert accepted; page cutoffs - 22 3/4.
Mechanical Specifications: Type page 13 x 21 1/4; E - 6 cols, 2 1/16, 1/8 between; A - 6 cols, 2 1/16, 1/8 between; C - 8 cols, 1 7/16, 3/16 between.
Areas Served: Monroe and Pike Counties
Delivery Method: Newsstand, Carrier, RacksEquipment & Software: BUSINESS EQUIPMENT: IBM/AS-400 BUSINESS SOFTWARE: Lawson CLASSIFIED EQUIPMENT: Hardware — PC, Novell/ Network, APP/Mac Quadra 800, APP/Mac II; Printers — Okidata/393 Plus; CLASSIFIED SOFTWARE: Dewar/Sys IV. DISPLAY EQUIPMENT: Hardware — PC; DISPLAY SOFTWAREAd Make-up Applications — Dewar/Ad Dummy; Layout Software — MEI/ ALS. EDITORIAL EQUIPMENT: Hardware — PC, IBM/PC 350; Printers — HP/LaserJet 5si EDITORIAL SOFTWARE: Dewar/View 1.4, Microsoft/Word 6.0, QPS/QuarkXPress 3.31. PRODUCTION SOFTWARE: PC, QPS/ QuarkXPress.

SUNBURY

THE DAILY ITEM

200 Market St, Sunbury, Pa., 17801-3402, Northumberland; gen tel (570) 286-5671; adv tel (570) 286-5671; ed tel (570) 286-5671; gen fax (570) 286-2570; adv fax (570) 988-5438; ed fax (570) 286-7695; gen/nat adv e-mail pbennett@dailyitem.com; disp adv e-mail pbennett@dailyitem.com; class adv e-mailpbennett@dailyitem.com; ed e-mail news@dailyitem.com; web site www.dailyitem.com
- 750,000(views) 275,589(visitors)
Group: Community Newspaper Holdings, Inc.
Published: Mon, Tues, Wed, Thur, Fri, Sat, Sun
Weekday Frequency: m
Saturday Frequency: m
Circulation: 14,232; 14,083(sat); 17,184(sun)
Last Audit: AAM December 31, 2017
Advertising Rate (weekday/saturday): Open inch rate $27.00
Advertising Rate (sunday): Open inch rate $30.00
News services: AP, ONS, MCT, TMS. **Established:** 1937
Own Printing Facility?: Yes
Commercial Printers?: Yes
Special Editions: Real Estate Guide (Monthly); Today's Woman (Quarterly).
Special Weekly Sections: Lifetyle, Business, Home, Real Estate (Sun); Schools (Mon); Health (Tue); Auto, Entertainment (Thur); Religion, TV (Sat)
Syndicated Publications: Relish (Monthly); Parade (S); American Profile (Weekly).
Pub... Frank Leto
Sr. Adv. Dir.................................. Patty Bennett
Audience Dir............................ Norman Sinclair
Ed.... Dennis Lyons
Managing Ed./Online News............. David Hillard
Managing /Features .... John Zaktansky
Ed. City Editor................................ Bill Bowman
Todd Stanford
News Ed./ Weekend Ed.................... Eric Pehowic
Reporter.................................... Emma Ginader
Reporter.................................. Eric Scicchitano
Reporter................................ Francis Scarcella
Reporter...................................... Joe Sylvester
Reporter.................................... Justin Strawser
Reporter............................... Karen Blackledge
Reporter...................................... Marcia Moore
Reporter... Rick Dandes
Classified Advertising........................ Carla Treon
Prodn. Mgr., Distr............................. Brett Neidig
Prodn. Mgr., Pressroom .... Thomas Hosey
Production Mgr. .... Lori Seebold
Sports Reporter .... Scott Dudinksie
Sports Reporter .... Todd Hummel
Market Information: ADS; TMC.
Mechanical Available: Offset; Black and 4 ROP colors; insert accepted; page cutoffs - 22 3/4.
Mechanical Specifications: Type page 13 1/4 x 21; E - 6 cols, 2 1/16, 1/8 between; A - 6 cols, 2 1/16, 1/8 between; C - 9 cols, 1 5/16, 1/8 between.
Delivery Method: Mail, Newsstand, Carrier, RacksEquipment & Software: PRESSROOM EQUIPMENT: Lines — TKS/double width offset (1 half deck) 1979; TKS/double width (2:1 folder; 1 non-reversing 10); Folders — 2-TKS/2:1; Pasters —3-TKS/Core Tension 1979, 5-TKS/3-arm Core Tension 1979Reels & Stands — Press Control System 1979.; MAILROOM EQUIPMENT: Counter Stackers — 2-Id, 2/PPC; Inserters & Stuffers — AM/ Sheridan 630; Tying Machines — Power Strap/PSN5; Wrapping Singles — Power Strap/SP-555; Address Machine — Machtronic, Wm; BUSINESS EQUIPMENT: IBM/AS-400 CLASSIFIED EQUIPMENT: Hardware — IBM/PC; CLASSIFIED SOFTWARE: Enterprise. DISPLAY EQUIPMENT: Hardware — IBM/RS 6000 with Raid Drive; Printers — HP/LaserJet; Other Hardware — 2-Flatbed Scanner, Umax DISPLAY SOFTWAREAd Make-up Applications — Microsoft/Office Suite, QPS/ QuarkXPress, Adobe/Photoshop; Layout Software — Mk/Managing Editor. EDITORIAL EQUIPMENT: Hardware — 2-IBM/RS-6000/ Kk, Polaroid/35mm Scanner; Printers — HP/ LaserJet EDITORIAL SOFTWARE: HI/ Jazbox, Adobe/Photoshop, Adobe/Illustrator. PRODUCTION EQUIPMENT: Hardware — Caere/OmniPage Pro; Cameras — 2-Konica/Spartan; Scanners — Kk, Polaroid PRODUCTION SOFTWARE: HI/Jazbox.

SWARTHMORE

DELAWARE COUNTY DAILY TIMES

639 S Chester Rd, Swarthmore, Pa., 19081-2315, Delaware; gen tel (610) 622-8800; adv tel (610) 622-8860; ed tel (610) 622-8810; gen fax (610) 622-8829; adv fax (610) 622-8889; ed fax (610) 622-8887; gen/nat adv e-mail paadvertising@digitalfirstmedia.com; disp adv e-mail paadvertising@digitalfirstmedia.com; class adv e-mailclassifieds@delcotimes.com; ed e-mail editor@delcotimes.com; web site www.delcotimes.com
670,774(visitors)
Group: Digital First Media
Published: Mon, Tues, Wed, Thur, Fri, Sat, Sun
Weekday Frequency: m
Saturday Frequency: m
Circulation: 20,148; 18,044(sat); 20,265(sun)
Last Audit: AAM June 30, 2016
Advertising Rate (weekday/saturday): Open inch rate $72.40
Advertising Rate (sunday): Open inch rate $72.40
News services: AP, Robert Hitchings & Co., U.S. Suburban Press Inc.. **Established:** 1876
Special Editions: Easter Dine Out (Apr); Back-to-School (Aug); Great Gifting (Dec); Swimsuit Guide (Feb); Super Bowl Auto (Jan); 55 & Up (Jul); Father's Day Gift Pages (Jun); Prom Guide (Mar); Mother's Day Gift Guide (May); Where to Dine Thanksgiving (Nov); Energy & Home I
Special Weekly Sections: Business (Daily); Auto (Mon); Restaurant Reviews (Wed); Auto, Entertainment, Church (Fri); Travel, Food, Real Estate (Sun)
Syndicated Publications: USA WEEKEND Magazine (S).
Ed.... Phil Heron
Sports Ed. .... Rob Parent
Sr. Pub....................................... Edward Condra
Cir. Dir. .... Joseph Forst
Adv. Mgr. .... Richard L. Crowe
Market Information: Split run; TMC.
Mechanical Available: Offset; Black and 3 ROP colors; insert accepted - flexi, product samples (flat), cardstock; page cutoffs - 22 3/4.
Mechanical Specifications: Type page 10 1/4 x 13; E - 5 cols, 2, between; A - 6 cols, 1 9/16, 1/33 between; C - 8 cols, 1 3/16, 1/33 between.Equipment & Software: PRESSROOM EQUIPMENT: Lines — 5-HI/1650 double width 1976; 1-HI/1650 double width 1992; Press Drive — SCR/ DC 460-Volt, 3 phase, 300 h.p.; Folders — HI/1650; Pasters —4-MEGReels & Stands — 1-Rewinder/Reel Stand.; MAILROOM EQUIPMENT: Counter Stackers — 2-HL/ Monitor, 2-HL/HT; Inserters & Stuffers — 2-GMA/SLS 1000 6:1, 1-KAN/480 6:1; Tying Machines — 2/Dynaric, 1-/MLN, 2-/ Spirit; Wrapping Singles — 1-/Na; Control System — GMA; Address Machine — 1-/ Na.; BUSINESS EQUIPMENT: IBM/AS-400 BUSINESS SOFTWARE: insi CLASSIFIED EQUIPMENT: Hardware — PC, APP/Mac, AST/Bravo LC 5133; Minolta/3700, X/7017; Printers — Okidata/2410; CLASSIFIED SOFTWARE: Cx, Intertext. DISPLAY EQUIPMENT: Hardware — APP/Mac Quadra 840 AU, APP/Mac 8500-150; Printers — HP, ECR/VRL 36HS, NewGen/ Imager 12; DISPLAY SOFTWAREAd Make-up Applications — Multi-Ad 4.0; Layout Software — MEI/ALS & CLS. EDITORIAL EQUIPMENT: Hardware — PC/Lf/AP Leaf Picture Desk, Polaroid/SprintScan EDITORIAL SOFTWARE: ATS with Microsoft Windows, QPS/QuarkXPress, Adobe/Photoshop, ELS. PRODUCTION EQUIPMENT: Hardware — Bidco/Imager, ECR/4550, Konica/Autokon, Sharp; Cameras

— C/Spartan Vertical, BIDCO - Konica; Scanners — 1-ECR/Autokon PRODUCTION SOFTWARE: MEI/ALS 1.7, MEI/CLS 1.6, MEI/ELS 1.6.

TITUSVILLE

THE TITUSVILLE HERALD

209 W Spring St, Ste B, Titusville, Pa., 16354-1687, Crawford; gen tel (814) 827-3634; gen fax (814) 827-2512; gen/nat adv e-mail advertising@titusvilleherald.com; disp adv e-mail advertising@titusvilleherald.com; class adv e-mailadvertising@titusvilleherald.com; ed e-mail news@titusvilleherald.com; web site www.titusvilleherald.com

Group: The Titusville Herald
Published: Mon, Tues, Wed, Thur, Fri, Sat
Weekday Frequency: m
Saturday Frequency: m
Circulation: 4,000; 4,000(sat)
Last Audit: Sworn/Estimate/Non-Audited September 30, 2017
Advertising Rate (weekday/saturday): Open inch rate $9.60
News services: AP. **Established:** 1865
Own Printing Facility?: Yes
Special Editions: The Golden Years (Apr); Football (Aug); Recipe Book (Dec); Growth & Progress (Feb); Coupons (Jan); Oil Heritage Week (Jul); Graduation (Jun); Spring Preview & Bridal (Mar); Discover (May); Thanksgiving (Nov); Auto Promo (Oct); Spartansburg Fair (Sept).
Special Weekly Sections: Business, Finance, Entertainment (Daily); Best Food (Wed); Religion (Fri); Home, Family (Sat)
Office Mgr. ....Karol Hartley
Pub./Adv. Dir. ....Michael Sample
Graphic Coord. ....Dave Ohmer
Mng. Ed. ....Stella Ruggiero
Reporter...Tom Boyle
Reporter...Mary Hill
Prodn. Mgr., Mailroom............ Paula Vandervort
Market Information: ADS; TMC.
Mechanical Available: Offset; Black and 3 ROP colors; insert accepted.
Mechanical Specifications: Type page 11 5/8 x 21 1/4; E - 6 cols, 1 5/6, 1/8 between; A - 6 cols, 1 5/6, 1/8 between; C - 9 cols, 1 5/6, 1/16 between.
Areas Served: 16354 16404 16341
Delivery Method: Mail, Newsstand, Carrier, RacksEquipment & Software: BUSINESS EQUIPMENT: Bs/20 CLASSIFIED EQUIPMENT: Hardware — APP/iMac, APP/Mac G4; Printers — HP 8150; CLASSIFIED SOFTWARE: Baseview. DISPLAY EQUIPMENT: Hardware — Apple/Imac ; Printers — Oki Data 8800 HP 8150; DISPLAY SOFTWAREAd Make-up Applications — Adobe CS 5; EDITORIAL EQUIPMENT: Hardware — 5-APP/iMac, ; Printers — Oki Data 8800 HP 8150 PRODUCTION SOFTWARE: Indesign 5.0
Note: Printing contracted with Corry (PA) Journal.

TOWANDA

THE DAILY REVIEW

116 Main St, Towanda, Pa., 18848-1832, Bradford; gen tel (570) 265-2151; adv tel (570) 265-2151; ed tel (570) 265-2151; gen fax (570) 265-1647; adv fax (570) 265-6130; ed fax (570) 265-1647; gen/nat adv e-mail reviewads@thedailyreview.com; disp adv e-mail reviewads@thedailyreview.com; class adv e-mailsrought@thedailyreview.com; ed e-mail reviewnews@thedailyreview.com; web site www.thedailyreview.com

Group: Sample Media Group
Published: Mon, Tues, Wed, Thur, Fri, Sat, Sun
Weekday Frequency: m
Saturday Frequency: m
Circulation: 7,356; 7,356(sat); 8,774(sun)
Last Audit: CAC September 30, 2017
Advertising Rate (weekday/saturday): Call for pricing
Advertising Rate (sunday): Call for pricing
Online Advertising Rate: Call for pricing
News services: AP, Washington Post **Established:** 1879

Own Printing Facility?: Yes
Commercial Printers?: Yes
Special Editions: Spring Home Improvement II (Apr); Medical Directory (Aug); Winter Sports Profile (Dec); Women In Business (Feb); Bridal (Jan); Troy Fair (Jul); Graduation (Jun); Spring Tour Guide (Mar); Human Services (May); Our Schools (Monthly); Senior Style II (Nov);
Special Weekly Sections: Best Food Days (Wed/Sun); Nascar (Fri); Senior's Column (S).
Syndicated Publications: Relish (Monthly); (Sat); American Profile (Weekly), Parade (Weekly).
Digital Platform - Mobile: Apple, Android, Windows
Digital Platform - Tablet: Apple iOS, Android, Windows 7, Kindle, Nook, Kindle Fire
Circulation Supervisor...................Debbie Bump
Regional Director of Production .. Brian Schlosser
Managing Editor .... Kelly Andrus
Classified Advertising Manager......... Sue Rought
Editor-in-Chief ....Matt Hicks
General Manager ....Dave Barry
Owner/Publisher .... Kelly Luvison
Circulation Director ....Bill Kurtz
Market Information: TMC.
Mechanical Available: Offset; Black and ROP colors; insert accepted; page cutoffs - 22.
Mechanical Specifications: Type page 13 x 20 3/4; E - 6 cols, 1 13/16, 1/6 between; A - 6 cols, 1 13/16, 1/6 between; C - 10 cols, 1 1/16, 1/8 between.
Areas Served: 13812, 13827, 14892, 16901, 16910, 16914, 16925, 12626, 16232, 16933, 16936, 16945, 16947, 17101, 17701, 17724, 17735, 17765, 18614, 18616, 18623, 18626, 18628, 18629, 18630, 18632, 18657, 18801, 18810, 18814, 18815, 18817, 18818, 18828, 18829, 18830, 18831, 18832, 18833, 18837, 18839, 18840, 18845, 18846, 18848, 18850, 18851, 18853, 18854
Delivery Method: Mail, Newsstand, Carrier, RacksEquipment & Software: PRESSROOM EQUIPMENT: Lines — DgM/430.; MAILROOM EQUIPMENT: Counter Stackers — 1-BG/Count-O-Veyor; Inserters & Stuffers — 9-MM/227; Tying Machines — 4-Dynaric/Strapping Machines; Address Machine — 1-Ch/538-525.; BUSINESS EQUIPMENT: IBM BUSINESS SOFTWARE: Hermes, Vision Data, Microsoft/Excel, Microsoft/Word CLASSIFIED EQUIPMENT: Hardware — CText; Printers — HP/LaserJet 4; CLASSIFIED SOFTWARE: Vision Data DISPLAY EQUIPMENT: Hardware — 3-APP/Power Mac 6100-66, 1-APP/Power Mac 7200-75, 1-APP/Power Mac 7200-120; Printers — APP/Mac LaserWriter Plus MODIA, NewGen/Turbo PS 880, HP/LaserJet 4, NewGen/DesignXpress 6; DISPLAY SOFTWAREAd Make-up Applications — QPS/QuarkXPress 3.32, Multi-Ad/Creator 4.0, Aldus/FreeH; EDITORIAL EQUIPMENT: Hardware — CText; Printers — HP/DeskJet 400 EDITORIAL SOFTWARE: XYQUEST/XyWrite III. PRODUCTION EQUIPMENT: Hardware — 2-ECR/VRL 36 Scriptsetter (PC level2 ECR/RIP), 1-Nu/Flip Top 40UP, Adobe/Photoshop 4.0, ECR/VRL 34 Scriptsetters; Cameras — 1-R/24-580; Scanners — Microtek/MS-II, 2-Polaroid/SprintScan 35, 2-Umax/Vista S-8, Umax/Vista S-12 PRODUCTION SOFTWARE: QPS/Qua

TYRONE

THE DAILY HERALD

1067 Pennsylvania Ave, Tyrone, Pa., 16686-1513, Blair; gen tel (814) 684-4000; adv tel (814)684-4000; ed tel (814)684-4000; gen fax (814) 684-4238; adv fax (814)684-4238; ed fax (814)684-4238; gen/nat adv e-mail ads@thedalyherald.net; disp adv e-mail ads@thedailyherald.net; class adv e-mailclassifieds@thedailyherald.net; ed e-mail astine@thedailyherald.net; web site www.thedailyherald.net

Group: Sample News Group LLC
Published: Mon, Tues, Wed, Thur, Fri, Sat, Sun
Weekday Frequency: e
Saturday Frequency: m
Circulation: 1,737; 1,737(sat)
Last Audit: Sworn/Estimate/Non-Audited September 30, 2017
Advertising Rate (weekday/saturday): Open inch

rate $8.65
News services: Landon Media Group.
Established: 1867
Own Printing Facility?: Yes
Special Editions: Home & Garden (Aug); Christmas Opening (Dec); Wedding (Feb); Business Direct (May); Home & Gardening (Sept).
Special Weekly Sections: TV Week (Fri).
Pres./Pub. ....George R. Sample
VP & Gen Mgr. ....John Cook
Ed. ....Julie White
Adv. Dir. ....Baretta Taylor
Adv. Sales Mgr. ....Linda Daniels
Circ. Mgr. ....Joyce Alley
Mark Palmer
Neal Pattison
Market Information: ADS; TMC.
Mechanical Available: Offset; Black and 3 ROP colors; insert accepted; page cutoffs - 21 1/2.
Mechanical Specifications: Type page 13 x 21 1/2; E - 6 cols, 2 1/16, 1/8 between; A - 6 cols, 2 1/16, 1/8 between; C - 9 cols, 1 3/8, 1/16 between.
Delivery Method: Mail, Newsstand, Carrier, RacksEquipment & Software: CLASSIFIED EQUIPMENT: Hardware — Mk/1100 Plus; CLASSIFIED SOFTWARE: Mk/1100 Plus. DISPLAY EQUIPMENT: Hardware — Mk, APP/Mac; Printers — APP/Mac LaserWriter; DISPLAY SOFTWAREAd Make-up Applications — Mk/Mycro-Comp AdWriter.; EDITORIAL EQUIPMENT: Hardware — Mk/550 EDITORIAL SOFTWARE: Mk/550. PRODUCTION EQUIPMENT: Hardware — APP/Mac LaserWriter; Scanners — APP/Mac Scanner, AG/Scanner.

UNIONTOWN

HERALD-STANDARD

8 E Church St, # 18, Uniontown, Pa., 15401-3563, Fayette; gen tel (724) 439-7500; adv tel (724) 439-7520; ed tel (724) 439-7555; gen fax (724) 439-7528; adv fax (724) 439-7528; ed fax (724) 439-7559; gen/nat adv e-mail swallach@heraldstandard.com; disp adv e-mail swallach@heraldstandard.com; class adv e-mailswallach@heraldstandard.com; ed e-mail jgarofalo@heraldstandard.com; web site www.heraldstandard.com

Group: Ogden Newspapers Inc.
Published: Mon, Tues, Wed, Thur, Fri, Sun
Weekday Frequency: m
Circulation: 13,845; 17,595(sun)
Last Audit: AAM June 30, 2017
Advertising Rate (weekday/saturday): Open inch rate $47.70
Advertising Rate (sunday): Open inch rate $50.00
News services: AP, SHNS.
Own Printing Facility?: No
Commercial Printers?: No
Special Weekly Sections: Health (Mon); Food (Wed);, Entertainment (Thurs); Real Estate (Fri); Outdoors (Fri.), Education (Sun);
Digital Platform - Mobile: Apple, Android, Windows
Digital Platform - Tablet: Apple iOS, Android, Windows 7, Kindle Fire
Pub. ....Bob Pinarski
Market Information: Split run; TMC; Zoned editions.
Mechanical Available: Offset; Black and 3 ROP colors; insert accepted; page cutoffs - 22.
Mechanical Specifications: Type page 11 x 21 1/2; E - 6 cols, 2 1/16, 1/8 between; A - 6 cols, 2 1/16, 1/8 between; C - 6 cols, 1 5/16, 1/8 between.
Areas Served: Uniontown/Fayette/15401
Delivery Method: Newsstand, Carrier, RacksEquipment & Software: PRESSROOM EQUIPMENT: Lines — 8-HI/845; MAILROOM EQUIPMENT: Counter Stackers — 1-HPS/Dual Carrier; Inserters & Stuffers — KAN/320 6 station; Tying Machines — 1-MLN/Sure Tyer.; BUSINESS EQUIPMENT: 2-DEC/PDP 11-70, SCS/Layout 8000 CLASSIFIED EQUIPMENT: Hardware — 1-DEC/PDP 11-70.; DISPLAY EQUIPMENT: Hardware — APP/Mac II; Printers — HP/LaserJet; DISPLAY SOFTWARELayout Software — SCS/Layout 8000, Unix/SCO, SCS/Lynx. EDITORIAL EQUIPMENT: Hardware — 2-DEC/PDP 11-70, 8-APP/Mac IIcx/AP/GraphicsNet; Printers — 1-Compaq/LA-180

EDITORIAL SOFTWARE: TMS/CMS 5.3. PRODUCTION EQUIPMENT: Hardware —2-COM/8600, 2-MON/1016 HS, 1-LE; Cameras — 1-Bo, 1-K/V241; Scanners — 1-HP, 1-Sharp, 1-Microtek PRODUCTION SOFTWARE: QPS/QuarkXPress 3.2.

WARREN

TIMES OBSERVER

205 Pennsylvania Ave W, Warren, Pa., 16365-2412, Warren; gen tel (814) 723-8200; adv tel (814) 723-1400; ed tel (814) 723-8200; gen fax (814) 723-9543; adv fax (814) 723-6922; ed fax (814) 723-6922; gen/nat adv e-mail advertising@timeobserver.com; disp adv e-mail advertising@timesobserver.com; class adv e-mailclassified@timesobserver.com; ed e-mail editorial@timesobserver.com; web site www.timesobserver.com

- 742,993(views) 63,009(visitors)
Group: Ogden Newspapers Inc.
Published: Mon, Tues, Wed, Thur, Fri, Sat
Weekday Frequency: m
Saturday Frequency: m
Circulation: 7,282; 7,541(sat)
Last Audit: AAM June 30, 2016
Advertising Rate (weekday/saturday): Open inch rate $24.03
News services: AP.
Own Printing Facility?: No
Special Editions: Coupon Books (Quarterly).
Special Weekly Sections: TV Times (Fri); Best Food Day (Sat); Spotlite (Thur) Living Page (Mon); Food, Spotlight Entertainment Guide, Movies, Theatre, Music, Outdoors, Books, Automotive (Thurs); TV Times (Fri); Food, Automotive (Sat).
Syndicated Publications: USA WEEKEND Magazine (Sat).
Digital Platform - Mobile: Apple, Android, Windows
Adv. Mgr., Classified ....Jack Albaugh
Publisher - Circulation Director........Bob Patchen
Managing Editor .... Eric Paddock
Food Ed. ....Diana Paddock
City Editor ....Tom Schultz
Sports Ed. ....Jon Sitler
Market Information: TMC; Zoned editions.
Mechanical Available: Offset; Black and 3 ROP colors; insert accepted; page cutoffs - 21 1/2.
Mechanical Specifications: Type page 11 37/50 x 21 1/2; E - 6 cols, 1 17/20, between; A - 6 cols, 1 17/20, between; C - 9 cols, 1 1/5, between.
Delivery Method: Mail, Newsstand, Carrier, RacksEquipment & Software: PRESSROOM EQUIPMENT: Lines — 5-G/Urbanite; Press Drive — Fin/100 h.p.; Folders — G/1/2.; MAILROOM EQUIPMENT: Counter Stackers — 1-BG/Count-O-Veyor; Tying Machines — 2/Sa, Gd, 1-/Nichiro Kogyo/Strapper; Wrapping Singles — Olson/Bostitcher; Address Machine — St.; CLASSIFIED EQUIPMENT: Hardware — APP/Mac Quadra; Printers — ECR/Imagesetter; CLASSIFIED SOFTWARE: DTI/ClassSpeed, DTI/AdSpeed, DTI, Adobe/Photoshop 2.5. DISPLAY EQUIPMENT: Hardware — APP/Mac Quadra 650; Printers — APP/Mac LaserWriter; Other Hardware — AP AdSend DISPLAY SOFTWAREAd Make-up Applications — DTI/AdSpeed, DTI, Adobe/Photoshop; Layout Software — DTI/SpeedPlanner, DTI. EDITORIAL EQUIPMENT: Hardware — APP/Mac Quadra; Printers — APP/Mac LaserWriter, ECR/Imagesetter EDITORIAL SOFTWARE: DTI/PageSpeed, DTI/Speedwriter, Adobe/Photoshop 3.0, Caere/OmniPage 2.1. PRODUCTION EQUIPMENT: Hardware — Caere/OmniPage 2.1; Cameras — 1-B/Commodore 24, 1-R/432MK II; Scanners — 1-EC PRODUCTION SOFTWARE: DTI/SpeedPlanner, DTI.

WASHINGTON

OBSERVER-REPORTER

122 S Main St, Washington, Pa., 15301-4904, Washington; gen tel (724) 222-2200; adv tel (724) 222-2200; ed tel (724) 222-2200; gen fax (724) 225-2077; adv fax (724)

222-3982; ed fax (724) 225-2077; gen/nat adv e-mail sales@observer-reporter.com; disp adv e-mail mtalerico@observer-reporter.com; class adv e-mailmtmiller@observer-reporter.com; ed e-mail newsroom@observer-reporter.com; web site www.observer-reporter.com
Published: Mon, Tues, Wed, Thur, Fri, Sat, Sun
Weekday Frequency: m
Saturday Frequency: m
Circulation: 21,152; 21,152(sat); 28,620(sun)
Last Audit: AAM September 30, 2016
Advertising Rate (weekday/saturday): Open inch rate $42.50
Advertising Rate (sunday): Open inch rate $45.50
Online Advertising Rate: (Modular Rates) In Line Banner- $12.00; In Story- $12.00; Leaderboard- $10.00; Skyscraper- $10.00; Bottom Banner- $6.00;
News services: AP, NYT. **Established:** 1808
Own Printing Facility?: Yes
Commercial Printers?: No
Special Editions: Health & Fitness (Apr); College & Pro Football (Aug); Monthly Planner (Dec); Spring Home Improvement (Mar); Christmas Gift Guide (Nov); Fall Home Improvements (Sept).
Special Weekly Sections: Weekend Entertainment, Religion (Fri); Home Section (Sun); Business, Financial (Mon-Sat)
Syndicated Publications: USA WEEKEND Magazine (S); American Profile, Spry, (Weekly); Total Health, Southpointe Today, Energy Report (Monthly); Living in Washington County, South Hills Living, Greene County Living (bimonthly).
Digital Platform - Mobile: Apple, Android, Windows, Blackberry
Digital Platform - Tablet: Apple iOS, Android, Windows 7, Blackberry Tablet OS, Kindle, Nook, Kindle Fire
Pres./Pub. .... Thomas P. Northrop
CFO .... David F. Lyle
Director of News .... Lucy S. Northrop
Adv. Dir. .... Matt Miller
Retail Sales Mgr. .... Matt Talerico
Circ. Dir. .... Bridget Vilencia
Mng. Ed. .... Park Burroughs
Bus. Ed. .... Mike Bradwell
City/Metro Ed. .... Elizabeth Rogers
Entertainment/Amusements Ed. Denise Bachman
Asst. News Ed .... Brant Newman
Sports Ed. .... Chris Dugan
Systems Mgr. .... Dan Fennell
Prodn. Mgr., Mailroom .... Gerald Hickman
Prodn. Mgr./Foreman, Pressroom . James Helicke
National Accounts .... Rob Anders
Bess Dunlevy
Lucy Corwin
Nancy Milinovich
Market Information: TMC; Zoned editions.
Mechanical Available: MAN/Roland Offset, Mediaman; Black and 3 ROP colors; insert accepted; page cutoffs - 22.
Mechanical Specifications: Type page 13 x 21; E - 6 cols, 2, 3/16 between; A - 6 cols, 2, 3/16 between; C - 9 cols, 1 5/16, 1/8 between.
Areas Served: 15301
Delivery Method: Mail, Newsstand, Carrier, RacksEquipment & Software: PRESSROOM EQUIPMENT: Lines — MAN/Roland Mediaman (3 half decks) 1993; Folders — 2-MAN/2:1; Pasters —MEG/2-45; Reels & Stands — 5-G/Reel.; MAILROOM EQUIPMENT: Counter Stackers — 2/Compass, 1-/QWI; Inserters & Stuffers — 1-GMA/SLS 2000 16:2; Tying Machines — 2-EAM-Mosca, 3-/Dynaric; Address Machine — 1-/KR, 5-/Wm.; BUSINESS EQUIPMENT: Axil/Unix Sun Clone, Vision Data BUSINESS SOFTWARE: Database, Word Processing, Microsoft/Word 6.0, Microsoft/Excel 5.0 CLASSIFIED EQUIPMENT: Hardware — Axil/Unix Sun Clone; Printers — C.Itoh/1000, Dataproducts, Dataproducts/Typhoon; CLASSIFIED SOFTWARE: Vision Data. DISPLAY EQUIPMENT: Hardware — 3-APP/Mac Quadra 650, 1-APP/Mac Centris 610, 2-APP/Power Mac PC; DISPLAY SOFTWAREAd Make-up Applications — Multi-Ad/Creator, QPS/QuarkXPress 7.1; Layout Software — MEI/ALS. EDITORIAL EQUIPMENT: Hardware — APP/Mac 9500/APP/Macs, APP/Mac PowerBooks EDITORIAL SOFTWARE: Baseview IQ. PRODUCTION EQUIPMENT: Hardware — 2-MON/Lasercomp, Mk/21, 1-X/P26 LaserPrinter, XIT/Schooner-Imagesetter, ECR/Pelbox 1045, 2-ECR/4550; Cameras — 1-C/Spartan III; Scanners — 1-ECR/Autokon News Graphics PRODUCTION SOFTWARE: QPS/QuarkXPress.

WAYNESBORO

THE RECORD HERALD

30 Walnut St, Waynesboro, Pa., 17268-1644, Franklin; gen tel (717) 762-2151; adv tel (717) 762-2151; ed tel (717) 762-2151; gen fax (717) 762-3824; adv fax (717) 762-3824; ed fax (717) 762-3824; gen/nat adv e-mail denise@therecordherald.com; disp adv e-mail advertising@therecordherald.com; class adv e-mailclassified@therecordherald.com; ed e-mail news@therecordherald.com; web site www.therecordherald.com
Group: New Media Investment Group
Published: Mon, Tues, Wed, Thur, Fri, Sat
Weekday Frequency: e
Saturday Frequency: m
Circulation: 8,005; 8,005(sat)
Last Audit: Sworn/Estimate/Non-Audited September 30, 2017
Advertising Rate (weekday/saturday): Open inch rate $15.27
News services: AP. **Established:** 1824
Special Editions: Home Improvement No. 1 (Apr); Back-to-School (Aug); Gift Guides (3 times) (Dec); Progress No. 1 (Feb); Bridal No. 1 (Jan); Spotlight Newcomers (Jul); Golden Years (Mar); Bridal No. 2 (May); Gift Guides (3 times) (Nov); Financial (Oct); Home Improvement No
Special Weekly Sections: Best Food Day (Wed); TV (Sat).
Syndicated Publications: Relish (Monthly); American Profile (Weekly).
Pub. .... Pat Patterson
Adv. Mgr., Classified .... Shirley Gossert
Circ. Mgr. .... Barbara Paterno
Ed .... Shawn Hardy
Educ. Ed .... Nancy Mace
Sports Ed. .... Scott Weaver
Data Processing Mgr. .... Nicole Kype
Prodn. Supt. .... Jay Wetzel
Prodn. Foreman, Pressroom .... Darious Walter
Adv. Mng. .... Denise Ingram
Mechanical Available: Offset; Black and 3 ROP colors; insert accepted; page cutoffs - 22 3/4.
Mechanical Specifications: Type page 13 x 21 1/2; E - 6 cols, 2 1/14, 1/6 between; A - 6 cols, 2 1/14, 1/6 between; C - 8 cols, 1 1/2, 1/6 between.Equipment & Software: PRESSROOM EQUIPMENT: Lines — 4-G/Urbanite 1964; Folders — 1-G/500.; MAILROOM EQUIPMENT: Tying Machines — 2/OVL; Address Machine — 1-/Ch.; BUSINESS EQUIPMENT: IBM/Sys 36 CLASSIFIED EQUIPMENT: Hardware — Mk/1100 Plus; Printers — APP/Mac LaserWriter; CLASSIFIED SOFTWARE: Mk/1100 Plus. DISPLAY EQUIPMENT: Hardware — APP/Mac IIsi, APP/Mac IIci; Printers — APP/Mac LaserWriter IIf; DISPLAY SOFTWAREAd Make-up Applications — Aldus/PageMaker; Layout Software — APP/Mac. EDITORIAL EQUIPMENT: Hardware — Mk/1100 Plus/Lf/AP Leaf Picture Desk; Printers — APP/Mac LaserWriter EDITORIAL SOFTWARE: Mk/1100 Plus. PRODUCTION EQUIPMENT: Hardware — Nu/Flip Top FT40V3UPNS, APP/Mac LaserWriter Pro 630; Cameras — C, VG/Graphline 760, K/Vertical 24; Scanners — HP/LaserJet Plus.

WEST CHESTER

DAILY LOCAL NEWS

250 N Bradford Ave, West Chester, Pa., 19382-1912, Chester; gen tel (610) 696-1775; adv tel (610) 430-1134; ed tel (610) 430-1130; gen fax (610) 430-1180; adv fax (610) 430-1190; ed fax (610) 430-1194; gen/nat adv e-mail paadvertising@digitalfirstmedia.com; disp adv e-mail jbatog@dailylocal.com; class adv e-mailmdenatale@21st-centurymedia.com; ed e-mail tmurray@dailylocal.com; web site www.dailylocal.com
- 4,000,000(views) 503,592(visitors)
Group: Digital First Media
Published: Mon, Tues, Wed, Thur, Fri, Sat, Sun
Weekday Frequency: m
Saturday Frequency: m
Circulation: 14,244; 11,740(sat); 15,305(sun)
Last Audit: AAM September 30, 2016
Advertising Rate (weekday/saturday): Full Pg 1/8 $295.00
News services: AP.
Own Printing Facility?: Yes
Special Editions: Fitness/Summer Fun (Apr); Back-to-School (Aug); Last Minute Gift Guide (Dec); Cutest Baby (Feb); Education Guide (Jan); Chester County Guide (Jul); Father's Day (Jun); Design-an-Ad (Mar); MADD Poster Contest (May); Employment Monthly (Monthly); Mature Lif
Special Weekly Sections: Best Food Days (Wed); Religion, Entertainment, Real Estate (Fri); Travel, Tabloid, TV (Sun); Business (Weekly); Women's Health (Monthly); Senior Citizen (Bi-Monthly)
Syndicated Publications: USA WEEKEND Magazine (Sat).
Digital Platform - Mobile: Apple, Android, Windows, Blackberry
Digital Platform - Tablet: Apple iOS, Android, Windows 7
Pub. .... Edward Condra
Cir. Dir. .... Joseph Forst
Adv. Mgr. .... Jen Batog
Class. Supv. .... Mary DeNatale
Ed. .... Andy Hachadorian
Market Information: TMC.
Mechanical Available: Offset; Black and 3 ROP colors; insert accepted - single sheet; page cutoffs - 22 3/4.
Mechanical Specifications: Type page 12 x 21 1/2; E - 6 cols, 1 7/8, 1/8 between; A - 6 cols, 1 7/8, 1/8 between; C - 10 cols, 1 3/16, 3/32 between.
Delivery Method: Mail, Newsstand, Carrier, RacksEquipment & Software: PRESSROOM EQUIPMENT: Lines — 10-G/Urbanite; Press Drive — 2-Fin/125H Drives; Folders — G/Urbanite 700; Pasters —7-Enkel/Autoweb 1991. MAILROOM EQUIPMENT: Counter Stackers — 2-HL/Monitor; Inserters & Stuffers — 1-GMA/SLS 1000 10:1; Tying Machines — 2/Power Strap/PSN-6; Address Machine — Ch.; BUSINESS EQUIPMENT: 2-IBM/Sys 400 BUSINESS SOFTWARE: INSI CLASSIFIED EQUIPMENT: Hardware — PPI; Printers — Bidco; CLASSIFIED SOFTWARE: PPI. DISPLAY EQUIPMENT: Hardware — APP/Power Mac 8100; Printers — Bidco/486 PC-RTI RIP, Ultre/486 PC-Spreadsheet RIP; Other Hardware — Kk/RFS 2035 Scanner, Lf/Leafscan 35 Scanner, 8-Umax/Vista Scanner DISPLAY SOFTWAREAd Make-up Applications — QPS/QuarkXPress 3.3, APP/Mac Appleshare 4.0; Layout Software — APP/Mac Netw EDITORIAL EQUIPMENT: Hardware — CNI/Open, APP/Mac Network/Kodak/Scanner; Printers — Bidco/Imagesetter EDITORIAL SOFTWARE: CNI/Open, Lf/AP Leaf Picture Desk. PRODUCTION EQUIPMENT: Hardware — Caere/OmniPage Pro 2.0, 1-Nu/Flip Top FT40APNS; Cameras — C/Spartan II; Scanners — Digi-Colour/Sys 3000, Lf/Leafscan 35, Kk/2035, Microtek/8003, Umax/Vista PRODUCTION SOFTWARE: QPS/QuarkXPress 3.3, Adobe/Photoshop 4.0.
Note: The Daily Local News also prints the Phoenixville (PA) Phoenix (m), a Journal Register Newspaper.

WILKES BARRE

THE CITIZENS' VOICE

75 N Washington St, Wilkes Barre, Pa., 18701-3109, Luzerne; gen tel (570) 821-2000; adv tel (570) 821-2030; ed tel (570) 821-2056; gen fax (570) 821-2249; adv fax (570) 825-2882; ed fax (570) 821-2247; gen/nat adv e-mail maltavilla@citizensvoice.com; disp adv e-mail szremba@citizensvoice.com; class adv e-mailclassified@timesshamrock.com; ed e-mail citydesk@citizensvoice.com; web site www.citizensvoice.com
- 4,000,000(views) 487,410(visitors)
Group: Times-Shamrock Communications
Published: Mon, Tues, Wed, Thur, Fri, Sat, Sun
Weekday Frequency: m
Saturday Frequency: m
Circulation: 23,134; 23,134(sat); 24,381(sun)
Last Audit: AAM December 31, 2016
Advertising Rate (weekday/saturday): Open inch rate $38.07
Advertising Rate (sunday): $38.07
News services: AP, Papert (Landon).
Own Printing Facility?: Yes
Commercial Printers?: Yes
Special Editions: Home & Improvement (Apr); Pigskin Preview (Aug); Christmas Shopping Guide (Dec); Bridal (Feb); Super Bowl Preview (Jan); Estate Planning (Jul); Graduation (Jun); Today's Woman (Mar); Who's Who in Wyoming Valley (May); Thanksgiving Holiday Shopping Guide (
Special Weekly Sections: Weekend (Fri); Regional (S); Best Food Day (Sat).
Syndicated Publications: Relish (Monthly); USA WEEKEND Magazine (S); American Profile (Weekly).
Digital Platform - Mobile: Apple, Android
Digital Platform - Tablet: Apple iOS, Android
Pub. .... W. Scott Lynett
Pub. .... Danial Haggerty
Adv. Dir. .... Mark Altavilla
Coord. .... Judi Shaver
Asst. Circ. Dir. .... Joe Neaoon
Executive Editor .... Larry Holeva
Editorial Page Ed. .... Jim Gittens
Web Ed. .... Shanon Rushton
News Ed. .... Leonarda Bilbow
Sports Ed. .... Neil Corbett
Wire Ed. .... Michael McGlynn
Photo Ed. .... Mark Moran
Mgmt. Info Servs. Mgr. .... Dennis Briggs
Prodn. Mgr., Mailroom .... John McGurk
Mechanical Available: Offset; Black and 3 ROP colors; insert accepted; page cutoffs - 22 3/4.
Mechanical Specifications: Type page 10 1/2 x 13; E - 5 cols, 2, 1/8 between; A - 5 cols, 2, 1/8 between; C - 10 cols, 1 1/16, 1/8 between.
Delivery Method: Mail, Newsstand, Carrier, RacksEquipment & Software: PRESSROOM EQUIPMENT: Lines — 8-G/Urbanite; Folders — G/1000.; MAILROOM EQUIPMENT: Counter Stackers — 3-QWI/300, 1/HL; Inserters & Stuffers — 1-Biliner/8:1; Tying Machines — 4-MLN/Spirits, 2-/Sterling; BUSINESS EQUIPMENT: 1-IBM/RISC 6000 BUSINESS SOFTWARE: Vision Data, Accts receivable 6.2, Accts payable 5.0, Gen ledger 5.0, Circ 3.9 CLASSIFIED EQUIPMENT: Hardware — 1-Sun/Ultra 10, 4-GB/Tape Drives (Backup); Printers — 1-HP/5M; CLASSIFIED SOFTWARE: Unisys. DISPLAY EQUIPMENT: Hardware — 1-APP/Mac 9600, 1-APP/Mac 9500, 1-APP/iMac, 2-APP/Mac 8500, APP/Mac 8100, 5-APP/Mac G3, APP/Mac G4; DISPLAY SOFTWAREAd Make-up Applications — Multi-Ad/Creator 2 1.5, Adobe/Acrobat 4.0, Adobe/Illustrator 8.0, Caere/OmniPage 3.0, Microsoft/Word 9.8, Adobe/Photoshop 6.0, Adobe/; EDITORIAL EQUIPMENT: Hardware — 2-HP/Netserver LD, 20-HP/Vectra VLS Pentium 233 mhz/1-Everex/Notebook, 2-APP/Power Mac 8100, 3-APP/Mac Power Book 190, APP/Power Book G3; Printers — 1-HP EDITORIAL SOFTWARE: Microsoft/Windows NT Server 4.0, Microsoft/SQL Server 6.5, Micros PRODUCTION EQUIPMENT: Hardware — Caere/OmniPage 3.0, Douthitt/Gemini; Scanners — 1-Epson/836L, 3-HP/ScanJet 6100C, 1-HP/ScanJet 4c, 2-HP/ScanJet G300 PRODUCTION SOFTWARE: QPS/QuarkXPress 4.04, Adobe/In Design.
Note: The Wilkes-Barre Citizens' Voice (mS) has a combination rate of $132.39 (m) and $133.68 (S) with the Scranton Times-Tribune (mS). Individual newspaper rates not made available.

TIMES LEADER

15 N Main St, Wilkes Barre, Pa., 18701-2604, Luzerne; gen tel (570) 704-3953; adv tel (570) 829-7130; ed tel (570) 829-7242; gen fax (570) 829-2002; adv fax (570) 829-2002; ed fax (570) 829-5537; gen/nat adv e-mail lbyrnes@civitasmedia.com; web site www.timesleader.com
538,857(visitors)
Group: Civitas Media, LLC-OOB
Published: Mon, Tues, Wed, Thur, Fri, Sat, Sun

Weekday Frequency: m
Saturday Frequency: m
Circulation: 19,784; 20,065(sat); 24,668(sun)
Last Audit: AAM March 31, 2016
Advertising Rate (weekday/saturday): Open inch rate $64.92
Advertising Rate (sunday): Open inch rate $99.56
News services: AP, MCT, DF, DJ, NYT.
Special Editions: Profile (Apr); Football (Aug); Gift Guide (Dec); Bride & Groom (Feb); How to Guide (Jul); Best of Times (Jun); Spring Home Improvement (Mar); Best & Brightest (May); Focus on Women (Nov); Fall Home Improvement (Oct).
Special Weekly Sections: The Guide (Fri); Consumer (Mon); Travel (S); Health (Tues); Food (Wed). Entertainment, Business/ Financial, Arts, Living, Automotive (Daily); Style, Local, Sports, Real Estate, Help Wanted (Daily & Sun); Best Food Day (Sun & Wed); Family/Kids (Thurs); Entertainment, Weekend guide (Fri); Religion, Travel (Sat); Travel, People, Grocer PP Day (Sun)
Syndicated Publications: Parade (S).
Ed./Pub. .... Richard L. Connor
Vice Pres./CFO .... Allison Uhrin
Adv./Mktg. Vice Pres. .... Kim Dudick
Circ. Vice Pres. .... Dick Dehavan
Executive Editor .... George Spohr
Ed. .... Rich Connor
Night Ed. .... Joe Healey
News Editor .... Dan Burnett
Prodn. Mgr., Pre Press .... Shelly Mccann
Market Information: TMC; Zoned editions.
Mechanical Available: Offset; Black and 3 ROP colors; insert accepted - min 7 3/4 x 5 1/2; page cutoffs - 22.
Mechanical Specifications: Type page 12 1/2 x 21; E - 6 cols, 2 1/16, 1/8 between; A - 6 cols, 2 1/16, 1/8 between; C - 10 cols, 1 3/8, 1/16 between.Equipment & Software: PRESSROOM EQUIPMENT: Lines — MAN/Roland double width (20 couples, offset; 3 tower, 1996; Folders — MAN/Roland; Pasters —MEG; Reels & Stands — MEG; Control System — MAN/ Rolland.; MAILROOM EQUIPMENT: Counter Stackers — 2-QWI/300, 3-QWI/350; Inserters & Stuffers — 2-GMA/SLS 1000; Tying Machines — 2/Dynaric; Wrapping Singles — 2-/QWI; Address Machine — 1-/Wm, 1-/Ch, 1-Mc/2000 PB Folder.; BUSINESS EQUIPMENT: HP/3000-928, HP/3000-918, HP/MPE-IY BUSINESS SOFTWARE: Microsoft/Office 5.0, Boreland/Parabox 4.0 CLASSIFIED EQUIPMENT: Hardware — 2-Pentium/Dual Processing Servers/266; Printers — 1-HP/III, 1-C.Itoh, 2-Dataproducts/ Typhoon; CLASSIFIED SOFTWARE: PPI/ Microsoft Windows NT, SQL 3.11. DISPLAY EQUIPMENT: Hardware — 1-APP/Mac NZM 486 DX66 with Novell fileserver; Printers — ECR/1045 CS, 2-Pre-Press/ Panther Pro Imagesetter, 2-Dataproducts/ Typhoon; DISPLAY SOFTWAREAd Make-up Applications — Multi-Ad/Creator, QPS/ QuarkXPress, Adobe/Illustrator, Adobe/ Photoshop, Aldus/FreeHand, 2-Dataproducts; EDITORIAL EQUIPMENT: Hardware — 22-PC 486-66MHz fileserver, 2-PC 286, 5-PC 386, 30-Pentium/PC 133MHZ; Printers — 2-Pre Press/Panther 46, 1-HP/ III, 1-Panasonic, ECR/Pelbox 1045CS, 2-Dataproducts/Typhoon EDITORIAL SOFTWARE: CCI 6.7.0.2AQ, Solaris/9. PRODUCTION EQUIPMENT: Hardware — Caere/OmniPage, Na/NP40; Scanners - 2-AG/1200 dpi, 6-HP/ScanJet PRODUCTION SOFTWARE: CCI/Editorial Sys. 6.7.0.2AQ, MEI/CLS, QPS/QuarkXPress 4.1, MEI/ALS 4.1.7.

YORK

THE YORK DISPATCH

205 N George St, York, Pa., 17401-1107, York; gen tel (717) 854-1575; adv tel (717) 767-6397; gen fax (717) 843-2958; adv fax (717) 764-6130; ed fax (717) 843-2814; gen/ nat adv e-mail news@yorkdispatch.com; ed e-mail news@yorkdispatch.com; web site www.yorkdispatch.com
- 8,137,364(views) 1,603,024(visitors)
Published: Mon, Tues, Wed, Thur, Fri
Weekday Frequency: e
Circulation: 12,227
Last Audit: AAM September 30, 2014
Advertising Rate (weekday/saturday): Open inch rate $87.35
News services: NYT, LAT-WP, AP, MNS, NEA, SHNS.
Special Weekly Sections: Best Food (Wed); Entertainment, Flipside (Thur); Entertainment (Fri); Business, Finance, Style, Local, Sports, Auto, Real Estate, Help Wanted (Daily);
Owner .... Phil Buckner
Bus. Mgr. .... Teresa Hoover
Mng. Ed. .... Mark Franklin
City Ed. .... Gayle Eubank
Editorial Page Ed. .... Patrick Delany
Entertainment/Weekend Ed. .... Mel Barber
News/Design Ed. .... John Sincoe
Sports Ed. .... Steve Heiser
Style Ed. .... Melissa Barber
Data Processing Mgr. .... Charles Burkhardt
Mgmt. Info Servs./Online Mgr. .... Scott Miller
Pres./Pub. .... Fred Uffelman
VP, Sales/Marketing .... Bryan Kelley
Market Information: Split run; TMC; Zoned editions.
Mechanical Available: Offset; Black and 3 ROP colors; insert accepted - all; page cutoffs - 22 3/4.Equipment & Software: PRESSROOM EQUIPMENT: Lines — 8-G/Metro 1991, 2-G/Metro CIC 1991; Pasters —8-G/ RTP. MAILROOM EQUIPMENT: Counter Stackers — 4-HL/Monitor HT II; Inserters & Stuffers — 2-HI/1472; Tying Machines — 4/ MLN.; BUSINESS EQUIPMENT: 11-HP/928 RL BUSINESS SOFTWARE: CJ, DB, Vesoft CLASSIFIED EQUIPMENT: Hardware — HI; Printers — C.Itoh/CI 400; CLASSIFIED SOFTWARE: HI, HI/Pagination. DISPLAY EQUIPMENT: Hardware — 1-APP/Power Mac 7100, DEC/Alpha NT Server, 1-APP/ Mac 650 Quadra, 2-APP/Power Mac 8600, 3-APP/Power Mac G3; Printers — 2-HP/ LaserJet 4MV, HP/LaserJet 4MV; Other Hardware — AP AdSend, ImageNet, Ad DISPLAY SOFTWAREAd Make-up Applications — QPS/QuarkXPress 3.3, Adobe/Photoshop; EDITORIAL EQUIPMENT: Hardware — AT, Dell/HI/Pagination; Printers — Textronix/600 EDITORIAL SOFTWARE: AT, HI. PRODUCTION EQUIPMENT: Hardware — 2-MON/3850, 2-C/R660; Cameras — 1-C/Spartan III; Scanners — ECR/1000, ECR/2045.
Note: For detailed advertising, circulation, printing and production information, see York Newspaper Company listing. Advertising in the York Dispatch automatically includes advertising in the York Daily Record (m).

YORK DAILY RECORD/YORK SUNDAY NEWS

1891 Loucks Rd, York, Pa., 17408-9708, York; gen tel (717) 767-6397; adv tel (717) 767-4237; ed tel (717) 771-2000; gen fax (717) 764-6130; adv fax (717) 767-3567; ed fax (717) 771-2009; gen/ nat adv e-mail news@ydr.com; disp adv e-mail tkeeler@mediaonepa.com; class adv e-mailclassified@mediaonemarketplace.com; ed e-mail news@ydr.com; web site www.ydr.com
- 1,800,000(views) 400,000(visitors); web site 2 www.inyork.com - 1,100,000(views) 145,000(visitors); web site 3 www.gametimepa.com - 350,000(views) 45,000(visitors); web site 4www.yorkblog.com - 140,000(views) 65,000(visitors)
Group: Gannett
Published: Mon, Tues, Wed, Thur, Fri, Sun
Weekday Frequency: m
Saturday Frequency: m
Circulation: 17,408; 39,958(sun)
Last Audit: AAM September 30, 2017
Advertising Rate (weekday/saturday): Open inch rate $83.35
Advertising Rate (sunday): Open inch rate $87.52
Online Advertising Rate: 300x250, 728x90 $12 cpm
News services: AP, McClatchy. **Established:** 1796
Own Printing Facility?: Yes
Commercial Printers?: Yes
Special Weekly Sections: Best Food Day (Sun & Wed); Entertainment (AM&PM), Flipside (Thurs); Travel, HomeSource (Sun); Business/ Financial, Style, Local, Sports, Automotive, Real Estate & Help Wanted (Daily)
Syndicated Publications: USA WEEKEND Magazine (S).
Digital Platform - Mobile: Apple, Android
Digital Platform - Tablet: Apple iOS
Exec. Asst. to Pub. .... Donna Mandl
Editor .... James McClure
Mng. Ed. .... Randy Parker
Asst. Mng. Ed., Features/Niche/Social Media Buffy Andrews-Gross
Asst. Mng. Ed., Metro .... Susan Martin
Assistant Managing Editor for Sports .. Lyzz Jones
Bus. Ed. and Weekly/Web Editor .... Cathy Hirko
Editorial Ed. .... Scott Fisher
AME - Visual and MultiMedia .... Brad Jennings
News Editor .... Tom Barstow
Publisher .... Sara Glines
Christine Loman
Dan Herman
Scott Blanchard
Market Information: TMC; Zoned editions.
Mechanical Specifications: SAU
Areas Served: York and Adams Counties
Delivery Method: Mail, Newsstand, Carrier, RacksEquipment & Software: PRESSROOM EQUIPMENT: Lines — 8 units Goss Metro; Press Drive — Fincor; Folders — 2-2:1; Pasters —GossControl System — Fincor; MAILROOM EQUIPMENT: Counter Stackers — 3-Idab; Inserters & Stuffers — 1 Magnapack 2 - 14/72; Tying Machines — 3 Dynaric; BUSINESS EQUIPMENT: Dell BUSINESS SOFTWARE: Windows CLASSIFIED EQUIPMENT: Hardware — Dell; Printers — HP; CLASSIFIED SOFTWARE: AdBase ATEX DISPLAY EQUIPMENT: Hardware — MAC; Printers — Misc.; DISPLAY SOFTWAREAd Make-up Applications — C2; EDITORIAL EQUIPMENT: Hardware — Dell/Sun/ HI/Pagination; Printers — HP/4000 EDITORIAL SOFTWARE: HI. PRODUCTION EQUIPMENT: Hardware — MAC; Scanners — Misc.
Note: For detailed advertising, circulation, printing and production information, see York Newspaper Company listing. Advertising in the York Daily Record automatically includes advertising in the York Dispatch (e).

RHODE ISLAND

NEWPORT

THE NEWPORT DAILY NEWS

101 Malbone Rd, Newport, R.I., 02840-1340, Newport; gen tel (401) 849-3300; adv tel (401) 849-3300; gen fax (401) 849-3335; adv fax (401) 849-3335; ed fax (401) 849-3306; gen/nat adv e-mail Abrams@NewportRI.com; disp adv e-mail Abrams@NewportRI.com; class adv e-mailndnadvertising@newportri.com; ed e-mail editor@newportri.com; web site www.newportdailynews.com
- 284,068(views) 42,146(visitors)
Group: GateHouse Media, Inc.
Published: Mon, Tues, Wed, Thur, Fri, Sat
Weekday Frequency: m
Saturday Frequency: m
Circulation: 12,738; 12,738(sat)
Last Audit: CAC March 31, 2015
Advertising Rate (weekday/saturday): Open inch rate $23.25
Online Advertising Rate: Open Rate $23.25 per. Col. In.; Leaderboard 728x90 $8 CPM; Super Skyscraper 300x600 $12 CPM; Medium Rectangle 300x250 $12 CPM; Leaderboard 728x90 $12 CPM; Super Skyscraper 300x600 $15 CPM
News services: AP, McClatchy. **Established:** 1846
Own Printing Facility?: Yes
Commercial Printers?: Yes
Special Editions: Health and Fitness, Newport County Chamber of Commerce Quarterly, Winter Festival, 50 Plus, Spring Home and Garden, Spring Dining Guide, Summer Activity Guide, Newport Flower Show, Tennis Hall of Fame Championships, Back to School, Fall Sports Preview, F all Home and Garden, Fall Dining Guide, Holiday Gift Guide, Last Minute Gift Guide
Publisher .... William F. Lucey
City Ed. .... M. Catherine Callahan
News Ed. .... Harvey B. Peters
Sports Ed. .... Scott P. Barrett
Operations Mgr. .... Kevin F. Schoen
Editor .... Joanthan Zins
Advertising Director .... Lynn Abrams
Market Information: ADS; Split run; TMC; Zoned editions.
Mechanical Available: Offset; Black and 3 ROP colors; insert accepted; page cutoffs - 22 3/4.
Mechanical Specifications: Type page 12 1/2 x 21 1/2; E - 6 cols, 2 1/16, 1/8 between; A - 6 cols, 2 1/16, 1/8 between; C - 8 cols, 1 9/16, 1/16 between.
Areas Served: Aquidneck Island - Newport, Middletown, Portsmouth, Tiverton
Delivery Method: CarrierEquipment & Software: PRESSROOM EQUIPMENT: Lines — 10-G/ Urbanite; Registration System — Burgess/ Carlson. MAILROOM EQUIPMENT: Counter Stackers — 1-HL/Monitor HT; Inserters & Stuffers — 1-S/624P; Tying Machines — 1-MLN/ML2, 1-MLN/Suretyer; Address Machine — 1/KR.; BUSINESS SOFTWARE: Vision Data CLASSIFIED SOFTWARE: Vision Data. DISPLAY SOFTWAREAd Make-up Applications — Vision Data; Layout Software — Layout/8000 EDITORIAL SOFTWARE: ACI/Open Pages. PRODUCTION EQUIPMENT: Hardware —

PAWTUCKET

THE TIMES

23 Exchange St, Pawtucket, R.I., 02860-2026, Providence; gen tel (401) 722-4000; adv tel (401) 722-4000; ed tel (401) 722-4000; gen fax (401) 727-9250; adv fax (401) 727-9252 (display); ed fax (401) 727-9280; gen/nat adv e-mail mlbosiak@woonsocketcall.com; disp adv e-mail advertising@pawtuckettimes.com; class adv e-mailclassified@woonsocketcall.com; ed e-mail editor@pawtuckettimes.com; web site www.pawtuckettimes.com
- 122,000(views) 57,000(visitors)
Group: RISN Operations Inc.
Published: Mon, Tues, Wed, Thur, Fri, Sat
Weekday Frequency: m
Saturday Frequency: m
Circulation: 3,303; 5,539(sat)
Last Audit: AAM September 30, 2014
Advertising Rate (weekday/saturday): Open inch rate $21.71
Online Advertising Rate: Skyscraper OR Big Box-$320/month-42,000 Ad Views; $250/ month-33,000 Ad Views; $175/month 24,000 Ad Views; $99/month-14,000 Ad Views. Skyscraper OR Bottom Banner-$320/ month-51,000 Ad Views; $250/month-40,000 Ad Views;$175/month-28,000;$99/ month-16,000 Ad Views; Weather Box Tile, OR Mini Banner- $320/month-64,000 Ad Views; $250/month 50,000 Ad Views; $175/ month-35,000 Ad Views; $99/month-19,000 Ad Views.
News services: AP. **Established:** 1885
Own Printing Facility?: No
Commercial Printers?: No
Special Editions: Spring Car Care (Apr); Bus Schedule (Aug); Holiday Gift Guide I & II (Dec); Business Profile (Feb); Bridal Showcase (Jan); Who's the Best-Ballot (Jul); Business Review (Jun); Profile-Massachusetts (Mar); Momentum (May); Monthly Kid's Tab (Monthly); Holida
Special Weekly Sections: Homes, TV, Religion (Sat); Health (Tues); Food (Wed).
Syndicated Publications: USA WEEKEND Magazine (Sat).
Controller .... Kathleen Kneeham
Adv. Mgr., Classified .... Diane Ames
Exec. Ed. .... Bianca Pavoncello
Managing Ed./News Ed. .... David Pepin
Sports Ed. .... Eric Benevides
Asst. Ed. .... Donna Kirwan
Adv. Dir./Gen. Mgr./Pub. .... Marylynn Bosiak
Market Information: TMC.
Mechanical Available: Offset; Black and 4 ROP colors; insert accepted; page cutoffs - 21 1/4.
Mechanical Specifications: Type page 12 x 21 1/2; E - 6 cols, 1 7/8, 3/16 between; A - 6 cols, 1 7/8, 3/16 between; C - 9 cols, 1 3/8, 1/8 between.

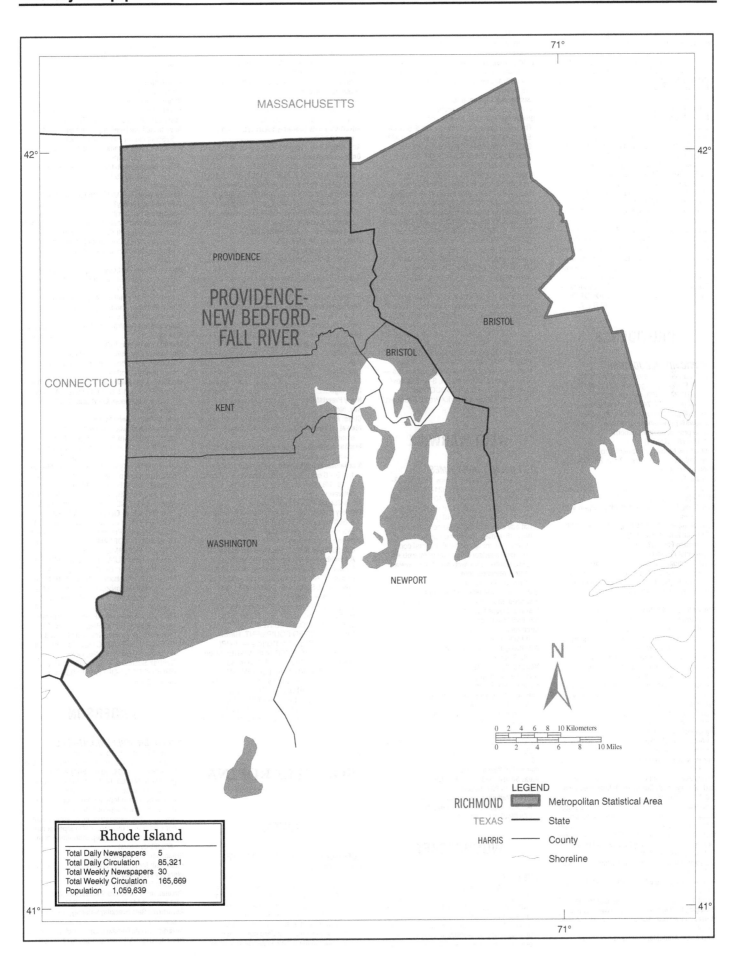

MASSACHUSETTS

CONNECTICUT

PROVIDENCE

PROVIDENCE-
NEW BEDFORD-
FALL RIVER

KENT

BRISTOL

BRISTOL

WASHINGTON

NEWPORT

71°

42°

42°

41°

41°

71°

0 2 4 6 8 10 Kilometers
0 2 4 6 8 10 Miles

N

Rhode Island

Total Daily Newspapers	5
Total Daily Circulation	85,321
Total Weekly Newspapers	30
Total Weekly Circulation	165,669
Population	1,059,639

LEGEND

RICHMOND	Metropolitan Statistical Area
TEXAS	State
HARRIS	County
	Shoreline

Areas Served: East Providence etc.
Delivery Method: Carrier, RacksEquipment & Software: MAILROOM EQUIPMENT: Tying Machines — 1-MLN/ML2-EE.; BUSINESS EQUIPMENT: IBM/Sys 36, IBM/AS 400 BUSINESS SOFTWARE: INSI CLASSIFIED EQUIPMENT: Hardware — Compaq/PC Desk Pro CLS; Printers — HP/Laserjet, Xante/Accel-O-Writer; CLASSIFIED SOFTWARE: PPI/Classifield. DISPLAY EQUIPMENT: Hardware — APP/Mac IIcx, APP/Mac SE, APP/Mac Plus, 2-APP/ Mac G3, 2-APP/Power Mac 6100; Printers — LaserWriter, Xante/Ultra 4000; Other Hardware — Zip drives, Scan DISPLAY SOFTWAREAd Make-up Applications — QPS/QuarkXPress, Adobe/Illustrator, Multi-Ad/Creator, FreeHand, Adobe/ Photoshop; EDITORIAL EQUIPMENT: Hardware — Compaq/Desk Pro PC/OCR Scanner, X/RFS 2035; Printers — APP/ Mac LaserWriter II, Xante/Accel-A-Writer EDITORIAL SOFTWARE: Microsoft/Office 97, QPS/QuarkXPress 4.0, Adobe/Photoshop 4.0. PRODUCTION EQUIPMENT: Hardware — 2-Linotype-Hell/Linotron 202-N, Hyphen/ Dash 72E, Ultra/4000; Cameras — 1-C/ Spartan III, 1-R/Mark II, R/432; Scanners — HP/Flatbed B&W Scanner PRODUCTION SOFTWARE: MEI/CLS 2.5.2, ALS 2.7.

PROVIDENCE

THE PROVIDENCE JOURNAL

75 Fountain St, Providence, R.I., 02902-0050, Providence; gen tel (401) 277-7000; ed tel (401) 277-7303; adv fax (401) 277-7802; ed fax (401) 277-7439; gen/nat adv e-mail letters@providencejournal.com; ed e-mail pjnews@providencejournal.com; web site www.providencejournal.com
1,155,752(visitors)
Group: New Media Investment Group
Published: Mon, Tues, Wed, Thur, Fri, Sat, Sun
Weekday Frequency: m
Saturday Frequency: m
Circulation: 64,432; 76,486(sat); 84,239(sun)
Last Audit: AAM June 30, 2016
Advertising Rate (weekday/saturday): Open inch rate $286.00
News services: AP, LAT-WP, MCT, SHNS, TMS, CQ, DJ. **Established:** 1829
Own Printing Facility?: Yes
Commercial Printers?: Yes
Special Editions: Family Fun (February); Summer Guide (May); Summer Food (June); Fall Guide (September); Student/Athlete Honor Roll (July); CVS Charity Classic (June);
Special Weekly Sections: Thrive (health and fitness), Monday; Connect (music, TV, technology gadgets), Tuesday; Food, Wednesday; Go! (things to do), Thursday; Movies, Friday; Decor (home and gardening), Saturday; Real Estate, Saturday; Homes, Sunday; Consumer, (personal finance), Sunday; The Rhode Islander, Sunday; All About You (fashion, self-care, relationships); Cars, Wednesday, Saturday and Sunday.
Syndicated Publications: Parade (S).
Digital Platform - Mobile: Apple, Android, Windows, Blackberry
Digital Platform - Tablet: Apple iOS, Android, Windows 7, Blackberry Tablet OS, Kindle, Nook, Kindle Fire
Vice Pres. & Editorial Pages Ed. .... Edward C. Achorn
Deputy Executive Editor .... Susan Areson
Asst. Managing Ed. Commerce & Consumer Desk John Kostrzewa
Executive Ed. .... Dave Butler
Mang. Ed. Visuals .... Michael Delaney
Managing Ed. Ops .... Kurt Mayer
Asst. Managing Ed. Breaking News ... Jack Khorey
Asst. Manag. Ed. Breaking News/Social Media ..... Pamela Reinsel Cotter
Assistant Managing Editor, Production .... Gary Zebrun
Assistant Managing Editor, Multi-platform ... Maria Caporizzo
Sports Ed. .... Michael McDermott
Managing Ed. Features .... Alan Rosenberg
Market Information: ADS; Split run; TMC; Zoned editions.
Mechanical Available: Flexographic; Black and 3 ROP colors; insert accepted - some customer inserts are printed in-house; page cutoffs - 22.
Mechanical Specifications: Type page 12 x 21; E - 6 cols, 1 43/50, 1/6 between; A - 6 cols, 1 43/50, 1/6 between; C - 9 cols, 1 23/100, 1/8 between.
Areas Served: The entire state of Rhode Island and southeastern Massachusetts
Delivery Method: Mail, Newsstand, RacksEquipment & Software: PRESSROOM EQUIPMENT: Lines — 6-W&H/Flexo 1987, 2-MOT/Flexo Tower 1992; 6-W&H/Flexo 1987, 2-MOT/Flexo Tower 1992; 6-W&H/ Flexo 1987, 2-MOT/Flexo Tower 1992; Pasters —18, 6Reels & Stands — 18, 6.; MAILROOM EQUIPMENT: Counter Stackers — QWI/501; Inserters & Stuffers — GMA/SLS-2000; Tying Machines — Dynaric/NP-3000; Wrapping Singles — 1/ St.; BUSINESS EQUIPMENT: 450-Dell/ XP PC BUSINESS SOFTWARE: Oracle CLASSIFIED EQUIPMENT: Hardware — AT/IAS, 2-AT/CLSPAG; Printers — HP, Data Printers; CLASSIFIED SOFTWARE: AT. DISPLAY EQUIPMENT: Hardware — 40-APP/Mac, In-house system, 110-PC; Printers — HP/LaserJet Printers; Other Hardware — 3-X/Scanner, 2-Tesca/Scanner, 1-Eversmart, 6-Desktop Scanners DISPLAY SOFTWARELayout Software — MEI/ALS, HI. EDITORIAL EQUIPMENT: Hardware — 112-At, 204-PC, 45-APP/Mac; Printers — HP EDITORIAL SOFTWARE: AT, XYQUEST/ XyWrite, QPS/QuarkXPress. PRODUCTION EQUIPMENT: Hardware — 3-Pre Press/ Panterras, Konica/Black Magic; Scanners — Nikon/35mm, 8-Microtek/III, 3-X, 1-Scitex/ EverSmart, 2-Tecsa PRODUCTION SOFTWARE: QPS/QuarkXPress, Alfaquest/ Print Express CPM.

WEST WARWICK

KENT COUNTY DAILY TIMES

1353 Main St, West Warwick, R.I., 02893-3859, Kent; gen tel (401) 821-7400; adv tel (401) 789-9744; ed tel (401) 789-9744 ext. 209; gen fax (401) 828-0810; adv fax (401) 828-0810; ed fax (401) 828-0810; gen/ nat adv e-mail jboucher@ricentral.com; disp adv e-mail jboucher@ricentral.com; class adv e-mailjboucher@ricentral.com; ed e-mail kceditor@ricentral.com; web site www.ricentral.com; web site 2 http://www.kentcountytimes.com
Group: RISN Operations Inc.
Southern Rhode Island Newspapers
Published: Mon, Tues, Wed, Thur, Fri, Sat
Weekday Frequency: All day
Saturday Frequency: All day
Circulation: 949; 1,104(sat)
Last Audit: CAC June 30, 2017
Advertising Rate (weekday/saturday): Open inch rate $14.03
News services: 1892
Own Printing Facility?: Yes
Commercial Printers?: No
Special Weekly Sections: Wedding, Anniversary (Mon); Senior (Tue); Best Food (Wed); Arts, Entertainment, Fashion, Health (Thur); Home (Fri); Religion (Sat)
Reg. Pub. .... Jody Boucher
Cir. Dir. .... Phil Rowell
Art Dir. .... Jim Buchanan
Ed. .... Jeremiah Ryan
Mechanical Specifications: Call for Info
Areas Served: 02893, 02896, 02886,, 02817, 02818, 02827, 02831
Delivery Method: Newsstand, Carrier, RacksEquipment & Software: MAILROOM EQUIPMENT: Tying Machines — 2/Bu.;

WOONSOCKET

THE CALL

75 Main St, Woonsocket, R.I., 02895-4312, Providence; gen tel (401) 762-3000; adv tel (401) 767-8505; ed tel (401) 767-8550; gen fax (401) 767-8509; adv fax (401) 767-8509; ed fax (401) 765-2834; gen/nat adv e-mail dbenjamin@woonsocketcall.com; disp adv e-mail ads@WoonsocketCall.com; class adv e-mailclassified@woonsocketcall.com; ed e-mail editor@woonsocketcall.com; web site www.woonsocketcall.com
- 253,000(views) 113,000(visitors)
Group: RISN Operations Inc.
Published: Mon, Tues, Wed, Thur, Fri, Sat, Sun
Weekday Frequency: m
Saturday Frequency: m
Circulation: 3,899; 3,899(sat); 5,399(sun)
Last Audit: AAM March 31, 2017
Advertising Rate (weekday/saturday): Open inch rate $26.53
Advertising Rate (sunday): Open inch rate $29.75
Online Advertising Rate: Skyscraper OR Bottom Banner-$320/month-51,000 Ad Views; $250/ month-40,000 Ad Views; $175/month 28,000 Ad Views; $99/month-16,000 Ad Views; Weather Box, Tild, OR Mini Banner-$320/ month-64,000 Ad Views; $250/month-50,000 Ad Views;$175/month-35,000 Ad Views;$99/ month-19,000 Ad Views
News services: AP. **Established:** 1892
Own Printing Facility?: No
Commercial Printers?: Yes
Special Editions: Chamber of Commerce Annual Report (Jan).
Special Weekly Sections: Pets(Mon); Health(Tue); Food(Wed); Entertainment (Thur); Auto (Fri); Real Estate (Sat); TV, Then and Now (Sun);
Syndicated Publications: USA WEEKEND Magazine (S).
Digital Platform - Mobile: Android, Windows
Digital Platform - Tablet: Android, Windows 7, Blackberry Tablet OS
Controller .... Kathie Needham
Pub. .... Jody Boucher
Gen. Mgr. .... Paul Palange
Ed. .... Seth Bromley
Dist. Mgr. .... Jorge Londono
Nat. / Preprint Mgr. .... Denise Benjamin
Adv. Mgr. .... Diane Ames
Class. Adv. .... Christina Bevilacqua
Market Information: Split run; TMC; Zoned editions.
Mechanical Available: Offset; Black and 3 ROP colors; insert accepted; page cutoffs - 22 3/4.
Mechanical Specifications: Type page 12 x 21 1/2; E - 6 cols, 1 7/8, 1/8 between; A - 6 cols, 1 7/8, 1/8 between; C - 9 cols, 1 5/16, 1/16 between.
Areas Served: Providence County
Delivery Method: Newsstand, CarrierEquipment & Software: PRESSROOM EQUIPMENT: Lines — 7-G/Urbanite U-615 single width (mono; 1-3 color unit) 1994; Press Drive — C.E.S./200 h.p.-PLC; Pasters —5-Enkel/ AutowebReels & Stands — 5; Registration System — Stoesser/center pin. MAILROOM EQUIPMENT: Counter Stackers — QWI/351; Inserters & Stuffers — 2-MM/227E; Tying Machines — 1/MLN, 1-Dynaric/NP 1500; Wrapping Singles — HL/Monitor; Address Machine — X/Chesire 525; BUSINESS EQUIPMENT: Dell BUSINESS SOFTWARE: INSI CLASSIFIED EQUIPMENT: Hardware — Compaq/Desk Pro; Printers — 1-HP/ Laserjets; CLASSIFIED SOFTWARE: Vision Data DISPLAY EQUIPMENT: Hardware — Mac G4; EDITORIAL EQUIPMENT: Hardware — 12-Compaq/Desk Pro; Printers — HP 5200 EDITORIAL SOFTWARE: Agile/Teambase 1.0.2.8. PRODUCTION EQUIPMENT: Hardware — ECRM CTP PRODUCTION SOFTWARE: Quark 6.5 Multi Ad Creator

SOUTH CAROLINA

AIKEN

EVENING POST INDUSTRIES' AIKEN COMMUNICATIONS

326 Rutland Dr NW, Aiken, S.C., 29801-4010, Aiken; gen tel (501) 730-4554; adv tel (501) 730-4554; ed tel (803) 648-2311; gen fax (803) 644-2383; adv fax (803) 644-2383; ed fax (803) 644-2383; gen/nat adv e-mail dbell@aikenstandard.com; disp adv e-mail dbell@aikenstandard.com; class adv e-mailddaniell@aikenstandard.com; ed e-mail mystory@aikenstandard.com; web site www.aikenstandard.com
- 1,179,650(views) 162,731(visitors)
Group: Evening Post Publishing Newspaper Group
Published: Mon, Tues, Wed, Thur, Fri, Sat, Sun
Weekday Frequency: m
Saturday Frequency: m
Circulation: 11,112; 11,112(sat); 13,122(sun)
Last Audit: AAM September 30, 2017
Advertising Rate (weekday/saturday): Inserts: $25cpm flat rate; ROP: $5.25pci
Advertising Rate (sunday): Inserts: $25cpm flat rate; ROP: $5.25pci
Online Advertising Rate: $10cpm ROS; pencil pushdowns, $275 for 1- 24 hr.; $500 for 2 in a month.
News services: AP, MCT. **Established:** 1867
Own Printing Facility?: Yes
Commercial Printers?: Yes
Special Editions: Masters Golf Tournament (Apr); Football (Aug); Brides Book (Jan); Horse Industry (Mar); Christmas Gift Guide (Nov); Medical Directory (June); Discover Aiken (Sept).
Special Weekly Sections: Religious Page (Fri); Home Hunter (S); Auto (Sat); Entertainment (Thur); Health (Wed).
Digital Platform - Mobile: Apple, Android
Digital Platform - Tablet: Apple iOS, AndroidRhonda Overby
Sales and Special Projects Man. ...... Diane Daniell
Man ed. .... Mike Harris
Market Information: TMC.
Mechanical Available: Offset; Black and 3 ROP colors; insert accepted - poly bags, sample bags; page cutoffs - 22.
Mechanical Specifications: Type page 13 1/8 x 21; E - 6 cols, 1 5/6, 1/6 between; A - 6 cols, 1 5/6, 1/6 between; C - 8 cols, 1 1/3, 1/6 between.
Areas Served: Aiken County
Delivery Method: Mail, Newsstand, Carrier, RacksEquipment & Software: PRESSROOM EQUIPMENT: Lines — 13-G/Community; Folders — 1-G/SSC.; MAILROOM EQUIPMENT: Tying Machines — It, Mosca/ Strapper; Control System — Buskco Inkjet Labeler; BUSINESS EQUIPMENT: Sun/ Ultra 450-256MB, Sun/Ultra 5, 10-XT, 2-APP/ Mac G-3 BUSINESS SOFTWARE: Vision Data 6.0, Vision Data 6.3 CLASSIFIED EQUIPMENT: Hardware — Sun/Ultra 450 Server 256MB; Printers — Genicom/4492XT; CLASSIFIED SOFTWARE: Vision Data 5.4. DISPLAY EQUIPMENT: Printers — HP/ LaserJet 4MV, AU/APS 2000, AU/APS-6-84 ACS Imagesetter; DISPLAY SOFTWAREAd Make-up Applications — QPS/QuarkXPress 4.1, Adobe/Photoshop 6.0, Adobe/Illustrator 9.0; Layout Software — APP/Power Mac G3. EDITORIAL EQUIPMENT: Hardware — APP/ Macs; Printers — AU/APS-6-84, Konica/EV Jetsetter 5100 EDITORIAL SOFTWARE: Dragx 3.6, Baseview/NewsEdit Pro 3.3, QTools 2.5.1. PRODUCTION EQUIPMENT: Hardware — Universal/26, Color Central; Scanners — Epson/2580 Photo PRODUCTION SOFTWARE: Baseview/IQ Server 3.1.8.

ANDERSON

ANDERSON INDEPENDENT-MAIL

1000 Williamston Rd, Anderson, S.C., 29621-6508, Anderson; gen tel (864) 224-4321; adv tel (864) 260-1204; ed tel (864) 260-1244; gen fax (864) 260-1276; adv fax (864) 260-1350; ed fax (864) 260-1276; gen/nat adv e-mail beckt@independentmail.com; disp adv e-mail beckt@independentmail.com; class adv e-mailclassifiedads@independentmail.com; ed e-mail newsroom@independentmail.com; web site www.independentmail.com
476,989(visitors)
Group: Journal Media Group
Published: Mon, Tues, Wed, Thur, Fri, Sat, Sun
Weekday Frequency: m
Saturday Frequency: m
Circulation: 16,240; 16,240(sat); 24,455(sun)
Last Audit: AAM December 31, 2015
Advertising Rate (weekday/saturday): Open inch rate $59.85
Advertising Rate (sunday): Open inch rate $67.09
News services: AP, The Newspaper Network,

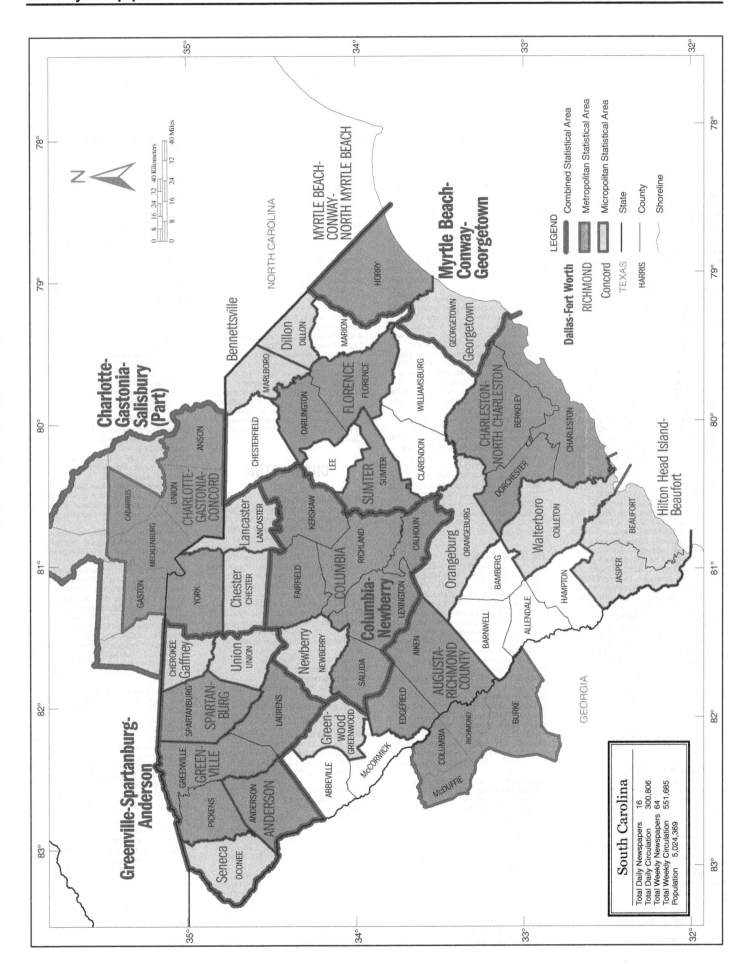

Charlotte-Gastonia-Salisbury (Part)

Greenville-Spartanburg-Anderson

Myrtle Beach-Conway-North Myrtle Beach

Myrtle Beach-Conway-Georgetown

Columbia-Newberry

NORTH CAROLINA

GEORGIA

TEXAS

LEGEND

Combined Statistical Area
Metropolitan Statistical Area
Micropolitan Statistical Area
State
County
Shoreline

Dallas-Fort Worth
RICHMOND
Concord
HARRIS

South Carolina

Total Daily Newspapers	16
Total Daily Circulation	300,806
Total Weekly Newspapers	64
Total Weekly Circulation	551,685
Population	5,024,369

Bennettsville

Gaffney

Union

Green-wood

Seneca

Hilton Head Island-Beaufort

NYT, SHNS, NEA. **Established:** 1899
Special Editions: Home Decorating (Apr); College Football Preview (Aug); HGTV Winter (Dec); NASCAR Preview (Feb); Homebuilders Tab (Jan); YMCA (Jul); South Carolina Factbook (Jun); HGTV Spring (Mar); High School Graduation Tab (May); Food Network Holiday Guide (Nov); YMCA
Special Weekly Sections: Automotive (Fri); Business (S); Automotive (Sat); Be (Thur); Food (Wed).
Syndicated Publications: Parade (S).
Pub. & CRO .... Susan Kelly-Gilbert
Exec. Ed. .... Steve Mullins
Content Editor .... Alison Newton
Ed., HomeTown People .... Willie Mattress
City Ed. .... Mike Alexieff
Night Ed. .... Colleen Cozak
IT Mgr. .... Bill Bussey
Sales Support & Pagination .... Beck Tyrrell
Dir. Digital Media .... Kathy Nelson
Dir. Circulation Sales .... Pete Barend
Mktg. Mgr. .... Chase Heatherly
Market Information: ADS; TMC; Zoned editions.
Mechanical Available: Offset; Black and 3 ROP colors; insert accepted - all; page cutoffs - 22 3/4.
Mechanical Specifications: Type page 10 1/2 x 21 1/2; E - 6 cols, 1 13/20, 1/8 between; A - 6 cols, 1 13/20, 1/8 between; C - 9 cols, 1 1/10, 7/100 between.
Areas Served: Anderson, pickens, upstate south carolina
Delivery Method: CarrierEquipment & Software: PRESSROOM EQUIPMENT: Lines — 10-G/Urbanite 1972; 6-Didde/ Minicom-17 1995; 2-Ryobi/3302 1997; Press Drive — 2-HP/100 Motors 1972; Folders — 2-G/2:1; Pasters —8-Cary 1980Control System — 1992; MAILROOM EQUIPMENT: Counter Stackers — 1-QWI/350, 1-QWI/450; Inserters & Stuffers — 1-GMA/SLS 1000; Tying Machines — 1-MLN/280, 1/OVL, 2-MLN/2CC, 2-Dynaric/NP 1500, Dynaric/ DZ400; Wrapping Singles — 2-QWI/00300; Control System — TMSI Drive/Navigator Convey; BUSINESS EQUIPMENT: HP/3000, 16-IBM/PC, DEC/200 NT Server, 3-DEC/ PC BUSINESS SOFTWARE: Peoplesoft 7.59, Accounting, HMRS CLASSIFIED EQUIPMENT: Hardware — HP; HP/ Office Jet Fax; Printers — Epson/LQ-1170; CLASSIFIED SOFTWARE: III/Tecs 2. DISPLAY EQUIPMENT: Hardware — APP/ Mac G4; Printers — Canon/Color Laser Copier; Other Hardware — AGFA Duoscan 11 x 17, 7-AGFA Scanner 8 1/2 x 11, HP Scanjet DISPLAY SOFTWAREAd Make-up Applications — Multi-Ad, QPS/ QuarkXPress, Adobe/Photoshop; Layout Software — Media Command. EDITORIAL EQUIPMENT: Hardware — HP/APP/Server, Kk/35 Scanner, Nikon/LS2000 Coolscan, Nikon/Digital Imaging System, AG/Flatbed Sacnner Duoscan 11 x 17; Printers — HP/ Postscript Laser Printer EDITORIAL SOFTWARE: DBEdit, QPS/QuarkXPress 4.11. PRODUCTION EQUIPMENT: Hardware — 1-Kk/Trendsetter News SA1423, 1-Kk/ Trendsetter News SA1512 PRODUCTION SOFTWARE: QPS/QuarkXPress 4.03, AG/ Duoscan 11 x 17, 7-AG/Scanner 8 1/2 x 11, HP/Scanjet.

BLUFFTON

THE BEAUFORT GAZETTE

10 Buck Island Rd, Bluffton, S.C., 29910-5937, Beaufort; gen tel (843) 524-3183; adv tel (843) 706-8202; ed tel (843) 524-3183; gen fax (843) 524-8728; gen/nat adv e-mail bosborn@islandpack.com; disp adv e-mail bosborn@islandpack.com; class adv e-mailbosborn@islandpack.com; ed e-mail sborton@islandpack.com; web site www.beaufortgazette.com
Group: The McClatchy Company
Published: Mon, Tues, Wed, Thur, Fri, Sat, Sun
Weekday Frequency: m
Saturday Frequency: m
Circulation: 4,642; 4,642(sat); 5,026(sun)
Last Audit: AAM September 30, 2017
Advertising Rate (weekday/saturday): Open inch rate $42.00
Advertising Rate (sunday): Open inch rate $46.00
News services: AP.
Special Editions: Garden & Home Improvement (Apr); Football (Aug); Coupon Pages (Dec); Income Tax (Feb); Bridal (Jan); Water Festival (Jul); Hurricane (Jun); Spring Tour of Homes (Mar); Gullah Festival (May); Cookbook/ Gift Guide (Nov); Fall Tour of Homes (Oct); Coupon Page
Special Weekly Sections: Health, Sports (Mon); Neighbors (Tue);; Sports, Neighbors (Wed); Military, The Guide (Fri); Auto, Religion (Sat); Travel, Book, Art, Home, Real Estate, Brides, Sports, TV (Sun); Business, Stocks, Finance (Daily)
Syndicated Publications: TV Week, Wall St. Journal, Parade (S).
Digital Platform - Mobile: Apple, Android
Digital Platform - Tablet: Apple iOS, Android
Pres./Pub. .... Sara Johnson Borton
Adv. Dir. .... Sandy Gilles
Ed .... Jeff Kidd
Features Ed. .... Tom Robinette
Photographer .... Bob Sofaly
Sports Ed. .... Lance Hanlin
Prodn. Dir. .... William King
Nat'l Adv. Dir .... Lorrie Anderson
Exec. Ed. .... Brian Tolley
Market Information: TMC.
Mechanical Available: Offset; Black and 3 ROP colors; insert accepted; page cutoffs - 22 3/4.
Mechanical Specifications: Type page 13 x 21; E - 6 cols, 2 1/16, 1/8 between; A - 6 cols, 2 1/16, 1/8 between; C - 9 cols, 1 3/8, 1/8 between. Equipment & Software: PRESSROOM EQUIPMENT: Lines — 6-G/Urbanite; Folders — 1-G/Urbanite.; MAILROOM EQUIPMENT: Counter Stackers — KAN, QWI; Inserters & Stuffers — 2/GMA; Tying Machines — 2-/ MLN, 1-/Power Strap, 1-/Dynaric.; BUSINESS EQUIPMENT: HP BUSINESS SOFTWARE: CJ CLASSIFIED EQUIPMENT: Hardware — Cx, 4-APP/Mac; CLASSIFIED SOFTWARE: Cx, Baseview. DISPLAY EQUIPMENT: Hardware — 4-APP/Mac; Printers — 2-APP/ Mac; DISPLAY SOFTWAREAd Make-up Applications — Baseview; Layout Software — 4-APP/Mac. EDITORIAL EQUIPMENT: Hardware — 22-APP/Mac/APP/Mac Scanner; Printers — 2-APP/Mac EDITORIAL SOFTWARE: Baseview. PRODUCTION EQUIPMENT: Hardware — APP/Mac, 2-AG/Accuset; Cameras — SCREEN PRODUCTION SOFTWARE: Baseview, QPS/QuarkXPress.

THE ISLAND PACKET

10 Buck Island Rd, Bluffton, S.C., 29910-5937, Beaufort; gen tel (843) 706-8100; adv tel (843) 706-8100; ed tel (843) 706-8111; gen fax (843) 706-5050; adv fax (843) 706-5050; ed fax (843) 706-3070; gen/nat adv e-mail ads@islandpacket.com; disp adv e-mail ads@islandpacket.com; class adv e-mailarobbins@islandpacket.com; ed e-mail newsroom@islandpacket.com; web site www.islandpacket.com
- 1,795,182(views) 260,356(visitors)
Group: The McClatchy Company
Published: Mon, Tues, Wed, Thur, Fri, Sat, Sun
Weekday Frequency: m
Saturday Frequency: m
Circulation: 15,626; 15,626(sat); 17,680(sun)
Last Audit: AAM March 31, 2016
Advertising Rate (weekday/saturday): Open inch rate $42.00
Advertising Rate (sunday): Open inch rate $46.00
Online Advertising Rate: 300x25 -$15 cpm; Leaderboard 728x90-$12 cpm, Floorboard $25 cpm
News services: AP, MCT, NYT, Pony Wire, SHNS. **Established:** 1970
Own Printing Facility?: Yes
Commercial Printers?: Yes
Special Editions: Health & Fitness, Hilton Head Happenings (May); Hurricane, Readers' Choice (June); Newcomers Packet (July); Back to School (Aug); Woman (Sept); Holiday Gift Guide (Nov); Health Care Directory (Dec)
Special Weekly Sections: Schools, Education, sports, Lowcountry Life (Mon); Health, Fitness, Sports, business (Tue); Food (Wed); Military (Thur); The Guide, Sports, Business, Life (Fri); Auto, Faith, Values (Sat); Book, Social, Homes, Sports (Sun)
Syndicated Publications: Parade (S).
Digital Platform - Mobile: Apple, Android
Digital Platform - Tablet: Apple iOS, Android
Pub./Pres. .... Sara Johnson Borton
Finance Dir. .... Cindy Paulbee
HR Dir. .... Jolie Bagonzi
Adv. Dir. .... Sandy Gills
Adv. Mgr., Classified .... Susan Green
Mktg. Dir. .... Beth Patton
Mng. Ed. .... Sally Mahan
City Ed. .... Don McClaude
Editorial Page Ed. .... Janet Smith
Features Ed. .... Tom Robinette
Sports Ed. .... Lincee Hanlin
New Media Dir. .... David Feld
Prodn. Dir. .... William King
Exec. Ed. .... Brian Tolley
Mechanical Available: Offset; Black and 3 ROP colors; insert accepted; page cutoffs - 21.
Mechanical Specifications: Type page 11 5/8 x 21; E - 6 cols, 1 4/5, 1/8 between; A - 6 cols, 1 4/5, 1/8 between; C - 9 cols, 1 1/5, 1/8 between.
Delivery Method: Mail, Newsstand, Carrier, RacksEquipment & Software: BUSINESS EQUIPMENT: 1-HP/3000 Series 58 CLASSIFIED EQUIPMENT: Hardware — CD, APP/Mac; Printers — HP/LaserJet 4Plus; CLASSIFIED SOFTWARE: Baseview/ Classified. DISPLAY EQUIPMENT: Hardware — 9-APP/Power Mac; Printers — Graphic Enterprises/Pagescan 3, HP/ Laser 4V; DISPLAY SOFTWAREAd Make-up Applications — Multi-Ad/Creator 4.01, QPS/ QuarkXPress 4.04, Aldus/FreeHand 8.0, Adobe/Photoshop 5.5, Adobe/Illustrator 5.0; Layout Software — APP/Mac. EDITORIAL EQUIPMENT: Hardware — CD, APP/Mac; Printers — HP/LaserJet 4MV EDITORIAL SOFTWARE: Baseview/IQue. PRODUCTION EQUIPMENT: Hardware — Caere/ OmniPage 3.0, AG/Accuset 1500; Cameras — 1-Nu; Scanners — Polaroid/SprintScan 35, Microtek/Scanmaker III, Microtek/ Scanmaker 6002S, Microtek/Scanmaker IV PRODUCTION SOFTWARE: QPS/ QuarkXPress 3.31.

CHARLESTON

THE POST AND COURIER

134 Columbus St, Charleston, S.C., 29403-4809, Charleston; gen tel (843) 577-7111; adv tel (843) 937-5468; ed tel (843) 937-5527; gen fax (843) 937-5463; adv fax (843) 937-5463; ed fax (843) 937-5545; gen/nat adv e-mail jdrolet@postandcourier.com; disp adv e-mail jdrolet@postandcourier.com; class adv e-mailmmandel@postandcourier.com; ed e-mail editor@postandcourier.com; web site www.postandcourier.com
- 8,000,000(views) 1,400,000(visitors); web site 2 lowcountryparent.com - 15,000(views) 1,500(visitors); web site 3 lowcountrypaws.com - 10,000(views) 1,000(visitors)
Group: Evening Post Publishing Newspaper Group
Published: Mon, Tues, Wed, Thur, Fri, Sat, Sun
Weekday Frequency: m
Saturday Frequency: m
Circulation: 54,286; 54,686(sat); 64,532(sun)
Last Audit: AAM March 31, 2017
Advertising Rate (weekday/saturday): Non-Modular Open inch rate $81.72, Modular $78.22
Advertising Rate (sunday): Non-Modular Open inch rate $89.95, Modular $71.06
Online Advertising Rate: Leaderboard (728x90): 10,000 impressions = $120.00; 25,000 impressions = $300.00; 50,000 impressions = $500
News services: AP, NYT. **Established:** 1803
Own Printing Facility?: Yes
Commercial Printers?: Yes
Special Editions: Southeastern Wildlife; Komen Race for the Cure; Cooper River Bridge Run; Volvo Cup Open; Spoleto; My Charleston Visitor Guide, My Charleston Holiday; Boat Parade; Holocaust; Progress SC; Pigskin Preview
Special Weekly Sections: Business (Mon); Automotive (Fri); Real Estate (Sat); Health (Mon); Food (Weds); Entertainment (Thurs); Home & Real Estate, Arts & Culture (Sun); People, Real Estate (Sat); Faith and Values (Sat)
Syndicated Publications: Parade
Proprietary Publications: Lowcountry Parent (monthly); Tideline (bi-monthly); North Charleston Magazine (3x/yr)
Digital Platform - Mobile: Apple, Android
Digital Platform - Tablet: Apple iOS, Android, Kindle, Kindle Fire
Dir., Audience Development .... Kurt Knapek
Editorial Page Ed. .... Charles Rowe
Pub. .... Pamela Browning
Communications and Community Relations Mgr. .. Robie Scott
Executive Editor .... Mitch Pugh
Senior Director, Interactive Sales .... Brad Boggs
President of Shared Services .... Ron Cartledge
Retail Advert. .... Jamie Drolet
Assist. to Pub .... Becky Baulch
Managing Ed. .... Rick Nelson
News Prod. Ed. .... Betsy Miller
Assoc. Ed. .... Elsa McDowell
Bus. and Tech. Ed. .... John McDermott
Sales and Mktg. Mgr .... Andy Morgan
Transportation/Distrb. Mgr. .... Lisa Rule
Strategic Mktg. Dir. .... Chris Zoeller
VP of Audience Development for Evening Post Industries .... John Posluszny
VP of Evening Post Publishing Newspaper Group .. Lynn McLamb
Feature's Ed. .... Theresa Taylor
Adv. Dir. .... Scott Embry
Market Information: Split run; TMC; Zoned editions.
Mechanical Available: Offset; Black and 3 ROP colors; Sticky Notes accepted; insert accepted - card stock, outserts, poly bags; page cutoffs - 22.
Mechanical Specifications: Page Size:
10.625" wide x 21"
Editorial Specs:
6 columns (10.625" or 10 5/8") wide.
Individual column width is 1.667"
with 1/8" between columns
ROP Ad Specs:
6 columns 10.625" wide.
Individual column width is 1.667"
with 1/8" between columns
Classified Ad Specs:
9 columns (10.625" or 10 5/8") wide.
Individual column width is 1.069"
with 1/8" between columns
Areas Served: Tri-County Area (Berkeley, Dorchester and Charleston Counties) plus out-lying areas such as Colleton County, Clarendon, Beaufort and Orangeburg, Columbia
Delivery Method: Mail, Newsstand, Carrier, RacksEquipment & Software: PRESSROOM EQUIPMENT: Lines — 10-G/Metroliner (7 half decks)
1979; 10-G/Metroliner (7 Half Decks) 1988; Press Drive — 10-Fin/5126 75 h.p., 10-Fin/5135 100 h.p.; Folders — 2-G/3:2 Double; Reels & Stands — 20; Control System — Goss; Registration System — CCI PRESSROOM SOFTWARE: Goss Press controls MAILROOM EQUIPMENT: Counter Stackers — 2-QWI/400; 4-QWI/500; 2QWI/ Packman; Inserters & Stuffers — 1-HI/2299, 1-HI/1472 1-Titan G60; Tying Machines — 8/ StraPak, 11-SAM/Mosca ROM 2, Wrapping Singles — 4-QWI Vipers, — Controls 1-QWI/CrossBelt; Address Machine — 7 Video Jet Lablers;1 Kodak 5220 Labeler; 3 5203HS Accraply applicators MAILROOM SOFTWARE:Miracom BUSINESS EQUIPMENT: Dell PowerEdge R720/ Win2013 Server/VMWare BUSINESS SOFTWARE: Brainworks A/R, Oracle Fusion AP/GL, Creditron Remittance Processing CLASSIFIED EQUIPMENT: Dell PowerEdge R720/Win2013 Server/VMWare CLASSIFIED SOFTWARE: Brainworks AdPerks, Quark 9.5,Pongrass pagination, Noble Systems call management DISPLAY EQUIPMENT: Dell PowerEdge R720/Win2013 Server/ VMWare, HP Designjet proofers DISPLAY SOFTWAREXpance (PC client), Asura, Creative Suite 6.0, SCS Layout-8000 EDITORIAL EQUIPMENT: Amazon Web Service EDITORIAL SOFTWARE: NewsCycle Mediaware Center, Creative Suite 6.0, BRS News Archive, Newscycle online CMS PRODUCTION EQUIPMENT: Hardware — 2 AGFA Advantage DL platesetters; AGFA Newsdrives; 2 Nela VCPm benders; AGFA RIPs, various HP Designjet proofers PRODUCTION SOFTWARE: ProImage Newsway, AGFA Arkitex Producer and Director, Newsdrive, RIP, Optiink, Autoink and Sublima software. Claro color management

CIRCULATION EQUIPMENT: Hosted CIRCULATION SOFTWARBrainworks CircSmart, Noble Systems call management, Satori mail processing

COLUMBIA

THE STATE

1401 Shop Rd, Columbia, S.C., 29201-4843, Richland; gen tel (800) 888-5353; adv tel (803) 771-8450; ed tel (803) 771-8451; gen fax (803) 771-8430; adv fax (803) 771-8430; ed fax (803) 771-8430; gen/nat adv e-mail bheller@thestate.com; disp adv e-mail llibet@thestate.com; class adv e-mailstateclassified@thestate.com; ed e-mail sbrook@thestate.com; web site www.thestate.com
- 12,000,000(views) 1,700,000(visitors)

Group: The McClatchy Company
Published: Mon, Tues, Wed, Thur, Fri, Sat, Sun
Weekday Frequency: m
Saturday Frequency: m
Circulation: 48,469; 49,469(sat); 61,266(sun)
Last Audit: AAM December 31, 2016
Advertising Rate (weekday/saturday): Open inch rate $158.00
News services: AP, LAT-WP, NYT, MCT. **Established:** 1891
Own Printing Facility?: Yes
Commercial Printers?: Yes
Special Editions: Summer Fun (Apr); Welcome Back USC (Aug); A New Year, A New You (Dec); Body, Health & More (Feb); 20 Under 40 (Jan); CBJ Book of Lists (Jul); Readers Choice (Jun); Rooms & Blooms (Mar); Living Here (May); Faith Guide (Nov); Midlands Health (Oct); CareerBu
Special Weekly Sections: The Extra [TMC] (Wed); Weekend Section (Fri); TV Weekly (Sun)
Syndicated Publications: Weekend (Fri); Lake Murray Columbia Magazine (Monthly); Go Gamecocks (Other); Sunday Comics (S); Wedding Book (Semi-yearly).
Digital Platform - Mobile: Apple, Android, Windows, Blackberry
Digital Platform - Tablet: Apple iOS, Android, Windows 7, Blackberry Tablet OS
Exec. Ed. .... Brian Tolley
Mng. Ed. .... Steve Brook
Managing Ed. for Online .... Gary Ward
Asst. Metro Ed. .... Dawn Kujawa
Assoc. Ed. .... Cindi Scoppe
Assoc. Ed. .... Warren Bolton
Asst. Mng. Ed. .... Eileen Waddell
Info Systems Site Mgr. .... Derek Lawson
Vice Pres., HR .... Diane Frea
Single Copy Mgr. .... Richard Curtis
Pres./Pub. .... Sara Johnson Borton
Market Information: Split run; TMC; Zoned editions.
Mechanical Available: Offset; Black and 3 ROP colors; insert accepted; page cutoffs - 22 1/2.
Mechanical Specifications: Type page 13 x 21; E - 6 cols, 2 1/16, 1/8 between; A - 6 cols, 2 1/16, 1/8 between; C - 10 cols, 1 3/16, 1/16 between.
Areas Served: The State circulates in 26 of 43 counties in South Carolina. Richland, Lexington and southern Kershaw counties make up the core market. The city of Columbia is in Richland County and contains the South Carolina State Capitol, The University of South Carolina and the U.S. Army's Fort Jackson. The city of Lexington is located in Lexington County.
Delivery Method: Mail, CarrierEquipment & Software: PRESSROOM EQUIPMENT: Lines — 14-G/HO (8-decks); 9-G/HO (5 decks); Reels & Stands — 23-G/CT-50; Control System — DEC/11-84, G/MPCS.; MAILROOM EQUIPMENT: Counter Stackers — 4-HL/Systems, 6-HL/HT Stacker; Inserters & Stuffers — 1-HI, SLS 2000; Tying Machines — 8-/MLN, 2-/Power Strap, 2-/Dynaric; Address Machine — 1-Ch/N-3000, 2-Ch/539.; CLASSIFIED EQUIPMENT: Hardware — 2-IBM/RS 6000, AT/Enterprise 50-seat; Printers — 3-All/3850; CLASSIFIED SOFTWARE: AT 4.5.2, Sysdeco Enterprise. DISPLAY EQUIPMENT: Hardware — APP/Mac, Sun ; Printers — V/5000, V/5300E, All/3850; DISPLAY SOFTWAREAd Make-up Applications — QPS/QuarkXPress, Cascade/Adobe InDesign; Layout Software — MEI/ALS 8000. EDITORIAL EQUIPMENT: Hardware — Dell/SAN; Printers — AU/APS 5, 3-All/3850 Kodak CTP EDITORIAL SOFTWARE: CCI PRODUCTION EQUIPMENT: Hardware — WL/Anocoil Processor, 1-AU/5u, AU/APS-6, III/3850, 1-P/ML26, 1-LE/TEK26, 3-LS/2600; Cameras — 1-C/Marathon, 1-C/Spartan III; Scanners — CD/645IE PRODUCTION SOFTWARE: QPS/QuarkXPress.

FLORENCE

MORNING NEWS

310 S Dargan St, Florence, S.C., 29506-2537, Florence; gen tel (843) 317-6397; adv tel (843) 317-7257; gen fax (843) 317-7291; adv fax (843) 317-7290; ed fax (843) 317-7292; gen/nat adv e-mail pgray@florencenews.com; disp adv e-mail pgray@florencenews.com; class adv e-mailclloyd@florencenews.com; ed e-mail cnews@florencenews.com; web site www.scnow.com 900,000(visitors)

Group: BH Media Group
Published: Mon, Tues, Wed, Thur, Fri, Sat, Sun
Weekday Frequency: m
Saturday Frequency: m
Circulation: 13,611; 13,611(sat); 18,216(sun)
Last Audit: AAM March 31, 2017
Advertising Rate (weekday/saturday): Open inch rate $50.00
Advertising Rate (sunday): Open inch rate $53.00
News services: AP, SHNS.
Special Editions: Car Care Directory (Apr); Back-To-School (Aug); Christmas Guide (Dec); Furniture Selection (Feb); Super Bowl Preview (Jan); Grilling Made Easy (Jul); Summer Daze (Jun); Speed-Darlington Race (Mar); Mother's Day Gift Guide (May); Chamberlink (Monthly); Bas
Special Weekly Sections: Best Food Days (Wed/Sun);
Syndicated Publications: USA WEEKEND Magazine (S).
Controller .... John McElwee
Adv. Mgr., Interactive Sales .... Michelle Marlowe
Circ. Dir. .... David Johnson
News Ed. .... Kimberly Ginfrida
Sports Ed. .... Sam Bundy
Asst. Sports Ed. .... Mark Haselden
Prodn. Dir. .... John Barlow
Prodn. Foreman, Mailroom .... Ray Reynolds
Prodn. Foreman, Pressroom .... Mark Attaway
Pub. .... Mark Blum
VP, Adv. .... Mark Wilson
Reg. Pub. .... Joseph Craig
Prod. Dir. .... Gary Snider
Regional Adv. Dir. .... Robin Walker
Market Information: TMC.
Mechanical Available: Offset; Black and 3 ROP colors; insert accepted - card stock; page cutoffs - 20 3/4.
Mechanical Specifications: Type page 12 x 20 1/2; E - 6 cols, 2 1/16, 1/8 between; A - 6 cols, 2 1/16, 1/8 between; C - 9 cols, 1 5/16, 1/8 between.Equipment & Software: PRESSROOM EQUIPMENT: Lines — 12-DGM/850 single width 1998; 12-DGM/850 single width; Press Drive — 2-GE/150 h.p., 4; Folders — 1-DGM/1050, 1-DGM/1030.; MAILROOM EQUIPMENT: Counter Stackers — MSI/220, Id, C/Marathon, Compass; Inserters & Stuffers — MM/308 Biliner, GMA/SLS 1000; Tying Machines — MLN/Spirit, Samuel/NT 1000; Wrapping Singles — Id/Bottom wrap; BUSINESS EQUIPMENT: HP/K900 Server BUSINESS SOFTWARE: Unix/Informix, Newzware, Microsoft/Word, Microsoft/Excel, Microsoft/Power Point CLASSIFIED EQUIPMENT: Hardware — PC; Printers — APP/Mac LaserWriter; CLASSIFIED SOFTWARE: HI/AdPower. DISPLAY EQUIPMENT: Hardware — APP/Mac; Printers — 1-Xante/8300; Other Hardware — PixelCraft/11 x 17 Scanner 8200 DISPLAY SOFTWAREAd Make-up Applications — Multi-Ad/Creator2 1.5, Adobe/Illustrator 6.0, Aldus/FreeHand 7.0, Search, Macromedia/FreeHand 7.0, Search; Layout Software — 1-Page Director, 1-MEI/ALS. EDITORIAL EQUIPMENT: Hardware — PC/Umax/Scanner, APP/Mac Workstation, Photo Scanner, APP/Server; Printers — LaserWriter/II NTX, Xante/Accel-a-Writer. PRODUCTION EQUIPMENT: Hardware — Caere/OmniPage, Pre Press/Panther Pro 46 (with Punch); Cameras — COM/C618C, COM/C660C, COM/C680C; Scanners — COM/C680C PRODUCTION SOFTWARE: Multi-Ad/Creator 2 1.5, QPS/QuarkXPress 3.32.

GREENVILLE

THE GREENVILLE NEWS

305 S Main St, Greenville, S.C., 29601-2605, Greenville; gen tel (864) 298-4100; adv tel (864) 298-4216; ed tel (864) 298-4321; gen fax (864) 298-4805; adv fax (864) 298-4023; ed fax (864) 298-4395; gen/nat adv e-mail krogers@greenvillenews.com; disp adv e-mail krogers@greenvillenews.com; ed e-mail localnews@greenvillenews.com; web site www.greenvilleonline.com

Group: Gannett
Published: Mon, Tues, Wed, Thur, Fri, Sat, Sun
Weekday Frequency: m
Saturday Frequency: m
Circulation: 38,890; 41,194(sat); 56,650(sun)
Last Audit: AAM September 30, 2016
Advertising Rate (weekday/saturday): Open inch rate $160.25
Advertising Rate (sunday): Open inch rate $176.25
News services: AP, LAT-WP, MCT, SHNS, TMS, GNS. **Established:** 1874
Special Editions: Guide to Greenville (Apr); High School Football (Aug); Late Christmas Gift Guide (Dec); Southern Home & Garden (Feb); Spring Bride (Jan); Best of the Upstate (Jul); Early Christmas Gift Guide (Nov); Progress (Oct).
Special Weekly Sections: TV, Community, Sports, Business, Lifestyle (Daily); Technology, Health, Lifestyle (Tue); City, Lifestyle, Food (Wed); Kids, NASCAR, Fashion, Lifestyle (Thur); Weekend, Entertainment (Fri); Auto, Religion (Sat); TV, Home, Business, Careers, Comics, Lifestyles, Art, Travel (Sun)
Syndicated Publications: USA WEEKEND Magazine (S).
Editorial Page Ed. .... Beth Padgett
Food Ed. .... Wanda Owings
Mng. Ed. .... Bill Fox
Reporter .... David Dykes
VP Market Devl and New Media .... Susan Schwartzkopf
City people writer .... Donna Walker
VP, Marketing .... Susan Schwartzkopf-Deanne
VP, Sales, General Mgr. .... Orestes Baez
Content Strategist .... Dave Hennigan
Exec. Ed. .... Katrice Hardy
Market Information: ADS; Split run; TMC; Zoned editions.
Mechanical Available: Offset; Black and 3 ROP colors; insert accepted - as requested; page cutoffs - 22.
Mechanical Specifications: Type page 11 5/8 x 21; E - 6 cols, 1 5/6, 1/8 between; A - 6 cols, 1 5/6, 1/8 between; C - 10 cols, 1 1/9, 1/20 between.Equipment & Software: PRESSROOM EQUIPMENT: Lines — 8-G/Metroliner double width 1983; 4-G/Headliner double width 1992, 4-G/Headliner double width 1984; Pasters —G/Hall EffectReels & Stands — 16; Control System — G/PCS II; Registration System — Hand Wheel/Side MAILROOM EQUIPMENT: Counter Stackers — 4-QWI/350, 4-QWI/400; Inserters & Stuffers — 14-GMA/SLS, 26-GMA/SLS; Tying Machines — 8/Dynaric, 3-EAM-Mosca; Control System — GMA/SAM; Address Machine — 3-Wm/hand labelers, 1-/KR; BUSINESS EQUIPMENT: IBM/Netinity PC Server, IBM/AS-400 BUSINESS SOFTWARE: Gannett, Genesys/V01 M08: Advertising, Gannett, Genesys/V01 M08: Circulation, Microsoft/Exchange Server 2000 E-mail System, Microsoft/Office 2000: Desktop Suite, Lawson/R6 (GL and AP): Finance, Cyb CLASSIFIED EQUIPMENT: Hardware — Dell/Pentium 133; HI/CPAG; Printers — Epson/DFX 5000; CLASSIFIED SOFTWARE: HI/windows cash. DISPLAY EQUIPMENT: Hardware — 2-Dell/Pentium; Printers — 2-HP/LaserJet 5; Other Hardware — HI/3-8900 Scanner Interface PCs, HI/Autocopy SIPC, APP/Super Mac G7, 4-HS/Images WS DISPLAY SOFTWAREAd Make-up Applications — SCS/Layout 8000 7.03; Layout Software — SCS/Layout 8000. EDITORIAL EQUIPMENT: Hardware — HI/XP-21/Lf/AP Server, 110-HI/Newsmaker Editorial terminal, AU/108S, AU/3850, 70-Ethernet Network; Printers — Typhoon/Graphics pagescan 3 EDITORIAL SOFTWARE: HI/8900, HI/XP-21 Newsmaker. PRODUCTION EQUIPMENT: Hardware — Konica, LE, X/7650, Scitex, Eskoscan/20245; Cameras — C/Spartan III; Scanners — 2-X/7650, Eskoscan/20245 PRODUCTION SOFTWARE: HI/Newsmaker Pagination 8.4.

GREENWOOD

THE INDEX-JOURNAL

610 Phoenix St, Greenwood, S.C., 29646-3253, Greenwood; gen tel (864) 223-1411; adv tel (864) 943-2509; ed tel (864) 223-1811; gen fax (864) 223-7331; ed fax (864) 223-7331; gen/nat adv e-mail bduncan@indexjournal.com; disp adv e-mail bduncan@indexjournal.com; class adv e-mailbduncan@indexjournal.com; ed e-mail rwhiting@indexjournal.com; web site www.indexjournal.com

Published: Mon, Tues, Wed, Thur, Fri, Sat, Sun
Weekday Frequency: m
Saturday Frequency: m
Circulation: 11,054; 11,054(sat); 12,369(sun)
Last Audit: AAM September 30, 2015
Advertising Rate (weekday/saturday): Open inch rate $23.10
Advertising Rate (sunday): Open inch rate $24.95
News services: AP, NEA. **Established:** 1919
Own Printing Facility?: Yes
Commercial Printers?: Yes
Special Editions: Parents Magazine (Spring & Fall) School Children ages 1-5 (Monthly)
Special Weekly Sections: Best Food Day (Wed);
Syndicated Publications: Parade (S).
CEO/Pres./Pub. .... Judith M. Burns
Exec. News Ed. .... Richard Whiting
Web Page Ed. .... Bob Simmonds
Prodn. Foreman, Mailroom .... Kevin Coleman
Circ. Mgr. .... Albert Ashley
Business Mgr. .... Nichole Varnum
Advertising Director .... Ed Gunderson
Market Information: Split run; TMC.
Mechanical Available: Offset; Black and 3 ROP colors; insert accepted; page cutoffs - 22 3/4.
Mechanical Specifications: Type page 13 x 21 1/2; E - 6 cols, 1 5/6, 1/8 between; A - 6 cols, 1 5/6, 1/8 between; C - 6 cols, 1 5/6, 1/8 between.
Areas Served: Counties of: Greenwood, Abbeville, McCormick,
Delivery Method: Carrier, RacksEquipment & Software: PRESSROOM EQUIPMENT: Lines — HI/Cotrell 845 1971; 5-HI/Cotrell 845 1971; 1-HI/Cotrell 845 1987; Control System — 1-1971.; MAILROOM EQUIPMENT: Counter Stackers — BG/109; Inserters & Stuffers — 2/MM; Tying Machines — MLN.; CLASSIFIED EQUIPMENT: Hardware — FSI, Microsoft/Windows NT Server; CLASSIFIED SOFTWARE: Mk, Oaracle/8, FSI/Advance Sales, QPS/QuarkXPress. DISPLAY EQUIPMENT: Hardware — APP/Mac; Printers — LaserMaster/1200, APP/Mac LaserWriter NTX; Other Hardware — APP/Mac CD-Rom, APP/Mac Scanner. EDITORIAL EQUIPMENT: Hardware — Mk, Microsoft/Windows NT Server EDITORIAL SOFTWARE: Oracle/8, FSI/METS, QPS/QuarkXPress, Mk. PRODUCTION EQUIPMENT: Hardware — 1-Nat; Cameras — 1-VG/Daylighter, 1-C/Spartan III.

MYRTLE BEACH

THE SUN NEWS

914 Frontage Rd E, Myrtle Beach, S.C., 29577-6700, Horry; gen tel (843) 626-8555; adv tel (843) 626-0240; ed tel (843) 626-0319; gen fax (843) 626-0208; adv fax (843) 626-0328; ed fax (843) 626-0356; gen/nat adv e-mail display@thesunnews.com; disp adv e-mail display@thesunnews.com; class adv e-mailclassifieds@thesunnews.com; ed e-mail spedersen@thesunnews.com; web

site www.myrtlebeachonline.com
- 11,100,000(views) 578,953(visitors)
Group: The McClatchy Company
Published: Mon, Tues, Wed, Thur, Fri, Sat, Sun
Weekday Frequency: m
Saturday Frequency: m
Circulation: 28,450; 28,452(sat); 37,881(sun)
Last Audit: AAM September 30, 2016
Advertising Rate (weekday/saturday): Open inch rate $62.00
Advertising Rate (sunday): Open inch rate $71.72
Online Advertising Rate: 1 Color $36.00/M (Full-Run); $43.00/M (Part Run); 2 Colors $41.00/M (Full-Run); $48.00/M (Part Run); Full Color $46.00/M (Full-Run); $53.00/M (Part Run).
News services: AP, NYT, MCT. **Established:** 1936
Special Editions: Home Improvement (Apr); Community Resource Guide (Aug); NASCAR (Feb); Volunteer of the Year (Jan); Health-Themed 2 (Jun); Myrtle Beach Hospitality Job Fair (Mar); Graduation (May); Design An Ad (Nov); Health-Themed 3 (Oct); Finance (Sept).
Special Weekly Sections: Best Food, Health, Dining Out (Wed); Neighbors (Thur); Entertainment (Fri); Homes, Gardens (Sat); Travel, Real Estate, People, Arts, Books, TV (Sun); Money, Business (Tue-Sun);
Syndicated Publications: Parade (S).
Digital Platform - Mobile: Apple, Android, Windows, Blackberry
Digital Platform - Tablet: Apple iOS, Android, Windows 7, Other
Pub...Mark Webster
VP, Adv....Fred Benson
Ed...Carolyn Murray
Op. Mgr......................................Lynette Dudley
Audience Dev. Dir. ....Jake Gervin
Market Information: ADS; Split run; TMC; Zoned editions.
Mechanical Available: Offset; Black and 3 ROP colors; insert accepted - spadea; page cutoffs - 21.
Mechanical Specifications: Type page 11 1/2 x 21; E - 6 cols, 1 11/16, 1/6 between; A - 6 cols, 1 11/16, 1/6 between; C - 10 cols, 1 1/20, 1/6 between.
Areas Served: Horry County
Delivery Method: Mail, Newsstand, Carrier, RacksEquipment & Software: PRESSROOM EQUIPMENT: Lines — 6-G/Headliner offset double width (4 half decks); Folders — 1-G/3:2, 1-KAN/Quarterfolder Labeler; Pasters —6-G/CT50; Control System — 1-G/MPCS.; MAILROOM EQUIPMENT: Counter Stackers — HL/Monitors, HL/HT, HL/HT II, S/Olympian, QWI/400; Inserters & Stuffers — 1-MM/275, S/472-NP100 Gripper System; Tying Machines — 1/MLN, 1-/Power Strap, 3-/Dynaric; Address Machine — 1-/Quarterfolder Labeler, KAN/600.; BUSINESS EQUIPMENT: HP/3000 model 947, HP/9000 model E55 BUSINESS SOFTWARE: CJ CLASSIFIED EQUIPMENT: Hardware — 1-Cybergraphics, 1-Cybergraphics; CLASSIFIED SOFTWARE: MS/NT 4.0, Cyber$ell. DISPLAY EQUIPMENT: Hardware — 16-APP/Mac, Sun/Sparc 10; Printers — QMS/2060; Other Hardware — 16-Flatbed Scanners DISPLAY SOFTWAREAd Make-up Applications — QPS/QuarkXPress 4.0, GEAC, All/Ad Manager; Layout Software — GEAC/World Class Series. EDITORIAL EQUIPMENT: Hardware — 5-AT, DEC/Alpha/8-APP/Mac; Printers — 2-QMS/2060, 1-HP/5000, 2-HP/1050C EDITORIAL SOFTWARE: AT 4.5.3, GEAC/Cybergraphics, GEAC/Cybernews, GEAC/Cyberpage 1.4.3. PRODUCTION EQUIPMENT: Hardware — Caere/OmniPage 3.0, 1-Nu/Flip Top FT40APRNS63, Adobe/Photoshop 5.5, C/66F; Cameras — 1-R/500, 1-C/Spartan II 1244 PRODUCTION SOFTWARE: Cybergraphics, AU/Oman NT.

ORANGEBURG

THE TIMES AND DEMOCRAT

1010 Broughton St, Orangeburg, S.C., 29115-5962, Orangeburg; gen tel (803) 533-5500; adv tel (803) 534-3352; ed tel (803) 534-1060; gen fax (803) 533-5557; adv fax (803) 533-5526; ed fax (803) 533-5595; gen/nat adv e-mail kfraser@timesanddemocrat.com; disp adv e-mail kfraser@timesanddemocrat.com; ed e-mail lharter@timesanddemocrat.com; web site www.theTandD.com
- 1,700,000(views) 220,000(visitors)
Group: Lee Enterprises, Inc.
Published: Mon, Tues, Wed, Thur, Fri, Sat, Sun
Weekday Frequency: m
Saturday Frequency: m
Circulation: 7,911; 7,911(sat); 8,773(sun)
Last Audit: AAM March 31, 2016
Advertising Rate (weekday/saturday): Open inch rate $23.95
Advertising Rate (sunday): Open inch rate $25.14
News services: AP. **Established:** 1881
Own Printing Facility?: Yes
Commercial Printers?: No
Special Editions: Home Improvement (Apr); Football (Aug); Greetings (Dec); Progress (Feb); Bridal (Jan); Car Care (Jun); Spring Fashion (Mar); Health & Fitness (May); Gift Guide (Nov); Car Care (Oct).
Special Weekly Sections: Sports, Local, Classifieds (Daily); Farm, Garden, Events (Mon); Business, NIE, Marketplace, Health (Tue); Best Food Day, Business, Markets (Wed); Business, Arts, Leisure, Community, Markets (Thur); Church, Markets, Religion (Fri); Classifieds, Real Estate, Sports, Outdoors, TV, Comics, Weddings, Home Decor, Special Sections, Local, Kids (Sun)
Syndicated Publications: Relish (Monthly); USA WEEKEND Magazine (S); American Profile (Weekly).
Digital Platform - Mobile: Apple, Android, Windows, Blackberry
Digital Platform - Tablet: Apple iOS, Android, Windows 7, Blackberry Tablet OS, Kindle, Nook, Kindle Fire
Pub./Adv. Dir...........................Cathy C. Hughes
Controller..................................Barbara Beach
Adv. Dir...Kayla Wiser
Mktg./Promo.....................................Carla Hall
City Ed.......................................Jeanne Crader
Editorial Page Ed................................Lee Harter
Features Ed................................Wendy Crader
Photographer..................................Larry Hardy
Regl. Ed......................................Carol Barker
Sports Ed........................................Brian Linder
Asst. Pub................................Georgianne Walton
Mgmt. Info Servs. Mgr. ....Jerry Harvill
Prodn. Mgr.....................................Jim Spears
Prodn. Mgr., Distr...............Barbara West-Ravenell
Prodn. Foreman, Pressroom............Russell Cain
Nat'l Adv. Mgr....................................Missy Hutto
Market Information: TMC; Zoned editions.
Mechanical Available: Offset; Black and 3 ROP colors; insert accepted; page cutoffs - 21.
Mechanical Specifications: Type page 13 x 21; E - 6 cols, 2 1/16, 1/8 between; A - 6 cols, 2 1/16, 1/8 between; C - 9 cols, 1 1/4, 1/8 between.
Delivery Method: Mail, Newsstand, Carrier, RacksEquipment & Software: PRESSROOM EQUIPMENT: Lines — 7-G/Urbanite; Folders — 1-G/Urbanite w/balloon former; Registration System — Stoesser/Register Systems. MAILROOM EQUIPMENT: Counter Stackers — 2-Id/Marathon, TMSI/HT2 Stacker; Inserters & Stuffers — 1/MM; Tying Machines — 2-Si, 1-/OVL.; BUSINESS EQUIPMENT: Sun/Microsys 410 CLASSIFIED EQUIPMENT: Hardware — 4-Sun/Microsys 4-110, 3-Sun/Sparc Station; CLASSIFIED SOFTWARE: IslandWrite 4.1, HP/LaserJet IIlp. DISPLAY EQUIPMENT: Hardware — APP/Mac, APP/Mac G3; Printers — 1-HP/Laserjet 4050N, 1-HP/Laserjet 5000GN, 1-HP Laserjet 4V; Other Hardware — 1-Epson/836 XL Color Scanner, 1-HP/Sc DISPLAY SOFTWAREAd Make-up Applications — QPS/QuarkXPress 4.04, Adobe/Illustrator 8.0, Adobe/Acrobat 4.0, Adobe/Photoshop 5.5; EDITORIAL EQUIPMENT: Hardware — PC, APP/Mac, APP/Mac G3/1-APP/Mac Scanner, 1-Artec/Viewstation ATIZ scanner, 1-AGFA/Horizon flatbed scanner, 1-Epson/836 XL Color Scanner, 1-HP/Scanjet 5p Scanner; Printers — 1-Lexmark/Optra Lxi, 1-HP/Laserjet IIlp EDITORIAL SOFTWARE: Lotu PRODUCTION EQUIPMENT: Hardware — Caere/OmniPage 8.0, 1-LE; Cameras — 1-C PRODUCTION SOFTWARE: QPS/QuarkXPress 4.04.

ROCK HILL

THE HERALD

132 W Main St, Rock Hill, S.C., 29730-4430, York; gen tel (803) 329-4000; adv tel (803) 329-4322; ed tel (803) 329-4073; gen fax (803) 909-4202; adv fax (803) 329-4028; ed fax (803) 329-4021; gen/nat adv e-mail webmaster@heraldonline.com; disp adv e-mail mpettus@heraldonline.com; class adv e-mailssancickle@heraldonline.com; ed e-mail posmundson@heraldonline.com; web site www.heraldonline.com
- 3,000,000(views) 500,000(visitors)
Group: The McClatchy Company
Published: Mon, Tues, Wed, Thur, Fri, Sat, Sun
Weekday Frequency: m
Saturday Frequency: m
Circulation: 13,693; 13,949(sat); 16,914(sun)
Last Audit: AAM June 30, 2015
Branch Offices: Fort Mill Times, The Lake Wyli Pilot, (York) Enquirer-Herald
Advertising Rate (weekday/saturday): Open inch rate $29.56
Advertising Rate (sunday): Open inch rate $32.04
Online Advertising Rate: Ruler (300x100): $4.00 CPM; Medium Rectangle (300x250): $8.00 CPM; Leaderboard (728x90): $7.00 CPM
News services: AP, LAT-WP, McClatchy, DF, SHNS, NYT. **Established:** 1872
Own Printing Facility?: No
Commercial Printers?: Yes
Special Editions: Come See Me (Apr); Back-to-School (Aug); Last Minute Gift Guide (Dec); York County Magazine (Feb); Health Horizons (Jan); Health Horizons (Jun); Newspapers in Education Student Stories (Mar); Emergency Medical Services (May); Wrap-up Christmas Early (Nov)
Special Weekly Sections: Automotive (Fri); TV Herald (S); Home & Real Estate (Sat); Star Watch (Wed).
Syndicated Publications: Parade (Fri).
Digital Platform - Mobile: Apple, Android, Blackberry
Digital Platform - Tablet: Apple iOS, Windows 7, Blackberry Tablet OS
Pres./Pub.....................................Debbie Abels
Adv. Mgr.................................Sonya Van Sickle
Ed....Paul Osmundson
Editorial Page Ed..........................James Werrell
Photo Ed...Andy Burriss
Advertising Director.......................Mary Pettus
Market Information: ADS; TMC.
Mechanical Available: Offset; Black and 3 ROP colors; insert accepted - books, envelopes; page cutoffs - 22 3/4.
Mechanical Specifications: Type page 11 1/2 x 21 1/2; E - 6 cols, 1 13/16, 1/8 between; A - 6 cols, 1 13/16, 1/8 between; C - 9 cols, 1 1/6, 1/16 between.
Areas Served: York, Chester, Lancaster, South Carolina
Delivery Method: Mail, Newsstand, Carrier, RacksEquipment & Software: PRESSROOM EQUIPMENT: Lines — 10-G/Urbanite, 1-DEV; Press Drive — 2-GE/150 h.p. DC; Folders — G/Urbanite 1000 Series 2:1; Reels & Stands — 2; MAILROOM EQUIPMENT: Counter Stackers — Id, HL, QWI; Inserters & Stuffers — HI/848, HI/1372; Tying Machines — NT 40 Samuel; Address Machine — Wink Jet; BUSINESS EQUIPMENT: HP/3000-918 RX BUSINESS SOFTWARE: CJ CLASSIFIED EQUIPMENT: Hardware — 1-APP/Power Mac 7300/266, 6-APP/Power Mac G3/300; Printers — HP/Laser Jet 4300 dtns; CLASSIFIED SOFTWARE: Baseview/Ad Manager/Pro 2.0.6. DISPLAY EQUIPMENT: Hardware — 5-APP/Mac G4, 11-APP/Mac G3; Printers — HP/Laserjet 8000N; Other Hardware — Scanners, Film Scanners (35 mm), digital cameras DISPLAY SOFTWAREAd Make-up Applications — Adobe/Photoshop 7.0, QPS/QuarkXPress 4.1, Macromedia/Freehand 10; Layout Software — Managing Editor/ALS, ALS/Page Di EDITORIAL EQUIPMENT: Hardware — APP/iMac, 15-APP/Mac G4, 3-APP/Mac G3, 23-APP/iMac/Nikon/LS-3510AF, Kk/RFS 2035 Plus; Printers — HP/Laser Jet 8100 EDITORIAL SOFTWARE: News Edit/Pro I QUE 3.4.3. PRODUCTION EQUIPMENT: Hardware — Caere/OmniPage Pro 8, Accuset/1500 Plus, HP/Laserjet 8000N PRODUCTION SOFTWARE: QPS/QuarkXPress 4.0.

SENECA

DAILY JOURNAL/MESSENGER

210 W North 1st St, Seneca, S.C., 29678-3250, Oconee; gen tel (864) 882-2375; gen fax (864) 882-2381; web site www.upstatetoday.com
Published: Tues, Wed, Thur, Fri, Sat
Weekday Frequency: m
Saturday Frequency: m
Circulation: 9,676; 9,676(sat)
Last Audit: Sworn/Estimate/Non-Audited September 30, 2017
Advertising Rate (weekday/saturday): (Modular Rates) Back Cover- $1440; Inside Front/Inside Back- $1200; Page 3,5,7- $1080; Full Page- $900; 2/3 Page- $810; 1/2 Page- $660; 1/3 Page- $570; 1/6 Page- $354
News services: AP, DF, DJ.
Own Printing Facility?: Yes
Commercial Printers?: Yes
Syndicated Publications: American Profile (Weekly).
Owner...Jerry Edwards
Office Mgr......................................Linda Garren
Circ. Dir...Scott Nickels
Graphics Coord................................Vicki Tymon
Sports Ed....................................Steven Bradley
Pressroom Mgr..............................Michael Watts
Pub....Hal Welch
Adv. Dir........................................Pierce Sandra
Mechanical Available: Offset; Black and 3 ROP colors; insert accepted; page cutoffs - 22.
Mechanical Specifications: Type page 11 1/2 x 21; E - 6 cols, 1 13/16, between; A - 6 cols, 1 13/16, between; C - 6 cols, 1 13/16, between.
Delivery Method: Newsstand, Carrier, Racks

SPARTANBURG

HERALD-JOURNAL

189 W Main St, Spartanburg, S.C., 29306-2334, Spartanburg; gen tel 864-562-7470; adv tel (864) 582-4511; ed tel (864) 582-4511 ext. 7210; adv fax (864) 594-6349; ed fax (864) 594-6350; gen/nat adv e-mail caralyn.bess@shj.com; disp adv e-mail caralyn.bess@shj.com; class adv e-mailnancy.hogsed@shj.com; ed e-mail chris.horeth@shj.com; web site www.goupstate.com
- 4,300,000(views) 499,512(visitors)
Group: New Media Investment Group
Published: Mon, Tues, Wed, Thur, Fri, Sat, Sun
Weekday Frequency: m
Saturday Frequency: m
Circulation: 10,624; 10,624(sat); 11,158(sun)
Last Audit: AAM March 31, 2016
Newspaper Reps: Michael Smith, Exec. Ed.
Caralyn Bess, Dir. of Adv.
Rick Bremmer, Reg. Dir. of Finance
Ken Smith, Dir. of Ops.
Marlene Smith, Dir. of HR
Advertising Rate (weekday/saturday): Open inch rate $63.19
Advertising Rate (sunday): Open inch rate $65.09
News services: AP, NYT, MCT. **Established:** 1842
Own Printing Facility?: No
Commercial Printers?: No
Special Editions: Football (3) Prep, College, Band (Aug); Stroller Cookbook (Oct) Gift Guide (Dec); Auto Racing (Feb); Prime Time (Jun); Lawn & Garden/Home Improvement (Mar); Showcase of Homes (May); Automotive Showcase (Nov); Arts Council (Sept).
Special Weekly Sections: Best Food (Wed); Financial (Tue-Sun); Entertainment (Thur); Real Estate, Lifestyle (Fri); Religion (Sat); Travel (Sun)
Proprietary Publications: Spartanburg Magazine
Digital Platform - Mobile: Apple, Android, Windows
Digital Platform - Tablet: Apple iOS, Android, Windows 7
Ent. Writer......................................Jose Franco
Dir. of Cir....Ken Smith
Exec. Ed...Mike Smith
Night Ed.......................................Dan Sullivan
Pub...Larry Riley
Dir. of Adv......................................Caralyn Bess

Assist.City Ed. .... Jason Spencer
Reg. Dir. of Finance .... Rick Bremmer
Dir .of HR .... Marlene Smith
Sports Ed. .... Robert Dalton
Asst. Managing Ed./Dig. .... Tom Priddy
Pub. .... Kevin Drake
Market Information: TMC.
Mechanical Available: Offset; Black and 3 ROP colors; insert accepted; page cutoffs - 22.
Mechanical Specifications: Type page 13 x 21 1/4; E - 6 cols, 2 1/16, 1/8 between; A - 6 cols, 2 1/16, 1/8 between; C - 9 cols, 1 3/8, 1/16 between.
Areas Served: Spartanburg, Cherokee & Union Counties
Delivery Method: Mail, Newsstand, Carrier, RacksEquipment & Software: PRESSROOM EQUIPMENT: Lines — 8-G/Headliner (4 color decks); Folders — 1-G/3:2; Pasters —G/CT 45. MAILROOM EQUIPMENT: Counter Stackers — 3-Id/2000; Inserters & Stuffers — 1-HI/1472; Tying Machines — 3/ Power Strap/PSN5; Address Machine — 1-/KR.; BUSINESS EQUIPMENT: IBM/ AS-400 36 BUSINESS SOFTWARE: INSI, Microsoft/Excel CLASSIFIED EQUIPMENT: Hardware — AT/Series 4; Printers — Dataproducts/8500; CLASSIFIED SOFTWARE: AT/IAS. DISPLAY EQUIPMENT: Hardware — 9-APP/Mac Quadra Graphics Workstation; Printers — APP/Mac LaserWriter II NTX, APP/Mac Select 360F; Other Hardware — 1-Hayes/ Accura 144, Fox/144 Data Modem. DISPLAY SOFTWAREAd Make-up Applications — QPS/QuarkXPress 3.3.1, Multi-Ad, Adobe/ Photoshop 3.0.4; EDITORIAL EQUIPMENT: Hardware — AT/Series 4/APP/Mac II fx, APP/Mac IIci, AG/Arcus Scanners, 2-APP/ Power Mac 8100-80; Printers — APP/Mac LaserWriter NTX, HP/4MV EDITORIAL SOFTWARE: AT. PRODUCTION EQUIPMENT: Hardware — Typereader 1.1, 2-Pre Press/Panther Pro, 1-APP/Mac Scanner; Cameras — 1-C/Spartan; Scanners — ECR/Autokon 1000DE, 3-AG/Arcus, 2-Umax/2400x. CIRCULATION EQUIPMENT: DTI

SUMTER

THE SUMTER ITEM

20 N Magnolia St, Sumter, S.C., 29150-4940, Sumter; gen tel (803) 774-1200; adv tel (803) 774-1256; ed tel (803) 774-1226; gen fax (803) 775-1024; adv fax (803) 774-1288; ed fax (803) 774-1210; gen/nat adv e-mail angela@theitem.com; disp adv e-mail Jack@theitem.com; class adv e-mailKathy@theitem.com; ed e-mail news@theitem.com; web site www.theitem.com
- 1,000,000(views) 100,000(visitors)
Group: Creative Circle Media Solutions
The Iris Digital Agency
Published: Tues, Wed, Thur, Fri, Sat, Sun
Weekday Frequency: m
Saturday Frequency: m
Circulation: 10,113; 10,113(sat); 11,307(sun)
Last Audit: VAC June 30, 2016
Advertising Rate (weekday/saturday): Modular: starting at cube sizes - $35 plus
Advertising Rate (sunday): Modular: starting at cube sizes- $35 plus
Online Advertising Rate: Leaderboard top $375/ Corner peel back $475/Right Rail /ROS $350/ Center Banner $250/ Anchor $175/
News services: AP, SC Press **Established:** 1894
Own Printing Facility?: No
Commercial Printers?: Yes
Special Editions: Gift Guide (Dec); Bride & Groom (Jan); Weddings (Jun); Home & Gardens (Mar); Readers Choice (June);Summertime (May); Parade of Shops (Nov); Extraordinary Women (Oct);Life is Good (Jan); Chamber Guide (July); Meet the Professionals (September); Football Guide (Aug)
Special Weekly Sections: Local Events & Activities (Fri); The Mini Page (Mon); History/ Community (S); Religion (Thursday); Kids Scoop (Thur); Career Connection (Tues); Recipes & Ideas (Wed). Clarendon Sun (Thurs)
Syndicated Publications: Parade (S); Relish, Spree, Athlon Sports
Digital Platform - Mobile: Apple, Windows
Digital Platform - Tablet: Apple iOS, Windows 7
Co-Pres .... Graham Osteen
Ed. & Pub./VP .... Jack Osteen
CEO .... Larry Miller
Co-Pres .... Kyle Osteen
Chairman .... Hubert D. Osteen
Feat. Ed. .... Ivy Moore
Univ. Desk Mgr. .... Rhonda Barrick
Managing Ed. .... Rick Carpenter
Sports Ed. .... Dennis Brunson
Jeff West
Market Information: TMC; Zoned editions.
Mechanical Available: Offset; Black and 3 ROP colors; insert accepted - min. 4 x 6; page cutoffs - 21 1/2.
Mechanical Specifications: Type page 12 1/2 x 21 1/2; E - 6 cols, 2 1/16, 1/6 between; A - 6 cols, 2 1/16, 1/6 between; C - 8 cols, 1 1/2, 1/12 between.
Areas Served: Sumter County, Clarendon County, Lee County
Delivery Method: Mail, Newsstand, Carrier, RacksEquipment & Software: MAILROOM EQUIPMENT: Counter Stackers — 1-BG/ Count-O-Veyor, 2/QWI; Inserters & Stuffers — 1-MM/6:1; Tying Machines — 2-/ Dynaric; Wrapping Singles — 1-/QWI; Address Machine — 1-/KAN; CLASSIFIED EQUIPMENT: Hardware — Newsware; Printers — Various; DISPLAY EQUIPMENT: Hardware — APP/Mac; Printers — HP/ LaserJet IV, HP/DeskWriter C, APP/ Mac Personal LaserWriter; DISPLAY SOFTWAREAd Make-up Applications — QPS/QuarkXPress, Multi-Ad/Creator, Aldus/ FreeHand, Adobe/Illustrator, In-Design, Microsoft/Word, Microsoft/Excel 4.0, Claris/ MacDraw II; EDITORIAL EQUIPMENT: Hardware — Newsware; Printers — Various PRODUCTION EQUIPMENT: Hardware — 2-ECR/Pelbox 3850, Adobe/Photoshop, 1-Konica/4000, 1-Digi-Colour; Cameras — 1-Nu; Scanners — 1-AU, 5-Flatbed/Scanner.
Note: OPC News, LLC - Clay Today, Ponte Vedra Recorder, Car Connection (Northern Florida)
Las Cruces (NM) Bulletin; Gulf Coast Newspapers (Southern Alabama)

UNION

UNION DAILY TIMES

201 N Herndon St, Union, S.C., 29379-2210, Union; gen tel (864) 427-1234; adv tel (864) 427-1234; ed tel (864) 427-1234; gen fax (864) 427-1237; adv fax (864) 427-1237; ed fax (864) 427-1237; gen/nat adv e-mail dmcmurray@civitasmedia.com; disp adv e-mail dmcmurray@civitasmedia.com; ed e-mail pedwards@civitasmedia.com; web site www.uniondailytimes.com
- 119,450(views) 23,408(visitors)
Group: Civitas Media, LLC-OOB
Published: Tues, Wed, Thur, Fri, Sat
Weekday Frequency: e
Saturday Frequency: m
Circulation: 6,409; 6,409(sat)
Last Audit: Sworn/Estimate/Non-Audited September 30, 2017
Branch Offices: Civitas Media Group
Advertising Rate (weekday/saturday): Open inch rate $12.50
Online Advertising Rate: Above the Fold: $14.40; Below the Fold: $11.70; Mobile: $22.50
News services: NEA, AP. **Established:** 1850
Own Printing Facility?: Yes
Commercial Printers?: No
Special Editions: Gardening (Apr); Football (Aug); Christmas (Dec); FYI-For Your Information (Jan); Graduation (May); Uniquely Union Festival (Oct); NASCAR Prime Time (Seniors) (Quarterly).
Syndicated Publications: American Profile (Sat).
Mng. Ed. .... Charles Warner
Market Information: Split run; TMC.
Mechanical Available: Offset; Black and 3 ROP colors; insert accepted; page cutoffs - 21 1/2.
Mechanical Specifications: Type page 12 1/2 x 21 1/2; E - 6 cols, 2, 1/8 between; A - 6 cols, 2, 1/8 between; C - 9 cols, 1 1/3, 1/8 between.
Areas Served: Union County
Delivery Method: MailEquipment & Software: PRESSROOM EQUIPMENT: Lines — 9-KP/News King (KJ-8 balloon former); Press Drive — GE/100 h.p.; Control System — 8-ATR/Tensioning System 1981.; MAILROOM EQUIPMENT: Counter Stackers — 1-BG/Count-O-Veyor; Inserters & Stuffers — KANSA; Tying Machines — 2-Miller/Bevco Strapmatic.; BUSINESS EQUIPMENT: PC BUSINESS SOFTWARE: BSI CLASSIFIED EQUIPMENT: Hardware — APP/Mac; Accuset/1200; Printers — APP/ Mac LaserWriter II NTX, HP/LaserJet; CLASSIFIED SOFTWARE: Baseview. DISPLAY EQUIPMENT: Hardware — APP/ Mac; Printers — APP/Mac LaserWriter II NTX, Accuset/1200, HP/LaserJet; DISPLAY SOFTWAREAd Make-up Applications — QPS/QuarkXPress, Aldus/PageMaker, Aldus/ FreeHand, Adobe/Photoshop, Baseview; Layout Software — APP/Mac Quadra. EDITORIAL EQUIPMENT: Hardware — APP/Mac/Accuset/1200, Konica/Jetsetter 3100; Printers — APP/Mac LaserWriter II NTX EDITORIAL SOFTWARE: Baseview. PRODUCTION EQUIPMENT: Hardware — Accuset, Konica/Jetsetter 3100; Cameras — SCREEN; Scanners — AG/Arcus, Abaton, Nikon PRODUCTION SOFTWARE: QPS/ QuarkXPress 3.32.

SOUTH DAKOTA

ABERDEEN

ABERDEEN AMERICAN NEWS

124 S 2nd St, Aberdeen, S.D., 57401-4010, Brown; gen tel (605) 225-5555; ed tel (605) 622-2300; gen fax (605) 229-7532; adv fax (605) 229-3954; ed fax (605) 225-0421; gen/nat adv e-mail corwig@aberdeennews.com; disp adv e-mail corwig@aberdeennews.com; class adv e-mailclassified@aberdeennews.com; ed e-mail swaltman@aberdeennews.com; web site www.aberdeennews.com
Group: Schurz Communications Inc
Published: Mon, Tues, Wed, Thur, Fri, Sat, Sun
Weekday Frequency: m
Saturday Frequency: m
Circulation: 11,485; 11,485(sat); 12,801(sun)
Last Audit: CAC September 30, 2013
Advertising Rate (weekday/saturday): Open inch rate $27.20
Advertising Rate (sunday): Open inch rate $29.75
News services: AP, MCT. **Established:** 1885
Special Editions: Back-to-School (Aug); Christmas Gift Guide (Dec); Dakota Decades (Other); Spring Car Care (Spring).
Special Weekly Sections: Scrapbook, Education, Humor (Mon); College Sports, American Profile (Tue); Taste (Wed); Out and About, Entertainment, Prep Sports (Thur); Farm, Outdoors (Fri) Church (Sat); Comics, Dakota Living (Sun)
Syndicated Publications: Relish (Monthly); USA Weekend (Sat); Parade (S); American Profile (Weekly).
Dir., Finance .... Lori Salfrank
Dir., HR .... Amy Jones
Adv. Dir. .... Christy Orwig
Circ. Dir. .... David Nelson
Sports Ed. .... John Papendick
Women's Ed. .... Jeff Bahr
Management Info Service Mgr. ...... Marcia Sebert
Prod. Mgr. .... Terry Salfrank
Pub .... Cory Bollinger
Adv. Sales Mgr. .... Dee McKibben
Market Information: TMC.
Mechanical Available: Offset; Black and 3 ROP colors; insert accepted; page cutoffs - 22 3/4.
Mechanical Specifications: Type page 12 1/2 x 21 1/2; E - 6 cols, 2, 1/8 between; A - 6 cols, 2, 1/8 between; C - 9 cols, 1 1/4, 1/8 between. Equipment & Software: PRESSROOM EQUIPMENT: Lines — 7-G/Urbanite single width 1973; MAILROOM EQUIPMENT: Counter Stackers — 1-Id/NS440, 1-QWI/350, QWI/400; Inserters & Stuffers — 1-MM/227S (10 station); Tying Machines — 1/Power Strap/PSN6E; Address Machine — 1-Ch/528-010; BUSINESS EQUIPMENT: 1-HP/3000-5Y 937 RX BUSINESS SOFTWARE: CJ, GEAC/AIM 8.02, GEAC/CIS 4.0.1.H, GEAC/2.09.M CLASSIFIED EQUIPMENT: Hardware — DTI; Printers — HP/Laserjet 5000; CLASSIFIED SOFTWARE: DTI/ ClassSpeed. DISPLAY EQUIPMENT: Hardware — APP/Mac G3; DISPLAY SOFTWAREAd Make-up Applications — Multi-Ad/Creator 4.01, QPS/QuarkXPress 4.1; Layout Software — DTI/Speed Planner. EDITORIAL EQUIPMENT: Hardware — DTI; Printers — HP/Laserjet 5000 EDITORIAL SOFTWARE: DTI. PRODUCTION EQUIPMENT: Hardware — 2-AU/APS-6600, 1-AU/APS-6-82-ACS, AU/APS6-84ACS, Pre Press/Panther Plus 46, Pre Press/Panther Pro 62; Cameras — 1-B/4000, 1-C/Spartan II; Scanners — Lf/Leafscan 35 PRODUCTION SOFTWARE: QPS/QuarkXPress 3.3.

BROOKINGS

BROOKINGS REGISTER

312 5th St, Brookings, S.D., 57006-1924, Brookings; gen tel (605) 692-6271; gen fax (605) 692-2979; gen/nat adv e-mail registeradvertising@brookingsregister.com; disp adv e-mail registeradvertising@brookingsregister.com; class adv e-mailregisteradvertising@brookingsregister.com; web site www.brookingsregister.com
Group: News Media Corp.
Published: Mon, Tues, Wed, Thur, Fri, Sat, Sun
Weekday Frequency: e
Saturday Frequency: m
Circulation: 4,263; 4,263(sat)
Last Audit: Sworn/Estimate/Non-Audited September 30, 2017
Advertising Rate (weekday/saturday): Open inch rate $18.00
News services: AP. **Established:** 1882
Special Editions: Our Town (Aug); Business People (Jun); Progress (Mar).
Special Weekly Sections: Local, Community, Regional, national, World, Sports, Editorial, Opinion, Classifieds, Public Notices (Daily); Best ood (Mon); Business, Celebrations (Tue); Agriculture (Wed); Religion (Thur); Outdoor (Fri); TV (Sat)
Syndicated Publications: American Profile (Weekly).
Mgr. .... Kendra Deibert
Adv. Dir. .... William McMacken
News Ed. .... Doug Kott
Managing Ed. .... Ken Curley
Circ. Mgr. .... Steve Kleinsasser
Market Information: TMC.
Mechanical Available: Offset; Black and 3 ROP colors; insert accepted; page cutoffs - 22 3/4.
Mechanical Specifications: Type page 13 x 21 1/2; E - 6 cols, 2, 3/16 between; A - 6 cols, 2, 3/16 between; C - 6 cols, 2, 3/16 between. Equipment & Software: PRESSROOM EQUIPMENT: Lines — 5-G/Community 1971; Folders — 1-G/SC (with upper former).; MAILROOM EQUIPMENT: Tying Machines — 3/Bu; Address Machine — Ch.; BUSINESS SOFTWARE: DSI/Paper Trak 2000 CLASSIFIED EQUIPMENT: Hardware — APP/Power Mac 6100; Dest/PC Scan 2000; Printers — APP/Mac LaserWriter Plus, Xante/1200; CLASSIFIED SOFTWARE: SMS, Baseview/Class Ad. DISPLAY EQUIPMENT: Hardware — APP/Mac SE, APP/Mac with Radius monitors, APP/Power Mac 7100; Printers — APP/Mac LaserWriter Plus, Xante/1200; Other Hardware — QPS/ QuarkXPress. DISPLAY SOFTWAREAd Make-up Applications — Claris/MacDraw, Aldus/FreeHand, Multi-Ad/Creator; Layout Software — QPS/QuarkXPress. EDITORIAL EQUIPMENT: Hardware — APP/Mac/ Dest/PC Scan 2000, Polaroid/SprintScan, APP/Power Mac with Adobe/Photoshop; Printers — APP/Mac Laserwriter II, APP/Mac LaserWriter Plus, Xante/1200 EDITORIAL SOFTWARE: QPS/QuarkXPress, WriteNow. PRODUCTION EQUIPMENT: Hardware — APP/Mac LaserWriter Plus NTX, Xante/1200; Cameras — B/Horizontal PRODUCTION SOFTWARE: QPS/QuarkXPress.

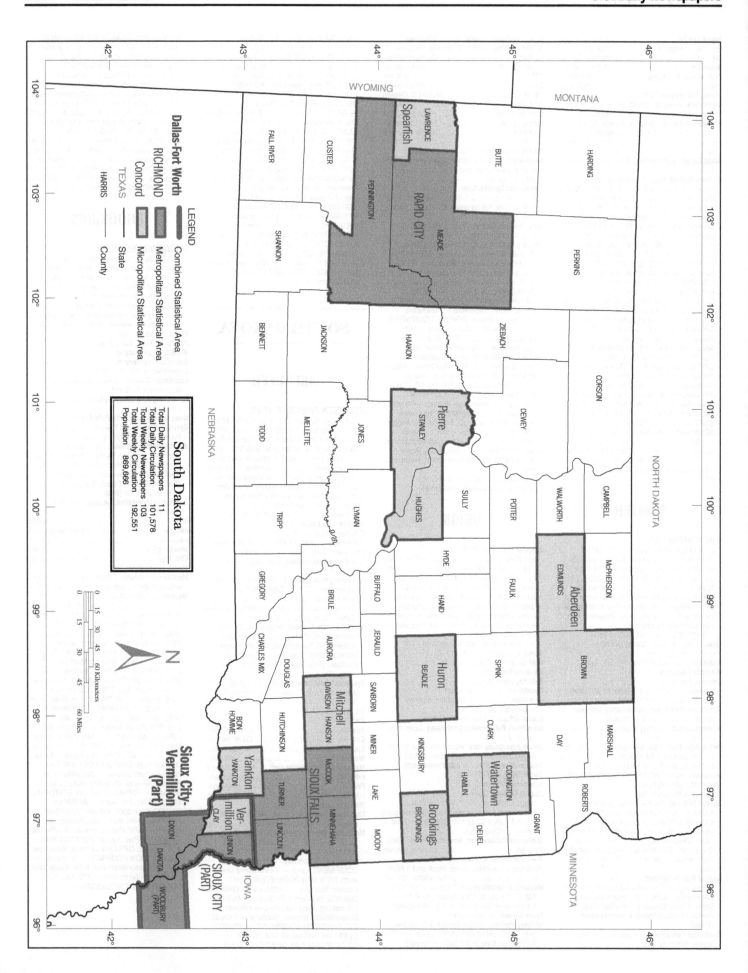

LEGEND

Dallas-Fort Worth — Combined Statistical Area
RICHMOND — Metropolitan Statistical Area
Concord — Micropolitan Statistical Area
TEXAS — State
HARRIS — County

South Dakota

Total Daily Newspapers	11
Total Daily Circulation	101,578
Total Weekly Newspapers	103
Total Weekly Circulation	192,551
Population	869,666

0 15 30 45 60 Kilometers
0 15 30 45 60 Miles

N

HURON

THE DAILY PLAINSMAN

49 3rd St SE, Huron, S.D., 57350-2015, Beadle; gen tel (605) 352-6401; adv tel (605) 353-7421; ed tel (605) 353-7425; gen fax (605) 353-7457; adv fax (605) 353-7422; ed fax (605) 352-7754; gen/nat adv e-mail medemail@aol.com; disp adv e-mail medemail@aol.com; class adv e-mailclassifieds.plainsman@midconetwork.com; ed e-mail editor.plainsman@midconetwork.com; web site www.plainsman.com

Group: Metro Newspaper Advertising Services, Inc.
News Media Corp.
Published: Tues, Wed, Thur, Fri, Sat, Sun
Weekday Frequency: m
Saturday Frequency: m
Circulation: 5,377; 5,377(sat); 5,740(sun)
Last Audit: Sworn/Estimate/Non-Audited September 30, 2017
Advertising Rate (weekday/saturday): Open inch rate $18.15
Advertising Rate (sunday): Open inch rate $18.15
News services: AP.
Own Printing Facility?: Yes
Commercial Printers?: Yes
Special Editions: Hunting (Oct); How to Guide (July); Real Estate Guide (Quarterly);
Special Weekly Sections: Best Food (Wed)
Syndicated Publications: Parade (S).
Pub./Adv. Dir. .... Mark Davis
Political Ed.................................Roger Larsen
Regl. Ed.................................. Crystal Pugsley
Sports Ed. .... Mike Carroll
Ed.. Sean Kelley
Circ. Mgr./Marketing Mgr. .... Kimberly Davis
Market Information: Split run; TMC; Zoned editions.
Mechanical Available: Offset; Black and 3 ROP colors; insert accepted - card, envelope, single sheet; page cutoffs - 13.
Mechanical Specifications: Type page 13 x 21 1/2; E - 6 cols, 2 1/16, 1/8 between; A - 6 cols, 2 1/16, 1/8 between; C - 8 cols, 1 9/16, 1/16 between.
Delivery Method: Mail, Newsstand, Carrier, RacksEquipment & Software: PRESSROOM EQUIPMENT: Lines — 7-G/Community; Folders — 1-G/SC.; MAILROOM EQUIPMENT: Tying Machines — 1-/Bu; Address Machine — 1-/Ch.; BUSINESS EQUIPMENT: 5-IBM BUSINESS SOFTWARE: DSI CLASSIFIED EQUIPMENT: Hardware — 4-PC; Printers — 1-APP/Mac Laser; CLASSIFIED SOFTWARE: APT. DISPLAY EQUIPMENT: Hardware — 4-PC; Printers — 1-Xante/1200 dpi 11 x 17 Laser; Other Hardware — 1-Flatbed Scanner. DISPLAY SOFTWAREAd Make-up Applications — Multi-Ad/Creator, QPS/QuarkXPress 4.0, Adobe/Illustrator; EDITORIAL EQUIPMENT: Hardware — 10-PC, 3-APP/Power Mac, 3-PC Pagination Stations/Polaroid/SprintScan 35; Printers — 1-APP/Mac Laser, 1-LaserMaster/XLO EDITORIAL SOFTWARE: APT, QPS/QuarkXPress 4.0, Adobe/Photoshop 3.0. PRODUCTION EQUIPMENT: Hardware — 1-Nu; Cameras — 1-Nikon, 1-SCREEN/Horizontal.

MADISON

THE MADISON DAILY LEADER

214 S Egan Ave, Madison, S.D., 57042-2911, Lake; gen tel (605) 256-4555; gen fax (605) 256-6190; gen/nat adv e-mail ads@madisondailyleader.com; disp adv e-mail ads@madisondailyleader.com; class adv e-mailclassifieds@madisondailyleader.com; ed e-mail news@madisondailyleader.com; web site www.DailyLeaderExtra.com
Published: Mon, Tues, Wed, Thur, Fri
Weekday Frequency: e
Circulation: 2,750
Last Audit: Sworn/Estimate/Non-Audited October 1, 2017
Advertising Rate (weekday/saturday): Open inch rate $7.30
News services: AP, South Dakota Newspaper Association **Established:** 1880
Own Printing Facility?: Yes
Commercial Printers?: Yes
Special Editions: Prairie Village Jamboree (Aug); Business Review & Forecast (Feb); Bridal Guide (Jan); Homeland Garden (May); Senior Scene (Oct).
Special Weekly Sections: Business (Mon); Best Food (Tue); Agriculture, Health, Fitness (Wed); Real Estate (Fri)
Marketing Mgr. ....Melissa Hegg
City Reporter ....Chuck Clement
Pub...Jon M. Hunter
Sports Ed. .... Larry Leeds
Managing Ed. .... Marcia Schoeberl
Tech. Manager.................................... Jeff Boldt
Classifieds...Alysia Sly
Reporter.. Jane Utecht
Market Information: Split run; TMC.
Mechanical Available: Offset; Black and 3 ROP colors; inserts accepted; page cutoffs - 22 3/4.
Mechanical Specifications: Type page 13 1/10 x 21; E - 6 cols, 2 1/14, 1/8 between; A - 6 cols, 2 1/14, 1/8 between; C - 6 cols, 2 1/14, 1/8 between.
Areas Served: Lake County, Miner County, Moody County, Kingsbury County, Brookings County, McCook County and Minnehaha County.
Delivery Method: Mail, Newsstand, Carrier, RacksEquipment & Software: PRESSROOM EQUIPMENT: Lines — 10 units combo QuadStack/Goss single width; Folders — Atlas; MAILROOM EQUIPMENT: Counter Stackers — 1/BG; Inserters & Stuffers — 1-Mueller-Martini; Tying Machines — 2-/Bu; Wrapping Singles — 1-/Bu; Address Machine — 1-W'Ink Jet; BUSINESS SOFTWARE: Synaptic/Advanced, CYMA/AP, CYMA/Payroll, CYMA/GL CLASSIFIED EQUIPMENT: Hardware — PC; CLASSIFIED SOFTWARE: QPS/QuarkXPress. InDesign DISPLAY SOFTWAREAd Make-up Applications — QPS/QuarkXPress, Adobe/Photoshop, Adobe/Illustrator; EDITORIAL EQUIPMENT: Hardware — PC EDITORIAL SOFTWARE: Suntype/Editorial, Adobe/Photoshop 5.0, QPS/QuarkXPress 4.0. PRODUCTION EQUIPMENT: Hardware — Kodak Trendsetter CTP PRODUCTION SOFTWARE: Evo/Preps IT SOFTWARE:EFI/PSI

MITCHELL

THE DAILY REPUBLIC

120 S Lawler St, Mitchell, S.D., 57301-3443, Davison; gen tel (605) 996-5514; adv tel (605) 996-5515; ed tel (605) 996-5516; gen fax (605) 996-7793; ed fax (605) 996-5020; gen/nat adv e-mail dailyads@mitchellrepublic.com; disp adv e-mail dailyads@mitchellrepublic.com; class adv e-maildailyclass@mitchellrepublic.com; ed e-mail dailynews@mitchellrepublic.com; web site www.mitchellrepublic.com
Group: Forum Communications Co.
Published: Mon, Tues, Wed, Thur, Fri, Sat
Weekday Frequency: m
Saturday Frequency: m
Circulation: 9,453; 9,453(sat)
Last Audit: VAC September 30, 2015
Advertising Rate (weekday/saturday): Open inch rate $18.55
News services: AP.
Special Editions: Car Care Series (Apr); Progress (Aug); Farm & Ranch (Feb); Bridal (Jan); Rodeo (Jul); Bridal (Jun); Home Improvement Series (Mar); Lawn & Garden (May); Christmas Preview (Nov); Hunting Guide (Oct); Fall Home Improvement Series (Sept).
Special Weekly Sections: Best Food Day (Tues)
Syndicated Publications: Relish (Monthly); Parade (S).
Bus. Mgr. .... Annette Kroger
Pub... Korrie Wenzel
Asst. Ed. .... Seth Tupper
Sports Ed. .... Leah Rado
Internet/Systems Mgr. ....Jessy Stroud
Prod. Foreman, Press-room ...... Richard Popejoy
Adv. Dir.... Lorie Hasen
Circ. Mgr...Adam Kaus
Market Information: TMC.
Mechanical Available: Offset; Black and 3 ROP colors; insert accepted; page cutoffs - 22 3/4.
Mechanical Specifications: Type page 13 x 21 1/2; E - 6 cols, 2 1/16, 1/8 between; A - 6 cols, 2 1/16, 1/8 between; C - 9 cols, 1 1/2, 1/16 between.Equipment & Software: PRESSROOM EQUIPMENT: Lines — 7-G/Community; Registration System — Duarte/Pin System. MAILROOM EQUIPMENT: Tying Machines — 2/Carlson; Address Machine — 1-/KR.; BUSINESS EQUIPMENT: ATT, Digital BUSINESS SOFTWARE: Collier-Jackson Inc, Cort CLASSIFIED EQUIPMENT: Hardware — Micron/6200 Prioris PC; Printers — AU/108-2, Dataproducts/Typhoon 16; CLASSIFIED SOFTWARE: MS/Windows 95, APT/ACT. DISPLAY EQUIPMENT: Hardware — APP/Mac; Printers — AU/108-2, Dataproducts/Typhoon 16; Other Hardware — Color Flatbed Scanner, Lf/Leafscan 35 DISPLAY SOFTWAREAd Make-up Applications — Multi-Ad, QPS/QuarkXPress, Adobe/Illustrator, Aldus/FreeHand; Layout Software — 2-HAS, APP/Mac. EDITORIAL EQUIPMENT: Hardware — Micron/6200 Prioris PC/APP/Mac; Printers — AU/108-2, Dataproducts/Typhoon 16 EDITORIAL SOFTWARE: Windows 95, APT/ACT. PRODUCTION EQUIPMENT: Hardware — Nu/Ultra-Plus Flip Top, Dataproducts/Typhoon 16, DTI/Devotec 20; Cameras — 1-R/Press 500, 1-DSA/C-680-C; Scanners — Lf PRODUCTION SOFTWARE: CD, QPS/QuarkXPress 3.32.

PIERRE

CAPITAL JOURNAL

333 W Dakota Ave, Pierre, S.D., 57501-4512, Hughes; gen tel (605) 224-7301; gen fax (605) 224-9210; gen/nat adv e-mail julie.furchner@capjournal.com; disp adv e-mail audrey.lucas@capjournal.com; class adv e-mailjennifer.bieser@capjournal.com; ed e-mail nick.lowrey@capjournal.com; web site www.capjournal.com
Group: Wick Communications
Published: Mon, Tues, Wed, Thur, Fri
Weekday Frequency: e
Circulation: 4,100
Last Audit: Sworn/Estimate/Non-Audited September 30, 2017
Advertising Rate (weekday/saturday): Open inch rate $12.86
News services: AP. **Established:** 1889
Special Editions: 4-H Finals Rodeo Booklet (Aug); Bridal Tab (Feb); Legislative (Jan); Crazy Days Downtown (Jul); Fourth of July Rodeo (Jun); Home & Garden/Real Estate Tab (Mar); Graduation Brochure (May); Chamber Brochure (Nov); Fire Prevention Tab (Oct); Hunting Guide Bo
Special Weekly Sections: Best Food Day (Tue); Entertainment, TV, Auto, Real Estate (Fri)
Syndicated Publications: Reminder Plus (Wed).
Managing Ed. .... Lance Nixon
Productions Mgr. ....Ray Pfeffer
Asst. Managing Ed..........................Nick Lowrey
Sports Ed...Gidal Kaiser
Circ Mgr..Ray Taylor
Adv Consultant..............................Laura Fischbach
Adv. Consultant ....Julie Furchner
Adv Consultant...........................April Schroeder
Market Information: ADS; TMC.
Mechanical Available: Offset; Black and 3 ROP colors; insert accepted; page cutoffs - 22 3/4.
Mechanical Specifications: Type page 13 x 21 1/2; E - 6 cols, 2 1/16, 1/8 between; A - 6 cols, 2 1/16, 1/8 between; C - 8 cols, 1 9/16, 1/8 between.Equipment & Software: PRESSROOM EQUIPMENT: Lines — 7-G/Community.; MAILROOM EQUIPMENT: Tying Machines — 2-Bu/String Tyer, OVL; Address Machine — 1-Ch/Model E base, 1-/Wm.; BUSINESS EQUIPMENT: 6-IBM/AT CLASSIFIED EQUIPMENT: Hardware — Imac; Printers — APP/Mac LaserWriter; CLASSIFIED SOFTWARE: MediaSpan DISPLAY EQUIPMENT: Printers — APP/Mac LaserWriter, Xante; Other Hardware — Epson/800 Scanner DISPLAY SOFTWARELayout Software — APP/Mac. EDITORIAL EQUIPMENT: Hardware — PC; Printers — APP/Mac LaserWriter, Xante/8200. EDITORIAL SOFTWARE: InDesign PRODUCTION EQUIPMENT: Hardware — TextBridge; Cameras — Nikon; Scanners — Polaroid/SprintScan, AG/Arcus II, Epson/800.

RAPID CITY

RAPID CITY JOURNAL

507 Main St, Rapid City, S.D., 57701-2733, Pennington; gen tel (605) 394-8300; adv tel (605) 394-8331; ed tel (605) 394-8314; gen fax (605) 394-8446; adv fax (605) 394-8462; ed fax (605) 394-8463; gen/nat adv e-mail news@rapidcityjournal.com; disp adv e-mail brandyn.crawford@rapidcityjournal.com; class adv e-mailbrandyn.crawford@rapidcityjournal.com; ed e-mail bart.pfankuch@rapidcityjournal.com; web site www.rapidcityjournal.com
- 6,141,454(views) 1,637,855(visitors)
Group: Lee Enterprises, Inc.
Published: Mon, Tues, Wed, Thur, Fri, Sat, Sun
Weekday Frequency: m
Saturday Frequency: m
Circulation: 16,686; 16,686(sat); 21,234(sun)
Last Audit: AAM March 31, 2016
Advertising Rate (weekday/saturday): Open inch rate $53.76
Advertising Rate (sunday): Open inch rate $61.95
Online Advertising Rate: Floating Bar Ad $32 CPM; Home Page $34 CPM; ROS $14 CPM
News services: AP, LAT-WP, SHNS. **Established:** 1878
Commercial Printers?: Yes
Special Weekly Sections: Black Hills Weekend (Fri); Health & Fitness (Mon); Living (S); Religion (Sat); Home & Garden (Thur); Sports (Tues); Food (Wed).
Syndicated Publications: Relish (Monthly); Parade (S); Athlon Sports (Monthly).
Digital Platform - Mobile: Apple, Android, Windows
Prodn. Dir......................................Mark Gibbens
Publisher.................................Shannon Brinker
Managing Editor ....Jim Stasiowski
Market Information: Split run; TMC; Zoned editions.
Mechanical Available: Offset; Black and 3 ROP colors; insert accepted; page cutoffs - 22.
Mechanical Specifications: Type page 11 5/8 x 21; E - 6 cols, 2 1/16, 1/8 between; A - 6 cols, 2 1/16, 1/8 between; C - 9 cols, 1 3/8, 1/8 between.
Areas Served: Western SD, Eastern WY, Northern NE
Delivery Method: Mail, CarrierEquipment & Software: PRESSROOM EQUIPMENT: Lines — 5-G/Headliner double width (4-color decks); 8-G/Community single width; Reels & Stands — 5; MAILROOM EQUIPMENT: Counter Stackers — 4-HL/monitor; Inserters & Stuffers — 1-MM/227E, 1-HI/1372; Tying Machines — 5/MLN; Address Machine — 1-/Ch.; CLASSIFIED EQUIPMENT: Hardware — PC; CLASSIFIED SOFTWARE: CText, Microsoft/Windows NT. DISPLAY EQUIPMENT: Hardware — APP/Power Mac; Other Hardware — ALS. DISPLAY SOFTWAREAd Make-up Applications — Multi-Ad/Creator, Adobe/Photoshop, QPS/QuarkXPress; EDITORIAL EQUIPMENT: Hardware — PC EDITORIAL SOFTWARE: Quick Wire, QPS/QuarkXPress, Microsoft/Word, Microsoft/Windows NT. PRODUCTION EQUIPMENT: Hardware — Nu/FlipTop, Na/FX VIII; Cameras — C/Spartan III; Scanners — Umax, AG PRODUCTION SOFTWARE: QPS/QuarkXPress 4.1.

SIOUX FALLS

ARGUS LEADER

200 S Minnesota Ave, Sioux Falls, S.D., 57104-6314, Minnehaha; gen tel (605) 331-2200; adv tel (605) 331-2355; ed tel (605) 331-2332; gen fax (605) 331-2260; adv fax (605) 331-2371; ed fax (605) 331-2294; gen/nat adv e-mail editor@argusleader.com; disp adv e-mail allegals@argusleader.com; class adv e-mailClassifieds@argusleader.com; ed e-mail editor@argusleader.com; web site www.argusleader.com
- 4,800,000(views) 550,000(visitors)
Group: Gannett

Published: Mon, Tues, Wed, Thur, Fri, Sat, Sun
Weekday Frequency: m
Saturday Frequency: m
Circulation: 25,485; 25,485(sat); 36,341(sun)
Last Audit: AAM June 30, 2017
Advertising Rate (weekday/saturday): Open inch rate $74.00
Online Advertising Rate: Leaderboard (728x90): $7.00; LRG Rectangle (300x250): $8.00; Half Page (300x600): $16.00
News services: AP, GNS, MCT. **Established:** 1881
Pres./Pub. .... Randell Beck
Dir., Admin./Controller .... Greg Robinson
Principal HR Business Partner .... Jean Healy
Advertising Director .... Kelly Redfearn
Executive Editor .... Maricarrol Kueter
Managing Editor .... Patrick Lalley
Consumer Exp. Dir./News .... Cory Myers
Sports Editor .... Stu Whitney
Circulation Director .... Owen Hotvet
Marketing Director .... Sherry Szadziewicz
Production Manager .... Allen Jungels
IT Manager .... Mike Golden
Adv. Mgr., Retail .... Kristi Grooms
Mechanical Available: Offset; Black and 3 ROP colors; insert accepted - inquire; page cutoffs - 22 3/4.
Mechanical Specifications: Type page 12 1/2 x 21 1/2; E - 6 cols, 2 1/16, 1/8 between; A - 6 cols, 2 1/16, 1/8 between; C - 10 cols, 1 7/32, 1/16 between.
Areas Served: Minnehaha, Lincoln, Turner, McCook
Delivery Method: Mail, Newsstand, Carrier, RacksEquipment & Software: PRESSROOM EQUIPMENT: Lines — 10-HI/1650; Pasters —7-HI/Auto. MAILROOM EQUIPMENT: Counter Stackers — 5-QWI/400; Inserters & Stuffers — 1-HI/632; Tying Machines — 4-Dynaric/NP-1500; Control System — ICN; Address Machine — 1/Ch; BUSINESS EQUIPMENT: Mac & PC CLASSIFIED EQUIPMENT: Hardware — Mac & PC; Printers — HP/Laserjet 4; CLASSIFIED SOFTWARE: Mactive/AdBase DISPLAY EQUIPMENT: Hardware — Mac & PC; DISPLAY SOFTWAREAd Make-up Applications — Indesign, Photoshop; Layout Software — 1-MEI/ALS, 13-MEI/ALS Page Director EDITORIAL EQUIPMENT: Hardware — Mac & PC EDITORIAL SOFTWARE: QPS/QuarkXPress 4.11, Copy Desk 2.11, QPS 2.11. PRODUCTION EQUIPMENT: Hardware — AP/Server PRODUCTION SOFTWARE: Indesign

SPEARFISH

BLACK HILLS PIONEER

315 Seaton Cir, Spearfish, S.D., 57783-3212, Lawrence; gen tel (605) 642-2761; adv tel (605) 642-2761; ed tel (605) 642-2761; gen fax (605) 642-9060; adv fax (605) 642-9060; ed fax (605) 642-9060; gen/nat adv e-mail dru@bhpioneer.com; disp adv e-mail dru@bhpioneer.com; class adv e-mailclassifieds@bhpioneer.com; ed e-mail news@bhpioneer.com; web site www.bhpioneer.com
Group: Seaton Group
Published: Mon, Tues, Wed, Thur, Fri, Sat
Weekday Frequency: e
Saturday Frequency: m
Circulation: 4,300; 4,300(sat)
Last Audit: Sworn/Estimate/Non-Audited September 30, 2017
Advertising Rate (weekday/saturday): Open inch rate $12.55
News services: AP. **Established:** 1876
Special Editions: Home Improvement (Apr); Deadwood Rodeo (Aug); Valentine's Day (Feb); New Year's Eve (Jan); 4th of July (Jul); Belle Fourche All Car Rally (Jun); St. Patrick's Day (Mar); Mother's Day (May); Christmas Greetings (Nov); Halloween (Oct); Football Contest (Sep
Special Weekly Sections: Best Food Day (Tue); Real Estate (Wed); Entertainment (Thur); Kids, Lifestyles (Fri); Black Hills State University (Sat)
Syndicated Publications: American Profile (Weekly).
Circ. Mgr. .... Scott Lister
Pub. .... Letitia Lister
Ed. .... Mark Watson
Adv. Sales .... Dru Thomas
Classifieds Adv. Mgr. .... Kari King
Market Information: TMC.
Mechanical Available: Offset; Black and 3 ROP colors; insert accepted - all sizes; page cutoffs - 22 3/4.
Mechanical Specifications: Type page 10 1/4 x 13 1/2; E - 5 cols, 1, 1/12 between; A - 5 cols, 1, 1/12 between; C - 5 cols, 1, 1/12 between.
Areas Served: 57783, 57754, 57732, 57793, 57785, 57779, 57717Equipment & Software: PRESSROOM EQUIPMENT: Lines — 4-G; MAILROOM EQUIPMENT: Tying Machines — 3/Bu; Wrapping Singles — 1-/Bu; Address Machine — 1-/Wm.; BUSINESS EQUIPMENT: APP/Mac II, IBM/XT, APP/Mac, RSK/Tandy 100 CLASSIFIED EQUIPMENT: Hardware — 1-APP/Mac.; DISPLAY SOFTWARELayout Software — 2-APP/Mac. EDITORIAL EQUIPMENT: Hardware — 7-APP/Mac, 7-HI/Compuedit format, 1-APP/Mac/APP/Mac Scanners; Printers — 3-APP/Mac LaserWriter, 1-NewGen/LaserWriter 1200 dpi, 2-HP. PRODUCTION EQUIPMENT: Hardware — B, APP/Mac LaserWriter Plus, APP/Mac NT, APP/Mac NTX; Cameras — 1-B/4000; Scanners — 2-APP/Mac Scanner.

WATERTOWN

WATERTOWN PUBLIC OPINION

120 3rd Ave NW, Watertown, S.D., 57201-2311, Codington; gen tel (605) 886-6901; gen fax (605) 886-4280; disp adv e-mail advertise@thepublicopinion.com; ed e-mail news@thepublicopinion.com; web site www.thepublicopinion.com
- 300,000(views) 100,000(visitors)
Group: Schurz Communications Inc
Published: Mon, Tues, Wed, Thur, Fri, Sat
Weekday Frequency: e
Saturday Frequency: m
Circulation: 9,079; 9,967(sat)
Last Audit: AAM June 30, 2016
Advertising Rate (weekday/saturday): Open inch rate $17.80 for Local and $29.00 for National
Online Advertising Rate: $8/CPM local $11/CPM National
News services: AP. **Established:** 1887
Own Printing Facility?: Yes
Commercial Printers?: Yes
Special Editions: Home & Garden (Apr); Family Resource (Aug); Sports (Aug), Sports (Dec); Farm Show (Feb); Bridal Showcase (Jan); Senior Focus (Jul); Health Tab (Jun); Health Tab (Mar); Winter Car Care (Oct); Fall Sportsman (Sept)
Special Weekly Sections: GoTV Guide, Business Spotlight (Tues); Real Estate Guide, Travel and Events, Good Health, Wedding Page (Weds); Outdoors, Church, Engagements and Anniversaries, Discover Downtown Watertown, Here' s My Card, NFL, NASCAR (Thurs); Farm, Focus on Business, Casino Directory, Coupon Page (Fri); Home Builders (Sat)
Syndicated Publications: Parade (Sat)., Relish (1st Wed of the month)
Digital Platform - Mobile: Apple, Android
Digital Platform - Tablet: Apple iOS, Android, Windows 7, Blackberry Tablet OS, Kindle, Nook, Kindle Fire
Pub. .... Mark S. Roby
Dir., Admin. .... Chris Carter
Sales & Marketing Mgr. .... Tim Oviatt
Circ. Mgr. .... Maureen Linn
Managing Ed. .... Roger Whittle
Sports Ed. .... Roger Merriam
Online Mgr. .... J.T. Fey
Prodn. Mgr., Press .... Dan Sumner
Market Information: ADS; Split run; TMC available.
Mechanical Available: Offset; Black and 3 ROP colors; insert accepted; page cutoffs - 21 1/2.
Mechanical Specifications: Type page 10 7/8 x 21 1/2; E - 6 cols, 10 7/8, 3/16 between; A - 6 cols, 10 7/8, 3/16 between; C - 8 cols, 10 7/8, 1/8 between.
Areas Served: 57201- Codington County Clark County, Day County, Deuel County, Grant County, Hamlin County, Kingsbury County, Roberts County, Big Stone (MN) County, Lac Qui Parle (MN) County, Traverse (MN) County, Yellow Medicine (MN)
Delivery Method: Mail, Newsstand, Carrier, RacksEquipment & Software: PRESSROOM EQUIPMENT: Lines — 5-HI/Cotrell 845 single width; Folders — 1-G and 1-quarterfolder. MAILROOM EQUIPMENT: Tying Machines — 1-Bu/18, 1-Malow/40-M; Address Machine — 1-KAN/650.; Inserter — KAN/480 CLASSIFIED EQUIPMENT: Hardware — APP/Mac; Printers — HP & XEROX Laserprinters CLASSIFIED SOFTWARE: Media Span/AD Manager Pro IV; InDesign CS6.1 (vers 8.1) DISPLAY EQUIPMENT: Hardware — APP/Mac; Printers — HPs; Other Hardware — AG/Flatbed Scanner. DISPLAY SOFTWAREInDesign CS6.1 (vers 8.1) EDITORIAL EQUIPMENT: Hardware — APP/Mac; Printers — HPs EDITORIAL SOFTWARE: InDesign CS6.1 (vers 8.1) PRODUCTION EQUIPMENT: Hardware — Kodak CtP; Cameras — 1-B/1822 PRODUCTION SOFTWARE: InDesign CS6.1 (vers 8.1) CIRCULATION EQUIPMENT: Hardware — MAC CIRCULATION SOFTWARMediaSpan - Circ Pro 5.3.3

YANKTON

YANKTON DAILY PRESS & DAKOTAN

319 Walnut St, Ste 2, Yankton, S.D., 57078-4344, Yankton; gen tel (605) 665-7811; adv tel (605) 665-7811; ed tel (605) 665-7811; gen fax (605) 665-1721; adv fax (605) 665-0288; ed fax (605) 665-1721; gen/nat adv e-mail micki.schievelbein@yankton.net; disp adv e-mail jim.gevens@yankton.net; class adv e-mailtera.schmidt@yankton.net; ed e-mail kelly.hurtz@yankton.net; web site www.yankton.net
- 1,028,000(views) 126,000(visitors)
Group: Yankton Media Inc.
Published: Mon, Tues, Wed, Thur, Fri, Sat
Weekday Frequency: m
Saturday Frequency: m
Circulation: 8,600; 8,600(sat)
Last Audit: Sworn/Estimate/Non-Audited September 30, 2017
Advertising Rate (weekday/saturday): Open inch rate $17.48
Online Advertising Rate: Leaderboard Position 'A' ROS: $11/1000 impressions (728x90); Medium Block Position 'B' ROS: $8/1000 impressions (300x250) ; Medium Block Position 'C' ROS: $5/1000 impressions (300x250)
News services: AP. **Established:** 1861
Own Printing Facility?: Yes
Special Editions: Spring Fashion Tab (Apr); Back-to-School Tab (Aug); Christmas Gift Ideas (Dec); Yankton Health (Feb); Progress (Jun); Weeder's Digest (Mar); Graduation Tab (May); Turkey Give-Away (Nov); Fall Fashion Tab (Oct); Fall Football (Sept). Her Voice Womens Magazine (6x year)
Special Weekly Sections: Business (Mon); Dining & Entertainmeng (Tues); Dining & Entertainment (Thurs); Food, Religion, TV & Entertainment (Fri); Outdoors, Agriculture (Sat)
Syndicated Publications: Relish (Monthly); USA WEEKEND Magazine (Sat); American Profile (Weekly).
Digital Platform - Mobile: Apple, Android, Windows, Blackberry
Digital Platform - Tablet: Apple iOS, Android, Windows 7, Blackberry Tablet OS, Kindle, Nook, Kindle Fire
Ed./Pub. .... Gary Wood
Bus. Mgr. .... Tonya Schild
Adv. Dir. .... Micki Schievelbein
Mng. Ed. .... Kelly Hertz
Regional Ed. .... Randy Dockendorf
Sports Ed. .... James Cimburek
New Media Director .... Beth Rye
Mechanical Available: Offset; Black and 3 ROP colors; insert accepted - packaged material, samples 1/4 thick & under; page cutoffs - 22 3/4.
Mechanical Specifications: Type page 13 x 21 1/2; E - 6 cols, 2 1/16, 1/8 between; A - 6 cols, 2 1/16, 1/8 between; C - 6 cols, 2 1/16, 1/8 between.
Areas Served: Yankton County, Clay County, Bon Homme county, Hutchinson county, Turner County, and various parts of Nebraska
Delivery Method: Mail, Carrier, RacksEquipment & Software: MAILROOM EQUIPMENT: Tying Machines — 2-Bu/1900, 1-Malow/40; Address Machine — 1/X, Ch/515.; BUSINESS EQUIPMENT: Unix/80486 BUSINESS SOFTWARE: PBS CLASSIFIED EQUIPMENT: Hardware — APP/Mac; Printers — APP/Mac ImageWriter, APP/Mac LaserWriter; CLASSIFIED SOFTWARE: Baseview. DISPLAY EQUIPMENT: Hardware — APP/Mac, APP/Mac IIcx, APP/Mac IIsi, APP/Mac SE, APP/Mac with Radius Monitor, 2-APP/Mac Quadra 800, 3-APP/Power Mac 6100, 1-APP/Power Mac 9500-132; Printers — APP/Mac LaserWriter IIq, MON/Express Master 1270; Other Hardware — Other DISPLAY SOFTWAREAd Make-up Applications — Multi-Ad/Creator; EDITORIAL EQUIPMENT: Hardware — APP/Mac/NewGen/Imager Plus; Printers — APP/Mac LaserWriter, MON/ExpressMaster 1270 EDITORIAL SOFTWARE: QPS/QuarkXPress, Baseview/NewsEdit. PRODUCTION EQUIPMENT: Hardware — Caere/OmniPage 2.0, APP/Mac; Cameras — B/Caravel; Scanners — APP/Mac, Nikon, APP/Mac Scanner PRODUCTION SOFTWARE: QPS/QuarkXPress 3.3.

TENNESSEE

ATHENS

THE DAILY POST-ATHENIAN

320 S Jackson St, Athens, Tenn., 37303-4715, McMinn; gen tel (423) 745-5664; gen fax (423) 745-8295; gen/nat adv e-mail sheila.watson@dailypostathenian.com; disp adv e-mail sheila.watson@dailypostathenian.com; class adv e-mailpatricia.mckenzie@dailypostathenian.com; ed e-mail autumn.hughes@dailypostathenian.com; web site www.dailypostathenian.com/
Group: Adams Publishing Group, LLC
Published: Mon, Tues, Wed, Thur, Fri
Weekday Frequency: e
Circulation: 10,000
Last Audit: Sworn/Estimate/Non-Audited September 30, 2017
Advertising Rate (weekday/saturday): Open inch rate $12.50
News services: AP. **Established:** 1848
Own Printing Facility?: Yes
Commercial Printers?: No
Special Editions: Health & Fitness (Apr); Football Contest Pages (Aug); Friendly Fellow Greetings (Dec); Boy Scout Salute (Feb); Income Tax Guide (Jan); Crime Prevention (Jul); Dairy Salute (Jun); Farming Salute (Mar); Keepsake (May); Holiday Cookbook (Nov); Car Care Guide
Special Weekly Sections: Best Food, Education (Wed); Business (Thur); TV, Religion, Weekend (Fri)
Syndicated Publications: Entertainment (Fri).
Pub .... Jeff Schumacher
Adv. Dir. .... Charlie Price
Mng. Ed. .... Richard Edwards
Editorial Writer .... Doug Headrick
Circ. Mgr. .... Tom Cogdell
Lifestyles Ed. .... Autumn Hughes
Sports Ed. .... Jack Slayton
Data Processing Mgr. .... Scott Wall
Prodn. Supt., Pressroom .... James King
Market Information: TMC.
Mechanical Available: Offset; Black and 3 ROP colors; insert accepted - in-house printing; page cutoffs - 22.
Mechanical Specifications: Type page 10 x 21; E - 6 cols, 1.5625, 1/8 between; A - 6 cols, 1.5625, 1/8 between; C - 6cols, 1 5/32, 1/8 between.
Areas Served: 37371
Delivery Method: Newsstand, Carrier, RacksEquipment & Software: PRESSROOM EQUIPMENT: Lines — 8-G; MAILROOM EQUIPMENT: Tying Machines — 2-/MLN, 1-/Mosca; Address Machine — 1-KR/Single Head.; BUSINESS EQUIPMENT: 1-Flex Cache/20386 DT BUSINESS SOFTWARE: Visiondata 6.3 CLASSIFIED EQUIPMENT: Hardware — Intel/Suntype; Printers — APP/Mac Laser Writer Pro

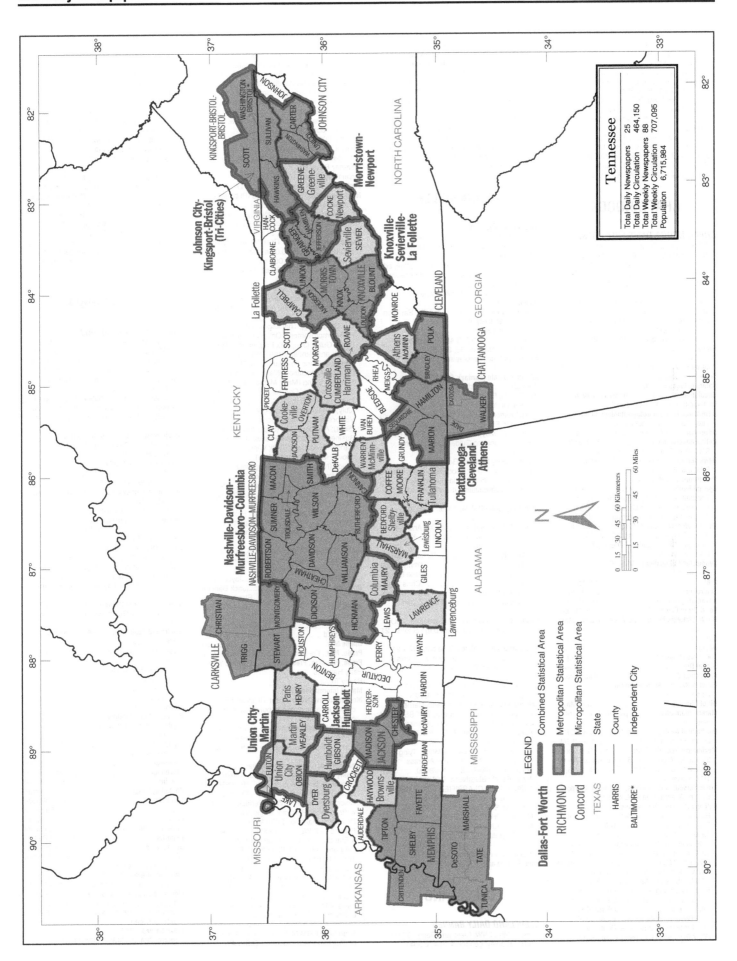

Tennessee

Total Daily Newspapers	25
Total Daily Circulation	464,150
Total Weekly Newspapers	88
Total Weekly Circulation	707,095
Population	6,715,984

LEGEND

Combined Statistical Area
Metropolitan Statistical Area
Micropolitan Statistical Area
State
County
Independent City

Dallas-Fort Worth
RICHMOND
Concord
TEXAS
HARRIS
BALTIMORE*

630, Okidata/Microline 591; CLASSIFIED SOFTWARE: SUN/Suntype 4.2. DISPLAY EQUIPMENT: Hardware — APP/Mac G3; Printers — Dataproduct/Typhoon 8; DISPLAY SOFTWAREAd Make-up Applications — Indesign; Layout Software — APP/Mac G3. EDITORIAL EQUIPMENT: Hardware — 1-Mk, APP/Mac-PC Server NT, 16-APP/Mac G3 & G4, Pentium 11/400 mhz/MON/Imagesetter, ECR/Imagesetter, News Express/Scriptsetter VRL36; Printers — 2-Dataproduct/Typhoon 8 EDITORIAL SOFTWARE: FSI 1.3.0. PRODUCTION EQUIPMENT: Hardware — 1-Nu, 1-Power/PC 8100; Cameras — 1-C/Spartan II PRODUCTION SOFTWARE: FSI 5.0.0.0.

CHATTANOOGA

CHATTANOOGA TIMES FREE PRESS

400 E 11th St, Chattanooga, Tenn., 37403-4203, Hamilton; gen tel (423) 756-6900; adv tel (423)757-6517; ed tel (423) 757-6357; gen fax (423) 757-6337; adv fax (423) 757-6861; ed fax (423) 757-6383; gen/nat adv e-mail lkahana@timesfreepress.com; disp adv e-mail lkahana@timesfreepress.com; class adv e-maildfarmer@timesfreepress.com; ed e-mail agerber@timesfreepress.com; web site www.timesfreepress.com
- 11,133,826(views) 1,613,539(visitors)

Group: NAN LLC
WEHCO Media, Inc.
Published: Mon, Tues, Wed, Thur, Fri, Sat, Sun
Weekday Frequency: m
Saturday Frequency: m
Circulation: 62,403; 47,363(sat); 60,239(sun)
Last Audit: AAM June 30, 2017
Advertising Rate (weekday/saturday): Open inch rate $63.91 and $73.37(Sat)
Advertising Rate (sunday): Open inch rate $84.52
Online Advertising Rate: Leaderboard (728x90) $16.00; In Story (300x250) $15.00
News services: AP, CNS, DF, NYT, SHNS. **Established:** 1869
Own Printing Facility?: Yes
Special Editions: Home Improvements (Apr); Football (Aug); Progress (Feb); Products & Services (Jul); Gift Guide (Nov); Health Trends (Oct); Home Improvements (Sept).
Special Weekly Sections: Chatanooga Weekend (Fri); Lifestyle (Mon); Arts & Travel (S); Lifestyle (Sat); Health & Fitness (Thur); Lifestyle (Wed).
Syndicated Publications: Relish (Monthly); Parade (S).
Pres. .... Jeff DeLoach
Controller .... Paul Abraham
Advertising Director .... Leslie Kahana
Ed. & Dir of Content .... Alison Gerber
Dir. of Strategic Marketing & Audience Dev. .. Mark Jones
Circ. Dir. .... Carroll Duckworth
Region Ed. .... Alex Chambliss
Free Press Page Ed. .... Clint Cooper
Digital Dir. .... Ed Bourn
Production Dir. .... Gary Webb
Major & National Account Executive
Dennis Parker
Dir of Circ Ops .... Frank Maier
Market Information: ADS; Split run; TMC; Zoned editions.
Mechanical Available: Flexo; Black and 3 ROP colors; insert accepted; page cutoffs - 22 3/4.
Mechanical Specifications: Type page 12 1/2 x 21 1/2; E - 6 cols, 2 1/16, 1/8 between; A - 6 cols, 2 1/16, 1/8 between; C - 9 cols, 1 1/3, 1/12 between.
Areas Served: Chattanooga, Nashville, Myrtle Beach, Atlanta, Dalton, Cleveland
Delivery Method: Mail, Newsstand, Carrier, RacksEquipment & Software: PRESSROOM EQUIPMENT: Lines — 10-MAN/Flexoman 1999; Pasters —9-G/Automatic 1972, 10-HOE/Auto 1999Reels & Stands — 9-1972, 10; Control System — 1999; MAILROOM EQUIPMENT: Counter Stackers — 4-Id/2100, 1/QWI, 3-Id/2220; Inserters & Stuffers — 2-MM/375; Tying Machines — 8-/Power Strap; Wrapping Singles — Addressing machine ; 2-/Ch.; BUSINESS EQUIPMENT: IBM/RS-6000, IBM/RS 6000 BUSINESS SOFTWARE: PBS, Lawson CLASSIFIED EQUIPMENT: Hardware — Pentium/III PC, APP/Mac G4; Printers — HP/5000; CLASSIFIED SOFTWARE: DTI. DISPLAY EQUIPMENT: Hardware — APP/Mac G3; DISPLAY SOFTWARELayout Software — Mk/Managing Editor, Mk/Ad Director. EDITORIAL EQUIPMENT: Hardware — 25-APP/Mac G4, 85-APP/iMac; Printers — HP, APP/Mac, NewGen, LaserMaster/Unity 1800 XL EDITORIAL SOFTWARE: Baseview/IQue, Baseview/NewsEdit IQue. PRODUCTION EQUIPMENT: Hardware — 2-OVAC, Na/FP II, 1-Konica/Jetsetter; Cameras — 2-C; Scanners — 1-Sharp/JX-610, Kk, 2-ECR/Autokon, 2-Kk, 1-Duoscan, 1-Arcus PRODUCTION SOFTWARE: QPS/QuarkXPress 4.01.

CLARKSVILLE

THE LEAF-CHRONICLE

200 Commerce St, Clarksville, Tenn., 37040-5101, Montgomery; gen tel (931) 552-1808; adv tel (931) 245-0275; ed tel (931) 245-0282; gen fax (931) 552-5859; ed e-mail cssmith@gannett.com; web site www.theleafchronicle.com
- 3,700,000(views) 302,800(visitors)

Group: Gannett
Published: Mon, Tues, Wed, Thur, Fri, Sat, Sun
Weekday Frequency: m
Saturday Frequency: m
Circulation: 9,273; 9,273(sat); 13,685(sun)
Last Audit: AAM June 30, 2016
Advertising Rate (weekday/saturday): Open inch rate $35.54
Advertising Rate (sunday): $48.19
News services: AP. **Established:** 1808
Own Printing Facility?: Yes
Commercial Printers?: Yes
Special Editions: Football (Aug);Fact Book (Aug); Salute to Fort Campbell (Jun); Vacation/Outdoors (May); Christmas Gift Guide (Nov); Higher Education Guide (Sept) Health (monthly)
Special Weekly Sections: Go-Weekly Entertainment (Fri); Food Days (Mon, Wed); Living Well (Wed) Sunday Living (Sun)
Syndicated Publications: USA WEEKEND Magazine (S).
Digital Platform - Mobile: Apple, Android, Windows, Blackberry
Digital Platform - Tablet: Apple iOS, Android, Windows 7, Blackberry Tablet OS, Kindle, Nook, Kindle Fire
Ed./Gen. Mgr. .... Richard Stevens
Bus. Ed. .... Jimmy Settle
Sr. Ed./Digital .... Alane Megna
Sr. Ed./News .... Chris Smith
Sales/Marketing Dir. .... Carol Daniels
Market Information: Split run; TMC; Zoned editions.
Mechanical Available: Offset; Black and 3 ROP colors; insert accepted - all; page cutoffs - 21 1/2.
Mechanical Specifications: Type page 12 x 21 1/2; E - 6 cols, 2, 1/6 between; A - 6 cols, 2, 1/6 between; C - 10 cols, 1 1/4, 1/12 between.
Areas Served: 37040, 37043, 37042, 37171, 37010, 37191, 37079, 37061, 42223
Delivery Method: Mail, Newsstand, Carrier, RacksEquipment & Software: PRESSROOM EQUIPMENT: Lines — 10-G/Urbanite; Folders — 1, 1.; MAILROOM EQUIPMENT: Counter Stackers — 1-Id/2000; Inserters & Stuffers — 1-HI/624, 1-MM/227; Tying Machines — 2-MLN/ML2EE; Address Machine — 1-MG/602, 1-Am/8000, 1-AVY/5209.; BUSINESS EQUIPMENT: 1-IBM/AS-400 CLASSIFIED EQUIPMENT: Hardware — Mk; 3-IBM/Selectric II.; DISPLAY SOFTWARELayout Software — Mk. EDITORIAL EQUIPMENT: Hardware — Mk. PRODUCTION EQUIPMENT: Hardware — 3M/Pyrofax, 1-LE/PC13; Cameras — 1-B/24, 1-ECR/Autokon; Scanners — 1-Graphic Enterprises/PageScan III.
Note: Printed at GPS/Nashville

CLEVELAND

CLEVELAND DAILY BANNER

1505 25th St NW, Cleveland, Tenn., 37311-3610, Bradley; gen tel (423) 472-5041; adv tel (423) 472-5041; gen fax (423) 476-1046; adv fax (423) 476-1046; ed fax (423) 614-6529; gen/nat adv e-mail advertising@clevelandbanner.com; disp adv e-mail advertising@clevelandbanner.com; classifieds@clevelandbanner.com; class adv e-mailadvertising@clevelandbanner.com; ed e-mail news@clevelandbanner.com; sports@clevelandbanner.com; lifestyles@clevelandbanner.com; web site www.clevelandbanner.com
- 700,000(views) 80,000(visitors)

Group: Cleveland Newspapers, Inc.
Published: Mon, Tues, Wed, Thur, Fri, Sun
Weekday Frequency: e
Circulation: 8,826; 10,364(sun)
Last Audit: AAM December 31, 2017
Newspaper Reps: Stephen Crass (Pub) Jack Bennett (Advertising Director)
Advertising Rate (weekday/saturday): Open inch rate $11.50 for National and $9.90 for Local
Advertising Rate (sunday): $11.50
Online Advertising Rate: Cost flat net by size = 300X250 pixels $240.00 a month. 728 X 90 pixels flat net =$400.00a mounth.
News services: AP. **Established:** 1854
Own Printing Facility?: Yes
Commercial Printers?: No
Special Editions: Baby (Apr); Christmas Greeting (Dec); Progress (Feb); Auto Winterize (Jan); Bride (Jun); Girl Scouts Page (Mar); Spring Car Care (May); Thanksgiving (Nov); Fall Home Improvement (Oct); Football (Sept); Bridal Guide (Jan); Tax Preparation (Jan); Health and Fitness (Mar); Park Care (Mar); Financial Planning (Mar); Ocoe Regional Builders Association (Mar); Graduation (May); Summer Living (May); Mother's Day Special (May); Readers' Choice(Jun); Fathers day (Jun); Back to School (July); Medical Journal (July); Distinguished Young Women (July); Visitor's Guide (Aug); Foothills Country Fair (Sept); All About Pets (Sept); Women in Business (Oct); Apple Festival (Oct); Breast Cancer Awareness (Oct); Winter Sports (Nov); Holiday Recipes (Nov); Holiday Gift Guide (Nov); Christmas Song Book (Dec); Last Minute Holiday Gift Guide (Dec)
Special Weekly Sections: Lifestyles (S); Lifestyles (Wed); Health (S); Education (S); Church News (Fri); School Page (Tues)
Syndicated Publications: American Profile (Fri); Parade maganize(S); Avalon (Sports) (Tues)
Digital Platform - Mobile: Apple, Android, Windows
Digital Platform - Tablet: Apple iOS, Android, Windows 7, Blackberry Tablet OS, Kindle, Nook, Kindle Fire, Other
Credit Mgr. .... Joyce Taylor
Dir., Adv./Promo. .... Jack Bennett
Ed. .... Stephen Crass
Assoc. Ed. .... Gwen Swiger
Librarian .... Mary Matthews
Sports Ed. .... Richard Roberts
Women's Ed. .... Bettie Marlowe
Online Mgr. .... Jim Bryant
Prodn. Mgr., Pre Press .... Carrie Pettit
Prodn. Foreman, Pressroom .... Richard Yarber
Patty Hawkins
Bailey Trena
Market Information: TMC.
Mechanical Available: Offset; Black and 3 ROP colors; insert accepted - polybags; page cutoffs - 21 1/2.
Mechanical Specifications: Type page 11 5/8 x 21 1/2; E - 6 cols, 1 5/6, 1/8 between; A - 6 cols, 1 5/6, 1/8 between; C - 6 cols, 1 5/6, 1/8 between.
Areas Served: Cleveland & Bradley Co
Delivery Method: Mail, Newsstand, Carrier, RacksEquipment & Software: PRESSROOM EQUIPMENT: Lines — 1-WPC/Quadra-Color single width, 4-WPC/Perfector single width; 5-WPC/Perfector single width; Press Drive — 2-Marathon/200 AMP Drives; Folders — 2-Web Leader/Marc-25; Reels & Stands — 9-Web Leader/Marc-25 roll stand.; MAILROOM EQUIPMENT: Tying Machines — Strapex.; BUSINESS EQUIPMENT: 1-Sun/Ultra 5 CLASSIFIED EQUIPMENT: Hardware — 4-APP/Mac; IPC/HSPTR; CLASSIFIED SOFTWARE: Media Span DISPLAY EQUIPMENT: Mac minis, iMacs, Macbooks, Mac Pro Server G-Speed Q TB Firewire, Xerox Phaser Printer, Accel-A-Writer 4N Printer, Epson Scanner, ECRM Mako News CTP, Raptor 68 Polymer Plate Processor DISPLAY SOFTWAREAd Make-up Applications — QPS/QuarkXPress 5.01, News-Edit PRO, Quark Copy Desk, Photoshop Adobe Illustrator, Adobe Acrobat, Word, Multi Ad/Creator 4; Adobe Acrobat, Microsoft Word for Mac EDITORIAL EQUIPMENT: Hardware — Mac Mini; Printers — 1-Xante/Accel-a-Writer 4N, Xerox Phaser 5550DN BW laser printer, Epson Perfection V600 Scanner, Marware Sportfolio Sleeve for 11" MacBook Air case, Kingston FCR-HS219/1 card reader, Iomega GCS1808KITU KVM Switch EDITORIAL SOFTWARE: News Edit Pro,
Quark Copy Desk PRODUCTION EQUIPMENT: Mac minis, iMacs, Macbooks, Mac Pro Server G-Speed Q TB Firewire, Xerox Phaser Printer, Accel-A-Writer 4N Printer, Epson Scanner, ECRM Mako News CTP, Raptor 68 Polymer Plate Processor PRODUCTION SOFTWARE: Ad Make-up Applications — QPS/QuarkXPress 5.01, News-Edit PRO, Quark Copy Desk, Photoshop Adobe Illustrator, Adobe Acrobat, Word, Multi Ad/Creator 4; Adobe Acrobat, Microsoft Word for Mac CIRCULATION SOFTWARDTI

COLUMBIA

COLUMBIA DAILY HERALD

1115 S Main St, Columbia, Tenn., 38401-3733, Maury; gen tel (931) 388-6464; gen fax (931) 388-1003; adv fax (931) 388-4101; disp adv e-mail cduncan@c-dh.net; ed e-mail newsroomc@c-dh.net; web site www.columbiadailyherald.com
- 412,000(views) 68,000(visitors); web site 2 http://advertisernews.biz/; web site 3 http://brentwoodlife.net/; web site 4http://franklinlife.net/

Group: New Media Investment Group
Published: Mon, Tues, Wed, Thur, Fri, Sun
Weekday Frequency: m
Circulation: 7,864; 9,680(sun)
Last Audit: AAM March 31, 2016
Branch Offices: Spring Hill Tennessee
Advertising Rate (weekday/saturday): Open inch rate $13.85
Advertising Rate (sunday): 13.85
Online Advertising Rate: $10.00 per CPM
News services: AP, NEA. **Established:** 1848
Own Printing Facility?: Yes
Commercial Printers?: Yes
Special Editions: Spring Fashion (Apr); Football (Aug); Christmas Greetings (Dec); Bridal (Jun); Graduation (May); Christmas Gift Guide (Nov); Fall Fashion (Sept); Healthy Living (monthly).
Special Weekly Sections: Church Page (Fri); Showtime TV Guide (S); Best Food Day (Wed).
Syndicated Publications: USA WEEKEND Magazine (S).
Proprietary Publications: The Daily Herald Value Guide
The Advertiser News
Franklin Life
Brentwood Life
Man Mag
Healthy Living
Best Of Maury County
Digital Platform - Mobile: Apple, Android, Blackberry
Digital Platform - Tablet: Apple iOS, Android, Kindle, Kindle Fire
Publisher .... Mark Palmer
Office Mgr. .... Betty Stewart
Adv. Dir. .... Craig Duncan
Photo Dept. Mgr. .... Susan Thurman
Sports Ed. .... Marion Wilhoite
IT Dir. .... Fay Hunt
Copy editor .... Alex Miller
Circulation Director .... Fred Schmidt
Reporter .... Samantha Ballard
Sports writer .... Justin Lamb
Ed. .... James Bennett
Market Information: ADS; TMC
Mechanical Available: Offset; Black and 3 ROP colors; insert accepted; page cutoffs - 21 1/2.
Mechanical Specifications: Type page 11 x 21 1/2; E - 6 cols, 1.639", 1/8 between; A - 6 cols, 2 1/16, 1/8 between; C - 8 cols, 1.2, 1/16 between.
Areas Served: 38401; 38402,38482,38483,38474,38461,

8451,37174,37179,38462,38483,38472,370 91,37034
Delivery Method: Mail, Newsstand, Carrier, RacksEquipment & Software: PRESSROOM EQUIPMENT: Lines — 13 unit-/Community; MAILROOM EQUIPMENT: Counter Stackers — Quipp 500; Inserters & Stuffers — Muller 227; Tying Machines — 1 Signode LBX 2000 2 Ty-Tech; Address Machine — Dispensamatic 6 in ; BUSINESS EQUIPMENT: PC/ Mac's BUSINESS SOFTWARE: MPA CLASSIFIED EQUIPMENT: Hardware — Apple; iMacG5; Printers — HP LaserJet; CLASSIFIED SOFTWARE: Ad Manager Pro 4 DISPLAY EQUIPMENT: Hardware — Apple G5; Printers — HP/LaserJet 5100; DISPLAY SOFTWAREAd Make-up Applications — Adobe Suite; EDITORIAL EQUIPMENT: Hardware — APP/Mac, Baseview; Printers — 4-APP/Mac LaserWriter II, 3-APP/Mac LaserWriter Plus. EDITORIAL SOFTWARE: News Engin, Indesign, Quark PRODUCTION EQUIPMENT: Hardware — 2-Mk/Ad Touch, 2-Mk/TouchWriter Plus; Cameras — 1-C/Spartan II; Scanners — 1-APP/ Mac. PRODUCTION SOFTWARE: Panther Fastrack, Plate Setter Raptor 68 Processors

COOKEVILLE

HERALD-CITIZEN

1300 Neal St, Cookeville, Tenn., 38501-4330, Putnam; gen tel (931) 526-9715; gen fax (931) 526-1209; gen/nat adv e-mail advertising@herald-citizen.com; disp adv e-mail advertising@herald-citizen.com; class adv e-mailclassified@herald-citizen.com; ed e-mail editor@herald-citizen.com; web site www.herald-citizen.com
Group: Cleveland Newspapers, Inc.
Published: Mon, Tues, Wed, Thur, Fri, Sun
Weekday Frequency: e
Circulation: 9,352; 11,173(sun)
Last Audit: AAM September 30, 2011
Advertising Rate (weekday/saturday): Open inch rate $12.73
Advertising Rate (sunday): Open inch rate $12.73
News services: AP.
Special Editions: Cookeville Cookoff Community Festival (Aug); Home Show (Feb); Progress (Jan); Venture Tourist Magazine (May); Holidays in Upper Cumberland (Nov).
Special Weekly Sections: Best Food Day (Mon); Local School (Thur); Church, Religious (Fri); Auto (Fri/Sun); Real Estate, Stage, Studio, news, Weddings, Engagements, Farm, Business, News (Sun)
Syndicated Publications: Relish (Monthly); Focus TV Tab (S).
Adv. Mgr. .... David Shelton
Circ. Mgr. .... Keith McCormick
Wire Ed. .... Bob McMillan
Prodn. Mgr. .... Mike DeLapp
Market Information: ADS; TMC; Zoned editions.
Mechanical Available: Offset; Black and 3 ROP colors; insert accepted; page cutoffs - 22 3/4.
Mechanical Specifications: Type page 13 x 21 1/2; E - 6 cols, 2 1/16, 1/8 between; A - 6 cols, 2 1/16, 1/8 between; C - 6 cols, 2 1/16, 1/8 between.Equipment & Software: PRESSROOM EQUIPMENT: Lines — WPC/Leader (4 b/w units;; WPC/Leader (3 b/w units); Reels & Stands — 7-WPC/ Leader; Control System — WPC/Leader.; MAILROOM EQUIPMENT: Tying Machines — MLN/Spirit, Strapex, Minimatic/351; Address Machine — 3/Dispensa-Matic/16.; BUSINESS EQUIPMENT: RSK/4000LX, DEC/XL-466 BUSINESS SOFTWARE: PBS/ MediaPlus CLASSIFIED EQUIPMENT: Hardware — IBM, RSK/Tandy; PB/phone modem; Printers — Panasonic/KX-P1624, APP/Mac LaserWriter Plus; CLASSIFIED SOFTWARE: CText. DISPLAY EQUIPMENT: Hardware — 2-APP/Mac Quadra 700, APP/Mac Quadra; Printers — APP/Mac LaserPrinter, HP/LaserJet; DISPLAY SOFTWAREAd Make-up Applications — Multi-Ad/Creator, Adobe/Illustrator.; EDITORIAL EQUIPMENT: Hardware — Mk; Printers — APP/Mac LaserPrinter, Epson/ Epl 7500 EDITORIAL SOFTWARE: Mk. PRODUCTION EQUIPMENT: Hardware — HP, AG/Arcus Plus Scanner, V/3990; Cameras — SCREEN; Scanners — Umax/ UC 840 PRODUCTION SOFTWARE: QPS/ QuarkXPress 3.3.

DYERSBURG

STATE GAZETTE

294 US Highway 51 Byp N, Dyersburg, Tenn., 38024-3659, Dyer; gen tel (731) 285-4091; adv tel (731) 285-4091 ext. 116; ed tel (731) 285-4091 x111; gen fax (731) 285-9747; adv fax (731) 285-9747; ed fax (731) 285-9747; gen/nat adv e-mail krambo@stategazette.com; disp adv e-mail krambo@stategazette.com; class adv e-mailkrambo@stategazette.com; ed e-mail srouse@stategazette.com; web site www.stategazette.com - 254,000(views) 18,000(visitors)
Group: Rust Communications
Published: Mon, Tues, Wed, Thur, Fri, Sun
Weekday Frequency: e
Circulation: 7,900; 7,900(sun)
Last Audit: Sworn/Estimate/Non-Audited September 30, 2017
Advertising Rate (weekday/saturday): Open inch rate $9.90; Open inch rate $11.09 (Wed)
Advertising Rate (sunday): Open inch rate $9.90
Online Advertising Rate: 10000 impressions-$330.00; 20000 impressions- $430.00
News services: AP. **Established:** 1865
Special Editions: Home Improvement (Apr); Family Business (Aug); Home for the Holidays (Dec); Progress (Feb); NASCAR (Jan); Kitchen & Bath (Jul); Seniors Tab (Jun); Lawn & Garden (Mar); Spring Fashion (May); Holiday Shopping Guide (Nov); Newspaper Week Tab (Oct); Newcomers
Special Weekly Sections: Food (Fri); TV Entertainer (S); Food (Wed).
Syndicated Publications: Relish (Monthly); Parade (S); American Profile (Weekly).
Publisher .... Shelia Rouse
Bus. Mgr. .... Jina Jeffries
Circ. Dir. .... Terry Brock
Mng. Ed. .... Mike Smith
Pressroom Mgr. .... Robert Pollard
Market Information: TMC.
Mechanical Available: Offset; Black and 3 ROP colors; insert accepted - single cards or sheets; page cutoffs - 22 3/4.
Mechanical Specifications: Type page 13 x 21 1/2; E - 6 cols, 2 1/16, 1/8 between; A - 6 cols, 2 1/16, 1/8 between; C - 8 cols, 1 9/16, 1/16 between.
Areas Served: Dyer County
Delivery Method: MailEquipment & Software: PRESSROOM EQUIPMENT: Lines — 8-G.; MAILROOM EQUIPMENT: Tying Machines — 1-Yamada/Tom; Address Machine — 1/ El.; BUSINESS EQUIPMENT: APP/ Mac BUSINESS SOFTWARE: Baseview CLASSIFIED SOFTWARE: Baseview. DISPLAY SOFTWARELayout Software — APP/Mac. EDITORIAL SOFTWARE: Baseview. PRODUCTION EQUIPMENT: Hardware — 2-COM/8400; Cameras — 1-R/401.

ELIZABETHTON

ELIZABETHTON STAR

300 N Sycamore St, Elizabethton, Tenn., 37643-2742, Carter; gen tel (423) 542-4151; adv tel (423) 542-4151; ed tel (423) 297-9064; gen fax (423) 542-2004; adv fax (423) 542-2004; ed fax (423) 542-2004; gen/nat adv e-mail shirley.nave@elizabethton.com; disp adv e-mail shirley.nave@elizabethton.com; class adv e-mailshirley.nave@elizabethton.com; ed e-mail rozella.hardin@elizabethton.com; web site www.elizabethton.com
Group: Boone Newspapers, Inc.
Published: Mon, Tues, Wed, Thur, Fri, Sun
Weekday Frequency: e
Circulation: 9,366; 9,366(sun)
Last Audit: Sworn/Estimate/Non-Audited September 30, 2017
Advertising Rate (weekday/saturday): Open inch rate $15.00
Advertising Rate (sunday): Open inch rate $15.00
News services: AP, Papert (Landon). **Established:** 1926
Special Editions: Christmas Gift Guide (Other).
Special Weekly Sections: Best Food (Tue); Auto (Wed); School (Thur); School, Church (Fri); Amusements, Builders (Sun)
Syndicated Publications: American Profile (S).
Pub .... Lynn Richardson
Prodn. Supt. .... Delaney Scalf
Circ. Mgr. .... Kathy Scalf
Asst. to Pub .... Patsy Johnson
Adv. Mgr. .... Shirley Nave
Adv. Dir. .... Bill Parsons
Ed. .... Rozella Hardin
Market Information: Zoned editions.
Mechanical Available: Offset; Black and 3 ROP colors; insert accepted; page cutoffs - 22 5/8.
Mechanical Specifications: Type page 13 x 21 1/2; E - 6 cols, 2 1/16, 1/8 between; A - 6 cols, 2 1/16, 1/8 between; C - 9 cols, 1 1/2, 1/8 between.Equipment & Software: PRESSROOM EQUIPMENT: Lines — 8-HI/V-15A.; MAILROOM EQUIPMENT: Address Machine — KR/Inserter.; BUSINESS EQUIPMENT: 1-IBM/3600 CLASSIFIED EQUIPMENT: Hardware — APP/Mac; Printers — APP/Mac LaserWriter, HP; CLASSIFIED SOFTWARE: Baseview. DISPLAY EQUIPMENT: Hardware — APP/ Mac; Printers — HP, NewGen; DISPLAY SOFTWAREAd Make-up Applications — QPS/QuarkXPress.; EDITORIAL EQUIPMENT: Hardware — APP/Mac EDITORIAL SOFTWARE: Baseview. PRODUCTION EQUIPMENT: Hardware — 1-COM/8400, 3-APP/Mac Plus, 2-APP/Mac LaserWriter, ECR; Cameras — III/Spartan

GREENEVILLE

THE GREENEVILLE SUN

121 W Summer St, Greeneville, Tenn., 37743-4923, Greene; gen tel (423) 638-4181; adv tel (423) 638-4185; gen fax (423) 638-3645; adv fax (423) 638-7348; gen/nat adv e-mail artie.wehenkel@greenevillesun.com; disp adv e-mail artie.wehenkel@greenevillesun.com; class adv e-mailartie.wehenkel@greenevillesun.com; ed e-mail michael.reneau@greenevillesun.com; web site www.greenevillesun.com - 900,000(views) 60,000(visitors)
Group: Adams Publishing Group, LLC
Published: Mon, Tues, Wed, Thur, Fri, Sat
Weekday Frequency: e
Saturday Frequency: m
Circulation: 10,500; 10,500(sat)
Last Audit: USPS September 26, 2017
Advertising Rate (weekday/saturday): Open inch rate $21.25 for Local
Advertising Rate (sunday): Same as above.
Online Advertising Rate: $10 CPM
News services: AP. **Established:** 1897
Own Printing Facility?: Yes
Commercial Printers?: Yes
Special Editions: Administrative Professionals Week (Apr); Greene Co. Guidebook (Aug); Christmas Greetings (Dec); Ladies Classic Basketball Tournament (Dec); Calendar Girls (Jan); Bridal Edition (Jan); Benchmarks (Mar); TN Greene (May); Salute To Industry (Oct; Pigskin Preview (Aug); Basketball (Nov); Car Care (Oct); Cheerleaders & Bands (Sept); People's Choice Awards (Nov); Greene County Partnership Directory (Jan).
Special Weekly Sections: Health (Mon); TV Week (Sat); Business (Thur); Maturity (Seniors) (Tues); Agriculture (Wed); Faith (Fri); Education (Wed).
Syndicated Publications: Athlon Sports, American Profile, Spry (Monthly).
Proprietary Publications: The Greeneville Neighbor News is published each Wednesday as a free distribution publication carrier delivered to non-subscribers.
Digital Platform - Mobile: Apple
Digital Platform - Tablet: Apple iOS
Pub .... Gregg K. Jones
Dir. Online Opp. .... Brian Cutshall
Adv. Dir. .... Arthur D. Wehenkel
Lifestyle Ed. .... Sarah Gregory
Circ/Prod. Mgr. .... Dale Long
Ed .... Michael Reneau
Assoc. Ed. .... Kristen Early
Gen. Mgr. .... John E Cash
Market Information: TMC.
Mechanical Available: Offset; Black and 3 ROP colors; insert accepted; page cutoffs - 22 3/4.
Mechanical Specifications: Type page 10 x 21 1/2; E - 6 cols, between; A - 6 cols, between; C - 6 cols, between.
Areas Served: 37743, 37745, 37616, 37641, 37681, 37711, 37809, 37810, 37818, 37656.
Delivery Method: Mail, Newsstand, Carrier, RacksEquipment & Software: PRESSROOM EQUIPMENT: Lines — 8-G/Urbanite; MAILROOM EQUIPMENT: Counter Stackers — 1-HI/Graphics, RS/25; Inserters & Stuffers — 1-MM/227E; Tying Machines — 1/ Nichiro Kogyo/Semi-Ace; Address Machine — 1-DEC/LA 180, Ch/525E Stamping machine.; BUSINESS EQUIPMENT: ALR BUSINESS SOFTWARE: Vision Data CLASSIFIED EQUIPMENT: Hardware — 4-Sun/Publishing.; DISPLAY EQUIPMENT: Hardware — APP/Mac; Printers — 3-APP/ Mac LaserWriter; DISPLAY SOFTWAREAd Make-up Applications — Adobe InDesign CS2; Layout Software — APP/Mac. EDITORIAL EQUIPMENT: Hardware — 1-Mk/4001, Mk/Mycro-Comp 1100 Plus, APP/ Mac; Printers — 1-APP/Mac LaserWriter Plus EDITORIAL SOFTWARE: FSI/Edit 1.10. PRODUCTION EQUIPMENT: Hardware — Caere/Omni Page Pro 7.0, 2-Ultre, Hyphen/ RIP; Cameras — 1-C/Spartan II; Scanners — Lf/Leafscan 45, Lf/Leafscan 35, Sharp/ J600 Flatbed PRODUCTION SOFTWARE: FSI/Edit 1.1.0.
Note: Best of Preps Event (May)

JACKSON

THE JACKSON SUN

245 W Lafayette St, Jackson, Tenn., 38301-6126, Madison; gen tel (731) 427-3333; adv tel (731) 425-9610; ed tel (731) 425-9686; gen fax (731) 425-9604; adv fax (731) 425-9604; ed fax (731) 425-9639; gen/nat adv e-mail contactus@jacksonsun.com; web site www.jacksonsun.com
Group: Gannett
Published: Mon, Tues, Wed, Thur, Fri, Sat, Sun
Weekday Frequency: m
Saturday Frequency: m
Circulation: 12,446; 12,446(sat); 19,822(sun)
Last Audit: AAM March 31, 2016
Advertising Rate (weekday/saturday): Open inch rate $61.75
Advertising Rate (sunday): Open inch rate $74.42
News services: AP, GNS. **Established:** 1879
Own Printing Facility?: Yes
Commercial Printers?: Yes
Special Editions: Football (Aug); Fact Book (Feb); How To (Jan); Back-to-School (Jul); NAIA (Mar); Apple (Monthly); Home Builders (Nov); Design An Ad (Oct).
Special Weekly Sections: Health, Fitness, Technology (Mon); Family, Parenting (Tue); Best Food (Wed); Entertainment, Magazine, Education (Thur); Home, Garden (Fri); Expanded Sports, Automotive, Religion (Sat); Business, Finance, TV, Amusement, Comics, Travel, Living, Real Estate, NFL (Sun); Business, Your Town (Daily)
Syndicated Publications: TV Week (own, newsprint) (S); Weekend Plus (Thur).
Digital Platform - Mobile: Apple, Android
Pub./Pres. .... Roy Heatherly
Finance Mgr. .... Tammy Gilliam
Credit Mgr. .... Betty Allen
Adv. Dir. .... Ron Prince
Adv. Mgr., Display .... Sarah Scott
Dir., Market Devel. .... Cathy Garrett
Circ. Mgr. .... Alice Sellers
Exec. Ed. .... Steve Coffman
Editorial Page Ed. .... Tom Bohs
Chief Content Ed. .... Kelly South
Sports Ed. .... Brandon Shields
Online Mgr. .... Martin Jelinek
Prodn. Servs. Mgr. .... Brad Isaacs
Prodn. Mgr., Commercial Print Shop . Beth Walker
Prodn. Mgr., Bldg. .... Andy Curtis
Nat'l Adv. Rep. .... Leesa Raines
Exec. Ed. .... Steve Coughman
Market Information: Split run; TMC.
Mechanical Available: Offset (KBA Comet 70); Black and 3 ROP colors; insert accepted - all; page cutoffs - 21 1/2.
Mechanical Specifications: Type page 11 5/8 x 20 1/4; E - 6 cols, 1 4/5, 7/24 between; A - 6 cols, 1 4/5, 7/24 between; C - 9 cols, 1 1/5, 1/12 between.

Delivery Method: Mail, Newsstand, Carrier, RacksEquipment & Software: PRESSROOM EQUIPMENT: Lines — KBA/Comet 70 single width (4 color) 5 towers 2001; MAILROOM EQUIPMENT: Counter Stackers — 2-QWI/400, 1-QWI/SJ200, 1-QWI/SJ350; Inserters & Stuffers — S/NP630; Tying Machines — 1-MLN/MAG-330, 1-Dynaric/NP2, 2-Dynaric/NP3; Wrapping Singles — Addressing machine 1/Cheshire; BUSINESS EQUIPMENT: IBM/AS-400 RISC CLASSIFIED EQUIPMENT: Hardware — DTI/Unix; 6-Toshiba/1100 portable; Printers — HP/5si; CLASSIFIED SOFTWARE: DTI 4.2.3. DISPLAY EQUIPMENT: Hardware — APP/Mac G3, APP/Mac G4; Printers — HP/5si; DISPLAY SOFTWAREAd Make-up Applications — Multi-Ad/Creator 2; Layout Software — DTI/PlanBuilder. EDITORIAL EQUIPMENT: Hardware — DTI/Unix/6-Toshiba/1100 portable; Printers — HP/5si EDITORIAL SOFTWARE: DTI 4.3. PRODUCTION EQUIPMENT: Hardware — Caere/OmniPage Pro, Konica/3650, Konica/6500; Scanners — Kk/Professional PRODUCTION SOFTWARE: DTI/PlanBuilder V7.

JOHNSON CITY

JOHNSON CITY PRESS

204 W Main St, Johnson City, Tenn., 37604-6212, Washington; gen tel (423) 929-3111; adv tel (423) 929-3111; ed tel (423) 929-3111; gen fax (423) 929-1674; adv fax (423) 929-9097; ed fax (423) 929-7484; gen/nat adv e-mail adsales@johnsoncitypress.com; disp adv e-mail adsales@johnsoncitypress.com; class adv e-mailadsales@johnsoncitypress.com; ed e-mail newsroom@johnsoncitypress.com; web site www.johnsoncitypress.com

Group: Sandusky Newspapers, Inc.
Published: Mon, Tues, Wed, Thur, Fri, Sat, Sun
Weekday Frequency: m
Saturday Frequency: m
Circulation: 18,049; 18,049(sat); 19,845(sun)
Last Audit: AAM June 30, 2017
Advertising Rate (weekday/saturday): Open inch rate $42.80
Advertising Rate (sunday): Open inch rate $45.67
News services: AP, NYT. **Established:** 1934
Own Printing Facility?: Yes
Commercial Printers?: No
Special Editions: Bristol Motor Speedway Tab-Ford City 500 (Apr); Bristol Motor Speedway Tab-Sharpie 500 (Aug); Christmas Gifts (Dec); Children's Valentines (Feb); Wedding Guide (Jan); Progress (Mar); Outdoor Recreation (May); Thanksgiving (Nov); Car Care (Oct); School (Se
Special Weekly Sections: Best Food (Wed/Sat); TV, Entertainment (Daily); Stocks (Tue-Sat); TV (Fri); Church, Mutual Funds, Classifieds, Auto (Sat); Tempo, Business, Sports, Travel (Sun)
Syndicated Publications: Parade (S).
Digital Platform - Mobile: Apple, Android
Digital Platform - Tablet: Apple iOS, Android
Pub. .... Justin Wilcox
Adv. Sales Mgr. .... Bill Cummings
Circ. Dir. .... Phil Hensley
Mng. Ed. .... John Molley
Editorial Page Ed. .... Robert Houk
Educ./School Ed. .... Sam Watson
Photo Dept. Mgr. .... Lee Talbert
Religion Ed. .... Robert Pierce
Sports Ed. .... Kelly Hodge
Travel Ed. .... Jan Hearn
Sue Legg
Alan Broyles
Sharon Salyers
Sales/Mktg Dir. .... Richard Clark
Mechanical Available: Offset; Black and 3 ROP colors; insert accepted - samples up to 13 x 11 x 1/8; page cutoffs - 22 3/4.
Mechanical Specifications: Type page 13 x 21 1/2; E - 6 cols, 2 1/16, 1/8 between; A - 6 cols, 2 1/16, 1/8 between; C - 9 cols, 1 3/8, 1/16 between.
Areas Served: 37605, 37615, 37604
Delivery Method: Newsstand, Carrier, RacksEquipment & Software: PRESSROOM EQUIPMENT: Press Drive — GE/DC-300; Reels & Stands — 6; Control System — 1986; MAILROOM EQUIPMENT: Counter Stackers — 1/QWI; Inserters & Stuffers — 1-HI/48P (8-Intol), 1-/MM 5:1; Tying Machines — 2-/MLN; Address Machine — 1-/KAN.; BUSINESS EQUIPMENT: IBM/RISC-6000 BUSINESS SOFTWARE: Vision Data CLASSIFIED EQUIPMENT: Hardware — Sun/Ultra 250-300 mhz; APP/Mac G3, QMS/2060 Laserprinter; Printers — 1-Centronics, HP/Laser Printer; CLASSIFIED SOFTWARE: Vision Data/Total Advertising. DISPLAY EQUIPMENT: Hardware — 4-APP/Mac G4, APP/Mac G3, 3-APP/Mac G3; Printers — 3-QMS/2060; DISPLAY SOFTWAREAd Make-up Applications — Multi-Ad/Creator 3.8.; EDITORIAL EQUIPMENT: Hardware — 30-ECR, 30-APP/iMac, 14-APP/Mac G4; Printers — 1-Centronics, 3-Qms/Laser Printers EDITORIAL SOFTWARE: ECR, Baseview. PRODUCTION EQUIPMENT: Hardware — Caere/OmniPage Pro 8.0, 1-AG/II, Nikon/Cool Scan; Cameras — 1-Robinson/480, 1-C/Sparton; Scanners — 1-AG/II PRODUCTION SOFTWARE: Baseview, QPS/QuarkXPress 4.1.

KINGSPORT

KINGSPORT TIMES-NEWS

701 Lynn Garden Dr, Kingsport, Tenn., 37660-5607, Sullivan; gen tel (423) 246-8121; adv tel (423) 392-1328 (Retail); ed tel (423) 392-1322; gen fax (423) 392-1385; adv fax (423) 392-1392; ed fax (423) 392-1385; gen/nat adv e-mail gcoleman@timesnews.net; disp adv e-mail retail@timesnews.net; class adv e-mailclassifieds@timesnews.net; ed e-mail news@timesnews.net; web site www.timesnews.net
- 4,556,884(views) 306,826(visitors)

Group: Sandusky Newspapers, Inc.
Published: Mon, Tues, Wed, Thur, Fri, Sat, Sun
Weekday Frequency: All day
Saturday Frequency: m
Circulation: 25,706; 23,798(sat); 29,606(sun)
Last Audit: AAM September 30, 2017
Newspaper Reps: Advertising Director — Billy Kirk
VP of Finance — Debbie Salyers
Content Director — Stephanie McClellan
Dirculation Director — John Quaintance
Director of Operations — Tim Archer
Marketing Director — Diana Meredith
Advertising Rate (weekday/saturday): Open inch rate $55.00
Advertising Rate (sunday): Open inch rate $57.20
Online Advertising Rate: Contact for specifics
News services: AP, MCT, CQ. **Established:** 1916
Own Printing Facility?: Yes
Commercial Printers?: Yes
Special Editions: American Home & Garden (Apr); Football Preview (Aug); Christmas Gallery of Gifts (3 times) (Dec); Chamber Annual Report (Feb); Celebrating Diversity (Jan); Readers Choice V (Jun); Progress (Mar); Spring Tune-Up (May);
Special Weekly Sections: Best Food (Wed/Sun); Entertainment (Thur); Religion (Fri); Business, Travel, Technology (Sun)
Syndicated Publications: Relish
Digital Platform - Mobile: Apple, Android, Windows
Digital Platform - Tablet: Apple iOS, Android
VP Finance .... Debbie Salyers
City Ed. .... Stephanie McLellan
Dan Strickler
Vice President, Sales .... Clark Richard
Display Mgr. .... Billy Kirk
Nat'l Adv. Mgr. .... Lynn Brooks
Publisher .... Rick Thomason
Market Information: Split run; TMC; Zoned editions.
Mechanical Available: Offset; Black and 3 ROP colors; insert accepted; page cutoffs - 23 9/16.
Mechanical Specifications: Type page 12 x 22 1/2; E - 6 cols, 2, 1/6 between; A - 6 cols, 2, 1/6 between; C - 9 cols, 1 3/8, 1/4 between.
Areas Served: 37660, 24251, 37642, 37645, 37617, 37659,37601,24244,24290
Delivery Method: Mail, Newsstand, Carrier, RacksEquipment & Software: PRESSROOM EQUIPMENT: Lines — 4-G/Metro 3077 (2 half decks) 1970; Press Drive — Fincor; Folders — 1-G/2:1.; MAILROOM EQUIPMENT: Counter Stackers — 1 Quipp 300; 2 Quipp 400; 2 Quipp 500-C; Inserters & Stuffers — Goss 630 18-head; K&M G60 32-head; Tying Machines — 4 GoPackaging; 2 Samuel; Control System — Miracom; Address Machine — Wm; BUSINESS EQUIPMENT: DEC BUSINESS SOFTWARE: Atex WCS CIS-Circulation Atex Adbase-Retail & Class Adv. SBS-AP, GL, Payroll & HR CLASSIFIED EQUIPMENT: Hardware — Dell & HP; Printers — HP Laserjet 4300; HP Laserjet 4; CLASSIFIED SOFTWARE: Atex AdBase DISPLAY EQUIPMENT: Hardware — HP & Dell; Printers — HP/4000N; HP/9500 hdn; DISPLAY SOFTWAREAd Make-up Applications — Adobe CS; Layout Software — SCS/Layout 8000. EDITORIAL EQUIPMENT: Hardware — 32-Dell/OptiFlex, & HP;Dell/Latitude, 27-Dell/PE4400; Printers — 2-X/Laser Printer, 1 HP 601n EDITORIAL SOFTWARE: Libercus PRODUCTION EQUIPMENT: Hardware — 2 AGFA; Scanners — Umax/Astra 1200A, Sharp/JX-610, Nikon/3510 AF, Umaz/PowerLook 2100XL, Epson/Perfection 1200 Photo, Epson/ES 1200C PRODUCTION SOFTWARE: AGFA Advantage/NSL

KNOXVILLE

KNOXVILLE NEWS SENTINEL

2332 News Sentinel Dr, Knoxville, Tenn., 37921-5766, Knox; gen tel (865) 521-8181; adv tel (865)342-6453; ed tel (865) 342-6300; adv fax (865) 342-6509; ed fax (865) 342-6400; gen/nat adv e-mail kns@knoxnews.com; disp adv e-mail ads@knoxnews.com; ed e-mail jack.mcelroy@knoxnews.com; web site www.knoxnews.com
- 8,110,967(views) 1,319,705(visitors)

Group: Journal Media Group
Published: Mon, Tues, Wed, Thur, Fri, Sat, Sun
Weekday Frequency: m
Saturday Frequency: m
Circulation: 62,002; 62,002(sat); 78,962(sun)
Last Audit: AAM June 30, 2017
Advertising Rate (weekday/saturday): Open inch rate Local Rates: $59.54(M-F), $70.05 (Th-Sat); National: $93.27 (M-W), $109.73 (Th-Sat)
Advertising Rate (sunday): $84.06 for Local and $131.68 for National
News services: AP, SHNS, NEA, LAT-WP, INS Bizwire, PR Newswire. **Established:** 1888
Own Printing Facility?: Yes
Commercial Printers?: Yes
Special Editions: Employer Spotlight (Apr); Prep Football (Aug); Fox 43 Winter Adventures (Dec); Childrens' Miracle Network Radiothon (Feb); Employer Spotlight (Jan); Employer Spotlight (Jul); Lenoir City Arts & Crafts Festival (Jun); Home Show (Mar); A Day in the Life (Ma
Special Weekly Sections: Preview (Fri); Science (Mon); Real Estate (S); Faith & Family (Sat); Style (Thur); Schools (Tues); Food (Wed).
Syndicated Publications: Parade (S).
Digital Platform - Mobile: Apple, Android, Windows, Blackberry
Digital Platform - Tablet: Apple iOS, Android, Windows 7, Blackberry Tablet OS, Kindle, Nook, Kindle Fire
Pres./Pub. .... Patrick Birmingham
Dir., Finance .... Paul Abraham
Dir., HR .... Debi Welch
Adv. Mgr., Retail .... Nancy Nabors
Classified Adv. Mgr. .... Brenda Crisp
Mktg. Dir. .... Lisa Duncan
Ed. .... Jack McElroy
Ed., Special Publications .... Wade Saye
Deputy Mng. Ed. .... Tom Chester
Asst. Mng. Ed., Graphics .... Michael Apuan
Bus. Ed. .... David Keim
Columnist .... Sam Venable
Editorial Page Ed. .... Hoyt Canady
Asst. Editorial Page Ed. .... Jan Avent
Entertainment Ed. .... Chuck Campbell
Film Ed. .... Betsy Pickle
Home Furnishings Ed. .... Susan Alexander
Librarian .... James Gill
Bruce Hartmann
Senior Director, Circulation Sales .. Heather Price
Market Information: ADS; Split run; TMC; Zoned editions.
Mechanical Available: Offset; Black and 3 ROP colors; insert accepted - Post-it notes; page cutoffs - 23 9/16.
Mechanical Specifications: Type page 13 x 22 1/2; E - 6 cols, 1 5/6, 1/8 between; A - 6 cols, 1 5/6, 1/8 between; C - 10 cols, between.
Areas Served: East Tennessee
Delivery Method: Mail, CarrierEquipment & Software: PRESSROOM EQUIPMENT: Lines — 12-MAN/Regioman (4 pages wide); Folders — 2-MAN/3:2; Control System — MAN.; MAILROOM EQUIPMENT: Counter Stackers — 6-GMA/Combi Stacks, 4-Compass; Inserters & Stuffers — 2-GMA; Tying Machines — 3-Dynaric/1500; Wrapping Singles — 2-GMA, 1-Dynaric/Strapper.; BUSINESS SOFTWARE: Cobol, Unisys, Unisys CLASSIFIED EQUIPMENT: Hardware — Compaq/Proliant 8500, 4-PPRO/550 Client, Compaq/4000 DeskPro; Printers — HP/5si mx, HP/8100, HP/8150; CLASSIFIED SOFTWARE: Unisys/AD2000. DISPLAY EQUIPMENT: Hardware — Compaq/Proliant 8500 Server 4-550 Client, Compaq 4000 Deskpro; Printers — HP/8100, HP/8150, HP/5si mx; DISPLAY SOFTWAREAd Make-up Applications — Baseview/Ad Manager, Multi-Ad/Creator.; EDITORIAL EQUIPMENT: Hardware — Compaq/Proliant server 7000, 4-PPRO/400 Client, Compaq/EN 400; Printers — HP/5si, HP/5si mx, HP/6L, HP/755 EDITORIAL SOFTWARE: ATS/Newsdesk. PRODUCTION EQUIPMENT: Hardware — 1-Burgess/Consolux, 1-Scitex/Eversmart Pro, AP/Picture Desk; Scanners — Scitex/Eversmart Jazz PRODUCTION SOFTWARE: ATS, Media Desk.

LEBANON

THE LEBANON DEMOCRAT

402 N Cumberland St, Lebanon, Tenn., 37087-2306, Wilson; gen tel (615) 444-3952; gen fax (615) 444-1358; ed fax (615) 444-0899; gen/nat adv e-mail mrodgers@lebanondemocrat.com; disp adv e-mail rop@lebanondemocrat.com; class adv e-mailclassified@lebanondemocrat.com; ed e-mail jfelkins@lebanondemocrat.com; web site www.lebanondemocrat.com
- 750,000(views) 130,000(visitors)

Group: Sandusky Newspapers, Inc.
Published: Tues, Wed, Thur, Fri, Sat
Weekday Frequency: m
Saturday Frequency: m
Circulation: 7,236; 7,236(sat)
Last Audit: Sworn/Estimate/Non-Audited October 23, 2017
Newspaper Reps: George Coleman, publisher
Jared Felkins, editor
Shelagh Mason, business manager
Wes Ritter, advertising director
Mark Rodgers, production manager
Advertising Rate (weekday/saturday): Open inch rate $12.00
News services: NEA, AP. **Established:** 1888
Own Printing Facility?: Yes
Commercial Printers?: Yes
Special Weekly Sections: Best Food (Wed); Agriculture (Tue); Lifestyles (Wed); Business (Thur); Religion, Real Estate (Fri); TV, Sports (Sat);
Syndicated Publications: USA WEEKEND Magazine (Fri).
Proprietary Publications: East of the City magazine
Digital Platform - Mobile: Apple, Android, Windows, Blackberry
Digital Platform - Tablet: Apple iOS, Android, Windows 7, Blackberry Tablet OS, Kindle, Nook, Kindle Fire
Mgr., Accounting .... Shelagh Mason
Sports Ed. .... Andy Reed
Prod. Mgr. .... Mark Rodgers
Prodn. Foreman, Pressroom .... Richard Knowles
Publisher .... George Coleman
Editor .... Jared Felkins
Advertising Director .... Wes Ritter
Market Information: TMC; Zoned editions.
Mechanical Available: Offset; Black and 3 ROP colors; insert accepted; page cutoffs - 22 1/2.
Mechanical Specifications: Type page 13 x 21 1/2; E - 6 cols, 2 1/16, 1/8 between; A - 6 cols, 2 1/16, 1/8 between; C - 6 cols, 2 1/16, 1/8 between.

Areas Served: Lebanon/Wilson County/37087
Mt. Juliet/Wilson County/37121
Watertown/Wilson County/37184
Delivery Method: Mail, Newsstand, Carrier, RacksEquipment & Software: PRESSROOM EQUIPMENT: Lines — 8-G/Community (color stock); MAILROOM EQUIPMENT: Counter Stackers — 1/Newstack; Tying Machines — Bu; Address Machine — 1-/Ch.; BUSINESS EQUIPMENT: Vision Data CLASSIFIED EQUIPMENT: Hardware — APP/Mac; CLASSIFIED SOFTWARE: Baseview. DISPLAY SOFTWARELayout Software — APP/Mac, APP/Mac IIcx, APP/Power Mac. EDITORIAL EQUIPMENT: Hardware — Mk EDITORIAL SOFTWARE: Mk. PRODUCTION EQUIPMENT: Hardware — 1-Nu/Flip Top FT40L, PrePress/Panther Plus Imagesetter, APP/Mac NTX, P; Cameras — 1-R/400, SCREEN/Companica.

MARYVILLE

THE DAILY TIMES

307 E Harper Ave, Maryville, Tenn., 37804-5724, Blount; gen tel (865) 981-1100; adv tel (865) 981-1150; ed tel (865) 981-1143; gen fax (865) 981-1175; adv fax (865)981-1156; ed fax (865)981-1175; gen/nat adv e-mail evelyn.sandlin@thedailytimes.com; disp adv e-mail evelyn.sandlin@thedailytimes.com; class adv e-mailclassifieds@thedailytimes.com; ed e-mail frank.trexler@thedailytimes.com; web site www.thedailytimes.com
- 750,000(views) 100,000(visitors)

Group: Adams Publishing Group, LLC
Published: Mon, Tues, Wed, Thur, Fri, Sat, Sun
Weekday Frequency: m
Saturday Frequency: m
Circulation: 15,861; 15,861(sat); 17,731(sun)
Last Audit: AAM March 31, 2015
Advertising Rate (weekday/saturday): Open inch rate $24.00
News services: AP. **Established:** 1883
Own Printing Facility?: No
Commercial Printers?: No
Special Editions: Townsend Traveler (Apr); Football Round-up (Aug); Progress (Feb); Father's Day (Jun); Home Improvement (Mar); Brides (May); Car Care (Oct); Fall Home Improvement (Sept).
Special Weekly Sections: Real Estate (Wed); TV Times (Mon); Religious News (Sat); Food (Wed).Weekend Entertainment (Thu)
Syndicated Publications: USA WEEKEND Magazine (S),
Relish, Athlon Sports
Proprietary Publications: Blount County HORIZON magazine
Digital Platform - Mobile: Apple, Android, Windows
Digital Platform - Tablet: Apple iOS, Android, Windows 7, Kindle
Adv. Dir.....................Evelyn Sandlin
Circulation Director....................Bryan Sandmeier
Mng. Ed.....................Frank Trexler
City/Metro Ed.....................Bob Norris
Editorial Page Ed.....................Dean Stone
Entertainment/Amusements Ed. Steven Wildsmith
Features Ed.....................Melanie Tucker
News Ed.....................Richard Dodson
Sports Ed.....................Marcus Fitzsimmons
IT Director....................Tim Malone
Publisher....................Carl Esposito
Asst. Mng. Ed.....................Amanda Greever
Prodn. Mgr., Pre Press....................David Ledford
Buzz Trexler
Market Information: Nonsubscriber product - Times Too!
Mechanical Available: Offset; Black and 3 ROP colors.
Mechanical Specifications: Type page 11 x 21.
Areas Served: Blount County
Delivery Method: Mail, Newsstand, Carrier, RacksEquipment & Software: BUSINESS EQUIPMENT: Windows PCs BUSINESS SOFTWARE: Vision Data CLASSIFIED EQUIPMENT: Hardware — Macintosh; Printers — Konica Minolta CLASSIFIED SOFTWARE: Vision Data DISPLAY EQUIPMENT: Hardware — Macintosh; Printers — Konica Minolta DISPLAY SOFTWAREAd Make-up Applications — Vision Data; Layout Software — Adobe/ Photoshop, InDesign EDITORIAL EQUIPMENT: Hardware — Macintosh; Printers — Konica/Minolta EDITORIAL SOFTWARE: MediaSpan PRODUCTION EQUIPMENT: Scanners — Kk/RFS 2035 Plus, Microtek/ScanMaker 3 PRODUCTION SOFTWARE: Adobe InDesign

MEMPHIS

THE COMMERCIAL APPEAL

495 Union Ave, Memphis, Tenn., 38103-3217, Shelby; gen tel (901) 529-2211; adv tel (901) 529-2251; web site www.commercialappeal.com
- 7,500,000(views) 785,380(visitors)

Group: Gannett
Published: Mon, Tues, Wed, Thur, Fri, Sat, Sun
Weekday Frequency: m
Saturday Frequency: m
Circulation: 59,325; 60,512(sat); 95,738(sun)
Last Audit: AAM September 30, 2016
Newspaper Reps: Mark Russell, Editor
News services: GNS, AP **Established:** 1840
Own Printing Facility?: No
Commercial Printers?: Yes
Special Editions: Memphis Most (Sept.)
President....................Mike Jung
Editor....................Mark Russell
Advertising Sales Director....................Tommy Ewing
Circulation Director....................Ken McCloud
Sales Manager-Territories.... Michelle Thompson
Adv. Sales Manager....................Darlene Hardy
Advertising Sales Director, Automotive.Ann-Marie Johnson
Client Strategy Manager....................Jordan Tucker
Sr. Manager, Newspaper Production Ehren Lowers
Consumer Sales Manager....................Keith Powers
Site Director....................Danny Bowen
Executive Administrator....................Glenn Edwards
Areas Served: Memphis TN & Surrounding communities
Delivery Method: Mail, Newsstand, Carrier, RacksEquipment & Software: PRESSROOM EQUIPMENT: Harland Simon MAILROOM EQUIPMENT: Prism BUSINESS SOFTWARE: Genesys

THE DAILY NEWS

193 Jefferson Ave, Memphis, Tenn., 38103-2322, Shelby; gen tel (901) 523-1561; adv tel (901) 528-5283; ed tel (901) 523-8501; gen fax (901) 526-5813; adv fax (901) 526-5813; ed fax (901) 526-5813; gen/nat adv e-mail advertising@memphisdailynews.com; disp adv e-mail leah@memphisdailynews.com; class adv e-mailleah@memphisdailynews.com; ed e-mail joverstreet@memphisdailynews.com; web site www.memphisdailynews.com
- 300,000(views) 100,000(visitors)

Group: The Daily News Publishing Co.
Published: Mon, Tues, Wed, Thur, Fri
Weekday Frequency: m
Circulation: 1,000
Last Audit: Sworn/Estimate/Non-Audited September 30, 2017
Advertising Rate (weekday/saturday): Open inch rate $13.50 (legal)
Online Advertising Rate: Leaderboard (728x90): $550/month; Side Position (250x250): $400/ month
News services: CNS **Established:** 1886
Publisher....................Eric Barnes
Marketing Director....................Leah Sansing
Associate Publisher/Exec. Ed...James Overstreet
Areas Served: Madison, Tipton, Fayette, Shelby
Delivery Method: Mail

MORRISTOWN

CITIZEN TRIBUNE

1609 W 1st North St, Morristown, Tenn., 37814-3724, Hamblen; gen tel (423) 581-5630; gen fax (423) 581-3061; ed fax (423) 581-8863; gen/nat adv e-mail ads@citizentribune.com; disp adv e-mail ads@citizentribune.com; class adv e-mailads@citizentribune.com; web site www.citizentribune.com
- 500,000(views) 80,000(visitors)

Group: Lakeway Publishers, Inc.
Published: Mon, Tues, Wed, Thur, Fri, Sun
Weekday Frequency: e
Circulation: 17,444; 22,494(sun)
Last Audit: AAM June 30, 2017
Advertising Rate (weekday/saturday): Open inch rate $21.09
Advertising Rate (sunday): Open inch rate $21.92
Online Advertising Rate: $10.00 per M
News services: AP, U.S. Suburban Press Inc.. **Established:** 1966
Own Printing Facility?: Yes
Commercial Printers?: Yes
Special Editions: Christmas, Graduation, 50th Anniversary Edition
Special Weekly Sections: Entertainment, TV (Daily); Best Food (Wed); Church (Fri); Lakeway Living, Entertainment, Business, Sports (Sun)
Syndicated Publications: Relish (Monthly); Parade (S).
Proprietary Publications: Wink Magazine Monthly, Over 50, Monthly.
Digital Platform - Mobile: Apple, Android, Windows, Blackberry
Digital Platform - Tablet: Apple iOS, Android, Windows 7, Blackberry Tablet OS, Kindle, Nook, Kindle Fire
President....................R. Jack Fishman
Mng. Ed.....................John Gullion
Features Ed.....................Stan Johnson
Health/Medical Ed.....................Bob Moore
Travel Ed.....................Denise Williams
Prodn. Mgr.....................Ricky Ball
Sales/Mktg Dir.....................Mike Walker
Publisher....................Mike Fishman
Circ. Dir.....................Don Lovelace
Market Information: TMC.
Mechanical Available: Offset; Black and 3 ROP colors; insert accepted; page cutoffs - 22 3/4.
Mechanical Specifications: Type page 11 5/8 x 21 1/2; E - 6 cols, 1 5/6, 1/8 between; A - 6 cols, 1 5/6, 1/8 between; C - 8 cols, 1 19/50, 1/8 between.
Areas Served: Morristown, Hamblen County, Jefferson County, Cocke County, Greene County, Hawkins County,
Hancock County, Grainger County, Claiborne County.
Delivery Method: Mail, Newsstand, Carrier, RacksEquipment & Software: PRESSROOM EQUIPMENT: Lines — 5-G/U; MAILROOM EQUIPMENT: Counter Stackers — 1/ BG; Inserters & Stuffers — 4-/MM; Tying Machines — 1-/MLN.; BUSINESS EQUIPMENT: 1-DEC/11-70 EDITORIAL EQUIPMENT: Hardware — 1-Ik/Minitek II (CPS 1020). PRODUCTION EQUIPMENT: Hardware — 1-Nu; Cameras — 1-C, 1-Cl.

MURFREESBORO

THE DAILY NEWS JOURNAL

201 E Main St, Ste 400, Murfreesboro, Tenn., 37130-3753, Rutherford; gen tel (615) 893-5860; adv tel (615) 893-5860; ed tel (615) 893-5860; gen fax (615) 896-8702; adv fax (615) 896-8702; ed fax (615) 896-8702; gen/nat adv e-mail slupton@tennessean.com; disp adv e-mail adcopy@dnj.com; ed e-mail mragland@dnj.com; web site www.dnj.com
- 2,500,000(views) 350,000(visitors)

Group: Gannett
Published: Mon, Tues, Wed, Thur, Fri, Sat, Sun
Weekday Frequency: m
Saturday Frequency: m
Circulation: 7,112; 7,112(sat); 10,300(sun)
Last Audit: AAM September 30, 2017
Advertising Rate (weekday/saturday): Open inch rate $22.66
Advertising Rate (sunday): Open inch rate $27.19
News services: AP, U.S. Suburban Press Inc.. **Established:** 1849
Own Printing Facility?: Yes
Commercial Printers?: Yes
Special Editions: R.County
Murfreesboro Magazine
Readers Choice
Special Weekly Sections: Movie Review (Fri); Job Solutions (Mon); Sports (S); Public Record (Sat); Health & Fitness (Thur); Seniors (Tues); Best Food Day (Wed).
Syndicated Publications: Parade
Digital Platform - Mobile: Apple, Android
Digital Platform - Tablet: Apple iOS, Android
Sports Ed.....................Tom Kreager
Nat'l Adv. Mgr.....................Sean Lupton
News Dir.....................Mealand Ragland
Market Information: ADS; Zoned editions.
Mechanical Available: Offset; Black and 3 ROP colors; insert accepted; page cutoffs - 22 3/4.
Mechanical Specifications: Type page 12 x 21 1/2; E - 6 cols, 2, 1/8 between; A - 6 cols, 2, 1/8 between; C - 9 cols, 1, 1/8 between.
Delivery Method: Newsstand, Carrier, RacksEquipment & Software: PRESSROOM EQUIPMENT: Lines — 5-G/Urbanite 1974, 4-DEV/Horizon 1985; MAILROOM EQUIPMENT: Counter Stackers — 1-HI/ RS-2517; Inserters & Stuffers — 6/MM; Tying Machines — 6-/MLN; Address Machine — 2-/KR.; BUSINESS EQUIPMENT: 6-IBM/ PC XT BUSINESS SOFTWARE: Foxbase, Acctmate CLASSIFIED EQUIPMENT: Hardware — 1-APP/Mac fileserver, 5-APP/ Mac LC III; Printers — 1-APP/Mac 630 Pro Printer; CLASSIFIED SOFTWARE: APP/Mac Appleshare 4.0, Baseview/ Class Manager. DISPLAY EQUIPMENT: Hardware — 2-APP/Mac Quadra 800, 1-APP/Mac 51, 4-APP/Mac Quadra 650; Printers — 2-APP/Mac LaserWriter NTX, 2-APP/Mac LaserWriter IIf, APP/Mac LaserWriter 630 Pro; Other Hardware — CD-Rom, 2-SyQue DISPLAY SOFTWAREAd Make-up Applications — QPS/QuarkXPress 3.3, Multi-Ad/Creator, Typeset; EDITORIAL EQUIPMENT: Hardware — APP/Mac/1-APP/ Mac Quadra 650, 1-APP/Mac SE 30, AP/ Wire, 1-Scanmaker/II Scanner; Printers — 1-APP/Mac LaserWriter 810 EDITORIAL SOFTWARE: QPS/QuarkXPress 3.31. PRODUCTION EQUIPMENT: Hardware — Caere/OmniPage, APP/Mac LaserWriter NTX; Cameras — C/Spartan II; Scanners — APP/Mac One Scanner PRODUCTION SOFTWARE: QPS/QuarkXPress 3.31.

NASHVILLE

THE TENNESSEAN

1100 Broadway, Nashville, Tenn., 37203-3116, Davidson; gen tel (615) 259-8000; adv tel (615) 259-8818; ed tel (615) 259-8095; gen fax (615) 259-8875; adv fax (615) 259-8820; ed fax (615) 259-8093; gen/nat adv e-mail rateinfo@tennessean.com; disp adv e-mail adv@tennessean.com; class adv e-mailslupton@tennessean.com; ed e-mail manastasi@gannett.com; web site www.tennessean.com
- 20,000,000(views) 4,000,000(visitors); web site 2 www.tnmediasolutions.com

Group: Gannett
Published: Mon, Tues, Wed, Thur, Fri, Sat, Sun
Weekday Frequency: m
Saturday Frequency: m
Circulation: 70,760; 70,618(sat); 115,459(sun)
Last Audit: AAM September 30, 2017
Advertising Rate (weekday/saturday): Open inch rate $43.65
Advertising Rate (sunday): Open inch rate $43.65
Online Advertising Rate: Standard Display (blended) $13
Banner $17
Pre-roll $20
Mobile $17
News services: NYT, LAT-WP, MCT, SHNS, GNS. **Established:** 1812
Own Printing Facility?: Yes
Commercial Printers?: Yes
Special Editions: Football(sept), Hockey(sept), FYI Magazine (Sept), Toast of Music City (July)
Special Weekly Sections: Best Food, Living, Food (Mon); Living, Health (Tue); Shopping (Wed); Metro Mix (Thur); Movies, Living, Style (Fri); Religion (Sat); Travel, Life, Home, Sports, Business, Comics (Sun)
Syndicated Publications: PARADE Magazine
Digital Platform - Mobile: Apple, Android
Digital Platform - Tablet: Apple iOS, Android
Regional Finance Director....................Bob Engel
Gen. Mgr. GPS Production Nashville.......... Thom Gregory
Pres./Pub.....................Laura Hollingsworth
Vice Pres., Circ.....................Jay Winkler
Consumer Exper. Dir.....................Lance Williams
Director of News & Editor....................Maria De Varenne
Sr. HR Business Partner....................Helen Jacobs
Manager, National/Major Accounts... Sean Lupton
Content Strategist....................Duane Gang

Daphne Lowell
Music Reporter................................ Juli Thanki
Photographer................................ Shelley Mays
Director of Sales..........................Shelley Davis
???? ????
Regional Sales Manager...............Dan Douglas
Key Accounts Mgr.......................Kimberly Hood
VP, Sales.. John Ward
Music Writer................................ Peter Cooper
Frank Sutherland
Consumer Experience Director........ David Anesta
Peter Antone
Market Information: ADS; Split run; TMC; Zoned editions.
Mechanical Available: Offset; Black and 3 ROP colors; insert accepted; page cutoffs - 22, 21.5
Mechanical Specifications: Type page 10 x 21 3/16; 10 x 20 1/2
Areas Served: Middle Tennessee
Delivery Method: Mail, Newsstand, Carrier, RacksEquipment & Software: PRESSROOM EQUIPMENT: Lines — 10-G/Colorliner; 10-G/Colorliner; 48-MAN/Uniset 70; Press Drive — G/Fincor, MAN/Baumuller; Folders — 4-G/3:2, 2-MAN/2:3:3; Pasters —20-G/CT50, 9-MAN; Control System — G/APCS MAN/PECOM; MAILROOM EQUIPMENT: Counter Stackers — 10-QWI/400, 2-QWI/500; Inserters & Stuffers — 2-KM/2299, 1-KM/1472; Tying Machines — 14-OVL/Strap; Control System — Quipp Newscom, BURT Mountain; Address Machine — 1-Ch/596, 2-VIP/9100; BUSINESS EQUIPMENT: 2-IBM/AS-400 BUSINESS SOFTWARE: Microsoft Office CLASSIFIED EQUIPMENT: Hardware — DELL; CLASSIFIED SOFTWARE: ATEX Mactive EDITORIAL EQUIPMENT: Hardware — Dell/Server/205-Intel/PC EDITORIAL SOFTWARE: CCI Newsgate PRODUCTION EQUIPMENT: Hardware — 3-AGFA CL, DL Platesetters PRODUCTION SOFTWARE: CCI Newsgate, Newsway
Note: The Tennessean is owned by Gannett Co., Inc. which owns more than 110 daily newspapers.

OAK RIDGE

THE OAK RIDGER

785 Oak Ridge Tpke, Oak Ridge, Tenn., 37830-7076, Anderson; gen tel (865) 482-1021; adv tel (865) 482-7355; ed tel (865) 220-5502; gen fax (865) 220-5460; adv fax (865) 220-5539; ed fax (865) 482-7834; gen/nat adv e-mail advertising@oakridger.com; disp adv e-mail advertising@oakridger.com; class adv e-mailadvertising@oakridger.com; ed e-mail editor@oakridger.com; web site www.oakridger.com
Group: New Media Investment Group
Published: Mon, Tues, Wed, Thur, Fri
Weekday Frequency: e
Circulation: 7,554
Last Audit: Sworn/Estimate/Non-Audited September 30, 2017
Advertising Rate (weekday/saturday): Open inch rate $15.15
Advertising Rate (sunday): Open inch rate $17.20
News services: AP. **Established:** 1949
Special Editions: Women in Business (Apr); Football (Aug); Greetings (Dec); Progress (Feb); Bride (Jan); Bride (Jun); Gardening (Mar); Outdoor (May); Cooking (Oct); Silver Salute (Sept).
Special Weekly Sections: Weekend Sports, Local (Mon); Business, American Profile (Tue); Best Food, Health (Wed); Garden, Weekend Entertainment (Thur); Real Estate, Weddings, Religion (Fri); Daily TV (Mon-Fri)
Syndicated Publications: USA WEEKEND Magazine (Fri); Relish (Monthly); American Profile (Weekly).
Major Acct...................................Carol Skyberg
Circ. Dir...Steve Traud
Publisher.........................Darrell G. Richardson
News Ed..................................... Tank Johnston
Photographer................................. Scott Fraker
Market Information: TMC.
Mechanical Available: Offset; Black and 3 ROP colors; insert accepted - any; page cutoffs - 22 3/4.
Mechanical Specifications: Type page 11 5/8 x 21 1/2; E - 6 cols, 1 13/16, 1/8 between; A - 6 cols, 1 13/16, 1/8 between; C - 9 cols, 1 3/16, 1/8 between.Equipment & Software: PRESSROOM EQUIPMENT: Reels & Stands — 2-DEV/4-high, 1-DEV/3-high.; MAILROOM EQUIPMENT: Counter Stackers — BG/Count-O-Veyor; Inserters & Stuffers — KAN/480; Tying Machines — 1-MLN/Spirit, 1-Si.; BUSINESS EQUIPMENT: NCR/Unix BUSINESS SOFTWARE: NCR/SMS Business Applications CLASSIFIED EQUIPMENT: Hardware — APP/Mac, 2-PEC; Printers — APP/Mac LaserWriter; CLASSIFIED SOFTWARE: Baseview. DISPLAY EQUIPMENT: Hardware — APP/Power Macs; Printers — 1-APP/Mac LaserWriter 630 Pro; DISPLAY SOFTWARELayout Software — Multi-Ad/Creator. EDITORIAL EQUIPMENT: Hardware — APP/Mac; Printers — MON/1270 Imager, 2-APP/Mac LaserWriter, 1999-Pre Press/Panther 46 EDITORIAL SOFTWARE: Baseview/NewsEdit Pro. PRODUCTION EQUIPMENT: Hardware — 1-Nat/A-250; Cameras — 1-C.

PARIS

THE PARIS POST-INTELLIGENCER

208 E Wood St, Paris, Tenn., 38242-4139, Henry; gen tel (731) 642-1162; gen fax (731) 642-1165; gen/nat adv e-mail advertising@parispi.net; disp adv e-mail advertising@parispi.net; class adv e-mailadvertising@parispi.net; ed e-mail mwilliams@parispi.net; web site www.parispi.net
- 100,000(views) 58,250(visitors)
Published: Mon, Tues, Wed, Thur, Fri
Weekday Frequency: m
Circulation: 4,193
Last Audit: Sworn/Estimate/Non-Audited December 18, 2017
Advertising Rate (weekday/saturday): Open inch rate $10.49
News services: AP, NEA, KFS, Universal Press. **Established:** 1866
Own Printing Facility?: No
Commercial Printers?: No
Special Editions: Brides (Jan); Future Farmers (Feb); Home/lawn/garden (Mar); Cooking school (Mar); Tourism (Apr); Miss Spring (Apr); Graduation (May); Community leaders (Jun); Reader's Choice (Jul); Football (Aug); Fair (Aug); Business Anniversary (Sep); 4-H (Oct); Factbook (Oct); Basketball (Nov); Holiday Gifts (Nov); Last-minute gifts (Dec); Year in review (Dec)
Special Weekly Sections: Best Food, Farm (Wed); Business (Thur); Outdoors, Genealogy (Fri); TV (Daily); Senior, Health (Bi-weekly)
Digital Platform - Tablet: Apple iOS
Bus. Mgr................................Evonne Williams
Circ. Mgr........................................ Tim Forrest
Pub./Ed..................................Michael Williams
News Ed.....................................Glenn Tanner
Outdoors Ed.......................... Steve McCadams
Sports Ed.................................. Tommy Priddy
Prodn. Supt..............................Jimmy Williams
Office Mgr...............................Daniel Williams
Advertising sales......................... Adam Barker
Market Information: Split run.
Mechanical Available: Offset; Black and 3 ROP colors; insert accepted - do not accept mini catalogs; page cutoffs - 22 3/4.
Mechanical Specifications: Type page 11 5/8 x 21 1/2; E - 6 cols, 1 5/6, 1/8 between; A - 6 cols, 1 5/6, 1/8 between; C - 9 cols, 1 3/16, 3/32 between.
Areas Served: Henry County, TN
Delivery Method: Mail, Carrier, Racks

SEVIERVILLE

THE MOUNTAIN PRESS

119 River Bend Dr, Sevierville, Tenn., 37876-1943, Sevier; gen tel (865) 428-0746; adv tel (865) 428-0748; ed tel (865) 428-0748; gen fax (865) 453-4913; disp adv e-mail jwhaley@themountainpress.com; ed e-mail editor@themountainpress.com; web site www.themountainpress.com
- 194,131(views) 32,559(visitors)
Group: Paxton Media Group, LLC
Published: Tues, Wed, Thur, Fri, Sat, Sun
Weekday Frequency: m
Saturday Frequency: m
Circulation: 5,077; 5,077(sat); 5,463(sun)
Last Audit: Sworn/Estimate/Non-Audited September 30, 2017
Advertising Rate (weekday/saturday): Open inch rate $21.11
News services: AP. **Established:** 1882
Own Printing Facility?: Yes
Commercial Printers?: Yes
Special Editions: Football (Aug); Medical Directory (Mar), Health & Fitness (Jan); Newcomer's Guide (Jul); Graduation (May); Reader's Choice (Oct); Breast Cancer Awareness (Oct.).
Special Weekly Sections: Spotlight (F).
Syndicated Publications: Spry (Monthly)
Digital Platform - Mobile: Apple
Digital Platform - Tablet: Apple iOS, Android
Pub...................................Jana M. Thomasson
Adv. Dir... Joi Whaley
Production Dir.................. R. Thomas McCarter
Circulation Sales Manager....... Tammy McGaha
Editor... Rhonda Bletner
Market Information: TMC on Wednesday 15,300
Mechanical Available: Offset; Black and 3 ROP colors; insert accepted; page cutoffs - 22 3/4.
Mechanical Specifications: Type page 10 x 21; 6 columns
Delivery Method: Mail, Newsstand, Carrier, RacksEquipment & Software: PRESSROOM EQUIPMENT: Lines — 9-G/Community single width; Press Drive — 2-HP/50; Folders — G/SSC; Registration System — Duarte/Pin System. MAILROOM EQUIPMENT: Tying Machines — 2-Malow/50; Address Machine — KR/211.; BUSINESS EQUIPMENT: APP/Mac BUSINESS SOFTWARE: Baseview CLASSIFIED EQUIPMENT: Printers — QMS/1660E; CLASSIFIED SOFTWARE: Baseview/Class. DISPLAY EQUIPMENT: Printers — HP/5000; Other Hardware — ECR/VRL 36 HS DISPLAY SOFTWAREAd Make-up Applications — Multi-Ad/Creator 4.0; Layout Software — APP/Mac 4400, APP/Mac 200. EDITORIAL EQUIPMENT: Hardware — Editorial System, APP/Power Mac; Printers — NewGen/Imager Plus 12, ECR/VRL 36 HS-Mako, QMS/1660 EDITORIAL SOFTWARE: Baseview, QPS/QuarkXPress 4.1. PRODUCTION EQUIPMENT: Hardware — 2-APP/Mac LaserWriter, Nu/Flip Top FT40UPNS, 1-NewGen/Imager Plus 12, Polaroid/SprintScan; Cameras — Spartan/III Chemco.

SHELBYVILLE

SHELBYVILLE TIMES-GAZETTE

323 E Depot St, Shelbyville, Tenn., 37160-4027, Bedford; gen tel (931) 684-1200; ed tel (931) 684-1200 ext. 218; gen fax (931) 685-0289; ed fax (931)685-0289; gen/nat adv e-mail ssmith@t-g.com; disp adv e-mail ssmith@t-g.com; class adv e-mailclassified@t-g.com; ed e-mail sfowler@t-g.com; web site www.t-g.com
Group: Rust Communications
Published: Tues, Wed, Thur, Fri, Sun
Weekday Frequency: e
Circulation: 6,566; 6,566(sun)
Last Audit: Sworn/Estimate/Non-Audited September 30, 2017
Advertising Rate (weekday/saturday): Open inch rate $11.25
Advertising Rate (sunday): Open inch rate $15.85
News services: AP, NEA, **Established:** 1948
Own Printing Facility?: Yes
Commercial Printers?: Yes
Special Editions: Private Property (Apr); Back-to-School (Aug); Fashion (Fall); Jaycees (Jan); Dairy (Jun); Farm (Mar); Bride (May); Sports (Monthly); Gift Guide (Nov).
Special Weekly Sections: American Profile, Horse,Farm, Questions Answered (Tue); Business (Wed); Entertainment (Thur); Faith, Garden, Sports (Fri); Life, Leisure, Foods, Family, Parenting, TV, Comics (Sun); TV (Tue-Fri,Sun)
Syndicated Publications: Relish (Monthly); Parade (S); American Profile (Weekly).
Digital Platform - Mobile: Apple
Pub.... Hugh Jones
Gen. Mgr...................................William Mitchell
Bus. Mgr...................................... Becky McBee
Display Adv. Mgr................Sandra (Sissy) Smith
City Ed....................................... John I. Carney
Ed...Sadie Fowler
Circ. Dir................................Olene Standfield
Market Information: TMC.
Mechanical Available: Offset; Black and 3 ROP colors; insert accepted.
Areas Served: 37060
Delivery Method: Mail, Newsstand, Carrier, RacksEquipment & Software: PRESSROOM EQUIPMENT: Lines — 6-KP/Color King Web (Non heat O.S.) 1963.; MAILROOM EQUIPMENT: Tying Machines — 2/Bu.; CLASSIFIED EQUIPMENT: Hardware — Mac; CLASSIFIED SOFTWARE: Baseview/Class Pro. DISPLAY EQUIPMENT: Hardware — Mac; DISPLAY SOFTWARELayout Software — InDesign EDITORIAL EQUIPMENT: Hardware — Mac

UNION CITY

THE MESSENGER

613 E Jackson St, Union City, Tenn., 38261-5239, Obion; gen tel (731) 885-0744; gen fax (731) 885-0782; gen/nat adv e-mail advertising@ucmessenger.com; disp adv e-mail advertising@ucmessenger.com; class adv e-mailucclass@ucmessenger.com; ed e-mail dcritch@ucmessenger.com; web site www.nwtntoday.com
Published: Mon, Tues, Wed, Thur, Fri
Weekday Frequency: e
Circulation: 8,335
Last Audit: Sworn/Estimate/Non-Audited September 30, 2017
Advertising Rate (weekday/saturday): Open inch rate $8.50
News services: AP.
Own Printing Facility?: Yes
Commercial Printers?: Yes
Special Weekly Sections: Business (Mon); Church (Thur); Farm (Tues); Food (Wed).
Pres./Pub................................. David Critchlow
Vice Pres./Office Mgr.............. F. Scott Critchlow
Bus. Mgr....................................Penella Davis
Adv. Mgr., Classified................Glenda Langford
Adv. Mgr., Retail....................... Gloria Chesteen
Farm Ed... Donna Ryder
Sports Ed...................................Mike Hutchens
Women's Ed..............................Darlene Hayes
Online Mgr.................................. Jeremy Leckey
Prodn. Mgr., Pressroom......................Rob Smith
Prodn. Mgr., Mailroom/Post Press John Travatham
Prodn. Mgr., Pre Press...................David Fuzzell
Market Information: TMC.
Mechanical Available: Offset; Black and 3 ROP colors; insert accepted; page cutoffs - 22.
Mechanical Specifications: Type page 11 5/8 x 21; E - 6 cols, 1 13/16, 1/8 between; A - 6 cols, 1 13/16, 1/8 between; C - 9 cols, 1 3/16, 1/8 between.
Delivery Method: Mail, Newsstand, Carrier, RacksEquipment & Software: PRESSROOM EQUIPMENT: Lines — DGM/6 mono; Folders — 2-SLN/2:1, 2-DGM/430.; MAILROOM EQUIPMENT: Counter Stackers — BG/108, 2-BG/Count-D-Veyor; Tying Machines — 2/Bu, 2-/Signode; Address Machine — 1-/Dispensa-Matic.; BUSINESS EQUIPMENT: APP/Mac, Baseview CLASSIFIED EQUIPMENT: Hardware — 2-APP/Mac 4400; Printers — APP/Mac LaserWriter, ECR/Imagesetter; CLASSIFIED SOFTWARE: Baseview. DISPLAY EQUIPMENT: Hardware — 2-APP/Mac G3; Printers — APP/Mac LaserWriter, GCC/Elite XL, ECR/Imagesetter, HP/5simx-Konica/Jetsetter; DISPLAY SOFTWAREAd Make-up Applications — Multi-Ad/Creator.; EDITORIAL EQUIPMENT: Hardware — 2-APP/Mac 6200, 8-APP/Mac G3, 2-APP/Mac 7200, 1-APP/Mac G4; Printers — HP/LaserJet 5simx, Konica/Jetsetter EDITORIAL SOFTWARE: Baseview/NewsEdit Pro. PRODUCTION EQUIPMENT: Hardware — ECR/VR 36 Imagesetter, Nu/631; Cameras — 1-C/Spartan; Scanners — Umax/Vista 56, Umax/Vista 56E, Lf/Leafscan 35 PRODUCTION SOFTWARE: QPS/QuarkXPress 3.32.

TEXAS

ABILENE

ABILENE REPORTER-NEWS

101 Cypress St, Abilene, Texas, 79601-5816, Taylor; gen tel (325) 673-4271; adv tel (325) 670-5280; ed tel (325) 676-6764; gen fax (325) 676-6797; ed fax (325) 670-5242; gen/nat adv e-mail advertising@reporternews.com; disp adv e-mail advertising@reporternews.com; class adv e-mailclassifieds@reporternews.com; ed e-mail doug.williamson@reporternews.com; web site www.reporternews.com
- 1,206,959(views) 277,311(visitors)

Group: Journal Media Group
Published: Mon, Tues, Wed, Thur, Fri, Sat, Sun
Weekday Frequency: m
Saturday Frequency: m
Circulation: 10,926; 10,926(sat); 13,054(sun)
Last Audit: AAM March 31, 2017
Advertising Rate (weekday/saturday): Open inch rate $50.00; $59.47 (Fri)
Advertising Rate (sunday): Open inch rate $59.47
News services: AP, NYT, SHNS. **Established:** 1881
Own Printing Facility?: Yes
Commercial Printers?: Yes
Special Editions: Kickoff (Aug); Big Country Farm and Ranch Show (Feb); Reader's Choice Awards (Jul); Ft. Griffin Fandangle (Jun); Rattlesnake Round-up (Mar); Western Heritage Classic (May); City Sidewalks (Nov); Health Source Directory (July)
Special Weekly Sections: TMC (Wed); Leisure Life (Thur); Spiritual (Fri); Family, Real Estate, Home (Sat); Travel, TV, Auto (Sun); News, Life, Business, Sports, Classified, Local (Daily)
Syndicated Publications: Abilene Magazine (Other); Parade (S).
Digital Platform - Mobile: Apple, Android, Windows, Blackberry
Digital Platform - Tablet: Apple iOS, Android, Windows 7, Blackberry Tablet OS, Kindle, Nook, Kindle Fire
CFO ..... Carla Draper
Circ. Dir. ..... David Rowe
Ed. ..... Barton Cromeens
Editorial Page Ed. ..... Sidney Levesque
Online Dir. ..... Dann Reagan
Prodn. Dir., Opns. ..... Mike Hall
Prodn. Mgr. ..... Christian Wells
Prodn. Mgr., Mailroom (Nights) .. Scott Pentecost
Prodn. Mgr., Pressroom ..... David Nunez
Ed. ..... Doug Williamson
Ad. Director ..... Dave Hedge
Pub./VP, Sales & Mktg ..... David J. Hedges
Circ. Sales Dir. ..... Tim Ritter
Market Information: ADS; Split run; TMC; Zoned editions.
Mechanical Available: Black and 3 ROP colors; insert accepted; page cutoffs - 21.
Mechanical Specifications: Type page 11 5/8 x 21; E - 6 cols, 1 5/6, 1/8 between; A - 6 cols, 1 5/6, 1/8 between; C - 10 cols, 1 5/64, 1/6 between.
Delivery Method: Mail, Newsstand, Carrier, RacksEquipment & Software: PRESSROOM EQUIPMENT: Lines — 3-G/Community single width 1984; 7-G/Headliner double width (offset, open fountain, 4 1/2 deck) 1984; 8-Didde/Web single width 1997; Press Drive — 4-GE/150LP motor; Folders — 2-Regent/2:1, 1-G/506, 1-G/Jaws; Pasters —G/Auto. MAILROOM EQUIPMENT: Counter Stackers — 1-Id, 2-QWI/350; Inserters & Stuffers — KAN/760 Inserters, 1-KAN/4-head Multifeeder; Tying Machines — 1-OVL/JP-80, 2/Dynaric; Address Machine — 1-/Scitex Ink Jet; BUSINESS EQUIPMENT: HP/3000 937LX CLASSIFIED EQUIPMENT: Hardware — Compaq/Proliant 2500; Printers — 1-HP/4000N, HP/2567, 2-HP/5 si; CLASSIFIED SOFTWARE: SII/Sys 25, AT/Enterprise 1.411. DISPLAY EQUIPMENT: Hardware — HP/3000; Printers — HP/LaserJet II, HP/2567; DISPLAY SOFTWAREAd Make-up Applications — CJ/Aim; Layout Software — MEI/ALS. EDITORIAL EQUIPMENT: Hardware — Compaq/Proliant 3000; Printers — HP/Laser Jet 4000 EDITORIAL SOFTWARE: DPS/DBEdit. PRODUCTION EQUIPMENT: Hardware — 2-Nu/Flip Top, 3-Nat, 1-W, 1-Pre Press/Panther Pro 46 Imagesetter, 1-Pre Press/Panther Pro Imagesetter 5300W, 1-Pre Press/Panther Pro 46115; Cameras — 2-C; Scanners — APP/Mac, PixelCraft/Pro Imager 8000 PRODUCTION SOFTWARE: DPS DB Edit.

AMARILLO

AMARILLO GLOBE-NEWS

900 S Harrison St, Amarillo, Texas, 79101-3424, Potter; gen tel (806) 376-4488; adv tel (806) 345-3231; ed tel (806) 345-3358; gen fax (806) 376-9217; adv fax (806) 372-3717; ed fax (806) 373-0810; gen/nat adv e-mail cindy.brown@amarillo.com; disp adv e-mail cindy.brown@amarillo.com; class adv e-mailcindy.ledesma@amarillo.com; ed e-mail michele.mcaffrey@amarillo.com; web site www.amarillo.com
- 4,500,000(views) 480,000(visitors)

Group: GateHouse Media, Inc.
Published: Mon, Tues, Wed, Thur, Fri, Sat, Sun
Weekday Frequency: m
Saturday Frequency: m
Circulation: 21,476; 21,476(sat); 27,524(sun)
Last Audit: AAM September 30, 2016
Advertising Rate (weekday/saturday): Open inch rate $56.49
Advertising Rate (sunday): Open inch rate $65.29
News services: AP, MCT, LAT-WP, DF. **Established:** 1909
Special Editions: Best of Amarillo, Discover Amarillo, Pigskin Preview
Special Weekly Sections: Best Food Day (Wed); Religion (Sat); Farm, Oil, Rea Estate, Business, Arts, Entertainment (Sun)
Syndicated Publications: Amarillo Magazine (Monthly); Parade (S); Relish (Monthly); Athlon (Monthly)
Digital Platform - Mobile: Apple, Android, Windows
Digital Platform - Tablet: Apple iOS
Pub. ..... Les Simpson
Personnel Dir. ..... Valerie Bintliff
Adv. Dir. ..... Mike Distelhorst
Bus. Ed. ..... Jim McBride
Director of Visual Content ... Michael Schumacher
Prodn. Dir., Opns. ..... Mike O'Connor
Ed. ..... Lee Wolverton
VP of Audience ..... Ric Anderson
Nat'l Acc. Mgr. ..... Dewey Shanks
Market Information: Split run; TMC; Zoned editions.
Mechanical Available: Offset; Black and 3 ROP colors; insert accepted; page cutoffs - 22 3/4.
Mechanical Specifications: Type page 13 x 21 1/2; E - 6 cols, 2 1/16, 1/8 between; A - 6 cols, 2 1/16, 1/8 between; C - 10 cols, 1 3/16, 1/8 between.
Areas Served: 79101 and beyond
Delivery Method: Mail, Newsstand, Carrier, RacksEquipment & Software: PRESSROOM EQUIPMENT: Lines — 6-G/Metro (3 half decks) 1979; Folders — G/3:1; Reels & Stands — 6; MAILROOM EQUIPMENT: Counter Stackers — 4-QWI/300; Inserters & Stuffers — 2-GMA/SLS 1000 18:1; Tying Machines — 4-Dynaric/NP-2, 2-Dynaric/Turntable; Wrapping Singles — 2-QWI/Cobra wraps; Control System — PMS; Address Machine — Wm.; BUSINESS EQUIPMENT: 4-IBM/Sys II, 10-Memorex/Telex 11918 BUSINESS SOFTWARE: Lotus 1-2-3, WordPerfect CLASSIFIED EQUIPMENT: Hardware — APP/Mac; CLASSIFIED SOFTWARE: DTI. DISPLAY EQUIPMENT: Hardware — 16-APP/Power Mac; Printers — APP/Mac LaserWriter II, Xante/Accel-a-Writer; Other Hardware — APP/Mac Scanner, Procom/Tape Back-up, NEC/CD-Rom, AP AdSend, Micronet/Optical Drive, Iomega/Jazz Drive, DISPLAY SOFTWAREAd Make-up Applications — Multi-Ad/Creator, Adobe/Illustrator; EDITORIAL EQUIPMENT: Hardware — 32-Gateway/2000, 13-APP/Mac; Printers — Okidata/Microline 320 EDITORIAL SOFTWARE: MPS. PRODUCTION EQUIPMENT: Hardware — AG/Accuset 1000, 1-Nu/Flip Top, AG/Accuset 1500, Xante; Cameras — 2-C/Spartan III; Scanners — AG/Horizon, 4-Microtek/Scanmaker E6 PRODUCTION SOFTWARE: DTI/Adobe Indesign 3.1.

ATHENS

ATHENS DAILY REVIEW

201 S Prairieville St, Athens, Texas, 75751-2541, Henderson; gen tel (903) 675-5626; adv tel (903) 675-5626; ed tel (903) 675-5626; gen fax (903) 675-9450; adv fax (903) 675-6870; ed fax (903) 675-9450; gen/nat adv e-mail adrretail@athensreview.com; disp adv e-mail adrretail@athensreview.com; class adv e-mailadrclass2@athensreview.com; ed e-mail editor@athensreview.com; web site www.athensreview.com

Group: Community Newspaper Holdings, Inc.
Published: Tues, Wed, Thur, Fri, Sat
Weekday Frequency: e
Saturday Frequency: m
Circulation: 4,400; 4,600(sun)
Last Audit: Sworn/Estimate/Non-Audited September 30, 2017
Advertising Rate (weekday/saturday): Open inch rate $12.46
Advertising Rate (sunday): Open inch rate $12.46
News services: AP. **Established:** 1901
Special Editions: Feb: Bridal
March: Business Card Dir., Livestock Show Edition
May: Graduation Edition, Backyard Vacations
Aug: Football Preview
Sept: Business Card Directory, How-to-Guide
Oct: Outdoor Guide, Recipe Guide
Nov: Veterans, Medical Directory
Special Weekly Sections: Best Food Days (Sun/Tue);
Syndicated Publications: HC Magazine: quarterly
Digital Platform - Tablet: Kindle
Pub ..... Lange Svehlak
Nat'lAdv. Dir. ..... Andi Green
Circ. Mgr. ..... Ginger McDaniel
Ed. ..... Jayson Larson
Sports Ed. ..... Benny Rogers
Ed. ..... Jeff Riggs
Classified Adv. Mgr. ..... Nita Sawicki
Areas Served: 75751,,75752, 75124, 75143, 75148, 75147, 75156, 75163, 75756, 75778, 75770,
Delivery Method: Mail, RacksEquipment & Software: PRESSROOM EQUIPMENT: Lines — 6-HI/V-15A (upper former); MAILROOM EQUIPMENT: Tying Machines — 2/Bu; Address Machine — 1-KR/215 (with 211).; CLASSIFIED EQUIPMENT: Hardware — Baseview/Mac; CLASSIFIED SOFTWARE: Baseview. DISPLAY EQUIPMENT: Printers — 2-Pre Press/Panther Imagesetter; DISPLAY SOFTWARELayout Software — APP/Mac. EDITORIAL EQUIPMENT: Hardware — APP/Mac EDITORIAL SOFTWARE: Baseview. PRODUCTION EQUIPMENT: Cameras — 1-Acti/183 PRODUCTION SOFTWARE: QPS/QuarkXPress8

AUSTIN

AUSTIN AMERICAN-STATESMAN

305 S Congress Ave, Austin, Texas, 78704-1200, Travis; gen tel (512) 445-3500; adv tel (512) 445-3742; ed tel (512) 445-3851; gen fax 512-445-1784; adv fax (512) 443-4047; ed fax (512) 445-3679; gen/nat adv e-mail national@statesman.com; disp adv e-mail shary.garza@coxinc.com; class adv e-mailshary.garza@coxinc.com; ed e-mail news@statesman.com; web site www.statesman.com
2,256,161(visitors)

Group: New Media Investment Group
Published: Mon, Tues, Wed, Thur, Fri, Sat, Sun
Weekday Frequency: m
Saturday Frequency: m
Circulation: 97,205; 92,771(sat); 120,408(sun)
Last Audit: AAM December 31, 2016
Advertising Rate (weekday/saturday): Open inch rate $129.60
Advertising Rate (sunday): Open inch rate $152.60
News services: AP, Cox News Service, MCT, LAT-WP, NNS, NYT, TMS. **Established:** 1871
Special Editions: High School & College Football (Aug); Gift Guide (Dec); Healthcare (Jan); This is Austin (Jul); SXSW (Mar); Diversity (Nov); Pro Football Preview (Oct); Austin City Limits Music Festival (Sept).
Special Weekly Sections: Food (Wed); Technology (Mon);Entertainment, Auto (Thur); Entertainment, Health (Fri); Auto, Weekly, Real Estate (Sun); Business, Living, Arts (Daily)
Syndicated Publications: Parade (S); Vista (Sat).
Digital Platform - Mobile: Apple, Android
Digital Platform - Tablet: Apple iOS, Android, Blackberry Tablet OS, Kindle, Nook, Kindle Fire
Vice Pres./CFO ..... Eddie Burns
Vice Pres., Fulfillment/Group Lead ..... Harry Davis
Circ. Dir. ..... Jana Dobson
Ed. ..... Debbie Hiott
Editorial Page Ed. ..... Arnold Garcia
Photo Dir. ..... Zach Ryall
Controller ..... Craig Wohlfort
Adv. Dir. ..... Colleen Brewer
Market Information: Split run; TMC; Zoned editions.
Mechanical Available: Offset; Black and 3 ROP colors; insert accepted; page cutoffs - 22.
Mechanical Specifications: Type page 12 1/2 x 21; E - 6 cols, 2, 1/6 between; A - 6 cols, 2, 1/6 between; C - 10 cols, 1 1/5, 1/9 between.
Areas Served: All of Central Texas
Delivery Method: Carrier, RacksEquipment & Software: PRESSROOM EQUIPMENT: Lines — 9-G/Metroliner double width (5 half decks) 1981; 9-G/Metroliner double width (5 half decks) 1981; 9-G/Metroliner double width (5 half decks) 1984, KBA/(2 Towers); 7-KBA/Towers (43 Couples); Folders — 4-G/3:2, 1-G/2:5:5; MAILROOM EQUIPMENT: Counter Stackers — 9-QWI/351, 3-HL/Monitor; Inserters & Stuffers — 1-S/1472, 1-S/1372, 1-GMA/SLS 2000 30:2, 1-GMA/SLS 1000 14:1; Tying Machines — 9-QWI/NS45 Strap, 2/Oval Strap; Address Machine — 2-Scitex.; BUSINESS EQUIPMENT: 1-IBM/7060-H30, Sun/3500 BUSINESS SOFTWARE: Microsoft/Windows XP, Microsoft/NT, Lawson CLASSIFIED EQUIPMENT: Hardware — AT; Ad Fast/Ad Fax (Future Tense), Ad On Time; Printers — HP; CLASSIFIED SOFTWARE: AT. DISPLAY EQUIPMENT: Hardware — APP/Mac; Printers — HP; Other Hardware — 6-Harlequin, AU, 1-AU/108, 1-AU/3850, 2-AU/3850 Wide DISPLAY SOFTWAREAd Make-up Applications — DTI/AdSpeed 4.3; Layout Software — DTI/Plan Builder. EDITORIAL EQUIPMENT: Hardware — APP/Mac, Sun/Enterprise 4000; Printers — HP EDITORIAL SOFTWARE: DTI/PageSpeed, DTI/SpeedPlanner. PRODUCTION EQUIPMENT: Hardware — 2-BKY, 2-WL/Lith-X-Pozer III, 1-GJ/550; Cameras — 1-C/Newspager I; Scanners — 1-Nikon/Pro Imager 8000, 1-Epson/1640 PRODUCTION SOFTWARE: DTI/AdSpeed 5.5, DTI/ImageSpeed 4.3, DTI/PageSpeed, DTI/Speed Planner 4.3.

BAYTOWN

THE BAYTOWN SUN

1301 Memorial Dr, Baytown, Texas, 77520-2401, Harris; gen tel (281) 422-8302; adv tel (281) 425-8036; ed tel (281) 425-8013; gen fax (281) 427-6283; adv fax (281) 427-6283; ed fax (281) 427-6283; gen/nat adv e-mail carol.skewes@baytownsun.com; disp adv e-mail carol.skewes@baytownsun.com; class adv e-mailjessica.rodriguez@baytownsun.com; ed e-mail janie.gray@baytownsun.com; web site baytownsun.com

Group: Southern Newspapers Inc.
Published: Tues, Wed, Thur, Fri, Sun
Weekday Frequency: m
Saturday Frequency: m
Circulation: 4,126; 4,572(sun)
Last Audit: CAC March 31, 2017
Advertising Rate (weekday/saturday): Open inch rate $57.34
Advertising Rate (sunday): Open inch rate $57.34
News services: AP, NEA, CNS, TMS. **Established:** 1922
Own Printing Facility?: Yes
Commercial Printers?: No

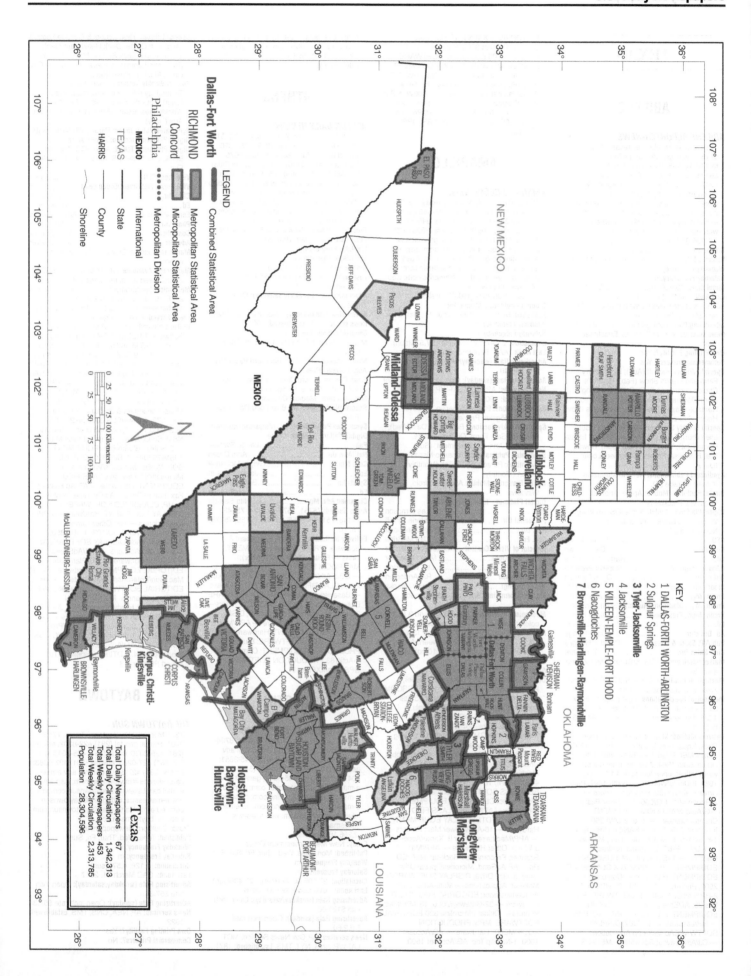

LEGEND

Dallas-Forth Worth — Combined Statistical Area

RICHMOND — Metropolitan Statistical Area

Concord — Micropolitan Statistical Area

Philadelphia ••••• — Metropolitan Division

MEXICO — International

TEXAS — State

HARRIS — County

— Shoreline

KEY

1 DALLAS-FORTH WORTH-ARLINGTON
2 Sulphur Springs
3 Tyler-Jacksonville
4 Jacksonville
5 KILLEEN-TEMPLE-FORT HOOD
6 Nacogdoches
7 Brownsville-Harlingen-Raymondville

Texas

Total Daily Newspapers	67
Total Daily Circulation	1,342,313
Total Weekly Newspapers	453
Total Weekly Circulation	2,313,785
Population	28,304,596

Special Editions: Forecast (Feb); Back-to-School (Jul); Coastal Views (Jun); Forecast (Mar); Outdoors (Sept).
Special Weekly Sections: Arts & Entertainment (Fri); TV Guide (S); Religious (Sat); Business (Tues); Best Food Days (Wed).
Syndicated Publications: USA WEEKEND Magazine (S); American Profile (Weekly).
Circ. Mgr. .... Joshua Hart
Business Manager/HR .... Sandy Denson
Ed. / Pub. .... Janie Gray
Adv. Mgr. .... Gordon Gallatin
Mng. Ed. .... David Bloom
Sports Ed. .... Dave Rogers
Market Information: ADS; TMC; Zoned editions.
Mechanical Available: Offset; Black and 3 ROP colors; insert accepted; page cutoffs - 21.
Mechanical Specifications: Type page 12 1/2 x 21; E - 6 cols, 2 1/16, 1/8 between; A - 6 cols, 2 1/16, 1/8 between; C - 9 cols, 1 5/16, 1/8 between.
Delivery Method: Mail, Newsstand, Carrier, RacksEquipment & Software: CLASSIFIED EQUIPMENT: Printers — APP/Mac LaserWriter II NTX; CLASSIFIED SOFTWARE: Mk/Proprietary. DISPLAY EQUIPMENT: Hardware — 2-APP/Mac IIcx, 2-APP/Mac IIsi; Printers — APP/Mac LaserWriter II NTX; DISPLAY SOFTWAREAd Make-up Applications — Mk/Proprietary; Layout Software — Mk/4000. EDITORIAL EQUIPMENT: Hardware — Mk/4000, 13-Mk/AT/APP/Mac Quadra 700; Printers — APP/Mac LaserWriter II NTX EDITORIAL SOFTWARE: Mk/Proprietary. PRODUCTION EQUIPMENT: Hardware — APP/Mac LaserWriter II NTX; Cameras — 1-C/Spartan III.

BEAUMONT

THE BEAUMONT ENTERPRISE

380 Main St, Beaumont, Texas, 77701-2331, Jefferson; gen tel (409) 880-0773; adv tel (409) 838-2819; ed tel (409) 838-2802; gen fax (409) 880-0757; adv fax (409) 838-2865; ed fax (409) 880-0757; gen/nat adv e-mail dvalentine@beaumontenterprise.com; disp adv e-mail dvalentine@beaumontenterprise.com; class adv e-mailchatcher@hearstnp.com; ed e-mail tkelly@hearstnp.com; web site www.beaumontenterprise.com - 6,000,000(views) 250,000(visitors); web site 2 SoutheastTexas.com - 7,000,000(views) 285,000(visitors)
Group: Hearst Communications, Inc.
Published: Mon, Tues, Wed, Thur, Fri, Sat, Sun
Weekday Frequency: m
Saturday Frequency: m
Circulation: 18,477; 18,477(sat); 26,422(sun)
Last Audit: AAM June 30, 2016
Branch Offices: Jasper Texas
Advertising Rate (weekday/saturday): Open inch rate $23
Advertising Rate (sunday): Open inch rate $27
Online Advertising Rate: $8 CPM
News services: HN, NYT, AP. **Established:** 1880
Own Printing Facility?: Yes
Commercial Printers?: No
Special Editions: Football Glossy Magazine(Aug); Readers Choice awards (April), Everything Book (Oct)
Special Weekly Sections: Health Plus (Wed.), CAT5-arts/entertainment (Thurs.), Food (Tues.), Auto (Fri.), Real Estate (Sunday), extra!(Sunday), Hardin County News (Wed.) Jasper News Boy (Wed.)
Proprietary Publications: VIP Glossy Magazine (mthly)
VIP Homes Glossy Magazine (bi-annual)
EventsBook Glossy Magazine (mthly)
Digital Platform - Mobile: Apple, Android, Windows, Blackberry
Digital Platform - Tablet: Apple iOS, Android, Windows 7, Blackberry Tablet OS, Kindle, Nook, Kindle Fire
Circ. Dir., Opns .... Jeffrey Reedy
Ed. .... Timothy M. Kelly
Editorial Page Ed. .... Tom Taschinger
Managing Editor .... Ashley Sanders
Mgmt. Info Servs. Mgr. .... Freddie Campbell
Publisher .... Mark Adkins
Circulation Director .... Paul Banister
Chief Revenue Officer .... Craig Hatcher
Advertising Director .... Donna Valentine
Market Information: Split run; TMC;
Mechanical Available: Offset; Black and 3 ROP colors; insert accepted - card, tab, standard; page cutoffs - 22 3/4.
Mechanical Specifications: Type page 11 1/2 x 21 1/2; E - 6 cols, 1 3/4, 1/8 between; A - 6 cols, 1 3/4, 1/8 between; C - 9 cols, 1 1/6, 1/8 between.
Areas Served: Beaumont/Port Arthur (Jefferson County)
Orange/Vidor (Orange County)
Lumberton (Hardin County)
Jasper (Jasper County)
Delivery Method: Mail, Newsstand, Carrier, RacksEquipment & Software: PRESSROOM EQUIPMENT: Lines — 9-G/Cosmo 3502 (double balloon); Pasters —7-G/Automatic. MAILROOM EQUIPMENT: Counter Stackers — 2-QWI/300; Inserters & Stuffers — 1-S/72P, HI/12 Hopper; Tying Machines — 2-Dynaric/NPI; Wrapping Singles — 2-Id.; BUSINESS SOFTWARE: ADMARC, Discus CLASSIFIED EQUIPMENT: Hardware — APT, Gateway, ALR/8200; Gateway/PC E1000; Printers — IBM/Network 17 printer; CLASSIFIED SOFTWARE: APT. DISPLAY EQUIPMENT: Printers — Xante/Accel-A-Writer 3G; Other Hardware — Pixelcraft/8000 Flatbed Scanner, Polaroid/Sprintscan Negative Scanner DISPLAY SOFTWAREAd Make-up Applications — QPS/QuarkXPress 4.0, Multi-Ad/Creator G2, Adobe/Photoshop 5.5; Layout Software — OS 8.5, APP/Mac G3, Multi-Ad/Creator. EDITORIAL EQUIPMENT: Hardware — APT, Gateway, ALR/8200/Gateway/PC 3200, Gateway/PC 4200; Printers — HP/5000 EDITORIAL SOFTWARE: APT. PRODUCTION EQUIPMENT: Hardware — 2-ECR/Knockout (Harlequin RIP), 1-Nu/Flip Top FT40UPNS, 2-C/OL Conveyor System PRODUCTION SOFTWARE: QPS/QuarkXPress 4.0.
Note: High School Athletic Awards SoutheastTexas.com

BIG SPRING

BIG SPRING HERALD

PO Box 1431, Big Spring, Texas, 79721-1431, Howard; gen tel (432) 263-7331; gen fax (432) 264-7205; gen/nat adv e-mail advertising@bigspringherald.com; disp adv e-mail advertising@bigspringherald.com; class adv e-mailadvertising@bigspringherald.com; ed e-mail editor@bigspringherald.com; web site www.bigspringherald.com - 700,000(views)
Group: Horizon Publications Inc.
Published: Mon, Tues, Wed, Thur, Fri, Sun
Weekday Frequency: e
Circulation: 4,337; 5,364(sun)
Last Audit: Sworn/Estimate/Non-Audited September 30, 2017
Advertising Rate (weekday/saturday): Open inch rate $16.55
Advertising Rate (sunday): Open inch rate $17.85
News services: AP. **Established:** 1904
Own Printing Facility?: Yes
Commercial Printers?: Yes
Special Editions: Football (Aug); Year In Review (Jan); Community Guide (Jul); Rodeo (Jun); Progress (Mar); Christmas Shopping Guide (Nov).
Special Weekly Sections: Health, Medical (Mon); Food, Entertainment (Wed); Youth (Tue); Church, Civic (Fri); Business, TV (Sun)
Syndicated Publications: TV-Leisure (newsprint) (Other); American Profile (S).
Pub .... Glenn Stifflemire
Bookkeeper .... Rachael Martinez
Adv. Mgr., Retail .... Rick Nunez
Circ. Mgr. .... Robert Smith
News Ed. .... Bill McClellan
Prodn. Mgr. .... Tony Hernandez
Market Information: TMC.
Mechanical Available: Offset; Black and 3 ROP colors; insert accepted; page cutoffs - 22 3/4.
Mechanical Specifications: Type page 12 1/2 x 21 1/2; E - 6 cols, 1 3/4, 1/16 between; A - 6 cols, 1 3/4, 1/16 between; C - 9 cols, 1 1/8, 1/16 between.
Areas Served: 79720 plus
Delivery Method: Mail, Newsstand, Carrier, RacksEquipment & Software: PRESSROOM EQUIPMENT: Lines — 8-G/Community 1974; MAILROOM EQUIPMENT: Tying Machines — Delta/Strapping AQ7.; BUSINESS EQUIPMENT: 1-IBM/PC-XT, IBM/PC-AT, 1-IBM/PC BUSINESS SOFTWARE: PBS CLASSIFIED EQUIPMENT: Hardware — 2-APP/Power Mac 180-35; Printers — APP/Mac LaserWriter 16-600PS; CLASSIFIED SOFTWARE: Baseview. DISPLAY EQUIPMENT: Hardware — APP/Mac Performa 6200, APP/iMac; Printers — Xante/Accel-a-Writer 8300; Other Hardware — 1-EZ/Photo Scanner DISPLAY SOFTWAREAd Make-up Applications — QPS/QuarkXPress, Adobe/Illustrator, Aldus/FreeHand, Baseview/NewsEdit; Layout Software — APP/Mac Performa 6200, APP/iMac. EDITORIAL EQUIPMENT: Hardware — APP/Mac, 10-APP/Mac Performa 6200/1-PowerBook/190 Laptop, Umax/1200 Scanner, 1-Polaroid/SprintScan 35-LE; Printers — 1-APP/Mac 16/1600 PS, 1-Laserwriter/II EDITORIAL SOFTWARE: QPS/QuarkXPress, Adobe/Illustrator, Aldus/FreeHand, Baseview/Ne PRODUCTION EQUIPMENT: Hardware - Roconex; Cameras — 1-R/500.

BORGER

BORGER NEWS-HERALD

207 S Main St, PO, Borger, Texas, 79007-4715, Hutchinson; gen tel (806) 273-5611; adv tel (806) 273-2552; ed tel (806) 273-2552; gen fax (806) 273-2552; gen/nat adv e-mail publisher@borgernewsherald.com; disp adv e-mail publisher@borgernewsherald.com; class adv e-mailclassifieds@borgernewsherald.com; ed e-mail editor@borgernewsherald.com; web site www.borgernewsherald.com - 40,000(views)
Group: Horizon Publications Inc.
Published: Mon, Tues, Wed, Thur, Fri, Sun
Weekday Frequency: m
Saturday Frequency: m
Circulation: 2,750; 3,000(sun)
Last Audit: Sworn/Estimate/Non-Audited September 30, 2017
Newspaper Reps: Tom Hinde - Publisher
Branch Offices: None
Advertising Rate (weekday/saturday): Open inch rate $10.50
Advertising Rate (sunday): Open inch rate $10.50
Online Advertising Rate: Please call
News services: AP **Established:** 1926
Own Printing Facility?: Yes
Commercial Printers?: Yes
Special Editions: County Livestock Show (Feb.) Tourism Guide (Apr.) Graduate (May) Best of the Best (July) HOPE Gala (Aug.) Patriots (Sep.) Education (Sep.) Cancer Awareness (Oct.) Veteran's Day (Nov.) Holiday Shopping Guide (Dec.)
Special Weekly Sections: Church (Fri); TV (Sun); Business (Daily)
Syndicated Publications: Relish (Monthly); TV tab (S); American Profile (Bi-Weekly).
Digital Platform - Mobile: Other
Digital Platform - Tablet: Other
Publisher .... Tom Hinde
Market Information: TMC
Mechanical Available: Offset; Black and 3 ROP colors; insert accepted - cards, catalogs; page cutoffs - 22 3/4.
Mechanical Specifications: Type page 13 x 21 1/2; E - 6 cols, 2 1/16, 1/8 between; A - 6 cols, 2 1/16, 1/8 between; C - 8 cols, 1 1/2, 1/8 between.
Areas Served: Hutchinson County, TX.
Delivery Method: Mail, Newsstand, Carrier, RacksEquipment & Software: PRESSROOM EQUIPMENT: Lines — 6-G; MAILROOM EQUIPMENT: Tying Machines — 1-Bu/77011.; BUSINESS EQUIPMENT: 1-IBM/PS2 MODEL 30, 1-Unisys/5000-50 CLASSIFIED SOFTWARE: Baseview. DISPLAY EQUIPMENT: Other Hardware — Raster/Ops. DISPLAY SOFTWAREAd Make-up Applications — Multi-Ad/Creator; EDITORIAL SOFTWARE: Baseview. PRODUCTION EQUIPMENT: Hardware — 1-Nu; Cameras — Acti; Scanners — APP/Mac Scanner.

BRENHAM

BRENHAM BANNER-PRESS

2430 S Chappell Hill St, Brenham, Texas, 77833-6098, Washington; gen tel (979) 836-7956; adv tel (979) 836-7956; gen fax (979) 830-8577; adv fax (979) 836-0727; ed fax (979) 830-8577; gen/nat adv e-mail mmueck@brenhambanner.com; disp adv e-mail retail@brenhambanner.com; class adv e-mailclassified@brenhambanner.com; ed e-mail edit@brenhambanner.com; web site www.brenhambanner.com - 1,311,312(views) 483,706(visitors)
Group: Hartman Newspapers LP
Published: Tues, Wed, Thur, Fri, Sun
Weekday Frequency: e
Circulation: 5,730; 5,860(sun)
Last Audit: CVC June 30, 2015
Advertising Rate (weekday/saturday): Open inch rate $8.70
Advertising Rate (sunday): Open inch rate $9.24
Online Advertising Rate: Run of site $100.00 CPM; Banner $300.00 CPM; Homepage $400.00 CPM
News services: AP, NEA. **Established:** 1866
Own Printing Facility?: Yes
Commercial Printers?: Yes
Special Editions: Visitor's Guide (Apr); Back-to-School (Aug); Gift Guide (Dec); Progress (Jan); Real Estate Guide (Mar); Graduation (May); Cookbook (Nov); Businesswomen (Oct); Visitor's Guide (Sept); Spring Sports Recap (June); Dining Guide (June)
Special Weekly Sections: Food (Tue); Church (Fri);
Syndicated Publications: Relish (Monthly); TV Guide/Scene (S)
Digital Platform - Mobile: Apple
Digital Platform - Tablet: Apple iOS
Office Mgr. .... Annell Meyer
Gen. Mgr. .... Danny Hukel
Adv. Director .... Helen Nowicki
Features Ed. .... Bud Chambers
Editor .... Arthur Hahn
Teen-Age/Youth Ed. .... Melissa Mccaghren
Women's Ed. .... Melissa Mcaghren
Publisher .... Michael Mueck
Market Information: TMC.
Mechanical Available: Offset; Black and 3 ROP colors; insert accepted; page cutoffs - 22 3/4.
Mechanical Specifications: Type page 11.625 x 21, 6 cols.
Areas Served: Brenham, Burton, Washington, Chappell Hill, Round Top, Carmine
Delivery Method: Mail, Newsstand, Carrier, RacksEquipment & Software: PRESSROOM EQUIPMENT: Lines — 5-WPC/Leader.; MAILROOM EQUIPMENT: Counter Stackers — BG; Inserters & Stuffers — 3/KAN; Tying Machines — 2-/MLN.; BUSINESS EQUIPMENT: APP/Mac BUSINESS SOFTWARE: Baseview CLASSIFIED EQUIPMENT: Hardware — APP/Mac; Imagesetter; Printers — APP/Mac LaserWriter II NTX, Okidata/Microline 320; CLASSIFIED SOFTWARE: Baseview, QPS. DISPLAY EQUIPMENT: Hardware — Baseview; Printers — APP/Mac LaserWriter II NTX; Other Hardware — Imagesetter DISPLAY SOFTWAREAd Make-up Applications — QPS/QuarkXPress; Layout Software — QPS/QuarkXPress. EDITORIAL EQUIPMENT: Hardware — APP/Mac/Imagesetter; Printers — APP/Mac LaserWriter II NTX EDITORIAL SOFTWARE: Baseview, QPS. PRODUCTION EQUIPMENT: Hardware — B; Cameras — C/Spartan II PRODUCTION SOFTWARE: QPS/QuarkXPress.

BROWNSVILLE

THE BROWNSVILLE HERALD

1135 E Van Buren St, Brownsville, Texas, 78520-7055, Cameron; gen tel (956) 542-4301; adv tel (956) 982-6651; ed tel (956) 982-6628; gen fax (956) 982-4201; adv fax (956) 982-4201; ed fax (956) 542-0840; gen/nat adv e-mail lmedrano@brownsvilleherald.com; disp adv e-mail lmedrano@brownsvilleherald.com; class adv e-maillmedrano@brownsvilleherald.com; ed e-mail rhenry@brownsvilleherald.com; web

site www.brownsvilleherald.com
Group: AIM Media Texas LLC
Published: Mon, Tues, Wed, Thur, Fri, Sat, Sun
Weekday Frequency: m
Saturday Frequency: m
Circulation: 10,031; 10,031(sat); 11,684(sun)
Last Audit: AAM September 30, 2016
Advertising Rate (weekday/saturday): Open inch rate $23.79
Advertising Rate (sunday): Open inch rate $27.48
News services: AP, MCT.
Special Editions: Mother's Day (Apr); Back-to-School (Aug); Christmas Gift Guide (Dec); Golden Years (Feb); Health & Fitness (Jan); Today's Women (Jul); Home & Garden (Mar); Spring Car Care (May); Welcome Winter Texans (Nov); National Car Care (Oct); Fall Fashion (Sept).
Special Weekly Sections: El Extra (Fri); Business (S); Education Extra (Wed).
Syndicated Publications: Parade (S).
Digital Platform - Mobile: Apple, Android, Windows
Digital Platform - Tablet: Apple iOS, Android
Pub. .... Frank Escobedo
Business Manager .... Melva Juarez
Advertising Director .... Linda Medrano
Editor .... Ryan Henry
Circulation Director .... Gonzalez Abe
IT Systems Manager .... Odie Carden
Education Services Director . Dr. Sandy McGehee
Market Information: Split run; TMC; Zoned editions.
Mechanical Available: Offset; Black and 3 ROP colors; insert accepted; page cutoffs - 22 3/4.
Mechanical Specifications: Type page 13 x 21; E - 6 cols, 2 1/16, 1/8 between; A - 6 cols, 2 1/16, 1/8 between; C - 10 cols, 1 1/4, 1/16 between.
Delivery Method: Newsstand, Carrier, RacksEquipment & Software: PRESSROOM EQUIPMENT: Lines — 6-HI/Cotrell 845; 4-HI/Cotrell 845; Folders — 2-HI/2:1.; MAILROOM EQUIPMENT: Tying Machines — 2-Si; Address Machine — 1/Ch.; BUSINESS EQUIPMENT: 1-IBM CLASSIFIED EQUIPMENT: Hardware — APT.; DISPLAY SOFTWARELayout Software — APT. EDITORIAL EQUIPMENT: Hardware — APT. PRODUCTION EQUIPMENT: Hardware — 2-Tegra/Varityper, Nu/Lithoplate; Cameras — 1-C.

BRYAN

THE EAGLE
1729 Briarcrest Dr, Bryan, Texas, 77802-2712, Brazos; gen tel (979) 776-4444; adv tel (979) 776-4444 ext. 300; ed tel (979) 776-4444 ext. 401; gen fax (979) 774-0496; adv fax (979) 774-0053; ed fax (979) 776-8923; gen/nat adv e-mail news@theeagle.com; disp adv e-mail advertising@theeagle.com; ed e-mail news@theeagle.com; web site www.theeagle.com
 - 2,531,143(views) 504,463(visitors); web site 2 aggiesports.com - 267,517(views) 52,968(visitors); web site 3 myaggienation.com - 60,732(views) 18,926(visitors); web site 4shopbrazos.com - 59,822(views) 28,656(visitors)
Group: BH Media Group
Published: Mon, Tues, Wed, Thur, Fri, Sat, Sun
Weekday Frequency: m
Saturday Frequency: m
Circulation: 13,088; 13,088(sat); 15,188(sun)
Last Audit: AAM March 31, 2016
Newspaper Reps: Rod Armstrong, Financial Director
Kelly Brown, Editor
Sean Lewis, Advertising Director
Greg Parker, Circulation Director
Mark Wilson, Production Director
Advertising Rate (weekday/saturday): Open inch rate $30.00
News services: AP. **Established:** 1889
Own Printing Facility?: Yes
Commercial Printers?: Yes
Special Editions: Back-to-School (Aug); Bridal Showcase (Jan); Senior Adults (Jun); Lawn & Garden (Mar); Holiday on the Brazos (Nov); Home Builders (Oct).
Special Weekly Sections: Business (S); Religion Pages (Sat); Entertainment (Thur); Best Food Days (Wed).

Syndicated Publications: Parade (S); American Profile (Weekly); Athlon (Weekly); Relish (M monthly)
Digital Platform - Mobile: Apple, Android
Digital Platform - Tablet: Apple iOS
Pub. .... Crystal Dupre
Finance Dir. .... Rod Armstrong
Circ. Dir. .... Greg Parker
Dir. Mail Mgr. .... Wayne Nedbalek
Exec. Ed. ....Kelly Brown
Ed. Page Ed. ....Robert C. Borden
News Ed. ....Darren Benson
Sports Ed. ....Robert Cessna
Mgmt. Info Servs. Mgr. .... Ben Tedrick
Prod. Dir. ....Mark Manning
Mailroom Mgr. ....Donald Crawford
Pre Press Mgr. ....Tammy Zimmerman
Market Information: TMC
Mechanical Available: Offset; Black and 3 ROP colors; insert accepted - any; page cutoffs - 22 3/4.
Mechanical Specifications: Type page 11 5/8 x 21 1/2; E - 6 cols, 2 1/16, 1/8 between; A - 6 cols, 2 1/16, 1/8 between; C - 9 cols, 1 3/8, 1/16 between.
Areas Served: 77845, 77801, 77802, 77803, 77807, 77808, 77850,77840, 77837, 77856, 77868, 77836, 77864, 77871
Delivery Method: Mail, Newsstand, Carrier, RacksEquipment & Software: PRESSROOM EQUIPMENT: Lines — 9-G/Urbanite single width 1979; Press Drive — Fin/125 h.p. motor.; MAILROOM EQUIPMENT: Counter Stackers — 2-Id/NS660 Counter Stacker, 1-QWI/400; Inserters & Stuffers — 1-NP/1372; Tying Machines — 1-MLN/ML2EE, MLN/SP 330, Sterling/GP30C; Address Machine — 1-KR/12.; BUSINESS EQUIPMENT: HP/3000, PC Network BUSINESS SOFTWARE: PeopleSoft, Microsoft/Office CLASSIFIED EQUIPMENT: Hardware, APP/Mac, APP/Mac G3, APP/iMac 400SE; 1-APP/Mac Server; Printers — HP/LaserJet 4MV; CLASSIFIED SOFTWARE: Baseview/Ad Manager Pro 2.2. DISPLAY EQUIPMENT: Hardware — APP/Mac 7300-200, APP/Mac G3, APP/Mac G4; Printers — HP/LJ 4MV, HP/LJ5000; DISPLAY SOFTWAREAd Make-up Applications — QPS/QuarkXPress 4.12, Adobe/Photoshop 5.5; Layout Software — Baseview/Page Director, MEI/ALS 2.1. EDITORIAL EQUIPMENT: Hardware — Ethernet, Printers — Dell PC, HP/LaserJet 4MV, HP/LJ 5000 EDITORIAL SOFTWARE: QPS/QuarkXPress 4.11, Adobe/Photoshop 5.5, Baseview/NewsEdit Pro 3.2, Baseview/Ique Server 3.3. PRODUCTION EQUIPMENT: Hardware — 1-Nu/FT40 APNS, 1-Douthitt/Gemini 29X40, 1-Nu/FT40 APNS; Cameras — 1-C/Spartan II; Scanners — HP/ScanJet 4c, Nikon/1000-35, Lf/Leafscan 35, AII/APS Scan 3750, Microtek/ScanMaker 9600XL, AU/Copydot PRODUCTION SOFTWARE: QPS/QuarkXPress 4.11, Adobe/PageM

CLEBURNE

CLEBURNE TIMES-REVIEW
108 S Anglin St, Cleburne, Texas, 76031-5602, Johnson; gen tel 817-645-2441; adv tel (817)645-2441; ed tel (817)645-2441; gen fax 817-556-0879; adv fax (817) 556-0879; ed fax (817)645-4020; gen/nat adv e-mail ralexander@trcle.com; disp adv e-mail ralexander@trcle.com; class adv e-mailtslade@trele.com; ed e-mail dgosser@trcle.com; web site www.cleburnetimesreview.com
 - 350,000(views) 82,000(visitors)
Group: Community Newspaper Holdings, Inc.
Published: Tues, Wed, Thur, Fri, Sat
Weekday Frequency: e
Saturday Frequency: e
Circulation: 2,400; 2,700(sat)
Last Audit: Sworn/Estimate/Non-Audited September 1, 2017
Advertising Rate (weekday/saturday): Open inch rate $10.00
Advertising Rate (sunday): Open inch rate $10.00
News services: AP. **Established:** 1904
Own Printing Facility?: No
Commercial Printers?: No
Special Editions: Football (Aug); Whistle Stop Christmas (Dec); Chamber of Commerce

(monthly); Cleburne This Is Texas (Jan)
Special Weekly Sections: Best Food Days (T)
Syndicated Publications: Relish (Monthly); USA WEEKEND Magazine (S); American Profile (Weekly).
Digital Platform - Mobile: Apple, Android, Windows
Digital Platform - Tablet: Apple iOS, Android, Windows 7, Blackberry Tablet OS, Kindle, Nook, Kindle Fire
Pub./ Adv. Dir. .... Kay Helms
Managing Editor .... Dale Gosser
News Editor ....Monica Faram
Market Information: TMC.
Mechanical Available: Offset; Black and 3 ROP colors; insert accepted; page cutoffs - 22 3/4.
Mechanical Specifications: Type page 10 1/4 x 21 1/4; E - 6 cols, 1 9/16, 1/8 between; A - 6 cols, 1 9/16, 1/8 between; C - 6 cols, 1 9/16, 1/8 between.
Areas Served: 76031 76033 76009 76028 76058 76059 76044 76050 76093 76036
Delivery Method: Mail, Newsstand, RacksEquipment & Software: PRESSROOM EQUIPMENT: Lines — 6-G/Community 1976; MAILROOM EQUIPMENT: Tying Machines — 1/MLN; Address Machine — Wm.; BUSINESS EQUIPMENT: PC, DOS BUSINESS SOFTWARE: Brainworks CLASSIFIED EQUIPMENT: Hardware — APP/Power Mac; CLASSIFIED SOFTWARE: Baseview/Ad Manager Pro. DISPLAY EQUIPMENT: Hardware — APP/Power Mac; Printers — 1-APP/Mac LaserWriter, Pre Press/Panther, HP/11x17 LaserPrinter; DISPLAY SOFTWAREAd Make-up Applications — Indesign; Layout Software — APP/Power Mac. EDITORIAL EQUIPMENT: Hardware — APP/Power Mac; Printers — Pre Press/Panthers, HP/11x17 LaserPrinter EDITORIAL SOFTWARE: Baseview/NewsEdit Pro. PRODUCTION EQUIPMENT: Hardware — Pre Press/VT1200, Adobe/Photoshop 4.0.1, Pre Press/Panther Pro; Cameras — AG, Epson/Digital, Kk/Digital; Scanners — Umax/Vista 12 PRODUCTION SOFTWARE: Indesign

CLUTE

THE FACTS
720 S Main St, Clute, Texas, 77531-5411, Brazoria; gen tel (979) 265-7411; adv tel (979)265-7411; ed tel (979)265-7411; gen fax (979) 265-9052; adv fax (979)265-9052; ed fax (979)265-9052; gen/nat adv e-mail cindy.cornette@thefacts.com; disp adv e-mail cindy.cornette@thefacts.com; class adv e-mailclassifieds@thefacts.com; ed e-mail michael.morris@thefacts.com; web site www.thefacts.com
 - 2,517,502(views) 718,935(visitors)
Group: Southern Newspapers Inc.
Published: Mon, Tues, Wed, Thur, Fri, Sat, Sun
Weekday Frequency: m
Saturday Frequency: m
Circulation: 12,457; 12,457(sat); 13,498(sun)
Last Audit: AAM March 30, 2015
Advertising Rate (weekday/saturday): Open inch rate $16.60
Advertising Rate (sunday): Open inch rate $17.90
News services: AP, NEA. **Established:** 1913
Own Printing Facility?: Yes
Commercial Printers?: Yes
Special Editions: Fishing (Apr); Fashion (Aug); Chamber of Commerce (Feb); Bridal (Jan); Profile/Progress (Jul); Fishing Fiesta (Jun); Spring Fashion (Mar); Brazoria County Fair (Oct); Football (Sept).
Special Weekly Sections: Best Food Day (Wed); Entertainment (Fri); Religion (Sat); Lifestyle (Wed/Sun); Outdoor (Thur/Sun); Business, Sports (Daily)
Syndicated Publications: USA WEEKEND Magazine (S).
Digital Platform - Mobile: Apple, Android
Digital Platform - Tablet: Apple iOS, Android
Pub./Ed. ....Bill Cornwell
Gen. Mgr. .... Judy Starnes
Adv. Dir. .... Cindy Cornette
Managing Ed. .... Yvonne Mintz
Info Servs./Online Mgr. .... Waylon Smart
Prodn. Mgr. .... Frankie Ramirez
Prodn. Mgr., Mailroom ....Glenn Blount
Business Mgr. ....Gloria Ashworth

Circ. Mgr. .... Beth Swintek
Market Information: TMC; Zoned editions.
Mechanical Available: Offset; Black and 3 ROP colors; insert accepted; page cutoffs - 22 3/4.
Mechanical Specifications: Type page 13 x 21; E - 6 cols, 2 1/16, 1/8 between; A - 6 cols, 2 1/16, 1/8 between; C - 9 cols, 1 3/8, 1/16 between.
Delivery Method: Mail, Newsstand, Carrier, RacksEquipment & Software: PRESSROOM EQUIPMENT: Lines — G/Urbanite 35 1993; Press Drive — A/C Drive Motors w/ Belt to Drive Shaft; Folders — G/500; Reels & Stands — Roll/Stands.; MAILROOM EQUIPMENT: Counter Stackers — HL/Monitor; Inserters & Stuffers — HI; Tying Machines — MLN; Address Machine — Miller, Bevgo.; BUSINESS SOFTWARE: Quattro/Pro, FileMaker Pro CLASSIFIED EQUIPMENT: Hardware — 7-APP/Power Mac 7300, 1-APP/Power Mac 7100, 1-APP/Mac Quadra 650; Printers — APP/Mac LaserWriter IIq, TI/Omni 800, LaserMaster/Unity, APP/Mac LaserWriter 16/600; CLASSIFIED SOFTWARE: Baseview, Adobe/Photoshop, Adobe/Illustrator. DISPLAY EQUIPMENT: Hardware — 3-APP/Mac IIci, 2-APP/Power Mac 7100, 2-APP/Power Mac 8600; Printers — APP/Mac LaserWriter IIq, APP/Mac LaserWriter 16/600; Other Hardware — HP/ DISPLAY SOFTWAREAd Make-up Applications — Aldus/PageMaker, QPS/QuarkXPress, Multi-Ad/Creator, Adobe/Illustrator, Adobe/Photoshop; EDITORIAL EQUIPMENT: Hardware — 7-PC, 5-APP/Mac Centris 650, 2-APP/Mac IIc, 1-APP/Power Mac 8500, APP/Mac Quadra, 2-APP/Power Mac 7100, 1-APP/Power Mac 8600/Lf/AP Leaf Picture Desk, 2-Umax/Scanner, 1-Nikon/Coolscan 1000, 1-APP/Mac 1400 Laptop; Printers — APP/Mac PRODUCTION EQUIPMENT: Hardware — APP/Mac LaserWriter IIq, APP/Mac LaserWriter Pro 630, ECR/3850, 2-APP/Mac LaserWriter 16/600PS; Cameras — C/Spartan III with Transport; Scanners — ECR/Autokon 1000 PRODUCTION SOFTWARE: QPS/QuarkXPress 3.32.

CONROE

THE COURIER OF MONTGOMERY COUNTY
100 Avenue A, Conroe, Texas, 77301-2946, Montgomery; gen tel (281) 378-1950; adv tel (281) 378-1950; ed tel (281) 378-1950; gen fax (936) 521-3301; adv fax (936) 521-3392; ed fax (936) 521-3302; gen/nat adv e-mail bmiller-fergerson@hcnonline.com; disp adv e-mail tlegg@hcnonline.com; class adv e-mailejames@hcnonline.com; ed e-mail adubois@hcnonline.com; web site www.yourconroenews.com
 - 2,700,000(views) 900,000(visitors)
Group: Hearst Communications, Inc.
Published: Mon, Tues, Wed, Thur, Fri, Sat, Sun
Weekday Frequency: m
Saturday Frequency: m
Circulation: 9,244; 8,430(sat); 8,532(sun)
Last Audit: AAM March 15, 2015
Advertising Rate (weekday/saturday): $22.50
News services: U.S. Suburban Press Inc., AP. **Established:** 1892
Own Printing Facility?: No
Commercial Printers?: No
Special Editions: Back-to-School (Aug); Last Minute Gifts (Dec); Progress (Feb); Bridal (Jan); Montgomery County Magazine (Jul); Montgomery County Fair (Mar); Mother's Day (May); Holiday Cookbook (Nov); Answer Book (Oct); High School Football (Sept).
Special Weekly Sections: Best Food Days (Wed/Sun)
Syndicated Publications: USA WEEKEND Magazine (S).
Digital Platform - Mobile: Apple, Android
Digital Platform - Tablet: Apple iOS, Android
Exec. Ed. ....Andy DuBois
Pub. ....Brenda Miller-Fergerson
Grp. Pub. ....Jim Fredricks
Gen. Sales Mgr. ....Corey Turner
Adv. Dir. ....Charles Lee
Adv. Mgr. .... Karen Maurmann
Circ. Dir. .... Rod Mcfarland
City Ed. .... Nancy Flake

Features Ed. ....Sandra Bosse
Sports Ed. ....Mike Jones
Mgmt. Info Servs. Mgr. ....Ann Toppel
Asst. Opns. Mgr. ....Kelly Lawson
Pub. ....Jason Joseph
Major/Nat'l Sr. Acct. Mgr. ....Tom Legg
Market Information: ADS; Split run; Zoned editions.
Mechanical Available: Offset; Black and 3 ROP colors; insert accepted - all; page cutoffs - 22 3/4.
Mechanical Specifications: 10.388" x 20.5"
Areas Served: Montgomery County
Delivery Method: Carrier, RacksEquipment & Software: PRESSROOM EQUIPMENT: Lines — 10-G/C; MAILROOM EQUIPMENT: Counter Stackers — 1/BG; Inserters & Stuffers — MM/227-Z; Tying Machines — 2-/Malow.; BUSINESS EQUIPMENT: IBM/MS-DOS CLASSIFIED EQUIPMENT: Hardware — IBM/MS-DOS; Printers — HP; CLASSIFIED SOFTWARE: Dewar. DISPLAY EQUIPMENT: Hardware — APP/Mac; Printers — AG/Accuset, Lexmark; DISPLAY SOFTWAREAd Make-up Applications — QPS/QuarkXPress 4.0, Adobe/Photoshop 4.0; Layout Software — Dewar. EDITORIAL EQUIPMENT: Hardware — IBM/MS-DOS, APP/Mac G3; Printers — APP EDITORIAL SOFTWARE: Microsoft/Word, QPS/QuarkXPress 3.32, Adobe/Photoshop. PRODUCTION EQUIPMENT: Hardware — 1-Nu, 1-BKY; Cameras — 1-C/Spartan III; Scanners — SCREEN/1350 PRODUCTION SOFTWARE: Dewar.

CORPUS CHRISTI

CORPUS CHRISTI CALLER-TIMES

820 N Lower Broadway St, Corpus Christi, Texas, 78401-2025, Nueces; gen tel (361) 884-2011; adv tel (361) 886-4301; ed tel (361) 886-3787; gen fax (361) 886-3732; adv fax (361) 886-3670; gen/nat adv e-mail hornc@caller.com; disp adv e-mail hornc@caller.com; class adv e-mailclassifieds@caller.com; web site www.caller.com 502,082(visitors)
Group: Journal Media Group
Published: Mon, Tues, Wed, Thur, Fri, Sat, Sun
Weekday Frequency: m
Saturday Frequency: m
Circulation: 26,280; 29,346(sat); 36,797(sun)
Last Audit: AAM March 31, 2016
Advertising Rate (weekday/saturday): Open inch rate $80.00
Advertising Rate (sunday): Open inch rate $100.00
News services: AP, NYT, MCT, SHNS. **Established:** 1883
Special Editions: South Texas Football (Aug); Best of Best (Dec); Horizons (Jan); Mi Vida (Monthly); Best of Best (Sept).
Special Weekly Sections: Health (Mon); Ladies Only (Tue); Best Food (Wed); Arts (Thur); Weekend (Fri); Home, Garden (Sat); Homes,Travel, Business, Hola (Sun)
Syndicated Publications: Parade (S).
Vice Pres., HR ....Arthur Acuna
Pub./CRO ....Libby Averyt
CFO ....Michelle Koesema
Exec. Sec. ....Sylvia Perez
Credit Mgr. ....Debra Villarreal
Mktg. Dir. ....Steve Arnold
Circ. Vice Pres ....Jeff Deloach
Circ. Opns. Mgr. ....Bob Gage
Ed. ....Shane Fitzgerald
Editorial Page Ed. ....Sandy Moorhead
Features Ed. ....Cynthia Wilson
Librarian ....Allison Ehrlich
Bus. Ed. ....Tom Whitehurst
Asst. Metro Ed. ....Allison Pollan
News Ed. ....Jen Deselms
Sports Ed. ....John Allen
Television Ed. ....Tina Vasquez
Pres./Pub. ....Darrell Coleman
Nat'l Sales Mgr. ....Chris Horn
Market Information: Split run; TMC; Zoned editions.
Mechanical Available: Offset; Black and 3 ROP colors; insert accepted - small product samples with prior approval; page cutoffs - 22.
Mechanical Specifications: Type page 11 1/2 x 20 5/8; E - 6 cols, 1 5/6, 1/8 between; A - 6 cols, 1 5/6, 1/8 between; C - 10 cols, 1 1/16, 1/16 between.Equipment & Software: PRESSROOM EQUIPMENT: Lines — 9-G/Metroliner double width (offset; 5 half decks) 1994; 8-Tandemer/Narrow Web 1992; 10-HI/V15; Press Drive — Fin/Incom; Folders — 1-G/3:2; Pasters —G/AutoReels & Stands — 9; Control System — G/PCS.; MAILROOM EQUIPMENT: Counter Stackers — 3-HL/Monitor, 2-HL/Monitor; Inserters & Stuffers — 1-GMA/SLS 1000 10:2, 1-KAN/7:1; Tying Machines — 2/MLN, 2-/Dynaric; Address Machine — 3-Wm/III, 2-/BH, 1-/Ink Jet Printer.; BUSINESS EQUIPMENT: HP/3000-947 BUSINESS SOFTWARE: GEAC 7016, MCBA 2.0, GEAC/CIS 6.06, GEAC/Aim CLASSIFIED EQUIPMENT: Hardware — HP/Net Server LH4; Konica/K550 Processor; Printers — HP/LaserJet 5si; CLASSIFIED SOFTWARE: CText. DISPLAY EQUIPMENT: Printers — HP/8000 N; Other Hardware — CD-Rom, ScanView/ScanMate 5000. DISPLAY SOFTWAREAd Make-up Applications — Multi-Ad/Creator, Adobe/Illustrator, Adobe/Photoshop, Managing Editor/ALS; EDITORIAL EQUIPMENT: Hardware — PC P350; Printers — HP/5si EDITORIAL SOFTWARE: Microsoft/NT, SQL/DPS Editorial. PRODUCTION EQUIPMENT: Hardware — 2-Konica/Powermatic 66f, Pre Press/Panther Pro, 1-W/Auto Unit; Cameras — 1-ECR/8400, 1-B/2000, 2-C/Spartan III; Scanners — ScanView/ScanMate 5000, Kk/RFS 2035, Umax/Mirage 16L, Umax/Super Vista S-12 PRODUCTION SOFTWARE: DPS/Ad Tracker.

CORSICANA

CORSICANA DAILY SUN

405 E Collin St, Corsicana, Texas, 75110-5325, Navarro; gen tel (903) 872-3931; adv tel (903) 872-3931; ed tel (903) 872-3931; gen fax (903) 872-6878; adv fax (903) 872-6878; ed fax (903) 872-6878; gen/nat adv e-mail advertising@corsicanadailysun.com; disp adv e-mail advertising@corsicanadailysun.com; class adv e-mailadvertising@corsicanadailysun.com; ed e-mail dailysun@corsicanadailysun.com; web site www.corsicanadailysun.com - 500,000(views) 75,000(visitors)
Group: Community Newspaper Holdings, Inc.
Published: Tues, Wed, Thur, Fri, Sat
Weekday Frequency: m
Saturday Frequency: m
Circulation: 5,690; 5,690(sat); 6,544(sun)
Last Audit: Sworn/Estimate/Non-Audited September 30, 2017
Advertising Rate (weekday/saturday): Open inch rate $13.50
Advertising Rate (sunday): Open inch rate $13.50
News services: AP. **Established:** 1895
Own Printing Facility?: No
Commercial Printers?: Yes
Special Editions: Football (Aug); Progress (Jun); Newcomers (Sept).
Special Weekly Sections: Best Food Fay, Business (Tue); Church (Fri); Business (Thur); Farm, Business, Living, Minipage, Entertainment (Sun)
Syndicated Publications: Relish (Monthly); USA WEEKEND Magazine (S).
Digital Platform - Mobile: Apple, Android, Windows, Blackberry
Digital Platform - Tablet: Apple iOS, Android, Windows 7, Blackberry Tablet OS
Circ. Mgr. ....David Smith
Photo Ed. ....Chris Smith
Data Processing Mgr. ....Deana Pawlowski
Adv. Dir. ....Karen Davis
Acct. Exec. ....Terri Anderson
Publisher ....Jake Mienk
Bus. Mgr. ....Sharon Brown
Ed. ....Thomas Martinez
Market Information: Split run; TMC; Zoned editions.
Mechanical Available: Offset; Black and 3 ROP colors; insert accepted; page cutoffs - 22 3/4.
Mechanical Specifications: Type page 13 3/4 x 21 1/2; E - 6 cols, 2 1/16, 1/8 between; A - 6 cols, 2 1/16, 1/8 between; C - 9 cols, 1 3/8, 1/16 between.
Delivery Method: MailEquipment & Software: PRESSROOM EQUIPMENT: Lines — 5-G/Urbanite.; MAILROOM EQUIPMENT: Counter Stackers — 1/BG; Tying Machines — 2-/MLN; Address Machine — 1-/KR.; BUSINESS EQUIPMENT: 1-MDS, 1-HP, 3-IBM/AT CLASSIFIED EQUIPMENT: Hardware - APP/Mac.; EDITORIAL EQUIPMENT: Hardware — 7-APP/Mac; Printers — 1-APP/Mac LaserWriter IIq, 1-APP/Mac LaserWriter IIf EDITORIAL SOFTWARE: Baseview/NewsEdit, QPS/QuarkXPress. PRODUCTION EQUIPMENT: Hardware — 1-Nat/225; Cameras — SCREEN, 1-C.

DALLAS

THE DALLAS MORNING NEWS

508 Young St, Dallas, Texas, 75202-4808, Dallas; gen tel (214) 977-8222; ed tel (214) 977-8205; adv fax (214) 977-7644; ed fax (972) 263-0456; gen/nat adv e-mail jricks@dmnmedia.com; disp adv e-mail jmerves@dmnmedia.com; class adv e-mailmmayer@dmnmedia.com; ed e-mail asktheeditor@dallasnews.com; web site www.dallasnews.com; web site 2 guidelive.com
Group: A.H. Belo Corporation
Published: Mon, Tues, Wed, Thur, Fri, Sat, Sun
Weekday Frequency: m
Saturday Frequency: m
Circulation: 223,553; 225,742(sat); 303,045(sun)
Last Audit: AAM March 31, 2017
News services: AP, NYT, Washington Post, Tribune News Service, Getty **Established:** 1885
Own Printing Facility?: Yes
Commercial Printers?: Yes
Special Weekly Sections: Guide (Fri); Travel (Sun); Points (Sun); Comics.
Syndicated Publications: Parade (Sun).
Proprietary Publications: Top 100 magazine 1X per year
Al Dia (Weds/Sat)
Briefing (Weds/Sat)
Holiday Entertaining (Nov)
Premium Magazines (4X per year)
Digital Platform - Mobile: Apple, Android
Digital Platform - Tablet: Apple iOS, Android, Kindle, Nook, Kindle Fire
Publisher and CEO ....Moroney James
Vice President/Editorial Page Editor. Keven Willey
Circulation Director ....Gene Chavez
Assistant Managing Editor/Features & Community Engagement ....Tom Huang
Managing Editor, Al Dia ....Alfredo Carbajal
Chief Digital Officer/SVP ....Nicki Purcell
Gen. Mgr. Recruitment, Real Estate & Gen. Classifieds ....Michael Mayer
VP Production ....Bill May
SVP/Business Development & Niche Products Grant Moise
Editor ....Mike Wilson
Sr. Dir., Audience Development ....Angie Grissom
President, BMG ....Alison Draper
Vice President/Managing Editor ......Robyn Tomlin
Deputy Managing Editor/News & Business.... Keith Campbell
Director of News Operations ....Mark Konradi
Assistant Managing Editor/Sports..... Gary Leavell
Director of Photography ....Marcia Allert
Editor/The Daily ....Denise Bieber
Market Information: Split run; TMC; Zoned editions.
Mechanical Available: Offset; Black and 3 ROP colors; insert accepted; page cutoffs - 22.
Mechanical Specifications: Type page 11 5/8 x 21; E - 6 cols, 1 5/6, 1/8 between; A - 6 cols, 1 5/6, 1/8 between; C - 10 cols, 1 3/32, 1/16 between.
Delivery Method: Mail, Newsstand, Carrier, RacksEquipment & Software: PRESSROOM EQUIPMENT: Lines — 1-TKS/Offset double width 1985; 1-TKS/Offset double width 1985; 1-TKS/Offset double width 1987; 1-TKS/Offset double width 1988; 1-TKS/Offset double width 1989; 1-TKS/Offset double width 1990; 1-Wifag/Offset double width 2000; Kodak Platemaking Imagers and Processors, Nela Benders and Sortation PRESSROOM SOFTWARE: ABB Press Controls
Copytrack MAILROOM EQUIPMENT: Counter stackers - 20 Quipp 350, 3 Quipp 400, 2 Quipp 500; Inserters & Stuffers - 4-GMA/SLS 1000A 28:2, 1 GMA/SLS 2000 8:2, 1 GMA/SLS 2000 14:2, 1 GMA/SLS 2000 18:2, 1 GMA/SLS 2000 8:2; Collators - 2 Prim-Hall 80 station; Tying Machines - 28 Dynaric NP-2, 6 Dynaric 5000, 11 Dynaric 5000X
MAILROOM SOFTWARE:Control System - 6 Fast Technology Insert Controls, 2 Quipp Newscom Insert Controls; 1 Winlincs Insert Controls; Burt planning
BUSINESS EQUIPMENT: Dell Servers - Windows, Unix, ESX BUSINESS SOFTWARE: PeopleSoft, Hyperion, Essbase, Kronos, Cognos, MasterTax,
Workday CLASSIFIED EQUIPMENT: Dell Servers - Linux, Windows CLASSIFIED SOFTWARE: Newscycle Adbase DISPLAY EQUIPMENT: Dell Servers - Windows, Unix DISPLAY SOFTWARENewscycle Adbase, DFP EDITORIAL EQUIPMENT: Dell Servers - Windows, Unix EDITORIAL SOFTWARE: CCI Newsgate, CCI Escenic, CNI Addesk, MerlinOne IT EQUIPMENT: Dell Servers - Windows, Unix IT SOFTWARE:CA Client Manager, VMWare, McAfee, Red Hat, Netbackup, SolarWinds CIRCULATION EQUIPMENT: Dell Servers - Windows, Unix CIRCULATION SOFTWARNewscycle DSI

DEL RIO

DEL RIO NEWS-HERALD

2205 N Bedell Ave, Del Rio, Texas, 78840-8007, Val Verde; gen tel (830) 775-1551; adv tel (830) 775-1551; ed tel (830) 775-1551; gen fax (830) 774-2610; gen/nat adv e-mail claudia.deleon@delrionewsherald.com; disp adv e-mail claudia.deleon@delrionewsherald.com; class adv e-mailclaudia.deleon@delrionewsherald.com; ed e-mail claudia.deleon@delrionewsherald.com; web site www.delrionewsherald.com - 10,000(views)
Group: Metro Newspaper Advertising Services, Inc.
Southern Newspapers Inc.
Published: Tues, Wed, Thur, Fri, Sun
Weekday Frequency: m
Circulation: 2,252; 2,515(sun)
Last Audit: CAC March 31, 2017
Advertising Rate (weekday/saturday): Open inch rate $14.80
Advertising Rate (sunday): Open inch rate $15.25
Online Advertising Rate: 85.00 p/thous
News services: AP, NEA. **Established:** 1929
Own Printing Facility?: Yes
Commercial Printers?: Yes
Special Weekly Sections: Best Food Days (Tue/Sun)
Syndicated Publications: Parade (S).
Digital Platform - Mobile: Apple, Android, Blackberry, Other
Digital Platform - Tablet: Apple iOS, Android, Windows 7, Blackberry Tablet OS, Kindle, Nook, Kindle Fire, Other
Managing Ed. ....Brian Argabright
AR rep
Josie Garcia
Market Information: ADS; TMC.
Mechanical Available: Offset; Black and 3 ROP colors; insert accepted; page cutoffs - 22 3/4.
Mechanical Specifications: Type page 13 x 21 1/2; E - 6 cols, 2 1/16, 1/8 between; A - 6 cols, 2 1/16, 1/8 between; C - 9 cols, 1 3/8, 1/16 between.
Areas Served: Del Rio Val Verde 78840
Delivery Method: Mail, Newsstand, Carrier, RacksEquipment & Software: PRESSROOM EQUIPMENT: Lines — 7-G/Community; Folders — 1-G/Community.; MAILROOM EQUIPMENT: Tying Machines — MLN; Address Machine — 1/KR.; BUSINESS EQUIPMENT: IBM, AT, XT, PC BUSINESS SOFTWARE: pbs, CLASSIFIED EQUIPMENT: Hardware — Mk.; CLASSIFIED SOFTWARE: newscycle DISPLAY SOFTWARELayout Software — Mk/Ad Touch. EDITORIAL EQUIPMENT: Hardware — Mk/1100 System. EDITORIAL SOFTWARE: newscycle,adobe PRODUCTION EQUIPMENT: Hardware - 1-COM/Computype II, 1-COM/4961, 2-COM/8400; Cameras — 1-C/Spartan III. PRODUCTION SOFTWARE: newscycle,adobe CIRCULATION SOFTWARcirc pro

DENTON

DENTON RECORD-CHRONICLE

314 E Hickory St, Denton, Texas, 76201-4272, Denton; gen tel (940) 387-3811; adv tel (940) 566-6858; ed tel (940) 566-6879; gen fax (940) 566-6846; adv fax (940) 566-6846; ed fax (945) 566-6888; gen/nat adv e-mail skelley@dentonrc.com; disp adv e-mail drcretailad@dentonrc.com; class adv e-mailClassads@dentonrc.com; ed e-mail drc@dentonrc.com; web site www.dentonrc.com
- 1,272,407(views) 188,009(visitors)

Group: A.H. Belo Corporation
Published: Mon, Tues, Wed, Thur, Fri, Sat, Sun
Weekday Frequency: m
Saturday Frequency: m
Circulation: 7,521; 7,310(sat); 9,945(sun)
Last Audit: AAM March 31, 2015
Advertising Rate (weekday/saturday): Open inch rate $36.50
Advertising Rate (sunday): Open inch rate $40.00
Online Advertising Rate: Open Rate Banner: $7.00; Open Rate Tower: $7.00; Open Rate Medium Rectangle: $7.00
News services: AP. **Established:** 1903
Own Printing Facility?: No
Commercial Printers?: No
Special Editions: Denton Time, Kid Life, Denton Business Chronicle, RealEstate, DealFinder, The A Train
Special Weekly Sections: Entertainment Chronicle (Thur).
Syndicated Publications: Parade (Sunday)
Digital Platform - Mobile: Apple
Digital Platform - Tablet: Apple iOS
Pub. .... Bill Patterson
Features Ed. .... Lucinda Breeding
Ad. Director .... Sandra Hammond
Market Information: TMC.
Mechanical Available: Offset Black and 3 ROP colors; insert accepted - card, single sheet; page cutoffs - 22 3/4.
Mechanical Specifications: Type page 13 x 21 1/2; E - 6 cols, 2 1/16, 1/6 between; A - 6 cols, 2 1/16, 1/6 between; C - 9 cols, 1 3/8, 1/8 between.
Areas Served: Northern Denton County including the city of Denton, TX
Delivery Method: CarrierEquipment & Software: BUSINESS EQUIPMENT: Atex CLASSIFIED EQUIPMENT: Atex DISPLAY EQUIPMENT: Atex DISPLAY SOFTWAREAtex EDITORIAL EQUIPMENT: CCI Newsgate 3 PRODUCTION EQUIPMENT: Apple/Indesign CIRCULATION EQUIPMENT: DSI

DESOTO

FOCUS DAILY NEWS

1337 Marilyn Ave, Desoto, Texas, 75115-6414, Dallas; gen tel (972) 223-9175; adv tel (972) 223-9175; ed tel (972) 223-2998; gen fax (972) 223-9202; adv fax (972) 223-9202; ed fax (972) 223-9202; gen/nat adv e-mail focusnews@wans.net; disp adv e-mail focusnews@wans.net; class adv e-mailfocusnews@wans.net; ed e-mail editor@focusdailynews.com; web site www.focusdailynews.com; web site 2 testdrivereport.com

Published: Tues, Wed, Thur, Fri, Sun
Weekday Frequency: m
Circulation: 37,387; 49,890(sun)
Last Audit: USPS December 12, 2017
Advertising Rate (weekday/saturday): Open inch rate $50 Daily
Advertising Rate (sunday): Open inch rate $55.00
Online Advertising Rate: Horizontal banner (600x250): $400.00 per month; Vertical banner (160x600): $300.00 per month
News services: 1987
Own Printing Facility?: Yes
Commercial Printers?: Yes
Special Editions: Back of School, Football, Bridal, SEMA, Progress, Graduation, Readers Choice, Football Pre-Season Special, Back to School, Bridal, Holiday Gift Guide, Mothers Day, Fathers Day, Graduation, Veterans Day
Special Weekly Sections: Automotive, Lifestyles
Digital Platform - Mobile: Apple, Android
Digital Platform - Tablet: Apple iOS, Android, Kindle, Nook, Kindle Fire
Pub. .... Marlon Hanson
Ed. .... Joshua Johnson
Prodn. Mgr. .... Alex Hanson
Circ. Mgr. .... Ginger Bolton
Digital Operations Director .... Kristin Barclay
Market Information: Dallas/FT Worth Southern Suburban
Mechanical Available: Full page 11.5x21
Mechanical Specifications: Type page 11 1/2 x 21; E - 6 cols, 1 3/4, between; A - 6 cols, 1 3/4, between; C - 6 cols, 1 3/4, between.
Areas Served: 75115, 75104, 75116, 75137, 75165, 75146, 75104, 75051, 75050, 75154, 75237, 75234
Delivery Method: Newsstand, Carrier, RacksEquipment & Software: PRESSROOM EQUIPMENT: Goss Communty MAILROOM EQUIPMENT: PC BUSINESS EQUIPMENT: PC CLASSIFIED EQUIPMENT: PC DISPLAY EQUIPMENT: PC DISPLAY SOFTWAREQuark Xpress EDITORIAL EQUIPMENT: PC EDITORIAL SOFTWARE: Quark Xpres PRODUCTION EQUIPMENT: Harlequin

EL PASO

EL PASO TIMES

500 W Overland Ave, Ste 150, El Paso, Texas, 79901-1108, El Paso; gen tel (915) 546-6100; adv tel (915) 546-6250; ed tel (915) 546-6124; gen fax (915) 546-6284; adv fax (915) 546-6404; ed fax (915) 546-6415; gen/nat adv e-mail advertising@elpasotimes.com; disp adv e-mail advertising@elpasotimes.com; class adv e-mailadvertising@elpasotimes.com; ed e-mail news@elpasotimes.com; web site www.elpasotimes.com
- 3,505,161(views) 640,785(visitors); web site 2 www.elpasoymas.com - 4,579(views) 1,769(visitors)

Group: Gannett
Published: Mon, Tues, Wed, Thur, Fri, Sat, Sun
Weekday Frequency: m
Saturday Frequency: m
Circulation: 29,939; 28,465(sat); 44,965(sun)
Last Audit: AAM September 30, 2017
Advertising Rate (weekday/saturday): Modular $43.65/ Full page $5500
Advertising Rate (sunday): Modular $43.65 / Full page $5500
Online Advertising Rate: Starting from $11.00 CPM
News services: AP, GNS, LAT-WP, Thunderdome **Established:** 1881
Own Printing Facility?: Yes
Commercial Printers?: Yes
Special Editions: Healthcare Directory (Apr); Football (Aug); Last Minute Gift Guide (Dec); Legal Directory (Feb); Women in Business (Jan); Career Tab + Expo (Jul); Family-Owned Business (Jun); Sport Utility Vehicles (Mar); Career Tab + Expo (May); Early Christmas Gift Gui
Special Weekly Sections: Living (Mon-Fri); Best Food Day (Wed); Entertainment (Fri); Real Estate, Travel, TV, Living (Sun); Business (Tues - Sun)
Syndicated Publications: Eastside Reporter (Fri); USA WEEKEND Magazine (S). Relish Magazine.
Proprietary Publications: El Paso y Mas
Digital Platform - Mobile: Apple, Android, Windows, Blackberry, Other
Digital Platform - Tablet: Apple iOS, Android, Windows 7, Blackberry Tablet OS, Kindle, Nook, Kindle Fire
Dir., HR .... Malena Field
Circ. Mgr., Transportation .... Randy Waldrop
VP of Production .... Patsy Hernandez
Executive Editor .... Robert Moore
Victor Kolenc
President .... Lilia Jones
Sales Director .... Salvador Hernandez
Market Information: ADS; Split run; TMC; Hispanic
Mechanical Available: Black and 3 ROP colors; inserts accepted; page cutoffs - 22.
Mechanical Specifications: Type page 10 x 21; E - 6 cols, 1 1/3, 1/6 between; A - 6 cols, 1 1/3, 1/6 between; C - 8 cols, 1 1/6, 1/2 between.
Delivery Method: Mail, Newsstand, Carrier, RacksEquipment & Software: PRESSROOM EQUIPMENT: Lines — G/Metrocolor (23 couples) double width 1997; G/Metrocolor (23 couples) double width 1997; Pasters —G/Digital; Reels & Stands — CT/50; Control System — G/MPCS.; MAILROOM EQUIPMENT: Counter Stackers — 6-QWI/351; Inserters & Stuffers — GMA/5652000 24:2, GMA/562000 20:2; Tying Machines — 5-Dynaric/NP 500; Control System — GMA/SAM; Address Machine — 1-Cheshire/Labeler; BUSINESS EQUIPMENT: Dell dekstops and Laptops; Canon, HP Multifunction Printers, iPad, Cisco IP Phone BUSINESS SOFTWARE: MS Office, JD Edwards, AdBase, Crystal, ImageNow, Outlook Soft CLASSIFIED EQUIPMENT: Dell desktops and Laptops; Canon, HP Multifunction Printers, iPads, Cisco IP Phone CLASSIFIED SOFTWARE: Microsoft Office, Adbooker, Ranger Data, Crystal, Cisco Agent, Shoom, eProofs, WebToCash DISPLAY EQUIPMENT: Dell desktops and Laptops; Canon, HP Multifunction Printers, iPads, Cisco IP Phone DISPLAY SOFTWAREMicrosoft Office, Adbooker, Ranger Data, Crystal, Cisco Agent, Shoom, eProofs, WebToCash EDITORIAL EQUIPMENT: Dell desktops and Laptops; Canon, HP Multifunction Printers, iPads, Cisco IP Phone, Apple Desktop and Laptops, Microfilm Machine, Scanners, Camaras, iPhones EDITORIAL SOFTWARE: QPS. SaxoTech, Quark, Copy Desk, Quark Express, Adobe creative suit, DC4 PRODUCTION EQUIPMENT: Dell desktops and Laptops; Canon, HP Multifunction Printers, iPads, Cisco IP Phone, Apple Desktop and Laptops, Microfilm Machine, Scanners, Camaras, iPhones PRODUCTION SOFTWARE: Goss, Arkitex, SAM, Cisco IP Phones, Adtrac, IT EQUIPMENT: Dell desktops and Laptops; Canon, HP Multifunction Printers, iPads, Cisco IP Phone, Apple Desktop and Laptops, Microfilm Machine, Scanners, Camaras, iPhones, Switches, Routers, Servers, Exchange, File servers, CCM, CCS, Firewalls, ASA files, Cores, Cisco 4500 3560, IT SOFTWARE:VPN, Facebook, Tout, Cisco IP Phones, Crystal, Exchange, CCN, IPCC, Unity, Backup exec, symantec, CIRCULATION EQUIPMENT: Dell desktops and Laptops; Chatterbox, Canon, Subscriber concierge, HP Multifunction Printers, iPads, Cisco IP Phone, Apple Desktop and Laptops, Microfilm Machine, Scanners, Camaras, iPhones; CIRCULATION SOFTWARMicrosoft Office, Crystal, Cisco Agent, WebToCash, Orchestrator, DTI - GUI, WinSpc,

ENNIS

THE ENNIS DAILY NEWS

213 N Dallas St, Ennis, Texas, 75119-4011, Ellis; gen tel (972) 875-3801; adv tel (972) 875-3801; ed tel (972) 875-3801; gen fax (972) 875-9747; adv fax (972) 875-9747; ed fax (972) 875-9747; gen/nat adv e-mail keven@ennisdailynews.com; disp adv e-mail advertising@ennisdailynews.com; class adv e-mailclassifieds@ennisdailynews.com; ed e-mail editor@ennisdailynews.com; web site www.ennisdailynews.com
- 100,000(views) 30,000(visitors)

Published: Tues, Wed, Thur, Fri, Sun
Weekday Frequency: e
Circulation: 3,214; 3,214(sun)
Last Audit: Sworn/Estimate/Non-Audited September 30, 2017
Advertising Rate (weekday/saturday): Open inch rate $9.50
Advertising Rate (sunday): Open inch rate $11.00
Online Advertising Rate: Call for details.
News services: AP **Established:** 1891
Own Printing Facility?: Yes
Commercial Printers?: Yes
Special Editions: Football program (July-August); Discover (September-October);
Holiday Hometown (October-November);Thanksgiving (November); Christmas (December); Family Guide (January); Medical Guide (February); Hometown Living (glossy) 6x per year.
Proprietary Publications: Hometown Living (bi-monthly)
Digital Platform - Mobile: Apple, Android
Digital Platform - Tablet: Apple iOS, Kindle
Market Information: TMC
Mechanical Available: Offset; Black and 3 ROP colors; insert accepted; page cutoffs - 21 1/2.
Mechanical Specifications: Type page 10 x 21 1/2; E - 6 cols. .167 inch gutters.
Areas Served: Ellis County
Delivery Method: Newsstand, Carrier, RacksEquipment & Software: PRESSROOM EQUIPMENT: Lines — 6-G/Community single width; Folders — 1-G/2:1.; MAILROOM EQUIPMENT: Tying Machines — 1/Strap Tyer.; CLASSIFIED EQUIPMENT: Hardware — PC; Printers — TI/Micro Laser; CLASSIFIED SOFTWARE: BMF. DISPLAY EQUIPMENT: Hardware — APP/Mac; Printers — GCC; DISPLAY SOFTWAREAd Make-up Applications — QPS.; EDITORIAL EQUIPMENT: Hardware — APP/Mac; Printers — GCC/XL20/600 EDITORIAL SOFTWARE: QPS. PRODUCTION EQUIPMENT: Hardware — Reconex, 1-COM/7200; Cameras — 1-B; Scanners — AG/Snap Scan, Minolta/Quick Scan.

FORT WORTH

FORT WORTH STAR-TELEGRAM

808 Throckmorton St, Fort Worth, Texas, 76102-6315, Tarrant; gen tel (817) 390-7400; adv tel (817) 390-7765; ed tel (817) 390-7150; gen fax (817) 336-7789; adv fax (817) 390-7869; ed fax (817) 390-7321; gen/nat adv e-mail marketguidefeedback@star-telegram.com; disp adv e-mail mediakit@star-telegram.com; class adv e-mailmediakit@star-telegram.com; ed e-mail jwilley@star-telegram.com; web site www.star-telegram.com
2,190,375(visitors)

Group: The McClatchy Company
Published: Mon, Tues, Wed, Thur, Fri, Sat, Sun
Weekday Frequency: m
Saturday Frequency: m
Circulation: 101,680; 92,485(sat); 175,585(sun)
Last Audit: AAM March 31, 2016
Advertising Rate (weekday/saturday): Open inch rate $455.00
Advertising Rate (sunday): Open inch rate $495.00
News services: Newspapers First, MCT, LAT-WP, SHNS, DJ (Dow Jones). **Established:** 1906
Special Editions: Summer Vacation (Apr); Football (Aug); Gift Guide III (Dec); Texas Golf & Resort (Feb); Stock Show I (Jan); Education (Jul); Primetime (Jun); Primetime (Mar); Top 25 (May); Healthcare (Monthly); Primetime (Nov); The Answer Book (Oct); Fall Home & Garden S
Special Weekly Sections: TV (Daily); Best Food Day (Wed); Weekend (Fri); Religion, TV Supplement (Sat); Travel (Sun)
Syndicated Publications: StarTime (Fri); Tarrant Business (Mon); Relish (Monthly); TV Star (weekly TV Guide) (S).
Pres./Pub. .... Gary Wortel
Vice Pres./CFO .... Roger Provost
Sr. Vice Pres., Adv. .... Michael J. Winter
Circ. Vice Pres. .... Dolan Stidom
Circ. Dir., Arlington .... Terry Foley
Circ. Dir., Sales/Training .... Lonna Hoffman
Sr. Vice Pres./Exec. Ed. .... Jim Witt
Vice Pres./Assoc. Ed. .... Bob Ray Sanders
Mng. Ed., Enterprise .... Kathy Vetter
Mng. Ed., Investigations .... Lois Norder
Asst. Mng. Ed., Bus. .... Steve Kaskovich
Asst. Mng. Ed., Features .... Catherine Mallette
Asst. Mng. Ed., Gov't Affairs .... John Gravois
Mng. Ed., Sports .... Celeste Williams
Majors/Nat'l Sales Dir. .... James Burda
VP .... Craig Diebel
Editorial Dept .... Charean Williams
Mng. Ed./News .... Lee Williams
VP of Audience Dev. Cir. .... Christian Lee
Market Information: Split run; TMC; Zoned editions.
Mechanical Available: Offset; Black and 3 ROP colors; insert accepted; page cutoffs - 22.
Mechanical Specifications: Type page 11 5/8 x 21 1/4; E - 6 cols, 2 1/14, 1/6 between; A - 6 cols, 2 1/14, 1/6 between; C - 6 cols, 1 1/5, 1/6 between.Equipment & Software: PRESSROOM EQUIPMENT: Lines — 11-G/

Headliner (with 8 half decks) 1986, 2-G/Metro Color Tower 1999; 11-G/Headliner (with 8 half decks) 1986, 2-G/Metro Color Tower 1999; 11-G/Headliner(w/8 half decks) 1986, 2-G/Metro Color Tower 1999; 11-G/Headliner (; MAILROOM EQUIPMENT: Counter Stackers — 17-HL/Monitor, 2-QWI/351, 6-QWI/351; Inserters & Stuffers — 3-HI/72P, 2-HI/630; Tying Machines — 18-Dynaric/NP2, 3-Dynaric/Am-9000, 3/Bu; Wrapping Singles — 3-Signode/HLS; Address Machine — 2-/Ch, 1-/MM, 2-/Video jet; BUSINESS EQUIPMENT: DEC, DEC/4100 CLASSIFIED EQUIPMENT: Hardware — IBM/RS 6000; Printers — Lexmark; CLASSIFIED SOFTWARE: CText. DISPLAY EQUIPMENT: Hardware — APP/Mac; Printers — APP/Mac LaserWriter III, HP, QMS, Lexmark; DISPLAY SOFTWAREAd Make-up Applications — Mk/Page Director, Mk/Ad Director, QPS/QuarkXPress, Adobe/Photoshop, Adobe/Illustrator; Layout Software — MEI. EDITORIAL EQUIPMENT: Hardware — Compaq/Pentium, Dell/Pentium; Printers — Epson, HP, Lexmark EDITORIAL SOFTWARE: Dewar. PRODUCTION EQUIPMENT: Hardware — 4-AU/3850, 2-AU/F108, 1-AU/30 double truck, 6-Gluntz & Jensen; Cameras — 1-Acti, 1-C/New, 1-C/Marathon; Scanners — 4-Scanmate/Scanview PRODUCTION SOFTWARE: QPS/QuarkXPress, Adobe/Photoshop, Adobe/Illustrator, Macromedia/Freehand.

GAINESVILLE

GAINESVILLE DAILY REGISTER

306 E California St, Gainesville, Texas, 76240-4006, Cooke; gen tel (940) 665-5511; gen fax 940-668-7257; adv fax (940) 665-0920; ed fax (940) 665-1499; gen/nat adv e-mail sales2@gainesvilleregister.com; disp adv e-mail sales1@gainesvilleregister.com; class adv e-mailclassifiedsgdr@ntin.net; ed e-mail editor@gainesvilleregister.com; web site www.gainesvilleregister.com 40,000(visitors)

Group: Community Newspaper Holdings, Inc.
Published: Tues, Wed, Thur, Fri, Sat
Weekday Frequency: m
Saturday Frequency: m
Circulation: 5,011; 5,019(sun)
Last Audit: USPS September 30, 2006
Advertising Rate (weekday/saturday): Open inch rate $12.92
News services: AP. **Established:** 1890
Own Printing Facility?: Yes
Commercial Printers?: Yes
Special Weekly Sections: Arts (Tue); Best Food Days (Wed); Agriculture (Thur); Church, Religion (Fri); Living (Daily)
Syndicated Publications: Relish (Monthly); USA WEEKEND Magazine (S); American Profile (Weekly).
Digital Platform - Mobile: Apple, Android
Digital Platform - Tablet: Apple iOS, Android
Bus. Mgr. .... Bernice Trimble
Circ. Mgr. .... Jack Bills
Pub .... Jim Perry
Managing Ed. .... Darin Allred
Pub .... Lisa Chappell
Market Information: Serving all of Cooke Co., Texas
Mechanical Available: Offset; Black and 3 ROP colors; insert accepted; page cutoffs - 19.
Mechanical Specifications: Type page 12 x 21 1/2; E - 6 cols, 1.56 inches , 1/8 between; C - 7 cols, 1.32 inches1/8 between.
Areas Served: 76240, 76272, 76250, 76252, 76273, 73459, 76265, 76233, 76238, 76239, 76263, 76266, 76253, 76258, 73448
Delivery Method: MailEquipment & Software: PRESSROOM EQUIPMENT: Lines — 24-G/Community.;

GALVESTON

THE GALVESTON COUNTY DAILY NEWS

8522 Teichman Rd, Galveston, Texas, 77554-9119, Galveston; gen tel (409) 683-5200; adv tel (409) 683-5224; ed tel (409) 683-5239; gen fax (409) 744-6268; adv fax (409) 744-7679; ed fax (409) 740-3421; gen/nat adv e-mail advertising@galvnews.com; disp adv e-mail advertising@galvnews.com; class adv e-mailadvertising@galvnews.com; ed e-mail newsroom@galvnews.com; web site www.galvnews.com

Group: Southern Newspapers Inc.
Published: Mon, Tues, Wed, Thur, Fri, Sat, Sun
Weekday Frequency: m
Saturday Frequency: m
Circulation: 17,926; 17,926(sat); 19,385(sun)
Last Audit: AAM March 31, 2016
Advertising Rate (weekday/saturday): Open inch rate $31.50
Advertising Rate (sunday): Open inch rate $33.60
News services: AP. **Established:** 1842
Own Printing Facility?: Yes
Commercial Printers?: Yes
Special Editions: Seniors Over 55 (Annually); Calendar of Events (Monthly); Dining Guide (Semi-yearly).
Special Weekly Sections: Sports, TV Page, Business, Entertainment, Auto, Our County, Real Estate (Daily); Best Food, lifestyle (Wed); Entertainment (Fri); Auto, Our Faith, Real Estate (Sat); Lifestyle, Travel, Real Estate, Jobs (Sun)
Syndicated Publications: Relish (Monthly); USA WEEKEND Magazine (S).
Bus. Mgr. .... D'Lorah Collier
Adv. Mgr., Retail .... Debbie Keith
Circ. Mgr. .... Yvonne Mascorro
Ed. .... Heber Taylor
Assoc. Ed. .... Michael A. Smith
Community News Editor .... Angela Taylor
Online Ed. .... Greg Mefford
Prodn. Foreman, Pressroom .... Brett Baker
Sports Editor .... Jordan Gordwin
Advertising Director .... Scott Moon
News Editor .... Melissa Rivera
Photo Editor
Jennifer Reynolds
Lifestyle Ed. .... Michael Smith
Sports Ed. .... Joshua Buckley
Ad. Director .... John Flowers
Pub. .... Leonard Woolsey
Market Information: TMC.
Mechanical Available: Offset; Black and 3 ROP colors; insert accepted - all; page cutoffs - 22 3/4.
Mechanical Specifications: Type page 13 x 21 1/2; E - 6 cols, 2 1/16, 1/8 between; A - 6 cols, 2 1/16, 1/8 between; C - 9 cols, 1 3/8, 1/16 between.
Areas Served: 77550, 77551, 77554, 77568, 77590, 77591, 77563
Delivery Method: Mail, Newsstand, Carrier, RacksEquipment & Software: PRESSROOM EQUIPMENT: Lines — 8-HI/Cotrell 845 1980; Folders — 1-HI/2:1, G/Urbanite.; MAILROOM EQUIPMENT: Counter Stackers — 1/S; Inserters & Stuffers — 1-/S; Tying Machines — 1-/MLN; Address Machine — 1-/KAN.; BUSINESS EQUIPMENT: Data General CLASSIFIED EQUIPMENT: Hardware — APP/Mac, DEC; Printers — Unified/Laser; CLASSIFIED SOFTWARE: DEC. DISPLAY EQUIPMENT: Hardware — APP/Mac, 2-APP/Mac IIg; Printers — LaserMaster; DISPLAY SOFTWAREAd Make-up Applications — Multi-Ad/Director; Layout Software — Mk/Ad Director, Mk/Managing Editor. EDITORIAL EQUIPMENT: Hardware — APP/Mac; Printers — APP/Mac LaserWriter IIg, AG/Imagesetters EDITORIAL SOFTWARE: Microsoft/Word, QPS/QuarkXPress, Custom-Developed. PRODUCTION EQUIPMENT: Hardware — 1-Nu, AG/Star 400, 2-AG/1000 Imagesetter; Cameras — C/Spartan III; Scanners — ECR, RZ/Diadem.

GREENVILLE

HERALD-BANNER

2305 King St, Greenville, Texas, 75401-3257, Hunt; gen tel (903) 455-4220; adv tel (903)455-4220; ed tel (903) 455-4220; gen fax (903) 455-6281; adv fax (903) 455-3100; ed fax (903) 455-6281; gen/nat adv e-mail publisher@heraldbanner.com; disp adv e-mail advertising@heraldbanner.com; class adv e-mailclassifieds@heraldbanner.com; ed e-mail editor@heraldbanner.com; web site www.heraldbanner.com - 19,000(views)

Group: Community Newspaper Holdings, Inc.
Published: Tues, Wed, Thur, Fri, Sat, Sun
Weekday Frequency: m
Saturday Frequency: m
Circulation: 7,945; 7,945(sat); 8,621(sun)
Last Audit: Sworn/Estimate/Non-Audited September 30, 2017
Advertising Rate (weekday/saturday): Open inch rate $13.30
Advertising Rate (sunday): Open inch rate $15.80
News services: AP. **Established:** 1869
Special Weekly Sections: TV Tabloid (S).
Syndicated Publications: Relish (Monthly); USA WEEKEND Magazine (S).
Pub. .... Lisa Chappell
Bus. Mgr. .... Mary Standfield
Adv. Dir. .... Leslie McMannis
Circ. Dir. .... Robert Spillers
Ed. .... Daniel Walker
Mng. Ed. .... Warren Morrison
Features Ed. .... Carol Ferguson
Sports Ed. .... David Claybourn
Prodn. Mgr. .... David Benini
Derek Price
Market Information: TMC.
Mechanical Available: Offset; Black and 3 ROP colors; insert accepted; page cutoffs - 22 3/4.
Mechanical Specifications: Type page 13 x 21 1/2; E - 6 cols, 1 5/6, 1/8 between; A - 6 cols, 1 4/5, 1/8 between; C - 9 cols, 1 4/5, 1/16 between.
Areas Served: Hunt County
Delivery Method: Carrier, RacksEquipment & Software: PRESSROOM EQUIPMENT: Lines — 8-G/Community 1974; Folders — 1-G/SC; Control System — VEE ARC/PWM 7000 1974.; MAILROOM EQUIPMENT: Counter Stackers — BG/108; Inserters & Stuffers — KAN; Tying Machines — 1-MLN/ML2EE, Dynaric/5580.; BUSINESS EQUIPMENT: IBM, EKI/Televideo CLASSIFIED EQUIPMENT: Hardware — 3-APP/Mac LC; Printers — Okidata/Microline 320; CLASSIFIED SOFTWARE: QPS/QuarkXPress 3.1. DISPLAY EQUIPMENT: Hardware — APP/Mac Quadra 700, APP/Power Mac G3; Printers — APP/Mac LaserWriter IIg, APP/Mac LaserWriter 16-600; Other Hardware — APP/Mac CD-Rom Driver CDSC Plus, Iomega/100MB Zip Drive DISPLAY SOFTWAREAd Make-up Applications — QPS/QuarkXPress 3.32, Adobe/Illustrator 3.0; Layout Software — APP EDITORIAL EQUIPMENT: Hardware — APP/Mac Classic, APP/Mac LC, APP/Mac IIsi, APP/Power Mac G3/Hayes/Smart modem 9600, Express/28.8; Printers — APP/Mac LaserWriter IIg, APP/Mac LaserWriter 16-600, APP/Mac LaserWriter 8500 EDITORIAL SOFTWARE: QPS/QuarkXPress 3.32, Baseview/N PRODUCTION EQUIPMENT: Hardware — Nat/A-250, APP/Mac Quadra 700, APP/Power Mac G-3; Cameras — SCREEN/Rollmatic C-475-D, SCREEN/Companica 680C; Scanners — APP/Mac One Scanner, Mita/DC-1656 Copier, Polaroid/SprintScan 35, Umax/Vista S-12.

HARLINGEN

VALLEY MORNING STAR

1310 S Commerce St, Harlingen, Texas, 78550-7711, Cameron; gen tel (956) 430-6200; gen fax (956)421-9862; adv fax (956) 430-6231; ed fax (956) 430-6233; gen/nat adv e-mail bmendell@rgvmedianetwork.com; disp adv e-mail ccastillo@valleystar.com ; class adv e-mailccastillo@valleystar.com ; ed e-mail lseiser@valleystar.com ; web site http://www.valleymorningstar.com/ - 720,000(views) 250,000(visitors); web site 2 myvalleystar.com

Group: AIM Media Texas LLC
Published: Mon, Tues, Wed, Thur, Fri, Sat, Sun
Weekday Frequency: m
Saturday Frequency: m
Circulation: 10,405; 10,405(sat); 11,838(sun)
Last Audit: AAM March 31, 2017
Advertising Rate (weekday/saturday): Open inch rate $17.73 (Mon-Tues); $20.86 (Wed-Sat)
Advertising Rate (sunday): $23.36
Online Advertising Rate: $10/CPM
News services: AP, MCT, TMS. **Established:** 1911
Own Printing Facility?: Yes
Commercial Printers?: Yes
Special Weekly Sections: Thursday Health & Wellness
Syndicated Publications: Parade, Relish, Athlon Sports, USA
Digital Platform - Mobile: Apple, Android
Digital Platform - Tablet: Apple iOS, Android
Acct. Mgr. .... Melva Juarez
Adv. Ops. Mgr. .... Peggy Elder
Circ. Dir. .... Rusty Hall
Sports Ed. .... Dave Favila
Pub./AD Dir. .... Lilia Castillo Jones
Adv. Dir. .... Christina Castillo
Ed. .... Lisa Seiser
Market Information: Super Sunday Non Sub product
Mechanical Available: Offset; Black and 3 ROP colors; insert accepted - all; page cutoffs - 22 3/4.
Mechanical Specifications: Type page 13 x 21; E - 6 cols, 2 1/16, 1/8 between; A - 6 cols, 2 1/16, 1/8 between; C - 10 cols, 1 1/4, 1/16 between.
Areas Served: Cameron & Willacy Counties
Delivery Method: Newsstand, Carrier, RacksEquipment & Software: PRESSROOM EQUIPMENT: Lines — 6-HI/Cotrell 845; 6-HI/Cotrell 845; Folders — 2-H/2:1; Pasters —8-Jardis/FP 4540. MAILROOM EQUIPMENT: Counter Stackers — Id, QWI; Tying Machines — 2-MLN/MLN2, Dynaric.; BUSINESS EQUIPMENT: Prosig, 4-PC 4DX2-66, SCSI, 7-Compaq/486 BUSINESS SOFTWARE: Brainworks, Southware CLASSIFIED EQUIPMENT: Hardware — APT; Printers — HP/4000.; DISPLAY EQUIPMENT: Hardware — 1-Compaq; Printers — HP/5si; DISPLAY SOFTWAREAd Make-up Applications — APT; Layout Software — 1-Compaq, APT. EDITORIAL EQUIPMENT: Hardware — APT/AP/Photo Server; Printers — HP/5000. PRODUCTION EQUIPMENT: Hardware — ECR/3850, ECR/4550; Cameras — 1-C/Spartan III; Scanners — 3-HP/Scanner PRODUCTION SOFTWARE: APT.

HENDERSON

HENDERSON DAILY NEWS

1711 US Highway 79 S, Henderson, Texas, 75654-4509, Rusk; gen tel (903) 657-2501; adv tel (903) 657-2501; ed tel (903) 657-2501; gen fax (903) 657-2452; adv fax (903) 657-2452; ed fax (903) 657-0056; gen/nat adv e-mail leslinebarger@hendersondailynews.com; disp adv e-mail leslinebarger@hendersondailynews.com; class adv e-mailclassifieds@hendersondailynews.com; ed e-mail rsalmon@hendersondailynews.com; web site www.hendersondailynews.com

Group: Hartman Newspapers LP
Published: Mon, Tues, Wed, Thur, Fri, Sun
Weekday Frequency: e
Circulation: 6,039; 7,206(sun)
Last Audit: Sworn/Estimate/Non-Audited September 30, 2017
Advertising Rate (weekday/saturday): Open inch rate $9.60
Advertising Rate (sunday): Open inch rate $9.60
News services: AP, NEA. **Established:** 1930
Own Printing Facility?: Yes
Commercial Printers?: Yes
Special Weekly Sections: Business (Mon); Religion (Fri); Women (Sun)
Syndicated Publications: Relish (Monthly); TV Magazine (S).
Digital Platform - Mobile: Apple, Android, Windows, Blackberry, Other
Digital Platform - Tablet: Apple iOS, Android, Windows 7, Blackberry Tablet OS, Kindle, Nook, Kindle Fire, Other
Pub./Nat'l Adv. Mgr. .... Les Linebarger
Accountant .... Nancy Harris
Circ. Mgr. .... John Garrison
News Ed. .... Tony Floyd
Sports Ed. .... Hughes Ellis
Prodn. Mgr. .... Joy Slaymaker
Ed. .... Matthew Prosser
Circ. Mgr. .... Jade Causey
Market Information: TMC.
Mechanical Available: Offset; Black and 3 ROP colors; insert accepted; page cutoffs - 21 1/2.
Mechanical Specifications: Type page 13 x 21 1/2; E - 6 cols, 2 1/16, 1/8 between; A - 6 cols, 2 1/16, 1/8 between; C - 8 cols, 1 3/8,

1/16 between.
Delivery Method: Mail, Newsstand, Carrier, RacksEquipment & Software: PRESSROOM EQUIPMENT: Lines — 6-HI/V-15A (upper former).; MAILROOM EQUIPMENT: Tying Machines — 1-Bu/64808.; CLASSIFIED SOFTWARE: Baseview/Class Manager. DISPLAY EQUIPMENT: Hardware — APP/Mac.; EDITORIAL EQUIPMENT: Hardware — APP/Mac/4-APP/Mac. PRODUCTION EQUIPMENT: Hardware — 3-APP/Mac LaserWriter Plus; Cameras — R/500; Scanners — 2-COM/MDR.

HOUSTON

HOUSTON CHRONICLE
4747 Southwest Fwy, Houston, Texas, 77027-6901, Harris; gen tel (713) 362-7171; adv tel (713) 224-6868; ed tel (713) 362-7491; gen fax (713) 362-3575; adv fax (713) 362-7835; ed fax (713) 362-6806; gen/nat adv e-mail info@chron.com; disp adv e-mail classifieds@chron.com; class adv e-mailinfo@chron.com; ed e-mail news@chron.com; viewpoints@chron.com; web site www.chron.com
- 132,527,944(views) 27,911,552(visitors)
Group: Hearst Communications, Inc.
Published: Mon, Tues, Wed, Thur, Fri, Sat, Sun
Weekday Frequency: m
Saturday Frequency: m
Circulation: 225,120; 211,136(sat); 345,214(sun)
Last Audit: AAM September 30, 2016
Advertising Rate (weekday/saturday): Open inch rate $595.24
Online Advertising Rate: Run of site $5.00 CPM
News services: AP, MCT, HN, NYT, CQ, Bloomberg, EFE, Getty Images, Sports Network, Financial Content. **Established:** 1901
Special Editions: Baseball (Apr); Football (Aug); Super Bowl (Feb); How-To Guide (Jul); Houston Open (Mar); Chronicle Top 100 (May); Health (Monthly); Holiday Guide (Nov); NBA Preview (Oct).
Special Weekly Sections: Houston Belief (Fri); InMotion (Other); Color Comics (S); New Homes (Sat); Preview/Dining Guide (Thur); Flavor (Wed).
Syndicated Publications: Zest (ROP) (S).
Digital Platform - Mobile: Apple, Android, Windows, Blackberry
Digital Platform - Tablet: Apple iOS, Android, Windows 7, Blackberry Tablet OS, Kindle, Nook, Kindle Fire
Chief Financial Officer .... John Perdigao
Executive VP/Multi-Market Advertising .Michael C. LaBonia
Vice President, Recruitment Advertising ...... Mario Barson
Vice President, Consumer Sales & Services .... Michael Gorman
Vice President, Operations .... Michael H. Sacks
Vice President, Audience Development & Planning Linda Schaible
Outlook Editor .... Veronica Flores-Panlagua
Executive Vice President/Sales ...... Rob Cravaritis
Editor, Executive Vice President/News .... Nancy Barnes
Managing Editor .... Steve Proctor
Executive Producer/Director, Digital Content .... Andrea G. Mooney
Director .... Greg Cox
Editor .... Jeff Cohen
Senior Ed. .... Maria Carrillo
Chief Operating Officer .... Paul Barbetta
Pub./Pres. .... Jack Sweeney
Market Information: ADS; Split run; TMC; Zoned editions.
Mechanical Available: Offset; Black and 3 ROP colors; insert accepted - cards, bags; page cutoffs - 22 3/4, 22, 21.
Mechanical Specifications: Type page 12 3/4 x 21 1/4; E - 6 cols, 1/6 between; A - 6 cols, 1/6 between; C - 6 cols, between.
Areas Served: Austin, Brazoria, Chambers, Fort Bend, Galveston, Harris, Liberty, Montgomery, San Jacinto, Waller
Delivery Method: Mail, Newsstand, Carrier, RacksEquipment & Software: PRESSROOM EQUIPMENT: Lines — 12-G/Metro 1978; 12-G/Metro 1979; 12-G/Metroliner 1984; 12-G/Metro 1978; 12-G/Metroliner 1984; 12-G/Metroliner 1982; Press Drive — Fincor;

Folders — 6G/3:2; Pasters —Simplified TensionReels & Stands — 60 reel stands; Control System — Denex; Registration System — Web/Tech. MAILROOM EQUIPMENT: Counter Stackers — Quipp 350 to 550; Inserters & Stuffers — 5-HI/1372P, 3-HI/Model 630 30 head, 1-G 22-99; Tying Machines — Dynaric; Control System — Burt/Enternet; Address Machine — 6-Sitma/Plastic Wrap w/18 head, 1/KR; BUSINESS EQUIPMENT: IBM BUSINESS SOFTWARE: Microsoft CLASSIFIED EQUIPMENT: Hardware — SII, PC, Sun/Enterprise 3000, Sun/Enterprise 4000, Sun/450; DP/CD Merge System; Printers — HP/LaserJet; CLASSIFIED SOFTWARE: SII, CKP. DISPLAY EQUIPMENT: Hardware — Sun; Other Hardware — AdSat, AP, One Vision/Assura, One Vision/Solvera DISPLAY SOFTWAREAd Make-up Applications — Sun/Breeze; Layout Software — Cx, AdControl. EDITORIAL EQUIPMENT: Hardware — SII, Sun/Microsys/AU/APS 5, Lf/AP Leaf Picture Desk, APP/Mac, Sun/Phoenix T-1, Merlin/Photo Archive, Fox/Prodatabase, BH/Proquest Publisher; Printers — QMS/2060, HP/Laserjet EDITORIAL SOFTWARE: DTI/Newspaper Systems Millenium Editoria PRODUCTION EQUIPMENT: Hardware — 4 AGFA Polaris CTp, 4 NELA VPB benders & sorter WL/Offset, 2-WL/Lith 7, 2-WL/Lith-X-Pozer, Scitex/342, AG/Horizon Flatbed, APP/Mac All Platform, Avanta/25 Imagers, Avanta/30 Imagers PRODUCTION SOFTWARE: ProImage

HUNTSVILLE

THE HUNTSVILLE ITEM
1409 10th St, Huntsville, Texas, 77320-3805, Walker; gen tel (936) 295-5407; gen fax (936) 435-0135; gen/nat adv e-mail huntsvilleitem@gmail.com; disp adv e-mail rhaldeman@itemonline.com; ed e-mail huntsvilleitem@gmail.com; web site www.itemonline.com
- 225,000(views) 88,800(visitors)
Group: Community Newspaper Holdings, Inc.
Published: Tues, Wed, Thur, Fri, Sun
Weekday Frequency: m
Saturday Frequency: m
Circulation: 3,800; 3,800(sat); 4,000(sun)
Last Audit: Sworn/Estimate/Non-Audited December 18, 2017
Advertising Rate (weekday/saturday): Open Rate $15.00 PCI
Advertising Rate (sunday): Open Rate $16.00 PCI
News services: AP. **Established:** 1850
Own Printing Facility?: Yes
Commercial Printers?: Yes
Special Editions: Walker County Proud (Progress Edition - February); Rodeo Tab (March); Fair Winners (April); Reader's Choice (May); Newcomer's Guide (June); Football Preview (August); (September); Breast Cancer Awareness (October); Inspiring Women in Business (October); Holiday Wrap,(November); Veterans Day Section (November); Moments & Memories Magazine (November); Holiday Coloring Book (December)
Special Weekly Sections: Teleview (S).
Syndicated Publications: Texas Dept. Corrections News Roundup (Monthly); USA WEEKEND Magazine (S); American Profile (Weekly);Magazine (Monthly).
Digital Platform - Mobile: Apple, Android, Windows, Blackberry
Digital Platform - Tablet: Apple iOS, Android, Windows 7, Blackberry Tablet OS, Kindle, Nook, Kindle Fire
Director of Audience Development . Polly Johnson
Editor .... Tom Waddill
Mailroom Mgr. .... Christina Blount
Pub./Adv. Dir. .... Rita Haldeman
Market Information: TMC.
Mechanical Available: Offset; Black and 3 ROP colors; insert accepted - all; page cutoffs - 22 3/4.
Mechanical Specifications: Type page 13 x 21 1/2; E - 6 cols, 2 1/16, 1/8 between; A - 6 cols, 2 1/16, 1/8 between; C - 9 cols, 1 3/8, 1/16 between.

Areas Served: 77320, 77340, 77342, 77358, 77334, 77873, 77367, 77876, 75862, 77864, 77359, 77364, 77831, 77852
Delivery Method: Mail, Newsstand, Carrier, RacksEquipment & Software: PRESSROOM EQUIPMENT: Lines — 10-G/Community single width 1991; Folders — G/SSC (with upper and lower former) 1991.; MAILROOM EQUIPMENT: Counter Stackers — 1-BG/Count-O-Veyor 108; Inserters & Stuffers — MM/7 Station; Tying Machines — 1-MLN/MLI-EE-ML-MS; CLASSIFIED EQUIPMENT: Hardware — Mk, APP/Mac; CLASSIFIED SOFTWARE: Baseview/Ad Manager Pro. DISPLAY SOFTWARELayout Software — APP/Mac. EDITORIAL EQUIPMENT: Hardware — Mk, APP/Mac EDITORIAL SOFTWARE: Baseview/NewsEdit, InDesign PRODUCTION EQUIPMENT: Hardware — V, Pre Press/Panther Pro 46; Cameras — 1-SCREEN/C-260; Scanners — Unimax PRODUCTION SOFTWARE: QPS/QuarkXPress 4.0.

KERRVILLE

KERRVILLE DAILY TIMES
429 Jefferson St, Kerrville, Texas, 78028-4412, Kerr; gen tel (830) 896-7000; adv tel (830)896-7000; ed tel (830)896-7000; gen fax (830) 896-1150; adv fax (830) 896-1150; ed fax (830) 896-1150; gen/nat adv e-mail advertising@dailytimes.com; disp adv e-mail advertising@dailytimes.com; class adv e-mailadvertising@dailytimes.com; ed e-mail niece.bell@dailytimes.com; web site www.dailytimes.com
Group: Southern Newspapers Inc.
Published: Mon, Tues, Wed, Thur, Fri, Sun
Weekday Frequency: m
Circulation: 5,872; 7,159(sun)
Last Audit: AAM March 31, 2015
Advertising Rate (weekday/saturday): Open inch rate $16.80
Advertising Rate (sunday): Open inch rate $16.80
News services: AP. **Established:** 1910
Special Editions: Football (Aug); Christmas (Dec); Brides (Mar); Graduation (May); Hunting & Wild Game Guide (Nov); New Car (Oct).
Special Weekly Sections: Women in Business (Mon); Best Food Day (Wed); Business in Review, Entertainment (Thur); Religion (Fri); Business (Sun)
Syndicated Publications: Real Estate (Monthly); Parade (S); American Profile (Weekly).
Circ. Dir. .... Jack Parker
Pub./Ed. .... Mike Graxiola
Mng. Ed. .... Carlina Villalpando
Photographer .... Tom Holden
Adv. Dir. .... Jennifer McCullough
Press Mgr. .... Ricky Carrington
Market Information: ADS; TMC.
Mechanical Available: Offset; Black and 3 ROP colors; insert accepted - 8 x 10 min.; page cutoffs - 22 3/4.
Mechanical Specifications: Type page 11 5/8 x 21 1/2; E - 6 cols, 1 13/16, 1/8 between; A - 6 cols, 1 13/16, 1/8 between; C - 9 cols, 1 1/8, 1/8 between.Equipment & Software: PRESSROOM EQUIPMENT: Lines — 6-G/Community single width; Folders — 1-G/SC.; MAILROOM EQUIPMENT: Counter Stackers — KAN; Inserters & Stuffers — KAN/380; Tying Machines — 1-Us/Q, 1-Us/TE, 1/Md.; BUSINESS SOFTWARE: PBC CLASSIFIED EQUIPMENT: Hardware — APP/iMac; CLASSIFIED SOFTWARE: Baseview/Class Pro. DISPLAY EQUIPMENT: Hardware — APP/Mac G3, APP/Mac G4; Printers — HP/4M; DISPLAY SOFTWARELayout Software — QPS/QuarkXPress. EDITORIAL EQUIPMENT: Hardware — APP/Mac G4/4-APP/Mac G4, Nikon/Coolscan; Printers — HP/4M EDITORIAL SOFTWARE: Baseview/NewsEdit Pro. PRODUCTION EQUIPMENT: Hardware — Anitec/Imagesetter; Cameras — 1-SCREEN/Companica 680C

KILLEEN

KILLEEN DAILY HERALD
1809 Florence Rd, Killeen, Texas, 76541-

8977, Bell; gen tel (254) 634-2125; adv tel (254) 501-7500; ed tel (254) 501-7540; gen fax (254)200-7640; adv fax (254) 200-7632; ed fax (254) 200-7640; gen/nat adv e-mail nationals@kdhnews.com; disp adv e-mail aedwards@kdhnews.com; class adv e-mailaedwards@kdhnews.com; ed e-mail news@kdhnews.com; web site www.kdhnews.com
- 88,000(views)
Group: Frank Mayborn Enterprises, Inc.
Published: Mon, Tues, Wed, Thur, Fri, Sat, Sun
Weekday Frequency: m
Saturday Frequency: m
Circulation: 10,524; 10,524(sat); 14,707(sun)
Last Audit: AAM March 31, 2016
Advertising Rate (weekday/saturday): Open inch rate $24.93
Online Advertising Rate: Please call for detailed pricing
News services: AP, Landon Media Group. **Established:** 1890
Own Printing Facility?: Yes
Commercial Printers?: Yes
Special Editions: Car Care (Apr); UMHB Sports (Aug); Wrap it Up 2 (Dec); Progressive (Feb); Boat Show (Jan); Mile Maker (Jul); 100 Best (Jun); Design An Ad (Mar); Festival of Flags (May); UCT Birthday (Nov); AUSA (Oct); Medical Directory (Sept).
Special Weekly Sections: Weekender (Fri); TV Book (S); Dollar Saver (Wed).
Syndicated Publications: Parade, Athlon sports
Proprietary Publications: Fort Hood Herald
Copperas Cove Herald
Harker Heights Herald
Tex Appeal Magazine
Homefront Magazine
Digital Platform - Mobile: Apple, Android, Windows
Digital Platform - Tablet: Apple iOS, Android, Windows 7, Kindle, Kindle Fire
Pub. ....Sue Mayborn
Gen. Mgr. ....Terry E. Gandy
Bus. Mgr. ....Rodney Sparks
Adv. Mgr. .... Tiffany Muller
Mng. Ed. .... Olga Pena
Asst. Mng. Ed. ....David Miller
Sports Ed. ....Mark Miller
Coord., Telecommun. ....Jason Browne
Market Information: ADS; TMC.
Mechanical Available: Offset; Black and 3 ROP colors; insert accepted - subject to publisher's approval; page cutoffs - 22 3/4.
Mechanical Specifications: Type page 13 x 21 1/2; E - 6 cols, 2 1/16, 1/8 between; A - 6 cols, 2 1/16, 1/8 between; C - 9 cols, 1 3/8, 1/16 between.
Areas Served: Killeen, Florence, Nolanville, Ft. Hood, Copperas Cove, Gatesville, Harker Heights and Belton
Delivery Method: Mail, Newsstand, Carrier, RacksEquipment & Software: PRESSROOM EQUIPMENT: Lines — 7-G/Urbanite 1978, 3-G/Urbanite 1985.; MAILROOM EQUIPMENT: Counter Stackers — 1/HL; Inserters & Stuffers — 1-/S; Tying Machines — 1-/MLN, 1-/EC; Address Machine — 2-/St.; BUSINESS EQUIPMENT: Dell BUSINESS SOFTWARE: MAS 90, AR-2000 CLASSIFIED EQUIPMENT: Hardware — ALR; Printers — GCC/Elite 808; CLASSIFIED SOFTWARE: APT. DISPLAY EQUIPMENT: Hardware — ALR; Printers — GCC/Elite 808; DISPLAY SOFTWAREAd Make-up Applications — APT; Layout Software — APT. EDITORIAL EQUIPMENT: Hardware — ALR/Lf/AP Leaf Picture Desk, Lf/Leafscan 35, Linotype-Hell/L 190, Mark/40 EX, SCREEN/Katana 5055; Printers — GCC/Elite 808 EDITORIAL SOFTWARE: APT. PRODUCTION EQUIPMENT: Hardware — Textbridge/Pro, Linotronic/Mark 40EX Postscript, SCREEN/Katana 5055, SCREEN/LD-M1060; Cameras — 1-C/Spartan III; Scanners — 1-Lf, Umax, SCREEN/Cezanne, Nikon/2000 PRODUCTION SOFTWARE: QPS/QuarkXPress, APT.

LAREDO

LAREDO MORNING TIMES
111 Esperanza Dr, Laredo, Texas, 78041-2607, Webb; gen tel (956) 728-2500; adv tel (956) 728-2512; ed tel (956) 728-2563;

gen fax (956) 723-1227; adv fax (956) 728-2593; ed fax (956) 724-3036; gen/nat adv e-mail bill@lmtonline.com; disp adv e-mail ads@lmtonline.com; ed e-mail ngeorgiou@lmtonline.com; web site www.lmtonline.com
Group: Hearst Communications, Inc.
Published: Mon, Tues, Wed, Thur, Fri, Sat, Sun
Weekday Frequency: m
Saturday Frequency: m
Circulation: 12,043; 12,043(sat); 14,147(sun)
Last Audit: AAM December 31, 2015
Advertising Rate (weekday/saturday): Open inch rate $51.35
Advertising Rate (sunday): Open inch rate $52.70
News services: AP, LAT-WP, NYT, MCT, HN, CNS. **Established:** 1881
Own Printing Facility?: No
Special Editions: Fall Fashion (Aug); Washington's Birthday (Feb); Border Olympics (Spring); Border Olympics (Summer).
Special Weekly Sections: Business (Mon); Best Food Day, La Familia, El Mercadito Shopper, Comics (Wed); Youth, Campus (Thur); Entertainment (Fri); Fashion, Society, Art of Living (Sun); El Tiempo de Laredo (Daily)
Syndicated Publications: USA WEEKEND Magazine (S); American Profile (Weekly).
Pub...William B. Green
Controller..Joe Vied
Adv. Dir................................... Adriana Devally
Photo Dept. Mgr............................Cuate Santos
Sunday Ed................................. Odie Arambula
Ed...Diana Fuentes
Market Information: Split run; TMC; Zoned editions.
Mechanical Available: Offset; Black and 3 ROP colors; insert accepted - pocket book size (5 x 7).
Mechanical Specifications: Type page 13 7/8 x 21; E - 6 cols, 2 1/16, 1/8 between; A - 6 cols, 2 1/16, 1/8 between; C - 6 cols, 2 1/16, 1/8 between.
Delivery Method: Mail, Newsstand, CarrierEquipment & Software: PRESSROOM EQUIPMENT: 1-Multi-Lith/1250; Folders — 1, 1. MAILROOM EQUIPMENT: Tying Machines — 2-Bu/PAT 27,744; Address Machine — 1-Am/Class 640, 1-Am/4000.; BUSINESS EQUIPMENT: 1-NCR/8200 CLASSIFIED EQUIPMENT: Hardware — M, 3-CRT terminal; 4-IBM/71, 1-NCR/memory unit, Dewar; Printers — 1-NCR/Lineprinter.; EDITORIAL EQUIPMENT: Hardware — AT, 14-IBM/71. PRODUCTION EQUIPMENT: Hardware — 1-Am/450, 2-Am/430, 1-Comp/Set 4510; Cameras — 1-C/Spartan II, 1-VG/320; Scanners — ECR/Autokon 5200.

LONGVIEW

LONGVIEW NEWS-JOURNAL

320 E Methvin St, Longview, Texas, 75601-7323, Gregg; gen tel (903) 237-7744; adv tel (903) 237-7736; ed tel (903) 237-7744; gen fax (903) 757-3742; adv fax (903) 236-3874; ed fax (903)237-3742; gen/nat adv e-mail ljobe@news-journal.com; disp adv e-mail cdean@news-journal.com; class adv e-mailhchatelain@news-journal.com; ed e-mail rbrack@news-journal.com; web site www.news-journal.com
- 1,750,000(views) 425,000(visitors); web site 2 mycharmonline.com - 6,600(views) 1,865(visitors); web site 3 Etvarsity.com - 165,000(views) 36,000(visitors)
Group: Texas Community Media LLC
Published: Mon, Tues, Wed, Thur, Fri, Sat, Sun
Weekday Frequency: m
Saturday Frequency: m
Circulation: 16,990; 16,990(sat); 19,349(sun)
Last Audit: AAM June 30, 2016
Newspaper Reps: Stephen McHaney
Pat Kinney
Denise Lytle
Branch Offices: 320 E. Methvin St., Longview, TX
Advertising Rate (weekday/saturday): 31.04 plus color
Advertising Rate (sunday): 39.09 plus color
Online Advertising Rate: $9 -$22/m
News services: AP, NYT **Established:** 1871
Own Printing Facility?: Yes
Commercial Printers?: Yes
Special Editions: Progress (March-April), AlleyFest (May), Great Texas Balloon Race (July), The Zone (August)
Special Weekly Sections: Religion (Sat), Business (Sun), Lifestyles (Sun), Health (Th), Taste (Wed), REW (Fri), @Play (Th)
Syndicated Publications: USA Weekend (Sun), American Profile (Mon), Relish (monthly Tuesday), Spry (monthly Thur), Athlon Sports (monthly Sun)
Proprietary Publications: Charm (every other month)
Pub.....................................Stephen McHaney
Sports Ed. ....Jack Stallard
Chief Photographer..........................Kevin Green
Prodn. Mgr. ....Janet Owens
Bindery Mgr.............................Terresa Garrison
Circ. Dir. ....Josh Hart
HR Dir. .... Pat Kinney
Dana Morton
Chief Financial Officer.....................Denise Lytle
Ed. Dir.... Ric Brack
Reg. Pub... Jerry Pye
Adv. Mgr.... Debbi Knoll
Adv. Dir... Larry Jobe
Market Information: TMC
Mechanical Available: Columns..... Points Layout Inches.................. Reproduction Size Inches
1 123 .... 1.71
1.71
2 252 .... 3.5
3.5
3 381 .... 5.29
5.29
4 510 .... 7.08
7.08
5 639 .... 8.88
8.88
6 768 .... 10.67
10.67
13 (Double Truck) 1596
22.17 .... 22.17
Areas Served: 75455 75563 75571 75601 75602 75603 75604 75605 75606 75607 75630 75631 75633 75638 75640 75644 75645 75647 75650 75651 75652 75654 75656 75657 75661 75662 75668 75670 75672 75683 75684 75686 75691 75692 75693 75755 75765
Delivery Method: Mail, Newsstand, Carrier, RacksEquipment & Software: PRESSROOM EQUIPMENT: DGM 850 16 units with 2 folders MAILROOM EQUIPMENT: SLS 1000 BUSINESS SOFTWARE: Brainworks CLASSIFIED SOFTWARE: Brainworks EDITORIAL EQUIPMENT: PC and Macintosh EDITORIAL SOFTWARE: Tera Digital Publishing GN3 IT EQUIPMENT: Dell
EMC IT SOFTWARE:Tera
Brainworks
SBS CIRCULATION SOFTWARBrainworks CircSmart

LUBBOCK

LUBBOCK AVALANCHE-JOURNAL

710 Avenue J, Lubbock, Texas, 79401-1808, Lubbock; gen tel (806) 762-8844; adv tel (806) 766-8616; ed tel (806) 766-8701; gen fax (806) 765-8770; adv fax (806) 765-5826; ed fax (806) 744-9603; gen/nat adv e-mail robin.morse@lubbockonline.com; disp adv e-mail shoni.wiseman@lubbockonline.com; class adv e-mailrobin.morse@lubbockonline.com; ed e-mail stephen.beasley@lubbockonline.com; web site www.lubbockonline.com
Group: GateHouse Media, Inc.
Published: Mon, Tues, Wed, Thur, Fri, Sat, Sun
Weekday Frequency: m
Saturday Frequency: m
Circulation: 25,014; 27,039(sat); 32,001(sun)
Last Audit: AAM September 30, 2016
Advertising Rate (weekday/saturday): Open inch rate $69.95
Advertising Rate (sunday): Open inch rate $74.55
News services: AP, MCT, LAT-WP. **Established:** 1900
Special Editions: Medical Directory (Aug); 50 Plus (Fall); Best of Lubbock (Jul); Life in Lubbock (Jun); 50 Plus (Spring); Sharing The Season (Winter).
Special Weekly Sections: Business, Industrial Review (Mon); Best Food Day (Wed); Entertainment (Fri); Special Section Calendar, Religion, Creative Living, TV, Real Estate (Sat); Entertainment, Agriculture, Local Daily News, Travel, Business (Sun)
Syndicated Publications: Relish (Monthly); USA WEEKEND Magazine (S).
Pub..................................... Stephen A. Beasley
Div. Controller..........................Charlene Harris
Dir., HR..................................Shelby Caballero
Adv. Dir., Sales................................ Jeff Brown
Adv. Mgr., Classified Sales............. Sarah Kelley
Retail Sales Mgr............................... Kevin Dyer
Dir., Consumer Mktg.........................Julia Childs
Circ. Mgr.............................. Brandon Hughes
Circ. Dir. ....James Grimmett
Ed... Terry Greenberg
Mng. Ed. ....Mel Tittle
Asst. Mng. Ed., News/Features....... Karen Brehm
Asst. Mng. Ed., Sports/Design .Courtney Linehan
Bus./Finance Ed...................Chris Van Wagenen
Editorial Page Ed. .... Joe Hughes
Entertainment Ed. .... Bill Kerns
Editorial Writer/Columnist ....Joe Gulick
Features Ed............................ Shelly Gonzales
News Ed............................ David (Crash) Daniel
Photo Dept. Mgr....................................Zack Long
Production Dir. .... Kristi Holt
Adv. Sales.. Robin Morse
Retail Adv. Dir. .... Shoni Wiseman
Market Information: TMC.
Mechanical Available: Offset; Black and 3 ROP colors; insert accepted; page cutoffs - 22 7/8.
Mechanical Specifications: Type page 11 5/8 x 21 1/2; E - 4 cols, 1/8 between; A - 6 cols, 1 5/6, 1/8 between; C - 9 cols, between.Equipment & Software: PRESSROOM EQUIPMENT: Lines — 12-G/Metro; Pasters —G/Automatic. MAILROOM EQUIPMENT: Counter Stackers — 4/T.M.S.I, 2-/H.T.; Inserters & Stuffers — 2-GMA/1000 18:2; Tying Machines — 4-/Dynaric; Wrapping Singles — 2-/Dynaric; Address Machine — 1-/Ch.; BUSINESS EQUIPMENT: 56-IBM/PC-AT, 1-APP/Mac SE, 1-APP/Mac IIfx, Dell/Optiplex GX270 BUSINESS SOFTWARE: MPS, DTI CLASSIFIED EQUIPMENT: Hardware — Gateway/2000 G6-233, DTI; Proteon/LAN; Printers — Toshiba/P351, 2-Xante, Konica/EV9200; CLASSIFIED SOFTWARE: MPS, DTI. DISPLAY EQUIPMENT: Hardware — 4-APP/Power PC 9100; Printers — AG/Imager 1000/1500, 2-Xante, Konica/EV9200; Other Hardware — CD-Rom, DISPLAY SOFTWAREAd Make-up Applications — APP/Mac, Adobe/Photoshop, Multi-Ad/Creator 3.0.1, Adobe/Acrobat, QuarkXpress, Adobe/Illustrator, Adobe/InDesign, Adobe/Distiller; EDITORIAL EQUIPMENT: Hardware — Gateway/2000, Gateway/P5-200, Gateway/G6-233, Gateway/2000, PS-60, 1-APP/Mac SE, 5-APP/Power Mac 8100-80, 1-APP/Mac IIfx, 5-APP/Mac 9100/APP/Mac IIfx, Proteon/LAN, Asanti/Eathernet; Printers — Toshiba/P351, APP/Mac LaserWriter II, PRODUCTION EQUIPMENT: Hardware — Accuset/1000, Accuset/1500, 2-Xante, Konica/EV9200; Cameras — Epson/1640 XL; Scanners — 1-AG/T2000XL, UMAX, HP/Scanjet.

LUFKIN

THE LUFKIN DAILY NEWS

300 Ellis at Herndon, Lufkin, Texas, 75904, Angelina; gen tel (936) 632-6631; adv tel (936) 631-2630; ed tel (936) 631-2623; gen fax (936) 632-6655; adv fax (936) 632-6655; ed fax (936) 632-6655; gen/nat adv e-mail tkedrowicz@lufkindailynews.com; disp adv e-mail tkedrowicz@lufkindailynews.com; class adv e-mailsdoyle@lufkindailynews.com; ed e-mail aadams@lufkindailynews.com; web site www.lufkindailynews.com
- 805,000(views) 9,700(visitors)
Group: Southern Newspapers Inc.
Published: Mon, Tues, Wed, Thur, Fri, Sat, Sun
Weekday Frequency: m
Saturday Frequency: m
Circulation: 7,125; 7,125(sat); 8,730(sun)
Last Audit: AAM March 31, 2017
Advertising Rate (weekday/saturday): Open inch rate $36.00
Advertising Rate (sunday): Open inch rate $41.00
News services: AP. **Established:** 1907
Own Printing Facility?: Yes
Commercial Printers?: Yes
Special Editions: Parade of Homes (Annually); Back-to-School (Aug); Christmas Shopping Guide (Dec); Progress (Feb); Graduation (May).
Special Weekly Sections: Travel (Fri); Technology (Mon); Lifestyle (S); NASCAR (Sat); Food (Wed).
Syndicated Publications: USA Weekend (S); American Profile (Weekly); Athon Sports (Weekly); Relish (Monthly); Spry (Monthly)
Proprietary Publications: Charm Magazine, Business Link both semi-monthly magazines
Digital Platform - Mobile: Apple, Android, Blackberry
Digital Platform - Tablet: Apple iOS, Android, Blackberry Tablet OS, Kindle, Kindle Fire
Pub...Greg Shrader
Adv. Dir................................. Tammy Kedrowicz
Circ. Dir. ....Jennifer Ricks
Ed.... Andy Adams
Lifestyles Ed.............................Beverly Johnson
News Ed.... Jeff Pownall
Photo Ed. ....Joel Andrews
Sports Ed. .... Josh Havard
Data Processing Mgr................. Renee Guajardo
Production. Mgr., Mailroom................. Billy Ricks
Prodn. Mgr., Pre Press.................. Robin Nevills
Prodn. Foreman, Pressroom.............Steve Reed
Business Manager..........................Jennifer Bess
Nacogdoches Adv. Mgr................... Staci Hodges
Market Information: ADS; TMC.
Mechanical Available: Offset; Black and 3 ROP colors; insert accepted; page cutoffs - 22 3/4.
Mechanical Specifications: Type page 11 5/8 x 21; E - 6 cols, 1 5/6, 1/8 between; A - 6 cols, 1 5/6, 1/8 between; C - 9 cols, 1 3/16, 1/8 between.
Areas Served: 75901,75904,75941,75949,75969,75980,75925,75976,75944,75937,75939,75929,75926,75845.
Delivery Method: Mail, Newsstand, Carrier, RacksEquipment & Software: PRESSROOM EQUIPMENT: Lines — 7-G/Urbanite 1979, 1-G/Urbanite (3 color) 1979; Press Drive — 2-Fin/Digital 100 h.p. DC motor; MAILROOM EQUIPMENT: Counter Stackers — QWI/200; Inserters & Stuffers — 2-MM/227S 6:1; Tying Machines — 2-MLN/MLI-EE.; BUSINESS EQUIPMENT: 1-HP/9000, HP/8175S BUSINESS SOFTWARE: DTI, Geac/Vision Shift CLASSIFIED EQUIPMENT: Hardware — 2-APP/Power Mac 7100-66, APP/Mac G4; Kk/DC 120 Digital Camera, APP/Mac One Scanner, HP/ScanJet 4C; Printers — HP/2100 DN; CLASSIFIED SOFTWARE: MediaSpan Class Manager DISPLAY EQUIPMENT: Hardware — Power Computing/Pro 2001 (Mac Clone), APP/Mac G4; Printers — APP/Mac LaserWriter, Epson/Stylus Color 3000, HP/2100N; Other Hardware — Kk/DC 120 Digital Camera, HP/ScanJet 4C, Kk/DC265 Zoom Digital Cameras DISPLAY SOFTWAREAd Make-up Applications — DTI/AdSpeed 4.2; Layout Software — D EDITORIAL EQUIPMENT: Hardware — APP/Mac G3, APP/Mac G4 700/1-Nikon/RS 3500, Howtek/ScanMaster II, Nikon/Digital Camera; Printers — HP/8150 EDITORIAL SOFTWARE: MediaSpan NewsEdit Pro PRODUCTION EQUIPMENT: Hardware — Konica/JetSetter 6100, Adobe/Photoshop; Cameras — Spartan III; Scanners — Microtek/60025, 1-Nikon/L5-3510 PRODUCTION SOFTWARE: MediaSpan Production Manager Pro, Puzzle Flow CIRCULATION EQUIPMENT: APP/Mac G% CIRCULATION SOFTWARMediaSpan Circulation Pro

MARSHALL

MARSHALL NEWS MESSENGER

309 E Austin St, Marshall, Texas, 75670-3475, Harrison; gen tel (903)903-7914; adv tel (903) 927-5973; ed tel (903) 935-7914; gen fax (903) 935-6242; adv fax (903) 935-6242; ed fax (903) 935-6242; gen/nat adv e-mail awalker@news-journal.com; disp adv e-mail dgray@news-journal.com; class adv e-maildgray@news-journal.com; ed e-mail cshields@marshallnewsmessenger.com; web site www.marshallnewsmessenger.com
Group: Cox Media Group
Texas Community Media Group
Published: Tues, Wed, Thur, Fri, Sat, Sun
Weekday Frequency: m
Saturday Frequency: m

Circulation: 4,517; 4,517(sat); 4,713(sun)
Last Audit: AAM March 31, 2014
Advertising Rate (weekday/saturday): Open inch rate $24.26
Advertising Rate (sunday): Open inch rate $39.32
News services: AP. **Established:** 1877
Special Weekly Sections: Generations (Tue); Food, Education (Wed); Weekend (Thur); Religion, NASCAR (Sat); Business, Books (Sun)
Syndicated Publications: Parade (S); American Profile (Weekly).
Bus. Mgr. .... Dana Morton
District Mgr. .... Chris Kundtson
Ed. .... Phil Latham
Asst. News Ed. .... D.D. Turner
Features Ed. .... Robin Richardson
Adv. Sales Exec. .... Bethany Dean
Adv. Dir. .... Andrew Walker
Circ. Dir. .... Josh Hart
Pub. .... Jerry Pye
Adv. Sales Exec. .... Johnnie Fancher
Market Information: Split run; TMC.
Mechanical Available: Offset; Black and 4 ROP colors; insert accepted - single sheet; page cutoffs - 22 3/4.
Mechanical Specifications: Type page 13 3/4 x 21 1/4; E - 6 cols, 1 5/6, 1/8 between; A - 6 cols, 1 5/6, 1/8 between; C - 9 cols, 1 9/50, 1/8 between.Equipment & Software: BUSINESS EQUIPMENT: IBM/PC-AT CLASSIFIED EQUIPMENT: Hardware — APP/iMac; Printers — TI/Omni 800 line printer; CLASSIFIED SOFTWARE: DTI/ ClassSpeed 1.3.2. DISPLAY EQUIPMENT: Hardware — APP/Mac G4; Printers — APP/ Mac LaserJet; DISPLAY SOFTWAREAd Make-up Applications — Aldus/PageMaker 5.0, Adobe/Illustrator 5.5.; EDITORIAL EQUIPMENT: Hardware — Mk/4000, APP/ Mac IIcx, APP/Mac Quadra 610/APP/ Mac Scanner, Lf/LeafScan 35, Lf/AP Leaf Picture Desk; Printers — TI/Omni 800 line printer, 2-Xante/8200, APP/Mac LaserWriter Plus, V/4990 EDITORIAL SOFTWARE: Mk/Ace 1.3.2, Mk/NewsTouch AT, QPS/ PRODUCTION EQUIPMENT: Hardware — 2-APP/Mac Radius, 2-APP/Mac IIcx.

MCALLEN

THE MONITOR

1400 E Nolana Ave, McAllen, Texas, 78504-6111, Hidalgo; gen tel (956) 686-4343; adv tel (956) 683-4113; ed tel (956) 683-4400; gen fax (956) 683-4201; adv fax (956) 683-4121; ed fax (956)-683-4401; gen/nat adv e-mail bmendell@rgvmedianetwork.com; disp adv e-mail bearly@themonitor.com; class adv e-maildsilva@rgvmedianetwork.com; ed e-mail csanchez@themonitor.com; web site www.themonitor.com
- 1,600,000(views) 260,000(visitors); web site 2 www.brownsvilleherald.com - 600,000(views) 80,000(visitors); web site 3 valleymorningstar.com - 520,000(views) 70,000(visitors)
Group: AIM Media Texas LLC
Published: Mon, Tues, Wed, Thur, Fri, Sat, Sun
Weekday Frequency: m
Saturday Frequency: m
Circulation: 20,822; 18,821(sat); 24,258(sun)
Last Audit: AAM March 31, 2017
Newspaper Reps: Jeremy Halbreich, Owner-Chairman, CEO
Rick Starks, Owner- President/COO
Stephan Wingert - Publisher/Regional VP
Armando Martinez- HR Director
Debbie Grant- CFO/ Controller
Advertising Rate (weekday/saturday): Open inch rate $42.69
Advertising Rate (sunday): Open inch rate $50.37
Online Advertising Rate: $12.50 CPM
News services: AP. **Established:** 1909
Own Printing Facility?: Yes
Commercial Printers?: Yes
Special Editions: B-T-S, HS Football (Aug); Business Directory (Apr), Hurricane (Jun.);
Special Weekly Sections: Religious Directory (Fri); Festiva
Syndicated Publications: Parade (S).Sprye (W); Athlon (F); American Profile (F); Relish (W)
Proprietary Publications: South Texas Outdoors (Feb., Jun., Sept., Nov.)
RGV Sports (May, Aug., Dec.) Park Book (Oct.), Guide Book (Nov.)
Digital Platform - Mobile: Apple, Android, Windows, Blackberry
Digital Platform - Tablet: Apple iOS, Android
Pub. .... Stephan Wingert
Dir., Finance & Controller .... Debbie Grant
Rgl. HR Dir. .... Armando Martinez
Gen. Mgr./Rgl. Adv. Mgr. RGV Media .... Benita Mendell
Commercial Print Director .... Walt Bartlick
Editor .... Carlos Sanchez
Regional Director of Information Technology Doug Fullerton
Regional Production Director .... Ernie Cortez
Circ. Dir. .... Robert Levrier
Contact Center Manager .... Dan Silva
Advertising Director .... Bob Early
Market Information: ADS.
Mechanical Available: Offset; Black and 3 ROP colors; insert accepted - all; page cutoffs - 21 inch.
Mechanical Specifications: Type page 10.25" x 20"; E - 6 cols, each column 1.608", .12" between; FP - 6 cols, 10.25" .12" between; C - 10 cols, 1 col .0975", .06" between. C FP 10 cols 10.25" x 20")
Areas Served: Hidalgo County,
Delivery Method: Mail, Newsstand, Carrier, RacksEquipment & Software: PRESSROOM EQUIPMENT: Goss Universal 45 PRESSROOM SOFTWARE: ABB MAILROOM EQUIPMENT: Inserting machine — 1-GMA/SLS 2000 14:2; SLS/1000;12:2; Tying Machines —Quipp Pacman Counter stackers and strapper. BUSINESS EQUIPMENT: Brainworks/AR Package;Cisco BUSINESS SOFTWARE: Newscycle Solutions APT, Quick Books; Enterprise CLASSIFIED EQUIPMENT: Hardware — DELL HP Printers CLASSIFIED SOFTWARE: APT. DISPLAY EQUIPMENT: Hardware — DELL HP Printers; DISPLAY SOFTWAREAd Make -up applications— APT EDITORIAL EQUIPMENT: Hardware — DELL HP Printers — HP/5000 EDITORIAL SOFTWARE: APT. MIcrosoft Word, In Design PRODUCTION EQUIPMENT: Hardware — Prolmage Impositioning Software, 2 Creo thermal news setters, Nela conveyor & Plate Punch bender. PRODUCTION SOFTWARE: APT. Adobe, In Design IT EQUIPMENT: Dell HP; Cisco IT SOFTWARE:Microsoft, Adobe CIRCULATION EQUIPMENT: DTI

MIDLAND

MIDLAND REPORTER-TELEGRAM

201 E Illinois Ave, Midland, Texas, 79701-4852, Midland; gen tel (432) 687-8813; adv tel (432) 687-8894; ed tel (432) 687-8855; gen fax (432)682-3793; ed fax (432) 570-7650; gen/nat adv e-mail jhouston@mrt.com; disp adv e-mail jhouston@mrt.com; class adv e-mailmrtclassified@mrt.com; ed e-mail news@mrt.com; web site www.mrt.com
- 2,000,000(views) 310,000(visitors)
Group: Hearst Communications, Inc.
Published: Mon, Tues, Wed, Thur, Fri, Sat, Sun
Weekday Frequency: m
Saturday Frequency: m
Circulation: 10,292; 10,292(sat); 12,314(sun)
Last Audit: AAM June 30, 2017
Newspaper Reps: Stewart Doreen I Editor in Chief
Mary Dearen I Managing Editor
Mercedes Cordero I Online Editor
Oscar LeRoy I Sports Editor
Trevor Hawes I Asst. Managing Editor
John Maddox I Production Director
Advertising Rate (weekday/saturday): Open inch rate $23.50
Advertising Rate (sunday): Open inch rate $27.50
News services: AP, HN, NYT. MCT, Bloomberg **Established:** 1929
Own Printing Facility?: Yes
Commercial Printers?: Yes
Special Editions: Youth Services (Apr); Back-to-School (Aug); Christmas Gift Guide (Dec); Primetime (Every other month); Outlook (Feb); Best of Midland (Jul); Senior Directory (Jun); Spring Home & Garden (Mar); Family Health (Nov); Oil (Oct); Fall Home & Garden (Sept); Football pre-view (Aug.)
Special Weekly Sections: Education (Tuesday), Health (Wednesday); Products, Services (Tue); Best Food Day, (Wed); Weekender (Thur); Religion, Lifestyle (Fri); Oil and Gas, Arts, Entertainment (Sun)
Syndicated Publications: Relish (Monthly); American Profile (Weekly).
Digital Platform - Mobile: Apple, Android, Windows
Digital Platform - Tablet: Apple iOS, Android, Windows 7
Ed. .... Stewart Doreen
Managing Ed. .... Mary Dearen
Oil/Gas Ed. .... Mella McEwen
Photo Ed. .... Tim Fischer
Mgr., Info Systems .... Lynn Kmiec
Online Mgr. .... Nancy Adamson
Prodn. Dir. .... John Maddox
Pub. .... Jeffrey Shabram
IT Dir. .... Brett Hrebicek
Adv. Dir. .... Jeri Houston
Market Information: TMC.
Mechanical Available: Offset; Black and 3 ROP colors; insert accepted - free-standing stock cards, envelope inserts; page cutoffs - 22 3/4.
Mechanical Specifications: Type page 11.00 x 21 1/2; E - 6 cols, 1.52, 0.9 between; A - 5 cols, 1.94, 0.9 between; C - 10 cols, 0.95, 0.10 between.
Areas Served: Midland, Odessa, Permian Basin
Delivery Method: Mail, Newsstand, Carrier, RacksEquipment & Software: PRESSROOM EQUIPMENT: Lines — 6-HI/1650 double width 1974; MAILROOM EQUIPMENT: Counter Stackers — 1-QWI/350; 1-Quipp/501 Inserters & Stuffers — S/48P (9 head); - Strappers 2-Dynaric NP 4000 - 1 Dynaric NP 1500
Computers - 1 PC (Windows 7) MAILROOM SOFTWARE:MS Office Suite - 2010 Standard BUSINESS EQUIPMENT: Computers -
5 -PC's (Windows 7 Professional & Windows XP)
Access to IBM Mainframe & IBM AS-400
Printers -
HP LaserJet P4515TN
Kyocera ECO SYS FS-1128 MFP
(Access to Kyocera TaskAlfa 400ci) BUSINESS SOFTWARE: ATEX AdBase Suite - AdBase 3.5
ATEX AdBase PGL PageLayout Applications
ATEX PGL Ad Distributor Application
Citrix (Web Interface for AdBase)
Edgil (Tokenization for AdBase Finance Applications and Marketing G2)
Affinity 4.0 (Advertising Ad Production)
TownNews (BLOX CMS - mywesttexas.com)
LocalEdge (Advertising Application)
Microsoft Office Suites - 2003, 2007, 2010
DISCUS (IBM Mainframe)
ADMARC (IBM Mainframe - Legacy system)
Hyperion (IBM AS400)
CLASSIFIED EQUIPMENT: Computers -
17 - PC's (Windows 7 Professional & Windows XP)
Printers -
Kyocera TaskAlfa 400ci CLASSIFIED SOFTWARE: ATEX AdBase Suite - AdBase 3.5
Citrix (Web Interface for AdBase)
Edgil (Tokenization for AdBase Finance Applications and Marketing G2)
Affinity 4.0 (Advertising Ad Production)
LocalEdge (Advertising Application)
Microsoft Office Suites - 2003, 2007, 2010
DISPLAY EQUIPMENT: Computers -
7 PC's - Windows 7 & Windows XP
6 iMacs - OSX
Printer -
Kyocera TaskAlfa 400ci DISPLAY SOFTWAREATEX AdBase Suite - AdBase 3.5
ATEX AdBase PGL PageLayout Applications
ATEX PGL Ad Distributor Application
Citrix (Web Interface for AdBase)
Edgil (Tokenization for AdBase Finance Applications and Marketing G2)
Affinity 4.0 (Advertising Ad Production)
TownNews (BLOX CMS - mywesttexas.com)
LocalEdge (Advertising Application)
Microsoft Office Suites - 2003, 2007, 2010, Mac Office 2008
EDITORIAL EQUIPMENT: Computers — 28 PC's - Windows 7 & Windows XP
Printers -
Kyocera TASKalfa 400ci KX
EDITORIAL SOFTWARE: Baseview NewsEdit 3.2
Software Construction Company - SCC Photo Archives
Microsoft Office Suite - 2010 Standard
Adobe Design Premium CS5.5 (InDesign for PageLayout)
AdBase PGL PageLink (to interface InDesign to AdBase PGL PageLayout)
Adobe Creative Design Premium 2.0
Quark 7.3 & 7.5
PRODUCTION EQUIPMENT: 2- AGFA - Advantage N-SL CTP with 2- VCF Processors
Computers -
3 - PC's - Windows 7 Professional
Printers -
Kyocera TASKalfa 400ci KX
PRODUCTION SOFTWARE: ATEX AdBase Suite - AdBase 3.5
ATEX AdBase PGL PageLayout Applications
Baseview NewsEdit 3.2
Software Construction Company - SCC Photo Archives
Microsoft Office Suite - 2010 Standard
Adobe Design Premium CS5.5 (InDesign for PageLayout)
AdBase PGL PageLink (to interface InDesign to AdBase PGL PageLayout)
Adobe Creative Design Premium 2.0
Quark 7.5
Microsoft Office Suite - 2010 Standard
IT EQUIPMENT: Servers -
Windows Server 2003 - SP3 - 6 (2 - Domain Controller Server, Firewall Server, 3 Application and File Servers)
Windows 7 Professional - 4 (CTP Controller Servers)
Windows XP - SP3 - 1 (AdBase Ad Distributor Server)
Mac OSX and OS9 - 2 (Baseview NewsEdit & Transporter Servers)
Sun Microsystems Unix -1 (Affinity SFTP Server)
Linux - 2 (Alert Logic Network Traffic Servers)
Network Devices -
1 - Cisco 3800 Series Router
5 - HP Procurve Switch 2810 48G 0/100/1000 Gigabit Switches,
1 - Cisco Catalyst 2950 10/100 24 Port Switch
Computers (MRT) -
75 PC's/8 Macs - Windows 7, Windows XP, Mac OSX
Printers (Network) -
3 - Kyocera TaskAlfa 400ci
2 - Kyocera ECO SYS FS-1128 MFP,
2 - HP LaserJet P4515TN,
1 - HP LaserJet Color 3600N
Telephone System -
Siemens HiPath 4000 (Survivoribility Unit)
IT SOFTWARE:Supported Software
Microsoft Server 2003
ATEX AdBase Suite - AdBase 3.5
ATEX AdBase PGL PageLayout Applications
ATEX PGL Ad Distributor Application
Citrix (Web Interface for AdBase)
Edgil (Tokenization for AdBase Finance Applications and Marketing G2)
Affinity 4.0 (Advertising Ad Production)
Marketing G2 (Circulation Applications)
Baseview NewsEdit 3.2 (Editorial Application)
Baseview Transporter 3.0 (Editorial Application)
AP WebFeeds Agent v2.2
AP Exchange (Web App)
TownNews (BLOX CMS - mywesttexas.com)
LocalEdge (Advertising Application)
Microsoft Office Suites - 2003, 2007, 2010, Mac Office 2008
Adobe Design Premium CS5.5
Adobe Web Premium CS5.5
Adobe Creative Suite 2 Premium
Adobe CS3.3 Premium
DISCUS (IBM Mainframe)
ADMARC (IBM Mainframe - Legacy system)
Hyperion (AS400)
CIRCULATION EQUIPMENT: Computers -
10 PC's - Windows 7 Professional and Windows XP
Printers -
HP LaserJet P4515TN,
HP LaserJet Color 3600N,
(access to Kyocera TaskAlfa 400ci)
CIRCULATION SOFTWARMicrosoft Office

Suites - 2003, 2007, 2010 Standard
DISCUS
Marketing G2

MINERAL WELLS

MINERAL WELLS INDEX
300 SE 1st St, Mineral Wells, Texas, 76067-5331, Palo Pinto; gen tel (940) 325-4465; adv tel (940) 325-4465; ed tel (940) 325-4465 ext. 3416; gen fax (940) 325-2020; adv fax (940)325-2020; ed fax (940) 325-2020; gen/nat adv e-mail adv@mineralwellsindex.com; disp adv e-mail adv@mineralwellsindex.com; class adv e-mailadv@mineralwellsindex.com; ed e-mail editor@mineralwellsindex.com; web site www.mineralwellsindex.com
Group: Community Newspaper Holdings, Inc.
Published: Tues, Wed, Thur, Fri, Sun
Weekday Frequency: m
Circulation: 3,500; 3,500(sun)
Last Audit: Sworn/Estimate/Non-Audited December 18, 2017
Advertising Rate (weekday/saturday): Open inch rate $12.50
Advertising Rate (sunday): Open inch rate $12.50
News services: AP. **Established:** 1900
Special Editions: Back-to-School (Aug); Christmas Gift Guide (Dec); Rodeo (May); Economic Development (Oct); Best of Mineral Wells (Sept).
Syndicated Publications: Relish (Monthly); TV Book (S); American Profile (Weekly).
General Manager & Editor ....David May
Market Information: ADS; TMC.
Mechanical Available: Offset; Black and 3 ROP colors; insert accepted - all; page cutoffs - 22 3/4.
Mechanical Specifications: Type page 13 3/4 x 21 1/2; E - 6 cols, 2, 1/8 between; A - 6 cols, 2, 1/8 between; C - 8 cols, 1 1/2, 1/8 between.Equipment & Software: PRESSROOM EQUIPMENT: Lines — 6-G/Community.; MAILROOM EQUIPMENT: Tying Machines — MC/Poly Strapper; CLASSIFIED EQUIPMENT: Hardware — APP/Mac G3; Printers — GCC/20-800; CLASSIFIED SOFTWARE: QPS/QuarkXPress, Multi-Ad/CAMS. EDITORIAL EQUIPMENT: Hardware — 5-APP/Mac G3; Printers — GCC/20-800 EDITORIAL SOFTWARE: Multi-Ad/Creator, QPS/QuarkXPress.

MOUNT PLEASANT

MOUNT PLEASANT DAILY TRIBUNE
210 S Van Buren Ave, Mount Pleasant, Texas, 75455-4440, Titus; gen tel (903) 572-1705; adv tel (903) 237-8863; ed tel (903)237-8863; gen fax (903) 572-6026; adv fax (903)572-6026; ed fax (903)572-6026; gen/nat adv e-mail kdaffern@tribnow.com; disp adv e-mail kdaffern@tribnow.com; class adv e-mailkdaffern@tribnow.com; ed e-mail valerie.reddell@tribnow.com; web site www.dailytribune.net
Group: Fenice Community Media
Published: Tues, Wed, Thur, Fri, Sun
Weekday Frequency: e
Circulation: 2,500; 3,100(sat); 4,988(sun)
Last Audit: Sworn/Estimate/Non-Audited September 30, 2017
Advertising Rate (weekday/saturday): Open inch rate $16.50
Advertising Rate (sunday): Open inch rate $17.50
News services: AP, NEA. **Established:** 1941
Own Printing Facility?: No
Commercial Printers?: No
Special Editions: Progress (Jan); Rodeo (Jun); Graduation (May); Women in Business (Oct); Modern Living (Quarterly); Football (Sept).
Special Weekly Sections: Real Estate, Sports (Daily); Religion (Fri); Agriculture, Business, Lifestyles (Sun)
Syndicated Publications: TV Viewing (Fri); Color Comics (S); American Profile (Weekly).
Market Information: ADS; TMC.
Mechanical Available: Offset; Black and 3 ROP colors; insert accepted; page cutoffs - 22 3/4.
Mechanical Specifications: Type page 13 x 21; E - 6 cols, 2 1/16, 1/8 between; A - 6 cols, 2 1/16, 1/8 between; C - 8 cols, 1 9/16, 1/16 between.

Areas Served: 75455Equipment & Software: PRESSROOM EQUIPMENT: Lines — 5-HI/V-15A 1984; 2-HI/V-15A 1993.; MAILROOM EQUIPMENT: Tying Machines — 2/Bu; Address Machine — 1-/KAN.; BUSINESS EQUIPMENT: PC BUSINESS SOFTWARE: BMF CLASSIFIED EQUIPMENT: Hardware — PC; Printers — APP/Mac LaserWriter; CLASSIFIED SOFTWARE: BMF. DISPLAY EQUIPMENT: Printers — APP/Mac LaserWriter; DISPLAY SOFTWAREAd Make-up Applications — Aldus/PageMaker; Layout Software — APP/Mac. EDITORIAL EQUIPMENT: Hardware — PC; Printers — APP/Mac LaserWriter EDITORIAL SOFTWARE: WordPerfect. PRODUCTION EQUIPMENT: Hardware — APP/Mac LaserWriter.

NACOGDOCHES

THE DAILY SENTINEL
4920 Colonial Dr, Nacogdoches, Texas, 75965-3021, Nacogdoches; gen tel (936)564-8361; adv tel (936)558-3210; ed tel (936)558-3202; gen fax (936)560-4267; adv fax (936)560-4267; ed fax (936)560-4267; gen/nat adv e-mail prains@dailysentinel.com; disp adv e-mail prains@dailysentinel.com; class adv e-mailclassifieds@dailysentinel.com; ed e-mail jedwards@dailysentinel.com; web site www.dailysentinel.com - 350,000(views) 20,000(visitors)
Group: Southern Newspapers Inc.
Published: Mon, Tues, Wed, Thur, Fri, Sat, Sun
Weekday Frequency: m
Saturday Frequency: m
Circulation: 5,500; 5,500(sat); 6,000(sun)
Last Audit: Sworn/Estimate/Non-Audited August 31, 2017
Newspaper Reps: Southern Newspapers Inc
Advertising Rate (weekday/saturday): $9.60 Nac only, $22.75 combo with Lufkin Daily news
Advertising Rate (sunday): $11.55Nac only, $26.00 combo with Lufkin Daily News
Online Advertising Rate: $8 - $5 cpm and by ad size
News services: AP Established: 1899
Own Printing Facility?: No
Commercial Printers?: Yes
Special Editions: Football (August) Progress (March) Outdoors (Fall) Charm Magazine (12x year) Nacogdoches Magazine (6x a year)
Special Weekly Sections: Food Day (W) Business (S) Education (W) Lifestyle (S)
Digital Platform - Mobile: Apple, Android
Digital Platform - Tablet: Apple iOS, Android, Kindle Fire
Publisher ....Debi Ryan
Sports ....Kevin Gore
City Editor ....Paul Bryant
Market Information: TMC.
Mechanical Available: Offset; Black and 3 ROP colors; insert accepted; page cutoffs - 22 3/4.
Mechanical Specifications: Type page 13 x 21 1/4; E - 6 cols, 2 1/16, 1/8 between; A - 6 cols, 2 1/16, 1/8 between; C - 9 cols, 1 5/16, 1/8 between.
Areas Served: Nacogdoches, County, Texas as primary.
Delivery Method: Mail, Newsstand, Carrier, RacksEquipment & Software: CLASSIFIED EQUIPMENT: Hardware — Wyse/150ES; Printers — TI/880; CLASSIFIED SOFTWARE: DTI/ClassSpeed. DISPLAY EQUIPMENT: Hardware — APP/Mac, APP/Mac NTX; Other Hardware — APP/Mac Scanner DISPLAY SOFTWAREAd Make-up Applications — DTI/AdSpeed; Layout Software — DTI/AdSpeed. EDITORIAL EQUIPMENT: Hardware — APP/Mac; Printers — APP/Mac LaserWriter NTX, HP/4MV LaserJet EDITORIAL SOFTWARE: DTI/PageSpeed. PRODUCTION EQUIPMENT: Hardware — APP/Mac NTX; Scanners — Lf/Leafscan.

NEW BRAUNFELS

NEW BRAUNFELS HERALD-ZEITUNG
549 Landa St, New Braunfels, Texas, 78130-6109, Comal; gen tel (830) 625-9144; ed tel (830) 625-9144 ext. 220; gen fax (830) 625-1224; ed fax (830) 606-3413; gen/nat adv e-mail advertising@herald-zeitung.com; disp adv e-mail david.compton@herald-zeitung.com; class adv e-mailclassifieds@herald-zeitung.com; ed e-mail editorial@herald-zeitung.com; web site www.herald-zeitung.com
Group: Southern Newspapers Inc.
Published: Tues, Wed, Thur, Fri, Sat, Sun
Weekday Frequency: m
Saturday Frequency: m
Circulation: 6,574; 6,574(sat); 7,501(sun)
Last Audit: CAC March 31, 2017
Advertising Rate (weekday/saturday): Open inch rate $15
Advertising Rate (sunday): Open inch rate $15
News services: AP. **Established:** 1852
Own Printing Facility?: Yes
Commercial Printers?: Yes
Special Editions: Medical Tab (Apr); Visitors' Guide (Aug); Babies on Parade (Feb); Chamber Tab (Jan); Visitors' Guide (Jul); Visitors' Guide (Jun); Visitors' Guide (Mar); Small Business (May); Wurstfest Guide (Oct).
Special Weekly Sections: TV Listings, Food, Home, Sports, Planner, Comics, Weather Classifieds (Daily); Entertainment (Thur); Church (Sat); Wedding, Engagements (Sun)
Syndicated Publications: American Profile, Spry
Proprietary Publications: New Braunfels Monthly Magazine, Two Rivers Weekly Review
Prodn. Mgr. ....Henry Coello
Circ. Dir. ....Joe Hayden
Pub. ....David Compton
Bus. Mgr. ....Jennifer Leal
Managing Editor ....Keith Domke
Circ. Asst. Mgr. ....Lee Stahle
Managing Ed. ....Chris Lykins
Mng. Ed. ....Gerard MacCrossan
News Ed. ....Autumn Phillips
Sports Ed. ....Chris Hossman
Pressroom Supvr. ....Gus Elbel
Pub. ....Neice Bell
Adv. Dir. ....David Burck
Business Mgr.........................Rosie Willingham
Mechanical Available: Offset; Black and 3 ROP colors; insert accepted; page cutoffs - 21.
Areas Served: Comal County, TX
Delivery Method: Mail, Newsstand, Carrier, RacksEquipment & Software: PRESSROOM EQUIPMENT: Lines — G/Community.; MAILROOM EQUIPMENT: Tying Machines — Dynaric.; BUSINESS SOFTWARE: Quattro, Microsoft/Word CLASSIFIED EQUIPMENT: Hardware — Mk; Printers — TI; CLASSIFIED SOFTWARE: Mk. DISPLAY EQUIPMENT: Printers — 1-APP/Mac LaserPrinter; DISPLAY SOFTWAREAd Make-up Applications — Microsoft/Word, QPS/QuarkXPress 4.1.; EDITORIAL EQUIPMENT: Hardware — APP/Mac G3 EDITORIAL SOFTWARE: Microsoft/Word, QPS/QuarkXPress. PRODUCTION EQUIPMENT: Hardware — 1-Nu; Cameras — R PRODUCTION SOFTWARE: QPS/QuarkXPress

ODESSA

ODESSA AMERICAN
222 E 4th St, Odessa, Texas, 79761-5122, Ector; gen tel (432)337-4661; adv tel (432) 333-7602; ed tel (432) 333-7764; gen fax (432) 334-8671; adv fax (432) 334-8641; ed fax (432) 333-7742; gen/nat adv e-mail sreeves@oaoa.com; disp adv e-mail ckerley@oaoa.com; class adv e-mailoaclassified@oaoa.com; ed e-mail ldennis@oaoa.com; web site www.oaoa.com - 1,300,000(views) 300,000(visitors)
Group: AIM Media Texas LLC
Published: Mon, Tues, Wed, Thur, Fri, Sat, Sun
Weekday Frequency: m
Saturday Frequency: m
Circulation: 10,483; 10,178(sun)
Last Audit: AAM March 31, 2017
Advertising Rate (weekday/saturday): Open inch rate $28.89

Advertising Rate (sunday): Open inch rate $31.90
Online Advertising Rate: Open Rate - $25 cpm - add $5 cpm for flash or page specific requests.
News services: AP, MCT. **Established:** 1927
Own Printing Facility?: Yes
Commercial Printers?: Yes
Special Editions: Graduation (June); Football (Aug); Oil Show (Oct - every other year); Holiday Happenings (Dec).
Special Weekly Sections: Best Food Day (Wed); Auto, Real Estate (Thur); Weekly, Entertainment (Fri); Church (Sat); Business, Oil & Gas, Finance (Sun)
Syndicated Publications: Parade (S), Relish, Spry, American Profile
Digital Platform - Mobile: Apple, Android
Digital Platform - Tablet: Apple iOS, Android
Editor ....Laura Dennis
Prod. Foreman, Mail room ....Gary Hesson
Director of Advertising & Marketing - Coye Kerley
Nat'l Adv. Coord.........................Stacey Reeves
Market Information: ADS; Split run; TMC.
Mechanical Available: Offset; Black and 3 ROP colors; insert accepted; page cutoffs - 21.5.
Mechanical Specifications: Type page 10 x 21 1/2; E - 6 cols, 1.528", 1/12 between; A - 6 cols, 1.528", 1/12 between; C - 9 cols, 1", 1/12 between.
Areas Served: Ector, Midland, Andrews, Crane, Pecos, Reeves, Upton, Ward and Winkler counties.
Delivery Method: Mail, Newsstand, Carrier, RacksEquipment & Software: PRESSROOM EQUIPMENT: Lines — 6-HI/1650 double width 1976; Press Drive — 2-CH/150 HP; Folders — 2-HI/2:1; Pasters —MEG/Flying. MAILROOM EQUIPMENT: Counter Stackers — QWI; Inserters & Stuffers — 1-GMA/SLS 1000A 8:1; Tying Machines — 2-Dynaric/NP 1500; BUSINESS EQUIPMENT: 1-Compaq/Proliant BUSINESS SOFTWARE: Great Plains, AR2000, Vision Data CLASSIFIED EQUIPMENT: Hardware — Compaq/Pentium 350mhz; Printers — QMS/2060; CLASSIFIED SOFTWARE: Microsoft/Word 7.0, QPS/QuarkXPress 4.0, APT/ACT. DISPLAY EQUIPMENT: Hardware — Dell/Pentium 800 mhz; Printers — QMS/2060, ECR/VR 36, Konica/VRL4550; Other Hardware — CD-Rom, Umax/Powerlook DISPLAY SOFTWAREAd Make-up Applications — QPS/QuarkXPress, Adobe/Illustrator, Adobe/Photoshop; Layout Software — Microsoft/Windows NT, QPS/QuarkXPress, Adobe/Indesign. EDITORIAL EQUIPMENT: Hardware — Compaq/Pentium 350mhz; Printers — HP/8100 EDITORIAL SOFTWARE: Microsoft/Word 7.0, QPS/QuarkXPress 4.0, APT/ACT. PRODUCTION EQUIPMENT: Hardware — ECR/VR 36, ECR/VR 36, Konica/VRL 4550; Cameras — C/Spartan II; Scanners — Umax/Powerlook PRODUCTION SOFTWARE: APT/ACT.

PALESTINE

PALESTINE HERALD-PRESS
519 N Elm St, Palestine, Texas, 75801-2927, Anderson; gen tel (903) 729-0281; gen fax (903) 729-1057; gen/nat adv e-mail jmienk@palestineherald.com; disp adv e-mail jmienk@palestineherald.com; class adv e-mailcveretto@palestineherald.com; ed e-mail jmienk@palestineherald.com; web site www.palestineherald.com
Group: Community Newspaper Holdings, Inc.
Published: Tues, Wed, Thur, Fri, Sun
Weekday Frequency: m
Saturday Frequency: m
Circulation: 5,013; 6,200(sun)
Last Audit: Sworn/Estimate/Non-Audited September 30, 2017
Advertising Rate (weekday/saturday): Open inch rate $10.30
News services: AP. **Established:** 1849
Own Printing Facility?: Yes
Commercial Printers?: Yes
Special Editions: Graduation - May Holiday Gift Guide - November OctoberFest -October
Special Weekly Sections: Entertainment (Fri); Community (S); Weekend (Sat); Best Food Day (Tues); Community (Wed).
Syndicated Publications: American Profile

(Weekly).
Parade
Bus. Mgr. ....Liz Falesch
Circ. Mgr. ....Candy Facklaeo
Mng. Ed. ....Angie Alvardo
Features Ed. ....Cheril Vermon
Sports Ed. ....Scott Tyler
Prodn. Mgr. ....Jim Buckley
Publisher ....Jake Mienk
Ed. ....Thomas Martínez
Market Information: TMC.
Mechanical Available: Offset; Black and 3 ROP colors; insert accepted; page cutoffs - 22 1/2.
Mechanical Specifications: Type page 13 x 21 1/2; E - 6 cols, 2 1/16, 1/8 between; A - 6 cols, 2 1/16, 1/8 between; C - 9 cols, 1 3/8, 1/8 between.
Areas Served: Anderson County
Delivery Method: MailEquipment & Software: PRESSROOM EQUIPMENT: Lines — 7-HI/V-15A 1973; 8-HI/V-15A 1999; Press Drive — 75hp and 60 hp; MAILROOM EQUIPMENT: Tying Machines — Bu.; BUSINESS EQUIPMENT: 1-HP/3700 BUSINESS SOFTWARE: CJ CLASSIFIED EQUIPMENT: Hardware — 2-APP/iMac; Printers — Okidata/Microline 320; CLASSIFIED SOFTWARE: Baseview. DISPLAY EQUIPMENT: Hardware — 2-APP/Mac Yosemite G3, APP/Power Mac 7350/180; DISPLAY SOFTWAREAd Make-up Applications — QPS/QuarkXPress 4.0, Multi-Ad/Creator, Adobe/Photoshop; Layout Software — Baseview/Ad Force, APP/Power Mac 8100/100. EDITORIAL EQUIPMENT: Hardware — 2-Ethernet/10T Hub, 6-APP/Mac Yosemite G3, 4-APP/Mac Quadra 800, APP/Mac Apple share IP Manager/LE/2100 Rapid Access Processor, Glunz & Jensen/720 Processor; Printers — 2-APP/Mac LaserWriter Pro 630 EDITORIAL SOFTWARE: Baseview, QPS/QuarkX PRODUCTION EQUIPMENT: Hardware — 1-Nu, Pre Press/Panther Plus VR Imagesetter; Cameras — B; Scanners — 2-Microtek/II XE, 2-Pre Press/Panther Plus RIP (1-VR & 1-IR), Microtek/Scanmaker 6400 XL PRODUCTION SOFTWARE: Baseview/NewsEdit Pro IQue 3.2.1, QPS/QuarkXPress 4.02.

PAMPA

THE PAMPA NEWS
403 W Atchison Ave, Pampa, Texas, 79065-6303, Gray; gen tel (806) 669-2525; adv tel (806) 669-2525; ed tel (806) 669-2525; gen fax (806) 669-2520; adv fax (806) 669-2520; ed fax (806) 669-2520; gen/nat adv e-mail rwoods@thepampanews.com; disp adv e-mail rwoods@thepampanews.com; class adv e-mailclassified1@thepampanews.com; ed e-mail jclee@thepampanews.com; web site www.thepampanews.com
Published: Tues, Wed, Thur, Fri, Sat
Weekday Frequency: m
Saturday Frequency: m
Circulation: 4,100; 4,100(sat)
Last Audit: Sworn/Estimate/Non-Audited September 30, 2017
Advertising Rate (weekday/saturday): Open inch rate $12.35
News services: AP. **Established:** 1906
Own Printing Facility?: Yes
Commercial Printers?: Yes
Special Editions: Christmas Greetings/Letters to Santa
Gray County Visitor's Guide
Pride and Progress
Football Guide
Area Dining Guide
Gray County Church Directory
Special Weekly Sections: Church (Wed); Women (Sat)
Syndicated Publications: Gray County Visitor's Guide (Annually).
Circ. Mgr. ....Sue Pribble
Pub./Adv. Mgr. ....ReDonn Woods
Classified Mgr. ....Beverly Taylor
Editor ....John Lee
Ed. ....Timothy Howsare
Production Mgr. ....Marcus Elkins
Mechanical Available: Offset; Black and 3 ROP colors; insert accepted; page cutoffs - 21 1/2.
Mechanical Specifications: Type page 10 3/8 x

21; E - 6 cols, 1 5/8, 1/8 between; A - 6 cols, 1 5/8, 1/8 between; C - 9 cols, 1 1/16, 1/16 between.
Areas Served: 79065
Delivery Method: Mail, Newsstand, RacksEquipment & Software: PRESSROOM EQUIPMENT: Lines — 6-G/Suburban.; MAILROOM EQUIPMENT: Tying Machines — 1/Bu; Address Machine — 1-/Dispensa-Matic (computer labels).; PRODUCTION EQUIPMENT: Hardware — APP/Mac, Pre Press/Panther

PARIS

THE PARIS NEWS
5050 SE Loop 286, Paris, Texas, 75460-6576, Lamar; gen tel (903) 785-8744; adv tel (903) 785-8744; ed tel (903) 785-8744; gen fax (903) 785-1263; adv fax (903) 785-1263; ed fax (903) 785-1263; gen/nat adv e-mail bren.garrett@theparisnews.com; disp adv e-mail bren.garrett@theparisnews.com; class adv e-mailmyriah.nance@theparisnews.com; ed e-mail editor@theparisnews.com; web site www.theparisnews.com
Group: Southern Newspapers Inc.
Published: Mon, Tues, Wed, Thur, Fri, Sun
Weekday Frequency: e
Circulation: 5,147; 5,660(sun)
Last Audit: CAC March 31, 2017
Advertising Rate (weekday/saturday): Open inch rate $18.70
Advertising Rate (sunday): Open inch rate $19.00
News services: AP. **Established:** 1869
Own Printing Facility?: Yes
Commercial Printers?: Yes
Special Editions: Brides (Apr); Newcomer's Guide (Aug); Greetings (Dec); Home Furnishings (Feb); Quarterly Farm & Ranch Review (Jun); Quarterly Farm & Ranch Review (Mar); Progress (May); Car Care (Nov); New Car (Oct); Football (Sept).
Special Weekly Sections: Business & Industry (Mon); NASCAR (Tue); Outdoors, Spotlight on Business (Thur); Religion, Entertainment Weekly (Fri); Business, lifestyle (Sun); Senior (First Sunday); Farm, Ranch, Lifestyles (Quarterly)
Syndicated Publications: TV & Entertainment Guide (Fri); Parade (S).
Digital Platform - Mobile: Apple, Android
Digital Platform - Tablet: Apple iOS, Android
Bus. Mgr. ....Relan Walker
Adv. Dir. ....Mel Parker
Circ. Mgr. ....Scott Baendy
Online Ed. ....Mary Madewell
Sports Ed. ....Van Hilburn
Prodn. Mgr., Mailroom ....Tammy Barnes
Prodn. Mgr., Pressroom ....Fred Downs
Pub. ....JD Davidson
Adv. Sales Rep. ....Sheryl Smith
Managing Ed. ....Connie Beard
Market Information: ADS; TMC.
Mechanical Available: Offset; Black and 3 ROP colors; insert accepted - standard; page cutoffs - 21 1/2.
Mechanical Specifications: Type page 11 5/8 x 21 1/2; E - 6 cols, 2 5/8, 1/8 between; A - 6 cols, 2 5/8, 1/8 between; C - 9 cols, 1 3/8, 1/8 between.
Delivery Method: Mail, Newsstand, Carrier, RacksEquipment & Software: PRESSROOM EQUIPMENT: Lines — 8-G/Community 1974.; MAILROOM EQUIPMENT: Tying Machines — MLN/ML2 Et; Address Machine — Uarco/4930.; BUSINESS EQUIPMENT: 1-Compaq/Proliant 1600, 5-HP/Vectra VL2 BUSINESS SOFTWARE: Netware, Circ CLASSIFIED EQUIPMENT: Hardware — APP/Mac; Printers — APP/Mac LaserWriter II NTX; CLASSIFIED SOFTWARE: Baseview. DISPLAY EQUIPMENT: Hardware — APP/Mac; Printers — APP/Mac LaserWriter Pro 630, APP/Mac LaserWriter 1600-600; Other Hardware — APP/Mac Scanner DISPLAY SOFTWAREAd Make-up Applications — Multi-Ad/Creator; Layout Software — APP/Mac. EDITORIAL EQUIPMENT: Hardware — APP/Mac/AG/Accuset 1000, Microtek/ScanMaker III, Polaroid/SprintScan; Printers — APP/Mac LaserWriter EDITORIAL SOFTWARE: QPS/QuarkXPress, Baseview/NewsEdit. PRODUCTION EQUIPMENT: Hardware — Caere/OmniPage Pro, AG/

Accuset 1000, APP/Mac LaserWriter 1600-600; Cameras — LE, R/500; Scanners — Microtek/ScanMaker III, Microtek/ScanMaker II, Polaroid/SprintScan PRODUCTION SOFTWARE: QPS/QuarkXPress 3.32.

PLAINVIEW

PLAINVIEW HERALD
820 Broadway St, Plainview, Texas, 79072-7316, Hale; gen tel (806) 296-1340; adv tel (806) 296-1320; ed tel (806) 296-1353; gen fax (806) 296-1363; adv fax (806) 296-1363; ed fax (806) 296-1363; gen/nat adv e-mail cortega@hearstnp.com; disp adv e-mail cortega@hearstnp.com; class adv e-mailcmcgill@hearstnp.com; ed e-mail william.carroll@hearstnp.com; web site www.myplainview.com
Group: Hearst Communications, Inc.
Published: Tues, Wed, Thur, Fri, Sun
Weekday Frequency: m
Circulation: 5,000; 6,000(sun)
Last Audit: Sworn/Estimate/Non-Audited February 4, 2018
Newspaper Reps: Carmen Ortega, advertising director
William Carroll, editor
Charles Lawson, circulation direction
Skip Leon, sports editor
Advertising Rate (weekday/saturday): Open inch rate $18.21
Advertising Rate (sunday): Open inch rate $18.21
News services: AP, HN, NYT. **Established:** 1889
Own Printing Facility?: No
Commercial Printers?: No
Special Editions: Back-to-School (Aug); Honor Roll (Mar).
Special Weekly Sections: Agriculture (Wed, Sun); Best Food Day (Thur); Church, Religion (Fri); Agriculture, Business (Sun)
Syndicated Publications: Relish (Monthly); Parade (S); American Profile (Weekly).
Digital Platform - Mobile: Apple, Android, Windows
Digital Platform - Tablet: Apple iOS, Android, Windows 7, Blackberry Tablet OS, Kindle, Nook, Kindle Fire
Prodn. Mgr., Mailroom ....Charles Lawson
Prodn. Supvr., Pre Press ....Carol McGill
Adv. Dir. ....Carmen Ortega
Class. Acct. Exec. ....Roijon Johnson
Ed ....William Carroll
Sports Ed. ....Skip Leon
Market Information: SMC.
Mechanical Available: Offset; Black and 3 ROP colors; insert accepted; page cutoffs - 21 1 you/2.
Areas Served: Hale County, Swisher County, Briscoe County, Lamb County, Floyd County, Castro County (Texas)
Delivery Method: Mail, Newsstand, Carrier, RacksEquipment & Software: CLASSIFIED SOFTWARE: FSI.

PORT ARTHUR

PORT ARTHUR NEWS
2349 Memorial Blvd, Port Arthur, Texas, 77640-2822, Jefferson; gen tel (409) 721-2417; ed tel (409) 721-2431; gen fax (409)724-6849; gen/nat adv e-mail ed.kestler@panews.com; disp adv e-mail ed.kestler@panews.com; class adv e-mailclassads@panews.com; ed e-mail panews@panews.com; web site www.panews.com
Group: Boone Newspapers, Inc.
Published: Tues, Wed, Thur, Fri, Sat, Sun
Weekday Frequency: m
Saturday Frequency: m
Circulation: 8,138; 8,138(sat); 9,000(sun)
Last Audit: AAM March 31, 2017
News services: AP. **Established:** 1897
Own Printing Facility?: Yes
Commercial Printers?: Yes
Special Editions: Family-Owned Business (Jan); Visitor's Guide (May); Cav-oil-cade (Oct).
Special Weekly Sections: Best Food Day (Wed); Entertainment (Fri)
Syndicated Publications: American Profile (Fri); Relish (Monthly); USA WEEKEND Magazine (S).

Digital Platform - Mobile: Apple, Android, Windows, Blackberry
Digital Platform - Tablet: Apple iOS, Android, Windows 7, Blackberry Tablet OS, Kindle, Nook, Kindle Fire
Publisher ....Rich Macke
Editorial Page Ed. ....Roger Cowles
Mechanical Available: Offset; Black and 3 ROP colors; insert accepted - news color; page cutoffs - 22 3/4.
Mechanical Specifications: Type page 11 5/8 x 21 1/2; E - 6 cols, 1 5/6, 1/8 between; A - 6 cols, 1 5/6, 1/8 between; C - 9 cols, 1 3/16, 1/16 between.
Delivery Method: Mail, Newsstand, Carrier, RacksEquipment & Software: PRESSROOM EQUIPMENT: Lines — 6-G/Urbanite (3 color); 4-G/Urbanite (balloon former); Press Drive — 2-HP/100; Folders — 2-G/2:1; Reels & Stands — G.; MAILROOM EQUIPMENT: Counter Stackers — 2/BG, 1-/HL; Inserters & Stuffers — 2-MM/227; Tying Machines — 2-MLN/ML2EE, 1-MLN/2AHS; Address Machine — 1-/CH; BUSINESS EQUIPMENT: PBS CLASSIFIED EQUIPMENT: Hardware — APP/Mac; Printers — APP/Mac LaserWriter; CLASSIFIED SOFTWARE: Baseview. DISPLAY EQUIPMENT: Hardware — APP/Mac; Printers — Imagesetters; DISPLAY SOFTWAREAd Make-up Applications — Multi-Ad, QPS/QuarkXPress; Layout Software — 8-APP/Mac G3. EDITORIAL EQUIPMENT: Hardware — APP/Mac, 1-APP/Mac; Printers — 1-APP/Mac LaserPrinter, Imagesetters/1270 Resolution EDITORIAL SOFTWARE: Baseview. PRODUCTION EQUIPMENT: Hardware — Laser Red/460 HS Imagesetters, 1-Nu/Flip Top FT40V4UPNS, 2-Douthitt; Cameras — 1-C/Spartan II, 1-C/Spartan III; Scanners — Microteks PRODUCTION SOFTWARE: QPS/QuarkXPress.

ROSENBERG

FORT BEND HERALD
1902 4th St, Rosenberg, Texas, 77471-5140, Fort Bend; gen tel 281-342-4474; gen fax 281-342-3219; gen/nat adv e-mail leehart@herald-coaster.com; disp adv e-mail leehart@fbherald.com; class adv e-mailclassad@fbherald.com; ed e-mail swilley@fbherald.com; web site www.fbherald.com
Group: Hartman Newspapers LP
Published: Mon, Tues, Wed, Thur, Fri, Sun
Weekday Frequency: e
Circulation: 7,003; 7,450(sun)
Last Audit: CVC June 30, 2009
Advertising Rate (weekday/saturday): Open inch rate $16.30
Advertising Rate (sunday): Open inch rate $16.30
News services: AP. **Established:** 1892
Own Printing Facility?: Yes
Commercial Printers?: Yes
Special Weekly Sections: Sports, Comics, Classifieds, Editorial (Daily); Business (Wed); Entertainment, TV, Religion, Church, Weddings, Engagements (Sun)
Syndicated Publications: Relish (Monthly); American Profile (Weekly).
Pres. ....Clyde C. King
Gen. Mgr. ....Lee Hartman
Sports Ed. ....Gary Martin
Prodn. Mgr. ....Stephanie Welch
Managing Ed. ....Scott Reese Willey
Circ. Dir. ....Bill Shannon
Adv. Dir. ....Dennis Garrison
Market Information: TMC.
Mechanical Available: Offset; Black and 3 ROP colors; insert accepted; page cutoffs - 22 3/4.
Mechanical Specifications: Type page 11.625 x 21, 6 cols.
Areas Served: HOUSTON—GALVESTON—BRAZORIA, TX CMSA
Delivery Method: Mail, Newsstand, Carrier, RacksEquipment & Software: PRESSROOM EQUIPMENT: Lines — WPC/Atlas-Leader single width 1992; WPC/Atlas-Leader single width 1992.; MAILROOM EQUIPMENT: Tying Machines — Wilton/Strap Pack SS-80.; BUSINESS EQUIPMENT: Macintosh BUSINESS SOFTWARE: Ad Manager Pro CLASSIFIED EQUIPMENT: Hardware — Macintosh; Printers — ECR/Scriptsetter, HP/LaserJet 4V; CLASSIFIED SOFTWARE:

Baseview. DISPLAY EQUIPMENT: Hardware — Macintosh; Printers — Xerox; Other Hardware — HP/Scanner. DISPLAY SOFTWAREAd Make-up Applications — Adobe Creative Suite; EDITORIAL EQUIPMENT: Hardware — APP/Mac/HP/Flatbed Scanner; Printers — ECR/Scriptsetter EDITORIAL SOFTWARE: Baseview.

SAN ANGELO

SAN ANGELO STANDARD-TIMES

34 W Harris Ave, San Angelo, Texas, 76903-5838, Tom Green; gen tel (325) 659-8201; adv tel (325) 659-8209; ed tel (325)659-8249; gen fax (325) 659-8171; adv fax (325) 659-8172; ed fax (325) 659-8173; gen/nat adv e-mail kate.rushing@gosanangelo.com; disp adv e-mail kate.rushing@gosanangelo.com; class adv e-mailkate.rushing@gosanangelo.com; ed e-mail mike.kelly@gosanangelo.com; web site www.gosanangelo.com 323,047(visitors)

Group: Journal Media Group
Published: Mon, Tues, Wed, Thur, Fri, Sat, Sun
Weekday Frequency: m
Saturday Frequency: m
Circulation: 14,205; 14,205(sat); 16,989(sun)
Last Audit: AAM December 31, 2015
Advertising Rate (weekday/saturday): Open inch rate $44.79
Advertising Rate (sunday): Open inch rate $48.11
News services: AP, SHNS. **Established:** 1884
Special Editions: San Angelo Living (annual); Blitz football preview (Fridays during football season); San Angelo Stockshow and Rodeo (annual)
Special Weekly Sections: Business (Mon); Alternate Health, Education (Tue); Best Food (Wed); Viewpoints (Thur); Arts, Entertainment (Fri); Religion, Auto (Sat); TV (Sun);
Syndicated Publications: My San Angelo (local news weekly, broadsheet) (Other); Parade (S); Hunting (annual); Senior Sourcebook (annual)
Digital Platform - Mobile: Apple, Android
Digital Platform - Tablet: Apple iOS, Kindle, Kindle Fire
HR Dir. ....Monty Stanley
Ed. .... Tim Archuleta
Columnist .... Rick Smith
Pub./Adv. Dir. .... Jeff DeLoach
Adv. Dir. .... Pam Hammer
Nat'l Acct. Exec. ....Kate Rushing
Circ. Sales Mgr. ....Jimmy Baugh
Market Information: Split run; TMC; Zoned editions.
Mechanical Available: Offset; Black and 3 ROP colors; insert accepted; page cutoffs - 22 3/4.
Mechanical Specifications: Type page 11 5/8 x 21 1/2; E - 6 cols, 2 1/16, 1/8 between; A - 6 cols, 2 1/16, 1/8 between; C - 10 cols, 1 3/16, 4/5 between.
Areas Served: 76821, 76825, 76837, 76849, 76856, 76859, 76861, 76866, 76875, 76886, 76901, 76903, 76904, 76905, 76908, 76930, 76932, 76933, 76934, 76935, 76936, 76937, 76941, 76943, 76945, 76950, 76951, 76957, 76958, 78624, 79567, 79739
Delivery Method: Mail, Carrier, RacksEquipment & Software: PRESSROOM EQUIPMENT: Lines — 3-G/Cosmo double width 1980; Pasters —6, 2. MAILROOM EQUIPMENT: Counter Stackers — 1/KAN; BUSINESS EQUIPMENT: HP/3000-937 RX BUSINESS SOFTWARE: PeopleSoft CLASSIFIED EQUIPMENT: Hardware — APP/iMac, APP/Mac G3; APP/Mac G4 Server; Printers — 1-APP/Mac LaserWriter, 1-Lexmark/Optma LX Plw; CLASSIFIED SOFTWARE: Baseview/AMP 2.1. DISPLAY EQUIPMENT: Hardware — 7-APP/Mac G4, 10-APP/Power G3, Dell/Power Edge 4300; Printers — HP/5si MX, HP/750C Plotter, 2-HP/DeskJet 1200 c-ps, HP/DeskJet 1600C, HP/755C Plotter; DISPLAY SOFTWAREAd Make-up Applications — Multi-Ad/Creator II, Adobe/Photoshop 6.0, Adobe/Illustrator 5.5; EDITORIAL EQUIPMENT: Hardware — Austin/APP/Power Mac G3; Printers — 1-Panasonic/KX P2411I, X/DC 220 EDITORIAL SOFTWARE: III 2.39. PRODUCTION EQUIPMENT: Hardware — APP/Mac NT Server, 2-Pre Press/

Panther Pro 46; Cameras — C/Spartan II; Scanners — Kk/2035, AG/Arcus Flatbed, Nikon/Coolscan PRODUCTION SOFTWARE: QPS/QuarkXPress 3.3, MEI/CLS 2.6, QPS/QuarkXPress 4.1.

SAN ANTONIO

SAN ANTONIO EXPRESS-NEWS

301 Avenue E, San Antonio, Texas, 78205-2006, Bexar; gen tel (210) 250-3000; adv tel (210) 250-2500; ed tel (210) 250-3171; gen fax (210) 250-3125; adv fax (210) 250-2360; ed fax (210) 250-3125; gen/nat adv e-mail rmccutcheon@express-news.net; disp adv e-mail rmccutcheon@express-news.net; class adv e-mailmurias@express-news.net; ed e-mail mleary@express-news.net; web site www.mySA.com

- 60,000,000(views) 3,335,707(visitors)

Group: San Antonio Express-News
Published: Mon, Tues, Wed, Thur, Fri, Sat, Sun
Weekday Frequency: m
Saturday Frequency: m
Circulation: 86,366; 83,218(sat); 149,636(sun)
Last Audit: AAM December 31, 2016
Advertising Rate (weekday/saturday): Open inch rate $120
Advertising Rate (sunday): Open inch rate $162
Online Advertising Rate: 300 x 250 - $20 CPM 728 x 90 - $20 CPM
News services: AP, NYT, LAT-WP, Bloomberg, MCT, GNS. **Established:** 1865
Special Editions: Higher Education Handbook, Rodeo, Readers Choice, Guide to San Antonio, Spurs Nation
Special Weekly Sections: Health, Fitness, Elders, Business (Mon); Mom's, Business, Kids, Family, Animals, Pets (Tues), Stock (Tues-Sat), Live Music, TV (Wed); Style (Thurs), Entertainment, Auto (Fri); Religion, Drive, Trends (Sat), Real Estate, Technology, Travel, Arts, Comics, Taste, Home (Sun)
Digital Platform - Mobile: Apple, Android, Windows, Blackberry
Digital Platform - Tablet: Apple iOS, Android, Windows 7, Blackberry Tablet OS
EVP, Advertising and Marketing .... Raymond McCutcheon
Publisher .... Susan Lynch Pape
Sr. VP/Editor .... Michael Leary
Managing Editor .... Jamie Stockwell
Executive Digital Media Producer .... Cory Heikkila
VP of Circulation .... Joseph Braunschweig
Market Information: Community Publications
Mechanical Available: Offset; Black and 3 ROP colors; insert accepted; page cutoffs - 22" and folded
Mechanical Specifications: Type of Page: Broadsheet
Full Page Ad Size: 9.94" x 21"
Columns: 6 col   1 col = 1.54"
Space between columns: .14"
Type of Page: Tab
Full Page Ad Size: 9.94" x 9.75"
Columns: 6 col.   1 col. = 1.54"
Space between columns: .14"
All measures are the same for both ROP and Classified pages
Areas Served: 78238, 78229, 78240, 78251, 78253, 78250, 78254, 78006, 78023, 78249, 78255, 78256, 78015, 78257, 78228,78201, 78212, 78216, 78209, 78213, 78230, 78234, 78217, 78202, 78205, 78208, 78215, 78231, 78248, 78258, 78259, 78260, 78232, 78247, 78261, 78218, 78219, 78233, 78239, 78109, 78244, 78108, 78148, 78154, 78266, 78203, 78204, 78210, 78220, 78214, 78221, 78224, 78222, 78223, 78235, 78245, 78207, 78211, 78225, 78226, 78237, 78227, 78236, 78242, 78002, 78101, 78112, 78152, 78069, 78073, 78252, 78263, 78264Equipment & Software: PRESSROOM EQUIPMENT: Lines — 3-G/Colorliner double width (8 units) 1994; 3-G/Colorliner doble width (8 units); 3-G/Colorliner double width (8 units); Folders — 4, 2-G/Sovereign 3:2 Single, 1-G/Sovereign 3:2 Double; Pasters —30-G/CT50Reels & Stands — 30; MAILROOM EQUIPMENT: Counter Stackers — 9-QWI/300, 4-QWI/SJ201A; Inserters & Stuffers — 3-HI/72P, 1-GMA/SLS 1000; Tying Machines — 8/Power Strap, 6-Sterling/Tying Machine.; BUSINESS EQUIPMENT: 1-B/4955, 1-V/340, Bs, IBM/ES9000-150 BUSINESS

SOFTWARE: Admarc (7.0): Adv (input & ordering) CLASSIFIED EQUIPMENT: Hardware — SII; 100-PC Terminals, 100-NT/NT Client; DISPLAY EQUIPMENT: Hardware — APP/Macs, APP/Power Mac, APP/Mac G3; Printers — MON/Proofers, Canon/Fieny, Iris; Other Hardware — MON/Imagesetters, Futuro/3850 DISPLAY SOFTWAREAd Make-up Applications — QPS/QuarkXPress 4.4; Layout Software — SCS/Layout 8000. EDITORIAL EQUIPMENT: Hardware — Unix/Enterprise 6000 Servers NT desktops/Graphic Enterprise/Page Scan; Printers — HP/LaserJet, Canon/350, HP/3500 Color, HP/4000, HP/8000, HP/5000 EDITORIAL SOFTWARE: Newsgate PRODUCTION EQUIPMENT: Hardware — 2-MON/ExpressMaster 3850, 2-MON/Lasercomp Express, Futuro; Cameras — 2-Newspagers, 1-C/Spartan III; Scanners — CD/636 Drum, CD/240 Drum, EskoFot/26365 Copydot PRODUCTION SOFTWARE: QPS/QuarkXPress, CCI/Layout Champ, Newsdesk. CIRCULATION SOFTWARNewscycle

SAN MARCOS

SAN MARCOS DAILY RECORD

1910 S Interstate 35, San Marcos, Texas, 78666-5901, Hays; gen tel (512) 392-2458; adv tel (512)392-2458; ed tel (512) 392-2458; gen fax (512) 392-1514; adv fax (512) 392-4655; ed fax (512) 392-1514; gen/nat adv e-mail mholt@sanmarcosrecord.com; disp adv e-mail mholt@sanmarcosrecord.com; class adv e-mailmholt@sanmarcosrecord.com; ed e-mail dsweat@wimberleyview.com; web site www.sanmarcosrecord.com

Group: Moser Community Media
Published: Tues, Wed, Thur, Fri, Sun
Weekday Frequency: e
Circulation: 5,000; 4,100(sun)
Last Audit: USPS October 1, 2017
Advertising Rate (weekday/saturday): Open inch rate $9.35
Advertising Rate (sunday): Open inch rate $11.00
News services: AP. **Established:** 1912
Own Printing Facility?: Yes
Commercial Printers?: Yes
Special Editions: Back-to-School (Aug); Progress (Feb).
Special Weekly Sections: Best Food Day (Wed); Wellness, Grocery Ads (Tue); Living (Wed); Cultural Arts (Thur); Earth Talks (Fri)
Syndicated Publications: USA WEEKEND Magazine (S); American Profile (Weekly).
Digital Platform - Mobile: Apple, Android
Digital Platform - Tablet: Apple iOS, Android
Circ. Dir. .... Karen George
News Ed. .... Anita Miller
Sports Editor .... Joe Vozzelli
Prodn. Supvr. .... Karen Ray
Pub. .... Don Moore
Adv. Dir. .... Marcy Holt
Exec. Ed. .... David Short
Production Dir. .... Chris Urbanovsky
Market Information: TMC.
Mechanical Available: Offset; Black and 3 ROP colors; insert accepted; page cutoffs - 22 3/4.
Mechanical Specifications: Type page 13 x 21 1/2; E - 6 cols, 2 1/16, 1/8 between; A - 6 cols, 2 1/16, 1/8 between; C - 9 cols, 1 3/8, 1/16 between.
Areas Served: San Marcos, Hays, 78666
Delivery Method: Newsstand, Carrier, RacksEquipment & Software: PRESSROOM EQUIPMENT: Lines — 7-G/Community; MAILROOM EQUIPMENT: Tying Machines — 1/Bu; Address Machine — 1-/El.; BUSINESS EQUIPMENT: DPT/1100, IBM EDITORIAL EQUIPMENT: Hardware — EKI/Televideo. PRODUCTION EQUIPMENT: Hardware — 1-COM/4961, 1-COM/2961, 1-COM/Unisetter; Cameras — 1-C/J75CC; Scanners — EKI/Televideo.

SEGUIN

THE SEGUIN GAZETTE

1012 Schriewer, Seguin, Texas, 78155-7473, Guadalupe; gen tel (830) 379-5402; gen fax (830) 379-8328; gen/nat adv e-mail elizabeth.

engelhardt@seguingazette.com; disp adv e-mail elizabeth.engelhardt@seguingazette.com; class adv e-mailclassifieds@seguingazette.com; ed e-mail editor@seguingazette.com; web site www.seguingazette.com

- 500,000(views) 150,000(visitors)

Group: Southern Newspapers Inc.
Published: Tues, Wed, Thur, Fri, Sun
Weekday Frequency: m
Circulation: 2,591; 3,363(sun)
Last Audit: CAC March 31, 2017
Advertising Rate (weekday/saturday): Open inch rate $10.95
Advertising Rate (sunday): Open inch rate $11.95
News services: AP. **Established:** 1888
Own Printing Facility?: No
Commercial Printers?: No
Special Weekly Sections: Sports, TV, Comics, health, Education, Seniors (Daily); Real Estate, Auto (Tue, Wed, Thur, Sun); Agriculture, Health, TV, Weddings, Engagements, Outdoor, Business, Lifestyle, Opinions, Entertainment (Sun); Senior (Tue); Business, Lifestyle, Opinions (Wed); Entertainment, Garden, Agriculture, Best Food Day (Thur); Church, lifestyle, Opinions (Fri)
Syndicated Publications: Weekly TV Guide (S); American Profile (S); USA Weekend (F); Relish; Spry
Digital Platform - Mobile: Apple, Android, Windows, Blackberry
Digital Platform - Tablet: Apple iOS, Android, Windows 7, Blackberry Tablet OS, Kindle, Nook, Kindle Fire
Business Manager .... Maggie Clarkson
Managing Editor .... Travis Webb
President, Editor & Publisher .... Jeff Fowler
Advertising Director .... Elizabeth Engelhardt
Circulation Director .... Brenda Mrazek
Creative Director ....Hannah Ruiz
Areas Served: City of Seguin; Guadalupe and Comal counties
Delivery Method: Mail, Newsstand, Carrier, Racks

SHERMAN

HERALD DEMOCRAT

603 S. Sam Rayburn Fwy., Sherman, Texas, 75090, Grayson; gen tel (903) 893-8181; gen fax (903) 868-1930; ed fax (903) 868-2106; gen/nat adv e-mail advertising@heralddemocrat.com; disp adv e-mail advertising@heralddemocrat.com; class adv e-mailclassified@heralddemocrat.com; ed e-mail news@heralddemocrat.com; web site www.heralddemocrat.com

Group: New Media Investment Group
Published: Mon, Tues, Wed, Thur, Fri, Sun
Weekday Frequency: m
Circulation: 12,147; 13,862(sun)
Last Audit: AAM March 31, 2016
Advertising Rate (weekday/saturday): Open inch rate $27.30
Advertising Rate (sunday): Open inch rate $29.30
News services: AP, SHNS. **Established:** 1879
Own Printing Facility?: Yes
Commercial Printers?: Yes
Special Editions: Home Improvement (Apr); Home Improvement (Aug); Christmas Greetings (Dec); Home Improvement (Jul); Car Care (Jun); Chamber of Commerce Industrial Review (Mar); Brides (May); Christmas Gift Guide (Nov); Car Care (Oct); Football (Sept).
Special Weekly Sections: Best Food Day (Wed); Business (Daily); Religion (Fri)
Syndicated Publications: Relish (Monthly); USA WEEKEND Magazine (S).
Pub. ....John P. Wright
Credit Mgr. .... Dianne Harp
Adv. Mgr., Classified .... Jennifer Parker
Adv. Dir./Nat'l Dir. .... Wes King
Circ. Dir. .... Mike Brezina
News/Wire Ed. ....Darrell McCorstin
Sports Ed. .... Bill Spinks
Mailroom Supvr. .... Raymond Hodge
Prodn. Mgr., Composing .... Teresa Redd
Prodn. Mgr., Pressroom .... Mike Harkey
Ed. .... Jonathan Cannon
Market Information: TMC; Zoned editions.
Mechanical Available: Offset; Black and 3 ROP colors; insert accepted; page cutoffs - 22 3/4.

Mechanical Specifications: Type page 11 5/8 x 21 1/2; E - 6 cols, 1 3/4, 3/16 between; A - 6 cols, 1 3/4, 3/16 between; C - 9 cols, 1 1/4, 1/8 between.
Areas Served: 75090, 75091, 75092, 75020, 75021
Delivery Method: Mail, Newsstand, Carrier, RacksEquipment & Software: PRESSROOM EQUIPMENT: Lines — 7-G/Urbanite 1973, 1-G/Urbanite 1989; MAILROOM EQUIPMENT: Counter Stackers — 1-MRS/1220, 1/QWI; Inserters & Stuffers — 1-/1372PS; Tying Machines — 2-MLN/ML2EE.; BUSINESS EQUIPMENT: 1-Unisys/5000, 1-HP/3000 927LX BUSINESS SOFTWARE: CJ CLASSIFIED EQUIPMENT: Hardware — APP/Mac; Printers — 1-APP/Mac LaserPrinter; CLASSIFIED SOFTWARE: Baseview. DISPLAY EQUIPMENT: Hardware — APP/Mac; DISPLAY SOFTWAREAd Make-up Applications — Baseview; Layout Software — MEI/ALS. EDITORIAL EQUIPMENT: Hardware — APP/Mac; Printers — 2-Pre Press/Panther Pro EDITORIAL SOFTWARE: NewsEngin PRODUCTION EQUIPMENT: Hardware — 2-Pre Press/Panther Pro Imagesetter

SNYDER

SNYDER DAILY NEWS

3600 College Ave, Snyder, Texas, 79549-4637, Scurry; gen tel (325) 573-5486; gen fax (325) 573-0044; gen/nat adv e-mail advertising@snyderdailynews.com; disp adv e-mail advertising@snyderdailynews.com; class adv e-mailclassified@snyderdailynews.com; ed e-mail barkley@snyderdailynews.com; web site www.snyderdailynews.com - 120,000(views) 450(visitors)
Published: Mon, Tues, Wed, Thur, Fri, Sat
Weekday Frequency: e
Saturday Frequency: e
Circulation: 3,400; 3,400(sun)
Last Audit: Sworn/Estimate/Non-Audited November 27, 2017
Advertising Rate (weekday/saturday): Open inch rate $9.25
Advertising Rate (sunday): Open inch rate $9.25
News services: Associated Press **Established:** 1950
Own Printing Facility?: Yes
Commercial Printers?: Yes
Special Editions: Christmas Greetings (Dec); Football (Aug.); Graduation (May); various others.
Special Weekly Sections: Best Food Day (Tue); Oil, Farm (Thurs)
Digital Platform - Mobile: Apple, Android
Digital Platform - Tablet: Apple iOS, Android
Asst. Pub. .... Wade Warren
Adv. Mgr., Classified .... Donna Browning
Sports Ed. .... Larry McCarthy
Pub. .... Bill Crist
Business Mgr. .... Christie Adams
Ed. .... Ben Barkley
Market Information: TMC.
Mechanical Available: Offset; Black and 3 ROP colors; insert accepted; page cutoffs - 21.
Mechanical Specifications: Type page 14 1/2 x 21; E - 6 cols, 2 1/16, 1/8 between; A - 6 cols, 2 1/16, 1/8 between; C - 6 cols, 2 1/16, 1/8 between.
Areas Served: 79549+
Delivery Method: Mail, Newsstand, Carrier, RacksEquipment & Software: PRESSROOM EQUIPMENT: Lines — 6-G/Community; Folders — 1-G/SC.; BUSINESS EQUIPMENT: TI CLASSIFIED EQUIPMENT: Hardware — FSI.; EDITORIAL EQUIPMENT: Hardware — FSI.

STEPHENVILLE

STEPHENVILLE EMPIRE-TRIBUNE

702 E South Loop, Stephenville, Texas, 76401-5314, Erath; gen tel (254) 965-3124; adv tel (254) 965-3124; ed tel (254) 965-3124; gen fax (254) 965-4269; adv fax (254) 965-4269; ed fax (254) 965-4269; gen/nat adv e-mail ssimmons@empiretribune.com; disp adv e-mail ssimmons@empiretribune.com; class adv e-mailswoods@empiretribune.com; ed e-mail svandenberge@empiretribune.com; web site www.yourstephenvilletx.com
Group: New Media Investment Group
Published: Tues, Wed, Thur, Fri, Sun
Weekday Frequency: m
Circulation: 4,752; 4,500(sun)
Last Audit: Sworn/Estimate/Non-Audited September 30, 2017
Advertising Rate (weekday/saturday): Open inch rate $14.95
Advertising Rate (sunday): Open inch rate $15.40
News services: AP, General Media. **Established:** 1900
Own Printing Facility?: No
Commercial Printers?: No
Special Editions: Progress (Feb); Mature Time (Monthly).
Special Weekly Sections: Best Food day (Tue); Religion (Fri); Lifestyles, Wedding, Engagements, Agriculture, 4-H, TV, Comics, Real Estate, Outdoors, Business, Movie, Entertainment (Sun)
Syndicated Publications: American Profile (S). SPRY, Atholon Sports
Pub. .... Jerry Pye
Co-Pub .... Judy Terry
Managing Ed. .... Jimmy Gelvan
Circ. Mgr. .... Jessie Frausto
Market Information: TMC.
Mechanical Available: Offset; Black and 3 ROP colors; insert accepted - product samples; page cutoffs - 23.
Mechanical Specifications: Type page 11 x 21 1/2; E - 6 cols, 1/8 between; A - 6 cols, 1/8 between; C - 10 cols, 1/8 between.
Areas Served: 76401
Delivery Method: Mail, Newsstand, Carrier, RacksEquipment & Software: PRESSROOM EQUIPMENT: Lines — 7-G/Community Offset 1972; Folders — 1-G/SC (with upper former).; MAILROOM EQUIPMENT: Tying Machines — MLN/Strapper (plastic).; BUSINESS EQUIPMENT: IBM BUSINESS SOFTWARE: Microsoft/Word, Microsoft/Excel, Microsoft/Outlook, Microsoft/Windows 98 CLASSIFIED EQUIPMENT: Hardware — APP/Mac; Printers — APP/Mac; CLASSIFIED SOFTWARE: Baseview/AdManager Pro. DISPLAY EQUIPMENT: Hardware — APP/Mac; Printers — APP/Mac Laser, 3-HP/4MV; DISPLAY SOFTWAREAd Make-up Applications — PBS; Layout Software — APP/Mac, QPS/QuarkXPress. EDITORIAL EQUIPMENT: Hardware — APP/Mac; Printers — APP/Mac Laser EDITORIAL SOFTWARE: QPS/QuarkXPress 4.0. PRODUCTION EQUIPMENT: Hardware — APP/Mac Laser, Imagesetter; Cameras — C/Spartan II Roll Camera

SULPHUR SPRINGS

SULPHUR SPRINGS NEWS-TELEGRAM

401 Church St, Sulphur Springs, Texas, 75482-2681, Hopkins; gen tel (903) 885-8663; gen fax (903) 885-8768; gen/nat adv e-mail angie@ssecho.com; disp adv e-mail ashley@ssecho.com; class adv e-mailclassified-ads@ssecho.com; ed e-mail editor@ssecho.com; web site www.myssnews.com
Group: Echo Publishing Co., Inc.
Published: Mon, Tues, Wed, Thur, Fri, Sun
Weekday Frequency: e
Circulation: 5,860; 6,118(sun)
Last Audit: Sworn/Estimate/Non-Audited September 30, 2017
Advertising Rate (weekday/saturday): Open inch rate $11.48
Advertising Rate (sunday): Open inch rate $11.48
News services: AP.
Special Weekly Sections: Best Food Day (Tue); Business (Thur); TV (Fri); Variety, Real Estate (Sun)
Pres./Pub. .... Scott Keys
Vice Pres. .... Jim Butler
Sec./Treasurer .... Carolyn Keys
Gen. Mgr. .... Butch Burney
Circ. Mgr. .... Kristi Hayes
News Ed. .... Faith Huffman
Sports Ed. .... Bobby Burney
MIS Mgr./Websmaster .... Davy Moseley
Adv. Dir. .... Leslie McCullough
Adv. Sales .... JR Foreman
Adv. Sales Rep. .... Jeremy Reynolds
Classified Sales .... Sara Cessna
Market Information: TMC.
Mechanical Available: Offset; Black and 3 ROP colors; insert accepted; page cutoffs - 22 1/2.
Mechanical Specifications: Type page 13 x 21; E - 6 cols, 2 1/16, 1/8 between; A - 6 cols, 2 1/16, 1/8 between; C - 6 cols, 2 1/16, 1/8 between.
Areas Served: 75482, 75478, 75471, 75420, 75433, 75481, 75431, 75437, 75497, 75494, 75440Equipment & Software: PRESSROOM EQUIPMENT: Lines — 7-HI/Cotrell V-15A; 8-KP/Color King; MAILROOM EQUIPMENT: Counter Stackers — 1/BG; Inserters & Stuffers — 1-/KR; Tying Machines — 1-/Bu, 1-/Cn; Address Machine — 1-/KR.; BUSINESS EQUIPMENT: 2-Northstar/Horizon, 2-IBM CLASSIFIED EQUIPMENT: Hardware — 2-APP/Mac SE.; EDITORIAL EQUIPMENT: Hardware — APP/Mac SE, APP/Mac SE30, APP/Mac Classic, APP/Mac fx, APP/Mac si, 2-APP/Power Mac 8100. PRODUCTION EQUIPMENT: Hardware — 3-APP/Mac LaserWriter Plus, 1-LaserMaster/1200 Laser Printer, ECR; Cameras — 1-Acti; Scanners — 4-APP/Mac SE PRODUCTION SOFTWARE: QPS/QuarkXPress.

SWEETWATER

SWEETWATER REPORTER

112 W 3rd St, Sweetwater, Texas, 79556-4430, Nolan; gen tel (325) 236-6677; adv tel (325)236-6677; ed tel (325)236-6677; gen fax (325) 235-4967; adv fax (325)235-4967; ed fax (325)235-4967; gen/nat adv e-mail business@sweetwaterreporter.com; disp adv e-mail business@sweetwaterreporter.com; class adv e-mailbusiness@sweetwaterreporter.com; ed e-mail publisher@sweetwaterreporter.com; web site www.sweetwaterreporter.com
Group: Horizon Publications Inc.
Published: Mon, Tues, Wed, Thur, Fri, Sun
Weekday Frequency: m
Saturday Frequency: m
Circulation: 4,176; 4,176(sun)
Last Audit: Sworn/Estimate/Non-Audited September 30, 2017
Advertising Rate (weekday/saturday): Open inch rate $9.75
Advertising Rate (sunday): $11.80
News services: AP. **Established:** 1881
Own Printing Facility?: Yes
Special Editions: AJRA National Finals Tab (Jul); Rattlesnake Tab (Mar) Hometown Heroes(Sep)
Special Weekly Sections: Church News (Fri); Business (S); Grocery Inserts (Tues).
Syndicated Publications: American Profile (Weekly).
Pub. .... Sharon Friedlander
Bus. Mgr. .... Danica Hickson
Adv. Sales Mgr. .... Brenda Morales
Adv. Sales Mgr. .... Justin Ramirez
Composing Mgr. .... Pablo Rodriguez
Prodn. Mgr., Pressroom .... Bleu Reyes
Ed. .... Tatiana Rodriguez
Ad Dir. .... Rick Nunez
Gen. Mgr. / Adv. Dir. .... Zela Armstrong
Market Information: ADS; TMC.
Mechanical Available: Offset; Black and 3 ROP colors; insert accepted - all; page cutoffs - 22.
Mechanical Specifications: Type page 12 x 21 1/2; E - 6 cols, 2 1/16, 1/8 between; A - 6 cols, 2 1/16, 1/8 between; C - 8 cols, 1 1/2, 1/8 between.
Areas Served: 79506, 79512, 79526, 79535, 79536, 79537, 79543, 79545, 79546, 79556
Delivery Method: Mail, Carrier, RacksEquipment & Software: PRESSROOM EQUIPMENT: Lines — 5-G 1963, 1-G 1977.; MAILROOM EQUIPMENT: Tying Machines — 1/Bu; Address Machine — 1-/Wm.; BUSINESS EQUIPMENT: Acer/PCs BUSINESS SOFTWARE: ARWorks CLASSIFIED EQUIPMENT: Hardware — APP/Mac; Printers — Okidata/320; CLASSIFIED SOFTWARE: Baseview. DISPLAY EQUIPMENT: Printers — 2-APP/Mac LaserWriter II NTX; DISPLAY SOFTWARELayout Software — Baseview. EDITORIAL EQUIPMENT: Hardware — APP/Mac; Printers — NewGen/LaserWriters EDITORIAL SOFTWARE: QPS/QuarkXPress. PRODUCTION EQUIPMENT: Hardware — 2-NewGen/Laserwriter; Cameras — 1-R/500.

TEMPLE

TEMPLE DAILY TELEGRAM

10 S 3rd St, Temple, Texas, 76501-7619, Bell; gen tel (254) 778-4444; adv tel (254) 778-4444; gen fax (254) 771-3516; adv fax (254) 778-2117; ed fax (254) 778-4444; gen/nat adv e-mail advertiz@tdtnews.com; disp adv e-mail advertiz@tdtnews.com; class adv e-mailtdtads@tdnews.com; ed e-mail tdt@tdtnews.com; web site www.tdtnews.com - 606,000(views) 138,000(visitors)
Group: Frank Mayborn Enterprises, Inc.
Published: Mon, Tues, Wed, Thur, Fri, Sat, Sun
Weekday Frequency: m
Saturday Frequency: m
Circulation: 13,096; 13,096(sat); 15,997(sun)
Last Audit: AAM March 31, 2016
Advertising Rate (weekday/saturday): Open inch rate $24.50
Advertising Rate (sunday): Open inch rate $26.50
Online Advertising Rate: 728X90 (300x100 mobile) - $15 per thousand 300 x 250 (same for mobile) - $15 per thousand 468 x 60 (300x50 mobile) - $12.50 per thousand
News services: AP. **Established:** 1907
Own Printing Facility?: Yes
Commercial Printers?: Yes
Special Editions: Tex Appeal Bridal (Jan); Day For Women (Feb.); TABA Home and Garden Expo (Feb.); Roll of Honor (Feb.); Home and Garden (Mar.); Parade of Homes (Apr.); Family Owned Business (Apr.); Tex Appeal Women in Business (May); Community Guide (June); Tex Appeal Brides (July); Football Preview (Aug.); Tex Appeal Medical (Sept.); Readers Choice (Nov.); Holiday Gift Guide (Nov.); Holiday Favorite Finds (Dec.).
Special Weekly Sections: Farm (Mon); Business (Tue); Best Food (Wed); Auto, Entertainment (Thur); Auto (Fri); Church, Auto, Employment, Real Estate (Sat); Best Food, Arts, Entertainment, Employment, Real Estate (Sun); Editorials, Comics, TV (Daily)
Syndicated Publications: Parade (S); Relish (monthly); Athlon Sports (monthly)
Proprietary Publications: Tex Appeal Magazine (monthly); TDT Homes Magazine (monthly).
Digital Platform - Mobile: Apple, Android
Digital Platform - Tablet: Apple iOS, Android
Gen. Mgr. .... Don Cooper
Adv. Dir. .... Lauren Ballard
Retail Adv. Mgr. .... Gary Garner
Editor and Publisher .... Sue Mayborn
Assistant Managing Editor .... Jerry Prickett
Mechanical Available: Offset; Black and 3 ROP colors; insert accepted - hi-fi rolls; page cutoffs - 22 3/4.
Mechanical Specifications: Type page 11 5/8 x 21 1/2; E - 6 cols, 1 13/16, 1/8 between; A - 6 cols, 1 13/16, 1/8 between; C - 9 cols, 1 3/16, 1/16 between.
Areas Served: 76501 .... Temple
76502 .... Temple
76504 .... Temple
76508 .... Temple
76511 .... Bartlett
76513 .... Belton
76518 .... Buckholts
76519 .... Burlington
76520 .... Cameron
76522 .... Copperas Cove
76527 .... Florence
76528 .... Eddy-Gatesville
76530 .... Granger
76534 .... Holland
76537 .... Jarrell
76539 .... Kempner
76541 .... Killeen
76542 .... Killeen
76543 .... Harker Heights/Killeen
76544 .... Fort Hood
76548 .... Harker Heights
76549 .... Killeen
76550 .... Lampasas
76554 .... Little River Academy
76557 .... Moody
76559 .... Nolanville
76567 .... Rockdale

76569....................Rogers
76570....................Rosebud
76571....................Salado
76579....................Troy
76656....................Lott
Delivery Method: Mail, Newsstand, Carrier, RacksEquipment & Software: PRESSROOM EQUIPMENT: Lines — 10-G/Urbanite; Folders — 1-G/2:1; MAILROOM EQUIPMENT: Counter Stackers — 3-HL/ Monitor; Inserters & Stuffers — 1-GMA/SLS 1000 8:2; Tying Machines — 1-MLN/Plastic, 1-MLN/2E.; BUSINESS EQUIPMENT: 7-Dell/ Pentium III BUSINESS SOFTWARE: Mas 90, IBM/AR 2000 CLASSIFIED EQUIPMENT: Hardware — ALR/Pentium II, ALR/Fileserver; 1-Microtek/b&w Scanner with OCR, 1-Kk/40 Digital Camera, 1-QuickTake/150 Digital Camera, 1-ABS/486; Printers — Okidata/320; CLASSIFIED SOFTWARE: APT. DISPLAY EQUIPMENT: Hardware — 1-APP/Mac 7100 Image Workstation, APP/Mac SE, 1-APP/ Mac 7200-120 Image Workstation; Printers — 1-LaserMaster/XLO Postscript Typesetter; Other Hardware — 2-Microtek/Scanner 1200 dpi color (11x17), 1-Microtek/Scanner 1200 dpi color (8 1/2x14), 1 EDITORIAL EQUIPMENT: Hardware — ALR/Pentium II, 1-Nikon/Coolscan; Printers — Okidata/320, 1-Okidata/591, 1-Okidata/321, 1-Epson/ Stylus Pro, HP/LaserJet IID EDITORIAL SOFTWARE: APT. PRODUCTION EQUIPMENT: Hardware — 1-L/190 Postscript Imagesetter Full Page, BKY/30A, 1-Konica/EV Jetsetter, 2-Elite XL Postscript; Cameras — 1-C/Spartan II PRODUCTION SOFTWARE: APT, QPS/QuarkXPress 4.0.

TYLER

TYLER MORNING TELEGRAPH

410 W Erwin St, Tyler, Texas, 75702-7133, Smith; gen tel (903) 597-8111; adv tel (903) 597-8111; ed tel (903) 597-8111; gen fax (903) 596-6368; adv fax (903) 597-4987; ed fax (903) 595-0335; gen/nat adv e-mail advertising@tylerpaper.com; disp adv e-mail advertising@tylerpaper.com; class adv e-mailclassifieds@tylerpaper.com; ed e-mail apollan@tylerpaper.com; web site www. tylerpaper.com
Group: TBB Printing Ltd.
Published: Mon, Tues, Wed, Thur, Fri, Sat, Sun
Weekday Frequency: m
Saturday Frequency: m
Circulation: 13,957; 13,957(sat); 16,660(sun)
Last Audit: AAM September 30, 2017
Advertising Rate (weekday/saturday): Open inch rate $28.33
Advertising Rate (sunday): Open inch rate $32.77
News services: AP, SHNS. **Established:** 1929
Special Editions: Business & Industry (Apr); Football (Aug); Christmas Greetings (Dec); Engineer's Week (Feb); Pillars of Progress (Jan); Parade of Homes (Jul); Senior Citizens (Jun); TALC (Mar); Discover Summer (May); Rose Festival (Oct); Clubs & Organizations (Sept).
Special Weekly Sections: Business (Mon); Best Food Days (Wed/Sun); SAG (Thur)
Syndicated Publications: Parade (S).
Pub. ....Nelson Clyde
CFO....................Thomas Clyde
Vice Pres., Sales/Mktg.....................Art McClelland
Adv. Mgr., Nat'l ....Robin Land
Adv. Mgr., Ops....................Jasper Curtis
Circ. Dir. ....Jerry Rives
Exec. Ed.....................Jim Giametta
Mng. Ed. ....Dave Berry
Asst. Mng. Ed.....................Richard Loomis
Asst. Mng. Ed.....................Danny Mogle
Bus. Ed.....................Greg Junek
Community Ed. ....Joyce Turner
Educ. Ed.....................Betty Waters
Librarian....................Diane May
Religion Ed. ....Patrick Butler
Sports Ed. ....Phil Hicks
Travel Ed.....................Terry Cannon
Adv. Dir. ....David R. Stringer
Prod. & Dist. Dir. ....Matt Milling
Editor....................Carlina Villalpando
Circ. Mgr.....................Mary Suits
Mechanical Available: Offset; Black and 3 ROP colors; insert accepted - hi fi, spadea; page cutoffs - 22 3/4.
Mechanical Specifications: Type page 11 5/8 x 21 1/2; E - 6 cols, 1 5/6, 1/8 between; A - 6 cols, 1 5/6, 1/8 between; C - 9 cols, 1 3/16, 1/8 between.
Areas Served: Smith, Henderson, Anderson, Cherokee, Rusk, Gregg, Wood, and Van Zandt countiesEquipment & Software: PRESSROOM EQUIPMENT: Lines — 12-HI/845N single width 1974; Press Drive — SECO/Warner Baldor; Folders — 2-HI/ RBC-2; Control System — Entertron/PLC.; MAILROOM EQUIPMENT: Counter Stackers — 3/HL, 2-QWI/401; Inserters & Stuffers — 1-K & M/1372; Tying Machines — 3-OVL/415, 1-OVL/515; Control System — K & M/Image PC, QWI/Program 32; Address Machine — 1-KR/215; BUSINESS EQUIPMENT: Advanced Publishing Technology BUSINESS SOFTWARE: Advanced Publishing Technology CLASSIFIED EQUIPMENT: Hardware — Novell/Network (PC Based) Client Server 4.1; Printers — Tektronix/ Phaser 600; CLASSIFIED SOFTWARE: Brainworks. DISPLAY EQUIPMENT: Hardware — 6-PC; Printers — Tektronix/ Phaser 600; Other Hardware — AP AdSend, XYQUEST/88 mg. removable, Micronet 1650 (1.3 removable optical drive), Zip Drives 100mb DISPLAY SOFTWAREAd Make-up Applications — QPS/QuarkXPress, Adobe/Illustrator, Adobe/Photoshop; Layout Software — Advanced Pub. T EDITORIAL EQUIPMENT: Hardware — Novell/Network (PC Based) Client Server 4.1; Printers — ECR/VRL 36, Tektronix/Phaser 600 EDITORIAL SOFTWARE: Advanced Pub. Technology/Automated Complete Typesetting. PRODUCTION EQUIPMENT: Hardware — Text Bridge/Pro, Macro/JetSetter; Cameras — 3-Kk/DC50, Digital Cameras; Scanners — Lf/Leafscan, Umax/Flatbed, Epson/Flatbed, Visioneer/Single Sheet Scanner, Kk/Film Scanner, Konica/Scanner PRODUCTION SOFTWARE: APT, MEI/ALS, QPS/ QuarkXPress.

VERNON

THE VERNON DAILY RECORD

3214 Wilbarger St, Vernon, Texas, 76384-7927, Wilbarger; gen tel (940) 552-5454; adv tel (940)552-5454; ed tel (940)552-5454; gen fax (940) 553-4823; adv fax (940)553-4823; ed fax (940)553-4823; gen/nat adv e-mail advertising@vernonrecord.com; disp adv e-mail advertising@vernonrecord.com; class adv e-mailclassified@vernonrecord.com; ed e-mail publisher@vernonrecord.com; web site www.vernonrecord.com
Group: Vernon Record, Inc.
Published: Mon, Tues, Wed, Thur, Fri, Sun
Weekday Frequency: e
Circulation: 2,400; 2,500(sun)
Last Audit: Sworn/Estimate/Non-Audited December 18, 2017
Advertising Rate (weekday/saturday): Open inch rate $9.90
Advertising Rate (sunday): Open inch rate $12.90
News services: AP. **Established:** 1908
Own Printing Facility?: Yes
Commercial Printers?: Yes
Special Weekly Sections: Best Food Day (Tue)
Treasurer....................Keith McCormick
Prodn. Mgr. ....Charles Ashley
Pres./Pub.....................Bret McCormick
Classified & New Media Dir. ....Teri McCormick
Ed.....................Payton McCormick
Managing Editor ....Daniel Walker
Advertising Director ....Shelby McCormick
Lifestyle editor ....Joyce Ashley
Sports Editor....................Chance Baskerville
Market Information: Split run;
Mechanical Available: Offset; Black and 3 ROP colors; insert accepted; page cutoffs - 22 3/4.
Mechanical Specifications: Type page 13 x 21; E - 6 cols, 2 1/16, 1/8 between; A - 6 cols, 2 1/16, 1/8 between; C - 6 cols, 2 1/16, 1/8 between.
Areas Served: 76384, 76385, 79252, 79225, 79227
Delivery Method: Newsstand, Carrier, RacksEquipment & Software: PRESSROOM EQUIPMENT: Lines — 6-G/Community 1986.; MAILROOM EQUIPMENT: Tying Machines — Bu.; Address Machine — Yes; BUSINESS EQUIPMENT: PC CLASSIFIED EQUIPMENT: Hardware — FSI; Printers — Xante/Accel-a-Writer; CLASSIFIED SOFTWARE: FSI. DISPLAY EQUIPMENT: Hardware — FSI; Printers — Xante/Accel-a-Writer; DISPLAY SOFTWAREAd Make-up Applications — FSI; Layout Software — FSI. EDITORIAL EQUIPMENT: Hardware — FSI EDITORIAL SOFTWARE: FSI. PRODUCTION EQUIPMENT: CTP

VICTORIA

VICTORIA ADVOCATE

311 E Constitution St, Victoria, Texas, 77901-8140, Victoria; gen tel (361) 580-6557; adv tel (361) 574-1241; ed tel (361) 574-1222; gen fax (361) 574-1216; adv fax (361) 574-1225; ed fax (361) 574-1220; gen/nat adv e-mail tbonner@vicad.com; disp adv e-mail tbonner@vicad.com; class adv e-mailtbonner@vicad.com; ed e-mail newsroom@vicad.com; web site www. victoriaadvocate.com
Group: Victoria Advocate Publishing Co.
Published: Mon, Tues, Wed, Thur, Fri, Sat, Sun
Weekday Frequency: m
Saturday Frequency: m
Circulation: 22,212; 22,212(sat); 24,511(sun)
Last Audit: AAM September 30, 2016
Advertising Rate (weekday/saturday): Open inch rate $65.45
Advertising Rate (sunday): Open inch rate $68.05
News services: AP, NYT. **Established:** 1846
Special Editions: Looking Good, Feeling Food (Aug); Holiday Inspirations (Dec); Livestock (Feb); Home Product Show (Mar); Meet Your Local Merchants (May); All In Good Taste (Nov); Farm & Ranch (Oct).
Special Weekly Sections: Good Living, Big Wed (Wed); Seniors, Entertainment (Thur); Home,Garden, Travel (Fri); Church, Auto (Sat); Farm, Oil & Gas, Lifestyles, Money (Sun)
Syndicated Publications: Parade (S).
Sec./Treasurer....................Catherine McHaney
VP....................Stephen McHaney
Ed.....................Chris Cobler
Other....................Becky Cooper
Pres.....................John M. Roberts
Photo Ed. ....Frank Tilley
Pub. ....Dan Easton
Feat. Ed. and Diversity Reporter ....Ortega J.R.
Nat'l Adv. Mgr.....................Thomas Bonner
Cir. Dir. ....Kevin Thaete
Market Information: Split run; TMC; Zoned editions.
Mechanical Available: Offset; Black and 3 ROP colors; insert accepted; page cutoffs - 22 3/4.
Mechanical Specifications: Type page 11 5/8 x 21 1/2; E - 6 cols, 1 5/6, 1/8 between; A - 6 cols, 1 5/6, 1/8 between; C - 9 cols, 1 3/8, 1/16 between.
Areas Served: 78648, 78682, 78959, 78629, 78614, 78677, 78159, 78956, 78935, 78962, 77442, 77434, 77435, 77485, 77441, 77488, 77461, 77406, 77469, 77420, 77417, 77406, 77494, 77407, 77498, 77479, 77469, 77430, 77486, 77422, 77975, 77984, 77995, 77964, 77994, 77954, 78164, 78141, 77963, 77905, 77904, 77901, 77968, 77951, 78340, 78393, 78377, 77990, 77979, 77983, 77957, 77962, 77971, 77455, 77437, 77432, 77458, 77419, 77465, 77456, 77440, 77468, 77482, 78102, 78389, 78387, 78370, 78390, 78374, 78362, 78336, 78382, 78982Equipment & Software: PRESSROOM EQUIPMENT: Lines — 6-HI/N1650 (5 Registron Reels & Stands) 1978; Press Drive — Haley/ Controls/Emerson; Folders — 2-HI/2:1; Reels & Stands — 5-HI/Registron; Control System — Haley/Emerson.; MAILROOM EQUIPMENT: Counter Stackers — 1-Id/550, 1-Id/2100, 2-Id/2000; Inserters & Stuffers — 2/AM Graphics/848; Tying Machines — 1-MLN/ML2-EE, 1-OVL/JP80, 1-OVL/JP40, 1-OVL/415-A.; BUSINESS EQUIPMENT: Compaq/Prosignia 300 BUSINESS SOFTWARE: SBS Business Software, PPI Advertising Software CLASSIFIED EQUIPMENT: Hardware — Compaq; Printers — HP/5si; CLASSIFIED SOFTWARE: PPI. DISPLAY EQUIPMENT: Hardware — IBM.; EDITORIAL EQUIPMENT: Hardware — IBM; Printers — 3-HP/Laser SL, 1-Epson/ Color EDITORIAL SOFTWARE: CNI/Agile Teambase Special Edition. PRODUCTION EQUIPMENT: Hardware — Kk/XL-7700 Printer, QPS, Lf/AP Leaf Picture Desk; Scanners — Nikon/35AF, Kk/2055 Plus, 2-AG/Arcus.

WACO

WACO TRIBUNE-HERALD

900 Franklin Ave, Waco, Texas, 76701-1906, McLennan; gen tel (254) 757-5788; adv tel (254) 757-5830; ed tel (254) 757-5701; gen fax (254) 757-6906; adv fax (254) 756-6906; ed fax (254) 757-0302; gen/ nat adv e-mail rprince@wacotrib.com; disp adv e-mail rprince@wacotrib.com; class adv e-mailclassifieds@wacotrib.com; ed e-mail letters@wacotrib.com; web site www. wacotrib.com
- 4,255,000(views) 400,000(visitors)
Group: BH Media Group
Published: Mon, Tues, Wed, Thur, Fri, Sat, Sun
Weekday Frequency: m
Saturday Frequency: m
Circulation: 22,504; 23,583(sat); 27,431(sun)
Last Audit: AAM June 30, 2016
Advertising Rate (weekday/saturday): Open inch rate $51.52
Advertising Rate (sunday): Open inch rate $53.17
Online Advertising Rate: Call for quote
News services: AP, NYT **Established:** 1892
Own Printing Facility?: No
Commercial Printers?: No
Special Editions: Garden & Landscape (Apr); Back-to-School (Aug); Christmas Gift Guide (Dec); Spring Fashion (Feb); Bridal (Jan); This is Central Texas (Jul); Business & Industry (May); Seniors (Monthly); Health Directory (Nov); New Cars (Oct); Home Furnishings (Sept).
Special Weekly Sections: Business in Review (Mon); Health, Fitness (Tue); Best Food Day (Wed); Home, Entertainment (Thur); Movies (Fri); Religion, Auto (Sat); Focus, Neighbor, Farm, Ranch, Business, Real Estate, Travel, Books, Family, Wedding, Announcements, TV (Sun);
Syndicated Publications: Waco Today (Monthly); Startime (local TV supplement) (S).
Digital Platform - Mobile: Apple, Android
Digital Platform - Tablet: Apple iOS, Android
Bus./Finance Ed.....................Mike Copeland
City Ed. ....Bill Whitaker
Chief Photographer....................Rod Aydelotte
Radio/Television Ed. ....Chris Oliver
Systems Ed. ....Freida Jackson
Pub....................Jim Wilson
Nat'l Sales Rep.....................Kristy Ferlet-Helton
Adv. Sales Mgr. ....Ana Lozano-Harper
Editor....................Steve Boggs
Market Information: Split run; TMC; Zoned editions.
Mechanical Specifications: Type page 13 x 21 1/4; E - 6 cols, 2, 1/6 between; A - 6 cols, 2, 1/6 between; C - 9 cols, 1 3/8, 1/12 between.
Areas Served: 76621, 76622, 76624, 76513, 76626, 76629, 76630, 76520, 76632, 76633, 76634, 76635, 75110, 76637, 76638, 76639, 76524, 76640, 75840, 76641, 76528, 76642, 76531, 76643, 76645, 76648, 76055, 76538, 76653, 76654, 76655, 76656, 76656, 76660, 76661, 76664, 76657, 76665, 76667, 76557, 76671, 76673, 76561, 76676, 76678, 76680, 76682, 76570, 75860, 76501, 76687, 76579, 76689, 76701, 76704, 76705, 76706, 76707, 76708, 76710, 76711, 76712, 76691, 76692, 76693
Delivery Method: Mail, Newsstand, Carrier, RacksEquipment & Software: BUSINESS EQUIPMENT: Dell Desktops, HP Printers BUSINESS SOFTWARE: DSI, CLASSIFIED EQUIPMENT: Dell Desktops, Ricoh and HP Printers CLASSIFIED SOFTWARE: Atex Adbase DISPLAY EQUIPMENT: Dell Desktops Printers — HP/LaserJet, APP/Mac LaserWriter 8500, Epson/Stylus; DISPLAY SOFTWAREAtex Adbase EDITORIAL EQUIPMENT: Dell Desktops and Laptops. Ricoh and HP Printers
Canon Cameras EDITORIAL SOFTWARE: TCMS PRODUCTION EQUIPMENT: Hardware — Dell Desktops, Ricoh and HP Printers PRODUCTION SOFTWARE: TCMC, Adobe Creative Suite IT EQUIPMENT:

Dell Servers IT SOFTWARE:Windows 10 CIRCULATION EQUIPMENT: Hardware — Dell Desktops, Ricoh and HP Printers CIRCULATION SOFTWARNewsCycle - DSI

WAXAHACHIE

WAXAHACHIE DAILY LIGHT

200 W Marvin Ave, Waxahachie, Texas, 75165-3040, Ellis; gen tel (972) 937-3310; gen fax (972) 937-1139; gen/nat adv e-mail sbrooks@waxahachietx.com; disp adv e-mail sbrooks@waxahachietx.com; class adv e-mailsrexrode@waxahachietx.com; ed e-mail tsmith@waxahachietx.com; web site www.waxahachieTX.com

Group: New Media Investment Group
Published: Tues, Wed, Thur, Fri, Sun
Weekday Frequency: m
Circulation: 4,500; 5,200(sun)
Last Audit: Sworn/Estimate/Non-Audited September 30, 2017
Advertising Rate (weekday/saturday): Open inch rate $12.25
Advertising Rate (sunday): Open inch rate $12.25
News services: AP. **Established:** 1867
Own Printing Facility?: Yes
Commercial Printers?: Yes
Special Editions: Profile (Feb); Newcomers (Jul); Gingerbread Trail (Jun); Football (Sept).
Special Weekly Sections: School Zone (Tue); Best Food Days (Wed/Sun); Business, Finance, Entertainment (Thur); Auto, Health, Religion (Fri); Real Estate, Employment (Sun)
Syndicated Publications: American Profile (Weekly).
Parade Magazine
Market Information: TMC.
Mechanical Available: Offset; Black and 4 ROP colors; insert accepted; page cutoffs - 22 3/4.
Mechanical Specifications: Type page 13 x 21 1/2; E - 6 cols, 1 5/6, 1/8 between; A - 6 cols, 1 5/6, 1/8 between; C - 10 cols, 1 5/6, 1/8 between.
Areas Served: 75165, 75167,75125, 75152, 75154, 76064, 76065, 76651
Delivery Method: Mail, Newsstand, Carrier, RacksEquipment & Software: PRESSROOM EQUIPMENT: Lines — 6-G/Community (upper former); Folders — 1-G/Community SC.; MAILROOM EQUIPMENT: Tying Machines — 4-/Sa, 1-/MLN; Address Machine — 1-Am/1900.; BUSINESS EQUIPMENT: Gateway BUSINESS SOFTWARE: PBS, Accounting CLASSIFIED EQUIPMENT: Hardware — APP/Mac SE30; CLASSIFIED SOFTWARE: Baseview. DISPLAY EQUIPMENT: Printers — HP/4MV; DISPLAY SOFTWAREAd Make-up Applications — QPS/QuarkXPress, Adobe/Photoshop; Layout Software — APP/Mac, APP/Mac II, APP/Mac G3, APP/Mac G4. EDITORIAL EQUIPMENT: Hardware — APP/Mac SE30, APP/Mac G3, APP/Mac G4; Printers — HP/4MV EDITORIAL SOFTWARE: QPS/InDesign, Adobe/Photoshop. PRODUCTION EQUIPMENT: Hardware — PrePress/CTP; Cameras — 1-C/Spartan III.

WEATHERFORD

THE WEATHERFORD DEMOCRAT

512 Palo Pinto St, Weatherford, Texas, 76086-4128, Parker; gen tel (817) 594-7447; adv tel (817) 594-7447 ext. 213; ed tel (817) 594-7447 ext. 234; gen fax (817) 594-9734; adv fax (817)594-9734; ed fax (817)594-9734; gen/nat adv e-mail jthompson@weatherforddemocrat.com; disp adv e-mail jthompson@weatherforddemocrat.com; class adv e-mailclassad@trcle.com; ed e-mail editor@weatherforddemocrat.com; web site www.weatherforddemocrat.com

Group: Community Newspaper Holdings, Inc.
Published: Tues, Wed, Thur, Fri, Sun
Weekday Frequency: m
Circulation: 3,740; 4,122(sun)
Last Audit: AAM September 30, 2014
Advertising Rate (weekday/saturday): Open inch rate $12.50
Advertising Rate (sunday): Open inch rate $12.50
News services: AP. **Established:** 1895
Special Editions: Christmas Gift Guides (Dec); Chamber of Commerce (Feb); Frontier Days (Jul); Christmas Gift Guides (Nov); Football (Sept).
Special Weekly Sections: Best Food Day (Wed); Church, Outdoors (Fri); Lifestyle, Business, Seniors, School (Sun)
Syndicated Publications: Relish (Monthly); USA WEEKEND Magazine (S); American Profile (Weekly).
Bus. Mgr. .... Sharon George
Circ. Mgr. .... Janette Fant
Sports Ed. .... Gregg Webb
Pub .... Julie Killion
Ed. .... Margarita Venegas
Adv. Dir. .... Tamara Smart
Pub .... Jeff Smith
Pub .... Keith Hansen
Mechanical Available: Offset; Black and 3 ROP colors; insert accepted - card; page cutoffs - 23.
Mechanical Specifications: Type page 13 x 21 1/2; E - 6 cols, 2 1/16, 1/8 between; A - 6 cols, 2 1/16, 1/8 between; C - 8 cols, 1 1/2, 1/8 between.
Areas Served: 76086, 76087, 76088, 76085, 76066, 76008, 76082, 76487
Delivery Method: Mail, CarrierEquipment & Software: PRESSROOM EQUIPMENT: Lines — 8-G/Community; Folders — 6-G/2:1.; MAILROOM EQUIPMENT: Tying Machines — 1-Mk/ACE 420, 1/MLN.; BUSINESS EQUIPMENT: Unisys/3105-00 CLASSIFIED EQUIPMENT: Hardware — 2-APP/Mac G3; Printers — APP/Mac LaserPrinter NT; CLASSIFIED SOFTWARE: Baseview/Class Manager Pro, Baseview/Class Flow. DISPLAY EQUIPMENT: Hardware — 2-APP/Power Mac; Printers — APP/Mac LaserPrinter NT; DISPLAY SOFTWARELayout Software — Adforce. EDITORIAL EQUIPMENT: Hardware — 8-APP/Power Mac; Printers — GCC EDITORIAL SOFTWARE: Baseview/NewsEdit Pro. PRODUCTION EQUIPMENT: Hardware — GCC, 6-APP/Mac G4; Cameras — Acti; Scanners — APP/Mac, 4-Umax.

WICHITA FALLS

WICHITA FALLS TIMES RECORD NEWS

1301 Lamar St, Wichita Falls, Texas, 76301-7032, Wichita; gen tel (940) 720-3491; adv tel (940) 720-3418; ed tel (940) 767-8341; gen fax (940) 720-3414; adv fax (940) 720-3453; ed fax (940) 767-1741; gen/nat adv e-mail tracyk@timesrecordnews.com; disp adv e-mail stew@wtr.com; web site www.timesrecordnews.com
207,521(visitors)

Group: Journal Media Group
Published: Mon, Tues, Wed, Thur, Fri, Sat, Sun
Weekday Frequency: m
Saturday Frequency: m
Circulation: 14,841; 14,841(sat); 18,381(sun)
Last Audit: AAM December 31, 2015
Advertising Rate (weekday/saturday): Open inch rate $40.86
Advertising Rate (sunday): Open inch rate $47.29
News services: AP. **Established:** 1907
Special Weekly Sections: What's Cookin' (Wed); Business (Tue/Thur); Entertainment, Air Force Base (Fri); Religion (Sat); Arts, Living, Technology, Women (Sun)
Syndicated Publications: Parade (S).
Relish
Athalon
Mktg./Promo. Dir. .... Jackie Riley
Circ. Dir. .... Don Boyd
Bus./Oil Ed. .... Angel Riggs
Librarian .... Jill Sexton
Radio/Television Ed. .... Lana Sweeten Shults
Regl. Ed. .... Suzanne Moore
Dir., Information Systems .... Bill Lindemann
Pub .... Darrell Coleman
Nat'l Accts. Mgr. .... Kathy Tracy
Retail Adv. Mgr. .... Stewart Swartz
Pub .... Swayne Bivona
Publisher .... Dwayne Bivona
Circ. Sales Dir. .... Richard Carlson
Ed .... Deanna Watson
Market Information: Split run; TMC; Zoned editions.
Mechanical Available: Offset; Black and 3 ROP colors; insert accepted - all; page cutoffs - 22 3/4.
Mechanical Specifications: Type page 13 x 21 1/2; E - 6 cols, 2 1/16, 1/8 between; A - 6 cols, 2 1/16, 1/8 between; C - 10 cols, 1 1/10, 1/16 between.Equipment & Software: PRESSROOM EQUIPMENT: Lines — 7-G/Cosmo 1984.; MAILROOM EQUIPMENT: Counter Stackers — 3-Id, HL; Inserters & Stuffers — 3/MM; Tying Machines — 4-/MLN; Address Machine — 1-/KR.; BUSINESS EQUIPMENT: HP/3000 CLASSIFIED EQUIPMENT: Hardware — Ik; Printers — NewGen; CLASSIFIED SOFTWARE: Ik. DISPLAY EQUIPMENT: Hardware — APP/Mac; Printers — NewGen, Tegra; DISPLAY SOFTWAREAd Make-up Applications — Multi-Ad/Creator 3.6.3; Layout Software — CJ/Layout 80. EDITORIAL EQUIPMENT: Hardware — Ik/APP/Mac; Printers — NewGen. PRODUCTION EQUIPMENT: Hardware — Nat, Tegra; Cameras — C; Scanners — ECR, Umax PRODUCTION SOFTWARE: QPS/QuarkXPress 3.3.1.

UTAH

LOGAN

THE HERALD JOURNAL

75 W 300 N, Logan, Utah, 84321-3971, Cache; gen tel (435) 752-2121; adv tel (435) 752-2121 x 351; ed tel (435)752-2121 ext. 320; gen fax (435) 753-6642; adv fax (435) 753-6642; ed fax (435)753-6642; gen/nat adv e-mail cliechty@hjnews.com; disp adv e-mail cliechty@hjnews.com; class adv e-mailhjclass@hjnews.com; ed e-mail cmcollum@hjnews.com; web site www.hjnews.com
- 1,117,273(views) 259,000(visitors)

Group: Pioneer Newspapers Inc
Published: Tues, Wed, Thur, Fri, Sat, Sun
Weekday Frequency: m
Saturday Frequency: m
Circulation: 10,624; 10,624(sat); 11,158(sun)
Last Audit: AAM March 31, 2016
Advertising Rate (weekday/saturday): Open inch rate $15.90
Advertising Rate (sunday): Open inch rate $16.60
News services: AP, CSM. **Established:** 1930
Own Printing Facility?: No
Special Editions: Home & Garden (Apr); Football (Aug); Sidewalk Days (Jul); Customer Appreciation Days (Jun); Progress (Mar); Tourist (May); Basketball (Nov); Hunter's Guide (Sept).
Special Weekly Sections: Food (Tue); Technology (Wed); Faith (Thur); Cache Magazine, Outdoors (Fri); Enterprise (Sun);
Syndicated Publications: Parade (S).
Digital Platform - Mobile: Apple, Android, Windows
Digital Platform - Tablet: Apple iOS, Android, Windows 7
City Ed. .... Tyler Ricks
Managing Ed. .... Charles McCollum
News Editor .... Chuck Nunn
Sports Ed. .... Shawn Harrison
Pub .... Michael Starn
Adv. Dir. .... Kyle Ashby
Circ. Mgr. .... Jason McNeely
Market Information: ADS; TMC; Zoned editions.
Mechanical Available: Offset; Black and 3 ROP colors; insert accepted; page cutoffs - 21 1/2.
Mechanical Specifications: Type page 12 x 20 1/2; E - 6 cols, 2, 1/8 between; A - 6 cols, 2, 1/8 between; C - 9 cols, 1 3/8, 1/16 between.
Delivery Method: Mail, Newsstand, Carrier, RacksEquipment & Software: PRESSROOM EQUIPMENT: Lines — 20-Dauphin/440 2001; Folders — 1-Dauphin/1035 with Quarterfold 2001; Pasters —3-Tandem/Jardis 50 2001. MAILROOM EQUIPMENT: Counter Stackers — BG/108, 2-QWI/SJ400, 3-QWI/SJ300, BG/Count-O-Veyor, Rima/RS25; Inserters & Stuffers — SUR; Tying Machines — 2-Samuel/NP30.; BUSINESS EQUIPMENT: Sun/Sparc workstation BUSINESS SOFTWARE: Microsoft/Word, Microsoft/Works 5.0 CLASSIFIED EQUIPMENT: Hardware — APP/iMac; Printers — Tektronix/Phaser 740, HP/LaserJet 6MP, Epson/Ink Jets; CLASSIFIED SOFTWARE: Baseview/AdManager Pro 2.1.1. DISPLAY EQUIPMENT: Hardware — 1-HP/Net Server; Printers — HP/LaserJet 6MP, HP/LJ 5000; Other Hardware — 6-Zip Drives 100 DISPLAY SOFTWAREAd Make-up Applications — QPS/QuarkXPress 4.0, Adobe/Photoshop 5.5, Adobe/Illustrator 9.0, APP/Mac Appleshare; Layout Software — 1-APP/Mac G3, 3-APP/Power Mac G4, 1-Power Compu EDITORIAL EQUIPMENT: Hardware — APP/Mac Centris 660AU, APP/Mac G4 400mhz, APP/Mac G3 350mhz, APP/Mac G4 350mhz, APP/Mac G3 300mhz, APP/Power Mac 7500, APP/Power Mac 8500, APP/Power Mac, APP/Mac Centris 650/HP/1050c, Tektronix/740; Printers — HP/5000, HP/1050C, HP PRODUCTION EQUIPMENT: Hardware — Offset, 2-APP/Power Mac G4 400mhz; Cameras — Nikon/DI-DIX; Scanners — COM, 1-Nikon/Scantouch 210, 2-Nikon/Super Coolscan LS1000, Epson/536XL PRODUCTION SOFTWARE: QPS/QuarkXPress 4.11.

OGDEN

STANDARD-EXAMINER

332 Standard Way, Ogden, Utah, 84404-1371, Weber; gen tel (801) 625-4400; adv tel (801) 625-4333; ed tel (801) 625-4544; gen fax (801) 625-4508; adv fax (801) 625-4508; ed fax (801) 625-4299; gen/nat adv e-mail advertise@standard.net; disp adv e-mail advertise@standard.net; class adv e-maildnewman@standard.net; ed e-mail news@standard.net; web site www.standard.net
- 3,500,000(views) 400,000(visitors)

Published: Mon, Tues, Wed, Thur, Fri, Sat, Sun
Weekday Frequency: m
Saturday Frequency: m
Circulation: 29,316; 28,338(sat); 31,968(sun)
Last Audit: AAM September 30, 2017
Advertising Rate (weekday/saturday): Open inch rate $43.05 (Mon-Thur); $46.93 (Fri)
Advertising Rate (sunday): Open inch rate $46.93
News services: AP, MCT, SHNS, DJ, LAT-WP. **Established:** 1888
Own Printing Facility?: Yes
Commercial Printers?: Yes
Special Editions: Parade of Homes (Aug); Neighborhoods (Dec); Bride & Groom (Jan); Pioneer Days (Jul); Home & Garden (Mar); Coupon Power (Monthly); Auto Guide (Nov); Car Care (Oct); Health & Fitness (Quarterly); Homemaker's School (Sept).
Special Weekly Sections: TMC (Mon); Outdoor (Wed); Military (Thur); Classifieds, Auto, Entertainment (Fri); Religion, Real Estate, Entertainment (Sat);Best Food Day, Life Styles, Travel, Business, Help Wanted (Sun); Seniors, Women, Outdoors (Monthly);
Syndicated Publications: Relish (Monthly); USA WEEKEND Magazine (S); American Profile (Weekly).
Exec. Asst. to the Pub. .... Anne Paul
Adv. Mgr., Classified .... David Newman
Retail Adv. Mgr. .... Jared Bird
Adv. Mgr., Major/Nat'l .... Julie Hartman
Adv. Supvr., Classified Telephone Sales .... Karie Gardner
Mgr., Creative .... Brad Roghaar
Circ. Dir. .... Ron Thornburg
Features Ed. .... Vanessa Zimmer
Graphics Ed. .... Andy Howell
Cuba Tucker
Mrkting Dir. .... Karla Woodward
Pub .... Brandon Erlacher
Market Information: TMC; Zoned editions.
Mechanical Available: Offset; Black and 3 ROP colors; insert accepted - product samples; page cutoffs - 21 1/2.
Mechanical Specifications: Type page 11 1/2 x 20 1/2; E - 6 cols, 1 5/6, 1/8 between; A - 6 cols, 1 5/6, 1/8 between; C - 9 cols, 1 1/3, 1/8 between.
Delivery Method: Mail, Newsstand, Carrier, RacksEquipment & Software: PRESSROOM EQUIPMENT: Lines — 6-KBA/Comet (6 towers, 48 couples) single width; Press Drive — Indramet/Shaftless; Reels & Stands — Amal/AR-80; Registration System — Quad Tech/RGS 5. MAILROOM EQUIPMENT:

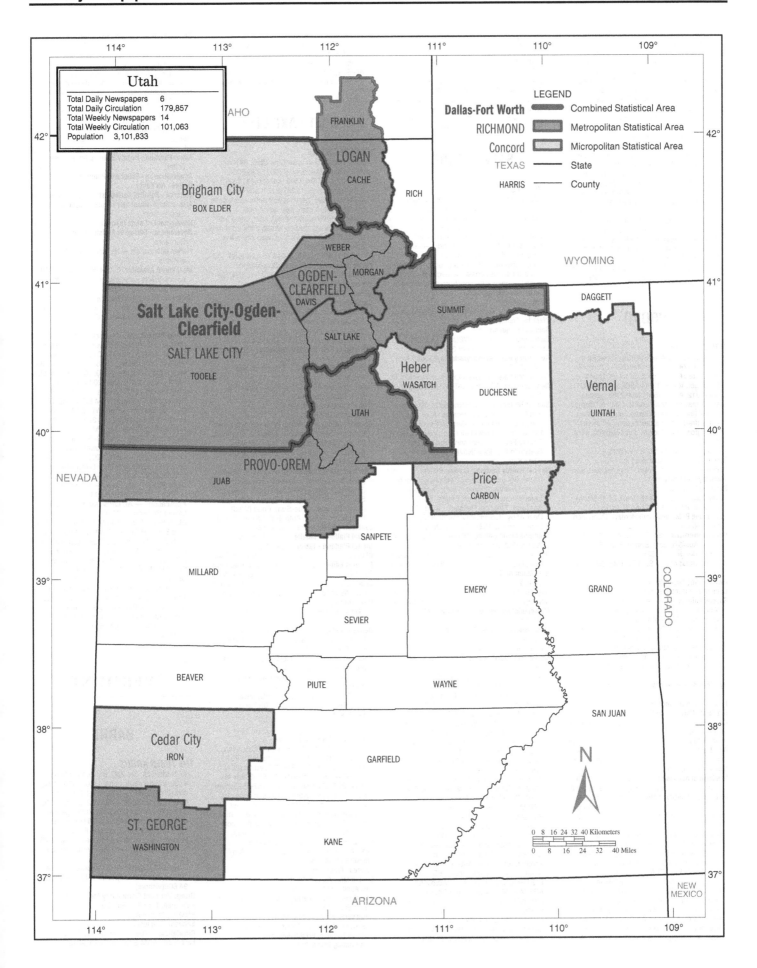

Utah

Total Daily Newspapers	6
Total Daily Circulation	179,857
Total Weekly Newspapers	14
Total Weekly Circulation	101,063
Population	3,101,833

LEGEND

Dallas-Fort Worth — Combined Statistical Area

RICHMOND — Metropolitan Statistical Area

Concord — Micropolitan Statistical Area

TEXAS — State

HARRIS — County

IDAHO

FRANKLIN

LOGAN

CACHE

RICH

Brigham City

BOX ELDER

WEBER

OGDEN-CLEARFIELD

MORGAN

DAVIS

SUMMIT

WYOMING

DAGGETT

Salt Lake City-Ogden-Clearfield

SALT LAKE CITY

SALT LAKE

TOOELE

Heber

WASATCH

DUCHESNE

Vernal

UINTAH

UTAH

PROVO-OREM

JUAB

Price

CARBON

NEVADA

SANPETE

MILLARD

EMERY

GRAND

SEVIER

COLORADO

BEAVER

PIUTE

WAYNE

SAN JUAN

Cedar City

IRON

GARFIELD

N

ST. GEORGE

WASHINGTON

KANE

0 8 16 24 32 40 Kilometers

0 8 16 24 32 40 Miles

ARIZONA

NEW MEXICO

Counter Stackers — 2-Id/2100, 2-QWI/2100; Inserters & Stuffers — GMA/SLS 2000; Tying Machines — 2/Dynaric; Control System — Ferag/Single Gripper; Address Machine — Marconi; BUSINESS EQUIPMENT: 42-PC BUSINESS SOFTWARE: WordPerfect, Microsoft/Office, ADP, Great Plains CLASSIFIED EQUIPMENT: Hardware — SII/Sys 66, 23-SII/Coyote 3, 3-SII, 3-SII/Echo, iQue, Tandem/CLX, Sun; Printers — 1-HP/5si, 1-HP/4L; CLASSIFIED SOFTWARE: SII/Classified, SII/ICP Sys. DISPLAY EQUIPMENT: Hardware — SII/Sys 66, 5-SII/Coyote III, 1-Umax/C600; Printers — 1-HP/5si; DISPLAY SOFTWAREAd Make-up Applications — SII/Classified, CZAR II; Layout Software — SII/IAL, SCS Layout 8000. EDITORIAL EQUIPMENT: Hardware — Tandem/CLX, Sun, 7-APP/Servers, 70-Baseview/NewsEditPro, 12-Baseview/NewsEditPro IQ/APP/Mac IIfx, AP/GraphicsNet, APP/Mac One Scanner, HP/ScanJet IIc; Printers — 1-HP/5si, 1-HP/3si, 2-HP/4, HP/II, 4-HP/8100. PRODUCTION EQUIPMENT: Hardware — Caere/OmniPage, Na/20, WL, HP/Laser Jet Series IV, 3-AJ/Graphic Ripps PRODUCTION SOFTWARE: SII/System 66, SCS.

PROVO

DAILY HERALD
86 N University Ave, Ste 300, Provo, Utah, 84601-4474, Utah; gen tel (801) 373-5050; adv tel (801) 344-2957; ed tel (801) 344-2935; gen fax (801)344-2982; adv fax (801) 356-3012; ed fax (801) 344-2985; gen/nat adv e-mail tfrantz@heraldextra.com; disp adv e-mail tfrantz@heraldextra.com; class adv e-mailtfrantz@heraldextra.com; ed e-mail stitrington@heraldextra.com; web site www.heraldextra.com
- 305,003(views) 19,631(visitors)
Group: Ogden Newspapers Inc.
Published: Mon, Tues, Wed, Thur, Fri, Sat, Sun
Weekday Frequency: m
Saturday Frequency: m
Circulation: 13,521; 13,451(sat); 21,436(sun)
Last Audit: AAM September 30, 2015
Advertising Rate (weekday/saturday): Open inch rate $60.00
Online Advertising Rate: Banner Ad-$15 cpm; Video Ads-$20 cpm; Bottom Slide Banner-$15; Video Preroll- $25
News services: AP, CNS, MCT, TMS. **Established:** 1873
Own Printing Facility?: No
Commercial Printers?: No
Special Editions: Summer Recreation & Travel (Apr); Football (Aug); Gift Guide (Dec); Valentine's Day (Feb); Father's Day (Jun); Progress (Mar); Provo Open (May); Home Interiors (Oct); Best of Utah Valley (Sept).
Special Weekly Sections: Wheels (Fri); TV Magazine (Sat); UV-Utah Valley's Weekly Entertainment Guide (Thur); Best Food Day (Tues).
Syndicated Publications: Relish (Monthly) Parade
Digital Platform - Mobile: Apple, Android
Digital Platform - Tablet: Apple iOS
Circ. Dir. .... Stephen Kelsey Michele Bates
Sports Editor .... Jared Lloyd
Adv. Cord. .... Lisa Llewelyn
Pub. .... Rhett Long
Market Information: TMC.
Mechanical Available: Offset; Black and 3 ROP colors; insert accepted; page cutoffs - 21 3/8.
Mechanical Specifications: Type page 11 5/8 x 21 1/2; E - 6 cols, 1 3/4, 1/8 between; A - 6 cols, 1 3/4, 1/8 between; C - 10 cols, 1 1/8 between.
Areas Served: Utah CountyEquipment & Software: BUSINESS EQUIPMENT: IBM/PC, PBS, APP/Mac BUSINESS SOFTWARE: Microsoft/Excel, Microsoft/Word, Lotus, PBS/MediaPlus CLASSIFIED EQUIPMENT: Hardware — APP/Mac, 15-APP/Mac; CLASSIFIED SOFTWARE: Baseview/Ad Manager Pro, Baseview/Ad Manager pro 2.0.6. DISPLAY EQUIPMENT: Hardware — Dell/PC, APP/Mac 7200, APP/Mac G4; Printers — 1-HP/5000, HP/5si; DISPLAY SOFTWARELayout Software — MEI/ALS,

MEI/ALS 4.0. EDITORIAL EQUIPMENT: Hardware — 30-APP/Mac, 40-APP/Mac/2-AU/3850, 2-AG/Accuset 1000-1500; Printers — 2-HP/8150 EDITORIAL SOFTWARE: Baseview/NewsEdit IQUE 3.2.3. PRODUCTION EQUIPMENT: Cameras — COM/680C, AG/Repromaster 2200; Scanners — AG/Focus Colorscanner, Nikon/3500 Slide Scanner, 3-Nikon/Coolscan, Nikon/Scantouch 1200 PRODUCTION SOFTWARE: QPS/QuarkXPre

SAINT GEORGE

THE SPECTRUM
275 E Saint George Blvd, Saint George, Utah, 84770-2954, Washington; gen tel (435) 674-6200; adv tel (435) 674-6261; ed tel (435) 674-6286; gen fax (435) 674-6265; adv fax (435) 674-6264; ed fax (435) 674-6265; gen/nat adv e-mail advertising@thespectrum.com; disp adv e-mail advertising@thespectrum.com; class adv e-mailclassifieds@thespectrum.com; ed e-mail skiggins@thespectrum.com; web site www.thespectrum.com
Group: Gannett
Published: Mon, Tues, Wed, Thur, Fri, Sat, Sun
Weekday Frequency: m
Saturday Frequency: m
Circulation: 11,494; 12,678(sat); 14,840(sun)
Last Audit: AAM December 31, 2015
Advertising Rate (weekday/saturday): Open inch rate $21.96
Advertising Rate (sunday): Open inch rate $24.65
News services: AP, GNS, LAT-WP. **Established:** 1963
Special Editions: Spring Home & Garden (Apr); Iron County Parade of Homes (Aug); Last Minute Gifts (Dec); St. George Parade of Homes (Feb); Bridal Fair (Jan); Washington County Fair (Jul); Tuacahn Tabloid (Jun); Getting in the Spirit (Nov); Complete Health (Oct); Kids Toda
Special Weekly Sections: Career Builder (Mon); Southwest Living, Technology, Food, Home (Tue/Wed); Auto (Thur); Outdoors, Entertainment (Fri); Real Estate (Sat); Business, Finance, Religion, Living, TV (Sun); Dear Abby , Community, Weather, Stocks, Entertainment, Public Forum (Daily)
Syndicated Publications: Where It's @ (Fri); USA WEEKEND Magazine (S).
Online Ed. .... Todd Seifert
Online Mgr. .... Jackie Hermans
Nat'l/Major Acct. Exec. .... Brent Bowden
Pres./Pub. .... Rhett Long
Reg. Fin. Dir. .... Conrad Velin
Adv. Mgr. .... Jeremy Browning
Market Information: ADS; Split run; TMC; Zoned editions.
Mechanical Available: Offset; Black and 3 ROP colors; insert accepted - print, insert, deliver; page cutoffs - 22 3/4.
Mechanical Specifications: Type page 12 x 21 1/2; E - 6 cols, 1 1/9, 1/8 between; A - 6 cols, 1 1/9, 1/8 between; C - 6 cols, 1 1/9, 1/8 between.Equipment & Software: PRESSROOM EQUIPMENT: Lines — 9-G/Community; Folders — 1-G/2:1.; MAILROOM EQUIPMENT: Counter Stackers - QWI/301W, BG/Count-O-Veyor; Inserters & Stuffers — 5-MM/227; Tying Machines — 1-OVL/415; Address Machine — Cheshire/534.; BUSINESS SOFTWARE: Newzware CLASSIFIED EQUIPMENT: Hardware — APP/Mac; Kk/Digital Imaging; Printers — HP/4MV, Pre Press/Panther Pro 46; CLASSIFIED SOFTWARE: Baseview. DISPLAY EQUIPMENT: Hardware — APP/Mac, PC; Printers — HP/4MV, Pre Press/Panther Pro; Other Hardware — 3-Umax/680 Scanner, ECR/Autokon Large Forma DISPLAY SOFTWAREAd Make-up Applications — Multi-Ad, QPS/QuarkXPress, Adobe/Photoshop, Adobe/Acrobat, Adobe/PageMaker, Archetype/Corel Draw, Adobe/Illustrator; EDITORIAL EQUIPMENT: Hardware — Microsoft/NT, APP/Mac, Mac/Nikon/Super Coolscan, Canon/Digital; Printers — Canon/LBP860, Pre Press/Panther, Pre Press/Pro 46, HP/5000 GN EDITORIAL SOFTWARE: QPS/QuarkXPress 4.1, Baseview/NewsEdit Pro 3.4. PRODUCTION EQUIPMENT:

Hardware — Caere/OmniPage, Pre Press/Panther Plus, Adobe/Photoshop, Caere/OmniPage; Scanners — Umax/680 Color Flatbed, Lf/Leafscan 35, ECR/Autokon 3850, AG/SnapScan PRODUCTION SOFTWARE: QPS/QuarkXPress 3.3, QPS/QuarkXPress 4.1.

SALT LAKE CITY

DESERET NEWS
55 N 300 W, Salt Lake City, Utah, 84101-3502, Salt Lake; gen tel (801) 236-6000; adv tel (801) 204-6300; ed tel (801) 237-2100; gen fax (801) 237-2121; adv fax (801)204-6395; gen/nat adv e-mail service@mediaoneutah.com; disp adv e-mail advertising@mediaoneutah.com; class adv e-mailservice@mediaoneutah.com; ed e-mail dwilks@deseretnews.com; web site www.deseretnews.com
- 33,183,470(views) 5,449,751(visitors)
Group: Newspaper Agency Corporation
Published: Mon, Tues, Wed, Thur, Fri, Sat, Sun
Weekday Frequency: m
Saturday Frequency: m
Circulation: 36,485; 43,852(sat); 113,840(sun)
Last Audit: Sworn/Estimate/Non-Audited September 30, 2017
Branch Offices: Advertising Office: 4770 S 5600 W. West Valley City UT 84118-7400
Advertising Rate (weekday/saturday): Open inch rate $202.77
Advertising Rate (sunday): Open inch rate $239.12
News services: AP, CSM, CT, LAT-WP, NNS, NYT. **Established:** 1850
Own Printing Facility?: Yes
Commercial Printers?: Yes
Special Editions: Education Week, LDS General Conference, Mormons in America, Olympics, Outdoor Retailer, Rugby, Sports Picks, Sundance Film Festival, Utah Blaze, Utah Grizzlies
Special Weekly Sections: Family (Mon); Sports (Mon-Sun); Health, Science, Education (Tue); Religion, Real Estate (Sat); Lifestyles, Society, Arts, Travel, TV Comics, Employment (Sun); Business (Tue-Sun); Food (Wed); Recreation (Thur); Auto, Entertainment (Fri)
Syndicated Publications: Parade (S).
Digital Platform - Mobile: Apple, Android
Digital Platform - Tablet: Apple iOS
CFO .... Michael Todd
Features Editor .... Christine Rappleye
Photo Ed. .... Chuck Wing
Sports Ed. .... Kent Condon
Church News Ed. .... Sarah Weaver
News Director .... Brian West
Market Information: ADS; Split run; TMC; Zoned editions.
Delivery Method: Mail, Newsstand, Carrier, RacksEquipment & Software: EDITORIAL SOFTWARE: DTI.
Note: For advertising, circulation, production personnel and information on production and printing, see Salt Lake City Newspaper Agency Corp. The Deseret News (mS) and The Salt Lake Tribune (mS) have a combination rate of $253.50(d) and $298.90(S).

THE SALT LAKE TRIBUNE
90 S 400 W, Ste 700, Salt Lake City, Utah, 84101-1431, Salt Lake; gen tel (801) 257-8742; adv tel (801) 237-2815; ed tel (801) 257-8742; gen fax (801) 207-8800; adv fax (801) 237-2519; ed fax (801) 257-8525; gen/nat adv e-mail advertising@sltrib.com; disp adv e-mail advertising@sltrib.com; class adv e-mailclassifieds@sltrib.com; ed e-mail editor@sltrib.com; web site www.sltrib.com
- 26,092,548(views) 2,838,700(visitors)
Group: Huntsman Family Investments
Published: Mon, Tues, Wed, Thur, Fri, Sun
Weekday Frequency: m
Saturday Frequency: m
Circulation: 78,417; 91,879(sun)
Last Audit: AAM September 30, 2016
Advertising Rate (weekday/saturday): Open inch rate $239.12
News services: AP, GNS, MCT, LAT-WP, CQ, Scripps McClatchy, West Wire, Religious News Service. **Established:** 1871
Own Printing Facility?: No

Special Editions: Yard & Home (Apr); Football (Aug); Christmas Gift (Dec); Wedding (Feb); Health & Fitness (Jan); Franklin Quest Golf (Jul); Father's Day (Jun); Progress (Mar); Seniors I (May); Early Bird Gift (Nov); Home & Garden (Oct); Focus on Business (Sept).
Special Weekly Sections: Business Pages (Fri); TV Book (S); Business Pages (Sat); Business Pages (Thur); Recreation Pages (Tues); Business Pages (Wed).
Syndicated Publications: Parade (S).
Pub. .... Dean Singleton
Ed. .... Nancy Conway
Administration - Deputy Editor, Editorial Page Editor .... Tim Fitzpatrick
Administration - Editor and Publisher . Terry Orme
Online - Art Editor .... Todd Adams
Editorial - Political Cartoonist .... Pat Bagley
Arts, entertainment and culture - Reporter ... Kathy Stephenson
Government - Courts reporter .... Tom Harvey
Government - Computer Assisted Reporting ... Tony Semerad
Market Information: ADS; Split run; TMC; Zoned editions.
Mechanical Available: Offset; Black and 3 ROP colors; insert accepted - various, call for information; page cutoffs - 22 3/4.
Mechanical Specifications: Type page 13 3/4 x 21 1/2; E - 6 cols, 2 1/4, 1/6 between; A - 6 cols, 2 1/4, 1/6 between; C - 10 cols, 1 1/4, 1/6 between.
Delivery Method: Mail, Newsstand, Carrier, RacksEquipment & Software: PRESSROOM EQUIPMENT: Lines — 10-G/Metro double width (5 color decks) 1978; 10-G/HO double width (5 color decks) 1989; 10-G/HO double width (W/5 color decks); 20-G/Urbanite single width 1987; Folders — 3-Imperial/Folder 3.2, 1.; MAILROOM EQUIPMENT: Counter Stackers — 8/QWL, 2-/HL, 2-Id; Inserters & Stuffers — S/1372, HI/1372, AM Graphics/2299; Tying Machines — 2-/Dynaric, 2-/Power Strap, 8-/Power Strap; Wrapping Singles — 2-/Power Strap; Control System — ARS/1372, Icom/2299; BUSINESS EQUIPMENT: CJ CLASSIFIED EQUIPMENT: Hardware — PC.; DISPLAY EQUIPMENT: Hardware — APP/Mac; DISPLAY SOFTWAREAd Make-up Applications — AT, QPS/QuarkXPress, All; Layout Software — MEI/ALS 8000, All. EDITORIAL EQUIPMENT: Hardware — APP/mac EDITORIAL SOFTWARE: XYQUEST/XyWrite, DTI. PRODUCTION EQUIPMENT: Hardware — WL, Nu/Flip Tops; Cameras — DSA; Scanners — Scitex/340 EZ Scanner PRODUCTION SOFTWARE: DT4.
Note: For advertising, circulation, production personnel and information on production and printing, see Salt Lake City Newspaper Agency Corp. The Salt Lake Tribune (mS) and The Deseret News (mS) have a combination rate of $253.50(d) and $298.90(S).

VERMONT

BARRE

THE TIMES ARGUS
47 N Main St, Ste 200, Barre, Vt., 05641-4168, Washington; gen tel (802) 479-0191; adv tel (802) 479-0191; ed tel (802) 479-0191; gen fax (802) 479-4032; adv fax (802) 479-4097; ed fax (802) 479-4096; gen/nat adv e-mail colleen.flanagan@timesargus.com; disp adv e-mail colleen.flanagan@timesargus.com; ed e-mail steven.pappas@timesargus.com; web site www.timesargus.com
- 948,899(views) 5,592(visitors); web site 2 www.vermonttoday.com - 443,194(views) 94,609(visitors)
Group: Vermont Community Media LLC
Published: Thur, Fri, Sat, Sun
Weekday Frequency: m
Saturday Frequency: m
Circulation: 5,796; 5,796(sat); 6,276(sun)
Last Audit: AAM September 30, 2013

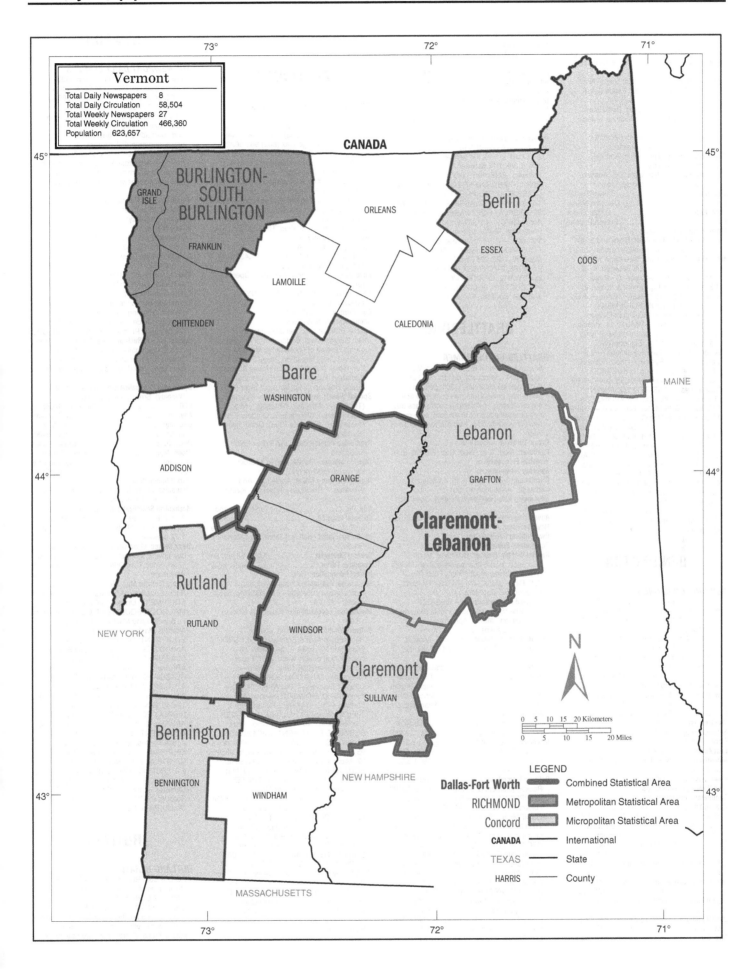

Vermont

Total Daily Newspapers	8
Total Daily Circulation	58,504
Total Weekly Newspapers	27
Total Weekly Circulation	466,360
Population	623,657

CANADA

GRAND ISLE

BURLINGTON-SOUTH BURLINGTON

FRANKLIN

ORLEANS

Berlin

ESSEX

COOS

LAMOILLE

CHITTENDEN

CALEDONIA

MAINE

Barre

WASHINGTON

Lebanon

GRAFTON

ADDISON

ORANGE

Claremont-Lebanon

Rutland

RUTLAND

WINDSOR

NEW YORK

Claremont

SULLIVAN

Bennington

BENNINGTON

WINDHAM

NEW HAMPSHIRE

MASSACHUSETTS

N

0   5   10   15   20 Kilometers
0   5   10   15   20 Miles

LEGEND

Dallas-Fort Worth	Combined Statistical Area
RICHMOND	Metropolitan Statistical Area
Concord	Micropolitan Statistical Area
CANADA	International
TEXAS	State
HARRIS	County

Advertising Rate (weekday/saturday): Open inch rate $14.25

Advertising Rate (sunday): Open inch rate $15.50

News services: AP, NYT, McLatchy. **Established:** 1806

Special Editions: Christmas Gift Guide (Nov).

Special Weekly Sections: Real Estate (Wed); Real Estate, Business (Thur); Art, Entertainment (Fri); Church, Real Estate (Sat); Auto, Business, Agriculture, Living, Health (Sun)

Syndicated Publications: Relish (Monthly); Vermont Sunday Magazine (S).

Digital Platform - Mobile: Apple, Android, Windows, Blackberry

Digital Platform - Tablet: Apple iOS, Android, Blackberry Tablet OS, Kindle Fire

Circ. Dir. ....Shawn Stabell
Pub. ....Deborah Morse
Exec. Asst. ....Mac Slivka
Ed. ....Steven Pappas

Market Information: TMC.

Mechanical Available: Offset; Black and 3 ROP colors; insert accepted; page cutoffs - 22 3/4.

Mechanical Specifications: Type page 11 5/8 x 21 1/4; E - 6 cols, 2, 3/8 between; A - 6 cols, 1 13/16, 3/16 between; C - 9 cols, 1 1/8, 1/8 between.Equipment & Software: PRESSROOM EQUIPMENT: Lines — 4-G/Urbanite; MAILROOM EQUIPMENT: Counter Stackers — BG/Count-O-Veyor 108, 1-S/Olympian, 1-MM/310-14; Inserters & Stuffers — 1-S/1472, Heidleberg; Tying Machines — MLN/2A, Signode/Tyer, Alaebond Tyer; Wrapping Singles — 2-S/Eclipse; Control System — Icon; Address Machine — Addressing m; BUSINESS EQUIPMENT: Sun BUSINESS SOFTWARE: Vision Data CLASSIFIED EQUIPMENT: Hardware — Vision Data; 5-APP/Mac G3.; DISPLAY EQUIPMENT: Hardware — 1-APP/Mac SE, 8-APP/Mac G3, 4-CD-Rom; Printers — HP/8500; DISPLAY SOFTWAREAd Make-up Applications — Multi-Ad/Creator, QPS/QuarkXPress 4.0, Adobe/Photoshop 5.0; Layout Software — MEI/ALS. EDITORIAL EQUIPMENT: Hardware — ACI; Printers — HP, Xante EDITORIAL SOFTWARE: Open Pages. PRODUCTION EQUIPMENT: Hardware — 2-Nu/Flip Top FT40UPNS; Cameras — 1-C/Spartan III; Scanners — Nikon/Coolscan, 2-Umax PRODUCTION SOFTWARE: American Computer Innovators, QPS/QuarkXPress.

BENNINGTON

BENNINGTON BANNER

425 Main St, Bennington, Vt., 05201-2141, Bennington; gen tel (802) 442-7567; adv tel (800) 245-0254; ed tel (802)447-7567 ext. 115; gen fax (802) 442-3413; adv fax (413)499-3419; ed fax (802)442-3413; gen/nat adv e-mail rmorin@benningtonbanner.com; disp adv e-mail rmorin@benningtonbanner.com; class adv e-mailsinopoli@benningtonbanner.com; ed e-mail kwhitcomb@benningtonbanner.com; web site www.benningtonbanner.com

Group: Birdland Acquisition LLC.

Published: Mon, Tues, Wed, Thur, Fri, Sat

Weekday Frequency: m

Saturday Frequency: m

Circulation: 3,423; 3,920(sat)

Last Audit: AAM June 30, 2017

Advertising Rate (weekday/saturday): Open inch rate $22.90

News services: AP. **Established:** 1905

Own Printing Facility?: Yes

Commercial Printers?: Yes

Special Editions: Spring Home & Garden (Apr); Business & Industry (Feb); Christmas Gift Guide (Nov); Fall Home Improvement (Oct); Bennington Antique Car Show (Sept).

Special Weekly Sections: Best Food Day (Mon/Thur); Business, Sports, Pet (Mon); Education (Tue); Health, Fitness (Wed); Entertainment (Thur)

Syndicated Publications: USA WEEKEND Magazine (Sat); American Profile (Weekly).

Digital Platform - Mobile: Apple, Android, Blackberry

Digital Platform - Tablet: Apple iOS, Android, Windows 7, Blackberry Tablet OS, Kindle

Circ. Dir. ....Christopher Oldham

Managing Ed. ....Adam Samrov
Local News Ed. ....Mark Rondeau
Interactive Media Dir. ....Bernard Re
Adv. Mgr. ....Bob Morin
Adv. Sales Coord. ....Missy Place
Adv. Sales Mgr. ....Susan Plaisance
Pub. ....Alan English

Market Information: ADS; TMC.

Mechanical Available: Offset; Black and 3 ROP colors; insert accepted - any; page cutoffs - 22 3/4.

Mechanical Specifications: Type page 13 x 21 1/4; E - 6 cols, 2 1/16, 1/8 between; A - 6 cols, 2 1/16, 1/8 between; C - 9 cols, 1 3/8, 1/16 between.Equipment & Software: BUSINESS EQUIPMENT: DEC/PDP 11-73 BUSINESS SOFTWARE: GEAR CLASSIFIED EQUIPMENT: Printers — 1-TI/810 Printer; CLASSIFIED SOFTWARE: PPI. DISPLAY SOFTWAREAd Make-up Applications — QPS/QuarkXPress, Adobe/Photoshop, Multi-Ad/Creator; Layout Software — APP/Power Mac. EDITORIAL EQUIPMENT: Hardware — APP/Power Mac/2-AST/PC 286 Premium, 1-Leading Edge/286, 2-PC 386SX EDITORIAL SOFTWARE: QPS/QuarkXPress. PRODUCTION EQUIPMENT: Hardware — 2-APP/Power Mac, Konica/Imagesetter.

BRATTLEBORO

BRATTLEBORO REFORMER

62 Black Mountain Rd, Brattleboro, Vt., 05301-9241, Windham; gen tel (802) 254-2311; gen fax (802) 257-1305; gen/nat adv e-mail news@reformer.com; disp adv e-mail advertising@reformer.com; class adv e-mailclassifieds@reformer.com; ed e-mail news@reformer.com; web site www.reformer.com

Group: Birdland Acquisition LLC.

Published: Mon, Tues, Wed, Thur, Fri, Sat, Sun

Weekday Frequency: m

Saturday Frequency: m

Circulation: 3,827; 3,827(sat); 4,656(sun)

Last Audit: AAM June 30, 2017

Advertising Rate (weekday/saturday): Open inch rate $25.30

Advertising Rate (sunday): Open inch rate $26.20

News services: AP. **Established:** 1913

Own Printing Facility?: Yes

Commercial Printers?: Yes

Special Weekly Sections: Business (Mon); Education, Home Improvement (Tue); Health (Wed); Entertainment (Thur); Food (Thur/Sat); Real Estate, Auto (Fri/Sat); TV (Sat); Employment (Sat/Mon)

Syndicated Publications: USA WEEKEND Magazine (Sat); American Profile (Weekly).

Digital Platform - Mobile: Apple, Android, Windows, Blackberry

Digital Platform - Tablet: Apple iOS, Android, Windows 7, Blackberry Tablet OS, Kindle, Nook, Kindle Fire

VP Adv. ....Jordan Brechenser
Day Mng. Ed. ....Bob Audette
Pub. ....Alan English
Pres. ....Fredric Rutberg
Night Mng. Ed. ....Melani Winters

Market Information: TMC.

Mechanical Available: Offset; Black and 3 ROP colors; insert accepted; page cutoffs - 22 3/4.

Mechanical Specifications: Type page 13 x 21 1/4; E - 6 cols, 2 1/16, 1/8 between; A - 6 cols, 2 1/16, 1/8 between; C - 9 cols, 1 3/8, 1/16 between.

Delivery Method: Mail, Newsstand, Carrier, RacksEquipment & Software: PRESSROOM EQUIPMENT: Lines — 8-G/Community; Folders — 2-G/SSC.; MAILROOM EQUIPMENT: Counter Stackers — 1/Fg; Tying Machines — 1-/MLN, 1-/OVL; Address Machine — Wm.; BUSINESS EQUIPMENT: DEC/PDP 11-73 BUSINESS SOFTWARE: Vision Data CLASSIFIED EQUIPMENT: Hardware — 2-Dewar/Sys II; CLASSIFIED SOFTWARE: Dewar. DISPLAY EQUIPMENT: Hardware — 3-Dewar/Discovery, PC 386; DISPLAY SOFTWAREAd Make-up Applications — Dewar, Aldus/PageMaker, Archetype/Corel Draw; Layout Software — Dewar/Discovery. EDITORIAL EQUIPMENT: Hardware — 2-Dewar/Sys II EDITORIAL SOFTWARE: Dewar. PRODUCTION

EQUIPMENT: Hardware — C; Cameras — C/Marathon; Scanners — Panasonic/505.

BURLINGTON

THE BURLINGTON FREE PRESS

100 Bank St Ste 700, Suite 700, Burlington, Vt., 05401-4946, Chittenden; gen tel (802) 863-3441; adv tel (802) 660-1819; ed tel (802) 865-0940; gen fax (802) 862-5622; adv fax (802) 863-4702; ed fax (802) 660-1802; gen/nat adv e-mail tamjohnson@burlingtonfreepress.com; disp adv e-mail tamjohnson@burlingtonfreepress.com; class adv e-mailBFPclass@gannett.com; ed e-mail estigliani@.burlingtonfreepress.com; web site www.burlingtonfreepress.com

Group: Gannett.

Published: Mon, Tues, Wed, Thur, Fri, Sat, Sun

Weekday Frequency: m

Saturday Frequency: m

Circulation: 16,869; 16,869(sat); 21,436(sun)

Last Audit: AAM March 31, 2017

Advertising Rate (weekday/saturday): Open inch rate $81.10

News services: AP, GNS, LAT-WP, NYT. **Established:** 1827

Own Printing Facility?: Yes

Commercial Printers?: Yes

Special Editions: Discover Jazz Festival (April); Gift Guides (Dec); Bridal (Jan); Food Festival (Jun); Festival of Fools (July); Maritime Festival (July) Marathon (May); Summer Fun Guide (May); Vermont House & Home (Monthly); Fall Fun Guide (September); Giving Season (Nov); Vermont Skier (Oct).

Special Weekly Sections: Innovate- Business (Thursday); Weekend (Thursday); Food & Wine (Friday); Wheels (Fri); Outdoor (Sat); Home (Sat); BTV Arts (Sun); Green Life (Sunday)

Syndicated Publications: USA WEEKEND Magazine (S).

Digital Platform - Mobile: Apple, Android, Windows, Blackberry

Digital Platform - Tablet: Apple iOS, Android, Windows 7, Blackberry Tablet OS, Kindle, Nook, Kindle Fire

Adv. Dir. ....Tammy Shannon
Editorial Page Ed. ....Aki Soga
Dir., IT ....Trevor Chase
Media Specialist - National Sales ....Marianne Green
Content Strategist ....Adam Silverman
Executive Editor ....Denis Finley

Market Information: TMC.

Mechanical Available: Offset; Black and 3 ROP colors; insert accepted - free standing; page cutoffs - 22 3/4.

Mechanical Specifications: Type page 6 col x 13.58"

Delivery Method: Newsstand, Carrier, RacksEquipment & Software: PRESSROOM EQUIPMENT: Lines — 5-G/Metro (2 color decks) double width 1967; Press Drive — 6-Fin/3260 1989; Pasters —G/Automatic. MAILROOM EQUIPMENT: Counter Stackers — 2-QWI/SJ20X, 1-HI/Rima RS-30, 2-QW/501; Inserters & Stuffers — 1-HI/1472A, 2-Dynaric/NP-3; Tying Machines — 1-MLN/2A, 1-MLN/2EE, 2/Power Strap; Address Machine — KR; BUSINESS EQUIPMENT: 1-IBM/AS-400 BUSINESS SOFTWARE: Microsoft/Windows 95, Microsoft/Windows NT, Microsoft/Office 97, Microsoft/Windows 2000 CLASSIFIED EQUIPMENT: Hardware — 17-PC P111; Printers — HP/LaserJet; CLASSIFIED SOFTWARE: HI/Ad Power. DISPLAY EQUIPMENT: Printers — 1-HP/800, 1-QMS/Magicolor 330; Other Hardware — 2-Umax 16/DL DISPLAY SOFTWAREAd Make-up Applications — QPS/QuarkXPress 4.11; Layout Software — 3-APP/G3, 20-APP/Mac G4, 15-APP/G4. EDITORIAL EQUIPMENT: Hardware — 13-PC P300, 37-PC P100 EDITORIAL SOFTWARE: HI/NMP Newsmaker HI/NME Newsmaker Edit. PRODUCTION EQUIPMENT: Hardware — 2-MON/Express Master 6000, 1-OCE/Thermal Proofer 9000G, 1-Alfa Quest/Proof Xpress II PRODUCTION SOFTWARE: HI/NMP Newsmaker, HI/CPAG Classified Pagination.

NEWPORT

THE NEWPORT DAILY EXPRESS

178 Hill St, Newport, Vt., 05855-9430, Orleans; gen tel (802) 334-6568; adv tel (802)334-6568; ed tel (802)334-6568; gen fax (802) 334-6891; adv fax (802)334-6891; ed fax (802)334-6891; gen/nat adv e-mail advertising@newportvermontdailyexpress.com; disp adv e-mail advertising@newportvermontdailyexpress.com; class adv e-mailclassified@newportvermontdailyexpress.com; ed e-mail editor@newportvermontdailyexpress.com; web site www.newportvermontdailyexpress.com

Group: Horizon Publications Inc.

Published: Mon, Tues, Wed, Thur, Fri

Weekday Frequency: m

Circulation: 5,000

Last Audit: Sworn/Estimate/Non-Audited September 30, 2017

Advertising Rate (weekday/saturday): Open inch rate $10.95

News services: AP. **Established:** 1936

Own Printing Facility?: Yes

Commercial Printers?: Yes

Special Editions: Spring Home Improvement (Apr); Gardening (May); June Dearie and Vacation Guide (June); Bridal (Feb); Menu Guide (July); Progress (Sept); Car Care(Oct).

Special Weekly Sections: Best Food Days (Mon); Arts, Entertainment, Travel (Wed); Auto, Travel (Thur); Health, Real Estate, Religion, Best Food Day (Fri); Home, Living, Women (Daily)

Syndicated Publications: American Profile (Weekly). SmartSource (Friday)

CFO ....Roland L. McBride
Adv. Dir. ....Marilyn Gardyne
Circ. Mgr. ....Sadie Watters
Mng. Ed. ....Steve Blake
Pres., Opns. ....David Radler
Prodn. Mgr. ....Karen Bartleson
Circ. Mgr. ....Carol Temple
Pub. ....Patricia Sears

Market Information: TMC.

Mechanical Available: Offset; Black and 3 ROP colors; insert accepted; page cutoffs - 22 3/4.

Mechanical Specifications: Type page 13 1/8 x 21 1/2; E - 6 cols, 2 1/5, 1/12 between; A - 6 cols, 2 1/8, 1/12 between; C - 6 cols, 2 1/8, 1/12 between.

Areas Served: Greensboro, Holland, Irasburg, Jay, Lowell, Morgan, Newport City, Newport Town, North Troy, Orleans, Troy, Westfield, Westmare

Delivery Method: Mail, Newsstand, Carrier, RacksEquipment & Software: PRESSROOM EQUIPMENT: Lines — 4-G/Community; MAILROOM EQUIPMENT: Counter Stackers — Bundle Tying Machines 1/Saxmyer; Address Machine — Wm.; BUSINESS EQUIPMENT: Synaptic/Micro Solutions, Acct/100, Okidata/393 Plus, Sun/Suntype CLASSIFIED EQUIPMENT: Hardware — APP/Mac; Printers — Okidata/320 Turbo; CLASSIFIED SOFTWARE: QPS/Class Flo 4.0. DISPLAY EQUIPMENT: Hardware — 2-ScrippSat/PC; Printers — APP/Mac Laser 12-640; Other Hardware — 2-Scanners/E6 DISPLAY SOFTWARELayout Software — APP/Mac G3, Multi-Ad/Creator. EDITORIAL EQUIPMENT: Hardware — APP/Mac/Adobe/Photoshop, Sprint/ScanMaker E6; Printers — APP/Mac Laser 8500 EDITORIAL SOFTWARE: QPS/QuarkXPress 4.0. PRODUCTION EQUIPMENT: Hardware — Paper Port/Strobe Scanner; Cameras — 1-K/241; Scanners — HP/ScanJet PRODUCTION SOFTWARE: QPS/QuarkXPress 4.0.

RUTLAND

RUTLAND HERALD

PO Box 668, Rutland, Vt., 05702-0668, Rutland; gen tel (800) 498-4296; adv tel (802) 747-6126; ed tel (802) 747-6133; gen fax (802) 775-2423; adv fax (802) 775-2423; ed fax (802) 773-0311; disp adv e-mail ads@rutlandherald.com; ed e-mail letters@rutlandherald.com; web site www.

rutlandherald.com
- 1,437,912(views) 172,888(visitors); web site 2 www.vermonttoday.com - 443,194(views) 5,248(visitors)
Group: Maine Today Media Inc.
Published: Thur, Fri, Sat, Sun
Weekday Frequency: m
Saturday Frequency: m
Circulation: 11,200; 11,200(sat); 12,609(sun)
Last Audit: AAM September 30, 2013
Advertising Rate (weekday/saturday): Open inch rate $24.90
Advertising Rate (sunday): Open inch rate $26.50
News services: AP, NYT, MCT. **Established:** 1794
Own Printing Facility?: Yes
Special Editions: Spring Car Care (Apr);Summer Camp Guide, Sping Sports, Vermont State Fair (Aug); Best fthe Best Readers Choice, Graduation (Jun); Business Outlook (Mar); VT Home and Properties (Monthly); Gift Guide (Nov); Fall Vermont
Special Weekly Sections: TV (Daily); Best Food, Business (Mon); Weekend (Fri); Weekly TV (Sat); Vermont, Comics (Sun)
Syndicated Publications: Relish (Monthly); Parade Magazine (S).
Digital Platform - Mobile: Apple, Android, Windows, Blackberry
Digital Platform - Tablet: Apple iOS, Android, Windows 7, Blackberry Tablet OS, Kindle Fire
Bus. Office Mgr. .... Deborah Morse
Circ. Dir. .... Shawn Stabell
Adv. Sales Mgr. .... Duguay Tim
Content Ed. .... Rich Alcott
Market Information: Split run; TMC; Zoned editions.
Mechanical Available: Offset; Black and 3 ROP colors; insert accepted; page cutoffs - 22 3/4.
Mechanical Specifications: Image 10 x 21 1/4; SAU for 22" Web
Areas Served: Rutland County and Southern Vermont
Delivery Method: Mail, Newsstand, Carrier, RacksEquipment & Software: BUSINESS EQUIPMENT: Vision Data, SUN. HP PC Workstations BUSINESS SOFTWARE: Vision Data CLASSIFIED EQUIPMENT: Hardware — Vision Data SUN, HP PC Workstations; Vision Data; Printers — HP; CLASSIFIED SOFTWARE: Vision Data. DISPLAY EQUIPMENT: Hardware — HP PC; Printers — HP; DISPLAY SOFTWAREAd Make-up Applications — Adobe Creative Suite; Layout Software — ALS-Managing Editor. EDITORIAL EQUIPMENT: Hardware — HP PC; Printers — HP EDITORIAL SOFTWARE: Saxotech Media ware Center PRODUCTION EQUIPMENT: Cameras — Nikon Digital; Scanners — Nikon PRODUCTION SOFTWARE: Adobe Indesign Saxotech

SAINT ALBANS

ST. ALBANS MESSENGER

281 N Main St, Saint Albans, Vt., 05478-2503, Franklin; gen tel (802) 524-9771; adv tel (802)524-9771 ext. 104; ed tel (802)524-9771 ext. 108; gen fax (802) 527-1948; adv fax (802)527-1947; ed fax (802)527-1948; gen/nat adv e-mail ads@samessenger.com; disp adv e-mail ads@samessenger.com; class adv e-mailclassifieds@samessenger.com; ed e-mail news@samessenger.com; web site www.samessenger.com
- 52,000(views)
Group: Vermont Publishing Corp.
Published: Mon, Tues, Wed, Thur, Fri, Sat
Weekday Frequency: e
Saturday Frequency: m
Circulation: 5,695; 5,930(sat)
Last Audit: Sworn/Estimate/Non-Audited September 30, 2017
Advertising Rate (weekday/saturday): Open inch rate $20.00
News services: AP. **Established:** 1861
Special Editions: Energy (Fall); Dairy (Jun); Meet Your Business and Professional Communities (May); Christmas (Nov); Home Improvements (Spring); Sports (Winter).
Special Weekly Sections: Best Business (Mon): Health (Tue); Travel, Entertainment (Thur); Auto (Fri); Food, TV (Sat)
Gen. Mgr. .... Suzanne Lynn
Adv. Dir. .... Jeremy Read
Ed. .... Gary Rutkowski
Pub. .... Emerson Lynn
Sports Ed. .... Josh Kaufmann
Prodn. Mgr. .... Lynne Fletcher
Press Mgr. .... Alex Domina
Market Information: TMC; Zoned editions.
Mechanical Available: Offset; Black and 3 ROP colors; insert accepted - any; page cutoffs - 22 3/4.
Mechanical Specifications: Type page 13 1/2 x 21; E - 6 cols, 2 1/16, 1/8 between; A - 6 cols, 2 1/16, 1/8 between; C - 6 cols, 2 1/16, 1/8 between.
Areas Served: St. Albans, Franklin County
Equipment & Software: PRESSROOM EQUIPMENT: Lines — 6-Wd/240; Folders — 1-Wd/2:1.; MAILROOM EQUIPMENT: Counter Stackers — 1/BG; Wrapping Singles — 2-/Us; Address Machine — 1-/Am.; BUSINESS EQUIPMENT: RSK/TRS 80 CLASSIFIED EQUIPMENT: Hardware — APP/Mac Plus.; EDITORIAL EQUIPMENT: Hardware — 17-APP/Mac Plus; Printers — 4-APP/Mac LaserWriter Plus. PRODUCTION EQUIPMENT: Hardware — 1-B/3200, 1-Nat/250; Cameras — 1-Nu/20-24, 1-K/18-20 V241; Scanners — AG/FJF74/2200, Densitometer, Entre/Scanner.

SAINT JOHNSBURY

THE CALEDONIAN-RECORD

190 Federal St, PO Box 8, Saint Johnsbury, Vt., 05819-5616, Caledonia; gen tel (802) 748-8121; adv tel (802) 748-8121; ed tel (802) 748-8121; gen fax (802) 748-1613; adv fax (802) 748-1613; ed fax (802) 748-1613; gen/nat adv e-mail news@caledonian-record.com; disp adv e-mail adv@caledonian-record.com; class adv e-mailadv@caledonian-record.com; ed e-mail news@caledonian-record.com; web site www.caledonianrecord.com
- 650,000(views) 150,000(visitors)
Published: Mon, Tues, Wed, Thur, Fri, Sat
Weekday Frequency: m
Saturday Frequency: m
Circulation: 6,694; 6,694(sat)
Last Audit: Sworn/Estimate/Non-Audited December 18, 2017
Branch Offices: St. Johnsbury, Littleton
Advertising Rate (weekday/saturday): Open inch rate $9.00
Advertising Rate (sunday): NA - No Sunday publication
Online Advertising Rate: Home page: Home page lrg tile (2) $249; Home-News ROS Tiles (15) $225; Inside pages: ROS 300x90 tiles (5) $149; All inside pages: inside banner 600x90 (3) $149; in-story 300x250 (2) $199; Bottom Banner 600x90 (ROS) $149;
News services: AP. **Established:** 1837
Own Printing Facility?: No
Commercial Printers?: Yes
Special Editions: Business Recognition (Jan); Bridal (Jan); Presidents' Day Auto (Feb); Real Estate/Home Improvement (Apr); Summer Guide (Jun); Sports Year in Review (Jun); Car Care (Sept); Winter Guide (Oct); Christmas Gift Guide (Nov);
Special Weekly Sections: School (Mon); Business (Sat); Health Beat (Thur); Family Page (Wed)., Entertainment (Fri), Youth Sports (Tue)
Digital Platform - Mobile: Apple, Android, Windows
Digital Platform - Tablet: Apple iOS, Android, Windows 7, Kindle Fire, Other
Pres. .... Mark M. Smith
Pub./VP .... Todd Smith
Bookkeeper .... Judy Burke
Exec. Ed. .... Dana Gray
City/Metro Ed. .... Andrew McGregor
Pub. .... Todd M. Smith
Educ. Services Dir. .... Rosie Smith
Picture Ed. .... Peter Lynch
Sports Ed. .... Michael Beniash
Adv. Dir./Online Mgr. .... Michael Gonyaw
Dig. Services Dir. .... Glen Jardine
Market Information: Northeastern Vermont and Northern New Hamlshire Burlington/ Plattsburgh DMA
Mechanical Specifications: Type page 10 7/8 x 21; E - 6 cols per page, each col. 1.708" with 1/8" between columns
Areas Served: Vermont Counties: Caledonia, Essex, Orleans
NH Counties: Grafton, Coos
Delivery Method: Mail, Newsstand, Carrier, RacksEquipment & Software: BUSINESS EQUIPMENT: Various HP BUSINESS SOFTWARE: Quickbooks, Vision Data CLASSIFIED EQUIPMENT: Hardware — Various HP; Printers — Various HP; CLASSIFIED SOFTWARE: Vision Data DISPLAY EQUIPMENT: Hardware — Various HP, 1 Mac G3; Printers — Various HP; Other Hardware — Epson/G36 Flatbed Scanner, Nikon/CoolScan III DISPLAY SOFTWAREAd Make-up Applications — QPS/QuarkXPress 8.02, Adobe/Photoshop CS2, Adobe/Acrobat 7; Layout Software — Falcon EDITORIAL EQUIPMENT: Hardware — Various HP'S Mac G3/Nikon/CoolScan III, AG/Arcus II Scanner; Printers — Various HP EDITORIAL SOFTWARE: GPS PRODUCTION EQUIPMENT: Scanners — AG/Arcus II, Epson/636 Pro, Nikon/CoolScan III PRODUCTION SOFTWARE: FAlcon

VIRGINIA

BRISTOL

BRISTOL HERALD COURIER

320 Bob Morrison Blvd, Bristol, Va., 24201-3812, Bristol City; gen tel (276) 669-2181; adv tel (276) 645-2525; ed tel (276) 645-2534; gen fax (276) 669-3696; adv fax (276) 645-2527; ed fax (276) 669-3696; gen/nat adv e-mail mary.whelchel@roanoke.com; disp adv e-mail smaxwell@bristolnews.com; class adv e-mailclassifieds@bristolnews.com; ed e-mail letters@bristolnews.com; web site www.heraldcourier.com
- 2,100,000(views) 450,000(visitors); web site 2 SWVAToday.com - 500,000(views) 45,000(visitors)
Group: BH Media Group
Published: Mon, Tues, Wed, Thur, Fri, Sat, Sun
Weekday Frequency: m
Saturday Frequency: m
Circulation: 17,802; 17,802(sat); 21,715(sun)
Last Audit: AAM March 31, 2017
Branch Offices: Abingdon, VA, Richlands, VA, Marion, VA, Wytheville, VA, Floyd VA
Advertising Rate (weekday/saturday): Open inch rate $54.25
News services: AP, SHNS. **Established:** 1870
Own Printing Facility?: Yes
Commercial Printers?: Yes
Special Editions: NASCAR (April & August) Football (Aug)Bristol Magazine (Quarterly)
Syndicated Publications: Relish (Monthly); American Profile (M); Athlon Sports (Monthly) Spry (Monthly)
Proprietary Publications: Bristol Magazine (qtrly)
Digital Platform - Mobile: Apple, Android
Digital Platform - Tablet: Apple iOS, Android
Mng. Ed. .... Rob Walters
Market Information: TMC; Zoned editions.
Mechanical Available: Offset; Black and 3 ROP colors; insert accepted; page cutoffs - 21.
Mechanical Specifications: Type page 9 7/8 x 19 3/4; E - 6 cols, 1 9/16, 1/8 between; A - 6 cols, 1 9/16, 1/8 between; C - 10 cols, 15/16, 1/16 between.
Areas Served: Bristol, Tennessee 37620
Bristol, Virginia 24201
Delivery Method: Mail, Newsstand, Carrier, RacksEquipment & Software: PRESSROOM EQUIPMENT: KBA Comet- 5 towers, 3 wide configuration
EAE/KBA press controls
Screen CTP MAILROOM EQUIPMENT: Counter Stackers —4 Quipp 500; 3 Gammerleir. Inserters & Stuffers — 1-K&M G3, , HI/1372; Tying Machines Dynaric, Signode; Barstrom Labeling system; MM 1510 5 head stitch and trim CLASSIFIED EQUIPMENT: Hardware — SIA; Polaroid/ SprintScan 35, Kk/DC 40 Digital Camera; Printers — 2-LaserMaster/1200, 2-ECR/4550; CLASSIFIED SOFTWARE: Dewar/Disc IV. DISPLAY EQUIPMENT: Hardware — APP/ Mac, 1-APP/Mac IIci, APP/Mac Quadra 650, 4-APP/Power Mac 9500; Printers — LaserMaster/1200, LaserMaster/Unity 1800, PMR, 2-ECR/4550; Other Hardware — 4-HP/ ScanJet IIP, Polaroid/SprintScan 35 DISPLAY SOFTWAREAd Make-up Applications — QPS/QuarkXPress; Layout Software — APP/Power M EDITORIAL EQUIPMENT: Hardware — SIA/Okidata/393, HP/ScanJet IIP, APP/Mac Quadra 650, 5-IBM/Laptop, Kk/ DC 40 Digital Camera, 2-Polaroid/SprintScan 35, APP/Power Mac 9500, 2-APP/Power Mac 9500; Printers — 2-LaserMaster/1200, 2-ECR/4550 EDITORIAL SOFTWARE: Dewar/Disc IV.

CHARLOTTESVILLE

THE DAILY PROGRESS

685 Rio Rd W, Charlottesville, Va., 22901-1413, Albemarle; gen tel (434) 978-7200; adv tel (434) 978-7209; ed tel (434) 978-7240; gen fax (434) 978-7204; adv fax (434) 978-7204; ed fax (434) 978-7252; gen/ nat adv e-mail fdubec@dailyprogress.com; disp adv e-mail fdubec@dailyprogress.com; class adv e-mailclassfied@dailyprogress.com; ed e-mail rjiranek@dailyprogress.com; whester@dailyprogress.com; web site www.dailyprogress.com
- 1,432,758(views) 309,135(visitors)
Group: BH Media Group
Published: Mon, Tues, Wed, Thur, Fri, Sat, Sun
Weekday Frequency: m
Saturday Frequency: m
Circulation: 15,777; 15,777(sat); 18,314(sun)
Last Audit: AAM September 30, 2016
Advertising Rate (weekday/saturday): Open inch rate $57.88 for National
Advertising Rate (sunday): $61.36 for National
News services: AP, LAT-WP. **Established:** 1892
Own Printing Facility?: No
Commercial Printers?: No
Special Editions: Homestyle; Silver Linings (Every other month); Charlotetsville Women; Graduation (May); How To Guide (May); Reader's Choice (July); Welcome Guide (Aug); Enterprise (Quarterly); Creative Home (Oct)
Special Weekly Sections: Best Food Day (S); Best Food Day (Wed); Select TV (Sat)
Syndicated Publications: USA WEEKEND Magazine (S).
Digital Platform - Mobile: Apple, Android, Windows
Digital Platform - Tablet: Apple iOS, Kindle
Editor .... Wes Hestor
Chief Photojournalist .... Andrew Shurtleff
Regional Circulation Director .... Steve Cook
Adv. Mgr .... Teresa Lamb
Asst. City Ed. .... Elliott Robinson
Sports Ed. .... John Shifflett
Features Ed. .... Jane Dunlap Norris
Photojournalist .... Ryan Kelly
Circ. Dir. .... Charles F. Doucet
Classified Coord .... Dana Hubbard
Regional Adv. Dir. .... Lowell Miller
Ed. .... Wes Hester
Pub. .... Rob Jiranek
Market Information: TMC; Zoned editions.
Mechanical Available: Offset; Black and 3 ROP colors; insert accepted; page cutoffs - 22.
Mechanical Specifications: Type page 12 1/2 x 21; E - 6 cols, 2, 1/8 between; A - 6 cols, 2, 1/8 between; C - 9 cols, 1 1/8, 1/16 between.
Areas Served: Albemarle County
Delivery Method: Mail, Newsstand, Carrier, RacksEquipment & Software: BUSINESS EQUIPMENT: HP CLASSIFIED EQUIPMENT: Hardware — 5-Compaq; NewGen, Imager Plus/12; Printers — HP/ LaserPrinter; CLASSIFIED SOFTWARE: ACT. DISPLAY SOFTWARELayout Software — DTI/AD Makeup II, Adobe/Photoshop. EDITORIAL EQUIPMENT: Hardware — HP/2-NewGen, Lf/Leafscan for Color Seperation; Printers — 4-APP/Mac Laser II NTX EDITORIAL SOFTWARE: ACT. PRODUCTION EQUIPMENT: Hardware — WL/Plater, 1-NewGen, Image Plus 12; Cameras — 1-C/Spartan III L270, SCREEN; Scanners — RZ.

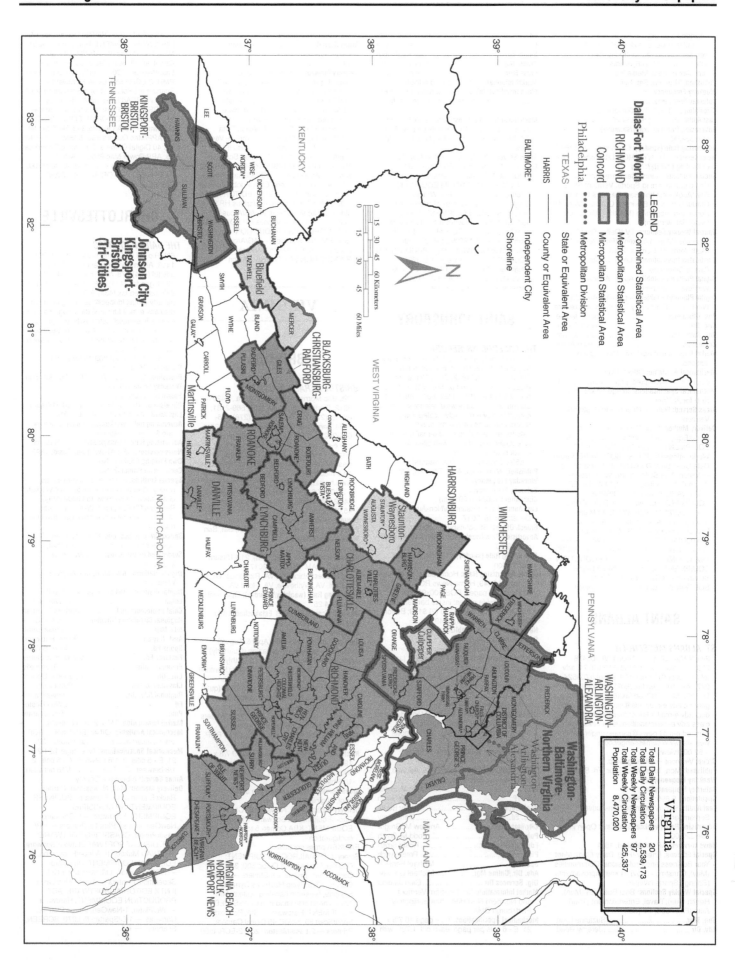

LEGEND

Dallas-Fort Worth — Combined Statistical Area
RICHMOND — Metropolitan Statistical Area
Concord — Micropolitan Statistical Area
Philadelphia — Metropolitan Division

BALTIMORE* — State or Equivalent Area
HARRIS — County or Equivalent Area
TEXAS — Independent City
Shoreline

Virginia

Total Daily Newspapers	20
Total Daily Circulation	2,539,173
Total Weekly Newspapers*	97
Total Weekly Circulation	425,337
Population	8,470,020

Johnson City-
Kingsport-
Bristol
(Tri-Cities)

KINGSPORT-
BRISTOL-
BRISTOL

Washington-
Baltimore-
Northern Virginia

WASHINGTON-
ARLINGTON-
ALEXANDRIA

Washington-
Arlington-
Alexandria

VIRGINIA BEACH-
NORFOLK-
NEWPORT NEWS

BLACKSBURG-
CHRISTIANSBURG-
RADFORD

Bluefield

ROANOKE

LYNCHBURG

DANVILLE

Staunton-
Waynesboro

HARRISONBURG

WINCHESTER

Culpeper

CHARLOTTESVILLE

RICHMOND

CULPEPER

CULPEPER STAR-EXPONENT

122 W Spencer St, Culpeper, Va., 22701-2628, Culpeper; gen tel (540) 825-0771; adv tel (540) 825-0771 ext. 4100; ed tel (540) 825-0771 ext. 4125; gen fax (540) 825-0778; adv fax (540) 825-5211; ed fax (540)825-0778; gen/nat adv e-mail lgore@dailyprogress.com; disp adv e-mail lgore@dailyprogress.com; class adv e-mailclassifieds@dailyprogress.com; ed e-mail mmckenna@starexponent.com; web site www.dailyprogress.com

Group: BH Media Group
Published: Mon, Tues, Wed, Thur, Fri, Sat, Sun
Circulation: 3,883; 3,883(sat); 4,374(sun)
Last Audit: AAM March 31, 2016
Adv. Mgr. ....Lynn Gore

DANVILLE

DANVILLE REGISTER & BEE

700 Monument St, Danville, Va., 24541-1512, Danville City; gen tel (434) 793-2311; adv tel (434)791-7926; ed tel (434)791-7990; gen fax (434) 799-0595; adv fax (434) 799-0595; ed fax (434)799-0595; gen/nat adv e-mail jrandell@registerbee.com; disp adv e-mail jrandell@registerbee.com; class adv e-mailclassifieds@newsadvance.com; ed e-mail rbenson@registerbee.com; web site www.godanriver.com

Group: BH Media Group
World Media Enterprises, Inc.
Published: Mon, Tues, Wed, Thur, Fri, Sat, Sun
Weekday Frequency: m
Saturday Frequency: m
Circulation: 9,934; 9,934(sat); 12,930(sun)
Last Audit: AAM March 31, 2017
Advertising Rate (weekday/saturday): Open inch rate $28.85
Advertising Rate (sunday): Open inch rate $32.20
News services: AP.
Special Editions: Chamber of Commerce Tab (Monthly); Postive Parenting (Quarterly).
Special Weekly Sections: Best Food Days (Wed/Sun)
Syndicated Publications: USA WEEKEND Magazine (S).
Pub.... Steve Kaylor
Promos. Mgr./NIE Dir. ....Janet Miller
Assistant Editor..........................Charles Wilborn
Editorial Page Ed. .... Robert Benson
Audiotex Mgr. ....Don Webb
Regl. Dir., Info Servs. .... Tony Canody
Prodn. Mgr....................................... Gloria Clark
Major/Nat'l Accts. Mgr. ....LaJuan Lewis
Sales Manager .... Debra Brown
Cir. Dir. ....Douglas Johnson
Market Information: ADS; TMC.
Mechanical Available: Offset; Black and 3 ROP colors; insert accepted - all; page cutoffs - 22 3/4.
Mechanical Specifications: Type page 13 x 21 1/2; E - 6 cols, 2 1/16, 1/8 between; A - 6 cols, 2 1/16, 1/8 between; C - 9 cols, 1 3/8, 1/16 between.Equipment & Software: PRESSROOM EQUIPMENT: Lines — 11-G/Urbanite 1215-1244 single width 1978, 2-G/Urbanite 1214-1244 single width 1993; Registration System — Duarte/Pin Registration. MAILROOM EQUIPMENT: Counter Stackers — 1-HL/Monitor, 1-Id/2000, 1-Id/2100; Inserters & Stuffers — HI/48P; Tying Machines — 1-MLN/ML, 1-MLN/Spirit, 1-MLN/SP330; Address Machine — 1-MM/Minuteman quarter folder.; BUSINESS EQUIPMENT: DEC/XL-590, Data Sciences CLASSIFIED EQUIPMENT: Hardware — 4-SII/Synthesis 66, Roadrunner/PC 486; Printers — 1-APP/Mac IIG; CLASSIFIED SOFTWARE: Pongrass/Page Integrator. DISPLAY EQUIPMENT: Hardware — 7-APP/Mac 7200-90, 6-Mk/Flatbed Scanner; Other Hardware — 6-APP/Mac Flatbed scanner DISPLAY SOFTWAREAd Make-up Applications — Adobe/Photoshop, Multi-Ad/Creator; Layout Software — 1-APP/Power Mac 8500-120 fileserver. EDITORIAL EQUIPMENT: Hardware — 1-SII/Synthesis 66XR, 20-Roadrunner/PC 486, 4-APP/Mac, 1-APP/Mac fileserver/1-APP/Power Mac 8500-120 fileserver; Printers — 3-APP/Mac LaserPrinter, 2-APP/Mac LaserWriter Pro EDITORIAL SOFTWARE: SII/Synthesis 66 XR. PRODUCTION EQUIPMENT: Hardware — 2-Accuset/Laser Imager, 1-AU/APS 6600 (Hitachi Engine), APP/Mac Quadra 840 AV, Microtek/Flatbed Scanner, Lf/Leafscan 35, Lf/Leafscan 45; Cameras — 1-C/Pager, 1-C/Spartan III PRODUCTION SOFTWARE: QPS/QuarkXPress 3.1.

FREDERICKSBURG

THE FREE LANCE-STAR

616 Amelia St, Fredericksburg, Va., 22401-3887, Fredericksburg City; gen tel (540) 374-5000; adv tel (540) 374-5460; ed tel (540) 374-5400; gen fax (540) 373-8450; ed fax (540) 373-8455; gen/nat adv e-mail information@freelancestar.com; disp adv e-mail advertising@freelancestar.com; class adv e-mailclassifieds@freelancestar.com; ed e-mail newsroom@freelancestar.com; web site www.freelancestar.com
- 560,000(views) 60,000(visitors); web site 2 www.fredericksburg.com - 4,300,000(views) 450,000(visitors)

Group: BH Media Group
Published: Mon, Tues, Wed, Thur, Fri, Sat, Sun
Weekday Frequency: m
Saturday Frequency: m
Circulation: 26,568; 27,678(sat); 30,735(sun)
Last Audit: AAM September 30, 2017
Advertising Rate (weekday/saturday): Open inch rate $27.40 (M-F); $30.10 (Sat)
Advertising Rate (sunday): $31.50
News services: AP, MCT. **Established:** 1885
Own Printing Facility?: Yes
Commercial Printers?: Yes
Special Editions: Bride & Groom (Feb); Parenting(Feb;
Horse Scene(Mar); Garden Week (Apr);
Spring Home Guide (May);
Wedding Guide (Jun); Guide To Living (July)
; Back To School (Aug);
High School Football (Aug);
Holiday Gift Guide (Nov); Holiday Trimming (Dec);.
Special Weekly Sections: House & Home (Fri); Viewpoints (Sun); Town & Country (Tues); Weekender (Thur); Food & Life (Wed); Stars & Stripes (Fri)Farm & Garden 1st Friday each month; Living Well 3rd Friday each month.
Digital Platform - Mobile: Apple, Android, Windows, Blackberry
Digital Platform - Tablet: Apple iOS, Android, Windows 7, Blackberry Tablet OS, Kindle, Nook, Kindle Fire
Editor... Phil Jenkins
Executive Assistant/HR Generalist........ Samantha Ashley
HR Dir.... Gayle P Yanez
Bus. Mgr. .... Karen Harris
Adv. Dir....................................... William P. Smith
Managing Editor ....Betty Snider
Life Ed. ....Katherine Shapleigh
Circulation Director........................ Timothy Krier
Classified Call Ctr. Sales Mgr............. Opal Curtis
Graphics/Design Dir. ....Catherine Davis
Editorial Page Editor .... James Toler
Pub.... Dale Lachniet
Ops. Dir.... Gary Snider
Market Information: TMC; Zoned editions.
Mechanical Available: Offset; Black and 3 ROP colors; insert accepted - Post-it ads; page cutoffs - 21.
Mechanical Specifications: Type page 11 5/16 x 20 1/2; E - 6 cols, 1 4/5, 1/8 between; A - 6 cols, 1 4/5, 1/8 between; C - 9 cols, 1 1/5, between.
Areas Served: NDM-22401, 22405, 22406, 22407, 22408, 22412, 22427, 22448, 22485, 22501, 22514, 22534, 22535, 22538, 22546, 22551, 22553, 22554, 22556, 22565, 22580
Delivery Method: Mail, Newsstand, Carrier, RacksEquipment & Software: PRESSROOM EQUIPMENT: Lines — 2 Unit 72" Triplewide Goss FPS Press-2010; 2 Unit 72" Triplewide Goss FPS Press-2010; 1 11 Meter Goss Conti Webb Dryer; Folders — 2 Goss 5:5:2 Folders and 1 Goss Quarterfold; Pasters —4 Goss Contiweb PastersControl System — Goss Omnicon; Registration System — QIPC Registration and Cut-Off MAILROOM EQUIPMENT: Counter Stackers — 4 Ferag Smart Stacks; Inserters & Stuffers — 1 32 Pocket Goss Magnapack with 2 DTP; Tying Machines — 6 Samuel Tiers; Wrapping Singles — 1 CMC JWR30; Control System — Goss Omnicon; Address Machine — Inline Domino Inkjet; CLASSIFIED EQUIPMENT: Hardware — 15-Xterms, 1-Sun/Enterprise 250; Printers — HP/4000; CLASSIFIED SOFTWARE: Vision Data 6.0. DISPLAY EQUIPMENT: Hardware — 2-APP/Mac G3, 16-APP/PowerMac G4/450; Printers — 1-HP/5Simx, 1-Tektronix/Phaser 780, 1-HP/8100; DISPLAY SOFTWAREAd Make-up Applications — Multi-Ad/Creator 4.04, AG/AdTracking 6.x, Binuscan; Layout Software — SCS/Layout 8000. EDITORIAL EQUIPMENT: Hardware — 2-Dell/PowerEdge 6300, 1-Dell/Poweredge 4300; Printers — 1-HP/4000, 1-HP/8100 EDITORIAL SOFTWARE: Tera/GN3 B85, Binuscan. PRODUCTION EQUIPMENT: Hardware — 2 Kodak News Generation 300 Thermal Imagers — NELA Optical Punch/Bend and Plate Sortation System CIRCULATION EQUIPMENT: HP Dell
Zerox CIRCULATION SOFTWARDTI

HARRISONBURG

DAILY NEWS-RECORD

231 S Liberty St, Harrisonburg, Va., 22801-3621, Harrisonburg City; gen tel (540) 574-6200; adv tel (540) 574-6220; gen fax (540) 574-6299; adv fax (540) 433-5503; gen/nat adv e-mail ads@dnronline.com; disp adv e-mail sturner@dnronline.com; ed e-mail kirkwood@dnronline.com; web site www.dnronline.com
- 1,000,000(views) 220,000(visitors)

Group: Byrd Newspapers
Published: Mon, Tues, Wed, Thur, Fri, Sat
Weekday Frequency: m
Saturday Frequency: m
Circulation: 24,323; 24,938(sat)
Last Audit: AAM March 31, 2016
Advertising Rate (weekday/saturday): Open inch rate $32.00
Online Advertising Rate: $7.50 per M for leaderboard
$6.00 per M for Other spots
News services: AP. **Established:** 1913
Own Printing Facility?: Yes
Commercial Printers?: Yes
Special Editions: Spring Car and Motorcycle Care (Apr); Community Guide (Aug); First Night (Dec); Valentines Day (Feb); Honor Roll of Business (Jan); Flag Insert (Jul); Graduation (Jun); Home & Garden (Mar); Our Valley (May); Real Estate Showcase (Monthly); Yuletide Gift G
Special Weekly Sections: TV Week (Fri);
Digital Platform - Mobile: Apple, Android
Digital Platform - Tablet: Apple iOS, Android, Kindle
Adv. Dir........................................ Steven Turner
Circ. Dir. .... Thomas Bridges
Ed., Gen Mgr., & Pub. .... Peter S. Yates
Mng. Ed. .... R. Cort Kirkwood
Mgmt. Info Servs. Mgr. .... Penny Anderson
Sports Ed. ....James Sacco
Market Information: TMC.
Mechanical Available: Offset; Black and 3 ROP colors; insert accepted; page cutoffs - 21 1/2.
Mechanical Specifications: Type page 11 1/8 x 21 1/2; E - 6 cols, 1 3/4, 1/8 between; A - 6 cols, 1 3/4, 1/8 between; C - 9 cols, 1 1/8, 1/8 between.
Areas Served: City of Harrisonburg and Counties of Rockingham, Shenandoah, Page, and Augusta in Virginia plus Hardy and Pendleton Counties in W.VA
Delivery Method: Mail, Newsstand, Carrier, RacksEquipment & Software: PRESSROOM EQUIPMENT: Lines — 8-G/Urbanite; Control System — Fin.; MAILROOM EQUIPMENT: Counter Stackers — 3-QWI/501; Inserters & Stuffers — 1-MM/227S, 1-MM/227S; Tying Machines — 1-Sterling/MR45CHDR, 1-Sterling/MR50CH, 1-Sterling/GP30, 1-Sterling/GP30; Address Machine — 1/Ch, 1-/BH; BUSINESS EQUIPMENT: 10-Vision Data, 2-IBM/PC, 1-Inteva/PC CLASSIFIED EQUIPMENT: Hardware — Sun/Enterprise 250; Printers — HP/5000; CLASSIFIED SOFTWARE: Vision Data/Total Advertising. DISPLAY EQUIPMENT: Hardware — Compaq; Printers — HP/5000; DISPLAY SOFTWAREAd Make-up Applications — Multi-Ad; Layout Software — APT. EDITORIAL EQUIPMENT: Hardware — Compaq; Printers — HP/5000 EDITORIAL SOFTWARE: Apt/Act 2001. PRODUCTION EQUIPMENT: Hardware — LE; Scanners — Tecsa PRODUCTION SOFTWARE: APT/ACT.

LYNCHBURG

THE NEWS & ADVANCE

101 Wyndale Dr, Lynchburg, Va., 24501-6710, Lynchburg City; gen tel (434) 385-5400; adv tel (434) 385-5450; ed tel (434) 385-5555; gen fax (434) 385-5472; adv fax (434) 385-5472; ed fax (434) 385-5538; gen/nat adv e-mail ads@newsadvance.com; disp adv e-mail ads@newsadvance.com; class adv e-mailclassifiedads@newsadvance.com; ed e-mail cglickman@newsadvance.com; web site www.newsadvance.com

Group: BH Media Group
Published: Mon, Tues, Wed, Thur, Fri, Sat, Sun
Weekday Frequency: m
Saturday Frequency: m
Circulation: 18,531; 18,531(sat); 23,751(sun)
Last Audit: AAM March 31, 2017
Advertising Rate (weekday/saturday): Open inch rate $56.10
Advertising Rate (sunday): Open inch rate $60.18
News services: AP, NYT. **Established:** 1866
Own Printing Facility?: Yes
Commercial Printers?: Yes
Special Editions: Greater Lynchburg Chamber of Commerce Report (); Garden Week (Apr); Kaleidoscope (Aug); Last Minute Gifts (Dec); Best of Health (Every other month); Progress (Feb); Bride & Groom (Jan); How-To-Guide (Jul); Summer Living (Jun); Who's Who in Construction (M
Special Weekly Sections: Best Food, Arts (Wed/Sun); Community (Tue/Thur); TV, Entertainment, Auto (Fri); Religion, Auto (Sat); Auto, Real Estate, Travel, Business, Health, Technology (Sun)
Digital Platform - Mobile: Apple, Android
Digital Platform - Tablet: Apple iOS, Android, Other
Managing Editor ....Caroline Glickman
Editorial Page/Opinion. Ed. ....Logan Anderson
Sports Ed. ....Chris Morris
Sales Support.................................Sue Scruggs
Digital Sales....................................Dean Smith
Adv. Dir. ....Ronald McBride
Circ. Dir. ....Stephanie Eubank
Regional Ad Director .... Kevin Smith
Market Information: Split run; TMC.
Mechanical Available: Offset; Black and 3 ROP colors; insert accepted; page cutoffs - 22 3/4.
Mechanical Specifications: Type page 13 x 21 1/2; E - 5 cols, 2 1/2, 13/100 between; A - 6 cols, 2 1/25, 1/6 between; C - 9 cols, 1 3/8, 1/20 between.
Areas Served: Lynchburg City, Campbell County, Amherst County, Appomattox County, Bedford CountyEquipment & Software: PRESSROOM EQUIPMENT: Lines — 5-HI/1650 1974; Press Drive — 2-Fin/250 h.p.; Folders — HI/2:1.; MAILROOM EQUIPMENT: Counter Stackers — 2/QWI; Inserters & Stuffers — 1-HI/1372; Tying Machines — 1-/Dyanric, 1-Si; Address Machine — 1-/KR.; BUSINESS EQUIPMENT: APT CLASSIFIED EQUIPMENT: Hardware — 10-EKI/Televideo; Printers — 1-NewGen/480; CLASSIFIED SOFTWARE: EKI. DISPLAY EQUIPMENT: Hardware — 1-PC 386 fileserver; Printers — 1-NewGen/1200T, 1-NewGen/480, 1-NewGen/Turbo Plus 1200B; Other Hardware — 2-Microtek/600 scanner, 1-HP/ScanJet IIC. DISPLAY SOFTWAREAd Make-up Applications — DTI, QPS/QuarkXPress, Adobe/Photoshop, Adobe/Illustrator; EDITORIAL EQUIPMENT: Hardware — HP/PC/1-Lf/AP Leaf Picture Desk, 1-Lf/Leafscan 35; Printers — 1-NewGen/1200T, HP/4MV, QMS/2060 EDITORIAL SOFTWARE: APT/Editorial System, QPS/QuarkXPress, Microsoft/Word. PRODUCTION EQUIPMENT: Hardware — 1-Graham/GNS 28, 1-BKY/5000, NewGen/1200T; Cameras — 1-C/Spartan III. CIRCULATION

SOFTWARNewscycle Solutions: DSI

MARTINSVILLE

MARTINSVILLE BULLETIN

204 Broad St, Martinsville, Va., 24112-3704, Martinsville City; gen tel (276) 638-8801; gen fax (276) 638-4153; ed fax (276) 638-7409; gen/nat adv e-mail advertising@martinsvillebulletin.com; disp adv e-mail advertising@martinsvillebulletin.com; class adv e-mailclassified@martinsvillebulletin.com; ed e-mail info@martinsvillebulletin.com; web site www.martinsvillebulletin.com

Group: BH Media Group
Published: Mon, Tues, Wed, Thur, Fri, Sun
Weekday Frequency: m
Circulation: 10,540; 12,142(sun)
Last Audit: AAM December 31, 2016
Advertising Rate (weekday/saturday): Open inch rate $17.72
Advertising Rate (sunday): Open inch rate $18.54
News services: NEA, AP. **Established:** 1889
Own Printing Facility?: No
Commercial Printers?: Yes
Special Editions: Race (Apr); Football (Aug); Christmas Greetings (Dec); Brides (Feb); Health & Fitness (Jan); Graduation (Jun); Spring (Mar); Real Estate (May); Christmas Shopping (Nov);Pastor's Appreciation (Oct); Medicine and Health (July)
Special Weekly Sections: Best Food Day (Wed); Entertainment (Fri); Business (Sun)
Syndicated Publications: Parade (S).
Chrmn. of the Bd. .... Antoinette M. Haskell
Pres./Pub. .... Robert H. Haskell
Vice Pres./Gen. Mgr. .... George H. Harris
Vice Pres. .... Elizabeth H. Haskell
Bus. Mgr. .... Tammy Foster
Adv. Mgr. .... Tammy Jones
Circ. Mgr. .... Matthew Dishman
Mng. Ed. .... Amanda Buck
Editorial Writer .... Ginny Wray
Food/Women's Ed. .... Holly Kozelski
Librarian .... Sue Carter
Photo Ed. .... Mike Wray
Prodn. Mgr. .... George Harris
Ed. .... Brian Carlton
Market Information: TMC.
Mechanical Available: Offset; Black and 3 ROP colors; insert accepted; page cutoffs - 22 3/4.
Mechanical Specifications: Type page 11 2/3 x 21 1/2; E - 6 cols, 1 4/5, 1/8 between; A - 6 cols, 1 4/5, 1/8 between; C - 9 cols, 1 1/4, 1/8 between.
Delivery Method: Mail, Newsstand, Carrier, RacksEquipment & Software: PRESSROOM EQUIPMENT: Lines — 5-G/Urbanite U-920; 5-DEV/2400.; MAILROOM EQUIPMENT: Counter Stackers — HI/Rima RS255; Inserters & Stuffers — KAN/480; Tying Machines — MLN, Dynaric, Interlake.; BUSINESS EQUIPMENT: IBM/PCs BUSINESS SOFTWARE: MSSI CLASSIFIED EQUIPMENT: Hardware — APP/Mac; Printers — 2-AU/Laser Film Imager, 3-Okidata; CLASSIFIED SOFTWARE: Baseview. EDITORIAL EQUIPMENT: Hardware — APP/Mac/Lf/Leafscan 35, AG/Flatbed Scanner; Printers — 2-AU/Laser Film Imager, 3-Okidata EDITORIAL SOFTWARE: Baseview. PRODUCTION EQUIPMENT: Hardware — AU, W; Scanners — Lf/Leafscan 35, Leica/Flatbed, AU/Drum Scanner PRODUCTION SOFTWARE: Baseview.

MC LEAN

USA TODAY

7950 Jones Branch Dr, Mc Lean, Va., 22108-0003, Fairfax; gen tel (703)854-3400; adv tel (703) 854-6000; ed tel (703)854-6000; gen/nat adv e-mail advertising@usatoday.com; disp adv e-mail advertising@usatoday.com; ed e-mail editor@usatoday.com; web site www.usatoday.com

Group: Gannett
Published: Mon, Tues, Wed, Thur, Fri, Sat, Sun
Weekday Frequency: m
Circulation: 2,081,202; 1,070,875(sat); 1,113,840(sun)
Last Audit: AAM December 31, 2016
News services: Crain Communications, AP, GNS, RN, AFP, DJ, UPI. **Established:** 1982
Own Printing Facility?: Yes
Commercial Printers?: Yes
Digital Platform - Mobile: Apple, Android, Windows
Digital Platform - Tablet: Apple iOS, Android, Windows 7, Kindle, Nook, Kindle Fire
Chief Content Officer .... Joanne Lipman
President & Publisher .... John Zidich
Editor in Chief .... Patty Michalski
Executive Editor .... Beryl Love
General Manager .... Susan Motiff
Editor, Editorial Page .... Bill Sternberg
Standards & Ethics Ed. .... Brent Jones
Chief Revenue Officer .... Kevin Gentzel
Chief Product Officer .... Daniel Bernard
Pres, Sports Media Group .... David Morgan
VP Marketing .... Tom Miller
Delivery Method: Mail, Newsstand, Carrier, Racks
Note: USA TODAY does not sell advertising on an inch rate basis: advertisers can purchase the specific sizes offered by the newspaper. Classified advertising is sold at a line rate.

NEWPORT NEWS

DAILY PRESS

703 Mariners Row, Newport News, Va., 23606-4432, Newport News City; gen tel (757) 247-4600; adv tel (757) 247-4678; ed tel (757) 247-4730; gen fax (757) 247-7899; adv fax (757) 247-4651 (retail); ed fax (757) 245-4675; gen/nat adv e-mail jalger@dailypress.com; disp adv e-mail jalger@dailypress.com; class adv e-mailclassified@dailypress.com; ed e-mail news@dailypress.com; web site www.dailypress.com
- 7,500,000(views) 715,320(visitors)

Group: Tronc, Inc.
Published: Mon, Tues, Wed, Thur, Fri, Sat, Sun
Weekday Frequency: m
Saturday Frequency: m
Circulation: 41,376; 34,402(sat); 80,965(sun)
Last Audit: AAM December 31, 2016
Branch Offices: Virginia Gazette, Tidewater Review
Advertising Rate (weekday/saturday): 1/8 Pg $115.12
Advertising Rate (sunday): 1/8 Pg $145.53
Online Advertising Rate: Average $9.00 CPM; Rich Media $700.00/Day
News services: AP, MCT, TMS. **Established:** 1896
Own Printing Facility?: No
Commercial Printers?: No
Special Editions: H.S. All Stars (Apr); H.S. Football (Aug); H.S. All Stars (Dec); Home Expo (Feb); H.S. All Stars (Jul); Prime Time (Jun); New Cars-Trucks-Vans (Mar); Guide to Pre-Owned Vehicles (May); College Basketball (Nov); New Cars (Oct); Arts Calendar (Quarterly); P
Special Weekly Sections: Entertainment (Mon); Shopping, Deals (Tue); Best Food Day (Wed); Home, Garden, Town Square (Thur); Entertainment, Auto (Fri); Auto, Entertainment, Religion, Real Estate, Health (Sat); Arts, Home, Travel, Real Estate (Sun); Business, Finance, Local, National (Daily)
Syndicated Publications: Hampton Roads Mom & Me (Monthly); MyTime for Hampton Roads Women (Other); TV Hampton Roads Magazine (S).
Digital Platform - Mobile: Apple, Android, Windows, Blackberry
Digital Platform - Tablet: Apple iOS, Android, Windows 7, Blackberry Tablet OS, Kindle, Nook, Kindle Fire
HR Dir. .... Keith Potts
Dir., Consumer Mktg. .... David Messick
Circ. Mgr. .... Todd Hubbard
Pub. .... Marisa Porto
Admin./Planning Mgr. .... Cindy Laraway
Features Ed. .... Karen Morgan
Dave Hendrickson
VP, Adv. .... Amy Powers
Dir., Adv. Sales .... Jerry E. Alger
Market Information: ADS; Split run; TMC; Zoned editions.
Mechanical Available: Offset; Black and full color ROP colors; insert accepted - product samples; page cutoffs - 22.
Mechanical Specifications: Type page 10 1/2 x 21; E - 6 cols, 1 19/32, 1/10 between; A - 6 cols, 1 19/32, 1/10 between; C - 10 cols, 1 3/32, 3/32 between.
Areas Served: Tidewater
Delivery Method: Mail, Newsstand, CarrierEquipment & Software: PRESSROOM EQUIPMENT: Lines — 16-G/3346-3347 (8 color half decks); MAILROOM EQUIPMENT: Counter Stackers — 6-GMA/CombiStacks, 4-QWI/401 Stackers, 2-Gammerler/Stackers; Inserters & Stuffers — 1-GMA/SLS3000 14:2, 1-GMA/SLS3000 30:2 (dual delivery); Tying Machines — 3-Dynaric/Tyer NP2, 1-Dynaric/NP3000; Control System — GMA/SA; BUSINESS EQUIPMENT: Admarc, IBM/CICS, CJ, Open Pages, CCI, Advision BUSINESS SOFTWARE: Microsoft/Office CLASSIFIED EQUIPMENT: Hardware — Dell/Pentium, Advision/GX110, ALPS/GX110; Printers — HP/8000; CLASSIFIED SOFTWARE: CText/ADV 5.1. DISPLAY EQUIPMENT: Hardware — Sun, Ultra II; Printers — HP/4000, HP/551, Canon/Fiery; DISPLAY SOFTWAREAd Make-up Applications — QPS/QuarkXPress 4.1; Layout Software — SCS/Layout 8000. EDITORIAL EQUIPMENT: Hardware — 130-Pentium/PC, 15-APP/Power Mac EDITORIAL SOFTWARE: Open Pages. PRODUCTION EQUIPMENT: Hardware — 3-AII/3850 Typesetter, AP/Server; Scanners — 1-GEI/Tecsa Scanners, 2-Umax/2100 XL PRODUCTION SOFTWARE: Open Pages, ALPS 5.1.

NORFOLK

THE VIRGINIAN-PILOT

150 W Brambleton Ave, Norfolk, Va., 23510-2018, Norfolk City; gen tel (757) 446-2983; adv tel (757) 662-1455; ed tel (757) 446-9000; gen fax (757) 446-2983; adv fax (757) 446-2983; ed fax (757) 446-2983; gen/nat adv e-mail kelly.till@pilotonline.com; disp adv e-mail kelly.till@pilotonline.com; class adv e-mailkelly.till@pilotonline.com; ed e-mail steve.gunn@pilotonline.com; web site www.pilotonline.com
- 12,259,378(views) 1,659,758(visitors); web site 2 www.thevirginianpilot.com; web site 3 www.hamptonroads.com

Group: Landmark Communications, Inc.
Published: Mon, Tues, Wed, Thur, Fri, Sat, Sun
Weekday Frequency: m
Saturday Frequency: m
Circulation: 106,913; 95,645(sat); 139,013(sun)
Last Audit: AAM December 31, 2016
Advertising Rate (weekday/saturday): Open inch rate $266.00 (Mon-Fri); $286 (Sat)
Advertising Rate (sunday): Open inch rate $286.00
Online Advertising Rate: Standard ad units Mobile Banner $12.00 CPM
News services: AP, MCT, LAT-WP, Landmark News Service. **Established:** 1866
Own Printing Facility?: Yes
Commercial Printers?: Yes
Special Editions: Career Day (Apr); Hurricane Alert (Aug); Technical Career Banners (Feb); African American Today (Feb); Forecast (Jan); Discover Hampton Roads (Jul); Scholastic Achievement (Jun); Discover the Albemarle (Mar); Spring Outer Banks Vacation Guide (May); Auto Show (Nov); Career Day (Oct);
Special Weekly Sections: Your Business (Mon); Best Food (Wed/Sun); Auto, Pulse, Entertainment, Arts (Fri); Home, Real Estate (Sat); Gracious Living (Sun)
Syndicated Publications: Parade (S); dash (1st Wed)
Digital Platform - Mobile: Apple, Android, Windows
Digital Platform - Tablet: Apple iOS, Kindle, Nook, Kindle Fire, Other
Pub. .... Pat Richardson
Exec. Ed. .... Steve Gunn
Sr. Ed. .... William Henry
Sr. Ed. .... Jeff Reece
Production Ed. .... Dan Duke
Ops. Dir. .... Reno David
Adv. Ops. Mgr. .... Charmel Shock Peters
Business Develop. Mgr. .... Alan Levenstein
Nat'l Acct. Exec. .... Lynn Rea
Adv. Dir. .... Kelly Warren-Till
Acquisition Manager .... Mary Mcchesney
Market Information: ADS; Split run; TMC; Zoned editions.
Mechanical Available: Offset; Black and 3 ROP colors; insert accepted; page cutoffs - 22 3/4.
Mechanical Specifications: Type page 11 1/2 x 21 1/2; E - 6 cols, 1 4/5, 1/8 between; A - 6 cols, 1 4/5, 1/8 between; C - 10 cols, 1 9/16, 1/16 between.
Areas Served: South Hampton Roads, NE North Carolina
Delivery Method: Mail, Newsstand, Carrier, RacksEquipment & Software: PRESSROOM EQUIPMENT: Lines — 30-G/Metro offset double width; Press Drive — FINCOR DRIVE SHAFT; Folders — 5-G/Metro 3:2 Imperial Folder (with double delivery); Pasters —30-G/Tension SystemReels & Stands — 30; Control System — Goss PCS; Registration System — Quad-tec PRESSROOM SOFTWARE: Goss PCS, AGFA MAILROOM EQUIPMENT: Counter Stackers — 14 SMS Ferag; Inserters & Stuffers — 3 Goss Magna-Pak Inserters; Tying Machines — 15 Mosca Z-5 Tyers; Control System — Omnizone; Address Machine — 4 Kodak Printers; MAILROOM SOFTWARE:Omnizone BUSINESS EQUIPMENT: 13-IBM/4381, 1-IBM/AS-400 B60 (midrange) CLASSIFIED EQUIPMENT: Hardware — 35-AT.; DISPLAY SOFTWARELayout Software — 3-Sun, AT/R2, 28-AT. EDITORIAL EQUIPMENT: Hardware — 200-AT, 10-APP/Mac Portable, 20-IBM/Portable, 40-IBM/Compatable, 12-AT/News Layout, 36-APP/Mac Page Design, 10-Tandem/Portable EDITORIAL SOFTWARE: Adobe InDesign PRODUCTION EQUIPMENT: Hardware — 2-AG/Avantra 30E, 2-K&F/PlatXpress with Vision Bender PRODUCTION SOFTWARE: All/Oman.

PETERSBURG

THE PROGRESS-INDEX

15 Franklin St, Petersburg, Va., 23803-4503, Petersburg City; gen tel (804) 722-5137; adv tel (804) 732-3456; ed tel (804) 732-3456; gen fax (804) 861-9452; adv fax (804) 861-9452; ed fax (804) 732-8417; gen/nat adv e-mail acoleman@progress-index.com; disp adv e-mail acoleman@progress-index.com; class adv e-mailads@progress-index.com; ed e-mail bcouturier@progress-index.com; web site www.progress-index.com

Group: New Media Investment Group
Published: Mon, Tues, Wed, Thur, Fri, Sat, Sun
Weekday Frequency: m
Saturday Frequency: m
Circulation: 6,154; 6,154(sat); 7,728(sun)
Last Audit: AAM June 30, 2017
Advertising Rate (weekday/saturday): Open inch rate $24.05
Advertising Rate (sunday): Open inch rate $24.05
News services: Associated Press, McClathy, NYT
Commercial Printers?: Yes
Special Editions: Spring Fix-up (Apr); Cruisin' (Aug); Dear Santa (Dec); Life Underwriters (Feb); First Aid (Jan); Customer Appreciation (Jul); School's Out-Summer Fun Guide (Jun); Progress (Mar); Dining Guide (May); Holiday Happenings (Nov); Fall Fix-up (Oct); Literacy Ta
Special Weekly Sections: Home, Garden (Mon); Best Food Day (Tue); NASCAR (Wed); Arts, Entertainment (Thur); Auto (Fri); Technology (Sat); Science, Health (Sun)
Syndicated Publications: Relish (Monthly); USA WEEKEND Magazine (S); American Profile (Weekly).
Mgr., Accounting .... Peggy Simon
Circ. Dir. .... Bob Seals
Photo Dept. Mgr., ... Patrick Kane
Sports Ed. .... Tom Dozier
Wire Ed. .... Cathy Ballou
Prodn. Mgr., Pressroom .... Ron Shifflet
Managing Ed. .... Brian Couturier
Sunday Ed. .... Brian Courtier
Adv. Dir. .... Baretta Taylor
Online Adv. Exec. .... Lauren Andrews
Pub .... Craig Richards
Adv. Sales Asst. .... Alice Coleman
Market Information: TMC.
Mechanical Available: Offset; Black and 3 ROP colors; insert accepted; page cutoffs - 23 1/4.
Mechanical Specifications: Type page 13 x 21 1/2; E - 6 cols, 2 1/16, 1/8 between;

A - 6 cols, 2 1/16, 1/8 between; C - 9 cols, 1 5/16, 1/8 between.Equipment & Software: PRESSROOM EQUIPMENT: Lines — 8-G/Community; Folders — 1-G/SSC.; MAILROOM EQUIPMENT: Tying Machines — 1/MLN, 1-/MLN.; BUSINESS EQUIPMENT: ATT CLASSIFIED EQUIPMENT: Hardware — Mk, APP/Mac; Printers — TI; CLASSIFIED SOFTWARE: Mk/4000, Multi-Ad/Creator, QPS/QuarkXPress. DISPLAY EQUIPMENT: Hardware — 2-APP/Mac; Printers — V/5100; DISPLAY SOFTWAREAd Make-up Applications — Multi-Ad/Creator, QPS/QuarkXPress, Aldus/FreeHand; Layout Software — APP/Mac. EDITORIAL EQUIPMENT: Hardware — APP/Mac; Printers — TI EDITORIAL SOFTWARE: QPS/QuarkXPress 3.11. PRODUCTION EQUIPMENT: Hardware — 2-V/5100, 1-V/5300, 1-V/Panther Plus; Cameras — SCREEN/C-690-C

PULASKI

THE SOUTHWEST TIMES (PULASKI, VA)

34 5th St NE, Pulaski, Va., 24301-4608, Pulaski; gen tel (540) 980-5220; adv tel (540)980-5220 ext. 316; ed tel (540)980-5220 ext. 312; gen fax (540) 980-3618; adv fax (540)980-3618; ed fax (540)980-3618; gen/nat adv e-mail brenda@southwesttimes.com; disp adv e-mail brenda@southwesttimes.com; class adv e-mailclassified@southwesttimes.com; ed e-mail editor@southwesttimes.com; web site www.southwesttimes.com

Group: Fackelman Newspapers
Published: Tues, Wed, Thur, Fri, Sun
Weekday Frequency: m
Circulation: 5,500; 5,500(sun)
Last Audit: Sworn/Estimate/Non-Audited October 1, 2017
Advertising Rate (weekday/saturday): Open inch rate $12.00
Advertising Rate (sunday): Open inch rate $12.00
News services: AP. **Established:** 1906
Own Printing Facility?: No
Commercial Printers?: No
Special Editions: Football (Aug); Fair (Jul); Pulaski County tourism (May); Graduation (May); quarterly quality-of-life magazine
Special Weekly Sections: Religion (Fri); Best Food Day (S); Best Food Day (Wed).
Pub............Brenda Adams
Managing Editor............Lynn Adams
Market Information: TMC.
Areas Served: 24301, 24084, 24141, 24312, 24382, 24347
Delivery Method: Mail, Newsstand, Racks

RICHMOND

RICHMOND TIMES-DISPATCH

300 E Franklin St, Richmond, Va., 23219-2214, Richmond City; gen tel (804) 649-6000; adv tel (804) 649-6251; ed tel (804) 649-6305; gen fax (804)775-8019; adv fax (804) 775-8019; ed fax (804) 819-5520; gen/nat adv e-mail addispatch@timesdispatch.com; disp adv e-mail addispatch@timesdispatch.com; class adv e-mailaddispatch@timesdispatch.com; ed e-mail pmudd@timesdispatch.com; web site www.timesdispatch.com
1,301,601(visitors)

Group: BH Media Group
Published: Mon, Tues, Wed, Thur, Fri, Sat, Sun
Weekday Frequency: m
Saturday Frequency: m
Circulation: 86,824; 94,185(sat); 111,642(sun)
Last Audit: AAM March 31, 2017
Advertising Rate (weekday/saturday): Open inch rate $184.00
Advertising Rate (sunday): Open inch rate $230.00
News services: AP, Business Wire, LAT-WP, Media General News, NYT, SHNS, Bloomberg, MCT. **Established:** 1850
Special Editions: Monument Avenue 10K (Apr); Discover Richmond (Aug); Holiday Books (Dec); Super Bowl (Feb); Year-End Stock Report (Jan); New Homes (Mar); Race Week (Sun) (May); UVA-Tech Game (Nov); Medical Jobs (Oct); Race Week (Sun) (Sept).
Special Weekly Sections: Best Food (Wed); Metro Business (Mon); Weekend (Thur); Home, Garden, Auto (Fri); Real Estate, Home, Garden (Sat); Real Estate, Travel (Sun)
Syndicated Publications: Parade (S).
Pres./Pub.............Thomas A. Silvestri
Hand over production plant............Sam Hightower
Controller............Raymond McDowell
Mgr., Pre Press Design Servs.............Karen Dillon
Classified Adv. Mgr.............Scott Christino
Telephone Sales Mgr.............Terry Hall
Vice Pres., Circ.............David B. Kirkman
Circ. Mgr., Metro............Thomas C. Smith
VP, Revenue & Business Development............John W. Kelly
Regional Sales Director............Erin Brooks
Editor............Paul Whelan
Major/Nat'l Acct. Mgr.............LaJuan Lewis
Delivery Mgr.............Scott Payne
Online Brand Director............Nicole McMullin
Market Information: ADS; Split run; TMC; Zoned editions.
Mechanical Available: Offset; Black and 3 ROP colors; insert accepted; page cutoffs - 22.
Mechanical Specifications: Type page 11 5/8 x 21; E - 6 cols, 2 1/16, 1/8 between; A - 6 cols, 2 1/16, 1/8 between; C - 10 cols, 1 1/4, 1/18 between.Equipment & Software: PRESSROOM EQUIPMENT: Lines — 36-MHI/Print couples (4 reversible half decks; 2 mono units); 36-MHI/Print couples (4 reversible half decks; 2 mono units); 36-MHI/Print couples (4 reversible half decks; 2 mono units); Folders — 2-MHI/180-page; Reels & Stands — Reels & Stands and Stands; MAILROOM EQUIPMENT: Counter Stackers — 11-Id/2100, 4/QWI, 3-HL/SH, 2-Rima/RS3100, 13-QWI/500; Inserters & Stuffers — 1-S/b-72P, 4-S/22-99, AM Graphics; Tying Machines — 13-/Dynaric; Control System — Id/Newssort, Id/Newslink; Address Machine — Ch/539, C; BUSINESS EQUIPMENT: HP/917, HP/935, HP/950, HP/949, HP/947 BUSINESS SOFTWARE: CJ, Visimage, Omnidex CLASSIFIED EQUIPMENT: Hardware — AT/Enterprise RS 6000, 1-Clarion Raid; 2-IBM/RS 6000 Workstations; Printers — 2-HP/5000TN; CLASSIFIED SOFTWARE: APP/Order Entry 1.4.172, Oracle/Database 7.3.4. DISPLAY EQUIPMENT: Hardware — 2-HP/Vectras, 2-Cascade/450E SunServers, 2-RAID/D1000; Printers — HP/LaserJet 4200, Xerox/Fiery color printer; Other Hardware — 1-HP/1055cm Full-Page Color, cm Full-Page Color-HP/1050, 1-C-Color/Color Management DISPLAY SOFTWAREAd Make-up Applications — SCS/Layout 8000 8.0; EDITORIAL EQUIPMENT: Hardware — 6-Sun/Ultra II servers, Client/200-PC 3.40/2-Dell/NAS Servers; Printers — HP/MV4, 4-HP/LaserJet 2200, X EDITORIAL SOFTWARE: HI/NME 4.0, Microsoft/Windows XP. PRODUCTION EQUIPMENT: Hardware — 2-WL/3, AII/3850, 4-AG/Alpha Harlequin RIP; Scanners — 4-Epson PRODUCTION SOFTWARE: HI/Newsmaker Pagination 2.05.12, AT/Classified Pagination 5.76.

ROANOKE

THE ROANOKE TIMES

201 Campbell Ave SW, Roanoke, Va., 24011-1105, Roanoke City; gen tel (540) 981-3211; adv tel (540) 981-3145; ed tel (540) 981-3113; gen/nat adv e-mail mary.whelchel@roanoke.com; disp adv e-mail adinfo@roanoke.com; class adv e-mailclassified@roanoke.com; ed e-mail editor@roanoke.com; web site www.roanoke.com
- 6,000,000(views) 1,500(visitors)

Group: BH Media Group
Published: Mon, Tues, Wed, Thur, Fri, Sat, Sun
Weekday Frequency: All day
Saturday Frequency: All day
Circulation: 45,717; 45,724(sat); 55,216(sun)
Last Audit: AAM June 30, 2017
Advertising Rate (weekday/saturday): Cost per inch w/color weekday $57.29
Advertising Rate (sunday): $67.01
Online Advertising Rate: $10.00
News services: AP, Washington Post News Service **Established:** 1886
Own Printing Facility?: Yes
Commercial Printers?: Yes
Special Weekly Sections: Sunday Business, TV Weekly (Friday). New River Valley (Part Run, Friday/Sunday), Laker Weekly (part run, Wednesday)
Proprietary Publications: Carriers, Racks and OTC Single Copy Sales
Digital Platform - Mobile: Apple, Android, Windows, Blackberry, Other
Digital Platform - Tablet: Apple iOS, Android, Windows 7, Blackberry Tablet OS, Kindle, Nook, Kindle Fire, Other
National and Majors Director............Mary Whelchel
Editorial Page Editor............Dwayne Yancey
Editor I............Liz Hock
Executive Editor............Lawrence McConnell
Publisher............Terry Jamerson
Design and Presentation Editor............Andrew Svec
Regional H/R Director............Karla Hernandez
Business Manager............David Weaver
Managing Editor............Lee Wolverton
Controller............Emily Wood
VP of Advertising............Jamie Kinnaird
Regional Circulation Director............Linnie Pride
Market Information: Southwest VA (including Roanoke and Blacksburg Metro Area, Giles and Floyd, Christiansburg, Radford, Pulaski, Smith Mountain Lake, Bedford and Franklin County.
Areas Served: Roanoke and New River Valley's MSAs
Delivery Method: Mail, Newsstand, Carrier, Racks

STAUNTON

THE NEWS LEADER

11 N Central Ave, Staunton, Va., 24401-4212, Staunton City; gen tel (540) 213-9199; adv tel (540) 213-9199; ed tel (540) 213-9128; gen fax (540) 885-8779; adv fax (540) 885-8779; ed fax (540) 885-1904; gen/nat adv e-mail ads@newsleader.com; disp adv e-mail ads@newsleader.com; class adv e-mailads@newsleader.com; ed e-mail news@newsleader.com; web site www.newsleader.com

Group: Gannett
Published: Mon, Tues, Wed, Thur, Fri, Sat, Sun
Weekday Frequency: m
Saturday Frequency: m
Circulation: 9,938; 9,938(sat); 12,051(sun)
Last Audit: AAM September 30, 2017
Advertising Rate (weekday/saturday): Open inch rate $41.15
Advertising Rate (sunday): Open inch rate $45.43
News services: GNS, AP, LAT-WP. **Established:** 1904
Special Editions: Home & Garden (Apr); Football (Aug); Bride's World (Feb); America's Birthday (Jun); Fact Book (Mar); Graduation (May).
Special Weekly Sections: Weather, TV (Daily); NASCAR (Thur); Faith, Value (Fri); History (Sat); Lifestyles, Home, Real Estate (Sun)
Syndicated Publications: USA WEEKEND Magazine (S).
Pub.............Roger Watson
Controller............Wilma Raybin
Admin., HR............Susan Armstong
Adv. Mgr.............Tricia Bryant
Adv. Mgr., Retail............Mark Chamberlin
Adv. Servs. Mgr.............Amy Smith
Circ. Dir.............Kathy Myers
Exec. Ed.............David Fritz
Sports Ed.............Hubert Grim
Online Content Developer............Chris Beard
Prodn. Dir.............Bryce Connelly
Major Accts. Rep.............Jim McCloskey
Reg. Controller............Jean Wysocki
Market Information: TMC; Zoned editions.
Mechanical Available: Offset; Black and 3 ROP colors; insert accepted; page cutoffs - 21 1/2.
Mechanical Specifications: Type page 13 x 21 1/4; E - 6 cols, 2 1/16, 1/8 between; A - 6 cols, 2 1/16, 1/8 between; C - 9 cols, 1 3/8, 1/16 between.Equipment & Software: PRESSROOM EQUIPMENT: Lines — 6-G/Urbanite; 1-AM/1650 MC Offset; Press Drive — 2-HP/100; Folders — 1-G/Urbanite.; MAILROOM EQUIPMENT: Counter Stackers — 1-Id/2000, 1-QWI/350; Inserters & Stuffers — GMA/Alphaliner; Tying Machines — 1/Bu, 1-MLN/MA, 1-/Akebono, 1-/Power Strap; Control System — GMA; Address Machine — 1-KR/Mailer, 1-KR/Quarter Folder; BUSINESS EQUIPMENT: IBM/AS-400 BUSINESS SOFTWARE: Lotus 3.1, Microsoft/Office CLASSIFIED SOFTWARE: Baseview. DISPLAY EQUIPMENT: Hardware — APP/Mac; Printers — Linotronic, ECR/Imagesetter, HP, APP/Mac LaserPrinter; Other Hardware — Adobe, Harlequin RIP, Microsoft/Windows NT DISPLAY SOFTWAREAd Make-up Applications — Baseview; Layout Software — APP/Mac, QPS/QuarkXPress. EDITORIAL EQUIPMENT: Hardware — APP/Mac Server, APP/Mac workstation EDITORIAL SOFTWARE: QPS/QuarkXPress. PRODUCTION EQUIPMENT: Hardware — 1-LE/LD-2600A, Harlequin, Linotronic/Ultre, ECR; Cameras — 1-C/Spartan II, 1-R/432, ECR; Scanners — 1-ECR/Autokon 1000, AG/Horizon Plus, Umax, Microtek, Nikon, Flatbed/Scanner PRODUCTION SOFTWARE: QPS/QuarkXPress 3.32.

STRASBURG

NORTHERN VIRGINIA DAILY

152 N Holliday St, Strasburg, Va., 22657-2143, Shenandoah; gen tel (540) 465-5137; adv tel (540) 465-5137; ed tel (540) 456-5137; gen fax (540) 465-6153; adv fax (540) 465-6166; ed fax (540) 465-6164; gen/nat adv e-mail mgochenour@nvdaily.com; disp adv e-mail classifieds@nvdaily.com; class adv e-mailclassifieds@nvdaily.com; ed e-mail news@nvdailiy.com; web site www.nvdaily.com
- 900,000(views) 175,000(visitors)

Group: Ogden Newspapers Inc.
Published: Mon, Tues, Wed, Thur, Fri, Sat
Weekday Frequency: m
Saturday Frequency: m
Circulation: 7,999; 8,988(sat)
Last Audit: AAM September 30, 2017
Advertising Rate (weekday/saturday): Open inch rate $17.12 for National; $14.55 for Local
Advertising Rate (sunday): N/A
News services: AP, SHNS. **Established:** 1932
Own Printing Facility?: No
Commercial Printers?: No
Special Editions: Discover the Valley/Tourism (Apr); Football (Aug); Bridal (Jan); Winchester County Guide (Jul); Farm & Home (Mar); Warren County Guide (May); Restaurants & Recipes (Nov); Winterize Home & Auto (Oct); Outdoors (Sept).
Special Weekly Sections: Wedding & Engagements (Mon); Real Estate/Home (Sat); Weekend + More (Thur); NASCAR (Wed).
Syndicated Publications: American Profile (Mon); USA WEEKEND Magazine (Sat).
Digital Platform - Mobile: Apple, Android
Digital Platform - Tablet: Apple iOS, Android
Preprint Adv.............Beverly George
Pub./Gen Mgr.............Mike Gochenour
Ed.............Linda Ash
District Sales Mgr.............Will Alsworth
Market Information: TMC.
Mechanical Available: Offset; Black and 3 ROP colors; insert accepted; page cutoffs - 22 3/4.
Mechanical Specifications: Type page 10x 21; E - 6 cols, 2 1/16, 1/8 between; A - 6 cols, 1 5/8, 1/8 between; C - 9 cols, 1 3/8, 1/16 between.
Areas Served: Counties of: Shenandoah, Warren, Frederick, Clarke, Paige in Virginia. Hampshire, Hardy West Virginia.
Delivery Method: Mail, Newsstand, Carrier, RacksEquipment & Software: PRESSROOM EQUIPMENT: Lines — 6-G/Urbanite 1978; 2-DEV/Horizon 1985; Reels & Stands — 6; MAILROOM EQUIPMENT: Counter Stackers — BG/Count-O-Veyor; Inserters & Stuffers — KAN; Tying Machines — Dynaric/Strapper; Address Machine — 2/St.; CLASSIFIED EQUIPMENT: Hardware — SUN/Server, APP/eMac Workstation, ON X11; Printers — HP/4 Plus; CLASSIFIED SOFTWARE: Vison Data/Classified Pagination System. DISPLAY EQUIPMENT: Hardware — APP/Mac G4 500 MHZ Dual Processors; Printers — HP/4100, HP 1700d, HP/4300; Other Hardware — Umax powerbook 21 DISPLAY SOFTWAREAd Make-up Applications — Corel Draw, QPS/QuarkXPress 4.11, Adobe/Photoshop, Baseview/Production Manager

Pro, Adobe/Typesetter 3, Adobe/Acrobat 5.0; EDITORIAL EQUIPMENT: Hardware — APP/Mac G4 400 MHZ Towers, APP/Mac G4 933 Mhz, APP/Mac 800Mhz/LiMax/Scanner, Nikon/Scanner; Printers — HP/4000 EDITORIAL SOFTWARE: Baseview/Newsedit Pro IQUE, QPS/QuarkXPress 4.11, Adobe/Photoshop. PRODUCTION EQUIPMENT: Hardware — Nu/Flip Top FT40V6 UPNS, ECR, HP/1700D, ECRM/EVJet 6200, ECRM/EVJet 3100; Cameras — 1-B/18 x 24; Scanners — Nikon/CoolScan, Umax/UTA 11 8 1/2 x 14 Page Scanner PRODUCTION SOFTWARE: Baseview/Managing Editor, ALS/Page Director 40.4, Adobe/Quark 4.11

SUFFOLK

SUFFOLK NEWS-HERALD
130 S Saratoga St, Suffolk, Va., 23434-5323, Suffolk City; gen tel (757) 539-3437; adv tel (757) 539-3437; ed tel (757) 539-3437; gen fax (757) 539-1123; adv fax (757) 539-3000; ed fax (757) 539-1123; gen/nat adv e-mail dana.snow@suffolknewsherald.com; disp adv e-mail dana.snow@suffolknewsherald.com; class adv e-mailhope.rose@suffolknewsherald.com; ed e-mail res.spears@suffolknewsherald.com; web site www.suffolknewsherald.com
Group: Boone Newspapers, Inc.
Published: Tues, Wed, Thur, Fri, Sat, Sun
Weekday Frequency: m
Saturday Frequency: m
Circulation: 80; 101(sat); 100(sun)
Last Audit: Sworn/Estimate/Non-Audited September 15, 2017
Advertising Rate (weekday/saturday): Open inch rate $25.15
Advertising Rate (sunday): Open inch rate $25.15
News services: 1873
Own Printing Facility?: No
Commercial Printers?: No
Special Editions: The Great Outdoors (Apr); Football (Aug); Christmas Greetings (Dec); Progress (Feb); Year in Review (Jan); Summer Lifestyles (Jul); June Bride (Jun); Home Improvement (Mar); Senior Citizens (May); Buckle Up for Safety Coloring Book (Nov); Peanut Festival
Special Weekly Sections: Food (Tue); Home, Garden (Wed); Military (Thur); Business (Fri); Religion (Sat); Leisure (Sun);
Proprietary Publications: Suffolk Living magazine Western Branch Magazine
Bus. Mgr. ....Cathy Daughtrey
Adv. Dir. ....Earl Jones
Pub. ....John Carr
Editor ....R.E Spears III
Circ. Mgr. ....Cathy Daughtrey
Adv. Rep. ....Hope Rose
News Editor ....Tracy Agnew
Market Information: Split run; TMC.
Mechanical Available: Offset; Black and 3 ROP colors; insert accepted; page cutoffs - 22 3/4.
Mechanical Specifications: Type page 11.25 x 21.5, 6 cols.
Areas Served: SUFFOLK
Chesapeake
Isle of Wight County
Delivery Method: Mail, Newsstand, Carrier, RacksEquipment & Software: PRESSROOM EQUIPMENT: Lines — 6-G/Community (24 pg b/w capacity).; MAILROOM EQUIPMENT: Tying Machines — 1/Us.; BUSINESS EQUIPMENT: 2-EKI/Televideo 950 CLASSIFIED EQUIPMENT: Hardware — APP/iMac; Printers — HP/5000; CLASSIFIED SOFTWARE: Baseview. DISPLAY EQUIPMENT: Hardware — APP/Mac G4; Printers — HP/5000; DISPLAY SOFTWAREAd Make-up Applications — QPS/QuarkXPress; Layout Software — APP/Mac G4. EDITORIAL EQUIPMENT: Hardware — HP; Printers — HP/5000 EDITORIAL SOFTWARE: QPS/QuarkXPress. PRODUCTION EQUIPMENT: Hardware — APP/Mac LaserPrinter PRODUCTION SOFTWARE: QPS/QuarkXPress.

WAYNESBORO

THE NEWS VIRGINIAN
1300 W Main St, Waynesboro, Va., 22980-2414, Waynesboro City; gen tel (540) 949-8213; adv tel (540) 949-8213; ed tel (540) 949-8216; gen fax (540) 949-6173; adv fax (540) 941-8859; ed fax (540) 942-4542; gen/nat adv e-mail mgads@newsvirginian.com; disp adv e-mail mgads@newsvirginian.com; class adv e-mailmgads@newsvirginian.com; ed e-mail nvnews@newsvirginian.com; web site www.newsvirginian.com
Group: BH Media Group
Published: Mon, Tues, Wed, Thur, Fri, Sat, Sun
Weekday Frequency: m
Saturday Frequency: m
Circulation: 4,201; 4,201(sat); 4,545(sun)
Last Audit: AAM September 30, 2016
Advertising Rate (weekday/saturday): Open inch rate $23.85
Advertising Rate (sunday): Open inch rate $27.26
News services: AP, NEA, TMS, Media General News Service.
Special Editions: Tourist Guide (Fall); Bridal Guide (Jan); Senior Lifestyles (Jun); Home & Garden (Mar); Hunting (Oct); Tourist Guide (Spring); Tourist Guide (Summer).
Special Weekly Sections: Best Food Days (Wed/Sun); Real Estate (Thur)
Syndicated Publications: USA WEEKEND Magazine (S); TV Time (Sat).
Interim Pub. ....Lawrence McConnell
Bus. Mgr. ....Denise Carter
Adv. Dir. ....Sherry Suggs
Circ. Dir. ....Paul Wash
Sports Ed. ....Jim Sacco
Pub. ....James Stratton
Bus. Develop sales Rep. ....Patti Butler
Classifieds Adv. Mgr. ....Stephanie Twitty
Mng. Ed. ....Rob Longley
Market Information: TMC.
Mechanical Available: Offset; Black and 3 ROP colors; insert accepted - Post-its, polybags, samples; page cutoffs - 22.
Mechanical Specifications: Type page 10 7/8 x 20 3/4; E - 6 cols, 1 73/100, 1/10 between; A - 6 cols, 1 73/100, 1/10 between; C - 10 cols, 1 2/25, 1/8 between.Equipment & Software: PRESSROOM EQUIPMENT: Lines — 4-G/Urbanite; MAILROOM EQUIPMENT: Tying Machines — 1-Bu/42409, 1/MLN.; BUSINESS SOFTWARE: Vision Data CLASSIFIED EQUIPMENT: Hardware — Mk/3000, 7-PC Microsystem; CLASSIFIED SOFTWARE: HI/AdPower, Microsoft/Word 6.0, QPS/QuarkXPress 4.1. DISPLAY EQUIPMENT: Printers — 2-APP/Mac LaserWriter; Other Hardware — HP/ScanJet Flatbed, APP/Mac Scanner. DISPLAY SOFTWAREAd Make-up Applications — QPS/QuarkXPress, Adobe/Photoshop, Caere/OmniPage, Ofoto; EDITORIAL EQUIPMENT: Hardware — Mk/3000, 10-PC Microsystem; Printers — HP/4MV Postscript, HP/4 Plus EDITORIAL SOFTWARE: Microsoft/Word 6.0, QPS/QuarkXPress 4.1, ACT. PRODUCTION EQUIPMENT: Hardware — Visioneer/Paper Port, Caere/OmniPage; Cameras — 1-B/24 x 24, COM/M, 1-LE/R 20 x 24 PRODUCTION SOFTWARE: QPS/QuarkXPress, Adobe/Photoshop, Caere/OmniPage.

WINCHESTER

THE WINCHESTER STAR
2 N Kent St, Winchester, Va., 22601-5038, Winchester City; gen tel (540) 667-3200; adv tel (540) 665-4950; ed tel (540) 665-4941; gen fax (540) 667-0012; adv fax (540) 667-0012; ed fax (540) 667-1649; gen/nat adv e-mail ads@winchesterstar.com; disp adv e-mail ads@winchesterstar.com; class adv e-mailads@winchesterstar.com; ed e-mail news@winchesterstar.com; web site www.winchesterstar.com
Group: Ogden Newspapers Inc.
Published: Mon, Tues, Wed, Thur, Fri, Sat
Weekday Frequency: m
Saturday Frequency: m
Circulation: 15,911; 18,433(sat)
Last Audit: AAM September 30, 2017
Advertising Rate (weekday/saturday): Open inch

rate $25.00
News services: AP, Washington Post **Established:** 1896
Own Printing Facility?: Yes
Special Editions: Christmas Gifts (Dec); Bridal (Feb); Our Community (Gov't) (Jan); Planting (Mar); Graduation (May); Real Estate Guide (Monthly); College & Pro Football (Sept).
Special Weekly Sections: Best Food Days (Wed/Sat); Business (Tue/Thur); Weekend, Church (Fri); Stocks (Sat)
Syndicated Publications: PARADE Magazine (Sat).
American Profile (Wed)
Athlon Sports (monthly)
Digital Platform - Mobile: Android
Digital Platform - Tablet: Android
Gen. Mgr. ....Thomas W. Byrd
Circ. Mgr. ....Bill Green
Mng. Ed. ....Maria Montgomery
Online Ed. ....Bobby Ford
Editorial Page Ed. ....Adrian O'Connor
Prodn. Foreman, Pressroom ....Glen Stickel
Systems Mgr. ....Joyce Williams
Adv. Manager ....Chrissy Hill
Production Mgr ....Kristen Colebank
Market Information: Split run; Zoned editions.
Mechanical Available: Offset; Black and 3 ROP colors; insert accepted; page cutoffs - 21 1/2.
Mechanical Specifications: Type page 13 x 21 1/2; E - 6 cols, 2, 1/5 between; A - 6 cols, 2, 1/5 between; C - 9 cols, 1 5/16, 1/5 between.
Delivery Method: Mail, Newsstand, Carrier, RacksEquipment & Software: PRESSROOM EQUIPMENT: Lines — 8-G/Urbanite U-1327 single width 1981; Folders — 1-G/Double former; Control System — 1-Ebway/SU 300.; MAILROOM EQUIPMENT: Counter Stackers — 1-HL/Dual Carrier, 2-QWI/501; Inserters & Stuffers — GMA/Alphaliner; Tying Machines — 2-EAM-Mosca, 1-Samuel/Automatic; Address Machine — 2-Am/1900; BUSINESS EQUIPMENT: IBM/Sys 3600 CLASSIFIED EQUIPMENT: Hardware — Dell/2300; Printers — CText/ALPS ALQ324E, NewGen/Turbo PS-400, HP/Laserjet 5000; CLASSIFIED SOFTWARE: SCS/Admax, SCS/Classpag. DISPLAY EQUIPMENT: Hardware — 2-Dell/4300 Server; Printers — HP/LaserJet 4000N, C.Itoh/CI-1000SQE; DISPLAY SOFTWAREAd Make-up Applications — SCS/Admax; Layout Software — Layout/8000. EDITORIAL EQUIPMENT: Hardware — COM, Dell/Optiplex-GS, Dell/2100, Dell/200, 2-Dell/PowerEdge 4200 Server/1-APP/Mac Quadra 700, 1-APP/Mac SE; Printers — HP/LaserJet 4000N, NewGen/Design Express 6 EDITORIAL SOFTWARE: Falcon/Indesign PRODUCTION EQUIPMENT: Hardware — 4-Xante/8200, Konica, 2-ECR; Cameras — C/Spartan III, SCREEN; Scanners — Microtek/ScanMaker III, HP ScanJet II cx PRODUCTION SOFTWARE: Good News.

WASHINGTON

BELLINGHAM

THE BELLINGHAM HERALD
1155 N State St, Ste 200, Bellingham, Wash., 98225-5024, Whatcom; gen tel (360) 676-2600; adv tel (360) 676-2660; ed tel (360) 676-2660; adv fax n/a; ed fax n/a; gen/nat adv e-mail advertising@bellinghamherald.com; disp adv e-mail advertising@bellinghamherald.com; class adv e-mailclassifieds@bellinghamherald.com; ed e-mail newsroom@bellinghamherald.com; web site www.bellinghamherald.com 648,000(visitors)
Group: The McClatchy Company
Published: Mon, Tues, Wed, Thur, Fri, Sat, Sun
Weekday Frequency: m
Saturday Frequency: m
Circulation: 15,752; 15,752(sat); 19,662(sun)
Last Audit: AAM March 31, 2016
Advertising Rate (weekday/saturday): Open inch rate $47
Advertising Rate (sunday): Open inch rate $58

Online Advertising Rate: 300x250 $10.00 CPM; 728x90 $8.00 CPM; 300x100 $7.00 CPM
News services: AP, MCT, NYT, WaPo, McClatchy **Established:** 1890
Own Printing Facility?: No
Commercial Printers?: No
Special Editions: Prime Time (Jan, March, May, July, Sept, Nov); Bellingham Families (March, May, Sept, Nov); Whatcom Weddings (Jan); Ski to Sea (May); Northwest Washington Fair Program (Aug); Whatcom Health Magazine (May); Northwest Homes (Bi Weekly); Photo Calendar (Dec); BIA Homeshow Program (Feb)
Special Weekly Sections: Best Food (Tue); Entertainment (Thur); TV, Major Dept. Store Adv. (Sun)
Syndicated Publications: Parade (Sun); Relish (Monthly)
Digital Platform - Mobile: Apple, Android
Digital Platform - Tablet: Apple iOS, Android, Other
Exec. Ed. ....Julie Shirley
Business Ed. ....Dave Gallagher
Senior Editor Sports and Features David Rasbach
Nat'l Retail Adv. ....Jill Wyatt
General Manager and Vice President of Advertising Rusty Dodge
Sr. Ed./News ....John Mangalonzo
Sr. Ed./Audiene ....Jim Donaldson
Market Information: ADS; Split run; TMC.
Mechanical Available: Offset; Black and 3 ROP colors; insert accepted - single sheet card stock; page cutoffs - 22 3/4.
Mechanical Specifications: 1 col: 1.5278" wide 6 col: 10" wide
Full pg height: 20.125"
Areas Served: 98220, 98225, 98226, 98227, 98229, 98239, 98231, 98240, 98244, 98247, 98248, 98262, 98264, 98266, 98281, 98295, 98276
Delivery Method: Mail, Newsstand, Carrier, RacksEquipment & Software: EDITORIAL SOFTWARE: CCI Newsgate

BREMERTON

KITSAP SUN
545 5th St, Bremerton, Wash., 98337-1413, Kitsap; gen tel (360) 377-3711; adv tel (360) 377-9210; ed tel (360) 415-2679; gen fax (360) 377-9237; adv fax (360) 377-9237; ed fax (360) 415-2681; gen/nat adv e-mail ad-support@kitsapsun.com; disp adv e-mail ad-support@kitsapsun.com; class adv e-mailclassifieds@kitsapsun.com; ed e-mail David.Nelson@kitsapsun.com; web site www.kitsapsunmedia.com
Group: Journal Media Group
Published: Mon, Tues, Wed, Thur, Fri, Sat, Sun
Weekday Frequency: m
Saturday Frequency: m
Circulation: 16,363; 16,705(sat); 18,718(sun)
Last Audit: AAM March 31, 2017
Advertising Rate (weekday/saturday): Open inch rate $50.09
Advertising Rate (sunday): Open inch rate $54.24
News services: AP, SHNS. **Established:** 1935
Special Editions: Visitor's Guide (Apr); 5 Days til Christmas (Dec); Home & Garden (May); Festival of Trees (Nov); Football (Oct).
Special Weekly Sections: News, Sports (Mon); Business (Tue); Food (Wed); Business, Home, Garden, Sports (Thur); Arts, Entertainment, Seniors, Auto, Business, Military (Fri); Auto, Business, Health, Real Estate (Sat); Business, Employment, Travel, TV, News, Real Estate, Family (Sun); Weather (Daily)
Syndicated Publications: USA WEEKEND Magazine (S).
Credit Mgr. ....Robin Alexander
Dir., Adv./Mktg. ....Mike Stevens
Nat'l Adv. Mgr. ....Don Dosa
Pres./Pub. ....Charles Horton
Ed. ....David Nelson
Entertainment Writer ....Michael Moore
Environmental/Tech. Writer Christopher Dunagan
Sports Ed. ....Chuck Stark
Submitted Content Ed. ....Jim Campbell
Opns. Dir. ....Ron Muhleman
Pre Press Mgr. ....Randi Watson
Classified Adv. Mgr. ....Barry Weaver
Circ. Dir. ....Hugh Hirata
Market Information: ADS; TMC; Zoned editions.

LEWISTON
NEZ PERCE
ASOTIN

IDAHO

PEND
OREILLE

SPOKANE
SPOKANE

Pullman
WHITMAN

GARFIELD

COLUMBIA

STEVENS

LINCOLN

ADAMS

Walla Walla
WALLA WALLA

FERRY

FRANKLIN

CANADA

OKANOGAN

Moses Lake
GRANT

KENNEWICK-
RICHLAND-
PASCO

BENTON

DOUGLAS

WENATCHEE
CHELAN

Ellensburg
KITTITAS

YAKIMA
YAKIMA

OREGON

KLICKITAT

BELLINGHAM
WHATCOM

MOUNT VERNON-ANACORTES
SKAGIT

Oak Harbor

**Seattle-Tacoma-
Olympia**

Seattle-Bellevue-
Everett
KING

SEATTLE-TACOMA-
BELLEVUE

SNOHOMISH

Tacoma
PIERCE

SAN
JUAN

ISLAND

KITSAP

Centralia
LEWIS

SKAMANIA

MULTNOMAH

PORTLAND-
VANCOUVER-
BEAVERTON

CLACKAMAS

Port Angeles
CLALLAM

JEFFERSON

BREMERTON-SILVERDALE

Shelton
MASON

OLYMPIA
THURSTON

LONGVIEW
COWLITZ

CLARK

WASHINGTON

COLUMBIA

YAMHILL

Aberdeen
GRAYS HARBOR

PACIFIC

WAHKIAKUM

LEGEND

Combined Statistical Area
Metropolitan Statistical Area
Micropolitan Statistical Area
Metropolitan Division
International
State
County
Shoreline

Dallas-Fort Worth
RICHMOND
Concord
Philadelphia

CANADA
TEXAS
HARRIS

N

60 Miles

60 Kilometers

0 15 30 45

0 15 30 45

Washington

Total Daily Newspapers	20
Total Daily Circulation	556,185
Total Weekly Newspapers	117
Total Weekly Circulation	1,243,712
Population	7,405,473

Mechanical Available: Web Offset; Black and 4 ROP colors; insert accepted - we-prints, product sample bags; page cutoffs - 22 3/4.
Mechanical Specifications: Type page 10 1/2 x 21 1/2; E - 6 cols, 1 14/25, 1/8 between; A - 6 cols, 1 14/25, 1/8 between; C - 9 cols, 1 7/100, 1/8 between.Equipment & Software: PRESSROOM EQUIPMENT: Lines — 5-HI/N1650 double width 1993; Press Drive — GE/200h.p.; Folders — 2-G/2:1; Reels & Stands — 4-G/double.; MAILROOM EQUIPMENT: Counter Stackers — 2-HL/Monitor, 1-HL/HT II; Inserters & Stuffers — GMA/SLS 1000 8:1; Tying Machines — 1-MLN/ML2, 1-MLN/MLEE, 1/Power Strap/PSNG; Address Machine — 1-KR/Quarter Folder, Ch.; BUSINESS EQUIPMENT: IBM/AS-400 CLASSIFIED EQUIPMENT: Hardware — PC Network; Printers — Epson; CLASSIFIED SOFTWARE: Dewar/Information Sys, XYQUEST/XyWrite. DISPLAY EQUIPMENT: Hardware — APP/Mac; Printers — APP/Mac LaserWriter, Hyphen/Pelbox Typesetter, AG/Select Set 5000, Hyphen/Ultra Typesetter; DISPLAY SOFTWAREAd Make-up Applications — Multi-Ad/Creator 3.8, Mk/Ad Director, QPS/QuarkXPress 3.32, Adobe/Photoshop 3.0, Adobe/PageMaker 6.0, Adobe/Illustrator 6; EDITORIAL EQUIPMENT: Hardware — APP/Mac/Microtek/Scanner, Nikon/FilmScanner, Kk/FilmScanner, Lf/AP Leaf Picture Desk; Printers — Hyphen/Typesetters, TI EDITORIAL SOFTWARE: QPS/QuarkXPress, Adobe/Photoshop 3.0, Adobe/Illustrator 6.0, P.INK. PRODUCTION EQUIPMENT: Hardware — 1-BKY/Ascor, 1-Burgess, SpectraSet/3100; Cameras — 1-Acti/24V, 1-R/432 Mark II; Scanners — Microtek PRODUCTION SOFTWARE: QPS/QuarkXPress.

COUPEVILLE

WHIDBEY NEWS TIMES

PO Box 1200, Coupeville, Wash., 98239-1200, Island; gen tel (360) 675-6611; adv tel (360) 675-6611; ed tel (360) 675-6611; gen/nat adv e-mail lmozes@whidbeynewsgroup.com; disp adv e-mail mhansen@whidbeynewsgroup.com; ed e-mail kgraves@whidbeynewsgroup.com; web site www.whidbeynewstimes.com
Group: Black Press Group Ltd.
Sound Publishing, Inc.
Published: Tues, Wed, Thur, Fri, Sat
Circulation: 13,394; 6,498(sat)
Last Audit: CAC March 31, 2016
Advertising Rate (weekday/saturday): Open inch rate $19.70
News services: 1908
Digital Platform - Mobile: Apple, Android, Windows, Blackberry
Digital Platform - Tablet: Apple iOS, Android, Windows 7, Blackberry Tablet OS, Kindle, Nook, Kindle Fire
Pub. ....Keven R. Graves
Ed. ....Megan Hansen
Nat'l Sales Dir. .... Stephen Barrett
Areas Served: Island County
Delivery Method: Mail, Newsstand, Racks

ELLENSBURG

DAILY RECORD

401 N Main St, Ellensburg, Wash., 98926-3107, Kittitas; gen tel (509) 925-1414; adv tel (509)925-1414; ed tel (509)925-1414; gen fax (509) 925-5696; adv fax (509)925-5696; ed fax (509)925-5696; gen/nat adv e-mail rsmith@kvnews.com; disp adv e-mail rsmith@kvnews.com; class adv e-mailclassified2@kvnews.com; ed e-mail jmarkell@kvnews.com; web site www.kvnews.com
Group: Adams Publishing Group, LLC
Published: Mon, Tues, Wed, Thur, Fri, Sat, Sun
Weekday Frequency: e
Saturday Frequency: m
Circulation: 5,523; 5,523(sat)
Last Audit: Sworn/Estimate/Non-Audited September 30, 2017
Advertising Rate (weekday/saturday): Open inch

rate $13.85 for Local and $16 for National
Online Advertising Rate: Half page 42.50 CPM; Leaderboard & In Story 37.50 cpm; Footer 22.50
News services: AP. **Established:** 1883
Own Printing Facility?: No
Commercial Printers?: No
Special Editions: Conservation/Agriculture (Apr); Fair Guide (Aug); Spring Visitor's Guide (May); Holiday Gift Guide (Nov); Rodeo (Sept); KV Living (April, July, Jan, Oct);
Special Weekly Sections: Religion (Sat); Business (Thurs), Food (Tues), Entertainment (Thurs), Outdoors (Fri)
Syndicated Publications: American Profile (Fri); Relish (Monthly); Parade (S).
Digital Platform - Mobile: Apple, Android, Blackberry
Editor/General Manager ....Joanna Markell
Telecom Mgr. ....Richard Dalton
Advertising sales manager ....Robyn Smith
Advertising process manager/national accts .. Pam Shuart
Circulation director .... Josh Crawford
Market Information: TMC.
Mechanical Available: Offset; Black and 3 ROP colors; insert accepted; page cutoffs - 22 3/4.
Mechanical Specifications: Type page 12 15/16 x 21; E - 6 cols, 2, 1/6 between; A - 6 cols, 2, 1/6 between; C - 9 cols, 1 1/2, 1/12 between.
Delivery Method: Mail, Newsstand, Carrier, RacksEquipment & Software: PRESSROOM EQUIPMENT: Lines — 2-G/Community 1968, 2-G/Community 1969, 2-G/Community 1980.; BUSINESS EQUIPMENT: Sun/Sparc Station 10 BUSINESS SOFTWARE: PBS CLASSIFIED EQUIPMENT: Hardware — APP/Mac; Printers — Okidata/Microline 320 Turbo; CLASSIFIED SOFTWARE: Baseview. DISPLAY EQUIPMENT: Hardware — APP/Mac; Printers — Xante/Accel-a-writer 8200; Other Hardware — Konica/EV-Jetsetter, Konica/K-550 processor. DISPLAY SOFTWAREAd Make-up Applications — QPS/QuarkXPress 3.3.2, Adobe/Photoshop 5.0, Aldus Freehand 8.0, Adobe/PageMaker 6.5, Multi Ad Creator, ALS/Managing Editor; EDITORIAL EQUIPMENT: Hardware — APP/Mac/APP/Mac; Printers — Xante/Accel-a-Writer 8200 EDITORIAL SOFTWARE: Baseview, QPS/QuarkXPress, Adobe/Photoshop, Caere/OmniPage. PRODUCTION EQUIPMENT: Hardware — Caere/OmniPage Pro 8.0, Konica/EV-Jetsetter; Cameras — APP/Mac QuickTake 150, Olympus/620-L; Scanners — Sprint/Scan 35, Epson/ES-1200, Umax/Astra 12205 PRODUCTION SOFTWARE: QPS/QuarkXPress 3.32.

EVERETT

THE HERALD

1213 California St, Everett, Wash., 98201-3445, Snohomish; gen tel (425) 339-3000; adv tel (425) 339-3030; ed tel (425) 339-3400; gen fax (425) 339-3049; adv fax (425) 339-3049; ed fax (425) 339-3435; gen/nat adv e-mail advertising@heraldnet.com; disp adv e-mail advertising@heraldnet.com; class adv e-mailclassified@heraldnet.com; ed e-mail editor@heraldnet.com; web site www.heraldnet.com
Group: The Washington Post
Black Press Group Ltd.
Published: Mon, Tues, Wed, Thur, Fri, Sat, Sun
Weekday Frequency: m
Saturday Frequency: m
Circulation: 32,045; 32,045(sat); 39,474(sun)
Last Audit: AAM March 31, 2015
Advertising Rate (weekday/saturday): Open inch rate $71.04
Advertising Rate (sunday): Open inch rate $81.63
News services: AP, LAT-WP, Scripps McClatchy News Service. **Established:** 1901
Own Printing Facility?: Yes
Commercial Printers?: Yes
Special Editions: Herald Health (Quarterly);
Special Weekly Sections: Business (Mon); Health (Tue); Best Food (Wed); Home and Garden (Thur); Arts, Entertainment, Automotive (Fri); Travel (Sat); Money, Real Estate (Sun)
Syndicated Publications: Relish (Monthly); Access (S).
Circ. Opns. Mgr. .... Jere Grubb
Exec. Ed. .... Neal Pattison

Herald Business Journal Editor ....Jim Davis
Features/Food Ed. ....Melanie Munk
Librarian/TV Ed. ....Bill Pedigo
Sports Ed. .... Kevin Brown
Josh O'Connor
City Ed. .... Robert Frank
Diane Shaver
Pub. ....David Dadisman
Adv. Dir. .... Pilar Linares
Retail Adv. Mgr. ....Carrie Radcliff
Dir., Nat'l and Regional Sales..... Stephen Barrett
Market Information: Split run; TMC; Zoned editions.
Mechanical Available: Offset; Black and 3 ROP colors; insert accepted; page cutoffs - 22.
Mechanical Specifications: Type page 13 x 21; E - 6 cols, 2 1/16, 1/8 between; A - 6 cols, 2 1/16, 1/8 between; C - 10 cols, 1 3/16, 1/8 between.
Areas Served: 98011, 98012, 98019, 98020, 98021, 98026, 98036, 98037, 98043, 98072, 98087, 98133, 98155, 98201, 98203, 98204, 98205, 98208, 98223, 98236, 98239, 98241, 98249, 98251, 98252, 98253, 98256, 98258, 98260, 98270, 98271, 98272, 98273, 98274, 98275, 98277, 98282, 98290, 98292, 98294, 98296
Delivery Method: Newsstand, Carrier, RacksEquipment & Software: PRESSROOM EQUIPMENT: Lines — 9-G/Metrocolor double width 1993; Folders — 2, G/3:2; Reels & Stands — 3-G/Ct-50 RIP; Control System — Rockwell/Automation Print View.; MAILROOM EQUIPMENT: Counter Stackers — 3/QWI, 2-Gammerler/KL 503/1; Inserters & Stuffers — 1-MM/227E, 1-/AM Graphics/NP 630, 1-G/Heidelberg 1280; Tying Machines — 5-/Dynaric; Address Machine — 3-KR/Paper Labeler, Scitex/Ink Jet; CLASSIFIED EQUIPMENT: Hardware — 1-DEC/Micro VAX 4000-200, 25-HP/Pentium II; CLASSIFIED SOFTWARE: Cybergraphics/Genesis 7.7. DISPLAY EQUIPMENT: Hardware — 22-APP/Power Mac; DISPLAY SOFTWARELayout Software — MEI/ALS. EDITORIAL EQUIPMENT: Hardware — 70-HP/Pentium II, 4-APP/Power Mac, 2-HP/NT fileserver EDITORIAL SOFTWARE: QPS/QuarkXPress 4.0, Microsoft/Word 6.0, APT/ACT. PRODUCTION EQUIPMENT: Hardware — 1-AG/Selectset 5000, 1-III/3850, 1-ECR/Scriptwriter; Cameras — 1-C/Marathon, 1-R/400, 1-R/475; Scanners — X/7650, 1-SCREEN/1030 PRODUCTION SOFTWARE: QPS/QuarkXPress 4.0.

KENNEWICK

TRI-CITY HERALD

333 W Canal Dr, Kennewick, Wash., 99336-3811, Benton; gen tel (509) 582-1500; adv tel (509) 582-1460; ed tel (509) 582-1523; gen fax (509) 582-1453; adv fax (509) 582-1401; ed fax (509) 582-1510; gen/nat adv e-mail ads@tricityherald.com; disp adv e-mail ads@tricityherald.com; class adv e-mailads@tricityherald.com; ed e-mail news@tricityherald.com; web site www.tricityherald.com
- 3,233,688(views) 493,812(visitors)
Group: McClatchy
Published: Mon, Tues, Wed, Thur, Fri, Sat, Sun
Weekday Frequency: m
Saturday Frequency: m
Circulation: 23,719; 22,995(sat); 28,785(sun)
Last Audit: AAM December 31, 2015
Advertising Rate (weekday/saturday): Open inch rate $60.64
Advertising Rate (sunday): Open inch rate $60.64
Online Advertising Rate: 300x250 $10cpm; 728x90 $10cpm; 300x100 $7cpm;Homepage only $15cpm; Floorboard $15cpm; Mobile $10cpm; Pre-roll video $25cpm; Ruler add 300x100 $8cpm.
News services: Metro Suburbia Inc./Newhouse Newspapers, LAT-WP, MCT, NYT, McClatchy. **Established:** 1947
Own Printing Facility?: No
Commercial Printers?: No
Special Editions: Healthy Living (Quarterly); Wine Press Northwest (Quarterly); Living TC (Quarterly)
Special Weekly Sections: Trends, Leisure (Mon); Family, Friends (Tue); Food, Nutrition (Wed); health, Fitness (Thur); Entertainment,

Arts (Fri); Outdoors, Auto, Religion (Sat); Desert Living, Real Estate, Travel, Voices, TV, Business (Sun); Business, Sports, Mid-Columbia (Daily)
Syndicated Publications: Parade (S).
Digital Platform - Mobile: Apple, Android
Digital Platform - Tablet: Apple iOS, Android
Controller .... Gerald Hug
Chief Photographer ....Bob Brawdy
Exec. Ed. ....Laurie Williams
Publisher .... Gregg McConnell
Adv. Dir. ....Sean Flaherty
Market Information: ADS; TMC.
Mechanical Available: Offset; Black and 3 ROP colors; insert accepted - all; page cutoffs - 21.
Mechanical Specifications: Type page 11 1/2 x 21; E - 6 cols, 1 3/4, 3/16 between; A - 6 cols, 1 3/4, 3/16 between; C - 9 cols, 1 3/16, 1/8 between.
Delivery Method: Mail, Newsstand, Carrier, RacksEquipment & Software: PRESSROOM EQUIPMENT: Lines — 6-MAN/MediaMan 1992; 7-G/Community 1982; Reels & Stands — 4-MEG.; MAILROOM EQUIPMENT: Counter Stackers — 4-Id/2000; Inserters & Stuffers — GMA/SLS 1000, HI/1372; Tying Machines — 1/Power Strap, 1-/Power Strap, 2-/Power Strap; Address Machine — 1-Ch/520-E.; BUSINESS EQUIPMENT: DEC/Micro VAX 4000 Model 50, SCS, Dell/4200 BUSINESS SOFTWARE: SCS, CJ: Circ (TMC), People Soft Financials CLASSIFIED EQUIPMENT: Hardware — SCS, Dell/4200; CLASSIFIED SOFTWARE: SCS/AdMax 8.0.3, SCS/ClassPag 3.96. DISPLAY EQUIPMENT: Hardware — Dell/Poweredge 4400; DISPLAY SOFTWAREAd Make-up Applications — Multi-Ad/Creator 4.0.3, Aldus/FreeHand 10, Adobe/Photoshop 6.x; Layout Software — SCS/Layout 8000. EDITORIAL EQUIPMENT: Hardware — 4-APP/Mac G3-400 EDITORIAL SOFTWARE: QPS/QuarkXPress 3.32, Baseview/News Edit Pro. PRODUCTION EQUIPMENT: Hardware — Nat/A-340, Kk/2035+ 35mm Scanner; Cameras — 1-C/1211, DAI/C-690-AX.

LONGVIEW

THE DAILY NEWS

770 11th Ave, Longview, Wash., 98632-2412, Cowlitz; gen tel (360) 577-2500; adv tel (360) 577-2500; ed tel (360) 577-2500; gen fax (360) 577-2536; adv fax (360) 577-2536; ed fax (360) 577-2538; gen/nat adv e-mail squaife@tdn.com; disp adv e-mail squaife@tdn.com; class adv e-mailahurse@tdn.com; ed e-mail andre@tdn.com; web site www.tdn.com
Group: Lee Enterprises, Inc.
Published: Mon, Tues, Wed, Thur, Fri, Sat, Sun
Weekday Frequency: m
Saturday Frequency: m
Circulation: 12,155; 12,155(sat); 13,422(sun)
Last Audit: AAM December 31, 2016
Advertising Rate (weekday/saturday): Open inch rate $29.35
Advertising Rate (sunday): Open inch rate $32.88
News services: AP, LAT-WP. **Established:** 1923
Special Editions: Thanksgiving (Other).
Special Weekly Sections: Business (Daily); Health, Lifestyle, Neighbors (Tue); Sasquatch, Best Food (Wed); Entertainment (Thur); Outdoor, TV (Fri); Religious. Auto (Sat); Travel, Real Estate, TV (Sun)
Syndicated Publications: Real Estate (Monthly); Parade (S).
Adv. Mgr., Retail ....Steve Quaife
City Ed. ....Andre Stepankowsky
Community Ed. ....Brenda McCorkle
Features Reporter ....Tom Paulu
Librarian .... Donna Yardley
Regl. Ed. .... Nancy Edwards
Pub. .... Rick Parrish
Managing Ed. ....John Markon
Business Mgr. ....Marianne Chambers
Copy Editor .... Mike Yantis
Market Information: ADS; TMC; Zoned editions.
Mechanical Available: Offset; Black and 3 ROP colors; insert accepted - Product Sample Bags; page cutoffs - 22 3/4.
Mechanical Specifications: Type page 11 1/8 x 21 1/2; E - 6 cols, 1 11/16, 1/8 between; A - 6 cols, 1 11/16, 1/8 between; C - 9 cols, 1 1/8, 1/16 between.Equipment & Software:

PRESSROOM EQUIPMENT: Lines — 4-G/Urbanite single width 1970; 3-G/Urbanite single width 1970; Folders — 2-G/Urbanite.; MAILROOM EQUIPMENT: Counter Stackers — 1-Id/Marathoner, 2-TMSI/Compass; Inserters & Stuffers — 2-MM/227 5:1; Tying Machines — 1-MLN/2EE, 2-MLN/2A, 3-MLN/2; Wrapping Singles — 2-Windab/UP720 Bottom Wrap; Address Machine — KR/215 Mailing System; BUSINESS EQUIPMENT: Sun/Sparc BUSINESS SOFTWARE: Vision Data CLASSIFIED EQUIPMENT: Hardware — Sun/Sparc workstations; Printers — HP/4050, Printronix/Line Printer; CLASSIFIED SOFTWARE: Vision Data/Classified. DISPLAY EQUIPMENT: Hardware — 8-APP/Mac G3, G4 Power Computing 8.01, 2-Sun/Servers; Other Hardware — Sharp/JX-600 Scanner, HP/ScanJet, HP/ScanJet CX, 2-Umax/S-12 Scanner, 1-HP/5000, 1-HP/2500 Color Proofer DISPLAY SOFTWARELayout Software — SCS/Layou EDITORIAL EQUIPMENT: Hardware — 2-Micron, 25-Dell/PC, APP/Mac Workstations/Umax/Astra 1200; Printers — HP/5000, HP/4050 EDITORIAL SOFTWARE: Lotus/Notes News Engin 4.6. PRODUCTION EQUIPMENT: Hardware — 1-Wd, 2-ECR/Scriptsetter RIP, 1-1PT Turbo Rip; Cameras — 1-C/Spartan II; Scanners — Nikon/LS-3510AF, Epson, Nikon/Coolscan PRODUCTION SOFTWARE: QPS/QuarkXPress 4.04.

MOSES LAKE

COLUMBIA BASIN HERALD

813 W 3rd Ave, Moses Lake, Wash., 98837-2008, Grant; gen tel (509) 765-4561; adv tel (509) 765-4561; ed tel (509) 765-4561; gen fax (509) 765-8659; adv fax (509) 765-8659; ed fax (509) 765-8659; gen/nat adv e-mail rblack@columbiabasinherald.com; disp adv e-mail rblack@colmbiabasinherald.com; class adv e-mailrblack@columbiabasinherald.com; ed e-mail editor@columbiabasinherald.com; web site www.columbiabasinherald.com

Group: Hagadone Corporation
Published: Mon, Tues, Wed, Thur, Fri
Weekday Frequency: e
Circulation: 4,406
Last Audit: Sworn/Estimate/Non-Audited October 5, 2017
Advertising Rate (weekday/saturday): Open inch rate $17.80
News services: AP. **Established:** 1941
Own Printing Facility?: Yes
Commercial Printers?: Yes
Special Editions: Create Your Own Adventure (Apr); Fair Tab (Aug); Lighted Ag Parade (Dec); Night on the Town (Feb); Spokane Boat Show (Jan); Home Buyers Guide (Jun); Spring Fair (Mar); All City Real Estate Guide (May); Horse & Rider (Monthly); Holiday Directory (Nov); His
Special Weekly Sections: Best Food Day (Tue); Community (Wed); Editorial, Travel (Thur); Business, Bits & Pieces, Religious, Hunting, Fishing (Fri)
Bus. Mgr. ..... Denise Lembcke
Nat'l Adv. Mgr. ..... Joyce McLanahan
Prodn. Supt. ..... Curt Weaver
Sales Manager ..... Rosalie Black
Circ. Dir. ..... Tom Hinde
Mng. Ed. ..... Bill Stevenson
Market Information: ADS; TMC.
Mechanical Available: Offset; Black and 3 ROP colors; insert accepted - others accepted; page cutoffs - 22 3/4.
Mechanical Specifications: Type page 13 x 21 1/2; E - 6 cols, 1 5/6, 1/8 between; A - 6 cols, 1 5/6, 1/8 between; C - 8 cols, 1 1/3, 1/8 between.
Delivery Method: Mail, Newsstand, Carrier, RacksEquipment & Software: MAILROOM EQUIPMENT: Tying Machines — 1/Bu, 1-/El; Address Machine — Ch/730S.; CLASSIFIED EQUIPMENT: Hardware — Mac/G4; Printers — HP/4200; CLASSIFIED SOFTWARE: Baseview 2.1.4. DISPLAY EQUIPMENT: Hardware — Mac/G4; Printers — HP/4200; DISPLAY SOFTWAREAd Make-up Applications — Baseview 2.1.4; Layout Software — Adforce. EDITORIAL EQUIPMENT: Hardware — Mac/G4; Printers — HP/4200 EDITORIAL SOFTWARE: Quark 4.0. PRODUCTION EQUIPMENT: Hardware — 2-Fr, 1-P, 1-Ma, 1-Fi; Cameras — 1-K.

MOUNT VERNON

SKAGIT VALLEY HERALD

1215 Anderson Rd, Mount Vernon, Wash., 98274-7615, Skagit; gen tel (360) 424-3251; adv tel (360) 416-2128; ed tel (360) 416-2160; gen fax (360) 424-5300; adv fax (360)424-5300; ed fax (360) 428-0400; gen/nat adv e-mail dpetit@skagitpublishing.com; disp adv e-mail dpetit@skagitpublishing.com; class adv e-maildpetit@skagitpublishing.com; ed e-mail editor@skagitpublishing.com; web site www.goskagit.com

Group: Adams Publishing Group, LLC
Published: Mon, Tues, Wed, Thur, Fri, Sat, Sun
Weekday Frequency: m
Saturday Frequency: m
Circulation: 12,100; 12,100(sat); 12,823(sun)
Last Audit: AAM December 31, 2016
Advertising Rate (weekday/saturday): Open inch rate $23.45
Advertising Rate (sunday): Open inch rate $25.45
Online Advertising Rate: Leaderboard: $12 per cpm; Big Box: $14 per cpm; Half Page: $18 per cpm
News services: AP, MCT, LAT-WP. **Established:** 1884
Own Printing Facility?: Yes
Commercial Printers?: Yes
Special Editions: Builders Assoc. Home Show (Apr); Anacortes Arts & Crafts (Aug); Bridal (Feb); Highland Games (Jul); Spring Home & Garden (Mar); Holiday Gift Guide (Nov); Swan (Woman of the Year) (Oct);
Special Weekly Sections: Business (Tue); best Food Day (Wed); Entertainment (Thur); Home & Garden (Fri); Religion (Sat); Skagit Living (Sun)
Syndicated Publications: TV Week Magazine (Weekly)
Digital Platform - Mobile: Apple, Android, Windows, Blackberry
Digital Platform - Tablet: Apple iOS, Android, Windows 7, Blackberry Tablet OS, Kindle, Nook, Kindle Fire
Pres. ..... Leighton P. Wood
Adv. Dir. ..... Mark Dobie
Adv. Mgr., Classified/Inside Sales ..... Jeanette Kales
Adv. Mgr., Co-op ..... Katie Sundermeyer
Adv. Mgr., Display ..... Deb Bundy
Adv. Mgr., Majors/Natl. Accts. ..... Stephanie Harper
Circ. Dir. ..... Manny Nevarez
Mng. Ed., Administration ..... Colette Weeks
Photo Ed. ..... Scott Terrell
Sports Ed. ..... Dan Ruthemeyer
Interactive Media Mgr. ..... Patrick Dougherty
Prodn. Dir. ..... Tom Larsen
Pub. ..... L. Stedem Wood
Ed. ..... Don Nelson
Market Information: ADS; TMC.
Mechanical Available: Offset; Black and 3 ROP colors; insert accepted - cards; page cutoffs - 22 3/4.
Mechanical Specifications: Type page 10 x 20 1/2; E - 6 cols, 1 19/32, 3/32 between; A - 6 cols, 1 19/32, 3/32 between; C - 6 cols, 1 19/32, 3/32 between.
Delivery Method: Mail, Newsstand, Carrier, RacksEquipment & Software: PRESSROOM EQUIPMENT: Lines — 16-G/Community; Folders — 2, G/Community; Registration System — Stoesser/Register System. MAILROOM EQUIPMENT: Counter Stackers — 2-MM/310-20; Inserters & Stuffers — 2-MM/5-pocket; Tying Machines — 2/Gd, 1-MLN/ML2EE, 2-MLN/2A; Address Machine — Ch/525; BUSINESS EQUIPMENT: IBM, Unix BUSINESS SOFTWARE: MSSI, PBS CLASSIFIED EQUIPMENT: Hardware — APP/Power Mac 7200; APP/Mac Scanner for OCR; Printers — APP/Mac, Epson/LQ870, APP/Mac LaserWriter NTX; CLASSIFIED SOFTWARE: Baseview/Class Manager Plus 3.21. DISPLAY EQUIPMENT: Hardware — APP/Mac 8-Quadra 700, APP/Power Mac 7100, APP/Mac Quadra 605, APP/Mac G4; Printers — APP/Mac LaserWriter 8500, APP/Mac LaserWriter 16-600, Harlequin/GSI Rip, AG/9800; Other Hardware — Canon/ DISPLAY SOFTWAREAd Make-up Applications — QPS/QuarkXPress 4.1, Adobe/Photoshop 5.5; EDITORIAL EQUIPMENT: Hardware — APP/Mac G4/Nikon/LS-3510 Negative Scanner, HP/ScanJet IIcx; Printers — APP/Mac LaserWriter IIg EDITORIAL SOFTWARE: Baseview/NewsEdit 3.3.2, QPS/QuarkXPress 4.1. PRODUCTION EQUIPMENT: Hardware — Mac PRODUCTION SOFTWARE: CS 5

OLYMPIA

THE OLYMPIAN

111 Bethel St NE, Olympia, Wash., 98506-4365, Thurston; gen tel (360) 754-5400; adv tel (360) 754-5457; ed tel (360) 754-5420; gen fax (360) 357-0207; adv fax (360) 357-0740; ed fax (360) 357-0202; gen/nat adv e-mail jdzaran@theolympian.com; disp adv e-mail jdzaran@theolympian.com; ed e-mail news@theolympian.com; web site www.theolympian.com
- 2,872,129(views) 468,509(visitors)

Group: The McClatchy Company
Published: Mon, Tues, Wed, Thur, Fri, Sat, Sun
Weekday Frequency: m
Saturday Frequency: m
Circulation: 16,859; 17,009(sat); 21,521(sun)
Last Audit: AAM December 31, 2016
Advertising Rate (weekday/saturday): Open inch rate $43 for Local and $67 for National
Advertising Rate (sunday): $53 for Local and $83 for National
Online Advertising Rate: $8 CPM
News services: AP, MCT, LAT-WP, NYT, Bloomberg **Established:** 1889
Own Printing Facility?: No
Commercial Printers?: No
Special Editions: After Christmas Sale (Dec); Tour of Homes (Jul); Source Book (Jun); Holiday Gift Guide (Nov); Best of South Sound (Oct)
Special Weekly Sections: TV Week (S); Weekend (Fri)
Syndicated Publications: Parade (S).
Digital Platform - Mobile: Apple, Android, Windows
Digital Platform - Tablet: Apple iOS, Android, Windows 7, Kindle, Kindle Fire
VP Circ. ..... Phil Schroder
Features Ed. ..... Dusti Demarest
Sr. Ed. ..... Jerre Redecker
Online Producer ..... Tammy McGee
VP Finance ..... Jennifer Matts-Sprague
Adv. Dir. ..... John Dzaran
HR Dir. ..... Norine Mullen
Market Information: TMC; Zoned editions.
Mechanical Available: Offset; Black and 3 ROP colors; insert accepted - with prior approval; page cutoffs - 22 3/4.
Mechanical Specifications: Type page 11 5/8 x 21 1/2; E - 6 cols, 1 3/4, 1/6 between; A - 6 cols, 1 3/4, 1/6 between; C - 9 cols, 1 3/4, 1/8 between.
Areas Served: 98501-98597, 98433
Delivery Method: Mail, Newsstand, Carrier, RacksEquipment & Software: CLASSIFIED SOFTWARE: AdBase DISPLAY SOFTWAREAd Make-up Applications — AdBase; Layout Software — MEI/ALS EDITORIAL EQUIPMENT: Hardware — IBM, Netfinity/5500/HP/8000; Printers — Tegra/5300B, Pre Press/Panther Pro 62 EDITORIAL SOFTWARE: CCI Newsgate PRODUCTION EQUIPMENT: Hardware — Caere/OmniPage 3.0, Pre Press/Panther Pro 62, Intellitune; Scanners — Polaroid/SprintScan, Kk/RSF 2350, Umax/PowerLook II, 1-TECSA/Fullpage 2570, 1-TECSA/Fullpage 2570 PRODUCTION SOFTWARE: APT, Adobe/QuarkXPress 4.1, MEI/CLS 3.0.

PORT ANGELES

PENINSULA DAILY NEWS

305 W 1st St, Port Angeles, Wash., 98362-2205, Clallam; gen tel (360) 452-2345; adv tel (360) 417-3540; ed tel (360) 417-3531; gen fax (360) 417-3521; adv fax (360) 417-3554; ed fax (360) 417-3521; gen/nat adv e-mail sbarrett@soundpublishing.com; disp adv e-mail sperry@peninsuladaiynews.com; class adv e-mailsperry@peninsuladailynews.com; ed e-mail news@peninsuladailynews.com; web site www.peninsuladailynews.com
- 1,200,000(views) 270,000(visitors)

Group: Black Press Group Ltd.
Published: Mon, Tues, Wed, Thur, Fri, Sun
Weekday Frequency: m
Circulation: 10,736; 12,208(sun)
Last Audit: AAM March 31, 2017
Branch Offices: Sequim office, 147-B W. Washington St., Sequim, WA 98382
Port Townsend/Jefferson County office, 1939 E. Sims Way, Port Townsend, WA 98368
Forks office,490 S. Forks Ave., Forks, WA 98331
Advertising Rate (weekday/saturday): Open inch rate $27.80
Advertising Rate (sunday): Open inch rate $29.85
News services: AP. New York Times News Service. **Established:** 1916
Own Printing Facility?: No
Commercial Printers?: No
Special Editions: Spring/Summer Viz Guide (May); Fairs (Aug); Christmas Gift Guide (Dec); Health and Welness (quarterly); Spring Home (Mar); Travel (May); New Cars (Nov); Fall-Winter Visitors Guide (Oct).
Special Weekly Sections: Best Food Day (Wed); Entertainment, Real Estate (Fri); Women, Real Estate (Sun)
Syndicated Publications: Relish (monthly) and Spry (monthly)
Proprietary Publications: Living on the Peninsula (quarterly)
Digital Platform - Mobile: Apple
Digital Platform - Tablet: Apple iOS
Circulation Marketing, Sequim and Jefferson County ..... Jasmine Birkland
Director of Circulation ..... Michelle Lynn
Publisher and Editor ..... John C. Brewer
Letters to Editors/Commentary ..... Paul Gottlieb
Photo Chief ..... Keith Thorpe
Executive Editor ..... Leah Leach
Nat'l Sales Dir. ..... Stephen Barrett
Managing Editor ..... Michael Foster
Sports Editor ..... Lee Horton
Advertising Director ..... Steve Perry
Publisher ..... Terry Ward
Market Information: ADS; Split run; TMC; Zoned editions for Clallam and Jefferson counties.
Mechanical Available: Offset; Black and 3 ROP colors; insert accepted - cards, 70 lb. stock; page cutoffs - 22.
Mechanical Specifications: 22-inch web; 6-col ROP
Areas Served: 98362, 98363, 98365, 98368, 98382, 98331, 98305, 98320, 98324,98325, 98326, 98334, 98339, 98343, 98350, 98357, 98365, 98376, 98381, 98399
Delivery Method: Mail, Carrier, RacksEquipment & Software: PRESSROOM EQUIPMENT: (Printed at Sound Publishing Inc., Everett, WA) MAILROOM EQUIPMENT: Inserts done at Sound Publishing Inc., Everett, WA BUSINESS EQUIPMENT: PC/Macs CLASSIFIED EQUIPMENT: Hardware — PC; CLASSIFIED SOFTWARE: AdPay DISPLAY EQUIPMENT: Hardware — Macs; DISPLAY SOFTWAREAd Make-up Applications — Multi-Ad/Creator; Quark; Adobe Suite; EDITORIAL EQUIPMENT: Hardware — MediaSpan/Macs EDITORIAL SOFTWARE: Adobe Suite PRODUCTION EQUIPMENT: Hardware — 3-AG/Accuset 1000; Cameras — None

SEATTLE

SEATTLE DAILY JOURNAL OF COMMERCE

83 Columbia St, Seattle, Wash., 98104-1432, King; gen tel (206) 622-8272; adv tel (206)622-8272; ed tel (206)622-8272; gen fax (206) 622-8416; adv fax (206)622-8416; ed fax (206)622-8416; gen/nat adv e-mail advertising@djc.com; disp adv e-mail advertising@djc.com; class adv e-mailclassifieds@djc.com; ed e-mail editor@djc.com; web site www.djc.com

Published: Mon, Tues, Wed, Thur, Fri, Sat
Weekday Frequency: m
Saturday Frequency: m
Circulation: 4,500; 4,500(sat)
Last Audit: Sworn/Estimate/Non-Audited September 30, 2017
Advertising Rate (weekday/saturday): Open inch rate $22.00

News services: AP, Business Wire. **Established:** 1893
Own Printing Facility?: Yes
Commercial Printers?: No
Special Weekly Sections: Travel (Fri); Heavy Equipment (Mon); Plan Bulletin (Sat); Real Estate (Thur); Environment (Tues); Architecture & Engineering (Wed).
Pub.....Phil Brown
Adv. Mgr.....Jeff Mosely
Circ. Mgr.....Val Valdez
Ed.....Laura Heberlein
Asst. Ed.....Trista Allen
Mng. Ed.....Maude Scott
Construction Ed.....Ben Minnick
Real Estate Ed.....Lynn Porter
Travel Ed.....John Silver
IT Dir.....John Elliott
Prodn. Mgr.....Nancy Slaney
Prodn. Foreman, Pressroom....David Elleby
Market Information: TMC.
Mechanical Available: Offset; Black and 3 ROP colors; insert accepted; page cutoffs - 22 3/4.
Mechanical Specifications: Type page 15 x 21 1/2; E - 7 cols, 2, 1/6 between; A - 7 cols, 2, 1/6 between; C - 8 cols, 1 2/3, 1/4 between.
Delivery Method: Mail, NewsstandEquipment & Software: PRESSROOM EQUIPMENT: Lines — 5-Econ/Web 1979.; MAILROOM EQUIPMENT: Counter Stackers — KR/3-Station Inserter; Tying Machines — Bu, EAM-Mosca; Wrapping Singles — Manual; Address Machine — KR/Label Head.; BUSINESS EQUIPMENT: Microsoft/Windows BUSINESS SOFTWARE: PBS CLASSIFIED EQUIPMENT: Hardware — AST; Printers — Panasonic/KX-P1624, HP/LaserJet 4M; CLASSIFIED SOFTWARE: PBS. DISPLAY EQUIPMENT: Hardware — PC, APP/Mac; Printers — HP; DISPLAY SOFTWARELayout Software — QPS/QuarkXPress. EDITORIAL EQUIPMENT: Hardware — PCs; Printers — 1-HP/LaserWriter EDITORIAL SOFTWARE: News Engine. PRODUCTION EQUIPMENT: Hardware — Nu/Flip Top FT4OV3UPNS, LE/Line 17; Cameras — 2-SCREEN/ Auto Companica LE, R; Scanners — Umax/840 MaxVision (color) PRODUCTION SOFTWARE: QPS/QuarkXPress.

THE SEATTLE TIMES

1000 Denny Way, Ste 501, Seattle, Wash., 98109-5323, King; gen tel (206) 464-2988; adv tel (206)464-2400; ed tel (206)464-8284; gen fax (206) 464-2239; adv fax (206)464-2239; ed fax (206)464-8284; gen/nat adv e-mail advertising@seattletimes.com; disp adv e-mail advertising@seattletimes.com; class adv e-mailadvertising@seattletimes.com; ed e-mail dshelton@seattletimes.com; web site www.seattletimes.com - 47,800,204(views) 7,916,375(visitors); web site 2 www.seattletimescompany.com
Group: The Seattle Times
Published: Mon, Tues, Wed, Thur, Fri, Sat, Sun
Weekday Frequency: m
Saturday Frequency: m
Circulation: 185,749; 185,749(sat); 284,633(sun)
Last Audit: AAM March 31, 2017
Advertising Rate (weekday/saturday): Open inch rate $165
Advertising Rate (sunday): Open inch rate $220
Online Advertising Rate: Digital standard ads: 300x250, 728x90, ROS, $6.00 CPM
Digital Large Ad Sizes: 300x600, 970x250, ROS, $11.00 CPM
News services: 1896
Own Printing Facility?: Yes
Commercial Printers?: Yes
Special Weekly Sections: NW Sunday, Real Estate, NW Traveler, Pacific NW (Sun); Best Food (Wed); Gardening (Thur); Weekend Plus, Homes (Sat)
Digital Platform - Mobile: Apple, Android, Other
Digital Platform - Tablet: Apple iOS, Android
Mng Ed....Michele Matassa Flores
Sr. VP, Finance....Buster Brown
Managing Ed.....Jim Simon
Managing Ed.....Michele Matassa Flores
Assistant Managing Ed., Visuals....Leon Espinoza
Deputy Mng. Ed.....Lynn Jacobson
Exec. Ed.....Don Shelton
Delivery Method: Mail, Newsstand, Carrier, Racks

SPOKANE

THE SPOKESMAN-REVIEW

999 W Riverside Ave, Spokane, Wash., 99201-1005, Spokane; gen tel (509) 459-5000; adv tel (509) 459-5095; ed tel (509) 459-5400; gen fax (509) 459-5234; adv fax (509) 459-5083; ed fax (509) 459-5482; gen/nat adv e-mail MikeD@spokesman.com; disp adv e-mail MikeD@spokesman.com; class adv e-mailScottB@spokesman.com; ed e-mail robc@spokesman.com; web site www.spokesman.com - 3,354,242(views) 679,685(visitors); web site 2 www.spokane7.com - 85,090(views) 28,017(visitors); web site 3 www.nwprepsnow.com - 350,181(views) 29,412(visitors); web site 4www.spokesmanjobs.com - 46,640(views) 4,325(visitors)
Published: Mon, Tues, Wed, Thur, Fri, Sat, Sun
Weekday Frequency: m
Saturday Frequency: m
Circulation: 71,127; 71,127(sat); 76,654(sun)
Last Audit: AAM March 31, 2017
Advertising Rate (weekday/saturday): $98.91 Local General and $79.13 Retail
Advertising Rate (sunday): $111.29 Local General and $89.03 Retail
Online Advertising Rate: $12.00 CPM
News services: Associated Press, MCT **Established:** 1883
Own Printing Facility?: Yes
Commercial Printers?: No
Special Editions: Fishing (April); Golf Tab (June); Activities Guide (May); Holiday Shopping (Nov); Live Well (April/Oct) Fair Guide (August/Sept)
Special Weekly Sections: TV Week (Sun); Automotive (Sat); Food in Today Section (Wed); 7 Entertainment (Fri); Real Estate and Jobs (Sun); LiveWell (Tue); Boomer (Mon); Outdoors (Thu); Pinch (Sun); Pinch (Wed)
Syndicated Publications: Parade (Sun); Athlon Sports (Thu -1x per month); Dash (Wed - 1x per month)
Digital Platform - Mobile: Apple, Android, Windows, Blackberry
Digital Platform - Tablet: Apple iOS, Android, Windows 7, Blackberry Tablet OS, Kindle, Nook, Kindle Fire
Editor....Gary Graham
City Editor....Addy Hatch
Dir. Production/IT....Laurie Lunzer
Senior Editor....Geoff Pinnock
Dir., Sales and Mktg.....Kathleen Coleman
Mgr., HR....Connie Bantz
Prodn. Mgr., Packaging Ctr.....Lenny Kerstetter
Prodn. Mgr., Pressroom....Steve Heidal
Prod.. Mgr.. Prepress....Jim Groh
Director of Advertising....Michael Dixon
Rob Curley
Market Information: ADS; Split run; TMC; Zoned editions.
Mechanical Available: Offset; Black and 3 ROP colors; insert accepted - some product samples; page cutoffs - 22 3/4.
Mechanical Specifications: Type page 9 5/8" x 21 1/2; E - 6 cols, 1 7/8 , 1/8 between; , A & C - 6 cols, 1 9/16, 1/10 between.
Areas Served: 83801-99344
Delivery Method: Newsstand, Carrier, RacksEquipment & Software: PRESSROOM EQUIPMENT: Lines — 6-G/Metro (4 decks) double width 1981 1-TKS Tower - 1995; 6-G/Metro (4 decks) double width 1981 1-TKS Tower - 1996; Press Drive — 2 - Fincor - 1980; Folders — 2 - Imperial 3.2's with Double-out capability; Pasters —12-G/Metro 1980, 2-TKS 1996Reels & Stands — 1980 Goss-Metro; Control System — TKS/NPC; Registration System — Manual PRESSROOM SOFTWARE: Software - TNPC running on RHEL 3.0
X-term touchscreens
EDG Press Drives
Smith PPI Dampening System MAILROOM EQUIPMENT: Counter Stackers — 2-QWV/500, 4-QWV/350, 2-QWV.359; Inserters & Stuffers — 1-G/630 (26 head), 1-G/632 (14 head), 1-G/632 (14 head); Tying Machines — 9-Dynaric/NP1500; Control System — G/OMNI Zone; Address Machine — 2-Video Jet Printers with Prism Software; MAILROOM SOFTWARE:Software -OmniZone application
MS-SQL Server 2005
MS Visual Studio 2005 CLASSIFIED EQUIPMENT: Hardware — 2 Dell Power R710, Windows 2003 Servers; CLASSIFIED SOFTWARE: Newscycle Solutions Classified MS-SQL Server 2005 DISPLAY EQUIPMENT: Hardware — 3 Dell PE R420; 2 Dell PE 1950 DISPLAY SOFTWARENewscycle Solutions Media Plus AR—
Ad Make-up Applications — PMP 5.1 Server; Layout Software — SCS/Layout 8000. EDITORIAL EQUIPMENT: Hardware — 3 Dell R510, RedHat Enterprise 5.6, Clustered; Printers — Lexmark/Laser printer; Plotters — HP T1200 PS EDITORIAL SOFTWARE: CCI Newsgate PRODUCTION EQUIPMENT: Hardware — 2-Krause Laser Jets 170 with Krause Bluefin processors. Newsflo: 2 Dell 1950, Windows 2003 Server; Scanners — Epson 10000 XL; TNPC/TKS on 2 Dell 1850 PE servers PRODUCTION SOFTWARE: CCI NewsDesk. PMP 5.5 application using Sun MySQL 5.1, PolkaDots-Newsflo PrePage IT 8.0, Approve IT, Move IT. CIRCULATION EQUIPMENT: Red Hat in VMWare CIRCULATION SOFTWARNewscycle Solutions CIRC

SUNNYSIDE

DAILY SUN NEWS

600 S 6th St, Sunnyside, Wash., 98944-2111, Yakima; gen tel (509) 837-4500; adv tel (509) 837-4500; ed tel (509) 837-4500; gen fax (509) 837-6397; adv fax (509) 837-6397; ed fax (509) 837-6397; gen/nat adv e-mail bstory@dailysunnews.com; disp adv e-mail bstory@dailysunnews.com; ed e-mail editor@dailysunnews.com; web site www.sunnyside.net
Group: Eagle Newspapers, Inc.
Published: Mon, Tues, Wed, Thur, Fri
Weekday Frequency: e
Circulation: 3,818
Last Audit: Sworn/Estimate/Non-Audited September 30, 2017
Advertising Rate (weekday/saturday): Open inch rate $9.00
News services: 1901
Special Editions: Auto Car Care (Apr); Sports Review (Aug); Letters to Santa (Dec); Presidents' Day (Feb); Reflections Year-in-Review (Jan); Vacation Getaway (Jul); Vacation Getaway (Jun); Easter (Mar); Graduation (May); Holiday Gift Guide (Nov); Women in Business (Oct); F
Special Weekly Sections: Sunshine Days (Weekly).
Syndicated Publications: American Profile (Fri).
Pub.....Tim J. Graff
Circ. Mgr.....Debbie Guerrero
News Ed.....Bob Story
Adv. Sales....Kim Taylor Morris
Market Information: TMC.
Mechanical Available: Offset; Black and 1 ROP colors; insert accepted; page cutoffs - 22 3/4.
Mechanical Specifications: Type page 10 1/3 x 16 1/2; E - 5 cols, 1 93/100, 1/6 between; A - 5 cols, 1 93/100, 1/6 between; C - 5 cols, 1 93/100, 1/6 between.Equipment & Software: PRESSROOM EQUIPMENT: Lines — 5-G/Community (with sc folder), 1-G/OUP; Registration System — Stoesser/PinSystem. MAILROOM EQUIPMENT: Tying Machines — Bu, Cypack, Mosca/Strapper; Address Machine — Wm.; BUSINESS EQUIPMENT: Mitac BUSINESS SOFTWARE: Synaptic, Cyma IV, Microsoft/Windows 98, Microsoft/Office 97, MS/Outlook e-mail CLASSIFIED EQUIPMENT: Hardware — 2-Pentium; Micron/Dot Matrix; Printers — NewGen/1200 dpi; CLASSIFIED SOFTWARE: Synaptic. DISPLAY EQUIPMENT: Hardware — APP/Power Mac 640-132, 1-APP/Power Mac Pro 240, 2-APP/Power Mac G3; Printers — X; DISPLAY SOFTWAREAd Make-up Applications — Aldus/PageMaker 6.5, Broderbund/Typestyler, Adobe/Illustrator 8, Adobe/Photoshop 6, Macromedia/Freehand 8.; EDITORIAL EQUIPMENT: Hardware — 3-APP/Mac Quadra, 3-APP/Power Mac/Pre Press/Panther Pro Imagesetter; Printers — APP/Mac LaserPrinter NTX, NewGen/1200 x 1200 dpi, X, Design/XL Laspr Printer EDITORIAL SOFTWARE: Microsoft/Word 5.1. PRODUCTION EQUIPMENT: Hardware — APP/Mac LaserWriter, Pre Press/Panther Pro; Cameras — Nu/SST 20 x 24; Scanners — Microtek/Scanner PRODUCTION SOFTWARE: Adobe/PageMaker 6.5.

TACOMA

THE NEWS TRIBUNE

1950 S State St, Tacoma, Wash., 98405-2817, Pierce; gen tel (253) 597-8742; adv tel (253) 597-8487; ed tel (253) 597-8686; gen fax (253) 597-8263; ed fax (253) 597-8274; gen/nat adv e-mail john.dzaran@thenewstribune.com; disp adv e-mail john.dzaran@thenewstribune.com; class adv e-mailjohn.dzaran@thenewstribune.com; ed e-mail newstips@thenewstribune.com; web site www.thenewstribune.com 1,260,980(visitors)
Group: The McClatchy Company
Published: Mon, Tues, Wed, Thur, Fri, Sat, Sun
Weekday Frequency: m
Saturday Frequency: m
Circulation: 54,604; 53,317(sat); 74,653(sun)
Last Audit: AAM June 30, 2016
Advertising Rate (weekday/saturday): Open inch rate $99.70
Advertising Rate (sunday): Open inch rate $99.70
Online Advertising Rate: $8
News services: AP, LAT-WP, MCT, McClatchy, Bloomberg, NYT **Established:** 1880
Own Printing Facility?: Yes
Commercial Printers?: No
Special Weekly Sections: Go (Fri); 50+ (Monthly); SouthSound TV (S); Adventure (S).
Syndicated Publications: Parade (S).
Digital Platform - Mobile: Apple, Android, Windows
Digital Platform - Tablet: Apple iOS, Android, Windows 7, Kindle, Kindle Fire
Exec. Ed.....Karen Peterson
Mng. Ed.....Dale Phelps
Crime/Breaking News Team Leader....Randy McCarthy
Editorial Page Editor....Matt Misterek
Production Manager....Wes Corey
VP Advertising....John Dzaran
Asst. Mng. Ed., Online....Ian Swenson
Market Information: ADS; Split run.
Mechanical Available: Offset; Black and 3 ROP colors; insert accepted; page cutoffs - 22 3/4.
Mechanical Specifications: Type page 10 x 21.5"; E - 6 cols, 1.562", .125"between; A - 6 cols, 1.562", .125"between; C - 6 cols, 1.562", .125"between.
Delivery Method: Mail, Newsstand, Carrier, RacksEquipment & Software: PRESSROOM EQUIPMENT: Lines — 9-G/Metro double width (5 half decks, 1 stack unit); 9-G/Metro double width (5 half decks, 1 stack unit); Press Drive — AAB-DC drives; Folders — 4-G/Metro 3:2; Reels & Stands — 18; MAILROOM EQUIPMENT: Counter Stackers — 3/HL, 6-QWI/301, 2Harris RIMA; Inserters & Stuffers — 1-;2-GMA/SLS 1000A 24:2; Tying Machines — 6-Signode, 6 Dynaric, 4 Ovalstrap; Control System — Prism. BURT; BUSINESS EQUIPMENT: Dell Servers BUSINESS SOFTWARE: ATEX Mactive 2.26 CLASSIFIED EQUIPMENT: Hardware — Dell Servers; Mixture of Dell/HP laptops and workstations; Printers — HP and Brother ; CLASSIFIED SOFTWARE: Mactive 2.26 DISPLAY EQUIPMENT: Hardware — Dell Servers; Other Hardware — Imagitex/Scanners, ECR/Autokon Scanners, Graphic Enterprise/Full-page Proofer DISPLAY SOFTWAREAd Make-up Applications — MEI Adtrack; EDITORIAL EQUIPMENT: Hardware — Sun V880 Sun Solaris 9/Mac's and PC's; Printers — Okidata/393, HP/LaserJet IV, APP/Mac LaserWriters EDITORIAL SOFTWARE: CCI Newsgate PRODUCTION EQUIPMENT: Hardware — 2-Nu/Flip Top FTUP, AG, Nikon, 1-Lf/AP Leaf Picture Desk PRODUCTION SOFTWARE: Unisys 10.2.

VANCOUVER

THE COLUMBIAN

701 W 8th St, Vancouver, Wash., 98660-3008, Clark; gen tel (360) 694-3391; adv tel

(360) 735-4497; ed tel (360) 735-4564; gen fax (360) 735-4503; adv fax (360) 735-4494; ed fax (360) 735-4598; gen/nat adv e-mail metrodesk@columbian.com; disp adv e-mail advertising@columbian.com; class adv e-mailclassified@columbian.com; ed e-mail letters@columbian.com; web site www.columbian.com
  - 2,460,700(views) 652,000(visitors); web site 2 Mobile app - 674,000(views) 7,000(visitors)
Published: Mon, Tues, Wed, Thur, Fri, Sat, Sun
Weekday Frequency: m
Saturday Frequency: m
Circulation: 27,569; 26,177(sat); 31,667(sun)
Last Audit: AAM March 31, 2016
Advertising Rate (weekday/saturday): Open inch rate $70.00
Advertising Rate (sunday): $77.00
Online Advertising Rate: ROS $10 cpm 300x600 guar. position $15 cpm
News services: AP, CNS, MCT - LAT, WP - Bloomberg. **Established:** 1890
Own Printing Facility?: Yes
Commercial Printers?: Yes
Special Editions: Jan: 4th Quarter Economic Update; Economic Forecast; Live well. Feb: Focus 50+; Portrait; Birthday review. March: Best of Clark County. April: Live Well; Summer Camps; First Quarter Economic Update. May: Focus 50+; Destination NW. June: At Home. July: Live Well; Second Quarter Economic Update. August: Clark County Fair. Focus 50+; Education Guide. Sept: Answer Book. Oct: Live Well; Breast Cancer Awareness; Third Quarter Economic Update. Nov: Focus 50"; Home for the Holidays I. Dec: Home for the Holidays II.
Special Weekly Sections: Weekend (Fri); Cruise Control (Sat) Real Estate, Recruitment (Sun)
Syndicated Publications: Parade (S)
Digital Platform - Mobile: Apple, Android
Digital Platform - Tablet: Apple iOS, Android, Kindle
Pub. ....Scott Campbell
Finance Manager/Treasurer .....Brandon Zarzana
HR Mgr. ....Denise Sandvig
Adv. Dir. ....Teresa Keplinger
Circ. Mgr., Promo./Sales ....Rachel Rose
Circ. Mgr., Single Copy ....Peter Geloff
Managing Editor ....Craig Brown
Metro Team Editor ....Mark Bowder
Sports Editor ....Micah Rice
Advertising Sales Mgr. ....Laura Wenrick
Circ.Systems Admin ....Greg Hartgrave
Editorial Page Editor ....Greg Jayne
Metro Team Editor ....John Hill
Dir. of Community Outreach ....Jody Campbell
News Editor ....Merridee Hanson
Home Delivery Mgr. ....Tony Myers
Circulation Manager ....Ben Campbell
IT Mgr. ....Brian MacKay
Production Manager ....Cris Matta
Photo Editor ....Amanda Cowan
Digital Marketing Manager ....Kristeen Millett
Market Information: TMC
Mechanical Available: Offset G/Metro; Black and 4 ROP colors; insert accepted; page cutoffs - 22 3/4.
Mechanical Specifications: 6 units; 4 half decks; Open Fountain ink system; 2 Uniflow 2:1 folders; 4 former boards.
Max. 44" web width.
Areas Served: 98601, 98604, 98606, 98607, 98629, 98642, 98660, 98661, 98662, 98663, 98664, 98665, 98671, 98674, 98675, 98682, 98683, 98684, 98685, 98686
Delivery Method: Mail, Newsstand, Carrier, RacksEquipment & Software: PRESSROOM EQUIPMENT: Lines — 6-G/Metro Double Width; 11-G/SSC Community; Press Drive — 7-Control Technique Mentor II; Folders — 2-G/Metro Uniflow 2:1, 1-G/SSC Community; Pasters —2-MEG, 6-G; Reels & Stands — 4-G/SSC Community.; MAILROOM EQUIPMENT: Counter Stackers — 5-Quipp 501N, 1-Gammerler/KL 5000; Inserters & Stuffers — 2-Muller SLS3000 12:1 and 10:1; Tying Machines — 5-Dynaric NP5000's; Wrapping Singles — 5 Quipp Viper bottom wraps; Address Machine — 2-Kodak 5120 Inkjet Printers; BUSINESS EQUIPMENT: Acer/HP/SuperMicro BUSINESS SOFTWARE: Newscycle Circulation, Newscycle Advertising, ADP, MS Dynamics CLASSIFIED EQUIPMENT: Hardware — Acer/HP/Mac; Printers — HP/Laserjet, Xerox DocCentre; CLASSIFIED

SOFTWARE: Newscycle Mediaplus DISPLAY EQUIPMENT: Hardware — Acer/HP; Printers — HP/Laserjet, Xerox DocCentre, HP/DesignJet; DISPLAY SOFTWAREAd Make-up Applications — Adobe/InDesign; Layout Software — SCS/Layout 8000 — SCS Track EDITORIAL EQUIPMENT: Hardware — Acer/HP/Mac; Printers — HP/Laser/Ricoh EDITORIAL SOFTWARE: Newscycle Content, WordPress Web Platform PRODUCTION EQUIPMENT: Hardware — Agfa AdvantageN SL CTP, Agfa AdvantageN SA CTP, VCF 85 Chem Free processors, Nela Vision Bender; Scanners — ScanMaker 9800XL PRODUCTION SOFTWARE: Adobe Indesign CSS, Adobe Photoshop CSS, Adobe Illustrator CSS, Adobe Flash CSS, Newscycle/Media Plus - Classified Pagination, Layout 8000 NewsWayX
OnColor IT EQUIPMENT: Supermicro IT SOFTWARE:VMware CIRCULATION EQUIPMENT: Supermicro CIRCULATION SOFTWARNewscycle Circulation

WALLA WALLA

WALLA WALLA UNION-BULLETIN

112 S 1st Ave, Walla Walla, Wash., 99362-3011, Walla Walla; gen tel (509) 525-3300; adv tel (509) 525-3304; ed tel (509) 525-3303; gen fax (509) 525-1232; adv fax (509) 525-1232; ed fax (509) 525-1232; gen/nat adv e-mail advertising@wwub.com; disp adv e-mail advertising@wwub.com; class adv e-mailadvertising@wwub.com; ed e-mail letters@wwub.com; web site www.union-bulletin.com
Group: The Seattle Times
Published: Mon, Tues, Wed, Thur, Fri, Sun
Weekday Frequency: e
Circulation: 9,104; 10,395(sun)
Last Audit: AAM September 30, 2015
Advertising Rate (weekday/saturday): Open inch rate $24.00
Advertising Rate (sunday): Open inch rate $24.72
News services: AP. **Established:** 1869
Own Printing Facility?: Yes
Commercial Printers?: No
Special Editions: On the Grow (Oct); The Lifesyle (monthly); Visitors Guide (Mar); Family Forum (Quarterly)
Special Weekly Sections: TV (Mon); Best Food (Tue); Enterprise, Business, Outdoor (Wed); Entertainment (Thur); Religion, Perspective, Panorama (Sun)
Syndicated Publications: Parade (S).
Controller ....Bill Thyken
Adv. Dir. ....Jay Brodt
Circ. Mgr. ....Michael Cibart
Ed. ....Rick Doyle
Editorial Page Ed. ....Rick Eskil
Asst. News Ed. ....Alasdair Stewart
Political Ed. ....Andy Porter
Sports Ed. ....Jim Buchan
Wire Ed. ....Catherine Hicks
Systems Specialist ....Josh Gesler
Pub. ....Rob Blethen
Nat'l Adv. Rep. ....Kandi Suckow
Publisher ....Brian Hunt
HR Mgr ....Steven Butcher
Prod. Supervisor ....James Blethen
Market Information: ADS; TMC.
Mechanical Available: Offset; Black and 3 ROP colors; insert accepted; page cutoffs - 22 3/4.
Mechanical Specifications: Type page 11 1/2 x 21 1/2; E - 6 cols, 1 5/6, 1/8 between; A - 6 cols, 1 5/6, 1/16 between; C - 9 cols, 1 9/50, 1/8 between.
Areas Served: 99323, 99324, 99328, 99329, 99347, 99348, 99359, 99360, 99361, 99362, 97813, 97862, 97886
Delivery Method: Mail, Newsstand, Carrier, RacksEquipment & Software: PRESSROOM EQUIPMENT: Lines — 5-G/Urbanite 1969; MAILROOM EQUIPMENT: Counter Stackers — 1/MM; Inserters & Stuffers — 2-MM/5 heads; Tying Machines — Dynaric; BUSINESS EQUIPMENT: 1-HP/3000 BUSINESS SOFTWARE: Adv, Circ, Accts payable, Gen ledger CLASSIFIED EQUIPMENT: Hardware — 4-PC; CLASSIFIED SOFTWARE: Cybergraphics. DISPLAY EQUIPMENT: Hardware — 4-PC; Other Hardware — X/Scanner DISPLAY

SOFTWAREAd Make-up Applications — QPS/QuarkXPress; Layout Software — MEI/AdForce. EDITORIAL EQUIPMENT: Hardware — 20-PC EDITORIAL SOFTWARE: Cybergraphic. PRODUCTION EQUIPMENT: Hardware — 2-Nu; Cameras — 1-C/Marathon, SCREEN; Scanners — 2-Nikon/Cool Scan PRODUCTION SOFTWARE: Cybergraphic.

WENATCHEE

THE WENATCHEE WORLD

14 N Mission St, Wenatchee, Wash., 98801-2250, Chelan; gen tel (509) 663-5161; adv tel (509) 664-7130; ed tel (509) 661-6391; gen fax (509)665-1182; adv fax (509) 663-9110; ed fax (509) 663-1183; gen/nat adv e-mail newsroom@wenatcheeworld.com; disp adv e-mail advertising@wenatcheeworld.com; class adv e-mailadvertising@wenatcheeworld.com; ed e-mail newsroom@wenatcheeworld.com; web site www.wenatcheeworld.com
Group: Wick Communications
Published: Tues, Wed, Thur, Fri, Sun
Weekday Frequency: e
Circulation: 15,001; 16,841(sun)
Last Audit: CAC September 30, 2014
Advertising Rate (weekday/saturday): Open inch rate $30.00
Advertising Rate (sunday): $30.00
News services: AP, McClatchy **Established:** 1905
Own Printing Facility?: Yes
Commercial Printers?: Yes
Special Weekly Sections: Business World (monthly); Foothills magazine (every other month); Lake Chelan (June-Aug)
Syndicated Publications: Faith & Family (Fri); TV World (S); Go! Entertainment (Thur); Food (Tues); Your News (Weds and Sun); Business (Sun); Agriculture (Sun)
Chairman emeritus ....Wilfred R. Woods
Ed. ....Cal Fitzsimmons
Editorial Page Ed. ....Kelli Scott
Features Ed. .... Marco Martinez
Don Seabrook
Joe Pitt
Personnel Manager ....Gretchen Woods
Circulation and Production Director .... Wyatt Gardiner
Controller ....Rob Torbett
Director of Technology and Communications .... Michael Everson
Andrea Andrus
Market Information: Certified Audit of Circulation
Mechanical Available: Offset; Black and 3 ROP colors; insert accepted; page cutoffs - 21 1/2.
Mechanical Specifications: Type page 11 5/6 x 20 7/20; E - 6 cols, 1 5/6, 1/6 between; A - 6 cols, 1 5/6, 1/6 between; C - 8 cols, 1 19/50, 1/9 between.
Areas Served: 98801, 98802, 98826, 98815, 98816
Delivery Method: Mail, Newsstand, CarrierEquipment & Software: PRESSROOM EQUIPMENT: Lines — KBA/Comet 4 over 4 32 couples 1999; Pasters — Amal/AR 60 CControl System — KBA/Drive-Tronic.; MAILROOM EQUIPMENT: Counter Stackers — 1-BG/Count-O-Veyor 108, Rima/RS30, Rima RS/3117 SL; Inserters & Stuffers — 1-MM/227S, 2-MM/227E; Tying Machines — 2-MLN/2EE, 1-Dynaric/1500, 2-Dynaric/NP1; Wrapping Singles — 1-MM/1509; BUSINESS EQUIPMENT: 1-PBS/SBS CLASSIFIED EQUIPMENT: Hardware — APP/Mac G3; Printers — 2-HP/4050; CLASSIFIED SOFTWARE: Baseview/Ad Manager Pro 2.0. DISPLAY EQUIPMENT: Hardware — APP/Mac; Printers — 1-Okidata/Printer, HP/4050; DISPLAY SOFTWAREAd Make-up Applications — QPS/QuarkXPress 3.32; Layout Software — MEI/ALS. EDITORIAL EQUIPMENT: Hardware — 43-APP/Mac/Telecopier; Printers — 2-HP/LaserJet, 2-Laserwriter/12-640 EDITORIAL SOFTWARE: Baseview/NewsEdit Pro 2.22. PRODUCTION EQUIPMENT: Hardware — WL/Plater 30D, 2-Pre Press/Panther Pro 36 Imagesetter with online processor; Scanners — Microtek/300Z Scanner, 2-APP/Mac, 1-Nikon/Slide Scanner, Epson/836XL PRODUCTION SOFTWARE: QPS/QuarkXPress.

YAKIMA

YAKIMA HERALD-REPUBLIC

114 N 4th St, Yakima, Wash., 98901-2707, Yakima; gen tel (509) 248-1251; adv tel (509) 452-7355; ed tel 509.577.7724; adv fax 509.577.7766; ed fax (509) 577-7767; gen/nat adv e-mail advertising@yakimaherald.com; disp adv e-mail advertising@yakimaherald.com; class adv e-mailclassads@yakimaherald.com; ed e-mail opinion@yakimaherald.com; web site www.yakimaherald.com
  - 4,120,000(views) 331,159(visitors); web site 2 509Autos.com - 16,892(views) 2,551(visitors); web site 3 509employment.com - 17,765(views) 2,728(visitors); web site 4elsoldeyakima.com - 6,026(views) 2,830(visitors)
Group: The Seattle Times
Published: Mon, Tues, Wed, Thur, Fri, Sat, Sun
Weekday Frequency: m
Saturday Frequency: m
Circulation: 21,661; 21,661(sat); 24,410(sun)
Last Audit: AAM December 31, 2016
Advertising Rate (weekday/saturday): Open inch rate $29.69
Advertising Rate (sunday): Open inch rate $29.69
Online Advertising Rate: Billboard 970x250 - $12.00
Medium Rectangle Banner 300x250 - $12.00
Leaderboard 728x90 - $10.00
High Impact or Rich Media - $30.00
Mobile Wide Banner 320x50 - $10.00
YHR Online Targeting - $2.50
News services: AP, MCT, LAT-WP, NEA, TMS. **Established:** 1889
Own Printing Facility?: Yes
Commercial Printers?: Yes
Special Editions: 509HomeFinder (Monthly)
509Autos (Biweekly)
Children's Yearbook (Jan)
How To Guide (Feb)
College Bound (Apr)
Spring Home & Garden (Apr)
Graduates (May)
Central Washington Sports Hall of Fame (Jun)
Readers' Choice Guide (Jul, Sept)
Prep Football (Aug)
Breast Cancer Awareness (Oct)
Women in Business (Oct)
Holiday Gift Guide (Nov)
Veterans Day (Nov)
Special Weekly Sections: Business
Outdoors
Auto
Faith
Home
Garden
Proprietary Publications: El Sol de Yakima (Weekly)
Playdate (Jan,Mar, May, Jul, Sept, Nov)
Yakima Magazine (Jan, Mar, Apr, May, Jun, Jul, Sept, Nov, Dec)
ReDiscover Yakima Valley
Quinceanera Magazine
Yakima Valley Bride Magazine (Jul, Dec)
Pub. ....Robert Crider
HR Dir. .... Maria Barajas
Adv. Dir. ....Jennine Perkinson
Mng. Ed. .... Alison Bath
Op. Dir. ....Roger Stanley
Digital Content Director ....Paul Crawford
Senior Circulation Manager ..... Tammy Fahsholtz
Finance Director .... Bill Thyken
Editor, El Sol de Yakima ....Gloria Ibanez
Market Information: ADS; TMC.
Mechanical Available: CTP, CMYK Process, Insert accepted - single sheet & multiple page inserts produced in house; page cut off 20.5
Mechanical Specifications: Tyoe Page
Thru Feb 2018 - 12.5 x 20.5
March 2018 - 10.125 x 20.5
6 Columns, 1/8" gutter
Areas Served: 98901, 98902, 98903, 98908, 98920, 98921, 98922, 98923, 98926, 98930, 98932, 98933, 98934, 98935, 98936, 98937, 98938, 98939, 98940, 98941, 98942, 98944, 98947, 98948, 98951, 98952, 98953, 99350
Delivery Method: Mail, Newsstand, Carrier, RacksEquipment & Software: PRESSROOM EQUIPMENT: Lines — 4.5 KBA Comet; Folders — 2-KF3; Reels & Stands — 7-Amal.; MAILROOM EQUIPMENT: Inserters & Stuffers — 2-GMA/1000

Control System — Lincs
Muller Martini Sticher
Offline 1/4 Folder CLASSIFIED SOFTWARE: Brainworks

WEST VIRGINIA

BECKLEY

THE REGISTER HERALD

801 N Kanawha St, Beckley, W.Va., 25801-3822, Raleigh; gen tel (304) 255-4400; adv tel (304) 255-4425; ed tel (304) 255-4462; gen fax (304) 255-4427; adv fax (304) 256-5641; ed fax (304) 256-5625; gen/nat adv e-mail tharris@registerherald.com; disp adv e-mail tharris@register-herald.com; class adv e-maildslone@register-herald.com; ed e-mail dcain@register-herald.com; web site www.register-herald.com

Group: Community Newspaper Holdings, Inc.
Published: Mon, Tues, Wed, Thur, Fri, Sat, Sun
Weekday Frequency: m
Saturday Frequency: m
Circulation: 15,414; 15,414(sat); 17,069(sun)
Last Audit: AAM September 30, 2014
Advertising Rate (weekday/saturday): Open inch rate $39.68
Advertising Rate (sunday): Open inch rate $40.26
Online Advertising Rate: $15 per column inch
News services: AP. **Established:** 1981
Special Weekly Sections: Entertainment, TV, Life (Daily); Childrens (Mon); Best Food (Wed); TV, Track (Fri); Church (Sat); Outdoor (Sun)
Syndicated Publications: Relish (Monthly); Parade (S).
Pub.....Frank Wood
Bus. Dir.....Drema Radford
Adv. Mgr., Classified....Diana Slone
Adv. Mgr., Retail....Charles Jessup
Circ. Dir.....Randy Taylor
Circ. Dir., Single Copy Sales....Mark Bowling
Ed.....Butch Antolini
Mng. Ed.....Dawn Keyes
Online Ed.....Mary Spillwell
Chief Photographer....Rick Barbero
Regl. Ed.....Pat Hanna
Sports Ed.....David Morrison
Vice Special Editions Ed.....Judy Karbonit
Women's Ed.....Bev Davis
Systems Mgr.....John Hart
Ed.....Richard Kelley
Adv. Dir.....Tammy Harris
Market Information: ADS; Split run; TMC; Zoned editions.
Mechanical Available: Offset; Black and 3 ROP colors; insert accepted - special inserts upon request; page cutoffs - 22 3/4.
Mechanical Specifications: Type page 13 x 21 3/4; E - 6 cols, 2 1/16, 1/8 between; A - 6 cols, 2 1/16, 1/8 between; C - 9 cols, 1 11/32, 1/16 between.Equipment & Software: PRESSROOM EQUIPMENT: Lines — 10-G/Urbanite 1981; Press Drive — 2-Fin/150 h.p.; MAILROOM EQUIPMENT: Counter Stackers — 1-Id, 1/Olympian; Inserters & Stuffers — GMA/9 pockets, MM/7 pockets; Tying Machines — 2-Dynaric/NP 30; Wrapping Singles — St; Address Machine — Chegier.; BUSINESS EQUIPMENT: IBM/AS-400 BUSINESS SOFTWARE: Oracle, NewzWare CLASSIFIED EQUIPMENT: Hardware — CText, DEC/486; Printers — 2-Tegra/Varityper 5100e, 1-Tegra/Varityper 6990, 2-Pre Press/Panther Pro 36; CLASSIFIED SOFTWARE: CText, CText/ALPS Pagination. DISPLAY EQUIPMENT: Hardware — 1-APP/Mac LC III; Printers — Tegra/Varityper 5100e, 1-Tegra/Varityper 6990, 2-Pre Press/Panther Pro 36; DISPLAY SOFTWAREAd Make-up Applications — Microsoft/Word, Multi-Ad/Creator, QPS/QuarkXPress, Adobe/Photoshop, Aldus/Freehand; Layout Software — 5-APP/Mac Centris 650. EDITORIAL EQUIPMENT: Hardware — CText, DEC, APP/Power Mac 8100-00/1-Tegra/Varityper 6990, 2-Pre Press/Panther Pro 36; Printers — 2-Tegra/Varityper 5100e EDITORIAL SOFTWARE: CText, QPS/QuarkXPress 3.31r5. PRODUCTION EQUIPMENT: Hardware — 2-Tegra/Varityper 5100e Laserprinter, 1-Tegra/Varityper 6990 Laser, APP/Power Mac 8100-100; Cameras — C/Spartan III, C/Newspager; Scanners — 2-Lf/Leafscan 35, 2-Flatbed, Microtek/Scanmaker III PRODUCTION SOFTWARE: CText, QPS/QuarkXPress 7.0.

BLUEFIELD

BLUEFIELD DAILY TELEGRAPH

928 Bluefield Ave, Bluefield, W.Va., 24701-2744, Mercer; gen tel (304) 327-2800; adv tel (304) 327-2816; ed tel (304) 327-2811; gen fax (304) 325-6179; adv fax (304) 327-6179; ed fax (304) 327-6179; gen/nat adv e-mail thale@bdtonline.com; disp adv e-mail thale@bdtonline.com; class adv e-mail@bdtonline.com; ed e-mail sperry@bdtonline.com; web site www.bdtonline.com
- 1,781,832(views) 260,000(visitors)

Group: Community Newspaper Holdings, Inc.
Published: Mon, Tues, Wed, Thur, Fri, Sat, Sun
Weekday Frequency: m
Saturday Frequency: m
Circulation: 10,031; 10,031(sat); 11,684(sun)
Last Audit: AAM September 30, 2016
Advertising Rate (weekday/saturday): Open inch rate $44.00
Advertising Rate (sunday): Open inch rate $44.00
News services: AP, Scripps Howard News Digest. **Established:** 1896
Own Printing Facility?: Yes
Commercial Printers?: Yes
Special Editions: Bluefield Chamber (Apr); Football (Aug); Holiday Cookbook (Dec); Senior Citizens (Feb); Super Bowl (Jan); Business Profiles (Jul); Bridal (Jun); Lawn & Garden (Mar); Mt. Festival (May); Holiday Lifestyles (Nov); Women in the Area (Oct); Home Improvement (
Special Weekly Sections: Best Food (Wed/Sun); TV, Weekend (Fri); Business (Sun)
Syndicated Publications: Parade (S).
Adv. Dir.....Terri Hale
Exec. Ed.....Tom Colley
Mng. Ed.....Samantha Perry
Fred Schmidt
Pub.....Darryl Hudson
Retail Adv. Mgr.....Natalie Fanning
Market Information: ADS; TMC.
Mechanical Available: Offset; Black and 3 ROP colors; insert accepted - spadea wrap; page cutoffs - 22 3/4.
Mechanical Specifications: Type page 13 x 21 1/2; E - 6 cols, 2 1/16, 1/8 between; A - 6 cols, 2 1/16, 1/8 between; C - 9 cols, 1 3/8, 1/11 between.
Delivery Method: Mail, Newsstand, Carrier, RacksEquipment & Software: PRESSROOM EQUIPMENT: Lines — 6-G/Cosmo double width; Reels & Stands — 5; MAILROOM EQUIPMENT: Counter Stackers — HL/2; Inserters & Stuffers — MM/2; Tying Machines — 1/Power Strap, 1-/Power Strap.; BUSINESS EQUIPMENT: 7-ATT/3B25100, Newsware 5.1 BUSINESS SOFTWARE: Microsoft/Office 97, Microsoft/Office 98, Microsoft/Office 2000, Oracle/Version 1.0, Newsware 5.1 CLASSIFIED EQUIPMENT: Hardware — 3-EKI/Televideo; CLASSIFIED SOFTWARE: CText. DISPLAY EQUIPMENT: Hardware — 3-APP/Mac IIci, 2-APP/Mac Quadra 950; Printers — 2-V/5100, 1-V/5300E; DISPLAY SOFTWAREAd Make-up Applications — Multi-Ad/Creator; Layout Software — APP/Mac. EDITORIAL EQUIPMENT: Hardware — 25-EKI/Televideo, Baseview; Printers — Pre Press/Panthers EDITORIAL SOFTWARE: Baseview/NewsEdit Pro. PRODUCTION EQUIPMENT: Hardware — Nu, Graham/Sub., Xante/Accel-A-Writer; Cameras — C/Spartan III, SCREEN/C-680C; Scanners — Nikon, MK, Umax PRODUCTION SOFTWARE: QPS/QuarkXPress 4.0.

CHARLESTON

THE CHARLESTON GAZETTE-MAIL

1001 Virginia St E, Charleston, W.Va., 25301-2816, Kanawha; gen tel (304) 348-4800; adv tel (304) 348-4860; ed tel (304) 348-5100; gen fax (304) 348-1233; adv fax (304) 348-5118; ed fax (304) 348-1233; gen/nat adv e-mail gazette@wvgazettemail.com; disp adv e-mail michael.moncada@cnpapers.com; class adv e-mailjamie@cnpapers.com; ed e-mail robbyers@wvgazettemail.com; web site www.wvgazettemail.com
- 3,958,273(views) 816,356(visitors)

Group: HD Media Company LLC
Published: Mon, Tues, Wed, Thur, Fri, Sat, Sun
Weekday Frequency: m
Saturday Frequency: m
Circulation: 47,504; 38,654(sat); 47,504(sun)
Last Audit: AAM September 30, 2016
Advertising Rate (weekday/saturday): Open inch rate $81.25
Advertising Rate (sunday): Open inch rate $97.85
Online Advertising Rate: Open CPM Discount: Leaderboard (728x90 pixels)-$15; Big Box (336x280 pixels)-$17; Big Box Half 9336x600 pixels-$5; Banner (468x60 pixels)-$5; Skyscraper (160x600 pixels0-$5
News services: AP, MCT. **Established:** 1873
Own Printing Facility?: Yes
Commercial Printers?: No
Special Editions: Home & Garden (Apr); Dance (Aug); Outlook (Feb); Bridal (Jan); WV Home Show (Mar); Fall Home Improvement (Oct); Hunting (Sept).
Special Weekly Sections: Auto, Religion (Sat); Best Food Day, Entertainment, Travel (Sun)
Syndicated Publications: PARADE (Sun)
Proprietary Publications: Putnam Review (Wed)
Digital Platform - Mobile: Apple, Android, Windows
Digital Platform - Tablet: Apple iOS, Android, Windows 7, Kindle, Kindle Fire
Major/Nat'l Accts.....John McGucken
Nat'l Adv. Mgr.....Lisa Skeens
Editorial Page Ed.....Dawn Miller
Market Information: Split run; TMC; Zoned editions.
Mechanical Available: Offset; Black and 3 ROP colors; insert accepted - all; page cutoffs - 22 3/4.
Mechanical Specifications: Type page 12 1/4 x 21 3/4; E - 6 cols, 1 7/8, 1/9 between; A - 6 cols, 1 7/8, 1/9 between; C - 9 cols, between.
Areas Served: The State Newspaper
Delivery Method: Mail, Newsstand, Carrier, RacksEquipment & Software: PRESSROOM EQUIPMENT: Lines — 11-G/Metro offset (double width) 1973; MAILROOM EQUIPMENT: Counter Stackers — 7/QWI; Inserters & Stuffers — HI; Tying Machines — 4-/Dynaric; Wrapping Singles — PM; Control System — Icon; Address Machine — 2-/KR, AVY.; BUSINESS EQUIPMENT: IBM/AS 400 BUSINESS SOFTWARE: JD Edwards GL, APP/Neasi-Weber Admarc 6.4 CLASSIFIED EQUIPMENT: Hardware — Dell/PC, 14-Dell/PC; CLASSIFIED SOFTWARE: TECS-2. DISPLAY EQUIPMENT: Hardware — Dell/PC; DISPLAY SOFTWAREAd Make-up Applications — SCC/Layout 8000; Layout Software — SCS/Layout 8000, 2-Dell/PC. EDITORIAL EQUIPMENT: Hardware — IBM/Netfinity, 2-IBM/Netfinity/Dell/PC; Printers — HP/8100 EDITORIAL SOFTWARE: Microsoft/Word. PRODUCTION EQUIPMENT: Hardware — AP Leafdesk, 3-Prepress Panther 4600 Imagesetters, 2-Ap Leafdesk; Scanners — 1-Graphic Enterprise TESCA PRODUCTION SOFTWARE: QPS/QuarkXPress 4.0, 50-IBM PC.
Note: For detailed general management, business personnel & production information, see Charleston Newspapers listing. The Saturday Gazette-Mail and the Sunday Gazette-Mail are published jointly by the Daily Mail Publishing Co. and the Daily Gazette Co.

CLARKSBURG

THE EXPONENT TELEGRAM

324 Hewes Ave, Clarksburg, W.Va., 26301-2744, Harrison; gen tel (304) 626-1400; adv tel (304) 626-1430; ed tel (304) 626-1473; gen fax (304) 624-4188; adv fax (304) 622-3629; ed fax (304) 624-4188; gen/nat adv e-mail advertising@theet.com; disp adv e-mail advertising@theet.com; class adv e-mailclassified@theet.com; ed e-mail news@theet.com; web site www.theet.com
- 1,200,000(views) 500,000(visitors); web site 2 Wvnews.com - 1,500,000(views)

Published: Tues, Wed, Thur, Fri, Sat, Sun
Weekday Frequency: m
Saturday Frequency: m
Circulation: 10,966; 10,966(sat); 14,076(sun)
Last Audit: AAM March 31, 2017
Advertising Rate (weekday/saturday): Open inch rate $20.40
Advertising Rate (sunday): Open inch rate $21.83
Online Advertising Rate: $10 CPM
News services: AP. **Established:** 1927
Own Printing Facility?: Yes
Commercial Printers?: Yes
Special Weekly Sections: Best Food Day (Wed)
Syndicated Publications: Parade (S).
Digital Platform - Mobile: Apple, Android, Windows
Digital Platform - Tablet: Apple iOS, Android, Windows 7
Operations Director....Robert Gaston
Executive Editor....John Miller
President....Brian Jarvis
Pub.....Andy Kniceley
Key Account Manager....Mia Biafore
Business Manager....Steve Ball
Advertising Director....Tammy Heitz
Digital Director....Chad Everson
Market Information: TMC.
Mechanical Available: Goss Urbanite Full-Color Offset;
insert accepted; page cutoffs - 21 3/4.
Mechanical Specifications: Type page 13 5/8 x 20; E - 6 cols, 2 1/8, 1/6 between; A - 6 cols, 2 1/8, 1/6 between; C - 10 cols, 1 1/4, 1/12 between.
Areas Served: Harrison, Marion, Lewis, Doddridge, Taylor, Upshur and Barbour Counties
Delivery Method: Mail, Newsstand, Carrier, RacksEquipment & Software: PRESSROOM EQUIPMENT: Lines — 1-G/High Speed Straight Line; H/Right Angle; Folders — 1, 1.; MAILROOM EQUIPMENT: Counter Stackers — KAN/MSI; Inserters & Stuffers — MM; Tying Machines — 1/Bu, 1-/Power Strap.; BUSINESS EQUIPMENT: IBM/Sys 36 BUSINESS SOFTWARE: IBM/Sys 36 CLASSIFIED EQUIPMENT: Hardware — CD/2330; Printers — Okidata; CLASSIFIED SOFTWARE: CD/TOPS. DISPLAY EQUIPMENT: Hardware — Dell/PC; Printers — C.Itoh/5000, HP/Laser; DISPLAY SOFTWAREAd Make-up Applications — SCS/Layout 8000; Layout Software — SCS/Layout 8000. EDITORIAL EQUIPMENT: Hardware — CD/2330/5-Leading Edge/D-2 EDITORIAL SOFTWARE: CD/TOPS. PRODUCTION EQUIPMENT: Hardware — 1-LE/Verter, APP/Mac Sys 7.5, Multi-Ad/Creator, Adobe/Photoshop; Cameras — 1-C/Spartan III; Scanners — Microtek/Flatbed, Microtek/35mm, Adobe/Photoshop PRODUCTION SOFTWARE: CD, Magician Plus, APP/Mac Quadra 950, APP/Mac Quadra 800, APP/Mac Sys 7.5.

ELKINS

THE INTER-MOUNTAIN

520 Railroad Ave, Elkins, W.Va., 26241-3861, Randolph; gen tel (304) 636-2121; adv tel (304) 636-2127; ed tel (304) 636-2124; gen fax (304) 636-2620; adv fax (304) 636-3695; ed fax (304) 636-8252; gen/nat adv e-mail publisher@theintermountain.com; disp adv e-mail addirector@theintermountain.com; class adv e-mailclassifieds@theintermountain.com; ed e-mail newsroom@theintermountain.com; web site www.theintermountain.com
- 214,863(views) 26,412(visitors)

Group: Ogden Newspapers Inc.
Published: Mon, Tues, Wed, Thur, Fri, Sat
Weekday Frequency: e
Saturday Frequency: m
Circulation: 5,761; 6,524(sat)
Last Audit: AAM March 31, 2017
Branch Offices: Buckhannon, WV
Advertising Rate (weekday/saturday): Open inch rate $25.36 for National and $14.59 Local
Advertising Rate (sunday): Open inch rate $25.36 for National and $14.59 Local
Online Advertising Rate: These vary depending

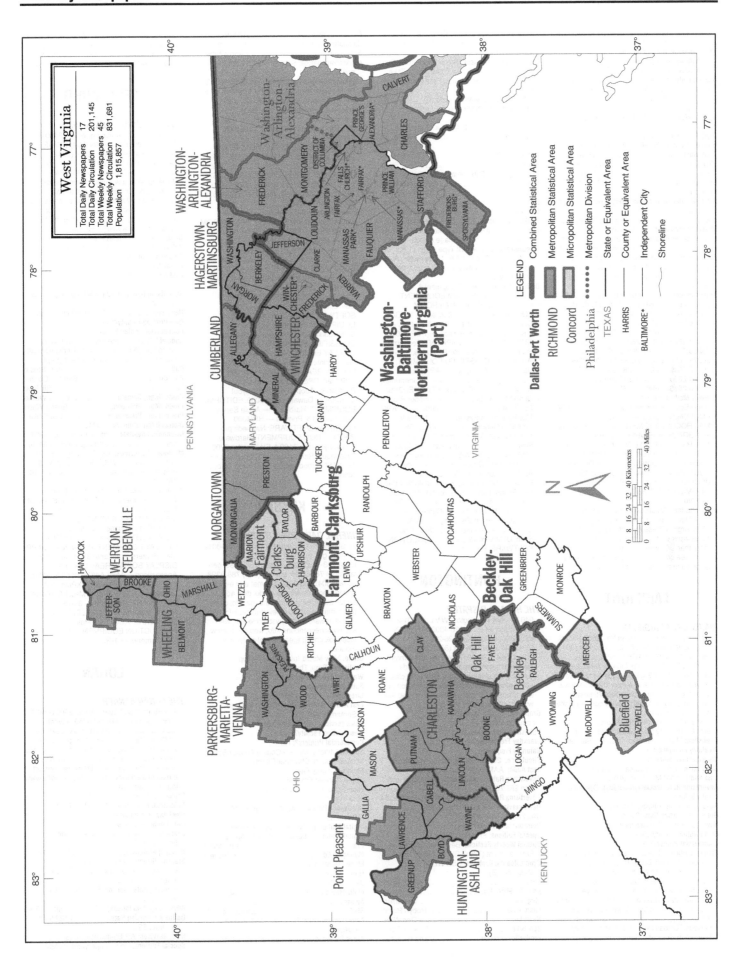

West Virginia

Total Daily Newspapers	17
Total Daily Circulation	201,145
Total Weekly Newspapers	45
Total Weekly Circulation	831,681
Population	1,815,857

LEGEND

Combined Statistical Area
Metropolitan Statistical Area
Micropolitan Statistical Area
Metropolitan Division
State or Equivalent Area
County or Equivalent Area
Independent City
Shoreline

Dallas-Fort Worth
RICHMOND
Concord
Philadelphia
TEXAS
HARRIS
BALTIMORE*

upon size, placement, targeting and package selection from $2 to $27 CPM.
News services: AP. **Established:** 1892
Own Printing Facility?: Yes
Commercial Printers?: Yes
Special Editions: The semi-annual Dining Guide, Visitors Guide and more. We also offer annual sports books for fall, winter and spring.
Special Weekly Sections: Inter-Tainment, a TV and local entertainment supplement
Digital Platform - Mobile: Apple, Android
Digital Platform - Tablet: Apple iOS, Android
Prod. Supervisor............................... Dave Ickes
Mng. Dir................................... Heather Henline
Dir. of Cir. .... Mindy Bond
Business Office Mgr. .... Robin Wilson
Exec. Ed................................. Matthew Burdette
Dir. of Creative/Commercial Print Services.. Joyce Becker
Adv. Dir..............................Michelle Hammonds
Market Information: Zoned editions.
Mechanical Available: Offset; Black and 3 ROP colors; insert accepted; page cutoffs - 22 3/4.
Mechanical Specifications: Type page 13 x 22; E - 6 cols, 2 1/16, 1/8 between; A - 6 cols, 2 1/16, 1/8 between; C - 6 cols, 2 1/16, 1/8 between.
Areas Served: 24915 24920 24927 24934 24944 24954 26209 26264 26273 26282 26291 26294 26201 26210 26215 26218 26222 26228 26234 26236 26237 26343 26372 26452 26238 26250 26275 26405 26416 26224 26230 26241 26253 26254 26257 26259 26263 26267 26270 26273 26276 26278 26280 26283 26285 26293 26296 26260 26269 26271 26287 26289 26292 26804 26807 26814 26818 26836 26847 26855 26866 26884 26886
Delivery Method: Mail, Newsstand, Carrier, RacksEquipment & Software: PRESSROOM EQUIPMENT: Lines — 8-HI/Cotrell V-15A; MAILROOM EQUIPMENT: Counter Stackers — 1-BG/108; BUSINESS EQUIPMENT: 1-NCR CLASSIFIED EQUIPMENT: Hardware — 1-COM/350.; DISPLAY EQUIPMENT: Hardware — 1-COM/Display IV.; EDITORIAL EQUIPMENT: Hardware — 8-COM/350. PRODUCTION EQUIPMENT: Hardware — 1-COM/2961, 1-COM/Trendsetter; Cameras — 1-Nu.
Note: The Inter-Mountain was named the 2014 Newspaper of the Year through the West Virginia Press Association's Better Newspaper Contest. It also has garnered more than 30 awards per year for each of the past three consecutive years, often winning recognition as a paper of General Excellence.

FAIRMONT

TIMES WEST VIRGINIAN

300 Quincy St, Fairmont, W.Va., 26554-3136, Marion; gen tel (304) 367-2500; adv tel (304) 367-2515; ed tel (304)367-2523; gen fax (304) 367-2569; adv fax (304)367-2569; ed fax (304)367-2569; gen/nat adv e-mail tdye@timeswv.com; disp adv e-mail tdye@timeswv.com; class adv e-mailclassified@timeswv.com; ed e-mail mpoe@timeswv.com; web site www.timeswv.com
- 359,000(views) 26,960(visitors)
Group: Community Newspaper Holdings, Inc.
Published: Mon, Tues, Wed, Thur, Fri, Sat, Sun
Weekday Frequency: m
Saturday Frequency: m
Circulation: 6,590; 6,590(sat); 7,245(sun)
Last Audit: AAM March 31, 2016
Advertising Rate (weekday/saturday): Open inch rate $16.60
Advertising Rate (sunday): $22.05
Online Advertising Rate: $15K
News services: AP. **Established:** 1976
Own Printing Facility?: Yes
Commercial Printers?: Yes
Special Editions: Senior Times, Year in Review, Superbowl (Jan); Bridal Tab, Class of 2019 (Feb); Taste of Home, Annual Report (Mar); Home Improvement, Consumer How To Guide, Senior Times (Apr); Three Rivers Festival (May); Business Review (June); What the Flag Means to Me, Rodeo Tab, Senior Times (July); Back to School, Hs Football Tab, College Football (Aug); Silver Pages (Sept), Women in Business, Senior Times (Oct); Veteran's Bonus Edition, Christmas Catalog, Miners Bonus Edition (Nov); December Last Minute Gift Guide (Dec)
Special Weekly Sections: Stock Page (Tues-Sun); Daily Grind (Mon); Cold Pizza (Tues); Take Five (Wed); Ticket (Thurs); Faith Journey (Sat)
Syndicated Publications: Parade (S).
Digital Platform - Mobile: Apple, Android, Windows, Blackberry
Digital Platform - Tablet: Apple iOS, Android, Windows 7, Blackberry Tablet OS, Kindle, Nook, Kindle Fire
Community Ed. .... John Veasey
Prodn. Mgr. .... James Short
Prodn. Foreman, Pressroom........... Gerald Price
Publisher... Kelly Miller
Adv. Dir......................................Craig Richards
Pub... Frank Wood
Gen. Mgr...Misty Poe
Market Information: TMC; Zoned editions.
Mechanical Available: Offset; Black and 3 ROP colors; insert accepted; page cutoffs - 22 3/4.
Mechanical Specifications: Type page 11 63/100 x 21 1/2; E - 6 cols, 1 5/6, 1/8 between; A - 6 cols, 1 5/6, 1/8 between; C - 9 cols, 1 5/6, 1/16 between.
Delivery Method: CarrierEquipment & Software: PRESSROOM EQUIPMENT: Lines — 7-G/Urbanite; MAILROOM EQUIPMENT: Counter Stackers — 1-BG/Count-O-Veyor 109; Inserters & Stuffers — 1-KAN/480; Tying Machines — 1-SP/330, 1/Gd.; BUSINESS EQUIPMENT: Pentium/PC BUSINESS SOFTWARE: Lotus, WordPerfect CLASSIFIED EQUIPMENT: Hardware — APP/Mac G3, APP/Mac Pagination System; Printers — TI/Lineprinter, HP/405N; CLASSIFIED SOFTWARE: QPS/QuarkXPress, Baseview/Ad Manager Pro. EDITORIAL EQUIPMENT: Hardware — APP/Mac Pagination System, APP/MAC G3/APP/Mac Quadra 950, Lf/Leafscan 35, APP/Mac G3, APP/Server NT, Nikon/Cool Scan; Printers — TI/Lineprinter, HP/4050 EDITORIAL SOFTWARE: Baseview/News Edit Pro, QPS/QuarkXPress, Baseview, Adobe/Photoshop PRODUCTION EQUIPMENT: Hardware — 1-COM/IV, Lf/AP Leaf Picture Desk, ApServer NT, APP/Mac G3, Pre Press/Panther Pro 36, 3-HP/4050N, PrePress/Panther Plus 46; Cameras — 1-R/500, C, SCREEN/Companica 680; Scanners — Lf/Leafscan 35, Nikon/Cool Scan, UMAX/PowerLook III PRODUCTION SOFTWARE: Equipment

HUNTINGTON

THE HERALD-DISPATCH

946 5th Ave, Huntington, W.Va., 25701-2004, Cabell; gen tel (304) 526-4002; adv tel (304) 526-6696; ed tel (304) 526-2787; gen fax (304) 526-2857; adv fax (304) 526-2863; ed fax (304) 526-2857; gen/nat adv e-mail cjessup@herald-dispatch.com; disp adv e-mail cjessup@herald-dispatch.com; class adv e-maillwaddell@herald-dispatch.com; ed e-mail editor@herald-dispatch.com; web site www.herald-dispatch.com
Group: HD Media Company LLC
Champion Industries
Published: Mon, Tues, Wed, Thur, Fri, Sat, Sun
Weekday Frequency: m
Saturday Frequency: m
Circulation: 20,387; 20,387(sat); 24,604(sun)
Last Audit: AAM December 31, 2016
Advertising Rate (weekday/saturday): Open inch rate $82.73
Advertising Rate (sunday): Open inch rate $98.54
News services: AP **Established:** 1909
Own Printing Facility?: Yes
Commercial Printers?: Yes
Special Editions: Progress (Mar);
Special Weekly Sections: Best Food (Wed/Sun); Entertainment (Thur); Style, Leisure (Sun);
Syndicated Publications: USA WEEKEND Magazine (S).
Pub.... Ed Dawson
Adv. Dir./Mktg. Dir. .... Amy Howat
Mng. Ed. .... Les Smith
Features Ed..................................Robyn Rison
News Ed...Don Willis
Sports Ed. .... Rick McCann
Production Director.................... David Hamilton
Operations manager....................Jeff Hutchinson
Circulation Director........................ Fred Schmidt
Nat'l Sales .... Angie Nibert
Market Information: Split run; TMC; Zoned editions.
Mechanical Available: Letterpress; Black and 3 ROP colors; insert accepted - any through a HI/1472 hopper; page cutoffs - 21 1/2.
Mechanical Specifications: Type page 13 x 21 1/2; E - 6 cols, 2, 1/6 between; A - 6 cols, 2, 1/6 between; C - 10 cols, 1 1/5, 1/10 between.
Areas Served: 25502, 25503, 25504, 25506, 25507, 25510, 25514, 25515, 25520, 25526, 25530, 25535, 25537, 25541, 25545, 25550, 25555, 25557, 25559, 25560, 25570, 25571, 25701, 25702, 25703, 25704, 25705, 41101 41102, 41129, 41230, 45619, 45623, 45638, 45669, 45678, 45680
Delivery Method: Mail, Newsstand, Carrier, RacksEquipment & Software: PRESSROOM EQUIPMENT: Lines — 6-Wd/Metropolitan double width (3 half decks) 1957; Press Drive — 5-GE/Motors 1994; Folders — 1-SC/3:2, 1-SC/Folder 2:1.; MAILROOM EQUIPMENT: Counter Stackers — HL/HT, HL/Monitor; Inserters & Stuffers — HI/1472 (13 Heads); Tying Machines — 2/Power Strap/PSD 5; BUSINESS EQUIPMENT: Dell, Linux Red Hat server BUSINESS SOFTWARE: Newzware CLASSIFIED EQUIPMENT: Hardware — Subsystem, Dell/Workstations; Printers — HP/4000; CLASSIFIED SOFTWARE: AdPower DISPLAY EQUIPMENT: Hardware — APP/Macs; Printers — HP/4000; DISPLAY SOFTWAREAd Make-up Applications — APP/Mac, QPS/QuarkXPress, Adobe/Photoshop, Adobe/Illustrator; Layout Software — Dewar/Layout 8000. EDITORIAL EQUIPMENT: Hardware — Apple Server X version 10.5; Printers — HP/4000 EDITORIAL SOFTWARE: Newsedit pro PRODUCTION EQUIPMENT: Hardware — 1-EV-jetsetter 7100 1-EV-jetsetter 6200 2 Harlequin Rips, version 7.2; Scanners — 1- 11X17 flatbed scanner 1- 8.5X11 flatbed scanner

KEYSER

MINERAL DAILY NEWS-TRIBUNE

21 Shamrock Dr, Keyser, W.Va., 26726-6012, Mineral; gen tel (304) 788-3333; adv tel (304) 788-3333; ed tel (301) 786-4488; gen fax (304) 788-3398; adv fax (304) 788-3398; ed fax (304) 788-3398; gen/nat adv e-mail advertising@newstribune.info; disp adv e-mail advertising@newstribune.info; class adv e-mailclassified@newstribune.info; ed e-mail newsroom@newstribune.info; web site www.newstribune.info; web site 2 www.facebook.com/pages/mineral-daily-news-tribune
Group: New Media Investment Group
Published: Tues, Thur, Fri, Sat
Weekday Frequency: m
Saturday Frequency: m
Circulation: 3,935; 4,064(sat)
Last Audit: Sworn/Estimate/Non-Audited September 19, 2017
News services: AP. **Established:** 1885
Own Printing Facility?: No
Commercial Printers?: No
Special Editions: Mineral County Answer Book
Mineral County Chamber Directory
Mineral County Fair
Apple Harvest Festival
High School Football Preview
Year in Review
Syndicated Publications: American Profile (Weekly).
Digital Platform - Mobile: Apple, Android
Digital Platform - Tablet: Apple iOS, Android
Pub.. Kelly Miller
Managing Ed. ....Liz Beavers
Mary Lou Weaver
Barbara High
Jessica Evans
Multi-Media Ad Exec .... Tracy Bean
Sports Editor...................................Nick Carroll
Staff...Sandy Canfield
Market Information: Split run; TMC; Zoned editions.
Areas Served: 26726, 21562, 26750, 26710, 26717, 26753, 26719, 21557
Delivery Method: Mail, Newsstand, Carrier, RacksEquipment & Software: DISPLAY SOFTWARELayout Software — 1-APP/Mac.

LEWISBURG

WEST VIRGINIA DAILY NEWS

188 Foster St, Lewisburg, W.Va., 24901-2099, Greenbrier; gen tel (304) 645-1206; adv tel (304) 645-1206; ed tel (304) 645-1206; gen fax (304) 645-7104; adv fax (304) 645-7104; ed fax (304) 645-7104; gen/nat adv e-mail dailynewsad@suddenlinkmail.com; disp adv e-mail dailynewsad@suddenlinkmail.com; class adv e-maildailynewsad@suddenlinkmail.com; ed e-mail wvdailynews@suddenlinkmail.com; web site www.wvdailynews.net
Group: Moffitt Newspapers
Published: Mon, Tues, Wed, Thur, Fri
Weekday Frequency: e
Circulation: 4,100
Last Audit: Sworn/Estimate/Non-Audited September 30, 2017
Advertising Rate (weekday/saturday): Open inch rate $7.00
News services: NEA, TMS. **Established:** 1969
Own Printing Facility?: Yes
Commercial Printers?: Yes
Special Editions: Home Improvement (Apr); State Fair (Aug); Bridal (Jan); Christmas Gift Guide (Nov); Home Improvement (Sept).
Pub...Judy Steele
Adv. Dir. .... Barbara Cordial
Ed...Bill Frye
Prodn. Mgr., Camera.................... Peggey Weikle
Prodn. Mgr., Mailroom.................... Susan Wade
Prodn. Mgr., Pressroom .... Lea Ballard
Market Information: ADS; TMC.
Mechanical Available: Offset; Black and 1 ROP colors; insert accepted; page cutoffs - 21 1/2.
Mechanical Specifications: Type page 13 x 21 1/2; E - 6 cols, 2 1/16, 1/8 between; A - 6 cols, 2 1/16, 1/8 between; C - 6 cols, 2 1/16, 1/8 between.
Delivery Method: Mail, Newsstand, Carrier, RacksEquipment & Software: PRESSROOM EQUIPMENT: Lines — 5-G/Community.; MAILROOM EQUIPMENT: Tying Machines — 1-/CE, 1-/Signode.; BUSINESS EQUIPMENT: 2-Leading Edge/MOD 2 DISPLAY EQUIPMENT: Hardware — 3-APP/Mac; Printers — 1-Xante/3N, 1-Xante/8300; DISPLAY SOFTWAREAd Make-up Applications — Multi-Ad/Creator 3.6, Aldus/PageMaker 6.0, QPS/QuarkXPress 5.0; Layout Software — 3-APP/Mac. EDITORIAL EQUIPMENT: Hardware — 3-APP/Mac; Printers — X/N 2025 EDITORIAL SOFTWARE: Aldus/PageMaker 5.0. PRODUCTION EQUIPMENT: Hardware — 1-P; Cameras — 1-R.

LOGAN

THE LOGAN BANNER

435 Stratton St, Logan, W.Va., 25601-3913, Logan; gen tel (304) 752-6950; adv tel (304)752-6950 ext. 305; gen fax (304) 752-1239; adv fax (304) 752-1239; gen/nat adv e-mail rrichards@civitasmedia.com; disp adv e-mail rrichards@civitasmedia.com; class adv e-mailrrichards@civitasmedia.com; ed e-mail msparks@civitasmedia; web site www.loganbanner.com
Group: HD Media Company LLC
Published: Mon, Tues, Wed, Thur, Fri, Sun
Weekday Frequency: e
Circulation: 9,579; 9,751(sun)
Last Audit: Sworn/Estimate/Non-Audited September 30, 2017
Newspaper Reps: B.j. Beaty, Robin Richards
Branch Offices: The Coal Valley News, Williamson Daily News, Gilbert Times, Independent Herald.
Advertising Rate (weekday/saturday): Open inch rate $17.40
Advertising Rate (sunday): Open inch rate $17.40
Online Advertising Rate: Banner Ad 12 Month Contract $5.25
News services: AP. **Established:** 1888
Special Editions: Home Improvement (Apr);

Football Signature Pages (Aug); Christmas Songbook (Dec); Basketball Pages (Feb); A-Z (Jul); Father's Day Photos (Jun); Girl Scout Page (Mar); Mother's Day Photos (May); Veteran's Day Page (Nov); Hunting (Oct); Football Pages (Sept
Special Weekly Sections: Entertainment (Daily); Best Food (Mon, Wed, Sun); Religion (Fri); Auto (Fri/Sun); Church, TV, Real Estate (Sun)
Syndicated Publications: Parade (S).
Pub. .... James Jenkins
Mng. Ed. .... Michael Browning
Sports Ed. .... Paul Adkins
Webmaster .... Martha Sparks
Prodn. Foreman, Composing .... Gaynell Hughes
Adv. Sales .... Robin Richards
Adv. Sales .... Anthony Sheppard
Circ Rep .... Katie Elkins
Asst Dir .... Ed Martin
Market Information: TMC.
Mechanical Available: Offset; Black and 3 ROP colors; insert accepted - all; page cutoffs - 22 3/4.
Mechanical Specifications: Type page 13 3/4 x 21 1/2; E - 6 cols, 2 1/16, 1/8 between; A - 6 cols, 2 1/16, 1/8 between; C - 9 cols, 1 3/8, 1/16 between.
Areas Served: Logan, Mingo, Boon, WyomingEquipment & Software: MAILROOM EQUIPMENT: Counter Stackers — 1/Fg; Inserters & Stuffers — 3-/DG; Tying Machines — 1-Ty-Tech/Tyer; Address Machine — 2-/Am.; CLASSIFIED EQUIPMENT: Printers — APP/Mac LaserWriter Pro 600; CLASSIFIED SOFTWARE: QPS/QuarkXPress. EDITORIAL EQUIPMENT: Hardware — 5-APP/Mac Quadra 610; Printers — APP/Mac LaserWriter Pro 600 EDITORIAL SOFTWARE: QPS/QuarkXPress. PRODUCTION EQUIPMENT: Hardware — 2-APP/Mac LaserWriter Pro 600, AG/Arcus Plus Scanner; Cameras — R/500.

MARTINSBURG

THE JOURNAL

207 W King St, Martinsburg, W.Va., 25401-3211, Berkeley; gen tel (304) 263-8931; adv tel (304) 263-8931 ext 110; ed tel (304) 263-3381; gen fax (304) 263-8058; adv fax (304) 267-2829; ed fax (304) 267-2903; gen/nat adv e-mail jgelestor@journal-news.net; disp adv e-mail bbarnes@journal-news.net; class adv e-mailsphillips@journal-news.net; ed e-mail mheath@journal-news.net; web site www.journal-news.net - 725,000(views) 110,103(visitors)
Group: Ogden Newspapers Inc.
Published: Mon, Tues, Wed, Thur, Fri, Sat, Sun
Weekday Frequency: m
Saturday Frequency: m
Circulation: 10,279; 10,279(sat); 11,780(sun)
Last Audit: AAM March 31, 2017
Advertising Rate (weekday/saturday): Open inch rate $36.00
Advertising Rate (sunday): Open inch rate $39.00
Online Advertising Rate: Top leaderboard $16.00; Right Rectangle $16.00; Center Banner $11.00; Left Skyscraper $16.00
News services: AP. **Established:** 1907
Own Printing Facility?: Yes
Commercial Printers?: Yes
Special Editions: Home Show (Apr); Fall Sports Tab (Aug); Christmas Songbook (Dec); Welcome Home (Feb); Bridal (Jan); Welcome Home (Jul); Welcome Home (Jun); Spring Sports Tab (Mar); Mother's Day Tab (May); Welcome Home (Nov); Halloween Safety (Oct); Welcome Home (Sept).
Special Weekly Sections: Health (Mon); Kids (Tue); Food, Recipes (Wed); Entertainment, Weekend (Thur); Home, Garden, Real Estate (Fri); Religion (Sat); Business (Sun); Neighborhood (Daily)
Syndicated Publications: Parade (S).
Pub. .... Craig Bartoldson
Chief Photographer .... Ron Agnir
Sports Ed. .... Rick Kozlowski
Online Mgr. .... Nicholas Werder
Editor .... Chris Kinsler
Adv. Dir. .... Judy Gelestor
Retail Adv. Mgr. .... Pam Fawley-Martin
Editor .... Mary Heath
Market Information: Split run; TMC; Zoned editions.
Mechanical Available: Offset; Black and 3 ROP colors; insert accepted - all; page cutoffs - 20.5
Mechanical Specifications: Type page 11 4/5 x 21 1/2; E - 6 cols, 1 7/8, 1/8 between; A - 6 cols, 1 7/8, 1/8 between; C - 8 cols, 1 5/16, 1/16 between.
Areas Served: Berkeley, Jefferson and Morgan County WV
Delivery Method: Newsstand, Carrier, RacksEquipment & Software: BUSINESS EQUIPMENT: NCR, Unix CLASSIFIED EQUIPMENT: Hardware — Umax/C500-240; NCR/UNIX, 2-Sun; Printers — HP/8150 DN; CLASSIFIED SOFTWARE: ONI/Class 0.5.4. DISPLAY EQUIPMENT: Hardware — Umax/C500-200, APP/Power Mac G3, 6-APP/Mac G4, Sun/Ultra Sparc Server 690 MP; Printers — APP/Mac LaserWriter NTX, 2-HP/8150 DN, 2-HP/8000 N, MON/ExpressMaster 2000, Konica/EV Jetsetter 4500 Imagesetter; Other Hardware — APP/Power Mac 6100-66, EDITORIAL EQUIPMENT: Hardware — APP/Mac G4, 6-Umax/C500/APP/Mac Centris 610, APP/Mac Centris 650, APP/Mac PC 6100-66, APP/Mac G-3 Workgroup Server; Printers — HP/8000 N EDITORIAL SOFTWARE: ONI/Class 0.5.4.

MORGANTOWN

THE DOMINION POST

1251 Earl L Core Rd, Morgantown, W.Va., 26505-5881, Monongalia; gen tel (304) 292-6301; adv tel (304) 291-9449; ed tel (304) 291-9425; gen fax (304) 291-2326; adv fax (304) 292-3704; ed fax (304) 291-2326; gen/nat adv e-mail ads@dominionpost.com; disp adv e-mail ads@dominionpost.com; class adv e-maildavis@dominionpost.com; ed e-mail newsroom@dominionpost.com; web site www.dominionpost.com
Group: Greer Industies
Published: Mon, Tues, Wed, Thur, Fri, Sat, Sun
Weekday Frequency: m
Saturday Frequency: m
Circulation: 12,537; 12,537(sat); 15,105(sun)
Last Audit: AAM March 31, 2017
Advertising Rate (weekday/saturday): Open inch rate $36.32
Advertising Rate (sunday): Open inch rate $41.14
Online Advertising Rate: Front -page ear dimensions:224x177 pixels- 52 week contract $75, 26 week contract $85; Front-page skyscraper 160x600 pixels: 52 week contrack $60. 26 week contract $70; Front page jumbo banner 738x90 pixels: 52 week contract $45, 26 week contract $55; Front page half banner 360x90 pixels: 52 week contract $30, 26 week contract $35.
News services: AP, MCT, NEA. **Established:** 1923
Own Printing Facility?: Yes
Commercial Printers?: Yes
Special Editions: Auto Care (Tab) (Apr); College Football (Aug); Xmas Gift Guide (3 times) (Dec); Health Fair (Tab) (Feb); Chamber of Commerce (Tab) (Jan); West Virginia's Birthday Party (Tab) (Jun); Progress (Mar); Summer Fun (May); Basketball (Nov); Goal Post (Oct); Buck
Special Weekly Sections: Best Food Days (Wed/Sun); Entertainment (Thur); Travel, Auto, Real Estate (Sun)
Syndicated Publications: Parade (S).
Digital Platform - Mobile: Apple, Android, Windows, Blackberry
Digital Platform - Tablet: Apple iOS, Android, Windows 7, Blackberry Tablet OS, Kindle, Nook, Kindle Fire, Other
Vice Pres./Sec./Treasurer .... James M. Troy
Controller .... Brian D. Cole
Owner/Pub. .... David A. Raese
Adv. Dir. .... Eric Wilson
Mktg. Assistant .... Courtney Dlugos
Circ. Single Copy Sales Mgr. .... Mike Campbell
Newspaper In Education Coordinator .... Joe Duley
Circ. Operations Mgr. .... Joseph Duley
Senior Reporter .... David Beard
Editor .... Geri Ferrara
Editorial Page Ed. .... Randy Vealey
Online Coord. .... David Whisler
Prodn. Mgr., Distr. .... Mike Bonnette
Prodn. Dir., Pre Press/Systems .. Chris Halterman
Nat'l Acct. Exec. .... Donna Davis
Market Information: TMC.
Mechanical Available: Offset; Black and 3 ROP colors; insert accepted; page cutoffs - 22 3/4.
Mechanical Specifications: Type page 13 1/4 x 21 1/2; E - 6 cols, 2 1/16, 1/8 between; A - 6 cols, 2 1/16, 1/8 between; C - 9 cols, 1 3/8, 1/16 between.
Areas Served: Marion, Monongalia, Preston
Delivery Method: Mail, Newsstand, Carrier, RacksEquipment & Software: PRESSROOM EQUIPMENT: Lines — 12-G/Urbanite; MAILROOM EQUIPMENT: Counter Stackers — 1/QWI, 1-QWI/400 1-QWI/500; Inserters & Stuffers — SLS1000; Tying Machines — 1-/MLN; Address Machine — KAN.; BUSINESS EQUIPMENT: Oracle BUSINESS SOFTWARE: Vision Data, DSI CLASSIFIED EQUIPMENT: Hardware — Miles 33; Printers — QMS/860 Laser; CLASSIFIED SOFTWARE: Miles 33 DISPLAY EQUIPMENT: Hardware — APP/Mac; DISPLAY SOFTWARELayout Software — DSI EDITORIAL EQUIPMENT: Hardware — Miles 33 31 PC, 10-APP/Mac; Printers — QMS/860 Laser EDITORIAL SOFTWARE: Miles 33 PRODUCTION EQUIPMENT: Hardware — 2-Newsmatic ECRM/CTP PRODUCTION SOFTWARE: Adobe CS5

MOUNDSVILLE

MOUNDSVILLE DAILY ECHO

713 Lafayette Ave, Moundsville, W.Va., 26041-2143, Marshall; gen tel (304) 845-2660; adv tel (304) 845-2660; ed tel (304) 845-2660; gen fax (304) 845-2661; adv fax (304) 845-2661; ed fax (304) 845-2661; gen/nat adv e-mail mdsvecho@gmail.com; disp adv e-mail mdsvecho@gmail.com; class adv e-mailmdsvecho@gmail.com; ed e-mail mdsvecho@gmail.com; web site www.facebook.com/moundsvilledailyecho
Published: Mon, Tues, Wed, Thur, Fri
Weekday Frequency: e
Circulation: 3,902; 3,902(sat)
Last Audit: Sworn/Estimate/Non-Audited September 30, 2017
Branch Offices: None/Privately Owned.
Advertising Rate (weekday/saturday): Open inch rate $4.17
News services: AP. **Established:** 1891
Own Printing Facility?: Yes
Commercial Printers?: No
Special Weekly Sections: Best Food Day (Wed)
Pub./Gen. Mgr. .... Charlie Walton
Adv. Rep. .... Susan Cooley
Adv. Rep. .... Melanie Murdock
Mechanical Available: Offset; Black and ROP colors; insert accepted; page cutoffs - 22 3/4.
Mechanical Specifications: Type page 15 1/8 x 21 5/8; E - 7 cols, 2, 1/8 between; A - 7 cols, 2, 1/8 between; C - 7 cols, 2, 1/8 between.
Areas Served: 26038, 15370, 20151, 23060, 27106, 29464, 32127, 33803, 43747, 43947, 43950, 44450, 15143, 26155, 25305, 26101, 26170, 26505, 26003, 26031, 26041, 26033, 26039, 26055, 26041
Delivery Method: Mail, Newsstand, Carrier, RacksEquipment & Software: PRESSROOM EQUIPMENT: Control System — GE/SCR. MAILROOM EQUIPMENT: Address Machine — 2-Am/Dispensa-Matic.; BUSINESS EQUIPMENT: 1-PC 586 DISPLAY EQUIPMENT: Hardware — PC; Printers — APP/Mac LaserWriter; DISPLAY SOFTWAREAd Make-up Applications — Aldus/PageMaker 3.01, Microsoft/Windows 3.1, Archetype/Corel Draw 3.0.; EDITORIAL EQUIPMENT: Hardware — PC; Printers — APP/Mac LaserWriter EDITORIAL SOFTWARE: Aldus/PageMaker 3.01, Microsoft/Windows 3.1. PRODUCTION EQUIPMENT: Hardware — APP/Mac Laser Plus; Cameras — R.

PARKERSBURG

PARKERSBURG NEWS & SENTINEL

519 Juliana St, Parkersburg, W.Va., 26101-5135, Wood; gen tel (304) 485-1891; adv tel (304) 485-1891; ed tel (304) 485-1891; gen fax (304) 485-2061; adv fax (304) 485-2061; ed fax (304) 485-2061; gen/nat adv e-mail advertising@newsandsentinel.com; disp adv e-mail advertising@newsandsentinel.com; class adv e-mailclassified@newsandsentinel.com; ed e-mail editorial@newsandsentinel.com; web site www.newsandsentinel.com - 1,400,000(views) 140,000(visitors)
Group: Ogden Newspapers Inc.
Published: Mon, Tues, Wed, Thur, Fri, Sat, Sun
Weekday Frequency: e
Circulation: 16,956; 16,411(sat); 20,767(sun)
Last Audit: AAM December 31, 2016
Advertising Rate (weekday/saturday): Open inch rate $89.79
Advertising Rate (sunday): Open inch rate $97.63
News services: AP.
Own Printing Facility?: Yes
Special Editions: Seniors (Monthly).
Special Weekly Sections: Food (Thur); Religion (Sat); TV, Food (Sun)
Syndicated Publications: Free Time (Entertainment) (Fri); Parade (S); Religion Tab (Sat).
Digital Platform - Mobile: Apple, Android
Digital Platform - Tablet: Apple iOS, Android
Pub. .... James T. Spanner
Circ. Dir. .... Joe Tranquill
Exec. Ed. .... James Smith
Mng. Ed. .... Paul LaPann
City Ed. .... Jess Mancini
Editorial Page Ed. .... Larry Cox
Film/Theater Ed. .... Brett Dunlap
Sports Ed. .... Dave Poe
Opns. Mgr. .... Chris Smith
Art Smith
Pub. .... Jim Spanner
Nat'l Adv. Mgr. .... Kim Geibel
Ad. Mgr. .... Jason Rollins
Adv. Dir. .... Matthew Tranquill
Market Information: TMC.
Mechanical Available: Offset; Black and 3 ROP colors; insert accepted; page cutoffs - 21 3/4.
Mechanical Specifications: Type page 12 1/2 x 21 3/4; E - 6 cols, 2 1/16, 1/8 between; A - 6 cols, 2 1/16, 1/8 between; C - 8 cols, 1 9/16, 1/16 between.
Delivery Method: Mail, Newsstand, Carrier, RacksEquipment & Software: PRESSROOM EQUIPMENT: Lines — 12-Urbinite; Folders — 2-Urbinite.; MAILROOM EQUIPMENT: Counter Stackers — 2-Quipp/401; Inserters & Stuffers — 1-HI/NP 1372; Tying Machines — MLN/ML2EE, 1/Power Strap/TS2504.; CLASSIFIED EQUIPMENT: Hardware — PC; CLASSIFIED SOFTWARE: Microsoft/Windows NT 4.0. DISPLAY EQUIPMENT: Hardware — 2-APP/Mac G3; Printers — APP/Mac 8500, ECR/VRL 36; DISPLAY SOFTWAREAd Make-up Applications — QPS/QuarkXPress, Multi-Ad/Creator.; EDITORIAL EQUIPMENT: Hardware — PC; Printers — HP/6M EDITORIAL SOFTWARE: Microsoft/Windows NT 4.0. PRODUCTION EQUIPMENT: Hardware — 1-WL/30B, ECR/VRL 36; Cameras — 1-K/N243, 1-C/Newspager.

POINT PLEASANT

POINT PLEASANT REGISTER

200 Main St, Point Pleasant, W.Va., 25550-1030, Mason; gen tel (304) 675-1333; adv tel (304) 675-1333; ed tel (304) 675-1333; gen fax (304) 675-5234; adv fax (304) 675-5234; ed fax (304) 675-5234; gen/nat adv e-mail jschultz@civitasmedia.com; disp adv e-mail jschultz@civitasmedia.com; class adv e-mailpprclassified@civitasmedia.com; ed e-mail news@mydailyregister.com; web site www.mydailyregister.com - 169,000(views) 25,000(visitors)
Group: Civitas Media, LLC-OOB
Published: Mon, Tues, Wed, Thur, Fri, Sat
Weekday Frequency: e
Saturday Frequency: m
Circulation: 3,918; 3,918(sat)
Last Audit: Sworn/Estimate/Non-Audited September 30, 2017
Advertising Rate (weekday/saturday): Open inch rate $13.50
News services: AP.
Own Printing Facility?: Yes
Special Weekly Sections: Church Page (Fri); Farm Page (Sun)
Circ. Mgr. .... David Lucas
Sports Ed. .... Larry Crum
Pub. .... Sammy Lopez

Adv. Mgr... Julia Schultz
Ed... Michael Johnson
Reg. Dir. .... Bud Hunt
Market Information: TMC.
Mechanical Available: Offset; Black and 3 ROP colors; insert accepted; page cutoffs - 21 1/4.
Mechanical Specifications: Type page 13 x 21 1/4; E - 6 cols, 2 1/16, 1/8 between; A - 6 cols, 2 1/16, 1/8 between; C - 8 cols, 1 1/2, 1/8 between.
Delivery Method: Mail, Newsstand, Carrier, RacksEquipment & Software: BUSINESS EQUIPMENT: IBM, IBM/AS-400 CLASSIFIED EQUIPMENT: Hardware — APP/Mac; CLASSIFIED SOFTWARE: Baseview. EDITORIAL EQUIPMENT: Hardware — APP/Mac Quadra 650, APP/Mac Quadra 610; Printers — APP/Mac LaserWriter Pro EDITORIAL SOFTWARE: Baseview. PRODUCTION EQUIPMENT: Hardware — Caere/OmniPage; Scanners — HP/ScanJet Plus.
Note: Printed at the Gallipolis (OH) Daily Tribune. For pressroom information, see the Gallipolis Daily Tribune listing.

WHEELING

THE INTELLIGENCER

1500 Main St, Wheeling, W.Va., 26003-2826, Ohio; gen tel (304) 233-0100; adv tel (304) 233-0100; ed tel (304) 233-0100; gen fax (304) 214-9377; adv fax (304) 233-0327; ed fax (304) 232-1399; gen/nat adv e-mail pbennett@theintelligencer.net; disp adv e-mail pbennett@theintelligencer.net; class adv e-mailshiggins@theintelligencer.net; ed e-mail Jmccabe@theintelligencer.net; web site www.theintelligencer.net - 1,021,969(views) 128,436(visitors)
Group: Ogden Newspapers Inc.
Published: Mon, Tues, Wed, Thur, Fri, Sat, Sun
Weekday Frequency: m
Saturday Frequency: m
Circulation: 11,258; 16,832(sat); 22,032(sun)
Last Audit: AAM March 31, 2017
Advertising Rate (weekday/saturday): Open inch rate $116.48
Advertising Rate (sunday): Open inch rate $126.22
News services: AP. **Established:** 1852
Own Printing Facility?: Yes
Commercial Printers?: Yes
Special Editions: Progress Edition (Feb.) Shale Play (Bi-Monthly) Football Preview (Aug.) Boomers & Beyond (Monthly) OV Parent (Monthly) Ohio Valley Real Estate (Monthly)
Special Weekly Sections: Entertainment (Fri); NFL Report (Mon); Best Food Day (Tue); Chalk Talk (Football Season (Thur); Faith (Sat)
Syndicated Publications: TV Book (own, local, newsprint) (S).
Digital Platform - Mobile: Apple, Android, Windows
Digital Platform - Tablet: Apple iOS, Android, Windows 7, Blackberry Tablet OS, Kindle, Nook, Kindle Fire
Pub...G. Ogden Nutting
Gen. Mgr..................................... Perry A. Nardo
Controller...............................Charles Deremer
Adv. Mgr., Classified....................Shelly Higgins
Adv. Dir...Pam Bennett
Circ. Dir. ....Dave Kahkbaugh
Bus./Finance Ed............................John McCabe
City Ed., News-Register..............Heather Ziegler
Editorial Page Ed., News-Register J. Michael Myer
Entertainment Ed. .... Betsy Bethel
Features Ed....................................Linda Comins
Food/Women's Ed.............................Phyllis Sigal
News Ed., Intelligencer......... Jennifer Compston
Market Information: ADS; ; TMC; Zoned editions.
Mechanical Available: Offset; Black and 3 ROP colors; insert accepted; page cutoffs - 22"
Mechanical Specifications: Print Area 10" x 21 6 col format
Areas Served: 26003
Delivery Method: Newsstand, Carrier, RacksEquipment & Software: PRESSROOM EQUIPMENT: Lines — DGM; DGM; MAILROOM EQUIPMENT: Counter Stackers — 2-HL/Monitor, 1-HL/HI II; Inserters & Stuffers — S/1372; Tying Machines — 2-MLN/2EE, 1-MLN/2, 1-MLN/2A; Wrapping Singles — Sa; Address Machine — Ch.; BUSINESS EQUIPMENT: NCR S20 BUSINESS SOFTWARE: In house CLASSIFIED EQUIPMENT: Hardware — PC; CLASSIFIED SOFTWARE: Microsoft/Windows NT. DISPLAY EQUIPMENT: Hardware — 4-APP/Mac G3, 2-Konica/Knock Out Imagesetter; Printers — 2-Konica/Knock Out Imagesetter; Other Hardware — 2-APP/Mac 8500 DISPLAY SOFTWAREAd Make-up Applications — QPS/QuarkXPress 3.31, Adobe/Photoshop 3.05, Multi-Ad/Creator 3.7, AP AdSend; Layout Software — APP/Mac, Multi-Ad/Creator EDITORIAL EQUIPMENT: Hardware — PC EDITORIAL SOFTWARE: Microsoft/Windows NT. PRODUCTION EQUIPMENT: Hardware — 2-APP/Mac LaserWriter NTX, 2-MON/1270 Imagesetter, 2-Konica/4550 Imagesetters; Cameras — 1-C/Pager, 1-AG/2024; Scanners — HP IIci, Kk/RFS-2035, Nikon/Coolscan, Umax PRODUCTION SOFTWARE: QPS/QuarkXPress 3.31.

WILLIAMSON

WILLIAMSON DAILY NEWS

38 West Second Avenue, Williamson, W.Va., 25661-3500, Mingo; gen tel (304) 235-4242; adv tel (304) 235-4242; ed tel (304) 235-4242; gen fax (304) 235-0730; adv fax (304) 235-0730; ed fax (304) 235-0730; gen/nat adv e-mail wdn.ads@heartlandpublications.com; disp adv e-mail wdn.ads@heartlandpublications.com; class adv e-mailwdn.classified@heartlandpublications.com; ed e-mail jbyers@heartlandpublications.com; web site www.williamsondailynews.com
Group: HD Media Company LLC
Published: Mon, Tues, Wed, Thur, Fri, Sat, Sun
Weekday Frequency: m
Saturday Frequency: m
Circulation: 8,028; 8,028(sat); 8,028(sun)
Last Audit: Sworn/Estimate/Non-Audited September 30, 2017
Advertising Rate (weekday/saturday): Open inch rate $13.30
Advertising Rate (sunday): Open inch rate $13.30
News services: AP. **Established:** 1912
Special Editions: Visitor's Guide (Jun); Golden News (Monthly); Red Ribbon Salute (Oct); Bride's Guide (Semi-yearly).
Special Weekly Sections: Best Food Day (Wed); Church (Sat); Auto (Sun)
Syndicated Publications: Golden News (Monthly); Parade (S).
Bus. Mgr..................................Raitchell Lipps
Mgr., Mktg./Promo. ....Drew Martin
Science Ed......................................Loretta Tackett
Prodn. Foreman, Composing......Clifford Marcum
Kathy Everett
Pub...Joshua Byers
Circ. Mgr...................................Bernadean Perry
Market Information: ADS; TMC.
Mechanical Available: Offset; Black and 3 ROP colors; insert accepted - single sheets, envelopes, samples; page cutoffs - 21 1/2.
Mechanical Specifications: Type page 13 x 21 3/4; E - 6 cols, 1 5/6, 1/8 between; A - 6 cols, 1 5/6, 1/8 between; C - 9 cols, between.
Equipment & Software: PRESSROOM EQUIPMENT: Lines — 6-KP/Daily King.; MAILROOM EQUIPMENT: Counter Stackers — 1/BG; Inserters & Stuffers — 4-DG/320; Tying Machines — 1-Bu/42409; Address Machine — 1-/Am, 1-/KR.; BUSINESS EQUIPMENT: Solomon/PC CLASSIFIED EQUIPMENT: Hardware — Server; Printers — APP/Mac LaserWriter 16-600PS; CLASSIFIED SOFTWARE: APP/Mac Pro, APP/Mac Class Pro. DISPLAY EQUIPMENT: Printers — AG/Accuset, Star/400 RIP, APP/Mac LaserWriter 16-600 PS; DISPLAY SOFTWAREAd Make-up Applications — QPS/QuarkXPress 3.32, Adobe/Freehand 5.0, Adobe/Photoshop 4.0; Layout Software — APP/Power Mac 9500. EDITORIAL EQUIPMENT: Hardware — Server; Printers — 3-APP/Mac LaserWriter 16-600 PS EDITORIAL SOFTWARE: Baseview. PRODUCTION EQUIPMENT: Hardware — 2-COM/Unisetters, AG/Accuset, Star/400 RIP; Cameras — 1-B/24x24, 1-DAI/24x24; Scanners — Nikon/Coolscan, AG/Arcus Flatbed PRODUCTION SOFTWARE: QPS/QuarkXPress 3.32.

WISCONSIN

ANTIGO

ANTIGO DAILY JOURNAL

612 Superior St, Antigo, Wis., 54409-2049, Langlade; gen tel (715) 623-4191; adv tel (715) 623-4191; ed tel (715) 623-4191; gen fax (715) 623-4193; adv fax (715) 623-4193; ed fax (715) 623-4193; gen/nat adv e-mail adj@dwave.net; disp adv e-mail adj@dwave.net; class adv e-mailadj@dwave.net; ed e-mail adj@dwave.net; web site www.antigodailyjournal.com
Group: Berner Brothers Publishing Company Inc.
Published: Mon, Tues, Wed, Thur, Fri, Sat
Weekday Frequency: e
Saturday Frequency: m
Circulation: 5,660; 5,760(sat)
Last Audit: Sworn/Estimate/Non-Audited September 30, 2017
Advertising Rate (weekday/saturday): Open inch rate $6.78
News services: AP **Established:** 1905
Own Printing Facility?: Yes
Commercial Printers?: No
Special Editions: Fitness & Health (Jan.); Bridal Guide (Feb.); Getting to Know You (March); Spring Home & Garden (April); Graduation (May); 4-H Youth Fair Days (July); Back to Back-to-School (Aug.); Northwoods Recreation (Sept.); Holiday Recipes (Nov.); Christmas Magazine (Nov.)
Special Weekly Sections: Local (Daily); Best Food (Mon); Around Town (Thur); TV (Sat)
Pub./Ed./Adv. Dir. .... Fred A. Berner
Reporter...Debbie Igl
Teen-Age/Youth Ed............................. Lisa Haefs
Pressman..................................Allan Gelhausen
Classifieds Adv. Mgr.......................... Sue Blahnik
Adv. Sales Consultant...................Cathy Wallace
Laura Harvey
Market Information: TMC.
Mechanical Available: Offset; Black and 3 ROP colors; insert accepted; page cutoffs - 22 3/4.
Mechanical Specifications: Type page 11.625 x 21; E - 6 cols, 1 13/16, 1/8 between; A - 6 cols, 1 13/16, 1/8 between; C - 6 cols, 1 3/8, 1/16 between.
Delivery Method: Mail, Newsstand, Carrier, RacksEquipment & Software: PRESSROOM EQUIPMENT: Lines — 5-G/Community.; MAILROOM EQUIPMENT: Tying Machines — 1/Bu; Address Machine — Stepper; BUSINESS EQUIPMENT: PC/Business Mac/Production CLASSIFIED EQUIPMENT: Hardware — Mac; Printers — HP; CLASSIFIED SOFTWARE: Baseview. DISPLAY EQUIPMENT: Hardware — MAC; Printers — HP; EDITORIAL EQUIPMENT: Hardware — Mac; Printers — HP EDITORIAL SOFTWARE: Baseview. PRODUCTION EQUIPMENT: Hardware — Mac; Scanners — HP, Epson PRODUCTION SOFTWARE: QuarkXpress, Adobe Photoshop

APPLETON

POST-CRESCENT

306 W Washington St, Appleton, Wis., 54911-5452, Outagamie; gen tel (920) 993-1000; adv tel (920) 996-7224; ed tel (920) 993-7155; gen fax (920) 730-1893; adv fax (920) 954-1945; ed fax (920) 733-1945; gen/nat adv e-mail pcads@appleton.gannett.com; disp adv e-mail pcads@appleton.gannett.com; class adv e-mailclassified@wisinfo.com; ed e-mail pcnews@postcrescent.com; web site www.postcrescent.com - 3,785,989(views) 543,900(visitors); web site 2 www.foxcitieshub.com
Group: Gannett
Published: Mon, Tues, Wed, Thur, Fri, Sat, Sun
Weekday Frequency: m
Saturday Frequency: m
Circulation: 32,405; 32,405(sat); 45,208(sun)
Last Audit: AAM March 31, 2016
Branch Offices: Neenah, WI; Madison, WI.
Advertising Rate (weekday/saturday): Open inch rate $89.90
Advertising Rate (sunday): Open inch rate $128.30
News services: MCT, Landon Media Group, AP, Gannett. **Established:** 1853
Own Printing Facility?: Yes
Commercial Printers?: Yes
Special Editions: Homes and More Magazine (monthly),
Employment features (quarterly)
Best of the Valley (Sept. & Oct.)
Spring Home and Garden (April)
Fall Home and Garden (Sept.)
Prep football preview (Aug)
Prep basketball preview (Nov)
Special Weekly Sections: Sports, Outdoor, Business, Travel (Sun); Business (Mon/Sun); Best Food (Wed); Entertainment (Thur); Home (Sat)
Syndicated Publications: USA WEEKEND Magazine (S).
Digital Platform - Mobile: Apple, Android
Digital Platform - Tablet: Apple iOS, Android, Kindle
Pres./Pub.......................................Genia Lovett
Vice Pres., Finance.........................Mike Seeber
News Director..............................Jason Adrians
Editor/Opinion...............................Larry Gallup
Editor/Sports & Features............. Ed Berthiaume
Consumer Experience Director.......Terry Lipshetz
Newsroom assistant..................Denise Wagner
Adv. Dir....Steve Broas
Editor/Digital................................Joel Christopher
Reporter/Fox Cities............................Jim Collar
Editor/Local enterprise............. Andy Thompson
Senior Director/Distribution-Wisconsin.......... Amy Leitzke
Distribution Director.....................Mark Johnson
Digital Manager.............................Steve Teofilo
VP/Adv. Dir./Interim Pub.................Steven Broas
Nat'l Sales ....Ray Stevens
James Fitzhenry
Pamela Henson
Market Information: ADS; TMC; Zoned editions.
Mechanical Available: Offset; Black and 3 ROP colors; insert accepted; page cutoffs - 21 1/2.
Mechanical Specifications: Type page 11 1/8 x 20 5/8; E - 6 cols, 1 3/4, 1/8 between; A - 6 cols, 1 3/4, 1/8 between; C - 10 cols, 1 1/20, 1/8 between.
Areas Served: 54911, 54913, 54914, 54915, 54190, 54136, 54140, 53014, 53061, 54106, 54110, 54113, 54129, 54131, 54165, 54170, 54929, 54981, 54940, 54942, 54944, 54945, 54947, 54949, 54952, 54956, 54961, 54981, 54983
Delivery Method: Newsstand, Carrier, RacksEquipment & Software: PRESSROOM EQUIPMENT: 8 (32 Couples)-2000; 8 (32 Couples)-2000; Registration System — Prazision/Comet EP. MAILROOM EQUIPMENT: Counter Stackers — 8-Compass/180; Inserters & Stuffers — 3-Printroll/GMA; Tying Machines — 7/Strapmaster; Wrapping Singles — 3-Dynaric/D2100; Control System — GMA; BUSINESS EQUIPMENT: iSeries BUSINESS SOFTWARE: Gannett Genesys CLASSIFIED EQUIPMENT: Hardware — Sun Unix; CLASSIFIED SOFTWARE: Mediaspan Ad Power DISPLAY EQUIPMENT: Hardware — Outsourced; DISPLAY SOFTWAREAd Make-up Applications — Outsourced, Adobe InDesign CS4; Layout Software — SCS Layout 8000 EDITORIAL SOFTWARE: CCI Europe NewsGate PRODUCTION EQUIPMENT: Hardware — AGFA

ASHLAND

THE ASHLAND DAILY PRESS

122 3rd St W, Ashland, Wis., 54806-1661, Ashland; gen tel (715) 682-2313; adv tel (715)682-2313; ed tel (715) 685-4510; gen fax (715) 682-4699; adv fax (715)682-4699; ed fax (715)682-4699; gen/nat adv e-mail bnorth@ashlanddailypress.net; disp adv e-mail bnorth@ashlanddailypress.net; class adv e-mailhjuoni@ashlanddailypress.net; ed e-mail lservinsky@ashlanddailypress.net; web site www.apg-wi.com
Group: Adams Publishing Group, LLC
Published: Mon, Wed, Thur, Fri, Sat
Weekday Frequency: m

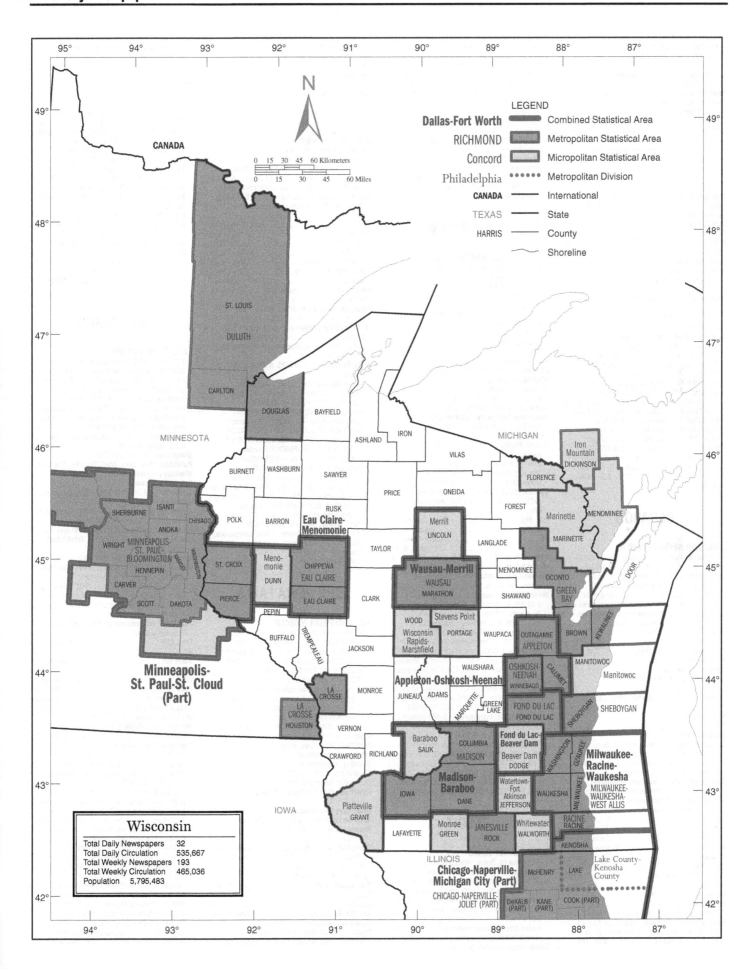

LEGEND

Dallas-Fort Worth — Combined Statistical Area
RICHMOND — Metropolitan Statistical Area
Concord — Micropolitan Statistical Area
Philadelphia — •••••• Metropolitan Division
CANADA — International
TEXAS — State
HARRIS — County
— Shoreline

Wisconsin

Total Daily Newspapers	32
Total Daily Circulation	535,667
Total Weekly Newspapers	193
Total Weekly Circulation	465,036
Population	5,795,483

Saturday Frequency: m
Circulation: 6,153; 6,153(sat)
Last Audit: Sworn/Estimate/Non-Audited October 1, 2017
Advertising Rate (weekday/saturday): Open inch rate $12.60
News services: Tribune News Service
Own Printing Facility?: Yes
Special Editions: Spring Car Care & Home Improvement (Apr); Bayfield County Fair Tab (Aug); Football Preview section (Aug), Red Clay Classic (Sept. Oct.) Whitetail Section (Nov.) Basketball Preview section (Dec) Songs of Christmas/Gift Guide & Holiday Greetings (Dec); Valentine's Day Gift Tab (Feb); Father's Day Gifts (Jun); Graduation Gift Guides (May)
Managing Editor ....David LaPorte
Editor ....Larry Servinsky
Sports Editor.........................Garett Greenwald
Staff Writer...................................Rick Olivo
Advertising ....Heidi Westerlund
Reporter....................................Sara Chase
Legals....................................Karen Petras
Sports Reporter...........................Jake Brown
Market Information: Split run.
Mechanical Available: Offset; Black and 3 ROP colors; insert accepted; page cutoffs - 22 3/4.
Mechanical Specifications: Type page 11 5/8 x 21 1/2; E - 6 cols, 1 5/6, 1/8 between; A - 6 cols, 1 5/6, 1/8 between; C - 6 cols, 1 5/6, 1/8 between.
Delivery Method: Mail, Newsstand, Carrier, RacksEquipment & Software: PRESSROOM EQUIPMENT: Lines — 8 (single width)-G/Community; Press Drive — HP/60 Motor; Folders — SC/Folder.; MAILROOM EQUIPMENT: Tying Machines — 3/Bu.; BUSINESS EQUIPMENT: 2-RSK/12, 2-RSK/3000 HD, APP/Power Mac BUSINESS SOFTWARE: Quickbooks 5.0 CLASSIFIED EQUIPMENT: Hardware — APP/Mac.; DISPLAY SOFTWARELayout Software — APP/Mac. EDITORIAL EQUIPMENT: Hardware — APP/Mac. PRODUCTION EQUIPMENT: Hardware — 1-NuArc/Flip Top; Cameras — AG/2200II, 1-B; Scanners — Microtek/E6 PRODUCTION SOFTWARE: Baseview.

BARABOO

BARABOO NEWS REPUBLIC
714 Matts Ferry Rd, Baraboo, Wis., 53913-3152, Sauk; gen tel (608) 356-4808; adv tel (608) 745-3800; gen fax (608) 356-0344; gen/nat adv e-mail bnr-news@capitalnewspapers.com; disp adv e-mail mmeyers@capitalnewspapers.com; class adv e-mailmmeyers@capitalnewspapers.com; web site www.wiscnews.com/bnr
Group: Lee Enterprises, Inc.
Capital Newspapers
Published: Mon, Tues, Wed, Thur, Fri, Sat
Weekday Frequency: m
Saturday Frequency: m
Circulation: 2,522; 2,647(sat)
Last Audit: AAM June 30, 2017
Advertising Rate (weekday/saturday): Open inch rate $20.10
News services: AP.
Own Printing Facility?: Yes
Commercial Printers?: No
Special Weekly Sections: Business, Society, Sports (Daily); Technology (Mon); Recreation (Wed); Entertainment (Thur); Entertainment, Home, Travel, TV, Food (Sat)
Syndicated Publications: Relish (Monthly); Parade (Sat); American Profile (Weekly).
Digital Platform - Mobile: Apple, Android
Digital Platform - Tablet: Apple iOS, Android
Ed........................................Todd Krysiak
Pub........................................Matt Meyers
Circ. Dir. ....Teresa Klinger
Asst. Ed..............................Andrew Analore
Feature Ed............................Ben Bromley
Sports Ed. ....Pete Watson
Prodn. Mgr., Mailroom........Nancy Preston
Adv. Dir. ....Jon Denk
Market Information: TMC.
Mechanical Available: Offset; Black and 3 ROP colors; insert accepted; page cutoffs - 21 3/4.
Mechanical Specifications: Type page 13 x 21 1/2; E - 6 cols, 1 7/8, 1/8 between; A - 6 cols, 1 7/8, 1/8 between; C - 9 cols, 1 3/16, 1/8

between.
Areas Served: Sauk County
Delivery Method: Mail, Newsstand, RacksEquipment & Software: PRESSROOM EQUIPMENT: Lines — 12-G/Community 1998.; MAILROOM EQUIPMENT: Counter Stackers — 1/MM; Inserters & Stuffers — 2-KAN/8; Tying Machines — 1-/Bu; Address Machine — VideoJet.; BUSINESS EQUIPMENT: SMS CLASSIFIED SOFTWARE: Baseview. DISPLAY EQUIPMENT: Printers — APP/Mac LaserPrinter.; EDITORIAL SOFTWARE: Baseview. PRODUCTION EQUIPMENT: Hardware — 2-Nu; Cameras — B/Vertical; Scanners — 3-COM/2961HS, 1-COM/7200, 1-COM/4 PRODUCTION SOFTWARE: QPS/QuarkXPress 4.0.

BEAVER DAM

DAILY CITIZEN, BEAVER DAM
805 Park Ave, Beaver Dam, Wis., 53916-2205, Dodge; gen tel (920) 887-0321; adv tel (920) 887-0321; ed tel (920) 887-0321; gen/nat adv e-mail szeinemann@capitalnewspapers.com; disp adv e-mail dc-ads@capitalnewspapers.com; class adv e-maildc-ads@capitalnewspapers.com; ed e-mail dc-news@capitalnewspapers.com; web site www.wiscnews.com
Group: Lee Enterprises, Inc.
Capital Newspapers
Published: Mon, Tues, Wed, Thur, Fri, Sat
Weekday Frequency: e
Saturday Frequency: m
Circulation: 5,482; 6,533(sat)
Last Audit: AAM June 30, 2017
Advertising Rate (weekday/saturday): Open inch rate $11.60 (Mon-Fri); $12.60 (Sat)
News services: AP, NYT.
Special Weekly Sections: Entertainment, Family (Wed, Thur); Religion (Fri); Arts, Entertainment, Family, Food, Health, Living, Travel (Sat); Business, Financial (Mon-Sat); Home (3rd Sat); Bridal (1st/3rd Sat)
Syndicated Publications: Relish (Monthly); USA WEEKEND Magazine (Sat); American Profile (Weekly).
Gen. Mgr...............................Scott Zeinemann
Circ. Dir. ....Teresa Klinger
Ed. ....Aaron Holbrook
Pub........................................James Kelsh
Editorial Page Ed. ....Jim Kelsh
Market Information: TMC; Zoned editions.
Mechanical Available: Offset; Black and 3 ROP colors; insert accepted; page cutoffs - 22 3/4.
Mechanical Specifications: Type page 15 1/4 x 21 3/8; E - 6 cols, 2 1/16, 1/8 between; A - 8 cols, 1 9/16, 1/8 between; C - 8 cols, 1 3/8, 1/16 between.Equipment & Software: PRESSROOM EQUIPMENT: Lines — 12-G/Community; 20-G/Community; Folders — 5-G/Community; Pasters -7-MEG. MAILROOM EQUIPMENT: Counter Stackers — 5-BG/Count-O-Veyor 104-108; Inserters & Stuffers — 4-MM/227E, 6-MM/227; Tying Machines — 4/Bu, 1-/CYP; Address Machine — 2-/Am, 1-/Kk.; BUSINESS EQUIPMENT: 10-IBM/PS2, 6-APP/Mac II CLASSIFIED EQUIPMENT: Hardware — 3-APP/Mac II.; DISPLAY SOFTWARELayout Software — 5-APP/Mac II. EDITORIAL EQUIPMENT: Hardware — 2-APP/Mac Plus, 8-APP/Mac II EDITORIAL SOFTWARE: Concept. PRODUCTION EQUIPMENT: Hardware — 1-Nu/Flip Top FT40LNS, 1-Nu/Flip Top FT40UPNS; Cameras — 1-B/Commodore PRODUCTION SOFTWARE: Concept.

BELOIT

BELOIT DAILY NEWS
149 State St, Beloit, Wis., 53511-6251, Rock; gen tel (608) 365-8811; adv tel (608)364-9235; gen fax (608) 365-1420; adv fax (608) 365-1420; gen/nat adv e-mail advertising@beloitdailynews.com; disp adv e-mail tcolling@beloitdailynews.com; class adv e-mailkboreen@beloitdailynews.com; ed e-mail bbarth@beloitdailynews.com; web site www.beloitdailynews.com
Group: Hagadone Corporation

Published: Mon, Tues, Wed, Thur, Fri, Sat
Weekday Frequency: e
Saturday Frequency: m
Circulation: 9,309
Last Audit: Sworn/Estimate/Non-Audited September 30, 2017
Advertising Rate (weekday/saturday): Open inch rate $34.60
Online Advertising Rate: call.
News services: AP, United Media Service.
Established: 1848
Own Printing Facility?: Yes
Commercial Printers?: Yes
Special Editions: MDA Tub Run, Summer Bridal Tab, 2013 Tourism, 2013 Source Book, Savvy, Yearbook, Legends of Sports, Adopt a Pet, Bridal Directory, Home Improvement
Special Weekly Sections: Best Food (Sat/Wed); Business (Tue); Weekend Entertainment, Real Estate, Health, TV (Fri)
Pub...................................Kent D. Eymann
City Ed. ....Clint Wolf
Editorial Page Ed. ....Bill Barth
Sports Ed. ....James Franz
Prodn. Mgr., Post Press ....Dave Shaw
Prodn. Mgr., Pressroom ....Tim Sager
Business Manager ....Angie Meade
Director of Business Development.....Todd Colling
Market Information: Split run; TMC.
Mechanical Available: Offset; Black and 3 ROP colors; insert accepted; page cutoffs - 21 1/2.
Mechanical Specifications: Type page 11 5/8 x 21 1/2; E - 6 cols, 1 5/6, 1/8 between; A - 6 cols, 1 5/6, 1/8 between; C - 8 cols, 1 9/25, 1/8 between.
Areas Served: 53511, 53525, 61080, 61072, 61073
Delivery Method: Mail, Newsstand, Carrier, RacksEquipment & Software: PRESSROOM EQUIPMENT: Lines — 6-G/Urbanite; Folders — 1-G/2:1.; MAILROOM EQUIPMENT: Tying Machines — 1-MLN/Plastic Strap.; BUSINESS EQUIPMENT: 1-DEC/TC 3800 BUSINESS SOFTWARE: Micro/VMS 5.1 CLASSIFIED EQUIPMENT: Hardware — Mac; Mac; Printers — OTC/850X2; CLASSIFIED SOFTWARE: NCS DISPLAY EQUIPMENT: Hardware — Mac; Printers — HP, Toshiba; DISPLAY SOFTWAREAd Make-up Applications — Multi-Ad/Creator, Indesign; EDITORIAL EQUIPMENT: Hardware — Mac/Mac; Printers — HP EDITORIAL SOFTWARE: NCS PRODUCTION EQUIPMENT: Hardware — Mac computers, ECRM CTP plate setter.; Cameras — None; Scanners — Dest top PRODUCTION SOFTWARE: NCS

CHIPPEWA FALLS

THE CHIPPEWA HERALD
321 Frenette Dr, Chippewa Falls, Wis., 54729-3372, Chippewa; gen tel (715) 723-5515; adv tel (715) 723-5515; ed tel (715) 723-5515; gen fax (715) 723-9644; adv fax (715) 723-9644; ed fax (715) 723-9644; gen/nat adv e-mail publisher@chippewa.com; disp adv e-mail advertising@chippewa.com; ed e-mail news@chippewa.com; web site www.chippewa.com; www.chippewavalleynewspapers.com
- 1,031,169(views) 149,863(visitors)
Group: Lee Enterprises, Inc.
Published: Mon, Tues, Wed, Thur, Sat, Sun
Weekday Frequency: m
Saturday Frequency: m
Circulation: 3,578; 3,578(sat); 3,568(sun)
Last Audit: AAM March 31, 2016
Advertising Rate (weekday/saturday): Open inch rate $15.42
Advertising Rate (sunday): Open inch rate $15.42
News services: AP, DJ, TMS. **Established:** 1870
Special Editions: Chippewa Valley Business Report (Quarterly).
Special Weekly Sections: Dining, Entertainment (Thur); Real Estate (Sat); Best Food, Auto, Business, TV, Travel (Sun)
Syndicated Publications: Parade (S).
Circ. District Mgr. ....Adam Polden
Editor.......................................Ross Evavold
Circ Dir ....Bill Lenardson
Adv. Dir. & Gen. Mgr. ....Stacia King
Market Information: ADS; TMC.
Mechanical Available: Offset; Black and 3 ROP colors; insert accepted - any; page cutoffs

- 21 1/2.
Mechanical Specifications: Type page 12 1/2 x 21 1/2; E - 6 cols, 2 1/16, 1/8 between; A - 6 cols, 2 1/16, 1/8 between; C - 6 cols, 2 1/16, 1/8 between.
Areas Served: Chippewa County, WisocnsinEquipment & Software: PRESSROOM EQUIPMENT: Lines — G/4-hi, 2-DEV/Flexicolor; Folders — 4-G/2:1.; MAILROOM EQUIPMENT: Counter Stackers — 2/BG; Inserters & Stuffers — USA/Leader; Tying Machines — 2-/Bu, 1-/It; Address Machine — KR.; CLASSIFIED EQUIPMENT: Hardware — Gateway; CLASSIFIED SOFTWARE: APT. DISPLAY EQUIPMENT: Other Hardware — Nikon/Coolscan DISPLAY SOFTWAREAd Make-up Applications — Multi-Ad/Creator, QPS/QuarkXPress; Layout Software — 2-APP/Mac, APP/Power Mac. EDITORIAL EQUIPMENT: Hardware — APP/Power Macs/Nikon/Coolscan; Printers — APP/Mac LaserPrinter EDITORIAL SOFTWARE: Baseview. PRODUCTION EQUIPMENT: Hardware — 2-COM/Laserwriter, Pre Press/Panther Pro; Cameras — SCREEN; Scanners — HP/ScanJet Plus, 2-Nikon/Coolscan PRODUCTION SOFTWARE: QPS/QuarkXPress.

EAU CLAIRE

LEADER-TELEGRAM
701 S Farwell St, Eau Claire, Wis., 54701-3831, Eau Claire; gen tel (715) 833-9200; adv tel (715) 833-7420; ed tel (715) 833-9203; gen fax (715) 833-9244; adv fax (715) 833-9244; ed fax (715) 858-7308; gen/nat adv e-mail dan.graaskamp@ecpc.com; disp adv e-mail dan.graaskamp@ecpc.com; class adv e-maildan.graaskamp@ecpc.com; ed e-mail gary.johnson@ecpc.com; web site www.leadertelegram.com
Group: Eau Claire Press Co.
Published: Mon, Tues, Wed, Thur, Fri, Sat, Sun
Weekday Frequency: m
Saturday Frequency: m
Circulation: 18,260; 19,006(sat); 21,241(sun)
Last Audit: AAM March 31, 2017
Advertising Rate (weekday/saturday): Open inch rate $33.10 (Mon-Fri); $34.70 (Sat)
Advertising Rate (sunday): Open inch rate $37.40
News services: AP, SHNS, MCT. **Established:** 1912
Special Editions: Impressions (Quarterly).
Special Weekly Sections: Business (Tue); Health, Business (Wed); Entertainment, Business (Thur); Outdoors, Business (Fri); Real Estate, Home, Religion (Sat); Entertainment, Travel, Lifestyles, Moments in Life, Business, Sports, Main News, Comics (Sun)
Syndicated Publications: USA WEEKEND Magazine (Sat).
Pres./CEO ....Pieter Graaskamp
VP.......................................Daniel Graaskamp
Sales Dir. ....Kathy Hayden
Circ. Dir. ....Mike Carlson
Ed. ....Don Huebscher
Food Ed.................................Blythe Wachter
Local News Ed..........................Gary Johnson
Mktg. / Promo Mgr. ....Brian Sandy
Market Information: Split run; TMC.
Mechanical Available: Offset; Black and ROP colors; insert accepted - all; page cutoffs - 22.
Mechanical Specifications: Type page 12 1/2 x 21; E - 6 cols, 1 13/16, 1/8 between; A - 6 cols, 1 13/16, 1/8 between; C - 9 cols, 1 3/16, 1/8 between.Equipment & Software: PRESSROOM EQUIPMENT: Lines — 14-DGM/850 single width 1998; Folders — 1-G/Half, 1-G/Quarter.; MAILROOM EQUIPMENT: Counter Stackers — 2-QWI/350; Inserters & Stuffers — 1-GMA/10:1; Tying Machines — 2/MLN; Wrapping Singles — Mailroom Control System GMA; Address Machine — 2-/KR; BUSINESS EQUIPMENT: 1-HP, 2-Dell Poweredge 6300, 1-Dell Poweredge 6400 BUSINESS SOFTWARE: Mactive CLASSIFIED EQUIPMENT: Hardware — 10-PC, Microsoft/Windows NT 4.0; Printers — Canon/BX-II, HP/LJ 4ML; CLASSIFIED SOFTWARE: Mactive. DISPLAY EQUIPMENT: Hardware — MS/NT PC 4.0 wka, 2-APP/Mac G3; Printers — 1-Canon/BX-II, Epson/Stylus Color 3000, 1-AGFA; DISPLAY SOFTWAREAd

Make-up Applications — Adobe/Illustrator, QPS/QuarkXPress, Adobe/Photoshop; Layout Software — Mactive. EDITORIAL EQUIPMENT: Hardware — 35-PC; Printers — Canon/BXII, HP/LS9700 EDITORIAL SOFTWARE: Microsoft/Word, QPS/QuarkXPress 4.11rl, ATS/Mediadesk. PRODUCTION EQUIPMENT: Hardware — 1-AG/5000 Recorder, 1-AG/Phoenix 2250, 1-AG/Avatru 44; Cameras — 1-Liberator; Scanners — 2-Nikon, 2-Epson/Expressions 800XL PRODUCTION SOFTWARE: QPS/QuarkXPress 4.11rl, Adobe/Illustrator 5.5,6.5.

FOND DU LAC

THE FOND DU LAC REPORTER

N6637 Rolling Meadows Dr, Fond Du Lac, Wis., 54937-9471, Fond Du Lac; gen tel (920) 922-4600; adv tel (920)922-4600; ed tel (920)922-4600; gen fax (920) 922-5388; adv fax (920) 922-3552; ed fax (920) 922-3552; gen/nat adv e-mail advertising@fdlreporter.com; disp adv e-mail advertising@fdlreporter.com; class adv e-mailadvertising@fdlreporter.com; ed e-mail treporter@fdlreporter.com; web site www.fdlreporter.com

Group: Gannett
Published: Mon, Tues, Wed, Thur, Fri, Sat, Sun
Weekday Frequency: e
Circulation: 8,529; 840(sat); 11,081(sun)
Last Audit: AAM March 31, 2016
Advertising Rate (weekday/saturday): Open inch rate $51.40
Advertising Rate (sunday): Open inch rate $62.90
News services: AP, GNS. **Established:** 1856
Own Printing Facility?: No
Commercial Printers?: Yes
Special Editions: Answer Book (Oct).
Special Weekly Sections: Weather, Community/State, Nation/World, Opinion, Community, Records, Waupun News Daily, Obituaries, Entertainment, Travel, Comics, Sports (Daily); Business, Home Town, Advice, Farm, Outdoor, Home & Garden, Driving/Destinations, Color Comics, TV Book, Real Estate (Sun); Great Community Photo Page, Advice (Mon); Business, Seniors, Technology (Tue); Home, Garden, Food, Best Food Day, NIE (Wed); Business, Advice, GOLF, Entertainment, Women (Thur); Business, Church, NASCAR (Fri)
Syndicated Publications: USA WEEKEND Magazine (S).
Photo Dept. Mgr. .... Pat Flood
Sports Ed. .... Paul Keup
Pub. .... Bill Hackney
Adv. Dir. .... Karen Befus
Market Information: ADS; TMC.
Mechanical Available: Offset; Black and 3 ROP colors; insert accepted - Newspac; page cutoffs - 21 1/2.
Mechanical Specifications: Type page 11 5/8 x 21 1/2; E - 6 cols, 1 5/6, 1/8 between; A - 6 cols, 1 5/6, 1/8 between; C - 9 cols, 1 1/4, 1/16 between.
Delivery Method: Mail, Newsstand, CarrierEquipment & Software: PRESSROOM EQUIPMENT: Lines — 7-G/Urbanite single width 1977; 1-Ik/Sheet Fed Press 1992; 12-G/Urbanite; 7-G/Urbanite; Folders — 1-G/Half, 1-G/Quarter, 2-G/Folders-Half Width, 2-1998; Pasters —8-Enkel/Auto Splicers MAILROOM EQUIPMENT: Counter Stackers — HL/Monitor HT, 2/HL, 2-/MRS; Inserters & Stuffers — 2-GMA/SLS 1000 2:12; Tying Machines — OVL, 2-/Samuel, 1-/Dynaric, 2-OVL/415; Wrapping Singles — 2-/Samuel, 2-Id; Address Machine — Video Jet/Ink Jet, Ch.; BUSINESS EQUIPMENT: ATT, Oracle BUSINESS SOFTWARE: IBM CLASSIFIED EQUIPMENT: Hardware — 1-HI; CLASSIFIED SOFTWARE: Ad Power. DISPLAY EQUIPMENT: Hardware — APP/Mac II, APP/Mac IIcx, APP/Mac IIci, 5-APP/Power Mac; Printers — APP/Mac LaserWriter II, V/5060W, Tegra/Varityper Rm.3; DISPLAY SOFTWAREAd Make-up Applications — Multi-Ad/Creator, Adobe/Illustrator, Aldus/Freehand, QPS/QuarkXPress; Layout Software — Ethernet, Appletalk/Network. EDITORIAL EQUIPMENT: Hardware — Atex/Pagination System; Printers — HP/P1180. PRODUCTION EQUIPMENT: Hardware — LaserJet 4mv, Digital Darkroom, Adobe/Photoshop, V/Film Recorder; Cameras — Auto/Companica 690D; Scanners — AG/StudioScan PRODUCTION SOFTWARE: CText.

FORT ATKINSON

DAILY JEFFERSON COUNTY UNION

28 Milwaukee Ave W, Fort Atkinson, Wis., 53538-2018, Jefferson; gen tel (920) 563-5553; adv tel (920) 563-5553; ed tel (920) 563-5553; gen fax (920) 563-2329; adv fax (920) 563-2329; ed fax (920) 563-2329; gen/nat adv e-mail advertising@dailyunion.com; disp adv e-mail rgrindstaff@dailyunion.com; class adv e-mailclassifieds@dailyunion.com; ed e-mail Cspangler@dailyunion.com ; web site www.dailyunion.com
- 400,000(views) 60,000(visitors)

Group: W.D. Hoard & Sons Publishing
Published: Mon, Tues, Wed, Thur, Fri
Weekday Frequency: e
Circulation: 7
Last Audit: Sworn/Estimate/Non-Audited September 29, 2017
Advertising Rate (weekday/saturday): Open inch rate $14.30
Advertising Rate (sunday): n/a
Online Advertising Rate: $299/Month with one-year commitment
News services: AP. **Established:** 1870
Own Printing Facility?: No
Commercial Printers?: Yes
Special Editions: Home Improvement (Apr); Health (Monthly); Christmas (Dec); Money Matters (Jan); Bridal (Mar); Car Care (Oct); Home Improvement (Sept).
Special Weekly Sections: Union Extra shopper (Wed); Business (Tue); Best Food (Wed); Senior Citizen (Fri)
Pres./Pub. .... Brian V. Knox
Managing Editor .... Christine Spangler
Adv. Mgr./Business Mgr. .... Robb Grindstaff
Circulation Director .... Brian Knox II
Market Information: TMC.
Mechanical Available: Offset; Black and 3 ROP colors; insert accepted; page cutoffs - 21".
Mechanical Specifications: Type page 11.125 X 19.5; E - 6 cols, 1.75" per col, 0.125" between; C - 8 cols, 1.281", 0.125" between.
Areas Served: 53538, 53549, 53190, 53038, 53523, 53551, 53178, 53156
Delivery Method: Mail, Newsstand, Carrier, RacksEquipment & Software: BUSINESS SOFTWARE: Pre1 SmartPublisher CLASSIFIED SOFTWARE: Pre1 SmartPublisher DISPLAY SOFTWAREPre1 SmartPublisher EDITORIAL SOFTWARE: Town News Blox TCMS PRODUCTION SOFTWARE: Creative Cloud CIRCULATION SOFTWARNewsCycle (MediaSpan) CircPro

GREEN BAY

GREEN BAY PRESS-GAZETTE

435 E Walnut St, Green Bay, Wis., 54301-5001, Brown; gen tel (920) 435-4411; adv tel (920) 431-8293; ed tel (920) 431-8400; gen fax (920) 431-8665; adv fax (920) 431-8308; ed fax (920) 431-8379; gen/nat adv e-mail online@greenbaypressgazette.com; disp adv e-mail prepress@greenbaypressgazette.com; class adv e-mailclassified@wisinfo.com; ed e-mail localnews@greenbaypressgazette.com; web site www.greenbaypressgazette.com
- 6,023,000(views) 637,000(visitors)

Group: Gannett
Published: Mon, Tues, Wed, Thur, Fri, Sat, Sun
Weekday Frequency: m
Saturday Frequency: m
Circulation: 36,282; 41,148(sat); 54,116(sun)
Last Audit: AAM March 31, 2016
Advertising Rate (weekday/saturday): Open inch rate $79.10
News services: MCT, AP, GNS. **Established:** 1915
Own Printing Facility?: Yes
Special Editions: Design an Ad (Apr); Menu Guide (Aug); Last Minute Gifts (Dec); Bridal (Feb); Home & Garden (Jan); Home & Garden (Jul); Bridal (Jun); Home & Garden (Mar); Health First (Monthly); Home & Garden (Nov); Coupon Book (Oct); Coupon Book (Semi-monthly); Home & Ga
Special Weekly Sections: Finally Friday (Fri); Careers (S); On the Road and Off (Sat); Weekend (Thur); Careers (Wed).
Syndicated Publications: USA WEEKEND Magazine (S).
Digital Platform - Mobile: Apple, Android, Windows
Digital Platform - Tablet: Apple iOS, Android
News Ed. .... Peter Frank
Circ. Dir. .... Scott Daily
President & Publisher .... Scott Johnson
Controller .... Tom Ricci
IT Dir. .... Phil Legler
Exec Editor .... Robert Zizzo
Content Coash .... Karl Ebert
Community Engagement Editor .... Peter Frank
Market Information: Split run; Zoned editions.
Mechanical Available: DiLitho; Black and 3 ROP colors; insert accepted - bags; page cutoffs - 23 9/16.
Mechanical Specifications: Type page 11 5/8 x 20 3/4; E - 6 cols, 1 5/6, 1/8 between; A - 6 cols, 1 5/6, 1/8 between; C - 9 cols, 1 6/25, 1/16 between.
Delivery Method: Mail, Carrier, RacksEquipment & Software: PRESSROOM EQUIPMENT: Lines — 6-G/Mark II double width, 2-G/Mark I double width 1969; Press Drive — CH/60 h.p.; Folders — 2-G/2:1; Reels & Stands — G/3-Arm.; MAILROOM EQUIPMENT: Counter Stackers — 4/HL, QWI/Hall; Inserters & Stuffers — HI/1472, S/NP630; Tying Machines — 2-MLN/2A, 2-/Dynaric, 1-/Power Strap; Wrapping Singles — QWI/Hall; Control System — Ic, HL/Spec 09; Address Machine — Dispensa-Matic-V4.; BUSINESS EQUIPMENT: IBM/AS-400 BUSINESS SOFTWARE: Microsoft/Office 97 CLASSIFIED EQUIPMENT: Hardware — Sun; Printers — AU/APS; CLASSIFIED SOFTWARE: HI/AdPower 1.2. DISPLAY EQUIPMENT: Hardware — APP/Mac; Printers — 3-AU/APS Software RIP & Imagesetter, AU/Sierra 3850; Other Hardware — Umax/Scanner, 2-Nikon/Slide Scanner, 2-Epson, 1-Hel/Sapphire DISPLAY SOFTWAREAd Make-up Applications — Multi-Ad/Creator, Adobe/Photoshop, QPS/QuarkXPress; Layout Software — 10-APP/Mac. EDITORIAL EQUIPMENT: Hardware — 28-AT/7000, 60-AT/Prestige 4.2.1/4-APP/Mac EDITORIAL SOFTWARE: AT, Aldus/Freehand, QPS/QuarkXPress, Adobe/Photoshop. PRODUCTION EQUIPMENT: Hardware — 3-AU/Software RIP & Imagesetter, 5-LE; Cameras — 1-C/Marathon, 1-B/Admiral; Scanners — 1-Hel/Sapphire, 1-ECR/Autokon 1000, 1-X/1200 dpi, 3-Umax/Color 1200 DPI, 2-Epson, 2-Nikon/Slide Scanner PRODUCTION SOFTWARE: QPS/QuarkXPress 3.5, AT.

JANESVILLE

THE JANESVILLE GAZETTE - GAZETTEXTRA

1 S Parker Dr, Janesville, Wis., 53545-3928, Rock; gen tel (608) 754-3311; adv tel (608)755-8344; ed tel (608)755-8293; gen fax (608) 754-8038; adv fax (608) 754-8179; ed fax (608) 755-8349; gen/nat adv e-mail retailad@gazettextra.com; disp adv e-mail retailad@gazettextra.com; class adv e-mailclassads@gazettextra.com; ed e-mail newsroom@gazetteextra.com; web site www.gazetteextra.com

Published: Mon, Tues, Wed, Thur, Fri, Sat, Sun
Weekday Frequency: m
Saturday Frequency: m
Circulation: 14,081; 14,081(sat); 18,199(sun)
Last Audit: AAM March 31, 2017
Advertising Rate (weekday/saturday): Open inch rate $50.94
Advertising Rate (sunday): Open inch rate $58.07
News services: AP, MCT. **Established:** 1845
Own Printing Facility?: Yes
Special Editions: Home & Garden (Apr); Football (Aug); Bride's (Feb); Progress Week (Jan); 4-H Fair (Jul); Spring Car Care (Mar); Summer Fun Vacation Tab (May); Building & Remodeling (Monthly); Xmas Opener (Nov); Auto Show (Oct); Parade of Homes (Sept).
Special Weekly Sections: Best Food (Wed/Sun); Entertainment (Thur); Travel (Sun); Real Estate, Coupon (Monthly)
Syndicated Publications: USA WEEKEND Magazine (S).
CEO/Pub. .... Sidney H. Bliss
Benefits Mgr. .... Jennifer Revels
Sec. .... Pam Milheiser
Adv. Mgr., Retail .... Tom Bradley
Director of Circulation .... Lon Haneal
Ed. .... Sid Schwartz
Bus. Ed. .... James Leute
Community Living Ed. .... Shelly Birkelo
Design Ed. .... Andrew Beaumont
Editorial Page Ed. .... Greg Peck
Educ. Reporter .... Frank Schultz
Asst. Features Ed. .... Ann Fiore
Graphics Ed./Art Dir. .... Tony DiNicola
Sports Ed. .... David Wedeward
Photo Ed. .... Bill Olmsted
Women's Ed. .... Rochelle Birkelo
Dir., Online Services .... Jonathan Lindquist
Adv. Dir. .... Dan White
Mary Jo Villa
Market Information: ADS; TMC.
Mechanical Available: Offset; Black and 3 ROP colors; insert accepted; page cutoffs - 22 3/4.
Mechanical Specifications: Type page 13 x 21 1/2; E - 6 cols, 2 1/16, 1/8 between; A - 6 cols, 2 1/16, 1/8 between; C - 9 cols, 1 3/8, 1/16 between.
Delivery Method: Newsstand, Carrier, RacksEquipment & Software: PRESSROOM EQUIPMENT: Lines — 4-G/Metro; Folders — 1-G/2:1.; MAILROOM EQUIPMENT: Counter Stackers — 1-Id/2000, 1-Id/2200; Inserters & Stuffers — GMA/SLS 1000 8 x 1; Tying Machines — MLN/Spirit; Address Machine — BH/1530; BUSINESS EQUIPMENT: 1-HP/3000 BUSINESS SOFTWARE: CJ CLASSIFIED EQUIPMENT: Hardware — Tandem/CLX; CLASSIFIED SOFTWARE: SII. DISPLAY EQUIPMENT: Hardware — 2-APP/Mac 840AV, 2-APP/Mac 6100, 2-APP/Mac 8100; Printers — GCC/1200p Laser Printer; DISPLAY SOFTWAREAd Make-up Applications — Adobe/Photoshop, Multi-Ad/Creator, QPS/QuarkXPress.; EDITORIAL EQUIPMENT: Hardware — Tandem/CLX/1-APP/Mac IIci, APP/Power Mac 8100 Color Darkroom, Epson/Color Dye Subprinter EDITORIAL SOFTWARE: SII. PRODUCTION EQUIPMENT: Hardware — 2-Pre Press/Panther Pm 36 with Mac RIP, APP/Mac Quadra 950; Cameras — 1-B/Commodore; Scanners — 4-Epson/Flatbed, 1-HP/Flatbed, Kk/Neg Scanner.

KENOSHA

KENOSHA NEWS

5800 7th Ave, Kenosha, Wis., 53140-4131, Kenosha; gen tel (262) 657-1000; adv tel (262) 657-1500; ed tel (262) 656-6279; gen fax (262) 656-1820; adv fax (262) 657-5101; ed fax (262) 657-8455; gen/nat adv e-mail ads@kenoshanews.com; class adv e-mailclassad@kenoshanews.com; ed e-mail newsroom@kenoshanews.com; web site www.kenoshanews.com

Group: United Communications Corporation
Published: Mon, Tues, Wed, Thur, Fri, Sat, Sun
Weekday Frequency: m
Saturday Frequency: m
Circulation: 17,851; 17,851(sat); 20,991(sun)
Last Audit: AAM September 30, 2016
Advertising Rate (weekday/saturday): Open inch rate $27
Advertising Rate (sunday): open inch rate $29.20
News services: AP, LAT-WP, SHNS. **Established:** 1894
Own Printing Facility?: No
Commercial Printers?: Yes
Special Editions: Lawn & Garden (Apr); Bridal (Aug); Tax (Feb); Bridal (Jan); Home Improvement (Mar); New Car (Nov); Fall Car Care (Oct); Home Improvement (Sept), Gift Guide (Nov./Dec.), Best of Tab, Graduation Tab
Special Weekly Sections: Get Out (Fri); Color Comics (S).
Syndicated Publications: Spry, Parade (S).
Digital Platform - Mobile: Apple, Android, Windows, Blackberry
Digital Platform - Tablet: Apple iOS, Android, Blackberry Tablet OS, Kindle Fire
CFO .... Ronald J. Montemurro

Asst. Adv. Dir. .... Dennis Serpe
Circ. Asst. Mgr., Delivery/Collections .... Mark Kretschmer
Asst. Mng. Ed., Nights ....John Sloca
Bus. Writer ....Deneen Smith
Editorial Page Ed. .... Steve Lund
Chief Photographer ....Kevin Poirier
Sports Ed. ....David Marran
Web Servs. Supvr. .... Terry Maraccini
Cir. Mgr. .... Jim De Marco
Prodn. Mgr., Opns. ....Delia Chiappetta
Adv. Dir. .... Ed Gambardella
Controller .... Francesco Angelini
IT Manager .... Trevor Daly
Ed. .... Joe Potente
Managing Ed. ....Mike Larsen
Pub .... Randall Rickman
Market Information: TMC.
Mechanical Available: Black and 3 ROP colors; insert accepted - any; page cutoffs - 20 inches
Mechanical Specifications: Type page 10.875 inches x 20 inches
Areas Served: 53104, 53105, 53109, 53128, 53139, 53140, 53142, 53143, 53144, 53147, 53157, 53158, 53159, 53168, 53170, 53177, 53179, 53181, 53182, 53192, 53402, 53403, 53404, 53405, 53406, 60002, 60031, 60046, 60048, 60083, 60087, 60096, 60099
Delivery Method: Newsstand, Carrier, RacksEquipment & Software: PRESSROOM EQUIPMENT: Lines — production off-site.; MAILROOM EQUIPMENT: — production off-site; CLASSIFIED EQUIPMENT: Hardware — SIA/NT 4.0; Printers — HP/6MP; CLASSIFIED SOFTWARE: Unysis/ Ad Management Systems 3. DISPLAY EQUIPMENT: Hardware — APP/Mac G4; Printers — HP/5Si; Other Hardware — Umax/Scanner, CNI/Ad Tracking DISPLAY SOFTWAREAd Make-up Applications — Multi-Ad/Creator 6.0; Layout Software — SCS/Layout 8000. EDITORIAL EQUIPMENT: Hardware — SIA; Printers — Kyocera/Royal, 4P5si EDITORIAL SOFTWARE: CTEXT/ Dateline Expressline, HP/5Si. PRODUCTION EQUIPMENT: Hardware — production off site PRODUCTION SOFTWARE: In-Design Suite

LA CROSSE

LA CROSSE TRIBUNE

401 3rd St N, La Crosse, Wis., 54601-3267, La Crosse; gen tel (608) 782-9710; adv tel (608) 791-8213; ed tel (608) 782-9710; gen fax (608) 782-9723,; adv fax (608) 782-9721; ed fax (608) 782-9723; gen/nat adv e-mail ads@lacrossetribune.com; disp adv e-mail ads@lacrossetribune.com; class adv e-mailads@lacrossetribune.com; ed e-mail rusty.cunningham@lee.net; web site www.lacrossetribune.com - 4,008,251(views) 586,000(visitors)
Group: Lee Enterprises, Inc.
Published: Mon, Tues, Wed, Thur, Fri, Sat, Sun
Weekday Frequency: m
Saturday Frequency: m
Circulation: 20,942; 27,178(sat); 29,489(sun)
Last Audit: AAM March 31, 2016
Advertising Rate (weekday/saturday): Open inch rate $35.96
Advertising Rate (sunday): Open inch rate $44.08
News services: AP, MCT, Metro Suburbia, Inc./ Newhouse Newspapers. **Established:** 1902
Own Printing Facility?: Yes
Commercial Printers?: Yes
Special Editions: Football (Aug); Gift Guide (Dec); Winter Getaway (Feb); Winter Getaway (Jan); Graduation (May); Coupon Book (Monthly); Christmas Opening (Nov); Credit Unions (Oct); Ourtime (Quarterly); Super Saver Coupons (Semi-monthly); Kids Fest (Sept).
Special Weekly Sections: Best Food, Travel, Family, Real Estate, Auto, Home, Business, Family (Sun); A+ Achievers (Tue); Health (Wed); Outdoors, Entertainment, Auto (Thur); Religion, TV (Sat)
Syndicated Publications: Relish (Monthly); Parade (S).
Digital Platform - Mobile: Apple, Android, Windows, Blackberry, Other
Digital Platform - Tablet: Apple iOS, Android, Windows 7, Blackberry Tablet OS, Kindle, Nook, Kindle Fire, Other
Group Publisher .... Michael Burns
Editorial Page Ed. .... Mark Wehrs
Online Ed. .... Marc Wehrs
Sports Ed. .... Jeff Brown
Cir. Dir. ....Bill Lenardson
Robin Noth
Adv. Dir. / Gen. Mgr. .... Stacia King
Market Information: TMC.
Mechanical Available: Offset; Black and 3 ROP colors; insert accepted - sample bags, self-adhesive notes; page cutoffs - 21 3/4.
Mechanical Specifications: Type page 11 5/8 x 21 1/2; E - 6 cols, 1 13/16, 1/8 between; A - 6 cols, 1 13/16, 1/8 between; C - 6 cols, 1 13/16, 1/8 between.
Areas Served: 52151, 52160, 52172, 53821, 53929, 54601, 54603, 54612, 54614, 54615, 54616, 54618, 54619, 54621, 54623, 54624, 54626, 54627, 54629, 54630, 54632, 54634, 54636, 54639, 54642, 54644, 54648, 54650, 54651, 54653, 54656, 54658, 54660, 54661, 54665, 54666, 54667, 54669, 54670, 54747, 54773, 55919, 55921, 55925, 55941, 55943, 55947, 55971, 55974, 55987Equipment & Software: PRESSROOM EQUIPMENT: Lines — 9-DGM/850, 5-G/Urbanite single width 1999; 4-Lincoln/ink pumps; Folders — 1-G/2:1, 1-Web/Specialties Quadra Folder 1996, 1-DGM/1030 1999.; MAILROOM EQUIPMENT: Counter Stackers — 2-HL/ Dual Carrier, 2-HL/Monitor, 1-Gammler/ STC 70; Inserters & Stuffers — MM/227, 1-S/1372; Tying Machines — 2-MLN/ML2EE, 2/Dynaric, 1-Mosca/Portable Strapper; Wrapping Singles — 1-/QWI; Control System — Addressing machine Ch/525E, BH/1530.; BUSINESS EQUIPMENT: 1-IBM/AS-400 CLASSIFIED EQUIPMENT: Hardware — 3-Compaq/Server, 1-Netwave, 22-Microsoft/Windows NT; Printers — HP/8000N; CLASSIFIED SOFTWARE: CText. DISPLAY EQUIPMENT: Printers — HP/5Si MX; DISPLAY SOFTWAREAd Make-up Applications — Multi-Ad/Creator 6.5, QPS/ QuarkXPress 4.1, Adobe/Illustrator 8.0, Adobe/Photoshop 7.0, Layout 8000 8; Layout Software — 10-Compaq/Server, 1-Netwave, 5-Microsoft/Windows NT/2000, 25-APP/ Mac G3/G4. EDITORIAL EQUIPMENT: Hardware — 6-Compaq/Server, 1-Netwave, 4-Microsoft/2000 XP; Printers — HP/8000N EDITORIAL SOFTWARE: APT, Microsoft/ Word XP 4.1, QPS/QuarkXPress CopyDesk 2.09. PRODUCTION EQUIPMENT: Hardware — Offset, 1-Pre Press/Panther Pro 62, Wing-Lynch, LE/LD 2600A; Cameras — 3-Canon/ EOS 1D; Scanners — 1-Microtek/ScanMaker 8700 PRODUCTION SOFTWARE: QPS/ QuarkXPress 4.1, HI/CPAG.

MADISON

WISCONSIN STATE JOURNAL, MADISON

1901 Fish Hatchery Rd, Madison, Wis., 53713-1248, Dane; gen tel (608) 252-6100; adv tel (608) 252-6000; ed tel (608) 252-6200; gen fax (608) 252-6119; adv fax (608) 256-6333; ed fax (608) 252-4155; gen/nat adv e-mail jschroeter@madison.com; disp adv e-mail jschroeter@madison.com; class adv e-mailswheeler@madison.com; ed e-mail cnpress@madison.com; web site http://host.madison.com/wsj/
Group: Lee Enterprises, Inc.
Capital Newspapers
Published: Mon, Tues, Wed, Thur, Fri, Sat, Sun
Weekday Frequency: m
Saturday Frequency: m
Circulation: 62,868; 59,616(sat); 81,273(sun)
Last Audit: AAM March 31, 2017
Advertising Rate (weekday/saturday): Open inch rate $112.43
Advertising Rate (sunday): Open inch rate $169.54
News services: Metro Suburbia Inc./Newhouse Newspapers, NYT, MCT. **Established:** 1839
Own Printing Facility?: Yes
Special Weekly Sections: Work, Career (Thur); Taste, Food (Fri); Business (Sat); Arts, Entertainment, Lifestyle, Travel, Recreation, Books, Home, Garden, Outdoors (Sun)
Syndicated Publications: Comics (S).
Dir., HR .... Debbie Reed
Ed. ....John Smalley
Online Director ....Tim Kelley
Managing Ed. .... Teryl Franklin
City Ed. .... Phil Glende
Gen. Mgr. .... Todd Sears
Circ. Dir. .... Phil Stoddard
Ops. Dir. .... Rob Strabala
Nat'l Adv. Dir. .... Jeff Schroeter
VP; Adv., Sales and Mktg. ....Joe Allen
Pub .... John Humenik
Market Information: ADS; Split run; TMC; Zoned editions.
Mechanical Available: Black and 3 ROP colors; insert accepted - samples, coupons, catalogs; page cutoffs - 23 3/4.
Mechanical Specifications: Type page 11 5/8 x 21 1/2; E - 6 cols, 1 5/6, 1/8 between; A - 6 cols, 2 1/16, 1/8 between; C - 10 cols, 1 1/6, between.
Delivery Method: Mail, Newsstand, Carrier, RacksEquipment & Software: PRESSROOM EQUIPMENT: Lines — 17-G/Metro double width 1975; 5-G/Community (2-Four H16A; 4-single width) 1994; Folders — 3-G/ Imperial 3:2, 2-G/Community SSE; Reels & Stands — 15-G/Metro; Registration System — Web Tech/Auto Registration. MAILROOM EQUIPMENT: Counter Stackers — 7-Id/ N5550, BG/Count-O-Veyor; Inserters & Stuffers — 2-HI/1372, GMA/SLS 2000; Tying Machines — 5-Dynaric/NP2; Wrapping Singles — 4-Bu/Strapper; Control System — GMA; Address Machine — 2-Ch/545, 5/ CH, 4-/Ideal; BUSINESS EQUIPMENT: IBM/AS-400 BUSINESS SOFTWARE: Microsoft/Office CLASSIFIED EQUIPMENT: Hardware — 56-Pentium/PC; Printers — HP/ LaserJet; CLASSIFIED SOFTWARE: Insiight 5.0. DISPLAY EQUIPMENT: Hardware — Sun/fileservers, Dell/450L; DISPLAY SOFTWAREAd Make-up Applications — HI/PLS 2.0; Layout Software — DEC/ Layout 80, HI/PLS Ad Display System. EDITORIAL EQUIPMENT: Hardware — Sun/ fileservers, Dell/Workstations/Dell/Latitude Laptops, Nikon/Digital Camera; Printers — HP/LaserJet EDITORIAL SOFTWARE: HI/Newsmaker 2.6. PRODUCTION EQUIPMENT: Hardware — AU/APS-108-S, 3-AU/3850; Cameras — 1-C/Newspaper, 2-DSA; Scanners — 3-AG/Horizon Plus, AG/XL 2000, AG/Scanner, Tecsa/Scanner PRODUCTION SOFTWARE: HI 2.0.

MANITOWOC

HERALD TIMES REPORTER

902 Franklin St, Manitowoc, Wis., 54220-4514, Manitowoc; gen tel (920) 684-4433; adv tel (920)684-4433; ed tel (920)686-2130; gen fax (920) 684-4416; adv fax (920) 686-2961; ed fax (920) 686-2103; gen/nat adv e-mail MantyAds@smgpo.gannett.com; disp adv e-mail MantyAds@smgpo.gannett.com; class adv e-mailclassified@wisinfo.com; ed e-mail htrnews@htrnews.com; web site www.htrnews.com
Group: Gannett
Published: Mon, Tues, Wed, Thur, Fri, Sat, Sun
Weekday Frequency: e
Saturday Frequency: e
Circulation: 8,399; 8,399(sat); 9,965(sun)
Last Audit: AAM March 31, 2016
Advertising Rate (weekday/saturday): Open inch rate $38.50 (Mon-Fri); $37.40 (Sat)
Advertising Rate (sunday): Open inch rate $38.50
News services: AP, NEA, SHNS, GNS. **Established:** 1898
Own Printing Facility?: No
Special Editions: Annual Business Issue (March) 50+ (monthly)
Special Weekly Sections: Sports, Business, Classified, Opinion, TV, Advice, Comics (Sun); Health, Sports (Mon), Lifestyle (Tue); Food, Sports (Wed); Lifestyle, Arts, Entertainment, Sports, Dining (Thur); Lifestyle, Religion, Sports, Youth (Fri); Sports, Lifestyle (Sat)
Syndicated Publications: USA WEEKEND Magazine (S).
Adv. Dir. ....Lowell Johnson
Business, City of Manitowoc ....Charles Matthews
Ed. .... Mike Knuth
Gen. Mgr. .... Bill Hackney
VP Finance .... Mike Seeber
Pub .... Scott Johnson
Market Information: TMC.
Mechanical Available: Offset; Black and 3 ROP colors; insert accepted - card stuffs; page cutoffs - 21 1/2.
Mechanical Specifications: Type page 11 5/8 x 20 1/4; E - 6 cols, 1 13/16, 1/8 between; A - 6 cols, 1 13/16, 1/8 between; C - 9 cols, 1 3/16, 1/16 between.
Areas Served: 54220, 54221
Delivery Method: CarrierEquipment & Software: MAILROOM EQUIPMENT: Tying Machines — 1/Bu, 1-/MLN.; BUSINESS EQUIPMENT: Oracle, PBS CLASSIFIED EQUIPMENT: Hardware — AT.; DISPLAY SOFTWAREAd Make-up Applications — PBS; Layout Software — ALS. EDITORIAL EQUIPMENT: Hardware — AT, DEC/Nikon/ Scanners; Printers — Pre Press/Panther, AGFA/CTP AG EDITORIAL SOFTWARE: QPS/QuarkXPress 3.32, Dewar/Dewarview. PRODUCTION SOFTWARE: Lf/AP Leaf Picture Desk, Adobe/Photoshop.

MARINETTE

EAGLEHERALD - EHEXTRA.COM

1809 Dunlap Ave, Marinette, Wis., 54143-1706, Marinette; gen tel (715) 735-6611; adv tel (715)735-6611 ext. 114; ed tel (715) 735-6611 ext. 155; gen fax (715) 735-7580; adv fax (715) 735-6562; ed fax (715) 735-0229; gen/nat adv e-mail khofer@eagleherald.com; disp adv e-mail khofer@eagleherald.com; class adv e-mailmmacdonald@eagleherald.com; ed e-mail news@eagleherald.com; web site www.ehextra.com
Group: The Gazette - gazettextra.com
Published: Mon, Tues, Wed, Thur, Fri, Sat
Weekday Frequency: m
Saturday Frequency: m
Circulation: 7,589; 7,589(sat)
Last Audit: Sworn/Estimate/Non-Audited September 30, 2017
Advertising Rate (weekday/saturday): Open inch rate $28.08
News services: AP. **Established:** 1867
Own Printing Facility?: Yes
Special Editions: Football Preview (Aug); Christmas Gift Guide (Dec); People Making A Difference (Dec.); Menominee County Fair (Jul); Home Improvement (Mar); Graduation (May); Insights (Oct); Home Improvement (Sept).
Special Weekly Sections: From the Past (Mon); Health (Wed); Boomers & Beyond (Thur); Outdoors (Fri); Business (Sat)
Syndicated Publications: American Profile Spry
Editor .... Dan Kitkowski
Sports Ed. .... Jody Korch
Prodn. Mgr., Press .... Roger Zink
Gen. Mgr. .... Dan White
Business manager ....Kathy Springberg
Ad manager .... Kelly Hofer
associate night editor ....Tim Greenwood
news and online editor .... Penny Mullins
staff writer .... Lisa Reed
photographer .... Rick Gebhard
Page designer .... Melissa Kowalczyk
Market Information: ADS; TMC.
Mechanical Available: Offset; Black and 3 ROP colors; insert accepted - any; page cutoffs - 22 3/4.
Mechanical Specifications: Type page 10 x 21 1/2; E - 6 cols, 1 5/6, 1/8 between; A - 6 cols, 1 5/6, 1/8 between; C - 6 cols, 1 5/6, 1/8 between.Equipment & Software: PRESSROOM EQUIPMENT: Lines — 6-G/Urbanite Single Width; 4-G/ Community Single Width; Folders — 1-G/2:1, 1-G/4:1.; MAILROOM EQUIPMENT: Tying Machines — 2/Bu, 1-Sa/SR1A.; BUSINESS EQUIPMENT: IBM BUSINESS SOFTWARE: Vision Data CLASSIFIED SOFTWARE: Baseview. DISPLAY SOFTWARELayout Software — 3-APP/Mac. EDITORIAL EQUIPMENT: Hardware — 1-APP/Mac EDITORIAL SOFTWARE: Baseview. PRODUCTION EQUIPMENT: Hardware — 1-3M/Deadliner, 3M/Pyrofax.

MARSHFIELD

MARSHFIELD NEWS-HERALD MEDIA

144 N Central Ave, Marshfield, Wis., 54449-2107, Wood; gen tel (715) 384-3131; adv tel (715)898-7004; ed tel (715)845-0655; gen fax (715) 387-4175; adv fax (715)387-4175; ed fax (715)387-4175; gen/nat adv e-mail taramondloch@marshfieldnewsherald.com; disp adv e-mail taramondloch@marshfieldnewsherald.com; class adv e-mailclassified@wisinfo.com; ed e-mail mtreinen@gannett.com; web site www.marshfieldnewsherald.com

Group: Gannett
Published: Mon, Tues, Wed, Thur, Fri, Sat, Sun
Weekday Frequency: e
Saturday Frequency: e
Circulation: 6,027; 6,027(sat)
Last Audit: AAM June 30, 2017
Advertising Rate (weekday/saturday): Open inch rate $28.20
News services: AP. **Established:** 1927
Own Printing Facility?: No
Commercial Printers?: No
Special Editions: Fairs (Aug); Basketball (Nov); Valentine's (Feb); Taxes (Jan); Hub City Days (Jul); Spring Builders & Auto (Mar); Dairyfest (May); Deer Hunting (Nov); Fall Auto (Oct); Fall Home Improvements (Sept)., Made in Central Wisconson (Sept); Academic All-Stars (April); Holiday Gift Guide (Dec); Home and Garden (April-Sept)
Special Weekly Sections: TV Listings (Mon-Fri); Food Recipes (Wed); Entertainment Page (Thur); Healthy Lifestyle (Mon); Homeroom Page (Sat); Home (Sat)
Digital Platform - Mobile: Apple, Android
Digital Platform - Tablet: Apple iOS, Android
Multimedia Photojournalist .. Megan McCormick
Opns. Mgr. .... Terri Hansen
Adv Mgr .... Tara Mondioch
Gen Mgr .... Mike Beck
Market Information: Split run; TMC.
Mechanical Available: Offset; Black and 3 ROP colors; insert accepted - anything 11 1/4 wide, 14 deep or less; page cutoffs - 21 1/2.
Mechanical Specifications: Type page 13 1/2 x 22 1/2; E - 6 cols, 2 1/16, 1/8 between; A - 6 cols, 2 1/16, 1/8 between; C - 8 cols, 1 1/2, 1/8 between.
Areas Served: Portions of Clark, Marathon, Taylor and Wood counties
Delivery Method: Carrier, RacksEquipment & Software: PRESSROOM EQUIPMENT: Lines — 6-G/Urbanite; MAILROOM EQUIPMENT: Counter Stackers — 1-BG/108; Tying Machines — 2/Bu; Address Machine — 2-Am/4000, St/labeler.; BUSINESS EQUIPMENT: NCR/Tower CLASSIFIED EQUIPMENT: Hardware — 4-COM.; DISPLAY SOFTWARELayout Software — 2-APP/Mac Radius Two Page Display, 1-APP/Mac Radius Full Page Display. EDITORIAL EQUIPMENT: Hardware — 1-COM. PRODUCTION EQUIPMENT: Hardware — 2-APP/Mac LaserWriter II; Cameras — 1-B.

MILWAUKEE

MILWAUKEE JOURNAL SENTINEL

333 W State St, Milwaukee, Wis., 53203-1305, Milwaukee; gen tel (414) 224-2000; adv tel (414) 224-2498; ed tel (414) 224-2047; gen fax (414) 224-2287; adv fax (414) 224-2485; ed fax (414) 224-2047; gen/nat adv e-mail btschacher@journalsentinel.com; disp adv e-mail btschacher@journalsentinel.com; class adv e-mailbtschacher@journalsentinel.com; ed e-mail jsedit@journalsentinel.com; web site www.jsonline.com - 20,562,000(views) 1,659,000(visitors)

Group: Journal Media Group
Published: Mon, Tues, Wed, Thur, Fri, Sat, Sun
Weekday Frequency: m
Saturday Frequency: m
Circulation: 152,944; 140,362(sat); 238,247(sun)
Last Audit: AAM March 31, 2017
Advertising Rate (weekday/saturday): Open inch rate $347.00
Advertising Rate (sunday): Open inch rate $484.00
News services: LA Times Sportswire, AP, MCT, LAT-WP, NYT, Entertainment News Service, Bloomberg. **Established:** 1882
Special Editions: Adult Education-Reinvention (Jan); Martin Luther King (Jan); Milwaukee NARI (Feb); College & Career Guide (Feb); Auto Show (1) (Feb); Auto Show (2) (Feb); Sports Show (March); Baseball Preview (Mar); Beer Week (April); CN Home Garden and Landscape (April); Nurse of the Year (April); Summer Getaways(May); Great Milwaukee Summer (May); Top Workplaces(May); Patio Dining (June); Summerfest (June); Adult Education-Reinvention (2) (July); State Fair (July); Make-A-Wish (Aug); Arts Season Preview (Aug); Packers Preview (Sept); Milwaukee NARI (2) (Sept); Martin Luther King (2) (Sept); College & Career Guide (2); Carol Deptolla's Top 30 Dining (Sept); Milwaukee Film (Sept); Think Pink (Sept); Wine and Dine (Nov); Holiday Lights (Nov); Winter Getaways (Nov)
Special Weekly Sections: Sports, TV, Business, Entertainment (Daily); Food (Wed); Wheels (Sat); Art, Books, Music, Travel, Entree, Sports, Business, Classified, Comics, TV, Employment, Real Estate (Sun)
Syndicated Publications: Holiday (Nov) (Other); USA WEEKEND Magazine (S).
Digital Platform - Mobile: Apple, Android
Digital Platform - Tablet: Apple iOS, Android
Pub./Gen. Mgr./Adv. Dir. .... Steve Lyles
Ed. in Chief .... Scott Peterson
Chrmn. of the Bd. .... Steven Smith
Pres./Pub. .... Elizabeth Brenner
Mng. Ed. .... Debi Eimer
Sr. Vice Pres./CFO .... Ken McNamee
Vice Pres., Info Technologies/CIO James Herzfeld
Admin Asst. .... Katie Zurn
Vice Pres., Legal .... Paul E. Kritzer
Reg. News Ed. .... Jim Riccioli
Vice Pres., Commun. .... Robert Dye
Vice Pres./Controller .... Claudia Booth
Vice Pres., HR .... James Spangler
Adv. Sr. Vice Pres. .... Richard Dobson
Adv. Vice Pres. .... Jandell Herum
Adv. Vice Pres., Pre Press .... Kristin Baker
Adv. Dir., Classified .... Marilyn Tanious
Adv. Dir., Display .... Andy Narrai
Vice Pres., Mktg. .... Tom Pierce
Gen. Mgr., Direct Mktg. .... Scott Pompe
Circ. Sr. Vice Pres. .... Mark Thomas
Circ. Asst. Dir., Distr. .... Darnell Rupnow
Sr. VP/Ed. .... George Stanley
Majors Nat'l Acct. Dir. .... Christopher Grow
Journal Media Group, Sr. Dir., Digital Tech.& Analytics .... James Conigliaro
Manager, Digital Yield .... Metcalf Sam
VP Cir., Audience & Customer Care ..... Kelly Wood
VP, Advertising .... Dani Longoria
Alison Laffe
Sr. Dir., Marketing .... David Ledlie
Journal Media Group, Sr. Dir., Dig. Rev. & Products .... Craig Besant
Pres .... Chris Stegman
Market Information: Split run; TMC; Zoned editions.
Mechanical Available: DiLitho; Black and 3 ROP colors; insert accepted - product samples when pre-approved; page cutoffs - 22 3/4.
Mechanical Specifications: Type page 13 x 21 7/16; A - 6 cols, 2 1/16, 1/8 between; C - 10 cols, 1 1/4, 1/16 between.
Areas Served: Waukesha County
Delivery Method: Mail, Newsstand, Carrier, RacksEquipment & Software: PRESSROOM EQUIPMENT: Lines — 9-H/Colormatic double width 1962; 9-H/Colormatic double width 1962; 9-H/Colormatic double width 1967; 9-H/Colormatic double width 1967; Folders — 8-H/2:1; Reels & Stands — 36-H; Control System — H/Reflex drive (; MAILROOM EQUIPMENT: Counter Stackers — 12-HL/Dual Carrier, 2-HL/Monitor, 5-TMSI/Compass 180; Inserters & Stuffers — 1-HI/1372P, 1-HI/1472P, 1-GMA/SLS 1000, 1-HI/1472, 1-GMA/SLS 2000; Tying Machines — 28/Dynaric; Wrapping Singles — 5-HL/3/4 wrap, 5-Id/3-4 wrap, 2-5/; BUSINESS SOFTWARE: Ross, CJ, Discus CLASSIFIED EQUIPMENT: Hardware — 2-Sun/Enterprisr 4500, 3-Dell/1300; Printers — HP/Laser Jet 4000, HP/Laser Jet 5000, HP/Laser Jet 6000; CLASSIFIED SOFTWARE: Mactive/Ad Base 2.10.17. DISPLAY EQUIPMENT: Hardware — 3-APP/Mac; Printers — HP/LaserJet 4000, HP/Laser Het 5000; Other Hardware — CNI DISPLAY SOFTWAREAd Make-up Applications — ALS; Layout Software — ALS. EDITORIAL EQUIPMENT: Hardware — SII/Tandem, 6-Tandem/K1000 Himalaya; Printers — HP/Laser Jet 4000, HP/Laser Jet 5000, HP/Laser Jet 6000 EDITORIAL SOFTWARE: SII/Coyote, Coyote/3. PRODUCTION EQUIPMENT: Hardware — 5-MON/Express, MAS/1000, 5-Konica/Processor, 1-MON/Futuro, 1-Carnfelot/Processor; Cameras — 1-C/Marathon, 1-C/Olympia, 2-C/Newspager; Scanners — 2-Pro/Imager 8000, Linotype-Hell/Linocolor Opal, 1-Scitex/Eversmart Supreme PRODUCTION SOFTWARE: HI/CPAG

MONROE

THE MONROE TIMES

1065 4th Ave W, Monroe, Wis., 53566-1318, Green; gen tel (608) 328-4202; adv tel (608) 328-4202; ed tel (608) 328-4202; gen/nat adv e-mail lhughes@themonroetimes.com; disp adv e-mail lhughes@themonroetimes.com; class adv e-maillhughes@themonroetimes.com; ed e-mail editor@themonroetimes.com; web site www.themonroetimes.com - 760,186(views) 59,513(visitors); web site 2 www.mymonroeshoppingnews.com - 10,979(views) 3,369(visitors); web site 3 www.myfreeportshoppingnews.com - 6,851(views) 3,403(visitors); web site 4stateline411.com - 2,898(views) 1,707(visitors)

Published: Mon, Tues, Wed, Thur, Fri, Sat
Weekday Frequency: All day
Saturday Frequency: All day
Circulation: 3,186; 3,180(sat)
Last Audit: CVC September 30, 2016
Newspaper Reps: Wisconsin Newspaper Association
Branch Offices: Bliss Communications
Advertising Rate (weekday/saturday): Open inch rate $34.00
Online Advertising Rate: Banner $259, Tiles $103, Search Sponsor $186
News services: AP. **Established:** 1898
Own Printing Facility?: No
Commercial Printers?: No
Special Editions: Home (Feb)Ag Week (March) Sports preview (March)Source (May) Graduation (May)Dairy Month (June) Fair(July)Sports Preview (August) Sports Preview (Nov)Holiday (Nov)
Special Weekly Sections: On Entertainment (Thursday)
Syndicated Publications: Spry (Monthly); American Profile (Sat).
Digital Platform - Mobile: Apple, Android
Digital Platform - Tablet: Apple iOS, Android
Vice Pres./Gen. Mgr. .... Carl C. Hearing
Office Mgr. .... Connie Flint
Adv. Mgr., Retail .... Laura Hughes
Editorial Page Ed. .... Mary Jane Grenzow
Circulation Manager .... Tina Curan
Market Information: ADS; TMC.
Mechanical Available: Offset; Black and full color ROP colors; insert accepted.
Mechanical Specifications: Type page 11 x 20; E - 6 cols, 1 3/4, 1/8 between; A - 6 cols, 1 3/4, 1/8 between; C - 9 cols, 1 1/8, 1/16 between.
Areas Served: 53566, 53522, 53550, 53502 53520, 53570, 53574, 53508, 61060, 61089, 61087, 53587, 53599, 53541, 53504, 53516, 53530, 53586
Delivery Method: MailEquipment & Software: BUSINESS SOFTWARE: Vision Data

OSHKOSH

OSHKOSH NORTHWESTERN

224 State St, Oshkosh, Wis., 54901-4839, Winnebago; gen tel (920) 235-7700; adv tel (920) 426-6639; ed tel (920) 426-6687; gen fax (920) 235-1316; adv fax (920) 235-1316 (Class); ed fax (920) 235-1316; gen/nat adv e-mail oshkoshad@thenorthwestern.com; disp adv e-mail oshkoshad@thenorthwestern.com; class adv e-mailoshkoshad@thenorthwestern.com; ed e-mail oshkoshnews@thenorthwestern.com; web site www.thenorthwestern.com

Group: Gannett
Published: Mon, Tues, Wed, Thur, Fri, Sat, Sun
Weekday Frequency: m
Saturday Frequency: m
Circulation: 10,218; 10,218(sat); 14,609(sun)
Last Audit: AAM March 31, 2016
Advertising Rate (weekday/saturday): Open inch rate $51.40 (Mon-Fri); $49.90 (Sat)
Advertising Rate (sunday): Open inch rate $62.90
News services: AP, GNS, MCT.
Special Editions: Lawn-Garden-Home (Apr); Football (Aug); Holiday Greetings (Dec); Bridal (Jan); Experimental Aircraft (Jul); Parade of Homes (Jun); Mid-WI Fun Guide (May); Basketball (Nov); Home Interiors (Oct); Answer Book (Sept).
Special Weekly Sections: Main, Local, Lifestyle, Sports, Classified, Business (Daily); Best Food (Sat); Stocks, Outdoors, Building, Business, Travel, TV (Sun)
Syndicated Publications: USA WEEKEND Magazine (S).
Adv. Dir. .... Lisa O'Halloran
Circ. Dir. .... Ryan Lenz
Mng. Ed. .... Jim Fitzhenry
City Ed. .... Carl Ebert
Chief Photographer .... Joe Sienkiewicz
Nat'l Adv. Rep. .... Lori Stubbe
GM/Adv. Dir. .... Karen Befus
Market Information: ADS; Split run; TMC.
Mechanical Available: Offset; Black and 3 ROP colors; insert accepted; page cutoffs - 22 3/4.
Mechanical Specifications: Type page 13 x 22; E - 6 cols, 1 5/6, 1/8 between; A - 6 cols, 1 5/6, 1/8 between; C - 9 cols, 1 3/16, 1/8 between.
Equipment & Software: PRESSROOM EQUIPMENT: Lines — 5-HI/1660 1979; Pasters —5-MEG/D500. MAILROOM EQUIPMENT: Tying Machines — 1/Dynaric.; BUSINESS EQUIPMENT: 1-Sun/Sparcstation 20 BUSINESS SOFTWARE: PBS, Media Plus, SBS CLASSIFIED EQUIPMENT: Hardware — 6-Pentium/PC, 2-Compaq/fileserver Pentium 150; Printers — 1-HP/4MP; CLASSIFIED SOFTWARE: Harris/Classified, Informatel/Classified Pagination, Novell/Network 4.1, Novell/SFT III. DISPLAY EQUIPMENT: Hardware — 1-APP/Mac G3, 1-APP/Mac G4, 1-APP/Mac Quadra 700, 1-APP/Mac IIci, 1-APP/Mac IIfx; Printers — HP/5000N, HP/8500; Other Hardware — PLI/128 floptical, 1-CD-Rom Player, CD-Writer DISPLAY SOFTWAREAd Make-up Applications — QPS/QuarkXPress, Aldus/Freehand, Adobe/Photoshop; Layout Software — Other EDITORIAL EQUIPMENT: Hardware — 1-APP/Power Mac 6100, 10-Pentium/200, 4-Pentium/100, 13-Pentium/166, 6-Compaq/fileserver Pentium 200 dual processors/Lf/Leafscan 35, APP/Mac 8100-100, APP/Mac IIfx, APP/Mac 8500-180; Printers — 1-HP/5000, AU/6600 EDITORIAL SOFTWARE: ATEX/D PRODUCTION EQUIPMENT: Hardware — Caere/OmniPage; Scanners — Umax/PowerLook PRODUCTION SOFTWARE: ATEX/Dewarview.

PORTAGE

DAILY REGISTER

1640 La Dawn Dr, Portage, Wis., 53901-8822, Columbia; gen tel (608) 745-3500; adv tel (608) 745-3571; ed tel (608) 745-3511; gen fax (608) 742-8346; adv fax (608) 745-4718; ed fax (608) 742-8346; gen/nat adv e-mail pdr-news@capitalnewspapers.com; disp adv e-mail mmeyers@madison.com; class adv e-mailmmeyers@madison.com; web site www.portagedailyregister.com

Group: Lee Enterprises, Inc.
Published: Mon, Tues, Wed, Thur, Fri, Sat
Weekday Frequency: m
Saturday Frequency: m
Circulation: 3,461; 3,560(sat)
Last Audit: Sworn/Estimate/Non-Audited November 30, 2017
Advertising Rate (weekday/saturday): Open inch rate $20.10
Online Advertising Rate: $7.00 cpm
News services: AP. **Established:** 1886
Own Printing Facility?: Yes
Commercial Printers?: Yes
Special Weekly Sections: Best Food Day (Wed); Entertainment (Fri)
Syndicated Publications: Best Time (Monthly); Parade (Sat); American Profile (Weekly).
Digital Platform - Mobile: Apple, Android,

Windows
Digital Platform - Tablet: Apple iOS, Android
Circ. Dir .... Teresa Klinger
Sports Ed. .... Travis Houslet
Pub. .... Matt Meyers
Adv. Dir. .... Jon Denk
Ed. .... Kerry Lechner
Market Information: TMC.
Mechanical Available: Offset; Black and 3 ROP colors; insert accepted; page cutoffs - 22 3/4.
Mechanical Specifications: Type page 12 1/8 x 21 1/2; E - 6 cols, 1 7/8, 1/8 between; A - 6 cols, 1 7/8, 1/8 between; C - 9 cols, 1 3/16, 1/16 between.
Areas Served: Columbia County
Delivery Method: Mail, Newsstand, Carrier, Racks

RACINE

THE JOURNAL TIMES

212 4th St, Racine, Wis., 53403-1005, Racine; gen tel (262) 634-3322; adv tel (262) 634-3322; ed tel (262) 634-3322; gen fax (262) 631-1702; adv fax (262) 631-1705; ed fax (262) 634-9194; gen/nat adv e-mail donna.mueller@lee.net; disp adv e-mail donna.mueller@lee.net; class adv e-maildonna.mueller@lee.net; ed e-mail stephanie.jones@lee.net; web site www.journaltimes.com
Group: Lee Enterprises, Inc.
Published: Mon, Tues, Wed, Thur, Fri, Sat, Sun
Weekday Frequency: m
Saturday Frequency: m
Circulation: 17,622; 17,622(sat); 20,640(sun)
Last Audit: AAM September 30, 2016
Advertising Rate (weekday/saturday): Open inch rate $46.75
Advertising Rate (sunday): Open inch rate $50.94
Online Advertising Rate: ROS $20 cpm; Section Specific $25cpm;
News services: AP, MCT.
Special Weekly Sections: Best Food Day (Mon); Health (Wed); Entertainment (Thur/Sun); Home & Garden (Fri); Religion (Sat); Travel (Sun)
Syndicated Publications: Relish (Monthly); Parade (S); American Profile (Weekly).
Pub. .... Mark Lewis
Major/Nat'l Accts. Rep. .... Heidi Ward
Circ. Mgr. .... Mathew Johnsrud
Circ. Mgr., Pennysaver .... Arne Arnold
News Ed. .... Tom Farley
Asst. News Ed. .... Heather Gascoigne
Photo Dir. .... Mark Hertzberg
Reporter .... Jeffrey Wilford
Sports Ed. .... Susan Shemanske
Prodn. Supvr., Pressroom .... Carl Simon
Adv. Dir. .... Donna Melby
Adv. Dir. .... Donna Mueller
Ed. .... Steve Lovejoy
Market Information: TMC; Zoned editions.
Mechanical Available: Flexo (direct); Black and 3 ROP colors; insert accepted - product samples; page cutoffs - 22 3/4.
Mechanical Specifications: Type page 13 x 21 1/2; E - 6 cols, 2 1/16, 1/8 between; A - 6 cols, 2 1/16, 1/8 between; C - 10 cols, 1 1/4, 1/16 between.Equipment & Software: PRESSROOM EQUIPMENT: Lines — 1-MOT/Colormax double width (Flexo 1-5 Impression Unit) 1994; 1-MOT/Colormax double width (Flexo 1-5 Impression Unit) 1995; 1-MOT/Colormax double width (Flexo 1-3 Impression Unit) 1995; Folders — 2-G/2:1; Reels & Stands — G/Re; MAILROOM EQUIPMENT: Counter Stackers — 3-Compass/180, HL/Monitor HT; Inserters & Stuffers — 1372 HI/Inserter; Tying Machines — 1/Power Strap/PNS6, 1-/Power Strap/PNS5, 2-Dynaric/NP2; Wrapping Singles — 2-QWI/Viper, Powerstrap w/ siderollers, Bottom wrapppers; BUSINESS EQUIPMENT: IBM/AS-400 BUSINESS SOFTWARE: WordPerfect, Microsoft/Excel, Microsoft/Word, XYQUEST/XyWrite, Paradox CLASSIFIED EQUIPMENT: Hardware — Compaq/Proliant; Printers — HP/2000C, OCE/9400; CLASSIFIED SOFTWARE: HI 3.6, CText/advision, Sybase. DISPLAY EQUIPMENT: Hardware — 2-APP/OSX Server; Printers — HP/2000C, OCE/9400; Other Hardware — HP/855OC DISPLAY SOFTWAREAd Make-up Applications — Quark/4.11, Adobe/Photoshop, Adobe/Illustrator; Layout Software — Managing Editor/ALS. EDITORIAL EQUIPMENT: Hardware — APP/Mac G3/2-AG/Avantra Select set 25, 2-APP/OSX Servers, Harlequin/NT RIPs; Printers — OCC/9400, HP/2000C, HP/8500C EDITORIAL SOFTWARE: HI 8.0, Baseview/IQue. PRODUCTION EQUIPMENT: Hardware — 2-AG/Avantra 25, 1-Na/FX VIII; Cameras — C/Spartan III; Scanners — Epson/836XL, Lf/Leafscan 35, Polaroid/SprintScan PRODUCTION SOFTWARE: QPS/QuarkXPress 4.0.

RHINELANDER

THE NORTHWOODS RIVER NEWS

232 S Courtney St, Stop 14, Rhinelander, Wis., 54501-3319, Oneida; gen tel (715) 365-6397; adv tel (715) 365-6397; ed tel (262) 306-5043; gen fax (715) 365-6367; adv fax (715) 365-6367; ed fax (715) 365-6367; gen/nat adv e-mail advertising@rivernewsonline.com; disp adv e-mail advertising@rivernewsonline.com; class adv e-mailclassified@rivernewsonline.com; ed e-mail news@rivernewsonline.com; web site www.rivernewsonline.com
- 112,524(views) 607,352(visitors)
Group: Northwoods Media LLC
Published: Mon, Tues, Wed, Thur, Fri, Sun
Weekday Frequency: e
Circulation: 5,302; 5,302(sun)
Last Audit: Sworn/Estimate/Non-Audited September 30, 2017
Advertising Rate (weekday/saturday): Open inch rate $7.25
Online Advertising Rate: Top Banner (650x80 pixels) $179/mo.; Bottom Banner (940x80 pixels) $79/mo. (ROS) Homepage Tile (300x150 pixels) $99/mo.; Super Box (240x340 pixels) $179/mo. (ROS*); Medium Tile (240x140 pixels) $79/mo.; Big Box (240x240 pixels) $149/mo. (ROS*)
News services: AP. **Established:** 1882
Own Printing Facility?: No
Commercial Printers?: No
Special Editions: Spring Home Improvement Guide (Apr); Fall Home Improvement Guide (Aug); Christmas Church Service (Dec); Valentine's Day (Feb); Financial Planning & Tax Time Feature (Jan); Customer Appreciation Sale (Jul); Father's Day Gift Guide (Jun); Progress (Mar); Mo
Special Weekly Sections: UP NORTH (Fri).
Syndicated Publications: Best Years (Monthly); Parade (S).
Digital Platform - Mobile: Apple, Android
Digital Platform - Tablet: Apple iOS, Android
Pub./Ed. .... Gregg Walker
Assoc. Ed. .... Heather Schaefer
Adv. Dir. .... Jan Juedes
Gen. Mgr. .... Wendi Ell
Circ. Mgr. .... Corey Richter
Sports Ed. .... Jeremy Mayo
Subscriptions .... Susan Taves
Market Information: TMC.
Mechanical Available: Offset; Black and 3 ROP colors; insert accepted - any; page cutoffs - 21 1/2.
Mechanical Specifications: Type page 11 5/8 x 21 1/2; E - 6 cols, 1 5/6, 1/8 between; A - 6 cols, 1 5/6, 1/8 between; C - 6 cols, 1 5/6, 1/8 between.
Areas Served: Oneida County
Delivery Method: Mail, Newsstand, CarrierEquipment & Software: PRESSROOM EQUIPMENT: Lines — 4-G/Community; MAILROOM EQUIPMENT: Tying Machines — 1-Bu/69175.; BUSINESS EQUIPMENT: 4-Mk/Acer CLASSIFIED EQUIPMENT: Hardware — PC; Printers — QMS/810; CLASSIFIED SOFTWARE: Suntype. DISPLAY EQUIPMENT: Hardware — APP/Mac; Printers — 2-QMS/810, 1-Unity/1800x60; Other Hardware — Nikon/Coolscan, HP/3c ScanJet DISPLAY SOFTWAREAd Make-up Applications — QPS/QuarkXPress; Layout Software — Multi-Ad. EDITORIAL EQUIPMENT: Hardware — APP/MacPrinters — 2-QMS/810 EDITORIAL SOFTWARE: Baseview. PRODUCTION EQUIPMENT: Hardware — 2-QMS/Laserprinter; Cameras — 1-K/241, 1-K/V2 41; Scanners — HP/ScanJet 3C.

SHAWANO

SHAWANO LEADER

1464 E Green Bay St, Shawano, Wis., 54166-2258, Shawano; gen tel (715) 526-2121; adv tel (715) 526-7012; ed tel (715) 526-7019; gen fax (715) 524-3941; adv fax (715)524-3941; ed fax (715)524-3941; gen/nat adv e-mail ckennedy@wolfrivermedia.com; disp adv e-mail ckennedy@wolfrivermedia.com; class adv e-mailclassifieds@wolfrivermedia.com; ed e-mail gmellis@wolfrivermedia.com; web site www.shawanoleader.com
Group: Wolf River Media/division of BlueLine Media Holdings
Metro Suburbia, Inc./Newhouse Newspapers
BlueLine Media Holdings
Published: Wed, Thur, Fri, Sat
Weekday Frequency: m
Saturday Frequency: m
Circulation: 6,525; 6,906(sun)
Last Audit: Sworn/Estimate/Non-Audited September 30, 2017
Advertising Rate (weekday/saturday): Open inch rate $16.78
News services: AP. **Established:** 1881
Own Printing Facility?: Yes
Commercial Printers?: Yes
Special Editions: Sports (Aug); Packer Pre-Game (Fall); Finance (Jan); Dairy (Jun); Home Improvement (Mar); Vacation (May); Seniors (Monthly); Christmas Opener (Nov).
Special Weekly Sections: Education (Wed); Business (Thur); Religion, Entertainment (Fri); Weekend, Lifestyle, Engagements, Entertainment, Home, Health, Science, Outdoor, Auto (Sat)
Syndicated Publications: Parade (Weekly).
CEO/Pres./Pub. .... Paul Seveska
Group Controller .... Berni Hollinger
Editorial Director .... Roger Bartel
vice president production .... Bob Perini
Regional Advertising Director .... Chris Kennedy
Market Information: TMC.
Mechanical Available: Offset; Black and 3 ROP colors; insert accepted; page cutoffs - 22 3/4.
Mechanical Specifications: Type page 12 x 21 1/2; E - 6 cols, 1 13/16, 1/6 between; A - 6 cols, 1 13/16, 1/6 between; C - 9 cols, 1 1/8, 1/8 between.
Areas Served: shawano, okono falls, ect.
Delivery Method: Mail, Newsstand, Carrier, RacksEquipment & Software: PRESSROOM EQUIPMENT: 11-G/SSC Community 1989; 8-G/SCC Community single width 2001; Folders — 1, 2-G/SSC; Control System — Phnuematic/RGS IV. MAILROOM EQUIPMENT: Counter Stackers — Amerigraph/RS-12; Tying Machines — 5-Bu/Tyer; Wrapping Singles — Bu, Sitma/5-into-1; Address Machine — Ch/Video jet 4000 JsII, 3/Ch.; BUSINESS EQUIPMENT: Sun/Server BUSINESS SOFTWARE: Vision Data CLASSIFIED EQUIPMENT: Hardware — Baseview; 2-APP/Mac; Printers — APP/Mac LaserWriter Plus, HP/4 Laser; CLASSIFIED SOFTWARE: APP/Mac. DISPLAY EQUIPMENT: Hardware — APP/Mac 8100-80, APP/Mac 7100-80, APP/Mac IIci, APP/Mac 9600, APP/Mac 96 4GB-HD; Printers — Pre Press/Panther Pro 46, Pre Press/Panther CTP, HP/DesignJet 755CM, HP/LaserJet IV; DISPLAY SOFTWAREAd Make-up Applications — Multi-Ad/Creator 3.7, QPS/QuarkXPress 3.31; Layout Software — Mult EDITORIAL EQUIPMENT: Hardware — APP/Mc G3, APP/iMac; Printers — HP/LaserJet EDITORIAL SOFTWARE: Baseview/NewsEditPro. PRODUCTION EQUIPMENT: Hardware — 1-Nu/Flip Top, Pre Press/Panther Pro 46, Pre Press/Panther CTP; Cameras — B, AG PRODUCTION SOFTWARE: Adobe/Photoshop, QPS/QuarkXPress, After Dark, Color Expert, Multi-Ad/Creator, Baseview.

SHEBOYGAN

THE SHEBOYGAN PRESS

632 Center Ave, Sheboygan, Wis., 53081-4621, Sheboygan; gen tel (920) 457-7711; adv tel (920) 453-5120; ed tel (920) 457-7711; gen fax (920) 457-0178; adv fax (920) 457-7043; ed fax (920) 457-3573; gen/nat adv e-mail news@sheboyganpress.com; disp adv e-mail ads@sheboyganpress.com; class adv e-mailclassified@wisinfo.com; ed e-mail editor@sheboyganpress.com; web site www.sheboyganpress.com
Group: Gannett
Published: Mon, Tues, Wed, Thur, Fri, Sat, Sun
Weekday Frequency: m
Saturday Frequency: m
Circulation: 12,053; 12,053(sat); 15,213(sun)
Last Audit: AAM March 30, 2016
Advertising Rate (weekday/saturday): Open inch rate $51.40 (Mon-Fri); $49.90 (Sat)
Advertising Rate (sunday): Open inch rate $62.90
News services: AP, GNS. **Established:** 1907
Own Printing Facility?: No
Commercial Printers?: Yes
Special Editions: Newspapers in Education (Apr); Football (Aug); Packers (Dec); Bridal Showcase (Jan); Graduation (Jun); Basketball (Nov); Fall Building (Oct); You (Mag.) (Quarterly); Packers (Sept.); Moxy (Monthly); Lake Shore Living (Monthly)
Special Weekly Sections: Food (Tue); Home, Garden, Entertainment, Weekend, Conservation (Thur); Beliefs, Religion (Fri); Beliefs, Travel, Outdoors (Sun)
Syndicated Publications: USA WEEKEND Magazine (S).
Retail Adv. Mgr. .... David Liebelt
Ed. .... Dan Benson
City Gov't .... Bob Petrie
Community Ed. .... Jennifer Kuszynski
Editorial Page Ed. .... Joe Gulig
Photo Lab .... Bruce Halmo
Presentation Ed. .... Robert Farina
Transportation Supvr. .... Allen Burgard
Sports Ed. .... Brandon Reid
Market Information: ADS; TMC.
Mechanical Available: Offset; Black and 3 ROP colors; insert accepted - sample packs; page cutoffs - 22 3/4.
Mechanical Specifications: Type page 12 x 22 3/4; E - 6 cols, 1 5/6, 1/6 between; A - 6 cols, 1 5/6, 1/6 between; C - 9 cols, 1 1/20, 1/8 between.
Delivery Method: Mail, Newsstand, Carrier, RacksEquipment & Software: PRESSROOM EQUIPMENT: Lines — 5-G/Headliner Anti-Friction double width Letterpress 1954; Folders — 2-G/2:1.; MAILROOM EQUIPMENT: Tying Machines — 1/Bu, 2-Wilton Pro/Standard 80; Address Machine — KAN/550 2.; BUSINESS EQUIPMENT: CTS, IBM/36 CLASSIFIED EQUIPMENT: Hardware — AText; Printers — Pre Press/Panther; CLASSIFIED SOFTWARE: AText. DISPLAY EQUIPMENT: Hardware — 4-Dewar/386 PC, 2-Dewar/PC 286, AText; Printers — APP/Mac Printer IIXL; DISPLAY SOFTWARELayout Software — ALS. EDITORIAL EQUIPMENT: Hardware — AText/APP/Mac IIci, APP/Mac SE 30; Printers — Pre Press/Panther EDITORIAL SOFTWARE: Prestige. PRODUCTION EQUIPMENT: Hardware — AG PRODUCTION SOFTWARE: QPS/QuarkXPress 4.0.

STEVENS POINT

STEVENS POINT JOURNAL

1200 3rd St, Stevens Point, Wis., 54481-2855, Portage; gen tel (715) 344-6100; adv tel (888)774-7744; ed tel (715)744-0655; gen fax (715) 344-7229; adv fax (715)344-7229; ed fax (715)344-7229; gen/nat adv e-mail lbolle@gannett.com; disp adv e-mail lbolle@gannett.com; class adv e-mailclassified@wisinfo.com; ed e-mail mtreinen@gannett.com; web site www.stevenspointjournal.com
Group: Gannett
Published: Mon, Tues, Wed, Thur, Fri, Sat, Sun
Weekday Frequency: e
Saturday Frequency: e
Circulation: 6,207; 6,207(sat); 306(sun)
Last Audit: AAM June 30, 2016
Advertising Rate (weekday/saturday): Open inch rate $31.10
News services: AP, GNS.
Special Editions: Packer Final (Fall).
Special Weekly Sections: Stocks (Mon-Sat);

High School Highlights (Mon); Parent & Child (Tue); Arts (Wed); Dining, Entertainment, TV Listings, Health, Auto (Thur); Real Estate, Area Church (Fri); Best Food Day, Church, Home, Food Kids (Sat)
Gen. Mgr. ....Mark Baldwin
Adv. Mgr., Classified ....Barb Soik
Editorial Page Ed. ....Lisa Nellessen-Lara
Lifestyles Ed. ....Jamie Jung
News Ed. ....Harold Goodridge
Picture Ed. ....Doug Wojcik
Sports Ed. ....Scott Williams
Prodn. Mgr. ....Kevin Kusava
Prodn. Mgr., Pre Press ....Robin Spindler
Prodn. Supt., Pressroom ....Gary Moyer
News Reporter ....Sari Lesk
Adv. Dir. ....Mary Jo Johnson
Adv. Services Mgr. ....Janie Hytry
Gen. Mgr. / Dir. of Sales
Laurie Bolle
Market Information: TMC.
Mechanical Available: Offset; Black and 4 ROP colors; insert accepted; page cutoffs - 22.
Mechanical Specifications: Type page 12 1/2 x 21; E - 6 cols, 2 1/16, 1/8 between; A - 6 cols, 2 1/16, 1/8 between; C - 9 cols, 1 2/3, 1/8 between.Equipment & Software: PRESSROOM EQUIPMENT: Lines — 12-G/Community; MAILROOM EQUIPMENT: Counter Stackers — 1/BG; Inserters & Stuffers — 1-/KAN; Tying Machines — 4-/Bu; Address Machine — 2-/Ch; BUSINESS EQUIPMENT: PC LAN BUSINESS SOFTWARE: Synaptic, Gyma CLASSIFIED EQUIPMENT: Hardware — Baseview; Printers — 2-HP/5M; CLASSIFIED SOFTWARE: I-Que Server 3.16. DISPLAY SOFTWARELayout Software — MEI/ALS. EDITORIAL EQUIPMENT: Hardware — Baseview; Printers — 2-HP/5M EDITORIAL SOFTWARE: Baseview/Ad Manager Pro 2.06. PRODUCTION EQUIPMENT: Hardware — Caere/Omni Page Pro 6.0, 2-Caere/Panther Pro 46; Cameras — 2-R PRODUCTION SOFTWARE: QPS/QuarkXPress 4.1.

WATERTOWN

WATERTOWN DAILY TIMES

113 W Main St, Watertown, Wis., 53094-7623, Jefferson; gen tel (920) 261-4949; adv tel (920)261-4949; ed tel (920) 261-5161; gen fax (920) 261-5102; adv fax (920)261-5102; ed fax (920)261-5102; gen/nat adv e-mail judyk@wdtimes.com; disp adv e-mail judyk@wdtimes.com; class adv e-mailclassified@wdtimes.com; ed e-mail news1@wdtimes.com; web site www.wdtimes.com
Published: Mon, Tues, Wed, Thur, Fri, Sat, Sun
Weekday Frequency: e
Saturday Frequency: m
Circulation: 9,287; 9,287(sat)
Last Audit: Sworn/Estimate/Non-Audited September 30, 2017
Advertising Rate (weekday/saturday): Open inch rate $15.27
News services: AP. **Established:** 1895
Own Printing Facility?: No
Commercial Printers?: Yes
Special Editions: Earth Day (Apr); Child Care/Back to School (Aug); Christmas Greetings (Dec); Financial (Feb); Bridal Section (Jan & June); Senior Style (May); Spring Home Improvement (Mar); Summer Life Styles (May); Christmas Open (Nov); Fall Tune Up (Oct); Health and Fitness (Jan); Games and Activities (Feb); Design and Ad (April); Graduation (May)'; June Dairy (June); Hunting (Aug)
Special Weekly Sections: Best Food Day (Mon); Commerce, Children's, American Profile (Tue); Agriculture, Business (Wed); Dining, Entertainment, Outdoors (Thur); Real Estate (Fri); Auto (Sat)
Syndicated Publications: USA WEEKEND Magazine (Sat); American Profile (Weekly); Spry (Monthly); Relish (Monthly)
Digital Platform - Mobile: Apple, Android
Digital Platform - Tablet: Apple iOS, Kindle, Kindle Fire
Vice Pres. ....Patricia L. Clifford
Sec. ....Margaret A. Krueger
Treasurer/Bus. Mgr. ....Ralph H. Krueger
Gen. Mgr. ....Kevin Clifford
Adv. Dir., Retail/Nat'l ....Judy A. Kluetzmann
Adv. Mgr., Classified ....Mark Shingler
Circ. Dir. ....Mark D. Kuehl
Ed. ....James M. Clifford
Editorial Page Ed. ....Thomas L. Schultz
Photo Ed. ....John Hart
Sports Ed. ....Kevin Wilson
Prodn. Mgr. ....Gregory J. Thrams
Market Information: Split run; TMC.
Mechanical Available: Offset; Black and 3 ROP colors; insert accepted; page cutoffs - 22 3/4.
Mechanical Specifications: Type page 11 5/8 x 21 1/2; E - 6 cols, 1 5/6, 1/8 between; A - 6 cols, 1 5/6, 1/8 between; C - 8 cols, 1 1/3, 1/8 between.
Delivery Method: Mail, Newsstand, Carrier, RacksEquipment & Software: PRESSROOM EQUIPMENT: Lines — 5-G/Community 1971; 1-G/Community 1984; 1-G/Community 1989; Folders — 1-G/Community.; MAILROOM EQUIPMENT: Tying Machines — 2-Ty-Tech/TM45; Address Machine — St/1600-2344.; BUSINESS EQUIPMENT: ATT/382-500 CLASSIFIED EQUIPMENT: Hardware — APP/Mac; Printers — Okidata; CLASSIFIED SOFTWARE: Baseview. DISPLAY EQUIPMENT: Hardware — APP/Mac, Baseview/Ad Manager Pro; Printers — APP/Mac LaserWriter; DISPLAY SOFTWAREAd Make-up Applications — QPS/QuarkXPress, Adobe/Illustrator.; EDITORIAL EQUIPMENT: Hardware — APP/Mac; Printers — Okidata, 3-APP/Mac LaserWriter, Xante/3G EDITORIAL SOFTWARE: Baseview 2.0.6. PRODUCTION EQUIPMENT: Hardware — 30-Nu/Flip Top FT40APRNS, APP/Power Mac G3, Nikon/Coolscan, APP/Power Mac 7200, APP/Power Mac 200; Cameras — B/Horizontal; Scanners — APP/Mac One Scanner, Microtek/ScanMaker, Nikon/Coolscan PRODUCTION SOFTWARE: QPS/QuarkXPress 6.1, Adobe/Photoshop.

WAUKESHA

THE FREEMAN

PO Box 7, 801 N Barstow St, Waukesha, Wis., 53187-0007, Waukesha; gen tel (262) 542-2500; adv tel (262) 513-2621; ed tel (262) 513-2671; gen fax (262) 542-6082; adv fax (262) 542-6082; ed fax (262) 542-8259; gen/nat adv e-mail jbaumgart@conleynet.com; disp adv e-mail jbaumgart@conleynet.com; class adv e-mailjbaumgart@conleynet.com; ed e-mail ppaige@conleynet.com; web site www.gmtoday.com
Group: Conley Media LLC
Published: Tues, Wed, Thur, Fri, Sat
Weekday Frequency: e
Saturday Frequency: m
Circulation: 9,386; 10,649(sat)
Last Audit: CVC March 31, 2017
Advertising Rate (weekday/saturday): $22.65
News services: AP. **Established:** 1858
Own Printing Facility?: Yes
Commercial Printers?: Yes
Special Editions: Tax Directory (Apr); Health/Medical Directory (Aug); Holiday Fun (Dec); Tax Directory (Feb); License Plate Contest (Jan); Antique Directory (Jul); Sidewalk Sale (Jun); National Women's History Month (Mar); National Home Decorating Month (May); Coupon Book
Special Weekly Sections: Best Food (Wed); Home, Real Estate, Leisure, Auto (Thur); Brides, TV, Auto (Sat); Easy Living, Health (Monthly); Resources, Summer Fun, Fall (Annually)
Syndicated Publications: Relish (Monthly); USA WEEKEND Magazine (Sat); American Profile (Weekly).
Adv. Mgr. ....Jim Baumgart
Circ. Mgr., Mktg./Promo ....Tom Badger
Publisher & Ed. in Chief ....Bill Yorth
Automotive Ed. ....Mary Carlson
Online/Mgmt. Info Servs. Mgr. ....Hays Goodman
Prodn. Coord., Mailroom ....Joe Rocha
Dist. Circ. Director ....Tim Haffemann
Editorial Page Ed. ....Shana Duffy
Prepress Mgr. ....Patricia Scheel
Market Information: ADS; TMC; Zoned editions.
Mechanical Available: Web Offset; Black and 3 ROP colors; insert accepted - single sheets, product samples; page cutoffs - 22 3/4.
Mechanical Specifications: Type page 13 x 21 1/2; E - 6 cols, 2, 3/16 between; A - 6 cols, 2, 3/16 between; C - 9 cols, 1 3/8, 1/16 between.
Areas Served: MILWAUKEE—RACINE, WI CMSA
Delivery Method: Mail, Newsstand, Carrier, RacksEquipment & Software: PRESSROOM EQUIPMENT: Lines — 8-G/Urbanite.; MAILROOM EQUIPMENT: Counter Stackers — 2/MM, Id; Inserters & Stuffers — 2-/MM; Tying Machines — 2-/Dynaric; Address Machine — KR.; BUSINESS EQUIPMENT: APP/iMac BUSINESS SOFTWARE: Microsoft/Office 97, Microsoft/Office 2000, Oracle, PBS CLASSIFIED EQUIPMENT: Hardware — APP/iMac; Printers — HP/Laserjet 4000N; CLASSIFIED SOFTWARE: Concept/Classworks. DISPLAY EQUIPMENT: Hardware — APP/Mac; Printers — HP/Laserjet 4000N; DISPLAY SOFTWAREAd Make-up Applications — Concept/AdNet.; EDITORIAL EQUIPMENT: Hardware — APP/Mac G3; Printers — GCC/Elite 1208, HP/Laserjet 5M EDITORIAL SOFTWARE: Adobe/Illustrator, Adobe/Photoshop, Concept/Adworks, Concept/Copy Works. PRODUCTION EQUIPMENT: Hardware — NU/FT 40V6UPNS, 2-Violet Laser/VSP85-S.

WAUSAU

THE WAUSAU DAILY HERALD

800 Scott St, Wausau, Wis., 54403-4951, Marathon; gen tel (715) 842-2101; adv tel (715) 845-0754; ed tel (715) 845-0661; gen fax (715) 848-9360; adv fax (715) 848-9360; ed fax (715) 848-9361; gen/nat adv e-mail opinions@wausaudailyherald.com; disp adv e-mail shehir@gannett.com; class adv e-mailclassified@wisinfo.com; ed e-mail mbaldwin@wausau.gannett.com; web site www.wausaudailyherald.com
Group: Gannett
Published: Mon, Tues, Wed, Thur, Fri, Sat, Sun
Weekday Frequency: e
Saturday Frequency: e
Circulation: 12,232; 12,232(sat); 30,576(sun)
Last Audit: AAM June 30, 2016
Advertising Rate (weekday/saturday): Open inch rate $51.40 (Mon-Fri); $49.90 (Sat)
Advertising Rate (sunday): Open inch rate $62.90
News services: AP, GNS. **Established:** 1907
Own Printing Facility?: Yes
Commercial Printers?: No
Special Editions: Career Choices (Apr); Prep Football (Aug); Sidewalk Sale (Jul); Summer Events (May); Real Estate Guide (Monthly); Thanksgiving (Nov); Forest Forever (Oct); Escape (May and Sept); You Magazine (Bi-Monthly); Thirteen for Thirteen (Monthly); Hmong Connections (Quarterly); Senior Living (Quarterly); Pets (March); Academic Excellence (Oct-May); Volunteer (April); Made in Central Wisconsin (Sept); Online Auction (April & Oct); Reader's Choice Awards (March-May); Athletes of the Year (May); Graduation (June)
Special Weekly Sections: News, Sports, Business, Classifieds (Daily); Travel, Stock, Outdoors (Sun); Health, Fitness, Follow-ups (Mon); Lifestyle, Senior, Technology (Tue); Best Food day, Nutrition, Diet, Youth Sports (Wed); Family, Outdoors, Weekend, Entertainment (Thur); Religion, Xpressions (Fri); Homestyle, Real Estate Guide (sat)
Syndicated Publications: HomeStyle (Every other month); CW Business (Monthly); USA WEEKEND Magazine (S).
Pres./Pub. ....Michael Beck
Adv. Dir. ....Scott Hehir
Exec. Ed. ....Mark Treinen
Librarian ....Debra Siburt
Opinion Page Ed. ....Pete Wasson
Photo Dept. Ed. ....Rob Orcutt
Sports Ed. ....Chris Schulte
Television Ed. ....Cathy Emerson
Prodn. Mgr., Distr. Ctr. ....Glenn Palder
Market Information: ADS; TMC.
Mechanical Available: Offset; Black and 3 ROP colors; insert accepted; page cutoffs - 22 3/4.
Mechanical Specifications: Type page 11 13/100 x 21 1/2; E - 6 cols, 1 3/4, 1/8 between; A - 6 cols, 1 3/4, 1/8 between; C - 10 cols, 1 1/20, 7/100 between.
Delivery Method: Mail, Newsstand, Carrier, RacksEquipment & Software: PRESSROOM EQUIPMENT: Lines — 4-G/Metro double width (Hump on 3-10 side) 1968; 2-G/Metro double width 5-10; Folders — 1-G/2:1; Pasters —G/Flying Paster. MAILROOM EQUIPMENT: Counter Stackers — 3-QWI/401 Narrow; Inserters & Stuffers — HI/1372, HI/Alphaliner; Tying Machines — 2/Power Strap; Address Machine — Ch.; BUSINESS EQUIPMENT: 1-IBM/AS-400 CLASSIFIED EQUIPMENT: Hardware — APP/Mac G3; Printers — TI/810, HP/LaserJet 5M, HP/LaserJet 400N; CLASSIFIED SOFTWARE: Baseview. DISPLAY EQUIPMENT: Hardware — APP/Mac; Printers — HP/8000 Laser, HP/2500C Color, HP/1050C DesignJet; Other Hardware — CD, XYQUEST/44 DISPLAY SOFTWAREAd Make-up Applications — Quark 4.1, Adobe/Illustrator; Layout Software — APP/Mac. EDITORIAL EQUIPMENT: Hardware — Mk/6000/Mk; Printers — APP/Mac LaserPrinter EDITORIAL SOFTWARE: Mk/ACE II, Caere/OmniPage. PRODUCTION EQUIPMENT: Hardware — Nu, Ultra/Plus; Cameras — 2-Tesca Copydot; Scanners — 1-AG/Duoscan, 1-AG/Duoscan T1200 PRODUCTION SOFTWARE: QPS/QuarkXPress, Baseview/Newsedit Pro.

WEST BEND

THE DAILY NEWS

100 S 6th Ave, West Bend, Wis., 53095-3309, Washington; gen tel (262) 306-5000; adv tel (414) 333-8635; ed tel (262) 306-5043; gen fax (262) 338-1984; adv fax (262) 338-1984; ed fax (262) 338-1984; gen/nat adv e-mail hrogge@conleynet.com; disp adv e-mail hrogge@conleynet.com; class adv e-mailclassifieds@conleynet.com; ed e-mail dailynews@conleynet.com; web site www.gmtoday.com
Group: Conley Media LLC
Published: Tues, Wed, Thur, Fri, Sat
Weekday Frequency: All day
Saturday Frequency: m
Circulation: 7,454; 7,776(sat)
Last Audit: CVC March 31, 2017
Branch Offices: No other branch office for the Daily News.
Advertising Rate (weekday/saturday): Open inch rate $14.27
Advertising Rate (sunday): N/A
Online Advertising Rate: We do have online options, but at this point in time we offer our gmtoday spots as value added to our print clients.
News services: AP, NYT. **Established:** 1856
Own Printing Facility?: Yes
Commercial Printers?: Yes
Special Editions: Honoring Veteran's section (May/Sept) Dairyland Bike Tour (June) Senior Citizens (Aug); Christmas Gift Guide (Dec); County Fair (Jul); Home Improvement (Mar); Christmas Opening (Nov); Fall Home Improvement (Sept).
Special Weekly Sections: School, Health, Fitness (Tue); Best Food, Outdoors (Wed); Entertainment, Recreation (Thur); Religion, American Profile, Food, NASCAR, Real Estate (Fri); Parenting, Trends, Technology, Travel, Photo, recipes (Sat)
Syndicated Publications: Relish (Monthly); USA WEEKEND Magazine (Sat); American Profile (Weekly). Redplum (Sat) SmartSource (Sat)
Digital Platform - Mobile: Apple, Android
Digital Platform - Tablet: Apple iOS, Android
Circ. Mgr. ....Kim Kleba
Composing Mgr. ....Scot Wiesner
Pub. /Adv. Mgr. ....Heather Rogge
Market Information: TMC.
Mechanical Available: Offset; Black and ROP colors; insert accepted - smaller units than full-page, tabs, booklets; page cutoffs - 23 9/16.
Mechanical Specifications: Type page 13 x 21 1/2; E - 6 cols, 2 1/6, 1/8 between; A - 6 cols, 2 1/6, 1/8 between; C - 9 cols, 1 3/8, 1/16 between.
Areas Served: Washington County
Delivery Method: Mail, NewsstandEquipment & Software: PRESSROOM EQUIPMENT: Lines — 8-G/Community; 10-G/Community; Folders — G/SC.; MAILROOM EQUIPMENT:

Tying Machines — 1-Bu/St, 1/Power Strap; Address Machine — 1-SAC/JR.; BUSINESS EQUIPMENT: 1-IBM/PC-XT, ATT CLASSIFIED EQUIPMENT: Hardware — 4-Mk/6000; Printers — V/5100; CLASSIFIED SOFTWARE: Mk/ACE II. DISPLAY EQUIPMENT: Hardware — APP/Mac IIci; DISPLAY SOFTWAREAd Make-up Applications — QPS, Aldus, Multi-Ad, QPS/QuarkXPress; Layout Software — APP/Mac IIci. EDITORIAL EQUIPMENT: Hardware — Mk/6000/Mk/Magitronic II; Printers — 2-V/5100 EDITORIAL SOFTWARE: Mk/Ace II. PRODUCTION EQUIPMENT: Hardware — Lf/AP Leaf Picture Desk, V; Cameras — SCREEN/Companica 680; Scanners — 1-SCREEN/680C. IT EQUIPMENT: Mac format

Note: Conley attends job fairs on a regular basis to promote our weekly jobs circulation.

WISCONSIN RAPIDS

DAILY TRIBUNE

220 1st Ave S, Wisconsin Rapids, Wis., 54495-4154, Wood; gen tel (715) 423-7200; adv tel (715) 422-6716; ed tel (715) 422-6723; gen fax (715) 421-1545; adv fax (715) 422-6758; ed fax (715) 421-1545; gen/nat adv e-mail tmondloch@marshfieldnewsherald.com; disp adv e-mail tmondloch@marshfieldnewsherald.com; class adv e-mailclassified@marshfieldnewsherald.com; ed e-mail editor@wisconsinrapidstribune.com; web site www.wisconsinrapidstribune.com

Group: Gannett
Published: Mon, Tues, Wed, Thur, Fri, Sat, Sun
Weekday Frequency: e
Saturday Frequency: m
Circulation: 6,378; 6,378(sat); 377(sun)
Last Audit: AAM June 30, 2017
Advertising Rate (weekday/saturday): Open inch rate $32.00
Advertising Rate (sunday): Open inch rate $32.00
News services: AP.
Special Editions: Boating Guide (Apr); Rivercities Fun Fest (Aug); Sports (Dec); Health Pages (Every other month); Badger State Games (Feb); Bridal Tab (Jan); Water Ski Tourney (Jul); Father's Day Honor Roll (Jun); Boating Guide (Mar); Graduation Tab (May); Sports (Nov); R
Special Weekly Sections: Best Food Day (Tue); Weekend Sports (Mon); Business, Stock (Tue-Sat); Agriculture (Wed); Dining, Entertainment, Outdoor (Thur); TV, Travel, Church, Religion (Fri); Seniors (Sat)
Exec. Ed. .... Allen Hicks
Photo Chief .... Tom Loucks
Religion Ed. .... Jamie Jung
Sports Ed. .... Jery Rhoden
Gen. Mgr. .... Matt Wolk
VP Finance .... Mike Seeber
Adv. Dir. .... Noelle Klomp
Market Information: TMC.
Mechanical Available: Offset; Black and 3 ROP colors; insert accepted; page cutoffs - 21.
Mechanical Specifications: Type page 11 5/8 x 21 1/2; E - 6 cols, 1 5/6, 1/6 between; A - 6 cols, 1 5/16, 1/6 between; C - 9 cols, 1 1/5, 2/25 between.Equipment & Software: PRESSROOM EQUIPMENT: Lines — 10-G/Community 1989.; MAILROOM EQUIPMENT: Tying Machines — 1/MLN.; CLASSIFIED EQUIPMENT: Hardware — APP/Mac G3; Printers — HP/5000; CLASSIFIED SOFTWARE: Baseview. DISPLAY EQUIPMENT: Hardware — APP/Mac; Printers — HP/5000; DISPLAY SOFTWAREAd Make-up Applications — QPS/QuarkXPress; Layout Software — APP/Mac. EDITORIAL EQUIPMENT: Hardware — APP/Mac G3, APP/iMacPrinters — HP/5000 EDITORIAL SOFTWARE: QPS/QuarkXPress, Baseview/IQUE. PRODUCTION EQUIPMENT: Hardware — Caere/OmniPage Pro, AP; Scanners — Epson PRODUCTION SOFTWARE: QPS/QuarkXPress.

WYOMING

CASPER

CASPER STAR-TRIBUNE

170 Star Ln, Casper, Wyo., 82604-2883, Natrona; gen tel (307) 266-0500; adv tel (307) 266-0588; ed tel (307) 266-0575; gen fax (307) 266-0501; adv fax (307) 266-0501; ed fax (307) 266-0568; gen/nat adv e-mail janet.johnson@trib.com; disp adv e-mail janet.johnson@trib.com; class adv e-mailjanet.johnson@trib.com; ed e-mail editors@trib.com; web site www.trib.com - 2,100,347(views) 398,355(visitors)

Group: Lee Enterprises, Inc.
Published: Mon, Tues, Wed, Thur, Fri, Sat, Sun
Weekday Frequency: m
Saturday Frequency: m
Circulation: 16,856; 16,009(sat); 18,279(sun)
Last Audit: AAM September 30, 2016
Advertising Rate (weekday/saturday): Open inch rate $41.96
Advertising Rate (sunday): Open inch rate $46.16
News services: AP, NYT.
Special Editions: Football (Aug); Bridal Guide (Jan); College National Finals Rodeo (Jun); Growing Tomorrows (Mar); Discover Casper (May); Holiday Guide (Nov).
Special Weekly Sections: Science, Technology (Mon); Health (Tue); Enjoy!, Food (Wed); Open Spaces, Business (Thur); Family, Weekender (Fri); Religion, NASCAR (Sat); Home, Garden (Sun)
Syndicated Publications: Relish (Monthly); Sunday Comics (S); American Profile (Weekly).
Pub .... Tom Biermann
Outside Sales Rep .... Marvin Rone
Ad Dir .... Janet Johnson
Marketing & Digital Dir .... Nicole Ott
Controller .... Jeff Hansen
Exec. Ed. .... Dale Bohren
Sports Ed. .... Ross Jacobsen
Ed .... Mandy Burton
Market Information: TMC.
Mechanical Available: Offset; Black and 3 ROP colors; insert accepted; page cutoffs - 22 3/4.
Mechanical Specifications: Type page 12 x 21 1/2; E - 6 cols, 1 13/16, 1/8 between; A - 6 cols, 1 13/16, 1/8 between; C - 9 cols, 1 7/32, 1/16 between.Equipment & Software: PRESSROOM EQUIPMENT: Lines — 9-G/Cosmo offset double width; Reels & Stands — 5; MAILROOM EQUIPMENT: Counter Stackers — 3/HL; Inserters & Stuffers — 2-/MM; Tying Machines — 2-/MLN.; BUSINESS EQUIPMENT: 2-Sun, 1-Unix/PC CLASSIFIED EQUIPMENT: Hardware — 1-Sun/Sparc.; DISPLAY SOFTWARELayout Software — SCS, ECR/Pelbox. EDITORIAL EQUIPMENT: Hardware — 1-Sun/Sparc. PRODUCTION EQUIPMENT: Hardware — 1-Nu, 2-COM/8600, LaCie; Cameras — 2-SCREEN/Companica; Scanners — 2-Data Copy/730GS.

CHEYENNE

WYOMING TRIBUNE-EAGLE

702 W Lincolnway, Cheyenne, Wyo., 82001-4359, Laramie; gen tel (307) 634-3361; adv tel (307) 633-3151; ed tel (307) 634-3361; gen fax (307) 633-3191; adv fax (307) 633-3191; ed fax (307) 633-3189; gen/nat adv e-mail wlopez@wyomingnews.com; disp adv e-mail wlopez@wyomingnews.com; class adv e-mailclass1@wyomingnews.com; ed e-mail bmartin@wyomingnews.com; web site www.wyomingnews.com

Group: Adams Publishing Group, LLC
Published: Mon, Tues, Wed, Thur, Fri, Sat, Sun
Weekday Frequency: m
Saturday Frequency: m
Circulation: 13,864; 13,864(sat); 14,901(sun)
Last Audit: AAM September 30, 2012
Advertising Rate (weekday/saturday): Open inch rate $25.70
Advertising Rate (sunday): Open inch rate $25.70
News services: NEA, AP, MCT. **Established:** 1894
Own Printing Facility?: Yes
Commercial Printers?: Yes
Special Editions: Football (Aug); Estate Planning (Feb); Cheyenne Frontier Days (Jul); Investing (Jun); Entrepreneurs (May); Home Improvement (Sept).
Special Weekly Sections: Finance (Mon); Religion (Sat); Family, Milestones, Schools, Travel, Science (Sun)
Syndicated Publications: USA WEEKEND Magazine (Sat).
Pres./Pub. .... L. Michael McCraken
Vice Pres./Sec. .... Ronald M. Brown
Treasurer/Controller .... Larry D. Catalano
Adv. Dir. .... Scott P. Walker
Adv. Mgr., Classified .... Lashay Hernandez
Adv. Mgr., Nat'l .... Cynthia M. Marek
Circ. Dir. .... Gina Larsen
Mng. Ed. .... D. Reed Eckhardt
Editorial Page Ed. .... Scott W. Smith
Features Ed. .... C.J. Putnam
Sports Ed. .... Robert Gagliardi
Prodn. Dir. .... James K. Thompson
Prodn. Mgr., Mailroom .... Joyce Girardin
Prodn. Foreman, Pressroom .. Larry E. Bechtholdt
Market Information: TMC.
Mechanical Available: Offset; Black and 3 ROP colors; insert accepted - printing available, also bags and samples; page cutoffs - 22 3/4.
Mechanical Specifications: Type page 11 5/8 x 21 1/2; E - 6 cols, 2 1/16, 1/8 between; A - 6 cols, 1 13/16, 1/8 between; C - 9 cols, 1 1/4, 1/16 between.
Delivery Method: Mail, Newsstand, Carrier, RacksEquipment & Software: PRESSROOM EQUIPMENT: Lines — 8-G/Urbanite 1010 (1 color unit) 1972; Folders — 1-G/Urbanite SU.; MAILROOM EQUIPMENT: Counter Stackers — S; Inserters & Stuffers — GMA/SLS 1000; Tying Machines — MLN; Address Machine — Mg; BUSINESS EQUIPMENT: Sun/Ultra 10 BUSINESS SOFTWARE: PBS, SBS CLASSIFIED EQUIPMENT: Hardware — 6-Dell; CLASSIFIED SOFTWARE: Automated Complete Typesetting System. DISPLAY EQUIPMENT: Hardware — 18-Dell/NT Workstation, 1-Dell/Laptop; Printers — Tegra/Varityper 5300 H, Pre Press/Panther Pro, Konica/9100; DISPLAY SOFTWAREAd Make-up Applications — QPS/QuarkXPress 4.01, Adobe/Illustrator 8.0, Adobe/Photoshop 5.0; Layout Software — Automated Complete Typesetting System. EDITORIAL EQUIPMENT: Hardware — 25-Dell EDITORIAL SOFTWARE: Automated Complete Typesetting System. PRODUCTION EQUIPMENT: Hardware — P, 1-Nu, QPS, Photoshop; Cameras — C/Spartan III; Scanners — Microtek/Flatbed, HP/ScanJet II, Nikon/4000 PRODUCTION SOFTWARE: QPS/QuarkXPress 4.01, Automated Complete Typesetting System, Konica/9100.

GILLETTE

THE NEWS-RECORD

1201 W 2nd St, Gillette, Wyo., 82716-3301, Campbell; gen tel (307) 682-9306; adv tel (307) 682-9306 ext. 217; ed tel (307) 686-9306; gen fax (307) 686-9306; adv fax (307) 686-9306; ed fax (307) 686-9306; gen/nat adv e-mail newsad@vcn.com; disp adv e-mail newsad@vcn.com; class adv e-mailclassified@gillettenewsrecord.com; ed e-mail news@gillettenewsrecord.com; web site www.gillettenewsrecord.com

Published: Mon, Tues, Wed, Thur, Fri, Sun
Weekday Frequency: e
Circulation: 6,479; 6,479(sun)
Last Audit: Sworn/Estimate/Non-Audited September 30, 2017
Advertising Rate (weekday/saturday): Open inch rate $14.50
Advertising Rate (sunday): Open inch rate $14.50
News services: AP. **Established:** 1904
Own Printing Facility?: Yes
Commercial Printers?: Yes
Special Editions: Health and Fitness(Jan);Do you wanna get away(Feb); Your Money(Jan) Hometown Business(Feb); Living 50+ (March); Here's my card(March); Spring on the road (April); Think Green (Earth Day); Home&Garden (May); Summer Guide (June) Energy Update (June); Health&Fitness (July) Hunting Guide(Booklet) (August); Parenting Guide/Cooler Days (Sept); Health&Fitness (Oct); Holiday Gift Guide (Nov); Home for the Holidays (Dec) Letters to Santa (Dec); Winter sports/Fall Sports/Christmas Greetings (Dec); Hunting Guide (Fall) Bridal Guide (April); Big Boys Toys (June); Home and Garden Issue(May)
Special Weekly Sections: Best Food (Tue); Business Section, Living, TV, Food (Sun)
Syndicated Publications: Health & Fitness Tab (Monthly); What's On (local entertainment and TV) (S); American Profile (Weekly).
Pres. .... Betty Kennedy
Bus. Mgr. .... Valerie Kettrey
Mng. Ed. .... Deb Holbert Sutton
Editorial Page Ed. .... Ann Franscell
Sports Ed. .... Kathy Brown
Prodn. Mgr. .... Mike Urlaub
Ann Turner
Adv. Mgr. .... Mandi Gideon
Circ. Mgr. .... Shauna Glasser
Pub./Ed. .... Ann Kennedy-Turner
Market Information: TMC.
Mechanical Available: Offset; Black and 3 ROP colors; insert accepted; page cutoffs - 22 3/4.
Mechanical Specifications: Type page 13 x 21; E - 6 cols, 2 1/16, 1/8 between; A - 6 cols, 2 1/16, 1/8 between; C - 8 cols, 1 1/2, 1/8 between.
Areas Served: Campbell County
Delivery Method: MailEquipment & Software: PRESSROOM EQUIPMENT: Lines — 6-G; Folders — 1-G/2:1.; MAILROOM EQUIPMENT: Tying Machines — 1/Bu, Felins/F16, Allpack/351.610.001; Address Machine — 1-/El.; CLASSIFIED EQUIPMENT: Hardware — 3-APP/Power Mac G3, 1-APP/iMac; 1-Nikon/ScanTouch 210; Printers — 1-Epson/Stylus Color 850 Ne; CLASSIFIED SOFTWARE: Baseview/AdManagerPro 2.0.5, QPS/QuarkXPress 4.0, Caere/OmniPage Pro 8.0. DISPLAY EQUIPMENT: Hardware — 1-APP/Power Mac G3, 1-APP/Mac Server G3; Printers — HP/LaserJet 4MV; Other Hardware — 1-Polaroid/SprintScan 35, 1-HP/ScanJet IIcx DISPLAY SOFTWAREAd Make-up Applications — QPS/QuarkXPress 3.32, Adobe Illustrator 8.0, Adobe/Photoshop 5.0, APP/AdSend 1.4.5, Adobe/Acrobat 4.0; EDITORIAL EQUIPMENT: Hardware — 1-Mk, 9-APP/Power Mac G3, 1-APP/Mac Blue G3, 1-APP/Mac Server Blue G3, 1-APP/Power Mac 7100/80/1-Polaroid/SprintScan 35 Plus, 1-HP/ScanJet 3c, 1-Iomega/Jaz Drive; Printers — 1-HP/LaserJet 4MV, 1-ECR/Scriptsetter VRL 36 PRODUCTION EQUIPMENT: Hardware — 1-LE; Cameras — 1-SCREEN/Companica PRODUCTION SOFTWARE: QPS/QuarkXPress 3.31.

LARAMIE

LARAMIE BOOMERANG

320 E Grand Ave, Laramie, Wyo., 82070-3712, Albany; gen tel (307) 742-2176; adv tel (307) 742-2176; ed tel (307) 742-2176; gen fax (307) 742-2046; adv fax (307) 742-2046; ed fax (307) 742-2046; gen/nat adv e-mail sarah@laramieboomerang.com; disp adv e-mail sarah@laramieboomerang.com; class adv e-mailclassads@laramieboomerang.com; ed e-mail news@laramieboomerang.com; web site www.laramieboomerang.com

Group: Adams Publishing Group, LLC
Published: Tues, Wed, Thur, Fri, Sat, Sun
Weekday Frequency: m
Saturday Frequency: m
Circulation: 5,233; 5,233(sat); 5,233(sun)
Last Audit: Sworn/Estimate/Non-Audited September 30, 2017
Advertising Rate (weekday/saturday): Open inch rate $13.45
Advertising Rate (sunday): $13.70
Online Advertising Rate: Poster $10.00 CPM; Leaderboard $8.00 CPM; Rectangles $6.00 CPM
News services: AP. **Established:** 1881
Own Printing Facility?: Yes
Commercial Printers?: Yes
Special Editions: Cute Pets (Jan); Bridal (Feb); Laramie Map (Feb); Home Improvement (Mar); Healthpro (Apr); Detour: Travel &

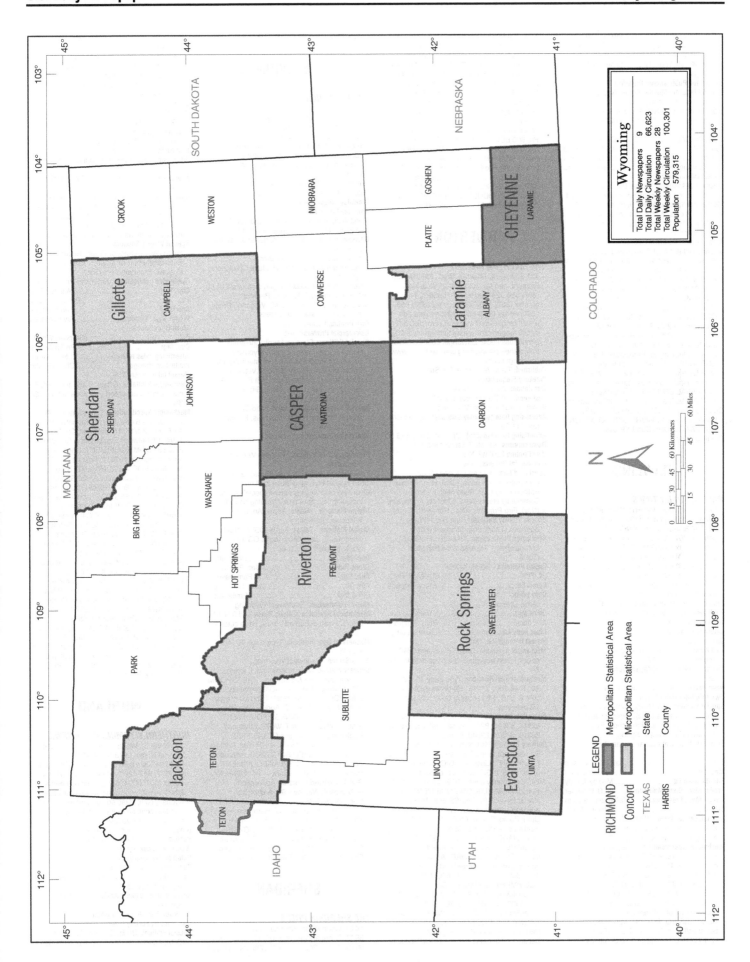

Wyoming

Total Daily Newspapers	9
Total Daily Circulation	66,623
Total Weekly Newspapers	28
Total Weekly Circulation	100,301
Population	579,315

LEGEND

RICHMOND	Metropolitan Statistical Area
Concord	Micropolitan Statistical Area
TEXAS	State
HARRIS	County

Rec (May); High School Graduation (May); Senior Living (Jun); Halloween (Oct); Cowboy Basketball (Nov); Seasons Greetings (Dec).
Special Weekly Sections: Entertainment/TV Listings
Syndicated Publications: Parade (S).
Digital Platform - Mobile: Apple, Android, Windows, Blackberry
Digital Platform - Tablet: Apple iOS, Android, Windows 7, Blackberry Tablet OS, Kindle, Nook, Kindle Fire
Bus. Office Mgr. ....Dianne Gallatin
Sports Ed. ....Robert Hammond
Adv. Mgr. ....Darcie Hoffland
Graphic Design Mgr. ....Brandon Crago
Market Information: TMC.
Mechanical Available: Offset; Black and 3 ROP colors; insert accepted; page cutoffs - 22 3/4.
Mechanical Specifications: Type page 13 x 21 1/2; E - 6 cols, 2 1/16, 1/4 between; A - 6 cols, 2 1/16, 1/4 between; C - 6 cols, 2 1/16, 1/4 between.
Areas Served: Laramie County
Delivery Method: Mail, Newsstand, Carrier, RacksEquipment & Software: PRESSROOM EQUIPMENT: Lines — 6-G/Community.; BUSINESS EQUIPMENT: PC BUSINESS SOFTWARE: Cyma CLASSIFIED EQUIPMENT: Hardware — PC; Printers — Okidata/320; CLASSIFIED SOFTWARE: QPS/QuarkXPress. DISPLAY EQUIPMENT: Hardware — 2-APP/Mac Centris 650; Printers — HP/5; Other Hardware — Sharp/ JX320 Scanner, PLI/Multisession CD Drive, PLI/Infinity 88 Removable. DISPLAY SOFTWAREAd Make-up Applications — QPS/QuarkXPress, Adobe/Photoshop, Fifth Generation Systems/Suitcase, CTA/Textpert; EDITORIAL EQUIPMENT: Hardware — PC EDITORIAL SOFTWARE: QPS/QuarkXPress. Creative Suite PRODUCTION EQUIPMENT: Hardware — 2-ECR/VRL36 PRODUCTION SOFTWARE: QPS/QuarkXPress.
Creative Suite

RAWLINS

RAWLINS DAILY TIMES
522 W Buffalo St, Rawlins, Wyo., 82301-5623, Carbon; gen tel (307) 324-3411; adv tel (307) 324-3411; ed tel (307) 324-3411; gen fax (307) 324-2797; adv fax (307)324-2797; ed fax (307)324-2797; gen/nat adv e-mail ads@rawlinstimes.com; disp adv e-mail ads@rawlinstimes.com; class adv e-mailclassifieds@rawlinstimes.com; ed e-mail editor@rawlinstimes.com; web site www.rawlinstimes.com
Group: Adams Publishing Group, LLC
Published: Tues, Wed, Thur, Fri, Sat
Weekday Frequency: m
Saturday Frequency: m
Circulation: 4,000; 4,000(sat)
Last Audit: Sworn/Estimate/Non-Audited September 30, 2017
Advertising Rate (weekday/saturday): Open inch rate $8.25
News services: AP. **Established:** 1889
Own Printing Facility?: Yes
Special Editions: Fair (Aug); Hunter's (Sept); Holiday Greetings (Dec); Explore Carbon county (May); Local High School Sports Previews (Fall, Winter, Spring)
Syndicated Publications: American Profile (Weekly).
Sec. ....Larry D. Catalano
Mng. Ed. ....Jessy Mullen
Bus./Finance Ed. ....Missey Turney
Prodn. Mgr., Distr./Mailroom ........L.B. Brantner
Prodn. Mgr., Pressroom .... Jefferson Haworth
publisher ....Holly P. Dabb
Mechanical Available: Offset; Black and 3 ROP colors; insert accepted - special arrangements; page cutoffs - 22 5/8.
Mechanical Specifications: Type page 10 1/2 x 14; E - 5 cols, 2 1/16, 1/8 between; A - 5 cols, 2 1/16, 1/8 between; C - 5 cols, 2 1/16, 1/8 between.Equipment & Software: PRESSROOM EQUIPMENT: Lines — 6-HI/ Cotrell V-15A; MAILROOM EQUIPMENT: Address Machine — 1-Data/Star 486-335X, Microsoft/Wordperfect Labels 6.0.; BUSINESS EQUIPMENT: MaxTech, Synaptic/Micro Solutions BUSINESS SOFTWARE: Synaptic/Micro Solutions

4.06 CLASSIFIED EQUIPMENT: Hardware — Synaptic/Micro Solutions; CLASSIFIED SOFTWARE: Synaptic/Micro Solutions, SunType. DISPLAY SOFTWAREAd Make-up Applications — QPS/QuarkXPress, Adobe; Layout Software — APP/Mac 75-100, APP/ Mac 6100-66, Power Computing/Power Tower 225. EDITORIAL EQUIPMENT: Hardware — Synaptic/Micro Solution; Printers — 2-APP/Mac LaserWriter II NTX, APP/Mac LaserWriter Pro 2-640, APP/Mac LaserWriter Pro 600 EDITORIAL SOFTWARE: Synaptic/ Micro Solutions, SunType. PRODUCTION EQUIPMENT: Hardware — APP/Mac LaserWriter Pro 600, 2-APP/Mac LaserWriter II; Cameras — 1-Argyle/23; Scanners — APP/Mac, 2-Nikon/ScanTouch, 2-Nikon/ Coolscan PRODUCTION SOFTWARE: QPS/ QuarkXPress 3.31, QPS/QuarkXPress 4.0.

RIVERTON

THE RIVERTON RANGER
421 E Main St, Riverton, Wyo., 82501-4438, Fremont; gen tel (307) 856-2244; adv tel (307) 856-2244; ed tel (307) 856-2244; gen fax (307) 856-0189; adv fax (307) 856-2560; ed fax (307) 856-0189; gen/nat adv e-mail rangerads@wyoming.com; disp adv e-mail rangerads@wyoming.com; class adv e-mailclassified@dailyranger.com; ed e-mail fremontnews@wyoming.com; web site www.dailyranger.com
Published: Tues, Wed, Thur, Fri, Sun
Weekday Frequency: e
Circulation: 7,200; 10,400(sun)
Last Audit: USPS October 1, 2017
Branch Offices: Lander (Wyoming)
Advertising Rate (weekday/saturday): Open inch rate $11.25
Advertising Rate (sunday): Open inch rate $16.30
News services: AP, MCT. **Established:** 1953
Own Printing Facility?: Yes
Commercial Printers?: Yes
Special Editions: Fair and Rodeo (Aug); Christmas (Dec); Bridal (Jan); Rendezvous-Balloon Rally (Jul); State Mining (Jun); Community Roots (Mar); Election; Agriculture (Nov); Fire Prevents (Oct); Hunt-Fish (Sept).
Special Weekly Sections: Best Food (Wed); Business (Thur); Entertainment (Fri)
Syndicated Publications: American Profile (S); Entertainment, TV Area-wide Schedule (Tues).
Digital Platform - Tablet: Kindle
Ed./Pub. ....Steven R. Peck
Sports Ed. ....Bruce Tippetts
Copy Editor
Jamie Drendel
Office Mgr. ....Tracy Coston
Adv. Coord. ....Ruth Urbigkeit
Classifieds Adv. Mgr. ....Luanne Luther
Market Information: TMC.
Mechanical Available: Offset; Black and 3 ROP colors; insert accepted - all; page cutoffs - 22 3/4.
Mechanical Specifications: Type page 13 x 21 1/2; E - 6 cols, 2 1/16, 1/8 between; A - 6 cols, 2 1/16, 1/8 between; C - 6 cols, 2 1/16, 1/8 between.
Areas Served: 82501, 82510, 82512. 82513. 82514, 82515, 82516, 82520, 82523, 82524, 82310, 82604, 82649, 82443
Delivery Method: Mail, Newsstand, Carrier, RacksEquipment & Software: PRESSROOM EQUIPMENT: Lines — 6-G/Community offset 1973; 2-G/Community offset 1983; 2-G/Community offset 1999; Folders — 1-G/ Suburban.; MAILROOM EQUIPMENT: Tying Machines — 2; BUSINESS EQUIPMENT: 3-IBM/PC, Pentium BUSINESS SOFTWARE: Quick Books CLASSIFIED EQUIPMENT: Hardware — PC, Mac; CLASSIFIED SOFTWARE: account scout DISPLAY EQUIPMENT: Hardware — APP/Mac iMac Intel; DISPLAY SOFTWAREAd Make-up Applications — QPS/QuarkXPress 3.3, Adobe/Photoshop.; EDITORIAL EQUIPMENT: Hardware — 6-Scoop Editorial/3-APP/Mac G4; Printers — 2-APP/ Mac 8500, LaserMaster/1800, APP/Mac LaserPro EDITORIAL SOFTWARE: Scoop/ Editorial. PRODUCTION EQUIPMENT: Hardware — Caere/OmniPage, Magic/ Separator; Cameras — 1-Nu PRODUCTION

SOFTWARE: QPS/QuarkXPress 8.5.

ROCK SPRINGS

ROCKET-MINER
215 D St, Rock Springs, Wyo., 82901-6234, Sweetwater; gen tel (307) 362-3736; gen fax (307) 382-2763; gen/nat adv e-mail jades@ rocketminer.com; disp adv e-mail jades@ rocketminer.com; class adv e-mailpublisher@ rocketminer.com; ed e-mail editor@ rocketminer.com; web site www.rocketminer.com
Group: Adams Publishing Group, LLC
Published: Tues, Wed, Thur, Fri, Sat, Sun
Weekday Frequency: m
Saturday Frequency: m
Circulation: 6,000; 6,500(sat); 6,500(sun)
Last Audit: USPS September 30, 2011
Newspaper Reps: Deb Sutton, general manager and editor
Jeff Robertson, group publisher
Advertising Rate (weekday/saturday): Open inch rate $12.50
Advertising Rate (sunday): Open inch rate $12.50
Online Advertising Rate: $250 Per Month
News services: AP, NEA, TMS, Wyoming Press Association. **Established:** 1883
Own Printing Facility?: Yes
Commercial Printers?: Yes
Special Editions: Election (Aug); Christmas (Dec); Bridal (Feb); Western Wyoming Review of Progress (Mar); Western Wyoming Vacation (May);Hunting (Sept); Veterans (Nov); Winter Sports (Dec); Fall Sports (Aug); Fair (July) Graduation (May); Gift Guide (Dec.); Letters to Santa (Dec.)
Special Weekly Sections: Best Food Day (Wed); Religion (Sun); Business, Finance, Entertainment (Daily)
Syndicated Publications: Parade
Spry
Proprietary Publications: Wellness Wyoming magazine
University of Wyoming football magazine
University of Wyoming basketball magazine
Overview of Wyo. Legislature/special section including four southern Wyoming dailies.
Digital Platform - Mobile: Apple, Android, Windows, Blackberry
Digital Platform - Tablet: Apple iOS, Android, Windows 7, Blackberry Tablet OS, Kindle, Nook, Kindle Fire, Other
Gen. Mgr./Ed. ....Deb Sutton
Group Pub. ....Jeff Robertson
Circ. Mgr. ....Pam Haynes
Adv. Dir. ....Jade Stevenson
Office Mgr. ....Emily Nash
Market Information: Southwest Wyoming
Mechanical Available: Offset; Black and 3 ROP colors; insert accepted - most; page cutoffs - 20.
Mechanical Specifications: Type page 10.955 x 19.75
Areas Served: Southwest Wyoming
Delivery Method: Mail, Newsstand, Carrier, RacksEquipment & Software: PRESSROOM EQUIPMENT: Lines — 5-G/Community 1974; MAILROOM EQUIPMENT: Tying Machines — 1-It/MS-AF, 1-Us/TE; Address Machine — 2-Am/4000.; BUSINESS EQUIPMENT: IBM BUSINESS SOFTWARE: Advanced Publishing Technologies CLASSIFIED EQUIPMENT: Hardware — HP, IBM; Printers — HP; CLASSIFIED SOFTWARE: Microsoft/ Windows 98 APT DISPLAY EQUIPMENT: Hardware — IBM; Printers — HP; DISPLAY SOFTWAREAd Make-up Applications — Microsoft/Windows 95, Archetype/ Corel Draw, QPS; Layout Software — APT EDITORIAL EQUIPMENT: Hardware — HP, IBM/HP; Printers — HP EDITORIAL SOFTWARE: Quark, apt PRODUCTION EQUIPMENT: Hardware — CTP Thermal; Cameras — Kodak DH; Scanners — none PRODUCTION SOFTWARE: CREO

SHERIDAN

THE SHERIDAN PRESS
144 E Grinnell Plz, Sheridan, Wyo., 82801-3933, Sheridan; gen tel (307) 672-2431; adv tel (307) 672-2431; ed tel (307)672-2431; gen

fax (307) 672-7950; adv fax (307)672-7950; ed fax (307)672-7950; gen/nat adv e-mail beth@thesheridanpress.com; disp adv e-mail beth@thesheridanpress.com; class adv e-mailclassified@thesheridanpress.com; ed e-mail editor@thesheridanpress.com; web site www.thesheridanpress.com
Group: Seaton Group
Published: Mon, Tues, Wed, Thur, Fri, Sat
Weekday Frequency: e
Saturday Frequency: m
Circulation: 3,523; 3,362(sat)
Last Audit: VAC June 30, 2014
Advertising Rate (weekday/saturday): Open inch rate $15.00
News services: AP, MCT, NEA, TMS. **Established:** 1887
Special Editions: Bridal Issue (Feb); Senior Health & Leisure (Jan); Sheridan-WY Rodeo (Jun); Home Improvement (Mar); Big Horn Mountain Tourist and Recreation Guide (May); Christmas (Nov); Hunting (Sept).
Special Weekly Sections: Best Food (Tue); Youth (Wed); Outdoor (Thur); Smart Living, Entertainment (Fri); Church, Business, Options, Entertainment (Sat)
Syndicated Publications: American Profile (Sat).
Circ. Mgr. ....Annette Bryl
Ed. ....Patrick Murphy
Sports Ed. ....Ken Hamerik
Prodn. Mgr., Systems ....Alvin Nielsen
Mark Blumenshine
Pub. ....Stephen Woody
Circ. Mgr. ....Phillip Ashley
advertising sales manager ....lisa marton
Production Manager .... Chad Riegler
Market Information: TMC.
Mechanical Available: Offset; Black and 3 ROP colors; insert accepted - all; page cutoffs - 22 3/4.
Mechanical Specifications: Type page 12 3/4 x 21 1/2; E - 6 cols, 2 1/16, 1/8 between; A - 6 cols, 2 1/16, 1/8 between; C - 7 cols, 1 3/4, 1/8 between.Equipment & Software: PRESSROOM EQUIPMENT: Lines — 9-G/Community 1975, 2; Folders — 1-G/ SC.; MAILROOM EQUIPMENT: Tying Machines — 1-Samuel/SA 625 Strapping, MLN, Signode.; BUSINESS EQUIPMENT: Pentium BUSINESS SOFTWARE: Baseview CLASSIFIED EQUIPMENT: Hardware — 4-APP/Power Mac, 4-APP/G4; Printers — Xante/Accel-a-Writer 39; CLASSIFIED SOFTWARE: Baseview 4.0. DISPLAY EQUIPMENT: Hardware — 2-APP/Power Mac; DISPLAY SOFTWAREAd Make-up Applications — Multi-Ad/Creator II, Adobe/ Photoshop 7.0, Adobe/Illustrator 10.; EDITORIAL EQUIPMENT: Hardware — 3-APP/G4, 5-APP/Power Mac/2-APP/Mac 30SE, APP/Power Mac fileserver; Printers — Xante/Accel-a-Writer 39 EDITORIAL SOFTWARE: Baseview 1.1, QPS/ QuarkXPress 3.32r5, APP/Mac Appleshare 5.0.2. PRODUCTION EQUIPMENT: Hardware — ECR/VRL 36; Cameras — Acti; Scanners — 1-Epson/836XL, Epson/1680, Nikon/4000 PRODUCTION SOFTWARE: QPS/QuarkXPress 3.32r5.

WORLAND

NORTHERN WYOMING DAILY NEWS
201 N 8th St, Worland, Wyo., 82401-2614, Washakie; gen tel (307) 347-3241; adv tel (307) 347-3241; ed tel (307)347-3241; gen fax (307) 347-4267; adv fax (307) 347-4267; ed fax (307)347-4267; gen/nat adv e-mail ads@wyodaily.com; disp adv e-mail ads@ wyodaily.com; class adv e-mailclassads@ wyodaily.com; ed e-mail editor@wyodaily. com; web site wyodaily.com
Group: Stevenson Newspapers
Published: Tues, Wed, Thur, Fri, Sat
Weekday Frequency: m
Saturday Frequency: m
Circulation: 3,468; 3,468(sat)
Last Audit: Sworn/Estimate/Non-Audited September 30, 2017
Advertising Rate (weekday/saturday): Open inch rate $12.50
News services: AP. **Established:** 1905
Own Printing Facility?: Yes
Special Editions: Bridal Section (Jan); FFA (Feb); Agriculture (Mar); Lawn and Garden

(April); Arts and Academics (May); Mothers day (June); Graduation edition (June); Big Horn Basin (July); Barley Agriculture (Sept); Trucking (Oct); Hunting (Oct); Breast cancer (Nov); Sugar Beet (Nov); Christmas (Dec)
Special Weekly Sections: Real Estate, Auto, Business, Finance (Daily); Best Food (Wed); Entertainment (Fri/Sat)
Syndicated Publications: Country Review (own,

newsprint) (S); American Profile (Weekly).
Adv. Mgr... Dustin Fuller
Pub....Lee Lockhart
Office Mgr./Circ. Mgr........................ Dennis Koch
People Page Ed........................ Christine Weber
Special Projects Ed................... Susan Lockhart
Prodn. Supt.....................................John Elliott
Market Information: TMC.
Mechanical Available: Offset; Black and 3 ROP

colors; insert accepted; page cutoffs - 22 3/4.
Mechanical Specifications: Type page 13 x 21 1/2; E - 6 cols, 2 1/16, 1/8 between; A - 6 cols, 2 1/16, 1/8 between; C - 6 cols, 2 1/16, 1/8 between.
Areas Served: Big Horn Basin, Mails out of state.
Delivery Method: MailEquipment & Software: PRESSROOM EQUIPMENT: Lines — 4-G/ Community; MAILROOM EQUIPMENT: Tying

Machines — 1-Bu/BT 16 String Tyer; Address Machine — 2/Wm.; BUSINESS EQUIPMENT: 2-IBM/OS 2 CLASSIFIED EQUIPMENT: Hardware — DP/Imaging 2355.; DISPLAY SOFTWARELayout Software — 1-COM/350. EDITORIAL EQUIPMENT: Hardware — DP/ Imaging 2355. PRODUCTION EQUIPMENT: Hardware — 1-Nu/Flip Top FT40; Cameras — 1-SCREEN.

DAILY NEWSPAPERS PUBLISHED IN CANADA

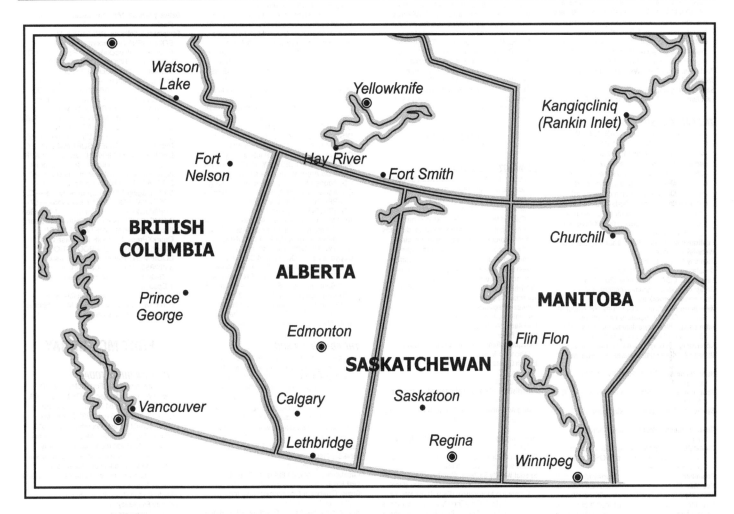

ALBERTA

CALGARY

CALGARY HERALD
215 16 St. S.E, Calgary, AB, T2E 7P5, Canada; gen tel (403) 235-7100; adv tel (403) 235-7168; ed tel (403) 235-7546; gen fax (403) 235-7379; adv fax (403) 235-8647; ed fax (403) 235-7379; gen/nat adv. e-mail submit@calgaryherald.com; disp adv e-mail advertising@calgaryherald.com; class adv e-mailwww.calgaryherald.com/ placeanad; ed e-mail Letters@calgaryherald. com; web site 1 www.calgaryherald.com - 20,218,957(views) 921,000(visitors)
Published: Mon, Tues, Wed, Thur, Fri, Sat
Weekday Frequency: m
Saturday Frequency: m

Circulation 82,670; 80,934(sat)
Last Audit: AAM September 30, 2017
Group: Postmedia Network Inc.
Newspaper Reps: Thibaud Wallaert, GM of Discomm Media
Branch Offices: Vancouver, BC
Toronto, ON
Montreal, QC
Eastern Canada
Advertising - Weekday/Saturday: M-W $9.53/ line; Thurs $10.01/line; Fri $11.45/line; Sat $10.59/line
Online Advertising Rates: Call for current rates

News services: AP, Bloomberg, Postmedia News, CP, Reuters, Daily Telegraph
Established: 1883
Special Weekly Sections: Spring Fashion (Neighbours) (Apr); Back To School (Neighbours) (Aug); BOMA (Dec); Calgary Foundation (Feb); Neighbours' Weddings (Jan); Discover the Columbia Valley (Jul); Energy (Jun); CRHBA Home Renovation Tour (Mar); Environment Week (May); Neighbours-
Syndicated Publications: Swerve (Arts, culture,

lifestyle on Friday), TV Times (Fri)
Digital Platform - Mobile: Apple, Android, Windows
Digital Platform - Tablet: Apple iOS, Android, Windows 7, Blackberry Tablet OS, Kindle
Publisher................................. Guy Huntingford
Dir. of Sales .... Ed Huculak
Adv. Mgr., Classified .... Chad Moore
Ed. in Chief................................Lorne Motley
Exec. Producer .... Monica Zurowski
Editorial Page Ed. .... David Marsden
Tablet Senior Prod. .... Tom Babin
Print. Ed...................................... Paul Harvey
Dist. Mgr. .... Gerry Turgeon
Adv. Sales & Operations Mgr. ....Bill Eshleman
Adv. Sales Mgr. ....Laura Linnell
Adv. Exec. Asst. .... Caroline Noseworthy
Local Ad. Service Team Leader..............Debi Tetz
Market information: ADS; Split run; Zoned editions.
Mechanical available: Offset; Black and 3 ROP colors; insert accepted - Poly Bags; page cutoffs - 22.
Mechanical Specifications: Type page 10 1/2 x 22.16; E - 5 cols, 2 3/16, 1/6 between; A -

10 cols, 1, 1/6 between; C - 10 cols, 1, 1/6 between.
Areas Served: Calgary
Delivery Method: Mail, Newsstand, Carrier, Racks
Equipment & Software PRESSROOM EQUIPMENT:Pressroom Lines — 9-G/Metro double width 1981, 2-G/Metro double width 1998; 9-G/Metro double width 1981, 2-G/ Metro double width 1998; Pasters — G/Metro; Reels & Stands — G/Metro. MAILROOM EQUIPMENT:Counter Stackers — 4-QWI/300, 2-QWI/350, 2-QWI/350; Inserters & Stuffers — Heidelberg/2299; Bundle Tying Machines — 6/Dynaric, 1-/Constellation, 1-/Dynamic; Wrapping Singles — 1-St/PM 720; Mailroom Control System — ICON/NT, QWI/Bundle Distribution Cont BUSINESS EQUIPMENT:Hardware — 3-DEC/VAX 4000-100 BUSINESS SOFTWARE:In-house CLASSIFIED EQUIPMENT:Hardware — Cybergraphics; Printers — HP/4S1 CLASSIFIED SOFTWARE:Cybergraphics. DISPLAY EQUIPMENT:Hardware — APP/ Macs DISPLAY SOFTWARE:Ad Make-Up

Applications — Multi-Ad/Creator, QPS/ QuarkXPress; Layout Software — ALS/30. EDITORIAL EQUIPMENT:Hardware — APP/ Mac G3, APP/iMac, APP/Mac Power Book; Printers — QMS/11 x 17 x 2, QMS/11 13 x 24 EDITORIAL SOFTWARE:QPS, Quark/ Copy Desk, Quickwire. PRODUCTION EQUIPMENT:Hardware — 2-AU/APS-108 C-6, 2-AU/APS-3850 SST, 1-WL, 2-LE/On-line Processor; Scanners — Topaz, 1-HI/ Opal Ultras, Linotype-Hell, Eskofot/2024 PRODUCTION SOFTWARE:QPS 1.12, QPS/ QuarkXPress, Multi-Ad/Creator.

METRO CALGARY

3030 3 Avenue N.E., Suite 110, Calgary, AB, T2A 6T7, Canada; gen tel 403-444-0136; adv tel (403)444-0136; ed tel (403)444-0136; gen/ nat adv. e-mail Adinfocalgary@metronews.ca; disp adv e-mail Adinfocalgary@metronews.ca; class adv e-mailclassified@metronews.ca; ed e-mail calgaryletters@metronews.ca; web site 1 metronews.ca
Published: Mon, Tues, Wed, Thur, Fri, Sat, Sun
Weekday Frequency: m
Saturday Frequency: m
Last Audit: CCAB September 30, 2015

THE CALGARY SUN

2615 12th St. NE, Calgary, AB, T2E 7W9, Canada; gen tel (403) 410-1010; adv tel (403) 250-4220; ed tel (403) 250-4161; gen fax (403) 250-4176; adv fax (403) 250-4258; ed fax (403) 250-4176; gen/nat adv. e-mail dal.lewis@sunmedia.ca; disp adv e-mail dal.lewis@sunmedia.ca; class adv e-mailcalgarysun.classifieds@sunmedia.ca; ed e-mail cal-news@sunmedia.ca; web site 1 www.calgarysun.com - 8,000,000(views) 700,000(visitors)
Published: Mon, Tues, Wed, Thur, Fri, Sat, Sun
Weekday Frequency: m
Saturday Frequency: m
Circulation 23,353; 26,312(sat); 35,700(sun)
Last Audit: CCAB September 30, 2015
Group: Quebecor Communications, Inc.
Postmedia Network Inc.
Newspaper Reps: Susan Courtney, VP, National Sales at QMI Corporate Sales Offices
Advertising - Weekday/Saturday: Open Line Rate $3.35 (Mon-Thurs); $3.44 (Fri/Sat)
Advertising - Sunday: Open Line Rate $4.07
Online Advertising Rates: Rates on Request

News services: CP, UPI, RN, GNS, CNW. **Established:** 1980
Special Weekly Sections: The Edge (Dec-April) (Monthly).
Syndicated Publications: TV Magazine (S); F.A.S.T. (Sat).
Digital Platform - Mobile: Apple, Android, Windows, Blackberry
Digital Platform - Tablet: Apple iOS, Android, Windows 7, Blackberry Tablet OS, Kindle, Nook, Kindle Fire
Controller....Murray Matieshen
Pub./Adv. Dir.....Ed Huculak
Mktg. Mgr.....Diane Wensel
Circ. Dir.....Bruce MacPherson
Ed.-in-Chief....Jose Rodriguez
Mng. Ed.....Martin Hutson
City Ed.....Dave Naylor
Info Servs. Mgr.....Chris Gibson
Prodn. Mgr., Pre Press....Sheldon Ball
Asst. Dir. of Sales....Dal Lewis
Exec. Asst.....Lori McCarry
Prod. Mgr.....Gayle Quillchini
Market information: TMC.
Mechanical available: Offset; Black and 3 ROP colors; insert accepted; page cutoffs - 22 3/4.
Mechanical Specifications: Type page 10.3330 x 11.4290; E - 6 cols, 1 1/2, 1/6 between; A - 8 cols, 1 3/16, 1/6 between; C - 8 cols, 1 3/16, 1/6 between.
Areas Served: Alberta
Equipment & Software PRESSROOM EQUIPMENT:Pressroom Lines — 3-G/ HO (mono), 4-G/decks 1992; Folders — G/ Imperial; Pasters — 6-G/CT50 RTP; Reels & Stands — 6-G/CT-50. MAILROOM EQUIPMENT:Counter Stackers — 3/ HL, 3-/QWI; Inserters & Stuffers — 1-/ HI, 1-/S; Bundle Tying Machines — 2-/ Dynaric, 2-/MLN; Wrapping Singles — 1-/ QWI, 1-/NJP, 1-/SH; Address Machine — Dm; Other Equipment — KAN/Quarter Folder, 1-MM/321 Stitcher-Trimmer, Polar/ CLASSIFIED EQUIPMENT:Hardware — 2-DEC/PDP 11-70/9-CT/90; Printers — 1-Chelgraph/PPT-600 CLASSIFIED SOFTWARE:Composition Systems. DISPLAY EQUIPMENT:Hardware — 2-APP/Power Mac 7500, 2-APP/Power Mac 8100, 2-APP/ Mac Quadra 840AV/2-HP/Scanner, Scitex; Printers — ECR/VR30, 1-Canon/Color Copier DISPLAY SOFTWARE:Ad Make-Up Applications — Multi-Ad/Creator, QPS/ QuarkXPress 3.3, Scitex, Adobe/Photoshop; Layout Software — 7-APP/Mac EDITORIAL EQUIPMENT:Hardware — 2-Sun/Sparc 10-151, 1-Sun/Sparc 10-51, 1-Sun/Sparc 10-41/14-APP/Mac PowerBook 150, 14-APP/ Mac Quadra 610, 18-APP/Mac Quadra 650, 4-APP/Mac Quadra 700, 8-APP/Mac Quadra 800, 2-APP/Mac Quadra 840 AV, 2-APP/Power Mac 7100, 4-APP/Mac D PRODUCTION EQUIPMENT:Hardware — 2-Polychrome, Harlequin, 4-DEC/Alpha with AU RIPs; Cameras — C/Spartan III, 1-AG; Scanners — Scitex/Smart Plus, 2-Scitex/340L, Howtek/D4000.
Note: Corporate rates are offered on a collective basis between the Edmonton, Calgary and Toronto markets.

EDMONTON

EDMONTON JOURNAL

10006 - 101 St., Edmonton, AB, T5J 0S1, Canada; gen tel (780) 429-5100; adv tel (780) 429-5400; ed tel (780) 429-5386; gen fax (780) 429-5500; adv fax (780) 498-5602; ed fax (780) 429-5500; gen/nat adv. e-mail rpaterson@postmedia.com; disp adv e-mail rpaterson@postmedia.com; class adv e-mailclassifieds@edmontonjournal.com; ed e-mail miype@postmedia.com; web site 1 www.edmontonjournal.com - 10,100,000(views) 730,000(visitors)
Published: Mon, Tues, Wed, Thur, Fri, Sat
Weekday Frequency: m
Saturday Frequency: m
Circulation 74,306; 75,498(sat)
Last Audit: AAM September 30, 2017
Group: Postmedia Network Inc.
Newspaper Reps: Thibaud Wallaert, GM at Discomm Media
Branch Offices: Vancouver, BC
Toronto, BC
Montreal, QC
Advertising - Weekday/Saturday: Modular sizes. Call for pricing.
Online Advertising Rates: Leaderboard $20; Big Box $25; Top Layer $45

News services: Postmedia Network **Established:** 1903
Special Editions: Destination West (Annually); Recreation Property (Other).
Special Weekly Sections: Golf-Masters (Apr); RV Showcase (Aug); Babies of the Year (Dec); Edmonton Motorshow (Feb); Banff Winter Festival (Jan); Golf-The Open Championship (Jul); Golf-U.S. Open (Jun); Alberta Health & Wellness Report (Mar); BC Report - Wine, Golf, Spa (May); Cana
Syndicated Publications: What's On (Fri); Body & Health (Mon); Sunday Reader (S); Real Estate Marketplace (Sat); At Home (Thur); Look (Tues); Working (Wed).
Digital Platform - Mobile: Apple, Android
Digital Platform - Tablet: Apple iOS
Adv. Mgr., Classified....Joseph Wuest
Adv. Mgr., Sales Planning/Nat'l Sales....Gordon Deeks
Deputy Ed., Readership/Features..Barb Wilkinson
Culture Ed.....Keri Sweetman
Vice Pres., Finance....David Becker
Vice Pres., HR....Ken Wickenberg
Credit Mgr.....David Marshall
Adv. Mgr., Retail Multi-Market Sales Ian Newman
Vice Pres., Mktg.....Patricia Hutchison
Mktg. Research Mgr.....Cindy Mah
Circ. Vice Pres., Reader Servs.....Douglas Wass
At Home/Look Ed.....Chris Standring
Digital Ad. Delivery Tech.....Janice Fehr
Ed.-in-Chief....Mark Goodhand
Special Feat.....Louise Lozeau
Adv. Services & Digital Mgr.....Lyn Propp
Managing Editor....Stephanie Coombs
Regional Vice-President Sales Prairie Region John Caputo
Director of Integrated Programs and Strategy.... Sandra Marocco
Market information: ADS; TMC.
Mechanical available: Cold Web Offset; Black and 3 ROP colors; insert accepted - Post-it notes, Tag-a-longs, Poly bags, Belly bands; page cutoffs - 23 9/16.
Mechanical Specifications: Type page 9.8330 x 19.2780; E - 5 cols, 2 1/20, 1/8 between; A - 10 cols, 1 1/16, 1/8 between; C - 10 cols, 1 1/16, 1/8 between.
Areas Served: Northern Alberta

Delivery Method: Mail, Newsstand
Equipment & Software PRESSROOM EQUIPMENT:Pressroom Lines — 11-G/ Metroliner (6 half decks); 11-G/Metroliner (6 half decks); Press Control System — G/ PCS. MAILROOM EQUIPMENT:Counter Stackers — 8-HL/Monitor, 8/QWI 401; Inserters & Stuffers — 4-Fg/Drum; Bundle Tying Machines — 16-Dynaric/NP 1500; Wrapping Singles — Manual. BUSINESS EQUIPMENT:Hardware — 2-DEC/VAX 4000 BUSINESS SOFTWARE:MS Office/ Exchange/Outlook 97-2000, Keaterm CLASSIFIED EQUIPMENT:Hardware — PC, DEC/VAX 4000, APP/Mac CLASSIFIED SOFTWARE:Cybergraphics/Genesis 22. DISPLAY EQUIPMENT:Hardware — APP/ Mac G4/CD-Rom, Canon/Digital Still Camera, Alpha/NT RIP; Printers — APP/ Mac LaserWriter DISPLAY SOFTWARE:Ad Make-Up Applications — Adobe/Illustrator CS, Adobe/Photoshop CS, Adobe/InDesign CS, Adobe/Acrobat PDF 6.0; Layout Software — APP/Mac, SCS/Layout 8000. EDITORIAL EQUIPMENT:Hardware — APP/Mac G3, APP/Mac G4, APP/iMac, APP/iBook; Printers — HP/5simmx, Graphic Enterprises, Page San III/Broadsheet Printer EDITORIAL SOFTWARE:QPS/QuarkXPress 3.32, QPS/ Copydesk 1.12, Quickwire 4.09, Adobe/ Photoshop 5.5, Adobe/Illustrator 6, Adobe/ CS. PRODUCTION EQUIPMENT:Hardware — 2-Southern/Litho; Scanners — PixelCraft 8200, 2-Linotype-Hell/Saphires, 2-Kk 2035, 2-HI/Opal Scanner, 2-ECR/2045C PRODUCTION SOFTWARE:Southam/Ad Trak, AU/Softpip, SCS/Linx, Asura 6.0.

THE EDMONTON SUN

10006 101 St, Edmonton, AB, T5J 0S1, Canada; gen tel (780) 468-0100; adv tel (780) 468-0114; ed tel (780) 468-0281; gen fax (780) 468-0139; adv fax (780) 468-0128; ed fax (780) 468-0139; gen/nat adv. e-mail ted.dakin@sunmedia.ca; disp adv e-mail ted.dakin@sunmedia.ca; ed e-mail edm-mailbag@sunmedia.ca; web site 1 www.edmontonsun.com - 10,000,000(views)
Published: Mon, Tues, Wed, Thur, Fri, Sat, Sun
Weekday Frequency: m
Saturday Frequency: m
Circulation 23,321; 23,822(sat); 31,804(sun)
Last Audit: CCAB September 30, 2016
Group: Quebecor Communications, Inc.
Postmedia Network Inc.
Newspaper Reps: Susan Courtney, VP National Sales, QMI Corporate Sales Office
Advertising - Weekday/Saturday: Open line rate $3.44 (Mon-Thurs); $3.53 (Fri/Sat)
Advertising - Sunday: Open line rate $4.12
Online Advertising Rates: Rates on request
News services: RN, CP, AP, SHNS, LAT-WP, TMS. **Established:** 1978
Special Weekly Sections: Saturday Home Improvement (Monthly).
Syndicated Publications: Car Market (Fri); Comics (S); Travel (Sat); Fashion (Tues); Food (Wed).
Digital Platform - Mobile: Apple, Android, Windows, Blackberry
Digital Platform - Tablet: Apple iOS
Pub. & CEO....David Black
Controller....Gunther Motsch
Adv. Dir.....Bob Paterson
Circ. Dir.....Nigel Wainwright
Ed. in Chief....Steve Serviss
City Ed.....Nicole Bergot
Editorial Page Ed.....Mike Jenkinson
News Ed.....Tony Saloway
Photo Dept. Mgr.....Tom Baraid
Info. Serv. Mgr.....Glenn Kaiser
Prodn. Dir.....Will Stephani
Ed.-in-Chief....Dave Breakenridge
Pub.....John Caputo
Asst. Adv. Director & Distribution....Ted Dakin
Retail Adv. Mgr.....Jean Figeat
VP of Operations, Western Canada....Craig Martin
Pub.....Gordon Norrie
Adv. Dir.....Gord Schwinghamer
Mgr., Customer Contact Centre .Catherine Stokes
Prod. Mgr.....Dru Warwick
Market information: Split run.
Mechanical available: Offset; Black and 3 ROP colors; insert accepted; page cutoffs - 22 3/4.
Mechanical Specifications: Type page 11 1/4 x 13 1/2; E - 8 cols, 1 1/6, 7/50 between; A - 8 cols, 1 1/6, 7/50 between; C - 8 cols, 1 1/6, 7/50 between.
Areas Served: Edmonton

Delivery Method: Mail, Newsstand, Carrier, Racks
Equipment & Software PRESSROOM EQUIPMENT:Pressroom Lines — G/Metro (7 units; 3 half decks) 1981; Folders — 1-G/ Double. MAILROOM EQUIPMENT:Counter Stackers — 3-G/Stackmaster, 3-Id; Inserters & Stuffers — 2-S/72P; Bundle Tying Machines — 2/MLN, MLN/News 90; Wrapping Singles — 3-/Cyclops; Address Machine — 3-MVP/BW50, 1-AVY/Labeler. BUSINESS EQUIPMENT:Hardware — 3-IBM CLASSIFIED EQUIPMENT:Hardware — Sun/Enterprise 3000, 3-Sun/Enterprise 450/ Ricoh/fax CLASSIFIED SOFTWARE:CSI, CJ. DISPLAY EQUIPMENT:Hardware — 2-APP/ Mac 7100 PPC; Printers — 2-HP/LaserJet III, APP/Mac LaserWriter Pro 63 DISPLAY SOFTWARE:Ad Make-Up Applications — Mk/Managing Editor; Layout Software — CJ. EDITORIAL EQUIPMENT:Hardware — 57-APP/Mac/2-Ricoh/fax; Printers — 1-NewGen, 2-QMS, 2-HP/LaserJet, 1-Tektronix/Phaser III pix EDITORIAL SOFTWARE:QPS/ QuarkXPress 3.3, P.INK/Database 2030, P.INK/Software 2.3.2. PRODUCTION EQUIPMENT:Hardware — 2-Howson, 3-III/3850, CCC 700i, Canon; Cameras — 2-C/Spartan Horizontal; Scanners — 1-Epson/Flatbed.
Note: Corporate rates are available on a collective basis between Sun Media Market newspapers across Canada.

FORT MCMURRAY

FORT MCMURRAY TODAY

8223 Manning Ave., Fort McMurray, AB, T9H 1V8, Canada; gen tel (780) 743-8186; adv tel (780) 743-8186 ext. 733245; ed tel (780) 743-8186 ext. 733243; gen fax (780) 468-0139; adv fax (866) 485-8461; ed fax (780) 715-3820; gen/nat adv. e-mail wsomerville@postmedia.com; disp adv e-mail wsomerville@postmedia.com; class adv e-mailrhonda.kaiser@sunmedia.ca; ed e-mail olivia.condon@sunmedia.ca; web site 1 www.fortmcmurraytoday.com
Published: Mon, Tues, Wed, Thur, Fri
Weekday Frequency: e
Saturday Frequency: m
Circulation 1,577
Last Audit: AAM March 31, 2016
Group: Quebecor Communications, Inc.
Postmedia Network Inc.
Newspaper Reps: Susan Courtney, VP National Sales at QMI Corporate Sales Office
Advertising - Weekday/Saturday: Open line rate $1.66 (Mon-Thurs); $1.92 (Fri); $0.90 (Sat)
News services: CP. **Established:** 1974
Own Printing Facility?: Y
Special Weekly Sections: Mystery Face (Apr); Back to School (Aug); Child's Christmas Eve (Dec); Your Money (Feb); Minor Hockey Week (Jan); Summer Sizzler (Jul); Environment (Jun); Slogan & Logo Contest (Mar); Forestry Week (May); Christmas Song Book (Nov); Fire Prevention Week (O
Digital Platform - Mobile: Apple, Android, Windows, Blackberry
Digital Platform - Tablet: Apple iOS
Pub.....Mary-Ann Kostiuk
Adv. Mgr.....Megan Kerton
Circ. Mgr.....Sonya Lacroixe
Acting Mng. Ed.....Erika Beauchesne
Circ. Mgr.....Amy Avery
Mng. Ed.....Erika Beauchesme

Market information: Split run; TMC.
Mechanical available: Offset; Black and 3 ROP colors; insert accepted; page cutoffs - 22 3/4.
Mechanical Specifications: Type page 11 7/16 x 21 3/16; E - 6 cols, 1 3/4, 1/8 between; A - 6 cols, 1 3/4, 1/8 between; C - 9 cols, 1 1/4, 1/8 between.
Areas Served: Edmonton

Delivery Method: Mail, Newsstand, Carrier, Racks
Equipment & Software PRESSROOM EQUIPMENT:Pressroom Lines — 7-G/Community; Folders — 1-G/Suburban 2:1. MAILROOM EQUIPMENT:Counter Stackers — 1-BG/Count-O-Veyor; Bundle Tying Machines — 2-Weld Loc/SP-505; Address Machine — Bostich, Polar, CAT. BUSINESS EQUIPMENT:Hardware — 4-NCR/Tower CLASSIFIED EQUIPMENT:Hardware — APP/Mac CLASSIFIED SOFTWARE:Baseview, QPS. DISPLAY EQUIPMENT:Hardware — APP/Mac, NEC/600 DISPLAY SOFTWARE:Ad Make-Up Applications — Mk/Ad Touch, APP/Mac SE IIs; Layout Software — APP/Mac. EDITORIAL EQUIPMENT:Hardware — APP/Mac EDITORIAL SOFTWARE:Microsoft, QPS. PRODUCTION EQUIPMENT:Hardware — 2-M/Linotron 202W, 1-Fuji; Cameras — 1-Acti.

GRANDE PRAIRIE

DAILY HERALD-TRIBUNE

10604 100 St., Grande Prairie, AB, T8V 6V4, Canada; gen tel (780) 532-1110; adv tel (780) 513-3991; ed tel (780) 513-3995 ext. 726251; gen fax (780) 532-2120; adv fax (866) 485-8461; ed fax (780) 532-2120; gen/nat adv. e-mail peter.meyerhoffer@sunmedia.ca; disp adv e-mail jane.mcrae@sunmedia.ca; class adv e-maildarlene.fritz@sunmedia.ca; ed e-mail lclow@postmedia.com; web site 1 www.dailyheraldtribune.com
Published: Mon, Tues, Wed, Thur, Fri
Weekday Frequency: m
Circulation 2,733
Last Audit: AAM March 2, 2016
Group: Quebecor Communications, Inc.
Postmedia Network Inc.
Newspaper Reps: Susan Courtney, VP Nation Sales
QMI Corporate Sales Office
Advertising - Weekday/Saturday: Open inch rate $1.69 (e-fri)
Online Advertising Rates: Call to inquire.
News services: QMI Agency **Established:** 1913
Own Printing Facility?: Y
Commercial Printers?: Y
Special Weekly Sections: Tourist Book (Apr); Business Review (Feb); On The Land (Mar); Homes (Monthly); Visitor's Guide (Other). Weekly Auto Guide, Holiday specials, Back To School, Agriculture
Syndicated Publications:
Digital Platform - Mobile: Apple
Digital Platform - Tablet: Apple iOS, Blackberry Tablet OS, Kindle
Publisher/Plant Manager .... Peter Meyerhoffer
Office Mgr. .... Margaret Steele
Adv. Mgr., Nat'l .... Fern Hickson
Ed. .... Diana Rinne
Sports Ed. .... Terry Farrell
Reg. Mng. Ed. .... Fred Rinne
Market information: Split run; TMC.
Mechanical available: Offset; Black and 3 ROP colors; insert accepted - door hangers, belly wraps, stickies; page cutoffs - 23.
Mechanical Specifications: Type page 10.3330 x 11.4290; E - 10 cols, 1 1/16, 1/8 between; A - 10 cols, 1 1/16, 1/8 between; C - 10 cols, 1 1/16, 1/8 between.
Areas Served: Grand Prairie

Delivery Method: Mail, Newsstand, Carrier, Racks
Equipment & Software PRESSROOM EQUIPMENT:Pressroom Lines — 10-G/Community (8 down; 2 stack; Balloon former); Press Drive — G/Community. MAILROOM EQUIPMENT:Counter Stackers — 1/BG, CH; Bundle Tying Machines — 1-/Sa, 2-/Sivaron; Address Machine — 1-/Am, 1-/IBM; Other Equipment — Kansa/480. BUSINESS EQUIPMENT:Hardware — 2-NCR CLASSIFIED EQUIPMENT:Hardware — Mk. DISPLAY EQUIPMENT:Hardware — 1-Mk, Datacopy DISPLAY SOFTWARE:Ad Make-Up Applications — QPS, Aldus/PageMaker; Layout Software — 5-APP/Mac. EDITORIAL EQUIPMENT:Hardware — Mk. PRODUCTION EQUIPMENT:Hardware — ECR/PelBox, 1-Nu/Flip Top; Cameras — 1-Acti PRODUCTION SOFTWARE:QPS 3.2.

LETHBRIDGE

THE LETHBRIDGE HERALD

504 7th St. S., Lethbridge, AB, T1J 2H1, Canada; gen tel (403) 328-4411; adv tel (430) 328-4410; ed tel (403) 328-4418; gen fax (403) 328-4536; adv fax (430) 329-8089; ed fax (403) 329-9355; gen/nat adv. e-mail bhancock@lethbridgeherald.com; disp adv e-mail bhancock@lethbridgeherald.com; class adv e-mailnvaneden@lethbridgeherald.com; ed e-mail bhancock@lethbridgeherald.com; web site 1 www.lethbridgeherald.com - 700,000(views) 95,000(visitors)
Published: Mon, Tues, Wed, Thur, Fri, Sat, Sun
Weekday Frequency: m
Saturday Frequency: m
Circulation 21,292; 13,186(sat); 10,737(sun)
Last Audit: AAM June 30, 2017
Group: Alta. Newspaper Group, Ltd
Horizon Publications Inc.
Newspaper Reps: Alvin Chow, Dir., Glacier Media

Mark Gravel, Sales Mgr., Postmedia Integrated Adv.

Greg Morton, VP & GM, Postmedia Integrated Adv.
Advertising - Weekday/Saturday: Open inch rate $2.08 (Mon-Th); $2.35 (F-Sat)
Advertising - Sunday: Open inch rate $2.08
Online Advertising Rates: Rates on request.
News services: AP, CP, CSM, MCT. **Established:** 1905
Own Printing Facility?: Y
Commercial Printers?: Y
Special Editions: Southern Alberta Business (Other).
Special Weekly Sections: Wheelers auto section among others
Syndicated Publications: Wheelers (Fri); Suntimes (Thursday TMC)
Digital Platform - Mobile: Apple, Android, Windows, Blackberry
Digital Platform - Tablet: Apple iOS, Android, Windows 7, Blackberry Tablet OS, Kindle, Nook, Kindle Fire
News Desk Ed. .... Randy Jensen
Prodn. Mgr., Commercial Print .... Don Winkler
Retail Sales Mgr. .... Brian Hancock
Senior VP & Group Pub. .... Mike Hertz
Multi-Market/National Adv. Sales .... Chris Tunke
Prod. & Systems Mgr. .... Ryan Turner
Market information: ADS; TMC; Zoned editions.
Mechanical available: Offset; Black and 3 ROP colors; insert accepted - samples, catalogs; page cutoffs - 21 1/2.
Mechanical Specifications: Type page 10 x 21 1/2; E - 10 cols, 1 1/16, 1/16 between; A - 10 cols, 1 1/16, 1/16 between; C - 10 cols, 1 1/16, 1/16 between.
Areas Served: SW Alberta

Delivery Method: Newsstand, Carrier, Racks
Equipment & Software PRESSROOM EQUIPMENT:Pressroom Lines — 7-G/Urbanite (1-3 color unit) single width 1973; Folders — G/Cole Quarter, G/Suburban Half, G/Urbanite Quarter. MAILROOM EQUIPMENT:Bundle Tying Machines — 3-MLN/2; Wrapping Singles — 1-MLN/MS-7; Address Machine — 1/Am; Other Equipment — MM/Stitcher-Trimmer. BUSINESS EQUIPMENT:Hardware — HP/9000, Unix System BUSINESS SOFTWARE:IBM/Newzware, Microsoft/Office CLASSIFIED EQUIPMENT:Hardware — Mircosoft/Windows NT Server 4.0, MS/NT Server 4.0, Acer/Altos 930/11-APP/Mac; Printers — Okidata/Turbo, Okidata/LaserPrinter, Okidata/Microline CLASSIFIED SOFTWARE:Baseview/AdManager Pro 2.0.2. DISPLAY EQUIPMENT:Hardware — APP/Mac, G-3/266; Printers — 2-APP/Mac LaserPrinter, 1-APP/Mac Color StyleWriter DISPLAY SOFTWARE:Ad Make-Up Applications — QPS 4.03, Adobe/Photoshop 5.0, Adobe/Illustrator 7.0, Archetype/Designer, Multi-Ad/Creator 3.5, Archetype/Designer 3.1, QPS/QuarkXPress EDITORIAL EQUIPMENT:Hardware — APP/Mac G3 Server/4-APP/Mac PowerBook G-3, 8-APP/Mac G3-266, 15-APP/Mac G3-233; Printers — 2-Genicom/Model 3810 SP, 1-GCC/Elite LaserPrinter EDITORIAL SOFTWARE:Baseview/NewsEdit Pro IQ, QPS/QuarkXPress 4.03. PRODUCTION EQUIPMENT:Hardware — 1-Pre Press/Panther Pro; Cameras — C/Spartan III, Companica/680C Vertical; Scanners — 2-Kk/RFS-2035, 2-AG/Arcus II flatbed PRODUCTION SOFTWARE:QPS/QuarkXPress, APP/Mac 4.03.

MEDICINE HAT

MEDICINE HAT NEWS

3257 Dunmore Rd S.E., Medicine Hat, AB, T1A 7E6, Canada; gen tel (403) 527-1101; adv tel (403) 527-1101; ed tel (403)528-5691; gen fax (403) 528-5696; adv fax (403) 527-0737; ed fax (403) 527-1244; gen/nat adv. e-mail lgove@medicinehatnews.com; disp adv e-mail lgove@medicinehatnews.com; class adv e-mailmattson@medicinehatnews.com; ed e-mail ksandford@medicinehatnews.com; web site 1 www.medicinehatnews.com
Published: Mon, Tues, Wed, Thur, Fri, Sat
Weekday Frequency: m
Saturday Frequency: m
Circulation 11,519; 11,519(sat)
Last Audit: AAM December 31, 2017
Group: Alta. Newspaper Group, Ltd
Horizon Publications Inc.
Newspaper Reps: Alvin Chow - Dir., Postmedia Integrated Adv.

Mark Gravel - Sales Mgr., Postmedia Integrated Adv.

Greg Morton - VP & GM, Postmedia Integrated Adv.
Advertising - Weekday/Saturday: Open inch rate $1.48 (M-Th); $1.59 (F-Sat)
Online Advertising Rates: Call to inquire
News services: CP. **Established:** 1887
Own Printing Facility?: Y
Commercial Printers?: Y
Special Weekly Sections: Homes & Gardens (Apr); Education (Aug); Christmas (Dec); Stampede (Jul); Progress (Mar); Car Care (Oct); Fall Shopping (Sept).
Syndicated Publications: TV Times (Fri); Homes (Sat); Wheels (Thur).
Pub. .... Michael Hertz
Circ. Dir. .... Gordon Waterhouse
City Ed. .... Kerri Hamel
Sports Ed. .... Sean Rooney
Prod. Mgr. .... Tom Peterson
Mng. Ed. .... Kerri Sanford
National & Multi-Market Sales .... Chris Tunke
Market information: Split run; TMC.
Mechanical available: Offset; Black and 3 ROP colors; insert accepted; page cutoffs - 22 3/4.
Mechanical Specifications: Type page 10 1/2 x 21 1/2; E - 10 cols, 1 1/16, 1/8 between; A - 10 cols, 1 1/16, 1/8 between; C - 10 cols, 1 1/16, 1/8 between.
Areas Served: Bow Island AB, Seven Persons AB, Foremost AB, Red Cliff AB, Walsh AB, Irvine AB, Brooks AB, Ralston AB, Mapoe Creek SAskatchewqn, Leader Saskatchewan, Swift Current Saskatchewqn
Delivery Method: Mail, Newsstand, Carrier, Racks
Equipment & Software PRESSROOM EQUIPMENT:Pressroom Lines — 10-G/Community single width; Folders — G/SC (upper former, 1/4 folder), BG/Count-O-Veyor 109; Press Registration System — Duarte/Pin Registration. MAILROOM EQUIPMENT:Inserters & Stuffers — KAN/480; Bundle Tying Machines — 2-Sa/S1120, 1/MLN, 1-/Ca; Other Equipment — 1-Challenge/3K Trimmer, 1-Lawson/Seriebb 3K Trimmer. CLASSIFIED EQUIPMENT:Hardware — 5-RSK/Tandy 3000, RSK/Tandy VGM 100 CLASSIFIED SOFTWARE:Baseview, Quickwire. DISPLAY EQUIPMENT:Printers — 1-QMS/860 plus/HP/ScanJet IIC scanner, Abaton/300, PixelCraft/Scanner. DISPLAY SOFTWARE:Ad Make-Up Applications — Adobe/Illustrator 6.0 EDITORIAL EQUIPMENT:Hardware — APP/Power Mac 7100-80; Printers — Select/360, QMS/1600, Fuji/Imagesetter, AU/Imagesetter EDITORIAL SOFTWARE:Quickwire, QPS/QuarkXPress. PRODUCTION EQUIPMENT:Hardware — Caere/OmniPage Pro, AU/Imagesetter; Cameras — 1-B/Caravel; Scanners — PixelCraft, Umax PRODUCTION SOFTWARE:QPS/QuarkXPress 3.31.

RED DEER

RED DEER ADVOCATE

2950 Bremner Ave., Red Deer, AB, T4R 1M9, Canada; gen tel (403) 343-2400; adv tel (403) 314-4343; ed tel (403) 314-4333; gen fax (403) 341-4772; adv fax (403) 342-4051; ed fax (403) 341-6560; gen/nat adv. e-mail advertising@reddeeradvocate.com; disp adv e-mail advertising@reddeeradvocate.com; class adv e-mailclassified@reddeeradvocate.com; ed e-mail editorial@reddeeradvocate.com; web site 1 www.reddeeradvocate.com
Published: Mon, Tues, Wed, Thur, Fri, Sat
Weekday Frequency: e
Saturday Frequency: m
Circulation 9,960; 10,237(sat)
Last Audit: AAM June 30, 2015
Group: Black Press Group Ltd.
Advertising - Weekday/Saturday: Open inch rates $2.32 (Mon-Th); $2.48 (Fri-Sat)
Online Advertising Rates: Leaderboard $20; Big Box $15
News services: CP, AP, SHNS. **Established:** 1894
Syndicated Publications: TV Today (Fri); Local Sports (Mon); Outdoor (Other); Color Comics (Sat); Food (Thur); Community Focus (Tues); Wheels (Wed).
Pub. .... Fred Gorman
Bus. Mgr. .... Dan Relkow
Adv. Dir. .... Callum Scott
Adv. Mgr., Classified .... Patricia Stamm
Adv. Mgr., Major Accts. .... Richard Smalley
Circ. Mgr. .... Allan Melbourne
Mng. Ed. .... Joe McLaughlin
Prodn. Mgr. .... Scott Williamson
Insert Mgr .... Randy Holt
Mng. Ed. .... John Stewart
Market information: Split run; TMC.
Mechanical available: Offset; Black and 3 ROP colors; insert accepted - envelopes & cards 8 x 11; page cutoffs - 22 3/4.
Mechanical Specifications: Type page 11 7/10 x 21 1/2; E - 6 cols, 1 13/16, 1/8 between; A - 6 cols, 1 13/16, 1/8 between; C - 9 cols, 1 1/8, 1/8 between.
Areas Served: Central Alberta

Delivery Method: Newsstand, Carrier
Equipment & Software PRESSROOM EQUIPMENT:Pressroom Lines — 40-G/Suburban, 32-G/Urbanite single width; Folders — 2; Reels & Stands — 2-G/Urbanite, 2-G/Suburban. MAILROOM EQUIPMENT:Counter Stackers — KAN; Inserters & Stuffers — 2-KAN/480; Bundle Tying Machines — 2-Gd/Oval Strapping Model EX-415; Wrapping Singles — 1/Poly-Bag; Other Equipment — MM/Saddle Stitcher. BUSINESS EQUIPMENT:Hardware — Sun/Sparc 20 BUSINESS SOFTWARE:Sun, PBS CLASSIFIED EQUIPMENT:Hardware — IBM CLASSIFIED SOFTWARE:AdTaker. DISPLAY EQUIPMENT:Hardware — APP/Mac/Syquest/drives; Printers — APP/Mac LaserPrinter DISPLAY SOFTWARE:Ad Make-Up Applications — QPS, Multi-Ad; Layout Software — APP/Mac. EDITORIAL EQUIPMENT:Hardware — APP/Mac/2-X/Copier; Printers — APP/Mac LaserPrinter EDITORIAL SOFTWARE:QPS, Baseview/NewsEdit. PRODUCTION EQUIPMENT:Hardware — WL/300, Adobe/Photoshop; Cameras — 1-Acti/24B, 1-Acti/204; Scanners — Nikon.

BRITISH COLUMBIA

DAWSON CREEK

DAWSON CREEK MIRROR

901-100th Ave., Dawson Creek, BC, V1G 1W2, Canada; gen tel (250) 782-4888; adv tel (250) 782-4888; ed tel (250) 782-4888; gen fax (250) 782-6300; adv fax (250) 782-6300; ed fax (250) 782-6300; gen/nat adv. e-mail jkmet@dcdn.ca; disp adv e-mail jkmet@dcdn.ca; class adv e-mailnpalfy@dcdn.ca; ed e-mail editor@dcdn.ca; web site 1 www.dawsoncreekmirror.ca
Published: Mon, Tues, Wed, Thur, Fri
Weekday Frequency: e
Circulation 2,004
Last Audit: Sworn/Estimate/Non-Audited September 30, 2017
Group: Glacier Media Group
Newspaper Reps: Wanda Yu - VP, Glacier Media Sales Office
Advertising - Weekday/Saturday: Open inch rate $0.89
Advertising - Sunday: Open inch rate $0.89
Online Advertising Rates: Rates on request.
News services: SNS. **Established:** 1930
Special Weekly Sections: Christmas (Other).
Adv. Dir./Assoc. Pub. ....Nicole Palfy
Circ. Mgr. .... Margot Owens
Mng. Ed. .... Alison McMeans
Prodn. Mgr., Pre Press .... Travis Hind
Reg. Mgr. .... William Julian
Market information: Split run; TMC; Zoned editions.
Mechanical available: Offset; Black and 3 ROP colors; insert accepted; page cutoffs - 21.
Mechanical Specifications: Type page 9.55 x 11 1/2; E - 10 cols, 1 1/16, 1/16 between.
Areas Served: Dawson Creek & Surrounding areas
Delivery Method: Mail, Carrier, Racks
Equipment & Software MAILROOM EQUIPMENT:Bundle Tying Machines — 1/Weld Loc. CLASSIFIED EQUIPMENT:Hardware — 1-APP/Mac; Printers — APP/Mac LaserWriter II. DISPLAY EQUIPMENT:Printers — APP/Mac LaserWriter IIg DISPLAY SOFTWARE:Layout Software — 4-APP/Mac. EDITORIAL EQUIPMENT:Hardware — APP/Mac/ APP/Mac LaserWriter II. PRODUCTION EQUIPMENT:Hardware — COM/Headliner; Cameras — K/Vertical 240; Scanners — Umax PRODUCTION SOFTWARE:QPS/ QuarkXPress 3.3.

FORT SAINT JOHN

ALASKA HIGHWAY NEWS

9916 98th St., Fort Saint John, BC, V1J 3T8, Canada; gen tel (250) 785-5631; adv tel (250) 785-5631; ed tel (250) 785-5631; gen fax (250) 785-3522; adv fax (250) 785-3522; ed fax (250) 785-3522; gen/nat adv. e-mail rwallace@ahnfsj.ca; disp adv e-mail rwallace@ahnfsj.ca; class adv e-mailbpiper@ahnfsj.ca; ed e-mail editor@ahnfsj.ca; web site 1 www.alaskahighwaynews.ca
Published: Mon, Tues, Wed, Thur, Fri
Weekday Frequency: e
Circulation 3,790
Last Audit: Sworn/Estimate/Non-Audited September 30, 2017
Group: Glacier Media Group
Advertising - Weekday/Saturday: Open inch rate $1.06
News services: SNS, CP, AP. **Established:** 1940
Reg. Mgr. .... William Julian
Adv. Mgr. .... Ryan Wallace
Mng. Ed. .... Alison McMeans
Market information: TMC.
Mechanical available: Offset; Black and 3 ROP colors; insert accepted; page cutoffs - 22 3/4.
Mechanical Specifications: Type page 13 x 21 1/2; E - 10 cols, 1 1/16, 1/8 between; A - 10 cols, 1 1/16, 1/8 between; C - 8 cols, 1 1/2, 1/8 between.
Areas Served: Fort St. John, Cecil Lake, Goodlow, Charlie Lake, Montney, North Pine, Rose Prairie, Taylor, Hudson's Hope, Baldonnel and Farmington
Delivery Method: Mail, Carrier
Equipment & Software MAILROOM EQUIPMENT:Bundle Tying Machines — 1-Tom/Tying machine. CLASSIFIED EQUIPMENT:Hardware — 1-Mk/1100. EDITORIAL EQUIPMENT:Hardware — APP/Mac EDITORIAL SOFTWARE:QPS/ QuarkXPress 4.1. PRODUCTION EQUIPMENT:Hardware — 1-Nu/Flip Top; Cameras — 1-B/Caravel; Scanners — COM PRODUCTION SOFTWARE:QPS/ QuarkXPress 4.1.

KELOWNA

THE DAILY COURIER

550 Doyle Ave., Kelowna, BC, V1Y 7V1, Canada; gen tel (250) 762-4445; adv tel (250) 470-0761; ed tel (250) 470-0741; gen fax (250) 762-3866; ed fax (250) 762-3866; gen/nat adv. e-mail krista.frasz@ok.bc.ca; disp adv e-mail krista.frasz@ok.bc.ca; class adv e-mailkrista.frasz@ok.bc.ca; ed e-mail Letters@ok.bc.ca; web site 1 www.kelownadailycourier.ca 110,000(visitors)
Published: Mon, Tues, Wed, Thur, Fri, Sat, Sun
Weekday Frequency: m
Saturday Frequency: m
Circulation 7,076; 7,176(sat); 6,964(sun)
Last Audit: CCAB September 16, 2016
Group: Continental Newspapers LTD
Newspaper Reps: Terry Armstrong - Group Publisher/VP
Okanagan Valley Newspaper Group
Advertising - Weekday/Saturday: Open inch rate $2.23
Advertising - Sunday: Open inch rate $2.23
Online Advertising Rates: Rates on request.
News services: CP. **Established:** 1904
Own Printing Facility?: Y
Commercial Printers?: Y
Digital Platform - Mobile: Apple, Android, Windows
Pub. .... Terry Armstrong
Adv. Dir. .... Krista Frasz
Bus. Ed. .... Steve MacNaull
Sports Ed. .... Dave Trifunov
Market information: Paid daily/TMC
Mechanical available: Offset; Black and 3 ROP colors; insert accepted;
Mechanical Specifications: Broadsheet
Areas Served: Central Okanagan

Delivery Method: Mail, Newsstand, Carrier, Racks
Equipment & Software PRESSROOM EQUIPMENT:Pressroom Lines — 17-G/ Community (3 color, Balloon); Press Drive — Fin/50 h.p. & 60 h.p. motors; Folders — G/ SC 518. MAILROOM EQUIPMENT:Bundle Tying Machines — Terminator; Other Equipment — Fox/321 Stitcher-Trimmer. CLASSIFIED EQUIPMENT:Hardware — APP/Mac, DEC CLASSIFIED SOFTWARE:QPS/QuarkXPress, CText. DISPLAY EQUIPMENT:Hardware — PBS; Printers — ATT/477, DEC/VT 400 DISPLAY SOFTWARE:Layout Software — MEI/ ALS. EDITORIAL EQUIPMENT:Hardware — APP/Mac; Printers — Pre Press/ Panther Pro, DEC/VT 1200 EDITORIAL SOFTWARE:QPS/QuarkXPress 3.3. PRODUCTION EQUIPMENT:Hardware — Caere/OmniPage 3.0, Kodamatic/520 Processor; Cameras — Nikon/3510 AF, Polaroid/SprintScan, Microtek; Scanners — QPS/QuarkXPress 3.3.

NANAIMO

NANAIMO DAILY NEWS

2575 McCullough Rd, Nanaimo, BC, V9S 5W5, Canada; gen tel (250) 729-4200; adv tel (250) 729-4248; ed tel (250) 729-4224; gen fax (250) 729-4256; adv fax (250) 729-4263; ed fax (250) 729-4288; gen/nat adv. e-mail ARosato-Taylor@nanaimodailynews.com; disp adv e-mail arosato-taylor@nanaimodailynews.com; class adv e-mailclassifieds@van.net; ed e-mail news@nanaimodailynews.com; web site 1 www.nanaimodailynews.com 227,000(visitors)
Published: Mon, Tues, Wed, Thur, Fri, Sat
Weekday Frequency: m
Saturday Frequency: m
Circulation 10,000
Last Audit: Sworn/Estimate/Non-Audited September 30, 2017
Newspaper Reps: Wanda Yu - VP, Glacier Media Group Sales
Advertising - Weekday/Saturday: Open inch rate $1.11 (M/Tu/W/F/Sa); $1.27 (Th)
Online Advertising Rates: Rates on request
News services: Postmedia News **Established:** 1874
Own Printing Facility?: Y
Commercial Printers?: Y
Digital Platform - Mobile: Apple, Android, Windows, Blackberry
Digital Platform - Tablet: Apple iOS, Android, Windows 7, Blackberry Tablet OS, Kindle, Nook, Kindle Fire
Pub. .... Hugh Nicholson
Circ. Dir. .... Les Gould
Mng. Ed. .... Mark MacDonald
Bus. Mgr. .... Rachel Mason
Sales and Mktg. Mgr. .... Andrea Rosato-Taylor
Deputy Ed. .... Philip Wolf
Mechanical Specifications: 10.50 x 21.50
Areas Served: Nanaimo, BC

Delivery Method: Mail, Newsstand, Carrier

PENTICTON

PENTICTON HERALD

186 Nanaimo Ave W #101, Penticton, BC, V2A 1N4, Canada; gen tel (250) 492-4002; adv tel (250) 490-0880 ext. 120; ed tel (250) 490-0880 ext. 300; gen fax (250) 492-2403; adv fax (250) 490-4829; ed fax (250) 492-2403; gen/nat adv. e-mail accounting@pentictonherald.ca; disp adv e-mail accounting@pentictonherald.ca; class adv e-mailaccounting@pentictonherald.ca; ed e-mail editor@pentictonherald.ca; web site 1 www.pentictonherald.ca - 160,000(views) 55,000(visitors)
Published: Mon, Tues, Wed, Thur, Fri, Sat, Sun
Weekday Frequency: m
Saturday Frequency: m
Circulation 3,993; 4,132(sat)
Last Audit: CCAB September 30, 2017
Group: Horizon Publications Inc.
Continental Newspapers LTD
Newspaper Reps: Postmedia Integrated Adv.
Advertising - Weekday/Saturday: Open inch rate $1.11
Advertising - Sunday: Open inch rate $1.11
Online Advertising Rates: Rates on request.
News services: CP, SNS. **Established:** 1910
Special Weekly Sections: Home Improvement (Apr); Home Improvement (Mar); Home Improvement (Sept).
Syndicated Publications: Real Estate (Fri); Business (Mon); TV Weekly (Thur); Business (Wed).
Sales Mgr. .... Ed Kennedy
Circ. Mgr. .... Shannon Haggard
Mng. Ed. .... James Millerjames
Sports Ed. .... Dave Crompton
GM .... Andre Martin
Mng. Ed. .... Paul Varga
Market information: TMC.
Mechanical available: Offset; Black and 3 ROP colors; insert accepted - coupons, envelopes, small catalogs; page cutoffs - 21 1/2.
Mechanical Specifications: Type page 11 x 21 1/2; E - 6 cols, 2 1/16, 1/8 between; A - 10 cols, 1 1/16, 1/8 between; C - 8 cols, 1 1/3, 1/8 between.
Areas Served: South Okanagan
Delivery Method: Mail, Newsstand, Carrier, Racks
Equipment & Software MAILROOM EQUIPMENT:Bundle Tying Machines — 1-Gd/OVL; Address Machine — ATT. BUSINESS EQUIPMENT:Hardware — PBS CLASSIFIED EQUIPMENT:Hardware — CText. DISPLAY EQUIPMENT:Hardware — APP/Mac DISPLAY SOFTWARE:Ad Make-Up Applications — QPS/QuarkXPress. EDITORIAL EQUIPMENT:Hardware — APP/Mac EDITORIAL SOFTWARE:QPS. PRODUCTION EQUIPMENT:Hardware — Pre Press/Panther; Cameras — Acti PRODUCTION SOFTWARE:QPS.

PORT ALBERNI

ALBERNI VALLEY TIMES

4918 Napier St., Port Alberni, BC, V9Y 3H5, Canada; gen tel (250) 723-8171; adv tel (250) 723-8171; ed tel (250) 729-4200; gen fax (250) 723-0586; adv fax (250) 723-0586; ed fax (250) 723-0586; gen/nat adv. e-mail kris.patterson@avtimes.net; disp adv e-mail kris.patterson@avtimes.net; ed e-mail eric.plummer@avtimes.net; web site 1 www.avtimes.net
Published: Mon, Tues, Wed, Thur, Fri
Weekday Frequency: e
Circulation 2,740
Last Audit: AAM March 31, 2015
Group: Black Press Group Ltd.
Newspaper Reps: Wanda Yu - VP, Glacier Media Group Sales
Advertising - Weekday/Saturday: Open inch rate $1.13 (M, W, F); $1.23 (Tues., EMC); $1.23 (Thu)
Online Advertising Rates: Rates on request.
News services: SNS, CP. **Established:** 1967
Special Editions: Weekender Magazine (own, offset) (Fri).
Special Weekly Sections: Salmon Derby (Aug); Christmas (Dec); Car Care (Fall); Travel (Feb); Salmon Derby (Jul); New Auto Supplement (Mar); Vacation (May); Remembrance Day (Nov); New Auto Supplement (Oct); Car Care (Spring).
Pub. .... Hugh Nicholson
Bus. Mgr. .... Debbie Reid
Circ. Mgr. .... Carla Groeneveld
Ed. .... Heather Thomson
Pub. .... Rick Major
Sales Mgr. .... Kris Patterson
Market information: ADS; TMC.
Mechanical available: Offset; Black and 3 ROP colors; insert accepted - flyers for one customer as part of press run; page cutoffs - 21.
Mechanical Specifications: Type page 10 1/2 x 21 1/2; E - 10 cols, 1, 1/4 between; A - 10 cols, 1, 1/4 between; C - 10 cols, 1, 1/4 between.
Areas Served: Communities in the Alberni Valley

Delivery Method: Mail, Newsstand, Carrier, Racks
Equipment & Software BUSINESS EQUIPMENT:Hardware — Nomads CLASSIFIED EQUIPMENT:Printers — APP/Mac LaserWriter. DISPLAY EQUIPMENT:Hardware — APP/Mac G3, APP/Mac 7200; Printers — APP/ Mac LaserWriter, APP/Mac 8500. EDITORIAL EQUIPMENT:Hardware — APP/Mac Plus System. PRODUCTION EQUIPMENT:Hardware — 3-APP/Mac, APP/ Mac LaserWriter; Cameras — 2-K/V.

PRINCE GEORGE

THE PRINCE GEORGE CITIZEN

150 Brunswick St., Prince George, BC, V2L 2B3, Canada; gen tel (250) 562-2441; adv tel (250) 960-2757; ed tel (250) 562-2441; gen fax (250) 562-9201; adv fax (250) 562-9201; ed fax (250) 562-9201; gen/nat adv. e-mail ads@pgcitizen.ca; disp adv e-mail ads@pgcitizen.ca; class adv e-mailcls@pgcitizen.ca; ed e-mail news@pgcitizen.ca; web site 1 www.princegeorgecitizen.com
Published: Mon, Tues, Wed, Thur, Fri, Sat
Weekday Frequency: m
Saturday Frequency: m
Circulation 6,236; 6,423(sat)
Last Audit: AAM December 31, 2017
Group: Glacier Media Group
Newspaper Reps: Wanda Yu - VP, Glacier Media

Group Sales
Advertising - Weekday/Saturday: Open inch rate $1.56 (M-W); $1.74 (Th); $1.56 (Fri, Sat)
Online Advertising Rates: Big Box, Leaderboard: $25

News services: CP. **Established:** 1916
Special Weekly Sections: Home Improvement (Apr); Parkwood Place Back to School (Aug); Boxing Week Savings (Dec); Cougars Den (Feb); Cougars Den (Jan); Home and Garden (Jul); Father's Day (Jun); Making a Difference (Mar); Mother's Day (May); Central Interior Business (Nov); Cougar
Syndicated Publications: TV Times (Fri); Homes (Sat); Motoring Trends (Thur).
Pub...Hugh Nicholson
Sales Mgr.......................................Lu Verticchio
Pub...Colleen Sparrow
Sports Ed.......................................Jim Swanson
Prodn. Mgr., Mailroom/Pressroom...........George Lesniewicz
Prodn. Foreman, Pressroom.............Kevin Eikum
Ed...Neil Godbout
Circ. Mgr......................................Alan Ramsay
Adv. Mgr....Dave Smith
Market information: Split run; TMC; Zoned editions.
Mechanical available: Offset; Black and 3 ROP colors; insert accepted; page cutoffs - 22 3/4.
Mechanical Specifications: Type page 10.9170 x 21 1/2; E - 5 cols, 2 1/4, 3/8 between; A - 10 cols, 1 1/16, 1/8 between; C - 8 cols, 1 3/4, 1/8 between.
Areas Served: City of Prince George

Delivery Method: Mail, Newsstand, Carrier, Racks
Equipment & Software PRESSROOM EQUIPMENT:Pressroom Lines — 6-G/11RB single width; Folders — 1 MAILROOM EQUIPMENT:Counter Stackers — 1-BG/109, 1-MM/310; Inserters & Stuffers — 1-MM/227; Bundle Tying Machines — 2/MLN; Other Equipment — 1-MM/1528. BUSINESS EQUIPMENT:Hardware — DEC/PDP 11-44 CLASSIFIED EQUIPMENT:Hardware — CText, 9-RSK/Tandy 3000 LAN; Printers — 1-APP/LaserWriter II NTX. DISPLAY EQUIPMENT:Hardware — APP/Mac II, APP/Power Mac 7100-66; Printers — APP/Mac LaserWriter, 2-AU/APS-6-108 DISPLAY SOFTWARE:Ad Make-Up Applications — Multi-Ad/Creator 3.6, QPS/QuarkXPress 3.3; Layout Software — SCS/Layout 8000. EDITORIAL EQUIPMENT:Hardware — CText, 2-RSK/Tandy 4000, 27-RSK/Tandy 3000 (PC LAN), 7-RSK/Tandy 4000 (PC LAN) EDITORIAL SOFTWARE:QPS/QuarkXPress. PRODUCTION EQUIPMENT:Hardware — Canon; Cameras — 1-C/Auto Companica 690C PRODUCTION SOFTWARE:QPS/QuarkXPress 3.3.

TRAIL

TRAIL DAILY TIMES
1136 Cedar Ave, Trail, BC, V1R 4B8, Canada; gen tel (250) 368-8551; adv tel (250) 364-1416; ed tel (250) 364-1242; gen fax (250) 368-8550; adv fax (250) 368-8550; gen/nat adv. e-mail nationals@trailtimes.ca; disp adv e-mail l.hart@trailtimes.ca; class adv e-mailnationals@trailtimes.ca; ed e-mail editor@trailtimes.ca; web site 1 www.trailtimes.ca
Published: Tues, Wed, Thur, Fri
Weekday Frequency: e
Circulation 1,335
Last Audit: VAC February 28, 2016
Group: Black Press Group Ltd.
Advertising - Weekday/Saturday: Open inch rate $18.90
Online Advertising Rates: Leaderboard $20; Big Box $15
News services: SNS, CP. **Established:** 1895
Own Printing Facility?: N
Commercial Printers?: N
Syndicated Publications: West Kootenay Advertiser (TMC Thursdays).
Circ. Mgr................................Michelle Bedford
Editor..Guy Bertrand
classifieds..........................Jeanine Margoreeth
sales...Dave Dykstra
Group Publisher............................Eric Lawson

Market information: Split run; TMC.
Mechanical available: Offset; Black and 3 ROP colors; insert accepted; page cutoffs - 14.
Mechanical Specifications: Type page 10 1/4 x 14; E - 6 cols, 1 1/2, 1/8 between; A - 6 cols, 10 1/4, 1/8 between; C - 6 cols, 10 1/4, 1/8 between.
Areas Served: Rossland, Trail, Warfield, Montrose & Fruitvale Communities

Delivery Method: Mail, Newsstand, Carrier
Equipment & Software EDITORIAL EQUIPMENT:Hardware — APP/Power Mac G3; Printers — LexMark/Optra S 1650, Optra S 1650 EDITORIAL SOFTWARE:In-Design, Adobe/Photoshop 4.0. PRODUCTION EQUIPMENT:Hardware — 1-COM/7200, 2-COM/4961, 1-COM/Unisetter; Cameras — 1-AG.

VANCOUVER

THE PROVINCE
#400 - 2985 Virtual Way, Vancouver, BC, V5M 4X7, Canada; gen tel (604) 605-2000; adv tel 1 (877) 699-8222; ed tel 1-877-979-9901; adv fax (604) 605-2206; ed fax (604) 605-2323; gen/nat adv. e-mail adinquiries@sunprovince.com; disp adv e-mail adinquiries@sunprovince.com; class adv e-mailadinquiries @ sunprovince.com; ed e-mail vantips@postmedia.com; web site 1 www.theprovince.com; web site 2 www.postmediasolutions.com
Published: Mon, Tues, Wed, Thur, Fri, Sun
Weekday Frequency: m
Saturday Frequency: m
Circulation 99,515; 112,608(sun)
Last Audit: AAM December 31, 2016
Group: Postmedia Network Inc.
Newspaper Reps: HAROLD MUNRO, Editor-in-chief
JASON LUDWIG, Regional VP Distribution Services
CLAYTON MOORE, Director, Sales
LEZA MALONEY, Director, Marketing
News services: 1898
Own Printing Facility?: N
Syndicated Publications: Westcoast Homes & Design Magazine (6 times a year in Sunday edition)
Digital Platform - Mobile: Apple, Android, Windows
Digital Platform - Tablet: Apple iOS, Android, Blackberry Tablet OS, Kindle Fire, Other
Deputy Editor...............................Paul Chapman
Weekend Editor...............................Hardip Johal
Editor-in-Chief...............................Harold Munro
Managing Editor...................Valerie Casselton
City Editor..................................Cassidy Olivier
Editorial Page Editor...................Gordon Clark
Areas Served: British Columbia
Delivery Method: Mail, Newsstand, Carrier, Racks

THE VANCOUVER SUN
#400 - 2985 Virtual Way, Vancouver, BC, V5M 4X7, Canada; gen tel (604) 605-2000; adv tel 604-605-7355; ed tel (604) 605-2030; gen fax (604) 605-2443; adv fax (604) 605-2206; ed fax (604) 605-2323; gen/nat adv. e-mail bkeller@postmedia.com; disp adv e-mail tcopeman@postmedia.com; class adv e-mailadinquiries @ sunprovince.com; ed e-mail vantips@postmedia.com; web site 1 www.vancouversun.com - 9,000,000(views) 1,900,000(visitors)
Published: Mon, Tues, Wed, Thur, Fri, Sat
Weekday Frequency: m
Saturday Frequency: m
Circulation 123,395; 141,294(sat)
Last Audit: AAM December 31, 2016
Group: Postmedia Network Inc.
News services: SOU, CP, AP, RN, TSS, NYT. **Established:** 1898
Own Printing Facility?: N
Syndicated Publications: TV Times (Fri); Color Comics (Sat).
Digital Platform - Mobile: Apple, Android
Digital Platform - Tablet: Apple iOS, Android
Ed. in Chief................................Harold Munro
Mng. Ed...............................Valerie Casselton
Deputy Editor...............................Paul Chapman

Mechanical available: Web Offset; Black and 3 ROP colors; insert accepted; page cutoffs - 22.
Mechanical Specifications: Type page 12 1/2 x 22; E - 6 cols, 2 1/16, 1/8 between; A - 6 cols, 2 1/16, 1/8 between; C - 10 cols, 1 1/4, 1/16 between.
Areas Served: Vancouver, BC

Delivery Method: Mail, Newsstand, Carrier, Racks
Equipment & Software PRESSROOM EQUIPMENT:Pressroom Lines — ManRoland Colorman XI Nine Towers 62 printing couples; ManRoland Colorman XI Nine Towers 62 printing couples; Press Drive — Seimens DC Drives Shafted press line; Folders — 2/1 Rotary Folders; Pasters — 26 Manroland CD15 Two arm Reelstand's; Reels & Stands — 26 Manroland CD15 Two arm Reelstand's; Press Control System — E.A.E; Press Registration System — None MAILROOM EQUIPMENT:Counter Stackers — 14 Quipp stackers and Viper Bottomwrappers; Inserters & Stuffers — Four 14 pocket Muller-Martini (GMA) SLS 2000 inserters ; Bundle Tying Machines — 28 Dynaric strappers with 14 turntables; Wrapping Singles — None ; Mailroom Control System — Muller-Martini Sams System BUSINESS EQUIPMENT:Hardware — HP Wintel Clients Apple Clients HP Intel Servers BUSINESS SOFTWARE:MS Windows XP Mac OS X MS Windows Server CLASSIFIED EQUIPMENT:Hardware — HP Inetl Servers; Printers — HP Printers CLASSIFIED SOFTWARE:HP DSS Software Atex Genera Cyber$ell EDITORIAL EQUIPMENT:Hardware — HP Wintel Clients Apple Clients HP Intel Servers; Printers — HP Printers EDITORIAL SOFTWARE:MS Windows XP Mac OS X MS Windows Server PRODUCTION EQUIPMENT:Hardware — HP Wintel Clients HP Intel Servers PRODUCTION SOFTWARE:PPI Saxotech
Note: The Vancouver Sun (m) and The Province (mS) have a combination rate of $17.22(m-mon-thur) & $21.99(m-fri, sat & S) per Agate line. For advertising, circulation, promotion, accounting, human resources, mechanical, personnel and production specifications, s

VICTORIA

VICTORIA TIMES COLONIST
2621 Douglas St., Victoria, BC, V8T 4M2, Canada; gen tel (250) 380-5211; adv tel (250) 380-5289; ed tel (250) 380-5201; gen fax (250) 380-5353; adv fax (250) 380-5253; ed fax (250) 380-5353; gen/nat adv. e-mail pmiranda@timescolonist.com; disp adv e-mail jscriven @ timescolonist.com; class adv e-mailclassified@timescolonist.com; ed e-mail letters@timescolonist.com ; web site 1 www.timescolonist.com - 7,000,000(views) 1,880,000(visitors); web site 2 readerschoice.timescolonist.com - 100,000(views) 5,000(visitors)
Published: Tues, Wed, Thur, Fri, Sat, Sun
Weekday Frequency: m
Saturday Frequency: m
Circulation 72,549; 56,633(sat); 56,577(sun)
Last Audit: AAM December 31, 2017
Group: Glacier Media Group
Newspaper Reps: Glacier Media National Advertising
Advertising - Weekday/Saturday: Open inch rate $4.32 (Fri-Sat); $3.58 (Sun-Thurs)
Online Advertising Rates: Big Box, Leaderboard: $25

News services: CP, McClatchy **Established:** 1980
Own Printing Facility?: Y
Commercial Printers?: Y
Special Editions: Discover Vancouver Island Arts Guide
Island Events
Planned Giving
Menu Guide
Special Weekly Sections: Homes
Driving
Travel
Entertainment

TC Extra
Islander
Syndicated Publications: TV Scene (Fri); Comics (S)
Proprietary Publications: Capital magazine
Capital Home magazine
Capital Christmas magazine
Digital Platform - Mobile: Apple, Android
Digital Platform - Tablet: Apple iOS, Android
Dir., Finance.....................Catherine McConnell
Dir. Adv....................................David Whitman
Circ. Mgr., Distr./Mktg.................Bruce Cousins
Ed. in Chief.................................Dave Obee
Market information: ADS; Split run; TMC.
Mechanical available: Offset; Black and 3 ROP colors; insert accepted; page cutoffs - 22 3/4.
Mechanical Specifications: Type page 11 9/16 x 21 7/8; E - 5 cols, 2 5/16, 1/8 between; A - 10 cols, 1 1/16, 3/32 between; C - 10 cols, 1 1/16, 3/32 between.
Areas Served: Vancouver Island, British Columbia

Delivery Method: Mail, Newsstand, Carrier, Racks
Equipment & Software PRESSROOM EQUIPMENT:Pressroom Lines — 9-G/Colorliner double width (35 couples) 1989; Folders — 2-G/2:3; Reels & Stands — G/RTP50; Press Control System — G/APCS. MAILROOM EQUIPMENT:Counter Stackers — 1-MM/288, 1-MM/388; Inserters & Stuffers — 2-MM/308 Biliner; Bundle Tying Machines — 2-OVL/JP-80; Wrapping Singles — 2-K-Jack/Filmwraps; Mailroom Control System — PC Interface with PBS System; Address Machine — 1/LinePrinter. BUSINESS EQUIPMENT:Hardware — HP/9000-D380 BUSINESS SOFTWARE:Microsoft/Excel, Microsoft/Word, Microsoft/Windows 95, AccPac, PBS, SITG CLASSIFIED EQUIPMENT:Hardware — APP/iMac CLASSIFIED SOFTWARE:Newscycle DISPLAY EQUIPMENT:Apple DISPLAY SOFTWARE:Ad Make-Up Applications — SCS/Layout 8000; Layout Software — Multi-Ad/Creator, QPS/QuarkX, Adobe CS EDITORIAL EQUIPMENT:Hardware — Apple PowerPC, HP EDITORIAL SOFTWARE:Baseview/NewsEdit IQ, XPress, Binuscan PRODUCTION EQUIPMENT:Hardware — Caere/OmniPage, APP/Mac, Adobe/Photoshop, Pre Press/ECRM Mako, Pre Press/Polkadots, ResourceSpace/Archive; Cameras — QPS/QuarkXPress, Multi-Ad, Adobe/Photoshop, Adobe/Illustrator-Streamline.

MANITOBA

BRANDON

BRANDON SUN
501 Rosser Ave., Brandon, MB, R7A 0K4, Canada; gen tel (204) 727-2451; adv tel (204)571-7424; ed tel (204) 571-7430; gen fax (204) 725-0976; adv fax (204)725-0976; ed fax (204) 727-0385; gen/nat adv. e-mail ads@brandonsun.com+; disp adv e-mail gparker@brandonsun.com; class adv e-mailclass@brandonsun.com; ed e-mail mgoerzen@brandonsun.com; web site 1 www.brandonsun.com
Published: Mon, Tues, Wed, Thur, Fri, Sat
Weekday Frequency: m
Saturday Frequency: m
Circulation 12,856; 14,115(sat)
Last Audit: AAM June 30, 2017
Group: FP Canadian Newspapers
Advertising - Weekday/Saturday: Space rates(Mon-Fri): open line rate $2.65
Advertising - Sunday: (Sat-Sun) Space rates: open line rate $3.27
News services: CP. **Established:** 1882
Own Printing Facility?: Y
Commercial Printers?: N
Syndicated Publications: Weekend magazine each Saturday

Publisher..Eric Lawson
Sales and Marketing Manager.......... Glen Parker
Mng. Ed................................. James O'Connor
Distribution................................ Ernie Cameron
Ed....Matt Goerzen
Mechanical Specifications: Broadsheet
Areas Served: Brandon & Surrounding area of Southwestern Manitoba
Delivery Method: Mail, Newsstand, Carrier, Racks

PORTAGE LA PRAIRIE

THE DAILY GRAPHIC

1941 Saskatchewan Ave. W., Portage la Prairie, MB, R1N 0R7, Canada; gen tel (204) 857-3427; adv tel (204) 857-3427; ed tel (204) 857-3427; gen fax (204) 239-1270; adv fax (204) 239-1270; ed fax (204) 239-1270; gen/nat adv. e-mail cindy.makarchuk@sunmedia.ca; disp adv e-mail cindy.makarchuk@sunmedia.ca; class adv e-mailportagedailygraphic.classifieds@sunmedia.ca; ed e-mail mdumont@postmedia.com; web site 1 www.portagedailygraphic.com
Published: Mon, Tues, Wed, Thur, Fri, Sat
Weekday Frequency: e
Circulation 2,382; 2,382(sat)
Last Audit: Sworn/Estimate/Non-Audited September 30, 2017
Group: Postmedia Network Inc.
Advertising - Weekday/Saturday: Rates on request
Online Advertising Rates: Rates on request
News services: CP. **Established:** 1895
Own Printing Facility?: Y
Syndicated Publications: TV Guide (Sat).
Digital Platform - Mobile: Apple, Android, Windows, Blackberry
Digital Platform - Tablet: Apple iOS, Android, Windows 7, Blackberry Tablet OS
Ed....Mickey Dumont
Market information: TMC.
Mechanical available: Offset; Black and 3 ROP colors; insert accepted; page cutoffs - 21.
Mechanical Specifications: Type page 14 1/2 x 21; E - 6 cols, 2 1/8, 1/8 between; A - 6 cols, 2 1/8, 1/8 between; C - 6 cols, 2 1/8, 1/8 between.
Areas Served: Portage la Prarie
Equipment & Software PRESSROOM EQUIPMENT:Pressroom Lines — 7-G/Community; Folders — G/SSC, G/SC. MAILROOM EQUIPMENT:Counter Stackers — 2-BG/Count-O-Veyor; Bundle Tying Machines — MLN, Gd/Constellation; Address Machine — St/Label Mailer, IBM/Label System 36. BUSINESS EQUIPMENT:Hardware — IBM/Sys 36 CLASSIFIED EQUIPMENT:Hardware — APP/Mac. DISPLAY SOFTWARE:Ad Make-Up Applications — APP/Mac System 7.5 3; Layout Software — APP/Mac Desktop. EDITORIAL EQUIPMENT:Hardware — APP/Mac G4 EDITORIAL SOFTWARE:APP/Mac System 7.5 3. PRODUCTION EQUIPMENT:Hardware — 1-WL, Fuji/PI 2800 Imagesetter; Cameras — 1-Kk; Scanners — LE, Nikon/LS 1000.

WINNIPEG

THE WINNIPEG SUN

1700 Church Ave., Winnipeg, MB, R2X 3A2, Canada; gen tel (204) 694-2022; adv tel (204) 632-2722; ed tel (204) 632-2774; gen fax (204)694-2347; adv fax (204) 632-8709; ed fax (204) 697-0759; gen/nat adv. e-mail daria.zmiyiwsky@sunmedia.ca; disp adv e-mail daria.zmiyiwsky@sunmedia.ca; class adv e-mailwpgsun.classified@sunmedia.ca; ed e-mail mark.hamm@sunmedia.ca; web site 1 www.winnipegsun.com - 8,500,000(views) 234,000(visitors)
Published: Mon, Tues, Wed, Thur, Fri, Sat, Sun
Weekday Frequency: m
Saturday Frequency: m
Circulation 14,110; 15,331(sat); 16,786(sun)
Last Audit: CCAB September 30, 2015
Group: Quebecor Communications, Inc. Postmedia Network Inc.
Advertising - Weekday/Saturday: Open line rate $2.48
Advertising - Sunday: Open line rate $2.48
Online Advertising Rates: Rates available upon request
News services: CP. **Established:** 1980
Syndicated Publications: ENT (S).
Digital Platform - Mobile: Apple, Android, Windows, Blackberry
Publisher/Director of Sales................Kevin Klein
Publisher/Director of Sales........ Daria Zmiyiwsky
Ed. in Chief....................................Mark Hamm
Prodn. Mgr....................................Ken Waterman
Advertising Strategist..................Darice Morries
Director of Marketing.................Carolyne Braid
Interim Director of Circulation.....Bonny Brennan
Director of Operation.........................Bob Doroz
Editor in Chief.............................Stephen Ripley
Mechanical available: Offset; Black and 3 ROP colors; insert accepted; page cutoffs - 22 3/4.
Mechanical Specifications: Type page 10 7/16 x 14 1/4; E - 8 cols, 1 5/32, 1/8 between; A - 8 cols, 1 5/32, 1/8 between; C - 8 cols, 1 5/32, 1/8 between.
Areas Served: Winnepeg, Manitoba
Delivery Method: Mail, Newsstand, Carrier, Racks
Equipment & Software PRESSROOM EQUIPMENT:Pressroom Lines — 10-G/Urbanite single width 1997; Folders — 1-G/Half, 1-DGM/Quarter; Pasters — 6 MAILROOM EQUIPMENT:Counter Stackers — 2-HL/Monitor; Inserters & Stuffers — 2-KAN/760; Bundle Tying Machines — 3/MLN. BUSINESS EQUIPMENT:Hardware — DEC/486-66, DEC/P5, Pentium/OEM BUSINESS SOFTWARE:Accpac 6.15, Microsoft/MSOffice 2000/97, Lotus/SS ME CLASSIFIED EQUIPMENT:Hardware — 7-APP/Mac; Printers — X/Docucolor 12, 332 ST CLASSIFIED SOFTWARE:Baseview, Ad Manager Pro. DISPLAY EQUIPMENT:Hardware — COM/MD7 350 MCS with preview, 2-APP/Mac DISPLAY SOFTWARE:Ad Make-Up Applications — Baseview/Display Manager, Managing Editor/ALS, QPS/QuarkXPress 4.11; Layout Software — APP/Mac, Baseview/ALS, QPS/QuarkXPress 4.11. EDITORIAL EQUIPMENT:Hardware — APP/Mac G3, APP/Mac G4, APP/iMac, APP/Mac PPC 7300, APP/Mac PPC 7600, APP/Mac PPC 8600, APP/Mac PPC 6100, APP/Mac PPC 7100, Quadra/840 AU; Printers — X/Docucolor 12, 332 ST, Xante, APP/Mac LaserWriter EDITORIAL SOFTWARE:QPS/QuarkXPress 4.11, Baseview/ PRODUCTION EQUIPMENT:Hardware — COM/MCS work stations, AM Graphics, APP/Mac G4, Compaq/DeskPro 8600, AG/25XT Imagesetters, AG/Apogee Typan NT; Cameras — DS/240, B/4000; Scanners — Hel/DB-300, COM/8400, AG/TS5000, Polaroid/SprintScan, AG/T2000 PRODUCTION SOFTWARE:QPS/QuarkXPress 4.1

WINNIPEG FREE PRESS

1355 Mountain Ave., Winnipeg, MB, R2X 3B6, Canada; gen tel (204) 697-7122; adv tel (204) 697-7332; ed tel (204) 697-7301; gen fax (204) 697-7370; adv fax (204) 697-7370; ed fax (204) 697-7412; gen/nat adv. e-mail advertis@freepress.mb.ca; disp adv e-mail fp.advertising@freepress.mb.ca; class adv e-mailwfpclass@freepress.mb.ca; ed e-mail letters@freepress.mb.ca; web site 1 www.winnipegfreepress.com - 11,000,000(views) 1,200,000(visitors)
Published: Mon, Tues, Wed, Thur, Fri, Sat
Weekday Frequency: m
Saturday Frequency: m
Circulation 67,688; 93,410(sat)
Last Audit: AAM March 31, 2015
Advertising - Weekday/Saturday: Open line rate(Mon-Fri): $7.51, (Sat): $9.48"
Online Advertising Rates: CPM: Mobile Site $41; iPad App $41; iPhone App $41; Mobile bundle $41
News services: CP, AP, MCT, NYT, LAT-WP, SHNS. **Established:** 1874
Special Weekly Sections: Golf Guide (Apr); Continuing Education (Aug); Christmas Supplement #2 (Dec); Youth Publication (Feb); Mutual Funds (Jan); Town & Country (MC Icelandic) (Jul); MCC Relief Sale (Jun); Parade of Homes (Mar); Cottage Reflections (May); Christmas Song Sheets &
Syndicated Publications: TV Plus (Sat); Neighbours (Wed).
VP Sales and Marketing.................Laurie Finley
Publisher..Bob Cox
Creative Services Manager.........Christine Fehler
Assistant Credit Manager......................John Hill
VP Digital Media.........................Sandra Kukreja
Editor..Paul Samyn
Pre-press Supervisor............. Debbie Thompson
Director of National Sales..............Kim Warburton
Director of Online Editorial Operations..........John Sullivan
Market information: Split run; TMC; Zoned editions.
Mechanical available: Letterpress (direct); Black and 3 ROP colors; insert accepted; page cutoffs - 22 3/4.
Mechanical Specifications: Type page 13 x 22 1/8; E - 6 cols, 2 1/16, 1/8 between; A - 10 cols, 1 1/16, 1/8 between; C - 10 cols, 1 1/4, 1/8 between.
Areas Served: Winnepeg & Manitoba
Delivery Method: Mail, Newsstand, Carrier, Racks
Equipment & Software PRESSROOM EQUIPMENT:Pressroom Lines — 7-G/Mark I; 7-G; 7-G/Mark I; Folders — 4; Pasters — 7-G/Digital, 14; Reels & Stands — 7, 14. MAILROOM EQUIPMENT:Counter Stackers — 2-CH/MK-IV, 1-SH/257S; Inserters & Stuffers — 1-S/24P; Bundle Tying Machines — 7/MLN; Wrapping Singles — 1-/St. BUSINESS EQUIPMENT:Hardware — 1-IBM/Sys 34 CLASSIFIED SOFTWARE:MeD/CSI-107. EDITORIAL EQUIPMENT:Hardware — 1-CSI/PDP 1170, 1-HAS/2330 EDITORIAL SOFTWARE:HAS/Magician Plus, MeD/CSI-103, MeD/CSI-105. PRODUCTION EQUIPMENT:Hardware — 2-Na/Superstar, 3-COM, 1-Fuji; Cameras — 2-C/SP-3; Scanners — 2-ECR/Autokon.

NEW BRUNSWICK

CARAQUET

L'ACADIE NOUVELLE

476 St-Pierre O, Caraquet, NB, E1W 1B7, Canada; gen tel (506) 727-4444; adv tel (506) 383-7433; ed tel (506) 727-0502; gen fax (506) 727-0530; adv fax (506) 383-7440; ed fax (506) 727-7620; gen/nat adv. e-mail jean-michel.godin@acadiemedia.com; disp adv e-mail jean-michel.godin@acadiemedia.com; class adv e-mailcharline.godin-landry@acadiemedia.com; ed e-mail gaetan.chiasson@acadienouvelle.com; web site 1 www.acadienouvelle.com
Published: Mon, Tues, Wed, Thur, Fri, Sat
Weekday Frequency: m
Saturday Frequency: m
Circulation 20,152; 20,152(sat)
Last Audit: Sworn/Estimate/Non-Audited September 30, 2017
Advertising - Weekday/Saturday: Open line rate(Mon-Fri): $1.18, (Sa t): $1.32
Online Advertising Rates: Rates available upon request
News services: CP. **Established:** 1984
Syndicated Publications: Seniors (Mon); Seniors (S); Show (Sat); Seniors (Thur); Seniors (Tues); Food (Wed).
Digital Platform - Mobile: Apple
Digital Platform - Tablet: Apple iOS
Pub./General Manager................ Francis Sonier
Dir. of Sales.................... Jean-Charles Gallant
News Manager.........................Gaetan Chiasson
Comptroller.................................. Liette Landry
Operations Manager......................... Denis Jean
Director of Marketing and Innovation Andre Wilson
Market information: ADS; Split run.
Mechanical available: Offset; Black and 3 ROP colors; insert accepted; page cutoffs - 14 3/16.
Mechanical Specifications: Type page 10 3/8 x 12 1/8; E - 10 cols, 1/6 between; A - 5 cols, 1 15/16, 1/6 between; C - 10 cols, 1/6 between.
Equipment & Software PRESSROOM EQUIPMENT:Pressroom Lines — 6-HI/D-150. MAILROOM EQUIPMENT:Bundle Tying Machines — 2/OVL, 1-/Nichiro Kogyo/Model EX311; Address Machine — 4-/Wm. BUSINESS EQUIPMENT:Hardware — IBM BUSINESS SOFTWARE:AccPac CLASSIFIED EQUIPMENT:Hardware — PC CLASSIFIED SOFTWARE:Informatel. DISPLAY EQUIPMENT:Hardware — APP/Mac; Printers — AG/Selectset 5000 DISPLAY SOFTWARE:Ad Make-Up Applications — QPS/QuarkXPress, Adobe/Illustrator. EDITORIAL EQUIPMENT:Hardware — COM, APP/Mac EDITORIAL SOFTWARE:Mk. PRODUCTION EQUIPMENT:Hardware — Enco/Negative Plate Processor Model N-322.

FREDERICTON

THE DAILY GLEANER

984 Prospect St, Fredericton, NB, E3B 2T5, Canada; gen tel (506) 458-6435; adv tel (506)859-4945; ed tel (506) 452-6671; gen fax (506) 452-7405; adv fax (506) 452-7405; ed fax (506) 452-7405; gen/nat adv. e-mail nationaladvertising@brunswicknews.com; disp adv e-mail nationaladvertising@brunswicknews.com; class adv e-mailnationaladvertising@brunswicknews.com; web site 1 www.telegraphjournal.com
Published: Mon, Tues, Wed, Thur, Fri, Sat
Weekday Frequency: m
Saturday Frequency: m
Circulation 16,050; 16,050(sat)
Last Audit: CMCA June 30, 2014
Group: Brunswick News, Inc. University Press of New Brunswick
Advertising - Weekday/Saturday: Open line rate(Mon-Thurs): $1.87, (Fri): $2.08, (Sat): $2.02
News services: CP. **Established:** 1880
Special Weekly Sections: Gardening (Apr); First Snow of Winter (Dec); Bridal (Jan); Woodstock Old Home Week (Jul); Creative Ad.Venture (Jun); Home Improvement (Mar); Downtown (Monthly); Fall Car Care (Oct); Northside (Other).
Syndicated Publications: TV/Radio Guide (Fri); Real Estate Guide (Mon); Cars Plus B/S (Wed).
Digital Platform - Mobile: Apple, Android
Digital Platform - Tablet: Apple iOS, Android, Windows 7, Blackberry Tablet OS, Kindle, Nook, Kindle Fire
National Customer Service Coordinator...Amanda Bona
NB Distributor................................Terra Coates
NB Distributor................... Lois-Anne McGregor
Director of National Sales..............Kelly Madden
Interactive Advertising Manager..... Carrie Moore
Market information: Split run; TMC.
Mechanical available: Offset; Black and 3 ROP colors; insert accepted; page cutoffs - 22 5/8.
Mechanical Specifications: Type page 11 1/2 x 21 1/2; E - 5 cols, 1, 1/6 between; A - 10 cols, 1, 1/6 between; C - 5 cols, 1, 1/6 between.
Areas Served: Fredericton, New Brunswick
Equipment & Software PRESSROOM EQUIPMENT:Pressroom Lines — 8-G/Urbanite single width 1979, 4-G/Urbanite single width 1990; Folders — G/2:1; Reels & Stands — 2-G/4 High. MAILROOM EQUIPMENT:Counter Stackers — 3/HL; Inserters & Stuffers — 1-HI/NP630; Bundle Tying Machines — 2-/Gd, 3-/Gd; Address Machine — 2-Panasonic/1925S PC. BUSINESS SOFTWARE:Great Plains Dynamics CLASSIFIED EQUIPMENT:Hardware — PCs CLASSIFIED SOFTWARE:HI/AdPower 3, HI/Cash System. DISPLAY EQUIPMENT:Hardware — PCs, APP/Mac G4 DISPLAY SOFTWARE:Ad Make-Up Applications — QPS/QuarkXPress, Adobe/Photoshop, Adobe/Illustrator, Adobe/Acrobat; Layout Software — SCS/Layout 8000. EDITORIAL EQUIPMENT:Hardware — PCs/2-CD/Electronic Picture Desk EDITORIAL SOFTWARE:HI/NewsMaker 4. PRODUCTION EQUIPMENT:Hardware —

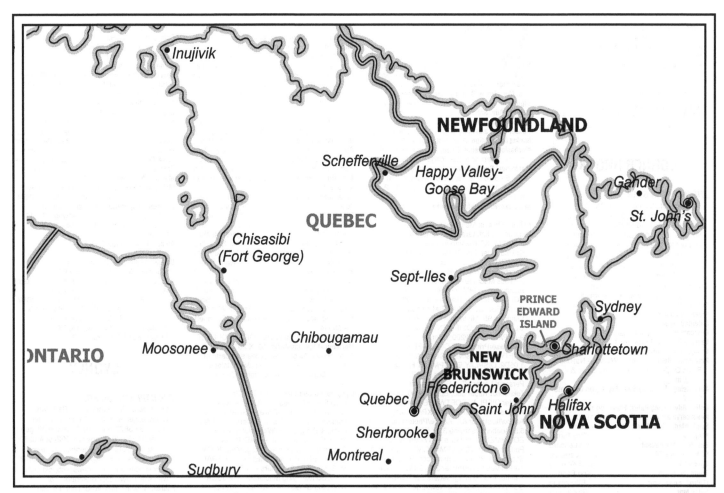

2-MON/3850, 1-Nu.

MONCTON

TIMES & TRANSCRIPT

939 Main St., Moncton, NB, E1C 8P3,
Canada; gen tel (506) 859-4945; adv tel
(506) 859-4900; ed tel (506) 859-4901;
gen fax (506) 859-4975; adv fax (506) 859-
4899; ed fax (506) 859-4904; gen/nat adv.
e-mail nationaladvertising@timestranscript.
com; disp adv e-mail bona.amanda@
brunswicknews.com; class adv e-mailbona.
amanda@brunswicknews.com; ed e-mail
news@timestranscript.com; web site 1 www.
telegraphjournal.com
Published: Mon, Tues, Wed, Thur, Fri, Sat
Weekday Frequency: m
Saturday Frequency: m
Circulation 28,812; 28,812(sat)
Last Audit: CMCA June 30, 2014
Group: Brunswick News, Inc.
Moncton Publishing
Advertising - Weekday/Saturday: Open line
rate(M-Th): $3.96, (Fri): $4.21, (Sat): $4.42
Online Advertising Rates: Rates available upon
request
News services: CP, SHNS. **Established:** 1983
Special Weekly Sections: Christmas Cookbook
(Dec); Outlook (Mar).
Syndicated Publications: TV Showtime (Fri);
Color Comic (Sat); Homes (Thur).
NB Distributor..................................Terra Coates
National Service Coordinator .... Amanda Leblanc
NB Distributor....................Lois-Anne McGregor
National Sales Director ....Kelly Madden
NB Distributor...........................Ashley McDavid
Market information: Split run; TMC; Zoned
editions.
Mechanical available: Offset; Black and 3 ROP
colors; insert accepted; page cutoffs - 22.
Mechanical Specifications: Type page 13 x 21
1/2; E - 5 cols, 2 1/4, 1/8 between; A - 10

cols, 1 1/16, 1/8 between; C - 5 cols, 2 1/4,
1/8 between.
Areas Served: Moncton
Equipment & Software PRESSROOM
EQUIPMENT:Pressroom Lines — G/
Headliner double width; G/Headliner double
width; G/Headliner double width; Pasters
— 6-G/RT-50.; Reels & Stands — G/3:2, G/
Jaw MAILROOM EQUIPMENT:Counter
Stackers — 1/HL, 1-Gammerler/KL 503/1, 3-/
HI, Olympian; Inserters & Stuffers — NP/630,
HI, 26-/Hopper; Bundle Tying Machines — 2-/
MLN, 1-/Dynamic; Wrapping Singles —
3-ARPAC/55 GI; Other Equipment — 1-MM/
Presto. BUSINESS EQUIPMENT:Hardware
— PBS CLASSIFIED EQUIPMENT:Hardware
— 6-Compaq/Prolinea 575; Printers — HP/
LaserJet 4MV CLASSIFIED SOFTWARE:HI/
Cash 5.1. DISPLAY EQUIPMENT:Hardware
— APP/Mac; Printers — Tektronix/Phaser
300, 1-MON/Page Master II DISPLAY
SOFTWARE:Ad Make-Up Applications —
QPS/QuarkXPress 3.3, Multi-Ad/Creator
3.5.2, Adobe/Photoshop 4.0, Adobe/Illustrator
7.0; Layout Software — PBS. EDITORIAL
EQUIPMENT:Hardware — Compaq/2000-30
Deskpro/8-APP/Power Mac, 3-Canon/
Digital Cameras; Printers — HP/LaserJet
4MT, MON/Page Master 600, MON/Proof
Express EDITORIAL SOFTWARE:HI/
NewsMaker Editorial 2.61. PRODUCTION
EQUIPMENT:Hardware — Kk, Solo/Listener;
Cameras — 3-Kk/DC53, 10-Kk/DC50;
Scanners — PixelCraft/7860C, 2-Umax/
Powerlook, 8-Umax/Super Vistor S-12,
2-Polaroid/SprintScan 35 PRODUCTION
SOFTWARE:HI/NewsMaker Pagination 1.6.

SAINT JOHN

NEW BRUNSWICK TELEGRAPH-JOURNAL

210 Crown St., Saint John, NB, E2L 3V8,
Canada; gen tel 1 (506) 632-8888; adv
tel 1 (888) 443-2459; ed tel 1 (506) 632-

8888; gen fax 1 (506) 645-3295; adv fax 1
(506) 645-3295; ed fax 1 (506) 645-3295;
gen/nat adv. e-mail cressman.mark@
brunswicknews.com; disp adv e-mail tobon.
johnl@brunswicknews.com; class adv
e-mailclassified@brunswicknews.com; ed
e-mail TJnewsroom@brunswicknews.com;
web site 1 www.telegraphjournal.com
Published: Mon, Tues, Wed, Thur, Fri, Sat
Weekday Frequency: m
Saturday Frequency: m
Circulation 26,863; 26,863(sat)
Last Audit: Sworn/Estimate/Non-Audited
September 30, 2017
Group: Brunswick News, Inc.
Branch Offices: Saint John, NB
Moncton, NB
Fredericton, NB
Miramichi, NB
Sussex, NB
St. Stephen, NB
Woodstock, NB
Grand Falls, NB
Edmundston, NB
Bathurst, NB
Campbellton, NB
Advertising - Weekday/Saturday: Open inch rate
$3.47 (M-Th); $3.70 (Fri); $3.88 (Sat)
Online Advertising Rates: Rates on request.
News services: Canadian Media Connection, DJ,
LAT-WP, Presslink, SOU. **Established:** 1862
Own Printing Facility?: Y
Commercial Printers?: Y
Special Weekly Sections: Spring Fashions
(Apr); Focus on Education (Aug); Christmas
Greetings (Dec); Brides (Feb); January
Discount (Jan); Travel Guide (Jul); NB Travel
Guide (Jun); Time for Thought (Mar); Auto
Dealer Profiles (May); Remembrance Day
(Nov); Fire Prevention (Oct);
Syndicated Publications: Showtime TV Guide
(Fri); Travel (Sat).
VP & Publisher ....James C. Irving
General Manager .... Kevin Curnock
Sr. Director of Distribution & Logistics .... Sean
Watson

Editor in Chief...........................Wendy Metcalfe
Head of Sales ....Mark Cressman
Director of IT ....Eric Falkjar
Creative Director....................Sylvie Robichaud
Adv. Mgr.............................Michael Horncastle
Editor - Administration ....David Spragg
Bus. Ed. ....David Stonehouse
Editorial Page Ed. ....Eric Mark
Prod. Mgr........................................ James Cole
Market information: ADS; TMC; Zoned editions.
Mechanical available: Letterpress (direct); Black
and 3 ROP colors; insert accepted - product
samples; page cutoffs - 21.
Mechanical Specifications: Type page 11.5 x
21; E - 6 cols, 1/8 between; A - 10 cols, 1
1/16, 1/8 between; C - 10 cols, 1 1/16, 1/8
between.
Delivery Method: Mail, Newsstand, Carrier,
Racks
Equipment & Software BUSINESS
EQUIPMENT:Hardware — 4-Mk/
Compaq Deskpro, Pentium/PC, 2-Sun/
Enterprise 450, 4-Sun/Sparc 5 BUSINESS
SOFTWARE:Microsoft/Office 97,
Telemagic, PBS/Circulation, PBS/Media
Plus CLASSIFIED EQUIPMENT:Hardware
— 2-APP/Mac G3, 6-Compaq/Deskpro
PIII/HP/Laserjet 4, HP/Laserjet 4000,
Lexmark/3200; Printers — Okidata/
OL840 CLASSIFIED SOFTWARE:DTI/
Class Speed 5.01, DTI/PlanBuilder 6.3,
DTI/SpeedPlanner 4.3, Microsoft/Office
97. DISPLAY EQUIPMENT:Hardware
— 22-Compaq/Deskpro PIII, 1-Toshiba/
Laptop; Printers — HP/Laserjet 4, HP/
LaserJet 5000 DISPLAY SOFTWARE:Ad
Make-Up Applications — DTI/ClassSpeed
5.01, Microsoft/Office 97, Telemagic 3.5;
Layout Software — PBS. EDITORIAL
EQUIPMENT:Hardware — 18-APP/Mac G3,
2-APP/Mac G4, 19-Compaq/DeskPro PIII,
3-Toshiba/Laptop PII, 1-Compaq/Laptop PIII,
1-APP/Mac Powerbook/APP/Mac Powermac
7200/180, APP/Mac Powermac 8100/80,
5-Sun/Sparc 5; Printers — HP/Laserjet
4MV, HP/Laserjet 4000, PRODUCTION
EQUIPMENT:Hardware — 8-Caere/

OmniPage, Digital camera card reader; Cameras — Kk/DCS520; Scanners — 2-Epson/Expression 836XL PRODUCTION SOFTWARE:DTI/AdSpeed 4.3, DTI/PageSpeed 4.3, DTI/SpeedPlanner 4.3.

NEWFOUNDLAND

CORNER BROOK

THE WESTERN STAR

106 West St., Corner Brook, NL, A2H 6E7, Canada; gen tel (709) 634-4348; adv tel (709) 637-4652; ed tel (709) 634-4669; gen fax (709) 637-4675; adv fax (709) 637-4675; ed fax (709) 634-9824; gen/nat adv. e-mail advertising@thewesternstar.com; disp adv e-mail advertising@thewesternstar.com; class adv e-mailadvertising@thewesternstar.com; ed e-mail newsroom@thewesternstar.com; web site 1 www.thewesternstar.com
Published: Mon, Tues, Wed, Thur, Fri, Sat
Weekday Frequency: m
Saturday Frequency: m
Circulation 3,382; 3,411(sat)
Last Audit: CCAB October 1, 2017
Group: Transcontinental Media
Newspaper Reps: Cameron Watson - National Sales Dir., Canadian Primedia Sales & Mktg. Inc.
Advertising - Weekday/Saturday: Open inch rate $1.27
Online Advertising Rates: Rates on request.
News services: Aditus. **Established:** 1900
Syndicated Publications: Star Scene (Sat).
Mng. Ed. ....Troy Turner
Bus. Mgr./Accountant ....Gladys Leonard
Editorial Page Ed. ....Ray Sweetapple
Sports Ed. ....David Kearsey
Prodn. Foreman ....Ken Bennett
IT/Prod. Supervisor ....BIll Boland
Sales Mgr. ....Gloria Hunt
Market information: TMC.
Mechanical available: Offset; Black and 1 ROP colors; insert accepted.
Mechanical Specifications: Type page 11 x 21.5; E - 6 cols, 2 1/16, 1/8 between.
Areas Served: Western Newfoundland
Equipment & Software PRESSROOM EQUIPMENT:Pressroom Lines — 8-G/Community Single Width 1980. MAILROOM EQUIPMENT:Bundle Tying Machines — 1/Whig, 1-/Gd; Address Machine — 1-/Am. CLASSIFIED EQUIPMENT:Hardware — HI. EDITORIAL EQUIPMENT:Hardware — HI. PRODUCTION EQUIPMENT:Hardware — 2-COM/Unisetter.

SAINT JOHN'S

THE TELEGRAM

430 Topsail Rd, Saint John's, NL, A1E 4N1, Canada; gen tel (709) 364-6300; adv tel (709) 748-0829; ed tel (709) 364-2323; gen fax (709) 364-9333; adv fax (709) 364-9333; ed fax (709) 364-3939; gen/nat adv. e-mail sales@thetelegram.com; disp adv e-mail sales@thetelegram.com; class adv e-mailclass@thetelegram.com; ed e-mail telegram@thetelegram.com; web site 1 www.thetelegram.com
Published: Mon, Tues, Wed, Thur, Fri, Sat
Weekday Frequency: m
Saturday Frequency: m
Circulation 11,344; 15,825(sat)
Last Audit: CCAB September 30, 2017
Group: Transcontinental Media
Newspaper Reps: Ron Clark - CEO, Canadian Primedia Sales & Mktg. Inc.
Advertising - Weekday/Saturday: Open inch rate $1.53 (M-T); $1.58 (F); $2.01 (Sat)
Online Advertising Rates: Rates on request.
News services: CP, CSM. **Established:** 1879
Digital Platform - Mobile: Apple
Digital Platform - Tablet: Apple iOS
Controller ....Keith Gover

Interim Pub./Adv. Mgr. ....Keith Connolly
Mng. Ed. ....Kerry Hann
Assoc. Ed. ....Pam Frampton
Prod. Mgr. ....Ian Kirby
News Ed. ....Russell Wangersky
Sports Ed. ....Robin Short
Prodn. Mgr., Mailroom ....Don Mackey
Circ. Mgr., Home Delivery Sales .....Dean Jacobs
Digital Dir. ....Gerry Carew
National Adv. Sales ....Joann Chaulk
Multimedia Retail Adv. Mgr. ....Todd Foote
Reader Sales and Mktg. Mgr. ....Leo Gosse
Market information: ADS; Split run; TMC.
Mechanical available: Offset; Black and 3 ROP colors; insert accepted; page cutoffs - 21 1/2.
Mechanical Specifications: Type page 11 x 21 1/2; E - 5 cols, 2 1/6, 1/6 between; A - 10 cols, 1, 1/12 between; C - 10 cols, 1, 1/12 between.
Areas Served: Newfoundland and Labrador

Delivery Method: Mail, Newsstand
Equipment & Software PRESSROOM EQUIPMENT:Pressroom Lines — 7-G/Cosmo (offset) double width. MAILROOM EQUIPMENT:Counter Stackers — 1-Id; Bundle Tying Machines — 2-Gd/Q; Address Machine — 1-Am/6250; Other Equipment — MM/Trimmer. BUSINESS EQUIPMENT:Hardware — HP/9000 BUSINESS SOFTWARE:Microsoft/Windows 95, Microsoft/Office, PBS CLASSIFIED EQUIPMENT:Hardware — 9-APP/Mac 7300/200; Printers — 2-APP/Mac LaserPrinter 360 CLASSIFIED SOFTWARE:Baseview/Class Manager Pro 1.05D2. DISPLAY EQUIPMENT:Hardware — 6-APP/Mac G3; Printers — APP/Mac Personal Laser NT, 1-HP/LaserJet 4MV, Tektronix/Phaser 380, Epson 3000/1-HP/4mv Printer DISPLAY SOFTWARE:Ad Make-Up Applications — QPS/QuarkXPress 4.1, Adobe/Illustrator 8.0, Adobe/Photoshop 5.5, Adobe/Streamline 3.07 EDITORIAL EQUIPMENT:Hardware — 17-APP/Mac Performa 580, 18-APP/Mac G3/1-Umax/1260 Scanner, 1-Polaroid/SprintScan; Printers — 1-APP/Mac LaserPrinter 360, 2-Pre Press/Panther Pro 36 Imagesetters EDITORIAL SOFTWARE:Baseview/NewsEdit Pro IQ 2.05. PRODUCTION EQUIPMENT:Hardware — 1-Nu, 2-APP/Mac G-3; Cameras — 1-Nu/SST 2024 C, ECR/Autokon 1000; Scanners — CD, 2-Nikon/3510 Slide, 1-Nikon/Coolscan, 3-Umax/1260 Flatbed PRODUCTION SOFTWARE:QPS/QuarkXPress 4.0.3, Fifi/Quark Extension.

NOVA SCOTIA

HALIFAX

THE CHRONICLE HERALD

2717 Joseph Howe Dr, Halifax, NS, B3J 2T2, Canada; gen tel (902) 426-2811; adv tel (902) 426-2811; ed tel (902) 426-2811; gen fax (902) 426-1170; adv fax (902) 426-1170; ed fax (902) 426-1158; gen/nat adv. e-mail advertising@herald.ca; disp adv e-mail advertising@herald.ca; class adv e-mailclassified@herald.ca; ed e-mail newsroom@herald.ca; web site 1 www.thechronicleherald.ca
Published: Mon, Tues, Wed, Thur, Fri, Sat, Sun
Weekday Frequency: m
Saturday Frequency: m
Circulation 88,893; 85,246(sat); 97,283(sun)
Last Audit: AAM September 30, 2011
Group: The Chronicle Herald Ltd.
Advertising - Weekday/Saturday: 1/100 p.: $146 (M-F); $160 (Sat)
Online Advertising Rates: Rates on request.
News services: CP, LAT-WP, NYT, Times of London, AP. **Established:** 1875
Own Printing Facility?: Y
Commercial Printers?: Y
Special Editions: Homes Etc. (Other); Comics (Sat).
Special Weekly Sections: Wheels (Thursdays),

Homes (Fridays), Entertainment
Syndicated Publications: Herald Magazine
Digital Platform - Mobile: Apple, Android
Digital Platform - Tablet: Apple iOS, Android
Pub. ...................................G.W. Dennis
Pub./CEO/Vice Pres. ....Sarah Dennis
Dir., Cor. Admin. ....Mary Lou Croft
HR Mgr. ....Theresa Williams
Purchasing ....Ken Jennex
Adv. Mgr., Retail Sales ....Paul Jacquart
Mktg. Mgr. ....Pam Nauss-Redden
Research Analyst/ROP Specialist ....Tracey King
Dir., Dist. and Log. ....Jim LaPierre
Dir., News Admin. ....Terry O'Neil
Dir., News Content ....Dan Leger
Asst. Dir., Design ....John Howitt
Asst. Dir., Newsroom ....Frank De Palma
Assignment Ed., Day ....Brian Ward
Assignment Ed., Night ....Eva Hoare
Books Ed. ....Christine Soucie
Editorial Page Ed. ....Robert Howse
Entertainment Ed. ....Greg Guy
Lifestyle Ed. ....Margaret MacKay
Director of Sales ....Barry Saunders
Vice Pres., Bus. Devel. ....Bruce MacCormack
Sales Dir. ....Nancy Cook
Mgr., Bus. Devel. ....Alex Liot
Ed. ....Claire McIlveen
Senior Mktg. Mgr. ....Jennifer Punch
VP Operations ....Ian Scott
Dir., Mktg. and Prod. Devel. .....Shawn Woodford
Market information: ADS; Split run; TMC; Zoned editions.
Mechanical available: WIPAG OF 370 OFFSET
Mechanical Specifications: 10" X 20"
Areas Served: All of Nova Scotia and parts of New Brunswick and Price Edward Island
Delivery Method: Mail, Newsstand, Carrier, Racks
Equipment & Software PRESSROOM EQUIPMENT:Pressroom Lines — WIFAG OF 370 PCV; Press Drive — SHAFTLESS; Folders — WIFAG 2:5:5; Pasters — WIFAG; Reels & Stands — 5-Wifag/Autopasters; Press Control System — EAE; Press Registration System — Wifag. MAILROOM EQUIPMENT:Counter Stackers — FERAT MTS; Inserters & Stuffers — FERAG MSD; Bundle Tying Machines — MOSCA; Wrapping Singles — 1-K/Pac, 1-K/Pac; Mailroom Control System — FERAG; Address Machine — Addressing mach CLASSIFIED EQUIPMENT:Hardware — Sun/Enterprise 3000, 2-Ultra/Sparc, APP/Mac 8500, APP/Mac 7600; Printers — GCC/Elite CLASSIFIED SOFTWARE:HI/Linopress 4.2. DISPLAY EQUIPMENT:Hardware — Sun/Enterprise 3000, 2-Ultra/Sparc, APP/Mac 8500, APP/Mac 7600; Printers — Asente, HP/2500, 2-AII/3850, 2-AII/NT-Rip DISPLAY SOFTWARE:Ad Make-Up Applications — CCI ADDESIC; Layout Software — SCS LAYOUT 8000 EDITORIAL EQUIPMENT:Hardware — CCI NEWSGATE/2-CD/EPD, In-house News Photo Archive System; Printers — GCC/Elite, 2-AII/NT-Rip, 2-AII/3850 EDITORIAL SOFTWARE:HI/Linopress 4.2, CCI/Newsdesk. PRODUCTION EQUIPMENT:Hardware — AG/3850 CTP Advantage, 2-AII/NT Rip; Scanners — Sharp XJ610, 1-ECR/Autokon 1000, Linotype-Hell/Opal, 2-Polaroid/Sprint Scan, Kk/2035 PRODUCTION SOFTWARE:HI/Linopress 4.2, CCI/Newsdesk.

NEW GLASGOW

THE NEWS

352 E. River Rd., New Glasgow, NS, B2H 5E2, Canada; gen tel (902) 752-3000; adv tel (902) 752-3000; ed tel (902) 752-3000; gen fax (902) 752-1945; adv fax (902) 928-1515; gen/nat adv. e-mail news@ngnews.ca; ed e-mail news@ngnews.ca; web site 1 www.ngnews.ca
Published: Mon, Tues, Wed, Thur, Fri, Sat
Weekday Frequency: m
Saturday Frequency: m
Circulation 4,495; 4,495(sat)
Last Audit: CMCA December 31, 2013
Group: Transcontinental Media
Newspaper Reps: Ron Clark - CEO, Canadian Primedia Sales & Mktg.
Advertising - Weekday/Saturday: 2A: $62.82 (M-

W, Fri, & Sat), $69.11 (Thurs)
Online Advertising Rates: Rates on request.
News services: CP. **Established:** 1911
Own Printing Facility?: Y
Commercial Printers?: N
Special Weekly Sections: Fishing (Apr); Brides (May); Business (Monthly); Car Care (Oct); Cookbook (Sept).
Digital Platform - Mobile: Apple, Android
Digital Platform - Tablet: Apple iOS, Android
Pub. ....Richard Russell
Controller ....Bernadine Hyson
Circ. Dir. ....Paul MacDonald
Ed. ....Dave Glenen
Sales Mgr. ....Inez Forbes
Prod. Mgr. ....Nancy Samson
Market information: ADS; TMC.
Mechanical available: Offset; Black and 3 ROP colors; insert accepted; page cutoffs - 22 3/4.
Mechanical Specifications: Type page 10 1/4 x 14; E - 5 cols, 2 1/8, 1/8 between; A - 10 cols, 1, 1/8 between; C - 8 cols, 1 1/3, 1/8 between.
Areas Served: Pictou County

Delivery Method: Newsstand, Carrier
Equipment & Software MAILROOM EQUIPMENT:Bundle Tying Machines — Gd; Address Machine — Mailrite/Computer. BUSINESS EQUIPMENT:Hardware — IBM/Newzware CLASSIFIED SOFTWARE:Mk. DISPLAY SOFTWARE:Ad Make-Up Applications — Mk. PRODUCTION EQUIPMENT:Cameras — B.

SYDNEY

THE CAPE BRETON POST

255 George St., Sydney, NS, B1P 6K6, Canada; gen tel (902) 564-5451; adv tel (902) 563-3873; ed tel (902) 563-3838; gen fax (902) 562-7077; adv fax (902) 564-6280; ed fax (902) 562-7077; gen/nat adv. e-mail edit@cbpost.com; disp adv e-mail adman@cbpost.com; ed e-mail news@cbpost.com; web site 1 www.capebretonpost.com
Published: Mon, Tues, Wed, Thur, Fri, Sat
Weekday Frequency: m
Saturday Frequency: m
Circulation 13,503; 13,972(sat)
Last Audit: CCAB September 30, 2017
Group: Transcontinental Media
Newspaper Reps: Ron Clark - CEO, Canadian Primedia Sales & Mktg. Inc.
Advertising - Weekday/Saturday: Open inch rate $1.84
Online Advertising Rates: Rates on request.
News services: AP, CP, SOU. **Established:** 1901
Special Weekly Sections: Fishing (Apr); Tourist (Aug); Brides (Feb); Tourist (Jul); Tourist (Jun); Automobile (May); Computers (Nov); Hunting (Oct); Home Improvement (Sept).
Syndicated Publications: Family (Fri); Health (Mon); Style (Sat); Entertainment/Arts (Thur); Food (Tues); Seniors (Wed).
Bus. Mgr. ....Shaw Robinson
Adv. Dir., Serv. ....Robert Edshaw
Adv. Mgr., Classified ....Helen Mccoy
Adv. Mgr. ....Rob EdShaw
Circ. Mgr., Promotional ....Matt Dawson
Mng. Ed. ....Fred Jackson
Editorial Page Ed. ....Doug McGee
News Ed. ....Steve Macinnis
Sports Ed. ....Bob Duchemin
Online Mgr. ....Heather MacKenzie
Prodn. Mgr. ....Paul Bruce
Prodn. Mgr., Pressroom ....Paul King
Ed. Dir. ....Tom Ayers
Pub. ....Anita Delazzer
Dir., Reader Sales and Dist. ....Helen MacCoy
Retail Sales Mgr. ....Scott MacQuarrie
IT/Systems Mgr. ....Vernon O'Quinn
Dir., Sales & Mktg. ....Robert Redshaw
Market information: ADS; TMC.
Mechanical available: Offset; Black and 3 ROP colors; insert accepted - product samples; page cutoffs - 21.
Mechanical Specifications: Type page 10 1/2 x 21 1/2; E - 6 cols, 2 1/4, 3/16 between; A - 10 cols, 1 1/16, 3/16 between; C - 10 cols, 1 1/16, 3/16 between.
Areas Served: Cape Breton Island
Equipment & Software PRESSROOM EQUIPMENT:Pressroom Lines — 8-G/Urbanite; Folders — 1 MAILROOM

EQUIPMENT:Counter Stackers — 1/
MSI; Bundle Tying Machines — 3-Gd/
Constellation; Address Machine — 1-/Am.
BUSINESS EQUIPMENT:Hardware — PC,
Newzware BUSINESS SOFTWARE:Lotus,
Microsoft/Windows 3.1, HP CLASSIFIED
EQUIPMENT:Hardware — APP/Mac
CLASSIFIED SOFTWARE:Baseview/
Class Manager Pro. DISPLAY
EQUIPMENT:Hardware — 4-APP/Power
Mac 8100 DISPLAY SOFTWARE:Ad Make-
Up Applications — Metro/AdCreation Tool
Kit, QPS/QuarkXPress, Adobe/Photoshop,
Adobe/Illustrator; Layout Software — ALS.
EDITORIAL EQUIPMENT:Hardware
— APP/Mac/Polaroid/Slide Scanners,
2-Umax/Scanner; Printers — Xante/1200
dpi EDITORIAL SOFTWARE:Baseview/
NewsEdit IQ, Baseview, QPS/QuarkXPress.
PRODUCTION EQUIPMENT:Hardware —
Pre Press/Panther; Cameras — Nu/18x24;
Scanners — QPS/QuarkXPress with
MetroAd Creation Tool Kit.

TRURO

THE DAILY NEWS
6 Louise St., Truro, NS, B2N 5C3, Canada;
gen tel (902) 893-9405; adv tel (902) 893-
9405; ed tel (902) 893-9405; gen fax (902)
893-0518; adv fax (902) 895-6104; ed fax
(902) 893-0518; gen/nat adv. e-mail news@
trurodaily.com; disp adv e-mail bpearson@
trurodaily.com; ed e-mail cfleming@trurodaily.
com; web site 1 www.trurodaily.com
Published: Mon, Tues, Wed, Thur, Fri, Sat
Weekday Frequency: m
Saturday Frequency: m
Circulation 4,378; 4,378(sat)
Last Audit: CMCA December 31, 2013
Group: Transcontinental Media
Newspaper Reps: Ron Clark - CEO, Canadian

Primedia Sales & Mktg.
Advertising - Weekday/Saturday: 2A: $62.82 (M-
F), $65.63 (Sat)
News services: CP. **Established:** 1891
Own Printing Facility?: Y
Commercial Printers?: N
Special Weekly Sections: Automotive (Fall); Stay
& Play (Jul); Stay & Play (Jun); Industrial
(Mar); Brides (May); Fashion (Spring);
Outdoors (Summer); Energy (Winter).
Digital Platform - Mobile: Apple, Android
Digital Platform - Tablet: Apple iOS, Android
Pub. ....Richard Russell
Office Mgr. ....Bernadine Hyson
Adv. Mgr. ....Bruce Pearson
Circ. Mgr. ....Paul MacDonald
Mng. Ed. ....Dave Glennen
Assignment Ed. ....Frank Cassidy
Prodn. Mgr. ....Dave Conrad
Newsroom Mgr. ....Sherry Martell
Market information: ADS; TMC; Zoned editions.
Mechanical available: Offset; Black and 3 ROP
colors; insert accepted - packaging, booklets,
samples; page cutoffs - 22 3/4.
Mechanical Specifications: Type page 10 1/4 x
14; E - 5 cols, 2 1/4, 1/16 between; A - 10
cols, 2 1/5, 1/16 between; C - 8 cols, 1 1/3,
1/16 between.
Delivery Method: Newsstand, Carrier
Equipment & Software MAILROOM
EQUIPMENT:Bundle Tying Machines
— 1-Gd/Oval Strapper. BUSINESS
EQUIPMENT:Hardware — Dell BUSINESS
SOFTWARE:PBS CLASSIFIED
EQUIPMENT:Hardware — Mac; Printers
— assorted CLASSIFIED SOFTWARE:Mk.
EDITORIAL EQUIPMENT:Hardware — Mac
EDITORIAL SOFTWARE:Mk. PRODUCTION
EQUIPMENT:Hardware — Mac

ONTARIO

BARRIE

THE BARRIE EXAMINER
571 Bayfield St., Barrie, ON, L4M 4Z9,
Canada; gen tel (705) 726-6537; adv tel
(705)726-6537 ext. 513358; ed tel (705)
726-6537 ext. 513245; gen fax (705)
726-7706; adv fax (705) 726-5414; ed
fax (705) 725-7717; gen/nat adv. e-mail
jhammill@postmedia.com; disp adv e-mail
jhammill@postmedia.com; class adv
e-mailthebarrieexaminer.classifieds@
sunmedia.ca; ed e-mail ntaylor@postmedia.
com; web site 1 www.thebarrieexaminer.com
Published: Mon, Tues, Wed, Thur, Fri, Sat
Weekday Frequency: m
Saturday Frequency: m
Circulation 4,602; 4,700(sat)
Last Audit: BPA December 30, 2010
Group: Postmedia Network Inc.
Quebecor Communications, Inc.
Newspaper Reps: Susan Courtney - VP, QMI
Corporate Sales Office
Advertising - Weekday/Saturday: Open inch rate
$1.33
News services: CP. **Established:** 1864
Ed. ....Brain Rodnick
Retail Sales Rep. ....Michelle Kennedy
Circ. Mgr. ....Scott Murphy
Mng. Ed. ....Mike Beaudin
Pub. and GM. ....Sandy Davies
Dist. Mgr. ....April McLean
News Ed. ....Brian Rodnick
Market information: Split run; TMC; Zoned
editions.
Mechanical available: Offset; Black and 3 ROP

colors; insert accepted; page cutoffs - 21 1/2.
Mechanical Specifications: Type page 11.5 x
20.5; E - 6 cols, 2 1/16, 1/8 between; A - 6
cols, 2 1/16, 1/8 between; C - 9 cols, 1 1/3,
1/8 between.
Equipment & Software EDITORIAL
EQUIPMENT:; Printers — 3-TTS.
PRODUCTION EQUIPMENT:Hardware
— 7-L.

BELLEVILLE

INTELLIGENCER
199 Front St. Ste 535, Belleville, ON, K8N
5H5, Canada; gen tel (613) 962-9171; adv
tel (613) 962-9171; ed tel (613) 962-9171;
gen fax (613) 962-9652; adv fax (613) 962-
9652; ed fax (613) 962-9652; gen/nat adv.
e-mail gerry.drage@sunmedia.ca; disp adv
e-mail gerry.drage@sunmedia.ca; class adv
e-mailintelligencer.classifieds@sunmedia.ca;
ed e-mail brice.mcvicar@sunmedia.ca; web
site 1 www.intelligencer.ca
Published: Mon, Tues, Wed, Thur, Fri, Sat
Weekday Frequency: e
Saturday Frequency: m
Circulation 5,907; 5,946(sat)
Last Audit: CCAB September 30, 2015
Group: Quebecor Communications, Inc.
Postmedia Network Inc.
Advertising - Weekday/Saturday: Open inch rate
$1.63
Online Advertising Rates: Tile: $249
News services: CP, AP. **Established:** 1870
Syndicated Publications: Prime Time-Seniors
(Mon); Dressing Up (Thur); Pulse (Tues);
Cookin' (Wed).
Digital Platform - Mobile: Apple, Android
Digital Platform - Tablet: Apple iOS, Android
Pres. ....John Knowles
Mng. Ed. ....Bill Glisky
Adv. Dir. ....Lisa Grills

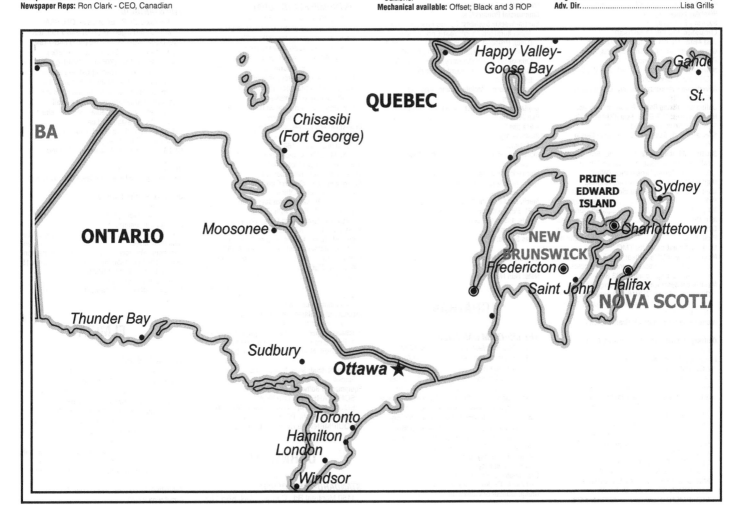

Circ. Mgr. .... Tim Devine
City Ed. .... Christopher Malette
Lifestyles Ed. .... Linda O'Connor
Sports Ed. .... Ady Vos
Dist. Mgr. .... Jason Hawley
Market information: ADS; TMC.
Mechanical available: Offset; Black and 3 ROP colors; insert accepted; page cutoffs - 21 1/2.
Mechanical Specifications: Type page 11.5 x 20 1/2; E - 6 cols, 2 1/16, 1/8 between; A - 6 cols, 2 1/16, 1/8 between; C - 9 cols, 1 1/4, between.
Areas Served: Belleville, Ontario

Delivery Method: Mail, Newsstand, Carrier, Racks
Equipment & Software PRESSROOM EQUIPMENT:Pressroom Lines — 7-G/ Urbanite. MAILROOM EQUIPMENT:Bundle Tying Machines — 2/Gd; Address Machine — 2-/Am. BUSINESS EQUIPMENT:Hardware — ATT CLASSIFIED EQUIPMENT:Hardware — CText, 6-COM, Baseview. EDITORIAL EQUIPMENT:Hardware — CText, CD/ EPD, ECR/Autokon Graphic System/ Nikon/Color Scanners. PRODUCTION EQUIPMENT:Hardware — 2-COM.

BRANTFORD

BRANDTFORD EXPOSITOR

195 Henry St. Bld 4, Unit 1, Brantford, ON, N3S 5C9, Canada; gen tel (519) 756-2020; adv tel (519) 756-2020; ed tel (519) 756-2020; gen fax (519) 756-3285; adv fax (519) 756-3285; ed fax (519) 756-3285; gen/nat adv. e-mail adam.giles@sunmedia.ca; disp adv e-mail adam.giles@sunmedia.ca; class adv e-mailbrandtfordexpositor.classifieds@sunmedia.ca; ed e-mail knovak@postmedia.com; web site 1 www.brantfordexpositor.ca
Published: Mon, Tues, Wed, Thur, Fri, Sat
Weekday Frequency: m
Saturday Frequency: m
Circulation 11,288; 11,567(sat)
Last Audit: CCAB September 30, 2015
Group: Quebecor Communications, Inc. Postmedia Network Inc.
Newspaper Reps: Susan Courtney - VP, QMI Corporate Sales Office
Advertising - Weekday/Saturday: Open inch rate $1.62
Online Advertising Rates: Rates on request.
News services: CP, SOU. **Established:** 1852
Special Editions: Weekender (Sat).
Special Weekly Sections: Community Guide (Other).
Syndicated Publications: TV Times (Fri); Sports (Mon); Comics (Sat); Showcase (Thur); Midweek (Tues); Crossroads (Wed).
Digital Platform - Mobile: Apple, Android
Digital Platform - Tablet: Apple iOS, Android
Pub .... Ken Koyama
Mng. Ed. .... Jeff Dertinger
Adv. Dir. .... Adam Giles
Circ. Dir. .... Andrea Foster
Prod. Mgr. .... Kyle Butler
Market information: ADS; TMC.
Mechanical available: Offset; Black and 3 ROP colors; insert accepted - product samples, catalogues; page cutoffs - 23 3/8.
Mechanical Specifications: Type page 11 1/2 x 22 1/2; E - 5 cols, 2 3/16, 1/6 between; A - 10 cols, 1 1/16, 1/12 between; C - 8 cols, 1 3/8, 1/12 between.
Areas Served: Brantford & Brant County

Delivery Method: Mail, Newsstand, Carrier, Racks
Equipment & Software PRESSROOM EQUIPMENT:Pressroom Lines — 8-G/ Metro 3183 double width (3 half decks); 8-G/ Metro 3184 double width (3 half decks); 8-G/Metro 3185 double width (3 half decks); Folders — 4-G/3:2. MAILROOM EQUIPMENT:Inserters & Stuffers — Manual; Mailroom Control System — HL/Dock console; Other Equipment — Rolmaster/Conveyor System. BUSINESS EQUIPMENT:Hardware — DEC/9200, PC CLASSIFIED EQUIPMENT:Hardware — APP/Mac G3; Printers — APP/ Mac LaserWriter II NTX CLASSIFIED SOFTWARE:Baseview. DISPLAY EQUIPMENT:Hardware — APP/Mac G3, APP/Mac G4; Printers — 3-APP/Mac LaserWriter II NTX, QMS/860 600dpi laser/ Nikon/35mm Scanner, 1-Umax/1200 DPI Scanner, 3-Umax/600 DPI Scan DISPLAY SOFTWARE:Ad Make-Up Applications — QPS/QuarkXPress 3.31, Aldus/Freehand 5.0, Adobe/Photoshop 3.01 EDITORIAL EQUIPMENT:Hardware — APP/Mac G3, APP/Mac G4/Umax/600 DPI Scanner; Printers — ECR/PelBox Imagesetter EDITORIAL SOFTWARE:QPS/QuarkXPress. PRODUCTION EQUIPMENT:Hardware — Calera/Wordscan, APP/Mac G3; Scanners — APP/Mac G3, Nikon, Umax PRODUCTION SOFTWARE:SCG/Ad Trac System, SCS/ Linx, QPS/QuarkXPress 3.31.

BROCKVILLE

THE BROCKVILLE RECORDER AND TIMES

2479 Parkedale Ave., Brockville, ON, K6V 3H2, Canada; gen tel (613) 342-4441; adv tel (613)342-4441 ext. 500251; ed tel (613) 342-4441 ext. 500107; gen fax (613) 342-4456; adv fax (613) 342-4542; ed fax (613) 342-4542; gen/nat adv. e-mail jeff.lawson@sunmedia.ca; disp adv e-mail jeff.lawson@sunmedia.ca; class adv e-mailrecorder.classifieds@sunmedia.ca; ed e-mail dgordanier@postmedia.com; web site 1 www.recorder.ca
Published: Mon, Tues, Wed, Thur, Fri
Weekday Frequency: e
Saturday Frequency: m
Circulation 9,615
Last Audit: CMCA December 31, 2013
Group: Postmedia Network Inc. Quebecor Communications, Inc.
Advertising - Weekday/Saturday: Open inch rate $1.50
News services: CP, AP, RN. **Established:** 1821
Own Printing Facility?: N
Commercial Printers?: N
Special Weekly Sections: Spring Fashion (Apr); Agricultural tab (Aug); Year-End Review (Dec); Prescott Fashion (Jan); Who's Who 1 (Jul); Spring Car Care (Mar); Boating (May); Ottawa Senators (Monthly); Christmas Gift Guide 1 (Nov); **Syndicated Publications:** Real Estate (Fri)
Digital Platform - Mobile: Apple, Android, Windows
Digital Platform - Tablet: Apple iOS, Android
Pub./Adv. Dir. .... Jeff Lawson
Managing Ed. .... Derek Gordanier
Business Mgr. .... Lori Abrams
Dist. Mgr. .... Lesley Longchamps
Market information: Split run; TMC; Zoned editions.
Mechanical available: Offset; Black and 3 ROP colors; insert accepted - up to 13 1/2 x 11 1/2; page cutoffs - 22 3/8.
Mechanical Specifications: Type page 11 1/2 x 21 3/8; E - 6 cols, 1 3/4, 1/8 between; A - 6 cols, 1 3/4, 1/8 between; C - 6 cols, 1 3/4, 1/8 between.
Areas Served: Brockville

Delivery Method: Mail, Newsstand, Carrier, Racks
Note: Sun News TV

CHATHAM

THE CHATHAM DAILY NEWS

138 King St. West, Chatham, ON, N7M 1E3, Canada; gen tel (519) 354-2000; adv tel (519) 354-2000; ed tel (519) 354-2000; gen fax (519) 354-3448; adv fax (519) 354-3448; ed fax (519) 354-3448; gen/nat adv. e-mail arodrigues@postmedia.com; disp adv e-mail arodrigues@postmedia.com; class adv e-mailchathamdailynews.classifieds@sunmedia.ca; ed e-mail pepp@postmedia.com; web site 1 www.chathamdailynews.ca
Published: Mon, Tues, Wed, Thur, Fri, Sat
Weekday Frequency: e
Saturday Frequency: m
Circulation 4,658; 4,724(sat)
Last Audit: CCAB September 30, 2015
Group: Quebecor Communications, Inc. Postmedia Network Inc.
Newspaper Reps: Susan Courtney - VP QMI Corporate Sales Office
Advertising - Weekday/Saturday: Open inch rate $0.99 (M-Sat)
Online Advertising Rates: Rates on request.
News services: QMI Reuters **Established:** 1865
Own Printing Facility?: N
Special Editions: Home Hunting Guide (Mon).
Digital Platform - Mobile: Apple, Android
Digital Platform - Tablet: Apple iOS, Android
Pub./Adv. Mgr. .... Dean Muharrem
Mng. Ed. .... Rod Hilts
Market information: ADS; TMC.
Mechanical available: Offset; Black and 3 ROP colors; insert accepted - single sheet, stitched or inserted; page cutoffs - 22 3/4.
Mechanical Specifications: Type page 11 1/2 x 20 1/2; E - 5 cols, 2 1/4, 1/8 between; A - 10 cols, 1 1/8, 1/8 between; C - 6 cols, 1 1/4, 1/8 between.
Areas Served: Chatham-Kent

Delivery Method: Mail, Newsstand, Carrier, Racks
Equipment & Software PRESSROOM EQUIPMENT:Pressroom Lines — 7-G/ Urbanite. MAILROOM EQUIPMENT:Bundle Tying Machines — 1/Gd, 1-/WT; Address Machine — 1-/El. CLASSIFIED EQUIPMENT:Hardware — 1-Hx/ HS43, 3-Hx, Baseview. DISPLAY EQUIPMENT:Hardware — APP/Mac. EDITORIAL EQUIPMENT:Hardware — 2-Hx/HS43, 1-DEC/PDP 11-04, APP/Mac EDITORIAL SOFTWARE:Hx. PRODUCTION EQUIPMENT:Hardware — 1-Nat, APP/Mac System, L2R/1800 HT; Cameras — 1-B; Scanners — 2-Hx.

COBOURG

NORTHUMBERLAND TODAY

99 King St. West, Cobourg, ON, K9A 4L1, Canada; gen tel (905) 372-0131; adv tel (905) 372-0131; ed tel (905) 372-0131; gen fax (905) 372-4966; adv fax (905) 372-4966; ed fax (905) 372-4966; gen/nat adv. e-mail michael.everson@sunmedia.ca; disp adv e-mail michael.everson@sunmedia.ca; class adv e-mailnorthumberlandtoday.classifieds@sunmedia.ca; ed e-mail sharielynn.fleming@sunmedia.ca; web site 1 www.northumberlandtoday.com
Published: Mon, Tues, Wed, Thur, Fri
Weekday Frequency: e
Circulation 3,168; 3,168(sat)
Last Audit: CMCA December 31, 2013
Group: Postmedia Network Inc. Quebecor Communications, Inc.
Newspaper Reps: Susan Courtney - VP, QMI Corporate Sales Office
Advertising - Weekday/Saturday: Open inch rate $0.92 (M,-W, Fri); $1.28 (Th)
Online Advertising Rates: Rates on request.
News services: SOU. **Established:** 1843
Digital Platform - Mobile: Apple, Android
Digital Platform - Tablet: Apple iOS, Android
Pub./Adv. Dir. .... Mark Holmes
Class. Adv. Mgr. .... Julie Hall
Mng. Ed. .... Sharrie Lynn Fleming
Ed .... Jeff Gard
Pub .... Darren Murphy
Market information: TMC.
Mechanical available: Offset; Black and 3 ROP colors; insert accepted.
Mechanical Specifications: Type page 11 1/2 x 20 1/2; E - 6 cols, 2 1/16, 1/8 between.
Areas Served: Northumberland County

Delivery Method: Mail, Newsstand, Carrier, Racks
Equipment & Software CLASSIFIED SOFTWARE:Mk. EDITORIAL EQUIPMENT:Hardware — Mk EDITORIAL SOFTWARE:Mk. PRODUCTION EQUIPMENT:Hardware — LE/Processor, Ik.

CORNWALL

STANDARD-FREEHOLDER

1150 Montreal Rd., Cornwall, ON, K6H 1E2, Canada; gen tel (613) 933-3160; adv tel (613) 933-3160; ed tel (613) 933-3160; gen/nat adv. e-mail ksammon@postmedia.com; disp adv e-mail ksammon@postmedia.com; class adv e-mailcsf.classifieds@sunmedia.ca; ed e-mail hrodrigues@postmedia.com; web site 1 www.standard-freeholder.com
Published: Mon, Tues, Wed, Thur, Fri, Sat
Weekday Frequency: m
Saturday Frequency: m
Circulation 5,000; 5,000(sat)
Last Audit: Sworn/Estimate/Non-Audited September 30, 2017
Group: Postmedia Network Inc.
Online Advertising Rates: Rates on request.
News services: CP, AP. **Established:** 1941
Own Printing Facility?: N
Commercial Printers?: N
Special Weekly Sections: Home & Garden (Apr); Brides (Feb); Progress (Mar); Car Care (Oct).
Digital Platform - Mobile: Apple, Android, Windows
Digital Platform - Tablet: Apple iOS, Android
Market information: Split run; TMC; Zoned editions.
Mechanical available: Offset; Black and 3 ROP colors; insert accepted - 36 pages max.; page cutoffs - 22 3/4.
Mechanical Specifications: Type page 11 1/2 x 20 1/2; E - 6 cols, 2 1/16, 1/8 between; A - 6 cols, 2 1/16, 1/8 between; C - 9 cols, 1 1/3, 1/8 between.
Areas Served: City of Cornwall, S,D&G and Akwesasne

Delivery Method: Mail, Newsstand, Carrier, Racks
Equipment & Software CLASSIFIED SOFTWARE:HI.

ELLIOT LAKE

THE STANDARD

14 Hillside Dr. S., Elliot Lake, ON, P5A 1M6, Canada; gen tel (705) 848-7195; adv tel (705) 848-7195; ed tel (705) 848-7195; gen fax (705) 848-0249; adv fax (866) 485-8461; ed fax (705) 848-0249; gen/nat adv. e-mail kjohansen@postmedia.com; disp adv e-mail kjohansen@postmedia.com; class adv e-maillelliotlakestandard.classifieds@sunmedia.ca; ed e-mail kmcsheffrey@postmedia.com; web site 1 www.elliotlakestandard.ca
Published: Mon, Tues, Wed, Thur, Fri, Sat
Circulation 2,743; 2,743(sat)
Last Audit: Sworn/Estimate/Non-Audited September 30, 2017
Group: Postmedia Network Inc.
Advertising - Weekday/Saturday: Open inch rate $9.80
Online Advertising Rates: $20/m
News services: 1957
Own Printing Facility?: Y
Commercial Printers?: Y
Man. Ed. .... Kevin McSheffrey
General Manager .... Karsten Johansen
Circulation Manager .... Lolene Patterson
Mechanical Specifications: Type page 10 1/4 x 15 E - 9 cols, 1" wide. 1/8" between
Areas Served: P5A 1M6
Delivery Method: Mail, Newsstand, Carrier, Racks

ELMIRA

THE OBSERVER

20-B Arthur St. N, Elmira, ON, N3B 1Z9, Canada; gen tel (519) 669-5790; adv tel (519) 669-5790 ext. 104; ed tel (519) 669-5790 ext. 103; gen fax (519) 669-5753; adv fax (519) 669-5753; ed fax (519) 669-5753; gen/nat adv. e-mail info@woolwichobserver.com; disp adv e-mail ads@woolwichobserver.com; class adv e-mailads@woolwichobserver.com; ed e-mail editor@woolwichobserver.com; web site 1 www.Observerxtra.com - 70,000(views) 15,000(visitors)
Published: Mon, Tues, Wed, Thur, Fri, Sat
Circulation 8,070

Last Audit: CMCA September 30, 2017
Group: Cathedral Communications Inc.
Newspaper Reps: Joe Merlihan - Publisher
Donna Rudy - Sales Manager
Steve Kannon - Editor
Pat Merlihan - Production Manager
Advertising - Weekday/Saturday: $1.05 per agate line
Advertising - Sunday: $1.05
News services: 1996
Own Printing Facility?: N
Commercial Printers?: Y
Pub. Joe Merlihan
Ed. Steve Kannon
Adv. Mgr. Donna Rudy
Areas Served: Township of Woolwich, Township of Wellesley, Waterloo
Delivery Method: Mail, Carrier, Racks

FORT FRANCES

FORT FRANCES DAILY TIMES

116 First St. E., Fort Frances, ON, P9A 3M7, Canada; gen tel (807) 274-5373; adv tel (807) 274-5373; ed tel (807) 274-5373; gen fax (807) 274-7286; adv fax (807) 274-7286; ed fax (807) 274-7286; gen/nat adv. e-mail jpierce@fortfrances.com; disp adv e-mail jpierce@fortfrances.com; class adv e-mailads@fortfrances.com; ed e-mail mbehan@fortfrances.com; web site 1 www.fftimes.com
Published: Mon, Tues, Thur, Fri
Weekday Frequency: e
Circulation 2,500
Last Audit: Sworn/Estimate/Non-Audited September 30, 2017
Group: Fort Frances Times Ltd.
Advertising - Weekday/Saturday: Open inch rate $1.18
Online Advertising Rates: Top Header Banner $199/month; Large Box $199/month; Skyscraper $149/month
News services: CP. **Established:** 1930
Special Weekly Sections: Farm Agriculture (Apr); B.A.S.S. Tournament (Jul); Fun in the Sun (Jun); Outdoor Living (May); Christmas Shopping (Nov); Farm Agriculture (Oct).
Syndicated Publications: Food Recipe (Thur).
Pub. James R. Cumming
Adv. Mgr. Debbie Ballard
Circ. Mgr. Pam Munn
Ed. Michael Behan
Online Mgr. Corey Westover
Prodn. Mgr. Don Cumming
Adv. Mgr. Debbie Logan
Market information: ADS; TMC.
Mechanical available: Offset; Black and 3 ROP colors; insert accepted; page cutoffs - 16.
Mechanical Specifications: Type page 10 1/4 x 15; E - 5 cols, 2 1/16, 1/8 between; A - 5 cols, 2 1/16, 1/8 between; C - 5 cols, 2 1/16, 1/8 between.
Areas Served: Fort Frances
Delivery Method: Mail
Equipment & Software PRESSROOM EQUIPMENT:Pressroom Lines — 4-HI/Cotrell V-15AB. MAILROOM EQUIPMENT:Counter Stackers — 1-BG/Count-O-Veyor; Bundle Tying Machines — 1/Bu; Address Machine — 1-/Am, 1-/Gp. BUSINESS EQUIPMENT:Hardware — 2-IBM, APP/Mac CLASSIFIED EQUIPMENT:Hardware — APP/Mac CLASSIFIED SOFTWARE:Baseview/Class Manager. DISPLAY EQUIPMENT:Hardware — APP/Mac DISPLAY SOFTWARE:Ad Make-Up Applications — Baseview/Ad Manager Pro; Layout Software — APP/Mac. EDITORIAL EQUIPMENT:Hardware — APP/Mac; Printers — Xante, V, Screen/3050, Imagesetters. PRODUCTION EQUIPMENT:Hardware — XD/Copy GS Plus; Cameras — 1-DS/CD240, DAI; Scanners — XD/Copy GS Plus, 1-Datacopy/GS Plus, HEL/Sapphire Scanner with Line Color Software PRODUCTION SOFTWARE:QPS.

GUELPH

THE GUELPH MERCURY TRIBUNE

367 Woodland Road, Unit 1, Guelph, ON, N1H 7K9, Canada; gen tel (519) 822-4310; adv tel (519) 823-6010; ed tel (519) 823-6060; gen fax (519) 767-1681; adv fax (519) 822-4272; ed fax (519) 767-1681; gen/nat adv. e-mail hdunbar@guelphmercurytribune.com; disp adv e-mail hdunbar@guelphmercurytribune.com; class adv e-mailclassifieds@metroland.com; ed e-mail editor@guelphmercurytribune.com; web site 1 www.guelphmercury.com
Published: Mon, Tues, Wed, Thur, Fri, Sat
Weekday Frequency: e
Saturday Frequency: m
Circulation 8,410; 8,932(sat)
Last Audit: CCAB December 31, 2013
Group: Metroland Media Group Ltd.
Newspaper Reps: Thibaud Wallaert - GM, Dicomm Media
Branch Offices: Toronto, ON
Advertising - Weekday/Saturday: 100,000: $1.59
Online Advertising Rates: Rates on request.
News services: CP. **Established:** 1854
Digital Platform - Mobile: Apple, Android, Windows, Blackberry
Mng. Ed. Phil Andrews
Circ. Mgr. Peter Hill
Prodn. Mgr. Daryl Warner
Prodn. Foreman, Mailroom Steven Cowley
Adv. Dir./Gen. Mgr. C David Kruse
Pub. Paul McCuaig
Market information: Split run; TMC.
Mechanical available: Offset; Black and 3 ROP colors; insert accepted; page cutoffs - 22 3/4.
Mechanical Specifications: Type page 10 1/2 x 21.1400; E - 6 cols, 2 1/16, 1/8 between; A - 6 cols, 2 1/16, 1/8 between; C - 9 cols, 1 1/3, 1/8 between.
Areas Served: Guelph & Wellington Counties

Delivery Method: Mail, Newsstand, Carrier
Equipment & Software PRESSROOM EQUIPMENT:Pressroom Lines — 7-G; Folders — 1 MAILROOM EQUIPMENT:Bundle Tying Machines — 1/Gd; Address Machine — 1-/Am. BUSINESS EQUIPMENT:Hardware — ATT CLASSIFIED EQUIPMENT:Hardware — 4-HAS. EDITORIAL EQUIPMENT:Hardware — HAS, HI. PRODUCTION EQUIPMENT:Hardware — 1-Nu; Cameras — 1-B, 1-Nu.

HAMILTON

THE HAMILTON SPECTATOR

44 Frid St., Hamilton, ON, L8N 3G3, Canada; gen tel (905) 526-3333; adv tel (905) 526-3438; ed tel (905) 526-3420; gen fax (905) 526-1696; adv fax (905) 522-1696; ed fax (905) 526-1395; gen/nat adv. e-mail sazzopardi@thespec.com; disp adv e-mail sazzopardi@thespec.com; class adv e-mailclassifieds@metroland.com; ed e-mail letters@thespec.com; web site 1 www.thespec.com - 6,200,000(views) 813,000(visitors)
Published: Mon, Tues, Wed, Thur, Fri, Sat
Weekday Frequency: m
Saturday Frequency: m
Circulation 64,755; 68,850(sat)
Last Audit: CCAB September 30, 2017
Group: Metroland Media
Metroland Media Group Ltd.
Newspaper Reps: Thibaud Wallaert - GM, Discomm Media
Branch Offices: Toronto, ON
Advertising - Weekday/Saturday: Open inch rate $7.29 (Mon-Fri); $8.62(Sat)
Online Advertising Rates: Rates on request.
News services: CP, UPI, LAT-WP, AP. **Established:** 1846
Special Weekly Sections: Auction Advantage (Apr); Talent Show (Aug); Christmas Gift Guide 3 (Dec); Career Pathways (Feb); Personal Finance (Jan); Reader's Choice (Jul); Golf Shoot-Out (Jun); Travel Ontario (Mar); Minor Sports (May); Christmas Gift Guide 1 (Nov); Fall Car Care (Oc
Syndicated Publications: Fashion (Fri); Spectator TV (Sat); Home & Garden (Thur); Car & Trucks (Tues); Food (Wed).
Digital Platform - Mobile: Apple, Android, Windows, Blackberry
Pub. Neil Oliver
Ed. in Chief Paul Berton
Vice Pres., Bus. Admin. Derek Fleming
Dir., HR Jamie Poehlman
Dir. of Digital Susan Azzopardl
Adv. Vice Pres. Kelly Montague
Director of Operations Bill Repath
Adv. Mgr., Retail Sales Pauline Lewis
Adv. Mgr., Class. Cathryn Easterbrook
Circ. Mgr., Home Delivery Cathy Burse
Jackie Dekar
Dist. Mgr. Patricia Allen
VP, Circ. & Mktg. Gary Myers
VP Prod Dean Zavarise
Market information: ADS; Split run; TMC.
Mechanical available: Offset; Black and 3 ROP colors; insert accepted - min. 50lbs. bookstack single sheet, max.3/8 thick; page cutoffs - 23 9/16.
Mechanical Specifications: Type page 10 1/2 x 21.9290; E - 6 cols, 2 1/16, 1/8 between; A - 10 cols, 1 1/16, 1/12 between; C - 10 cols, 1 1/16, 1/12 between.
Areas Served: Hamilton, Burlington, Stoney Creek, Dundas, Ancaster, Grimsby, Flamborough, Glanbrook & Surrounding areas
Delivery Method: Mail, Newsstand, Carrier
Equipment & Software PRESSROOM EQUIPMENT:Pressroom Lines — 8-G/Metro 3183 double width (3 half decks) 1976; 8-G/Metro 3184 double width (3 half decks) 1976; 8-G/Metro 3185 double width (3 half decks) 1976; Press Drive — Fin; Folders — 4-G/3:2. MAILROOM EQUIPMENT:Counter Stackers — 2-HL/HT2, 4-QWI/Hall, 3-QWI/Sport, 2-QWI/Sport 2; Inserters & Stuffers — 4-GMA/SLS 1000 8:1, Fg/Gripper, HI (on-line); Bundle Tying Machines — 2/Power Strap/PSN5, 4-/Power Strap/PSN6, 2-Newstyer/2000, 4-Dynaric/NP3; Wrapping Singles — Wrapping singles BUSINESS EQUIPMENT:Hardware — 2-DEC/VAX 6220 CLASSIFIED EQUIPMENT:Hardware — Cybergraphics, DEC/VAX 4000, PCs CLASSIFIED SOFTWARE:Cybergraphics, HI/PLS. DISPLAY EQUIPMENT:Hardware — HI/8900, APP/Mac Quadra 700, APP/Mac Quadra 950, Microtek/Scanners, APP/Mac IIsi, Abaton/Scan 300-85; Printers — HP/Laserwriter II DISPLAY SOFTWARE:Ad Make-Up Applications — HI/Layout, QPS/QuarkXPress, Multi-Ad/Creator, Aldus/Freehand, Adobe/Photoshop, Ofoto, Broderbund/Type EDITORIAL EQUIPMENT:Hardware — APP/Mac/APP/Mac Graphics System EDITORIAL SOFTWARE:QPS 1.12. PRODUCTION EQUIPMENT:Hardware — 2-AU/3850, 1-Au/108-C, III/Automatic with KFM Vision Bender; Cameras — 1-C/1211, 1-C/1270; Scanners — 1-ECR, 1-PixelCraft, 1-Kk, 1-Epson PRODUCTION SOFTWARE:QPS/QuarkXPress 3.3, Adobe/Photoshop.

KENORA

KENORA DAILY MINER & NEWS

33 Main St. S., Kenora, ON, P9N 3X7, Canada; gen tel (807) 468-5555; adv tel (807) 468-5555 ext. 226; ed tel (807)468-5555 ext. 243; gen fax (807) 468-4318; adv fax (807)468-4318; ed fax (807)468-4318; gen/nat adv. e-mail candice.withers@sunmedia.ca; disp adv e-mail candice.withers@sunmedia.ca; class adv e-mailkenora.classifieds@sunmedia.ca; ed e-mail lloyd.mack@sunmedia.ca; web site 1 www.kenoradailyminerandnews.com
Published: Mon, Tues, Wed, Fri
Weekday Frequency: m
Circulation 2,700
Last Audit: Sworn/Estimate/Non-Audited September 30, 2017
Group: Postmedia Network Inc.
Quebecor
Newspaper Reps: Susan Courtney - VP, QMI Coporate Sales
Advertising - Weekday/Saturday: Open line rate $0.86
Online Advertising Rates: Rates on request
News services: 1881
Own Printing Facility?: Y
Commercial Printers?: Y
Ed. Lloyd Mack
Circ. Mgr. Alicia McLeod
Pub. Daria Zmiyiwsky
Mechanical Specifications: 10.3330 x 11.4290 inches
10 col x 160 lines
Areas Served: P9N 3X7
Delivery Method: Mail, Newsstand, Carrier, Racks

KINGSTON

THE KINGSTON WHIG-STANDARD

6 Cataraqui St., Kingston, ON, K7L 4Z7, Canada; gen tel (613) 544-5000; adv tel (613) 544-5000; ed tel (613) 544-5000; gen fax (613) 530-4122; adv fax (613) 530-4121 (Class); ed fax (613) 530-4122; gen/nat adv. e-mail aalmeida@postmedia.com; disp adv e-mail aalmeida@postmedia.com; class adv e-mailthewhig.classifieds@sunmedia.ca; ed e-mail steve.serviss@sunmedia.ca; web site 1 www.thewhig.com
Published: Mon, Tues, Wed, Thur, Fri, Sat
Weekday Frequency: m
Saturday Frequency: m
Circulation 14,419; 15,911(sat)
Last Audit: CCAB September 30, 2015
Group: Quebecor Communications, Inc.
Postmedia Network Inc.
Newspaper Reps: Susan Courtney - VP, QMI Corporate Sales
Advertising - Weekday/Saturday: Open inch rate $1.68 (M-F); $1.93 (Sat)
Online Advertising Rates: Rates on request.
News services: CP, AP, SOU. **Established:** 1834
Special Weekly Sections: Home & Garden (Apr); Back to School (Aug); Baby of the Year (Dec); Brides (Feb); Managing Your Money (Jan); Dining Guide (Jul); Vacation Guide (May); Mutual Funds (Monthly); Christmas (Nov); Women in Business (Oct); Fall Activity Guide (Sept).
Syndicated Publications: Entertainment (Fri); Fashion (Mon); Companion/Travel (Sat); Entertainment (Thur); Health (Tues); Food (Wed).
Digital Platform - Mobile: Apple, Android
Digital Platform - Tablet: Apple iOS, Android
Pub./Adv. Dir. Liza Nelson
Ntn'l Sales Mike Healey
Mng. Ed. Derek Shelly
Prod. Mgr. Sean Daly
Ed. Mike Beaudin
Regional Dir., Circ. & Dist. Jeff Lundy
Market information: TMC.
Mechanical available: Offset; Black and 3 ROP colors; insert accepted; page cutoffs - 22 3/4.
Mechanical Specifications: Type page 11 1/2 x 21; E - 5 cols, 2 3/16, 3/16 between; A - 10 cols, 1, 1/16 between; C - 8 cols, 1 1/3, 1/8 between.
Areas Served: Kingston & Surrounding areas

Delivery Method: Mail, Newsstand, Carrier, Racks
Equipment & Software PRESSROOM EQUIPMENT:Pressroom Lines — 10-G/Urbanite single width 1992; Folders — 1, 1-SU/Jaw Folder w/ 1/4 Folder; Pasters — 7 MAILROOM EQUIPMENT:Counter Stackers — 2-HL/HT II; Inserters & Stuffers — GMA/SLS 1000; Bundle Tying Machines — 1/OVL, 2-OVL/JP-40; Mailroom Control System — PMS-6; Address Machine — 2-/Wm; Other Equipment — 2-MM/Saddle Stitcher H325. BUSINESS EQUIPMENT:Hardware — 5-IBM, Service Bureau CLASSIFIED EQUIPMENT:Hardware — 1-Cybergraphics; Printers — QMS/860 CLASSIFIED SOFTWARE:Cybergraphics. DISPLAY EQUIPMENT:Hardware — APP/Mac/ECR/Autokon Scanner, Nikon/Scanner, Kk/Scanner, Horizon/Scanner; Printers — APP/LaserWriter II NTX, 2-AU/APS-6-108, Lexmark/Optra N DISPLAY SOFTWARE:Ad Make-Up Applications — QPS/QuarkXPress, Aldus/Freehand, Adobe/Illustrator; Layout Software — SCS/Layout 80 EDITORIAL EQUIPMENT:Hardware — APP/Mac; Printers — QMS/860 EDITORIAL SOFTWARE:QPS. PRODUCTION EQUIPMENT:Hardware — Caere/OmniPage, Aqualith/32; Scanners — 1-ECR/Autokon 1000 PRODUCTION SOFTWARE:QPS/QuarkXPress.

KITCHENER

THE RECORD

160 King St. East, Kitchener, ON, N2G 4E5, Canada; gen tel (519) 895-5552; adv tel (519) 894-1500 (Class); ed tel (519) 895-5602; gen fax (519) 894-3912; adv fax (519) 894-1258; ed fax (519) 894-3829; gen/nat adv. e-mail cschmidt@therecord.com; disp adv e-mail cschmidt@therecord.com; class adv e-mailclassifieds@metroland.com; ed e-mail mmarks@therecord.com; web site 1 www.therecord.com
Published: Mon, Tues, Wed, Thur, Fri, Sat
Weekday Frequency: m
Saturday Frequency: m
Circulation 49,167; 51,719(sat)
Last Audit: BPA December 31, 2013
Group: Metroland Media Group Ltd.
Newspaper Reps: Thibaud Wallaert
Branch Offices: Toronto, ON
Advertising - Weekday/Saturday: 500,000: $2.19 (Mon-Thurs); $2.30 (Fri); $2.58 (Sat)
Online Advertising Rates: Rates on request.
News services: CP, LAT-WP, NYT. **Established:** 1878
Special Weekly Sections: Financial Forum (Monthly).
Syndicated Publications: Wheels (Fri); TV Week (Sat); Entertainment Tab (Thur); Small Business (Wed).
Digital Platform - Mobile: Apple, Android, Windows, Blackberry
Pub. .... Paul McCuaig
Ed-in-Chief .... Lynn Haddrall
Dir. Adv. & Circ. .... Donna Luelo
Dir. Prod. and Dist. .... Paul McKeon
Class. Mgr. .... Sandra Lennox
Mng. Ed. .... Melinda Marks
Mailroom Mgr. .... Mike Handfield
Bus. Ed. .... Ron DeRuyter
City Ed. .... Neil Ballantyne
Editorial Page Ed. .... John Roe
Librarian .... Johanna Neufeld
Online Ed. .... Karlo Berkovich
National Adv./Admin. Supervisor Cathy Weisbrod
Market information: Split run; TMC.
Mechanical available: Offset; Black and 3 ROP colors; insert accepted - envelopes; page cutoffs - 22.
Mechanical Specifications: Type page 10 1/2 x 21.9290; E - 10 cols, 1 1/16, 1/16 between; A - 10 cols, 1 1/16, 1/16 between; C - 10 cols, 1 1/16, 1/16 between.
Areas Served: Waterloo Region

Delivery Method: Mail, Newsstand, Carrier, Racks
Equipment & Software MAILROOM EQUIPMENT:Counter Stackers — 4-QWI/401, HL; Inserters & Stuffers — 2-GMA/SLS 2000 12:2; Bundle Tying Machines — 4-Dynaric/NP-3, 1-MLN/ML0AE-16977, 2/Power Strap; Wrapping Singles — 4-QWI/Viper Bottom Wrap. BUSINESS EQUIPMENT:Hardware — Admarc, Cybergraphics 4096, Discus, Intel/ Layout 8000, QPS, Quicktrac, Smartstream CLASSIFIED EQUIPMENT:Hardware — 2-DEC/VAX 4000-60; Printers — HP/LaserJet IV CLASSIFIED SOFTWARE:Cybergraphics. DISPLAY EQUIPMENT:Hardware — DEC/ VAX 4105 Lluster; Printers — C.Itoh/300, 1-Mannesman/660, 1-Mannesman/690 DISPLAY SOFTWARE:Ad Make-Up Applications — SCS/Layout 8000; Layout Software — SCS/Layout 8000. EDITORIAL EQUIPMENT:Hardware — APP/Mac, PC; Printers — 1-NewGen/660B, 1-NewGen/ Xcelerwriter EDITORIAL SOFTWARE:QPS/ QuarkXPress 4, QPS. PRODUCTION EQUIPMENT:Hardware — Calera/Wordscan.

LONDON

THE LONDON FREE PRESS

369 York St., London, ON, N6A 4G1, Canada; gen tel (519) 679-1111; adv tel (519) 679-1111; ed tel (519) 679-1111; gen fax (519) 667-4523; adv fax (519) 667-4523; ed fax (519) 667-4620; gen/nat adv. e-mail carolyn.johnson@sunmedia.ca; disp adv e-mail carolyn.johnson@sunmedia.ca; class adv e-maillfpress.classifieds@sunmedia.ca; ed e-mail joe.ruscitti@sunmedia.ca; web site 1 www.lfpress.com
Published: Mon, Tues, Wed, Thur, Fri, Sat
Weekday Frequency: m
Saturday Frequency: m
Circulation 41,830; 45,176(sat)
Last Audit: AAM June 30, 2016
Group: Quebecor Communications, Inc. Postmedia Network Inc.
Advertising - Weekday/Saturday: Open inch rate $6.43 (M-F); $7.84 (Sat.)
Online Advertising Rates: Rates on request.
News services: GNS, CP, Canada News Wire. **Established:** 1855
Special Editions: M Magazine For Men (Every other month); Home Magazine (Quarterly); TV Magazine (Sat); Decor Magazine (Semi-yearly).
Special Weekly Sections: Garden Center Book (Apr); Continuing Education (Aug); Countdown to Christmas (Dec); Campbook (Feb); Health Guide (Jan); National Fishing Week (Jun); Fashion Statement (Mar); Escapes (May); Downtown Living (Monthly); Holiday Shopping (Nov); Hot Toys (Oct);
Syndicated Publications: Wheels (Fri); Business Monday (Mon); Homes (Sat); Ticket (Thur).
Digital Platform - Mobile: Apple, Android
Digital Platform - Tablet: Apple iOS, Android
Pub./CEO, Digital & Print .... Susan Muszak
Adv. Dir. .... Lisa Catania Chiaramida
Adv. Mgr., Retail .... Jerry Pilkey
Adv. Mgr., Auto/Real Estate .... Chris Kubinski
Adv. Mgr., Digital .... Jim Heaven
Circ. Dir., Reader Sales/Serv./Mktg. .... Sherri Scott
Ed.-in-Chief .... Joe Ruscitti
News Ed. .... Howard Burns
Mgmt. Info Servs. Mgr. .... Glen Besley
Dir., Operations .... John Pacitto
Dir., Reader Sales, Service & Mktg. Sherri Walker
Market information: TMC.
Mechanical available: Offset; Black and 3 ROP colors; insert accepted - poly bags, outsert packages, sampling; page cutoffs - 22 3/4.
Mechanical Specifications: Type page 11 1/2 x 21 1/2; E - 6 cols, 1 3/4, 3/16 between; A - 10 cols, 2 1/4, 1/8 between; C - 10 cols, 2 1/4, 1/8 between.
Areas Served: London, Southwestern Ontario

Delivery Method: Mail, Newsstand, Carrier, Racks
Equipment & Software PRESSROOM EQUIPMENT:Pressroom Lines — G/ Headliner offset; 9-G/Urbanite single width 1979; Folders — G/Offset 2:1, G/Letterpress; Pasters — G/Digital Predrive, Butler/ Splicers; Reels & Stands — G/Simplified Tension. MAILROOM EQUIPMENT:Counter Stackers — 6-Id/2000; Inserters & Stuffers — 5-GMA/SLS 1000; Bundle Tying Machines — 5/Power Strap; Wrapping Singles — Manual; Address Machine — 1-/Ch; Other Equipment — HI/Trimmer. BUSINESS EQUIPMENT:Hardware — 2-Alpha/1000 BUSINESS SOFTWARE:Cobol CLASSIFIED EQUIPMENT:Hardware — Compaq/ PC P111-400 EN; Printers — HP/4050 N CLASSIFIED SOFTWARE:Adacus. DISPLAY EQUIPMENT:Hardware — APP/ Mac G3; Printers — HP/LaserJet, HP/4050 N DISPLAY SOFTWARE:Ad Make-Up Applications — Managing Editor/ALS, Managing Editor/CLS, QPS/QuarkXPress; Layout Software — MEI/ALS 4.1.6, MEI/ CLS 3.0.1, QPS/QuarkXPress 4.11. EDITORIAL EQUIPMENT:Hardware — APP/Mac, APP/Mac G3; Printers — Xante EDITORIAL SOFTWARE:QPS/ Quark Publishing System 2.08, QPS/ Copydesk 2.08, QPS/QuarkXPress 4.11. PRODUCTION EQUIPMENT:Hardware — 2-C, 4-Imagesetter, 4-RIP, P; Scanners — ECR/M2045, Epson, Scitex/Smart 340, PixelCraft/7650 C, PixelCraft/8000 PRODUCTION SOFTWARE:QPS.

NIAGARA FALLS

NIAGARA FALLS REVIEW

4424 Queen St, Niagara Falls, ON, L2E 2L3, Canada; gen tel (905) 358-5711; adv tel (905) 358-5711; ed tel (905) 358-5711; gen fax (905)356-0785; adv fax (905)356-0785; ed fax (905) 374-0461; gen/nat adv. e-mail jumacdonald@postmedia.com; disp adv e-mail jumacdonald@postmedia.com; class adv e-mailniagarafallsreview.classifieds@sunmedia.com; ed e-mail ascott@postmedia.com; web site 1 www.niagarafallsreview.ca
Published: Mon, Tues, Wed, Thur, Fri, Sat
Weekday Frequency: m
Saturday Frequency: m
Circulation 7,090; 7,138(sat)
Last Audit: CCAB September 30, 2015
Group: Quebecor Communications, Inc.
Newspaper Reps: Susan Courtney - VP, QMI Corporate Sales
Advertising - Weekday/Saturday: Open line rate $1.32 (M-W, Fri); $1.50 (Th); $1.41 (Sat)
Online Advertising Rates: Rates on request.
News services: CP. **Established:** 1879
Special Weekly Sections: Niagara-on-the-Lake Tourist Guide (Apr); Niagara Family Fun Tourist Guide (Aug); Niagara Family Fun Tourist Guide (Jul); Niagara Family Fun Tourist Guide (Jun); Niagara Family Fun Tourist Guide (May); Winter Festival of Lights (Oct).
Syndicated Publications: Home Buyer's Guide (Real Estate) (Sat).
Digital Platform - Mobile: Apple, Android
Digital Platform - Tablet: Apple iOS, Android
Pub. .... Michael Cressman
Adv. Mgr. .... Mark Smith
Ed. in Chief .... Steven Gallagher
Mng. Ed. .... Cory Larocque
Senior Group Pub. .... Judy Bullis
Mng. Ed. .... Peter Conradi
Market information: ADS; TMC.
Mechanical available: Offset; Black and 3 ROP colors; insert accepted - product samples, non-newsprint publications; page cutoffs - 22 3/4.
Mechanical Specifications: Type page 11 1/2 x 20 1/2; E - 10 cols, 1 1/16, 1/16 between; A - 10 cols, 1 1/16, 1/16 between; C - 9 cols, between.
Areas Served: Niagara Falls & Fort Eerie

Delivery Method: Mail, Newsstand, Carrier, Racks
Equipment & Software PRESSROOM EQUIPMENT:Pressroom Lines — 7-G/ Urbanite; Press Drive — 2-G/Motor; Folders — 1, 1. MAILROOM EQUIPMENT:Counter Stackers — 1/KAN; Inserters & Stuffers — 1-/ KAN; Bundle Tying Machines — 1-/OVL. BUSINESS EQUIPMENT:Hardware — SITG BUSINESS SOFTWARE:HP, Epson, NEC CLASSIFIED EQUIPMENT:Hardware — APP/Mac; Printers — HP CLASSIFIED SOFTWARE:QPS. DISPLAY EQUIPMENT:Hardware — APP/Mac; Printers — HP DISPLAY SOFTWARE:Layout Software — APP/Mac, MEI/ALS. EDITORIAL EQUIPMENT:Hardware — APP/Mac; Printers — HP EDITORIAL SOFTWARE:QPS/ QuarkXPress 4.0. PRODUCTION EQUIPMENT:Hardware — 2-COM/9400 Laser, LE/1200; Cameras — 1-C/Spartan II 1244, ECR/Autokon 1000; Scanners — HP/ Scantec PRODUCTION SOFTWARE:CD 3.1.

NORTH BAY

NUGGET

259 Worthington St. W., North Bay, ON, P1B 3B5, Canada; gen tel (705) 472-3200; adv tel (705) 472-3200; ed tel (705) 472-3200; gen fax (705) 472-1438; adv fax (705) 472-1438; ed fax (705) 472-1438; gen/nat adv. e-mail rdawson@postmedia.com; disp adv e-mail rdawson@postmedia.com; class adv e-mailnugget.classifieds@sunmedia.ca; ed e-mail msandford@postmedia.com; web site 1 www.nugget.ca
Published: Mon, Tues, Wed, Thur, Fri, Sat
Weekday Frequency: e
Saturday Frequency: e
Circulation 7,189; 7,444(sat)
Last Audit: CCAB September 30, 2015
Group: Quebecor Communications, Inc. Postmedia Network Inc.
Newspaper Reps: Susan Courtney - VP, QMI Corporate Sales Office
Advertising - Weekday/Saturday: Open inch rate $1.53 (M-Th); $1.58 (F-Sa)
Online Advertising Rates: Rates on request.
News services: CP, SOU, Fin. Times, Can. Bus. Wire. **Established:** 1907
Special Editions: Weekly TV Times Mini Tab (Fri); Vintage Times (Monthly); Weekly Broadsheet (Sat); Parenting (Semi-monthly).
Special Weekly Sections: Car Care (Apr); Boys & Girls of Summer (Aug); Baby Review (Dec); Cookbook (Jun); Brides (Mar); Home & Garden (May); New Car (Nov); Fall Car Care (Oct); Community Guide (Sept).
Syndicated Publications: Real Estate (Fri); Weekender (Sat); Entertainment (Thur); Business (Tues); Food (Wed).
Digital Platform - Mobile: Apple, Android
Digital Platform - Tablet: Apple iOS, Android
Pub. .... Dan Johnson
Mng. Ed. .... Bruce Cowan
Adv. Dir. .... Steve Page
Prodn. Mgr., Post Press .... Paul Chapman
Prodn. Foreman, Pressroom .... Steve Hevenor
Market information: TMC; Zoned editions.
Mechanical available: Web Offset; Black and 3 ROP colors; insert accepted - product samples; page cutoffs - 22 3/4.
Mechanical Specifications: Type page 11 1/2 x 20; E - 5 cols, 2 1/16, 1/8 between; A - 10 cols, 1 1/16, 1/8 between; C - 9 cols, 1 3/16, 1/8 between.
Areas Served: North Bay

Delivery Method: Mail, Newsstand, Carrier, Racks
Equipment & Software PRESSROOM EQUIPMENT:Pressroom Lines — 13-G/ Community; Folders — G/SSC, G/Community. MAILROOM EQUIPMENT:Counter Stackers — BG/Count-O-Veyor 108, MM/285; Inserters & Stuffers — 13-KAN/760; Bundle Tying Machines — 2/Stappers; Other Equipment - Trimmer (3 knife). BUSINESS EQUIPMENT:Hardware — PCs BUSINESS SOFTWARE:Microsoft/Excel, Microsoft/Word CLASSIFIED EQUIPMENT:Hardware — PC, APP/Mac; Printers — XIT/Laser Printer 11x17 CLASSIFIED SOFTWARE:CText. DISPLAY EQUIPMENT:Hardware — DEC/ VAX; Printers — DEC/LG02 DISPLAY SOFTWARE:Ad Make-Up Applications — SCS/Layout 8000; Layout Software — SCS/Layout 8000. EDITORIAL EQUIPMENT:Hardware — APP/Mac/Kk/ Negscanner; Printers — Xante EDITORIAL SOFTWARE:QPS/QuarkXPress 5, Microsoft/ Office Suite, Adobe/Photoshop, QPS. PRODUCTION EQUIPMENT:Hardware — Caere/OmniPage, APP/Mac, Adobe/ Photoshop, Adobe/Illustrator; Scanners — Epson/Negative Scanner.

ORILLIA

ORILLIA PACKET

425 West St. N., Suite 15, Orillia, ON, L3V 7R2, Canada; gen tel (705) 325-1355; adv tel (705) 325-1355 ; ed tel (705) 325-1355; gen fax (705) 325-4033; adv fax (705) 325-7691 (Classified); ed fax (705) 325-4033; gen/ nat adv. e-mail nicole.parkes@sunmedia.ca; disp adv e-mail jocelyn.hill@sunmedia.ca; class adv e-mailorilliapacket.classifieds@sunmedia.ca; ed e-mail ntaylor@postmedia.com; web site 1 www.orilliapacket.com
Published: Mon, Tues, Wed, Thur, Fri, Sat
Weekday Frequency: m
Saturday Frequency: m
Circulation 5,336; 5,407(sat)
Last Audit: BPA December 30, 2010
Group: Postmedia Network Inc. Sun Media Corp.
Newspaper Reps: Susan Courtney - VP National Sales, QMI Corporate Sales Office
Advertising - Weekday/Saturday: Open inch rate $1.57 (M-W, F, Sat); $2.03 (Th)
Online Advertising Rates: Rates on request.
News services: Sun Media **Established:** 1870
Own Printing Facility?: N
Commercial Printers?: Y
Digital Platform - Mobile: Apple, Android
Digital Platform - Tablet: Apple iOS, Android
Publisher/General Manager .... John Hammill
Mng. Ed. .... Randy Lucenti
Circ. Mgr. .... Scott Murphy
Pre-Press Mgr. .... April Barber
Market information: ADS; TMC.

Mechanical available: Offset; Black and 3 ROP colors; insert accepted; page cutoffs - 22 3/4.
Mechanical Specifications: Type page 11 1/2 x 20 1/2; E - 6 cols, 2 1/16, 1/8 between; A - 6 cols, 2 1/16, 1/8 between; C - 9 cols, 1 1/3, 1/8 between.
Areas Served: City of Orillia, Rama First Nation and the townships of Ramara, Severn and Oro-Medonte

Delivery Method: Mail, Newsstand, Carrier, Racks
Equipment & Software MAILROOM EQUIPMENT:Bundle Tying Machines — 1/Gd; Address Machine — 1-/El. EDITORIAL EQUIPMENT:Hardware — CD/Pagination/APP/Mac Graphic. PRODUCTION EQUIPMENT:Hardware — F/Plate Maker; Cameras — 1-B/3000.

OTTAWA

LE DROIT

47 Rue Clarence, Bureau 222, Ottawa, ON, K1G 3J9, Canada; gen tel (613) 562-7747; adv tel (514) 285-6884; ed tel (613) 562-0111; gen fax (613) 562-7572; adv fax (613) 562-7539; ed fax (613) 562-7539; gen/nat adv. e-mail production@ledroit.com; disp adv e-mail production@ledroit.com; class adv e-mailpetitesannonces@ledroit.com; ed e-mail tirage@ledroit.com; web site 1 www.lapresse.ca/le-droit
Published: Mon, Tues, Wed, Thur, Fri, Sat
Weekday Frequency: m
Saturday Frequency: m
Circulation 27,903; 28,928(sat)
Last Audit: AAM March 31, 2016
Group: Le Droit Ltee
Newspaper Reps: Marc Giguere - GM, Gesca Media Sales

Robert Laplante - Pres., Media-Corps Inc.
Advertising - Weekday/Saturday: Frequency 5: $70.00, $75.00 (Sat); Frequency 4: $105.00, $110.00 (Sat.); Frequency 3: $190.00, $200.00
Online Advertising Rates: Rates on request.
News services: CP, AFP. **Established:** 1884
Syndicated Publications: Weekend (entertainment) (Fri); TV Guide (Sat); Societe (Living) (Thur); Internet and Science (Tues).
Digital Platform - Mobile: Apple, Android
Digital Platform - Tablet: Apple iOS, Android
Pres., Ed. .... Jacques Pronovost
Comptroller .... Patrice Dellehuneur
Dir., Sales/Promo. .... Claude Tremblay
Ed. in Chief .... Andre Lorocque
Arts Ed. .... Valerie Lessard
Editorial Page Ed. .... Pierre Jury
News Ed. .... John Jajnon
Sports Ed. .... Marc Brassard
Online Mgr. .... Antonie Boulet
Prodn. Mgr., Computer Systems .Louis Simoneau
Prod. Cord. .... Raymond Begin
Sales & Mktg. Dir. .... Eric Brousseau
Mng. Ed. .... Jean Gagnon
Circ. Dir. .... Robert Schiffo
Market information: TMC; Zoned editions.
Mechanical available: Offset; Black and 3 ROP colors; insert accepted; page cutoffs - 15.
Mechanical Specifications: Type page 10 1/4 x 14 1/4
Areas Served: Ottawa & Surrounding areas

Delivery Method: Mail, Newsstand, Carrier
Equipment & Software PRESSROOM EQUIPMENT:Pressroom Lines — 10-RKW/Creusotloire (2 1/2 units; 3 Quad units) single width; 3-RKW/Creusotloire color single width 1998; Folders — 2 MAILROOM EQUIPMENT:Counter Stackers — MM/Wamack, MM; Inserters & Stuffers — MM/2 4:1; Bundle Tying Machines — OVL/JP-80. BUSINESS EQUIPMENT:Hardware — Sun CLASSIFIED EQUIPMENT:Hardware — 2-Dell/Power Edge 4100-200 Server, 16-Dell; Printers — HP/LaserJet 4M Plus CLASSIFIED SOFTWARE:SCS/AdMax, Unix/SCO. DISPLAY EQUIPMENT:Hardware — 2-Star Max, 2-APP/Power Mac 7200/120, 1-APP/Power Mac 7300-180, 1-APP/Mac G3-333 Server, 3-APP/Power Mac G3-233, 1-APP/Mac G3-266, 1-Dell/Optiplex Pentium II/400; Printers — APP/Mac LaserWriter 8500, HP/LaserJet II, Tex Tronix/Phaser 300i EDITORIAL EQUIPMENT:Hardware — 4-APP/Power Mac, APP/Mac G3-333 Server, 24-APP/Mac, 9-APP/Power Mac G3-266/25-RSK/Tandy 1100 FD, 7-APP/Mac PowerBook; Printers — 1-HP/5MP, 1-APP/Mac LaserWriter Pro 630 EDITORIAL SOFTWARE:Baseview/NewsEdit Pro DB, APP/Mac, OS. PRODUCTION EQUIPMENT:Hardware — STF/Auto OCR, Adobe/Rips, APP/Mac 9500, Comulus/DataBase; Cameras — B; Scanners — 1-Nikon/Coolscan, 1-Kk/2035, AG/Horizon, AG/Duo Scan PRODUCTION SOFTWARE:QPS/QuarkXPress 3.32, SCS/Linx 4.0.

THE OTTAWA CITIZEN

1101 Baxter Rd., Ottawa, ON, K2C 3M4, Canada; gen tel (613) 829-9100; adv tel (613) 596-3590; ed tel (613) 596-3664; gen fax (613) 726-5852; adv fax (613) 726-5895; ed fax (613) 726-1198; gen/nat adv. e-mail adinquiries@ottawacitizen.com; disp adv e-mail adinquiries@ottawacitizen.com; class adv e-mailclassified@ottawacitizen.com; ed e-mail letters@thecitizen.canwest.com; web site 1 www.ottawacitizen.com - 6,600,000(views) 891,000(visitors)
Published: Mon, Tues, Wed, Thur, Fri, Sat
Weekday Frequency: m
Saturday Frequency: m
Circulation 88,577; 80,177(sat)
Last Audit: AAM March 31, 2017
Group: Postmedia Network Inc.
Newspaper Reps: Thibaud Wallaert - GM, Discomm Media
Branch Offices: Vancouver, BC
Toronto, ON
Montreal, QC
Advertising - Weekday/Saturday: Open inch rate $9.09 (Mon-Fri); $12.22 (Sat)
Online Advertising Rates: Leaderboard $18; Big Box $27; Tall Block $40
News services: CP, AP, SOU, LAT-WP, NYT, MCT, RN, SHNS, Bloomberg, HN, Independent, Telegraph. **Established:** 1845
Special Weekly Sections: New Homes Interiors & Lifestyles (Apr); Local Business Profile (Aug); Winter Travel Directory (Dec); March Break Destination (Feb); National Ski Week (Jan); Taste Of Ottawa (Jul); Armed Forces (Jun); High Tech Report (Mar); Ottawa Business Show (May); Ski
Syndicated Publications: Wheels (Fri); High Tech (Mon); TV Times (Sat); Style (Thur); Food (Wed).
Digital Platform - Mobile: Apple, Android
Digital Platform - Tablet: Apple iOS, Android
Pub. & Ed.-in-Chief .... Gerry Nott
Ed. .... Andrew Potter
Vice Pres., HR/Finance .... Deborah Bennett
Dir. of Finance .... Shirley Tam
VP Mktg. and Reader Sales .... Paul Sarkozy
Circ. Mgr., Systems Admin. ....Robert Littlemore
VP Mftg. and Dist. .... Patrick Brennan
Prod. Mgr. .... Don Joly
VP, Adv. Sales .... Ryan Shortt
Sales Planning Cord .... Laurie Stanul
Market information: ADS; Split run; TMC.
Mechanical available: Offset; Black and 3 ROP colors; insert accepted; page cutoffs - 23 3/4.
Mechanical Specifications: Type page 10 1/2 x 22; E - 6 cols, 2 1/16, 1/8 between; A - 10 cols, 1 1/16, 1/8 between; C - 10 cols, 1 1/16, 1/8 between.
Areas Served: Ottawa & Surrounding areas

Delivery Method: Mail, Newsstand, Carrier, Racks
Equipment & Software PRESSROOM EQUIPMENT:Pressroom Lines — 9-G/Metro Offset 1973; 9-G/Metro Offset 1973; 9-G/Metro Offset 1994; Folders — 3-G/3:2; Reels & Stands — 24 MAILROOM EQUIPMENT:Counter Stackers — 6-QWI/300, 2-SH/257; Inserters & Stuffers — 3/AM Graphics/NP 630; Bundle Tying Machines — 5-/Power Strap/PSN-6, 2-/Dynaric. BUSINESS EQUIPMENT:Hardware — Compaq/DeskPro 5120 BUSINESS SOFTWARE:Microsoft/Office 6.0 CLASSIFIED EQUIPMENT:Hardware — PCs/Sharp/610 scanner CLASSIFIED SOFTWARE:Cybergraphics. DISPLAY EQUIPMENT:Hardware — APP/Mac DISPLAY SOFTWARE:Ad Make-Up Applications — QPS/QuarkXPress; Layout Software — SCS/Layout 8000. EDITORIAL EQUIPMENT:Hardware — PC 386, PC 486, APP/Mac ci, APP/Power Mac 6100-66, APP/Mac Power Book 150; Printers — AU/APS 6, V/VT-600, APP/Mac LaserWriters, HP/LaserJet 4 PWS EDITORIAL SOFTWARE:DEC, QPS/QuarkXPress, QPS/Quark Dispatch, QPS/Quark Copy Desk, QuickWire. PRODUCTION EQUIPMENT:Hardware — 1-Nu/Flip Top FTUP, 1-All/Sierra, 1-All/3850, 1-DAI/LD-2600; Scanners — 1-Sharp/Flatbed, 4-Nikon/Negative Scanner, 1-ECR, 3-Epson, 1-PixelCraft PRODUCTION SOFTWARE:QPS.

THE OTTAWA SUN

18A Antares Dr., Ottawa, ON, K2E 1A9, Canada; gen tel (613) 739-7000; adv tel (613) 739-7100; ed tel (613) 739-5113; gen fax (613) 739-9383; adv fax (613) 739-8044; ed fax (613) 739-8041; gen/nat adv. e-mail jstewart@postmedia.com; disp adv e-mail jstewart@postmedia.com; class adv e-mailottawasun.classifieds@sunmedia.ca; ed e-mail michelle.waters@sunmedia.ca; web site 1 www.ottawasun.com - 10,000,000(views)
Published: Mon, Tues, Wed, Thur, Fri, Sat, Sun
Weekday Frequency: m
Saturday Frequency: m
Circulation 25,923; 23,408(sat); 25,711(sun)
Last Audit: CCAB September 30, 2015
Group: Quebecor Communications, Inc.
Postmedia Network Inc.
Newspaper Reps: Susan Courtney - VP National Sales, QMI Corporate Sales Office
Advertising - Weekday/Saturday: Open inch rate $2.65
Advertising - Sunday: Open inch rate $2.89
Online Advertising Rates: Leaderboard $25; Big Box $25; Skyscraper $20

News services: AP, CP, GNS, RN. **Established:** 1988
Special Editions: Show Time (S).
Special Weekly Sections: Welcome Home (Renovation Guide) (Monthly).
Syndicated Publications: Car Market (Thur).
Digital Platform - Mobile: Apple, Android, Windows, Blackberry
Digital Platform - Tablet: Apple iOS, Android, Windows 7, Blackberry Tablet OS
Adv. Sales Dir. .... Bruce Holmes
Classified Mgr. .... Marietta D'Alessio
Circ. Dir. .... George Norlock
Mng. Ed. .... Don Ermen
Prodn. Dir. .... Charles Stapley
Prodn. Mgr. .... Tracey Legault
Pub., CEO .... Rick Gibbons
Dist. Dir. .... Randy Hayley
Editor .... Keith Bonnell
Market information: TMC.
Mechanical available: Offset; Black and 3 ROP colors; insert accepted - 11 x 13 1/2, single sheets must be folded; page cutoffs - 13 1/2.
Mechanical Specifications: Type page 10.3330 x 11.4290; E - 8 cols, 1 3/16, 1/8 between; A - 8 cols, 1 3/16, 1/8 between; C - 8 cols, 1 3/16, 1/8 between.
Areas Served: Ottawa & Surrounding areas

Delivery Method: Mail, Newsstand, Carrier, Racks
Equipment & Software PRESSROOM EQUIPMENT:Pressroom Lines — 10-G/Urbanite single width 1989; 4-G/Urbanite single width 1995; Folders — 2-G/Urbanite 2:1; Pasters — 8 MAILROOM EQUIPMENT:Counter Stackers — 1-Id, 1-Id, 1-Id; Inserters & Stuffers — 2-MM/227, 1-HI/1372; Bundle Tying Machines — 2/MLN, 1-/Dynamic.; Address Machine — ATT/Computer Print Out. BUSINESS EQUIPMENT:Hardware — Pentium/PCs BUSINESS SOFTWARE:Lotus, WordPerfect 6.0, Microsoft/Office 98 CLASSIFIED EQUIPMENT:Hardware — Compaq/Pentium; Printers — X/2025, X/432 ST, QMS/1725 CLASSIFIED SOFTWARE:Multi-Ad 4.0, Aldus/Freehand 9.0, Adobe/Illustrator 8.0. DISPLAY EQUIPMENT:Hardware — APP/Power Mac 8600, APP/Mac G3, APP/Mac G4; Printers — X/2825, X/DC12 DISPLAY SOFTWARE:Ad Make-Up Applications — Multi-Ad/Creator 4.0, Adobe/Illustrator 8.0, Aldus/Freehand 7.0, QPS/QuarkXPress 3.32, Adobe/Photoshop 5.5; Layout Software — MEI/ALS. EDITORIAL EQUIPMENT:Hardware — APP/iMac, APP/Power Mac, APP/iBook, APP/Mac G4; Printers — X/2025, X/432 ST EDITORIAL SOFTWARE:QPS/QuarkXPress 3.3.1, Adobe/Illustrator 8.0, Phoenix/Client, Aldus/Freehand 9.0, Newsline/Solo (5X), Adobe/Photoshop 4.0, Adobe/Photoshop 5.0. PRODUCTION EQUIPMENT:Hardware — 2-Burgess/Plate Burners, III/3850, LE/1800; Cameras — ECR/Autokon, Marathon/Horizontal; Scanners — Kk/Neg Scanner PRODUCTION SOFTWARE:Mk/Ad Director 2.0.

OWEN SOUND

OWENSOUND SUN TIMES

290 9th St., East, Owen Sound, ON, N4K 5P2, Canada; gen tel (519) 376-2250; adv tel (519) 376-2250; ed tel (519) 376-2250; gen fax (519) 372-1861; adv fax (519) 372-1861; ed fax (519) 372-1861; gen/nat adv. e-mail lkazarian@postmedia.com; disp adv e-mail lkazarian@postmedia.com; class adv e-mailowensoundsuntimes.classifieds@sunmedia.ca; ed e-mail doug.edgar@sunmedia.ca; web site 1 www.owensoundsuntimes.com
Published: Mon, Tues, Wed, Thur, Sat
Weekday Frequency: e
Saturday Frequency: e
Circulation 12,884; 12,884(sat)
Last Audit: CMCA December 31, 2013
Group: Postmedia Network Inc.
Quebecor Communications, Inc.
Newspaper Reps: Susan Courtney - VP National Sales, QMI Corporate Sales Office
Advertising - Weekday/Saturday: Open inch rate $1.24 (M-Th); $1.38 (Sat)
Online Advertising Rates: Rates on request.
News services: CP, SOU. **Established:** 1922
Special Weekly Sections: Home Improvement 1 (Apr); Back to School (Aug); Xmas Greetings (Dec); Business Outlook (Feb); Brides (Jan); The Sale (Jul); Home Improvement 2 (May); Xmas Gift Guide (Nov); Almanac (Oct); Financial Planning 1 (Sept).
Syndicated Publications: Real Estate (Fri); Sports (Mon); Auto (Thur); Seniors (Tues); Lifestyles (Wed).
Digital Platform - Mobile: Apple, Android
Digital Platform - Tablet: Apple iOS, Android
Pub.
Cheryl McMenemy
Adv. Dir. .... Louise Kazarian-Hodder
Circ. Mgr. .... Brent Radbourne
Mng. Ed. .... Doug Edgar
Grey Bruce Group Pub. .... Marie David
Market information: ADS; TMC.
Mechanical available: Offset; Black and 3 ROP colors; insert accepted - envelopes, samples; page cutoffs - 21 3/4.
Mechanical Specifications: Type page 11 1/2 x 20 1/2; E - 5 cols, 2 3/16, 1/8 between; A - 10 cols, 1, 1/8 between; C - 5 cols, 2 3/16, 1/8 between.
Areas Served: Grey & Bruce Counties

Delivery Method: Mail, Newsstand, Carrier, Racks
Equipment & Software PRESSROOM EQUIPMENT:Pressroom Lines — 5-G/Community single width (1 Community 4-high); Folders — 1-G/SC. MAILROOM EQUIPMENT:Counter Stackers — 2/BG; Inserters & Stuffers — MM/8-into-1; Bundle Tying Machines — MLN. BUSINESS EQUIPMENT:Hardware — 1-Compaq/LTE 286, 1-IBM/PS2 Model 60, 2-IBM/PS2 Model 30 BUSINESS SOFTWARE:Lotus 2.2 CLASSIFIED EQUIPMENT:Hardware — APP/Mac/1-APP/Mac LaserScanner CLASSIFIED SOFTWARE:CText 6.0. DISPLAY EQUIPMENT:Hardware — 1-APP/Mac, 5-APP/Mac fx, 5-APP/Power PC 7600/1-APP/Mac Scanner, 1-AG/Horizon Scanner, 1-ECR/Autokon; Printers — 3-APP/Mac LaserPrinter DISPLAY SOFTWARE:Ad Make-Up Applications — QPS/QuarkXPress, Adobe/Illustrator, Aldus/Freehand, Adobe/Photoshop EDITORIAL EQUIPMENT:Hardware — 5-APP/Mac

Quadra 950/Smith Corona/XDS 20; Printers — 3-APP/Mac LaserWriter EDITORIAL SOFTWARE:APP/Mac, QPS/QuarkXPress. PRODUCTION EQUIPMENT:Hardware — ECR/Imagesetter, AU/APS108; Scanners — AG/Repromaster-3000 PRODUCTION SOFTWARE:Ad Trac 2.1.

PEMBROKE

THE DAILY OBSERVER

186 Alexander Street, Pembroke, ON, K8A 4L9, Canada; gen tel (613) 732-3691; adv tel (613) 732-3691; ed tel (613) 732-3691; gen fax (613) 732-1022; adv fax (613) 732-2645; ed fax (613)732-1022; gen/nat adv. e-mail jim.kwiatkowski@sunmedia.ca; disp adv e-mail jim.kwiatkowski@sunmedia.ca; class adv e-mailthedailyobserver.classifieds@sunmedia.ca; ed e-mail anthony.dixon@sunmedia.ca; web site 1 www.thedailyobserver.ca
Published: Tues, Wed, Thur, Fri, Sat
Weekday Frequency: m
Saturday Frequency: m
Circulation 4,179; 4,772(sat)
Last Audit: BPA December 31, 2012
Group: Postmedia Network Inc.
Quebecor Communications, Inc.
Newspaper Reps: Susan Courtney - VP National Sales, QMI Corporate Sales Office
Advertising - Weekday/Saturday: Open inch rate $1.04 (T-Sat)
News services: CP, SOU. **Established:** 1855
Own Printing Facility?: N
Commercial Printers?: Y
Syndicated Publications: Home Finder (Thursday)
Digital Platform - Mobile: Apple, Android, Windows, Blackberry
Digital Platform - Tablet: Apple iOS, Android, Windows 7, Blackberry Tablet OS
Circ. Mgr. .... David Bell
Editorial Page Ed. .... Peter Lapinskie
Prodn. Mgr., Mailroom .... Lisa Bell
Pub./Adv. Mgr. .... Jim Kwiatkowski
Market information: ADS; TMC.
Mechanical available: Offset; Black and 3 ROP colors; insert accepted; page cutoffs - 21 1/2.
Mechanical Specifications: Type page 11 1/2 x 20 1/2; E - 5 cols, 2 1/4, 1/8 between; A - 10 cols, 1 1/16, 1/8 between; C - 8 cols, 1 5/16, 1/8 between.
Areas Served: Upper Ottawa Valley
Delivery Method: Mail, Newsstand, Carrier, Racks
Equipment & Software MAILROOM EQUIPMENT:Bundle Tying Machines — 1/Gd, TS/210; Address Machine — Mail Rite. DISPLAY EQUIPMENT:Printers — Xante DISPLAY SOFTWARE:Layout Software — APP/Mac, QPS/QuarkXPress. EDITORIAL EQUIPMENT:Hardware — APP/Mac; Printers — 2-F EDITORIAL SOFTWARE:QPS/QuarkXPress, APP/Mac, Baseview. PRODUCTION EQUIPMENT:Hardware — COM/II 316, COM/II 40348.

PETERBOROUGH

THE PETERBOROUGH EXAMINER

60 Hunter St., East, Peterborough, ON, K9H 1G5, Canada; gen tel (705) 745-4641; adv tel (705) 745-4641; ed tel (705) 745-4641; gen fax (705) 745-3361; adv fax (705) 745-3361; ed fax (705) 741-3217; gen/nat adv. e-mail dmurphy@postmedia.com; disp adv e-mail dmurphy@postmedia.com; class adv e-mailthepeterbouroughexaminer.classifieds@sunmedia.ca; ed e-mail kmgordon@postmedia.com; web site 1 www.thepeterboroughexaminer.com
Published: Mon, Tues, Wed, Thur, Fri, Sat
Weekday Frequency: e
Saturday Frequency: m
Circulation 8,642; 8,878(sat)
Last Audit: CCAB September 30, 2015
Group: Quebecor Communications, Inc.
Postmedia Network Inc.
Newspaper Reps: Susan Courtney - VP National Sales, QMI Corporate Sales Office
Advertising - Weekday/Saturday: Open inch rate $1.94 (M-Sa); $2.42 (Th)
Online Advertising Rates: Rates on request.
News services: Hollinger Inc., AP, RN.
Established: 1847
Special Editions: TV Channels (Sat).
Special Weekly Sections: Cook Book (Dec); Brides (Jan); Progress (Mar); Home Improvement (May); Seniors Monthly (Monthly); Cook Book (Spring).
Digital Platform - Mobile: Apple, Android
Digital Platform - Tablet: Apple iOS, Android
Pub. .... Darren Murphy
Mng. Ed. .... Jim Hendry
Adv. Mgr. .... Gerry Drage
Circ. Mgr. .... Marg Knot
Buss. Mgr. .... Stefanie Lynch
Class. .... Cindy Jacobs
Prod. Supervisor .... Wayne Willis
Market information: ADS; TMC.
Mechanical available: Offset; Black and 3 ROP colors; insert accepted - samples, tags, etc.; page cutoffs - 22 3/4.
Mechanical Specifications: Type page 11 1/2 x 20 1/2; E - 5 cols, 2 1/4, 1/16 between; A - 10 cols, 1 1/16, 1/16 between; C - 8 cols, 1 1/3, 1/16 between.
Areas Served: Peterborough, Ontario
Delivery Method: Mail, Newsstand, Carrier
Equipment & Software MAILROOM EQUIPMENT:Bundle Tying Machines — 3/OVL. BUSINESS EQUIPMENT:Hardware — ATT CLASSIFIED EQUIPMENT:Hardware — Intel/386 CLASSIFIED SOFTWARE:CText/Classified Pagination (Alps-0S2), CText/Adept (Ad building). DISPLAY EQUIPMENT:Hardware — Intel/386 DISPLAY SOFTWARE:Ad Make-Up Applications — SCS/Layout 8000; Layout Software — SCS/Layout 8000. EDITORIAL EQUIPMENT:Hardware — Intel/486, Intel/386/1-APP/Mac IIcx, 2-APP/Mac Quadra, 1-APP/Mac Quadra 950, 1-Sharp/JX-610 flatbed scanner, 2-CD/Newsline 2644 Picture Desk, 2-Nikon/3500 Scanner, 2-AG/Arcus Flatbed Scanner; Printers — APP/Mac LaserWriter EDITORIAL SOFTWARE:Softwar PRODUCTION EQUIPMENT:Hardware — 2-V/Series 6000 Imagesetter, 1-QMS/860 Print System; Cameras — 1-DS/Horizontal Page Camera C-260-D; Scanners — 2-Nikon/3500 PRODUCTION SOFTWARE:QPS/QuarkXPress 3.1.

SAINT CATHARINE'S

ST. CATHARINES STANDARD

10-1 St. Paul St., Saint Catharine's, ON, L2R 7L4, Canada; gen tel (905) 684-7251; adv tel (905) 684-7251; ed tel (905) 684-7251; gen fax (905) 684-6032; adv fax (905) 684-6032; ed fax (905) 684-6032; gen/nat adv. e-mail john.tobon@sunmedia.ca; disp adv e-mail john.tobon@sunmedia.ca; class adv e-mailclassifieds@stcatharinesstandard.ca; ed e-mail ascott@postmedia.com; web site 1 www.stcatharinesstandard.ca
Published: Mon, Tues, Wed, Thur, Fri, Sat
Weekday Frequency: e
Saturday Frequency: e
Circulation 10,425; 11,215(sat)
Last Audit: AAM June 30, 2016
Group: Postmedia Network Inc.
Quebecor Communications, Inc.
Newspaper Reps: Susan Courtney - VP National Sales, QMI Corporate Sales Office
Advertising - Weekday/Saturday: Open inch rate $2.21 (M-W, F, Sat); $2.87 (Th)
Online Advertising Rates: Rates on request.
News services: QMI Agency **Established:** 1891
Own Printing Facility?: Y
Special Weekly Sections: Autonet, Homes
Digital Platform - Mobile: Apple, Android
Digital Platform - Tablet: Apple iOS, Android
Pub. .... Mark Cressman
Adv. Mgr. .... Mike Thompson
Ed. in Chief .... Peter Conradi
Mng. Ed. .... Erica Bajer
Prodn. Mgr., Mailroom .... Keith Matheson
Reg. Promo. & Comm. Relations Dir. .... Daria Zmiyiwsky
Market information: TMC.
Mechanical available: Black and 3 ROP colors; insert accepted - self-adhesive notes; page cutoffs - 22 3/4.
Mechanical Specifications: Type page 11 1/2 x 20 1/2; E - 5 cols, 2 1/4, 1/8 between; A - 10 cols, 1 1/16, 1/8 between; C - 10 cols, 1 1/16, 1/8 between.
Areas Served: Southern Ontario, Canada
Delivery Method: Newsstand, Carrier
Equipment & Software MAILROOM EQUIPMENT:Inserters & Stuffers — KAN DISPLAY SOFTWARE:Ad Make-Up Applications — SCS/Layout 8000; Layout Software — SCS/Layout 8000. EDITORIAL EQUIPMENT:Hardware — 4-Compaq/Proliant ML530/APP/Power Mac 7300, APP/Mac 7200, APP/Mac 8500, AP/PictureDesk, 6-APP/Mac G4; Printers — 2-HP/LaserJet 4MV EDITORIAL SOFTWARE:Microsoft/Windows NT 4.0, Microsoft/Windows 2000.

SAINT THOMAS

ST. THOMAS TIMES-JOURNAL

16 Hincks St., Saint Thomas, ON, N5R 5Z2, Canada; gen tel (519) 631-2790; adv tel (519) 631-2790; ed tel (519) 631-2790; gen fax (519) 631-5653; adv fax (519) 631-5653; ed fax (519) 631-5653; gen/nat adv. e-mail linda.leblanc@sunmedia.ca; disp adv e-mail linda.leblanc@sunmedia.ca; class adv e-mailst.thomastj.class@sunmedia.ca; ed e-mail don.biggs@sunmedia.ca; web site 1 www.stthomastimesjournal.com
Published: Mon, Tues, Wed, Thur, Fri, Sat
Weekday Frequency: e
Saturday Frequency: m
Circulation 4,165; 4,069(sat)
Last Audit: BPA December 30, 2010
Group: Postmedia Network Inc.
Quebecor Communications, Inc.
Newspaper Reps: Susan Courtney - VP National Sales, QMI Corporate Sales Office
Advertising - Weekday/Saturday: Open inch rate $1.07 (M-F); $1.18 (Sat)
Online Advertising Rates: Rates on request.
News services: CP, AP, RN. **Established:** 1882
Special Weekly Sections: Calendar (Annually); The Great Outdoors (Apr); Back to School (Aug); Christmas Wishbook II (Dec); Hearty Strokes (Feb); All Aboard (Jan); London Profile (Jul); Tourist Guide (Mar); She's My Mom (May); Christmas Crafts (Nov); City Directory (Oct); 911 Serv
Syndicated Publications: TV Tab (Fri).
Digital Platform - Mobile: Apple, Android
Digital Platform - Tablet: Apple iOS, Android
Pub./Adv. Mgr. .... Bev Ponton
Page Ed. .... Ian McCallum
Pub./Adv. Mgr. .... Linda LeBlanc
Office Mgr. .... Julie Tapsell
Market information: TMC.
Mechanical available: Offset; Black and 3 ROP colors; insert accepted; page cutoffs - 12 1/5.
Mechanical Specifications: Type page 10 1/4 x 11 1/2; E - 6 cols, 1 3/8, 1/8 between; A - 6 cols, 1 3/8, 1/8 between; C - 7 cols, 1 1/3, 1/8 between.
Areas Served: St. Thomas, Canada
Delivery Method: Mail, Carrier
Equipment & Software PRESSROOM EQUIPMENT:Pressroom Lines — 8-G/Community 1981; Folders — 1-G/Quarter 1993. MAILROOM EQUIPMENT:Counter Stackers — BG/Count-O-Veyor, BG/209; Bundle Tying Machines — 2/Gd, 1-/Dynaric; Address Machine — 1-/El. BUSINESS EQUIPMENT:Hardware — ATT/3B2-500 CLASSIFIED EQUIPMENT:Hardware — APP/Power Mac/QMS/86 Print System, QMS/Print System; Printers — APP/Mac LaserWriter Pro 630 CLASSIFIED SOFTWARE:Baseview. DISPLAY EQUIPMENT:Hardware — APP/Power Mac; Printers — QMS/Laser Printers, HP/LaserJet 5si/MX DISPLAY SOFTWARE:Ad Make-Up Applications — QPS/QuarkXPress, Adobe/Photoshop, Adobe/Illustrator/; Layout Software — Other Equipment; DTI/Imagesetter, P/Processor. EDITORIAL EQUIPMENT:Hardware — APP/Mac Quadra 610/QMS/860 Print System; Printers — QMS/860 EDITORIAL SOFTWARE:QPS/QuarkXPress, Baseview/NewsEdit. PRODUCTION EQUIPMENT:Hardware — QMS/860 Laser Printer, APP/Mac, Epson/Stylus Colour 3000, Fugi/PI 2800 Imagesetter; Cameras — Acti, Kk/Digital Science DC 50 Zoom; Scanners — Umax/UC840, Epson/Expression 636.

SARNIA

THE OBSERVER

140 South Front St., Sarnia, ON, N7T 7M8, Canada; gen tel (519) 344-3641; adv tel (519) 344-3641; ed tel (519) 344-3641; gen fax (519) 322-2961; adv fax (519)322-2961; ed fax (519) 332-2951; gen/nat adv. e-mail linda.leblanc@sunmedia.ca; disp adv e-mail linda.leblanc@sunmedia.ca; class adv e-mailtheobserver.classifieds@sunmedia.ca; ed e-mail pepp@postmedia.com; web site 1 www.theobserver.ca
Published: Mon, Tues, Wed, Thur, Fri, Sat
Weekday Frequency: e
Saturday Frequency: m
Circulation 10,501; 11,499(sat)
Last Audit: CCAB December 31, 2013
Group: Postmedia Network Inc.
Quebecor Communications, Inc.
Newspaper Reps: Susan Courtney - VP National Sales, QMI Corporate Sales Office
Advertising - Weekday/Saturday: Open inch rate $1.49 (M-F); $1.64 (Sa)
Online Advertising Rates: Rates on request.
News services: 1853
Commercial Printers?: N
Digital Platform - Mobile: Apple, Android
Digital Platform - Tablet: Apple iOS, Android, Kindle
Pub./Sales Dir. .... Linda Leblanc
Mng. Ed. .... Rod Hilts
Office Mgr. .... Barb Mcbride
Circ. .... Marc Roberts
Prod. Mgr. .... Gary Squire
Mechanical available: Letterpress (direct); Black and 3 ROP colors; insert accepted; page cutoffs - 21 1/2.
Mechanical Specifications: Type page 11 1/2 x 20 1/2; E - 6 cols, 2 1/16, 1/8 between.
Areas Served: Sarnia & Lambton County
Delivery Method: Newsstand, Carrier

SAULT SAINTE MARIE

THE SAULT STAR

145 Old Garden River Rd., Sault Sainte Marie, ON, P6A 5M5, Canada; gen tel (705) 759-3030; adv tel (705) 759-3030; ed tel (705) 759-3030; gen fax (705) 759-5947; adv fax (705) 759-5947; ed fax (705) 759-5947; gen/nat adv. e-mail mkennedy@postmedia.com; disp adv e-mail mkennedy@postmedia.com; class adv e-mailsaultstar.classifieds@sunmedia.ca; ed e-mail frupnik@postmedia.com; web site 1 www.saultstar.com
Published: Mon, Tues, Wed, Thur, Fri, Sat
Weekday Frequency: e
Saturday Frequency: m
Circulation 7,569; 7,640(sat)
Last Audit: CCAB September 30, 2015
Group: Postmedia Network Inc.
Quebecor Communications, Inc.
Newspaper Reps: Susan Courtney - VP National Sales, QMI Corporate Sales Office
Advertising - Weekday/Saturday: Open inch rate $1.75 (M-F); $1.93 (Sat)
Online Advertising Rates: Rates on request.
News services: 1912
Own Printing Facility?: Y
Commercial Printers?: Y
Special Weekly Sections: Fall Fashion (Aug); Christmas Greetings (Dec); RRSP (Feb); Brides '07 (Jan); Station Mall Side Walk Sale (Jul); Side Walk Sale (Jun); Car Care (May); Home Front (Monthly); Queenstown Christmas (Nov); Station Mall (Oct); Brides (Sept).
Syndicated Publications: TV Times (Fri); Comics (Sat); Classified (Wed).
Digital Platform - Mobile: Apple, Android
Digital Platform - Tablet: Apple iOS, Android
Pres./Pub. .... Lou Maulucci
Ed. .... Frank Rupnik

Mgr., Admin. ....Jackie DePasquale
Adv. Mgr. ....Mike Kennedy
Dir., Reader Sales/Serv. ....Bruno Vit
City Ed. ....Jeff Ougler
Data Processing Mgr. ....Steve Shooks
Prodn. Mgr. ....Kevin Caron
Prodn. Foreman, Pressroom ....Gary Graham
Market information: ADS; TMC.
Mechanical available: Offset; Black and 3
ROP colors; insert accepted - Samples,
Catalogues; page cutoffs - 22 3/4.
Mechanical Specifications: Type page 11 1/2
x 20 1/2; E - 5 cols, 2 9/50, 1/8 between;
A - 10 cols, 1, 1/8 between; C - 10 cols, 1,
1/8 between.
Areas Served: Sault Ste. Marie

Delivery Method: Newsstand, Carrier, Racks
Equipment & Software PRESSROOM
EQUIPMENT:Pressroom Lines — 8-G/
Urbanite; Folders — 1 MAILROOM
EQUIPMENT:Counter Stackers — BG/Count-
O-Veyor; Inserters & Stuffers — 1-KAN/320
8 station, 1-MM/Saddle Stitcher, MM/
Quarter; Bundle Tying Machines — 1-MLN/
ML2EE, 6-Gd/Q; Address Machine — 1/
WM; Other Equipment — MM/Minuteman.
BUSINESS EQUIPMENT:Hardware — PBS
BUSINESS SOFTWARE:Smart Stream
CLASSIFIED EQUIPMENT:Hardware —
Compaq/File servers, Compaq; Printers
— APP/Mac LaserWriter NTX CLASSIFIED
SOFTWARE:Baseview. DISPLAY
EQUIPMENT:Hardware — ACER; Printers
— HP/4050 DISPLAY SOFTWARE:Layout
Software — SCS/Layout 8000. EDITORIAL
EQUIPMENT:Hardware — Compaq/
fileservers, APP/Mac, Compaq; Printers —
QMS/860, APP/Mac LaserWriter NTX, APP/
Mac LaserWriter IIg, AU/APS-108-12C, HP/
Laserjet 9000, HP/Laxerjet 4050 EDITORIAL
SOFTWARE:NT, Baseview, APP/Mac
System 9.2 3, QPS, Microsoft/Window-NT.
PRODUCTION EQUIPMENT:Hardware
— 2-Nu/Flip Top FT4OUP, 4-APP/
Mac LaserPrinter, 2-AU/APS 108-12C;
Cameras — 1-C/Spartan III; Scanners —
APP/Mac, APP/Mac G3 PRODUCTION
SOFTWARE:QPS/QuarkXPress 3.1, Ad
Tracking 3.0.

SIMCOE

THE SIMCOE REFORMER
50 Gilbertson Dr., Simcoe, ON, N3Y 4L2,
Canada; gen tel (519) 426-5710; adv tel
(519) 426-5710; ed tel (519) 426-5710;
gen fax (519) 426-9255; adv fax (519) 426-
9255; ed fax (519) 426-9255; gen/nat adv.
e-mail sdowns@bowesnet.com; disp adv
e-mail sdowns@bowesnet.com; class adv
e-mailsimcoereformer.classifieds@sunmedia.
ca; ed e-mail knovak@postmedia.com; web
site 1 www.simcoereformer.ca
Published: Mon, Tues, Wed, Thur, Fri
Weekday Frequency: e
Circulation 8,950
Last Audit: Sworn/Estimate/Non-Audited
September 30, 2017
Group: Postmedia Network Inc.
Quebecor Communications, Inc.
Newspaper Reps: Susan Courtney - VP National
Sales, QMI Corporate Sales Office
Advertising - Weekday/Saturday: Open inch rate
$1.17
News services: CP. **Established:** 1858
Digital Platform - Mobile: Apple, Android
Digital Platform - Tablet: Apple iOS, Android
Pub. ....Ken Koyoma
Mng. Ed. ....Kim Novak
Adv. Mgr. ....Sue Downs
Circ. Mgr. ....Andrew Kiss
Circ. ....Andrew Foster
Prod. Mgr. ....Deb Campbell
Market information: TMC; Zoned editions.
Mechanical available: Offset; Black and 3 ROP
colors; insert accepted; page cutoffs - 21 1/2.
Mechanical Specifications: Type page 11 1/2 x
20 1/2; E - 6 cols, 2 1/15, 1/8 between; A - 6
cols, 2 1/15, 1/8 between; C - 9 cols, 1 1/3,
1/8 between.
Areas Served: Simcoe, Ontario

Delivery Method: Mail, Newsstand, Carrier
Equipment & Software PRESSROOM

EQUIPMENT:Pressroom Lines — 6-G;
Folders — 1-G/Quarter and Half fold.
MAILROOM EQUIPMENT:Bundle
Tying Machines — 2/Bu, 2-/Strapper;
Address Machine — ATT. BUSINESS
EQUIPMENT:Hardware — ATT CLASSIFIED
EQUIPMENT:Hardware — Mk. DISPLAY
SOFTWARE:Layout Software — APP/Mac.
EDITORIAL EQUIPMENT:Hardware — Mk.
PRODUCTION EQUIPMENT:Hardware —
1-Fuji/360F; Cameras — 2-R.

STRATFORD

THE STRATFORD BEACON HERALD
789 Eerie St., Stratford, ON, N4Z 1A1,
Canada; gen tel (519) 271-2222; adv tel
(519) 271-2222; ed tel (519) 271-2222; gen
fax (519) 271-1026; adv fax (519) 271-1031;
ed fax (519)271-1026; gen/nat adv. e-mail
carmstrong@postmedia.com; disp adv e-mail
carmstrong@postmedia.com; ed e-mail
burquhart@postmedia.com; web site 1 www.
stratfordbeaconherald.com
Published: Mon, Tues, Wed, Thur, Fri, Sat
Weekday Frequency: e
Saturday Frequency: m
Circulation 6,643; 6,643(sat)
Last Audit: Sworn/Estimate/Non-Audited
September 30, 2017
Group: Postmedia Network Inc.
Quebecor Communications, Inc.
Newspaper Reps: Susan Courtney - VP National
Sales, QMI Corporate Sales Office
Advertising - Weekday/Saturday: Open inch rate
$1.02
News services: CP **Established:** 1923
Own Printing Facility?: N
Commercial Printers?: N
Special Weekly Sections: Festival (May).
Digital Platform - Mobile: Apple, Android
Digital Platform - Tablet: Apple iOS, Android
Mng. Ed. ....Bruce Urquhart
Circ. Mgr. ....Barb Boyne
Credit Mgr. ....Janice Humphrey
Prodn. Mgr. ....Leigh McCann
Reporter ....Galen Simmons
Sports Editor ....Cory Smith
Terry Bridge
Reporter ....Jonathan Juha
Advertising Director ....Curtis Armstrong
Market information: TMC.
Mechanical available: Offset; Black and 3 ROP
colors; insert accepted; page cutoffs - 22 3/4.
Mechanical Specifications: Type page 11 1/2 x
20 1/2; E - 6 cols, 1 13/16, 1/8 between; A - 6
cols, 3 3/4, 1/8 between; C - 6 cols, between.
Areas Served: Stratford, Ontario
Delivery Method: Mail, Newsstand, Carrier
Equipment & Software PRESSROOM
EQUIPMENT:Pressroom Lines —
8-SLN/Offset 1988. MAILROOM
EQUIPMENT:Counter Stackers — BG/108;
Bundle Tying Machines — 1/Nichiro Kogyo/
TS-210; Wrapping Singles — Beacon.
BUSINESS EQUIPMENT:Hardware
— 1-DEC/1123 CLASSIFIED
EQUIPMENT:Hardware — APP/Mac
G3; Printers — 1-XIT/Schooner, 2-XIT/
Clipper CLASSIFIED SOFTWARE:CAMS
4.0. DISPLAY EQUIPMENT:Hardware —
APP/Mac 4.0; Printers — 2-XIT/Clipper,
1-XIT/Schooner, 2-Xante, 1-Lexmark/
Optra DISPLAY SOFTWARE:Ad Make-
Up Applications — Multi-Ad 4.0, QPS/
QuarkXPress 3.3, Adobe/Photoshop 4.0,
Caere/OmniPage Pro 8.0. EDITORIAL
EQUIPMENT:Hardware — APP/Mac NT
Server; Printers — 2-Xante, 1-Lexmark/
Optra, 2-XIT/Clipper, 1-Schooner EDITORIAL
SOFTWARE:QPS/QuarkXPress, Microsoft/
Windows NT Server 4.0, HP/Netserver.
PRODUCTION EQUIPMENT:Hardware
— Caere/OmniPro 8.0, 2-XIT/Clippers
LaserPrinter, 2-Xante/LaserPrinter,
1-Lexmark/LaserPrinter; Cameras —
1-Acti/204; Scanners — 5-Scanmaker
Scanner PRODUCTION SOFTWARE:QPS/
QuarkXPress 4.0.

STURGEON FALLS

THE TRIBUNE
206 King St., Sturgeon Falls, ON, P2B
1R7, Canada; gen tel (705) 753-2930; gen
fax (705) 753-5231; gen/nat adv. e-mail
tribune@westnipissing.com; web site 1 www.
westnipissing.com
Published: Mon, Tues, Wed, Thur, Fri, Sat
Circulation 6,683
Last Audit: CCAB September 30, 2015
Advertising - Weekday/Saturday: agate line=$0.70
News services: 1968
Own Printing Facility?: Y
Commercial Printers?: Y
Special Editions: Bridal, Financial planning,
Women's Day, Volunteer Week, Mother's Day,
Spring Home, Yard and Garden, Automotive,
St-Jean Baptiste, Graduation, Summer
Festivals, Back to School, Fall Home, Winter
Automotive, Christmas Wishes...
Special Weekly Sections: TV Guide, crossword &
horoscope; classifieds
Ed. ....Suzanne Gammon
Prodn. Mgr. ....Jason Steven
Circulation and accounts ....Linda Birmingham
Mechanical Specifications: Type page 10 1/4 x
14; E - 6 cols, 1 1/2, 1/4 between; A - 6 cols,
1 1/2, 1/4 between.
Delivery Method: Mail, Newsstand

SUDBURY

THE SUDBURY STAR
128 Pine Street Suite 201, Sudbury, ON,
P3C 1X3, Canada; gen tel (705) 674-5271;
adv tel (705) 674-5271 ext. 505250; ed
tel (705)674-5271 ext. 505232; gen fax
(705) 674-0624; adv fax (705)674-0624;
ed fax (705)674-0624; gen/nat adv. e-mail
kjohansen@postmedia.com; disp adv e-mail
kjohansen@postmedia.com; class adv
e-mailthesudburystar.classifieds@sunmedia.
com; ed e-mail dmacdonald@postmedia.
com; web site 1 www.thesudburystar.com
Published: Mon, Tues, Wed, Thur, Fri, Sat
Weekday Frequency: e
Saturday Frequency: m
Circulation 8,399; 8,994(sat)
Last Audit: CCAB September 30, 2015
Group: Postmedia Network Inc.
Advertising - Weekday/Saturday: Open inch rate
$2.09
Online Advertising Rates: $20 - CPM
News services: CP. **Established:** 1909
Special Editions: Weekend Alive (Fri).
Syndicated Publications: TV Listings (Fri); Travel
(Sat); Real Estate Guide (Thur).
Publisher / Ad Director ....Karsten Johansen
Circ. Mgr. ....Dave Pacquett
Office Mgr. ....Mary Valade
City Ed. ....Don MacDonald
News Ed. ....Andrew Low
Sports Ed. ....Bruce Heidman
???? ????
Pub./Adv. Dir. ....David Kilgour
Market information: ADS; Split run; TMC; Zoned
editions.
Mechanical available: Letterpress; Black and
3 ROP colors; insert accepted - all; page
cutoffs - 21 1/2.
Mechanical Specifications: Type page 11 1/2 x
21 1/2; E - 5 cols, 2 1/6, 1/8 between; A - 10
cols, 1 1/64, 1/8 between; C - 10 cols, 1 1/64,
1/8 between.
Areas Served: Northern Ontario

Delivery Method: Mail, Newsstand
Equipment & Software PRESSROOM
EQUIPMENT:Pressroom Lines —
Multilith/1850; 10-G/Urbanite 1999.
MAILROOM EQUIPMENT:Bundle Tying
Machines — 3-Acme/P5N250APB, Gd Oval
Strapping; Wrapping Singles — Manual;
Address Machine — 1/Am. BUSINESS
EQUIPMENT:Hardware — IBM/Sys 34
CLASSIFIED EQUIPMENT:Hardware
— 1-APP/iMac, 4-APP/Mac Power Mac
G3; Printers — APP/Mac LaserWriter
Pro 60 CLASSIFIED SOFTWARE:Ad
Manager Pro 1.05, APP/Mac 8.1. DISPLAY
EQUIPMENT:Hardware — 2-Compaq/
Desktop Pro 575, Touch; Printers —

Samsung/ML-4600 DISPLAY SOFTWARE:Ad
Make-Up Applications — Lotus 123,
WordPerfect; Layout Software — NewzWare.
EDITORIAL EQUIPMENT:Hardware —
1-Acer/Veriton S100, 1-APP/iMac Power Mac
8600-300, 10-APP/Power Mac 7300-200,
Mitsubishi/Diamond Scan 15VX, Mitsubushi/
Diamond Pro 91TXV/Microtech/Card Reader,
Poloroid/SprintScan 35 Plus, Umax/Astra
1200S flat-bed scanner; Printers — Printe
PRODUCTION EQUIPMENT:Hardware —
Graham, Laser Red 1800HT 2, Newsline
Solo/Listener, Hoechst/Encomatic; Cameras
— B/3-in-1, 4-Kk/DC26S Zoom; Scanners —
ECR/Autokon, Microtec Photo Card Reader,
Umax/Astra 1200S 2, Umax/Astra 2400S
PRODUCTION SOFTWARE:Adobe/Acrobat
4.0, Adobe/Pagemake

THUNDER BAY

THE CHRONICLE-JOURNAL
75 S. Cumberland St., Thunder Bay, ON, P7B
1A3, Canada; gen tel (807) 343-6200; adv tel
(807) 343 6219; ed tel (807) 343-6215; gen
fax (807) 345-5991; adv fax (807) 345-3582;
ed fax (807) 343-9409; gen/nat adv. e-mail
skabir@chroniclejournal.com; disp adv e-mail
skabir@chroniclejournal.com; class adv
e-mailclassifieds@chroniclejournal.com; ed
e-mail editor@chroniclejournal.com; web site
1 www.chroniclejournal.com
Published: Mon, Tues, Wed, Thur, Fri, Sat, Sun
Weekday Frequency: m
Saturday Frequency: m
Circulation 15,956; 17,306(sat); 15,657(sun)
Last Audit: AAM September 30, 2015
Group: Continental Newspapers LTD
Horizon Publications Inc.
Newspaper Reps: Alvin Chow - Dir., Integrated
Adv., Postmedia Network Inc.

Mark Gravel - Sales Mgr., Integrated Adv.,
Postmedia Network Inc.

Greg Morton - VP/GM, Postmedia Network Inc.
Branch Offices: Kelowna, BC
Advertising - Weekday/Saturday: Open inch rate
$2.32 (M-F); $2.55 (Sat)
Advertising - Sunday: Open inch rate $2.32
Online Advertising Rates: Rates on request
News services: CP, AP. **Established:** 1899
Own Printing Facility?: Y
Commercial Printers?: Y
Special Editions: Outdoor Guide, Horizons
Special Weekly Sections: Building & Home
Improvement (Apr); Dining Guide (Aug);
Weddings By Design (Jul); Transportation
Week (May); Shop Canada (Monthly); Under
the Tree (Nov); Weddings By Design (Oct);
Garden Time (Spring).
Syndicated Publications: TV Scene (Sat).
Pub. ....Colin J. Bruce
Managing Ed. ....Greg Giddens
Dir., Finance ....Hilda Caverly
Pub./GM ....Clint Harris
Circ. Dir. ....Harry Brown
Editorial Page Ed. ....Ian Pattison
News Ed. ....Joanne Kushnier
Sports Ed. ....John Nagy
Systems/Traffic Mgr. ....Dave Wadson
Prodn. Foreman, Pressroom ....Joe St. Lawrence
Mng. Ed. ....Julio Gomes
Mgr., Adv. ....Steve Benoit
Market information: TMC; Zoned editions.
Mechanical available: Offset; Black and 3 ROP
colors; insert accepted; page cutoffs - 22 3/4.
Mechanical Specifications: Type page 10 1/2 x
21 1/2; E - 6 cols, 1/8 between; A - 10 cols,
1 1/6, 1/8 between; C - 6 cols, 1 3/4, 1/8
between.
Delivery Method: Mail, Newsstand, Carrier,
Racks
Equipment & Software PRESSROOM
EQUIPMENT:Pressroom Lines — 10-G/
Urbanite single width 1977; Press Drive
— 2-DC Motors/100 h.p.; Folders — 1
MAILROOM EQUIPMENT:Counter Stackers
— Id; Inserters & Stuffers — 1-MM/Alphaliner;
Bundle Tying Machines — 2/Akibono, 2-Gd/
Constellation; Wrapping Singles — 2-/IDAB
Baggers; Other Equipment — MM/Saddle
Stitcher. BUSINESS EQUIPMENT:Hardware
— HP, IBM/Newzware BUSINESS
SOFTWARE:Microsoft/Excel 98 CLASSIFIED

EQUIPMENT:Hardware — HAS, APP/Power Mac 4400; Printers - APP/Mac LaserWriter 8500 CLASSIFIED SOFTWARE:QPS/ QuarkXPress 3.3.2, Baseview/Adman Pro 1.050. DISPLAY EQUIPMENT:Hardware — APP/Power Mac, Polaroid/SprintScan (35), APP/Mac G4; Printers — Pre Press/ Panther Catara 46, Pre Press/Panther Pro 46, HP/5000, APP/Mac 8500 DISPLAY SOFTWARE:Ad Make-Up Applications — QPS/QuarkXPress 3.32, Adobe/Photoshop 5.5, Adobe/Illustrator 8.0, Aldus/Freehand 8.0. EDITORIAL EQUIPMENT:Hardware — APP/Mac Performa, APP/Power Mac 7200, APP/Power Mac 8500, G3; Printers — Pre Press/Panther Catara, Pre Press/Panther Pro 46, HP/5000 EDITORIAL SOFTWARE:QPS/ QuarkXPress 3.32, Baseview/ NewsEditPro IQ 2.2. PRODUCTION EQUIPMENT:Hardware — WL Plate Processor, Pre Press/Panther Catara 46, Pre Press/Panther Pro 46, HP/5000, APP/ Mac 8500; Cameras — ACTI/125; Scanners — Linotype Hell Ultr 2, Polaroid/SprintScan (35), AGFA Snapscan E25 PRODUCTION SOFTWARE:QPS/QuarkXPress 3.2, Baseview/News

TIMMINS

THE TIMMINS DAILY PRESS

187 Cedar St. South, Timmins, ON, P4N 7G1, Canada; gen tel (705) 268-5050; adv tel (705) 268-5050; ed tel (705) 268-5050; gen fax (705) 268-7373; adv fax (705) 268-7373; ed fax (705) 268-7373; gen/nat adv. e-mail tdp.advertising@sunmedia.ca; disp adv e-mail tdp.advertising@sunmedia.ca; class adv e-mailtimminspress.classifieds@sunmedia.ca; ed e-mail tperry@postmedia.com; web site 1 www.timminspress.com
Published: Mon, Tues, Wed, Thur, Fri, Sat
Weekday Frequency: m
Saturday Frequency: m
Circulation 6,634; 6,714(sat)
Last Audit: BPA December 30, 2010
Group: Postmedia Network Inc.
Quebecor Communications, Inc.
Newspaper Reps: Susan Courtney - VP National Sales, QMI Corporate Sales Office
Advertising - Weekday/Saturday: Open inch rate $1.22 (M-Th); $1.29 (F-Sat)
Online Advertising Rates: Rates on request.
News services: CP. **Established:** 1934
Special Editions: Mining (Annually).
Special Weekly Sections: Business & Industry North (Monthly); Frontier Mining (Quarterly).
Syndicated Publications: TV Scene (Fri).
Pub. .... Lisa Wilson
Mng. Ed. .... Thomas Perry
City Ed. .... Wayne Snider
Circ. Mgr. .... Gio Crispo
Adv. Mgr. .... Anne Laferriere
Circ. Mgr. .... Dean Lessard
Market information: TMC.
Mechanical available: Offset; Black and 3 ROP colors; insert accepted; page cutoffs - 22 3/4.
Mechanical Specifications: Type page 11 1/2 x 20 1/2; E - 6 cols, 2 1/16, 1/8 between; A - 6 cols, 2 1/16, 1/8 between; C - 9 cols, 1 1/3, 1/8 between.
Areas Served: Northeastern Ontario

Delivery Method: Mail, Newsstand
Equipment & Software PRESSROOM EQUIPMENT:Pressroom Lines — 8-G/ Community; Folders — 1 MAILROOM EQUIPMENT:Bundle Tying Machines — 1/ Gd; Other Equipment — MM/Minuteman. CLASSIFIED EQUIPMENT:Hardware — CText. EDITORIAL EQUIPMENT:Hardware — CText. PRODUCTION EQUIPMENT:Hardware — CD; Cameras — 1-Nu.

TORONTO

NATIONAL POST

365 Bloor St East, Toronto, ON, M4W3L4, Canada; gen tel (416) 383-2300; adv tel (800) 668-5617; ed tel (416) 383-2300; gen fax (416) 442-2209; adv fax (416) 386-2696; ed fax (416) 383-2443; gen/nat adv. e-mail queries@nationalpost.com; disp adv e-mail advqueries@nationalpost.com; web site 1 www.nationalpost.com
Published: Mon, Tues, Wed, Thur, Fri, Sat
Weekday Frequency: m
Saturday Frequency: m
Circulation 72,487; 81,948(sat)
Last Audit: AAM September 30, 2016
Group: Postmedia Network Inc.
Advertising - Weekday/Saturday: Open inch rate $15.46
Online Advertising Rates: Big Box: $45 Leaderboard: $45
News services: APP, AP, CP, DJ, NYT, RN. **Established:** 1998
Own Printing Facility?: Y
Commercial Printers?: N
Special Weekly Sections: FP Executive, FP Entrepreneur, Legal Post, FP Mining, Post Driving, Post Movies, Weekend Post, Post Homes
Syndicated Publications: Financial Post Magazine, Post Homes Magazine
Digital Platform - Mobile: Apple, Android, Windows, Blackberry
Digital Platform - Tablet: Apple iOS, Android, Windows 7, Blackberry Tablet OS, Kindle, Nook, Kindle Fire
Editor .... Anne Marie Owens
SVP, Community Publishing Group + Reader Sales + Service .... Craig Barnard
Senior VP, National Post .... Gerry Nott
Chief Revenue Officer .... Paula Festas
President .... Gordon Fisher
Market information: Split run; TMC; Zoned editions.
Mechanical available: Offset; Black and 3 ROP colors; insert accepted - min. 6 x 8; page cutoffs - 21 3/4.
Mechanical Specifications: Type page 10 4/5 x 21 3/4; E - 6 cols, 1 1/16, between; A - 10 cols, 1 1/16, between; C - 10 cols, 1 1/16, between.
Areas Served: Entire Canadian area
Delivery Method: Newsstand, Carrier
Equipment & Software BUSINESS EQUIPMENT:Hardware — In-house Southam System-Vax based BUSINESS SOFTWARE:Microsoft/Office, Microsoft/ Exchange DISPLAY EQUIPMENT:Hardware — APP/Mac G3; Printers — HP DISPLAY SOFTWARE:Ad Make-Up Applications — QuickTrac 6.0, QPS/QuarkXPress 3.32; Layout Software — SCS/Layout-8000, ALS. EDITORIAL EQUIPMENT:Hardware — APP/Mac G3/Au/Apscom; Printers — HP, Xante, Graphic Enterprises/ EDITORIAL SOFTWARE:QPS 1.12, QPS/QuarkXPress 3.32. PRODUCTION EQUIPMENT:Hardware — Au/APS-3850, T/One Merlin; Scanners — Eskoscan/2024, Eskoscan/2636, Epson, Kk PRODUCTION SOFTWARE:QPS/ QuarkXPress 3.32, QuickTrac, SCS, Linx.

THE EPOCH TIMES

344 Consumers Rd, Toronto, ON, M2J 1P8, Canada; gen tel (416) 298-1933; adv tel (416) 986-3525; ed tel (416) 298-1933; gen fax (416) 298-1299; adv fax (416) 298-1299; ed fax (416) 298-1299; gen/nat adv. e-mail canada_ads@epochtimes.com; disp adv e-mail canada_ads@epochtimes.com; class adv e-mailethan.guo@epochtimes.com; ed e-mail newsdesk@epochtimes.com; web site 1 www.theepochtimes.com/n2/#ca
Published: Mon, Tues, Wed, Thur, Fri, Sat, Sun
Weekday Frequency: m
Saturday Frequency: m
Last Audit: CCAB September 30, 2017
Group: Epoch Times Media Inc.
Advertising - Weekday/Saturday: 1/32 p.: $188; 1/16 p.: $314; 1/8 p.: $522
Online Advertising Rates: Rates on request.
News services: 2000
Senior Director of Sales Development ... Leah Lan
Mechanical Specifications: Type page 11 x 20 1/4

THE GLOBE AND MAIL

444 Front St. W., Toronto, ON, M5V 2S9, Canada; gen tel (416) 585-5000; gen fax (416) 585-5698; gen/nat adv. e-mail advertising@globeandmail.com; ed e-mail newsroom@globeandmail.com; web site 1 www.theglobeandmail.com - 62,000,000(views) 5,734,000(visitors)
Published: Mon, Tues, Wed, Thur, Fri, Sat
Weekday Frequency: m
Saturday Frequency: m
Circulation 213,520; 284,998(sat)
Last Audit: AAM September 30, 2016
Newspaper Reps: Ediz Binder - Mktg. and Sales Dev. Mgr., Publicitas North America
Branch Offices: Vancouver, BC
Montreal, QC
Advertising - Weekday/Saturday: Open inch rate $31.88 (Mon-Fri); $35.06 (Sat)
Online Advertising Rates: Rates available upon request

News services: AFP, CP, DJ, Economist, NYT, RN, SHNS, TMS. **Established:** 1844
Special Weekly Sections: Report on Mutual Funds (Monthly); Gusto (Other).
Syndicated Publications: Travel (Sat); Technology (Thur); Travel (Wed); Globe Television (Weekly).
Digital Platform - Mobile: Apple, Android, Blackberry
Digital Platform - Tablet: Apple iOS
Public Ed. .... Sylvia Stead
Commentary Ed. .... Natasha Hassan
Globe Review Ed. .... Andrew Gorham
Photo Ed. .... Moe Doiron
Report on Bus. Ed. .... Michael Babad
Ed.-in-Chief .... David Walmsley
VP, Mktg. .... Sean Humphrey
VP, Operations .... Perry Nixdorf
CRO .... Andrew Saunders
Market information: ADS; Split run.
Mechanical available: Offset; Black and 3 ROP colors; insert accepted - magazines, product samples; page cutoffs - 22 3/4.
Mechanical Specifications: Type page 9.88 x 20; E - 6 cols, 1 13/16, 3/16 between; A - 6 cols, 1 13/16, 3/16 between; C - 6 cols, 1 13/16, 3/16 between.
Areas Served: Entire Canadian region

Delivery Method: Mail, Newsstand, Carrier
Equipment & Software BUSINESS EQUIPMENT:Hardware — BUSINESS SOFTWARE:Oracle CLASSIFIED EQUIPMENT:Hardware — HI/Ad / Power; Printers — HP/7970. DISPLAY SOFTWARE:Ad Make-Up Applications — HI; Layout Software — HI/8300 Pagination System. EDITORIAL EQUIPMENT:Hardware — AT, HI/NMP Pagination System, CCI/ Ethernet EDITORIAL SOFTWARE:AT. PRODUCTION EQUIPMENT:Hardware — HI/Images Graphic Subsystem, Prosetter; Scanners — ECR/Autokon 2045, Sharp/600, Nikon, Linotype-Hell, AG.

THE TORONTO SUN

365 Bloor St. E., 6th Floor, Toronto, ON, M4W 3L4, Canada; gen tel (416) 947-2222; adv tel (416) 947-2333; ed tel (416) 947-2211; gen fax (416) 368-0374; adv fax (416) 947-3139; ed fax (416) 947-1664; gen/ nat adv. e-mail torsun.retail@sunmedia.ca; disp adv e-mail torsun.retail@sunmedia.ca; class adv e-mailtorontosun.classifieds@sunmedia.ca; ed e-mail torsun.citydesk@sunmedia.ca; web site 1 www.torontosun.com - 30,000,000(views)
Published: Mon, Tues, Wed, Thur, Fri, Sat, Sun
Weekday Frequency: m
Saturday Frequency: m
Circulation 86,462; 80,194(sat); 95,172(sun)
Last Audit: CCAB September 30, 2015
Group: Postmedia Network Inc.
Newspaper Reps: Bill Bratt - Adv. Dir., Digital & Print Ad Sales, QMI Corporate Sales Office

Susan Courtney - VP National Sales, QMI Corporate Sales Office

Advertising - Weekday/Saturday: Open line rate $6.97
Advertising - Sunday: Open inch rate $10.09
Online Advertising Rates: Big Box/Leaderboard/ SkyScraper $1700/100,000 Imp

News services: QMi, AFP, RN, Wenn News, TSN **Established:** 1971
Own Printing Facility?: N
Commercial Printers?: N
Special Editions: Tribute (Every other month).
Special Weekly Sections: TV Book
Digital Platform - Mobile: Apple, Android, Blackberry
Digital Platform - Tablet: Apple iOS, Android, Kindle
Deputy Editor .... Kevin Hann
Cor. Dir., HR .... Chris Krygiel
Sr. Assoc. Ed. .... Lorrie Goldstein
Cartoonist .... Andrew Donato
Travel Ed. .... Robin Robinson
Sports Ed. .... Bill Pierce
Corporate Entertainment Editor Kevin Williamson
Lifestyle/Food Ed. .... Rita DeMontis
News Research Dept. .... Julie Kirsh
VP & CIO, Info Serv. .... Richard Roy
Vice President, Advertising Sales Darren Murphy
Sales Director/Director of Promotion Lesley Annett
Vice President, Finance .... Piero Menicucci
Executive Assistant to the Publisher .... Christina Fleming
Comment Editor .... Adrienne Batra
Pub. .... Mike Power
Corporate VP, Reader Sales & Services .... Steve Angelevski
Adv. Dir. .... Bill Bratt
Mechanical available: Printing Process: Cold Web OffSET
Mechanical Specifications: Format Tabloid, Live Area 10.3330" x 11.4290" Column Width 0.8330" Column Depth 160 agate lines x 10 columns
Areas Served: Toronto and surrounding areas - including Kingston, Windsor, Sudbury, Hamilton, Niagara
Delivery Method: Newsstand, Carrier
Equipment & Software BUSINESS EQUIPMENT:Hardware — IBM xseries Dell Blades HP EVA EMC San BUSINESS SOFTWARE:DTI CLASSIFIED EQUIPMENT:Hardware — Dell Blades HP EVA EMC San/DTI MediaPlus; Printers — Sharp CLASSIFIED SOFTWARE:DTI MediaPlus DISPLAY EQUIPMENT:Hardware — Dell Blades HP EVA EMC San; Printers — Sharp DISPLAY SOFTWARE:Ad Make-Up Applications — Indesign / QuarkXPress, Adobe/Illustrator; Layout Software — MediaSpectrum EDITORIAL EQUIPMENT:Hardware — Dell Blades HP EVA EMC San/APP/Mac/PCs; Printers — Sharp EDITORIAL SOFTWARE:MediaSpan Jazzbox PRODUCTION EQUIPMENT:Hardware — Dell Blades; Cameras — Nikon PRODUCTION SOFTWARE:Newsway

TORONTO STAR

1 Yonge St., Toronto, ON, M5E 1E6, Canada; gen tel (416) 367-2000; adv tel (416) 777-7777; ed tel (416) 869-4300; gen fax (416) 869-4328; adv fax 416-814-3270; ed fax (416) 869-4328; gen/nat adv. e-mail adinfo@thestar.ca; disp adv e-mail adinfo@thestar.ca; class adv e-mailstarad@thestar.ca; ed e-mail igentle@thestar.ca; web site 1 www.thestar.com - 61,000,000(views) 3,300,000(visitors)
Published: Mon, Tues, Wed, Thur, Fri, Sat, Sun
Weekday Frequency: m
Saturday Frequency: m
Circulation 132,896; 224,394(sat); 158,652(sun)
Last Audit: CCAB September 30, 2017
Group: Torstar
Advertising - Weekday/Saturday: One (2" x 1"): $846.87, $1,101.35 (Sat); Two (2" x 2"): $1,629.53, $2,119.39 (Sat); Three (2" x 2-13/16"): $2,299.59, $2,989.89 (Sat)
Advertising - Sunday: One (2" x 1"): $593.49; Two (2" x 2"): $1,140.78; Three (2" x 2-13/16"): $1,610.38
Online Advertising Rates: Rates on request.
News services: CP, TR, WP, TMS, NYT, Bloomberg, Getty Images **Established:** 1892
Own Printing Facility?: Y
Commercial Printers?: Y
Special Editions: Starweek (Sat).
Special Weekly Sections: Travel, Wheels, New In Homes, Condos, Comics, NYT Weekly
Syndicated Publications: Golf, Do-It (Home Improvement), various special section opportunities.
Digital Platform - Mobile: Apple, Android, Windows, Blackberry
Digital Platform - Tablet: Apple iOS, Android, Kindle, Nook, Kindle Fire
Pub. .... John Cruickshank
Ed. in Chief .... Michael Cooke
Managing Ed. .... Irene Gentle
CIO, Metroland & Star Media Group, Group IT,

Torstar Corporation .... Paula Sinclair
VP & CFO .... Peter Bishop
VP, Adv. .... Sandy Muir
Adv. Grp. Dir., Home/Automotive/Sports/ Entertainment .... Norm Laing
Adv. Grp. Dir., Nat'l/Technology .... Carolyn Sadler
Adv. Mgr., Mktg. Research/Info .... Jim Fahey
Adv. Mgr., Syndicate .... Robin Graham
Vice Pres., Mktg. .... Sandy MacLeod
Dir. Cir. .... Terry Willows
Circ. Mgr., Home Delivery .... Brenda Yarwood
EVP-Torstar Printing Group .... Dean Zavarise
Asst. Mng. Ed., Entertainment/Life .... John Ferri
Dir., Creative Mktg .... Lorne Silver
Mng. Ed. .... Jane Davenport
Market information: Split run; TMC.
Mechanical available: Offset; Black and 3 ROP colors; insert accepted; page cutoffs - 22.
Mechanical Specifications: Type page 10 1/2 x 20.8120; E - 6 cols, 1 3/4, 1/6 between; A - 10 cols, 1 1/16, 1/12 between; C - 10 cols, 1 1/16, 1/12 between.
Areas Served: Greater Toronto area
Delivery Method: Mail
Equipment & Software PRESSROOM EQUIPMENT:Pressroom Lines — 12-MAN/ Colorman (60 printing couples) 1992; 12-MAN/Colorman (60 printing couples) 1992; 12-MAN/Colorman (60 printing couples) 1992 MAILROOM EQUIPMENT:Counter Stackers — 9-HL/II; Inserters & Stuffers — 6/ AM Graphics/630; Bundle Tying Machines — 6-/Power Strap, 14-Dynaric/NP3, 18-/ Power Strap/inserting; Wrapping Singles — 18-/Power Strap/Three Quarter Wrap, 9-/ Power Strap/PSN 250; Mailroom Control System — Mailroom control sys BUSINESS EQUIPMENT:Hardware — Hitachi/EX 80, HP/client server system, Sun/client server system BUSINESS SOFTWARE:Microsoft/ PC Products, Discus, CCI Adobe, Quark CLASSIFIED EQUIPMENT:Hardware — Hitachi/Ex 80, Dell PCs, Dell Servers, Sun Servers, ; Printers — HP, Cannon, Xerox CLASSIFIED SOFTWARE:CCI, ADS DISPLAY EQUIPMENT:Hardware — Sun, DELL, Apple, NEC's ; Printers — HP, Cannon, Xerox DISPLAY SOFTWARE:Ad Make-Up Applications — NW/Admarc , ADS; Layout Software — TEDS, In-house. EDITORIAL EQUIPMENT:Hardware — Dell PC, MAC PC/CCI/Pagination System; Printers — 16-HP/LaserJet EDITORIAL SOFTWARE:CCI Newsgate, SCC PRODUCTION EQUIPMENT:Hardware — Prima, Newsway ; Scanners — Epson PRODUCTION SOFTWARE:CCI/Layout Champ, CCI/AD Champ.

WELLAND

WELLAND TRIBUNE

228 East Main St., Welland, ON, L3B 5P5, Canada; gen tel (905) 732-2411; adv tel (905) 732-2411; ed tel (905) 732-2411; gen fax (905) 732-4883; adv fax (905) 732-0965; ed fax (905) 732-3660; gen/nat adv. e-mail aldo.donofrio@sunmedia.ca; disp adv e-mail aldo.donofrio@sunmedia.ca; class adv e-mailplaceit.sun@sunmedia.ca; ed e-mail ascott@postmedia.com; web site 1 www. wellandtribune.ca
Published: Mon, Tues, Wed, Thur, Fri, Sat
Weekday Frequency: m
Saturday Frequency: m
Circulation 8,347; 8,381(sat)
Last Audit: CCAB December 31, 2013
Group: Postmedia Network Inc.
Quebecor Communications, Inc.
Newspaper Reps: Susan Courtney - VP National Sales, QMI Corporate Sales Office
Advertising - Weekday/Saturday: Open inch rate $1.24 (M-Fri); $1.61 (Th)
Online Advertising Rates: Rates on request.
News services: CP. **Established:** 1863
Special Weekly Sections: Cookbook (Aug); Progress (Feb); Fashion (Monthly).
Syndicated Publications: Television Listings Guide (Fri); Homes (Sat).
Pub. .... John Tobon
Adv. Dir. .... Julia Coles
Mng. Ed. .... Dan Dakin
Circ. Mgr. .... Karin Vanderzee
Sports Ed. .... Bernd Frank
Senior Group Pub. .... Judy Bullis
Prod. Mgr. .... Lydia Kinos
Market information: TMC.
Mechanical available: Offset; Black and 3 ROP colors; insert accepted - Post It; page cutoffs - 22 3/4.
Mechanical Specifications: Type page 11 1/2 x 21; E - 10 cols, 1 1/16, between; A - 10 cols, 1 1/16, between; C - 9 cols, 1 5/16, between.
Areas Served: Port Colborne, Wainfleet, Welland & Pelham

Delivery Method: Mail, Carrier, Racks
Equipment & Software PRESSROOM EQUIPMENT:Pressroom Lines — 12-G/ Urbanite single width; Folders — 2, 1-G/ with balloon upper former; Reels & Stands — 7 MAILROOM EQUIPMENT:Counter Stackers — 2-Id; Inserters & Stuffers — 1/ KAN; Bundle Tying Machines — Gd, OVL. BUSINESS EQUIPMENT:Hardware — PC BUSINESS SOFTWARE:Microsoft/Office CLASSIFIED EQUIPMENT:Hardware — APP/Mac; Printers — App, HP CLASSIFIED SOFTWARE:QPS/QuarkXPress. DISPLAY EQUIPMENT:Hardware — PC; Printers — Ap, HP DISPLAY SOFTWARE:Ad Make-Up Applications — Managing Editor/ALS; Layout Software — Baseview. EDITORIAL EQUIPMENT:Hardware — APP/Mac/ Imagesetter; Printers — APP, HP EDITORIAL SOFTWARE:QPS/QuarkXPress 3.3. PRODUCTION EQUIPMENT:Hardware — ECR/Knockout, ECR/Stingray; Cameras — 1-Liberator; Scanners — Microtek/ScanMaker PRODUCTION SOFTWARE:QPS 3.3.

WINDSOR

THE WINDSOR STAR

300 Ouellette Ave, Windsor, ON, N9A 7B4, Canada; gen tel (519) 255-5768; adv tel (519) 255-5768; ed tel (519) 255-5743; gen fax (519) 255-5250; adv fax (519) 255-5778; ed fax (519) 255-5515; gen/nat adv. e-mail adinquiries@windsorstar.com; disp adv e-mail adinquiries@windsorstar.com; class adv e-mailwww.windsorstar.com/placeanad; ed e-mail evanwageningen@postmedia. com; web site 1 www.windsorstar.com - 5,800,000(views) 219,000(visitors)
Published: Mon, Tues, Wed, Thur, Fri, Sat
Weekday Frequency: m
Saturday Frequency: m
Circulation 48,676; 49,947(sat)
Last Audit: AAM March 31, 2017
Group: Postmedia Network Inc.
Newspaper Reps: Thibaud Wallaert - GM, Discomm Media
Branch Offices: Vancouver, BC
Toronto, ON
Montreal, QC
Advertising - Weekday/Saturday: Open inch rate $8.16 (M-Fri); $9.79 (Sat)
Online Advertising Rates: Leaderboard $20; Big Box $30; Top Layer $45

News services: Postmedia Network Newspapers, CP, SOU, LAT-WP, SHNS. **Established:** 1888
Own Printing Facility?: Y
Commercial Printers?: Y
Special Weekly Sections: Car Care (Apr); Christmas Greetings (Dec); Bridal Feature (Feb); Financial Investment Review (Jan); Fun in the Sun (Jun); Automotive Report (Mar); Garden Feature (May); Forever Young (Monthly); Senior Citizens Days (Nov); Automotive Report (Oct); Symphony
Syndicated Publications: TV Times (Sat).
Digital Platform - Mobile: Apple, Android
Digital Platform - Tablet: Apple iOS, Android
Ed.-in-Chief .... Marty Beneteau
Dir., Mfg. .... Doug Shillington
Personnel Mgr. .... Louise Veres
Dir. of Adv. .... Ken Stewart
Adv. Mgr., Classified .... Maggie Saunders
Dir. Digital sales & Mktg. .... Beverly Becker
Editorial Page Ed. .... John Coleman
Entertainment Ed. .... Ted Shaw
Metro Ed. .... Jim Potter
Sports Ed. .... Mark Falkner
Dir., Audience Development/Customer Service Bob Thwaites
Market information: Split run; TMC.
Mechanical available: Offset; Black and 3 ROP colors; insert accepted - hi-fi, partials, zones, catalogs; page cutoffs - 22.
Mechanical Specifications: Type page 11.4090 x 21.2140; E - 6 cols, 2 1/16, 1/8 between; A - 6 cols, 2 1/16, 1/8 between; C - 10 cols, 1 7/32, 1/12 between.
Areas Served: Windsor & Essex County

Delivery Method: Newsstand, Carrier, Racks
Equipment & Software PRESSROOM EQUIPMENT:Pressroom Lines — 7-KB/ Colora double width 1996; Folders — 1-KB/MOT/3:2, 1; Pasters — KB/EAE; Reels & Stands — KB/EAE. MAILROOM EQUIPMENT:Counter Stackers — 4-QWI/351; Inserters & Stuffers — 1-Dynaric/ NP630-2, 1-Dynaric/NP630-4; Bundle Tying Machines — 4-Id/Pwa 5750 plastic wrap, 4-QWI/Cobra Underwrap; Mailroom Control System — HI/Prima. BUSINESS EQUIPMENT:Hardware — DEC/Micro VAX 3800, DEC/Micro VAX CLASSIFIED EQUIPMENT:Hardware — HP, HP; Printers — Graphic Enterprises CLASSIFIED SOFTWARE:SyD, Cybergraphics. DISPLAY EQUIPMENT:Hardware — APP/ Mac; Printers — Graphic Enterprises DISPLAY SOFTWARE:Ad Make-Up Applications — QPS/QuarkXPress, Adobe/ Photoshop; Layout Software — SCS/Layout 8000, Southam/Ad Track. EDITORIAL EQUIPMENT:Hardware — APP/Mac; Printers — HP, APP/Mac EDITORIAL SOFTWARE:QPS 1.1. PRODUCTION EQUIPMENT:Hardware — AU/3850 Sierra, Nu/Flip Top; Cameras — ECR.

WOODSTOCK

WOODSTOCK SENTINEL-REVIEW

16 Brock St., Woodstock, ON, N4S 3B4, Canada; gen tel (519) 537-2341; adv tel (519) 537-2341; ed tel (519) 537-2341; gen fax (519) 537-8542; adv fax (519) 537-8542; ed fax (519) 537-8542; gen/ nat adv. e-mail dcarter@postmedia.com; disp adv e-mail dcarter@postmedia.com; class adv e-mailwoodstocksentinelreview. classifieds@sunmedia.ca; ed e-mail burquhart@postmedia.com; web site 1 www. woodstocksentinelreview.com
Published: Mon, Tues, Wed, Thur, Fri
Weekday Frequency: m
Circulation 6,000
Last Audit: Sworn/Estimate/Non-Audited September 30, 2017
Group: Postmedia Network Inc.
Quebecor Communications, Inc.
Newspaper Reps: Susan Courtney - VP National Sales, QMI Corporate Sales Office
Advertising - Weekday/Saturday: Open inch rate $1.05
News services: UPI. **Established:** 1854
Special Weekly Sections: Spring Home Improvement (Apr); Brides (Jan); Tourist Guide (Jun); Annual Business & Industrial Review (Mar); Home & Garden (May); Holiday Gift Guide (Nov); Fall Home Improvement (Oct); Agriculture (Quarterly).
Syndicated Publications: Sports (Thur).
Pub. .... Andrea Demeer
Adv. Mgr. .... Rosaline Bruyns
Ed. .... Bruce Urquhart
Sports Ed. .... Cory Smith
Prodn. Mgr. .... Debbie Campbell
Circ. Mgr. .... Mike Sissing
Market information: ADS; TMC.
Mechanical available: Offset; Black and full color ROP colors; insert accepted - samples; page cutoffs - 21 1/2.
Mechanical Specifications: Type page 11 1/2 x 20 1/2; E - 6 cols, 1 9/16, 1/8 between; A - 10 cols, 15/16, 2/16 between; C - 10 cols, 15/16, 2/16 between.
Areas Served: City of Woodstock & Oxford County

Delivery Method: Mail, Newsstand, Carrier
Equipment & Software PRESSROOM EQUIPMENT:Pressroom Lines — 8-G/Community. MAILROOM EQUIPMENT:Bundle Tying Machines — Gd/Q 200A, Gd/RM 174 Strap BUSINESS EQUIPMENT:Hardware — 5-ATT CLASSIFIED EQUIPMENT:Hardware — 1-HI, HAS. DISPLAY EQUIPMENT:Hardware — APP/Mac; Printers — APP/Mac DISPLAY SOFTWARE:Layout Software — APP/ Mac Graphics System. EDITORIAL EQUIPMENT:Hardware — 1-HI, 12- HAS/HAS/Pagination. PRODUCTION EQUIPMENT:Hardware — 2-COM/MCS 8400, 2-COM/9400 Laser; Cameras — B/2000; Scanners — Microtek.

PRINCE EDWARD ISLAND

CHARLOTTETOWN

THE GUARDIAN

165 Prince St., Charlottetown, PE, C1A 4R7, Canada; gen tel (902) 629-6000; adv tel (902) 629-6068; ed tel (902) 629-6039; gen fax (902) 566-3808; adv fax (902) 566-9830; ed fax (902) 566-3808; gen/nat adv. e-mail twilson@theguardian.pe.ca; disp adv e-mail twilson@theguardian.pe.ca; class adv e-mailclass@theguardian.pe.ca; ed e-mail newsroom@theguardian.pe.ca; web site 1 www.theguardian.pe.ca - 3,000,000(views) 270,000(visitors)
Published: Mon, Tues, Wed, Thur, Fri, Sat
Weekday Frequency: m
Saturday Frequency: m
Circulation 14,240; 14,822(sat)
Last Audit: CCAB December 31, 2013
Group: Transcontinental Media
Newspaper Reps: Ron Clark - CEO, Canadian Primedia Sales & Mktg. Inc.
Advertising - Weekday/Saturday: Open inch rate $1.27 (M-F); $1.34 (Sat)
Online Advertising Rates: Rates on request.
News services: Hollinger Inc., CP. **Established:** 1887
Special Weekly Sections: Emergency Preparedness (Apr); Old Home Week (Aug); Last Minute Gift Guide (Dec); Winter Carnival (Feb); Road Builders (Jan); Grads 2008 (Jul); PEI Council of the Disabled (Jun); Christmas Cookbook (Mar); Leave A Legacy (May); Seniors (Monthly); Shop Kensi
Syndicated Publications: Real Estate Guide (Thur).
Digital Platform - Mobile: Apple, Android, Windows, Blackberry
Digital Platform - Tablet: Apple iOS, Android
Pub. .... Don Brander
Bus. Mgr. .... Ron Kelly
Adv. Dir. .... Heather Tedford
Dir., Reader Sales & Dist. .... Ron Lund
Mng. Ed. .... Gary J. MacDougall
Editorial Page Ed. .... Bill McGuire
Features Ed. .... Carolyn Drake
News Ed. .... Wayne Thibodeau
Sports Ed. .... Jason Malloy
Market information: ADS.
Mechanical available: Offset; Black and 2 ROP colors; insert accepted - poly bags, samples; page cutoffs - 22 3/4.
Mechanical Specifications: Type page 10 1/2 x 21 1/2; E - 5 cols, 2 1/4, 1/8 between; A - 10 cols, 1 3/32, 1/8 between; C - 6 cols, 1 5/6, 1/8 between.
Areas Served: Prince Edward

Delivery Method: Mail, Newsstand, Carrier, Racks
Equipment & Software PRESSROOM EQUIPMENT:Pressroom Lines — G/ Community (8 units; 1 stack unit) 1976; Folders — G/SC. MAILROOM EQUIPMENT:Bundle Tying Machines — 2-Gd/Ex 311; Address Machine — 2/ Am. BUSINESS EQUIPMENT:Hardware — Newzware CLASSIFIED EQUIPMENT:Hardware — Baseview, 3-APP/ Mac CLASSIFIED SOFTWARE:HP/4. DISPLAY EQUIPMENT:Hardware — 2-APP/ Mac; Printers — HP/LaserJet, 2-HP/4MV DISPLAY SOFTWARE:Ad Make-Up Applications — QPS/QuarkXPress 4.0; Layout Software — Ad-Force. EDITORIAL

EQUIPMENT:Hardware — 28-HAS, 32-APP/Mac, 2-MS/NT Server/Poloroid/SprintScan, Wing Lynch/Film Processor; Printers — 2-HP/4MV EDITORIAL SOFTWARE:HAS 2.5. PRODUCTION EQUIPMENT:Hardware — 1-B, Polaroid/SprintScan; Cameras — 1-B, 1-SCREEN; Scanners — AG, Sprint Scan PRODUCTION SOFTWARE:QPS/QuarkXPress 4.0.

SUMMERSIDE

THE JOURNAL PIONEER

316 Water St., Summerside, PE, C1N 4K5, Canada; gen tel (902) 436-2121; adv tel (902) 432-8238; ed tel (902) 432-8216; gen fax (902) 436-3027; adv fax (902) 436-0784; ed fax (902) 436-3027; gen/nat adv. e-mail pramsay@journalpioneer.com; disp adv e-mail pramsay@journalpioneer.com; class adv e-mailcgallant@journalpioneer.com; ed e-mail bworks@journalpioneer.com; web site 1 www.journalpioneer.com

Published: Mon, Tues, Wed, Thur, Fri, Sat
Weekday Frequency: m
Saturday Frequency: m
Circulation 5,387; 5,703(sat)
Last Audit: CCAB September 30, 2015
Group: Transcontinental Media
Newspaper Reps: Canadian Primeda Sales & Mktg Inc.
Advertising - Weekday/Saturday: Open inch rate $.86
Online Advertising Rates: Rates on request.
News services: CP. **Established:** 1865
Syndicated Publications: TV Guide (local, newsprint) (Thurs).
Pub./GM....Sandy Rundle
Adv. Mgr.....Paul Ramsay
Dir., Reader Sales/Serv.....Ron Lund
Sports Ed.....Jason Simmonds
Managing Editor....Brad Works
Circ. Dir.....Ed Kennedy
Prod. Supervisor....Jason Matheson
Mng. Ed.....Mike Turner
Market information: ADS; TMC.
Mechanical available: Offset; Black and 3 ROP colors; insert accepted; page cutoffs - 22 3/4.
Mechanical Specifications: Type page 11 x 21; E - 5 cols, 2 1/8, 1/8 between; A - 10 cols, 1 1/16, between; C - 5 cols, 2 1/8, between.
Areas Served: Prince County, Prince Edward Island

Delivery Method: Mail, Newsstand, Carrier, Racks
Equipment & Software PRESSROOM EQUIPMENT:Pressroom Lines — 6-G/Community, 3-G/Community Color; Folders — 1 MAILROOM EQUIPMENT:Bundle Tying Machines — 1-Pak/F16; Wrapping Singles — Weld-Loc/Strapping; Address Machine — 1-EI/3301. CLASSIFIED EQUIPMENT:Hardware — APP/Mac LC, APP/Mac; Printers — APP/Mac Stylewriter CLASSIFIED SOFTWARE:Claris/FileMaker Pro, QPS, Microsoft/Word, QPS/QuarkXPress. DISPLAY EQUIPMENT:Hardware — 2-APP/Mac IIci; Printers — 2-APP/Mac LaserWriter II DISPLAY SOFTWARE:Ad Make-Up Applications — Multi-Ad/Creator, QPS, Microsoft/Word, Adobe/Illustrator, Zedcor/Deskpaint, Adobe/Streamline; Layout Software — APP/Mac. EDITORIAL EQUIPMENT:Hardware — 8-APP/Mac, 2-APP/Mac IIci/Ven-Tel/Modem(1200 baud); Printers — APP/Mac LaserWriter II EDITORIAL SOFTWARE:QPS/QuarkXPress, Microsoft/Word. PRODUCTION EQUIPMENT:Hardware — 1-P/SQ24; Cameras — 1-B.

QUEBEC

MONTREAL

LA PRESSE

7 Rue St. Jacques, Montreal, QC, H2Y 1K9, Canada; gen tel (514) 285-7272; adv tel (514) 285-6874; ed tel (514) 285-7070; gen fax (514) 285-6808; gen/nat adv. e-mail commentaires@lapresse.ca; ed e-mail forum@lapresse.ca; web site 1 www.lapresse.ca

Published: Mon, Tues, Wed, Thur, Fri, Sun
Weekday Frequency: m
Saturday Frequency: m
Circulation 257,656; 263,959(sun)
Last Audit: AAM December 31, 2017
Group: Gesca Ltd.
Newspaper Reps: Marc Giguere, GM; Simon Jennings, Pres.; Merida Lake, GM; France-Elaine Nolet, Adv. Mgr, - Gesca Media Sales

Robert Laplante - Pres., Media-Corps Inc.
Advertising - Weekday/Saturday: Frequency 4: $503.00, $835.00 (Sat); Frequency 3: $850.00, $1,388.00 (Sat); Frequency 2: $1,623.00, $2,702.00 (Sat)
Online Advertising Rates: Rates on request.
News services: AFP, CP, AP, UPI, DJ, RN. **Established:** 1884
Special Editions: Tele-Presse TV-Radio Tab Magazine (Sat).
Special Weekly Sections: Plus Weekend Review (Other).
Pub....Guy Crevier
Vice Pres., Personnel/Labor Rel.....Jacques Tousignant
Vice Pres., Commun.....Caroline Jamet
Asst. to Pres./Legal Counsel....Philippe-Denis Richard
Controller....Robert Julien
Adv. Dir., Retail....Yves Lalonde
Vice Pres., Mktg.....Jean Durocher
Dir., Promo.....Christiane Dube
Circ. Dir.....Jocelyn Godbout
Vice Pres./Ed.....Philippe Cantin
Mng. Ed.....Eric Trottier
Books Ed.....Jocelyne Lepage
Editorial Dir.....Andre Pratte
Educ. Ed.....Marie Allard
Finance Ed.....Jon Sebastian Gagmom
Music Ed., Classical....Claude Gingras
Music Ed., Pop....Alain Brunet
Ottawa Bureau....Gilles Toupin
Photo Ed.....Benoit Giguere
Market information: Split run.
Mechanical available: Letterpress - Napp Plates; Black and 3 ROP colors; insert accepted; page cutoffs - 23 9/16.
Mechanical Specifications: Type page 10.0625 x 21; E - 5 cols, 2 3/16, 3/16 between; A - 10 cols, 1 1/16, 3/16 between; C - 10 cols, 1 1/16, 3/32 between.
Equipment & Software PRESSROOM EQUIPMENT:Pressroom Lines — 36-G/Headliner double width; Folders — 4 MAILROOM EQUIPMENT:Counter Stackers — 7/HL; Inserters & Stuffers — 1-S/72P, 1-HI/632; Bundle Tying Machines — 7-/Power Strap; Wrapping Singles — 6-Mosca/(ACME). BUSINESS EQUIPMENT:Hardware — 2-IBM/4381 CLASSIFIED EQUIPMENT:Hardware — 2-APP/Mac II. DISPLAY EQUIPMENT:Hardware — 8-HI/8300, 4-Zenith, 4-AT, 8-IBM/PS2 30 DISPLAY SOFTWARE:Layout Software — SCS/Layout 8000. EDITORIAL EQUIPMENT:Hardware — IBM/PS2-LAN, 85-IBM/PS2-30-286, COM/Ethernet/HI/Images Picture Desk 3, 2-Sun/Sparc, 3-HI/KM, 1-X/Scanner EDITORIAL SOFTWARE:AT 3.6, AT/40. PRODUCTION EQUIPMENT:Hardware — Na, 2-ECR/Autokon-1000; Scanners — 2-Eskofot PRODUCTION SOFTWARE:HI.

LE DEVOIR

1265 Berri, 8th Floor, Montreal, QC, H2K 4X4, Canada; gen tel (514) 985-3333; adv tel (514) 985-3399; ed tel (514)985-3333; gen fax (514) 985-3360; adv fax (514) 985-3390; ed fax (514) 985-3360; gen/nat adv. e-mail lmillette@ledevoir.com; disp adv e-mail lmillette@ledevoir.com; class adv e-mailpetitesannonces@ledevoir.com; ed e-mail redaction@ledevoir.com; web site 1 www.ledevoir.com

Published: Mon, Tues, Wed, Thur, Fri, Sat
Weekday Frequency: m
Saturday Frequency: m
Circulation 70,182; 91,289(sat)
Last Audit: AAM March 31, 2017
Group: Le Devoir Inc.
Newspaper Reps: Phil Goddard - Partner, Consumer Media Solutions - CMS
Advertising - Weekday/Saturday: Open inch rate $2.08; $2.84 (Sat)
Online Advertising Rates: Rates on request.
News services: CP, AP, LE Monde, RN, AFP, CNW, Telbec. **Established:** 1910
Syndicated Publications: L'Agenda (Sat).
Pub.....Bernard Descoteaux
Vice Pres., Bus./Finance....Catherine Laberge
Dir., Promo.....Jose Chrisffaro
Circ. Dir.....Carolyn Simard
Ed. in Chief....Josee Boileau
Economics Ed.....Gerard Berube
Cultural Pages....Michel Belair
Prodn. Dir.....Christian Goulet
Info. Mgr.....Roland-Yves Carignan
VP, Adv. Sales....Lise Millette
Asst. Sales Mgr.....Vincent Spiridigliozzi
Market information: TMC.
Mechanical available: Offset; Black and 3 ROP colors; insert accepted; page cutoffs - 21 3/4.
Mechanical Specifications: Type page 11.875 x 20.75; E - 6 cols, 2 1/16, 1/8 between; A - 6 cols, 2 1/16, 1/8 between; C - 9 cols, 1 5/16, 1/6 between.
Equipment & Software BUSINESS EQUIPMENT:Hardware — PC System BUSINESS SOFTWARE:AccPac, Informatel CLASSIFIED EQUIPMENT:Hardware — Novell/486 server CLASSIFIED SOFTWARE:Informatel. DISPLAY EQUIPMENT:Hardware — APP/Macs; Printers — QMS/860 DISPLAY SOFTWARE:Ad Make-Up Applications — QPS/QuarkXPress, Aldus/Freehand, Adobe/Illustrator, Adobe/Streamline, Adobe/Photoshop; Layout Software — APP/Macs. EDITORIAL EQUIPMENT:Hardware — APP/Mac/Sharp/11x17 scanner, AG/Arcus, Nikon/3510AF, Radius/Vision Video Capture; Printers — AG/Selectset 5000, AG/Selectset 7000, QMS/860, APP/Mac LaserWriter IIg, HP EDITORIAL SOFTWARE:Baseview/NewsEdit, QPS/QuarkXPress, Adobe/Photoshop PRODUCTION EQUIPMENT:Hardware — AG/Selectset 5000, AG/Selectset 7000; Scanners — AG/Arcus, Sharp, 2-Nikon/LS 3510AF.
Note: All printing and distribution of Le Devoir Inc. is outsourced.

LE JOURNAL DE MONTREAL

4545 Rue Frontenac, Montreal, QC, H2H 2R7, Canada; gen tel (514) 521-4545; adv tel (514) 521-4545; ed tel (514) 521-4545; gen fax (514) 521-4416; adv fax (514)521-4416; ed fax (514)521-4416; gen/nat adv. e-mail Marc.Couture@quebecormedia.com; disp adv e-mail Marc.Couture@quebecormedia.com; class adv e-mailclassees@quebecormedia.com; ed e-mail jdq-scoop@quebecormedia.com; web site 1 www.journaldemontreal.com

Published: Mon, Tues, Wed, Thur, Fri, Sat, Sun
Weekday Frequency: m
Saturday Frequency: m
Circulation 171,560; 188,875(sat); 176,638(sun)
Last Audit: CCAB September 30, 2015
Group: Quebecor Communications, Inc.
Newspaper Reps: Susan Courtney - VP National Sales, QMI Corporate Sales Office
Advertising - Weekday/Saturday: Open inch rate $12.01 (M-F); $13.84 (Sat)
Advertising - Sunday: Open inch rate $12.01
Online Advertising Rates: Rates on request.
News services: CP, Telbec, DJ, CNW, AFP. **Established:** 1964
Syndicated Publications: Cahier Week-End (Sat).
Pres./Pub.....Lyne Robipaille
Adv. Mgr.....Gilles Lamoureux
VP, Comm. & Promo.....Denise Lareau
Circ. Mgr.....Christianne Benjamin
Ed.-in-Chief....Dany Doucet
News Ed.....Serge LaBrosse
Sports Ed.....Denis Poissant
Data Processing Mgr.....Luc Trudel
Audiotex Mgr., Servs.....Marie Andre Lessard
VP, Prodn.....Denis Tetrault
VP, Sales....Marc Bourassa
Dir., Research & Mktg.....Andre Phaneuf
Market information: TMC.
Mechanical available: Offset; Black and 3 ROP colors; insert accepted; page cutoffs - 22 3/4.
Mechanical Specifications: Type page 10 7/32 x 12 19/32; E - 8 cols, 1 3/16, 1/8 between; A - 8 cols, 1 3/16, 1/8 between; C - 8 cols, 1 3/16, 1/8 between.
Equipment & Software PRESSROOM EQUIPMENT:Pressroom Lines — 12-G/Cosmo double width 1984; 18-G/Metro double width 1984; Folders — 2-G/2:1, 3-G/3:2; Pasters — 10-G/Cosmo, 15-G/Metro. MAILROOM EQUIPMENT:Counter Stackers — 6-RKW/40; Bundle Tying Machines — 6-MLN/85495; Wrapping Singles — 2-Ideal/7100. BUSINESS EQUIPMENT:Hardware — DEC/VAX/4000-300 CLASSIFIED EQUIPMENT:Hardware — 2-Sun/Sparc 10-51, 42-PC, CText/Advision, CText/Alps; Printers — 2-QMS/860 CLASSIFIED SOFTWARE:Unix/OS-2 2.1, CText/Advision, CText/Alps. DISPLAY EQUIPMENT:Hardware — DEC/VAX 4000-300, Open Voll 5.5-2; Printers — AU/APS 1560 DISPLAY SOFTWARE:Ad Make-Up Applications — QPS/QuarkXPress 3.32; Layout Software — SCS/Layout 8000. EDITORIAL EQUIPMENT:Hardware — DEC/PDP 11-70, 50-DEC/VAX, APP/Mac Power PC 8550-/200; Printers — 4-HP/5000 EDITORIAL SOFTWARE:TMS, QPS 1.12. PRODUCTION EQUIPMENT:Hardware — 3-AU/F/08-C, 3-AU/F108FC, Coatsworth Communications; Scanners — Eskofot/8200S, Chromograph/2000, 2-PixelCraft/7650, 2-PixelCraft 8000 PRODUCTION SOFTWARE:QPS/QuarkXPress 3.32.

MONTREAL GAZETTE

1010 Sainte-Catherine St. W., Suite 200, Montreal, QC, H3B 5L1, Canada; gen tel (514) 987-2222; adv tel (514) 987-2350; gen fax (514) 987-2270; adv fax (514) 987-2380; gen/nat adv. e-mail gazadv@montrealgazette.com; disp adv e-mail gazadv@montrealgazette.com; class adv e-mailclassifieds@montrealgazette.com; web site 1 www.montrealgazette.com - 7,300,000(views) 1,000,000(visitors); web site 2 www.hockeyinsideout.com - 1,300,000(views) 106,000(visitors)

Published: Mon, Tues, Wed, Thur, Fri, Sat
Weekday Frequency: m
Saturday Frequency: m
Circulation 72,916; 83,310(sat)
Last Audit: AAM March 31, 2017
Group: Postmedia Network Inc.
Newspaper Reps: Postmedia Network Inc.; Dicomm Media; Publicitas North America.
Advertising - Weekday/Saturday: Open line rate $7.87 (Monday-Friday).
Advertising - Sunday: Open line rate $9.91 (Saturday).
Online Advertising Rates: Available upon request: cassels@montrealgazette.com.
News services: Bloomberg, Postmedia News Service, CP, AP. **Established:** 1778
Own Printing Facility?: N
Commercial Printers?: N
Special Weekly Sections: Montreal Gazette West Island; TVtimes.
Digital Platform - Mobile: Apple, Android
Digital Platform - Tablet: Apple iOS, Android
Dir., Finance, Postmedia....Mario Belluscio
Mgr, Admin– Eastern Region....Donna Dudka
Dir., Integrated Adv.....Giancarlo Lanzetta
Research Manager....David Klimek
Regional Vice-President, Advertising - Eastern Canada
Stéphane Le Gal
Director, Integrated Adv. & Strategy, 3i..Charlene Assels
Editor, Montreal Gazette & Vice-President, Editorial, Eastern Region, Postmedia
Lucinda Chodan
Manager, Advertising Sales....Sean Duckett
Executive Producer, Print....Jeff Blond

Editorial Page Editor .... Edie Austin
Newsroom Administrator ....June Thompson
Yves Levasseur
Areas Served: (Primarily) Montreal Census Metropolitan Area.
Delivery Method: Mail, Newsstand, Carrier, Racks
Equipment & Software CLASSIFIED EQUIPMENT:Operations outsourced. EDITORIAL EQUIPMENT:MacBook Pro (13" & 15") and MacBook Air (11"). EDITORIAL SOFTWARE:SaxoPress 7, InDesign, Adobe/Photoshop. IT EQUIPMENT:Hardware — HP Compaq 8000 Elite SFF; Dell Monitors; Printers — HP 4345 MFP. CIRCULATION EQUIPMENT:Hardware — HP Compaq 8000 Elite SFF; Dell 17; Printers — HP 9050 MFP.

QUEBEC

LE SOLEIL

410 Blvd. Charest East, Quebec, QC, G1K 7J6, Canada; gen tel (418) 686-3233; adv tel (418) 686-3435; ed tel (418) 686-3209; gen fax (418) 686-3225; adv fax (418) 686-3260; ed fax (418) 686-3374; disp adv e-mail marketing@lesoleil.com; ed e-mail redaction@lesoleil.com; web site 1 www.lesoleil.ca
Published: Mon, Tues, Wed, Thur, Fri, Sat, Sun
Weekday Frequency: m
Saturday Frequency: m
Circulation 66,826; 76,888(sat); 72,202(sun)
Last Audit: AAM March 31, 2016
Group: Gesca Ltd.
Newspaper Reps: Marc Giguere, GM; Simon Jennings, Pres.; Merida Lake, GM - Gesca Media Sales

Robert Laplante - Pres., Media-Corps Inc.
Advertising - Weekday/Saturday: 4/7 v. (8.11" x 9.64"): $6,332 (M-F), $7,089 (Sat)
Advertising - Sunday: 4/7 v. (8.11" x 9.64"): $6,332
Online Advertising Rates: Rates on request.
News services: CP, AFP, NYT, TELBEC, CN Wire, RN, AP. **Established:** 1816
Special Editions: WEM (week-end magazine) (Fri); Tele-Magazine (Mon); Dimanche Magazine (S); Le Soleil Tele-Magazine (Sat); Actualite Magazine (Thur); Mode Magazine (Tues); Plein Air (openair) (Wed).
Syndicated Publications: Entertainment (Fri); Automobile (Mon); Entertainment (S); Entertainment (Sat).
Pres. .... Claude Daniel
Bus. Mgr. .... Gilles Ouellet
Supvr. .... Therese Cote
VP, Adv. .... Louis Gendron
Cartoonist .... Andre-Philippe Cote
Editorial Page Ed. .... Pierre-Paul Noreau
Librarian .... Yves Bellefleur
Music Ed. .... Daphne Bedard
Online Ed. .... Michel Samson
Real Estate .... Gilles Angers
Sports Dir. .... Maurice Dumas
Travel Ed. .... Raymond Tardif
Prodn. Dir. .... Gilles Garneau
Prodn. Mgr., Graphic Arts .... Line Baillargeon
Pub./Pres. & Ed. .... Claude Gagnon
VP, Circ. .... Benoit Jobin
Prod. Mgr. .... Patrick Paluck
Market information: ADS.
Mechanical available: Letterpress (direct); Black and 3 ROP colors; insert accepted; page cutoffs - 23 3/4.
Mechanical Specifications: Type page 10.18 x 13.92; E - 5 cols, 2 1/16, 1/8 between; A - 10 cols, 3/16 between; C - 10 cols, 1/16 between.
Equipment & Software BUSINESS EQUIPMENT:Hardware — Sun/Enterprise 3000, Microsoft/NT Server 2000 BUSINESS SOFTWARE:Solaris 2.6, UShare 5.0.1 CLASSIFIED EQUIPMENT:Hardware — APP/Mac 6100, 11-HP/LC/Electronic Mail Box, TTS, Umax/300; Printers — QMS CLASSIFIED SOFTWARE:Cenoad 1.33, QPS/QuarkXPress 4.1. DISPLAY EQUIPMENT:Hardware — APP/Power Mac G4; Printers — 1-C.Itoh/5000, 2-Printronics, 5-Fuji/4500, APP/Mac Pro DISPLAY SOFTWARE:Ad Make-Up Applications — Service Bureau; Layout Software — Managing Editor/ALS 2.5. EDITORIAL EQUIPMENT:Hardware — 6-APP/Mac IIvx, 2-APP/Mac SE, 7-APP/Power Mac 8100, 18-APP/Power Mac 6100, 4-APP/Mac Quadra 700, 1-APP/Mac IIfx, 1-APP/Mac Quadra 800, 1-APP/Mac IIx, 1-APP/Mac SE30, 3-APP/Mac LC II, 10-APP/Mac Power Book, 13-LC/475/3-APP/Mac Laser PRODUCTION EQUIPMENT:Hardware — AU

SAGUENAY

LE QUOTIDIEN

1051, Boul. Talbot, Saguenay, QC, G7H 5C1, Canada; gen tel (418) 545-4474; adv tel (418) 549-4444; ed tel (418) 545-4474; gen fax (418) 690-8805; adv fax (418) 690-8824; ed fax (418) 690-8805; gen/nat adv. e-mail annonces@lequotidien.com; disp adv e-mail annonces@lequotidien.com; class adv e-mailclassees@lequotidien.com; ed e-mail redaction@lequotidien.com; web site 1 www.lapresse.ca/le-quotidien/ - 720,000(views) 140,000(visitors)
Published: Mon, Tues, Wed, Thur, Fri, Sat, Sun
Weekday Frequency: m
Saturday Frequency: m
Circulation 22,816; 22,897(sat); 25,547(sun)
Last Audit: AAM March 31, 2016
Group: Gesca Ltd.
Newspaper Reps: Marc Giguere - GM, Gesca Media Sales

Robert Laplante - Pres., Media-Corps Inc.
Advertising - Weekday/Saturday: Frequency 5: $54.00; Frequency 4: $114; Frequency 3: $194
Online Advertising Rates: Rates on request
News services: CP. **Established:** 1884
Special Weekly Sections: Le Cahier Economique (Oct).
Digital Platform - Mobile: Apple, Android
Digital Platform - Tablet: Apple iOS, Android
Pub. .... Michel Simard
Dir. Sales & Mktg. .... Linda Cantin
Ed. in Chief .... Denis Bouchard
Info. Mgr. .... Francois St-Gelais
Prodn. Mgr., Distr. .... Bernard Bellei
Prod./Circ. Mgr. .... Jean Simard
Prod. Dir. .... Sylvaine Tremblay
Market information: Split run; TMC; Zoned editions.
Mechanical available: Offset; Black and 3 ROP colors; insert accepted; page cutoffs - 21 1/2.
Mechanical Specifications: Type page 10.18 x 13.92; E - 5 cols, 1 15/16, 1/8 between; A - 10 cols, 15/16, 1/8 between; C - 5 cols, 1 15/16, 1/8 between.
Areas Served: French Canada
Equipment & Software PRESSROOM EQUIPMENT:Pressroom Lines — 12-G/Urbanite; Press Drive — Westinghouse/Litholine; Folders — G/SSC; Pasters — 7-Martin/Automatic; Press Control System — 1-SC/200 Litho. MAILROOM EQUIPMENT:Counter Stackers — MM; Bundle Tying Machines — 1/MLN; Address Machine — 1-/Am. BUSINESS EQUIPMENT:Hardware — IBM, Sun/Sparc, IBM/AS-400, HP BUSINESS SOFTWARE:Microsoft/Windows NT 4 CLASSIFIED EQUIPMENT:Hardware — 4-Mk, APP/Mac, Power PC 4400; Printers — APP/Mac, HP/4050 CLASSIFIED SOFTWARE:Baseview/Class Manager. DISPLAY EQUIPMENT:Hardware — APP/Mac G3, APP/Mac G3-333; Printers — QMS/860, Canon/ImageClass C2100/Sharp/JX450 scanners 2, Umax/Mirage II scanner DISPLAY SOFTWARE:Ad Make-Up Applications — Adobe/Illustrator 8.01, Adobe/Photoshop 5.0, QPS/QuarkXPress 4.1; Layout Software — Minimac. EDITORIAL EQUIPMENT:Hardware — APP/Mac LC475, Centris/650, APP/Mac PPC 6100, APP/Mac PPC 7300, APP/Mac Power Book/Lf/AP Picture Desk, APP/Mac Quadra 800; Printers — HP/LaserJet 5M, HP/4050 EDITORIAL SOFTWARE:C, Cenotext 1.1.2. PRODUCTION EQUIPMENT:Hardware — Olec/OV45HD, Kk/Polychrome Graphics SN32, Accuset/1000; Cameras — 1-B, 1-R; Scanners — Cp, Umax/Mirage II PRODUCTION SOFTWARE:QPS/QuarkXPress 4.1, Informatel/Geometry.

SHERBROOKE

LA TRIBUNE

1950 Rue Roy, Sherbrooke, QC, J1K 2X8, Canada; gen tel (819) 564-5450; adv tel (819) 564-5450; ed tel (819) 564-5454; gen fax (819) 564-5480; adv fax (819) 564-5482; ed fax (819) 564-8098; gen/nat adv. e-mail latribune@latribune.qc.ca; disp adv e-mail latribune@latribune.qc.ca; class adv e-maillatribune@latribune.qc.ca; ed e-mail latribune@latribune.qc.ca; web site 1 www.cyberpresse.ca
Published: Mon, Tues, Wed, Thur, Fri, Sat, Sun
Weekday Frequency: m
Saturday Frequency: m
Circulation 23,507; 23,325(sat); 2,022(sun)
Last Audit: AAM March 31, 2017
Group: Gesca Ltd.
Newspaper Reps: Marc Giguere - GM, Gesca Media Sales
Advertising - Weekday/Saturday: Frequency 5: $108.00; Frequency 4: $204; Frequency 3: $346
Online Advertising Rates: Rates on request.
News services: CP. **Established:** 1910
Special Editions: Weekend Magazine (Sat).
Pres./Ed. .... Louis Boisvert
Adv. Asst. Mgr. .... Alain LeClerc
Circ. Mgr. .... Andre Custeau
Newsroom Dir. .... Louis Eric Allard
Photo Dept. Mgr. .... Renee Marquis
Radio/Television Ed. .... Andre Laroche
Sports Ed. .... Sonia Bolduc
Prodn. Mgr. .... Andre Roberge
Asst. Prod. Mgr. .... Steve Rancourt
Prod. Mgr. .... Rene Beliveau
Pub & Pres. .... Louise Boisvert
Ed.-in-Chief .... Maurice Cloutier
Adv. Dir. .... Sylvain Denault
Market information: TMC.
Mechanical available: Offset; Black and 3 ROP colors; insert accepted; page cutoffs - 22 3/4.
Mechanical Specifications: Type page 10 1/4 x 14 1/4; E - 5 cols, 1 1/16, 1/16 between; A - 10 cols, 1 1/16, 1/16 between; C - 10 cols, 1 1/16, 1/16 between.
Equipment & Software PRESSROOM EQUIPMENT:Pressroom Lines — 6-G/Cosmo 3526 (Web Press Offset). MAILROOM EQUIPMENT:Counter Stackers — 1/HL; Bundle Tying Machines — 1-MLN/ML2EE, 1-MLN/MLL2A; Wrapping Singles — 2-Gd/Q7070; Address Machine — 1-Am/6400, 1-Am/2605. BUSINESS EQUIPMENT:Hardware — IBM/AS-400 CLASSIFIED EQUIPMENT:Hardware — HI/Cash, PCs CLASSIFIED SOFTWARE:Unix. DISPLAY EQUIPMENT:Hardware — HI/8900, Sun/Server XP21; Printers — X/Proofer, AU/Typesetter, HP/2500 DISPLAY SOFTWARE:Layout Software — SCS/Layout 8000. EDITORIAL EQUIPMENT:Hardware — HI/8900, Sun/Server XP21. PRODUCTION EQUIPMENT:Hardware — 2-AU/APS108C, Turbo 3850; Cameras — 1-C/Spartan II-2606, 1-C/Spartan III, 1-III/VGC-TC; Scanners — 1-ECR/Autokon, 3-X, 1-AG.

THE RECORD

1195 Galt East, Sherbrooke, QC, J1H 1Y7, Canada; gen tel (819) 569-9525; adv tel (819) 569-9511; ed tel (819) 569-6345; gen fax (819) 821-3179; adv fax (819) 821-3179; ed fax (819) 821-3179; class adv e-mailclassad@sherbrookerecord.com; ed e-mail newsroom@sherbrookerecord.com; web site 1 www.sherbrookerecord.com
Published: Mon, Tues, Wed, Thur, Fri
Weekday Frequency: m
Circulation 4,392
Last Audit: AAM September 30, 2011
Group: Alta. Newspaper Group, Ltd
Newspaper Reps: Marnie Owston - Adv. Cord, Quebec Community Newspapers Assoc.

Alvin Chow, Dir; Mark Gravel, Sales Mgr.; Greg Morton, VP - Postmedia Network Inc.
Advertising - Weekday/Saturday: Open inch rate $1.19 (M-Th); $1.24 (Fri)
Online Advertising Rates: Rates on request.
News services: CP, Telbec. **Established:** 1897
Special Weekly Sections: Annual Review (Apr); Fashions (Fall); Ski (Jan); Holiday (Jun); Fashions (Spring); County Fairs (Summer).
Pub. .... Sharon Mccully
Ed. .... Daniel Coulombe
Prodn. Mgr. .... Sheila Bell
Prodn. Mgr., Composing .... Francine Thibault
Ed. .... John Edwards
Circ. Mgr. .... Laurie Schoolcraft
Market information: TMC.
Mechanical available: Black and 3 ROP colors; insert accepted; page cutoffs - 13 15/16.
Mechanical Specifications: Type page 10 1/4 x 11.9375; E - 5 cols, 1 7/8, 1/8 between; A - 5 cols, 1 7/8, 1/8 between; C - 5 cols, 1 7/8, 1/8 between.
Areas Served: Eastern Townships of Quebec
Equipment & Software MAILROOM EQUIPMENT:Bundle Tying Machines — 3/Bu; Address Machine — 1-Am/1955B. EDITORIAL EQUIPMENT:; Printers — 3-COM/AKI. PRODUCTION EQUIPMENT:Hardware — 1-COM/ACM9000, 2-COM/2961HS, 1-COM/7200, 1-COM/4961; Cameras — 1-Nu.

TROIS-RIVIERES

LE NOUVELLISTE

1920 rue Bellefeuille, Trois-Rivieres, QC, G9A 3Y2, Canada; gen tel (819) 376-2501; gen fax (819) 376-0946; disp adv e-mail pub@lenouvelliste.qc.ca; ed e-mail information@lenouvelliste.qc.ca; web site 1 www.lapresse.ca/le-nouvelliste
Published: Mon, Tues, Wed, Thur, Fri, Sat
Weekday Frequency: m
Saturday Frequency: m
Circulation 31,123; 32,662(sat)
Last Audit: AAM March 31, 2016
Group: Gesca Ltd.
Newspaper Reps: Marc Giguere - GM, Gesca Media Sales

Robert Laplante - Pres., Media-Corps Inc.
Advertising - Weekday/Saturday: Frequency 5: $96.00; Frequency 4: $194; Frequency 3: $324
Online Advertising Rates: Rates on request.
News services: Target Media Inc., AP, AFP, RN, UPI, Telbec, Laserphoto. **Established:** 1920
Special Editions: Nouvelliste Plus (Sat).
Special Weekly Sections: Tourist (Other).
Mgr., Personnel .... Marc Auger
Adv. Dir. .... Yves Neault
Mktg./Promo. Dir. .... Ginette Panneton
Circ. Mgr. .... Patrick Giassom
Ed. .... Marc Rochette
Ed.-in-Chief .... Stephen Frappier
Prodn. Mgr. .... Raymond Pitre
Prodn. Mgr., Printing .... Pierre Cote
Pres./Ed. .... Raymond Tardif
Pres./Ed. .... Alain Turcotte
Market information: Split run.
Mechanical available: Offset; Black and 3 ROP colors; insert accepted - roll-fed; page cutoffs - 22 3/4.
Mechanical Specifications: Type page 10 1/4 x 14.28; E - 10 cols, 1 1/16, 1/12 between; A - 10 cols, 1 1/16, 1/12 between; C - 10 cols, 1 1/16, 1/12 between.
Equipment & Software PRESSROOM EQUIPMENT:Pressroom Lines — 6-HI/1600 1982; 8-HI/V-15 1989; Folders — KAN/1/4 folder 1994; Pasters — 4-MEG, 4. MAILROOM EQUIPMENT:Counter Stackers — 2-MM/CS25, 1-MM/S70; Bundle Tying Machines — 3-Si; Address Machine — 1-Head/R-4800-X, CH/Base 522. BUSINESS EQUIPMENT:Hardware — IBM/AS-400, IBMs BUSINESS SOFTWARE:Dun & Bradstreet 4.0 CLASSIFIED EQUIPMENT:Hardware — HI/Cash, 2-HI/XP-21/AU/Rip; Printers — AU/3850 CLASSIFIED SOFTWARE:HI/PEN, HI/XP-21, HI/2100. DISPLAY EQUIPMENT:Hardware — HI/2100, HI/XP-21; Printers — AU/3850 DISPLAY SOFTWARE:Ad Make-Up Applications — HI/2100, HI/XP-21; Layout Software — SCS/Layout 8000. EDITORIAL EQUIPMENT:Hardware — 2-HI/XP-21/AU/Rip; Printers — AU/3850 EDITORIAL SOFTWARE:HI/PEN, HI/XP-21, HI/2100. PRODUCTION EQUIPMENT:Hardware — WL/Litho Plater, 2-X/Power PC 8100; Cameras — 2-X/Scanner 7650, 2-X/8000 PRODUCTION SOFTWARE:HI/2100 2.1.

VANIER

LE JOURNAL DE QUEBEC

450 Bechard Ave., Vanier, QC, G1M 2E9, Canada; gen tel (418) 683-1573; gen fax (418) 683-8886; adv fax (418) 683-1027; ed fax (418) 688-8181; web site 1 lejournaldequebec.canoe.ca
Published: Mon, Tues, Wed, Thur, Fri, Sat, Sun
Weekday Frequency: m
Saturday Frequency: m
Circulation 78,487; 86,211(sat); 80,947(sun)
Last Audit: CCAB September 30, 2017
Group: Quebecor Communications, Inc.
Newspaper Reps: Susan Courtney - VP National Sales, QMI Corporate Sales Office
Advertising - Weekday/Saturday: Open inch rate $6.60 (M-F), $7.03 (Sat)
Advertising - Sunday: Open inch rate $6.60
Online Advertising Rates: Rates on request.
News services: PC, UPI, Canada News Wire, Telbec, AFP.
Special Weekly Sections: Mode (Apr); La rentree (Aug); Informatique/Electronique (Dec); Reer (Feb); La Mariee (Jan); 50% (Jul); Sante Mieux-etre (Jun); Formule 1 (Mar); Golf (May); Sports d'hiver (Nov); Automobile (Oct); Votre Argent et Vous (Sept).
Syndicated Publications: Automotive (Mon); Tele-Haire (TV listings) (Other); Entertainment (Sat); Fashion (Tues); Food and Health (Wed).
Vice Pres., Finance.....................Andre Berube
Controller...................................Louis Ouellet
Adv. Vice Pres., Sales...................Daniel Houde
Mgr., Promo..........................Pierre Villeneuve
Circ. Mgr.................................Marc Couture
Entertainment Ed. ....Karen Vezilleneube
Gen. Ed...................................Donald Charette
Data Processing Mgr. ....Louis Chretien
VP, Adv...................Jean Pierre Robitaille
Prodn. Mgr., Pre Press...............Maurice Vezina
Prodn. Mgr., Pressroom ....Ulric Kusik

Pub............................Louise Cordeau
Circ. Mgr. ....Georges Leveille
Ed.-in-chief ....Sebastian Menard
Market information: Zoned editions.
Mechanical available: Offset; Black and 3 ROP colors; insert accepted - all; page cutoffs - 22.
Mechanical Specifications: Type page 10.2187 x 12.5710; E - 8 cols, 1 1/6, 1/8 between; A - 8 cols, 1 1/6, 1/8 between; C - 8 cols, 1 1/6, 1/8 between.
Equipment & Software PRESSROOM EQUIPMENT:Pressroom Lines — 11-G/Urbanite 5000 Series single width 1990; 11-G/Urbanite 5000 Series single width 1990; Folders — 2-G/Urbanite 1990; Pasters — 16-MEG/Flying DME Pasters 1990. MAILROOM EQUIPMENT:Counter Stackers — 2/FG; Bundle Tying Machines — 3-/Cyclops, 2-/Power Strap; Wrapping Singles — 2-/RKW; Mailroom Control System — 1-/HL. BUSINESS EQUIPMENT:Hardware — Micro Vax/3000/80 CLASSIFIED EQUIPMENT:Hardware — 1-DEC/PDP 11-70, DEC/VT 173C; Printers — 1-DEC/Letterwriter CLASSIFIED SOFTWARE:CMS 2.3. DISPLAY EQUIPMENT:Hardware — 20-APP/Mac Power PC; Printers — Xante/8200, Xante/8300, Accel-A-Writer, Au/Aps 2000 DISPLAY SOFTWARE:Ad Make-Up Applications — QPS/QuarkXPress 3.32, Adobe/Illustrator 6.0, Adobe/Photoshop 5.0. EDITORIAL EQUIPMENT:Hardware — DEC/PDP 11-70, 37-DEC/VT-72, 16-APP/Mac LC, 15-APP/Mac PowerBook 100/10-APP/Mac Power PC 6500; Printers — 2-Printronix EDITORIAL SOFTWARE:TMS/V5-3. PRODUCTION EQUIPMENT:Hardware — 2-AU/APS Micro 5, 2-AU/APS 7 AV25; Cameras — 1-Acti, 1-R; Scanners — 2-AG/Horizon Plus, 1-AG/Horizon Ultra, 1-Umax PRODUCTION SOFTWARE:QPS/QuarkXPress 3.32.

SASKATCHEWAN

MOOSE JAW

THE MOOSE JAW TIMES-HERALD

44 Fairford St. W., Moose Jaw, SK, S6H 1V1, Canada; gen tel (306) 692-6441; adv tel (306) 692-6441; ed tel (306) 692-6441; gen fax (306) 692-2101; adv fax (306) 694-1216; ed fax (306) 692-2101; gen/nat adv. e-mail advertising@mjtimes@sk.ca; disp adv e-mail advertising@mjtimes@sk.ca; class adv e-mailclassifieds@mjtimes@sk.ca; ed e-mail lisa.goudy@mjtimes@sk.ca; web site 1 www.mjtimes.sk.ca
Published: Mon, Tues, Wed, Thur, Fri, Sat
Weekday Frequency: e
Saturday Frequency: m
Circulation 7,447
Last Audit: Sworn/Estimate/Non-Audited September 30, 2017
Group: Transcontinental Media
Newspaper Reps: Ron Clark - CEO, Canadian Primedia Sales & Mktg. Inc.
Advertising - Weekday/Saturday: Open inch rate $2.13
Online Advertising Rates: Rates on request.
News services: CP, AP, Toronto Star Syndicate.
  Established: 1889
Own Printing Facility?: N
Special Weekly Sections: Year-End Review (Dec); Minor Hockey Special (Jan); Progress (Jul); Christmas Specials (Nov); Vacation Guide (Other); and more
Syndicated Publications: Color Comics (Sat).
GM/Pub.............................Rob Clark
Bus. Mgr.........................Polly Veroba
Adv. Mgr.........................Glenn Haug

Adv. Supvr., Classified ....Judy Ellis
Mng. Ed. ....Lesley Sheppard
Prodn. Mgr., Pre Press.................Wanda White
Pub....................................Nancy Johnson
Circ. Mgr. ....Doug Lix
Mng. Ed. ....Lyndsay McCready
Market information: ADS; TMC.
Mechanical available: Offset; Black and 3 ROP colors; insert accepted; page cutoffs - 21.5"
Mechanical Specifications: Type page 10.333 x 21.500
Delivery Method: Newsstand, Carrier

PRINCE ALBERT

PRINCE ALBERT DAILY HERALD

30 10th St E, Prince Albert, SK, S6V 0Y5, Canada; gen tel (306) 764-4276; adv tel (306) 764-4276; ed tel (306) 764-4276; gen fax (306) 763-3331; adv fax (306) 763-6747; ed fax (306) 763-3331; gen/nat adv. e-mail classifieds@paherald.sk.ca; disp adv e-mail classifieds@paherald.sk.ca; class adv e-mailclassifieds@paherald.sk.ca; ed e-mail editorial@paherald.sk.ca; web site 1 www.paherald.sk.ca
Published: Mon, Tues, Wed, Thur, Fri, Sat
Weekday Frequency: e
Saturday Frequency: m
Circulation 4,942; 5,190(sat)
Last Audit: BPA October 1, 2011
Group: Transcontinental Media
Advertising - Weekday/Saturday: Open inch rate $1.56 (mon-thurs)
Advertising - Sunday: n/a
News services: CP, SNS, Leader-Star.
  Established: 1894
Special Weekly Sections: Car Care (Fall); Winter Festival (Feb); Brides (Jan); Progress (Mar); Cookbook (Nov); Chamber of Commerce (Quarterly).
Syndicated Publications: Entertainment

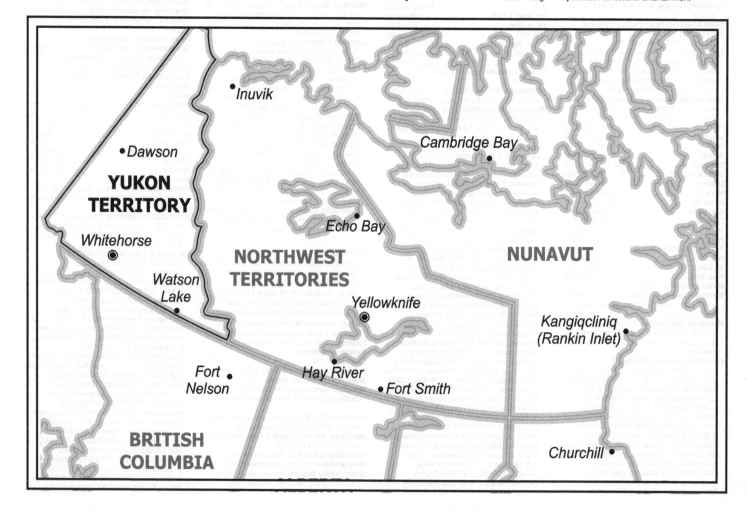

Guide (local, newsprint) (Fri); Rural Roots (agriculture) (S).
Publisher ....John Morash
Advertising Manager ....Mitzi Munro
Editor ....Perry Bergson
Circulation Manager ....Lorraine Brassard
Market information: ADS; TMC.
Mechanical available: Offset; Black and 3 ROP colors; insert accepted; page cutoffs - 22 3/4.
Mechanical Specifications: Type page 11 1/2 x 21 1/2; E - 5 cols, 2 1/8, 1/8 between; A - 10 cols, 1 1/16, 1/8 between; C - 10 cols, 1 1/16, 1/8 between.
Areas Served: Prince Albert, Saskatchewan

Delivery Method: Mail, Newsstand, Carrier, Racks
Equipment & Software PRESSROOM EQUIPMENT:Pressroom Lines — 8-G/Community single width 1974; Folders — 1 MAILROOM EQUIPMENT:Inserters & Stuffers — KAN/6 pocket; Bundle Tying Machines — 1-Gd/Q; Mailroom Control System — ATT; Address Machine — 1/El; Other Equipment — Cole/3 bladetrimmer. BUSINESS EQUIPMENT:Hardware — ATT CLASSIFIED EQUIPMENT:Hardware — APP/Mac CLASSIFIED SOFTWARE:Baseview. DISPLAY EQUIPMENT:Hardware — APP/Mac; Printers — APP/Mac DISPLAY SOFTWARE:Ad Make-Up Applications — Multi-Ad/Creator. EDITORIAL EQUIPMENT:Hardware — APP/Mac; Printers — 3-COM, APP/Mac EDITORIAL SOFTWARE:QPS/QuarkXPress 4.1, Adobe/Photoshop 5.0, Macromedia/Freehand 5.0. PRODUCTION EQUIPMENT:Hardware — Ultra/94E Imagesetter; Cameras — 1-B; Scanners — Polaroid/PrintScan, Umax/Vista PRODUCTION SOFTWARE:QPS/QuarkXPress 4.1.

REGINA

THE LEADER-POST
1964 Park St., Regina, SK, S4P 3G4, Canada; gen tel (306) 781-5211; adv tel (306) 781-5251; ed tel (306) 781-5300; gen fax (306) 565-2588; adv fax (306) 781-5350; ed fax (306) 565-2588; gen/nat adv. e-mail advertising@leaderpost.com; disp adv e-mail advertising@leaderpost.com; class adv e-mailclassifieds@leaderpost.com; ed e-mail sripley@leaderpost.com; web site 1 www.leaderpost.com - 1,500,000(views) 101,000(visitors)
Published: Mon, Tues, Wed, Thur, Fri, Sat
Weekday Frequency: m
Saturday Frequency: m
Circulation 33,279; 33,895(sat)
Last Audit: AAM September 30, 2015
Group: Postmedia Network Inc.
Newspaper Reps: Vancouver, BC
Toronto, ON
Montreal, QC
Branch Offices: Thibauld Wallaert - GM, Discomm Media
Advertising - Weekday/Saturday: Open inch rate $3.71 (M-Th); $4.43 (F-Sat)
Online Advertising Rates: Rates on request.
News services: CP, AP. **Established:** 1883

Special Editions: Weekender (Sat).
Special Weekly Sections: International Dance Day (Apr); Around Town (Aug); Activity Planner (Dec); Golf Expo (Feb); World No Smoking Day (Jan); Get Away In Saskatchewan (Jul); Career Frontiers (Jun); A Place To Call Home (Mar); Southeast Vacation Guide (May); Real Estate Coloring
Syndicated Publications: Driver's Seat (Fri); Real Estate (Sat); Entertainment (Thur); Careers (Weekly).
Digital Platform - Mobile: Apple, Android, Windows, Blackberry
Digital Platform - Tablet: Apple iOS, Android
Pub. ....Marty Klyne
Mgr., HR ....Twyla Clermont-Anderson
Adv. Dir. ....Les Wagman
Ed. in Chief. ....Janice Dockham
Deputy Ed., Online ....Kevin Blevins
Assoc. Ed. ....Marlon Marshall
City Coord. ....Veronica Rhodes
Finance Ed. ....Bruce Johnstone
Librarian ....Sue Marshall
News Coord. ....Chris Harbron
Photo Dept. Mgr. ....Roy Antal
Sports Ed. ....Rob Vanstone
Prodn. Mgr., Bldg. ....Brad Montague
Prodn. Foreman, Pre Press. ....Cal Martin
Prodn. Mgr., Pressroom/Distr. ....Bill Ruddy
Pub. ....Alan Allnut
Dir., Reader Sales & Service ....Jeff Epp
Prod. Mgr. ....Rhonda Exner
VP, Mktg. ....Rick Fraser
Regional VP, Adv. Sales ....Jeff Funtasz
Ed.-in-Chief, Saskatchewan ....Rob McLaughlin
Nat'l Sales Mgr., SK. ....Cindy Zawislak
Market information: TMC; Zoned editions.
Mechanical available: Letterpress (offset); Black and 3 ROP colors; insert accepted - samples, sticky notes; page cutoffs - 21 3/4.
Mechanical Specifications: Type page 10 1/2 x 21 1/2; E - 5 cols, 2 3/16, 1/8 between; A - 10 cols, 1/8 between; C - 10 cols, 1/8 between.
Areas Served: Saskatchewan

Delivery Method: Mail, Newsstand, Racks
Equipment & Software PRESSROOM EQUIPMENT:Pressroom Lines — 8-G/Metroliners double width (4-black; 4-color decked) 1985; Folders — 2-G/3:2; Pasters — 8; Press Registration System — G/pin system. MAILROOM EQUIPMENT:Counter Stackers — 3/KAN, 1-MM/227, 1-ld; Inserters & Stuffers — 1-MM/Gintol, 2-KAN/480 8 into 1; Bundle Tying Machines — 1-Si/MLNZ, 1-/Acme, 1-/Mini-mark, 3-Dynaric/NP 15000; Wrapping Singles — 2-/RKW, 2-/QWI (bottom wrap); Address Machine — 2-Am/2 BUSINESS EQUIPMENT:Hardware — PBS/MediaPlus, DEC/486 DX2 66 BUSINESS SOFTWARE:SCS/Layout 8000 CLASSIFIED EQUIPMENT:Hardware — 6-PC/21-PC; Printers — HP CLASSIFIED SOFTWARE:Cybersell 2.9. DISPLAY EQUIPMENT:Hardware — PC P4/12-APP/Mac; Printers — HP/8150 DISPLAY SOFTWARE:Ad Make-Up Applications — MS Office, Sam, Mk/Ad Director; Layout Software — SCS/Layout 8000. EDITORIAL EQUIPMENT:Hardware — 5-APP/Mac G3/40-APP/Mac G3; Printers — HP/8150 EDITORIAL SOFTWARE:Baseview/Newsedit 3.2.2. PRODUCTION EQUIPMENT:Hardware — 1-Au/APS 3850, 1-Au/APS Sierra, Pre Press/Panther Pro 46,

1-V; Scanners — Umax, Kk/Negscanner, AG/Arcus, AG/Horizon Ultra, Pusup-Eskofot 2024 PRODUCTION SOFTWARE:QPS/QuarkXPress 4.11.

SASKATOON

SASKATOON STARPHOENIX
204 5th Ave. N., Saskatoon, SK, S7K 2P1, Canada; gen tel (306) 657-6397; adv tel (306) 657-6340; ed tel (306) 657-6231; gen fax (306) 657-6437; adv fax (306) 657-6208; ed fax (306) 657-6437; gen/nat adv. e-mail mluczka@postmedia.com; disp adv e-mail mluczka@thestarphoenix.com; class adv e-mailsdyck@thestarphoenix.com; ed e-mail letters@thestarphoenix.com; web site 1 www.thestarphoenix.com - 3,000,000(views) 200,000(visitors)
Published: Mon, Tues, Wed, Thur, Fri, Sat
Weekday Frequency: m
Saturday Frequency: m
Circulation 38,270; 39,009(sat)
Last Audit: AAM March 31, 2017
Group: Postmedia Network Inc.
Advertising - Weekday/Saturday: Open inch rate $4.73
Online Advertising Rates: Leaderboard: $20; Big Box $25

News services: CP, AP, NYT, CanWest News Service. **Established:** 1902
Syndicated Publications: TV Times (Fri); Saskatoon Sun (S); Saskatoon Shopper (Wed).
Digital Platform - Mobile: Apple, Android, Windows, Blackberry
Digital Platform - Tablet: Apple iOS, Android
Pub./Ed. in Chief ....Rob McLaughlin
VP., Adv. Sales ....Rick Fraser
Prod. Mgr. ....Jeff Golding
Circ. Dir. ....Mark Kotellnikof
Mgr., HR ....Sharon Wacker
Ed ....Heather Persson
Market information: ADS; TMC.
Mechanical available: Black and full color ROP colors; insert accepted - catalogues,sample products.
Areas Served: Saskatoon

Delivery Method: Mail, Newsstand, Carrier

YUKON TERRITORY

WHITEHORSE

WHITEHORSE STAR
2149 2nd Ave., Whitehorse, YT, Y1A 1C5, Canada; gen tel (867) 668-2002; adv tel (867) 668-2060; ed tel (867) 667-4481; gen fax (867) 668-7130; adv fax (867) 668-7130; ed fax (867) 668-7130; gen/nat adv. e-mail advertising@whitehorsestar.com; disp adv e-mail advertising@whitehorsestar.com;

class adv e-mailclassifieds@whitehorsestar.com; ed e-mail editor@whitehorsestar.com; web site 1 www.whitehorsestar.com - 225,000(views) 26,000(visitors)
Published: Mon, Tues, Wed, Thur, Fri
Weekday Frequency: e
Circulation 1,359
Last Audit: AAM June 30, 2015
Advertising - Weekday/Saturday: The column inch rate varies from $19.77 down to $17.00 depending on the size of the advertisement.
Online Advertising Rates: Rates on request.
News services: CP **Established:** 1900
Own Printing Facility?: Y
Commercial Printers?: N
Special Editions: -Xmas Greetings (Dec); -Yukon Quest (Feb). 1000 km Dog Sled Race from Whitehorse to Fairbanks or vice versa. -Yukon River Quest (June) from Whitehorse to Dawson City in Canoes, Kayaks etc.
Digital Platform - Mobile: Apple
Digital Platform - Tablet: Apple iOS
Pub. ....Jackie Pierce
Adv./Sales Mgr. ....Michele Pierce
Circ. Mgr. ....John Stuckey
Editor ....Jim Butler
Photo Ed. ....Vince Fedoroff
Wire Ed ....Eric Murphy
Head Pressman ....Don Campbell
Circulation Assistant ....Joni Pierce
Reporter ....Chuck Tobin
Reporter ....Stephanie Waddle
Reporter ....Emily Blake
Reporter ....Taylor Blewett
Advertising Rep. ....McKayla Morgan
Accounts ....Pat Wilson
Market information: Split run; TMC.
Mechanical available: Offset Web; Black and 3 ROP colors; insert accepted; page cutoffs - 14 1/2.
Mechanical Specifications: Type page 10.3750 x 13.5710; E - 5 cols, 1 17/20, 1/6 between; A - 5 cols, 1 17/20, 1/6 between; C - 6 cols, 1 1/2, 1/6 between.
Areas Served: Yukon

Delivery Method: Mail, Newsstand, Carrier, Racks
Equipment & Software PRESSROOM EQUIPMENT:Pressroom Lines — 1965-Community/2; 2-G/Community 1975; 2-G/Community 1985. MAILROOM EQUIPMENT:Inserters & Stuffers — Kansa; Address Machine — 1/PB. BUSINESS EQUIPMENT:Hardware — IBM BUSINESS SOFTWARE:AccPac CLASSIFIED EQUIPMENT:Hardware — APP/Mac; Printers — XEROX CLASSIFIED SOFTWARE:InDesign, Adobe Illustrator, QuarkXPress, Adobe PhotoShop, Adobe/Acrobat , Microsoft Word, Epsom scanner DISPLAY EQUIPMENT:Hardware — APP/Mac DISPLAY SOFTWARE:Layout Software — QPS/QuarkXPress, Adobe/Photoshop, InDesign, Illustrator etc., EDITORIAL EQUIPMENT:Hardware — APP/Mac on Ethernet, APP/Mac Server; Printers — XEROX EDITORIAL SOFTWARE:APP/Mac, OS 9.1. PRODUCTION EQUIPMENT:Hardware — Adobe/Acrobat; Cameras — B/Horizontal; Scanners — Umax/Astra PRODUCTION SOFTWARE:QPS/QuarkXPress 4.1, Adobe/Photoshop. CIRCULATION EQUIPMENT:Binder, Postal equipment etc. etc.

ONLINE ONLY NEWSPAPERS IN THE UNITED STATES

ARIZONA

TUCSON

TUCSONSENTINEL.COM
1960 N. Painted Hills, Tuscon, AZ, 85745, Pima, USA; tel (520) 302-5989; e-mail ads@tucsonsentinel.com; ed e-mail news@tucsonsentinel.com
Web Site: tucsonsentinel.com
Established: 2009
Pub./Ed............................Dylan Smith
News/Engagement Ed........Maria Coxon-Smith

ARKANSAS

FAYETTEVILLE

THE FAYETTEVILLE FLYER
205 N College Ave, Fayetteville, AR, 72701-4238, Washington, USA; tel (479) 966-4860; adv tel (479) 387-1002; e-mail contact@fayetteville flyer.com
Web Site: www.fayettevilleflyer.com
Mthly Avg Views: 200,000
Mthly Avg Unique Visitors: 75,000
Group: Wonderstate Media, LLC
Dustin Bartholomew
Todd GillCo-Owners

CALIFORNIA

BERKELEY

THE BERKELEY DAILY PLANET
3023 Shattuck Ave, Berkeley, CA, 94705, Alameda, USA; tel (510) 845-8440; ed e-mail news@berkeleydailyplanet.com
Web Site: berkeleydailyplanet.com
Pub. ....Mike O'Malley
Ed. ....Becky O'Malley

CITRUS HEIGHTS

SACRAMENTO PRESS
PO Box 7981, Citrus Heights, CA, 95621, CA, USA; tel (916) 572-7609; e-mail advertising@sacramentopress.com; ed e-mail newstip@sacramentopress.com
Web Site: sacramentopress.com
Established: 2008
Digital Platform - Mobile: Apple, Android, Windows, Blackberry
Digital Platform - Tablet: Apple iOS, Android, Windows 7, Blackberry Tablet OS, Kindle, Kindle Fire
Editor ....Bethany Harris
Editorial Assistant..................Cesar Alexander

IRVINE

SOUTH COAST EDITOR
5319 University Drive, Suite 227, Irvine, CA,

92612, Orange, USA; tel (949) 287-8330; e-mail editor@southcoasteditorcom
Web Site: http://southcoasteditor.com
Ed. ....Saboohi Currim

COLORADO

LOVELAND

COLONEL
398 Wildbriar Lane, Loveland, CO, 80537, Larimer, USA; tel (970) 669-3272; adv tel (970) 669-3272; ed tel 9706693272; e-mail gary@berthoudrecorder.com; adv e-mail gary@berthoudrecorder.com; ed e-mail gary@berthoudrecorder.com
Web Site: www.berthoudrecorder.com
Pub, ed, reporter, photographer Gary Wamsley

CONNECTICUT

HARTFORD

THE CONNECTICUT MIRROR
36 Russ Street, Hartford, CT, 06106, Hartford, USA; tel (860) 218-6380; adv tel (860) 218-6380; ed tel (860) 490-4313; e-mail bputterman@ctmirror.org; adv e-mail bputterman@ctmirror.org; ed e-mail calbert@ctmirror.org
Web Site: www.ctmirror.org
Mthly Avg Views: 500,000
Mthly Avg Unique Visitors: 82,000
Advertising: 2013
Established: 2009
Group: The Connecticut News Project, Inc.
Digital Platform - Mobile: Apple, Android, Windows
Digital Platform - Tablet: Apple iOS, Android, Windows 7
Ed. ....Claude Albert
Capital Bur. Chief...................Mark Pazniokas
CEO / Publisher....................Bruce Putterman

NEW HAVEN

THE NEW HAVEN INDEPENDENT
51 Elm St., Suite 307, New Haven, CT, 06510, New Haven, USA; tel (203) 624-8007; ed e-mail editor@newhavenindependent.org
Web Site: newhavenindependent.org
Ed. ....Paul Bass
Managing Editor ....Melissa Bailey

ILLINOIS

CHICAGO

PEOPLE'S WORLD
3339 S Halsted St, Chicago, IL, 60608-6882, Cook, USA; tel (773) 446-9920; fax (773) 446-9928; e-mail contact@peoplesworld.org
Web Site: www.peoplesworld.org
Ed.-in-Chief..................................John Wojcik

Mng. Ed................................Mariya Strauss

THE ONION
212 W Superior St., Suite 200, Chicago, IL, 60654-3562, Cook, USA; tel (312) 751-0503; fax (312) 751-4137; e-mail advertising@theonion.com
Web Site: theonion.comJoe Randazzo

INDIANA

FORT WAYNE

THE JOURNAL GAZETTE
600 W MAIN ST, FORT WAYNE, IN, 46802-1498, IN, USA; tel (260) 461-8773; adv tel (260) 461-8350; ed tel (260) 461-8773; fax (260) 461-8648; adv fax (260) 461-8489; ed fax (260) 461-8648; e-mail advertising@fwn.fortwayne.com; adv e-mail advertising@fwn.fortwayne.com; ed e-mail jgnews@jg.net
Web Site: www.journalgazette.net
Advertising: Open inch rate $81.65 (Mon-Thur); $95.90 (Fri-Sat)
Established: 1863
Digital Platform - Mobile: Apple, Android
Digital Platform - Tablet: Apple iOS, Android
Pres./Pub....................................Julie Inskeep
Assistant Metro Ed./day city Ed.. Jim Chapman
Managing Ed..................................Jim Touvell
Features Ed. ....Terri Richardson
News Technology Mgr..........Tom Pellegrene Jr.
Ed. ....Sherry Skufca
Note: For detailed production and mechanical information, see Fort Wayne Newspapers Inc. listing.

KENTUCKY

ABERDEEN

BEECH TREE NEWS
PO Box 140, Aberdeen, KY, 42201-0140, Butler, USA; tel (270) 526-9527; fax (270) 526-2178; e-mail diane@beechtreenews.com
Web Site: www.beechtreenews.com
Advertising: Strip Ad-1mth run/$125, 6mth/$112, 12mth/$93.75. Block Ad-1mth/$250, 6mth/$225, 12mth/$187.50
Established: 2009Diane Dyer
John Embry

LOUISA

LEVISA LAZER
1328 Gene Wilson Blvd, Louisa, KY, 41230-9681, Lawrence, USA; tel (606) 638-0123
Web Site: www.thelevisalazer.com
Established: 2008
Ed. ....Mark Grayson

RUSSELLVILLE

THE LOGAN JOURNAL
2575 Bowling Green Rd, Russellville, KY, 42276-9617, Logan, USA; tel (270) 772-1544; e-mail jimturner@loganjournal.com
Web Site: www.loganjournal.comJim Turner

MARYLAND

COLUMBIA

BALTIMORE POST-EXAMINER
PO Box 2094, Columbia, MD, 21045-2094, Howard, USA; tel (443) 745-4363; e-mail BaltimorePostExaminer@gmail.com
Web Site: baltimorepostexaminer.com
Mthly Avg Unique Visitors: 100,000
Established: 2012
Pub ....Timothy Maier
Note: Sister site is Los Angeles Post-Examiner

MINNESOTA

MINNEAPOLIS

MINNPOST
900 6th Avenue SE, Suite 220, Minneapolis, MN, 55414, Hennepin, USA; tel (612) 455-6950; adv tel (612) 455-6953; fax (612) 455-6960; e-mail info@minnpost.com
Web Site: minnpost.com
Mthly Avg Views: 1,000,000
Mthly Avg Unique Visitors: 450,000
Established: 2007
Publisher & CEO ....Andrew Wallmeyer
Web Editor............................Corey Anderson
Ad. Director.............................Sally Waterman
Editor ....Andrew Putz
Note: MinnPost is a 501(c)3 nonprofit corporation.

MONTANA

MISSOULA

NEW WEST
415 N Higgins Ave, Suite 103, Missoula, MT, 59802, Missoula, USA; tel (877) 343-5207; e-mail advertise@newwest.net; ed e-mail info@newwest.net
Web Site: newwest.net

NEW JERSEY

ATLANTIC HIGHLANDS

ATLANTIC HIGHLANDS HERALD
25 Second Avenue, Atlantic Highlands, NJ, 07716, Monmouth, USA; e-mail allan@ahherald.com
Web Site: ahherald.com
Mthly Avg Views: 30,000
Mthly Avg Unique Visitors: 15,000
Established: 1999
Digital Platform - Mobile: Apple, Android, Windows, Blackberry
Digital Platform - Tablet: Apple iOS, Android, Windows 7, Blackberry Tablet OS, Kindle,

Nook, Kindle Fire
Pub. & Ed..........................Allan Dean
Note: We exclude many foreign visitors and bots.

UNION

VAILSBURG LEADER
1291 Stuyvesant Ave, Union, NJ, 07083-3823, Union, USA; tel (908) 686-7700; fax (908) 686-4169; e-mail ads@thelocalsource.com; adv e-mail class@thelocalsource.com; ed e-mail editorial@thelocalsource.com
Web Site: www.essexnewsdaily.com
Established: 1949
Group: Worrall Community Newspapers, Inc.
Pub. ....David Worrall
Gen. Mgr..............................Raymond Worrall
Adv. Mgr.................................Peter Worrall
Nancy Worrall
Note: E-Edition Only

NEW YORK

BATAVIA

THE BATAVIAN
200 E. Main St., Suite 5, Batavia, NY, 14020, NY, USA; tel (585) 250-4118; e-mail lisa@thebatavian.com; adv e-mail lisa@thebatavian.com; ed e-mail billie@thebatavian.com
Web Site: thebatavian.com
Mthly Avg Views: 1,500,000
Mthly Avg Unique Visitors: 120,000
Established: 2008
Digital Platform - Mobile: Apple, Android
Digital Platform - Tablet: Apple iOS, Android
Pub ....Howard Owens
Ed. ....Billie Owens
Sales/Mktg. Coord. ....Lisa Ace

NEW YORK

GOTHAM GAZETTE
299 Broadway, Suite 700, New York, NY, 10007, Manhattan, USA; tel (212) 227-0342; fax (212) 227-0345; e-mail advertise@gothamgazette.com; ed e-mail info@gothamgazette.com
Web Site: gothamgazette.com
Established: 1999
Group: Citizens Union Foundation
Exec. Ed. ....Ben Max

THE FISCAL TIMES
712 5th Ave, Fl 17, New York, NY, 10019-4108, Manhattan, USA; tel (212) 313-9680; fax (877) 291-7606; e-mail info@thefiscaltimes.com
Web Site: www.thefiscaltimes.com
Ed.-in-Chief...............................Jacqueline Leo
Acct. Mgr.....................................Jeff Czaplicki

THE HUFFINGTON POST
770 Broadway, New York, NY, 10012, Manhattan, USA; tel (212) 652-6400; e-mail blogteam@huffingtonpost.com
Web Site: huffingtonpost.com
Managing Editor ....Karen Mahabir
Pres. ....Arianna Huffington
Ed.-in-Chief...............................Lydia polgreen

THE NEW YORK SUN
105 Chambers St., 2nd Floor, New York, NY, 10007-3516, Manhattan, USA; tel (212) 406-2000; adv tel (212) 901-2700; fax (212) 571-9836; e-mail inquiries@nysun.com; adv e-mail advertising@nysun.com; classified@nysun.com; ed e-mail editor@nysun.com
Web Site: www.nysun.com

Dir., Classified ....John Garrett
Circ. Dir. ....Linda Seto
Ed...Seth Lipsky
Mng. Ed.....................................Ira Stoll
Art Ed..Dave Propson
Bus. Ed. ....Richard Thomson
Features Ed. ....Emily Gitter
Sports Ed.....................Michael Woodsworth

PELHAM

THE PELHAMS-PLUS
P.O. Box 8605, Pelham, NY, 10803, Westchester, USA; tel (914) 738-8717; e-mail maggieklein@pelhamweekly.com
Web Site: www.pelhamwplus.com
Advertising: $80-$100 per month
Established: 1992
Group: Klein Information Resources, Inc.
Digital Platform - Mobile: Apple, Android, Windows, Blackberry
Digital Platform - Tablet: Apple iOS, Android
Ed. ....Margaret A. Klein

PENNSYLVANIA

BALA CYNWYD

PHILADELPHIA JEWISH VOICE
327 Pembroke Road, Bala Cynwyd, PA, 19004, Montgomery, USA; tel (610) 649-1454; adv tel (215) 849-2312; ed tel (610) 649-0998; fax (610) 649-0255; e-mail ads@pjvoice.org; adv e-mail ads@pjvoice.org; ed e-mail editor@pjvoice.com
Web Site: pjvoice.org
Mthly Avg Views: 10,000
Mthly Avg Unique Visitors: 9,000
Advertising: Ronit Treatman
Established: 2005
Digital Platform - Mobile: Apple, Android, Windows, Blackberry, Other
Digital Platform - Tablet: Apple iOS, Android, Windows 7, Blackberry Tablet OS, Kindle, Nook, Kindle Fire, Other
Pub ....Daniel Loeb
Food Editor ....Ronit Tretman
President ....Bonnie Squires
VP...Ken Myers

CLEARFIELD

GANT DAILY
219 S 2nd St, Clearfield, PA, 16830-2205, Clearfield, USA; tel (814) 765-5256; fax (814) 765-5631; e-mail dkilmer@gantdaily.com; adv e-mail sales@gantdaily.com; ed e-mail jshirey@gantdaily.com
Web Site: www.gantdaily.com
Mthly Avg Unique Visitors: 300,000
Established: 2006
Group: Gant Media LLC
Digital Platform - Mobile: Apple, Android, Windows, Blackberry
Digital Platform - Tablet: Apple iOS, Android, Windows 7, Blackberry Tablet OS, Kindle, Nook, Kindle Fire
Pres. ....Christene Dahlem
Ed. ....Jessica Shirey
Adv./Digital Media Sales...............Ray Serafini
Bus. Dev't. Mgr....................Morgan Dubensky

LINGLESTOWN

LINGLESTOWN GAZETTE
6204 Elmer Ave., Linglestown, PA, 17112, Dauphin, USA; tel (717) 512-0722; e-mail linglestowngazette@gmail.com
Web Site: linglestowngazette.com
Mthly Avg Views: 300
Mthly Avg Unique Visitors: 2,000

Ed./Pub...Bill Bostic

PHILADELPHIA

PHILLYVOICE.COM
1430 Walnut St, Philadelphia, PA, 19102, Philadelphia, USA; tel (26) 519-4500; e-mail Sales@PhillyVoice.com
Web Site: PhillyVoice.com
Group: WWB Holdings, LLC
Exec. Dir ....Lexie Norcross
Exe. Ed......................................Matt Romanoski
Exec. Ed. ....Bob McGovern
VP of Sales/Mktg. ....Hal Donnelly

RHODE ISLAND

WARWICK

RHODY BEAT
1944 Warwick Avenue, Warwick, RI, 02889, Kent, USA; tel (401) 732-3100; fax (401) 732-3110; e-mail suzannew@rhodybeat.com; adv e-mail sueh@rhodybeat.com
Web Site: rhodybeat.com
Group: Beacon Communications, Inc
Gen. Mgr. ....Richard G. Fleischer
Pub./Beacon Ed............................John Howell

TENNESEE

CHATTANOOGA

CHATTANOOGAN.COM
100 Cherokee Boulevard, #109, Chattanooga, TN, 37405, Hamilton, USA; tel (423) 266-2325; e-mail news@chattanoogan.com
Web Site: chattanoogan.com
Pub. ....John Wilson

TEXAS

AUSTIN

THE TEXAS TRIBUNE
823 Congress Ave., Suite 1400, Austin, TX, 78701, Travis, USA; tel (512) 716-8600; adv tel (512) 716-8634 ; fax (512) 716-8601; e-mail ahinkle@texastribune.org
Web Site: texastribune.org
Mthly Avg Views: 3,632,933
Mthly Avg Unique Visitors: 617,068
Ed.-in-Chief............................Emily Ramshaw
Exec. Editor ....Ross Ramsey
Development Director.............Maggie Gilburg
CRO & Advertising ....April Hinkle

CORPUS CHRISTI

COASTAL BEND LEGAL & BUSINESS NEWS
526 Mediterranean Drive, Corpus Christi, TX, 78418-3967, Nueces, USA; tel 361-937-4907; fax 361-937-1849; e-mail info@cblnews.com; adv e-mail info@cblnews.com; ed e-mail cblnews@cblnews.com

Web Site: www.cblnews.com
Advertising: 1/8 Pg $75.00
Established: 1981
Pub./Ed./Adv. Dir.......................Kim Gutierrez

MARBLE FALLS

DAILYTRIB.COM
1007 AVENUE K, MARBLE FALLS, TX, 78654-5039, Burnet, USA; tel (830) 693-7152; fax (830) 693-3085; e-mail advertising@thepicayune.com; adv e-mail advertising@thepicayune.com; ed e-mail editor@thepicayune.com
Web Site: www.dailytrib.com
Mthly Avg Views: 89,000
Mthly Avg Unique Visitors: 21,500
Established: 1991
Group: Victory Publishing Co., Ltd.
Associate Publisher.....................Mandy Wyatt
Pres./Pub./Adv. Sales ....Amber Weems

SPRING

THE PAPER
23503 Briarcreek Blvd., Spring, TX, 77373, Harris, USA; tel (832) 296-6887; adv tel (832) 296-6887; ed tel 8322966887; e-mail bobgunner@gmail.com; adv e-mail bobgunner@gmail.com; ed e-mail bobgunner@gmail.com
Web Site: thepapermagazine.com
Advertising: 2008
Established: 2008
Digital Platform - Mobile: Other
Pub./Ed...Bob Gunner

VIRGINIA

FRONT ROYAL

LIFESITENEWS.COM
4 Family Life Lane, Front Royal, VA, 22630, Warren, USA; tel (888) 678-6008; adv tel (888) 678-6008 ext 928; fax (540) 635-4374; e-mail cmaagad@lifesitenews.com; adv e-mail cmaagad@lifesitenews.com; ed e-mail editor@lifesitenews.com
Web Site: www.lifesitenews.com
Mthly Avg Views: 4,000,000
Mthly Avg Unique Visitors: 2,200,000
Established: 1997
Digital Platform - Mobile: Apple, Android, Windows, Blackberry
Digital Platform - Tablet: Apple iOS, Android, Windows 7, Blackberry Tablet OS, Kindle, Nook, Kindle Fire
Adv. Mgr....................................Clare Maagad
Editor / Journalist.......................Patrick Craine
US Bureau Chief ....Benjamin Johnson
Managing Ed.............................John Jalsevac
Ed. & Chief.........................John-Henry Westen
Managing Director ....Steve Jalsevac
Journalist / Photographer ....Lisa Bourne
Journalist ....Claire Chretien
Journalist ....Doug Bean
Journalist ....Peter Baklinski
Journalist ....Doug Mainwaring
Rome Correspondent ....Diane Montagna
Journalist ....Lianne Laurence
Journalist ....Fr. Mark Hodges

WARRENTON

FAUQUIER NOW
50 Culpeper St, Suite 3, Warrenton, VA, 20188, Fauquier, USA; tel (540) 359-6574; e-mail Ellen@FauquierNow.com
Pub. ....Ellen Emerson
Ed. ....Lawrence Emerson

WASHINGTON

SEATTLE

CROSSCUT
401 Mercer St, Seattle, WA, 98109, King,
USA; tel (206) 382-6137; fax (206) 443-6691;
e-mail advertising@crosscut.com
Web Site: crosscut.com
Ed.-in-Chief.................................Greg Hascom
Exec. Mgr.........................Tamara Power-Drutis
Acc. Mgr....................................Jonah Fruchter
Ed. ....Joe Copeland

SEATTLE POST-INTELLIGENCER
2901 3rd Ave, Suite 120, Seattle, WA,

98121, King, USA; tel (206) 448-8030; adv
tel (206) 448-8036; ed tel (206) 464-2496;
fax (206) 515-5577; adv fax (206) 493-0993
; ed fax (206) 382-6760; e-mail advertising@
seattlepi.com; ed e-mail citydesk@seattlepi.
com
Web Site: www.seattletimes.com
Established: 2009
Group: Metro Newspaper Advertising Services,
Inc.
Digital Platform - Mobile: Apple, Android
Digital Platform - Tablet: Apple iOS, Android
Assoc. Pub./ Editorial Ed. ....Ryan Blethen
Mng. Ed......................................Suki Dardarian
Exec. Prod. ....Sarah Rupp
Dir. of Visuals............................Denise Clifton
Exec. News Ed..........................Leon Espinoza
Sr. VP, Bus. Ops...................Michael Shepard
Sr. VP, Finance...........................Buster Brown
VP, Public Affairs.............................Jill Mackie
VP/CFO ....Eileen Takeuchi
Dir., Labor Rel./Safety ....Chris Biencourt
Mktg. Dir., New Media...............Anna Bertrand
Aerospace/Boeing Reporter......Dominic Gates

WEST VIRGINIA

HUNTINGTON

HUNTINGTONNEWS.NET
528 Ridgewood Rd, Huntington, WV, 25701-
4852, Cabell, USA; tel (304) 654-0087; adv
tel (304) 840-1555; ed tel (304) 544-8160;
e-mail hnn.ads@gmail.com; ed e-mail
trutherford@huntingtonnews.net
Web Site: www.huntingtonnews.net
Established: 2000
Pub./Owner.................................. Matt Pinson
Ed. .... Tony Rutherford
Adv. Dir....................................Dale Anderson II

WISCONSIN

KOHLER

MYSHEBOYGAN.COM
P.O. Box 33, Kohler, WI, 53044, Sheboygan,
USA; tel (920) 917-6311; e-mail ads@
mysheboygan.com; ed e-mail news@
mysheboygan.com
Web Site: mysheboygan.com
Mthly Avg Views: 100,000
Established: 2012
Digital Platform - Mobile: Apple, Android
Digital Platform - Tablet: Apple iOS, Android,
Kindle
News Dir. ....Jane Van Treeck

Section II

U.S. and Canadian Daily Newspaper Groups and Special Services

U.S. NEWSPAPER GROUPS

A

A.H. BELO CORPORATION — 400 S Record St, Dallas, TX, 75202-4806, USA; tel (214) 977-6606; fax (214) 977-6603; e-mail blc@belo.com; web site www.belo.com
Est.: 1842
Chrmn. of the Bd./CEO — Robert W. Decherd;
Exec. Vice Pres., Law & Government/Sec. — Guy H. Kerr;
Exec. Vice Pres. — Donald F. (Skip) Cass;
Sr. Vice Pres./Chief Accounting Officer — Carey Hendrickson;
Sr. Vice Pres., Bus. Devel. — Edward Olkkola;
Vice Pres., Techn. — W. Craig Harper;
Newspapers:Denton Record-Chronicle, TX
The Dallas Morning News, TX

ADAMS PUBLISHING GROUP, LLC — 704 S 7th Ave, Virginia, MN, 55792-3086; tel (218) 750-2615; fax (419) 782-2944; e-mail crescent@crescent-news.com; web site www.adamspg.com
Est.: 1887
Ed. — Peter Bodley;
Mktg. Dir. — Bob Cole;
Reg. Pres. — Christopher Knight;
Reg. Pub. — Sam Gett;
Pres. & Pub. — David Fike;
Reg. Pub. — Chad Hjelming;
Reg. Pub. — Julie Frazier;
Pub. — John D. Worthington;
Adv. Mgr. — Mary Anne Pfeiffer;
Adv. Mgr. — Mark Ryan;
Ed. — Debbie Horne;
Circ. Mgr. — Betty Lentz;
Ed. — Dennis Van Scoder;
Sports Ed. — Bruce Hefflinger;
Prepress Mgr. — Beverly Stahl;
Gen. Mgr. — Steve VanDemark;
I.T. Director — Adam Breckler;
Pres. — Carl Esposito; Newspapers:APG Media of Tennessee/North Carolina, TN
The Avery Journal-Times, NC
The Blowing Rocket, NC
The Pilot, NC
Anacortes American, WA
Belgrade News, MT
Bozeman Daily Chronicle, MT
Cecil Whig, MD
Daily Record, WA
Eastern Shore Bargaineer, MD
Eau Claire Press Co., WI
Herald and News, OR
Idaho State Journal, ID
Kuna Melba News, ID
Lake County Examiner, OR
News-Herald, TN
Preston Citizen, ID
Skagit Valley Herald, WA
Stanwood Camano News, WA
Teton Valley News, ID
The Advocate & Democrat, TN
The Ashe Mountain Times, NC
The Daily Post-Athenian, TN
The Daily Times, TN
The Greeneville Sun, TN
The Herald-News, TN
The Maryland Independent, MD
The Nickel, OR
The Rogersville Review, TN
The Watauga Mountain Times, NC
Watauga Democrat, NC
Aitkin Independent Age, MN
Mille Lacs Messenger, MN
Faribault Daily News, MN
Bargain Hunter, MN
The Ashland Daily Press, WI
The Newport Plain Talk, TN
The Bay Times, MD
Gladwin County Record, MI

The Times Record, MD
Hibbing Daily Tribune, MN
Mesabi Daily News, MN
Andrews Gazette, MD
Wyoming Business Report, WY
Rawlins Daily Times, WY
Bayfield County Journal, WI
Post Register, ID
Kenyon Leader, MN
Rock Springs Rocket Miner, WY
The Chisholm Tribune Press, MN
Anoka County Shopper, MN
Kent County News, MD
Laramie Boomerang, WY
The Enterprise, MD
Wyoming Tribune-Eagle, WY
Brooklyn Center/Brooklyn Park Sun-Post, MN
Co-pilot, MN
Blaine-Spring Lake Park Life, MN
Minnetonka/Deephaven/Hopkins Sun Sailor, MN
Le Sueur News-Herald, MN
St. Louis Park Sun Sailor, MN
Logan Daily News, OH
Richfield Sun-Current, MN
Anoka County Union Herald, MN
Bloomington Sun-Current, MN
Crescent Extra, OH
Minnesota River Valley Shopper, MN
The Caledonia Argus, MN
Carver County News, MN
Champlin-Dayton Press, MN
Lonsdale News - Review, MN
Columbia Heights/Fridley Sun Focus, MN
Northfield Weekender, MN
North Crow River News, MN
Northfield News, MN
South Crow River News, MN
Robbinsdale/Crystal/New Hope/Golden Valley Sun-Post, MN
Sawyer County Record, WI
Dairyland Peach, MN
Owatonna People's Press, MN
Dakota County Tribune, MN
The Avenue News, MD
St. Peter Herald, MN
The Post Review, MN
Eden Prairie Sun-Current, MN
The Challis Messenger, ID
Edina Sun-Current, MN
Park Falls Herald, WI
The Le Center Leader, MN
Excelsior/Shorewood/Chanhassen Sun Sailor, MN
Forest Lake Times, MN
Isanti County News, MN
Waseca Area Shopper, MN
The Laker, MN
The Vinton County Courier, OH
Mille Lacs County Times, MN
Waseca County News, MN
Monticello Times, MN
Morrison County Record, MN
Perry County Tribune, OH
Mounds View/New Brighton Sun Focus, MN
Owatonna Area Shopper, MN
Norwood Young America Times, MN
Price County Review, WI
Lonsdale Area News-Review, MN
Osseo-Maple Grove Press, MN
The Calvert Recorder, MD
The Pioneer, MN
The Crescent-News, OH
Wayzata/Orono/Plymouth/Long Lake Sun Sailor, MN
Princeton Union-Eagle, MN
The Leader, MN
Faribault Area Shopper, MN
Scotsman, MN
St. Croix Valley Peach, MN
The Early Bird, WI
Star News, MN
Stillwater Gazette, MN
The Circleville Herald, OH

Sun Thisweek Apple Valley, MN
The Dorchester Star, MD
Thisweek Burnsville-Eagan Sun, MN
Queen Anne's Record Observer, MD
Sun Thisweek Lakeville, MN
Rice Lake Chronotype, WI
Town & Country Shopper, GA
The Waconia Patriot, MN
Rocket-Miner, WY
Spooner Advocate, WI
Star Democrat, MD
Newark Post, DE
The Enterprise, MD
Dundalk Eagle, MD
Enquirer Gazette, MD
Pentagram, VA
Tester, MD
The Journal, MD
Quarterdeck, DC
Joint Base Journal, DC
Southern Maryland Advertiser, MD
South Potomac Pilot, VA
The Bargainer, MD
The Standard, MD

ADVANCE PUBLICATIONS, INC. — 950 W Fingerboard Rd, Staten Island, NY, 10305-1453, USA; tel (718) 981-1234; fax (718) 981-1456; web site www.advance.net
Chrmn. of the Bd. — S.I. Newhouse;
Pres. — Donald E. Newhouse;
Pub., Staten Island Advance — Caroline Diamond Harrison;
Executive VP — Mark Newhouse;
Newspapers:The Patriot-News, PA
The Warren Reporter, NJ
South Advance, MI
Beaverton Leader, OR
Sun News, OH
Forest Grove Leader, OR
The US, PA
The Ann Arbor News, MI
The Kalamazoo Gazette, MI
Advantage, GA
Bayonne Journal (OOB) , NJ
Cadence, MI
Chronicle Shopping Guide (OOB), MI
Cranford Chronicle, NJ
Davison Flagstaff, MI
Duncannon Record, PA
Grand Blanc News, MI
Grand Valley Advance, MI
Hillsboro Argus, OR
Hunterdon County Democrat, NJ
Independent Press, NJ
Juniata Sentinel, PA
Kearny Weekly, NJ
Southeast Advance, MI
Metuchen/Edison Review, NJ
Northwest Advance, MI
Northeast Advance, MI
Penasee Globe, MI
Perry County Times, PA
Press-Register, AL
Record Press, NJ
Secaucus Journal (OOB) , NJ
Ledger Somerset Observer, NJ
South Plainfield Reporter, NJ
Southwest Advance, MI
Staten Island Advance, NY
Suburban News, NJ
Sun Scoop Journal, OH
The Advance, GA
The Bay City Times, MI
The Birmingham News, AL
The Burton News, MI
The Community Journal, MI
The Express-Times, PA
The Fenton Press, MI
The Flint Journal, MI
The Flint Township News, MI
The Flushing Observer, MI
The Gloucester County Times, NJ
The Grand Rapids Press, MI

The Huntsville Times, AL
The Jackson Citizen Patriot, MI
The Jersey Journal, NJ
The Mississippi Press, MS
The Muskegon Chronicle, MI
The News of Cumberland County, NJ
The News-Sun, PA
The Oregonian, OR
The Post-Standard, NY
The Reporter, NJ
The Republican, MA
The Saginaw News, MI
Star-Gazette, NJ
The Swartz Creek News, MI
The Times, NJ
The Times-Picayune, LA
South Jersey Times , NJ
Waterfront Journal, NJ
The Plain Dealer, OH
The Star-Ledger, NJ

AIM MEDIA INDIANA — 2980 N National Rd, Ste A, Columbus, IN, 47201-3234, USA; tel (812) 372-7811; web site www.therepublic.comEst.: 1872
CFO — Jeff Rogers;
Dir., Info. Servs. and human resources — Karen Fox Thompson;
Publisher — Chuck Wells;
Newspapers:Amherst News-Times, OH
Bellville Star & Tri-Forks Press, OH
Daily Advocate, OH
Daily Reporter, IN
Englewood Independent, OH
Fairborn Daily Herald, OH
Galion Inquirer, OH
Gallipolis Daily Tribune, OH
Hillsboro Times-Gazette, OH
Huber Heights Courier, OH
Macon County Times, TN
Miami County Advocate, OH
Sentinel-Tribune, OH
The Lima News, OH
The Register-Herald, OH
News Journal Star, OH
Republic Extra, IN
The Portsmouth Daily Times, OH
Daily Journal, IN
The Republic, IN
Pendleton Times-Post, IN
Brown County Democrat, IN
The Jackson County Banner, IN
The (Columbus) Republic, IN
Daily Journal, IN
The (Seymour) Tribune, IN
The Jackson County Banner, IN

AIM MEDIA TEXAS LLC — 1400 E Nolana Ave, McAllen, TX, 78504-6111, USA; tel (956) 683-4060; e-mail manager@aimmediatx.com; web site www.aimmediatexas.com
Newspapers:The Brownsville Herald, TX
Valley Morning Star, TX
The Monitor, TX
Odessa American, TX

AMERICAN COMMUNITY NEWSPAPERS LLC — 33 2nd St NE, # 280, Osseo, MN, 55369-1252, USA; tel (763) 425-3323; fax 763-425-2945; web site www.americancommunitynewspapers.com
Est.: 1998
CEO — Gene Carr;
CFO — David Kosofsky;
Cor. Controller — Richard D. Hendrickson;
Newspapers:Osseo-Maple Grove Press, MN
Champlin-Dayton Press, MN
North Crow River News, MN
Eden Prairie Sun-Current, MN
Sunnyvale View, TX
Columbia Heights/Fridley Sun Focus, MN
Eagan/Apple Valley/Rosemount Sun Thisweek, MN

Edina Sun-Current, MN
Excelsior/Shorewood/Chanhassen Sun Sailor, MN
Lakeville Sun-Current, MN
Monticello Shopper, MN
Monticello Times, MN
Northwest Columbus News, OH
Ramsey County Sun Focus (OOB), MN
Robbinsdale/Crystal/New Hope/Golden Valley Sun-Post, MN
Suburban News Publications, OH
The Big Walnut News, OH
The Times, OH
Wayzata/Orono/Plymouth/Long Lake Sun Sailor, MN

APG MEDIA OF TENNESSEE/NORTH CAROLINA — 103 W Summer St, Greeneville, TN, 37743-4923, USA; tel (423) 638-4181; fax (423) 639-9701; web site www.greenevillesun.com
Parent Co.: Adams Publishing Group, LLC
President of APG East and Publisher of The Greeneville Sun — Gregg K. Jones;
VP of Human Resources of Adams Publishing Group — Jo Ann Hopson;
Chief Revenue Officer of APG Media of TN/NC, and General Manager of The Greeneville Sun. — John E. Cash;
President of APG Media of TN/NC and Publisher of The Daily Times — Carl Esposito; Newspapers:The Connection, TN
Note: APG Media of TN/NC publishes three daily and eleven non-daily general circulation newspapers in East Tennessee and the High Country of Western North Carolina. The company also publishes tourism publications in the Great Smoky Mountains region, operates a brochure distribution company, and publishes monthly hotel/motel travel guides and websites throughout the southeastern United States. The company also owns and operates The High Road Agency, a full service marketing solutions firm based out of Tri-Cities TN/VA.

B

BEACON COMMUNICATIONS, INC — 1944 Warwick Ave, Warwick, RI, 02889-2448, USA; tel (401) 732-3100; fax (401) 732-3110; web site www.warwickonline.com
Est.: 1968
Publisher — John Howell;
General Manager — Richard Fleischer;
Newspapers:Cranston Herald, RI
Warwick Beacon, RI
Johnston Sun Rise, RI
Pennysaver, RI
Rhody Beat, RI

BH MEDIA GROUP — 1314 Douglas St, Ste 1500, Omaha, NE, 68102-1848, USA; e-mail berkshire@berkshirehathaway.com; web site www.berkshirehathaway.com
Scott Searl; Jeff Shabram; Thomas Kastrup;
Corporate Director — Jeffrey Carney;
SR. VICE PRESIDENT, COO — Doug Hiemstra;
VICE PRESIDENT, BH MEDIA MIDWEST GROUP — Alex Skovgaard;
Regional Sales Director, NC Group of BH Media — Jason Propst;
Vice President — Dale Lachniet;
Sr. Vice President, COO — Hiemstra Doug;
Newspapers:Bellevue Leader, NE
Advantage, NE
The Free Lance-Star, VA
Kearney Hub, NE
Star-Herald, NE
The Grand Island Independent, NE
The North Platte Telegraph, NE
Tulsa Business & Legal News, OK
Valley News Today, IA
Waco Tribune-Herald, TX
Market Weekly, NE
Smyth County News & Messenger, VA
Lexington Clipper-Herald, NE
Tulsa World, OK

Midlands Newspapers, Inc., NE
News & Record, NC
Powhatan Today, VA
Richlands News-Press, VA
Rockingham Now, NC
The Waverly News, NE
Gering Courier, NE
Shore News Today, NJ
Culpeper Star-Exponent, VA
The Burg, VA
Lake City News & Post, SC
Pow, NC
The Eagle, TX
The Enterprise Ledger, AL
The Eden News, NC
The Press of Atlantic City, NJ
The Messenger, NC
Wahoo Newspaper, NE
The Buffalo News, NY
The Roanoke Times, VA
Morning News, SC
The News & Advance, VA
Omaha World-Herald, NE
Bristol Herald Courier, VA
The Dothan Eagle, AL
News & Messenger, VA
Independent Tribune, NC
Jackson County Floridan, FL
The News Herald, NC
The Daily Progress, VA
The Hickory Daily Record, NC
The McDowell News, NC
Winston-Salem Journal, NC
Hernando Today (OOB), FL
Statesville Record & Landmark, NC
Opelika-Auburn News, AL
Richmond Times-Dispatch, VA
The News Virginian, VA
Dothan Progress, AL
Atlantic City Weekly, NJ
Mechanicsville Local, VA
Goochland Gazette, VA
The Greene County Record, VA
Madison Eagle, NJ
Orange County Review, VA
Danville Register & Bee, VA
The Floyd Press, VA
Bland County Messenger, VA
Wytheville Enterprise, VA
Martinsville Bulletin, VA
The Franklin News-Post, VA
Mooresville Tribune, NC
Army Flier, AL
Eufaula Tribune, AL
The Hartsville Messenger, SC
Gretna Breeze, NE
Papillion Times, NE
Ralston Recorder, NE
The Ashland Gazette, NE
The Clarinda Herald-Journal, IA
The Daily Nonpareil, IA
York News-Times, NE
The Eden News, NC
The Reidsville Review, NC
The Suncoast News, FL

BIGFOOT MEDIA, INC. — 2076 University Ave, Berkeley, CA, 94704-1006, USA; tel (510) 841-5600; fax (510) 841-5695Est.: 1999Newspapers:San Mateo Daily Journal, CA

BIRDLAND ACQUISITION LLC. — 20803 Biscayne Blvd, Ste 301, Aventura, FL, 33180-1431, USANewspapers:Bennington Banner, VT
Brattleboro Reformer, VT
Manchester Journal, VT
New England Newspapers Inc, MA
The Berkshire Eagle, MA

BLOCK COMMUNICATIONS, INC. — 405 Madison Ave, Ste 2100, Toledo, OH, 43604-1224, USA; tel (419) 724-6212; fax (419) 724-6167; e-mail info@blockcommunications.com; web site www.blockcommunications.com
Est.: 1900
Chrmn. — Allan Block;
Pres. — Gary Blair; Newspapers:Pittsburgh Post-Gazette, PA
The Blade, OH
Note: Block Communications Inc. is a

privately held media company which operates cable television in Toledo and Sandusky, Ohio, four television stations, a telecom business and a residential security business. Block Communications also owns The Blade located i

BOONE NEWSPAPERS, INC. — 15222 Freemans Bend Rd, Northport, AL, 35475-3800, USA; tel (205) 330-4100; fax (205) 330-4140; e-mail bni@boonenewspapers.com; web site www.boonenewspapers.com
Chrmn. of the Bd./CEO/Dir. — James B. Boone;
Pres./COO — Todd H. Carpenter;
Sr. Vice Pres. — William T. Beckner;
Sr. Vice Pres. — David D. Churchill;
Vice Pres. — Jason Cannon;
Vice Pres. — Joseph C. Davis;
Vice Pres. — Michele Cox Gerlach;
Vice Pres. — Michael R. Kelley;
Vice Pres. — Dennis M. Palmer;
Vice Pres. — Joseph C. Davis;
VP — Kevin Cooper;
Vice Pres. — Tim Prince;
Newspapers:Americus Times-Recorder, GA
Claiborne Progress, TN
LaGrange Daily News, GA
The Advocate-Messenger, KY
The Interior Journal, KY
The Jessamine Journal, KY
The Stanly News & Press, NC
The Winchester Sun, KY
Cordele Dispatch, GA
Daily Leader, MS
Dowagiac Daily News, MI
The Farmville Herald, VA
The State Journal, KY
Washington Daily News, NC
Pelham Reporter, AL
The Madison Record, AL
Albert Lea Tribune, MN
Alabaster Reporter, AL
Alexander City Outlook, AL
Andalusia Star-News, AL
Atmore Advance, AL
Austin Daily Herald, MN
Butler County News, AL
Cassopolis Vigilant, MI
Dadeville Record, AL
Demopolis Times, AL
Eclectic Observer, AL
Edwardsburg Argus, MI
The Fergus Falls Daily Journal, MN
Franklin County Times, AL
Freeborn County Shopper, MN
Gates County Index, NC
Hartselle Enquirer, AL
Lowndes Signal, AL
Miss-lou Buyers Guide, MS
Mower County Shopper, MN
Natchez Newspapers, Inc., MS
Post-searchlight Extra, GA
Roanoke-Chowan News-Herald, NC
Shelby County Reporter, AL
Suffolk News-Herald, VA
The Brewton Standard, AL
The Clanton Advertiser, AL
The Greenville Advocate, AL
The Ironton Tribune, OH
The Leader, MI
The Luverne Journal, AL
The Troy Messenger, AL
The Natchez Democrat, MS
The Post-Searchlight, GA
The Roanoke-chowan's Shopper Weekly, NC
The Tidewater News, VA
Tribune Shopping News, MN
Weekender, MN
The Selma Times-Journal, AL
The Tallassee Tribune, AL
Blackbelt Gazette, AL
The Wetumpka Herald, AL
Elizabethton Star, TN
The Madison County Record, AR
Bogalusa Daily News, LA
L'Observateur, LA
Port Arthur News, TX
Tryon Daily Bulletin, NC
Salisbury Post, NC
The Vicksburg Post, MS

Picayune Item, MS
The Oxford Eagle, MS
Niles Daily Star, MI

BRADFORD PUBLISHING CO. — 43 Main St, Bradford, PA, 16701-2019, USA; tel (814) 368-3173; fax (814) 362-6510; e-mail info@bradfordera.com; web site www.bradfordera.com
Pres. — John H. Satterwhite;Newspapers:Olean Times Herald, NY
The Bradford Era, PA

BREHM COMMUNICATIONS, INC. — 16644 W Bernardo Dr, Ste 300, San Diego, CA, 92127-1901, USA; tel (858) 451-6200; fax (858) 451-3814; e-mail debbiel@brehmmail.com; web site www.brehmcommunications.com
Est.: 1919
Pres — William Brehm;
Controller — Jeff Johnson;
Execu Asst — Debbie Lindsay;
VP-Sales and Mktg — Thomas Kirk;
Dir, Human Resources — Sara Salinas;
Interactive Media & Technology Mgr — Ryan Schuyler;
Real Estate Mgr — Barbara Schuyler;
Newspapers:Auburn Journal, CA
Big Bear Grizzly, CA
Wine Country This Week, CA
Laughlin Entertainer, AZ
Wabash And Edwards Today, IN
Desert Entertainer, CA
Big Bear Shopper, CA
Bullhead City Booster, AZ
Desert Trail, CA
Emery County Progress, UT
Grizzly Weekender, CA
Hi-Desert Star, CA
Mohave Valley Daily News, AZ
Mountain News & Crestline Courier-News, CA
Needles Desert Star, CA
Warrick County Today, IN
Oakland City Journal, IN
Auburn Trader, CA
Gibson County Today, IN
Loomis News, CA
Richfield Reaper, UT
Wickenburg Sun, AZ
Sun Advocate, UT
Vernal Express, UT
Uintah Basin Standard, UT
Placer Herald, CA
Colfax Record, CA
Observation Post, CA
Barstow Log, CA
Laughlin Nevada Times, AZ
Folsom Telegraph, CA
Lincoln News Messenger, CA
El Dorado Hills Telegraph, CA
Note: Subsidiaries: The Democrat Co.; Gull Communications, Inc.; Hi-Desert Publishing Co., Inc.; News West Publishing Company Inc.; Gold Country Media, Inc.; Wine Country Publications, Inc.; Princeton Publishing, Inc.; Mt. Carmel Register Co.; Warrick Publishing Co., Inc.

BRYAN PUBLISHING CO. — 127 S Walnut St, Bryan, OH, 43506-1718, USA; tel (419) 636-1111; fax 419-636-8937Newspapers:Northwest Signal, OH
The Bryan Times, OH

BYRD NEWSPAPERS — 2 N Kent St, Winchester, VA, 22601-5038, USA; tel (540) 667-3200Parent Co.: Ogden Newspapers Inc.
Newspapers:Daily News-Record, VA

C

CALKINS MEDIA — 8400 Bristol Pike, Levittown, PA, 19057, USA; tel (215) 949-4011; fax (215) 949-4021; e-mail feedback@calkins-media.com; web site www.phillyburbs.com

Parent Co.: GateHouse Media, Inc.
COO — Michael Scobey;
Sr. Vice Pres. — Micheal White;
Sec. to Pres. — Carolyn Crawford;
Dir., Adv./Mktg. — Kim Noble;
Dir., Information Servs. — Edward E. Emberger;
Dir., Interactive Media — Robert R. Kellagher;
Director of Corporate Development & Strategic Partnerships — Myra Cortado;
Vice Pres./Chief Digital Officer — Guy Tasaka; Shirley Ellis;
Director — Sandra Hardy;
Exec. Editor — Patricia Walker;
Production Director — Bob Braun;
Audience Development Director & GM — Steve Todd;
CEO — Mark Contreras;
General Manager — Jake Volcsko;
VP of Publishing/President and Publisher — Michael Jameson; Stanley M. Ellis;
VP/Director — Stan Ellis; Newspapers:The Intelligencer, PA
Ellwood City Ledger, PA
Greene County Messenger, PA
Bucks County Courier Times, PA
South Dade News Leader, FL
Note: Calkins Media also owns and operates the ABC affiliate TV station in Sarasota, Florida.

CAPITAL NEWSPAPERS — 1901 Fish Hatchery Rd, Madison, WI, 53713-1248, USA; tel (608) 252-6200; fax (608) 252-6028; e-mail customerservice@madison.com; web site www.capitalnewspapers.com
Pres./Pub. — Clayton Frink;
CFO — Pam Wells;
Chrmn., Board — John H. Lussier;
Treasurer — Philip Blake;
Ed. — Paul Fanlund;
Production Dir. — Robert Strabala; Julie Belschner;
VP of Advertising, Sales & Marketing — Joe Allen; Newspapers:Columbus Journal, WI
Juneau County Star-Times, WI
Monday-mini, WI
Reedsburg Times-Press, WI
Sauk Prairie Eagle, WI
Shopper Stopper, WI
Shopping Reminder, WI
Tri-county, WI
Wisconsin Dells Events, WI
Baraboo News Republic, WI
Daily Citizen, Beaver Dam, WI
Wisconsin State Journal, Madison, WI
Note: Capital Newspapers is partially owned by Lee Enterprises Inc. Capital Newspapers owns five daily newspapers and 16 non-daily publications.

CENTRAL MISSOURI NEWSPAPERS INC. — 210 Monroe St, Jefferson City, MO, 65101-3210, USA; tel (573) 761-0281; web site www.centralmonewspapers.com
Gen Mgr — Todd Frantz; Newspapers:The Lake Today OOB, MO

CLEVELAND NEWSPAPERS, INC. — 525 Office Park Dr, Mountain Brk, AL, 35223-2413, USA; tel (205) 870-1684; fax (205) 870-9531 Est.: 1956
Chrmn. of Bd./Vice Pres. — C. Lee Walls; Newspapers:Chatsworth Times, GA
Cleveland Daily Banner, TN
Daily Mountain Eagle, AL
Herald-Citizen, TN
St. John Valley Times, ME
The Bolivar Commercial, MS
The Daily Tribune News, GA

CNHI, LLC — 445 Dexter Ave, Montgomery, AL, 36104-3775, USA; tel (334) 293-5800; web site www.cnhi.com
Sr. VP — Mike Beatty; Newspapers:Crossroads Supersaver, IL
North Coast, MI
The Madison County Advertiser, KY

COLORADO COMMUNITY MEDIA — 9137 Ridgeline Blvd, Ste 210, Highlands Ranch, CO, 80129-2752, USA; tel (303) 566-4100; fax (303) 566-4098; web site www.coloradocommunitymedia.com
Est.: 2000
Pub. — Gerard Healey; John Tracy;
Newspapers:Wheat Ridge Transcript, CO
Douglas County News Press, CO
Northglenn-Thornton Sentinel, CO
Castle Rock News Press, CO
Centennial Citizen, CO
Elbert County News, CO
The Englewood Herald, CO
Lone Tree Voice, CO
Highlands Ranch Herald, CO
Parker Chronicle, CO
Littleton Independent, MA
South Platte Independent, CO
Arvada Press, CO
Lakewood Sentinel, CO
Golden Transcript, CO
Westminster Window, CO
Northglenn-Thornton Sentinel, CO
Castle Pines News Press, CO

COMMUNITY MEDIA GROUP — 805 S Logan St, West Frankfort, IL, 62896-2637, USA; tel (618) 937-6412; fax (618) 932-3848; web site www.communitymediagroup.com
Chrmn./Pres./CEO — Larry J. Perrotto;
Vice Chrmn. — John H. Satterwhite;
Exec. Vice Pres. — John D. Perrotto;
Exec. Vice Pres. — Mark J. Perrotto;
Exec. Vice Pres. — Joan R. Williams;
Vice Pres. — Paul Barrett;
VP Accounting — Kristen Ahlberg;
Newspapers:Barr's Post Card News, IA
Bonny Buyer, IA
Daily Gate City, IA
Fort Madison Daily Democrat, IA
Hancock County Journal-Pilot, IL
The Progress, PA
Ludington Daily News, MI
Ludington Shopper's Edition, MI
Cedar Falls Times (OOB), IA
The Star-News, CA
The Hoopeston Chronicle, IL
Ossian Bee, IA
Fayette Leader, IA
Colonie/Loudonville Spotlight, NY
Fayette County Union, IA
The Leader-Vindicator, PA
Neoga News (OOB), IL
The Spotlight, NY
The Elgin Echo, IA
Oblong Gem (OOB), IL
Bremer County Independent, IA
Tri-County Sunday, PA
Atlantic News Telegraph, IA
Audubon County Advocate Journal, IA
Bremer-butler Super Shopper, IA
Finger Lakes Times, NY
Fountain County Neighbor, IN
Free Press-Courier, PA
Indiana Spirit, IN
Iosco County News Herald, MI
Lafayette Leader, IN
Messenger, IN
News Times, IN
Oceana's Herald-Journal, MI
Port Allegany Reporter-Argus, PA
Rensselaer Republican, IN
Shopper's Reminder, IA
The Chronicle, IL
The Extra, IL
The News-Gazette, IN
The Newton County Enterprise, IN
The Oelwein Daily Register, IA
The News Reminder, IN
The Reporter (OOB), IL
The Wellsboro Gazette, PA
Times-Republic, IL
White Lake Beacon, MI
Oscoda Press, MI
Vinton Livewire, IA
Kankakee Valley Post-News, IN
The Review-Republican, IN
Olean Times Herald, NY
Independence Bulletin Journal, IA
The Courier Express, PA

Jeffersonian Democrat, PA
Bradford Era, PA
Note: Community Media Group owns ten daily newspapers, 23 weekly and 18 shopper publications.

COMMUNITY NEWSPAPER HOLDINGS, INC. — 445 Dexter Ave, Ste 7000, Montgomery, AL, 36104-3892, USA; tel (334) 293-5800; fax (334) 293-5913; web site www.cnhi.com
Pres./CEO — Donna Barrett;
Executive VP/COO — F. Steve McPhaul;
Senior VP, Revenue — Jack Robb;
Senior VP, Audience Development — Linwood Pride;
Executive VP/COO — Keith Blevins;
Chief Digital Officer/VP — Matthew Ipsan;
Chief Financial Officer — Jennifer Pustaver;
Vice Pres., Digital Sales — Dee Dee Mathis;
Regional Executive — Henry Bird;
Director, Internal Audit — Nick Stanfill;
Senior Vice President — Robyn McCloskey;
Senior Vice President & Senior Controller — Chris Cato; Newspapers:Laurel Leader-Call, MS
Herald-Banner, TX
Royse City Herald Banner, TX
Cooperstown Crier, NY
Rockwall County Herald Banner, TX
Chickasha News, OK
The Herald-Tribune, IN
Herald Journal, IN
Pharos-Tribune, IN
The Goshen News, IN
Tribune-Star Publishing Co., Inc., IN
Marion County Reminder, IA
Oskaloosa Shopper, IA
Princeton Times, WV
Skyline, MS
The Free Press, MN
Ad Express, IA
Rutherford Weekly, NC
Enid News & Eagle, OK
The Randolph Guide, NC
Glasgow Daily Times, KY
Gloucester Daily Times, MA
Suwannee Democrat, FL
Pauls Valley Democrat, OK
Ad-Express & Daily Iowegian, IA
The Salem News, MA
The Ada News , OK
Albion Advertiser, NY
Allied News, PA
Woodward News, OK
Andover Townsman, MA
The Eagle-Tribune, MA
Athens Daily Review, TX
Bluefield Daily Telegraph, WV
Branford News, FL
Bravo Extra, PA
Carriage Towne News, NH
Cleburne Times-Review, TX
Clinton Herald, IA
Coffee County News (OOB), GA
Commerce Journal, TX
Commercial News, IL
Corsicana Daily Sun, TX
Crossville Chronicle, TN
Daily Union, IL
Effingham Daily News, IL
Gainesville Daily Register, TX
Greensburg Daily News, IN
Greenup County News-Times, KY
Hartshorne Sun, OK
Hendricks County Flyer, IN
Hometown, IN
Image, IN
Jasper News, FL
Kokomo Tribune, IN
Madison County Direct, IN
McAlester News-Capital, OK
Mineral Wells Index, TX
Montgomery Herald, WV
Moore American, IN
Muskogee Phoenix, OK
New Castle News, PA
Niagara Gazette, NY
Norman Transcript, OK
North Jefferson News, AL
Oskaloosa Herald, IA

Palestine Herald-Press, TX
Mineral Wells Index, TX
Parker County Shopper, TX
Pella Chronicle, IA
Press-Republican, NY
Traverse City Record-Eagle, MI
Register-News, IL
Route 66, OK
Rushville Republican, IN
Sapulpa Daily Herald, OK
Shopper's Edge, OK
St. Clair News-Aegis, AL
Star Beacon, OH
Star Shopper, TX
Stilwell Democrat Journal, OK
Tahlequah Daily Press, OK
The Claremore Daily Progress, OK
The Commonwealth-Journal, KY
The Cullman Times, AL
The Cumberland Times-News, MD
The Daily Citizen, GA
The Daily Independent, KY
The Daily Item, PA
The Daily News, MA
The Daily Star, NY
The Pryor Times, OK
The Danville News, PA
The Duncan Banner, OK
The Eastern Oklahoma County News, OK
The Edmond Sun, OK
News and Tribune, IN
The Express-Star, OK
The Fayette Tribune, WV
The Greensburg Times, IN
The Herald, PA
The Herald Bulletin, IN
The Huntsville Item, TX
The Joplin Globe, MO
The Knoxville Journal-Express, IA
The Meadville Tribune, PA
The Meridian Star, MS
The Moultrie Observer, GA
Stillwater News Press, OK
The News-Courier, AL
The Poplarville Democrat, MS
The Register Herald, WV
The Reporter, IN
The Richmond Register, KY
The Sentinel-Echo, KY
The Star, TX
The Sun/Sunday Sun, OK
The Tifton Gazette, GA
The Tribune Star, IN
The Tribune-Democrat, PA
The Tuttle Times, OK
The Union-Recorder, GA
The Washington Times, DC
The Wayne County Outlook, KY
The Weatherford Democrat, TX
The Weekend Flyer, IN
Thomasville Times-Enterprise, GA
Times West Virginian, WV
Times-Tribune, KY
Tribune, IN
Lockport Union-Sun & Journal, NY
Valdosta Daily Times, GA
Westville Reporter, OK
Zionsville Times Sentinel, IN
Jacksonville Daily Progress, TX
The Haverhill Gazette, MA
Derry News, NH
Olive Hill Times, KY
Grayson Journal-Enquirer, KY
The Daily Southerner, NC
The Morehead News, KY
The Ottumwa Courier, IA
Mayo Free Press, FL
The Times-Leader, NC
The Times Tribune, TX

COMMUNITY NEWSPAPERS, INC. — PO Box 792, Athens, GA, 30606-6003, USA; tel (706) 548-0010; fax (706) 548-0808; web site www.cninewspapers.com
Est.: 1967
Chrmn. — Tom Wood;
Pres. — William H. Dink NeSmith;
CFO — Mark Major;
Corporate Marketing Director / Major Account Manager — Joel Jenkins; Eric NeSmith;
Newspapers:Andrews Journal, NC

Cherokee Scout, NC
The Elberton Star, GA
Bay View NOW, WI
Clay County Progress, NC
North Shore NOW, WI
Brookfield-Elm Grove NOW, WI
Crossroads Chronicle, NC
Dawson News & Advertiser (OOB), GA
Lake City Reporter, FL
Cudahy NOW, WI
News-Leader, FL
Elm Grove NOW, WI
Palatka Daily News, FL
Fox Point NOW, WI
The Clayton Tribune, GA
Franklin NOW, WI
The Dahlonega Nugget, GA
Germantown NOW, WI
Glendale NOW, WI
The Franklin Press, NC
Oak Creek-Franklin-Greendale-Hales Corners NOW, WI
The Graham Star, NC
Greenfield-West Allis NOW, WI
The Hartwell Sun, GA
Hales Corners NOW, WI
The Highlander, NC
Menomonee Falls-Germantown NOW, WI
The News Leader, GA
Mequon NOW, WI
The Northeast Georgian, GA
Mitchell News-Journal, NC
Muskego-New Berlin NOW, WI
The Telfair Enterprise, GA
New Berlin NOW, WI
The Toccoa Record, GA
Oak Creek NOW, WI
Tribune & Georgian, GA
Nassau County Record, FL
South Milwaukee NOW, WI
St. Francis NOW, WI
White County News, GA
The Smoky Mountain Times, NC
Wauwatosa NOW, WI
West Allis NOW, WI
Note: Community Newspapers Inc. maintains 28 subscriber newspapers and affliates in Georgia, Florida and North Carolina. Also, select non-duplicating TMC's are available.

COMMUNITY PUBLISHERS, INC. — 900 SE 5th St, Ste 22, Bentonville, AR, 72712-6090, USA; tel (479) 271-3782; fax (479) 271-3788; e-mail commpub.com; web site www.commpub.com
Parent Co.: Phillips Media Group LLC
Est.: 1982
Pres. — Steve Trolinger;
Exec. Vice Pres. — Michael Brown;
Vice Pres. — Dave Berry;
CFO — Tom Bruns;
Prodn. Mgr. — Charles Heidelberg; Ronnie Bell; Roger Frye; David Guay;
Newspapers:Harrison Daily Times, AR
Community Publishers, Inc./Neighbor News, AR
Bolivar Herald-Free Press, MO
Cedar County Republican/Stockton Journal, MO
Collinsville News, OK
Coweta American (OOB), OK
Owasso Reporter, OK
Sand Springs Leader, OK
Skiatook Journal, OK
South County Mail, MO
The Newton County Times, AR
The Republic Monitor, MO
Wagoner Tribune, OK
South County Leader - (OOB), OK
Broken Arrow Ledger, OK
Tulsa Business Journal, OK
Note: Community Publishers Inc. owns the Harrison Daily Times in Harrison, AR and one daily business newspaper plus 20 weekly and semi-weekly community newspapers as well as three commercial printing plants.

CONLEY MEDIA LLC — 115 Monroe St, Beaver Dam, WI, 53916-2436, USA; tel (920) 885-7800; fax (920) 887-2779; e-mail hrd@

conleynet.com; web site www.gmtoday.com
Est.: 1970
Pres./CEO — James E. Conley;Newspapers:Milwaukee Post, WI
Washington County Post, WI
The Daily News, WI
Greater Milwaukee Jobs, WI
The Freeman, WI
The Hartford Times Press, WI
Oconomowoc Enterprise, WI
Ozaukee County Guide, WI
News Graphic, WI
Note: Conley Publishing Group Ltd. is a printing and publishing corporation with locations throughout Wisconsin, Colorado and Arizona. Conley Publishing publishes nine non-daily publications along with two daily newspapers in WI. Conley also publishes lifestyle magazines.

CONSOLIDATED PUBLISHING CO. — PO Box 189, Anniston, AL, 36202-0189, USA; tel (256) 235-9200; fax (256) 241-1980; web site www.annistonstar.com
Chrmn. — H. Brandt Ayers;
Pres. — Phillip A. Sanguinetti;
Vice Pres. — Chris Waddle;
Controller/Treasurer — Scott Calhoun;
Multimedia Advertising Director — David Bragg;
Social Media Consultant — Chris Pittman;
Newspapers:The Anniston Star, AL
Piedmont Journal, AL
The Cleburne News, AL
The Daily Home, AL
The Jacksonville News, AL
The Saint Clair Times, AL
Note: Consolidated Publishing Co. also owns three weekly publications: the Jacksonville (AL) News, Heflin (AL) The Cleburne News and Pell (AL) The Saint Clair Times.

COOKE COMMUNICATIONS FLORIDA, LLC — 3420 Northside Dr, Key West, FL, 33040-4254, USA; tel (305) 292-7777 Ext. 204; e-mail ttodd@keysnews.com; web site www.keysnews.com
Est.: 1876
Director of Advertising — Tommy Todd;Newspapers:Florida Keys Free Press, FL
Key West Citizen, FL
Keys Style Magazine, FL
Health File Magazine, FL
Paradise (The Entertainment Paper), FL
Bridal Magazine of the Florida Keys, FL
Home Magazine Spring & Fall, FL
Menu Guide , FL

COX MEDIA GROUP — 6205 Peachtree Dunwoody Rd, Fl 9, Atlanta, GA, 30328-4524, USA; tel (678) 645-0000; fax (678) 645-5002; web site www.coxnewspapers.com
Est.: 1898
Chrmn./CEO, Cox Enterprises Inc. — James C. Kennedy;
Pres./COO, Cox Enterprises Inc. — Jimmy Hayes;
Pres. — Sandy Schwartz;
Exec. Vice Pres./CFO, Cox Enterprises Inc. — John Dyer;
Exec. Vice Pres. — Douglas Franklin;
Vice Pres./CFO — Melody Darch;
Vice Pres./CIO — Christopher Caneles;
Vice Pres./HR — Susan S. Davidson;
Vice Pres., Adv. — Cathy B. Coffey;
Vice Pres., Circ. — Al Smith;
Vice Pres., Mktg./Grp. Vice Pres., Community Newspapers — Caroline C. John;
Vice Pres., Newsprint Supply — Mark Mansfield;
Vice Pres., Digital Media — Leon Levitt;
Gen. Mgr., COXnet — John Reetz;
Dir., Classified/Internet Adv. — Dean Welch;
Dir., Newsprint Supply — Greg Tant;
Nat'l Online Sales Mgr. — Bill Sullivan;
Vice Pres., Opns. — Stanley P. Richmond;
Newspapers:MundoHispánico Newspaper, GA
Westlake Picayune, TX

Florida Pennysaver, FL
Lake Travis View, TX
Marshall News Messenger, TX
The Bastrop Advertiser, TX
The Daily Advance, NC
The Daily Sentinel, CO
The Nickel, CO
The Pflugerville Pflag, TX
The Smithville Times, TX
Note: Cox Newspapers Inc. also owns Valpak; Cox Custom Media, and PAGAS. Cox Newspapers also has 50% ownership of Trader Publishing Co. and 33% of SP Newsprint. Cox Newspapers is a subsidiary of Cox Enterprises, Inc. and owns Austin Community Newspapers Gro

D

DAILY CAMERA — 2500 55th St, Ste 210, Boulder, CO, 80301-5740, USA; tel (303) 442-1202; fax (303) 449-9358; e-mail jstravolemos@prairiemountainmedia.com; web site www.dailycamera.com Parent Co.: Digital First Media Est.: 1890
Pub. — Al Manzi;
Mgr., Mktg./Promo./New Media — Jill Stravolemos;
Exec. Ed. — Kevin Kaufman;
City Ed. — Matt Sebastian;

DIGITAL FIRST MEDIA — 101 W. Colfax Ave, Fl 11, Denver, CO, 80202-5177, USA; tel (215) 504-4200; fax (215) 867-2174; e-mail rvenengas@journalregister.com; web site www.digitalfirstmedia.com
CFO — Michael J. Koren;
Pub — Sharon Ryan;
CEO — Steven B. Rossi;
EVP Sales & Digital — Chris Loretto;
EVP, Operations — Bill Higginson;
VP., Prodn. — William J. Higginson;
EVP & Chief Human Resources Officer — Robert Monteleone; Newspapers:Boston Herald, MA
Mid Michigan Buyer's Guide, MI
Press-Telegram, CA
Southern California News Group, CA
The Orange County Register, CA
The Press-Enterprise, CA
The Detroit News, MI
Advance of Bucks County, PA
Clear Lake Observer-American, CA
Grunion Gazette, CA
The Leader and The Kalkaskian, MI
The Willits News, CA
Tri-City Weekly, CA
Lake County's Penny Saver, CA
Oneida-madison Pennysaver, NY
South County News, CA
The Jack County Herald (OOB), TX
The Ukiah Daily Journal, CA
Ambler Gazette, PA
Prairie Mountain Publishing, CO
Bristol Pilot, PA
The Mendocino Beacon, CA
County Press, PA
The Advisor & Source, MI
Fort Bragg Advocate-News, CA
Garnet Valley Press, PA
The Canon City Daily Record, CO
Glenside News, PA
The Foothills Trader, CT
Montgomery Life, PA
News of Delaware County, Town Talk, Garnet Valley Press, Springfield Press, County PRess, PA
Montgomery Media, PA
Newtown Advance, PA
North Penn Life, PA
Perkasie News-Herald, PA
Public Spirit, PA
Piedmonter, CA
Souderton Independent, PA
Springfield Sun, PA
The Berkeley Voice, CA
The Boyertown Area Times, PA
Marin Independent Journal, CA
The Community Connection, PA

The Denver Post, CO
The Globe, PA
The Montclarion, CA
News-Herald, MI
Los Angeles Daily News, CA
The Hamburg Area Item, PA
The Review, PA
The Star Group, Inc., TX
Akron News-Reporter, CO
Times Chronicle, PA
Willow Grove Guide, PA
The Bay Voice, MI
Alameda Journal, CA
The Chelsea Standard, MI
Colorado Daily, CO
The Macomb Daily, MI
East Bay Times, CA
The Oakland Press, MI
Daily Camera, CO
The Reporter, PA
Loveland Reporter-Herald, CO
West Hartford News, CT
Alpena Star, MI
Blue Water Voice, MI
Longmont Times-Call, CO
Community News, NY
Daily Local News, PA
Fairfield Minuteman, CT
Ile Camera, MI
Burlington Record, CO
The Macomb Voice, MI
Main Line Suburban Life, PA
Chico Enterprise-Record, CA
Main Line Times, PA
Press & Guide, MI
Estes Park Trail-Gazette, CO
Shoreline Times, CT
Fort Morgan Times, CO
Southern Chester County Times Record, PA
Fremont Bulletin, CA
The Central Record, NJ
The Litchfield County Times, CT
Hometown Shopper, CA
The North Macomb Voice, MI
Julesburg Advocate, CO
The Recorder, PA
Berksmont News, PA
The Phoenix Reporter & Item, PA
The View, MI
Lake County Record-Bee, CA
Tri-County Record, PA
The Lamar Ledger, CO
Marin Independent Journal, CA
Palo Alto Daily News, CA
The Middletown Press, CT
Bellows Falls Town Crier, VT
Royal Oak Daily Tribune (OOB), MI
Morning Sun, MI
Heritage Newspapers, Inc., MI
The Oneida Daily Dispatch, NY
The Mercury News, CA
The Saratogian, NY
San Mateo County Times (OOB), CA
The Record, NY
Daily Freeman, NY
Santa Cruz Sentinel, CA
Sentinel & Enterprise, MA
The News-Herald, OH
St. Paul Pioneer Press, MN
The Morning Journal, OH
Delaware County Daily Times, PA
The Mercury, PA
The Brush News-Tribune, CO
The Times Herald, PA
The Daily Democrat, CA
The Trentonian, NJ
Main Line Media News, PA
The Monterey County Herald, CA
The Reporter, PA
Journal-Advocate, CO
The Sun, MA
Times-Standard , CA
Tri-Valley Herald/San Ramon Valley Herald (OOB), CA
Vallejo Times-Herald, CA
The Journal - Albany, El Cerrito, Kensington, CA
Press-Telegram (Long Beach), CA
Longmont Weekly (OOB), CO
Palos Verdes Peninsula News, CA
Ft Bragg Advocate-News, CA
Broomfield Enterprise, CO

Willits News, CA
Redwood Times, CA
Impacto, CA
Valley Journal, CA
Tri-City Weekly, CA
The Penny Slaver, CA
Clear Lake Ovserver, CA
Salinas Weekly, CA
Royal George Shopping News, CO
Rome Observer (OOB), NY
Morning Star Publishing Company, MI
Freedom Communications, Inc., CA
Note: Journal Register Company is a
newspaper company that owns 22daily
newspapers, including the New Haven
Register, and 346 non-daily publications.
All of the company's operations in six
geographic areas: Connecticut, Greater
Philadelphia, Greater Cleveland,

DOW JONES & COMPANY — 1211 Avenue
of the Americas, New York, NY, 10036-8701,
USA; tel (212) 416-2000; web site www.
dowjones.com
  Est.: 1882
  CEO — Leslie Hinton;
  Pres., Dow Jones Online — Gordon McLeod;
  Exec. Vice Pres./CFO — Stephen Daintith;
  Exec. Vice Pres., Enterprise Media Grp. —
  Clare Hart;
  Exec. Vice Pres./Gen. Counsel — Mark H.
  Jackson;
  Sr. Vice Pres., Local Media Grp. — John N.
  Wilcox;
  Sr. Vice Pres./Chief HR Officer — Greg
  Giangrande;
  Sr. Vice Pres., Special Projects — Ian
  Weston;
  Vice Pres., Commun. — Linda E. Dunbar;
  Vice Pres., Security — Joseph J.
  Cantamessa;
  Ed. in Chief — Robert Thomson;
  Newspapers:The Wall Street Journal, NY
  Dow Jones Local Media Group, NY
  Note: Dow Jones is the world's premier
  publisher of business news and information
  in every form of media

DOW JONES LOCAL MEDIA GROUP — 40
Mulberry St, Middletown, NY, 10940-6302,
USA; tel (845) 341-1100; web site www.
dowjoneslmg.comParent Co.: Dow Jones &
Company
  Est.: 1936
  CFO — Jonathan Kahan;
  Chief Operating Officer — William T.
  Kennedy;
  Senior Vice President, Advertising Sales
  — Molly Evans;
  Senior Vice President, Printing & Distribution
  — Don Waterman;
  Senior Vice President, Product Marketing
  — Kurt Lozier;
  Senior VP, Advertising Sales — Molly Evans;
  Vice Pres., Human Resources — Patricia
  Gatto;
  Treasurer — Chet D. Krinsky;
  Ed. — Ken Hall;
  Vice Pres., Information Servs. — John
  Treglia;
  Vice Pres., Opns./Adv. — Zeke Fleet;
  Circulation Director — Kelvin Parker;
  National & Major Accounts Manager —
  Gregory Appel; Newspapers:Medford Nickel,
  OR
  Nantucket Today, MA
  Barnstable Patriot, MA
  The Inquirer and Mirror, MA
  Exeter News-Letter, NH
  The Hampton Union, NH
  The York Weekly, NH
  York County Coast Star, NH
  The Advocate, MA
  Middleboro Gazette, MA
  The Chronicle, MA
  The Spectator, MA

E

E. W. SCRIPPS CO. — 312 Walnut St, Ste
2800, Cincinnati, OH, 45202-4019, USA; tel
(513) 977-3000; fax (513) 977-3090; e-mail
michele.roberts@scripps.com; web site www.
scripps.com
  COO — Richard A. Boehne;
  Sr. Vice Pres./Newspapers — Timothy E.
  Stautberg;
  Sr. VP/CFO/Treasurer — Tim Wesolowski;
  Pres. & CEO — Adam Symson;
  Board Member — Roger Ogden;
  Chief Administrative Officer — Lisa Knutson;
  Director of Digital Sales, Newspapers — Jay
  Horton;
  Senior Director, Digital Revenue — Tom Sly;
  VP, Strategic Planning & Development —
  Robin Davis;
  VP, Finance & Administration — Mike Hales;
  VP/Content, Newspapers — Mizell Stewart;
  Michele Roberts;
  Sr. Analyst/Systems Engineer
   — Donald Murray;
  Sr. Systems Analyst — Todd Nakamura;
  Newspapers:Metro Pulse, TN
  Anderson Valley Post, CA
  Jupiter Courier, FL
  Note: The E. W. Scripps Company is a
  diverse media concern with interests in
  newspaper publishing, broadcast television,
  cable television programming and interactive
  media.

EAGLE MEDIA — 114 W Diamond St, Butler,
PA, 16001-5747, USA; tel (724) 282-8000; fax
(724) 282-1280; e-mail news@butlereagle.com;
web site www.butlereagle.com
  Mng. Ed. — Chris Morelli;Newspapers:Butler
  Eagle, PA
  Pittsburgh City Paper, PA

EAGLE NEWSPAPERS, INC. — 4901 Indian
School Rd NE, Salem, OR, 97305-1128, USA;
web site www.eaglenewspapers.com
  Newspapers:Daily Sun News, WA
  The Dalles Daily Chronicle, OR
  Hood River News, OR
  Idaho County Free Press, ID
  Omak-Okanogan County Chronicle, WA
  The Polk County Itemizer-Observer, OR
  The Enterprise, WA
  Moneysaver-lewis Clark Edition, ID
  Moneysaver-palouse Edition, ID

ELWOOD PUBLISHING CO., INC. — 317
S Anderson St, Elwood, IN, 46036-2018, USA;
tel (765) 552-3355; fax (765) 552-3358; e-mail
elpub@elwoodpublishing.com; web site www.
elwoodpublishing.com
  Pub. — Bob Nash;Newspapers:Alexandria
  Times-Tribune, IN
  Leader-Tribune Review East, IN
  Leader-Tribune Review West, IN

EMMERICH NEWSPAPERS, INC. — PO
Box 16709, Jackson, MS, 39236-6709, USA;
tel (601) 957-1122; fax (601) 957-1533; e-mail
wyatt@northsidesun.com; web site www.
northsidesun.com
  Pres./CEO — J. Wyatt
  Emmerich;Newspapers:Charleston Sun
  Sentinel, MS
  The Choctaw Plaindealer, MS
  The Hattiesburg Post, MS
  The Petal News, MS
  The Star-Herald, MS
  Clarke County Tribune, MS
  Delta Democrat Times, MS
  Dumas Clarion, AR
  Enterprise-Journal, MS
  Madison Journal, LA
  Northside Sun, MS
  Scott County Times, MS
  Simpson County News, MS
  Southwest Sun, MS
  The Charleston Sun-Sentinel, MS
  The Clarksdale Press Register, MS

The Columbian-Progress, MS
The Conservative, MS
The Enterprise-Tocsin, MS
The Era-Leader, LA
The Greenwood Commonwealth, MS
The Magee Courier, MS
The Winona Times, MS
The Yazoo Herald, MS
The Laurel Chronicle, MS
Carrollton Conservative, MS
The Newton County Appeal, MS
Newto County Appeal, MS
Kosciusko Star-Herald, MS
Winston County Journal, MS
Note: Emmerich Newspapers Inc. also owns
26 community newspapers primarily in
Mississippi.

EO MEDIA GROUP — 1400 Broadway St NE,
Salem, OR, 97301-0504, US; tel (503) 364-
4431; e-mail hwright@eomediagroup.com; web
site www.eomediagroup.com
  Parent Co.: EO Media Group
  Est.: 1875
  COO — Heidi Wright;Newspapers:Hermiston
  Herald, OR
  Capital Press, OR
  Chinook Observer, WA
  Oregon Coast Today, OR
  East Oregonian, OR
  The Daily Astorian, OR
  Seaside Signal, OR
  Cannon Beach Gazette, OR
  Coast River Business Journal, OR
  Blue Mountain Eagle, OR
  Wallowa County Chieftain, OR

**EVENING POST PUBLISHING
NEWSPAPER GROUP** — 134 Columbus
St, Charleston, SC, 29403-4809, USA; tel
(843) 577-7111; fax (843) 937-5788; e-mail
dherres@postandcourier.com; web site www.
charleston.net
  Pres., Evening Post Community Publications
  Grp. — Dan Herres;
  Vice Pres., Evening Post Community
  Publications Grp. — Kathy Wilkinson;
  Newspapers:Evening Post Industries' Aiken
  Communications, SC
  Waccamaw Times, SC
  Berkeley Independent, SC
  Summerville Journal-Scene, SC
  The Clemmons Courier, NC
  The Georgetown Times, SC
  The News, SC
  The Post and Courier, SC
  The Star, SC
  Moultrie News, SC
  The Gazette, SC
  Note: Evening Post Community Publications
  Group, Inc. also owns the Buenos Aires
  (Argentina) Herald (mS) and operates 11
  television stations as well as Solo Syndicate,
  LTD. in London. The company also owns
  and manages timberland in Soth Carolina
  through White

F

FACKELMAN NEWSPAPERS — PO Box
910, 238 Market Street, Jennings, LA, 70546-
0910, USA; tel (337) 824-3011; fax n/a; e-mail
marcrichard8@gmail.com
  Est.: 1966
  Chairman — Ann F. Nixon;
  President — Frank E. Nixon;
  Vice President — Marc A. Richard;
  Treasurer — Broward E. Ratliff;
  Vice President - Operations — Dona H.
  Smith; Newspapers:Jennings (LA) Daily
  News, LA
  Ruston (LA) Daily Leader, LA
  The Southwest Times (Pulaski, VA), VA
  Note: Fackelman Newspapers shares
  ownership of the Crowley (LA) Post-Signal
  with B I Moody III (The Moody Company).
  In addition, this partnership owns one
  weekly newspaper in Louisiana. Fackelman
  Newspapers is also affiliated with two weekly

and one twice-weekly newspapers in Texas,
two weekly newspapers in Florida, one
weekly and one
  twice-weekly newspapers in Missouri, one
weekly newspaper in Louisiana and several
TMC publications.

FENICE COMMUNITY MEDIA — 211 W
3rd St, Taylor, TX, 76574-3518, USA; tel (512)
352-8285; fax (512) 352-8295; e-mail granite@
granitepub.com; web site www.granitepub.com
  Est.: 1978
  Founder — Jim Chionsini;
  CEO — Brandi Chionsini;
  Newspapers:Madisonville Meteor, TX
  Bandera Bulletin, TX
  Boerne Star, TX
  Elgin Courier, TX
  The Light & Champion, TX
  The Gonzales Inquirer, TX
  The Colorado County Citizen, TX
  The Hutto News, TX
  The Fort Stockton Pioneer, TX
  The Vindicator, TX
  Hill Country News, TX
  Mount Pleasant Daily Tribune, TX
  The Sealy News, TX
  The Navasota Examiner, TX
  Taylor Press, TX
  Note: Granite Publications also owns the
  Mount Pleasant Daily Tribune, a 5-day daily
  in Mount Pleasant, Texas.

FINDLAY PUBLISHING CO. — 701 W
Sandusky St, Findlay, OH, 45840-2325, USA;
tel (419) 422-5151; fax (419) 422-2937; web
site www.thecourier.com
  Est.: 1836
  Pres./Publisher — Karl L. Heminger;
  Vice Pres/Treasurer — Kurt F. Heminger;
  Audience Development Director — Kim
  Wilhelm;
  Vice President. Broadcast — David Glass;
  Newspapers:The Courier, OH
  The Review Times, OH
  Note: The Findlay Publishing Co. owns two
  daily newspapers as well as the Findlay
  (OH) Courier Plus. Findlay also owns seven
  broadcast radio stations.

FORUM COMMUNICATIONS CO. — 101
5th St N, Fargo, ND, 58102-4826, USA; tel
(701) 235-7311; fax (701) 241-5406; e-mail
wmarcil@forumcomm.com; web site www.
forumcomm.com
  CFO — John Hajostek;
  Pub. — William C. Marcil;
  President & CEO — Bill   Marcil
  Jr.;
  Director of Circulation — Christopher
  Berdahl; Jill Colosky;
  Dir. of Finance — Jon Buller;
  Pres./CEO — Lloyd Case; Frederick Greer;
  Dennis Doeden; Newspapers:Echoland -
  Piper Shopper, MN
  Perham Focus, MN
  Farmington Rosemount Independent Town
  Pages, MN
  Echo Journal, MN
  Agweek, ND
  The Bulletin, MN
  Lake Area Press, MN
  Advertizer, ND
  Sunday Reminder, MN
  River Falls Journal, WI
  Intercom, MN
  Park Rapids Enterprise Express, MN
  Duluth News Tribune, MN
  Echo-Press, MN
  Enterprise Bulletin, MN
  Hastings Star Gazette, MN
  InForum, ND
  Lake County News-Chronicle, MN
  Lakeland Shopping Guide, MN
  Morris Sun Tribune, MN
  New Richmond News, WI
  New York Mills Herald, MN
  Osakis Review, MN
  Park Rapids Enterprise, MN
  Pierce County Herald, WI

Republican Eagle, MN
South Washington County Bulletin, MN
The American, MN
Detroit Lakes Tribune, MN
Worthington Daily Globe, MN
The Daily Republic, SD
Superior Telegram, WI
The Detroit Lakes Tribune, MN
The Farmington Independent, MN
The Hancock Record, MN
The Jamestown Sun, ND
The Pine Journal, MN
The Bemidji Pioneer, MN
The Rosemount Town Pages, MN
The Metro Weekly, ND
Wadena Pioneer Journal, MN
West Central Tribune, MN
West Fargo Pioneer, ND
Woodbury Bulletin, MN
Grand Forks Herald, ND
Duluth Budgeteer News, MN
Brainerd Dispatch, MN
Brainerd Dispatch, MN
The Forum, LA
The Hudson Star-Observer, WI
Note: Forum Communications Co. owns eleven daily newspapers and 28 non-daily publications. Forum Communications also owns several television and radio stations, a commerical printing division and a new media division.

FRANK MAYBORN ENTERPRISES, INC.
— 10 S 3rd St, Temple, TX, 76501-7619, USA; tel (254) 778-4444; fax (254) 774-9391; e-mail tdt@temple-telegram.com; web site www. tdtnews.com
Est.: 1979
Pres. — Sue Mayborn;Newspapers:Killeen Daily Herald, TX
Temple Daily Telegram, TX

G

GANNETT — 7950 Jones Branch Dr, Mc Lean, VA, 22107-0002, USA; tel (703) 854-6000; fax (703) 854-2001; e-mail gcishare@gannett.com; web site www.gannett.com
Est.: 1906
President and CEO, Gannett — Robert J. Dickey;
Chief Revenue Officer — Kevin Gentzel;
Chief Product Officer — David Payne;
Chief Strategy Officer — Maribel Wadsworth;
Chief Financial Officer — Alison Engel;
Chief Legal Officer — Barbara Wall;
President of Domestic Publishing — John Zidich;
Chief Technology Officer — Jamshid Khazenie;
Chief Marketing Officer — Andy Yost;
CEO Newsquest — Henry Faure Walker;
Chief People Officer — David Harmon;
Newspapers:Detroit Free Press, MI
Evansville Courier & Press, IN
Lehigh Acres News-Star, FL
Record Searchlight, CA
The Daily Times, NM
The Gleaner, KY
The Journal News, NY
The Lebanon Daily News, PA
The Record, NJ
The Tennessean, TN
Ventura County Star, CA
Wilmington News Journal, OH
Media Network of Central Ohio, OH
Las Cruces Sun-News, NM
Action Advertiser, WI
Action Sunday, WI
Ross County Advertiser, OH
Best - Central, FL
Door County Real Estate Guide, WI
Best - North, FL
Visalia Times-Delta, CA
Eastern Shore News, VA
Tri-County Press, OH
Loveland Herald, OH
Indian Hill Journal, OH
Forest Hills Journal, OH

Eastern Hills Journal, OH
St. John's Recorder, FL
Best - South, FL
Living - Kettle Moraine Sunday, WI
Bethel Journal, OH
Asbury Park Press, NJ
News-Record, WI
Lakeshore Chronicle, WI
Newark-licking Advertiser, OH
Milford-Miami Advertiser, OH
Pickaway County Advertiser, OH
Wausau Buyers Guide, WI
Delhi Press, OH
Lancaster/fairfield Advertiser, OH
Hilltop Press, OH
Hocking Valley Advertiser, OH
Price Hill Press, OH
Rockland County Express, NY
Coshocton County Advertiser, OH
Local Living, IN
South Lyon Herald, MI
The Cincinnati Enquirer, OH
Northwest Press, OH
The Antigo Area Shopper, WI
Maryland Beachcomber, MD
Mukwonago Publications, WI
Appeal Tribune, OR
Tribune-Gazette, WI
Reno Gazette-Journal, NV
The Baxter Bulletin, AR
Times Press, WI
Baltic Beacon, SD
Gallatin News Examiner, TN
Home News Tribune, NJ
Pelican Press, FL
Williamston Enterprise, MI
Toms River Observer-Reporter, NJ
Daily World, LA
Add Sheet, IA
The Daily Journal, NJ
Campbell County Recorder, KY
Great Falls Tribune, MT
North English Record, IA
Atlantic County Record, NJ
The Commercial Appeal, TN
Star Press Union, IA
Outlook, OH
The Greenville News, SC
Marengo Pioneer-Republican, IA
Pensacola News Journal, FL
The Livingston County Daily Press & Argus, MI
Topics North Central, IN
Towne Courier, MI
Iowa City Press-Citizen, IA
The Jackson Sun, TN
Fairview Observer, TN
The Wausau Daily Herald, WI
Beacon Mailbag (OOB) , NJ
Forest County Beacon, WI
Nashville Record, TN
The Source Sampler, MI
Journal and Courier, IN
Western Hills Press, OH
Ottawa County Outlook, OH
The Erlanger Recorder, KY
Courier News, NJ
Ankeny Register & Press Citizen, IA
Wright Way Shopper, MN
Delta-Waverly Community News, MI
Oconto County Reporter, WI
Blue Water Shopper, MI
Ocean Pines Independent, MD
The Salinas Californian, CA
Mainland Journal, NJ
Stewart-Houston Times, TN
Stayton Mail, OR
Pennysaver, HI
Chillicothe Gazette, OH
The Des Moines Register, IA
The Spectrum, UT
Robertson County Times, TN
The Times, NY
Springfield News-Leader, MO
The Advocate, OH
Portland Review & Observer, MI
Palladium-Item, IN
The News Leader, VA
The Courier-Journal, KY
The Sumner County Shopper, TN
The Marion Star, OH
USA TODAY, VA

The Pataskala Standard, OH
Madison County Herald, MS
Beachcomber, DE
Tuckerton Beacon, NJ
Grinnell Pennysaver, IA
The Daily Advertiser, LA
Fort Thomas Recorder, KY
Chincoteague Beacon, VA
San Juan Sun, NM
Lake Orion Eccentric, MI
The Daily News Journal, TN
Colorado Connection, CO
The Patent Trader, NY
Review Press (OOB), NY
Community Journal Clermont, OH
News Journal, OH
The Delaware Wave, DE
Democrat and Chronicle, NY
Lamoille County Advertiser, VT
Extra, IA
Montezuma Republican, IA
Eagle-Gazette Media, OH
Oconto County Beacon, WI
TN Media, TN
The Courier-Post, NJ
Poughkeepsie Journal, NY
Air Force Times, VA
The Coloradoan, CO
The Noblesville Ledger, IN
Green Bay Press-Gazette, WI
The Green Bay News-Chronicle, WI
West Bloomfield Eccentric, MI
Northeast Suburban Life, OH
Lansing State Journal, MI
Windsor Beacon, CO
The Hendersonville Star News, TN
Times Herald, MI
The News-Star, LA
Delaware Coast Press, DE
Community Snapshot, WI
Tribune-Times, SC
Door County Advocate, WI
The Shopping News, MN
The Fond du Lac Reporter, WI
Stevens Point Journal, WI
Garden City Observer, MI
The News-Messenger, OH
The Leaf-Chronicle, TN
Times Recorder, OH
Daily Record, NJ
Topics Northeast, IN
The Granville Sentinel, OH
Buyers' Digest, VT
The Coshocton Tribune, OH
Chittenden County Advertiser, VT
Bulletin Board, AL
Record-Herald and Indianola Tribune, IA
Beach Haven Times, NJ
The Burlington Free Press, VT
Ashland City Times, TN
Brandon Valley Challenger, SD
The Asheville Citizen-Times, NC
The Indianapolis Star, IN
Pennypower Shopping News, MO
The Desert Sun, CA
Novi News, MI
The Lacey Beacon, NJ
Post-Crescent, WI
Oshkosh Northwestern, WI
Franklin-grand Isle County Advertiser, VT
Mason Valley News/The Leader-Courier, NV
The News Journal, DE
Somerset Herald, MD
Sunday Kewaunee County Chronicle (OOB), WI
Island Weekly, HI
Dickson Shopper, TN
Florence Recorder, KY
Poweshiek County CR, IA
The Southwest Copper Shopper, NM
Desert Valley Times, NV
Dell Rapids Tribune, SD
St. Cloud Times, MN
The Star Press, IN
Egg Harbor News, NJ
Black Mountain News, NC
Consumers Press, MT
Daily Tribune, WI
Telegraph-Forum, OH
Star Advocate, FL
Clinton News, MS
The Dickson Herald, TN

Prattville Progress, AL
The Sheboygan Press, WI
Weekly Item, IN
Record Journal, NJ
Carencro News, LA
News-Record and Sentinel, NC
The Beacon, NJ
Hammonton News, NJ
Hattiesburg American, MS
Argus Leader, SD
USA WEEKEND - New York, NY (OOB), NY
Florida Today, FL
The Times, LA
Press & Sun-Bulletin, NY
The Ithaca Journal, NY
The Arizona Republic, AZ
Tucson Citizen (OOB), AZ
Star-Gazette, NY
Tulare Advance-Register, CA
Federal Times, VA
Arizona Business Gazette, AZ
Army Times, VA
Battle Creek Enquirer, MI
Montgomery Advertiser, AL
De Pere Journal, WI
Marine Corps Times, VA
Journal Tribune, IA
Poweshiek County Chronicle-Republican, IA
Boone Community Recorder, KY
News Herald, OH
Birmingham Eccentric, MI
South Kenton Recorder, KY
Redford Observer, MI
The Clarion-Ledger, MS
Farmington Observer, MI
Northville Record, MI
Herald Times Reporter, WI
Lakes/forest Beacon, WI
Marshfield News-Herald Media, WI
The Town Talk, LA
Canton Observer, MI
Livonia Observer, MI
Milford Times, MI
Westland Observer, MI
Cheatham County Money Saver, TN
Statesman Journal, OR
Kewaunee County Star-News, WI
Observer & Eccentric Media, MI
Plymouth Observer, MI
South Oakland Eccentric, MI
Tallahassee Democrat, FL
The Daily Times, MD
Alamogordo Daily News, NM
Current-Argus, NM
Deming Headlight, NM
Silver City Sun-News, NM
The Evening Sun, PA
York Daily Record/York Sunday News, PA
El Paso Times, TX
Public Opinion, PA
Note: Gannett Co. Inc.'s portfolio includes 92 daily local market newspapers, USA TODAY, and their related digital platforms and non-daily publications, and Newsquest, a leading U.K. regional news provider.

GATEHOUSE MEDIA, INC. — 175 Sully's
Trail #3, Corporate Crossings Office Park, Pittsford, NY, 14534-4560, USA; tel (585) 598-0030; fax (585) 248-2631; web site www. gatehousemedia.com
Parent Co.: New Media Investment Group
Est.: 1997
CEO — Michael E. Reed;
Pres./COO — Kirk Davis;
Sr. Vice Pres./CFO — Melinda A. Janik;
CIO — Paul Ameden;
Vice Pres., Sales & Marketing — Brad Harmon;
Senior Vice Pres., Content/News Opns. — Brad Dennison;
Regional VP - Midwest — Gloria Fletcher;
Regional VP - Atlantic — James O'Rourke;
Regional VP - Western — Nick Monico;
Regional VP - New England — Rick Daniels;
Regional VP - Great Lakes — Kevin Kampman;
Reg. Pub. — Scott Harrell;
Vice President, Content and Audience — Arkin David; Crystal Barrett;
Director, Major & National Accounts — Anna

St. Charles;
VP Circulation/Consumer Marketing — Paul Felicissimo;
VP of Sales and Digital Services — Michael Petrak;
VP of Sales Productivity — Rebecca Capparelli;
VP Publishing - Community East — Brad Harmon; Alice Coyle; Charles Goodrich; Jesse Floyd;
National Acct. Sales Mgr. — Eliot Putnam; William Down; Megan Reynolds;
VP, Adv. — John Bordeleau;
Director of National Sales — Gregory Appel;
SR Director of Digital Strategy — Rich Hoover;
New England Reg. Pub. — Peter D. Meyer;
Newspapers:Calkins Media, PA
The Newport Daily News, RI
The Register-Guard, OR
Alice Echo-News Journal, TX
The Helena Arkansas Daily World, AR
Lehigh Valley Business, PA
The Bee, KS
The Hays Daily News Extra, KS
Beaver County Times, PA
Miami News-record, OK
Times2, AL
Long Island Business News, NY
Beauregard Daily News, LA
Burlington County Times, NJ
Bluffton Today, SC
Amarillo Globe-News, TX
The Wayne Independent, PA
Ashland Times-Gazette, OH
Athens Banner-Herald, GA
Aurora Advocate, OH
Cuyahoga Falls News-Press, OH
Hudson Hub-Times, OH
Juneau Empire, AK
Log Cabin Democrat, AR
Lubbock Avalanche-Journal, TX
Peninsula Clarion, AK
Savannah Morning News, GA
The Augusta Chronicle, GA
The Fayetteville Observer, NC
The Florida Times-Union, FL
The Leesville Daily Leader, LA
The St. Augustine Record, FL
The Topeka Capital-Journal, KS
homer News, AK
The Hawk Eye, IA
Cherokee County News-Advocate, KS
Record-Courier, OH
StarNews, NC
The Alliance Review, OH
Ad Sack, TX
The Daily Jeffersonian, OH
The Columbus Dispatch, OH
Eldorado Daily Journal, IL
Stow Sentry, OH
Arizona Capitol Times, AZ
The Daily Record, OH
Columbia Daily Tribune, MO
The Journal Record, OK
The Apalachicola Carrabelle Times, FL
The Salina Journal, KS
St. Charles County Business Record, MO
St. Louis Daily Record, MO
The Garden City Telegram, KS
The Hays Daily News, KS
The Hutchinson News, KS
The Ottawa Herald, KS
Crestview News Bulletin, FL
Pocono Record Plus, PA
Alma Journal, AR
The Daily Record, MO
Freer Press, TX
Missouri Lawyers Media, MO
Nueces County Record-Star, TX
Perry Chief, IA
Ellis County Trading Post, TX
Hockessin Community News, DE
Tonopah Times-Bonanza and Goldfield News, NV
Bent County Democrat, CO
Argus-Sentinel, IL
Penny Press 1, NE
Abington Mariner, MA
Access Shoppers' Guide, MI
Allston-Brighton TAB, MA

Amesbury News, MA
Easton Journal, MA
Framingham TAB, MA
Hopkinton Crier, MA
Kingston Reporter, MA
Medfield Press, MA
Natick Bulletin & TAB, MA
Nebraska City News-Press, NE
Needham Times, MA
Newburyport Current, MA
Newton Tab, MA
North Shore Sunday, MA
Norwood Transcript & Bulletin, MA
Rockland Standard, MA
Salem Gazette, MA
Saugus Advertiser, MA
Scituate Mariner, MA
West Michigan Senior Times, MI
Sharon Advocate, MA
Shrewsbury Chronicle, MA
Somerville Journal, MA
Stoneham Sun, MA
Sudbury Town Crier, MA
The Dedham Transcript, MA
The Harvard Post, MA
The Sentinel, MA
The Villager, MA
The Westborough News, MA
Tri-Town Transcript, MA
Wakefield Observer, MA
Watertown TAB, MA
Wayland Town Crier, MA
Wellesley Townsman, MA
West Roxbury Transcript, MA
Weston Town Crier, MA
Westwood Press, MA
Weymouth News, MA
Wilmington Advocate, MA
Winchester Star, MA
Woburn Advocate, MA
Bridgewater Independent, MA
Catskill Shopper - Eastern Sullivan County, NY
Catskill Shopper - Ulster County, NY
Fort Leavenworth Lamp, KS
Horseheads Shopper, NY
Milford Beacon, DE
Provincetown Banner, MA
Sandwich Broadsider, MA
Stoughton Journal, MA
Swampscott Reporter, MA
The Bulletin, MA
Town & Country Shopper, MN
Victor Post, NY
Wareham Courier, MA
Wayne Post, NY
Your Valley, NY
Andover American, KS
Sunflower Shopper's Guide, KS
Times & Courier, MA
Allegany County Pennysaver, NY
Arlington Advocate, MA
Ashland TAB, MA
Ashley News, IL
Bargain Hunter, CA
Belmont Citizen-Herald, MA
Big Nickel, MO
Billerica Minuteman, MA
Braintree Forum, MA
Brookline TAB, MA
Brown County Reminder, MN
Burlington Union, MA
Cajun Gazette, LA
Cambridge Chronicle & TAB, MA
Cambridge Chronicle IN ILLINOIS, IL
Chelmsford Independent, MA
Chilli Corthe Cho Cho Advertiser, IL
Chronicle Ad-viser, NY
Chronicle Shopper, KS
Classified Plus, MA
Cohasset Mariner, MA
Community News, NY
Corning Leader, NY
Courier-Gazette, NY
Courier-Journal, NY
Daily Midway Driller, CA
Danvers Herald, MA
Dover Post, DE
Dover-Sherborn Press, MA
Dunsmuir News, CA
East Peoria Times-Courier, IL
Fort Folk Guardian, LA

Fulton County Shopper, IL
Gardner Chronicle, IL
Gateway Shoppers Guide, MI
Genesee Country Express, NY
Geneseeway Shopper, NY
Geneseo Republic, IL
Gentry County Shopper, MO
Georgetown Record, MA
Gonzales Weekly Citizen, LA
Granite Falls-Clarkfield Advocate-Tribune, MN
Hamburg Reporter, IA
Hamilton-Wenham Chronicle, MA
Harwich Oracle, MA
Hingham Journal, MA
Hockessin Community News, DE
Holbrook Sun, MA
Holliston TAB, MA
Pennesaverplus, NY
Hudson Sun, MA
Images of Herkimer County (OOB), NY
Ipswich Chronicle, MA
Kansas City Kansan (OOB), KS
Lexington Minuteman, MA
Lincoln Journal, MA
Linn County Leader, MO
Littleton Independent, MA
Logan County Shopper, IL
McDonough County Voice, IL
Malden Observer, MA
Marblehead Reporter, MA
Marlborough Enterprise, MA
Marshfield Mariner, MA
Maryville Penny Press, MO
Medford Transcript, MA
Money Stretcher, IL
Montevideo American-News, MN
Mt. Shasta Herald, CA
Nevada County Picayune, AR
Newport Independent, AR
Newton Press-Mentor, IL
Newton TAB, MA
North Andover Citizen, MA
Old Colony Memorial, MA
Pembroke Mariner & Express, MA
Pennysaver, IL
PeoriaTimes-Observer, IL
Post South, LA
Raynham Journal, MA
Reading Advocate, MA
Redwood Falls Livewire, MN
Roselle Itasca Press, IL
Roseville Independent, IL
Si Trader, IL
Shoppers Fair, MI
Sleepy Eye Herald-Dispatch, MN
Smyrna/Clayton Sun-Times, DE
Springfield Shopper, IL
St. James Leader-Journal OOB, MO
St James Plaindealer, MN
Steuben Courier-Advocate, NY
Syracuse Journal-Democrat, NE
Tazewell County Shopper, IL
Tewksbury Advocate, MA
The Advantage, IL
The Beacon-Villager, MA
The Blade, IL
The Bolton Common, MA
The Cape Codder, MA
The Chronicle-Express, NY
The Clay County Advocate-Press, IL
The Commercial Express, MI
The Concord Journal, MA
The Country Gazette, MA
The Derby Reporter, KS
The Donaldsonville Chief, LA
The Extra, IA
The Fowler Tribune, CO
The Gurdon Times, AR
The Jackson Star News, WV
The Marceline Press, MO
The Middletown Transcript, DE
The Progress, IL
The Redwood Falls Gazette, MN
The Register, MA
Gallatin Democrat, IL
The Shopper, NY
The Shopper, MN
The Star Shopper, IL
The Star-herald, WV
The Sussex Countian, DE
The Times Record, IL

The Moscow Villager, PA
The Walpole Times, MA
The Weekly, MO
Timesaver Shopping Guide, NY
Today's Shopper, WV
Tri-county Buyer's Guide, MI
Weed Press, CA
Wellington Daily News, KS
Westborough News, MA
Westford Eagle, MA
The Money Stretcher White County, IL
White Hall Journal, AR
Whitman Times, MA
Wyandotte County Shopper, KS
The Suburbanite, OH
Carbondale News, PA
Livingston Shopping News, IL
Bedford Minuteman, MA
Canton Journal, MA
Halifax-Plympton Reporter, MA
Hanover Mariner, MA
Duxbury Reporter, MA
Norton Mirror, MA
Mansfield News, MA
Melrose Free Press, MA
Carver Reporter, MA
Norwell Mariner, MA
Randolph Herald, MA
The Gridley Herald, CA
Waltham News Tribune, MA
Kiowa County Signal, KS
Beverly Citizen, MA
The Sun-Times, AR
Woodford Times, IL
Brockport Post, NY
Mackinaw Journal, MI
Weekly Mail, IL
Eldora Herald-Ledger, IA
The Gridley Shopping News, CA
Suburban Life Publications, IL
The Fairbury Blade, IL
The News Eagle, PA
Aurora Advertiser, MO
Vicksburg Commercial-Express, MI
Oquawka Current, IL
Jackson Herald, WV
Norris City Banner, IL
Community Newspaper Co. - South, MA
The Spokesman, IL
Morton Times-News, IL
Washington Times Reporter, IL
The McDonough County Voice, IL
Penny Press, NE
Big Aa Shopper, MO
Chillicothe Times-Bulletin, IL
Messenger Post Media, NY
Times News Group, IL
Flashes Publishers, MI
Springfield Advertiser, IL
Tip-off Shopping Guide, MI
St. John News, KS
The Echo-Pilot, PA
Glen Rose Reporter, TX
Edinburg Review, TX
Valley Town Crier, TX
Note: GateHouse Media Inc. is owned by Fortress Investment Group LLC.

H

HAGADONE CORPORATION — 111 S 1st St, Coeur D Alene, ID, 83814-2794, USA; tel (208) 667-3431; fax (208) 664-7206; e-mail info@hagadone.com; web site www.hagadone.com
Est.: 1966
Chrmn. of the Bd. — Duane B. Hagadone;
President — Bradley D. Hagadone;
CFO — Mont Garman;
Mgr., MIS Dept. — Judd Jones;
Newspapers:Advertiser, MT
Daily Inter Lake, MT
Hungry Horse News, MT
Basin Business Journal Farm News, WA
The Sun Tribune, WA
Mineral Independent, MT
Beloit Daily News, WI
Bonner County Daily Bee, ID
Clark Fork Valley Press, MT
Coeur d'Alene Press, ID
Columbia Basin Herald, WA

Lake County Leader, MT
Priest River Times, ID
Shoshone News-Press, ID
The Western News, MT
West Shore News, ID
My Stateline Shopper, WI
The Whitefish Pilot, MT
Bonners Ferry Herald, ID
Note: Hagadone Corp., also owns a Printing, Hospitality and Real Estate Division.

HALIFAX MEDIA — 2339 Beville Rd, Daytona Beach, FL, 32119-8720, USA; tel 386-265-6700; fax 386-265-6750; e-mail info@halifaxmediagroup.com; web site www.halifaxmediagroup.comThomas Boni;
Rgl. Controller
— Robert Delaney; Newspapers:The Destin Log, FL
Santa Rosa Press Gazette, FL
The Havelock News, NC
The Star, FL
The Walton Sun, FL
West Volusia Pennysaver, FL
Holmes County Times-Advertiser, FL
South Lake Press, FL

HARTMAN NEWSPAPERS LP — 1914 4th St, Rosenberg, TX, 77471-5140, USA; tel (281) 342-8691; fax (281) 342-6968
Parent Co.: Hartman Newspapers, L.P.
Est.: 1974
Bill Hartman;
Pres. — Clyde C. King;
Vice Chairman — Fred B. Hartman;
Controller — Mark Thormaehlen;
Newspapers:Brenham Banner-Press, TX
Fort Bend Herald, TX
Henderson Daily News, TX
The Katy Times, TX
The Kaufman Herald, TX
El Campo Leader-News, TX
Wharton Journal-Spectator, TX
East Bernard Express, TX
The Rockport Pilot, TX
Port Lavaca Wave, TX
Alvin Advertiser, TX

HAYNES PUBLISHING CO. — 170 S Penn Ave, Oberlin, KS, 67749-2243, USA; tel (785) 475-2206; fax (785) 475-2800; e-mail obherald@nwkansas.com; web site www.nwkansas.com
Est.: 1879
Pres. — Stephen C. Haynes;
CFO — Cynthia A. Haynes;
Newspapers:Country Advocate, KS
St. Francis Herald, KS
Goodland Star-News, KS
The Norton Telegram, KS
Oberlin Herald, The, KS
Bird City Times, KS
Colby Free Press, KS
Note: Company publishes six newspapers and two shoppers in Northwest Kansas.

HEARST COMMUNICATIONS, INC. — 300 W 57th St, New York, NY, 10019-3741, USA; tel (212) 649-2000; fax (806) 296-1315; web site www.hearst.com
Est.: 1887
Vice Chrmn./CEO — Frank Bennack;
Pres., Hearst Newspapers — Steven R. Swartz;
Sr. Vice Pres., Finance — John M. Condon;
Vice Pres., Digital Media — Neeraj Khemlani;
Sr. Vice Pres. — Mark E. Aldam;
Newspapers:Atascocita Observer, TX
New Haven Register, CT
The Register Citizen, CT
The Dolphin, CT
Times Union, NY
Connecticut Post, CT
Darien News, CT
Deer Park Broadcaster, TX
Eastex Advocate, TX
The Advocate, CT
Bellaire Examiner, TX
The Daily Commercial Recorder, TX
The Courier of Montgomery County, TX

The Hour, CT
Cypress Creek Mirror, TX
El Tiempo de Laredo, TX
New Canaan News, CT
East Montgomery County Observer, TX
Laredo Morning Times, TX
Fairfield Citizen, CT
Fort Bend Sun, TX
Friendswood Journal, TX
Westport News, CT
Humble Observer, TX
Huron Daily Tribune, MI
Kingwood Observer, TX
Lake Houston Observer, TX
The Beaumont Enterprise, TX
Magnolia Potpourri, TX
Memorial Examiner, TX
The Canyon News, TX
River Oaks Examiner, TX
New Milford Spectrum, CT
Sugar Land Sun, TX
Bay Area Citizen, TX
The Hardin County News, TX
The Examiners, TX
The Pennysaver, NY
Pasadena Citizen, TX
The Vassar Pioneer Times, MI
Midland Daily News, MI
The Rancher, TX
Midland Reporter-Telegram, TX
Tomball Potpourri, TX
Norwalk Citizen (OOB), CT
Tribune Recorder Leader, MI
Edwardsville Intelligencer, IL
Muleshoe Journal, TX
Houston Chronicle, TX
San Francisco Chronicle, CA
The News-Times, CT
Plainview Herald, TX
Greenwich Time, CT
Note: The Hearst Corporation is a diversified communications company, with interests in magazine, newspaper and business publishing; television and radio stations; newspaper comics and features syndication; cable TV networks; television production and syndicati

HORIZON PUBLICATIONS INC. — 1120 N Carbon St, Ste 100, Marion, IL, 62959-1055, USA; tel (618) 993-1711; fax (618) 997-4018; web site www.horizonpublicationsinc.com
Est.: 1999
Exec. Vice Pres./CFO — Roland McBride;Newspapers:Big Spring Herald, TX
Poteau Daily News, OK
The Chronicle-Journal, ON
The Shoppers Guide, OK
Mammoth Times, CA
Auglaize Merchandiser, OH
Berne Shopping News, IN
Bulldog Beat, MS
Deer Park Tribune, WA
Malvern Daily Record, AR
Post And Mail Shopping News, IN
Statesman Examiner, WA
The Post and Mail (Tuesday), IN
The Saline Courier TMC
Daily Times Leader, MS
Inyo Register, CA
Malvern Daily TMC
Morning News, ID
Bingham County Bargains, ID
Starkville Daily News, MS
The Community Post, OH
The Evening Leader, OH
The Monroeville News, IN
The Newport Daily Express, VT
The Observer News Enterprise, NC
The Post & Mail, IN
Valley City Times-Record, ND
Wapakoneta Daily News, OH
The Saline Courier, AR
Decatur Daily Democrat, IN
Custer County Chief, NE
Antlers American, OK
Guymon Daily Herald, OK
The Kane Republican, PA
The Punxsutawney Spirit, PA
The Ridgway Record, PA
The Daily Press, PA

Borger News-Herald, TX
Sweetwater Reporter, TX
Penticton Herald, BC
The Lethbridge Herald, AB
Medicine Hat News, AB

HUNTSMAN FAMILY INVESTMENTS — 500 S Huntsman Way, Salt Lake City, UT, 84108-1235, USA; tel (801) 584-5921; e-mail ben@hfinvestments.com; web site www.hfinvestments.com
Partner — Benjamin Wu;Newspapers:The Salt Lake Tribune, UT

I

IMPREMEDIA LLC — 1 Metrotech Ctr, 18th Floor, Brooklyn, NY, 11201-3948, USA; tel (212) 807-4785; fax (212) 807-4746; e-mail john.paton@impremedia.com; web site www.impremedia.com
Chrmn./CEO — John Paton;
Vice Chrmn. — Jose Lozano;
CEO & Pub./CEO, La Opinion — Monica Lozano;
CEO, ImpreMedia Digital — Arturo Duran;
Sr. Vice Pres., Sales — Erich Linker;
Sr. Vice Pres., Online Sales — Liz Saracheck; Newspapers:La Opinion - Contigo, CA
La Raza Newspaper, IL
Sunday Dispatch, PA
Vista Magazine (Headquarters)-OOB, NY
El Diario La Prensa, NY
Hoy, NY
La Opinion, CA
El Mensajero, CA
La Prensa, FL
Vista Magazine-OOB, FL
The Dallas Post, PA

INDEPENDENT NEWSMEDIA INC. USA — 110 Galaxy Dr, Dover, DE, 19901-9262, USA; tel (302) 674-3600; fax (877) 377-2424; e-mail newsroom@newszap.com; web site www.newszap.comEst.: 1953
Chrmn. of the Bd./CEO — Joe Smyth;
Corp. Pres. — Tamra Brittingham;
Pres., Opns. — Ed Dulin;
Vice Pres., Adv. — Darel LaPrade;
Dir., Research/Devel. — Chris Engel;
Exec. Asst. — Sheila Clendaniel;
Pub. — Greg Tock; Newspapers:Daily News-Sun, AZ
Surprise Today, AZ
Glendale Today, AZ
Glendale-peoria Today, AZ
Caloosa Belle, FL
Dorchester Banner, MD
Immokalee Bulletin, FL
Salisbury Independent, MD
Biltmore Independent (OOB), AZ
The Clewiston News, FL
Crisfield-Somerset County Times, MD
Delaware State News, DE
East Mesa Independent (OOB), AZ
Glades County Democrat, FL
Apache Junction/Gold Canyon Independent, AZ
Milford Chronicle, DE
Okeechobee News, FL
Peoria Independent, AZ
Queen Creek Independent, AZ
Scottsdale Independent, AZ
Sun City Independent, AZ
Surprise Independent, AZ
Sussex Post, DE
Town of Paradise Valley Independent, AZ
The Harrington Journal, DE
Note: Independent Newspapers Inc. owns three daily newspapers and 25 weekly publications.

INDEPENDENT PUBLICATIONS INC — 945 E Haverford Rd, Bryn Mawr, PA, 19010-3814, USA; tel (610) 527-6330; fax (610) 527-9733; web site www.independentpublicationsinc.com
Pres./CEO — Andrew T. Bickford;

Sr. Vice Pres./Treasurer — Charles E. Catherwood;
President — William McLean;
Newspapers:Hollis Brookline Journal, NH
The News Leader, FL
Osceola News-Gazette, FL
Pasco Shopper, FL
Sumter Shopper, FL
Triangle News Leader, FL

IOWA NEWSPAPERS, INC. — 317 5th St, Ames, IA, 50010-6101, USA; tel (515) 232-2160; fax (515) 232-2364; e-mail news@amestrib.com; web site www.amestrib.com
Chrmn. — Verle Burgason;
Pres. — John Goossen;
Vice Pres./Controller — Pat Snyder;
Circ. Dir. — Daniel Cronin;
Newspapers:Northeast Dallas County Record (OOB), IA
Story County Advertiser, IA
The Tri-County Times, IA

J

JOHNSON NEWSPAPER CORP. — 260 Washington St, Watertown, NY, 13601-4669, USA; tel (315) 782-1000; fax (315) 661-2520; e-mail news@wdt.net; web site www.watertowndailytimes.com
Est.: 1861
Chrmn. of the Bd./CEO — John B. Johnson;
Pres./COO — Harold B. Johnson;
CFO — Ray Weston; Jill Van Hoesen;
Editor, VP of News Operations
— Tim Farkas; Newspapers:Carthage Republican Tribune, NY
Ogdensburg Journal/Advance News, NY
The Daily Mail, NY
The Daily News, NY
Chatham Courier, NY
The Ravena News-Herald, NY
The Drummer Pennysaver, NY
Jefferson County Pennysaver, NY
Journal and Republican, NY
Register-Star, NY
The Malone Telegram, NY
Watertown Daily Times, NY
Ogdensburg Journal, NY
Daily Courier-Observer

JOURNAL MEDIA GROUP — 333 W State St, Milwaukee, WI, 53203-1305, USA; tel (414) 224-2000; web site www.jc.com
Vice President/General Counel — Hillary Ebach;Newspapers:Anderson Independent-Mail, SC
Naples Daily News, FL
North Shore NOW, WI
Bay View NOW, WI
Brookfield-Elm Grove NOW, WI
Cudahy NOW, WI
Elm Grove NOW, WI
Fox Point NOW, WI
Franklin NOW, WI
Germantown NOW, WI
Glendale NOW, WI
Oak Creek-Franklin-Greendale-Hales Corners NOW, WI
Greenfield-West Allis NOW, WI
Hales Corners NOW, WI
Menomonee Falls-Germantown NOW, WI
Mequon NOW, WI
Muskego-New Berlin NOW, WI
New Berlin NOW, WI
Oak Creek NOW, WI
South Milwaukee NOW, WI
St. Francis NOW, WI
Wauwatosa NOW, WI
West Allis NOW, WI
Wisconsin State Farmer, WI
Kitsap Sun, WA
Milwaukee Journal Sentinel, WI
Knoxville News Sentinel, TN
Abilene Reporter-News, TX
Corpus Christi Caller-Times, TX
Metroparent, WI
San Angelo Standard-Times, TX
Wichita Falls Times Record News, TX

K

KPC MEDIA GROUP, INC. — 102 N Main St, Kendallville, IN, 46755-1714, USA; tel (260) 347-0400; fax (260) 347-7281; e-mail helpdesk@kpcmedia.com; web site www.kpcnews.com

Parent Co.: KPC Media Inc.
Est.: 1911
Principal Owner — George O. Witwer;
President — Terry Housholder;
CEO — Randy Mitchell; Grace Householder;
CFO — Rick Mitchell;
IT Manager — Brent Folkner;
Production Manager — Gary Craiger;
Regional Advertising Director — Joy Newman; Newspapers:The Advance Leader, IN
Greater Fort Wayne Business Weekly, IN
Churubusco News, IN
The Butler Bulletin, IN
The Herald Republican, IN
The Star, IN
Smart Shopper, IN
Smart Shopper, IN
The News Sun, IN
The Garrett Clipper, IN
Albion New Era, IN
Northwest News, IN
INIWhitley County, IN
INIFort Wayne Publications (5 zones), IN
Note: KPC Media Group publishes: 3 dailies - The News Sun, The Star and The Herald Republican. 6 paid weeklies - The Albion New Era, Churubusco News, Northwest News, The Garrett Clipper, Butler Bulletin and Advance-Leader. Fort Wayne Business Weekly, INIFort Wayne Publications (5 publications direct mailed to 90,000 residence in Fort Wayne). One free direct mail weekly in Whitley County (13,000), one Northeast Regional Shopper (42,000), Three phone books covering 4 north east Indiana counties. Commercial printing and mailing operation.

L

LAKEWAY PUBLISHERS, INC. — 1609 W 1st North St, Morristown, TN, 37814-3724, USA; tel (423) 581-5630; fax (423) 581-3061; e-mail copyboy@lcs.net; web site www.lakewaypublishersinc.com

Parent Co.: Lakeway Publishers, Inc.
Est.: 1966
Pub. — R. Michael Fishman;
Vice Pres., Middle TN/Cor. Sec./Treasurer — Jeffrey Fishman;
President — R. Jack Fishman;
Newspapers:Citizen Tribune, TN
The Tullahoma News, TN
The Elk Valley Times, TN
Grundy County Herald, TN
Manchester Times, TN
Moore County News, TN
Bowling Green Times, MO
The Elsberry Democrat, MO
The Hermann Advertiser-Courier, MO
The Lincoln County Journal, MO
Louisiana Press Journal, MO
The Centralia Fireside Guard, MO
The Vandalia Leader, MO
Northern Neck News, VA
The Caroline Progress, VA
Westmoreland News, VA
Northumberland Echo, VA
Herald-Progress, VA
The Central Virginian, VA
Osceola News-Gazette, FL
Clermont News Leader, FL
The News Leader, FL
Triangle News Leader, FL
The Civil War Courier, TN
Newstime, MO
Note: Lakeway Publishers Inc. also own the Morristown (TN) Citizen Tribune, a daily publication.

LANCASTER MANAGEMENT, INC. — 645 Walnut St, Gadsden, AL, 35901-7102, USA; tel (256) 543-3417; fax (256) 543-3548; e-mail mschuver@lminews.com; web site www.lminews.com

Pres. — Charles W. Lancaster;
Vice Pres. — Michael F. Schuver;
Vice Pres. — Jeff R. Selsor; John Lancaster; Ben Lancaster; Newspapers:Ashley News Observer, AR
Floyd County Times, KY
The Hazard Herald, KY
DeQueen Bee, AR
Eudora Enterprise, AR
Chicot Spectator, AR
The Mena Star, AR
The Waldron News, AR
The McDuffie Progress, GA
Monroe County News, IA
Albia Union-Republican, IA
The Chariton Leader, IA
Chariton Herald-Patriot, IA
The Humeston News Era, IA
Moravia Union, IA
Georgetown News-Graphic, KY
The Murray Ledger & Times, KY
The Paintsville Herald, KY
The Appalachian News-Express, KY
Sea Coast Echo, MS
Stone County Enterprise, MS
Branson Tri-Lakes News, MO
The Moore County News-Press, TX
The Hopewell News, VA
Note: Lancaster Management Inc. owns one daily newspapers and more than 30 weekly and shopper publications.

LANDMARK COMMUNICATIONS, INC. — 150 W Brambleton Ave, Norfolk, VA, 23510-2018, USA; tel (757) 446-2010; fax (757) 446-2004; e-mail info@landmarkinteractive.com; web site www.landmarkinteractive.com; www.landmarkinteractive.com

Chrmn. of the Bd./CEO — Frank Batten;
Vice Chrmn. — Richard F. Barry;
Pres./COO — Decker Anstrom;
Exec. Vice Pres./Sec./Gen. Counsel — Guy Friddell;
Exec. Vice Pres./Pres., Landmark Publishing Grp. — R. Bruce Bradley;
Exec. Vice Pres., HR — Charlie W. Hill;
Vice Pres., Finance — Colleen Pittman;
Operations Director — David Reno;
Newspapers:Bedford Bullet, VA
The Virginian-Pilot, VA
The Sentinel-News, KY
Brighton Standard Blade, CO
Casey County News, KY
Central Kentucky News-Journal, KY
Citrus County Chronicle, FL
Columbine Courier, CO
Commerce City Express, CO
Cynthiana Democrat, KY
Fort Lupton Press, CO
Grant County News and Express, KY
Harriman Record, TN
La Salle Leader (OOB), CO
LaRue County Herald News, KY
Lancaster News, SC
Lebanon Enterprise, KY
Lincoln's Country Shopper, IN
Lincolnland Shopping Guide, IN
Los Alamos Monitor, NM
Marketplace, KY
Mason-dixon Marketplace, MD
Morgan County News, TN
Chester News & Reporter, SC
Carrollton News-Democrat, KY
Owenton News-Herald, KY
Oldham Era, KY
Opinion-Tribune, IA
Pageland Progressive-Journal, SC
Pioneer News, KY
Red Oak Express, IA
River City Trading Post, KY
Riverland News, FL
Rockwood Times, TN
Sentinel News Plus, KY
Spencer County Journal-Democrat, IN
Spencer Magnet, KY
Sumter County Times, FL

The Anderson News, KY
The Brunswick Beacon, NC
The Leader-union Publishing Co., IL
The News-Enterprise, KY
The Shopper, TN
Trimble Banner, KY
Williston Pioneer Sun News, FL
Note: Landmark Communications Inc. has a 49.9% interest in Capital-Gazette Communications Inc. in Annapolis, MD. Landmark owns and operates two CBS affiliated television stations and cable channel networks. Landmark is also 50% owner, with Cox Communications,

LANDMARK COMMUNITY NEWSPAPERS, LLC — 601 Taylorsville Rd, Shelbyville, KY, 40065-9125, USA; tel (502) 633-4334; fax (502) 633-4447; web site www.lcni.com

Parent Co.: Landmark Media Enterprises, LLC
Est.: 1973
Pres. — Michael G. Abernathy;
Adv. Dir. — Tony Martinette;
Exec. VP. — Daniel Sykes;
Editorial Director — John Nelson;
Newspapers:Galax Gazette, VA
The Anderson News, KY
Bedford Bulletin, VA
Brighton Standard Blade, CO
The Brunswick Beacon, NC
The Canyon Courier, CO
Carrollton News-Democrat, KY
Casey County News, KY
Cedar Key Beacon, FL
Central Kentucky News-Journal, KY
Chester News & Reporter, SC
Chiefland Citizen, FL
Clear Creek Courant, CO
Commerce City Sentinel Express, CO
Cynthiana Democrat, KY
Declaration, VA
Fort Lupton Press, CO
Gadsden County Times, FL
Grant County News and Express, KY
Henry County Local, KY
Kentucky Standard, KY
La Follette Press, TN
Lancaster News, SC
LaRue County Herald News, KY
Lebanon Enterprise, KY
Morgan County News, TN
Mount Vernon Democrat, IN
Oldham Era, KY
Opinion-Tribune, IA
Owenton News-Herald, KY
Pageland Progressive-Journal, SC
Perry County News, IN
Pioneer News, KY
The Record, KY
Red Oak Express, IA
Riverland News, FL
Roane County News, TN
The Sentinel-News, KY
Spencer County Journal-Democrat, IN
Spencer Magnet, KY
Springfield Sun, KY
Sumter County Times, FL
Trimble Banner, KY
The Leader-Union, IL
The Wakulla News, FL
Williston Pioneer Sun News, FL
Gazette Plus, VA
Sentinel News Plus, KY

LEE ENTERPRISES, INC. — 201 N Harrison St, Ste 600, Davenport, IA, 52801-1918, USA; tel (563) 383-2100; fax (563) 328-4319; e-mail information@lee.net; web site www.lee.net
Est.: 1890
Chairman/Pres./CEO — Kevin Mowbray;
Exec. Chairman — Mary Junck;
VP/CFO/Treasurer — Ronald Mayo;
VP, Publishing — Michael R. Gulledge;
VP, Commun. — Daniel K. Hayes;
VP, Publishing — Greg R. Veon;
VP, Strategy — Greg P. Schermer;
VP, IT — Michele White;
VP, Audience — Suzanna Frank;
VP, Digital — James Green;
VP, Digital Sales — Paul Farrell;

VP, HR — Astrid Garcia; Charles Arms;
Newspapers:Ad Extra, IL
Moline Dispatch Publishing Company, L.L.C, IL
Arizona Daily Sun, Flagstaff, AZ
The Dispatch-Argus, IL
Fremont Area Shopper, NE
The Philomath Express, OR
Missoula Independent, MT
Dunn County Big Buck, WI
Flagstaff Live!, AZ
Badgerland Values Columbia County, WI
Country Folks - East Zone, NY
The Post-Star, NY
Hot Springs Star, SD
The World, OR
Quad-City Times, IA
The Dunn County News, WI
Arizona Daily Star, AZ
Democrat News, MO
Santa Maria Times, CA
The Lompoc Record, CA
The Sentinel, CA
Napa Valley Register, CA
The Times-News, ID
Elko Daily Free Press, NV
The Pantagraph, IL
The Southern Illinoisan, IL
Herald & Review, Decatur, IL
Journal Gazette & Times-Courier, IL
The Times of Northwest Indiana, IN
Globe Gazette, Mason City, IA
Muscatine Journal, IA
Sioux City Journal, IA
The Courier, IA
The Ledger Independent, KY
Daily Journal, Park Hills, MO
St. Louis Post-Dispatch, MO
Billings Gazette, MT
The Montana Standard, MT
Helena Independent Record, MT
Missoulian, MT
Ravalli Republic, MT
The Bismarck Tribune, ND
Lincoln Journal Star, NE
Beatrice Daily Sun, NE
The Columbus Telegram, NE
Fremont Tribune, NE
The Citizen, Auburn, NY
Albany Democrat-Herald, OR
Corvallis Gazette-Times, OR
The Sentinel, PA
The Times and Democrat, SC
Rapid City Journal, SD
The Daily News, WA
Wisconsin State Journal, Madison, WI
Daily Citizen, Beaver Dam, WI
Baraboo News Republic, WI
Daily Register, WI
The Journal Times, WI
La Crosse Tribune, WI
Winona Daily News, MN
The Chippewa Herald, WI
Casper Star-Tribune, WY
Meade County Times-Tribune, SD
Mitchell County Press-News, IA
Pennysaver, ND
Jackson County Chronicle, WI
Five Cities Times Press Recorder (OOB), CA
Times-Press-Recorder (OOB), CA
Bettendorf News, IA
Lee Agri-Media, Bismarck, ND
The Kingsburg Recorder, CA
La Crosse Foxxy Shopper, WI
Midwest Messenger, NE
Burt County Plaindealer, NE
Coulee News, WI
Suburban Journals of Greater St. Louis, MO
Lebanon Express, OR
Forest City Summit, IA
The Plattsmouth Journal, NE
Neighborhood Extra, NE
Illinois Suburban Journals, IL
Mandan News, ND
The Chadron Record, NE
The Banner-Press, NE
Mini Nickel Classifieds, MT
The Schuyler Sun, NE
The Garden Island, Lihue, HI
The Weekly Calistogan, CA
Tri-county Foxxy Shopper, WI
Casper Journal, WY

Distinctive Properties, CA
Onalaska Holmen Courier-Life, WI
Note: Lee Enterprises is a leading provider of local news and information and advertising in 50 markets, with 46 daily newspapers and a joint interest in four others, rapidly growing digital products and nearly 300 specialty publications in 22 states. Lee's markets include St. Louis, MO; Lincoln, NE; Madison, WI; Davenport, IA; Billings, MT; Bloomington, IL; and Tucson, AZ. Lee Common Stock is traded on the New York Stock Exchange under the symbol LEE.

LEWIS NEWSPAPERS — 302 S Cross St, Robinson, IL, 62454-2137, USA; tel (618) 544-2101; fax (618) 544-9533; e-mail news@robdailynews.com; web site www.robdailynews.com
Est.: 1919
Pub. — Kathleen Lewis;Newspapers:Daily News, IL
Daily Record, IL
Lawrence County News, IL
The Robinson Constitution, IL
Note: Lewis Newspapers also owns the Robinson (IL) Constitution and the Lawrence (IL) County News, two weekly newspapers, and the Lawrenceville (IL) Daily Record.

LORAIN COUNTY PRINTING & PUBLISHING CO. — 225 East Ave, Elyria, OH, 44035-5634, USA; tel (440) 329-7000; fax (440) 329-7272; e-mail ctnews@chroniclet.com; web site www.chroniclet.com
Est.: 1927
President and CEO — Paul Martin; Jeff Pfeiffer; Newspapers:Chronicle-Telegram, OH
The Medina County Gazette, OH
North Ridgeville Press, OH

LSN PUBLISHING COMPANY LLC — 600 Jefferson St, Ste 913, Lafayette, LA, 70508, USA; tel (337) 266-2154; fax (337) 266-2127; web site www.louisianastatenewspapers.com
Chairman — B.I. Moody III;
Pres. — Kevin Moody;
COO — Darrell Guillory;
Newspapers:Abbeville Meridional, LA
Avoyelles Journal, LA
Franklin Banner-Tribune, LA
The Basile Weekly, LA
The Bayou Journal, LA
Bunkie Record, LA
Caldwell Watchman, LA
Church Point News, LA
The Crowley Post-Signal, LA
The Daily Review, LA
The Delhi Dispatch, LA
The Eunice News, LA
Gueydan Journal, LA
The Kaplan Herald, LA
Kinder Courier News, LA
The Mamou Acadian Press, LA
The Marksville Weekly News, LA
The Oakdale Journal, LA
The Rayne-Acadian Tribune, LA
Richland Beacon-News, LA
Teche News, LA
Tensas Gazette, LA
Ville Platte Gazette, LA
The West Carroll Gazette, LA
Note: Louisiana State Newspapers owns four daily newspapers and 19 weekly publications.

M

MAINE TODAY MEDIA INC. — 1 City Ctr, Fl 5, Portland, ME, 04101-4070, USA; tel (207) 791-6650; web site www.mainetoday.com
Pres./Pub. — Richard L. Connor;Newspapers:Rutland Herald, VT
Kennebec Journal, ME
Morning Sentinel, ME
Portland Press Herald / Maine Sunday Telegram, ME

MAINSTREET MEDIA GROUP, LLC — 6400 Monterey Rd, Gilroy, CA, 95020-6628, USA; tel (408) 842-6400; fax (408) 842-7105; e-mail clake@mainstreetmg.comParent Co.: Mainstreet Media Group Holdings, LLC
Est.: 2003
COO, CFO & General Counsel — Chris Lake;Newspapers:Amador Ledger-Dispatch, CA
The Gilroy Dispatch, CA
The Pinnacle (OOB), CA
La Jolla Light, CA
Santa Cruz Good Times, CA
San Diego Suburban News (OOB), CA
Solana Beach Sun, CA
Del Mar Times, CA
Rancho Bernardo News-Journal, CA
Rancho Santa Fe Review, CA
Carmel Valley News, CA
Poway News Chieftan, CA
Note: Mainstreet Media Group owns 12 weekly newspapers, clustered in San Diego and south of San Jose.

MCNAUGHTON NEWSPAPERS — 1250 Texas St, Fairfield, CA, 94533-5748, USA; tel (707) 425-4646; fax (707) 425-5924; web site www.dailyrepublic.com
Pres./CEO — Foy McNaughton;
Vice Pres. — R. McNaughton;
Adv. Dir. — Sharon Guy;
Ed. — Debra DeAngelo; Newspapers:Daily Republic, CA
The Davis Enterprise, CA
Village Life, CA
Winters Express, CA
Mountain Democrat, CA
Note: McNaughton also owns the El Dorado Gazette, Georgetown Gazette & Town Crier, Folsom Life Folsom, the Village Life and the Winters Express all weekly publications located in California.

MESSENGER POST MEDIA — 73 Buffalo St, Canandaigua, NY, 14424-1001, USA; tel (585) 394-0770; fax (585) 394-1675; e-mail bkesel@messengerpostmedia.com; web site www.mpnnow.com
Parent Co.: GateHouse Media, Inc.
Est.: 1970
Pub. — Brian Doane;
Exe. Ed. — Brian Doane;
Mng. Ed./Content — Allison Cooper;
Mng. Ed./Presentation — Kevin Frisch;
Adv. Dir. — Beth Kesel;
Production Director — Brian Ambor;
Newspapers:Webster Post, NY
Brighton-Pittsford Post, NY
Irondequoit Post, NY
Penfield Post, NY
Greece Post, NY
Rush-Henrietta Post, NY
East Rochester-Fairport Post, NY
Gates-Chili Post, NY

MORGAN CITY NEWSPAPERS LLC — 1014 Front St, Morgan City, LA, 70380-3226, USA; tel (985) 384-8370; fax (985) 384-4255; web site www.daily-review.com
Est.: 1872
Pub. — Steve Shirley;
Gen. Mgr. — Andy Shirley; Newspapers:The Daily Review, LA
Franklin Banner-Tribune, LA
Note: Morgan City Newspapers LLC also owns the St. Mary Journal, a twice a week publication located in Morgan City, LA.

MORRIS COMMUNICATIONS CO. LLC — 725 Broad St, Augusta, GA, 30901-1336, USA; tel (888) 622-6358; fax (706) 722-7125; e-mail morrismarketing@morris.com; web site www.morris.com
Parent Co.: Morris Communications Company, LLC
CEO — William S. Morris III;
Sr. Vice Pres., Finance/Sec./Treasurer — Craig S. Mitchell; Newspapers:The Alaska Star, AK
Note: Morris Communications Company, LLC

is part of a privately held media company with diversified holdings that include newspaper, magazine, and cable television. Morris's holdings numerous magazines and specialized publications, visitor (travel and tourism) publications, including Where Magazine, Wheretraveler.com, and Where Guestbooks and provides cable television, internet, broadband, and telephone services.

N

NEW ENGLAND NEWSPAPERS INC — 75 S Church St, Pittsfield, MA, 01201-6157, USA; tel (413) 447-7311; fax (413) 499-3419; e-mail news@berkshireeagle.com
Parent Co.: Birdland Acquisition LLC.
Est.: Roots dating back to 1789
Asst. Editor-Berkshire Eagle — Jennifer Huberdeau;
CCSEO — Warren C. Dews Jr.;
Page Des./Copy Ed. — Mitchell Chapman;
Newspapers:Berkshire Eagle, MA
Bennington Banner, VT
Manchester Journal, VT
Brattleboro Reformer, VT
UpCountry Magazine, MA

NEW MEDIA INVESTMENT GROUP — 1345 Avenue of the Americas, Fl 46, New York, NY, 10105-4302, USA; tel (212) 479-3160; e-mail ir@newmediainv.com
Newspapers:Akron Beacon Journal, OH
Austin American-Statesman, TX
GateHouse Media, Inc., NY
Palm Beach Daily News, FL
The Palm Beach Post, FL
Alive, OH
Bedford Now, MI
Columbia Daily Tribune, MO
Rochester Business Journal, NY
Times Record, AR
McPherson Sentinel, KS
Dodge City Daily Globe, KS
The Newton Kansan, KS
The Morning Sun, KS
The Pratt Tribune, KS
Bastrop Daily Enterprise, LA
Cheboygan Daily Tribune, MI
Ames Tribune, IA
Crookston Daily Times, MN
Taunton Daily Gazette, MA
The Courier, MI
The Daily Reporter, MI
Hillsdale Daily News, MI
Cape Cod Times, MA
The Leavenworth Times, KS
Ionia Sentinel-Standard, MI
Sault Ste. Marie Evening News, MI
The Enterprise, MA
Rolla Daily News, MO
The Monroe News, MI
Milford Daily News, MA
The Daily Register, IL
Benton Evening News, IL
The Journal-Standard, IL
Olney Daily Mail, IL
The Daily Leader, IL
The Herald News, MA
The Standard-Times, MA
Hannibal Courier-Post, MO
Daily Guide, MO
Stuttgart Daily Leader, AR
The Evening Tribune, NY
The Carmi Times, IL
The Observer-Dispatch, NY
Times-News, NC
Daily Review Atlas, IL
The State Journal-Register, IL
The Daily American, IL
Devils Lake Journal, ND
The Repository, OH
Telegram & Gazette, MA
Pekin Daily Times, IL
Journal Star, IL
The Holland Sentinel, MI
Sturgis Journal, MI
The Oak Ridger, TN
The Courier-Tribune, NC

The Progress-Index, VA
The Moberly Monitor-Index, MO
The Star, NC
Neosho Daily News, MO
La Junta Tribune-Democrat, CO
The Ledger, FL
The Daily Commercial, FL
Daily Messenger, NY
Ocala Star-Banner, FL
Sarasota Herald-Tribune, FL
Lake Sun Leader, MO
Daily Comet, LA
Foster's Daily Democrat, NH
Hope Star, AR
The Record Herald, PA
Metrowest Daily News, MA
The Patriot Ledger, MA
The Gadsden Times, AL
The Daily Telegram, MI
Mineral Daily News-Tribune, WV
The Ardmoreite, OK
Mail Tribune, OR
The Kinston Free Press, NC
The Sun Journal, NC
The Times Herald-Record, NY
Wellsville Daily Reporter, NY
The Gaston Gazette, NC
Siskiyou Daily News, CA
The Bulletin, CT
Pocono Record, PA
Columbia Daily Herald, TN
Herald-Journal, SC
Daily Press, CA
The Butler County Times-Gazette, KS
The Daily News, NC
The Dispatch, NC
Miami News-Record, OK
Daytona Beach News-Journal, FL
The News Herald, FL
News Chief, FL
Northwest Florida Daily News, FL
The Gainesville Sun, FL
The Examiner / Examiner Weekend, MO
Kirksville Daily Express, MO
Mexico Ledger, MO
Pine Bluff Commercial, AR
Star-Courier, IL
Lincoln Courier, IL
The Marion Daily Republican, IL
Brownwood Bulletin, TX
Waxahachie Daily Light, TX
Shawnee News-Star, OK
Du Quoin Evening Call, IL
The Register-Mail, IL
Erie Times-News, PA
The Herkimer Telegram, NY
Daily Ledger, IL
Times-News, NC
Rockford Register Star, IL
The Times-Reporter, OH
The Independent, OH
The Carthage Press, MO
Examiner-Enterprise, OK
The Ashland Daily Tidings, OR
The Tuscaloosa News, AL
Portsmouth Herald, NH
Arkadelphia Siftings Herald, AR
Herald Democrat, TX
Boonville Daily News, MO
Constitution-Tribune, MO
The Daily Independent, CA
The Leader, NY
The Providence Journal, RI
The Record, CA
Stephenville Empire-Tribune, TX
Thisweek Newspapers, MN

NEWS MEDIA CORP. — 211 E Il Route 38, Rochelle, IL, 61068-2303, USA; tel (815) 562-2061; fax (815) 562-2161; web site www.newsmediacorporation.com
Est.: 1975
Pres. — John C. Tompkins;
Vice Pres. — Michael Tompkins;
Gen. Mgr. — John Shank;
Controller — Michael Rand;
Newspapers:Arizona Silver Belt, AZ
Ashton Gazette, IL
Center Post-Dispatch, CO
Ogle County Life, IL
The Lingle Guide, WY

Copper Country News, AZ
Lake Powell Chronicle, AZ
Register-Pajaronian, CA
The Rustler, CA
Gonzales Tribune, CA
Soledad Bee, CA
Greenfield News, CA
Paso Robles Press, CA
Atascadero News, CA
Valley Courier, CO
The Monte Vista Journal, CO
The Mineral County Miner, CO
The South Fork Tines, CO
The Del Norte Prospector, CO
The Conejos County Citizen, CO
The Rochelle News Leader, IL
Clinton Journal, IL
The Amboy News, IL
Mendota Reporter, IL
News-Times, OR
Siuslaw News, OR
Cottage Grove Sentinel, OR
Brookings Register, SD
Moody County Enterprise, SD
The Daily Plainsman, SD
The Redfield Press, SD
The Record Delta, WV
Mountain Statesman, WV
Taylor County Value Guide, WV
The Torrington Telegram, WY
The Lusk Herald, WY
The Platte County Record-Times, WY
Guernsey Gazette, WY
The Business Farmer, NE
Sublette Examiner, WY
The Pinedale Roundup, WY
Uinta County Herald, WY
Bridger Valley Pioneer, WY
The Kemmerer Gazette, WY

NEWS-PRESS & GAZETTE CO. — 825 Edmond St, , Saint Joseph, MO, 64501-2737, USA; tel (816) 271-8500; fax (816) 271-8695; e-mail dennis.ellsworth@npgco.com; web site www.newspressnow.com
Parent Co.: NPG Newspapers Inc.
Est.: 1918
Chief Executive Officer — David R. Bradley;
President — Brian Bradley;
Exec. Vice-President, COO- Newspapers —
Stacey Hill; Newspapers:Atchison Globe, KS
The Daily Star Journal - Warrensburg
Hiawatha World, KS
The Miami County Republic, KS
St. Joseph News-Press, MO
Courier Tribune, MO
Note: News-Press & Gazette Co. also owns the newspapers in Atchison, Hiawatha, Louisburg, Osawatomie, Paola, Kansas and Missouri newspapers in St. Joseph, Smithville, Liberty, Kearney, & Warrensburg.

NEWSPAPERS OF NEW ENGLAND — 1 Monitor Dr, Concord, NH, 03301-1834, USA; tel (603) 224-5301; fax (603) 224-6949; web site www.concordmonitor.com
Chrmn. — John Kuhns;
Pres./CEO — Aaron Julian;
CFO — Dan McClory;
Pub. — Geordie Wilson; Tundra Solsek;
VP/Digital — Ernesto Burden;
Newspapers:Concord Monitor, NH
Monadnock Ledger-Transcript, NH
Valley News, NH
The Recorder, MA
Valley Advocate, MA
Note: Newspapers of New England also owns the Peterborough (NH) Monadnock Ledger, a weekly publication.

NORTH JERSEY COMMUNITY NEWSPAPERS — 1 Garret Mountain Plz, Woodland Park, NJ, 07424-3320, USA; tel (973) 569-7000; fax (973) 569-7129; web site www.northjersey.com
Parent Co.: North Jersey Media Group Inc.
Est.: 2003
VP/Pub. — Janice Friedman;
VP/Pub. — Michael Lawson;
Pres. — Stephen A Borg; Newspapers:Aim

Jefferson
Aim Vernon, NJ
Aim West Milford, NJ
Argus, NJ
Belleville Times, NJ
Bloomfield Life, NJ
Bogota Bulletin, NJ
Cliffside Park Citizen, NJ
Clifton Journal, NJ
Community News, NJ
Edgewater View, NJ
Fort Lee Suburbanite, NJ
Franklin Lakes/Oakland Suburban News, NJ
The Gazette, NJ
Glen Ridge Voice, NJ
Glen Rock Gazette, NJ
Hackensack Chronicle, NJ
The Item of Millburn and Short Hills, NJ
Leonia Life, NJ
Little Ferry Local, NJ
Mahwah Suburban News, NJ
Midland Park Suburban News, NJ
The Montclair Times, NJ
Neighbor News, NJ
Northern Valley Suburbanite, NJ
Nutley Sun, NJ
Parsippany Life, NJ
Pascack Valley Community Life, NJ
Passaic Valley Today, NJ
Ramsey Suburban News, NJ
Ridgefield Park Patriot, NJ
The Ridgewood News, NJ
South Bergenite, NJ
Suburban News, NJ
Suburban Trends, NJ
Teaneck Suburbanite, NJ
Town Journal, NJ
Town News, NJ
Twin-Boro News, NJ
Verona-Cedar Grove Times, NJ
Waldwick Suburban News, NJ
Wayne Today, NJ
Wyckoff Suburban News, NJ
Englewood Suburbanite, NJ
Tenafly Suburbanite, NJ

O

OAHU PUBLICATIONS INC. — 500 Ala Moana Blvd, Ste 7-500, Honolulu, HI, 96813-4930, USA; tel (808) 529-4818; web site www.oahupublications.com
Parent Co.: Black Press Group Ltd.
Newspapers:Honolulu Star-Advertiser, HI
MidWeek Oahu, HI
Metro HNL (OOB), HI
USA Today Hawaii Edition , HI
Street Pulse, HI
The Garden Island, Kauai, HI
Kauai Midweek, HI
Hawaii Tribune-Herald, HI
West Hawaii Today, HI
North Hawaii News, HI
Hawaii Army Weekly, HI
Marine Star, HI
Ho`okele (Navy & Air Force), HI

OGDEN NEWSPAPERS INC. — 1500 Main St, Wheeling, WV, 26003-2826, USA; tel (304) 233-0100; fax (304) 233-9397; e-mail myer@news-register.net; web site www.oweb.com
Est.: 1800
Publisher — G. Ogden Nutting;
Pres./CEO — Robert M. Nutting;
Vice Pres. — William O. Nutting;
Vice Pres. — William C. Nutting;
Treasurer/CFO — Duane D. Wittman;
Newspapers:Adirondack Daily Enterprise, NY
Byrd Newspapers, VA
Page News & Courier, VA
The Shenandoah Valley-Herald, VA
The Warren Sentinel, VA
The Winchester Star, VA
Daily Herald, UT
Herald-Standard, PA
The Frederick News-Post, MD
Independent, MN
Independent Shopper's Review, MN
Lawrence Journal-World, KS

Northern Virginia Daily, VA
Cape Coral Breeze, FL
The Lake Placid News, NY
The Leader-Herald, NY
The Maui Bulletin, HI
Lee County Shopper, FL
Island Reporter, FL
Sanibel-Captiva Islander, FL
Sanibel - Captiva Shopper's Guide, FL
Captiva Current, FL
The Pine Island Eagle, FL
Fort Myers Beach Observer, FL
Fort Myers Beach Bulletin, FL
The Maui News, HI
The News-Sentinel, IN
The Messenger, IA
Times-Republican, IA
Consumer News, IA
The Daily Freeman-Journal, IA
The Dysart Reporter, IA
Estherville News, IA
Reporter-Democrat, IA
Tama County Shopper, IA
The Tama News-Herald, IA
Toledo Chronicle, IA
The Traer Star-Clipper, IA
Reinbeck Courier, IA
Northern-Sun Print, IA
Pennysaver, IA
The Alpena News, MI
The Daily Mining Gazette, MI
The Daily News, MI
Daily Press, MI
The Mining Journal, MI
Up Action News, MI
Action Shopper, MI
Advertiser, MI
Sentinel, MN
The Journal, MN
Faribault County Register, MN
New Ulm Shopper/post Review, MN
Minot Daily News, ND
Pierce County Tribune, ND
The Post-Journal, NY
The Observer, NY
The Westfield Republican, NY
Sentinel-News, NY
The Advertiser-Tribune, OH
Herald-Star, OH
The Marietta Times, OH
Morning Journal, OH
The Review, OH
The Times Leader, OH
The Tribune Chronicle, OH
Salem News, OH
Boardman Town Crier, OH
Williamsport Sun-Gazette/Lock Haven
Express, PA
Times Observer, PA
The Express, PA
The Sentinel, PA
Altoona Mirror, PA
County Observer, PA
East Lycoming Shopper, PA
The Luminary, PA
The Intelligencer, WV
The Inter-Mountain, WV
The Journal, WV
Parkersburg News & Sentinel, WV
Wetzel Chronicle, WV
Tyler Star News, WV
Weirton Daily Times, OH
The Shepherdstown Chronicle, WV
Green Tab, WV
Bedford Journal, NH
Mahoning Valley Parent Magazine, OH
Poland Town Crier, OH
The Milford Cabinet, NH
The Trading Post, ND
Merrimack Journal, NH
Austintown Town Crier, OH
Gasparilla Gazette (OOB), FL
Westfield Republican, NY
Canfield Town Crier, OH
The Emmetsburg Reporter, IA
Town Crier Shopper, MN
Quality Guide, NY
Note: Nutting Newspapers also publishes the Capper's, Grit, Mother Earth News, Brave Hearts, The Herb Companion, Herbs for Health, Farm Collector, Gas Engine Magazine, and Steam Traction.

OMAHA WORLD-HERALD — 1314 Douglas St, Ste 1500, Omaha, NE, 68102-1848, USA; tel (402) 444-1000; fax (402) 444-1231; e-mail phil.taylor@owh.com; web site www.omaha.com
Parent Co.: BH Media Group
Est.: 1885
Pres. & CEO, Pub. — Terry J. Kroeger;
Dir., Digital Development — Jeff Carney;
Dir., Production — Kristy Gerry;
CFO/Sr. Vice Pres. — Duane Polodna;
Sr. VP/Gen. Counsel — Scott Searl;
Exec VP — Doug Hiemstra;
Finance Dir./Controller — Mike Kirk;
Chief Revenue Officer — Thom Kastrup;
Director of Local Sales — Brett Snead;
Adv. Mgr., Custom Publishing/Events — Tam Webb;
Classified Employment Manager — Aaron Consalvi;
Director of Classified Advertising — Deb McChesney;
Mgr., Suburban Newspapers — Paul Swanson;
VP of Advertising — Keely Byars;
Dir Community Relations — Susan Violi;
Executive Editor — Melissa Matczak;
General Manager — Phil Taylor; @ SectionHead:P

PADDOCK PUBLICATIONS — PO Box 280, Arlington Heights, IL, 60006-0280, USA; tel (847) 427-4300; web site www.dailyherald.com
Newspapers:Carbondale Times, IL
Daily Herald, IL
Northwestern News, IL
Randolph County Herald Tribune, IL
Ridgeway News, IL
Steeleville Ledger, IL
The Girard Gazette, IL
The Herald News, IL
The Panhandle Press, IL
Virden Recorder, IL
Reflejos Bilingual Publications, IL

PAGE-SHENANDOAH NEWSPAPER CORP. — 231 S Liberty St, Harrisonburg, VA, 22801-3621, USA; tel (540) 574-6200; fax (540) 574-6299; web site www.shenvalleynow.comParent Co.: Page Shenandoah Newspaper Corporation
Est.: 1896
Pub. — Thomas T. Byrd;
Pres — Peter S. Yates;
Ed and Gen Mgr — Randy Arrington;
Note: Byrd Newspapers owns Rockingham Publishing Co. , publisher of the Daily News-Record and The Winchester Evening Star. Inc, publisher of The Winchester (VA) Star. Several weekly newspapers are also included in the group.

PAXTON MEDIA GROUP, LLC — 201 S 4th St, Paducah, KY, 42003-1524, USA; tel (270) 575-8600; fax (270) 442-8188; e-mail classified@sanfordherald.com; web site www.sanfordherald.com
Est.: 1896
Pres./CEO — David M. Paxton;
VP/CFO — Richard E. Paxton;
Asst. — Milinda Harnice; Newspapers:Daily Herald, NC
Grayson County News-Gazette, KY
The Current Bargain, IN
The Villa Rican, GA
The Standard, IN
West Georgia Weekly, GA
Princeton Daily Clarion, IN
Chronicle-Tribune, IN
Elkhart Truth, IN
Mount Carmel Register, IL
The Mayfield Messenger, KY
Metropolis Planet, IL
Paragould Daily Press, AR
Peru Tribune, IN
South Haven Tribune, MI
Harbor Country News, MI
Douglas County Sentinel, GA
The Courier, AR
The Daily Citizen, AR

The Daily Corinthian, MS
The Daily Courier, NC
Daily Dispatch, NC
Griffin Daily News, GA
Paragould Daily Press, AR
The Daily Star, LA
The Enquirer-Journal, NC
High Point Enterprise, NC
Herald-Sanford, NC
Herald-Argus, IN
The Messenger, KY
Messenger-Inquirer, KY
The Mountain Press, TN
The Shelbyville News, IN
News Dispatch, IN
Connersville News-Examiner, IN
News-Topic, NC
Wabash Plain Dealer, IN
The Paducah Sun, KY
The Jonesboro Sun, AR
Vincennes Sun-Commercial, IN
The Times, IN
Times-Georgian, GA
Huntington Herald-Press, IN
The Courier-Times, IN
Thomasville Times, NC
Marshall County Tribune-Courier, KY
Archdale-Trinity News, NC
McLean County News, KY
Franklin Favorite, KY
Metropolis Planet, IL
Portland Leader, TN
The Mayfield Messenger, KY
Gateway Beacon, GA
The Cadiz Record, KY
Note: Paxton Media Group LLC owns 31
daily newspapers and 13 paid non-daily
publications. Paxton Media also owns and
operates an NBC-affiliated television station
in Paducah, KY.

PIONEER NEWSPAPERS INC — 221 1st
Ave W, Ste 405, Seattle, WA, 98119-4238,
USA; tel (206) 284-4424; fax (206) 282-2143;
e-mail jwampler@pioneernewsgroup.com; web
site www.pioneernewsgroup.com
    Est.: 1976
    Pres. — Mike Gugliotto;
    CFO — Jeffrey Hood;
    Corp. Controller — Fred Eberlein;
    Internal Auditor & Advertising Systems
    Support — Larry Wells;
    Information & Circulation Systems Mgr. —
    Julie Hughes;
    Payroll & Finance Analyst — Sue Persh;
    Jeff Wampler;
    Human Resources Director — Megan
    Berg; Eric Johnston; Jeff Avgeris;
    Newspapers:Messenger-Index, ID
    Idaho Press, ID
    Stanwood Camano Advertiser, WA
    The Argus, WA
    The Herald Journal, UT
    Idaho Press-Tribune, ID
    The Leader, UT
    Lone Peak Lookout OOB, MT
    The News-Examiner, ID
    The Standard-Journal, ID
    The West Yellowstone News OOB*, MT
    Note: Pioneer News Group owns eight daily
    newspapers and 15 publications throughout
    the northwestern United States.

PRAIRIE MOUNTAIN PUBLISHING — 2500
55th St, Ste 210, Boulder, CO, 80301-5740,
USA; tel (303) 442-1220; web site www.
dailycamera.com
    Parent Co.: Digital First Media
    Est.: 1890
    Pres. and CEO — Albert Manzi;
    Vice Pres.; Marketing and Advertising —
    Jill Stravolemos; Newspapers:Broomfield
    Enterprise, CO
    Akron News-Reporter, CO
    The Brush News-Tribune, CO
    Burlington Record, CO
    Julesburg Advocate, CO
    Canon City Shopper, CO

PRINCETON PUBLISHING CO., INC. —
100 N Gibson St, Princeton, IN, 47670-1855,
USA; tel (812) 385-2525; fax (812) 386-6199;
e-mail lrembee@pdclarion.com; web site www.
pdclarion.com
    Est.: 1846
    Pub./CEO — Jeff Schumacher;
    Ed. — Andrea Howe; Newspapers:Oakland
    City Journal, IN
    Weekender, IN
    Note: Princeton Publishing Co., Inc. is owned
    by Brehm Communications Inc.

Q

QUINCY MEDIA, INC. — 130 S 5th St,
Quincy, IL, 62301-3916, USA; tel (217)
223-5100; fax (217) 223-5019; e-mail info@
quincyinc.com; web site www.careers@quincy.
com
    Pres./CEO — Ralph M. Oakley;
    Controller — David A. Graff;
    VP/CFO — Brad Eaton;
    Asst. to Pres./CEO — Morey Taraska;
    Dir., HR — Jena Schulz;
    Dir., Facilities/Capital Project/Broadcast
    Engineering — Brady Dreasler;
    Dir., Opns. Support — Brenda Wiskirchen;
    VP, Newspapers & Interactive — Mary
    Winters;
    IT Mgr. — Michael Funk; Newspapers:The
    Quincy Herald-Whig, IL
    New Jersey Herald, NJ
    Note: Quincy Newspapers Inc. also owns
    New Jersey Herald, twelve television stations
    and two radio stations.

R

RAY BARNES NEWSPAPERS, INC. — 201
E Columbus St, Kenton, OH, 43326-1583,
USA; tel (419) 674-4066; fax (419) 673-1125;
web site www.kentontimes.com
    Chrmn. of the Bd. — Jack L. Barnes;
    Pres. — Charles Barnes;
    Newspapers:Leader-Tribune Review East, IN
    The Elwood Call-Leader, IN
    Leader-Tribune Review West, IN
    The Daily Chief-Union, OH
    The Kenton Times, OH
    Tipton County Tribune, IN

RECORD PUBLISHING COMPANY, LLC
— 1050 W Main St, Kent, OH, 44240-2006,
USA; tel (330) 541-9400; fax (330) 296-2698;
e-mail rwaite@dixcom.com; web site www.
recordpub.com
    Est.: 1832
    General Manager — Waite Ron;
    Pub. — David Dix; Newspapers:Streetsboro
    Gateway News (OOB), OH
    Nordonia Hills News Leader, OH
    Tallmadge Express, OH
    Twinsburg Bulletin, OH
    Record-Courier, OH
    Note: Record Publishing Co. is part of Dix
    Communications which is owned by the
    Wooster Republican Printing Co. Through
    it's subsidiaries, Alliance Publishing Co.
    LLC, Ashland Publishing Co. LLC, Defiance
    Publishing LLC, Frankfort Publishing Co.,
    Jeffersonian C

RISN OPERATIONS INC. — 508 Main St,
Wilmington, DE, 19804-3911, USA
    Newspapers:Chariho Times, RI
    Coventry Courier, RI
    East Greenwich Pendulum, RI
    Kent County Daily Times, RI
    Narragansett Times, RI
    Standard-Times, RI
    The Call, RI
    The Porterville Recorder, CA
    The Times, RI
    Yuma Sun, AZ

ROCKINGHAM PUBLISHING CO. — 231
S Liberty St, Harrisonburg, VA, 22801-3621,
USA; tel (540) 574-6200; fax (540) 574-6299;
e-mail business@dnronline.com; web site
www.dnronline.com
    Est.: 1913
    Pres. — Thomas T. Byrd;
    Gen. Mgr. — Peter S. Yates; Newspapers:The
    Valley Banner, VA
    Rocktown Weekly, VA
    Note: Rockingham Publishing Co. is owned
    by Byrd Newspapers which also owns one
    daily and three weekly newspapers.

ROME NEWS-TRIBUNE — 305 E 6th Ave,
305 E 6th Ave, Rome, GA, 30161-6007, USA;
tel (706) 346-5279; fax (706) 232-9632; e-mail
romenewstribune@romenewstribune.com; web
site 305 E 6th ave
    Parent Co.: Times Journal, Inc
    Est.: 1843
    Publisher — Otis Raybon;Newspapers:The
    Calhoun Times, SC
    Catoosa County News, GA
    Rome News-Tribune, GA
    Cherokee County Herald, AL
    Walker County Plus, GA
    Walker County Messenger, GA
    Polk Standard Journal, GA
    Note: Rome News-Tribune is published by
    Rome News Media,LLC and owned by Times
    Journal, Inc in Marietta Ga. and publishes
    the Rome News-Tribune a daily newspaper
    in Rome, GA as well as five area weekly
    newspapers, Rome Life Magazine,and www.
    romenews-tribune.com.

RUST COMMUNICATIONS — 301 Broadway
St, Cape Girardeau, MO, 63701-7330, USA;
tel (573) 335-6611; fax (573) 334-9258; e-mail
editor@mccookgazette.com; web site www.
mccookgazette.com
    Est.: 1883
    Chrmn. — Gary W. Rust;
    Co-Pres./Pub. — Jon K. Rust;
    Co-Pres. — Rex D. Rust;
    Vice Pres./COO — Wally Lage;
    Vice Pres., Opns. — Jim Maxwell;
    Vice President of Production — David Guay;
    Newspapers:Big Nickel, NE
    The Fort Scott Tribune, KS
    Remsen Bell-Enterprise, IA
    Southeast Missourian, MO
    Southeast Missourian Plus, MO
    The Daily Statesman, MO
    The Daily Dunklin Democrat, MO
    Daily Dunklin Democrat Extra, MO
    The Marshall Democrat-News, MO
    The Monett Times, MO
    The Nevada Daily Mail, MO
    Daily American Republic, MO
    Standard Democrat, MO
    The Democrat Argus, MO
    Cassville Democrat, MO
    Scott County Signal, MO
    The Concordian, MO
    Delta News Citizen, MO
    Missourian-News, MO
    The Steele Enterprise, MO
    South Missourian-News, MO
    The Banner-Press, MO
    Puxico Press, MO
    Blytheville Courier News, AR
    Lovely County Citizen, AR
    Carroll County News, AR
    The Town Crier, AR
    The Osceola Times, AR
    Clay County Times-Democrat, AR
    The News, AR
    Poinsett County Democrat, AR
    State Gazette, TN
    Marshall County Tribune, TN
    Shelbyville Times-Gazette, TN
    The Brazil Times, IN
    Banner-Graphic, IN
    Greene County Daily World, IN
    Cherokee Chronicle Times, IA
    Le Mars Daily Sentinel, IA
    The Daily Reporter, IA
    Pilot Tribune, IA
    Dickinson County News, IA

McCook Daily Gazette, NE
Shoppers Guide, IA

S

S.A.W. ADVISORS, LLC — 11513 Charlotte
Ln, Frisco, TX, 75035-8339, USA
    Newspapers:Lake Cities Sun, TX
    McKinney Courier-Gazette, TX
    The Colony Courier Leader, TX
    Lewisville Leader, TX
    Rowlett Lakeshore Times, TX
    Frisco Enterprise, TX
    Little Elm Journal, TX
    Coppell Gazette, TX
    Allen American, TX
    Flower Mound Leader, TX
    Mesquite News, TX
    Celina Record, TX
    Carrollton Leader, TX

SAMPLE MEDIA GROUP — 201 N Lehigh
Ave, Sayre, PA, 18840-2246, USA
    Newspapers:Blairsville Dispatch, PA
    Daily Courier, PA
    Leader Times, PA
    The Daily Review, PA

SAMPLE NEWS GROUP LLC — 28 W South
St, Corry, PA, 16407-1810, USA; tel (814)
665-8291
    CEO — George Sample;
    Graphics/I.T. Manager — David Coyle;
    Newspapers:Citizen (OOB), NH
    Morning Times, PA
    The Huntingdon Daily News, PA
    The Palladium-Times, NY
    The Standard-Journal, PA
    The Times Record, ME
    The Latrobe Bulletin, PA
    The Daily Herald, PA
    Journal-Tribune, ME
    The Bedford Gazette, PA
    Corry Journal, PA
    Ocean City Sentinel, NJ
    Gettysburg Times, PA
    The Shippensburg News-Chronicle, PA
    The Mountaineer-Herald, PA
    The Portage Dispatch, PA
    The Star-Courier, PA

SANDUSKY NEWSPAPERS, INC. — 17
Executive Park Rd, Ste 3A, Hilton Head Island,
SC, 29928-4738, USA; tel (843) 842-9162; fax
(843) 842-9617
    Chrmn/CEO — David Rau;
    Vice Pres./Gen. Counsel/CFO — Peter Vogt;
    President and COO — Doug Phares;
    Newspapers:Sandusky Register, OH
    Norwalk Reflector, OH
    Hilltop Times, UT
    Grand Haven Tribune, MI
    The Lebanon Democrat, TN
    Mt. Juliet News, TN
    The Hartsville Vidette, TN
    Herald & Tribune, TN
    The Erwin Record, TN
    Kingsport Times-News, TN
    Johnson City Press, TN
    The Tomahawk, TN

SCHURZ COMMUNICATIONS INC — 1301
E Douglas Rd, Mishawaka, IN, 46545-1732,
USA; tel (574) 247-7237; fax (574) 247-7238;
web site www.schurz.com
    Est.: 1872
    Sr VP and CFO — Gesumino A. Agostino;
    President and CEO — Todd F. Schurz;
    VP Digital Media — J.B. Ozuna;
    VP of Human Resources and Corporate
    Development — Scott Schurz;
    VP of Publishing — Cory Bollinger;
    Director of Strategic Planning and
    Corporate Development — Chris Dautel;
    Newspapers:Farm Forum, SD
    Watertown Public Opinion, SD
    The Times-Mail, IN
    The Herald-Mail, MD

The Herald Times, IN
Charlevoix Courier, MI
The Reporter Times, IN
Gaylord Herald Times, MI
The Mooresville-Decatur Times, IN
Petoskey News-Review, MI
South Bend Tribune, IN
Daily American, PA
Aberdeen American News, SD
Northern Michigan Review, Inc., MI
Herald-mail Express, MD
The Public Opinion, SD

SEACOAST MEDIA GROUP — 111 NH Ave, Portsmouth, NH, 03801-2864, USA
Andrew Chernoff; John Tabor;Newspapers:The Hampton Union, NH
The York Weekly, NH
Exeter News-Letter, NH
York County Coast Star, NH

SHAW MEDIA — 3200 E Lincolnway, Sterling, IL, 61081-1773, USA; tel (815) 284-4000; fax (815) 301-1727; e-mail tshaw@shawmedia.com; web site www.shawmedia.com
Est.: 1851
Pres. and COO
— John Rung;
CFO
Treasurer — Terri Swegle;
Chairman — Ryan McKibben;
Secretary/Admin. Asst. — Peggy Campbell;
Corp Strategy Coor — Peter Shaw;
CEO — John Rung; Newspapers:The Times, IL
Berwyn Suburban Life, IL
Jasper County Tribune, IA
The Telegraph, IL
West Chicago Suburban Life, IL
Bureau County Republican, IL
Downers Grove Suburban Life, IL
Geneva Chronicle, IL
Glen Ellyn Suburban Life, IL
St. Charles Chronicle, IL
Hinsdale Suburban Life, IL
Villa Park Suburban Life, IL
Westmont Suburban Life, IL
Addison Suburban Life, IL
Elmhurst Suburban Life, IL
Carol Stream Suburban Life, IL
LaGrange Suburban Life, IL
Tonica News, IL
Creston News Advertiser, IA
Daily Chronicle, IL
The Midweek, IL
Forreston Journal, IL
Kane County Chronicle, IL
Morris Herald-News, IL
Mt. Morris Times, IL
Newton Daily News, IA
Oregon Republican Reporter, IL
Osceola Sentinel-Tribune, IA
Lake County Journal, IL
Southwest Iowa Advertiser, IA
Tri-County Press, IL
Northwest Herald, IL
Daily Gazette, IL
McHenry County Magazine, IL
Kane County Magazine, IL
Valley Life, IL
SV Weekend, IL
The Review, IL
The Advertiser, IA
Jasper County Advertiser, IA
Sunrise Edition, IA
Batavia Chronicle, IL
Herald Life, IL
Putnam County Record, IL
Wheaton Suburban Life, IL
Lombard Suburban Life, IL
Lemont Suburban Life, IL
Woodridge Suburban Life, IL
The Herald-News, IL
The Prairie Advocate News, IL
Jasper County Tribune, IA
Illinois Valley Scene, IL
Kendall County Record, ID
Oswego Ledger, IL
Plano Record, IL
Sandwich Record, IL
Elburn Herald

Sugar Grove Herald
Note: Brand Promise: Relevant Information, Marketing Solutions, Community Advocates.

SHEARMAN CORPORATION — 4900 Highway 90 E, Lake Charles, LA, 70615-4037, USA; tel (337) 494-4033; fax (337) 494-4013; e-mail atinsley@americanpress.com; web site www.americanpress.com
Est.: 1895
Pres. — Thomas B. Shearman;
Bus. Mgr. — Anita Tinsley;
Newspapers:American Press, LA
Southwest Daily News, LA
Vinton News, LA
Hobbs News-Sun, NM
The Chronicle-News, CO

SHELBY COUNTY NEWSPAPERS, INC — 115 N Main St, Columbiana, AL, 35051-5359, USA; tel (205) 669-3131; fax (205) 669-4217
General Manager — Katie McDowell;Newspapers:Shelby County Reporter, AL
Alabaster Reporter, AL
Pelham Reporter, AL

SMALL NEWSPAPER GROUP — 8 Dearborn Sq, Kankakee, IL, 60901-3909, USA; tel (815) 937-3300; fax (815) 937-3301; web site www.sngnews.com
Pres. — Len Robert Small;
Executive Vice President — Thomas P. Small;
Vice Pres. — Robert Hill;
CIRCULATION AND AUDIENCE DIRECTOR
— Rebecca Meyer;
General Manager/Production Director —
Kevin Norden;
Network Operations Director — Wade LeBeau;
Business Manager — Cindy Liptak;
Distribution Manager — Ronald Blackwell;
Editor at Large — Mike Frey;
VP-Finance — Sally Hendron;
Newspapers:The Daily Journal, IL
Post-Bulletin, MN
Note: Small Newspaper Group Inc. owns Agri-News in IA and MN, and Rochester Magazine.

SOUTHERN CALIFORNIA NEWS GROUP — 21860 Burbank Blvd, Ste 200, Woodland Hills, CA, 91367-7439, USA; tel (818) 713-3883; web site www.socalnewsgroup.com
Parent Co.: Digital First Media
Est.: 1878
Pres. & Pub. — Ron Hasse;
SVP & Exec Ed — Frank Pine;
Chief Revenue Officer — Tom Kelly;
VP, Mktg — Bill VanLaningham;
CFO — Dan Scofield;
Sr. Dir HR — Rosemaria Altieri;
VP Operations — Jon Merendino;
Newspapers:Excelsior Los Angeles, CA
Daily Breeze, CA
La Prensa, CA
The Whittier Daily News, CA
Pasadena Star-News, CA
The Facts (Redlands), CA
San Gabriel Valley Tribune, CA
The Sun, CA
Press-Telegram, CA
Los Angeles Daily News, CA
Inland Valley Daily Bulletin, CA
Excelsior Orange County, CA
Note: Two reputable and trusted news sources, Los Angeles News Group and Freedom Communications, have united to establish Southern California News Group (SCNG), the largest local news provider in the five-county Los Angeles metropolitan area. With 11 daily local newspapers and more than two dozen community weeklies, the SCNG is a leader in circulation among top news publications nationwide.

SOUTHERN COMMUNITY NEWSPAPERS, INC. — PO Box 603, Lawrenceville,

GA, 30046-0603, USA; tel (770) 963-9205; fax (770) 277-5277; web site www.southerncommunitynewspapers.com/
Newspapers:Clayton News Daily, GA
Henry Daily Herald, GA
The Rockdale Citizen, GA
The Albany Herald, GA
Gwinnett Daily Post, GA

SOUTHERN NEWSPAPERS INC. — 5701 Woodway Dr, Ste 131, Houston, TX, 77057-1589, USA; tel (713) 266-5481; e-mail lwalls@sninews.com; web site www.sninews.com
Est.: 1951
Treasurer — Ruby Barrow;
CEO — Lissa Walls;
Pres.
— Dolph Tillotson; Newspapers:Sand Mountain Shopper's Guide, AL
The Lawton Constitution, OK
The Bay City Tribune, TX
The Baytown Sun, TX
Del Rio News-Herald, TX
The Facts, TX
The Times-Journal, AL
The Galveston County Daily News, TX
Kerrville Daily Times, TX
The Lufkin Daily News, TX
New Braunfels Herald-Zeitung, TX
The Paris News, TX
Sand Mountain Reporter, AL
The Seguin Gazette, TX
The Daily Sentinel, AL
The Daily Sentinel, TX
The Independent, TN
News Telegram, TX

SOUTHERN RHODE ISLAND NEWSPAPERS — 187 Main St, Wakefield, RI, 02879-3504, USA; tel (401) 789-9744; fax (401) 789-1550; web site www.ricentral.com
Publisher — Nanci Batson;Newspapers:Kent County Daily Times, RI
Chariho News, RI
Coventry Courier, RI
Narragansett Times, RI
East Greenwich Pendulum, RI
Standard-Times, RI
Note: Southern Rhode Island Newspapers is owned by RISN (Rhode Island Suburban Newspapers) Operations.

STAR COMMUNITY NEWSPAPERS — 624 Krona Dr, Ste 170, Plano, TX, 75074-8304, USA; tel (972) 424-6565; fax (972) 398-4470; web site www.starlocalnews.com
Parent Co.: Times Media Group
Est.: 1901
Publisher — Roger Will;Newspapers:Colony-Courier Leader, TX
The Leader, Flower Mound, Highland Village, Lewisville, TX
Note: Owned by 1013 Communication, Star Community Newspapers are sister papers of Houston Community Newspapers.

SUN COAST MEDIA GROUP INC — 23170 Harborview Rd, Punta Gorda, FL, 33980-2100, USA; tel (941) 206-1000; e-mail info@sun-herald.com; web site www.yoursun.com/
President/CEO/COO — David Dunn-Rankin;
Ad Director/PGH — Leslee Peth;
VP/Polk Operations
Publisher/Heartland Newspapers — Jim Gouvellis;
President/News-Sun & Highlands Sun —
Glen Nickerson;
Publisher/North Port Sun — Steve Sachkar;
Publisher, Englewood Sun — Carol Moore;
Publisher, Arcadian — Joe Gallimore;
Publisher, Venice Gondolier Sun — Tim Smolarick; Newspapers:Charlotte Sun, FL
Highlands News-Sun, FL
Arcadian, FL
Englewood Sun, FL
North Port Sun, FL
The Polk County News and Democrat, FL
Venice Gondolier Sun, FL
News-Sun, FL

SUN PUBLICATIONS OF FLA. — 7060 Havertys Way, Lakeland, FL, 33805-1413, USA; tel (863) 583-1202; fax (863) 583-1212; e-mail rmiller@sunpubfla.com; web site www.sunpubfla.com
Commercial Print Manager — Robin Miller;Newspapers:Clermont News Leader, FL
The News Leader, FL
Pasco Shopper, FL
Sumter Shopper, FL
Triangle News Leader, FL
Osceola News-Gazette, FL

SUN-TIMES MEDIA GROUP INC. — 30 N Racine Ave, Chicago, IL, 60607-2183, USA; tel (312) 321-3000; fax (312) 321-6426; e-mail metro@suntimes.com; web site www.suntimes.com
CEO
— Edwin Eisendrath;
Editor-in-Chief — Chris Fusco;
SVP, Digital News Products — Carol Fowler;
Chief Digital Strategist — Matthew Watson;
SVP, Advertising — Alison Laffe;
Chief Operating Officer — Nykia Wright;
Newspapers:Chicago Sun-Times, IL
The Straight Dope (website only), IL

SUPERIOR PUBLISHING COMPANY — PO Box 408, 148 East Third Street, Superior, NE, 68978-0408, USA; tel (402) 879-3291; fax (402) 879-3463; e-mail tse@superiorne.com; web site www.superiorne.com
Est.: 1900
Pub — BILL Blauvelt;Newspapers:The Superior Express, NE
Jewell County Record, KS
Nuckolls County Locomotive-Gazette, NE
Note: Superior Publishing Company owns 3 weekly newspapers and one newsletter.

SWIFT COMMUNICATIONS, INC. — 580 Mallory Way, Carson City, NV, 89701-5360, USA; tel (775) 850-7676; fax (775) 850-7677; e-mail info@swiftcom.com; web site www.swiftcom.com
Chrmn., Bd. — Richard K. Larson;
Pres./CEO — Arne L. Hoel;
President & COO — Robert L. Brown;
Cor. Controller — Bill J. Waters;
Cor. Dir. — Debbie Spieker-Martin;
AUDIENCE DEVELOPMENT DIRECTOR
— Trisha Woodside; James Morgan; Valerie Richardson; Newspapers:Craig Daily Press, CO
Steamboat Pilot, CO
Steamboat Today, CO
Sierra Sun, CA
Tahoe Daily Tribune, CA
The Union, CA
Nevada Appeal, NV
North Lake Tahoe Bonanza, NV
The Record-Courier, NV
The News-Review, OR
The Eagle Valley Enterprise, CO
Glenwood Springs Post Independent, CO
Grand Junction Free Press, CO
Greeley Daily Tribune, CO
Sky-Hi News, CO
Snowmass Sun, CO
Summit Daily News, CO
The Aspen Times, CO
Citizen Telegram, CO
Vail Daily, CO
Windsor Now, CO
Valley Journal, CO
Lahontan Valley News & Fallon Eagle Standard, NV
Note: Swift Newspapers Inc. also publishes two farm and ranch magazines as well as Northern Nevada Business Weekly.

T

TALLAPOOSA PUBLISHERS, INC. — 548 Cherokee Rd, Tallapoosa County, Alexander City, AL, 35010-2503, USA; tel (256) 234-

4281; fax (256) 234-6550; web site www.
booonenewspapers.com
> Parent Co.: Tallapoosa Publishers Inc.
> Bus. Mgr. — Angela Mullins;
> Editor — Mitch Sneed;
> Pres./Pub. — Steve Baker;
> Advertising Director — Tippy Hunter;
> Newspapers:Tallassee Tribune, AL

TENNESSEE VALLEY MEDIA CO., INC.
— 201 1st Ave SE, Decatur, AL, 35601-2333,
USA; tel (256) 353-4612; fax (256) 340-2366;
web site www.decaturdaily.com
> Pres./Pub. — Barrett C. Shelton Jr.;
> Gen. Mgr. — Clint Shelton;
> Newspapers:Redston Rocket, AL
> The Moulton Advertiser, AL
> Courier Journal, AL

THE CONNECTICUT NEWS PROJECT, INC.
— 36 Russ St, Hartford, CT, 06106-1520, USA;
tel (860) 2186380; e-mail publisher@ctmirror.
org; web site 36 Russ Street
> Parent Co.: The Connecticut News Project
> Est.: 2010
> CEO and Publisher — Bruce
> Putterman;Newspapers:The Connecticut
> Mirror, CT

THE DOLAN COMPANY — 222 S 9th St,
Ste 2300, Minneapolis, MN, 55402-3363,
USA; tel (612) 317-9420; web site www.
thedolancompany.com
> Newspapers:Daily Journal of Commerce, OR
> The Daily Record, MD
> North Carolina Lawyers Weekly, NC
> The Mecklenburg Times, NC
> Daily Journal of Commerce, OR

THE EDWARD A. SHERMAN PUBLISHING
CO. — 101 Malbone Rd, Newport, RI, 02840-
1340, USA; tel (401) 849-3300; fax (401) 849-
3306; e-mail circDept@newportRI.com; web
site www.newportdailynews.com
> Est.: 1846
> Mng Ed — Jonathan Zins;Newspapers:The
> Independent, RI
> Newport Mercury, RI

THE FAYETTEVILLE FLYER — 205 N
College Ave, Fayetteville, AR, 72701-4238,
USA; tel (479) 966-4860; e-mail contact@
fayettevilleflyer.com; web site www.
fayettevilleflyer.com
> Parent Co.: Wonderstate Media, LLC
> — Dustin Bartholomew;
> — Todd Gill; Co-Owners

THE FISCAL TIMES — 712 5th Ave, Fl
17, New York, NY, 10019-4108, USA; tel
(212) 313-9680; fax (877) 291-7606; e-mail
info@thefiscaltimes.com; web site www.
thefiscaltimes.com
> Ed.-in-Chief — Jacqueline Leo;
> Acct. Mgr. — Jeff Czaplicki; @
> RecordHead:The Gazette - gazettextra.com
> — 1 S Parker Dr, Janesville, WI, 53545-3928,
> USA; tel (608) 754-3311; fax (608) 754-
> 8038; e-mail sbliss@gazettextra.com; web
> site www.gazettextra.comParent Co.: Bliss
> Communications, IncEst.: 1845
> Pres./Chrmn./CEO — Sidney H. Bliss;
> VP Strategic Operations — Mary Jo Villa;
> VP Financial Operations — Pam Schmoldt;
> Director of Technical Services & Facilities —
> Chad Lette;
> Ed. — Sid Schwartz;
> Vice President Printing Operations — Tony
> Smithson;
> Director of Advertising Operations — Tom
> Bradley;
> Director of Circulation — Rudy Frank;
> Director of Digital Advertising — Laura Feit;
> Vice President & General Manager-
> EagleHerald — Kathy Springberg;
> Newspapers:EagleHerald - ehextra.com, WI
> Walworth County Shopper Advertiser, WI
> Stateline News, WI
> Messenger, WI

THE McCLATCHY COMPANY — 2100 Q St,
Sacramento, CA, 95816-6816, USA; tel (916)
321-1855; fax (916) 321-1869; web site www.
mcclatchy.com
> Est.: 1857
> VP/Sec./Gen. Counsel — Karole Morgan-
> Prager;
> VP, Interactive Media — Chris Hendricks;
> VP, News and Washington Ed. — Anders
> Gyllenhaal;
> Controller — Hai Nguyen;
> Nat. Digital Sales Mgr. — Monica Woodworth;
> National Sales Mgr. — Julie Lambert;
> VP of Adv. — Kim Nussbaum;
> Pres./CEO — Craig Forman;
> Newspapers:The Fresno Bee, CA
> The Herald-Sun, NC
> Merced Sun-Star, CA
> The Modesto Bee, CA
> The Sacramento Bee, CA
> The Tribune, CA
> Bradenton Herald, FL
> Miami Herald, FL
> El Nuevo Herald, FL
> Columbus Ledger-Enquirer, GA
> The Telegraph, GA
> Idaho Statesman, ID
> The Wichita Eagle, KS
> The Sun Herald, MS
> The Kansas City Star, MO
> The Charlotte Observer, NC
> The News & Observer, NC
> Centre Daily Times, PA
> The Beaufort Gazette, SC
> The Herald, SC
> The Island Packet, SC
> The State, SC
> The Sun News, SC
> Fort Worth Star-Telegram, TX
> The Bellingham Herald, WA
> The Olympian, WA
> The News Tribune, WA
> Mansfield News-Mirror, TX
> The Peninsula Gateway, WA
> Lee's Summit Journal, MO
> Livingston Chronicle, CA
> Bee Niche Products, CA
> Keesler News, MS
> Vida en el Valle, CA
> Herald Values, CA
> Almaden Resident, CA
> Atwater Signal, CA
> Berkeley Voice (duplicate), CA
> Campbell Reporter, CA
> Cass County Democrat-Missourian, MO
> El Cerrito Albany Journal, CA
> Florida Keys Keynoter, FL
> Fort Mill Times, SC
> Lamorinda Sun, CA
> Los Banos Enterprise, CA
> O'Fallon Progress, IL
> Pinckneyville Democrat, IL
> Rose Garden Resident, CA
> Salinas Valley Weekly, CA
> Saratoga News, CA
> Sierra Star, CA
> Sparta News-Plaindealer, IL
> Sun-Bulletin, CA
> The Cambrian, CA
> The Cary News, NC
> The Chowchilla News, CA
> The Clovis Independent, CA
> The Cupertino Courier, CA
> The Keller Citizen, TX
> The Olathe News, MO
> The Puyallup Herald, WA
> The Reporter, FL
> The Sunnyvale Sun, CA
> Valley Times (OOB), CA
> The Enquirer-Herald, SC
> The Telegraph, GA
> Note: The McClatchy Company is a leading
> news and information provider, offering a
> wide array of print and digital products in
> each of the markets it serves. As the third
> largest newspaper company in the United
> States, McClatchy's operations include 30
> daily newspapers, community newspapers,
> websites, mobile news and advertising, niche
> publications, direct marketing and direct mail
> services. McClatchy's largest newspapers
> include The Miami Herald, The Sacramento

Bee, the Fort Worth Star-Telegram, The
Kansas City Star, The Charlotte Observer
and The News & Observer in Raleigh, N.C.
McClatchy is listed on the New York Stock
Exchange under the symbol MNI.

THE NEW YORK TIMES CO. — 620 8th
Ave, New York, NY, 10018-1618, USA; tel (212)
556-1234; fax (212) 556-4011; web site www.
nytco.com
> Est.: 1896
> Pub. — Stephen Dunbar-Johnson;
> Chrmn., The New York Time Co./ Pub., The
> New York Times — Arthur O. Sulzberger;
> Vice Chrmn., The New York Times Co./Pub.,
> International Herald Tribune — Michael
> Golden;
> Pres./CEO — Janet L. Robinson;
> CIO — Joseph Seibert;
> Sr. Vice Pres., Digital Opns. — Martin A.
> Nisenholtz;
> Sr. Vice Pres., Finance/Cor. Controller —
> Anthony Benten;
> Vice Pres./Deputy Gen. Counsel — Kenneth
> A. Richieri;
> Vice Pres./Treasurer — Laurena Emhoff;
> Vice Pres., Finance/Cor. Devel. — James C.
> Lessersohn;
> Vice Pres., Internal Audit — Philip A. Ciuffo;
> Vice Pres., Labor Rel. — Terry L. Hayes;
> Vice Pres., Compensation/Benefits — Ann
> S. Kraus;
> Vice Pres., Orgn./Devel. — Neal Roberts;
> Vice Pres., Forest Pdct. — Jennifer C. Dolan;
> Cor. Sec./Sr. Counsel — Rhonda L. Brauer;
> Pres., Broadcast Media Grp. — Robert H.
> Eoff;
> Pres., New York Times — Scott Heekin-
> Canedy;
> Pres., Boston Globe — Richard J. Daniel;
> Sr. Vice Pres. — James M. Follo;
> Newspapers:The New York Times, NY
> The New York Times News Service &
> Syndicate
> Note: The New York Times Co. publishes The
> New York Times, the International Herald
> Tribune, The Boston Globe as well as 16
> other newspapers. The New York Times Co.
> also owns more than 40 web sites and two
> New York City radio stations.

THE NEWS-GAZETTE — 15 E Main St,
Champaign, IL, 61820-3625, USA; tel
(217) 351-5252; fax (217) 351-5291; e-mail
advertising@news-gazette.com; web site www.
news-gazette.com
> Est.: 1852
> Pres. — John Foreman;
> Columnist — Tom Kacich;
> Librarian — Carolyn Vance;
> Photo Ed. — Darrell Hoemann;
> Ed. — Jim Rossow;
> Circ. Dir. — Pete Jones;
> CEO/Pub. — John Reed;
> VP/Dir. HR — Tracy Nally;
> VP/Gen. Mgr. Radio — Mike Haile;
> Adv. Dir. — Tom Zalabak;
> Adv. Sales Mgr. & National Sales — Jackie
> Martin;
> Customer Care Center Manager — Denny
> Santarelli;
> Opinions Page Ed. — Jim Dey;
> Features Ed. — Tony Mancuso;
> Dir. of Market Dev. — Amy George;
> Adv. Services Mgr. — Alice Vaughan;
> Online Ed. — Niko Dugan;
> Newspapers:Independent News, IL
> The Leader, IL
> Leroy Farmer City Press, IL
> Mahomet Citizen, IL
> Ford County Record, IL
> Piatt County Journal-Republican, IL
> Rantoul Press, IL
> The Regional, IL

THE RECORD-JOURNAL PUBLISHING
CO. — 500 S Broad St, 2nd Floor, Meriden,
CT, 06450-6643, USA; tel (203) 235-1661; fax
(203) 235-6345; e-mail newsroom@record-
journal.com; web site www.myrecordjournal.

com
> Est.: 1867
> Pres./Pub. — Eliot C. White;
> Executive VP and Assistant Publisher — Liz
> White;
> Sr. Vice President & Editor — Ralph
> Tomaselli;
> Senior VP and CRO — Shawn Palmer;
> Newspapers:Record-Journal, CT
> Berlin Citizen, CT
> The Plainville Citizen, CT
> The Southington Citizen, CT
> Town Times, CT
> The North Haven Citizen
> The Cheshire Citizen
> The Westerly Sun, RI
> The Mystic River Press, CT
> Note: The Record-Journal Publishing Co.
> also owns The Westerly Sun and eight
> weekly newspapers.

THE SEATTLE TIMES — 1000 Denny Way,
Ste 501, Seattle, WA, 98109-5323, USA; tel
(206) 464-2988; fax (206) 464-2239; e-mail
advertising@seattletimes.com; web site www.
seattletimes.com
> Parent Co.: The Seattle Times
> Est.: 1896
> Mng Ed — Michele Matassa Flores;
> Sr. VP, Finance — Buster Brown;
> Managing Ed. — Jim Simon;
> Managing Ed. — Michele Matassa Flores;
> Assistant Managing Ed., Visuals — Leon
> Espinoza;
> Deputy Mng. Ed. — Lynn Jacobson;
> Exec. Ed. — Don Shelton;
> Newspapers:Newcastle News, WA
> The Seattle Times, WA
> Sammamish Review, WA
> Walla Walla Union-Bulletin, WA
> The Issaquah Press, WA
> Yakima Herald-Republic, WA
> SnoValley Star, WA

THE WESTFIELD NEWS GROUP LLC —
62 School St, Westfield, MA, 01085-2835,
USA; tel (413) 562-4181; web site www.
thewestfieldnews.com
> Newspapers:Pennysaver, MA
> The Westfield News , MA

TIMES COMMUNITY NEWS (TCN) — 202
W 1st St, Los Angeles, CA, 90012-4299,
USA; tel (818) 637-3200; fax (818) 241-1975;
e-mail gnp@latimes.com; web site www.
glendalenewspress.com
> Editor — Dan Evans;
> CFO — Gordon Tomaske;
> Gen. Mgr. — Tom Johnson;
> Bus. Mgr. — Debbie Feyerabend;
> Opns. Mgr. — Neil McAnally;
> Exec. Ed. — John Canalis;
> Newspapers:Burbank Leader, CA
> Park Labrea News & Beverly Press, CA
> La Canada Valley Sun, CA
> Huntington Beach Independent (OOB), CA
> Note: Times Community News (TCN) is
> owned by the Los Angeles Times.

TIMES MEDIA GROUP — PO Box 10528,
Reno, NV, 89510-0528, USA; tel (775) 333-
0004; e-mail info@freedom.com; web site www.
freedom.com
> Est.: 1955
> Pres. — Randy Miller;
> Owner, President — Eric Spitz;
> Owner, Publisher — Aaron Kushner;
> Dir., Strategy and Development — Emily
> Martin; Newspapers:Capistrano Valley
> News, CA
> Deer Park Broadcaster, TX
> Orange County Catholic, CA
> Fountain Valley View, CA
> Huntington Beach Wave, CA
> West University Examiner, TX
> Colony-Courier Leader, TX
> Irvine World News, CA
> San Clemente Sun Post, CA
> Spring Observer, TX
> Aliso Viejo News, CA

The Woodlands Villager, TX
Anaheim Bulletin, CA
East Valley Tribune, AZ
Dana Point News, CA
Eastex Advocate, TX
Fullerton News-Tribune, CA
Brea-La Habra Star-Progress, CA
Star Community Newspapers, TX
Laguna News-Post, CA
Ahwatukee Foothills News, AZ
Laguna Niguel News, CA
Laguna Woods Globe, CA
Orange City News, CA
Placentia News Times, CA
Saddleback Valley News, CA
Sun-Post News, CA
The Tustin News, CA
Yorba Linda Star, CA
Santa Ana Register (OOB), CA
Rancho Canyon News (OOB), CA
Plano Star-Courier, TX
Saddleback Valley News
Humble Observer, TX
Atascocita Observer, TX
Kingwood Observer, TX
Los Angeles Register (OOB)
East Montgomery County Observer, TX
Garden Grove Journal
Lake Houston Observer, TX
Long Beach Register
Cleveland Advocate, TX
The Current (Newport Beach & Costa Mesa)
Dayton News, TX
The Long Beach Register (OOB), CA
Tomball Potpourri, TX
Magnolia Potpourri, TX
Cypress Creek Mirror, TX
Ladera Post (OOB), CA
Pasadena Citizen, TX
Mojave Desert News, CA
Bay Area Citizen, TX
Saddleback Valley News - Mission Viejo, CA
Hesperia Star, CA
Pearland Journal, TX
Friendswood Journal, TX
Rancho Santa Margarita News (OOB), CA
River Oaks Examiner, TX
Bellaire Examiner, TX
Colusa County Sun-Herald, CA
Memorial Examiner, TX
Corning Observer, CA
The Rancher, TX
Sugar Land Sun, TX
Willows Journal (OOB), CA
Scuppernong Reminder, NC
The Hickory News, NC
The Mid-Valley Town Crier, TX
The Shopper, NC
Note: Freedom Communications is headquartered in Santa Ana, Calif.

TIMES-SHAMROCK COMMUNICATIONS
— 149 Penn Ave, Scranton, PA, 18503-2055, USA; tel (570) 348-9100; fax (570) 348-9149; web site www.thetimes-tribune.com
Est.: 1895
Pub. — William R. Lynett;
COO — Don Farley;
CEO — George Lynett Jr;
CEO — Bobby Lynett;
CEO — Matthew Haggerty;
Pub. — Edward Lynett;
Pub. — George Lynett; Newspapers:The Times-Tribune, PA
The Citizens' Voice, PA
The Republican-Herald, PA
Wyoming County Press Examiner, PA
The Valley Advantage, PA
The Pocono Shopper, PA
Hazleton Standard-Speaker, PA

TIOGA PUBLISHING COMPANY — 25 East Ave, Wellsboro, PA, 16901-1618, USA; tel 570-724-2287; web site www.tiogapublishing.com
Newspapers:The Wellsboro Gazette, PA
Free Press-Courier, PA

TN MEDIA — 1100 Broadway, Nashville, TN, 37203-3116, USA; tel (615) 259-8000; fax (615) 259-8875; e-mail rateinfo@tennessean.

com; web site www.tennessean.com
Parent Co.: Gannett
Est.: 1812
VP, Finance — Bob Engel;
Gen. Mgr. GPS Production Nashville — Thom Gregory;
Pres./Pub. — Laura Hollingsworth;
Vice Pres., Circ. — Jay Winkler;
Key Accounts Mgr. — Kimberly Hood;
Consumer Exper. Dir. — Lance Williams;
Director of News & Editor — Maria De Varenne;
VP, Sales — John Ward;
Sr. HR Business Partner — Helen Jacobs;
Music Writer — Peter Cooper; Frank Sutherland;
Manager, National/Major Accounts — Sean Lupton;
Consumer Experience Director — David Anesta;
Content Strategist — Duane Gang; Daphne Lowell;
Music Reporter — Juli Thanki; Peter Antone;
Photographer — Shelley Mays;
Director of Sales — Shelley Davis;
Newspapers:Ashland City Times, TN
Cheatham County Money Saver, TN
The Dickson Herald, TN
Dickson Shopper, TN
Fairview Observer, TN
The Hendersonville Star News, TN
Gallatin News Examiner, TN
Robertson County Times, TN
Stewart-Houston Times, TN
Nashville Record, TN
The Sumner County Shopper, TN
Note: The Tennessean is owned by Gannett Co., Inc. which owns more than 90 daily newspapers.

TRIB TOTAL MEDIA, INC. — 503 Martindale St, DI Clark Building, Suite 250, Pittsburgh, PA, 15212-5746, USA; tel (412) 321-6460; web site www.tribtotalmedia.com/
Est.: 1889
Pub. — Richard M. Scaife;
Pres./CEO — Ralph Martin;
Exec. Dir. Sales — William M. Cotter;
Pres/CEO — Jennifer Bertetto ;
CFO — Jennifer Walters; Gary Mazzotta;
Janet Corrinne-Harvey; Lindsay Berdell;
Exec. Dir. Prodn. — Keith Bertetto;
Prodn. Dir. — Shawn Callahan;
Board Chairman — H. Yale Gutnick;
Newspapers:Pittsburgh Tribune-Review, PA
Tribune-Review, PA
Valley News Dispatch, PA
Buttermilk Falls, PA
The Times Express, PA
Murrysville Star, PA
Norwin Star, PA
Penn-Trafford Star, PA
Pine Creek Journal, PA
Plum Advance Leader, PA
Sewickley Herald, PA
South Hills Record, PA
The Dispatch, PA
The Herald, PA
The Jeannette Spirit, PA
The Times-Sun, PA
The Independent-Observer, PA
The Ligonier Echo, PA
The Mount Pleasant Journal, PA
The Signal Item, PA
McKnight Journal, PA
North Journal, PA
Cranberry Journal, PA
Bridgeville Area News, PA
Shaler Journal, PA
Hampton Journal, PA
Penn Hills Progress, PA

TRIBUNE-REVIEW PUBLISHING CO.
— 622 Cabin Hill Dr, Greensburg, PA, 15601-1657, USA; tel (724) 838-5124; fax (724) 834-1151; e-mail info@tribweb.com; web site www. tribLIVE.com
Chrmn./Pres. — Ralph Martin;
Sr. Vice. Pres./CFO — Raymond Hartung;
COO — Nickolas F. Monico;
COO — Trish Hooper; Newspapers:Penn

State New Kensington:Communications Dept, PA
The Daily News (OOB), PA
The Valley Independent (OOB), PA
Valley News Dispatch, PA

TRONC, INC. — 435 N Michigan Ave, Chicago, IL, 60611-4066, USA; tel (312) 222-9100; fax (208) 746-7341; web site www. tribpub.com
Est.: 1892
Executive Chairman — Dr. Patrick Soon-Shiong
Newspapers:Baltimore Messenger-OOB, MD
News-Press, CA
St. Louis/Southern Illinois Labor Tribune, MO
Milton Record-Transcript, MA
Hoy Los Angeles, CA
Hoy Fin de Semana, CA
Dorchester Argus-Citizen, MA
Arbutus Times, MD
Jamaica Plain Citizen, MA
Hyde Park Tribune, MA
South Boston Tribune, MA
Crown Point Star, IL
Los Angeles Times, CA
Chicago Tribune, IL
The Baltimore Sun, MD
Orlando Sentinel, FL
The Morning Call, PA
Daily Press, VA
Hoy LLC, CA
Howard County Times, MD
Jeffersonian, MD
Northeast Booster Reporter-OOB, MD
The Aegis, MD
The Weekender, MD

U

UNITED COMMUNICATIONS CORPORATION — 5800 7th Ave, Kenosha, WI, 53140-4131, USA; tel (262) 657-1000; fax (262) 657-6226; e-mail tschmitz@ ucclocalmedia.com; web site www. ucclocalmedia.com"Parent Co.: United Communications Corporation
Est.: 1969
Chairman/Dir. — Elizabeth Brown;
CEO/President — Lucy Brown Minn;
Chief Operating Officer — Tom Yunt;
Publisher-Kenosha News — Randy Rickman;
CFAO — Tina Schmitz; Newspapers:Zion Benton News, IL
Kenosha News, WI
The Sun Chronicle, MA
Lake Geneva Regional News, WI
Bargaineer, WI
Note: United Commmunications Corp. operates the following dailies: The Kenosha News (WI) and The Sun Chronicle (MA). Weeklies: the (WI) Bargaineer, The Zion Benton News (IL), Lake Geneva Regional News (WI) and the Foxboro (MA) Reporter. UCC also operates two television stations; KEYC-TV/Fox 12 NEYC (MN), WWNY-TV, FOX 28 WNYF and MeTV (NY)

V

VIRGINIA NEWS GROUP — 1602 Village Market Blvd SE, Ste 360, Leesburg, VA, 20175-4721, USA; tel (703) 777-1111; web site www. virginianewsgroup.com
Est.: 1963
Peter W. Arundel;Newspapers:Loudoun Times-Mirror, VA
TimesDigital

W

WEHCO MEDIA, INC. — 115 E Capitol Ave, Little Rock, AR, 72201-3819, USA; tel (501) 378-3400; fax (501) 376-8594; web site www.

wehco.com/
Digital Media Sales Mgr. — Penny Nelson;
President — Lea Nathaniel;
Online Dir. — Matthew Costa; Judy Nethercutt; Newspapers:Arkansas Democrat-Gazette, AR
Northwest Arkansas Newspapers LLC, AR
Banner-News, AR
El Dorado News-Times / Sunday News, AR
The Sentinel-Record, AR
Camden News, AR
Northwest Arkansas Democrat-Gazette, AR
The Fulton Sun, MO
News Tribune, MO
Chattanooga Times Free Press, TN
Texarkana Gazette, AR
La Prensa Libre, AR
The Free Weekly, AR
The Times of Northeast Benton County, AR
The Weekly Vista, AR
Washington County Enterprise-Leader, AR
Westside Eagle Observer, AR
California Democrat, MO
McDonald County Press, MO
The Lake Today OOB, MO

WESTERN NEWS&INFO, INC. — 1748 S Arizona Ave, Yuma, AZ, 85364-5727, USA; tel (928) 783-3311; fax (928) 783-3313; e-mail urnumber1@westernnews.com; web site www. westernnews.com
Est.: 1958
Pres./CEO — Joseph E. Soldwedel;
Sr. Vice Pres. — Blake DeWitt;
Vice Pres./CFO — David Montgomery;
Vice Pres./Dir., HR — D.J. Johnson;
Vice Pres./CEO, Prescott Newspapers Inc. — Kit Atwell; Newspapers:Desert Shopper, CA
Kudos, AZ
Navajo-Hopi Observer, AZ
Palo Verde Valley Times, CA
Quartzsite Times, CA
Smart Shopper, AZ
Camp Verde Bugle, AZ
The Daily Courier, AZ
The Verde Independent, AZ
Prescott Valley Tribune, AZ
Chino Valley Review, AZ
Big Bug News (OOB), AZ
Kingman Daily Miner, AZ
Williams-Grand Canyon News, AZ
The Parker Pioneer, AZ
Today's News-Herald, AZ
Smart Buyer, AZ
Smart Shopper Ash Fork, AZ
Smart Shopper, AZ
River Extra, AZ
Note: Western Newspapers Inc. shares 50% ownership of the Lake Havasu City (AZ) Today's News Herald (mS), and the weekly Parker (AZ) Parker Pioneer (w) with Wick Communicatons.

WICK COMMUNICATIONS — 333 W Wilcox Dr, Ste 302, Sierra Vista, AZ, 85635-1791, USA; tel (520) 458-0200; fax (520) 458-6166; web site www.wickcommunications.com
Est.: 1984
Sec./Treasurer — Robert J. Wick;
Pres. / CEO — Francis Wick;
Dig. Media Mgr. — Alessia Alaimo;
CFO — Ron Parra;
COO — Nickolas Monico; Newspapers:The Wenatchee World, WA
Today's News-Herald, AZ
Frontiersman, AK
Anchorage Press, AK
Arizona Range News, AZ
The Copper Era, AZ
The Daily Territorial, AZ
The Douglas Dispatch, AZ
Eastern Arizona Courier, AZ
Green Valley News & Sahuarita Sn, AZ
Nogales International, AZ
The Parker Pioneer, AZ
San Pedro Valley News-Sun, AZ
Sahuarita Sn, AZ
Wick Communications - Herald/Review, AZ
Sierra Vista Herald - Sunday Bravo Shopper, AZ
Half Moon Bay Review, CA

The Montrose Daily Press, CO
Independent-Enterprise, ID
The Daily Iberian, LA
Sidney Herald, MT
News-Monitor, ND
The Daily News, ND
Williston Daily Herald, ND
Argus Observer, OR
Treasure Valley Reminder, OR
Capital Journal, SD
Reminder Plus, SD
Note: Wick Communications shares 50% ownership of the Lake Havasu City (AZ) Today's News-Herald (mS), and the weekly Parker (AZ) Pioneer with Western Newspapers Inc.

WOMACK PUBLISHING CO. — 30 N Main St, Lynchburg, VA, 24513-0001, USA; tel (434) 432-1654; fax (434) 432-1005; web site www.womackpublishing.com
  Chrmn. — Charles Zan Womack;
  Pres./COO — Diane C. White;
  HR Mgr. — Ron Cox;
  Accounting Mgr. — Jim Glidewell;
  Circ. Mgr. — Shirley Adkins;
  Editorial Dir. — Tim Davis;
  Press Opns. Mgr. — Randy Velvin;
  Newspapers:Altavista Journal, VA
  Brunswick Times-Gazette, VA

Caswell Messenger, NC
Independent Messenger, VA
Lake Gaston Gazette-Observer, NC
The Mebane Enterprise, NC
Montgomery Herald, NC
The News of Orange County, NC
The News Progress, VA
Smith Mountain Eagle, VA
South Hill Enterprise, VA
Star-Tribune, VA
Times-Virginian, VA
The Union Star, VA
Warren Record, NC

WONDERSTATE MEDIA, LLC — 205 N College Ave, Fayetteville, AR, 72701-4238, USA; tel (479) 966-4860; e-mail contact@fayettevilleflyer.com; web site www.fayettevilleflyer.com
  — Dustin Bartholomew;
  — Todd Gill; Co-OwnersNewspapers:The Fayetteville Flyer, AR

WORLDWEST LLC — 609 New Hampshire St, Lawrence, KS, 66044-2243, USA; tel (785) 843-1000; fax (785) 832-7207
  Est.: 1994
  Owner — Dan Simons;
  Cor. Sec. — Ralph D. Gage;

Co-Mgr. — Dolph C. Simons;
General Manager - Steamboat Pilot & Today — Scott Stanford;
Publisher - Craig Daily Press — Bryce Jacobson;
Publisher - Payson Roundup — John Naughton;
COO — Suzanne Schlicht;
Note: WorldWest LLC owns the Payson (AZ) Roundup, Craig (CO) Daily Press, and the Steamboat (CO) Pilot & Today, all weekly publications. The company also owns the Steamboat (CO) Today, and the Craig (CO) Daily Press, both daily publications, and Steamboat TV18, a leased access cable television station.

WWB HOLDINGS, LLC — 50 S 16th St, Philadelphia, PA, 19102-2516, USA; tel (267) 519-4500; e-mail lexie@phillyvoice.com; web site www.phillyvoice.com
  Mng. Dir. — Lexie Norcross;Newspapers:PhillyVoice.com, PA

Y

YELLOWSTONE COMMUNICATIONS —

401 S Main St, Livingston, MT, 59047-3418, USA; tel (406) 222-2000; fax (406) 222-8580; e-mail enterprise@livent.net; web site www.livingstonenterprise.com
  Pres. — John Sullivan;
  Comptroller — Scott Squillace;
  Mktg. Dir. — Jim Durfey; Newspapers:Big Horn County News, MT
  The Big Timber Pioneer, MT
  Carbon County News, MT
  Dillon Tribune, MT
  The Independent Press, MT
  Glendive Ranger-Review, MT
  Judith Basin Press, MT
  Laurel Outlook, MT
  Lewistown News-Argus, MT
  The Livingston Enterprise, MT
  Miles City Star, MT
  The Stillwater County News, MT
  The Terry Tribune, MT
  Park County Super Shopper, MT
  Note: Yellowstone Newspapers owns two daily newspapers, two twice weeklies and seven weekly newspapers. Yellowstone also owns KATL, an AM radio station in Miles City, Montana Best Times, a monthly senior publication and two commerical job and web printing plan

---

CANADIAN NEWSPAPER GROUPS

A

ALTA. NEWSPAPER GROUP, LTD — 504 Seventh St. S. Lethbridge AB, T1J 2H1, Canada; tel (403) 328-4411; fax (403) 328-4536
  Vice Pres./Gen. Mgr. — Bob Carey
  Circ. Dir. — Tony LeBlanc
  Newspapers:The 40-mile County Commentator, AB
  The Lethbridge Herald, AB
  The Southern Sun Times, AB
  Medicine Hat News, AB
  The Sunny South News, AB
  The Taber Times, AB
  Vauxhall Advance, AB
  The Maple Creek News, SK
  Maple Creek & Southwest Advance Times, SK
  The Lethbridge Shopper, AB
  The Medicine Hat Shopper, AB
  The Shaunavon Standard, SK
  Brome County News, QC
  The Record, QC
  Note: Southern Alberta Newspaper Group owns two daily newspapers, four weekly newspapers and three shopper publication.

B

BLACK PRESS GROUP LTD. — #310-5460 152nd St. Surrey BC, V3S 5J9, Canada; tel (604) 575-2744; fax (604) 575-5329; web site www.blackpress.ca
Est.: 1975
  Chair/Founder — David Black
  Pres. and CEO — Rick O'Connor
  Pres., Group Ops — Randy Blair
  VP Finance — Frank Hanson
  Newspapers:100 Mile House Free Press, BC
  Alberni Valley News, BC
  Shuswap Market News, BC
  The Abbotsford News, BC
  The Agassiz-harrison Observer, BC
  Alberni Valley Times, BC
  The Aldergrove Star, BC
  Arrow Lakes News, BC

The Ashcroft-cache Creek Journal, BC
Barriere Star Journal, BC
The Boundary Creek Times, BC
Burns Lakes District News, BC
Caledonia Courier, BC
The Campbell River Mirror, BC
The Castlegar News, BC
The Chilliwack Progress, BC
North Thompson Times, BC
Cloverdale Reporter, BC
Comox Valley Record, BC
Cranbrook Daily Townsman, BC
Eagle Valley News, BC
Golden Star, BC
Goldstream Gazette, BC
The Grand Forks Gazette, BC
The Kimberley Daily Bulletin, BC
Northern Sentinel - Kitimat, BC
Kootenay Advertiser, BC
The Ladysmith Chronicle, BC
The Lake Cowichan Gazette, BC
Lakeshore News, BC
Langley Advance, BC
Langley Times, BC
The Maple Ridge News, BC
Maple Ridge & Pitt Meadow Times, BC
Mission City Record, BC
Monday Magazine, BC
Nanaimo News Bulletin, BC
Nelson Star, BC
North Island Gazette, BC
North Island Midweek, BC
Oak Bay News, BC
Parksville Qualicum Beach News, BC
The Peace Arch News, BC
The Peninsula News Review, BC
Penticton Western News, BC
Quesnel Cariboo Observer, BC
Revelstoke Review, BC
Rossland News, BC
Saanich News, BC
Salmon Arm Observer, BC
Princeton Similkameen Spotlight, BC
The Smithers Interior News, BC
The Sooke News Mirror, BC
Summerland Review, BC
Surrey Now-leader, BC
The Terrace Standard, BC
The Free Press, BC
Tri-city News, BC

Westerly News, BC
Trail Daily Times, BC
Vanderhoof Omineca Express, BC
Victoria News, BC
The Williams Lake Tribune, BC
The Yukon Review, OK
The Bashaw Star, AB
Castor Advance, AB
Eckville Echo, AB
Ponoka News, AB
Red Deer Advocate, AB
Red Deer Express, AB
Rimbey Review, AB
Stettler Independent, AB
Sylvan Lake News, AB
Leduc-wetaskiwin Pipestone Flyer, AB
The Arlington Times, WA
Kent Reporter, WA
Bainbridge Island Review, WA
Bellevue Reporter, WA
Bellingham Business Journal, WA
Bothell/Kenmore Reporter, WA
Bremerton Patriot-OOB, WA
Central Kitsap Reporter, WA
Covington-Maple Valley-Black Diamond Reporter, WA
The Enumclaw Courier-Herald, WA
Federal Way Mirror, WA
Forks Forum, WA
The Islands' Sounder, WA
The Islands' Weekly, WA
Issaquah/Sammamish Reporter, WA
The Journal of the San Juan Islands, WA
Kirkland Reporter, WA
The Marysville Globe, WA
Mercer Island Reporter, WA
Okanogan Valley Gazette-Tribune, WA
Peninsula Daily News, WA
Port Orchard Independent, WA
Redmond Reporter, WA
Renton Reporter, WA
The Sequim Gazette, WA
Snoqualmie Valley Record, WA
South Whidbey Record, WA
Tacoma Daily Index, WA
Tukwila Reporter, WA
Vashon-Maury Island Beachcomber, WA
Veterans' Life-OOB, WA
The Whidbey Examiner, WA
Whidbey News Times, WA

Friday Forward, AB
Honolulu Star-Advertiser, HI
Oahu Publications Inc., HI
The Daily World, WA
The Herald, WA
BOnny Lake Sumner Courier, WA
Boulevard Chinese, BC
Chemainus Valley, BC
Clearwater Times, BC
Coast Mountian News, BC
Cowichan Valley News, BC
Creston Valley Advance, BC
Haida Gwaii Observer, BC
Hawaii Tribune-Herald, HI
Hope Standard, BC
Houston Today, BC
Kaua'i Midweek, HI
Keremeos Review, BC
Kingston Community , WA
Lacombe Express, AB
Lake Country Calendar, WA
Metro HNL, HI
Midweek, HI
North Delta Reporter, BC
North Kitsap Herald, WA
SF Weekly, CA
Street Pulse, HI
Garden ISland, HI
The Northern View, BC
San Francisco Examiner, CA
Vernon Morning Star, BC
West Hawaii Today, HI
Note: In the U.S., Black Press owns Sound Publishing Inc. and Oahu Publications, publishers of the Honolulu Star Advertiser as well as the Akron Beacon Journal and San Francisco Examiner and SF Weekly newspapers.

G

GLACIER MEDIA GROUP — 2188 Yukon Street Vancouver BC, V5Y 3P1, Canada; tel (604) 872-8565; fax (604) 638-2453; e-mail info@glaciermedia.ca; web site www.glaciermedia.ca
Est.: 1999
  Chairman — Sam Grippo

Pres./CEO — Jonathan J.L. Kennedy
Dir. — Bruce W. Aunger
Pres., Comm. Media — Peter Kvarnstrom
CFO — Orest Smysnuik
Newspapers: New Westminster Record, BC
The Northern Horizon, BC
The Westender, BC
Alaska Highway News, BC
Assiniboia Times, SK
Barrhead Leader, AB
Bonnyville Nouvelle, AB
Bowen Island Undercurrent, BC
Bridge River Lillooet News, BC
Burnaby Now, BC
Canora Courier, SK
Carlyle Observer, SK
Carstairs Courier, AB
Coast Reporter, BC
The Deloraine Times And Star, MB
Delta Optimist, BC
The Didsbury Review (OOB), AB
Elk Point Review, AB
Southeast Lifestyles, SK
Estevan Mercury, SK
Flin Flon Reminder, MB
The Humboldt Journal, SK
Innisfail Province, AB
The Kamsack Times, SK
Lac La Biche Post, AB
Melita New Era, MB
North Shore News, BC
Okotoks Western Wheel, AB
Olds Albertan, AB
Pique Newsmagazine, BC
Powell River Peak, BC
Preeceville Progress, SK
The Prince George Citizen, BC
Redvers Optimist (OOB), SK
The Reston Recorder, MB
Richmond News, BC
Rocky Mountain Outlook, AB
Rocky View Weekly, AB
Souris Plaindealer, MB
Squamish Chief, BC
St. Albert Gazette, AB
St. Paul Journal, AB
Sundre Round-up, AB
Battlefords News-optimist, SK
Kipling Citizen, SK
Dawson Creek Mirror, BC
Yorkton News Review, SK
The Outlook, SK
The Tisdale Recorder, SK
Parkland Review, SK
Thompson Citizen/nickel Belt News, MB
Victoria Times Colonist, BC
Tri-city News, BC
The Vancouver Courier, BC
Virden Empire-advance, MB
The Westlock News, AB
Westman Journal, MB
Weyburn Review, SK
Weyburn This Week, SK
The Whistler Question, BC
Yorkton This Week, SK

M

METROLAND MEDIA GROUP LTD. —
3125 Wolfedale Rd. Mississauga ON, L5C
1W1, Canada; tel (905) 281-5656; fax (905)
279-5103; e-mail result@metroland.com; web
site www.metroland.com
  Pres. — Ian Oliver
  Vice Pres. — Kathie Bride
  Sr. Vice Pres. — Tim Whittaker
  Sr. Vice Pres. — Ian McLeod
  Vice Pres. — Ian Proudfoot
  Vice Pres., HR — Brenda Biller
  Vice Pres. — Joe Anderson
  Vice Pres. — Bruce Danford
  Vice Pres. — Ron Lenyk
  Vice Pres. — Ken Nugent
  Vice Pres. — Carol Peddie
  Gordon Paolucci
  Vice President — Kukle Terry
  Ed-In-Chief — Lois Tuffin
  John Willems
  Scott Miller Cressman
  Tracy Magee-Graham

Editor-In-Chief — Haggert Peter
VP, Business Development & Acquisitions —
Terry Kukle
Newspapers: Belleville News, ON
Fort Erie Post, ON
Independent & Free Press, ON
Ajax-pickering News Advertiser, ON
The Alliston Herald, ON
Almaguin News, ON
Ancaster News, ON
Arnprior Chronicle-Guide, ON
Arthur Enterprise News, ON
The Aurora Banner, ON
The Barrie Advance, ON
Beach-Riverdale Mirror, ON
Belleville News Emc, ON
Bloor West Villager, ON
Bracebridge Examiner, ON
Bradford & West Gwillimbury Topic, ON
Brampton Guardian, ON
Brant News, ON
The Brighton Independent, ON
Brock Citizen, ON
The Burlington Post, ON
Caledon Enterprise, ON
Cambridge Times, ON
The Carleton Place-almonte Canadian
Gazette Emc, ON
City Centre Mirror, ON
Clarington This Week, ON
Dundas Star News, ON
Express, ON
The East York Mirror, ON
The Elmira Independent, ON
The Erin Advocate, ON
Etobicoke Guardian, ON
Times Advocate, ON
The Fergus-elora News Express, ON
The Flamborough Review, ON
The Frontenac Gazette, ON
The Georgina Advocate, ON
Glanbrook Gazette, ON
The Gravenhurst Banner, ON
The Grimsby Lincoln News, ON
The Guelph Mercury Tribune, ON
Guelph Tribune, ON
Hamilton Mountain News, ON
The Hamilton Spectator, ON
Huntsville Forester, ON
Innisfil Journal, ON
Kanata Kourier-standard Emc, ON
Kawartha Lakes This Week, ON
Kemptville Advance Emc, ON
Kingston Heritage Emc, ON
Kitchener Post, ON
The Listowel Banner, ON
Manotick News Emc, ON
Markham Economist & Sun, ON
The Mirror, ON
The Milton Canadian Champion, ON
Minto Express, ON
Mississauga News, ON
The Mount Forest Confederate, ON
The Muskokan, ON
Nepean-barrhaven News Emc, ON
New Hamburg Independent, ON
The Newmarket Era-banner, ON
North York Mirror, ON
Northumberland News, ON
Niagara This Week, ON
Oakville Beaver, ON
The Orangeville Banner, ON
Orillia Today, ON
Orleans News Emc, ON
Oshawa-whitby This Week, ON
Ottawa East Emc, ON
Ottawa South Emc, ON
Ottawa West Emc, ON
The Parkdale Villager, ON
Parry Sound Beacon Star, ON
Parry Sound North Star, ON
The Perth Courier Emc, ON
Peterborough This Week, ON
The Port Perry Star, ON
Quinte West Emc, ON
The Renfrew Mercury Emc, ON
The Richmond Hill Liberal, ON
The Grand River Sachem, ON
The Scarborough Mirror, ON
Smiths Falls Record News Emc, ON
South Asian Focus, ON
St. Lawrence News, ON

St. Mary's Journal Argus, ON
St. Thomas/elgin Weekly News, ON
The Stayner Sun, ON
The Stittsville News, ON
Stoney Creek News, ON
Stratford Gazette, ON
Collingwood Connection, ON
Uxbridge Times-journal, ON
Vaughan Citizen, ON
Walkerton Herald-times, ON
Waterloo Chronicle, ON
The Record, ON
West Carleton Review, ON
The Wingham Advance-times, ON
The York Guardian, ON

P

POSTMEDIA NETWORK INC. — 365 Bloor
Street East Toronto ON, M4W 3L4, Canada;
tel (416) 383-2300; e-mail corporateinquiries@
canwest.com; web site www.postmedia.com
Parent Company:
  Postmedia Network Canada Corp.
Est.: 2010
Newspapers: National Post, ON
  The Record-gazette, AB
  The Calgary Sun, AB
  Calgary Herald, AB
  Daily Herald-Tribune, AB
  The Edmonton Sun, AB
  Edmonton Journal, AB
  The Province, BC
  The Vancouver Sun, BC
  The Winnipeg Sun, MB
  The Barrie Examiner, ON
  The Stratford Beacon Herald, ON
  The Chatham Daily News, ON
  The Daily Observer, ON
  The Timmins Daily Press, ON
  Brandtford Expositor, ON
  Intelligencer, ON
  Kenora Daily Miner & News, ON
  The Kingston Whig-Standard, ON
  The London Free Press, ON
  Nugget, ON
  Northumberland Today, ON
  The Ottawa Citizen, ON
  The Ottawa Sun, ON
  Orillia Packet, ON
  The Observer, ON
  The Peterborough Examiner, ON
  The Brockville Recorder and Times, ON
  The Sault Star, ON
  Woodstock Sentinel-Review, ON
  The Simcoe Reformer, ON
  St. Thomas Times-Journal, ON
  Standard-Freeholder, ON
  St. Catharines Standard, ON
  The Sudbury Star, ON
  Owensound Sun Times, ON
  The Toronto Sun, ON
  Welland Tribune, ON
  The Windsor Star, ON
  Montreal Gazette, QC
  The Leader-Post, SK
  Saskatoon StarPhoenix, SK
  Airdrie Echo, AB
  Bow Valley Crag & Canyon, AB
  The Camrose Canadian, AB
  Cochrane Times, AB
  Cold Lake Sun, AB
  Devon Dispatch News, AB
  Drayton Valley Western Review, AB
  Edmonton Examiner, AB
  Edson Leader, AB
  Fairview Post, AB
  Fort McMurray Today, AB
  The Fort Saskatchewan Record, AB
  The Grove Examiner, AB
  Hanna Herald, AB
  The High River Times, AB
  The Hinton Parklander, AB
  Lacombe Globe, AB
  Leduc Representative, AB
  Lloydminster Meridian Booster, AB
  The Nanton News, AB
  Pincher Creek Echo, AB
  Sherwood Park/strathcona County News, AB
  The Stony Plain Reporter, AB

Strathmore Standard, AB
Vulcan Advocate, AB
Wetaskiwin Times, AB
The Whitecourt Star, AB
Vermilion Standard, AB
The Melfort Journal, SK
Nipawin Journal, SK
Northeast Sun, CA
The Daily Graphic, MB
Central Plains Herald Leader, MB
The Interlake Spectator, MB
Morden Times, MB
The Red River Valley Echo, MB
Selkirk Journal, MB
The Stonewall Argus & Teulon Times, MB
The Valley Leader, MB
Winkler Times, MB
Chatham This Week, ON
Clinton News-record, ON
Cochrane Times-post, ON
The County Weekly News, ON
Courier Press, ON
Delhi News-record, ON
Elgin County Market, ON
The Enterprise-bulletin, ON
Age Dispatch Focus, ON
Fort Erie Shopping Times, ON
The Fort Erie Times, ON
The Reporter, ON
Goderich Signal-star, ON
In Port News, ON
The Ingersoll Times, ON
The Kincardine News, ON
Kingston Community News, WA
The Kingsville Reporter, ON
Lake Of The Woods Enterprise, ON
Lake Shore Shopper, ON
Londoner, ON
The Lakeshore News, ON
The Lucknow Sentinel, ON
The Mid-north Monitor, ON
The Mitchell Advocate, ON
Napanee Guide, ON
The News, ON
The Niagara Advance, ON
Northern News, ON
The Northern Times, ON
The Norwich Gazette, ON
Paris Star, ON
Pennysaver, ON
The Petrolia Topic, ON
The Post, ON
Oxford Shopping News/review, ON
Sarnia & Lambton County This Week, ON
Sault Ste. Marie This Week, ON
The Huron Expositor, ON
Shoreline Beacon, ON
Shoreline Week, ON
The Standard, ON
The Strathroy Age Dispatch, ON
Thorold Niagara News, ON
The Tillsonburg News, ON
The Tilbury Times, ON
Timmins Times, ON
Times-reformer, ON
Trentonian, ON
The Weekender, ON
What's Up Muskoka, ON
The Wiarton Echo, ON

Q

QUEBECOR COMMUNICATIONS, INC.
— 999 De Maisonneuve Blvd. W. Ste. 1100
Montreal QC, H3A 3L4, Canada; tel (514)
877-5334; fax (514) 954-3624; e-mail serge.
sasseville@quebecor.com; web site www.
quebecor.com
  Vice Pres. — Tony Ross
  Newspapers: Le Journal De Joliette, QC
  The Observer, ON
  The Edmonton Sun, AB
  The Mitchell Advocate, ON
  The Weekender, ON
  Shoreline Beacon, ON
  The Valley Leader, MB
  Le Pharillon, QC
  Dunnville Chronicle, ON
  Le Saint-laurent Portage, QC
  Le Point, QC

L'avant-poste Gaspesien, QC
The Enterprise-bulletin, ON
Times-reformer, ON
The Barrie Examiner, ON
The Brockville Recorder and Times, ON
The Timmins Daily Press, ON
Northern News, ON
Le Reveil, QC
Le Citoyen De La Vallee De L'or, QC
Niagara Falls Review, ON
The Daily Observer, ON
St. Catherines Shopping News, ON
Pincher Creek Echo, AB
Le Journal Des Pays D'en Haut Le Vallee, QC
Oxford Shopping News/review, ON
Cochrane Times, AB
L'eclaireur-progres/beauce Nouvelles, QC
The Melfort Journal, SK
Le Reveil, QC
Winkler Times, MB
Kingston This Week, ON
Daily Herald-Tribune, AB
The Markdale Standard, ON
The Calgary Sun, AB
The Spirit of Bothwell, ON
Information Du Nord L'annonciation, QC
Plein Jour Sur Manicouagan, QC
Chronicle, ON
The Chatham Daily News, ON
Lloydminster Meridian Booster, AB
The Petrolia Topic, ON
The Huron Expositor, ON
Information Du Nord Mont Tremblant, QC
The Post, ON
The Peterborough Examiner, ON
The Examiner, ON
Information Du Nord Sainte-agathe, QC
Niagara Shopping News, ON
Airdrie Echo, AB
L'echo Du Nord, QC
Le Courrier Du Sud/south Shore Courier, QC
Sarnia This Week, ON
Lindsay Post (OOB), ON
Bow Valley Crag & Canyon, AB
Napanee Guide, ON
West Niagara News, ON
Le Rimouskois, QC
Age Dispatch Focus, ON
St. Catharines Standard, ON
Welland Tribune, ON
Nipawin Journal, SK
The Tillsonburg News, ON
Strathmore Standard, AB
Banff Crag & Canyon OOB* (2013), AB
The Strathroy Age Dispatch, ON
Nugget, ON
Fort Erie Shopping Times, ON
Objectif Plein Jour, QC
Woodstock Sentinel-Review, ON
Morden Times, MB
Meadow Lake Progress, SK
Crowsnest Pass Promoter (OOB), AB
The Kinistino Birch Hills Post Gazette (OOB), SK
Colborne Chronicle, ON
Northumberland Today, ON
Le Journal de Saint-Hubert (OOB), QC
Drayton Valley Western Review, AB
Le Mirabel, QC
Plein Jour De Charlevoix, QC
Owensound Sun Times, ON
Leamington Post, ON
The Interlake Spectator, MB
Peuple De Lotbiniere, QC
Central Plains Herald Leader, MB
Trentonian, ON
Brandtford Expositor, ON
The Kingston Whig-Standard, ON
Selkirk Journal, MB
The Mayerthorpe Freelancer, AB
The Red River Valley Echo, MB
La Sentinelle de Chibougamau, QC
Les Actualites, QC
Le Port Cartois, QC
Paris Star, ON

The Wiarton Echo, ON
Intelligencer, ON
Brossard Eclair, QC
Edmonton Examiner, AB
The Stratford Beacon Herald, ON
The Niagara Advance, ON
Journal Le Peuple, QC
L'information, QC
Fairview Post, AB
Hanna Herald, AB
Edson Leader, AB
The Stonewall Argus & Teulon Times, MB
Clinton News-record, ON
Barry's Bay This Week, ON
Le Journal de Montreal, QC
The Sault Star, ON
The Beausejour Review, MB
The Ingersoll Times, ON
St. Thomas Times-Journal, ON
The Simcoe Reformer, ON
Le Journal de Quebec, QC
The London Free Press, ON
Timmins Times, ON
The Lucknow Sentinel, ON
What's Up Muskoka, ON
L'echo De La Baie, QC
Fort McMurray Today, AB
Le Progres-echo, QC
The Fort Erie Times, ON
Beauce Media, QC
La Voix Gaspesienne, QC
Lac du Bonnet Leader, MB
Delhi News-record, ON
The Winnipeg Sun, MB
Le Peuple Cote-sud, QC
Lake Shore Shopper, ON
Welland Shopping News, ON
Amherstburg Echo (OOB), ON
The Northern Times, ON
The Ottawa Sun, ON
The Reporter, ON
Sault Ste. Marie This Week, ON
Leduc Representative, AB
Standard-freeholder Complimentary, ON
Lacombe Globe, AB

T

THE CHRONICLE HERALD — 2717 Joseph Howe Dr Halifax NS, B3J 2T2, Canada; tel (902) 426-2811; fax (902) 426-1170; e-mail advertising@herald.ca; web site www. thechronicleherald.ca
Parent Company:
The Chronicle Herald Ltd.
Est.: 1875
Pub. — G.W. Dennis
Pub./CEO/Vice Pres. — Sarah Dennis
Dir., Cor. Admin. — Mary Lou Croft
HR Mgr. — Theresa Williams
Purchasing — Ken Jennex
Adv. Mgr., Retail Sales — Paul Jacquart
Mktg. Mgr. — Pam Nauss-Redden
Research Analyst/ROP Specialist — Tracey King
Dir., Dist. and Log. — Jim LaPierre
Dir., News Admin. — Terry O'Neil
Dir., News Content — Dan Leger
Asst. Dir., Design — John Howitt
Asst. Dir., Newsroom — Frank De Palma
Assignment Ed., Day — Brian Ward
Assignment Ed., Night — Eva Hoare
Books Ed. — Christine Soucie
Editorial Page Ed. — Robert Howse
Entertainment Ed. — Greg Guy
Lifestyle Ed. — Margaret MacKay
Director of Sales — Barry Saunders
Vice Pres., Bus. Devel. — Bruce MacCormack
Sales Dir. — Nancy Cook
Mgr., Bus. Devel. — Alex Liot
Ed. — Claire McIlveen
Senior Mktg. Mgr. — Jennifer Punch
VP Operations — Ian Scott

Dir., Mktg. and Prod. Devel. — Shawn Woodford

TORSTAR — One Yonge St. Toronto ON, M5E 1P9, Canada; tel (416) 869-4010; fax (416) 869-4183; e-mail torstar@torstar.ca; web site www.torstar.ca
Chrmn. of the Bd. — Frank Ialobucci
Pres./CEO — Dr. Robert Prichard
Exec. Vice Pres./CFO — David P. Holland
Newspapers: Ajax-pickering News Advertiser, ON
Cowichan Valley Citizen, BC
Creston Valley Advance, BC
Hope Standard, BC
Houston Today, BC
Invermere Valley Echo, BC
Kelowna Capital News, BC
Keremeos Review, BC
Lake Country Calendar, BC
The Morning Star, BC
Ancaster News, ON
Annex Guardian, ON
Arthur Enterprise News, ON
Beach-Riverdale Mirror, ON
Bloor West Villager, ON
Bracebridge Examiner, ON
Brampton Guardian, ON
Brock Citizen, ON
Caledon Enterprise, ON
Cambridge Times, ON
Clarington This Week, ON
Collingwood Connection, ON
Dresden-Bothwell Leader-Spirit (OOB), ON
Dundas Star News, ON
Etobicoke Guardian, ON
Guelph Tribune, ON
Huntsville Forester, ON
Independent & Free Press, ON
Kawartha Lakes This Week, ON
Markham Economist & Sun, ON
Minto Express, ON
New Hamburg Independent, ON
Niagara This Week, ON
North York Mirror, ON
Northumberland News, ON
Oakville Beaver, ON
Orillia Today, ON
Oshawa-whitby This Week, ON
Peterborough This Week, ON
Shopping News, ON
St. Mary's Journal Argus, ON
Stoney Creek News, ON
The Barrie Advance, ON
The Burlington Post, ON
The East York Mirror, ON
The Elmira Independent, ON
The Erin Advocate, ON
The Fergus-elora News Express, ON
The Flamborough Review, ON
The Georgina Advocate, ON
The Gravenhurst Banner, ON
The Grimsby Lincoln News, ON
The Listowel Banner, ON
The Milton Canadian Champion, ON
The Mirror, ON
The Muskokan, ON
The Newmarket Era-banner, ON
The Orangeville Banner, ON
The Port Perry Star, ON
The Richmond Hill Liberal, ON
The Scarborough Mirror, ON
The Stayner Sun, ON
The Wasaga Sun, ON
The Wingham Advance-times, ON
The York Guardian, ON
Times Advocate, ON
Toronto Star, ON
Uxbridge Times-journal, ON
Walkerton Herald-times, ON
Waterloo Chronicle, ON
Note: Torstar owns Metroland Media Group, which owns three daily newspapers.

TRANSCONTINENTAL MEDIA — 1 Place

Ville Marie, Ste. 3315 Montreal ON, H3B 3N2, Canada; tel (514) 954-4000; fax (514) 954-4016; e-mail info@transcontinental.ca; web site www.transcontinental.com
Est.: 1976
Exec. Chrmn. of the Bd. — Remi Marcoux
Pres./CEO — Francois Olivier
CFO — Benoit Huard
Pres., Trancontinental Media Inc. — Natalie Larivi
Vice Pres./Chief Legal Officer/Cor. Sec. — Christine Desaulniers
Vice Pres. Corp. Devel. — Isabelle Marcoux
Sr. Vice Pres., Transcontinental Media Inc./ Newspapaper Grp. — Marc N. Ouellette
Media Relations Dir. — Nessa Brendergast
Newspapers: Amherst Daily News, NS
Broadview Express, SK
Charlesbourg Express, QC
Cites Nouvelles, QC
Courrier-ahuntsic, QC
Courrier-laval, QC
Courrier-sud, QC
Grenfell Sun, SK
Hants Journal, NS
Harbour Breton Coaster, NL
Hebdo Rive Nord, QC
Hebdo Du St. Maurice, QC
Journal L'actuel, QC
L'action, QC
L'artisan, QC
L'avenir De L'erable, QC
L'echo De La Tuque, QC
L'echo De Maskinonge, QC
L'express, QC
L'hebdo Journal, QC
L'hebdo Mekinac/des Chenaux, QC
La Nouvelle, QC
La Petite Nation, QC
La Revue De Gatineau, QC
La Voix Populaire, QC
La Voix Du Sud, QC
Le Courrier Bordeaux/cartierville, QC
Le Lac St. Jean, QC
Northern Pen, NL
Prince Albert Daily Herald, SK
Progres Saint-leonard, QC
Radville Deep South Star, SK
Register, NS
Saint-laurent News, QC
The Advance, NS
The Advertiser, NS
The Advertiser, NL
The Aurora, NL
The Cape Breton Post, NS
The Citizen-record, NS
The Coast Guard, NS
The Compass, NL
The Daily News, NS
The Daily News, NS
The Gander Beacon, NL
The Gulf News, NL
The Labradorian, NL
The Moose Jaw Times-Herald, SK
The News, NS
The Nor'wester, NL
The Packet, NL
The Pilot, NL
The Sackville Tribune-post, NB
The Southern Gazette, NL
The Southwest Booster, SK
The Spectator, NS
The Star, ON
The Telegram, NL
The Vanguard, NS
The Western Star, NL
The Westmount Examiner, QC
Transcontinental Medias, QC
The Digby County Courier, NS
The Chronicle, QC
L'etoile Du Lac, QC
The Oxbow Herald, SK
The Georgian, NL
The Journal Pioneer, PE
Seaway News, ON
The Guardian, PE

PROFESSIONAL, BUSINESS AND SPECIAL SERVICES DAILIES

AGRICULTURAL

AGWEEK(AGRICULTURAL)
375 2nd Ave North, Grand Forks, ND, 58201, Grand Forks; gen tel (800) 477-6572 ext. 1236; web site www.agweek.com
Group:
Forum Communications Co.
Ed. Lisa Gibson
Director Kirsten Stromsodt
Managing Ed. Bianca Bina

THE DELMARVA FARMER(AGRICULTURAL)
7913 Industrial Park Rd, Easton, MD, 21601-8603, Talbot; gen tel 410-822-3965; gen fax 410-822-5068; gen e-mail editorial@americanfarm.com; web site www. americanfarm.com
Established: 1978
Pub. Ralph Hostetter

URNER BARRY'S PRICE-CURRENT
(mon to fri) (Agricultural)
PO Box 389, Toms River, NJ, 08754-0389, Ocean; gen tel (732) 240-5330; gen fax (732) 341-0891; gen e-mail help@urnerbarry.com; web site www.urnerbarry.com
Advertising Rate:
Open inch rate $17.00
Pres. Paul B. Brown

APPAREL

WOMEN'S WEAR DAILY
(mon to fri) (Apparel)
750 3rd Ave Fl 8, New York, NY, 10017-2703, New York; gen tel (212) 630-3800; gen fax (212) 630-4606; adv fax (212) 630-4580; web site www.wwd.com
Circulation: 56,562(pd);
ABC
September 30, 2011
Advertising Rate:
Open inch rate $322.00
Established: 1910
Chrmn./Editorial Dir. Patrick McCarthy
Pres./CEO, Fairchild Fashion Grp. Gina Sanders
Robert Sauerberg
Pub. Christine Guilfoyle
Dale Reich
Ed. in Chief Ed Nardoza
Mng. Ed. Richard Rosen
Mng. Ed., Special Reports Dianne Pogoda
Prodn. Mgr., Distr. Cristina Mojca

ARCHITECTURE

DAILY JOURNAL OF COMMERCE
(mon to fri) (Architecture)
921 SW Washington St Ste 210, Portland, OR, 97205-2810, Multnomah; gen tel (503) 226-1311; adv tel (503) 226-1311; gen fax (503) 226-1315; adv fax (503) 802-7219; ed fax (503) 802-7239; gen e-mail newsroom@djcoregon.com; adv e-mail rynni.henderson@djcoregon.com; ed e-mail stephanie.basalyga@djcoregon.com; web site www.djcoregon.com
Group:

The Dolan Company
Advertising Rate:
Open inch rate $25.00
News services:
AP, RN, TMS.
Established: 1872
Digital Platform - Mobile:
Apple, Android
Ed. Stephanie Basalyga
Publisher/Vice President Rynni Henderson

DAILY JOURNAL OF COMMERCE
(mon to fri) (Architecture)
3445 N. Causeway Blvd. Suite 901, Metairie, LA, 70002, Jefferson; gen tel (504) 834-9292; gen fax (504) 832-3534; gen e-mail mail@ nopg.com; adv e-mail anne.lovas@nopg. com; ed e-mail greg.larose@nopg.com; web site www.djcgulfcoast.com
Advertising Rate:
Email or call for rates
Established: 1922
Gen. Mgr. Anne Lovas
Managing Editor Greg Larose
Pub Lisa Blossman
Asst. Data Ed. Rebecca Naquin
Pub. Mark Singletary

DODGE CONSTRUCTION NEWS CHICAGO
(mon to fri) (Architecture)
130 E Randolph St Fl 14, Chicago, IL, 60601-6207, Cook; gen tel (312) 233-7499; gen fax (312) 233-7486; web site www. mediacourier.net
Advertising Rate:
Open inch rate $34.00
Established: 1946
Ed. Craig Barner

THE DAILY NEWS
(mon to fri) (Architecture)
193 JEFFERSON AVE, MEMPHIS, TN, 38103-2339, Shelby; gen tel (901) 523-1561; adv tel (901) 528-5283; ed tel (901) 523-8501; gen fax (901) 526-5813; adv fax (901) 526-5813; ed fax (901) 526-5813; gen e-mail advertising@memphisdailynews.com; adv e-mail leah@memphisdailynews.com; ed e-mail joverstreet@memphisdailynews.com; web site www.memphisdailynews.com
Group:
The Daily News Publishing Co.
Circulation: 1,000(pd); 2,000(fr);
USPS
September 30, 2017
Advertising Rate:
Open inch rate $13.50 (legal)
News services:
CNS.
Established: 1886
Publisher Eric Barnes
Marketing Director Leah Sansing
Associate Publisher/Exec. Ed. James Overstreet

THE DAILY REPORTER
(mon to fri) (Architecture)
225 E. Michigan St., Suite 300, Milwaukee, WI, 53202, Milwaukee; gen tel (414) 276-0273; ed tel (414) 225-1807; gen fax (414) 276-4416; gen e-mail news@dailyreporter. com; adv e-mail squinn@dailyreporter.com; ed e-mail dshaw@dailyreporter.com; web site www.dailyreporter.com
Group:
BridgeTower Media
Circulation: 3,105(pd)
News services:
AP.
Established: 1897
Digital Platform - Mobile:
Apple, Android, Windows
Digital Platform - Tablet:
Apple iOS, Android, Windows 7

Associate Publisher/Editor Joe Yovino
Advertising Director Susan Quinn
Managing Editor Dan Shaw

TULSA BUSINESS & LEGAL NEWS(ARCHITECTURE)
315 S. Boulder, Tulsa, OK, 74103-4422, Tulsa; gen tel (918) 581-8306; adv tel (918) 581-8525; ed tel (918) 581-8306; gen e-mail news@tulsabusiness.com; adv e-mail legalnews@oklaweeklygroup.com; ed e-mail news@tulsabusiness.com; web site www. tulsabusiness.com
Group:
BH Media Group
Established: 1909
Editor Lesa Jones

BANKING

AMERICAN BANKER
(mon to fri) (Banking)
1 State St Fl 26, New York, NY, 10004-1483, New York; gen tel (212) 803-8200; adv tel (212) 803-8691; ed tel (212) 803-8399; gen fax (212) 843-9600; gen e-mail Liesbeth. Severiens@sourcemedia.com; adv e-mail Liesbeth.Severiens@sourcemedia.com; ed e-mail Dean.Anason@sourcemedia.com; web site www.americanbanker.com
Circulation: 2,373(pd);
AAM
September 30, 2014
Advertising Rate:
$6,280 (1/2P); $3,735 (1/4P); $3,370 (1/8P)
News services:
AP, RN, UPI.
Established: 1835
Digital Platform - Mobile:
Apple, Android, Windows, Blackberry
Digital Platform - Tablet:
Apple iOS
CEO James Malkin
SVP, Conferences John DelMauro
Ed. in Chief Neil Weinberg
Ed.-in-chief Marc Hochstein
Managing Ed. Dean Anason
Contributing Editor Daniel Wolfe
Washington Bureau Chief, Regulation & Reform Rob Blackwell
Deputy Bureau Chief, Regulation & Reform Joe Adler
Editor, Comm. Banking Paul Davis
Deputy Editor, Merger & Acquisitions Robert Barba
Ed., Technology Penny Crosman
Deputy Editor, Bankthink Sarah Todd
Ed., News Alan Kline
Co-Chief, Copy Desk Neil Cassidy
Co-Chief, Copy Desk Mark Sanborne
Senior Art Director Michael Chu
Ed., American Banker Online Christopher Wood
Asst. Ed., American Banker Online Brian Lewis
Asst. Ed., American Banker Online Yong Lim
Managing Ed., American Banker Online Zanub Saeed
Asst. Ed., American Banker Online Gary Siegel
Adv., Northeast Liesbeth Severiens
Adv., Southeast David Cleworth
Adv., Midwest Jeff Dembski
Adv., West Sara Culley
Assoc. Dir. of Classified Sales JoAnne Kao
Mktg. Dir. Jeannie Nguyen
Mktg. Cord. Ashley Tavoularis
Dist. Mgr. Michael Candemeres
Reprints, Circ/Cust. Service Joylyn Yaw
CEO, SourceMedia Douglas Manoni

CFO, SourceMedia Rebecca Knoop
Chief Mktg. & Digital Officer Minna Rhee
EVP & CCO David Longobardi
EVP & Managing Dir., Banking & Capital Markets Karl Elken
EVP & Managing Dir, Professional Services Group Adam Reinebach
SVP, Human Resources/Office Management Ying Wong

BROOKLYN DAILY EAGLE & DAILY BULLETIN
(mon to fri) (Banking)
16 Court St Ste 1208, Brooklyn, NY, 11241-1012, Kings; gen tel (718) 858-2300; gen fax (718) 858-8281; gen e-mail publisher@brooklyneagle.net; web site www. brooklyneagle.net
Advertising Rate:
Open inch rate $24.00
Pub. J.D. Hasty
Adv. Mgr. Patricia Higgins
Adv. Mgr., Legal Daniel Doctorow
Adv. Mgr., Special Projects Ted Cutler
Sam Howe
Mng. Ed. Ron Geberer

DAILY RECORD
(mon to fri) (Banking)
3323 Leavenworth St, Omaha, NE, 68105-1900, Douglas; gen tel (402) 345-1303; gen fax (402) 345-2351; gen e-mail lhenningsen@omahadailyrecord.com; adv e-mail diane@omahadailyrecord.com; ed e-mail lorraine@omahadailyrecord.com; web site www.omahadailyrecord.com
Advertising Rate:
Open inch rate $7.25
News services:
Associated Press, Creators Syndicate, U.S. News Syndicate.
Established: 1886
Publisher Lynda K. Henningsen
Editor Lorraine Boyd
Production Brian Henningsen
Advertising (Classified, Display, Website) Diane Bilek
Legal Editor/Legal Notices Mary Mosher
Legal Notice Judy Boyd
Note:
Bona fide paid circulation in Douglas County in excess of 300 copies, printed in Omaha, NE

INVESTOR'S BUSINESS DAILY
(m-mon to fri) (Banking)
12655 Beatrice St, Los Angeles, CA, 90066-7303, Los Angeles; gen tel (310) 448-6700; adv tel (310) 448-6700; ed tel (310) 448-6373; gen fax (310) 577-7301; adv fax (310) 577-7301; ed fax (310) 577-7350; ed e-mail IBDnews@investors.com; web site www. investors.com
Circulation: 113,547(pd); 5,572(fr);
AAM
December 31, 2015
News services:
AP.
Established: 1984
Vice Pres., Customer Rel. Margo Schuster
Director, Advertising Operations Kathy Murray
Adv. Mgr., Opns. (E. Coast) Janice Janendo
Exec. Ed. Chris Gessel
Mng. Ed. Susan Warfel
Technology Bureau Chief, Silicon Valley Mike Krey
Assoc. Ed. Terry Jones
Graphic Arts Ed. Mary Ann Edwards
New America Ed. Ken Hoover
Mutual Funds/Personal Finance Ed. Doug Rogers
To The Point Ed. Ed Carson
Prodn. Ed. Mark Sharar

Vice Pres., Mktg. Ralph Perrini
Vice Pres., Internet Mktg. Harlan Ratzky
Circ. Vice Pres. Doug Fuller
Ed. Wesley F. Mann
Leaders Ed. Bucky Fox
To The Point Ed. Ken Popovich
Vice Pres./Nat'l Adv. Dir. Terri Chiodo
Asst. Ed. Ken Brown

MIAMI DAILY BUSINESS REVIEW
(mon to fri) (Banking)
PO Box 10589, Miami, FL, 33101-0589,
Miami-Dade; gen tel (305) 377-3721; adv
tel (305) 347-6623; ed tel (305) 347-6694;
gen fax (305) 374-8474; adv fax (305) 347-
6644; ed fax (305) 347-6626; gen e-mail
DailyBusinessReview@alm.com; adv e-mail
ccurbelo@alm.com; ed e-mail dlyons@alm.
com; web site www.dailybusinessreview.com
Group:
ALM Media
Advertising Rate:
Varies: http://www.dailybusinessreview.com/
advertising.jsp;
N/A(Sun)
News services:
AP, Bloomberg, Florida News Service.
Established: 1926
Group Publisher, FL/GA/TX Chris Mobley
Associate Publisher/Chief Financial Officer
Jeff Fried
Director of Advertising Carlos Curbelo
Editor-in-Chief David Lyons
Business Editor Jay Rees
Law Editor Catherine Wilson
Director of Creative Services John Michael
Rindo
Director of Operations & MIS Guillermo
Garcia
Web Administrator John Hernandez
Vice President/Miami-Dade Legal & Court
Relations Sookie Williams
Note:
See Daily Business Review editions in
Broward and Palm Beach, FL.

PALM BEACH DAILY BUSINESS REVIEW
(mon to fri) (Banking)
1 SE 3rd Ave, Suite 900, Miami, FL, 33131-
1700, Miami-Dade; gen tel (305) 377-3721;
adv tel (305) 347-6623; ed tel (305) 347-
6694; gen fax (561) 820-2077; adv fax (305)
347-6644; ed fax (305) 347-6626; gen e-mail
DailyBusinessReview@alm.com; adv e-mail
ccurbelo@alm.com; ed e-mail dlyons@alm.
com; web site www.dailybusinessreview.com
Group:
ALM Media
Advertising Rate:
http://www.dailybusinessreview.com/
advertising.jsp;
N/A(Sun)
News services:
AP, Bloomberg, Florida News Service.
Established: 1979
Group Publisher, FL/GA/TX Chris Mobley
Associate Publisher/Chief Financial Officer
Jeff Fried
Editor-in-Chief David Lyons
Vice President/Broward & Palm Beach
Legals Deborah Mullin
Director of Advertising Carlos Curbelo
Group Subscriptions Manager Annette
Martinez
Web Administrator John Hernandez
Business Editor Jay Rees
Law Editor Cathy Wilson
Director of Client Development Stephanie
Hemmerich
Audience Development Manager Adam
Kaplan
Note:
See Daily Business Reviews editions in
Broward and Miami, FL.

THE DAILY NEWS
(mon to fri) (Banking)
193 JEFFERSON AVE, MEMPHIS, TN,
38103-2339, Shelby; gen tel (901) 523-1561;
adv tel (901) 528-5283; ed tel (901) 523-
8501; gen fax (901) 526-5813; adv fax (901)

526-5813; ed fax (901) 526-5813; gen e-mail
advertising@memphisdailynews.com; adv
e-mail leah@memphisdailynews.com; ed
e-mail joverstreet@memphisdailynews.com;
web site www.memphisdailynews.com
Group:
The Daily News Publishing Co.
Circulation: 1,000(pd); 2,000(fr);
USPS
September 30, 2017
Advertising Rate:
Open inch rate $13.50 (legal)
News services:
CNS.
Established: 1886
Publisher Eric Barnes
Marketing Director Leah Sansing
Associate Publisher/Exec. Ed. James
Overstreet

THE DAILY RECORD
(mon to fri) (Banking)
11 E SARATOGA ST STE 1, BALTIMORE,
MD, 21202-2199, Baltimore City; gen tel
(443) 524-8100; adv tel (443) 524-8100;
ed tel (443) 524-8150; gen fax (410)
752-2894; adv fax (410) 752-2894; ed
fax (410) 752-2894; gen e-mail suzanne.
huettner@thedailyrecord.com; adv e-mail
advertising@thedailyrecord.com; ed e-mail
tbaden@thedailyrecord.com; web site www.
thedailyrecord.com
Group:
The Dolan Company
Circulation: 2,572(pd); 384(fr)
March 31, 2014
Advertising Rate:
Open inch rate $510.00/Day
Established: 1888
Publisher Suzanne Fischer-Huettner
Comptroller Maria Kelly
Audience Dev. Dir. Tracy Bumba
Admin. Asst. Shelby Carter
Ed. Thomas Baden Jr.
Digital Ed. Jason Whong
Legal Ed. Danny Jacobs
Sr. Photographer Maximilian Franz
Special Products Ed. Jessica Gregg
Acc. Mgr. Darice Miller
Acc. Mgr. Terri Thompson
Mktg. and Event Coord. Haley Poling

THE DAILY RECORD
(mon to fri) (Banking)
PO Box 3595, Little Rock, AR, 72203-
3595, Pulaski; gen tel (501) 374-5103; gen
fax (501) 372-3048; gen e-mail bobby@
dailydata.com; adv e-mail jedwards@
dailydata.com; ed e-mail editor@dailydata.
com; web site www.dailyrecord.us
Circulation: 3,210(pd); 25(fr);
USPS
October 4, 2011
Advertising Rate:
Column Inch Rate - $20.00
News services:
NNS, TMS, DRNW, INS.
Established: 1925
Pub. Bill F. Rector
Adv./Mktg. Dir. Jay Edwards
Gen. Mgr. Bobby Burton
Comptroller Robin Hill

THE LEGAL INTELLIGENCER
(mon to fri) (Banking)
1617 John F Kennedy Blvd Ste 1750,
Philadelphia, PA, 19103-1854, Philadelphia;
gen tel (215) 557-2300; adv tel (215) 557-
2359; ed tel (215) 557-2489; gen fax (215)
557-2301; adv fax (215) 557-2301; ed fax
(215) 557-2301; gen e-mail HGREZLAK@
ALM.COM; adv e-mail dchalphin@alm.com;
ed e-mail hgrezlak@alm.com; web site www.
thelegalintelligencer.com
Group:
ALM Media
News services:
AP.
Established: 1843
Publisher Hal Cohen
Associate Publisher Donald Chalphin

Note:
See media kit for market information.

THE RECORD REPORTER
(Mon`Wed`Fri) (Banking)Maricopa; gen tel
(602) 417-9900; gen fax (602) 417-9910; gen
e-mail Diane_Heuel@dailyjournal.com ; adv
e-mail record_reporter@dailyjournal.com; ed
e-mail diane_heuel@dailyjournal.com; web
site www.recordreporter.com
Group:
DAILY JOURNAL CORPORATION
Established: 1914
Digital Platform - Mobile:
Apple, Android, Blackberry
Digital Platform - Tablet:
Apple iOS, Android, Windows 7, Blackberry
Tablet OS
Pub. Diane Heuel
Ed. Christopher Gilfillan
Method of Printing:
Tabloid

TULSA BUSINESS & LEGAL NEWS(BANKING)
315 S. Boulder, Tulsa, OK, 74103-4422,
Tulsa; gen tel (918) 581-8306; adv tel (918)
581-8525; ed tel (918) 581-8306; gen e-mail
news@tulsabusiness.com; adv e-mail
legalnews@oklaweeklygroup.com; ed e-mail
news@tulsabusiness.com; web site www.
tulsabusiness.com
Group:
BH Media Group
Established: 1909
Editor Lesa Jones

BUILDING

DAILY JOURNAL OF COMMERCE
(mon to fri) (Building)
3445 N. Causeway Blvd. Suite 901, Metairie,
LA, 70002, Jefferson; gen tel (504) 834-9292;
gen fax (504) 832-3534; gen e-mail mail@
nopg.com; adv e-mail anne.lovas@nopg.
com; ed e-mail greg.larose@nopg.com; web
site www.djcgulfcoast.com
Advertising Rate:
Email or call for rates
Established: 1922
Gen. Mgr. Anne Lovas
Managing Editor Greg Larose
Pub Lisa Blossman
Asst. Data Ed. Rebecca Naquin
Pub. Mark Singletary

DAILY RECORD
(mon to fri) (Building)
3323 Leavenworth St, Omaha, NE,
68105-1900, Douglas; gen tel (402) 345-
1303; gen fax (402) 345-2351; gen e-mail
lhenningsen@omahadailyrecord.com; adv
e-mail diane@omahadailyrecord.com; ed
e-mail lorraine@omahadailyrecord.com; web
site www.omahadailyrecord.com
Advertising Rate:
Open inch rate $7.25
News services:
Associated Press, Creators Syndicate, U.S.
News Syndicate.
Established: 1886
Publisher Lynda K. Henningsen
Editor Lorraine Boyd
Production Brian Henningsen
Advertising (Classified, Display, Website)
Diane Bilek
Legal Editor/Legal Notices Mary Mosher
Legal Notice Judy Boyd
Note:
Bona fide paid circulation in Douglas County
in excess of 300 copies, printed in Omaha,
NE

TACOMA DAILY INDEX
(mon to fri) (Building)

402 Tacoma Ave S Ste 200, Tacoma, WA,
98402-5400, Pierce; gen tel (253) 627-4853;
adv tel (253) 627-4853; ed tel (253) 627-
4853; gen fax (253) 627-2253; adv fax (253)
627-2253; ed fax (253) 627-2253; gen e-mail
legals@tacomadailyindex.com; adv e-mail
publisher@tacomadailyindex.com; ed e-mail
editor@tacomadailyindex.com; web site
www.tacomadailyindex.com
Group:
Black Press Group Ltd.
Advertising Rate:
Open inch rate $9.65
News services:
American Court & Commercial Printing.
Established: 1890
Pub. Ken Spurrell
Matthews Todd

THE DAILY NEWS
(mon to fri) (Building)
193 JEFFERSON AVE, MEMPHIS, TN,
38103-2339, Shelby; gen tel (901) 523-1561;
adv tel (901) 528-5283; ed tel (901) 523-
8501; gen fax (901) 526-5813; adv fax (901)
526-5813; ed fax (901) 526-5813; gen e-mail
advertising@memphisdailynews.com; adv
e-mail leah@memphisdailynews.com; ed
e-mail joverstreet@memphisdailynews.com;
web site www.memphisdailynews.com
Group:
The Daily News Publishing Co.
Circulation: 1,000(pd); 2,000(fr);
USPS
September 30, 2017
Advertising Rate:
Open inch rate $13.50 (legal)
News services:
CNS.
Established: 1886
Publisher Eric Barnes
Marketing Director Leah Sansing
Associate Publisher/Exec. Ed. James
Overstreet

THE DAILY REPORTER
(mon to fri) (Building)
225 E. Michigan St., Suite 300, Milwaukee,
WI, 53202, Milwaukee; gen tel (414) 276-
0273; ed tel (414) 225-1807; gen fax (414)
276-4416; gen e-mail news@dailyreporter.
com; adv e-mail squinn@dailyreporter.com;
ed e-mail dshaw@dailyreporter.com; web
site www.dailyreporter.com
Group:
BridgeTower Media
Circulation: 3,105(pd)
News services:
AP.
Established: 1897
Digital Platform - Mobile:
Apple, Android, Windows
Digital Platform - Tablet:
Apple iOS, Android, Windows 7
Associate Publisher/Editor Joe Yovino
Advertising Director Susan Quinn
Managing Editor Dan Shaw

THE RECORD REPORTER
(Mon`Wed`Fri) (Building)Maricopa; gen tel
(602) 417-9900; gen fax (602) 417-9910; gen
e-mail Diane_Heuel@dailyjournal.com ; adv
e-mail record_reporter@dailyjournal.com; ed
e-mail diane_heuel@dailyjournal.com; web
site www.recordreporter.com
Group:
DAILY JOURNAL CORPORATION
Established: 1914
Digital Platform - Mobile:
Apple, Android, Blackberry
Digital Platform - Tablet:
Apple iOS, Android, Windows 7, Blackberry
Tablet OS
Pub. Diane Heuel
Ed. Christopher Gilfillan
Method of Printing:
Tabloid

TULSA BUSINESS & LEGAL NEWS(BUILDING)
315 S. Boulder, Tulsa, OK, 74103-4422,

Tulsa; gen tel (918) 581-8306; adv tel (918) 581-8525; ed tel (918) 581-8306; gen e-mail news@tulsabusiness.com; adv e-mail legalnews@oklaweeklygroup.com; ed e-mail news@tulsabusiness.com; web site www.tulsabusiness.com
Group:
BH Media Group
Established: 1909
Editor Lesa Jones

BUSINESS

GREATER BATON ROUGE BUSINESS REPORT(BUSINESS)
PO Box 1949, Baton Rouge, LA, 70821-1949, East Baton Rouge; gen tel (225) 928-1700; gen fax (225) 928-5019; adv fax (225) 926-1329; ed fax (225) 923-3448; ed e-mail editors@businessreport.com; web site www.businessreport.com
Circulation: 2,768(pd); 6,898(fr);
Sworn
October 1, 2013
Established: 1982Nancy Breitenbach

DAILY COMMERCIAL RECORD
(mon to fri) (Business)
706 Main St Bsmt, Dallas, TX, 75202-3699, Dallas; gen tel (214) 741-6366; gen fax (214) 741-6373; gen e-mail dcr@dailycommercialrecord.com; web site www.dailycommercialrecord.com
Advertising Rate:
Open inch rate $14.76
Pub. E. Nuel Cates Jr.
Ed. Emily Cates

DAILY COURT REVIEW
(mon to fri) (Business)
PO Box 1889, Houston, TX, 77251-1889, Harris; gen tel (713) 869-5434; ed tel (713) 869-5434; gen fax (713) 869-8887; ed e-mail editor@dailycourtreview.com; web site www.dailycourtreview.com
Advertising Rate:
Open inch rate $16.80
News services:
RN, National Newspaper Association, Texas Press Association.
Established: 1889
Pub. Tom Morin
Editor Michael Clements

DAILY JOURNAL OF COMMERCE
(mon to fri) (Business)
921 SW Washington St Ste 210, Portland, OR, 97205-2810, Multnomah; gen tel (503) 226-1311; adv tel (503) 226-1311; gen fax (503) 226-1315; adv fax (503) 802-7219; ed fax (503) 802-7239; gen e-mail newsroom@djcoregon.com; adv e-mail rynni.henderson@djcoregon.com; ed e-mail stephanie.basalyga@djcoregon.com; web site www.djcoregon.com
Group:
The Dolan Company
Advertising Rate:
Open inch rate $25.00
News services:
AP, RN, TMS.
Established: 1872
Digital Platform - Mobile:
Apple, Android
Ed. Stephanie Basalyga
Publisher/Vice President Rynni Henderson

DAILY RECORD
(mon to fri) (Business)
3323 Leavenworth St, Omaha, NE, 68105-1900, Douglas; gen tel (402) 345-1303; gen fax (402) 345-2351; gen e-mail lhenningsen@omahadailyrecord.com; adv e-mail diane@omahadailyrecord.com; ed e-mail lorraine@omahadailyrecord.com; web

site www.omahadailyrecord.com
Advertising Rate:
Open inch rate $7.25
News services:
Associated Press, Creators Syndicate, U.S. News Syndicate.
Established: 1886
Publisher Lynda K. Henningsen
Editor Lorraine Boyd
Production Brian Henningsen
Advertising (Classified, Display, Website) Diane Bilek
Legal Editor/Legal Notices Mary Mosher
Legal Notice Judy Boyd
Note:
Bona fide paid circulation in Douglas County in excess of 300 copies, printed in Omaha, NE

DAILY REPORT
(mon to fri) (Business)
190 Pryor St SW, Atlanta, GA, 30303-3607, Fulton; gen tel (404) 521-1227; gen fax (404) 523-5924; gen e-mail fcdr@amlaw.com; web site www.dailyreportonline.com
Advertising Rate:
Open inch rate $1,800.00 (page)
Established: 1890
Office Mgr. Sarah Wagner
Adv. Dir. Mischelle Grant
Assoc. Pub. Ed Bean
Mng. Ed. Jonathan Ringel
Art. Dir. Jason Bennitt
Pub. Wayne Curtis

FINANCE AND COMMERCE
(tues to sat) (Business)
730 2nd Ave S Ste 100, Minneapolis, MN, 55402-5767, Hennepin; gen tel (612) 333-4244; adv tel (612) 584-1545; ed tel (612) 584-1526; gen fax (612) 333-3243; gen e-mail info@finance-commerce.com; web site www.finance-commerce.com
Advertising Rate:
Open inch rate $12.00
News services:
AP.
Established: 1887
Vice Pres./Pub. Steve Jahn
Bus. Mgr. Joann Barquest
Jeanne Reiland
Prodn. Mgr. Nancy Spangler

METROPOLITAN NEWS-ENTERPRISE
(mon to fri) (Business)
210 S Spring St, Los Angeles, CA, 90012-3710, Los Angeles; gen tel (213) 346-0033; gen fax (213) 687-3886; gen e-mail news@metnews.com; web site www.metnews.com
Advertising Rate:
Open inch rate $6.00
News services:
AP.
Established: 90012
Co-Pub. Jo-Ann W. Grace
Co-Pub. Rodger M. Grace
Gen. Mgr. S. John Babigan
Asst. Mgr. Vahn C. Babigan

THE DAILY COMMERCIAL RECORDER
(mon to fri) (Business)
P.O. Box 2171, San Antonio, TX, 78297, Bexar; gen tel (210) 250-2438; gen fax (210) 250-2360; gen e-mail dcr@primetimenewspapers.com; web site www.primetimenewspapers.com
Group:
Hearst Communications, Inc.
Advertising Rate:
Open inch rate $25.00
News services:
ACCN, Creator Syndicates, LAT-WP, National American Press Syndicate, NYT..
General Sales Manager Mickey Urias
Legal Coordinator Cindy Castillo

THE DAILY DEAL
(mon to fri) (Business)
14 Wall St Fl 15, New York, NY, 10005-2139, New York; gen tel (212) 313-9200; adv tel

(212) 313-9264; gen fax (212) 545-8442; ed fax (212) 313-9293; gen e-mail advertising@thedeal.com; ed e-mail epaisley@thedeal.com; ed e-mail rteitelman@thedeal.com; web site www.thedeal.com
Pres./Pub. Kevin Worth
COO Robert Clark
CFO Kurt Streams
Adv. Sr. Mgr. Mike Danforth
Tom Spanos
Dir., Cor. Commun. Martha Brown
Circ. Vice Pres. Jeff Hartford
Circ. Sr. Mgr. Carol Harms
Ed. in Chief Robert Teitelman
Exec. Ed. Yvette Kantrow
Asst. Mng. Ed. Josh Karlen
Asst. Mng. Ed. Frances A. McMorris
Asst. Mng. Ed. Richard Morgan
Asst. Mng. Ed. John E. Morris
Asst. Mng. Ed. Alain Sherter
Asst. Mng. Ed. Robert Walzer
Art/Design Dir. Lawrence R Gendron
Statistics Ed. Anthony Baldo
Dir., Info Techology Adam S. Feinberg
Thomas Groppe

THE DAILY JOURNAL
(mon to fri) (Business)
1114 W 7th Ave Ste 100, Denver, CO, 80204-4455, Denver; gen tel (303) 756-9995; adv tel (303) 584-6737; ed tel (303) 584-6724; gen fax (303) 756-4465; adv fax (303) 584-6717; ed fax (303) 756-4465; web site www.colorado.construction.com
Advertising Rate:
Open inch rate $25.20
Established: 1897Open inch rate $25.20
John
Adv. Dir. John Rhoades
Adv. Mgr. Michael Branigan
Ed. Melissa Leslie
Mark Shaw

THE DAILY LEGAL NEWS
(mon to fri) (Business)
501 Texas St Rm M103, Shreveport, LA, 71101-5403, Caddo; gen tel (318) 222-0213; web site www.dailylegalnews.net
Advertising Rate:
Open inch rate $15.00/wk (3 1/2" x 1"), $25.00/2wk, $35.00/3wk
Pub. Lee Ann Bryce

THE DAILY LEGAL NEWS AND CLEVELAND RECORDER
(tues to sat) (Business)
2935 Prospect Ave E, Cleveland, OH, 44115-2688, Cuyahoga; gen tel (216) 696-3322; gen fax (216) 696-6329; gen e-mail dln@dln.com; adv e-mail ads@dln.com; ed e-mail editor@dln.com; web site www.dln.com
Advertising Rate:
Open inch rate $16.00
News services:
AP, National Newspaper Association, Ohio Newspaper Association.
Established: 1885
Sec./Gen. Counsel John D. Karlovec
Controller Frederick Davis
Richard Karlovec
Mng. Ed. Jeffrey B. Karlovec
editor@dln.com Lisa Cech
Prodn. Mgr. Terry Machovina
Kurt Gutwein

THE DAILY NEWS
(mon to fri) (Business)
193 JEFFERSON AVE, MEMPHIS, TN, 38103-2339, Shelby; gen tel (901) 523-1561; adv tel (901) 528-5283; ed tel (901) 523-8501; gen fax (901) 526-5813; adv fax (901) 526-5813; ed fax (901) 526-5813; gen e-mail advertising@memphisdailynews.com; adv e-mail leah@memphisdailynews.com; ed e-mail joverstreet@memphisdailynews.com; web site www.memphisdailynews.com
Group:
The Daily News Publishing Co.
Circulation: 1,000(pd); 2,000(fr);
USPS

September 30, 2017
Advertising Rate:
Open inch rate $13.50 (legal)
News services:
CNS.
Established: 1886
Publisher Eric Barnes
Marketing Director Leah Sansing
Associate Publisher/Exec. Ed. James Overstreet

THE DAILY RECORD
(mon to fri) (Business)
PO Box 1062, Louisville, KY, 40201-1062, Jefferson; gen tel (502) 583-4471; gen fax (502) 585-5453; gen e-mail janicep@nacms-c.com
Advertising Rate:
Open inch rate $1.20 (legal line)
News services:
National Association of Credit Management.
Established: 40201
Pub. Connie J. Cheak
Mng. Ed. Janice Prichard

THE DAILY RECORD
(mon to fri) (Business)
PO Box 30006, Rochester, NY, 14603-3006, Monroe; gen tel (585) 232-6920; gen fax (585) 232-2740; gen e-mail kevin.momot@nydailyrecord.com; web site www.nydailyrecord.com
Advertising Rate:
Open inch rate $.90 (agency line), $.75 (retail line)
News services:
American Court & Commercial Newspapers, National Newspaper Association.
Established: 14603-3006
Chrmn./CEO James P. Dolan
Vice Pres./Pub. Kevin Momot
CFO Scott Pollei
Tara Buck

THE DAILY RECORD
(mon to fri) (Business)
PO Box 3595, Little Rock, AR, 72203-3595, Pulaski; gen tel (501) 374-5103; gen fax (501) 372-3048; gen e-mail bobby@dailydata.com; adv e-mail jedwards@dailydata.com; ed e-mail editor@dailydata.com; web site www.dailyrecord.us
Circulation: 3,210(pd); 25(fr);
USPS
October 4, 2011
Advertising Rate:
Column Inch Rate - $20.00
News services:
NNS, TMS, DRNW, INS.
Established: 1925
Pub. Bill F. Rector
Adv./Mktg. Dir. Jay Edwards
Gen. Mgr. Bobby Burton
Comptroller Robin Hill

THE DAILY RECORDER
(mon to fri) (Business)
PO Box 1048, Sacramento, CA, 95812-1048, Sacramento; gen tel (916) 444-2355; adv tel (800) 652-1700; gen fax (916) 444-0636; gen e-mail daily_recorder@dailyjournal.com; ed e-mail jt_long@dailyjournal.com; web site www.dailyjournal.com
Advertising Rate:
Open inch rate $26.00
News services:
AP, dj.
Established: 1901
Pres./Pub. Jerry Salzman
Cor. Office Dir. Raymond Chagolla
Personnel Dir. Dorothy Salzman
Ed. Michael Gottlieb
Tom Barragan
Prodn. Designer Houay Keobouth

THE DAILY REPORTER
(mon to fri) (Business)
225 E. Michigan St., Suite 300, Milwaukee, WI, 53202, Milwaukee; gen tel (414) 276-0273; ed tel (414) 225-1807; gen fax (414)

276-4416; gen e-mail news@dailyreporter.com; adv e-mail squinn@dailyreporter.com; ed e-mail dshaw@dailyreporter.com; web site www.dailyreporter.com
Group:
BridgeTower Media
Circulation: 3,105(pd)
News services:
AP.
Established: 1897
Digital Platform - Mobile:
Apple, Android, Windows
Digital Platform - Tablet:
Apple iOS, Android, Windows 7
Associate Publisher/Editor Joe Yovino
Advertising Director Susan Quinn
Managing Editor Dan Shaw

THE DAILY TRANSCRIPT
(m-mon to fri) (Business)
PO Box 85469, San Diego, CA, 92186-5469, San Diego; gen tel (619) 232-4381; adv tel (619) 232-4381; ed tel (619) 232-4381; gen fax (619) 239-5716; adv fax (619) 239-4312; ed fax (619) 236-8126; gen e-mail editor@sddt.com; adv e-mail sales@sddt.com; ed e-mail editor@sddt.com; web site www.sddt.com
Circulation: 6,404(pd)
March 31, 1998
Advertising Rate:
Open inch rate $100.00
News services:
AP, Bloomberg..
Established: 1886
Pub./CEO Robert Loomis
Mgr., HR Patricia Techaira
Dir., Mktg. Christine Tran
Circ. Mgr. Shelley Barry
Adv. Dir., Classified Andrea Lane
Ed. in Chief Joe Guerin
Circ. Mgr. Shelly Barry
Joseph Schmitt
Ed. Joseph Guerin
Exec. Ed. George Chamberlin
Real Estate Ed. Richard Spaulding
Dir., Info Systems Joey Schmitt
Prodn. Mgr. Steve Lovelace
Cathy Krueger

THE JOURNAL RECORD
(mon to fri) (Business)
PO Box 26370, Oklahoma City, OK, 73126-0370, Oklahoma; gen tel (405) 235-3100; adv tel (405) 278-2830; ed tel (405) 278-2850; gen fax (405) 278-6907; ed fax (405) 278-2890; ed e-mail news@journalrecord.com; web site www.journalrecord.com
Group:
GateHouse Media, Inc.
Circulation: 2,800(pd); 69(fr);
VAC
December 31, 2012
Advertising Rate:
Open inch rate $18.62
News services:
AP.
Established: 1903
Bus. Mgr. Terri Vanhooser
Editor and Associate Publisher Ted Streuli
Advertising Director Sarah Barrow

THE LEGAL INTELLIGENCER
(mon to fri) (Business)
1617 John F Kennedy Blvd Ste 1750, Philadelphia, PA, 19103-1854, Philadelphia; gen tel (215) 557-2300; adv tel (215) 557-2359; ed tel (215) 557-2489; gen fax (215) 557-2301; adv fax (215) 557-2301; ed fax (215) 557-2301; gen e-mail HGREZLAK@ALM.COM; adv e-mail dchalphin@alm.com; ed e-mail hgrezlak@alm.com; web site www.thelegalintelligencer.com
Group:
ALM Media
News services:
AP.
Established: 1843
Publisher Hal Cohen
Associate Publisher Donald Chalphin
Note:

See media kit for market information.

THE LOS ANGELES DAILY JOURNAL
(mon to fri) (Business)
915 E 1st St, Los Angeles, CA, 90012-4042, Los Angeles; gen tel (213) 229-5300; gen fax (213) 229-5481; ed fax (213) 229-5462; web site www.dailyjournal.com
Advertising Rate:
Open inch rate $69.16 (page)
News services:
AP, NYT, CNS, McClatchy.
Chrmn. of the Bd. Charles T. Munger
Vice Chrmn. of the Bd. J.P. Guerin
Pub. Gerald Salzman
Adv. Dir. Audrey Miller
Ramond Chagolla
Ed. Martin Berg

THE RECORD REPORTER
(Mon`Wed`Fri) (Business)Maricopa; gen tel (602) 417-9900; gen fax (602) 417-9910; gen e-mail Diane_Heuel@dailyjournal.com ; adv e-mail record_reporter@dailyjournal.com; ed e-mail diane_heuel@dailyjournal.com; web site www.recordreporter.com
Group:
DAILY JOURNAL CORPORATION
Established: 1914
Digital Platform - Mobile:
Apple, Android, Blackberry
Digital Platform - Tablet:
Apple iOS, Android, Windows 7, Blackberry Tablet OS
Pub. Diane Heuel
Ed. Christopher Gilfillan
Method of Printing:
Tabloid

THE ST. LOUIS COUNTIAN
(mon to sat; S) (Business)
319 N 4th St, Saint Louis, MO, 63102-1906, Saint Louis City; gen tel (314) 421-1880; adv tel (314) 421-1880; ed tel (314) 421-1880; gen fax (314) 421-0436; adv fax (314) 421-0436; ed fax (314) 421-0436; adv e-mail carol.prycma@thedailyrecord.com; ed e-mail willc@thedailyrecord.com; web site www.thedailyrecord.com
Advertising Rate:
Open inch rate $6.56
News services:
RN.
Pub. Richard Gard
Bus. Mgr. Amanda Passmore
Adv. Dir. Amy Burdge
Circ. Mgr. Stacey Fish
William B. Connaghan
Prodn. Mgr. John M. Reno

WYOMING BUSINESS REPORT
(Business)Laramie; gen tel (307) 633-3193; gen fax (307) 633-3191; adv e-mail bnelson@wyomingbusinessreport.com; web site www.wyomingbusinessreport.com
Group:
Adams Publishing Group, LLC
Pub. Dir of Sals Belinda Nelson
Controller Dionne Roccaforte

COMMERCE

COMMERCIAL RECORDER
(mon to fri) (Commerce)
PO Box 11038, Fort Worth, TX, 76134, Tarrant; gen tel (817) 255-0779; adv tel (817) 255-0779; ed tel (817) 255-0779; gen fax (817) 926-5377; gen e-mail johnybska@gmail.com; adv e-mail johnybska@gmail.com; ed e-mail johnybska@gmail.com; web site www.commercialrecorder.com
Advertising Rate:
Open inch rate $9.00
Established: 1903
Publisher Janet R. Ratcliff
Editor n Chief

Assoc. Publisher John Bondurant

DAILY RECORD
(mon to fri) (Commerce)
3323 Leavenworth St, Omaha, NE, 68105-1900, Douglas; gen tel (402) 345-1303; gen fax (402) 345-2351; gen e-mail lhenningsen@omahadailyrecord.com; adv e-mail diane@omahadailyrecord.com; ed e-mail lorraine@omahadailyrecord.com; web site www.omahadailyrecord.com
Advertising Rate:
Open inch rate $7.25
News services:
Associated Press, Creators Syndicate, U.S. News Syndicate.
Established: 1886
Publisher Lynda K. Henningsen
Editor Lorraine Boyd
Production Brian Henningsen
Advertising (Classified, Display, Website) Diane Bilek
Legal Editor/Legal Notices Mary Mosher
Legal Notice Judy Boyd
Note:
Bona fide paid circulation in Douglas County in excess of 300 copies, printed in Omaha, NE

DAILY SHIPPING NEWS
(mon to fri) (Commerce)
4106 SE Llewellyn St, Portland, OR, 97222-5870, Clark; gen tel (360) 254-5504; gen fax (360) 254-7145; gen e-mail dsnews@europa.com; web site www.wwshipper.com
Advertising Rate:
Open inch rate $10.00
Established: 98607
Pub. Jim Egger

DETROIT LEGAL NEWS
(mon to fri) (Commerce)
1409 Allen Dr Ste B, Troy, MI, 48083-4003, Oakland; gen tel (248) 577-6100; adv tel (248) 577-6100; ed tel (248) 577-6100; gen fax (248) 577-6111; adv fax (248) 577-6111; ed fax (248) 967-5532; gen e-mail editor@legalnews.com; adv e-mail paul@legalnews.com; ed e-mail editor@legalnews.com; web site www.legalnews.com
Advertising Rate:
Open inch rate $23.00
News services:
AP.
Pub. Susanne Favale
Treasurer Richard J. Swiftney
Adv. Dir. Paul A. Arlon
Circ. Mgr. Christina Jacobs
Brian Cox
Prodn. Mgr., Pre Press Jessica Mosier

THE DAILY NEWS
(mon to fri) (Commerce)
193 JEFFERSON AVE, MEMPHIS, TN, 38103-2339, Shelby; gen tel (901) 523-1561; adv tel (901) 528-5283; ed tel (901) 523-8501; gen fax (901) 526-5813; adv fax (901) 526-5813; ed fax (901) 526-5813; gen e-mail advertising@memphisdailynews.com; adv e-mail leah@memphisdailynews.com; ed e-mail joverstreet@memphisdailynews.com; web site www.memphisdailynews.com
Group:
The Daily News Publishing Co.
Circulation: 1,000(pd); 2,000(fr);
USPS
September 30, 2017
Advertising Rate:
Open inch rate $13.50 (legal)
News services:
CNS.
Established: 1886
Publisher Eric Barnes
Marketing Director Leah Sansing
Associate Publisher/Exec. Ed. James Overstreet

THE DAILY RECORD
(mon to fri) (Commerce)
11 E SARATOGA ST STE 1, BALTIMORE,

MD, 21202-2199, Baltimore City; gen tel (443) 524-8100; adv tel (443) 524-8100; ed tel (443) 524-8150; gen fax (410) 752-2894; adv fax (410) 752-2894; ed fax (410) 752-2894; gen e-mail suzanne.huettner@thedailyrecord.com; adv e-mail advertising@thedailyrecord.com; ed e-mail tbaden@thedailyrecord.com; web site www.thedailyrecord.com
Group:
The Dolan Company
Circulation: 2,572(pd); 384(fr)
March 31, 2014
Advertising Rate:
Open inch rate $510.00/Day
Established: 1888
Publisher Suzanne Fischer-Huettner
Comptroller Maria Kelly
Audience Dev. Dir. Tracy Bumba
Admin. Asst. Shelby Carter
Ed. Thomas Baden Jr.
Digital Ed. Jason Whong
Legal Ed. Danny Jacobs
Sr. Photographer Maximilian Franz
Special Products Ed. Jessica Gregg
Acc. Mgr. Darice Miller
Acc. Mgr. Terri Thompson
Mktg. and Event Coord. Haley Poling

THE DAILY REPORTER
(mon to fri) (Commerce)
580 S High St Ste 316, Columbus, OH, 43215-5659, Franklin; gen tel (614) 224-4835; gen fax (614) 224-8649; gen e-mail editor@sourcenews.com; ed e-mail editor@thedailyreporteronline.com; web site www.thedailyreporteronline.com
Advertising Rate:
Open inch rate $3,880.00 (Page)
News services:
AP.
Established: 1896
Pres. Ed Frederickson
Vice Pres./Pub. Dan Shillingburg
Adv. Mgr., Sales Jeff Zeigler
Editor Cindy Ludlow
Assoc. Ed. Chris Bailey

THE JOURNAL RECORD
(mon to fri) (Commerce)
PO Box 26370, Oklahoma City, OK, 73126-0370, Oklahoma; gen tel (405) 235-3100; adv tel (405) 278-2830; ed tel (405) 278-2850; gen fax (405) 278-6907; ed fax (405) 278-2890; ed e-mail news@journalrecord.com; web site www.journalrecord.com
Group:
GateHouse Media, Inc.
Circulation: 2,800(pd); 69(fr);
VAC
December 31, 2012
Advertising Rate:
Open inch rate $18.62
News services:
AP.
Established: 1903
Bus. Mgr. Terri Vanhooser
Editor and Associate Publisher Ted Streuli
Advertising Director Sarah Barrow

THE RECORD REPORTER
(Mon`Wed`Fri) (Commerce)Maricopa; gen tel (602) 417-9900; gen fax (602) 417-9910; gen e-mail Diane_Heuel@dailyjournal.com ; adv e-mail record_reporter@dailyjournal.com; ed e-mail diane_heuel@dailyjournal.com; web site www.recordreporter.com
Group:
DAILY JOURNAL CORPORATION
Established: 1914
Digital Platform - Mobile:
Apple, Android, Blackberry
Digital Platform - Tablet:
Apple iOS, Android, Windows 7, Blackberry Tablet OS
Pub. Diane Heuel
Ed. Christopher Gilfillan
Method of Printing:
Tabloid

TULSA BUSINESS & LEGAL

NEWS(COMMERCE)
315 S. Boulder, Tulsa, OK, 74103-4422,
Tulsa; gen tel (918) 581-8306; adv tel (918)
581-8525; ed tel (918) 581-8306; gen e-mail
news@tulsabusiness.com; adv e-mail
legalnews@oklaweeklygroup.com; ed e-mail
news@tulsabusiness.com; web site www.
tulsabusiness.com
Group:
BH Media Group
Established: 1909
Editor Lesa Jones

CONSTRUCTION

AMERICAN METAL MARKET
(mon to fri) (Construction)
225 Park Ave S Fl 6, New York, NY, 10003-
1604, New York; gen tel (212) 213-6202; adv
tel (646) 274-6213; ed tel (212) 213-6202;
gen fax (212) 213-1804; adv fax (412) 471-
7203; ed fax (212) 213-6202; gen e-mail
ammnews@amm.com; adv e-mail kross@
amm.com; ed e-mail jisenberg@amm.com;
web site www.amm.com
Advertising Rate:
Open inch rate $36.48 (page)
News services:
RN, AP, PRN, Bridge News, Business Wire..
Established: 1882Raju Daswani
Pricing Dir. Derek Lundquist
Mng. Ed. Jo Isenberg-O'loughlin
Sen. Vice Pres./Ed in Chief David Brooks
Michael Greenlund

DAILY COMMERCIAL NEWS AND CONSTRUCTION RECORD
(mon to fri) (Construction)
500 Hood Rd., 4th Fl., Markham, ON, L3R
9Z3; gen tel (905) 752-9292; gen fax (905)
752-5450; gen e-mail bev.akerfeldt@cmdg.
com; adv e-mail cindy.littler@cmdg.com;
ed e-mail john.leckie@cmdg.com; web site
www.dcnonl.com
Advertising Rate:
Open inch rate $63.00 (Canadian)
Vice Pres./Pub. Andrew Cook
Circ. Mgr. Rod Oyco
Ed. Tarin Elbert
Todd McGill
Adv. Sales Mgr.-Display Elena Langlois

DAILY JOURNAL OF COMMERCE
(mon to fri) (Construction)
921 SW Washington St Ste 210, Portland,
OR, 97205-2810, Multnomah; gen tel (503)
226-1311; adv tel (503) 226-1311; gen
fax (503) 226-1315; adv fax (503) 802-
7219; ed fax (503) 802-7239; gen e-mail
newsroom@djcoregon.com; adv e-mail
rynni.henderson@djcoregon.com; ed e-mail
stephanie.basalyga@djcoregon.com; web
site www.djcoregon.com
Group:
The Dolan Company
Advertising Rate:
Open inch rate $25.00
News services:
AP, RN, TMS.
Established: 1872
Digital Platform - Mobile:
Apple, Android
Ed. Stephanie Basalyga
Publisher/Vice President Rynni Henderson

DAILY JOURNAL OF COMMERCE
(mon to fri) (Construction)
3445 N. Causeway Blvd. Suite 901, Metairie,
LA, 70002, Jefferson; gen tel (504) 834-9292;
gen fax (504) 832-3534; gen e-mail mail@
nopg.com; adv e-mail anne.lovas@nopg.
com; ed e-mail greg.larose@nopg.com; web
site www.djcgulfcoast.com
Advertising Rate:
Email or call for rates
Established: 1922

Gen. Mgr. Anne Lovas
Managing Editor Greg Larose
Pub Lisa Blossman
Asst. Data Ed. Rebecca Naquin
Pub. Mark Singletary

DAILY RECORD
(mon to fri) (Construction)
3323 Leavenworth St, Omaha, NE,
68105-1900, Douglas; gen tel (402) 345-
1303; gen fax (402) 345-2351; gen e-mail
lhenningsen@omahadailyrecord.com; adv
e-mail diane@omahadailyrecord.com; ed
e-mail lorraine@omahadailyrecord.com; web
site www.omahadailyrecord.com
Advertising Rate:
Open inch rate $7.25
News services:
Associated Press, Creators Syndicate, U.S.
News Syndicate.
Established: 1886
Publisher Lynda K. Henningsen
Editor Lorraine Boyd
Production Brian Henningsen
Advertising (Classified, Display, Website)
Diane Bilek
Legal Editor/Legal Notices Mary Mosher
Legal Notice Judy Boyd
Note:
Bona fide paid circulation in Douglas County
in excess of 300 copies, printed in Omaha,
NE

DODGE CONSTRUCTION NEWS CHICAGO
(mon to fri) (Construction)
130 E Randolph St Fl 14, Chicago, IL,
60601-6207, Cook; gen tel (312) 233-7499;
gen fax (312) 233-7486; web site www.
mediacourier.net
Advertising Rate:
Open inch rate $34.00
Established: 1946
Ed. Craig Barner

DODGE CONSTRUCTION NEWS GREENSHEET
(mon to fri) (Construction)
1333 S Mayflower Ave Fl 3, Monrovia, CA,
91016-4066, Los Angeles; gen tel (626) 932-
6161; ed tel (626) 932-6175; gen fax (626)
932-6163; ed fax (626) 932-6163; web site
www.construction.com
Advertising Rate:
Open inch rate $36.90 (display); $25.00
(classified)
Established: 91016
Pub. James McGraw

THE DAILY JOURNAL
(mon to fri) (Construction)
1114 W 7th Ave Ste 100, Denver, CO, 80204-
4455, Denver; gen tel (303) 756-9995; adv
tel (303) 584-6737; ed tel (303) 584-6724;
gen fax (303) 756-4465; adv fax (303) 584-
6717; ed fax (303) 756-4465; web site www.
colorado.construction.com
Advertising Rate:
Open inch rate $25.20
Established: 1897Open inch rate $25.20
John
Adv. Dir. John Rhoades
Adv. Mgr. Michael Branigan
Ed. Melissa Leslie
Mark Shaw

THE DAILY NEWS
(mon to fri) (Construction)
193 JEFFERSON AVE, MEMPHIS, TN,
38103-2399, Shelby; gen tel (901) 523-1561;
adv tel (901) 528-5283; ed tel (901) 523-
8501; gen fax (901) 526-5813; adv fax (901)
526-5813; ed fax (901) 526-5813; gen e-mail
advertising@memphisdailynews.com; adv
e-mail leah@memphisdailynews.com; ed
e-mail joverstreet@memphisdailynews.com;
web site www.memphisdailynews.com
Group:
The Daily News Publishing Co.
Circulation: 1,000(pd); 2,000(fr);
USPS

September 30, 2017
Advertising Rate:
Open inch rate $13.50 (legal)
News services:
CNS.
Established: 1886
Publisher Eric Barnes
Marketing Director Leah Sansing
Associate Publisher/Exec. Ed. James
Overstreet

THE DAILY REPORTER
(mon to fri) (Construction)
225 E. Michigan St., Suite 300, Milwaukee,
WI, 53202, Milwaukee; gen tel (414) 276-
0273; ed tel (414) 225-1807; gen fax (414)
276-4416; gen e-mail news@dailyreporter.
com; adv e-mail squinn@dailyreporter.com;
ed e-mail dshaw@dailyreporter.com; web
site www.dailyreporter.com
Group:
BridgeTower Media
Circulation: 3,105(pd)
News services:
AP.
Established: 1897
Digital Platform - Mobile:
Apple, Android, Windows
Digital Platform - Tablet:
Apple iOS, Android, Windows 7
Associate Publisher/Editor Joe Yovino
Advertising Director Susan Quinn
Managing Editor Dan Shaw

TULSA BUSINESS & LEGAL NEWS(CONSTRUCTION)
315 S. Boulder, Tulsa, OK, 74103-4422,
Tulsa; gen tel (918) 581-8306; adv tel (918)
581-8525; ed tel (918) 581-8306; gen e-mail
news@tulsabusiness.com; adv e-mail
legalnews@oklaweeklygroup.com; ed e-mail
news@tulsabusiness.com; web site www.
tulsabusiness.com
Group:
BH Media Group
Established: 1909
Editor Lesa Jones

COURT

COMMERCIAL RECORDER
(mon to fri) (Court)
PO Box 11038, Fort Worth, TX, 76134,
Tarrant; gen tel (817) 255-0779; adv tel (817)
255-0779; ed tel (817) 255-0779; gen fax
(817) 926-5377; gen e-mail johnybska@
gmail.com; adv e-mail johnybska@gmail.
com; ed e-mail johnybska@gmail.com; web
site www.commercialrecorder.com
Advertising Rate:
Open inch rate $9.00
Established: 1903
Publisher Janet R. Ratcliff
Editor n Chief
Assoc. Publisher John Bondurant

COURT & COMMERCIAL RECORD(COURT)
41 E Washington St Ste 200, Indianapolis,
IN, 46204-3517, Marion; gen tel (317) 363-
5408; adv fax (317) 263-5259; gen e-mail
judy.smith@ibj.com; adv e-mail karuta@ibj.
com; web site www.courtcommercialrecord.
com
Group:
IBJ Media Corporation
Advertising Rate:
Notice of Administration: $82.00, Adoptions:
$132.00, Car Sales: $44.00, Determine
Heirship: $132.00, Dissolution of Corporation:
$52.00, Foundation Report: $72.00,
Guardianship Notice: $132.00, Final Account
or Intermediate Account: $68.00, Name
Change: $132.00, Summons Notice of Suit:
$132.00
Established: 1895

Ed./Pub. Kelly Lucas
Adv. Mgr. Judy Smith
Circulation Manager Bill Wright

DAILY RECORD
(mon to fri) (Court)
3323 Leavenworth St, Omaha, NE,
68105-1900, Douglas; gen tel (402) 345-
1303; gen fax (402) 345-2351; gen e-mail
lhenningsen@omahadailyrecord.com; adv
e-mail diane@omahadailyrecord.com; ed
e-mail lorraine@omahadailyrecord.com; web
site www.omahadailyrecord.com
Advertising Rate:
Open inch rate $7.25
News services:
Associated Press, Creators Syndicate, U.S.
News Syndicate.
Established: 1886
Publisher Lynda K. Henningsen
Editor Lorraine Boyd
Production Brian Henningsen
Advertising (Classified, Display, Website)
Diane Bilek
Legal Editor/Legal Notices Mary Mosher
Legal Notice Judy Boyd
Note:
Bona fide paid circulation in Douglas County
in excess of 300 copies, printed in Omaha,
NE

DETROIT LEGAL NEWS
(mon to fri) (Court)
1409 Allen Dr Ste B, Troy, MI, 48083-4003,
Oakland; gen tel (248) 577-6100; adv tel
(248) 577-6100; ed tel (248) 577-6100; gen
fax (248) 577-6111; adv fax (248) 577-6111;
ed fax (248) 967-5532; gen e-mail editor@
legalnews.com; adv e-mail paul@legalnews.
com; ed e-mail editor@legalnews.com; web
site www.legalnews.com
Advertising Rate:
Open inch rate $23.00
News services:
AP.
Pub. Susanne Favale
Treasurer Richard J. Swiftney
Adv. Dir. Paul A. Arlon
Circ. Mgr. Christina Jacobs
Brian Cox
Prodn. Mgr., Pre Press Jessica Mosier

MISSOURI LAWYERS MEDIA(COURT)
319 N 4th St Fl 5, 5th Floor, Saint Louis,
MO, 63102-1907, Saint Louis City; gen tel
(314) 421-1880; adv tel (314) 558-3260;
ed tel (314) 558-3220; gen fax (314) 621-
1913; adv fax (314) 421-7080; ed fax (314)
621-1913; gen e-mail kathi.cartwright@
molawyersmedia.com; adv e-mail johnny.
aguirre@molawyersmedia.com; ed e-mail
fred.ehrlich@molawyersmedia.com; web site
www.molawyersmedia.com
Group:
GateHouse Media, Inc.
Circulation: 4,500(pd); 10,820(fr)
October 1, 2013
Advertising Rate:
Full Page $2,360.00
Established: 1890
Digital Platform - Mobile:
Apple, Android, Windows
Digital Platform - Tablet:
Apple iOS, Android, Windows 7
Prod. Mgr. John Reno
Pub. Liz Irwin

TACOMA DAILY INDEX
(mon to fri) (Court)
402 Tacoma Ave S Ste 200, Tacoma, WA,
98402-5400, Pierce; gen tel (253) 627-4853;
adv tel (253) 627-4853; ed tel (253) 627-
4853; gen fax (253) 627-2253; adv fax (253)
627-2253; ed fax (253) 627-2253; gen e-mail
legals@tacomadailyindex.com; adv e-mail
publisher@tacomadailyindex.com; ed e-mail
editor@tacomadailyindex.com; web site
www.tacomadailyindex.com
Group:
Black Press Group Ltd.
Advertising Rate:

Open inch rate $9.65
News services:
American Court & Commercial Printing.
Established: 1890
Pub. Ken Spurrell
Matthews Todd

THE DAILY COMMERCIAL RECORDER
(mon to fri) (Court)
P.O. Box 2171, San Antonio, TX, 78297,
Bexar; gen tel (210) 250-2438; gen
fax (210) 250-2360; gen e-mail dcr@
primetimenewspapers.com; web site www.
primetimenewspapers.com
Group:
Hearst Communications, Inc.
Advertising Rate:
Open inch rate $25.00
News services:
ACCN, Creator Syndicates, LAT-WP, National
American Press Syndicate, NYT..
General Sales Manager Mickey Urias
Legal Coordinator Cindy Castillo

THE DAILY EVENTS
(mon to fri) (Court)
PO Box 1, Springfield, MO, 65801-0001,
Greene; gen tel (417) 866-1401; gen fax
(417) 866-1491; gen e-mail info@dailyevents.
com; web site www.thedailyevents.com
News services:
American Court & Commercial Newspapers.
Established: 1881
Editor Wendy Greyowl
Associate Editor Susan Barnes
Court Reporter Andrea Donohue
Circulation Manager Jasmin Adams
Court Reporter Lindsey Wheeler
Publisher Jeff Schrag

THE DAILY LEGAL NEWS
(mon to fri) (Court)
501 Texas St Rm M103, Shreveport, LA,
71101-5403, Caddo; gen tel (318) 222-0213;
web site www.dailylegalnews.net
Advertising Rate:
Open inch rate $15.00/wk (3 1/2" x 1"),
$25.00/2wk, $35.00/3wk
Pub. Lee Ann Bryce

THE DAILY NEWS
(mon to fri) (Court)
193 JEFFERSON AVE, MEMPHIS, TN,
38103-2339, Shelby; gen tel (901) 523-1561;
adv tel (901) 528-5283; ed tel (901) 523-
8501; gen fax (901) 526-5813; adv fax (901)
526-5813; ed fax (901) 526-5813; gen e-mail
advertising@memphisdailynews.com; adv
e-mail leah@memphisdailynews.com; ed
e-mail joverstreet@memphisdailynews.com;
web site www.memphisdailynews.com
Group:
The Daily News Publishing Co.
Circulation: 1,000(pd); 2,000(fr);
USPS
September 30, 2017
Advertising Rate:
Open inch rate $13.50 (legal)
News services:
CNS.
Established: 1886
Publisher Eric Barnes
Marketing Director Leah Sansing
Associate Publisher/Exec. Ed. James
Overstreet

THE DAILY RECORD
(mon to fri) (Court)
PO Box 3595, Little Rock, AR, 72203-
3595, Pulaski; gen tel (501) 374-5103; gen
fax (501) 372-3048; gen e-mail bobby@
dailydata.com; adv e-mail jedwards@
dailydata.com; ed e-mail editor@dailydata.
com; web site www.dailyrecord.us
Circulation: 3,210(pd); 25(fr);
USPS
October 4, 2011
Advertising Rate:
Column Inch Rate - $20.00
News services:

NNS, TMS, DRNW, INS.
Established: 1925
Pub. Bill F. Rector
Adv./Mktg. Dir. Jay Edwards
Gen. Mgr. Bobby Burton
Comptroller Robin Hill

THE DAILY RECORD
(mon to fri) (Court)
PO Box 1062, Louisville, KY, 40201-1062,
Jefferson; gen tel (502) 583-4471; gen
fax (502) 585-5453; gen e-mail janicep@
nacms-c.com
Advertising Rate:
Open inch rate $1.20 (legal line)
News services:
National Association of Credit Management.
Established: 40201
Pub. Connie J. Cheak
Mng. Ed. Janice Prichard

THE DAILY RECORD
(mon to fri) (Court)
11 E SARATOGA ST STE 1, BALTIMORE,
MD, 21202-2199, Baltimore City; gen tel
(443) 524-8100; adv tel (443) 524-8100;
ed tel (443) 524-8100; gen fax (410)
752-2894; adv fax (410) 752-2894; ed
fax (410) 752-2894; gen e-mail suzanne.
huettner@thedailyrecord.com; adv e-mail
advertising@thedailyrecord.com; ed e-mail
tbaden@thedailyrecord.com; web site www.
thedailyrecord.com
Group:
The Dolan Company
Circulation: 2,572(pd); 384(fr)
March 31, 2014
Advertising Rate:
Open inch rate $510.00/Day
Established: 1888
Publisher Suzanne Fischer-Huettner
Comptroller Maria Kelly
Audience Dev. Dir. Tracy Bumba
Admin. Asst. Shelby Carter
Ed. Thomas Baden Jr.
Digital Ed. Jason Whong
Legal Ed. Danny Jacobs
Sr. Photographer Maximilian Franz
Special Products Ed. Jessica Gregg
Acc. Mgr. Darice Miller
Acc. Mgr. Terri Thompson
Mktg. and Event Coord. Haley Poling

THE DAILY REPORTER
(mon to fri) (Court)
580 S High St Ste 316, Columbus, OH,
43215-5659, Franklin; gen tel (614) 224-
4835; gen fax (614) 224-8649; gen e-mail
editor@sourcenews.com; ed e-mail editor@
thedailyreporteronline.com; web site www.
thedailyreporteronline.com
Advertising Rate:
Open inch rate $3,880.00 (Page)
News services:
AP.
Established: 1896
Pres. Ed Frederickson
Vice Pres./Pub. Dan Shillingburg
Adv. Mgr., Sales Jeff Zeigler
Editor Cindy Ludlow
Assoc. Ed. Chris Bailey

THE DAILY REPORTER
(mon to fri) (Court)
225 E. Michigan St., Suite 300, Milwaukee,
WI, 53202, Milwaukee; gen tel (414) 276-
0273; ed tel (414) 225-1807; gen fax (414)
276-4416; gen e-mail news@dailyreporter.
com; adv e-mail squinn@dailyreporter.com;
ed e-mail dshaw@dailyreporter.com; web
site www.dailyreporter.com
Group:
BridgeTower Media
Circulation: 3,105(pd)
News services:
AP.
Established: 1897
Digital Platform - Mobile:
Apple, Android, Windows
Digital Platform - Tablet:
Apple iOS, Android, Windows 7

Associate Publisher/Editor Joe Yovino
Advertising Director Susan Quinn
Managing Editor Dan Shaw

THE DAILY TERRITORIAL
(m-mon to fri) (Court)
2900 E BROADWAY BLVD STE 113,
TUCSON, AZ, 85716-5344, Pima; gen tel
(520) 294-1200; adv tel (520) 294-1200; ed
tel (520) 294-1200; gen fax (520) 294-4040;
adv fax (520) 294-4040; ed fax (520) 295-
4071; gen e-mail editor@azbiz.com; adv
e-mail advertising@azbiz.com; ed e-mail
dhatfield@azbiz.com; web site www.azbiz.
com
Group:
Wick Communications
Circulation: 753(pd);
Sworn
September 30, 2017
Advertising Rate:
Open inch rate $5.45
News services:
American Newspaper Representatives Inc...
Established: 1966
Pub. Thomas Lee
Adv. Dir. Jill A'Hearn
Adv. Mgr., Legal Monica Akyol
Circ. Dir. Laura Horvath
Ed. David Hatfield
Art Dir. Andrew Arthur
Prodn. Mgr. Greg Day

THE LOS ANGELES DAILY JOURNAL
(mon to fri) (Court)
915 E 1st St, Los Angeles, CA, 90012-4042,
Los Angeles; gen tel (213) 229-5300; gen fax
(213) 229-5481; ed fax (213) 229-5462; web
site www.dailyjournal.com
Advertising Rate:
Open inch rate $69.16 (page)
News services:
AP, NYT, CNS, McClatchy.
Chrmn. of the Bd. Charles T. Munger
Vice Chrmn. of the Bd. J.P. Guerin
Pub. Gerald Salzman
Adv. Dir. Audrey Miller
Ramond Chagolla
Ed. Martin Berg

THE RECORD REPORTER
(Mon`Wed`Fri) (Court)Maricopa; gen tel
(602) 417-9900; gen fax (602) 417-9910; gen
e-mail Diane_Heuel@dailyjournal.com ; adv
e-mail record_reporter@dailyjournal.com; ed
e-mail diane_heuel@dailyjournal.com; web
site www.recordreporter.com
Group:
DAILY JOURNAL CORPORATION
Established: 1914
Digital Platform - Mobile:
Apple, Android, Blackberry
Digital Platform - Tablet:
Apple iOS, Android, Windows 7, Blackberry
Tablet OS
Pub. Diane Heuel
Ed. Christopher Gilfillan
Method of Printing:
Tabloid

THE RECORDER
(mon to fri) (Court)
1035 Market St Ste 500, San Francisco,
CA, 94103-1650, San Francisco; gen tel
(415) 749-5400; adv tel (415) 749-5444;
gen fax (415) 749-5449; adv fax (415) 749-
5566; ed fax (415) 749-5549; gen e-mail
recorder_editor@alm.com; web site www.
therecorder.com
Advertising Rate:
Open inch rate $3,200.00 (Full Page Display)
News services:
AP.
Established: 1877
Pub. Chris Braun
Controller Janice Tang
Adv. Mgr., Classified Patrick Vigil
Adv. Mgr., Display Jim Tamietti
Robert Salapuddin
Adv. Coord., Display Heather Ragsdale
Mktg. Dir. John Cosmides

Circ. Mgr. Ed Vergara
Scott Graham
Mng. Ed. George Forcier
Prodn. Mgr./Art Dir. Tess Herrmann

THE ST. LOUIS COUNTIAN
(mon to sat; S) (Court)
319 N 4th St, Saint Louis, MO, 63102-1906,
Saint Louis City; gen tel (314) 421-1880; adv
tel (314) 421-1880; ed tel (314) 421-1880;
gen fax (314) 421-0436; adv fax (314) 421-
0436; ed fax (314) 421-0436; adv e-mail
carol.prycma@thedailyrecord.com; ed e-mail
willc@thedailyrecord.com; web site www.
thedailyrecord.com
Advertising Rate:
Open inch rate $6.56
News services:
RN.
Pub. Richard Gard
Bus. Mgr. Amanda Passmore
Adv. Dir. Amy Burdge
Circ. Mgr. Stacey Fish
William B. Connaghan
Prodn. Mgr. John M. Reno

TOLEDO LEGAL NEWS
(mon to fri) (Court)
PO Box 6816, Toledo, OH, 43612-0816,
Lucas; gen tel (419) 470-8600; gen fax (419)
470-8602; gen e-mail tlnmain@bex.net; web
site www.toledolegalnews.com
Circulation:
December 15, 2017
Advertising Rate:
Open inch rate $12.00
Established: 1894
V.P. Finance Jim Schubargo

TULSA BUSINESS & LEGAL NEWS(COURT)
315 S. Boulder, Tulsa, OK, 74103-4422,
Tulsa; gen tel (918) 581-8306; adv tel (918)
581-8525; ed tel (918) 581-8306; gen e-mail
news@tulsabusiness.com; adv e-mail
legalnews@oklaweeklygroup.com; ed e-mail
news@tulsabusiness.com; web site www.
tulsabusiness.com
Group:
BH Media Group
Established: 1909
Editor Lesa Jones

CREDIT

CHICAGO DAILY LAW BULLETIN
(mon to fri) (Credit)
415 N State St, Chicago, IL, 60654-4674,
Cook; gen tel (312) 644-7800; gen fax (312)
644-4255; gen e-mail displayads@lbpc.com;
web site www.lawbulletin.com
Advertising Rate:
Open inch rate $26.40 (Classified),
$2,588.00 (Full Page Display)
News services:
AP, NYT.
Pres./CEO Brewster Macfarland
Exec. Vice Pres. Neil Breen
James Banich
Consultant Bernie Judge
Adv. Sr. Dir., Sales/Mktg. Mark Menzies
Mng. Ed. Stephen Brown
Fred Faulkner
Adam Music
Patrick Milhizer
Chmn. Sandy Macfarland

DAILY RECORD
(mon to fri) (Credit)
3323 Leavenworth St, Omaha, NE,
68105-1900, Douglas; gen tel (402) 345-
1303; gen fax (402) 345-2351; gen e-mail
lhenningsen@omahadailyrecord.com; adv
e-mail diane@omahadailyrecord.com; ed
e-mail lorraine@omahadailyrecord.com; web

site www.omahadailyrecord.com
Advertising Rate:
Open inch rate $7.25
News services:
Associated Press, Creators Syndicate, U.S.
News Syndicate.
Established: 1886
Publisher Lynda K. Henningsen
Editor Lorraine Boyd
Production Brian Henningsen
Advertising (Classified, Display, Website)
Diane Bilek
Legal Editor/Legal Notices Mary Mosher
Legal Notice Judy Boyd
Note:
Bona fide paid circulation in Douglas County
in excess of 300 copies, printed in Omaha,
NE

THE RECORD REPORTER
(Mon`Wed`Fri) (Credit)Maricopa; gen tel
(602) 417-9900; gen fax (602) 417-9910; gen
e-mail Diane_Heuel@dailyjournal.com ; adv
e-mail record_reporter@dailyjournal.com; ed
e-mail diane_heuel@dailyjournal.com; web
site www.recordreporter.com
Group:
DAILY JOURNAL CORPORATION
Established: 1914
Digital Platform - Mobile:
Apple, Android, Blackberry
Digital Platform - Tablet:
Apple iOS, Android, Windows 7, Blackberry
Tablet OS
Pub. Diane Heuel
Ed. Christopher Gilfillan
Method of Printing:
Tabloid

TULSA BUSINESS & LEGAL NEWS(CREDIT)
315 S. Boulder, Tulsa, OK, 74103-4422,
Tulsa; gen tel (918) 581-8306; adv tel (918)
581-8525; ed tel (918) 581-8306; gen e-mail
news@tulsabusiness.com; adv e-mail
legalnews@oklaweeklygroup.com; ed e-mail
news@tulsabusiness.com; web site www.
tulsabusiness.com
Group:
BH Media Group
Established: 1909
Editor Lesa Jones

ENTERTAINMENT

DAILY VARIETY
(mon to fri) (Entertainment)
5900 Wilshire Blvd Ste 3100, Los Angeles,
CA, 90036-5805, Los Angeles; gen tel (323)
617-9100; adv tel (323) 857-6600; ed tel
(323) 965-4476; adv fax (323) 932-0393; adv
e-mail advertising@variety.com; web site
www.variety.com
Circulation:
N/A
Advertising Rate:
Open inch rate $216.00
News services:
DJ, AP.
Grp. Vice Pres./Pub. Charles C. Koones
CMO, Variety Entertainment Grp. Madelyn
Hammond
Peter Bart
Adv. Dir., West Coast Sales Craig Hitchcock
Dan Hart
Circ. Dir. Christopher Wessel
Circ. Mgr. Joseph Brescia
Grp. Ed. Timothy M. Gray
Ed. Leo Wolinsky
Mng. Ed. Ted Johnson
Assoc. Ed. Phil Gallo
Assoc. Ed., Special Reports Stuart Levine
Asst. Mng. Ed. Kirstin Wilder
Deputy News Ed. Cynthia Littleton
Sr. Ed. Lindsay Chaney
Sr. Ed. Patricia Saperstein

Sr. Ed., Special Reports Steve Chagollan
Sr. Ed., Special Reports Sharon Swart
Michael Schneider

THE HOLLYWOOD REPORTER
(mon to fri) (Entertainment)
5700 Wilshire Blvd Ste 500, Suite 500, Los
Angeles, CA, 90036-3767, Los Angeles;
gen tel (323) 525-2000; adv fax (323) 525-
2372; ed fax (323) 525-2377; web site www.
hollywoodreporter.com
Advertising Rate:
Open inch rate $100.00(fri)(classified)
News services:
AP. Eric Mika
Vice Pres./Assoc. Pub., Sales/Mktg. Rose
Einstein
Audience Mktg. Dir. Katie Fillingame
Ed. Elizabeth Guider
David Morgan
Mng. Ed. Mike Barnes
Vice Pres., Digital Content Scott McKenzie
Film Ed. Gregg Kilday
Steve Brennan
News Ed Erik Pedersen
.Nellie Andreeva

FINANCE

AMERICAN BANKER
(mon to fri) (Finance)
1 State St Fl 26, New York, NY, 10004-1483,
New York; gen tel (212) 803-8200; adv tel
(212) 803-8691; ed tel (212) 803-8399; gen
fax (212) 843-9600; gen e-mail Liesbeth.
Severiens@sourcemedia.com; adv e-mail
Liesbeth.Severiens@sourcemedia.com; ed
e-mail Dean.Anason@sourcemedia.com;
web site www.americanbanker.com
Circulation: 2,373(pd);
AAM
September 30, 2014
Advertising Rate:
$6,280 (1/2P); $3,735 (1/4P); $3,370 (1/8P)
News services:
AP, RN, UPI.
Established: 1835
Digital Platform - Mobile:
Apple, Android, Windows, Blackberry
Digital Platform - Tablet:
Apple iOS
CEO James Malkin
SVP, Conferences John DelMauro
Ed. in Chief Neil Weinberg
Ed.-in-chief Marc Hochstein
Managing Ed. Dean Anason
Contributing Editor Daniel Wolfe
Washington Bureau Chief, Regulation &
Reform Rob Blackwell
Deputy Bureau Chief, Regulation & Reform
Joe Adler
Editor, Comm. Banking Paul Davis
Deputy Editor, Merger & Acquisitions Robert
Barba
Ed., Technology Penny Crosman
Deputy Editor, Bankthink Sarah Todd
Ed., News Alan Kline
Co-Chief, Copy Desk Neil Cassidy
Co-Chief, Copy Desk Mark Sanborne
Senior Art Director Michael Chu
Ed., American Banker Online Christopher
Wood
Asst. Ed., American Banker Online Brian
Lewis
Asst. Ed., American Banker Online Yong Lim
Managing Ed., American Banker Online
Zanub Saeed
Asst. Ed., American Banker Online Gary
Siegel
Adv., Northeast Liesbeth Severiens
Adv., Southeast David Cleworth
Adv., Midwest Jeff Dembski
Adv., West Sara Culley
Assoc. Dir. of Classified Sales JoAnne Kao
Mktg. Dir. Jeannie Nguyen
Mktg. Cord. Ashley Tavoularis
Dist. Mgr. Michael Candemeres

Reprints, Circ/Cust. Service Joylyn Yaw
CEO, SourceMedia Douglas Manoni
CFO, SourceMedia Rebecca Knoop
Chief Mktg. & Digital Officer Minna Rhee
EVP & CCO David Longobardi
EVP & Managing Dir., Banking & Capital
Markets Karl Elken
EVP & Managing Dir, Professional Services
Group Adam Reinebach
SVP, Human Resources/Office Management
Ying Wong

DAILY RECORD
(mon to fri) (Finance)
3323 Leavenworth St, Omaha, NE,
68105-1900, Douglas; gen tel (402) 345-
1303; gen fax (402) 345-2351; gen e-mail
lhenningsen@omahadailyrecord.com; adv
e-mail diane@omahadailyrecord.com; ed
e-mail lorraine@omahadailyrecord.com; web
site www.omahadailyrecord.com
Advertising Rate:
Open inch rate $7.25
News services:
Associated Press, Creators Syndicate, U.S.
News Syndicate.
Established: 1886
Publisher Lynda K. Henningsen
Editor Lorraine Boyd
Production Brian Henningsen
Advertising (Classified, Display, Website)
Diane Bilek
Legal Editor/Legal Notices Mary Mosher
Legal Notice Judy Boyd
Note:
Bona fide paid circulation in Douglas County
in excess of 300 copies, printed in Omaha,
NE

INVESTOR'S BUSINESS DAILY
(m-mon to fri) (Finance)
12655 Beatrice St, Los Angeles, CA, 90066-
7303, Los Angeles; gen tel (310) 448-6700;
adv tel (310) 448-6700; ed tel (310) 448-
6373; gen fax (310) 577-7301; adv fax (310)
577-7301; ed fax (310) 577-7350; ed e-mail
IBDnews@investors.com; web site www.
investors.com
Circulation: 113,547(pd); 5,572(fr);
AAM
December 31, 2015
News services:
AP.
Established: 1984
Vice Pres., Customer Rel. Margo Schuster
Director, Advertising Operations Kathy
Murray
Adv. Mgr., Opns. (E. Coast) Janice Janendo
Exec. Ed. Chris Gessel
Mng. Ed. Susan Warfel
Technology Bureau Chief, Silicon Valley
Mike Krey
Assoc. Ed. Terry Jones
Graphic Arts Ed. Mary Ann Edwards
New America Ed. Ken Hoover
Mutual Funds/Personal Finance Ed. Doug
Rogers
To The Point Ed. Ed Carson
Prodn. Ed. Mark Sharar
Vice Pres., Mktg. Ralph Perrini
Vice Pres., Internet Mktg. Harlan Ratzky
Circ. Vice Pres. Doug Fuller
Ed. Wesley F. Mann
Leaders Ed. Bucky Fox
To The Point Ed. Ken Popovich
Vice Pres./Nat'l Adv. Dir. Terri Chiodo
Asst. Ed. Ken Brown

THE DAILY LEGAL NEWS
(mon to fri) (Finance)
501 Texas St Rm M103, Shreveport, LA,
71101-5403, Caddo; gen tel (318) 222-0213;
web site www.dailylegalnews.net
Advertising Rate:
Open inch rate $15.00/wk (3 1/2" x 1"),
$25.00/2wk, $35.00/3wk
Pub. Lee Ann Bryce

THE DAILY NEWS
(mon to fri) (Finance)

193 JEFFERSON AVE, MEMPHIS, TN,
38103-2339, Shelby; gen tel (901) 523-1561;
adv tel (901) 528-5283; ed tel (901) 523-
8501; gen fax (901) 526-5813; adv fax (901)
526-5813; ed fax (901) 526-5813; gen e-mail
advertising@memphisdailynews.com; adv
e-mail leah@memphisdailynews.com; ed
e-mail joverstreet@memphisdailynews.com;
web site www.memphisdailynews.com
Group:
The Daily News Publishing Co.
Circulation: 1,000(pd); 2,000(fr);
USPS
September 30, 2017
Advertising Rate:
Open inch rate $13.50 (legal)
News services:
CNS.
Established: 1886
Publisher Eric Barnes
Marketing Director Leah Sansing
Associate Publisher/Exec. Ed. James
Overstreet

THE DAILY RECORD
(mon to fri) (Finance)
PO Box 1062, Louisville, KY, 40201-1062,
Jefferson; gen tel (502) 583-4471; gen
fax (502) 585-5453; gen e-mail janicep@
nacms-c.com
Advertising Rate:
Open inch rate $1.20 (legal line)
News services:
National Association of Credit Management.
Established: 40201
Pub. Connie J. Cheak
Mng. Ed. Janice Prichard

THE DAILY RECORD
(mon to fri) (Finance)
PO Box 3595, Little Rock, AR, 72203-
3595, Pulaski; gen tel (501) 374-5103; gen
fax (501) 372-3048; gen e-mail bobby@
dailydata.com; adv e-mail jedwards@
dailydata.com; ed e-mail editor@dailydata.
com; web site www.dailyrecord.us
Circulation: 3,210(pd); 25(fr);
USPS
October 4, 2011
Advertising Rate:
Column Inch Rate - $20.00
News services:
NNS, TMS, DRNW, INS.
Established: 1925
Pub. Bill F. Rector
Adv./Mktg. Dir. Jay Edwards
Gen. Mgr. Bobby Burton
Comptroller Robin Hill

THE LOS ANGELES DAILY JOURNAL
(mon to fri) (Finance)
915 E 1st St, Los Angeles, CA, 90012-4042,
Los Angeles; gen tel (213) 229-5300; gen fax
(213) 229-5481; ed fax (213) 229-5462; web
site www.dailyjournal.com
Advertising Rate:
Open inch rate $69.16 (page)
News services:
AP, NYT, CNS, McClatchy.
Chrmn. of the Bd. Charles T. Munger
Vice Chrmn. of the Bd. J.P. Guerin
Pub. Gerald Salzman
Adv. Dir. Audrey Miller
Ramond Chagolla
Ed. Martin Berg

THE ST. LOUIS COUNTIAN
(mon to sat; S) (Finance)
319 N 4th St, Saint Louis, MO, 63102-1906,
Saint Louis City; gen tel (314) 421-1880; adv
tel (314) 421-1880; ed tel (314) 421-1880;
gen fax (314) 421-0436; adv fax (314) 421-
0436; ed fax (314) 421-0436; adv e-mail
carol.prycma@thedailyrecord.com; ed e-mail
willc@thedailyrecord.com; web site www.
thedailyrecord.com
Advertising Rate:
Open inch rate $6.56
News services:
RN.
Pub. Richard Gard

Bus. Mgr. Amanda Passmore
Adv. Dir. Amy Burdge
Circ. Mgr. Stacey Fish
William B. Connaghan
Prodn. Mgr. John M. Reno

TULSA BUSINESS & LEGAL NEWS(FINANCE)
315 S. Boulder, Tulsa, OK, 74103-4422,
Tulsa; gen tel (918) 581-8306; adv tel (918)
581-8525; ed tel (918) 581-8306; gen e-mail
news@tulsabusiness.com; adv e-mail
legalnews@oklaweeklygroup.com; ed e-mail
news@tulsabusiness.com; web site www.
tulsabusiness.com
Group:
BH Media Group
Established: 1909
Editor Lesa Jones

GOVERNMENT

DAILY JOURNAL OF COMMERCE
(mon to fri) (Government)
3445 N. Causeway Blvd. Suite 901, Metairie,
LA, 70002, Jefferson; gen tel (504) 834-9292;
gen fax (504) 832-3534; gen e-mail mail@
nopg.com; adv e-mail anne.lovas@nopg.
com; ed e-mail greg.larose@nopg.com; web
site www.djcgulfcoast.com
Advertising Rate:
Email or call for rates
Established: 1922
Gen. Mgr. Anne Lovas
Managing Editor Greg Larose
Pub Lisa Blossman
Asst. Data Ed. Rebecca Naquin
Pub. Mark Singletary

DAILY RECORD
(mon to fri) (Government)
3323 Leavenworth St, Omaha, NE,
68105-1900, Douglas; gen tel (402) 345-
1303; gen fax (402) 345-2351; gen e-mail
lhenningsen@omahadailyrecord.com; adv
e-mail diane@omahadailyrecord.com; ed
e-mail lorraine@omahadailyrecord.com; web
site www.omahadailyrecord.com
Advertising Rate:
Open inch rate $7.25
News services:
Associated Press, Creators Syndicate, U.S.
News Syndicate.
Established: 1886
Publisher Lynda K. Henningsen
Editor Lorraine Boyd
Production Brian Henningsen
Advertising (Classified, Display, Website)
Diane Bilek
Legal Editor/Legal Notices Mary Mosher
Legal Notice Judy Boyd
Note:
Bona fide paid circulation in Douglas County
in excess of 300 copies, printed in Omaha,
NE

METROPOLITAN NEWS-ENTERPRISE
(mon to fri) (Government)
210 S Spring St, Los Angeles, CA, 90012-
3710, Los Angeles; gen tel (213) 346-0033;
gen fax (213) 687-3886; gen e-mail news@
metnews.com; web site www.metnews.com
Advertising Rate:
Open inch rate $6.00
News services:
AP.
Established: 90012
Co-Pub. Jo-Ann W. Grace
Co-Pub. Rodger M. Grace
Gen. Mgr. S. John Babigan
Asst. Mgr. Vahn C. Babigan

ROLLCALL
(Daily) (Government)
77 K St NE Fl 8, Suite 100, Washington, DC,

20002-4681, District Of Columbia; gen tel
(202) 650-6500; gen fax (202) 824-0902; web
site www.rollcall.com
Publisher Laurie Battaglia

SAN FRANCISCO DAILY JOURNAL
(mon to fri) (Government)
44 Montgomery St Ste 500, San Francisco,
CA, 94104-4607, San Francisco; gen tel
(415) 296-2400; gen fax (415) 296-2440; web
site www.dailyjournal.com
Advertising Rate:
Open inch rate $754.00 (quarter page)
News services:
AP.
Ed. Linda Hubbell

THE DAILY COMMERCIAL RECORDER
(mon to fri) (Government)
P.O. Box 2171, San Antonio, TX, 78297,
Bexar; gen tel (210) 250-2438; gen
fax (210) 250-2360; gen e-mail dcr@
primetimenewspapers.com; web site www.
primetimenewspapers.com
Group:
Hearst Communications, Inc.
Advertising Rate:
Open inch rate $25.00
News services:
ACCN, Creator Syndicates, LAT-WP, National
American Press Syndicate, NYT..
General Sales Manager Mickey Urias
Legal Coordinator Cindy Castillo

THE DAILY NEWS
(mon to fri) (Government)
193 JEFFERSON AVE, MEMPHIS, TN,
38103-2339, Shelby; gen tel (901) 523-1561;
adv tel (901) 528-5283; ed tel (901) 523-
8501; gen fax (901) 526-5813; adv fax (901)
526-5813; ed fax (901) 526-5813; gen e-mail
advertising@memphisdailynews.com; adv
e-mail leah@memphisdailynews.com; ed
e-mail joverstreet@memphisdailynews.com;
web site www.memphisdailynews.com
Group:
The Daily News Publishing Co.
Circulation: 1,000(pd); 2,000(fr)
USPS
September 30, 2017
Advertising Rate:
Open inch rate $13.50 (legal)
News services:
CNS.
Established: 1886
Publisher Eric Barnes
Marketing Director Leah Sansing
Associate Publisher/Exec. Ed. James
Overstreet

THE DAILY RECORD
(mon to fri) (Government)
11 E SARATOGA ST STE 1, BALTIMORE,
MD, 21202-2199, Baltimore City; gen tel
(443) 524-8100; adv tel (443) 524-8100;
ed tel (443) 524-8150; gen fax (410)
752-2894; adv fax (410) 752-2894; ed
fax (410) 752-2894; gen e-mail suzanne.
huettner@thedailyrecord.com; adv e-mail
advertising@thedailyrecord.com; ed e-mail
tbaden@thedailyrecord.com; web site www.
thedailyrecord.com
Group:
The Dolan Company
Circulation: 2,572(pd); 384(fr)
March 31, 2014
Advertising Rate:
Open inch rate $510.00/Day
Established: 1888
Publisher Suzanne Fischer-Huettner
Comptroller Maria Kelly
Audience Dev. Dir. Tracy Bumba
Admin. Asst. Shelby Carter
Ed. Thomas Baden Jr.
Digital Ed. Jason Whong
Legal Ed. Danny Jacobs
Sr. Photographer Maximilian Franz
Special Products Ed. Jessica Gregg
Acc. Mgr. Darice Miller
Acc. Mgr. Terri Thompson
Mktg. and Event Coord. Haley Poling

THE DAILY RECORDER
(mon to fri) (Government)
PO Box 1048, Sacramento, CA, 95812-1048,
Sacramento; gen tel (916) 444-2355; adv tel
(800) 652-1700; gen fax (916) 444-0636; gen
e-mail daily_recorder@dailyjournal.com; ed
e-mail jt_long@dailyjournal.com; web site
www.dailyjournal.com
Advertising Rate:
Open inch rate $26.00
News services:
AP, dj.
Established: 1901
Pres./Pub. Jerry Salzman
Cor. Office Dir. Raymond Chagolla
Personnel Dir. Dorothy Salzman
Ed. Michael Gottlieb
Tom Barragan
Prodn. Designer Houay Keobouth

THE DAILY REPORTER
(mon to fri) (Government)
225 E. Michigan St., Suite 300, Milwaukee,
WI, 53202, Milwaukee; gen tel (414) 276-
0273; ed tel (414) 225-1807; gen fax (414)
276-4416; gen e-mail news@dailyreporter.
com; adv e-mail squinn@dailyreporter.com;
ed e-mail dshaw@dailyreporter.com; web
site www.dailyreporter.com
Group:
BridgeTower Media
Circulation: 3,105(pd)
News services:
AP.
Established: 1897
Digital Platform - Mobile:
Apple, Android, Windows
Digital Platform - Tablet:
Apple iOS, Android, Windows 7
Associate Publisher/Editor Joe Yovino
Advertising Director Susan Quinn
Managing Editor Dan Shaw

THE JOURNAL RECORD
(mon to fri) (Government)
PO Box 26370, Oklahoma City, OK, 73126-
0370, Oklahoma; gen tel (405) 235-3100; adv
tel (405) 278-2830; ed tel (405) 278-2850;
gen fax (405) 278-6907; ed fax (405) 278-
2890; ed e-mail news@journalrecord.com;
web site www.journalrecord.com
Group:
GateHouse Media, Inc.
Circulation: 2,800(pd); 69(fr);
VAC
December 31, 2012
Advertising Rate:
Open inch rate $18.62
News services:
AP.
Established: 1903
Bus. Mgr. Terri Vanhooser
Editor and Associate Publisher Ted Streuli
Advertising Director Sarah Barrow

LAW

AKRON LEGAL NEWS
(mon to fri) (Law)
60 S Summit St, Akron, OH, 44308-1775,
Summit; gen tel (330) 376-0917; adv tel
(330) 376-0917; gen fax (330) 376-7001;
gen e-mail aln97@apk.net; web site www.
akronlegalnews.com
Advertising Rate:
Open inch rate $11.00
News services:
AP.
Pres./Pub. John L.
Vice Pres./Gen. Mgr. Robert Heffern
Ed. Susan Maybury
Gen. Mngr. Jason Crosten

BAY COUNTY LEGAL NEWS
(thur) (Law)
PO Box 278, Bay City, MI, 48707-0278,

Bay; gen tel (989) 893-6344; adv tel (989)
893-6344; ed tel (989) 893-6344; gen fax
(989) 893-2991; adv fax (989) 893-2991; ed
fax (989) 893-2991; gen e-mail bcdem@
sbcglobal.net; adv e-mail bcdem@sbcglobal.
net; ed e-mail bcdem@sbcglobal.net; web
site www.bclegalnews.com
Circulation: 900(pd)
January 7, 2004
Advertising Rate:
Open inch rate $5.00
Established: 1892
Gen. Mgr. Carol DeVeau

BROOKLYN DAILY EAGLE & DAILY BULLETIN
(mon to fri) (Law)
16 Court St Ste 1208, Brooklyn, NY,
11241-1012, Kings; gen tel (718) 858-
2300; gen fax (718) 858-8281; gen e-mail
publisher@brooklyneagle.net; web site www.
brooklyneagle.net
Advertising Rate:
Open inch rate $24.00
Pub. J.D. Hasty
Adv. Mgr. Patricia Higgins
Adv. Mgr., Legal Daniel Doctorow
Adv. Mgr., Special Projects Ted Cutler
Sam Howe
Mng. Ed. Ron Geberer

CHICAGO DAILY LAW BULLETIN
(mon to fri) (Law)
415 N State St, Chicago, IL, 60654-4674,
Cook; gen tel (312) 644-7800; gen fax (312)
644-4255; gen e-mail displayads@lbpc.com;
web site www.lawbulletin.com
Advertising Rate:
Open inch rate $26.40 (Classified),
$2,588.00 (Full Page Display)
News services:
AP, NYT.
Pres./CEO Brewster Macfarland
Exec. Vice Pres. Neil Breen
James Banich
Consultant Bernie Judge
Adv. Sr. Dir., Sales/Mktg. Mark Menzies
Mng. Ed. Stephen Brown
Fred Faulkner
Adam Music
Patrick Milhizer
Chmn. Sandy Macfarland

CINCINNATI COURT INDEX
(mon to fri) (Law)
119 W Central Pkwy Fl 2, Cincinnati, OH,
45202-1075, Hamilton; gen tel (513) 241-
1450; gen fax (513) 684-7821; gen e-mail
support@courtindex.com; web site www.
courtindex.com
Advertising Rate:
Open inch rate $9.00
News services:
AP.
Ed. Mark Veatty

DAILY COMMERCE
(e-mon to fri) (Law)
PO Box 54026, Los Angeles, CA, 90054-
0026, Los Angeles; gen tel (213) 229-5300;
adv tel (213) 229-5511; ed tel (213) 229-
5558; gen fax (213) 229 5481; adv fax (213)
229 5481; ed fax (213) 229-5462; gen e-mail
audreymiller@dailyjournal.com; web site
www.dailyjournal.com
Circulation: 1,254(pd)
September 24, 1998
Advertising Rate:
Open inch rate $12.00
News services:
AP, LAT-WP, NYT..
Established: 1888
Pub. Gerald L. Salzman
Adv. Rep. Audrey Miller
Circ. Mgr. Ray Chagolla
Ed. Lisa Churchill
Mgmt. Info Servs. Mgr. Ky Tu
Prodn. Mgr. Manuel Azuiler

DAILY COMMERCIAL RECORD
(mon to fri) (Law)
706 Main St Bsmt, Dallas, TX, 75202-3699, Dallas; gen tel (214) 741-6366; gen fax (214) 741-6373; gen e-mail dcr@dailycommercialrecord.com; web site www.dailycommercialrecord.com
Advertising Rate:
Open inch rate $14.76
Pub. E. Nuel Cates Jr.
Ed. Emily Cates

DAILY COURT REPORTER
(mon to fri) (Law)
120 W 2nd St Ste 418, Dayton, OH, 45402-1602, Montgomery; gen tel (419) 470-8602; gen fax (937) 341-5020; gen e-mail info@thedailycourt.com; web site www.dailycourt.com
Circulation:
December 12, 2017
Advertising Rate:
Open inch rate $12.00
News services:
American Court & Commercial Newspapers.
Pres./Pub. Jeffrey Foster
Editorial Mgr. Virginia Steitz

DAILY COURT REVIEW
(mon to fri) (Law)
PO Box 1889, Houston, TX, 77251-1889, Harris; gen tel (713) 869-5434; ed tel (713) 869-5434; gen fax (713) 869-8887; ed e-mail editor@dailycourtreview.com; web site www.dailycourtreview.com
Advertising Rate:
Open inch rate $16.80
News services:
RN, National Newspaper Association, Texas Press Association.
Established: 1889
Pub. Tom Morin
Editor Michael Clements

DAILY JOURNAL OF COMMERCE
(mon to fri) (Law)
921 SW Washington St Ste 210, Portland, OR, 97205-2810, Multnomah; gen tel (503) 226-1311; adv tel (503) 226-1311; gen fax (503) 226-1315; adv fax (503) 802-7219; ed fax (503) 802-7239; gen e-mail newsroom@djcoregon.com; adv e-mail rynni.henderson@djcoregon.com; ed e-mail stephanie.basalyga@djcoregon.com; web site www.djcoregon.com
Group:
The Dolan Company
Advertising Rate:
Open inch rate $25.00
News services:
AP, RN, TMS.
Established: 1872
Digital Platform - Mobile:
Apple, Android
Ed. Stephanie Basalyga
Publisher/Vice President Rynni Henderson

DAILY LEGAL NEWS
(mon to fri) (Law)
100 E Federal St Ste 126, Youngstown, OH, 44503-1834, Mahoning; gen tel (330) 747-7777; gen fax (330) 747-3977; gen e-mail john@akronlegalnews.com; web site www.dlnnews.com
Advertising Rate:
Open inch rate $5.00
Pres. John Burleson
Office Mgr. Kim Pierson
Adv. Dir. Ellen Dellaserra

DAILY RECORD
(mon to fri) (Law)
3323 Leavenworth St, Omaha, NE, 68105-1900, Douglas; gen tel (402) 345-1303; gen fax (402) 345-2351; gen e-mail lhenningsen@omahadailyrecord.com; adv e-mail diane@omahadailyrecord.com; ed e-mail lorraine@omahadailyrecord.com; web site www.omahadailyrecord.com
Advertising Rate:

Open inch rate $7.25
News services:
Associated Press, Creators Syndicate, U.S. News Syndicate.
Established: 1886
Publisher Lynda K. Henningsen
Editor Lorraine Boyd
Production Brian Henningsen
Advertising (Classified, Display, Website) Diane Bilek
Legal Editor/Legal Notices Mary Mosher
Legal Notice Judy Boyd
Note:
Bona fide paid circulation in Douglas County in excess of 300 copies, printed in Omaha, NE

DAILY REPORT
(mon to fri) (Law)
190 Pryor St SW, Atlanta, GA, 30303-3607, Fulton; gen tel (404) 521-1227; gen fax (404) 523-5924; gen e-mail fcdr@amlaw.com; web site www.dailyreportonline.com
Advertising Rate:
Open inch rate $1,800.00 (page)
Established: 1890
Office Mgr. Sarah Wagner
Adv. Dir. Mischelle Grant
Assoc. Pub. Ed Bean
Mng. Ed. Jonathan Ringel
Art. Dir. Jason Bennitt
Pub. Wayne Curtis

FINANCE AND COMMERCE
(tues to sat) (Law)
730 2nd Ave S Ste 100, Minneapolis, MN, 55402-5767, Hennepin; gen tel (612) 333-4244; adv tel (612) 584-1545; ed tel (612) 584-1526; gen fax (612) 333-3243; gen e-mail info@finance-commerce.com; web site www.finance-commerce.com
Advertising Rate:
Open inch rate $12.00
News services:
AP.
Established: 1887
Vice Pres./Pub. Steve Jahn
Bus. Mgr. Joann Barquest
Jeanne Reiland
Prodn. Mgr. Nancy Spangler

FULTON COUNTY DAILY REPORT(LAW)
190 PRYOR ST SW, ATLANTA, GA, 30303-3685, Fulton; gen tel (404) 521-1227; adv tel (404) 419-2870; adv fax (404) 419 - 2819; gen e-mail lsimcoe@alm.com; web site www.dailyreportonline.com
Group:
ALM
Circulation: 2,805(pd); 225(fr);
VAC
December 31, 2016
Digital Platform - Mobile:
Apple, Android, Windows, Blackberry
Editor Ed Bean
Group Publisher Wayne Curtis
Systems Director Scott Pitman
Regional Editor-in-Chief George Haj
Mng. Ed. Jonathan Ringel

GARFIELD COUNTY LEGAL NEWS(LAW)
302 E Maine Ave, Enid, OK, 73701-5746, Garfield; gen tel (580) 234-4739; adv tel (580) 234-4739; ed tel (580) 234-4739; gen fax (580) 237-3237; adv fax (580) 237-3237; ed fax (580) 237-3237; gen e-mail info@garfieldcountylegalnews.com; ed e-mail publisher@garfieldcountylegalnews.com; web site www.garfieldcountylegalnews.com
Advertising Rate:
$50.00 ($0.15 per word) (Notice to Creditors)
Established: 1913

MIAMI DAILY BUSINESS REVIEW
(mon to fri) (Law)
PO Box 10589, Miami, FL, 33101-0589, Miami-Dade; gen tel (305) 377-3721; adv tel (305) 347-6623; ed tel (305) 347-6694; gen fax (305) 374-8474; adv fax (305) 347-6644; ed fax (305) 347-6626; gen e-mail

DailyBusinessReview@alm.com; adv e-mail ccurbelo@alm.com; ed e-mail dlyons@alm.com; web site www.dailybusinessreview.com
Group:
ALM Media
Advertising Rate:
Varies: http://www.dailybusinessreview.com/advertising.jsp;
N/A(Sun)
News services:
AP, Bloomberg, Florida News Service.
Established: 1926
Group Publisher, FL/GA/TX Chris Mobley
Associate Publisher/Chief Financial Officer Jeff Fried
Director of Advertising Carlos Curbelo
Editor-in-Chief David Lyons
Business Editor Jay Rees
Law Editor Catherine Wilson
Director of Creative Services John Michael Rindo
Director of Operations & MIS Guillermo Garcia
Web Adminstrator John Hernandez
Vice President/Miami-Dade Legal & Court Relations Sookie Williams
Note:
See Daily Business Review editions in Broward and Palm Beach, FL.

MISSOURI LAWYERS MEDIA(LAW)
319 N 4th St Fl 5, Saint Louis, MO, 63102-1907, Saint Louis City; gen tel (314) 421-1880; adv tel (314) 558-3260; ed tel (314) 558-3220; gen fax (314) 621-1913; adv fax (314) 421-7080; ed fax (314) 621-1913; gen e-mail kathi.cartwright@molawyersmedia.com; adv e-mail johnny.aguirre@molawyersmedia.com; ed e-mail fred.ehrlich@molawyersmedia.com; web site www.molawyersmedia.com
Group:
GateHouse Media, Inc.
Circulation: 4,500(pd); 10,820(fr)
October 1, 2013
Advertising Rate:
Full Page $2,360.00
Established: 1890
Digital Platform - Mobile:
Apple, Android, Windows
Digital Platform - Tablet:
Apple iOS, Android, Windows 7
Prod. Mgr. John Reno
Pub. Liz Irwin

NEW YORK LAW JOURNAL
(mon to fri) (Law)
120 Broadway Fl 5, New York, NY, 10271-1100, New York; gen tel (212) 457-9400; gen fax (212) 417-7705; gen e-mail cservice@nylj.com; web site www.nylj.com
Advertising Rate:
Open inch rate $99.40
News services:
AP.
Established: 10271
Pres./CEO William L. Pollak
CFO Eric Lundberg
Pub. George Dillehay
Adv. Vice Pres., Nat'l Steve Lincoln
Martha Sturgeon
Circ. Mktg. Mgr. Michael Bennett
Ed. in Chief Rex Bossert

PALM BEACH DAILY BUSINESS REVIEW
(mon to fri) (Law)
1 SE 3rd Ave, Suite 900, Miami, FL, 33131-1700, Miami-Dade; gen tel (305) 377-3721; adv tel (305) 347-6623; ed tel (305) 347-6694; gen fax (561) 820-2077; adv fax (305) 347-6644; ed fax (305) 347-6626; gen e-mail DailyBusinessReview@alm.com; adv e-mail ccurbelo@alm.com; ed e-mail dlyons@alm.com; web site www.dailybusinessreview.com
Group:
ALM Media
Advertising Rate:
http://www.dailybusinessreview.com/advertising.jsp;
N/A(Sun)
News services:

AP, Bloomberg, Florida News Service.
Established: 1979
Group Publisher, FL/GA/TX Chris Mobley
Associate Publisher/Chief Financial Officer Jeff Fried
Editor-in-Chief David Lyons
Vice President/Broward & Palm Beach Legals Deborah Mullin
Director of Advertising Carlos Curbelo
Group Subscriptions Manager Annette Martinez
Web Administrator John Hernandez
Business Editor Jay Rees
Law Editor Cathy Wilson
Director of Client Development Stephanie Hemmerich
Audience Development Manager Adam Kaplan
Note:
See Daily Business Reviews editions in Broward and Miami, FL.

PITTSBURGH LEGAL JOURNAL
(mon to fri) (Law)
436 7th Ave Ste 4, Pittsburgh, PA, 15219-1827, Allegheny; gen tel (412) 402-6623; gen fax (412) 320-7965; gen e-mail JPULICE@SCBA.ORG; web site www.pittsburghlegaljournal.com
Group:
Pennsylvania NewsMedia Association
Advertising Rate:
Open inch rate $8.75
Established: 1853
Exec. Dir. David Blaner

SAINT PAUL LEGAL LEDGER
(mon to thur) (Law)
332 Minnesota St Ste E1432, Saint Paul, MN, 55101-1309, Ramsey; gen tel (651) 222-0059; ed tel (651) 602-0575; gen fax (651) 222-2640; gen e-mail steve.jahn@finance-commerce.com; web site www.legal-ledger.com
Advertising Rate:
Open inch rate $12.00 (legal)
News services:
AP.
Established: 55101-1163
Pub. Patrick Boulay
Bus. Mgr. Barbara St. Martin
Adv. Mgr., Display Jay Kodytek
Bill Wolfe
Prodn. Supvr., Pressroom Mike Wolfe

SAN FRANCISCO DAILY JOURNAL
(mon to fri) (Law)
44 Montgomery St Ste 500, San Francisco, CA, 94104-4607, San Francisco; gen tel (415) 296-2400; gen fax (415) 296-2440; web site www.dailyjournal.com
Advertising Rate:
Open inch rate $754.00 (quarter page)
News services:
AP.
Ed. Linda Hubbell

ST. JOSEPH DAILY COURIER
(mon to fri) (Law)
1020 S 10th St, Saint Joseph, MO, 64503-2407, Buchanan; gen tel (816) 279-3441; gen fax (816) 279-2091; gen e-mail sjdailycourier@sbcglobal.net
Pres./Pub. Bill Cunningham

ST. LOUIS DAILY RECORD
(mon to sat; S) (Law)
PO Box 88910, Saint Louis, MO, 63188-1910, Saint Louis City; gen tel (314) 421-1880; adv tel (314) 421-1880; ed tel (314) 421-1880; gen fax (314) 421-0436; adv fax (314) 421-7080; ed fax (314) 421-0436; gen e-mail editcopy@thedailyrecord.com; adv e-mail johnny.aguirre@molawyersmedia.com; ed e-mail fred.ehrlich@molawyersmedia.com; web site www.molawyers.com
Group:
GateHouse Media, Inc.
Advertising Rate:
Open inch rate $6.56

News services:
RN.
Digital Platform - Mobile:
Apple, Android, Windows
Digital Platform - Tablet:
Apple iOS, Android, Windows 7
Bus. Mgr. Amanda Passmore
Prodn. Mgr. John M. Reno

THE DAILY COMMERCIAL RECORDER
(mon to fri) (Law)
P.O. Box 2171, San Antonio, TX, 78297,
Bexar; gen tel (210) 250-2438; gen
fax (210) 250-2360; gen e-mail dcr@
primetimenewspapers.com; web site www.
primetimenewspapers.com
Group:
Hearst Communications, Inc.
Advertising Rate:
Open inch rate $25.00
News services:
ACCN, Creator Syndicates, LAT-WP, National
American Press Syndicate, NYT..
General Sales Manager Mickey Urias
Legal Coordinator Cindy Castillo

THE DAILY EVENTS
(mon to fri) (Law)
PO Box 1, Springfield, MO, 65801-0001,
Greene; gen tel (417) 866-1401; gen fax
(417) 866-1491; gen e-mail info@dailyevents.
com; web site www.thedailyevents.com
News services:
American Court & Commercial Newspapers.
Established: 1881
Editor Wendy Greyowl
Associate Editor Susan Barnes
Court Reporter Andrea Donohue
Circulation Manager Jasmin Adams
Court Reporter Lindsey Wheeler
Publisher Jeff Schrag

THE DAILY JOURNAL
(mon to fri) (Law)
1114 W 7th Ave Ste 100, Denver, CO, 80204-
4455, Denver; gen tel (303) 756-9995; adv
tel (303) 584-6737; ed tel (303) 584-6724;
gen fax (303) 756-4465; adv fax (303) 584-
6717; ed fax (303) 756-4465; web site www.
colorado.construction.com
Advertising Rate:
Open inch rate $25.20
Established: 1897Open inch rate $25.20
John
Adv. Dir. John Rhoades
Adv. Mgr. Michael Branigan
Ed. Melissa Leslie
Mark Shaw

THE DAILY LEGAL NEWS
(mon to fri) (Law)
501 Texas St Rm M103, Shreveport, LA,
71101-5403, Caddo; gen tel (318) 222-0213;
web site www.dailylegalnews.net
Advertising Rate:
Open inch rate $15.00/wk (3 1/2" x 1"),
$25.00/2wk, $35.00/3wk
Pub. Lee Ann Bryce

THE DAILY LEGAL NEWS AND CLEVELAND RECORDER
(tues to sat) (Law)
2935 Prospect Ave E, Cleveland, OH, 44115-
2688, Cuyahoga; gen tel (216) 696-3322; gen
fax (216) 696-6329; gen e-mail dln@dln.com;
adv e-mail ads@dln.com; ed e-mail editor@
dln.com; web site www.dln.com
Advertising Rate:
Open inch rate $16.00
News services:
AP, National Newspaper Association, Ohio
Newspaper Association.
Established: 1885
Sec./Gen. Counsel John D. Karlovec
Controller Frederick Davis
Richard Karlovec
Mng. Ed. Jeffrey B. Karlovec
editor@dln.com Lisa Cech
Prodn. Mgr. Terry Machovina
Kurt Gutwein

THE DAILY NEWS
(mon to fri) (Law)
193 JEFFERSON AVE, MEMPHIS, TN,
38103-2339, Shelby; gen tel (901) 523-1561;
adv tel (901) 528-5283; ed tel (901) 523-
8501; gen fax (901) 526-5813; adv fax (901)
526-5813; ed fax (901) 526-5813; gen e-mail
advertising@memphisdailynews.com; adv
e-mail leah@memphisdailynews.com; ed
e-mail joverstreet@memphisdailynews.com;
web site www.memphisdailynews.com
Group:
The Daily News Publishing Co.
Circulation: 1,000(pd); 2,000(fr);
USPS
September 30, 2017
Advertising Rate:
Open inch rate $13.50 (legal)
News services:
CNS.
Established: 1886
Publisher Eric Barnes
Marketing Director Leah Sansing
Associate Publisher/Exec. Ed. James
Overstreet

THE DAILY RECORD
(mon to fri) (Law)
PO Box 30006, Rochester, NY, 14603-
3006, Monroe; gen tel (585) 232-6920;
gen fax (585) 232-2740; gen e-mail kevin.
momot@nydailyrecord.com; web site www.
nydailyrecord.com
Advertising Rate:
Open inch rate $.90 (agency line), $.75
(retail line)
News services:
American Court & Commercial Newspapers,
National Newspaper Association.
Established: 14603-3006
Chrmn./CEO James P. Dolan
Vice Pres./Pub. Kevin Momot
CFO Scott Pollei
Tara Buck

THE DAILY RECORD
(mon to sat; S) (Law)
405 E 13th St Ste 101, Kansas City, MO,
64106-2830, Jackson; gen tel (816) 931-
2002; adv tel (816) 931-2002; gen fax (816)
561-6675; adv fax (816) 561-6675; gen
e-mail mail@kcdailyrecord.com; adv e-mail
johnny.aguirre@molawyersmedia.com
Group:
GateHouse Media, Inc.
Advertising Rate:
Open inch rate $9.80
Bus. Mgr. Amanda Passmore
Kansas City Office Mgr. Peter Crawford
Prodn. Mgr. John Reno

THE DAILY RECORD
(mon to fri) (Law)
PO Box 3595, Little Rock, AR, 72203-
3595, Pulaski; gen tel (501) 374-5103; gen
fax (501) 372-3048; gen e-mail bobby@
dailydata.com; adv e-mail jedwards@
dailydata.com; ed e-mail editor@dailydata.
com; web site www.dailyrecord.us
Circulation: 3,210(pd); 25(fr);
USPS
October 4, 2011
Advertising Rate:
Column Inch Rate - $20.00
News services:
NNS, TMS, DRNW, INS.
Established: 1925
Pub. Bill F. Rector
Adv./Mktg. Dir. Jay Edwards
Gen. Mgr. Bobby Burton
Comptroller Robin Hill

THE DAILY RECORD
(mon to fri) (Law)
PO Box 1062, Louisville, KY, 40201-1062,
Jefferson; gen tel (502) 583-4471; gen
fax (502) 585-5453; gen e-mail janicep@
nacms-c.com
Advertising Rate:
Open inch rate $1.20 (legal line)

News services:
National Association of Credit Management.
Established: 40201
Pub. Connie J. Cheak
Mng. Ed. Janice Prichard

THE DAILY RECORDER
(mon to fri) (Law)
PO Box 1048, Sacramento, CA, 95812-1048,
Sacramento; gen tel (916) 444-2355; adv tel
(800) 652-1700; gen fax (916) 444-0636; gen
e-mail daily_recorder@dailyjournal.com; ed
e-mail jt_long@dailyjournal.com; web site
www.dailyjournal.com
Advertising Rate:
Open inch rate $26.00
News services:
AP, dj.
Established: 1901
Pres./Pub. Jerry Salzman
Cor. Office Dir. Raymond Chagolla
Personnel Dir. Dorothy Salzman
Ed. Michael Gottlieb
Tom Barragan
Prodn. Designer Houay Keobouth

THE DAILY REPORTER
(mon to fri) (Law)
225 E. Michigan St., Suite 300, Milwaukee,
WI, 53202, Milwaukee; gen tel (414) 276-
0273; ed tel (414) 225-1807; gen fax (414)
276-4416; gen e-mail news@dailyreporter.
com; adv e-mail squinn@dailyreporter.com;
ed e-mail dshaw@dailyreporter.com; web
site www.dailyreporter.com
Group:
BridgeTower Media
Circulation: 3,105(pd)
News services:
AP.
Established: 1897
Digital Platform - Mobile:
Apple, Android, Windows
Digital Platform - Tablet:
Apple iOS, Android, Windows 7
Associate Publisher/Editor Joe Yovino
Advertising Director Susan Quinn
Managing Editor Dan Shaw

THE DAILY TERRITORIAL
(m-mon to fri) (Law)
2900 E BROADWAY BLVD STE 113,
TUCSON, AZ, 85716-5344, Pima; gen tel
(520) 294-1200; adv tel (520) 294-1200; ed
tel (520) 294-1200; gen fax (520) 294-4040;
adv fax (520) 294-4040; ed fax (520) 295-
4071; gen e-mail editor@azbiz.com; adv
e-mail advertising@azbiz.com; ed e-mail
dhatfield@azbiz.com; web site www.azbiz.
com
Group:
Wick Communications
Circulation: 753(pd);
Sworn
September 30, 2017
Advertising Rate:
Open inch rate $5.45
News services:
American Newspaper Representatives Inc...
Established: 1966
Pub. Thomas Lee
Adv. Dir. Jill A'Hearn
Adv. Mgr., Legal Monica Akyol
Circ. Dir. Laura Horvath
Ed. David Hatfield
Art Dir. Andrew Arthur
Prodn. Mgr. Greg Day

THE INTER-CITY EXPRESS
(mon to fri) (Law)
1109 Oak St Ste 103, Oakland, CA, 94607-
4917, Alameda; gen tel (510) 272-4747; gen
fax (510) 465-1576
Pub. Nell Fields
Adv. Dir. Dan Gougherty
Adv. Mgr., Legal Tonya Peacock
Ed. Tom Barkley
Ronald McNees

THE JOURNAL RECORD
(mon to fri) (Law)
PO Box 26370, Oklahoma City, OK, 73126-
0370, Oklahoma; gen tel (405) 235-3100; adv
tel (405) 278-2830; ed tel (405) 278-2850;
gen fax (405) 278-6907; ed fax (405) 278-
2890; ed e-mail news@journalrecord.com;
web site www.journalrecord.com
Group:
GateHouse Media, Inc.
Circulation: 2,800(pd); 69(fr);
VAC
December 31, 2012
Advertising Rate:
Open inch rate $18.62
News services:
AP.
Established: 1903
Bus. Mgr. Terri Vanhooser
Editor and Associate Publisher Ted Streuli
Advertising Director Sarah Barrow

THE LEGAL INTELLIGENCER
(mon to fri) (Law)
1617 John F Kennedy Blvd Ste 1750,
Philadelphia, PA, 19103-1854, Philadelphia;
gen tel (215) 557-2300; adv tel (215) 557-
2359; ed tel (215) 557-2489; gen fax (215)
557-2301; adv fax (215) 557-2301; ed fax
(215) 557-2301; gen e-mail HGREZLAK@
ALM.COM; adv e-mail dchalphin@alm.com;
ed e-mail hgrezlak@alm.com; web site www.
thelegalintelligencer.com
Group:
ALM Media
News services:
AP.
Established: 1843
Publisher Hal Cohen
Associate Publisher Donald Chalphin
Note:
See media kit for market information.

THE LOS ANGELES DAILY JOURNAL
(mon to fri) (Law)
915 E 1st St, Los Angeles, CA, 90012-4042,
Los Angeles; gen tel (213) 229-5300; gen fax
(213) 229-5481; ed fax (213) 229-5462; web
site www.dailyjournal.com
Advertising Rate:
Open inch rate $69.16 (page)
News services:
AP, NYT, CNS, McClatchy.
Chrmn. of the Bd. Charles T. Munger
Vice Chrmn. of the Bd. J.P. Guerin
Pub. Gerald Salzman
Adv. Dir. Audrey Miller
Ramond Chagolla
Ed. Martin Berg

THE RECORD REPORTER
(Mon`Wed`Fri) (Law)Maricopa; gen tel (602)
417-9900; gen fax (602) 417-9910; gen
e-mail Diane_Heuel@dailyjournal.com ; adv
e-mail record_reporter@dailyjournal.com; ed
e-mail diane_heuel@dailyjournal.com; web
site www.recordreporter.com
Group:
DAILY JOURNAL CORPORATION
Established: 1914
Digital Platform - Mobile:
Apple, Android, Blackberry
Digital Platform - Tablet:
Apple iOS, Android, Windows 7, Blackberry
Tablet OS
Pub. Diane Heuel
Ed. Christopher Gilfillan
Method of Printing:
Tabloid

THE RECORDER
(mon to fri) (Law)
1035 Market St Ste 500, San Francisco,
CA, 94103-1650, San Francisco; gen tel
(415) 749-5400; adv tel (415) 749-5444;
gen fax (415) 749-5449; adv fax (415) 749-
5566; ed fax (415) 749-5549; gen e-mail
recorder_editor@alm.com; web site www.
therecorder.com
Advertising Rate:
Open inch rate $3,200.00 (Full Page Display)

News services:
AP.
Established: 1877
Pub. Chris Braun
Controller Janice Tang
Adv. Mgr., Classified Patrick Vigil
Adv. Mgr., Display Jim Tamietti
Robert Salapuddin
Adv. Coord., Display Heather Ragsdale
Mktg. Dir. John Cosmides
Circ. Mgr. Ed Vergara
Scott Graham
Mng. Ed. George Forcier
Prodn. Mgr./Art Dir. Tess Herrmann

THE ST. LOUIS COUNTIAN

(mon to sat) (S) (Law)
319 N 4th St, Saint Louis, MO, 63102-1906,
Saint Louis City; gen tel (314) 421-1880; adv
tel (314) 421-1880; ed tel (314) 421-1880;
gen fax (314) 421-0436; adv fax (314) 421-
0436; ed fax (314) 421-0436; adv e-mail
carol.prycma@thedailyrecord.com; ed e-mail
willc@thedailyrecord.com; web site www.
thedailyrecord.com
Advertising Rate:
Open inch rate $6.56
News services:
RN.
Pub. Richard Gard
Bus. Mgr. Amanda Passmore
Adv. Dir. Amy Burdge
Circ. Mgr. Stacey Fish
William B. Connaghan
Prodn. Mgr. John M. Reno

TULSA BUSINESS & LEGAL NEWS(LAW)

315 S. Boulder, Tulsa, OK, 74103-4422,
Tulsa; gen tel (918) 581-8306; adv tel (918)
581-8525; ed tel (918) 581-8306; gen e-mail
news@tulsabusiness.com; adv e-mail
legalnews@oklaweeklygroup.com; ed e-mail
news@tulsabusiness.com; web site www.
tulsabusiness.com
Group:
BH Media Group
Established: 1909
Editor Lesa Jones

MEDICAL

LOUISIANA MEDICAL NEWS

(Monthly) (Medical)
PO Box 60010, Lafayette, LA, 70596-
0010, Lafayette; gen tel (337) 235-5455;
gen fax (337) 232-2959; adv e-mail
brandycav@gmail.com; ed e-mail editor@
medicalnewsinc.com; web site www.
louisianamedicalnews.com

MUNICIPAL BONDS

DAILY JOURNAL OF COMMERCE

(mon to fri) (Municipal Bonds)
3445 N. Causeway Blvd. Suite 901, Metairie,
LA, 70002, Jefferson; gen tel (504) 834-9292;
gen fax (504) 832-3534; gen e-mail mail@
nopg.com; adv e-mail anne.lovas@nopg.
com; ed e-mail greg.larose@nopg.com; web
site www.djcgulfcoast.com
Advertising Rate:
Email or call for rates
Established: 1922
Gen. Mgr. Anne Lovas
Managing Editor Greg Larose
Pub Lisa Blossman
Asst. Data Ed. Rebecca Naquin
Pub. Mark Singletary

DAILY RECORD

(mon to fri) (Municipal Bonds)
3323 Leavenworth St, Omaha, NE,
68105-1900, Douglas; gen tel (402) 345-
1303; gen fax (402) 345-2351; gen e-mail
lhenningsen@omahadailyrecord.com; adv
e-mail diane@omahadailyrecord.com; ed
e-mail lorraine@omahadailyrecord.com; web
site www.omahadailyrecord.com
Advertising Rate:
Open inch rate $7.25
News services:
Associated Press, Creators Syndicate, U.S.
News Syndicate.
Established: 1886
Publisher Lynda K. Henningsen
Editor Lorraine Boyd
Production Brian Henningsen
Advertising (Classified, Display, Website)
Diane Bilek
Legal Editor/Legal Notices Mary Mosher
Legal Notice Judy Boyd
Note:
Bona fide paid circulation in Douglas County
in excess of 300 copies, printed in Omaha,
NE

TULSA BUSINESS & LEGAL NEWS(MUNICIPAL BONDS)

315 S. Boulder, Tulsa, OK, 74103-4422,
Tulsa; gen tel (918) 581-8306; adv tel (918)
581-8525; ed tel (918) 581-8306; gen e-mail
news@tulsabusiness.com; adv e-mail
legalnews@oklaweeklygroup.com; ed e-mail
news@tulsabusiness.com; web site www.
tulsabusiness.com
Group:
BH Media Group
Established: 1909
Editor Lesa Jones

MUNICIPAL FINANCE

DAILY RECORD

(mon to fri) (Municipal Finance)
3323 Leavenworth St, Omaha, NE,
68105-1900, Douglas; gen tel (402) 345-
1303; gen fax (402) 345-2351; gen e-mail
lhenningsen@omahadailyrecord.com; adv
e-mail diane@omahadailyrecord.com; ed
e-mail lorraine@omahadailyrecord.com; web
site www.omahadailyrecord.com
Advertising Rate:
Open inch rate $7.25
News services:
Associated Press, Creators Syndicate, U.S.
News Syndicate.
Established: 1886
Publisher Lynda K. Henningsen
Editor Lorraine Boyd
Production Brian Henningsen
Advertising (Classified, Display, Website)
Diane Bilek
Legal Editor/Legal Notices Mary Mosher
Legal Notice Judy Boyd
Note:
Bona fide paid circulation in Douglas County
in excess of 300 copies, printed in Omaha,
NE

THE BOND BUYER

(mon to fri) (Municipal Finance)
1 State St Fl 26, New York, NY, 10004-1483,
New York; gen tel (212) 803-8200; adv tel
(212) 843-9617; gen fax (212) 803-1592; adv
fax (212) 843-9617; ed fax (212) 843-9614;
gen e-mail michael.stanton@sourcemedia.
com; web site www.bondbuyer.com
Advertising Rate:
Open inch rate $168.00
CEO Jim Malkin
Pub. Michael Stanton
Adv. Dir., Legal Bill Baneky
Ed. in Chief Amy Resnick

PUBLIC NOTICE

DAILY JOURNAL OF COMMERCE

(mon to fri) (Public Notice)
3445 N. Causeway Blvd. Suite 901, Metairie,
LA, 70002, Jefferson; gen tel (504) 834-9292;
gen fax (504) 832-3534; gen e-mail mail@
nopg.com; adv e-mail anne.lovas@nopg.
com; ed e-mail greg.larose@nopg.com; web
site www.djcgulfcoast.com
Advertising Rate:
Email or call for rates
Established: 1922
Gen. Mgr. Anne Lovas
Managing Editor Greg Larose
Pub Lisa Blossman
Asst. Data Ed. Rebecca Naquin
Pub. Mark Singletary

DAILY JOURNAL OF COMMERCE

(mon to fri) (Public Notice)
921 SW Washington St Ste 210, Portland,
OR, 97205-2810, Multnomah; gen tel (503)
226-1311; adv tel (503) 226-1311; gen
fax (503) 226-1315; adv fax (503) 802-
7219; ed fax (503) 802-7239; gen e-mail
newsroom@djcoregon.com; adv e-mail
rynni.henderson@djcoregon.com; ed e-mail
stephanie.basalyga@djcoregon.com; web
site www.djcoregon.com
Group:
The Dolan Company
Advertising Rate:
Open inch rate $25.00
News services:
AP, RN, TMS.
Established: 1872
Digital Platform - Mobile:
Apple, Android
Ed. Stephanie Basalyga
Publisher/Vice President Rynni Henderson

DAILY RECORD

(mon to fri) (Public Notice)
3323 Leavenworth St, Omaha, NE,
68105-1900, Douglas; gen tel (402) 345-
1303; gen fax (402) 345-2351; gen e-mail
lhenningsen@omahadailyrecord.com; adv
e-mail diane@omahadailyrecord.com; ed
e-mail lorraine@omahadailyrecord.com; web
site www.omahadailyrecord.com
Advertising Rate:
Open inch rate $7.25
News services:
Associated Press, Creators Syndicate, U.S.
News Syndicate.
Established: 1886
Publisher Lynda K. Henningsen
Editor Lorraine Boyd
Production Brian Henningsen
Advertising (Classified, Display, Website)
Diane Bilek
Legal Editor/Legal Notices Mary Mosher
Legal Notice Judy Boyd
Note:
Bona fide paid circulation in Douglas County
in excess of 300 copies, printed in Omaha,
NE

MISSOURI LAWYERS MEDIA(PUBLIC NOTICE)

319 N 4th St Fl 5, 5th Floor, Saint Louis,
MO, 63102-1907, Saint Louis City; gen tel
(314) 421-1880; adv tel (314) 558-3260;
ed tel (314) 558-3220; gen fax (314) 621-
1913; adv fax (314) 421-7080; ed fax (314)
621-1913; gen e-mail kathi.cartwright@
molawyersmedia.com; adv e-mail johnny.
aguirre@molawyersmedia.com; ed e-mail
fred.ehrlich@molawyersmedia.com; web site
www.molawyersmedia.com
Group:
GateHouse Media, Inc.
Circulation: 4,500(pd); 10,820(fr)
October 1, 2013
Advertising Rate:
Full Page $2,360.00

Established: 1890
Digital Platform - Mobile:
Apple, Android, Windows
Digital Platform - Tablet:
Apple iOS, Android, Windows 7
Prod. Mgr. John Reno
Pub. Liz Irwin

THE DAILY COMMERCIAL RECORDER

(mon to fri) (Public Notice)
P.O. Box 2171, San Antonio, TX, 78297,
Bexar; gen tel (210) 250-2438; gen
fax (210) 250-2360; gen e-mail dcr@
primetimenewspapers.com; web site www.
primetimenewspapers.com
Group:
Hearst Communications, Inc.
Advertising Rate:
Open inch rate $25.00
News services:
ACCN, Creator Syndicates, LAT-WP, National
American Press Syndicate, NYT..
General Sales Manager Mickey Urias
Legal Coordinator Cindy Castillo

THE DAILY NEWS

(mon to fri) (Public Notice)
193 JEFFERSON AVE, MEMPHIS, TN,
38103-2339, Shelby; gen tel (901) 523-1561;
adv tel (901) 528-5283; ed tel (901) 523-
8501; gen fax (901) 526-5813; adv fax (901)
526-5813; ed fax (901) 526-5813; gen e-mail
advertising@memphisdailynews.com; adv
e-mail leah@memphisdailynews.com; ed
e-mail joverstreet@memphisdailynews.com;
web site www.memphisdailynews.com
Group:
The Daily News Publishing Co.
Circulation: 1,000(pd); 2,000(fr);
USPS
September 30, 2017
Advertising Rate:
Open inch rate $13.50 (legal)
News services:
CNS.
Established: 1886
Publisher Eric Barnes
Marketing Director Leah Sansing
Associate Publisher/Exec. Ed. James
Overstreet

THE DAILY RECORD

(mon to sat) (S) (Public Notice)
405 E 13th St Ste 101, Kansas City, MO,
64106-2830, Jackson; gen tel (816) 931-
2002; adv tel (816) 931-2002; gen fax (816)
561-6675; adv fax (816) 561-6675; gen
e-mail mail@kcdailyrecord.com; adv e-mail
johnny.aguirre@molawyersmedia.com
Group:
GateHouse Media, Inc.
Advertising Rate:
Open inch rate $9.80
Bus. Mgr. Amanda Passmore
Kansas City Office Mgr. Peter Crawford
Prodn. Mgr. John Reno

THE DAILY RECORD

(mon to fri) (Public Notice)
PO Box 3595, Little Rock, AR, 72203-
3595, Pulaski; gen tel (501) 374-5103; gen
fax (501) 372-3048; gen e-mail bobby@
dailydata.com; adv e-mail jedwards@
dailydata.com; ed e-mail editor@dailydata.
com; web site www.dailyrecord.us
Circulation: 3,210(pd); 25(fr);
USPS
October 4, 2011
Advertising Rate:
Column Inch Rate - $20.00
News services:
NNS, TMS, DRNW, INS.
Established: 1925
Pub. Bill F. Rector
Adv./Mktg. Dir. Jay Edwards
Gen. Mgr. Bobby Burton
Comptroller Robin Hill

THE DAILY RECORD

(mon to fri) (Public Notice)

11 E SARATOGA ST STE 1, BALTIMORE, MD, 21202-2199, Baltimore City; gen tel (443) 524-8100; adv tel (443) 524-8100; ed tel (443) 524-8150; gen fax (410) 752-2894; adv fax (410) 752-2894; ed fax (410) 752-2894; gen e-mail suzanne. huettner@thedailyrecord.com; adv e-mail advertising@thedailyrecord.com; ed e-mail tbaden@thedailyrecord.com; web site www. thedailyrecord.com
Group:
The Dolan Company
Circulation: 2,572(pd); 384(fr)
March 31, 2014
Advertising Rate:
Open inch rate $510.00/Day
Established: 1888
Publisher Suzanne Fischer-Huettner
Comptroller Maria Kelly
Audience Dev. Dir. Tracy Bumba
Admin. Asst. Shelby Carter
Ed. Thomas Baden Jr.
Digital Ed. Jason Whong
Legal Ed. Danny Jacobs
Sr. Photographer Maximilian Franz
Special Products Ed. Jessica Gregg
Acc. Mgr. Darice Miller
Acc. Mgr. Terri Thompson
Mktg. and Event Coord. Haley Poling

THE DAILY REPORTER

(mon to fri) (Public Notice)
225 E. Michigan St., Suite 300, Milwaukee, WI, 53202, Milwaukee; gen tel (414) 276-0273; ed tel (414) 225-1807; gen fax (414) 276-4416; gen e-mail news@dailyreporter. com; adv e-mail squinn@dailyreporter.com; ed e-mail dshaw@dailyreporter.com; web site www.dailyreporter.com
Group:
BridgeTower Media
Circulation: 3,105(pd)
News services:
AP.
Established: 1897
Digital Platform - Mobile:
Apple, Android, Windows
Digital Platform - Tablet:
Apple iOS, Android, Windows 7
Associate Publisher/Editor Joe Yovino
Advertising Director Susan Quinn
Managing Editor Dan Shaw

THE JOURNAL RECORD

(mon to fri) (Public Notice)
PO Box 26370, Oklahoma City, OK, 73126-0370, Oklahoma; gen tel (405) 235-3100; adv tel (405) 278-2830; ed tel (405) 278-2850; gen fax (405) 278-6907; ed fax (405) 278-2890; ed e-mail news@journalrecord.com; web site www.journalrecord.com
Group:
GateHouse Media, Inc.
Circulation: 2,800(pd); 69(fr);
VAC
December 31, 2012
Advertising Rate:
Open inch rate $18.62
News services:
AP.
Established: 1903
Bus. Mgr. Terri Vanhooser
Editor and Associate Publisher Ted Streuli
Advertising Director Sarah Barrow

THE LEGAL INTELLIGENCER

(mon to fri) (Public Notice)
1617 John F Kennedy Blvd Ste 1750, Philadelphia, PA, 19103-1854, Philadelphia; gen tel (215) 557-2300; adv tel (215) 557-2359; ed tel (215) 557-2489; gen fax (215) 557-2301; adv fax (215) 557-2301; ed fax (215) 557-2301; gen e-mail HGREZLAK@ ALM.COM; adv e-mail dchalphin@alm.com; ed e-mail hgrezlak@alm.com; web site www. thelegalintelligencer.com
Group:
ALM Media
News services:
AP.
Established: 1843

Publisher Hal Cohen
Associate Publisher Donald Chalphin
Note:
See media kit for market information.

THE RECORD REPORTER

(Mon`Wed`Fri) (Public Notice)Maricopa; gen tel (602) 417-9900; gen fax (602) 417-9910; gen e-mail Diane_Heuel@dailyjournal.com ; adv e-mail record_reporter@dailyjournal. com; ed e-mail diane_heuel@dailyjournal. com; web site www.recordreporter.com
Group:
DAILY JOURNAL CORPORATION
Established: 1914
Digital Platform - Mobile:
Apple, Android, Blackberry
Digital Platform - Tablet:
Apple iOS, Android, Windows 7, Blackberry Tablet OS
Pub. Diane Heuel
Ed. Christopher Gilfillan
Method of Printing:
Tabloid

TULSA BUSINESS & LEGAL NEWS(PUBLIC NOTICE)

315 S. Boulder, Tulsa, OK, 74103-4422, Tulsa; gen tel (918) 581-8306; adv tel (918) 581-8525; ed tel (918) 581-8306; gen e-mail news@tulsabusiness.com; adv e-mail legalnews@oklaweeklygroup.com; ed e-mail news@tulsabusiness.com; web site www. tulsabusiness.com
Group:
BH Media Group
Established: 1909
Editor Lesa Jones

REAL ESTATE

BROOKLYN DAILY EAGLE & DAILY BULLETIN

(mon to fri) (Real Estate)
16 Court St Ste 1208, Brooklyn, NY, 11241-1012, Kings; gen tel (718) 858-2300; gen fax (718) 858-8281; gen e-mail publisher@brooklyneagle.net; web site www. brooklyneagle.net
Advertising Rate:
Open inch rate $24.00
Pub. J.D. Hasty
Adv. Mgr. Patricia Higgins
Adv. Mgr., Legal Daniel Doctorow
Adv. Mgr., Special Projects Ted Cutler Sam Howe
Mng. Ed. Ron Geberer

DAILY JOURNAL OF COMMERCE

(mon to fri) (Real Estate)
921 SW Washington St Ste 210, Portland, OR, 97205-2810, Multnomah; gen tel (503) 226-1311; adv tel (503) 226-1311; gen fax (503) 226-1315; adv fax (503) 802-7219; ed fax (503) 802-7239; gen e-mail newsroom@djcoregon.com; adv e-mail rynni.henderson@djcoregon.com; ed e-mail stephanie.basalyga@djcoregon.com; web site www.djcoregon.com
Group:
The Dolan Company
Advertising Rate:
Open inch rate $25.00
News services:
AP, RN, TMS.
Established: 1872
Digital Platform - Mobile:
Apple, Android
Ed. Stephanie Basalyga
Publisher/Vice President Rynni Henderson

DAILY RECORD

(mon to fri) (Real Estate)
3323 Leavenworth St, Omaha, NE, 68105-1900, Douglas; gen tel (402) 345-1303; gen fax (402) 345-2351; gen e-mail

lhenningsen@omahadailyrecord.com; adv e-mail diane@omahadailyrecord.com; ed e-mail lorraine@omahadailyrecord.com; web site www.omahadailyrecord.com
Advertising Rate:
Open inch rate $7.25
News services:
Associated Press, Creators Syndicate, U.S. News Syndicate.
Established: 1886
Publisher Lynda K. Henningsen
Editor Lorraine Boyd
Production Brian Henningsen
Advertising (Classified, Display, Website) Diane Bilek
Legal Editor/Legal Notices Mary Mosher
Legal Notice Judy Boyd
Note:
Bona fide paid circulation in Douglas County in excess of 300 copies, printed in Omaha, NE

MIAMI DAILY BUSINESS REVIEW

(mon to fri) (Real Estate)
PO Box 10589, Miami, FL, 33101-0589, Miami-Dade; gen tel (305) 377-3721; adv tel (305) 347-6623; ed tel (305) 347-6694; gen fax (305) 374-8474; adv fax (305) 347-6644; ed fax (305) 347-6626; gen e-mail DailyBusinessReview@alm.com; adv e-mail ccurbelo@alm.com; ed e-mail dlyons@alm. com; web site www.dailybusinessreview.com
Group:
ALM Media
Advertising Rate:
Varies: http://www.dailybusinessreview.com/ advertising.jsp;
N/A(Sun)
News services:
AP, Bloomberg, Florida News Service.
Established: 1926
Group Publisher, FL/GA/TX Chris Mobley
Associate Publisher/Chief Financial Officer Jeff Fried
Director of Advertising Carlos Curbelo
Editor-in-Chief David Lyons
Business Editor Jay Rees
Law Editor Catherine Wilson
Director of Creative Services John Michael Rindo
Director of Operations & MIS Guillermo Garcia
Web Adminstrator John Hernandez
Vice President/Miami-Dade Legal & Court Relations Sookie Williams
Note:
See Daily Business Review editions in Broward and Palm Beach, FL.

PALM BEACH DAILY BUSINESS REVIEW

(mon to fri) (Real Estate)
1 SE 3rd Ave, Suite 900, Miami, FL, 33131-1700, Miami-Dade; gen tel (305) 377-3721; adv tel (305) 347-6623; ed tel (305) 347-6694; gen fax (561) 820-2077; adv fax (305) 347-6644; ed fax (305) 347-6626; gen e-mail DailyBusinessReview@alm.com; adv e-mail ccurbelo@alm.com; ed e-mail dlyons@alm. com; web site www.dailybusinessreview.com
Group:
ALM Media
Advertising Rate:
http://www.dailybusinessreview.com/ advertising.jsp;
N/A(Sun)
News services:
AP, Bloomberg, Florida News Service.
Established: 1979
Group Publisher, FL/GA/TX Chris Mobley
Associate Publisher/Chief Financial Officer Jeff Fried
Editor-in-Chief David Lyons
Vice President/Broward & Palm Beach Legals Deborah Mullin
Director of Advertising Carlos Curbelo
Group Subscriptions Manager Annette Martinez
Web Administrator John Hernandez
Business Editor Jay Rees
Law Editor Cathy Wilson
Director of Client Development Stephanie

Hemmerich
Audience Development Manager Adam Kaplan
Note:
See Daily Business Reviews editions in Broward and Miami, FL.

THE DAILY NEWS

(mon to fri) (Real Estate)
193 JEFFERSON AVE, MEMPHIS, TN, 38103-2339, Shelby; gen tel (901) 523-1561; adv tel (901) 528-5283; ed tel (901) 523-8501; gen fax (901) 526-5813; adv fax (901) 526-5813; ed fax (901) 526-5813; gen e-mail advertising@memphisdailynews.com; adv e-mail leah@memphisdailynews.com; ed e-mail joverstreet@memphisdailynews.com; web site www.memphisdailynews.com
Group:
The Daily News Publishing Co.
Circulation: 1,000(pd); 2,000(fr);
USPS
September 30, 2017
Advertising Rate:
Open inch rate $13.50 (legal)
News services:
CNS.
Established: 1886
Publisher Eric Barnes
Marketing Director Leah Sansing
Associate Publisher/Exec. Ed. James Overstreet

THE DAILY RECORD

(mon to fri) (Real Estate)
11 E SARATOGA ST STE 1, BALTIMORE, MD, 21202-2199, Baltimore City; gen tel (443) 524-8100; adv tel (443) 524-8100; ed tel (443) 524-8150; gen fax (410) 752-2894; adv fax (410) 752-2894; ed fax (410) 752-2894; gen e-mail suzanne. huettner@thedailyrecord.com; adv e-mail advertising@thedailyrecord.com; ed e-mail tbaden@thedailyrecord.com; web site www. thedailyrecord.com
Group:
The Dolan Company
Circulation: 2,572(pd); 384(fr)
March 31, 2014
Advertising Rate:
Open inch rate $510.00/Day
Established: 1888
Publisher Suzanne Fischer-Huettner
Comptroller Maria Kelly
Audience Dev. Dir. Tracy Bumba
Admin. Asst. Shelby Carter
Ed. Thomas Baden Jr.
Digital Ed. Jason Whong
Legal Ed. Danny Jacobs
Sr. Photographer Maximilian Franz
Special Products Ed. Jessica Gregg
Acc. Mgr. Darice Miller
Acc. Mgr. Terri Thompson
Mktg. and Event Coord. Haley Poling

THE DAILY RECORD

(mon to fri) (Real Estate)
PO Box 3595, Little Rock, AR, 72203-3595, Pulaski; gen tel (501) 374-5103; gen fax (501) 372-3048; gen e-mail bobby@ dailydata.com; adv e-mail jedwards@ dailydata.com; ed e-mail editor@dailydata. com; web site www.dailyrecord.us
Circulation: 3,210(pd); 25(fr);
USPS
October 4, 2011
Advertising Rate:
Column Inch Rate - $20.00
News services:
NNS, TMS, DRNW, INS.
Established: 1925
Pub. Bill F. Rector
Adv./Mktg. Dir. Jay Edwards
Gen. Mgr. Bobby Burton
Comptroller Robin Hill

THE DAILY REPORTER

(mon to fri) (Real Estate)
225 E. Michigan St., Suite 300, Milwaukee, WI, 53202, Milwaukee; gen tel (414) 276-

0273; ed tel (414) 225-1807; gen fax (414) 276-4416; gen e-mail news@dailyreporter.com; adv e-mail squinn@dailyreporter.com; ed e-mail dshaw@dailyreporter.com; web site www.dailyreporter.com
Group:
BridgeTower Media
Circulation: 3,105(pd)
News services:
AP.
Established: 1897
Digital Platform - Mobile:
Apple, Android, Windows
Digital Platform - Tablet:
Apple iOS, Android, Windows 7
Associate Publisher/Editor Joe Yovino
Advertising Director Susan Quinn
Managing Editor Dan Shaw

THE JOURNAL RECORD
(mon to fri) (Real Estate)
PO Box 26370, Oklahoma City, OK, 73126-0370, Oklahoma; gen tel (405) 235-3100; adv tel (405) 278-2830; ed tel (405) 278-2850; gen fax (405) 278-6907; ed fax (405) 278-2890; ed e-mail news@journalrecord.com; web site www.journalrecord.com
Group:
GateHouse Media, Inc.
Circulation: 2,800(pd); 69(fr);
VAC
December 31, 2012
Advertising Rate:
Open inch rate $18.62
News services:
AP.
Established: 1903
Bus. Mgr. Terri Vanhooser

Editor and Associate Publisher Ted Streuli
Advertising Director Sarah Barrow

THE LEGAL INTELLIGENCER
(mon to fri) (Real Estate)
1617 John F Kennedy Blvd Ste 1750, Philadelphia, PA, 19103-1854, Philadelphia; gen tel (215) 557-2300; adv tel (215) 557-2359; ed tel (215) 557-2489; gen fax (215) 557-2301; adv fax (215) 557-2301; ed fax (215) 557-2301; gen e-mail HGREZLAK@ALM.COM; adv e-mail dchalphin@alm.com; ed e-mail hgrezlak@alm.com; web site www.thelegalintelligencer.com
Group:
ALM Media
News services:
AP.
Established: 1843
Publisher Hal Cohen
Associate Publisher Donald Chalphin
Note:
See media kit for market information.

THE RECORD REPORTER
(Mon`Wed`Fri) (Real Estate)Maricopa; gen tel (602) 417-9900; gen fax (602) 417-9910; gen e-mail Diane_Heuel@dailyjournal.com ; adv e-mail record_reporter@dailyjournal.com; ed e-mail diane_heuel@dailyjournal.com; web site www.recordreporter.com
Group:
DAILY JOURNAL CORPORATION
Established: 1914
Digital Platform - Mobile:
Apple, Android, Blackberry
Digital Platform - Tablet:
Apple iOS, Android, Windows 7, Blackberry

Tablet OS
Pub. Diane Heuel
Ed. Christopher Gilfillan
Method of Printing:
Tabloid

TULSA BUSINESS & LEGAL NEWS(REAL ESTATE)
315 S. Boulder, Tulsa, OK, 74103-4422, Tulsa; gen tel (918) 581-8306; adv tel (918) 581-8525; ed tel (918) 581-8306; gen e-mail news@tulsabusiness.com; adv e-mail legalnews@oklaweeklygroup.com; ed e-mail news@tulsabusiness.com; web site www.tulsabusiness.com
Group:
BH Media Group
Established: 1909
Editor Lesa Jones

SPORTS

DAILY RACING FORM
(mon to sat; S) (Sports)
708 3rd Ave Fl 12, New York, NY, 10017-4129, New York; gen tel (212) 366-7600; adv tel (212) 366-7607; ed fax (212) 366-7718; gen e-mail Daily Racing Form publishes several editions nationwide.; adv e-mail advert@drf.com; ed e-mail editor@drf.com; web site www.drf.com
Advertising Rate:
Open inch rate $21.75 (national)

News services:
RN, UPI.
Pres./Gen. Mgr. Jim Kostas
Pub. Steven Crist
Dir., HR Jim Hajney
Jeffery Burch
Circ. Mgr. Joel Brady
Ed. in Chief Rich Rosenbush
Irwin Cohen
Note:
Daily Racing Form publishes several editions nationwide.

THE DAILY NEWS
(mon to fri) (Sports)
193 JEFFERSON AVE, MEMPHIS, TN, 38103-2339, Shelby; gen tel (901) 523-1561; adv tel (901) 528-5283; ed tel (901) 523-8501; gen fax (901) 526-5813; adv fax (901) 526-5813; ed fax (901) 526-5813; gen e-mail advertising@memphisdailynews.com; adv e-mail leah@memphisdailynews.com; ed e-mail joverstreet@memphisdailynews.com; web site www.memphisdailynews.com
Group:
The Daily News Publishing Co.
Circulation: 1,000(pd); 2,000(fr);
USPS
September 30, 2017
Advertising Rate:
Open inch rate $13.50 (legal)
News services:
CNS.
Established: 1886
Publisher Eric Barnes
Marketing Director Leah Sansing
Associate Publisher/Exec. Ed. James Overstreet

Section III

News, Pictures and Syndicate Services

NEWS, PICTURES AND SYNDICATE SERVICES

A

ACCURACY IN MEDIA — 4350 E West Hwy , Ste 555 , Bethesda , 20814-4582 , USA (202) 364-4401; fax (202) 364-4098; e-mail info@aim.org; web site www.aim.org
Chrmn. — Donald K. Irvine
Special Projects Dir. — Deborah Lambert
Exec. Secretary — Roger Aronoff

ACCUWEATHER, INC. — 385 Science Park Rd, State College, PA, 16803-2215, USA (814) 237-0309; fax (814) 235-8609; e-mail sales@accuweather.com; info@accuwx.com; web site www.accuweather.com
Founder & President — Dr. Joel N. Myers
CEO — Barry Lee Myers
Sr. VP, Chief Meteorologist — Elliot Abrams
Sr. VP, Forensics — Dr. Joseph Sobel
COO — Evan A. Myers
Sr. VP, Special Initiatives — Michael Steinberg
Chief Strategy Officer — James Candor
Chief Marketing Officer — John Dokes

ADLINK-INTERNATIONAL LTD — Global Advertising Services, 16 Upper Woburn Street, London, WC1H 0AF, United Kingdom; tel ; tel (44 -) 330 606 1438; fax 330 606 1468; e-mail info@adlinkinternational.com; web site www.adlinkinternational.com
Mng. Dir. — Shamlal PuriNote: Publishers Representatives, Advertising services in Africa, Middle East, Far East, Caribbean, Europe, Press Freedom in Africa, Editorial services, Special Supplements.

ADVERTISING WORKSHOP — University of Oklahoma-Gaylord/Amc, Herbert School of Journalism & Mass Co , Norman , 73019-0001 , USA (405) 325-5209; fax (405) 325-7565; e-mail javery@ou.edu; web site www.ou.edu/gaylord
Self-Syndicator — Jim Avery
Staff Asst. — Kelly StormNote: University of Oklahoma-Gaylord/AMC, Herbert School of Journalism & Mass Communication

AGENCE FRANCE-PRESSE - WASHINGTON, DC — 1500 K St NW , Ste 600 , Washington , 20005-1200 , USA (202) 289-0700; fax (202) 414-0634; e-mail afp-us@afp.com; web site www.afp.com
Mktg & Sales Dir., North America — Gilles Tarot
Senior Account Manager — Sue Lisk

AGENCIA PRENSA INTERNACIONAL INC. — 112 W 9th St , Ste 518 , Los Angeles , 90015-1529 , USA 213-800-9896; fax (213) 388-0563; e-mail prensa@agenciapi.com; web site www.agenciapi.com
Media Mgr. — Javier Rojas
Ed. — Antonio Nava

AGEVENTURE NEWS SERVICE — 2199 Astor St , Apt 503 , Orange Park , 32073-5619 , USA (904) 629-6020; e-mail demko@demko.com; web site www.demko.com
Ed.-in-Chief — David J. Demko

ALAN LAVINE, INC. — 10199 Willow Ln , Palm Beach Gardens , 33410-5141 , USA (561) 630-7112; e-mail mwliblav@aol.com
Chrmn./Pres. — Alan Lavine
Mktg. Mgr. — Gail Liberman

ALM — 120 Broadway , Fl 5 , New York , 10271-1100 , USA (212) 457-9400; web site www.alm.com
Pres./CEO — William L. Pollak
Sr. Vice Pres. — Jack Berkowitz
Vice Pres., Licensing/Bus. Devel. — Ellen Sigel
Editorial Dir. — Aric Press
Chief Digital Officer — Jeffrey Litvack

ALTERNET — 77 Federal St , San Francisco , 94107-1414 , USA (415) 284-1420; fax (415) 284-1414; e-mail info@alternet.org; web site www.alternet.org
Pub./Exec. Ed. — Don Hazen
Bus. Mgr. — Leigh Johnson
Sr. Ed. — Tai Moses
Mng. Ed. — Davina Baum

AMERICAN CROSSWORD FEDERATION — PO Box 69 , Massapequa Park , 11762-0069 , USA (561) 989-0550; e-mail snpuzz@aol.com; web site www.stanxwords.com
Pres./Ed. in Chief — Stanley Newman
Vice Pres./Sales Dir. — Joseph Vallely

AMERICAN FEDERATION OF TEACHERS — 555 New Jersey Ave NW , Washington , 20001-2029 , USA (202) 879-4400; fax (202) 879-4545; e-mail aftpres@aol.com; online@aft.org; web site www.aft.org
Pres. — Randi Weingarten
Sec./Treasurer — Antonia Portese
Exec. Vice Pres. — Lorretta Johnson

AMPERSAND COMMUNICATIONS — 2311 S Bayshore Dr , Miami , 33133-4728 , USA (305) 285-2200; e-mail amprsnd@aol.com; web site www.ampersandcom.com
Ed. — George Leposky
Mng. Partner — Rosalie E. Leposky

ANCHORED DREAMS — 1301 Drier Pl , Highland Park , 08904-3614 , USA (732) 985-7613; e-mail azjaffe@optonline.net; az@azriela.com; web site www.azrielajaffe.com
Author/Self-Syndicator — Jaffe Azriela

ANDREWS MCMEEL SYNDICATION — 1130 Walnut St , Kansas City , 64106-2109 , USA (816) 581-7500; e-mail press@amuniversal.com; web site http://syndication.andrewsmcmeel.com/
Vice Pres. of Sales — John Vivona
Office Manager — Jan Flemington

ANTIQUE DETECTIVE SYNDICATE — 5808 Royal Club Dr , Boynton Beach , 33437-4264 , USA (561) 364-5798; e-mail antique2@bellsouth.net
Pres./Writer — Anne Gilbert

ANTIQUES & COLLECTIBLE SELF-SYNDICATED COLUMN — PO Box 597401 , Chicago , 60659-7401 , USA (773) 267-9773; e-mail thecapecod@aol.com; web site www.anitagold.com
Author/Creator/Owner — Anita Gold

AP DIGITAL AND COMMERCIAL SERVICES — 450 W 33rd St , New York , 10001-2603 , USA (212) 621-1997; fax (212) 621-1955; web site www.apimages.com
Vice Pres. — Ian Cameron

ARRIGONI TRAVEL SYNDICATION — 15 Rock Ridge Rd , Fairfax , 94930-1413 , USA (415) 456-2697; fax (415) 456-2697; e-mail patarrigoni@comcast.net; web site www.travelpublishers.com
Pres. — Patricia ArrigoniNote: Creeators Syndicate freelancer

ARTISTMARKET.COM — 35336 Spring Hill Rd , Farmington Hills , 48331-2044 , USA (248) 661-8585; fax (248) 788-1022; e-mail info@artistmarket.com; web site www.artistmarket.com
CEO/Ed. — A. David Kahn

ARTIZANS.COM SYNDICATE — 11136 - 75 A St. NW, Edmonton, AB, T5B 2C5, Canada (780) 471-6112; fax (877) 642-8666; e-mail sales@artizans.com; support@artizans.com; web site www.artizans.com; www.dialanartist.com
Pres. — Malcolm Mayes

ASHLEIGH BRILLIANT — 117 W Valerio St , Santa Barbara , 93101-2927 , USA (805) 682-0531; e-mail ashleigh@ashleighbrilliant.com; web site www.ashleighbrilliant.com
Pres. — Ashleigh Brilliant
Vice Pres. — Dorothy Brilliant

ASSOCIATED PRESS — 200 Liberty St., New York, NY, 10281, USA (877) 836-9477; e-mail info@ap.org; web site www.ap.org
Pres./CEO — Gary Pruitt
Sen. V.P./HR — Jessica Bruce
Senior V.P./Exec. Ed. — Sally Buzbee
Senior V.P./ CFO — Ken Dale
Senior V.P./CTO — Gianluca D'Aniello
Senior V.P./ Revenue, Americas — Dave Gwizdowski
Senior V.P./Gen. Counsel, Corp. Sec. — Karen Kaiser
Senior V.P./Strategic Planning — Jim Kennedy
Senior V.P. Revenue, Int.'l — Daisy VeerasinghamNote: U.S. States and Territories:

ALABAMA
Birmingham: (205) 251-4221
Montgomery: (334) 262-5947

ALASKA
Anchorage: (907) 272-7549
Juneau: (907) 586-1515

ARIZONA
Phoenix: (602) 258-8934

ARKANSAS
Little Rock: (501) 225-3668

CALIFORNIA
Sacramento: (916) 448-9555
Los Angeles: (213) 626-1200
San Diego: (619) 231-9365
San Francisco: (415) 495-1708

COLORADO
Denver: (303) 825-0123

CONNECTICUT
Hartford: (860) 246-6876
New Haven: (203) 964-9270

DISTRICT OF COLUMBIA
Washington: (202) 641-9000

FLORIDA
Cape Canaveral: (212) 621-1699
Orlando: (407) 425-4547
Tallahassee: (850) 224-1211
West Palm Beach: (305) 594-5825
Miami: (305) 594-5825

GEORGIA
Atlanta: (404) 653-8460

HAWAII
Honolulu: (808) 536-5510

IDAHO
Boise: (208) 343-1894

ILLINOIS
Springfield: (217) 789-2700
Chicago: (312) 781-0500

INDIANA
Indianapolis: (317) 639-5501

IOWA
Des Moines: (515) 243-3281
Iowa City: (319) 337-5615

KANSAS
Topeka: (785) 234-5654
Wichita: (316) 263-4601

KENTUCKY
Frankfort: (502) 227-2410
Louisville: (502) 583-7718

LOUISIANA
Baton Rouge: (225) 343-1325
New Orleans: (504) 523-3931

MAINE
Augusta: (207) 622-3018
Portland: (207) 772-4157

MARYLAND
Baltimore: (410) 837-8315

MASSACHUSETTS
Boston: (617) 357-8100

MICHIGAN
Lansing: (517) 482-8011
Traverse City: (231) 929-4180
Detroit: (313) 259-0650

MINNESOTA
Minneapolis: (612) 332-2727
St. Paul: (651) 222-4821

MISSISSIPPI
Jackson: (601) 948-5897

MISSOURI
Columbia: (573) 884-9934
Jefferson City: (573) 636-9415
St. Louis: (314) 241-2496
Kansas City: (816) 421 4844

MONTANA
Billings: (406) 896-1528
Helena: (406) 442-7440

NEBRASKA
Lincoln: (402) 476-2525
Omaha: (402) 391-0031

NEVADA
Carson City: (775) 322-3639
Las Vegas: (702) 382-7440
Reno: (775) 322-3639

NEW HAMPSHIRE
Concord: (603) 224-3327

NEW JERSEY
Newark: (973) 642-0151
Atlantic City: (609) 645-2063
Trenton: (609) 392-3622

NEW MEXICO
Albuquerque: (505) 822-9022

NEW YORK
New York: (212) 621-1500
Albany: (518) 458-7821
Buffalo: (716) 852-1051

NORTH CAROLINA

Charlotte: (704) 334-4624
Raleigh: (919) 510-8937

NORTH DAKOTA
Bismarck: (701) 223-8450
Fargo: (701) 235-1908

OHIO
Cincinnati: (513) 241-2386
Cleveland: (216) 771-2172
Columbus: (614) 885-2727
Toledo: (419) 255-7113

OKLAHOMA
Oklahoma City: (405) 525-2121
Tulsa: (918) 584-4346

OREGON
Portland: (503) 228-2169

PENNSYLVANIA
Allentown: (610) 207-9297
Harrisburg: (717) 238-9413
Philadelphia: (215) 561-1133
Pittsburgh: (412) 281-3747
State College: (814) 238-3649

PUERTO RICO
San Juan: (717) 793-5833 or (305) 594-1845

RHODE ISLAND
Providence: (401) 274-2270

SOUTH CAROLINA
Charleston: (843) 722-1660
Columbia: (803) 799-5510

SOUTH DAKOTA
Pierre: (605) 224-7811

TENNESSEE
Memphis: (901) 525-1972
Nashville: (615) 373-9988

TEXAS
Austin: (512) 472-4004
Dallas: (972) 991-2100
Fort Worth: (817) 348-0367
Lubbock: (806) 765-0394
San Antonio: (210) 222-2713
Houston: (281) 872-8900

UTAH
Salt Lake City: (801) 322-3405

VERMONT
Montpelier: (802) 229-0577

VIRGINIA
Richmond: (804) 643-6646
McLean: (703) 761-0187

WASHINGTON
Olympia: (360) 753-7222
Seattle: (206) 682-1812
Spokane: (800) 300-8340
Yakima: (509) 453-1951

WEST VIRGINIA
Charleston: (304) 346-0897

WISCONSIN
Milwaukee: (414) 225-3580
Madison: (608) 255-3679

WYOMING
Cheyenne: (307) 632-9351

ASSOCIATED PRESS INFORMATION SERVICES — 450 W 33rd St, New York, NY, 10001-2603, USA (212) 621-1500; fax (212) 621-7520; e-mail info@ap.org; web site www. ap.org
Dir. Sales — Ted Mendelsohn

ASSOCIATED PRESS MANAGING EDITORS ASSOCIATION — 450 W 33rd St, New York, NY, 10001-2603, USA (212) 621-1838; fax (212) 506-6102; e-mail apme@ ap.org; web site www.apme.com
Gen. Mgr. — Sally JacobsenNote: Elections held in Oct

ATLANTIC FEATURE SYNDICATE — 16 Slayton Rd , Melrose , 02176-4222 , USA (781) 665-4442; e-mail lynn@ offthemarkcartoons.com; web site www. offthemark.com
Pres. — Mark Parisi
Mktg. Dir. — Lynn Reznick

AUTOEDITOR SYNDICATION — 186 Cypress Point Rd , Half Moon Bay , 94019-2212 , USA ; tel ; tel (United States - HALF MOON BAY) (650) 726-2386; fax (650) 726-2386; e-mail brian@autoeditor.com; web site 186 CYPRESS POINT ROAD
Ed./Pub. — Brian DouglasNote: Automotive editorial website

AUTOWRITERS ASSOCIATES, INC. (MOTOR MATTERS) — PO Box 3305 , Wilmington , 19804-4305 , USA (302) 998-1650; e-mail info@motormatters.biz; web site www.motormatters.biz
Pres. — Connie Keane
Contributor, Rolling Homes — Julianne Crane
Contributor, Ask the Auto Doctor — Junior Damato
Contributor, FreeWheeling — Evelyn Kanter
Contributor, Get Off the Road — Dan Lyons
Contributor, Bonus Wheels, New on Wheels — Sue Mead
Contributor, FreeWheeling — Kate McLeod
Contributor, Classic Classics — Vern Parker
Contributor, Truck Talk — Tim Spell
Contributor, 2-Wheeling Today, New On Wheels, Bonus Wheels — Arv Voss
Editor, Contributor, Women Auto Know — Brandy Schaffels
Contributor, New On Wheels, Get Off the Road, Bonus Wheels — Frank Aukofer
Contributor, Classic Classics, New on Wheels, Bonus Wheels — Steve Wheeler
Contributor, New On Wheels, Down the Road, Bonus Wheels — Lyndon Conrad Bell
Joe Michaud
Lynn WalfordNote: Motor Matters is an automotive marketing content communications service with expertise in automotive editorial-advertorial curation, distribution, and syndication partnerships. Goals are to help publications maximize advertising to in-market new car buyers and recapture buyers in the used car segments with engaging content. Strengths are rooted in accuracy, credibility, and clarity in messaging. Plus, we are eagle-eyed editors and fierce under deadlines.
Motor Matters delivers high-quality, easy-to-read, engaging automotive content. Solutions include new/used car buyers guides, expert reviews, consumer-interest trends and automotive niche articles (www. motormatters.biz).

B

BANKRATE.COM — 11760 US Highway 1 , Ste 200 , North Palm Beach , 33408-3003 , USA (561) 630-2400; fax (561) 625-4540; web site www.bankrate.com
President & CEO (Former) — Tom Evans
Sr. Vice Pres./Chief Revenue Officer — Donald M. Ross
Sr. Vice Pres., Finance/CFO — Robert J. DeFranco
Sr. Vice Pres./Chief Mktg./Commun. Officer — Bruce Zanca
Mktg. Dir. — Beth Planakis

BASIC CHESS FEATURES — 102 Blatchley Rd , Windsor , 13865-3304 , USA (607) 775-0587; e-mail slyman@tds.net
Pres. — Shelby Lyman

BEAVER CREEK FEATURES — 3508 W

151st St , Cleveland , 44111-2105 , USA (216) 251-1389; e-mail dnorman@bge.net; web site www.sites.google.com/site/wallyswoods
Artist/Owner — Dean Norman

BIG RING MEDIA TEAM, INC. — PO Box 231 , Madison , 47250-0231 , USA (812) 265-6313; fax (812) 418-3368; e-mail info@bigringwriting.com; web site www. bigringwriting.com
Dir. — Richard Ries
Admin. Asst. — Julie Ries

BIOFILE — 995 Teaneck Rd , Apt 3N , Teaneck , 07666-4543 , USA (201) 833-2350; fax (201) 833-2350; e-mail mrbiofile@aol.com; web site www.thebiofile.com
Ed. — Mark (Scoop) Malinowski

BLACK PRESS SERVICE, INC. — 375 5th Ave , New York , 10016-3323 , USA ; tel ; tel (001 - 212) (212) 686-6850; fax (212) 686-7308; e-mail news@blackradionetwork.com; web site www.blackradionetwork.com
Pres. — Jay R. Levy
Sales Mgr. — Peter Knight
Ed. — Roy Thompson
Assoc. Ed. — Bill Baldwin

BLACK STAR PUBLISHING CO., INC. — 333 Mamaroneck Ave, # 175, White Plains, NY, 10605-1440, USA (212) 679-3288; e-mail sales@blackstar.com; web site www.blackstar. com
Pres. — Ben Chapnick
Vice Pres. — John P. Chapnick

BLOOMBERG NEWS — 27 Fl., Cheung Kong Ctr., 2 Queens Rd. Central, Hong Kong, Hong Kong

BLOOMBERG NEWS — Yusen Bldg., 1st Fl., 2-3-2 Marunouchi, Tokyo, 100, Japan

BLOOMBERG NEWS — 100 Business Park Dr , Skillman , 08558-2601 , USA

BLOOMBERG NEWS — 1 Macquarie Pl., Level 36, Gtwy. 36, Sydney, NSW, 2000, Australia

BLOOMBERG NEWS — 1399 New York Ave NW , Fl 11 , Washington , 20005-4749 , USA

BLOOMBERG NEWS — Neue Mainzer Strasse 75, Frankfurt, 60311, Germany

BLOOMBERG NEWS — 161 Bay St., Ste. 4300, Toronto, ON, M5J 2S1, Canada

BLOOMBERG NEWS — 731 Lexington Ave , New York , 10022-1331 , USA

BLOOMBERG NEWS — 111 S Wacker Dr , Ste 4950 , Chicago , 60606-4418 , USA

BLOOMBERG NEWS — 7 Rue Scribe, Paris, 75009, France

BLOOMBERG NEWS — Pierre 3., Ste, 101 , San Francisco , 94111, USA

BLOOMBERG NEWS — Capital Square, 23 Church St., 12th Fl., Singapore, 49481, Singapore

BROADCAST NEWS LIMITED — 840 Howe St., Ste. 250, Vancouver, BC, V6Z 2L2, Canada (604) 687-1662; fax (604) 687-5040
Bureau Chief — Jill St. Louis

BROADCAST NEWS LIMITED — 36 King St. E., Toronto, ON, M5C 2L9, Canada (416) 364-0321; fax (416) 364-8896; web site www.

thecanadianpress.com
News Editor — Ellen Huebert
CFO — David Ross
Gen. Exec./Client Liaison — Terry Scott
Sales/Mktg. Dir. — Charles Messina
Sandra Clarke

CANADIAN PRESS, THE - TORONTO, ON — 36 King St. E., Toronto, ON, M5C 2L9, Canada (416) 364-0321; fax (416) 364-0207; e-mail info@thecanadianpress.com; web site www.thecanadianpress.com
Chrmn. — John Honderich
News Editor — Ellen Huebert
Legislature Correspondent — Keith Leslie
Pres. — Eric Morrison
CFO — David Ross
Chief, Ontario Servs. — Wendy McCann
Vice Pres., Broadcasting — Terry Scott
Vice Pres., French Servs. — Jean Roy
Dir., HR — Paul Woods
Office Mgr. — Sharon Hockin
Exec. Dir. — Philipe MercureNote: Elections held in April

BROADCAST NEWS LIMITED — 1050 rue Des Parlementaires, Bureau 207, Quebec City, QC, G1R 5A4, Canada (418) 646-5377; fax (418) 523-9686
Correspondent — Martin Ouellett

BROADCAST NEWS LIMITED — 165 Sparks St., Ste. 800, Ottawa, ON, K1P 5B9, Canada (613) 238-4142; fax (613) 232-5163
Bureau Chief — Robert Russo

BROADCAST NEWS LIMITED — Rm. 335, Press Gallery, Regina, SK, S4S 0B3, Canada (306) 585-1024; fax (306) 585-1027
Saskatchewan Correspondent — Jay Branch

BROADCAST NEWS LIMITED — The Press Gallery, Box 6000, Queen St., Fredericton, NB, E3B 5H1, Canada (506) 457-0746; fax (506) 457-9708
New Brunswick Correspondent — Kevin Bissett

BROADCAST NEWS LIMITED — 1888 Brunswick St., Ste. 100, Halifax, NS, B3J 3J8, Canada (902) 422-9284; fax (902) 565-7588
Bureau Chief — Dean Beeby
Legislative Reporter — Murray Brewster

BROADCAST NEWS LIMITED — 215 St. Jacques W., Ste. 100, Montreal, QC, H2Y 1M6, Canada (514) 849-8008; fax (514) 282-6915
Quebec Correspondent — Peter Ray

BROADCAST NEWS LIMITED — PO Box 10109, 106th St., Ste. 504, Edmonton, AB, T5J 3L7, Canada (780) 428-6490; fax (780) 428-0663
Bureau Chief — Kathy Bell

BROADCAST NEWS LIMITED — 386 Broadway Ave., Ste. 101, Winnipeg, MB, R3C 3R6, Canada (204) 988-1781; fax (204) 942-4788
Manitoba Correspondent — Steve Lambert

CANADIAN PRESS, THE - CALGARY, AB — 131 9 Avenue SW, Suite 310, Calgary, AB, T2P 1K1, Canada (403) 543-7238; fax (403) 262-7520; e-mail calgary@thecanadianpress. com; web site www.thecanadianpress.com
National Correspondent — Bill Graveland
National Business Correspondent — Lauren Krugel
Business reporter — Dan Healing

BUSINESS NEWSFEATURES — 417 Lexington Rd , Grosse Pointe Farms , 48236-2820 , USA (313) 929 - 0800; e-mail cmeyering@ameritech.net
Writer, Computer Columns — Robert H. Meyering

Ed. — Carl E. Meyering

BUSINESS WIRE - BOSTON, MA — 2
Center Plz , Ste 500 , Boston , 02108-1921 ,
USA (617) 742-2760; fax (617) 742-2782;
e-mail news@businesswire.com; web site
Business Wire - Boston, MA
Pres./COO — Cathy Baron Tamraz

BUSINESS WIRE - CLEVELAND, OH —
1001 Lakeside Ave E , Ste 1525 , Cleveland ,
44114-1193 , USA (800) 769-0220; fax (800)
827-0237; web site www.businesswire.com
Midwest Reg. Mgr. — Jill Connor

BUSINESS WIRE - DENVER, CO — 1725
Blake St , Ste 100 , Denver , 80202-5917 ,
USA (800) 308-0166; fax (303) 830-2442; web
site www.businesswire.com
Vice Pres. — Dylan Frusciano

BUSINESS WIRE - LOS ANGELES, CA —
12100 Wilshire Blvd , Ste 780 , Los Angeles ,
90025-1281 , USA (800) 237-8212; fax (310)
820-7363; web site www.businesswire.com
Mgr., Southwest Reg. — Mike Iannuzzi
Nat'l Dir., Mktg. Programs — Tom Becktold

BUSINESS WIRE - NEW YORK, NY — 40
E 52nd St, Fl 14, New York, NY, 10022-5911,
USA (212) 752-9600; fax (212) 752-9698; web
site www.businesswire.com
Vice Pres., New York Reg. — Phyllis
Dantuono
Pres./CEO — Cathy Baron Tamraz

BUSINESS WIRE - SAN FRANCISCO, CA
— 44 Montgomery St , Fl 39 , San Francisco ,
94104-4602 , USA (415) 986-4422; fax (415)
788-5335; e-mail news@businesswire.com;
web site www.businesswire.comCathy Baron
Tamraz
Co-Chief Opns. — Gregg Castano
Vice Pres., Global Media — news@
businesswire.com Neil

C

CAGLE CARTOONS, INC. — PO Box 22342 ,
Santa Barbara , 93121-2342 , USA (805) 969-
2829; e-mail cari@cagle.com; web site www.
caglecartoons.com
Pres./CEO — Daryl Cagle
Exec. Ed./Mktg. Dir. — Cari Dawson
BartleyNote: Cagle Cartoons, Inc. does not
accept unsolicited submissions.

**CANADIAN ARTISTS SYNDICATE
INCORPORATED** — 5 Ramsgate Lane, Suite
116, Halifax, NS, B3P 2S6, Canada 902) (902)
407-3440; e-mail rvroom@artistssyndicate.ca;
web site www.artistssyndicate.ca
President — Richard Vroom

**CANADIAN PRESS, THE - EDMONTON,
AB** — Cornerpoint, 10109 106th St., Ste.
504, Edmonton, AB, T5J 3L7, Canada (780)
428-6490; fax (780) 428-0663; web site www.
thecanadianpress.com
Bureau Chief — Heather Boyd

**CANADIAN PRESS, THE - FREDERICTON,
NB** — Press Gallery, 96 Saint John St,
Fredericton, NB, E3B 1C5, Canada (506)
457-0746; fax (506) 457-9708; web site www.
thecanadianpress.com
Correspondent — Kevin Bissett

CANADIAN PRESS, THE - HALIFAX, NS —
1888 Brunswick St., Ste. 701, Halifax, NS, B3J
3J8, Canada (902) 422-8496; fax (902) 425-
2675; web site www.thecanadianpress.com
Bureau Chief — Dean Beeby

CANADIAN PRESS, THE - MONTREAL, QC

— 215 St. Jacques St., Ste. 100, Montreal, QC,
H2Y 1M6, Canada (514) 849-3212; fax (514)
282-6915; e-mail info@thecanadianpress.com;
web site www.thecanadianpress.com
Pres. — Eric Morrison
Vice Pres.-French Serv. — Claude Papineau

CANADIAN PRESS, THE - OTTAWA, ON
— 165 Sparks St., Ste. 800, Ottawa, ON, K1P
5P7, Canada (613) 238-4142; fax (613) 238-
4452; e-mail ottowa@thecanadianpress.com;
web site www.thecanadianpress.com
Bureau Chief — Robert Russo

**CANADIAN PRESS, THE - QUEBEC
CITY, QC** — 1050 Des Parlementaires,
Ste. 2, Quebec City, QC, G1R 5J1, Canada
(418) 646-5377; fax (418) 523-9686; e-mail
info@thecanadianpress.com; web site www.
thecanadianpress.com
Director — Jean Roy

**CANADIAN PRESS, THE - REGINA,
SK** — Legislative Bldg., Press Gallery, Rm.
335, Regina, SK, S4S 0B3, Canada (306)
585-1024; fax (306) 585-1027; e-mail info@
thecanadianpress.com; web site www.
thecanadianpress.com
Correspondent — Stephanie Graham

**CANADIAN PRESS, THE - SAINT JOHN'S,
NL** — 139 Water St., Ste. 901, The Fortis
Bldg., Saint John's, NL, A1C 1B2, Canada
(709) 576-0687; fax (709) 576-0049; web site
www.thecanadianpress.com
Correspondent — Michelle MacAfee

**CANADIAN PRESS, THE - VANCOUVER,
BC** — 840 Howe St., Ste. 250, Vancouver, BC,
V6Z 2L2, Canada (604) 687-1662; fax (604)
687-5040; web site www.thecanadianpress.
com
Bureau Chief — Wendy Cox

CANADIAN PRESS, THE - VICTORIA, BC
— Press Gallery, Rm. 360, Victoria, BC, V8V
1X4, Canada (250) 384-4912; fax (250) 356-
9597; e-mail dirk.meissner@thecanadianpress.
com; web site www.thecanadianpress.com
Correspondent — Dirk Meissner

**CANADIAN PRESS, THE - WASHINGTON,
DC** — 1100 13th St NW , Washington , 20005-
4051 , USA (202) 638-3367; fax (202) 638-
3369; web site www.thecanadianpress.com
Bureau Chief — Robert Russo

CANADIAN PRESS, THE - WINNIPEG, MB
— 386 Broadway Ave., Ste. 101, Winnipeg, MB,
R3C 3R6, Canada (204) 988-1781; fax (204)
942-4788; e-mail info@thecanadianpress.com;
web site www.thecanadianpress.com
Manitoba Correspondent — Steve Lambert

CAPITAL CONNECTIONS — 1698 32nd St
NW , Washington , 20007-2969 , USA (202)
337-2044; fax (202) 338-4750; e-mail karen@
karenfeld.com; web site www.karenfeld.com
Owner/Editor — Karen Feld

CAPITOL NEWS SERVICE — 530 Bercut Dr ,
Ste E , Sacramento , 95811-0101 , USA (916)
445-6336; fax (916) 443-5871; e-mail editor@
senior-spectrum.com; web site www.senior-
spectrum.comSusan Carlson

CAREER SOURCE/COLUMN — PO Box 94 ,
Birmingham , 48012-0094 , USA (248) 647-
3662; e-mail sgsilver2002@yahoo.com; sheryl.
silver@yahoo.com
Owner/Author — Sheryl Silver

CARTOON RESOURCE — 3568 Cascade Rd
SE , Grand Rapids , 49546-2141 , USA (616)
551-2238; e-mail andrew@cartoonresource.

com; web site www.cartoonresource.com
Creative Dir. — Andrew Grossman
Mktg. Dir. — Nancy TerrellNote: Cartoon
Resource delivers customized editorial art
with rapid turn-around.

CARTOONEWS, INC. — 15 Central Park W ,
New York , 10023-7708 , USA (212) 980-0855;
fax (212) 980-1664; e-mail cartoonews@aol.
com; luriestudios@aol.com; web site www.
luriecartoon.com
Pres. — T.R. Fletcher
Vice Pres., Sales — L. Raymond
Admin. Dir. — Lisa Duval
Accountant/CPA — John Schmitt

**CARTOONISTS & WRITERS SYNDICATE/
CARTOON ARTS INTERNATIONAL - NEW
YORK, NY** — 67 Riverside Dr , Apt 7A , New
York , 10024-6136 , USA (212) CARTOON
(277-8666); e-mail cwss@cartoonweb.com;
web site www.nytsyn.com/cartoons
Pres. — Jerry Robinson

**CARTOONISTS & WRITERS SYNDICATE/
CARTOON ARTS INTERNATIONAL -
RANCHO PALOS VERDES, CA** — 28028
Lobrook Dr , Rancho Palos Verdes , 90275-
3132 , USA (212) 227-8666; fax (310) 541-
9017; e-mail cwsmedia@cartoonweb.com; web
site www.nytsyn.com/cartoons
Pres. — Jerry Robinson
Vice Pres./Ed. — Jens Robinson
Assoc. Ed. — Bojan Jovanovic

CATHOLIC NEWS SERVICE — 3211 4th St
NE , Washington , 20017-1104 , USA (202)
541-3250; e-mail cns@catholicnews.com; web
site www.catholicnews.com
Director/Editor in Chief — Tony Spence
General News Editor — Julie Asher
Features Editor — Edmond Brosnan
Library/Information Services/Archives —
Katherine M. Nuss
Web Editor — James LackeyNote: Catholic
news since 1920.

CINEMAN SYNDICATE — 31 Purchase St,
Ste 203, Rye, NY, 10580-3013, USA (914) 967-
5353; e-mail cinemansyndicate@verizon.net;
web site www.minireviews.com
Pub./Ed./Co-Owner — John P. McCarthy

**CITY NEWS SERVICE, INC. - LOS
ANGELES, CA** — 11400 W Olympic Blvd ,
Ste 780 , Los Angeles , 90064-1553 , USA
(310) 481-0407; fax (310) 481-0416; e-mail
citynews@pacbell.net; info@socalnews.com;
web site www.socalnews.com
Pres. — Doug Faigin
Ed. — Lori Streifler
City Ed. — Marty Sauerzopf

**CITY NEWS SERVICE, INC. - SAN DIEGO,
CA** — 202 C St , Rm 13A , San Diego ,
92101-4806 , USA (619) 231-9097; fax (619)
231-9633; e-mail fdrim@fdcglobal.net
Bureau Chief — Kelly Wheeler
Ed. — Lori Streifler

CLARIN CONTENIDOS — Tacuari 1840,
Buenos Aires, CA, 1139, Argentina; tel ; tel
(54 - 11) 4309-7216; fax 4309-7635; e-mail
contenidos@clarin.com; web site www.
clarincontenidos.com.ar
Ed. — Matilde Sanchez
Photo Editor — Agustin Beltrame
Ed. — Hernan DiMenna

CLASSICSTOCK / ROBERTSTOCK — 4203
Locust St , Philadelphia , 19104-5228 , USA
(215) 386-6300; fax (215) 386-3521; e-mail
robertag@classicstock.com; web site www.
classicstock.com
Pres., ClassicStock — H. Armstrong Roberts
Vice Pres., Creative — Roberta Groves

CLEAR CREEK FEATURES — PO Box 3289 ,
Grass Valley , 95945-3289 , USA (530) 272-
7176; e-mail clearcreekrancher@yahoo.com
Author/Self-Syndicator/Pub. — Mike
Drummond

COLLINS COMMUNICATIONS — 21-07
Maple Ave , Fair Lawn , 07410-1524 , USA
(201) 703-0911; fax (201) 703-0211; e-mail
stepoutmag@aol.com; web site www.so-mag.
com
Publisher — Lawrence Collins
Editor — Dan Lorenzo

**COMMUNICATION INTERNATIONAL/
NATIONAL NEWS** — 1423 N Orange Grove
Ave , West Hollywood , 90046-3901 , USA
(323) 876-1668; fax (323) 876-1404; e-mail
bonnie@bonniechurchill.com; web site www.
bonniechurchill.com
Pres. — Hillary Bekins
Lead Columnist — Bonnie Churchill

COMMUNITY FEATURES — 1733
Dawsonville Hwy , Gainesville , 30501-1531 ,
USA (770) 287-3798; fax (770) 287-0112;
e-mail commfeat@charter.net; web site www.
communityfeatures.com
— Christina Smith
— Bill JohnsonCo-OwnersNote: Community
Features sells and maintains church and
Bible verse pages, and offers features for
religious pages.

COMPUTERUSER — 220 S 6th St , Ste 500 ,
Minneapolis , 55402-4501 , USA (612) 339-
7571; e-mail editor@computeruser.com; web site
www.computeruser.com
Ed. — Dan Heilman
Vice Pres., Publishing — Nathaniel
Opperman

CONGRESSIONAL QUARTERLY, INC. — 77
K St NE , Fl 8, Washington, DC, 20002-4681,
USA (202) 650-6500; fax (202) 650-6741;
e-mail sales@cq.com; web site www.cq.com
Editorial Director — Mike Mills
Sr Vice pres./CFO — Douglas Wallen
Sr. Vice Pres., Sales — Jim Gale
Executive Vice President and Managing
Director — Keith White
SVP, Advertising — Mark Walters
SVP, legislative services and publisher —
Meg Hargreaves
Vice President and Publisher, advocacy,
state and transcripts
— Barkley Kern
Exec. Ed., News — Susan Benkelman

**CONSULATE GENERAL OF SWEDEN
IN NEW YORK** — 445 Park Ave , Fl 21 ,
New York , 10022-2606 , USA (212) 888-
3000; fax (212) 888-3125; e-mail newyork@
consulateofsweden.org; web site www.
swedennewyork.com

CONTENT THAT WORKS — 4410 N
Ravenswood Ave , Ste 101 , Chicago , 60640-
5873 , USA (773) 728-8351; fax (773) 728-
8326; e-mail info@contentthatworks.com; web
site www.contentthatworks.com
CEO — Paul A. Camp
COO — Jenn Goebel
Vice Pres., Sales — Dan Dalton
Editorial Director — Mary Connors

**CONTINENTAL FEATURES/CONTINENTAL
NEWS SERVICE** — 501 W Broadway ,
Ste A PMB 265 , San Diego , 92101-
3562 , USA (858) 492-8696; e-mail
continentalnewsservice@yahoo.com; web site
www.continentalnewsservice.com
Ed. in-Chief — Gary P. SalamoneNote: CF/
CNS publishes (1) Continental Newstime
general-interest newsmagazine as an
available newspaper insert, with its
individual newspaper features also marketed
separately; (2) the children's newspaper,

Kids' Newstime approximately 154-158 times a year; (3) a Northern California community newspaper regularly and a San Diego News Edition intermittently; (4) CF/CNS has launched special, periodic, on-line Washington D.C., Chicago, Atlanta, Honolulu, Miami, Anchorage, Minneapolis, Rochester (N.Y.), Houston, Seattle, and Boston News Editions; and (5) CF/CNS now offers a Country Neighbor Edition of Continental Newstime for our rural friends in the West and East.

CORBIS — 250 Hudson St , New York , 10013-1413 , USA (212) 375-7600; fax (212) 375-7700; e-mail media@corbis.com; web site www.corbis.com
Office Mgr. — Thomas Depuoz

CRAIN NEWS SERVICE (INCLUDES AUTOMOTIVE NEWS SYNDICATE) — 1155 Gratiot Ave , Detroit , 48207-2732, USA (313) 446-6000; fax (313) 446-8030; e-mail info@crain.com; web site www.crain.com
Editorial Asst. — Dan Jones

CREATIVE CIRCLE MEDIA SYNDICATION — 945 Waterman Ave , East Providence , 02914-1342 , USA ; tel ; tel (01 - 401) 455-1555; fax (401) 272-1150; e-mail info@creativecirclemedia.com; web site www.creativecirclemedia.com
Pres. — Bill Ostendorf

CREATIVE COMIC PRODUCTIONS — 1608 S Dakota Ave , Sioux Falls , 57105-1819 , USA (605) 336-9434; e-mail smoments7@aol.com ; web site www.creativecomics.net
Owner/Mgr. — Ken Alvine

CREATORS — 737 3rd St , Hermosa Beach , 90254-4714 , USA (310) 337-7003; fax (310) 337-7625; e-mail sales@creators.com; info@creators.com; web site www.creators.com
CEO — Rick Newcombe
National Sales Director — Margo Sugrue
Sales Director — Mary Ann Veldman
Vice President of Operations — Marianne Sugawara
Sales Administrator — Sheila Telle
Editor — Jessica Burtch
Editor — Anthony Zurcher
Associate, Business Development, Operations & Sales — Anica Wong
Head of development, programming and technology — Brandon Telle
Managing Editor — David Yontz
Associate, Business Development, Operations & Sales — Gunner Coil
Editor — Mikaela Conley
Editor — Simone Slykhous
Head of accounting — Sarah Follette
Production; Animator — Pete Kaminski
Accounting/finance analyst — Katie Ransom
President & COO — Jack Newcombe

CRICKET COMMUNICATIONS, INC. — PO Box 527 , Ardmore , 19003-0527 , USA (610) 924-9158; fax (610) 924-9159; e-mail crcktinc@aol.com
Pres./Pub. — Edwin Marks
Vice Pres./Ed. — Mark E. Battersby
Mng. Ed. — E. Arthur Stern

CRITICS, INC. — Dublin , 43017, USA (614) 408-3865; e-mail info@criticsinc.com; web site www.criticsinc.com
Pub./Ed. — Aris T. Christofides
Commun. Dir. — Lori Pearson
Contributing Ed. — Teressa L. Elliott
Contributing Ed. — Wade R. Gossett
Bus. Mgr. — Ethan Cuhulinn

CURT SCHLEIER REVIEWS — 646 Jones Rd , River Vale , 07675-6034 , USA (201) 391-7135; e-mail writa1@me.com
Pres./Ed. — Curt Schleier

D

DAIL ADVERTISING SERVICE — 1701 Wayne Memorial Dr, Goldsboro, NC, 27534-2239, USA (919) 736-0447; fax (919) 736-0483; e-mail dailadvertising@bellsouth.net
Nat'l Rep. — Annette W. Dail

DAVE GOODWIN & ASSOCIATES — 721 86th St , Miami Beach , 33141-1115 , USA 305) (305) 865-0158; e-mail davegoodwi@aol.com; web site www.davegoodwin.weebly.com
Author/Owner — Dave Goodwin
Writer — Ari Goodwin

DEG SYNDICATION — 25 Columbus Cir , # 55E , New York , 10019-1107 , USA (212) 2090847; fax ; e-mail expert@deg.com; web site www.deg.com
Pres./Writer — Marisa D'Vari

DERUS MEDIA SERVICE, INC. — 7702 Cass Ave , Ste 110 , Darien , 60561-5080 , USA (630) 649-9058

DISABILITY NEWS SERVICE — 13703 Southernwood Ct , Chantilly , 20151-3345 , USA (703) 437-6635

DIVORCE REALITY GROUP — 135 E Bennett St , Ste 29 , Saline , 48176-1747 , USA (734) 668-2001; fax (734) 668-1200; e-mail dell@divorcebalance.com; web site www.divorcepeers.com
Divorce Mediator — Dell Deaton

DOING BIZ IN — 1865 River Falls Dr , Roswell , 30076-5114 , USA (770) 998-9911; e-mail info@thewritepublicist.com; web site www.thewritepublicist.com
Creator/Writer — Regina Lynch-Hudson

DORK STORM PRESS/SHETLAND PRODUCTIONS — PO Box 45063 , Madison , 53744-5063 , USA (608) 222-5522; fax (608) 222-5585; e-mail john@kovalic.com; web site www.kovalic.com
Office Mgr. — Alexander Schiller
Ed. — Eleanor Williams
Business Manager — Alex Aulisi

DOW JONES NEWSWIRES - BOGOTA, COLOMBIA — Calle 93B No. 13-30 Oficina 301, Bogota, Colombia; tel ; tel (57 - 481-1785; fax 483-5623; e-mail datanewsdj@hotmail.com; web site www.dowjones.com/djnewswires.asp
Correspondent — Richard Sanders
Sales Exec. — Martha De Rengifo

DOW JONES NEWSWIRES - BRUSSELS, BELGIUM — Blvd. Brand Whitlock 87, Brussels, 1200, Belgium; tel ; tel (32 - 2) 285-0130; fax 741 1429; e-mail dirk.geeraerts@dowjones.com; vanessa.stolk@dowjones.com; web site www.dowjones.com/djnewswires.asp
Rep. — Vanessa Stolk
Correspondent — Peter Greiff
Acct. Mgr. — Dirk Geeraerts

DOW JONES NEWSWIRES - BUENOS AIRES, ARGENTINA — Leandro N. Alem 712, Piso 4, Buenos Aires, 1001, Argentina; tel ; tel (54 - 1) 4314-8788; fax 4311-0083; e-mail ana.del-riccio@dowjones.com; web site www.dowjones.com/djnewswires.asp
Correspondent — Michelle Wallin
Sales Exec. — Ana Del-Riccio

DOW JONES NEWSWIRES - FRANKFURT, GERMANY — Wilhem Leuschner Strasse 78, Frankfurt, D-60329, Germany; tel ; tel (49 - 69) 29 725 200; fax 29 725 222; web site www.dowjones.com/djnewswires.asp
Ed. — Fridrich Geiger

DOW JONES NEWSWIRES - HONG KONG, HONG KONG — 25F Central Plz., 18 Harbour Rd., Wanchai, Hong Kong, Hong Kong; tel ; tel (852 - 2573 7121; e-mail djnews.hk@dowjones.com; web site www.dowjones.com
Correspondent — Jeffrey Ng

DOW JONES NEWSWIRES - KUALA LUMPUR, MALAYSIA — Ste. 21A-8-2, 8th Floor, Faber Imperial Ct., Jalan Sultan Ismail, Kuala Lumpur, 50250, Malaysia; tel ; tel (60 - 3) (65) 6415-4200; fax (65) 6225-8959; e-mail janet.leau@dowjones.com
Correspondent — Matthew Geiger
Acct. Mgr. — Janet Leau

DOW JONES NEWSWIRES - LONDON, UNITED KINGDOM — Commodity Quay, E. Smithfield, London, E1W 1AZ, United Kingdom; tel ; tel (44 - 20) 726-7903; fax 726-7855; e-mail adam.howes@dowjones.com; web site www.dowjones.com
Regl. Sales Mgr. — Adam Howes

DOW JONES NEWSWIRES - LONDON, UNITED KINGDOM — 12 Norwich St., London, EC4A 1QN, United Kingdom; tel ; tel (44 - 227) 842-9550; fax 842-9551
Correspondent — Bhushan Bahree
Sales Mgr. — Sarah Money

DOW JONES NEWSWIRES - MADRID, SPAIN — Espronceda 32 1st Planta, Madrid, 28003, Spain; tel ; tel (34 - 91) 395-8120; fax 399-1930
Bureau Chief — Santiago Perez

DOW JONES NEWSWIRES - MANILA, PHILIPPINES — 12/F Tower One & Exchange Plaza Ayala Triangle, Ayala Ave, Makati City, Manila, Philippines; tel ; tel (63 - 2) 574-616; fax 885-0293; e-mail Lilian.Karununean@dowjones.com; web site www.djnewswires.com
Correspondent — Lilian Karununean

DOW JONES NEWSWIRES - MEXICO CITY, MEXICO — Av. Issac Newton No. 286, Piso 9, Col. Chapultepec Morales, Mexico City, 11560, Mexico 55) (525) 254-5581; fax (525) 254-7510
Correspondent — Peter R. Fritsch

DOW JONES NEWSWIRES - MILANO, ITALY — Via Burigozzo 5, Milano, 20122, Italy; tel ; tel (39 - 02) 7601-5386; fax 5821 9752
Correspondent — Susan Peiffer

DOW JONES NEWSWIRES - NEW YORK, NY — 1155 Avenue of the Americas , Fl 7 , New York , 10036-2758 , USA (609) 520-4000; e-mail SpotNews@dowjones.com; web site www.djnewswires.com
Correspondent — Gregory White

DOW JONES NEWSWIRES - NEW YORK, NY — 1211 Avenue of the Americas , New York , 10036-8701 , USA (212) 416-2400; fax (212) 416-2410; e-mail spotnews@priority.dowjones.com; web site www.djnewswires.com
Vice Pres./Gen. Mgr. — Tim Turner
Vice Pres., Sales/Mktg. — James Donoghue
Mng. Ed., Dow Jones Newswire Americas — Neal Lipschutz

DOW JONES NEWSWIRES - PARIS, FRANCE — 6-8 Boulevard Haussmann, Paris, 75009, France; tel ; tel (33 - 1) 7036 5502; fax 4017-1781; e-mail thierry.cadin@dowjones.com
Reg'l Sales Mgr. — Thierry Cadi
Correspondent — David Pearson

DOW JONES NEWSWIRES - SAO PAULO, BRAZIL — Rua Joaquim Floriano 488. 6 andar, Sao Paulo, 04534 002, Brazil; tel ; tel (55 - 11) 256-0520; fax 3044-2813; e-mail ana.gresenberg@dowjones.com
Correspondent — John Wright

Sales Exec. — Ana Gresenberg

DOW JONES NEWSWIRES - SINGAPORE, SINGAPORE — 10 Anson Rd., Ste. 32-09/10 Int'l Plz., Singapore, 079903, Singapore; tel ; tel (65 - 6415-4200; fax 6225-8959; e-mail hweekun.ho@dowjones.com
Correspondent — Lim Mui Khi
Regl. Sales Mgr. — Hwee-Kun Ho

DOW JONES NEWSWIRES - SYDNEY, AUSTRALIA — Level 10 56 Titt St., Sydney, 2000, Australia; tel ; tel (61 - 2) 8272 4600; fax 8272 4601; web site www.dowjones.com
Correspondent — Ian McDonald
Regl. Sales Mgr. — Tom Rustowski

DOW JONES NEWSWIRES - TOKYO, JAPAN — Marunouchi Mitsui Bldg. 1F, 2-2-2, Marunouchi Chiyoda-ku, Tokyo, 100 0004, Japan; tel ; tel (81 - 3) 5220 2730; fax 5220-2746; e-mail masashi.takeuchi@dowjones.com
Sales Mgr. — Masashi Takeuchi

DOW JONES NEWSWIRES - WASHINGTON, DC — 1025 Connecticut Ave NW , Ste 800 , Washington , 20036-5419 , USA (202) 862-9272; fax (202) 862-6621
Bureau Chief — Rob Wells

DOW JONES NEWSWIRES - ZURICH, SWITZERLAND — Sihlquai 253, Postfach 1128, Zurich, 8031, Switzerland; tel ; tel (41 - 43) 960 5870; fax 960 5701; e-mail sarah.money@dowjones.com; penny.greenwood@awp.ch
Sr. Acct. Mgr. — Penny Greenwood

DOWN TO BUSINESS - COLUMN — 836 Buttonwood Ct , Marco Island , 34145-2310 , USA ; tel ; tel (1 - 9782702590) 9782702590; e-mail andy.singer@singerexecutivedevelopment.com; web site www.singerexecutivedevelopment.comNote: Weekly and well liked business column sent out every Tuesday. Discusses any and all aspects of business.

DR. BEE EPSTEIN-SHEPHERD — PO Box 221383 , Carmel , 93922-1383 , USA (831) 625-3188; fax (831) 625-0611; e-mail drbeemm@aol.com; web site www.drbee.com
Mental Skills Coach/Writer — Dr. Bee Epstein-Shepherd

DSENTERTAINMENT/NORTH SHORE PUBLISHING — PO Box 318 , Vermilion , 44089-0318 , USA (440) 967-0293; fax (440) 967-0293; e-mail dave@northshorepublishing.com; dave@thecomedybook.com; web site www.thecomedybook.com; www.davelaughs.com; www.beatlesincleveland.com; www.northshorepublishing.com
Author/Award-Winning Humor Columnist — Dave Schwensen

DUNKEL SPORTS RESEARCH SERVICE — PO Box 133 , Mount Vernon , 22121-0133 , USA (202) 253-3899; e-mail dunkelratings@msn.com; web site www.dunkelindex.com
— Richard H. Dunkel Jr.
— Bob DunkelCo-Ed./Co-Owners

E

EARTH TALK: QUESTIONS & ANSWERS ABOUT OUR ENVIRONMENT — 28 Knight St , Norwalk , 06851-4719 , USA (203) 854-5559/x106; fax (203) 866-0602; e-mail earthtalkcolumn@emagazine.com; web site www.earthtalk.org
Pub./Exec. Ed. — Doug Moss

EAST-WEST NEWS BUREAU — 531 Main

St , Ste 902 , El Segundo , 90245-3060 , USA

ED FISCHER PRODUCTION — 215 Elton Hills Dr NW , Apt 56 , Rochester , 55901-2497 , USA (651) 491-3613; e-mail ed.fischer.toons@gmail.com; web site www.edfischer.com
Self-Syndicator plus 3,500 cartoons on a variety of subjects for papers, books, advertising, newsletters,magazines. 28 awards — Ed FischerNote: 75 newspapers pay to receive 9 Ed Fischer cartoons a week plus Cartoonstock. Com sells my cartoons world-wide plus selling 500,000 books

EDITOR'S COPY SYNDICATE — 6620 35th Ct E , Sarasota , 34243-2730 , USA ; e-mail christianssims@yahoo.com
Ed./Pub. — Edward H. Sims
Bus. Mgr. — Bente Christensen
Circ. Mgr. — Christian Sims

EFE NEWS SERVICES - ALGIERS, ALGERIA — 4 Ave. Pasteur, 1st Fl., Algiers, 16000, Algeria; tel ; tel (213 - 2) 173 5680; fax 174 0456; e-mail javiergarcia@efe.com
Rep. — Javier Garcia

EFE NEWS SERVICES - BEIJING, CHINA — Julong Garden, 7-14 L. Xinzhongjie, 68 Dongcheng, Beijing, 100027, China; tel ; tel (86 - 10) 6553 1198; fax 6552 7861; web site www.efe.es
Rep. — Paloma Caballero

EFE NEWS SERVICES - BERLIN, GERMANY — Reinhardtstrasse 58, Berlin, NY, 10117, Germany; tel ; tel (49 - 30) (206) 039-860; fax (206) 039-840; e-mail berlin@efe.comNoelia López

EFE NEWS SERVICES - BOGOTA, COLOMBIA — Calle 67 No 7-35, Bogota, Colombia; tel ; tel (57 - 1) 321 48 55; fax 321 47 51; e-mail efecol@efebogota.com.co
Rep. — Esther Rebollo

EFE NEWS SERVICES - BRUSSELS, BELGIUM — Residence Palace, Rue de la Loi, 155, Brussels, 1040, Belgium; tel ; tel (32 - 2) 285-4831; fax 230-9319; e-mail bruselas@efe.com
Rep. — Jose Manuel Sanz

EFE NEWS SERVICES - BUENOS AIRES, ARGENTINA — Av. Alicia Moreau de Justo 1720, Buenos Aires, 1107, Argentina; tel ; tel (54 - 11) 43 11 12 11; fax 43 12 75 18; e-mail redaccion@can.com.ar
Rep. — Mar Marin

EFE NEWS SERVICES - CAIRO, EGYPT — 4 Mohamed Mazhar, 3 - apt. 5. Zamalek, Cairo, Egypt; tel ; tel (20 - 2) 738-0792; fax 361-2198
Rep. — Grace Augustine

EFE NEWS SERVICES - GENEVA, SWITZERLAND — Bureau 49, Palas des Nations B, Ave. Paix, Geneva, 1211, Switzerland; tel ; tel (41 - 22) 7336273; e-mail ginebra@efe.com; web site www.efe.com
Bureau Chief — Celine Aemisegger

EFE NEWS SERVICES - GUATEMALA CITY, GUATEMALA — 8 Ave. 8-56 Zone 1, Edif. 10-24, Segundo Nivel, Oficina 203, Guatemala City, Guatemala; tel ; tel (502 - 2) 51 94 84; fax 51 84 59; e-mail guatemala@acan-efe.com
Rep. — Carlos Arrazola

EFE NEWS SERVICES - LA PAZ, BOLIVIA — Avda. Sanchez Lima, 2520. Edificio Anibal - MZ 01, La Paz, 7403, Bolivia; tel ; tel (591 - 2) 235-9837; fax 239-1441; e-mail efebol@entelnet.bo
Rep. — Soledad Alvarez

EFE NEWS SERVICES - LIMA, PERU — Mauel Gonzalez Olaechea, 207, Lima, 27, Peru; tel ; tel (51 - 1) 441 24 22; fax 421 13 72; e-mail lima@efe.com
Rep. — Javier Otazu

EFE NEWS SERVICES - LISBON, PORTUGAL — Rua Castilho, 13 D, 5A, Lisbon, DC, 1250 066, Portugal; tel ; tel (351 - 21) 351 39 30; fax 351 39 38; e-mail lisboa@efe.com
Rep. — Emilio Crespo

EFE NEWS SERVICES - LONDON, UNITED KINGDOM — 299 Oxford St. 6th Fl., London, W1C 2DZ, United Kingdom; tel ; tel (44 - 20) 7493 7313; fax 7493-7114
Rep. — Joaquin Rabago

EFE NEWS SERVICES - MANAGUA, NICARAGUA — Garden City S-22, Managua, Nicaragua; tel ; tel (505 - 2) 49 11 66; fax 49 59 28; e-mail nicaragua@acan-efe.com
Rep. — Philadelphus Martinez

EFE NEWS SERVICES - MANILA, PHILIPPINES — Unit 1006, 88 Corporate Center, 141 Sedeno corner, Manila, 1227, Philippines; tel ; tel (63 - 2) 843 1986; fax 843 1973; e-mail manila@efe.com; web site www.efe.es
Bureau Chief — Miguel Frau Rovira
Ed. — Marco Zabaleta

EFE NEWS SERVICES - MEXICO CITY, MEXICO — Lafayette, 69, Colonia Ave., Mexico City, 011590, Mexico; tel ; tel (52 - 55) 5545 8256; fax 5254 1412
Sales Mgr. — Alejandro Amezcua
Rep. — Manuel Fuentes

EFE NEWS SERVICES - MONTEVIDEO, URUGUAY — Wilson Ferreira Aldunate 1294, Montevideo, 11100, Uruguay; tel ; tel (598 - 2) 902 03 38; fax 902 67 26; e-mail montevideo@efe.com
Rep. — Raul Cortes

EFE NEWS SERVICES - MOSCOW, RUSSIA — Ria Novosti International Press Center, Zubovski blvd. 4, Moscow, 119021, Russia; tel ; tel (7 - 495) 637 5137; fax 637 5137; e-mail efemos@gmail.com
Rep. — Miguel Bas

EFE NEWS SERVICES - NEW DELHI, INDIA — 48, Hanuman Road. Instituto Cervantes building, Connaught Place, New Delhi, 110001, India; tel ; tel (91 - 11) 41501999; e-mail india@efe.com; web site www.efe.com
Correspondent — Moncho Torres

EFE NEWS SERVICES - PANAMA CITY, PANAMA — Avda. Samuel Lewis y Manuel Icaza. Edif. Comosa 22, Panama City, 0834 00749, Panama; tel ; tel (507 - 2) 23 90 14; fax 64 84 42; e-mail panama@acan-efe.com
Rep. — Hernan Martin

EFE NEWS SERVICES - PARIS, FRANCE — 10 rue St. Marc, Buro. 165, Paris, 75002, France; tel ; tel (33 - 1) 44 82 65 40; fax 40 39 91 78; e-mail paris@efe.com; web site www.efe.com
Rep. — Javier Alonso

EFE NEWS SERVICES - QUITO, ECUADOR — Edificio Platinum Oficinas, piso 8 C. Carlos Padilla s/n, Quito, 4043, Ecuador; tel ; tel (593 - 2) 251-9466; fax 225-5769; e-mail redacquito@efe.com
Rep. — Enrique Ibanez

EFE NEWS SERVICES - RABAT, MOROCCO — 14, rue de Kairoajne, Apt. 13,

5 ME (Angle rue d'Alger), Rabat, Morocco; tel ; tel (212 - 537) 723 218; fax 732 195; e-mail efe@menara.ma
Director — Javier Otazu
Rep. — Enrique Rubio

EFE NEWS SERVICES - RIO DE JANEIRO, BRAZIL — Praia de Botafogo, 228 Rm. 605 B, Rio de Janeiro, AL, 22359-900, Brazil; tel ; tel (55 - 212) 553-6355; fax 553-8823; e-mail rio@efebrasil.com.br; web site www.efe.com
Rep. — Jaime Ortega

EFE NEWS SERVICES - ROME, ITALY — Via dei Canestrari, 5-2, Rome, 00186, Italy; tel ; tel (39 - 06) 683-4087; fax 687-4918; e-mail roma@efe.com
Director — Javier Alonso

EFE NEWS SERVICES - SAN JOSE, COSTA RICA — Avda., 10 Calles 19/21 n. 1912, Apanado 8.4930, San Jose, 1000, Costa Rica; tel ; tel (506 - 2222-6785; fax 2233-7681; e-mail costarica@acan-efe.com; web site Curridabat
Director — Nancy De Lemos

EFE NEWS SERVICES - SAN SALVADOR, EL SALVADOR — Condominio Balam Quitze, Local 17. 2. P. General Sta., San Salvador, El Salvador; tel ; tel (503 - 263 7063; fax 263 5281; e-mail elsalvador@acan-efe.com
Rep. — Laura Barros

EFE NEWS SERVICES - SANTIAGO, CHILE — Almirante Pastene, 333 - office 502, Santiago, Chile; tel ; tel (56 - 2) 632-4946; fax 519-3912; e-mail redaccion@agenciaefe.tie.cl
Rep. — Manuel Fuentes

EFE NEWS SERVICES - SANTURCE, PUERTO RICO — Edificio Cobian's Plz., Of. 214, Av Ponce de León 1607, San Juan, PR, 00909, Puerto Rico (787) 721-8821; e-mail redacpr@efe.com
Head of Puerto Ricos Bureau — Cristina Ozaeta

EFE NEWS SERVICES - TEGUCIGALPA, HONDURAS — Col. Elvel, Segunda Calle, Apt. 2012, Tegucigalpa, Honduras; tel ; tel (504 - 231 1730; fax 231 1772; e-mail honduras@acan-efe.com
Rep. — German Reyes

EFE NEWS SERVICES - VIENNA, AUSTRIA — Rechte Wienzeile 51/16, Vienna, 1050, Austria; tel ; tel (43 - 1) 368 4174; fax 369 8842; e-mail viena@efe.com
Rep. — Ramon Santaularia

EFE NEWS SERVICES - WASHINGTON, D.C — 1252 National Press Building. 529, 14 Street, NW , Washington D.C. 20045 , Washington Post , 20045, USA ; tel ; tel ((202) - 202) 745 76 92; fax (202) 393 41 18 / 19; e-mail info@efeamerica.com; web site www.efe.com
Business Development Director — Manuel Ortega

EFE NEWS SERVICES - WASHINGTON, DC — 529 14th St NW , Washington , 20045-1217 , USA (202) 745-7692; fax (305) 262-7557; e-mail info@efeamerica.com; web site www.efe.com
Pres. — Jose Antonio Vera
Vice Pres. — Maria Luisa Azpiazu
Sales and Business Dev. Dir. — Rafael Carranza
Bureau Chief-Miami — Mar Gonzalo
Bureau Chief- New York — Elena Moreno
Marketing Coordinator — Marcela RomeroNote: EFE is the leading Spanish-language news agency and the fourth largest in the world.

ELIZABETH S. SMOOTS — 5735 27th Ave NE , Seattle , 98105-5511 , USA ; e-mail doctor@practicalprevention.com; web site www.practicalprevention.com
Self-Syndicator — Elizabeth S. Smoots MD

EUROPA PRESS NEWS SERVICE — Paseo de la Castellana, 210, Madrid, 28046, Spain; tel ; tel (91 - 359-2600; fax 350-3251; e-mail noticias@europapress.es; web site www.europapress.es

EXHIBITOR RELATIONS CO. — 1262 Westwood Blvd , Los Angeles , 90024-4801 , USA (310) 441-7400; fax (310) 475-0316; e-mail info@ercboxoffice.com; web site www.ercboxoffice.com
Pres. — Robert Bucksbaum
Box Office Analyst — Jeff Bock

F

FAMILY ALMANAC — 420 Constitution Ave NE , Washington , 20002-5924 , USA (202) 544-5698; fax (202) 544-5699; e-mail marguerite.kelly@gmail.com; web site www.margueritekelly.com
Columnist of Family Almanac, WA Post and other papers — Marguerite KellyNote: retired free-lance columnist of Family Almanac which ran in the Washington Post for 35 years and was syndicated in other papers for nearly that long.

FAMILY FEATURES EDITORIAL SYNDICATE, INC. — 5825 Dearborn St, Mission, KS, 66202-2745, USA (913) 722-0055, (800) 800-5579; fax (913) 789-9228; e-mail support@familyfeatures.com, jmillett@familyfeatures.com; web site www.familyfeatures.com
Owner — Dianne Hogerty
President — Brian Agnes
Pres. — Dena Klein
CEO — Diane Hogerty
Media Manager — Jennifer Millett

FASHION SYNDICATE PRESS — PO Box 727 , Woodstock , 05091-0727 , USA (917) 749-8421; fax (212) 242-4604; e-mail fashionshowroom@yahoo.com; web site www.fashionsyndicatepress.com
Owner — Andres Aquino
Ed. — Elaine Hallgren
Prodn. Art Dir. — Justin AlexanderNote: Films, video and photos syndication.

FEATURE PHOTO SERVICE, INC. — 450 7th Ave , Ste 1700 , New York , 10123-0096 , USA (212) 944-1060; fax (212) 944-7801; e-mail editor@ndn.com; web site https://www.featurephoto.com
Pres./CEO — Oren Hellner
Office Mgr. — Marla EdwardsNote: Photo distribution via: AP, FeaturePhoto.com, NewsCom and 25+ worldwide media partners

FEATUREWELL.COM — 238 W 4th St , New York , 10014-2610 , USA (212) 924-2283; e-mail featurewell@featurewell.com; sales@featurewell.com; contactus@featurewell.com; web site www.featurewell.com
Founder/CEO — David Wallis
CTO — Marc Deveaux

FINANCIAL TIMES — 1 Southwark Bridge, London, SE1 9HL, United Kingdom; tel ; tel (44 - 20) 7775 6248; fax 873-3070; e-mail synd.admin@ft.com; web site www.ft.com
Synd. Mgr. — Sophie DeBrito
Picture Synd. — Richard Pigden

FNA NEWS — PO Box 11999 , Salt Lake City , 84147-0999 , USA (801) 355-3336; e-mail rng2@utah.edu; web site www.fnanews.com

com
Mng. Ed. — Richard Goldberger
Energy Ed./Houston Bureau Chief — K. Rossi
Health/Wellness Ed./Los Angeles Bureau Chief — Connie Levy
Legal Affairs Ed. — Larry Long
Photo Bureau Chief — Matt D'Alessandro
Travel/Society Ed. — Cindy Richey
Technology Ed. — Marlon U. Stones
Washington Bureau Chief — Jenyfer Morris

FOCUS ON STYLE — PO Box 532 , New York , 10276-0532 , USA (212) 473-8353; e-mail information@focusonstyle.com; web site www.sharonhaver.com; www.focusonstyle.com
Syndicated Columnist, Newspaper/Online — Sharon Haver

FOOD NUTRITION HEALTH NEWS SERVICE — 1712 Taylor St NW , Washington , 20011-5313 , USA ; tel ; tel (+01 - 202) (202) 723-2477; e-mail goody.solomon@verizon.net; web site www.fnhnews.com
Owner/Exec. Ed./Author — Goody L. Solomon

FOTOPRESS INDEPENDENT NEWS SERVICE INTERNATIONAL — 266 Charlotte St., Ste. 297, Peterborough, ON, K9J 2V4, Canada (705) 745-5770; fax (705) 745-9459; e-mail kubikjohn@fotopressnews.org; web site www.fotopressnews.org
Opns. Dir. — John M. Kubik
Accts. Administrator — Steven Brown
South America Journalist — Hugo Fernandez
Central America Photo Journalist — Vincent Delgado
North America Journalist — Elizabeth McKinney Bennett
North America Journalist — Frederick Brown
North America Journalist — Irene Clark
North America Journalist — Jarrett Dubois
North America Journalist — Barbara Jividen
North America Journalist — Jacquelyn Johnson
North America Journalist — Kevin G. Marty
North America Photographer — Lauren McFaul
Australia Artist — Peter Kozak
Africa Journalist — Mulenga Chola
Africa Journalist — Luis Managonde
Africa Photographer — Nariz Bhugaloo
United Kingdom Journalist — Gordon Irving
United Kingdom Journalist — Robert O'Connor
Japan Journalist — Edward Neilam
Japan Photo Journalist — Naohiro Kimura

G

GANNETT NEWS SERVICE - ALBANY, NY — 150 State St , Albany , 12207-1646 , USA (518) 436-9781; fax (518) 436-0130
Bureau Chief — Joe Spector
Account Executive — Robert Hauptman
Account Executive — Keith Zurenda
President of Sales — Mary Murcko
VP, Gannett National Sales, USCP — Howard Griffin

GANNETT NEWS SERVICE - BATON ROUGE, LA — 900 N 3rd St , Baton Rouge , 70802-5236 , USA (225) 342-7333
Bureau Chief — Mike Hasten

GANNETT NEWS SERVICE - MCLEAN, VA — 7950 Jones Branch Dr , Mc Lean , 22108-0003 , USA (703) 854-6000; fax (703) 854-2152; e-mail candrews@gns.gannett.com; web site www.gannett.com
Office Mgr. — Marie Marino
Mng. Ed., Features/Graphics/Photography — Jeannette Barrett-Stokes
Mng. Ed., News — Phil Pruitt
Copy Desk Chief — Bev Winston

Asst. Copy Desk Chief — Michelle Washington
Regl. Ed. — Laura Rehrmann
Regl. Ed. — Val Ellicott
Regl. Ed. — Theresa Harrah
Regl./Database Ed. — Robert Benincasa
News/Sports/Technology Ed. — Craig Schwed
Photo Ed. — Jeff Franko
Special Projects Ed. — Linda Dono
Nat'l Correspondent, Defense/Security — John Yaukey
Nat'l Ed./Correspondent, Politics — Chuck Raasch
Sports Correspondent — Mike Lopresti
Regl. Correspondent, California/Nevada — Doug Abrahms
Regl. Correspondent, Colorado/Montana/Idaho — Faith Bremner
Regl. Correspondent, Delaware/Maryland/Vermont — Erin Kelly
Regl. Correspondent, Florida/Georgia — Larry Wheeler
Regl. Correspondent, Indiana/Illinois — Maureen Groppe

GARY JAMES — 111 Shearin Ave , East Syracuse , 13057-1847 , USA , e-mail garyjames111@hotmail.com; web site www.famousinterview.com
Feature Interviewer/ Investigative Journalist — Gary JamesNote: I also write for the website: www.classicbands.com
See: Rock And Roll Interviews And: www.famousinterview.com Click: Interviews

GEORGE WATERS, USA ; E-MAIL GEORGE@GEORGEWATERS.NET; WEB SITE WWW.GEORGEWATERS.NET
Humor Columnist — George Waters

DEUTSCHE PRESSE-AGENTUR (DPA) — 405 E 42nd St , Rm L0219 , New York , 10017-3507 , USA (212) 319-6626; fax (212) 753-6168; e-mail None; web site www.dpa.com
English Correspondent
International Marketing and Sales Head — Rainer Finke

GET FIT WITH THE WORLD'S FITTEST MAN — 2707 3rd Ave , San Diego , 92103-6269 , USA (858) 375-6150; e-mail info@gutcheckfitness.com; web site www.gutcheckfitness.com
Pres./Author — Joe Decker

GLENMOOR ENTERPRISE MEDIA GROUP — 75 N Main St , No 203 , Willits , 95490-3107 , USA (707) 367-4608; fax (707) 459-6106; e-mail glenmoorent@yahoo.com
Gen. Mgr. — Ron C. Moorhead

GLOBAL HORIZONS — 1330 New Hampshire Ave NW , Apt 609 , Washington , 20036-6311 , USA (202) 363-1270; e-mail edflattau@msn.com; web site www.edflattau.com
Pres. — Edward Flattau
Ed. — Pam Ebert

GLOBAL INFORMATION NETWORK — 220 5th Ave , Fl 8 , New York , 10001-7708 , USA ; tel ; tel (1 - 212) (212) 244-3123; e-mail ipsgin@igc.org
Exec. Dir. — Lisa Vives

GLOBE PHOTOS, INC. — 24 Edmore Ln S , West Islip , 11795-4016 , USA (631) 661-3131; fax (631) 321-4063; e-mail requests@globephotos.com; web site www.globephotos.com
Pres. — Mary Beth Whelan
Vice Pres. — Raymond D. Whelan

GLOBE SYNDICATE — 499 Richardson Rd , Strasburg , 22657-5236 , USA (540) 635-3229; e-mail publisher@globesyndicate.com; web

site www.globesyndicate.com
Ed./Pub. — Gavin Bourjaily
Asst. Pub./Assoc. Ed. — M.F. Bourjaily, III

GOLF PUBLISHING SYNDICATE — 2743 Saxon St , Allentown , 18103-2825 , USA (610) 437-4982; e-mail info@galvgolf.com; web site www.galvgolf.com
Pres. — Karl D. Gilbert

GOT INFLUENCE? PUBLISHING — 190 Dundee Rd , Inverness , 60010-5254 , USA (847) 359-7860; e-mail info@GotInfluenceInc.com; web site www.GotInfluenceInc.com
Founder/Self-Syndicator/Columnist — Dan Seidman

H

HEALTHY MINDS — 3709 Crestbrook Rd , Mountain Brk , 35223-1512 , USA (205) 969-2963; fax (205) 969-1972; e-mail wfleisig@hotmail.com
Writer/Self-Syndicator — Dr. Wayne Fleisig

HEARST NEWS SERVICE — 700 12th St NW , Ste 1000 , Washington , 20005-3994 , USA (202) 263-6400; fax (202) 263-6441; e-mail chuck@hearstdc.com; web site www.hearst.com
Bureau Chief — David McCumber

HEART TONES — PO Box 304 , P. O. Box 304 , Lumberton , 28359-0304 , USA (913) 433-3877; e-mail info@hearttones.com; web site www.hearttones.com
Pres./Founder — Gloria Thomas-Anderson
Public Relations Director — Tracee Jackson
Webmaster and Graphics Specialist — Tammy Iroku

HIGH COUNTRY NEWS — 119 Grand Ave , PO Box 1090, Paonia , 81428-9905 , USA (970) 527-4898; fax (970) 527-4897; e-mail hcnsyndicate@hcnsyndicate.org; web site www.hcn.org
Ed. in Chief — Jonathan Thompson
Syndicate Representative — JoeAnn Kalenak
Exec. Dir. — Paul Larmer

HISPANIC LINK NEWS SERVICE — 1420 N St NW , Washington , 20005-2843 , USA (202) 234-0280; fax (202) 234-4090; e-mail editor@hispaniclink.org; web site www.hispaniclink.org
Pub. — Carlos Ericksen-Mendoza
Capitol Hill Ed. — Patricia Guadalupe

HOLLISTER KIDS — 763 W Lancaster Ave , Ste 250 , Bryn Mawr , 19010-3401 , USA (484) 829-0024; fax (484) 829-0027; e-mail contactus@hollisterkids.com; web site www.hollisterkids.com
Pres. — Kim Landry
Vice Pres. — Peter Landry
Art Dir. — Heidi Karl

HOLLYWOOD NEWS SERVICE — 13636 Ventura Blvd , Ste 303 , Sherman Oaks , 91423-3700 , USA (818) 986-8168; fax (818) 789-8047; e-mail editor@newscalendar.com; web site www.newscalendar.com
Ed. in Chief — Carolyn Fox
Mng. Ed. — Susan Fox
Fujita Greg
Margaret Miller
John Carlin
John Fox
Editor — Sindy SaitoNote: Hollywood News Service is an entertainment wire service and does not accept solicitations for new features.

HOME IMPROVEMENT TIME, INC. — 7425 Steubenville Pike , Oakdale , 15071-9311 , USA (412) 787-2881; fax (412) 787-3233; e-mail info@homeimprovementtime.com; web

site www.homeimprovementtime.com
President — Carole C. Stewart
Website Marketing Manager — Jeff Stewart

HOT TOPICS PUBLICATIONS, INC. — PO Box 183 , Wyncote , 19095-0183 , USA (215) 635-1120; e-mail nie@hottopicshotserials.com; web site www.hottopicshotserials.com
Pres. — Deborah Carroll
Vice Pres. — Ned Carroll

HURST SPORTS MEDIA — 2740 N Pine Grove Ave , Apt 4C , Chicago , 60614-6101 , USA (773) 871-3918; e-mail hurstsportsmedia@yahoo.com; web site www.hurstsportsmedia.blogspot.com
Owner/Editor/Columnist — Bob Hurst

I

IMORTGAGEGUIDE.COM LLC — PO Box 5795 , Scottsdale , 85261-5795 , USA (480) 905-8000; fax (480) 905-8190; e-mail info@imortgageguide.com; web site www.imortgageguide.comNote: Revenue-sharing content for real estate/print and online

INDEPENDENCE FEATURE SYNDICATE — 727 E 16th Ave , Denver , 80203-2048 , USA (303) 279-6536; fax (303) 279-4176; e-mail mike@i2i.org; web site www.independenceinstitute.org
Pres. — Jon Caldara
Research Dir. — David Kopel
Media/Publications Mgr. — Mike Krause

INMAN NEWS — 4225 Hollis St , Emeryville , 94608-3507 , USA ; tel ; tel (1 - 720) (720)635-9065; e-mail amber@inman.com; web site 4225 Hollis Street
Assoc. Ed. — Andrea Brambila
Ed. In Chief — Amber Taufen
Assoc. Ed. — Caroline Feeney

INTERNATIONAL PHOTO NEWS — 2902 29th Way , West Palm Beach , 33407-6742 , USA (561) 683-9090; fax (561) 683-9090; e-mail jay@jaykravetz.com
— Jay N. Kravetz
— Cheryl DupreeEd.s

INTERNATIONAL PUZZLE FEATURES — 4507 Panther Pl , Charlotte , 28269-3189 , USA (704) 921-1818; fax (704) 597-1331; e-mail publisher@cleverpuzzles.com; web site www.cleverpuzzles.com
Owner — Pat Battaglia

J

J FEATURES — PO Box 70 , Cohasset , 02025-0070 , USA (781) 383-9858; fax (781) 383-6688; e-mail jfeatures@aol.com
Columnist — Chuck A. Jaffe
Syndicate Mgr. — Susan Biddle Jaffe

J.D. CROWE — 212 Fig Ave , Fairhope , 36532-1415 , USA (251) 219-5676; fax (251) 219-5799; e-mail jdcrowe@AL.com; web site http://connect.al.com/user/jcrowe/posts.html
Statewide Editorial Cartoonist, AL.com & Alabama Media Group — J.D. CroweNote: Artizans.com

JAMES RAIA — 122 43rd St , Sacramento , 95819-2102 , USA (916) 508-5122; e-mail james@jamesraia.com; web site www.jamesraia.com
Self-Syndicator — James RaiaNote: The Weekly Driver is a automotive column featuring new and vintage car reviews and automotive news, www.theweeklydriver.com. It appears on Sunday in two newspapers in the Bay Area News Group as well as monthly

in Gulfshore Business, a monthly business magazine in Naples, Florida.

JANDON FEATURES — 2319 S 105th Ave , Omaha , 68124-1821 , USA (402) 502-4367; e-mail jan@riggenbach.info; web site www.midwestgardening.com
Columnist — Jan RiggenbachNote: Garden columns and features for Midwestern U.S. newspapers only. Midwest Gardening, 1tw illus. 450 words; Garden Variety, 1tw illus. 200 words.

JASON LOVE (HUMOR FEATURES) — 165 N 5th St , Apt 208 , Port Hueneme , 93041-3061 , USA (805) 271-9560; e-mail mail@jasonlove.com; web site www.jasonlove.com
Sole Proprietor — Jason Love
Office Mgr. — Yahaira Quintero
Agent — Philippe Marquis
Writer — Rima Rudner
Illustrator — Vladimir Stankovski
Illustrator — Jose Angel (Gogue) Rodriguez
Illustrator — Thaum Blumel

JEWISH TELEGRAPHIC AGENCY, INC. — 24 W 30th St , 4 , New York , 10001-4443 , USA (212) 643-1890; fax (212) 643-8498; e-mail newsdesk@jta.org; web site www.jta.org

JIJI PRESS AMERICA LTD. — 120 W 45th St , Ste 1401 , New York , 10036-4062 , USA (212) 575-5830; fax (212) 764-3950; e-mail edit@jijiusa.com; web site www.jiji.com
Pres. — Hiroshi Masuda

JOE HARKINS — 2595 John F Kennedy Blvd , Jersey City , 07306-6014 , USA (201) 985-2105; e-mail joe@travelthenet.com; web site www.travelthenet.com
Self-Syndicator — Joe Harkins

JONATHON ALSOP (BOSTON WINE SCHOOL) — 1354 Commonwealth Ave , Allston , 02134-3809 , USA (617) 784-7150; fax (888) 833-9528; e-mail jalsop@BostonWineSchool.com; web site www.bostonwineschool.com
Wine Writer/Self-Syndicator — Jonathon Alsop

JOURNAL PRESS SYNDICATE — 545 W End Ave , Apt 2C , New York , 10024-2723 , USA (212) 580-8559; e-mail ijbnyc@aol.com
Ed. — Irwin J. Breslauer
Mng. Ed. — John Lynker
Automotive Ed. — Todd Lewis
Comics Ed. — William Kresse

K

KAREN M. ENGBERG, M.D. — 334 S Patersons Ave Ste 120 , Goleta , 93111 , USA (805) 683-0055; fax (805) 683-0149; e-mail kengbergmd@aol.com; web site www.jacksonmedicalgroup.com
Self-Syndicator — Karen M. Engberg, M.D.

KEISTER WILLIAMS NEWSPAPER SERVICES, INC. — 1807 Emmet St N, Ste 6B, Charlottesville, VA, 22901-3616, USA (434) 293-4709; fax (434) 293-4884; e-mail ky@kwnews.com; web site www.kwnews.com
Pres./Treasurer — Walton C. (Ky) Lindsay
Vice Pres., Mktg. — Meta L. Nay
Admin. — Carol Lindsay
Pres. — Walton Lindsay

KEYSTONE PICTURES — 408 N El Camino Real , San Clemente , 92672-4717 , USA (949) 481-3747; fax (949) 481-3941; e-mail info@zumapress.com; web site www.zumapress.com
Dir. — Scott McKiernan

KID SCOOP — PO Box 1802 , Sonoma , 95476-1802 , USA (707) 996-6077; fax (707) 938-8718; e-mail thescoop@kidscoop.com; web site www.kidscoop.com
Pres./CEO — Vicki Whiting

KING & KANGO KOMIX & ILLUSTRATIONS — PO Box 7914 , Vallejo , 94590 , USA (707) 704-2086; e-mail Tuckyart@att.net; web site www.tuckyart.com
Pub. — Tucky McKey

KING FEATURES SYNDICATE — 300 W 57th St , 41 , New York, NY, 10019-3741, USA (212) 969-7550; fax (646) 280-1550; e-mail kfs-public-relations@hearst.com; web site www.kingfeatures.com
VP., Gen. Mgr. — Keith McCloat
Gen. Mgr., King Feat. Weekly Service — Inside Sales — David Cohea
Dir., PR — Claudia Smith
Sr. Sales Consultant/Printing & New England Newspaper Sales — Jack Walsh
Inside Sales Mgr — Dennis Danko
Sales Mgr., New Media Inside Sales — Michael Mancino
VP, Syndication Sales — John Killian
Editorial Dir., King Feat. Weekly Service — Jim Clarke
Gen. Mgr., Syndication — Brendan Burford
SE Sales — Randy Noble
Executive Editor — Diana Smith
Senior Comics Editor — Evelyn Smith
Senior Features Editor — Chris Richcreek
Western Region Sales — Curtis Trammell
International Sales Consultant — Robin Graham
Sales Coordinator — Monique Prioleau
President — C.J. Kettler

KYODO NEWS INTERNATIONAL, INC. — 780 3rd Ave , Rm 1103 , New York , 10017-2158 , USA (212) 508-5440; fax (212) 508-5441; e-mail kni@kyodonews.com; web site www.kyodo.co.jp; www.kyodonews.com
Vice President — Toshi Mitsudome

L

LEVIN REPRESENTS — 2402 4th St , Apt 6 , Santa Monica , 90405-3664 , USA (310) 392-5146; fax (310) 392-3856; e-mail deblevin@aol.com; web site www.callahanonline.com
Pres. — Deborah Levin

LISTENING, INC. — 105 E 3rd St , Hobart , 46342-4308 , USA (219) 947-5478; e-mail info@familiesbesafe.com; web site listeninginc.com
Pres. — Patricia Work Bennett
Vice Pres. — Richard Bennett

LITERARY FEATURES SYNDICATE — 92 East St , North Grafton , 01536-1806 , USA (508) 839-4404; e-mail nick@gentlymad.com
Pres. — Constance V. Basbanes
Mng. Ed./Columnist — Nicholas A. Basbanes

LONA O'CONNOR — 2751 S Dixie Hwy , West Palm Beach , 33405-1233 , USA (561) 820-4100; e-mail lona_oconnor@pbpost.com; web site www.palmbeachpost.com
Author, journalist — Lona O'Connor

M

MAGNUM PHOTOS, INC. — 12 W 31st St , 11 , New York , 10001-4415 , USA (212) 929-6000; fax (212) 929-9325; e-mail photography@magnumphotos.com; web site www.magnumphotos.com

MAKING IT PRODUCTIONS — 2200 Pacific Coast Hwy , Ste 206 , Hermosa Beach , 90254-2701 , USA 310-469-8429; e-mail krobinson@makingit.com; web site www.makingit.com
Cartoonist/Owner — Keith Robinson
Artists Representative — Emily Reichbach
Archivist — Karen Overstreet
Office Manager — Mary HayesNote: With Universal uClick: gocomics.com/making-it

MALE CALL — 721 Shore Acres Dr , Mamaroneck , 10543-4214 , USA (914) 698-0721; e-mail lois.fenton @prodigy.net
Columnist/Advice, Men's Business & Social Dress Consultant/Men's Personal Shopper, Blogger — Lois FentonNote: Columnist/Advice, Men's Business & Social Dress Consultant/Men's Personal Shopper, Blogger

MARION JOYCE — 52 Sagamore Rd , Bronxville , 10708-1544 , USA (914) 961-2020; fax (914) 793-3434
Pres. — Marion Joyce

MARKET NEWS INTERNATIONAL — 40 Fulton St , 5 , New York , 10038-5092 , USA (212) 669-6400; fax (212) 608-3024; e-mail tony@marketnews.com; web site www.marketnews.com
Mng. Ed. — Tony Mace
Washington Bureau Chief — Denis Gulino
London Bureau Chief/European Ed. — Kevin Woodfield
managing editor — John Carter
Clive TillbrookNote: Market News Service has bureaus in New York, Chicago, Washington DC, London, Frankfurt, Berlin, Paris, Brussels, Beijing, Tokyo, Singapore and Sydney.

MARKS & FREDERICK ASSOC., LLC — 11 Green Hill Rd , Kent , 06757-1246 , USA (860) 927-3948; fax (860) 927-3062; e-mail info@mfamedia.com; web site www.mfamedia.com
Pres. — Ted MarksNote: Marks & Frederick Associates represents various publishing interests in Europe and Asia.

MATURE LIFE FEATURES — 3911 Kendall St , San Diego , 92109-6130 , USA (858) 483-3412; e-mail cecilscag@aol.com; web site www.maturelifefeatures.com
Ed. in Chief/Financial Ed. — Cecil F. Scaglione
Book Ed. — Beverly Rahn Scaglione
Nat'l Affairs/Health Ed. — James B. Gaffney
Travel Ed. — Igor Lobanov

MEADOWLANDS MEDIA GROUP — 20 Nevins St , Rutherford , 07070-2819 , USA (201) 939-7875; fax (201) 896-8619; e-mail salfino@comcast.net; web site www.rotoaction.com
Pres. — Catherine Salfino
Columnist — Michael Salfino
Columnist — David Ferris

MEDIA GENERAL SYNDICATION SERVICES — 418 N Marshall St , Winston Salem , 27101-2815 , USA (800) 457-1156; fax (336) 727-7461; e-mail jsarver@wsjournal.com
Rep. — Jodi Stephenson Sarver

MEGALO MEDIA — PO Box 1503 , New York , 10021-0042 , USA (212) 861-8048; e-mail megalomedia@lawtv.com; web site www.megalomedia.biz; www.crossword.org
Pres. — J. Baxter Newgate
Ed./Vice Pres. — Sandy Applegreen
Assoc. Ed. — Paul Merenbloom
Puzzle Ed. — Arthur Wynne

METRO EDITORIAL SERVICES — 519 8th Ave, 18, New York, NY, 10018-4577, USA (212) 947-5100; fax (212) 714-9139; e-mail mes@metro-email.com; web site www.mcg.

metrocreativeconnection.com
Publisher — Robert Zimmerman
Exec. Vice Pres./Mktg. Dir. — Debra Weiss
Mktg. Mgr. — Lauren Lekoski
VP, Sales — Jo Ann Shapiro
Regional Sales Mgr. — Lou Ann Sornson
Regional Sales Mgr. — Tina Dentner
Regional Sales Mgr. — Cathy Agee
Regional Sales Mgr. — Gwen Tomaselli
Regional Sales Mgr. — Jennifer Steiner
Joann JohnsonNote: Metro is a leading provider of advertising, creative and editorial resources designed to help media companies make money with their print, online, and mobile products. We provide ready-to-use images, ads, stock-quality photos, logos/trademarks, auto photos, marketing/sales materials, copyright-free features, print templated sections, online e-Sections, and groundbreaking digital ad development tools, plus custom image, ad design and editorial services.

MIC INSURANCE SERVICES — 170 Kinnelon Rd , Rm 11 , Kinnelon , 07405-2324 , USA (973) 492-2828; fax 973-492-9068; web site www.micinsurance.com
Pres./Author — Irene C. Card
Sec./Treasurer/Author — Betsy ChandlerNote: Medical Insurance Claims, Inc. changed name to MIC Insurance Services

MIDWEST FEATURES SYNDICATE — PO Box 259623 , Madison , 53725-9623 , USA (608) 274-8925; e-mail info@roadstraveled.com; web site www.roadstraveled.com; www.marybergin.com
Columnist — Mary BerginNote: Producing since 2002 weekly travel columns, with art, usually about America's Heartland, especially the Upper Midwest.

MIKO'S PACIFIC NEWS SERVICE — 33280 E Nimrod St , Solon , 44139-4433 , USA (203) 378 2893; e-mail bmiko@pacificdialogue.com; web site www.pacificdialogue.com
Ed. — Robert J. Miko

MILITARY UPDATE — PO Box 231111 , Centreville , 20120-7111 , USA (703) 830-6863; e-mail tomphilpott@militaryupdate.com; web site www.militaryupdate.com
Self-Syndicator — Tom PhilpottNote: For daily newspapers near military bases across the country, Military Update has for 20 years covered breaking news affecting service members — active, reserve, retirees and family members.

MILLIGAN SYNDICATE — 981 Longmeadow Ct , Lake Barrington , 60010-9120 , USA (847) 381-1593
— Molly Milligan
— Annie MilliganEd.sNote: Milligan Syndicate has retired. Thank you for years of service. Molly Milligan

MORRIS NEWS SERVICE — 229 Peachtree St NE , Ste 202 , Atlanta , 30303-1600 , USA (404) 589-8424; fax (404) 589-8429; e-mail john.winters@morris.com; web site www.morrisnewsservice.com

MOTOR NEWS MEDIA CORP. — 3710 SE Capitol Cir , Ste F , Grimes , 50111-5046 , USA (515) 986-1155; e-mail motornewsmedia@live.com; web site www.motornewsmedia.com
Pres./CEO — Kenneth J. ChesterNote: automotive news and photography service.

MOVE, INC. — 30700 Russell Ranch Rd , Westlake Village , 91362-9500 , USA (805) 557-2300; fax (805) 557-2680; e-mail corporateinfo@move.com; web site www.marketing.move.com
Chrmn. — Joe F. Hanauer

CEO — W. Michael Long

N

NATIONAL NEWS BUREAU — PO Box 43039 , Philadelphia , 19129-3039 , USA ; tel ; tel (+01 - 215) (215) 849-9016; fax 215-754-4488; e-mail nnbfeature@aol.com; fashionnnb@aol.com; travelnnb@aol.com; foodandwinennb@aol.com; booksnnb@aol.com; web site www.nationalnewsbureau.com
Pub./Ed. in Chief — Harry Jay Katz
Fashion/Beauty/Lifestyles Ed. — Debra Renee Cruz
Features Ed. — Andy EdelmanNote: We specialize in fashion, food, wine, theater, movie reviews, celebrity interviews, Our "BEST" series from kitchen appliances to household items, travel to exotic, romantic destinations, men and women's apparel.

NEW ENGLAND NEWS SERVICE, INC. — 66 Alexander Rd , Newton , 02461-1831 , USA 617-244-3075; e-mail nenewsnow@rcn.com
Bureau Chief — Milton J. Gun
Staff — Lee Ann Jacob
Staff — Eleanor Margolis
Staff — Howard Neal
Staff — Kate Tattlebaum
Corresp. — Steve Richards

NEW LIVING SYNDICATE — 99 Waverly Ave , Apt 6D , Patchogue , 11772-1922 , USA (631) 751-8819; e-mail charvey@newliving.com; web site www.newliving.com
Pub./Ed. in Chief — Christine Lynn Harvey

NEW YORK PRESS PHOTOGRAPHERS ASSOCIATION — 225 W 36th St , Ste 1-P , New York , 10018-7525 , USA ; tel ; tel ((212) 889-6633 - (212) 889-6634); e-mail office@nyppa.org; web site www.nyppa.org

NEWS LICENSING — The News Building, 13th Floor,, 1 London Bridge, London, SE1 9GF, United Kingdom; tel ; tel (44 - 207) 711 7888; fax n/a; e-mail enquiries@newslicensing.co.uk; web site www.newslicensing.co.uk
Licensing Sales Mngr. — Darren Hendry

NEWSCOM — 375 S Chipeta Way , Ste B , Salt Lake City , 84108-1261 , USA (801) 584-3900; fax (202) 383-6190; e-mail sales@newscom.com; web site www.newscom.com
Gen. Mgr. — Bill Creighton
Sales Mgr. — Tom Bannon
IP Rel. Mgr. — Lily Cheung
Mktg. Dir. — Ericka Calvert

NEWSFINDER — 1700 E Racine Ave , Waukesha , 53186-6934 , USA , (262) 544-5252; e-mail nf-support@newsfinder.com; web site www.newsfinder.com
Gen. Mgr. — Sandy Hamm
Acct. Mgr. — Linda Kalinowski
Account Manager — Colleen HammNote: Full AP wire of stories and photos for non-daily publications.

NEWSUSA, INC. — 1069 W Broad St, Ste 205, Falls Church, VA, 22046-4610, USA (703) 462-2700; web site www.newsusa.com
Vice Pres., Sales — Richard Rothstein
Pub. — Rick SmithNote: www.newsusa.com/articles
Free RSS feed of articles for websites

NORTH AMERICA SYNDICATE — 300 W 57th St , Fl 41 , New York , 10019-3741 , USA (212) 969-7550; fax (646) 280-1550; e-mail kfs-public-relations@hearst.com; web site www.kingfeatures.com
Pres. — T.R. Shepard III
Vice Pres./Gen. Mgr. — Keith McCloat
VP, Syndication Sales — John Killian
Gen. Mgr., King Feat. Weekly Service —

David Cohea
Sr. Sales Consultant/Printing & New England Newspaper Sales — Jack Walsh
PR Dir. — Claudia Smith
Inside Sales Mgr. — Dennis Danko
Sales Mgr., New Media Inside Sales Rep — Michael Mancino
Gen. Mgr., Syndication — Brendan Burford
Editorial Dir., King Feat. Weekly Service — Jim Clarke
SE Sales — Randy Noble
West Coast Sales — Curtis Trammell
International Sales Consultant — Robin Graham
Executive Editor — Diana Smith
Senior Features Editor — Chris Richcreek
Senior Comics Editor` — Evelyn Smith
Sales Coordinator — Monique PrioleauNote: North America Syndicate is an affiliated company of King Features Syndicate.

NORTH AMERICAN PRECIS SYNDICATE, INC. — 415 Madison Ave, Fl 12, New York, NY, 10017-7947, USA (212) 867-9000; fax (800) 990-4329; e-mail service@napsnet.com; info@napsnet.com; web site www.napsnet.com
Pres. — Dorothy York
Vice Pres., Media Rel. — Gary Lipton
Ed. in Chief — Candace Leiberman
Serv. Mgr. — Yauling Wagner

O

OASIS NEWSFEATURES, INC. — PO Box 2144 , Middletown , 45402 , USA (800) 245-7515; e-mail kwilliams@oasisnewsfeatures.com; web site www.oasisnewsfeatures.com
Exec. Ed. — Kevin Williams

ON THE HOUSE SYNDICATION, INC. — 2420 Sand Creek Rd , C-1318 , Brentwood , 94513-2707 , USA (925) 432-7246 x24; fax (925) 420-5690; e-mail info@onthehouse.com; web site www.onthehouse.com
Pres./Co-Host — James Carey
Vice Pres./Co-Host — Morris Carey
Affiliate Rel. Dir. — Sylvie Castaniada

P

PACIFIC NEWS SERVICE — 209 9th St , Ste 200 , San Francisco , 94103-6800 , USA ; tel ; tel ((415) 503-4170 - (415) 503-0970); e-mail eshore@newamericamedia.org; web site www.newamericamedia.org

PAPPOCOM — 3 Birch Ledge Rd , Glen , 03838-6453 , USA (603) 383-6729; e-mail info@waynegouldpuzzles.com; web site www.waynegouldpuzzles.com
Dir. — Wayne Gould
Mgr. — Scott Gould

PARENT TO PARENT — 2464 Taylor Rd , Ste 131 , Wildwood , 63040-1222 , USA (636) 236-6236 ; fax (636) 458-7688; e-mail editor@parenttoparent.com; web site www.parenttoparent.com
Owner — Jodie Lynn
Personal Assistant
Assistant Editor — Kyle JohnsonNote: Self syndicated

PEARY PERRY ENTERPRISES — 2002 N Greens Blvd , Richmond , 77406-6673 , USA ; tel ; tel (001 - 512) (512) 653-8545; fax 832-201-9818; e-mail pperry@pearyperry.com; web site www.pearyperry.com
Self-Syndicator/Columnist
Local & National Publications
www.pearyperry.com
— Peary PerryNote: Political column- 'A Nation of Fools'
General commentary on life (satire) - 'Letters From North America'

Trivia column- 'Ponder Points'

PEDIATRIC POINTS — 5 Chain Bridge Dr , Newburyport , 01950-1723 , USA (978) 476-9121; fax (978) 521-8372; e-mail carolynroybornstein@gmail.com; web site www.carolynroybornstein.com
MD — Carolyn Roy-Bornstein

PHOTOSOURCE INTERNATIONAL — 1910 35th Ave , Osceola , 54020-5602 , USA (715) 248-3800; fax (715) 248-3800; e-mail psi2@photosource.com; web site www.photosource.com
Editorial Dir. — Jeri EnghNote: N/A

PLAIN LABEL PRESS — 1690 Carman Mill Dr , Manchester , 63021-7107 , USA (636) 207-9880; fax (636) 207-9880; e-mail mail@plainlabelpress.com; web site www.creativeon-line.com/syndicate
Vice Pres./Mng. Ed. — Ed Chermoore
Submissions Ed. — Laura Meyer

PR NEWSWIRE — 350 Hudson St, Ste 300, New York, NY, 10014-4504, USA 1.888-776-0942; e-mail MediaInquiries@prnewswire.com; web site www.prnewswire.com
Audience Relations Manager — Christine Cube
SVP, Global Operations — Dave Haapaoja
VP, Strategic Communications & Content — Victoria Harres

PRACTICAL ECOMMERCE — 125 S Park St , Ste 430 , Traverse City , 49684-3610 , USA (231) 946-0606; e-mail kmurdock@practicalecommerce.com; web site http://www.practicalecommerce.com
Pub and Ed — Kerry Murdock
Senior Contributing Editor — Armando Roggio

PRESS ASSOCIATES, INC. — 2605 P St NW , Ste A , Washington , 20007-5029 , USA (202) 898-4825; e-mail press_associates@yahoo.com
Ed. in Chief — Mark J. Gruenberg
Ed. — Janet Brown
Cartoonist — Dick Belland
Accounting — Martha Turner

PUNCH IN TRAVEL, FOOD, WINE & ENTERTAINMENT NEWS SYNDICATE — 400 E 59th St , Apt 9F , New York , 10022-2344 , USA (212) 755-4363; e-mail info@punchin.com; web site www.punchin.com
Pres./Mng. Ed. — Nancy Preiser
Contributing Writer — Betty Andrews
Contributing Writer — Bob Andrews
Contributing Writer — John Edwards
Contributing Writer — Bette Johns
Contributing Writer — Nina Lindt
Contributing Writer — Tom Weston

Q

Q SYNDICATE — 20222 Farmington Rd , Livonia , 48152-1412 , USA (734) 293-7200; fax (734) 293-7201; e-mail qsyndicate@pridesource.com; web site www.qsyndicate.com
Pres. — Susan Horowitz
CFO — Jan Stevenson
Ed. — Christopher AzzopardiNote: Q Syndicate provides content and community to the gay and lesbian press.

R

RAFFERTY CONSULTING GROUP — 45775 Indian Wells Ln , Indian Wells , 92210-8835 , USA (760) 776-9606; fax (760) 776-9608;

e-mail rrafferty@raffertyconsulting.com; web site www.raffertyconsulting.com
Pres. — Renata J. Rafferty

REEL TO REAL CELEBRITY PROFILES — 8643 N Fielding Rd , Milwaukee , 53217-2427 , USA ; web site david.fantle@gmail.com; web site www.reeltoreal.com
— David Fantle
— Tom JohnsonCreator/WritersNote: We specialize in interviews with stars that have a track record and appeal to 50 plus readers. We do not need to be pitched reality stars or young "flavor of the month" stars who desperately need some press.

RELIGION NEWS SERVICE — 529 14th St NW , Ste 1009 , Washington , 20045-2001 , USA (202) 463-8777; fax (202) 662-7154; e-mail info@religionnews.com; web site www.religionnews.com
Senior Editor — David E. Anderson
Editor-in-Chief — Kevin Eckstrom
Editorial/Publishing Consultant — Tracy Gordon
Production Editor — Adelle Banks
Associate Editor — Daniel Burke
National Correspondent — Lauren Markoe
Bus./Sales Mgr. — Claudia M. Sans Werner
Bus. Coord. — David Shaw

REUTERS — 3 Times Sq , Fl 17 , New York , 10036-6564 , USA

REUTERS — 311 S Wacker Dr , Ste 1200 , Chicago , 60606-6623 , USA

REUTERS MEDIA — 3 Times Sq, New York, NY, 10036-6564, USA (646) 223-4000; fax (646) 223-4393; e-mail rosalina.thomas@thomsonreuters.com; web site www.reuters.com/newsagency
Vice Pres./Head of Sales - The Americas, Reuters News Agency, Thomson Reuters — Ms. Rosalina Thomas
Publishing Solutions Specialist — Melissa Metzger
Global Director of Marketing — Bipasha Ghosh

RICK HOROWITZ — 4014 N Morris Blvd , Shorewood , 53211-1844 , USA (414) 963-9333; e-mail rickhoro@execpc.com; web site www.huffingtonpost.com/rick-horowitz/
Self-Syndicator — Rick Horowitz
Webmaster — Charlie White

RON BERNTHAL — PO Box 259 , Hurleyville , 12747-0259 , USA ; tel ; tel (1 - (845) 292-3071; fax (845) 434-4806; e-mail ronbernthal@wjffradio.org
Self-Syndicator, Travel/Historic Preservation Audio Programs — Ron Bernthal

S

SAM MANTICS ENTERPRISES — 3650 Mockingbird Dr , Vero Beach , 32963-1514 , USA (772) 492-9032; fax (772) 492-9032; e-mail jancook@myvocabulary.com; web site www.syndicate.com; myvocabulary.com; www.rootonym.com
Pres./Cartoon Ed. — Carey Orr Cook
Bus. Devel. — Jan Cook
Sr. Vice Pres., Mktg./Sales — Keith Cook
Internet/Web Ed. — Kylie Cook
Prodn. Mgr. — Brad Cook
Senior Ed. — Corry CookNote: We syndicate vocabulary word puzzles, word games and educational activities (K-12+.)

SCHWADRON CARTOON & ILLUSTRATION SERVICE — PO Box 1347 , Ann Arbor , 48106-1347 , USA (734) 665-8272; fax (734) 665-8272; e-mail schwaboo@comcast.net; web site www.

schwadroncartoons.com
  Ed. — Harley Schwadron
  Sec. — Sally Booth

SCRIPPS HOWARD NEWS SERVICE
— 1090 Vermont Ave NW , Ste 1000 ,
Washington , 20005-4965 , USA (202) 408-
1484; fax (202) 408-5950; web site www.shns.
com
  Ed./Gen. Mgr. — Peter Copeland
  Chief Tech. Officer/Webmaster — David
  Johnson
  Sales & Mktg. Contact/Sr. Vice Pres. & Gen.
  Mgr., United Media — Lisa Klem Wilson
  Desk Ed. — Bob Jones
  Sports Ed. — John Lindsay

**SCRIPPS-MCCLATCHY WESTERN
SERVICES** — 1090 Vermont Ave NW , Ste
1000 , Washington , 20005-4965 , USA (202)
408-1484; fax (202) 408-5950

SENIOR WIRE NEWS SERVICE — 2377
Elm St , Denver , 80207-3206 , USA (303)
355-3882; e-mail clearmountain@tde.com; web
site www.seniorwire.net
  Pub./Ed. — Allison St. ClaireNote: Contact
  through website or email. Use submission
  or query and subject of article in subject line
  for editorial matter. Paste stories into email
  rather than as an attachment.

SERVICEQUALITY.US — 1063 Todos Santos
Sta , Concord , 94522, USA (925) 798-
0896; fax (925) 215-2320; e-mail support@
servicequality.us; web site www.service-quality.
com
  Pres. — Dr. Jeffrey S. Kasper

SHARPNACK, JOE — PO Box 3325 , Iowa
City , 52244-3325 , USA (319) 512 9705;
e-mail sharptoons@yahoo.com; web site www.
sharptoons.com
  Self-Syndicator — Joe Sharpnack

SIPA NEWS SERVICE — 59 E 54th St , New
York , 10022-4211 , USA (212) 758-0740; fax
(212) 593-5194; e-mail info@leadersmag.com;
web site www.leadersmag.com
  Chrmn./Ed. in Chief — Henry O. Dormann
  Vice Pres./Exec. Ed. — Darrell Brown

SLIGHTLY OFF! — 24730 Illini Dr , Plainfield ,
60544-2435 , USA (815) 954-5817; e-mail
deb@slightlyoff.com; web site www.slightlyoff.
com
  Author/Owner — Deb DiSandro

SOVFOTO/EASTFOTO — 263 W 20th St , Apt
3 , New York , 10011-3542 , USA (212) 727-
8170; fax (212) 727-8228; e-mail info@sovfoto.
com; web site www.sovfoto.com
  President — Vanya Edwards

SPECTRUM FEATURES SYNDICATE —
2351 Wyda Way , Apt 1113 , Sacramento ,
95825-1609 , USA (916)417-1688; e-mail
editor@greeleyandstone.com; web site www.
greeleyandstone.com
  Ed. in Chief — Walter Brasch
  Exec. Ed. — Rose Renn
  Assoc. Ed. — Matt Gerber
  Art/Prodn. Dir. — Mary Jayne Reibsome
  Dir. of Mktg. — Diana Saavedra

SPRINGER FOREIGN NEWS SERVICE
— 500 5th Ave , Ste 2800 , New York , 10110-
0002 , USA (212) 983-1983

STADIUM CIRCLE FEATURES — 82 Nassau
St , Ste 521 , New York , 10038-3703 , USA
(917) 267-2493; e-mail info@paperpc.net; web
site www.paperpc.com
  Ed./Columnist — Robert AnthonyNote: Home
  of the Paper PC blog: www.paperpc.com .
  Twitter: @newyorkbob
  Pinterest: Top 250 worldwide with 1.2 million

followers: www.paperpcpicks.com

STARCOTT MEDIA SERVICES, INC. —
6906 Royalgreen Dr , Cincinnati , 45244-4004 ,
USA (513) 231-6034; e-mail dulley@dulley.
com; contact@dulley.com; web site www.
dulley.com
  Pres. — James T. Dulley

STATE NET — 2101 K St, Sacramento, CA,
95816-4920, USA (916) 444-0840; fax (916)
446-5369; e-mail info@statenet.com; web site
www.statenet.com
  — Laurie Stinson
  — Jud ClarkPres.s

**STRAIGHT DOPE - WRAPPORTS/SUN-
TIMES MEDIA, INC.** — 350 N Orleans St ,
Chicago , 60654-1975 , USA ; e-mail cecil@
straightdope.com; web site www.straightdope.
com
  Creator/Writer — Cecil Adams
  Editor/General Mgr — Ed ZottiNote: Direct
  business inquiries to:
  webmaster@straightdope.com

SUN FEATURES — 1100 Garden View Rd ,
Apt 122 , Encinitas , 92024-1360 , USA (760)
652-5302; e-mail jlk@sunfeatures.com; web
site www.sunfeatures.com
  Pres. — Joyce Lain Kennedy
  Vice Pres. — Tim K. Horrell

SYLVIA DI PIETRO — 55 W 14th St , Apt
4H , New York , 10011-7409 , USA (212)
242-8800; fax (212) 633-6298; e-mail info@
sylviadipietro.com; web site www.sylviadipietro.
com
  Self-Syndicator — Sylvia Di Pietro

T

**TAIPEI ECONOMIC & CULTURAL OFFICE,
PRESS DIVISION - NEW YORK, NY** — 1E
E 42nd St , Fl 11 , New York , 10017-6904 ,
USA ; tel ; tel (002 - 212) (212) 557-5122; fax
(212) 557-3043; e-mail roctaiwan@taipei.org;
web site www.taiwanembassy.org
  Contact — Ching Yi Ting

**TAIPEI ECONOMIC & CULTURAL
REPRESENTATIVE OFFICE, PRESS
DIVISION - WASHINGTON, DC** — 4201
Wisconsin Ave NW , Washington , 20016-
2146 , USA (202) 895-1800; fax (202) 362-
6144; e-mail tecroinfodc@tecro.us; web site
http://www.roc-taiwan.org/US
  Dir. Press — Frank Wang

**TAIPEI ECONOMIC AND CULTURAL
OFFICE IN CHICAGO** — 55 W Wacker Dr ,
Ste 1200 , Chicago , 60601-1797 , USA ; tel
; tel (1 - (312) 616-0100; fax (312) 616-1486;
e-mail teco@tecochicago.org; web site www.
taiwanembassy.org
  Deputy Director — Justin Lee

TELEGRAPH MEDIA GROUP — 111
Buckingham Palace Road, London, SW1W
0DT, United Kingdom; tel ; tel (44 - 20) 020
7931 1010 ; e-mail syndication@telegraph.
co.uk; web site www.telegraph.co.uk/
syndication
  Content Partnerships Director — Sophie
  HanburyNote: Syndication manages
  all commercial licensing and content
  partnerships for all print publications and
  digital platforms for The Telegraph Media
  Group.

THE BOOKWORM SEZ, LLC — W5556
State Road 33 , La Crosse , 54601-7158 , USA
(608) 782-2665; fax (608) 787-8222; e-mail
bookwormsez@yahoo.com; bookwormsez@
gmail.com; web site www.bookwormsez.com
  Book Reviewer — Terri SchlichenmeyerNote:

Book reviewer ONLY; work with more than
250 publications in print and online.

**THE CHRISTIAN SCIENCE MONITOR
NEWS SERVICE** — 210 Massachusetts Ave ,
Boston , 02115-3012 , USA (617) 450-2123;
e-mail syndication@csmonitor.com; web site
www.csmonitor.comAndy Bickerton

THE CLASSIFIED GUYS — 12 Bates Pl ,
Danbury , 06810-6803 , USA (203) 798-0462;
e-mail comments@classifiedguys.com; web
site www.classifiedguys.com
  — Duane Holze
  — Todd HolzeCo-Pres.s

THE FUNNY PAGES — 4185 Bonway
Dr , Pensacola , 32504-7701 , USA (850)
484-8622; fax (850) 484-8622; e-mail
thejoker@thefunnypages.com; web site www.
thefunnypages.com
  Creator — Phillip A. Ryder

THE GELMAN FEATURE SYNDICATE — PO
Box 399 , Roscoe , 12776-0399 , USA (607)
498-4700
  Owner/Ed. — Bernard Gelman

**THE JERUSALEM POST FOREIGN
SERVICE** — The Jerusalem Post Bldg.,
Jerusalem, 91000, Israel; tel ; tel (972 - 2)
5315666; fax 5389527; e-mail ads@jpost.co.il;
web site www.jpost.com
  Editor in Chief — Steve Linde
  Managing Ed. — David Brinn

THE NAME GAME INTERNATIONAL, INC.
— 401 SW 54th Ave , Plantation , 33317-3628 ,
USA (954) 321-0032; fax (954) 321-8617;
e-mail namegameco@aol.com
  Pres. — Melodye Hecht Icart
  Vice Pres., Sales/Dev. — Mitchell J. Free

**THE NEW YORK TIMES NEWS SERVICE
& SYNDICATE** — 620 8th Ave , Fl 20 , New
York , 10018-1618 , USA ; tel ; tel (1 - 212)
(212) 556-1927; e-mail nytsyn-sales@nytimes.
com; web site www.nytsyn.com
  Managing Ed, News Services — Ray
  Krueger
  Marketing Manager — Andrea Mariano
  Regional Director, US & Canada — Aidan
  McNulty
  Regional Director, Latin America, Mexico &
  the Caribbean — Christopher Lalime
  Regional Director, Europe, Middle East &
  Africa — Cass Adamson
  Regional Director, Asia Pacific — Whye-Ko
  Tan
  Vice President and Executive Editor, News
  Service & Syndicate — Nancy Lee
  Managing Editor, Images — Sergio Florez
  Editorial Director, News Service & Syndicate
  — Anita Patil
  Vice President, Licensing & Syndication —
  Alice Ting
  Managing Editor, Syndicate — Patti Sonntag
  General Manager, News Services & Print
  Innovation — Michael Greenspon

THE NEWS ITEM — 707 N Rock St ,
Shamokin , 17872-4930 , USA (570) 644-
6397; fax (570) 648-7581; e-mail publisher@
newsitem.com; web site www.newsitem.com
  Ed. — Andy Hentzelman
  Pub. — Greg Zyla

**THE NYT NEWS SERVICE/SYNDICATE
- PHOTOS & GRAPHICS** — 620 8th Ave ,
Fl 9 , New York , 10018-1618 , USA (212)
556-4204; fax (212) 556-3535; web site www.
nytsyn.com
  Managing Editor/Images — Sergio Florez

THE ROMANTIC SYNDICATED COLUMN
— PO Box 1567 , Cary , 27512-1567 , USA
(919) 701-9818; e-mail column@theromantic.

com; web site www.theromantic.com
  Writer — Michael Webb

**THE SCIENCE ADVICE GODDESS-
AMY ALKON** — 171 Pier Ave , Ste 280 ,
Santa Monica , 90405-5311 , USA ; e-mail
adviceamy@aol.com; web site http://www.
advicegoddess.com
  Syndicated science-based advice columnist
  on love, dating, sex, relationships. Science-
  based manners expert. Upcoming book,
  "Unf*ckology" - a "science-help" book on how
  to transform to live with guts and confidence.
  @amyalkon on Twitter. — Amy Alkon
  Vice Pres., Syndication — Lucy FurryNote:
  Award-winning science-based nationally-
  syndicated advice columnist. Author of
  science-based books including "Good
  Manners For Nice People Who Sometimes
  Say F*ck" (St. Martin's Press, 2014). Next
  book, "Unf*ckology," "science-help" on
  how to live with guts and confidence (Jan
  2018). Weekly science podcast featuring
  the luminaries of behavioral science talking
  about their books. Speaking engagements
  through Macmillan.

THE WALL STREET JOURNAL SUNDAY
— 1211 Avenue of the Americas , New York ,
10036-8701 , USA (212) 597-5733; fax (212)
597-5633; e-mail wsj.ltrs@wsj.com; web site
www.wsj.
  Vice Pres., Partner Businesses — Paul Bell
  Dir., Sales — Steven Townsley
  Ed. — David Crook

**THE WASHINGTON POST WRITERS
GROUP** — 1301 K St NW , Washington ,
20071-0004 , USA (202) 334-5375; fax (202)
334-5669; e-mail syndication@washpost.com;
web site https://syndication.washingtonpost.
com/
  Ops. Mgr. — Karen H. Greene
  Dir., Sales & Mktg. — Maria Gatti
  Comics Ed. — Amy Lago
  CEO/General Manager — Richard
  Aldacushion
  Sr. Systems Admin. — Rob Cleland
  Mgr., Editorial Prod. — Sophie Yarborough
  Sales Mgr. — Brian Patten

THE WEATHER UNDERGROUND, INC.
— 185 Berry St , Ste 5501 , San Francisco ,
94107-1761 , USA (415) 983-2602; fax (415)
543-5044; e-mail chuck@wunderground.com;
web site www.wunderground.com
  Pres. — Alan Steremberg
  Office Mgr. — Brian Read
  Vice Pres. Sales/Mktg. — Andria Stark

THE WILD SIDE — 2222 Fish Ridge Rd ,
Cameron , 26033-1367 , USA (304) 686-2630;
e-mail sshalaway@aol.com; web site http://
scottshalaway.googlepages.com/
  Nature Writer, Wildlife Biologist — Scott
  ShalawayNote: Provide a 700-word weekly
  column about nature, wild birds, and
  conservation to newspapers

THE WITZZLE CO. — PO Box 866933 ,
Plano , 75086-6933 , USA (972) 398-3897; fax
(972) 398-8154; e-mail care@kaidy.com; web
site www.mathfun.com
  Owner/Pres. — Louis Y. Sher

THINK GLINK INC. — 361 Park Ave , Ste
200 , Glencoe , 60022-1585 , USA 847-242-
0550; e-mail ilyce@ThinkGlink.com; web site
www.thinkglink.com; www.lawproblems.com;
www.expertrealestatetips.net
  Pub. — Ilyce R. Glink
  Ed. — Samuel J. TamkinNote: We offer
  a thrice weekly written column, called
  "Real Estate Matters," and a daily (M-F)
  video column called "The Real Estate
  Minute." Samples are available at http://
  thinkglinkpublishing.com/real-estate-minutes/.
  The REMs are available via a simple widget
  and can be customized. If you are looking

to design a deep, content-rich online real estate section, we can help with that, too. Contact Sam Tamkin (sam@thinkglink.com) for details.

THIS MODERN WORLD — PO Box 150673 , Brooklyn , 11215-0673 , USA (718) 768-2522; e-mail tom.tomorrow@gmail.com; web site www.thismodernworld.com
Creator — Dan PerkinsNote: Please do not send submissions for syndication.

THIS SIDE OF 60 — PO Box 332 , North Newton, 67117-0332 , USA (316) 283-5231; e-mail vsnider@southwind.net; web site www.thisside60.comSnider VadaNote: Motivational column about empowerment in mature years

TMS SPECIALTY PRODUCTS — 435 N Michigan Ave, Ste 1400, Chicago, IL, 60611-7551, USA (800) 637-4082; fax (312) 527-8256; e-mail ctrammell@tribune.com; web site www.tmsspecialtyproducts.com
Gen. Mgr. — Marco Buscaglia
Sales manager — Curtis Trammell
Mng. Ed. — Mary Elson
Art Dir. — Todd RectorNote: TMS Specialty Products provides articles and images suitable for use in advertorial sections, niche publications and other targeted media, as well as custom ordered content, including local and paginated products.

TOM & JOANNE O'TOOLE, TRAVEL JOURNALISTS/PHOTOGRAPHERS — 4603 Wood St , Willoughby , 44094-5821 , USA (440) 942-5455; e-mail traveljournalists@hotmail.com
Journalist/Photographer — Thomas J. O'Toole
Journalist — Joanne R. O'Toole

TORSTAR SYNDICATION SERVICES — One Yonge St., Toronto, ON, M5E 1E6, Canada (416) 869-4994 (Sales); fax (416) 869-4587; e-mail syndicate@torstar.com; web site www.torstarsyndicate.com; www.tsscontent.ca;www.getstock.com
Managing Director — Robin Graham
Sales Representative
Torstar Syndication Services
GetStock.com — Ted Cowan
Account Information — Evi Docherty
Sales Asst. — Joanne MacDonald
Associate Director, Business Development — Julie Murtha

TRADE NEWS SERVICE (FATS AND OILS) — 3701 State Route 21 , Canandaigua , 14424-9020 , USA (585) 396-0027; e-mail tns@rochester.rr.com; web site www.fats-and-oils.com
Sr. Ed. — Dennis C MaxfieldNote: Serving the fats and oils industry exclusively, since 1914.

TRAVELIN' LIGHT — 4001 W Kings Row St , Muncie, 47304-2431 , USA (937) 423-3517; e-mail kelsey@travelin-light.com; web site www.travelin-light.com
Writer/Photographer — Kelsey Timmerman
Cartoonist — Geoff Hassing

TRIBUNE CONTENT AGENCY — 435 N Michigan Ave, Ste 3, Chicago, IL, 60611-6229, USA (800) 637-4082; e-mail tcasales@tronc.com; web site www.tribunecontentagency.com
Dir., US Syndication Sales — Scott Cameron
Sales Dir. — Rick DeChantal
Director of Operations — Karen Eich
VP Sales — Wayne Lown
Editor / General Manager — John Barron
Marketing Manager — Matt Maldre

TRIBUNE MEDIA SERVICES ENTERTAINMENT PRODUCTS — 40 Media Dr , Queensbury , 12804-4086 , USA (800) 833-9581; fax (518) 792-4414;

e-mail cyung@tribune.com; web site www.tribunemediaentertainment.com
Exec. Dir., Newspapers — Cameron Yung
Gen. Mgr., Sales/Mktg. — Kathleen Tolstrup
Account Executive — Ken Hyatt

TRIBUNE NEWS SERVICE — 435 N Michigan Ave , Ste 3 , Chicago , 60611-6229 , USA (800) 637-4082; e-mail tcasales@tronc.com; web site www.tribunenewsservice.com
Sales Dir. — Rick DeChantal
VP Sales — Wayne Lown
Ed., Gen. Mgr. — John Barron
Assoc. Ed. — Zach Finken

TRIVIA GUY BY GUINNESS HOLDER — 282 Spring Dr , Spartanburg , 29302-3248 , USA (864) 621-7129; e-mail trivguy@bellsouth.net, wc@triviaguy.com; web site www.triviaguy.com, www.patreon.com/triviaguy
Trivia Guinness World Record Holder/Syndicated Columnist — Wilson CaseyNote: "It's NOT just trivia, it's trivia WITH the Guinness World Record holder."

Content provider by subscription since 2000 with nationwide references.

DAILIES: 6 multiple choice trivia questions (with answers) 7x/week available 365 days/yr running the gamut of categories and interests.

WEEKLIES: 20 multiple choice trivia questions (with answers) 1x/wk available 52 weeks/yr running the gamut of categories and interests.

Catered versions also available such as 2x/wk, 3x/wk, 1x/month, just Sundays Biblical-flavored, etc.

Holidays and special occasion days throughout year are topical flavored.

Feature has proven track record and is size-adaptable, meaning subscribers may run less questions than supplied.

TV TIMES/NEW ENGLAND MOTORSPORTS SYNDICATION — 1324 Belmont St , Ste 102 , Brockton , 02301-4435 , USA (781) 784-7857; fax (781) 784-7857; e-mail lmodestino@hotmail.com; web site www.enterprisenews.com/tracktalk
Author — Lou ModestinoNote: My webpage changed for 2012 and beyond

U

U-BILD NEWSPAPER FEATURES — 821 S Tremont St , Ste B , Oceanside , 92054-4158 , USA (800) 828-2453; fax (760) 754-2356; e-mail ktaylor@u-bild.com; web site www.u-bild.com
Pres. — Kevin Taylor
Features Ed. — Jeffrey Reeves

UNITED FEATURE SYNDICATE (DIV. OF UNITED MEDIA) — 200 Madison Ave , New York , 10016-3903 , USA (800) 221-4816; fax (212) 293-8600; web site www.unitedfeatures.com; www.comics.com
Pres./CEO — Douglas R. Stern
Sr. Vice Pres./Gen. Mgr. — Lisa Klem Wilson
Exec. Dir., Pub. Rel. — Mary Anne Grimes
Exec. Ed. — Suma CM
Sales/Admin. Mgr. — Carmen Puello
Regl. Sales Mgr. — Colette Cogley
Regl. Sales Mgr. — Ron O'Neal
Regl. Sales Mgr. — Jim Toler
Customer Serv. Rep — Dawn Gregory
Sales Mgr., Int'l/E-rights — Emily Stephens
Reprint Rights Sales — Reprint Rights Coord.
Vincent Marciano

UNITED MEDIA/EW SCRIPPS — 312 Walnut St , Ste 2800 , Cincinnati, 45202-4019 , USA (513) 977-3000; fax (513) 977-3024; web site www.scripps.com
General Manager, United Media — Vincent Marciano
Senior Analyst/ Systems Engineer — Donald MurrayNote: United Media's operations were outsourced to Universal Uclick in Kansas City, Mo., June 1, 2011. Please direct all inquiries to Universal Uclick.

UNITED PRESS INTERNATIONAL — 1200 N Federal Hwy , Ste 200 , Boca Raton , 33432-2813 , USA 202-898-8000; e-mail media@upi.com; web site www.upi.com
President — Nicholas Chiaia
Chief Content Officer — Charlene Pacenti
Business Manager — Franco FernandezNote: United Press International is a leading provider of news, photos and information to millions of readers around the globe via UPI.com and its licensing services. With a history of reliable reporting dating back to 1907, today's UPI is a credible source for the most important stories of the day, continually updated - a one-stop site for U.S. and world news, as well as entertainment, trends, science, health and stunning photography. UPI also provides insightful reports on key topics of geopolitical importance, including energy and security. UPI is based in Washington, D.C., and Boca Raton, Fla.

UNIVERSAL UCLICK INTERNATIONAL DIVISON — 1130 Walnut St , Kansas City , 64106-2109 , USA (816) 581-7500; e-mail sales@amuniversal.com; web site www.amuniversal.com
Pres. — Kerry Slagle
Mng. Dir., Latin America — Milka Pratt

V

VOTERAMA IN CONGRESS - THOMAS VOTING REPORTS — PO Box 363 , Washington , 22747-0363 , USA (202) 332-0857; e-mail info@voterama.info; web site www.voterama.info
Pub./Ed. — Mr. Richard G. ThomasNote: Covers House and Senate legislative actions and members' voting records and campaign-finance data for U.S. news media — a finished editorial product transmitted daily and weekly in text, graphic and online formats.

W

W.D. FARMER RESIDENCE DESIGNER, INC. — 5238 Rocky Hill Dr SW , Lilburn , 30047-6631 , USA (770) 934-7380; fax (770) 934-1700; e-mail wdfarmer@wdfarmerplans.com; vstarkey@wdfarmerplans.com; web site www.wdfarmer.com; www.wdfarmerplans.com/featurehomes; www.wdfplans.com
Designer — W.D. Farmer
Pres. — Vickie Starkey

WAGNER INTERNATIONAL PHOTOS, INC. — 62 W 45th St , Fl 6 , New York , 10036-4208 , USA (212) 827-0500; fax (212) 944-9536; e-mail larry@nycphoto.com; info@nycphoto.com; web site www.nycphoto.com
Adv. Mgr. — Larry Lettera
Chief Photographer — Jeff Connell

WASHINGTON MONTHLY LLC — 1200 18th St NW , Ste 330 , Washington , 20036-2556 , USA (202) 955-9010; fax (202) 955-9011; e-mail editors@washingtonmonthly.com; web site www.washingtonmonthly.com
Publisher — Diane Straus Tucker
VP, Operations & Marketing — Carl Iseli

VP Cir. — Claire Iseli
Founding Ed. — Charles Peters
Ed. in Chief — Paul Glastris
Adv. Mgr. — Ambi Ambachew

WASHINGTON POST NEWS SERVICE WITH BLOOMBERG NEWS — 1301 K St NW , Washington , 20071-0004 , USA ; tel ; tel (+1 - (800) 879-9794 ext. 1; e-mail syndication@washpost.com; web site syndication.washingtonpost.com
Sales Mgr./North America — Brian Patten
Dir., Int. Sales & Marketing — Maria Gatti
Marketing Representative/Northeast & South — Jim Toler
Senior Systems Administrator — Robert Cleland
Marketing Representative/Midwest & West — Gabriella Ferrufino
General Manager/Editorial Director — Richard Aldacushion
Marketing Representative/Midwest — Sally Ragsdale

WATAUGA CONSULTING, INC. — 192 Abbey Rd , Boone , 28607-8606 , USA (828) 773-3481; e-mail info@supin.com; web site www.supin.comJeanne SupinNote: Helping you make changes that matter.

WEATHER UNDERGROUND, INC., THE — 185 Berry St , Ste 5501 , San Francisco , 94107-1761 , USA (415) 983-2602; fax (415) 543-5044; e-mail press@wunderground.com; web site www.wunderground.com
Press & Media — Andria Stark

WERNER RENBERG — PO Box 496 , Chappaqua , 10514-0496 , USA (914) 241-2038; fax (914) 242-0470; e-mail werren@att.net
Self-Syndicator — Werner Renberg

WHITEGATE FEATURES SYNDICATE — 71 Faunce Dr , Ste 1 , Providence , 02906-4805 , USA (401) 274-2149; e-mail webmaster@whitegatefeatures.com; staff@whitegatefeatures.com; web site www.whitegatefeatures.com
Pres./CEO — Ed Isaac
Vice Pres./Gen. Mgr. — Steve Corey
Office Mgr. — Mari Howard
Talent Dir./Special Projects Mgr. — Eve Green

WIECK — 1651 N Collins Blvd , Ste 100 , Richardson , 75080-3604 , USA (972) 392-0888; fax (972) 934-8848; e-mail info@wieck.com; web site www.wieck.com
Chrmn. — James Wieck
Pres. — Tim Roberts
Sr. VP — Marc Newman

WILD BILL'S CARTOON SHOW! — 179 Old Cement Rd , Lot B40 , Montoursville, 17754-8252 , USA (570) 494-6789; fax 866 923 0401; e-mail wildbill@wildbillsartshow.net; web site www.wildbillsartshow.net
Creator — Bill Stanford

WINGO, LLC — 12161 Ken Adams Way, Ste 110J, Wellington, FL, 33414-3194, USA (561) 379-2635; e-mail sat@amerimarketing.com; web site www.wingopromo.com; www.amerimarketing.com
Pres. — Scott Thompson

WIRELESS FLASH NEWS, INC. — PO Box 633030, San Diego , 92163-3030 , USA (619) 220-7191; fax (619) 220-8590; e-mail newsdesk2@flashnews.com; web site www.flashnews.com
Mng. Ed. — Patrick Glynn
Sr. Ed. — Monica Garske
Sales/Mktg. Mgr. — David Louie

WOMBANIA — 249 Kensington Ave. N.,

Hamilton, ON, L8L 7N8, Canada (905) 544-6174; e-mail wombania@wombania.com; web site www.wombania.com; www.comics.wombania.com
  Owner/Cartoonist — Peter Marinacci
  Ed. — R.L.B. HartmannNote: Color and B&W weekly comic strip since 2003

WORLD FEATURES SYNDICATE — 5842 Sagebrush Rd , La Jolla , 92037-7037 , USA , (858) 456-6215; e-mail info@worldfeaturessyndicate.com; web site www.worldfeaturessyndicate.com
  Sales Dir. — Tom Robbins
  Ed. — Ronald A. Sataloff

Sr. Assoc. Ed./Columnist — Karl A. Van Asselt
Assoc. Ed. — Ernie A. Gomez

WORLD IMAGES NEWS SERVICE — 14741 Green Park Way , Centreville , 20120-3126 , USA ; tel ; tel (USA - Centreville) 703-380-2808; e-mail jack@winsphoto.com; web site http://www.winsphoto.com
  CEO/Chief Photographer — Jack SykesNote: International photo agency

WORLDWATCH/FOREIGN AFFAIRS SYNDICATE — 14421 Charter Rd , Apt 5C ,

Jamaica , 11435-1292 , USA (718) 591-7246; e-mail jjmcolumn@earthlink.net
  Editor — John J. Metzler

Y

YELLOWBRIX — 200 North Glebe Road, Ste. 1025, Ste 1025 , Arlington, VA, 22203, USA (703) 548-3300; fax (703) 548-9151; e-mail info@yellowbrix.com; web site www.yellowbrix.com
  Founder/Pres./CEO — Jeffrey P. Massa
  Adv. Mgr. — Tom Hargis

Z

ZUMA PRESS, INC. — 408 N El Camino Real , San Clemente , 92672-4717 , USA , tel ; tel (United States - San Clemente); e-mail zinfo@zumapress.com; web site 408 N El Camino Real
  CEO/Founder — Scott McKiernan
  News Dir./Picture Desk Mgr. — Ruaridh Stewart
  CTO — Patrick Johnson
  CFO — Julie Mason

NEWSPAPER COMIC SECTION GROUPS AND NETWORKS

BUSINESS INFORMATION GROUP — 80 Valleybrook Drive, Toronto, ON, M3B 2S9, Canada; tel (416) 442-5600; fax (416) 442-2191; web site www.bizinfogroup.ca
  Pres. — Bruce Creighton

METRO NEWSPAPER ADVERTISING SERVICES, INC. — 8 W 38th St, 8 W. 38th St., 4th Fl., New York, NY, 10018-6229, USA; tel (212) 576-9510; fax (212) 576-9526; e-mail billh@metrosn.com; web site www.metrosn.com
  Chairperson & CEO — Phyllis Cavaliere
  SVP Client Services — Tack Prashad
  President/COO — Michael Baratoff
  Sr. Vice Pres./Midwest Sales Dir. — Carl Berg
  Exec. Dir. — Tom Vorel
  Sr. Vice Pres., Eastern Adv. — Bill Huck
  Sr. Vice Pres., Finance — Nili DeBono
  Sr. Vice Pres./Eastern Region — William Huck
  New Ventures Development — Frank Grasso
  Senior VP, Operations — Kim Viggiano
  Included in the following newspapers: Akron (OH) Beacon Journal; Albuquerque (NM) Journal/Tribune; Allentown (PA) Morning Call; Atlanta (GA) Journal-Constitution; Austin (TX) American-Statesman; Bangor (ME) Daily News; Bay City (MI) Times; Beaumont (TX) Enterprise; Biloxi (MS) Sun Herald; Birmingham (AL) News; Bloomington (IN) Herald-Times; Boston (MA) Globe; Boston (MA) Herald; Brockton (MA) Enterprise; Camden (NJ) Courier-Post; Cedar Rapids (IA) Gazette; Charleston (SC) Post & Courier; Charlotte (NC) Observer; Chattanooga (TN) Times Free Press; Chicago (IL) Sun-Times; Chicago (IL) Tribune; Cincinnati (OH) Enquirer; Cleveland (OH) Plain Dealer;

Colorado Springs (CO) Gazette; Columbus (GA) Ledger-Enquirer; Corpus Christi (TX) Caller-Times; Corsicana (TX) Daily Sun; Dallas (TX) Morning News; Danbury (CT) News-Times; Dayton (OH) Daily News; Daytona Beach (FL) News-Journal; Del Rio (TX) News-Herald; Detroit (MI) News & Free Press; El Paso (TX) Times; Elmira (NY) Star-Gazette; Erie (PA) Times-News; Fargo (ND) Forum; Flint (MI) Journal; Fort Lauderdale (FL) South Florida Sun-Sentinel; Fort Myers (FL) News-Press; Fort Worth (TX) Star-Telegram; Fresno (CA) Bee; Grand Rapids (MI) Press; Green Bay (WI) Press-Gazette; Greensboro (NC) News & Record; Greenville (SC) News; Hackensack (NJ) Record; Harrisburg (PA) Patriot-News; Hartford (CT) Courant; Honolulu (HI) Advertiser; Houston (TX) Chronicle; Indianapolis (IN) Star; Jackson (MS) Clarion-Ledger; Jackson (TN) Sun; Jacksonville (FL) Florida Times-Union; Knoxville (TN) News Sentinel; Kansas City (MO) Star; Lancaster (PA) Sunday News; Las Vegas (NV) Review Journal & Sun; Lewiston (ME) Sunday Sun-Journal; Little Rock (AR) Arkansas Democrat-Gazette; Long Island (NY) Newsday; Longview (TX) News-Journal; Los Angeles (CA) Times; Louisville (KY) Courier-Journal; Lowell (MA) Sun; Lubbock (TX) Avalanche-Journal; Macon (GA) Telegraph; Madison (WI) Wisconsin State Journal; Memphis (TN) Commercial Appeal; Merrillville (IN) Post-Tribune; Miami (FL) Herald; Milwaukee (WI) Journal Sentinel; Minneapolis (MN) Star Tribune; Mobile (AL) Press-Register; Modesto (CA) Bee; Monterey (CA) Monterey County Herald; Muncie (IN) Star Press; Munster (IN) Times; Muskegon (MI) Chronicle; Myrtle Beach (SC) Sun News; Nashville (TN) Tennessean; New Haven (CT) Register; New Orleans (LA) Times-Picayune;

New York (NY) Daily News; Newark (NJ) Star-Ledger; Newport News (VA) Daily Press; Norfolk (VA) Virginian-Pilot; North Andover (MA) Eagle-Tribune; Oakland (CA) Tribune; Ontario (CA) Inland Valley Daily Bulletin; Pasadena (CA) Star-News; Philadelphia (PA) Inquirer; Phoenix (AZ) Arizona Republic; Pittsburgh (PA) Post-Gazette; Pittsburgh (PA) Tribune-Review; Pleasanton (CA) Tri-Valley Herald; Port Arthur (TX) News; Portland (ME) Maine Sunday Telegram; Portland (OR) Oregonian; Providence (RI) Journal; Pueblo (CO) Chieftain; Raleigh (NC) News & Observer; Reading (PA) Eagle; Richmond (VA) Times-Dispatch; Riverside (CA) Press-Enterprise; Roanoke (VA) Times; Rochester (NY) Democrat & Chronicle; Sacramento (CA) Bee; Saginaw (MI) News; Saint Louis (MO) Post-Dispatch; Saint Paul (MN) Pioneer Press; Saint Petersburg (FL) Times; San Antonio (TX) Express-News; San Bernardino (CA) County Sun; San Diego (CA) Union-Tribune; San Francisco (CA) Chronicle; San Jose (CA) Mercury News; San Mateo (CA) County Times; Santa Ana (CA) Orange County Register; Santa Barbara (CA) News-Press; Santa Rosa (CA) Press Democrat; Savannah (GA) Morning News; Shreveport (LA) Times; South Bend (IN) Tribune; Springfield (IL) State Journal-Register; Springfield (MA) Republican; Springfield (OH) News-Sun; Staten Island (NY) Advance; Stockton (CA) Record; Tacoma (WA) News Tribune; Tampa (FL) Tribune and Times; Toledo (OH) Blade; Torrance (CA) Daily Breeze; Trenton (NJ) Times; Troy (NY) Record; Tulsa (OK) World; Waco (TX) Tribune-Herald; Washington (DC) Post; Waterbury (CT) Republican-American; West Palm Beach (FL) Palm Beach Post; White Plains (NY) Journal News; Wichita

(KS) Eagle; White Plains (NY) Journal
Circ. 32,083,450 Sworn/Estimate/Non-AuditedNote: Metro has been creating networks for national advertisers since 1932. It places advertising for represented newspapers through its Sunday Magazine, Metro-Puck Comics and Metro ROP Networks. Please see these entries in Section V of the Year Book.

METRO NEWSPAPER ADVERTISING SERVICES, INC. — 160 Spear St, Ste 1875, San Francisco, CA, 94105-5146, USA; tel (310) 798-4986; fax (310) 564-7633; e-mail kathy@metrosn.com; web site www.metrosn.com
  Mgr. — Kathy Jahns
  Sr. Vice Pres. — Ali Nazem
  Circ. Sworn/Estimate/Non-Audited

METRO-PUCK COMICS NETWORK - NEW YORK — 28 Wells Ave, Ste 4, Yonkers, 10701-7045, USA; tel (212) 576-9510; fax (212) 576-9526; e-mail getinfo@metrosn.com; web site www.metrosn.com
  EVP Client Services — Tack Prashad
  Circ. (Sun) Sworn/Estimate/Non-Audited

WYOMING COLOR COMIC GROUP — 702 W Lincolnway, Cheyenne, 82001-4359, USA; tel 307-633-6164; fax (307) 633-3191; web site www.wyomingnews.com
  Controller — Larry Catalano
  Included in the following newspapers: Cheyenne (WY) Wyoming Sunday Tribune-Eagle; Laramie (WY) Boomerang; Rawlins Daily (WY) Times
  Circ. (Mon, Tues, Wed, Thur, Fri, Sat, Sun) Sworn/Estimate/Non-AuditedNote: Circ varieries only Cheyenne is an ABC paper

NEWSPAPER DISTRIBUTED MAGAZINES AND TMC PUBLICATIONS

AMERICAN PROFILE - CHICAGO, IL — 500 N Michigan Ave, Ste 910, Chicago, 60611-3741, USA; tel (312) 440-0333; fax (312) 948-0555; web site www.americanprofile.com
  Group: Publishing Group of America
  Executive Director, Integrated Media — Nanci Davidson
  Circ. 10,000,000; Sworn/Estimate/Non-Audited September 30, 2017

AMERICAN PROFILE - FRANKLIN, TN — 341 Cool Springs Blvd, Ste 400, Franklin, 37067-7224, USA; tel (615) 468-6021; web site

www.americanpub.com
  Nashville/West Coast Assoc. Pub. — Frank Zier
  Circ. ; Sworn/Estimate/Non-Audited September 30, 2017

AMERICAN PROFILE - LOS ANGELES, CA — 6255 W Sunset Blvd, Ste 705, Los Angeles, 90028-7408, USA; tel (323) 467-5906; fax (323) 467-7180; web site www.americanprofile.com
  Adv Sales Rep. — Debbie Siegel
  Circ. ; Sworn/Estimate/Non-Audited September 30, 2017

AMERICAN PROFILE - NEW YORK, NY — 60 E 42nd St, Ste 1111, New York, 10165-1111, USA; tel (212) 478-1900; fax (646) 865-1921; web site www.americanprofile.com
  Sr. Vice Pres./Grp. Pub. — Amy Chernoff
  Adv. Dir. — Shannon Hay
  Assoc. Ed., Direct Response — Linda Rich
  Member Newspapers: Aberdeen (SD) American News; Abilene (KS) Reflector-Chrnoicle; Alamogordo (NM) Daily News; Albuquerque (NM) Journal; Alexander City (AL) Outlook; Alice (TX) Echo-News Journal; Alliance (NE) Times-Herald; Alliance (OH) Review; Alton (IL) Telegraph; Altus (OK) Times; Andalusia (AL) Star-News; Ardmore

(OK) Daily Ardmoreite; Arkadelphia (AR) Daily Siftings Herald; Ashland (WI) Daily Press; Ashtabula (OH) Star Beacon; Athens (AL) News-Courier; Athens (OH) Messenger; Athens (TX) Daily Review; Atlantic (IA) News-Telegraph; Attleboro (MA) Sun Chronicle; Augusta (KS) Daily Gazette; Baker City (OR) Herald; Baraboo (WI) News-Republic; Bartlesville (OK) Examiner-Enterprise; Bastrop (LA) Daily Enterprise; Batavia (NY) Daily News; Batesville (AR) Guard; Baytown (TX) Sun; Beatrice (NE) Daily Sun; Beaver Dam (WI) Daily Citizen; Bedford (PA) Gazette; Bennington (VT) Banner; Benton (AR) Courier; Benton (IL) Evening News;

Big Rapids (MI) Pioneer; Big Spring (TX) Herald; Billings (MT) Gazette; Blackfoot (ID) Morning News; Bloomington (IL) Pantagraph; Bloomsburg (PA) Press Enterprise; Boone (IA) News-Republican; Boonville (MO) Daily News & Record; Borger (TX) News-Herald; Bowling Green (KY) Daily News; Brainerd (MN) Dispatch; Brattleboro (VT) Reformer; Brenham (TX) Banner-Press; Brookings (SD) Register; Brooksville (FL) Hernando Today; Brownwood (TX) Bulletin; Brunswick (GA) News; Bryan (OH) Times; Bryan (TX) Eagle; Bullhead City (AZ) Mohave Valley Daily News; Burley (ID) South Idaho Press; Burlington (NC) Times-News; Burlington (IA) Hawk Eye; Cadillac (MI) News; Camden (AR) News; Camdenton (MO) Lake Sun Leader; Canon City (CO) Daily Record; Canton (IL) Daily Ledger; Carbondale (IL) Southern Illinoisan; Carlisle (PA) Sentinel; Carlsbad (NM) Current-Argus; Carroll (IA) Daily Times Herald; Carson City (NV) Nevada Appeal; Cartersville (GA) Daily Tribune News; Carthage (MO) Press; Casa Grande (AZ) Dispatch; Casper (WY) Star-Tribune; Catskill (NY) Daily Mail; Cedar Rapids (IA) Gazette; Centerville (IA) Ad Express & Daily Iowegian; Chanute (KS) Tribune; Charlotte Harbor (FL) Sun; Cheboygan (MI) Daily Tribune; Circleville (OH) Herald; Clanton (AL) Advertiser; Claremont (NH) Eagle Times; Claremore (OK) Daily Progress; Cleburne (TX) Times-Review; Cleveland (MS) Bolivar Commercial; Cleveland (TN) Daily Banner; Clinton (IA) Herald; Coeur d'Alene (ID) Press; Coffeyville (KS) Journal; Coldwater (MI) Daily Reporter; Columbia City (IN) Post & Mail; Columbus (NE) Telegram; Conway (AR) Log Cabin Democrat; Coos Bay (OR) World; Corry (PA) Journal; Council Bluffs (IA) Daily Nonpareil; Craig (CO) Daily Press; Creston (IA) News Advertiser; Crookston (MN) Daily Times; Crystal Lake (IL) Northwest Herald; Cullman (AL) Times; Cumming (GA) Forsyth County News; Cushing (OK) Daily Citizen; Danville (KY) Advocate-Messenger; Decatur (IN) Daily Democrat; Defiance (OH) Crescent-News; Delphos (OH) Daily Herald; Deming (NM) Headlight; Demopolis (AL) Times; Derby (KS) Reporter; Devils Lake (ND) Journal; Dover (NH) Foster's Daily Democrat; Du Quoin (IL) Evening Call; Duncan (OK) Banner; Dunn (NC) Daily Record; Durant (OK) Daily Democrat; Dyersburg (TN) State Gazette; Easton (MD) Star-Democrat; Edmond (OK) Sun; Effingham (IL) Daily News; El Centro (CA) Imperial Valley Press; El Dorado (AR) News-Times; El Dorado (KS) Times; Elizabethton (TN) Star; Elkton (MD) Cecil Whig; Ellensburg (WA) Daily Record; Elyria (OH) Chronicle-Telegram; Fairfield (CA) Daily Republic; Fairfield (IA) Ledger; Fallon (NV) Lahontan Valley News; Faribault (MN) Daily News; Farmington (NM) Daily Times; Fort Atkinson (WI) Daily Jeffersonian County Union; Fort Madison (IA) Daily Democrat; Fort Morgan (CO) Times; Fort Payne (AL) Times Journal; Frankfort (KY) State Journal; Frederick (MD) News-Post; Freeport (IL) Journal-Standard; Fremont (NE) Tribune; Gainesville (TX) Daily Register; Galion (OH) Inquirer; Gallup (NM) Independent; Gastonia (NC) Gaston Gazette; Geneva (IL) Kane County Chronicle; Gastonia (NC) Gaston Gaz
Circ. 9,801,887; BPA June 30, 2008

AMERICAN PROFILE - NORTHVILLE, MI
— 22185 Heatheridge Ln, Northville, 48167-9300, USA; tel (248) 991-1810; web site www.americanprofile.com
Auto Adv. Mgr. — Jim Main
Circ. ; Sworn/Estimate/Non-Audited September 30, 2017

ASSOCIATION OF ALTERNATIVE NEWSMEDIA
— 1156 15th St NW, Ste 1005, Washington, DC, 20005-1722, USA; tel 289-8484; fax (202) 289-2004; e-mail web@aan.org; web site www.altweeklies.com
Dir. of Meetings — Debra Silvestrin
Int. Exec. Dir. — Jason Zaragoza
Circ. ; Sworn/Estimate/Non-Audited September 30, 2017
Note Annual convention held in summer.

MALVERN DAILY TMC
— 219 Locust St, Malvern, 72104-3721, USA; tel (501) 337-7523; fax (501) 337-1226; e-mail mdrecord@sbcglobal.net; web site www.malvern-online.com
Group: Horizon Publications Inc.
Bus. Mgr. — Kim Taber
Adv. Dir. — Richard Folds
Circ. Mgr. — Kathi Ledbetter
News Ed. — Mark Bivens
Online Ed. — James Liegh
Sports Ed. — LaJuan Monney
Composing Mgr. — Jessica Mathis
Circ. ; Sworn/Estimate/Non-Audited September 30, 2006

MARTINEZ NEWS-GAZETTE
— 802 Alhambra Ave, Martinez, 94553-1604, USA; tel (408) 603-5640; fax (925) 228-1536; e-mail rickj64@gmail.com
Circ. ; Sworn/Estimate/Non-Audited September 30, 2017

METRO NEWSPAPER ADVERTISING SERVICES, INC.
— 8 W 38th St, 8 W. 38th St., 4th Fl., New York, NY, 10018-6229, USA; tel (212) 576-9510; fax (212) 576-9526; e-mail billh@metrosn.com; web site www.metrosn.com
Chairperson & CEO — Phyllis Cavaliere
SVP Client Services — Tack Prashad
President/COO — Michael Baratoff
Sr. Vice Pres./Midwest Sales Dir. — Carl Berg
Exec. Dir. — Tom Vorel
Sr. Vice Pres., Eastern Adv. — Bill Huck
Sr. Vice Pres., Finance — Nili DeBono
Sr. Vice Pres./Eastern Region — William Huck
New Ventures Development — Frank Grasso
Senior VP, Operations — Kim Viggiano
Member Newspapers: Akron (OH) Beacon Journal; Albuquerque (NM) Journal/Tribune; Allentown (PA) Morning Call; Atlanta (GA) Journal-Constitution; Austin (TX) American-Statesman; Bangor (ME) Daily News; Bay City (MI) Times; Beaumont (TX) Enterprise; Biloxi (MS) Sun Herald; Birmingham (AL) News; Bloomington (IN) Herald-Times; Boston (MA) Globe; Boston (MA) Herald; Brockton (MA) Enterprise; Camden (NJ) Courier-Post; Cedar Rapids (IA) Gazette; Charleston (SC) Post & Courier; Charlotte (NC) Observer; Chattanooga (TN) Times Free Press; Chicago (IL) Sun-Times; Chicago (IL) Tribune; Cincinnati (OH) Enquirer; Cleveland (OH) Plain Dealer; Colorado Springs (CO) Gazette; Columbus (GA) Ledger-Enquirer; Corpus Christi (TX) Caller-Times; Corsicana (TX) Daily Sun; Dallas (TX) Morning News; Danbury (CT) News-Times; Dayton (OH) Daily News; Daytona Beach (FL) News-Journal; Del Rio (TX) News-Herald; Detroit (MI) News & Free Press; El Paso (TX) Times; Elmira (NY) Star-Gazette; Erie (PA) Times-News; Fargo (ND) Forum; Flint (MI) Journal; Fort Lauderdale (FL) South Florida Sun-Sentinel; Fort Myers (FL) News-Press; Fort Worth (TX) Star-Telegram; Fresno (CA) Bee; Grand Rapids (MI) Press; Green Bay (WI) Press-Gazette; Greensboro (NC) News & Record; Greenville (SC) News; Hackensack (NJ) Record; Harrisburg (PA) Patriot-News; Hartford (CT) Courant; Honolulu (HI) Advertiser; Houston (TX) Chronicle; Indianapolis (IN) Star; Jackson (MS) Clarion-Ledger; Jackson (TN) Sun; Jacksonville (FL) Florida Times-Union; Knoxville (TN) News Sentinel; Kansas City (MO) Star; Lancaster (PA) Sunday News; Las Vegas (NV) Review Journal & Sun; Lewiston (ME) Sunday Sun-Journal; Little Rock (AR) Arkansas Democrat-Gazette; Long Island (NY) Newsday; Longview (TX) News-Journal; Los Angeles (CA) Times; Louisville (KY) Courier-Journal; Lowell (MA) Sun; Lubbock (TX) Avalanche-Journal; Macon (GA) Telegraph; Madison (WI) Wisconsin State Journal; Memphis (TN) Commercial Appeal; Merrillville (IN) Post-Tribune; Miami (FL) Herald; Milwaukee (WI) Journal Sentinel; Minneapolis (MN) Star Tribune; Mobile (AL) Press-Register; Modesto (CA) Bee; Monterey (CA) Monterey County Herald; Muncie (IN) Star Press; Munster (IN) Times; Muskegon (MI) Chronicle; Myrtle Beach (SC) Sun News; Nashville (TN) Tennessean; New Haven (CT) Register; New Orleans (LA) Times-Picayune; New York (NY) Daily News; Newark (NJ) Star-Ledger; Newport News (VA) Daily Press; Norfolk (VA) Virginian-Pilot; North Andover (MA) Eagle-Tribune; Oakland (CA) Tribune; Ontario (CA) Inland Valley Daily Bulletin; Pasadena (CA) Star-News; Philadelphia (PA) Inquirer; Phoenix (AZ) Arizona Republic; Pittsburgh (PA) Post-Gazette; Pittsburgh (PA) Tribune-Review; Pleasanton (CA) Tri-Valley Herald; Port Arthur (TX) News; Portland (ME) Maine Sunday Telegram; Portland (OR) Oregonian; Providence (RI) Journal; Pueblo (CO) Chieftain; Raleigh (NC) News & Observer; Reading (PA) Eagle; Richmond (VA) Times-Dispatch; Riverside (CA) Press-Enterprise; Roanoke (VA) Times; Rochester (NY) Democrat & Chronicle; Sacramento (CA) Bee; Saginaw (MI) News; Saint Louis (MO) Post-Dispatch; Saint Paul (MN) Pioneer Press; Saint Petersburg (FL) Times; San Antonio (TX) Express-News; San Bernardino (CA) County Sun; San Diego (CA) Union-Tribune; San Francisco (CA) Chronicle; San Jose (CA) Mercury News; San Mateo (CA) County Times; Santa Ana (CA) Orange County Register; Santa Barbara (CA) News-Press; Santa Rosa (CA) Press Democrat; Savannah (GA) Morning News; Shreveport (LA) Times; South Bend (IN) Tribune; Springfield (IL) State Journal-Register; Springfield (MA) Republican; Springfield (OH) News-Sun; Staten Island (NY) Advance; Stockton (CA) Record; Tacoma (WA) News Tribune; Tampa (FL) Tribune and Times; Toledo (OH) Blade; Torrance (CA) Daily Breeze; Trenton (NJ) Times; Troy (NY) Record; Tulsa (OK) World; Waco (TX) Tribune-Herald; Washington (DC) Post; Waterbury (CT) Republican-American; West Palm Beach (FL) Palm Beach Post; White Plains (NY) Journal News; Wichita (KS) Eagle; White Plains (NY) Journal
Circ. 8,237,412; Sworn/Estimate/Non-Audited March 31, 2007
Note Metro has been creating networks for national advertisers since 1932. It places advertising for represented newspapers through its Sunday Magazine, Metro-Puck Comics and Metro ROP Networks. Please see these entries in Section V of the Year Book.

METRO NEWSPAPER ADVERTISING SERVICES, INC.
— 160 Spear St, Ste 1875, San Francisco, CA, 94105-5146, USA; tel (310) 798-4986; fax (310) 564-7633; e-mail kathy@metrosn.com; web site www.metrosn.com
Mgr. — Kathy Jahns
Sr. Vice Pres. — Ali Nazem
Circ. ; Sworn/Estimate/Non-Audited September 30, 2017

MOLINE/ROCK ISLAND/QUAD CITY METRO UNIT
— 1720 5th Ave, Moline, 61265-7907, USA; tel (309) 764-4344; e-mail advertising@qconline.com; web site www.qconline.com
CRO — Val Yazbec
Ed. — Jerry Taylor
Adv. Dir. — Kelly Johannes
Member Newspapers: Moline (IL) Dispatch; Rock Island (IL) Argus
Circ. 39,625; CAC March 31, 2015

PARADE
— 60 E 42nd St, Ste 820, New York, 10165-0820, USA; tel (212) 478-1910; e-mail sales@amgparade.com; web site www.parade.com
Group: AMG/Parade
Sr. Vice Pres., Newspaper Rel. — David Barber
Circ. 22,000,000; GfK MRI September 1, 2017

PARADE PUBLICATIONS, INC. - BLOOMFIELD HILLS, MI
— 100 W Long Lake Rd, Bloomfield Hills, 48304-2773, USA; tel (248) 540-9820; fax (248) 540-9891; e-mail det_sales@parade.com; web site www.parade.com
Vice Pres., Adv. — Mike DeBartolo
Circ. ; Sworn/Estimate/Non-Audited September 30, 2017

PARADE PUBLICATIONS, INC. - CHICAGO, IL
— 500 N Michigan Ave, Ste 910, Chicago, 60611-3741, USA; tel (312) 661-1620; fax (312) 661-0776; e-mail chi_sales@parade.com; web site www.parade.com
Vice Pres./Mid-Western Mgr. — Eric Karaffa
Circ. ; Sworn/Estimate/Non-Audited September 30, 2017

PARADE PUBLICATIONS, INC. - LOS ANGELES, CA
— 6300 Wilshire Blvd, Los Angeles, 90048-5204, USA; tel (323) 965-3649; fax (323) 965-4971; web site www.parade.com
Acct. Dir. — Greg Hancock
Circ. ; Sworn/Estimate/Non-Audited September 30, 2017

PARADE PUBLICATIONS, INC. - SAN FRANCISCO, CA
— 50 Francisco St, Ste 400, San Francisco, 94133-2114, USA; tel (415) 955-8222; fax (415) 397-0562; e-mail sf_sales@parade.com; web site www.parade.com
Adv. Contact — Bill Murray
Circ. ; Sworn/Estimate/Non-Audited September 30, 2017

RELISH - CHICAGO, IL
— 500 N Michigan Ave, Ste 910, Chicago, 60611-3741, USA; tel (312) 948-0333; fax (312) 948-0555; web site www.pubgroup.com
Adv. Coord. — Andrea Blank
Circ. ; Sworn/Estimate/Non-Audited September 30, 2017

RELISH - FRANKLIN, TN
— 341 Cool Springs Blvd, Ste 400, Franklin, 37067-7224, USA; tel (615) 468-6000; fax (615) 468-6100; web site www.pubgroup.com
Nashville/West Coast Assoc. Pub. — Frank Zier
Circ. ; Sworn/Estimate/Non-Audited September 30, 2017

RELISH - LOS ANGELES, CA
— 300 Corporate Pointe, Ste 340, Culver City, 90230-8713, USA; tel (310) 216-7270; fax (310) 216-7212; web site www.relishmag.com
Acct. Mgr. — Jamie Relis
Circ. ; Sworn/Estimate/Non-Audited September 30, 2017

RELISH - NEW YORK, NY
— 60 E 42nd St, Ste 1115, New York, 10165-1115, USA; tel (212) 478-1900; fax (646) 865-1921; web site www.relishmag.com
Sr. Vice Pres./Grp. Pub. — Amy Chernoff
Adv. Dir. — Shannon Hay
Assoc. Ed., Direct Response — Linda Rich
Member Newspapers: Aberdeen (SD) American News; Alamogordo (NM) Daily News; Albany (OR) Democrat-Herald; Albert Lea (MN) Tribune; Albuquerque (NM) Journal; Amarillo (TX) Globe-News; Americus (GA) Times-Recorder; Ames (IA) Tribune; Annapolis (MD) Capital; Ardmore (OK) Daily Ardmoreite; Ashland (KY) Daily Independent; Ashland (WI) Daily Press; Ashtabula (OH) Star Beacon; Athens (AL) News-Courier; Athens (GA) Banner-Herald; Athens (TX) Daily Review; Attleboro (MA)

Sun Chronicle; Augusta (GA) Chronicle; Austin (MN) Daily Herald; Baraboo (WI) News-Republic; Barre (VT) Times Argus; Baton Rouge (LA) Advocate; Beatrice (NE) Daily Sun; Beaver Dam (WI) Daily Citizen; Beckley (WV) Register-Herlad; Bellingham (WA) Herald; Bemidji (MN) Pioneer; Beverly (MA) Salem News; Billings (MT) Gazette; Bismarck (ND) Tribune; Bloomington (IL) Pantagraph; Blytheville (AR) Courier News; Borger (TX) News-Herald; Bowling Green (KY) Daily News; Brainerd (MN) Dispatch; Brazil (IN) Times; Brenham (TX) Banner-Press; Bridgeport (CT) Post; Brooksville (FL) Hernando Today; Bryan (OH) Times; Bryan (TX) Eagle; Burlington (IA) Hawk Eye; Camden (AR) News; Canon City (CO) Daily Record; Cape Girardeau (MO) Southeast Missourian; Carbondale (IL) Southern Illinoisan; Cartersville (GA) Daily Tribune News; Casper (WY) Star-Tribune; Cedar Rapids (IA) Gazette; Centerville (IA) Ad Express & Daily Iowegian; Chattanooga (TN) Times Free Press; Cherokee (IA) Chronicle Times; Chickasha (OK) Express-Star; Chico (CA) Enterprise-Record; Claremore (OK) Daily Progress; Coeur d'Alene (ID) Press; Cleburne (TX) Times-Review; Colorado Springs (CO) Gazette; Columbus (NE) Telegram; Cookeville (TN) Herald-Citizen; Coos Bay (OR) World; Corsicana (TX) Daily Sun; Corvallis (OR) Gazette-Times; Covina (CA) San Gabriel Valley Tribune; Creston (IA) News Advertiser; Crystal Lake (IL) Northwest Herald; Cullman (AL) Times; Cumberland (MD) Times-News; Dalton (GA) Daily Citizen; Danbury (CT) News-Times; Davenport (IA) Quad-City Times; Davis (CA) Enterprise; Dexter (MO) Daily Statesman; Dickinson (ND) Press; Dodge City (KS) Daily Globe; Dothan (AL) Eagle; Dubuque (IA) Telegraph Herald; Duncan (OK) Banner; Dyersburg (TN) State Gazette; Easton (MD) Star-Democrat; Easton (PA) Express-Times; Edmond (OK) Sun; El Centro (CA) Imperial Valley Press; El Dorado (AR) News-Times; Elizabethtown (KY) News Enterprise; Elko (NV) Daily Free Press; Elkton (MD) Cecil Whig; Ellensburg (WA) Daily Record; Eureka (CA) Times-Standard; Everett (WA) Daily Herald; Fargo (ND) Forum; Faribault (MN) Daily News; Fayetteville (NC) Observer; Flagstaff (AZ) Arizona Daily Sun; Fort Worth (TX) Star-Telegram; Frederick (MD) News-Post; Fremont (CA) Argus; Fremont (NE) Tribune; Gainesville (TX) Daily Register; Gallup (NM) Independent; Galveston (TX) County Daily News; Geneva (IL) Kane County Chronicle; Glasgow (KY) Daily Times; Glens Falls (NY) Post-Star; Gloucester (MA) Daily Times; Grand Forks (ND) Herald; Grand Island (NE) Independent; Greencastle (IN) Banner-Graphic; Greenfield (MA) Recorder;

Greensburg (IN) Daily News; Greenville (TX) Herald-Banner; Hackensack (NJ) Record; Hagerstown (MD) Herald Mail; Hanford (CA) Sentinel; Hannibal (MO) Courier-Post; Hayward (CA) Daily Review; Henderson (TX) Daily News; Hibbing (MN) Daily Tribune; Hillsdale (MI) Daily News; Hobbs (NM) News-Sun; Holland (MI) Sentinel; Hopkinsville (KY) New Era; Hot Springs (AR) Sentinel-Record; Huntsville (TX) Item; Independence (MO) Examiner; International Falls (MN) Daily Journal; Jacksonville (FL) Florida Times-Union; Jamestown (ND) Sun; Johnstown (PA) Tribune-Democrat; Jonesboro (GA) News Daily; Kankakee (IL) Daily Journal; Kearney (NE) Hub; Kellogg (ID) Shoshone News-Press; Kennett (MO) Daily Dunklin Democrat; Kerrville (TX) Daily Times; Kingman (AZ) Daily Miner; Klamath Falls (OR) Herald and News; Kokomo (IN) Tribune; La Crosse (WI) Tribune; Lakeport (CA) Lake County Record-Bee; Lancaster (PA) Intelligencer Journal & New Era; Las Vegas (NM) Optic; Laurel (MS) Leader-Call; Las Vegas (N

Circ. 12,005,646; BPA June 30, 2008

SPOTLIGHT — 250 Yonge St, Winston Salem, 27101, USA; tel (800) 457-1156; fax (336) 727-7461; web site www.starwatch.com
Bus. Mgr. — Alan Cronk
Sales Agent — Jody Stephenson Sarver
Circ. ; Sworn/Estimate/Non-Audited
September 30, 2017

STAR WATCH — 418 N Marshall St, Winston Salem, 27101-2815, USA; tel (336) 727-7406; fax (800) 430-0532; web site www.starwatch.com
Sales Agent — Jody Stephenson Sarver
Exec. Ed. — Alan Cronk
Circ. ; Sworn/Estimate/Non-Audited
September 30, 2017

THE SALINE COURIER TMC — 321 N Market St, Benton, 72015-3734, USA; tel (501) 315-8228; fax (501) 315-1230; e-mail news@bentoncourier.com; web site www.bentoncourier.com
Group: Horizon Publications Inc.
Bus. Mgr. — Vicki Dorsch
Assoc. Ed. — Lynda Hollenback
Prodn. Mgr. — Patricia Stuckey
Publisher — Terri Leifeste
Addvertising Director — David Wills
Editor — Megan Reynolds
Circ. ; Sworn/Estimate/Non-Audited
September 30, 2001

TMS SPECIALTY PRODUCTS — 435 N Michigan Ave, Ste 1400, Chicago, IL, 60611-7551, USA; tel (800) 637-4082; fax (312) 527-8256; e-mail ctrammell@tribune.com; web site

www.tmsspecialtyproducts.com
Gen. Mgr. — Marco Buscaglia
Sales manager — Curtis Trammell
Mng. Ed. — Mary Elson
Art Dir. — Todd Rector
Circ. ; Sworn/Estimate/Non-Audited
September 30, 2017
Note TMS Specialty Products provides articles and images suitable for use in advertorial sections, niche publications and other targeted media, as well as custom ordered content, including local and paginated products.

TRIBUNE MEDIA SERVICES TV LOG - CHICAGO, IL — 435 N Michigan Ave, Ste 1300, Chicago, 60611-4037, USA; tel (312) 222-3394; web site www.tribunemediaservices.comDavid D.
Member Newspapers: Allentown (PA) Morning Call; Arlington (IL) Daily Herald; Athens (GA) Daily News & Banner Herald; Atlanta (GA) Journal & Constitution; Atlantic City (NJ) Press; Bakersfield (CA) Californian; Baltimore (MD) Sun; Bangor (ME) News; Beaver (PA) County Times; Belleville (IL) News-Democrat; Bellevue (WA) Journal American; Boston (MA) Globe; Boston (MA) Herald; Boulder (CO) Daily Camera; Bridgeport (CT) Connecticut Post; Bridgewater (NJ) Courier News; Buffalo (NY) News; Canton (OH) Repository; Charlotte (NC) Observer; Chicago (IL) Sun-Times; Chicago (IL) Tribune; Cleveland (OH) Plain Dealer; Columbia (SC) State; Columbus (OH) Dispatch; Dallas (TX) News; Dayton (OH) News; Daytona Beach (FL) News-Journal; Denver (CO) Post; Denver (CO) Rocky Mountain News; Detroit (MI) Free Press; Detroit (MI) News; Durham (NC) Sun; Evansville (IN) Courier & Press; Everett (WA) Herald; Fort Lauderdale (FL) Sun-Sentinel; Fort Myers (FL) News Press; Fort Worth (TX) Star-Telegram; Fresno (CA) Bee; Galveston (TX) Daily News; Gary (IN) Post-Tribune; Glens Falls (NY) Post Star; Greensburg (PA) Tribune Review; Hackensack (NJ) Bergen County Record; Hartford (CT) Courant; Houston (TX) Chronicle; Indianapolis (IN) Star; Jacksonville (FL) Florida Times-Union; Jersey City (NJ) Jersey Journal; Kansas City (MO) Star; Kenosha (WI) News; Little Rock (AR) Democrat-Gazette; Long Beach (CA) Press Telegram; Long Island (NY) Newsday; Los Angeles (CA) Daily Breeze; Los Angeles (CA) Daily News; Lowell (MA) Sun; Los Angeles (CA) Times; Macomb (IL) Daily Journal; Mesa (AZ) Tribune; Miami (FL) Herald; Milwaukee (WI) Journal Sentinel; Minneapolis (MN) Star Tribune; Modesto (CA) Bee; Morristown (NJ) Daily Record; New Haven (CT) Register; New York (NY) Daily News; New York (NY) Post; Newport

News (VA) Daily Press; Norfolk (VA) Virginian Pilot; Oakland (MI) Press; Oklahoma City (OK) Oklahoman & Times; Omaha (NE) World-Herald; Orange County (CA) Register; Orlando (FL) Sentinel; Palm Springs (CA) Desert Sun; Pasadena (CA) Star News; Philadelphia (PA) Daily News; Philadelphia (PA) Inquirer; Pittsburgh (PA) Post-Gazette; Port Huron (MI) Times Herald; Quincy (MA) Patriot Leader; Racine (WI) Journal Times; Raleigh (NC) News & Observer; Reading (PA) Eagle; Riverside (CA) Press; Rome (GA) News Tribune; Sacramento (CA) Bee; Salt Lake City (UT) Deseret News; Salt Lake City (UT) Tribune; San Antonio (TX) Express News; San Francisco (CA) Chronicle; San Francisco (CA) Examiner; San Jose (CA) Mercury News; Springfield (MO) News-Leader; St. Louis (MO) Post-Dispatch; St. Paul (MN) Pioneer Press; St. Petersburg (FL) Times; Trenton (NJ) Times; Tucson (AZ) Arizona Star; Vancouver (WA) Columbian; Washington (DC) Post; Washington (DC) Times; West Palm Beach (FL) Post; Wichita (KS) Eagle; Wilkes Barre (PA) Times-Leader; Wilmington (DE) News Journal; Worcester (MA) Telegram & Gazette; Youngstown (OH) Vindicator;
Circ. 32,853,868; Sworn/Estimate/Non-Audited July 23, 1999

TRIBUNE MEDIA SERVICES TV LOG - LOS ANGELES, CA — 5800 W Sunset Blvd, Los Angeles, 90028-6607, USA; tel (310) 581-5011; fax (310) 581-8025; web site www.tribunemediaservices.com
Circ. ; Sworn/Estimate/Non-Audited
September 30, 2017

TRIBUNE MEDIA SERVICES TV LOG - QUEENSBURY, NY — 40 Media Dr, Queensbury, 12804-4086, USA; tel (518) 792-9914; fax (212) 210-2863; web site www.tribunemediaservices.com
Circ. ; Sworn/Estimate/Non-Audited
September 30, 2017

TVTIMES — 250 Yonge St., Toronto, ON, M5B 2L7, Canada; tel (416) 593-6556; fax (416) 593-7329; e-mail tvtimes3@canwest.com; web site www.canwest.com
Dir., Newspaper Sales — Quin Millar
Member Newspapers: Windsor (ON) Star; Victoria (BC) Times-Colonist; Vancouver (BC) Sun; Saskatoon (SK) Star Phoenix; Regina (SK) Leader Post; Prince George (BC) Citizen; Ottawa (ON) Citizen; Montreal (QC) Gazette; Medicine Hat (AB) News; Kamloops (BC) Daily News; Edmonton (AB) Journal; Calgary (AB) Herald; Winnipeg (BC) Free Press
Circ. 1,124,839; ABC September 30, 2007

Section IV

Mechanical and Interactive Equipment, Supplies and Services

EQUIPMENT, SUPPLIES AND SERVICES
COMPANIES SERVING THE NEWSPAPER INDUSTRY

A

A & A RESEARCH
690 Sunset Blvd, Kalispell, MT, 59901-3641, USA; tel (406) 752-7857; fax (406) 752-0194; e-mail fireowl@in-tch.com
Pres.—Judith Doonan
Research Dir.—E.B. Eiselein
Industry: Market Research; Research Studies;

A-AMERICAN MACHINE & ASSEMBLY (PRESS PARTS DIV.)
2620 Auburn St, Rockford, IL, 61101-4222, USA; tel (815) 965-0884; fax (815) 965-1049; e-mail sales@a-americanpressparts.com; web site www.a-americanpressparts.com
Pres.—Mark Keller
Vice Pres., Opns.—Tom Sweeney
Industry: Complete line of repair / replacement parts for printing presses, folders and RTP's Large inventories of mechanical consumable parts including, Knives, Slitters, Knife Box Components, Nip (Gain) Rings, Folding Blades, spindles, gears and much, much more. Also stocking many pneumatic and electrical components. In house manufacturing allows for shortened lead time and the quality you expect.

A-KORN ROLLER, INC.
3545 S Morgan St, Chicago, IL, 60609-1590, USA; tel (773) 254-5700; fax (773) 650-7355; e-mail a-kornroller@a-kornroller.com; web site www.a-kornroller.com
Pres.—Michael Koren
Industry: Roll Cleaning Equipment; Roll Coverings; Roller Grinders; Roller Grinding Services; Rollers; Rollers: Dampening;

AAA PRESS INTERNATIONAL
3160 N Kennicott Ave, Arlington Heights, IL, 60004-1426, USA; tel (847) 818-1100; fax (800) 678-7983; e-mail info@aaapress.com; web site www.aaapress.com
Pres.—Jack Ludwig
Vice Pres., Sales/Mktg.—Mark Hahn
Industry: Cameras & Accessories; Circulation Equipment & Supplies; Equipment Dealers (New); Equipment Dealers (Used); Imagesetters; Plate Mounting & Register Systems; Press Accessories, Parts & Supplies; Presses: Flexographic; Proofing Systems; Rewinders

ABB INC.
9011 Bretshire Dr, Dallas, TX, 75228-5105, USA; tel (214) 328-1202; web site www.abb/printing.com
Nat'l Sales/Mktg. Dir.—Jeff Gelfand
Industry: Drives & Controls; Press Control Systems; Plate workflow, System Integration Services;

ABB LTD.
Affolternstr. 44, PO Box 8131, Zurich, N/A, CH-8050, Switzerland; tel 41 43 317-7111; fax 41 43 317-4420; e-mail engage.abb@ch.abb.com; web site www.abb.com
CEO—Joseph Hogan
CFO—Michel Demare

ABB, INC. (PRINTING SYSTEMS)
16250 W Glendale Dr, New Berlin, WI, 53151-2858, USA; tel (262) 785-3206; fax (262) 785-6295; web site www.abb.com/printing
Vice Pres.-Paper Drives Systems/Printing—Rick Hepperla
Nat'l Sales/Mktg. Dir.-Printing Systems—Jeffrey Gelfand

Mgr.-Sales Applications/Printing Drives Systems—Hans Wirth
Industry: Drives & Controls; Press Control Systems; System Integration Services

ACCRAPLY, INC.
3580 Holly Ln N Ste 60, Plymouth, MN, 55447-1367, USA; tel (763) 557-1313; fax (763) 519-9656; web site www.accraply.com
Vice Pres., Sales—Dave Hansen
Industry: Label Printing Machines

ACCUFAST PACKAGE PRINTING SYSTEMS
125 Wolf Rd Ste 318, Albany, NY, 12205-1221, USA; tel (518) 283-0988; fax (518) 283-0977; e-mail sales@accufastpps.com; web site www.accufastpps.com
Pres.—Ken St. John
Mgr.—Meg Flanigan
Industry: Label Printing Machines; Mailroom Systems & Equipment;

ACER AMERICA
333 W San Carlos St Ste 1500, San Jose, CA, 95110-2738, USA; tel (408) 533-7700; fax (408) 533-4555; web site www.acer.com
Pres., Pan America Opns.—Rudi Schmidleithner
CFO—Ming Wang
Industry: Computers: Laptop & Portable

ACS CAPITAL
6633 Boulevard 26 Ste 107, North Richland Hills, TX, 76180-1523, USA; tel (817) 284-3060; fax (817) 284-3061; e-mail leaseguy@waymark.net
Contact—Stuart Kelley

ACUTECH LLC
PO Box 543, Granger, IN, 46530, USA; tel (574) 262-8228; web site www.acu-tech.net
Managing Director—Joe Bella
Industry: Plate Cylinder Lock Ups
Web Register Systems
Used Plate Benders
Legacy Press and Pre Press equipment Repair and Services
Used Presses
Used Auxiliary Equipment
Installation

AD-A-NOTE
1000 RockPointe Blvd, Pittsburgh, PA, 15084-2806, USA; tel (724) 889-7707; e-mail Bruce@ad-a-note.com; web site www.ad-a-note.com
Executive Vice President —Bruce Barna
Industry: Sticky Notes

ADHESIVES RESEARCH, INC.
PO Box 100, Glen Rock, PA, 17327-0100, USA; tel (717) 235-7979; fax (717) 235-8320; web site www.adhesivesresearch.com
Vice Pres., Commercial Devel.—George Cramer
Industry: Adhesives

ADI/PDM TRADE GROUP
PO Box 220, Sylvania, GA, 30467-0220, USA; tel (912) 564-2400; fax (912) 564-2402; e-mail jlmcd1492@aol.com; web site www.arcdoyle.com
Pres.—Jim McDonald
Industry: Computers: Storage Devices; Counting, Stacking, Bundling Machines; Feeding, Folding, Delivery Equipment; Folding Machines; Material Handling Equipment: Automatic Guided Vehicles; Material Handling Equipment: Palletizing

Machines; Material Handling Equipment: Pallets & Palletizers; Presses: Flexographic; Solvent Recovery Systems

ADOBE SYSTEMS, INC.
345 Park Ave, San Jose, CA, 95110-2704, USA; tel (408) 536-6000; fax (408) 537-6000; web site www.adobe.com
Sr. Vice Pres., Global Mktg.—Ann Lewnes
Dir., Worldwide Adv.—Jennifer Reynolds

ADVANCE GRAPHICS EQUIPMENT OF YORK, INC.
4700 Raycom Rd, Dover, PA, 17315-1303, USA; tel (717) 292-9183; fax (717) 292-0196; e-mail info@ageyork.com; web site www.ageyork.com
Industry: Counting, Stacking, Bundling Machines; Cutters & Trimmers; Feeding, Folding, Delivery Equipment; Folding Machines; In-Line Trimming Systems; Inserting Equipment (Includes Stuffing Machines); Numbering Machines; Three Knife Trimmer; Web Press - Special Equipment

ADVANCE SYSTEMS, INC.
PO Box 9428, Green Bay, WI, 54308-9428, USA; tel (920) 468-5477; fax (920) 468-0931; e-mail asi_sales@advancesystems.com; web site www.advancesystems.com
Pres.—William Henry
Office Mgr.—Chelly Pierquet
Sales/Mktg. Mgr.—Mike Sellers
Industry: Dryers: Film and Papers; Drying Systems

ADVANCED INTERACTIVE MEDIA GROUP, LLC
402 Spring Valley Rd, Altamonte Springs, FL, 32714, USA; tel (407) 788-2780; fax (866) 611-6551; e-mail pzollman@aimgroup.com; web site www.aimgroup.com
Founding Principal—Peter M. Zollman
Editorial Director—Jim Townsend
Europe Director—Katja Riefler
Principal, director of consulting—Rob Paterson
Diana Bogdan
Industry: Consulting Services
Industry Trade Publication
Conferences — Automotive advertising, recruitment advertising and technology

ADVANCED TECHNICAL SOLUTIONS, INC.
PO Box 386, Maynard, MA, 01754-0386, USA; tel (978) 849-0533; fax (978) 849-0544; e-mail info@atsusa.com; web site www.atsusa.com
Exec. Vice Pres.—Bill Page
Industry: Computers: Hardware & Software Integrators; Input & Editing Systems; Publishing Systems; Software: Advertising (Includes Display; Classified); Software: Circulation; Software: Editorial; Software: Press/Post Press

ADVANTEX MARKETING INTERNATIONAL, INC.
600 Alden Road, Suite 606 , Markham, ON, L3R 0E7, Canada; tel (416) 481-5657; fax (416) 481-5692; e-mail info@advantex.com; web site www.advantex.com
Pres.—Kelly Ambrose
Industry: Consulting Services: Circulation; Consulting Services: Marketing; Promotion Services

ADVERTISING CHECKING BUREAU, INC.
675 Third Ave. Suite 2905, New York, NY,

10017, USA; tel (212) 684-3377; fax (212) 684-3381; e-mail sales@acbcoop.com; web site www.acbcoop.com
Pres./CEO—Brian T. McShane
VP., Nat'l Sales—John Portelli
Industry: Library Retrieval Systems; Market Research; Research Studies;Co-op advertising management

AEC, INC.
1100 E Woodfield Rd Ste 550, Schaumburg, IL, 60173-5135, USA; tel (847) 273-7700; fax (847) 273-7804; e-mail dazzarello@corpemail.com; web site www.aecinternet.com
Pres.—Tom Breslin
Industry: Architects/Engineers (Includes Design/Construction Firms); Press Accessories, Parts & Supplies

AECOM
303 E Wacker Dr Ste 1400, Chicago, IL, 60601-5214, USA; tel (312) 373-7700; fax (312) 373-7710; web site www.aecom.com
Office Mgr.—Betty Hendricks
Industry: Architects/Engineers (Includes Design/Construction Firms); Consulting Services: Equipment; Consulting Services: Production;

AG INDUSTRIES, INC.
1 American Rd, Cleveland, OH, 44144-2398, USA; tel (216) 252-6737; fax (216) 252-6773; web site www.agifixtures.com
Mktg./Adv. Coord.—Sandy Saunders
Industry: Newspaper Dispensers (Mechanical/Electronic)

AGFA MONOTYPE CORPORATION
985 Busse Rd, Elk Grove Village, IL, 60007-2400, USA; tel (847) 718-0400; fax (847) 718-0500; e-mail steve.kuhlman@agfamonotype.com; web site www.agfamonotype.com
Mgr., Sales/Mktg.—Steve Kuhlman
Industry: Consulting Services: Computer; Software: Design/Graphics; Type, Fonts

AIRLOC LLC
PO Box 260, Franklin, MA, 02038-0260, USA; tel (508) 528-0022; fax (508) 528-7555; e-mail info@airloc.com; web site www.airloc.com
Engineering Mgr.—Philip Littlewood
Industry: Vibration Isolation & Machine Leveling Mounts

AIRSYSTEMS, INC.
16528 Westgrove Dr, Addison, TX, 75001-5627, USA; tel (972) 931-0711; fax (972) 250-2034; e-mail emcor_info@emcorgroup.com
Pres.—Milton Lemaster
Industry: Inks; Controllers: Press

ALAR ENGINEERING CORPORATION
9651 196th St, Mokena, IL, 60448, USA; tel (708) 479-6100; fax (708) 479-9059; e-mail nancyc@alarcorp.com; web site www.alarcorp.com
President—Paula Jackfert
Vice Pres., Int'l Sales—Vickey Gorski
Sales Mgr.—Steve Gorski
Industry: Waste Water Treatment Systems

ALCATEL-LUCENT
600 Mountain Ave # 2F-147, New Providence, NJ, 07974-2008, USA; tel (908) 582-3000; fax (908) 582-2576; e-mail execoffice@alcatel-lucent.com; web site www.alcatel-lucent.com

CEO—Ben Verwaayen
Pres., Bell Labs—Jeong H. Kim

ALFA CTP SYSTEMS INC.

554 Clark Rd Ste 2, Tewksbury, MA, 01876-1631, USA; tel (603) 689-1101; fax 978-429-0870; e-mail info@alfactp.com; web site www.alfactp.com
President—Tony Ford
VP Operations—Keith Roeske
Paul Norton
Industry: Imagesetters; Plates: Offset (Computer to Plate); Proofing Systems; Software: Pagination/Layout; Typesetters: Laser;

ALFAQUEST TECHNOLOGIES

1150 Rose Rd, Lake Zurich, IL, 60047-1567, USA; tel (847) 427-8800; fax (847) 427-8860; e-mail keith.roeske@alfactp.com; web site www.alfactp.com
Vice President Of Operations—Keith Roeske
Industry: Computers: Hardware & Software Integrators; Imagesetters; Interfaces; Laser Printers; Multiplexers/Routers; Output Management and Preflight Software; Photo Archiving; Platemakers: Laser; Raster Image Processors;

ALL SYSTEMS COLOR, INC.

2032 S Alex Rd Ste A, West Carrollton, OH, 45449-4023, USA; tel (937) 859-9701; fax (937) 859-9709; e-mail steveo@allsystemscolour.com; web site www.allsystemscolour.com
CEO—George Dick
Gen. Mgr.—Steve Orf
Industry: Color Proofing; Color Seperation Scanners; Color Seperations, Positives; Prepress Color Proofing Systems

ALL SYSTEMS GO

2 Cedar St Ste 1, Woburn, MA, 01801-6352, USA; tel (781) 932-6700; fax (781) 932-6711; e-mail info@allsysgo.com; web site www.allsysgo.com
Pres.—Richard Pape
Industry: Computers: Hardware & Software Integrators; Computers: Laptop & Portable; Computers: Storage Devices; Consulting Services: Advertising; Consulting Services: Circulation; Consulting Services: Computer; Consulting Services: Equipment; Consulting Services: Marketing; Imagesetters; Software: Design/Graphics

ALLIANCE RUBBER CO.

PO Box 20950, Hot Springs, AR, 71903-0950, USA; tel (501) 262-2700; fax (501) 262-3948; e-mail sales@alliance-rubber.com; web site www.rubberband.com
Director Sales & Marketing—Joan Dennis
Sheryl Koller
Industry: Rubber Band Manufacturer

AMERGRAPH CORPORATION

520 Lafayette Rd, Sparta, NJ, 07871-3447, USA; tel (973) 383-8700; fax (973) 383-9225; e-mail sales@amergraph.com; web site www.amergraph.com
Pres.—Robert Lesko
Industry: Exposure Lamps; Film & Paper; Film Processing Machines; Ink Bleeding Equipment; Ink Pumping Systems; Offset Plate-Making Service & Equipment; Plate Exposure Units; Plate Processors; Platemakers: Offset (Computer to Plate); Processors: Film & Paper; Vacuum Frames

AMERICAN CONSULTING SERVICES

440 NE 4th Ave, Camas, WA, 98607-2173, USA; tel (800) 597-9798; fax (360) 833-4620; e-mail info@toma.com; web site www.toma.com
Pres.—Mark Rood
Industry: Consulting Services: Advertising

AMERICAN FIDELITY ASSURANCE CO.

PO Box 25523, Oklahoma City, OK, 73125-0523, USA; tel (405) 523-2000; web site

www.afadvantage.com
Chrmn./CEO/Pres.—William B. Cameron
Div. Mktg. Mgr.—Bob Fleet
Industry: Insurance

AMERICAN GRAPHIC ARTS, INC.

PO Box 240, Elizabeth, NJ, 07206-0240, USA; tel (908) 351-6906; fax (908) 351-7156; web site www.agamachinery.com
Pres.—John Jacobson
Industry: Equipment Dealers (Used); Gluing Systems

AMERICAN INK JET CORP.

13 Alexander Rd Ste 1, Billerica, MA, 01821-5098, USA; tel (978) 670-9200; fax (978) 667-9200; e-mail info@amjet.com; web site www.amjet.com
Pres./CEO—Michael Andreottola
Industry: Inks

AMERICAN INTERNATIONAL COMMUNICATIONS, INC.

101425 Overseas Hwy #922, Key Largo, FL, 33037-4505, USA; tel (305) 453-5456; fax (305) 453-5455; e-mail pkaic@aol.com
Pres./CEO—Paul Keever
Industry: Telephone Automated Inbound Programs, Product information, Answering Services, Voice & video Conferencing, Voice Mail, Games, Horoscope, Health info; Voice Over IP; System Programming; Internet; Web site building; Consulting Services; 30 years in business.

AMERICAN NEWSPAPER REPRESENTATIVES

2075 W Big Beaver Rd Ste 310, Troy, MI, 48084-3439, USA; tel (248) 643-9910; fax (248) 643-9914; e-mail accountsales@gotoanr.com; web site www.anrinc.net
Pres.—John Jepsen
Exec. Vice Pres./COO—Robert Sontag
Regl. Sales Mgr., Minneapolis—Melanie Cox
Hilary Howe
Industry: Consulting Services: Advertising

AMERICAN OPINION RESEARCH

279 Wall St., Research Pk., Princeton, NJ, 8540, USA; tel (609) 683-4035; fax (609) 683-8398; e-mail acasale@imsworld.com; web site www.imsworld.com
Chrmn./CEO—Tony Casale
Pres.—Lois Kaufman
Industry: Consulting Services: Advertising; Consulting Services: Circulation; Consulting Services: Editorial; Consulting Services: Marketing

AMERICAN ROLLER CO.

1440 13th Ave., Union Grove, WI, 53182, USA; tel (262) 878-2445; fax (262) 878-2241; e-mail info@americanroller.com; web site www.americanroller.com
Pres.—Dan Cahalane
Industry: Roll Coverings; Rollers; Rollers: Dampening;

AMERICAN ULTRAVIOLET CO., INC.

212 S Mount Zion Rd, Lebanon, IN, 46052-9479, USA; tel (765) 483-9514; fax (765) 483-9525; web site www.auvco.com
Sales Rep.—Jack Slattery
Industry: Press Accessories, Parts & Supplies

ANOCOIL CORPORATION

PO Box 1318, Vernon Rockville, CT, 06066-1318, USA; tel (860) 871-1200; fax (860) 872-0534; web site www.anocoil.com
CEO—H.A. Fromson
Pres.—David Bujese
Vice Pres., Anocoil—Timothy A. Fromson
Vice President- Sales—Bud Knorr
Industry: Chemicals: Plate Processing; Plates: Offset (Computer to Plate); Plates: Offset (Conventional)

ANYGRAAF USA

10451 Mill Run Cir Ste 400, Owings Mills,

MD, 21117-5594, USA; tel (240) 379-6620; e-mail andy.hunn@anygraaf.fi; web site www.anygraaf.com
Managing Dir. —Andy Hunn
SALES DIR.—Bill Ryker
Industry: Proofing Systems

APPLE, INC.

1 Infinite Loop, Cupertino, CA, 95014-2084, USA; tel (408) 996-1010; fax (408) 996-0275; web site www.apple.com
CEO—Timothy Cook
Sr. Vice Pres., Worldwide Pdct. Mktg.—Philip W. Schiller

APPLIED INDUSTRIAL MACHINERY

1930 SE 29th St, Oklahoma City, OK, 73129-7626, USA; tel (405) 672-2222; fax (405) 672-2272
Pres.—Robert Gilson
Industry: Equipment Dealers (New); Feeding, Folding, Delivery Equipment; Folding Machines; In-Line Trimming Systems; Three Knife Trimmer; Web Press - Special Equipment

ARC INTERNATIONAL

10955 Withers Cove Park Dr, Charlotte, NC, 28278-0020, USA; tel (704) 588-1809; fax (704) 588-9921; web site www.arcinternational.com
Pres.—Mike Foran
Gen. Mgr.—Steven Wilkinson
Vice Pres., Cor. Sales—Steve Woodard
Industry: Cleaners & Solvents; Platemakers: Flexographic (Computer to Plate); Platemakers: Laser; Roll Coverings; Rollers

ARCH CHEMICALS, INC.

PO Box 10099, Mesa, AZ, 85216-0099, USA; tel (480) 987-7000; web site www.archchemicals.com
Pres.—Mike Campbell
Dir., Sales—Mario Stanghellini
Vice Pres., Int'l Mktg.—Jim LaCasse
Industry: Acid Dispensing Systems; Chemicals: Plate Processing; Chemicals: Pressroom;

ARCO ENGINEERING, INC. (NEWSPAPER DIV.)

3317 Gilmore Industrial Blvd, Louisville, KY, 40213-2174, USA; tel (502) 966-3134; fax (502) 966-3135; e-mail sales@arcoengineering.com; web site www.arcoengineering.com
Pres.—James Gunn
Industry: Belts, Belting, V-Belts; Equipment Dealers (New); Equipment Dealers (Used); Gauges, Measuring; Noise Control; Pasters; Reels & Tensions; Reels (Inlcudes Paper Reels); Scanners: Color B & W, Plates, Web; Tension & Web Controls

ARPAC GROUP

9511 River St, Schiller Park, IL, 60176-1019, USA; tel (847) 678-9034; fax (847) 671-7006; e-mail info@arpacgroup.com; web site www.arpacgroup.com
Pres.—Michael Levy
Industry: Bundling and Tying Machines; Conveyors; Shrink Wrapping Equipment

ARROW PRINTING CO.

PO Box 2898, Salina, KS, 67402-2898, USA; tel (785) 825-8124; fax (785) 825-0784; e-mail arrow@arrowprintco.com; web site www.arrowprintco.com
Pres.—Kent Fellers
Adv. Mgr.—Dennis Suelter
Industry: Consulting Services: Advertising; Offset Camera, Darkroom Equipment; Offset Plate Files; Photo Proofing Systems; Platemakers: Offset (Conventional); Plates: Offset (Conventional); Prepress Color Proofing Systems; Presses: Offset; Processors: Film & Paper; Scanners: Color B & W, Plates, Web

ARTBEATSEXPRESS

PO Box 709, Myrtle Creek, OR, 97457-0110,

USA; tel (541)863-4429; fax (541)863-4547; e-mail info@artbeats.com; web site www.artbeatsEXPRESS.com
Pres.—Phil Bates
COO—Laura Hollifield
Adv./Mktg. Mgr.—Julie Hill
Global Dist. Mgr.—Peggy Nichols
Dir., Tech.—Bob Hayes
Industry: Royalty Free Stock Media

ASHWORTH BROTHERS, INC.

450 Armour Dl, Winchester, VA, 22601-3459, USA; tel (540) 662-3494; fax (540) 662-3150; web site www.ashworth.com
Vice Pres. Mktg.—Joe Lackner
Mktg. Mgr.—Tim Jones
Industry: Belts, Belting, V-Belts; Conveyors;

ASTECH INTERMEDIA

999 18th St Ste 2240, Denver, CO, 80202-2442, USA; tel (303) 296-9966; fax (303) 296-9969; e-mail ter@astech-intermedia.com; web site www.smartfocus.com
Pres./CEO—Tom Ratkovich
Dir., Client Servs.—Tia Talbert
Industry: Consulting Services: Advertising; Consulting Services: Circulation; Consulting Services: Computer; Consulting Services: Marketing; Marketing Database Design and Implementation; Software: Circulation; Training: Sales & Marketing

ATEX

87 Castle Street, Reading, N/A, RG1 7SN, United Kingdom; tel 118 958 7537; fax 118 958 7537; e-mail info@atex.com; web site www.atex.com
Sr. Vice Pres./Chief Integration Officer—Peter Marsh
Sr. Vice Pres., Sales Americas—Malcolm McGrory
Industry: Software: Advertising (Includes Display; Classified); Software: Asset Management; Software: Circulation; Software: Editorial; Software: Pagination/Layout;

ATEX NORTH AMERICA

410 N Wickham Rd, Melbourne, FL, 32935-8648, USA; tel (321) 254-5559; fax (321) 254-4392; e-mail adbase.support-services.us@atex.com; web site www.atex.com
CEO of North America—Scott Roessler
Vice Pres., Product Mgmt.—Lars Jiborn
Vice Pres., Mktg.—Steve Roessler
Industry: Consulting Services: Advertising; Software: Advertising (Includes Display; Classified); Software: Business (Includes Administration/Accounting);

ATEX NORTH AMERICA

6767 N Wickham Rd Ste 111, Melbourne, FL, 32940-2024, USA; tel (813) 739-1700; fax (813) 739-1710; e-mail info@atex.com; web site www.atex.com
CEO—John Hawkins
CEO, Atex North America—Scott Rossler
Sales Mgr.—Malcom McGregory
Industry: Software: Advertising (Includes Display; Classified); Software: Business (Includes Administration/Accounting); Software: Circulation; Software: Editorial; Software: Pagination/Layout;

ATLAS SPECIALTY LIGHTING

7304 N Florida Ave, Tampa, FL, 33604-4889, USA; tel (813) 238-6481; fax (813) 238-6656; web site www.asltg2.com
Mgr.—Ralph Felten
Industry: Lighting Equipment

AUTOLOGIC INFORMATION INTERNATIONAL

1050 Rancho Conejo Blvd, Thousand Oaks, CA, 91320-1717, USA; tel (805) 498-9611; fax (805) 499-1167; e-mail abrunner@autologic.com; web site www.autologic.com
Pres.—Al Brunner
Vice Pres., Software Engineering—Ratan Bhaunani

Vice Pres., Mfg.—Doug Arlt
Dir., Americas Opns.—Jack Embree
Mktg. Mgr.—Tom LeJeune
Industry: Archiving Systems; Computers: Hardware & Software Integrators; Facsimilie/Fax Transmission Systems; Multiplexers/Routers; Platemakers: Direct; Platemakers: Flexographic (Computer to Plate); Publishing Systems; Scanners: Color B & W, Plates, Web; Software: Advertising (Includes Display; Classified); Software: Electronic Data Interchange; Typesetters: Laser

AUTOMATED MAILING SYSTEMS CORP.
PO Box 541326, Dallas, TX, 75354-1326, USA; tel (972) 869-2844; fax (972) 869-2735; e-mail amsco@amscodallas.com; web site www.amscodallas.com
Vice Pres.—Scott Helsley
Mktg. Mgr—Thomas Helsley
Industry: Addressing Machines; Bundling and Tying Machines; Inserting Equipment (Includes Stuffing Machines); Mailroom Systems & Equipment; Strapping Machines

AWS, A THERMAL CARE DIVISION
5680 W. Jarvis Ave., Niles, IL, 60714, USA; tel (630) 595-3651; fax (630) 595-5433; e-mail info@thermalcare.com; web site www.thermalcare.com
Mktg. Servs. Mgr.—Audrey Guidarelli
Industry: Circulation Equipment & Supplies; Ink Fountains & Accessories; Ink Pumping Systems; Press Accessories, Parts & Supplies

AYERS/JOHANEK PUBLICATION DESIGN, INC.
6449 Meadowview Ter S, Zionsville, PA, 18092-2091, USA; tel 610-928-1111; e-mail ayers@publicationdesign.com; web site www.publicationdesign.com
Partner—John Johanek

B

B & L MACHINE & DESIGN
PO Box 743, Effingham, IL, 62401-0743, USA; tel (217) 342-3918; fax (217) 342-2081; e-mail info@blmachinedesign.com; web site www.blmachinedesign.com
Pres.—Larry Hines
Mktg. Mgr.—Lara Westjohn
Prodn. Mgr., Mfg.—Jim Strange
Industry: Presses: Offset; Training: Press Operation & Maintenance

B E & K, INC.
PO Box 2332, Birmingham, AL, 35201-2332, USA; tel (205) 972-6000; fax (205) 972-6300; web site www.bek.com
Industry: Architects/Engineers (Includes Design/Construction Firms)

B.H. BUNN CO.
2730 Drane Field Rd, Lakeland, FL, 33811-1325, USA; tel (863) 647-1555; fax (863) 686-2866; e-mail info@bunntyco.com; web site www.bunntyco.com
Pres.—John R. Bunn
Industry: Bundling and Tying Machines; Strapping Machines;

BADGER FIRE PROTECTION
944 Glenwood Station Ln Ste 303, Charlottesville, VA, 22901-1480, USA; tel (800) 446-3857; fax (800) 248-7809; e-mail vmodic@badgerfire.com; web site www.badgerfire.com
Sales/Mktg. Dir.—Alan Owens
Industry: Fire Protection

BAIRD MANUFACTURING
Hwy. 79 East, Clarendon, AR, 72029, USA; tel (800) 682-2278
Industry: Cart Distribution Systems

BALDOR ELECTRIC CO.
PO Box 2400, Fort Smith, AR, 72902-2400, USA; tel (479) 646-4711; fax (479) 648-5752; e-mail charlie_hubbard@baldor.com; web site www.baldor.com
Chrmn./CEO—John McFarland
Pres./COO—Ronald E. Tucker
Cor. Commun. Dir.—Charles G. Hubbard
Vice Pres., Sales—Randy Colip
Vice Pres., Mktg.—Randy Breaux
Industry: Drives & ControlsMotors

BALDWIN AMERICAS
3350 West Salt Creek, Arlington Heights, IL, 60005, USA; tel 913-888-9800; e-mail csrteam@baldwintech.com; web site www.baldwintech.com/home
Sales Contact—Denise Jabotte
Industry: Sales, Service, and Parts; Sheetfed and Web, Blanket Cleaner/Washer (Automatic); UV/IR/LED Drying Systems; Web Printing Controls (WPC) systems; Press Accessories, Parts & Supplies, Cleaning Cloth; @RecordHead:Baldwin Technology Company, Inc.
3041 Woodcreek Dr Ste 102, Downers Grove, IL, 60515-5418, USA; tel 630-595-3651; fax 630-595-5433; e-mail info@baldwintech.com; web site www.baldwintech.com
Vice President, Baldwin Americas Sales & Marketing—Donald Gustafson
Industry: UV & LED Curing and IR Drying Systems; Automatic Blanket Cleaners; Circulation Equipment & Supplies; Dampening Systems; Environmental Control Systems; Fluid Management Systems: Pressroom; Ink Controls, Computerized; Press Accessories, Parts & Supplies; Recirculators; Solvent Recovery Systems; Powder Applicators; Gluing Systems; Anti-Offset Powder; Blanket Cleaning Cloth Consumables; UV Lamps

BALEMASTER
980 Crown Ct, Crown Point, IN, 46307-2732, USA; tel (219) 663-4525; fax (219) 663-4591; e-mail sales@balemaster.com; web site www.balemaster.com
Sales Mgr.—Mike Connell
Industry: Baling Machines

BARRY FRENCH
3 Ashlawn Rd, Assonet, MA, 02702-1105, USA; tel (508) 644-5772; e-mail barryfrench@yahoo.com
Owner—Barry French
Industry: Brokers & Appraisers; Consulting Services: Financial;

BASF CORP.
12 Thompson Rd, East Windsor, CT, 06088-9696, USA; tel (860) 623-9901; fax (860) 623-4657; web site www.basf.com
HR—Allan Bailie
Industry: Adhesives

BASF CORPORATION
100 Park Ave, Florham Park, NJ, 07932-1089, USA; tel (973) 245-6000; fax (973) 245-6714; web site www.basf.us
CEO—Hans U. Engel
Industry: chemical

BATON LOCK & HARDWARE CO., INC.
11521 Salinaz Ave, Garden Grove, CA, 92843-3702, USA; tel (714) 590-6969; fax (714) 590-6960; e-mail info@batonlockusa.com; web site www.batonlockusa.com
Pres.—Hwei Ying Chen
Industry: Calibration Software/Hardware

BAUMER ELECTRIC LTD.
122 Spring St Ste C6, Southington, CT, 06489-1534, USA; tel (860) 621-2121; fax (860) 628-6280; e-mail sales.us@baumerelectric.com; web site www.baumerelectric.com/usa
Pdct. Mgr.—Jeremy Jones
Mrkt.—Kristian Santamaria

Industry: Controls: Photo Electric; Newspaper Couter; Totalizing Systems; Web Break Detector

BAUMFOLDER CORP.
1660 Campbell Rd, Sidney, OH, 45365-2480, USA; tel (937) 492-1281; fax (937) 492-7280; e-mail baumfolder@baumfolder.com; web site www.baumfolder.com
Pres.—Janice A. Benanzer
Dir., Sales/Mktg.—Mark Pellman
Industry: Belts, Belting, V-Belts; Collating Equipment; Counting, Stacking, Bundling Machines; Cutters & TrimmersCutters & Trimmers; Delivery Equipment; Feeding, Folding, Delivery Equipment; Folding Machines; Inserting Equipment (Includes Stuffing Machines); Pumps (Air, Ink, Vacuum)

BAUMULLER
429 Hayden Station Rd Ste B, Windsor, CT, 06095-1340, USA; tel (860) 243-0232; fax (860) 286-3080; e-mail info@baumuller.com; web site www.baumuller.com
Industry: Motors

BECKART ENVIRONMENTAL, INC.
6900 46th St, Kenosha, WI, 53144-1779, USA; tel (262) 656-7680; fax (262) 656-7699; e-mail inbox@beckart.com; web site www.beckart.com
Pres.—Thomas M. Fedrigon
Mgr., Mktg./Sales—Dan Fedrigon
Industry: Wastewater Treatment

BEK SYSTEMS, INC.
1001 W Republic Dr Ste 9, Addison, IL, 60101-3016, USA; tel (630) 248-4334; e-mail info@beksystems.com; web site www.beksystems.com
Pres.—Paul Englram
Industry: Ink Bleeding Equipment; Ink Fountains & Accessories; Ink Pumping Systems; Ink Recovery Systems; Offset Fountain Controls;

BELL & HOWELL SCANNERS
760 S Wolf Rd, Wheeling, IL, 60090-6232, USA; tel (847) 675-7600; fax (847) 423-7503; web site www.bellhowell.com
Pres.—George Marton
Industry: Mailroom Systems & Equipment; Publishing Systems

BELLATRIX SYSTEMS, INC.
1015 SW Emkay Dr, Bend, OR, 97702-1010, USA; tel (541) 382-2208; fax (541) 385-3277; e-mail frontoffice@bellatrix.net; web site www.bellatrix.net
President and CEO—Steve Morris
Sr. Vice Pres., Sales/Mktg.—William Raven
Industry: Circulation Equipment & Supplies; Electronic Coin Totalizers for Newspaper Vending machines, Credit Card Systems for newspaper vending machines

BELT CORPORATION OF AMERICA
253 Castleberry Industrial Dr, Cumming, GA, 30040-9051, USA; tel (800) 235-0947; fax (770) 887-4138; e-mail sales@beltcorp.com; web site www.beltcorp.com
Pres.—William C. Levensalor
Sales Mgr.—Rich Blais
Inside Sales Supvr.—Mike Bridges
Industry: Belts, Belting, V-Belts

BELTING INDUSTRIES CO., INC.
PO Box 310, Kenilworth, NJ, 07033-0310, USA; tel (908) 272-8591; fax (908) 272-3825; e-mail info@beltingindustries.com; web site www.beltingindustries.com
Chrmn.—Webb A. Cooper
Pres.—Scott Cooper
COO—Gene Hobson
Controller—Paul West
Sales Mgr.—Jeff Smith
Industry: Belts, Belting, V-Belts

BENDER MACHINE, INC.
2150 E 37th St, Vernon, CA, 90058-1491,

USA; tel (323) 232-1790; fax (323) 232-6456; e-mail info@bendermachine.com; web site www.bendermachine.com
Mktg. Mgr.—Bruce Perry
Acct. Mgr.—Doug Martin
Industry: Newsprint; Newsprint Handeling Equipment; Roller Grinders; Roller Grinding Services;

BERTING COMMUNICATIONS
6330 Woburn Dr, Indianapolis, IN, 46250, USA; tel 317-849-5408; fax (317) 849-5408; e-mail bob@bobberting.com; web site 6330 Woburn Drive
Pres.—Bob Berting
Vice Pres.—Barbara Berting
Graphic Artist—Don Cooper
Industry: Publisher Consultant Services:Merchant Advertising Seminars; Marketing; Training: Sales & Marketing—webinars,tele-seminars

BETA SCREEN CORP.
707 Commercial Ave, Carlstadt, NJ, 07072-2602, USA; tel (201) 939-2400; fax (201) 939-7656; e-mail info@betascreen.com; web site www.betascreen.com
Pres.—Arnold Serchuk
Contact—Larry Goldberg
Industry: Calibration Software/Hardware; Color Proofing; Color Viewing Equipment; Dark Room Equipment; Densitometers; Gauges, Measuring; Layout Tables, Light Tables & Workstations; Optical Products; Static Eliminators; Tables (Dot, Etch, Opaquing, Register, Retouching, Stripping)

BISHAMON INDUSTRIES CORP.
5651 E Francis St, Ontario, CA, 91761-3601, USA; tel (909) 390-0055; fax (909) 390-0060; e-mail info@bishamon.com; web site www.bishamon.com
Pres.—Wataru Sugiura
Vice Pres., Sales/Mktg.—Bob Clark
Industry: Mailroom Systems & Equipment; Material Handling Equipment: Vehicle Loading; Newsprint Handeling Equipment; Paper Handeling Equipment;

BLOWER APPLICATION CO., INC.
PO Box 279, Germantown, WI, 53022-0279, USA; tel (800) 959-0880; fax (262) 255-3446; e-mail info@bloapco.com; web site www.bloapco.com
Pres.—John Stanislowski
CEO—Michael J. Young
Mgr., Sales—Ric Johnson
Industry: Cutters & Trimmers; In-Line Trimming Systems; Paper Shredders; System Installations;

BLUE HERON PAPER CO.
419 Main St, Oregon City, OR, 97045-1809, USA; tel (503) 650-4211; fax (503) 650-4512; e-mail customerservice@blueheronpaper.com.; web site www.blueheronpaper.com
Pres. / CEO—Michael A Siebers
Mgr., Sales/Mktg.—Jon E. Melkerson
Industry: Newsprint

BOB RAY & ASSOCIATES, INC.
3575 Morreim Dr, Belvidere, IL, 61008-6307, USA; tel (815) 547-9393; fax (815) 547-5572; e-mail chuck@bobray.com; web site www.bobray.com
Pres.—Chuck Britton
Vice Pres., Admin.—Nolen G. Lee
Vice Pres., Sales—John R. Steker
Technical Sales Mgr.—John F. Nicoli

BOB WEBER, INC.
23850 Commerce Park Rd., Cleveland, OH, 44122, USA; tel (800) 399-4294; fax (800) 837-8973; e-mail info@bob-weber.com; web site www.bob-weber.com
Director of Marketing—Leslie DiVincenzo
Senior Technician—Steve Fondriest
Business Development Director—Bill Weber
Industry: Equipment Dealers (New) - BWI Series CTP; Printing Consumables - Plates

and Chemistry; Used PrePress Equipment; Platesetters; CTP; Computer-to-plate; Plate Processors; Raster Image Processors; Workflow RIPS; Xitron RIPs, Plate Readers

BODINE ELECTRIC
201 Northfield Rd, Northfield, IL, 60093-3311, USA; tel (773) 478-3515; fax (773) 478-3232; web site www.bodine-electric.com
Pres.—John Bodine
Industry: Motors

BOSCH REXROTH
5150 Prairie Stone Pkwy, Hoffman Estates, IL, 60192-3707, USA; tel (847) 645-3600; fax (847) 645-6201; web site www.boschrexroth-us.com
Pres./CEO—Berend Bracht
Industry: Press Control Systems

BOTTCHER AMERICA CORP.
4600 Mercedes Dr, Belcamp, MD, 21017-1225, USA; tel (800) 637-8120; fax (410) 273-7174; e-mail support@boettcher-systems.com; web site www.bottcher.com
Vice Pres., Mktg.—Wayne Porter
Alan Fischer
Industry: Rollers

BOWE BELL + HOWELL
3791 S Alston Ave, Durham, NC, 27713-1880, USA; tel (919) 767-4401; e-mail marketing@bowebellhowell.com; web site www.bowebellhowell.com
Pres.—George Marton
Exec. Vice Pres.—Frank Gozzo
Vice Pres., Sales—Scott Turner
Industry: Mailroom Systems & Equipment

BRADY & PAUL COMMUNICATIONS
7 Orange St, Newburyport, MA, 01950-2805, USA; tel (978) 463-2255; e-mail bradybrady@aol.com; contact@johnbrady.info; web site www.bradyandpaul.com; www.johnbrady.info
Pres.—John Brady
Designer—Greg Paul
Industry: Art & Layout Equipment and Services; Consulting Services: Editorial;

BRAINWORKS SOFTWARE DEVELOPMENT CORP.
100 S Main St Ste 102, Sayville, NY, 11782-3148, USA; tel (631) 563-5000; fax (631) 563-6320; e-mail info@brainworks.com; web site www.brainworks.com
President—John Barry
Director of Sales—Rick Sanders
Business Development Manager—Frank Collinsworth
Business Development Manager—Matt Griffith
Industry: Pagination Systems; Software: Advertising (Includes Display; Classified, Preprints and Digital); Software: Business (Includes Administration/Accounting); Software: Design/Graphics; Software: Pagination/Layout; System Integration Services; Software: Circulation Software; Digital Subscriptions, CRM; Digital Advertising; Software: Customer Relationship Management (CRM); iPad Application

BROCK SOLUTIONS U.S. INC.
8080 Tristar Dr Ste 126, Irving, TX, 75063-2823, USA; tel (972) 373-2500; fax (972) 444-0352; e-mail info@brocksolutions.com; hr@brocksolutions.com; web site www.brocksolutions.com
Project Mgr.—Bill Mctuire
Industry: Addressing Machines; Consulting Services: Production;

BRODIE SYSTEM, INC.
1539 W. Elizabeth Ave., Linden, NJ, 07036, USA; tel (908) 862-8620; fax (908) 862-8632; e-mail customerservice@brodiesystem.com; web site www.brodiesystem.com
Pres.—Thomas W. Nielsen

Eng.—Nicholas Lloyd
Prodn. Mgr., Opns.—John Farrell
Industry: Cylinder Repair; Ink Fountains & Accessories; Press Accessories, Parts & Supplies; Roller Grinding Services; Rollers; Rollers: Dampening;

BROWN MANNSCHRECK BUSINESS SYSTEM
5901 NE Woodbine Rd, Saint Joseph, MO, 64505-9353, USA; tel 816-387-8180; fax 816-364-7925; e-mail customerservice@browncompanies.net; web site www.browncompanies.net/
CEO—Steven Pitluck
Vice Pres.—Craig Greer
Vice Pres., Sales—Cathie Wayman
Industry: Sales and design Office Furniture

BROWN'S WEB PRESS SERVICE & MACHINE SHOP
PO Box 326, Mexico, MO, 65265-0326, USA; tel (573) 581-6275; fax (573) 581-7278; e-mail lgbrown59@gmail.com
Pres.—L.G. Brown
Vice President—Gena Brown
Industry: Cylinder Repair; Drives & Controls; Equipment Dealers (Used); Erectors & Riggers; Press Rebuilding; Press Repairs; Presses: Offset; Roller Grinding Services;

BRUCE BELL & ASSOCIATES
PO Box 400, Canon City, CO, 81215-0400, USA; tel (800) 359-7738; e-mail info@surview.com; web site www.surview.com
Opns. Dir.—Terri Madigan
Director, Sales and Customer Service—G. Alain Chamot
Industry: Computers: Hardware & Software Integrators; Computers: Laptop & Portable; Consulting Services: Advertising; Consulting Services: Marketing; Software: Advertising (Includes Display; Classified)

BST PRO MARK
650 W Grand Ave Ste 301, Elmhurst, IL, 60126-1026, USA; tel (630) 833-9900; fax (630) 833-9909; e-mail sales@bstpromark.com; web site www.bstpromark.com
Vice Pres., Mktg.—John Thome
Industry: Color Management Software; Color Registration; Color Viewing Equipment; Press Accessories, Parts & Supplies; Produciton Control Systems; Web Cleaners; Web Guides

BUFFALO TECHNOLOGY INC.
11100 Metric Blvd Ste 750, Austin, TX, 78758-4072, USA; tel (512) 349-1580; fax (512) 339-7272; e-mail sales@buffalotech.com; web site www.buffalotech.com
PR—Jay Pechek
Industry: Computers: Hardware & Software Integrators; Computers: Local Area Network (LANS); Computers: Storage Devices;

BUHRS AMERICAS, INC.
6404 Glacier Ln N, Osseo, MN, 55311-4153, USA; tel (763) 557-9100; fax (763) 557-9700; e-mail info.americas@buhrs.com; web site www.buhrs.com
Pres.—Michael Aumann
Industry: Automatic Plastic Bagging Equipment; Feeding, Folding, Delivery Equipment; Folding Machines; Inserting Equipment (Includes Stuffing Machines); Mailroom Systems & Equipment; Newspaper Couter; Software: Press/Post Press;

BULBTRONICS
45 Banfi Plz N, Farmingdale, NY, 11735-1539, USA; tel (631) 249-2272; fax (631) 249-6066; e-mail bulbs@bulbtronics.com; web site www.bulbtronics.com
Vice Pres., Sales—Lee Vestrich
Mgr., Mktg.—Beckie Mullin
Industry: Lighting Equipment

BURGESS INDUSTRIES, INC.
7500 Boone Ave N Ste 111, Brooklyn Park, MN, 55428-1026, USA; tel (763) 553-7800;

fax (763) 553-9289; e-mail djburgess@burgessind.com; web site www.burgessind.com
Pres./CEO—Dennis Burgess
Nat'l Pdct. Mgr.—Joe Stein
Nat'l Sales Dir.—Richard Fream
Industry: Color Proofing; Color Registration; Controls: Exposure; Controls: Register; Light Integrators; Plate Bending Systems; Plate Mounting & Register Systems; Proofing Systems; Static Eliminators; Vacuum Frames

BURNISHINE PRODUCTS
25392 W Park Ct, Lake Villa, IL, 60046-9710, USA; tel 847-356-0222; fax 847-306-3550; e-mail rgiza@burnishine.com; web site www.burnishine.com
Graphic Arts Customer Service—Patty Vick
President—Roger Giza
Industry: Offset Fountain Solutions; Plate Cleaners; Miscellaneous Pressroom Chemicals

BURT TECHNOLOGIES, INC.
32156 Castle Ct Ste 206, Evergreen, CO, 80439-9500, USA; tel (303) 674-3232; fax (303) 670-0978; e-mail info@burtmountain.com; sales@burtmountain.com; support@burtmountain.com; web site www.burtmountain.com
Founder/Pres.—Jim Burt
CEO—Rich Burt
Burt Response Center Manager—Billy Calva
Industry: Computers: Hardware & Software Integrators; Inserting Equipment (Includes Stuffing Machines); Interfaces; Mailroom Systems & Equipment; Software: Press/Post Press; Training: Post Press

BUSCH, INC.
516 Viking Dr, Virginia Beach, VA, 23452-7316, USA; tel (757) 463-7800; fax (757) 463-7407; e-mail marketing@buschusa.com; web site www.buschpump.com
Pres.—Charles Kane
Mktg. Specialist—Linda Katz
Industry: Pumps (Air, Ink, Vacuum)

BUTLER AUTOMATIC
41 Leona Dr, Middleboro, MA, 02346-1404, USA; tel (508) 923-0544; fax (508) 923-0886; e-mail butler@butlerautomatic.com; web site www.butlerautomatic.com
Vice Pres., Engineering—John Clifford
Industry: Conveyors; Counting, Stacking, Bundling Machines; Cutters & Trimmers; Flying Pasters; Material Handling Equipment; Palletizing Machines; Pasters; Roll Handling Equipment; Splicers, Automatic; Tension & Web Controls;

C

CACHET FINE ART PHOTOGRAPHIC PAPER
11661 Martens River Cir Ste D, Fountain Valley, CA, 92708-4212, USA; tel (714) 432-6331; fax (714) 432-7102; e-mail onecachet@aol.com; web site www.onecachet.com
Pres.—Ike Royer
Industry: Chemicals: Photographic; Dark Room Equipment; Film & Paper: Filters (Photographic);

CANADIAN WEB CONSULTANTS LTD.
57 Hiawatha Dr., Port Sydney, ON, P0B 1L0, Canada; tel (705) 385-8016; e-mail canadaoffice@cwc4webs.com; web site www.cwc4webs.com
Pres.—Stephen Tweddle
Vice Pres.—Michele Belanger
Office Mgr.—Lorraine Bell
Industry: Consulting Services: Equipment; Consulting Services: Production; Erectors & Riggers;

CANNON EQUIPMENT
324 Washington St W, Cannon Falls,

MN, 55009-1142, USA; tel (800) 533-2071; fax (651) 322-1583; e-mail info@cannonequipment.com; web site www.cannonequipment.com
Pres.—Chuck Gruber
Nat'l Sales Mgr./Newspaper Handling Systems—Pat Geraghty
Industry: Cart Distribution Systems; Circulation Equipment & Supplies; Conveyors; Mailroom Systems & Equipment;

CANON USA, INC.
1 Canon Park, Melville, NY, 11747-3036, USA; tel (632) 330-5000; e-mail mediacontact@cusa.canon.com; web site www.usa.canon.com
Pres./CEO, Canon U.S.A., Inc.—Yoroku Adachi
Exec. Vice Pres./Gen. Counsel Admin./Reg'l Opns.—Seymour Liebman
Sr. Vice Pres./Gen Mgr., Sales Mktg./Admin.—Tod D. Pike
Adv. Dir., Cameras/Camcorders, Dir., Mktg. Serv./Adv.—Rick Booth

CAPCO MACHINERY SYSTEMS, INC.
PO Box 11945, Roanoke, VA, 24022-1945, USA; tel (540) 977-0404; fax (540) 977-2781; web site www.capcomachinery.com
Pres.—Edward E. West
Vice Pres., Finance—Amy S. West
Industry: Roller Grinders

CAPITA TECHNOLOGIES
17600 Gillette Ave, Irvine, CA, 92614-5715, USA; tel (949) 260-3000; fax (949) 851-9875; e-mail sales@capita.com; web site www.capita.com
CEO—Charles Granville
Exec. Vice Pres., Techn./Opns.—Imelda Ford
Industry: Software: Pagination/Layout; System Integration Services;

CAPITAL TRACK CO.
1364 Cardwell Sq S, Columbus, OH, 43229-9022, USA; tel (614) 221-4110; fax (614) 225-9832; web site www.capitaltrack.com
Adv. Contact—Matt Caldwell
Industry: Consulting Services: Equipment; Newsprint Handling Equipment; Paper Handling Equipment; Roll Handling Equipment;

CAPROCK DEVELOPMENTS, INC.
PO Box 95, Morris Plains, NJ, 07950-0095, USA; tel (973) 267-9292; fax (973) 292-0614; e-mail info@caprockdev.com; web site www.caprockdev.com
President—Alan Schwartz
Industry: Densitometers; Exposure Lamps; Gauges, Measuring; Lighting Equipment; Offset Blanket Thickness Gauge; Optical Products; Paper Testing Instruments; Testing Instruments;

CARIWEB PRODUCTS
PO Box 1349, Harlingen, TX, 78551-1349, USA; tel (956) 423-5766; fax (956) 748-3417; e-mail cariwebproducts@aol.com
Pres.—Jose Henderson
Industry: Tape Splicing Equipment

CARLSON DESIGN CONSTRUCT
34 Executive Park Ste 250, Irvine, CA, 92614-4707, USA; tel (949) 251-0455; fax (949) 251-0465; e-mail carlson@carlson-dc.com; web site www.carlson-dc.com
Vice Pres., Mktg—Tom Ryan
Industry: Architects/Engineers (Includes Design/Construction Firms)

CASCADE CORP.
PO Box 20187, Portland, OR, 97294-0187, USA; tel (503) 669-6300; fax (800) 693-3768; web site www.cascorp.com
Chrmn.—C. Calvert Knudson
Pres./CEO—Robert C. Warren
Sr. Vice Pres.-Finance/CFO—Andy Anderson
Vice Pres., HR—Greg Anderson

Mgr.,Cust. Srvs—Todd Finney
Mgr., Customer Info Serv.—Eric Fioler
Industry: Material Handling Equipment: Truck Loaders; Paper Handeling Equipment;

CATALYST PAPER (USA), INC.
2200 6th Avenue, Suite 800, Seattle, WA, 98121-2312, USA; tel (206) 838-2070; fax (206) 838-2071; web site www.catalystpaper.com
Sales Director—James Hardt
VP International Sales—Mark Petersen
SVP Sales & Marketing—Sean Curran
Industry: Newsprint; Paper: Coated Groundwood Offset; Paper: Groundwood Specialties; Paper: Specialty Printing Paper;

CATALYST PAPER CORP.
3600 Lysander Ln., 2nd Fl., Richmond, BC, V7B 1C3, Canada; tel (604) 247-4400; fax (604) 247-0512; e-mail contactus@catalystpaper.com; web site www.catalystpaper.com
Vice-President and General Manager Newsprint and International—Jim Bayles
Industry: Manufacturing

CCI EUROPE, INC.
600 Townpark Ln NW Ste 350, Kennesaw, GA, 30144-3758, USA; tel (770) 420-1100; fax 1 770 420 5558; e-mail info@ccieurope.com; web site www.ccieurope.com
CEO—Dan Korsgaard
Vice Pres., Project Sales—Jorgen Valker
Vice Pres., Mktg.—Torben Juul
President, CCI US—Carsten Boe Jensen
Industry: Software: Advertising (Includes Display; Classified); Software: Asset Management; Software: Business (Includes Administration/Accounting); Software: Design/Graphics; Software: Editorial; Software: Electronic Data Interchange; Software: Pagination/Layout; Software: Workflow Management/Tracking; System Integration Services; Training: Keyboard Operation;

CCI EUROPE, INC.-GEORGIA BRANCH
600 Townpark Ln NW Ste 350, Kennesaw, GA, 30144-3758, USA; tel (770) 420-1100; fax (770) 420-5588; e-mail info@ccieurope.com; web site www.ccieurope.com
Pres.—Carsten Boe Jensen
Sales—Jorgen Valkaer
Industry: Content Management Systems

CELEBRO
151 W 4th St Ste 201, Cincinnati, OH, 45202-2746, USA; tel (513) 665-3777; fax (513) 768-8958; e-mail info@celebro.com; web site www.gmti.com
Pres./CEO—Steve Fuschetti
Vice Pres., Celebro Opns.—Tom Foster
Dir., Implementation Servs.—Michael Hibert
Industry: Computers: Hardware & Software Integrators; Electronic Ad Delivery; Software: Advertising (Includes Display; Classified); Software: Electronic Data Interchange

CENTRAL GRAPHICS
1302 Enterprise Dr, Romeoville, IL, 60446-1016, USA; tel (630) 759-1696; fax (630) 759-1792; e-mail cgi@cgipressparts.com; web site www.cgipressparts.com/
Pres.—Jim Crivellone
Sales/Opns. Mgr.—Pat Murphy
Industry: Belts, Belting, V-Belts; Copper Plating Drums; Cylinder Repair; Equipment Dealers (Used); Folder Knives; Pin Register Systems; Press Accessories, Parts & Supplies; Presses: Offset; Roller Grinding Services; Rollers: Dampening;

CH2MHILL LOCKWOOD GREENE
9191 S Jamaica St, Englewood, CO, 80112-5946, USA; tel (888) 242-6445; web site www.ch2m.com/corporate/default.asp
Contact—Monique Plumley
Industry: Architects/Engineers (Includes Design/Construction Firms); Material Handling Equipment: Automatic Guided Vehicles;

CHANNELNET
3 Harbor Dr Ste 206, Sausalito, CA, 94965-1491, USA; tel (415) 332-4704; fax (415) 332-1635; e-mail info@channelnet.com; web site www.softad.com; www.channelnet.com
Founder/CEO—Paula George Tompkins
CFO—Kevin Kelly
Sr. Dir., Professional Servs.—Mike Behr
Industry: Consulting Services: Advertising; Software: Advertising (Includes Display; Classified);

CHAPEL HILL MANUFACTURING CO.
PO Box 208, Oreland, PA, 19075-0208, USA; tel (215) 884-3614; fax (215) 884-3617; e-mail sales@chapelhillmfg.com; web site www.chapelhillmfg.com
Pres./Vice Pres., Mktg.—John Seeburger
Vice Pres., Sales—J. Robert Seeburger
Industry: Dampening Systems

CHAUNCEY WING'S SONS, INC.
P.O. Box 420, Marion, MA, 02738, USA; tel (508) 748-1680; e-mail info@chaunceywing.com; web site www.chaunceywing.com
President—Anne C. Wing
Industry: Repairs & parts for Wing Mailers

CHEMETRON FIRE SYSTEMS
16 W 361 S Frontage Road, Burr Ridge, IL, 60527-5857, USA; tel (708) 748-1503; fax (708) 748-2847; e-mail info@chemetron.com; web site www.chemetron.com
Mgr.—John Powers
Industry: Architects/Engineers (Includes Design/Construction Firms); Fire Protection; System Installations; System Integration Services; Telecommunications;

CHF FOTO SUPPLY
70 Worth St, South Hackensack, NJ, 07606-1420, USA; tel (201) 488-9033; e-mail chf@chffoto.com
—Charlie Wimpfheimer
—Michael GreenCo-Owners
Industry: Cameras & Accessories; Film & Paper: Filters (Photographic);

CHUCK BLEVINS & ASSOC.
8396 Northhampton Ct, Naple, FL, 34120, USA; tel (239) 595-3840; e-mail chuckblevins@aol.com; web site www.chuckblevins.com
Industry: Consulting Services: Equipment; Consulting Services: Ergonomics; Consulting Services: Production; Mailroom Systems & Equipment; Press Systems and equipment

CHURCH RICKARDS, WHITLOCK & CO., INC.
10001 W Roosevelt Rd, Westchester, IL, 60154-2664, USA; tel (708) 345-7500; fax (708) 345-1166; e-mail crwfred@aol.com
Pres.—Fred C. Hohnke
Regl. Mgr.—Daniel Demjanik
Reg. Mgr.—Tim Solt
Industry: Consulting Services: Circulation; Consulting Services: Human Resources; Insurance;

CIRCULATION DEVELOPMENT, INC.
PO Box 6, Wentzville, MO, 63385-0006, USA; tel (800) 247-2338; fax (800) 400-4453; e-mail increase@circulation.net; web site www.circulation.net
Chrmn.—Bill Wesa
Pres.—Jim Oden
Vice Pres.—Rob Oden
Mktg. Dir.—Carmen Salvati
Dir., Info. Servs.—David Wesa
Industry: Consulting Services: Circulation; Consulting Services: Marketing;

CIRCULATION SOLUTIONS, INC.
PO Box 1575, Auburn, AL, 36831-1575, USA; tel (334) 826-6847; e-mail van@circulationsolutions.com
Pres.—Van Dozier
Sec.—Wyndol Smith

Industry: Circulation Equipment & Supplies; Consulting Services: Circulation; Newspaper Marketing;

CLARK MATERIAL HANDLING CO.
700 Enterprise Dr, Lexington, KY, 40510-1028, USA; tel (859) 422-6400; fax (859) 422-7408; web site www.clarkmhc.com
Pres.—Dennis Lawrence
Dir., HR—Sherry Myers
Industry: Equipment Dealers (New); Equipment Dealers (Used); Lift Trucks; Material Handling Equipment: Palletizing Machines; Material Handling Equipment: Pallets & Palletizers; Material Handling Equipment: Truck Loaders; Material Handling Equipment: Vehicle Loading;

CLIPPER BELT LACER CO.
2525 Wisconsin Ave, Downers Grove, IL, 60515-4241, USA; tel 800-323-3444; fax 630-971-1180; e-mail info@flexco.com; web site www.flexco.com
Gen. Mgr.—Nancy Ayres
Treasurer—Bro Ballentine
Sales Mgr.—Dick Reynolds
Mktg. Mgr.—John H. Meulenberg
Pdct. Mgr.—Beth Miller
Industry: Belts, Belting, V-Belts; Cutting Tools;

CNI CORP.
468 Route 13 S Ste A, Milford, NH, 03055-3488, USA; tel (603) 673-6600; fax (603) 672-6633; e-mail sales@cnicorp.com; web site www.cnicorp.com
Pres.—Jon Dickinson
Scott Snow
Bill Suplee
Industry: Consulting Services: Production; Data Communication; Input & Editing Systems; Optical Character Recognition (OCR); Pagination Systems; Prepress Color Proofing Systems; Publishing Systems; Training: Keyboard Operation; Typesetters: Laser; Word Processing System;

COAST GRAPHIC SUPPLY
1112 Casitas ct., Ventura, CA, 93004, USA; tel (805) 642-5585; e-mail coastgraphic@earthlink.net; web site www.coastgraphicsupply.com
Pres.—James Cagnina
Industry: Digital printing & proofing: Supplies & equipment Ink & Bulk Ink Systems Sublimation Ink Paper & Blanks Chemicals: Plate Processing; Chemicals: Pressroom; Composing Room Equipment & Supplies; Densitometers; Film & Paper: Contact; Film & Paper: Phototypesetting;

COLD JET, INC.
455 Wards Corner Rd Ste 100, Loveland, OH, 45140-9033, USA; tel (513) 831-3211; e-mail info@coldjet.com; web site www.coldjet.com; www.dryiceblasting.com
Pres./CEO—Gene Cooke
Industry: Cleaners & Solvents

COLORVISION, INC.
5 Princess Rd, Lawrenceville, NJ, 08648-2301, USA; tel (609) 895-7430; fax (609) 895-8110; e-mail info@colovision.com; web site www.datacolor.com
Vice Pres. Mktg./Sales—Brian Levey
Industry: Software: Electronic Data Interchange

COLTER PETERSON
414 E 16th St, Paterson, NJ, 07514-2638, USA; tel (515) 276-4528; fax (515) 276-8324; e-mail sales@colterpeterson.com; web site www.colterpeterson.com
Vice President—Vince Payne
Industry: Paper Cutters, Material Handling, Perfect Binders and & Three Knife Trimmers

COMMODITY RESOURCE & ENVIRONMENT
116 E Prospect Ave, Burbank, CA, 91502-2035, USA; tel (818) 843-2811; fax (818) 843-2862; e-mail info@creweb.com

www.creweb.com
Pres.—Larry Dewitt
Industry: Hazardous Waste Disposal Services; Silver Recovery

COMMUNICATIONS MANAGEMENT SERVICE, INC.
30 Nutmeg Dr, Trumbull, CT, 06611-5453, USA; tel (203) 377-3000; fax (203) 377-2632; e-mail dan@bargainnews.com; web site www.bargainnews.com
Pres.—John F. Roy
Vice Pres.—Daniel F. Rindos
New Media Sales Dir.—Daniel Firoa
Industry: Consulting Services: Circulation; Consulting Services: Marketing; Newspaper Marketing;

COMPUTER TALK TECHNOLOGY, INC.
225 E. Beaver Creek Rd., Ste. 310, Richmond Hill, ON, L4B 3P4, Canada; tel (905) 882-5000; fax (905) 882-5501; e-mail info@icescape.com; web site www.computer-talk.com
Mktg. Dir.—Robert Moore
Pres./CEO—Mandle Cheung
Mktg. Mgr.—Lindsay Aitken
Industry: Software: Electronic Data Interchange; System Integration Services;

COMPUTER TREE PROFESSIONAL TRAINING
121 Peddycord Park Dr., Kernersville, NC, 27284, USA; tel (336) 768-9820; e-mail sales@computertree.com; web site www.computertree.com
Pres.—Bob Young
Vice President—Joe Young
Industry: As an Apple Authorized Training Center (AATC), ComputerTree Professional Training provides skills training, certification training, and testing at our own facilities in North Carolina and Georgia or on-site anywhere.

COMTEL INSTRUMENTS CO.
37000 Plymouth Rd, Livonia, MI, 48150-1132, USA; tel (734) 542-1300; fax (734) 542-1353; e-mail comtelcorp@comtel.com; web site www.comtel.com
Industry: Software: Electronic Data Interchange

CONLEY PUBLISHING SYSTEMS
PO Box 478, Beaver Dam, WI, 53916-0478, USA; tel (920) 887-3731; fax (920) 887-0439; e-mail concept@conleynet.com; web site www.conleynet.com
Pres.—James E. Conley
Industry: Input & Editing Systems; Pagination Systems; Phototypesetting Fonts; Publishing Systems; Software: Advertising (Includes Display; Classified); Software: Design/Graphics; Software: Editorial; Software: Pagination/Layout; Typesetting Programs;

CONSOLIDATED STORAGE COS.
225 Main St, Tatamy, PA, 18085-7059, USA; tel 800-323-0801; fax 888-859-2121; e-mail info@equipto.com; web site www.equipto.com; catalog.equipto.com, www.clubstor.comies.com"
President—Robert Ammerman
Industry: Material handling and storage equipment including modular drawer cabinets, other storage cabinets, shelving , shelving with drawers, bulk storage racks, workcenters and work benches, mezzanine and deckover units, stairways, carts and small parts storage units, pallet rack, mobile aisle systems

CONTINENTAL PRODUCTS
PO Box 760, Mexico, MO, 65265-0760, USA; tel 1-800-325-0216; e-mail mail@continentalproducts.com; web site www.continentalproducts.com
Vice Pres., Sales/Mktg.—Vince Fuemmeler
Mgr., Sales—Don Price
Industry: Circulation Equipment & Supplies; Newspaper Bags; Tubes, Racks (Includes Racks: Motor Route Tubes);

CONTROL ENGINEERING CO.
2306 Newport Blvd, Costa Mesa, CA, 92627-1548, USA; tel (949) 722-7821; e-mail ccarrillo@controlengineering.com; web site www.controlengineering.com
Engineering Mgr.—Carlos Carrillo
Industry: Cabinets; Conveyors; Material Handling Equipment: Automatic Guided Vehicles; Material Handling Equipment: Truck Loaders; Newsprint Handling Equipment; Paper Handeling Equipment;

CRAFTSMEN MACHINERY CO., INC.
PO Box 2006, Framingham, MA, 01703-2006, USA; tel (508) 376-2001; fax (508) 376-2003; e-mail sales@craftsnmenmachinery.com; web site www.craftsmenmachinery.com
Pres./Chief Exec. Officer—Sherwin Marks
Industry: Core Cutters, Restorers, Rounders; Dark Room Equipment; Densitometers; Folder Knives; Gauges, Measuring; Presses: Offset;

CREATIVE CIRCLE MEDIA SOLUTIONS
945 Waterman Ave., East Providence, RI, 02914, USA; tel (401) 272-1122; e-mail info@creativecirclemedia.com; web site www.creativecirclemedia.com
Pres & founder—Bill Ostendorf
Design director—Lynn Rognsvoog
IT director—Tim Benson
Industry: Software: web CMS, advertising, native content; Consulting; Outsourcing; Training; Web and print redesigns; print editorial production platform.

CREATIVE HOUSE PRINT MEDIA CONSULTANTS
PO Box 160, Sheldon, IA, 51201-0160, USA; tel (712) 324-5347; fax (712) 324-2345; e-mail pww@iowainformation.com
Pres.—Peter W. Wagner
Sec./Treasurer—Jeff Wagner
Industry: Consulting Services: Advertising; Circulation; Design; Promotion Ideas; Advertising Design

CREO
3 Federal St, Billerica, MA, 01821-3500, USA; tel (978) 439-7000; fax (781) 275-3430; e-mail info@creoservers.com; web site www.creo.com
Pres., Creo Americas—Larry Letteney
CEO—Amos Michelson
Vice Pres.-HR—Darcy O'Grady
Vice Pres., Global Mktg.—Boudewijn Neijens
Industry: Color Proofing; Color Seperation Scanners; Computers: Hardware & Software Integrators;

CRIBB, GREENE & COPE
825 Great Northern Blvd, Helena , MT, 59601, USA; tel (406) 579-2925; fax (866) 776-8010; e-mail jcribb@cribb.com; web site www.cribb.com
Managing Dir.—John T. Cribb
MD.—Gary Greene
Market Analyst—Bill Wilke
Director—Randy Cope
Associate—John Thomas Cribb
Industry: Brokers, Consultants & Appraisers

CRYOGENESIS (A DIV. OF WM & C SERVICES, INC.)
2140 Scranton Rd, Cleveland, OH, 44113-3544, USA; tel (216) 696-8797; fax (216) 696-8794; e-mail cryogen@cryogenesis-usa.com; web site www.cryogenesis-usa.com
Pres.—James Becker
Vice Pres., Sales—John R. Whalen
Industry: Cleaners & Solvents; Roll Cleaning Equipment;

CYGNET STORAGE SOLUTIONS, INC.
1880 Santa Barbara Ave Ste 220, San Luis Obispo, CA, 93401-4482, USA; tel 805-781-3580; fax 805-781-3583; e-mail waynea@cygnet.com
Vice Pres., Mktg.—Wayne Augsburger

Industry: Archiving Systems; Disk Drive Sales/Repair; Files, Storage; Library Retrieval Systems; Software: Asset Management; Storage Retrieval Systems;

D

D & R ENGINEERING
12629 Prairie Ave, Hawthorne, CA, 90250-4611, USA; tel (310) 676-4896; fax (310) 676-3420
Owner—Daws Waffer
Industry: Counting, Stacking, Bundling Machines; Gluing Systems; Web Cleaners; Web Offset Remoisturizers; Web Press - Special Equipment;

DAC SYSTEMS
4 Armstrong Park Rd., Bldg II, Shelton, CT, 6484, USA; tel (203) 924-7000; fax (203) 944-1618; e-mail sales@dacsystems.com; web site www.dacsystems.com
Pres.—Mark Nickson
Industry: Audiotex Systems & Software; Facsimilie/Fax Transmission Systems; Integrated Fax Servers; Optical Character Recognition (OCR); Speech Recognition; Telecommunications;

DAIGE PRODUCTS, INC.
1 Albertson Ave Ste 5, Albertson, NY, 11507-1444, USA; tel (800) 645-3323; e-mail info@daige.com; web site www.daige.com
Pres.—Ike Harris
Industry: Adhesive Wax Coaters; Adhesives;

DAIL ADVERTISING SERVICE
PO Box 10278, Goldsboro, NC, 27532-0278, USA; tel (919) 736-0447; fax (919) 736-0483; e-mail dailadvertising@bellsouth.net
Nat'l Rep.—Annette W. Dail
Industry: Consulting Services: Advertising

DAN-BAR, INC.
2502 JMT Industrial Dr. Suite 104, Apopka, FL, 32703-6542, USA; tel (407) 292-0600; fax (407) 292-0602; e-mail dcmdanbar@aol.com; contact@danbarinc.com; web site www.danbarinc.com
Pres.—Dan Baratta
Industry: Automatic Plastic Bagging Equipment; Baling Machines; Collating Equipment; System Installations;

DANFOSS GRAHAM
8800 W Bradley Rd, Milwaukee, WI, 53224-2820, USA; tel (414) 355-8800; fax (414) 355-6117; web site www.danfoss.com
Pres./CEO—Niels B. Christiansen
Industry: Drives & Controls; Motors;

DARIO DESIGNS, INC.
318 Main St. Ste 120, Northborough, MA, 01532, USA; tel (508) 877-4444; fax (508) 877-4474; e-mail dario@dariodesigns.com; web site www.dariodesigns.com
Pres.—Dario Dimare
VP—David Ehrhardt
Industry: Architects/Engineers (Includes Design/Construction Firms)

DATA ENGINEERING LTD.
Sorvaajankatu 13, Helsinki, N/A, 00880, Finland; tel 358 9 759 1988; fax 358 9 786 626; e-mail data@dataengineering.fi; web site www.dataengineering.fi
Mgr.—Marco Aueinen
Industry: Ink Controls, Computerized; Proofing Systems;

DATAFEST TECHNOLOGIES, INC.
5961 S Redwood Rd, Salt Lake City, UT, 84123-5261, USA; tel (801) 261-4608; e-mail sales@datafest.com; web site www.datafest.com
Pres.—Scott A. Clawson
Industry: Software: Advertising (Includes Display; Classified); Software: Business

(Includes Administration/Accounting);

DAY INTERNATIONAL
1333 N Kirk Rd, Batavia, IL, 60510-1444, USA; tel (630) 526-9903; fax (630) 526-9926
Industry: Chemicals: Pressroom; Chemicals: Roller Cleaning; Cleaners & Solvents; Dampening Systems; Offset Chemicals & Supplies; Offset Fountain Solutions; Offset Prevention-Materials & Equipment; Plate Cleaners; Press Accessories, Parts & Supplies; Rollers: Dampening;

DAY INTERNATIONAL
15151 Prater Dr Ste L, Covington, GA, 30014-4961, USA; tel (770) 787-5080; fax (770) 787-4589; web site www.rotadyne.com
Mgr., Customer Serv.—Rita Harper
Industry: Blanket Mounting and Bars

DAY-GLO COLOR CORP.
4515 Saint Clair Ave, Cleveland, OH, 44103-1268, USA; tel (216) 391-7070; fax (216) 391-7751; e-mail dayglo@dayglo.com; web site www.dayglo.com
Vice Pres., Sales—Mark Wright
Industry: Inks

DEAN MACHINERY INTERNATIONAL, INC.
6855 Shiloh Rd E, Alpharetta, GA, 30005-8372, USA; tel (678) 947-8550; fax (678) 947-8554; e-mail sales@deanmachinery.com; web site www.deanmachinery.com
Pres.—Walter Dean
Industry: Adhesive Wax Coaters; Brokers & Appraisers; Equipment Dealers (Used); Label Printing Machines; Presses: Flexographic; Presses: Offset; Presses: Rotogravure;

DECISIONMARK CORP.
818 Dows Rd Ste 100, Cedar Rapids, IA, 52403-7000, USA; tel (319) 365-5597; fax (319) 365-5694; e-mail sales@decisionmark.com; web site www.decisionmark.com
Pres./CEO—Jack Perry
Vice Pres., Pdct. Devel.—Mick Rinehart
Vice Pres., Opns.—Herb Skoog
Industry: Software: Advertising (Includes Display; Classified); Software: Circulation; Software: Editorial;

DEE-PAUL GRAPHIC SERVICES
10006 Karmont Ave, South Gate, CA, 90280-5417, USA; tel (562) 928-5747
Pres.—Diana Howard
Nat'l Sales Mgr.—Art Contreras

DEMATICS
507 Plymouth Ave NE, Grand Rapids, MI, 49505-6029, USA; tel (877) 725-7500; fax (616) 913-7701; e-mail usinfo@dematic.com; web site www.dematic.us
Pres.—John Baysore
Vice Pres., Field Sales—S. Buccella
Mgr., Purchasing—R. Klaasen
Industry: Conveyors; Material Handling Equipment: Automatic Guided Vehicles; Material Handling Equipment: Truck Loaders;

DENEX, INC.
135 W Illinois Ave, Southern Pines, NC, 28387-5808, USA; tel (910) 692-5463; fax (910) 222-3100; e-mail gcarroll@denexinc.com; web site www.denex.se; www.denex.com
Pres.—Gary J. Carroll
Industry: Laser Printers

DENNIS STORCH CO.
175 W 72nd St Apt 8G, New York, NY, 10023-3208, USA; tel (212) 877-2622; e-mail dstorch@aol.com; web site www.dennis-storch.com
President—Dennis Storch
Industry: Printing Equipment Dealer. Used Presses and Offset Presses.

DESCARTES SYSTEMS GROUP
120 Randall Dr., Waterloo, ON, N2V 1C6, Canada; tel (519) 746-8110; fax (519) 747-0082; e-mail info@descartes.com; web site www.descartes.com
CEO—Arthur Mesher
CFO—Stephanie Ratza
Exec. Vice Pres., Solutions/Servs.—Chris Jones
Exec. Vice Pres., Cor. Devel./Gen. Counsel—Scott J. Pagan
Exec. Vice Pres., Global Field Opns.—Edward J. Ryan
Exec. Vice Pres., Information Servs.—Raimond Diederik
Industry: Computers: Hardware & Software Integrators

DESIGN SCIENCE, INC.
140 Pine Ave Fl 4, Long Beach, CA, 90802-9440, USA; tel (562) 432-2920; fax (562) 432-2857; e-mail sales@dessci.com; web site www.dessci.com
Pres.—Paul Topping
Industry: Input & Editing Systems; Type, Fonts;

DESKNET, INC.
10 Exchange Pl Ste 2040, Jersey City, NJ, 07302-3935, USA; tel 201-946-7080; web site www.desknetinc.com
Pres.—Brian Fitzsimons
Vice Pres.-Mktg./Sales—Thomas C. Triumph
Industry: Software: Asset Management; Software: Design/Graphics; Software: Editorial; Software: Electronic Data Interchange; Software: Pagination/Layout; Software: Workflow Management/Tracking; System Integration Services;

DEVLIN ELECTRONICS LTD.
D1 Grafton Way, Basingstoke, Basingstoke, N/A, RG22 6HZ, United Kingdom; tel +44 1256 467 367; fax +44 1256 840 048; e-mail sales@devlin.co.uk; web site www.devlin.co.uk
Mng. Dir.—Martin Baker
Industry: Composing Room Equipment & Supplies; Interfaces;

DIENAMIC MICROPRINT
71 King St., Ste.3024, Saint Catharine's, ON, L2R 3H7, Canada; tel (905) 688-5593; fax (905) 688-6132; e-mail microprint@vaxxine.com; web site www.dienamicmis.com
Pres.—Mark Porter
Vice Pres.-Finance—Lori Walsh
Industry: Mailroom Systems & Equipment

DIGITAL COLLECTIONS
312 Elm St Fl 20, Cincinnati, OH, 45202-2739, USA; tel (513) 665-3777; fax (513) 768-8958; e-mail mtucker@gmti.gannett.com; web site www.gmti.com
Pres./CEO—Steve Fuschetti
Vice Pres., Installations/Support—Bill Mahlock
Dir., Sales & Marketing—Michael Tucker
Industry: Digital Asset Management Systems: Full service contractor; Hardware & Software Integrators; Content Aggregation and Distribution; Semantic Engine Services; Archive Content Management software.

DIGITAL TECHNOLOGY INTERNATIONAL
350 S 400 W Ste 200, Lindon, UT, 84042-1923, USA; tel (801) 853-5000; fax (801) 853-5001; e-mail dtinfo@dtint.com; web site www.dtint.com
Pres./COO—Jeff Carpenter
CEO—Don Oldham
CFO—Geoff Walker
Vice Chrmn.—Levor Oldham
Technical Dir.—Jim Knudsen
Industry: Archiving Systems; Software: Advertising (Includes Display; Classified); Software: Asset Management; Software: Business (Includes Administration/Accounting); Software: Circulation; Software: Design/Graphics; Software: Editorial; Software: Pagination/Layout; System Integration Services

DIGITAL TECHNOLOGY INTERNATIONAL
7900 International Dr Ste 800, Minneapolis, MN, 55425-1581, USA; tel (651) 639-0662; fax (651) 639-0306; e-mail info@dtint.com; web site www.dtint.com
Vice president, marketing—Steve Nilan
Exec. Vice Pres.—Bud DePietto
Vice Pres., Opns.—Mary Olson
Industry: Software: Advertising (Includes Display; Classified); Software: Business (Includes Administration/Accounting); Software: Circulation;

DIRECT REPRODUCTION CORP.
34 S Macquesten Pkwy, Mount Vernon, NY, 10550-1704, USA; tel (914) 665-6515; fax (914) 665-6518; e-mail Technical@LRADX.com; web site www.lradx.com/site/
Pres.—Ronald L. Russo
Industry: Color Proofing; Color Registration; Masking Materials; Offset Negative Masking Paper; Prepress Color Proofing Systems;

DIRKS, VAN ESSEN & MURRAY
119 E Marcy St Ste 100, Santa Fe, NM, 87501-2092, USA; tel (505) 820-2700; fax (505) 820-2900; web site www.dirksvanessen.com
Pres.—Owen D. Van Essen
Exec. Vice Pres.—Philip W. Murray
Vice Pres.—Sara April
Analyst—Holly Myers
Industry: Brokers & Appraisers; Consulting Services: Financial;

DIVERSIFIED PHOTO/GRAPHICS SUPPLY
333 W Alondra Blvd Ste C, Gardena, CA, 90248-2428, USA; tel (800) 544-1609; fax (310) 328-8518; e-mail orders@diversifiedimaging.net; web site www.diversifiedimaging.net
Opns. Mgr.—Bruce Benton
Industry: Automatic Film Processors; Cameras & Accessories; Chemicals: Photographic; Enlargers (Photographic); Equipment Dealers (New); Film & Paper: Filters (Photographic); Inks; Lenses (Camera); Photography: Digital/Electronic Cameras; Processors: Film & Paper;

DOMINO AMJET, INC.
1290 Lakeside Dr, Gurnee, IL, 60031-2499, USA; tel (847) 244-2501; fax (847) 244-1421; e-mail marketing@dominoamjet.com; web site www.domino-printing.com
Industry: Addressing Machines; Label Printing Machines; Laser Printers; Numbering Machines

DOMTAR, INC.
395 de Maisonneuve Blvd. W., Montreal, QC, H3A 1L6, Canada; tel (514) 848-5400; fax (514) 848-6878; web site www.domtar.com
Chrmn.—Brian Levitt
Pres./CEO—Raymond Royer
Industry: Paper: Specialty Printing Paper

DOUTHITT CORP.
245 Adair St, Detroit, MI, 48207-4287, USA; tel (313) 259-1565; fax (313) 259-6806; e-mail em@douthittcorp.com; web site www.douthittcorp.com
Int'l Sales—Mark W. Diehl
Industry: Controls: Exposure; Exposure Lamps; Layout Tables, Light Tables & Workstations; Light Integrators; Offset Plate-Making Service & Equipment; Pin Register Systems; Plate Exposure Units; Platemakers: Flexographic (Traditional); Platemakers: Offset (Computer to Plate); Vacuum Frames;

DRAKE COMMUNICATIONS, INC.
202 W McCart St. Ste 200, Krum, TX, 76249-5580, USA; tel (214) 206-3333
Pres.—Cecil Drake
Vice Pres.—L.G. Drake
Industry: Elections Interactive Voice Response (IVR) Information systems

DUNHILL INTERNATIONAL LIST CO.,

INC.
6400 Congress Ave Ste 1750, Boca Raton, FL, 33487-2898, USA; tel (561) 998-7800; fax (561) 998-7880; e-mail dunhill@dunhillintl.com; web site www.dunhills.com
Pres.—Robert Dunhill
Vice Pres.—Candy Dunhill
Vice Pres.—Cindy Dunhill
Industry: Mailing List Compiler
Mailing List Broker
Email List Broker

DUNNING PHOTO EQUIPMENT, INC.
605 W Needles Ave, Bixby, OK, 74008-4131, USA; tel (918) 366-4917; fax (918) 366-4918; e-mail ernie@dunningphoto.com; web site www.dunningphoto.com
Pres.—Ernie Dunning
Industry: Dark Room Equipment; Processors: Film & Paper;

DYC SUPPLY CO.
5740 Bayside Rd, Virginia Beach, VA, 23455-3004, USA; tel (800) 446-8240; fax (757) 486-5689; e-mail kevink@d-y-c.com; web site www.dyc.com
Pres.—Joseph Martinez
Asst. Mktg. Mgr.—Marc Banks
Industry: Blankets; Offset Blankets, Blanket Wash;

DYNARIC, INC.
5740 Bayside Rd, Virginia Beach, VA, 23455-3004, USA; tel (800) 526-0827; fax (757) 363-8016; e-mail gd@dynaric.com; web site www.dynaric.com
Pres.—Joseph Martinez
Asst. Mktg. Mgr.—Marc Banks
Industry: PLASTIC STRAPPING AND STRAPPING EQUIPMENT

E

E.I. DU PONT DE NEMOURS & CO.
1007 Market St, Wilmington, DE, 19898-1100, USA; tel (302) 774-1000; fax (302) 355-4013; e-mail contact@dupont.com; web site www2.dupont.com
Chrmn./Pres./CEO—Ellen J. Kullman
Exec., Vice Pres./CFO—Jeffrey L. Keefer
Exec. Vice Pres./Chief Innovation Officer—Thomas M. Connelly
Exec. Vice Pres./COO—Richard R. Goodmanson
Exec. Vice Pres./Human Resources—W. Donald Johnson
Grp. Vice Pres., Chief Mktg./Sales Officer—Diane H. Gulyas
Vice Pres./Controller—Barry J. Niziolek
Vice Pres., DuPont Sales Effectiveness—Harry Parker
Vice Pres./Treasurer—Susan M. Stalnecker
Vice Pres./CMO/Chief Sales Officer—Cynthia C. Green
Industry: Color Analyzers; Color Proofing; Color Registration; Color Separation Scanners; Color Viewing Equipment; Controls: Register; Phototypesetting Interface Equipment; Prepress Color Proofing Systems; Press Control Systems;

E/DOC SYSTEMS
6949 Appling Farms Pkwy, Memphis, TN, 38133-4731, USA; tel (901) 367-9500; fax (901) 367-9510; web site www.edocsystems.com
Pres.—Tom Pease
Industry: Facsimilie/Fax Transmission Systems; Laser Printers;

EAM-MOSCA CORP.
675 Jaycee Dr., Valmont Industrial Pk., Hazle Township, PA, 18202-1155, USA; tel (570) 459-3426; fax (570) 455-2442; e-mail info@eammosca.com; web site www.eammosca.com
Sales Admin.—Pam Kuzmak

VP, Sales—Edward Martin
Pres.—Dan Dreher
Industry: Bundling and Tying Machines; Strapping Machines;

EARMARK
1125 Dixwell Ave, Hamden, CT, 06514-4788, USA; tel (203) 777-2130; fax (203) 777-2886; e-mail staff@earmark.com; web site www.earmark.com
Industry: Wireless Radio Communication Headsets

EASTMAN KODAK CO.
343 State St, Rochester, NY, 14650-0002, USA; tel (800) 698-3324; fax (585) 724-1089; web site www.kodak.com
Chrmn./CEO—Antonio Perez
Pres./COO—Philip J. Faraci
Exec. Vice Pres./CFO—Frank Sklarsky
Vice Pres., Global Logistics—Etienne Bourgeois
Vice Pres./Dir., Brand/Market Devel.—Claude H. Denker
Vice Pres./Chief Diversity Officer—Essie L. Calhoun
Vice Pres./Dir., Health/Safety/Environment—David Kiser
Dir., Cor. Media Rel.—Gerard Meuchner
Dir., Interactive Mktg./Convergence—Thomas Hoehn
Mgr., Film/Worldwide Strategic Prdct. Grp.—Larry Morgan
Industry: Cameras & Accessories; Film & Paper: Contact; Film & Paper: Filters (Photographic); Film & Paper: Phototypesetting; Microfilming; Offset Plate-Making Service & Equipment; Photo Proofing Papers; Plate Processors; Plates: Offset (Conventional); Processors: Film & Paper;

ECLIPSE SERVICES (DIV. OF QUADRIVIUM, INC.)
7721 Beech Lane, Wyndmoor, PA, 19038-7615, USA; tel 484-462-4300; fax 207-373-0723; e-mail sales@eclipseservices.com; web site www.eclipseservices.com
President—Jeanette MacNeille
Industry: Software: Advertising (Includes Display; Classified, Online); Software: Business (Includes Administration/Accounting). New: Available on iPhone, iPad for sales reps.

ECRM
554 Clark Rd, Tewksbury, MA, 01876-1631, USA; tel (978) 851-0207; fax (978) 851-7016; e-mail sales@ecrm.com; web site www.ecrm.com
President&CEO—Richard Black
Industry: Imagesetters; Platemakers: Offset (Computer to Plate); Prepress Color Proofing Systems; Processors: Film & Paper; Proofing Systems;

ED BARON & ASSOCIATES, INC.
PO Box 3203, Oakton, VA, 22124-9203, USA; tel (703) 620-1725; fax (703) 620-9037; e-mail edbaron@edbaron.com; web site www.edbaron.com
Pres.—Ed Baron
Industry: Consulting Services: Advertising; Consulting Services: Circulation; Consulting Services: Financial; Consulting Services: Marketing; Training: Sales & Marketing

EDGIL ASSOCIATES, INC.
222 Rosewood Dr Ste 210, Danvers, MA, 01923-4520, USA; tel (800) 457-9932; fax (978) 667-6050; e-mail sales@edgil.com; web site www.edgil.com
Dir., Sales—Sean Callahan
Industry: Payment Processing

EDITOR & PUBLISHER MAGAZINE
18475 Bandilier Circle, Fountain Valley, CA, 92708, USA; tel 949-660-6150; fax 949-660-6172; e-mail circulation@editorandpublisher.com; web site www.editorandpublisher.com
Publisher—Duncan McIntosh

Editor-in-Chief—Jeff Fleming
Managing Editor—Nu Yang
Director of Advertising—Janette Hood
Circulation Director—Amelia Salazar
Industry: Trade Publications

EDIWISE
2227 S. Millway, Ste. 200, Mississauga, ON, L5L 3R6, Canada; tel (905) 820-3084; fax (905) 820-1498; e-mail ericw@ediwise.com; web site www.ediwise.comEric Wee
Industry: Computers: Hardware & Software Integrators; Newsprint; Newsprint Handeling Equipment; Paper Handeling Equipment; Software: Asset Management; Software: Business (Includes Administration/Accounting); Software: Electronic Data Interchange

EGENOLF MACHINE, INC. (EGENOLF CONTRACTING & RIGGING)
350 Wisconsin St, Indianapolis, IN, 46225-1536, USA; tel (317) 637-9891; fax (317) 631-8153; e-mail egenolfma@gmail.com
Pres.—James Egenolf
Industry: Press Rebuilding; Press Repairs;

ELAPLAN BUCHHOLZ GMBH & CO.
D-24217, Schonberg, N/A, N/A, Germany; tel +49 4344 309 158; fax +49 4344 309 172; e-mail info@uniton.de; web site www.elaplan.de
Mng. Dir.—Hans-Herbert Buchholz
Industry: Facsimilie/Fax Transmission Systems; Press Control Systems;

ELCORSY TECHNOLOGY, INC.
4405 Poirier Blvd., Saint Laurent, QC, H4R 2A4, Canada; tel (888) 352-6779; fax (514) 337-0042; e-mail marketing@elcorsy.com; web site www.elcorsy.com
Vice Pres., Mktg.—Pierre Castegnier
Sales Rep.—Robert Jollet
Industry: Inks; Presses: DiLitho;

ELECTRONIC SYSTEMS ENGINEERING CO.
1 E Eseco Rd, Cushing, OK, 74023-5531, USA; tel (918) 225-1266; fax (918) 225-1284; e-mail wallace@eseco-speedmaster.com; web site www.eseco-speedmaster.com
CFO—Ed Handlin
Pres.—Wallace Hallman
Industry: Color Analyzers; Dark Room Equipment; Densitometers; Enlargers (Photographic); Film & Paper: Film Processing Machines;

ELECTRONIC TELE-COMMUNICATIONS, INC.
1915 Mac Arthur Rd, Waukesha, WI, 53188-5702, USA; tel (262) 542-5600; fax (262) 542-1524; e-mail etc_mkt@etcia.com; web site www.etcia.com
Pres./CEO—Dean W. Danner
Vice Pres., Sales—Joseph A. Voight
Industry: Telecommunications

ENGINEERING PRODUCTS CO., INC.
3278 Pleasant Hill Rd, Genoa, IL, 60135, USA; tel (815) 784-4020; fax (815) 784-4020; web site www.engineeringproductco.com
Owner—Jamie Courtney
Industry: Conveyors

EPUBLISH4ME
1375 Gateway Blvd, Boynton Beach, FL, 33426-8304, USA; tel (561) 370-3336; e-mail sales@epublish4me.com; web site www.epublish4me.com
Senior Account Executive—Nicholas Koriakin
Industry: Advertising

ERGOTRON, INC.
1181 Trapp Rd Ste 100, Saint Paul, MN, 55121-1266, USA; tel (651) 681-7600; fax (651) 681-7715; e-mail sales@ergotron.com; web site www.ergotron.com
Pres.—Pete Segar

Industry: Cabinets; Computers: Local Area Network (LANS); Computers: Storage Devices; Consulting Services: Ergonomics;

ERNEST SCHAEFER, INC.
731 Lehigh Ave, Union, NJ, 07083-7626, USA; tel (908) 964-1280; fax (908) 964-6787; e-mail eschaefe@aol.com; web site www.ernestschaeferinc.com
Pres.—Ernest Schaefer
Industry: Type, Fonts, Letters, Cover Board, Book Glue.

ESKO-GRAPHICS
8535 Gander Creek Dr, Miamisburg, OH, 45342-5436, USA; tel (937) 454-1721; fax (937) 454-1522; web site www.esko.com
Division Mgr., Printers Systems—Tony Wiley
Mktg. Commun. Mgr.—Carrie Woryk
Industry: Software: Design/Graphics

ESSEX PRODUCTS GROUP
30 Industrial Park Rd, Centerbrook, CT, 06409-1019, USA; tel (800) 394-7130; fax (860) 767-9137; e-mail sales@epg-inc.com; web site www.epg-inc.com
Pres.—Peter Griffin
Operations Mgr.—Matt Strand
Industry: Ink Controls, Computerized

EURO-KNIVES USA
11516 W 90th St, Overland Park, KS, 66214-1710, USA; tel (913) 648-7860; fax (913) 859-0334; e-mail al@euro-knivesusa.com; rob@euro-knivesusa.com; web site www.euro-knivesusa.com/index.php
Owner—Al Elton
Sales Mgr.—Rob Elton
Industry: Cut-off knives, slitters, Tucker's, grippers, pin screws, cutting sticks, cheekwoods

EWERT AMERICA ELECTRONICS LTD.
869 Pickens Industrial Dr Ste 12, Marietta, GA, 30062-3164, USA; tel 678-996-2411; fax 770-421-0731; e-mail ceickhoff@eaeusa.com; web site www.eaeusa.com
CM, COO—Chris Eickhoff
Industry: Computers: Hardware & Software Integrators; Drives & Controls; Press Control Systems; Software: Workflow Management/Tracking;
Closed loop ink density controls
System Installations; System Integration Services; Training: Press Operation & Maintenance;

EXTRATEC CORP.
5930 Muncaster Mill Rd, Rockville, MD, 20855-1734, USA; tel (301) 924-5150; fax (301) 924-5151; e-mail sales@extratek.com
Pres.—Regis E. Finn
Industry: Environmental Control Systems

F

FAKE BRAINS, INC.
791 Southpark Dr Ste 300, Littleton, CO, 80120-6401, USA; tel (303) 791-3301; fax (303) 470-5218; e-mail sales@fakebrains.com; web site www.fakebrains.com
Pres.—Pat Pfeifer
VP/Sales Dir.—Lisa Pfeifer
Industry: Software: Advertising (Includes Display; Classified, Digital Media); Software: Business (Includes Administration/Accounting); Software: CRM (Customer Relations); Software: Cloud; Software: OnPremise

FANUC ROBOTICS AMERICA, INC.
3900 W Hamlin Rd, Rochester Hills, MI, 48309-3253, USA; tel 888-326-8287; fax 847-898-5001; e-mail marketing@fanucrobotics.com; web site www.fanucrobotics.com
Sr. Mktg. Analyst—Cathy Powell
Industry: Conveyors; Material Handling Equipment: Palletizing Machines; Newsprint

Handeling Equipment; Paper Handeling Equipment; Roll Handeling Equipment;

FELINS, INC.
8306 W Parkland Ct, Milwaukee, WI, 53223-3832, USA; tel (800) 843-5667; fax (414) 355-7759; e-mail salesteam@felins.com; web site www.felins.com
Industry: Bundling and Tying Machines; Mailroom Systems & Equipment; Strapping Machines;

WRH GLOBAL AMERICAS
24 World's Fair Dr. Unit G, Somerset, NJ, 08873, USA; tel (856) 842-0600; fax (732) 356-1637; e-mail info@wrh-global-americas.com; web site www.wrh-global-americas.com
VP—Barry Evans
CEO—Rene Luchsinger
Industry: Provider of Ferag Systems, Service and Spare Parts

FIBERWEB
842 SE Main St, Simpsonville, SC, 29681-7118, USA; tel (864) 963-2106; e-mail sdavis@fiberweb.com; web site www.fiberwebgraphics.com
Area Mgr.—Shawn Davis
Industry: Cleaners & Solvents; Plate Cleaners; Press Accessories, Parts & Supplies;

FIFE CORPORATION
PO Box 26508, Oklahoma City, OK, 73126-0508, USA; tel (405) 755-1600; fax (405) 755-8425; e-mail fife@fife.com; web site www.fife.com
Mgr.—Marcel Hage
Industry: Visual Display Terminals; Web Break Detector; Web Guides; Web Press - Special Equipment;

FINCOR AUTOMATION, INC.
3750 E Market St, York, PA, 17402-2798, USA; tel (717) 751-4300; fax (717) 751-4263
Sales Mgr., Printing—Lee Hankey
Industry: Drives & Controls; Press Control Systems;

FKI LOGISTEX
9301 Olive Blvd, Saint Louis, MO, 63132-3207, USA; tel (314) 993-4700; fax (314) 995-2400; web site www.fkilogistex.com
Industry: Material Handling Equipment: Palletizing Machines; Remanufactures Equipment

FLEMING ENTERPRISES
928 S Blue Mound Rd, Fort Worth, TX, 76131-1402, USA; tel (817) 232-9575; fax (817) 847-6705; web site www.flemingenterprises.net
Owner—Jeff M. Fleming
Office Manager—Patrick Fleming
Industry: Drives & Controls; Drying Systems; Equipment Dealers (Used); Erectors & Riggers; Feeder Press; Feeding, Folding, Delivery Equipment; Produciton Control Systems; Roll Handeling Equipment; Roller Grinders; Tension & Web Controls;

FLEXOGRAPHIC TECHNICAL ASSOCIATION
3920 Veterans Memorial Hwy Ste 9, Bohemia, NY, 11716-1074, USA; tel (631) 737-6020; fax (631) 737-6813; e-mail membership@flexography.org; web site www.flexography.org
Pres.—Mark Cisternino
Pub., FLEXO Mag.—Robert Moran
Membership & Buss. Dev. Dir.—Jay Kaible
Education Director—Joe Tuccitto
Marketing Manager—Eileen Cosma
Industry: Trade Publications; Training: Post Press; Training: Pre Press; Training: Press Operation & Maintenance;

FLINT GROUP
14909 N Beck Rd, Plymouth, MI, 48170-2411, USA; tel (734) 781-4600; fax (734)

781-4699; e-mail info@na.flintgrp.com; web site www.flintgrp.com
Pres., North Amer.—Bill Miller
Vice Pres./Gen. Mgr., News Ink/Pub. Div.—Mike Green
Vice Pres., Bus./Technical Devel.—Norm Harbin
Industry: Ink Pumping Systems; Ink Storage Tanks; Inks;

FLINT GROUP.
14909 North Beck, Plymouth, MI, 48170, USA; tel (734) 781-4600; fax (734) 781-4699; e-mail info@flintgrp.com; web site www.flintgrp.com
Industry: Printing inks (including coldset UV; black and color; and soy-based options); Offset fabric and Metalback Blankets; Blanket Mounting and Bars; Pressroom Chemicals including Washes Fountain Solutions, Cleaners and more; Pressroom Supplies; Digital inks; and more.

FLYNN BURNER CORP.
PO Box 431, New Rochelle, NY, 10802-0431, USA; tel (914) 636-1320; fax (914) 636-3751; web site www.flynnburner.com
Pres.—Julian Modzeleski
Vice Pres.—Dom Medina
Industry: Web Press - Special Equipment

FORREST CONSULTING
725 Kenilworth Ave, Glen Ellyn, IL, 60137-3805, USA; tel (630) 730-9619; e-mail fasttrackhelp@strategicbusinessleader.com; web site www.strategicbusinessleader.com
Pres.—Lee Crumbaugh
Industry: Consulting Services: Advertising; Consulting Services: Circulation; Consulting Services: Financial; Consulting Services: Marketing;

FORTEC, INC.
613 N 36th St, Milwaukee, WI, 53208-3826, USA; tel (414) 344-1900; fax (414) 935-3309; e-mail email@fortec.com; web site www.fortec.com
Pres.—Jack Olson
Industry: Newspaper Dispensers (Mechanical/Electronic); Tubes, Racks (Includes Racks: Motor Route Tubes);

FOSTER MFG. CO.
204B Progress Dr, Montgomeryville, PA, 18936-9616, USA; tel 267-413-6220; fax 267-413-6227; e-mail information@fostermfg.com; web site www.fostermfg.com
Pres.—Ted Borowsky
Industry: Archiving Systems; Art & Layout Equipment and Services; Cabinets; Color Viewing Equipment; Composing Room Equipment & Supplies; Cutters & Trimmers; Cutting Tools; Dark Room Equipment; Files, Storage; Layout Tables, Light Tables & Workstations; Offset Plate Files; Photo Archiving; Plastic Folders; Prepress Color Proofing Systems; Proofing Systems; Storage Retrieval Systems; Tables (Dot, Etch, Opaquing, Register, Retouching, Stripping)

FOX BAY INDUSTRIES, INC.
4150 B Pl NW Ste 101, Auburn, WA, 98001-2449, USA; tel (253) 941-9155; fax (253) 941-9197; e-mail info@foxbay.com; sales@foxbay.com; web site www.foxbay.com
Pres.—Ladele Walker
Sales Mgr.—Wayne Walker
Industry: Consulting Services: Ergonomics

FRANKLIN WIRE WORKS, INC.
910 E Lincoln Ave, Belvidere, IL, 61008-2928, USA; tel (815) 544-6676; fax (815) 547-5356; web site www.franklindisplay.com
Sales Mgr.—Dick Boyett
Industry: Circulation Equipment & Supplies

FRY COMMUNICATIONS, INC.
800 W. Church Rd., Mechanicsburg, PA, 17055, USA; tel (800) 334-1429; e-mail info@frycomm.com; web site www.frycomm.com

com
Chairman of the Board—Henry Fry
VP Sales—Kevin Quinn
CEO—Mike Lukas
VP Manufacturing—Mike Weber
Industry: Publishing Systems; Trade Publications; Commercial Printer

FUJI PHOTO FILM USA/GRAPHIC SYSTEMS DIV.
850 Central Ave, Hanover Park, IL, 60133-5422, USA; tel (630) 259-7200; fax (630) 259-7078; e-mail contact@fujifilms.com; web site www.fujifilm.com
Pres., Industrial Imaging Markets Grp.—Tim Combs
Sr. Vice Pres./Gen. Mgr., PhotoImaging Grp.—Bill Diminno
Industry: Chemicals: Plate Processing; Color Proofing; Film & Paper: Contact; Film & Paper: Duplicating; Film & Paper: Filters (Photographic); Imagesetters; Plates: Offset (Computer to Plate); Proofing Systems; Plates: Offset (Conventional); Scanners: Color B & W, Plates, Web;

FUJIFILM GRAPHIC SYSTEMS USA, INC.
309 Fellowship Road Suite 200, Mt. Laurel, NJ, 08504, USA; tel (856) 488-7200; fax (856) 488-7690; web site www.fujifilmgs.com
Mktg. Mgr.—Tim Combs
Industry: Blankets; Chemicals: Pressroom; Color Management Software; Imagesetters; Inks; Offset Chemicals & Supplies; Platemakers: Flexographic (Computer to Plate); Plates: Offset (Conventional); Proofing Systems; Software: Press/Post Press;

FUJIFILM GRAPHIC SYSTEMS USA, INC.
30962 San Benito St, Hayward, CA, 94544-7935, USA; tel (510) 487-1701; fax (510) 471-0453; web site www.fujifilmgs.com
Reg'l Sales Mgr.—Richard Cay

FUJIFILM GRAPHIC SYSTEMS USA, INC.
850 Central Ave, Hanover Park, IL, 60133-5422, USA; tel (630) 259-7200; fax (630) 259-7078; web site www.fujifilmgs.com
Reg'l Sales Mgr.—John Briar

FUJIFILM GRAPHIC SYSTEMS USA, INC.
11150 Hope St, Cypress, CA, 90630-5236, USA; tel (714) 933-3300; fax (714) 899-4707; web site www.fujifilmgs.com
Reg'l Sales Mgr.—Richard Payne

FUJIFILM GRAPHIC SYSTEMS USA, INC.
436 Hayden Station Rd, Windsor, CT, 06095-1302, USA; tel (860) 298-0509; fax (860) 298-0296; web site www.fujifilmgs.com
Reg'l Sales Mgr.—Tony Aquino
Acnt. Mgr.—Lorna Borghese

FUJIFILM GRAPHIC SYSTEMS USA, INC.
2507 W Erie Dr Ste 103, Tempe, AZ, 85282-3117, USA; tel (602) 437-4944; fax (602) 437-8483; web site www.fujifilmgs.com
Reg'l Sales Mgr.—Richard Pyane

FUJIFILM GRAPHIC SYSTEMS USA, INC.
3926 Willow Lake Blvd, Memphis, TN, 38118-7040, USA; tel (901) 363-6260; fax (866) 435-6901; web site www.fujifilmgs.com
Reg'l Sales Mgr.—Tommy Greene

FUJIFILM GRAPHIC SYSTEMS USA, INC.
1650 Magnolia Dr, Cincinnati, OH, 45215-1976, USA; tel (513) 563-6700; fax (513) 563-0377; web site www.fujifilmgs.com
Reg'l Sales Mgr.—Kurt Paskert

FUJIFILM GRAPHIC SYSTEMS USA, INC.
8680 Greenwood Pl, Savage, MD, 20763-9718, USA; tel (301) 362-0600; fax (301) 317-7480; e-mail jchumley@fujifilmgs.com; web site www.fujifilmgs.com
Reg'l Sales Mgr.—Rod Ambrose

FUJIFILM GRAPHIC SYSTEMS USA, INC.
1101 W Cambridge Circle Dr, Kansas City, KS, 66103-1311, USA; tel (816) 241-2782; fax (816) 241-3232; web site www.fujifilmgs.com
Reg'l Sales Mgr.—Richard H. Brown

FUJIFILM GRAPHIC SYSTEMS USA, INC.
330 Westway Pl Ste 446, Arlington, TX, 76018-1025, USA; tel (817) 784-6474; fax (817) 467-7351; web site www.fujifilmgs.com
Reg'l Sales Mgr.—Randy Sullivan

FUJIFILM GRAPHIC SYSTEMS USA, INC.
5165 S Towne Dr, New Berlin, WI, 53151-7955, USA; tel (262) 796-8721; fax (262) 796-9589; web site www.fujifilmgs.com
Reg'l Sales Mgr.—Mark Harpke

FUJIFILM HUNT CHEMICALS U.S.A., INC.
40 Boroline Rd, Allendale, NJ, 07401-1616, USA; tel (201) 236-8633; fax (201) 995-2299; web site www.fujihuntusa.com
Vice Pres.—Scott Clouston
Pres.—Albert Adrts
Industry: Chemicals: Photographic; Chemicals: Pressroom;

FUJIFILM NORTH AMERICA CORPORATION
850 Central Ave., Hanover Park, IL, 60133, USA; tel (866) 378-1429; fax (765) 482-0288; web site www.fujifilmus.com
VP Corp. Accounts & Newspapers—Lane Palmer
Newspaper Acct. Mgr., SE Region—Lorna Borghese
Newspaper Acct. Mgr., NW Reg.—Bob Veyera
Newspaper Support Specialist—Michael Mossman
Newspaper Acct. Mgr., SW Reg.—Jurgen Gruber
Newspaper Acct. Mgr., NE Reg.—J. Faulkner
Industry: Plates
Chemistry
Films
Pressroom products
CTP equipment
Processors
Workflow
Proofing supplies
Safety equipment
Service
Color management

FULCO, INC.
30 Broad St., Denville, NJ, 07834, USA; tel (973) 627-2427; fax 973-627-5872; e-mail support@fulcoinc.com; web site www.fulcoinc.com
Owner/Pres.—Jim Duffy
Client Services Director—Dave Ross
Industry: Subscription Fulfillment

G

G&K-VIJUK INTERNATIONAL
715 N Church Rd, Elmhurst, IL, 60126-1415, USA; tel (630) 530-2203; fax (630) 530-2245; e-mail guk-vijuk@guk-vijuk.com; web site www.guk-vijuk.com
Op. Mgr.—Rick Jasnica
Sales Mgr.—Kevin Boivin
Industry: Folding Machines

G.T. SPECIALTIES
PO Box 6383, Albuquerque, NM, 87197-6383, USA; tel (505) 343-0600; fax (505) 343-0606; e-mail Sales@gt-specialties.com; web site www.gt-specialties.com
Owner—Louis Nunez
Industry: Offset Press, New made in USA grippers, Recondition grippers with a Diamond Coating

GAMMERLER (US) CORP.
431 Lakeview Ct Ste B, Mt Prospect, IL, 60103, Canada; tel 224 361-8300; fax (224) 361-8301; web site www.gammerler.com; e-mail joe.jastrzebski@gammerler.com
Managing Director—Joe Jastrzebski
Industry: Conveyors; Counting, Stacking, Bundling Machines; Cutters & Trimmers; Feeding, Folding, Delivery Equipment; Gluing Systems; In-Line Trimming Systems; Mailroom Systems & Equipment; Material Handling Equipment: Palletizing Machines; Material Handling Equipment: Pallets & Palletizers;

GAMMERLER AG
Lietenstr. 26, Geretsried-Gelting, N/A, D-82538, Germany; tel +49 8171 404-326; fax +49 8171 404-244; e-mail dietrich.lauber@gammerler.de; web site www.gammerler.com
Sales Mgr.—Dietrich Lauber

GANNETT MEDIA TECHNOLOGIES INTERNATIONAL (GMTI)
312 Elm St Ste 2G, Cincinnati, OH, 45202-2763, USA; tel (513) 665-3777; fax (513) 768-8958; e-mail gmti-info@gmti.gannett.com; web site www.gmti.com
Pres./CEO—Steve Fuschetti
Industry: Archiving Systems; Computers: Hardware & Software Integrators; Library Retrieval Systems; Marketing Database Design and Implementation; Photo Archiving; Software: Advertising (Includes Display; Classified); Storage Retrieval Systems;

GE INSTRUMENT CONTROL SYSTEMS, INC.
PO Box 7126, Pensacola, FL, 32534-0126, USA; tel (850) 474-4646; fax (850) 968-0563
Sales—Sharon Stall
Industry: Architects/Engineers (Includes Design/Construction Firms); Controls: Exposure; Controls: Photo Electric; Controls: Register;

GENERAL BINDING CORP.
4 Corporate Dr, Lake Zurich, IL, 60047-8924, USA; tel 800-723-4000; fax 800-914-8178; web site www.gbcconnect.com
Industry: Paper Shredders

GENERAL DATACOMM, INC.
6 Rubber Ave, Naugatuck, CT, 06770-4117, USA; tel (203) 729-0271; fax (203) 723-2883; web site www.gdc.com
CFO—William Henry
Industry: Computers: Hardware & Software Integrators; Telecommunications;

GEORGIA-PACIFIC CORP.
133 Peachtree St NE Ste 3700, Atlanta, GA, 30303-1862, USA; tel (404) 652-4000; fax (404) 230-1674; e-mail gpfinance@gapac.com; web site www.gp.com
Chrmn.—Dave Robertson
Pres./CEO—Jim Hannan
Pres., Recycled Fibers—Simon H. Davies
Pres., N. American Retail Bus.—John P. O'Donnell
Pres., Chemicals—Richard G. Urschel
Pres., Dixie—Sean R. Fallmann
Exec. Vice Pres., Global Consumer Pdcts.—Kathleen A. Walters
Exec. Vice Pres., Wood Pdcts.—Ronald L. Paul
Sr. Vice Pres., Commun. government and Pub. Aff.—Sheila M. Weidman
Vice Pres., Mktg. Commun.—Rob Lorys
Dir., Mktg. Servs.—Chris Beyer
Brand Mktg. Dir., Brawny—Gino Biondi
Vice Pres., Information Resources/CIO—H. James Dallas
Industry: Photostat: Paper

GERRARD OVALSTRAPPING
4020 Gault Ave S, Fort Payne, AL, 35967-7567, USA; tel (256) 845-1928; fax (256) 845-1490; e-mail usa_info@goval.com; web site www.goval.com

Mgr.—Neena Wilson
Industry: Strapping Machines

GILBANE BUILDING CO.
7 Jackson Walkway, Providence, RI, 02903-3694, USA; tel (401) 456-5800; fax (401) 456-5930; web site www.gilbaneco.com
Chrmn./CEO—Paul J. Choquette
Pres./COO—Thomas F. Gilbane
Exec. Vice Pres.—William Gilbane
Sr. Vice Pres.-Mktg./Sales—Alfred K. Potter
Sr. Vice Pres./Mgr.-Central Reg.—Walter Mckelvey
Sr. Vice Pres./Mgr., Southwest—Wandell Holmes
Sr. Vice Pres./Mgr., Mid Atlantic—Bruce Hoffman
Sr. Vice Pres./Mgr.-North East Reg.—George Cavallo
Industry: Architects/Engineers (Includes Design/Construction Firms)

GLOBAL PRESS MANAGEMENT SERVICES, LLC.
63 Coryell St Ste A, Lambertville, NJ, 08530-1715, USA; tel (609) 773-0401; fax (609) 773-0403; e-mail epadilla@globalpressmanagement.com; web site www.globalpressmanagement.com
CEO—Edward R. Padilla
Industry: Consulting Services: Equipment; Folding Machines; Press Accessories, Parts & Supplies; Press Engineers; Press Rebuilding; @RecordHead:Global Turnkey Systems, Inc.
2001 US Highway 46 Ste 203, Parsippany, NJ, 07054-1315, USA; tel (973) 331-1010; fax (973) 331-0042; e-mail sales@gtsystems.com; web site www.gtsystems.com
Pres./CEO—Al Alteslane
Industry: Computers: Hardware & Software Integrators; Computers: Local Area Network (LANS); Consulting Services: Circulation; Consulting Services: Computer; Software: Circulation; Software: Electronic Data Interchange; Subscription Fulfillment Software; System Installations; System Integration Services;

GLOBIX CORP.
95 Christopher Columbus Dr Fl 16, Jersey City, NJ, 07302-2927, USA; tel (212) 334-8500; fax (212) 625-8650; e-mail support@qualitytech.com; web site www.qualitytech.com
Pres./CEO/COO—Kurt Van Wagenen
Gen. Mgr.—Shelagh Montgomery
Industry: Computers: Hardware & Software Integrators; Computers: Laptop & Portable; Computers: Local Area Network (LANS); Computers: Storage Devices;

GLUNZ & JENSEN, INC.
500 Commerce Drive, Quakertown, PA, 18951, USA; tel (267) 405-4000; fax (267) 227-3615; e-mail gj-americas@glunz-jensen.com; web site www.glunz-jensen.com
VP Sales—Michael Bugge'
Industry: Offset Platemaking: processors for thermal, UV and violet plates
Offset Plate: plate stackers and conveyors
Flexo Platemaking: exposure units, processors, dryers, light finishers, automated plate making plate mounting, sleeve trimming and plate cleaning equipment
CtP: inkjet computer to plate system

GO PLASTICS/STREETSMART LLC
515 Brown Industrial Pkwy, Canton, GA, 30114-8013, USA; tel 866-366-6166; fax 877-894-9966; e-mail brianb@goplastics.com; web site www.goplastics.com
Dir.-Sales/Mktg.—Brian Bauman
Adv. Customer Info Serv.—Michelle Gollob
Industry: Circulation Equipment & Supplies; Newspaper Dispensers (Mechanical/Electronic);

GOLD COUNTY ADVISORS, INC.
604 Sutter St Ste 394, Folsom, CA, 95630-2698, USA; tel (916) 673-9778; fax (888)

933-0807; e-mail jeff@goldcountryadvisors.com; web site www.goldcountryadvisors.com
Principal—Jeffrey Potts
Industry: Brokers & Appraisers, Merger & Acquisition Advisors for the newspaper business.

GOSS INTERNATIONAL CORPORATION
121 Technology Dr, Durham, NH, 03824-4716, USA; tel 603-749-6600; fax 603-750-6860; e-mail info@gossinternational.com; web site www.gossinternational.com
Chrmn.—Ed Padilla
CEO—Jochen Meissner
CFO—Joseph Gaynor
Sr. Vice Pres., Global Sales—Richard Schultz
Mktg. Mgr.—Cecilia Chou
Greg Norris
Industry: Press Accessories, Parts & Supplies; Press Rebuilding; Press Repairs; Presses: Offset;

GRAFIKAMERICA
1285 W King St, York, PA, 17404-3409, USA; tel (717) 843-3183; fax (717) 845-8828; e-mail sales@grafikam.com
Pres.—Ward Walsh
Industry: Color Registration; Controls: Register; Ink Controls, Computerized; Tension & Web Controls; Web Offset Remoisturizers;

GRAPHIC ARTS BLUE BOOK ONLINE
2000 Clearwater Dr, Oak Brook, IL, 60523-8809, USA; tel 800/323-4958, x8333; fax 678/680-1667; e-mail info@gabb.com; web site www.gabb.com
Global Marketing Director—Mary Miller
Industry: Trade Publications

GRAPHIC MACHINE SALES, INC.
8917 Hickory Ln, Wonder Lake, IL, 60097-9179, USA; tel (815) 382-1914; e-mail graphic@stans.net; web site www.graphicmachinesales.com
Pres.—James Anzelmo
Industry: Used web presses and auxiliaries

GRAPHIC ROLL COVERINGS
300-B, Newkirk Road, Richmond Hill, ON, L4C 3G7, Canada; tel (905) 475-2357; fax (905) 475-3421; e-mail info@graphicroller.com; web site www.graphicroller.com
Pres.—Brian Venis
Industry: Ink Rollers; Rollers; Dampening; Rollers; UV; Nylon Roller Coating; Chrome Roller Coating; Split Nip Folder Rolls; Infeed Nip Rolls; Grater Wrap-Roller Covering; Ink Fountains & Accessories; Press Accessories, Parts & Supplies; Roller Grinding Services; @RecordHead:Graphic System Services, Inc.
1201 Ardmore Ave, Itasca, IL, 60143-1187, USA; tel (630) 860-5959; fax (630) 860-6515; e-mail info@jardis.com; web site www.jardis.com
Pres.—Allan Jardis
Mgr.—Gary Klawinski
Industry: Architects/Engineers (Includes Design/Construction Firms); Consulting Services: Equipment; Ink Pumping Systems; Pasters; Press Accessories, Parts & Supplies; Pumps (Air, Ink, Vacuum); Remanufactures Equipment; Splicers, Automatic; Tension & Web Controls; Web Press - Special Equipment;

GRAPHIC TECHNOLOGY, INC. (GTI)
PO Box 3138, Newburgh, NY, 12550-0651, USA; tel (845) 562-7066; fax (845) 562-2543; e-mail sales@gtilite.com; web site www.gtilite.com
Pres.—Frederic McCurdy
Vice Pres., Sales/Mktg.—Robert McCurdy
Sales/Mktg Coord.—Linda Sutherland
Industry: Art & Layout Equipment and Services; Color Viewing Equipment; Layout Tables, Light Tables & Workstations; Lighting Equipment; Press Accessories, Parts & Supplies;

GRAPHICS MICROSYSTEMS, INC.
1655 Science Pl, Rockwall, TX, 75032-6202, USA; tel (972) 290-3120; fax (972) 722-1128; e-mail avt@avt-inc.com; web site www.avt-inc.com
Southern Regional Sales Mgr.—Bill Fleck
Industry: Color Registration; Controls: Register; Densitometers; Ink Controls, Computerized; Press Control Systems;

GRAPHLINE
30 Main St Ste 300, Danbury, CT, 06810-3006, USA; tel (800) 998-3200; fax (954) 724-2255; e-mail marketing@graphline.com; web site www.graphline.com
Pres./CEO—Michael Ostroff
Exec. Vice Pres./CFO—Ray Domis
Vice Pres.,Marketing/Operations—Ralph Theile
Dir., Mktg.—Tom Brancato
Industry: Chemicals: Photographic; Chemicals: Plate Processing; Film & Paper: Contact; Densitometers; Film & Paper: Duplicating; Film & Paper: Film Processing Machines; Imagesetters; Laser Printers; Platemakers: Direct;

GREAT SOUTHERN CORP. (SIRCO DIV.)
PO Box 18710, Memphis, TN, 38181-0710, USA; tel (901) 365-1611; fax (901) 365-4498; e-mail info@gsmemphis.com; web site www.gsmemphis.com
Pres.—Scott Vaught
Industry: Circulation Equipment & Supplies; Newspaper Bags;

GRIMES, MCGOVERN & ASSOCIATES
10 West 15th Street, New York City, NY, 10011, USA; tel (917) 881—6563; e-mail lgrimes@mediamergers.com; web site www.mediamergers.com
Chmn.—Larry Grimes
V.P., Head of Newspaper Division—Julie Bergman
Senior Associate-Northeast/New England—John Szefc
Senior Associate- Southeast/South—David Slavin
Owner, CEO—John McGovern
Senior Associate-Southern States—Lewis Floyd
Founder—Walter Grimes
Sr. Assoc.-SW/Plains—Gary Borders
Sr. Assoc.-CANADA-Mag. & Newspapers—Gord Carley
Sr. Advisor-Newspapers—Joe Bella
Sr. Assoc.-Western/Mtn. States—Ken Amundson
Senior Associate-Sales Nationwide—Ken Blum
Industry: Brokers & Appraisers; Consulting Services: Advertising; Consulting Services: Financial; Consulting Services: Human Resources; Consulting Services: Marketing;

GSP, INC.
PO Box 2358, Westerly, RI, 02891-0922, USA; tel (401) 348-0210; fax (401) 348-0689; e-mail gspmystic@gsptoday.com; web site www.gsptoday.com
Pres.—Jens E. Ljungberg
Vice Pres.—Maurice Blanchet
Controller—Mary Ponte
Industry: Presses: Offset; Web Press - Special Equipment; Labeling Equipment

H

H & M PASTER SALES & SERVICE, INC.
21828 87th Ave SE Ste D, Woodinville, WA, 98072-8054, USA; tel 425-892-1093; fax 425-892-1096; e-mail steve@bjmach.com; web site www.bjmach.com
Pres.—Steven Bjorklund
Industry: Adhesives; Gluing Systems; Pasters; Web Press - Special Equipment;

H.R. SLATER CO., INC.
2050 W 18th St, Chicago, IL, 60608-1816, USA; tel (312) 666-1855; fax (312) 666-1856; e-mail hrslatercompany@aol.com
Pres.—Robert Kurzka
Office Mgr.—William C. St. Hilaire
Industry: Delivery Equipment; Gauges, Measuring; Mailroom Systems & Equipment; Newsprint Handeling Equipment; Paper Handeling Equipment;

HADRONICS
4570 Steel Pl., Cincinnati, OH, 45209, USA; tel (513) 321-9350; fax (513) 321-9377; e-mail sales@hadronics.com; web site www.hadronics.com
VP., Sales—Jeff McCarty
Industry: Copper Plating Drums; Cylinder Repair; Dampening Systems; Ink Fountains & Accessories; Roller Grinding Services; Rollers; Rollers: Dampening;

HALL CONTRACTING SERVICES, INC.
33530 Pin Oak Pkwy., Avon Lake, OH, 44012, Avon Lake; tel (440) 930-0050; fax (440) 930-0025; e-mail hcs@hallcontractingservices.com; web site www.hallcontractingservices.com
CEO—Robert Bowers
Vice President of Operations—Tom Julius
Director of Sales—Larry Wojcik
Industry: New Press controls;Equipment Dealer (Used); Erectors & Riggers; Press Engineers; Press Rebuilding; Press Repairs; Remanufactures Equipment; Web Width Change mods;

HAMILTON CIRCULATION SUPPLIES CO.
PO Box 398, Beecher, IL, 60401-0398, USA; tel 708-946-2208; fax (708) 946-3733; e-mail info@hamiltoncirculation.com; web site www.theservicechamps.com
Pres.—Joseph M. Beaudry
Vice Pres.—Thomas P. Hamilton
Pat Stein
Vice Pres.—Susan Beaudry
Administration—Carrie Dolan
Industry: Adhesives; Circulation Equipment & Supplies; Delivery Equipment; Material Handling Equipment: Pallets & Palletizers; Newspaper Bags; Newspaper Dispensers (Mechanical/Electronic); Newspaper Marketing; Rack Display Cards; Software: Circulation; Tubes, Racks (Includes Racks: Motor Route Tubes);

HARLAND SIMON
210 W 22nd St Ste 138, Oak Brook, IL, 60523-4061, USA; tel (630) 572-7650; fax (630) 572-7653; e-mail sales@harlandsimon.com; web site www.harlandsimon.com
Managing Director - Americas—John Staiano
Industry: Color Proofing; Drives & Controls; Ink Controls, Computerized; Mailroom Systems & Equipment; Inserting Systems (Includes Stuffing Machines); Press Control Systems; Press Data Accumulators; Produciton Control Systems; Software: Pagination/Layout; Software: Press/Post Press; Software: Workflow Management/Tracking;

HARPER CORPORATION OF AMERICA
PO Box 38490, Charlotte, NC, 28278-1008, USA; tel 800-438-3111; fax (704) 588-3819; e-mail customer@harperimage.com; web site www.harperimage.com
President—Margaret Harper Kluttz
VP of Operations—Lee Kluttz
VP of Sales—Alan Rogers
Industry: Anilox manufacturer

HARRIS CORP.
1025 W Nasa Blvd # A11-0, Melbourne, FL, 32919-0001, USA; tel (321) 727-9100; web site www.harris.com
Pres./CEO/Chrmn.—Howard L. Lance
COO—Robert K. Henry
Sr. Vice Pres./CFO—Gary L. McArthur
Vice Pres., Investor Rel.—Pamela Padgett
Treasurer—Charles J. Greene
Industry: Business Computers; Data

Communication; Facsimilie/Fax Transmission Systems; Pagination Systems; Input & Editing Systems; Press Control Systems; Publishing Systems; Visual Display Terminals;

HART INDUSTRIES
43 Doran St, East Haven, CT, 06512-2212, USA; tel (203) 469-6344; fax (203) 469-6592; e-mail steve@hartindus.com; web site www.hartindus.com
Pres.—Steve Mancuso
Industry: Dark Room Equipment; Environmental Control Systems; Silver Recovery; Wastewater Treatment;

HEAT AND CONTROL, INC.
21121 Cabot Blvd, Hayward, CA, 94545-1177, USA; tel 800-227-5980; fax (510) 259-0600; e-mail info@heatandcontrol.com; web site www.heatandcontrol.com
Chrmn./CEO—Andy Caridis
Pres.—Tony Caridis
Dir., Mktg.—Audrey Waidelich
Industry: Counting, Stacking, Bundling Machines

HEIDELBERG USA
1000 Gutenberg Dr, Kennesaw, GA, 30144, USA; tel 437-7388; e-mail info@heidelberg.com; web site www.heidelberg.com/us
Senior Vice President, Equipment—Felix Mueller
Industry: Manufacturing

HEIDELBERG USA, INC.
1000 Gutenberg Dr NW, Kennesaw, GA, 30144-7028, USA; tel (888) 472-9655; e-mail info@heidelberg.com; web site www.us.heidelberg.com
Sr. Vice Pres., HR/Gen. Counsel—Susan Nofi
Sr. Vice Pres., Finance—Thomas Topp
President—Harald Weimer
Sr. V.P. Equipment Marketing—Andrew Rae
Sr. V.P. Service—Ulrich Koehler
Industry: Sheetfed offset presses; digital production presses; wide format inkjet; prepress software and CtP output systems; inkjet proofing systems; color managmnt business and production managment software; cutters, stitchers, folders, binders, and other postpress package producing systems; all consumables including plates, inks, coating solutions, blanket washes, and much more.

HERCO GRAPHIC PRODUCTS
PO Box 369, Wauconda, IL, 60084-0369, USA; tel (800) 235-5541; fax (815) 578-9593; e-mail hercographics@aol.com; web site www.hercographics.com
Dir. Sales—Christine Polanzi
Industry: Roll Coverings; Rollers;

HERMAN H. STICHT CO., INC.
45 Main St Ste 401, Brooklyn, NY, 11201-1084, USA; tel (718) 852-7602; fax (718) 852-7915; e-mail stichtco@aol.com; web site www.stichtco.com
Pres.—Paul H. Plotkin
Industry: Static Eliminators

HEWLETT-PACKARD CO.
3000 Hanover St, Palo Alto, CA, 94304-1185, USA; tel (650) 857-1501; fax (650) 857-5518; e-mail hp-leads@hp.com; web site www.hp.com
Chrmn./Pres./CEO—Mark Hurd
CMO—Michael Mendenhall
Exec. Vice Pres., Enterprise Bus.—Ann Livermore
Exec. Vice Pres., Worldwide Mktg., Personal Systems Grp.—Richard Gerstein
Vice Pres., Mktg.—Tariq Hassan
Vice Pres., Brand Strategy—Glenna Patton
Dir., Mktg., Small/Midsize Bus.—Brian Burch

HEWLETT-PACKARD CO.
3600 Army Post Rd, Des Moines, IA, 50321-2906, USA; tel (952) 944-9330; fax (952)

943-8622; e-mail info@colorspan.com; web site www.colorspan.com
Dir., Mktg.—Bruce Butler
Industry: Inks

HEXAGON METROLOGY, INC.
250 Circuit Dr, North Kingstown, RI, 02852-7441, USA; tel (401) 886-2000; fax (401) 886-2727; web site www.hexagonmetrology.com
Adv. Mgr.—William Fetter
Industry: Gauges, Measuring

HFW INDUSTRIES
PO Box 8, Buffalo, NY, 14207-0008, USA; tel (716) 875-3380; fax (716) 875-3385; web site www.hfwindustries.com
Pres.—John Watson
Manufacturing Manager—Ron Jurewicz
Industry: Cylinder reconditioning

HONEYWELL, INC.
101 Columbia Rd, Morristown, NJ, 07960-4658, USA; tel (973) 455-2000; fax (973) 455-4002; e-mail lois.sills@honeywell.com; web site www.honeywell.com
CEO—Dave Cote
Industry: Fire Protection; Humidifiers; Press Control Systems;

HORIZONS, INC.
18531 S Miles Rd, Cleveland, OH, 44128-4237, USA; tel 1.800.482.7758; e-mail info@horizonsisg.com; web site www.horizonsisg.com
Pres.—Herb Wainer
Vice Pres., Mktg.—Wayne Duignan
Industry: Adhesives; Chemicals: Photographic; Input & Editing Systems; Label Printing Machines;

HOWTEK
98 Spit Brook Rd Ste 100, Nashua, NH, 03062-5737, USA; tel 937-431-1464; fax 937-431-1465; e-mail sales@icadmed.com; web site www.icadmed.com
Pres.—Ken Ferry
Industry: Color Seperation Scanners

HUDSON-SHARP
975 Lombardi Ave, Green Bay, WI, 54304-3735, USA; tel (920) 494-4571; e-mail sales@hudsonsharp.com; web site www.hudsonsharp.com
CEO—Rod Drummond
Industry: Automatic Plastic Bagging Equipment

HURLETRON, INC.
1820 Tempel Dr., Libertyville, IL, 60048, USA; tel (847) 680-7022; fax (847) 680-7338; e-mail sales@hurletron.com; web site www.hurletron.com
Gen. Mgr.—Steve J. Siler
Asst. Gen. Mgr./Dir.of Sales—Kevin Oakes
Industry: Adhesives; Controls: Register;

I

I-MANY, INC.
1735 Market St Ste 3700, Philadelphia, PA, 19103-7527, USA; tel (800) 832-0228; e-mail info@imany.com; web site www.imany.com
Pres./CEO—John A. Rade
Industry: Consulting Services: Financial

ICANON ASSOCIATES, INC.
2321 N Penn Rd Ste C, Hatfield, PA, 19440-1972, USA; tel (800) 544-4450; e-mail sales@icanon.com; web site www.newzware.com
Pres.—Joe Lewinski
Dir., Mktg.—Gary Markle
Engineering—Mike Hanson
Industry: Computers: Hardware & Software Integrators; Consulting Services: Computer; Consulting Services: Financial; Software: Advertising (Includes Display; Classified);

Software: Business (Includes Administration/
Accounting); Software: Circulation; Software:
Editorial; Software: Pagination/Layout;

IDEAFISHER SYSTEMS, INC.
5640 SE Riverside Way, Vancouver, WA,
98661-7175, USA; tel 360-450-6888;
e-mail info@ideafisher.com; web site www.
ideafisher.com
—Marsh Fisher
—Mark EffingerCEOs
Industry: Software: Advertising (Includes
Display; Classified)

IGS KNIVES, INC.
760 W Wallick Ln, Red Lion, PA, 17356-8859,
USA; tel (717) 244-6753; fax (717) 244-6529;
e-mail info@igsknives.com; web site www.
igsknives.com
Corporate Sec—Katie Howard
Industry: Web Press - Special Equipment

IKS KLINGELNBERG GMBH
In der Fleute 18, 42897 Remscheid, N/A,
N/A, Germany; tel 2191 969-0; fax 2191 969-
111; e-mail info@interknife.com; web site
www.interknife.com
Pres./CEO—Thomas Meyer

IMAPRO CORP.
400 St. Laurent Blvd, Ottawa, ON, K1G 6C4,
Canada; tel (613) 738-3000; fax (613) 738-
5038; e-mail sales@imapro.com; web site
www.imapro.com
Pres.—Fred Andreone
Industry: Computers: Hardware & Software
Integrators; Computers: Local Area Network
(LANS); Disk Drive Sales/Repair; Dryers:
Film and Papers; Software: Pagination/
Layout;

IMC AMERICA
1285 W King St, York, PA, 17404-3409, USA;
tel (717) 845-4807; fax (717) 845-8828;
e-mail imcsales@imcamerica.com; web site
www.imcamerica.com
Pres.—Ward Walsh
Vice Pres., Mktg./Sales—Ric Mayle
Industry: Blanket Cleaner/Washer (Automatic);
Conveyors; Counting, Stacking, Bundling
Machines; Cutters & Trimmers; In-Line
Trimming Systems; Material Handling
Equipment: Automatic Guided Vehicles;
Material Handling Equipment: Palletizing
Machines; Paper Handling Equipment; Roll
Handling Equipment;

IMPACT RACKS, INC.
12 Wheatland Dr., Mechanicsburg, PA,
17050, USA; tel (717) 200-1213; e-mail
impactracks@aol.com
Pres.—John Knowles
VP—Stefan Knowles
Industry: Circulation Equipment & Supplies;
Newspaper Dispensers (Mechanical/
Electronic); Remanufactures Equipment;
Strapping Machines; Tubes, Racks (Includes
Racks: Motor Route Tubes);

IMPAK (A DIV. OF PAKON, INC.)
5950 Clearwater Dr Ste 100, Minnetonka,
MN, 55343-8986, USA; tel (952) 936-9500;
fax (952) 936-9509; e-mail salesinfo@pakon.
com; web site www.pakon.com
Sales/Mktg. Mgr.—Juan Palacios
Industry: Scanners: Color B & W, Plates, Web

IMSI
25 Leveroni Ct Ste B, Novato, CA, 94949-
5726, USA; tel 415-483-8000; fax 415-884-
9023; e-mail sales@imsisoft.com; web site
www.imsidesign.com
Chrmn./CEO—Royal Farros
COO—Robert Mayer
Industry: Software: Design/Graphics; Software:
Electronic Data Interchange; Software:
Pagination/Layout;

INDUSTRIAL ACOUSTICS CO.
1160 Commerce Ave, Bronx, NY, 10462-

5537, USA; tel (718) 931-8000; fax (718)
863-1138; e-mail newyork@iac-acoustics.
com; web site www.industrialacoustics.com
Pres.—Kenneth Delasho
Industry: Environmental Control Systems

INDUSTRIAL NOISE CONTROL, INC.
401 Airport Rd, North Aurora, IL,
60542-1818, USA; tel (630) 844-1999;
fax (630) 966-9710; e-mail sales@
industrialnoisecontrol.com; web site www.
industrialnoisecontrol.com
Pres.—Mark Rubino
Industry: Architects/Engineers (Includes Design/
Construction Firms); Noise Control;

INFORMATICA DALAI SA DE CV
Prolongacion A. Reyes 4508, Col. Villa del
Rio, Monterrey, N/A, 64850, Mexico; tel +52
81 365-4077; fax +52 81 365-5990; web site
www.dalai.com
Devel. Mgr.—Gerardo Trevino
Mng. Dir.—Juan Lauro Aguirre
Adv. Mgr.—David Valdez
Industry: Pagination Systems; Software:
Advertising (Includes Display; Classified);
Software: Asset Management; Software:
Editorial;

INGERSOLL-RAND-ARO FLUID PRODUCT DIV.
PO Box 151, Bryan, OH, 43506-0151, USA;
tel (419) 636-4242; fax (419) 633-1674;
e-mail arowebleads@irco.com; web site
www.ingersollrandproducts.com
Chrmn./Pres.—Herbert L. Henkel
Industry: Ink Bleeding Equipment; Ink Pumping
Systems; Pumps (Air, Ink, Vacuum);

INLAND NEWSPAPER MACHINERY LLC
2298 W Layton Dr, Olathe, KS, 66061, USA;
tel 522-4889; e-mail inmc1@inlandnews.com;
web site www.inlandnews.com
Sales Admin.—Ann Campbell
Pres.—Beau Campbell
Industry: Brokers & Appraisers; Consulting
Services: Equipment; Equipment Dealers
(New); Equipment Dealers (Used); Press
Rebuilding; Press Repairs; Presses: Offset;
Remanufactures Equipment;

INNOTEK CORPORATION
9140 Zachary Ln N, Maple Grove, MN,
55369-4003, USA; tel (763) 488 9910; fax
(763)488 9904; e-mail sales@innotek-ep.
com; web site www.innotek-ep.com
CEO President—Dennis Burns
Vice Pres., Finance—David Kalina
Vice Pres., Sales—Lynn Hughes
Industry: Hydraulic & Pneumatic components
and systems. Contract manufacturing.

INNOVATIVE SYSTEMS DESIGN, INC.
222 Brunswick Blvd., Pointe-Claire, QC, H9R
1A6, Canada; tel (514) 459-0200; fax (514)
459-0300; e-mail sales@isd.ca; web site
www.isd.ca
Pres.—Jeff Tierney
Director of Sales and Marketing—Rob
Dumas
Sales Coord.—Monica Steibelt
Industry: Telecommunications

INSERT EAST, INC.
7045 Central Hwy, Pennsauken, NJ, 08109-
4312, USA; tel (856) 663-8181; fax (856)
663-3288; web site www.insertseast.com
Owner—Gino Maiale
Pres.—Nick Maiale
Plant Mgr.—Frank Oliveti
Industry: Circulation Equipment & Supplies

INSURANCE SPECIALTIES SERVICES, INC.
946 Town Ctr, New Britain, PA, 18901-5182,
USA; tel 800-533-4579; fax 215-918-0507;
e-mail info@issisvs.com; web site www.
issisvs.com
Pres.—Kenneth P. Smith

Sales—Kathy Liney
Industry: Insurance

INTER-CONTINENTAL GRAPHICS, INC.
11351 Bent Pine Dr, Fort Myers, FL, 33913-
8110, USA; tel (239) 561-6401; fax (239)
561-6402; e-mail jv@intercontinentalweb.
com; web site www.intercontinentalweb.com
Pres.—Judith E. Wenzel
Dir., Sales—John F. Velilla
Industry: Blankets; Counting, Stacking, Bundling
Machines; Plates: Offset (Conventional);
Press Accessories, Parts & Supplies; Press
Control Systems; Presses: Offset; Reels &
Tensions; Rollers; Splicers, Automatic;

INTERACTIVE DATA REAL-TIME SERVICES, INC.
32 Crosby Dr, Bedford, MA, 01730-1448,
USA; tel 781-687-8500; fax 781-687-8005;
e-mail sales.us@interactivedata.com; web
site www.interactivedata-rts.com
Pres.—Mark Hopsworth
Mktg. Mgr.—Azriane Carnan
Industry: Consulting Services: Financial

INTERCONTINENTAL ENGINEERING CO.
25944 Northline Rd, Taylor, MI, 48180-4413,
USA; tel (734) 946-9931; fax (734) 946-9992
Pres.—Michael Schwartz
Dir.—Somendra Khosla
Industry: Presses: Offset

INTERLINK
PO Box 207, Berrien Springs, MI, 49103-
0207, USA; tel (269) 473-3103; fax (206)
984-2240; e-mail info@ilsw.com; web site
www.ilsw.com
Founder—William E. Garber
President—Bradley Hill
Industry: Software: Circulation Management.
Software: Advertising Billing (Includes
Display; Classified)

INTERNATIONAL TRADEMARK ASSOCIATION
655 3rd Ave Fl 10, New York, NY, 10017-
5646, USA; tel (212) 642-1700; fax (212)
768-7796; e-mail info@inta.org; web site
www.inta.org
Exec. Dir.—Alan Drewsen
Devin Toporek

INTERSTATE DISTRIBUTOR CO.
11707 21st Avenue Ct S, Tacoma, WA,
98444-1236, USA; tel (253) 537-9455; e-mail
web_info@intd.com; web site www.intd.com
President & CEO—George Payne
Pres.—Gary McLean
Sec.—Dolores Fitzerald
Sr. Vice Pres., Sales/Mktg.—Peter M.
Carlander

INTRALOX, LLC
301 Plantation Rd, Harahan, LA, 70123-
5326, USA; tel (504) 733-0463; fax (504)
734-0063; web site www.intralox.com
Sales Mgr.—Edel Blanks
Industry: Conveyors

INX INTERNATIONAL INK CO.
150 N Martingale Rd Ste 700, Schaumburg,
IL, 60173-2009, USA; tel (630) 682-1800;
fax (847) 969-9758; e-mail general@
inxinternational.com; info@inxintl.com; web
site www.inxinternational.com
Chrmn.—M. Matsuzawa
Pres./CEO—Richard Clendenning
Sr. Vice Pres., Product/Mfg. Technology—Joe
Cichon
Sr. Vice Pres.-Gen. Affairs/Admin.—John
Carlson
Sr. Vice Pres.-Liquid Div.—Charles
Weinholzer
Sr. Vice Pres.-Metal Div.—Kenneth
O'Callaghan
Sr. Vice Pres.-Offset Div./COO—George
Polasik
Dir., PR—Betty Leavitt

Industry: Chemicals: Pressroom; Cleaners &
Solvents; Consulting Services: Marketing;
Ink Bleeding Equipment; Ink Fountains &
Accessories; Ink Pumping Systems; Ink
Storage Tanks; Inks;

IPC
618 148TH CT. N.E., BRADENTON, FL,
34212, USA; tel (941) 484-3622; fax 877-
290-7176; e-mail charlie@ipcpoly.com; web
site www.ipcpoly.com
Pres.—Charlie Hencye
Asst. Mgr.—Cheryl Hencye
Industry: Newspaper Poly Bags, RACKS
& Supplies, Single Copy Items,
PROMOTIONAL ITEMS, Twine, Rubber
Bands, Business Cards

ITW HOBART BROTHERS CO.
400 Trade Sq E, Troy, OH, 45373-2463, USA;
tel (937) 332-4000; fax (937) 332-5224; web
site www.hobartbrothers.com
Welding Equip. Mgr.—Dean Phillips
Adv./Commun. Mgr.—Debbie Doench
Industry: Motors

J

J. THOMAS MCHUGH CO., INC.
12931 Ford Dr, Fishers, IN, 46038-2899,
USA; tel (317) 577-2121; fax (317) 577-2125;
e-mail tbryant@jtmchugh.com; web site
www.jtmchugh.com
Owner/CEO—Thomas J. Bryant
Industry: Blanket Mounting and Bars; Blankets;
Offset Blanket Thickness Gauge; Offset
Blankets, Blanket Wash;

JARDIS INDUSTRIES, INC.
1201 Ardmore Ave, Itasca, IL, 60143-1187,
USA; tel (630) 860-5959; fax (630) 860-6515;
e-mail info@jardis.com; web site www.jardis.
com
Pres.—Alan W. Jardis
Gen. Mgr.—Adam Jardis
Industry: Film and Papers; Drying Systems;
Festoon Splicers; Flying Pasters; Constant
tension Infeeds; Web guides; Plow folders;
Angle Bar arrangemdnts ; Custom designed
web handling Equipment;Offset and
Flexographic printing press for newspaper,
commercial , book and packaging
applications

JBT CORPORATION (FORMERLY FMC TECHNOLOGIES)
400 Highpoint Dr, Chalfont, PA, 18914-3924,
USA; tel (215) 822-4600; fax (215) 822-4553;
e-mail sgv.sales@jbtc.com; web site www.
jbtc-agv.com
Mktg. Mgr.—Mark Longacre
Industry: Material Handling Equipment:
Automatic Guided Vehicles; Newsprint
Handling Equipment; Paper Handling
Equipment; Roll Handling Equipment; Roll
Preparation Equipment; Software: Workflow
Management/Tracking; System Integration
Services;

JERVIS B. WEBB CO.
34375 W 12 Mile Rd, Farmington Hills,
MI, 48331-5624, USA; tel (248) 553-1000;
e-mail info@jerviswebb.com; web site www.
daifukuna.com
Sr. Vice Pres./CFO—John S. Doychich
Daifuku North America Holding
Company President and CEO—Aki
Nishimura
Industry: Computers: Hardware & Software
Integrators; Consulting Services: Equipment;
Conveyors; Mailroom Systems & Equipment;
Material Handling Equipment: Automatic
Guided Vehicles; Material Handling
Equipment: Vehicle Loading; Newsprint
Handling Equipment; Paper Handling
Equipment; Roll Handeling Equipment;
Storage Retrieval Systems;

JOHN JULIANO COMPUTER SERVICES

CO.
2152 Willive Pl., Decatur, GA, 30033, USA;
tel (404) 327-6010; fax (815) 301-8581;
e-mail info@jjcs.com; web site www.jjcs.com
Pres.—John Juliano
Principal Analyst—L. Carol Christopher
Industry: Consulting Services: Computer;
Consulting Services: Marketing;

JOHNSTONE ENGINEERING & MACHINE CO.
PO Box 66, Parkesburg, PA, 19365-0066,
USA; tel 610-593-6350; fax 610-593-2172;
e-mail jemco2@comcast.net
Sales Mgr.—Raymond E. Sullivan
President—Bill Haag
Industry: Reels & Tensions; Reels (Inlcudes
Paper Reels); Rewinders; Roll Handling
Equipment;

JUPITER IMAGES CORP.
6000 N Forest Park Dr, Peoria, IL, 61614-
3556, USA; tel (309) 688-8800; fax (309)
688-3075; e-mail sales@jupiterimages.com;
web site www.jupiterimages.com
Vice Pres., Opns.—Mark Nickerson
Industry: Software: Design/Graphics; Trade
Publications;

JUST NORMLICHT, INC.
2000 Cabot Blvd W Ste 120, Langhorne, PA,
19047-2408, USA; tel (267) 852-2200; fax
(267) 852-2207; e-mail sales@justnormlicht.
com; web site www.justnormlicht.com
Vice President—Eric Dalton
Industry: Color Proofing; Color Viewing
Equipment;

K

K & F INTERNATIONAL, INC.
12633 Industrial Park Dr, Granger, IN, 46530-
6884, USA; tel (574) 272-9950; fax (574)
277-6566; e-mail sales@k-f.com; web site
www.k-f.com
Gen. Mgr.—Kent Deal
Vice Pres., Sales—Al Brunner
Mktg. Coord.—Tim Scott
Coord., Int'l Sales—Linda Vervaet
Industry: Color Registration; Offset Plate-
Making Service & Equipment; Pin Register
Systems; Plate Bending Systems;
Plate Processors; Platemakers: Offset
(Conventional); 281;

K & M NEWSPAPER SERVICES, INC.
45 Gilbert St Ext, Monroe, NY, 10950-2815,
USA; tel (845) 782-3817; fax (845) 783-2972;
e-mail info@kmnewspaper.com; web site
www.kmnewspaper.com
Pres.—Mark Jacobs
Controller—Micki Jacobs
Office Mgr.—Karla Hahan
Vice Pres., Sales—Rick Walter
Industry: Belts, Belting, V-Belts; Controls: Photo
Electric; Conveyors; Mailroom Systems
& Equipment; Motors; Remanufactures
Equipment;

K-JACK ENGINEERING CO., INC.
PO Box 2320, Gardena, CA, 90247-0320,
USA; tel (310) 327-8389; fax (310) 769-6997;
e-mail kjack@kjack.com; web site www.
kjack.com
Pres.—Jack S. Chalabian
Vice Pres.—Jacqueline Chalabian-Jernigan
Vice Pres., Sales—Steven H. Chalabian
Industry: Cart Distribution Systems; Circulation
Equipment & Supplies; Delivery Equipment;
Newspaper Dispensers (Mechanical/
Electronic); Software: Circulation; Tubes,
Racks (Includes Racks: Motor Route Tubes);

KAIM & ASSOCIATES INTERNATIONAL MARKETING, INC.
102 Industrial Park Rd, Lodi, WI, 53555-
1374, USA; tel (608) 592-7404; fax (608)
592-7404; e-mail info@kaiminc.com; web site

www.kaiminc.com
Pres.—Wayne Kaim
Industry: Color Registration; Controls: Register;
Paper Shredders; Pasters; Reels & Tensions;
Roll Cleaning Equipment; Rollers; Tension
& Web Controls; Web Break Detector; Web
Cleaners;

KAMEN & CO. GROUP SERVICES
626 RXR Plz, Uniondale, NY, 11556-0626,
USA; tel (516) 379-2797; fax (516) 379-3812;
e-mail info@kamengroup.com; web site www.
kamengroup.com
Pres./CEO—Kevin Brian Kamen
Vice Pres.—Celeste Myers
Industry: Architects/Engineers (Includes Design/
Construction Firms); Brokers & Appraisers;
Circulation Equipment & Supplies; Consulting
Services: Advertising; Consulting Services:
Circulation; Consulting Services: Financial;
Consulting Services: Human Resources;
Consulting Services: Marketing; Training;
Sales & Marketing; Tubes, Racks (Includes
Racks: Motor Route Tubes);

KANALY TRUST CO.
5555 San Felipe St Ste 200, Houston, TX,
77056-2760, USA; tel (713)561-9300; fax
(713) 877-8744; e-mail kanaly@kanaly.com;
web site www.kanaly.com
Chairman/CEO—Drew Kanaly
Industry: Consulting Services: Financial

KANSA TECHNOLOGY, LLC
3700 Oakes Dr, Emporia, KS, 66801-5136,
USA; tel (620) 343-6700; fax (620) 343-2108;
e-mail marketing@kansa.com; web site www.
kansa.com
CEO—Jerry Waddell
Chief Operating Officer—Lonnie Worthington
Megan Kropff
Industry: Addressing Machines; Collating
Equipment; Conveyors; Counting, Stacking,
Bundling Machines; Feeding, Folding,
Delivery Equipment; Folding Machines;
Infeed Stackers; Inserting Equipment
(Includes Stuffing Machines); Mailroom
Systems & Equipment; Remanufactures
Equipment;

KASPAR WIRE WORKS, INC./SHO-RACK
PO Box 667, Shiner, TX, 77984-0667, USA;
tel (361) 594-2911; fax (361) 594-4264;
e-mail custserv@shorack.com; web site
www.shorack.com
Customer Service—Chris Stluka
Customer Service—David Vana
Gen. Mgr.—Morgan Barnett
Industry: Circulation Equipment & Supplies;
Cleaners & Solvents; Newspaper Dispensers
(Mechanical/Electronic); Software:
Circulation;

KBA NORTH AMERICA, INC. (KOENIG & BAUER AG)
2555 Regent Blvd, Dallas, TX, 75261, USA;
tel 469-532-8040; fax 469-532-8190; e-mail
na-marketing@kba,com; web site www.
kba.com
Pres./CEO—Mark Hischar
Vice Pres., Mktg.—Eric Frank
Vice-President of Sales & Service—Ulrich
Wicke
Executive Sales—Pernice Samuel
National Sales Manager—Bruce Richardson
Sales Director Web Presses—Schenker
Winfried
Digital Sales and Marketing Specialist—
Denise Prewitt
Regional Sales Dir. —Alex Stepanian
Industry: Flexogrpahic Press Conversion; Flying
Pasters; Pasters; Presses: Flexographic;
Presses: Offset; Reels & Tensions; Reels
(Inlcudes Paper Reels) Tension & Web
Controls;

KEENE TECHNOLOGY, INC. (KTI)
14357 Commercial Pkwy, South Beloit, IL,
61080-2621, USA; tel (815) 624-9899; fax
(815) 624-4223; e-mail info@keenetech.com;
web site www.keenetech.com

Office Mgr.—Kery Wallace
Industry: Rewinders; Splicers, Automatic;

KEISTER WILLIAMS NEWSPAPER SERVICES, INC.
PO Box 8187, Charlottesville, VA, 22906-
8187, USA; tel (434) 293-4709; fax (434)
293-4884; e-mail ky@kwnews.com; web site
www.kwnews.com
Pres./Treasurer—Walton C. (Ky) Lindsay
Vice Pres., Mktg.—Meta L. Nay
Admin.—Carol Lindsay
Pres.—Walton Lindsay
Industry: Consulting Services: Advertising;
Consulting Services: Marketing;

KEPES, INC.
9016 58th Pl Ste 600, Kenosha, WI, 53144-
7819, USA; tel (262) 652-7889; fax (262)
652-7787; e-mail inquire@kepes.com; web
site www.kepes.com
Pres./Sales Mgr.—Wayne Pagel
Mktg. Mgr.—John Slanchik
Industry: Equipment Dealers (Used); Feeding,
Folding, Delivery Equipment; Gluing
Systems; Remanufactures Equipment; Roll
Handling Equipment; Rollers;

KIDDER, INC.
270 Main St, Agawam, MA, 01001-1838,
USA; tel (413) 786-8692; fax (413) 786-8785;
e-mail kidderpress@worldnet.att.net
Pres.—Charles Rae
CFO—Thomas K. Trant
Vice Pres.-HR—John Rico
Vice Pres.-Engineering—Harris Barnard
Mktg. Mgr.—Cheryl N. Smith
Industry: Dryers: Film and Papers; Ink Fountains
& Accessories; Presses: Flexographic;
Rewinders;

KIMOTO TECH
1701 Howard St Ste G, Elk Grove Village,
IL, 60007-2479, USA; tel (847) 640-8022;
fax (847) 640-7942; e-mail info@kimototech.
com; web site www.kimototech.com
Sales Supvr.—Alex Jasinowski
Kimosetter Support —Serina Vartanian
Industry: Film & Paper: Filters (Photographic);
Film & Paper: Phototypesetting;

KINETIC CORPORATION
200 Distillery Commons Ste 200, Louisville,
KY, 40206-1987, USA; tel (502) 719-
9500; fax (502) 719-9569; e-mail info@
theTechnologyAgency.com; web site www.
theTechnologyAgency.com
Pres.—G. Raymond Schuhmann
Chief Brand Strategist—Cindi Ramm
Industry: Consulting Services: Production;
Photo Archiving; Preprint Service &
Production; Software: Asset Management;
Software: Design/Graphics; Software:
Pagination/Layout; Software: Workflow
Management/Tracking;

KIRK-RUDY, INC.
125 Lorraine Pkwy, Woodstock, GA, 30188-
2487, USA; tel (770) 427-4203; fax (770)
427-4036; web site www.kirkrudy.com
Pres.—Rick Marshal
Industry: Addressing Machines; Inserting
Equipment (Includes Stuffing Machines);
Mailroom Systems & Equipment;

KODAK GCG
401 Merritt 7 Ste 22, Norwalk, CT, 06851-
1068, USA; tel (203) 845-7115; fax (203)
845-7173; web site www.kodak.com
Sr. Cor. Vice Pres.—Andrew Copley
Industry: Chemicals: Photographic; Chemicals:
Plate Processing; Color Management
Software; Color Proofing; Film & Paper:
Contact; Film & Paper: Duplicating; Film
& Paper: Filters (Photographic); Offset
Plate-Making Service & Equipment; Plates:
Offset (Computer to Plate); Plates: Offset
(Conventional);

KOENIG & BAUER AKTIENGESELLSCHAFT

(KBA)
Postfach 6060, Wuerzburg, N/A, D 97010,
Germany; tel +49 931 909 4336; fax +49 931
909 6015; e-mail kba-wuerzburg@kba-print.
de; web site www.kba-print.de
Pres.—Helge Hansen
Dir., Mktg.—Klaus Schmidt
Industry: Flexogrpahic Press Conversion;
Flying Pasters; Press Control Systems;
Presses: Flexographic; Presses: Offset;
Presses: Rotogravure; Reels & Tensions;
Roll Handling Equipment; Roll Preparation
Equipment; Web Press - Special Equipment;

KOLBUS AMERICA, INC.
812 Huron Rd S Ste 750, Cleveland, OH,
44115-1126, USA; tel (216) 931-4940; fax
(216) 931-5101; e-mail robert.shafer@
kolbus.com; web site www.kolbus.com
Office Mgr.—Ruth Wilson
Pres./Dir., Sales/Distr. Americas—Robert
Shafer
Industry: Counting, Stacking, Bundling
Machines; Cutters & Trimmers; Material
Handling Equipment: Palletizing Machines;

KOMORI AMERICA CORP.
5520 Meadowbrook Industrial Ct, Rolling
Meadows, IL, 60008-3898, USA; tel 847-909-
7706; e-mail komori.american@attglobal.
net; contact@komori-america.com; web site
www.komori-america.us
Pres./COO, Komori America Cor.—Kosh
Miyao
Pdct. Mgr.—Doug Schardt
Industry: Presses: Offset; Proofing Systems;

KONICA MINOLTA BUSINESS SOLUTIONS
PO Box 81250, Mobile, AL, 36689-1250,
USA; tel (201) 825-4000; fax (251) 633-4460;
e-mail stephanie.ryan@bpus.konicaminolta.
us; web site www.konicaminolta.us
Chrmn./CEO—Shoei Yamana
Pres./COO—Stephen Fletcher
Inside Sale Dir.—Rick Gable
Corporate Contact—Stephanie Ryan
Rgl. Mgr.—Craig Underwood
Industry: Laser Printers

KONICA MINOLTA BUSINESS SOLUTIONS USA INC.
100 Williams Dr, Ramsey, NJ, 07446, USA;
tel 236-4399; e-mail pr@kmbs.konicaminolta.
us; web site 100 Williams DriveKristina
Marchitto
Industry: IT Services and Solutions and
Technology

KUBRA
5050 Tomken Rd., Mississauga, ON, L4W
5B1, Canada; tel (905) 624-2220; fax (905)
624-2886; web site www.kubra.com
Pres./CEO—Rick Watkin
Vice Pres., Opns.—Robert Iantorno
Vice Pres., Sales/Mktg.—Rick Huff
Sr. Vice Pres., Bus. Devel.—Mark Visic

KYE SYSTEMS CORP
12675 Colony Ct, Chino, CA, 91710-2975,
USA; tel 909) 628-8836; e-mail webmaster@
geniusnet.com.tw; web site www.geniusnet.
com
Pres.—Geoffrey Lin
Ken Chao
Industry: PC products, mobile phone and Tablet
PC, including mice, keyboards, graphics
tablets, touch pen, power banks, webcams,
speakers, headphones, microphones,
sleeves, backpacks, and professional gaming
gear, digital cameras, camcorders, vehicle
recorders, and projectors.

L

LANKFORD ENGINEERING, INC.
PO Box 80335, Lafayette, LA, 70598-0335,
USA; tel (337) 267-3131; fax (337) 261-2332;
e-mail infol@lankfordengr.com; web site

www.lankfordengr.com
Mgr.—Greg Laurent
Industry: Architects/Engineers (Includes Design/ Construction Firms); Consulting Services: Production; Flying Pasters; Maintenance, Plant & Equipment; Pasters; Reels & Tensions; Tension & Web Controls;

LASER PRODUCTS TECHNOLOGIES
3936 Circle Dr, Holmen, WI, 54636-9187, USA; tel 800-999-9749; e-mail info@lptnow.com; web site www.lptnow.com
Pres.—Michael Marty
Vice Pres.—Bob King
Industry: Laser Printers

LATIN AMERICAN DIV./FLINT INK
9100 S Dadeland Blvd Ste 1800, Miami, FL, 33156-7817, USA; tel (305) 670-0066; fax (305) 670-0060; web site www.flintink.com
Pres.—Jerko E. Rendic
Bus. Mgr.—Claudia Anderson
Regl. Sales Mgr., Brazil—Paul Chmielewicz
Regl. Sales Mgr., South America—Fernando Tavara
Regl. Sales Mgr., Central America/ Caribbean—Nestor Porto
Technical Serv. Mgr.—Al Miller
Industry: Blankets; Chemicals: Plate Processing; Chemicals: Pressroom; Chemicals: Roller Cleaning; Ink Pumping Systems; Ink Recovery Systems; Inks; Plates: Offset (Conventional); Presses: Offset;

LAUTERBACH GROUP
W.222 N.5710 Millerway, Sussex, WI, 53089, USA; tel (800) 558-2126; fax 262-820-1806; e-mail mascinfo@masclabels.com; web site www.masclabels.com
Pres.—Shane Lauterbach
Vice Pres. Mktg.—Rebecca Kerschinske
Bus. Mgr.—Elaine Schnier
Industry: Label Printing Machines

LAZER-FARE MEDIA SERVICES
PO Box 48114 RPO Lakewood, Winnipeg, MB, R2J 4A3, Canada; tel (204) 452-5023; fax (204) 272-3499; e-mail sales@lazerfare.com; web site www.lazerfare.com
Pres.—Kelly Armstrong
Industry: Archiving Systems; Consulting Services: Advertising; Consulting Services: Computer; Consulting Services: Editorial; Content and Digital Asset Management systems

LEARNING TREE INTERNATIONAL
400 Continental Blvd Ste 150, El Segundo, CA, 90245-5059, USA; tel (310) 417-9700; fax (310) 410-2952; e-mail uscourses@learningtree.com; web site www.learningtree.com
Chrmn.—David Collins
Pres./CEO—Nicholas Schacht
Industry: Training: Keyboard Operation

LEXISNEXIS
555 W 5th St Ste 4500, Los Angeles, CA, 90013-3003, USA; tel (213) 627-1130; e-mail lexisnexiscommunities@lexisnexis.com; web site www.lexisnexis.com
CEO, Lexis-Nexis Grp.—Andrew Prozes
Pres./CEO, Cor. & Fed. Mkts.—Kurt Sanford
Pres./CEO, U.S. Legal Mkts.—Michael Walsh
CEO, Risk Mgmt.—James M. Peck
Richard Sobelsohn

LINCOLN INDUSTRIAL
1 Lincoln Way, Saint Louis, MO, 63120-1578, USA; tel (314) 679-4200; fax (800) 424-5359; web site www.lincolnindustrial.com
Pres.—Bart Aitken
Vice Pres., Finance—Phillip Garton
Dir., Product Mgmt.—Pete Laucis
Vice Pres., Sales/Mktg.—Jim Hawk
Mgr., Mktg. Serv.—Roy Lotspeich
Industry: Lubricants; Pumps (Air, Ink, Vacuum);

LINDE LIFT TRUCK CORP.
2450 W 5th North St, Summerville, SC, 29483-9621, USA; tel (843) 875-8000; fax (843) 875-8362; web site www.lmh-na.com; www.lindelifttruck.com
Pres.—Brian Butler
Mktg. Dir.—Mark Rossler
Industry: Material Handling Equipment: Automatic Guided Vehicles; Material Handling Equipment: Truck Loaders; Material Handling Equipment: Vehicle Loading;

LISSOM CORP. INC.
PO Box 441, Bronxville, NY, 10708, USA; tel (914) 761-6360; e-mail hank@weboffsetpress.com; web site www.weboffsetpress.comHank Damhuis
Industry: Presses: Web Offset

LITCO INTERNATIONAL, INC.
PO Box 150, Vienna, OH, 44473, USA; tel 330-539-5433; fax (330) 539-5388; e-mail info@litco.com; web site www.litco.com/molded-wood-pallets
President—Gary L. Trebilcock
CEO—Lionel F. Trebilcock
Executive Vice President—Gary A. Sharon
Industry: Material Handling Equipment: Pallets & Palletizers

LITHCO INC.
9449 Jefferson Blvd, Culver City, CA, 90232-2913, USA; tel (310) 559-7770; e-mail lithco@lithcoinc.com; web site www.lithcoinc.com
Pres.—Gerald Gaebel
Office Mgr.—Sheila Martin
President—Jeff Simon
Industry: Gauges, Measuring; Layout Tables, Light Tables & Workstations; Optical Products; Prepress Color Proofing Systems; Rules;

LITHO RESEARCH, INC.
1621 W Carroll Ave, Chicago, IL, 60612-2501, USA; tel (312) 738-0292; fax (312) 738-2386
Pres.—Michael T. Miske
Industry: Environmental Control Systems; Offset Blankets, Blanket Wash; Offset Chemicals & Supplies; Plate Cleaners; Roll Cleaning Equipment; Static Eliminators;

LOCAL SEARCH ASSOCIATION
1720 W Detweiller Dr, Peoria, IL, 61615-1695, USA; tel (309) 690-5324; e-mail jill@thelsa.org; web site www.lsa.org
VP Prod. Dev.—Brian Dickerson
Business Development Manager—Alanda Hunt
Business Development Manager—Susan Wise
Sr. Vice Pres.—Jill Addy-Wright
Business Development Manager—Tammy Ramp
Business Development Manager—Jennifer Clough
Office Manager—Mary Armstrong
marketing coordinator—Kirstin Krupps
Industry: Art & Layout Equipment and Services; Consulting Services: Advertising; Editorial; Software: Design/Graphics; Software: Editorial: mobile

LOGETRONICS CORP.
6521 Arlington Blvd Ste 210, Falls Church, VA, 22042-3009, USA; tel (703) 536-9841; fax (703) 912-7745; e-mail loge@starpower.net
Pres.—Raymond Luca
Industry: Film & Paper: Film Processing Machines; Film & Paper: Film Roll Dispensers; Plate Coating Machines; Plate Exposure Units; Plate Processors; Plate Scanning Systems; Processors: Diffusion Transfer; Processors: Film & Paper; Remanufactures Equipment;

LORENTZEN & WETTRE
1055 Windward Ridge Pkwy Ste 160,

Alpharetta, GA, 30005-1729, USA; tel (770) 442-8015; fax (770) 442-6792; e-mail usa@lorentzen-wettre.com; web site www.lorentzen-wettre.com
Pres.—Phillip Westmoreland
Industry: Consulting Services: Production; Maintenance, Plant & Equipment; Paper Testing Instruments;

LYNNE MEENA CO.
130 St. Matthews Avenue, Suite 303, Louisville, KY, 40207, USA; tel (800) 818-1181
Industry: Advertising headlines. Rewrite your advertising headlines for more effective results.

LYON ENTERPRISES
4305 Cloud Dance, Santa Fe, NM, 87507, USA; tel (800) 243-1144; fax (505) 471-1665; e-mail ray@lyonenterprises.com; web site www.lyonenterprises.com
Pres.—Ray Lyon
Industry: Circulation Equipment & Supplies; Tubes, Racks (Includes Racks: Motor Route Tubes); Carrier Bags; Point of Purchase; Imprinted Merchandise

M

M.W. BURKE & ASSOCIATES, INC.
185 Front St Ste 207, Danville, CA, 94526-3340, USA; tel (925) 838-9070; fax (925) 838-4695; e-mail mwburke@aol.com
Pres./Chrmn.—M.W. (Maury) Burke
Industry: Consulting Services: Advertising; Consulting Services: Circulation; Consulting Services: Production; Prepress Color Proofing Systems;

MAC DERMID AUTOTYPE INC.
1675 Winnetka Cir, Rolling Meadows, IL, 60008-1372, USA; tel 800-323-0632; fax (847) 818-8280; e-mail autotypeusinfo@macdermid.com; web site www.macdermidautotype.com
Pres.—Peter Levinsohn
Industry: Chemicals: Photographic; Masking Materials; Plates: Offset (Computer to Plate)

MACDERMID PRINTING SOLUTIONS
245 Freight St, Atlanta, GA, 30336, USA; tel 800-729-6991; fax 404-505-3290; e-mail mpsproductinfo@macdermid.com; web site www.macdermid.com/printing
CEO—Dan Leever
Mgr., Nat'l Sales—Timothy Sener
Industry: Blanket Mounting and Bars; Blankets; Platemakers: Direct; Platemakers: Flexographic (Computer to Plate); Platemakers: Flexographic (Traditional); Platemakers: Letterpress; Plates: Flexographic (Conventional); Plates: Letterpress; Plates: Offset (Computer to Plate);

MACDERMID PRINTING SOLUTIONS
260 S Pacific St, San Marcos, CA, 92078-2430, USA; tel 760-510-6277; fax 760-510-6200; e-mail mpsproductinfo@macdermid.com; web site www.macdermid.com/printing
Publication Mktg. Mgr.—Tom Moore
Industry: Cleaners & Solvents; Color Management Software; Platemakers: Flexographic (Traditional); Platemakers: Letterpress; Plates: Flexographic (Conventional);

MACDONALD ADVERTISING SERVICES
302 Ferry St, Lafayette, IN, 47901-1185, USA; tel (765) 742-9012; e-mail info@macdonaldclassified.com; web site www.gomacdonald.com
Pres.—Patrick McDonald
Mng. Ed.—Andrew McGlothlen
Industry: Art & Layout Equipment and Services; Consulting Services: Advertising; Software: Design/Graphics; Trade Publications;

MAH MACHINE CO., INC.
3301 S Central Ave, Cicero, IL, 60804-3986, USA; tel (708) 656-1826; fax (708) 656-4152; e-mail info@mahmachine.com; web site www.mahmachine.com
Pres.—Martin Hozjan
Industry: Cylinder Repair; Equipment Dealers (New); Equipment Dealers (Used); Feeding, Folding, Delivery Equipment; Presses: Offset; Roller Grinding Services; Rollers; Rollers: Dampening;

MALOW CORP.
1835 S Nordic Rd, Mt Prospect, IL, 60056-5715, USA; tel (847) 956-0200; fax (847) 956-0935; web site www.malow.com
Sales Mgr.—Terry Luzader
Industry: Automatic Plastic Bagging Equipment; Bundling and Tying Machines; Strapping Machines;

MANAGING EDITOR, INC.
610 York Rd., Ste. 400, Jenkintown, PA, 19046, USA; tel (215) 886-5662; fax (215) 886-5681; e-mail info@maned.com; web site www.maned.com
Managing Director—Mark Leister
Head of Global Sales and Marketing—Mark Wasserman
Industry: Pagination Systems; Preprint Service & Production; Software: Advertising (Includes Display; Classified); Software: Editorial; Software: Pagination/Layout; Software: Workflow Management/Tracking; Digital Publishing;

MANASSY SALES INC.
6861 Yellowstone Blvd Ste 106, Forest Hills, NY, 11375-9404, USA; tel (718) 544-4739; fax (347) 642 8060; e-mail manassyparts@yahoo.com
Pres.—Joel Marcus
Industry: Press Accessories, Parts & Supplies; Rollers;

MANISTIQUE PAPERS, INC.
453 S Mackinac Ave, Manistique, MI, 49854-1399, USA; tel (906) 341-2175; fax (906) 341-5635; e-mail info@manistiquepapers.com; web site www.manistiquepapers.com
Gen. Mgr.—Jon Johnson
Comptroller—Linda Benedetto
Prodn. Mgr.—Tony Martin
Industry: Newsprint; Paper: Groundwood Specialties;

MANROLAND WEB SYSTEMS INC.
2150 Western Ct Ste 420, Lisle, IL, 60532-1973, USA; tel (630) 920-5850; fax (630) 920-5851; web site www.manroland-web.com
Marketing Manager—Denise Lease
CEO—Greg Blue
VP of Sales—Ron Sams
Industry: Material Handling Equipment: Automatic Guided Vehicles; Newsprint Handling Equipment; Press Accessories, Parts & Supplies; Press Control Systems; Presses: Flexographic; Presses: Offset; Reels (Includes Paper Reels); Roll Cleaning Equipment; Ink Jet & Digital Press Equipment; Folding & Finishing Equipment

MANUGRAPH DGM, INC.
PO Box 573, Elizabethville, PA, 17023-0573, USA; tel (717) 362-3243; web site www.dauphingraphic.com
CEO—Chris Lunt
Pres.—Brian LaBine
Vice Pres., Sales/Mktg.—David Moreland
Mgr., Inside Sales/Mktg.—David Lucas
Industry: Press Repairs; Presses: Offset; Remanufactures Equipment; Software: Workflow Management/Tracking; Training: Press Operation & Maintenance;

MARATEK ENVIRONMENTAL TECHNOLOGIES, INC.
60 Healey Rd., Unit 8-10, Bolton, ON, L7E 5A5, Canada; tel (905) 857-2738; e-mail cdarcel@maratek.com; web site www.

maratek.com/stor.pdf
Pres.—Colin Darcel
Mktg. Mgr.—Michelle Chouinard
Industry: Environmental Control Systems; Equipment Dealers (New); Fluid Handling: Pressroom; Ink Recovery Systems; Silver Recovery; Wastewater Treatment; Solvent Recovery Systems;

MARKEM-IMAJE
100 Chastain Center Blvd NW Ste 165, Kennesaw, GA, 30144-5561, USA; tel (770) 421-7700; fax (770) 421-7702; web site www.markem-imaje.com
President—Omar Kerbage
Gen. Mgr.—Jacques Desroches
Mgr., Mktg.—Alisha Howard
Industry: Addressing Machines; Inks; Label Printing Machines; Mailroom Systems & Equipment;

MARKETING PLUS, INC.
135 Green St, Woodbridge, NJ, 07095-2961, USA; tel (732) 694-1020; e-mail mpi@marketingplusinc.com; web site www.marketingplusinc.com
Pres./CEO—Monty Cerasani
Gen. Mgr.—Susan Taylor
Office Mgr.—John Saparito
HR Mgr.—Karen Marov
Vice Pres., Bus. Devel.—John Lederer
IT Mgr.—Phil Lyman
Industry: Consulting Services: Marketing; Market Research;

MARKETING STRATEGIES INCORPORATED
26 Genevieve Rd, East Weymouth, MA, 02189-1057, USA; tel (781) 340-6640; fax (781) 340-7640; e-mail info@marketingstrategies.org; web site www.marketingstrategies.org
Industry: Consulting Services: Advertising; Consulting Services: Marketing;

MARKZWARE SOFTWARE, INC.
1805 E Dyer Rd Ste 101, Santa Ana, CA, 92705-5742, USA; tel (949) 756-5100; e-mail info@markzware.com; web site www.markzware.com
Pres./CEO—Patrick Marchese
Public Relations—Mary Gay Marchese Patty Talley
Industry: Software: Editorial; Software: Electronic Data Interchange;

MARTIN AUTOMATIC, INC.
1661 Northrock Ct, Rockford, IL, 61103-1296, USA; tel (815) 654-4800; fax (815) 654-4810; e-mail info@martinauto.com; web site www.martinauto.com
Vice Pres., Sales—David A. Wright
Contract Admin.—Bob Sanderson
Contract Admin.—Tim Delhotal
Mktg. Mgr.—Tim Ward
Industry: Conversion Equipment; Flying Pasters; Newsprint Handeling Equipment; Pasters; Press Accessories, Parts & Supplies; Rewinders; Web Guides;

MARTIN YALE, INC.
251 Wedcor Ave, Wabash, IN, 46992-4201, USA; tel (260) 563-0641; fax (260) 563-4575; e-mail info@martinyale.com; web site www.martinyale.com
Pres.—Greg German
Industry: Cutters & Trimmers; Folding Machines; Label Printing Machines; Paper Handeling Equipment; Paper Shredders;

MASTER FLO TECHNOLOGY
1233 Tessier St., Hawkesbury, ON, K6A 3R1, Canada; tel (613) 636-0539; fax (613) 636-0762; e-mail info@mflo.com; web site www.mflo.com
President—Edward Desaulniers
Vice Pres., Opns—Tim Duffy
Industry: Circulation Equipment & Supplies; Dampening Systems; Delivery Equipment; Feeding, Folding, Delivery Equipment;

Ink Fountains & Accessories; Inserting Equipment (Includes Stuffing Machines); Material Handling Equipment: Pallets & Palletizers; Offset Fountain Controls; Press Accessories, Parts & Supplies; Recirculators;

MASTHEAD INTERNATIONAL, INC.
700 Quantum Rd NE, Rio Rancho, NM, 87124-4500, USA; tel 505-890-7103; fax 505-890-7104; e-mail info@masthead.net; web site www.masthead.net
Proj. Mgr./Estimator—Joel Birket

MASTHEAD INTERNATIONAL, INC.
3602 S 16th St, Phoenix, AZ, 85040-1311, USA; tel 602-276-5373; fax 602-276-8116; e-mail steve.stone@masthead.net; web site www.masthead.net
Branch Mgr.—Steve Stone
Bus. Devel. Mgr.—Kent Kraft
Industry: Controllers: Press; Drives & Controls; Erectors & Riggers; Pasters; Press Parts; Press Rebuilding; Press Repairs; Presses: Flexographic; Presses: Letterpress; Presses: Offset; Tension & Web Controls; Training: Press Operation & Maintenance; Web Width Changer;

MATTHEWS INTERNATIONAL CORP.
6515 Penn Ave, Pittsburgh, PA, 15206-4482, USA; tel (412) 665-2550; fax (412) 365-2055; e-mail info@matw.com; web site www.matthewsmarking.com; www.matw.com
Pres./CEO—Joseph C. Bartolacci
Industry: Laser Printers

MAXCESS
PO Box 26508, Oklahoma City, OK, 73126-0508, USA; tel (405) 755-1600; fax (405) 755-8425; e-mail sales@maxcessintl.com; web site www.maxcessintl.com
Brand Manager—Kasey Morales
Dir., Mktg./Sales—Stephanie Millman
Industry: Chemicals: Chuck (Paper Roll); Cutters & Trimmers; Cutting Tools; Drives & Controls; Reels & Tensions; Tension & Web Controls; Visual Display Terminals; Web Break Detector; Web Guides; Web Press - Special Equipment;

MAXX MATERIAL HANDLING LLC
315 E St, Hampton, VA, 23661-1209, USA; tel (757) 825-8100; fax (757) 825-8800; e-mail mhogan@maxxmh.com; web site www.maxxmh.com
Pres.—Randy Gilliland
Vice Pres.—Mark Hogan
Industry: Material Handling Equipment: Truck Loaders; Material Handling Equipment: Vehicle Loading;

MBM CORP.
PO Box 40249, North Charleston, SC, 29423-0249, USA; tel (843) 552-2700; fax (843) 552-2974; e-mail sales@mbmcorp.com; web site www.mbmcorp.com
Pres.—Ned Ginsburg
Industry: Cutters & Trimmers; Cutting Tools; Feeding, Folding, Delivery Equipment; Folding Machines; In-Line Trimming Systems;

MCCAIN BINDERY SYSTEMS
14545 W Edison Dr, New Lenox, IL, 60451-3672, USA; tel 815-462-9363; fax 815-462-1471; e-mail mccainbind@earthlink.net; web site www.mccainbindery.com
Pres.—Nancy Jones
Sales Manager—Bill Whitehead
National Service/ Product Manager—Chester Zurek
Vice Pres./Gen. Mgr.—Dennis Keem
Industry: Saddle Stitching, Side Sewers, Sheeters, Inserting Equipment (Includes Stuffing Machines); Bindery and Mailroom Systems & Equipment;

MCCAIN PRINTING CO.
525 Wilson St, Danville, VA, 24541-1490, USA; tel (434) 792-1331; fax (434) 793-5473; e-mail efsounders@mccainprint.com; web

site www.mccainprint.com
Owner—Eugene Sounders

MCCRRORY PUBLISHING
PO Box 5218, Fort Wayne, IN, 46895-5218, USA; tel 260-485-1812; fax 260-444-4951; e-mail info@mccpub.com; web site www.mccpub.com
Industry: Computers: Hardware & Software Integrators; Consulting Services: Computer; Consulting Services: Editorial; Software: Advertising (Includes Display; Classified); Software: Editorial; Software: Electronic Data Interchange; Software: Pagination/Layout; System Integration Services;

MCGRANN PAPER CORP.
2101 Westinghouse Blvd # A, Charlotte, NC, 28273-6310, USA; tel (704) 583-2101; fax (704) 369-2229; web site www.mcgrann.com
Owner/Pres.—Karl McGrann
Sales Rep.—Bob Marko
Sr. VP, Sales—Kirk Castle
Industry: Newsprint; Paper: Coated Groundwood Offset; Paper: Groundwood Specialties; Paper: Specialty Printing Paper;

MCGRANN PAPER CORPORATION
2101 Westinghouse Blvd, Charlotte, NC, 28273-6310, USA; tel 909-595-2727; fax 704-369-2227; web site www.mcgrann.com
Partner—Anthony V. Nanna
Industry: Paper - Marchant - Converter-Distributor

MCGRANN PAPER EAST
22476 Fisher Rd, Watertown, NY, 13601-1062, USA; tel (315) 788-4090; fax (315) 788-3388

MCI
22001 Loudoun County Pkwy, Ashburn, VA, 20147-6122, USA; tel (703) 206-5600; fax (703) 206-5601; e-mail info@mci.com; web site www.mci.com
Chrmn./CEO—Ivan Siedenberg
Pres., Opns./Tech.—Fred Briggs
Exec. Vice Pres./CFO—Robert Blakely
Exec. Vice Pres., HR—Daniel Casaccia
Exec. Vice Pres., Strategy/Cor. Devel.—Jonathan Crane
Sr. Vice Pres., Commun.—Grace Chentent
Sr. Vice Pres., Mktg./CMO—Nancy B. Gofus Shane King
Industry: Data Communication

MEDIA AMERICA BROKERS
1130 Piedmont Ave NE Ste. 912, Atlanta, GA, 30309-3783, USA; tel (404) 875-8787; e-mail lonwwilliams@aol.com
Owner—Lon W Williams
Industry: Brokers & Appraisers

MEDIA CYBERNETICS LP
401 N Washington St Ste 350, Rockville, MD, 20850-0707, USA; tel (301) 495-3305; fax 240-328-6193; e-mail info@mediacy.com; web site www.mediacy.com
Pres.—Doug Paxson
Industry: Optical Character Recognition (OCR)

MEDIA DATA TECHNOLOGY, INC. (MDTI)
20 Roundelay Rd, South Hadley, MA, 01075-1614, USA; tel (413) 534-3307; e-mail jpeters@mediadatatech.com
Pres.—John Peters
Industry: Software: Advertising (Includes Display; Classified)

MEDIA MARKETING, INC.
10955 Westmoor Dr Fl 4, Westminster, CO, 80021-2704, USA; tel (303) 440-7855; fax 303-440-8035; e-mail info@immediate.com; sales@immediate.com; web site www.immediate.com
Pres./CEO—James Theall
VP, Solutions—Charles Mauldin
VP, Sales—Patti Theall

Industry: Consulting Services: Advertising; Consulting Services: Marketing; Software: Advertising (Includes Display; Classified); Training: Sales & Marketing;

MEDIA MONITORS, INC.
445 Hamilton Ave Ste 700, White Plains, NY, 10601-1828, USA; tel (914) 428-5971; fax (914) 259-4541; e-mail jselig@mediamonitors.com; web site www.mediamonitors.com
Pres.—Philippe Generali
Sales Executive—John L. Selig
National Account Manager—Cheryl Lohr
VP, Sales—Frank Cammarata
Industry: Consulting Services: Advertising

MEDIA PROFESSIONAL INSURANCE
1201 Walnut St Ste 1800, Kansas City, MO, 64106-2247, USA; tel (816) 471-6118; fax (816) 471-6119; e-mail marketing@mediaprof.com; web site www.mediaprof.com
Sr. Vice Pres., Underwriting—Mary Schust
Industry: Insurance

MEDIA SALES PLUS, INC.
6400 Main Street, Suite 201, Williamsville, NY, 14221-5858, USA; tel (716) 250-6884; fax (716) 634-0574; web site www.mediasalesplus.com
Chief Executive Officer—Dominick Bordonaro
Client Partnerships—Debra Chase
Industry: A preeminent provider of multi-media advertising sales and support services.

MEDIASPAN
2725 S Industrial Hwy Ste 100, Ann Arbor, MI, 48104-6233, USA; tel 800.913.1299; e-mail info@mediaspangroup.com; web site www.mediaspangroup.com
Vice Pres., Sales & Mktg.—Ken Freedman
President—Dan Roberts
Vice Pres., Customer Servs.—Carla Green
Dir. of Sales, Western USA—Gary Schwartskopf
Technical Sales and Marketing Dir.—Geoff Kehrer
Industry: Software: Advertising (Includes Display; Classified); Software: Circulation; Software: Design/Graphics; Software: Editorial; Software: Pagination/Layout; Software: Press/Post Press;

MEDIASPAN GROUP INC.
2725 S Industrial Hwy Ste 100, Ann Arbor, MI, 48104-6233, USA; tel (734) 887-4400; fax (734) 887-4401; e-mail marketing@mediaspangroup.com; web site www.mediaspangroup.com
Coord., Domestic Sales—Kim Anderson
Industry: Consulting Services: Circulation; Consulting Services: Editorial; Consulting Services: Production; Library Retrieval Systems; Pagination Systems; Publishing Systems; Software: Circulation; Software: Editorial; Software: Pagination/Layout; Training: Design & Layout

MEENA COPY & LAYOUT
130 Saint Matthews Ave, Louisville, KY, 40207-3105, USA; tel (800) 818-1181; fax (800) 818-8329; e-mail lynnemeena@aol.com
Pres.—Lynne Meena
Industry: Consulting Services: Advertising: How to make a good ad better. Advertising; Design & Layout;

MEGADATA CORP.
1 Landmark Sq Ste 1900, Stamford, CT, 06901-2671, USA; tel 203-622-4086; web site www.passur.com
Media—Ron Dunsky
Pres.—Beck Gilbert
Industry: Data Communication; Input & Editing Systems;

MEGASYS INTERNATIONAL, INC.
45 Industrial Park Rd W Ste H, Tolland, CT,

06084-2839, USA; tel (860) 871-8713; fax (860) 871-8710; e-mail megasysint@aol.com; web site megasysinternational.com
Pres.—Fred McNutt
Industry: Bundling and Tying Machines; Composing Room Equipment & Supplies; Equipment Dealers (New); Equipment Dealers (Used); Folding Machines; Label Printing Machines; Paper Shredders; Photostat: Machines;

MEGTEC SYSTEMS
PO Box 5030, De Pere, WI, 54115-5030, USA; tel (920) 337-1410; fax (920) 558-5535; e-mail info@megtec.com; web site www.megtec.com
Mktg. Mgr.—Mary Van Vonderen
Industry: Dryers: Film and Papers; Drying Systems; Environmental Control Systems; Flying Pasters; Roll Handling Equipment;

MERCER HUMAN RESOURCE CONSULTING
70 Linden Oaks Ste 310, Rochester, NY, 14625-2804, USA; tel (585) 389-8701; fax (585) 289-8801; web site www.mercerhr.com
Mktg. Rep.—Jim Hardesty

MERLINONE, INC.
17 Whitney Rd., Quincy, MA, 02169, USA; tel (617) 328-6645; fax (617) 328-9845; e-mail info@merlinone.com; web site www.merlinone.com
Pres./CEO—David M. Tenenbaum
Merlin Sr. Acct. Rep.—Rande Simpson
VP of IT & Managed Services—Jeff Seidensticker
Dir., Cust. Support—Michael Kullen
Industry: Picture Desks, Archiving and Digital Asset Management systems for all your data types including audio, video, PDF's

MERRIMAC SOFTWARE ASSOCIATES
PO Box 28, South Tamworth, NH, 03883-0028, USA; tel 603-323-5077; fax (603) 218-2140; e-mail sales@merrsoft.com; web site www.merrsoft.com
Owner—Tom Vachon
Support Manager—Sabrina Fobes
Programmer—Jim Loughner
Industry: Publishing Software: Advertising (includes Display and Classified); Pagination/Layout; Circulation and Distribution; Commercial Sales; Management (includes Administration and Accounting);

MESA CORP.
4546 S 86th St Ste B, Lincoln, NE, 68526-9252, USA; tel (402) 489-9303; fax (402) 489-7524; e-mail info@mesacorp.com; sales@mesacorp.com; web site www.mesacorp.com
Vice Pres.-Sales/Mktg.—Thomas Manning
Industry: Storage Retrieval Systems

METAFIX, INC.
1925 46th Ave., Montreal, QC, H8T 2P1, Canada; tel (514) 633-8663; fax (514) 633-1678; e-mail sales@metafix.com; web site www.metafix.com
Industry: Environmental Control Systems; Silver Recovery;

METALS RECOVERY SERVICE
1660 Georgesville Rd., Columbus, OH, 43228, USA; tel (614) 870-9444; fax (614) 878-6000; e-mail sdahms@msitarget.com; web site www.msitarget.com
Vice Pres.—Steven P. Dahms
Industry: Silver Recovery

METRO EDITORIAL SERVICES
519 8th Ave Fl 18, New York, NY, 10018-4577, USA; tel (212) 947-5100; fax (212) 714-9139; e-mail mes@metro-email.com; web site www.mcg.metrocreativeconnection.com
Publisher—Robert Zimmerman
Exec. Vice Pres./Mktg. Dir.—Debra Weiss
Mktg. Mgr.—Lauren Lekoski

VP, Sales—Jo Ann Shapiro
Regional Sales Mgr.—Lou Ann Sornson
Regional Sales Mgr.—Tina Dentner
Regional Sales Mgr.—Cathy Agee
Regional Sales Mgr.—Gwen Tomaselli
Regional Sales Mgr.—Jennifer Steiner
Joann Johnson
Industry: Art & Layout Equipment and Services; Consulting Services: Advertising; Consulting Services: Editorial; Software: Design/Graphics; Software: Editorial;

METROLAND PRINTING/PUBLISHING & DISTRIBUTING LTD.
3125 Wolfedale Rd., Mississauga, ON, L5C 1W1, Canada; tel 905-281-5656; fax 905-279-5103; web site www.metroland.com
Vice Pres., HR—Brenda Biller
Industry: Presses: Offset; Publishing Systems;

METSO PAPER
PO Box 2771, York, PA, 17405-2771, USA; tel (717) 845-4807; fax (717) 845-8828; e-mail imcsales@imcamerica.com
Pres.—Ward Walsh
Vice Pres., Sales./Mktg.—Ric Mayle
Industry: Newsprint Handeling Equipment; Paper Handeling Equipment; Roll Handeling Equipment;

MICRO SYSTEMS SPECIALISTS, INC. (MSSI)
PO Box 347, Millbrook, NY, 12545-0347, USA; tel (845) 677-6150; fax (845) 677-6620; e-mail mssisoftware@cs.com; web site www.mssi-software.com
Pres.—Dawn Blackburn
Industry: Software: Advertising Billing; Software: Business (Includes Administration/Accounting); Software: Circulation

MICROFILM PRODUCTS CO.
266 Germonds Rd, West Nyack, NY, 10994-1320, USA; tel (845) 371-3700; fax (845) 371-3780; e-mail info@microfilmproducts.com; web site www.microfilmproducts.com
Pres.—Gary Moelis
Industry: Addressing Machines; Bundling and Tying Machines; Equipment Dealers (New); Equipment Dealers (Used); Folding Machines;

MICROTEK
9960 Bell Ranch Dr Ste 103, Santa Fe Springs, CA, 90670-6178, USA; tel (310) 687-5800; fax 562-903-7832; e-mail sales@microtek.com; web site www.microtekusa.com
Dir., Mktg.—Mary Ann Whitlock
Industry: Color Seperation Scanners; Scanners: Color B & W, Plates, Web;

MID-AMERICA GRAPHICS, INC.
PO Box 466, Harrisonville, MO, 64701-0466, USA; tel (816) 887-2414; fax (816) 887-2762; e-mail sales@midamericagraphics.com; web site www.midamericagraphics.com
Pres.—Charles George
Exec. Vice Pres.—William David George
Gen. Mgr.—Dan George
Sec.—Terri Widdle
Industry: Conveyors; In-Line Trimming Systems; Infeed Stackers; Inserting Equipment (Includes Stuffing Machines); Newsprint Handeling Equipment;

MIDLANTIC EQUIPMENT CO., INC.
567 Wyckoff Ave, Wyckoff, NJ, 07481-1336, USA; tel (201) 891-1448; fax (201) 891-2664; e-mail midequip@yahoo.com; web site www.agfa-imagesetters.com
Mktg. Mgr.—Arlene Vanderweert
Industry: Imagesetters

MIDSYSTEMS TECHNOLOGY LTD.
One Kingdom Street , London, N/A, W8 5SF, United Kingdom; tel (0)20 3320 5000; fax (0)20 3320 1771; e-mail sales@midsys.co.uk; web site www.misys.co.uk
Mng. Dir.—John Sussens

Industry: Produciton Control Systems

MIDWEST PUBLISHERS SUPPLY CO.
4640 N. Olcott Ave., Harwood Heights, IL, 60706, USA; tel (708) 867-4646; fax (708) 867-6954; e-mail info@mps-co.com
Pres.—James Rezabek
Industry: Art & Layout Equipment and Services; Blankets; Blue Line Grids; Chemicals: Pressroom; Composing Room Equipment & Supplies; Lift Trucks; Mailroom Systems & Equipment; Offset Chemicals & Supplies; Press Accessories, Parts & Supplies;

MILES 33
40 Richards Ave Ste 29, Norwalk, CA, 06854-2322, USA; tel (203) 838-2333; fax (203) 838-4473; e-mail info@miles33.com; web site www.miles33.com
Pres.—Chris Habasinski
VP Marketing and Western USA Sales—Albert De Bruijn
VP, Business Development—Edward Hubbard
Industry: Computers: Hardware & Software Integrators; Consulting Services: Advertising; Consulting Services: Editorial; Software: Advertising (Includes Display; Classified; Digital and Print); Software: Digital Asset Management; Software: Content Management Systems for newsroom and Web; Software: Pagination/Layout; Software: Ad Tracking; Software: Self Service Advertising; Software: Digital Video Ad Production; Software: Ipad and Android Apps; Software: Business Analytics/Datamining

MILLER-COOPER CO.
1545 Atlantic Ave, Kansas City, MO, 64116-3910, USA; tel 808-289-6246; e-mail info@mcink.com; web site www.mcink.com
Pres.—Debbie Nylund
Industry: Adhesives; Blankets; Chemicals: Pressroom; Inks;

MINNESOTA OPINION RESEARCH, INC. (MORI)
8500 Normandale Lake Blvd Ste 630, Minneapolis, MN, 55437-3809, USA; tel (952) 835-3050; fax (952) 835-3385; e-mail minneapolis@magid.com; web site www.moriresearch.com
Pres.—Ron Mulder
Vice Pres., Research—Brent Stahl
Industry: Consulting Services: Advertising; Consulting Services: Circulation; Consulting Services: Editorial; Consulting Services: Marketing; Market Research; Newspaper Marketing; Research Studies;

MIRACHEM CORP.
PO Box 14059, Phoenix, AZ, 85063-4059, USA; tel 808-847-3527; fax (602) 353-1411; e-mail cservice@mirachem.com; web site www.mirachem.com
COO—Pat Doughty
Sales Mgr.—Bob Boyle
Industry: Chemicals: Pressroom; Chemicals: Roller Cleaning; Cleaners & Solvents;

MIRACLE INDUSTRIES, INC.
118 Colebrook River Rd Ste 1, Winsted, CT, 06098-2241, USA; tel (203) 723-0928; fax (203) 723-0394
Pres.—John Chabot
Vice Pres., Sales/Mktg.—Phyllis Fennlly
Industry: Motors; Press Accessories, Parts & Supplies; Press Control Systems; Press Engineers; Presses: Offset; Roller Grinding Services; Web Break Detector; Web Press - Special Equipment;

MIRACOM COMPUTER CORP.
PO Box 44, Eastchester, NY, 10709, USA; tel (888) 309-0639; e-mail info@miracomcomputer.com; web site www.miracomcomputer.com
CEO—Judah Holstein
Vice President—Bill Harley
Director, Customer Service—Tom Whelan
Field Application Engineer—Ralph Valero

Project Engineer—Michael Dodds
Application Developer—Alex Gray
Inside Sales—Amy Arkawy
Finance Representative—Tina Dalton
Industry: Production Control Systems Planning Systems Inventory Systems Inkjet Labeling Systems

MISSOURI PRESS SERVICE, INC.
802 Locust St, Columbia, MO, 65201-7799, USA; tel (573) 449-4167; fax (573) 874-5894; e-mail mmaassen@socket.net; web site www.mopress.com
Industry: Newspapers. Consulting Services: Advertising; Consulting Services: Editorial;

MITCHELL'S
PO Box 2431, New York, NY, 10116-2431, USA; tel 800-662-2275; fax (212) 594-7254; e-mail papers@mitchellsny.com; web site www.mitchellsny.com
—Mitchell Newman
—Roy NewmanOwners
Industry: Delivery Equipment

MO-MONEY ASSOCIATES, INC.
3838 N Palafox St, Pensacola, FL, 32505-5222, USA; tel (850) 432-6301; fax (850) 434-5645; e-mail momoney@momoney.com; web site www.momoney.com
Pres.—Cliff Mowe
Mktg. Mgr.—Tom McVoy

MOBILE COMPUTING CORPORATION USA
6300 Northwest Dr., Unit# 1, Mississauga, ON, L4V 1J7, Canada; tel 800-392-8651; fax 905-676-9191; e-mail MCCMarketing@mobilecom.com; web site www.mobilecom.com
Sales Rep.—Les Feasey
Industry: Business Computers; Computers: Hardware & Software Integrators; Consulting Services: Circulation; Consulting Services: Computer; Software: Circulation;

MONACO SYSTEMS, INC.
100 Burtt Rd Ste 203, Andover, MA, 01810-5920, USA; tel (978) 749-9944; fax (978) 749-9977; e-mail corporateemail@xrite.com; web site www.monacosys.com
Dir.-Mktg.—Bonnie Fladung
Industry: Color Management Software; Software: Workflow Management/Tracking;

MORCOR SOLUTIONS, INC.
232 Dundas St. W., Ste. 201, Napanee, ON, K7R 2A8, Canada; tel (613) 354-2912; e-mail info@morcor.com; web site www.morcor.com
Pres.—Kenn Morrison
Industry: Software: Asset Management; Software: Workflow Management/Tracking; Training: Design & Layout; Training: Keyboard Operation; Training: Pre Press;

MOTTERSTITCH COMPANY, INC.
P.O. Box 97, Carolina, RI, 02812, USA; tel (401)364-6061; fax (401)364-6063; e-mail tom@motterstitch.com; web site www.motterstitch.com
President—Thomas Northup
Office Admin.—Linda Northup
Consultant—Roland Reuterfors
Consultant Engineer—Bengt Magnusson
Chief Engineer—David Mr. Gilman
Office Assist.—Adam Mr. Northup
Secretary—Cheryl Mrs. Bernat
Sales VP—David Northup
Industry: In-Line Stapling/Stitching Machine for Newspaper and Commercial Press, Stitching Wire Sales

MOUSER INSTITUTE SCHOOL OF ADVERTISING
PO Box 86, Nottoway, VA, 23955-0086, USA; tel (434) 292-1604; fax (434) 292-6672; e-mail cm@mouserinstitute.com; web site www.mouserinstitute.com

Pres.—Charles Mouser
Industry: Trade Publications

MSP COMMUNICATIONS

220 S 6th St Ste 500, Minneapolis, MN, 55402-4507, USA; tel (612) 339-7571; fax (612) 339-5806; e-mail edit@mspmag.com; web site www.mspmag.com
Pres.—Gary Johnson
Ed. in Chief—Brian Anderson
Industry: Trade Publications

N

N & L ENTERPRISES, INC.

306 Wynn Dr NW, Huntsville, AL, 35805-6113, USA; tel (256) 883-8700; fax (256) 880-8800; web site www.nlisc.com
Pres.—Bill Serrell
Industry: Composing Room Equipment & Supplies; Equipment Dealers (New); Equipment Dealers (Used); Facsimilie/Fax Transmission Systems; Proofing Systems;

N/S CORPORATION

235 W Florence Ave, Inglewood, CA, 90301-1293, USA; tel (800) 782-1582; e-mail info@nswash.com; web site www.nswash.com
CEO—Thomas Ennis
Pres.—Thomas G. Ennis
Mktg. Mgr.—Gary Avrech
Industry: Conveyors; Drying Systems; Environmental Control Systems;

NAMA GRAPHICS E, LLC

15751 Annico Dr Ste 2, Homer Glen, IL, 60491-4739, USA; tel (630) 668-6262; fax (262) 966-3852; e-mail rsnama@wi.rr.com; web site www.namagraphicse.com
—John Griffin
—Rick SmithOwners
Industry: Environmental Control Systems; Flying Pasters; Ink Fountains & Accessories; Rollers: Dampening;

NATIONAL GRAPHIC SUPPLY CORP.

226 N Allen St, Albany, NY, 12206-1799, USA; tel (518) 438-8411; fax (518) 438-0940; e-mail info@ngspcb.com; web site www.ngscorp.com
Vice Pres.-Nat'l Accts./Opns.—Roberta Berkowitz
Industry: Blankets; Cameras & Accessories; Chemicals: Photographic; Chemicals: Pressroom; Color Management Software; Film & Paper: Contact; Film & Paper: Duplicating; Film & Paper: Filters (Photographic); Film & Paper: Phototypesetting; Lenses (Camera);

NATIONAL MEDIA ASSOCIATES

PO Box 849, Ada, OK, 74821-0849, USA; tel (580) 421-9600; fax (580) 421-9960; e-mail bolitho@bolitho.com; web site www.nationalmediasales.com
Broker—Thomas C. Bolitho
Industry: Brokers & Appraisers; Consulting Services: Financial;

NATIONAL MEDIA ASSOCIATES

PO Box 2001, Branson, MO, 65615-2001, USA; tel (417) 338-6397; fax (417) 338-6510; e-mail Brokered1@gmail.com; web site www.nationalmediasales.com
Owner—Edward M. Anderson
Industry: Brokers & Appraisers; Consulting Services: Financial;

NATIONAL NEWSPAPER ASSOCIATION PUBLISHERS' AUXILIARY

900 Community Drive, Springfield, IL, 62703, USA; tel (217) 241-1400; e-mail pubaux@nna.org; web site www.nnaweb.org
Comm. Dir.—Stan Schwartz
Chief Operating Officer—Lynne Lance
Industry: Trade Publications

NB FINISHING, INC.

1075 Morse Ave, Schaumburg, IL, 60193-4503, USA; tel (847) 895-0900; fax (847) 895-0999; e-mail info@nbfinishing.com; web site www.nbfinishing.com
Pres.—Bruce Nichols
Mgr., Opns.—Dave Nichols
Industry: Plate Processors; Roller Grinding Services;

NEASI-WEBER INTERNATIONAL

25115 Avenue Stanford Ste 300, Valencia, CA, 91355-4806, USA; tel (818) 895-6900; fax (818) 830-0889; e-mail info@nwintl.com; web site www.nwintl.com
Pres.—Jim S. Weber
CEO—Dennis J. Neasi
Industry: Mailroom Systems & Equipment; Software: Advertising (Includes Display; Classified); Software: Circulation;

NELA

610 Whitetail Blvd, River Falls, WI, 54022-5209, USA; tel (715) 425-1900; fax (751) 425-1901; e-mail info@nela-usa.com; web site www.nela-usa.com
Pres.—David Klein
Mgr., Engineering—Bob Deis
Pdct. Mgr., Web & Sheetfed—Taag Erickson
Sales Dir.—Jurgen Gruber
Mktg. Mgr.—Katharina Gruber
Industry: Color Registration; Controls: Register; Offset Plate-Making Service & Equipment; Pin Register Systems; Plate Bending Systems; Plate Mounting & Register Systems; Press Accessories, Parts & Supplies; Punching Equipment; Web Press - Special Equipment;

NESBITT PUBLISHING LTD.

PO Box 160, Shoal Lake, MB, R0J 1Z0, Canada; tel 204-759-2644; fax 204-759-2521; e-mail smpnews@mymts.net
Chief Executive Officer—Gregory Nesbitt
Editor—Marcie Harrison
Advertising—Connie Kay
Publisher—Ryan Nesbitt
Industry: South Mountain Press community newspaper

NET-LINX AG

Kathe-Kollwitz-Ufer 76-79, Dresden, N/A, 01309, Germany; tel +49 351 3187 5888; fax +49 351 3187 5550; e-mail nxinfo@net-linx.com; web site www.net-linx.com
Pres.—Holm Hallbauer

NETWORK NEWSPAPER ADVERTISING, INC.

23811 Chagrin Blvd Ste LL25, Cleveland, OH, 44122-5525, USA; tel (216) 595-3990; fax (216) 595-3992; e-mail cccamh@aol.com
Pres.—Charles Hickman
Industry: Consulting Services: Advertising

NEWMAN INTERNATIONAL, LLC

5405 W 97th Cir, Overland Park, KS, 66207-3271, USA; tel (913) 648-2000; fax (913) 648-7750; e-mail j.newman@att.net; web site www.timsonsusedprintingpresses.com
Pres.—John T. Newman
Vice Pres.—Mary C. Newman
Industry: Presses: Offset; Web Press - Special Equipment;

NEWSCOLOR, LLC

PO Box 802, Silverton, OR, 97381-0802, USA; tel (503) 873-2414; e-mail sales@newscolor.com; web site www.newscolor.com
Mng. Dir.—Ron LaForge
Sales Dir.—Karen Barr
Industry: Color Proofing

NEWSCURRENTS

PO Box 52, Madison, WI, 53701-0052, USA; tel 608 836-6660; fax 608 836-6684; e-mail csis@newscurrents.com; web site www.newscurrents.com
Marketing Mgr.—Matt Cibula

Industry: NIE Print & Website Weekly Content

NEWSCYCLE SOLUTIONS

7900 International Drive Suite 800, Bloomington, MN, 55425, USA; tel 651-639-0662; e-mail info@newscycle.com; web site www.newscycle.com
Sales Director—Paul Mrozinski
VP., Business Relations—John Pukas
Rgl. Sales Dir.—Steve Moon
Rgl. Sales Dir.—Marc Thompson
Marketing Communications Mgr.—Lisa Speth
Asia-Pacific Bus. Mgr.—Bryan Hooley
Vice President of Market Development—Ken Freedman
Vice President of Marketing—Pete Marsh
Sales Director—Julie Maas
Sales Director—Chris McKee
Sales Director—Mike McLaughlin
Sales Engineer—Geoff Kehrer
Executive Sales Director, EMEA—Robert Bohlin
Industry: Software: Advertising (Includes Display; Classified); Software: Circulation; Software: Design/Graphics; Software: Editorial; Software: Pagination/Layout;

NEWSENGIN, INC.

15560 Golden Ridge Ct, Chesterfield, MO, 63017-5124, USA; tel (636) 537-8548; fax (636) 532-9408; web site www.newsengin.com
CEO—Jim Mosley
Pres.—George Landau
CTO—Virgil Tipton
Industry: Archiving Systems; News Wire Capture Systems; Software: Editorial; Software: Pagination/Layout;

NEWSPAPER ELECTRONICS CORP.

5737 Swope Pkwy, Kansas City, MO, 64130-4224, USA; tel (816) 523-5993; fax (816) 523-2820; e-mail sales@ne-corp.com; web site www.ne-corp.com
Pres.—Kelvin W. Perry
Dir., Special Markets—Vincent P. Jacks
Industry: Business Computers; Computers: Hardware & Software Integrators; Computers: Laptop & Portable; Computers: Local Area Network (LANS); Computers: Storage Devices; Consulting Services: Computer; Integrated Fax Servers;

NEWSPAPER SERVICES OF AMERICA

3025 Highland Pkwy Ste 700, Downers Grove, IL, 60515-5553, USA; tel (630) 729-7500; e-mail info@nsamedia.com; web site www.nsamedia.com
Industry: Consulting Services: Advertising

NEWSPRINT SALES CO.

PO Box 5224, Charlottesville, VA, 22905-5224, USA; tel (434) 972-7712; fax (434) 977-5902; e-mail rswift@brant-allen.com
Gen. Mgr.—Jacques Beauchesne
Gen. Sales Mgr.—Richard P. Swift
Industry: Newsprint

NEWSTECH CO. (DIV. OF ROVINTER, INC.)

675 NW 97th St, Miami, FL, 33150-1652, USA; tel (305) 757-5577; fax (305) 757-2255; e-mail newstech@newstech.com; web site www.newstech.com
Pres.—Oscar Rovito
Vice Pres.—Diego A. Rovito
Industry: Blankets; Film & Paper: Phototypesetting; Inks; Offset Chemicals & Supplies; Plate Mounting & Register Systems; Plate Processors; Plates: Offset (Computer to Plate); Plates: Offset (Conventional); Press Parts; Rollers;

NEWSVIEW SOLUTIONS

143 S Main St Fl 8, Salt Lake City, UT, 84111-1917, USA; tel (800) 897-3271; fax (801) 257-8818; e-mail info@newsviewsolutions.com; web site www.newsviewsolutions.com

Dir.-Sales—Mike Venso
Dir.-Tribune Solutions—Tony Semerad
Dir.-Mktg.—Kim McDaniel
Industry: Archiving Systems; Software: Asset Management; Software: Electronic Data Interchange; Software: Workflow Management/Tracking; Storage Retrieval Systems;

NIKON, INC.

1300 Walt Whitman Rd Fl 2, Melville, NY, 11747-3064, USA; tel (631) 547-4200; fax (631) 547-0299; web site www.nikonusa.com
Pres./CEO—Nobuyoshi Gokyu
Sr. Vice Pres.—David Lee
Gen. Mgr., Mktg. Pro Pdcts./Digital SLR Systems/Speedlights—Steve Heiner
Nat'l Mktg. Mgr., Nikon USA—William Giordano
Communications Coordinator—Kristina Kurtzke
Industry: Consumer Electronics

NISUS SOFTWARE, INC.

PO Box 1302, Solana Beach, CA, 92075-7302, USA; tel (858) 481-1477; fax (858) 764-0573
Industry: Word Processing System

NOBLE SYSTEM CORPORATION

1200 Ashwood Pkwy Ste 300, Atlanta, GA, 30338-4747, USA; tel (404) 851 1331; fax (404) 851 1421; e-mail info@noblesystems.com; web site www.noblesystems.com
Pres./CEO—Jim Noble Jr
COO—Rita Dearing
CFO—Jay S. Mayne
CTO—Mark M. Moore
Vice Pres., Sales/Mktg.—Christopher Saulkner
Industry: Omnichannel Contact Management Call Center Software Telecommunications

NORMAN X GUTTMAN, INC.

135 Green St, Woodbridge, NJ, 07095-2961, USA; tel (732) 636-8671; fax (732) 636-8673; web site www.advertoon.com
Pres.—Daniel Guttman
Industry: Inks; Roll Converters; Roller Grinding Services; Rollers; Rollers: Dampening; Tension & Web Controls;

NORTH ATLANTIC PUBLISHING SYSTEMS, INC.

66 Commonwealth Ave, Concord, MA, 01742-2974, USA; tel (978) 371-8989; fax (978) 371-5678; e-mail naps@napsys.com; xthelp@napsys.com; web site www.napsys.com
Retail Sales Mgr.—Andrew W. Koppel
Industry: Consulting Services: Editorial; Software: Asset Management; Software: Editorial; Software: Pagination/Layout; Software: Workflow Management/Tracking;

NORTH SHORE CONSULTANTS, INC.

613 Thorndale Ave, Elk Grove Village, IL, 60007-4334, USA; tel (773) 286-7245; fax (773) 286-1974; e-mail nsc@enescee.com; web site www.enescee.com
Pres.—Audrey Mysliwiec
Mgr.—Dennis B. Wojtecki
Industry: Adhesives; Flying Pasters; Splicers; Automatic; Tape Splicing Equipment;

NORTHEAST INDUSTRIES, INC.

2965 Tolemac Way, Prescott, AZ, 86305-2179, USA; tel 800-821-6257; fax (928) 443-0851; e-mail sam@neiinc.com; web site www.neiinc.com
Pres.—Sam W. Boyles
Industry: Consulting Services: Equipment; Presses: DiLitho; Presses: Flexographic; Presses: Letterpress; Presses: Offset;

NORTHERN GRAPHIC SUPPLY

64 Hardy Dr, Sparks, NV, 89431-6307, USA; tel (775) 359-6466; fax (775) 359-6966; e-mail 4ngs@sbcglobal.net

Pres.—Barbara Gouldstone
Industry: Newspaper Marketing

NORWOOD PAPER
7001 W 60th St, Chicago, IL, 60638-3101, USA; tel (773) 788-1508; fax (773) 788-1528; e-mail sales@norwoodpaper.com; web site www.norwoodpaper.com
President—Laura Martin
Vice President—Robert Zeman
COO—Kathleen Zemen
Industry: Newsprint; Paper: Coated Groundwood Offset; Paper: Groundwood Specialties; Paper: Specialty Printing Paper; Rewinders;

NOTEADS.COM, INC./POST-IT NOTE ADVERTISING
6906 Martin Way E, Olympia, WA, 98516-5567, USA; tel 800-309-7502; fax (800) 309-7503; e-mail john@noteads.com; web site www.noteads.com
President—John Grantham
Sales—Kristin Gustin
Industry: Consulting Services: Advertising

NRD LLC
PO Box 310, Grand Island, NY, 14072-0310, USA; tel (716) 773-7634; fax (716) 773-7744; e-mail sales@nrdinc.com; web site www.nrdinc.com
Director of Sales and Marketing—John Glynn
Industry: Static Eliminators

NUANCE
1 Wayside Rd, Burlington, MA, 01803-4609, USA; tel (781) 565-5000; fax (781) 565-5001; e-mail info@dragonsys.com; web site www.nuance.com
Mgr., Cor. Commun.—Renee Blodgett
Industry: Speech Recognition

NUANCE COMMUNICATIONS INC.
1 Wayside Rd, Burlington, MA, 01803-4609, USA; tel (781) 565-5000; fax (781) 565-5001; web site www.nuance.com
Chrmn./CEO—Paul Ricci
Exec. Vice Pres./CFO—Thomas Beaudoin
Sr. Vice Pres., Cor. Devel.—Richard Palmer
Sr. Vice Pres., Mktg.—Robert Weideman
Vice Pres., Opns.—Rick Broyles
Sr. Vice Pres., Worldwide Sales—Steve Chambers
Vice Pres., HR—Dawn Howarth

NUARC CO., INC.
6200 W Howard St, Niles, IL, 60714-3400, USA; tel (847) 967-4400; fax (847) 967-9664; e-mail nuarc@ccm.net; web site www.mrprint.com
Industry: Cameras & Accessories; Color Printing Frames; Controls: Exposure; Dark Room Equipment; Diffusion Transfer Processors; Offset Plate-Making Service & Equipment; Plate Exposure Units; Platemakers: Offset (Conventional); Processors: Diffusion Transfer; Proofing Systems;

NUS CONSULTING GROUP
PO Box 712, Park Ridge, NJ, 07656-0712, USA; tel (201) 391-4300; fax (201) 391-8158; e-mail contact@nusconsulting.com; web site www.nusconsulting.com
—Gary Soultanian
—Richard SoultanianCo-Pres.s
Industry: Telecommunications

O

OLEC
1850 E Saint Andrew Pl, Santa Ana, CA, 92705-5043, USA; tel (714) 881-2000; fax (714) 881-2001; e-mail sales@olec.com; web site www.olec.com
Mng. Dir.—Don Ohlig
Sales Mgr.—Al Mora
Vice Pres.,Electronics Sales—Gordon Quinn

Industry: Produciton Control Systems

OLYMPUS AMERICA, INC.
3500 Corporate Pkwy, Center Valley, PA, 18034-8229, USA; tel (888) 553-4448; fax (484) 896-7115; e-mail info@olympusamerica.com; web site www.olympusamerica.com
Pres./COO—F. Mark Gumz
Exec. Dir., Brand Devel.—Mark Huggins
Sr. PR Mgr.—Elizabeth Sullivan
Vice Pres., Mktg.—Michael J. Hunter

ONE CORP.
455 E Paces Ferry Rd NE Ste 350, Atlanta, GA, 30305-3315, USA; tel (404) 842-0111; fax (404) 848-0525; e-mail dboles@onecorp.com; web site www.onecorp.com; www.webpresses.com
Pres.—Durelle Boles
CFO—Jennifer Boles
Industry: Equipment Dealers (New); Equipment Dealers (Used); Web Offset Presses; Flying Pasters; Presses: Offset; Remanufactures Equipment; Splicers, Automatic;

OUTSOURCING USA
1200 Twin Stacks Dr, Dallas, PA, 18612, USA; tel (570) 674-5600; e-mail info@outsourcingusa.net; web site www.outsourcingusa.net
CEO—Lynn Banta
VP Business Development—Maureen Missal
VP of Information Systems—Tony Banta
Industry: Pre-press ad production services for both print and web

OVERLAND STORAGE, INC.
9112 Spectrum Center Blvd, San Diego, CA, 92123-1599, USA; tel (858) 571-5555; fax (858) 571-3664; e-mail sales@overlandstorage.com; web site www.overlandstorage.com
Pres—Eric Kelly
Vice Pres., HR—Veritta Wells
Vice Pres., Opns.—Mike Gawarecki
Vice Pres., Sales—Ravi Pendekanti
Industry: Computers: Storage Devices

P

PACESETTER GRAPHIC SERVICE CORP.
2672 Hickory Grove Rd NW, Acworth, GA, 30101-3643, USA; tel (800) 241-7970; fax 770-974-2980; web site www.pacesetterusa.com
Pres.—Robert Allen
Exec. Vice Pres.—Jeri Hammond
Industry: Blankets; Rollers; Rollers: Dampening;

PAGE
700 American Ave Ste 101, King Of Prussia, PA, 19406-4031, USA; tel (610) 592-0646; fax (610) 592-0647; web site www.pagecooperative.com
CEO—John Snyder
Office Mgr.—Evelyn Jayne
Industry: Composing Room Equipment & Supplies; Inks; Newsprint; Paper: Groundwood Specialties; Plates: Offset (Conventional);

PALOS SOFTWARE
520 Kearny Villa Way, Ste. 108, San Diego, CA, 92123-1869, USA; tel (858) 836-4400; e-mail marketing@palos.com; web site www.palos.com
Pres.—David Altomare
Industry: Software: Pagination/Layout

PAMARCO GLOBAL GRAPHICS
235 E 11th Ave, Roselle, NJ, 07203-2015, USA; tel (908) 241-1200; fax (908) 241-4009; web site www.pamarcoglobal.com
Pres./CEO—Terry Ford
Industry: Rollers

PAMARCO GLOBAL GRAPHICS
150 Marr Ave NW, Marietta, GA, 30060-1050, USA; tel (770) 795-8556; fax (770) 795-8943; e-mail info@pamarcoglobal.com; web site www.pamarcoglobal.com
Vice Pres., Mfg.—James Miller
Vice Pres., Sales/Mktg.—Greg Anderson
Industry: Press Accessories, Parts & Supplies; Presses: Offset; Rollers; Rollers: Dampening;

PAN AMERICAN PAPERS, INC.
5101 NW 37th Ave, Miami, FL, 33142-3232, USA; tel (305) 635-2534; fax (305) 635-2538; e-mail panampap@bellsouth.net; web site www.panampap.com
Sr. Vice Pres.—Jesus A. Roca
Industry: Newsprint; Paper: Specialty Printing Paper;

PANTONE, INC.
590 Commerce Blvd, Carlstadt, NJ, 07072-3098, USA; tel (201) 935-5500; fax (201) 935-3338; e-mail support@pantone.com; web site www.pantone.com
Pres.—Ron Potesky
Industry: Color Management Software; Software: Design/Graphics;

PARAGON TECHNOLOGIES INC.
101 Larry Holmes Dr Ste 500, Easton, PA, 18042-7723, USA; tel (610) 252-7321; fax (610) 252-3102; e-mail info@sihs.com; sales@sihs.com; web site www.sihs.com
Chrmn.—Theodore W. Myers
Industry: Conveyors; Mailroom Systems & Equipment; Material Handling Equipment: Automatic Guided Vehicles;

PARSONS CORPORATION
100 W Walnut St, Pasadena, CA, 91124-0001, USA; tel (626) 440-2000; fax (626) 440-2630; web site www.parsons.com
Chairman and CEO—Charles Harrington
Corporate Vice President, Marketing & Communications—Erin Kuhlman
Industry: Engineering, construction, technical, and professional services

PASTE-UP SUPPLY
10930 1/2 Grand Ave, Temple City, CA, 91780-3551, USA; tel (626) 448-4543
Owner—Pat Treanor
Industry: Adhesive Wax Coaters

PC INDUSTRIES
176 Ambrogio Dr., Gurnee, IL, 60031, USA; tel (847) 336-3300; fax (847) 336-3232; e-mail sales@pcindustries.com; web site www.pcindustries.com
Pres./Sales Mgr.—John Woolley
Industry: Cameras & Accessories; Color Registration; Controls: Register; Optical Character Recognition (OCR); Press Control Systems; Proofing Systems;

PDI PLASTICS
5037 Pine Creek Dr, Westerville, OH, 43081-4849, USA; tel (800)634-0017; fax (614) 890-0467; e-mail sales@pdisaneck.com; web site www.newsbags.com
Pres.—Frank Cannon
Exec. VP—Todd Wilson
Industry: Circulation Equipment & Supplies

PEMCO, INC.
3333 Crocker Ave, Sheboygan, WI, 53081-6425, USA; tel (920) 458-2500; fax (920) 458-1265; e-mail sales@pemco.kpl.net; web site www.pemco.kpl.net
Technical Sales Dir.—Jeff Bogel
Industry: Conversion Equipment; Conveyors; Cutters & Trimmers; Photostat: Paper; Reels & Tensions; Reels (Inlcudes Paper Reels); Roll Handeling Equipment; Splicers, Automatic; Tension & Web Controls; Web Guides;

PENCO PRODUCTS
1820 Stonehenge Drive, Greenville, PA,

27585, USA; tel 800-562-1000; e-mail general@pencoproducts.com; web site www.pencoproducts.com
Pres.—Greg Grogan
Mktg. Mgr.—Philip H. Krugler
Industry: Cabinets; Storage Retrieval Systems;

PERFORMANCE CONTRACTING GROUP
16400 College Blvd, Lenexa, KS, 66219-1389, USA; tel 1-800-255-6886; e-mail info@pcg.com; web site www.pcg.com

PERMA-FIX ENVIRONMENTAL SERVICES
8302 Dunwoody Pl Ste 250, Atlanta, GA, 30350-3390, USA; tel (770) 587-9898; fax (770) 587-9937; e-mail corporate@perma-fix.com; web site www.perma-fix.com
Pres./CEO—Lou Centofanti
Mgr.—Pam Ittah
Industry: Environmental Control Systems

PERRETTA GRAPHICS CORP.
46 Violet Ave, Poughkeepsie, NY, 12601-1521, USA; tel (845) 473-0550; fax (845) 454-7507; e-mail mailbox@perretta.com; service@perretta.com; web site www.perretta.com
Pres.—Christopher Perretta
Bus. Mgr., Int'l Sales—Bruce Quilliam
Vice Pres., Sales/Mktg.—Bruce L. Quilliam
Sales Mgr.—Jean Laird
Serv. Mgr.—Paul Jorde
Asst. Serv. Mgr.—Jordan Terziyski
Industry: Controls: Register; Ink Controls, Computerized; Keyless Inking Conversion & Add-ons; Web Press - Special Equipment;

PETCO ROLLER CO.
28041 N Bradley Rd, Lake Forest, IL, 60045-1163, USA; tel (847) 362-1820; fax (847) 362-1833; e-mail mail@petcorolls.com; web site www.petcorolls.com
Sales Mgr.—Dale Glen
Industry: Roll Coverings; Rollers; Rollers: Dampening;

PHELPS, CUTLER & ASSOCIATES
35 Barnard St Ste 300, Savannah, GA, 31401, USA; tel (912) 388-4692; fax (678) 826-4708; e-mail phelpscutler@aol.com; web site www.phelpscutler.com
Managing Partner—Louise Phelps
Industry: M&A Broker; Expert Witness on Valuation; General Operational Consulting: Print and Digital Revenue Strategies; Niche (print and digital websites) specialist; Circulation Consulting Services: Editorial; Consulting Services: Financial; Consulting Services: Human Resources; Consulting Services: Marketing;

PHOTO SYSTEMS, INC.
7200 Huron River Dr, Dexter, MI, 48130-1099, USA; tel (734) 426-9625; fax (734) 426-3780; e-mail sales@photosys.com; web site www.photosys.com
Pres.—Alan Fischer
Sales Mgr.—Nikki Calloway
Industry: Chemicals: Photographic; Chemicals: Plate Processing; Chemicals: Pressroom; Chemicals: Roller Cleaning; Film & Paper; Film Processing Machines;

PHOTOSOURCE INTERNATIONAL
Pine Lake Farm, 1910 35th Rd., Osceola, WI, 54020, USA; tel (800) 624-0266; fax (715) 248-3800; e-mail info@photosource.com; web site www.photosource.com
Pub.—Rohn Engh
Mng. Ed.—Angie Dober
Industry: Photography: Digital/Electronic Cameras; Trade Publications;

PITMAN CO.
611 River Dr, Center 3, Elmwood Park, NJ, 07407-1338, USA; tel (800) 540-2432 x4848; web site www.pitman.com
Pres.—Peter J. Moore
Sales Consultant—Dick Simonian
Industry: Color Proofing; Color Registration;

Color Seperation Scanners; Color Viewing Equipment; Dark Room Equipment; Plate Exposure Units; Plate Processors; Plates: Offset (Conventional); Scanners: Color B & W, Plates, Web;

PITMAN PHOTO SUPPLY
13911 S Dixie Hwy, Miami, FL, 33176-7234, USA; tel 800-252-3008; e-mail pitmanphoto@att.net; web site www.pitmanphotosupply.com
Pres.—Michael Werner
Sales Mgr.—Lowell H. Elsea
Industry: Cameras & Accessories; Chemicals: Photographic; Dark Room Equipment; Dryers: Film and Papers; Enlargers (Photographic); Film & Paper: Film Roll Dispensers; Film & Paper: Filters (Photographic); Fixing & Stop Baths; Lenses (Camera); Photography: Digital/Electronic Cameras;

PLUMTREE CO.
PO Box 14216, Savannah, GA, 31416-1216, USA; tel (912) 354-5155; fax (912) 354-1375; e-mail email@plumtreecompany.com; web site www.plumtreecompany.com
Pres.—Tim Cooper
Vice Pres., Sales—Julian Cooper
Industry: Consulting Services: Production; Mailroom Systems & Equipment; Newspaper Couter; Newspaper Marketing; Newsprint Handeling Equipment; Promotion Services; Software: Press/Post Press; Software: Workflow Management/Tracking; Totalizing Systems;

POLAROID HOLDING CO.
300 Baker Ave Ste 330, Concord, MA, 01742-2131, USA; tel (781) 386-2000; fax (781) 386-6243; e-mail marketing@polaroid.com; web site www.polaroid.com
CEO—Mary L. Jeffries
Vice Pres., Product Mgmt.—Jim Koestler
Vice Pres./Gen. Mgr., Digital Imaging—Jon Pollock
Vice Pres., Mktg.—Cheryl Mau
Media Rel.—Lorrie Parent

POLKADOTS SOFTWARE INC.
N/A, N/A, QC, N/A, Canada; tel (514) 595-6866; e-mail info@polkadots.ca; web site www.polkadots.ca
Pres.—Gilles Duhamel
VP—Sylvain Audet
Industry: Newspaper prepress automation, page pairing, ink optimizing, RIP, web growth compensation, internet proofing, internet job definition

PORTAGE NEWSPAPER SUPPLY CO.
655 Winding Brook Dr Ste 205, Glastonbury, CT, 06033-4364, USA; tel (877) 659-8318; fax (877) 806-6397; e-mail info@portagegraphic.com; web site www.portagenotebooks.com
Pres.—Robert Belter
Industry: Cutters & Trimmers

POYRY MANAGEMENT CONSULTING (USA) INC.
52 Vanderbilt Ave Rm 1405, New York, NY, 10017-0080, USA; tel (646) 651-1547; fax (212) 661-3830; web site www.poyry.us
Director—Soile Kilpi
Industry: Consulting Services: Management Consulting; Market Research; Market Strategy; paper; media

PPI MEDIA GMBH
Hindenburgstrasse 49, Hamburg, N/A, D-22297, Germany; tel +49 40 2274 3360; fax +49 40 2276 33666; e-mail media@ppimedia.de; web site www.ppimedia.de
CEO—Norbert Ohl
US Market Consultant—Steve Nilan
Sales Mgr.—Christian Finder
Product Mgr.—Jorg Kruse
Industry: Mailroom Systems & Equipment; Output Management and Preflight Software; Pagination Systems; Produciton Control Systems; Software: Advertising (Includes

Display; Classified); Software: Pagination/Layout; Software: Workflow Management/Tracking; System Integration Services;

PRAXAIR, INC.
39 Old Ridgebury Rd # M1, Danbury, CT, 06810-5103, USA; tel 1-800-772-9247; fax 1-800-772-9985; e-mail info@praxair.com; web site www.praxair.com
Chrmn./Pres./CEO—Stephen F. Angel
Nat'l Sales Mgr.—Scott McLaughlin
Plant Mgr.—Jim Drake
Exec. Vice Pres.—Ricardo Malfitano
Sr. Vice Pres./CFO—James Sawyer
Vice Pres., Procuremenet/Materials Mgmt.—John Stevens
Vice Pres., Strategic Planning/Mktg.—Sunil Mattoo
Vice Pres., Commun./Pub. Rel.—Nigel Muir
Industry: Rollers

PRESS-ENTERPRISE, INC. (COLOR GRAPHICS DEPT.)
3185 Lackawanna Ave, Bloomsburg, PA, 17815-3398, USA; tel (570) 784-2121; fax (570) 784-9226; web site www.pressenterpriseonline.com
Prodn. Mgr., Color Graphics—Bill Bason
Industry: Color Proofing; Color Seperations, Positives; Electronic Pre-Scan Systems; Input & Editing Systems;

PRESSLINE SERVICES, INC.
731 Prairie Dupont Dr, Dupo, IL, 62239, USA; tel (314) 682-3800; fax (314) 487-3150; web site www.pressline.info; www.presslineservices.com
Pres.—Jim Gore
Industry: Consulting Services: Equipment; Cylinder Repair; Press Rebuilding; Press Repairs; Web Width Changer;

PRESSROOM CLEANERS, INC.
5709 SOUTH 60TH STREET, SUITE 100B, OMAHA, NE, 68117-2204, USA; tel (402) 597-3199; fax (402) 597-8765; e-mail theresa@pressroomcleaners.com; web site www.pressroomcleaners.com
Pres.—Theresa Frangoulis
Office Mgr.—Angie Clarke
Industry: Industrial Cleaning Services

PRESSTEK, INC.
55 Executive Dr, Hudson, NH, 03051-4903, USA; tel (603) 595-7000; fax 603-594-9666 (Sales/Mktg.); e-mail info@presstek.com ; web site www.presstek.com; shop.presstek.com
Marketing Specialist—Jonelle Rexenes
Industry: Presstek DI Digital Offset Presses; ABDick Conventional Offset Presses Platemakers: Offset (Computer to Plate); Plates: Offset (Computer to Plate); Press Accessories, Parts & Supplies; Press Repairs; Presses: Offset; Processors: Film & Paper; Proofing Systems; Punching Equipment; Post Press

PRESTELIGENCE
8328 Cleveland Ave NW, North Canton, OH, 44720-4820, USA; tel (330) 305-6960; fax (330) 497-5562; e-mail info@presteligence.com; web site www.presteligence.com
Pres. & CEO—Bob Behringer
Controller—Melissa McBride
Dir. of Mktg.—Denise Franken
VP, Ops.—Randy Plant
Major Accnt. Mgr.—Jeff Bernhardt
Industry: Calibration Software/Hardware; Color Proofing; Multiplexers/Routers; Ink Controls, Computerized; Output Management and Preflight Software; Prepress Color Proofing Systems; Software: Advertising (Includes Display; Classified); Software: Press/Post Press; Software: Workflow Management/Tracking; System Integration Services; eTearsheets & eInvoices, e-Editions, Mobile Apps, High School Sports Platform and Web CMS

PRIM HALL ENTERPRISES, INC.
11 Spellman Rd, Plattsburgh, NY, 12901-5326, USA; tel (518) 561-7408; fax (518) 563-1472; e-mail sales@primhall.com; primhall@primhall.com; web site www.primhall.com
Pres.—John E. Prim
Vice Pres.—David E. Hall
Mktg. Coord.—Matt Demers
Industry: Collating Equipment; Conveyors; Mailroom Systems & Equipment; Paper Handeling Equipment; Three Knife Trimmer;

PRINTERS HOUSE AMERICAS LLC
10, Scindia House, Connaught Place, New Delhi, N/A, N/A, India; tel 91-11-23313071; fax 91-11-23356637; e-mail tphindia@bol.net.in; web site www.phaorient.com

PRINTERS' SERVICE/PRISCO/PRISCODIGITAL
26 Blanchard St., Newark, NJ, 07105-4784, USA; tel (973) 589-7800; fax (973) 589-3225; e-mail inquiries@prisco.com; web site www.prisco.com
Chrmn.—Richard B. Liroff
Pres.—Bruce Liroff
CFO—Russ Mantione
Vice Pres., Research/Technology—David Gerson
Vice Pres., Mktg.—Eric A. Gutwillig
President, PriscoDigital LLC—Steve Zunde
Vice Pres., Prodn./Mfg.—Joe Schleck
Senior VP—Michael White
Industry: Chemicals: Pressroom; Circulation Equipment & Supplies; Cleaners & Solvents; Lubricants; Offset Blankets, Blanket Wash; Offset Chemicals & Supplies; Offset Fountain Solutions; Plate Cleaners; Press Accessories, Parts & Supplies; Solvent Recovery Systems; Wide Format Inkjet systems, Wide Format Inkjet supplies, Automated Cutting Systems, Software

PRINTING PRESS SERVICES, INC.
Sellers St. Works, Preston Lancs, N/A, PR1 5EU, United Kingdom; tel +44 1772 797 050; fax +44 1772 705 761; e-mail stephenm@ppsi.co.uk; web site www.ppsi.co.uk
Pres.—Joe McManamon
Mng. Dir.-Press Division—Stephen McManamon
Mng. Dir.-Inking Systems Division—David McManamon
Office Mgr.—Marilyn Lloyd
Industry: Conversion Equipment; Drives & Controls; Equipment Dealers (New); Equipment Dealers (Used); Erectors & Riggers; Ink Controls, Computerized; Ink Fountains & Accessories; Presses: Offset; Splicers, Automatic;

PRINTING TECHNOLOGY, INC.
2337 Ember Woods Dr, Keller, TX, 76262-8825, USA; tel (817) 431-0132; fax (817) 431-0270; e-mail bissatpti@aol.com; web site www.webpressparts.com
Bus. Mgr.—Leigh Ann Bissbort
Industry: Cylinder Repair; Equipment Dealers (Used); Folder Knives; Ink Fountains & Accessories; Press Accessories, Parts & Supplies; Press Rebuilding; Press Repairs; Presses: Offset; Rollers; Rollers: Dampening;

PRINTMARK
432 Johnson Rd, East Montpelier, VT, 05651-4250, USA; tel (802) 229-9743; e-mail alex@printmark.net; web site www.printmark.net
Dir., Prodn.—Alex Brown
Industry: Consulting Services: Computer; Consulting Services: Editorial; Consulting Services: Production;

PRINTRONIX, INC.
15345 Barranca Pkwy, Irvine, CA, 92618-2216, USA; tel (714) 368-2300; fax (714) 368-2600; e-mail info@printronix.com; sales@printronix.com; web site www.printronix.com
Industry: Computers: Hardware & Software Integrators

PRINTSOFT AMERICAS, INC.
70 West Madison St. Three First National Plaza Suite 1400, Chicago, IL, 60602, USA; tel (630) 625-5400; fax (630) 625-5401; e-mail sales@printsoftamericas.com; web site www.printsoft.com
Nat'l Sales Mgr.—Daniel Sheedy
Industry: Laser Printers; Software: Circulation;

PRINTWARE
2935 Waters Rd Ste 160, Saint Paul, MN, 55121-1688, USA; tel (651) 456-1400; fax (651) 454-3684; e-mail sales@printwarellc.com; web site www.printwarellc.com
Pres.—Stan Goldberg
Vice Pres.-Sales/Mktg.—Tim Murphy
Industry: Offset Plate-Making Service & Equipment; Plate Processors; Platemakers: Offset (Conventional); Plates: Offset (Conventional);

PROIMAGE AMERICA, INC.
103 Carnegie Ctr Ste 300, Princeton, NJ, 08540-6235, USA; tel (609) 844-7576; fax (609) 895-2666; e-mail pia@new-proimage.com; web site www.new-proimage.com
President/CEO—John J. Ialacci
Vice President, Operations—Mike Monter
Vice President, Sales and Marketing—Rick Shafranek
Industry: Calibration Software/Hardware; Color Management; Consulting Services: Production; Software: Electronic Data Interchange; Software: Pagination/Layout; Software: Workflow Management/Tracking, Ripping, Imposition; Training: Automated Pre Press workflow; Ink Optimization; Press Registration; Content Management Systems; Tablet & Mobile Solutions

PROQUEST LLC
PO Box 1346, Ann Arbor, MI, 48106-1346, USA; tel (734) 761-4700; e-mail info@proquest.com; web site www.proquest.com
CEO—Marty Kahn
Sr. Vice Pres., Global Sales—Simon Beale
Sr. Vice Pres., Mktg.—Lynda James-Gilboe
Chris Cowan
Industry: Archiving Systems

PSC FLO-TURN, INC.
1050 Commerce Ave Ste 1, Union, NJ, 07083-5080, USA; tel (908) 687-3225; fax (908) 687-1715; e-mail info@psoturn.com; web site www.flow-turn.com
Pres.—Rod Chrysler
Industry: Conveyors

PUBLICATION DESIGN, INC.
6449 Meadowview Ter S, Zionsville, PA, 18092-2091, USA; tel (610) 928-1111; fax (610) 928-1110; e-mail ayers@publicationdesign.com; web site www.publicationdesign.com
Pres., V.P., Sec. Tres.—Robert Ayers
Industry: Publication Design & Layout Services

PUBLISHERS CIRCULATION FULFILLMENT INC.
303 Smith Street, Suite One, Farmingdale, NY, 11735, USA; tel (631) 2703133; e-mail sales@pcfcorp.com; web site www.pcfcorp.com
Pres./CEO—Jerry Giordana
VP of Growth and Development—Tom Dressler
James Cunningham
Industry: Newspaper Distribution Technology Services

PULSE RESEARCH, INC.
PO Box 2884, Portland, OR, 97208-2884, USA; tel (503) 626-5224; fax (503) 277-2184; e-mail info@pulsesearch.com; support@pulseresearch.com; web site www.pulseresearch.com
PRESIDENT—John W. Marling
CIO—John Bertoglio
Vice Pres., Sales—Denice Nichols
Vice Pres.—Andrew Dove

Vice Pres.—Brian Knapp
Industry: Consulting Services: Advertising; Consulting Services: Circulation; Consulting Services: Marketing;

Q

QUAD TECH
N64W23110 Main St, Sussex, WI, 53089-5301, USA; tel (414) 566-7500; fax (414) 566-9670; e-mail info@qtiworld.com; web site www.quadtechworld.com
Pres.—Karl Fritchen
Vice Pres.,Sales—Randy Freeman
Industry: Color Registration; Controls: Register; Ink Controls, Computerized; Press Control Systems; Web Break Detector;

QUADTECH
N64W23110 Main St, Sussex, WI, 53089-3230, USA; tel (414) 566-7500; fax (414) 566-9670; e-mail sales@quadtechworld.com; web site www.quadtechworld.com
Pres.—Karl Fritchen
Vice Pres., Bus. Devel.—Randy Freeman
Dir., Engineering/Gen. Mgr.,Commercial/Newspaper—Vince Balistrieri
Regional Sales Manager—Greg Kallman
Industry: Color Registration; Controls: Register; Ink Controls, Computerized; Press Control Systems; Web Break Detector;

QUARK, INC.
1225 17th St Ste 1200, Denver, CO, 80202-5503, USA; tel (303) 894-8888; fax (303) 894-3399; e-mail quarkxpress@quark.com; web site www.quark.com
Pres./CEO—Kamar Aulakh
Industry: Software: Asset Management; Software: Design/Graphics; Software: Editorial; Software: Pagination/Layout;

QUEBECOR WORLD
612, Rue Saint-Jacques, Montréal, N/A, H3C 4M8, Canada; tel (514) 380-1999; e-mail contact.us@quebecorusa.com; web site www.quebecor.com
Pres./CEO—Charles Cavell
Exec. Vice Pres., Sales—Brian Freschi
Dir. Cor. Commun.—Jeremy Roberts
Industry: Consulting Services: Production; Input & Editing Systems; Preprint Service & Production; Presses: Rotogravure;

QUICKWIRE LABS
300 Carlton St., Winnipeg, MB, R3B 2K6, Canada; tel (905) 785-0748; fax (204) 926-4686; e-mail bmiller@quickwire.com; web site www.quickwire.com
Gen. Mgr.—Bill Miller
Quicktrac Developer—Paul Medland
Integrator—Richard Bliss
Industry: Software: Advertising (Includes Display; Classified); Software: Editorial; Software: Pagination/Layout;

QUIPP SYSTEM, INC.
PO Box 71057, Chicago, IL, 60694-1057, USA; tel (800) 258-1390; fax (305) 623-0980; e-mail info@quipp.com; web site www.quipp.com
Vice Pres., Sales.—Angel Arrabal
Mktg. Mgr.—Leticia Gostisa
Vice Pres., Opns.—David Switalski
Industry: Conveyors; Material Handling Equipment: Pallets & Palletizers; Material Handling Equipment: Truck Loaders; Software: Press/Post Press; System Installations; System Integration Services; Training: Post Press;

R

R.B. INTERMARK, INC.
15 Kirkland Blvd., Ste. 108, Kirkland, QC, H9J 1N2, Canada; tel (514) 695-7172; fax (514) 695-2108; e-mail digitron.brimo@sympatico.ca
Pres.—Rene J. Brimo
Industry: Silver Recovery; Solvent Recovery Systems; Wastewater Treatment; Water Management Systems;

R.R. DONNELLEY & SONS CO.
111 S Wacker Dr Ste 3600, Chicago, IL, 60606-4300, USA; tel (312) 326-8000; fax (312) 326-8001; e-mail info@rrd.com; web site www.rrdonnelley.com
Pres./CEO—Thomas J. Quinlan
COO—John R. Paloian
Sr. Vice Pres., Mktg./Commun.—Douglas Fitzgerald

RAK SYSTEMS, INC.
5500 Plantation Rd, Theodore, AL, 36582-1702, USA; tel (251) 653-4080; fax (251) 653-1014; e-mail info@raksystems.com; web site www.raksystems.com
Pres.—Richard Kitzmann
Industry: Newspaper Racks, both coin operated and free distribution racks, new and used racks. Refurbishing of newspaper racks. Parts needed for newspaper racks.

RANDOM ACCESS
62 Birdsall St, Greene, NY, 13778-1049, USA; tel (607) 656-7584; e-mail marsland@aol.com
Pres.—William Marsland
Industry: Consulting Services: Computer; System Integration Services;

RANGER DATA TECHNOLOGIES INC.
360 E Maple Rd Ste X, Troy, MI, 48083-2707, USA; tel (248) 336-7300; fax (248) 336-8775; e-mail info@rangerdata.com; web site www.rangerdata.com
Sr. VP of Operations—George Willard
Director of Marketing & Customer Service—Grace Shields
National Dir. of Sales & Marketing—Dolores Gauthier
Industry: Software: Advertising (Includes Display; Classified)

REED BRENNAN MEDIA ASSOCIATES, INC.
628 Virginia Dr, Orlando, FL, 32803-1858, USA; tel (407) 894-7300; fax (407) 894-7900; e-mail rbma@rbma.com; web site www.rbma.com
VP—Jeff Talbert
Mgr., Mktg.—Timothy Brennan
King Features Weekly Service—David Cohea
Industry: Input & Editing Systems; Pagination Systems;

REEVES BROTHERS, INC.
PO Box 1531, Spartanburg, SC, 29304-1531, USA; tel (864) 576-1210; fax (864) 595-2270; web site www.trelleborg.com
CEO—Keith Dye
Industry: Blanket Mounting and Bars; Blankets;

REPUBLIC ROLLER CORP.
PO Box 330, Three Rivers, MI, 49093-0330, USA; tel (800) 765-5377; fax (269) 273-7655; e-mail bestroll@aol.com; web site www.republicroller.com
Pres.—G.L. Umphrey
Sales Mgr.—Bill Gross
Industry: Roll Coverings; Roller Grinding Services; Rollers; Rollers: Dampening;

RESEARCH USA, INC.
180 N Wacker Dr Ste 202, Chicago, IL, 60606-1600, USA; tel (800) 863-4800; fax (312) 658-0085; e-mail info@researchusainc.com; hr@researchusainc.com; web site www.researchusainc.com
Industry: Market Research

RESOLUTE FOREST PRODUCTS
111 Duke Street, Suite 5000, Montréal, QC, H3C 2M1, Canada; tel (514) 875-2160; fax (423) 336-7950; e-mail info@resolutefp.com;
web site www.resolutefp.com
VP, Sales-Southern Market—Devon Mike
Rgl. Mgr.—Garry Grissom
Industry: Pulp & Paper

RFC WIRE FORMS
525 Brooks St, Ontario, CA, 91762-3702, USA; tel (909) 984-5500; fax (909) 984-2322; e-mail rfccompany@aol.com; web site www.rfcwireforms.com
Pres.—Don Kemby
Gen. Mgr.—Greg Lunsmann
Industry: Rack Display Cards

RICHMOND/GRAPHIC PRODUCTS, INC.
20 Industrial Dr, Smithfield, RI, 02917-1502, USA; tel (401) 233-2700; fax (401) 233-0179; e-mail info@richmond-graphic.com; web site www.richmond-graphic.com
CEO—Hugh C. Neville
Controller—P.J. Griffee
Vice Pres., Sales/Mktg.—Frank Ragazzo
Industry: Art & Layout Equipment and Services; Exposure Lamps; Film & Paper: Film Processing Machines; Layout Tables, Light Tables & Workstations; Offset Plate-Making Service & Equipment; Plate Processors; Processors: Diffusion Transfer; Processors: Film & Paper; Tables (Dot, Etch, Opaquing, Register, Retouching, Stripping); Vacuum Frames;

RICKENBACHER MEDIA
6731 Desco Dr, Dallas, TX, 75225-2704, USA; tel (214) 384 2779; e-mail rmedia@msn.com; web site www.rickenbachermedia.com
Pres./Exec. Dir.—Ted Rickenbacher
Western States Dir.—Jim Afinowich
Industry: Brokers & Appraisers

RICOH CORP.
5 Dedrick Pl, West Caldwell, NJ, 07006-6398, USA; tel (973) 882-2000; fax (973) 808-7555; web site www.ricoh-usa.com
Pres.—Martin Brodigan

ROBERTSON EQUIPMENTS
1301 S Maiden Ln, Joplin, MO, 64801-3844, USA; tel (800) 288-1929; fax (417) 781-3704; e-mail sales@robertsonpress.com; web site www.robertsonpress.com
Owner—Bob Robertson
Pres.—Charles J. Robertson
Dir., Mktg.—Jason Bard
Parts Mgr.—Dave Reddick
Industry: Consulting Services: Computer; System Integration Services; Conveyors; Material Handling Equipment: Automatic Guided Vehicles; Material Handling Equipment: Truck Loaders;

ROBERTSON PRESS MACHINERY CO., INC.
1301 S Maiden Ln, Joplin, MO, 64801-3844, USA; tel (417) 673-1929; fax (417) 781-3704; e-mail sales@robertsonpress.com; web site www.robertsonpress.com
Pres.—Charles Robertson
Industry: Color Registration; Dampening Systems; Equipment Dealers (New); Equipment Dealers (Used); Press Accessories, Parts & Supplies; Press Rebuilding; Presses: Offset; Remanufactures Equipment; Tension & Web Controls; Web Press - Special Equipment;

ROCHESTER INSTITUTE OF TECHNOLOGY
69 Lomb Memorial Dr, Rochester, NY, 14623-5602, USA; tel (585) 475-2728; fax (585) 475-7029; e-mail spmofc@rit.edu; web site www.rit.edu
Admin. Chair—Patricia Sores
Industry: Abrasives; Cameras & Accessories; Consulting Services: Computer; Consulting Services: Equipment; Consulting Services: Production;

ROCKWELL AUTOMATION
PO Box 760, Milwaukee, WI, 53201-0760, USA; tel (262) 512-8200; fax (262) 512-8579; web site www.rockwellautomation.com
Mktg. Commun. Specialist—Michael Faase
Industry: Controllers: Press; Drives & Controls; Press Control Systems;

ROCONEX CORP.
20 Marybill Dr S, Troy, OH, 45373-1034, USA; tel (937) 339-2616; fax (937) 339-1470; e-mail info@roconex.com; web site www.roconex.com
Pres.—Tyrone Spear
Industry: Art & Layout Equipment and Services; Cabinets; Files, Storage; Layout Tables, Light Tables & Workstations; Offset Plate Holders; Plate Exposure Units; Platemakers: Offset (Conventional); Storage Retrieval Systems; Tables (Dot, Etch, Opaquing, Register, Retouching, Stripping);

ROGGEN MANAGEMENT CONSULTANTS, INC.
223 Egremont Plain Rd #603, North Egremont, MA, 01230, USA; tel (413) 528-2300; fax (413) 528-2300; e-mail mark.roggen@roggenconsultants.com; mnroggen@aol.com; web site www.roggenconsultants.com
Pres.—Mark N. Roggen
Industry: Newspaper Distribution & Logistics Consultant

ROLLEM CORP. OF AMERICA
95 Hoffman Ln Ste T, Islandia, NY, 11749-5020, USA; tel (516) 485-6655; fax (516) 485-5936; e-mail info@rollemusa.com; web site www.rollemusa.com
Vice Pres., Sales—Richard Nigro
Industry: Numbering Machines

ROOSEVELT PAPER
1 Roosevelt Dr, Mount Laurel, NJ, 08054-6312, USA; tel (856) 303-4100; fax (856) 642-1949; e-mail info@rooseveltpaper.com; web site www.rooseveltpaper.com
Pres.—David Kosloff
Vice Pres., Sales/Mktg.—Eric Conine
Mktg. Dir.—Lynn Perce
Industry: Newsprint; Paper: Coated Groundwood Offset; Paper: Specialty Printing Paper;

ROSBACK CO.
125 Hawthorne Ave, Saint Joseph, MI, 49085-2636, USA; tel (269) 983-2582; fax (269) 983-2516; e-mail rosbacksales@qtm.net; web site www.qtm.net/rosback
Pres.—Larry R. Bowman
Vice Pres., Sales/Mktg.—Ron F. Bowman
Industry: Adhesives; Collating Equipment; Equipment Dealers (New); Folding Machines;

ROTADYNE CORP.
8140 S Cass Ave, Darien, IL, 60561-5013, USA; tel (630) 769-9700; fax (630) 769-9255; e-mail rotadynecorp@rotadyne.com; web site www.rotadyne.com
Vice Pres., OEM Sales—John A. Costello
Vice Pres. Industrial Sales—John Kaminski
Vice Pres. Graphic Sales—John Breau
Industry: Blankets; Roll Coverings; Rollers; Rollers: Dampening;

ROTOFLEX MARK ANDY CANADA, INC.
420 Ambassador Dr., Mississauga, ON, L5T 2R5, Canada; tel (905) 670-8700; fax (905) 670-3402; e-mail sales@rotoflex.com; web site www.rotoflex.com
Vice Pres., Finance—Rod Allen
Dir., Mfg.—Brian Nicoll
Gen. Mgr./Vice Pres., Sales/Mktg.—Val Rimas
Industry: Conversion Equipment; Dies (Perforating and Slitting); Rewinders;

ROWLETT ADVERTISING SERVICE, INC.
PO Box 50, Goodlettsville, TN, 37070-0050,

USA; tel (615) 859-6609; fax (615) 851-7187;
e-mail rowlettadvertising@att.net; web site
www.rowlettadv.com
Pres.—Richard Rowlett
Sec./Treasurer—Mary Belcher
Industry: Church Page Advertising Sales

ROYAL CONSUMER INFORMATION PRODUCTS, INC.
2 Riverview Dr Ste 1, Somerset, NJ, 08873-
1150, USA; tel (732) 627-9977; fax (800)
232-9769; e-mail info@royalsupplies.com;
web site www.royal.com
Pres.—Salomon Suwalsky
Vice Pres., Sales (Royal)—Terry Setar
Mgr., Sales/Supplies—Wendy Donnelly
Industry: Facsimilie/Fax Transmission Systems;
Laser Printers;

RYCOLINE PRODUCTS, INC.
5540 N Northwest Hwy, Chicago, IL, 60630-
1134, USA; tel (773) 775-6755; fax (773)
775-9414; web site www.rycoline.com
Gen. Mgr.—Dennis Sweet
Industry: Blankets; Chemicals: Plate
Processing; Chemicals: Pressroom;
Circulation Equipment & Supplies; Cleaners
& Solvents; Offset Blanket Thickness Gauge;
Offset Blankets, Blanket Wash; Offset
Chemicals & Supplies; Offset Fountain
Solutions;

RYDER SYSTEM, INC.
11690 NW 105th St, Medley, FL, 33178-
1103, USA; tel (305) 500-3726; fax (305)
500-4339; web site www.ryder.com
Chrmn./Pres./CEO—Gregory Swienton
Sr. Vice Pres., Sales/Mktg.—Thomas
Renehan
Industry: Lift Trucks

S

SAKURAI USA
1700 Basswood Rd, Schaumburg, IL, 60173-
5318, USA; tel (847) 490-9400; fax (847)
490-4200; e-mail sales@sakurai.com; info@
sakurai.com; inquiry@sakurai.com; web site
www.sakurai.com
Vice Pres., Sales—Don Bence
Industry: Presses: Offset

SALES DEVELOPMENT SERVICES
600 N Cleveland Ave Ste 260, Westerville,
OH, 43082-7265, USA; tel (614) 794-
0500; fax (614) 961-3268; e-mail info@
salesdevelopment.com; web site www.
sdsinc.com
Vice Pres., Opns.—Christine Hunt
Industry: Consulting Services: Advertising;
Consulting Services: Computer; Consulting
Services: Marketing; Facsimilie/Fax
Transmission Systems; Integrated Fax
Servers; Market Research; Marketing
Database Design and Implementation;
Software: Advertising (Includes Display;
Classified); Trade Publications;

SALES TRAINING CONSULTANTS, INC.
5550 Glades Rd Ste 515, Boca Raton, FL,
33431, USA; tel (561) 482-8801; e-mail
akemper@salestrainingconsultants.com; web
site www.newspapertraining.com
Pres.—Alice Kemper
Consultant/Trainer—Diane Rossi
Consultant/Trainer—Denise Zagnoli
Consultant/Trainer—Margo Berman
Consultant/Trainer—Ed Baron
Consultant/Trainer—Anne Stein
Industry: Training: Sales, Leadership,
Subscription Retention (Stopbusters),
Customer Service

SAMUEL STRAPPING SYSTEM
1401 Davey Rd Ste 300, Woodridge, IL,
60517-4991, USA; tel (800) 323-4424; fax
(630) 783-8901; e-mail info@samuelsystem.
com; web site www.samuelsystems.com
Industry: Bundling and Tying Machines;

Strapping Machines;

SAMUEL, SON & CO.
735 Oval Ct., Burlington, ON, L7L 6A9,
Canada; tel (905) 279-9580; fax (905) 639-
2290; e-mail packaging@samuel.com; web
site www.goval.com
U.S. Manager of Inside Sales and
Administration—Kevin McEldowney
Industry: Baling Machines; Bundling and Tying
Machines; Conveyors; Counting, Stacking,
Bundling Machines; Flooring; Mailroom
Systems & Equipment; Roll Handling
Equipment; Strapping Machines;

SAP AMERICA, INC.
18101 Von Karman Ave Ste 900, Irvine, CA,
92612-0151, USA; tel (949) 622-2200; e-mail
press@sap.com; web site www.sap.com
CFO—Mark White
Vice Pres., Global Adv./Branding—Costanza
Tedesco
Sr. Dir., Social Media Mktg.—Brian Ellefritz
Industry: Software: Advertising (Includes
Display; Classified); Software: Circulation;

SAPPI FINE PAPER NORTH AMERICA
255 State St Fl 4, Boston, MA, 02109-2618,
USA; tel (617) 423-7300; fax (617) 423-5494;
e-mail info@sappi.com; web site www.sappi.
com
Pres./CEO—Mark Gardner
Vice Pres., Finance/CFO—Annette Luchene
Vice Pres., Sales—Bob Forsberg
Industry: Paper: Coated Groundwood Offset;
Paper: Groundwood Specialties; Paper:
Specialty Printing Paper; Photostat: Paper;

SAXMAYER CORP.
PO Box 10, Blissfield, MI, 49228-0010, USA;
tel (517) 486-2164; fax (517) 486-2055;
e-mail info@saxmayercorp.com; web site
www.erichbaumeister.com
Pres., Mktg./Sales—Michael Vennekotter
Vice Pres., Engineering/Mfg.—James
Fischer
Process Supvr., Information Technology—
Jeremy Sell
Industry: Newsprint Handling Equipment;
Strapping Machines;

SAXOTECH
302 Knights Run Ave Ste 1150, Tampa, FL,
33602-5974, USA; tel (603) 472-5825; fax
(603) 472-3082; e-mail ussales@saxotech.
com; web site www.ckp.com; www.saxotech.
com
Pres.—Pat Stewart
Mng. Partner/CFO—Dick Mooney
Vice Pres., Opns.—James Mooney
Dir., Sales—Jeff Rapson
Industry: Pagination Systems; Software:
Advertising (Includes Display; Classified);
Software: Editorial; Software: Pagination/
Layout;

SAXOTECH, INC.
302 Knights Run Ave Ste 1150, Tampa, FL,
33602-5974, USA; tel 813-221-1600; fax 813-
221-1604; e-mail info@saxotech.com; web
site www.saxotech.com
CEO—Anders Christiansen
Director of Marketing—Robert Payne
Vice Pres., Cor. Mktg.—Paul Harris
Industry: Archiving Systems; News Wire
Capture Systems; Pagination Systems; Photo
Archiving; Publishing Systems; Software:
Asset Management; Software: Editorial;
Software: Pagination/Layout; Software:
Workflow Management/Tracking;

SCA PROMOTIONS, INC.
3030 Lbj Fwy Ste 300, Dallas, TX, 75234-
2753, USA; tel (214) 860-3700; fax (214)
860-3480; e-mail info@scapromo.com; web
site www.scapromotions.com
Pres.—Robert D. Hamman
Vice Pres., Sales—Shiela Bryan
Industry: Insurance; Newspaper Marketing;
Promotion Services;

SCARBOROUGH RESEARCH
770 Broadway Ste 200, New York, NY,
10003-9551, USA; tel (646) 654-8400; fax
(646) 654-8440; e-mail info@scarborough.
com; web site www.scarborough.com
Pres./CEO—Robert L. Cohen
Exec. Vice Pres./Dir., Sales—Steven Seraita
Vice Pres., Mktg./Commun.—Deirdre
McFarland
VP, Analytics and Insights—Ronald Mulder
Cynthia Methvin
Industry: Consulting Services: Advertising;
Consulting Services: Marketing; Market
Research; Newspaper Marketing; Research
Studies; Software: Advertising (Includes
Display; Classified); Training: Keyboard
Operation;

SCHAEFER MACHINE CO., INC.
200 Commercial Dr, Deep River, CT, 06417-
1682, USA; tel (860) 526-4000; fax (860)
526-4654; e-mail schaefer01@snet.net; web
site www.schaeferco.com
Pres.—Bob Gammons
Vice Pres.—Virginia Gammons
Industry: Adhesives; Gluing Systems;

SCHAWK
1 N Dearborn St Ste 700, Chicago, IL,
60602-4340, USA; tel (312) 943-0400; fax
(312) 943-2450; web site www.schawk.com
Sales Mgr.—Jamie Mandarion
Industry: Color Management Software; Library
Retrieval Systems; Preprint Service &
Production; Storage Retrieval Systems;

SCHERMERHORN BROS. CO.
340 Eisenhower Ln N, Lombard, IL,
60148-5470, USA; tel (630) 627-9860;
fax (630) 627-1178; web site www.
schermerhornbrosco.com
Sales Contact—Dennis Jenkins
Industry: Circulation Equipment & Supplies

SCHLENK-BOTH INDUSTRIES
40 Nickerson Rd, Ashland, MA, 01721-1912,
USA; tel (508) 881-4100; fax (508) 881-1278;
e-mail customer.service@schlenkboth.com;
web site www.schlenk-both.com/
Pres.—Brian Kelly
Industry: Inks

SCHUR INTERNATIONAL A/S
J.W. Schurs Vej 1, Dk-8700 Horsens, N/A,
N/A, Denmark; tel +45 7627 2727; fax +45
7627 2700; e-mail sin@schur.com; web site
www.schur.com
Owner—Hans Schur

SCHUR PACKAGING SYSTEMS, INC.
545 Busse Rd, Elk Grove Village, IL, 60007-
2116, USA; tel (847) 619-0068; fax (847)
619-0353; e-mail spi@schur.com; web site
www.schur.com
Parts/Serv. Dir.—Magnus Wall
President—Dan Kemper
Technical Sales Dir.—Gert Jensen
Industry: Mailroom Systems & Equipment;

SCREEN (USA)
5110 Tollview Dr, Rolling Meadows, IL,
60008-3715, USA; tel (847) 870-7400; fax
(847) 870-0149; e-mail rsiwicki@screenusa.
com; web site www.screenusa.com
Pres—Mike Fox
CFO—Robert Bernstein
Application Support Mgr.—Richard Siwicki
Opns. Mgr.—Edvardo Navarro
Industry: Color Proofing; Color Seperation
Scanners; Imagesetters; Proofing Systems;
Raster Image Processors; Software:
Pagination/Layout; Tables (Dot, Etch,
Opaquing, Register, Retouching, Stripping);

SEMLER INDUSTRIES, INC. (PRESSROOM FLUIDS EQUIPMENT DIV.)
3800 Carnation St, Franklin Park, IL, 60131-
1202, USA; tel (847) 671-5650; fax (847)
671-7686; e-mail semler@semlerindustries.

com; web site www.semlerindustries.com
Pres.—Loren H. Semler
Dir. Sales—William E. Schulz
Industry: Circulation Equipment & Supplies;
Fluid Handling: Pressroom; Ink Recovery
Systems; Ink Storage Tanks; Wastewater
Treatment;

SHOOM, INC.
6345 Balboa Blvd Ste 247, Encino, CA,
91316-1580, USA; tel (800) 446-6646; fax
(818) 755-9943; e-mail info@shoom.com;
web site www.shoom.com
Vice Pres., Customer Serv.—Sharon Ryoji
Industry: Software: Electronic Data Interchange

SHREVE SYSTEMS
3080 Knolin Dr Ste 2, Bossier City, LA,
71112-2465, USA; tel (318) 424-9791; fax
(318) 424-9771; e-mail ssystems@bellsouth.
net; web site www.shrevesystems.com
Pres.—Rich Harold
Industry: Computers: Hardware & Software
Integrators

SHUTTLEWORTH, LLC
10 Commercial Rd, Huntington, IN, 46750-
9044, USA; tel (260) 356-8500; fax (260)
359-7810; e-mail inc@shuttleworth.com; web
site www.shuttleworth.com
Industry: Conveyors; Masking Materials; Paper
Handling Equipment; Roll Handling
Equipment;

SIEBERT, INC.
8134 47th St, Lyons, IL, 60534-1836, USA;
tel (708) 442-2010; fax (708) 447-9353;
e-mail customerservice@siebertinc.com;
web site www.siebertinc.com
Pres.—J.P. Mulcahy
Industry: Chemicals: Roller Cleaning; Cleaners
& Solvents;

SIEMENS COMMUNICATIONS GROUP
900 Broken Sound Pkwy NW, Boca Raton,
FL, 33487-3513, USA; tel (561) 923-5000;
web site www.siemens.com
CFO/CIO—Michael Kutschenreuter
Media Rel.—Bill Makley
Sr. Vice Pres., Sales/Serv.—J. Licata
Industry: Telecommunications

SIGNODE CORP.
3600 W Lake Ave, Glenview, IL, 60026-1215,
USA; tel (847) 724-7500; fax (847) 657-4261;
web site www.itw.com
Pres.—David Steer
Vice Pres.—R. Flaum
Dir., Mktg. Commun.—Jim Fallon
Industry: Strapping Machines

SIIX USA CORP.
651 Bonnie Ln, Elk Grove Village, IL, 60007-
1911, USA; tel (847) 593-3211; fax (847)
364-5290; e-mail bpusczan@siix-usa.com;
web site www.siix.co.jp
Mgr., Sales/Engineering—Steve Swanson
Industry: Scanners: Color B & W, Plates, Web

SIMCO INDUSTRIAL STATIC CONTROL PRODUCTS
2257 N Penn Rd, Hatfield, PA, 19440-1998,
USA; tel (215) 822-6401; fax (215) 822-3795;
e-mail simcoind@itw.com; customerservice@
simcomail.com; sales@simco.biz; web site
www.simco-static.com
Customer Serv. Mgr.—Ed Huber
Technical Rep.—Brian Mininger
Industry: Inserting Equipment (Includes
Stuffing Machines); Paper Cleaners; Press
Accessories, Parts & Supplies; Static
Eliminators; Testing Instruments;

SIMON MILLER SALES CO.
3409 W Chester Pike Ste 204, Newtown
Square, PA, 19073-4290, USA; tel (215)
923-3600; fax (215) 923-1173; e-mail info@
simonmiller.com; web site www.simonmiller.
com

Pres.—Joseph Levit
COO—Henri C. Levit
Vice Pres., Mktg.—David Donde
Industry: Newspaper Couter; Newspaper Marketing; Newsprint; Paper: Coated Groundwood Offset; Paper: Groundwood Specialties; Paper: Specialty Printing Paper; Roll Converters;

SITMA USA, INC.
45 Empire Dr, Saint Paul, MN, 55103-1856, USA; tel (651) 222-2324; fax (651) 222-4652; e-mail sitmausa@sitma.com; web site www.sitma.com
Mktg. Mgr.—Ann Butzer
Industry: Automatic Plastic Bagging Equipment; Collating Equipment; Conveyors; Counting, Stacking, Bundling Machines; Feeding, Folding, Delivery Equipment; Folding Machines; Inserting Equipment (Includes Stuffing Machines); Mailroom Systems & Equipment; Remanufactures Equipment; Shrink Wrapping Equipment;

SKO BRENNER AMERICAN
841 Merrick Rd # CS9320, Baldwin, NY, 11510-3331, USA; tel (516) 771-4400; fax (516) 771-7810; e-mail stu@skobrenner.com; web site www.skobrenner.com
CEO—Stuart Brenner
COO—Jon R. Lunn
Sr. Vice Pres.—Jim Graziano
Industry: Credit & Collections

SMITH PRESSROOM PRODUCTS, INC.
9215 Bond St., Overland Park, KS, 66214, USA; tel (913) 888-0695; fax (913) 888-0699; e-mail info@smithpressroomproducts.com; web site www.smithpressroomproducts.com
Pres.—Dennis Schupp
VP—Ross Hart
Industry: Blanket Cleaner/Washer (Automatic); Dampening Systems; Offset Fountain Controls; Offset Fountain Solutions; Pumps (Air, Ink, Vacuum); Recirculators; Solvent Recovery Systems; Wastewater Treatment; Water Management Systems; Web Offset Remoisturizers;

SNAP-ON BUSINESS SOLUTIONS
4025 Kinross Lakes Pkwy, Richfield, OH, 44286-9371, USA; tel (330) 659-1600; fax (330) 659-1601; e-mail info@snaponbusinesssolutions.com; web site www.snaponbusinesssolutions.com
Pres.—Mary Beth Siddons
Industry: Computers: Storage Devices; Developing and Processing

SOFTWARE BUSINESS SYSTEMS
7401 Metro Blvd Ste 550, Edina, MN, 55439-3033, USA; tel (952) 835-0100; fax (952) 835-7504; e-mail admin@sbsweb.com; web site www.sbsweb.com
Pres.—Curtis Cerf
Vice Pres., Customer Service—Amy Pumarlo
Industry: Software: Business (Includes Administration/Accounting); Payroll/HR; Procurement; System Installations; System Integration Services;

SOFTWARE CONSULTING SERVICES, LLC
630 Municipal Dr Ste 420, Nazareth, PA, 18064-8990, USA; tel (610) 746-7700; fax (610) 746-7900; e-mail sales@newspapersystems.com; web site www.newspapersystems.com
Pres.—Richard J. Cichelli
Vice Pres., Opns.—Curtis Jackson
Mktg. Dir.—Martha J. Cichelli
Industry: Software: Advertising (Includes Display; Classified); Page Design (dummying); Editorial; Digital Asset Management; Ad Tracking; Managed Services

SOLAR SYSTEMS
PO Box 859, Preston, WA, 98050-0859, USA; tel (425) 270-6100; fax (425) 270-6150; e-mail info@solarsystems.com; web site www.solarsystems.com

CFO—Jean McCall
Industry: Computers: Hardware & Software Integrators; Remanufactures Equipment; Storage Retrieval Systems;

SOLNA WEB USA, INC.
PO Box 15066, Lenexa, KS, 66285-5066, USA; tel (913) 492-9925; fax (913) 492-0170; e-mail rkerns@solnaweb.com; web site www.solnaweb.com
Pres.—Richard Kerns
Industry: Presses: Offset

SONOCO PRODUCTS CO.
PO Box 160, Hartsville, SC, 29551-0160, USA; tel (843) 383-7000; fax (843) 383-7008; web site www.sonoco.com
Pres.—Harris Deloach
Division Vice Pres., Sales—Don Gore
Industry: Newspaper Bags; Recycling Newsprint; Tubes, Racks (Includes Racks: Motor Route Tubes);

SOUTH BEND LATHE CORP.
1735 N Bendix Dr, South Bend, IN, 46628-1601, USA; tel (574) 289-7771; fax (574) 236-1210; e-mail sales@southbendlathe.com; web site www.southbendlathe.com
Pres.—Carmine Martino
Vice Pres.—Joseph Mittiga
Industry: Roller Grinders

SOUTHERN LITHOPLATE, INC.
PO Box 9400, Wake Forest, NC, 27588-6400, USA; tel (800) 638-7990; fax (919) 556-1977; e-mail info@slp.com; web site www.slp.com
Chrmn./CEO—Edward A. Casson
Sr. VP—Steve Mattingly
VP Sales—Ted McGrew
Dir. Global Technical Solutions—Gary Blakeley
Industry: Chemicals: Plate Processing; Chemicals: Pressroom; Film & Paper: Film Processing Machines; Film & Paper: Filters (Photographic); Offset Chemicals & Supplies; Offset Film; Offset Fountain Solutions; Plate Processors; Plates: Offset (Computer to Plate); Plates: Offset (Conventional);

SPARTANICS
3605 Edison Pl, Rolling Meadows, IL, 60008-1077, USA; tel (847) 394-5700; fax (847) 394-0409; e-mail sales@spartanico.com; web site www.spartanics.com
VP., Sales/Mktg.—Mike Bacon
Industry: Laser Cutting Machines, Die Cutting Machines, Screen Printing Lanes, Plastic Card Counting, Plastic Card Inspection, Registration Shears

SPECTRA LOGIC
6285 Lookout Rd # 100, Boulder, CO, 80301-3318, USA; tel (303) 449-6400; fax (303) 939-8844; e-mail sales@spectralogic.com; web site www.spectralogic.com
Dir., Cor. Mktg.—Molly Rector
Industry: Computers: Hardware & Software Integrators; Library Retrieval Systems;

SPECTRECOM CORPORATION
10226 Petit Ave, North Hills, CA, 91343-1018, USA; tel (818) 832-4111; fax (818) 832-8111; e-mail info@spectrecom.com; web site www.spectrecom.com
Pres.—Terry Allen
Vice Pres.—Sandra Allen
Industry: Consulting Services: Advertising; Consulting Services: Marketing; Market Research; Newspaper Marketing; Research Studies; Software: Advertising (Includes Display; Classified); Training: Keyboard Operation;

SPECTRUM HUMAN RESOURCE SYSTEMS CORP.
999 18th St Ste 200, Denver, CO, 80202-2424, USA; tel (303) 592-3200; fax (303) 595-9970; e-mail support@spectrumhr.com; web site www.spectrumhr.com

Pres.—Sybll Romley
Exec. Vice Pres.—Matthew Keitlen
Industry: Software: Asset Management; Software: Business (Includes Administration/Accounting);

SRDS, A KANTAR MEDIA COMPANY
1700 E Higgins Rd Ste 500, Des Plaines, IL, 60018-5610, USA; tel (847) 375-5000; fax (847) 375-5001; e-mail contact@srds.com; web site www.srds.com
CFO—Kevin McNally
President—Stephen Davis
Vice Pres., HR—Valerie LaMorte
VP, Information Sales & Client Service—Trish DeLaurier
Vice Pres., Pdct. Opns.—Gayle Paprocki
Vice Pres., Mktg./Bus. Devel.—Dave Kostolansky
VP Marketing Communications—Lindsay Morrison
Publisher—Ronald Speechley
Director, Data Services—June Levy
Sales Director, Southwest Region—John Cronan
Industry: Trade Publications

ST. LOUIS JOURNALISM REVIEW
PO Box 12474, Saint Louis, MO, 63132-0174, USA; tel (314) 991-1699; fax (314) 963-6104; e-mail sjreview@sbcglobal.net; web site www.sjreview.org
Ed.—Ed Bishop
Asst. Gen. Mgr.—Erica Burleson
Industry: Consulting Services: Editorial

STANFORD PRODUCTS
1139 S Broadway Ave, Salem, IL, 62881-2404, USA; tel (618) 548-2600; fax (618) 548-6782; web site www.stanfordproductsllc.com
Customer Serv. Mgr.—Deann Sager
Sales Mgr.—Tim Andrews
Sales Mgr.—Larry Boyles
Industry: Rewinders

STEEL CITY CORP.
1000 Hedstrom Dr, Ashland, OH, 44805-3587, USA; tel (800) 321-0350; fax (330) 797-2947; e-mail jsmith@scity.com; web site www.scity.com
National Sales Mgr.—Jim Smith
Customer Service—Deb Walker
Operations Manager—Scott VanGilder
Industry: In addition to offering traditional circulation and distribution supplies (Home Delivery/Single Copy), Steel City Corp. now offers a digital in-store display; providing publishers an opportunity to increase circulation and advertising revenue .The company also provides circulation marketing ideas via their Gaining Readers and Subscribers Program (G.R.A.S.P).

STERLING PACKAGING SYSTEMS
6275 Heisley Rd, Mentor, OH, 44060-1858, USA; tel (440) 358-7060; fax (440) 358-7061; web site www.polychem.com
Gen. Mgr.—Mihia Cojocaru
Industry: Bundling and Tying Machines; Consulting Services: Equipment; Conveyors; Mailroom Systems & Equipment; Remanufactures Equipment;

STERLING TYPE FOUNDRY
PO Box 50234, Indianapolis, IN, 46250-0234, USA; tel (317) 849-5665; fax (317) 849-1616; web site www.sterlingtype.com
Works Mgr.—David C. Churchman
Industry: Platemakers: Letterpress; Presses: Letterpress; Type, Fonts;

STEWART GLAPAT CORP.
PO Box 3030, Zanesville, OH, 43702-3030, USA; tel (740) 452-3601; fax (740) 452-9140; e-mail sglapat@adjustoveyor.com; web site www.adjustoveyor.com
C.E.O and Chairman—Charles T. Stewart
Sales Manager —David T. Stewart
Executive Vice President—Amy Stewart

President & C.O.O —William T. Stewart
Director of Engineering—Mike Hinton
Production Manager—Russ Lindamood
Purchasing Manager—Jerry Funk
Spare Parts Sales Mgr. —Ron Bachelor
Industry: Material Handling Equipment: Telescopic Conveyors, Truck Loaders & Unloaders

STM NETWORKS
2 Faraday, Irvine, CA, 92618-2737, USA; tel (949) 753-7864; fax (949) 273-6020; e-mail info@stmi.com; web site www.stmi.com
Chrmn.—Emil Youssefzadeh
COB—Faramarz Youssefzadeh
Vice Pres., Sales—Umar Javed
Vice Pres., Mktg.—Rick Forberg
Industry: Facsimilie/Fax Transmission Systems; Interfaces;

STOCK, FUND, OR ETF
122 Mill Pond Lane, PO Box 488, Water Mill, NY, 11976, USA; tel (631) 204-9100; fax (631) 204-0002; e-mail stevea@hamptons.com; web site www.VATinfo.org
Pres.—Steve Abramson
Vice Pres.—Jane E. Nichols
Office Mgr.—Joan Dalessandro
Industry: Process Color Reference Guides

STORAENSO
201 Broad St, Stamford, CT, 06901-2004, USA; tel (203) 359-5707; fax (203) 359-5858; web site www.storaenso.com
Mgr., Mktg.—Paul Lukaszewski
Industry: Paper: Coated Groundwood Offset

SUNSHINE PAPER CO.
12601 E 33rd Ave Ste 109, Aurora, CO, 80011-1839, USA; tel (303) 341-2990; fax (303) 341-2995; e-mail mgallagher@sunshinepaper.com; web site www.sunshinepaper.com
Vice Pres., Sales/Mktg.—Michael S. Gallagher
Adv. Customer Info Serv.—Geri Hancock
Industry: Calibrated Under-Packing made from Fiber Based, Synthetic, Compressible and Hybrid materials, ParaTex compressible under lay, Plate and Blanket Under-Packing, Offset Blanket Thickness Gauge; Offset Supplies; Ink Jet Papers and Substrates,

SUPERIOR HANDLING EQUIPMENT, INC.
8 Aviator Way, Ormond Beach, FL, 32174-2983, USA; tel (800) 721-4339; fax (386) 677-0022; e-mail info@superiorlifts.com; web site www.superiorlifts.com
President—Beth Vollmar
Industry: Material Handling Equipment: Truck Loaders; Material Handling Equipment: Vehicle Loading; Paper Handeling Equipment;

SUPERIOR LITHOPLATE OF INDIANA, INC.
PO Box 192, Rockville, IN, 47872-0192, USA; tel (765) 569-2094; fax (765) 569-2096; web site www.superiorlithoplate.com
Pres.—Robert T. Blane
Vice Pres.—Steven C. Blane
Office Mgr.—Miriam Blane
Nat'l Sales Mgr.—Thomas J. Casson
Industry: Chemicals: Plate Processing; Chemicals: Pressroom; Offset Chemicals & Supplies; Plate Cleaners; Platemakers: Offset (Conventional);

SUPPORT PRODUCTS, INC.
PO Box 1185, Effingham, IL, 62401-1185, USA; tel (217) 536-6171; fax (217) 536-6828; e-mail supprot@supportproducts.com; custserv@supportproducts.com; sales@supportproducts.com; web site www.supportproducts.com
CEO—Jim Calhoon
Dir., Sales—Rob Bradshaw
Industry: Adhesives; Chemicals: Roller Cleaning; Composing Room Equipment & Supplies; Ink Fountains & Accessories;

Layout Tables, Light Tables & Workstations; Masking Materials; Offset Blanket Thickness Gauge; Plate Cleaners; Rules; Static Eliminators;

SUPPORT SYSTEMS INTERNATIONAL CORP.

136 S 2nd St, Richmond, CA, 94804-2110, USA; tel (510) 234-9090; fax (510) 233-8888; e-mail sales@FiberMailbox.com; web site www.FiberOpticCableShop.com
Pres.—Ben Parsons
Industry: fiber optic cable assembly manufacturing; fiber optic related products.

SYNTELLECT, INC.

2095 W Pinnacle Peak Rd Ste 110, Phoenix, AZ, 85027-1262, USA; tel (602) 789-2800; fax (602) 789-2768; e-mail info.ie@enghouse.com; web site www.syntellect.com
Pres.—Steve Dodenhoff
CFO—Peter Pamplin
Vice Pres., Sales Americas—Keith Gyssler
Vice Pres., Pdct. Mktg.—Tricia Lester
Contact—Jackie Dasta
Industry: Computers: Hardware & Software Integrators; Computers: Local Area Network (LANS); Consulting Services: Advertising; Consulting Services: Circulation; Consulting Services: Equipment; Consulting Services: Marketing; Speech Recognition; Subscription Fulfillment Software; System Integration Services; Telecommunications;

SYSTEMS TECHNOLOGY, INC.

1351 E. Riverview Dr., San Bernardino, CA, 92408, USA; tel (909) 799-9950; fax (909) 796-8297; e-mail info@systems-technology-inc.com; web site www.systems-technology-inc.com
Pres.—John St. John
Sales. Dir.—Brad Siegel
Industry: Bundling and Tying Machines; Counting, Stacking, Compensating Stackers, Count-O-Veyors, Bundling Machines; Cutters & Trimmers; In-Line Trimming Systems; Material Handling Equipment: Palletizing Machines; Strapping Machines;
Conveyors

T

TAFT CONTRACTING CO. (NOT AFFILIATED W/TAFT EQPT. CO.)

9000 67th St, Hodgkins, IL, 60525-7606, USA; tel (708) 656-7500; fax (708) 656-8945; e-mail info@taftcontracting.com; web site www.taftcontracting.com
CEO—Richard J. Walsh
Pres., Sales—Michael Walsh
Vice Pres., Field Servs.—John Bianchi
Industry: Erectors & Riggers

TALLY GENICOM

14600 Myford Rd, Irvine, CA, 92606-1005, USA; tel (714) 368-2300; fax (714) 368-2335; e-mail info@printronix.com; web site www.tallygenicom.com
CEO—Randy Eisendach
Dir., Mktg.—Karen Jensen
Industry: Laser Printers

TALX CORP.

11432 Lackland Rd, Saint Louis, MO, 63146-3516, USA; tel (314) 214-7000; fax (314) 214-7588; e-mail moreinfo@talx.com; web site www.talx.com
CEO—William Canfield
Vice Pres., Market Devel.—Michael Smith
Industry: Speech Recognition

TAPCLICKS

3101 Tisch Way, Suite 1002, San Jose, CA, 95128-2533, USA; tel 408-725-2942; e-mail sales@tapclicks.com; web site www.tapclicks.com
Industry: Marketing Technology
Big Data
Marketing Analytics

TECH-ENERGY CO.

1111 Schneider, Cibolo, TX, 78108-3101, USA; tel (210) 658-0614; fax (210) 658-0653; e-mail techenergy@techenergy.com; web site www.techenergy.com
Pres.—John E. Pickard
Vice Pres.—Beth Benke
Sec.—Phyllis Pickard
Treasurer—Teresa Moeller
Serv. Mgr.—Louis Benke
Int'l Sales Mgr.—Rachel Bell
Nat'l Sales Mgr.—David N. Moeller
Industry: Blanket Mounting and Bars; Blankets; Ink Fountains & Accessories; Press Accessories, Parts & Supplies; Press Engineers; Press Rebuilding; Press Repairs; Presses: Letterpress; Presses: Offset; Rollers;

TECHNIDYNE CORP.

100 Quality Ave, New Albany, IN, 47150-7222, USA; tel (812) 948-2884; fax (812) 945-6847; e-mail spectrum@technidyne.com; web site www.technidyne.com
Pres./CEO—M. Todd Popson
Bus. Dir.—Paul M. Crawford
Vice Pres., Sales/Mktg.—Thomas Crawford
Mgr., Technical Servs.—Patrick Robertson
Industry: Color Analyzers; Color Management Software; Equipment Dealers (New); Equipment Dealers (Used); Paper Testing Instruments;

TECHNOLOGY INTEGRATORS

PO Box 334, Effingham, IL, 62401-0334, USA; tel 217-342-3981; fax 217-3421286; web site www.technologyintegrators.net; www.airstamping.com
Sales Engineer—Gene Williams
Sales Engineer—Troy Ramey
Acct. Exec.—Kim Schmidt
Industry: Press Accessories, Parts & Supplies; Vacuum Frames;

TECHNOTRANS AMERICA, INC.

1050 E Business Center Dr, Mount Prospect, IL, 60056-2180, USA; tel (847) 227-9200; fax (847) 227-9400; e-mail ttasales@technotrans.com; info@technotrans.com; web site www.technotrans.com
Vice Pres.—Thomas Carbery
Sales Admin.—Victoria Moore
Industry: Blanket Cleaner/Washer (Automatic); Dampening Systems; Dies (Perforating and Slitting); Water Management Systems; Web Offset Remoisturizers;

TEK-TOOLS, INC.

4040 McEwen Rd Ste 240, Dallas, TX, 75244-5032, USA; tel (972) 980-2890; fax (972) 866-0714; e-mail contact@tek-tools.com; web site www.tek-tools.com
Pres./CEO—Ken Barth
Dir., Sales—Cindy Whitley
Dir., Mktg.—Stephen Harding
Industry: Software: Advertising (Includes Display; Classified); Software: Editorial; Software: Electronic Data Interchange; Software: Workflow Management/Tracking;

TEL-AIRE PUBLICATIONS, INC.

3105 E John Carpenter Fwy, Irving, TX, 75062-4933, USA; tel (972) 438-4111; fax (972) 579-7483; e-mail sales@tel-aire.com; web site www.tel-aire.com
Pres.—David McGee
Industry: Trade Publications

TELESONIC PACKAGING CORP., AMES ENGINEERING DIV.

805 E 13th St, Wilmington, DE, 19802-5000, USA; tel (302) 658-6945; fax (302) 658-6946; e-mail telesonics@aol.com; web site www.telesoniconline.com
Pres.—Bernard Katz
Industry: Automatic Plastic Bagging Equipment; Shrink Wrapping Equipment; Packaging machinery

TELETYPE CO.

20 Park Plz, Boston, MA, 02116-4303, USA; tel (617) 542-6220; fax (617) 542-6289; e-mail info@teletype.com; web site www.teletype.com
—Marlene Winer
—Edward FreemanMktg. Mgr.s
Industry: Publishing Systems

TEMBEC

405 The West Mall, Ste. 800, Etobicoke, ON, M9C 5J1, Canada; tel (416) 775-2801; fax (416) 621-4303; web site www.tembec.com
Pres.—Chris Black
Account Executive—Earle Alain
VP, Sales & Marketing—Yardley Renee
Industry: Newsprint

TENSOR INTERNATIONAL LLC

10330 Argonne Woods Dr Ste 300, Woodridge, IL, 60517-5088, USA; tel (630) 739-9600; fax (630) 739-9339; e-mail info@ustensor.com; web site www.ustensor.com
Chief Operating Officer and V. P. of Sales—Michael Pavone
President—Mattias Andersson
Industry: Presses: Offset

TERA DIGITAL PUBLISHING

40 Richards Ave Ste 29, Norwalk, CT, 06854-2322, USA; tel (203) 838-2333; fax (203) 838-4473; e-mail info@miles33.com; web site www.teradp.com
Sr. VP Sales—Don Sullivan
VP Marketing and Sales for Western USA—Albert De Bruijn
Industry: Consulting Services: Editorial; Software: Editorial Content Management Systems; Software: Web Publishing; Software: Digital Asset Management/Archiving

TEUFELBERGER GMBH

Vogelweiderstrasse 50, Wels, N/A, 4600, Austria; tel 43 7242 4130; fax 43 7242 413100; e-mail fibersplastics@teufelberger.com; mailbox@teufelberger.com; web site www.teufelberger.com
Owner—Teufel Seuz
Mgr., Mktg./Sales Agriculture—Harald Katzinger
Industry: Bundling and Tying Machines; Counting, Stacking, Bundling Machines; Strapping Machines;

THE AUSTIN COMPANY

6095 Parkland Blvd Ste 100, Cleveland, OH, 44124-6140, USA; tel (440) 544-2600; fax (440) 544-2690; e-mail austin.info@theaustin.com; ne@theaustin.com; web site www.theaustin.com
Gen. Mgr.—Curt Miller
Vice Pres., Planning/Design—Duane Lofdahl
Sr. Vice Pres., Sales/Mktg. Gen. Mgr.—Michael G. Pierce
Sr. Newspaper Consultant—Michael Craft
Industry: Architects/Engineers (Includes Design/Construction Firms); Consulting Services: Equipment; Consulting Services: Financial; Consulting Services: Marketing; Consulting Services: Production; Mailroom Systems & Equipment; Maintenance, Plant & Equipment; Newsprint Handling Equipment; Roll Handling Equipment; System Integration Services

THE CANNON GROUP, INC.

5037 Pine Creek Dr, Westerville, OH, 43081-4849, USA; tel (614) 890-0343; fax (614) 890-0467; e-mail sales@pdisaneck.com; web site www.newsbags.com
Pres.—Frank Cannon
Industry: Circulation Supplies and Equipment

THE DOW CHEMICAL CO.

2030 Dow Ctr, Midland, MI, 48674-2030, USA; tel (989) 636-1000; fax (989) 636-3518; e-mail dowmedia.relations@dow.com; web site www.dow.com
Chrmn./Pres./CEO—Andrew Liveris

Vice Pres., Global Pub. Aff.—Matt Davis
Vice Pres./Treasurer—Fernando Ruiz
Industry: Adhesives; Cleaners & Solvents;

THE GAZETTE COMPANY

501 2nd Ave SE, Cedar Rapids, IA, 52401-1303, USA; tel (319) 398-8422; fax (319) 368-8505; e-mail customercare@thegazettecompany.com; web site www.thegazettecompany.com
Chrmn.—Joe Hadky
President and CEO—Chuck Peters
VP Sales & Marketing—Chris Edwards

THE HASKELL CO.

PO Box 44100, Jacksonville, FL, 32231-4100, USA; tel (904) 791-4500; fax (904) 791-4699; web site www.thehaskellco.com
Pres.—Steve Halverson
Resource Center Administrator—Sara Guthrie
Industry: Architects/Engineers (Includes Design/Construction Firms); Consulting Services: Equipment;

THE KEENAN GROUP, INC.

PO Box 458, Pleasant View, TN, 37146-0458, USA; tel (615) 746-2443; fax (615) 746-2270; e-mail info@keenangroup.com; web site www.keenangroup.com
Pres.—Robert P. Keenan
Vice Pres., Sales/Mktg.—Debra B. Keenan
Industry: Consulting Services: Advertising; Consulting Services: Circulation; Consulting Services: Equipment; Consulting Services: Marketing; Consulting Services: Production; Newspaper Bags; Newspaper Dispensers (Mechanical/Electronic); Newspaper Marketing;

THE NEWARK GROUP

312 E Ellawood Ave, Cedartown, GA, 30125-3902, USA; tel (770) 748-3715; fax (770) 748-7414
Vice Pres.—Mickey Thompson
Sales Mgr.—Randy Tillery
Industry: Newsprint Handling Equipment

THE SEYBOLD REPORT

130 W. Main Street, Suite 144-175, Trappe, PA, 19426, USA; tel 484 206-4233; e-mail contact@thejossgroup.com; web site www.seyboldreport.com
Publisher, Editor, Owner—Molly Joss
Industry: Trade Publications

THE SLATONITE

PO Box 667, Slaton, TX, 79364-0667, USA; tel 806-828-6201; fax 806-828-6202; e-mail slatonit@sbcglobal.net; web site www.slatonitenews.com
Ed./Pub.—Ken Richardson
Managing Editor—James Villanueva
Production Editor / advertising director—D'Etta Brown
Business Manager—Malva Richardson
Copy Editor—Gloria Olivares
Industry: newspaper, advertising

THE SOFTWARE CONSTRUCTION CO. (SCC)

3810 Hamby Rd, Alpharetta, GA, 30004-3953, USA; tel (770) 751-8500; fax (770) 772-6800; e-mail sales@sccmediaserver.com; web site www.sccmediaserver.com
CEO—Rick Marucci
Vice Pres.—Lee Funnell
Industry: Software: Digital Asset Management; Software: Multimedia Photo Story Archiving; Software: News Budgeting; Software: Workflow Management; Software: Assignment Tracking; Software: Syndicated Data Delivery

THE WELLMARK COMPANY

1903 SE 29th St, Oklahoma City, OK, 73129-7625, USA; tel (405) 672-6660; fax (405) 672-6661; e-mail twc@wellmarkco.com; web site www.wellmarkco.com

Pres.—Dick Pfieffer
VP Sales/Mktg.—Steve Lawson
Industry: Gauges, Measuring; Ink Storage Tanks;

THOUGHT EQUITY MANAGEMENT, INC.
1530 16th St Ste 600, Denver, CO, 80202-1447, USA; tel (720) 382-2869; fax (720) 382-2719; e-mail sales@thoughtequity.com; web site www.thoughtequity.com
Founder/CEO—Kevin Schaff
CTO—Mark Lemmons
Vice Pres., Mktg.—Mike Emerson
Vice Pres., Bus. Devel.—Frank Cardello
Industry: Electronic Ad Delivery

TIDLAND CORP.
2305 SE 8th Ave, Camas, WA, 98607-2261, USA; tel (360) 834-2345; fax (360) 834-5865; e-mail tidland@tidland.com; web site www.tidland.com
Media Mgr.—Kasey Morales
Mktg. Commun.—Michelle Pass
Industry: Chemicals: Chuck (Paper Roll); Consulting Services: Equipment; Conversion Equipment; Core Cutters, Restorers, Rounders; Cutters & Trimmers; Cutting Tools; Reels & Tensions; Reels (Inlcudes Paper Reels); Tension & Web Controls; Web Press - Special Equipment;

TILT-LOCK
12070 43rd St NE, Saint Michael, MN, 55376-8427, USA; tel (800) 999-8458; fax (763) 497-7046; e-mail sales@tiltlock.com; web site www.tiltlock.com
Sales Mgr.—Jerry Morton
Industry: Chemicals: Chuck (Paper Roll); Roll Handling Equipment;

TKM UNITED STATES, INC.
PO Box 75015, Cincinnati, OH, 45275-0015, USA; tel (859) 689-7094; fax (859) 689-7565; e-mail sales@tkmus.com; web site www.tkmus.com
Market Mgr.—Michael Clark
Industry: Cutters & Trimmers

TKS (USA), INC.
3001 E Plano Pkwy Ste 200, Plano, TX, 75074-7480, USA; tel (972) 983 0600; fax (972) 870-5857; e-mail sales@tkspress.com; web site www.tksusa.com
Vice President of Sales and Marketing—Mike Shafer
Industry: Presses: Offset and digital ink jet and gripper conveyor

TKS LTD.
26-24 Shiba 5-Chome Minato-Ku, Tokyo, N/A, 108-8375, Japan; tel +81 3 3451-8141; fax +81 3 3451-7425; e-mail overseas@tks-net.co.jp; web site www.tks-net.co.jp
Pres.—Noriyuki Shiba
Sales Chief Officer—Osamu Kurata

TNS GLOBAL
11 Madison Ave Ste 1201, New York, NY, 10010-3624, USA; tel (212) 991-6000; e-mail enquiries@tnsglobal.com; web site www.tnsglobal.com
—Leendert De Voogd
—Mark FrancasSales Rep.s
Industry: Consulting Services: Advertising; Consulting Services: Marketing; Market Research;

TOBIAS ASSOCIATES, INC.
PO Box 2699, Ivyland, PA, 18974-0347, USA; tel (800) 877-3367; fax (215) 322-1504; e-mail sales@tobiasinc.com; web site www.densitometer.com
Vice Pres.—Eric M. Tobias
Sales Mgr.—William D. Bender
Industry: Calibration Software/Hardware; Color Analyzers; Dark Room Equipment; Densitometers; Electronic Pre-Scan Systems; Press Accessories, Parts & Supplies; Testing Instruments;

TOLERANS AB SWEDEN
P.O Box 669, Tyreso, N/A, 135 26, Sweden; tel +46 8 4487030; fax +46 8 4487040; e-mail info@tolerans.com; web site www.tolerans.com
CEO—Jan Melin
Industry: Printing

TOWER PRODUCTS, INC.
PO Box 3070, Palmer, PA, 18043-3070, USA; tel (610) 253-6206; fax (610) 258-9695; e-mail info@towerproducts.com; web site www.towerproducts.com
Pres./CEO—Richard Principato
Industry: Chemicals: Pressroom; Chemicals: Roller Cleaning; Cleaners & Solvents; Fountain Solutions, Low VOC Cleaners

TRANSPORTATION CONSULTANTS, INC.
8302 Dunwoody Pl Ste 352, Atlanta, GA, 30350-3351, USA; tel (404) 250-0100; fax (404) 250-0253; e-mail tci@transpconsult.com; web site www.transpconsult.com
Pres.—Paul Gold
Industry: Consulting Services: Fleet Operations

TRAUNER CONSULTING SERVICES, INC.
1617 John F Kennedy Blvd Frnt, Philadelphia, PA, 19103-1856, USA; tel (215) 814-6400; fax (215) 814-6440; e-mail philadelphia@traunerconsulting.com; web site www.traunerconsulting.com
Mgr., New Bus.—Russ Thomas
Industry: Architects/Engineers (Includes Design/Construction Firms); Training: Keyboard Operation;

TRIBUNE MEDIA SERVICES
333 Glen St Ste 400, Glens Falls, NY, 12801-3564, USA; tel (518) 792-9914; fax (518) 761-7118; e-mail tvdata@tvdata.com; web site www.tvdata.com, www.clicktv.com
Pres.-Publishing Division—Roger Moore
CFO/Sr. Vice Pres.-New Bus. Devel.—Kenneth Carter
Sr. Vice Pres.-Sales—Kathleen Tolstrup
Sr. Vice Pres.-Info Systems—James McCormick
Vice Pres.-Opns.—John McVay
Vice Pres.-Newspaper/Sales—Cameron Yung
Vice Pres.-Newspaper Grp. Sales—Bill Callahan
Vice Pres.-Metro Newspaper Sales—John Dodds
Vice Pres.-Editorial—Rob Plocharczyk
Dir., Regl. Sales—Bill Ranney
Mgr.-Online Product—Kevin Joyce
Account Executive—Ken Hyatt
Industry: Software: Pagination/Layout; Training: Design & Layout;

TRUPROOF LTD.
Unit 7 Bldg. B Faircharm Trading Estate, London, N/A, SE8 3DX, United Kingdom; tel +44 181 694-8588; fax +44 181 443-288; e-mail info@truproof.co.uk; sales@truproof.co.uk
Mng. Dir.—G.M. Walden
Industry: Cabinets; Color Proofing; Color Viewing Equipment; Densitometers; Laser Printers; Layout Tables, Light Tables & Workstations; Prepress Color Proofing Systems; Storage Retrieval Systems;

TSA
2050 W Sam Houston Pkwy N, Houston, TX, 77043-2422, USA; tel (713) 935-1500; fax (713) 935-1555; e-mail info@tsa.com; web site www.tsa.com
Pres.—William C. Smith
Sales Mgr.—Steven Perry
Servs. Devel. Mgr.—Rick Valanta
Industry: Computers: Hardware & Software Integrators; Equipment Dealers (New); Equipment Dealers (Used);

U

U.S. PETROLON INDUSTRIAL
11442 Queens Dr, Omaha, NE, 68164-2229, USA; tel (402) 727-1577; fax (402) 445-8608; e-mail al@uspetrolon.com; web site www.uspetrolon.com
Regl. Distributor—Al Harrell
Industry: Fluid Handeling: Pressroom

UMAX TECHNOLOGIES, INC.
10460 Brockwood Rd, Dallas, TX, 75238-1640, USA; tel (214) 342-9799; fax (214) 342-9046; e-mail sales@umax.com; web site www.umax.com
Vice Pres., Mktg.—Tenny Sin
Sr. Line Mgr.—Linn Lin
Industry: Color Seperation Scanners; Scanners: Color B & W, Plates, Web;

UNICOM, INC.
PO Box 92730, Anchorage, AK, 99509-2730, USA; tel (907) 561-1674; fax (907) 563-3185; e-mail info@unicom-alaska.com; web site www.unicom-alaska.com
Vice Pres./Gen. Mgr.—Rob Taylor
Industry: Telecommunications

UNION RUBBER, INC.
PO Box 1040, Trenton, NJ, 08606-1040, USA; tel (609) 396-9328; fax (609) 396-3587; e-mail contact@best-testproducts.com; web site papercement.com
Pres.—Paul Neiber
Industry: Adhesives

UNIQUE PHOTO
123 US Highway 46, Fairfield, NJ, 07004-3225, USA; tel (973) 377-5555; fax (973) 377-8800; e-mail info@uniquephoto.com; sales@uniquephoto.com; web site www.uniquephoto.com
COO—Matthew Sweetwood
CFO—Jonathon Sweetwood
Industry: Cameras & Accessories; Chemicals: Photographic; Cutters & Trimmers; Dark Room Equipment; Developing and Processing; Film & Paper: Film Roll Dispensers; Film & Paper: Filters (Photographic); Lenses (Camera); Photography: Digital/Electronic Cameras; Photostat: Chemicals;

UNISYS CORP.
Unisys Way, Blue Bell, PA, 19424-0001, USA; tel (215) 986-6999; fax (215) 986-2312; e-mail info@unisys.com; investor@unisys.com; web site www.unisys.com
Chrmn./CEO—J. Edward Coleman
Sr. Vice Pres./CFO—Janet Brutschea Haugen
Vice Pres./Treasurer—Scott A. Battersby
Industry: Archiving Systems; Computers: Hardware & Software Integrators; Electronic Ad Delivery; Software: Advertising (Includes Display; Classified); Software: Business (Includes Administration/Accounting); Software: Editorial; Software: Pagination/Layout; Software: Workflow Management/Tracking; System Integration Services;

UNITED PAPER MILLS KYMMENE, INC.
1270 Avenue of the Americas Ste 203, New York, NY, 10020-1700, USA; tel (212) 218-8232; fax (212) 218-8240; web site www.upm.com
Pres.—Tapio Korpeinen
Exec. Vice Pres./CFO—Jyrki Salo
Industry: Newsprint

UNITED STATES POSTAL SERVICE
475 Lenfant Plz SW, Washington, DC, 20260-0004, USA; tel (202) 268-2500; fax (202) 268-5211; web site www.usps.gov; www.usps.com, www.usps.com/mailingonline
Chrmn.—James C. Miller
Postmaster General/CEO—John Potter
Deputy Postmaster General—Patrick R.

Donahoe
Exec. Vice Pres./CFO—Harold Walker
CMO—Anita J. Bizzotto
Exec. Vice Pres./Chief HR Officer—Anthony Vegliante
Sr. Vice Pres., Mktg. Devel.—John R. Wargo
Vice Pres., Product Devel.—Nicholas F. Barranca
Vice Pres./Treasurer—Robert Peterson
Mgr., Product Mktg.—Larry M. Speakes
Mgr., USPS Adv. Program/Media Planning—Al Gilbert
Industry: Mailroom Systems & Equipment

US INK
651 Garden St, Carlstadt, NJ, 07072-1609, USA; tel (201) 935-8666; fax (201) 933-3728; web site www.usink.com
Vice Pres., Sales—John C. Corcoran
Technical Dir.—Peter I. Ford
President—Michael Dodd
John Williams
Industry: Inks

USSPI MEDIA
424 E. State Pkwy., Ste. 228, Schaumburg, IL, 60173, USA; tel (847) 490-6000; fax (847) 843-9058; e-mail info@usspi.com; web site www.usspi.com
CEO—Phil Miller
VP Media Relations—Rick Baranski
Executive VP—Michelle Hammons
VP Sales—Barbara Ancona
Industry: Newspaper, email, digital solutions.

UTILIMASTER
603 Earthway Blvd, Bristol, IN, 46507-9182, USA; tel (574) 862-4561; fax (574) 862-4517; e-mail info@utilimaster.com; web site www.utilimaster.com
Sr. Vice Pres., Sales/Mktg.—John Marshall
Industry: Delivery Equipment

UV PROCESS SUPPLY, INC.
1229 W Cortland St, Chicago, IL, 60614-4805, USA; tel (773) 248-0099; fax (773) 880-6647; e-mail info@uvps.com; web site www.uvprocess.com
Pres.—Stephen Siegel
Industry: Color Analyzers; Drying Systems; Ink Bleeding Equipment; Ink Fountains & Accessories; Ink Pumping Systems; Ink Storage Tanks; Lubricants; Offset Chemicals & Supplies; Pumps (Air, Ink, Vacuum); Static Eliminators;

UVP, LLC
2066 W 11th St, Upland, CA, 91786-3509, USA; tel (909) 946-3197; fax (909) 946-3597; e-mail uvp@uvp.com; web site www.uvp.com
Pres.—Leighton Smith
Vice Pres., Mktg./Sales—Alex Waluszko
Commun. Mktg. Serv.—Kathy Buckman
Industry: Exposure Lamps; Inks;

V

VAN SON HOLLAND INK CORP. OF AMERICA
185 Oval Dr, Islandia, NY, 11749-1402, USA; tel (800) 645-4182; fax (800) 442-8744; e-mail info@vansonink.com; web site www.vansonink.com
Pres.—Joseph Bendowski
Industry: Inks

VEGRA USA
1621 W Carroll Ave, Chicago, IL, 60612-2501, USA; tel (312) 733-3400; fax (312) 738-2386; e-mail info@vegra.de; web site www.vegra.de
Vice Pres., Sales—Michael Miske
Industry: Chemicals: Pressroom; Core Strippers & Seperators; Dies (Perforating and Slitting); Offset Blankets, Blanket Wash; Offset Chemicals & Supplies; Offset Fountain Solutions; Static Eliminators;

VER-A-FAST CORPORATION
20545 Center Ridge Rd Ste 300, Rocky River, OH, 44116-3423, USA; tel (440) 331-0250; fax (440) 331-2701; e-mail bbensman@verafast.com; web site www.verafast.com
President—Robert Bensman
Exec. Vice Pres.—Cathy Soprano
Vice Pres., Mktg./Devel.—Nanette Kubera
Mktg./Research Specialist—James Tanner
Prodn. Mgr.—Carol Tanner
Computer Servs. Mgr.—Kim Taraba
Industry: Consulting Services: Circulation; Market Research; Research Studies; Telecommunications; Complete Data Services; Sunday Select; Complete Telemarketing Services Outbound

VERSAR INC.
6850 Versar Ctr Ste 1, Springfield, VA, 22151-4196, USA; tel (703) 750-3000; fax (703) 642-6807; e-mail info@versar.com; web site www.versar.com
Pres./CEO—Theodore M. Prociv
Industry: Architects/Engineers (Includes Design/ Construction Firms); System Installations;

VERTIS
250 W Pratt St Ste 1800, Baltimore, MD, 21201-6813, USA; tel (410) 528-9800; fax (410) 528-9289; e-mail info@vertisinc.com; web site www.vertisinc.com / www.vertis.co.uk
Industry: Software: Advertising (Includes Display; Classified)

VIDAR SYSTEMS CORP.
365 Herndon Pkwy Ste 105, Herndon, VA, 20170-6236, USA; tel (703) 471-7070; fax (703) 471-1165; e-mail medical@vidar.com; web site www.vidar.com
Industry: Scanners: Color B & W, Plates, Web

VIDEOJET TECHNOLOGIES INC.
1500 Mittel Blvd., Wood Dale, IL, 60191, USA; tel (630) 860-7300; fax (630) 582-1343; e-mail info@videojet.com; web site www.videojet.com
Industry: Addressing Machines; Inks; Label Printing Machines; Mailroom Systems & Equipment;

VISION DATA EQUIPMENT CORP.
1377 3rd St, Rensselaer, NY, 12144-1899, USA; tel (518) 434-2193; fax (518) 434-3457; e-mail sales@vdata.com; web site www.vdata.com
President—Dempsey Tom
Sales Mgr—Timothy Donnelly
Southwest U.S. Sales manager—Amy Weaver
Industry: Print & Digital Media Software: Total Advertising & sales management for print & web pubs. (Includes CRM, Sales, A/R/ Accounting, VisionWeb customer ad entry); Software: Total Circulation Management for print & web pubs; Software: Electronic Data Interchange; Software: Pagination/ Layout; Software: Ad tracking, production management; Software: Remote Workflow Management.

VOICEWORLD, INC.
11201 N 70th St, Scottsdale, AZ, 85254-5183, USA; tel (718) 252-3153; fax (480) 922-5572; e-mail prospects@voiceworld.com; web site www.voiceworld.com
Pres./Founder—Brian L. Berman
Industry: Business Computers; Consulting Services: Circulation; Telecommunications;

W

WALTER MEIER CLIMATE (USA), INC.
PO Box 698, Ogdensburg, NY, 13669-0698, USA; tel (315) 425-1255; fax (613) 822-7964; e-mail nortec@humidity.com; web site www.humidity.com
Pres.—Urs Schenk

Vice Pres., Sales—Gary Berlin
Vice Pres., Mktg.—Mike Hurley
Mktg. Coord.—Naomi Cassidy
Industry: Humidifiers

WALTERRY INSURANCE BROKERS
7411 Old Branch Ave, Clinton, MD, 20735-1323, USA; tel (301) 868-7200; fax (301) 868-2611; e-mail insurance@walterry.com; web site www.walterry.com
Dir., Mktg.—Walter J. Coady
Industry: Insurance

WEATHERLINE, INC.
12119 St. Charles Rock Rd., Saint Louis, MO, 63044, USA; tel (314) 291-1000; fax (314) 291-3226; e-mail info@weatherline.com; web site www.weatherline.com
Pres.—Richard H. Friedman
Exec. Vice Pres.—Michelle Parent
Sr. Vice Pres.—Nancy J. Friedman
Sr. Vice Pres.—Martha Murphy
Sr. Vice Pres.—Stephen L. Smith
Industry: Consulting Services: Advertising; Consulting Services: Marketing; Promotion Services;

WEB PRINTING CONTROLS, A BALDWIN COMPANY
3350 West Salt Creek Ln., Ste 110, Arlington Heights, IL, 60005, USA; tel 847-477-6323; e-mail mark.krueger@Baldwintech.com; web site www.wpcteam.com
Product Line Leader WPC—Herman Gnuechtel
Director Of Sales; WPC—Mark Krueger
Industry: Controls: Color Register; Color Density: Cut-off, Press controls, ribbon controls: Web Break Detector systems: Web Guides

WEBER SYSTEMS, INC.
23850 Commerce Park Rd., Ste. 108, Beachwood, OH, 44122-5829, USA; tel (432) 687-5445; fax (432) 687-5445; web site www.jeffweber.net
Pres.—Jeff Weber
Industry: Prepress Color Proofing Systems; Storage Retrieval Systems; Computers: Hardware & Software Integrators; Equipment Dealers (New); Equipment Dealers (Used); Software: Pagination/Layout;

WEBPRESS, LLC
PO Box 2274, Tacoma, WA, 98401-2274, USA; tel 253-620-4747; fax 253-722-0378; e-mail info@webpressllc.com; web site www.webpressllc.com
Operations Manager—Rick Guinn
President—Brian Haun
Customer Service/Parts—Brian Hilsendager
Sales—Jim Merek
Industry: Folding Machines; Presses: Offset; Remanufactures Equipment; Roll Handling Equipment; Web Press - Special Equipment;

WESCO GRAPHICS
410 E Grant Line Rd Ste B, Tracy, CA, 95376-2838, USA; tel (209) 832-1000; fax (209) 832-7800; e-mail jim@wescographics.com; web site www.wescographics.com
Pres.—Jim Estes
Vice Pres.—Betty Estes
Industry: Consulting Services: Equipment; Equipment Dealers (Used); Erectors & Riggers; Inserting Equipment (Includes Stuffing Machines); Press Rebuilding; Press Repairs; Presses: Offset; Reels & Tensions; Roll Handling Equipment; Web Press - Special Equipment;

WEST COAST COMPUTER SYSTEMS
2010 N Wilson Way, Stockton, CA, 95205-3126, USA; tel (209) 948-5499; e-mail sales@wccsys.com; web site www.wccsys.com
Sales/Mktg. Mgr.—Ed Kobrin
Application Software Mgr.—Simon Young
System Software Mgr.—Jim Ponder
Industry: Ink Storage Tanks; Lubricants; Offset

Chemicals & Supplies; Pumps (Air, Ink, Vacuum); Static Eliminators; Consulting Services: Marketing; Market Research;

WESTERN LITHOTECH
3433 Tree Court Industrial Blvd, Saint Louis, MO, 63122-6617, USA; tel (800) 325-3310; fax (636) 825-4681; e-mail kathy_may@westernlitho.com
Pres./CEO—William Streeter
Sr. Vice Pres., Sales/Mktg.—Lane Palmer
Vice Pres., Machinery Division—John Powers
Mgr., Nat'l Sales—Todd Socia
Mgr., Int'l Sales—Ernie Stokes
Mgr., US/Int'l Mktg.—Kathryn May
Prodn. Mgr., Newspaper Product—Keith Walker
Industry: Chemicals: Plate Processing; Offset Plate-Making Service & Equipment; Plate Cleaners; Plate Processors; Platemakers: Flexographic (Traditional); Platemakers: Letterpress; Platemakers: Offset (Computer to Plate); Platemakers: Offset (Conventional); Plates: Offset (Computer to Plate); Plates: Offset (Conventional);

WESTERN LITHOTECH
2625 N Neergard Ave, Springfield, MO, 65803-4993, USA; tel (800) 421-0051; fax (417) 831-0142; web site www.westernlithotech.com
Mktg. Mgr.—Keith Walker
OEM Sales Mgr., Machinery Division—Tony Petersen

WESTERN PRINTING MACHINERY
9229 Ivanhoe St, Schiller Park, IL, 60176-2348, USA; tel (847) 678-1740; fax (847) 678-6176; e-mail kmarkovich@wpm.com; web site www.wpm.com
Industry: Counting, Stacking, Bundling Machines; Cutters & Trimmers; Dies (Perforating and Slitting); Web Press - Special Equipment;

WESTERN QUARTZ PRODUCTS, INC.
2432 Spring St, Paso Robles, CA, 93446-1296, USA; tel (805) 238-3524; fax (805) 238-6811; e-mail info@westernquartz.com; web site www.westernquartz.com
Pres.—Jon Dallons
CFO—Katy Wetterstrand
Industry: UV Exposure Lamps

WESTERN ROLLER CORP.
63393 Nels Anderson Rd, Bend, OR, 97701-5743, USA; tel (541) 382-5643; fax (541) 382-0159; web site www.westernroller.com
Owner—Doug Collver
Industry: Delivery Equipment; Mailroom Systems & Equipment; Web Press - Special Equipment;

WHITE BIRCH PAPER
80 Field Point Rd Ste 1, Greenwich, CT, 06830-6416, USA; tel (203) 661-3344; fax (203) 661-3349; web site www.whitebirchpaper.com
Chrmn./CEO—Peter M. Brant
Sr. Vice Pres./CFO—Edward D. Sherrick
President & COO—Christopher M. Brant
Sr. Vice Pres., Sales—Russel Lowder
Industry: Newsprint; Paper: Groundwood Specialties;

WHITING TECHNOLOGIES
N/A, N/A, IL, N/A, USA; tel (630) 850-9680; e-mail fred@whitingtech.com; web site www.whitingtech.com
Pres.—Fred Whiting
Industry: Press Equipment

WHITNEY WORLDWIDE, INC.
553 Hayward Ave N Ste 250, Saint Paul, MN, 55128-9006, USA; tel (800) 597-0227; fax (651) 748-4000; e-mail whitney@whitneyworld.com; web site www.whitneyworld.com
CEO—Les Layton

Industry: Consulting Services: Circulation; Consulting Services: Marketing; Mailing List Compiler; Market Research; Newspaper Marketing;

WHITWORTH KNIFE COMPANY
508 Missouri Ave, Cincinnati, OH, 45226-1121, USA; tel (513) 321-9177; fax (513) 321-9938; e-mail sales@whitworthknifecompany.com; web site www.whitworthknifecompany.com
Owner—Ray Whitworth
Industry: Consulting Services: Production; Core Cutters, Restorers, Rounders; Core Strippers & Seperators; Cutters & Trimmers; Cutting Tools; Dies (Perforating and Slitting); Folder Knives; In-Line Trimming Systems; Ink Fountains & Accessories; Roller Grinders;

WIFAG
26, route de la Glâne, Fribourg, N/A, 1701, Switzerland; tel 426 1888; e-mail noel.mcevoy@wifag.com; web site www.wifag-polytype.com/
Director of Sales & Marketing—Noel McEvoy
Industry: Printing Presses: Offset & Digital, New & Preowned, Automation & Press Controls, Upgrades, Rertrofits and Service

WILLIAM DUNKERLEY PUBLISHING CONSULTANT
275 Batterson Dr., New Britain, CT, 06053, USA; tel (860) 827-8896; fax (508) 507-3021; e-mail wdpc@publishinghelp.com; web site www.publishinghelp.com
Principal—William Dunkerley
Industry: Consulting Services: Business Analysis; Consulting Services: Advertising; Consulting Services: Editorial; Consulting Services: Financial; Consulting Services: Marketing; Market Research

WILSON GREGORY AGENCY, INC.
PO Box 8, Camp Hill, PA, 17001-0008, USA; tel (717) 730-9777; fax (717) 730-9328; e-mail info@wilsongregory.com; web site www.wilsongregory.com
Chrmn./CEO—Ted Gregory
Pres.—Richard Hively
Vice Pres.—Todd Gregory
Vice Pres., Opns.—Mark Gregory
Industry: Consulting Services: Circulation; Insurance;

WINDMOELLER AND HOELSCHER CORP.
23 New England Way, Lincoln, RI, 02865-4200, USA; tel (401) 333-2770; fax (401) 333-6491; e-mail info@whcorp.com; web site www.whcorp.com
President—Andrew Wheeler
Vice President of Sales—Klaus Kleeman
Vice President of Service—Buch Javeed
Industry: Presses: Flexographic; Presses: Rotogravure;

WINTON ENGINEERING CO.
2303 W 18th St, Chicago, IL, 60608-1808, USA; tel (312) 733-5200; fax (312) 733-0446; e-mail d.allison@w-rindustries.com; web site ^www.w-rindustries.com
Vice Pres.—David Allison
Industry: Chemicals: Pressroom; Chemicals: Roller Cleaning; Cleaners & Solvents; Offset Chemicals & Supplies; Press Accessories, Parts & Supplies;

WOLK ADVERTISING, INC. (RETAIL CARPET AD SERVICE)
920 E Lincoln St, Birmingham, MI, 48009-3608, USA; tel (248) 540-5980; e-mail wolkadv@earthlink.net; web site www.flooringads.com
Pres.—Erv Wolk
Industry: Art & Layout Equipment and Services; Consulting Services: Advertising; Training: Design & Layout;

WPC MACHINERY CORP.
23872 N Kelsey Rd, Lake Barrington, IL, 60010-1563, USA; tel (630) 231-7721; fax

(630) 231-7827
Prodn. Mgr., Press Servs.—Mark Krueger
Industry: Consulting Services: Production;
Cylinder Repair; Drives & Controls; Erectors
& Riggers; Ink Fountains & Accessories;
Paper Handeling Equipment; Press
Rebuilding; Press Repairs; Rollers;

WRUBEL COMMUNICATIONS
12-32 River Rd, Fair Lawn, NJ, 07410-1802,
USA; tel (201) 796-3331; fax (201) 796-5083;
e-mail Chasnews@aol.com
Pres.—Charles Wrubel
Industry: Consulting Services: Advertising;
Consulting Services: Circulation; Consulting
Services: Editorial; Consulting Services:
Financial; Consulting Services: Marketing;

X

X-RITE INC.
4300 44th St SE, Grand Rapids, MI, 49512-
4009, USA; tel (616) 803-2100; fax (888)
826-3061; e-mail info@xrite.com; investor@
xrite.com; customerservice@xrite.com; web
site www.xrite.com
Pres./CEO/COO—Thomas J. Vacchiano
CFO—Mary E Chowning
Exec. Vice Pres./CFO—Raj Shah
CTO—Francis Lamy
Industry: Color Analyzers; Color Proofing; Color

Viewing Equipment; Densitometers; Ink
Controls, Computerized; Lighting Equipment;
Photo Proofing Systems; Proofing Systems;
Testing Instruments;

XERIUM TECHNOLOGIES INC.
14101 Capital Blvd, Youngsville, NC, 27596,
USA; tel 919-556-7235; fax 919-556-1063
Vice Pres., Sales—Kevin Frank
Industry: Roll Coverings; Roller Grinding
Services; Rollers;

XEROX (CORP. HEADQUARTERS)
PO Box 1600, Stamford, CT, 06904-1600,
USA; tel (800) ASK-XEROX (275-9376)
Chrmn. of the Bd./Chrmn.-Exec.
Committee—Paul Allaire
Pres./CEO—Anne Mulcahy
Industry: Scanners: Color B & W, Plates, Web

XEROX CORP.
6336 Austin Center Blvd., Ste.300, Austin,
TX, 78729, USA; tel (512) 343-5600; fax
(512) 343-5635; e-mail marketing@omnifax.
xerox.com; web site www.omnifax.com
Mgr.—Erin Hunt
Industry: Facsimilie/Fax Transmission Systems

XEROX CORP.
45 Glover Ave, Norwalk, CT, 06850-1203,
USA; tel (800) 275-9376; e-mail webmaster@

xerox.com; web site www.xerox.com
Chairman/CEO—Ursula Burns
Corporate Executive Vice President
General Counsel and Secretary—Don Liu
Corporate Executive Vice President
President, Xerox Services—Robert Zapfel
Corporate Executive Vice President
President, Xerox Technology —Jeff
Jacobson
Corporate Executive Vice President
Chief Financial Officer —Kathryn Mikells
Industry: Xerox provides business process
services, printing equipment, hardware
and software technology for managing
information — from data to documents. Learn
more at www.xerox.com.

XITRON
4880 Venture Dr Ste 500, Ann Arbor, MI,
48108-9559, USA; tel (734) 913-8080; fax
(734) 913-8088; e-mail xitronsales@xitron.
com; web site www.xitron.com
Executive Vice President—Bret Farrah
Marketing Coordinator—Jennifer Graustein
Industry: CtP RIPs and Workflows, High-Speed
Digital and Inkjet RIPs and workflows, Ink
Key Presetting software, Ctp Interfaces,
CtP TIFF Catchers, Prepress Software
Development

XPEDX PRINTING TECHNOLOGIES
6285 Tri Ridge Blvd, Loveland, OH, 45140-

8318, USA; tel (513) 965-2900; fax (901)
214-9674; web site www.xpedx.com
Pres.—Mary Laschinger
Vice Pres./Gen. Mgr.—John Torrey
Industry: Cutters & Trimmers; Paper Handeling
Equipment; Presses: Offset;

XYONICZ
6754 Martin St, Rome, NY, 13440-7119,
USA; tel (315) 334-4214; fax (315) 336-3177
Pres./Mgr., Mktg.—Ed Zionc
Industry: Equipment Dealers (New); Feeding,
Folding, Delivery Equipment; Mailroom
Systems & Equipment; Material Handling
Equipment: Truck Loaders; Newsprint
Handeling Equipment;

Y

YALE MATERIALS HANDLING CORP.
1400 Sullivan Dr, Greenville, NC, 27834-
9007, USA; tel (800) 233-9253; fax (252)
931-7873; e-mail ayinfo@yale.com; web site
www.yale.com
Pres.—Don Chance
Dir., Financial Servs.—Tina Goodwin
Vice Pres., Aftermarket Sales—Jay Costello
Dir., Dealer Devel.—Walt Nawicki
Industry: Lift Trucks

CATEGORIES OF EQUIPMENT, SUPPLIES AND SERVICES

A

**ABDICK CONVENTIONAL OFFSET
PRESSES PLATEMAKERS: OFFSET**
Presstek, Inc.

ABRASIVES
Rochester Institute of Technology

ACID DISPENSING SYSTEMS
Arch Chemicals, Inc.

AD TRACKING
Software Consulting Services, LLC

ADDRESSING MACHINES
Automated Mailing Systems Corp.
Brock Solutions U.S. Inc.
Domino Amjet, Inc.
Kansa Technology, LLC
Kirk-Rudy, Inc.
Markem-Imaje
Microfilm Products Co.
Videojet Technologies Inc.

ADHESIVE WAX COATERS
Daige Products, Inc.
Dean Machinery International, Inc.
Paste-Up Supply

ADHESIVES
Adhesives Research, Inc.
BASF Corp.
Chauncey Wing's Sons, Inc.
Daige Products, Inc.
H & M Paster Sales & Service, Inc.
Hamilton Circulation Supplies Co.
Horizons, Inc.
Hurletron, Inc.
Miller-Cooper Co.
North Shore Consultants, Inc.
Rosback Co.
Schaefer Machine Co., Inc.
Support Products, Inc.

The Dow Chemical Co.
Union Rubber, Inc.

ADVERTISING
ePublish4me
Media Sales Plus, Inc.

ADVERTISING DESIGN
Creative House Print Media Consultants

ANILOX MANUFACTURER
Harper Corporation of America

**ARCHITECTS/ENGINEERS (INCLUDES
DESIGN/CONSTRUCTION FIRMS)**
AEC, Inc.
AECOM
B E & K, Inc.
Carlson Design Construct
Ch2MHill Lockwood Greene
Chemetron Fire Systems
Dario Designs, Inc.
GE Instrument Control Systems, Inc.
Gilbane Building Co.
Graphic System Services, Inc.
Industrial Noise Control, Inc.
Kamen & Co. Group Services
Lankford Engineering, Inc.
Parsons, Inc.
The Austin Company
The Haskell Co.
Trauner Consulting Services, Inc.
Versar Inc.

**ARCHIVE CONTENT MANAGEMENT
SOFTWARE.**
Digital Collections

ARCHIVING SYSTEMS
Autologic Information International
Cygnet Storage Solutions, Inc.
Digital Technology International
Foster Mfg. Co.
Gannett Media Technologies International
(GMTI)

Lazer-fare Media Services
NewsEngin, Inc.
NewsView Solutions
ProQuest LLC
SAXOTECH, Inc.
Unisys Corp.
Xitron

**ART & LAYOUT EQUIPMENT AND
SERVICES**
Brady & Paul Communications
Foster Mfg. Co.
Graphic Technology, Inc. (GTI)
MacDonald Advertising Services
Metro Creative Graphics, Inc.
Midwest Publishers Supply Co.
Richmond/Graphic Products, Inc.
Roconex Corp.
Wolk Advertising, Inc. (Retail Carpet Ad
Service)

AUDIOTEX SYSTEMS & SOFTWARE
DAC Systems

AUTOMATIC BLANKET CLEANERS
Baldwin Technology Company, Inc.

AUTOMATIC FILM PROCESSORS
Diversified Photo/Graphics Supply

**AUTOMATIC PLASTIC BAGGING
EQUIPMENT**
Buhrs Americas, Inc.
Dan-Bar, Inc.
Hudson-Sharp
Malow Corp.
Muller Martini Mailroom Systems, Inc.
SITMA USA, Inc.
Telesonic Packaging Corp., Ames Engineering
Div.

B

BALING MACHINES
Balemaster
Dan-Bar, Inc.
Gerrard Ovalstrapping

BELTS, BELTING, V-BELTS
A-American Machine & Assembly (Press Parts
Div.)
Arco Engineering, Inc. (Newspaper Div.)
Ashworth Brothers, Inc.
Baumfolder Corp.
Belt Corporation of America
Belting Industries Co., Inc.
Central Graphics
Clipper Belt Lacer Co.
K & M Newspaper Services, Inc.

BINDERS
Heidelberg USA, Inc.

**BINDERY AND MAILROOM SYSTEMS &
EQUIPMENT**
McCain Bindery Systems

BINDERY EQUIPMENT
McCain Bindery Systems

**BLANKET CLEANER/WASHER
(AUTOMATIC)**
Baldwin Oxy-Dry Americas
grafikAmerica
IMC America
Smith Pressroom Products, Inc.
Technotrans America, Inc.

BLANKET MOUNTING AND BARS
Day International
Flint Group.
J. Thomas McHugh Co., Inc.
MacDermid Printing Solutions
Reeves Brothers, Inc.
Tech-Energy Co.

BLANKETS
DYC Supply Co.
Inter-Continental Graphics, Inc.
J. Thomas McHugh Co., Inc.
Latin American Div./Flint Ink
MacDermid Printing Solutions
Midwest Publishers Supply Co.
Miller-Cooper Co.
National Graphic Supply Corp.
Newstech Co. (Div. of Rovinter, Inc.)
Pacesetter Graphic Service Corp.
Reeves Brothers, Inc.
RotaDyne Corp.
Rycoline Products, Inc.
Tech-Energy Co.

BLUE LINE GRIDS
Midwest Publishers Supply Co.

BROKERS & APPRAISERS
Barry French
Cribb, Greene & Associates
Dean Machinery International, Inc.
Dirks, Van Essen & Murray
Grimes, W.B. & Co.
Hare Associates, Inc.
Inland Newspaper Machinery LLC
JP Media Partners
Kamen & Co. Group Services
Media America Brokers
National Media Associates
National Media Associates
Rickenbacher Media

BUNDLE DELIVERY EQUIPMENT
WRH Marketing Americas, Inc.

BUNDLING AND TYING MACHINES
Arpac Group
Automated Mailing Systems Corp.
B.H. Bunn Co.
EAM-Mosca Corp.
FELINS, Inc.
Gerrard Ovalstrapping
Malow Corp.
Megasys International, Inc.
Microfilm Products Co.
Muller Martini Corp.
Muller Martini Mailroom Systems, Inc.
Samuel Strapping System
Sterling Packaging Systems
Systems Technology, Inc.
Teufelberger GmbH
WRH Marketing Americas Americas, Inc

BUSINESS AND PRODUCTION MANAGMENT SOFTWARE
Heidelberg USA, Inc.

BUSINESS COMPUTERS
Harris Corp.
Mobile Computing Corporation USA
Newspaper Electronics Corp.
VoiceWorld, Inc.

C

CABINETS
Consolidated Storage Cos.
Control Engineering Co.
Ergotron, Inc.
Foster Mfg. Co.
Penco Products
Roconex Corp.
Thompson Cabinet Co.
Truproof Ltd.

CALIBRATION SOFTWARE/HARDWARE
Baton Lock & Hardware Co., Inc.
Beta Screen Corp.
Presteligence
ProImage America, Inc.
Tobias Associates, Inc.
Xitron

CAMERAS & ACCESSORIES
AAA Press International
CHF Foto Supply
Diversified Photo/Graphics Supply
Eastman Kodak Co.
National Graphic Supply Corp.
NuArc Co., Inc.
PC Industries
Pitman Photo Supply
Rochester Institute of Technology
Unique Photo

CART DISTRIBUTION SYSTEMS
Baird Manufacturing
Cannon Equipment
K-Jack Engineering Co., Inc.

CHEMICAL RECYCLING
Hart Industries

CHEMICALS
BASF Corporation

CHEMICALS: CHUCK (PAPER ROLL)
Maxcess
Tidland Corp.
Tilt-Lock

CHEMICALS: PHOTOGRAPHIC
Cachet Fine Art Photographic Paper
Diversified Photo/Graphics Supply
Fujifilm Hunt Chemicals U.S.A., Inc.
GraphLine
Horizons, Inc.
Kodak GCG
Mac Dermid Autotype Inc.
National Graphic Supply Corp.
Photo Systems, Inc.
Pitman Photo Supply
Unique Photo

CHEMICALS: PLATE PROCESSING
Anocoil Corporation
Arch Chemicals, Inc.
Fuji Photo Film USA/Graphic Systems Div.
GraphLine
Kodak GCG
Latin American Div./Flint Ink
Photo Systems, Inc.
Rycoline Products, Inc.
Southern Lithoplate, Inc.
Superior Lithoplate of Indiana, Inc.
Western LithoTech

CHEMICALS: PRESSROOM
Arch Chemicals, Inc.
Coast Graphic Supply
Day International
Duostat Co. (Affiliated with VGC Corp.)
Fujifilm Hunt Chemicals U.S.A., Inc.
INX International Ink Co.
Latin American Div./Flint Ink
Midwest Publishers Supply Co.
Miller-Cooper Co.
Mirachem Corp.
National Graphic Supply Corp.
Photo Systems, Inc.
Printers' Service/Prisco/PriscoDigital
Rycoline Products, Inc.
Southern Lithoplate, Inc.
Superior Lithoplate of Indiana, Inc.
Tower Products, Inc.
Vegra USA
Winton Engineering Co.

CHEMICALS: ROLLER CLEANING
Day International
Latin American Div./Flint Ink
Mirachem Corp.
Photo Systems, Inc.
Siebert, Inc.
Support Products, Inc.
Tower Products, Inc.
Winton Engineering Co.

CHROME ROLLER COATING
Graphic Printing Roller Ltd.

CHURCH PAGE ADVERTISING SALES
Rowlett Advertising Service, Inc.

CIRCULATION
Creative House Print Media Consultants

CIRCULATION CONSULTING SERVICES: EDITORIAL
Phelps, Cutler & Associates

CIRCULATION EQUIPMENT & SUPPLIES
AAA Press International
Alliance Rubber Co.
AWS, A Thermal Care Division
Baldwin Technology Company, Inc.
Bellatrix Systems, Inc.
Cannon Equipment
Circulation Solutions, Inc.
Continental Products
Franklin Wire Works, Inc.
Go Plastics/StreetSmart LLC
Great Southern Corp. (Sirco Div.)
Hamilton Circulation Supplies Co.
Impact Racks, Inc.
Insert East, Inc.
Kamen & Co. Group Services
Kaspar Wire Works, Inc./Sho-Rack
K-Jack Engineering Co., Inc.
Lyon Enterprises
Master Flo Technology
PDI Plastics
Printers' Service/Prisco/PriscoDigital
Rycoline Products, Inc.
Schermerhorn Bros. Co.
Semler Industries, Inc. (Pressroom Fluids Equipment Div.)

CIRCULATION SUPPLIES
Steel City Corp.

CIRCULATION SUPPLIES AND EQUIPMENT
The Cannon Group, Inc.

CLEANERS & SOLVENTS
ARC International
Cold Jet, Inc.
Cryogenesis (A Div. of WM & C Services, Inc.)
Day International
Fiberweb
INX International Ink Co.
Kaspar Wire Works, Inc./Sho-Rack
MacDermid Printing Solutions
Mirachem Corp.
Pressroom Cleaners
Printers' Service/Prisco/PriscoDigital
Rycoline Products, Inc.
Siebert, Inc.
The Dow Chemical Co.
Tower Products, Inc.
Winton Engineering Co.

CLOSED LOOP INK DENSITY CONTROLS SYSTEM INSTALLATIONS
Ewert America Electronics Ltd.

COLLATING EQUIPMENT
Baumfolder Corp.
Dan-Bar, Inc.
Kansa Technology, LLC
Prim Hall Enterprises, Inc.
Rosback Co.
SITMA USA, Inc.

COLOR ANALYZERS
E.I. du Pont de Nemours & Co.
Electronic Systems Engineering Co.
Technidyne Corp.
Tobias Associates, Inc.
UV Process Supply, Inc.
X-Rite Inc.

COLOR MANAGEMENT
ProImage America, Inc.

COLOR MANAGEMENT SOFTWARE
BST Pro Mark

Kodak GCG
MacDermid Printing Solutions
Monaco Systems, Inc.
National Graphic Supply Corp.
Pantone, Inc.
Schawk
Technidyne Corp.
Trumatch, Inc.

COLOR MANAGMENT
Heidelberg USA, Inc.

COLOR PRINTING FRAMES
NuArc Co., Inc.

COLOR PROOFING
All Systems Color, Inc.
Beta Screen Corp.
Burgess Industries, Inc.
Creo
Direct Reproduction Corp.
Duostat Co. (Affiliated with VGC Corp.)
E.I. du Pont de Nemours & Co.
Fuji Photo Film USA/Graphic Systems Div.
Harland Simon
Just Normlicht, Inc.
Kodak GCG
Konica Minolta Graphic Imaging USA
Newscolor, LLC
Pitman Co.
Press-Enterprise, Inc. (Color Graphics Dept.)
Presteligence
SCREEN (USA)
Truproof Ltd.
Xitron
X-Rite Inc.

COLOR REGISTRATION
BST Pro Mark
Burgess Industries, Inc.
Direct Reproduction Corp.
E.I. du Pont de Nemours & Co.
grafikAmerica
Graphics Microsystems, Inc.
K & F International, Inc.
Kaim & Associates International Marketing, Inc.
NELA
PC Industries
Pitman Co.
Quad Tech
QuadTech
Robertson Press Machinery Co., Inc.

COLOR SEPERATION SCANNERS
All Systems Color, Inc.
Creo
Duostat Co. (Affiliated with VGC Corp.)
E.I. du Pont de Nemours & Co.
Howtek
Microtek
Pitman Co.
SCREEN (USA)
UMAX Technologies, Inc.

COLOR SEPERATIONS, POSITIVES
All Systems Color, Inc.
Press-Enterprise, Inc. (Color Graphics Dept.)

COLOR VIEWING EQUIPMENT
Beta Screen Corp.
BST Pro Mark
E.I. du Pont de Nemours & Co.
Foster Mfg. Co.
Graphic Technology, Inc. (GTI)
Just Normlicht, Inc.
Pitman Co.
Truproof Ltd.
X-Rite Inc.

COMPLETE DATA SERVICES
Ver-A-Fast Corporation

COMPLETE TELEMARKETING SERVICES OUTBOUND
Ver-A-Fast Corporation

COMPOSING ROOM EQUIPMENT &

SUPPLIES
Coast Graphic Supply
Devlin Electronics Ltd.
Foster Mfg. Co.
Megasys International, Inc.
Midwest Publishers Supply Co.
N & L Enterprises, Inc.
PAGE
Support Products, Inc.
Thompson Cabinet Co.

COMPUTERS: HARDWARE & SOFTWARE INTEGRATORS
Advanced Technical Solutions, Inc.
alfaQuest Technologies
All Systems Go
Autologic Information International
Bruce Bell & Associates
Buffalo Technology Inc.
Burt Technologies, Inc.
Celebro
Creo
Descartes Systems Group
Duostat Co. (Affiliated with VGC Corp.)
EDIWISE
Ewert America Electronics Ltd.
Gannett Media Technologies International (GMTI)
General DataComm, Inc.
Global Turnkey Systems, Inc.
Globix Corp.
ICANON Associates, Inc.
Imapro Corp.
Jervis B. Webb Co.
McCrrory Publishing
Miles 33
Mobile Computing Corporation USA
Newspaper Electronics Corp.
Printronix, Inc.
Shreve Systems
Solar Systems
Spectra Logic
Syntellect, Inc.
TSA
Unisys Corp.
Weber Systems, Inc.

COMPUTERS: LAPTOP & PORTABLE
Acer America
All Systems Go
Bruce Bell & Associates
Globix Corp.
Newspaper Electronics Corp.

COMPUTERS: LOCAL AREA NETWORK (LANS)
Buffalo Technology Inc.
Ergotron, Inc.
Global Turnkey Systems, Inc.
Globix Corp.
Imapro Corp.
Newspaper Electronics Corp.
Support Systems International Corp.
Syntellect, Inc.

COMPUTERS: STORAGE DEVICES
ADI/PDM Trade Group
All Systems Go
Buffalo Technology Inc.
Consolidated Storage Cos.
Ergotron, Inc.
Globix Corp.
Newspaper Electronics Corp.
Overland Storage, Inc.
Snap-on Business Solutions
Thompson Cabinet Co.

COMPUTER-TO-PLATE
Bob Weber, Inc.

CONSULTING SERVICES
American International Communications, Inc.
Creative Circle Media Solutions
Meena Copy & Layout

CONSULTING SERVICES INDUSTRY TRADE PUBLICATION
Advanced Interactive Media Group, LLC

CONSULTING SERVICES: ADVERTISING
All Systems Go
American Consulting Services
American Newspaper Representatives
American Opinion Research
Arrow Printing Co.
ASTech InterMedia
Atex North America
Bruce Bell & Associates
ChannelNet
ComPlan Associates
Creative Brilliance Advertising, Marketing & Public Relation
Creative House Print Media Consultants
Dail Advertising Service
Ed Baron & Associates, Inc.
Forrest Consulting
Grimes, W.B. & Co.
Hare Associates, Inc.
Kamen & Co. Group Services
Keister Williams Newspaper Services, Inc.
Lazer-fare Media Services
M.W. Burke & Associates, Inc.
MacDonald Advertising Services
Marketing Strategies Incorporated
Media Marketing, Inc.
Media Monitors, Inc.
Metro Creative Graphics, Inc.
Miles 33
Minnesota Opinion Research, Inc. (MORI)
MultiAd
Network Newspaper Advertising, Inc.
Newspaper Services of America
NoteAds.com, Inc./Post-it Note Advertising
Print Marketing Concepts, Inc.
Pulse Research, Inc.
Sales Development Services
Scarborough Research
Spectrecom Corporation
Syntellect, Inc.
The Keenan Group, Inc.
TNS Global
Weatherline, Inc.
William Dunkerley Publishing Consultant
Wolk Advertising, Inc. (Retail Carpet Ad Service)
Wrubel Communications

CONSULTING SERVICES: BUSINESS ANALYSIS
William Dunkerley Publishing Consultant

CONSULTING SERVICES: CIRCULATION
Advantex Marketing International, Inc.
All Systems Go
American Opinion Research
ASTech InterMedia
Church Rickards, Whitlock & Co., Inc.
Circulation Development, Inc.
Circulation Solutions, Inc.
Communications Management Service, Inc.
ComPlan Associates
Creative Brilliance Advertising, Marketing & Public Relation
Ed Baron & Associates, Inc.
Forrest Consulting
Global Turnkey Systems, Inc.
Kamen & Co. Group Services
M.W. Burke & Associates, Inc.
MediaSpan Group Inc.
Minnesota Opinion Research, Inc. (MORI)
Mobile Computing Corporation USA
Pulse Research, Inc.
Syntellect, Inc.
The Keenan Group, Inc.
Ver-A-Fast Corporation
VoiceWorld, Inc.
Whitney Worldwide, Inc.
Wilson Gregory Agency, Inc.
Wrubel Communications

CONSULTING SERVICES: COMPUTER
Agfa Monotype Corporation
All Systems Go
ASTech InterMedia
ComPlan Associates
Global Turnkey Systems, Inc.
ICANON Associates, Inc.
John Juliano Computer Services Co.
Lazer-fare Media Services

McCrrory Publishing
Mobile Computing Corporation USA
Newspaper Electronics Corp.
Printmark
Random Access
Robertson Equipments
Rochester Institute of Technology
Sales Development Services

CONSULTING SERVICES: EDITORIAL
American Opinion Research
Brady & Paul Communications
ComPlan Associates
Hare Associates, Inc.
Lazer-fare Media Services
McCrrory Publishing
MediaSpan Group Inc.
Metro Creative Graphics, Inc.
Miles 33
Minnesota Opinion Research, Inc. (MORI)
Missouri Press Service, Inc.
North Atlantic Publishing Systems, Inc.
Printmark
St. Louis Journalism Review
Tera Digital Publishing
William Dunkerley Publishing Consultant
Wrubel Communications

CONSULTING SERVICES: EQUIPMENT
AECOM
All Systems Go
Capital Track Co.
Chuck Blevins & Assoc.
ComPlan Associates
Consolidated Storage Cos.
Global Press Management Services, LLC.
Graphic System Services, Inc.
Inland Newspaper Machinery LLC
Jervis B. Webb Co.
Northeast Industries, Inc.
Pressline Services, Inc.
Rochester Institute of Technology
Sterling Packaging Systems
Syntellect, Inc.
The Austin Company
The Haskell Co.
The Keenan Group, Inc.
Tidland Corp.
Wesco Graphics

CONSULTING SERVICES: ERGONOMICS
Chuck Blevins & Assoc.
Consolidated Storage Cos.
Ergotron, Inc.
Fox Bay Industries, Inc.

CONSULTING SERVICES: FINANCIAL
Barry French
ComPlan Associates
Dirks, Van Essen & Murray
Ed Baron & Associates, Inc.
Forrest Consulting
Grimes, W.B. & Co.
ICANON Associates, Inc.
I-many, Inc.
Interactive Data Real-Time Services, Inc.
Kamen & Co. Group Services
Kanaly Trust Co.
National Media Associates
National Media Associates
Phelps, Cutler & Associates
Print Marketing Concepts, Inc.
The Austin Company
William Dunkerley Publishing Consultant
Wrubel Communications

CONSULTING SERVICES: FLEET OPERATIONS
Transportation Consultants, Inc.

CONSULTING SERVICES: HUMAN RESOURCES
Church Rickards, Whitlock & Co., Inc.
Grimes, W.B. & Co.
Kamen & Co. Group Services
Phelps, Cutler & Associates

CONSULTING SERVICES: MANAGEMENT

CONSULTING
Poyry Management Consulting (USA) Inc.

CONSULTING SERVICES: MARKETING
Advantex Marketing International, Inc.
All Systems Go
American Opinion Research
ASTech InterMedia
Bruce Bell & Associates
Circulation Development, Inc.
Communications Management Service, Inc.
ComPlan Associates
Ed Baron & Associates, Inc.
Forrest Consulting
Grimes, W.B. & Co.
INX International Ink Co.
John Juliano Computer Services Co.
Kamen & Co. Group Services
Keister Williams Newspaper Services, Inc.
Marketing Plus, Inc.
Marketing Strategies Incorporated
Media Marketing, Inc.
Minnesota Opinion Research, Inc. (MORI)
NewsCurrents
Phelps, Cutler & Associates
Pulse Research, Inc.
Sales Development Services
Scarborough Research
Spectrecom Corporation
Syntellect, Inc.
The Austin Company
The Keenan Group, Inc.
TNS Global
Weatherline, Inc.
West Coast Computer Systems
Whitney Worldwide, Inc.
William Dunkerley Publishing Consultant
Wrubel Communications

CONSULTING SERVICES: PRODUCTION
AECOM
Brock Solutions U.S. Inc.
Chuck Blevins & Assoc.
CNI Corp.
ComPlan Associates
Kinetic Corporation
Lankford Engineering, Inc.
Lorentzen & Wettre
M.W. Burke & Associates, Inc.
MediaSpan Group Inc.
Plumtree Co.
Printmark
ProImage America, Inc.
Quebecor World
Rochester Institute of Technology
The Austin Company
The Keenan Group, Inc.
Whitworth Knife Company
WPC Machinery Corp.

CONSUMER ELECTRONICS
Nikon, Inc.

CONTENT AGGREGATION AND DISTRIBUTION
Digital Collections

CONTENT AND DIGITAL ASSET MANAGEMENT SYSTEMS
Lazer-fare Media Services

CONTENT MANAGEMENT SYSTEMS
CCI Europe, Inc.-Georgia Branch
ProImage America, Inc.

CONTROLLERS: PRESS
AirSystems, Inc.
Masthead International, Inc.
Rockwell Automation

CONTROLS: EXPOSURE
Burgess Industries, Inc.
Douthitt Corp.
GE Instrument Control Systems, Inc.
NuArc Co., Inc.

CONTROLS: PHOTO ELECTRIC
Baumer Electric Ltd.

GE Instrument Control Systems, Inc.
K & M Newspaper Services, Inc.

CONTROLS: REGISTER
Burgess Industries, Inc.
E.I. du Pont de Nemours & Co.
GE Instrument Control Systems, Inc.
grafikAmerica
Graphics Microsystems, Inc.
Hurletron, Inc.
Kaim & Associates International Marketing, Inc.
NELA
PC Industries
Perretta Graphics Corp.
Quad Tech
QuadTech
Web Printing Controls

CONVERSION EQUIPMENT
Martin Automatic, Inc.
Pemco, Inc.
Printing Press Services, Inc.
Rotoflex Mark Andy Canada, Inc.
Tidland Corp.

CONVEYORS
Arpac Group
Ashworth Brothers, Inc.
Butler Automatic
Cannon Equipment
Control Engineering Co.
Dematics
Engineering Products Co., Inc.
FANUC Robotics America, Inc.
Gammerler (US) Corp.
Gerrard Ovalstrapping
Hall Contracting Services, Inc.
IMC America
Intralox, LLC
Jervis B. Webb Co.
K & M Newspaper Services, Inc.
Kansa Technology, LLC
Mid-America Graphics, Inc.
Muller Martini Mailroom Systems, Inc.
N/S Corporation
Paragon Technologies Inc.
Pemco, Inc.
Prim Hall Enterprises, Inc.
PSC Flo-Turn, Inc.
Quipp System, Inc.
Robertson Equipments
Shuttleworth, LLC
SITMA USA, Inc.
Sterling Packaging Systems
Systems Technology, Inc.
WRH Marketing Americas Americas, Inc
WRH Marketing Americas, Inc.

CO-OP ADVERTISING MANAGEMENT
Advertising Checking Bureau, Inc.

COPPER PLATING DRUMS
A-American Machine & Assembly (Press Parts Div.)
Central Graphics
Hadronics

CORE CUTTERS, RESTORERS, ROUNDERS
Craftsmen Machinery Co., Inc.
Tidland Corp.
Whitworth Knife Company

CORE STRIPPERS & SEPERATORS
Vegra USA
Whitworth Knife Company

COUNTING, STACKING MACHINES
Systems Technology, Inc.

COUNTING, STACKING, BUNDLING MACHINES
ADI/PDM Trade Group
Advance Graphics Equipment of York, Inc.
Baumfolder Corp.
Butler Automatic
D & R Engineering
Gammerler (US) Corp.

Gerrard Ovalstrapping
Heat and Control, Inc.
IMC America
Inter-Continental Graphics, Inc.
Kansa Technology, LLC
Kolbus America, Inc.
Muller Martini Corp.
SITMA USA, Inc.
Teufelberger GmbH
Western Printing Machinery

CREDIT & COLLECTIONS
SKO Brenner American

CTP
Bob Weber, Inc.

CUTTERS & TRIMMERS
Advance Graphics Equipment of York, Inc.
Baumfolder Corp.
Blower Application Co., Inc.
Butler Automatic
Foster Mfg. Co.
Gammerler (US) Corp.
Heidelberg USA, Inc.
IMC America
Kolbus America, Inc.
Martin Yale, Inc.
Maxcess
MBM Corp.
Muller Martini Corp.
Pemco, Inc.
Portage Newspaper Supply Co.
Roconex Corp.
Systems Technology, Inc.
Tidland Corp.
TKM United States, Inc.
Unique Photo
Western Printing Machinery
Whitworth Knife Company
Xpedx Printing Technologies

CUTTING EQUIPMENT
Euro-Knives USA

CUTTING TOOLS
A-American Machine & Assembly (Press Parts Div.)
Clipper Belt Lacer Co.
Foster Mfg. Co.
Maxcess
MBM Corp.
Tidland Corp.
Whitworth Knife Company

CYLINDER REPAIR
Brodie System, Inc.
Brown's Web Press Service & Machine Shop
Central Graphics
Hadronics
MAH Machine Co., Inc.
Pressline Services, Inc.
Printing Technology, Inc.
WPC Machinery Corp.

D

DAMPENING SYSTEMS
Baldwin Technology Company, Inc.
Chapel Hill Manufacturing Co.
Day International
Duostat Co. (Affiliated with VGC Corp.)
Hadronics
Master Flo Technology
Robertson Press Machinery Co., Inc.
Smith Pressroom Products, Inc.
Technotrans America, Inc.

DARK ROOM EQUIPMENT
Beta Screen Corp.
Cachet Fine Art Photographic Paper
Craftsmen Machinery Co., Inc.
Dunning Photo Equipment, Inc.
Electronic Systems Engineering Co.
Foster Mfg. Co.
Hart Industries/Metafix Compliance Systems

NuArc Co., Inc.
Pitman Co.
Pitman Photo Supply
Tobias Associates, Inc.
Unique Photo

DATA COMMUNICATION
CNI Corp.
Harris Corp.
MCI
Megadata Corp.

DELIVERY EQUIPMENT
Baumfolder Corp.
H.R. Slater Co., Inc.
Hamilton Circulation Supplies Co.
K-Jack Engineering Co., Inc.
Master Flo Technology
Mitchell's
Utilimaster
Western Roller Corp.
WRH Marketing Americas Americas, Inc

DENSITOMETERS
Beta Screen Corp.
Bob Weber, Inc.
Caprock Developments, Inc.
Coast Graphic Supply
Craftsmen Machinery Co., Inc.
Duostat Co. (Affiliated with VGC Corp.)
Electronic Systems Engineering Co.
Graphics Microsystems, Inc.
GraphLine
Tobias Associates, Inc.
Truproof Ltd.
X-Rite Inc.

DESIGN
Creative House Print Media Consultants

DESIGN & LAYOUT
Meena Copy & Layout

DEVELOPING AND PROCESSING
Snap-on Business Solutions
Unique Photo

DIE CUTTING MACHINES
Spartanics

DIES (PERFORATING AND SLITTING)
Rotoflex Mark Andy Canada, Inc.
Technotrans America, Inc.
Vegra USA
Western Printing Machinery
Whitworth Knife Company

DIFFUSION TRANSFER PROCESSORS
NuArc Co., Inc.

DIGITAL ADVERTISING
Brainworks Software Development Corp.

DIGITAL AND PRINT
Miles 33

DIGITAL ASSET MANAGEMENT
Software Consulting Services, LLC

DIGITAL ASSET MANAGEMENT SYSTEMS: FULL SERVICE CONTRACTOR
Digital Collections

DIGITAL PRINTING & PROOFING
Coast Graphic Supply

DIGITAL PRODUCTION PRESSES
Heidelberg USA, Inc.

DIGITAL SUBSCRIPTIONS, CRM
Brainworks Software Development Corp.

DISK DRIVE SALES/REPAIR
Cygnet Storage Solutions, Inc.

Imapro Corp.

DRIVES & CONTROLS
ABB Inc.
ABB, Inc. (Printing Systems)
Brown's Web Press Service & Machine Shop
Danfoss Graham
Ewert America Electronics Ltd.
Fincor Automation, Inc.
Fleming Enterprises
Harland Simon
Masthead International, Inc.
Maxcess
Printing Press Services, Inc.
Rockwell Automation
WPC Machinery Corp.

DRIVES & CONTROLSMOTORS
Baldor Electric Co.

DRYERS: FILM AND PAPERS
Advance Systems, Inc.
Imapro Corp.
Jardis Industries, Inc.
Kidder, Inc.
MEGTEC Systems
Pitman Photo Supply

DRYING SYSTEMS
Advance Systems, Inc.
Baldwin Oxy-Dry Americas
Fleming Enterprises
Jardis Industries, Inc.
MEGTEC Systems
N/S Corporation
UV Process Supply, Inc.

E

EDITORIAL
Software Consulting Services, LLC

ELECTRONIC AD DELIVERY
Celebro
Thought Equity Management, Inc.
Unisys Corp.

ELECTRONIC PRE-SCAN SYSTEMS
Press-Enterprise, Inc. (Color Graphics Dept.)
Tobias Associates, Inc.

ENLARGERS (PHOTOGRAPHIC)
Diversified Photo/Graphics Supply
Electronic Systems Engineering Co.
Pitman Photo Supply

ENVIRONMENTAL CONTROL SYSTEMS
Baldwin Technology Company, Inc.
Extratec Corp.
Hart Industries
Hart Industries/Metafix Compliance Systems
Industrial Acoustics Co.
Litho Research, Inc.
Maratek Environmental Technologies, Inc.
MEGTEC Systems
Metafix, Inc.
N/S Corporation
Nama Graphics E, LLC
Parsons, Inc.
Perma-Fix Environmental Services

EQUIPMENT DEALERS (NEW)
AAA Press International
Applied Industrial Machinery
Arco Engineering, Inc. (Newspaper Div.)
Clark Material Handling Co.
Diversified Photo/Graphics Supply
Duostat Co. (Affiliated with VGC Corp.)
Inland Newspaper Machinery LLC
MAH Machine Co., Inc.
Maratek Environmental Technologies, Inc.
Megasys International, Inc.
Microfilm Products Co.
N & L Enterprises, Inc.
ONE Corp.
Printing Press Services, Inc.

Robertson Press Machinery Co., Inc.
Rosback Co.
Technidyne Corp.
TSA
Weber Systems, Inc.
XYonicz

EQUIPMENT DEALERS (USED)
AAA Press International
American Graphic Arts, Inc.
Arco Engineering, Inc. (Newspaper Div.)
Brown's Web Press Service & Machine Shop
Central Graphics
Clark Material Handling Co.
Dean Machinery International, Inc.
Fleming Enterprises
Hall Contracting Services, Inc.
Inland Newspaper Machinery LLC
Kepes, Inc.
MAH Machine Co., Inc.
Megasys International, Inc.
Microfilm Products Co.
N & L Enterprises, Inc.
ONE Corp.
Printing Press Services, Inc.
Printing Technology, Inc.
Robertson Press Machinery Co., Inc.
Technidyne Corp.
TSA
Weber Systems, Inc.
Wesco Graphics

EQUIPMENT DEALERS (USED) - PREPRESS EQUIPMENT
Bob Weber, Inc.

ERECTORS & RIGGERS
Brown's Web Press Service & Machine Shop
Fleming Enterprises
Hall Contracting Services, Inc.
Jardis Industries, Inc.
Masthead International, Inc.
Printing Press Services, Inc.
Taft Contracting Co. (not affiliated w/Taft Eqpt. Co.)
Wesco Graphics
WPC Machinery Corp.

ETEARSHEETS & EINVOICES
Presteligence

EXPERT WITNESS IN VALUATION
Phelps, Cutler & Associates

EXPOSURE LAMPS
Amergraph Corporation
Caprock Developments, Inc.
Douthitt Corp.
Richmond/Graphic Products, Inc.
UVP, LLC
Western Quartz Products, Inc.

F

FACSIMILIE/FAX TRANSMISSION SYSTEMS
Autologic Information International
DAC Systems
e/Doc Systems
ELAPLAN Buchholz GmbH & Co.
Harris Corp.
N & L Enterprises, Inc.
Royal Consumer Information Products, Inc.
Sales Development Services
STM Networks
Xerox Corp.

FEEDER PRESS
Fleming Enterprises

FEEDING, FOLDING, DELIVERY EQUIPMENT
ADI/PDM Trade Group
Advance Graphics Equipment of York, Inc.
Applied Industrial Machinery
Baumfolder Corp.

Buhrs Americas, Inc.
Fleming Enterprises
Gammerler (US) Corp.
Kansa Technology, LLC
Kepes, Inc.
MAH Machine Co., Inc.
Master Flo Technology
MBM Corp.
SITMA USA, Inc.
XYonicz

FILES, STORAGE
Consolidated Storage Cos.
Cygnet Storage Solutions, Inc.
Foster Mfg. Co.
Roconex Corp.

FILM & PAPER: CONTACT
Coast Graphic Supply
Eastman Kodak Co.
Fuji Photo Film USA/Graphic Systems Div.
GraphLine
Kodak GCG
National Graphic Supply Corp.

FILM & PAPER: DUPLICATING
Fuji Photo Film USA/Graphic Systems Div.
GraphLine
Kodak GCG
National Graphic Supply Corp.

FILM & PAPER: FILM PROCESSING MACHINES
Amergraph Corporation
Duostat Co. (Affiliated with VGC Corp.)
Electronic Systems Engineering Co.
GraphLine
LogEtronics Corp.
Photo Systems, Inc.
Richmond/Graphic Products, Inc.
Southern Lithoplate, Inc.

FILM & PAPER: FILM ROLL DISPENSERS
LogEtronics Corp.
Pitman Photo Supply
Unique Photo

FILM & PAPER: FILTERS (PHOTOGRAPHIC)
Cachet Fine Art Photographic Paper
CHF Foto Supply
Diversified Photo/Graphics Supply
Eastman Kodak Co.
Fuji Photo Film USA/Graphic Systems Div.
Kimoto Tech
Kodak GCG
National Graphic Supply Corp.
Pitman Photo Supply
Southern Lithoplate, Inc.
Unique Photo

FILM & PAPER: PHOTOTYPESETTING
Coast Graphic Supply
Eastman Kodak Co.
Kimoto Tech
National Graphic Supply Corp.
Newstech Co. (Div. of Rovinter, Inc.)

FIRE PROTECTION
Badger Fire Protection
Chemetron Fire Systems
Honeywell, Inc.

FIXING & STOP BATHS
Pitman Photo Supply

FLEXOGRPAHIC PRESS CONVERSION
KBA North America, Inc. (Koenig & Bauer AG)
Koenig & Bauer Aktiengesellschaft (KBA)

FLOORING
Gerrard Ovalstrapping

FLUID HANDELING: PRESSROOM
Maratek Environmental Technologies, Inc.
Semler Industries, Inc. (Pressroom Fluids

Equipment Div.)
U.S. Petrolon Industrial

FLUID MANAGEMENT SYSTEMS: PRESSROOM
Baldwin Technology Company, Inc.

FLYING PASTERS
Butler Automatic
Jardis Industries, Inc.
KBA North America, Inc. (Koenig & Bauer AG)
Koenig & Bauer Aktiengesellschaft (KBA)
Lankford Engineering, Inc.
Martin Automatic, Inc.
MEGTEC Systems
Nama Graphics E, LLC
North Shore Consultants, Inc.
ONE Corp.

FOLDER KNIVES
A-American Machine & Assembly (Press Parts Div.)
Central Graphics
Craftsmen Machinery Co., Inc.
Printing Technology, Inc.
Whitworth Knife Company

FOLDERS
Heidelberg USA, Inc.

FOLDING MACHINES
ADI/PDM Trade Group
Advance Graphics Equipment of York, Inc.
Applied Industrial Machinery
Baumfolder Corp.
Buhrs Americas, Inc.
G&K-Vijuk International
Global Press Management Services, LLC.
Kansa Technology, LLC
Martin Yale, Inc.
MBM Corp.
Megasys International, Inc.
Microfilm Products Co.
Rosback Co.
SITMA USA, Inc.
WebPress, LLC

FOUNTAIN SOLUTIONS, LOW VOC CLEANERS
Tower Products, Inc.

G

GAUGES, MEASURING
A-American Machine & Assembly (Press Parts Div.)
Arco Engineering, Inc. (Newspaper Div.)
Beta Screen Corp.
Caprock Developments, Inc.
Craftsmen Machinery Co., Inc.
H.R. Slater Co., Inc.
Hexagon Metrology, Inc.
Lithco Inc.
The Wellmark Company

GENERAL OPERATIONAL CONSULTING
Phelps, Cutler & Associates

GLUING SYSTEMS
American Graphic Arts, Inc.
Baldwin Technology Company, Inc.
D & R Engineering
Gammerler (US) Corp.
H & M Paster Sales & Service, Inc.
Kepes, Inc.
Schaefer Machine Co., Inc.

GRATER WRAP-ROLLER COVERING
Graphic Printing Roller Ltd.

H

HARDWARE & SOFTWARE INTEGRATORS
Digital Collections

HAZARDOUS WASTE DISPOSAL SERVICES
Commodity Resource & Environment

HUMIDIFIERS
Honeywell, Inc.
Walter Meier Climate (USA), Inc.

HYDRAULIC & PNEUMATIC COMPONENTS
Innotek Corporation

I

IMAGESETTERS
AAA Press International
alfa CTP Systems LLC
alfaQuest Technologies
All Systems Go
Bob Weber, Inc.
ECRM
Fuji Photo Film USA/Graphic Systems Div.
GraphLine
MidLantic Equipment Co., Inc.
SCREEN (USA)
Xitron

INFEED NIP ROLLS
Graphic Printing Roller Ltd.

INFEED STACKERS
Kansa Technology, LLC
Mid-America Graphics, Inc.

INK BLEEDING EQUIPMENT
Amergraph Corporation
BEK Systems, Inc.
Ingersoll-Rand-Aro Fluid Product Div.
INX International Ink Co.
UV Process Supply, Inc.

INK CONTROLS, COMPUTERIZED
Baldwin Technology Company, Inc.
Data Engineering Ltd.
Essex Products Group
grafikAmerica
Graphics Microsystems, Inc.
Harland Simon
Perretta Graphics Corp.
Presteligence
Printing Press Services, Inc.
Quad Tech
QuadTech
X-Rite Inc.

INK FOUNTAINS & ACCESSORIES
AWS, A Thermal Care Division
BEK Systems, Inc.
Brodie System, Inc.
Graphic Printing Roller Ltd.
Hadronics
INX International Ink Co.
Kidder, Inc.
Master Flo Technology
Nama Graphics E, LLC
Printing Press Services, Inc.
Printing Technology, Inc.
Support Products, Inc.
Tech-Energy Co.
UV Process Supply, Inc.
Whitworth Knife Company
WPC Machinery Corp.

INK JET & DIGITAL PRESS EQUIPMENT
Manroland Web Systems Inc.

INK JET PAPERS AND SUBSTRATES,
SunShine Paper Co.

INK OPTIMIZATION
ProImage America, Inc.

INK PUMPING SYSTEMS
Amergraph Corporation
AWS, A Thermal Care Division
BEK Systems, Inc.
Flint Group
Graphic System Services, Inc.
Ingersoll-Rand-Aro Fluid Product Div.
INX International Ink Co.
Latin American Div./Flint Ink
UV Process Supply, Inc.

INK RECOVERY SYSTEMS
BEK Systems, Inc.
Latin American Div./Flint Ink
Maratek Environmental Technologies, Inc.
Parsons, Inc.
Semler Industries, Inc. (Pressroom Fluids
Equipment Div.)

INK ROLLERS
Graphic Printing Roller Ltd.

INK STORAGE TANKS
Flint Group
INX International Ink Co.
Semler Industries, Inc. (Pressroom Fluids
Equipment Div.)
The Wellmark Company
UV Process Supply, Inc.
West Coast Computer Systems

INKJET PROOFING SYSTEMS
Heidelberg USA, Inc.

INKS
AirSystems, Inc.
American Ink Jet Corp.
Day-Glo Color Corp.
Diversified Photo/Graphics Supply
Elcorsy Technology, Inc.
Flint Group
Hewlett-Packard Co.
INX International Ink Co.
Latin American Div./Flint Ink
Markem-Imaje
Miller-Cooper Co.
Newstech Co. (Div. of Rovinter, Inc.)
Norman X Guttman, Inc.
PAGE
Schlenk-Both Industries
US Ink
UVP, LLC
Van Son Holland Ink Corp. of America
Videojet Technologies Inc.

IN-LINE STAPLING MACHINE
Motterstitch Company, Inc.

IN-LINE TRIMMING SYSTEMS
Advance Graphics Equipment of York, Inc.
Applied Industrial Machinery
Blower Application Co., Inc.
Gammerler (US) Corp.
IMC America
MBM Corp.
Mid-America Graphics, Inc.
Systems Technology, Inc.
Whitworth Knife Company

INPUT & EDITING SYSTEMS
Advanced Technical Solutions, Inc.
CNI Corp.
Conley Publishing Systems
Design Science, Inc.
Harris Corp.
Horizons, Inc.
Megadata Corp.
Press-Enterprise, Inc. (Color Graphics Dept.)
Quebecor World
Reed Brennan Media Associates, Inc.

INSERTING EQUIPMENT (INCLUDES STUFFING MACHINES)
Advance Graphics Equipment of York, Inc.

Automated Mailing Systems Corp.
Baumfolder Corp.
Buhrs Americas, Inc.
Burt Technologies, Inc.
Harland Simon
Kansa Technology, LLC
Kirk-Rudy, Inc.
Master Flo Technology
Mid-America Graphics, Inc.
Muller Martini Corp.
Muller Martini Mailroom Systems, Inc.
Simco Industrial Static Control Products
SITMA USA, Inc.
Wesco Graphics
WRH Marketing Americas Americas, Inc
WRH Marketing Americas, Inc.

INSURANCE
American Fidelity Assurance Co.
Church Rickards, Whitlock & Co., Inc.
Insurance Specialties Services, Inc.
Media Professional Insurance
SCA Promotions, Inc.
Walterry Insurance Brokers
Wilson Gregory Agency, Inc.

INTEGRATED FAX SERVERS
DAC Systems
Newspaper Electronics Corp.
Sales Development Services

INTERFACES
alfaQuest Technologies
Burt Technologies, Inc.
Devlin Electronics Ltd.
STM Networks

INTERNET
American International Communications, Inc.

IPAD APPLICATIONS
Brainworks Software Development Corp.

K

KEYLESS INKING CONVERSION & ADD-ONS
Perretta Graphics Corp.

L

LABEL PAPER & LABELS
Chauncey Wing's Sons, Inc.

LABEL PRINTING MACHINES
Accraply, Inc.
ACCUFAST Package Printing Systems
Dean Machinery International, Inc.
Domino Amjet, Inc.
Horizons, Inc.
Lauterbach Group
Markem-Imaje
Martin Yale, Inc.
Megasys International, Inc.
Videojet Technologies Inc.

LABELING EQUIPMENT
GSP, Inc.

LASER CUTTING MACHINES
Spartanics

LASER PRINTERS
alfaQuest Technologies
Denex, Inc.
Domino Amjet, Inc.
Duostat Co. (Affiliated with VGC Corp.)
e/Doc Systems
GraphLine
Konica Minolta Business Solutions
Laser Products Technologies
Matthews International Corp.
Printsoft Americas, Inc.

Royal Consumer Information Products, Inc.
Tally Genicom
Truproof Ltd.

LAYOUT TABLES, LIGHT TABLES & WORKSTATIONS
Beta Screen Corp.
Douthitt Corp.
Duostat Co. (Affiliated with VGC Corp.)
Foster Mfg. Co.
Graphic Technology, Inc. (GTI)
Lithco Inc.
Richmond/Graphic Products, Inc.
Roconex Corp.
Support Products, Inc.
Truproof Ltd.

LENSES (CAMERA)
Diversified Photo/Graphics Supply
National Graphic Supply Corp.
Pitman Photo Supply
Unique Photo

LIBRARY RETRIEVAL SYSTEMS
Advertising Checking Bureau, Inc.
Cygnet Storage Solutions, Inc.
Gannett Media Technologies International (GMTI)
MediaSpan Group Inc.
Schawk
Spectra Logic

LIFT TRUCKS
Clark Material Handling Co.
Midwest Publishers Supply Co.
Ryder System, Inc.
Yale Materials Handling Corp.

LIGHT INTEGRATORS
Burgess Industries, Inc.
Douthitt Corp.

LIGHTING EQUIPMENT
Atlas Specialty Lighting
Bulbtronics
Caprock Developments, Inc.
Graphic Technology, Inc. (GTI)
X-Rite Inc.

LUBRICANTS
Lincoln Industrial
Printers' Service/Prisco/PriscoDigital
UV Process Supply, Inc.
West Coast Computer Systems

M

M&A BROKER
Phelps, Cutler & Associates

MAILING LIST COMPILER
Whitney Worldwide, Inc.

MAILING LIST SERVICES
Dunhill International List Co., Inc.

MAILROOM SYSTEMS & EQUIPMENT
ACCUFAST Package Printing Systems
Automated Mailing Systems Corp.
Bell & Howell Scanners
Bishamon Industries Corp.
Bowe Bell + Howell
Buhrs Americas, Inc.
Burt Technologies, Inc.
Cannon Equipment
Chuck Blevins & Assoc.
Dienamic Microprint
FELINS, Inc.
Gammerler (US) Corp.
Gerrard Ovalstrapping
H.R. Slater Co., Inc.
Harland Simon
Jervis B. Webb Co.
K & M Newspaper Services, Inc.
Kansa Technology, LLC

Kirk-Rudy, Inc.
Markem-Imaje
Midwest Publishers Supply Co.
Muller Martini Corp.
Muller Martini Mailroom Systems, Inc.
Neasi-Weber International
Paragon Technologies Inc.
Plumtree Co.
ppi Media GmbH
Prim Hall Enterprises, Inc.
Quipp
Schur Packaging Systems, Inc.
SITMA USA, Inc.
Sterling Packaging Systems
The Austin Company
United States Postal Service
Videojet Technologies Inc.
Western Roller Corp.
XYonicz

MAINTENANCE, PLANT & EQUIPMENT
A-American Machine & Assembly (Press Parts Div.)
Lankford Engineering, Inc.
Lorentzen & Wettre
The Austin Company

MANAGED SERVICES
Software Consulting Services, LLC

MANUFACTURING
Catalyst Paper Corp.
Heidelberg USA

MARKET RESEARCH
A & A Research
Advertising Checking Bureau, Inc.
Marketing Plus, Inc.
Minnesota Opinion Research, Inc. (MORI)
Poyry Management Consulting (USA) Inc.
Research USA, Inc.
Sales Development Services
Scarborough Research
Spectrecom Corporation
TNS Global
Ver-A-Fast Corporation
West Coast Computer Systems
Whitney Worldwide, Inc.
William Dunkerley Publishing Consultant

MARKET STRATEGY
Poyry Management Consulting (USA) Inc.

MARKETING
Berting Communications

MARKETING DATABASE DESIGN AND IMPLEMENTATION
ASTech InterMedia
Gannett Media Technologies International (GMTI)
Sales Development Services

MASKING MATERIALS
Direct Reproduction Corp.
Mac Dermid Autotype Inc.
Shuttleworth, LLC
Support Products, Inc.

MATERIAL HANDLING EQUIPMENT: AUTOMATIC GUIDED VEHICLES
ADI/PDM Trade Group
Ch2MHill Lockwood Greene
Control Engineering Co.
Dematics
IMC America
JBT Corporation (formerly FMC Technologies)
Jervis B. Webb Co.
Linde Lift Truck Corp.
Manroland Web Systems Inc.
Paragon Technologies Inc.
Robertson Equipments

MATERIAL HANDLING EQUIPMENT: PALLETIZING MACHINES
ADI/PDM Trade Group
Butler Automatic

Clark Material Handling Co.
FANUC Robotics America, Inc.
FKI Logistex
Gammerler (US) Corp.
IMC America
Kolbus America, Inc.
Muller Martini Corp.
Muller Martini Mailroom Systems, Inc.
Systems Technology, Inc.

MATERIAL HANDLING EQUIPMENT: PALLETS & PALLETIZERS
ADI/PDM Trade Group
Clark Material Handling Co.
Gammerler (US) Corp.
Hamilton Circulation Supplies Co.
Litco International, Inc.
Master Flo Technology
Quipp System, Inc.

MATERIAL HANDLING EQUIPMENT: TRUCK LOADERS
Cascade Corp.
Clark Material Handling Co.
Control Engineering Co.
Dematics
Linde Lift Truck Corp.
MAXX Material Handling LLC
Quipp System, Inc.
Robertson Equipments
Stewart Glapat Corp.
Superior Handling Equipment, Inc.
XYonicz

MATERIAL HANDLING EQUIPMENT: VEHICLE LOADING
Bishamon Industries Corp.
Clark Material Handling Co.
Jervis B. Webb Co.
Linde Lift Truck Corp.
MAXX Material Handling LLC
Superior Handling Equipment, Inc.

MEDIA
Poyry Management Consulting (USA) Inc.

MICROFILMING
Eastman Kodak Co.

MISCELLANEOUS PRESSROOM CHEMICALS
Burnishine Products

MOTORS
A-American Machine & Assembly (Press Parts Div.)
Baumuller
Bodine Electric
Danfoss Graham
ITW Hobart Brothers Co.
K & M Newspaper Services, Inc.
Miracle Industries, Inc.

MULTIPLEXERS/ROUTERS
alfaQuest Technologies
Autologic Information International
Presteligence

N

NEWS WIRE CAPTURE SYSTEMS
NewsEngin, Inc.
SAXOTECH, Inc.

NEWSPAPER AND EMAIL ADVERTISING SALES
USSPI Media

NEWSPAPER BAGS
Continental Products
Great Southern Corp. (Sirco Div.)
Hamilton Circulation Supplies Co.
Sonoco Products Co.
The Keenan Group, Inc.

NEWSPAPER COUTER
Baumer Electric Ltd.
Buhrs Americas, Inc.
Plumtree Co.
Simon Miller Sales Co.

NEWSPAPER DISPENSERS (MECHANICAL/ELECTRONIC)
AG Industries, Inc.
Fortec, Inc.
Go Plastics/StreetSmart LLC
Hamilton Circulation Supplies Co.
Impact Racks, Inc.
Kaspar Wire Works, Inc./Sho-Rack
K-Jack Engineering Co., Inc.
The Keenan Group, Inc.

NEWSPAPER DISTRIBUTION CONSULTANT
Roggen Management Consultants, Inc.

NEWSPAPER DISTRIBUTION EQUIPMENT
IPC
RAK Systems, Inc.

NEWSPAPER MARKETING
Circulation Solutions, Inc.
Communications Management Service, Inc.
Hamilton Circulation Supplies Co.
Minnesota Opinion Research, Inc. (MORI)
Northern Graphic Supply
Plumtree Co.
SCA Promotions, Inc.
Scarborough Research
Simon Miller Sales Co.
Spectrecom Corporation
The Keenan Group, Inc.
Whitney Worldwide, Inc.

NEWSPAPER VENDING MACHINE PAYMENT SYSTEMS
Bellatrix Systems, Inc.

NEWSPAPER, ADVERTISING
The Slatonite

NEWSPAPERS. CONSULTING SERVICES: ADVERTISING
Missouri Press Service, Inc.

NEWSPRINT
Bender Machine, Inc.
Blue Heron Paper Co.
Catalyst Paper (USA), Inc.
EDIWISE
Manistique Papers, Inc.
McGrann Paper Corp.
Newsprint Sales Co.
Norwood Paper
PAGE
Pan American Papers, Inc.
Roosevelt Paper
Simon Miller Sales Co.
Tembec
United Paper Mills Kymmene, Inc.
White Birch Paper

NEWSPRINT HANDELING EQUIPMENT
Bender Machine, Inc.
Bishamon Industries Corp.
Capital Track Co.
Control Engineering Co.
EDIWISE
FANUC Robotics America, Inc.
H.R. Slater Co., Inc.
Jervis B. Webb Co.
Martin Automatic, Inc.
Metso Paper
Mid-America Graphics, Inc.
Muller Martini Corp.
Plumtree Co.
Saxmayer Corp.
The Austin Company
The Newark Group
XYonicz

NEWSPRINT HANDLING EQUIPMENT
JBT Corporation (formerly FMC Technologies)
Manroland Web Systems Inc.

NICHE (PRINT AND DIGITAL WEBSITES) SPECIALIST
Phelps, Cutler & Associates

NOISE CONTROL
Arco Engineering, Inc. (Newspaper Div.)
Industrial Noise Control, Inc.

NUMBERING MACHINES
Advance Graphics Equipment of York, Inc.
Domino Amjet, Inc.
Rollem Corp. of America
Web Printing Controls

NYLON ROLLER COATING
Graphic Printing Roller Ltd.

O

OFFSET AND METALBACK BLANKETS
Flint Group.

OFFSET BLANKET THICKNESS GAUGE
Caprock Developments, Inc.
J. Thomas McHugh Co., Inc.
Rycoline Products, Inc.
Support Products, Inc.

OFFSET BLANKETS, BLANKET WASH
DYC Supply Co.
J. Thomas McHugh Co., Inc.
Litho Research, Inc.
Printers' Service/Prisco/PriscoDigital
Rycoline Products, Inc.
Vegra USA

OFFSET CAMERA, DARKROOM EQUIPMENT
Arrow Printing Co.

OFFSET CHEMICALS & SUPPLIES
Day International
Litho Research, Inc.
Midwest Publishers Supply Co.
Newstech Co. (Div. of Rovinter, Inc.)
Printers' Service/Prisco/PriscoDigital
Rycoline Products, Inc.
Southern Lithoplate, Inc.
Superior Lithoplate of Indiana, Inc.
UV Process Supply, Inc.
Vegra USA
West Coast Computer Systems
Winton Engineering Co.

OFFSET FILM
Southern Lithoplate, Inc.

OFFSET FOUNTAIN CONTROLS
BEK Systems, Inc.
Master Flo Technology
Smith Pressroom Products, Inc.

OFFSET FOUNTAIN SOLUTIONS
Burnishine Products
Day International
Printers' Service/Prisco/PriscoDigital
Rycoline Products, Inc.
Smith Pressroom Products, Inc.
Southern Lithoplate, Inc.
Vegra USA

OFFSET NEGATIVE MASKING PAPER
Direct Reproduction Corp.

OFFSET PLATE FILES
Arrow Printing Co.
Foster Mfg. Co.

OFFSET PLATE HOLDERS
Roconex Corp.

OFFSET PLATE-MAKING SERVICE & EQUIPMENT
Amergraph Corporation
Douthitt Corp.
Eastman Kodak Co.
K & F International, Inc.
Kodak GCG
NELA
NuArc Co., Inc.
Printware
Richmond/Graphic Products, Inc.
Western LithoTech

OFFSET PREVENTION-MATERIALS & EQUIPMENT
Baldwin Oxy-Dry Americas
Day International

OFFSET SUPPLIES
SunShine Paper Co.

OPTICAL CHARACTER RECOGNITION (OCR)
CNI Corp.
DAC Systems
Media Cybernetics LP
PC Industries

OPTICAL PRODUCTS
Beta Screen Corp.
Caprock Developments, Inc.
Lithco Inc.

OUTPUT MANAGEMENT AND PREFLIGHT SOFTWARE
alfaQuest Technologies
ppi Media GmbH
Presteligence

OUTSOURCING
Creative Circle Media Solutions

P

PACKAGING MACHINERY
Telesonic Packaging Corp., Ames Engineering Div.

PAGE DESIGN (DUMMYING)
Software Consulting Services, LLC

PAGINATION SYSTEMS
Brainworks Software Development Corp.
CNI Corp.
Conley Publishing Systems
Harris Corp.
Informatica Dalai SA de CV
Managing Editor, Inc.
MediaSpan Group Inc.
ppi Media GmbH
Print Marketing Concepts, Inc.
Reed Brennan Media Associates, Inc.
Saxotech
SAXOTECH, Inc.

PAPER
Poyry Management Consulting (USA) Inc.

PAPER - MARCHANT - CONVERTER- DISTRIBUTOR
McGrann Paper Corporation

PAPER CLEANERS
Simco Industrial Static Control Products

PAPER CUTTERS
Colter Peterson

PAPER HANDLING EQUIPMENT
Bishamon Industries Corp.

Capital Track Co.
Cascade Corp.
Control Engineering Co.
EDIWISE
FANUC Robotics America, Inc.
H.R. Slater Co., Inc.
IMC America
Jervis B. Webb Co.
Martin Yale, Inc.
Metso Paper
Muller Martini Corp.
Prim Hall Enterprises, Inc.
Shuttleworth, LLC
Superior Handling Equipment, Inc.
WPC Machinery Corp.
Xpedx Printing Technologies

PAPER HANDLING EQUIPMENT
JBT Corporation (formerly FMC Technologies)

PAPER MATERIALS AND HANDLING
SunShine Paper Co.

PAPER SHREDDERS
Blower Application Co., Inc.
General Binding Corp.
Kaim & Associates International Marketing, Inc.
Martin Yale, Inc.
Megasys International, Inc.

PAPER TESTING INSTRUMENTS
Caprock Developments, Inc.
Lorentzen & Wettre
Technidyne Corp.

PAPER: COATED GROUNDWOOD OFFSET
Catalyst Paper (USA), Inc.
McGrann Paper Corp.
Norwood Paper
Roosevelt Paper
Sappi Fine Paper North America
Simon Miller Sales Co.
StoraEnso

PAPER: GROUNDWOOD SPECIALTIES
Catalyst Paper (USA), Inc.
Manistique Papers, Inc.
McGrann Paper Corp.
Norwood Paper
PAGE
Sappi Fine Paper North America
Simon Miller Sales Co.
White Birch Paper

PAPER: SPECIALTY PRINTING PAPER
Catalyst Paper (USA), Inc.
Domtar, Inc.
McGrann Paper Corp.
Norwood Paper
Pan American Papers, Inc.
Roosevelt Paper
Sappi Fine Paper North America
Simon Miller Sales Co.

PASTERS
Arco Engineering, Inc. (Newspaper Div.)
Butler Automatic
Graphic System Services, Inc.
H & M Paster Sales & Service, Inc.
Jardis Industries, Inc.
Kaim & Associates International Marketing, Inc.
KBA North America, Inc. (Koenig & Bauer AG)
Lankford Engineering, Inc.
Martin Automatic, Inc.
Masthead International, Inc.

PC PRODUCTS
KYE Systems Corp

PHOTO ARCHIVING
alfaQuest Technologies
Foster Mfg. Co.
Gannett Media Technologies International (GMTI)
Kinetic Corporation
SAXOTECH, Inc.

PHOTO PROOFING PAPERS
Eastman Kodak Co.

PHOTO PROOFING SYSTEMS
Arrow Printing Co.
X-Rite Inc.

PHOTOGRAPHY: DIGITAL/ELECTRONIC CAMERAS
Diversified Photo/Graphics Supply
PhotoSource International
Pitman Photo Supply
Unique Photo

PHOTOSTAT: CHEMICALS
Unique Photo

PHOTOSTAT: MACHINES
Megasys International, Inc.

PHOTOSTAT: PAPER
Georgia-Pacific Corp.
Pemco, Inc.
Sappi Fine Paper North America

PHOTOTYPESETTING FONTS
Conley Publishing Systems

PHOTOTYPESETTING INTERFACE EQUIPMENT
E.I. du Pont de Nemours & Co.
Xitron

PICTURE DESKS
MerlinOne, Inc.

PIN REGISTER SYSTEMS
Central Graphics
Douthitt Corp.
K & F International, Inc.
NELA

PLASTIC FOLDERS

PLASTIC STRAPPING
Dynaric, Inc.

PLATE BENDING SYSTEMS
Burgess Industries, Inc.
K & F International, Inc.
NELA

PLATE CLEANERS
Burnishine Products
Day International
Fiberweb
Litho Research, Inc.
Printers' Service/Prisco/PriscoDigital
Superior Lithoplate of Indiana, Inc.
Support Products, Inc.
Western LithoTech

PLATE COATING MACHINES
LogEtronics Corp.

PLATE EXPOSURE UNITS
Amergraph Corporation
Douthitt Corp.
LogEtronics Corp.
NuArc Co., Inc.
Pitman Co.
Roconex Corp.

PLATE LOCK UPS
Acutech LLC

PLATE MOUNTING & REGISTER SYSTEMS
AAA Press International
Burgess Industries, Inc.
NELA
Newstech Co. (Div. of Rovinter, Inc.)

PLATE PROCESSORS
Amergraph Corporation
Bob Weber, Inc.
Eastman Kodak Co.
K & F International, Inc.
LogEtronics Corp.
NB Finishing, Inc.
Newstech Co. (Div. of Rovinter, Inc.)
Pitman Co.
Printware
Richmond/Graphic Products, Inc.
Southern Lithoplate, Inc.
Western LithoTech

PLATE READERS
Bob Weber, Inc.

PLATE SCANNING SYSTEMS
LogEtronics Corp.

PLATEMAKERS: DIRECT
Autologic Information International
GraphLine
MacDermid Printing Solutions

PLATEMAKERS: FLEXOGRAPHIC (COMPUTER TO PLATE)
ARC International
Autologic Information International
MacDermid Printing Solutions

PLATEMAKERS: FLEXOGRAPHIC (TRADITIONAL)
Douthitt Corp.
MacDermid Printing Solutions
MacDermid Printing Solutions
Western LithoTech

PLATEMAKERS: LASER
alfaQuest Technologies
ARC International

PLATEMAKERS: LETTERPRESS
MacDermid Printing Solutions
MacDermid Printing Solutions
Sterling Type Foundry
Western LithoTech

PLATEMAKERS: OFFSET (COMPUTER TO PLATE)
Amergraph Corporation
Douthitt Corp.
ECRM
Western LithoTech

PLATEMAKERS: OFFSET (CONVENTIONAL)
Arrow Printing Co.
K & F International, Inc.
NuArc Co., Inc.
Printware
Roconex Corp.
Superior Lithoplate of Indiana, Inc.
Western LithoTech

PLATES: FLEXOGRAPHIC (CONVENTIONAL)
MacDermid Printing Solutions
MacDermid Printing Solutions

PLATES: LETTERPRESS
MacDermid Printing Solutions

PLATES: OFFSET (COMPUTER TO PLATE)
alfa CTP Systems LLC
Anocoil Corporation
Fuji Photo Film USA/Graphic Systems Div.
Kodak GCG
Mac Dermid Autotype Inc.
MacDermid Printing Solutions
Newstech Co. (Div. of Rovinter, Inc.)
Presstek, Inc.
Southern Lithoplate, Inc.
Western LithoTech

PLATES: OFFSET (CONVENTIONAL)
Anocoil Corporation
Arrow Printing Co.
Eastman Kodak Co.
Fuji Photo Film USA/Graphic Systems Div.
Inter-Continental Graphics, Inc.
Kodak GCG
Latin American Div./Flint Ink
Newstech Co. (Div. of Rovinter, Inc.)
PAGE
Pitman Co.
Printware
Southern Lithoplate, Inc.
Western LithoTech

PLATESETTERS
Bob Weber, Inc.

POST PRESS
Presstek, Inc.

POWDER APPLICATORS
Baldwin Technology Company, Inc.

PRE-PRESS AD PRODUCTION SERVICES FOR BOTH PRINT AND WEB
Outsourcing USA

PREPRESS COLOR PROOFING SYSTEMS
All Systems Color, Inc.
Arrow Printing Co.
CNI Corp.
Direct Reproduction Corp.
E.I. du Pont de Nemours & Co.
ECRM
Lithco Inc.
M.W. Burke & Associates, Inc.
Polkadots Software Inc.
Presteligence
Truproof Ltd.
Weber Systems, Inc.

PREPRESS SOFTWARE AND CTP OUTPUT SYSTEMS
Heidelberg USA, Inc.

PREPRINT SERVICE & PRODUCTION
Kinetic Corporation
Managing Editor, Inc.
Quebecor World
Schawk

PRESS ACCESSORIES
G.T. Specialties

PRESS ACCESSORIES, PARTS & SUPPLIES
AAA Press International
A-American Machine & Assembly (Press Parts Div.)
AEC, Inc.
American Ultraviolet Co., Inc.
AWS, A Thermal Care Division
Baldwin Oxy-Dry Americas
Baldwin Technology Company, Inc.
Brodie System, Inc.
BST Pro Mark
Central Graphics
Day International
Fiberweb
Global Press Management Services, LLC.
Goss International Corporation
Graphic Printing Roller Ltd.
Graphic System Services, Inc.
Graphic Technology, Inc. (GTI)
Inter-Continental Graphics, Inc.
Manassy Sales Inc.
Manroland Web Systems Inc.
Martin Automatic, Inc.
Master Flo Technology
Midwest Publishers Supply Co.
Miracle Industries, Inc.
NELA
Pamarco Global Graphics
Presstek, Inc.
Printers' Service/Prisco/PriscoDigital
Printing Technology, Inc.
Robertson Press Machinery Co., Inc.

Simco Industrial Static Control Products
Tech-Energy Co.
Technology Integrators
Tobias Associates, Inc.
Winton Engineering Co.

PRESS CONTROL SYSTEMS
ABB Inc.
ABB, Inc. (Printing Systems)
Bosch Rexroth
E.I. du Pont de Nemours & Co.
ELAPLAN Buchholz GmbH & Co.
Ewert America Electronics Ltd.
Fincor Automation, Inc.
Graphics Microsystems, Inc.
Harland Simon
Harris Corp.
Honeywell, Inc.
Inter-Continental Graphics, Inc.
Koenig & Bauer Aktiengesellschaft (KBA)
Manroland Web Systems Inc.
Miracle Industries, Inc.
PC Industries
Quad Tech
QuadTech
Rockwell Automation
Web Printing Controls

PRESS DATA ACCUMULATORS
Harland Simon

PRESS ENGINEERS
Global Press Management Services, LLC.
Hall Contracting Services, Inc.
Miracle Industries, Inc.
Tech-Energy Co.

PRESS PARTS
Masthead International, Inc.
Newstech Co. (Div. of Rovinter, Inc.)

PRESS REBUILDING
A-American Machine & Assembly (Press Parts Div.)
Brown's Web Press Service & Machine Shop
Egenolf Machine, Inc. (Egenolf Contracting & Rigging)
Global Press Management Services, LLC.
Goss International Corporation
Hall Contracting Services, Inc.
Inland Newspaper Machinery LLC
Masthead International, Inc.
Pressline Services, Inc.
Printing Technology, Inc.
Robertson Press Machinery Co., Inc.
Tech-Energy Co.
Wesco Graphics
WPC Machinery Corp.

PRESS REGISTRATION
ProImage America, Inc.

PRESS REPAIRS
Brown's Web Press Service & Machine Shop
Egenolf Machine, Inc. (Egenolf Contracting & Rigging)
Goss International Corporation
Hall Contracting Services, Inc.
Inland Newspaper Machinery LLC
Manugraph DGM, Inc.
Masthead International, Inc.
Pressline Services, Inc.
Presstek, Inc.
Printing Technology, Inc.
Tech-Energy Co.
Wesco Graphics
WPC Machinery Corp.

PRESS SYSTEMS AND EQUIPMENT
Chuck Blevins & Assoc.

PRESSES: DILITHO
Elcorsy Technology, Inc.
Northeast Industries, Inc.

PRESSES: FLEXOGRAPHIC
AAA Press International

ADI/PDM Trade Group
Dean Machinery International, Inc.
KBA North America, Inc. (Koenig & Bauer AG)
Kidder, Inc.
Koenig & Bauer Aktiengesellschaft (KBA)
Manroland Web Systems Inc.
Masthead International, Inc.
Northeast Industries, Inc.
Windmoeller and Hoelscher Corp.

PRESSES: LETTERPRESS
Masthead International, Inc.
Northeast Industries, Inc.
Sterling Type Foundry
Tech-Energy Co.

PRESSES: OFFSET
Arrow Printing Co.
B & L Machine & Design
Brown's Web Press Service & Machine Shop
Central Graphics
Craftsmen Machinery Co., Inc.
Dean Machinery International, Inc.
Goss International Corporation
GSP, Inc.
Inland Newspaper Machinery LLC
Intercontinental Engineering Co.
Inter-Continental Graphics, Inc.
KBA North America, Inc. (Koenig & Bauer AG)
Koenig & Bauer Aktiengesellschaft (KBA)
Komori America Corp.
Latin American Div./Flint Ink
MAH Machine Co., Inc.
Manroland Web Systems Inc.
Manugraph DGM, Inc.
Masthead International, Inc.
Metroland Printing/Publishing & Distributing Ltd.
Miracle Industries, Inc.
Newman International, LLC
Northeast Industries, Inc.
ONE Corp.
Pamarco Global Graphics
Presstek, Inc.
Printing Press Services, Inc.
Printing Technology, Inc.
Robertson Press Machinery Co., Inc.
Sakurai USA
Solna Web USA, Inc.
Tech-Energy Co.
Tensor International LLC
WebPress, LLC
Wesco Graphics
Xpedx Printing Technologies

PRESSES: OFFSET AND DIGITAL
TKS (USA), Inc.

PRESSES: ROTOGRAVURE
Dean Machinery International, Inc.
Koenig & Bauer Aktiengesellschaft (KBA)
Quebecor World
Windmoeller and Hoelscher Corp.

PRESSES: WEB OFFSET
Lissom Corp. Inc.

PRESSROOM CHEMICALS
Flint Group.

PRESSROOM PRODUCTS
Fujifilm North America Corporation

PRESSROOM SUPPLIES
Flint Group.

PRESSTEK DI DIGITAL OFFSET PRESSES
Presstek, Inc.

PRINT & DIGITAL MEDIA SOFTWARE
Vision Data Equipment Corp.

PRINTING
Tolerans AB Sweden

PRINTING EQUIPMENT DEALER
Dennis Storch Co.

PRINTING INKS
Flint Group.

PRINTING PRESSES
WIFAG

PROCESS COLOR REFERENCE GUIDES
Trumatch, Inc.

PROCESSORS: DIFFUSION TRANSFER
LogEtronics Corp.
NuArc Co., Inc.
Richmond/Graphic Products, Inc.

PROCESSORS: FILM & PAPER
Amergraph Corporation
Arrow Printing Co.
Bob Weber, Inc.
Diversified Photo/Graphics Supply
Dunning Photo Equipment, Inc.
Eastman Kodak Co.
ECRM
Glunz & Jensen, Inc.
LogEtronics Corp.
Presstek, Inc.
Richmond/Graphic Products, Inc.

PRODUCITON CONTROL SYSTEMS
BST Pro Mark
Fleming Enterprises
Harland Simon
Midsystems Technology Ltd.
Miracom Computer Corp.
OLEC
ppi Media GmbH

PROMOTION IDEAS
Creative House Print Media Consultants

PROMOTION SERVICES
Advantex Marketing International, Inc.
Plumtree Co.
SCA Promotions, Inc.
Weatherline, Inc.

PROOFING SYSTEMS
AAA Press International
alfa CTP Systems LLC
Anygraaf USA
Burgess Industries, Inc.
Data Engineering Ltd.
ECRM
Fuji Photo Film USA/Graphic Systems Div.
Komori America Corp.
Konica Minolta Graphic Imaging USA
N & L Enterprises, Inc.
NuArc Co., Inc.
PC Industries
Presstek, Inc.
SCREEN (USA)
X-Rite Inc.

PUBLICATION DESIGN & LAYOUT SERVICES
Publication Design, Inc.

PUBLISHER CONSULTANT SERVICES
Berting Communications

PUBLISHING SYSTEMS
Advanced Technical Solutions, Inc.
Autologic Information International
Bell & Howell Scanners
CNI Corp.
Conley Publishing Systems
Fry Communications
Harris Corp.
MediaSpan Group Inc.
Metroland Printing/Publishing & Distributing Ltd.
SAXOTECH, Inc.
TeleType Co.

PULP & PAPER
Resolute Forest Products

PUMPS (AIR, INK, VACUUM)
Baumfolder Corp.
Busch, Inc.
Graphic System Services, Inc.
Ingersoll-Rand-Aro Fluid Product Div.
Lincoln Industrial
Smith Pressroom Products, Inc.
UV Process Supply, Inc.
West Coast Computer Systems

PUNCHING EQUIPMENT
NELA
Presstek, Inc.

R

RACK DISPLAY CARDS
Hamilton Circulation Supplies Co.
RFC Wire Forms

RASTER IMAGE PROCESSORS
alfaQuest Technologies
Bob Weber, Inc.
SCREEN (USA)
Xitron

RECIRCULATORS
Baldwin Technology Company, Inc.
Master Flo Technology
Smith Pressroom Products, Inc.

RECYCLING NEWSPRINT
Sonoco Products Co.

REELS & TENSIONS
Arco Engineering, Inc. (Newspaper Div.)
Inter-Continental Graphics, Inc.
Jardis Industries, Inc.
Johnstone Engineering & Machine Co.
Kaim & Associates International Marketing, Inc.
KBA North America, Inc. (Koenig & Bauer AG)
Koenig & Bauer Aktiengesellschaft (KBA)
Lankford Engineering, Inc.
Maxcess
Pemco, Inc.
Tidland Corp.
Wesco Graphics

REELS (INCLUDES PAPER REELS)
Arco Engineering, Inc. (Newspaper Div.)
Jardis Industries, Inc.
Johnstone Engineering & Machine Co.
KBA North America, Inc. (Koenig & Bauer AG)
Manroland Web Systems Inc.
Pemco, Inc.
Tidland Corp.

REMANUFACTURES EQUIPMENT
FKI Logistex
Graphic System Services, Inc.
Hall Contracting Services, Inc.
HFW Industries
Impact Racks, Inc.
Inland Newspaper Machinery LLC
Jardis Industries, Inc.
K & M Newspaper Services, Inc.
Kansa Technology, LLC
Kepes, Inc.
LogEtronics Corp.
Manugraph DGM, Inc.
Muller Martini Mailroom Systems, Inc.
ONE Corp.
Robertson Press Machinery Co., Inc.
SITMA USA, Inc.
Solar Systems
Sterling Packaging Systems
WebPress, LLC

REPAIRS & PARTS FOR WING MAILERS
Chauncey Wing's Sons, Inc.

RESEARCH STUDIES
A & A Research
Advertising Checking Bureau, Inc.
Hare Associates, Inc.
Minnesota Opinion Research, Inc. (MORI)
Scarborough Research
Spectrecom Corporation
Ver-A-Fast Corporation

REWINDERS
AAA Press International
Johnstone Engineering & Machine Co.
Keene Technology, Inc. (KTI)
Kidder, Inc.
Martin Automatic, Inc.
Norwood Paper
Rotoflex Mark Andy Canada, Inc.
Stanford Products

ROLL CLEANING EQUIPMENT
A-Korn Roller, Inc.
Cryogenesis (A Div. of WM & C Services, Inc.)
Kaim & Associates International Marketing, Inc.
Litho Research, Inc.
Manroland Web Systems Inc.

ROLL CONVERTERS
Norman X Guttman, Inc.
Simon Miller Sales Co.

ROLL COVERINGS
A-Korn Roller, Inc.
American Roller Co.
ARC International
Herco Graphic Products
Petco Roller Co.
Republic Roller Corp.
RotaDyne Corp.
Xerium Technologies Inc.

ROLL HANDLING EQUIPMENT
Butler Automatic
Capital Track Co.
FANUC Robotics America, Inc.
Fleming Enterprises
Gerrard Ovalstrapping
Jervis B. Webb Co.
Johnstone Engineering & Machine Co.
Kepes, Inc.
Koenig & Bauer Aktiengesellschaft (KBA)
MEGTEC Systems
Metso Paper
Pemco, Inc.
Shuttleworth, LLC
The Austin Company
Tilt-Lock
WebPress, LLC
Wesco Graphics

ROLL HANDLEING EQUIPMENT
IMC America

ROLL HANDLING EQUIPMENT
JBT Corporation (formerly FMC Technologies)

ROLL PREPARATION EQUIPMENT
JBT Corporation (formerly FMC Technologies)
Koenig & Bauer Aktiengesellschaft (KBA)

ROLLER GRINDERS
A-Korn Roller, Inc.
Bender Machine, Inc.
Capco Machinery Systems, Inc.
Fleming Enterprises
South Bend Lathe Corp.
Whitworth Knife Company

ROLLER GRINDING SERVICES
A-Korn Roller, Inc.
Bender Machine, Inc.
Brodie System, Inc.
Brown's Web Press Service & Machine Shop
Central Graphics
Graphic Printing Roller Ltd.
Hadronics
MAH Machine Co., Inc.
Miracle Industries, Inc.

NB Finishing, Inc.
Norman X Guttman, Inc.
Republic Roller Corp.
Xerium Technologies Inc.

ROLLERS
A-Korn Roller, Inc.
American Roller Co.
ARC International
Bottcher America Corp.
Brodie System, Inc.
Hadronics
Herco Graphic Products
Inter-Continental Graphics, Inc.
Kaim & Associates International Marketing, Inc.
Kepes, Inc.
MAH Machine Co., Inc.
Manassy Sales Inc.
Newstech Co. (Div. of Rovinter, Inc.)
Norman X Guttman, Inc.
Pacesetter Graphic Service Corp.
Pamarco Global Graphics
Pamarco Global Graphics
Petco Roller Co.
Praxair, Inc.
Printing Technology, Inc.
Republic Roller Corp.
RotaDyne Corp.
Tech-Energy Co.
WPC Machinery Corp.
Xerium Technologies Inc.

ROLLERS: DAMPENING
A-Korn Roller, Inc.
American Roller Co.
Brodie System, Inc.
Central Graphics
Day International
Graphic Printing Roller Ltd.
Hadronics
MAH Machine Co., Inc.
Nama Graphics E, LLC
Norman X Guttman, Inc.
Pacesetter Graphic Service Corp.
Pamarco Global Graphics
Petco Roller Co.
Printing Technology, Inc.
Republic Roller Corp.
RotaDyne Corp.

RULES
Lithco Inc.
Support Products, Inc.

S

SALES AND DESIGN OFFICE FURNITURE
Brown Mannschreck Business System

SCANNERS: COLOR B & W, PLATES, WEB
Arco Engineering, Inc. (Newspaper Div.)
Arrow Printing Co.
Autologic Information International
Fuji Photo Film USA/Graphic Systems Div.
Impak (A Div. of Pakon, Inc.)
Microtek
Pitman Co.
Siix USA Corp.
UMAX Technologies, Inc.
VIDAR Systems Corp.
Xerox (Corp. Headquarters)

SEMANTIC ENGINE SERVICES
Digital Collections

SHEETFED OFFSET PRESSES
Heidelberg USA, Inc.

SHRINK WRAPPING EQUIPMENT
Arpac Group
Muller Martini Corp.
SITMA USA, Inc.
Telesonic Packaging Corp., Ames Engineering Div.

SILVER RECOVERY
Commodity Resource & Environment
Hart Industries
Hart Industries/Metafix Compliance Systems
Maratek Environmental Technologies, Inc.
Metafix, Inc.
Metals Recovery Service
R.B. Intermark, Inc.

SOFTWARE: AD TRACKING
Miles 33

SOFTWARE: AD TRACKING, PRODUCTION MANAGEMENT
Vision Data Equipment Corp.

SOFTWARE: ADVERTISING
Advanced Technical Solutions, Inc.
Atex
Atex North America
Atex North America
Autologic Information International
Brainworks Software Development Corp.
Bruce Bell & Associates
CCI Europe, Inc.
Celebro
ChannelNet
Conley Publishing Systems
Datafest Technologies, Inc.
Decisionmark Corp.
Digital Technology International
Digital Technology International
Eclipse Services (Div. of Quadrivium, Inc.)
Fake Brains, Inc.
Gannett Media Technologies International (GMTI)
ICANON Associates, Inc.
IdeaFisher Systems, Inc.
Informatica Dalai SA de CV
Interlink
Managing Editor, Inc.
McCrrory Publishing
Media Data Technology, Inc. (MDTI)
Media Marketing, Inc.
MediaSpan
Merrimac Software Associates
Micro Systems Specialists, Inc. (MSSI)
Miles 33
MultiAd
Neasi-Weber International
NEWSCYCLE Solutions
ppi Media GmbH
Presteligence
Quickwire Labs
Ranger Data Technologies Inc.
Sales Development Services
SAP America, Inc.
Saxotech
Scarborough Research
Software Consulting Services, LLC
Spectrecom Corporation
Tek-Tools, Inc.
Unisys Corp.
Vertis

SOFTWARE: ASSET MANAGEMENT
Atex
CCI Europe, Inc.
Cygnet Storage Solutions, Inc.
DeskNet, Inc.
Digital Technology International
EDIWISE
Informatica Dalai SA de CV
Kinetic Corporation
Morcor Solutions, Inc.
MultiAd
NewsView Solutions
North Atlantic Publishing Systems, Inc.
Quark, Inc.
SAXOTECH, Inc.
SPECTRUM Human Resource Systems Corp.
The Software Construction Co.

SOFTWARE: BUSINESS (INCLUDES ADMINISTRATION/ACCOUNTING)
Atex North America
Atex North America
Brainworks Software Development Corp.
CCI Europe, Inc.

Datafest Technologies, Inc.
Digital Technology International
Digital Technology International
Eclipse Services (Div. of Quadrivium, Inc.)
EDIWISE
Fake Brains, Inc.
ICANON Associates, Inc.
Merrimac Software Associates
Micro Systems Specialists, Inc. (MSSI)
Software Business Systems
SPECTRUM Human Resource Systems Corp.
Unisys Corp.

SOFTWARE: CIRCULATION
Advanced Technical Solutions, Inc.
ASTech InterMedia
Atex
Atex North America
Decisionmark Corp.
Digital Technology International
Digital Technology International
Fake Brains, Inc.
Global Turnkey Systems, Inc.
Hamilton Circulation Supplies Co.
ICANON Associates, Inc.
Interlink
Kaspar Wire Works, Inc./Sho-Rack
K-Jack Engineering Co., Inc.
MediaSpan
MediaSpan Group Inc.
Merrimac Software Associates
Micro Systems Specialists, Inc. (MSSI)
Mobile Computing Corporation USA
Neasi-Weber International
NEWSCYCLE Solutions
Printsoft Americas, Inc.
SAP America, Inc.

SOFTWARE: CIRCULATION MANAGEMENT
Vision Data Equipment Corp.

SOFTWARE: CIRCULATION SOFTWARE
Brainworks Software Development Corp.

SOFTWARE: CMS, ADVERTISING, NATIVE CONTENT
Creative Circle Media Solutions

SOFTWARE: COMMUNITY BUILDING
John Juliano Computer Services Co.

SOFTWARE: CONTENT MANAGEMENT SYSTEMS FOR NEWSROOM AND WEB
Miles 33

SOFTWARE: CUSTOMER RELATIONSHIP MANAGEMENT (CRM)
Brainworks Software Development Corp.

SOFTWARE: DESIGN/GRAPHICS
Agfa Monotype Corporation
All Systems Go
Artbeats
Brainworks Software Development Corp.
CCI Europe, Inc.
Conley Publishing Systems
DeskNet, Inc.
Digital Technology International
Esko-Graphics
IMSI
Jupiter Images Corp.
Kinetic Corporation
MacDonald Advertising Services
MediaSpan
Metro Creative Graphics, Inc.
MultiAd
NEWSCYCLE Solutions
Pantone, Inc.
Quark, Inc.
The Software Construction Co.

SOFTWARE: DIGITAL ASSET MANAGEMENT
Miles 33

SOFTWARE: DIGITAL ASSET

MANAGEMENT/ARCHIVING
Tera Digital Publishing

SOFTWARE: DIGITAL VIDEO AD PRODUCTION
Miles 33

SOFTWARE: EDITORIAL
Advanced Technical Solutions, Inc.
Atex
Atex North America
CCI Europe, Inc.
Conley Publishing Systems
Decisionmark Corp.
DeskNet, Inc.
Digital Technology International
ICANON Associates, Inc.
Informatica Dalai SA de CV
Managing Editor, Inc.
Markzware Software, Inc.
McCrrory Publishing
MediaSpan
MediaSpan Group Inc.
Metro Creative Graphics, Inc.
NEWSCYCLE Solutions
NewsEngin, Inc.
North Atlantic Publishing Systems, Inc.
Quark, Inc.
Quickwire Labs
Saxotech
SAXOTECH, Inc.
Tek-Tools, Inc.
The Software Construction Co.
Unisys Corp.

SOFTWARE: EDITORIAL CONTENT MANAGEMENT SYSTEMS
Tera Digital Publishing

SOFTWARE: ELECTRONIC DATA INTERCHANGE
Autologic Information International
CCI Europe, Inc.
Celebro
ColorVision, Inc.
Computer Talk Technology, Inc.
Comtel Instruments Co.
DeskNet, Inc.
EDIWISE
Global Turnkey Systems, Inc.
IMSI
Markzware Software, Inc.
McCrrory Publishing
NewsView Solutions
ProImage America, Inc.
Shoom, Inc.
Tek-Tools, Inc.
Vision Data Equipment Corp.

SOFTWARE: JREPORTER
John Juliano Computer Services Co.

SOFTWARE: MOBILE
John Juliano Computer Services Co.

SOFTWARE: MULTIPLE SERVICES
Xerox Corp.

SOFTWARE: PAGINATION/LAYOUT
alfa CTP Systems LLC
Atex
Atex North America
Brainworks Software Development Corp.
Capita Technologies
CCI Europe, Inc.
Conley Publishing Systems
DeskNet, Inc.
Digital Technology International
Harland Simon
ICANON Associates, Inc.
Imapro Corp.
IMSI
Kinetic Corporation
Managing Editor, Inc.
McCrrory Publishing
MediaSpan
MediaSpan Group Inc.
Merrimac Software Associates

Miles 33
MultiAd
NEWSCYCLE Solutions
NewsEngin, Inc.
North Atlantic Publishing Systems, Inc.
PALOS Software
ppi Media GmbH
ProImage America, Inc.
Quark, Inc.
Quickwire Labs
Saxotech
SAXOTECH, Inc.
SCREEN (USA)
Tribune Media Services
Unisys Corp.
Vision Data Equipment Corp.
Weber Systems, Inc.

SOFTWARE: PRESS/POST PRESS
Advanced Technical Solutions, Inc.
Buhrs Americas, Inc.
Burt Technologies, Inc.
Harland Simon
MediaSpan
Muller Martini Mailroom Systems, Inc.
Plumtree Co.
Presteligence
Quipp System, Inc.

SOFTWARE: REMOTE WORKFLOW MANAGEMENT.
Vision Data Equipment Corp.

SOFTWARE: SELF SERVICE ADVERTISING
Miles 33

SOFTWARE: SOCIAL MEDIA
John Juliano Computer Services Co.

SOFTWARE: WEB PUBLISHING
Tera Digital Publishing

SOFTWARE: WORKFLOW MANAGEMENT/ TRACKING
CCI Europe, Inc.
DeskNet, Inc.
Ewert America Electronics Ltd.
Harland Simon
JBT Corporation (formerly FMC Technologies)
Kinetic Corporation
Managing Editor, Inc.
Manugraph DGM, Inc.
Monaco Systems, Inc.
Morcor Solutions, Inc.
NewsView Solutions
North Atlantic Publishing Systems, Inc.
Plumtree Co.
ppi Media GmbH
Presteligence
SAXOTECH, Inc.
Tek-Tools, Inc.
The Software Construction Co.
Unisys Corp.

SOFTWARE: WORKFLOW MANAGEMENT/ TRACKING, RIPPING, IMPOSITION
ProImage America, Inc.

SOFTWARE:NEWS GATHERING
John Juliano Computer Services Co.

SOLVENT RECOVERY SYSTEMS
ADI/PDM Trade Group
Baldwin Oxy-Dry Americas
Baldwin Technology Company, Inc.
Maratek Environmental Technologies, Inc.
Printers' Service/Prisco/PriscoDigital
R.B. Intermark, Inc.
Smith Pressroom Products, Inc.

SOUTH MOUNTAIN PRESS COMMUNITY NEWSPAPER
Nesbitt Publishing Ltd.

SPEECH RECOGNITION
DAC Systems

Nuance
Syntellect, Inc.
TALX Corp.

SPLICERS, AUTOMATIC
Butler Automatic
Graphic System Services, Inc.
Inter-Continental Graphics, Inc.
Keene Technology, Inc. (KTI)
North Shore Consultants, Inc.
ONE Corp.
Pemco, Inc.
Printing Press Services, Inc.

SPLIT NIP FOLDER ROLLS
Graphic Printing Roller Ltd.

STACKERS AND TYING MACHINES
WRH Marketing Americas, Inc.

STATIC ELIMINATORS
Beta Screen Corp.
Burgess Industries, Inc.
Herman H. Sticht Co., Inc.
Litho Research, Inc.
NRD LLC
Simco Industrial Static Control Products
Support Products, Inc.
UV Process Supply, Inc.
Vegra USA
West Coast Computer Systems

STICKY NOTES
AD-A-NOTE

STITCHERS
Heidelberg USA, Inc.

STORAGE RETRIEVAL SYSTEMS
Consolidated Storage Cos.
Cygnet Storage Solutions, Inc.
Gannett Media Technologies International (GMTI)
Jervis B. Webb Co.
Mesa Corp.
Muller Martini Corp.
Muller Martini Mailroom Systems, Inc.
NewsView Solutions
Penco Products
Roconex Corp.
Schawk
Solar Systems
Truproof Ltd.
Weber Systems, Inc.
WRH Marketing Americas Americas, Inc
WRH Marketing Americas, Inc.

STRAPPING MACHINES
Automated Mailing Systems Corp.
B.H. Bunn Co.
EAM-Mosca Corp.
FELINS, Inc.
Gerrard Ovalstrapping
Gerrard Ovalstrapping
Impact Racks, Inc.
Malow Corp.
Samuel Strapping System
Saxmayer Corp.
Signode Corp.
Systems Technology, Inc.
Teufelberger GmbH

SUBSCRIPTION FULFILLMENT
Fulco, Inc.

SUBSCRIPTION FULFILLMENT SOFTWARE
Global Turnkey Systems, Inc.
Syntellect, Inc.

SUNDAY SELECT
Ver-A-Fast Corporation

SYSTEM INSTALLATIONS
Blower Application Co., Inc.
Chemetron Fire Systems

Dan-Bar, Inc.
Global Turnkey Systems, Inc.
Quipp System, Inc.
Software Business Systems
Versar Inc.

SYSTEM INTEGRATION SERVICES
ABB Inc.
ABB, Inc. (Printing Systems)
Brainworks Software Development Corp.
Capita Technologies
CCI Europe, Inc.
Chemetron Fire Systems
Computer Talk Technology, Inc.
DeskNet, Inc.
Digital Technology International
Ewert America Electronics Ltd.
Global Turnkey Systems, Inc.
JBT Corporation (formerly FMC Technologies)
McCrrory Publishing
ppi Media GmbH
Presteligence
Quipp System, Inc.
Random Access
Robertson Equipments
Software Business Systems
Syntellect, Inc.
The Austin Company
Unisys Corp.

SYSTEM PROGRAMMING
American International Communications, Inc.

T

TABLES (DOT, ETCH, OPAQUING, REGISTER, RETOUCHING, STRIPPING)
Beta Screen Corp.
Richmond/Graphic Products, Inc.
Roconex Corp.
SCREEN (USA)
Thompson Cabinet Co.

TABLET & MOBILE SOLUTIONS
ProImage America, Inc.

TAPE SPLICING EQUIPMENT
Cariweb Products
North Shore Consultants, Inc.

TELECOMMUNICATION
Noble System Corporation

TELECOMMUNICATIONS
Chemetron Fire Systems
DAC Systems
Drake Communications, Inc.
Earmark
Electronic Tele-Communications, Inc.
General DataComm, Inc.
Innovative Systems Design, Inc.
NUS Consulting Group
Siemens Communications Group
Support Systems International Corp.
Syntellect, Inc.
Unicom, Inc.
Ver-A-Fast Corporation
VoiceWorld, Inc.

TELEPHONE SERVICES
American International Communications, Inc.

TENSION & WEB CONTROLS
Arco Engineering, Inc. (Newspaper Div.)
Butler Automatic
Fleming Enterprises
grafikAmerica
Graphic System Services, Inc.
Kaim & Associates International Marketing, Inc.
KBA North America, Inc. (Koenig & Bauer AG)
Lankford Engineering, Inc.
Masthead International, Inc.
Maxcess
Norman X Guttman, Inc.
Pemco, Inc.
Robertson Press Machinery Co., Inc.

Tidland Corp.
Web Printing Controls

TESTING INSTRUMENTS
Caprock Developments, Inc.
Simco Industrial Static Control Products
Tobias Associates, Inc.
X-Rite Inc.

THREE KNIFE TRIMMER
Advance Graphics Equipment of York, Inc.
Applied Industrial Machinery
Prim Hall Enterprises, Inc.

TOTALIZING SYSTEMS
Baumer Electric Ltd.
Plumtree Co.

TRADE PUBLICATIONS
Editor & Publisher Magazine
Flexographic Technical Association
Fry Communications
Graphic Arts Blue Book Online
Jupiter Images Corp.
MacDonald Advertising Services
Mouser Institute School of Advertising
MSP Communications
National Newspaper Association Publishers' Auxiliary
PhotoSource International
Sales Development Services
SRDS, a Kantar Media Company
Tel-Aire Publications, Inc.
The Seybold Report

TRAINING
Computer Tree Professional Training
Creative Circle Media Solutions

TRAINING: AUTOMATED PRE PRESS WORKFLOW
ProImage America, Inc.

TRAINING: DESIGN & LAYOUT
MediaSpan Group Inc.
Morcor Solutions, Inc.
Tribune Media Services
Wolk Advertising, Inc. (Retail Carpet Ad Service)

TRAINING: KEYBOARD OPERATION
CCI Europe, Inc.
CNI Corp.
Learning Tree International
Morcor Solutions, Inc.
Scarborough Research
Spectrecom Corporation
Trauner Consulting Services, Inc.

TRAINING: POST PRESS
Burt Technologies, Inc.
Flexographic Technical Association
Muller Martini Mailroom Systems, Inc.

Quipp System, Inc.

TRAINING: PRE PRESS
Flexographic Technical Association
Morcor Solutions, Inc.

TRAINING: PRESS OPERATION & MAINTENANCE
B & L Machine & Design
Ewert America Electronics Ltd.
Flexographic Technical Association
Manugraph DGM, Inc.
Masthead International, Inc.

TRAINING: SALES & MARKETING
ASTech InterMedia
Creative Brilliance Advertising, Marketing & Public Relation
Ed Baron & Associates, Inc.
Kamen & Co. Group Services
Media Marketing, Inc.

TRAINING: SALES & MARKETING-- WEBINARS, TELE-SEMINARS
Berting Communications

TRAINING: SALES AND MARKETING
Sales Training Consultants, Inc.

TUBES, RACKS (INCLUDES RACKS: MOTOR ROUTE TUBES)
Continental Products
Fortec, Inc.
Hamilton Circulation Supplies Co.
Impact Racks, Inc.
Kamen & Co. Group Services
K-Jack Engineering Co., Inc.
Lyon Enterprises
Sonoco Products Co.

TYPE, FONTS
Agfa Monotype Corporation
Design Science, Inc.
Ernest Schaefer, Inc.
Sterling Type Foundry

TYPESETTERS: LASER
alfa CTP Systems LLC
Autologic Information International
CNI Corp.
Xitron

TYPESETTING PROGRAMS
Conley Publishing Systems

U

USED WEB PRESSES AND AUXILIARIES
Graphic Machine Sales, Inc.

UV & LED CURING AND IR DRYING

SYSTEMS
Baldwin Technology Company, Inc.

V

VACUUM FRAMES
Amergraph Corporation
Burgess Industries, Inc.
Douthitt Corp.
Richmond/Graphic Products, Inc.
Technology Integrators

VIBRATION ISOLATION & MACHINE LEVELING MOUNTS
AirLoc LLC

VISUAL DISPLAY TERMINALS
Fife Corporation
Harris Corp.
Maxcess

VOICE OVER IP
American International Communications, Inc.

W

WASTEWATER TREATMENT
Beckart Environmental, Inc.
Hart Industries
Hart Industries/Metafix Compliance Systems
Maratek Environmental Technologies, Inc.
R.B. Intermark, Inc.
Semler Industries, Inc. (Pressroom Fluids Equipment Div.)
Smith Pressroom Products, Inc.

WATER MANAGEMENT SYSTEMS
Alar Engineering Corp.
R.B. Intermark, Inc.
Smith Pressroom Products, Inc.
Technotrans America, Inc.

WEB AND PRINT REDESIGNS
Creative Circle Media Solutions

WEB BREAK DETECTOR
Baumer Electric Ltd.
Fife Corporation
Kaim & Associates International Marketing, Inc.
Maxcess
Miracle Industries, Inc.
Quad Tech
QuadTech
Web Printing Controls

WEB CLEANERS
BST Pro Mark
D & R Engineering
Kaim & Associates International Marketing, Inc.

WEB GUIDES
BST Pro Mark
Fife Corporation
Martin Automatic, Inc.
Maxcess
Pemco, Inc.
Web Printing Controls

WEB OFFSET PRESSES
ONE Corp.

WEB OFFSET REMOISTURIZERS
D & R Engineering
grafikAmerica
Smith Pressroom Products, Inc.
Technotrans America, Inc.

WEB PRESS - SPECIAL EQUIPMENT
Advance Graphics Equipment of York, Inc.
Applied Industrial Machinery
D & R Engineering
Fife Corporation
Flynn Burner Corp.
Graphic System Services, Inc.
GSP, Inc.
H & M Paster Sales & Service, Inc.
IGS Knives, Inc.
Koenig & Bauer Aktiengesellschaft (KBA)
Maxcess
Miracle Industries, Inc.
NELA
Newman International, LLC
Perretta Graphics Corp.
Robertson Press Machinery Co., Inc.
Tidland Corp.
WebPress, LLC
Wesco Graphics
Western Printing Machinery
Western Roller Corp.

WEB SITE BUILDING
American International Communications, Inc.

WEB WIDTH CHANGER
A-American Machine & Assembly (Press Parts Div.)
Hall Contracting Services, Inc.
Pressline Services, Inc.

WIDE FORMAT INKJET
Heidelberg USA, Inc.

WIDE FORMAT INKJET SYSTEMS & SUPPLIES
Printers' Service/Prisco/PriscoDigital

WORD PROCESSING SYSTEM
CNI Corp.
Nisus Software, Inc.

WORKFLOW RIPS
Bob Weber, Inc.

INTERACTIVE PRODUCTS AND SERVICES COMPANIES SERVING THE NEWSPAPER INDUSTRY

2

24/7 REAL MEDIA, INC.
132 W 31st St, Fl 9, New York, NY, 10001-3406, USA (212) 231-7100; fax (646) 259-4200; e-mail info@xaxis.com; web site www.247realmedia.com
Product or Service: Advertising/Marketing Agency

3

3M TOUCH SYSTEMS, INC.
300 Griffin Brook Dr, Methuen, MA, 01844-1873, USA (978) 659-9000; fax (978) 659-9100; web site www.3mtouch.com
Product or Service: Hardware/Software Supplier
Bus. Unit Mgr.—Chris Tsourides

A

AARON MARCUS AND ASSOCIATES.
1196 Euclid Ave, Berkeley, CA, 94708-1640, USA (510)599-3195; e-mail aaron.marcus@bamanda.com; web site www.bamanda.com
Product or Service: CD-ROM Designer/Manufacturer, Consultants, Graphic/Design Firm, POP/Kiosk Designer, Research

Principal—Aaron Marcus
Note: Available to author research and other publications, to be interviewed, or to give lectures/workshops

ACCUWEATHER, INC.
385 Science Park Rd, State College, PA, 16803-2215, USA (814) 237-0309; fax (814) 235-8609; e-mail sales@accuweather.com; info@accuwx.com; web site www.

accuweather.com

Product or Service: Multimedia/Interactive Products, Other Services, Online Service Provider and Internet Hosts

Founder & President—Dr. Joel N. Myers

CEO—Barry Lee Myers

Sr. VP, Chief Meteorologist—Elliot Abrams

Sr. VP, Forensics—Dr. Joseph Sobel

COO—Evan A. Myers

Sr. VP, Special Initiatives—Michael Steinberg

Chief Strategy Officer—James Candor

Chief Marketing Officer—John Dokes

ACT TELECONFERENCING, INC.

1526 Cole Blvd, Ste 300, Lakewood, CO, 80401-3410, USA (303) 233-3500; web site www.acttel.com

Product or Service: Multimedia/Interactive Products

Pres.—Peter Salas

ACTIVE DATA EXCHANGE

190 Brodhead Rd Ste 300, Lehigh Valley Industrial Pk. IV, Bethlehem, PA, 18017-8617, USA (610) 997-8100; fax (610) 866-7899; e-mail info@activedatax.com; web site www.activedatax.com

Product or Service: Publisher/Media

Pres./CEO—Susan C. Yee

COO—Kendra Hollinger

ADAPTIVE OPTICS ASSOCIATES, INC., A UNITED TECHNOLOGIES CO.

10 Wilson Rd, Cambridge, MA, 02138-1128, USA (617) 864-0201; fax (617) 864-5855; e-mail info@aoainc.com; web site www.mdatechnology.net

Product or Service: Hardware/Software Supplier

Pres.—Jeff Yourz

ADITYA BIRLA MINACS

34115 W 12 Mile Rd, Farmington Hills, MI, 48331-3368, USA (248) 553-8355; e-mail info@minacs.adityabirla.com; web site www.minacs.adityabirla.com

Product or Service: Telecommunications/Service Bureaus

COO—Anil Bhalia

CEO—Deepak Patel

ADOBE SYSTEMS, INC.

345 Park Ave, San Jose, CA, 95110-2704, USA (408) 536-6000; fax (408) 537-6000; web site www.adobe.com

Product or Service: Hardware/Software Supplier

Sr. Vice Pres., Global Mktg.—Ann Lewnes

Dir., Worldwide Adv.—Jennifer Reynolds

ADSTREAM AMERICA

115 W 18th St, New York, NY, 10011-4113, USA (845) 496-8283; fax (845) 496-8037; e-mail sales.us@adstream.com; web site www.adstream.com

Product or Service: Hardware/Software Supplier

Pres.—Michael Palmer

Business Mgr.—Kirk Brauch

ADTRAN

901 Explorer Blvd NW, Huntsville, AL, 35806-2807, USA (800) 923-8726; e-mail info@adtran.com; web site www.adtran.com

Product or Service: Hardware/Software Supplier

PR Dir.—Tammie Dodson

ADVANCE INTERNET, INC.

30 Journal Sq, Ste 400, Jersey City, NJ, 07306-4101, USA (201) 459-2888; fax (201) 653-1189; web site www.advance.net

Product or Service: Publisher/Media

Pres.—Peter Weinberger

Admin—Johanna Dell'Aquila

ADVANCED COMMUNICATION DESIGN, INC.

7901 12th Ave S, Minneapolis, MN, 55425-1017, USA (952) 854-4000; fax (952) 854-5774; e-mail sales@acdstar.com; web site www.acdstar.com

Product or Service: Multimedia/Interactive

Products

Pres./CEO—Marco Scibora

Customer Serv.—Geri Charleston

ADVANCED INTERACTIVE MEDIA GROUP, LLC

402 Spring Valley Rd, Altamonte Springs, FL, 32714-5845, USA (407) 788-2780; fax (866) 611-6551; e-mail pzollman@aimgroup.com; web site www.aimgroup.com

Product or Service: Consultants, Publisher/Media

Founding Principal—Peter M. Zollman

Editorial Director—Jim Townsend

Europe Director—Katja Riefler

Principal, director of consulting—Rob Paterson

Diana Bogdan

Note: The AIM Group is a global team of consulting experts in classified advertising, marketplaces and interactive media. We help publishers grow their businesses through strategic and tactical support. We publish Classified Intelligence Report, the international continuous advisory service that is often called "the bible of the classified advertising industry."

We work with news media publishers, dot-coms, print classified publishers, yellow page publishers, broadcasters and technology vendors worldwide to help develop, launch and grow revenue-generating services.

We are first and foremost "consultants who publish," not "publishers who do a little consulting on the side." Most of our consulting work is performed on a proprietary basis, so our clients often see only a small fraction of our work-product.

We offer solutions for companies planning their strategies, increasing revenue, market share, and in developing products and packing strategies to grow their business. We help build interactive products and services; we don't just talk about them based on flimsy research. We support investors and analysts trying to determine the health of a company, or to find companies ripe for investment or acquisition.

Our team includes long-time senior executives, so we work with senior executives to help them understand where their interactive-media and classified services need to evolve. We've been sales reps and sales managers, so we can help sales teams grow and develop traditional and interactive media services. Our writer / analysts get to the heart of the matter, and understand the business inside and out.

We work with clients globally. Our worldwide team of almost 40 people follows the evolution in interactive media and classified advertising more closely than anyone else.

ADVANCED PUBLISHING TECHNOLOGY

123 S Victory Blvd, Burbank, CA, 91502-2347, USA (818) 557-3035; fax (818) 557-1281; e-mail aptsales@advpubtech.com; web site www.advpubtech.com

Product or Service: Circulation, Editorial, Hardware/Software Supplier, Online Service Provider and Internet Hosts

Pres.—David Kraai

COO—Ken Barber

Online Product Mgr.—Diane Duren

Adv. Prod. Mgr.—Shellie Sommerson

Cir. Prod. Mgr.—Sid Kendrick

Ed. Prod. Mgr.—Joe Kennedy

ADVANCED TELECOM SERVICES, INC. (CANADA)

1150 1st Ave, Ste 105, King Of Prussia, PA, 19406-1350, USA (416) 800-2490; fax (610) 964-9117; e-mail sales@advancedtele.com; web site www.advancedtele.com

Product or Service: Telecommunications/Service Bureaus

Dir. of Marketing—Bob Bentz

ADVANCED TELECOM SERVICES, INC. (U.K.)

12-16 Clerkenwell Rd., London, EC1M 5PQ, United Kingdom 7608 7787; fax 7608 7788; e-mail uksales@advancedtele.co.uk; web site www.advancedtele.com

Product or Service: Telecommunications/Service Bureaus

Mng. Dir./Gen. Mgr.—Ian Scott

Dir., Sales—Cindy Aspland

ADVERTISING AGE

711 3rd Ave, New York, NY, 10017-4014, USA (212) 210-0100; fax (212) 210-0200; e-mail editor@adage.com; web site www.adage.com

Product or Service: Publisher/Media

Pub.—Allison Price Arden

AGILITY

15900 Morales Rd, Houston, TX, 77032-2126, USA (714) 617-6300; e-mail americas@logistics.com; web site www.agilitylogistics.com

Product or Service: Telecommunications/Service Bureaus

Sales—Pam Holdrup

AL BREDENBERG CREATIVE SERVICES

71 Franklin St, Danbury, CT, 06810-5483, USA (203) 791-8204; e-mail ab@copywriter.com; web site www.copywriter.com

Product or Service: Advertising/Marketing Agency

Contact—Al Bredenberg

ALLIANCE FOR AUDITED MEDIA

48 W Seegers Rd, Arlington Heights, IL, 60005-3900, USA (224) 366-6939; fax (224) 366-6949; web site www.auditedmedia.com/services/digital-services.aspx

Product or Service: Consultants, Trade Association, Web Site Auditor

VP, Digital Auditing Services—Steve Guenther

CEO, President and Managing Director—Tom Drouillard

AMASIS

1538 W Cullerton St, Chicago, IL, 60608-2918, USA (312) 850-9459; fax (312) 850-9459; e-mail amasis@amasis.com; web site www.amasis.com

Product or Service: Graphic/Design Firm

Head Designer—Tamara Manning

AMERICA ONLINE DIGITAL CITY, INC.

22000 Aol Way, Dulles, VA, 20166-9302, USA (877) 265-5622; web site www.aol.com

Product or Service: Publisher/Media

Pres./CEO—Ray Oglethrepe

Dir., Bus. Devel.—Bill McIntosh

AMERIKIDS USA

10 Leonard St, Apt 3SW, New York, NY, 10013-2961, USA (212) 941-8461; e-mail developer@amerikids.com; web site www.amerikids.com

Product or Service: Multimedia/Interactive Products

CEO—Lynn Rogoff

Media Producer—Mark Tabashnick

Note: We just launched Green Kids Media's Endanger Games http:// www.amerikids/com

AMPLIFIED.COM, INC.

1465 Northside Dr NW, Ste 110, Atlanta, GA, 30318-4220, USA (404) 351-0600; fax (404) 351-0645; e-mail parker@amplified.com

Product or Service: Publisher/Media

Pres.—Wayne Parker

ANIMATED SOFTWARE CO.

PO Box 1936, Carlsbad, CA, 92018-1936, USA (760) 720-7261; e-mail rhoffman@animatedsoftware.com; web site www.animatedsoftware.com

Product or Service: Multimedia/Interactive Products

Owner/Chief Programmer—Ace Hoffman

ANSWERS MEDIA INC.

30 N Racine Ave, Ste 300, Chicago, IL, 60607-2184, USA (312) 421-0113; fax (312) 421-1457; e-mail info@answersmediainc.com; web site www.answersmediainc.com

Product or Service: Multimedia/Interactive Products

Pres.—Jeff Bohnson

APCO WORLDWIDE

700 12th St NW, Ste 800, Washington, DC, 20005-3949, USA (202) 778-1000; fax (202) 466-6002; e-mail information@apcoworldwide.com; web site www.apcoworldwide.com

Product or Service: Advertising/Marketing Agency, Consultants

APDI-APPLICATION PROGRAMMING & DEVELOPMENT, INC.

1282 Smallwood Dr W, Ste 276, Waldorf, MD, 20603-4732, USA (301) 893-9115; fax (301) 645-5035; e-mail mburnett@apdi.net; web site www.apdi.net

Product or Service: Online Service Provider and Internet Hosts

Pres./CEO—Mark Burnett

APPLE, INC.

1 Infinite Loop, Cupertino, CA, 95014-2083, USA (408) 996-1010; fax (408) 996-0275; web site www.apple.com

Product or Service: Hardware/Software Supplier

CEO—Timothy Cook

Sr. Vice Pres., Worldwide Pdct. Mktg.—Philip W. Schiller

APPLIED ART & TECHNOLOGY

2430 106th St, Des Moines, IA, 50322-3763, USA (515) 331-7400; fax (515) 331-7401; e-mail mail@appliedart.com; info@appliedart.com; web site www.appliedart.com

Product or Service: Multimedia/Interactive Products

Media Mgr.—Jeanie Jorgensen

APTAS

1221 Auraria Pkwy, Denver, CO, 80204-1836, USA (303) 572-1122; fax (303) 572-1123; e-mail info@aptas.com; web site www.localmatters.com

Product or Service: Hardware/Software Supplier, Multimedia/Interactive Products, Publisher/Media

CEO—Perry Evans

ARC RESEARCH

14 Commerce Dr, Cranford, NJ, 07016-3505, USA (908) 276-6300; fax (908) 276-1301; web site www.arcresearch.com

Product or Service: Advertising/Marketing Agency, Consultants

Pres.—Sallie Bernard

Vice Pres.—Douglas Belt

ARCH COMMUNICATIONS, INC.

1327 Hampton Ave, Saint Louis, MO, 63139-3113, USA (314) 645-8000; fax (314) 645-8100; e-mail customer@archcom.net; web site www.archcom.net

Product or Service: Telecommunications/Service Bureaus

Pres.—David Brandstetter

ARIZONA REPUBLIC DIGITAL MEDIA

200 E Van Buren St, Phoenix, AZ, 85004-2238, USA (602) 444-8000; fax (602) 444-8044; web site www.azcentral.com

Product or Service: Publisher/Media

VP News Executive Editor—Nicole Carroll

ARLEN COMMUNICATIONS LLC

6407 Landon Ln, Bethesda, MD, 20817-5603, USA (301) 229 2199; e-mail garlen@arlencom.com; web site www.arlencom.com

Product or Service: Consultants

Pres.—Gary Arlen

ASBURY PARK PRESS
3601 Hwy 66, Neptune, NJ, 7754-, USA (732) 922-6000; fax (732) 922-0783; e-mail htowns@njpressmedia.com; web site www.app.com
Product or Service: Multimedia/Interactive Products, Publisher/Media

ASPECT COMMUNICATIONS
690 N McCarthy Blvd, Milpitas, CA, 95035-5134, USA (978) 250-7900; fax (408) 325-2260; web site www.aspect.com
Product or Service: Hardware/Software Supplier
Pres./CEO/Dir.—James D. Foy
Exec. Vice Pres., Finance/CFO—Michael J. Provenzano
Sr. Vice Pres., Mktg.—Laurie Cairns

ASSIGNMENT DESK
820 N Orleans St, Ste 205, Chicago, IL, 60610-3136, USA (312) 464-8600; fax (312) 464-8605; e-mail cya@assignmentdesk.com; web site www.assignmentdesk.com
Product or Service: Multimedia/Interactive Products, Telecommunications/Service Bureaus
Bus. Mgr.—Evelyn Beldam

ASSOCIATED PRESS INFORMATION SERVICES
450 W 33rd St, New York, NY, 10001-2603, USA (212) 621-1500; fax (212) 621-7520; e-mail info@ap.org; web site www.ap.org
Product or Service: Publisher/Media
Dir. Sales—Ted Mendelsohn

ASTECH INTERMEDIA
999 18th St, Ste 2240, Denver, CO, 80202-2442, USA (303) 296-9966; fax (303) 296-9969; e-mail ter@astech-intermedia.com; web site www.smartfocus.com
Product or Service: Online Service Provider and Internet Hosts
Pres./CEO—Tom Ratkovich
Dir., Client Servs.—Tia Talbert

AT&T, INC.
175 E Houston St, San Antonio, TX, 78205-2255, USA (210) 821-4105; fax (210) 351-2071; web site www.att.com
Product or Service: Telecommunications/Service Bureaus
Chrmn./CEO—Randall L. Stephenson
Pres./CEO, AT&T Directory Opns.—Dennis M. Payne
Sr. Exec. Vice Pres./CMO—Lea Ann Champion
SVP/Global Mktg. Officer—Cathy Coughlin Linda Hanacek

ATEX
87 Castle Street, Reading, RG1 7SN, United Kingdom 118 958 7537; fax 118 958 7537; e-mail info@atex.com; web site www.atex.com
Product or Service: Hardware/Software Supplier
Sr. Vice Pres./Chief Integration Officer—Peter Marsh
Sr. Vice Pres., Sales Americas—Malcolm McGrory

ATOMIC IMAGING, INC.
1501 N Magnolia Ave, Chicago, IL, 60642-2427, USA (312) 649-1800; fax (312) 642-7441; e-mail info@atomicimaging.com; web site www.atomicimaging.com
Product or Service: Graphic/Design Firm
Pres.—Ari Golan
Commun. Consultant—Nick Brown
Producer—Aigar Dombrouskis
Interactive Design—Jim Abreu

AUDIO SERVICE AMERICA PRODUCTIONS / FREEHOLD DIVISION
28 Ten Eyck Ave, Albany, NY, 12209-1518, USA (800) 723-4272; e-mail holdit@4asap.com; web site www.4asap.com

Product or Service: Advertising/Marketing Agency, Consultants, Multimedia/Interactive Products
Consultant—Kevin Childs
Mktg. Dir.—T. Raymond Gruno
Note: Production Division:
FreeHold Business Marketing Solutions

AUTHORLINK
103 Guadalupe Dr, Irving, TX, 75039-3334, USA (972) 402-0101; fax (866) 381-1587; e-mail dbooth@authorlink.com; web site www.authorlink.com
Product or Service: Multimedia/Interactive Products, Publisher/Media
Ed. in Chief—Doris Booth
Note: Authorlink specializes in e-book conversion and distribution. We also provide news and informatin for editors, agents, writers and readers.

AUTOMATED GRAPHIC SYSTEMS
4590 Graphics Dr, White Plains, MD, 20695-3122, USA (301) 843-1800; fax (301) 843-6339; e-mail info@ags.com; web site www.ags.com
Product or Service: CD-ROM Designer/Manufacturer
Pres.—Dustin Graupman
Controller—Teresa Willingham
Dir., New Technology—Mark Czajka

AUTONOMY, INC.
1 Market Plz, Fl 19, San Francisco, CA, 94105-1103, USA (415) 625-1400; fax (415) 243-9984; e-mail autonomy@autonomy.com; web site www.autonomy.com
Product or Service: Multimedia/Interactive Products
CEO—Michael Lynch
CTO—Richard Gaunt

B

B-LINKED, INC.
PO Box 3721, Chapel Hill, NC, 27515-3721, USA (919) 883-5362; e-mail tmelet@b-linked.com; web site www.adtransit.com
Product or Service: Online Service Provider and Internet Hosts
President—Todd Melet
VP of Technology—Michael-Anne Ashman

B/HI
11500 W Olympic Blvd, Ste 399, Los Angeles, CA, 90064-1530, USA (310) 473-4147; fax (310) 478-4727; e-mail info@bhimpact.com; web site www.bhimpact.com
Product or Service: Advertising/Marketing Agency
Partner—Dean Bender
Sr. Vice Pres.—Shawna Lynch
Managing Partner—Jerry Griffin

BACKE DIFITAL BRAND MARKETING
100 W Matsonford Rd, Bldg 101, Radnor, PA, 19087-4558, USA (610) 947-6900; fax (610) 896-9242; e-mail info@backemarketing.com; web site www.backemarketing.com
Product or Service: Advertising/Marketing Agency
Pres./CEO—John E. Backe
Sr. Vice Pres.—Malcolm Brown

BACKWEB
2077 Gateway Pl, Ste 500, San Jose, CA, 95110-1085, USA (408) 933-1700; fax (520) 962-4800; e-mail pr@backweb.com; web site www.backweb.com
Product or Service: Hardware/Software Supplier
Vice Pres., Mktg./Pdct. Mgmt.—Yishay Yovel

BBS COMPUTING
1315 E Ridge Rd, Rochester, NY, 14621-2004, USA (585) 544-3669; e-mail info@bbscomputing.co.uk; web site www.bbscomputing.com
Product or Service: Online Service Provider and

Internet Hosts
Pres.—Russell Frey

BEATLEY GRAVITT COMMUNICATIONS
9A W Grace St, Richmond, VA, 23220-5013, USA (888) 355-9151; fax (804) 359-5261; web site www.beatleygravitt.com
Product or Service: Graphic/Design Firm
Pres./Dir., Mktg.—Ed Lacy

BIAKELSEY
15120 Enterprise Ct, Chantilly, VA, 20151-1274, USA (800) 331-5086; e-mail info@biakelsey.com; web site www.kelseygroup.com
Product or Service: Publisher/Media
CEO—Neal Polachek

BKJ PRODUCTIONS
99 Washington St, Melrose, MA, 02176-6024, USA (781) 662-8800; e-mail info@bkjproductions.com; web site www.bkjproductions.com
Product or Service: Multimedia/Interactive Products
Pres.—Brian K. Johnson

BKR STUDIO, INC.
105 E Jefferson Blvd, Ste 800, South Bend, IN, 46601-1917, USA (574) 245-9576; e-mail info@bkrstudio.com; web site www.bkrstudio.com
Product or Service: Multimedia/Interactive Products
Pres.—Brian Rideout
Office Mgr.—Tina Merrill

BLACK STAR PUBLISHING CO., INC.
333 Mamaroneck Ave, # 175, White Plains, NY, 10605-1440, USA (212) 679-3288; e-mail sales@blackstar.com; web site www.blackstar.com
Product or Service: Advertising/Marketing Agency
Pres.—Ben Chapnick
Vice Pres.—John P. Chapnick

BLASS COMMUNICATIONS
17 Drowne Rd, Old Chatham, NY, 12136-3006, USA (518) 766-2222; fax (518) 766-2445; e-mail info@blasscommunications.com; web site www.blasscommunications.com
Product or Service: Advertising/Marketing Agency

BLUECIELO ECM SOLUTIONS
2400 Lake Park Dr SE, Ste 450, Smyrna, GA, 30080-7644, USA (404) 634-3302; fax (404) 633-4604; e-mail info@bluecieloecm.com; web site www.bluecieloecm.com
Product or Service: Hardware/Software Supplier
Contact—Karen Rhymer

BMC GROUP, INC.
477 Madison Ave, Fl 6, New York, NY, 10022-5827, USA (212) 310-5900; fax (212) 644-4552; web site www.bmcgroup.com
Product or Service: Hardware/Software Supplier
Sales Contact—Matt Morris

BRANFMAN LAW GROUP, P.C.
708 Civic Center Dr, Oceanside, CA, 92054-2504, USA (760) 637-2400; fax (760) 687-7421; e-mail info@branfman.com; web site www.branfman.com
Product or Service: Consultants
Owner—David Branfman
Assoc.—Mark Reichenthal

BREZE, INC.
3625 Quakerbridge Rd, Hamilton, NJ, 08619-1268, USA (609) 587-4200; fax (609) 936-9077; e-mail mail@breze.com; web site www.breze.com
Product or Service: Multimedia/Interactive Products
Vice Pres.—Jerry Konecny

BROADVISION
1700 Seaport Blvd, Ste 210, Redwood City, CA, 94063-5579, USA (650) 295-0716; fax (650) 364-3425; e-mail info@broadvision.com; web site www.broadvision.com
Product or Service: Hardware/Software Supplier
Dir.—Jean Mc Corthy

BUSINESS WIRE - NEW YORK, NY
40 E 52nd St, Fl 14, New York, NY, 10022-5911, USA (212) 752-9600; fax (212) 752-9698; web site www.businesswire.com
Product or Service: Online Service Provider and Internet Hosts
Vice Pres., New York Reg.—Phyllis Dantuono
Pres./CEO—Cathy Baron Tamraz

BUZZ360 LLC
17728 Kingsway Path, # 120, Lakeville, MN, 55044-5208, USA (612) 567 0396; e-mail info@buzz360.co; web site www.buzz360.co
Product or Service: Marketing
Note: A new world of Partner Marketing

C

C-T INNOVATIONS
11509 Commonwealth Dr, Louisville, KY, 40299-2379, USA (502) 814-5100; fax (502) 814-5110; web site www.ct-innovations.com
Product or Service: Telecommunications/Service Bureaus
Pres.—Robert Flynn

CABLEFAX DAILY LLC
4 Choke Cherry Rd, Fl 2, Rockville, MD, 20850-4024, USA (301) 354-2000; fax (301) 738-8453; e-mail sarenstein@accessintel.com; web site www.cablefax.com
Product or Service: Online Service Provider and Internet Hosts
Editorial Dir.—Seth Arenstein

CABLEVISION SYSTEMS CORPORATION
1111 Stewart Ave, Bethpage, NY, 11714-3533, USA (516) 803-2300; web site www.cablevision.com
Product or Service: Telecommunications/Service Bureaus
Chairman—Charles F. Dolan
President and CEO—James L. Dolan
Vice Chairman—Hank Ratner
Executive Vice President & General Counsel—David Ellen
Vice Chairman & CFO—Gregg Seibert
President, Local Media—Tad Smith
Sr. Advisor, Customer Care, Technology and Networks—Wilt Hildenbrand
President, Optimum Services—Kristin Dolan

CAPTURED DIGITAL, INC.
2520 Turquoise Cir, Ste B, Newbury Park, CA, 91320-1218, USA (805) 499-7333; fax (805) 499-4590; e-mail jobs@captureddigital.com; web site www.capturedimages.com
Product or Service: Telecommunications/Service BureausJohn Chater

CARL WALTZER DIGITAL SERVICES, INC.
873 Broadway, Ste 412, New York, NY, 10003-1234, USA (212) 475-8748; fax (212) 475-9359; e-mail wdigital@nyc.rr.com; web site www.waltzer.com
Product or Service: Telecommunications/Service Bureaus
Pres.—Carl Waltzer
Photographer—Bill Waltzer

CASCADE TECHNOLOGIES, INC.
1075 Eastern Ave, Somerset, NJ, 8873-, USA (732) 560-9008; fax (908) 626-1209; e-mail info@cascadetechnologies.com; web site www.cascadetechnologies.com
Product or Service: Telecommunications/Service Bureaus
Pres.—Vigdis Austad
Vice Pres.-Technology—Frank Joicy

Sales—Barbara Bishop
Mktg. Assoc.—Janice Harrison

CATALYST INTERNATIONAL, INC.
8989 N Deerwood Dr, Milwaukee, WI, 53223-2446, USA (414) 362-6800; fax (414) 362-6794; e-mail info@ctcsoftware.com; web site www.ctcsoftware.com
Product or Service: Hardware/Software Supplier
Contact—Mark Shupac

CBS MAXPREPS, INC.
4080 Plaza Goldorado Cir, Ste A, Cameron Park, CA, 95682-7455, USA (800) 329-7324; fax (530) 672-8559; e-mail sales@maxpreps.com; web site www.maxpreps.com
Product or Service: Multimedia/Interactive Products, Publisher/Media
Pres.—Andy Beal

CD TECHNOLOGY
1112 Walsh Ave, Santa Clara, CA, 95050-2646, USA (408) 982-0990; fax (408) 982-0991; web site www.cdtechnology.com
Product or Service: CD-ROM Designer/Manufacturer
Pres.—William W. Liu

CELEBRO
312 Elm St, Fl 20, Cincinnati, OH, 45202-2739, USA (513) 665-3777; fax (513) 768-8958; e-mail info@celebro.com; web site www.gmti.com
Product or Service: Hardware/Software Supplier
Pres./CEO—Steve Fuschetti
Vice Pres., Celebro Opns.—Tom Foster
Dir., Implementation Servs.—Michael Hibert

CENTURYTEL INTERACTIVE
8750 N Central Expy, Ste 720, Dallas, TX, 75231-6462, USA (214) 360-6280; fax (972) 996-0868; e-mail jd@centuryinteractive.com; web site www.centuryinteractive.com
Product or Service: Telecommunications/Service Bureaus
COO—Jack Doege

CGI GROUP, INC.
460 Totten Pond Rd, Ste 530, Waltham, MA, 02451-1944, USA (781) 810-4022; fax (781) 890-4361; e-mail web@cgi.com; web site www.cgi.com
Product or Service: Consultants
Global Mktg. Mgr.—Jennifer Peters

CHANNELNET
3 Harbor Dr, Ste 206, Sausalito, CA, 94965-1491, USA (415) 332-4704; fax (415) 332-1635; e-mail info@channelnet.com; web site www.softad.com; www.channelnet.com
Product or Service: Consultants, Hardware/Software Supplier
Founder/CEO—Paula George Tompkins
CFO—Kevin Kelly
Sr. Dir., Professional Servs.—Mike Behr

CHASE BOBKO, INC.
750 N 34th St, Seattle, WA, 98103-8801, USA (206) 547-4310; fax (206) 548-0749; e-mail information@chasebobko.com
Product or Service: Multimedia/Interactive Products
Pres.—Bob Boiko
CEO—Jayson Antonoff
Vice Pres.—Patricia Chase

CIBER, INC.
6363 S Fiddlers Green Cir, Ste 1400, Greenwood Village, CO, 80111-5024, USA (303) 220-0100; fax (303) 220-7100; web site www.ciber.com
Product or Service: Consultants
COO—Peter Cheesbrough

CINEMAN SYNDICATE
31 Purchase St, Ste 203, Rye, NY, 10580-3013, USA (914) 967-5353; e-mail cinemansyndicate@verizon.net; web site

www.minireviews.com
Product or Service: Publisher/Media
Pub./Ed./Co-Owner—John P. McCarthy

CITYSEARCH.COM
8833 W Sunset Blvd, West Hollywood, CA, 90069-2110, USA (310) 360-4500; e-mail customerservice@citygrid.com; web site www.citysearch.com
Product or Service: Multimedia/Interactive Products
CEO—Jay Herratti

CLARITAS
9444 Waples St, Ste 280, San Diego, CA, 92121-2985, USA (800) 234-5973; fax (858) 500-5800; e-mail Marketing@Claritas.com; web site www.claritas.com
Product or Service: Consultants, Research
Sr. VP—Dave Miller

COBBEY & ASSOCIATES FULL SERVICE MARKETING RESEARCH
PO Box 12, Carson City, NV, 89702-0012, USA (877) 433-3242; fax (775) 847-0327; e-mail cobbey@cobbey.com; web site www.cobbey.com
Product or Service: Consultants

COGENT COMMUNICATIONS, INC.
1015 31st St NW, Washington, DC, 20007-4406, USA (202) 295-4200; fax (202) 338-8798; e-mail info@cogentco.com; web site www.cogentco.com
Product or Service: Online Service Provider and Internet Hosts
Founder/CEO—Dave Schaeffer
Pres./COO—Reed Harrison
CFO—Tad Weed

COLLEGE PUBLISHER, INC.
31 Saint James Ave, Ste 920, Boston, MA, 02116-4155, USA (888) 735-5578; e-mail support@collegemedianetwork.com; web site www.collegepublisher.com
Product or Service: Hardware/Software Supplier
Contact—Chris Gillon

COMMGRAPHICS INTERACTIVE, INC.
9259 Pioneer Ct, Lincoln, NE, 68520-9307, USA (402) 432-1450; e-mail nwineman@commgraphics.com
Product or Service: Multimedia/Interactive Products
New Bus. Dir.—Neil Wineman

COMMUNICATION DESIGN
24 Caribou Ct, Monterey, CA, 93940-6303, USA (831) 373-3925; e-mail www.ittelson.com
Product or Service: Multimedia/Interactive Products
Prof—John C. Ittelson
Project Mgr.—Bobbi Kamil
Webmaster—Brendan Ittelson

COMMUNITECH SERVICES INC.
2340 S Arlington Heights Rd, Ste 360, Arlington Heights, IL, 60005-4517, USA (847) 981-1200; fax (847) 981-9085; e-mail info@communitechservices.com; web site www.communitechservices.com
Product or Service: Telecommunications/Service Bureaus
Vice Pres.—Barb Gendes Shact

COMPETENCE SOFTWARE
PO Box 353, Dove Creek, CO, 81324-0353, USA (727) 459-0531; web site www.competencesoftware.net
Product or Service: Multimedia/Interactive Products
Founder—Larry Byrnes
Vice Pres., Devel.—Mary Lou Dewyngaert
Vice Pres., Mkt. Devel.—Shannon Byrnes
Asst. to CEO—Jessica Byrnes

COMPUTER TALK TECHNOLOGY, INC.
225 E. Beaver Creek Rd, Suite 310, Richmond Hill, ON, L4B 3P4, Canada (905) 882-5000; fax (905) 882-5501; e-mail info@icescape.com; web site www.computer-talk.com
Product or Service: Hardware/Software Supplier
Mktg. Dir.—Robert Moore
Pres./CEO—Mandie Cheung
Mktg. Mgr.—Lindsay Aitken

COMTEX NEWS NETWORK
625 N Washington St, Ste 301, Alexandria, VA, 22314-1930, USA (703) 797-8135; fax (703) 820-2005; e-mail cs@comtex.com; web site www.comtex.com
Product or Service: Online Service Provider and Internet Hosts
Chrmn./Interim CEO—C.W. Gillmly
Pres.—Chip Brian
Vice Pres., Content—Kathy Ballard
Dir.—Pieter VanBennekom

CONGRESSIONAL QUARTERLY, INC.
77 K St NE, Fl 8, Washington, DC, 20002-4681, USA (202) 650-6500; fax (202) 650-6741; e-mail sales@cq.com; web site www.cq.com
Product or Service: Publisher/Media
Editorial Director—Mike Mills
Sr Vice pres./CFO—Douglas Wallen
Sr. Vice Pres., Sales—Jim Gale
Executive Vice President and Managing Director—Keith White
SVP, Advertising—Mark Walters
SVP, legislative services and publisher—Meg Hargreaves
Vice President and Publisher, advocacy, state and transcripts—Barkley Kern
Exec. Ed., News—Susan Benkelman

CONSERVIT CORPORATION
28 North Routh 12 Suite C, Fox Lake, IL, 60020-, USA (847) 629-5567; fax (847) 265-4915; e-mail sales@conservit.com; web site www.conservit.com
Product or Service: Telecommunications/Service Bureaus
Pres.—Peter F. Theis

CONVERGENT MEDIA SYSTEMS
190 Bluegrass Valley Pkwy, Alpharetta, GA, 30005-2204, USA (770) 369-9000; fax (770) 369-9100; e-mail convergent@convergent.com; web site www.convergent.com
Product or Service: Multimedia/Interactive Products
CEO—Bryan Allen
Vice Pres., Mktg.—Rick Hutcheson

CONVERGYS
201 E 4th St, Cincinnati, OH, 45202-4248, USA (513) 723-7000; e-mail marketing@convergys.com; web site www.convergys.com
Product or Service: Multimedia/Interactive Products
Sr. Dir., Mktg.—Keith Wolters

COPIA INTERNATIONAL LTD.
52 Salt Creek Rd, Roselle, IL, 60172-1420, USA (630) 388-6900; fax (630) 778-8848; e-mail sales@copia.com; web site www.copia.com
Product or Service: Hardware/Software Supplier, Other Services
Pres.—Steve Hersee
Vice Pres., Mktg.—Dorothy Gaden-Flanagan
VP, Eng.—Terry Flanagan

COREL
1600 Carling Ave., Ottawa, ON, K1Z 8R7, Canada (613) 728-8200; fax (613) 728-9790; web site www.corel.com
Product or Service: Hardware/Software Supplier
Sr. Vice Pres., Sales/Mktg.—Kevin Thornton

CORPORATE DISK COMPANY
4610 Prime Pkwy, McHenry, IL, 60050-7005, USA (815) 331-6000; fax (815) 331-6030; e-mail info@disk.com; web site www.disk.com
Product or Service: CD-ROM Designer/Manufacturer
Pres.—William Mahoney
Note: Specializing in CD and DVD Manufacturing along with all the related printing, packaging, technical, and fulfillment services. Providing complete start to finish solutions.

COSMOS COMMUNICATIONS, INC.
1105 44th Dr, Long Island City, NY, 11101-5107, USA (718) 482-1800; fax (718) 482-1968; web site www.cosmoscommunications.com
Product or Service: Graphic/Design Firm
Pres.—Arnold Weiss

CRAMP + TATE, INC.
230 S 15th St, Fl 2, Philadelphia, PA, 19102-3806, USA (215) 893-0500; fax (215) 893-0543; e-mail jeff.cramp@cramp.com; web site www.cramp.com
Product or Service: Advertising/Marketing Agency

CREATIVE CIRCLE MEDIA SOLUTIONS
945 Waterman Ave, East Providence, RI, 02914-1342, USA (401) 272-1122; e-mail info@creativecirclemedia.com; web site www.creativecirclemedia.com
Product or Service: Advertising/Marketing Agency, Circulation, Consultants, Editorial, Graphic/Design Firm, Hardware/Software Supplier, Marketing, Other Services, Online Service Provider and Internet Hosts
Pres & founder—Bill Ostendorf
Design director—Lynn Rognsvoog
IT director—Tim Benson
Note: Full service and custom software provider with a dynamic web CMS, user-contributed content, classifieds, hosting, pay wall, native content, QuickAds and print editorial production systems. We also provide strategic consulting, newsroom training, ad design training, new revenue ideas, high-end outsourcing services and extensive print and web redesigns.

CREATIVE DIRECT
10 Schalks Crossing Rd, Ste 501, Plainsboro, NJ, 08536-1612, USA (908) 239-8965
Product or Service: Advertising/Marketing Agency

CSTV ONLINE, INC.
2035 Corte Del Nogal, Ste 250, Carlsbad, CA, 92011-1465, USA (760) 431-8221; fax (760) 431-8108; e-mail customersupport@cstv.com; web site www.cstv.com
Product or Service: Multimedia/Interactive Products
Vice Pres., Sales—Tim Rivere
Dir., Finance—George Scott
Exec. Producer—Tom Keyes

CUSTOMER COMMUNICATIONS GROUP
165 S Union Blvd, Ste 260, Lakewood, CO, 80228-2241, USA (303) 986-3000; fax (303) 989-4805; e-mail info@customer.com; web site www.customer.com
Product or Service: Advertising/Marketing Agency
Pres.—Sandra Gudat

CYBER SALES ONE, INC.
PO Box 84, Bronxville, NY, 10708-0084, USA (917) 250-6074; e-mail albertcran@aol.com
Product or Service: Advertising/Marketing Agency
Pres./CEO—Albert H. Crane

CYBERCON.COM
210 N Tucker Blvd, Fl 7, Saint Louis, MO, 63101-1941, USA (314) 621-9991; fax (314)

241-1777; e-mail staff@cybercon.com; web site www.cybercon.com
Product or Service: Online Service Provider and Internet Hosts
Pres.—Joshua Chen

CYBERSMART
201 Lloyd Rd, Bernardsville, NJ, 07924-1711, USA (908) 221-1516; fax (908) 221-0617; e-mail information@cybersmart.org; web site www.cybersmart.org
Product or Service: Multimedia/Interactive Products
—Jim Teicher
—Mala BawerExec. Dir.s

CYBERTECH, INC.
935 Horsham Rd, Horsham, PA, 19044-1230, USA (215) 957-6220; fax (215) 674-8515; e-mail sales@cbrtech.com; web site www.cbrtech.com
Product or Service: Hardware/Software Supplier, POP/Kiosk Designer
Pres.—Ronald Schmidt
Sec./Treasurer—Lloyd Barnett

CYWAYS, INC.
19 Westchester Rd, Newton, MA, 02458-2519, USA (617) 965-9465; fax (617) 796-8997; e-mail support@cyways.com
Product or Service: Online Service Provider and Internet Hosts
Pres.—Peter H. Lemieux

D

D & H INFORMATION SERVICES, INC.
5720 Osuna Rd NE, Albuquerque, NM, 87109-2527, USA (505) 888-3620; fax (505) 888-3722; e-mail dhinfo@dhinfo.com; web site www.dhinfo.com

D-SQUARED STUDIOS, INC.
4312 Elm St, Dallas, TX, 75226-1133, USA (214) 746-6336; fax (214) 746-6338; e-mail doug.davis@d2studios.net; web site www.d2studios.net
Product or Service: Multimedia/Interactive Products
Pres.—Doug Davis

DAC SYSTEMS
4 Armstrong Park Rd, Shelton, CT, 6484-, USA (203) 924-7000; fax (203) 944-1618; e-mail sales@dacsystems.com; web site www.dacsystems.com
Product or Service: Telecommunications/Service Bureaus
Pres.—Mark Nickson

DANA COMMUNICATIONS
2 E Broad St, Hopewell, NJ, 08525-1810, USA (609) 466-9187; fax (609) 466-0285; e-mail bprewitt@danacommunications.com; web site www.danacommunications.com
Product or Service: Advertising/Marketing Agency

DANIEL LAMPERT COMMUNICATIONS CORP.
PO Box 151719, Altamonte Springs, FL, 32715-1719, USA (407) 327-7000; fax (407) 695-9014; e-mail service@dlc2.com; web site www.dlc2.com
Product or Service: Multimedia/Interactive Products, Online Service Provider and Internet Hosts
Pres.—Dan Lampert

DESIGN MEDIA, INC.
650 Alabama St, San Francisco, CA, 94110-2039, USA (415) 641-4848; fax (415) 641-5245; e-mail info@designmedia.com; web site www.designmedia.com
Product or Service: Multimedia/Interactive Products
Pres./CEO—Pamela May

Sr. Project Mgr.—Marlita Kahn
Sr. Project Mgr.—Barbara Berry
Project Mgr.—Wallace Murray
Project Mgr.—Alison DeGrassi
Office Mgr.—Cori Freeland
Sr. Web Developer—Rylan North

DESIGNORY.COM
211 E Ocean Blvd, Ste 100, Long Beach, CA, 90802-4850, USA (562) 624-0200; web site www.designory.com
Product or Service: Advertising/Marketing Agency

DESIGNORY.COM
200 E Randolph St, Ste 3620, Chicago, IL, 60601-6512, USA (312) 729-4500; web site www.designory.com
Product or Service: Advertising/Marketing Agency

DESIGNORY.COM
209 10th Ave S, Ste 409, Nashville, TN, 37203-0767, USA (615) 514-7514; web site www.designory.com
Product or Service: Advertising/Marketing Agency

DESKNET, INC.
10 Exchange Pl, Fl 20, Jersey City, NJ, 07302-3918, USA (201) 946-7080; e-mail sales@desknetinc.com; web site www.desknetinc.com
Product or Service: Consultants
Co-CEO—Michael Fitzsimons

DEV.KINNEY/MEDIAGRAPHICS, INC.
717 Spring St, Memphis, TN, 38112-1830, USA (901) 324-1658; fax (901) 323-7214; e-mail mediagraphics@devkinney.com; web site www.devkinney.com
Product or Service: Advertising/Marketing Agency
Pres.—J.D. Kinney
Vice Pres.—C.P. Kinney
Office Mgr.—Lynn Hastines

DEX MEDIA
2200 W Airfield Dr, Dallas, TX, 75261-4008, USA (919) 297-1600; web site www.dexmedia.com
Product or Service: Advertising/Marketing Agency, Marketing
Chrmn./CEO—Richard C. Notebaert
Vice Chrmn./CFO—Oren G. Shaffer
Pres./CEO, Qwest Dex—George Burnett
Exec. Vice Pres., Finance—Robin R. Szeliga
Sr. Vice Pres., Cor. Commun.—Joan H. Walker

DEX ONE CORP.
2200 W Airfield Dr, Dallas, TX, 75261-4008, USA (919) 297-1600; fax (919) 297-1285; e-mail info@dexone.com; web site www.dexone.com
Product or Service: Publisher/Media
Exec. Vice Pres./CFO—Steven M. Blondy
Sr. Vice Pres./CMO—Maggie LeBeau

DIALOGIC COMMUNICATIONS CORP.
730 Cool Springs Blvd, Ste 300, Franklin, TN, 37067-7290, USA (615) 790-2882; fax (615) 790-1329; e-mail sales@dccusa.com; bcarman@dccusa.com; web site www.dccusa.com
Product or Service: Telecommunications/Service Bureaus
Sales Rep.—Bill Carman

DIALOGIC CORP.
1515 State Rt 10, Parsippany, NJ, 07054-4538, USA (973) 967-6000; fax (973) 967-6006; e-mail sales@dialogic.com; web site www.dialogic.com
Product or Service: Telecommunications/Service Bureaus
Pres./CEO—Howard Bubb
Contact—Athena Mandros

DIGICONNECT
8004 Cedar Dr, Rogers, AR, 72756-7729, USA (877) 235-7714; fax (479) 595-8748; e-mail info@digiconow.com; web site www.digiconow.com
Product or Service: Telecommunications/Service Bureaus
CEO—Kim Gustafson

DIGITAL COLLECTIONS
312 Elm St, Fl 20, Cincinnati, OH, 45202-2739, USA (513) 665-3777; fax (513) 768-8958; e-mail mtucker@gmti.gannett.com; web site www.gmti.com
Product or Service: Consultants, Hardware/Software Supplier, Online Service Provider and Internet Hosts
Pres./CEO—Steve Fuschetti
Vice Pres., Installations/Support—Bill Mahlock
Dir., Sales & Marketing—Michael Tucker

DIGITAL DESIGN GROUP LIMITED
955 Milton St, Pittsburgh, PA, 15218-1031, USA (412) 243-9119; fax (412) 243-2285; e-mail rob@ddg-designs.com; web site www.ddg-designs.com
Product or Service: Multimedia/Interactive Products

DIRECT IMAGES INTERACTIVE, INC.
1933 Davis St, Ste 314, San Leandro, CA, 94577-1259, USA (510) 613-8299; e-mail info@directimages.com; web site www.directimages.com
Product or Service: Multimedia/Interactive Products
Producer/Dir.—Bill Knowland
Art Dir.—Beverly Knowland

DLS DESIGN
232 Madison Ave, Rm 800, New York, NY, 10016-2940, USA (212) 255-3464; e-mail info@dlsdesign.com; web site www.dlsdesign.com
Product or Service: Graphic/Design Firm
Pres.—David Schiffer

DOUBLECLICK
111 8th Ave, Fl 10, New York, NY, 10011-5210, USA (212) 271-2542; fax (212) 287-1203; e-mail publicrelations@doubleclick.net; web site www.doubleclick.com
Product or Service: Advertising/Marketing Agency

DOW JONES INTERACTIVE PUBLISHING
RR 1 Box 4300, Monmouth Junction, NJ, 08852-9801, USA (609) 520-4000; fax (609) 520-4662; e-mail marianne.krafinski@dowjones.com; web site www.dowjones.com
Product or Service: Multimedia/Interactive Products
CEO—Les Hinton

DREAMSCAPE DESIGN, INC.
10 Henson Pl, Ste A, Champaign, IL, 61820-7836, USA (217) 359-8484; fax (217) 239-5858; e-mail info@dreamscapedesign.com; web site www.dreamscapedesign.com
Product or Service: Advertising/Marketing Agency, CD-ROM Designer/Manufacturer, Consultants, Graphic/Design Firm, Multimedia/Interactive Products, POP/Kiosk Designer, Web Site Auditor

DREAMSCAPE DESIGN, INC.
125 S Wacker Dr, Chicago, IL, 60606-4424, USA (217) 359-8484; fax (217) 356-3378; web site www.dreamscapedesign.com
Product or Service: Graphic/Design Firm
Bus. Devel. Mgr.—Amy Moushon

DTN/THE PROGRESSIVE FARMER
2204 Lakeshore Dr, Ste 415, Birmingham, AL, 35209-8856, USA (800) 292-2340; e-mail onlinehelp@dtn.com; web site www.dtn.com
Product or Service: Online Service Provider and Internet Hosts, Publisher/Media

Ed.-in-Chief—Gregg Hillyer

DUNN SOLUTIONS GROUP
5550 Touhy Ave, Skokie, IL, 60077-3253, USA (847) 673-0900; fax (847) 673-0904; web site www.dunnsolutions.com
Product or Service: Multimedia/Interactive Products
Pres.—David Skwarczek

E

EASE CT SOLUTIONS
5995 Windward Pkwy, Alpharetta, GA, 30005-4184, USA (404) 338-2241; fax (404) 338-6101
Product or Service: Hardware/Software Supplier

EDGIL ASSOCIATES, INC.
222 Rosewood Dr, Ste 210, Danvers, MA, 01923-4520, USA (800) 457-9932; fax (978) 667-6050; e-mail sales@edgil.com; web site www.edgil.com
Product or Service: Hardware/Software Supplier
Dir., Sales—Sean Callahan

EDITOR & PUBLISHER INTERACTIVE
17782 Cowan, Ste C, Irvine, CA, 92614-6042, USA (949) 660-6150; fax (949) 660-6172; web site www.editorandpublisher.com
Product or Service: Publisher/Media

EDR/BEACHWOOD STUDIOS
23330 Commerce Park Rd, Beachwood, OH, 44122-, USA (216) 292-7300; fax (216) 292-0545; e-mail vrettas@edrmedia.com; web site www.edr.com
Product or Service: CD-ROM Designer/Manufacturer, Multimedia/Interactive Products, POP/Kiosk Designer
CEO—Peter Vrettas
Office Mgr.—Darcy Angell

ELECTRONIC TELE-COMMUNICATIONS, INC.
1915 Mac Arthur Rd, Waukesha, WI, 53188-5702, USA (262) 542-5600; fax (262) 542-1524; e-mail etc_mkt@etcia.com; web site www.etcia.com
Product or Service: Telecommunications/Service Bureaus
Pres./CEO—Dean W. Danner
Vice Pres., Sales—Joseph A. Voight

ELFWORKS 3D CONSTRUCTION CO.
1421 Page St, Alameda, CA, 94501-3822, USA (510) 769-9391; e-mail first_contact@elfworks.com; web site www.elfworks.com
Product or Service: Graphic/Design Firm
Owner—Erik Flom

EMERGENCE LABS, INC.
5150 N Royal Atlanta Dr, Tucker, GA, 30084-3047, USA (770) 908-5650; fax (770) 908-5673; web site www.emergencelabs.com
Product or Service: Advertising/Marketing Agency

EMPHASYS SOFTWARE
13475 Danielson St, Ste 220, Poway, CA, 92064-8858, USA (858) 268-7100; fax (858) 268-7111; e-mail service3d@emphasys-software.com; web site www.emphasys-software.com
Product or Service: Hardware/Software Supplier
Pres.—Kerry Burch

EN TECHNOLOGY CORP.
322 N Main St, Newport, NH, 03773-1496, USA (603) 863-8102; fax (603) 863-7316; e-mail sales@entechnology.com; web site www.entechnology.com
Product or Service: Telecommunications/Service Bureaus
Chrmn. of the Bd.—David Hall
Pres.—Patricia Gallup
Opns. Mgr.—Matt Cookson

ENIGMA

140 Kendrick St, Needham, MA, 02494-2739, USA (781) 370-5000; fax (781) 370-6000; e-mail infous@enigma.com; web site www.enigma.com
Product or Service: Hardware/Software Supplier
Chrmn./CEO—Johathan Yaron
Vice Pres., Mktg.—John Snow

ENVISION INTERACTIVE

901 5th Ave, Ste 3300, Seattle, WA, 98164-2024, USA (206) 225-0800; fax (206) 225-0801; e-mail info@envisioninc.com; web site www.envisioninc.com
Product or Service: Multimedia/Interactive Products

EPIC SOFTWARE GROUP, INC.

701 Sawdust Rd, The Woodlands, TX, 77380-2943, USA (281) 363-3742; fax (281) 419-4509; e-mail epic@epicsoftware.com; web site www.epicsoftware.com
Product or Service: Multimedia/Interactive Products
Pres.—Vic Cherubini

EPSILON

601 Edgewater Dr, Wakefield, MA, 01880-6237, USA (781) 685-6000; fax (781) 685-0830; web site www.epsilon.com
Product or Service: Advertising/Marketing Agency

EPSILON INTERACTIVE

11 W 19th St, Fl 9, New York, NY, 10011-4275, USA (212) 457-7000; fax (212) 457-7040; e-mail info@epsilon.com; web site www.epsilon.com
Product or Service: Advertising/Marketing Agency

EPUBLISH4ME

1375 Gateway Blvd, Boynton Beach, FL, 33426-8304, USA (561) 370-3336; e-mail sales@epublish4me.com; web site www.epublish4me.com
Product or Service: Advertising/Marketing Agency, Graphic/Design Firm, Multimedia/Interactive Products, Online Service Provider and Internet Hosts, Publisher/Media
Senior Account Executive—Nicholas Koriakin
Note: Digitize your pubs at http://www.epublish4me.com/?r=403. It automatically posts them on TitleStand where you can sell them by getting local and worldwide distribution (see http://titlestand.com/t).

Your PDFs are converted into digital 3-D page flipping revenue generator books, newspapers or magazines with video, audio, hyperlinks and extensive tracking where they can be read on Tablet, PC, Mac, iPad, iPhone, iTouch, iOS, Android and Kindle Fire.

Kind regards,

Nick.Koriakin@ePublish4me.com
561-370-3336

ESOFT

295 Interlocken Blvd, Ste 500, Broomfield, CO, 80021-8002, USA (866) 233-2296; e-mail info@esoft.com; web site www.esoft.com
Product or Service: Hardware/Software Supplier
CEO/Pres.—Jeff Finn
CTO—Patrick Walsh
Dir., Finance—Tim Olson
Vice Pres., Opns.—Jason Rollings

ET SRL ELETTRONICA TELECOMUNICAZIONI

Viale Veneto 4, Cinisello Balsamo, Milan, 20092, Italy 39 02 66033; fax 39 02 66033270; e-mail info@et_spa.com; web site www.et_spa.com
Product or Service: Hardware/Software Supplier
Mgr., Projects/Devel.—Marco Prandi
Commercial Mgr.—Massimo Fiocchi

EUR/ELECTRONIC URBAN REPORT

PO Box 412081, Los Angeles, CA, 90041-9081, USA (323) 254-9599; fax (323)-421-9383; e-mail editorial@eurweb.com; web site www.eurweb.com
Product or Service: Publisher/Media
Pub.—Lee Bailey

F

FAMILY FEATURES EDITORIAL SYNDICATE, INC.

5825 Dearborn St, Mission, KS, 66202-2745, USA (913) 722-0055, (800) 800-5579; fax (913) 789-9228; e-mail support@familyfeatures.com, jmillett@familyfeatures.com; web site www.familyfeatures.com
Product or Service: Multimedia/Interactive Products
Owner—Dianne Hogerty
President—Brian Agnes
Pres.—Dena Klein
CEO—Diane Hogerty
Media Manager—Jennifer Millett

FILESTREAM, INC.

PO Box 93, Glen Head, NY, 11545-0093, USA (516) 759-4100; fax (516) 759-3011; e-mail info@filestream.com ; support@filestream.com; server@filestream.com; reseller@filestream.com; web site www.filestream.com
Product or Service: Hardware/Software Supplier
Chrmn./CEO—Yao Chu

FILM ARTISTS ASSOCIATES

21044 Ventura Blvd, Ste 215, Woodland Hills, CA, 91364-6501, USA (818) 883-5008; fax (818) 386-9363
Product or Service: Advertising/Marketing Agency
Contact—Chris Dennis

FIRST DATA VOICE SERVICES

10910 Mill Valley Rd, Omaha, NE, 68154-3930, USA (402) 777-2100; fax (402) 222-7910; e-mail fdvsinfo@firstdata.com; web site www.callit.com/FDVSSite/contact.aspx
Product or Service: Telecommunications/Service Bureaus
Vice Pres., Devel.—James Harvey
Vice Pres., Sales—Bob Van Stry

FISHER PHOTOGRAPHY

2234 Cathedral Ave NW, Washington, DC, 20008-1504, USA (202) 232-3781; e-mail info@fisherphoto.com; web site www.fisherphoto.com
Product or Service: Graphic/Design Firm
Owner—Patricia Fisher
Contact—Wayne W. Fisher

FLI, INCORPORATED

400 Palisades Ave, Santa Monica, CA, 90402-2720, USA (310) 451-3307; fax (310) 451-4207; e-mail jcwills@fliinc.com; web site www.fliinc.com
Product or Service: Consultants
President/CEO—John Wills
Vice President—Jane Wills
Dir., Bus. Devel.—Susan Moore

FLIP YOUR LID

19626 Ventura Blvd, Ste 200, Tarzana, CA, 91356-6082, USA (818) 307-4165; e-mail jay@flipyourlid.com; web site www.flipyourlid.com
Product or Service: Multimedia/Interactive Products
Pres./CEO—Jay Jacoby

FOUR PALMS, INC.

11260 Roger Bacon Dr, Fl 4, Reston, VA, 20190-5227, USA (703) 834-0200; fax (703) 834-0219; e-mail info@fourpalms.com; web site www.fourpalms.com
Product or Service: Multimedia/Interactive

Products
Pres.—Pat Buteux

FRANK N MAGID ASSOCIATES

1 Research Ctr, Marion, IA, 52302-5868, USA (319) 377-7345; fax (319) 377-5861; e-mail Bhague@magid.com; web site www.magid.com
Product or Service: Consultants, Research
Exec. Vice Pres.—Bill Hague
Bill Day

FUJITSU TEN CORP. OF AMERICA

20100 S Western Ave, Torrance, CA, 90501-1307, USA (310) 327-2151; fax (310) 767-4355; e-mail info@lao.ten.fujitsu.com; web site www.fujitsu_ten.com
Product or Service: Multimedia/Interactive Products
Mktg., Dir.—Michael West

FUSEBOX, INC.

36 W 20th St, Fl 11, New York, NY, 10011-4241, USA (212) 929-7644; fax (212) 929-7947; e-mail info@fusebox.com; web site www.fusebox.com
Product or Service: Graphic/Design Firm

G

G2 DIRECT & DIGITAL

636 11th Ave, New York, NY, 10036-2005, USA (212) 537-3700; fax (212) 537-3737; e-mail steve.harding@geometry.com; web site www.g2.com
Product or Service: Advertising/Marketing Agency

GANNETT MEDIA TECHNOLOGIES INTERNATIONAL (GMTI)

312 Elm St, Fl 20, Cincinnati, OH, 45202-2739, USA (513) 665-3777; fax (513) 768-8958; e-mail gmti-info@gmti.gannett.com; web site www.gmti.com
Product or Service: Multimedia/Interactive Products
Pres./CEO—Steve Fuschetti

GCN PUBLISHING

194 Main St, Ste 2NW, Norwalk, CT, 06851-3502, USA (203) 665-6211; fax (203) 665-6212; e-mail info@gcnpublishing.com; web site www.gcnpublishing.com
Product or Service: Multimedia/Interactive Products
Vice Pres., Technology—Sean Fulton
Creative Dir.—Joanne Persico

GODFREY

40 N Christian St, Lancaster, PA, 17602-2828, USA (717) 393-3831; fax (717) 393-1403; e-mail curt@godfrey.com; web site www.godfrey.com
Product or Service: Advertising/Marketing Agency

GREAT!

3527 Knollhaven Dr NE, Brookhaven, GA, 30319-1908, USA (404) 303-7311; fax (404) 252-0697; e-mail dan@greattv.com; web site www.greattv.com
Product or Service: Telecommunications/Service Bureaus
CEO/Chief Creative Officer—Dan Smigrod

GRIFFIN CHASE OLIVER, INC.

25262 Monte Verde Dr, Laguna Niguel, CA, 92677-1535, USA (949) 495-1144; fax (815) 366-3885; e-mail info@griffinchaseoliver.com; web site www.griffinchaseoliver.com
Product or Service: POP/Kiosk Designer
CEO—Jim Redfield

H

HEALTHSTREAM

209 10th Ave S, Ste 450, Nashville, TN, 37203-0788, USA (615) 301-3100; fax (615) 301-3200; e-mail contact@healthstream.com; web site www.healthstream.com
Product or Service: Multimedia/Interactive Products
CEO—Robert A. Frist
Sr. Vice Pres., Finance—Arthur E. Newman

HEWLETT-PACKARD CO.

5400 Legacy Dr, Plano, TX, 75024-3105, USA (972) 604-6000; web site www.hp.com
Product or Service: Publisher/Media

HITCHCOCK FLEMING AND ASSOCIATES, INC.

500 Wolf Ledges Pkwy, Akron, OH, 44311-1022, USA (330) 376-2111; fax (330) 376-2808; e-mail jdeleo@teamhfa.com; web site www.teamhfa.com
Product or Service: Advertising/Marketing Agency

HOLDCOM

955 Lincoln Ave, Glen Rock, NJ, 07452-3226, USA (201) 444-6488; fax (201) 445-4653; e-mail info@holdcom.com; web site www.holdcom.com
Product or Service: Advertising/Marketing Agency
Pres.—Neil Fishman
CEO—Harvey Edelman

HOSKYNS & ASSOCIATES

3038 E Cactus Rd, Phoenix, AZ, 85032-7150, USA (602) 867-1324; fax (602) 867-3673
Product or Service: Multimedia/Interactive Products
Pres.—Donald Hoskyns
Creative Dir.—Curtiss Prickett

HOTWAX MULTIMEDIA, INC.

16 Stoney Brook Ct, Ramsey, NJ, 07446-1456, USA (201) 818-0001; e-mail info@hotwax.com; web site www.hotwax.com
Product or Service: Multimedia/Interactive Products
Owner—David R. Huber

HTS INTERACTIVE HEALTH CARE

434 NW 6th Ave, Ste 202, Portland, OR, 97209-3651, USA (503) 241-9315; fax (503) 241-8466; e-mail info@htshealthcare.com; web site www.htshealthcare.com
Product or Service: Multimedia/Interactive Products
Mng. Dir./Vice Pres.—Harvey Smythe
Creative Dir.—Charlie Levinson

HUTCHINSON ASSOCIATES, INC.

822 Linden Ave, Ste 200, Oak Park, IL, 60302-1562, USA (312) 455-9191; e-mail hutch@thisishutchinson.com; web site www.thisishutchinson.com
Product or Service: Advertising/Marketing Agency, Consultants, Graphic/Design Firm, Marketing, Other Services
Pres.—Jerry Hutchinson
Prod.—Doug White

I

IBM CORP.

1 New Orchard Rd, Armonk, NY, 10504-1722, USA (404) 236-2600; fax (404) 236-2626; web site www.ibm.com
Product or Service: Hardware/Software Supplier
Chrmn./Pres./CEO—Samuel J. Palmisano
Sr. Vice Pres./Grp. Exec., Sales—Frank Kern
Sr. Vice Pres., Strategy—J. Bruce Harreld
Vice Pres., Worldwide media/digital media—Marianne Caponnetto

Sr. Vice Pres., Dir. of Research—John E. Kelly III
Sr. Vice Pres., HR—J. Randall Macdonald
Sr. Vice Pres., Cor. Commun./Mktg.—Jon C. Iwata
Sr. Vice Pres./CFO—Mark Loughridge
Sr. Vice Pres., Enterprise Bus. Servs., IBM Global Servs.—Virginia M. Rometty
Sr. Vice Pres., Information Technology Servs., IBM Global Servs.—Michael E. Daniels
Sr. Vice Pres., Systems/Technology Grp.—Robert W. Moffatt
Vice Pres., Worldwide Adv.—Deirdre Bigley
Vice Pres., Mktg., IBM Global Servs.—Mary Garrett
Vice Pres., Worldwide Integrated Mktg. Commun.—Diane Brink
Vice Pres., Integrated Mktg. Commun., IBM Software Grp.—Mark A. Rosen
Gen. Mgr., Internet Application Servs.—John E. Patrick
Exec. Dir., Adv./Cor. Mktg.—Roger W. Adams
Dir., Media Opns.—J. Kosanke
Program Dir., GLBT Supplier Rel./Procurement—Irwin Drucker
Program Dir., GLBT Sales/Talent—Joseph Bertolotti
Tom Burke

ICENI TECHNOLOGY
Sackville Place 44-48 Magdalen St., Norwich, NR3 1JV, United Kingdom 603-628-289; fax 603-627-415; e-mail sales@iceni.com; web site www.iceni.com
Product or Service: Multimedia/Interactive Products
Dir.—Simon Crowfoot

ICONNICHOLSON
11 W 19th St, Fl 3, New York, NY, 10011-4280, USA (212) 274-0470; fax (888) 847-5321; web site www.iconnicholson.com
Product or Service: Multimedia/Interactive Products
CEO—Tom Nicholson

ILIO ENTERTAINMENT
5356 Sterling Center Dr, Westlake Village, CA, 91361-4612, USA (818) 707-7222; fax (818) 707-8552; e-mail info@ilio.com; web site www.ilio.com
Product or Service: Hardware/Software Supplier
—Shelly Williams
—Mark HiskeyCo-Owners

IMAGE ZONE, INC.
11 W 69th St, # 10, New York, NY, 10023-4720, USA (212) 924-8804; e-mail mail@imagezone.com; web site www.imagezone.com
Product or Service: Multimedia/Interactive Products
MD—Doug Ehrlich
Creative Dir.—Peter Smallman

IMAGEN, INC.
PO Box 814270, Dallas, TX, 75381-4270, USA (214) 232-3385; fax (419) 821-2047; e-mail al@imageninc.com; web site www.imageninc.com
Product or Service: Graphic/Design Firm
Pres.—Al Schmidt

IMERGY
48 W 38th St, Fl 6, New York, NY, 10018-0045, USA (212) 221-8585; fax (212) 869-3676
Product or Service: Multimedia/Interactive Products
Pres.—Flora W. Perskie
Vice Pres., Media Integration—Peter Mackey
Sr. Creative Dir.—Debra Leeds
Dir., Multimedia Productions—Richard Spitalny

INETUSA
PO Box 917208, Longwood, FL, 32791-7208, USA (321) 733-5391; fax (321) 723-4552; e-mail info@inetusa.com; web site www.inetusa.com
Product or Service: Multimedia/Interactive Products, Online Service Provider and Internet Hosts
Pres.—Tim Yandell

INFOCUS CORP.
13190 SW 68th Pkwy, Ste 200, Portland, OR, 97223-8368, USA (503) 207-4700; fax (503) 207-4707; e-mail info@infocus.com; web site www.infocus.com
Product or Service: Hardware/Software Supplier
Pres./CEO—John Harker
Sr. Vice Pres./Gen. Mgr., Americas—William D. Yavorsky
Vice Pres., Mktg./Strategy—Candace Petersen

INFOMEDIA, INC.
2081 Columbiana Rd, Vestavia Hills, AL, 35216-2139, USA (205) 823-4440; e-mail jason@infomedia.com; web site www.infomedia.com
Product or Service: Advertising/Marketing Agency, Consultants, Graphic/Design Firm, Marketing, Online Service Provider and Internet Hosts, Publisher/Media, Web Site Auditor
President—Jason Lovoy

INFORMATION PRESENTATION TECH.
825 Buckley Rd, Ste 200, San Luis Obispo, CA, 93401-8193, USA (805) 541-3000; fax (805) 541-3037; e-mail info@iptech.com; web site www.iptech.com
Product or Service: Multimedia/Interactive Products
Vice Pres., Sales/Mktg.—Olivia Favela

INFORONICS, INC.
25 Porter Rd, Littleton, MA, 01460-1434, USA (978) 698-7400; fax (978) 698-7500; web site www.inforonics.com
Product or Service: Multimedia/Interactive Products
Pres.—Bruce Mills
Vice Pres., Sales—Andy Kramer
Vice Pres., Opns.—Tom Pellegriti

INNOVATIVE SYSTEMS DESIGN, INC.
222 Brunswick Blvd, Pointe-Claire, QC, H9R 1A6, Canada (514) 459-0200; fax (514) 459-0300; e-mail sales@isd.ca; web site www.isd.ca
Product or Service: Telecommunications/Service Bureaus
Pres.—Jeff Tierney
Director of Sales and Marketing—Rob Dumas
Sales Coord.—Monica Steibelt

INTACTIX
14400 N 87th St, Scottsdale, AZ, 85260-3649, USA (480) 308-3000; fax (480) 308-3001; e-mail info@jda.com; web site www.jda.com
Product or Service: Hardware/Software Supplier
Sales Mgr.—Karen Storey

INTERACTIVE CONFERENCING NETWORK
42 Oak Ave, Tuckahoe, NY, 10707-4025, USA (914) 961-0700
Product or Service: Telecommunications/Service Bureaus
Owner—Steve Campus

INTERACTIVE EDUCATIONAL SYSTEMS DESIGN, INC.
33 W 87th St, New York, NY, 10024-3082, USA (631) 691-2606; e-mail iesdinc@aol.com; web site www.iesdinc.com
Product or Service: Consultants
Pres.—Ellen Bialo
Vice Pres.—Jay Sivin Kachala

INTERACTIVE INTERNATIONAL, INC.
290 W End Ave, New York, NY, 10023-8106, USA (212) 580-5015; fax (212) 580-5017;

e-mail ivie@erols.com; web site www.erols.com
Product or Service: Hardware/Software Supplier
Pres.—George M. Bulow

INTERACTIVE MEDIA ASSOCIATES
612 Main St, Boonton, NJ, 07005-1761, USA (973) 539-5255; fax (973) 917-4730; e-mail info@imedianinc.com; web site www.imedianinc.com
Product or Service: Consultants
Founder—Len Muscarella
Pres.—Sally Muscarella
Vice Pres./Creative Dir.—Michelle Camaron
Vice Pres., Bus. Devel.—Anthony Zarro
Dir., Devel.—Brian McGovern
Dir., Pjct. Mgmt.—Geri Ricciani

INTERACTIVE PICTURES CORPORATION (IPIX)
48 Western Ave, Cohoes, NY, 12047-3903, USA (518) 235-3455; e-mail support@ipix.com; web site https://www.ipix.com
Product or Service: Multimedia/Interactive Products
Contact—Mary Pam Claiborne

INTERACTIVE PUBLISHING CORP.
7639 Edarwood Cir, Boca Raton, FL, 33434-, USA (561) 483-7734; e-mail vicmilt@victormilt.com; web site www.victormilt.com
Product or Service: CD-ROM Designer/Manufacturer
CEO—Kim Milt
Creative Dir.—Victor Milt
Exec. Producer—Martin Ross

INTERALIA COMMUNICATIONS
701 24th Ave SE, Minneapolis, MN, 55414-2691, USA (952) 942-6088; fax (952) 942-6172; e-mail info@interalia.com; web site www.interalia.com
Product or Service: Telecommunications/Service Bureaus
Bus. Admin. Assoc.—Mary Mcracken

INTERCOM
3 Grogans Park Dr, Ste 200, The Woodlands, TX, 77380-2922, USA (800) 298-7070; fax (281) 364-7032; e-mail intercom@intercom-interactive.com; web site www.intercom-interactive.com
Product or Service: Multimedia/Interactive Products
Pres.—Bob Yeager
Gen. Mgr.—Margo Pearson

INTERNATIONAL DEMOGRAPHICS/THE MEDIA AUDIT
10333 Richmond Ave, Ste 200, Houston, TX, 77042-4142, USA (713) 626-0333; fax (713) 626-0418; e-mail tma@themediaaudit.com; web site www.themediaaudit.com
Product or Service: Advertising/Marketing Agency
Chrmn.—James B. Higginbotham
Pres.—Robert A. Jordan
Exec. Vice Pres., Sales—J. Phillip Beswick
Exec. Vice Pres./Sales Mgr.—Michael W. Bustell

IRON DESIGN
120 N Aurora St, Ste 5A, Ithaca, NY, 14850-4337, USA (607) 275-9544; fax (607) 275-0370; e-mail todd@irondesign.com; web site www.irondesign.com
Product or Service: Graphic/Design Firm

ISRAEL FAXX
611 Saint Andrews Blvd, The Villages, FL, 32159-2280, USA (352) 750-9420; e-mail dcanaan@israelfaxx.com; web site www.israelfaxx.com
Product or Service: CD-ROM Designer/Manufacturer, Publisher/Media
Contact—Don Canaan

J

JABLONSKI DESIGN, INC.
8 Daisy Way, Ste B, Paramus, NJ, 07652-4305, USA (201) 843-0228; e-mail info@jablonskidesign.com; web site www.jablonskidesign.com
Product or Service: Graphic/Design Firm
Pres.—Carl Jablonski

JDA SOFTWARE GROUP, INC.
14400 N 87th St, Scottsdale, AZ, 85260-3649, USA (480) 308-3000; fax (480) 308-3001; e-mail info@jda.com; web site www.jda.com
Product or Service: Hardware/Software Supplier
CEO—Hamish Brewer

JLM CD-ROM PUBLISHING CO.
189 Magnolia St, Ste 100, San Francisco, CA, 94123-2869, USA (415) 440-2668; fax (415)440-2668; e-mail jlee123@earthlink.net; web site www.jlmcdpublishing.com
Product or Service: CD-ROM Designer/Manufacturer, Multimedia/Interactive Products, Publisher/Media
Partner—Miguel Florez
CFO—Raymond Proca
Contact—James Lee

JUDSON ROSEBUSH CO.
15 China Circle Ct, Carmel, NY, 10512-4452, USA (212) 581-3000; e-mail info@rosebush.com; web site www.rosebush.com
Product or Service: Multimedia/Interactive Products
Pres.—Judson Rosebush

JUPITER IMAGES CORP.
6000 N Forest Park Dr, Peoria, IL, 61614-3556, USA (309) 688-8800; fax (309) 688-3075; e-mail sales@jupiterimages.com; web site www.jupiterimages.com
Product or Service: Hardware/Software Supplier
Vice Pres., Opns.—Mark Nickerson
Note: All-purpose art and idea service.

K

KEN PETRETTI PRODUCTIONS, LLC
33 Parkway, Maywood, NJ, 07607-1556, USA (201) 368-2296; fax (201) 368-1489; e-mail ken@kenpetretti.com; web site www.kenpetretti.com
Product or Service: Advertising/Marketing Agency, CD-ROM Designer/Manufacturer, Consultants, Graphic/Design Firm, Multimedia/Interactive Products, Online Service Provider and Internet Hosts, POP/Kiosk Designer, Publisher/Media, Web Site Auditor
Producer—Ken Petretti

KINETIC CORPORATION
200 Distillery Cmns, Ste 200, Louisville, KY, 40206-1987, USA (502) 719-9500; fax (502) 719-9569; e-mail info@theTechnologyAgency.com; web site www.theTechnologyAgency.com
Product or Service: Graphic/Design Firm
Pres.—G. Raymond Schuhmann
Chief Brand Strategist—Cindi Ramm

KING FEATURES SYNDICATE
300 W 57th St, Fl 41, New York, NY, 10019-3741, USA (212) 969-7550; fax (646) 280-1550; e-mail kfs-public-relations@hearst.com; web site www.kingfeatures.com
Product or Service: Publisher/Media
VP., Gen. Mgr.—Keith McCloat
Gen. Mgr., King Feat. Weekly Service
Inside Sales—David Cohea
Dir., PR—Claudia Smith
Sr. Sales Consultant/Printing & New England Newspaper Sales—Jack Walsh
Inside Sales Mgr.—Dennis Danko
Sales Mgr., New Media Inside Sales—

Michael Mancino
VP, Syndication Sales—John Killian
Editorial Dir., King Feat. Weekly Service—Jim Clarke
Gen. Mgr., Syndication—Brendan Burford
SE Sales—Randy Noble
Executive Editor—Diana Smith
Senior Comics Editor—Evelyn Smith
Senior Features Editor—Chris Richcreek
Western Region Sales—Curtis Trammell
International Sales Consultant—Robin Graham
Sales Coordinator—Monique Prioleau
President—C.J. Kettler

KIOSK INFORMATION SYSTEMS
346 S Arthur Ave, Louisville, CO, 80027-3010, USA (303) 466-5471; fax (303) 466-6730; e-mail sales@kiosk.com; web site www.kiosk.com
Product or Service: POP/Kiosk Designer
Pres.—Rick Malone
Vice Pres., Sales/Mktg.—Tom Weaver

KOBIE MARKETING, INC.
100 2nd Ave S, Ste 1000, Saint Petersburg, FL, 33701-4360, USA (727) 822-5353; fax (727) 822-5265; e-mail info@kobie.com; web site www.kobie.com
Product or Service: Advertising/Marketing Agency
CIO—Don Hughes
Project Mgr.—Robert Gilley

L

L-SOFT INTERNATIONAL, INC.
8100 Corporate Dr, Ste 350, Landover, MD, 20785-2231, USA (301) 731-0440; fax (301) 731-6302; e-mail sales@lsoft.com; web site www.lsoft.com
Product or Service: Hardware/Software Supplier
CEO—Eric Thomas
Vice Pres., Admin.—Donna Laster
Vice Pres., Software Eng.—Francoise Becker
Vice Pres., Computer Servs.—John Harlan

L@IT2'D (LATITUDE)
714 N Laurel Ave, Los Angeles, CA, 90046-7008, USA (323) 852-1425; fax (323) 856-0704; e-mail info@lati2d.com; web site www.lati2d.com
Product or Service: Graphic/Design Firm
CCO—Water Kerner

LARSON TEXTS, INC.
1762 Norcross Rd, Erie, PA, 16510-3838, USA (814) 824-6365; fax (814) 824-6377; e-mail eforsik@larsontexts.com; web site www.larsontexts.com
Product or Service: Multimedia/Interactive Products, Publisher/Media

LAUNCH AGENCY
4100 Midway Rd, Ste 2110, Carrollton, TX, 75007-1965, USA (972) 818-4100; fax (972) 818-4101; e-mail mboone@launchagency.com; web site www.launchagency.com
Product or Service: Advertising/Marketing Agency

LAURA SMITH ILLUSTRATION
6545 Cahuenga Ter, Hollywood, CA, 90068-2744, USA (323) 467-1700; fax (323) 467-1700; e-mail Laura@LauraSmithArt.com; web site www.laurasmithart.com
Product or Service: Editorial, Graphic/Design Firm, Marketing

LAZER-FARE MEDIA SERVICES
PO Box 48114 RPO Lakewood, Winnipeg, MB, R2J 4A3, Canada (204) 452-5023; fax (204) 272-3499; e-mail sales@lazerfare.com; web site www.lazerfare.com
Product or Service: Consultants, Hardware/Software Supplier
Pres.—Kelly Armstrong

LEXISNEXIS
555 W 5th St, Ste 4500, Los Angeles, CA, 90013-3003, USA (213) 627-1130; e-mail lexisnexiscommunities@lexisnexis.com; web site www.lexisnexis.com
Product or Service: Consultants
CEO, Lexis-Nexis Grp.—Andrew Prozes
Pres./CEO, Cor. & Fed. Mkts.—Kurt Sanford
Pres./CEO, U.S. Legal Mkts.—Michael Walsh
CEO, Risk Mgmt.—James M. Peck
Richard Sobelsohn

LIEBERMAN RESEARCH WORLDWIDE
1900 Avenue of the Stars, Ste 1600, Los Angeles, CA, 90067-4412, USA (310) 553-0550; fax (310) 553-4607; e-mail lrwonline@lrwonline.com; web site www.lrwonline.com
Product or Service: Advertising/Marketing Agency
Chairman and CEO—Dave Sackman

LIGHT FANTASTIC STUDIOS, INC.
618 Portland Ave, North Baldwin, NY, 11510-2642, USA (212) 604-0666; fax (212) 604-0666; e-mail info@lightfantasticstudios.com; web site www.lightfantasticstudios.com
Product or Service: Multimedia/Interactive Products
Pres./Creative Dir.—Paul Hollett
Art Dir.—Ray Rue
Designer—Ranee Chong

LOCAL SEARCH ASSOCIATION
1720 W Detweiller Dr, Peoria, IL, 61615-1612, USA (309) 690-5324; e-mail jill@thelsa.org; web site www.lsa.org
Product or Service: Consultants, Editorial, Graphic/Design Firm, Marketing, Other Services, Trade Association
VP Prod. Dev.—Brian Dickerson
Business Development Manager—Alanda Hunt
Business Development Manager—Susan Wise
Sr. Vice Pres.—Jill Addy-Wright
Business Development Manager—Tammy Ramp
Business Development Manager—Jennifer Clough
Office Manager—Mary Armstrong
marketing coordinator —Kirstin Krupps

LOGICAL DESIGN SOLUTIONS, INC.
200 Park Ave, Ste 210, Florham Park, NJ, 07932-1026, USA (973) 210-6300; fax (973) 971-0103; e-mail info@lds.com; web site www.lds.com
Product or Service: Multimedia/Interactive Products
Pres./CEO—Mimi Brooks
CFO—E. Bruce Lovenberg
Sr. Vice Pres., Bus. Devel.—Mauricio Barberi
Vice Pres., Pjct. Mgmt.—Ken Kuhl
Vice Pres., Techn.—Marty Burns
Vice Pres., Sales—John Fee
Vice Pres., Mktg.—Kevin Casey
Vice Pres., Client Servs.—Eric Dalessio
Vice Pres., Opns.—Gary Sikorski

LOGOPREMIUMS.COM
PO Box 295, Mount Kisco, NY, 10549-0295, USA (914) 244-0735; fax (914) 244-1995; e-mail info@logopremiums.com; web site www.logopremiums.com
Product or Service: Advertising/Marketing Agency
Project Mgr.—Jeff Levine

LUMINARE
65 Norfolk St, Unit 4, San Francisco, CA, 94103-4357, USA (415) 661-1436; e-mail info@luminare.com; web site www.luminare.com
Product or Service: CD-ROM Designer/Manufacturer
Pres.—Caitlin Curtin

M

M/C/C
8131 Lbj Fwy, Ste 275, Dallas, TX, 75251-1352, USA (972) 480-8383; fax (972) 669-8447; e-mail pam_watkins@mccom.com; web site www.mccom.com
Product or Service: Advertising/Marketing Agency
Pres.—Mike Crawford
SVP, Business and Media Strategy—Pam Watkins
SVP, Account Service—Jim Terry
Vice President, Account Supervisor—Shannon Sullivan
Vice President, Creative Director—Todd Brashear
Vice Pres., Creative Servs.—Greg Hansen
Vice Pres., Media/Prod. Svcs.—Karen Hansen
Pub. Rel. Mgr.—Michelle Metzger

M2 COMMUNICATIONS LTD.
PO Box 4030, Bath, ENG, BA1 0EE, United Kingdom 7047 0200; fax 7057 0200; e-mail info@m2.com; web site www.m2.com
Product or Service: Publisher/Media
Ed. in Chief—Jamie Ayres

MACTECH MAGAZINE
PO Box 5200, Westlake Village, CA, 91359-5200, USA (805) 494-9797; fax (805) 494-9798; e-mail press_releases@mactech.com; web site www.mactech.com
Product or Service: Publisher/Media
Pub.—Neil Ticktin
Ed. in Chief—Dave Mark
Reviews/KoolTools Ed.—Michael R. Harvey

MAGNACOM, INC.
615 Discovery Dr NW, Ste B, Huntsville, AL, 35806-2801, USA (256) 327-8900; fax (256) 327-8998; e-mail info@magnacom-inc.com; web site www.magnacom-inc.com
Product or Service: Telecommunications/Service Bureaus
Pres.—John Trainor

MALL MARKETING MEDIA
1877 W 4000 S, Roy, UT, 84067-3500, USA (801) 927-2600; fax (801) 927-2727; e-mail michael@mallmarketingmedia.com; web site www.mallmarketingmedia.com
Product or Service: Advertising/Marketing Agency
Vice Pres.—Kayla Vigil
Sales Mgr.—Michael O'Connell

MAPS.COM
120 Cremona Dr, Ste H, Santa Barbara, CA, 93117-5564, USA (805) 685-3100; fax (805) 685-3330; e-mail info@maps.com; web site www.maps.com
Product or Service: Online Service Provider and Internet Hosts
Pres.—John Serpa
Founder/Chrmn./CEO—Robert H. Temkin
Exec. Vice Pres.—Charles Regan
Vice Pres., Finance/Admin.—Anne Messner
Dir., Mktg.—Bruce Kurtz
Dir., Online Commerce—Bill Spicer
Dir., Mapping Servs.—Ed Easton
Dir., Tech./Project Devel.—Mitch McCoy
Dir., Education Mktg.—Erik Davis

MARCOLE ENTERPRISES, INC.
2920 Camino Diablo, Ste 200, Walnut Creek, CA, 94597-3966, USA (925) 933-9792; fax (925) 933-9795; e-mail dpava@marcole.com; web site www.marcole.com
Product or Service: Hardware/Software Supplier, Multimedia/Interactive Products, Online Service Provider and Internet Hosts, POP/Kiosk Designer
Vice Pres., Sales & Marketing—David Pava

MARKE COMMUNICATIONS, INC.
45 W 45th St, Fl 16, New York, NY, 10036-4602, USA (212) 201-0600; fax (212) 213-0785; web site www.marke.com
Product or Service: Advertising/Marketing Agency

MCCLATCHY INTERACTIVE
1100 Situs Ct, Raleigh, NC, 27606-5446, USA (919) 861-1200; fax (919) 861-1300; e-mail jcalloway@mcclatchyinteractive.com; web site www.mcclatchyinteractive.com
Product or Service: Publisher/Media
Vice Pres.—Christian A. Hendricks
Exec. Vice Pres./Gen. Mgr.—Fraser Van Asch
Vice President Strategic Development—James Calloway
Product Management Director—Kathy Lehmen
Senior Manager Mobile Initiatives—Damon Kiesow

MCI
22001 Loudoun County Pkwy, Ashburn, VA, 20147-6105, USA (703) 206-5600; fax (703) 206-5601; e-mail info@mci.com; web site www.mci.com
Product or Service: Online Service Provider and Internet Hosts, Telecommunications/Service Bureaus
Chrmn./CEO—Ivan Siedenberg
Pres., Opns./Tech.—Fred Briggs
Exec. Vice Pres./CFO—Robert Blakely
Exec. Vice Pres., HR—Daniel Casaccia
Exec. Vice Pres., Strategy/Cor. Devel.—Jonathan Crane
Sr. Vice Pres., Commun.—Grace Chentent
Sr. Vice Pres., Mktg./CMO—Nancy B. Gofus
Shane King

MCMONIGLE & ASSOCIATES
818 E Foothill Blvd, Monrovia, CA, 91016-2408, USA (626) 303-1090; fax (626) 303-5431; e-mail jamie@mcmonigle.com; web site www.mcmonigle.com
Product or Service: Advertising/Marketing Agency

MEDIA DESIGN GROUP
3250 Ocean Park Blvd, Ste 200, Santa Monica, CA, 90405-3250, USA (310) 584-9200; fax (310) 584-9725; e-mail info@mediadesigngroup.com; web site www.mediadesigngroup.com
Product or Service: CD-ROM Designer/Manufacturer
CEO—John D. Slack

MEDIA ENTERPRISES
360 E 1st St, # 605, Tustin, CA, 92780-3211, USA (714) 778-5336; e-mail john@media-enterprises.com; web site www.media-enterprises.com
Product or Service: Advertising/Marketing Agency, Consultants, Editorial, Graphic/Design Firm, Marketing, Multimedia/Interactive Products, Research, Trade Association
Principal—John Lemieux Rose

MEDIA LOGIC USA, LLC
59 Wolf Rd, Albany, NY, 12205-2612, USA (518) 456-3015; fax (518) 456-4279; e-mail jmcdonald@medialogic.com; web site www.medialogic.com
Product or Service: Advertising/Marketing Agency, Graphic/Design Firm, Marketing, Multimedia/Interactive Products
New Business—Jim McDonald
Press Mgr.—David Schultz

MEDIA MARKETING, INC.
10955 Westmoor Dr, Fl 4, Westminster, CO, 80021-2704, USA (303) 440-7855; fax 303-440-8035; e-mail info@immediate.com; sales@immediate.com; web site www.immediate.com
Product or Service: Hardware/Software Supplier
Pres./CEO—James Theall
VP, Solutions—Charles Mauldin
VP, Sales—Patti Theall
Note: Increasing Advertising Revenue by

Helping You Sell with Research Data and Manage Presentations

MEDIA SUPPLY, INC.
611 Jeffers Cir, Exton, PA, 19341-2525, USA (610) 884-4400; fax (610) 884-4500; e-mail info@mediasupply.com; web site www.mediasupply.com
Product or Service: CD-ROM Designer/Manufacturer
Sales Mgr.—Steven P. Derstine

MEDIABIDS, INC.
448 Main St, Winsted, CT, 06098-1528, USA (860) 379-9602; fax (860) 379-9617; e-mail info@mediabids.com; web site www.mediabids.com
Product or Service: Advertising/Marketing Agency, Multimedia/Interactive Products
President—Jedd Gould
Director, Media Relations—June Peterson
Note: MediaBids connects publications with thousands of advertisers nationwide. Additionally, MediaBids offers a unique performance-based print advertising program that provides publications with high-quality ads from national advertisers and a way to monetize unused inventory.

MERCURY CENTER
750 Ridder Park Dr, San Jose, CA, 95131-2432, USA (408) 920-5000; fax (408) 288-8060; e-mail tmooreland@sjmercury.com; web site www.mercurycenter.com
Product or Service: Online Service Provider and Internet Hosts
Dir., Mercury Center—Tom Mooreland

METHODOLOGIE, INC.
720 3rd Ave, Ste 800, Seattle, WA, 98104-1870, USA (206) 623-1044; fax (206) 625-0154; e-mail info@methodologie.com; web site www.methodologie.com
Product or Service: CD-ROM Designer/Manufacturer, Graphic/Design Firm, Multimedia/Interactive Products

METRO NEWSPAPER
550 S 1st St, San Jose, CA, 95113-2806, USA (408) 298-8000; fax (408) 279-5813; e-mail press@metronews.com; web site www.metroactive.com; www.metronews.com
Product or Service: Online Service Provider and Internet Hosts
Pres.—Dan Pulcrano

MICRO PERFECT CORP.
PO Box 285, Calverton, NY, 11933-0285, USA (631) 727-9639; fax (631) 727-9638; e-mail info@microperfect.com; web site www.microperfect.com
Product or Service: Hardware/Software Supplier
Mgr.—Gregory Fischer

MICROLOG CORP.
401 Professional Dr, Ste 125, Gaithersburg, MD, 20879-3468, USA (301) 540-5500; fax (301) 330-2450; e-mail sales@mlog.com; web site www.mlog.com
Product or Service: Hardware/Software Supplier
Pres./CEO/Dir.—W. Joseph Brookman
CTO—John C. Mears
Exec. Vice Pres., Worldwide Sales—Steve Feldman

MICROSOFT CORP.
1 Microsoft Way, Redmond, WA, 98052-8300, USA (425) 882-8080; fax (425) 936-7329; e-mail storesoc@microsoft.com; web site www.microsoft.com
Product or Service: Hardware/Software Supplier
Non-Exec. Chrmn.—William H. Gates
CEO—Steven A. Ballmer
COO—Kevin Turner
Chief Software Architect—Ray Ozzie
CIO—Tony Scott
CCO—Gayle Troberman
Pres., Platform Products/Servs. Div.—Kevin Johnson

Pres., Bus. Div.—Stephen Elop
Pres., Online Servs. Grp.—Qi Lu
Pres., Server/Tools Bus.—Bob Muglia
Pres., Windows Div.—Steven Sinofsky
CFO/Cor. Vice Pres., Windows Div.—Tami Reller
Cor. Vice Pres., Worldwide Retail Sales, Home Retail Div.—Mitchell Koch
Cor. Vice Pres., MSN Global Mktg.—Jane Boulware
Cor. Vice Pres., Retail Stores—David Porter
Sr. Vice Pres., Technical Strategy—Eric Rudder
Sr. Vice Pres., Cor. Mktg. Grp.—Mich Mathews
Sr. Vice Pres., Online Servs./Windows—Bill Veghte
Sr. Vice Pres./Gen. Mgr., MSN Int'l—Greg Nelson
Sr. Vice Pres., Interactive Entertainment Bus.—Don Mattrick

MICROVOICE APPLICATIONS, INC.
5100 Gamble Dr, Ste 375, Minneapolis, MN, 55416-1565, USA (612) 373-9300; fax (612) 373-9779; e-mail sales@mva.com; web site www.mva.com
Product or Service: Telecommunications/Service Bureaus
Nat'l Sales Mgr.—Rich Berg
Int'l Sales Mgr.—Mike James

MIDWEST DIGITAL COMMUNICATIONS
701 Walsh Rd, Madison, WI, 53714-1372, USA (608) 257-5673; fax (608) 257-5669; e-mail info@midwestdigital.com; web site www.midwestdigital.com
Product or Service: Advertising/Marketing Agency
CEO—Jay Jurado

MILES 33
40 Richards Ave, Pendegast Street, 5170, Norwalk, CT, 06854-2319, USA (203) 838-2333; fax (203) 838-4473; e-mail info@miles33.com; web site www.miles33.com
Product or Service: Hardware/Software Supplier, Multimedia/Interactive Products
Pres.—Chris Habasinski
VP Marketing and Western USA Sales—Albert De Bruijn
VP, Business Development—Edward Hubbard

MODERN DIGITAL
1921 Minor Ave, Seattle, WA, 98101-1415, USA (206) 623-3444; fax (206) 340-1548; e-mail info@moderndigital.com; web site www.moderndigital.com
Product or Service: CD-ROM Designer/Manufacturer
Vice Pres.—David Fassio

MORPACE INTERNATIONAL
31700 Middlebelt Rd, Ste 200, Farmington Hills, MI, 48334-2375, USA (248) 737-5300; fax (248) 737-5326; e-mail information@morpace.com; web site www.morpace.com
Product or Service: Consultants
Pres.—Jack McDonald
CEO—Francis Ward

MOTION CITY FILMS
1424 4th St, Ste 604, Santa Monica, CA, 90401-3447, USA (310) 434-1272; e-mail editor@motioncity.com; web site www.motioncity.com
Product or Service: Multimedia/Interactive Products
Producing Dir.—G. Michael Witt
Composer/Audio Engineer—Marty Blasick

MOTOROLA MOBILITY, LLC.
600 N US Highway 45, Libertyville, IL, 60048-1286, USA (847) 523-5000; fax (847) 523-8770; e-mail motorola@encompass.com; web site htttwww.motorola.com
Product or Service: Telecommunications/Service Bureaus

Sr. Vice Pres./Gen. Mgr., North American Reg.—Tim Cawley
Sr. Vice Pres./CTO—Ralph Pini
Sr. Vice Pres., Global Devices—Terry Vega
Sr. Dir., Global Web Mktg.—Ben Hill
Global Dir.,Media Commun./Pub. Aff.—Leslie Dance
CMO, Mobile Devices—Bill Ogle
Dir., Commun./Pub. Aff.—Alan Buddendeck
Dir., Emerging Consumer Mktg.—David Rudd

MOTOROLA SOLUTIONS, INC.
1303 E Algonquin Rd, Schaumburg, IL, 60196-4041, USA (847) 576-5000; fax (561) 739-2341; e-mail Training.NA@motorolasolutions.com; web site www.motorolasolutions.com
Product or Service: Telecommunications/Service Bureaus
Pres./CEO—Gregory Brown
Lead Independent Dir. of the Board—David Dorman

MOVIUS INTERACTIVE CORPORATION
11360 Lakefield Dr, Duluth, GA, 30097-1569, USA (770) 283-1000; fax (770) 497-3990; web site www.moviuscorp.com
Product or Service: Telecommunications/Service Bureaus
CEO—Oscar Rodriguez

MPI MEDIA GROUP
16101 108th Ave, Orland Park, IL, 60467-5305, USA (708) 460-0555; fax (708) 873-3177; e-mail info@mpimedia.com; web site www.mpimedia.com
Product or Service: Publisher/Media
Contact—Nicola Goelzhaeufer

MPS MEDIA PHONE SERVICE KG
Markenstrasse 21, Duesseldorf, D-40014, Germany 777 3237; fax 167 5994; e-mail hjkruse@mediaphone.de; web site www.mediaphone.de
Product or Service: Telecommunications/Service Bureaus
Mng. Dir.—Hans-Joachim Kruse

MRW COMMUNICATIONS, LLC.
6 Barker Square Dr, Pembroke, MA, 02359-2225, USA (781) 924-5282; fax (781) 926-0371; e-mail jim@mrwinc.com; web site www.mrwinc.com
Product or Service: Hardware/Software Supplier
Account Services Dir.—Jim Watts
Creative Dir., Copy—Tom Matzell
Creative Dir., Art—Kristen Balunas

MULTI-MEDIA COMMUNICATIONS
8160 E Butherus Dr, Ste 10, Scottsdale, AZ, 85260-2523, USA (508) 653-3392; fax (508) 651-9970; e-mail info@mmcom.com; web site www.mmcom.com
Product or Service: Multimedia/Interactive Products
Pres.—Don Baine

MULTIMEDIA RESEARCH GROUP, INC.
7320 E Butherus Dr, Ste 105, Scottsdale, AZ, 85260-2438, USA (888) 958-1472; fax (480) 685-4976; e-mail info@mrgco.com; web site www.mrgco.com
Product or Service: Consultants
Pres.—Gary Schultz

MULTIMEDIA RESOURCE GROUP
505 W Olive Ave, Ste 312, Sunnyvale, CA, 94086-7604, USA (408) 315-8720; fax (408) 277-0782; e-mail training@multigroup.com; web site www.multigroup.com
Product or Service: Consultants
Owner—Ken Durso

MUSE PRESENTATION TECHNOLOGIES
3510 S Susan St, Santa Ana, CA, 92704-6938, USA (800) 950-4955; fax (714) 850-1018; e-mail jimmuse@museprestech.com; web site www.museprestech.com

Product or Service: Other Services, POP/Kiosk Designer
Pres.—Joyce Logan
CEO—Jim Muse
Gen. Mgr.—Wil Bigelow

N

NEC CORPORATION OF AMERICA
6535 State Highway 161, Irving, TX, 75039-2402, USA (800) 240-0632; fax (888) 318-7932; e-mail info@neclease.com; web site www.necunifiedsolutions.com
Product or Service: Telecommunications/Service Bureaus
Gen. Mgr.—Albert F. Kelly

NETVILLAGE.COM, LLC.
342 Main St, Laurel, MD, 20707-7100, USA (301) 498-7797; fax (301) 498-8110; e-mail info@netvillage.com; web site www.netvillage.com
Product or Service: Hardware/Software Supplier, Online Service Provider and Internet Hosts
CEO—Harold Van Arnem
Pres./COO—Nathan Hammond
CTO—Stephen Bathurst
Controller—Tony Burgess

NETWORK TELEPHONE SERVICES
21135 Erwin St, Woodland Hills, CA, 91367-3713, USA (818) 992-4300; fax (818) 992-8415; e-mail sales@nts.net; web site www.nts.net
Product or Service: Telecommunications/Service Bureaus
Pres.—Gary Passon

NEW HORIZONS COMPUTER LEARNING CENTER
1900 S State College Blvd, Ste 450, Anaheim, CA, 92806-6163, USA (714) 940-8000; e-mail info.corp@newhorizons.com; web site www.newhorizons.com
Product or Service: Multimedia/Interactive Products
CEO—Mark Miller
Sr. Vice Pres., Mktg.—Heidi Rose
Vice. Pres., Mktg.—Mark Tucker

NEW MEDIA HOLLYWOOD
6150 Santa Monica Blvd, Los Angeles, CA, 90038-1712, USA (323) 957-5000; fax (323) 957-8500; e-mail info@nmh.com; web site www.nmh.com
Product or Service: Multimedia/Interactive Products
Pres.—Chris Speer

NEWMAN BROTHERS
112 E Pecan St, Ste 1330, San Antonio, TX, 78205-1536, USA (210) 226-0371; fax (210) 226-6506
Product or Service: Multimedia/Interactive Products
Owner—John Newman

NEWS MEDIA ALLIANCE
4401 Wilson Blvd Ste 900, Arlington, VA, 22203-4195, USA (571) 366-1000; fax (571) 366-1195; e-mail sheila.owens@naa.org; web site www.naa.org
Product or Service: Publisher/Media
Pres. & CEO—David Chavern
CFO—Robert Walden
VP of HRO—Sarah Burkman
SVP Bus. Dev.—Rich Schiekofer
VP of Audience Dev.—John Murray
Comm. Mgr.—Lindsey Loving
SVP of Public Policy—Paul Boyle
VP of Public Policy—Danielle Coffey
VP, Research & Industry Analysis—Jim Conaghan
Public Policy Mgr.—Kristina Zaumseil
Note: Elections held in April/May

NEWSCOM
145 S Spring St, Fl 10, Los Angeles, CA, 90012-4053, USA (213) 237-4643; fax (213) 237-7914; e-mail sales@newscom.com; web site www.newscom.com
Product or Service: Telecommunications/Service Bureaus
Gen Mgr.—Jay Brodsky
IP Rel. Dir.—Melanie Rockwell
Dir., Opns.—Dan Royal
Dir., Sales/Mktg.—Diana Backlund

NEWSCYCLE SOLUTIONS
7900 International Dr, Ste 800, Bloomington, MN, 55425-1581, USA 651-639-0662; e-mail info@newscycle.com; web site www.newscycle.com
Product or Service: Circulation, Consultants, Editorial, Hardware/Software Supplier, Multimedia/Interactive Products, Online Service Provider and Internet Hosts, Publisher/Media
Sales Director—Paul Mrozinski
VP., Business Relations —John Pukas
Rgl. Sales Dir.—Steve Moon
Rgl. Sales Dir.—Marc Thompson
Marketing Communications Mgr.—Lisa Speth
Asia-Pacific Bus. Mgr.—Bryan Hooley
Vice President of Market Development—Ken Freedman
Vice President of Marketing—Pete Marsh
Sales Director—Julie Maas
Sales Director—Chris McKee
Sales Director—Mike McLaughlin
Sales Engineer—Geoff Kehrer
Executive Sales Director, EMEA—Robert Bohlin
Note: Newscycle Solutions, which was formed by the combination of DTI, SAXOTECH, Atex AdBase and MediaSpan, delivers the most complete range of software solutions for the global news media industry, including news content management, advertising, circulation, audience, and analytics. Newscycle is a trusted technology partner serving more than 1,200 media companies with 8,000 properties across more than 30 countries on six continents. The company is headquartered in Bloomington, MN and has U.S. offices in Florida, Michigan and Utah; with international offices in Australia, Canada, Denmark, Germany, Malaysia, Norway, Sweden, and the United Kingdom. For more information, go to: http://www.newscycle.com.

NEWSPHERE
12412 SE 26th Pl, Bellevue, WA, 98005-4157, USA (425) 957-0219; web site www.newsphere.org
Product or Service: Publisher/Media
Ed.—Alan Boyle

NEWSSTAND, INC.
1835 Kramer Ln, Ste B150, Austin, TX, 78758-4230, USA (512) 334-5102; fax (512) 334-5199; e-mail support@newsstand.com; web site www.newsstand.com
Product or Service: Telecommunications/Service Bureaus

NEWSUSA, INC.
1069 W Broad St, Ste 205, Falls Church, VA, 22046-4610, USA (703) 462-2700; web site www.newsusa.com
Product or Service: Publisher/Media
Vice Pres., Sales—Richard Rothstein
Pub.—Rick Smith
Note: www.newsusa.com/articles
Free RSS feed of articles for websites

NEWTON MEDIA ASSOCIATES, INC.
824 Greenbrier Pkwy, Ste 200, Chesapeake, VA, 23320-3697, USA (757) 547-5400; fax (757) 547-7383; e-mail info@newtonmedia.com; web site www.newtonmedia.com
Product or Service: Advertising/Marketing Agency
Pres.—Steven Newton
Media Dir.—Janet Burke
Media Consultant—Aimee James

Account Executive/ Media Buyer—Aubry Winfrey
Director New Business Development—Steve Warnecke

NEXTCOM
5933 W Century Blvd, Ste 410, Los Angeles, CA, 90045-5471, USA (310) 360-1000; fax (310) 360-5000; e-mail customercare@nextcom.net; web site www.nextcom.net
Product or Service: Telecommunications/Service Bureaus
Opns. Mgr.—David Hajian

NICHOLSON KOVAC, INC.
600 Broadway Blvd, Kansas City, MO, 64105-1536, USA (816) 842-8881; fax (816) 842-6340; e-mail nk@nicholsonkovac.com; web site www.nicholsonkovac.com
Product or Service: Advertising/Marketing Agency

NICOLLET TECHNOLOGIES
7901 12th Ave S, Bloomington, MN, 55425-1017, USA (952) 854-3336; fax (952) 854-5774; e-mail info@nicollet.com; web site www.nicollet.com
Product or Service: Telecommunications/Service Bureaus
Pres.—Marco Scibora

NORTEL NETWORKS, INC.
4001 Chapel Hill Nelson Hwy, Research Triangle Park, NC, 27709-0158, USA (905) 863-7000; fax (905) 238-7350; e-mail NortelMediaRelations@nortel.com; web site www.nortel.com
Product or Service: Telecommunications/Service Bureaus

NORTH VALLEY DIVER PUBLICATIONS
585 Royal Oaks Dr, Redding, CA, 96001-0133, USA (530) 246-2009; e-mail nvdp@c-zone.net; web site www.northvalleydiver.com
Product or Service: Publisher/Media
CEO—Dan Bailey

NUANCE COMMUNICATIONS, INC.
1 Wayside Rd, Burlington, MA, 01803-4609, USA (781) 565-5000; fax (781) 565-5001; e-mail kevin.faulkner@nuance.com; web site www.nuance.com
Product or Service: Multimedia/Interactive Products
Pres.—Robert Schwager
CFO—Tim Ledwick
Sr. Vice Pres./Gen. Mgr., Int'l/Commun. Recording Systems—Ed Rucinski
Sr. Vice Pres./Gen. Mgr., Integrated Voice Systems—Bob Attanasio
Sr. Vice Pres., Mktg./Strategic Planning—Donald Fallati
Sr. Vice Pres., Worldwide Servs.—Joe Delaney
Sr. Vice Pres., Mfg./Logistics—Jim Davis

NY INFORMATION TECHNOLOGY CENTER
55 Broad St, Frnt 4, New York, NY, 10004-2565, USA (212) 482-0857; fax (212) 482-0815; e-mail nyitc@55broadst.com; web site www.55broadst.com
Product or Service: Multimedia/Interactive Products
Pres.—William C. Rudin
COO/Exec. Vice Pres.—John J. Gilbert
Dir.-Info Serv.—Jason Largever

O

O & J DESIGN, INC.
41 W 25th St, Fl 4, New York, NY, 10010-2085, USA (212) 242-1080; fax (212) 242-1081; e-mail info@oandjdesign.com; web site www.oandjdesign.com
Product or Service: Multimedia/Interactive Products

O'HALLORAN ADVERTISING, INC.
270 Saugatuck Ave, Westport, CT, 06880-6431, USA (203) 341-9400; fax (203) 341-8681; e-mail info@ohalloranagency.com; web site www.ohalloranagency.com
Product or Service: Advertising/Marketing Agency
CEO—James O'Halloran
Pres.—Kevin O'Halloran

OLIVE SOFTWARE, INC
3033 S Parker Rd, Ste 502, Aurora, CO, 80014-2921, USA 720-747-1220; e-mail info@olivesoftware.com; web site www.olivesoftware.com
Product or Service: Multimedia/Interactive Products, Online Service Provider and Internet Hosts

OMIX, INC. (ONLINE MARKETSPACE)
102 Vaquero Way, Emerald Hills, CA, 94062-3152, USA (650) 568-9800; fax (650) 368-6973; e-mail information@omix.com; web site www.omix.com
Product or Service: Online Service Provider and Internet Hosts
Pres./CTO—Terry Lillie
Vice Pres.—Kyle Hurlbut
Gen. Mgr.—Sandy Lillie
Dir., Bus. Devel.—Jim Chabrier
Dir., Mktg.—Maxine Lym
Creative Dir.—Jim Rodgers
Dir., Finance/Opns.—Gail Price

OPEN TEXT CORP.
275 Frank Tompa Dr, Waterloo, ON, N2L 0A1, Canada (519) 888-7111; fax (519) 888-0677; e-mail @opentext.com; web site www.opentext.com
Product or Service: Hardware/Software Supplier
—Tom Jenkins
—John ShackletonCEOs

ORACLE & SUN MICROSYSTEMS, INC.
500 Oracle Pkwy, Redwood City, CA, 94065-1677, USA (650) 506-7000; fax (408) 276-3804; e-mail oraclesales_us@oracle.com; web site www.oracle.com/us/sun
Product or Service: Hardware/Software Supplier
Chrmn.—Scott G. McNealy
Pres./CEO—Jonathan I. Schwartz
Exec. Vice Pres., Cor. Resources/CFO—Michael Lehman
Chief Acctg. Officer—Kalyani Chatterjee
Pres., Enterprise Servs.—Lawrence Hambly
Exec. Vice Pres., Sun Servs.—Don Grantham
Exec. Vice Pres., People/Places/Chief HR Officer—Crawford Beveridge
Exec. Vice Pres./CTO, SunLabs—Greg Papadopoulos
Exec. Vice Pres., Sun Software—Richard Green
Sr. Brand Strategist, Java—Tom Herbst
Sr. Dir., Brand Experience, Java—Rhodes Klement
Sr. Vice Pres., Brand/Global Commun./Integrated Mktg.—Ingrid Van der Hoogen
Vice Pres., Client Brand Mktg./Adv.—Scott Kraft

ORIGIN COMMUNICATIONS, INC.
4140 Regency Dr, Colorado Springs, CO, 80906-7200, USA (719) 785-9900; fax (719) 314-0168; e-mail info@origincom.com; web site www.origincom.com
Product or Service: Advertising/Marketing Agency, Consultants, Graphic/Design Firm
President—Randel Castleberry
Acct. Servs./Media Dir.—Jil Goebel

P

PAGE COOPERATIVE
1112 Moorefield Creek Rd SW, Vienna, VA, 22180-6245, USA (610) 687-3778; fax (610) 592-0647; e-mail info@pagecooperative.com; web site www.pagecooperative.com

Product or Service: Telecommunications/Service Bureaus
CEO—John Snyder
General Manager—Steve Schroeder
Accnt. Supervisor—Marcy Emory
Director—Graff Joan

PAGE INTERNATIONAL
21 Chatham Center S Dr, Savannah, GA, 31405-, USA (912) 964-7243; fax (912) 965-1225; e-mail info@pageint.com; web site www.page-int.com
Product or Service: Multimedia/Interactive Products
Pres.—Michael Clark
Vice Pres.—Terence Bower
Gen. Mgr.—Susan Vander Masp

PARTSRIVER, INC.
3155 Kearney St, Ste 210, Fremont, CA, 94538-2268, USA (510) 360-5361; fax (510) 413-0079; e-mail support@partsriver.com; web site www.partsriver.com
Product or Service: Hardware/Software Supplier
CEO—Horacio Woolcott
Chief Devel. Officer—Steve De Laet
CTO—Rishi Agarwal
Vice Pres., Servs./Content Mgmt.—Sherry Arnold

PC TODAY MAGAZINE
120 W Harvest Dr, Lincoln, NE, 68521-4408, USA (800) 247-4880; fax (402) 479-2104; e-mail feedback@pctoday.com; web site www.pctoday.com
Product or Service: Publisher/Media
Pres.—Thomas J. Peed
Coord./Mgr.—Mark Peery

PC WORLD
501 2nd St, Ste 600, San Francisco, CA, 94107-4133, USA (415) 243-0500; fax (415) 442-1891; e-mail webmaster@pcworld.com; web site www.pcworld.com
Product or Service: Publisher/Media
Assoc. Pub., PC World.com—Michael Carrol
Mgr., Online Ad Opns.—Brian Buizer
Mgr. Bus Devl—David Lake

PEARSON, INC.
330 Hudson St, New York, NY, 10013-1046, USA (212) 641-2400; e-mail susan.aspey@pearson.com; web site www.pearson.com
Product or Service: Multimedia/Interactive Products

PEIRCE-PHELPS, INC.
2000 N 59th St, Philadelphia, PA, 19131-3031, USA (215) 879-7000; fax (215) 879-5427; e-mail techhelp@peirce.com; web site www.peirce.com
Product or Service: Hardware/Software Supplier
Pres.—Brian Peirce

PENTON MEDIA
1166 Avenue of the Americas, Fl 10, New York, NY, 10036-2750, USA (212) 204-4200; fax (212) 206-3622; e-mail CorporateCustomerService@penton.com; web site www.penton.com
Product or Service: Publisher/Media
Comm. Mgr.—Eliane Kauck
Sr. Customer Service Mgr.—Bev Walter

PIXEL TOUCH
341 Bonnie Cir, Ste 101B, Corona, CA, 92880-2895, USA (951) 371-4360; fax (951) 549-0479; e-mail sales@pixeltouch.com; web site www.pixeltouch.com
Product or Service: Multimedia/Interactive Products
Pres.—Jim Stewart

POLYCOM, INC.
4750 Willow Rd, Pleasanton, CA, 94588-2959, USA (925) 924-6000; fax (925) 924-6100; e-mail Ryan.Batty@Polycom.com; web site www.polycom.com
Product or Service: Telecommunications/Service

Bureaus
Chrmn./Pres./CEO—Robert C. Hagerty

PR & MARKETING NEWS
110 William St, Fl 11, New York, NY, 10038-3901, USA (212) 621-4964; e-mail info@wrightsmedia.com; web site www.prandmarketing.com
Product or Service: Publisher/Media
Vice Pres./Pub.—Diane Schwartz

PR NEWSWIRE
350 Hudson St, Ste 300, New York, NY, 10014-4504, USA 1.888-776-0942; e-mail MediaInquiries@prnewswire.com; web site www.prnewswire.com
Product or Service: Multimedia/Interactive Products
Audience Relations Manager—Christine Cube
SVP, Global Operations—Dave Haapaoja
VP, Strategic Communications & Content—Victoria Harres

PRECISION ARTS ADVERTISING, INC.
57 Fitchburg Rd, Ashburnham, MA, 01430-1409, USA (978) 827-4552; e-mail sales@precisionarts.com; web site www.precisionarts.com
Product or Service: Advertising/Marketing Agency

PREMIERE GLOBAL SERVICES, INC.
3280 Peachtree Rd NE, Ste 1000, Atlanta, GA, 30305-2451, USA (404) 262-8400; e-mail auinfo@pgi.com; web site www.premiereglobal.com
Product or Service: Telecommunications/Service Bureaus
Chrmn./CEO—Boland T. Jones
Pres.—Theodore P. Schrafft
CFO—Michael E. Havener

PRESS+
25 W 52nd St, Fl 15, New York, NY, 10019-6104, USA (212) 332-6405; e-mail info@mypressplus.com; web site www.mypressplus.com
Product or Service: Consultants
Co-Founder—Steven Brill
Co-Founder—Gordon Crovitz
Matt Skibinski
Co-Founder—Leo Hindery
Director of Public Affairs—Cindy Rosenthal

PROCESS SOFTWARE
959 Concord St, Framingham, MA, 01701-4682, USA (508) 879-6994; fax (508) 879-0042; e-mail info@process.com; careers@process.com; international@process.com; web site www.process.com
Product or Service: Hardware/Software Supplier
Vice Pres., Sales—Mick McCarthy

PROJECTS IN KNOWLEDGE, INC.
290 W Mt Pleasant Ave, Ste 2350, Livingston, NJ, 07039-2763, USA (973) 890-8988; fax (973) 890-8866; e-mail rstern@projectsinknowledge.com; web site www.projectsinknowledge.com
Product or Service: Multimedia/Interactive Products
Pres.—Robert Stern
Sr. Vice Pres.—Patricia Peterson
Sr. Vice Pres.—Susan Hostetler
Vice Pres., Design Servs.—Adrian Holmes

PROLINE DIGITAL
PO Box 27682, Denver, CO, 80227-0682, USA (303) 761-3999; fax (303) 761-1818; e-mail info@prolinedigital.com; web site www.prolinedigital.com
Product or Service: CD-ROM Designer/Manufacturer
Pres.—Tony Marcon

PROQUEST DIALOG
789 E Eisenhower Pkwy, Ann Arbor, MI, 48108-3218, USA N/A; e-mail customer@dialog.com; web site proquest.com/go/pqd
Product or Service: Consultants, Other Services, Research

PROXIOS
707 E Main St, Ste 1425, Richmond, VA, 23219-2807, USA (804) 342-1200; fax (804) 342-1209; e-mail sales@proxios.com; web site www.proxios.com
Product or Service: Multimedia/Interactive Products
Pres.—Frank E. Butler

PTI MARKETING TECHNOLOGIES, INC.
201 Lomas Santa Fe Dr, Ste 300, Solana Beach, CA, 92075-1288, USA (858) 847-6600; fax (858) 793-4120; e-mail inquiries@pti.com; web site www.pti.com
Product or Service: Advertising/Marketing Agency
Pres./CEO—Coleman Kane
Sales Vice Pres.—Jim Van Natter

PULSE RESEARCH
1500 SW 11th Ave, Portland, OR, 97201-3532, USA (503) 626-5224; e-mail support@pulseresearch.com; web site www.pulseresearch.com
Product or Service: Consultants, Multimedia/Interactive Products, Web Site Auditor
Pres.—John Marling

PYRAMID STUDIOS
1710 Altamont Ave, Richmond, VA, 23230-4504, USA (804) 353-0700; fax (804) 355-5019; e-mail dhornstein@pyramidstudios.com; web site www.pyramidstudios.com
Product or Service: Multimedia/Interactive Products
Pres.—Bruce Hornstein

R

RANGER DATA TECHNOLOGIES INC.
360 E Maple Rd, Ste X, Troy, MI, 48083-2707, USA (248) 336-7300; fax (248) 336-8775; e-mail info@rangerdata.com; web site www.rangerdata.com
Product or Service: Hardware/Software Supplier
Sr. VP of Operations—George Willard
Director of Marketing & Customer Service—Grace Shields
National Dir. of Sales & Marketing—Dolores Gauthier

RAPP
437 Madison Ave, New York, NY, 10022-7001, USA (212) 817-6800; fax (212) 817-6750; e-mail social.rapp@rapp.com; web site www.rapp.com
Product or Service: Advertising/Marketing Agency

READING HORIZONS
1194 Flint Meadow Dr, Kaysville, UT, 84037-9564, USA (801) 295-7054; fax (801) 295-7088; e-mail info@readinghorizons.com; web site www.readinghorizons.com
Product or Service: Publisher/Media
Pres.—Tyson Smith

READMEDIA
418 Broadway, Albany, NY, 12207-2922, USA (518) 429-2800; fax (518) 429-2801; e-mail customerservice@eisinc.com; web site www.readmedia.com
Product or Service: Other Services
CEO/Pres.—Colin Mathews

RED HILL STUDIOS
1017 E St, Ste C, San Rafael, CA, 94901-2845, USA (415) 457-0440; fax (415) 457-0450; e-mail info@redhillstudios.com; web site www.redhillstudios.com
Product or Service: Graphic/Design Firm, Multimedia/Interactive Products, POP/Kiosk Designer

Creative Dir./Founder—Robert Hone
Dir. Business Development—Adrienne Macbeth

REECE & ASSOCIATES
4200 Northside Pkwy NW, Bldg 7, Atlanta, GA, 30327-3007, USA (404) 586-2100; fax (404) 586-2150; e-mail info@reeceassociates.com; web site www.reeceassociates.com
Product or Service: Multimedia/Interactive Products
—Gary Reece
—Lynda ReeceOwners

RENO REAL ESTATE CONSULTING GROUP
PO Box 12598, Reno, NV, 89510-2598, USA (801) 599-3183; fax (888) 771-7180; e-mail info@LivingInReno.com; web site www.LivingInReno.com
Product or Service: Consultants
Real Estate Consultant—Frank Borghetti
Note: Real Estate Investments Residential & Commercial

REUTERS MEDIA
3 Times Sq, New York, NY, 10036-6564, USA (646) 223-4000; fax (646) 223-4393; e-mail rosalina.thomas@thomsonreuters.com; web site www.reuters.com/newsagency
Product or Service: Multimedia/Interactive Products, Publisher/Media
Vice Pres./Head of Sales - The Americas, Reuters News Agency, Thomson Reuters—Ms. Rosalina Thomas
Publishing Solutions Specialist—Melissa Metzger
Global Director of Marketing—Bipasha Ghosh

RG CREATIONS, INC.
9638 Industrial Rd, San Carlos, CA, 94070-, USA (650) 596-0123; fax (650) 596-8590; e-mail bob@rgcreations.com; web site www.rgcreations.com
Product or Service: Graphic/Design Firm
Owner—Robert G. Fuller

RIBIT, INC.
4287 Belt Line Rd, Ste 135, Addison, TX, 75001-4510, USA (972) 239-8866; fax (972) 239-8788; e-mail ribit@ribit.com; web site www.ribit.com
Product or Service: Advertising/Marketing Agency, Marketing, Multimedia/Interactive Products
Pres./Founder—Robin Moss
Creative Dir.—Jason Landry
Multimedia Developer—Linda Krauss

RISDALL MARKETING GROUP
550 Main St, Ste 100, New Brighton, MN, 55112-3272, USA (651) 286-6700; fax (651) 631-2561; e-mail info@risdall.com; web site www.risdall.com
Product or Service: Advertising/Marketing Agency, Graphic/Design Firm, Marketing
Chrmn./CEO—John Risdall
Chrmn./Pres.—Ted Risdall
Vice Pres./Dir. Web Dev.—Joel Koenigs

RISI, INC.
4 Alfred Cir, Bedford, MA, 01730-2340, USA (781) 734-8900; fax (781) 271-0337; e-mail info@risi.com; web site www.risiinfo.com
Product or Service: Publisher/Media
CEO—Mike Cossey

S

SAME PAGE.COM
PO Box 325, Sanibel, FL, 33957-0325, USA (239) 395-7655; fax (239) 395-6745; e-mail press@same-page.com; web site www.same-page.com
Product or Service: Graphic/Design Firm

Pres.—Bruce Collen

SANTRONICS SOFTWARE
15600 SW 288th St, Ste 306, Homestead, FL, 33033-1200, USA (305) 248-3204; fax (305) 248-0394; e-mail sales@santronics.com; web site www.santronics.com
Product or Service: Hardware/Software Supplier
Pres.—Hector Santos
Dir., Mktg.—Andrea Santos

SAP AMERICA, INC.
18101 Von Karman Ave, Ste 900, Irvine, CA, 92612-0151, USA (949) 622-2200; e-mail press@sap.com; web site www.sap.com
Product or Service: Hardware/Software Supplier
CFO—Mark White
Vice Pres., Global Adv./Branding—Costanza Tedesco
Sr. Dir., Social Media Mktg.—Brian Ellefritz

SCALA, INC.
350 Eagleview Blvd, Ste 150, Exton, PA, 19341-1115, USA (610) 363-3350; fax (610) 363-4010; e-mail marc.rifkin@scala.com; web site www.scala.com
Product or Service: Hardware/Software Supplier
CEO—Gerard Bucas
Pres.—Robert Koolen
CFO—Anthony Maddalone
Dir. Training/Servs.—Marc Rifkin

SEALANDER & CO.
611 N Buckner Blvd, Dallas, TX, 75218-2708, USA (214) 321-8612; fax (214) 328-0779; e-mail john@sealander.com; web site www.sealander.com
Product or Service: Advertising/Marketing Agency
Owner—John Sealander

SILICON GRAPHICS, INC.
900 N McCarthy Blvd, Milpitas, CA, 95035-5128, USA (669) 900-8000; e-mail support@sgi.com; web site www.sgi.com
Product or Service: Hardware/Software Supplier
Pres./CEO—Mark Barrenechea
Sr. Vice Pres., Worldwide Sales/Mktg.—Tony Carrozza
Sr. Vice Pres./CFO—Jim Wheat
Vice Pres./CMO—George Skaff

SILVER OAKS COMMUNICATIONS
824 17th St, Moline, IL, 61265-2126, USA (309) 797-9898; fax (309) 797-9653; e-mail info@silveroaks.com; web site www.silveroaks.com
Product or Service: CD-ROM Designer/Manufacturer
System Mgr.—Charles Dostale

SIMBA INFORMATION
60 Long Ridge Rd, Ste 300, Stamford, CT, 06902-1841, USA (203) 325-8193; fax (203) 325-8975; e-mail customerservice@simbainformation.com; web site www.simbainformation.com
Product or Service: Publisher/Media
Pub.—Linda Kopp
Sr. Ed.—David Goddard
Sr. Ed.—Michael Norris
Sr. Ed.—Dan Strempel
Mng. Ed.—Kathy Mickey
Ed.—Karen Meaney

SLINGSHOT TECHNOLOGIES
1811 Chestnut St, Apt 304, Philadelphia, PA, 19103-3706, USA (800) 405-5755; fax (610) 277-1748; e-mail info@slingshot-tech.com; web site www.slingshot-tech.com
Product or Service: Telecommunications/Service Bureaus
Pres./CEO—Christopher S. Stephano

SMARTMAX SOFTWARE, INC.
8801 S Yale Ave, Ste 460, Tulsa, OK, 74137-3503, USA (918) 496-8103; fax (918) 491-0033; e-mail sales@sightmax.com; web site

www.smartmax.com
Product or Service: Hardware/Software Supplier
Pres.—Eric Weber

SOFTWARE & INFORMATION INDUSTRY ASSOCIATION

1090 Vermont Ave NW, Fl 6, Washington, DC, 20005-4930, USA (202) 289-7442; fax (202) 289-7097; e-mail piracy@siia.net; web site www.siia.net
Product or Service: Trade Association
Pres.—Ken Wasch

SOFTWARE CONSULTING SERVICES, LLC

630 Municipal Dr, Ste 420, Nazareth, PA, 18064-8990, USA (610) 746-7700; fax (610) 746-7900; e-mail sales@newspapersystems.com; web site www.newspapersystems.com
Product or Service: Hardware/Software Supplier
Pres.—Richard Cichelli
VP of Finance and HR—Susan Fenstermaker
VP and Gen. Man.—Kurt M. Jackson
Note: 800 number goes directly to the sales department

SOLO PHOTOGRAPHY, INC.

3503 NW 15th St, Miami, FL, 33125-1715, USA (305) 634-8820; fax (305) 635-9367; e-mail rp@solo-photography.com; web site www.solo-photography.com
Product or Service: Graphic/Design Firm, Publisher/Media
Pres.—Raul Pedroso

SOURCELINK

500 Park Blvd, Ste 1245, Itasca, IL, 60143-2610, USA (310) 208-2024; fax (310) 208-5681; e-mail info@sourcelink.com; web site www.sourcelink.com
Product or Service: Advertising/Marketing Agency
Vice Pres., Interactive Servs.—Scott L. Hilchey

SPANLINK COMMUNICATIONS

605 Highway 169 N, Minneapolis, MN, 55441-6407, USA (763) 971-2000; fax (763) 971-2300; e-mail support@spanlink.com; web site www.spanlink.com
Product or Service: Telecommunications/Service Bureaus
CEO—Scott Christian

SPAR ASSOCIATES, INC.

927 West St, Annapolis, MD, 21401-3653, USA (410) 263-8593; fax (410) 267-0503; e-mail info@sparusa.com; web site www.sparusa.com
Product or Service: Consultants, Hardware/Software Supplier
Pres.—Laurent C. Deschamps
Vice Pres., Opns.—Charles Greenwell

SPECIALTY SYSTEMS, INC.

1451 Route 37 W, Ste 1, Toms River, NJ, 08755-4969, USA (732) 341-1011; fax (732) 341-0655; e-mail contact@specialtysystems.com; web site www.specialtysystems.com
Product or Service: Hardware/Software Supplier
Vice Pres.—Bill Cabey

SPOTMAGIC, INC.

1700 California St, Ste 430, San Francisco, CA, 94109-0429, USA (415) 692-0117; e-mail info@spotmagic.com; web site www.spotmagic.com
Product or Service: Multimedia/Interactive Products
Founder, Affiliate Rel.—John Armstrong
Founder, Pub. Rel.—Robin Solis

SPRINT NEXTEL CORP.

6391 Sprint Pkwy, Overland Park, KS, 66251-6100, USA (703) 433-4000; e-mail boardinquiries@sprint.com; web site www.sprintnextel.com
Product or Service: Telecommunications/Service Bureaus

Non-Exec. Chrmn.—James Hance

Pres./CEO—Daniel R. Hesse
CFO—Robert Brust
Controller—William G. Arendt
CIO—Richard T.C. LeFave
Acting CMO—John Garcia
Chief Network Officer—Kathryn Walker
Sr. Vice Pres., Brand Adv.—Bill Morgan
Vice Pres./Chief Diversity Officer—David P. Thomas
Vice Pres., Cor. Mktg.—Mike Goff
Pres., Network Opns.—Steven Elfman

SS8 NETWORKS

750 Tasman Dr, Milpitas, CA, 95035-7456, USA (408) 944-0250; fax (408) 428-3732; e-mail info@ss8.com; web site www.ss8.com
Product or Service: Telecommunications/Service Bureaus
CEO—Dennis Haar
CFO—Kam Wong
CTO—Dr. Cemal Dikmen
President & COO—Faizel Lakhani
VP of Marketing —Tony Thompason

STATE NET

2101 K St, Sacramento, CA, 95816-4920, USA (916) 444-0840; fax (916) 446-5369; e-mail info@statenet.com; web site www.statenet.com
Product or Service: Online Service Provider and Internet Hosts
—Laurie Stinson
—Jud ClarkPres.s

STATS, LLC.

2775 Shermer Rd, Northbrook, IL, 60062-7700, USA (847) 583-2100; fax (847) 583-2600; e-mail sales@stats.com; web site www.stats.com
Product or Service: Multimedia/Interactive Products
Gen. Mgr.—Jim Morganthaler

STOK SOFTWARE, INC.

373 Smithtown Byp, Ste 287, Hauppauge, NY, 11788-2516, USA (631) 232-2228; e-mail customerservice@stok.com; web site www.stok.com
Product or Service: Telecommunications/Service Bureaus
Pres./Founder—Glenn Stok

STONEMAN LAW OFFICES LTD.

3724 N 3rd St, Ste 200, Phoenix, AZ, 85012-2035, USA (602) 263-9200; fax (602) 277-4883; e-mail request@patentdoc.com; web site www.patentdoc.com
Product or Service: Consultants
—Marty Stoneman
—Eric FishRegistered Patent Attorneys

SUMTOTAL SYSTEM INC.

110 110th Ave NE, Ste 700, Bellevue, WA, 98004-5867, USA (877) 868-2527 (Technical Support); fax (425) 455 3071; e-mail sales@click2learn.com; web site www.click2learn.com; www.asymetrix.com
Product or Service: Multimedia/Interactive Products
Vice Pres., Worldwide Sales/Alliances—Gary Millrood
Vice Pres., Professional Servs.—Ray Pitts

SUNGARD

680 E Swedesford Rd, Wayne, PA, 19087-1605, USA (800) 825-2518; fax (212) 406-2861; e-mail getinfo@sungard.com; web site www.sungard.com
Product or Service: Hardware/Software Supplier
Vice Pres., Mktg.—Nicole Burn
Pres.—Cristobal Conde

SUSSEX COUNTY ONLINE

PO Box 874, Ocean View, DE, 19970-0874, USA (302) 537-4198; e-mail emagill@scdel.net; web site www.sussexcountyonline.com
Product or Service: Consultants

Owner/Pub.—Eric Magill
Content Ed.—Kerin Magill

SYMANTEC CORP.

350 Ellis St, Mountain View, CA, 94043-2202, USA (650) 527-8000; e-mail info@symantec.com; web site www.symantec.com
Product or Service: Online Service Provider and Internet Hosts
Pres./CEO—Steve Bennett

SYNTELLECT, INC.

2095 W Pinnacle Peak Rd, Ste 110, Phoenix, AZ, 85027-1262, USA (602) 789-2800; fax (602) 789-2768; e-mail info.ie@enghouse.com; web site www.syntellect.com
Product or Service: Telecommunications/Service Bureaus
Pres.—Steve Dodenhoff
CFO—Peter Pamplin
Vice Pres., Sales Americas—Keith Gyssler
Vice Pres., Pdct. Mktg.—Tricia Lester
Contact—Jackie Dasta

T

TADIRAN TELECOM, INC.

265 Executive Dr, Ste 250, Plainview, NY, 11803-1743, USA (516) 632-7200; fax (516) 632-7210; web site www.tadirantele.com
Product or Service: Telecommunications/Service Bureaus
CEO—David Sopko

TALX CORP.

11432 Lackland Rd, Saint Louis, MO, 63146-3516, USA (314) 214-7000; fax (314) 214-7588; e-mail moreinfo@talx.com; web site www.talx.com
Product or Service: Telecommunications/Service Bureaus
CEO—William Canfield
Vice Pres., Market Devel.—Michael Smith

TAM COMMUNICATIONS

5610 Scotts Valley Dr, Ste 552B, Scotts Valley, CA, 95066-3473, USA (831) 439-1500; fax (831) 439-0298; e-mail susan@tamcom.com; web site www.tamcom.com
Product or Service: Advertising/Marketing Agency
Pres./CEO—Susan O'Connor Fraser

TARGETBASE

7850 N Belt Line Rd, Irving, TX, 75063-6062, USA (972) 506-3400; fax (972) 506-3505; e-mail info@targetbase.com; web site www.targetbase.com
Product or Service: Advertising/Marketing Agency
Pres./CEO—Mark Wright
Mng. Dir.—Robin Rettew

TECH IMAGE LTD.

1130 W Lake Cook Rd, Ste 250, Buffalo Grove, IL, 60089-1994, USA (847) 279-0022; fax (847) 279-8922; e-mail pr@techimage.com; web site www.techimage.com
Product or Service: Marketing
—Dan O'Brien
—Tom McFeeleyBlog Ed.s

TELECOMPUTE CORP.

4919 Upton St NW, Washington, DC, 20016-2349, USA (202) 789-7860; fax (800) 533-2329; e-mail warren@telecompute.com; web site www.telecompute.com
Product or Service: Telecommunications/Service Bureaus
Pres.—Warren Miller

TELEPERFORMANCE INTERACTIVE

502 W Germantown Pike, Ste 610, Plymouth Meeting, PA, 19462-1321, USA (610) 684-2701; fax (610) 941-9844; e-mail mcohen@teleperformance.com; web site www.teleperformance.com

Product or Service: Telecommunications/Service Bureaus
Pres.—Marc Cohen
COO—Jeffrey Cohen
Vice Pres., Sales—Charles Dowbird

TELEPHONE DOCTOR CUSTOMER SERVICE TRAINING

30 Hollenberg Ct, Bridgeton, MO, 63044-2454, USA (314) 291-1012; fax (314) 291-3710; e-mail info@telephonedoctor.com; web site www.telephonedoctor.com
Product or Service: Online Service Provider and Internet Hosts
Pres.—Nancy Friedman
Gen. Mgr./Vice Pres.—David Friedman

TELSPAN, INC.

101 W Washington St Ste 1200E, Pnc Center, Indianapolis, IN, 46204-3409, USA (317) 631-6565; fax (317) 687-1747; e-mail info@telspan.com; web site www.telspan.com
Product or Service: Telecommunications/Service Bureaus
Chrmn.—J. Bruce Laughrey
COO—Patrick Martin

THE ARBITRON CO.

142 W 57th St, New York, NY, 10019-3300, USA (212) 887-1300; fax (212) 887-1401; e-mail alisa.joseph@arbitron.com; web site www.arbitron.com
Product or Service: Telecommunications/Service Bureaus
Pres.—Steve Morris
Pres., Opns./Technology/Research/Devel.—Owen Charlebois
Gen. Mgr./Domestic Radio—Brad Kelly
Vice Pres., Sales, Advertiser/Agency Servs.—Carol Edwards
Pres., Sales/Mktg.—Pierre Bouvard

THE CREATORS MEDIA GROUP

2 Jackson St, Pleasantville, NY, 10570-3025, USA (914) 769-0676; fax (914) 769-0763; e-mail admin@creatorsmedia.com; web site www.creatorsmedia.com
Product or Service: Multimedia/Interactive Products
CEO—Anthony Trama

THE GAZETTE COMPANY

501 2nd Ave SE, Cedar Rapids, IA, 52401-1303, USA (319) 398-8422; fax (319) 368-8505; e-mail customercare@thegazettecompany.com; web site www.thegazettecompany.com
Product or Service: Multimedia/Interactive Products, Publisher/Media
Chrmn.—Joe Hadky
President and CEO—Chuck Peters
VP Sales & Marketing—Chris Edwards

THE NEXT WAVE

100 Bonner St, Dayton, OH, 45410-1306, USA (937) 228-4433; fax (937) 228-4111; e-mail surf@thenextwave.biz; web site www.thenextwave.biz
Product or Service: Advertising/Marketing Agency

THE PRESENTATION PROFESSOR

2276 S Beverly Glen Blvd, Unit 108, Los Angeles, CA, 90064-2440, USA (310) 286-0969; fax (310) 286-0970; e-mail tom@professorpowerpoint.com; web site www.professorppt.com
Product or Service: Multimedia/Interactive Products
Pres.—Tom Bunzel

THE SPORTS NETWORK

2200 Byberry Rd, Ste 200, Hatboro, PA, 19040-3739, USA (215) 441-8444; fax (215) 441-5767; e-mail info@sportsnetwork.com; web site www.sportsnetwork.com
Product or Service: Multimedia/Interactive Products, Publisher/Media

Pres./CEO—Mickey Charles
Nat'l Sales Mgr.—Ken Zajac
Dir., Technical Opns.—Bruce Michaels
Sales Associate—Bernie Greenberg

THE STEPHENZ GROUP
75 E Santa Clara St, Ste 900, San Jose, CA, 95113-1842, USA (408) 286-9899; fax (408) 286-9866; e-mail info@stephenz.com; web site www.stephenz.com
Product or Service: Advertising/Marketing Agency
Pres./CEO—Barbara Zenz
Vice Pres., Creative Servs.—Stephanie Paulson

THE TUCKER GROUP
19 Edgewood Rd, Sharon, MA, 02067-1938, USA (781) 784-0932; e-mail mtucker@tuckergroup.com
Product or Service: Advertising/Marketing Agency
Owner—Michael Tucker

THUNDERSTONE SOFTWARE LLC
815 Superior Ave E, Cleveland, OH, 44114-2706, USA (216) 820-2200; fax (216) 820-2211; e-mail info@thunderstone.com; web site www.thunderstone.com
Product or Service: Hardware/Software Supplier, Online Service Provider and Internet Hosts
CMO—Peter Thusat

TNS GLOBAL
11 Madison Ave, Ste 1201, New York, NY, 10010-3624, USA (212) 991-6000; e-mail enquiries@tnsglobal.com; web site www.tnsglobal.com
Product or Service: Advertising/Marketing Agency
—Leendert De Voogd
—Mark FrancasSales Rep.s

TOM O'TOOLE COMMUNICATION, INC.
115 79th St, Burr Ridge, IL, 60527-5954, USA (630) 789-8666; e-mail tom@tomotoole.com; web site www.tomotoole.com
Product or Service: Advertising/Marketing Agency
Pres.—Tom O'Toole

TOWNNEWS.COM
1510 47th Ave, Moline, IL, 61265-7021, USA (800) 293-9576; fax (309) 743-0830; e-mail info@townnews.com; web site www.townnews.com
Product or Service: Editorial, Graphic/Design Firm, Hardware/Software Supplier, Multimedia/Interactive Products, Other Services, Online Service Provider and Internet Hosts, Web Site Auditor
Exec Chairman—Marc Wilson
CEO—Brad Ward
Rgl. Sales Mgr.—Carol Grubbe
Tech. Sales Rep.—Teri Sutton
Reg. Sales Mgr.—Roger Lee
Dir./Buss. Dev.—Theresa Nelson
Sr. Tech. Sales Rep.—Marc Filby
Reg. Sales Mgr.—Loren Widrick
Dir./Product Mgmt.—Christine Masters
Dir. Mktg.—Aaron Gilllette
Reg. Sales Mgr.—David Sutton
Regional Sales Manager—John Montgomery
Note: No. 1 provider of Content Management Systems to U.S. daily newspapers, according to Reynolds Journalism Institute.

TRADEWINDS PUBLISHING
6695 Fox Ridge Cir, Davidson, NC, 28036-8090, USA (704) 896-9978; fax (615) 841-3288; e-mail wgray01@wgray.com; web site www.wgray.com
Product or Service: Publisher/Media
Ed.—Bill Gray

TREEHOUSE ONE INTERACTIVE
40310 Three Forks Rd, Magnolia, TX, 77354-4628, USA (512) 682-6943; fax (512) 682-6943; e-mail info@treehouse1.com; web site

www.treehouse1.com
Product or Service: Multimedia/Interactive Products
Contact—Brian K. Hecht

TRIBAL DDB
437 Madison Ave, Fl 8, New York, NY, 10022-7046, USA (212) 515-8321; fax (212) 515-8660; web site www.tribaldb.com
Product or Service: Advertising/Marketing Agency

TRIBUNE CONTENT AGENCY
435 N Michigan Ave, Ste 3, Chicago, IL, 60611-6229, USA (800) 637-4082; e-mail tcasales@tronc.com; web site www.tribunecontentagency.com
Product or Service: Multimedia/Interactive Products
Dir., US Syndication Sales—Scott Cameron
Sales Dir.—Rick DeChantal
Director of Operations—Karen Eich
VP Sales—Wayne Lown
Editor / General Manager—John Barron
Marketing Manager—Matt Maldre

TSANG SEYMOUR DESIGN, INC.
526 W 26th St, Rm 708, New York, NY, 10001-5524, USA (212) 352-0063; fax (212) 352-0067; e-mail info@tsangseymour.com; ps@tsangseymour.com; web site www.tsangseymour.com
Product or Service: Graphic/Design Firm
—Patrick Seymour
—Catarina TsangPrincipals

TV DATA (TRIBUNE MEDIA SERVICES)
333 Glen St, Glens Falls, NY, 12801-3666, USA (518) 792-9914; fax (518) 792-4414; e-mail tvdata@tvdata.com; web site www.clicktv.com; www.tvdata.com
Product or Service: Multimedia/Interactive Products
Vice Pres., Newspaper/Adv. Sales—Cameron Yung

TWO TWELVE
902 Broadway, Fl 20, New York, NY, 10010-6002, USA (212) 254-6670; fax (212) 254-6614; e-mail info@twotwelve.com; web site www.twotwelve.com
Product or Service: Graphic/Design Firm
Founder/Principal/Pres.—David Gibson
Principal—Ann Harakawa
CMO—Sarah Haun

TYJILL ENTERPRISES, INC.
1009 E Elm Tree Rd, Rossford, OH, 43460-1353, USA (419) 349-6513; fax (419) 666-4249; e-mail jappt@tyjill.com; web site www.tyjill.com
Product or Service: Multimedia/Interactive Products
Pres.—John J. Appt

U

ULEAD SYSTEMS, INC.
970 W 190th St, Ste 480, Torrance, CA, 90502-1015, USA (510) 979-7118; fax (310) 512-6408; e-mail info@corel.com; web site www.ulead.com
Product or Service: Hardware/Software Supplier
Vice Pres., American Sales—Mike Yanez

ULTITECH, INC.
0 Foot of Broad St, Ste 202, Stratford, CT, 06615-9201, USA (203) 375-7300; fax (203) 375-6699; e-mail ultitech@meds.com; web site www.meds.com
Product or Service: Multimedia/Interactive Products
Pres.—William J. Comcowich
Mgr., Opns.—Laura McClatchie

UNET 2 CORPORATION
84 Mount Misery Dr, Sag Harbor, NY, 11963-

3922, USA (631) 725-9513; fax (631) 725-9513; e-mail JMonaco@UNET2.net; web site www.UNET2.net
Product or Service: Editorial, Multimedia/Interactive Products, Online Service Provider and Internet Hosts, Publisher/Media
Pres.—James Monaco

UNISYS CORP.
Unisys Way, Blue Bell, PA, 19424-0001, USA (215) 986-6999; fax (215) 986-2312; e-mail info@unisys.com; investor@unisys.com; web site www.unisys.com
Product or Service: Hardware/Software Supplier
Chrmn./CEO—J. Edward Coleman
Sr. Vice Pres./CFO—Janet Brutschea Haugen
Vice Pres./Treasurer—Scott A. Battersby

UNITED MEDIA
1130 Walnut St, Kansas City, MO, 64106-2109, USA (816) 581-7340; fax (816) 581-7346; e-mail salesdirector@amuniversal.com; web site www.universaluclick.com
Product or Service: Publisher/Media
Pres.—Kerry Slagle

UNIVERSAL TECHNICAL SYSTEMS, INC.
202 W State St, Ste 700, Rockford, IL, 61101-1152, USA (815) 963-2220; fax (815) 963-8884; e-mail sales@uts.us.com; web site www.uts.us.com
Product or Service: Hardware/Software Supplier
Pres.—Jack Marathe

UPSHAW & ASSOCIATES
14 Altamira Ave, Kentfield, CA, 94904-1407, USA (415) 785-8735; fax (415) 507-9194; e-mail upshaw@upshawmarketing.com; web site www.brandbuilding.com
Product or Service: Consultants
Principal—Lynn B. Upshaw

USA 800, INC.
9808 E 66th Ter, Raytown, MO, 64133-5850, USA (816) 358-1303; fax (816) 358-8845; e-mail tdavis@usa-800.com; web site www.usa800.com
Product or Service: Telecommunications/Service Bureaus
Pres./CEO—Tom Davis
Exec. Vice Pres./CFO—Dan Quigley
Vice Pres./Dir., Techn.—Mike Langel

V

V! STUDIOS
8229 Boone Blvd, Ste 420, Vienna, VA, 22182-2651, USA (703) 760-0440; fax (703) 760-0417; e-mail operations@v-studios.com; web site www.v-studios.com
Product or Service: Online Service Provider and Internet Hosts
Vice Pres.—Cindy Benesch
Vice Pres., Promo.—Troy Benesch
Dir., Mktg./Sales—Jim Hatch

VERIO, INC.
1203 Research Way, Orem, UT, 84097-6207, USA (303) 645-1900; fax (303) 708-2490; e-mail veriomedia@verio.net; web site www.verio.com
Product or Service: Online Service Provider and Internet Hosts
Pres.—Kiyoshi Maeda

VERIZON COMMUNICATIONS, INC.
1095 Avenue of the Americas, New York, NY, 10036-6797, USA (212) 395-2121; fax (212) 719-3349; e-mail info@verizon.com; web site www.verizon.com
Product or Service: Telecommunications/Service Bureaus
Chrmn./CEO—Ivan G. Seidenberg
Vice Chrmn./Pres.—Lawrence Babbio
Grp. Pres., Int'l—Dan Petri
Exec. Vice Pres./CFO—Doreen Toben

Pres., Verizon Foundation—Patrick Gaston
Exec. Vice Pres., Pub. Affairs/Commun.—Thomas Tauke
Exec. Vice Pres., HR—Marc Reed
Exec. Vice Pres./CTO—Dick Lynch
Sr. Vice Pres., Strategy/Devel./Planning—John Diercksen
Sr. Vice Pres./Treasurer—Tom Bartlett
Sr. Vice Pres., Domestic Telecom HR—John Bell
Sr. Vice Pres., Mktg./Digital Media—John Harrobin
Sr. Vice Pres., Investor Rel.—Catherine Webster
CIO—Shaygan Kheradpir
Pres., Landline Opns.—Francis Shamoo
Pres., Wholesale Mkts.—Virginia Ruesterholz
Mgr., Hispanic Mktg.—Joe Paz

VERTICAL COMMUNICATIONS, INC.
4717 E Hilton Ave, Ste 400, Phoenix, AZ, 85034-6414, USA (480) 374-8900; fax (480) 998-2469; e-mail info@vertical.com; web site www.vertical.com
Product or Service: Hardware/Software Supplier
CEO—William Tauscher
Exec. Vice Pres./Gen. Mgr.—Dick Anderson
CFO—Ken Clinebell
CTO—Scott Pickett
Sr. Vice Pres., Bus. Dev.—Peter H. Bailey
Sr. Vice Pres., Dev.—Chris Brookins
Vice Pres., Sales—Jim Scanlon
Vice Pres., Sales-Distributed Enterprise Solutions—Ben Alves
Vice Pres., International Sales—Mel Passarelli

VERVE MOBILE
5973 Avenida Encinas, Ste 101, Carlsbad, CA, 92008-4477, USA (760) 479-0055; fax (760) 479-0056; e-mail info@vervewireless.com; web site www.vervewireless.com
Product or Service: Advertising/Marketing Agency, Multimedia/Interactive Products
Pres.—Tom Kenney
CMO—Greg Hallinan
Vice President, Publisher Services—Ray Green
SVP Publisher & Advertising Operations—Aimee Iriwn

VICORP.COM
101 E Park Blvd, Ste 600-15, Plano, TX, 75074-5483, USA (972) 596-2969; e-mail sales@vicorp.com; info@vicorp.com; web site www.vicorp.com
Product or Service: Hardware/Software Supplier
CEO—Brendan Treacy
COO—Lee Cottle

VNU EMEDIA
85 Broad St, New York, NY, 10004-2434, USA (646) 654-5550; fax (646) 654-5584; e-mail corporatepressinquiries@nielsen.com; web site www.vnuemedia.com
Product or Service: Publisher/Media
Pres., eMedia/Information Mktg.—Toni Nevitt
Vice Pres., eMedia—John Lerner
Vice Pres., Technology—Christian Evans
Dir., Sales—Eileen Long
Nat'l Sales Dir.—Jeff Green
Bus. Devel. Mgr.—Evan Ambinder

VOICE RETRIEVAL & INFORMATION SERVICES, INC.
3222 Skylane Dr, Ste 100, Carrollton, TX, 75006-2522, USA (972) 380-8400; fax (972) 380-0118; e-mail sales@vri.com; web site www.vri.com
Product or Service: Telecommunications/Service Bureaus
Customer Service Rep.—Melissa Guevara

VOICE TECHNOLOGIES GROUP, INC.
2350 N Forest Rd, Getzville, NY, 14068-1296, USA (716) 689-6700 ext. 255; fax (716) 689-6800; e-mail info@vtg.com; web site www.vtg.com
Product or Service: Telecommunications/Service Bureaus

Sales Dir.—Joseph Miller
Mktg. Serv. Mgr.—Cathryn Apenowich

VOICETEXT COMMUNICATIONS
211 E 7th St, Ste 1200, Austin, TX, 78701-3218, USA (512) 404-2300; fax (512) 479-6464; e-mail conference@voicetext.com; web site www.voicetext.com
Product or Service: Telecommunications/Service Bureaus
Pres.—Eileen Williams
Mgr., Audio Conference—Jennifer Mackin

VOICEWORLD
11201 N 70th St, Scottsdale, AZ, 85254-5183, USA (602) 922-5500; fax (602) 922-5572; e-mail brains@voiceworld.com; web site www.voiceworld.com
Product or Service: Hardware/Software Supplier
Pres.—Brian L. Berman

VOLT INFORMATION SCIENCES
1 Sentry Pkwy E, Ste 1000, Blue Bell, PA, 19422-2310, USA (610) 825-7720; fax (610) 941-6874; e-mail ssaha@volt.com; web site www.volt.com
Product or Service: Multimedia/Interactive Products
Pres.—Gerard Dipippo
Exec. Vice Pres./COO—Steven A. Shaw
Prodn. Mgr.—Bob Epstein

VOXWARE, INC.
300 American Metro Blvd, Ste 155, Hamilton, NJ, 08619-2371, USA (609) 514-4100; fax (609) 514-4101; e-mail marketing@voxware.com; web site www.voxware.com
Product or Service: Hardware/Software Supplier
Vice Pres., Sales/Bus. Devel.—Charlie Rafferty

W

WASHINGTONPOST.NEWSWEEK INTERACTIVE
1150 15th St NW, Washington, DC, 20071-0001, USA (202) 334-6000; fax (703) 469-2995; web site www.washingtonpost.com
Product or Service: Publisher/Media
Exec. Ed.—Marcus Brauchli

WESSAN INTERACTIVE
3033 N 93rd St, Omaha, NE, 68134-4715, USA (402) 572-8200; fax (402) 572-7244; e-mail sales@wessan.com; web site www.wessan.com
Product or Service: Consultants, Multimedia/Interactive Products, Other Services, Online Service Provider and Internet Hosts, Telecommunications/Service Bureaus
President & CEO—Michael Kepler
VP Sales & Marketing—Kevin Schaaf

WEST INTERACTIVE CORP.
11650 Miracle Hills Dr, Omaha, NE, 68154-4448, USA (402) 963-1300; fax (402) 963-1602; e-mail sales@west.com; web site www.westinteractive.com
Product or Service: Multimedia/Interactive Products
Pres.—Nancee Berger
Vice Pres., Sales/Mktg.—Mack McKenzie

WIDECOM GROUP, INC.
14 Lafayette Sq, Buffalo, NY, 14203-1929, USA (905) 712-0505; fax (905) 712-0506; e-mail info@widecom.com; widecom@widecom.com; web site www.widecom.com
Product or Service: Telecommunications/Service Bureaus
Vice Pres., Sales/Mktg.—Suneet Tuli

WINSTAR/NORTHWEST NEXUS, INC.
15821 NE 8th St, Ste W200, Bellevue, WA, 98008-3957, USA (206) 415-2500; fax (206) 415-2500; e-mail sales@nwnexus.com; web site www.nwnexus.net
Product or Service: Online Service Provider and Internet Hosts
Pres.—Ed Morin
Vice Pres.—Ralph Sims

WIRELESS COMMUNICATIONS ASSOCIATION INTERNATIONAL
1333 H St NW, Ste 700, Washington, DC, 20005-4707, USA (202) 452-7823; web site www.wcai.com
Product or Service: Trade Association
Pres.—Fred Cambell

WOLFF/SMG
1641 Commons Pkwy, Macedon, NY, 14502-

9190, USA (315) 986-1155; fax (315) 986-1157; e-mail info@wolff-smg.com; web site www.wolff-smg.com
Product or Service: Advertising/Marketing Agency, Consultants, Graphic/Design Firm, Multimedia/Interactive Products

WOODWARD COMMUNICATIONS, INC.
801 Bluff St, Dubuque, IA, 52001-4661, USA (563) 588-5685; e-mail tom.woodward@wcinet.com; web site www.wcinet.com
Product or Service: Advertising/Marketing Agency, Editorial, Marketing, Multimedia/Interactive Products, Online Service Provider and Internet Hosts, Publisher/Media, Research
CEO/Pres.—Tom Woodward
Note: WCI is a diversified, employee-owned company, composed of community media, agency and targeted business trade services. The corporation has seven operating divisions: TH Media, Woodward Community Media, Woodward Radio Group, Woodward Printing Services, Two Rivers Marketing, ON Communication, and WoodwardBizMedia.

WORLD INTERACTIVE NETWORK
3960 Broadway, Fl 4, New York, NY, 10032-1543, USA (212) 740-4400; fax (212) 795-8553; e-mail winnet@panix.com; web site www.winglobal.com
Product or Service: Multimedia/Interactive Products
Vice Pres./Gen. Mgr.—Claudia Soifer
Exec. Producer, Multimedia—Charles David Padro

WPA FILM LIBRARY
16101 108th Ave, Orland Park, IL, 60467-5305, USA (708) 460-0555; fax (708) 460 0187; e-mail sales@wpafilmlibrary.com; web site www.wpafilmlibrary.com
Product or Service: Publisher/Media
Dir., Sales—Diane Paradiso

X

XMISSION
51 E 400 S, Ste 200, Salt Lake City, UT, 84111-2753, USA (801) 539-0852; fax (801) 539-0853; e-mail info@xmission.com; web

site www.xmission.com
Product or Service: Online Service Provider and Internet Hosts
Founder—Howard Gordon
Pres.—Peter Ashdown
Gen. Mgr.—Sue Ashdown
Cor. Sales—Bret Jensen
Mktg. Mgr.—Bob Dobbs

XTIVIA
304 S 8th St, Ste 201, Colorado Springs, CO, 80905-1825, USA (888) 685-3101 ext. 2; fax (719) 685-3400; e-mail nir.gryn@xtivia.com; web site www.xtivia.com
Product or Service: Consultants
CEO—Nir Gryn

Y

Y2M: YOUTH MEDIA & MARKETING NETWORKS
31 Saint James Ave, Ste 920, Boston, MA, 02116-4155, USA (888) 738-5578; e-mail support@collegemedianetwork.com; web site www.y2m.com
Product or Service: Advertising/Marketing Agency
Vice Pres./Gen.Mgr.—Dina Witter Pradel
Dir., Strategic Devel./Opns.—Tom Peterson
Gen. Mgr.—Sara Steele-Rogers

Z

ZANE PUBLISHING, INC.
PO Box 1697, Woodstock, GA, 30188-1366, USA (770) 795-9195; fax (770) 795-8495; e-mail stewart.cross@zane.com; web site www.zane.com
Product or Service: CD-ROM Designer/Manufacturer
Pres./COO—Stewart Cross

ZHIVAGO MANAGEMENT PARTNERS
381 Seaside Dr, Jamestown, RI, 02835-2376, USA (401) 423-2400; e-mail kristin@zhivago.com; web site www.zhivago.com
Product or Service: Consultants
Pres.—Kristin Zhivago

CATEGORIES OF INTERACTIVE PRODUCTS AND SERVICES

A

ADVERTISING/MARKETING AGENCY
24/7 Real Media, Inc.
Al Bredenberg Creative Services
APCO Worldwide
Audio Service America Productions / FreeHold Division
Backe Difital Brand Marketing
Bender/Helper Impact
Black Star Publishing Co., Inc.
Blass Communications
Cramp + Tate, Inc.
Creative Direct
Customer Communications Group
Cyber Sales One, Inc.
Dana Communications
Designory.com
Dev.Kinney/MediaGraphics, Inc.
Dex Media
DoubleClick
Dreamscape Design, Inc.
Emergence Labs, Inc.
Epsilon
Epsilon Interactive
ePublish4me

Film Artists Associates
G2 Direct & Digital
Godfrey
Hitchcock Fleming and Associates, Inc.
Holdcom
Hutchinson Associates, Inc.
International Demographics/The Media Audit
Ken Petretti Productions, LLC
Kobie Marketing, Inc.
Launch Agency
Lieberman Research Worldwide
LOGOpremiums.com
M/C/C
Mall Marketing Media
Marke Communications, Inc.
McMonigle & Associates
Mediabids, Inc.
Midwest Digital Communications
Newton Media Associates, Inc.
Nicholson Kovac, Inc.
O'Halloran Advertising, Inc.
Origin Communications, Inc.
Precision Arts Advertising, Inc.
PTI Marketing Technologies, Inc.
Rapp
Ribit, Inc.
Risdall Marketing Group

Sealander & Co.
SourceLink
Tam Communications
Targetbase
The Next Wave
The Stephenz Group
The Tucker Group
TNS Global
Tom O'Toole Communication, Inc.
Tribal DDB
Verve Mobile
Wolff/SMG
Woodward Communications, Inc.
Y2M: Youth Media & Marketing Networks

C

CD-ROM DESIGNER/MANUFACTURER
Aaron Marcus and Associates, Inc.
Automated Graphic Systems
CD Technology
Corporate Disk Company
Dreamscape Design, Inc.
EDR/Beachwood Studios
interActive Publishing Corp.

Israel Faxx
JLM CD-ROM Publishing Co.
Ken Petretti Productions, LLC
Luminare
Media Design Group
Media Supply, Inc.
Methodologie, Inc.
Modern Digital
Proline Digital
Silver Oaks Communications
Zane Publishing, Inc.

CIRCULATION
NEWSCYCLE Solutions

CONSULTANTS
Aaron Marcus and Associates, Inc.
Advanced Interactive Media Group, LLC
APCO Worldwide
Arlen Communications LLC
Audio Service America Productions / FreeHold Division
Borghetti Consulting Group
Branfman Law Group, P.C.
CGI Group, Inc.
ChannelNet

Ciber, Inc.
Cobbey & Associates Full Service Marketing Research
Creative Circle Media Solutions
DeskNet, Inc.
Digital Collections
Dreamscape Design, Inc.
FLI, Incorporated
Frank Magid Associates
Hutchinson Associates, Inc.
Interactive Educational Systems Design, Inc.
Interactive Media Associates
Ken Petretti Productions, LLC
Lazer-fare Media Services
LexisNexis
Morpace International
Multimedia Research Group, Inc.
Multimedia Resource Group
NEWSCYCLE Solutions
Nielsen
Origin Communications, Inc.
Press+
ProQuest Dialog
Pulse Research
Spar Associates, Inc.
Stoneman Law Offices Ltd.
Sussex County Online
Upshaw & Associates
Wolff/SMG
Xtivia
Zhivago Management Partners

E

EDITORIAL
NEWSCYCLE Solutions

G

GRAPHIC DESIGN FIRM
Iron Design
Aaron Marcus and Associates, Inc.
Amasis
Atomic Imaging, Inc.
Beatley Gravitt Communications
Cosmos Communications, Inc.
Creative Circle Media Solutions
DLS Design
Dreamscape Design, Inc.
Dreamscape Design, Inc.
ELFWorks 3D Construction Co.
ePublish4me
Fisher Photography
Fusebox, Inc.
Hutchinson Associates, Inc.
Imagen, Inc.
Jablonski Design, Inc.
Ken Petretti Productions, LLC
Kinetic Corporation
L@it2'd (Latitude)
Laura Smith Illustration
Methodologie, Inc.
Origin Communications, Inc.
Red Hill Studios
RG Creations, Inc.
Risdall Marketing Group
Same Page.com
Solo Photography, Inc.
Tsang Seymour Design, Inc.
Two Twelve
Wolff/SMG

H

HARDWARE/SOFTWARE SUPPLIER
3M Touch Systems, Inc.
Adaptive Optics Associates, Inc., A United Technologies Co.
Adobe Systems, Inc.
Adstream America
ADTRAN
Advanced Publishing Technology
Apple, Inc.
Aptas
Aspect Communications

Atex
BackWeb
BlueCielo ECM Solutions
BMC Group, Inc.
BroadVision
Catalyst International, Inc.
Celebro
ChannelNet
College Publisher, Inc.
Computer Talk Technology, Inc.
Copia International Ltd.
Corel
Creative Circle Media Solutions
Cybertech, Inc.
Digital Collections
EASE CT Solutions
Edgil Associates, Inc.
Emphasys Software
Enigma
eSoft
ET Srl Elettronica Telecomunicazioni
Filestream, Inc.
IBM Corp.
ILIO Entertainment
Infocus Corp.
Intactix
Interactive International, Inc.
JDA Software Group, Inc.
Jupiter Images Corp.
Lazer-fare Media Services
L-Soft International, Inc.
MarCole Enterprises, Inc.
Media Marketing, Inc.
Micro Perfect Corp.
Microlog Corp.
Microsoft Corp.
Miles 33
MRW Communications, LLC.
netVillage.com, LLC.
NEWSCYCLE Solutions
Nielsen
Open Text Corp.
Oracle & Sun Microsystems, Inc.
PartsRiver, Inc.
Peirce-Phelps, Inc.
Process Software
Ranger Data Technologies Inc.
Santronics Software
SAP America, Inc.
Scala, Inc.
Silicon Graphics, Inc.
SmartMax Software, Inc.
Software Consulting Services, LLC
Spar Associates, Inc.
Specialty Systems, Inc.
SunGard
Thunderstone Software LLC
TownNews.com
Ulead Systems, Inc.
Unisys Corp.
Universal Technical Systems, Inc.
Vertical Communications, Inc.
Vicorp.com
VoiceWorld
Voxware, Inc.

M

MARKETING
Buzz360 LLC
Ribit, Inc.
Risdall Marketing Group
Tech Image Ltd.
Woodward Communications, Inc.

MULTIMEDIA/INTERACTIVE PRODUCTS
AccuWeather, Inc.
ACT Teleconferencing, Inc.
Advanced Communication Design, Inc.
Amerikids USA
Animated Software Co.
Answers Media Inc.
Applied Art & Technology
Aptas
Asbury Park Press
Assignment Desk
Audio Service America Productions / FreeHold Division
Authorlink

Autonomy, Inc.
BKJ Productions
BKR Studio, Inc.
Breze, Inc.
CBS MaxPreps, Inc.
Chase Bobko, Inc.
citysearch.com
CommGraphics Interactive, Inc.
Communication Design
Competence Software
Convergent Media Systems
Convergys
CSTV Online, Inc.
CyberSmart
Daniel Lampert Communications Corp.
Design Media, Inc.
Digital Design Group Limited
Direct Images Interactive, Inc.
Dow Jones Interactive Publishing
Dreamscape Design, Inc.
D-Squared Studios, Inc.
Dunn Solutions Group
EDR/Beachwood Studios
Envision Interactive
epic software group, Inc.
ePublish4me
Family Features Editorial Syndicate, Inc.
Flip Your Lid
Four Palms, Inc.
Fujitsu Ten Corp. of America
Gannett Media Technologies International (GMTI)
GCN Publishing
HealthStream
Hoskyns & Associates
Hotwax Multimedia, Inc.
HTS Interactive Health Care
Iceni Technology
IconNicholson
Image Zone, Inc.
Imergy
inetUSA
Information Presentation Tech.
Inforonics, Inc.
Interactive Pictures Corporation (IPIX)
InterCom
JLM CD-ROM Publishing Co.
Judson Rosebush Co.
Ken Petretti Productions, LLC
Larson Texts, Inc.
Light Fantastic Studios, Inc.
Logical Design Solutions, Inc.
MarCole Enterprises, Inc.
Media Enterprises
Media Logic USA, LLC
Mediabids, Inc.
Methodologie, Inc.
Miles 33
Motion City Films
Multi-Media Communications
New Horizons Computer Learning Center
New Media Hollywood
Newman Brothers
NEWSCYCLE Solutions
Nuance Communications, Inc.
NY Information Technology Center
O & J Design, Inc.
Page International
Pearson, Inc.
Pixel Touch
PR Newswire
Projects In Knowledge, Inc.
Proxios
Pulse Research
Pyramid Studios
Red Hill Studios
Reece & Associates
Reuters Media
Ribit, Inc.
SpotMagic, Inc.
STATS, LLC.
Sumtotal System Inc.
The Creators Media Group
The Gazette Company
The Presentation Professor
The Sports Network
Treehouse One Interactive
Tribune Content Agency
TV Data (Tribune Media Services)
TyJill Enterprises, Inc.
UltiTech, Inc.
Unet 2 Corporation

Verve Mobile
Volt Information Sciences
West Interactive Corp.
Wolff/SMG
World Interactive Network

O

ONLINE SERVICE PROVIDER AND INTERNET HOSTS
AccuWeather, Inc.
APDI-Application Programming & Development, Inc.
ASTech InterMedia
BBS Computing
B-Linked, Inc.
Business Wire - New York, NY
CableFAX Daily LLC
Cogent Communications, Inc.
Comtex News Network
Creative Circle Media Solutions
Cybercon.com
Cyways, Inc.
Digital Collections
DTN/The Progressive Farmer
ePublish4me
inetUSA
Ken Petretti Productions, LLC
Maps.com
MarCole Enterprises, Inc.
MCI
Mercury Center
Metro Newspaper
netVillage.com, LLC.
NEWSCYCLE Solutions
Omix, Inc. (Online Marketspace)
State Net
Symantec Corp.
Telephone Doctor Customer Service Training
Thunderstone Software LLC
TownNews.com
Unet 2 Corporation
V! Studios
Verio, Inc.
WinStar/Northwest Nexus, Inc.
XMission

OTHER SERVICES
AccuWeather, Inc.
D & H Information Services, Inc.
Muse Presentation Technologies
ProQuest Dialog
readMedia
TownNews.com

P

POP/KIOSK DESIGNER
Aaron Marcus and Associates, Inc.
Cybertech, Inc.
Dreamscape Design, Inc.
EDR/Beachwood Studios
Griffin Chase Oliver, Inc.
Ken Petretti Productions, LLC
Kiosk Information Systems
MarCole Enterprises, Inc.
Muse Presentation Technologies
Red Hill Studios

PUBLISHER/MEDIA
Active Data Exchange
Advance Internet, Inc.
Advanced Interactive Media Group, LLC
Advertising Age
America Online Digital City, Inc.
Amplified.com, Inc.
Aptas
Arizona Republic Digital Media
Asbury Park Press
Associated Press Information Services
Authorlink
BIAKelsey
CBS MaxPreps, Inc.
Cineman Syndicate
Congressional Quarterly, Inc.
Dex One Corp.
DTN/The Progressive Farmer

Editor & Publisher Interactive
ePublish4me
EUR/Electronic Urban Report
HEC Reading Horizons
Hewlett-Packard Co.
InfoMedia, Inc.
Israel Faxx
JLM CD-ROM Publishing Co.
Ken Petretti Productions, LLC
King Features Syndicate
M2 Communications Ltd.
MacTech Magazine
McClatchy Interactive
MPI Media Group
NEWSCYCLE Solutions
Newspaper Association of America
Newsphere
NewsUSA, Inc.
North Valley Diver Publications
PC Today Magazine
PC World
Penton Media
PR & Marketing News
Reuters Media
RISI, Inc.
Simba Information
Solo Photography, Inc.
The Gazette Company
The Sports Network
The Washington Times Corp.
Tradewinds Publishing
Unet 2 Corporation

United Media
VNU eMedia
Washingtonpost.Newsweek Interactive
Woodward Communications, Inc.
WPA Film Library

R

RESEARCH
ProQuest Dialog

T

TELECOMMUNICATIONS/SERVICE BUREAUS
Aditya Birla Minacs
Advanced Telecom Services, Inc. (Canada)
Advanced Telecom Services, Inc. (U.K.)
Agility
Arch Communications, Inc.
Assignment Desk
AT&T, Inc.
Cablevision Systems Corporation
Captured Digital, Inc.
Carl Waltzer Digital Services, Inc.
Cascade Technologies, Inc.
CenturyTel Interactive
CommuniTech Services Inc.

Conservit Corporation
C-T Innovations
DAC Systems
Dialogic Communications Corp.
Dialogic Corp.
Electronic Tele-Communications, Inc.
En Technology Corp.
First Data Voice Services
GREAT!
Innovative Systems Design, Inc.
Interactive Conferencing Network
Interalia Communications
MagnaCom, Inc.
MCI
MicroVoice Applications, Inc.
Motorola Mobility, LLC.
Motorola Solutions, Inc.
Movius Interactive Corporation
MPS Media Phone Service KG
NEC Corporation of America
Network Telephone Services
Newscom
NewsStand, Inc.
Nextcom
Nicollet Technologies
Nortel Networks, Inc.
PAGE Cooperative
Polycom, Inc.
Premiere Global Services, Inc.
Slingshot Technologies
Spanlink Communications
Sprint Nextel Corp.

SS8 Networks
Stok Software, Inc.
Syntellect, Inc.
Tadiran Telecom, Inc.
TALX Corp.
Telecompute Corp.
Teleperformance Interactive
TelSpan, Inc.
The Arbitron Co.
U.S. Netcom Corporation
USA 800, Inc.
Verizon Communications, Inc.
Voice Retrieval & Information Services, Inc.
Voice Technologies Group, Inc.
VoiceText Communications
Wessan Interactive
WideCom Group, Inc.

TRADE ASSOCIATION
Software & Information Industry Association
Wireless Communications Association
International

W

WEB SITE AUDITOR
Alliance for Audited Media/ImServices
Dreamscape Design, Inc.
Ken Petretti Productions, LLC
Pulse Research

Section V

Other Organizations and Industry Services

ADVERTISING/CIRCULATION NEWSPAPER PROMOTION SERVICES

A

ATLAS FLAGS, INC. — 2010 Weems Rd, Tucker, GA, 30084-5207, USA 770-938-0003; fax 770-493-4083; e-mail atlasflags@mindspring.com; web site www.atlasflags.com
President................................. Fary Rosenthal
Vice-President/Sales Mgr....Robert Rosenthal

C

CREATIVE MARKETING ASSOCIATES, INC. — 3100 Broadway Blvd, Ste 227, Kansas City, MO, 64111-2413, USA (816) 474-1400
Pres...Maynard Small

E

EYE CATCHER PRODUCTIONS — 2718 Wilshire Dr, Hollywood, CA, 90068-, USA 323-467-7011; e-mail frankpierson@gmail.com

F

FARAGO & ASSOCIATES — 29200 Northwestern Hwy, Ste 114, Southfield, MI, 48034-1055, USA (248)-436-4080; fax (248)-436-4058; e-mail info@faragoassoc.com; web site www.faragoassoc.com
President...................................Peter Farago
Dir. Finance ....Bruce MacDonald
Dir. Operations .... Scott Schofding
Production Mgr. Composing Graphics Michael Schofding

H

HOT OFF THE PRESS PROMOTIONS, INC. — 480 Luna Bella Ln, New Smyrna Beach, FL, 32168-5346, USA 386-423-8156; e-mail info@hot-promos.com; web site www.hotoffthepress.com
President.............................Harry Campbell
Vice-President....................Patricia Campbell

K

KNOWLEDGE UNLIMITED, INC — 2320 Pleasant View Rd, Middleton, WI, 53562-5521, USA (800) 356-2303; fax (800) 618-1570; e-mail csis@newscurrents.com; web site www.knowledgeunlimited.com
President................................ Judith Laitman

L

LYON ENTERPRISES — 4305 Cloud Dance, Santa Fe, NM, 87507-2591, USA (800) 243-1144; fax (505) 471-1665; e-mail ray@lyonenterprises.com; web site www.lyonenterprises.com
Pres....................................Ray Lyon

M

MARDEN-KANE, INC — 1055 Franklin Ave, Ste 300, Garden City, NY, 11530-2903, USA 516-365-3999; fax 516-365-5520; e-mail expert@mardenkane.com; web site www.mardenkane.com
CFO.................................... Alan Richter
Exec. Vice Pres. ....Leonard Bierman
Exec. Vice Pres. .... Paul Goldman
Exec. Vice Pres. .... Marc Wortsman
Vice-Pres............................Fae Savignano
Vice-Pres............................Jessie Auletti
Acct. Exec......................... Richard Facianella

N

NADBANK-NEWSPAPER AUDIENCE DATABANK — 890 Yonge St, Suite 200, Toronto, ON, M4W 3P4, Canada 416-923-3569; fax 416-923-4002; e-mail acrassweller@nadbank.com; web site www.nadbank.com
Exec. Dir. ....Anne Crassweller
Client Services Dir .... MeLing Johnston

NEWS AMERICA FSI — 2121 Avenue of the Stars, Los Angeles, CA, 90067-5010, USA 310-407-2500; fax 310-785-0862; web site www.newsamerica.comRobert Cole
Maggie Smith
Jessie Aversano

NEWS AMERICA FSI — 150 S 5th St, Ste 3400, Minneapolis, MN, 55402-4236, USA 612-395-7340; fax 612-376-0990; web site www.newsamerica.comRobert Cole
Jessie Aversano
Maggie Smith

NEWS AMERICA FSI — 3455 Peachtree Rd NE, Ste 950, Atlanta, GA, 30326-3258, USA 404-760-5950; fax 404-237-0705; web site www.newsamerica.comRobert Cole
Maggie Smith
Jessie Aversano

NEWS AMERICA FSI — 1185 Avenue of the Americas, Fl 27, New York, NY, 10036-2603, USA 212-782-8000; fax 212-575-5847; web site www.newsamerica.com
Sr. Vice President....................... Robert Cole
Office Mgr........................Maggie Smith
Sr. Vice President Marketing Jessie Aversano

NEWS AMERICA FSI — 20 Westport Rd, Wilton, CT, 06897-4549, USA 203-563-6600; fax (203) 563-6519 ; web site www.newsamerica.comMaggie Smith
Jessie Aversano
Robert Cole

NEWS AMERICA FSI — 303 E Wacker Dr, Fl 21, Chicago, IL, 60601-5212, USA 312-540-4100; fax (312) 616-3990; web site www.newsamerica.com
Sr. Vice- President marketingJessie Aversano
Sr. Vice President....................... Robert Cole
Office Mgr.................................Maggie Smith

NEWS AMERICA FSI — 2626 Howell St, Ste 960, Dallas, TX, 75204-0906, USA 214-981-0800; fax 214-953-3090; web site www.newsamerica.com
President................................Chris Mixson
Robert Cole
Maggie Smith
Jessie Aversano

S

SELECTIVE MARKETING — 1075 Nelsons Walk, Naples, FL, 34102-7834, USA 239-649-0013
President................................ John Mehaffey

SIMMONS MARKET RESEARCH BUREAU — 230 Park Ave S, New York, NY, 10003-1528, USA 212-598-4500; fax 212-598-5401; web site www.smrb.com
Chrmm/CEO ....William Engel
Pres/COO................................Chris Wilson
Exec. VP Simmons Local ....Craig Harper
Acct. Mgr...............................Jeremy Gabor
VP Integrated Mktg/Sales ....Gary Warech
Exec. VP Mktg/New Bus Dev ...Evan Goldfarb

V

VALASSIS COMMUNICATIONS, INC. — 6 Armstrong Rd, Ste 2, Shelton, CT, 06484-4722, USA 800-437-0479; web site www.valassis.comWilliam Hogg
Alan Schultz
Robert Recchia
Mary Broaddus
Richard Herpich

VALASSIS COMMUNICATIONS, INC. — 600 N Cockrell Hill Rd, Dallas, TX, 75211-1860, USA 214-353-6200; fax 612-338-3844; web site www.valassis.comAlan Schultz
Robert Recchia
Mary Broaddus
Richard Herpich
William Hogg

VALASSIS COMMUNICATIONS, INC. — 1575 Corporate Dr, Costa Mesa, CA, 92626-1467, USA 800-437-0479; web site www.valassis.comWilliam Hogg
Robert Recchia
Mary Broaddus
Richard Herpich
Alan Schultz

VALASSIS COMMUNICATIONS, INC. — 4216 Park Glen Rd, Saint Louis Park, MN, 55416-4758, USA 800-437-0479; e-mail pr@valassis.com; web site www.valassis.com
Pres/CEo....................................Alan Schultz
Vice-Pres/CFO.....................Robert Recchia
Exec. Asst............................. Mary Broaddus
Vice-Pres US Sales ....Richard Herpich
Vice-Pres MFG/Opns................William Hogg

W

WINGO, LLC — 12161 Ken Adams Way, Ste 110J, Wellington, FL, 33414-3194, USA (561) 379-2635; e-mail sat@amerimarketing.com; web site www.wingopromo.com; www.amerimarketing.com
Pres.....................................Scott Thompson

ASSOCIATIONS AND CLUBS - NATIONAL AND INTERNATIONAL

A

AAF COLLEGE CHAPTERS — 1101 Vermont Ave NW, Ste 500, Washington, DC, 20005-3521, USA (202) 898-0089; fax (202) 898-0159; e-mail education@aaf.org; aaf@aaf.org; web site www.aaf.org
Pres./CEO ....James Datri
Sr. Vice Pres........................Joanne Schecter
Note: Elections held in June

ACCREDITING COUNCIL ON EDUCATION IN JOURNALISM AND MASS COMMUNICATIONS — University of Kansas, 1435 Jayhawk Blvd., Lawrence, KS, 66045-0001, USA (785) 864-3973; fax (785)864-5225; e-mail sshaw@ku.edu; web site www.acejmc.org
Pres..................................... Peter Bhatia
Exec. Dir. ....Susanne Shaw
Vice President ....Paul Parsons

ADVERTISING MEDIA CREDIT EXECUTIVES ASSOCIATION INTERNATIONAL — PO Box 43514, Louisville, KY, 40253-0514, USA N/A; web site www.amcea.org
President................................Vickie Bolinger
Note: Elections held in May

AIGA, THE PROFESSIONAL ASSOCIATION FOR DESIGN — 233 Broadway, Rm 1740, New York, NY, 10279-1803, USA (212) 807-1990; e-mail general@aiga.org; web site www.aiga.org
Exec. Dir. .... Julie Anixter
CEO/CFO.............................. Hezron Gurley
Chief of Staff .... Amy Chapman
Note: AIGA is the professional association for design, a nonprofit organization dedicated to advancing design as a professional craft, strategic tool and vital cultural force. Founded in 1914, AIGA today serves more than 22,000 members through 66 chapters and 200 student groups across the United

States. AIGA stimulates thinking about design, demonstrates the value of design and empowers the success of designers at each stage of their careers.

ALLIANCE FOR AUDITED MEDIA (AAM) — 48 W Seegers Rd, Arlington Heights, IL, 60005-3900, USA (224) 366-6939; fax (224) 366-6949; web site www.auditedmedia.com
VP, Product Leadership................ Joe Hardin
EVP, Com. Dev. ....Brian Condon
Dir., Client Dev........................ Kevin Rehberg

AMERICAN ADVERTISING FEDERATION — 1101 Vermont Ave NW, Ste 500, Washington, DC, 20005-3521, USA (202) 898-0089; fax (202) 898-0159; e-mail aaf@aaf.org; web site www.aaf.org

AMERICAN ASSOCIATION OF INDEPENDENT NEWS DISTRIBUTORS — PO Box 70244, Washington, DC, 20024-0244, USA (202)678-8350; fax (202)889-9209; e-mail cnnorthrop@southwestdistribution.com; web site www.aaind.org
Pres... Cary Northrop

AMERICAN BUSINESS MEDIA — 201 E 42nd St Fl 7, Suite 2200, New York, NY, 10017-5704, USA (212) 661-6360; fax (212) 370-0736; e-mail info@abmmail.com; web site www.abmassociation.com
Note: Elections held in May

AMERICAN BUSINESS MEDIA AGRICULTURAL COUNCIL — 201 E 42nd St, Rm 2200, New York, NY, 10017-5714, USA (212) 661-6360; fax (212) 370-0736; e-mail info@abmmail.com; web site www.americanbusinessmedia.com
Exec. Dir.......................................Todd Hittle

AMERICAN FOREST & PAPER ASSOCIATION, INC. — 1111 19th St NW, Ste 800, Washington, DC, 20036-3652, USA (202) 463-2700; fax (202) 463-2040; e-mail info@afandpa.org; membership@afandpa.org; web site www.afandpa.org
Pres./CEO............................. Donna Harman

AMERICAN JEWISH PRESS ASSOCIATION — C/O Kca Association Management, 107 S. Southgate Dr., Washington, DC, 20036, USA 480-403-4602; fax 480-893-7775; e-mail info@aipa.org; web site www.ajpa.org
Pres......................................Elana Kahn-Oren
Assoc. Dir. ....Natasha Nadel
Exec. Dir. .... Toby Dershowitz
Note: Elections held in June

AMERICAN MARKETING ASSOCIATION — 311 S Wacker Dr, Ste 5800, Chicago, IL, 60606-6629, USA (312) 542-9000; fax (312) 542-9001; e-mail info@ama.org; web site www.marketingpower.com
Note: Elections held in spring

AMERICAN NEWS WOMEN'S CLUB, INC. — 1607 22nd St NW, Washington, DC, 20008-1921, USA (202) 332-6770; fax (202) 265-6092; e-mail anwclub@comcast.net; web site www.anwc.org
Pres.. Pam Ginsbach
Note: Elections held in May.

AMERICAN NEWSPAPER LAYOUT MANAGERS ASSOCIATION (ANLOMA) — 2442 Dr Martin Luther King Blvd, Fort Myers, FL, 33901-3904, USA (239) 335-0340; fax (239) 335-0205
Vice Pres.............................. Jonathan Tolton
Pres.................................. Robert Hammond
Note: Yearly Conference - March/April

AMERICAN PRESS INSTITUTE — 4401 Wilson Blvd, Ste 900, Arlington, VA, 22203-4195, USA (571) 366-1200; e-mail hello@pressinstitute.org; web site www.americanpressinstitute.org
Exec. Dir./Pres..................... Andrew B. Davis
Vice Pres., Programming/PersonnelCarol Ann Riordan
Dir., Tailored Solutions ....Elaine Clisham
Assoc. Dir. ....Mary Peskin
Deputy Director .... Jeff Sonderman
Editorial Coordinator ....Millie Tran
Executive Director ....Thomas Rosenstiel
Program Coordinator .... Kevin Loker
Tonda Rush
Content Strategy Program Manager.......... Liz Worthington
Senior Research Project Manager..........Jane Elizabeth

AMERICAN SOCIETY OF JOURNALISTS AND AUTHORS — 1501 Broadway, Ste 302, New York, NY, 10036-5501, USA (212) 997-0947; fax (212) 937-2315; e-mail staff@asja.org; web site www.asja.org
Exec. Dir. .... Alexandra Owens
Pres......................................Salley Shannon

AMERICAN SOCIETY OF NEWS EDITORS — 209 Reynolds Journalism Institute, Missouri School of Journalism, Columbia, MO, 65211-0001, USA (573)884-2405; fax (573)884-3824; e-mail asne@asne.org; web site www.asne.org
Exec. Dir. ....Teri Hayt
Comm. Mgr................................ Jiyoung Won
Sr. Info. Specialist.......... Megan Schumacher
Note: Elections held in June

ANGLO-AMERICAN PRESS ASSOCIATION OF PARIS — 67 Rue Halle, Paris, 75014, France; tel (33) 1 4545 7400; e-mail axelkrause@wanadoo.fr; web site www.aapafrance.com
Sec. Gen.................................... Axel Krause
British Co-Pres. ....Georgina Oliver
American Co-Pres................ Gregory Viscusi

ASIAN AMERICAN JOURNALISTS ASSOCIATION — 5 3rd St, Ste 1108, San Francisco, CA, 94103-3212, USA (415) 346-2051; fax (415) 346-6343; e-mail national@aaja.org; web site www.aaja.org
Contact.....................Annabelle Udo-O'Malley

ASSOCIATED PRESS MANAGING EDITORS ASSOCIATION — 450 W 33rd St, New York, NY, 10001-2603, USA (212) 621-1838; fax (212) 506-6102; e-mail apme@ap.org; web site www.apme.com
Gen. Mgr.................................Sally Jacobsen
Note: Elections held in Oct

ASSOCIATION FOR EDUCATION IN JOURNALISM AND MASS COMMUNICATION — 234 Outlet Pointe Blvd, Ste A, Columbia, SC, 29210-5667, USA (803) 798-0271; fax (803) 772-3509; e-mail aejmchq@aol.com; web site www.aejmc.org
Exec. Dir. ....Jennifer McGill
Note: Elections held in March; conventions in early August.

ASSOCIATION FOR WOMEN IN COMMUNICATIONS — 3337 Duke St, Alexandria, VA, 22314-5219, USA (703) 370-7436; fax (703) 342-4311; e-mail info@womcom.org; web site www.womcom.org
Exec. Dir. .... Pamela Valenzuela
Note: Group and individual memberships only from all communications disciplines

ASSOCIATION OF ALTERNATE POSTAL SYSTEMS — 1725 Oaks Way, Oklahoma City, OK, 73131-1220, USA (405) 478-0006; e-mail aaps@cox.net; web site www.aapsinc.org
Exec. Dir. ....John White
Pres..Michael Lynch
Note: Elections held at annual conference

ASSOCIATION OF ALTERNATIVE NEWSMEDIA — 1156 15th St NW, Ste 1005, Washington, DC, 20005-1722, USA 289-8484; fax (202) 289-2004; e-mail web@aan.org; web site www.altweeklies.com
Dir. of Meetings .... Debra Silvestrin
Int. Exec. Dir..........................Jason Zaragoza
Note: Annual convention held in summer.

ASSOCIATION OF AMERICAN EDITORIAL CARTOONISTS — 3899 N Front St, Harrisburg, PA, 17110-1583, USA (717) 703-3003; fax (717) 703-3008; e-mail info@pa-news.org; aaec@pa-news.org; web site www.editorialcartoonists.com
Manager...................................Teresa Shaak
Note: Elections held each year at the annual convention.

ASSOCIATION OF CANADIAN ADVERTISERS — 95 St Clair Ave. W., Ste. 1103, Toronto, ON, M4V 1N6, Canada (416) 964-3805; fax (416) 964-0771; web site www.acaweb.ca

ASSOCIATION OF FOOD JOURNALISTS, INC. — 7 Avenida Vista Grande, Ste B7 # 467, Santa Fe, NM, 87508-9207, USA 505-466-4742; e-mail caroldemasters@yahoo.com; web site www.afjonline.com
Exec. Dir. ....Carol DeMasters
Note: Election held in summer of even years

ASSOCIATION OF FREE COMMUNITY PAPERS — 7445 Morgan Rd, Ste 203, Liverpool, NY, 13090-3990, USA 877-203-2327; fax 781-859-7770; e-mail loren@afcp.org; web site www.afcp.org
Executive Director...................Loren Colburn
Administrative Assistant..............Alix Browne
Administrative Assistant......... Cassey Recore
Editor..................................... Dave Neuharth
Production Manager.............Barbara Holmes
Marketing Representative Wendy MacDonald

ASSOCIATION OF NATIONAL ADVERTISERS, INC. — 708 3rd Ave, 33rd Flr., New York, NY, 10017-4201, USA (212) 697-5950; fax (212) 687-7310; web site www.ana.net

ASSOCIATION OF NATIONAL ADVERTISERS, INC. — 2020 K St NW, Ste 660, Washington, DC, 20006-1900, USA (202) 296-1883; fax (202) 296-1430; web site www.ana.net

ASSOCIATION OF OPINION JOURNALISTS (FORMERLY THE NATIONAL CONFERENCE OF EDITORIAL WRITERS) — 801 3rd St S, Saint Petersburg, FL, 33701-4920, USA 727-821-9494; e-mail david.haynes@jrn.com; web site aoj.wildapricot.org

ASSOCIATION OF SCHOOLS OF JOURNALISM AND MASS COMMUNICATION — 234 Outlet Pointe Blvd, Ste A, Columbia, SC, 29210-5667, USA (803) 798-0271; fax (803) 772-3509; e-mail aejmchq@aol.com; web site www.asjmc.org
Exec. Dir. ....Jennifer McGill
Note: Elections held in April

B

BASEBALL WRITERS ASSOCIATION OF AMERICA — PO Box 610611, Bayside, NY, 11361-0611, USA (718) 767-2582; fax (718) 767-2583; e-mail bbwaa@aol.com; web site http://bbwaa.com
Secretary-Treasurer...............Jack O'Connell
Note: Elections held in Oct

BBM CANADA — 1500 Don Mills Rd., 3rd Fl., Toronto, ON, M3B 3L7, Canada (416) 445-9800; fax (416) 445-8644; e-mail info@bbm.ca; web site www.bbm.ca
Vice Pres., Western Servs. .... Catherine Kelly
Corp. Scrvs............................... Dorena Noce
Exec. Vice Pres./CFO..................Glen Shipp
Exec. Asst................................ Heather Gillis
Pres./CEO .... Jim Mac Leod
Vice Pres., Meter Servs. ....Randy Missen
Vice Pres., Quebec Servs..... Robert Langlois

BPA WORLDWIDE — 100 Beard Sawmill Rd, Fl 6, Shelton, CT, 06484-6156, USA (203) 447-2800; fax (203) 447-2900; web site www.bpaww.com
Chairman ....Carole A. Walker
Pres./CEO ....Glenn Hansen
Vice Pres., Commun. .... Karlene Lukeovitz
Sr. Vice Pres., Auditing.......... Richard Murphy
Sr. Vice Pres., Mktg. Servs...........Peter Black
Note: Elections held in May

CANADIAN PRESS, THE - TORONTO, ON — 36 King St. E., Toronto, ON, M5C 2L9, Canada (416) 364-0321; fax (416) 364-0207; e-mail info@thecanadianpress.com; web site www.thecanadianpress.com
Chrmn. .... John Honderich
News Editor..............................Ellen Huebert
Legislature Correspondent........... Keith Leslie
Pres.. Eric Morrison
CFO... David Ross
Chief, Ontario Servs............. Wendy McCann
Vice Pres., Broadcasting.............. Terry Scott
Vice Pres., French Servs.................Jean Roy
Dir., HR.......................................Paul Woods
Office Mgr............................... Sharon Hockin
Exec. Dir. ....Philipe Mercure
Note: Elections held in April

BUSINESS MARKETING ASSOCIATION — 1833 Centre Point Cir, Ste 123, Naperville, IL, 60563-4848, USA (630) 544-5054; fax (630) 544-5055; e-mail info@marketing.org; web site www.marketing.org
Membership Mgr. .... Kelly Staley
Exec. Dir. ....Patrick Farrey
Note: Elections held in June

C

CANADIAN BUSINESS PRESS — 2100 Banbury Cresent, Oakville, ON, L6H 5P6, Canada 905-844-6822; e-mail torrance@cbp.ca; web site www.cbp.ca
Executive Director.................... Trish Torrance

CANADIAN CIRCULATIONS AUDIT BOARD (CCAB, INC.) — 1 Concorde Gate Suite 800, SUITE 800, Toronto, ON, M3C 3N6, Canada (416) 487-2418; fax (416) 487-6405; e-mail info@bpaww.com; web site www.bpaww.com
Mktg. Mgr...Neil Ta
Note: Elections held in April

CANADIAN NEWS MEDIA ASSOCITION — 37 Front Street East Suite 200, Toronto, ON, M5E 1B3, Canada; tel (1) 416 (416) 923-3567; fax (416) 923-7206; e-mail info@newsmediacanada.ca; web site www.https://nmc-mic.ca
Chairman ....Bob Cox
Vice-Chairmain .... Craig Bernard
Note: News Media Canada was formed by the merger of the Canadian Newspaper Association and the Canadian Community Newspapers Association in 2017

CANADIAN PRINTING INK MANUFACTURERS ASSOCIATION — 52 Palmer Rd., Grimby, ON, L3M 5L4, Canada (905) 309-5883; fax (905) 309-5838; e-mail cpima@sympatico.ca; web site www.cpima.org
Exec. Dir./Sec./Treasurer........ Dorothea Nace
Pres..Neil Marshall
Vice Pres................................. Vivy da Costa
Note: Elections held in Aug. for a two year term

CATHOLIC PRESS ASSOCIATION — 205 W Monroe St, Ste 470, Chicago, IL, 60606-5011, USA (312) 380-6789; fax (312) 361-0256; e-mail cathjourn@catholicpress.org; web site www.catholicpress.org
  Exec. Dir................Timothy Walter
  Note: Elections held in Feb

COLLEGE MEDIA ASSOCIATION — 355 Lexington Ave, Fl 15, New York, NY, 10017-6603, USA 212-297-2195; e-mail info@collegemedia.org; web site www.collegemedia.org
  Executive Director.................Meredith Taylor
  Note: Elections held in Oct every two years.

COUNCIL FOR ADVANCEMENT AND SUPPORT OF EDUCATION — 1307 New York Ave NW, Ste 1000, Washington, DC, 20005-4726, USA (202) 328-2273; fax (202) 387-4973; e-mail memberservicecenter@case.org; web site www.case.org
  Exec. Dir...................Ben Patrusky
  Pres........................Cristine Russell
  Admin....................Diane McGurgan
  Pres.......................John Lippincott
  Note: Elections held in July.

COUNCIL FOR THE ADVANCEMENT OF SCIENCE WRITING, INC. — PO Box 910, Hedgesville, WV, 25427-0910, USA (304) 754-6786; e-mail info@casw.org; web site www.casw.org
  Admin.....................Diane McGurgan
  Pres.......................Alan Boyle
  Exec. Dir.................Rosalind Reid
  Note: Elections held in April. Not a membership organization.

D

DIGITAL CONTENT NEXT — 1350 Broadway, Rm 606, New York, NY, 10018-7205, USA (646) 473-1000; fax (646) 473-0200; e-mail info@online-publishers.org; web site www.online-publishers.org

DOG WRITERS' ASSOCIATION OF AMERICA — 173 Union Rd, Coatesville, PA, 19320-1326, USA (610) 384-2436; fax (610) 384-2471; e-mail dwaa@dwaa.org; web site www.dwaa.org
  Sec.........................Pat Santi
  Pres.......................Dr. Carmen Battaglia
  Pres.......................Carmen Battaglia
  Note: Elections held in Feb. Writers contest closes Sept. 1 each year

E

EPICOMM — 1800 Diagonal Rd, Ste 320, Alexandria, VA, 22314-2862, USA 703-836-9200; fax 703-548-8204; e-mail info@epicomm.org; web site www.epicomm.org
  President & CEO.................J. Ken Garner

EUROPEAN NEWSPAPER PUBLISHERS' ASSOCIATION — Square du Bastion 1A, Bte 3, 1050 Bruxelles, Belgium; tel (32) 2 551 0190; fax 551 0199; e-mail enpa@enpa.be; web site www.enpa.be
  Dir.........................Valtteri Niiranen
  Office Mgr.................Viviane Garceau
  Note: The ENPA is an association of European daily newspaper publishers organizations

F

FOREIGN PRESS ASSOCIATION — 333 E 46th St, Apt 1K, New York, NY, 10017-7426,

USA (212) 370-1054; fax (212) 370-1058; e-mail fpanewyork@aol.com
  Member....................Agnes Niemetz
  Pres.......................Alan Capper
  Vice Pres..................David Michaels
  Asst. Gen. Sec.............Hadar Harel
  Treasurer..................Jan Latus
  Asst. Treasurer............Roberto Socas
  Note: Elections held in Dec

FREEDOM FORUM — 555 Pennsylvania Ave NW, Washington, DC, 20001-2114, USA (202) 292-6100; e-mail news@freedomforum.org; info@newseum.org; web site www.freedomforum.org
  Chrmn./CEO................Charles L. Overby
  Sr. Vice Pres., Int'l Programs.........Chris Wells
  Vice Pres., Opns..............James Thompson
  Sr. Vice Pres., Devel.............Mary Kay Blake
  Sr. Vice Pres., Finance........Nicole Mandeville
  Vice Pres., Mktg............Susan Bennett
  Note: Not a membership organization

G

GRAPHIC COMMUNICATIONS CONFERENCE/INTERNATIONAL BROTHERHOOD OF TEAMSTERS — 25 Louisiana Ave NW, Washington, DC, 20001-2130, USA (202) 508-6800; fax (202) 508-6661; web site www.gciu.org
  Secretary-Treasurer/Vice President.....Robert Lacey
  Note: Elections held quadrennially.

GRAPHIC COMMUNICATIONS COUNCIL — 1899 Preston White Dr, Reston, VA, 20191-5458, USA (703) 264-7200; fax (703) 620-0994; e-mail npes@npes.org; web site www.npes.org
  Administrator..................Carol J. Hurlburt
  Asst. Dir., Membership......Carol Lee Hawkins

GRAVURE ASSOCIATION OF AMERICA — 8281 Pine Lake Rd, Denver, NC, 28037-8812, USA (201) 523-6042; fax (201) 523-6048; e-mail gaa@gaa.org; web site www.gaa.org
  Pres./CEO...................Bill Martin
  Exec. Dir..................Bernadette Carlson
  Dir.........................Michelle Jones Aronowitz
  Ed..........................Roger Ynosroza
  Note: Elections held in April

H

HEBDOS QUEBEC — 2550 Daniel-Johnson,, Bureau 345, Laval, QC, H7T 2L1, Canada 514 (514) 861-2088; fax (514) 861-1966; e-mail communications@hebdos.com; web site hebdos.com
  Exec. Dir..................Gilber Paquette

I

IDEALLIANCE — 1600 Duke St, Ste 420, Alexandria, VA, 22314-3421, USA (703)837-1070; e-mail http://idealliance.org; web site www.ipa.org
  Exec. Asst..................Donna McDevitt
  Pres.......................Steven Bonoff
  Note: Elections held in Oct.

INDEPENDENT FREE PAPERS OF AMERICA — 107 Hemlock Dr, Rio Grande, NJ, 08242-1731, USA (609) 408-8000; fax (609) 889-0141; web site www.ifpa.com
  Exec. Dir..................Gary Rudy
  Note: Elections held in Sept

INTER AMERICAN PRESS ASSOCIATION — 1801 SW 3rd Ave, Fl 7, Miami, FL, 33129-1500, USA (305) 634-2465; fax (305)635-2272;

e-mail info@sipiapa.org; web site www.sipiapa.org
  Librarian..................Alfonso Juarez
  Exec. Dir..................Julio Munoz
  Editor.....................Horacio Ruiz
  Note: Elections held in Nov

INTERMARKET AGENCY NETWORK — 5307 S 92nd St, Hales Corners, WI, 53130-1681, USA (414) 425-8800; fax (414) 425-0021; web site www.intermarketnetwork.com
  Exec. Dir..................Bill Eisner

INTERNATIONAL ADVERTISING ASSOCIATION, INC. — 747 3rd Ave, Fl 2, New York, NY, 10017-2878, USA 646-722-2612; fax 646 722 2501; e-mail iaa@iaaglobal.org; membership@iaaglobal.org; web site www.iaaglobal.org
  Mgr. IT.....................Karl Kam
  Exec. Dir..................Michael Lee
  Note: Elections held every two years at the IAA World-Advertising Congress. The IAA is a global partnership of advertisers, agencies, and media. The Association has 3,700 members in 95 countries, 105 corporate members, 65 organizational members and 61 chapters

INTERNATIONAL ASSOCIATION OF BUSINESS COMMUNICATORS (IABC) — 601 Montgomery St, Ste 1900, San Francisco, CA, 94111-2690, USA (415) 544-4700; fax (415) 544-4747; e-mail service_centre@iabc.com; web site www.iabc.com
  Pres./CEO..................Julie Freeman
  Note: Elections held at international conference

INTERNATIONAL ASSOCIATION OF SPORTS NEWSPAPERS (IASN) — 7 rue Geoffroy Saint Hilaire, Paris, 75005, France; tel (33) 1 47 42 85 29; fax 47 42 49 48; e-mail rcuccoli@press-iasn.org; web site www.press-iasn.org
  Sec. Gen...................Rosarita Cuccoli

INTERNATIONAL CENTER FOR JOURNALISTS — 1616 H St NW, Fl 3, Washington, DC, 20006-4903, USA (202) 737-3700; fax (202) 737-0530; e-mail editor@icfj.org; web site www.icfj.org
  Pres.......................Joyce Barnathan
  Vice Pres., Finance.....................Nancy Frye
  Vice Pres., Programs...............Patrick Butler
  Vice Pres., Development..........Vjollca Shtylla
  Vice Pres., New Initiatives....Sharon Moshavi
  Note: International Center for Journalists is not a membership organization.

INTERNATIONAL LABOR COMMUNICATIONS ASSOCIATION AFL/CIO/CLC — 815 16th St NW, Washington, DC, 20006-4101, USA (202) 637-5068; fax (202) 637-5069; e-mail ilca@aflcio.org; web site www.ilcaonline.org
  Pres.......................Steve Stallone
  Note: Elections held biennially.

INTERNATIONAL NEWSPAPER MARKETING ASSOCIATION, INC. — PO Box 740186, Dallas, TX, 75374-0186, USA (214) 373-9111; fax (214) 373-9112; e-mail inma@inma.org; web site www.inma.org
  Exec. Dir..................Earl J. Wilkinson
  Note: Elections held in May

INTERNATIONAL PRESS CLUB OF CHICAGO (IPCC) — PO Box 2498, Chicago, IL, 60690-2498, USA; tel (312-834-7728) Chicago 312-834-7228; e-mail info@ipcc.org; web site www.internationalpressclubofchicago.org
  President..................Wayne Toberman
  Note: Lunch meetings every Thursday monthly at Union League Club Chicago

INTERNATIONAL PRESS INSTITUTE — Spiegelgasse 2, Vienna, A-1010, Austria; tel (43) 1 512 9011; fax 512 9014; e-mail ipi@freemedia.at; web site www.freemedia.at
  Dir.........................David Dadge
  Note: Elections held annually on a rotation basis

INTERNATIONAL SOCIETY OF WEEKLY NEWSPAPER EDITORS — 3950 Newman Rd, Joplin, MO, 64801-1512, USA (417) 625-9736; fax (417) 659-4445; e-mail stebbins-c@mssu.edu; web site www.iswne.org
  Exec. Dir..................Chad Stebbins
  Note: Elections held in June or July at the annual conference.

INVESTIGATIVE REPORTERS AND EDITORS (IRE) — 141 Neff Annex, Columbia, MO, 65211-0001, USA (573) 882-2042; fax (573) 882-5431; e-mail info@ire.org; web site www.ire.org
  Exec. Dir..................Mark Horvit
  Note: Elections held in June

J

JAPAN NEWSPAPER PUBLISHERS & EDITORS ASSOCIATION — Nippon Press Center Bldg., 2-2-1 Uchisaiwai-cho, Chiyoda-ku, Tokyo, 100-8543, Japan; tel (+81) 3-3591-3462; fax -9743; e-mail editor@pressnet.or.jp; web site www.pressnet.or.jp/english/index.htm
  North American Rep.....................Ryuta Araki

K

KAPPA ALPHA MU HONORARY SOCIETY IN PHOTO JOURNALISM — 316F Lee Hills Hall, Columbia, MO, 65211-1370, USA 573-882-4821; fax 573-884-5400; e-mail kratzerb@missouri.edu; web site www.photojournalism.missouri.edu
  Chrmn......................David Rees
  Director of Photography, Assistant Professor . Brian Kratzer
  Note: An affiliate of the National Press Photographers Association. Elections held in the fall.

KAPPA TAU ALPHA NATIONAL HONOR SOCIETY FOR JOURNALISM & MASS COMMUNICATION — University of Missouri, 76 Gannett Hall, Columbia, MO, 65211-0001, USA (573) 882-7685; fax (573) 884-1720; e-mail umcjourkta@missouri.edu; web site www.kappataualpha.org
  P, Kent State University....................Jeff Fruit
  VP, Arkansas State.......................Holly Hunt
  Exec. Dir./Treasurer.................Beverly Horvit
  Note: Elections held every two years

L

LEAGUE OF ADVERTISING AGENCIES, INC. — 65 Reade St, Apt 3A, New York, NY, 10007-1841, USA (212) 528-0364; fax (212) 766-1181; web site www.adagencies.org
  Exec. Dir..................Deana Boles
  Pres.......................Lori Fabisiak
  Treasurer..................Mark Levit
  Sec........................Mindy Gale
  Vice Pres..................Richard Harrow
  Note: Elections held in May

LOCAL MEDIA ASSOCIATION — PO Box 450, Lake City, MI, 49651-0450, USA (888) 486-2466; fax (888) 317-0856; e-mail hq@localmedia.org; web site www.localmedia.org
  Vice President - Director of R & D Services Al Cupo
  President..................Nancy Lane
  Sales and Marketing Director........Conti Peter

Sales & Marketing Manager
.... Lindsey Estes
Classified Avenue Director of Sales... Deanna Lewis
Marketing Technology Manager ... Abdul Khan
Local Media Today Editor .... Deb Shaw
Accounting & Finance DirectorJanice Norman
Director of Broadcast Services ...Jack Zavoral
Note: Elections held in the fall

M

MARKETING ADVERTISING GLOBAL NETWORK — 1017 Perry Hwy, Ste 5, Pittsburgh, PA, 15237-2173, USA (412) 366-6850; fax (412) 366-6840; e-mail cheri@magnetglobal.org; web site www.magnetglobal.org
Executive Director .... Cheri Gmiter
Note: Elections held in Oct

MEDIA ALLIANCE — 2830 20th St Ste 102, Pacific Felt Factory, San Francisco, CA, 94110-2825, USA; tel (01) 415 746-9475; fax N/A; e-mail tracy@media-alliance.org; web site www.media-alliance.org
Exec. Dir. ....Tracy Rosenberg

MEDIA FINANCIAL MANAGEMENT ASSOCIATION — 550 W Frontage Rd, Ste 3600, Northfield, IL, 60093-1243, USA 847-716-7000; fax 847-716-7004; e-mail info@mediafinance.org; web site www.mediafinance.org
President & CEO........................Mary Collins
Director of Operations.................Jamie Smith

MEDIA HUMAN RESOURCES ASSOCIATION — 1800 Duke St, Alexandria, VA, 22314-3494, USA (800) 283-7476; fax (703) 535-6490; e-mail shrm@shrm.org; web site www.shrm.org
Pres.......................................Laurence O'Neil
Note: Elections held in June

N

NATIONAL ASSOCIATION OF BLACK JOURNALISTS — 1100 Knight Hall, Suite 3100, College Park, MD, 20742-0001, USA (301) 405-0248; fax (301) 314-1714; e-mail nabj@nabj.org; web site www.nabj.org
Exec. Dir. ....Karen Wynn Freeman
Pres..Kathy Times
Note: Elections held every two years

NATIONAL ASSOCIATION OF BROADCASTERS — 1771 N St NW, Washington, DC, 20036-2800, USA (202) 429-5300; fax (202) 429-4199; e-mail nab@nab.org; web site www.nab.org
Joint Board Chrmn. .... Bruce T. Reese
COO/CFO ....Janet McGregor
Note: Elections held once in two years.

NATIONAL ASSOCIATION OF CREDIT MANAGEMENT — 8840 Columbia 100 Pkwy, Columbia, MD, 21045-2100, USA (410) 740-5560; fax (410) 740-5574; e-mail info@nacm.org; web site www.nacm.org
Dir., Commun. ....Caroline Zimmerman
Treasurer...........................James E. Vanghel
Pres.................................Robin D. Schauseil
Note: Elections held in May

NATIONAL ASSOCIATION OF HISPANIC JOURNALISTS — 1050 Connecticut Ave NW, Fl 10, Washington, DC, 20036-5334, USA (202) 662-7145; fax (202) 662-7144; e-mail nahj@nahj.org; web site www.nahj.org
Interim Executive Director ....Anna M. Lopez Buck

NATIONAL ASSOCIATION OF HISPANIC PUBLICATIONS — 529 14th St NW, Ste 1126, Washington, DC, 20045-2120, USA (202) 662-7250; e-mail directory@nahp.org; web site www.nahp.org
Exec. Dir. .... Kerry Stackpole
Note: Elections held every two years

NATIONAL ASSOCIATION OF REAL ESTATE EDITORS (NAREE) — 1003 NW 6th Ter, Boca Raton, FL, 33486-3455, USA (561) 391-3599; fax (561) 391-0099; e-mail madkimba@aol.com; web site www.naree.org
Executive Director .... Mary Doyle-Kimball
Note: 63rd Annual Journalism Competition - Entry Deadline March 1, 2013 for work published in 2012. Platinum, Gold, Silver and Bronze Awards, plus awards for Best Freelance Collection and Best Young Journalist. 25 categories for journalists specializing in residential and commercial real estate, mortgage finance, green building, home design and urban planning. New category this year: "Best Breaking News Report."

NATIONAL ASSOCIATION OF REAL ESTATE PUBLISHERS — PO Box 5292, Florence, SC, 29502-5292, USA N/A; e-mail narep2014@gmail.com; web site www.narep.org
Secretary/Treasurer .... Sheila Stepp
Note: Elections held in May

NATIONAL ASSOCIATION OF SCIENCE WRITERS — PO Box 7905, Berkeley, CA, 94707-0905, USA 510-647-9500; e-mail director@nasw.org; web site www.nasw.org

NATIONAL CARTOONISTS SOCIETY — 341 N Maitland Ave, Ste 130, Maitland, FL, 32751-4761, USA (407) 647-8839; fax (407) 629-2502; e-mail crowsegal@crowsegal.com; web site www.reuben.org
Pres...Jeff Keane
Note: Elections held annually

NATIONAL FEDERATION OF PRESS WOMEN — 200 Little Falls St, Ste 405, Falls Church, VA, 22046-4302, USA 800-780-2715; fax (703) 237-9808; e-mail presswomen@aol.com; web site www.nfpw.org
Executive Director ....Carol Pierce
Note: Elections held odd years in June

NATIONAL LESBIAN AND GAY JOURNALISTS ASSOCIATION — 2120 L St NW, Ste 850, Washington, DC, 20037-1550, USA (202) 588-9888; fax (202) 588-1818; e-mail info@nlgja.org; web site www.nlgja.org
Pres......................................David Barrie
Note: Elections held annually

NATIONAL NEWSPAPER ASSOCIATION — 900 Community Drive, Springfield, IL, 62703, USA (217)241-1400; fax (217) 241-1301; e-mail lynne@nna.org; web site www.nna.org
Comm. Dir. .... Stan Schwartz
Chief Operating Officer .... Lynne Lance
CEO .... Sam Fisher
Note: Officer elections held in Sept/Oct during Annual Convention; annual Leadership Conference in March; annual Better Newspaper Contest entry deadline Spring

NATIONAL NEWSPAPER PUBLISHERS ASSOCIATION BLACK PRESS OF AMERICA — 1816 12th St NW, Washington, DC, 20009-4422, USA 202-588-8764; fax 202-588-8960; e-mail nnpadc@nnpa.org; web site www.nnpa.org
Interim Exec. Ed. .... Hazel Trice Edney
Note: Elections held every two years in June.

NATIONAL PAPER TRADE ASSOCIATION, INC. — 330 N Wabash Ave, Ste 2000, Chicago, IL, 60611-7621, USA (312) 321-4092;

fax (312) 673-6736; e-mail npta@gonpta.com; web site www.gonpta.com
Pres...Newell Holt
Note: Elections held in Oct

NATIONAL PRESS CLUB — 529 14th St NW, Washington, DC, 20045-1217, USA (202) 662-7500; fax (202) 662-7569; web site www.press.org
Exec. Dir. .... William McCarren
Note: Elections held in Nov

NATIONAL PRESS FOUNDATION — 1211 Connecticut Ave NW, Ste 310, Washington, DC, 20036-2709, USA (202) 663-7280; fax (202) 530-2855; e-mail npf@nationalpress.org; web site www.nationalpress.org
President and COO....................Bob Meyers

NATIONAL PRESS PHOTOGRAPHERS ASSOCIATION, INC. — 3200 Croasdaile Dr, Ste 306, Durham, NC, 27705-2588, USA (919) 383-7246; fax (919) 383-7261; e-mail info@nppa.org; web site www.nppa.org
Exec. Dir. ....Jim Straight
Membership Dir. .... Mindy Hutchison
Note: Elections held in June

NATIONAL RETAIL FEDERATION — 325 7th St Nw, Liberty Pl, Ste 1100, Washington, DC, 20004, USA (202) 783-7971; fax (202) 737-2849; web site www.nrf.com
CFO.................................... Carleen C. Kohut
Pres......................................Tracy Mullin
Note: Elections held in Jan

NATIONAL SCHOLASTIC PRESS ASSOCIATION — 2221 University Ave SE, Ste 121, Minneapolis, MN, 55414-3074, USA (612) 625-8335; fax 612-605-0072; e-mail info@studentpress.org; web site www.studentpress.org
Exec. Dir. .... Logan Aimone

NATIONAL WRITERS ASSOCIATION — 10940 S Parker Rd, Ste 508, Parker, CO, 80134-7440, USA (303) 841-0246; e-mail natlwritersassn@hotmail.com; web site www.nationalwriters.com
Exec. Dir. ....Sandy Whelchel

NATIVE AMERICAN JOURNALISTS ASSOCIATION — 395 W Lindsey St, Norman, OK, 73019-4201, USA (405) 325-1649; fax (405) 325-6945; e-mail info@naja.com; web site www.naja.com
Pres.................................... Cristina Azocar
Interim. Dir. .... Jeff Harjo
Note: Elections held in August

NEW YORK MEDIA CREDIT GROUP — 1100 Main St, Buffalo, NY, 14209-2308, USA 716-887-9547; fax 716-878-0479; e-mail robert.gagliardi@abc-amega.com
Regional Account Manager.. Robert Gagliardi
Pres...Nina Link
Dir................................. Vaughn P. Benjamin
Note: Elections held in March

NEWS MEDIA ALLIANCE — 4401 Wilson Blvd, Ste 900, Arlington, VA, 22203-4195, USA (571) 366-1000; fax (571) 366-1195; e-mail sheila.owens@naa.org; web site www.naa.org
Pres. & CEO.........................David Chavern
CFO.....................................Robert Walden
VP of HRO ....Sarah Burkman
SVP Bus. Dev. .... Rich Schiekofer
VP of Audience Dev...................John Murray
Comm. Mgr.........................Lindsey Loving
SVP of Public Policy......................Paul Boyle
VP of Public Policy .... Danielle Coffey
VP, Research & Industry Analysis............. Jim Conaghan
Public Policy Mgr................ Kristina Zaumseil
Note: Elections held in April/May

NEWS MEDIA CANADA — 37 Front Street East Suite 200, Toronto, ON, M5E 1B3, Canada (416) 923-3567; fax (416) 923-7206; e-mail info@newspaperscanada.ca; web site www.ccna.ca
Pres.......................................John Hinds

NEWSPAPER ASSOCIATION MANAGERS, INC. — 32 Dunham Rd, Beverly, MA, 01915-1844, USA 978-338-2555; e-mail mlpiper52@cmcast.net; web site www.nammanagers.com
Exec. Dir. ....Morley Piper
Finance Officer........................ Susan Daigle
Note: Elections held in Aug

NEWSPAPER CANADA — 890 Yonge Street Ste 200, Toronto, ON, M4W 3P4, Canada (416) 923-3567; fax (416) 923-7206; e-mail info@newspapercanada,ca; web site www.newspapercanada.ca

NORTH AMERICAN AGRICULTURAL JOURNALISTS — 6434 Hurta Ln, Bryan, TX, 77808-9283, USA (979) 845-2872; fax (979) 862-1202; e-mail ka-phillips@tamu.edu; web site www.naaj.net
Exec. Sec./Treasurer............ Kathleen Phillips
Note: Elections held in April

NORTH AMERICAN MATURE PUBLISHERS ASSOCIATION — 1140 Jupiter Rd, Camdenton, MO, 65020-4403, USA (877) 466-2672; fax (573) 873-9993; e-mail kzarky@maturepublishers.com; web site www.maturepublishers.com
Exec. Dir. ....Karen Zarky
Note: Election held in Nov

NPES — 1899 Preston White Dr, Reston, VA, 20191-5458, USA (703) 264-7200; fax (703) 620-0994; e-mail npes@npes.org; web site www.npes.org
Dir., Commun. .... Judy Durham
Pres.......................................Ralph Nappi
Chrmn. ....Tom Saggiomo
Note: NPES is the association for suppliers of printing, publishing and converting technologies. Elections held at fall meeting

O

ORGANIZATION OF NEWS OMBUDSMEN — 6336 Hawthorn Lane, Vancouver, BC, V6T 2J6, Canada (604) 353-6228; e-mail klapointe@newsombudsmen.org; web site www.newsombudsmen.org
Executive Director .... Kirk LaPointe

OUTDOOR ADVERTISING ASSOCIATION OF AMERICA (OAAA) — 1850 M St NW, Ste 1040, Washington, DC, 20036-5821, USA (202) 833-5566; fax (202) 833-1522; e-mail info@oaaa.org; web site www.oaaa.org
Pres. & CEO......................... Nancy Fletcher

OUTDOOR WRITERS ASSOCIATION OF AMERICA, INC. — 615 Oak St, Ste 201, Missoula, MT, 59801-2469, USA (406) 728-7434; fax (406) 728-7445; e-mail info@owaa.org; web site www.owaa.org
Executive Director ....Brandon Shuler
Note: Elections held in Spring

OVERSEAS PRESS CLUB OF AMERICA — 40 West 45 Street, New York, NY, 10036, USA (212) 626-9220; fax (212) 626-9210; e-mail info@opcofamerica.org; web site www.opcofamerica.org
Exec. Dir. .... Patricia Kranz
Note: Elections held in late summer

P

PRINTING INDUSTRIES OF AMERICA — 200 Deer Run Rd, Sewickley, PA, 15143-2324, USA (412) 741-6860; fax (412) 741-2311; e-mail printing@printing.org; web site www. printing.org
Mktg. Mgr...................................... Lisa Erdner
VP .... Gary Jones

PRINTING, PUBLISHING & MEDIA WORKERS SECTOR-CWA — 501 3rd St NW, Ste 950, Washington, DC, 20001-2760, USA (202) 434-1106; fax (202) 434-1482; e-mail bshippe@cwa-union.org; web site www.cwa-union.org
Pres... Larry Cohen
Note: Elections to be held at CWA convention in August 2008.

PROFESSIONAL FOOTBALL WRITERS OF AMERICA (PFWA) — 11345 Frontage Ave, Maryland Heights, MO, 63043-5000, USA (314) 298-2681; e-mail hbalzer@aol.com; web site www.pfwa.org
Secretary................................ Howard Balzer
Note: Elections held in Jan

PROMOTION MARKETING ASSOCIATION, INC. — 650 1st Ave, Ste 2-SW, New York, NY, 10016-3240, USA (212) 420-1100; fax (212) 533-7622; e-mail pma@pmalink.org; web site www.pmalink.org
Note: Elections held in June

PROMOTIONAL PRODUCTS ASSOCIATION INTERNATIONAL — 3125 Skyway Cir N, Irving, TX, 75038-3526, USA 972-252-0404; fax (972) 258-3004; e-mail pr@ppai.org; web site www.ppai.org
Vice Pres., Mktg./Commun. ...Paul Bellantone
Pres./CEO ....Steve Slagle

PUBLIC RELATIONS SOCIETY OF AMERICA, INC. — 33 Maiden Ln, Fl 11, New York, NY, 10038-5149, USA (212) 460-1400; (212) 995-0757; e-mail hq@prsa.org; web site www.prsa.org
Pres..............................Willam Murray
Note: Elections held in October

Q

QUILL AND SCROLL SOCIETY — 100 Adler Journalism Bldg Ste W111, Univ. of Iowa School of Journalism and Mass Comm., Iowa City, IA, 52242-2004, USA (319) 335-3457; fax (319) 335-3989; e-mail quill-scroll@uiowa.edu; web site www.uiowa.edu

R

RADIO TELEVISION DIGITAL NEWS ASSOCIATION — 529 14th St NW, Ste 1240, Washington, DC, 20045-2520, USA (770) 622-7011; fax (202) 223-4007; e-mail mikec@rtdna.org; web site www.rtdna.org
Exec. Dir. ....Mike Cavender
Awards, Membership and Programs Manager Katie Switchenko
Digital, Communications and Marketing Manager................................... Derrick Hinds
Manager of Membership and Programs Karen Hansen
Meetings and Events Manager . Noukla Ruble

REGIONAL REPORTERS ASSOCIATION — 1575 Eye St NW Suite 350, Washington, DC,

20008, USA (202) 408-2705; e-mail president@ rra.org; web site www.rra.org
Sec. .... Adrianne Flynn
Pres. ....Suzanne Struglinski

RELIGION NEWS ASSOCIATION — University of Missouri, 30 Neff Annex, Columbia, MO, 65211-0001, USA (740)263-7875; e-mail McCallen@RNA.org; web site www.RNA.org
Chief Ops. Officer................ Tiffany McCallen
Business Mgr............................. Amy Schiska

REPORTERS COMMITTEE FOR FREEDOM OF THE PRESS — 1101 Wilson Blvd, Ste 1100, Arlington, VA, 22209-2275, USA (703) 807-2100; fax (703) 807-2109; e-mail rcfp@rcfp.org; web site www.rcfp.org
Exec. Committee....................Dahlia Lithwick
Exec. Dir. .... Lucy A. Dalglish
Exec. Committee .... Neil Lewis
Exec. Committee........................ Tony Mauro

RTDNA - CANADA (RADIO TELEVISION DIGITAL NEWS ASSOCIATION) — 2800 - 14th Ave., Ste. 210, Markham, ON, L3R 0E4, Canada (416) 756 2213; fax (416) 491-1670; e-mail sherry@associationconcepts.ca; info@ rtdnacanada.com; web site www.rtdnacanada. com
Operations Manager ....Sherry Denesha
Note: Elections held in June

S

SALES AND MARKETING EXECUTIVES INTERNATIONAL — PO Box 1390, Sumas, WA, 98295-1390, USA (312) 893-0751; fax (604) 855-0165; e-mail willis.turner@smei.org; web site www.smei.org
Pres./CEO .... Willis Turner
Note: Elections held on a rolling basis

SOCIETY FOR FEATURES JOURNALISM — 1100 Knight Hall, College Park, MD, 20742-0001, USA (301) 314-2631; fax (301) 314-9166; e-mail aasfe@jmail.umd.edu; web site www.aasfe.org
Pres...................................... Denise Joyce
Exec. Dir. .... Kalyani Chadda
Note: Elections held in Sept./Oct

SOCIETY FOR NEWS DESIGN, INC. — 424 E Central Blvd, Ste 406, Orlando, FL, 32801-1923, USA (407) 420-7748; fax (407) 420-7697; e-mail snd@snd.org; web site www.snd.org
Exec. Dir. .... Stephen Komives
Note: Annual competition deadline is mid-January. Officer elections held in fall prior to annual workshop exhibition.

SOCIETY OF AMERICAN BUSINESS EDITORS AND WRITERS, INC. — 555 N Central Ave, Ste 302, Phoenix, AZ, 85004-1248, USA (602) 496-7862; fax (602) 496-7041; e-mail sabew@sabew.org; web site www.sabew.org
Note: Elections held in April

SOCIETY OF AMERICAN TRAVEL WRITERS, INC. — 7044 S 13th St, Oak Creek, WI, 53154-1429, USA (414) 908-4949; fax (414) 768-8001; e-mail satw@satw.org; web site www.satw.org
Exec. Dir. ....Nancy Short

SOCIETY OF ENVIRONMENTAL JOURNALISTS (SEJ) — PO Box 2492, Suite 301, Jenkintown, PA, 19046-8492, USA (215) 884-8174; fax (215) 884-8175; e-mail sej@sej.org; web site www.sej.org
Exec. Dir. .... Beth Parke

Note: Board elections held each fall

SOCIETY OF PROFESSIONAL JOURNALISTS — 3909 N Meridian St, Ste 200, Indianapolis, IN, 46208-4011, USA (317) 927-8000; fax (317) 920-4789; e-mail spj@spj.org; web site www.spj.org
Interim Executive Director.......... Tara Puckey

SOCIETY OF THE SILURIANS — PO Box 1195, Madison Square Station, New York, NY, 10159-1195, USA (212) 532-0887; e-mail silurians@aol.org; web site www.silurians.org
Membership Chairman .... Mort Sheinman
Editor, Silurian News..............Bernard Kirsch
Note: Elections of officers and board members held in May

SPECIAL LIBRARIES ASSOCIATION, NEWS DIVISION — 331 S Patrick St, Alexandria, VA, 22314-3501, USA (703) 647-4900; fax (703) 647-4901; e-mail sla@sla.org; web site www.sla.org
CEO .... Janice R. Lachance
COO/CFO .... Nancy A. Sansalone
Dir., Exec. Office Relations....Natasha Kenner
Note: Elections held in May

T

TECHNICAL ASSOCIATION OF THE GRAPHIC ARTS — 200 Deer Run Rd, Sewickley, PA, 15143-2324, USA (412) 259-1706; fax (412) 741-2311; e-mail taga@printing.org; web site www.taga.org
Managing Director...................... Mark Bohan
Note: Elections held in February

THE 4 A'S — 1065 Avenue of the Americas, Fl 16, New York, NY, 10018-0174, USA (212) 682-2500; fax (212) 682-8391; e-mail info@aaaa.com; web site www.aaaa.org
Pres. & CEO......................... Nancy Fletcher
Note: Election held in April

THE ADVERTISING COUNCIL, INC. — 815 2nd Ave, Fl 9, New York, NY, 10017-4500, USA (212) 922-1500; fax (212) 922-1676; e-mail info@adcouncil.org; web site www.adcouncil.org
Pres. & Chief Exec. Officer....... Lisa Sherman

THE ADVERTISING RESEARCH FOUNDATION (ARF) — 432 Park Ave S, Fl 6, New York, NY, 10016-8013, USA (212) 751-5656; fax (212) 319-5265; e-mail info@thearf.org; web site www.thearf.org
CEO & Pres.............................. Gayle Fuguitt
Note: Elections held in March

THE DIRECT MARKETING ASSOCIATION, INC. — 1120 Avenue of the Americas, New York, NY, 10036-6700, USA (212) 768-7277; fax (212) 302-6714; web site www.the-dma.org
CEO .... Lawrence M. Kimmel
Note: Elections held in Oct

THE NATIONAL SOCIETY OF NEWSPAPER COLUMNISTS, INC. — 205 Gun Hill St, Milton, MA, 02186-4026, USA 617 322-1420; e-mail director@columnists.com; web site www.columnists.com
Executive Director (as of January 2017)......... Suzette Standring
Note: Annual conference held in June.

THE NEWSGUILD-CWA — 501 3rd St NW Fl 6, Fl 6, Washington, DC, 20001-2760, USA (202) 434-7177; fax (202) 434-1472; e-mail guild@newsguild.org; web site www.newsguild.org
President.............................Bernard Lunzer

International Chairperson ..Martha Waggoner
Exec. VP ....Marian Needham

TRANS-CANADA ADVERTISING AGENCY NETWORK — 25 Sheppard Ave. West, Suite 300, Toronto, ON, M2N 6S6, Canada 416-221-8883; e-mail mabill@waginc.ca; web site www.tcaan.ca
Exec. Dir. ....Alice Zaharchuk
Mng. Dir./Treasurer.................Bill Whitehead

U

UNITED NATIONS CORRESPONDENTS ASSOCIATION — United Nations, Room S-308, New York, NY, 10017, USA (212) 963-7137; e-mail contactus@unca.com; web site www.unca.com
Pres.................................. Giam Paolo Pioli
1st Vice Pres. .... Louis Charbonneau
2nd Vice Pres. .... Masood Haider
Note: Elections held in Dec

W

WINNIPEG PRESS CLUB — C/O St. James Legion Branch #4, 1755 Portage Avenue, Winnipeg, MB, R3J 0E6, Canada (204) 800-1887; e-mail winnipegpressclub@outlook.com
VP ....Wendy Hart
Pres. ....Dwight MacAulay
Note: Since 2011, we have made our home at a local Royal Canadian Legion branch in Winnipeg, which has allowed us gracious use of their facilities. (Bar, meeting rooms, games room, food services).

We welcome visitors from press clubs and media organizations around the world. If you are planning to be in Winnipeg, please email winnipegpressclub@outlook.com, or call (204) 800-1887.

WORLD ASSOCIATION OF NEWSPAPERS AND NEWS PUBLISHERS (WAN-IFRA) — Rotfeder-Ring 11, Frankfurt am Main, 60327, Germany; tel (49) 69 240063-0; fax 240063-300; e-mail info@wan-ifra.org; web site www.wan-ifra.org
WAN-IFRA President ....Michael Golden
WAN-IFRA CEO................ Vincent Peyrègne
Note: Elections held every two years in June.

WORLD ASSOCIATION OF NEWSPAPERS AND NEWS PUBLISHERS (WAN-IFRA) — Rotfeder-Ring 11, Frankfurt, 60327, Germany; tel (49) 69 240063-0; fax 240063-300; e-mail info@wan-ifra.org; web site www.wan-ifra.org
.... Vincent Peyrègne
....................................Christoph RiessCEOs

WORLD PRESS INSTITUTE — 3415 University Ave W, Saint Paul, MN, 55114-1019, USA 612-205-7582; e-mail info@worldpressinstitute.org; web site www.worldpressinstitute.org
Exec. Dir. .... David McDonald

Y

YOUTH EDITORIAL ASSOCIATION — 4401 Wilson Blvd, Ste 900, Arlington, VA, 22203-4195, USA 571-366-1000; e-mail sandy.woodcock@naa.org; web site www.naafoundation.org
Director- NAA Foundation ...Sandy Woodcock

ASSOCIATIONS AND CLUBS - CITY, STATE AND REGIONAL

A

ADVERTISING CLUB OF GREATER NEW YORK — 989 Avenue of the Americas, 7th floor, New York, NY, 10018, USA; tel (212) 533-8080; fax (212) 533-1929; e-mail memberships@theadvertisingclub.org; web site www.theadvertisingclub.org
    Exec. Dir. ....Gina Grillo
    Note: Elections held in July

ALBERTA WEEKLY NEWSPAPERS ASSOCIATION — 3228 Parsons Rd, Edmonton, AB, T6N 1M2, Canada; tel (780) 434-8746; fax (780) 438-8356; e-mail info@awna.com; web site www.awna.com
    Exec. Dir. ....Dennis Merrell

ALLIED DAILY NEWSPAPERS OF WASHINGTON — 1110 Capitol Way S, Olympia, WA, 98501-2251, USA; tel (360) 943-9960; fax (360) 943-9962; e-mail anewspaper@aol.com
    Exec. Dir. ....Rowland Thompson

ARIZONA ASSOCIATED PRESS MANAGING EDITORS ASSOCIATION — 1850 N. Central Ave., Ste. 640, Phoenix, AZ, 85004, USA; tel (602) 258-8934; fax (602) 254-9573; e-mail aparizona@ap.org; web site www.ap.org/arizona
    Bureau Chief ....Michelle Williams
    Note: Elections held in the summer

ARKANSAS PRESS WOMEN ASSOCIATION, INC. — 1301 Golden Pond Rd, Little Rock, AR, 72223-9549, USA; tel 501-671-2126; fax 501-671-2121; e-mail arkpresswomen@yahoo.com; web site arkpresswomen.wordpress.com
    President ....Mary Hightower
    Treasurer..................................Terry Hawkins
    Note: Elections held in the fall of spring odd numbered years

ASSOCIATED COLLEGIATE PRESS — 2221 University Ave. SE, Ste. 121, Minneapolis, MN, 55414, USA; tel (612) 625-8335; fax (612) 626-0720; e-mail info@studentpress.org; web site www.studentpress.org
    Exec. Dir. .... Logan Aimone

ASSOCIATED PRESS — 184 High St #3, Boston, MA, 02110, USA; tel (617) 357-8100; fax (617) 338-8125; e-mail apboston@ap.org; web site www.ap.org/boston
    News Ed. ....William Kole
    Dir., Local Media ....Dwayne Desaulniers
    Pres. & CEO................................ Gary Pruitt

ASSOCIATED PRESS/CALIFORNIA-NEVADA NEWS EXECUTIVES — 221 S. Figueroa St., Ste. 300, Los Angeles, CA, 90012, USA; tel (213) 626-5833; e-mail losangeles@ap.org; web site www.ap.org/losangeles
    Bureau Chief, Los Angeles Anthony Marquez
    Bureau Chief, San Francisco ....John Raess
    Reg'l Vice Pres. Newyork..............Sue Cross
    Note: Elections held in May

ASSOCIATED PRESS/OKLAHOMA NEWS EXECUTIVES — 525 Central Park Dr., Ste. 202, Oklahoma City, OK, 73105, USA; tel (405) 525-2121; fax (405) 524-7465; e-mail apoklahoma@ap.org; web site www.ap.org/oklahoma
    Bureau Chief..................................Dale Leach

ATLANTIC COMMUNITY NEWSPAPERS

ATLANTIC COMMUNITY NEWSPAPERS ASSOCIATION — 7075 Bayers Rd., Ste. 216, Halifax, NS, B3L 2C2, Canada; tel (902) 832-4480; fax (902) 832-4484; e-mail info@newspapersatlantic.ca; web site www.acna.com
    Exec. Dir. ....Mike Kierstead

B

BRITISH COLUMBIA/YUKON COMMUNITY NEWSPAPERS ASSOCIATION — #9 West Broadway, Vancouver, BC, V5Y 1P1, Canada; tel (604) 669-9222; fax (604) 684-4713; e-mail info@bccommunitynews.com; web site www.bccommunitynews.com
    Gen. Mgr..........................George Affleck
    Note: Elections held in May

C

CAL WESTERN CIRCULATION MANAGERS' ASSOCIATION — 123 Sequoia Glen Ln, Novato, CA, 94947, USA; tel (415) 297-8836; e-mail cwcma@imblake.com; web site www.cwcma.org
    Executive Director .... Blake Webber
    Pres...................................... Aaron Kotarek
    Note: Election of officers is held during the annual meeting. Annual meeting is in June every year.

CALIFORNIA PRESS ASSOCIATION — Cal. Newspr. Publs. Assoc., 2000 O St., Suite 120, Sacramento, CA, 95811, USA; tel (916) 288-6000; web site www.cnpa.com
    Exec. Dir. .... Thomas Newton
    Note: Elections held in Dec

CAPITOL PRESS ASSOCIATION — PO Box 191, Raleigh, NC, 27602, USA; tel (919) 836-2858; e-mail smooneyh@ncinsider.com
    Mgr. ....Scott Mooneyham
    Note: Elections held in Jan

CCNMA: LATINO JOURNALISTS OF CALIFORNIA — ASU Walter Cronkite School of Journalism, 725 Arizona Ave. Ste. 404, Santa Monica, CA, 90401-1723, USA; tel (424) 229-9482; fax (424) 238-0271; e-mail ccnmainfo@ccnma.org; web site www.ccnma.org
    Executive Director ....Julio Moran

CENTRAL STATES CIRCULATION MANAGERS ASSOCIATION — 562 54th Street A, Moline, IL, 61265, USA; tel N/A; e-mail cscma@aol.com; web site www.cscma.com
    Board Chair
    ....Angie Lyons
    President .... Scott Kinter
    Secretary/Treasurer ....Jill Henderson
    Note: Elections held in April

COLORADO ASSOCIATED PRESS EDITORS AND REPORTERS — 1444 Wazee St., Ste. 130, Denver, CO, 80202-1395, USA; tel (303) 825-0123; fax (303) 892-5927; e-mail apdenver@ap.org; web site www.ap.org/colorado
    Bureau Chief ....Jim Clarke
    Note: Elections held in Feb

COMMUNITY PAPERS OF INDIANA — PO Box 1004, Crown Point, IN, 46308, USA; tel (219) 689-6262; fax (219) 374-7558
    Pub./Owner ....Shari Foreman
    Note: Elections held in April

COMMUNITY PAPERS OF MICHIGAN — 5000 Northwind Dr., Ste. 240, East Lansing, MI, 48823, USA; tel (517) 333-3355; fax (517) 333-3322; e-mail jackguza@cpapersmi.com;slkotecki@cpapersmi.com; web site www.communitypapersofmichigan.com
    Exec. Dir. ....Jack Guza

CONNECTICUT ASSOCIATED PRESS MANAGING EDITORS ASSOCIATION — 10 Columbus Blvd., Hartford, CT, 06106, USA; tel (860) 246-6876; fax (860) 727-4003; e-mail aphartford@ap.org; web site www.ap.org
    Bureau Chief ....William Kole

CONSEIL DE PRESSE DU QUEBEC — 1000, rue Fullum, Ste. A.208, Montreal, QC, H2K 3L7, Canada; tel (514) 529-2818; fax (514) 873-4434; e-mail info@conseildepresse.qc.ca; web site www.conseildepresse.qc.ca
    Contact..Guy Amyot
    Director of communication .... Julien Acosta

CUSTOMIZED NEWSPAPER ADVERTISING (IOWA) — 319 E 5th St, Des Moines, IA, 50309-1927, USA; tel (515) 244-2145; fax (515) 244-4855; web site www.cnaads.com; www.inanews.com
    Exec. Dir. .... Chris Mudge
    Acct. Exec.....................................Bryan Rohe
    Sales Dir. ....Ron Bode
    Sales Rep.....................................Bruce Adams
    Note: Represents 302 daily and weekly newspapers in Iowa and can place advertising in any newspaper in the country.

F

FLORIDA NEWSPAPER ADVERTISING & MARKETING EXECUTIVES — 610 Crescent Executive Court, Suite 112, Lake Mary, FL, 32746, USA; tel (321) 283-5273; e-mail hello@fname.org; web site www.fname.org
    Exec. Dir. ....Sandy Osteen

FLORIDA SOCIETY OF NEWSPAPER EDITORS — 336 E. College Ave. Suite 203, Tallahassee, FL, 32301, USA; tel (850) 222-5790; fax 850-224-6012; e-mail fpa-info@flpress.com; web site www.fsne.org
    Membership Coordinator .... Marcia Cyr
    Note: Elections held at June convention

FREE COMMUNITY PAPERS OF NEW ENGLAND — 100-1 Domino Drive, Concord, CT, 01742, USA; tel 877-423-6399; e-mail bne@fcpne.com; web site www.communitypapersne.com
    Admin. ....Lynn Duval

FREE COMMUNITY PAPERS OF NEW YORK — 750 W. Genesee St., Syracuse, NY, 13204, USA; tel (315) 472-6007; fax (315) 472-5919; e-mail ads@fcpny.com; web site www.fcpny.org
    Executive Director ....Dan Holmes
    Sales & Training ....Tom Cuskey

FREE LANCE JOURNALIST/BLOGGER — 121 South Street, 121 South Street, Churubusco, IN, 46723, USA; tel (260) 241-7737; e-mail vsade8@gmail.com
    Freelance writer/blogger
    2017-18 WPCI President; WPCI Communications Contest co-chair........ Vivian Sade

FREEDOM OF INFORMATION FOUNDATION OF TEXAS — 3001 N Lamar Blvd., Ste. 302, Austin, TX, 78705, USA; tel (512) 377 1575; fax (512) 377 1578; e-mail kelley.shannon@foift.org; web site www.foift.org
    Executive Director ....Kelley Shannon
    Note: Elections held in Dec

G

GREAT LAKES/MIDSTATES NEWSPAPER CONFERENCE, INC. — 1335 Dublin Rd., Suite 216-B, Colombus, OH, 43215, USA; tel (614) 486-6677; fax (614) 486-4940; e-mail glmsconf@comcast.net; web site www.ohionews.com
    Bus. Mgr./Sec./Treasurer..........Jack Gahagan
    Note: Elections held in Feb

H

HOLLYWOOD FOREIGN PRESS ASSOCIATION — 646 N. Robertson Blvd., West Hollywood, CA, 90069-5078, USA; tel (310) 657-1731; fax (310) 657-5576; e-mail info@hfpa.org; web site www.hfpa.org
    Head, Mktg..........................Michael Russell
    Pres.. Philip Berk

HOOSIER STATE PRESS ASSOCIATION — 41 E Washington St, Ste 101, Indianapolis, IN, 46204-3560, USA; tel (317) 803-4772; fax (317) 624-4428; web site www.hspa.com
    Exec. Dir./Gen. Counsel .... Stephen Key
    Adv. Dir. ....Pamela Lego
    Communications Specialist.........Milissa Tuley
    HSPA Foundation Dir.............. Karen Braeckel
    Office Mgr..............................Yvonne Yeadon
    Adv. Coord.............................Shawn Goldsby
    Note: Represents daily and weekly newspapers in Indiana

I

IDAHO PRESS CLUB — PO Box 2221, Boise, ID, 83701-2221, USA; tel (208) 389-2879; e-mail email@idahopressclub.org; web site www.idahopressclub.org
    Exec. Dir. ....Martha Borchers
    Note: IPC accepts individual memberships for reporters and public information officers in several areas. Elections and awards ceremony held in the spring. One annual seminars held in spring and fall

ILLINOIS ASSOCIATED PRESS MANAGING EDITORS — 10 S. Wacker Drive, Suite 2500, Chicago, IL, 60606, USA; tel (312) 781-0500; e-mail chifax@ap.org; web site www.ap.org

NOTE: ELECTIONS HELD IN SEPT

ILLINOIS WOMAN'S PRESS ASSOCIATION, INC. — PO Box 180150, Chicago, IL, 60618-9997, USA; tel (708) 296-8669; e-mail iwpa@gmail.com; web site www.iwpa.org
    Pres.................................Cora Weisenberger

INDIANA ASSOCIATED PRESS MANAGING EDITORS — 251 N. Illinois St., Ste. 1600,

Indianapolis, IN, 46204, USA; tel (317) 639-5501; e-mail indy@ap.org

INDIANAPOLIS PRESS CLUB FOUNDATION — PO Box 40923, Indianapolis, IN, 46240, USA; tel (317) 701-1130; e-mail jlabalme@indypress@att.net; web site www.indypressfoundation.org
Executive Director .... Jenny Labalme
Note: Elections held in January

INLAND PRESS ASSOCIATION — 701 Lee St., Ste. 925, Des Plaines, IL, 60016, USA; tel (847) 795-0380; fax (847) 795-0385; e-mail inland@inlandpress.org; web site www.inlandpress.org
Mgr. of Research & Member Services ... Karla Zander
Dir. of Membership and Programming ....Patty Slusher
Exec. Dir. ....Tom Slaughter
Ed. ....Mark Fitzgerald
Accounting Mgr......................Steve Hoffman
Note: Elections held in Oct

IOWA ASSOCIATED PRESS MEDIA EDITORS ASSOCIATION — 505 Fifth Ave., Ste. 1000, Des Moines, IA, 50309, USA; tel (515) 243-3281; fax (515) 243-3884; e-mail apdesmoines@ap.org; web site www.apiowa.org
Reg. Dir............................... Kia Breaux
Note: Elections held in June

IOWA NEWSPAPER ASSOCIATION, INC. — 319 E 5th St, Fl 2, Des Moines, IA, 50309-1927, USA; tel (515) 244-2145; fax (515) 244-4855; e-mail ina@inanews.com; web site www.inanews.com
Sales & Mktg. Dir........ Susan Patterson Plank
Business Mgr......................Brent Steemken
Comm. Dir.............................. Jodi Hulbert
Dev. Dir. ....Geof Fischer
Inside Sales Mgr...................Samantha Fett
Media Dir. ....Heidi Geisler
Program Dir. ....Jana Shepherd
Tech. & Digital Dev. Mgr............Susan James
Pres. ....Ryan Harvey
Sales & Mktg. Assist..........Kaitlyn Van Patten
Note: Elections held in May

K

KANSAS ASSOCIATED PRESS MANAGING EDITORS ASSOCIATION — Associated Press, 215 W. Pershing St., Ste. 221, Kansas City, MO, 64108, USA; tel (816) 421-4844; fax (816) 421-3590; e-mail apkansascity@ap.org; web site www.ap.org/kansas
Bureau Chief .... Randy Picht
Note: Elections held in Oct

KANSAS ASSOCIATED PRESS PUBLISHERS AND EDITORS — Associated Press, 215 W. Pershing St., Ste. 221, Kansas City, MO, 64108, USA; tel (816) 421-4844; fax (816) 421-3590
Bureau Chief ....Paul Stevens
Bd. Chrmn. .... Tom Bell
Note: Elections held in Dec

KANSAS PROFESSIONAL COMMUNICATORS — 2369 Road J5, Americus, KS, 66835, USA; tel 620-227-1807; fax 620 227-1806; e-mail kansasprocom@gmail.com; web site www.kansasprofessionalcommunicators.org
Pres. .... Jennifer Latzke
Professor, WSU Elliott School of Communication .... Les Anderson
Becky Funke
Wilma Moore-Black
Miller Jill
Note: We are the Kansas affiliate of the National Federation of Press Women.

KENTUCKY ASSOCIATED PRESS EDITORS ASSOCIATION — 525 W. Broadway, Louisville, KY, 40202, USA; tel (502) 583-7718; fax (502) 589-4831; e-mail ayeomans@ap.org; web site www.ap.org/kentucky
Note: Elections held in Nov

L

LEGISLATIVE CORRESPONDENTS ASSOCIATION OF NYS — 25 Eagle St., NYS Capital, Albany, NY, 12224, USA; tel (518) 455-2388; web site www.lcapressroom.com
President ....Matthew Hamilton

LOS ANGELES PRESS CLUB — 4773 Hollywood Blvd., Los Angeles, CA, 90027, USA; tel (323) 669-8081; fax (323) 669-8069; e-mail info@lapressclub.org; web site www.lapressclub.org
Exec. Dir. ....Diana Ljungaeus
Note: Elections held in Nov

LOUISIANA PRESS WOMEN, INC. — The Advocate, 7290 Blue Bonnet Rd., Baton Rouge, LA, 70810, USA; tel (225) 383-1111; fax (225) 388-0323; e-mail mshuler@theadvocate.com; web site www.theadvocate.com
Pres. ....David Manship
Note: Elections held even years

LOUISIANA-MISSISSIPPI ASSOCIATED PRESS MANAGING EDITORS ASSOCIATION — 125 south congress st. suite 1330, Jackson, MS, 39201, USA; tel 601-948-5897; fax 601-948-7975; e-mail jkme@ap.org ; web site www.ap.org
News Ed. ....Brian Schwaner

M

MAINE DAILY NEWSPAPER PUBLISHERS ASSOCIATION — 26 Elmwood Road, Cape Elizabeth, ME, 04107, USA; tel 207-799-2996; e-mail scostello@sunjournal.com; web site www.mainepressassociation.orgGary Gagne

NOTE: ELECTIONS HELD IN JUNE

MANITOBA COMMUNITY NEWSPAPER ASSOCIATION — 943 McPhillips Street, Winnipeg, MB, R2X 2J9, Canada; tel (204) 947-1691; fax (204) 947-1919; web site www.mcna.com

NOTE: ELECTIONS HELD AT ANNUAL APRIL CONVENTION

MARYLAND-DELAWARE-DC PRESS ASSOCIATION — 60 West St., Ste. 107, Annapolis, MD, 21401-2479, USA; tel (855) 721-6332; fax (855) 721-6332; e-mail rsnyder@mddc.com; web site www.mddcpress.com
Exec. Dir. ....Rebecca Snyder

MASSACHUSETTS NEWSPAPER PUBLISHERS ASSOCIATION — 7 S Street Ct., Rockport, MA, 01966, USA; tel (978) 546-3400; fax (978) 418-9161; e-mail info@masspublishers.org; web site www.masspublishers.org
Exec. Dir. ....Robert J. Ambrogi

METROPOLITAN NEW YORK FOOTBALL WRITERS ASSOCIATION — American Football Networks, Inc., P.O. Box 477, Roseland, NJ, 07068-0477, USA; tel (973) 364-0605; fax (973) 364-0425; e-mail americanfootballnetworks@gmail.com; web site www.mnyfwa.com
Pres..........................Dennis Wilson

MICHIGAN ASSOCIATED PRESS EDITORIAL ASSOCIATION — 300 River Pl., Ste. 2400, Detroit, MI, 48207, USA; tel (313) 259-0650; fax (313) 259-4966; e-mail apmichigan@ap.org; web site www.ap.org
Regional Director - East
...................................Eva Parziale

MICHIGAN PRESS ASSOCIATION — 827 N Washington Ave, Lansing, MI, 48906-5135, USA; tel (517) 372-2424; fax (517) 372-2429; e-mail mpa@michiganpress.org; web site www.michiganpress.org
Growth & Operations Manager Roselie Lucus
Public Affairs Manager ....Lisa McGraw
Design & Communications Specialist .... Sean Wickham
Mgr. ....Janet Mendler
Exec. Dir. ....James Tarrant
Adv. Dir. ....Paul Biondi
Note: Elections held in Jan

MID-ATLANTIC CIRCULATION MANAGERS ASSOCIATION — Daily Herald, PO Box 520, Roanoke Rapids, NC, 27870-0520, USA; tel (252) 537-2505; fax (252) 537-1887; web site www.midatlanticcma.org
Sec./Treasurer.........................Carol Moseley
President...........................Robyn Ashley
First Vice President ....Keven Zepezauer
Second Vice President............. David Adams
Representative ....Kevin Craig
Representative...... Patricia Speziale Edwards
Representative ....Sean Torain
Representative ....Clayton Hall
Note: Elections held in May

MID-ATLANTIC COMMUNITY PAPERS ASSOCIATION — 375 Jalappa Road, Hamburg, PA, 19526, USA; tel 800-450-7227; e-mail info@macpa.net; web site www.macpa.net
Exec. Dir. ....Alyse Mitten
Note: Elections Held in April for both Boards

MID-ATLANTIC NEWSPAPER ADVERTISING & MARKETING EXECUTIVES — 359-C Wando Place Drive, Mt. Pleasant, SC, 29464, USA; tel (509)540-1534; e-mail edwardrbryant@yahoo.com; web site www.midatlanticname.com
Exec. Dir. ....Terri Saylor
Note: Elections held in March

MIDWEST FREE COMMUNITY PAPERS — PO Box 1350, Iowa City, IA, 52244-1350, USA; tel (319) 341-4352; fax (319) 341-4358; e-mail mfcp@mchsi.com; web site www.mfcp.org
Office Mgr..................................Jori Hendon
Note: Classified advertising for 124 publications

MIDWEST TRAVEL WRITERS ASSOCIATION — 902 S. Randall Road, Suite C311, St. Charles, IL, 60174, USA; tel 888-551-8184; e-mail sylvia@forbesfreelance.com; web site www.mtwa.org
Active Dir. ....Carla Waldemar
Treasurer ....Rich Warren
Active Dir. ....Susan Pollack
Administrative Assistant .... Sylvia Forbes
Note: Elections held in Mar or April

MINNESOTA ASSOCIATED PRESS ASSOCIATION — 425 Portland Ave, Third Floor, Minneapolis, MN, 55488, USA; tel (612) 332-2727; fax (612) 342-5299; e-mail apminneapolis@ap.org; web site www.ap.org
News Ed. ....Doug Glass

MINNESOTA FREE PAPER ASSOCIATION — 21998 Hwy. 27, Little Falls, MN, 56345, USA; tel 320-630-5312; fax (320) 632-2348; e-mail terry@littlefalls.net; web site www.mfpa.com
Asst. Sec./Treasurer...................Terry Lehrke
Pres....................................Trevor Slette
Note: Elections held in Feb

MISSOURI ASSOCIATED PRESS MANAGING EDITORS — Associated Press, 215 W. Pershing, Ste. 221, Kansas City, MO, 64108, USA; tel (816) 421-4844; fax (816) 421-3590; e-mail apkansascity@ap.org; web site www.ap.org
Bureau Chief .... Randy Picht
Note: Elections held in April

MISSOURI PRESS WOMEN — 528 Pamela Ln., Kirkwood, MO, 63122-1138, USA; tel N/A; e-mail MPCNFPW@gmail.com; web site www.mpc-nfpw.org
treasurer...............................Janice Denham
Deborah Reinhardt

MONTANA ASSOCIATED PRESS ASSOCIATION — 321 Fuller Ave. #2, Helena, MT, 59601, USA; tel (406) 442-7440; fax (406) 442-5162; e-mail apmontana@ap.org; web site www.ap.org/montana
Bureau Chief ....Jim Clark
Note: Elections held in June every two years

N

NASJA EAST — 22 Cavalier Way, Latham, NY, 12110, USA; tel 518 339-5334; e-mail nasjaeast@nasja.org; web site http://www.nasja.org/east/index.cfm
Pres. .... Peter Hines

NATIONAL NEWSPAPER ASSOCIATION — 900 Community Drive, Springfield, IL, 62703, USA; tel (217)241-1400; fax (217) 241-1301; e-mail lynne@nna.org; web site www.nna.org
Comm. Dir. .... Stan Schwartz
Chief Operating Officer .... Lynne Lance
CEO .... Sam Fisher
Note: Officer elections held in Sept/Oct during Annual Convention; annual Leadership Conference in March; annual Better Newspaper Contest entry deadline Spring

NEBRASKA ASSOCIATED PRESS ASSOCIATION — 845 "S" Street, Lincoln, NE, 68508, USA; tel (402)476-2851; fax (402)476-2942; e-mail nebpress@nebpress.com; web site www.ap.org/nebraska
Bureau Chief .... Tina Heraldson
Note: Elections held in Sept

NENPA MARKETING & ADVERTISING COUNCIL — 370 Common St., Dedham, MA, 02026, USA; tel (781) 320-8050; fax (781) 320-8055; e-mail info@nenpa.com; web site www.nenpa.com
Exec. Dir. NENPA .... Dan Cotter
Note: Elections held in Oct

NEW ENGLAND ASSOCIATION OF CIRCULATION EXECUTIVES — 4 Trotting Rd., Chelmsford, MA, 1824, USA; tel (978) 256-0691; fax (978) 256-4873; e-mail neace@neace.com; web site www.neace.com
Sec. ....William H. Hoar
Note: Elections held in May

NEW ENGLAND NEWSPAPER & PRESS ASSOCIATION — 1 Arrow Drive, Suite 6, Woburn, MA, 01801, USA; tel (781) 281-2053; fax (339) 999-2174; e-mail info@nenpa.com; web site www.nenpa.com

NOTE: ELECTIONS HELD IN MARCH

NEW ENGLAND SOCIETY OF NEWSPAPER EDITORS — 370 Common Street, 3rd Floor Ste 319, Barletta Hall, Dedham, MA, 02026, USA; tel 781-320-8050; fax 781-320-8055; e-mail info@nenpa.com; web site www.nesne.org
Ed. ....George Geers
Note: Elections held in Nov

NEW JERSEY ASSOCIATED PRESS MANAGING EDITORS ASSOCIATION — 50 W. State St., Ste. 1114, Trenton, NJ, 8608, USA; tel (609) 392-3622; fax (609) 392-3525; e-mail aptrenton@ap.org; web site www.ap.org/nj
BC ....Sally Hale

NEW JERSEY LEGISLATIVE CORRESPONDENTS CLUB — Hackensack Record, Trenton, NJ, 8625, USA; tel (609) 292-5159; fax (609) 984-1888
Pres. ....Jim Hooker
Note: This group accepts news organizations with correspondents based in Trenton, N.J

NEW MEXICO PRESS WOMEN — 256 DP Rd., Los Alamos, NM, 87544, USA; tel (505) 662-4185; fax (505) 827-6496; e-mail lanews@lamonitor.com; web site www.newmexicopresswomen.org
Pres. ....Carol Clark
Note: Elections held May 1st of even numbered years

NEW ORLEANS PRESS CLUB — 846 Howard Avenue, New Orleans, LA, 70113, USA; tel 504-259-4687; e-mail info@pressclubneworleans.org; web site www.pressclubneworleans.org
Exec. Dir. .... Bill Langkopp
Note: Elections held in July

NEW YORK FINANCIAL WRITERS ASSOCIATION, INC. — PO Box 338, Ridgewood, NJ, 07451-0338, USA; tel (201) 612-0100; fax (201) 612-9915; e-mail nyfwa@aol.com; web site www.nyfwa.org
Exec. Mgr. .... Jane Reilly
Note: Elections held on fourth Wed. of Jan. Members are journalists in the business or financial media

NEW YORK NEWS PUBLISHERS ASSOCIATION — 252 Hudson Ave, Albany, NY, 12210, USA; tel (518) 449-1667; web site www.nynpa.org
Pres. .... Diane Kennedy

NEW YORK PRESS PHOTOGRAPHERS ASSOCIATION, INC. — PO Box 3346, New York, NY, 10008-3346, USA; tel (212) 889-6633; e-mail office@nyppa.org; web site www.nyppa.org
Trustee .... Ray Stubblebine
Secretary - Historian ....Marc Hermann
President ....Bruce Cotler
Vice President ....Todd Maisel
Note: Elections held every other year

NEW YORK SOCIETY OF NEWSPAPER EDITORS — 222 Waverly Avenue, Syracuse, NY, 13244, USA; tel (315) 443-2305; fax (315) 443-3946
Pres. ....Joann M. Crupi

NEW YORK STATE ASSOCIATED PRESS ASSOCIATION — 450 W. 33rd St., Albany, NY, 10001, USA; tel 212-621-1670; fax 212-621-1679; e-mail info@ap.org; web site www.ap.org
Bureau Chief ....Howard Goldberg
Note: Elections held in Sept

NEW YORK STATE CIRCULATION MANAGERS ASSOCIATION — 85 Civic Center Plz., Poughkeepsie, NY, 12601, USA; tel (845) 437-4738; fax (845) 437-4902; e-mail farrellb@poughkee.gannett.com; web site www.poughkeepsiejournal.com
Board Member .... Bill Farrell
Note: Elections held in May

NORTH CAROLINA PRESS CLUB — 200 Countryside Rd, Harmony, NC, 28634-9420, USA; tel (704)546-7900; e-mail suzyb3@gmail.com; web site www.nfpw.org
Past President .... Suzy Barile
Note: Elections held in March

NORTH DAKOTA ASSOCIATED PRESS — PO Box 1018, Bismarck, ND, 58502-5646, USA; tel (701) 223-8450; fax (701) 224-0158; e-mail apbismarck@ap.orgBlake Nicholson

NORTHERN ILLINOIS NEWSPAPER ASSOCIATION — Campus Life Building, Suite 130, DeKalb, IL, 60115, USA; tel (815) 753-4239; fax (815) 753-0708; web site www.ninaonline.org
Communications Coordinator .... Shelley Hendricks

NORTHERN STATES CIRCULATION MANAGERS ASSOCIATION — PO Box 220, Grand Rapids, MN, 55744, USA; tel (218) 326-6623; fax (218) 326-6627; e-mail ron.oleheiser@grandrapidsmn.com; web site www.grandrapidsmn.com
Pub. ....Ron Oleheiser
Note: Elections held in Sept

NORTHWEST INTERNATIONAL CIRCULATION EXECUTIVES — PO Box 778, La Conner, WA, 98257, USA; tel (360) 466-2006; fax (360) 466-2006; e-mail nice@galaxynet.com; web site www.nicex.org
Sec./Treasurer...............................Dale Irvine
Note: Management seminars sponsored in Oct. (non-dailies welcome). Elections held at annual conference in May

O

OHIO CIRCULATION MANAGERS ASSOCIATION — 1335 Dublin Rd., Suite 216-B, Columbus, OH, 43215, USA; tel (614) 486-6677; fax (614) 486-4940; e-mail bbarker@plaind.com; web site www.ohiocirculation.com
Committee Chair ....Kim Wilhelm
Note: Elections held in Oct

OHIO NEWSPAPER ADVERTISING EXECUTIVES — 1335 Dublin Rd. S., Ste. 216-B, Columbus, OH, 43215, USA; tel (614) 486-6677; fax (614) 486-6373; e-mail mhenry@adohio.net; web site www.adohio.net
Mgr. ....Mark Henry
Note: Elections held in Feb.

ONTARIO COMMUNITY NEWSPAPERS ASSOCIATION — 3228 South Service Rd. Ste 116, Burlington, ON, L7N 3H8, Canada; tel (905) 639-8720; fax (905) 639-6962; e-mail info@ocna.org; web site www.ocna.org
Executive Director .... Anne Lannan

ORANGE COUNTY PRESS CLUB — 1835 Newport Blvd., #A-109-538, Costa Mesa, CA, 92627, USA; tel (714) 564-1052; fax (714) 564-1047; e-mail OCPressClub@orangecountypressclub.com; web site www.ocpressclub.org
Sec./Treasurer........................Jean O. Pasco
Note: Elections held in July

OVERSEAS PRESS CLUB OF AMERICA — 40 West 45 Street, New York, NY, 10036, USA; tel (212) 626-9220; fax (212) 626-9210; e-mail info@opcofamerica.org; web site www.opcofamerica.org
Exec. Dir. .... Patricia Kranz
Note: Elections held in late summer

OVERSEAS PRESS CLUB OF PUERTO RICO (ESTABLISHED 1968) — 1399 Ave. Ana G. M?ndez, San Juan, PR, 00928-1345, Puerto Rico; tel (787) 525-8901; fax N/A; e-mail opcpr@yahoo.com; web site www.opcpr.wordpress.com
Pres. ....Ángel Rodríguez
Note: Martha Alonso - 787-408-3033

P

PACIFIC NORTHWEST ASSOCIATION OF WANT AD NEWSPAPERS (PNAWAN) & WESTERN REGIONAL ADVERTISING PROGRAM (WRAP) — 304 W 3rd Ave, C/O Exchange Publishing, Spokane, WA, 99201-4314, USA; tel (509) 922-3456; fax (509) 455-7940; e-mail Ads@PNAWAN.org; web site www.RegionalAds.org
Executive Director of the Pacific Northwest Association of Want Ad Newspapers (PNAWAN) & Western Regional Advertising Program (WRAP) .... Kylah Strohte
PNAWAN Office
Note: We are audited and verified by the Circulation Verification Council annually.

PNAWAN headquarters are located at the offices of hosting member publication, Exchange Publishing, in Spokane, WA.

PACIFIC NORTHWEST NEWSPAPER ASSOCIATION — 708 Tenth St., Sacramento, CA, 95814, USA; tel (888) 344-7662; fax (916) 288-6002; e-mail tom@cnpa.com; web site www.pnna.com
Exec. Dir. .... Jack Bates
Note: Elections held in the July

PENNSYLVANIA SOCIETY OF NEWS EDITORS — 3899 N. Front St., Harrisburg, PA, 17110, USA; tel (717) 703-3000; fax (717) 703-3001; e-mail teresas@pa-news.org; web site www.panewsmedia.org
President, PA Newspaper Association...... Teri Henning
Note: Elections held in May

PENNSYLVANIA WOMEN'S PRESS ASSOCIATION — 511 Lenox St., Stroudsburg, PA, 18360, USA; tel (717) 295-7869; e-mail pwpa@lancasteronline.com; web site www.pwpa.us

NOTE: ELECTIONS HELD IN MAY. ORGANIZATION ACCEPTS FREELANCERS

Q

QUEBEC COMMUNITY NEWSPAPERS ASSOCIATION — 189 Hymus Blvd., Suite 207, Pointe-Claire, QC, H9R 1E9, Canada; tel (514) 697-6330; fax (514) 697-6331; e-mail execdir@qcna.qc.ca; web site www.qcna.org
Executive Director ....Richard Tardif

S

SASKATCHEWAN WEEKLY NEWSPAPERS ASSOCIATION — 14-401 45th St. W., Saskatoon, SK, S7L 5Z9, Canada; tel (306) 382-9683; fax (306) 382-9421; e-mail swna@swna.com; web site www.swna.com
Tech. Officer .... Cameron Just
Commun.Coord.......................... Julie Schau
Office Mgr......................... Louise Simpson
Adv. Coord., Classified................Nicole Nater
Exec. Dir. ....Steve Nixon

SOCIETY OF CLASSIFIED ADVERTISING MANAGERS OF AMERICA, INC. — PO Box 531335, Mountain Brook, AL, 352530-1335, USA; tel (205) 592-0389; fax (205)599-5598; e-mail hrushing@usit.net; web site www.scama.com
Exec. Officer........................ Hugh J. Rushing
Note: Elections held in Feb

SOUTH CAROLINA ASSOCIATED PRESS — 1401 Shop Road, Suite B, Columbia, SC, 29201, USA; tel (803) 799-5510; fax (803) 252-2913; e-mail apcolumbia@ap.org
Bureau Chief .... Maryann Mrowca

SOUTHEASTERN ADVERTISING PUBLISHERS ASSOCIATION — 104 Westland Dr, Columbia, TN, 38401-6522, USA; tel (931) 223-5708; fax (888) 450-8329; e-mail info@sapatoday.com; web site www.sapatoday.com
Exec. Dir. .... Douglas Fry
Note: Classified advertising for 75 publications in 10 Southeastern states. Display Network also available.

SOUTHERN CIRCULATION MANAGERS ASSOCIATION — P.O. Box 1163, Kingsport, TN, 37662, USA; tel N/A; e-mail info@scmaonline.net; web site www.scmaonline.net
Sec. ....Debra Casciano
Treasurer...................................... Glen Tabor
Note: Elections held in April. Organization accepts shoppers as Associate Members

SOUTHERN NEWSPAPER PUBLISHERS ASSOCIATION — 3680 N. Peachtree Rd., Ste. 300, Atlanta, GA, 30341, USA; tel (404) 256-0444; fax (404) 252-9135; e-mail edward@snpa.org; web site www.snpa.org
Asst ED ....Cindy Durham
Exec. Dir. ....Edward VanHorn
Office Mgr..........................Paulette Sheffield
Charles H. Morris
Thomas A. Silvestri
David Dunn-Rankin
Note: Elections held at the annual convention in Oct.

SOUTHWEST CLASSIFIED ADVERTISING MANAGERS ASSOCIATION — Dallas Morning News, 508 Young St., Dallas, TX, 75265-5237, USA; tel 214-977-8222; e-mail jmckeon@dallasnews.com; web site www.dallasnews.com
President and General ManagerJohn Mckeon
General Manager, Recruitment, Real Estate, General Classifieds................ Michael Mayer

STATE HISTORICAL SOCIETY OF WISCONSIN — 816 State St., Madison, WI, 53706, USA; tel (608) 264-6534; fax (608) 264-6002; web site www.wisconsinhistory.org
Administrative Asst............Margaret T. Dwyer

T

TENNESSEE ASSOCIATED PRESS MANAGING EDITORS — John Siegenthaler Center, 1207 18th Avenue South, Suite 261-A, Nashville, TN, 37212, USA; tel (615) 373-9988; fax (615) 376-0947; e-mail apnashville@ap.org; web site www.ap.org/states/tennessee
Bureau Chief ....Adam Yeomans

TENNESSEE PRESS SERVICE, INC. — 625 Market St, Ste 1100, Knoxville, TN, 37902-2219, USA; tel (865) 584-5761; fax (865) 558-8687; e-mail info@tnpress.com; web site www.tnadvertising.biz
Exec. Dir. .... Greg Sherrill
Director of Advertising................. David Wells
Note: Elections held in June

TEXAS ASSOCIATED PRESS MANAGING EDITORS — The Dallas Morning News, 508 Young St., Dallas, TX, 75202, USA; tel (214) 977-8222; web site www.txapme.com
Deputy Mng. Ed...........................Leona Allen
Note: Elections held in March

TEXAS CIRCULATION MANAGEMENT ASSOCIATION — c/o PO Box 9577, The Woodlands, TX, 77387, USA; tel N/A; e-mail tcma@texascma.org; web site www.texascma.org
Secretary/Treasurer .... J W Smith

Note: America's First Circulation Sectional Founded September 18, 1913

TEXAS COMMUNITY MEDIA LLC — 1226 Newberry Drive, Allen, TX, 75013, USA; tel 972-741-6258; e-mail jack@tcnatoday.com; web site www.tcnatoday.com
Exec. Dir. ....Dick Colvin

THE AD CLUB — 9 Hamilton Pl., Boston, MA, 02108-3210, USA; tel (617) 262-1100; fax (617) 456-1772; e-mail newsfeed@adclub.org; web site www.adclub.org

THE AD CLUB — 22 Batterymarch Street, 1st Floor, Boston, MA, 02109, USA; tel 617-262-1100; web site www.adclub.org
Pres..Kathy Kiely

THE PRESS CLUB OF CLEVELAND — 28022 Osborn Road, Cleveland, OH, 44140, USA; tel 440-899-1222; e-mail pressclubcleveland@oh.rr.com; web site pressclubcleveland.com
President, Trustee ....Ed Byers
Executive Administrator ....Lynn Bracic

U

UNIVERSITY PRESS OF KENTUCKY — 663 S. Limestone St., Lexington, KY, 40508-4008,
USA; tel (859) 257-8419; fax (859) 323-1873; e-mail smwrin2@uky.edu; web site www.kentuckypress.com
Mktg. Dir. ....John Hussey
Dir..Stephen Wrinn
Note: Elections held in spring/fall of odd numbered years

UTAH-IDAHO-SPOKANE ASSOCIATED PRESS ASSOCIATION — 30 E. 100 South St., Ste. 200, Salt Lake City, UT, 84111, USA; tel (801) 322-3405; fax (801) 322-0051; e-mail apsaltlake@ap.org
Bureau Chief ....Jim Clarke
Note: Elections held in June

V

VALLEY PRESS CLUB, INC. — PO Box 5475, Springfield, MA, 01101-5475, USA; tel (413) 682-0007; e-mail info@valleypressclub.com; web site www.valleypressclub.com
Pres......................................Charlie Bennett
Note: Elections held in March

W

WASHINGTON ASSOCIATED PRESS NEWSPAPER EXECUTIVES ASSOCIATION — 3131 Elliott Ave., Ste. 750, Seattle, WA,
98121, USA; tel (206) 682-1812; fax (206) 621-1948; e-mail apseattle@ap.org; web site www.ap.org
Bureau Chief ....Nancy Trott
Note: Elections held in Oct./Nov

WASHINGTON PRESS ASSOCIATION — c/o 15642 129th Court SE, Renton, WA, 98058, USA; tel N/A; web site www.washingtonpressassociation.com
President ....Bill Virgin
Vice President ....Mike Maltais
Secretary....................................Sarah Smith

WEST TEXAS PRESS ASSOCIATION — 706 SW 10th St., Perryton, TX, 79070, USA; tel (806) 435-3631; fax (806) 435-2420; e-mail secretary@wtpa.org; web site www.wtpa.org
Secretary-Treasurer ....Mary Dudley
Note: Elections held at annual convention in July

WHITE HOUSE CORRESPONDENTS ASSOCIATION — 600 New Hampshire Ave., Ste. 800, Washington, DC, 20037, USA; tel 202-266-7453; fax (202) 266-7454; e-mail director@whca.net; web site www.whca.net
Executive Director ....Steven Thomma
Note: Elections held in July

WHITE HOUSE NEWS PHOTOGRAPHERS ASSOCIATION, INC. — PO Box 7119, Washington, DC, 20044-7119, USA; tel (202)
785-5230; e-mail info@whnpa.org; web site www.whnpa.org
Treasurer ....Jon Elswick
President ....Whitney Shefte
Vice President ....Jim Bourg
Note: Elections held in Mar.

WISCONSIN ASSOCIATED PRESS ASSOCIATION — 111 E. Wisconsin Ave., Ste.1925, Milwaukee, WI, 53202, USA; tel (414) 225-3580; e-mail apmlw@ap.org; web site www.ap.org
News Ed. ....Roger Schneider
Note: Elections held in May

WISCONSIN FREE COMMUNITY PAPERS — 101 S. Main St., Fond Du Lac, WI, 54935, USA; tel 800-727-8745; fax 920-922-0861; e-mail wcp@wisad.com; web site www.wisad.com
Exec. Dir. ....Janelle Anderson

WYOMING ASSOCIATED PRESS — 320 W. 25th St., Ste. 310, Cheyenne, WY, 82001, USA; tel (307) 632-9351; fax (307) 637-8538; web site www.ap.org
Bureau Chief ....Jim Clark

CIRCULATION AUDIT SERVICES

ALLIANCE FOR AUDITED MEDIA (AAM) — 48 W Seegers Rd, Arlington Heights, IL, 60005-3900, USA; tel (224) 366-6939; fax (224) 366-6949; web site www.auditedmedia.com
VP, Product Leadership — Joe Hardin
EVP, Com. Dev. — Brian Condon
Dir., Client Dev. — Kevin Rehberg
Established: 1914
Auditing of circulation for print and digital analytics to include web, mobile, and ad serving platforms.Profile:
The Alliance for Audited Media is the recognized leader in cross-media verification with unparalleled expertise across all brand platforms including web, mobile, email and print. More than 4,000 publishers, advertisers, agencies and technology vendors depend on our data-driven insights, technology certification audits and information services to transact with trust. Our leadership consists of top performers across each discipline, including directors of ad agencies, vice presidents of major national brands and publishers of leading newspapers and magazines.

Together, they are committed to setting universal benchmarks for media transparency

and excellence that elevate the entire industry.

BPA WORLDWIDE — 100 Beard Sawmill Rd, Shelton, CT, 06484-6150, USA; tel (203) 447-2800; fax (203) 447-2900; web site www.bpaww.com
Pres./CEO — Glenn Hansen
Sr. Vice Pres., Auditing — Richard J. Murphy
Established: 1930

CANADIAN CIRCULATIONS AUDIT BOARD (CCAB, INC.) — 1 Concorde Gate Suite 800, SUITE 800, Toronto, ON, M3C 3N6, Canada; tel (416) 487-2418; fax (416) 487-6405; e-mail info@bpaww.com; web site www.bpaww.com
Mktg. Mgr. — Neil Ta
Established: 1937Profile:
Bulk Distribution Audit; Select Distribution Audit.Note: Elections held in April

CANADIAN MEDIA CIRCULATION AUDIT — 37 Front Street East Suite, Toronto, ON, M5E 1B3, Canada; tel (416) 923-3567; fax (416) 923-7206; e-mail info@newspaperscanada.ca; web site www.newspaperscanada.ca
Pres. — John Hinds

MD — Tina Ongkeko
CMCA Manager — Winnie Legaspi
Established: 1919

CERTIFIED AUDIT OF CIRCULATIONS, INC. — 155 Willowbrook Blvd, Fl 4, Wayne, NJ, 07470-7032, USA; tel (973) 785-3000; fax (973) 785-8341; e-mail esodt@certifiedaudit.com; web site www.certifiedaudit.com
Dir., Opns. — David Roe
Audit Mgr. — Debbie Maragoudakis
Dir., Mktg. — Evelina Sodt
CEO — Mark Stoecklin
Established: 1956
Circulation Auditing
Readership, Reach and Advertising Value Research

CIRCULATION VERIFICATION COUNCIL — 338 S Kirkwood Rd, Unit 102, Saint Louis, MO, 63122-6166, USA; tel (314) 966-7711; fax (314) 822-0666; e-mail tbingaman@cvcaudit.com; web site www.cvcaudit.com
VP Audit Services — Jim Kennedy
Pres./CEO — Tim Bingaman
Receptionist — Sarah Black
Audit Coord. — Hannah Stevens
Buss. Mgr. — Darlene Lucy

Audit Coord. — Denise Baur
Established: 1992
Circulation Audits

SINGAPOREHAMPERS — Singapore, Robinson Road, Robinson Road, 068 876, Singapore; tel N/A; web site www.singaporehampersonline.comNote: http://www.singaporehampersonline.com

VERIFIED AUDIT CIRCULATION (VAC) — 1001 5th Ave, Ste 270, San Rafael, CA, 94901-2904, USA; tel (415) 461-6006; fax (415) 461-6007; e-mail info@verifiedaudit.com; web site www.verifiedaudit.com
CEO — Tim Prouty
VP Marketing and Sales — Alan Levy
Audit Mgr. — Jennifer Armor
Field Verification Mgr. — Josh Luck
Audit Mgr. — Tara Taylor
Audit Mgr. — Wren Tracy
Accountant — Julie Vega
Account Coord. — Julie Ghezzi
Established: 1951
Print and electronic media auditing, readership surveys research and field auditing.

CLIP ART SERVICES

B&B - BANKER & BRISEBOIS ADVERTISING — 901 Tower Dr, Ste 315, Troy, MI, 48098-2817, USA
(248) 519-9200; fax (248) 519-9206; e-mail bbinfo@bbfurnitureadvertising.com; web site www.bbfurnitureadvertising.com
Established: 1912
Pres. — Lee Gilmore

Profile:
Specializes in newspaper advertising for retail furniture dealers.
Furniture Ad Idea Services: Retail home furnishings ads available for ideas or to download online. Includes events, promotions, seasonal ads, departmental and positioning ads for lower-end to higher-end stores.

CENTURY FEATURES, INC. — 1420 Centre Ave, Apt 2213, Pittsburgh, PA, 15219-3535, USA
(412) 471-6533; fax (412) 765-3672
Contact — Charles Reichblum
I Bet You Didn't Know: Series of sports columns leased exclusively to automobile dealers, tire dealers, men's stores, etc; Calling

All Home Makers: Series of furniture columns leased to furniture stores; Interesting Facts: Leased exclusively to one sponso

COLEMAN ADVERTISING — PO Box 8807, Corpus Christi, TX, 78468-8807, USA
(361) 993-2277; e-mail

challengeradvertising@mail.com; web site www.challengeradvertising.com
Established: 1958
Owner — Zack Coleman
Profile:
Selling Church Page Advertising Weekly Sponsorships for Newspapers in the USA. Everyone in The Church and Support America: Advertising and selling programs with local weekly sponsorships; 3 X 4 col. SA6 proof series.

EZADSPRO — 302 Ferry St, Fl 2, Lafayette, IN, 47901-1185, USA
(765) 742-9012; fax (765) 742-2843; e-mail info@ezadspro.com; web site www.ezadspro.com
Managing Partner — Perry Rice
EZAdsPro Publisher: Online ad-building system exclusively designed for real estate and automotive classified advertising; Above the Fold publications: Industry news for advertising departments both in print, online and mobile.

JUPITER IMAGES CORP. — 6000 N Forest Park Dr, Peoria, IL, 61614-3556, USA
(309) 688-8800; fax (309) 688-3075; e-mail sales@jupiterimages.com; web site www.jupiterimages.com
Established: 1964
Vice Pres., Opns. — Mark Nickerson
All-purpose art and idea service.

JUPITERIMAGES — 232 E Pima St Ste 200-C, Tucson, AZ, 85712, USA
(520) 811-8101; fax (520) 881-1841; web site www.jupiterimages.com
Pres. — Peter Gariepy
Dir., Mktg. — Dan Burk
Clipart.com: Offers downloadable clip art via subscription.

KEISTER-WILLIAMS NEWSPAPER SERVICES, INC. — 1807 Emmet St N, # 6, Charlottesville, VA, 22901-3616, USA
(800) 293-4709; fax (434) 293-4884; e-mail kw@kwnews.com; web site www.kwnews.com
Established: 1939
Pres. — Walton C. Lindsay
Support the Church: Weekly series in two, three or four column glossy form. CD solicitation of sponsorship available through Keister in most states or by newspaper staff.

METRO EDITORIAL SERVICES — 519 8th Ave, Fl 18, New York, NY, 10018-4577, USA
(212) 947-5100; fax (212) 714-9139; e-mail mes@metro-email.com; web site www.mcg.metrocreativeconnection.com
Established: 1910
Publisher — Robert Zimmerman
Exec. Vice Pres./Mktg. Dir. — Debra Weiss
Mktg. Mgr. — Lauren Lekoski
VP, Sales — Jo Ann Shapiro
Regional Sales Mgr. — Lou Ann Sornson
Regional Sales Mgr. — Tina Dentner
Regional Sales Mgr. — Cathy Agee
Regional Sales Mgr. — Gwen Tomaselli
Regional Sales Mgr. — Jennifer Steiner
Joann Johnson
Profile:
Metro Creative Graphics, Inc. is the leading provider of advertising, creative, and editorial resources specifically designed to help media companies make money with their print, online, and mobile products. With an unparalleled dedication to providing the finest resources available for ready-to-use images, spec ads, ideas, stock-quality photos, logos/trademarks, auto manufacturer photos, marketing/sales materials and training tools, copyright-free editorial features, print templated sections, online e-Sections, and groundbreaking digital ad development tools — plus custom image, ad design, and editorial services — Metro is unmatched in serving the creative needs of today's media companies.

CREATIVE SERVICES FOR PRINT, ONLINE AND MOBILE:
MetroCreativeConnection.com (MCC) is your one-stop resource for all your creative images, ads, editorial and planning needs for online, mobile and print projects. Here, you will access the ultimate database of industry-specific material, comprised of the content from each of Metro's services. Conveniently delivered to you online in the MCC Libraries, it is accessible to an unlimited number of users, any time, anywhere, from any computer with Internet access. Easily search and download from the ever-growing collection of
images, hi-res photos and spec ad templates within MCC. You can also benefit from MCC's unique Project Organizer — save selections; connect people or departments with shared projects; create virtual teams for increased productivity and communication. MCC is the must-have resource to increase efficiency in your daily workflow, from planning to production. Complete ads are delivered in QuarkXPress® and InDesign® formats, with individual ad elements conveniently available for customizing in any other application. The services in the MCC Libraries include:

Metro® Newspaper Service – This indispensable resource of art, photos, ads and ideas is one that every publication needs to fulfill the daily creative demands of advertisers and production teams. With the in-depth compilation of timely images, ideas and spec ads, you are fully covered for every sellable event and important advertiser category. Corresponding Web ads are also provided for all key advertisers.

Metro Campaigns & Classified – Innovative ads, campaigns and promotions form the core of this service, including art and photos for your important automotive, recruitment and real estate print and online advertising needs. Further increase ad sales armed with campaigns for key advertisers, themed directories, self-promotion ads and circulation-building ideas, as well as print and Web ad combos.

MiAD Spec Ad Library – Spec ads sell, and this monthly service is ready to go with ad layouts based on popular advertising themes such as bridal, home, automotive services, health and fitness, pets, seniors and more. Themes correspond to at least one of the most saleable ad categories of the month, and complement one or more of the fully-templated section themes. Corresponding Web ads are also included for selected advertisers. Plus, all ads are MiAD enabled for immediate customization and presentation.

Metro Holiday Advertising Service – This guaranteed moneymaker for your holiday selling season contains holiday art, photos, covers, headings and ads covering the biggest end-of-year sales opportunities. Spanning the season from Thanksgiving through Christmas and New Year's, this is one complete, easy-to-sell package for boosting end-of-year revenue.

Metro Automotive Photos Library – In a single, easy-to-use location, this exceptional online service gives you a valuable archive of auto images from 2000 to present, for all makes and models. Choose from multiple, consistently lit views of each vehicle, color views for every manufacturer color, three interior shots of each vehicle, as well as location backgrounds
for use with any model, to satisfy your auto advertisers and ad designs.

Metro Logos & Trademarks Library – Choose from the thousands of color and black-and-white logos and trademarks you need to assist advertisers in connecting their businesses with the nationally known brands that consumers want, in one easy-to-use

location.

METRO EDITORIAL SERVICES:
Online e-Sections – Premium quality, online e-Sections — ready to go live and sell — help you improve your online presence and grow revenue with a program that takes minimal effort yet delivers a maximum return. Sites like these can change the game for you in terms of online advertisers, and visitors, who will flock to your timely and engaging online e-Sections. Say goodbye to old-fashioned section pdfs and hello to new online revenue.

Fully-templated Print Special Sections (TSS) – Two professionally-designed, fully-templated sections are available each month for key topics that are ready to present, sell and print. The time savings alone needed to create each of these dynamic sections is reason enough to subscribe. Each Templated Special Section corresponds to an online Metro e-Section so you also increase your opportunities for print and Web combination sales.

Metro Editorial Features – Get copyright-free, non-branded stories for print or online use in specialty and everyday pages and publications. Find features for themes such as home, health and pets, as well as general-interest, calendar- and event-related stories. In addition, benefit from bonus, reader-friendly content, perfect for sponsorships, including: Weekly crossword, word search, word scramble and Crypto Fun puzzles; Kids' Corner educational games and trivia; recipes; horoscopes; as well as daily Sudoku puzzles.

AD DEVELOPMENT SERVICES™ (ADS):
ADS is your go-to resource for print and online programs and tools that help increase productivity, cost-savings and revenue.

Metro e-Connect – Here is a multimedia advertising solution that you and your advertisers will love for driving cross-platform sales. Key features include: Online e-Sections (described above) and Storefronts. Storefronts give you a wide range of possibilities for creating Web sites, literally, for: Individual advertisers to highlight their business and timely offers; special events such as fairs; sports teams... you name it. Ready to implement through a user-friendly CMS, all e-Sections and Storefronts can be live in minutes so you can start selling and significantly increase online revenue.

Metro interactive Ad Designer™ (MiAD) Desktop & Mobile – With the revolutionary desktop version, you can make spec ads and finished ads with only a Web browser and an Internet connection. MiAD is simple to use, yet delivers sophisticated results, making it the perfect resource for easily and quickly creating spec ads for every sales call. For on-the-go help, MiAD mobileTM let's you create and present spec ads on a tablet. Ads from each of Metro's services are MiAD-enabled to provide the options needed for all advertisers.

Metro ADS On Demand™ (AOD) – Custom print, Web and mobile ads designed within your client specifications and deadline is what Metro ADS On Demand is all about. From the simplest to the most complex ad and design work, know that AOD is available to you with a convenient online order form, fast turnaround, no long-term contracts and no ad quantity commitments — the help you need, when you need it.

SALES IDEAS, PLANNING & TRAINING TOOLS:
These added-value resources are designed to help you get the most out of your Metro services with plan-ahead tools, training and ideas, ideas, ideas!

Metro Plus Business® – Monthly articles describe the "how-tos" of executing successful

ad and promotion ideas that other media publishers have already proven profitable for creating special sections, contests, themed pages, sales incentives, special events, Web pages, and more. Search, select and print stories from the MCC Plus Business Library, as
well as the popular MetroIdeas pages and Weekly Sales Tips e-mails.

Metro Interactive Planning Calendar – This indispensable tool puts a first-rate information resource at your fingertips. Continuously updated, this perpetual calendar of monthly, weekly and daily events, with contact information and sales tips, will help you seize every opportunity to generate revenue throughout the year.

Metro Client Services & Training – Our renowned Regional Managers and Client Services team is here to help answer your questions, provide technical support, and take custom requests. Ongoing e-mail communications, Webinars and training tools are a further extension to this valuable support component, as well as individual and group training.

Metro Print Books & e-Editions – View new service content from Metro Newspaper Service (MNS), Campaigns & Classified, and MiAD Spec Ad Library in our print book. Or, view them individually via e-Edition from which you can also print or download the entire issue. e-Editions are also available for the Web Ads Supplement (part of MNS) and Metro Editorial Services features.

NEWS USA, INC. — 1069 W Broad St, Ste 205, Falls Church, VA, 22046-4610, USA
(800) 355-9500; e-mail office@newsusa.com

NEWSUSA, INC. — 1069 W Broad St, Ste 205, Falls Church, VA, 22046-4610, USA
(703) 462-2700; web site www.newsusa.com
Established: 1987
Vice Pres., Sales — Richard Rothstein
Pub. — Rick Smith
Features: Print features, in AP style, carry the messages of Fortune 500 companies, nonprofit organizations, public relations agencies, smaller companies and individual entrepreneurs. Byline articles, evergreen features and seasonal and timely features ar

NORTH AMERICAN PRECIS SYNDICATE, INC. — 415 Madison Ave, Fl 12, New York, NY, 10017-7947, USA
(212) 867-9000; fax (800) 990-4329; e-mail service@napsnet.com; info@napsnet.com; web site www.napsnet.com
Established: 1958
Pres. — Dorothy York
Vice Pres., Media Rel. — Gary Lipton
Ed. in Chief — Candace Leiberman
Serv. Mgr. — Yauling Wagner
Featurettes (Free Filler/Feature Service): Free repro proofs, CD-ROMS or diskettes of cartoons, features and fillers from PR sources mailed once a week; free on behalf of 700 non-profit organizations, trade associations and government agencies to newspape

SYNDICATED AD FEATURES, INC. — 1 Foxhill Dr, Ste 110, Walpole, MA, 02081-4418, USA
(800) 783-5600; fax (508) 668-2168; e-mail info@synadinc.com; web site www.synadinc.com
Established: 1967
Pres. — David G. Margolis
Vice Pres./Eastern Regl. Sales Dir. — Bill Blumsack
Mid-Atlantic Regl. Sales Mgr. — Tim Wydro
Richard Ross
Office Mgr. — Susan Gundersen
Comptroller — Jodi Rutkowski
Profile:

Specialized ad agency
Personalized Columns: Ghostwrites feature columns for businesses and medical professions professionals that appear under the client's picture and by-line in his or her local newspaper on an exclusive basis. The program consists of a 52-week supply of informative, timely, highly ethical and different

columns/articles each week. It builds new and repeat customers/clients/patients. Also available on a client website and/or in a blog.

THOUGHT EQUITY MANAGEMENT, INC.
— 1530 16th St, Fl 6, Denver, CO, 80202-1447, USA
(720) 382-2869; fax (720) 382-2719; e-mail sales@thoughtequity.com; web site www.thoughtequity.com
Established: 2003
Founder/CEO — Kevin Schaff

CTO — Mark Lemmons
Vice Pres., Mktg. — Mike Emerson
Vice Pres., Bus. Devel. — Frank Cardello
Thought Equity Libraries: Supplier of motion content to newspaper, cable and broadcast companies. Thousands of affordable, top-quality ads and commercials are searchable and accessible online.

CLIPPING BUREAUS

ALLEN'S PRESS CLIPPING BUREAU —
215 W 6th St, Apt 1100, Los Angeles, CA, 90014-1931, USA; tel (213) 628-4214; fax (213) 627-0889; e-mail la@allenspcb.com; web site www.allenspress.4t.com
Office Mgr — Linda Wiser

ALLEN'S PRESS CLIPPING BUREAU —
657 Mission St, Ste 602, San Francisco, CA, 94105-4120, USA; tel (415) 392-2353; fax (415) 362-6208; web site www.allenspress.4t.com
Gen. Mgr. — John N. McCombs

ALLEN'S PRESS CLIPPING BUREAU
— 621 SW Alder St, Ste 540, Portland, OR, 97205-3620, USA; tel (503) 223-7824; fax (503) 223-3819; e-mail portland@allenspcb.com; web site www.allenspress.4t.com
Office Mgr — Whit Draper

ALLEN'S PRESS CLIPPING BUREAU —
1218 3rd Ave, Ste 1010, Seattle, WA, 98101-3290, USA; tel (206) 622-8312; fax (206) 622-5748; e-mail seattle@allenspcb.com; web site www.allenspress.4t.comEstablished: 1888
Regional Manager — Grace Chrystie

ARKANSAS NEWSPAPER CLIPPING SERVICE — 411 S Victory St, Ste 201, Little Rock, AR, 72201-2935, USA; tel (573) 474-1000; fax (573) 474-1001; e-mail sfrieling@newsgroup.comEstablished: 1995
Mgr. — Shirley Anderson

BURRELLESLUCE — 30 B Vreeland Road, # B, Florham Park, NJ, 7932, USA; tel (973) 992-6600 ; fax (973) 992-7675; e-mail inquiry@burrellesluce.com; web site www.burrellesluce.comEstablished: 1888
Chrmn./ CEO — Robert C. Waggoner
Pres./COO — John P. French
VP, Director of National Sales — Rick Melchers
Director of Publisher Services — Steven Townsley
Senior VP, Content Management — Daniel Schaible
Content Acquisition Specialist — Michael Lillis

CISION AB — Linnegatan 87A, Stockholm, SE-114 88, Sweden; tel 507 410 00; fax 507

417 17; e-mail support.se@cision.com; web site www.cision.com
Pres. — Hans Gieskes
Gen. Mgr. — Magnus Thell
Commun. Mgr. — Ulrika Nyberg

CISION CANADA LTD. — 150 Ferrand Dr., Ste. 1100, Toronto, ON, M3C 3E5, Canada; tel (416) 750-2220; fax (416) 750-2233; e-mail sales@cision.com; web site www.cision.com
Pres. — Phil Crompton
Gen. Mgr., Print Monitoring — Gary LaRose

CISION US, INC. — 332 S Michigan Ave, Chicago, IL, 60604-4434, USA; tel (866) 639-5087; fax (312) 922-3127; e-mail info.us@cision.com; web site www.cision.com
Vice Pres., Bus. Devel. — Michael Renderman
Exec.Dir. — Diana Eagen

COLORADO PRESS CLIPPING SERVICE
— 1120 N Lincoln St, Ste 912, Denver, CO, 80203-2138, USA; tel (303) 571-5117; fax (303) 571-1803; e-mail coloradopress@colopress.net; web site www.coloradopressassociation.com
CEO — Jerry Raehal

ILLINOIS PRESS CLIPPING BUREAU —
900 Community Dr, Springfield, IL, 62703-5180, USA; tel (217) 241-1300; fax (217) 241-1301; e-mail rkline@illinoispress.org; web site www.IllinoisPress.org
Executive Director — Sam Fisher

INTERNATIONAL PRESS CUTTING BUREAU — 224/236 Walworth Rd., London, ENG, SE17 1JE, UK; tel 7708 2113; fax 7701 4489; e-mail info@ipcb.co.uk; web site www.ipcb.co.uk
Sr. Partner/Gen. Mgr. — Robert Podro

IOWA PRESS CLIPPING BUREAU — 319 E. 5th St., Ste. 6, Ste 6, Des Moines, IA, 50309, USA; tel (573) 474-1000; e-mail service@newzgroup.com/ web site www.newzgroup.com/Group: Newz Group. Established: 1996
Director of Customer Service — Sarah Frieling

KANSAS PRESS CLIPPING SERVICE —
5423 SW 7th St, Topeka, KS, 66606-2330, USA; tel (573) 474-1000; e-mail service@

newzgroup.com; web site www.newzgroup.comGroup: Newz Group. Established: 2005
Director of Customer Service — Sarah Frieling

KENTUCKY PRESS CLIPPING SERVICE - NEWZ GROUP — 409 W. Vandiver, Bldg #3, Ste. 100, Bldg 3 # STE 100, Columbia, MO, 65202, USA; tel (573) 474-1000; fax (573) 474-1001; e-mail info@newzgroup.com; web site www.newzgroup.comGroup: Geotel. Established: 1995

MISSOURI PRESS CLIPPING BUREAU - NEWZ GROUP — 409 W. Vandiver, Bldg #3, Ste. 100, Bldg 3 # STE 100, Columbia, MO, 65202, USA; tel (573) 474-1000; fax (573) 474-1001; e-mail info@newzgroup.com; web site www.newzgroup.comGroup: Geotel. Established: 1995
President/CEO — Brad Buchanan
Mgr. — Lee Brooks

NEW ENGLAND NEWSCLIP AGENCY, INC.
— 30 Vreeland Rd, # B, Florham Park, NJ, 07932-1901, USA; tel (800) 631-1160; fax (973) 992-7675; e-mail mmckenna@burrellesluce.com; web site www.burrellesluce.comGroup: BurrellesLuce.
National Sales Manager — Michael McKenna

NEW MEXICO PRESS CLIPPING BUREAU - NEWZ GROUP — 409 W. Vandiver, Bldg #3, Ste. 100, Bldg 3 # STE 100, Columbia, MO, 65202, USA; tel (573) 474-1000; fax (573) 474-1001; e-mail info@newzgroup.com; web site www.newzgroup.comGroup: Geotel. Established: 1995

NEWZ GROUP — 409 Vandiver Dr, Bldg 3, Columbia, MO, 65202-3754, USA; tel (573) 474-1000; fax (573) 474-1001; e-mail info@newzgroup.com; web site www.newzgroup.comEstablished: 1991
Pres. — Brad Buchanan
Vice Pres. — Scott Buchanan
Vice President — Ian Buchanan

ROMEIKE LTD. — Romeike House, 290-296 Green Lanes, Palmers Green, London, N13 5TP, UK; tel 882 0155; fax 882 6716; web site www.romeike.com
— Giselle Bodie

— Michael HigginsMng. Dir.s

SOUTH CAROLINA PRESS CLIPPING BUREAU — 106 Outlet Pointe Blvd, Columbia, SC, 29210-5669, USA; tel (573) 474-1000; e-mail service@newzgroup.com; web site www.newzgroup.comGroup: Newz Group. Established: 1999
Director of Customer Service — Sarah Frieling

SOUTH DAKOTA NEWSPAPER ASSOCIATION — 1125 32nd Ave, Brookings, SD, 57006-4707, USA; tel (605) 692-4300; fax (605) 692-6388; e-mail sdna@sdna.com; web site www.sdna.comEstablished: 1882
Exec. Dir. — David Bordewyk
Advertising Sales Director — John Brooks
Business Manager — Nicole Herrig
Advertising Placement Coordinator — Sandy DeBeer

TENNESSEE PRESS SERVICE, INC. — 625 Market St, Ste 1100, Knoxville, TN, 37902-2219, USA; tel (865) 584-5761; fax (865) 558-8687; e-mail info@tnpress.com; web site www.tnadvertising.bizEstablished: 1947
Exec. Dir. — Greg Sherrill
Director of Advertising — David Wells

VIRGINIA CLIPPING SERVICE — 10195 Maple Leaf Ct, Ashland, VA, 23005-8136, USA; tel (804) 550-5114; fax (804) 550-5116; e-mail virginiaclipping@burrellesluce.com; web site www.vaclippingservice.com
Client Servs. Mgr. — Duska Adams

WEST VIRGINIA PRESS CLIPPING BUREAU - NEWZ GROUP — 409 W. Vandiver, Bldg #3, Ste. 100, Bldg 3 # STE 100, Columbia, MO, 65202, USA; tel (573) 474-1000; fax (573) 474-1001; e-mail info@newzgroup.com; web site www.newzgroup.comGroup: Geotel. Established: 1995

WYOMING NEWSPAPER CLIPPING SERVICE — 409 Vandiver Dr, Bldg 3 # STE 100, Columbia, MO, 65202-3754, USA; tel (573) 474-1000; fax (573) 474-1001; e-mail info@newzgroup.comGroup: Geotel. Established: 1995

ELECTRONIC CLIPPING BUREAUS

ASSOCIATED PRESS INFORMATION SERVICES—450 W 33rd St New York, NY 10001-2603, USA; tel (212) 621-1500; fax (212) 621-7520; e-mail info@ap.org; web site www.ap.org
Dir. Sales — Ted Mendelsohn

BURRELLESLUCE—30 B Vreeland Road # B Florham Park, NJ 7932, USA; tel (973) 992-6600 ; fax (973) 992-7675; e-mail inquiry@burrellesluce.com; web site www.burrellesluce.com Established: 1888
Chrmn./ CEO — Robert C. Waggoner

Pres./COO — John P. French
VP, Director of National Sales — Rick Melchers
Director of Publisher Services — Steven Townsley
Senior VP, Content Management — Daniel

Schaible
Content Acquisition Specialist — Michael Lillis

IOWA PRESS CLIPPING BUREAU—319 E. 5th St., Ste. 6 Ste 6 Des Moines, IA 50309,

USA; tel (573) 474-1000; e-mail service@
newzgroup.com; web site www.newzgroup.com/
Group:Newz Group.
Established: 1996
Director of Customer Service — Sarah
Frieling

**KENTUCKY PRESS CLIPPING SERVICE
- NEWZ GROUP**—409 W. Vandiver, Bldg #3,
Ste. 100 Bldg 3 # STE 100 Columbia, MO
65202, USA; tel (573) 474-1000; fax (573) 474-
1001; e-mail info@newzgroup.com; web site
www.newzgroup.com
Group:Geotel.
Established: 1995

**MISSOURI PRESS CLIPPING BUREAU
- NEWZ GROUP**—409 W. Vandiver, Bldg #3,
Ste. 100 Bldg 3 # STE 100 Columbia, MO
65202, USA; tel (573) 474-1000; fax (573) 474-
1001; e-mail info@newzgroup.com; web site
www.newzgroup.com
Group:Geotel.
Established: 1995
President/CEO — Brad Buchanan
Mgr. — Lee Brooks

**NEW MEXICO PRESS CLIPPING BUREAU
- NEWZ GROUP**—409 W. Vandiver, Bldg #3,
Ste. 100 Bldg 3 # STE 100 Columbia, MO
65202, USA; tel (573) 474-1000; fax (573) 474-

1001; e-mail info@newzgroup.com; web site
www.newzgroup.com
Group:Geotel.
Established: 1995

PROQUEST DIALOG—789 E Eisenhower
Pkwy Ann Arbor, MI 48108-3218, USA; e-mail
customer@dialog.com; web site proquest.com/
go/pqd

**WEST VIRGINIA PRESS CLIPPING
BUREAU - NEWZ GROUP**—409 W. Vandiver,
Bldg #3, Ste. 100 Bldg 3 # STE 100 Columbia,
MO 65202, USA; tel (573) 474-1000; fax (573)
474-1001; e-mail info@newzgroup.com; web
site www.newzgroup.com
Group:Geotel.
Established: 1995

YELLOWBRIX—200 North Glebe Road, Ste.
1025 Ste 1025 Arlington, VA 22203, USA ;
tel (703) 548-3300; fax (703) 548-9151; e-mail
info@yellowbrix.com; web site www.yellowbrix.
com
Founder/Pres./CEO — Jeffrey P. Massa
Adv. Mgr. — Tom Hargis

NEWSPAPER BROKERS AND APPRAISERS

ADMEDIA PARTNERS, INC. — 3 Park Ave,
Fl 31, New York, NY, 10016-5902, USA; tel
(212) 759-1870; fax (212) 888-4960; e-mail
info@admediapartners.com; web site www.
admediapartners.com; Established 1990
Mgr. Dir. — Seth R. Alpert
Principal — Oliver Schweitzer
Managing Dir. — Greg Smith
Managing Dir. — Andy Schoder
Managing Dir. — Adam Birnbaum
Managing Dir. — Mike Mortell

**ASSOCIATED TEXAS NEWSPAPERS,
INC.** — 4100 Jackson Ave, Apt 460, Austin,
TX, 78731-6067, USA; tel (512) 407-8283;
fax (512) 407-8289; e-mail Billberger@austin.
rr.com; web site www.hondoanvilherald.com;
Established 1886
Pres. — Bill Berger
Vice Pres. — Jeff Berger

CAPITAL ENDEAVORS, INC. — 232 W
Crogan St, Ste C, Lawrenceville, GA, 30046-
4853, USA; tel (770) 962-8399; fax (770) 962-
8640; e-mail davidstill@capitalendeavors.com;
web site www.capitalendeavors.com
Pres. — David R. Still

CBS ASSOCIATES — 423 Sutton Cir, Danville,
CA, 94506-1154, USA; tel (925) 736-6350; fax
(925) 736-3034
Contact — Carl B. Shaver

CRIBB, GREENE & COPE LLC — 825 Great
Northern Blvd, Ste 202, Helena, MT, 59601-
3340, USA; tel (406) 579-2925; fax (866) 776-
8010; e-mail jcribb@cribb.com; web site www.
cribb.com; Established 1923
Managing Dir. — John Cribb
Managing Dir. — Gary Greene
Dir. — Randy Cope
Assoc. — John Thomas Cribb

DIRKS, VAN ESSEN & MURRAY — 119 E
Marcy St, Ste 100, Santa Fe, NM, 87501-2092,
USA; tel (505) 820-2700; fax (505) 820-2900;
web site www.dirksvanessen.com; Established
1980
Pres. — Owen D. Van Essen
Exec. Vice Pres. — Philip W. Murray
Vice Pres. — Sara April
Analyst — Holly Myers

FOURNIER MEDIA SERVICES, INC. — 613
7th St, Prosser, WA, 99350-1459, USA; tel
(206) 409-9216; fax (509) 786-1779; e-mail
mutinybaydad@aol.com; web site www.
recordbulletin.com; Established 1982
Pres. — John L. Fournier

FRENCH, BARRY — 3 Ashlawn Rd, Assonet,
MA, 02702-1105, USA; tel (508) 644-5772;

e-mail barryfrench@yahoo.com; Established
1986
Pres. — Barry French

GAUGER MEDIA SERVICE, INC. — PO Box
627, Raymond, WA, 98577-0627, USA; tel (360)
942-3560; e-mail dave@gaugermedia.com; web
site www.gaugermedia.com; Established 1987
Pres/Broker — Dave Gauger

GOLD COUNTY ADVISORS, INC. — 604
Sutter St, Ste 394, Folsom, CA, 95630-2698,
USA; tel (916) 673-9778; fax (888) 933-0807;
e-mail jeff@goldcountryadvisors.com; web site
www.goldcountryadvisors.com; Established
2003
Principal — Jeffrey Potts

GRIMES, MCGOVERN & ASSOCIATES
— 10 W 15th St, Apt 903, New York, NY,
10011-6823, USA; tel (917) 881—6563; e-mail
lgrimes@mediamergers.com; web site www.
mediamergers.com; Established 1959
Chmn./Adv. — Larry Grimes
V.P., Head of Newspaper Division — Julie
Bergman
Senior Associate-Northeast/New England —
John Szefc
Senior Associate- Southeast/South — David
Slavin
Owner, CEO — John McGovern
Senior Associate-Southern States — Lewis
Floyd
Founder — Walter Grimes
Sr. Assoc.-SW/Plains — Gary Borders
Sr. Assoc.-CANADA-Mag. & Newspapers —
Gord Carley
Sr. Advisor-Newspapers — Joe Bella
Sr. Assoc.-Western/Mtn. States — Ken
Amundson
Senior Associate-Sales Nationwide — Ken
Blum

HARRIS WILLIAMS & CO. — 575 Market St,
Fl 31, San Francisco, CA, 94105-2854, USA;
tel (415) 288-4260; fax (415) 288-4269; e-mail
tarmstrong@harriswilliams.com; web site www.
harriswilliams.com
Mng. Dir. — Tiff B. Armstrong

HARRIS WILLIAMS & CO. — 1001 Haxall
Pt, Fl 9, Richmond, VA, 23219-3944, USA; tel
(804) 648-0072; fax (804) 648-0073; e-mail
kbaker@harriswilliams.com; web site www.
harriswilliams.com; Established 1999
Marketing Director — Kimberly Baker

HARVEY, FAYE — PO Box 1410, Lebanon,
MO, 65536-1410, USA; tel (417) 532-4809;
e-mail f_harvey@hotmail.com
Broker — Faye Harvey

HEMPSTEAD & CO., INC. — 807 N Haddon
Ave, Haddonfield, NJ, 08033-1749, USA; tel
(856) 795-6026; fax (856) 795-4911; e-mail
jeh@hempsteadco.com; web site www.
hempsteadco.com
Mng. Dir. — Mark Penny

JORDAN, EDMISTON GROUP, INC. — 150
E 52nd St, Fl 18, New York, NY, 10022-6260,
USA; tel (212) 754-0710; fax (212) 754-0337;
e-mail adamg@jegi.com; web site www.jegi.
com
CEO — Wilma Jordan
COO — Bill Hitzig
Mng. Dir. — Tolman Geffs
Mng. Dir. — Michael Marchesano
Mng. Dir. — Richard Mead
Mng. Dir. — Scott Peters
Vice Pres., Mktg. — Adam Gross

KAMEN & CO. GROUP SERVICES — 626
Rxr Plz, Uniondale, NY, 11556-0626, USA;
tel (516) 379-2797; fax (516) 379-3812;
e-mail info@kamengroup.com; web site www.
kamengroup.com; Established 1981
Pres./CEO — Kevin Brian Kamen
Vice Pres. — Celeste Myers

**KEVIN BRIAN KAMEN & CO. (KAMEN &
CO. GROUP SERVICES)** — 626 Rxr Plz,
Uniondale, NY, 11556-0626, USA; tel (516)
379-2797; fax (516) 379-3812; e-mail info@
KamenGroup.com; web site www.KamenGroup.
com; Established 1981
Pres./CEO — Kevin Brian Kamen
Vice Pres., New York — Gary R. Kamen
Vice Pres., Tampa — Rosalyn Kamen
Gen. Mgr., Los Angeles — Mathew Kamen
Office Mgr. — Mary Hiscock
Office Mgr. — Tom Horowitz

KNOWLES MEDIA BROKERAGE SERVICES
— PO Box 910, Carroll, IA, 51401-0910, USA;
tel (712) 792-2179; fax (712) 792-2309; e-mail
gregg.knowles@netzero.com; web site www.
media-broker.com; Established 1987
Owner — Gregg Knowles

MANAGEMENT PLANNING, INC. — 5401 S
Kirkman Rd, Ste 310, Orlando, FL, 32819-7937,
USA; tel (407) 599-0060; fax (407) 641-8778;
e-mail jgitto@mpival.com; web site www.
mpival.com
Vice Pres. — Joseph A. Gitto

MANAGEMENT PLANNING, INC. — 70
W Madison St, Ste 1400, Chicago, IL, 60602-
4267, USA; tel (312) 214-6141; fax (312) 214-
3110; e-mail sroberts@mpival.com; web site
www.mpival.com
Vice Pres. — Stephen J. Roberts

MANAGEMENT PLANNING, INC. — 300
Park Ave, Ste 1700, New York, NY, 10022-7402,
USA; tel (212) 572-6291; fax (212) 572-6499;
e-mail jhardwick@mpival.com; web site www.
mpival.com
Reg'l Dir. — John H. Hardwick

MANAGEMENT PLANNING, INC. — 10
Station St, Ste 3, Simsbury, CT, 06070-2258,
USA; tel (860) 651-8185; fax (860) 651-0032;
e-mail bcranshaw@mpival.com; web site www.
mpival.com
Vice Pres. — William O. Cranshaw
Gen. Mgr. — Harry.L Curtis

MANAGEMENT PLANNING, INC. — 101
Poor Farm Rd, Princeton, NJ, 08540-1941,
USA; tel (609) 924-4200; fax (609) 924-4573;
e-mail mpival.com; web site www.mpival.com
Pres. — Harry L. Curtis
Sr. Vice Pres. — Thomas A. Egan
Sr. Vice Pres. — Frank E. Koehl
Sr. Vice Pres. — Roy H. Meyers
Vice Pres. — Gerald P. Valentine

MANAGEMENT PLANNING, INC. — 77
Franklin St, Fl 5, Boston, MA, 02110-1510,
USA; tel (617) 482-6462; fax (617) 482-2515;
e-mail jweir@mpival.com; web site www.mpival.
com
Reg'l Dir. — Jeremy Weir

MAYO COMMUNICATIONS — 7248
Bernadine Ave, Fl 2, West Hills, CA, 91307-
1410, USA; tel (818) 340-5300; fax ; e-mail
Publicity@mayocommunications.com; web site
www.MAYOCommunications.com; Established
1995
CEO & President — Aida Mayo

MEDIA AMERICA BROKERS — 1130
Piedmont Ave NE, Apt 912, Atlanta, GA,
30309-3783, USA; tel (404) 875-8787; e-mail
lonwwilliams@aol.com; Established 1989
Owner — Lon W Williams

MEDIA SERVICES GROUP, INC. — 149 S
Roscoe Blvd, Ponte Vedra, FL, 32082-4127,
USA; tel (904) 285-3239; fax (904) 285-5618;
e-mail george@mediaservicesgroup.com; web
site www.mediaservicesgroup.com
Mng. Dir. — George R. Reed
Dir. — William H. Lytle
Dir. — Robert J. Maccini
Dir. — Thomas McKinley
Dir. — Gregory Merrill
Dir. — William L. Whitley
Dir. — Jody McCoy
Assoc. — Eddie Esserman
Assoc. — Stephan Sloan

NATIONAL MEDIA ASSOCIATES — PO Box 849, Ada, OK, 74821-0849, USA; tel (580) 421-9600; fax (580) 272-5070; e-mail bolitho@nationalmediasales.com; web site www.nationalmediasales.com; Established 1995
— Thomas Bolitho
— Edward AndersonPres.s

NATIONAL MEDIA ASSOCIATES — PO Box 2001, Branson, MO, 65615-2001, USA;

tel (417) 338-6397; fax (417) 338-6510; e-mail Brokered1@gmail.com; web site www.nationalmediasales.com; Established 1997
Owner — Edward M. Anderson

PHELPS, CUTLER & ASSOCIATES — 35 Barnard St, Ste 300, Savannah, GA, 31401-2515, USA; tel (912) 351-9122; fax (678) 826-

4708; e-mail phelpscutler@aol.com; web site www.phelpscutler.com; Established 1991
Pres. — Louise D. Phelps

RICKENBACHER MEDIA — 6731 Desco Dr, Dallas, TX, 75225-2704, USA; tel (214) 384 2779; e-mail rmedia@msn.com; web site www.rickenbachermedia.com; Established 1985
Pres./Exec. Dir. — Ted Rickenbacher
Western States Dir. — Jim Afinowich

VERONIS SUHLER STEVENSON — 55 E 52nd St, Fl 33, New York, NY, 10055-0007, USA; tel (212) 935-4990; fax (212) 381-8168; e-mail stevensonj@vss.com; web site www.vss.com
Co-Founder/Mng. Partner/Chrmn./Co-CEO — John J. Veronis
Co-Founder/Mng. Partner — John S. Suhler
Mng. Partner/Co-CEO — Jeffrey T. Stevenson

NEWSPAPER REPRESENTATIVES - FOREIGN

A

ADMARKET INTERNATIONAL (DIV. OF MARCOM INTERNATIONAL, INC.)
105 Woodrow Ave, Southport, CT, 06890-1121, USA
(203) 319-1000; fax (203) 319-1004; e-mail info@admarketintl.com; web site www.admarketintl.comEstablished: 1986
Pres./CEO — Nabil E. Fares
Acct. Exec. — Kristina Kalman
AdMarket International plans and places advertising in 15,000 media newspapers in over 200 countries worldwide

ADMAX INTERNATIONAL MEDIA
7326 McLaren Ave, West Hills, CA, 91307-2123, USA
(818) 715-9931; fax (253) 648-4574; e-mail admax@sbcglobal.net; web site www.admaxinternational.comEstablished: 1992
Pres. — Maria de los Angeles
Pres. — Edward G. Wilson
Media Dir. — Maria Teresa Perez
Acct. Exec. — Brad Brigg
Acct. Exec. — Simon English
Acct. Exec. — Larry Redd
Acct. Exec. — Julio Vender

ADVANTAGE NEWSPAPER CONSULTANTS
2850 Village Dr, Ste 102, Fayetteville, NC, 28304-3864, USA
(910) 323-0349; fax (910) 323-9280; e-mail info@newspaperconsultants.com; web site www.newspaperconsultants.comEstablished: 1996
President — Timothy O. Dellinger
General Mgr. — Susan M. Jolley
Exec. Dir. of Sales — Marie Smith
Advantage Newspaper Consultants (ANC) is recognized as the leader in TV Magazine advertising sales in the United States. ANC works with both independent publishers and major newspaper chains to increase their core product ad revenue using innovative campaigns and creative, seasoned sales professionals that produce quantifiable

results. Our sales manager's work with newspaper management to set goals and create an incentive plan which accelerates a TV Magazine sales campaign targeted towards finding key hidden revenue in their market in two weeks or less.

Using the same proven formula of enthusiastic joint sales calls and dedicated management support that has lead to thousands of successful TV magazine sales campaigns, ANC also offers a cross-platform advertising sales program - Total Market Reach (TMR) - which includes print, mobile and digital ad combo sales.

AXEL SPRINGER VERLAG AG
Axel Springer Platz 1, Hamburg, D-203, Germany; tel (49) 40
34700; fax 3472 5540; web site www.asv.de
Chrmn. — Mathias Dopfner

B

BRYDSON GLOBAL MEDIA SALES
301 W 53rd St, Apt 10E, New York, NY, 10019-5794, USA
(212) 586-7773; fax (212) 582-6353; e-mail brydmedia@aol.com; web site www.brydsonglobalmedia.comEstablished: 1980
Pres. — David Brydson

C

CHARNEY/PALACIOS & CO.
5201 Blue Lagoon Dr, Ste 200, Miami, FL, 33126-2065, USA
(786) 388-6340; fax (786) 388-9113; e-mail miami@publicitas.com; web site www.publicitas.com
CEO — Grace Palacios
Sales Mktg. Mgr. — Maria Jose Torres
Charney/Palacios is a subsidiary of Publicitas

D

DICOMM MEDIA
350 5th Ave, Fl 59, New York, NY, 10118-5999, USA
(646) 536-7206; fax (973) 335-1038; e-mail info@dicommintl.com; web site www.dicommintl.comEstablished: 1995
Gen. Mgr. — Thibaud Wallaert
A unique media sales firm which represents numerous different Canadian media companies and publishers. We also work with many clients on assisting with their planning and buying efforts in Canada across all media types including print, digital/mobile, broadcast, radio, out of home and any other medium available.

DOW JONES INTERNATIONAL MARKETING SERVICES
1155 Avenue of the Americas, Fl 7, New York, NY, 10036-2758, USA
(212) 597-5743; fax (212) 597-5833; web site www.dowjones.com
Exec. Asst. — Courtney Tate

L

LAWTON MEDIA INC.
102 SW 3rd St, Lawton, OK, 73501-4031, USA; tel (1)
(580) 353-0620; fax (580) 585-5140; e-mail srobertson@swoknews.com; web site www.swoknews.comEstablished: 1901
Pres. — David Hale

LEE & STEEL LLC
25 Burroughs Rd, Easton, CT, 06612-1409, USA
(203) 445-8900; fax (203) 445-1885; e-mail michael.lee@leeandsteel.comEstablished: 1991
CEO — Michael Lee

M

MARSTON WEBB INTERNATIONAL
60 Madison Ave, Ste 1212, New York, NY, 10010-1636, USA
(212) 684-6601; fax (212) 725-4709; e-mail marwebint@cs.com; web site www.marstonwebb.comEstablished: 1981
Pres. — Victor Webb
Vice Pres. — Madlene Olson
MWI also represents South African and Middle Eastern papers

MEMBER SERVICES COORDINATOR
37 Front St E, Suite 200, Toronto, ON, M5E 1B3, Canada
(416) 923-7724; e-mail adreach@ocna.org; web site www.adreach.ca
Group:
Ontario Community Newspapers Association
Member Services Coordinator — Kelly Gorven
Executive Director — Caroline Medwell

MULTIMEDIA, INC.
7061 Grand National Dr, Ste 127, Orlando, FL, 32819-8992, USA
(407) 903-5000; fax (407) 363-9809; e-mail info@multimediausa.com; web site www.multimediausa.com
Pres. — Fernando Mariano

P

PUBLICITAS NORTH AMERICA, INC.
330 7th Ave, Fl 5, New York, NY, 10001-5443, USA
(212)330-0720; fax (212) 599-8298; e-mail newyork@publicitas.com; web site www.publicitas.com
CFO — Joseph DeFalco

NEWSPAPER REPRESENTATIVES - NATIONAL

A

AD REPS
51 Church St, Boston, MA, 02116-5417, USA; tel (617) 542-6913; fax (617) 542-7227; e-mail adreps1@yahoo.com
Pres. — Steve Ganak

ADVANTAGE NEWSPAPER CONSULTANTS
2850 Village Dr, Ste 102, Fayetteville, NC, 28304-3864, USA; tel (910) 323-0349; fax (910) 323-9280; e-mail info@newspaperconsultants.comEstablished 1996
President — Timothy O. Dellinger
General Mgr. — Susan M. Jolley
Exec. Dir. of Sales — Marie Smith
Advantage Newspaper Consultants (ANC)

is recognized as the leader in TV Magazine advertising sales in the United States. ANC works with both independent publishers and major newspaper chains to increase their core product ad revenue using innovative campaigns and creative, seasoned sales professionals that produce quantifiable results. Our sales manager's work with newspaper management to set goals and create an incentive plan which accelerates

a TV Magazine sales campaign targeted towards finding key hidden revenue in their market in two weeks or less.

Using the same proven formula of enthusiastic joint sales calls and dedicated management support that has lead to thousands of successful TV magazine sales campaigns, ANC also offers a cross-platform advertising sales program - Total Market

Reach (TMR) - which includes print, mobile and digital ad combo sales.

ADVERTISING MEDIA PLUS, INC.
5397 Twin Knolls Rd, Ste 17, Columbia, MD, 21045-3256, USA; tel (410) 740-5077; fax (410) 740-5888; e-mail info@ampsinc.net; web site www.ampsinc.net
Group: Medinger Media LLC Established 2001
Owner and President — Daniel Medinger

AMERICAN NEWSPAPER REPRESENTATIVES, INC.
2075 W Big Beaver Rd, Ste 310, Troy, MI, 48084-3439, USA; tel (248) 643-9910; fax (248) 643-9914; web site www.gotoanr.comEstablished 1943
Pres. — John Jepsen
Exec. Vice Pres./COO — Robert Sontag
ANR represents over 9,000 daily and weekly community newspapers nationwide

AMERICAN NEWSPAPER REPRESENTATIVES, INC.
940 County Road B W, Roseville, MN, 55113-4405, USA; tel (651) 487-5778; e-mail mcox@anrinc.net; web site www.anrinc.net
Sales Mgr. — Melanie Cox

C

C-VILLE HOLDINGS LLC
308 E Main St, Charlottesville, VA, 22902-5234, USA; tel 434/817-2749; fax 434/817-2758; e-mail aimee@c-ville.com; web site www.c-ville.comEstablished 1995
Ed — Jessica Luck

CALIFORNIA NEWSPAPER SERVICE BUREAU (CNSB)
915 E 1st St, Los Angeles, CA, 90012-4050, USA; tel (213) 229-5500; fax (213) 229-5481; e-mail ari_gutierrez@dailyjournal.com; web site www.legaladstore.comEstablished 1888
Division Director
Government Advertising Division
Daily Journal Corporation and
California Newspaper Service Bureau — Ari Gutierrez
The Daily Journal Corporation is a publisher of legal and business publications, including the Los Angeles and San Francisco Daily Journals, distributed in major California cities.

Additionally, its in-house clearinghouse service provides ad placement services to government agencies, attorney's and other advertisers for legally mandated and outreach advertising including class action notices in any daily, community and/or ethnic publication and/or websites.

CAMPUS MEDIA GROUP
7760 France Ave S, Ste 800, Bloomington, MN, 55435-5929, USA; tel (952) 854-3100; e-mail info@campusmediagroup.com; web site www.campusmediagroup.comEstablished 2002
COO — Jason Bakker
Pres./CEO — Tom Borgerding
College marketing agency.

CENTRO INC.
11 E Madison St, 6th Fl., Chicago, IL, 60602-4574, USA; tel (312) 423-1565; e-mail socialmedia@centro.net; web site www.centro.netEstablished 2001
EVP, Customer Experience — Katie Risch
VP, Pub. Solutions — John Hyland

H

HARTE-HANKS COMMUNICATIONS, INC.
9601 McAllister Fwy, Ste 610, San Antonio, TX, 78216-4632, USA; tel (210) 829-9000; fax

(210) 829-9101; web site www.harte-hanks.com
Pres., Direct Mktg. — Gary Skidmore
Represents shopper publications

I

INTERSECT MEDIA SOLUTIONS
610 Crescent Executive Ct, Ste 112, Lake Mary, FL, 32746-2111, USA; tel (321) 283-5255; e-mail info@intersectmediasolutions.com; web site www.intersectmediasolutions.com
Group: Florida Press Association Established 1959
Pres./CEO — Dean Ridings
VP/CSO — Melanie Mathewson
Acct. Mgr. — Carolyn Klinger
Media Mgr. — Jessica Pitts
CFO — Mark Burger
General Counsel — Sam Morley

J

JOSEPH JACOBS ORGANIZATION
349 W 87th St, Ste 1, New York, NY, 10024-2662, USA; tel (212) 787-9400; fax (212) 787-8080; e-mail erosenfeld@josephjacobs.org; web site www.josephjacobs.orgEstablished 1919
Pres. — David Koch
Represents Jewish publications

L

LATINO 247 MEDIA GROUP
3445 Catalina Dr, Carlsbad, CA, 92010-2856, USA; tel (760) 434-1223; fax (760) 434-7476; e-mail kirk@whisler.com; web site www.latino247.newsEstablished 1996
Pres. — Kirk Whisler
General Manager — Ana Patiño
Accounting Manager — Ericka Benitez

M

MCNAUGHTON NEWSPAPERS
424 E State Pkwy, Ste 228, Schaumburg, IL, 60173-6406, USA; tel (847) 490-6000; fax (847) 843-9058; e-mail rickb@usspi.com; web site www.usspi.com
Vice President Media Relations — Rick Baranski
CEO — Philip Miller
Vice President Sales — Barbara Ancona
Executive Vice President — Michelle Hammons
Designs cost effective print and digital solutions for national/regional/local advertisers.

MEDIASPACE SOLUTIONS
904 Mainstreet, Hopkins, MN, 55343-7529, USA; tel (612) 253-3900; fax (612) 454-2848; e-mail bstcyr@mediaspace.com; web site www.mediaspacesolutions.comEstablished 1999
Chief Operating Officer — Randy Grunow
VP of Business Development & Marketing — Brian St. Cyr
Dir., Account Development — Tony Buesing
Sr. Med. Supervisor — Brian Kieser
Director of Media Development
  — Colin May
Buying Manager
  — Carol Wagner
Buying Supervisor
  — Jason Armstrong
Director Media Planning
  — Tom Johnson

METRO NEWSPAPER ADVERTISING

SERVICES, INC.
8 W 38th St, 8 W. 38th St., 4th Fl., New York, NY, 10018-6229, USA; tel (212) 576-9510; fax (212) 576-9526; e-mail billh@metrosn.com; web site www.metrosn.comEstablished 1932
Chairperson & CEO — Phyllis Cavaliere
SVP Client Services — Tack Prashad
President/COO — Michael Baratoff
Sr. Vice Pres./Midwest Sales Dir. — Carl Berg
Exec. Dir. — Tom Vorel
Sr. Vice Pres., Eastern Adv. — Bill Huck
Sr. Vice Pres., Finance — Nili DeBono
Sr. Vice Pres./Eastern Region — William Huck
New Ventures Development — Frank Grasso
Senior VP, Operations — Kim Viggiano
Metro has been creating networks for national advertisers since 1932. It places advertising for represented newspapers through its Sunday Magazine, Metro-Puck Comics and Metro ROP Networks. Please see these entries in Section V of the Year Book.

METRO NEWSPAPER ADVERTISING SERVICES, INC.
160 Spear St, Ste 1875, San Francisco, CA, 94105-5146, USA; tel (310) 798-4986; fax (310) 564-7633; e-mail kathy@metrosn.com; web site www.metrosn.com
Mgr. — Kathy Jahns
Sr. Vice Pres. — Ali Nazem

METRO SUBURBIA, INC./NEWHOUSE NEWSPAPERS
711 3rd Ave, Fl 6, New York, NY, 10017-4029, USA; tel (212) 697-8020; fax (212) 972-3146; e-mail johnt@metrosuburbia.com; web site www.metrosuburbia.com
Adv. Sales Mgr. — Kevin Drolet
Adv. Sales Mgr. — John Tingwall
Adv. Sales Mgr. — Chad Johnson
Pres. — Robert N. Schoenbacher
New York Sales Mgr. — John A. Colombo
Adv. Sales Mgr. — Jon Gold
Adv. Sales Mgr. — Brenda Goodwin-Garcia

METROLAND MEDIA GROUP LTD.
3125 Wolfedale Rd., Mississauga, ON, L5C 1W1, Canada; tel (905) 281-5656; fax (905) 279-5103; e-mail result@metroland.com; web site www.metroland.com
Pres. — Ian Oliver
Vice Pres. — Kathie Bride
Sr. Vice Pres. — Tim Whittaker
Sr. Vice Pres. — Ian McLeod
Vice Pres. — Ian Proudfoot
Vice Pres., HR — Brenda Biller
Vice Pres. — Joe Anderson
Vice Pres. — Bruce Danford
Vice Pres. — Ron Lenyk
Vice Pres. — Ken Nugent
Vice Pres. — Carol Peddie
Gordon Paolucci
Vice President — Kukle Terry
Ed-In-Chief — Lois Tuffin
John Willems
Scott Miller Cressman
Tracy Magee-Graham
Editor-In-Chief — Haggert Peter
VP, Business Development & Acquisitions — Terry Kukle

MOTIVATE, INC.
4141 Jutland Dr Ste 300, Suite 300, San Diego, CA, 92117-3658, USA; tel (866) 664-4432; e-mail marcia@MotivateROI.com; web site www.motivateROI.comEstablished 1977
Prtnr. — Marcia A. Hansen
CEO — Trevor Hansen
Motivate, Inc. represents the following target markets: Multicultural (Hispanic, African American, Asian); Youth, LGBTQ, Senior, Military.

N

NEWSPAPER NATIONAL NETWORK
41899 Waterfall Rd, Northville, MI, 48168-3267, USA; tel (248) 680-4676; fax (248) 680-4667
Sales Exec. — Larry Doyle

NEWSPAPER NATIONAL NETWORK LP
20 W 33rd St, Fl 7, New York, NY, 10001-3305, USA; tel 212-856-6300; fax 212-856-6343; e-mail rchelstowski@nnnlp.com; web site www.nnnlp.comEstablished 1994
President & CEO — Jason E. Klein
Sr. Vice Pres., Bus. Devel. — Paul C. Atkinson
CEO — Ray Chelstowski
SVP, Sales — Lynn Lehmkuhl
Vice Pres., Newspaper Rel. — Frank P. Grasso
Sr. Vice Pres., Sales — Lynn A. Lehmkuhl
Sr. Vice Pres., Mktg. — Mary Ellen Holden
Doug MacDonald
Sales Dir. — Jack Grandcolas
Sales Dir. — Mary Dowling
Sr. Vice Pres., Media/Opns. — Jerry Fragetti
Anthony Moreno
Marshall Genger

NEWSPAPERS FIRST, INC
4601 Sheridan St, Ste 317, Hollywood, FL, 33021-3433, USA; tel (954) 987-8666; fax (954) 963-0921
Vice Pres./Sales Mgr. — Lawrence J. Malloy

NEWSPAPERS FIRST, INC.
330 Madison Ave, Fl 11, New York, NY, 10017-5001, USA; tel (212) 692-7100; fax (212) 286-9004; web site www.newspapersfirst.comEstablished 1960
Pres./CEO — Bob Termotto
Sr. Vice Pres./CFO — Robert Termotto
Vice Pres., Southern Reg. — Darren Larson
Vice Pres., Eastern Reg. — Allen Dunstan

NEWSPAPERS FIRST, INC.
5757 Wilshire Blvd, Ste 570, Los Angeles, CA, 90036-3683, USA; tel (323) 549-9144; fax (323) 459-0944
Vice Pres./Sales Mgr. — Richard Riegle

NEWSPAPERS FIRST, INC.
8115 Preston Rd, Ste 640, Dallas, TX, 75225-6319, USA; tel (214) 696-8666; fax (214) 696-3416; web site www.newspapersfirst.com
Vice Pres./Sales Mgr. — Darren Larson

P

PHILADELPHIA AREA NEWSPAPERS
580 W Germantown Pike Ste 108, Plymouth Plz., Plymouth Meeting, PA, 19462-1370, USA; tel (610) 941-3555; fax (610) 941-1289; e-mail brian@phillyareapapers.com; web site www.phillyareapapers.comEstablished 1929
Pres. — R. Brian Hitchings
Acct. Supvr. — Donna DeFrangesco

PUBLICITAS MCGOWN INC.
8250 Boul Decarie Bureau 205, Montreal, QC, H4P 2P5, Canada; tel (514) 735-5191; fax (514) 342-9406; e-mail cynthia.jollymore@publicitas.com; web site www.publicitas.com
Mng. Dir. — Wayne Faint John
Vice Pres., Sales — Cynthia Jollymore
McGown/Intermac represents 25 U.S. daily newspapers

PUBLICITAS NORTH AMERICA, INC.
2701 Troy Center Dr, Ste 250, Continental Plz, Troy, MI, 48084, USA; tel (248) 720-2456; fax (248) 404-9609
Branch Dir. — Michael May

PUBLICITAS NORTH AMERICA, INC.
330 7th Ave, Fl 5, New York, NY, 10001-5443, USA; tel (212)330-0720; fax (212) 599-8298; e-mail newyork@publicitas.com; web site www.publicitas.com
CFO — Joseph DeFalco

PUBLICITAS NORTH AMERICA, INC.
330 7th Ave, Fl 18, New York, NY, 10001-5010, USA; tel (310) 601-7618; e-mail newyork@publicitas.com; web site www.publicitas.com
Senior Account Director — Francisca Hoogeveen

PUBLICITAS NORTH AMERICA, INC.
3400 Peachtree Rd NE, Ste 1700, Atlanta, GA, 30326-1187, USA; tel (404) 467-8783; fax (404) 262-3746; e-mail ppn-atlanta@publicitas.com
Branch Dir. — Sal Zammuto

PUBLICITAS NORTH AMERICA, INC.
26234 N 72nd Dr, Peoria, AZ, 85383-7331, USA; tel (623) 561-5692; fax (623) 561-5539; web site www.publicitas.com
Contact — Lisa Richmeier

PUBLICITAS NORTH AMERICA, INC.
970 N Kalaheo Ave Ste C107, Pali Palms Plaza, Kailua, HI, 96734-1871, USA; tel (808) 587-8300; fax (808) 587-8307; e-mail ppn-honolulu@publicitas.com; honolulu@publicitas.com; web site www.publicitas.com
Director Hawaii/Pacific — G. Robert Wiegand

PUBLICITAS NORTH AMERICA, INC.
13355 Noel Rd, Ste 1030, Dallas, TX, 75240-6602, USA; tel (972) 386-6187; e-mail ppn-dallas@publicitas.com
Branch Dir. — Jo Neese

PUBLICITAS NORTH AMERICA, INC.
1401 E Broward Blvd, Ste 204, Fort Lauderdale, FL, 33301-2116, USA; tel (954) 768-9992; fax (954) 768-9013
Branch Dir. — Brad Ames

PUBLICITAS NORTH AMERICA, INC.
32 Lincoln Park, San Anselmo, CA, 94960-2561, USA; tel 415-464-6899; e-mail sanfrancisco@publicitas.com; web site www.publicitas.com
Mgr. — Humberto Najar

PUBLISHERS REPRESENTATIVES OF FLORIDA, INC.
4601 W Kennedy Blvd, Ste 227, Tampa, FL, 33609-2519, USA; tel (813) 286-8299; fax (813) 287-0651; e-mail proftampa@aol.com
Mgr. — Rick Cammack
Pres. — Jim Gundry
Mgr. — Lee Knox

R

RE:FUEL
151 W 26th St, 12th Fl., New York, NY, 10001-6810, USA; tel 866-360-9688; e-mail info@refuelnow.com; web site www.refuelnow.comEstablished 1968
President/CEO — Andrew T. Sawyer
SVP, Sales — Greg Anthony
Director, Sales Strategy — Andrew O'Dell
re:fuel specializes in the military, college, Hispanic, African-American, ethnic and senior markets.

RIVENDELL MEDIA, INC.
1248 US Highway 22, Mountainside, NJ, 07092-2692, USA; tel (908) 232-2021 EXT 200; fax (908) 232-0521; e-mail info@rivendellmedia.com; web site www.rivendellmedia.comEstablished 1979
Pres. — Todd Evans
Represents LGBT publications and digital properties.

RUXTON GROUP/VMG ADVERTISING
1201 E Jefferson St, Phoenix, AZ, 85034-2300, USA; tel 1800-278-9866; fax 602.238-4805; e-mail ads@voicemediagroup.com; web site www.vmgadvertising.com
Group: Voice Media Group Established 1983
SVP Sale & Operations — Joe Larkin
SVP Sales — Susan Belair
Business Manager — Veronica Villela

S

SHELBY PUBLISHING CO. INC.
517 Green St NW, Gainesville, GA, 30501-3313, USA; tel (770) 534-8380; fax (678) 343-2197; web site www.theshelbyreport.comEstablished 1967
VP/Sales Mgr. Midwest — Geoffrey Welch
C. Ronald Johnston

T

THE NEWSPAPER NETWORK (TNN)
400 Interstate North Pkwy SE, Ste 1050, Atlanta, GA, 30339-5054, USA; tel (770) 988-1750; fax (770) 988-1756
Vice Pres., Sales (Southern Reg.) — Ann Robb
Vice Pres., Automotive Sales — June Holmes

THE NEWSPAPER NETWORK (TNN)
106 Outlet Pointe Blvd, Columbia, SC, 29210-5669, USA; tel 888-727-7377; fax 803-551-0903
Regl. Sales Mgr. — Cynthia Miller
Regl. Sales Exec. — LaTrecia Hopson
Regl. Sales Exec. — Stephanie Stanton

THE NEWSPAPER NETWORK (TNN)
350 5th Ave, Rm 1802, New York, NY, 10118-0110, USA; tel (212) 268-1540; fax (212) 268-1541
Regl. Sales Mgr. — Rita Jurczyk

TOWMAR REPRESENTACIONES S.A.
Presa Endho # 11, Col. Irrigacion, M.H., Mexico City, FL, 11500, Mexico; tel (55) 5395-5888; fax (55) 5395-4985; e-mail INFO@towmar.net; web site www.towmar.netEstablished 1967
Pres. — Juan Martinez Dugay
Pres. — Juan Martinez Dugay
VP, Sales — Cesar Quijas
New address

TRIBUNE 365
2839 Paces Ferry Rd SE, Ste 1105, Atlanta, GA, 30339-5770, USA; tel (770) 433-9554; fax (770) 433-1927; web site www.ctmgadvertise.com
Atlanta Mgr. — Gail Brinkman

TRIBUNE 365
19500 Victor Pkwy, Ste 100, Livonia, MI, 48152-7012, USA; tel (734) 464-6500; fax (734) 464-7188; web site www.ctmgadvertise.com
Detroit Mgr. — Mark Barrons

TRIBUNE 365
220 E 42nd St, Rm 400, New York, NY, 10017-5833, USA; tel 212-448-2620; e-mail kvansaun@tribune.com; web site www.tribune.com

Dir., Mktg. — Irina David
Account Director — Kimberly Michaud

TRIBUNE 365
3107 Stirling Rd, Ste 205, Fort Lauderdale, FL, 33312-8502, USA; tel (954) 989-8833; fax (954) 963-3395; web site www.ctmgadvertise.com
Florida Mgr. — Berry Werblow

TRIBUNE MEDIA NETWORK
12900 Preston Rd, Ste 615, Dallas, TX, 75230-1322, USA; tel (972) 789-6920; fax (972) 239-2737; web site www.tribunemediagroup.com
Southwestern Regl. Sales Dir. — Grant Moise

TRIBUNE MEDIA NETWORK
100 Bush St, Ste 925, San Francisco, CA, 94104-3920, USA; tel (415) 693-5600; fax (415) 391-4992; web site www.tribunemediagroup.com
Mgr. — Neal Zimmerman

TRIBUNE MEDIA NETWORK
202 W 1st St, Los Angeles, CA, 90012-4299, USA; tel (213) 237-2135; fax (213) 237-2007
Pres./CEO — Peter Liguori
Dir., Western Reg. — Richard Jones

V

VOICE MEDIA GROUP
969 N Broadway, Denver, CO, 80203-2705, USA; tel (602) 271-0040; e-mail joe.larkin@voicemediagroup.com; web site www.voicemediagroup.com
Sr. Vice Pres. Sales — Joe Larkin
Vice Pres., Sales — Susan Belair
Newspaper represents for 50 alternative newsweeklies

W

WIDE AREA CLASSIFIED
113 N Minnesota St, New Ulm, MN, 56073-1729, USA; tel 800-324-8236; fax 866-822-5487; e-mail info@wideareaclassifieds.com; web site www.wideareaclassifieds.comEstablished 1986
Exec. Dir. — Shannon Reinhart
Represents shopper publications in 50 states

NEWSPAPER REPRESENTATIVES - STATE

ADNETWORKNY — 109 Twin Oaks Dr, Ste D, Syracuse, NY, 13206-1204, USA; tel (315) 472-6007; fax (877) 790-1976; e-mail ads@fcpny.com; web site www.fcpny.comEst.: 1950
Exec. Dir. — Dan Holmes
Sales & Training Director — Tom Cuskey
AdNetworkNY is the advertising arm of Free Community Papers of NY (FCPNY), an association of free distribution publishers delivering to more than 3.2 million homes across the Empire State.
AdNetworkNY enables advertisers to reach all or parts of New York through classified, display and insert advertising. Low CPM's and high readership brings great value for your ad dollar.
Classified and display advertising

ALABAMA NEWSPAPER ADVERTISING SERVICE, INC. — 3324 Independence Dr, Ste 200, Birmingham, AL, 35209-5602, USA; tel (205) 871-7737; fax (205) 871-7740; e-mail mail@alabamapress.org; web site www.alabamapress.org
Exec. Dir. — Felicia Mason
Adv. Mgr. — Brad English

ALLIED DAILY NEWSPAPERS OF WASHINGTON — 1110 Capitol Way S, Olympia, WA, 98501-2251, USA; tel (360) 943-9960; fax (360) 943-9962; e-mail anewspaper@aol.com
Exec. Dir. — Rowland Thompson

ANA ADVERTISING SERVICES, INC. (ARIZONA NEWSPAPER ASSOCIATION) — 1001 N Central Ave, Ste 670, Phoenix, AZ, 85004-1947, USA; tel (602) 261-7655; fax (602) 261-7525; e-mail office@ananews.com; web site www.ananews.comEst.: 1931
Exec. Dir. — Paula Casey
Media Buyer — Cindy London
Communications Manager — Julie O'Keefe
Represents daily and weekly newspapers in Arizona

ARKANSAS PRESS SERVICES — 411 S Victory St, Little Rock, AR, 72201-2933, USA; tel (501) 374-1500; fax (501) 374-7509; e-mail info@arkansaspress.org; web site www.arkansaspress.orgEst.: 1873
Exec. Dir. — Tom Larimer
Adv. & Mktg. Dir. — Ashley Wimberley
The Arkansas Press Association is the trade association for the newspapers of Arkansas. We represent Arkansas newspapers will national advertisers and hand advertising placement for a broad spectrum of advertisers, including political and advocacy advertisers.
Represents daily and weekly newspapers in Arkansas

CNPA ADVERTISING SERVICES — 2000 O St, Ste 120, Sacramento, CA, 95811-5299, USA; tel (916) 288-6000; fax (916) 288-6003; e-mail bryan@cnpa.com; web site www.cnpa.com
Exec. Dir. — Jack Bates
Dir. — Sharla Trillo
Client Rel./Sales Mgr. — Patrice Bayard-Miller

COMMUNITY PAPERS OF FLORIDA — 12601 SE 53rd Terrace Rd, Belleview, FL, 34420-5106, USA; tel (352) 237-3409; fax (352) 347-3384; e-mail djneuharth@aol.com; web site www.communitypapersofflorida.comEst.: 1960
Executve Director — Dave Neuharth
Administrative Asst. — Barbara Holmes
Florida statewide association for free papers
Classified advertising in 82 community news and shopper publications in Florida.

COMMUNITY PAPERS OF MICHIGAN, INC. — 5000 Northwind Dr, Ste 240, East Lansing, MI, 48823-5032, USA; tel (800) 783-0267; fax (517) 333-3322; e-mail

jackguza@cpapersmi.com; web site www.communitypapersofmichigan.com
Pres. — Terry Roby
Exec.Dir. — Jack Guza
Office Mgr. — Stacy Kotecki
Display advertising for 90 publications in Michigan that in cooperation with Community Papers of Michigan reaches more than 2.5 million Michigan households. Classifed advertising reaches 1.7 million Michigan households

CUSTOMIZED NEWSPAPER ADVERTISING (IOWA) — 319 E 5th St, Des Moines, IA, 50309-1927, USA; tel (515) 244-2145; fax (515) 244-4855; web site www.cnaads.com; www.inanews.com
Exec. Dir. — Chris Mudge
Acct. Exec. — Bryan Rohe
Sales Dir. — Ron Bode
Sales Rep. — Bruce Adams
Represents 302 daily and weekly newspapers in Iowa and can place advertising in any newspaper in the country.

FLORIDA PRESS SERVICE, INC. — 336 E College Ave, Ste 203, Tallahassee, FL, 32301-1559, USA; tel (850) 222-5790; fax (850) 222-4498; e-mail fps-info@flpress.com; web site www.flpress.com
Pres./CEO — Dean Riddings
Florida Press is an intergrated, full service placement, research invoicing and verification firm owned and operated by all of Florida's newspapers. Our mission is to help our client advertisors coordinate multi-market newspaper campaigns quickly, effecie
Represents 42 daily and 135 weekly newspapers in Florida

GEORGIA NEWSPAPER SERVICE, INC. — 3066 Mercer University Dr, Ste 200, Atlanta, GA, 30341-4137, USA; tel (770) 454-6776; fax (770) 454-6778; e-mail mail@gapress.org; web site www.gapress.org
Exec. Dir. — Robin Rhodes
Represents daily and weekly newspapers in Georgia

GREAT NORTHERN CONNECTION — 8703 Midway Rd, Lena, WI, 54139-9769, USA; tel (920) 829-5145; e-mail classifieds@greatnorthernconn.com; web site www.greatnorthernconn.comEst.: 1985
Adv. Contact — Char Meier
Represents 35 publications in northeastern Wisconsin and upper peninsula Michigan

HITCHINGS & CO. — 580 W Germantown Pike, Ste 108, Plymouth Meeting, PA, 19462-1370, USA; tel (610) 941-3555; fax (610) 941-1289; e-mail brian@phillyareapapers.com; web site www.phillyareapapers.com
Pres. — Brian Hitchings
Acct. Supvr. — Donna DeFrangesco

INTERSECT MEDIA SOLUTIONS — 610 Crescent Executive Ct, Ste 112, Lake Mary, FL, 32746-2111, USA; tel (321) 283-5255; e-mail info@intersectmediasolutions.com; web site www.intersectmediasolutions.comEst.: 1959
Pres./CEO — Dean Ridings
VP/CSO — Melanie Mathewson
Acct. Mgr. — Carolyn Klinger
Media Mgr. — Jessica Pitts
CFO — Mark Burger
General Counsel — Sam Morley
Intersect Media Solutions is the advertising agency of the Florida Press Association. Our mission is to provide outstanding client services with innovative media solutions that reach relevant and prospective audiences, to promote our relationships with our media partners, and to be profitable in the pursuit.

KENTUCKY PRESS SERVICE, INC. — 101 Consumer Ln, Frankfort, KY, 40601-8489, USA; tel (502) 223-8821; fax (502) 875-2624; e-mail

dthompson@kypress.com; web site www.kypress.comEst.: 1959
Exec. Dir. — David Thompson
Controller — Bonnie Howard
Membership organization of all Kentucky newspapers
Represents daily and weekly newspapers in Kentucky

LOUISIANA PRESS ASSOCIATION — 404 Europe St, Baton Rouge, LA, 70802-6403, USA; tel (225) 344-9309; fax (225) 344-9344; e-mail pam@lapress.com; web site www.lapress.comEst.: 1880
Communications Dir. — Mike Rood
Exec. Dir. — Pamela Mitchell
Dir. of Ops. — Mitchell-Ann Droge
Adv. Dir. — Erin Palmintier
State Newspaper Trade Association

MACNET — PO Box 408, Hamburg, PA, 19526-0408, USA; tel (800) 450-7227; fax (610) 743-8500; e-mail info@macpa.net; web site www.macpa.net; www.macnetonline.com
Exec. Dir. — Alyse Mitten
Classified advertising for 360 publications in PA, OH, NY, NJ, DE, MD, WV, VA, Washington DC.

MANSI MEDIA — 3899 N Front St, Harrisburg, PA, 17110-1583, USA; tel (717) 703-3030; fax (717) 703-3033; e-mail sales@mansimedia.com; web site www.mansimedia.com
VP/Adv. — Lisa Knight
Chris Kazlauskas
Dir. Client Solutions — Wes Snider
Sr. Media Buyer — Ronaldo Davis
Dir., Interactive Media — Matthew Caylor
Account Manager — Lindsey Artz
Account Manager — Shannon Mohar
Director, Client Solutions — Brian Hitchings
Represents daily and weekly newspapers and their digital products anywhere in the U.S. and beyond.

MIDWEST FREE COMMUNITY PAPERS — PO Box 1350, Iowa City, IA, 52244-1350, USA; tel (319) 341-4352; fax (319) 341-4358; e-mail mfcp@mchsi.com; web site www.mfcp.orgEst.: 1955
Office Mgr. — Jori Hendon
Classified advertising for 124 publications

MISSISSIPPI PRESS SERVICES, INC. — 371 Edgewood Terrace Dr, Jackson, MS, 39206-6217, USA; tel (601) 981-3060; fax (601) 981-3676; e-mail mspress@mspress.org; web site www.mspress.orgEst.: 1866
Exec. Dir. — Layne Bruce
Member Services Manager — Monica Gilmer
Business Development Manager — Sue Hicks
Media Director — Andrea Ross
Represents daily and weekly newspapers in Mississippi

MNI — 827 N Washington Ave, Lansing, MI, 48906-5135, USA; tel (517) 372-2424; fax (517) 372-2429; e-mail mpa@michiganpress.org; web site www.michiganpress.orgEst.: 1868
Executive Director — Mike MacLaren
Growth & Operations Manager — Rose Lucas
Public Affairs Manager — Lisa McGraw
Represents print and digital media in Michigan

MONTANA NEWSPAPER ADVERTISING SERVICE, INC. — 825 Great Northern Blvd, Ste 202, Helena, MT, 59601-3340, USA; tel (406) 443-2850; fax (406) 443-2860; e-mail randy@mtnewspapers.com; web site www.mtnewspapers.comEst.: 1955
Accounting Specialist — Randy Schmoldt
Represents daily and weekly newspapers in Montana.

NEBRASKA PRESS ADVERTISING SERVICE — 845 S St, Lincoln, NE, 68508-1226, USA; tel (402) 476-2851; fax (402) 476-2942; e-mail nebpress@nebpress.com; web site www.nebpress.comEst.: 1879
Adv. Sales Dir. — Rob James
Exec. Dir., Nebraska Press Assoc. — Allen Beermann
Professional trade association that represents the daily and weekly newspapers in Nebraska.

NENPA AD NETWORK (NEW ENGLAND NEWSPAPER AND PRESS ASSOCIATION) — 1 Arrow Dr, Ste 6, Woburn, MA, 01801-2039, USA; tel (781) 281-2053; fax (339) 999-2174; e-mail info@nenpa.com; web site www.nenpa.comEst.: 1930
Executive Director — Linda Conway
Represents daily, weekly and specialty newspapers in the six New England states

NEW JERSEY NEWSMEDIA NETWORK (NJNN) — 810 Bear Tavern Rd, Ste 307, Ewing, NJ, 08628-1022, USA; tel (609) 406-0600; fax (609) 406-0399; e-mail njnn@njpa.org; web site www.njpa.org/njnnEst.: 1991
Adv. Dir. — Amy Lear
NJPA Exec Dir — George White
NJNN Networks Mgr — Diane Trent
Media planning and placement service for print and digital campaigns. Specializing in daily, weekly, ethnic and specialty pubs reaching New Jersey.

NEW MEXICO PRESS ASSOCIATION — 700 Silver Ave SW, Albuquerque, NM, 87102-3019, USA; tel (505) 275-1241; fax (505) 275-1449; e-mail info@nmpress.org; web site www.nmpress.org
Office Mgr. — Holly Aguilar
Elections held in Oct

NEW YORK NEWS PUBLISHERS ASSOCIATION — 252 Hudson Ave, Albany, NY, 12210-1802, USA; tel (518) 449-1667; fax (518) 449-1667; web site www.nynpa.comEst.: 1927
Pres. — Diane Kennedy
Education Services Dir. — Mary H. Miller
Dir. of Adv. & Event Mgmt. — Don Ferlazzo
NYNPA is the non-profit trade association representing the daily, weekly, and online newspapers of New York State. NYNPA monitors the New York State Legislature on behalf of the newspaper industry, opposing unfavorable legislation and working to craft new laws to open up government activities to public scrutiny. The Association also provides training and professional networking opportunities to its member publishers, advertising and marketing, and circulation staff. It organizes an annual contest to recognize excellence in journalism, provides curriculum guides and support to Newspaper in Education programs, and assists advertisers in placing advertising in member newspapers. Additionally, the association manages the New York Newspapers Foundation, which provides grants to literacy-oriented community organizations.
Represents daily newspapers in New York State. Offers statewide and regional newspaper advertising solutions to general public at discounted rates.

NEW YORK PRESS SERVICE — 1681 Western Ave, Albany, NY, 12203-4305, USA; tel (518) 464-6483; fax (518) 464-6489; e-mail nypa@nynewspapers.com; web site www.nynewspapers.comEst.: 1853
Adv. Rep., Classified Sales — Phil Anthony
Mktg. Dir. — Jill Van Dusen
New York Press Service is a nationwide newspaper advertising, buying and placement service. Market analysis, rate/coverage spreadsheets. Nine publications, ethnic, senior family, alternative and mainstream community newspapers. Target marketing

solutions
Represents weekly newspapers in New York

NORTH CAROLINA PRESS SERVICE, INC. — 5171 Glenwood Ave, Ste 364, Raleigh, NC, 27612-3266, USA; tel (919) 787-7443; fax (919) 787-5302; web site www.ncpress.comEst.: 1985
Exec. Dir. — Beth Grace
Member Services Director — Laura Nakoneczny
Director of Sales — Mark Holmes
Represents all daily and weekly newspapers in North Carolina

NORTH DAKOTA NEWSPAPER ASSOCIATION — 1435 Interstate Loop, Bismarck, ND, 58503-0567, USA; tel (701) 223-6397; fax (701) 223-8185; e-mail info@ndna.com; web site www.ndna.comEst.: 1885
Mktg. Dir. — Kelli Richey
Exec. Dir. — Steve Andrist
Adv. Dir. — Mike Casey
Adv./Public Notice Coord. — Colleen Park
Office Coord./Adv. Assist. — Shari Peterson
Pres., NDNA Ed. Foundation — Aaron Becher
Past President — Sara J. Plum
President — Harvey Brock
Second Vice President — Jill Denning Gackle
NDNA Director — Paul Erdelt
NDNA Director — Leah Burke
NDNA Director — Matt McMillan
Director — Frank Perea
Director — Karen Speidel
Advertising placed in 89 North Dakota newspapers and related publications. Statewide classified advertising and small space advertising programs.
Represents daily and weekly newspapers in North Dakota

OHIAD — PO Box 69, Covington, OH, 45318-0069, USA; tel (937) 473-2028; fax (937) 473-2500; e-mail dselanders@woh.rr.com; web site www.arenspub.com
Secreatary/Treasurer — Gary Godfrey
Classified advertising for 16 publications. In cooperation with Community Papers of Ohio.

OHIO NEWSPAPER SERVICES, INC. — 1335 Dublin Rd, Ste 216B, Columbus, OH, 43215-1000, USA; tel (614) 486-6677; fax (614) 486-4940; web site www.ohionews.org; www.adohio.netEst.: 1933
Executive Director
Ohio Newspaper Association — Dennis Hetzel
Acting Director of Advertising — Walt Dozier
Manager, Administrative Services — Sue Bazzoli
Manager of Communications & Content — Jason Sanford
Receptionist and Secretary — Ann Riggs
Advertising Coordinator — Patricia Conkle
Network Account Executive — Kathy McCutcheon
Advertising Account Executive — Casey Null
Represents all 81 daily and 154 weekly Ohio newspaper and affiliated websites.

OKLAHOMA PRESS SERVICE — 3601 N Lincoln Blvd, Oklahoma City, OK, 73105-5411, USA; tel (405) 524-4421; fax (405) 499-0048; e-mail sysop@okpress.com; web site www.okpress.com
Exec. Vice Pres. — Mark Thomas
Represents daily and weekly newspapers in Oklahoma

PACIFIC NORTHWEST ASSOCIATION OF WANT AD NEWSPAPERS (PNAWAN) & WESTERN REGIONAL ADVERTISING PROGRAM (WRAP) — 304 W 3rd Ave, C/O Exchange Publishing, Spokane, WA, 99201-4314, USA; tel (509) 922-3456; fax (509) 455-7940; e-mail Ads@PNAWAN.org; web site www.RegionalAds.orgEst.: 1977
Executive Director of the Pacific Northwest Association of Want Ad Newspapers

(PNAWAN) & Western Regional Advertising Program (WRAP) — Kylah Strohte
PNAWAN Office
PNAWAN is an association of 30 different publications throughout the greater Pacific Northwest region: Washington, Oregon, Idaho, Montana, Alberta & British Columbia. The combined total distribution is approximately 600,000 per week.
Reach a bigger audience & Advertise in local community papers throughout the Pacific Northwest region!

PNAWAN (Pacific NW Assoc. of Want Ad Newspapers) makes advertising on a regional scale easy and affordable.

Prices start at just $50 per Regional Ad!

Place both classified & display ads in up to 30 different publications throughout Washington, Oregon, Idaho, Montana, Alberta & British Columbia in just 1 easy phone call.

Our publications believe in high standards of quality and ethics in advertising. PNAWAN publications are well-known in their communities and have very loyal readerships.

Total weekly distribution: 537,006
We are audited and verified by the Circulation Verification Council annually.

Classified Ad Rates:

$6.25 per edition, minimum 8 editions required
(Note: Editions are calculated as number of weeks x number of running publications)

Examples:
8 publications x 1 week = $50
4 publications x 2 weeks = $50

12 publications x 1 week = $75
6 publications x 2 weeks = $75
16 publications x 1 week = $100
8 publications x 2 weeks = $100
....etc.

Maximum USA coverage: 23 pubs x 1 week = $143.75
Maximum coverage incl. Canada: 30 pubs x 1 week = $187.50

25 word max. Extra words = 10 cents per word per edition

Call today to place your Pacific Northwest Regional Ads! 509-922-3456 or 1-800-326-2223 (toll-free). Note: PNAWAN is hosted by member company, Exchange Publishing, so be sure to ask for PNAWAN Regional Ads when calling.

You may also email ads@pnawan.org for any inquiries, or contact the Executive Director of PNAWAN, Kylah Strohte, directly at Kylah@ExchangePublishing.com

More information about the Pacific Northwest Association of Want Ad Newspapers (PNAWAN) online at www.RegionalAds.org

Mission:
To unite, promote, and facilitate advertising between the free community newspaper publications of the Pacific Northwest so that our advertisers can easily reach a bigger audience.
We are audited and verified by the Circulation Verification Council annually.

PNAWAN headquarters are located at the offices of hosting member publication, Exchange Publishing, in Spokane, WA.

PUBLISHERS DEVELOPMENT SERVICE — PO Box 1256, Fond Du Lac, WI, 54936-1256, USA; tel (920) 922-4864; fax (920) 922-0861; e-mail janelle@pdsadnet.com; web site www.pdsadnet.comEst.: 1978
CEO — Janelle Anderson
Gen. Mgr. — Jeanne Schmal
Classified Sales Mgr. — Kathy Braun
Media placement firm specializing in print media in particular community papers. Display advertising for 122 publications. In cooperation with Wisconsin Free Community Papers

RESEAU SELECT/SELECT NETWORK — 25 Sheppard Ave W, Suite 500, Toronto, ON, M2N 6S7, Canada; tel (416) 733-7600; fax (416) 726-8519; e-mail inforeseauselect@tc.tc; web site www.reseauselect.com

RESEAU SELECT/SELECT NETWORK — 8000 Av Blaise-Pascal, Montreal, QC, H1E 2S7, Canada; tel (514) 643-2300; fax (514) 866-3030; e-mail inforeseauselect@tc.tc; web site www.reseauselect.comEst.: 1976
General Manager — François Laferrière
Represents more than 148 weekly French-language newspapers in Quebec, Ontario, Manitoba and New Brunswick

SOUTH CAROLINA PRESS SERVICES, INC. — 106 Outlet Pointe Blvd, Columbia, SC, 29210-5669, USA; tel (803) 750-9561; fax (803) 551-0903; e-mail rsavely@scpress.org; web site http://www.scnewspapernetwork.com/Est.: 1985
Director of Opertions — Randall Savely
Represents all South Carolina newspapers in placement of classified and display advertising

SOUTHEASTERN ADVERTISING PUBLISHERS ASSOCIATION — 104 Westland Dr, Columbia, TN, 38401-6522, USA; tel (931) 223-5708; fax (888) 450-8329; e-mail info@sapatoday.com; web site www.sapatoday.comEst.: 1979
Exec. Dir. — Douglas Fry
Classified advertising for 75 publications in 10 Southeastern states. Display Network also available.

SYNC2 MEDIA — 1120 N Lincoln St, Ste 912, Denver, CO, 80203-2138, USA; tel (303) 571-5117; fax (303) 571-1803; e-mail info@sync2media.com; web site www.sync2media.com
CEO — Jerry Raehal
Account Executive — Judy Quelch
Account Executive — Peyton Jacobson
Represents daily and weekly newspapers in Colorado

TEXCAP — 1226 Newberry Dr, Allen, TX, 75013-3669, USA; tel (972) 741-6258; fax (866) 822-4920; e-mail jack@tcnatoday.com; web site www.tcnatoday.comEst.: 1964
Exec. Dir. — Dick Colvin
Classified advertising for 109 publications. In cooperation with Texas Community Newspapers Assoc

WISCONSIN NEWSPAPER ASSOCIATION — 34 Schroeder Ct, Ste 220, Madison, WI, 53711-2528, USA; tel (608) 283-7620; fax (608) 283-7631; e-mail wna@wnanews.com; web site www.wnanews.comEst.: 1853
Exec. Dir. — Beth Bennett
Media Services Dir. — Denise Guttery
Communications Dir. — James Debilzen
Member Services Dir. — Julia Hunter
Represents 34 daily and over 225 weekly and specialty newspapers

TRADE UNIONS IN THE NEWSPAPER FIELD

COMMUNICATIONS WORKERS OF AMERICA — 501 3rd St NW, Washington, DC, 20001-2760, USA; tel (202) 434-1100; fax (202) 434-1279; web site www.cwa-union.org
Pres. — Larry Cohen
Sec./Treasure — Jeffrey Rechenbach

GRAPHIC COMMUNICATIONS INTERNATIONAL — 1900 L St NW, Washington, DC, 20036-5002, USA; tel (202) 721-0537; fax (202) 721-0641; e-mail webmessenger@gciu.org; web site gtedeschi@gciu.org
Pres. — George Tedeschi

Vice Pres. — Robert Lacey
Executive Assistant to the President — Richard Whitworth

INTERNATIONAL UNION OF OPERATING ENGINEERS — 1125 17th St NW, Washington, DC, 20036-4709, USA; tel (202) 429-9100; fax (202) 778-2688; web site www.iuoe.org
Gen. Pres. — Vincent J. Giblin
Gen. Sec./Treasurer — Christopher Hanley

SERVICE EMPLOYEES INTERNATIONAL UNION, CLC — 1800 Massachusetts Ave NW,

Washington, DC, 20036-1806, USA; tel (202) 730-7000; fax (202) 429-5660; web site www.seiu.org
Int'l Pres. — Andrew L. Stern
Sec./Treasurer — Anna Burger
Int'l Exec. Vice Pres. — Mary Kay Henry
Int'l Vice Pres. — Gerald Hudson
Int'l Exec. Vice Pres. — Eliseo Medina
Int'l Exec. Vice Pres. — Tom Woodruff

THE LABORERS' INTERNATIONAL UNION OF NORTH AMERICA — 905 16th St NW, Washington, DC, 20006-1703, USA; tel (202) 737-8320; fax (202) 737-2754; web site www.liuna.org

Gen. Pres. — Terence M. O'Sullivan
Gen. Sec./Treasurer — Armand E. Sabitoni

THE NEWSGUILD-CWA — 501 3rd St NW Fl 6, Fl 6, Washington, DC, 20001-2760, USA; tel (202) 434-7177; fax (202) 434-1472; e-mail guild@newsguild.org; web site www.newsguild.org
Established: 1933
President — Bernard Lunzer
International Chairperson — Martha Waggoner
Exec. VP — Marian Needham

UNITED NATIONS CORRESPONDENTS ASSOCIATION

UNITED NATIONS CORRESPONDENTS ASSOCIATION

UNITED NATIONS, NEW YORK
UNCA is a professional organization of nearly 200 journalists from dozens of countries representing scores of publications and

broadcasters from all regions of the world, plus the major global news agencies.
It represents reporters in dialogues with the U.N. Secretariat to resolve problems, such as disagreements over security concerns and access to news sources.
UNCA also sponsors related briefings by sources both inside and outside the United Nations and an annual gala dinner recognizing outstanding journalism and a Citizen of the World Award. It is associated

with the Dag Hammarskjold Fund for Journalists, (www.unjournalismfellowship) which sponsors journalists from developing countries for the duration of the annual General Assembly.

UNCA EXECUTIVE COMMITTEE
President – Pamela S. Falk (CBS News TV & Radio)
First Vice-President – Kahraman Haliscelik (TRT Turkish Radio & TV)

Second Vice-President – Masood Haider (Dawn)
Third Vice-President – Erol Avdovic (Webpublicapress)
Treasurer – Bouchra Benyoussef (Maghreb Arab Press)
Secretary – Seana Magee (Kyodo News)

EXECUTIVE

COMMITTEE

MEMBERS AT LARGE

Nabil Abi Saab (Alhurra TV)
Talal Al-Haj (Al-Arabiya TV)
Sherwin Bryce-Pease (South African Broadcasting)
Zhenqiu Gu (Xinhua News Agency)
Melissa Kent (CBC/Radio Canada)
Evelyn Leopold (Huffington Post Contributor)
Michelle Nichols (Reuters)
Valeria Robecco (ANSA News Agency)
Sangwon Yoon (Bloomberg)

REGULAR MEMBERS

A Dean Sam (TV Asahi America, Inc)
Abad Jose Angel (ANTENA 3 TV Spain (TV))
Abb0Ud Nizar (ALALAM TV and Al-khbar Daily)
Abbadi Abdelkader (Dossiers du Tadla; Columbia Paper)
Abed Morad Hashim (Al-Jazeera)
Abi Saab Nabil (Alhurra TV)
Acar Selcuk (Star Turkish Newspaper (D);)
Albayrak Nafiz (DHA (Dogan News Agency))
Al-Haj Anita (Al Arabiya News Channel)
Al-Haj Talal (Al Arabiya TV)
Ali Iftikhar (Associated Press of Pakistan)
Alrawi Khaldoun (Associated Press)
Amaba Ayano (Nippon TV)
André Viollaz (Agence France-Presse)
Ask Alf Ole (Aftenposten, Norwegian (D))
Avakian Florence (Armenian Radio)
Avdovic Erol (Radio Deutsche Welle, Germany (R))
Avni Benny (The New York Post; Kol Israel)
Bai Jie (Xinhua News Agency)
Barada Ali (An-Nahar)
Baris Behzat (Cumhuriyet Bizim Gazet, Istanbul (D))
Bases Daniel (Reuters)
Batson Roger Dale (Nippon TV)
Baumgarten George (Jewish Newspapers)
Benyoussef Bouchra (Maghreb Arab Press Agency)
Berrocal Frances Elaine (Mainichi Newspapers)
Besheer Margaret (Voice of America (R) (TV))
Bhalla Arvind (Daily Punjab Kesri, India)
Bian Chenguang (Science and Technology Daily)
Broeker Anja (ARD/WDR German TV)
Brooks Courtney Rose (Radio Free Europe/Radio Liberty)
Bryce-Pease Sherwin (South African Broadcasting)
Burchett Elisa (U.N. OBSERVER & Int. Report)
Burtis Farida (Syndicated Features, London (NA))
Carriba Victor (Prensa Latina)
Cespedes Marisa (Televisa NY (Mexican TV))
Chang Heidi (Hong Kong Phoenix Satellite TV)
Charbonneau Louis (Reuters)
Charles Ann (The Baltic Times (W))
Cianfanelli Renzo (RAC Associates LLC; Il Seccolo XIX;)
Cinar Ali (Turkish Journal)
Common David (CBC News)
Coombs Casey L (The Diplomatic Courier)
Darabi Afshar (Islamic Republic News Agency)

Dayani Dilshad (Rhythm Broadcasting)
De Lavarne Celhia Chaix (Radio France (R))
Deen Thalif (Inter Press Service (IPS))
Dergham Raghida (Al-Hayat, London (D))
Deyab Safie Eldin (Sphinx News Network (NA))
Ding Xiaoxi (The People's Daily)
Dironza Serena (ANSA News Agency)
Donnet Pierre-Antoine (Agence France-Presse)
Ebara Miki (NHK Japan Broadcasting (TV))
Edwards Steven (Postmedia News, National Post)
Eid Randa (Al Jazeera Television, New York (TV))
Elliott Joy (Carib News, New York)
Espinoza Cholene (Talk Radio/Media News Service)
Falk Pamela S (CBS News)
Farkas Alessandra (Corriere della Sera)
Farrell Naomi (World Union Press)
Fasulo Linda (NPR News, (R))
Fathi Tarek (Middle East News Agency)
Figueiredo Paulo Dias (LUSA - News Agency of Portugal)
Fitzgerald Denis (Saudi Press Agency)
Font Eva (Radio Francia Internacional)
Franco Widad (NHK Japan Broadcasting (TV))
Gabel Glenn (Al Jazeera Satellite Channel)
Gallavin Georgia (Fujisankei Communications)
Gallego Mercedes (Vocento Media Group (former ABC Madrid))
Galsim Raymund (Privilege Lifestyle Magazine(Canada) (M))
Geneste Alexandra (Le Monde)
Geni Joe (Yomiuri Shimbun)
Goyal Raghubir (Asia Today, Washington, DC (TV), Asia TV)
Gripiotis Mihalis (Hellenic Broadcasting Corp/ERT)
Gu Zhenqiu (Xinhua News Agency)
Guaita Anna (IL Messaggero (D))
Guerrero Maurizio (Notimex (NA))
Haider Masood (Dawn, Pakistan (D))
Haliscelik Kahraman (TRT Turkish Radio & Television)
Hauben Ronda (taz.de (Die Tageszeitung); The 4th Media)
Heilprin John (Associated Press)
Hernandez Daniel (Tokyo Shimbun/ Chunichi Shimbun)
Hopkins Marcelle (Al Jazeera Arabic)
Hou Minggu (China Central Television (TV))
Houngbo Herman (LC2 TV - Benin)
Huang Jishun (China Central Television)
Hurst Whitney (CNN)
Hvistendahl Else (Norwegian American Weekly;)
Ignatiou Michail (Ethnos Newspaper (D), Mega TV)
Jaber Juman Jamil (Al-Arabiya News Channel)
Jackson Flavia (Bloomberg News)
Jendoubi Saloua (Kuwait News Agency (NA))
Jha Lalit (Pajhwok Afghan News, Afghanistan(D))
Ji Yujie (China Central Television, New York)
Jiang GuangFu (Hong Kong Phoenix Satellite TV)
Kabbaj Abdellatif (Morrocan Press (TV/R))
Kalayci Sezai (Zaman Newspaper (D))
Kammerlander Annemarie (ARD German TV/New York Bureau)
Kant Ravi (TV Asia, New Jersey (TV))

Kashimoto Teruyuki (Tokyo Broadcasting System Intl.)
Kasuga Yoshiaki (The Asahi Shimbun)
Kawaguchi Traci Yuri (Tokyo Broadcasting System Intl.)
Kent Melissa (Canadian Broadcasting Corp/Radio-Canada)
Kikilo Vladimir (ITAR-TASS, Moscow (NA))
Kins Gloria Starr (Society & Diplomatic Review)
Klein Joseph A (Canada Free Press)
Kodani Hiromi (The Tokyo Shimbun)
Kolesa Kristina Sue (Al-Arabiya News Channel)
Konja Afaf (South-South News)
Koundakjian Harry L (AZTAG)
Krauss Mitchell (CBS News (TV) - Retired)
Lauria Joe (The Wall Street Journal (D), New York)
Le Tuyen QUANG (Vietnam News Agency)
Lederer Edith (Associated Press (NA))
Lee Matthew Russell (Inner City Press)
Leopold Evelyn (Huffington Post contributor, freelancer)
Li Wenjia (China Central Television)
Liu Chang (China Central Television, New York)
Lurie Ranan R (Cartoonews International Syndicate Edito)
Macfarquhar Neil (The New York Times, UN Bureau Chief)
Magee Seana (Kyodo News)
Mastrolilli Paolo (La Stampa)
Melzer Chris (DPA, German Press Agency)
Metzler John (Worldtribune.com (WEB),)
Mian Azim (GEO-TV, Pakistan/ The News International)
Miller Bill (Washington International)
Moran Benedict (Al Jazeera English)
Moreno Elena (EFE News Agency)
Mula Halil (RTV21 (TV))
Mumin Md Kausar (Weekly Akhon Samoy)
Mutiasari Tia (ANTARA News Agency)
Nader Samar (NTV (Lebanon))
Nalavala Nosh (MediaGlobal News Agency)
Nazzal Khawla (Emirates News Agency "WAM")
Nguyen Trung Huu (Vietnam News Agency)
Nguyen Tuan Anh (Vietnam News Agency)
Nguyen Tuyet J (German Press Agency DPA)
Noain Idoya (El Periodico)
Oikawa Jun (NHK Japan Broadcasting Corp.)
Orvis Patricia M (Newport Daily Express)
Osborne Thomas (U.S - UN Report)
Oshima Michael Haruto (TV Asahi America)
Ostwald Gisela (German Press Agency/DPA, Hamburg (NA))
Pak Cia (Scannews)
Panagos Dimitrios (GANP, Athens News Agency,)
Panayiotou Panayiotis (Athens News Agency (Greece))
Pandhi Vijay (The Himachal Times, Energy India)
Patterson Dan (Talk Radio/Media News Service)
Pavia Will (The Times of London)
Pfaeffle Walter (Austria Press Agentur (NA))
Pintozzi Liliana Faccioli (SKY TG24)
Pioli Giampaolo (LA NAZIONE)
Plesea Gabriel (Freelance Reporter)
Plett Barbara (British Broadcasting Corporation (BBC))
Pontecorboli Gianna (Lettera 22 (NA))
Proempers Klaus Heinz (ZDF German Television)

Qiong LIN (Xinhua News Agency)
Rankin Katharine Anne (Nikkei America (D))
Ratner Ellen (Talk Radio/Media News Service)
Reilly William M (Xinhua News Agency (NA))
Richter Cristelle (ARD German Television)
Rivera Karen Patricia (The Tokyo Shimbun)
Robecco Valeria (Quotidiano Nazionale (D))
Rodriguez Carmen-Maria (Radio Marti, (R))
Roth Richard (CNN (TV))
Roth Thomas Martin (ARD/WDR German TV)
Sabet Sadegh (Scannews)
Sahin-Sakar Ozlem (Anatolian Agency/A.A, (NA) Ankara, Turk)
Saloomey Kristen (Al Jazeera English TV)
Sarre Claudia (ARD German Radio Network)
Sawa Yasuomi (Kyodo News)
Schlesinger Stephen (Freelance)
Schmidt Thomas (ARD German Radio Network)
Schuh Trish (Esquire Magazine (MM))
Semprini Francesco (La Stampa)
Shakouri Ebrahim (I.R.I.B News)
Shen Hong (Xinhua News Agency)
Shen Ting (China Radio International)
Silverman Ken (Fuji TV Network News)
Singh Yoshita (Press Trust of India)
Sintes Fabienne (Radio France)
Smith Adele (Le Figaro (D))
Snow Anita (Associated Press)
Sofi Horacio (Freelance)
Springer Bevan (Freelance Correspondent)
Stapp Katherine (IPS)
Stea Carla (Global Research (I))
Teramoto Atsuko (The Mainichi Newspapers)
Toyama Kaoru (TV Asahi)
Toyoda Chiyoko (Fuji TV Network News)
Tsitsas Athanasios (Eleftherotypia; Antenna TV; Alitheia)
Ucciardo Frank (CBS News)
Uluc Dogan (Hurriyet, Istanbul (D))
Usher Graham (Al Ahram Weekly)
Utset Joaquin (EFE News Services (NA))
Vaccara Stefano (America Oggi, Oggi 7, Radio Radicale)
Valenzuela David (EFE News Services)
Villanti Benjamin Mark (The Asahi Shimbun, Reporter)
Vyas Rohit (TV Asia, USA (TV))
Wachtel Jonathan (Fox TV News, New York (TV))
Wakaki Noriko (Fujisankei Communications (TV))
Wang Lei (Xinhua News Agency)
Warren April Jan (The Yomiuri Shimbun)
Wei Wei (Xinhua News Agency)
Weschler Joanna (Security Council Report)
Williams Ian (Tribune, weekly, London UK;)
Witcher Timothy (Agence France-Presse)
Wu Yun (People's Daily)
Wu Zhiqiang (Xinhua News Agency)
Wurst James (LGMA - TV)
Xi Laiwang (The People's Daily)
Yan Huan (Xinhua News Agency)
Yanagisawa Michinobu (The Yomiuri Shimbun)
Yoshikata Yuji (The Yomiuri Shimbun (D))
Youssef Ezzat Ibrahim (Al-Ahram (D))
Youssef Sana (AL-Akhbar; Akhbar El-Yom; AkherSaa CAIRO)
Zakharchenko Ivan (RIA Novosti (NA))
Zehil Sylviane (L'Orient Le Jour)
Zeng Hu (Xinhua News Agency)
Zoupaniotis Apostolos (Cyprus (NA); CyBC; Kathimerini, Era-5)

U.S. STATE NEWSPAPER ASSOCIATIONS

A

ALABAMA PRESS ASSOCIATION — 3324 Independence Dr, Ste 200, Birmingham, AL,
35209-5602, USA; tel (205) 871-7737; fax (205) 871-7740; e-mail felicia@alabamapress.org; web site www.alabamapress.org
Exec. Dir. ....Felicia Mason

Adv. Mgr......................................Brad English
Senior Marketing Rep.............. Leigh Tortorici
Sales/Mktg Exec ....Amy Metzler
Member Services/Network Coordinator. Chris

McDaniel
Note: Elections held in Feb

ARIZONA NEWSPAPERS ASSOCIATION — 1001 N Central Ave, Ste 670, Phoenix, AZ, 85004-1947, USA; tel (602) 261-7655; fax (602) 261-7525; e-mail p.casey@ananews.com; web site www.ananews.com
Exec. Dir. .... Paula Casey
Communications Manager .... Julie O'Keefe
Ad Placement Manager .... Cindy London
Note: Elections held in Sept. Statewide and national one order/one bill advertising placement service

C

CALIFORNIA NEWS PUBLISHERS ASSOCIATION — 2701 K St, Sacramento, CA, 95816-5131, USA; tel (916) 288-6000; fax (916) 288-6002; web site www.cnpa.com
President .... William Johnson
VP, Sec/Trea .... Paulette Brown-Hinds
Exec. Dir. .... Thomas Newton
Gen. Counsel .... Jim Ewert
Dir. of Membership .... Simon Birch
Director of Advertising .... Cecelia Drake
Director of Affiliate Relations .... Joe Wirt
Director of Meetings .... Renee Smith

COLORADO PRESS ASSOCIATION — 1120 N Lincoln St, Ste 912, Denver, CO, 80203-2138, USA; tel (303) 571-5117; fax (303) 571-1803; e-mail colopress@colopress.net; web site www.coloradopressassociation.com
CEO .... Jerry Raehal
Office Man. .... Jean Creel
Membership and Projects .... Russell Bassett
Advertising .... Judy Quelch

CONNECTICUT DAILY NEWSPAPERS ASSOCIATION — 330 Main St, Fl 3, Hartford, CT, 06106-1851, USA; tel (860) 716-4461; fax (860) 541-6484; web site www.ctdailynews.com
Executive Director .... Chris VanDeHoef
Note: Elections held in April/May

F

FLORIDA PRESS ASSOCIATION — 1025 Greenwood Blvd, Ste 191, Lake Mary, FL, 32746-5410, USA; tel (321) 283-5255; e-mail fpa-info@flpress.com; web site www.flpress.com
Pres. & CEO .... Dean Ridings
VP, Strategy .... Carolyn Klinger
Gen. Counsel .... Sam Morley
Note: Association accepts free newsapers if they meet the requirements.
FPA is the parent company of Intersect Media Solutions

G

GEORGIA PRESS ASSOCIATION — 3066 Mercer University Dr, Ste 200, Atlanta, GA, 30341-4137, USA; tel (770) 454-6776; fax (770) 454-6778; e-mail mail@gapress.org; web site www.gapress.org
Exec. Dir. & Pub .... Robin Rhodes
Member Services Director . Mary Pat Hodges
Sales & Marketing Director .... Rick Hammell
Publications Editor .... Sean Ireland
Business Development Manager .... Michelle Pearson
President .... Mesha Wind
Note: Elections held at annual convention in June

H

HAWAII PUBLISHERS ASSOCIATION — 500 Ala Moana Blvd, Ste 7-500, Honolulu, HI, 96813-4930, USA; tel (808) 738-4992; fax (808) 664-8892; e-mail info@hawaiipublishersassociation.com; web site www.hawaiipublishersassociation.com
Executive Director .... Rick Asbach

HOOSIER STATE PRESS ASSOCIATION — 41 E Washington St, Ste 101, Indianapolis, IN, 46204-3560, USA; tel (317) 803-4772; fax (317) 624-4428; web site www.hspa.com
Exec. Dir./Gen. Counsel .... Stephen Key
Adv. Dir. .... Pamela Lego
Communications Specialist .... Milissa Tuley
HSPA Foundation Dir. .... Karen Braeckel
Office Mgr. .... Yvonne Yeadon
Adv. Coord .... Shawn Goldsby
Note: Represents daily and weekly newspapers in Indiana

I

ILLINOIS PRESS ASSOCIATION — 900 Community Dr, Springfield, IL, 62703-5180, USA; tel (217) 241-1300; fax (217) 241-1301; e-mail ipa@illinoispress.org; web site www.illinoispress.org
Exec. Dir. .... Dennis DeRossett
Adv. Dir. .... Jeffrey Holman
Dir. of Member Relations .... Lynne Lance
Dir. Gov. Relations .... Josh Sharp
Business Mgr. .... Carolyn Austin
Tech & Online Coord. .... Ron Kline
Dig. Adv. Mgr. .... Melissa Calloway
Admin Assist & Member Rel. .... Cindy Bedolli
Pub. .... Stan Shwartz
VP, Business Dev. .... Tony Scott
Note: The Illinois Press Advertising Service can place any newspaper product available in Illinois and has several well-established, low-cost networks.

IOWA NEWSPAPER ASSOCIATION, INC. — 319 E 5th St, Fl 2, Des Moines, IA, 50309-1927, USA; tel (515) 244-2145; fax (515) 244-4855; e-mail ina@inanews.com; web site www.inanews.com
Sales & Mktg. Dir. .... Susan Patterson Plank
Business Mgr. .... Brent Steemken
Comm. Dir. .... Jodi Hulbert
Dev. Dir .... Geof Fischer
Inside Sales Mgr. .... Samantha Fett
Media Dir. .... Heidi Geisler
Program Dir. .... Jana Shepherd
Tech. & Digital Dev. Mgr. .... Susan James
Pres. .... Ryan Harvey
Sales & Mktg. Assist .... Kaitlyn Van Patten
Note: Elections held in May

K

KANSAS PRESS ASSOCIATION — 5423 SW 7th St, Topeka, KS, 66606-2330, USA; tel (785) 271-5304; fax (785) 271-7341; e-mail info@kspress.com; web site www.kspress.com
Director of Member Services . Emily Bradbury
Admin. Assist./Adv. .... Lori Jackson
Exec. Dir. .... Doug Anstaett
Adv. Dir. .... Amber Jackson
Accountant .... Judy Beach
Note: Represents 28 daily and 185 weekly newspapers in Kansas

KENTUCKY PRESS ASSOCIATION, INC. — 101 Consumer Ln, Frankfort, KY, 40601-8489, USA; tel (502) 223-8821; fax (502) 226-3867; e-mail dthompson@kypress.com; web site www.kypress.com
Exec. Dir. .... David T. Thompson
Controller .... Bonnie Howard
Note: Elections held in Jan

L

LOUISIANA PRESS ASSOCIATION — 404 Europe St, Baton Rouge, LA, 70802-6403, USA; tel (225) 344-9309; fax (225) 344-9344; e-mail pam@lapress.com; web site www.lapress.com
Communications Dir. .... Mike Rood
Exec. Dir. .... Pamela Mitchell
Dir. of Ops .... Mitchell-Ann Droge
Adv. Dir. .... Erin Palmintier

M

MAINE PRESS ASSOCIATION — 26 Elmwood Rd, Cape Elizabeth, ME, 04107-1337, USA; tel 207-799-2996; fax (800) 799-6008; e-mail mainepressmail@gmail.com; web site www.mainepress.wordpress.com
.... Jeff Ham
.... Diane NortonExec. Dir.s
Note: Elections held in Sept

MANSI MEDIA — 3899 N Front St, Harrisburg, PA, 17110-1583, USA; tel (717) 703-3030; fax (717) 703-3033; e-mail sales@mansimedia.com; web site www.mansimedia.com
VP/Adv. .... Lisa Knight
Chris Kazlauskas
Dir. Client Solutions .... Wes Snider
Sr. Media Buyer .... Ronaldo Davis
Dir., Interactive Media .... Matthew Caylor
Account Manager .... Lindsey Artz
Account Manager .... Shannon Mohar
Director, Client Solutions .... Brian Hitchings
Note: Represents daily and weekly newspapers and their digital products anywhere in the U.S. and beyond.

MICHIGAN PRESS ASSOCIATION — 827 N Washington Ave, Lansing, MI, 48906-5135, USA; tel (517) 372-2424; fax (517) 372-2429; e-mail mpa@michiganpress.org; web site www.michiganpress.org
Growth & Operations Manager Roselie Lucus
Public Affairs Manager .... Lisa McGraw
Design & Communications Specialist .... Sean Wickham
Mgr. .... Janet Mendler
Exec. Dir. .... James Tarrant
Adv. Dir. .... Paul Biondi
Note: Elections held in Jan

MINNESOTA NEWSPAPER ASSOCIATION — 12 S 6th St, Ste 1120, Minneapolis, MN, 55402-1501, USA; tel (612) 332-8844; fax (612) 342-2958; e-mail info@mna.org; web site www.mna.org
Executive Director .... Lisa Hills
Managing Director .... Dan Lind
Asst. Exec. Dir. .... Barbara Trebisovsky
Advertising Account Manager .... Phil Morin
Note: Convention, trade show and elections in January.

MISSISSIPPI PRESS ASSOCIATION — 371 Edgewood Terrace Dr, Jackson, MS, 39206-6217, USA; tel (601) 981-3060; fax (601) 981-3676; e-mail mspress@mspress.org; web site www.mspress.org
Exec. Dir. .... Layne Bruce
Media Dir. .... Andrea Ross
Member Services Mgr. .... Monica Gilmer
Note: Elections held in June

MISSOURI PRESS ASSOCIATION — 802 Locust St, Columbia, MO, 65201-4888, USA; tel (573) 449-4167; fax (573) 874-5894; web site www.mopress.com
Missouri Press Service .... Ted Lawrence
Membership Services DirectorKristie Williams
Mark Maassen
Note: Elections held in Sep.

MONTANA NEWSPAPER ASSOCIATION — 825 Great Northern Blvd, Ste 202, Helena, MT, 59601-3340, USA; tel (406) 443-2850; fax (406) 443-2860; e-mail jim@mtnewspapers.com; web site www.mtnewspapers.com
Executive Director .... Jim Rickman
Business Development Manager .... Kev Campbell
Accounting Specialist .... Pamela Chriske

N

NEBRASKA PRESS ASSOCIATION/ NEBRASKA PRESS ADVERTISING SERVICE — 845 S St, Lincoln, NE, 68508-1226, USA; tel (402) 476-2851; fax (402) 476-2942; e-mail nebpress@nebpress.com; web site www.nebpress.com
Exec. Dir. .... Allen Beermann
Adv. Mgr., Nebr Press Adv. Service ... Carolyn Bowman
Office Mgr. .... Jenelle Plachy
Admin. Asst./Press Release Coord. .... Susan Watson
Adv. Sales Asst., Nebr. Press Adv. Service..... Violet Kirk
Note: Annual convention and election of officers held in April

NEVADA PRESS ASSOCIATION, INC. — 102 N Curry St, Carson City, NV, 89703-4934, USA; tel (775) 885-0866; fax (775) 885-8233; e-mail nevadapress@att.net; web site www.nevadapress.com
Exec. Dir. .... Barry Smith
Pres. .... Scott Sibley
Note: Elections held in Sept

NEW JERSEY PRESS ASSOCIATION — 810 Bear Tavern Rd, Ste 307, Ewing, NJ, 08628-1022, USA; tel (609) 406-0600; fax (609) 406-0300; e-mail njpress@njpa.org; web site www.njpa.org
Foundation Director .... John J. O'Brien
Executive Director .... George H. White
NJNN Director .... Amy C. Lear
Business Manager .... Scott Kutcher
Communications Manager Catherine Langley
Member Services Manager.... Peggy Stephan Arbitell
Accounting Coordinator .... Jane Hartsough
Marketing Specialist .... Julianne Mangano

NEW MEXICO PRESS ASSOCIATION — 700 Silver Ave SW, Albuquerque, NM, 87102-3019, USA; tel (505) 275-1241; fax (505) 275-1449; e-mail info@nmpress.org; web site www.nmpress.org
Office Mgr. .... Holly Aguilar
Note: Elections held in Oct

NEW YORK PRESS ASSOCIATION — 621 Columbia Street Ext, Ste 100, Cohoes, NY, 12047-3876, USA; tel (518) 464-6483; fax (518) 464-6489; e-mail nypa@nynewspapers.com; web site www.nynewspapers.com
Member Services Mgr. .... Richard Hotaling
VP Adv. .... Dave Worden
VP Adv. .... Doug Rea
Assist. Gen. Mgr. for Membership Systems Jill Van Dusen
Exec. Dir.
.... Michelle Rea
Controller .... Scott Lavigne
Note: Election of officers held in Sept; largest newspaper industry training convention and trade show in the country held in March or April

NEW YORK PRESS PHOTOGRAPHERS ASSOCIATION, INC. — PO Box 3346, New York, NY, 10008-3346, USA; tel (212) 889-6633; e-mail office@nyppa.org; web site www.nyppa.org
Trustee .... Ray Stubblebine
Secretary - Historian .... Marc Hermann
President .... Bruce Cotler
Vice President .... Todd Maisel
Note: Elections held every other year

NEWSPAPER ASSOCIATION OF IDAHO — 407 W Jefferson St, Boise, ID, 83702-6049, USA; tel (208) 345-9929; fax (208) 345-9928;

e-mail amber@rischpisca.com; web site www.
newspaperassociationofidaho.com
Dir.. Amber Hauge

NORTH CAROLINA PRESS ASSOCIATION
— 5171 Glenwood Ave, Ste 364, Raleigh, NC,
27612-3266, USA; tel (919) 787-7443; fax (919)
787-5302; e-mail laurie@ncpress.com; web site
www.ncpress.com

Publisher...................................Beth Grace
Editor.................................Laura Nakoneczny
Media Director ....Megan Dew
Office Manager ....Laurie Seals
President.................................. Mark Wilson
Vice President...........................Bart Adams
President................... Regina Howard-Glaspie
Vice President............................ Pat Taylor
NCPA Secretary/Treasurer........Tammy Dunn
NCPS Secretary/Treasurer .... Bill Moss
Immediate Past President.................Les High
President....................................Paul Mauney
Note: Elections held in July

NORTH DAKOTA NEWSPAPER ASSOCIATION
— 1435 Interstate Loop,
Bismarck, ND, 58503-0567, USA; tel (701) 223-
6397; fax (701) 223-8185; e-mail info@ndna.
com; web site www.ndna.com

Mktg. Dir. ....Kelli Richey
Exec. Dir. ....Steve Andrist
Adv. Dir. ....Mike Casey
Adv./Public Notice Coord...........Colleen Park
Office Coord./Adv. Assist......... Shari Peterson
Pres., NDNA Ed. Foundation ....Aaron Becher
Past President...........................Sara J. Plum
President.................................Harvey Brock
Second Vice President.....Jill Denning Gackle
NDNA Director ....Paul Erdelt
NDNA Director .... Leah Burke
NDNA Director ....Matt McMillan
Director.......................................Frank Perea
Director....................................Karen Speidel
Note: Represents daily and weekly
newspapers in North Dakota

O

OHIO NEWSPAPER ASSOCIATION — 1335
Dublin Rd, Ste 216B, Columbus, OH, 43215-
1000, USA; tel (614) 486-6677; fax (614) 486-
6373; e-mail dhetzel@ohionews.org; web site
www.ohionews.org

Exec. Dir. ....Dennis Hetzel
Mgr. Admin. Services ....Sue Bazzoli
Comm. Mgr....................Jason Sanford
Adv. Dir. .... Walt Dozier
Admin. Asst. .... Ann Riggs
Network Acct. Exec. & Digital Specialist Mitch
Colton
Program Support Asst....................Josh Park
Operations Manager ....Patricia Conkle
Note: Elections held in Feb

OKLAHOMA PRESS ASSOCIATION — 3601
N Lincoln Blvd, Oklahoma City, OK, 73105-
5411, USA; tel (405) 499-0020; fax (405) 499-

0048; e-mail swilkerson@okpress.com; web site
www.okpress.com

Executive Vice President..........Mark Thomas
Front Office/Building Manager ....Scott
Wilkerson
Sales Director..........................Landon Cobb
Member Services Director ....Lisa Sutliff
Creative Services Director ... Jennifer Gilliland
Digital Clipping Service Manager Keith Burgin
Advertising Manager .... Cindy Shea
Note: Elections held in June

OREGON NEWSPAPER PUBLISHERS ASSOCIATION
— 4000 Kruse Way Pl, Bldg
160, Lake Oswego, OR, 97035-5545, USA;
tel (503) 624-6397; fax (503) 639-9009; e-mail
onpa@orenews.com; web site www.orenews.
com

Exec. Dir. .... Laurie Hieb
Advertising Services Manager ....Linda
Hutcheson
Accounting Assistant......... Laurie Sterkowicz
Patricia Murphy
Edward Wistos
Jackie Thomas
Note: Elections held in June

P

PENNSYLVANIA NEWSMEDIA ASSOCIATION
— 3899 N Front St, Harrisburg,
PA, 17110-1583, USA; tel (717) 703-3000; fax
(717) 703-3001; e-mail info@pa-news.org; web
site www.panewsmedia.org

Vice President, Association Services .... Tricia
Greyshock
Vice President, Advertising..........Lisa Knight
Amanda Shafer
Bob Schnarrs
Chris Hagan
David Rhoads
Deborah Musselman
Diane Brinser
Kristin Bleiler
Lauren Fox
Communications Manager ....Lisa Strohl
Melissa Melewsky
Paula Knudsen
Rae Elise Williard
Sherid Virnig
Pres..Mark Cohen
Note: Represents daily, weekly, collegiate and
online newspapers in Pennsylvania & the U.S.

R

RHODE ISLAND PRESS ASSOCIATION —
University of Rhode Island, Journalism Dept.,
Kingston, RI, 2881, USA; tel (401) 874-4287;
fax (401) 874-4450; e-mail lllevin@uri.edu; web
site www.ripress.org

Secretary................................. Linda Levin
Treasurer...............................Fran Ostendorf
Note: Elections held in Jan

S

SOUTH CAROLINA PRESS ASSOCIATION
— 106 Outlet Pointe Blvd, Columbia, SC,
29210-5669, USA; tel (803) 750-9561; fax (803)
551-0903; e-mail scpress@scpress.org; web
site www.scpress.org

Adv. Dir. .... Alanna Ritchie
Director of Operations............Randall Savely
Executive Director .... Bill Rogers
Assistant Director ....Jen Madden
Note: Elections held in March.

SOUTH DAKOTA NEWSPAPER ASSOCIATION
— 1125 32nd Ave, Brookings,
SD, 57006-4707, USA; tel (605) 692-4300; fax
(605) 692-6388; e-mail sdna@sdna.com; web
site www.sdna.com

Exec. Dir. ....David Bordewyk
Advertising Sales Director..........John Brooks
Business Manager ....Nicole Herrig
Advertising Placement Coordinator ......Sandy
DeBeer
Note: Elections held in May

T

TENNESSEE PRESS ASSOCIATION, INC.
— 625 Market St, Ste 1100, Knoxville, TN,
37902-2219, USA; tel (865) 584-5761; fax (865)
558-8687; e-mail info@tnpress.com; web site
www.tnpress.com

Exec. Dir. .... Greg Sherrill
Advertising Dir............................. David Wells
Member Services Manager...... Robyn Gentile
Note: Elections held in June

TEXAS PRESS ASSOCIATION — 8800
Business Park Dr, Ste 100, Austin, TX, 78759-
7403, USA; tel (512) 477-6755; fax (512) 477-
6759; e-mail mhodges@texaspress.com; web
site www.texaspress.com

Exec. Dir. ....Micheal Hodges
Executive Vice President.......Donnis Baggett
Member Services Director .... Ed Sterling
Controller...........................Stephanie Hearne
Note: Elections held in June

U

UTAH PRESS ASSOCIATION, INC. — 9716
S 500 W, Sandy, UT, 84070-2565, USA; tel 801-
237-2376; e-mail upa@utahpress.com; web site
www.utahpress.com

Exec. Dir. .... Brian Allfrey
Advertising Coordinator .... Denice Page
Accounting ....Michael Wolsey
Note: Elections held in March

V

VERMONT PRESS ASSOCIATION —
Journalism Dept / 169 Jeanmarie Hall, St.
Michael's College, Colchester, VT, 05439-0001,
USA; tel (802) 654-2442; e-mail mdonoghue@
smcvt.edu; web site www.vtpress.org

Executive Director ....Mike Donoghue
Note: Elections held in the Fall

VIRGINIA PRESS ASSOCIATION, INC. —
11529 Nuckols Rd, Glen Allen, VA, 23059-5508,
USA; tel (804) 521-7570; fax (804) 521-7590;
web site www.vpa.net

Executive Director ....Betsy Edwards
Member Services Manager..... Janet Madison
Advertising Director.................Diana Shaban
Communications Manager ..... Jeremy Slayton
Assistant Executive Director ..Kim Woodward
Note: Elections held in April

W

WASHINGTON NEWSPAPER PUBLISHERS ASSOCIATION, INC.
— PO Box 389, Port
Townsend, WA, 98368-0389, USA; tel 360-344-
2938; e-mail fredobee@wnpa.com; web site
www.wnpa.com

Exec. Dir. ....Fred Obee
Member Services Director .... Janay Collins
Note: Elections held in Oct; officers installed
in Oct

WEST VIRGINIA PRESS ASSOCIATION, INC.
— 3422 Pennsylvania Ave, Charleston,
WV, 25302-4633, USA; tel (800) 235-6881; fax
(800) 526-6939; e-mail wvpress@wvpress.org;
web site www.wvpress.org

Exec. Dir. ....Don Smith
Adv. Dir. ....Toni Heady
Adv. Staff .... Dalton Walker
Note: The WVPA Annual Convention is held
in August.

WISCONSIN NEWSPAPER ASSOCIATION
— 34 Schroeder Ct, Ste 220, Madison, WI,
53711-2528, USA; tel (608) 283-7620; fax (608)
283-7631; e-mail wna@wnanews.com; web site
www.wnanews.com

Exec. Dir. ....Beth Bennett
Media Services Dir. ....Denise Guttery
Communications Dir. ....James Debilzen
Member Services Dir...................Julia Hunter
Note: Represents 34 daily and over 225
weekly and specialty newspapers

WYOMING PRESS ASSOCIATION — 2121
Evans Ave, Cheyenne, WY, 82001-3733, USA;
tel (307) 635-3905; fax (307) 635-3912; e-mail
wyopress@wyopress.org; web site www.
wyopress.org

Exec. Dir. ....Jim Angell
Deputy Dir....................................Cecilia Moats
Note: Elections held in Jan

CANADIAN NEWSPAPER ASSOCIATIONS

A

ALBERTA WEEKLY NEWSPAPERS ASSOCIATION
— 3228 Parsons Rd,
Edmonton, AB, T6N 1M2, Canada; tel (780)
434-8746; fax (780) 438-8356; e-mail info@
awna.com; web site www.awna.com

Exec. Dir. ....Dennis Merrell

ALLIANCE FOR AUDITED MEDIA CANADA
— 20 Bloor Street East, P.O. Box 75066,
Toronto, ON, M4W 3T3, Canada; tel 416-962-
5840; web site www.auditedmedia.com

VP/Gen. Mgr for AAM Canada.......Joan Brehl
Manager, Client Solutions .... Angie Sanna

ASSOCIATION DE LA PRESSE FRANCOPHONE
— 267 Dalhousie Street,
Ottawa, ON, K1N 7E3, Canada; tel (613) 241-

1017; fax (613) 241-6313; e-mail secretariat@
apf.ca; web site www.apf.ca

Gen. Mgr ....Adrien Cantin
Deputy Dir. of Special Events, Development
and Communications ....Caroline Cantin

ASSOCIATION OF CANADIAN ADVERTISERS
— 95 St Clair Ave. W., Ste.
1103, Toronto, ON, M4V 1N6, Canada; tel (416)

964-3805; fax (416) 964-0771; web site www.
acaweb.ca

ATLANTIC COMMUNITY NEWSPAPERS ASSOCIATION
— 7075 Bayers Rd., Ste.
216, Halifax, NS, B3L 2C2, Canada; tel (902)
832-4480; fax (902) 832-4484; e-mail info@
newspapersatlantic.ca; web site www.acna.com

Exec. Dir. ....Mike Kierstead

B

BBM CANADA — 1500 Don Mills Rd., 3rd Fl., Toronto, ON, M3B 3L7, Canada; tel (416) 445-9800; fax (416) 445-8644; e-mail info@bbm.ca; web site www.bbm.ca

   Vice Pres., Western Servs. .... Catherine Kelly
   Corp. Scrvs................................ Dorena Noce
   Exec. Vice Pres./CFO.................. Glen Shipp
   Exec. Asst................................. Heather Gillis
   Pres./CEO............................. Jim Mac Leod
   Vice Pres., Meter Servs. .... Randy Missen
   Vice Pres., Quebec Servs..... Robert Langlois

BRITISH COLUMBIA/YUKON COMMUNITY NEWSPAPERS ASSOCIATION — #9 West Broadway, Vancouver, BC, V5Y 1P1, Canada; tel (604) 669-9222; fax (604) 684-4713; e-mail info@bccommunitynews.com; web site www.bccommunitynews.com

   Gen. Mgr................................George Affleck
   Note: Elections held in May

CANADIAN PRESS, THE - TORONTO, ON — 36 King St. E., Toronto, ON, M5C 2L9, Canada; tel (416) 364-0321; fax (416) 364-0207; e-mail info@thecanadianpress.com; web site www.thecanadianpress.com

   Chrmn. .... John Honderich
   News Editor.............................Ellen Huebert
   Legislature Correspondent........... Keith Leslie
   Pres. .... Eric Morrison
   CFO.................................... David Ross
   Chief, Ontario Servs............. Wendy McCann
   Vice Pres., Broadcasting.............. Terry Scott
   Vice Pres., French Servs................Jean Roy
   Dir., HR.................................Paul Woods
   Office Mgr............................ Sharon Hockin
   Exec. Dir. .... Philipe Mercure
   Note: Elections held in April

C

CANADIAN BUSINESS PRESS — 2100 Banbury Cresent, Oakville, ON, L6H 5P6, Canada; tel 905-844-6822; e-mail torrance@cbp.ca; web site www.cbp.ca

   Executive Director .... Trish Torrance

CANADIAN CIRCULATIONS AUDIT BOARD (CCAB, INC.) — 1 Concorde Gate Suite 800, SUITE 800, Toronto, ON, M3C 3N6, Canada; tel (416) 487-2418; fax (416) 487-6405; e-mail info@bpaww.com; web site www.bpaww.com

   Mktg. Mgr..................................Neil Ta
   Note: Elections held in April

CANADIAN NEWS MEDIA ASSOCITION — 37 Front Street East Suite 200, Toronto, ON, M5E 1B3, Canada; tel (416) 923-3567; fax (416) 923-7206; e-mail info@newsmediacanada.ca; web site www.https://nmc-mic.ca

   Chairman .... Bob Cox

Vice-Chairmain .... Craig Bernard
Note: News Media Canada was formed by the merger of the Canadian Newspaper Association and the Canadian Community Newspapers Association in 2017

CANADIAN PRINTING INK MANUFACTURERS ASSOCIATION — 52 Palmer Rd., Grimby, ON, L3M 5L4, Canada; tel (905) 309-5883; fax (905) 309-5838; e-mail cpima@sympatico.ca; web site www.cpima.org

   Exec. Dir./Sec./Treasurer........ Dorothea Nace
   Pres. .... Neil Marshall
   Vice Pres. .... Vivy da Costa
   Note: Elections held in Aug. for a two year term

CONSEIL DE PRESSE DU QUEBEC — 1000, rue Fullum, Ste. A.208, Montreal, QC, H2K 3L7, Canada; tel (514) 529-2818; fax (514) 873-4434; e-mail info@conseildepresse.qc.ca; web site www.conseildepresse.qc.ca

   Contact............................... Guy Amyot
   Director of communication .... Julien Acosta

F

FEDERATION PROFESSIONNELLE DES JOURNALISTES DU QUEBEC — 1012 Mount Royal Ave., Suite 105, Montreal (Quebec), QC, H2X 1X6, Canada; tel (514) 522-6142; fax (514) 522-6071; e-mail info@fpjq.org; web site www.fpjq.org

   Exec. Dir............................. Caroline Locher
   Deputy Dir............ Emilia-Larivee Tourangeau
   Adv. Rep. .... Leslie Humblot

FLYER DISTRIBUTION STANDARDS ASSOCIATION — 1881 Yonge Street, Suite 800, Toronto, ON, M4S 3C4, Canada; tel (416) 922-6678 ext. 236; fax (416) 922-8011; web site www.fdsa-canada.org

   Manager, Special Projects ....Mary Markou

H

HEBDOS QUEBEC — 2550 Daniel-Johnson,, Bureau 345, Laval, QC, H7T 2L1, Canada; tel (514) 861-2088; fax (514) 861-1966; e-mail communications@hebdos.com; web site hebdos.com

   Exec. Dir. ....Gilber Paquette

M

MANITOBA COMMUNITY NEWSPAPER ASSOCIATION — 943 McPhillips Street, Winnipeg, MB, R2X 2J9, Canada; tel (204)

947-1691; fax (204) 947-1919; web site www.mcna.com

NOTE: ELECTIONS HELD AT ANNUAL APRIL CONVENTION

N

NEWS MEDIA CANADA — 37 Front Street East Suite 200, Toronto, ON, M5E 1B3, Canada; tel (416) 923-3567; fax (416) 923-7206; e-mail info@newspaperscanada.ca; web site www.ccna.ca

   Pres..John Hinds

NEWSPAPER CANADA — 890 Yonge Street Ste 200, Toronto, ON, M4W 3P4, Canada; tel (416) 923-3567; fax (416) 923-7206; e-mail info@newspapercanada,ca; web site www.newspapercanada.ca

NEWSPAPERS ATLANTIC — 7071 Bayers Road, Suite 331, Halifax, NS, B3L 2C2, Canada; tel (902) 402-3777; fax (902) 402-3777; e-mail mike@newspapersatlantic.ca; web site 7075 Bayers Road, Suite 216"

   Executive Director .... Mike Kierstead
   Value Advertising Manager........... Liz Keitner
   Advertising Coordinator ....Julia Manuel

O

ONTARIO COMMUNITY NEWSPAPERS ASSOCIATION — 3228 South Service Rd. Ste 116, Burlington, ON, L7N 3H8, Canada; tel (905) 639-8720; fax (905) 639-6962; e-mail info@ocna.org; web site www.ocna.org

   Executive Director .... Anne Lannan

ORGANIZATION OF NEWS OMBUDSMEN — 6336 Hawthorn Lane, Vancouver, BC, V6T 2J6, Canada; tel (604) 353-6228; e-mail klapointe@newsombudsmen.org; web site www.newsombudsmen.org

   Executive Director .... Kirk LaPointe

Q

QUEBEC COMMUNITY NEWSPAPERS ASSOCIATION — 189 Hymus Blvd., Suite 207, Pointe-Claire, QC, H9R 1E9, Canada; tel (514) 697-6330; fax (514) 697-6331; e-mail execdir@qcna.qc.ca; web site www.qcna.org

   Executive Director ....Richard Tardif

R

RTDNA - CANADA (RADIO TELEVISION DIGITAL NEWS ASSOCIATION) — 2800 - 14th Ave., Ste. 210, Markham, ON, L3R 0E4, Canada; tel (416) 756 2213; fax (416) 491-1670; e-mail sherry@associationconcepts.ca; info@rtdnacanada.com; web site www.rtdnacanada.com

   Operations Manager ....Sherry Denesha
   Note: Elections held in June

S

SASKATCHEWAN WEEKLY NEWSPAPERS ASSOCIATION — 14-401 45th St. W., Saskatoon, SK, S7L 5Z9, Canada; tel (306) 382-9683; fax (306) 382-9421; e-mail swna@swna.com; web site www.swna.com

   Tech. Officer .... Cameron Just
   Commun.Coord...........................Julie Schau
   Office Mgr...........................Louise Simpson
   Adv. Coord., Classified...............Nicole Nater
   Exec. Dir. ....Steve Nixon

T

THE CANADIAN ASSOCIATION OF JOURNALISTS — Box 745, Cornwall, ON, K6H 5T5, Canada; tel N/A; web site www.caj.ca

   ....Hugo Rodrigues
   .... Nick Taylor-VaiseyNat'l Dir.s

TRANS-CANADA ADVERTISING AGENCY NETWORK — 25 Sheppard Ave. West, Suite 300, Toronto, ON, M2N 6S6, Canada; tel 416-221-8883; e-mail mabill@waginc.ca; web site www.tcaan.ca

   Exec. Dir. ....Alice Zaharchuk
   Mng. Dir./Treasurer.................Bill Whitehead

W

WINNIPEG PRESS CLUB — C/O St. James Legion Branch #4, 1755 Portage Avenue, Winnipeg, MB, R3J 0E6, Canada; tel (204) 800-1887; e-mail winnipegpressclub@outlook.com

   VP ....Wendy Hart
   Pres....................................Dwight MacAulay
   Note: Since 2011, we have made our home at a local Royal Canadian Legion branch in Winnipeg, which has allowed us gracious use of their facilities. (Bar, meeting rooms, games room, food services).

We welcome visitors from press clubs and media organizations around the world. If you are planning to be in Winnipeg, please email winnipegpressclub@outlook.com, or call (204) 800-1887.

Section VI

E&P's Who's Where Directory of Newspaper People

E&P's Who's Where Directory of Newspaper People, is an alphabetical listing of all personnel from U.S. and Canadian daily and weekly newspapers and newspaper groups listed in Book 1 and 2 of the DataBook. It also includes personnel from News and Syndicate Services, shopper publications, and specialty and niche publications.

Each name is followed by a phone number to reach that person, the email address, the person's title, name of newspaper or company, city and state.

Index

A

A'Hearn, Jill ....(520) 295-4236
jahearn@azbiz.com, Adv. Dir., The Daily
Territorial, AZ, Tucson

ALMEN, Theodore ....(320) 264-3071
kbanner@tds.net, PUBLISHER, Lakes Area
Review, MN, New London

Aaron, Charlotte
vfusco@express-news.net, Gen. Mgr., Ad'
Smart (OOB), TX, San Antonio
vfusco@express-news.net, Vice Pres.,
Classified Adv., Bulverde News, TX, San
Antonio
vfusco@express-news.net, Vice Pres.,
Classified Adv., Fort Sam News Leader, TX,
San Antonio
vfusco@express-news.net, Vice Pres.,
Classified Adv., Kelly Observer, TX, San
Antonio
vfusco@express-news.net, Vice Pres.,
Classified Adv., Lackland Talespinner, TX,
San Antonio
vfusco@express-news.net, Vice Pres.,
Classified Adv., Medical Patriot, TX, San
Antonio
vfusco@express-news.net, Vice Pres.,
Classified Adv., North Central News, TX,
San Antonio
vfusco@express-news.net, Vice Pres.,
Classified Adv., Northeast Herald, TX, San
Antonio
vfusco@express-news.net, Vice Pres.,
Classified Adv., Randolph Wingspread, TX,
San Antonio
vfusco@express-news.net, Vice Pres.,
Classified Adv., Northwest Weekly, TX, San
Antonio

Aaron, Derek
sports@tjrcn.com, Ed, The Russell County
News-Register, KY, Russell Springs
sports@tjrcn.com, News/Sports Ed., The
Times Journal, KY, Russell Springs

Aaron, Joseph ....(847) 966-0606
Joescoop@aol.com, Ed. and Pub., Chicago
Jewish News, IL, Skokie

Aaron, Robin ....(903) 796-7133
raaron@casscountynow.com, Editor, Atlanta
Citizens Journal, TX, Atlanta

Abbot, Thomas
tabbott@journalregister.com, Pub., The
Mercury, PA, Pottstown

Abbott, Brandi ....(816) 324-3149
adsales@stjoelive.com, Ad Sales, Savannah
Reporter and Andrew County Democrat, MO,
Savannah

Abbott, Jeanne
abbottj@missouri.edu, Managing Ed.,
Columbia Missourian, MO, Columbia

Abbott, Thomas ....(610) 323-3000
tabbott@journalregister.com, Pub, Mercury
Sampler, PA, Pottstown

Abby, Tutor...............................(425) 388-9522
Editor-in-chief, Everett Community College,
WA, Everett

Abdelnour, Doug ....(740) 549-2200
Classified Mgr., Consumer News Service Inc.,
OH, Lewis Center

Abe, Gonzalez ....(956) 982-6660
agonzalez@brownsvilleherald.com, Circulation
Director, The Brownsville Herald, TX,
Brownsville

Abel, David
dabel@firstrealtymgt.com, Part-time Fac.,
Northeastern University, MA, Boston

Abel, Jananne ....(914) 939-6864
editor@westmorenews.com, Ed., America
Latina, NY, Port Chester
editor@westmorenews.com, Editor, Westmore
News, NY, Port Chester

Abel, Richard...........................(914) 939-6864
publisher@westmorenews.com, Publisher,
Westmore News, NY, Port Chester
publisher@westmorenews.com, Adv. Mgr.,
America Latina, NY, Port Chester

Abell, Gene ....(859) 231-3237
gabell@herald-leader.com, Sports Ed.,
Lexington Herald-Leader, KY, Lexington

Abeln, Steve ....(907) 644-5412
advertising@anchoragepress.com, Publisher,
Anchorage Press, AK, Anchorage

Abels, Debbie
dabels@heraldonline.com, Pres./Pub., The
Herald, SC, Rock Hill
dabels@heraldonline.com, Pub., The Enquirer-
Herald, SC, York

Abendroth, Betty ....(903) 849-3333
news@c-bstatesman.com, Owner / Publisher,
Chandler & Brownsboro Statesman, TX,
Chandler

Abercrombie, Karen W.
alamsgr@bellsouth.net, Pub. / Gen. Mgr.,
Alabama Messenger, AL, Birmingham

Abernathy, Gary ....(937) 393-3456 Ext. 1682
gabernathy@civitasmedia.com, Pub. / Ed.,
Hillsboro Times-Gazette, OH, Hillsboro

Abernathy, Michael G. ....(502) 513-1143
mabernathy@lcni.com, Pres., Landmark
Community Newspapers, LLC, KY,
Shelbyville

Abernethy, Julie
jabernethy@friendship.us, Hollins Univ., VA,
Roanoke

Abittan, Lori
lori@multimedianova.com, Ed., Insieme, QC,
Montreal

Abonyi, Susan
news@nmjlink.org, Ed., New Mexico Jewish
Link, NM, Albuquerque

Abraham, Betsy
babraham@antonmediagroup.com, Ed.,
Westbury Times, NY, Mineola

Abraham, Israel Khyri.................(508) 565-1190
iabraham@stonehill.edu, Chair, Stonehill
College, MA, Easton

Abraham, Joseph .... (845) 887-5200 ext. 119
joe@sc-democrat.com, Co-Editor, Sullivan
County Democrat, NY, Callicoon

Abraham, Paul ....(423) 757-6370
jdeloach@timesfreepress.com, Controller
, Chattanooga Times Free Press, TN,
Chattanooga
jdeloach@timesfreepress.com, Dir., Finance,
Knoxville News Sentinel, TN, Knoxville

Abraham Jr., Nate ....(803) 256-4015
NateAbraham@CarolinaPanorama.com, Pub.,
Carolina Panorama, SC, Columbia

Abrahamson, David
d-abrahamson@northwestern.edu, Prof.,
Northwestern University, IL, Evanston

Abram, Kelsie
ledge@uw.edu, Editor-in-Chief, The University
of Washington Tacoma Ledger Student
Newspaper, WA, Tacoma

Abramowitz, Roxanne.................(724) 626-3530
rabramowitz@tribweb.com, Mng. Ed., Daily
Courier, PA, Connellsville

Abrams, Drew Dara...................(650) 949-7372
Foothill College, CA, Los Altos Hills

Abrams, Ed ....(212) 457-7735
ed.abrams@metro.us, Metro US Exec./
National Sales Dir.
& Associate Publisher Metro New York, Metro
New York, NY, New York

Abrams, Lori...........(613) 342-44441, ext 500248
lori.abrams@sunmedia.ca, Business Mgr.,
The Brockville Recorder and Times, ON,
Brockville

Abrams, Lynn ....(401) 230-2311
Abrams@NewportRI.com, Advertising Director,
The Newport Daily News, RI, Newport

Abrams, Lynn..........................(401) 380-2311
abrams@newportri.com, Adv. Sales Mgr., The
Independent, RI, Newport

Abramson, Steve......................(631) 204-9100
stevea@hamptons.com, Pres., Stock, Fund, or
ETF, NY, Water Mill

Abreu, Jim
jim@atomicimaging.com, Interactive Design,
Atomic Imaging, Inc., IL, Chicago

Abshier, Bryce
bryce.abshier@starbanner.com, Nat'l Adv.
Acct. Exec., Ocala Star-Banner, FL, Ocala

Abssi, Michel...........................(323) 978-8888
info@beiruttimes.com, Ed., Beirut Times, CA,
Pasadena

Ace, Lisa ....(585) 250-4118
lisa@thebatavian.com, Sales/Mktg. Coord.,
The Batavian, NY, Batavia

Acevedo, Cynthia
cacevedo@sun-herald.com, Nat'l/Major Acct.
Sales, Charlotte Sun, FL, Punta Gorda

Acevedo, Melorie ....(415) 777-7473
macevedo@sfchronicle.com, MIS Director, San
Francisco Chronicle, CA, San Francisco

Acheson, Heather
heather.acheson@camaspostrecord.com,
Mng. Ed., Camas-Washougal Post Record,
WA, Camas
heather.acheson@camaspostrecord.com, Ed.,
At Your Leisure, WA, Camas

Achkar, Alan
aachkar@sbtinfo.com, Exec. Ed., South Bend
Tribune, IN, South Bend

Achorn, Edward C.....................(401) 277-7190
eachorn@providencejournal.com, Vice Pres. &
Editorial Pages Ed., The Providence Journal,
RI, Providence

Acker, Amber
amberacker@onlinecommercegroup.com,
Auburn Univ., AL, Montgomery

Acker, Stephen
acker.1@osu.edu, Assoc. Prof., Ohio State
University, OH, Columbus

Acker, Yvonda ....(620) 792-9239
Barton County Cmty. College, KS, Great Bend

Ackerman, Bonnie
hackerman@heraldprint.com, Adv. Dir.,
The New Washington Herald, OH, New
Washington

Ackerman, Kevin......................(330) 580-8550
kevin.ackerman@cantonrep.com, Ops. VP, The
Times-Reporter, OH, New Philadelphia
kevin.ackerman@cantonrep.com, Ops. Dir.,
The Repository, OH, Canton

Acor, Brett
bacor@postregister.com, Sales Dir., Post
Register, ID, Idaho Falls

Acosta, Gail ....(850) 939-8040
gail@navarrepress.com, Ad., Navarre Press,
FL, Navarre

Acosta, Julien
julien.acosta@conseildepresse.qc.ca, Director
of communication, Conseil de Presse du
Quebec, QC, Montreal

Acosta, Letty...........................(336) 727-7456
lacosta@wsjournal.com, Circulation Retention
Sales, Marketing & (N.I.E.) News In
Education, Winston-Salem Journal, NC,
Winston Salem

Acosta, Mark ....(951) 368-9362
macosta@pe.com, Metro Ed., The Press-
Enterprise, CA, Riverside
macosta@pe.com, VP, Audience, Lexington
Herald-Leader, KY, Lexington

Acosta, Rueben ....(505) 564-4671
racosta@daily-times.com, Cir. Dist. Mgr., The
Daily Times, NM, Farmington

Acra, Natalie ....(812) 663-3111 x7034
natalie.acra@greensburgdailynews.com, Adv.
Mgr., The Greensburg Times, IN, Greensburg
natalie.acra@greensburgdailynews.com,
Operations Mgr., Greensburg Daily News, IN,
Greensburg

Acton, Karen
kacton@somdnews.com, Pub., The Enquirer-
Gazette, MD, Waldorf
kacton@somdnews.com, Pub., The Enterprise,
MD, California
kacton@somdnews.com, Pub., The Maryland
Independent, MD, White Plains

Adachi, Yoroku
pr@cusa.canon.com, Pres./CEO, Canon
U.S.A., Inc., Canon USA, Inc., NY, New
Hyde Park

Adadie, Chuck ....(601) 403-1312
CABADIE@PRCC.EDU, Pearl River Commnity
College, MS, Poplarville

Adaime, Ivan
ivan.adaime@impremedia.com, General Mgr
Digital, El Diario La Prensa, NY, Brooklyn

Adair-Hodges, Erin ....ext. 255
Arts Ed., Weekly Alibi, NM, Albuquerque

Adam, Andrew.............................330-541-927
aadam@recordpub.com, Ed., Hudson Hub-
Times, OH, Kent

Adam, David
dadam@whig.com, Advisor, Quincy Univ., IL,
Quincy

Adam, Diane
greek@britsys.net, Prodn. Mgr., Greek Star,
IL, Chicago

Adamcik, Beth ....(641) 842-2155
advertising@journalexpress.net, Marketing
Consultant, Marion County Reminder, IA,
Knoxville

Adamian, John ....(860) 241-3444
jadamian@hartfordadvocate.com, Mng. Ed.,
New Haven Advocate (OOB), CT, New Haven
jadamian@hartfordadvocate.com, Mng. Ed.,
New Mass Media, Inc., CT, Hartford
jadamian@hartfordadvocate.com, Mng. Ed.,
New Haven Advocate, CT, New Haven

Adamiec, Sara
sadamiec@mtexpress.com, Adv. Rep., Idaho
Mountain Express, ID, Ketchum

Adamis, Tony .... (845) 331-5000 Ext. 01095
tadamis@freemanonline.com, Mng. Ed., Daily
Freeman, NY, Kingston

Adamo, Felix
fadamo@bakersfield.com, Chief Photographer,
The Bakersfield Californian, CA, Bakersfield

Adams, Allen ....(207) 942-2901
aadams@themainedge.com, Ed., The Maine
Edge, ME, Bangor

Adams, Bart ....(910) 230-2001
badams@mydailyrecord.com , Ed./Pub., The
Daily Record, NC, Dunn

Adams, Bart S.
badams@dunndailyrecord.com, Pub., Harnett
County News, NC, Lillington

Adams, Brooke
brooke@rushing-media.com, Circ. Mgr, The
Weekly Want Ads, LA, Houma

Adams, Cecil
cecil@straightdope.com, Creator/Writer,
Straight Dope - Wrapports/Sun-Times Media,
Inc., Chicago

Adams, Cheri ....(478) 987-1823
cadams@sunmulti.com, VP, Major Accts. Rep.,
The Houston Home Journal, GA, Perry

Adams, Chris
cadams@clarionnews.net, Ed., Clarion News,
IN, Corydon

Adams, Christie
christie.adams@sccpss.com, Adv. Mgr.,

Savannah Herald, GA, Savannah

Adams, Darrel .... **(620) 408-9918**
darrel.adams@dodgeglobe.com, Adv. Mgr., The Shopper's Weekly, KS, Dodge City

Adams, David .... **(252) 329-9516**
dadams@reflector.com, Circ. Dir., The Daily Reflector, NC, Greenville

Adams, David .... **(252) 329-9630**
dadams@reflector.com, Second Vice President, Mid-Atlantic Circulation Managers Association, NC, Roanoke Rapids

Adams, David .... **(309) 852-2181**
dadams@gatehousemedia.com, Circulation Dir., The Daily Reflector, NC, Greenville
dadams@gatehousemedia.com, Pub., Gallatin Democrat, IL, Shawneetown
dadams@gatehousemedia.com, Pub., Eldorado Daily Journal, IL, Harrisburg
dadams@gatehousemedia.com, Pub., The Register-Mail, IL, Galesburg
dadams@gatehousemedia.com, Pub., Daily Ledger, IL, Canton
dadams@gatehousemedia.com, Pub., The Daily Leader, IL, Pontiac
dadams@gatehousemedia.com, Pub., Star Courier, PA, Northern Cambria
dadams@gatehousemedia.com, Pub., Galva News, IL, Galva
dadams@gatehousemedia.com, Pub., Geneseo Republic, IL, Geneseo

Adams, Diane
dadams@ironmountaindailynews.com, NIE Coord., The Daily News, MI, Iron Mountain

Adams, Dorothy
lawcoadv@bellsouth.net, Circ. Mgr., Lawrence County Advocate, TN, Lawrenceburg

Adams, Duska .... **(804) 550-5114**
virginiaclipping@burrellesluce.com, Client Servs. Mgr., Virginia Clipping Service, VA, Ashland

Adams, Floyd
floyd.adams@savannah.chatham.k12.ga.us, Pub., Savannah Herald, GA, Savannah

Adams, Fred
GeneralManager@GrenadaStar.com, Gen. Mgr., Grenada Star, MS, Grenada
GeneralManager@GrenadaStar.com, Prodn. Mgr., Grenada Lake Herald, MS, Grenada

Adams, James .... **(603) 668-4321**
jadams@unionleader.com, Instr., Alabama State Univ., AL, Montgomery
jadams@unionleader.com, Prod. Mgr., The Sun/Sunday Sun, OK, Midwest City

Adams, Jane
info@greenecountymessenger.com, Gen. Mgr, Greene County Messenger, PA, Waynesburg

Adams, Jennifer
editor@theplainsman.com; opinion@theplainsman.com, Auburn Univ., AL, Auburn University

Adams, Joe .... **(615) 444-3952 ext. 12**
jadams@lebanondemocrat.com, Pub./Vice Pres., The Lebanon Democrat, TN, Lebanon

Adams, Joe
joe.adams@sonoco.com, Pub., The Hartsville Vidette, TN, Hartsville

Adams, Joe
mtjulietnews@tds.net, Pub., Mt. Juliet News, TN, Lebanon

Adams, Joseph H.
southstar@centurytel.net, Ed., The Ozark Southern Star, AL, Ozark

Adams, Kelly .... **(785) 295-5656**
kelly.adams@cjonline.com, Asst. Copy Chief, The Topeka Capital-Journal, KS, Topeka

Adams, Kenneth .... **(912) 356-0025**
news@savannahherald.net, Publisher, Savannah Herald, GA, Savannah

Adams, Kim .... **(319) 984-6179**
news@denveriaforum.com, Publisher, Denver

Forum, IA, Denver

Adams, Kim Edward .... **(319) 827-1128**
publisher@jesupcitizenherald.com, Pub., Jesup Citizen Herald, IA, Jesup

Adams, Lynn
editor@southwesttimes.com, Managing Editor, The Southwest Times (Pulaski, VA), VA, Pulaski

Adams, Mike .... **(910) 486-3558**
adamsm@fayettevillenc.com, Exec. Ed., The Fayetteville Observer, NC, Fayetteville

Adams, Nancy
nadams@polkio.com, Pub, The Polk County Itemizer-Observer, OR, Dallas

Adams, Paul
padams@hearstnp.com, Sports Ed., Huron Daily Tribune, MI, Bad Axe

Adams, Robert
monitor@omnitelcom.com, Ed., The Monitor Review, IA, Stacyville

Adams, Robert
rpa@aol.com, Ed., Monitor Review, MN, Adams

Adams, Robin .... **(863) 802-7558**
robin.adams@theledger.com, Health/Medical Ed., The Ledger, FL, Lakeland

Adams, Ron .... **(440) 245-6901 Ext. 90702**
radams@morningjournal.com, Controller, The News-Herald, OH, Willoughby
radams@morningjournal.com, CFO, The Morning Journal, OH, Lorain

Adams, Sarah
sadams@mckendree.edu, Editor in Chief, McKendree University, IL, Lebanon

Adams, Sarah .... **ext. 247**
sadams@sharonherald.com, News Ed., The Herald, PA, Sharon

Adams, Stephen .... **(205) 631-8716**
sadams@njeffersonnews.com, Sales, North Jefferson News, AL, Gardendale

Adams, Thomas
adams1@rose-hulman.edu, Advisor, Rose-Hulman Inst. of Technology, IN, Terre Haute

Adams, Todd .... **(801) 788-1549**
tadams@sltrib.com, Online - Art Editor, The Salt Lake Tribune, UT, Salt Lake City
tadams@sltrib.com, Sports Ed., The State Journal-Register, IL, Springfield

Adams, Todd .... **(208) 879-4445**
Reporter/photographer, The Challis Messenger, ID, Challis

Adams, Tom .... **(954) 574-5373**
TAdams@tribune.com, Pres./Pub., Hi-Riser - Broward, FL, Pompano Beach

Adams, Tom
tadams@tribune.com, Pub./Gen. Mgr., Boca Raton Forum, FL, Fort Lauderdale
tadams@tribune.com, Pub./Gen. Mgr., Coral Springs Focus (OOB), FL, Coral Springs
tadams@tribune.com, Plantation/Davie Forum, FL, Fort Lauderdale
tadams@tribune.com, Pres./Pub./Gen. Mgr., Oakland Park Gazette (OOB), FL, Fort Lauderdale
tadams@tribune.com, Pub./Gen. Mgr., Shalom - Broward, FL, Fort Lauderdale
tadams@tribune.com, Pub./Gen. Mgr., Shalom - Palm Beach, FL, Fort Lauderdale
tadams@tribune.com, Pub./Gen. Mgr., South Woodham Focus (OOB), FL, Fort Lauderdale
tadams@tribune.com, Pub./Gen. Mgr., Weston Gazette, FL, Fort Lauderdale
tadams@tribune.com, President, Lake Worth Forum, FL, Fort Lauderdale
tadams@tribune.com, President, Live Wellington, FL, Fort Lauderdale
tadams@tribune.com, President, Deerfield and Pompano Forum, FL, Fort Lauderdale
tadams@tribune.com, Pres./Pub., West Boca Forum, FL, Fort Lauderdale

Adams, Tom

tadams@tribune.com, Adv. Mgr., Jewish Journal - Broward Central, FL, Fort Lauderdale
tadams@tribune.com, Pres./Pub., Plantation/Davie Forum, FL, Fort Lauderdale
tadams@tribune.com, Pres./Pub., Royal Palm Forum (OOB), FL, Fort Lauderdale
tadams@tribune.com, Pres./Pub., East Side Forum, FL, Fort Lauderdale
tadams@tribune.com, Adv. Mgr., Jewish Journal Palm Beach South, FL, Fort Lauderdale
tadams@tribune.com, Pres./Pub., Margate / Coconut Creek Forum, FL, Fort Lauderdale
tadams@tribune.com, Pub./Pres., Boynton Forum, FL, Fort Lauderdale
tadams@tribune.com, Pres./Pub., Delray Beach Forum, FL, Fort Lauderdale
tadams@tribune.com, Sr. Adv. Mgr., Jewish Journal - Broward North, FL, Pompano Beach
tadams@tribune.com, Pres./Pub., The Forum - Sunrise & Tamarac, FL, Davie
tadams@tribune.com, Sales Mgr., Jewish Journal - Broward South, FL, Pompano Beach
tadams@tribune.com, Adv. Mgr., Jewish Journal - Miami Dade, FL, Pompano Beach
tadams@tribune.com, Adv. Mgr., Jewish Journal - Palm Beach North, FL, Pompano Beach

Adams, Tony .... **(513) 732-2511**
tadams@clermontsun.com, Pub., The Clermont Sun, OH, Batavia

Adams, Tony
asa3866@aol.com, Pub., The Brown County Press, OH, Mount Orab

Adamson, Cass .... **+44 (207) 061-3508**
cadamson@nytimes.com, Regional Director, Europe, Middle East & Africa, The New York Times News Service & Syndicate, New York

Adamson, Cass .... **+44 (207) 061-3508**
cadamson@nytimes.com, Regional Director, Europe, Middle East & Africa, The New York Times News Service & Syndicate, New York

Adamson, Donn .... **(573) 518-3638 ext. 143**
dadamson@dailyjournalonline.com, Sports Ed., Daily Journal, Park Hills, MO, Park Hills

Adamson, Lonnie .... **(864) 855-0355 ext. 36**
ladamson@civitasmedia.com, Gen. Mgr./Ed., The Pickens Sentinel, SC, Easley

Adamson, Nancy
nadamson@mrt.com, Online Mgr., Midland Reporter-Telegram, TX, Midland

Adamson, Pam
padamson@dailyhome.com, Adv. Dir., The Daily Home, AL, Talladega

Adcock, Jaquita .... **(806) 323-6461**
jaquita@canadianrecord.com, Adv. Sales, The Canadian Record, TX, Canadian

Addenbrooke, Erin .... **(303) 566-4074**
eaddenbrooke@coloradocommunitymedia.com, Adv. Dir., Westminster Window, CO, Westminster

Addenbrooke, Erin .... **(303) 566-4074**
eaddenbrooke@ourcoloradonews.com, Adv. Mgr., Lone Tree Voice, CO, Highlands Ranch
eaddenbrooke@ourcoloradonews.com, Adv. Dir., The Englewood Herald, CO, Highlands Ranch
eaddenbrooke@ourcoloradonews.com, Major Accts. Mgr., Northglenn-Thornton Sentinel, CO, Westminster
eaddenbrooke@ourcoloradonews.com, Adv. Dir., Parker Chronicle, CO, Highlands Ranch
eaddenbrooke@ourcoloradonews.com, Adv. Dir., Highlands Ranch Herald, CO, Highlands Ranch
eaddenbrooke@ourcoloradonews.com, Adv. Dir., Elbert County News, CO, Highlands Ranch
eaddenbrooke@ourcoloradonews.com, Adv. Dir., The Littleton Independent, CO, Highlands Ranch

Addiego, Walter
waddiego@sfchronicle.com, Movie Ed./Copy Ed., San Francisco Chronicle, CA, San Francisco

Addington, Joel .... **(904) 259-2400**
reporter@bakercountypress.com, Mng Ed., The Baker County Press, FL, Macclenny

Addleman, Brent
editor3@zitomedia.net, Ed., Daily Press, PA, Saint Marys

Addy-Wright, Jill
jaddywright@multiad.com, Sr. Vice Pres., Local Search Association, IL, Peoria

Adelman, Matt .... **(307) 358-2965**
publisher@douglas-budget.com, Pub./Ed., The Douglas Budget, WY, Douglas

Adelman, Matt .... **(307) 358-2965**
publisher@douglas-budget.com, Prod. Mgr., The Douglas Budget, WY, Douglas

Adelstein, Kevin .... **(216) 342-5206**
kevin@cjn.org, Pres. Pub. & CEO, Cleveland Jewish News, OH, Beachwood

Adkins, David .... **(812) 316-5384**
dadkins@suncommercial.com , Dis. Mgr., Vincennes Sun-Commercial, IN, Vincennes

Adkins, Jim
adkinsj@fayobserver.com, Circ. Dir., Carolina Flyer, NC, Fayetteville

Adkins, Jana .... **(661) 287-5599**
jana@signalscv.com, Mng. Ed., Santa Clarita Valley Signal, CA, Santa Clarita

Adkins, Mark .... **(409) 838-2898**
madkins@beaumontenterprise.com, Publisher, The Beaumont Enterprise, TX, Beaumont

Adkins, Marlene
madkins@j-adgraphics.com, Circ. Mgr., Battle Creek Shopper News, MI, Battle Creek

Adkins, Paul
padkins@loganbanner.com, Sports Ed., The Logan Banner, WV, Logan

Adkins, Shaun .... **(765) 575-4648**
sadkins@thecouriertimes.com, Home Delivery Mgr., The Courier-Times, IN, New Castle

Adkins, Shirley .... **(434) 432-1654 ext. 24**
shirleyadkins@womackpublishing.com, Circ. Mgr., Womack Publishing Co., VA, Lynchburg

Adkison, Lisa
ladkison@idahocountyfreepress.com, Adv. Rep., Idaho County Free Press, ID, Grangeville

Adkisson, Gary
gadkisson@paducahsun.com, Gen. Mgr., The Paducah Sun, KY, Paducah

Adkisson, Shana
editor@normantranscript.com, Ed, Moore American, OK, Norman

Adler, Joe .... **(571) 403-3832**
joe.adler@sourcemedia.com, Deputy Bureau Chief, Regulation & Reform, American Banker, NY, New York

Adolphoson, Sue
sadolphson@sfchronicle.com, Sunday Datebook Ed., San Francisco Chronicle, CA, San Francisco

Adrians, Jason ....**(920) 993-1000, ext. 1-237**
jadrians@gannett.com, News Director, Post-Crescent, WI, Appleton

Ads, Classified
bcclassifieds@blackpress.ca, Classifieds , The Lake Cowichan Gazette, BC, Duncan

Adsett, Dave .... **(519) 843-5410 ext. 530**
editor@wellingtonadvertiser.com, Ed., The Wellington Advertiser, ON, Fergus

Adsett, Dave
drayton@wellingtonadvertiser.com, Ed., The Community News, ON, Drayton

Adsett, William .... **(519) 843-5410 ext. 525**
info@wellingtonadvertiser.com, Pub., The

jpalderton@times-news.com, Ed., Beyond 50, MD

jpalderton@times-news.com, Ed., The Garrett County Weekender, MD, Cumberland

Aldoory, Linda
laldoory@umd.edu, Assoc. Prof., Pub. Rel./ Health Commun./Feminist Scholarship, University of Maryland, MD, College Park

Aleshire, Peter .... (928) 474-5251 x115
paleshire@payson.com, Ed., The Payson Roundup, AZ, Payson

Alessi, Steve
salessi@starledger.com, VP of Advertising, The Star-Ledger, NJ, Newark

Alexander, Alison
alison@uga.edu, Prof./Sr. Assoc. Dean, University of Georgia, GA, Athens

Alexander, Ashley ....(518) 873-6368
ashley@denpubs.com, Adv. Dir., The News Enterprise Sun, NY, Elizabethtown

ashley@denpubs.com, Adv. Dir., The Times of Ti Sun, NY, Elizabethtown

Alexander, Ashley ....(518) 873-6368
ashley@suncommunitynews.com, Advt Dir, The North Countryman Sun, NY, Elizabethtown

Alexander, Ashley ....(518) 873-6368
ashley@denpubs.com, Adv. Dir., The Valley News Sun, NY, Elizabethtown

Alexander, Ashley ....(518) 873-6368
ashley@suncommunitynews.com, Northern Adirondacks Publishing Group Mgr, Sun Community News, Published by:Denton Publications, Inc., NY, Elizabethtown

Alexander, Cesar
cesar.alexander@sacramentopress.com, Editorial Assistant, Sacramento Press, CA, Citrus Heights

Alexander, Dan ....(518) 873-6368
dj@denpubs.com, Gen. Mgr., The News Enterprise Sun, NY, Elizabethtown

dj@denpubs.com, Prod. Mgr., The Times of Ti Sun, NY, Elizabethtown

Alexander, Daniel ....(518) 873-6368
dj@suncommunitynews.com, Gen Mgr, Sun Community News, Published by:Denton Publications, Inc., NY, Elizabethtown

Alexander, Daniel E. .... (518) 873-6368 ext. 206
dan@suncommunitynews.com, Pres./Pub., The Adirondack Journal Sun, NY, Elizabethtown

dan@suncommunitynews.com, Pub., The News Enterprise Sun, NY, Elizabethtown

dan@suncommunitynews.com, Pub., Clinton County Free Today, NY, Plattsburgh

dan@suncommunitynews.com, Pub., The North Countryman Sun, NY, Elizabethtown

dan@suncommunitynews.com, Pub., The Valley News Sun, NY, Elizabethtown

dan@suncommunitynews.com, Pub., Tri-Lakes Free Trader, NY, Elizabethtown

dan@suncommunitynews.com, Pub., The Times of Ti Sun, NY, Elizabethtown

Alexander, Daniel E. .... (518) 873-6368 ext. 206
dan@suncommunitynews.com, Pub/Pres, Sun Community News, Published by:Denton Publications, Inc., NY, Elizabethtown

Alexander, Gayle ....(518) 873-6368 x207
gayle@suncommunitynews.com, Financial controller, Sun Community News, Published by:Denton Publications, Inc., NY, Elizabethtown

Alexander, Jon ....(563) 383-2320
jalexander@qctimes.com, Editorial Page Ed., Quad-City Times, IA, Davenport

Alexander, Justin
fashionshowroom@yahoo.com, Prodn. Art Dir., Fashion Syndicate Press, Woodstock

Alexander, Ken
newsroom@100milefreepress.net, Editor, 100 Mile House Free Press, BC, 100 Mile House

Alexander, Keri

kalexander@shoshonenewspress.com, Mgr./ Adv. Dir., Shoshone News-Press, ID, Osburn

Alexander, Mary .... (810) 766-6381
malexander@flintjounal.com, Adv. Mgr., Grand Blanc News, MI, Flint

malexander@flintjounal.com, Adv. Dir., The Flushing Observer, MI, Flint

Alexander, Misty
misty@moultonadvertiser.com, Ad Rep., The Moulton Advertiser, AL, Moulton

Alexander, Natasha ....(704) 669-3305
nalexander@gastongazette.com, Ad manager, The Gaston Gazette, NC, Gastonia

Alexander, Patrick ....(541) 921-0413
patrick@oregoncoasttoday.com, Ed., Oregon Coast Today, OR, Lincoln City

Alexander, Rachel
editor@fmtimes.com , Ed., Fort Morgan Times, CO, Fort Morgan

Alexander, Renae
ralexander@weaphersorddemocart.com, Adv. Mgr., Parker County Shopper, TX, Weatherford

Alexander, Richard ....(401) 847-4921
Ed., Newport Navalog, RI, Newport

Alexander, Robin........................(360) 792-3332
ralexander@kitsapsun.com, Credit Mgr., Kitsap Sun, WA, Bremerton

Alexander, Steven H.................(612) 673-7060
Steve.Alexander@startribune.com, Sr. VP, Circ., Star Tribune, MN, Minneapolis

Alexander, Susan
alexanders@knews.com, Home Furnishings Ed., Knoxville News Sentinel, TN, Knoxville

Alexsa, Debbie
newpaltztimes@ulsterpublishing.com, Ed., New Paltz Times, NY, New Paltz

Alfaro, Vanessa
valfaro@tracypress.com, Adv. Sales, Tracy Press, CA, Tracy

Alfers, Mike................................(620) 465-4636
malfers@ruralmessenger.com, Pub, Rural Messenger, KS, Haven

Alfonso, Melene
m.alfonso@scng.com, VP, Advertising, The Highlander - La Puente Edition, CA, Monrovia

Alfonso, Melene .... (818) 713-3330
malfonso@scng.com, VP Advertising, La Puente Highlander, CA, Monrovia

Alfonso, Melene
malfonso@scng.com, VP, Advertising, The Highlander - Glendora Edition, CA, Monrovia

Alfonso, Melene .... (818) 713-3330
malfonso@scng.com, VP Advertising, Rowland Heights Highlander, CA, Monrovia

Alfonso, Melene .... (818) 713-3330
melene.alfonso@dailynews.com , Adv. Vice Pres., Los Angeles Daily News, CA, Woodland Hills

Alfonso, Melene .... (818) 713-3330
malfonso@scng.com, Advertising Vice President, Diamond Bar Highlander, CA, Monrovia

Alford, Gina
galford@nickelads.com, Nickel Ads - Central Portland, OR, Portland

galford@nickelads.com, Nickel Ads - East Portland, OR, Portland

galford@nickelads.com, Nickel Ads - Mid Valley, OR, Portland

galford@nickelads.com, Nickel Ads - West Portland, OR, Portland

Alford, Jane
jalford@thelancasternews.com, Mng. Ed., Lancaster News, SC, Lancaster

Alford, Melissa
malford@lsj.com, Dir., HR, Lansing State

Journal, MI, Lansing

Alford, Moody R.
adrep@arkcity.net, Adv. Consultant, The Arkansas City Traveler, KS, Arkansas City

Alford, Nathan
alford@dnews.com, Pub., Northwest Market, ID, Moscow

alford@dnews.com, Pub./Ed., Moscow-Pullman Daily News, ID, Moscow

alford@dnews.com, Pub./Ed., Lewiston Morning Tribune, ID, Lewiston

Algarin, Matt ....(850) 654-8448
malgarin@waltonsun.com, Managing Ed., The Walton Sun, FL, Santa Rosa Beach

Alger, Jerry E.
jalger@dailypress.com, Dir., Adv. Sales, Daily Press, VA, Newport News

Algood, Charles ....ext. 120
callgood@sandmountainreporter.com, Prodn. Mgr., Sand Mountain Reporter, AL, Albertville

Alguire, Clint
calguire@alonovus.com, Sales Mgr, Tuscarawas Bargain Hunter, OH, Millersburg

calguire@alonovus.com, Adv. Dir., Holmes County Journal, OH, Millersburg

Ali, Fabby
taylor2039@aol.com, The San Antonio Observer, TX, San Antonio

Ali, Waseem..........................(210) 222-9220
wsmali@aol.com, President/CEO, The Tymes, TX, San Antonio

wsmali@aol.com, Advertising Manager, The San Antonio Observer, TX, San Antonio

Alido, Ronnie..........................(530) 225-8277
Ronnie.Alido@redding.com, Sup. of Press Ops., Record Searchlight, CA, Redding

Alison, Dale
dalison@thehawkeye.com, Mng. Ed., Hawk Eye Shopper, IA, Burlington

Alison, Dale
dalison@thehawkeye.com, Mng. Ed., The Hawk Eye, IA, Burlington

Alkon, Amy
flame777@aol.com, Syndicated science-based advice columnist on love, dating, sex, relationships. Science-based manners expert. Upcoming book, "Unf*ckology" - a "science-help" book on how to transform to live with guts and confidence. @amyalkon on Twitter., The Science Advice Goddess-Amy Alkon, Santa Monica

Allain, Pam ....(780) 778-3977
pamela.allain@sunmedia.ca, Reg. Dir. of Adv., The Mayerthorpe Freelancer, AB, Whitecourt

Allain, Pamela .... (780) 962-4257 ext. 307
pallain@postmedia.com, Pub., The Whitecourt Star, AB, Whitecourt

pallain@postmedia.com, Adv. Dir, Drayton Valley Western Review, AB, Drayton Valley

pallain@postmedia.com, Pub., The Grove Examiner, AB, Spruce Grove

pallain@postmedia.com, Pub., The Stony Plain Reporter, AB, Spruce Grove

Allaine, Elise
eallain@simcoe.com, Gen. Mgr., Innisfil Journal, ON, Barrie

Allaire, Nancy ....(819) 293-4551
nancy.allaire@transcontinental.ca, Ed., Courrier-sud, QC, Nicolet

Allam, Salah
allam@idirect.com, Pub., Canada & Arab World, ON, Toronto

Allard, Debora
debbie@thesciotovoice.com, Pub./Ed., The Scioto Voice, OH, Wheelersburg

Allard, Karen ....(517) 278-2318, ext. 29
kallard@thedailyreporter.com, Circ. Mgr., The Daily Reporter, MI, Coldwater

Allard, Louis Eric
latribune@latribune.qc.ca, Newsroom Dir., La

Tribune, QC, Sherbrooke

Allard, Mark
info@thesciotovoice.com, Circ. Mgr./Sports Ed., The Scioto Voice, OH, Wheelersburg

Allard, Rene
rene.allard@voicenews.com , Circ. Mgr. , Downriver Voice, MI, Clinton Township

rene.allard@voicenews.com, Circ. Mgr., The Armada Times, MI, Clinton Township

rene.allard@voicenews.com, Circ. Mgr., The Macomb Voice, MI, Clinton Township

rene.allard@voicenews.com, Circ. Mgr., The Bay Voice, MI, Clinton Township

rene.allard@voicenews.com , Circ. Mgr. , The North Macomb Voice, MI, Clinton Township

Alldredge, Ralph......................(209) 754-3861
pub.calent@gmail.com, Co-Pub., Tracy Press, CA, Tracy

pub.calent@gmail.com, Pub., Calaveras Californian, CA, San Andreas

Allegretto, Cindy ....(941) 361-4995
cindy.allegretto@heraldtribune.com., Web Ed., Sarasota Herald-Tribune, FL, Sarasota

Allegrezza, Nicole ....(631) 475-1000, ext. 21
advletters@optonline.net, Editor, Long Island Advance, NY, Patchogue

Allen, Andrew ....ext. 234
Adv. Mgr., Huntsville Forester, ON, Huntsville

Allen, Andrew .... (705) 789-5541 ext. 234
aallen@metrolandnorthmedia.com, Circ Mgr, Bracebridge Examiner, ON, Bracebridge

Allen, Anne .... (208) 639-3530
aallen@idahobusinessreview.com, Ed., Idaho Business Review, ID, Boise

Allen, Ben .... (603) 224-5301 ext. 369
ballen@cmonitor.com, Tech. Servs. Mgr., Concord Monitor, NH, Concord

Allen, Bill .... (705) 789-5541 ext. 243
ballen@metrolandnorthmedia.com, Pub./Gen. Mgr., Huntsville Forester, ON, Huntsville

ballen@metrolandnorthmedia.com, Reg'l Gen. Mgr., Parry Sound North Star, ON, Parry Sound

Allen, Bill
banner@muskoka.com, Gen. Mgr., The Gravenhurst Banner, ON, Gravenhurst

Allen, Bill .... (705) 789-5541 ext. 243
ballen@almaguinnews.com, Gen. Mgr., Almaguin News, ON, Burks Falls

Allen, Carolyn .... (601) 961-7167
callen@hickmanrealty.com, Credit Mgr., The Clarion-Ledger, MS, Jackson

Allen, Chris
callen@civitasmedia.com, Sports Ed., The Marshall Democrat-News, MO, Marshall

callen@civitasmedia.com, Assoc. Prof., University of Nebraska at Omaha, NE, Omaha

Allen, Clellie
editor@wakeweekly.com, Ed./Assit. Pub., The Wake Weekly, NC, Wake Forest

Allen, Craig ....(203) 330-6254
craig.allen@scni.com , Adv., Opns./Circ. Dir., The Advocate, CT, Stamford

craig.allen@scni.com , Assoc. Prof., Arizona State University, AZ, Tempe

craig.allen@scni.com , Vice Pres. Operations, Greenwich Time, CT, Old Greenwich

Allen, David ....(414) 229-4436
dsallen@uwm.edu, Professor and Director of Graduate Studies, University of Wisconsin-Milwaukee / Department of Journalism, Advertising, and Media Studies (JAMS), WI, Milwaukee

Allen, Donna............................(252) 329-9546
dallen@reflector.com, HR Dir., The Daily Reflector, NC, Greenville

Allen, Donna............................(252) 329-9546
dallen@reflector.com, HR Director, Cooke Communications North Carolina, LLC, NC,

Allen, Ed
Greenville

Allen, Ed
eallen@westlake-picayune.com, Ed., Lake Travis View, TX, Austin

Allen, Gary
gallen@newberggraphic.com, Ed., The Newberg Graphic, OR, Newberg

Allen, Gary
gallen@newberggraphic.com, Ed., Valley Classifieds, OR, Newberg

Allen, Gillian
features@theaggie.org, Features Editor, University of California, Davis, CA, Davis

Allen, Harold
harold.allen@flyergroup.com, Pub., The Weekend Flyer, IN, Avon

Allen, Harold .... (317) 272-5800 ext. 208
harold.allen@flyergroup.com, Pub., Hendricks County Flyer, IN, Avon

Allen, Heather .... (806) 872-2177
accounting@pressreporter.com, Bookkeeper, Lamesa Press Reporter, TX, Lamesa

Allen, Irene
irene@phillipscountyreview.com, Page Design, Phillips County Review, KS, Phillipsburg

Allen, James Preston ....(310) 519-1442 ext. #1
james@randomlengthsnews.com, Los Angeles Harbor College, CA, San Pedro

Allen, James Preston .... (310) 519-1016
james@randomlengthsnews.com, Pub., Random Lengths/harbor Independent News, CA, San Pedro
james@randomlengthsnews.com, Pub., Random Lengths News, CA, San Pedro

Allen, Jennifer
jallenvoice@yahoo.com, Adv. Mgr., Hot Springs Village Voice, AR, Hot Springs Village

Allen, Joe
jallen@madison.com, VP of Advertising, Sales & Marketing, Capital Newspapers, WI, Madison
jallen@madison.com, Star Tribune, MN, Minneapolis

Allen, Joe .... (608) 252-6274
jallen@madison.com, VP; Adv., Sales and Mktg., Wisconsin State Journal, Madison, WI, Madison

Allen, John..............................(361) 886-3745
allenj@caller.com, Sports Ed., Corpus Christi Caller-Times, TX, Corpus Christi

Allen, Karrie
kallen.chathamcourier@registerstar.com, Ed., Chatham Courier, NY, Hudson

Allen, Kay .... (580) 634-2154
kallen@civitasmedia.com, Cir. Mgr., Durant Daily Democrat, OK, Durant

Allen, Kristy .... (717) 253-9411
kallen@gburgtimes.com, Webmaster, Gettysburg Times, PA, Gettysburg

Allen, Leona .... (214) 977-8942
ldallen@dallasnews.com, Editorial Writer, The Dallas Morning News, TX, Dallas

Allen, Linda..........................(256) 840-3000
lallen@sandmountainreporter.com, Classifieds, Sand Mountain Reporter, AL, Albertville

Allen, Lisa
advertising@tumblerridgenews.com, Sales Mgr, Tumbler Ridge News, BC, Tumbler Ridge

Allen, Lois .... (616) 696-3655
classifieds@cedarspringspost.com, Pub., Cedar Springs Post, MI, Cedar Springs

Allen, Lorri .... (903) 566-6120
lorriallen@uttyler.edu, Adviser, Univ. of Texas at Tyler, TX, Tyler

Allen, Luchie Mendoza..... (818) 552-4503 ext. 204
luchie@balita.com, Pub., Weekend Balita/ Midweek Balita, CA, Glendale

Allen, Mark
editor@olneydailymail.com, Ed., The Advantage, IL, Olney

Allen, Matthew
matthew.allen@shelbycountyreporter.com, Adv. Mgr., Alabaster Reporter, AL, Columbiana
matthew.allen@shelbycountyreporter.com, Adv. Mgr., Pelham Reporter, AL, Columbiana
matthew.allen@shelbycountyreporter.com, Adv. Mgr., Shelby County Reporter, AL, Columbiana

Allen, Patricia
pallen@terryasphalt.com, Dist. Mgr., The Hamilton Spectator, ON, Hamilton

Allen, Penny
advertising@mountaineer.bz, Adv. Mgr., The Mountaineer, AB, Rocky Mountain House

Allen, Raymond .... ext. 258
rallen@michronicle.com, Prodn. Mgr., Michigan Chronicle, MI, Detroit

Allen, Robert
rec@pacesetterusa.com, Pres., Pacesetter Graphic Service Corp., GA, Acworth

Allen, Rod
r.allen@city.ac.uk, Dept. Head, City University, London, London

Allen, Ruby
business@thepiercecountytribune.com, Off. Mgr. , Pierce County Tribune, ND, Rugby

Allen, Sandra
sandra@spectrecom.com, Vice Pres., Spectrecom Corporation, CA, North Hills

Allen, Sean
sallen@brantnews.com, Ed, Brant News, ON, Brantford

Allen, Shane
sallen@gatehousemedia.com, Sr. Group Pub., Hope Star, AR, Hope

Allen, Shannon.............. (256) 840-3000 ext 124
sports@sandmountainreporter.com, Sports Editor, Sand Mountain Reporter, AL, Albertville

Allen, Sherhonda .... (256) 740-5732
sherhonda.allen@timesdaily.com, City Ed., Times Daily, AL, Florence

Allen, Stacey .... (416) 774-2300
sallen@insidetoronto.com, Dir. Adv. , North York Mirror, ON, Toronto

Allen, Stephen .... (812) 206-2106
stephen.allen@newsandtribune.com, Prod. Mgr., News and Tribune, IN, Jeffersonville
stephen.allen@newsandtribune.com, Prod. Mgr., Tribune, IN, New Albany

Allen, Sylvia
s.allen@brunswicktimes-gazette.com, Ed., Brunswick Times-Gazette, VA, Lawrenceville

Allen, Terese .... (810) 433-6778
tallen@tctimes.com, Marketing Director, Tri-County Times, MI, Fenton

Allen, Tina
composing@blackwelljournaltribune.net , Adv., Blackwell Journal-Tribune, OK, Blackwell

Allen, Todd
production@thewarrensentinel.com, Prod. Mgr., The Warren Sentinel, VA, Front Royal

Allen, Todd F.
todd@wakeweekly.com, Pub., The Wake Weekly, NC, Wake Forest

Allen, Trent
opnews@mts.net, Ed., Opasquia Times, MB, The Pas

Allen, Wade..........................(704) 669-3331
wallen@shelbystar.com, lifestyles reporter, The Star, NC, Shelby

Allen-Hoch, Chris
publisher@bainbridgereview.com, Pub., Sound Publishing, Inc., WA, Poulsbo

Allender, John

circulation@palatkadailynews.com, Circ. Dir., Palatka Daily News, FL, Palatka

Aller, Danny.............................(229) 888-9306
danny.aller@albanyherald.com, Sports Editor, The Albany Herald, GA, Albany

Allert, Marcia.........................(214) 977-8216
mallert@dallasnews.com, Director of Photography, The Dallas Morning News, TX, Dallas

Alley, Jason
jalley@digitalfirstmedia.com, Ed, The Chelsea Standard, MI, Southgate
jalley@digitalfirstmedia.com, Editor, News-Herald, MI, Southgate

Alley, Joyce
dherald@verizon.net, Circ. Mgr., The Daily Herald, PA, Tyrone

Alleyne, Shelley .... (604) 885-4811 ext. 260
classified@coastreporter.net, Class. Supv., Coast Reporter, BC, Sechelt

Alleyne-Morris, Kester
KAlleynemorris@chicagotribune.com, Asst. Subj. Ed., Nat., Chicago Tribune, IL, Chicago

Allfrey, Brian .... (801) 237-2379
ballfrey@utahpress.com, Exec. Dir., Utah Press Association, Inc., UT, Sandy

Allgood, Laren
lallgood@eprisenow.com, Account Exec., The Enterprise Ledger, AL, Enterprise

Allison, Anita
m.reporter@mchsi.com, Display Adv., The Momence Progress Reporter, IL, Momence

Allison, Bill .... (315) 470-2080
ballison@advancemediany.com, VP, Sales, The Post-Standard, NY, Syracuse

Allison, David .... (404) 249-1039
dallison@bizjournals.com, Ed., Atlanta Business Chronicle, GA, Atlanta

Allison, David
d.allison@w-rindustries.com, Vice Pres., Winton Engineering Co., IL, Chicago

Allison, Dean .... (814) 472-3038
St. Francis Univ., PA, Loretto

Allison, Jeff
jeff.allison@tryondailybulletin.com, Press Room Mgr., Tryon Daily Bulletin, NC, Tryon

Alliston, Becky
ealliston@wccnet.edu, Adv. Mgr., Washtenaw Community College, MI, Ann Arbor

Allman, Kevin
kevina@gambitweekly.com, Editor, Gambit, LA, New Orleans

Allman, Robert
rallman@kpcmedia.com, Pub., Churubusco News, IN, Churubusco

Allman, Robert L......................(260) 636-2727
newera@app-printing.com, Pub., Albion New Era, IN, Albion

Allman, Robert L.
nweditor@app-printing.com, Pub., Northwest News, IN, Huntertown

Allmond, Christi
callmond@fstribune.com, Circ. Asst., The Fort Scott Tribune, KS, Fort Scott

Allon, Tom
tallon@manhattanmedia.com, Pres., New York Press, NY, New York

Allsion, Jennifer .... (337) 363-3939
Circ. Mgr., Kinder Courier News, LA, Kinder

Allsop, Charlotte .... (503) 684-0360
callsop@commnewspapers.com, Class Sales Mgr., The Lake Oswego Review, OR, Lake Oswego

Alltop, David.........................(410) 770-4158
dalltop@chespub.com, Rgl. IT Mgr., The Star-Democrat, MD, Easton

Almen, Theodore J.

kbanner@tds.net, Ed., Kerkhoven Banner, MN, Kerkhoven

Almond, Tracey
talmond@stanlynewspress.com, Adv. Mgr., The Stanly News & Press, NC, Albemarle

Almquist, Terese
talmquist@newstopic.net, Pub., Caldwell Weekly, NC, Lenoir

Almquist, Terese .... (828) 610-8715
talmquist@newstopic.net, Pub./Adv. Dir., News-Topic, NC, Lenoir

Alnor, William M.
william.alnor@tamuk.edu, Journalism Dir., Texas A&M University-Kingsville, TX, Kingsville

Aloisio, Ann
aaloisio@heraldstandard.com, Major Nat'l Accts., Herald-Standard, PA, Uniontown

Alonso, Javier
paris@efe.com, Rep., EFE News Services - Paris, France, Paris

Alonso, Martha.........................(787) 408-3033
martharalonso@gmai;.com, Assistant Executive Director, Overseas Press Club of Puerto Rico (Established 1968), PR, San Juan

Alonzo, Anthony .... (291) 769-9292
Photojournalist, Northwest Indiana Catholic, IN, Merrillville

Alonzo, Jennifer
jfapublisher@gmail.com, Pub., Slv Lifestyles, CO, Monte Vista

Alonzo, Jennifer
jfa@amigo.net, Ed., The Del Norte Prospector, CO, Monte Vista

Alonzo, Jennifer.........................(719) 852-3531
jfa@amigo.net, Ed., The Mineral County Miner, CO, Monte Vista
jfa@amigo.net, Publisher, The Monte Vista Journal, CO, Monte Vista
jfa@amigo.net, Grp. Pub., Valley Publishing, CO, Monte Vista

Alonzo, Jennifer
jfapublisher@gmail.com, Pub./Ed., The South Fork Tines, CO, Monte Vista

Alonzo, Jennifer
jfa@amigo.net, Pub., The Conejos County Citizen, CO, Monte Vista

Alperstein, Neil
nalperstein@loyola.edu, Adv./PR, Loyola College, MD, Baltimore

Alpert, Seth R.
salpert@admediapartners.com, Mgr. Dir., AdMedia Partners, Inc., NY, New York

Alpher, David
dalpher@jewishexponent.com, Gen. Mgr., Jewish Exponent, PA, Philadelphia

Alpine, Dan Mac .... (978) 739-1303
ipswich@wickedlocal.com, Ed., Ipswich Chronicle, MA, Danvers

Alred, John
jalred@jaxnews.com, Ed., The Jacksonville News, AL, Anniston

Alred, John .... (256) 235-3531
news@cleburnenews.com, Pub., The Cleburne News, AL, Heflin

Alred, John
jalred@jaxnews.com, Pub., Piedmont Journal, AL, Anniston

Alsop, Jonathon .... (617) 784-7150
jalsop@invinoveritas.com, Wine Writer/Self-Syndicator, Jonathon Alsop (Boston Wine School), Allston

Alston, Beth................(229) 924-2751 ext. 1529
beth.alston@gaflnews.com, Executive Editor, Americus Times-Recorder, GA, Americus

Alston, Beth
beth.alston@gaflnews.com, Exec. Ed., Cordele

Dispatch, GA, Cordele

Alston, Mark .... **(919) 932-8780**
chclassified@nando.com, Adv. Dir., Chapel Hill News, NC, Durham

Alsworth, Will
walsworth@nvdaily.com, District Sales Mgr., Northern Virginia Daily, VA, Strasburg

Alt, Jason .... **(856) 486-2442**
jalt@gannettnj.com, Regional Ed., The Courier-Post, NJ, Cherry Hill

Alt, Jason .... **(856) 563-5254**
jalt@gannettnj.com, Reg. Ed., The Daily Journal, NJ, Vineland

Altavilla, Mark .... **ext. 2037**
marka@citizensvoice.com, Adv. Dir., The Citizens' Voice, PA, Wilkes Barre

Altena, Beth
squiremail@aol.com, Owner/Ed., Rockford Squire, MI, Rockford

Alters, Susie .... **(218) 855-5836**
susie.alters@brainerddispatch.com, Adv. Mgr., Echo Journal, MN, Pequot Lakes
susie.alters@brainerddispatch.com, Sales Dir./ Classified, Brainerd Dispatch, MN, Brainerd

Alters, Susie .... **(218) 855-5836**
susie.alters@brainerddispatch.com, Advertising Director, Echoland - Piper Shopper, MN, Brainerd

Alters, Susie .... **(218) 855-5836**
susie.alters@brainerddispatch.com, Advertising Director, Echoland Shopper, MN, Brainerd

Althauser, Allison .... **(770) 205-8965**
Aalthauser@forsythnews.com, Adv. Acct. Exec., Forsyth County News, GA, Cumming

Altieri, Rosemaria
raltieri@scng.com, Sr. Dir HR, Southern California News Group, CA, Woodland Hills
raltieri@scng.com, VP HR, Press-Telegram, CA, Long Beach

Altman, Dennis
altman@pop.uky.edu, Assoc. Prof., University of Kentucky, KY, Lexington

Altmeppen, Klaus-Dieter
klaus-dieter.altmeppen@ku-eichstaett.de, Chair, Catholic University, Eichstaett

Altomare, David
marketing@palos.com, Pres., PALOS Software, CA, San Diego

Altschiller, Howard
haltschiller@seacoastonline.com, Exec. Ed., The Hampton Union, NH, Portsmouth

Altschiller, Howard .... **(603) 610-1113**
haltschiller@seacoastonline.com , Ed., Exeter News-Letter, NH, Portsmouth
haltschiller@seacoastonline.com , Ed., York County Coast Star, NH, Portsmouth
haltschiller@seacoastonline.com , The York Weekly, NH, Portsmouth
haltschiller@seacoastonline.com , Ex. Ed., Foster's Daily Democrat, NH, Dover
haltschiller@seacoastonline.com , Exec. Ed., Portsmouth Herald, NH, Portsmouth

Alvarado, Mickey
managingeditor@tecumsehherald.com, Ed., The Tecumseh Herald, MI, Tecumseh

Alvardo, Angie
atawater@palestineherald.com, Mng. Ed., Palestine Herald-Press, TX, Palestine

Alvardo, Marco .... **(956) 546-5113**
Circ. Mgr., Bargain Book, TX, Brownsville

Alvarez, Christopher
calvarez@elhispanicnews.com, Prodn. Mgr., El Hispanic News, OR, Portland

Alvarez, Gloria
editorial@egpnews.com, Mng. Ed., Wyvernwood Chronicle, CA, Los Angeles
editorial@egpnews.com, Mng. Ed., City Terrace Comet, CA, Los Angeles
editorial@egpnews.com, Mng. Ed., Commerce Comet, CA, Los Angeles
editorial@egpnews.com, Mng. Ed., Eastside Sun, CA, Los Angeles
editorial@egpnews.com, Mng. Ed., Ela Brooklyn-Belvedere Comet, CA, Los Angeles
editorial@egpnews.com, Mng. Ed., Mexican American Sun, CA, Los Angeles
editorial@egpnews.com, Mng. Ed., Montebello Comet, CA, Los Angeles
editorial@egpnews.com, Mng. Ed., Monterey Park Comet, CA, Los Angeles
editorial@egpnews.com, Mng. Ed., Northeast Sun, CA, Los Angeles
editorial@egpnews.com, Mng. Ed., Vernon Sun, CA, Los Angeles
editorial@egpnews.com, Mng. Ed., Bell Gardens Sun, CA, Los Angeles

Alvarez, Soledad
efebol@entelnet.bo, Rep., EFE News Services - La Paz, Bolivia, La Paz

Alves, Ben
balves@vertical.com, Vice Pres., Sales-Distributed Enterprise Solutions, Vertical Communications, Inc., AZ, Phoenix

Alves, Chiara
aggienewmedia@gmail.com, New Media Manager, University of California, Davis, CA, Davis

Alves, Igor M. .... **(973) 817-7400**
imalves@24horasnewspaper.com , Marketing Director, 24 Horas, NJ, Newark

Alves, Kristen .... **(203) 789-5352**
kjohnson@nhregister.com, Promo. Mgr., New Haven Register, CT, New Haven

Alves, Sonia Paula
salves@24horasnewspaper.com, Ad. Director, 24 Horas, NJ, Newark

Alveshere, Terry
terry.alveshere@bismarcktribune.com, The Bismarck Tribune, ND, Bismarck

Alvesteffer, Terry .... **(616) 669-2700 ext. 173**
Circ. Mgr., South Advance, MI, Jenison

Alvey, Dan .... **(830) 693-7152**
Owner, The Picayune, TX, Marble Falls

Alvey, Jim
jalvey@baltsun.com, Dir. Direct Mktg., Towson Times, MD, Baltimore
jalvey@baltsun.com, Dir, Direct Mktg., Baltimore Messenger-OOB, MD, BALTIMORE
jalvey@baltsun.com, Dir., Direct Mktg., Arbutus Times, MD, Baltimore
jalvey@baltsun.com, Dir. Direct Mktg., The Record, MD, Bel Air
jalvey@baltsun.com, Dir., Direct Mktg., The Weekender, MD, Bel Air

Alvey, Lee
lee@thepicayune.com, Owner, The Picayune, TX, Marble Falls

Alvine, Ken .... **(605) 336-9434**
smoments7@aol.com, Owner/Mgr., Creative Comic Productions, Sioux Falls

Alvord, Karen .... **(315) 363-5100**
kalvord@journalregister.com, Gen. Mgr./ Adv. Dir., Oneida-madison Pennysaver, NY, Oneida
kalvord@journalregister.com, Adv. Dir., The Oneida Daily Dispatch, NY, Oneida

Alwin, Heather
colby.society@nwkansas.com, Society Ed., Colby Free Press, KS, Colby

Alwood, Edward
edward.alwood@quinnipiac.edu, Assoc. Prof., Quinnipiac University, CT, Hamden

Amador, Dava .... **(707) 526-8517**
dava.amador@pressdemocrat.com, Circ. Mgr., The Press Democrat, CA, Santa Rosa

Amador, Monica
sales@el-observador.com, Adv./Mktg. Dir., El Observador, CA, San Jose

Aman, Joe E. .... **(208) 337-4681 ext. 104**
joe@owyhee.com, Owner, The Owyhee Avalanche, ID, Homedale

Aman, Robert .... **(208) 337-4681 ext. 105**
rob@owyhee.com, Composition, The Owyhee Avalanche, ID, Homedale

Amarante, Joseph .... **(203) 789-5675**
news@nhregister.com, Radio/Television Ed., New Haven Register, CT, New Haven

Amato, Tom .... **(508) 676-2526**
tamato@heraldnews.com, Circ. Dir., Real Estate Guide, MA, Fall River

Amato, Tom .... **(508) 676-2526**
tamato@heraldnews.com, Circ. Dir., Taunton Daily Gazette, MA, Taunton

Amaya, Hermando .... **(702) 383-0388**
hamaya@reviewjournal.com, Ed., Las Vegas Weekly, NV, Henderson

Amaya, Hernando .... **(702) 387-2972**
hamaya@reviewjournal.com, Editor, El Tiempo, NV, Las Vegas

Ambachew, Ambi .... **(202) 955-9010**
ambi@washingtonmonthly.com, Adv. Mgr., Washington Monthly LLC, Washington

Ambis, Sharon
sharon.ambis@jjournal.com, Mktg. Dir., The Jersey Journal, NJ, Secaucus

Ambor, Brian
bambor@messengerpostmedia.com, Production Director, Messenger Post Media, NY, Canandaigua

Ambrogi, Robert J. .... **(978) 546-3400**
info@masspublishers.org, Exec. Dir., Massachusetts Newspaper Publishers Association, MA, Rockport
info@masspublishers.org, Exec. Dir., Massachusetts Newspaper Publishers Association, MA, 16 Mckays Dr.

Ambrose, Jim
jambrose@glaciermedia.ca, Publisher, The Marketplace, SK, Yorkton
jambrose@glaciermedia.ca, Publisher, Yorkton This Week, SK, YORKTON

Ambrose, Kelly
info@advantex.com, Pres., Advantex Marketing International, Inc., ON, Markham

Ambrose, Tricia .... **(440) 951-0000 ext. 707**
tambrose@news-herald.com, Ed., Chatter, OH, Willoughby
tambrose@news-herald.com, Exec. Ed., The News-Herald, OH, Willoughby

Ambrosia, John
ambrosia@pioneerlocal.com, Exec. Ed., Niles Herald-Spectator, IL, Chicago

Ambrosia, John
ambrosia@pioneerlocal.com, Exec. Ed., Morton Grove Champion, IL, Chicago

Ambry, Julie .... **(618) 239-2623**
jambry@bnd.com, Adv., Belleville News-Democrat, IL, Belleville

Ameden, Paul .... **(585) 598-0030**
pameden@gatehousemedia.com, CIO, GateHouse Media, Inc., NY, Pittsford

Ameen, Monica .... **(972) 488-3555**
mameen@unitedad.com, Circ. Dir., DallasChild, TX, Addison

Amero, Jeff
jeff.amero@newschief.com, Circ. Dir., News Chief, FL, Winter Haven

Amero, Pamela .... **(705) 444-1875 ext. 64**
pamero@simcoe.com, Adv. , Express, ON, Meaford
pamero@simcoe.com, Adv Mgr, Blue Mountains Courier-herald, ON, Meaford

Ames, Brad
bames@publicitas.com, Branch Dir., Publicitas North America, Inc., FL, Fort Lauderdale

Ames, Diane .... **(401) 767-8505**

dames@woonsocketcall.com, Adv. Mgr., Classified, The Times, RI, Pawtucket
dames@woonsocketcall.com, Adv. Mgr., The Call, RI, Woonsocket

Amlin, Brenda .... **(937) 652-1331 Ext. 1782**
bamlin@civitasmedia.com, Bus. Mgr., Urbana Daily Citizen, OH, Urbana

Ammann, Larry .... **(605) 692-9311**
shopper@brookings.net, Circ. Mgr., Town & Country Shopper, SD, Brookings

Ammerman, Robert .... **(610) 330-6501**
rammerman@csci-usa.com, President, Consolidated Storage Cos., PA, Tatamy

Ammerman, Steve
sammermann@wctrib.com, Publisher, West Central Tribune, MN, Willmar

Ammermann, Steve
sammermann@wctrib.com, Pub., Sunday Reminder, MN, Willmar

Amormino, Joseph
JAMORMINO@DNPS.COM, TECHNICAL SERVICES DIR., Detroit Free Press, MI, Detroit

Amos, Bob .... **(813) 259-7702**
ramos@tampatrib.com, Tampa Bay Times, FL, St Petersburg

Amos, Marcus .... **(812) 752-3171**
mamos@gbpnews.com, Ed., The Scott Co. Journal & Chronicle, IN, Scottsburg
mamos@gbpnews.com, Editor, The Giveaway, IN, Scottsburg

Amoss, Jim .... **(504) 826-3475**
jamoss@timespicayune.com, Ed., The Times-Picayune, LA, New Orleans

Amundson, Ken .... **(970) 215-3060**
ken.amundson@outlook.com, Sr. Associate-West- Mtn. States, W.B. Grimes & Company, MD, Gaithersburg

Amundson, Ken .... **(970) 215-3060**
ken.amundson@outlook.com, Sr. Assoc.-Western/Mtn. States, Grimes, McGovern & Associates, NY, New York

Amundson, Kenneth J .... **(970) 669-5050**
kamundson@reporter-herald.com, Gen. Mgr./ Ed., Loveland Reporter-Herald, CO, Loveland

Amy, Schaake
aschaake@edwpub.net, Adv. Mgr., Edwardsville Intelligencer, IL, Edwardsville

Anand, Sudhir
sudhir@weeklyvoice.com, Pub., The Weekly Voice, ON, Mississauga
sudhir@weeklyvoice.com, Awaaz Punjabi, ON, Mississauga

Anander, Lori
lanander.windhamjournal@registerstar.com, Ed., Windham Journal, NY, Catskill

Anander, Lori .... **(518) 943-2100, ext. 3331**
lanander.windhamjournal@thedailymail.net, Managing editor, Chatham Courier, NY, Hudson

Anason, Dean .... **(770) 621-9935**
dean.anason@sourcemedia.com, Managing Ed., American Banker, NY, New York

Anastasi, Michael .... **(626) 422-4305**
michael.anastasi@langnews.com, Exec. Ed./ VP, Azusa Herald Highlander, CA, Monrovia
michael.anastasi@langnews.com, Exec. Ed./VP, Glendora Press Highlander, CA, Monrovia
michael.anastasi@langnews.com, Exec. Ed./ VP, La Puente Highlander, CA, Monrovia
michael.anastasi@langnews.com, Exec. Ed./ VP, The Highlander - Rowland Heights Edition, CA, Monrovia
michael.anastasi@langnews.com, Exec. Ed./ VP, West Covina Highlander, CA, West Covina

Anastasia, Susan .... **(813) 657-4524**
Ed., Brandon News & Tribune, FL, Tampa

Ancona, Barbara .... **(646) 237-6929**

barbaraa@usspi.com, Vice President Sales, McNaughton Newspapers, IL, Schaumburg

Ancona, Barbara
barbaraa@usspi.com, VP Sales, USSPI Media, IL, Schaumburg

Anctil, Bill.............................(207) 689-2942
banctil@sunjournal.com, Adv. Sales, Sun Journal, ME, Lewiston

Anders, Rob ....(724) 229-2075
randers@observer-reporter.com, National Accounts, Observer-Reporter, PA, Washington

Andersen, Dennies ....(620) 582-5101
weststar@gmaxx.us, Ed./Pub., The Western Star, KS, Coldwater

Andersen, Erin
eandersen@journalstar.com, Families/Schools/Kids Reporter, Lincoln Journal Star, NE, Lincoln

Andersen, Gary
publisher@fairmontsentinel.com, Pub., Sentinel, MN, Fairmont

Andersen, Greg ....(415) 892-1516 x 19
gandersen@marinscope.com, Ed., San Rafael News Pointer, CA, Novato
gandersen@marinscope.com, Ed., Twin Cities Times, CA, Novato

Andersen, James
sports@thealpenanews.com, Sports Ed., The Alpena News, MI, Alpena

Andersen, Julian
mcr@mcrecord.com, Pub, Morrison County Record, MN, Little Falls

Andersen, Julian.......................(763) 712-2400
Pub., Coon Rapids Herald, MN, Coon Rapids
Pub., Dakota County Tribune, MN, Apple Valley

Andersen, Julian L.
pueproduction@ecm-inc.com, Pub., Town & Country Shopper, GA, Griffin

Anderson, Ally.........................(780) 385-6693
Production Manager, The Community Press, AB, Killam

Anderson, Andy
aanderson@cascorp.com, Sr. Vice Pres.-Finance/CFO, Cascade Corp., OR, Fairview

Anderson, Barbara.....................(319) 291-1546
Barb.Anderson@wcfcourier.com, Controller, The Courier, IA, Waterloo

Anderson, Barbara..............(650) 726-4424 x 313
barbanderson@hmbreview.com, Business, Circ. Mgr., Half Moon Bay Review, CA, Half Moon Bay

Anderson, Bill
mainlinenews@verizon.net, Pub., Mainline Newspapers, PA, Ebensburg

Anderson, Bill
banderson@metroland.com, Gen Mgr, Brampton Guardian, ON, Mississauga

Anderson, Bob
moultoneagle@sbcglobal.net, Pub., The Moulton Eagle, TX, Moulton

Anderson, Brenda......................(920) 356-6739
newsroom@langleytimes.com, Ed, Langley Times, BC, Langley

Anderson, Brian
banderson@spscommerce.com, Ed. in Chief, MSP Communications, MN, Minneapolis

Anderson, Bruce
ava@pacific.net, Ed., Anderson Valley Advertiser, CA, Boonville

Anderson, Calvin
calvin@crookstontimes.com, Adv. Mgr., Crookston Daily Times, MN, Crookston

Anderson, Casey .... ext. 22
casey@tucsonlocalmedia.com, Adv. Dir., Foothills News, AZ, Tucson

Anderson, Casey ....(520) 797-4384 ext. 22

casey@tucsonlocalmedia.com, Ad. Dir., Tucson Weekly, AZ, Tucson

Anderson, Cherie ....(831) 438-2500
cherie@pressbanner.com, Advertising Director, Press Banner, CA, Scotts Valley

Anderson, Chris
canderson@oregonian.com, Pub., Forest Grove Leader, OR, Portland
canderson@oregonian.com, Pub., Beaverton Leader, OR, Beaverton

Anderson, Clyde ....(870) 508-8028
clanderson@baxterbulletin.com, Distribution/Dock Supervisor, The Baxter Bulletin, AR, Mountain Home

Anderson, Corey
canderson@minnpost.com, Web Editor, MinnPost, MN, Minneapolis

Anderson, Craig ....(763) 712-3578
craig.anderson@ecm-inc.com, Dist. Mgr., Edina Sun-Current, MN, Eden Prairie

Anderson, Cristina.........(402) 371-1080 ext. 252
canderson@norfolkdailynews.com, Circ. Mgr., Norfolk Daily News, NE, Norfolk

Anderson, Dan
andersond@dailycamera.com, Bus. Mgr., The Canon City Daily Record, CO, Canon City

Anderson, Dana
valentinenews@valentinenews.com, Office Mgr., Valentine Midland News, NE, Valentine

Anderson, Daralyn
publisher@vashonbeachcomber.com, Pub., Vashon-Maury Island Beachcomber, WA, Vashon

Anderson, David
dstrauss@turley.com, Gen. Mgr., The Sentinel, MA, Belchertown

Anderson, David
danderson@ecube.com, Pub., The Boulder Monitor, MT, Boulder

Anderson, David
reapersp@richfieldreaper.com, Assoc. Ed., Richfield Reaper, UT, Richfield

Anderson, David E.
david.anderson@religionnews.com, Senior Editor, Religion News Service, Washington

Anderson, Deborah
deborahanderson@clipperpress.com, Pub., Duxbury Clipper, MA, Duxbury

Anderson, Deborah ....(781) 293-0420
deb@whpexpress.com, Pub, Plympton-Halifax Express, MA, Hanson
deb@whpexpress.com, Pub, Whitman-Hanson Express, MA, Hanson

Anderson, Dennis ....(970) 252-7022
dennisa@montrosepress.com, Adv. Dir., The Montrose Daily Press, CO, Montrose

Anderson, Dennis ....(309) 686-3159
danderson@pjstar.com, Exec. Ed., Journal Star, IL, Peoria

Anderson, Dennis ....(785) 832-7194
danderson@ljworld.com, Lawrence Journal-World, KS, Lawrence

Anderson, Dennis ....(907) 352-2255
dennis.anderson@frontiersman.com, Pub./Adv. Dir., Frontiersman, AK, Wasilla

Anderson, Dick
danderson@vertical.com, Exec. Vice Pres./Gen. Mgr., Vertical Communications, Inc., AZ, Phoenix

Anderson, Douglas
daa7@psu.edu, Dean/Prof./Co-Dir., Sports Journ. Ctr., The Pennsylvania State University, PA, University Park

Anderson, Edward
anderson@nationalmediasales.com, Pres., National Media Associates, OK, Ada

Anderson, Edward M. ....(417) 338-6397
Brokered1@gmail.com, Owner, National Media

Associates, MO, Branson

Anderson, Eric
cp.eanderson@gmail.com, Publisher/Sales/Production Manager, The Community Press, AB, Killam

Anderson, Eric.........................(780) 385-6693
vikingweeklyreview@gmail.com, Pub., The Weekly Review, AB, Viking

Anderson, George
ganderson@dddnews.com, Managing Ed., The Daily Dunklin Democrat, MO, Kennett

Anderson, Greg ....(617) 823-7861
grega@pamarcoglobal.com, Vice Pres., Sales/Mktg., Pamarco Global Graphics, GA, Marietta
grega@pamarcoglobal.com, Vice Pres., HR, Cascade Corp., OR, Fairview
grega@pamarcoglobal.com, Vice Pres., Engineering, SocialNet, Inc., CA, Mountain View

Anderson, Greg
ganderson@Salisburypost.com, Pub, Salisbury Post, NC, Salisbury

Anderson, Heather
editor@stonecountyenterprise.com, Ed./Pub., Stone County Enterprise, MS, Wiggins

Anderson, Holly
tribune@tiogand.com, Cir. , The Journal, ND, Crosby
tribune@tiogand.com, Cir. Mgr., Tioga Tribune, ND, Tioga

Anderson, J. Reed ....(701) 662-2127
randerson@devilslakejournal.com, G.M., Devils Lake Journal, ND, Devils Lake

Anderson, James
janderson@wasecacountynews.com, Lane Cmty. College, OR, Eugene

Anderson, James T.
Jim_Anderson@tamu-commerce.edu, Instr., Texas A&M University-Commerce, TX, Commerce

Anderson, Jan ....(406) 225-3821
janderson@jeffersoncountycourier.com, Ed., The Boulder Monitor, MT, Boulder

Anderson, Janelle ....ext. 108
janelle@pdsadnet.com, CEO, Publishers Development Service, WI, Fond Du Lac
janelle@pdsadnet.com, CEO, Publishers Development Service, WI, Fond du Lac

Anderson, Janelle ....ext. 105
janelle@wisad.com, Exec. Dir., Wisconsin Free Community Papers, WI, Fond du Lac

Anderson, Janet........................(317) 736-2797
Circ. Mgr., Calhoun County Reminder, IA, Rockwell City

Anderson, Janna
andersj@elon.edu, Assoc. Prof., Elon University, NC, Elon

Anderson, Jerry
dherald@st-tel.net, Pub., The Dighton Herald, KS, Dighton

Anderson, Jim
jimandersondesign@me.com, Graphic Designer, Gay Alliance, NY, Rochester

Anderson, Jim
janderson@ironmountaindailynews.com, News Ed., The Daily News, MI, Iron Mountain

Anderson, Joe
production@huntsvilleforester.com, Regl. Pub., Huntsville/muskoka Advance, ON, Huntsville

Anderson, Joe
publisher@simcoe.com, Pub., The Stayner Sun, ON, Wasaga Beach

Anderson, Joe ....(518) 290-3891
janderson@digitalfirstmedia.com, Circulation District Mgr., The Saratogian, NY, Saratoga Springs

Anderson, Joe

janderson@simcoe.com, Pub., The Wasaga Sun, ON, Wasaga Beach

Anderson, Joe
orillia@simcoe.com, Pub., Orillia Today, ON, Orillia

Anderson, Joe
janderson@simcoe.com, Pub., The Mirror, ON, Midland

Anderson, John ....(607) 324-1425 Ext. 205
johnanderson@eveningtribune.com, Editor, Genesee Country Express, NY, Dansville

Anderson, John
editor@wellsvilledaily.com, Ed., Allegany County Pennysaver, NY, Wellsville

Anderson, John ....(585) 343-8000 Ext. 1426
janderson@batavianews.com, Managing Editor, The Daily News, NY, Batavia

Anderson, John ....(607) 324-1425 Ext. 205
johnanderson@eveningtribune.com, Regional Ed., Wellsville Daily Reporter, NY, Wellsville

Anderson, Jon ....(218) 739-3308
jon@themidweek.com, Sales Manager, This Week's Shopping News, MN, Fergus Falls

Anderson, Jonathan ....(260) 925-2611
janderson@kpcmedia.com, Multimedia Sales Executive, The Star, IN, Auburn

Anderson, Julian
print.northbranch@ecm-inc.com, Pub., The Post Review, MN, Cambridge

Anderson, Julian
julian.anderson@ecm-inc.com, Pub., Scotsman, MN, Cambridge

Anderson, Julie ....(406) 271-5561
indobserv@3rivers.net, Office Mgr., Independent Observer, MT, Conrad

Anderson, Karen ....(541) 383-0324
kanderson@bendbulletin.com, CFO, Western Communications, Inc., OR, Bend

Anderson, Kelly
kanderson@homemagonline.com, Ed., Home Magazine, MN, Mankato

Anderson, Kerry
kamcjm@gmail.com, Pub/Advt Mgr, Tofield Mercury, AB, Tofield

Anderson, Kerry ....(780) 662-4046
vikingweeklyreview@gmail.com, Owner, The Weekly Review, AB, Viking

Anderson, Kerry
kamcjm@gmail.com, Pub., The Lamont Leader, AB, Lamont

Anderson, Kevin ....(705) 335-2283
newseditor@kapuskasingtimes.com, Managing Ed. , The Northern Times, ON, Kapuskasing
newseditor@kapuskasingtimes.com, Managing Ed., The Weekender, ON, Kapuskasing

Anderson, Kevin
kevin.anderson@sunmedia.ca, Regional Managing Editor, Timmins Times, ON, Timmins

Anderson, Kevin
KevinA@millelacsmessenger.com, Pub., Mille Lacs Messenger, MN, Isle

Anderson, Kevin ....(320) 676-3123
kevina@millelacsmessenger.com, Pub, Aitkin Independent Age, MN, Aitkin

Anderson, Kim
marketing@mediaspansoftware.com, Coord., Domestic Sales, MediaSpan Group Inc., MI, Ann Arbor

Anderson, Kirk ....(620) 855-3902
jacksoniannews@me.com, Ed, Golden Plains Publishing, KS, Cimarron

Anderson, Kristin ....(618) 497-8272
cjournal@egyptian.net, Co-Owner, County Journal, IL, Percy

Anderson, Kristin ....(618) 497-8272
cjournal@egyptian.net, Co-Owner, County

Journal, IL, Percy

Anderson, Leigh Anne.................**(404) 614-1205**
leigh.anderson@creativeloafing.com,
Marketing and Promotions Director, Creative
Loafing Atlanta, GA, Atlanta

Anderson, Les.........................**(316) 978-6065**
les.anderson@wichita.edu, Professor, WSU
Elliott School of Communication, Kansas
Professional Communicators, KS, Americus

Anderson, Linda......................**(406) 782-3820**
butte.news@butteweekly.com, Publisher/owner,
The Butte Weekly, MT, Butte

Anderson, Lisa
lkanderson@hngnews.com, Adv. Sales Rep.,
The Star, WI, Sun Prairie

Anderson, Logan......................**(434) 385-5549**
landerson@newsadvance.com, Editorial Page/
Opinion. Ed., The News & Advance, VA,
Lynchburg

Anderson, Loraine....................**(231) 933-1468**
landerson@record-eagle.com, Regl. Ed.,
Traverse City Record-Eagle, MI, Traverse City

Anderson, Mark
standard@sunflowertelco.com, Pub., The Leoti
Standard, KS, Leoti

Anderson, Mark
manderson@valleynewstoday.com, Adv.,
Weekly Times, IA, Shenandoah

Anderson, Mark
kirkand@ucom.net, Pub., Jacksonian, KS,
Cimarron

Anderson, Mark
bglover1955@gmail.com, Pub., The Oakley
Graphic, KS, Oakley

Anderson, Mark
mark@mcweekly.com, Managing Editor,
Monterey County Weekly, CA, Seaside

Anderson, Mark......................**(800) 658-3755**
Pub., Jetmore Republican, KS, Jetmore

Anderson, Mark......................**(620) 855-3902**
Pub, Edwards County Sentinel, KS, Kinsley

Anderson, Mark
editor@staplesworld.com, Ed., Staples World,
MN, Staples

Anderson, Matt
andersonpubl@unitelsd.com, Pub./Ed.,
Montrose Herald, SD, Canistota

Anderson, Matt
andersonpubl@unitelsd.com, Pub./Ed., The
Hartford Area News, SD, Canistota

Anderson, Matt
news@andersonpublications.com, Pub./Ed.,
The Humboldt Journal, SD, Canistota

Anderson, Melissa
ccr@utma.com, Cavalier County Republican,
ND, Langdon

Anderson, Michael
manderson@nmc.edu, Northwestern Michigan
College, MI, Traverse City

Anderson, Michele...................**(360) 650-6763**
Western Washington Univ., WA, Bellingham

Anderson, Nancy.....................**(605) 964-2100**
wreagle@westrivereagle.com, Gen. Mgr., West
River Eagle, SD, Eagle Butte

Anderson, Penny.....................**(540) 574-6255**
pander@dnronline.com, Mgmt. Info Servs.
Mgr., Daily News-Record, VA, Harrisonburg

Anderson, Raymond
rhanders@wisc.edu, Prof. Emer., University of
Wisconsin-Madison, WI, Madison

Anderson, Ric.........................**(702) 259-2333**
ric.anderson@lasvegassun.com, Managing
Ed., Las Vegas Sun, NV, Henderson
ric.anderson@lasvegassun.com, Mng. Ed.,
Boulder City News, NV, Henderson

Anderson, Richard.........**(207) 594-4401 ext. 326**
randerson@villagesoup.com, CEO, Village

Netmedia, Inc., ME, Rockland

Anderson, Richard
midweek@mnww.com, Pub., The Midweek,
Inc., MN, Fergus Falls

Anderson, Richard
rkanderson@mnww.com, This Week's
Shopping News, MN, Fergus Falls

Anderson, Rick
randerson@thedailyworld.com, Sports Ed., The
Daily World, WA, Aberdeen

Anderson, Rodrick
swdailysports@yahoo.com, Sports Ed.,
Southwest Daily News, LA, Sulphur

Anderson, Sam.......................**(604) 575-2400**
editor@cloverdalereporter.com, Ed., Cloverdale
Reporter, BC, Surrey

Anderson, Sandy.....................**(417) 926-5148**
ads1sandy@news-journal.net, Pub., Mountain
Grove News-Journal, MO, Mountain Grove

Anderson, Scott...............................**ext. 216**
sanderson@swbooster.com, Mng. Ed., The
Southwest Booster, SK, Swift Current

Anderson, Scott
sanderson@havredailynews.com, Prodn. Mgr.,
The Havre Daily News, MT, Havre

Anderson, Scott
sanderson@uvsj.com, Pub., The Standard-
Journal, ID, Rexburg

Anderson, Scott......................**(515) 663-6943**
sanderson@amestrib.com, Pub., Ames
Tribune, IA, Ames

Anderson, Shawny
sanderso@stmarys-ca.edu, Advisor, Saint
Mary's College of California, CA, Moraga

Anderson, Sherry
mpherald@harborside.com, Owner/Adv. Mgr.,
Myrtle Point Herald, OR, Myrtle Point

Anderson, Stefanie...................**(618) 579-1225**
sanderson@dailyherald.com, Sr. Vice Pres. /
General Manager / Southern Illinois Local
Media Group, Daily Herald, IL, Arlington
Heights

Anderson, Steve
anderssd@jmu.edu, Dir./Prof., James Madison
University, VA, Harrisonburg

Anderson, Sue........................**(541) 836-2241**
drainenterprise@earthlink.net, Pub./Owner,
Drain Enterprise, OR, Drain

Anderson, Sue...............**(928) 763-2505 ext. 6106**
suemvdn@npgcable.com, Bus. Mgr., Mohave
Valley Daily News, AZ, Bullhead City

Anderson, Ted..............**(519) 623-7395 ext. 232**
tanderson@cambridgetimes.ca, Adv. Mgr.,
Cambridge Times, ON, Cambridge

Anderson, Terry......................**(402) 374-2225**
terry.anderson@midwestproducer.com, News
Ed., Midwest Messenger, NE, Tekamah

Anderson, Tim
bmackey@inebraska.com, Assoc. Prof.,
University of Nebraska-Lincoln, NE, Lincoln
bmackey@inebraska.com, VP, Adv., Savannah
Morning News, GA, Savannah

Anderson, Tim........................**(229) 423-9331**
tandersonherald@gmail.com, Ed., The Herald-
Leader, GA, Fitzgerald

Anderson, Viola
violaa@dlnewspapers.com, Circ. Mgr., Detroit
Lakes Tribune, MN, Detroit Lakes
violaa@dlnewspapers.com, Circ. Mgr., The
Detroit Lakes Tribune, MN, Detroit Lakes

Anderson, William
mainlinenews@verizon.net, Pub., The
Mountaineer-Herald, PA, Ebensburg
mainlinenews@verizon.net, Pub., The
Mainliner, PA, Ebensburg
mainlinenews@verizon.net, Pub., The Journal,
PA, Ebensburg
mainlinenews@verizon.net, Pub., The Star-

Courier, PA, Northern Cambria
mainlinenews@verizon.net, Pub., The
Dispatch, PA, Ebensburg
mainlinenews@verizon.net, Pub., Mainline
Extra, PA, Ebensburg

Anderson, Zach
news.times@hcinet.net, Ed, The Starbuck
Times, MN, Glenwood

Anderson , John......................**(585) 593-2300**
johnanderson@eveningtribune.com, Rgl. Ed.,
The Evening Tribune, NY, Hornell

Anderson II, Dale...................**(304) 840-1555**
hnn.ads@gmail.com, Adv. Dir.,
HuntingtonNews.net, WV, Huntington

Anderson Witmer, Stephanie........**(717) 477-1521**
Asst. Prof./print & online media, Shippensburg
University/Communication/Journalism
Department , PA, Shippensburg

Andersson, Mattias
mattias.andersson@ustensor.com, President,
Tensor International LLC, IL, Woodridge

Andeweg, Logan
brenda@towncrierltd.com, Pub., Town Crier,
IA, Pella

Andrade, Becky......................**(828) 669-8727**
becky@blackmountainnews.com, Adv. Rep,
Black Mountain News, NC, Black Mountain

Andrade, Franklin G..........................**ext. 201**
frank@laoferta.com, Pub., La Oferta Review,
CA, San Jose

Andrade, Mary J..............................**ext. 202**
mary@laoferta.com, Ed., La Oferta Review,
CA, San Jose

Andrade, Veronica..........................**ext. 203**
veronica@laoferta.com, Adv. Dir., La Oferta
Review, CA, San Jose

Andre, Marilyn...........**(913) 367-0583 ext. 20408**
marilyna@npgco.com, Bus. Mgr./Circ.,
Atchison Globe, KS, Atchison

Andreas, Erika
locals@pctribune.com, Gen. Mgr, The Starbuck
Times, MN, Glenwood

Andreas, Karen.......................**(978) 946-2241**
kandreas@gloucestertimes.com, Pub.,
Gloucester Daily Times, MA, Gloucester

Andreas, Karen.......................**(978) 338-2671**
kandreas@salemnews.com, Pub., The Salem
News, MA, Beverly

Andreas, Karen.......................**(978) 946-2241**
kandreas@newburyportnews.com, Pub., The
Eagle-Tribune, MA, North Andover
kandreas@newburyportnews.com, Pub., The
Daily News, MA, Newburyport

Andreas, Karen
editor@derrynews.com, Pub., Derry News,
NH, Derry

Andreas, Karen.......................**(978) 946-2110**
kandreas@nobmg.com, Reg. Pub., Andover
Townsman, MA, Andover

Andreasen, Kim..............................**ext. 233**
kandreasen@putnamsentinel.com, Adv. Rep.,
Putnam County Sentinel, OH, Ottawa

Andreasen, Margaret
mcandrea@facstaff.wisc.edu, Prof. Emer.,
University of Wisconsin-Madison, WI,
Madison

Andreone, Fred.......................**(613) 738-3000**
sales@imapro.com, Pres., Imapro Corp., ON,
Rockcliffe

Andreottola, Michael
info@amjet.com, Pres./CEO, American Ink Jet
Corp., MA, Billerica

Andres, Cheryl
candres@putnamsentinel.com, Adv. Mgr.,
Putnam County Sentinel, OH, Ottawa
candres@putnamsentinel.com, Adv. Mgr.,
Putnam County Vidette, OH, Ottawa

Andres, Jeff.............................**(651) 464-4601**

jeff.andres@ecm-inc.com, Gen. Mgr., Forest
Lake Times, MN, Forest Lake

Andres, Jeff
jeff.andres@ecm-inc.com, Gen Mgr., St. Croix
Valley Peach, MN, Forest Lake

Andres, Jeff............................**(612) 267-3797**
jeff.andres@ecm-inc.com, Gen. Mgr., Princeton
Union-Eagle, MN, Princeton

Andres, Jeff............................**(612) 267-3797**
jeff.andres@ecm-inc.com, Rgl Gen. Mgr., Isanti
County News, MN, Cambridge

Andres, Jeff............................**(763) 691-6022**
jeff.andres@ecm-inc.com, Gen. Mgr., Mille
Lacs County Times, MN, Princeton
jeff.andres@ecm-inc.com, Gen. Mgr., Star
News, MN, Elk River

Andrews, Aimee
aimee@c-ville.com, Pub., C-ville Weekly, VA,
Charlottesville

Andrews, Brenda H.
njguide@gmail.com, Pub., Journal And Guide,
VA, Norfolk

Andrews, Clara Padilla
cpadilla@elhispanicnews.com, Pub., El
Hispanic News, OR, Portland

Andrews, Connie.....................**(610) 371-5006**
candrews@readingeagle.com, Promotions
Manager, Reading Eagle Company, PA,
Reading
candrews@readingeagle.com, Senior Dir of
Mktg, Reading Eagle, PA, Reading

Andrews, Deanna....................**(712) 762-4188**
deannaandrews605@yahoo.com, Prod. Mgr.,
Anita Tribune, IA, Anita

Andrews, Elliot...............**(256) 840-3000 ext 130**
advertising@sandmountainreporter.com,
Advertising Assistant, Sand Mountain
Reporter, AL, Albertville

Andrews, Emily......................**(419) 609-5805**
emilyandrews@tandemnetwork.com, Dir. of
Dig. Mktg, Norwalk Reflector, OH, Norwalk

Andrews, Gene.......................**(712) 762-4188**
gandrews@midlands.net, Pub./Gen. Mgr./Adv.
Mgr., Anita Tribune, IA, Anita

Andrews, Greg.......................**(317) 362-9267**
gandrews@ibj.com, Ed., Indianapolis Business
Journal, IN, Indianapolis

Andrews, Jannaya
jandrews@decaturdailydemocrat.com,
Associate Ed./News Ed., Decatur Daily
Democrat, IN, Decatur

Andrews, Kayla
kayla.andrews@baptiststandard.com, Bus.
Mgr., Baptist Standard, TX, Plano

Andrews, Larry
landrews@webbweekly.com, Gen. Mgr., Webb
Weekly, PA, South Williamsport

Andrews, Lauren
internetsales@progress-index.com, Online Adv.
Exec., The Progress-Index, VA, Petersburg

Andrews, Lehaina
ads@hayriverhub.com, Adv. Mgr., The Hub,
NT, Hay River

Andrews, Linda......................**(330) 580-8461**
linda.andrews@cantonrep.com, Controller, The
Repository, OH, Canton

Andrews, Mary Ann...................**(270) 777-4030**
mandrews@bgdailynews.com, Copy Editor,
Daily News, KY, Bowling Green

Andrews, Pat.........................**(954) 938-7105**
pandrews@miamiherald.com, Asst. Mng. Ed.,
Broward, Herald Values, FL, Miami

Andrews, Phil.........................**(519) 823-6050**
pandrews@guelphmercury.com, Mng. Ed., The
Guelph Mercury Tribune, ON, Guelph

Andrews, Tim
tim.andrews@state.or.us, Sales Mgr., Stanford
Products, IL, Salem

Andrews, Wells ....(928) 763-2505 Ext 2222
Gmco53@clippintheriver.com, General
Manager, Mohave Valley Daily News, AZ,
Bullhead City

Andrews, Wells
wandrews@uniondemocrat.com, Pub., The
Union Democrat, CA, Sonora

Andrews-Duve, Myles................(909) 703-0291
editorinchief@highlandernews.org, EIC, Univ.
of California, Riverside, CA, Riverside

Andrews-Gross, Buffy ....(717) 771-2052
buffy@ydr.com, Asst. Mng. Ed., Features/
Niche/Social Media, York Daily Record/York
Sunday News, PA, York

Andrich, Lauren
landrich@newsday.com, Newsday, NY, Melville

Andrist, Steve
stevea@ndna.com, Exec. Dir., North Dakota
Newspaper Association, ND, Bismarck

Andrus, Andrea........................(509) 664-7136
andrus@wenatcheeworld.com, The Wenatchee
World, WA, Wenatchee

Andrus, Kelly
kandrus@thedailyreview.com, Managing
Editor, The Daily Review, PA, Towanda

Andrus, Tiffany ....(269) 673-1701
tiffany.andrus@flashespublishers.com, Sales,
West Michigan Senior Times, MI, Holland

Andrzejewski, Chad ....(303) 715-3206
chad.andrzejewski@archden.org, Adv. Mgr.,
Denver Catholic Register, CO, Denver

Anesta, David
danesta@gannett.com, Consumer Experience
Director, TN Media, TN, Nashville
danesta@gannett.com, Consumer Experience
Director, The Tennessean, TN, Nashville

Anfinson, Reed W.
reed@monitor-news.com, Pub., Swift County
Monitor & News, MN, Benson

Angel, Kristi ....(406) 657-1251
kangel@billingsgazette.com, Mng. Ed., Billings
Gazette, MT, Billings

Angel, Roxanne ....(360) 378-5696
Pub., The Journal of the San Juan Islands, WA,
Friday Harbor

Angel, Stephanie
sangel@lsj.com, Mng. Ed., The Source
Sampler, MI, Lansing

Angel, Stephanie
sangel@lsj.com, Mng. Ed., Lansing State
Journal, MI, Lansing

Angel-Currier, Sylvia
angelsj@tdstelme.net, Pub., Rolling Thunder
Express, ME, Newport

Angeles, Maria de los................(818) 715-9931
admax@sbcglobal.net, Pres., Admax
International Media, CA, West Hills

Angelevski, Steve
steve.angelevski@sunmedia.ca, Corporate VP,
Reader Sales & Services, The Toronto Sun,
ON, Toronto

Angeli, Stefani
stefanie.angeli@newsday.com, Senior Director
National Sales
, Newsday, NY, Melville

Angelini, Francesco ....(262) 656-6210
fangelini@kenoshanews.com, Controller,
Kenosha News, WI, Kenosha

Angell, Darcy
angell@edr.com, Office Mgr., EDR/Beachwood
Studios, OH, Beachwood

Angell, Jim ....(307) 635-3905
wyopress@wyopress.org, Exec. Dir., Wyoming
Press Association, WY, Cheyenne

Angell, Susan ....(608) 208-1681
couriergraphics@hngnews.com, Graphics/
Prod. Coord., The Milton Courier, WI, Milton

Angelo, Jesse ....(212) 930-8271
jangelo@nypost.com, Pub. / CEO, New York
Post, NY, New York

Anger, Laura ....(231) 591-2609
Ferris State Torch., MI, Big Rapids

Angers, Gilles
gangers@lesoleil.com, Real Estate, Le Soleil,
QC, Quebec

Angilly, Paul
pangilly@centralctcommunications.com, Sports
Ed., The Bristol Press, CT, Bristol

Angius, James
james.angius@latimes.com, News Op., Exec.
News Ed., Los Angeles Times, CA, Los
Angeles

Anguiano, Richard ....(352) 867-4104
richard.anguiano@starbanner.com, Online
Community Editor, Ocala Star-Banner, FL,
Ocala

Angulo, Alba
alba@elmundonewspaper.com, Publisher, El
Mundo - Austin / San Antonio, TX, Austin

Anischik, Thomas J. ....(860) 241-3759
tanischik@courant.com, Sr. VP Ops Admin.,
The Hartford Courant, CT, Hartford

Ankeny, Ben
ben.ankeny@austindailyherald.com, Mktg.
Consultant, Austin Daily Herald, MN, Austin

Ankney, Bernie ....(205) 726-2465
rnankney@samford.edu, Chair, Samford
University, AL, Birmingham

Ann, Alexis............................(860) 599-1221
alexisinmystic@aol.com, Pub./Adv. Sales, The
Resident, CT, Pawcatuck

Ann, Hanna ....(507) 526-7324
ahanna@faribaultcountyregister.com, Circ.
Mng., Faribault County Register, MN, Blue
Earth

Annan-Brady, Rita ....(973) 226-8900
rannan-brady@recordernewspapers.com, New
Jersey Hills Media Group, NJ, Whippany

Annan-Brady, Rita
rannan-brady@recordernewspapers.com,
Lifestyles Ed., The Progress, NJ, Caldwell

Annand, Vanessa
advocate@athabasca.greatwest.ca, Ed., The
Athabasca Advocate, AB, Athabasca

Annett, Lesley ....(416) 946-2297
lesley.annett@sunmedia.ca, Sales Director/
Director of Promotion, The Toronto Sun, ON,
Toronto

Annis, Ron ....(541) 942-3325
graphics@cgsentinel.com, Prod. Mgr., Siuslaw
News, OR, Florence

Anokwa, Kwadwo
kanokwa@butler.edu, Dir., Butler Univ., IN,
Indianapolis

Anschutz, Philip F. ....(303) 298-1000
Chrmn./CEO, The Anschutz Co., CO, Denver

Anselm, Deborah ....(563) 383-2224
danselm@qctimes.com, Pub., Quad-City
Times, IA, Davenport

Anselm, Tom..........................(314) 831-4645
Sales Mgr., Independent News, MO, Florissant

Anstaett, Doug ....(785) 271-5304
danstaett@kspress.com, Exec. Dir., Kansas
Press Association, KS, Topeka

Antal, Natalie
natalie.antal@rochester.edu, Acting Managing
Editor, WATS, Simon Grad. School of Bus.,
NY, Rochester

Antal, Roy..............................(306) 781-5233
photography@leaderpost.canwest.ca, Photo
Dept. Mgr., The Leader-Post, SK, Regina

Anthes, Rob
news@mercerspace.com, Ed., Community
News Service - Hamilton Post, NJ, Lawrence

Anthony, Cliff ....(440) 366-7729
canthony@lorainccc.edu, Advisor, Lorain
County Cmty. College, OH, Elyria

Anthony, Greg
ganthony@refuelnow.com, SVP, Sales, re:fuel,
NY, New York

Anthony, Phil
nypa@nynewspapers.com, Adv. Rep.,
Classified Sales, New York Press Service,
NY, Albany

Anthony, Robbin
anthonro@uvu.edu, Bus. Mgr., Utah Valley
University, UT, Orem

Anthony, Robert ....(917) 267-2493
bob@paperpc.net, Ed./Columnist, Stadium
Circle Features, New York

Antilley, David
antilleyd@nsula.edu, Dir./Producer NSU 22,
Northwestern State University of Louisiana,
LA, Natchitoches

Anton, Angela
aanton@antonnews.com, Pub., Port
Washington News, NY, Port Washington

Anton, Angela
levittowntribune@antonnews.com, Pub.,
Levittown Tribune, NY, Mineola

Anton, Angela
oysterbayenterprisepilot@antonnews.com,
Pub., Oyster Bay Enterprise Pilot, NY,
Mineola

Anton, Angela
newhydeparkillustrated@antonnews.com, Pub.,
New Hyde Park Illustrated, NY, Mineola

Anton, Angela
mineolaamerican@antonnews.com, Pub.,
Mineola American, NY, Mineola

Anton, Angela
aanton@antonnews.com, Pub., Westbury
Times, NY, Mineola

Anton, Angela
manhassetpress@antonnews.com, Pub.,
Manhasset Press, NY, Mineola

Anton, Angela
a_anton@antonnews.com, Pub., Roslyn News,
NY, Mineola

Anton, Angela
manhassetpress@antonnews.com, Pub.,
Massapequan Observer, NY, Mineola

Anton, Angela S. ....(516) 747-8282
a_anton@antonnews.com, Pub., Great Neck
Record, NY, Mineola

Anton, Angela Susan ....(516) 747-8282
a.anton@antonnews.com, Pub., Farmingdale
Observer, NY, Mineola

Anton, Angela Susan
a_anton@antonnews.com, Pub., Floral Park
Dispatch, NY, Mineola

Anton, Angela Susan
a.anton@antonnews.com, Pub., Anton
Community Newspapers, NY, Mineola

Anton, Angela Susan
a_anton@antonnews.com, Pub., Garden City
Life, NY, Mineola

Antone, Peter
pantone@gannett.com, TN Media, TN,
Nashville
pantone@gannett.com, The Tennessean, TN,
Nashville

Antonelli, Lou ....(903) 427-4567
theclarksvilletimes@gmail.com, Managing
Editor, Clarksville Times, TX, Clarksville

Antonelli, Paul ....(518) 843-1100 Ext. 133
paul.antonelli@recordernews.com, Sports Ed.,
The Recorder, NY, Amsterdam

Antonich, Suzanne
suzanne.antonich@scripps.com, Gen. Mgr.,
Jupiter Courier, FL, Stuart

Antonich, Suzanne......................(863) 763-3134
Adv. Consultant, Glades County Democrat, FL,
Okeechobee

Antonopoulos, Spiros ....ext. 223
Web Ed., Weekly Alibi, NM, Albuquerque

Anyaegbunam, Chike
canya2@pop.uky.edu, Assoc. Prof., University
of Kentucky, KY, Lexington

Anyiam, Charles ....(310) 644-0315
canyiam@theafricantimes.com, Ed., The
African Times/USA, CA, Hawthorne

Anzalone, Joe ....(212) 210-2166
janzalone@nydailynews.com, Dir. of Multi-
Cultural Retail Sales Mgr., New York Daily
News, NY, New York

Anzelmo, James ....(815) 382-1914
graphic@stans.net, Pres., Graphic Machine
Sales, Inc., IL, Wonder Lake

Apa, Marnie
marnie@threeriversnews.com, Adv. Sales,
Three Rivers Commercial-News, MI, Three
Rivers

Apana, Lehia ....(808) 244-6350
lehia@mauinews.com, The Maui News, HI,
Wailuku

Apenowich, Cathryn
info@vtg.com, Mktg. Serv. Mgr., Voice
Technologies Group, Inc., NY, Getzville

Apfelbaum, Marianne ...... (802) 872-9000 ext. 118
vermontmaturity@aol.com, Ed & Pub, Vermont
Maturity Magazine, VT, Williston

Apfelbaum, Marianne ...... (802) 872-9000 ext. 118
marianne@willistonobserver.com, Sales Mgr.,
Williston Observer, VT, Williston

Apodaca, Alberto ....(212) 597-5612
alberto.apodaca@wsj.com, Lux. Adv., Sales
Dir., The Wall Street Journal, NY, New York

Apodaca, Ted ....(562) 431-1397 x 220
editor@newsenterprise.net, Ed., News
Enterprise, CA, Seal Beach

Appel, Gregory ....(518) 828-1616
Gappel@columbiagreenemedia.com,
Advertising Director, Register-Star, NY,
Hudson

Appel, Gregory ....(518) 828-1616 Ext. 2463
gappel@columbiagreenemedia.com, Exec. Ed.
, Register-Star, NY, Hudson
gappel@columbiagreenemedia.com,
Advertising Director, The Daily Mail, NY,
Hudson

Appel, Gregory
greg.appel@dowjones.com, nat'l Adv. Mgr.,
The Spectator, MA, New Bedford
greg.appel@dowjones.com, National & Major
Accounts Manager, Dow Jones Local Media
Group, NY, Middletown

Appel, Gregory
gappel@gatehousemedia.com, Director of
National Sales
, GateHouse Media, Inc., NY, Pittsford

Appen, Hans
hans@northfulton.com, Gen. Mgr., John's
Creek Herald, GA, Alpharetta

Appen, Ray ....(770) 442-3278
appen@northfulton.com, Pub., The Revue &
News, GA, Alpharetta
appen@northfulton.com, Pub., John's Creek
Herald, GA, Alpharetta
appen@northfulton.com, Pub., Milton Herald,
GA, Alpharetta
appen@northfulton.com, Pub., The Forsyth
Herald, GA, Alpharetta

Apperson, Glenda........................ext. 218
glenda.apperson@gaflnews.com, Prodn.
Foreman, Composing, The Moultrie
Observer, GA, Moultrie

Apple, Charity ....(336) 506-3057
capple@thetimesnews.com, Features Ed.,
Times-News, NC, Burlington

Appleford, Steve
steve.appleford@latimes.com, Feat. Ed., News-Press, CA, Los Angeles

Appler, Anita
amappler@grantky.com, Classified, Circulation Manager, Grant County News and Express, KY, Williamstown

Appleyard, Ernie .... (815) 625-3600 Ext. 720
eappleyard@saukvalley.com, Prodn. Mgr., The Telegraph, IL, Dixon

Appleyard, Ernie ....(815) 625-3600 ext. 5720
Production Dir., Daily Gazette, IL, Sterling

Appt, John J. ....(419) 255-3567
jappt@tyjill.com, Pres., TyJill Enterprises, Inc., OH, Rossford

April, Sara
sara@dirksvanessen.com, Vice Pres., Dirks, Van Essen & Murray, NM, Santa Fe

Aquino, Andres.........................(917) 749-8421
info@usafashionshows.com, Owner, Fashion Syndicate Press, Woodstock

Aquino, Jose
jaquino@santamariatimes.com, Web Developer, Santa Maria Times, CA, Santa Maria

Aquino, Tony
taquino@fujifilmgs.com, Reg'l Sales Mgr., Fujifilm Graphic Systems USA, Inc., CT, Windsor

Araguz, Nikki
media@houstonvoice.org, Opinion Editor, Houston Voice, TX, Houston

Arambula, Odie ....(956) 728-2561
odie@lmtonline.com, Sunday Ed., Laredo Morning Times, TX, Laredo

Aranda, William
assistantphotoeditor@dailylobo.com, Asst. Photo Ed., New Mexico Daily Lobo, NM, Albuquerque

Arango, German
newsdesk@eldiausa.com, Pub., La Subasta, TX, Houston

Arango, Gloria..........................(562) 499-1237
gloria.arango@langnews.com, V.P./HR, Pasadena Star-News, CA, Torrance

Arango, Gloria..........................(562) 499-1237
gloria.arango@langnews.com , VP, HR, Los Angeles Daily News, CA, Woodland Hills

Aratani, Lauren
herald@browndailyherald.com, The Brown Daily Herald, RI, Providence

Arbetter, Susan.........................(518) 449-2672
Pres., Legislative Correspondents Association of NYS, NY, Albany

Arbic, Janna LeHocky
janna.arbic@freeborncountyshopper.com, Sales Mgr., Freeborn County Shopper, MN, Albert Lea

ArbitalJacoby, Sheri
sarbitaljacoby@antonmediagroup.com, Mng. Ed., Great Neck Record, NY, Mineola

Arbogast, Joanne
jarbogast@dailyitem.com, Features Ed., The Daily Item, MA, Lynn

Arboleda, Carmen
ecuanews@inch.com, Adv. Mgr., Ecuador News, NY, Woodside

Arceneaux, Noah
noah.arceneaux@sdsu.edu, Asst. Prof., San Diego State University, CA, San Diego

Archangelo, Maria...........(802) 878-5282 ext 202
news@essexreporter.com, Editor, The Colchester Sun, VT, Colchester
news@essexreporter.com, Ed. and Co-publisher, The Essex Reporter, VT, Saint Albans

Archer, Greg
garcher@gtweekly.com, Ed., Santa Cruz Good

Times, CA, Santa Cruz

Archibald, Edward
ed@daily-jeff.com, Adv. Mgr., Jeffersonian Advantage, OH, Cambridge

Archibald, John
admin.syp@rogers.com, Adv. Mgr., Tottenham Times, ON, Beeton

Archibald, John
jarchibald@simcoeyorkprinting.com, Publisher, Simcoe-York Group, ON, Beeton

Archibald, Nellie
narchibald@journalpatriot.com, Adv. Mgr., The Wilkes Journal-Patriot, NC, North Wilkesboro

Archipley, Paul ....(425) 347-5634
publisher@mukilteobeacon.com, Pub., Mukilteo Beacon, WA, Mukilteo

Archipley, Paul ....(206) 542-4155
publisher@edmondsbeacon.com, Pub./Ed., Edmonds Beacon, WA, Mukilteo

Archuleta, Tim..........................(325) 659-8231
tarchuleta@gosanangelo.com, Ed., San Angelo Standard-Times, TX, San Angelo

Ard, Scott ....(408) 299-1828
sard@bizjournals.com, Ed., San Jose Business Journal, CA, San Jose

Arden-Hopkins, Christina
mail@cubapatriot.com, Pub., Cuba Patriot & Free Press, NY, Cuba

Ardis, Greg ....(410) 845-4607
gardis@dmg.gannett.com, Classified Key Rep., The Daily Times, MD, Salisbury

Arellano, Gustavo
garellano@ocweekly.com, Ed., Oc Weekly, CA, Fountain Valley

Arellano, Sandra
sarellano@ourcoloradonews.com, Circ. Mgr., The Littleton Independent, CO, Highlands Ranch
sarellano@ourcoloradonews.com, Circ. Mgr., Douglas County News Press, CO, Highlands Ranch
sarellano@ourcoloradonews.com, Circ. Mgr., Parker Chronicle, CO, Highlands Ranch

Arenas, Gail ....(787) 354-4029
andragale@aol.com, Executive Director, Overseas Press Club of Puerto Rico (Established 1968), PR, San Juan

Arendall, Audra ....(325) 773-5100
audra@thestamfordstar.com, Adv. Dir., The Stamford Star, TX, Stamford

Arendt, Britta ....(218) 326-6623
barendt@grhr.net, Ed., Grand Rapids Herald-Review, MN, Grand Rapids

Arendt, Britta
britta.arendt@mx3.com, Editor, Herald-review/manney's Shopper, MN, Grand Rapids

Arendt, John
news@summerlandreview.com, Ed., Summerland Review, BC, Summerland

Arenstein, Seth........................(301) 354-2000
sarenstein@accessintel.com, Editorial Dir., CableFAX Daily LLC, MD, Rockville

Arenz, Jeff
sports@murrayledger.com, Sports Ed., The Murray Ledger & Times, KY, Murray

Areson, Susan..........................(401) 277-7329
sareson@providencejournal.com, Deputy Executive Editor, The Providence Journal, RI, Providence

Arevalo, Gaby ....(410) 455-1262
Univ. of Maryland Baltimore County, MD, Baltimore

Arevalo, Kricket
delivery@threeriversnews.com, Circ., Three Rivers Commercial-News, MI, Three Rivers

Argabright, Brian ....(830) 703-3023
news@delrionewsherald.com, Managing Ed., Del Rio News-Herald, TX, Del Rio

Argentieri, Chris
chris.argentieri@latimes.com, Senior VP & Gen. Mgr. Ca. News Group, Los Angeles Times, CA, Los Angeles

Argue, Linda
largue@lsj.com, Circ. Mgr., Charlotte Shopping Guide, MI, Lansing
largue@lsj.com, Circ. Dir., Lansing State Journal, MI, Lansing

Arie, Mike ....(405) 238-6464
marie@pvdemocrat.com, Ed, Pauls Valley Democrat, OK, Pauls Valley

Arinde, Nayaba
nayaba.arinde@amsterdamnews.com, Editor, New York Amsterdam News, NY, New York

Arkawy, Amy...........................(888) 309-0639
amy@miracomcomputer.com, Inside Sales, Miracom Computer Corp., NY, Eastchester

Arke, Ed
earke@messiah.edu, Professor of Communications, Messiah College, PA, Mechanicsburg

Arland-Fye, Barb
arland-fye@davenportdiocese.org, Mng. Ed., The Catholic Messenger, IA, Davenport

Arlen, Gary.............................(301) 229-2199
garlen@arlencom.com, Pres., Arlen Communications LLC, MD, Bethesda

Arleth, Joe
voiceeditor@huskies.bloomu.edu, Bloomsburg Univ., PA, Bloomsburg

Armada, Bernard
bjarmada@stthomas.edu, Assoc. Prof., University of St. Thomas, MN, Saint Paul

Armantrout, Janet ....(925) 243-8013
editmail@compuserve.com, Ed./Prod. Mgr., The Independent, CA, Livermore

Armbruster, Doug ....(785) 822-1421
darmbruster@salina.com, Deputy Ed., The Salina Journal, KS, Salina

Armendariz, Bill...........(575) 564-2611 Ext. 2626
barmendariz@demingheadlight.com, Ed., Deming Headlight, NM, Deming

Armendariz, R.L.
editor@hispanianews.com, Ed., Hispania News, CO, Colorado Springs

Armendariz, Sami ....(719) 540-0222
Prodn. Mgr., Hispania News, CO, Colorado Springs

Armesto, Eladio Jose.................(786) 286-8787
patrianews@aol.com, Publisher, El Nuevo PATRIA, FL, Miami

Armesto, Eladio Jose.................(786) 286-8787
patrianews@aol.com, Pub, El Nuevo PATRIA, FL, Miami

Armesto, Sara P. ....(786) 286-8787
armesto.sp@gmail.com, Associate Ed., El Nuevo PATRIA, FL, Miami

Armfield, Tanya ....(318) 281-4422
tarmfield@bastropenterprise.com, Classified Adv. Mgr., Bastrop Daily Enterprise, LA, Bastrop

Armold, Kevin
karmold@intranix.com, Prod. Dir., Times-Republic, IL, Watseka

Armor, Jennifer............ (415) 461-6006, ext. 210
jlarmor@verifiedaudit.com, Audit Mgr., Verified Audit Circulation (VAC), CA, San Rafael

Arms, Charles
charles.arms@lee.net, Lee Enterprises, Inc., IA, Davenport

Armstong, Melissa
melissa@haliburtonpress.com, Sales Rep, Bancroft This Week, ON, Bancroft

Armstrong, Susan......................(540) 213-9105
sarmstrong@newsleader.com, Admin., HR, The News Leader, VA, Staunton

Armstrong, Beth
sentinel@whitesitesentinel.com, Adv. Mgr., The Review, IL, Port Byron

Armstrong, Colleen
carmstrong@islandssounder.com, Pub., The Islands' Sounder, WA, Eastsound

Armstrong, Curtis
carmstrong@postmedia.com, Advertising Director, The Stratford Beacon Herald, ON, Stratford

Armstrong, Dreama
darmstrong@reidsvillereview.com, Office Mgr., The Eden Daily News, NC, Reidsville

Armstrong, Harry G.
news@thegoldentimes.com, Ed., The Golden Times, NJ, Pitman

Armstrong, Jason
jarmstrong@mediaspace.com, Buying Supervisor
, Mediaspace Solutions, MN, Hopkins

Armstrong, Jeff........................(770) 683-1726
jarmstrong@newnan.com, Sports Writer, The Newnan Times-Herald, GA, Newnan

Armstrong, John
jarmstrong@spotmagic.com, Founder, Affiliate Rel., SpotMagic, Inc., CA, San Francisco

Armstrong, Kelly
kelly@lazerfare.com, Pres., Lazer-fare Media Services, MB, Winnipeg

Armstrong, Kevin ....(918) 495-7080
warmstrong@oru.edu, Advisor, Oral Roberts Univ., OK, Tulsa

Armstrong, Maggie
maggie@pdclarion.com, Class. Adv. Mgr., Princeton Daily Clarion, IN, Princeton

Armstrong, Mary ....(309) 690-5324
marmstrong@multi-ad.com, Office Manager, Local Search Association, IL, Peoria

Armstrong, Mary
marmstrong@seattleschild.com, Pub. Asst., Seattle's Child, WA, Lynnwood

Armstrong, Michael ....(907) 235-7767
michael.armstrong@homernews.com, Ed., homer News, AK, Homer

Armstrong, Rachel ....(505) 835-5996
New Mexico Inst. of Mining & Technology, NM, Socorro

Armstrong, Rick
rick.armstrong@wichita.edu, Assoc. Prof., Wichita State University, KS, Wichita

Armstrong, Robin ....ext. 119
rarmstrong@toledocitypaper.com, Accounting, Ann Arbor Family Press, OH, Toledo

Armstrong, Robin
rarmstrong@toledocitypaper.com, Admin. Acct., Toledo Area Parent News, OH, Toledo

Armstrong, Rod ....(979) 731-4613
rod.armstrong@theeagle.com, Finance Dir., The Eagle, TX, Bryan

Armstrong, Shell............(985) 876-3008, ext. 20
Exec. Ed., Tri-Parish Times & Business News, LA, Houma

Armstrong, Terry ....(250) 470-0721
terry.armstrong@ok.bc.ca, Pub., The Daily Courier, BC, Kelowna

Armstrong, Theresa
tarmstrong@civitasmedia.com, Gen Mgr/Ad Mgr, Grayson County News-Gazette, KY, Leitchfield

Armstrong, Tiff B......................(415) 288-4260
tarmstrong@harriswilliams.com, Mng. Dir., Harris Williams & Co., CA, San Francisco

Armstrong, Travis K. ....(805) 564-5161
voices@newspress.com, Editorial Page Ed., Santa Barbara News-Press, CA, Santa Barbara

Armstrong, Twila

advertising@almaguinnews.com, Adv. Rep., Almaguin News, ON, Burks Falls

Armstrong, Zela ....(325) 236-6677
publisher@sweetwaterreporter.com, General Manager / Ad Director, Nolan County Shopper, TX, Sweetwater
publisher@sweetwaterreporter.com, Gen. Mgr. / Adv. Dir., Sweetwater Reporter, TX, Sweetwater

Arneal, Nathan ....(402) 652-8312
nbeagle@gmail.com, Ed & Pub, North Bend Eagle, NE, North Bend

Arnett, Alyx
aarnett@kokomoperspective.com, Indiana Univ., IN, Kokomo

Arnett, Carol ....(314) 831-4645
Reporter, Independent News, MO, Florissant

Arnett, Josh ....(620) 241-2422
jarnett@mcphersonsentinel.com, Staff Writer, McPherson Sentinel, KS, McPherson

Arnett, Paul ....(808) 529-4786
parnett@staradvertiser.com, Sports Ed., Honolulu Star-Advertiser, HI, Honolulu

Arnett, Ronald C.
arnett@duq.edu, Chair/Prof., Duquesne University, PA, Pittsburgh

Arnold, Andrea ....(509) 935-8422
theindependent@centurytel.net, Office Mgr., The Independent, WA, Chewelah

Arnold, Arne ....(262) 631-1734
Circ. Mgr., Pennysaver, The Journal Times, WI, Racine

Arnold, Austin ....(419) 358-8010
editor@blufftonnews.com, Ed., The Bluffton News, OH, Bluffton

Arnold, Brian ....(707) 427-6969
Asst. Sports Ed., Daily Republic, CA, Fairfield

Arnold, Bruno
redaktion@neue.ch, Ed. in Chief, NEUE URNER ZEITUNG, Altdorf

Arnold, E. N. ....ext. 252
edarnold@peterboroughexaminer.com, Mng. Ed., The Examiner, ON, Peterborough

Arnold, Fred
fred@mcbattascompanies.com, Pub., The Belleville Telescope, KS, Belleville

Arnold, Jared ....(509) 935-8422
publisher@centurytel.net, Pub., The Independent, WA, Chewelah

Arnold, Jo ....(603) 594-1241
news@nashuatelegraph.com, Ed. Asst., The Telegraph, NH, Nashua

Arnold, Jodi
jarnold@newportindependent.com, Office Mgr./ Classifieds/Circ. Mgr., Newport Independent, AR, Newport

Arnold, Lance
lance.arnold@nicholls.edu, Instr., Nicholls State University, LA, Thibodaux

Arnold, Lorin
arnold@rowan.edu, Asst. Prof., Rowan Univ., NJ, Glassboro

Arnold, Melanie ....(305) 292-7777
marnold@keysnews.com, Dir, Adv., Florida Keys Free Press, FL, Tavernier

Arnold, Mike ....(352) 563-3393
marnold@chronicleonline.com, Mng. Ed., Citrus County Chronicle, FL, Crystal River

Arnold, Paige ....(806) 364-2030
business@herefordbrand.com, Accountant, The Hereford Brand, TX, Hereford

Arnold, Sally ....(806) 847-7803
briscoenews@gmail.com, Pub./Ed., Briscoe County News, TX, Silverton

Arnold, Steve ....(334) 240-0112
sdarnold@gannett.com , Content Strategist/ Digital Ed., Montgomery Advertiser, AL,
Montgomery

Arnold, Steve ....(361) 886-3624
arnolds@caller.com, Mktg. Dir., Corpus Christi Caller-Times, TX, Corpus Christi

Arnold, Theresa ....(250) 378-4241
publisher@merrittherald.com, Merritt Herald, BC, Merritt

Arnold, Traci ....(610) 371-5161
tarnold@readingeagle.com, Customer Service Manager, Reading Eagle Company, PA, Reading

Arnot, Lisa ....(978) 249-3535 ext. 600
larnot@atholnews.com, Office Mgr., Athol Daily News, MA, Athol

Arnst, Karl ....(361) 343-5214
sales@mysoutex.com, Adv. Dir., Refugio County Press, TX, Refugio

Arnst, Karl
news@mysoutex.com, Adv. Dir., Beeville Bee-Picayune, TX, Beeville

Arnst, Karl
karneseditor@mysoutex.com, Adv. Dir., The Karnes Countywide, TX, Karnes City

Arnst, Michelle
marnst@thepostnewspapers.com, Graphic Designer, The Post Newspapers - Medina, OH, Medina

Aronoff, Roger ....ext. 109
roger@aim.org, Exec. Secretary, Accuracy in Media, Bethesda

Aronowitz, Michelle Jones
maronowitz-jones@gaa.org, Dir., Gravure Association of America, NC, Denver

Arrabal, Angel
angel@quipp.com, Vice Pres., Sales, Quipp System, Inc., FL, Miami Lakes

Arrasmith, Denim ....(937) 556-5762
darrasmith@civitasmedia.com, Admin. Asst. , Wilmington News Journal, OH, Wilmington

Arrazola, Carlos
guatemala@acan-efe.com, Rep., EFE News Services - Guatemala City, Guatemala, Guatemala City

Arredondo, Cynthia
carredondo@currentargus.com, Multi. Med. Cons. , Current-Argus, NM, Carlsbad

Arrigo, Rene
bcpress@frontier.com, Adv. Mgr, The Brown County Press, OH, Mount Orab

Arrigoni, Patricia
patarrigoni@comcast.net, Pres., Arrigoni Travel Syndication, Fairfax

Arrington, Randy
editor@pagenewspaper.com, Ed./Gen. Mgr., The Shenandoah Valley-Herald, VA, Woodstock

Arroyo, Gladys
garroyo@suntimes.com, Adv. Vice Pres., Chicago Sun-Times, IL, Chicago

Arth, Shelley
shellyarth@socket.net, Pub., Saline County Citizen, MO, Marshall

Arthur, Andrew
andrewa@elrio.org, Art Dir., The Daily Territorial, AZ, Tucson

Arthur, Barbara
barthur@southhillenterprise.com, Office Mgr., South Hill Enterprise, VA, South Hill

Arthur, Barry ....(501) 378-3484
barthur@arkansasonline.com, Asst. Managing Ed., Arkansas Democrat-Gazette, AR, Little Rock

Arthur, Damon ....(530) 225-8226
darthur@redding.com, Multimedia Journalist, Record Searchlight, CA, Redding

Artis, James ....(615) 321-3268
sales1501@aol.com, VP Advert., Tennessee
Tribune, TN, Nashville

Artz, Lindsey ....(717) 703-3031
lindseya@mansimedia.com, Account Manager, MANSI Media, PA, Harrisburg

Arundel, Peter W. ....(703) 777-1111
parundel@virginianewsgroup.com, Chairman/ CEO, Fauquier Times, VA, Warrenton

Arundel, Peter W. ....(703) 777-1111
parundel@timespapers.com, Virginia News Group, VA, Leesburg
parundel@timespapers.com, Chairman/CEO, Virginia New Group, VA, Leesburg

Arvidson, Donna ....(406) 271-5561
Adv. Asst., Independent Observer, MT, Conrad

Arvig, Dana
darvig@montereyherald.com, Ad. Dir., The Monterey County Herald, CA, Monterey

Arviso Jr., Tom ....(928) 871-1135
tarviso@navajotimes.com, CEO/ Pub, Navajo Times Publishing Company, Inc., AZ, Window Rock

Asanin, Cedo
srbobran@excite.com, Gen. Mgr., Kanadski Srbroban, ON, Hamilton

Asbach, Jeff
jeffa@hometownfocus.us, Prodn. Mgr., Northland Shopper, MN, Virginia

Asbach, Rick ....(808) 738-4992
rasbach@hawaiipublishersassociation.com, Executive Director, Hawaii Publishers Association, HI, Honolulu

Asciolla, Nila
nila@newportthisweek.net, Adv. Exec., Newport This Week, RI, Newport

Ash, Blue ....(702) 403-0252
bash@luxurylv.com, Pub., Luxury Las Vegas magazine, NV, Las Vegas

Ash, Linda
lash@nvdaily.com, Ed., Northern Virginia Daily, VA, Strasburg

Ash, Nancy ....ext. 238
nash@sharonherald.com, Living/Lifestyle Ed., The Herald, PA, Sharon

Ashby, Cathy
cathya@journalpub.com, Assoc. Pub., Central Penn Parent, PA, Harrisburg

Ashby, Donna
dashby@viewnewspapers.net, Prod. Mgr, Grand Blanc View, MI, Davison
dashby@viewnewspapers.net, Prod. Mgr, Swartz Creek View, MI, Davison
dashby@viewnewspapers.net, Prod. Mgr, LA View, MI, Lapeer
dashby@viewnewspapers.net, Prod. Mgr, The Brown City Banner, MI, Sandusky
dashby@viewnewspapers.net, Prod. Mgr, Flint Township View, MI, Davison
dashby@viewnewspapers.net, Prod. Mgr, Township View, MI, Chesaning
dashby@viewnewspapers.net, Prod. Mgr, The Davison Index, MI, Davison
dashby@viewnewspapers.net, Prod. Mgr, Tri-County Citizen, MI, Sandusky

Ashby, Janice ....(812) 206-2103
janice.ashby@newsandtribune.com, Bus. Mgr., News and Tribune, IN, Jeffersonville
janice.ashby@newsandtribune.com, Business Mgr., Tribune, IN, New Albany

Ashby, Toni ....(503) 357-3181
tashby@fgnewstimes.com, Advertising Sales, Forest Grove News-Times, OR, Forest Grove

Ashcraft, Richie ....x 388
Richie.Ashcraft@gjsentinel.com, Web Editor, The Daily Sentinel, CO, Grand Junction

Ashenfelder, Dennis ....(570) 387-1234 Ext 1602
Bus. Office Mgr., Press Enterprise, PA, Bloomsburg

Asher, Gunilla ....(970) 429-9170
gunilla@aspentimes.com, Adv. Dir., The Aspen Times, CO, Aspen

Asher, Julie
jasher@catholicnews.com, General News Editor, Catholic News Service, Washington

Ashfield, Chris
publisher@grasslandsnews.ca, Group Publisher, The Melville Advance, SK, Melville

Ashfield, Chris
herald@whitewoodherald.sk.ca, Pub, The Whitewood Herald, SK, Whitewood

Ashford, Carolyn
publisher@pryordailytimes.com, Pub., The Pryor Times, OK, Claremore

Ashleigh, Fox
sports@sidneyherald.com, Sports Editor, Sidney Herald, MT, Sidney

Ashley, Bob
bashley@heraldsun.com, Ed., The Herald-Sun, NC, Durham

Ashley, Charles
vdr@vernonrecord.com, Prodn. Mgr., The Vernon Daily Record, TX, Vernon

Ashley, Robyn ....(704) 358-6172
rashley@charlotteobserver.com, President, Mid-Atlantic Circulation Managers Association, NC, Roanoke Rapids

Ashley, Samantha ....(540) 735-1956
sashley@freelancestar.com, Executive Assistant/HR Generalist, The Free Lance-Star, VA, Fredericksburg

Ashley, Tim ....(574) 658-4111
tashley@the-papers.com, Associate Editor, The Paper - Kosciusko Edition, IN, Milford

Ashley, Valarie ....(765) 348-0110
newstimes@comcast.net, Adv. Conslt. , News Times, IN, Hartford City

Ashley-Ward, Amelia
sunreporter@sbcglobal.net, Pub., California Voice, CA, San Francisco

Ashley-Ward, Amelia
sunmedia97@aol.com, Ed., Sun Reporter, CA, San Francisco

Ashley-Ward, Amelia
sunmedia97@aol.com, Ed., Metro Reporter, CA, San Francisco

Ashlock, Marcus
editor@thesyracusejournal.com, Owner/Ed., The Syracuse Journal, KS, Syracuse

Ashman, Michael-Anne ....(919) 699-1988
ashman@adtransit.com, VP of Technology, B-Linked, Inc., NC, Chapel Hill

Ashmore, Margo ....(612) 867-4874
Margo@MyNortheaster.com, Pub., Northeaster, MN, Minneapolis

Ashton, Jean ....(508) 909-4104
jashton@stonebridgepress.com, Adv. Mgr., The Webster Times, MA, Southbridge

Ashton, Jean ....(508) 909-4104
jashton@stonebridgepress.com, Adv. Mgr., Auburn News, MA, Southbridge

Ashton, Jean
jashton@stonebridgepress.com, Adv. Dir., Spencer New Leader, MA, Southbridge

Ashton, Jean ....(508) 909-4104
jashton@stonebridgepress.com, Adv., Blackstone Valley Tribune, MA, Southbridge
jashton@stonebridgepress.com, Adv. Mgr., Stonebridge Press, Inc., MA, Southbridge

Ashton, Jean ....(508) 909-4104
jashton@stonebridgepress.com, Ad. Director, Charlton Villager, MA, Southbridge
jashton@stonebridgepress.com, Display Adv. , Southbridge Evening News, MA, Southbridge
jashton@stonebridgepress.com, Adv. Mgr., Sturbridge Villager, MA, Southbridge
jashton@stonebridgepress.com, Dir. Sales/ Mktg., Sturbridge Villager, MA, Southbridge

Ashurst, Andy
editor@mitchellnews.com, Pub., Mitchell News-Journal, NC, Spruce Pine

Ashworth, Gloria

gloria.ashworth@thefacts.com, Business Mgr., The Facts, TX, Clute

Ashworth, Ruck
ruck.ashworth@andalusiastarnews.com, Adv. Mgr., Andalusia Star-News, AL, Andalusia

Askelson, Kristin
kristin@acadiananow.com, News Dir./Content Strategist, The Daily Advertiser, LA, Lafayette

Asleson, Glen
gasleson@mankatofreepress.com, Prodn. Dir., The Free Press, MN, Mankato

Asmundson, Carla .... (626) 544-0890
casmundson@scng.com, Classified Advertising Manager, La Puente Highlander, CA, Monrovia

Asmundson, Carla .... (626) 544-0890
casmundson@sgvn.com, Classified Advertising Manager, Diamond Bar Highlander, CA, Monrovia

Asmundson, Carla .... (626) 544-0890
casmundson@scng.com, Classified Advertising Manager, Rowland Heights Highlander, CA, Monrovia

Asnicar, Tammy
editor@roguriverpress.com, Ed., Rogue River Press, OR, Grants Pass

Aspland, Cindy
cindya@advancedtele.co.uk, Dir., Sales, Advanced Telecom Services, Inc. (U.K.), London

Assad, Naela El .... ext. 22
classifieds@irishvoice.com, Classified Mgr., Irish Voice, NY, New York

Assad, Samah
phreako1756@yahoo.com, Editor-in-Chief, Cleveland State Univ., OH, Cleveland

Assels, Charlene .... (514) 987-2222
cassels@montrealgazette.com, Director, Integrated Adv. & Strategy, 3i, Montreal Gazette, QC, Montreal

Assink, Michael
massink1@mlive.com, VP of Sales, The Jackson Citizen Patriot, MI, Jackson

Assink, Michael
massink@mbusinessreview.com, VP of Sales, The Grand Rapids Press, MI, Grand Rapids

Astrup, Joni .... (763) 241-3668
joni.astrup@ecm-inc.com, Assoc. Ed., Star News, MN, Elk River

Aswege, Scott .... (309) 757-4934
ashwish@qconline.com, Financial Analyst, The Dispatch-Argus, IL, Moline

Atcheson, Denice .... (805) 437-0404
datcheson@vcstar.com, Dir., Finance, Ventura County Star, CA, Camarillo

Atchison, Spring
ads@hfherald.com, Co-Pub./Own./Office Mgr./Adv. Mgr., Haxtun-Fleming Herald, CO, Haxtun

Aten, Tim
Tim.aten@naplesnews.com, News Ed., Naples Daily News, FL, Naples

Ater, Maureen .... (330) 580-8430
maureen.ater@cantonrep.com, Gen. Mgr., The Repository, OH, Canton
maureen.ater@cantonrep.com, Gen. Mgr., The Independent, OH, Massillon

Atheron, Dusty .... (970) 728-9788 ext.24
dusty@telluridenews.com, Assoc. Pub., The Norwood Post, CO, Telluride

Atherton, Debbie
circulation@newpraguetimes.com, Circ. Mgr., Lake Region Life, MN, New Prague

Atherton, Dusty
dusty@telluridedailyplanet.com, Assoc. Pub., Telluride Daily Planet; the Watch; The Norwood Post, CO, Telluride

Atkins, Campbell .... (936) 348-3505

campbell.atkins@madisonvillemeteor.com, Sports writer, Madisonville Meteor, TX, Madisonville

Atkins, Charlotte .... (706) 290-5279
catkins@gainesvilletimes.com, Publisher, The Times, GA, Gainesville

Atkins, Gary
atkinsg@seattleu.edu, Chair, Seattle University, WA, Seattle

Atkins, Jeanni
iatkins@olemiss.edu, Assoc. Prof., University of Mississippi, MS, University

Atkins, Joan .... (606) 783-5312
sports@trailblazeronline.net, Morehead State Univ., KY, Morehead
sports@trailblazeronline.net, Journalism Coord., Morehead State University, KY, Morehead

Atkins, Karen
news@fultonsun.com, Ed., The Fulton Sun, MO, Fulton

Atkins, Michael R. .... (705) 673-5667 Ext. 348
Pres., Northern Life, ON, Sudbury

Atkinson, Adam .... (315) 376-6851
jpapineau@lowville.com, Ed., Journal and Republican, NY, Lowville

Atkinson, Bill .... (931) 484-5145
batkinson@crossville-chronicle.com, GM/Marketing Director, Crossville Chronicle, TN, Crossville

Atkinson, Dan .... (617) 629-3385
datkinson@wickedlocal.com, Ed., Somerville Journal, MA, Somerville

Atkinson, Jill .... (530) 257-5321
jatkinson@lassennews.com, Adv. Mgr., Lassen County Times, CA, Susanville

Atkinson, Jill .... (530) 257-5321
jatkinson@lassennews.com, Adv. Mgr., Westwood Pinepress, CA, Susanville

Atkinson, Jo .... (308) 537-3636
ads@gothenburgtimes.com, Office Mgr., Gothenburg Times, NE, Gothenburg

Atkinson, Kassi
kassi@thetexasspur.com, Asst. Ed./Adv. Dir. , The Texas Spur, TX, Spur

Atkinson, Kate .... (204) 476-3401
news@neepawabanner.com, Ed, The Neepawa Banner And Press, MB, Neepawa

Atkinson, Kelly .... (416) 774-2338
katkinson@insidetoronto.com, Regl. Mgr., HR, The Scarborough Mirror, ON, Toronto

Atkinson, Larry
pcnews@pottercountynews.com, Pub., Potter County News, SD, Gettysburg

Atkinson, Larry .... (605) 230-0161
atkinson@mobridgetribune.com, Pub, Monday Reminder, SD, Mobridge

Atkinson, Larry .... (605) 845-3646
atkinson@mobridgetribune.com, Pub, Mobridge Tribune, SD, Mobridge

Atkinson, Paul C. .... (212) 856-6304
paulcatkinson@nnnlp.com, Sr. Vice Pres., Bus. Devel., Newspaper National Network LP, NY, New York

Atkinson, Rollie
rollie@sonomawest.com, Pub., The Windsor Times, CA, Healdsburg

Atlas, Nancy
jewishreporter@aol.com, Mng. Ed., Metrowest Jewish Reporter, MA, Framingham

Atlas, Nancy
jewishreporter@aol.com, Ed., The Jewish Reporter, MA, Framingham

Attaway, Mark .... (843) 317-7363
mattaway@florencenews.com, Prodn. Foreman, Pressroom, Morning News, SC, Florence

Atwell, Kit .... (928) 445-3333 ext. 1070
Vice Pres./CEO, Prescott Newspapers Inc., Western News&Info., Inc., AZ, Yuma

Atwell, Kit .... (928) 445-3333 ext. 1070
katwell@prescottaz.com, Co-Pub., Chino Valley Review, AZ, Chino Valley

Atwell, Shelly
shelly.atwell@camaspostrecord.com, Circ. Mgr., Camas-Washougal Post Record, WA, Camas

Atwell, Shelly
shelly.atwell@camaspostrecord.com, Circ. Mgr., At Your Leisure, WA, Camas

Atwood, Kelly .... (601) 477-4084
kelly.atwood@jcjc.edu, Newspaper Adviser, Jones County Junior College, MS, Ellisville

Aubé, Jean Nicolas .... (514) 636-7314
jeannicolas.aube@tc.tc, News Director, Cites Nouvelles, QC, Dorval

Aubé, Jean Nicolas .... (514) 636-7314
jeannicolas.aube@tc.tc, News Director, The Chronicle, QC, Dorval

Auclair, Phillippe
hm@hebdos.net, Dir., Les Hebdos Monteregiens, QC, Boucherville

Aucter, Cindy .... (315) 376-4997
caucter@lowville.com, Acct. Rep., Carthage Republican Tribune, NY, LOWVILLE

Audet, Diane .... ext. 304
diane.audet@quebecormedia.com, Pub., Le Reveil, QC, Saint-Georges

Audette, Bob .... (802) 254-2311, Ext. 160
raudette@reformer.com, Day Mng. Ed. , Brattleboro Reformer, VT, Brattleboro

Audette, Diane
office@crestonvalleyadvance.ca, Circ. Mgr., Creston Valley Advance, BC, Creston

Audus, James .... (620) 792-1211 ext. 234
jaudus@gbtribune.com, Press manager, Great Bend Tribune, KS, Great Bend

Aueinen, Marco
data@dataengineering.fi, Mgr., Data Engineering Ltd., Helsinki

Aufderheide, Patricia
paufder@american.edu, Prof., American University, DC, Washington

Aufill, Peyton .... (806) 323-6461
peyton@canadianrecord.com, Sports Ed, The Canadian Record, TX, Canadian

Aughenbaugh, Cindy .... (814) 765-5581 ext. 213
Circ. Mgr., The Progress, PA, Clearfield

Augherton, Ann
aaugherton@catholicherald.com, Mng. Ed., Arlington Catholic Herald, VA, Arlington

Augsburger, Wayne
sales@cygnet.com, Vice Pres., Mktg., Cygnet Storage Solutions, Inc., CA, San Luis Obispo

Augur, Jennifer .... (413) 662-5127
j.augur@mcla.edu, Massachusetts College of Liberal Arts, MA, North Adams

August, Hilary .... (231) 439-9322
Classifieds, Petoskey News-Review, MI, Petoskey

Auguste, Arnold .... (416) 656-3400
share@interlog.com, Pub., Share, ON, Toronto

Augustine, Grace
cairo@efe.com, Rep., EFE News Services - Cairo, Egypt, Cairo

Augustine, Larry D.
augustin@susqu.edu, Chair, Susquehanna University, PA, Selinsgrove

Aulakh, Kamar .... (303) 894-8888
quarkxpress@quark.com, Pres./CEO, Quark, Inc., CO, Denver

Ault, Heather .... (765) 213-5748
hault@muncie.gannett.com, Marketing Coord., The Star Press, IN, Muncie

Aultman, William J.
baultman@onlinechester.com, Pub., Chester News & Reporter, SC, Chester

Auman, Ann
auman@hawaii.edu, Assoc. Prof., University of Hawaii at Manoa, HI, Honolulu

Auman, Richard .... (610) 371-5151
rauman@readingeagle.com, Director of Circulation, Reading Eagle Company, PA, Reading

Auman, Richard D. .... (610) 371-5151
rauman@readingeagle.com, Circ. Dir., Reading Eagle, PA, Reading

Aumann, Michael
michaelaumann@buhrs.com, Pres., Buhrs Americas, Inc., MN, Plymouth

Ausburn, Leslie
jewishj@jfsatx.org, Ed., The Jewish Journal of San Antonio, TX, San Antonio

Austen, Garnet
kentpub.ads@ns.sympatico.ca, Pub., Mirror-examiner, NS, Middleton

Austin, Amy
aaustin@washcp.com, Pub., Washington City Paper, DC, Washington

Austin, Bruce
baagll@rit.edu, Chair, Rochester Institute of Technology, NY, Rochester

Austin, Carolyn .... (217) 241-1300 x 237
Business Mgr., Illinois Press Association, IL, Springfield

Austin, Edie .... (514) 987-2222
eaustin@montrealgazette.com, Editorial Page Editor, Montreal Gazette, QC, Montreal

Austin, Erica
eaustin@wsu.edu, Interim Dir./Prof., Washington State University, WA, Pullman

Austin, George .... ext. 103
editor@spectatornewsonline.com, Ed., The Spectator, MA, New Bedford

Austin, Jennifer .... (207) 990-8030
jaustin@bangordailynews.com, Project Coord. , Bangor Daily News, ME, Bangor

Austin, Julia .... (512) 477-0746 ext. 20
ausin@texasobserver.org, Assoc. Pub., The Texas Observer, TX, Austin

Austin, Larry
dispatch@wnypapers.com, Ed., Grand Island Pennysaver, NY, Grand Island

Austin, Larry
dispatch@wnypapers.com, Ed., Island Dispatch, NY, Grand Island

Austin, Manuel
aadist@aol.com, Pres., A & A Distribution, Inc., CA, San Jose

Austin, Miranda .... (304) 294-4144
Assistant Legal Editor, Mullens Advocate, WV, Mullens

Austin, Philip
newsroom@oneidadispatch.com, Pub., Pennysaver, NY, Oneida

Austin, Ronna .... ext. 7307
Oklahoma City Community College, OK, Oklahoma City

Austin, Sue .... (785) 822-1429
saustin@salina.com, Classified Consultant, The Salina Journal, KS, Salina

Austin, Tanya .... (506) 536-2500 ext 221
taustin@sackvilletribunepost.com, Circ/Class. Mgr, The Sackville Tribune-post, NB, Sackville

Austreng, Mike .... (320) 685-8621
csrecord@midconetwork.com, Ed., Cold Spring Record, MN, Cold Spring

Authur, Alan .... (505) 863-6811 ext. 226
sports@gallupindependent.com, Sports Ed., Gallup Independent, NM, Gallup

Backe, John E. .... ext. 6901
jebacke@backemarketing.com, Pres./CEO, Backe Difital Brand Marketing, PA, Radnor

Backer, Cathy .... (847) 486-7393
Mng. Ed., Wilmette Life, IL, Chicago

Backlund, Diana
diana@newscom.com, Dir., Sales/Mktg., Newscom, CA, Los Angeles

Backstrom, Steve .... (541) 742-7900
hcj@pinetel.com, Pub./Ed/Prod. Mgr., Hells Canyon Journal, OR, Halfway

Bacon, Cheryl M.
cheryl.bacon@jmc.acu.edu, Chair/Prof., Abilene Christian University, TX, Abilene

Bacon, Gregory
gbacon@observertoday.com, Managing Editor, The Observer, NY, Dunkirk

Bacon, Jake .... (908) 556-2258
jbacon@azdailysun.com, Photo Ed., Arizona Daily Sun, Flagstaff, AZ, Flagstaff

Bacon, Mike .... (847) 394-5700
mbacon@spartanics.com, VP., Sales/Mktg., Spartanics, IL, Rolling Meadows

Bacon, Shawn .... (608) 257-4990 ext. 131
sbacon@startrenting.com, Acct. Exec., Start Renting Magazine, WI, Madison

Bacza, Rick
rbacza@altoonamirror.com, Prodn. Mgr., Altoona Mirror, PA, Altoona

Badal, Ann
advertise@thetomahawk.com, Adv. Mgr., The Tomahawk, TN, Mountain City

Baden, Tom
tom.baden@thedailyrecord.com, Ed., Connecticut Post, CT, Bridgeport

Baden Jr., Thomas .... (443) 524-8150
tbaden@thedailyrecord.com, Ed., The Daily Record, MD, Baltimore

Bader, Andy
andy.bader@sunmedia.ca, Ed., The Mitchell Advocate, ON, Mitchell

Bader, Micah
micah.bader@albertleatribune.com, Sports Ed., Albert Lea Tribune, MN, Albert Lea

Badger, Andrea .... (765) 482-4650 ext. 125
andrea.badger@reporter.net, Copy Ed., The Reporter, IN, Lebanon

Badger, Tom .... (262) 513-2607
tbadger@conleynet.com, Circ. Mgr., Mktg./ Promo., The Freeman, WI, Waukesha

Badir, George .... (626) 844-7777
4beirut@gmail.com, Adv. Mgr., Beirut Times, CA, Pasadena

Badman, John .... (618) 463-2572
john_badman@thetelegraph.com, Photo Dept. Mgr., The Telegraph, IL, Alton

Badoud, John
jbadoud@scotsmanpress.com, Owner, Moravia Pennysaver (OOB), NY, Syracuse
jbadoud@scotsmanpress.com, Scotsman Pennysaver - Auburn (OOB), NY, Syracuse
jbadoud@scotsmanpress.com, Scotsman Pennysaver - Baldwinsville, NY, Syracuse
jbadoud@scotsmanpress.com, Scotsman Pennysaver - Camillus Solvay (OOB), NY, Syracuse
jbadoud@scotsmanpress.com, Scotsman Pennysaver - Cortland Sunday (OOB), NY, Syracuse
jbadoud@scotsmanpress.com, Scotsman Pennysaver - East Syracuse Minoa (OOB), NY, Syracuse
jbadoud@scotsmanpress.com, Scotsman Pennysaver - Geneva (OOB), NY, Syracuse
jbadoud@scotsmanpress.com, Scotsman Pennysaver - Liverpool, NY, Syracuse
jbadoud@scotsmanpress.com, Scotsman Pennysaver - Moravia (OOB), NY, Syracuse
jbadoud@scotsmanpress.com, Scotsman Pennysaver - NE Syracuse Edition (OOB),

NY, Syracuse
jbadoud@scotsmanpress.com, Scotsman Pennysaver - North Area (OOB), NY, Syracuse
jbadoud@scotsmanpress.com, Scotsman Pennysaver - North Syracuse Mattydale (OOB), NY, Syracuse
jbadoud@scotsmanpress.com, Scotsman Pennysaver - Pennywise, NY, Syracuse
jbadoud@scotsmanpress.com, Scotsman Pennysaver - Seneca Falls (OOB), NY, Syracuse
jbadoud@scotsmanpress.com, Scotsman Pennysaver - Skaneateles, NY, Syracuse
jbadoud@scotsmanpress.com, Scotsman Pennysaver - Sw Syracuse Edition, NY, Syracuse

Badoud, John
jbadoud@scotsmanpress.com, The Patriot Advertiser, NY, Fulton

Badran, Badran
badran.badran@zu.ac.ae, Prof., Zayed University, Al Ruwayyah

Baer, Theresa
editor@thesiuslawnews.com, Ed., Siuslaw News, OR, Florence

Baergen, Darrel
dbaergen.comm@hsutx.edu, Chair, Hardin-Simmons University, TX, Abilene

Baez, Orestes
obaez@gannett.com, VP of Sales, Digital & Marketing
, The Commercial Appeal, TN, Memphis

Bagale, Dawn
dbagale@elkintribune.com, Customer Service Rep, The Tribune, NC, Elkin

Baggerly-Hinojosa, Dr. Barbara ..... (956) 565-2425
mercedesenterprise@sbcglobal.net, Publisher/ Owner, Mercedes Enterprise, TX, Mercedes

Baggett, Debbie .... (530) 749-4714
dbaggett@appealdemocrat.com, Adv./Retail/ Mktg. Mgr., Colusa County Sun-Herald, CA, Marysville
dbaggett@appealdemocrat.com, Adv./Retail/ Mktg Dir., Corning Observer, CA, Marysville
dbaggett@appealdemocrat.com, Retail Adv. Dir./Mktg. Dir., Willows Journal (OOB), CA, Willows

Baggett, Donnis
dbaggett@texaspress.com, Executive Vice President, Texas Press Association, TX, Austin

Baggs, Mary
mary.baggs@starbanner.com, Community Relations , Ocala Star-Banner, FL, Ocala

Baggs, Norman .... (770) 535-6300
nbaggs@gainesvilletimes.com, Gen. Mgr., The Times, GA, Gainesville

Bagley, Dan
bagley@breakthroughs.com, Assoc. Prof., University of South Florida, FL, Tampa

Bagley, Jamie
jamie.lrnews@gmail.com, Little River News, AR, Ashdown

Bagley, Pat .... (801) 257-8806
bagley@sltrib.com, Editorial - Political Cartoonist, The Salt Lake Tribune, UT, Salt Lake City

Bagley, Quinton
editor.lrnews@gmail.com, Gen. Mgr., Little River News, AR, Ashdown

Bagnowski, Tom .... (212) 594-2266 ext. 112
Nowy Dziennik, NJ, Garfield

Bagonzi, Jolie
jbagonzi@islandpacket.com, HR Dir., The Island Packet, SC, Bluffton

Bagwell, Dan .... (205) 443-5632
dbagwell@bizjournals.com, Research Dir, Birmingham Business Journal, AL, Birmingham

Bagwell, Steve ....Ext. 226
sbagwell@newsregister.com, Mng. Ed., News-Register, OR, McMinnville

Bahl, Jamie
jbahl@wcinet.com, Natl./Rgl. Acct. Rep., Telegraph Herald, IA, Dubuque

Bahm, Carolyn .... (901) 433-9138
carolyn.bahm@journalinc.com, Ed, The Bartlett Express, TN, Bartlett

Bahney, Jennifer .... (740) 474-3131 Ext. 210
jbahnew@circlevilleherald.com, Asst. Ed., The Circleville Herald, OH, Circleville

Bahr, Jeff
jbahr@aberdeennews.com, Women's Ed., Aberdeen American News, SD, Aberdeen

Baier, Miriam .... (937) 651-1124
mbaier@examiner.org, Ed., Bellefontaine Examiner, OH, Bellefontaine

Baier, Rick A.
rickbaier@yahoo.com, Pub., Cissna Park News, IL, Cissna Park
rickbaier@yahoo.com, Pub., Rankin Independent, IL, Cissna Park

Bailenson, Jeremy
bailenson@stanford.edu, Asst. Prof., Stanford University, CA, Stanford

Bailes, Greg
onebusiness@observernewsonline.com, Bus. Office , The Observer News Enterprise, NC, Newton

Bailey, Andrew .... (250) 726-7029
andrew.bailey@westerlynews.ca, Ed, Westerly News, BC, Ucluelet

Bailey, Ashley
abailey@decaturdailydemocrat.com, Reporter, Decatur Daily Democrat, IN, Decatur

Bailey, Brad
bbailey@pressrepublican.com, Publisher, Press Extra, NY, Plattsburgh

Bailey, Brad .... (570) 420-4372
bbailey@poconorecord.com, Associate Pub and Adv. Dir., Pocono Record Plus, PA, Stroudsburg
bbailey@poconorecord.com, Adv. Dir., Pocono Record, PA, Stroudsburg

Bailey, Brad .... (518) 565-4130
bbailey@pressrepublican.com, Publisher, Press-Republican, NY, Plattsburgh

Bailey, Chris
bathcountynews@gmail.com, Pub./Ed., Bath County Bulletin, KY, Owingsville

Bailey, Chris
cbailey@sourcenews.com, Assoc. Ed., The Daily Reporter, OH, Columbus

Bailey, Christy .... (301) 645-9480
cbailey@somdnews.com, Adv. Mgr., The Enquirer-Gazette, MD, Waldorf

Bailey, Cindy
cinswind1290@fairpoint.net, Pub./Ed., GreeneSpeak, PA, Waynesburg

Bailey, Cindy .... (614) 221-2449 ext. 92
cindy@columbusalive.com, Circ. Mgr., Alive, OH, Columbus

Bailey, Dan .... (530) 246-2009
dbailey@c-zone.net, CEO, North Valley Diver Publications, CA, Redding

Bailey, Don
dbailey@macon.com, Pres./Pub., The Telegraph, GA, Macon

Bailey, Donna .... (937) 538-4821
dbailey@civitasmedia.com, Class. Adv. Sales Mgr., The Sidney Daily News, OH, Sidney

Bailey, Erin .... (631) 289-5911
St. Josephs College, NY, Patchogue

Bailey, Greg .... (256) 549-2057
greg.bailey@gasdentimes.com, Assoc. Ed., The Gadsden Times, AL, Gadsden

Bailey, James
execdiropag@gci.net, Execu Dir, Senior Voice, AK, Anchorage

Bailey, Jennifer .... (217) 477-5178
jbailey@dancomnews.com, Commercial News, IL, Danville

Bailey, Josh .... (231) 779-4138
jbailey@cadillacnews.com, Circ./Marketing Dir., Cadillac News, MI, Cadillac

Bailey, Josh .... (231) 779-4138
jbailey@cadillacnews.com, Sales and Marketing Leader, Northern Michigan News, MI, Cadillac

Bailey, Julie .... (818) 710-2960
Los Angeles Pierce College, CA, Woodland Hills

Bailey, Kathy
kbailey@isthmus.com, Dir., Admin., Isthmus, WI, Madison

Bailey, Lee
LBinfo@eurweb.com, Pres., Bailey Broadcasting Services, CA, Glendale
LBinfo@eurweb.com, Pub., EUR/Electronic Urban Report, CA, Los Angeles

Bailey, Melissa
m.bailey@newhavenindependent.org, Managing Editor, The New Haven Independent, CT, New Haven

Bailey, Michael
mbailey@enlabel.com, Production Ed., The Boston Globe, MA, Boston

Bailey, Rick
news@hillsororeporter.com, Ed., Hillsboro Reporter, TX, Hillsboro

Bailey, Shan
shan.bailey@sj-r.com, Asst. Circ. Mgr., Springfield Advertiser, IL, Springfield

Bailey, Shawn .... (204) 638-4420
dherald@mts.net, Ed., Dauphin Herald, MB, Dauphin

Bailey, Sheila
rubyfmccoy@yahoo.com, Adv. Mgr., The Industrial News, WV, Welch

Bailey, Sheryl .... (831) 385-4880 x 15
sheryl@southcountynewspapers.com, Adv. Mgr., Greenfield News, CA, King City

Bailey, Sheryl .... (831) 385-4880
sheryl@southcountynewspapers.com, Adv. Mgr., Gonzales Tribune, CA, King City

Bailey, Todd .... (575) 391-5440
editor@hobbsnews.com, Ed., Hobbs News-Sun, NM, Hobbs

Bailie, Allan
EHP_P_Info_Center@basf.com, HR, BASF Corp., CT, East Windsor

Bailon, Gilbert .... (314) 340-8387
gbailon@post-dispatch.com, Ed, St. Louis Post-Dispatch, MO, Saint Louis

Baim, Tracy
editor@windycitymediagroup.com, Ed., Black Lines, IL, Chicago
editor@windycitymediagroup.com, Publisher, Exec. Ed., Windy City Times, IL, Chicago
editor@windycitymediagroup.com, Ed., En La Vida, IL, Chicago
editor@windycitymediagroup.com, Pub., Nightspots, IL, Chicago

Baine, Don
dbaine@mmcom.com, Pres., Multi-Media Communications, AZ, Scottsdale

Baine, Wallace .... (831) 429-2427
wbaine@santa-cruz.com, Ent. Ed., Santa Cruz Sentinel, CA, Scotts Valley

Bair, James
bsheet@vicon.net, Gen. Mgr., The Bargain Sheet, PA, State College

Baird, Daniel
dbaird@oakvillebeaver.com, Dir., Adv., Oakville

Beaver, ON, Oakville

Baird, David .... (765) 641-4341
dabaird@anderson.edu, Anderson Univ., IN, Anderson

Baird, Diana
dbaird@messenger-index.com, Gen. Mgr., Messenger-Index, ID, Emmett

Baird, Linda B. .... (585) 258-2205
lbaird@gannett.com, HR Dir. Gannett East Group, Democrat and Chronicle, NY, Rochester

Bajackson, Bob
rb20@txstate.edu, Lectr./Dir., Student Pubs, Texas State University-San Marcos, TX, San Marcos

Bajackson, Bob .... (512) 245-3408
bobb8082002@yahoo.com, Advisor, Texas State Univ., TX, San Marcos

Bajer, Erica .... (905) 684-7251 ext. 1168
erica.bajer@sunmedia.ca, Mng. Ed., St. Catharines Standard, ON, Saint Catharine's

Bakan, George
sgn2@sgn.org, Pub., Seattle Gay News, WA, Seattle

Baker, Alan L. .... (207) 667-2576 ext. 230
abaker@ellsworthamerican.com, Pub., The Ellsworth American, ME, Ellsworth

Baker, Alan L. .... (207) 288-0556
info@mdislander.com, Pub., Mount Desert Islander, ME, Bar Harbor

Baker, Andrew .... (619) 594-7291
San Diego State Univ., CA, San Diego

Baker, Andrew
andbaker@snu.edu, Graphic Design, Southern Nazarene Univ., OK, Bethany

Baker, Barbara .... (816) 640-2251
Wcaddesign@embarqmail.com, Office Mgr., Weston Chronicle, MO, Weston

Baker, Ben
wiregrassfarmer@yahoo.com, Ed., Wiregrass Farmer, GA, Ashburn

Baker, Beth
bbaker@turley.com, Adv. Mgr., Barre Gazette, MA, Barre

Baker, Beth .... (800) 824-6548
bbaker@turley.com, Dir., Adv., Ware River News, MA, Ware

Baker, Beth
bbaker@turley.com, Adv. Mgr., Buy Line, MA, Palmer

Baker, Beth .... (800) 824-6548
bbaker@turley.com, Adv. Mgr., Agawam Advertiser News, MA, Feeding Hills

Baker, Beth
bbaker@turley.com, Ad. Director, Country Journal, MA, Huntington
bbaker@turley.com, Ad. Director, The Chicopee Register, MA, Chicopee
bbaker@turley.com, Ad. Director, The Holyoke Sun, MA, Chicopee
bbaker@turley.com, Ad. Director, The Journal Register, MA, Palmer
bbaker@turley.com, Ad. Director, Town Reminder, MA, South Hadley
bbaker@turley.com, Adv. Mgr., Wilbraham-Hampden Times, MA, Wilbraham

Baker, Beth
bbaker@turley.com, Adv. Mgr., The Register, MA, Wilbraham

Baker, Beth
bbaker@turley.com, Adv. Mgr., Shopping Guide, MA, Palmer

Baker, Beth
bbaker@turley.com, Ad. Director, The Sentinel, MA, Belchertown
bbaker@turley.com, Ad. Director, Quaboag Current, MA, Ware

Baker, Bridget .... (541) 485-1234

Baker, Martin

bridget.baker@registerguard.com, Pub. Rel. Dir., The Register-Guard, OR, Eugene

Baker, Chris Allen
cbaker@sctonline.net, Sports Ed., Scott County Times, MS, Forest

Baker, Chuck
cbaker@ajnews.com, Co-Publisher, The Apache Junction/Gold Canyon News, AZ, Apache Junction

Baker, Craig .... (815) 220-6971
cbaker@newstrib.com, Cor. Accounting Mgr., News-Tribune, IL, La Salle

Baker, Daniel
dbaker@lagrangenews.com, Ed., La Grange Shopper, GA, Lagrange

Baker, Darlene
dbaker@yrmg.com, Adv. Coord., The Newmarket Era-banner, ON, Newmarket

Baker, Dave .... (541) 338-2320
dave.baker@registerguard.com, Mng. Ed., The Register-Guard, OR, Eugene

Baker, David T.
dbaker@louisianaweekly.com, Webmaster, Louisiana Weekly, LA, New Orleans

Baker, Deb .... (712) 243-2624
Circ@ant-news.com, Circ. Dir., Atlantic News Telegraph, IA, Atlantic

Baker, Dee
dbaker@joplinglobe.com, Nat'l Coord., The Joplin Globe, MO, Joplin

Baker, Ed .... (404) 249-1009
ebaker@bizjournals.com, Pub., Atlanta Business Chronicle, GA, Atlanta

Baker, Frank .... (580) 548-8186
fbaker@eaglemkt.com, Marketing Director, Enid News & Eagle, OK, Enid

Baker, Gerard
gerard.baker@wsj.com, Editor in Chief, The Wall Street Journal, NY, New York

Baker, Janet .... (907) 486-3227 ext.610
jbaker@kodiakdailymirror.com, Circulation, Kodiak Daily Mirror, AK, Kodiak

Baker, Jessica .... (541) 942-3325
publisher@cgsentinel.com, Pub., Cottage Grove Sentinel, OR, Cottage Grove

Baker, Joe
karneseditor@mysoutex.com, Ed., The Karnes Countywide, TX, Karnes City

Baker, John
jbaker@canbyherald.com, Ed., The Canby Herald, OR, Canby

Baker, Judy
news@gcnews-star.com, Office Mgr., The Garvin County News Star, OK, Maysville

Baker, Ken
sales@osoyoostimes.com, Adv. Mgr., Osoyoos Times, BC, Osoyoos

Baker, Kent A. .... (712) 873-3141
record@wiatel.net, Pres, The Record, IA, Moville

Baker, Kimberly
kbaker@harriswilliams.com, Marketing Director, Harris Williams & Co., VA, Richmond

Baker, Lesley .... (580) 482-1221 Ext. 2078
lbaker@civitasmedia.com, Class., Altus Times, OK, Altus

Baker, Linda
Lbaker@molallapioneer.com, Circ. Mgr, Molalla Pioneer, OR, Molalla

Baker, Mark
mark.baker@lee.net, Pub., Advertiser, WI, Chippewa Falls

Baker, Mark
mark.baker@lee.net, Pub., Your Family Shopper, WI, Chippewa Falls

martin.baker@devlin.co.uk, Mng. Dir., Devlin Electronics Ltd., Basingstoke

Baker, Michelle
lifestyles@banner-tribune.com, Lifestyles Ed., Franklin Banner-Tribune, LA, Franklin

Baker, Nancy .... (336) 888-3558
nbaker@hpenews.com, Controller, High Point Enterprise, NC, High Point

Baker, Patty
placeads@americanclassifiedknoxville.com, Co-Owner, American Classifieds, TN, Knoxville

Baker, Reba
rebab@tds.net, Ed., Thousandsticks News, KY, Hyden

Baker, Robert .... (803) 414-8236
editorial@manninglive.com, Ed., The Manning Times, SC, Manning

Baker, Robert L.
bbaker@wcexaminer.com, Ed., Wyoming County Press Examiner, PA, Tunkhannock

Baker, Rusty .... (254) 757-2306 ext. 206
Adv. Mgr., American Classifieds, TX, Waco

Baker, Sarah .... (319) 398-7164
sarah.baker@kirkwood.edu, Kirkwood Community College, IA, Cedar Rapids

Baker, Steve .... (256) 234-4281
steve.baker@alexcityoutlook.com, President/Publisher, The Wetumpka Herald, AL, Alexander City

Baker, Steve .... ext. 111
publisher@capjournal.com, Pub., Reminder Plus, SD, Pierre

Baker, Steve
steve.baker@alexcityoutlook.com, Pres./Pub., Tallapoosa Publishers, Inc., AL, Alexander City

Baker, Terrie .... (308) 324-5511
terrie.baker@lexch.com, Pub., Lexington Clipper-Herald, NE, Lexington

Baker, Terrie
terrie.baker@nptelegraph.com, Pub., The North Platte Telegraph, NE, North Platte
terrie.baker@nptelegraph.com, Gen. Mgr., The Grand Island Independent, NE, Grand Island

Baker, Terrie L. .... (308) 324-5511 ext. 126
terrie.baker@lexch.com, Pub., People Plus, NE, Lexington

Baker, Vernon .... (606) 672-2841
rebab@tds.net, Pub., The Leslie County News, KY, Hyden

Baker-Nantz, Jamie
jbakernantz@fuse.net, Ed., Grant County News and Express, KY, Williamstown

Bakewell, Danny
geninfo@lasentinel.net, Pub., Los Angeles Sentinel, CA, Los Angeles

Bakke, Elaine .... (509) 493-2112
ebakke@eaglenewspapers.com, Pub., The Enterprise, WA, White Salmon

Bakke, Melissa .... (701) 777-2678
melissa.bakke@email.und.edu, Sales and Marketing Coordinator , Univ. of North Dakota, ND, Grand Forks

Bakke, Sverre .... (509) 493-2112
sbakke@eaglenewspapers.com, Ed. / Sports Ed., The Enterprise, WA, White Salmon

Bakken, Peggy .... (763) 424-7351
peggy.bakken@ecm-inc.com, Ed., North Crow River News, MN, Osseo

Bakken, Peggy
peggy.bakken@ecm-inc.com, Ed., Mounds View/New Brighton Sun Focus, MN, Eden Prairie
peggy.bakken@ecm-inc.com, Ed., Brooklyn Center/Brooklyn Park Sun-Post, MN, Osseo
peggy.bakken@ecm-inc.com, Ed., St. Louis Park Sun Sailor, MN, Osseo

Bakken, Peggy .... (952) 392-6822
pbakken@acnpapers.com, Ed., Robbinsdale/Crystal/New Hope/Golden Valley Sun-Post, MN, Eden Prairie

Bakken, Peggy .... (763) 424-7351
peggy.bakken@ecm-inc.com, Ed., Rockford Area News Leader, MN, Osseo

Bakken, Peggy .... (763) 424-7351
pbakken@acnpapers.com, Ed., Osseo-Maple Grove Press, MN, Osseo

Bakken, Peggy .... (320) 845-2700
aenterprise@albanytel.com, Co-Pub., Stearns-Morrison Enterprise, MN, Albany

Bakken, Peggy .... (763) 424-7351
peggy.bakken@ecm-inc.com, Ed., South Crow River News, MN, Osseo

Bakken, Peggy .... (763) 424-7351
sun.distribution@ecm-inc.com, Ed., Champlin-Dayton Press, MN, Osseo

Bakker, Jason
jason@campusmediagroup.com, COO, Campus Media Group, MN, Bloomington

Baklinski, Peter ....(888) 678-6008 x 931
pbaklinski@lifesitenews.com, Journalist, LifeSiteNews.com, VA, Front Royal

Bakner, Martin .... (814) 793-2144
accounting@mcheraldonline.com, Acct Mgr. , Morrisons Cove Herald, PA, Martinsburg

Bako, Olivia .... (780) 349-3033 Ext. 6
obako@westlock.greatwest.ca, Ed., The Westlock News, AB, Westlock

Bakoyannis, George .... (450) 978-9999
Prodn. Mgr., Nouvelles Parc Extension News, QC, Laval

Balakrishnan, Ajit
mail@indiaabroad.com, Pub., India Abroad, NY, New York

Balcazar, Kathy .... (630) 845-5355
kbalcazar@shawmedia.com, Ed., St. Charles Chronicle, IL, St Charles
kbalcazar@shawmedia.com, Ed., Batavia Chronicle, IL, St Charles

Balch, John
jbalch_leader@yahoo.com, Assoc. Ed., The Nashville News-Leader, AR, Nashville

Baldassari, Erin .... (617) 629-3390
ebaldassari@wickedlocal.com, Assist. Ed., Cambridge Chronicle & TAB, MA, Somerville

Balding, Timothy
timothy.balding@wan-ifra.org, Dir., Global Affairs, World Association of Newspapers and News Publishers (WAN-IFRA), Frankfurt am Main

Baldwin, Cecelia
cecelia.baldwin@sjsu.edu, Prof., San Jose State University, CA, San Jose

Baldwin, Chuck
cbaldwin@hcnonline.com, Hearst Communications, Inc., NY, New York

Baldwin, Elizabeth
ebaldwin@theunion.com, Circ. Dir., The Union, CA, Grass Valley

Baldwin, Janet .... (760) 951-6208
JBaldwin@vvdailypress.com, Classified Supervisor, Daily Press, CA, Victorville

Baldwin, Judy
jbaldwin@civitasmedia.com, Circ. Mgr., The Tribune, NC, Elkin

Baldwin, Lu Shep
lushep.baldwin@jonesmedia.biz, Event Marketing Director
, APG Media of Tennessee/North Carolina, TN, Greeneville

Baldwin, Mark .... (715) 345-2055
Gen. Mgr., Stevens Point Journal, WI, Stevens Point

Baldwin, Mark .... (815) 987-1358
mbaldwin@rrstar.com, Exec. Ed., Rockford

Register Star, IL, Rockford

Baldwin, Ralph........................(423) 252-1205
rbaldwin@xtn.net, COO, APG Media of
Tennessee/North Carolina, TN, Greeneville

Balentine, Ian ....(530) 344-5048
ibalentine@mtdemocrat.net, Adv. Dir.,
Mountain Democrat, CA, Placerville

Baleschrino, Richard.................(212) 217-4472
Fashion Inst. of Technology, NY, New York

Balfe, Nancy
nbalfe@dioceseofgreensburg.org, Circulation
Coordinator, The Catholic Accent, PA,
Greensburg

Balgenorth, Steve.....................(970) 871-4232
sbalgenorth@SteamboatToday.com, Circ. Dir.,
Steamboat Pilot, CO, Steamboat Springs
sbalgenorth@SteamboatToday.com, Circ. Dir.,
Steamboat Today, CO, Steamboat Springs

Balinsky, Derrick............ (607) 324-1425 Ext. 207
derrickbalinsky@eveningtribune.com, Sports
Ed., The Evening Tribune, NY, Hornell

Balke, Steve ....(830) 278-3335
sbalke@uvaldeleadernews.com, Adv. Dir.,
Uvalde Leader-News, TX, Uvalde

Balkun, John............................(973) 586-8178
Balkun@northjersey.com, Dir. Sports, Herald
News, NJ, Rockaway

Ball, Carmin ....(573) 468-6511
Office/Bus Mgr
, Sullivan Independent News, MO, Sullivan

Ball, Katharine ....(831) 754-4282
Digital Ed., The Salinas Californian, CA,
Salinas

Ball, Leah
leahball@kw.com, Art Dir., The Texas
Observer, TX, Austin

Ball, Mary.................... (765) 482-4650 Ext. 117
mary.ball@reporter.net, Adv. Rep., The
Reporter, IN, Lebanon

Ball, Ricky
ads@citizentribune.com, Prodn. Mgr., Citizen
Tribune, TN, Morristown

Ball, Steve ....(304) 626-1475
Sball@ theet.com, Business Manager, The
Exponent Telegram, WV, Clarksburg

Ballance, John ....(225) 388-0680
jballance@theadvocate.com, Photo Dir., The
Advocate, LA, Baton Rouge

Ballantine, Richard G.
rgb@durangoherald.com, Pub., Durango
Herald, CO, Durango

Ballantine, Robert C.
production@catholicfreepress.org, Adv. Mgr.,
The Catholic Free Press, MA, Worcester

Ballantyne, Neil
nballantyne@therecord.com, City Ed., The
Record, ON, Kitchener

Ballard, Debbie
dlogan@fortfrances.com, Adv. Mgr., Fort
Frances Daily Times, ON, Fort Frances

Ballard, Dorothy ....(918) 542-5533
dballard@miaminewsrecord.com, Managing
Editor, Miami News-record, OK, Miami

Ballard, Joe
jballard@hngnews.com, Reporter, Lodi
Enterprise & Poynette Press, WI, Lodi

Ballard, Kathryn........................(785) 462-3963
kballard@nwkansas.com, Sales/artist, Country
Advocate, KS, Colby

Ballard, Kathryn
kballard@nwkansas.com, Adv. Rep., Colby
Free Press, KS, Colby

Ballard, Kathy
kballard@comtex.com, Vice Pres., Content,
Comtex News Network, VA, Alexandria

Ballard, Lauren ....(254) 778-4444
laurenb@tdtnews.com, Adv. Dir., Temple Daily

Telegram, TX, Temple

Ballard, Mark..........................(225) 342-7279
mballard@theadvocate.com, CNB Ed., The
Advocate, LA, Baton Rouge

Ballard, Sally............... (260) 625-3879 ext. 207
circulation@thepostandmail.com, Circ. Mgr.,
The Post & Mail, IN, Columbia City
circulation@thepostandmail.com, Circu. , The
Post and Mail (Tuesday), IN, Columbia City

Ballard, Terry............... (317) 272-5800 ext. 180
terry.ballard@flyergroup.com, Prodn. Dir.,
Hendricks County Flyer, IN, Avon

Ballard, Terry
terry.ballard@flyergroup.com, Prodn. Dir., The
Weekend Flyer, IN, Avon

Ballare, Debbie
dballard@fortfrances.com, Adv. Mgr., Fort
Frances Times, ON, Fort Frances

Ballaway, Michael ....(413) 786-7747
mballway@turley.com, Mng Ed, Turley
Publications, Inc., MA, Palmer

Ballestrini, Janet M. .... (860) 442-2200 ext. 309
j.ballestrini@theday.com, Circ. Mgr., The Day,
CT, New London

Balling, Joshua ....(508) 228-0001
jballing@inkym.com, Assistant Editor, The
Inquirer and Mirror, MA, Nantucket

Balling, Joshua H.
jballing@inkym.com, Mng. Ed., The Inquirer
and Mirror, MA, Nantucket

Ballinger, Malcolm ....(850) 433-1166 ext. 26
malcolm@ballengerpublishing.com, Pub.,
Gosport, FL, Pensacola

Ballmer, Steven A.
stevenb@microsoft.com, CEO, Microsoft Corp.,
WA, Redmond

Ballou, Diana...........................(712) 563-2741
dianab@auduboncountynews.com,
Composition, Audubon County Advocate
Journal, IA, Audubon

Balzer, Howard ....(314) 298-2681
hbalzer@aol.com, Secretary, Professional
Football Writers of America (PFWA), MO,
Maryland Heights

Bamberg, Bob
news@alleghanynews.com, Ed, The Alleghany
News, NC, Sparta

Banal, Karen
karen.banal@ecm-inc.com, Classified Mgr.,
Dairyland Peach, MN, Sauk Centre

Banciella, Rick ....(305) 376-2052
rbanciella@miamiherald.com, Dir of Strategic
Advt, El Nuevo Herald, FL, Doral

Bandura, Rosemarie
production@peninsulanewsreview.com, The
Peninsula News Review, BC, Sidney

Bandy, Jowanna
j.bandy@ky-leadernews.com, Gen Mgr, Central
City Leader News, KY, Central City

Bandy, Steve
Steve.Bandy@CrowleyToday.com, Managing
Ed., The Crowley Post-Signal, LA, Crowley

Bane, Melissa ....(812) 523-7052
MBane@TribTown.com, Adv. Dir., The Tribune,
IN, Seymour

Baneky, Bill
william.baneky@sourcemedia.com, Adv. Dir.,
Legal, The Bond Buyer, NY, New York

Banerjee, Devin
devin.banerjee@stanfordalumni.org, Stanford
Univ., CA, Stanford

Bangert, Carol........................(765) 420-5226
cbangert@jconline.com, Content Strategist,
Journal and Courier, IN, Lafayette

Bangert, Lesli
lbangert@johnstownbreeze.com, Pub., The
Johnstown Breeze, CO, Johnstown

Bangert, Randy.......................(970) 392-4435
rbangert@greeleytribune.com, Ed., Windsor
Now, CO, Windsor
rbangert@greeleytribune.com, Ed., Greeley
Daily Tribune, CO, Greeley

Baniak, Peter ....(859) 231-3446
pbaniak@herald-leader.com, Ed., Lexington
Herald-Leader, KY, Lexington

Banister, Paul ....(409) 838-2812
Circulation Director, The Beaumont Enterprise,
TX, Beaumont

Bankenship, Robert
robert.blankenship@demopolistimes.com, Pub.
Ed., Blackbelt Gazette, AL, Demopolis

Banker, Dana
dbanker@sunsentinel.com, Mng. Ed., The
Gazette - Pembroke Pines & Miramar, FL,
Fort Lauderdale

Banko, Pete
pbanko@republicanherald.com, Ed., The
Republican-Herald, PA, Pottsville

Banks, Adelle...........................(202) 463-8777
adelle.banks@religionnews.com, Production
Editor, Religion News Service, Washington

Banks, Barbara ....(716) 897-0442
advertising@thechallengernews.com, Ed.,
Challenger Community News Corp., NY,
Buffalo

Banks, Bruce ....(517) 417-2041
prepress@lenconnect.com, Prepress Mgr., The
Daily Telegram, MI, Adrian

Banks, Cynthia ....(412) 263-1427
cbanks@post-gazette.com, National & Major
Accounts Mgr., Pittsburgh Post-Gazette, PA,
Clinton

Banks, Elizabeth
ebanks@frc.mass.edu, Hopkinton Crier, MA,
Framingham

Banks, Elizabeth ....(508) 634-7567
ebanks@wickedlocal.com, Managing Ed.,
Milford Daily News, MA, Milford

Banks, Marc ....(800) 526-0827
marcb@dynaric.com, Asst. Mktg. Mgr., DYC
Supply Co., VA, Virginia Beach
marcb@dynaric.com, Asst. Mktg. Mgr., Dynaric,
Inc., VA, Virginia Beach

Bankston, Norman ....(229) 226-2400
norman.bankston@gaflnews.com, Pub.,
Thomasville Times-Enterprise, GA,
Thomasville

Banner, Todd
todd.danner@bulletinreview.com, Sports Ed.,
Denison Bulletin & Review, IA, Denison

Banning, Stephen
sbanning@bradley.edu, Asst. Prof., Bradley
University, IL, Peoria

Banning, Troy
tbanning@freemanjournal.net, Sports Ed., The
Daily Freeman-Journal, IA, Webster City

Banov, Jessica ....(919) 460-2605
jbanov@newsobserver.com, Ed, Southwest
Wake News, NC, Cary

Banse, Michelle.......................(979) 732-2304
publisher@coloradocountycitizen.com, Pub.,
The Colorado County Citizen, TX, Columbus

Banta, Lucy .... (908) 232-2913 ext. 103
editor@njfamily.com, Mng. Ed., Morris County
Family, NJ, Mountainside

Banta, Lucy .... (908) 232-2913 ext. 103
editor@njfamily.com, Mng. Ed., Union County
Family, NJ, Mountainside

Banta, Lucy .... (908) 232-2913 ext. 103
editor@njfamily.com, Mng. Ed., New Jersey
Family, NJ, Summit

Banta, Lynn ....(570) 674-5600
info@outsourcingusa.net, CEO, Outsourcing
USA, PA, Dallas

Banta, Robin

graphics@lifeandleisurenj.com, Prod. Mgr., Life
& Leisure, NJ, Lincoln Park

Banta, Tony ....(570) 674-5600
tbanta@outsourcingusa.com, VP of Information
Systems, Outsourcing USA, PA, Dallas

Banton, Fiona ....(954) 262-8461
Nova Southeastern Univ., FL, Davie

Bantz, Connie
connieb@spokesman.com, Mgr., HR, The
Spokesman-Review, WA, Spokane

Banwell, Jeremy
jbanwell@gctelegram.com, Circ. Mgr., The
Garden City Telegram, KS, Garden City

Baohanah, Do
news@nguoi-viet.com, Pub., Nguoi Viet News,
CA, Westminster

Baptista, Nicole .... (415) 892-1516 x 13
nbaptista@marinscope.com, Ed., Novato
Advance, CA, Novato

Barajas, Maria ....(509) 577-7707
mbarajas@yakimaherald.com, HR Dir., Yakima
Herald-Republic, WA, Yakima

Baranczyk, Merle
merleb@avpsalida.com, Pub., The Mountain
Mail, CO, Salida

Baranczyk, Merle ....(719) 539-6691
merleb@avpsalida.com, Pub., Mountain Guide,
CO, Salida

Baranowski, Lori ....(815) 937-3394
lbaranowski@daily-journal.com, HR Asst.-
Benefits Coordinator, The Daily Journal, IL,
Kankakee

Baranowski, Tony
tonyb@iafalls.com, Adv. Mgr., Ackley World
Journal, IA, Ackley

Baranski, Bob
bbaranski@seattleweekly.com, Publisher,
Seattle Weekly, WA, Seattle

Baranski, Rick.................. (847) 490-6000 x207
rickb@usspi.com, Vice President Media
Relations , McNaughton Newspapers, IL,
Schaumburg

Baranski, Rick...............................ext. 207
rickb@usspi.com, VP Media Relations, USSPI
Media, IL, Schaumburg

Baratoff, Michael ....(212) 576-9511
michaelb@metrosn.com, President/COO,
Metro Newspaper Advertising Services, Inc.,
NY, New York

Baratta, Dan
dcmdanbar@aol.com, Pres., Dan-Bar, Inc.,
FL, Apopka

Baratta, Jennifer...........(815) 625-3600 ext. 5630
jbarratta@saukvalley.com, Adv. Dir., Daily
Gazette, IL, Sterling

Baratta, Jennifer .... (815) 625-3600 Ext. 630
jbaratta@saukvalley.com, Adv. Mgr., The
Telegraph, IL, Dixon

Baratta, Jennifer .... (815) 625-3600 ext. 630
jbaratta@svnmail.com, Adv. Dir., Forreston
Journal, IL, Dixon

Barba, Robert ....(312) 777-1364
robert.barba@sourcemedia.com, Deputy
Editor, Merger & Acquisitions, American
Banker, NY, New York

Barbalios, Anastasia
abarbalios@philadelphiaweekly.com, Mng. Ed.,
Philadelphia Weekly, NJ, Cherry Hill

Barbara, Smith
bsmith@breezenewspapers.com, Circulation
Director, Cape Coral Breeze, FL, Cape Coral

Barbarito, Gerald M. ....(561) 775-9500
Pub., Florida Catholic, FL, Orlando

Barbaro, Nick
barbaro@austinchronicle.com, Pub., Austin
Chronicle, TX, Austin

Barbati, Carl ....(973) 383-1253

cbarbati@njherald.com, Sports Ed., New Jersey Herald, NJ, Newton

Barbati, Duane ....(575) 437-7120 ext. 7134
dbarbati@alamogordonews.com, Mng. Ed., Alamogordo Daily News, NM, Alamogordo

Barbe, April
editor@jacksonvilleprogress.com, Ed., Jacksonville Daily Progress, TX, Jacksonville

Barbeau, Don
donb@abbynews.com, Adv Mgr, The Abbotsford News, BC, Abbotsford

Barber, April
april.barber@sunmedia.ca, Pre-Press Mgr., Orillia Packet, ON, Orillia

Barber, David ....(212) 450-7068
dave_barber@parade.com, Sr. Vice Pres., Newspaper Rel., Parade, New York

Barber, Dennis
info@startrenting.com, Adv.Mgr, Start Renting Magazine, WI, Madison

Barber, Doug
dmbarber@sunherald.com, Sports Ed., The Sun Herald, MS, Gulfport

Barber, Janet ....(918) 253-4322
news@delcojournal.com, Ed., Delaware County Journal, OK, Jay

Barber, Ken
kenb@tiac.net, COO, Advanced Publishing Technology, CA, Burbank

Barber, Lionel
lionel.barber@ft.com, Ed., FINANCIAL TIMES, Paris

Barber, Marsha
andrewse@madison.k12.ct.us, Assoc. Prof., Ryerson University, ON, Toronto

Barber, Mel
mbarber@yorkdispatch.com, Entertainment/Weekend Ed., The York Dispatch, PA, York

Barber, Natasha ....(320) 968-7220
Natasha@saukherald.com, Ed., Benton County News, MN, Foley

Barberi, Mauricio ....(973) 210-6318
mbarberi@lds.com, Sr. Vice Pres., Bus. Devel., Logical Design Solutions, Inc., NJ, Florham Park

Barbero, Rick
rbarbero@register-herald.com, Chief Photographer, The Register Herald, WV, Beckley

Barbetta, Paul ....(203) 330-6527
pbarbetta@hearst.com, Grp. Pub./Pres., Darien News, CT, Bridgeport
pbarbetta@hearst.com, Grp. Pub., Fairfield Citizen, CT, Bridgeport
pbarbetta@hearst.com, Grp. Pub./Pres., Westport News, CT, Bridgeport
pbarbetta@hearst.com, Group Pres./Pub., New Canaan News, CT, Bridgeport

Barbey, Peter
pbarbey@readingeagle.com, Pres. & CEO, Reading Eagle Company, PA, Reading

Barbey, Peter
pbarbey@readingeagle.com, Pres.CEO, Reading Eagle, PA, Reading

Barbieri, Tony
afb15@psu.edu, Foster Prof., Writing/Editing, The Pennsylvania State University, PA, University Park

Barboza, Robert
editor@chroniclenewsonline.com, Ed., The Chronicle, MA, New Bedford

Barbutes, James
circ@neiapapers.com, Circ. Mgr., The Oelwein Daily Register, IA, Oelwein

Barbuto, Dana ....(617) 786-7074
dbarbuto@ledger.com, Features Ed., The Patriot Ledger, MA, Quincy

Barbuto, Dana

dbarbuto@enterprisenews.com, Features Ed., The Enterprise, MA, Brockton

Barchak, Leonard
barchak@mcneese.edu, Prof., McNeese State University, LA, Lake Charles

Barclay, Becky ....(919) 739-7837
bbarclay@newsargus.com, Society/Women's Ed., Goldsboro News-Argus, NC, Goldsboro

Barclay, Kristin ....(972) 223-9175
Kristin@focusdailynews.com, Digital Operations Director, Focus Daily News, TX, Desoto

Barclay, Sheila
sbarclay@evdio.org, Prod. Tech., The Message, IN, Evansville

Barco, Manolo ....(305) 237-1255
Advisor, Miami Dade College, FL, Miami

Barcomb, Maurice ....(315) 789-3333
mbarcomb@fltimes.com, Circ. Dir., Finger Lakes Times, NY, Geneva

Bard, Jason
jbard@kingpress.com, Dir., Mktg., Robertson Equipments, MO, Joplin

Bard, Paula
editor@monahansnews.net, Ed., The Monahans News, TX, Monahans

Bardi, Joe
joe.bardi@creativeloafing.com, Managing Ed., Creative Loafing Tampa Bay, FL, Tampa

Bardole, Jacki ....(641) 322-3161
editor@acfreepress.com, Ed., Adams County Free Press, IA, Corning

Bardonner, Sharon ....(765) 659-4622
sbardonner@fltimes.com, Pub., The Times, IN, Frankfort

Bardwell, Jim ....(903) 845-2235
jbardwell@gladewatermirror.com, Pub./Ed., Gladewater Mirror, TX, Gladewater

Barebo, Mark ....(507) 285-7608
mbarebo@postbulletin.com, Adv. Dir., Post-Bulletin, MN, Rochester

Barefield, Nicole ....(850) 638-0212 ext. 4001
nbarefield@chipleypaper.com, Pub., Holmes County Times-Advertiser, FL, Chipley

Barenklau, Shon
news@bellevueleader.com, Pub., Air Pulse, NE, Bellevue

Barenklau, Shon ....(402) 537-4840
shon.barenklau@papilliontimes.com, Gen. Mgr./Pub., Market Weekly, NE, Wahoo

Barger, Bob
bob@meridianimpact.com, Adv. Mgr, Impact Of Hattiesburg, MS, Hattiesburg
bob@meridianimpact.com, Adv. Mgr, Impact Of Laurel, MS, Meridian

Barger, Debbie
dbarger@cableone.net, Off. Mgr., Silver Creek Herald, AZ, Holbrook

Barger, Jeannine ....(814) 765-9495 ext. 222
display@theprogressnews.com, Adv. Mgr., Display, The Progress, PA, Clearfield

Barger, Matthew ....(928) 524-6203
mbarger@cableone.net, Pub., The Tribune-News, AZ, Holbrook
mbarger@cableone.net, Pub., Silver Creek Herald, AZ, Holbrook

Bargfrede, Cory
cbargfrede@messengernews.net, Retail Adv Mgr, The Messenger, IA, Fort Dodge

Bargfrede, Cory ....(515) 573-2141 ext. 428
cbargfrede@messengernews.net, Adv. Mgr., Messenger Extra, IA, Fort Dodge

Bargfrede, Cory
cbargfrede@messengernews.net, Adv. Dir., The Daily Freeman-Journal, IA, Webster City
cbargfrede@messengernews.net, Adv. Dir., The Messenger, IA, Fort Dodge

Barham, Betsey ....(501) 505-1227
betsey.barham@thecabin.net, VP of Sales, Log Cabin Democrat, AR, Conway

Barhorst, Ken ....(937) 538-4818
kbarhorst@sidneydailynews.com, Sports Ed., The Sidney Daily News, OH, Sidney

Barichello, Derek ....(815) 431-4073
derekb@mywebtimes.com, News Editor, The Times, IL, Ottawa

Baril, Larry
lbaril@sunjournal.com, Acc. Exec., Sun Journal, ME, Lewiston

Barile, Dan
dbarile@farragutpress.com, Pub./Ed., Farragut Press, TN, Farragut

Barile, Suzy ....(704) 546-7900
suzyb3@gmail.com, Past President, North Carolina Press Club, NC, Harmony

Barker, Adam ....(731) 642-1162
abarker@parispi.net, Advertising sales, The Paris Post-Intelligencer, TN, Paris

Barker, Bill ....(239) 262-3161
bill.barker@naplesnews.com, President/Publisher, The Banner, FL, Naples
bill.barker@naplesnews.com, President/Publisher, Marco Eagle, FL, Naples
bill.barker@naplesnews.com, Pres./Pub., Naples Daily News, FL, Naples

Barker, Carol
cbarker@timesanddemocrat.com, Regl. Ed., The Times and Democrat, SC, Orangeburg

Barker, Dan
business@fmtimes.com, Bus. Ed., Fort Morgan Times, CO, Fort Morgan

Barker, Doug ....(360) 533-6039
dbarker@thedailyworld.com, Editor, The Daily World, WA, Aberdeen

Barker, Ed
ebarker@ajnews.com, Co-Publisher, The Apache Junction/Gold Canyon News, AZ, Apache Junction **Barker, Marilyn** ....(231) 723-3592
advocate@pioneergroup.net, Pub., Manistee News Advocate, MI, Manistee

Barker, Marilyn ....(231) 723-3592
mbarker@pioneergroup.com, Pub. / Gen. Mgr., West Shore Shopper's Guide, MI, Manistee

Barker, Marlys ....(515) 382-2161 ext. 205
mbarker@nevadaiowajournal.com, Gen. Mgr., The Tri-County Times, IA, Ames

Barker, Rene
circulation@lebanondailyrecord.com, Adv. Sales Mgr., Pulaski County Mirror, MO, Saint Robert

Barker, Sean ....(203) 789-5700
sbarker@nhregister.com, Sports Ed., New Haven Register, CT, New Haven

Barker, Valerie
valerie.barker@camoves.com, Lectr., San Diego State University, CA, San Diego

Barker, William ....(813) 259-7135
Tampa Bay Times, FL, St Petersburg

Barker Jr, Dennis ....(423) 623-6171
dennis.barker@newportplaintalk.com, Sports Editor, The Newport Plain Talk, TN, Newport

Barkin, Dan ....(919) 829-4562
dan.barkin@newsobserver.com, Ed., North Raleigh News, NC, Raleigh
dan.barkin@newsobserver.com, Deputy Managing Ed., The News & Observer, NC, Raleigh

Barkley, Elizabeth
elizabeth.barkley@msj.edu, Mount St. Joseph University, OH, Cincinnati

Barkus, Jen
jen.barkus@sj-r.com, Adv. Mgr., Springfield Advertiser, IL, Springfield

Barlow, Ava

betsy@theleonardgraphic.com, Adv. Dir., Leonard Graphic, TX, Leonard

Barlow, Bill ....(609) 365-6168
bbarlow@catamaranmedia.com, Ed., The Gazette, NJ, Pleasantville

Barlow, Bill ....(609) 624-8900 Ext. 240
bbarlow@catamaranmedia.com, Ed, Wildwood Leader, NJ, Marmora
bbarlow@catamaranmedia.com, Ed., Brigantine Beachcomber, NJ, Egg Harbor Township

Barlow, Bill ....(609) 365-6168
bbarlow@catamaranmedia.com, Ed., The Current, NJ, Egg Harbor Township

Barlow, John ....(843) 317-7360
jbarlow@florencenews.com, Prodn. Dir., Morning News, SC, Florence

Barlow, Keith ....(478) 453-1441
kbarlow@unionrecorder.com, Pub., Lake Oconee Breeze, GA, Milledgeville

Barlow, Keith E. ....(478) 453-1424
kbarlow@unionrecorder.com, Pub., The Union-Recorder, GA, Milledgeville

Barlow, Rhonda ....(856) 754-7103
rbarlow@njadvancemedia.com, VP Sales & Pub., South Jersey Times , NJ, Mullica Hill

Barmlett, Gini
Gini@tctrib.com, Ed, Tri-County News, OR, Junction City

Barna, Blair
blair@charlestoncitypaper.com, Adv. Dir., The Charleston City Paper, SC, Charleston

Barna , Bruce ....(724) 889-7707
Bruce@ad-a-note.com, Executive Vice President , AD-A-NOTE, PA, Pittsburgh

Barnable, Judy
judy@lemarssentinel.com, Data Processing Mgr., Le Mars Daily Sentinel, IA, Le Mars

Barnacle, Robert ....(218) 246-8533
drpub@paulbunyan.net, Ed., Deerpath Shopper, MN, Deer River

Barnard, Craig ....(416) 383-2315
cbarnard@nationalpost.com, SVP, Community Publishing Group + Reader Sales + Service, National Post, ON, Toronto

Barnard, Erik
ebarnard@mdn.net, Adv. Mgr., Online Sales, Midland Daily News, MI, Midland

Barnard, Jacky ....(805) 564-5120
jbarnard@newspress.com, Customer Serv. Mgr., Santa Barbara News-Press, CA, Santa Barbara

Barnard, Sara ....(504) 636-7421
sbarnard@theadvocate.com, Director of Sales/Marketing, The Advocate, LA, Baton Rouge

Barnathan, Joyce
jbarnathan@icfj.org, Pres., International Center for Journalists, DC, Washington

Barner, Craig
craig_barner@macgraw-hill.com, Ed., Dodge Construction News Chicago IL, Chicago

Barner, Mark R.
barner@niagara.edu, Chair/Assoc. Prof., Niagara University, NY, Niagara University

Barnes, Amy ....(330) 721-4005
abarnes@medina-gazette.com, Acct. Exec., The Medina County Gazette, OH, Medina

Barnes, Becky ....(859) 234-1035
bbarnes@cynthianademocrat.com, Ed., Cynthiana Democrat, KY, Cynthiana

Barnes, Brad
circulation@triplicate.com, Entertainment Writer, Columbus Ledger-Enquirer, GA, Columbus

Barnes, Charles
kceditor@kentontimes.com, Pres., Ray Barnes Newspapers, Inc., OH, Kenton

Barnes, David ....(419) 294-2332 Ext. 27
dcuads@dailychiefunion.com, Adv. Mgr., The Daily Chief-Union, OH, Upper Sandusky

Barnes, Deb ....(651) 407-1200
citizen@presspubs.com, The Lowdown - St. Croix Valley Area, MN, White Bear Lake

Barnes, Debra ....(651) 407-1200
citizen@presspubs.com, Ed., Forest Lake Lowdown, MN, White Bear Lake

Barnes, Denise Rolark ....(202) 561-4100
drbarnes@washingtoninformer.com, Publisher, Washington Informer, DC, Washington

Barnes, Eric.............................(901) 523-1561
ebarnes@memphisdailynews.com, Pub., The Memphis News, TN, Memphis

Barnes, Eric.............................(901) 528-5267
ebarnes@memphisdailynews.com, Pub, CEO, Hamilton County Herald, TN, Chattanooga

Barnes, Janet ....(509) 493-2112
jbarnes@eaglenewspapers.com, Class. / Circ. Mgr, The Enterprise, WA, White Salmon

Barnes, Jeff.............................(419) 294-2332
dcueditor@dailychiefunion.com, Pub. , The Daily Chief-Union, OH, Upper Sandusky

Barnes, Jeff
ktpublisher@kentontimes.com, Pub., The Kenton Times, OH, Kenton

Barnes, Keith
kbarnes@kenlynews.com, News Ed., Kenly News, NC, Kenly

Barnes, Kelli
manager@tylercountybooster.com, Mgr., Tyler County Booster, TX, Woodville

Barnes, Larry...........................(502) 624-1211
larry.barnes2@us.army.mil, Ed., Turret, KY, Fort Knox

Barnes, Mark
editor@kunamelba.com, Ed., Kuna Melba News, ID, Kuna

Barnes, Nancy
nancy.barnes@chron.com, Editor, Executive Vice President/News, Houston Chronicle, TX, Houston

Barnes, Nancy..........................(612) 673-4951
Nancy.Barnes@startribune.com, Ed./Sr. Vice Pres., Star Tribune, MN, Minneapolis

Barnes, Phyllis.........................(740) 772-9385
pbarnes@chillicothegazette.com, Ops. Mgr., Chillicothe Gazette, OH, Chillicothe

Barnett, Brooke
bbarnett@elon.edu, Assoc. Prof., Elon University, NC, Elon

Barnett, Catherine ....(707) 521-5202
catherine.barnett@pressdemocrat.com, Pub., The Press Democrat, CA, Santa Rosa

Barnett, Dave...........................(416) 774-2230
dbarnett@insidetoronto.com, Prodn. Dir., The East York Mirror, ON, Willowdale

Barnett, Kari ....(954) 596-5632
KABarnett@tribune.com, Editor, West Boca Forum, FL, Fort Lauderdale
KABarnett@tribune.com, Editor, Lake Worth Forum, FL, Fort Lauderdale
KABarnett@tribune.com, Editor, Live Wellington, FL, Fort Lauderdale

Barnett, Lloyd
lbarnett@cbrtech.com, Sec./Treasurer, Cybertech, Inc., PA, Horsham

Barnett, Morgan........................(361) 594-3327
mbarnett@kasparwireworks.com, Gen. Mgr., Kaspar Wire Works, Inc./Sho-Rack, TX, Shiner

Barnett, Ronnie ....(870) 633-3131
Circ. Mgr., East Arkansas Advertiser, AR, Forrest City

Barnett, Wren ....(704) 698-0021
Grimes, McGovern & Associates, NY, New York

Barney, Roger
roger@richfieldreaper.com, Prodn. Mgr., The Richfield Shopper, UT, Richfield

Barnhardt, Mike
ernews@davie-enterprise.com, Mng Ed., Davie County Enterprise-Record, NC, Mocksville

Barnhart, Carson.......................(435) 723-3471
classifieds@benewsjournal.com, Classifieds Manager, Box Elder News Journal, UT, Brigham City

Barnhill, Candace......................(214) 768-4111
cbarnhill@smu.edu, Int. Exec. Dir., Southern Methodist Univ., TX, Dallas

Barnum, John
johnbarnum@hpu.edu, Assoc. Prof., Hawaii Pacific University, HI, Honolulu

Barnwell, Jack
jbarnwell@ridgecrestca.com, Mng. Ed., The Daily Independent, CA, Ridgecrest

Baroja, Sandra ....(786) 286-8787
patrianews@aol.com, Food & Wine Editor, El Nuevo PATRIA, FL, Miami

Baron, Cydney
cbaron@pryordailytimes.com, Ed, The Pryor Times, OK, Claremore

Baron, Ed................................(703) 620-1725
edbaron@edbaron.com, Pres., Ed Baron & Associates, Inc., VA, Oakton
edbaron@edbaron.com, Consultant/Trainer, Sales Training Consultants, Inc., FL, Boca Raton

Baron, Martin...........................(202) 334-9198
martin.baron@washpost.com, Editor, The Washington Post, DC, Washington

Barquest, Joann
joann.barquest@finance-commerce.com, Bus. Mgr., Finance and Commerce, MN, Minneapolis

Barr, Bev ....(830) 796-9799
bcceditor@sbcglobal.net, Editor, Bandera County Courier, TX, Bandera

Barr, Clyde .... altnewsban@frontiernet.net
Ed., St. Elmo Banner, IL, Altamont

Barr, Clyde
news@altnewsban.com, Ed., The Altamont News, IL, Altamont

Barr, Debbie
prepress@yorktonthisweek.com, Prodn. Mgr., Yorkton This Week, SK, YORKTON

Barr, Karen....................(650) 237-2290 ext. 11
karen@newscolor.com, Sales Dir., Newscolor, LLC, OR, Silverton

Barr, Marc
mabarr@mtsu.edu, Prof., Middle Tennessee State University, TN, Murfreesboro

Barr, Rick
rbarr@catholiccincinnati.org, Prodn. Mgr., The Catholic Telegraph, OH, Cincinnati

Barr, Susan ....(760) 379-3667 x 14
editor@ksun.com, Ed., Kern Valley Sun, CA, Lake Isabella

Barr, Thomas J.
editor@pioneernews.net, Pub., Pioneer News, KY, Shepherdsville
editor@pioneernews.net, Ed., Pioneer News, KY, Shepherdsville

Barr, Tom...................(937) 382-2574 Ext. 2508
tbarr@civitasmedia.com, Editor, Wilmington News Journal, OH, Wilmington

Barr, Tom........................(937) 382-2574 x2508
tbarr@civitasmedia.com, Ed., News Journal Star, OH, Wilmington

Barr, Wayne.............................(413) 782-1580
Western New England College, MA, Springfield

Barra, Mark.............................(309) 467-3314
mbarra@mtco.com, Dir., Woodford Star, IL, Eureka

Barra, Mark...................(309) 467-3314 Ext 207
mbarra@mtco.com, Gen. Mgr., The Woodford County Journal, IL, Eureka

Barranca, Nicholas F.
nicholas.f.barranca@usps.gov, Vice Pres., Product Devel., United States Postal Service, DC, Washington

Barrand, Andy ....(517) 278-2318, ext. 27
abarrand@hillsdale.net, Managing Ed. , Hillsdale Daily News, MI, Hillsdale

Barrenechea, Mark
support@sgi.com, Pres./CEO, Silicon Graphics, Inc., CA, Milpitas

Barrera, Marcia ....(570) 253-3055
mbarrera@gatehousemedia.com, Circulation Coordinator, Carbondale News, PA, Honesdale

Barresi, Peter
pbarresi@uticaod.com, Circ. Mgr. , The Observer-Dispatch, NY, Utica

Barrett, Barbara
bbarrett@muncyluminary.com, Mng. Ed., The Luminary, PA, Hughesville

Barrett, Bengy..........................(606) 326-2669
bbarrett1@dailyindependent.com, Prodn. Mgr., Mailroom, The Daily Independent, KY, Ashland

Barrett, Crystal
cbarrett@gatehousemedia.com, Adv. Mgr. , Post South, LA, Plaquemine

Barrett, Crystal.........................(225) 644-6397
cbarrett@gatehousemedia.com, Advertising Manager, Gonzales Weekly Citizen, LA, Gonzales

Barrett, Crystal.........................(225) 644-6397
cbarrett@gatehousemedia.com, Nat'l Adv. Mgr., Gonzales Weekly Citizen, LA, Gonzales
cbarrett@gatehousemedia.com, GateHouse Media, Inc., NY, Pittsford

Barrett, Donna..........................(334) 293-5800
dbarrett@cnhi.com, Pres./CEO, Community Newspaper Holdings, Inc., AL, Montgomery

Barrett, Gretchen ....(609) 871-8051
gbarrett@calkins.com, Editorial Ed., Burlington County Times, NJ, Willingboro

Barrett, Julie
kradvertising@zitomedia.net, Adv.Dir., The Kane Republican, PA, Kane

Barrett, Melissa.........................(215) 755-2000
barrettm@einstein.edu, Adv. Dir., The Philadelphia Public Record, PA, Philadelphia

Barrett, Paul M.........................(315) 789-3333
pmbpub@aol.com, Pub., Finger Lakes Times, NY, Geneva

Barrett, Red.............................(954) 425-1022
rlbarrett@sun-sentinel.com, Digital Sales Dir., South Florida Sun-Sentinel, FL, Fort Lauderdale

Barrett, Scott P. ....(401) 380-2356
Barrett@NewportRI.com, Sports Ed., The Newport Daily News, RI, Newport

Barrett, Stephen ....(360) 394-5833
sbarrett@soundpublishing.com, Nat'l Sales Dir., Tukwila Reporter, WA, Kent
sbarrett@soundpublishing.com, Nat'l Sales Dir., Bothell/Kenmore Reporter, WA, Kirkland
sbarrett@soundpublishing.com, Nat'l Sales Dir., Redmond Reporter, WA, Kirkland
sbarrett@soundpublishing.com, Nat'l Sales Dir., The Whidbey Examiner, WA, Coupeville
sbarrett@soundpublishing.com, Nat'l Sales Dir., Forks Forum, WA, Forks
sbarrett@soundpublishing.com, Nat'l Sales Dir., Kent Reporter, WA, Kent
sbarrett@soundpublishing.com, Nat'l Sales Dir., Whidbey Crosswind, WA, Coupeville
sbarrett@soundpublishing.com, Nat'l Sales Dir., Renton Reporter, WA, Kent
sbarrett@soundpublishing.com, Nat'l sales Dir., The Arlington Times, WA, Marysville
sbarrett@soundpublishing.com, Nat'l Sales Dir., Covington-Maple Valley-Black Diamond Reporter, WA, Kent
sbarrett@soundpublishing.com, Nat'l Sales Dir., Bainbridge Island Review, WA, Bainbridge Island
sbarrett@soundpublishing.com, Nat'l Sales Dir., Kingston Community News, WA, Poulsbo
sbarrett@soundpublishing.com, Nat'l Sales Dir., Kirkland Reporter, WA, Kirkland
sbarrett@soundpublishing.com, Nat'l Sales Dir., Mercer Island Reporter, WA, Bellevue
sbarrett@soundpublishing.com, Nat'l Sales Dir., Okanogan Valley Gazette-Tribune, WA, Oroville
sbarrett@soundpublishing.com, Nat'l Sales Dir., Snoqualmie Valley Record, WA, Snoqualmie
sbarrett@soundpublishing.com, Nat'l Sales Dir., The Enumclaw Courier-Herald, WA, Enumclaw
sbarrett@soundpublishing.com, Nat'l Sales Dir., The Islands' Sounder, WA, Eastsound
sbarrett@soundpublishing.com, Nat'l Sales Dir., The Islands' Weekly, WA, Lopez Island
sbarrett@soundpublishing.com, Nat'l Sales Dir., The Journal of the San Juan Islands, WA, Friday Harbor
sbarrett@soundpublishing.com, Nat'l Sales Dir., Vashon-Maury Island Beachcomber, WA, Vashon
sbarrett@soundpublishing.com, Nat'l Sales Dir., Whidbey News Times, WA, Coupeville
sbarrett@soundpublishing.com, Nat'l Sales Dir., Bellevue Reporter, WA, Bellevue
sbarrett@soundpublishing.com, Nat'l Sales Dir., Issaquah/Sammamish Reporter, WA, Bellevue
sbarrett@soundpublishing.com, Nat'l Sales Dir., North Kitsap Herald, WA, Poulsbo
sbarrett@soundpublishing.com, Nat'l Sales Dir., Port Orchard Independent, WA, Port Orchard
sbarrett@soundpublishing.com, Nat'l Sales Dir., South Whidbey Record, WA, Coupeville
sbarrett@soundpublishing.com, Nat'l Sales Dir., The Sequim Gazette, WA, Sequim
sbarrett@soundpublishing.com, Nat'l Sales Dir., Central Kitsap Reporter, WA, Poulsbo
sbarrett@soundpublishing.com, Nat'l Sales Dir., Peninsula Daily News, WA, Port Angeles

Barrett, Stephen ....(360) 394-5833
sbarrett@soundpublishing.com, Dir., Nat'l and Regional Sales, The Herald, WA, Everett

Barrett, Steve
steve@greenemessenger.com, Ed., Greene County Messenger, PA, Waynesburg

Barriatua, Tony.........................(208) 726-8060
publisher@mtexpress.com, Production Mgr., Idaho Mountain Express, ID, Ketchum

Barrick, Rhonda........................(803) 774-1264
rhondab@theitem.com, Univ. Desk Mgr., The Sumter Item , SC, Sumter

Barrie, David
info@nlgja.org, Pres., National Lesbian and Gay Journalists Association, DC, Washington

Barringer, Richard .... ext. 21
District Mgr., Evergreen Country Shopper, WI, Ashland

Barringer, Richard
richard@evergreencountryshopper.com, Adv. Mgr., North Country Sun, MI, Ironwood

Barrios , Francisco ....(520) 364-3424
circulation@douglasdispatch.com, Circ. Mgr., The Douglas Dispatch, AZ, Douglas

Barron, James..........................(505) 986-3045
jbarron@sfnewmexican.com, Sports Ed., The Santa Fe New Mexican, NM, Santa Fe

Barron, John............................(312) 527-8154
jcbarron@tronc.com, Ed., Gen. Mgr., Tribune News Service, Chicago

Barron, John............................(312) 527-8154
jcbarron@tronc.com, Editor / General Manager, Tribune Content Agency, IL, Chicago

Barrons, Mark
mbarrons@tribune.com, Detroit Mgr., Tribune 365, MI, Livonia

Barros, Laura
elsalvador@acan-efe.com, Rep., EFE News Services - San Salvador, El Salvador, San Salvador

Barrow, Ruby ....(713) 266-5481
rbarrow@sninews.com, Treasurer, Southern Newspapers Inc., TX, Houston

Barrow, Sarah ....(405) 278-2830
sbarrow@journalrecord.com, Advertising Director, The Journal Record, OK, Oklahoma City

Barrows, R. Nathaniel W. ....(207) 367-2200
info@pbp.me, Pub & Owner, Castine Patriot, ME, Blue Hill

Barrows, R. Nathaniel W.
ia@penobscotbaypress.com, Ed., Island Ad-Vantages, ME, Stonington

Barrows, R. Nathaniel W.
wp@penobscotbaypress.com, Ed., The Weekly Packet, ME, Blue Hill

Barry, Dan
dbarry@sentinelnews.com, Adv. Mgr., Sentinel News Plus, KY, Shelbyville

Barry, Dan
dbarry@sentinelnews.com, Adv. Mgr., The Sentinel-News, KY, Shelbyville

Barry, Dave
troyps@epix.net, General Manager, Troy Pennysaver, PA, Troy

Barry, David
opennysaver@stny.rr.com, Gen. Mgr., Owego Pennysaver, NY, Owego

Barry, David ....(570) 644-6397
dbarry@tsweeklygroup.com, Rgl. Adv. Dir. , The News-Item, PA, Shamokin

Barry, John
jbarry@blockislandtimes.com, Adv. Mgr./Prodn. Mgr., The Block Island Times, RI, Block Island

Barry, John
jbarry@brainworks.com, President, Brainworks Software Development Corp., NY, Sayville

Barry, Judy
jbarry@tvimedia.com, Adv. Sr. Vice Pres., The Wall Street Journal, NY, New York

Barry, Mark L. ....ext. 301
m.barry@theday.com, Circ. Dir., The Day, CT, New London

Barry, Paul
paul.barry@vicksburgpost.com, Mng. Ed., The Vicksburg Post, MS, Vicksburg

Barry, Paul
production@columbianprogress.com, Prodn. Mgr., The Columbian-Progress, MS, Columbia

Barry, Shelly
shelley.barry@sddt.com, Circ. Mgr., The Daily Transcript, CA, San Diego

Barske, Emily
emily.barske@iowastatedaily.com, Editor in chief, Iowa State University, IA, Ames

Barstow, Tom ....(717) 771-2000
tbarstow@ydr.com, News Editor, York Daily Record/York Sunday News, PA, York

Bart, Peter
peter.bart@variety.com, Daily Variety, CA, Los Angeles

Bartanen, Michael
bartanmd@plu.edu, Chair, Pacific Lutheran University, WA, Tacoma

Bartel, Roger ....(715) 526 - 2121
rbartel@bluelinemediaholdings.com, Editorial Director, Shawano Leader, WI, Shawano

Bartels, Del

newsdesk@pioneer-review.com, Ed., The Pioneer-Review, SD, Philip

Bartels, Jared ....(970) 224-7786
jaredbartels@coloradoan.com, Finance Dir., Controller, The Coloradoan, CO, Fort Collins

Bartels, Susan
susan.bartels@mcbattascompanies.com, Adv Dir, The Belleville Telescope, KS, Belleville

Bartelt, Tom ....(307) 334-2867
lhbilling@luskherald.com, Office Mgr., The Lusk Herald, WY, Lusk

Barth, Bill
bbarth@beloitdailynews.com, Editorial Page Ed., Beloit Daily News, WI, Beloit

Barth, Bob ....(785) 295-1142
bob.barth@cjonline.com, Adv. Dir., The Topeka Capital-Journal, KS, Topeka

Barth, Cindy ....(407) 241-2889
cbarth@bizjournals.com, Ed., Orlando Business Journal, FL, Orlando

Barth, Ken ....(972) 980-2890
contact@tek-tools.com, Pres./CEO, Tek-Tools, Inc., TX, Dallas

Barth, Mary Ann ....(419) 542-7764
maryann@hicksvillenewstribune.com, Pub./Ed., The News-Tribune, OH, Hicksville

Barth, William ....(608) 364-9221 ext. 140
bbarth@beloitdailynews.com, Ed., My Stateline Shopper, WI, Beloit

Bartholomay, Lucy ....(617) 929-2619
bartholomay@gobe.com, Mng. Dir., Pdct. Innovation, The Boston Globe, MA, Boston

Bartholomew, Dustin
contact@fayettevilleflyer.com, Co-Owner, Wonderstate Media, LLC, AR, Fayetteville
contact@fayettevilleflyer.com, Co-Owner, The Fayetteville Flyer, AR, Fayetteville

Bartholow, Jim ....(740) 373-2121 Ext. 540
jbarthol@mariettatimes.com, Sr. Copy Ed., The Marietta Times, OH, Marietta

Bartle, James
Nuz4u@fidnet.com, Owner Mng. Ed., Sullivan Independent News, MO, Sullivan

Bartlett, Allen
albartlett@naplesnews.com, City Ed., Naples Daily News, FL, Naples

Bartlett, Jenna ....(541) 902-3524
jbartlett@thesiuslawnews.com, Publisher, Siuslaw News, OR, Florence

Bartlett, John ....(805) 466-2585 ext. 101
publisher@pasoroblespress.com, Pub., Paso Robles Press, CA, Paso Robles
publisher@pasoroblespress.com, Pub., Siuslaw News, OR, Florence
publisher@pasoroblespress.com, Pub., Atascadero News, CA, Atascadero

Bartlett, Michael ....(805) 466-2585 x105
mbartlett@atascaderonews.com, Gen. Mgr., Atascadero News, CA, Atascadero
mbartlett@atascaderonews.com, Gen. Mgr., Paso Robles Press, CA, Paso Robles

Bartlett, Tom
tbartlett@whitecase.com, Sr. Vice Pres./Treasurer, Verizon Communications, Inc., NY, New York

Bartley, Betty ....(317) 745-2777
therepublican@sbcglobal.net, Editor, The Republican, IN, Danville

Bartley, Randon W. ....(814) 849-5339 ext. 28
rbartley@thecourierexpress.com, Ed., Jeffersonian Democrat, PA, Brookville

Bartley, Randy ....(814) 849-5339
rbartley@thecourierexpress.com, Gen. Mgr., The Leader-Vindicator, PA, New Bethlehem

Bartley, Sam ....(276) 935-2123
virginiamountaineer@gmail.com, Pub./Ed., The Virginia Mountaineer, VA, Grundy

Bartlick, Walt ....(956) 683-4522

wbartlick@themonitor.com, Commercial Print Director, The Monitor, TX, McAllen

Bartolacci, Joseph C.
info@matw.com, Pres./CEO, Matthews International Corp., PA, Pittsburgh

Bartoldson, Craig ....(304) 263-8931
cbartoldson@journal-news.net, Pub., The Journal, WV, Martinsburg

Bartollacci, Nancy
nbartolacci@moberlymonitor.com, Classified Ads, The Moberly Monitor-Index, MO, Moberly

Bartolo, Tony
tbartolo@clevelandstatecc.edu, Adv. Mgr., Cleveland State Cmty. College, TN, Cleveland

Bartolone, Angela ....(954) 747- 3041
abartolone@sfparenting.com, Adv. Mgr., South Florida Parenting Magazine, NC, Durham

Barton, Bruce ....ext. 301
Ed., Los Altos Town Crier, CA, Los Altos

Barton, Chuck ....(209) 369-2761 ext. 248
chuckb@lodinews.com, Pressroom Foreman, Lodi News-Sentinel , CA, Lodi

Barton, Dan
kingstontimes@ulsterpublishing.com, Ed., Kingston Times, NY, Kingston
kingstontimes@ulsterpublishing.com, Ed., Mid-Hudson Post Pioneer, NY, New Paltz

Barton, Dan
kingstontimes@gmail.com, Ed., Saugerties Times, NY, Kingston

Barton, Katie
katieb@republicmonews.com, Ed., The Republic Monitor, MO, Republic

Barton, Kurtis ....(602) 271-0040
kurtis.barton@newtimes.com, Publisher, New Times, AZ, Phoenix

Barton, Shelley ....(812) 663-3111 x7022
shelley.barton@greensburgdailynews.com, Rushville Republican, IN, Rushville
shelley.barton@greensburgdailynews.com, HR/Accounting, Greensburg Daily News, IN, Greensburg

Barton, Stacie
editor@ky-leadernews.com, Ed, Central City Leader News, KY, Central City

Barton, Tom ....(912) 652-0324
tom.barton@savannahnow.com, Editorial Page Ed., Savannah Morning News, GA, Savannah

Bartrum, Neal ....(765) 671-7175
nbartrum@chronicle-tribune.com, Distr. Mgr., Chronicle-Tribune, IN, Marion

Bartscher, Larry ....ext. 219
lbartscher@norfolkdailynews.com, Adv. Mgr., Daily News Plus, NE, Norfolk

Bartz, Jeremiah ....(907) 352-2273
sports@frontiersman.com, Sports Ed., Frontiersman, AK, Wasilla

Bartz, Krista ....(406) 346-2149
Admin. Assistant/Bookkeeper, The Independent Press, MT, Forsyth

Baruzzi, Cara ....(203) 789-5748
Bus. Ed., New Haven Register, CT, New Haven

Bas, Miguel
efemos@gmail.com, Rep., EFE News Services - Moscow, Russia, Moscow

Basalyga, Stephanie
sbasalyga@djcOregon.com, Ed, Daily Journal of Commerce, OR, Portland
sbasalyga@djcOregon.com, Ed., Daily Journal of Commerce, OR, Portland

Basbanes, Nicholas A.
nick@gentlymad.com, Mng. Ed./Columnist, Literary Features Syndicate, North Grafton

Basham, John ....ext. 25
john@northcountrynow.com, Adv. Mgr., North

Country This Week, NY, Potsdam

Bashri, Maha
mbashri@bradley.edu, Asst. Prof., Bradley University, IL, Peoria

Basile, John
jbasile@wickedlocal.com, Mng. Ed. , Bourne Courier, MA, Hyannis

Basile, John ....(508) 375-4945
jbasile@wickedlocal.com, Ed., The Bulletin, MA, Yarmouth Port

Basile, John ....(508) 375-4945
jbasile@wickedlocal.com, Managing Ed., The Register, MA, Hyannis

Basinger, Chris ....ext. 628
cbasinger@newtondailynews.com, Prodn. Mgr., Commercial Printing, Newton Daily News, IA, Newton

Baskin, Mike ....(386) 681-2491
Advertising Director, Daytona Beach News-Journal, FL, Daytona Beach

Baskin, Shelley
comp.antlers.amer@sbcglobal.net, Adv. Mgr., Antlers American, OK, Antlers

Baskin, Steve ....(978) 946-2350
smilkone@eagletribune.com, Circ. Dir., Andover Townsman, MA, Andover

Basolo, Kristy ....(906) 227-2545
kbasolo@nmu.edu, Advisor, Northern Michigan Univiversity, MI, Marquette

Bason, Bill
bill.b@pressenterprise.net, Prodn. Mgr., Color Graphics, Press-Enterprise, Inc. (Color Graphics Dept.), PA, Bloomsburg

Bass, Aaron ....(419) 521-7343
abass@gannett.com, Sales Mgr., The Marion Star, OH, Marion

Bass, Alison ....(304) 293-0393
alison.bass@mail.wvu.edu, Assistant Professor, West Virginia University, WV, Morgantown

Bass, Fayline
fayline@theforumnews.com, Adv. Mgr/Gen. Mgr., The Forum, LA, Shreveport

Bass, Jeff
jeff.bass@marist.edu, Instr., Marist College, NY, Poughkeepsie

Bass, Mona
mbass@gazette.net, Corp. Classified Dir. , The Gazette - Damascus / Clarksburg, MD, Gaithersburg
mbass@gazette.net, Corp. Classified Dir., The Gazette - Silver Spring / Takoma Park / Burtonsville (OOB), MD, Gaithersburg
mbass@gazette.net, Corp. Classified Dir., The Gazette - Bethesda / Chevy Chase / Kensington (OOB), MD, Gaithersburg
mbass@gazette.net, Corp. Classified Dir., The Gazette - North / Central Prince George Co. (OOB), MD, Gaithersburg
mbass@gazette.net, Corp. Classified Dir., The Gazette - Potomac / North Potomac, MD, Gaithersburg
mbass@gazette.net, Corp. Classified Dir., The Gazette - Rockville / Aspen Hill / Wheaton (OOB), MD, Gaithersburg
mbass@gazette.net, Corp. Classified Dir., The Gazette - Gaithersburg / Mont. Village (OOB), MD, Gaithersburg
mbass@gazette.net, Corp. Classified Dir., The Gazette - Olney (OOB), MD, Gaithersburg
mbass@gazette.net, Corp. Classified Dir., The Gazette - Germantown / Poolsville / Boyds (OOB), MD, Gaithersburg

Bass, Mona
bassm@fayobserver.com, Adv. Mgr., Carolina Trader Autos, NC, Fayetteville

Bass, Paul
p.bass@newhavenindependent.org, Ed., The New Haven Independent, CT, New Haven

Bass, Sara ....(620) 694-5700 Ext. 100
sbass@hutchnews.com, Circ. Mgr., Opns.;

Marketing Director, The Hutchinson News, KS, Hutchinson

Bassett, Ann
echo@mrnews.ca, Circ. Mgr., The Mile Zero News, AB, High Level

Bassett, Ann
echo@mrnews.ca, The Echo-pioneer, AB, High Level

Bassett, Ann
echo@mrnews.ca, Office/Adv., The Echo-pioneer, AB, High Level

Bassett, Greg
gbassett@newszap.com, Ed./Gen. Mgr., Salisbury Independent, MD, Salisbury

Bassett, Russell........................**(720) 274-7173**
rbassett@colopress.net, Membership and Projects, Colorado Press Association, CO, Denver

Bassier, Peggy
pbassier@sbtinfo.com, Local Adv. Agr., South Bend Tribune, IN, South Bend

Bassler, Allan..........................**(814) 793-2144**
publisher@mcheraldonline.com, Publisher, Morrisons Cove Herald, PA, Martinsburg

Basso, Dan............................**(989) 725-5136**
drbasso@argus-press.com, Managing Ed., The Argus-Press, MI, Owosso

Bastian, Kris
kris@zanderpressinc.com, Adv. Mgr., The Brillion News, WI, Brillion

Bastian, Kris
kris@zanderpressinc.com, Circ. Mgr., Lake To Lake Shopper, WI, Brillion

Bastidas, Jose.........................**(760) 778-4781**
Jose.Bastidas@DesertSun.com, Prod., The Desert Sun, CA, Palm Springs

Baston, Adele.........................**(513) 768-8326**
abaston@enquirer.com, Account Mgr., Northwest Press, OH, Cincinnati

Bastrom, Gretchen..........**(617) 859-1400 ext. 244**
gretchen@improper.com, Office Mgr., The Improper Bostonian Magazine, MA, Boston

Batcha, Sarah.........................**(909) 483-9374**
sarah.batcha@langnews.com, Digital News Editor, Inland Valley Daily Bulletin, CA, Rancho Cucamonga

Batchelor, Paul.......................**(604) 605-2546**
pbatchelor@sunprovince.com, VP Sales, The Vancouver Sun, BC, Vancouver

Batdorff, John
jabii@pioneergroup.com, Pres./CEO, Pioneer Group, MI, Big Rapids

Bateman, Peter.......................**(502) 582-4291**
pbateman@courier-journal.com, VP, IT, The Courier-Journal, KY, Louisville

Batemarco, Kathy....................**(973) 569-7660**
kabatem@gannett.com, HR. Mgr., The Record, NJ, Woodland Park
kabatem@gannett.com, HR Man., Herald News, NJ, Rockaway

Bates, Carl............................**(205) 325-2237**
Adv. Dir., Bus. Devel., The Birmingham News, AL, Birmingham

Bates, David...........................**(207) 532-2281**
hptsales@bangordailynews.com, Sales Rep., Houlton Pioneer Times, ME, Houlton

Bates, Jack............................**(916) 288-6006**
jack@cnpa.com, Exec. Dir., CNPA Advertising Services, CA, Sacramento

Bates, Jack............................**(916) 288-6000**
jack@cnpa.com, Exec. Dir., Pacific Northwest Newspaper Association, CA, Sacramento

Bates, Jim.............................**(303) 954-1825**
jbates@denverpost.com, Night Ed., The Denver Post, CO, Denver

Bates, Kim............................**(419) 724-6050**
kimbates@theblade.com, City Ed., The Blade, OH, Toledo

Bates, Madilyn
madi.bates@ucdadvocate.com, Editor in Chief, Univ. of Colorado, CO, Denver

Bates, Michele.............**(318) 377-1866 ext. 107**
michelle@press-herald.com, Reporter, Minden Press Herald, LA, Minden

Bates, Stephen
stephen.bates@unlv.edu, Asst. Prof, University of Nevada, Las Vegas, NV, Las Vegas

Bates, Tom
kevin.wendt@htimes.com, Pub, The Huntsville Times, AL, Huntsville

Bates, Zack...............**(205) 755-5747, ext. 606**
zach.bates@clantonadvertiser.com, Marketing Consul, The Clanton Advertiser, AL, Clanton

Batey , Katie................**(270) 678-5171 Ext. 224**
Customer Service , Glasgow Daily Times, KY, Glasgow

Bath, Alison...........................**(509) 577-7703**
abath@yakimaherald.com, Mng. Ed., Yakima Herald-Republic, WA, Yakima

Bath, Tim...................**(765) 459-3121 Ex. 8596**
tim.bath@kokomotribune.com, Photo Ed., Kokomo Tribune, IN, Kokomo

Batiste, Fredrick.....................**(225) 771-5812**
fredrick_batiste@subr.edu, Publications Assistant/Advisor, Southern University, LA, Baton Rouge

Batog, Jen
jbatog@dailylocal.com, Adv. Mgr., Daily Local News, PA, West Chester

Batra, Adrienne.......................**(416) 947-8359**
adrienne.batra@sunmedia.ca, Comment Editor, The Toronto Sun, ON, Toronto

Batson, Nanci...............**(401) 789-9744 ext 105**
nbatson@ri-mediagroup.com, Publisher, Southern Rhode Island Newspapers, RI, Wakefield

Batson, Nanci...............**(401) 789-9744 ext 105**
nbatson@ri-mediagroup.com, Pub., Standard-Times, RI, Wakefield
nbatson@ri-mediagroup.com, Pub., Narragansett Times, RI, Wakefield

Batson, Nancy
nbatson@ri-mediagroup.com, Pub., East Greenwich Pendulum, RI, Wakefield

Battaglia, Carmen
cbattaglia@mindspring.com, Pres., Dog Writers' Association of America, PA, Coatesville

Battaglia, Dr. Carmen
cbattaglia@mindspring.com, Pres., Dog Writers' Association of America, PA, Coatesville

Battaglia, Laurie
lb@rollcall.com, Publisher, RollCall, DC, Washington

Battaglia, Pat..........................**(704) 921-1818**
publisher@cleverpuzzles.com, Owner, International Puzzle Features, Charlotte

Batten, Frank
fbattenj@lcimedia.com, Chrmn. of the Bd./CEO, Landmark Communications, Inc., VA, Norfolk

Batten, Steve
sbatten@pottsmerc.com, Adv. Mgr., Mercury Sampler, PA, Pottstown

Battersby, Mark E......................**(610) 924-9158**
crcktinc@aol.com, Vice Pres./Ed., Cricket Communications, Inc., Ardmore

Battista, Jocelyn.....................**(203) 354-1115**
jbattista@thehour.com, Classified Advertising Supervisor, The Hour, CT, Norwalk

Battistoni, Joe........................**(219) 933-4155**
joe.battistoni@nwi.com, VP of Sales., The Times of Northwest Indiana, IN, Munster

Battles, Lori
loripdjnews@yahoo.com, Legal / Bill., The Perry Daily Journal, OK, Perry

Batts, Lisa............................**(252) 265-7810**
lisa@wilsondaily.com, Mng. Ed., The Wilson Times, NC, Wilson

Bauer, Annette........................**(816) 632-6543**
editor@mycameronnews.com, Ed., The Citizen Observer, MO, Cameron

Bauer, Caleb
c.bauer@thecr.com, Reporter, The Commercial Review, IN, Portland

Bauer, David C.L......................**(217) 245-6121**
dbauer@myjournalcourier.com, Editor and publisher, Jacksonville Journal-Courier, IL, Jacksonville

Bauer, Doug
dbauer@lmtribune.com, Mng. Ed., Lewiston Morning Tribune, ID, Lewiston

Bauer, Eric
editorial@orangeleader.com, Pub., Smart Shopper, TX, Orange

Bauer, James R.
jrbauer@alltel.net, Bus. Mgr., The Daily Press, PA, Saint Marys

Bauer, Karen..........................**(701) 224-5522**
karen.bauer@bismarckstate.edu, Advisor, Bismarck State College, ND, Bismarck

Bauer, Margaret......................**(307) 756-3371**
mleader@collinscom.net, Pub./Ed./Adv. Mgr., Moorcroft Leader, WY, Moorcroft

Bauer, Rich..**ext. 226**
rbauer@leaderunion.com, Mng. Ed., The Leader-union Publishing Co., IL, Vandalia

Bauer, Steve...........................**(863) 494-0300**
Ed., Arcadian, FL, Arcadia

Bauer, Sue
sue.bauer@ecpc.com, Adv. Mgr., The Country Today, WI, Eau Claire

Bauer, Traci...........................**(585) 258-2615**
tbauer@democratandchronicle.com, VP, Digital Strategy & Development, Democrat and Chronicle, NY, Rochester

Bauer, Tyson
rbeditor@andrew.cmu.edu, Tepper School of Business at Carnegie Mellon University, PA, Pittsburgh

Baulch, Becky
bbaulch@postandcourier.com, Assist. to Pub, The Post and Courier, SC, Charleston

Baum, Davina
davina@afar.com, Mng. Ed., AlterNet, San Francisco

Baum, Margeret
sanmatean@smccd.net., College of San Mateo, CA, San Mateo

Baum , Ed......................**(914) 244-0533 ext. 15**
Ed., Record-Review, NY, Bedford Hills

Bauman, Brian.............**(866) 366-6166 ext. 202**
brianb@goplastics.com, Dir.-Sales/Mktg., Go Plastics/StreetSmart LLC, GA, Canton

Bauman, John
john.bauman@sunmedia.ca, Sales Mgr., Goderich Signal-star, ON, Goderich

Bauman, John
clinton.ads@bowesnet.com, Adv. Mgr., Clinton News-record, ON, Clinton

Bauman, Matt
mbaumann@readingeagle.com, Web Editor, Reading Eagle Company, PA, Reading

Baumann, Daniel
dbaumann@dailyherald.com, Chairman Emeritus, Daily Herald, IL, Arlington Heights

Baumann, Ellyn.......................**(507) 896-2107**
banner@acegroup.cc, Ed., The Houston Banner, MN, Houston

Baumann, Jim..........................**(847) 427-4555**
jbaumann@dailyherald.com, Vice Pres./Managing Editor, Daily Herald, IL, Arlington Heights

Baumann, Roberta...................**608-729-3697**
tribnews@hngnews.com, Mng. Ed., Waunakee Tribune, WI, Waunakee

Baumeister, Alan...........**(812) 482-2424 ext 151**
abaumeister@dcherald.com, Single Copy Sales & Print Distribution Manager, The Herald, IN, Jasper

Baumgardner, Letty..................**(530) 344-5049**
lettyb@mtdemocrat.net, Graphics Manager, Mountain Democrat, CA, Placerville

Baumgart, Jim........................**(262) 513-2621**
jbaumgart@conleynet.com, Adv. Mgr., The Freeman, WI, Waukesha

Baumgart, Jim
jbaumgart@conleynet.com, Advertising Manager, Oconomowoc Enterprise, WI, Waukesha

Baumgarten, Marjorie
marjorie@austinchronicle.com, Film Ed, Austin Chronicle, TX, Austin

Baumgarten, Mark
mbaumgarten@seattleweekly.com, Ed. in Chief, Seattle Weekly, WA, Seattle

Baumgartner, Paige
pbaumgartner@bnd.com, Belleville News-Democrat, IL, Belleville

Baumgartner, Ron.........**(574) 658-4111 ext. 2316**
rbaumgartner@the-papers.com, Pub., The Mail-Journal, IN, Milford

Baumgartner, Ron.........**(574) 658-4111 ext. 2316**
rbaumgartner@the-papers.com, Pub., The Paper - Kosciusko Edition, IN, Milford

Baumgartner, Ronald
rbaumgartner@the-papers.com, Pub., Senior Life (OOB), IN, Milford
rbaumgartner@the-papers.com, The Papers Incorporated, IN

Bautsch, Florence....................**(570) 628-6020**
fbautsch@republicanherald.com, Editorial Page Ed., The Republican-Herald, PA, Pottsville

Bawer, Mala
mala@cybersmart.org, Exec. Dir., CyberSmart, NJ, Bernardsville

Baxa, Jill..............................**(620) 241-2422**
jbaxa@mcphersonsentinel.com, Bookkeeper, McPherson Sentinel, KS, McPherson

Baxley, Cindy
cindybaxley@bellsouth.net, Ed., Clarke County Tribune, MS, Quitman

Baxley, Jaymie
jbaxley@civitasmedia.com, Features Ed., The Robesonian, NC, Lumberton

Baxter, John
john.baxter@bob.hsbc.com, Circ. Mgr., New York Press, NY, New York

Baxter, Julie...........................**(303) 410-2650**
baxterj@broomfieldenterprise.com, Ed., Broomfield Enterprise, CO, Boulder

Baxter, Laura
laura.baxter@militarynews.com, Pub., Peninsula Warrior- Air Force, VA, Norfolk

Baxter, Laura
sales@militarynews.com, Pub., Soundings, VA, Norfolk

Bay, Kathy
bcnews@ekns.net, Pub., The Bracken County News, KY, Brooksville

Bay , Sharon..........................**(619) 685-6970**
sharon@sandiegofamily.com, Publisher, San Diego Family Magazine, CA, San Diego

Bayard-Miller, Patrice................**(916) 288-6029**
patrice@cnpa.com, Client Rel./Sales Mgr., CNPA Advertising Services, CA, Sacramento

Bayer, Maxine .... ext. 14
mbayer@rvpublishing.com, Adv. Mgr., Senior Courier, IL, Machesney Park

Bayles, Cara
cara@weeklydig.com, News/Features Ed., Boston's Weekly Dig, MA, Boston

Bayles, Jim ....(604) 247-4766
jim.bayles@catalystpaper.com, Vice-President and General Manager Newsprint and International, Catalyst Paper Corp., BC, Richmond

Bayless, Eddie
ebayless@bastropenterprise.com, Gen. Mgr./ Retail Adv. Sales, Bastrop Daily Enterprise, LA, Bastrop

Baysore, John
LogisticsResults@Dematic.com, Pres., Dematics, MI, Grand Rapids

Bazinet, Benoit
bazinetb@Transcontinental.com, Pub., L'action, QC, Joliette

Bazinet, Benoit ....(450) 752-0447
bazinetb@transcontinental.ca, Action Mercredi, QC, Joliette
bazinetb@transcontinental.ca, Express Montcalm, QC, Saint Lin Laurentides

Bazinet, Benoit ....(450) 759-3664
bazinetb@transcontinental.ca, Action Mercredi, QC, Joliette

Bazzoli, Sue ....(614) 486-6677
sbazzoli@ohionews.org, Manager, Administrative Services, Ohio Newspaper Services, Inc., OH, Columbus

Bazzoli , Sue...............(614) 486-6677 ext. 1018
sbazzoli@ohionews.org, Mgr. Admin. Services, Ohio Newspaper Association, OH, Columbus

Beach, Charles ....(845) 358-1710
charles.beach@nyack.edu, Nyack College, NY, Nyack

Beach, Jeff...............................(320) 763-1211
jbeach@echopress.com, Ed., Echo-Press, MN, Alexandria

Beach, Jeff...............................(320) 763-3133
jbeach@echopress.com, Ed., Lakeland Shopping Guide, MN, Alexandria

Beach, Joe ....(503) 364-4431
jbeach@capitalpress.com, Ed., Capital Press, OR, Salem

Beach, Judy ....(785) 271-5304
Accountant, Kansas Press Association, KS, Topeka

Beach, Michael ....(505) 818-8904
mike.beach@gazette.com, The Gazette, CO, Colorado Springs

Beacom, Jamie .... (440) 998-2323 Ext. 140
jbeacon@starbeacon.com, Pub. / Adv. Dir., Star Beacon, OH, Ashtabula

Beager, Laurel
laurel@ifallsdailyjournal.com, Ed., The Journal, MN, International Falls

Beagle, Ben...........................(585) 243-0296
ben@livingstonnews.com, Gen Mgr/Mng. Ed., The Livingston County News, NY, Geneseo

Beagle, Tammie
tbeagle@westliberty.edu, West Liberty University, WV, West Liberty

Beagley, Harlan .... (509) 765-4561 ext. 214
hbeagley@columbiabasinherald.com, Pub., Columbia Basin Herald, WA, Moses Lake
hbeagley@columbiabasinherald.com, The Ridgway Record, PA, Ridgway

Beaird, Judy
argus@kkspc.com, Ed., The Astoria South Fulton Argus, IL, Astoria

Beal, Andy ....(530) 313-9203
andy@maxpreps.com, Pres., CBS MaxPreps, Inc., CA, Cameron Park

Beal, Julia

advertising@ominecaexpress.com, Prod., Caledonia Courier, BC, Fort St. James

Beal, Ron .... (440) 245-6901 Ext. 90711
rbeal@morningjournal.com, Adv. Dir. / Gen. Mgr., The Morning Journal, OH, Lorain

Beal, Tom
tbeal@azstarnet.com, Instr., University of Arizona, AZ, Tucson

Beale, Chip ....(937) 225-7390
chip.beale@coxinc.com, General Sales Manager - Digital, Dayton Daily News, OH, Franklin

Bealer, Cindy George
newsherald@thenews-messenger.com, Pub., Ottawa County Outlook, OH, Fremont

Beals, Gregg................. (620) 694-5700 Ext. 701
gbeals@hutchnews.com, Production Director, The Hutchinson News, KS, Hutchinson

Beam, Justin
jbeam@republicmedia.com, The Arizona Republic, AZ, Phoenix

Bean, Doug ....(888) 678-6008 x 947
dbean@lifesitenews.com, Journalist, LifeSiteNews.com, VA, Front Royal

Bean, Ed................................(404) 419-2830
ebean@alm.com, Editor, Fulton County Daily Report, GA, Atlanta
ebean@alm.com, Assoc. Pub., Daily Report, GA, Atlanta

Bean, Gerald A.
jbean@centurygroup.com, Owner, Century Group Newspapers, CA, Yucaipa

Bean, Greg .... ext. 8212
Exec. Ed., Tri-Town News, NJ, Manalapan

Bean, Joanna ....(719) 636-0273
joanna.bean@gazette.com, ManagingEditor, The Gazette, CO, Colorado Springs

Bean, Myra ....(662) 563-4591
psports@panolian.com, Sports Ed., The Panolian, MS, Batesville

Bean, Rick ....(336) 888-3500
rbean@hpenews.com, Pub., High Point Enterprise, NC, High Point

Bean, Rick
rbean@hpenews.com, Pub., The Herald-Sun, NC, Durham
rbean@hpenews.com, Pub., Archdale Trinity News, NC, High Point

Bean, Tracy .... (304) 788-3333 ext. 115
tbean@newstribune.info, Multi-Media Ad Exec, Mineral Daily News-Tribune, WV, Keyser

Beane, Pat ....(812) 331-4340
pbeane@heraldt.com, Sports Ed., The Herald Times, IN, Bloomington

Beanland, Rusty ....(210) 744-7363
rbeanland@tnolsa.com, Office Administrator, Thrifty Nickel, TX, San Antonio

Bear, H. T.................................(334) 737-2567
hbear@oanow.com, Prod. Dir, Opelika-Auburn News, AL, Opelika

Beard, Annette ....(479) 872-5168
prtnews@mc2k.com, Mng. Ed., The Times of Northeast Benton County, AR, Pea Ridge

Beard, Chris
chris@373design.com, Online Content Developer, The News Leader, VA, Staunton

Beard, Connie .... (903) 785-6960 ext 243
connie.beard@theparisnews.com, Managing Ed., The Paris News, TX, Paris

Beard, David............................(304) 291-9436
dbeard@dominionpost.com, Senior Reporter, The Dominion Post, WV, Morgantown

Beard, Elizabeth
ebeard@lsua.edu, Louisiana State Univ., LA, Alexandria

Beard, Fred
fbeard@ou.edu, Prof., University of Oklahoma,

OK, Norman

Beard, Jay .... (256) 840-3000 ext 119
jbeard@sandmountainreporter.com, Staff Writer, Sand Mountain Reporter, AL, Albertville

Beard, Michael ....(770) 718-3402
mbeard@gainesvilletimes.com, New Media Ed., The Times, GA, Gainesville

Beard, Susan
beard@northjersey.com, VP / HR, The Record, NJ, Woodland Park

Beardsley, Mark........................(706) 335-7204
mbeardsley@mainstreetnews.com, Ed., The Commerce News, GA, Jefferson

Beasley, Jarrod
jbeasley@bnd.com, Belleville News-Democrat, IL, Belleville

Beasley, Larry ....(202) 636-4845
lbeasley@washingtontimes.com, Pres. & CEO, The Washington Times, DC, Washington

Beasley, Stephen A.
stephen.beasley@lubbockonline.com, Pub., Lubbock Avalanche-Journal, TX, Lubbock

Beasley, Teresa
tbeasley@panola.edu, Panola College, TX, Carthage

Beason, Rhonda
rbeason@carmitimes.com, Circ. Mgr., The Carmi Times, IL, Carmi

Beattie, Chris
cbeattie@starlocalnews.com, Community Ed., McKinney Courier-Gazette, TX, Plano

Beattie, John ....(413) 731-5016
(413) 731-5016 Ext. 279, Dir. of Dig. Ops., The Republican, MA, Springfield

Beattie, Pamela ....(937) 552-2301
pbeattie@civitasmedia.com, Adv. Mgr., Vandalia Drummer News, OH, Vandalia
pbeattie@civitasmedia.com, Adv. Mgr., Englewood Independent, OH, Vandalia
pbeattie@civitasmedia.com, Adv. Mgr., Huber Heights Courier, OH, Vandalia

Beatty, Chad ....(518) 581-2480 x 212
cbeatty@saratogapublishing.com, Pub & Ed., Saratoga Today, NY, Saratoga Springs

Beatty, Mike
mbeatty@joplinglobe.com, Sr. VP, CNHI, LLC, AL, Montgomery
mbeatty@joplinglobe.com, Pub., The Joplin Globe, MO, Joplin

Beatty, Esq., Robert
robertbeatty@sfltimes.com, Pub., South Florida Times, FL, Fort Lauderdale

Beaty, James ....(918) 421-2023
jbeaty@mcalesternews.com, Mng. Ed., McAlester News-Capital, OK, McAlester

Beauchemin, Robert
rbeauchemin@lapensee.qc.ca, Adv. Rep., La Pensee De Bagot, QC, Acton Vale

Beauchesme, Erika
erika.beauchesne@sunmedia.ca, Mng. Ed., Fort McMurray Today, AB, Fort McMurray

Beauchesne, Erika
erika.beauchesne@sunmedia.ca, Acting Mng. Ed. , Fort McMurray Today, AB, Fort McMurray

Beauchesne, Jacques ....(804) 227-4001
Gen. Mgr., Newsprint Sales Co., VA, Charlottesville

Beaudette, Arthur
arthur@newsadvertiser.com, Gen. Mgr., Vegreville News Advertiser, AB, Vegreville

Beaudette, Dan........................(780) 632-2861
dan@newsadvertiser.com, Ed., Vegreville News Advertiser, AB, Vegreville

Beaudin, Mike
mike.beaudin@sunmedia.ca, Ed., The Kingston Whig-Standard, ON, Kingston

Beaudin, Mike..................................ext. 243
mbeaudin@bar.southam.ca, Mng. Ed., The Barrie Examiner, ON, Barrie

Beaudoin, Francois
francois.beaudoin@lavoixdelest.ca, Mng. Ed., La Voix De L'est Plus, QC, Granby

Beaudry, Glenn
gbeaudry@kelownacapnews.com, Circ. Mgr., Kelowna Capital News, BC, Kelowna

Beaudry, Joseph M. ....(708) 946-2208
jbeaudry@hamiltoncirculation.com, Pres., Hamilton Circulation Supplies Co., IL, Beecher

Beaudry, Susan
sbeaudry@hamiltoncirculation.com, Vice Pres., Hamilton Circulation Supplies Co., IL, Beecher

Beaulieu, Patria Ann ....(514) 636-7314
patriciaann.beaulieu@transcontinental.ca, Messager De Lachine / Dorval, QC, Dorval

Beaulieu, Patricia ....(514) 218-7772
patricia.beaulieu@neomedia.com, Regional Director , Le Journal De Joliette, QC, Joliette

Beaulieu, Patricia Ann ....(514) 636-7314
patriciaann.beaulieu@transcontinental.ca, Pub., Lachine Messenger, QC, Dorval
patriciaann.beaulieu@transcontinental.ca, Magazine De L'ile-des-soeurs, QC, Dorval
patriciaann.beaulieu@transcontinental.ca, Messager De Lasalle, QC, Lasalle
patriciaann.beaulieu@transcontinental.ca, Messager De Verdun, QC, Dorval

Beaulieu, Patricia-Ann.................(514) 636-7314
patricia-ann.beaulieu@tc.tc, Publisher, The Westmount Examiner, QC, Westmount

Beaulieu, Sarah........................(819) 575-7575
sarah.beaulieu@hebdosquebecor.com, Journal De Magog, QC, Sherbrooke
sarah.beaulieu@hebdosquebecor.com, Journal De Sherbrooke, QC, Sherbrooke

Beaumont, Andrew
abeaumont@gazetteextra.com, Design Ed., The Janesville Gazette - GazetteXtra, WI, Janesville

Beaupre, Christiane ....(800) 525-6752
info@leregional.com, Le Regional, ON, Brampton
info@leregional.com, Gen. Mgr., Le Rempart, ON, Windsor

Beaver, Dennis
thefactsnewspaper@excite.com, Pub., Facts News, WA, Seattle

Beavers, Jefferson...................(559) 278-8180
jbeavers@csufresno.edu, California State Univ., CA, Fresno

Beavers, Liz ....(304) 788-3333
lbeavers@newstribune.info, Ed., Today's Shopper, WV, Keyser
lbeavers@newstribune.info, Managing Ed., Mineral Daily News-Tribune, WV, Keyser

Beavers, Ron ....(785) 295-1258
ron.beavers@cjonline.com, Prod. , The Topeka Capital-Journal, KS, Topeka

Bebbington, Jim ....(937) 225-2217
jim.bebbington@coxinc.com, Shared Content Editor, Dayton Daily News, OH, Franklin

Bebee, Grant
gbebee@greatfallstribune.com, Gen. Mgr., Consumers Press, MT, Great Falls

Bechen, Brooke
bbechen@thedodgevillechronicle.com, Ed., The Dodgeville Chronicle, WI, Dodgeville

Becher, Aaron
abecher@forumcomm.com, Pres., NDNA Ed. Foundation, North Dakota Newspaper Association, ND, Bismarck

Bechtel, Katie
kbechtel@piquenewsmagazine.com, Circ Mgr, Pique Newsmagazine, BC, Whistler

Behrens, Kevin
kb@marysvillejt.com, Gen. Mgr., Marysville Journal-Tribune, OH, Marysville

Behresn, Kevin ....(937) 644-9111
kb@marysvillejt.com, Publisher, The Richwood Gazette, OH, Marysville

Behringer, Bob
bbehringer@presteligence.com, Pres. & CEO, Presteligence, OH, North Canton

Behul, Julius ....(905) 507-8004
editor@kanadskyslovak.ca, Editor-in-Chief, Kanadsky Slovak / The Canadian Slovak, ON, Mississauga

Behymer, Bruce ....(316) 281-7899
bruce@harveycountynow.com, Marketing Dude (sales manager), Buyer's Edge Of South Central Kansas, KS, Newton

Beideman, Jeff ....(215) 345-3076
Sports Ed., The Intelligencer, PA, Doylestown

Beierschmitt, Victoria ....(559) 583-2442
vbeierschmitt@hanfordsentinel.com, Adv. Mgr., The Sentinel, CA, Hanford

Beique, Paul ....(802) 654-6708
Instr., St. Michael's College, VT, Colchester
St. Michael's College, VT, Colchester

Beirne, Horton P. ....(540) 962-2121 ext. 13
virginianreview@aol.com, News Ed., Virginian Review, VA, Covington

Beirne, Mary Ann
vareviewads@aol.com, Adv. Dir., Virginian Review, VA, Covington

Beitler, Paul
sports@news-banner.com, Sports Ed., News-Banner, IN, Bluffton

Beitz, Mike ....(519) 271-2220 ext. 207
mbeitz@bowesnet.com, Wire Ed., The Stratford Beacon Herald, ON, Stratford

Beitz, Ryan ....(217) 774-2161 ext.255
ryan.beitz@shelbyvilledailyunion.com, Circ. Mgr./Off. Mgr., Daily Union, IL, Shelbyville

Bekins, Hillary
bonnie@bonniechurchill.com, Pres., Communication International/National News, West Hollywood

Bekken, Jon
jbekken@alb.edu, Albright College, PA, Reading

Belair, Susan
sue.belair@voicemediagroup.com, Vice Pres., Sales, Voice Media Group, CO, Denver

Belair, Susan ....(917) 822-4142
sue.belair@voicemediagroup.com, SVP Sales, Ruxton Group/VMG Advertising, AZ, Phoenix

Beland, Diane ....ext. 225
diane.beland@transcontinental.ca, Sales Coord., L'echo De Maskinonge, QC, Louiseville

Belanger, Michele
michelebelanger@cwc4webs.com, Vice Pres., Canadian Web Consultants Ltd., ON, Port Sydney

Belcher, Bob
belcher@corsicanadailysun.com, Ed., Star Shopper, TX, Corsicana

Belcher, Carol
Carol@centrevillepress.com, Bookkeeper, The Centreville Press, AL, Centreville

Belcher, Debbie ....ext. 225
dbelcher@coalfield.com, Office Mgr., The Coalfield Progress, VA, Norton

Belcher, Geoff
gbelcher@seacoastecho.com, News Ed, Sea Coast Echo, MS, Bay Saint Louis

Belcher, Mary ....(615) 859-6609
rowlettadvertising@att.net, Sec./Treasurer, Rowlett Advertising Service, Inc., TN, Goodlettsville

Belcher, Neal ....(859) 654-3333
nealb@falmouthoutlook.com, Publisher, The Shopper's Outlook (free Shopper), KY, Falmouth

Belcher, Scott
sbelcher@elkintribune.com, Advertising Rep, The Tribune, NC, Elkin

Beldam, Evelyn
cya@assignmentdesk.com, Bus. Mgr., Assignment Desk, IL, Chicago

Belden, Roxy ....(785) 822-1490
rbelden@saljournal.com, Business Office Mgr., The Salina Journal, KS, Salina

Belfour, Juanita ....(519) 348-8431 Ext. 203
madvocate.sales@sunmedia.ca, Adv. Mgr., The Mitchell Advocate, ON, Mitchell

Belha, Jamie ....(309) 797-0332
jbelha@qconline.com, Classified Telesales Supervisor, The Dispatch-Argus, IL, Moline

Belisle, Maggie
sales@westwindweekly.com, Adv. Sales Consult., Westwind Weekly News, AB, Magrath

Beliveau, Rene
rene.beliveau@latribune.qc.ca, Prod. Mgr., La Tribune, QC, Sherbrooke

Belknap, Holly ....(405) 756-3169
theshopper@valornet.com, Vice-Pres./ Publisher, Shopper News Note, OK, Lindsay

Bell, Alberta S. ....(978) 632-8000 ex. 16
albertabell@thegardnernews.com, Pres./Pub., The Gardner News, MA, Gardner

Bell, Alicia
advertising@mvdemocat.com, Adv. Sales , Mount Vernon Democrat, IN, Mount Vernon

Bell, Amy
amy.bell@lee.net, Controller, The Columbus Telegram, NE, Columbus

Bell, Blake
blake.bell@atmoreadvance.com, Pres./Pub., Atmore Advance, AL, Atmore

Bell, Carol ....(312) 225-2400
CFO, Dir. of Fin & Bus Op, Chicago Defender, IL, Chicago

Bell, Chris ....(785) 832-7137
cbell@ljworld.com, Lawrence Journal-World, KS, Lawrence

Bell, Dave
circulation@leaderunion.com, Pub., The Leader-union Publishing Co., IL, Vandalia

Bell, David ....(870) 423-6636
photos@cox-internet.com, Photographer, Carroll County News, AR, Berryville

Bell, David ....(613) 732-3692
circ@nrtco.net, Circ. Mgr., The Daily Observer, ON, Pembroke

Bell, David ....(928) 428-2560
editor@eacourier.com, Mng. Ed., Eastern Arizona Courier, AZ, Safford
editor@eacourier.com, Mng. Ed., The Copper Era, AZ, Safford

Bell, Donna ....(585) 258-2407
dbell@gannett.com, HR, The Ithaca Journal, NY, Ithaca
dbell@gannett.com, Community News Ed., The Saratogian, NY, Saratoga Springs

Bell, Donna ....(585) 258-2407
dbell@democratandchronicle.com, Sr. HR Business Partner, Democrat and Chronicle, NY, Rochester

Bell, Donna J.
telfairenterprise@windstream.net, Gen. Mgr., The Telfair Enterprise, GA, Mc Rae

Bell, Doug ....(303) 350-1039
doug@evergreenco.com, Ed., Clear Creek Courant, CO, Idaho Springs
doug@evergreenco.com, Ed., Columbine Courier, CO, Evergreen

Bell, Dustin
dbell@greeleytrib.com, Prodn. Mgr., Pre Press, Greeley Daily Tribune, CO, Greeley

Bell, Eva ....(606) 573-4510 Ext.1167
ebell@civitasmedia.com, Receptionist/ Classifieds/Legals, The Harlan Daily Enterprise, KY, Harlan

Bell, Jim
jim@thechetekalert.com, Pub./Ed., The Chetek Alert, WI, Chetek

Bell, Jim
jim@thechetekalert.com, Assoc. Pub., Barron News-Shield, WI, Barron
jim@thechetekalert.com, Pub., Bloomer Advance, WI, Bloomer

Bell, Jodi
jbell@pnj.com, Director of Sales , Pensacola News Journal, FL, Pensacola

Bell, John ....(215) 628-8330 ext. 210
jbell@montgomerynews.com, Adv. Mgr., South Jersey Parents Express, PA, Fort Washington

Bell, John ....(215) 628-8330 ext. 210
jbell@montgomerynews.com, Adv. Mgr., Parents' Express, PA, Fort Washington

Bell, John
john.bell@ey.com, Sr. Vice Pres., Domestic Telecom HR, Verizon Communications, Inc., NY, New York

Bell, Joseph ....(814) 773-3151
Ed., The Ridgway Record, PA, Ridgway
Editor, Shop Right, PA, Ridgway

Bell, Joseph ....(814) 837-2227
krnews1@verizon.net, Ed., The Kane Republican, PA, Kane

Bell, Kandice ....(770) 683-1724
kandice@newnan.com, Reporter, The Newnan Times-Herald, GA, Newnan

Bell, Kathy
kbell@cp.org, Bureau Chief, Broadcast News Limited, AB, Edmonton

Bell, Kristina
kbell@highpoint.edu, Lectr., High Point Univ., NC, High Point

Bell, Lindsey
lindsey@newsleaderonline.com, Society Ed, Carroll County News-Leader, TN, Huntingdon

Bell, Lorraine ....(705) 385-8016
lorrainebell@cwc4webs.com, Office Mgr., Canadian Web Consultants Ltd., ON, Port Sydney

Bell, Mark
newsshield@chibardun.net, Pub./Sports Ed., Barron News-Shield, WI, Barron

Bell, Pat ....(308) 381-9426
patricia.bell@theindependent.com, Adv. Dir., The Grand Island Independent, NE, Grand Island

Bell, Paul ....(212) 659-1212
paul.bell@dowjones.com, Vice Pres., Partner Businesses, The Wall Street Journal Sunday, New York

Bell, Rachel
rachel_bell@techenergy.com, Int'l Sales Mgr., Tech-Energy Co., TX, Cibolo

Bell, Roger
rogerbassistanteditor@gmail.com, Reg. Ed., The Prince George Journal, VA, Emporia

Bell, Sheila
production@sherbrookerecord.com , Prodn. Mgr., The Record, QC, Sherbrooke

Bell, Thom
thom.bell@albanyherald.com, Circulation Manager, The Albany Herald, GA, Albany

Bell, Thom
thom.bell@rockdalecitizen.com, Circ. Dir., The Rockdale Citizen, GA, Conyers

Bell, Thom ....(770) 963-9205 Ext. 1350
thom.bell@gwinnettdailypost.com, Vice President/Circulation Southern Community Newspapers, Inc., Gwinnett Daily Post, GA, Lawrenceville

Bell, Thom ....ext. 237
Circ. Dir., The Newton Citizen, GA, Conyers
Circ. Mgr., Clayton News Daily, GA, Jonesboro

Bell, Wayne
kgisales@gi.konicaminolta.us, Sr. Vice Pres., Konica Minolta Business Solutions USA Inc., NJ, Ramsey

Bella, Joe ....(574) 262-8228
jbella@mediamergers.com, Sr. Advisor-Newspapers, Grimes, McGovern & Associates, NY, New York

Bella, Joe ....1-(574) 276-1547
jbella@acu-tech.net, Managing Director, Acutech LLC, IN, South Bend

Bella, Michael J.
news@salisburypost.com, Prodn. Vice Pres., Opns., Salisbury Post, NC, Salisbury

Bellaby, Mara ....(321) 242-3573
mbellaby@floridatoday.com, Enterprise Editor / space, family, education, Florida Today, FL, Melbourne

Bellamy, Lee
lbellamy@timesnews.net, Adv. Mgr., Classified, Kingsport Times-News, TN, Kingsport

Bellan, Bernie ....(204) 229-5213
bebellan@shaw.ca, Publisher/Editor, Jewish Post & News, MB, Winnipeg

Bellantone, Paul
paulb@ppa.org, Vice Pres., Mktg./Commun., Promotional Products Association International, TX, Irving

Bellantoni, Christina
christina.bellantoni@latimes.com, Politics, Asst. Managing Ed., Los Angeles Times, CA, Los Angeles

Bellard, Chris
sales@thecoastalstar.com, Adv. Dir., The Coastal Star, FL, Ocean Ridge

Bellefleur, Yves ....(418) 686-3413
ybellefleur@lesoleil.com, Librarian, Le Soleil, QC, Quebec

Belles, Ed
ed@twptimes.com, Pub., The Township Times, MI, Breckenridge

Belles, Mike ....(209) 722-1812 ext. 493
belles@pspub.com, Vice Pres., Circ., Pacific Sierra Publishing, Inc., CA, Merced

Bellinger, Nathan ....(315) 769-2451
nbellinger@ogd.com, Adv. Acct. Exec. , Daily Courier-Observer/Advance News, NY, Massena

Bellinghausen, Pat ....(406) 657-1303
pbellinghausen@billingsgazette.com, Editorial Page Ed., Billings Gazette, MT, Billings

Bellotti, John
John_Bellotti@tamu-commerce.edu, Asst. Prof., Texas A&M University-Commerce, TX, Commerce

Bellows, Amy
advertise@myweeklysentinel.com, Adv., The Canton Independent Sentinel, PA, Canton

Bellune, Jerry
jerrybellune@yahoo.com, Ed. Emer., Lexington County Chronicle & The Dispatch-News, SC, Lexington

Bellune, MacLeod
lexchron@windstream.net, Adv. Mgr., Lexington County Chronicle & The Dispatch-News, SC, Lexington

Bellune, Mark
markbellune@yahoo.com, Managing Editor, Lexington County Chronicle & The Dispatch-News, SC, Lexington

Belluscio, Mario ....(514) 987-2222
mbelluscio@montrealgazette.com, Dir.,

Finance, Postmedia, Montreal Gazette, QC, Montreal

Belongie, Terrie ....(906) 789-9122 ext. 160
tbelongie@upaction.com, Gen. Mgr., Up Action News, MI, Escanaba

Belschner, Julie ....(608) 495-0276
jbelschner@capitalnewspapers.com, Capital Newspapers, WI, Madison

Belt, James C.
advertising@dallasexaminer.com, Adv. Mgr., Dallas Examiner, TX, Dallas

Belt, Mollie ....(214) 941-3100
mbelt@dallasexaminer.com, Publisher, The Dallas Examiner, TX, Dallas

Belt, Mollie Finch ....(214) 428-3446
mbelt@dallasexaminer.com, Pub., Dallas Examiner, TX, Dallas

Belter, Robert
info@portagephic.com, Pres., Portage Newspaper Supply Co., CT, Glastonbury

Belton, Jennifer
jbelton@dailynewsgroup.com, Adv. Mgr., Pacifica Tribune, CA, Novato
jbelton@dailynewsgroup.com, Adv. Sales Mgr., Palo Alto Daily News, CA, Menlo Park

Beltrame, Agustin 4309-7216
abeltrame@clarin.com, Photo Editor, Clarin Contenidos, CA, Buenos Aires

Belyea, Ron ....(207) 594-4401 ext. 250
rbelyea@villagesoup.com, COO, Village Netmedia, Inc., ME, Rockland

Bemis, Larry
Lbemis@parkecountysentinel.com, Ed., Parke County Sentinel, IN, Rockville

Bemis, Scott ....(303) 803-9210
sbemis@bizjournals.com, Pub., Denver Business Journal, CO, Denver

Benally, Olivia.........................(928) 871-1134
obenally@navajotime.com, Controller, Navajo Times Publishing Company, Inc., AZ, Window Rock

Benavides, Julie .... (765) 482-4650 ext. 101
julie.benavides@reporter.net, Classified Rep., The Reporter, IN, Lebanon

Benavides, M.E. ....(956) 982-6622
Sports Ed., The Brownsville Herald, TX, Brownsville

Benavides, Rachel
rbenavides@link.freedom.com, Ed., El Nuevo Heraldo, TX, Brownsville

Benavides, Tessa
tbenavides@saedpartnership.org, Our Lady of The Lake Univ., TX, San Antonio

Bence, Don
don@sakurai.com, Vice Pres., Sales, Sakurai USA, IL, Schaumburg

Bencini, Gaye
gaye@thehctimes.com, Co-Owner, The Hickman County Times, KY, Clinton

Bender, Dan
dbender@statesmanjournal.com, Metro Ed., Statesman Journal, OR, Salem

Bender, Dean
dean_bender@bhimpact.com, Partner, B/HI, CA, Los Angeles

Bender, Deb
deb@wcrecord.com, Cir. Mgr., The Walsh County Record, ND, Grafton

Bender, John
jbender@unl.edu, Assoc. Prof., University of Nebraska-Lincoln, NE, Lincoln

Bender, Quinn ....(250) 638-7283
newsroom@terracestandard.com, Editor, The Terrace Standard, BC, Terrace

Bender, Ralph
rbender@theadvocate.com, CEO, Capital City Press, LA

Bender, Tony
redhead@drtel.net, Ed., The Ashley Tribune, ND, Ashley

Bender, Valerie......................(559) 441-6766
vbender@fresnobee.com, Pub., Vida en el Valle, CA, Fresno
vbender@fresnobee.com, VP Custom Pub, The Fresno Bee, CA, Fresno

Bendowski, Joseph
info@vansonink.com, Pres., Van Son Holland Ink Corp. of America, NY, Islandia

Benedetto, Linda ....(906) 341-4211
lbenedetto@manistiquepapers.com, Comptroller, Manistique Papers, Inc., MI, Manistique

Benedict, Helen
helen.benedict@pearson.com, Prof., Columbia University, NY, New York

Benedict, Kim ....(580) 223-2200
kim.benedict@ardmoreite.com, Pub., The Ardmoreite, OK, Ardmore

Benek, Christopher ....(330) 569-5203
Hiram College, OH, Hiram

Benes, Nick .... (402) 371-1020 ext. 240
nbenes@norfolkdailynews.com, Asst. Sports Ed., Norfolk Daily News, NE, Norfolk

Beneteau, Marty ....(519) 255-5714
mbeneteau@windsorstar.com, Ed.-in-Chief, The Windsor Star, ON, Windsor

Benevides, Eric ....(401) 767-8543
sports@pawtuckettimes.com, Sports Ed., The Times, RI, Pawtucket

Benfatti, Giene
gbenfatti@recordernewspapers.com, Digital Media Advisor, New Jersey Hills Media Group, NJ, Whippany

Benfield, Jennifer
jbenfield@corbinnewsjournal.com, Circ. Mgr., News Journal, KY, Corbin

Bengelsdorf, Peter....................(631) 843-2728
Dir., Publishing Devel., Newsday, NY, Melville

Bengfort, James ....(405) 605-6789
jbengfort@okgazette.com, Associate Pub., Oklahoma Gazette, OK, Oklahoma City

Bengston, Rodney ....(216) 986-2369
rbengston@sunnews.com, Asst. Ed., Sun News, OH, Cleveland

Beni, John L. ....(210) 450-7115
john_beni@parade.com, Vice Chrmn./COO, Parade, New York

Beniash, Michael
beniashm@caledonian-record.com, Sports Ed., The Caledonian-Record, VT, Saint Johnsbury

Benisch, Christine ....(608) 764-0299
cbenisch@hngnews.com, Circ. Mgr., DeForest Times-Tribune, WI, Windsor

Benishek, Megan
mbenishek@pleasantonexpress.com, Ad Sales, Pleasanton Express, TX, Pleasanton

Benitez, Ericka ....(760) 434-1223
ericka@benitez.news, Accounting Manager, Latino 247 Media Group, CA, Carlsbad

Benjamin, Carol
carol.icsg@sbcglobal.net, Gen. Mgr., Ionia County Shoppers Guide, MI, Saranac

Benjamin, Cynthia ....(585) 258-2322
cbenjami@democratandchronicle.com, Community Content Ed., Democrat and Chronicle, NY, Rochester

Benjamin, Denise....................(401) 767-8513
dbenjamin@woonsocketcall.com, Nat./Preprint Mgr., The Call, RI, Woonsocket

Benjamin, Jim
jbenjam@utnet.utoledo.edu, Chair, University of Toledo, OH, Toledo

Benjamin, Lee Ellen..................(903) 796-7133

production@casscountynow.com, Designer, Atlanta Citizens Journal, TX, Atlanta

Benjamin, Louise
louben@k-state.edu, Assoc. Prof./Ross Beach Chair, Kansas State University, KS, Manhattan

Benjamin, Tim
tim@accesspress.org, Publisher/Editor, Access Press, MN, Saint Paul

Benjamin, Vaughn P.
vpbenjamin@cfoadvisors.com, Dir., NEW YORK MEDIA CREDIT GROUP, NY, Buffalo

Benke, George
benke@math.georgetown.edu, Circ. Mgr., Washington Parent Magazine, MD, Bethesda

Benke, Louis..........................(210) 658-0614
lbenke@techenergy.com, Serv. Mgr., Tech-Energy Co., TX, Cibolo

Benkelman, Susan....................(202) 419-8458
sbenkelman@cq.com, Exec. Ed., News, Congressional Quarterly, Inc., DC, Washington

Benko Wylie, Mari ....(559) 897-2828
mwylie@fresnobee.com, VP Finance, Visalia Times-Delta, CA, Visalia

Benn, Kimberly
kbenn@desalesmedia.org, Adv. Sales Exec., The Tablet, NY, Brooklyn

Bennack, Frank
fbennack@hearst.com, Vice Chrmn./CEO, Hearst Communications, Inc., NY, New York

Benner, Amelia........................(217) 586-2512
abenner@news-gazette.com, Ed., Mahomet Citizen, IL, Mahomet

Bennes, Melinda
circulation@devilslakejournal.com, Circ. Mgr., Devils Lake Journal, ND, Devils Lake

Bennett, Becky ....(717) 262-4813
bbennett@publicopinionnews.com, Ed., Public Opinion, PA, Chambersburg

Bennett, Beth ....(608) 283-7621
beth.bennett@wnanews.com, Exec. Dir., Wisconsin Newspaper Association, WI, Madison

Bennett, Beth
bbennett@ua.edu, Assoc. Prof./Chair, Commun. Studies, University of Alabama, AL, Tuscaloosa

Bennett, Beverly ....(601) 961-7144
Nat'l Acct. Coord., Madison County Herald, MS, Ridgeland
Adv. Pre Prints, The Clarion-Ledger, MS, Jackson

Bennett, Brenda...............................ext. 236
brenda.bennett@rockdalecitizen.com, Adv. Dir., The Rockdale Citizen, GA, Conyers

Bennett, Brenda...............................ext. 236
brenda.bennett@rockdalecitizen.com, Adv. Dir., The Newton Citizen, GA, Conyers

Bennett, Carlin
publisher@enterprisecourier.com, Publisher, East Prairie Eagle & Enterprise-Courier, MO, East Prairie

Bennett, Charles
cbennett@turley.com, Ed., Wilbraham-Hampden Times, MA, Wilbraham

Bennett, Charlie
cbennett@turley.com, Pres., Valley Press Club, Inc., MA, Springfield

Bennett, Chris B.
chrisb@mediumnews.net, Co-Pub., Seattle Medium, WA, Seattle

Bennett, Deborah ....(613) 596-8530
dbennett@thecitizen.southam.ca, Vice Pres., HR/Finance, The Ottawa Citizen, ON, Ottawa

Bennett, Denise
dbennett@uidaho.edu, Fac., University of Idaho, ID, Moscow

Bennett, Grace ....(313) 222-5976
gbennett@freepress.com, Admin. Mgr., Detroit Free Press, MI, Detroit

Bennett, James ....(931) 388-6464
jbennett@c-dh.net, Ed., Columbia Daily Herald, TN, Columbia

Bennett, John
progress@ClearwaterProgress.com, Pub./Owner, The Clearwater Progress, ID, Kamiah

Bennett, Karen
karen.bennett@nashville.gov, Belmont Univ., TN, Nashville

Bennett, Mark ....(812) 231-4377
mark.bennett@tribstar.com, Columnist, The Tribune Star, IN, Terre Haute

Bennett, Marlene
mbennett@michigannewspapers.com, Adv. Mgr., Gladwin Buyers Guide, MI, Gladwin

Bennett, Marty ....(269) 694-9431
shoppersguide@sbcglobal.net, Community Shoppers Guide, MI, Otsego

Bennett, Michael
bennettm@mfri.com, Pub., Niles Daily Star, MI, Niles

Bennett, Michael
mb@brigadecapital.com, Circ. Mktg. Mgr., New York Law Journal, NY, New York

Bennett, Pam ....(304) 233-0100
pbennett@theintelligencer.net, Adv. Dir., The Intelligencer, WV, Wheeling

Bennett, Patricia Work
Info@ParentsKeepKidsSafe.com, Pres., Listening, Inc., Hobart

Bennett, Patty
pbennett@dailyitem.com, Sr. Adv. Dir., The Daily Item, PA, Sunbury
pbennett@dailyitem.com, Adv. Dir., Scrapbook, PA, Sunbury
pbennett@dailyitem.com, Adv. Dir., The Daily Item, MA, Lynn

Bennett, Raechel ....(802) 246-6397
ads@commonsnews.org, Adv. Dir., The Commons, VT, Brattleboro

Bennett, Rayanne
monitor@dioceseoftrenton.org, Assoc. Pub., The Monitor, NJ, Trenton

Bennett, Rhonda ....(641) 872-1234
rbennett@corydontimes.com, Pub, The Humeston News Era, IA, Corydon

Bennett, Rhonda
rbennett@corydontimes.com, Pub, Corydon Times Republican, IA, Corydon

Bennett, Richard
elder-warrior@comcast.net, Vice Pres., Listening, Inc., Hobart

Bennett, Rob
rbennett@unionleader.com, Circ. Mgr., Goffstown News, NH, Manchester

Bennett, Ron
rbennett@burkeblue.com, Rgl. IT Dir., The News Herald, FL, Panama City

Bennett, Steve
info@symantec.com, Pres./CEO, Symantec Corp., CA, Mountain View

Bennett, Susan
news@freedomforum.org, Vice Pres., Mktg., Freedom Forum, DC, Washington

Bennett, Susan
progress@ClearwaterProgress.com, Pub./Owner, The Clearwater Progress, ID, Kamiah

Bennett Harvey, Helen ....(203) 789-5730
State/City Ed., New Haven Register, CT, New Haven

Benning, Marlo
marlo@inhnews.com, Co-Pub., The Verndale Sun, MN, Verndale

Benning, Ray

ray@inhnews.com, Co-Pub., The Verndale
Sun, MN, Verndale

Benning, Ray
news@inhnews.com, Pub., Independent News
Herald, MN, Clarissa

Benoit, Dale
dale@printall.net, Ed., Plaquemines Gazette,
LA, Belle Chasse

Benoit, Steve ....(807) 343-6277
sbenoit@chroniclejournal.com, Mgr., Adv., The
Chronicle-Journal, ON, Thunder Bay

Benoit, Todd ....(207) 990-8299
tbenoit@bangordailynews.com, V.P./C.O.O.,
Bangor Daily News, ME, Bangor

Bensman, Robert ....(440) 331-0250
bensmanbob@yahoo.com, President, Ver-A-
Fast Corporation, OH, Rocky River

Benson, Dan ....(920) 453-5125
dbenson@sheboyganpress.com, Ed., The
Sheboygan Press, WI, Sheboygan

Benson, Darren ....(949) 731-4653
darren.benson@theeagle.com, News Ed., The
Eagle, TX, Bryan

Benson, Fred ....(843) 443-2470
fbenson@thesunnews.com, VP, Adv., The Sun
News, SC, Myrtle Beach

Benson, Ian
ibenson14@wooster.edu, College of Wooster,
OH, Wooster

Benson, Jake ....(218) 624-3344
journal@proctormn.com, Ed., Proctor Journal,
MN, Proctor

Benson, Robert .... ext. 3090
rbenson@registerbee.com, Editorial Page Ed.,
Danville Register & Bee, VA, Danville

Benson, Tim ....(401) 272-1122
IT director, Creative Circle Media Solutions, RI,
East Providence

Benson, Wanda ....(615) 321-3268
sales1501@aol.com, Assoc. Pub., Tennessee
Tribune, TN, Nashville

Bent, Michelle ....(972) 992-1771
WestEssexTribune@gmail.com, Editor, West
Essex Tribune, NJ, Livingston

Bent, Rhiannon ....(435) 652-7816
bent@dixie.edu, Dixie State College, UT, Saint
George

Benten, Anthony ....(212) 556-1713
bentent@nytimes.com, Sr. Vice Pres., New
England Newspaper Group, NY, New York
bentent@nytimes.com, Sr. Vice Pres., Finance/
Cor. Controller, The New York Times Co., NY,
New York
bentent@nytimes.com, The New York Times,
NY, New York

Bentlage, Gay
gbentlage@bnd.com, Adv. Mgr., Highland
News Leader, IL, Highland

Bentle, Mike ....(978) 371-5757
mbentle@wickedlocal.com, Sales Mgr.,
Arlington Advocate, MA, Lexington

Bentle, Mike
mbentle@wickedlocal.com, Adv. Mgr., Belmont
Citizen-Herald, MA, Lexington

Bentley, Christina ....(606) 528-7898 Ext. 40
newsroom@thetimestribune.com, Web/Special
Pages Ed., Times-Tribune, KY, Corbin

Bentley, Clyde
bentleycl@missouri.edu, Assoc. Prof.,
University of Missouri, MO, Columbia

Bentley, Susan
susanbentley@westondemocrat.com, Adv. Dir.,
Weston Democrat, WV, Weston

Bento, Avery
apbento@willamette.edu, Advisor, Willamette
Univ., OR, Salem

Benton, Bruce

darrell@diversifiedphoto.com , Opns. Mgr.,
Diversified Photo/Graphics Supply, CA,
Gardena

Benton, Gary
peddlerads@bellsouth.net, Adv. Mgr., The
Peddler/advantage, TN, Paris

Benton, Gary
peddlerads@bellsouth.net, Peddler Advantage,
TN, Paris

Benton, Jackie
news@mackenzietimes.com, Pub/Ed, The
Times, BC, Mackenzie

Benton, Malena ....ext. 122
malena@lanoticia.com, Art. Dir., La Noticia,
NC, Charlotte

Benton, Melinda ....(541) 440-4687
melinda.benton@umpqua.edu, Umpqua Cmty.
College, OR, Roseburg

Benton, Nicholas F. ....(703) 532-3267
nfbenton@fcnp.com, Owner/Pub./Ed., Falls
Church News-Press, VA, Falls Church

Benton, Sherry Hagerman ....(406) 827-3421
ledgerads@blackfoot.net, Adv. Mgr., Sanders
County Ledger, MT, Thompson Falls

Bentz, Bob ....(416) 800-2490
bobb@advancedtele.com, Dir. of Marketing,
Advanced Telecom Services, Inc. (Canada),
PA, King Of Prussia

Benyr, Amanda ....(618) 239-2607
abenyr@bnd.com, Adv., Belleville News-
Democrat, IL, Belleville

Benz, Cole
therald@countrymedia.net, Ed. , The Herald,
ND, New England
therald@countrymedia.net, Ed., Adams County
Record, ND, Hettinger

Benz, Kim ....(312) 527-8473
kbenz@hoyllc.com, Director of Sales Strategy,
Hoy LLC, CA, Los Angeles

Benzie-Lourey, Marlana
askovamerican@scicable.com, Ed., Askov
American, MN, Askov

Benziger, Jeff
jbenziger@cerescourier.com, Ed., The Ceres
Courier, CA, Turlock

Bequeath, Tina ....(724) 775-3200 x111
tbequeath@timesonline.com, Controller,
Beaver County Times, PA, Beaver

Berblinger, Gary ....(573) 431-2010 ext. 3636
gberblinger@dailyjournalonline.com, Pub.,
Daily Journal, Park Hills, MO, Park Hills

Berdahl, Christopher
cberdahl@forumcomm.com, Director of
Circulation, Forum Communications Co.,
ND, Fargo

Berdell, Lindsay
lberdell@tribweb.com, Trib Total Media, Inc.,
PA, Pittsburgh

Bereuter, Cheyenne ....(325) 773-5100
cheyenne@thestamfordstar.com, Pub./Ed., The
Stamford Star, TX, Stamford

Berezansky, Bo ....(518) 439-4949 x 417
bo@spotlightnews.com, VP of Advertising,
Spotlight Newspapers, NY, Delmar
bo@spotlightnews.com, VP of Sales, Colonie/
Loudonville Spotlight, NY, Delmar
bo@spotlightnews.com, Ad., The Spotlight,
NY, Delmar

Berg, Amy
aberg@easyreader.info, Dispaly Sales, Easy
Reader, CA, Hermosa Beach

Berg, Barry ....(561) 820-4650
bberg@pbpost.com, Circ. Vice Pres., The Palm
Beach Post, FL, West Palm Beach

Berg, Carl
carlb@metrosn.com, Sr. Vice Pres./Midwest
Sales Dir., Metro Newspaper Advertising
Services, Inc., NY, New York

Berg, Janine ....(701) 642-8585
circulation@wahpetondailynews.com, Circ.
Clerk, The Daily News, ND, Wahpeton

Berg, Larry ....(734) 432-8000
bergl@valassis.com, VP of ROP Sales,
Valassis, MI, Livonia

Berg, Rich
rberg@mva.com, Nat'l Sales Mgr., MicroVoice
Applications, Inc., MN, Minneapolis

Berg, Tony
tberg@kcstar.com, Pres./Pub., The Kansas
City Star, MO, Kansas City

Bergen, Lori
bergen@txstate.edu, Prof./Dir., Texas State
University-San Marcos, TX, San Marcos

Bergendahl, Wendie
wendieb@meadvilletribune.com, Classifieds
Adv. Mgr., The Meadville Tribune, PA,
Meadville

Bergenheim, Roger ....(401) 680-4848
publisher@pbn.com, Pub., Providence
Business News, RI, Providence

Berger, Adam
aberger@actionshopperonline.com, Pub.,
Action Shopper, MI, Marquette

Berger, Angela
sales.theprogress@gmail.com, Adv. Mgr., The
Clearwater Progress, ID, Kamiah

Berger, Betsy ....(206) 768-6477
bberger@sccd.ctc.edu, South Seattle Cmty.
College, WA, Seattle

Berger, Bill ....(512) 407-8283
billberger@austin.rr.com, Pres., Associated
Texas Newspapers, Inc., TX, Austin

Berger, Charlotte
sales@newsandpressonline.com, Adv. Mgr.,
The News & Press, SC, Darlington

Berger, Eric
piedmontgazette@sbcglobal.net, Mng. Ed., The
Piedmont-Surrey Gazette, OK, Piedmont

Berger, Erik
orkarchechieftain@sbcglobal.net, Mng. Ed.,
Chieftain, OK, Piedmont

Berger, Jeff ....(830) 426-3346
anvil@hondo.net, Pub./Ed., Hondo Anvil
Herald, TX, Hondo

Berger, Jeff
anvil@hondo.net, Vice Pres., Associated Texas
Newspapers, Inc., TX, Austin

Berger, Jessica
jberger@westianet.net, Office Asst., Westside
Observer, IA, Westside

Berger, Lori ....(516) 569-4000, ext. 228
lberger@liherald.com, Adv. Manager
PrimeTime Xpress, Primetime, NY, Garden
City

Berger, Melanie ....(361) 865-3510
admanager@flatoniaargus.com, Office Mgr./
Reporter/Photo., The Flatonia Argus, TX,
Flatonia

Berger, Nancee
nrberger@west.com, Pres., West Interactive
Corp., NE, Omaha

Berger, Pam
pam@ominecaexpress.com, Pub./Sales Mgr.,
Caledonia Courier, BC, Fort St. James

Berger, Pam
publisher@ominecaexpress.com, Pub./Sales
Mgr, Vanderhoof Omineca Express, BC,
Vanderhoof

Berger, Teufel
fibersplastics@teufelberger.com, Owner,
Teufelberger GmbH, Wels

Bergeron, Parise
parise.bergeron@monteregieweb.com, Adv.
Rep., Journal La Voix, QC, Sorel

Bergeron, Tricia ....(831) 385-4880 x 21

editor@southcountynewspapers.com, Gen.
Mgr., The Rustler, CA, King City
editor@southcountynewspapers.com, Ed./Gen.
Mgr., Gonzales Tribune, CA, King City
editor@southcountynewspapers.com, Ed./Gen
Mgr., Greenfield News, CA, King City

Bergerson, Ginny ....(507) 444-2386
gbergerson@owatonna.com, Advertising
Director, Owatonna People's Press, MN,
Owatonna

Bergerson, Ginny ....(507) 344-6339
gbergerson@mankatofreepress.com, Adv. Dir.,
The Free Press, MN, Mankato

Bergerson, Ginny ....(507) 444-2386
gbergerson@owatonna.com, Ad Dir, Owatonna
Area Shopper, MN, Owatonna

Berggreen, Shu-Ling
shu-ling.berggreen@colorado.edu, Assoc.
Prof./Head, Media Studies seq., University of
Colorado, CO, Boulder

Bergin, Mary ....(608) 274-8925
info@roadstraveled.com, Columnist, Midwest
Features Syndicate, Madison

Bergland, Robert
bergland@missouriwestern.edu, Missouri
Western State University, MO, Saint Joseph

Bergman, Ashley
abergman@dailynews.net, Sales Associate,
The Hays Daily News, KS, Hays

Bergman, Julie ....(218) 230-8943
julie@wiktel.com, V.P., Head of Newspaper
Division, Grimes, McGovern & Associates,
NY, New York
julie@wiktel.com, Sr. Associate-Midwest/
Plains States, W.B. Grimes & Company, MD,
Gaithersburg
julie@wiktel.com, Senior Associate-Midwest,
Lewis Floyd- Grimes, W.B. & Co., AL, Gulf
Shores

Bergman, Kim ....(330) 841-1620
kbergman@tribtoday.com, Adv. Dir., Canfield
Town Crier, OH, Warren
kbergman@tribtoday.com, Adv. Dir., Poland
Town Crier, OH, Warren
kbergman@tribtoday.com, Adv. Dir., Boardman
Town Crier, OH, Warren
kbergman@tribtoday.com, Adv. Dir., Austintown
Town Crier, OH, Warren

Bergman, Rollin
exponent@grandforkspolaristel.net, Mng. Ed.,
The Exponent, MN, East Grand Forks

Bergman, Rollin ....(218) 782-2275
tribune@wiktel.com, Pub., Tribune, MN,
Greenbush

Berian, Lisa ....(478) 744-4245
lberrian@macon.com, Vp of Advertising, The
Telegraph, GA, Macon

Berkeley, Kaki ....(919) 836-5997
kberkeley@newsobserver.com, Adv. Dir.,
Clayton News-Star, NC, Raleigh
kberkeley@newsobserver.com, Adv Dir,
Southwest Wake News, NC, Cary
kberkeley@newsobserver.com, Adv. Mgr.,
Eastern Wake News, NC, Raleigh
kberkeley@newsobserver.com, Adv. Dir.,
Garner-Cleveland Record, NC, Raleigh
kberkeley@newsobserver.com, Ad. Dir., The
Cary News, NC, Raleigh
kberkeley@newsobserver.com, Adv. Mgr., The
Durham News, NC, Chapel Hill
kberkeley@newsobserver.com, Adv. Dir., The
Smithfield Herald-OOB, NC, SMITHFIELD

Berkery, Sheri ....(856) 486-2673
sberkery@gannettnj.com, Reg. Prod., The
Courier-Post, NJ, Cherry Hill

Berkovich , Karlo
kberkovich@therecord.com, Online Ed., The
Record, ON, Kitchener

Berkowitz, Roberta
info@ngspcb.com, Vice Pres.-Nat'l Accts./
Opns., National Graphic Supply Corp., NY,
Albany

Berkshire, Forrest
fberkshire@kystandard.com , Ed, Kentucky Standard, KY, Bardstown

Berlin, Eric
enquirerdemocrat@yahoo.com, Cir.Mgr, Enquirer Express, IL, Carlinville

Berlo, Trina
trina@creemore.com, Ed., Creemore Echo, ON, Creemore

Berman, Brian L.
brains@voiceworld.com, Pres., VoiceWorld, AZ, Scottsdale

Berman, Brian L.
brains@voiceworld.com, Pres./Founder, VoiceWorld, Inc., AZ, Scottsdale

Berman, Judith .... **(410) 332-6565**
jberman@baltsun.com, Sr. VP Sales & Mkting., Catonsville Times, MD, Baltimore
jberman@baltsun.com, Sr VP Sales & Mkting., Columbia Flier, MD, Columbia
jberman@baltsun.com, Sr VP Sales & Mkting, Baltimore Messenger-OOB, MD, BALTIMORE
jberman@baltsun.com, Sr. VP, Sales/Mktg, Arbutus Times, MD, Baltimore
jberman@baltsun.com, Sr VP Sales & Mkting, The Record, MD, Bel Air
jberman@baltsun.com, Sr VP Sales & Mkting, Northeast Booster Reporter-OOB, MD, TOWSON
jberman@baltsun.com, Sr VP Sales & Mkting, The Aegis, MD, Baltimore
jberman@baltsun.com, Sr VP Sales & Mkting, Jeffersonian, MD, Towson
jberman@baltsun.com, Sr. VP. Sales/Mktg., The Weekender, MD, Bel Air
jberman@baltsun.com, Sr VP Sales & Mkting, Howard County Times, MD, Columbia
jberman@baltsun.com, Sr VP Sales & Mkting, Owings Mills Times, MD, Baltimore
jberman@baltsun.com, Sr. VP, Sales/Mktg., Towson Times, MD, Baltimore

Berman, Margo
bermanm@fiu.edu, Assoc. Prof., Florida International University, FL, North Miami

Bernal, Katherine .... **ext. 254**
Prodn. Mgr., The Scarborough Mirror, ON, Toronto

Bernal, Katherine .... **(416) 493-4400 ext. 250**
Prodn. Mgr., The East York Mirror, ON, Willowdale

Bernard, Alain .... **(819) 379-1490**
alain.bernard@transcontinental.ca, Sales Mgr., L'hebdo Journal, QC, Trois-Rivieres

Bernard, Barry
bbernard@candgnews.com, Prod. Mgr., Warren Weekly, MI, Warren

Bernard, Barry
bbernard@candgnews.com, Prod. Mgr., Farmington Press, MI, Warren
bbernard@candgnews.com, Prod. Mgr., Rochester Post, MI, Warren
bbernard@candgnews.com, Prod. Mgr, Royal Oak Review, MI, Warren
bbernard@candgnews.com, Prod. Mgr, Southfield Sun, MI, Warren
bbernard@candgnews.com, Prod. Mgr, West Bloomfield Beacon, MI, Warren
bbernard@candgnews.com, Prod. Mgr, St. Clair Shores Sentinel, MI, Warren
bbernard@candgnews.com, Prod. Mgr, Birmingham-Bloomfield Eagle, MI, Warren
bbernard@candgnews.com, Prod. Mgr, Woodward Talk, MI, Warren
bbernard@candgnews.com, Prod. Mgr, Madison-Park News, MI, Warren
bbernard@candgnews.com, Prod. Mgr, The Eastsider, MI, Warren
bbernard@candgnews.com, Prod. Mgr, Macomb Chronicle, MI, Warren
bbernard@candgnews.com, Prod. Mgr, Fraser-Clinton Chronicle, MI, Warren
bbernard@candgnews.com, Prod. Mgr, Troy Times, MI, Warren
bbernard@candgnews.com, Prod. Mgr, Grosse

Pointe Times, MI, Warren
bbernard@candgnews.com, Prod. Mgr, Advertiser Times, MI, Warren
bbernard@candgnews.com, Prod. Mgr, Shelby-Utica News, MI, Warren
bbernard@candgnews.com, Prod. Mgr, Journal, MI, Warren

Bernard, Barry
bbernard@candgnews.com, Prodn. Mgr., Sterling Heights Sentry, MI, Warren

Bernard, Beth .... **(209) 223-8763**
bbarnard@ledger.news, Adv. Dir., Amador Ledger-Dispatch, CA, Jackson

Bernard, Cathy
cathybernard@canadafrancais.com, Pub., Le Guide De Cowansville, QC, Cowansville

Bernard, Daniel
d.bernard@elsevier.com, Gen. Mgr., WSJ.com, The Wall Street Journal, NY, New York
d.bernard@elsevier.com, Chief Product Officer, USA TODAY, VA, Mc Lean

Bernard, Eric
direction@oieblanc.com, Ed., La Petite Nation, QC, Saint Andre-Avellin

Bernard, Jim .... **(612) 673-4477**
jim.bernard@startribune.com, Sr. VP, Digital, Star Tribune, MN, Minneapolis

Bernard, Julie
julie.bernard@nopg.com, Production Mgr., New Orleans City Business, LA, Metairie

Bernard, Patrick
patrick.bernard@fandm.edu, Franklin & Marshall College, PA, Lancaster

Bernard, Ron
rbernard@crestonnews.com, Circ. Mgr., Southwest Iowa Advertiser, IA, Creston

Bernard, Sallie
sbernard@safeminds.org, Pres., ARC Research, NJ, Cranford

Bernat, Cheryl Mrs. .... **(401) 364-6061**
cheryl@motterstitch.com, Secretary, Motterstitch Company, Inc., RI, Carolina

Bernbry, Jacob
jacob@greenepublishing.com, Editor, Madison Enterprise-Recorder, FL, Madison
jacob@greenepublishing.com, Editor, Madison County Carrier, FL, Madison

Berneking, Meghan
mberneking@cincinnatisymphony.org, Xavier Univ., OH, Cincinnati

Berner, Fred .... **(715) 623-4191**
adj@dwave.net, Pub, Ed, Journal Express, WI, Antigo

Berner, Fred A. .... **(715) 623-4191**
adj@dwave.net, Pub./Ed./Adv. Dir., Antigo Daily Journal, WI, Antigo

Bernhard, Adam .... **(330) 972-5912**
business-manager@buchtelite.com, Business Manager, The University of Akron, OH, Akron

Bernhard, Andy
ab@parkrecord.com, Pub., Park Record, UT, Park City

Bernhardt, Jeff
jbernhardt@presteligence.com, Major Accnt. Mgr., Presteligence, OH, North Canton

Bernier, Gilbert .... **(418) 228-8858**
gilbert.bernier@quebecormedia.com, Gen. Mgr., L'eclaireur-progres/beauce Nouvelles, QC, Saint Georges
gilbert.bernier@quebecormedia.com, Beauce Media, QC, Sainte Marie-de-Beauce
gilbert.bernier@quebecormedia.com, Progres De Bellechasse, QC, Saint Georges

Berns, Francie
francie.berns@latimes.com, VP, Film Advertising , Los Angeles Times, CA, Los Angeles

Bernsee, Eric
ebernsee@bannergraphic.com, Ed., Banner-

Graphic, IN, Greencastle

Bernsen, Charles .... **(615) 354-1653**
charles@jewishnashville.org, Editor, The Jewish Observer, TN, Nashville

Bernstein, Sanford
sbernstein@rockawave.com, Gen. Mgr., The Wave, NY, Rockaway Beach

Bernstein Saylor, Hali .... **(702) 586-9523**
hsaylor@bouldercityreview.com, Ed, Boulder City Review, NV, Boulder City

Bernt, Joseph .... **(740) 593-2589**
berntj@ohiou.edu, Prof./Assoc. Dir., Grad. Studies/Research, Ohio University, OH, Athens

Bernthal, Ron .... **(845) 292-3071**
ronbernthal@wjffradio.org, Self-Syndicator, Travel/Historic Preservation Audio Programs, Ron Bernthal, Hurleyville

Berrian, Lisa .... **(478) 744-4245**
lberrian@macon.com, Adv. Mgr., Retail, The Telegraph, GA, Macon

Berrier, Kevin .... **(410) 857-8554**
kevin.berrier@carrollcountytimes.com, Commercial Printing Consultant , Carroll County Times, MD, Westminster

Berry, Abel
lavoznj@aol.com, Pub., La Voz, NJ, Elizabeth

Berry, Bobby .... **(478) 745-4141**
berryb@wcbi.com, COO - Morris Network, Morris Multimedia, Inc., GA, Savannah

Berry, Dave .... **(417) 777-9776**
daveb@mo.neighbornews.com, The Republic Monitor, MO, Republic
daveb@mo.neighbornews.com, Pub, The Marshfield Mail, MO, Marshfield

Berry, Dave
daveb@phillipsmedia.com, Pub., Nixa Enterprise (OOB), MO, Nixa
daveb@phillipsmedia.com, Vice Pres., Community Publishers, Inc., AR, Bentonville

Berry, Dave .... **(417) 468-2013**
mailads@cpimo.com, Pub., The Edge, MO, Marshfield

Berry, Dave
daveb@bolivarmonews.com, Pub., Christian County Headliner News, MO, Ozark
daveb@bolivarmonews.com, Pub, South County Mail, MO, Rogersville

Berry, Dave .... **(903) 596-6238**
dvberry@tylerpaper.com, Mng. Ed., Tyler Morning Telegraph, TX, Tyler

Berry, Dave
daveb@cpimo.com, Pub., Bolivar Herald-Free Press, MO, Bolivar

Berry, Dave .... **(417) 777-9776**
daveb@mo.neighbornews.com, Vice Pres., publisher, Community Publishers, Inc./Neighbor News, AR, Bolivar

Berry, John .... **(609) 429-7442**
jberry@21st-centurymedia.com, Ed., The Middletown Press, CT, Middletown
jberry@21st-centurymedia.com, Mng. Ed. , The Central Record, NJ, Medford

Berry, John .... **(609) 349-7442**
jberry@trentonian.com, Ed. , The Trentonian, NJ, Trenton

Berry, John .... **(860) 489-3121 ext. 333**
jberry@21st-centurymedia.com, Ed., West Hartford News, CT, New Haven
jberry@21st-centurymedia.com, Ed., The Register Citizen, CT, Torrington

Berry, John
jberry@enquirer.com, Major Sales & Marketing Manager, The Cincinnati Enquirer, OH, Cincinnati

Berry, Mike .... **(309) 852-2181**
mberry@starcourier.com, Assoc. Ed. , Star-Courier, IL, Kewanee

---

Berry, Patrick
patrickberry@thewestfieldnewsgroup.com, Pres., The Westfield News , MA, Westfield

Berry, Patrick
patrickberry@thewestfieldnewsgroup.com, President/Owner, Pennysaver, MA, Westfield

Berry, Paul
pberry@news-leader.com, Exec. Ed., Springfield News-Leader, MO, Springfield

Berry, Ryan .... **(937) 548-0851 ext. 224**
rberry@earlybirdpaper.com, Mng. Ed., The Early Bird, OH, Greenville

Berry, Stan
sberry@darnews.com, Editor, Daily American Republic, MO, Poplar Bluff

Berry, Tom
tberry@mayfield-messenger.com, Ed., The Mayfield Messenger, KY, Mayfield

Berry, Vivian .... **(308) 882-4453**
Accounts Payable manager , Imperial Republican, NE, Imperial

Berry, Wanda
wanda@franklinsun.com, Public Notice/Class., The Franklin Sun, LA, Winnsboro

Berry, Zuri .... **(617) 619-6514**
zuri.berry@bostonherald.com, Multimedia Ed., Boston Herald, MA, Boston

Berryhill, Michael
mberryhill@uh.edu, Asst. Prof., University of Houston, TX, Houston

Berryman, Mark
starexaminer@elberton.com, Mng. Ed., The Elberton Star, GA, Elberton

Bertelson, Kylie
kylie.bertelson@woodbinetwiner.com, Adv. Rep., The Woodbine Twiner, IA, Woodbine

Bertetto, Keith .... **(412) 321-6460**
Exec. Dir. Prodn., Trib Total Media, Inc., PA, Pittsburgh

Bertetto , Jennifer .... **(724) 779-7160**
jbertetto@tribweb.com, Pres/CEO, Trib Total Media, Inc., PA, Pittsburgh

Berthiaume, Ed. .... **(920) 993-1000**
eberthiaume@postcrescent.com, Editor/Sports & Features, Post-Crescent, WI, Appleton

Berthiaume, Johanne
j.berthiaume@journallavoix.net, Ed., Journal La Voix, QC, Sorel

Berting, Bob .... **(317) 849-5408**
bob@bobberting.com, Pres., Berting Communications, IN, Indianapolis

Bertling, Terry
tbertling@express-news.net, New Publications & Special Projects Ed., San Antonio Express-News, TX, San Antonio

Bertoglio, John
bertoglio@pulseresearch.com, CIO, Pulse Research, Inc., OR, Portland

Bertok, Mike
mikeb@mywebtimes.com, Adv. Dir., The Times, IL, Ottawa

Bertolotti, Joseph
mbertol@us.ibm.com, Program Dir., GLBT Sales/Talent, IBM Corp., NY, Armonk

Berton, Paul
pberton@thespec.com, Ed. in Chief, The Hamilton Spectator, ON, Hamilton

Bertosa, John
jbertosa@news-herald.com, Mng. Ed., The News-Herald, OH, Willoughby

Bertrand, Guy .... **(250) 364-1242 ext. 211**
editor@trailtimes.ca, Editor, Trail Daily Times, BC, Trail

Bertsch, Carolyn .... **(320) 363-7741**
assignmenteditor@thenewsleaders.com, Assignment Editor, Sartell Newsleader, MN, Saint Joseph

Bertsch, Carolyn .... (320) 363-7741
assignmenteditor@thenewsleaders.com,
Assignment Editor, St. Joseph Newsleader,
MN, Saint Joseph

Berube, Breandan
mnews@salmonpress.com, Ed., The Gilford
Steamer, NH, Meredith

Berube, Brendan
record@salmonpress.com, Ed., Plymouth
Record Enterprise, NH, Meredith

Besant, Craig .... (414) 224-2019
craig.besant@jmg.com, Journal Media Group,
Sr. Dir., Dig. Rev. & Products, Milwaukee
Journal Sentinel, WI, Milwaukee

Besley, Glen
gbesley@lfpress.com, Mgmt. Info Servs. Mgr.,
The London Free Press, ON, London

Besonen, Nancy .... (906) 524-6197
sentinel1886@gmail.com, Reporter, L'Anse
Sentinel, MI, Lanse

Bess, Caralyn .... (864) 562-7350
caralyn.bess@shj.com, Dir. of Adv., Herald-
Journal, SC, Spartanburg

Bess, Jennifer .... (936) 632-2607
jbess@lufkindailynews.com, Business
Manager, The Lufkin Daily News, TX, Lufkin

Bessen, Jeff .... (516) 569-4000 x201
Executive Ed., Franklin Square/Elmont Herald,
NY, Garden City
Ed., Nassau Herald, NY, Garden City

Besser, Suzanne
sbesser@beaconhilltimes.com, Mng. Ed., The
Beacon Hill Times, MA, Boston

Bessette, Alain .... (867) 873-6603
aquilon@internorth.com, Ed., L'aquilon, NT,
Yellowknife

Best, Bonitta
editor@triangletribune.com, Ed., The Triangle
Tribune, NC, Durham

Best, John
john@bayobserver.ca, Pub., The Bay Observer,
ON, Hamilton

Best, Kathy
editor@ravallirepublic.com, Ed., Ravalli
Republic, MT, Hamilton
editor@ravallirepublic.com, Ed., Missoulian,
MT, Missoula

Best, Peter
homesandestates@aol.com, Pub., Homes &
Estates Magazine, NJ, Morristown

Best, Robert R.
newspro@newsprogress.com, Pub., News-
Progress, IL, Sullivan

Best, Shannon .... (910) 249-4611
Media Dir., The Sampson Independent, NC,
Clinton

Besterfeldt, Kim
accounting@timesnewspapers.com, Circ. Mgr,
West End Word, MO, Saint Louis
accounting@timesnewspapers.com, Circ. Mgr,
South County Times, MO, Saint Louis
accounting@timesnewspapers.com, Circ. Mgr,
Webster-Kirkwood Times, Inc., MO, Saint
Louis

Beswick, Anne
abeswick@yrmg.com, Retail Adv. Mgr., The
Richmond Hill Liberal, ON, Markham

Betancourt, Jorge .... (702) 477-3847
jbetancourt@reviewjournal.com, Art Director,
El Tiempo, NV, Las Vegas

Betancourt-Lewis, Carmen .... (305) 358-1008
cblewis@miamitodaynews.com, VP, Miami
Today, FL, Miami

Beth, Kathrin
info@wochenpostusa.com, Pub.,
Nordamerikaniche Wochenpost, MI, Troy

Beth Carr, Mary
mcarr@alaskanewspapers.com, Adv. Rep., The

Cordova Times, AK, Cordova

Beth Futa, Lynsey .... (808) 529-4861
lfuta@marinestarhi.com, Ed, Marine Star, HI,
Mcbh Kaneohe Bay

Beth Jackson, Nancy
nancybeth.jackson@zu.ac.ae, Assoc. Prof.,
Zayed University, Al Ruwayyah

Bethke, Carla
CarlaB@milehighnews.com, Acct. Mgr.,
Milehigh Newspapers, CO, Golden

Bettis, Mitch .... (501) 372-1443
mbettis@abpg.com, Pub, Little Rock Family,
AR, Little Rock

Bettis, Mitch
mbettis@abpg.com, Pres., Arkansas Business
Publishing Group, AR
mbettis@abpg.com, Pub., Stuttgart Daily
Leader, AR, Stuttgart

Betts, Crystal
amy.ero@dallasobserver.com, Prod. Mgr.,
Dallas Observer, TX, Dallas

Betts, Patricia .... (828) 274-8888
pbetts@iwanna.com, Advertising Manager,
Iwanna, NC, Asheville

Betz, Emily .... (515) 628-5239
Central College, IA, Pella

Betz, Tim .... (330) 996-3599
tbetz@thebeaconjournal.com, Controller,
Akron Beacon Journal, OH, Akron

Betzner, Jessyka
Jessyka.Betzner@kokomotribune.com,
Customer Serice Rep./NIE Coord., Kokomo
Tribune, IN, Kokomo

Beutler, Patty
pbeutler@journalstar.com, Focus Ed., Lincoln
Journal Star, NE, Lincoln

Beveridge, Lici .... (601) 584-3104
lbeveridge@hattiesburgamerican.com,
Engagement Ed. , Hattiesburg American,
MS, Hattiesburg

Beverly, Cal
editor@thecitizen.com, Pub., The Citizen, GA,
Fayetteville

Beverly, Joyce
jbeverly@thecitizen.com, Adv. Sales Dir., The
Citizen, GA, Fayetteville

Bevil, Bob
spectator@centurytel.net, Pub., The Spectator,
AR, Ozark

Bevil, Pat .... (479) 667-2136
Circ. Mgr., The Spectator, AR, Ozark

Bevilacqua, Christina .... (401) 767-8503
classified@woonsocketcall.com, Class. Adv. ,
The Call, RI, Woonsocket

Bevins, Doug .... (203) 317-2228
dbevins@record-journal.com, Copy Desk
Chief, Record-Journal, CT, Meriden

Bewick, Michael
michael.bewick@timesheraldnewspapers.com,
Pub., Dearborn Times-Herald, MI, Dearborn

Bewley, Shelley .... (919) 836-5909
sbewley@newsobserver.com, Adv Sales Mgr,
Midtown Raleigh News, NC, Raleigh

Bexley, Kelly
kbexley@dothaneagle.com, Prodn. Mgr.,
Dothan Progress, AL, Dothan

Beyal, Duane .... (928) 871-1136
editor@navajotimes.com, Editor, Navajo Times
Publishing Company, Inc., AZ, Window Rock

Beyer, Bill
bbeyer@djcOregon.com, Adv. Mgr., Daily
Journal of Commerce, OR, Portland

Beym, Jessica .... (856) 754-7133
jbeym@njadvancemedia.com, Community
Editor, South Jersey Times , NJ, Mullica Hill

Beym, Jessica .... (856) 754-7133
jbeym@njadvancemedia.com, Comm. Ed.,

South Jersey Times , NJ, Mullica Hill

Bhalia, Anil
info@minacs.adityabirla.com, COO, Aditya
Birla Minacs, MI, Farmington Hills

Bhambri, Rajeev
rajeevb@indiaabroad.com, COO - US Media,
India Abroad, NY, New York

Bhatia, Peter .... (513) 768-8551
pbhatia@enquirer.com, Ed. & VP of Audience
Engagement, The Cincinnati Enquirer, OH,
Cincinnati

Bhatia, Peter
peterkbhatia@gmail.com, Pres, Accrediting
Council on Education in Journalism and
Mass Communications, KS, Lawrence

Bhatt, Nimit .... (410) 455-1261
Univ. of Maryland Baltimore County, MD,
Baltimore

Bhatti, Michelle
mbhatti@vancourier.com, Mktg Dir, The
Vancouver Courier, BC, Vancouver

Bhogal, Ramneek
jason.langslet@palmer.edu, Palmer College of
Chiropractic, IA, Davenport

Bhoj, Durga
durga.bhoj@latimes.com, Div. Mgr., Los
Angeles Times, CA, Los Angeles

Bhuiyan, Rafique .... (306) 999-3077
info@thejogajog.com, Chief Editor, The Weekly
Jogajog, SK, Regina

Bhuiyan, Serajul
sbhuiyan@lincoln.edu, Prof./Dir., Lincoln
University of the Commonwealth of
Pennsylvania, PA, Lincoln University

Biafore, Mia .... (304) 626-1463
mbiafore@theet.com, Key Account Manager,
The Exponent Telegram, WV, Clarksburg

Bialka, Mike
mike.bialka@brainerddispatch.com, Sports
Ed., Brainerd Dispatch, MN, Brainerd

Bialo, Ellen
ebialo@iesdinc.com, Pres., Interactive
Educational Systems Design, Inc., NY, New
York

Bialorucki, Joe .... (419) 724-6483
jbialorucki@toledoblade.com, Circulation
Manager, Operations, The Blade, OH, Toledo

Bianco, Deborah
dbianco@timesonline.com, Classifieds Adv.
Dir., Beaver County Times, PA, Beaver

Bice, Robin
ads@leader-call.net, Gen. Mgr., Laurel Leader-
Call, MS, Laurel

Bichard, Shannon
shannon.bichard@ttu.edu, Asst. Prof., Texas
Tech University, TX, Lubbock

Bickel, Amy .... (620) 694-5700 Ext. 320
abickel@hutchnews.com, Agland Ed. , The
Hutchinson News, KS, Hutchinson

Bickel, Eileen
ebickel@njnpublishing.com, Vice Pres., Adv.,
Suburban News, NJ, New Providence
ebickel@njnpublishing.com, Pub./Adv. Mgr.,
Hunterdon Observer, NJ, Flemington

Bickel, Eileen
union@njnpublishing.com, Pub., Cranford
Chronicle, NJ, New Providence

Bickel, Mark .... (239) 344-0347
mbickel@news-press.com, Consumer
Experience Dir., The Commercial Appeal,
TN, Memphis

Bickert, Tom .... (724) 775-3200 ext. 155
tbickert@timesonline.com, Mng. Ed., Content,
Beaver County Times, PA, Beaver

Bickford, Josh
jbickford@eastbaynewpapers.com, Ed., Bristol
Phoenix, RI, Bristol
jbickford@eastbaynewpapers.com, Ed.,

Barrington Times, RI, Bristol

Biderman, David
david.biderman@wsj.com, Director, The Wall
Street Journal, NY, New York

Bidinger, Elizabeth
elizabeth.bidinger@worcester.edu, Worcester
State College, MA, Worcester

Bieber, Alec
abieber@adirondackdailyenterprise.com,
Circ. Mgr., Adirondack Daily Enterprise, NY,
Saranac Lake

Bieber, Denise .... (214) 977-8823
dbeeber@dallasnews.com, Editor/The Daily,
The Dallas Morning News, TX, Dallas

Bieberly, Clifford
cbieberl@chaminade.edu, Dir., Chaminade,
University of Honolulu, HI, Honolulu

Biehn, Kristie
kbiehn@wasecacountynews.com, Adv.,
Waseca County News, MN, Waseca

Bielema, Charlene
cbielema@clintonherald.com, Ed., Clinton
Herald, IA, Clinton

Bielss, Gayle .... (254) 527-4424
Pub./Ed./Adv. Dir., Tribune-Progress, TX,
Bartlett

Bienvenu, Henri .... (337) 394-6232
Teche News, LA, Saint Martinville

Bierbauer, Charles
bierbauer@sc.edu, Prof./Dean, College of
Mass Commun. and Information Studies,
University of South Carolina, SC, Columbia

Biermann, Tom .... (309) 757-4924
Tom.Biermann@lee.net, General Manager, The
Dispatch-Argus, IL, Moline

Biermann, Tom .... (307) 266-0526
tom.biermann@trib.com, Pub, Casper Star-
Tribune, WY, Casper

Biesk, Joe
jbiesk@tribpub.com, Ed., Post-Tribune, IN,
Crown Point
jbiesk@tribpub.com, Ed., Lake County News-
Sun, IL, Gurnee
jbiesk@tribpub.com, Ed., The Herald News,
IL, Chicago

Biesk, Joe .... (312) 222-2425
jbiesk@tribpub.com, Ed., Daily Southtown,
IL, Aurora

Bigelow, Bill .... (541) 383-0359
bbigelow@bendbulletin.com, Sports Ed., The
Bulletin, OR, Bend

Biggs, Charles .... (918) 523-4425
charlesbiggs@tulsabeacon.com, Ed., Tulsa
Beacon, OK, Tulsa

Biggs, Don .... (519) 673-5005 ext. 516421
don.biggs@sunmedia.ca, Reg. Ed. , The
Strathroy Age Dispatch, ON, Strathroy

Biggs, John H.
tcnews@bellsouth.net, Pub., Tishomingo
County News, MS, Iuka

Biggs, Mark
markbiggs@missouristate.edu, Assoc. Prof.,
Missouri State University, MO, Springfield

Bikowicz, Pam .... (321) 402-0402
pbikowicz@osceolanewsgazette.com,
Accounting, Osceola News-gazette, FL,
Kissimmee

Bilbey, Ryan .... ext. 11
Gen. Mgr., Cass River Trader, MI, Vassar

Bilbney, Greg .... ext. 111
gbilbrey@robdailynews.com, Managing Ed.,
Daily News, IL, Robinson

Bilbow, Leonarda .... ext. 2067
lbilbow@citizensvoice.com, News Ed., The
Citizens' Voice, PA, Wilkes Barre

Bilbrey, Greg
gbilbrey@robdailynews.com, Ed., The

Robinson Constitution, IL, Robinson

Bilden, Karen
gleaner@invisimax.com, Ed., The Gleaner, ND, Northwood

Bilek, Diane
diane@omahadailyrecord.com, Advertising (Classified, Display, Website), Daily Record, NE, Omaha

Bilinski, James
jbilinski@ithacatimes.com, Pub., Newfield News, NY, Ithaca

Bilinski, James
jbilinski@ithacatimes.com, Pub., Ithaca Times, NY, Ithaca

Bilinski, James
jbilinski@ithacatimes.com, Pub., Ovid Gazette, NY, Ithaca

Bilinski, James
jbilinski@ithacatimes.com, Pub., The Trumansburg Free Press, NY, Ithaca

Bilinski, James
jbilinski@ithacatimes.com, Pub., Spencer Random Harvest Weekely, NY, Ithaca

Bilinski, James
jbilinski@ithacatimes.com, Pub., Finger Lakes Community Newspapers, NY, Ithaca

Bilinski, James
jbilinski@ithacatimes.com, Pub., The Interlaken Review, NY, Ithaca

Bill, Jeff .... (410) 332-6944
jeff.bill@baltsun.com, Photo Ed. , Carroll County Times, MD, Westminster

Biller, Brenda
mnebeluk@metroland.com, Vice Pres., HR, Metroland Printing/Publishing & Distributing Ltd., ON, Mississauga

Billeter, Robert
news@westondemocrat.com, Pub./Ed., Weston Democrat, WV, Weston

Billinghurst, Joel .... (905) 664-8800
jbillinghurst@metroland.com, Produ Mgr., Ancaster News, ON, Stoney Creek

Billings, Emily
ebillings@arkansasnews.com, Gen. Mgr., Jacksonville Patriot, AR, North Little Rock
ebillings@arkansasnews.com, Gen. Mgr., Maumelle Monitor, AR, North Little Rock
ebillings@arkansasnews.com, Gen. Mgr., The North Little Rock Times, AR, North Little Rock
ebillings@arkansasnews.com, Gen. Mgr., Hot Springs Village Voice, AR, Hot Springs Village
ebillings@arkansasnews.com, Gen Mgr., Sherwood Voice, AR, North Little Rock
ebillings@arkansasnews.com, Gen. Mgr., Carlisle Independent, AR, Carlisle
ebillings@arkansasnews.com, Gen. Mgr., Lonoke Democrat, AR, Lonoke

Billingsley, ReShonda .... (713) 663-6996
reshonda@defendermediagroup.com, Online Ed., Houston Defender Media Group, Formerly Houston Defender, TX, Houston

Billiot, Debbie
circulation@banner-tribune.com, Circ. Mgr., Franklin Banner-Tribune, LA, Franklin

Billips, Elizabeth
lizbillips@yahoo.com, Assoc. Ed., The True Citizen, GA, Waynesboro

Billman, Jeffery
jbillman@indyweek.com, Ed., Indy Week, NC, Durham

Bills, Robbie
rbills@timescourier.com, Sports Ed., Times-Courier, GA, Ellijay

Bilquist, Che'rell .... (913) 715-8920
cherell.bilquist@jocogov.org, Advertising Manager, The Best Times, KS, Olathe

Bilsky, Jenifer

jbilsky@postmedia.com, Adv Dir, Selkirk Journal, MB, Selkirk
jbilsky@postmedia.com, Adv Dir, The Interlake Spectator, MB, Stonewall
jbilsky@postmedia.com, Adv Dir, The Stonewall Argus & Teulon Times, MB, Stonewall

Bina, Bianca .... (800) 477-6572
Managing Ed., Agweek, ND, Grand Forks

Binford, Mira
mira.binford@quinnipiac.edu, Prof., Quinnipiac University, CT, Hamden

Bingaman, Tim .... (314) 966-7711
tbingaman@cvcaudit.com, Pres./CEO, Circulation Verification Council, MO, Saint Louis

Bingham, Nicole .... (317) 736-2730
Operations Coord., Daily Journal, IN, Franklin

Bingham, Shereen
sbingham@unomaha.edu, Prof./Asst. Dir., University of Nebraska at Omaha, NE, Omaha

Bingle, Jerry .... (574) 936-3101
jbingle@thepilotnews.com, Gen. Mgr., The Shopper, IN, Plymouth

Binns, Kelly .... (641) 842-2155
class@journalexpress.net, Cashier, Marion County Reminder, IA, Knoxville

Binstock, Jeff
jeff.binstock@globegazette.com, Circ. Mgr., Globe Gazette, Mason City, IA, Mason City

Bintliff, Valerie .... (806) 345-3333
valerie.bentliff@amarillo.com, Personnel Dir., Amarillo Globe-News, TX, Amarillo

Binyon, Alec .... (530) 894-2300
alecb@newsreview.com, General Manager, Chico News & Review, CA, Chico

Biondi, Paul .... (517) 372-2424
paul@michiganpress.org, Advertising Director, Real Detroit Weekly (OOB), MI, Royal Oak
paul@michiganpress.org, Adv. Dir., Michigan Press Association, MI, Lansing

Biondi, Roy
roy.biondi@wcfcourier.com, The Courier, IA, Waterloo
roy.biondi@wcfcourier.com, Pub., Globe Gazette, Mason City, IA, Mason City

Biondi, Roy .... (319) 291-1500
Roy.Biondi@wcfcourier.com, Pub., The Other Paper (OOB), OH, Columbus
Roy.Biondi@wcfcourier.com, Pub., The Courier, IA, Waterloo

Birch, Simon .... (916) 288-6001
simon@cnpa.com, Dir. of Membership, California News Publishers Association, CA, Sacramento

Bird, Greg
birdman@tmcvoice.com, Ed., The McCreary County Voice, KY, Whitley City

Bird, Henry
hbird@cnhi.com, Pub., Madison County Direct, IN, Anderson

Bird, Jared .... (801) 625-4388
jbird@standard.net, Retail Adv. Mgr., Standard-Examiner, UT, Ogden

Bird, Kenton
kbird@uidaho.edu, Dir./Assoc. Prof., University of Idaho, ID, Moscow

Bird, Micheal
mbird@post-journal.com, Pub., The Post-Journal, NY, Jamestown

Bird, Mike .... (716) 487-1111 ext. 201
mbird@post-journal.com, Publisher, The Westfield Republican, NY, Westfield
mbird@post-journal.com, Pub., Westfield Republican, NY, Westfield

Bird, Teresa .... (250) 723-6399
publisher@albernivalleynews.com, Publisher, Alberni Valley News, BC, Port Alberni

Bird, Walter
wbird@stonebridgepress.com, Exec. Ed., The Webster Times, MA, Southbridge

Bird-Meyer, Matt .... (660) 543-4430
bird-meyer@ucmo.edu, Adviser, University of Central Missouri, MO, Warrensburg

Birdsall, Leif
leif@rogueriverpress.com, Circ/Web Mgr, Rogue River Press, OR, Grants Pass

Birdsall, Pam .... (541) 582-1707
Pam@RogueRiverPress.com, Admin, Rogue River Press, OR, Grants Pass

Birdsell, Beth
bbirdsell@siouxcityjournal.com, Nat'l Adv. Mgr., Sioux City Journal, IA, Sioux City

Birkelo, Shelly
sbirkelo@gazetteextra.com, Community Living Ed., The Janesville Gazette - GazetteXtra, WI, Janesville

Birket, Joel
info@masthead.net, Proj. Mgr./Estimator, Masthead International, Inc., NM, Rio Rancho

Birkett, Greg .... (563) 588-0162
gbirkett@dbqadvertiser.com, President , Dubuque Advertiser, IA, Dubuque

Birkett, Kathleen
kbirkett@sunysullivan.edu, SUNY Sullivan, NY, Loch Sheldrake

Birkland, Jasmine .... (360) 683-3311
jbirkland@peninsuladailynews.com, Circulation Marketing, Sequim and Jefferson County , Peninsula Daily News, WA, Port Angeles

Birkland, Marilyn
mbirkland@stcloud.gannett.com, Adv. Mgr., Territory Retail Sales, St. Cloud Times, MN, Saint Cloud

Birkner, Peter .... (313) 343-5580
pbirkner@grossepointenews.com, Adv. Mgr., The Connection, MI, Grosse Pointe Woods

Birks, Dennis
dbirks@avpress.com, Prodn. Mgr., Opns., Antelope Valley Press, CA, Palmdale

Birmingham, Linda .... (705) 753-2930
tribune@westnipissing.com, Circulation and accounts, The Tribune, ON, Sturgeon Falls

Birmingham, Patrick .... (865) 342-6600
publisher@knoxnews.com, Pres./Pub., Knoxville News Sentinel, TN, Knoxville

Birnbaum, Adam
abirnbaum@grandwoodcapital.com, Managing Dir., AdMedia Partners, Inc., NY, New York

Bischof, Amii .... (574) 269-2932
warsaw@the-papers.com, Warsaw Office Manager, The Paper - Kosciusko Edition, IN, Milford

Bischof, Greg .... ext. 7244
Farm Reporter, Texarkana Gazette, AR, Texarkana

Bischoff, Donna .... (314) 340-8529
dbischoff@post-dispatch.com, VP, Adv. , St. Louis Post-Dispatch, MO, Saint Louis

Bischoff, Howard .... (650) 948-9000
Circulation Mgr, Los Altos Town Crier, CA, Los Altos

Bischoff, Howard ....ext. 306
Circ. Mgr., Los Altos Town Crier, CA, Los Altos

Bisconti, Dana .... (860) 241-3678
dbisconti@courant.com, Finance Director, The Hartford Courant, CT, Hartford

Bisha, Robin
rbisha@tlu.edu, Texas Lutheran Univ., TX, Seguin

Bishop, Alana .... (225) 647-4569
alana@alanatvl.com, Gonzales Weekly Citizen, LA, Gonzales

Bishop, Amy .... (614) 461-8739

(614) 469-6325, Adv. Dir., Alive, OH, Columbus

Bishop, Barbara .... (732) 906-2020
bbishop@cascadetechnologies.com, Sales, Cascade Technologies, Inc., NJ, Somerset

Bishop, Bojinka .... (740) 593-2675
Assoc. Prof., Ohio University, OH, Athens

Bishop, Ed
review@webster.edu, Ed., St. Louis Journalism Review, MO, Saint Louis

Bishop, Ian .... (202) 636-4719
ibishop@washingtontimes.com, Managing Ed. - Dig., The Washington Times, DC, Washington

Bishop, Melody .... (256) 263-7421
melody.bishop@timesdaily.com, Adv. Dir., Times Daily, AL, Florence

Bishop, Melody .... (540) 981-3145
melody.bishop@roanoke.com, Director of Advertising, The Roanoke Times, VA, Roanoke

Bishop, Peter
pbishop@metroland.com, Ed, Brock Citizen, ON, Cannington
pbishop@metroland.com, VP & CFO, Toronto Star, ON, Toronto

Bishop Holley, Martin D. .... (901) 373-1200
Pub., The West Tennessee Catholic, TN, Memphis

Bishop John, Brungardt .... (620) 227-1500
bishop@dcdiocese.org, Pub, The Southwest Kansas Catholic, KS, Dodge City

Bissbort, Leigh Ann .... (817) 379-5960
bissatpti@aol.com, Bus. Mgr., Printing Technology, Inc., TX, Fort Worth

Bissell, Kimberly
bissell@jn.ua.edu, Assoc. Prof., University of Alabama, AL, Tuscaloosa

Bissell, Shelly
sbissell@shawmedia.com, Adv. Dir., Classified, Kane County Chronicle, IL, Saint Charles

Bissell, Shelly .... (815) 526-4497
sbissell@shawmedia.com, Classified Mgr., Northwest Herald, IL, Crystal Lake

Bissett, Kevin .... (506) 457-0746
editorial@thecanadianpress.com, New Brunswick Correspondent, Broadcast News Limited, NB, Fredericton
editorial@thecanadianpress.com, Correspondent, Canadian Press, The - Fredericton, NB, NB, Fredericton

Bissinger, Kate
katherine-bissinger@utc.edu, Univ. of Tennessee Chattanooga, TN, Chattanooga

Bisson, Charlene .... (623) 445-2823
cbisson@newszap.com, Pub., White Mountain Independent, AZ, Show Low
cbisson@newszap.com, Pub., Gilbert Independent (OOB) , AZ, Apache Junction
cbisson@newszap.com, Pub., Biltmore Independent (OOB), AZ, Phoenix
cbisson@newszap.com, Pub., Scottsdale Independent, AZ, Phoenix
cbisson@newszap.com, Pub., Town of Paradise Valley Independent, AZ, Phoenix

Bisson, Charlene .... (623) 972-6101
cbisson@newszap.com, Pub, Sun City Independent, AZ, Sun City

Bitikofer, Dustin .... (314) 968-2699
delivery@timesnewspapers.com, circulation manager, South County Times, MO, Saint Louis

Bitikofer, Dustin .... (314) 968-2699
delivery@timesnewspaper.com, circulation manager, West End Word, MO, Saint Louis

Bitikofer, Dustin .... (314) 968-2699
circulation manager, Webster-Kirkwood Times, Inc., MO, Saint Louis

Bitikofer, Dwight .... (314) 968-2699
publisher@timesnewspapers.com, publisher,

West End Word, MO, Saint Louis

Bitikofer, Dwight .... (314) 968-2699
publisher@westendword.com, Pub., West End
Word, MO, Saint Louis
publisher@westendword.com, Pub., South
County Times, MO, Saint Louis
publisher@westendword.com, Pub., Webster-
Kirkwood Times, Inc., MO, Saint Louis

Bitker, Deb
dbitker@pilotindependent.com, Circ. Mgr, The
Pilot-Independent, MN, Walker

Bittick, Paul .... (805) 756-2537
pbittick@calpoly.edu, GM, California
Polytechnic State Univ., CA, San Luis Obispo

Bittner, Nancy
gutimes@westriv.com, Pub. / Ed. , Glen Ullin
Times, ND, Glen Ullin

Bivona, Dwayne .... (940) 720-3491
bivonad@timesrecordnews.com, Publisher,
Wichita Falls Times Record News, TX,
Wichita Falls

Bizzotto, Anita J.
abizzott@emai.usps.gov, CMO, United States
Postal Service, DC, Washington

Bjoin, Bob
heditor@harlannet.com, Ed., News-Advertiser,
IA, Harlan

Bjork, Becky
becky.bjork@myheraldreview.com, Adv. Dir.,
Sierra Vista Herald - Sunday Bravo Shopper,
AZ, Sierra Vista
becky.bjork@myheraldreview.com, Adv. Dir.,
Wick Communications - Herald/Review, AZ,
Sierra Vista

Bjork, Nick
nbjork@djcOregon.com, Pub., Daily Journal of
Commerce, OR, Portland

Bjorkgren, David
dbjorkgren@delconewsnetwork.com, Mng. Ed.,
News of Delaware County, Town Talk, Garnet
Valley Press, Springfield Press, County
PRess, PA, Swarthmore

Bjorklund, Steven .... (425) 892-1093
steve@bjmach.com, Pres., H & M Paster Sales
& Service, Inc., WA, Woodinville

Black, Chris .... (416) 775-2803
info@tembec.com, Pres., Tembec, ON,
Etobicoke

Black, David .... (780) 468-0214
david.black@edmsun.com, Pub. & CEO, The
Edmonton Sun, AB, Edmonton

Black, David .... 1-(250) 480-3220
Chair/Founder, Black Press Group Ltd., BC,
Surrey

Black, Gordon R. .... (541) 383-0339
gblack@bendbulletin.com, Pres., Western
Communications, Inc., OR, Bend

Black, Gwen .... (334) 393-9716
gblack@eprisenow.com, News Clerk, The
Enterprise Ledger, AL, Enterprise

Black, Jason .... (724) 626-3534
jblack@tribweb.com, Sports Ed., Daily Courier,
PA, Connellsville

Black, Jo Dee .... (406) 791-6502
Business Editor, Great Falls Tribune, MT, Great
Falls

Black, JoEllen .... (816) 776-5454 Ext. 12
publisher@richmond-dailynews.com, Pub.,
Richmond News, MO, Richmond

Black, Leah .... (518) 862-2056
editor@excitingread.com, Ed., Capital District
Parent, NY, Latham

Black, Louis
lblack@austinchronicle.com, Ed., Austin
Chronicle, TX, Austin

Black, Marty .... (808) 690-8849
mblack@staradvertiser.com, VP/Production,
Kauai Midweek, HI, Honolulu

mblack@staradvertiser.com, VP/Production,
MidWeek Oahu, HI, Honolulu

Black, Marty .... (808) 690-8849
mblack@staradvertiser.com, VP/Prod.,
Honolulu Star-Advertiser, HI, Honolulu

Black, Miguel
circulation@westender.com, Circ. Mgr., We
Vancouver Weekly, BC, Vancouver
circulation@westender.com, Circ Mgr, The
Westender, BC, Vancouver

Black, Oneida
oblack@garrardcentralrecord.com, Exec. Sec./
Adv. Mgr., Garrard Central Record, KY,
Lancaster

Black, Peter .... ext. 2802
pblack@bpaww.com, Sr. Vice Pres., Mktg.
Servs., BPA Worldwide, CT, Shelton

Black, Rosalie
rblack@columbiabasinherald.com, Sales
Manager, Columbia Basin Herald, WA,
Moses Lake

Blackburn, Angela
ablackburn@oakvillebeaver.com, Ed. , Oakville
Beaver, ON, Oakville

Blackburn, Dawn .... (845) 677-6150
mssisoftware@cs.com, Pres., Micro Systems
Specialists, Inc. (MSSI), NY, Millbrook

Blackburn, Gary
gary.blackburn@princeton.com.au, Pub.,
Gibson County Today, IN, Princeton

Blackburn, Peggy
news@thewetumpkaherald.com, Mng. Ed., The
Wetumpka Herald, AL, Alexander City

Blackburn, Peggy
news@thewetumpkaherald.com, Mng. Ed., The
Eclectic Observer, AL, Wetumpka

Blackburn, Rick
dixonpilotnews@yahoo.com, Co Publishers,
Dixon Pilot Newspaper and Print Shop, MO,
Dixon

Blackledge, Karen
kblackledge@dailyitem.com, Reporter, The
Danville News, PA, Danville
kblackledge@dailyitem.com, Reporter, The
Daily Item, PA, Sunbury

Blackman, Bob .... (563) 262-0552
sales@muscatinepost.com, Pub., The Post, IA,
Muscatine

Blackmon, Cleretta T.
mobilebeaconinc@bellsouth.net, Ed., Mobile
Beacon And Alabama Citizen, AL, Mobile

Blackmon, Jeff .... (806) 647-1234
Jeff@countystarnews.com, Adv. Dir., The
Castro County News, TX, Dimmitt

Blackwell, Karen .... (919) 419-6757
kblackwell@heraldsun.com, Office Mgr., The
Herald-Sun, NC, Durham

Blackwell, Laura
advertising@ldnews.net, Adv. Mgr./Pub., Burns
Lakes District News, BC, Burns Lake

Blackwell, Rob .... (571) 403-3834
rob.blackwell@sourcemedia.com, Washington
Bureau Chief, Regulation & Reform,
American Banker, NY, New York

Blackwell, Ronald .... (815) 937-3350
Distribution Manager, Small Newspaper Group,
IL, Kankakee

Blackwell, Steve
sblackwell@greercitizen.com, Pub./Adv. Mgr.,
The Greer Citizen, SC, Greer

Blade, Chris
cblade@postbulletin.com, Bus. Mgr., Post-
Bulletin, MN, Rochester

Bladine, Jeb
jbladine@newsregister.com, Pres./Pub, News-
Register, OR, McMinnville

Blaesser, Mike .... (831) 429-2417
mblaesser@santacruzsentinel.com, Internet

Dir., Santa Cruz Sentinel, CA, Scotts Valley

Blain, Rachel .... (519) 351-7331 ext.554701
rblain@postmedia.com, Office Mgr., Chatham
This Week, ON, Chatham

Blair, Brian .... (812) 379-5672
bblair@therepublic.com, Features Ed., The
Republic, IN, Columbus

Blair, Bruce
bblair@ocregister.com, VP, Circ., Laguna
Woods Globe, CA, Santa Ana

Blair, Bruce
bblair@ocregister.com, VP Cir., The Orange
County Register, CA, Santa Ana

Blair, Donna .... (530) 749-4702
dblair@appealdemocrat.com, Business
Manager
, Appeal Democrat, CA, Marysville

Blair, Gary .... (419) 724-6258
gblair@toledoblade.com, Pres., Block
Communications, Inc., OH, Toledo

Blair, Jan .... (309) 343-7181
jblair@register-mail.com, The Register-Mail,
IL, Galesburg

Blair, Kelly
sports@camdenarknews.com, Sports Ed.,
Camden News, AR, Camden

Blair, Louanen
lblair@hotlandpublication.com, Circ. Mgr.,
Focus, OH, Portsmouth

Blair, Marcus
mblair@carlalbert.edu, Carl Albert State
College, OK, Poteau

Blair, Morgan
chargertimes@uah.edu, Editor-in-Chief, Univ.
of Alabama Huntsville, AL, Huntsville

Blair, Paula .... ext. 169
paula.blair@duncanbanner.com, Adv. Mgr.,
Classified, The Duncan Banner, OK, Duncan

Blair, Rachelle
rblair@hngnews.com, Mng. Ed., Lodi
Enterprise & Poynette Press, WI, Lodi

Blair, Randy
rblair@blackpress.ca, Pres., Group Ops, Black
Press Group Ltd., BC, Surrey

Blair, Rhonda .... (605) 337-2571
cmcountynews@midstatesd.net, Pub./Ed.,
Charles Mix County News, SD, Geddes

Blais, George .... (780) 349-3033 Ext. 3
gblais@westlock.greatwest.ca, Pub., The
Westlock News, AB, Westlock

Blais, Jacques
boursiery@transcontinental.ca, Ed., Le
Regional De Hull, QC, Gatineau

Blais, Jacques
jackques.blais@transcontinental.ca, Pub./Gen.
Mgr., Week-end Outaouais, QC, Gatineau

Blais, Jacques
blaisj@trancontinental.ca, Gen. Mgr., La Revue
De Gatineau, QC, Gatineau

Blais, Laurie .... (603) 594-1212
getclassifieds@nashuatelegram.com, Class.
- Real Est. & Rec. Mgr., The Telegraph, NH,
Nashua

Blais, Mike .... (860) 495-8259
mblais@thewesterlysun.com, Sales Dir, The
Westerly Sun, CT, Pawcatuck

Blais, Rich
sales@beltcorp.com, Sales Mgr., Belt
Corporation of America, GA, Cumming

Blaisdell, Elisha .... (603) 734-9050
elisha@carriagetownenews.com, Ed., Carriage
Towne News, NH, Kingston

Blaisdell, John
blaisdellj@rhodes.edu, Rhodes College, TN,
Memphis

Blake, Anne .... (978) 632-8000 x34
ablake@thegardnernews.com, Adv. Rep. , The

Gardner News, MA, Gardner

Blake, Beth
beth@thenewstimes.com, Mng. Ed., Carteret
County News-Times, NC, Morehead City

Blake, Cheyenne
cheyenne@menastar.com, Composing
Manager, The Mena Star, AR, Mena

Blake, Emily .... (867) 667-4481
emily@whitehorsestar.com, Reporter,
Whitehorse Star, YT, Whitehorse

Blake, Heather
heather.blake@indianagazette.com, Indiana
Univ. of Pennsylvania, PA, Indiana

Blake, Kathy
kathy.blake@oakpress.com, Business Ed., The
Oakland Press, MI, Pontiac

Blake, Melissa .... (815) 825-2086 ext. 3450
mblake@kishwaukeecollege.edu, Kishwaukee
College, IL, Malta

Blake, Phil
pblake@meriter.com, Pub., Coverstory, WI,
Madison

Blakeley, Eddie .... (606) 784-4116
eblakeley@cnhi.com, Pub., The Morehead
News, KY, Morehead

Blakeley, Eddie .... (606) 326-2601
publisher@dailyindependent.com, Pub., The
Daily Independent, KY, Ashland

Blakeley, Gary .... (800) 638-7990
gblakeley@slp.com, Dir. Global Technical
Solutions, Southern Lithoplate, Inc., NC,
Youngsville

Blakely, Lindsey .... (870) 972-3186
Editor, Arkansas State Univ., AR, State
University

Blakemore, Brad .... (903) 567-4000
brad@vanzandtnews.com, Pub., Van Zandt
Newspapers LLC, TX, Canton

Blakemore, Christi
healdtonherald@att.net, Pub., Wilson Post-
Democrat, OK, Healdton

Blakemore, John S.
johnb@stephens.edu, Chair, Stephens
College, MO, Columbia

Blakley, Stewart
sblakley@lib.brenau.edu, Chair, Brenau
University, GA, Gainesville

Blanchard, Dean
dblanchard@theadvocate.com, Cir Dir., Capital
City Press, LA

Blanchard, Rebecca
rblanchard@berksmontnews.com, Ed., The
Boyertown Area Times, PA, Pottstown

Blanchard, Scott
sblanchard@ydr.com, York Daily Record/York
Sunday News, PA, York

Blanchard, Steve
steveb@watermarkonline.com, Ed., Watermark
Media, FL, Orlando

Blanchet, Maurice
mblanchet@gsptoday.com, Vice Pres., GSP,
Inc., RI, Westerly

Blanchet, Mike
mblanchet@sunjournal.com, Adv. Acct. Exec.,
Franklin Journal, ME, Farmington

Blanchet, Mike
mblanchet@sunjournal.com, Acc. Exec., Sun
Journal, ME, Lewiston

Blanchet, Stacy .... (207) 861-9210
mscommunity@centralmaine.com, Community
News Ed., Morning Sentinel, ME, Waterville

Blanchette, Ken .... ext. 239
Sports Ed., Townsend Times, MA, Devens

Blanco, Laurie
lblanco@ottawaherald.com, Adv. Dir., The
Ottawa Herald, KS, Ottawa

Bland, John A.
jbland@thetd.com, Ed., The Times Dispatch, AR, Walnut Ridge

Bland, Sherwood.....................**(336) 506-3095**
sbland@thetimesnews.com, Production Director, Times-News, NC, Burlington

Bland-Selix, Lisa
classified@theshoppersedge.net, Pub., Shopper's Edge, OK, Enid

Blane, Miriam
miriam@superiorlithoplate.com, Office Mgr., Superior Lithoplate of Indiana, Inc., IN, Rockville

Blane, Robert T.
robert@superiorlithoplate.com, Pres., Superior Lithoplate of Indiana, Inc., IN, Rockville

Blane, Steven C.
steve@superiorlithoplate.com, Vice Pres., Superior Lithoplate of Indiana, Inc., IN, Rockville

Blaner, David
dblainer@acba.org, Exec. Dir., Pittsburgh Legal Journal, PA, Pittsburgh

Blank, Debbie..............**(812) 934-4343 ext. 113**
TheHeraldTribune@batesvilleheraldtribune.com, Mng Ed., The Herald-Tribune, IN, Batesville

Blank, Holly.................**(516) 307-1045 Ext. 202**
hblank@theislandnow.com, Circ. Mgr., New Hyde Park Herald Courier, NY, Williston Park
hblank@theislandnow.com, Cir. Mgr., Williston Times, NY, Williston Park
hblank@theislandnow.com, Circulation Mgr, Great Neck News, NY, Williston Park

Blank, Steven...............**(516) 307-1045 Ext. 201**
sblank@theislandnow.com, Pub, New Hyde Park Herald Courier, NY, Williston Park

Blank, Steven...............**(516) 307-1045 Ext. 201**
sblank@theislandnow.com, Ed., Williston Times, NY, Williston Park

Blank , Steven..............**(516) 307-1045 Ext. 201**
sblank@theislandnow.com, Ed & Pub, Great Neck News, NY, Williston Park
sblank@theislandnow.com, Manhasset Times, NY, Williston Park
sblank@theislandnow.com, Port Washington Times, NY, Williston Park

Blankenship, Allison
allison@auburnvillager.com, Assoc. Ed, Auburn Villager, AL, Auburn

Blankenship, Anne
lifestyles@freemanjournal.net, Mng. Ed., The Daily Freeman-Journal, IA, Webster City

Blankenship, Bill.....................**(785) 295-1284**
bill.blankenship@cjonline.com, Arts/Ent. Ed., The Topeka Capital-Journal, KS, Topeka

Blankenship, Melissa
editor@oldhamera.com, Gen. Mgr./Ed. , Oldham Era, KY, La Grange

Blankenship, Melissa
publisher@oldhamera.com, Gen. Mgr., Marketplace, KY, La Grange

Blankenship, Robert
rblankenship@rensselaerrepublican.com, Pub., Rensselaer Republican, IN, Rensselaer

Blanks, Edel
customerservice@intralox.com, Sales Mgr., Intralox, LLC, LA, Harahan

Blanton, Mark
mark.kmherald@gmail.com, Adv. Rep, Kings Mountain Herald, NC, Kings Mountain

Blanton, Mark.........................**(704) 739-7496**
Sales Rep., The Cherryville Eagle, NC, Cherryville

Blaser, Randy.......................**(847) 486-7372**
blazer@pioneerlocal.com, Sr. Ed., Wilmette Life, IL, Chicago

Blaser, Randy.......................**(847) 486-7372**
blaser@pioneerlocal.com, Bureau Chief, Morton Grove Champion, IL, Chicago

Blasick, Marty
mb@motioncity.com, Composer/Audio Engineer, Motion City Films, CA, Santa Monica

Blaufuss, Turner.....................**(701) 642-8585**
sports@wahpetondailynews.com, Sports Ed. , The Daily News, ND, Wahpeton

Blaufuss, Turner.....................**(701) 642-8585**
sports@wahpetondailynews.com, Sports Ed. , The Daily News, ND, Wahpeton

Blauvelt, BILL.........................**(402) 879-3291**
tse@superiorne.com, Pub, Superior Publishing Company, NE, Superior

Blauvelt, Bill.........................**(785) 378-3191**
tse@superiorne.com, Pub., Jewell County Record, KS, Mankato

Blauvelt, Bill.........................**(402) 879-3291**
bblauvelt@windstream.net, Ed., The Superior Express, NE, Superior

Blay, Jeff.................**(905) 688-4332 ext. 1147**
jeff.blay@sunmedia.ca, Reporter, Thorold Niagara News, ON, Saint Catharine's

Blaylock, Jim.........................**(706) 868-1222**
jim.blaylock@augustachronicle, Visual Journalist, The Columbia County News-Times, GA, Evans

Blaylock, Scott.......................**(765) 675-2115**
Adv. Mgr., Leader-Tribune Review West, IN, Tipton
Adv. Mgr., Leader-Tribune Review East, IN, Tipton

Blazak, Jon
jblazak@nmsu.edu, New Mexico State Univ., NM, Las Cruces

Blazer, Phil
pblazer@blazermediagroup.com, Ed., Jewish News, CA, Encino

Blazucki, Sarah.......................**(215) 625-8501**
sarah@epgn.com, Editor, Philadelphia Gay News, PA, Philadelphia

Bleakley, Bill.........................**(405) 605-6789**
publisher@okgazette.com, CEO/Pres/Pub., Okcbiz, OK, Oklahoma City

Bleakley, Chad
cbleakley@okgazette.com, Circ. Mgr., Okcbiz, OK, Oklahoma City

Bleckburn, Chris
fchb.editor@yahoo.com, Owner, Floyd County Hesperian-Beacon, TX, Floydada

Bledsoe, Lori
Editor@thealpinesun.com, Ed., Alpine Sun, CA, Alpine

Bledsoe, Pamela...........**(229) 924-2751 ext 1519**
pamela.bledsoe@gaflnews.com, Ad Sales, Americus Times-Recorder, GA, Americus

Blegen, Dale
mail@desmetnews.com, Pub., The De Smet News, SD, De Smet

Blegen, Dale.........................**(605) 847-4421**
lptimes@iw.net, Pub., Lake Preston Times, SD, Lake Preston

Blessinger, Justin.....................**(605) 256-5278**
justin.blessinger@dsu.edu, Dakota State Univ., SD, Madison

Blethen, James.......................**(509) 526-8359**
jamesblethen@wwub.com, Prod. Supervisor, Walla Walla Union-Bulletin, WA, Walla Walla

Bletner, Rhonda
rbletner@themountainpress.com, Editor, The Mountain Press, TN, Sevierville

Blevins, Frederick
frederick.blevins@fiu.edu, Prof., Florida International University, FL, North Miami

Blevins, Betsy
betsy@theleonardgraphic.com, Pub./Ed., Leonard Graphic, TX, Leonard

Blevins, Chuck
crblevins@aol.com, Pres., Chuck Blevins & Assoc., FL, Naples

Blevins, Keith.........................**(334) 293-5800**
kblevins@cnhi.com, Executive VP/COO, Community Newspaper Holdings, Inc., AL, Montgomery

Blevins, Kevin.........................**(306) 781-5408**
kblevins@leaderpost.canwest.com, Deputy Ed., Online, The Leader-Post, SK, Regina

Blevins, Lynn
lynnb@harrisondaily.com, Managing Ed., Harrison Daily Times, AR, Harrison

Blewett, Steve
steve.blewett@mailserver.ewu.edu, Dir./Prof., Eastern Washington University, WA, Spokane

Blewett, Taylor.......................**(867) 667-4481**
taylor@whitehorsestar.com, Reporter, Whitehorse Star, YT, Whitehorse

Blick, Thomas Edward
blick@latech.edu, Head, Louisiana Tech University, LA, Ruston

Bliss, Erik
ebliss@manhattanmedia.com, Manhattan Media LLC, NY

Bliss, Nathen.........................**(952) 392-6894**
nbliss@acnpapers.comx, Adv. Dir., Wayzata/Orono/Plymouth/Long Lake Sun Sailor, MN, Eden Prairie

Bliss, Richard
rbliss@quickwire.com, Integrator, Quickwire Labs, MB, Winnipeg

Bliss, Sidney H.
sbliss@gazetteextra.com, CEO/Pub., The Janesville Gazette - GazetteXtra, WI, Janesville

Bliss, Sidney H........................**(608) 755-8207**
sbliss@gazettextra.com, Pres./Chrmn./CEO, The Gazette - gazettextra.com, WI, Janesville

Blizzard, Andy.........................**(561) 820-4696**
ablizzard@pbpost.com, VP, Revenue Develop., The Palm Beach Post, FL, West Palm Beach

Block, Allan
a.block@blockcommunications.com, Chrmn., Block Communications, Inc., OH, Toledo

Block, John Robinson.................**(412) 263-1861**
Chairman, Publisher & Editor-in-Chief, Pittsburgh Post-Gazette, PA, Clinton

Block, John Robinson.................**(419) 724-6176**
johnrblock@theblade.com, Ed. in Chief, The Blade, OH, Toledo

Block, Martin
mp-block@northwestern.edu, Prof., Northwestern University, IL, Evanston

Block, Michael.......................**(740) 450-6743**
kblock@gannett.com, Adv. Mgr., Coshocton County Advertiser, OH, Coshocton

Blodgett, Simon.......................**(717) 307-2448**
simon.blodgett@mercersburgjournal.com, Circ. Mgr, Mercersburg Journal, PA, Mercersburg

Blomstedt, Jeremy.........**(308) 345-4500 ext. 114**
editor2@ocsmccook.com, Assoc. Ed., McCook Daily Gazette, NE, Mc Cook

Blond, Jeff.........................**(514) 987-2222**
jblond@montrealgazette.com, Executive Producer, Print, Montreal Gazette, QC, Montreal

Blonde, Scott.................**(239) 574-1110 x110**
sblonde@breezenewspapers.com, Pub., Island Reporter, FL, Sanibel
sblonde@breezenewspapers.com, Pub., North Fort Myers Neighbor, FL, Cape Coral
sblonde@breezenewspapers.com, Sanibel - Captiva Shopper's Guide, FL, Cape Coral
sblonde@breezenewspapers.com, Pub, Sanibel-Captiva Islander, FL, Cape Coral
sblonde@breezenewspapers.com, Pub.,

Captiva Current, FL, Sanibel
sblonde@breezenewspapers.com, Publisher, Lee County Shopper, FL, Cape Coral

Blonde, Scott
sblonde@breezenewspapers.com, Pub., The Pine Island Eagle, FL, Bokeelia

Blonde, Scott.........................**(239) 574-1110**
sblonde@breezenewspapers.com, Pub. , Fort Myers Beach Observer, FL, Fort Myers Beach
sblonde@breezenewspapers.com, Pub., Cape Coral Breeze, FL, Cape Coral

Blood, Leslie
blood_l@fortlewis.edu, Ft. Lewis College, CO, Durango

Bloom, Betsy.........................**(906) 774-2772**
bbloom@ironmountaindailynews.com, Ed., The Daily News, MI, Iron Mountain

Bloom, Brian...................**(574) 533-2151 x301**
brian.bloom@goshennews.com, Pub., The Goshen News, IN, Goshen

Bloom, David
david.bloom@thecash-book.com, Asst. Pub., Cash-Book Journal/The Weekender, MO, Jackson

Bloom, David.........................**(281) 425-8016**
david.bloom@baytownsun.com, Mng. Ed., The Baytown Sun, TX, Baytown

Bloom, Debby
dbloom@dailyastorian.com, The Daily Astorian, OR, Astoria

Bloom, Karen
karenb@kpcnews.net, Adv. Dir., Smart Shopper, IN, Angola

Bloomfield, Michelle L......................**ext. 241**
mbloomfield@hickoryrecord.com, News Ed., The Hickory Daily Record, NC, Hickory
mbloomfield@hickoryrecord.com, News Ed., Pow, NC, Hickory

Bloomquist, Timothy M.
Tim@reviewmessenger.com, Ed./Pub., The Review Messenger, MN, Sebeka

Blose, F. Len.........................**(330) 841-1600**
lblose@tribToday.com, Gen. Mgr., The Tribune Chronicle, OH, Warren

Blossman, Lisa
lisa.blossman@nopg.com, Pub, Daily Journal of Commerce, LA, Metairie
lisa.blossman@nopg.com, Sales Mgr., New Orleans City Business, LA, Metairie

Blount, Christina.......................**(936) 295-5407**
cblount@itemonline.com, Mailroom Mgr., The Huntsville Item, TX, Huntsville

Blount, Donald W......................**(209) 546-8251**
dblount@recordnet.com, Mng. Editor, The Record, CA, Stockton

Blount, Glenn
glenn.blount@thefacts.com, Circ. Mgr., Buyer's Express, TX, Clute

Bloxsom, Bill
bbloxsom@hersamacorn.com, Sports Ed., Trumbull Times, CT, Shelton

Bloxsom, Bill
bbloxsom@hersamacorn.com, Sports Ed., Monroe Courier, CT, Shelton

Bloxsom, Bill
bbloxsom@hersamacorn.com, Sports Ed., Milford Mirror, CT, Shelton

Blubaugh, Bob.........................**(410) 857-7895**
bob.blubaugh@carrollcountytimes.com, News Ed. , Carroll County Times, MD, Westminster

Bludau, Kristie
tribuneherald@sbcglobal.net, Adv. Dir., Hallettsville Tribune-Herald, TX, Hallettsville

Blue, Greg
greg.blue@manroland-web.com, CEO, Manroland Web Systems Inc., IL, Lisle

Blue, Jerry.........................**(563) 422-3888**

jbblue@thefayettecountyunion.com, Vice President, Fayette County Union, IA, West Union

Blue, Tracy
tablue@voice-tribune.com, Pub., The Voice-Tribune, KY, Louisville

Bluhm, Warren
wbluhm@doorcountyadvocate.com, Assc. Ed., Door County Advocate, WI, Sturgeon Bay
wbluhm@doorcountyadvocate.com, Assoc. Ed., Kewaunee County Star-News, WI, Kewaunee

Blum, Ken .... (330) 682-3416
blummer@aol.com, Senior Associate-Sales Nationwide, Grimes, McGovern & Associates, NY, New York

Blum, Marc .... (609) 624-8900 Ext. 226
Pub., Brigantine Beachcomber, NJ, Egg Harbor Township

Blum, Mark .... (717) 240-7110
mblum@florencenews.com, Pub., Morning News, SC, Florence

Blume, Allan .... (919) 847-2127
editor@BRnow.org, Editor/President, Biblical Recorder, NC, Cary

Blumenshine, Mark .... (307) 672-2431
mark@thesheridanpress.com, The Sheridan Press, WY, Sheridan

Blumenstein, Rebecca
rebecca.blumenstein@wsj.com, Deputy Editor in Chief, The Wall Street Journal, NY, New York

Blumenthal, Susan K. .... (203) 775-9122
susan@ctpennysaver.com, Pub., Yankee Pennysaver, CT, Brookfield

Blumsack, Bill .... (781) 255-7773 ext. 16
billblumsack@syndicatedadfeatures.com, Vice Pres./Eastern Regl. Sales Dir., Syndicated Ad Features, Inc., MA, Walpole

Blunt, Ann
ann.blunt@timesreporter.com, Adv. Dir., The Times-Reporter, OH, New Philadelphia

Blunt, Ann
annblunt@stwnewspress.com, Adv. Dir., The Columbus Telegram, NE, Columbus

Blurton, Kevin .... (256) 740-5792
kevin.blurton@timesdaily.com, Prod. Dir., Times Daily, AL, Florence

Blussick, Jasmine .... (724) 949-1216
jblussick@observer-reporter.com, Adv. Mgr, The Almanac, PA, Pittsburgh

Bly, Joan .... (403) 758-6911
sales@westwindweekly.com, Office Admin., Westwind Weekly News, AB, Magrath

Bly, Sue
suebly84@gmail.com, Adv., Spring Valley Tribune, MN, Spring Valley

Blyden, Vincent
vincent.blyden@famu.edu, Prof., Florida A&M University, FL, Tallahassee

Blystone, Chuck .... (309) 820-3248
cblystone@pantagraph.com, Features Ed., The Pantagraph, IL, Bloomington

Blyth, Jennifer .... (250) 480-3239
editor@oakbaynews.com, Ed., Oak Bay News, BC, Victoria

Board, Fred
fboard@lmtribune.com, Gen. Mgr., Lewiston Morning Tribune, ID, Lewiston

Board, Fred .... (208) 848-2292
fboard@lmtribune.com, Gen. Mgr., Moscow-Pullman Daily News, ID, Moscow
fboard@lmtribune.com, Gen. Mgr., Northwest Market, ID, Moscow

Boardman, Liz .... (401) 380-2394
editorial@independentri.com, Managing Editor, The Independent, RI, Newport

Boath, Kimberley .... (203) 317-2312

kboath@record-journal.com, Ad. Dir., The Plainville Citizen, CT, Meriden

Boath, Kimberley .... (203) 317-2448
kboath@record-journal.com, Adv. Dir., Berlin Citizen, CT, Meriden
kboath@record-journal.com, Adv. Dir., Town Times, CT, Meriden
kboath@record-journal.com, Ad. Dir., The Southington Citizen, CT, Meriden

Bobbitt, Judi .... ext. 2248
jbobbitt@durhamregion.com, Regl. Ed., Oshawa-whitby This Week, ON, Oshawa

Boblett, Joanne .... (218) 792-5842
news@northlandpress.com, Publisher, Northland Press, MN, Crosslake

Boblett, Paul .... (218) 692-5842
news@northlandpress.com, Editor and Advertising Manager, Northland Press, MN, Crosslake

Bobo, L. Peyton
gazettenews@frontiernet.net, Co-Pub., West Alabama Gazette, AL, Millport

Bobo, L. Peyton .... (205) 759-3091
northportgazette@northportgazette.com, Co-Pub., The Northport Gazette, AL, Northport

Bobroff, Robert .... (407) 241-2897
rbobroff@bizjournals.com, Publisher, Orlando Business Journal, FL, Orlando

Bocamazo, Susan .... (617) 451-7300
sbocamazo@lawyersweekly.com, Pub., Massachusetts Lawyers Weekly, MA, Boston
sbocamazo@lawyersweekly.com, Pub, Rhode Island Lawyers Weekly, MA, Boston

Bock, Barbara .... (207) 791-6206
bbock@mainetoday.com, VP/Adv., Portland Press Herald / Maine Sunday Telegram, ME, Portland

Bock, David
dbock@hawaiitribune-herald.com, Publisher and Editor, Hawaii Tribune-Herald, HI, Hilo

Bock, Hope
hb5@evansville.edu, Prof., University of Evansville, IN, Evansville

Bock, Jeff .... (310) 441-7400
jeff@ercboxoffice.com, Box Office Analyst, Exhibitor Relations Co., Los Angeles

Bock, Jill
jillb@standard-democrat.com, News Ed., Standard Democrat, MO, Sikeston

Bock, Julie .... (509) 826-1110
jbock@omakchronicle.com, Circulation/classified manager, Omak-Okanogan County Chronicle, WA, Omak

Bockrath, Dan
letters@citybeat.com, Publisher, Cincinnati Citybeat, OH, Cincinnati

Bocquel, Bernard
bbocquel@mymts.net, Assoc. Ed, La Liberte, MB, Saint Boniface

Bode, Ron .... (319) 398-8213
ron.bode@gazettecommunications.com, Adv. Dir., The Penny Saver, IA, Cedar Rapids

Bode, Roy .... (830) 693-4367
roy.bode@highlandernews.com, Pub./Ed., The Highlander, TX, Marble Falls

Bodell, Jon .... (603) 224-5301 ext. 317
Copy Ed., Concord Monitor, NH, Concord

Boden, Dave
dboden@newstribune.info, Pub., Daily Courier, PA, Connellsville

Boden, Dave
dboden@newstribune.info, Pub., Today's Shopper, WV, Keyser

Bodette, John L.
jbodette@stcloudtimes.com, Exec. Ed., St. Cloud Times, MN, Saint Cloud

Bodiford, Vince .... (562) 431-1397
vbodiford@paramountjournal.org, Pub., The

Paramount Journal, CA, Paramount
vbodiford@paramountjournal.org, Exec. Pub., The Catalina Islander, CA, Avalon
vbodiford@paramountjournal.org, Pub., News Enterprise, CA, Seal Beach

Bodine, John
john.bodine@bodine-electric.com, Pres., Bodine Electric, IL, Chicago

Bodle, John
jbodle@mtsu.edu, Prof., Middle Tennessee State University, TN, Murfreesboro

Bodley, Peter .... (763) 712-3513
peter.bodley@ecm-inc.com, Ed., Anoka County Shopper, MN, Coon Rapids

Bodley, Peter .... (763) 712-3513
peter.bodley@ecm-inc.com, Mng. Ed., Coon Rapids Herald, MN, Coon Rapids

Bodoh, Dennis
denny.bodoh@lee.net, Gen. Mgr., Dunn County Big Buck, WI, Chippewa Falls

Bodoh, Denny
denny.bodoh@lee.net, Adv. Mgr., Dunn County Reminder, WI, Menomonie

Boeger, Rob
rboeger@window-media.com, Art Dir., Washington Blade, DC, Washington

Boehler, Mark .... (662) 287-6111 ext 340
editor@dailycorinthian.com, Ed., The Daily Corinthian, MS, Corinth

Boehm, Angele
angele.boehm@bulletinreview.com, Bookkeeper, Denison Bulletin & Review, IA, Denison

Boehme, Cami
cami@digitalslant.com, Adj. Instr., Utah State University, UT, Logan

Boehn, Willene
circulation@stuttgartdailyleader.com, Circ. Mgr., Stuttgart Daily Leader, AR, Stuttgart

Boehne, Richard A. .... (513) 977-3025
rboehne@scripps.com, COO, E. W. Scripps Co., OH, Cincinnati

Boeker, Denise .... same
same, The Petersburg Observer, IL, Petersburg

Boerckel, Larry
handl@augustashomes.com, Ed., Homes & Land of Augusta, GA, Martinez

Boerckel, Larry
handl@augustashomes.com, Ed., Home Guide, GA, Martinez

Boering, Stacie .... (915) 592-5222 ext. 291
sboering@nysaver.com, Adv. Mgr., Pennysaver, NY, Elmsford

Boettcher, Lee Gayle
buffaloexpress@goquest.com, Ed., Buffalo Express, TX, Buffalo

Bogart, Amber .... (315) 661-2506
abogart@ogd.com, Cir. CSR, Ogdensburg Journal/Advance News, NY, Ogdensburg
abogart@ogd.com, Cir. CSR, Daily Courier-Observer/Advance News, NY, Massena

Bogart, Stephanie .... (580) 482-1221 Ext. 2080
sbogart@civitasmedia.com, Adv. Sales Rep., Altus Times, OK, Altus

Bogdan, Diana
dianab@aimgroup.com, Advanced Interactive Media Group, LLC, FL, Altamonte Springs

Bogel, Jeff
sales@pemco.kpl.net, Technical Sales Dir., Pemco, Inc., WI, Sheboygan

Bogenschutz, Tim
tim.bogenschutz@brainerddispatch.com, Pub., Brainerd Dispatch, MN, Brainerd

Boger, David M.
ads@wynneprogressinc.com, Pub., Wynne Progress, AR, Wynne

Boggins, Stephanie

ads@reporternews.com, Adv. Mgr., Sound of Freedom, TX, Abilene

Boggs, Brad .... (843) 745-5883
bboggs@postandcourier.com, Senior Director, Interactive Sales, The Post and Courier, SC, Charleston

Boggs, Jerry
jboggs@news-graphic.com, Ed., Georgetown News-Graphic, KY, Georgetown

Boggs, Jerry
jboggs@news-expressky.com, Ed., The Mountain Bargain Hunter, KY, Pikeville

Boggs, Kris .... (815) 625-3600 ext. 233
kboggs@svnmail.com, HR, Forreston Journal, IL, Dixon

Boggs, Larry .... (724) 775-3200 ext. 221
lboggs@timesonline.com, Circ. Dir., Beaver County Times, PA, Beaver

Boggs, Steve
sboggs@weatherforddemocrat.com, Pub., Parker County Shopper, TX, Weatherford

Boggs , Steve
sboggs@wacotrib.com, Editor, Waco Tribune-Herald, TX, Waco

Boghossian, Sylva A.
armenianreporter@msn.com, Prodn. Mgr., Armenian Reporter International, Inc., NJ, Paramus

Bogich, Greg
bogichg@valassis.com, Senior VP of Digital Media
, Valassis, MI, Livonia

Bogle, Robert W. .... (215) 893-4050
info@phila-tribune.com, CEO Pres., Philadelphia Tribune, PA, Philadelphia

Bohan, Mark
mbohan@printing.org, Managing Director, Technical Association of the Graphic Arts, PA, Sewickley

Bohanan, Terri
terrib@edmondsun.com, Classi. Adv., The Edmond Sun, OK, Edmond

Bohenkamp, John .... (319) 758-8133
jbohnenkamp@thehawkeye.com, Sports Editor, The Hawk Eye, IA, Burlington

Bohl, Ken
ken.bohl@bismarcktribune.com, Circ. Dir., The Bismarck Tribune, ND, Bismarck

Bohl, Ken
ken.bohl@bismarcktribune.com, Circ. Mgr., Finder, ND, Bismarck

Bohl, Kristi
tribune@nccray.net, Pub. , Burke County Tribune, ND, Bowbells

Bohlman, Beth .... (701) 780-1218
bbohlman@gfherald.com, circulation director, Grand Forks Herald, ND, Grand Forks

Bohnson, Jeff
jbohnson@answersmediainc.com, Pres., Answers Media Inc., IL, Chicago

Bohren, Dale .... (307) 266-0516
dale.bohren@trib.com, Pub./Ed., Casper Journal, WY, Casper
dale.bohren@trib.com, Exec. Ed., Casper Star-Tribune, WY, Casper

Bohrer, Dave .... (601) 693-1551 est.3213
Ed., The Meridian Star, MS, Meridian

Boiko, Bob
information@chasebobko.com, Pres., Chase Bobko, Inc., WA, Seattle

Boise, Lee
lboise@windstream.net, Pub./Ed./Gen. Mgr., The Rural-Urban Record, OH, Columbia Station

Boisvert, Louis
abonnement@latribune.qc.ca, Pres./Ed., La Tribune, QC, Sherbrooke

Boisvert, Louise
louise.boisvert@latribune.qc.ca, Pub & Pres., La Tribune, QC, Sherbrooke

Boisvert, Louisse
lboisvert@latribune.qc.ca, Pub., La Voix De L'est Plus, QC, Granby

Boisvert, Paul .... **(306) 648-3479**
trib.editorial@sasktel.net, Ed, Gravelbourg Tribune, SK, Gravelbourg

Boivin, Kevin .... **(630) 530-2203**
kboivin@guk-vijuk.com, Sales Mgr., G&K-Vijuk International, IL, Elmhurst

Boland, Bill .... **(709) 637-4684**
bboland@thewesternstar.com, IT/Prod. Supervisor, The Western Star, NL, Corner Brook

Boland, Ryan
news@fultonsun.com, Sports Ed., The Fulton Sun, MO, Fulton

Bolander, Adam .... **(319) 291-1522**
Adam.Bolander@wcfcourier.com, Circ. Mgr. , The Courier, IA, Waterloo

Bolas, Rich .... **(623) 876-2523**
rbolas@yourwestvalley.com, Sports Ed., Daily News-Sun, AZ, Sun City

Boldan, Kelly
kboldan@wctrib.com, Mng. Ed., Sunday Reminder, MN, Willmar

Boldan, Kelly .... **(320) 235-1150**
kboldan@wctrib.com, Editor, West Central Tribune, MN, Willmar

Boldt, Jeff .... **(605) 256-4555**
jeff@madisondailyleader.com, Tech. Manager, The Madison Daily Leader, SD, Madison

Bolduc-Jacob, Marilaine
marilaine.bolduc-jacob@transcontinental.ca, Information Dir., Courrier-ahuntsic, QC, Saint Laurent

Boles, Becca
bboles@pnj.com, Dir., Market Devel., Pensacola News Journal, FL, Pensacola

Boles, Deana
lori@weinrichadv.com, Exec. Dir., League of Advertising Agencies, Inc., NY, New York

Boles, Durelle
dboles@onecorp.com, Pres., Gutenberg Printing Press Co., GA, Atlanta
dboles@onecorp.com, Pres., ONE Corp., GA, Atlanta
dboles@onecorp.com, Vice Pres., Boles, Morgan & Canino, Inc., AL, Florence

Boles, Lana .... **(541) 463-5655**
Lane Cmty. College, OR, Eugene

Bolich, Matt .... **(717) 248-6741**
mbolich@lewistownsentinel.com, Adv. Dir., The Sentinel, PA, Lewistown

Bolinger, Vickie .... **(619) 293-1198**
vickie.bolinger@utsandiego.com, President, Advertising Media Credit Executives Association International, KY, Louisville

Bolitho, Jake .... **(309) 734-3176**
jbolitho@reviewatlas.com, Ed., Daily Review Atlas, IL, Monmouth

Bolitho, Nick .... **(978) 739-1350**
nbolitho@cnc.com, Adv. Dir., Waltham News Tribune, MA, Needham
nbolitho@cnc.com, Adv. Dir., Sandwich Broadsider, MA, Yarmouth Port
nbolitho@cnc.com, Adv. Dir., Harwich Oracle, MA, Orleans
nbolitho@cnc.com, Adv. Dir., Pembroke Mariner & Express, MA, Marshfield
nbolitho@cnc.com, Adv. Dir., Natick Bulletin & TAB, MA, Framingham
nbolitho@cnc.com, Adv. Dir., The Westborough News, MA, Framingham
nbolitho@cnc.com, Adv. Dir., The Raynham Call, MA, Taunton
nbolitho@cnc.com, Adv. Dir., Provincetown Banner, MA, Provincetown

nbolitho@cnc.com, Adv. Dir., Avon Messenger, MA, Brockton
nbolitho@cnc.com, Adv. Dir., Bridgewater Independent, MA, Raynham
nbolitho@cnc.com, Adv. Dir., Wareham Courier, MA, Plymouth
nbolitho@cnc.com, Adv. Dir., The Lakeville Call, MA, Brockton
nbolitho@cnc.com, Adv. Dir., Shrewsbury Chronicle, MA, Framingham
nbolitho@cnc.com, Adv. Dir., Beverly Citizen, MA, Danvers
nbolitho@cnc.com, Adv. Dir., The Villager, MA, Framingham
nbolitho@cnc.com, Adv. Dir., Norwood Transcript & Bulletin, MA, Needham
nbolitho@cnc.com, Adv. Dir., Stoughton Journal, MA, Raynham
nbolitho@cnc.com, Adv. Dir., Cape Ann Beacon, MA, Danvers
nbolitho@cnc.com, Adv. Dir., The Bulletin, MA, Yarmouth Port
nbolitho@cnc.com, Adv. Dir., Woburn Advocate, MA, Concord
nbolitho@cnc.com, Adv. Dir., West Roxbury Transcript, MA, Needham
nbolitho@cnc.com, Adv. Dir., Randolph Herald, MA, Randolph
nbolitho@cnc.com, Adv. Dir., Southwick Suffield News, MA, Feeding Hills
nbolitho@cnc.com, Adv. Dir. , Mansfield News, MA, Marshfield
nbolitho@cnc.com, Adv. Dir. , The Register, MA, Hyannis
nbolitho@cnc.com, Adv. Dir., Brookline TAB, MA, Needham
nbolitho@cnc.com, Adv. Dir., Newton Tab, MA, Needham
nbolitho@cnc.com, Adv. Dir., Bourne Courier, MA, Hyannis
nbolitho@cnc.com, Adv. Dir., Medfield Press, MA, Needham
nbolitho@cnc.com, Adv. Dir., Norton Mirror, MA, Raynham
nbolitho@cnc.com, Adv. Dir., Westwood Press, MA, Needham
nbolitho@cnc.com, Adv. Dir., Easton Journal, MA, Raynham
nbolitho@cnc.com, Adv. Dir., Kingston Reporter, MA, Plymouth
nbolitho@cnc.com, Adv. Dir., Old Colony Memorial, MA, Plymouth
nbolitho@cnc.com, Adv. Dir., Sharon Advocate, MA, Needham
nbolitho@cnc.com, Adv. Dir., The Country Gazette, MA, Milford
nbolitho@cnc.com, Adv. Dir., Somerville Journal, MA, Somerville
nbolitho@cnc.com, Adv. Dir., Tewksbury Advocate, MA, Concord
nbolitho@cnc.com, Adv. Dir., Allston-Brighton TAB, MA, Needham
nbolitho@cnc.com, Adv. Dir., The Bolton Common, MA, Concord
nbolitho@cnc.com, Adv. Dir., Holbrook Sun, MA, Randolph
nbolitho@cnc.com, Adv. Dir., Lincoln Journal, MA, Concord
nbolitho@cnc.com, Adv. Dir., Marlborough Enterprise, MA, Framingham
nbolitho@cnc.com, Adv. Dir., Stoneham Sun, MA, Somerville
nbolitho@cnc.com, Adv. Dir., Lexington Minuteman, MA, Lexington
nbolitho@cnc.com, Adv. Dir., Watertown TAB, MA, Needham
nbolitho@cnc.com, Adv. Dir., North Shore Sunday, MA, Danvers
nbolitho@cnc.com, Adv. Dir., Scituate Mariner, MA, Marshfield
nbolitho@cnc.com, Adv. Dir., Hopkinton Crier, MA, Framingham
nbolitho@cnc.com, Adv. Dir., Reading Advocate, MA, Danvers
nbolitho@cnc.com, Adv. Dir., The Concord Journal, MA, Concord
nbolitho@cnc.com, Adv. Dir., North Attleboro Free Press, MA, North Attleboro
nbolitho@cnc.com, Adv. Dir., Ashland TAB, MA, Framingham
nbolitho@cnc.com, Adv. Dir., Chelmsford Independent, MA, Concord

nbolitho@cnc.com, Adv. Dir., Wilmington Advocate, MA, Concord
nbolitho@cnc.com, Adv. Dir., Wayland Town Crier, MA, Framingham
nbolitho@cnc.com, Adv. Dir., Salem Gazette, MA, Danvers
nbolitho@cnc.com, Adv. Dir., Norwell Mariner, MA, Marshfield
nbolitho@cnc.com, Adv. Dir., Newburyport Current, MA, Danvers
nbolitho@cnc.com, Adv. Dir., Medford Transcript, MA, Danvers
nbolitho@cnc.com, Adv. Dir., Cambridge Chronicle & TAB, MA, Somerville
nbolitho@cnc.com, Adv. Dir., Dover-Sherborn Press, MA, Needham
nbolitho@cnc.com, Adv. Dir., Hanover Mariner, MA, Marshfield
nbolitho@cnc.com, Adv. Dir., Wakefield Observer, MA, Danvers
nbolitho@cnc.com, Adv. Dir., Wellesley Townsman, MA, Needham
nbolitho@cnc.com, Adv. Dir. , Needham Times, MA, Needham
nbolitho@cnc.com, Adv. Dir., Burlington Union, MA, Concord
nbolitho@cnc.com, Adv. Dir., Weston Town Crier, MA, Framingham
nbolitho@cnc.com, Adv. Dir., Cohasset Mariner, MA, Hingham
nbolitho@cnc.com, Adv. Dir., Braintree Forum, MA, Randolph
nbolitho@cnc.com, Adv. Dir., Holliston TAB, MA, Framingham
nbolitho@cnc.com, Adv. Dir., Malden Observer, MA, Danvers
nbolitho@cnc.com, Adv. Dir., Marblehead Reporter, MA, Marblehead
nbolitho@cnc.com, Adv. Dir., North Andover Citizen, MA, Danvers
nbolitho@cnc.com, Adv. Dir., Tri-Town Transcript, MA, Danvers
nbolitho@cnc.com, Adv. Dir., Littleton Independent, MA, Concord
nbolitho@cnc.com, Adv. Dir., Westford Eagle, MA, Concord
nbolitho@cnc.com, Adv. Dir., Ipswich Chronicle, MA, Danvers
nbolitho@cnc.com, Adv. Dir., Rockland Standard, MA, Marshfield
nbolitho@cnc.com, Adv. Dir., Swampscott Reporter, MA, Marblehead
nbolitho@cnc.com, Adv. Dir., Weymouth News, MA, Randolph
nbolitho@cnc.com, Adv. Dir., Hamilton-Wenham Chronicle, MA, Danvers
nbolitho@cnc.com, Adv. Dir., Danvers Herald, MA, Danvers
nbolitho@cnc.com, Adv. Dir., Georgetown Record, MA, Danvers
nbolitho@cnc.com, Adv. Dir., Canton Journal, MA, Raynham
nbolitho@cnc.com, Adv. Dir., Winchester Star, MA, Lexington
nbolitho@cnc.com, Adv. Dir., Hingham Journal, MA, Hingham
nbolitho@cnc.com, Adv. Dir., The Beacon-Villager, MA, Concord
nbolitho@cnc.com, Adv. Dir., Melrose Free Press, MA, Danvers
nbolitho@cnc.com, Adv. Dir., Hudson Sun, MA, Framingham
nbolitho@cnc.com, Adv. Dir., The Walpole Times, MA, Walpole
nbolitho@cnc.com, Adv. Dir., Carver Reporter, MA, Plymouth
nbolitho@cnc.com, Adv. Dir., Times & Courier, MA, Concord
nbolitho@cnc.com, Adv. Dir., Amesbury News, MA, Danvers

Bolitho, Thomas .... **(580) 421-9600**
bolitho@nationalmediasales.com, Pres., National Media Associates, OK, Ada

Bolitho, Thomas C. .... **(580) 421-9600**
bolitho@nationalmediasales.com, Broker, National Media Associates, OK, Ada

Bolitho, Tom
times.chickasaw@chickasaw.net, Ed., Chickasaw Times, OK, Ada

Bolle, Laurie .... **(715) 845-0622**
lbolle@gannett.com, Classified Mgr., Kewaunee County Star-News, WI, Kewaunee
lbolle@gannett.com, Gen. Mgr. / Dir. of Sales , Stevens Point Journal, WI, Stevens Point

Bollinger, Cory .... **(812) 331-4251**
mmaloney@heraldt.com, Pub., The Mooresville-Decatur Times, IN, Martinsville

Bollinger, Cory .... **(605) 622-2202**
cbollinger@aberdeennews.com, Adv. Dir., The Herald Times, IN, Bloomington
cbollinger@aberdeennews.com, Pub., Aberdeen American News, SD, Aberdeen

Bollinger, Cory .... **(812) 331-4251**
cbollinger@schurz.com, VP of Publishing, Schurz Communications Inc, IN, Mishawaka

Bollinger, Josh .... **(443) 239-1392**
jbollinger@chespub.com, News Ed. , The Star-Democrat, MD, Easton

Bollman, Stacy
classifieds@befordgazette.com, Class. , The Bedford Gazette, PA, Bedford

Bologna, Michael .... **(516) 569-4000 ext. 211**
mikeb@liherald.com, Vice Pres., Opns., Richner Communications, Inc., NY, Garden City

Bologna, Michael .... **ext. 211**
mbologna@liherald.com, Vice Pres., Opns., Primetime, NY, Garden City

Bologna, Michael .... **(516) 569-4000 x211**
Gen. Mgr., Lynbrook/East Rockaway Herald, NY, Garden City

Bolognese, Rick .... **(203) 789-5301**
rbolognese@newhavenregister.com, Produ Dir, The Dolphin, CT, Groton

Bolt, Lynn
classifieds@wltribune.com, Class. Mgr, The Williams Lake Tribune, BC, Williams Lake

Bolton, Bart .... **(217) 788-1485**
bart.bolton@sj-r.com, The State Journal-Register, IL, Springfield

Bolton, Bo
news@monroejournal.com, Pub., The Monroe Journal, AL, Monroeville

Bolton, Jean .... **(910) 484-6200**
jbolton@upandcomingmag.com, Vice Pres., Opns., Up & Coming Weekly, NC, Fayetteville

Bolton, Jodie
news@monroejournal.com, Art Dir., The Monroe Journal, AL, Monroeville

Bolton, John .... **(520) 618-7868**
bolton@azstarnet.com, Starnet Online Ed., Arizona Daily Star, AZ, Tucson

Bolton, Linda
lbolton@aberdeenpublishing.com, Mng. Dir., Osoyoos Times, BC, Osoyoos

Bolton, Linda .... **(250) 498-3711**
lbolton@aberdeenpublishing.com, Pub., Oliver Chronicle, BC, Oliver

Bolton, Steve
comanchetimes@pldi.net, Ed., Comanche Times, OK, Comanche

Bolton, Tom .... **ext. 2228**
tbolton@pulitzer.net, Exec. Ed., Santa Maria Times, CA, Santa Maria

Bolton, Tom .... **(805) 739-2229**
Exec. Ed., The Lompoc Record, CA, Santa Maria

Bolus, Shelly .... **(970) 728-9788 ext.16**
shelly@telluridenews.com, Office Mgr., The Norwood Times, CO, Telluride
shelly@telluridenews.com, Office Mgr., Telluride Daily Planet; the Watch; The Norwood Post, CO, Telluride

Bolyard, Gary A. .... **(304) 329-0090**
ppigary@atlanticbb.net, Pub., The Preston County Journal, WV, Kingwood

Bolyard, Kelly .... **(808) 930-8659**

kbolyard@westhawaiitoday.com, Advertising Director, West Hawaii Today, HI, Kailua Kona

Bolyard, Tina M.
ppitina@atlanticbb.net, Ed., The Preston County Journal, WV, Kingwood

Bolz, Barbara J.
bolzbj@udmercy.edu, Chair, University of Detroit Mercy, MI, Detroit

Bomstad, Sharon
sbomstad@wctrib.com, Features Ed., West Central Tribune, MN, Willmar

Boname, Mickayla ....(850) 638-0212 Ext. 4003
mboname@chipleypaper.com, Adv., Holmes County Times-Advertiser, FL, Chipley

Bonanny, Brett ....(570) 740-0638
Luzerne County Cmty. College, PA, Nanticoke

Bond, Amanda
pickettpress@twlakes.net, Pub./Ed., Pickett County Press, TN, Byrdstown

Bond, David
dbond@miningjournal.net, Graphics Mgr., The Mining Journal, MI, Marquette

Bond, Dianne
bookkeeping@mcduffieprogress.com, Office Mgr./Circ. Mgr., The McDuffie Progress, GA, Thomson

Bond, Ginny
gbond@firstfreedombank.com, Adv. Dir., The Wilson Post, TN, Lebanon

Bond, James D.
mspaper@mychoice.net, Pub., Money Stretcher, IL, Galatia

Bond, Jesse P. ....(315) 789-3333
production@fltimes.com, Production Mgr., Finger Lakes Times, NY, Geneva

Bond, Jill ....(765) 459-3121 Ex. 8578
jill.bond@kokomotribune.com, Managing Ed., Kokomo Tribune, IN, Kokomo

Bond, Mindy .... (304) 636-2121, ext. 124
mbond@theintermountain.com, Dir. of Cir., The Inter-Mountain, WV, Elkins

Bonde, Alysoun ....(530) 752-9888
University of California, Davis, CA, Davis

Bondurant, Jay ....(540) 586-8612
jbondurant@bedfordbulletin.com, Pub., Bedford Bullet, VA, Bedford
jbondurant@bedfordbulletin.com, Pub./Adv. Mgr., Bedford Bulletin, VA, Bedford

Bondurant, John
recorder@flash.net, Editor n Chief
Assoc. Publisher, Commercial Recorder, TX, Fort Worth

Bone, Dianne L. .... (843) 546-4148 ext. 232
dbone@gtowntimes.com, Bus. Mgr., Georgetown Communications, Inc., SC, Georgetown

Bonebrake, Linda ....(530) 926-5214
Office Mgr., Voice Of The Mountain, CA, Mount Shasta

Boney, Thomas E.
alamancenews@mail.com, Pub./Ed., The Alamance News, NC, Graham

Bonfiglio, Dawn ....(330) 996-3285
dbonfiglio@thebeaconjournal.com, IT Director, Akron Beacon Journal, OH, Akron

Bongiorni, Tami ....(330) 672-6306
Kent State Univ., OH, Kent

Bongo, Jane
jane@clearwatergazette.com, Ed., Clearwater Beacon, FL, Seminole

Boni, Katie
kmb20@albion.edu, Features Editor, Albion College, MI, Albion

Boni, Thomas
tboni@crestviewbulletin.com, Halifax Media, FL, Daytona Beach
tboni@crestviewbulletin.com, Ed., Crestview

News Bulletin, FL, Crestview

Bonifant, Drew ....(207) 621-5638
dbonifant@centralmaine.com, Sports Writer , Morning Sentinel, ME, Waterville

Bonifanti, Terry
tbonifanti@timesshamrock.com, Features Ed., The Times-Tribune, PA, Scranton

Bonin, Paula
jdngm@jenningsdailynews.net, Gen. Mgr./ Adv. Mgr., Jennings (LA) Daily News, LA, Jennings

Bonitabitus, Carmel ....(480) 966-0845
Cbonitatibus@times-standard.com, Prod. Mgr., Tri-City Weekly, CA, Eureka

Bonitatibus, Carmel ....(707) 441-0544
cbonitatibus@times-standard.com, Advertising Director/Production Director, Times-Standard , CA, Eureka

Bonn, Jim
jbonn@oleantimesherald.com, Pub., Olean Times Herald, NY, Olean

Bonnar, Stephanie
ads@newslj.com, Graphic Designer, News Letter Journal, WY, Newcastle

Bonnell, Keith
keith.bonnell@sunmedia.ca, Editor, The Ottawa Sun, ON, Ottawa

Bonner, Dave
dave@powelltribune.com, Pub., The Powell Tribune, WY, Powell

Bonner, Ken
Ken.Bonner@thedailysentinel.com, Adv. Dir., The Daily Sentinel, AL, Scottsboro

Bonner, Thomas
tbonner@vicad.com, Nat'l Adv. Mgr., Victoria Advocate, TX, Victoria

Bonner, Toby
toby@powelltribune.com, Adv. Mgr./Gen. Mgr., The Powell Tribune, WY, Powell

Bonnette, Mike ....(304) 296-7753
mailroom@dominionpost.com, Prodn. Mgr., Distr., The Dominion Post, WV, Morgantown

Bonoff, Steven
sbonoff@idealliance.org, Pres., Idealliance, VA, Alexandria

Bonsack, Laurie
wellsmir@bevcomm.net, Ed., Wells Mirror, MN, Wells

Bonsall, Jeanna
jbonsall@turley.com, Adv. Rep., The Tantasqua Town Common, MA, Palmer

Bonspiel, Steve
steveb@easterndoor.com, Ed./Pub., The Eastern Door, QC, Kahnawake

Bonza, Ed ....(470) 578-6470
ebonza@kennesaw.edu, Kennesaw State University, GA, Kennesaw

Boogert, John ....(814) 231-4640
jboogert@centredaily.com, Exec. Ed. , Centre Daily Times, PA, State College

Book, Constance
cbook@elon.edu, Assoc. Dean/Assoc. Prof., Elon University, NC, Elon

Booker, Amy ....(251) 867-4876
amy.booker@brewtonstandard.com, Advert. Rep, The Brewton Standard, AL, Brewton

Boom, Brian ....(901) 872-2286
brian.bloom@journalinc.com, Pub./Adv. Dir., The Millington Star, TN, Memphis

Boone, James B.
JIM.BOONE@BOONENEWSPAPERS. COM, Chrmn. of the Bd./CEO/Dir., Boone Newspapers, Inc., AL, Northport

Boone, Jean Patterson ....(804) 644-0496
jeanboone@richmondfreepress.com, Pres./ Pub., Richmond Free Press, VA, Richmond

Boone, Kenneth ....(256) 234-4281 ext. 27

kenneth.boone@alexcityoutlook.com, Pub., Alexander City Outlook, AL, Alexander City

Boone, Kenneth
kenneth.boone@alexcityoutlook.com, Pub., Dadeville Record, AL, Alexander City

Boone, Rozaan ....(718) 320-3300, Ext. 3375
cctimes@riverbaycorp.com, Ed., Co-op City Times, NY, Bronx

Boonjathai, Kimberly
phoenixnews@luc.edu, Loyola Univ., IL, Chicago

Booth, Doris ....(972) 402-0101
dbooth@authorlink.com, Ed. in Chief, Authorlink, TX, Irving

Booth, Dorothy ....(517) 592-2122
Dorothy@theexponent.com, Adv. Mgr., The Exponent, MI, Brooklyn

Booth, Jim ....(727) 893-8420
jbooth@tampabay.com, Sr. Ed., Tampa Bay Times, FL, St Petersburg

Booth, Kyle ....(941) 361-4996
kyle.booth@heraldtribune.com, Front Page Ed., Sarasota Herald-Tribune, FL, Sarasota

Booth, Ray
rbooth@daily-jeff.com, Exec. Ed., New Concord Area Leader, OH, Cambridge
rbooth@daily-jeff.com, Prodn. Mgr., The Daily Jeffersonian, OH, Cambridge

Booth, Ray
rbooth@daily-jeff.com, Mng. Ed., Barnesville Enterprise, OH, Barnesville

Booth, Ray H.
rbooth@daily-jeff.com, Exec. Ed., The Daily Jeffersonian, OH, Cambridge

Booth, Sally ....(734) 426-8433
Sec., Schwadron Cartoon & Illustration Service, Ann Arbor

Booth, Tom ....(508) 676-2560
tbooth@heraldnews.com, Adv. Dir., Real Estate Guide, MA, Fall River

Booth-Ehle, Margaret
mbehle@pa.net, Pub., The Franklin Shopper, PA, Chambersburg

Boothe, Jason
jason@washcountynews.com, Washington County News, AL, Citronelle

Boothe, Kay ....(936) 687-2424
kboothe@messenger-news.com, Ed., The Messenger, TX, Grapeland

Boothroyd, Greg
ads@smokymountainnews.com, Adv. Dir., Smoky Mountain News, NC, Waynesville

Booze, Melinda
Boozem@evangel.edu, Evangel University, MO, Springfield

Bope, Kathy
perhameb@eot.com, Bus. Mgr., Enterprise Bulletin, MN, Perham

Bopp, David ....(308) 497-2153
Ed., Spalding Enterprise, NE, Spalding

Bopp, David ....(308) 358-0440
crpress@hotmail.com, Ed., Cedar Rapids Press, NE, Cedar Rapids

Borah, Richard
richard@sooperads.com, Sooper Ads, ID, Twin Falls

Borak, Jeffrey ....(413) 496-6212
jborak@berkshireeagle.com, Ent. Ed. , The Berkshire Eagle, MA, Pittsfield

Borchers, Martha ....(208) 389-2879
email@idahopressclub.org, Exec. Dir., Idaho Press Club, ID, Boise

Borde, Desaree ....(575) 538-5893 Ext. 5808
dborde@scsun-news.com, Multi. Med. Acct. Exec. , Silver City Sun-News, NM, Silver City

Bordeleau, John ....(978) 739-1335
VP, Adv., GateHouse Media, Inc., NY, Pittsford

Bordelon, Michael ....(337) 363-3939
vpgaz@centurytel.net, Editor, Ville Platte Gazette, LA, Ville Platte

Bordelon, Ted
pawirenews@bsmphilly.com, Mng. Ed., The Midweek Wire, PA, Bensalem

Borden, Barb ....(204) 697-7389
barb.borden@freepress.mb.ca, Sales Manager, The Sou'wester, MB, Winnipeg

Borden, Barb ....(204) 697-7389
barb.borden@freepress.mb.ca, Sales Mgr, The Times, MB, Winnipeg

Borden, Barb ....(204) 697-7389
barb.borden@freepress.mb.ca, Sales Manager, The Headliner, MB, Winnipeg

Borden, Barb ....(204) 697-7389
barb.borden@freepress.mb.ca, Sales Manager, The Lance, MB, Winnipeg

Borden, Barb ....(204) 697-7389
barb.borden@freepress.mb.ca, Sales Mgr, The Herald, MB, Winnipeg

Borden, Barb ....(204) 697-7389
barb.borden@freepress.mb.ca, Sales Mgr, The Metro, MB, Winnipeg

Borden, Robert C. ....(979) 731-4621
robert.borden@theeagle.com, Ed. Page Ed., The Eagle, TX, Bryan

Borders, Gary ....(903) 237-8863
garyb@mediamergers.com, Sr. Assoc.-SW/ Plains, Grimes, McGovern & Associates, NY, New York

Bordewyk, David ....(605) 692-4300
daveb@sdna.com, Exec. Dir., South Dakota Newspaper Association, SD, Brookings

Bordner, Jean
jeanb@news-banner.com, Adv. Sales Mgr., News-Banner, IN, Bluffton

Bordok, David
dbordok@hammondstar.com, Pressroom Supervisor, The Daily Star, LA, Hammond

Bordonado, Gilles ....(450) 964-4444
gbordonado@larevue.qc.ca, Pub./Pres./CEO., La Revue De Terrebonne, QC, Terrebonne

Bordonado, Gilles ....(450) 964-4444
gbordonado@larevue.qc.ca, Président, Le Trait D'union, QC, Terrebonne

Bordonaro, Dominick ....(716) 250-6884
dbordonaro@mediasalesplus.com, Chief Executive Officer, Media Sales Plus, Inc., NY, Williamsville

Bordonaro, Greg .... (860) 236-9998 ext. 139
gbordonaro@HatfordBusiness.com, Ed., Hartford Business Journal, CT, Hartford

Boreman, Deb .... (419) 281-0581 Ext. 230
dboreman@times-gazette.com, Cir. Mgr., Ashland Times-Gazette, OH, Ashland

Boreman, Deborah .... (419) 281-0581 ext. 230
dboreman@times-gazette.com, Circulation Director, Ashland Publishing Co. LLC, OH, Ashland

Boren, Elizabeth ....(615) 444-3952
eboren@lebanondemocrat.com, Circ. Mgr., The Lebanon Democrat, TN, Lebanon

Boren, Jim ....(559) 441-6307
jboren@fresnobee.com, Exe. Ed/Senior V.P, The Fresno Bee, CA, Fresno
jboren@fresnobee.com, Exec. Ed./Sen. VP, The Clovis Independent, CA, Fresno

Boren, Julie
publisher@campbellpublications.net, Publisher, Campbell Publishing Co., Inc., IL, Jerseyville

Boren, Julie
publisher@campbellpublications.net, Pub., Greene Prairie Press, IL, Carrollton

Boren, Julie
info@enquirerdemocrat.com, Pub., Coal Country Times, IL, Carlinville
info@enquirerdemocrat.com, Pub., Macoupin

County Enquirer Democrat, IL, Carlinville

Boren, Julie
publisher@campbellpublications.net, Pub./Ed.,
The Weekly Messenger, IL, Pittsfield

Boren, Julie
publisher@campbellpublications.net, Pub.,
Calhoun News-Herald, IL, Hardin
publisher@campbellpublications.net, Pub.,
Jesey County Journal, IL, Jerseyville

Boren, Julie.............................(217) 285-2345
Pub., Scott County Times, IL, Winchester

Borer, Eric...................(909) 593-3511 ext. 4292
borere@ulv.edu, University of La Verne, CA,
La Verne

Borg, Jennifer A.........................(973) 569-7680
BorgJ@northjersey.com, VP/Corp Secretary
& General Counsel , Herald News, NJ,
Rockaway

Borg, Malcom..........................(973) 569-7306
borgm@northjersey.com, Chairman, The
Record, NJ, Woodland Park

Borg, Stephen..........................(973) 569-7270
borgs@northjersey.com, Pres., Su Guia, NJ,
Clifton

Borg, Stephen..........................(973) 569-7270
borgs@northjersey.com, Pres., Mahwah
Suburban News, NJ, Ridgewood

Borg, Stephen A.......................(973) 569-7306
borgs@northjersey.com, Pres., North Jersey
Deals, NJ, Woodland Park
borgs@northjersey.com, Pres., North Jersey
Community Newspapers, NJ, Woodland Park

Borg, Stephen A.......................(973) 569-7270
BorgS@northjersey.com, Herald News, NJ,
Rockaway

Borgen, Kari...........................(541) 523-3673
kborgen@wescompapers.com, Regional
Publisher, The Observer, OR, La Grande

Borgen, Kari...........................(541) 523-3673
kborgen@bakercityherald.com, Pub., Baker
City Herald, OR, Baker City
kborgen@bakercityherald.com, Interim
Publisher, The Union Democrat, CA, Sonora

Borgerding, Tom
emailus@campusmediagroupinc.com,
Pres./CEO, Campus Media Group, MN,
Bloomington

Borges, Craig...........................(508) 236-0337
news@thesunchronicle.com, Business, The
Sun Chronicle, MA, Attleboro

Borghese, Lorna.......................(570) 690-2344
lborghese@fujifilm.com, Accnt. Mgr., Fujifilm
Graphic Systems USA, Inc., CT, Windsor
lborghese@fujifilm.com, Newspaper Acct.
Mgr., SE Region, Fujifilm North America
Corporation, IL, Hanover Park

Borghetti, Frank.......................(801) 599-3183
frank@borghetti.com, Real Estate Consultant,
Reno Real Estate Consulting Group, NV,
Reno

Borham, Roger
info@thearthurgraphic.com; recordherald@
consolidated.net, Ed., Arthur Graphic
Clarion, IL, Arthur
info@thearthurgraphic.com; recordherald@
consolidated.net, Ed., Southern Piatt Record
Herald, IL, Arthur

Borise, Stephanie.....................(203) 964-2420
sborise@hearstmediact.com, Business Editior,
Greenwich Time, CT, Old Greenwich

Borkowski, Lee.......................(608) 647-2911
lborkowski@wcinet.com, General Manager,
Richland Center Shopping News, WI,
Richland Center

Borkowski, Lee
lborkowski@wcinet.com, General manager,
Oregon Observer, WI, Oregon

Borkowski, Lee.......................(608) 845-9559
lborkowski@wcinet.com, Regional Publisher,

Great Dane Shopping News, WI, Verona

Borkowski, Lee.......................(608) 845-9559
lborkowski@wcinet.com, Gen. Mgr., The
Fitchburg Star, WI, Verona

Borkowski, Lee
lborkowski@wcinet.com, Regional Publisher,
Wisconsin-iowa Shopping News, WI, Prairie
Du Chien

Bormann, Bruce J.
nwh@ltbroadband.net, Ed., North Weld Herald,
CO, Eaton

Bormann, Jean........................(563) 659-3121
obsgm@iowatelecom.net, Adv. Mgr., The
Observer, IA, De Witt

Born-Smith, Linda........................ ext. 10
lborn@mcphersonsentinel.com, Adv. Dir.,
Classified, McPherson Sentinel, KS,
McPherson

Borom, Damon........................(216) 999-6603
dborom@plaind.com, Prodn. Mgr., Machinists/
Engineers, The Plain Dealer, OH, Brooklyn

Boroshok, Jon
j.boroshok@snhu.edu, Southern New
Hampshire Univ., NH, Manchester

Boroson, Rebecca
editor@jewishmediagroup.com, Ed., Jewish
Standard, NJ, Teaneck

Borovik, Dmitry........................(416) 774-2238
dborovik@insidetoronto.com, Sales Rep.,
North York Mirror, ON, Toronto

Borowski, Neill........................(607) 798-1127
nborowski@stargazette.com, Exec. Ed. , Star-
Gazette, NY, Elmira
nborowski@stargazette.com, Exec. Ed., Press
& Sun-Bulletin, NY, Binghamton

Borowski, Neill A.......................(607) 798-1186
nborowski@ithacajournal.com, Exec. Ed., The
Ithaca Journal, NY, Ithaca

Borowsky, Ted
information@fostermfg.com, Pres., Foster Mfg.
Co., PA, Montgomeryville

Borrell, A. Joseph......................(717) 477-1521
Dept. Chairman, Shippensburg University/
Communication/Journalism Department , PA,
Shippensburg

Borsuk, Ken................. (203) 861-9191 ext. 112
editor@greenwichpost.com, Ed., Greenwich-
Post, CT, Darien

Bortel, Robert..........................(419) 372-2606
rbortel@bgsu.edu, Bowling Green State Univ.,
OH, Bowling Green

Borthwick, Ian........................(616) 331-2484
advertising@lanthorn.com, Advertising
Manager, Grand Valley State Univ., MI,
Allendale

Borton, Sara Johnson................(843) 706-8105
sborton@islandpacket.com, Pub./Pres., The
Island Packet, SC, Bluffton

Borton, Sara Johnson
sborton@islandpacket.com, Pres./Pub., The
Beaufort Gazette, SC, Bluffton

Bos, David
dbos@niagarathisweek.com, Gen. Mgr.,
Niagara This Week, ON, Thorold

Bosak, Chris...........................(203) 354-1047
cbosak@thehour.com, Co-Managing Editor,
Bus. Ed., The Hour, CT, Norwalk

Bosak, Maria..........................(204) 589-5871
presstr@mts.net, Ed., Ukrainsky Holos, MB,
Winnipeg

Boselly, Julie..........................(425) 483-0606
julie@woodinville.com, Pub., The Woodinville
Weekly, WA, Woodinville

Bosiak, Marylynn.....................(401) 767-8500
mlbosiak@woonsocketcall.com, Adv. Dir./Gen.
Mgr./Pub., The Times, RI, Pawtucket

Boss, Grant............................(603) 668-4321

gbosse@unionleader.com, Editorial Page
Ed., New Hampshire Union Leader/New
Hampshire Sunday News, NH, Manchester

Bossart, Sherrie
sbossart@athensmessenger.com, Adv. Mgr.,
Messenger Consumer Services, OH, Athens

Bosse, Leigh
granitequill@mcttelecom.com, Pub.,
Messenger, NH, Hillsborough

Bosse, Sandra
sbosse@hcnonline.com, Features Ed., The
Courier of Montgomery County, TX, Conroe

Bossey, Steve..........................(810) 762-5616
Mott Cmty. College, MI, Flint

Bossick, David.............(231) 845-5182 ext.312
dbossick@ludingtondailynews.com, Sports Ed.,
Ludington Daily News, MI, Ludington

Bossley, Ashley
ashley.bossley@vermiliontoday.com, Classified
Sales Rep., Abbeville Meridional, LA,
Abbeville

Bostwick, Charles....................(661) 267-4119
cbostwick@avpress.com, Ed., Antelope Valley
Press, CA, Palmdale

Bostwick, Charles....................(661) 267-4119
cbostwick@avpress.com, Mng. Ed., Antelope
Valley Press Express, CA, Palmdale

Bosworth, Robert H.
rbosworth@thequincysun.com, Ed. & Pub. ,
The Quincy Sun, MA, Quincy

Both, Kristene........................(973) 290-4343
College of St. Elizabeth, NJ, Morristown

Botta, Renee
renee.botta@du.edu, Assoc. Prof./Dir., Mass
Commun. Grad. Studies, University of
Denver, CO, Denver

Bottome, Abigail......................(978) 232-2050
observer@endicott.edu, Endicott College, MA,
Beverly

Bottomly, Therese...................(503) 221-8434
theresebottomly@news.oregonian.com, Mng.
Ed., News, The Oregonian, OR, Portland

Bottrell, Andrew
abottrell@nptelegraph.com, Sports Ed., The
North Platte Telegraph, NE, North Platte

Bottrell, Kevin
kbottrell@nwkansas.com, Ed, Goodland Star-
News, KS, Goodland

Bottrell, Kevin
kbottrell@nwkansas.com, Ed., The Delphos
Republican, KS, Glasco

Bottrell, Lizz
oxbow.herald@sasktel.net, Editor, The Oxbow
Herald, SK, Oxbow

Bouchard, Renel.....................(450) 347-0323
renel.bouchard@canadafrancais.com, Gen.
Mgr., Journal L'avenir & Des Rivieres, QC,
Farnham
renel.bouchard@canadafrancais.com, Journal
Le Richelieu, QC, Sainte Jean sur Richelieu

Bouchard, Renel
renel.bouchard@canadafrancais.com, Gen.
Mgr., Le Canada Francais, QC, Sainte Jean
sur Richelieu

Bouchard, Roxanne
administration@la-liberte.mb.ca, Office Admin.,
La Liberte, MB, Saint Boniface

Bouchard, Sophie....................(418) 908-3438
lenic@spirimedia.com, Nic, QC, Saint Augustin
de Desmaures

Boucher, Jody..............(401) 789-9744 ext 105
jboucher@ricentral.com, Adv. Mgr., Standard-
Times, RI, Wakefield

Boucher, Jody
jboucher@ricentral.com, Adv. Mgr./Pub.,
Narragansett Times, RI, Wakefield

Boucher, Jody.........................(401) 789-9744

jboucher@ricentral.com, Reg. Pub., Kent
County Daily Times, RI, West Warwick
jboucher@ricentral.com, Pub., The Call, RI,
Woonsocket
jboucher@ricentral.com, Adv. Dir., East
Greenwich Pendulum, RI, Wakefield

Boucher, Jody..............(401) 789-9744 ext. 105
jboucher@ricentral.com, Regional Pub./Adv.
Dir., Coventry Courier, RI, Wakefield

Boucher, Jody.........................(401) 789-9744
jboucher@ricentral.com, Adv. Mgr./Pub.,
Chariho Times, RI, Wakefield

Boucher, Judy.........................(618) 239-2500
jboucher@bnd.com, Newsroom, Belleville
News-Democrat, IL, Belleville

Boucly, Chris
cboucly@ocregister.com, Events Ed., Laguna
News-Post, CA, Santa Ana

Boudreau, Joyce
jboudreau@catholictranscript.org, Circ. Supvr.,
The Catholic Transcript, CT, Bloomfield

Boudreaux, Brigette
jdnads@bellsouth.net, Composing Mgr.,
Jennings (LA) Daily News, LA, Jennings

Bouffard, Kevin.......................(863) 802-7591
kevin.bouffard@theledger.com, Agriculture
Reporter
, The Ledger, FL, Lakeland

Boufford, John
comp@alconareview.com , Prodn. Mgr., Alcona
County Review, MI, Harrisville

Boukari, Ellen
ellen@alachuatoday.com, Executive Editor,
Alachua County Today, FL, Alachua

Boulanger, Yannick....................(450) 581-5120
boulangery@transcontinental.ca, Chief Ed.,
Hebdo Rive Nord, QC, Repentigny

Boulay, Patrick
patrick.boulay@legal-ledger.com, Pub., Saint
Paul Legal Ledger, MN, Saint Paul

Bouley, RoxAnne......................(218) 927-3761
rbouley@aitkinage.com, Operations Manager,
Bargain Hunter, MN, Isle

Bouley, RoxAnne......................(218) 927-3761
rbouley@aitkinage.com, Operations Mgr.
, Mille Lacs Messenger, MN, Isle

Bouley, Roxanne.....................(218) 927-3761
rbouley@aitkinage.com, Operations Mgr.,
Aitkin Independent Age, MN, Aitkin

Bouley, Roxanne.....................(218) 927-3761
rbouley@aitkinage.com, Advertising
Coordinator, Bargain Hunter, MN, Isle

Boulianne, Guylaine
guylaine.boulianne@journalhautecotenord.
com, Sec., Journal Haute Cote-nord, QC,
Forestville

Boultinghouse, Douglas.............(870) 325-6412
ccherald@tds.net, Circulation Manager/Graphic
Arts, Cleveland County Herald, AR, Rison

Boulware, Dorothy
webeditor@afro.com, Ed., Every Wednesday,
MD, Baltimore

Bouquot, Terry........................(513) 755-5110
terry.bouquot@coxinc.com, Sr. Director, Sales,
Dayton Daily News, OH, Franklin

Bourantas, John
jbourantas@washingtontimes.com, Asst. Mng.
Ed., The Washington Times, DC, Washington

Bourassa, Marc............(514) 521-4545 ext. 2470
marc.bourassa@quebecormedia.com, VP,
Sales, Le Journal de Montreal, QC, Montreal

Bourbonnais, Denis
denis.bourbonnais@monteregieweb.com,
Ed. in Chief, Le Journal Saint-francois, QC,
Salaberry-de-Valleyfield

Bourbonnais, Yves......................... ext. 246
ybourbonnais@groupejcl.com, Dir., Prodn., Le
Groupe Jcl Inc., QC, Saint Eustache

Bourcier, Robert......................**(514) 643-2300**
robert.bourcier@tc.tc, Production manager,
Cites Nouvelles, QC, Dorval

Bourcier, Robert......................**(514) 636-2300**
robert.bourcier@tc.tc, Production Manager,
The Chronicle, QC, Dorval

Bourdages, Lise......................**(450) 964-4444**
ventes@larevue.qc.ca, Coordonnatrice aux
ventes, Le Trait D'union, QC, Terrebonne

Bourdages, Lise......................**(450) 964-4444**
ventes@larevue.qc.ca, Sales Coord, La Revue
De Terrebonne, QC, Terrebonne

Bourg, Jim
info@whnpa.org, Vice President, White House
News Photographers Association, Inc., DC,
Washington

Bourgeault, Sylvie
sbourgeault@echosvedettes.ca, Gen. Mgr.,
Echos Vedettes, QC, Montreal

Bourgeois, Etienne
etienne.bourgeois@kodak.com, Vice Pres.,
Global Logistics, Eastman Kodak Co., NY,
Rochester

Bourjaily, Gavin......................**(540) 635-3229**
dist@globesyndicate.com, Ed./Pub., Globe
Syndicate, Strasburg

Bourkland, Doug
dbourkland@mcleodusa.net, American
Classifieds - Boise, ID, Boise

Bourkoulas, Alexis......................**(248) 398-3400**
abourkoulas@metroparent.com, Gen. Mgr.,
Metro Parent Magazine, MI, Ferndale

Bourn, Ed
ebourn@tfponline.com, Digital Dir.,
Chattanooga Times Free Press, TN,
Chattanooga

Bourne, Andi......................**(406) 677-2155**
Pathfinder@seeleylake.com, Editor &
Publisher, Seeley Swan Pathfinder, MT,
Seeley Lake

Bourne, Lisa......................**(888) 678-6008 x941**
lbourne@lifesitenews.com, Journalist /
Photographer, LifeSiteNews.com, VA, Front
Royal

Bourne, Nathan......................**(406) 677-2155**
nathan@seeleylake.com, Mailing &
Advertising, Seeley Swan Pathfinder, MT,
Seeley Lake

Bourque, Justin......................**(337) 321-6760**
justin.bourque@daily-iberian.com, District Mgr.,
The Daily Iberian, LA, New Iberia

Bourque, Sandy
sbourque@nnenews.com, Controller, Concord
Monitor, NH, Concord

Boursier, Yannick
yannick.boursier@tc.tc, Pub./Ed., Le Bulletin,
QC, Gatineau

Bousquet, Kim
kim.bousquet@nonpareilonline.com, Religion
Ed., The Daily Nonpareil, IA, Council Bluffs

Boutwell, Ken
kenbou@olemiss.edu, Asst. Prof., University of
Mississippi, MS, University

Bouvard, Pierre
pierre.bouvard@arbitron.com, Pres., Sales/
Mktg., The Arbitron Co., NY, New York

Bouzan, Jeniece
jbouzan@gulfcoastnewspapers.com, Adv.
Consultant, The Onlooker, AL, Foley

Bovat, Sara
shbova14@g.holycross.edu, Co-Editor-in-
Chief, College of the Holy Cross, MA,
Worcester

Bowden, Bill......................**(931) 879-4040**
fencourier@twlakes.net, Pub./Ed., Fentress
Courier, TN, Jamestown

Bowden, Brent
bbowden@thespectrum.com, Nat'l/Major Acct.

Exec., The Spectrum, UT, Saint George

Bowden, Steve......................**(617) 619-6476**
steve.bowden@bostonherald.com, Dir. of
Information Systems, Boston Herald, MA,
Boston

Bowder, Mark......................**(360) 735-4512**
mark.bowder@columbian.com, Metro Team
Editor, The Columbian, WA, Vancouver

Bowe, Nathan......................**(218) 847-3151**
nbowe@dlnewspapers.com, Ed., Lake Area
Press, MN, Detroit Lakes
nbowe@dlnewspapers.com, Ed., Detroit Lakes
Tribune, MN, Detroit Lakes

Bowell, Stephen
The False Creek News, Mng. Ed., The False
Creek News, BC, Vancouver

Bowell, Stephen
news@communitydigest.ca, Managing Editor,
Community Digest, BC, N. Vancouver

Bowen, Danny......................**(901) 529-5898**
danny.bowen@commercialappeal.com, Site
Director, The Commercial Appeal, TN,
Memphis

Bowen, Dennis
dbowen@dailypress.net, Circ. Mgr., Daily
Press, MI, Escanaba

Bowen, Dennis..........**(906) 786-2021 ext. 116**
dbowen@dailypress.net, Circ. Mgr., Up Action
News, MI, Escanaba

Bowen, Ernie......................**(806) 270-0822**
redriverskibum@msn.com, Ass. Ed./Phot., The
Hansford County Reporter-Statesman, TX,
Spearman

Bowen, Keith......................**(530) 852-0296**
keithb@goldcountrymedia.com, Auburn
Journal, CA, Auburn

Bowen, Les......................**(585) 335-2271**
lesbowen@dansvilleonline.com, General
Manager, Pennesaverplus, NY, Hornell

Bowen, Max......................**(781) 433-8354**
mbowen@wickedlocal.com, Ed., Westwood
Press, MA, Needham

Bowen, Max......................**(781) 433-8354**
mbowen@wickedlocal.com, Ed., Medfield
Press, MA, Needham

Bowen, Mike......................**(410) 770-4124**
mbowen@chespub.com, Rgl. Plant & Prod. Dir.
, The Star-Democrat, MD, Easton

Bowens, John
jbowen@register-mail.com, Production Mgr.,
Oquawka Current, IL, Oquawka

Bowerman, Dan......................**(563) 383-2450**
dbowerman@qctimes.com, Asst. Managing
Ed., Quad-City Times, IA, Davenport

Bowers, Alexandra
abowers@charlestownbridge.com, Mng.
Ed., The Charlestown Patriot-Bridge, MA,
Charlestown

Bowers, Brandon......................**(928) 453-4237**
bbowers@havasunews.com, Ed, Today's
News-Herald, AZ, Lake Havasu City

Bowers, Judi......................**(909) 866-3456 ext. 133**
jbowers.grizzly@gmail.com, General Manager,
Grizzly Weekender, CA, Big Bear Lake

Bowers, Judi......................**(909) 866-3456 x 133**
jbowers.grizzly@gmail.com, Pub., Big Bear
Grizzly, CA, Big Bear Lake

Bowers, Maggie......................**(770) 683-1762**
maggie@newnan.com, Feat. Ed., The Newnan
Times-Herald, GA, Newnan

Bowers, Mike......................**(573) 336-0234**
mbrame@springfi.gannett.com, Adv. Mgr.,
Guidon, MO, Saint Robert
mbrame@springfi.gannett.com, Ed., Fort
Leonard Wood Guidon, MO, Fort Leonard
Wood

Bowers, Robert......................**(440) 930-0050**
rbowers@hallcontractingservices.com, CEO,

Hall Contracting Services, Inc., OH, Avon
Lake

Bowers, Scott......................**(815) 987-1451**
sbowers@rrstar.com, Pub., The Star Shopper,
IL, Rockford

Bowers, Michelle......................**(613) 354-6641**
napaneeproduction@gmail.com, Prodn. Mgr.,
The Napanee Beaver, ON, Napanee

Bowers, Michelle
m.bowes@napaneebeaver.com, Prodn. Mgr.,
The Picton Gazette, ON, Picton

Bowie, Tara......................**(250) 499-2653**
editor@keremeosreview.com, Ed., Keremeos
Review, BC, Keremeos

Bowker, Chrissie......................**(778) 225-0022**
publisher@comoxvalleyrecord.com, Pub, North
Island Midweek, BC, Courtenay
publisher@comoxvalleyrecord.com, Pub.,
Comox Valley Record, BC, Courtenay

Bowler, Burl......................**(406) 487-5303**
2leader@nemont.net, Adv. Mgr., Daniels
County Leader, MT, Scobey

Bowlin, Cindy
cindyb@capegazette.com, Adv. Mgr., Cape
Gazette, DE, Lewes

Bowling, Janis
janis.bowling@heraldbulletin.com, Newsroom
Coord., The Herald Bulletin, IN, Anderson

Bowman, Bill......................**ext. 107**
bbowman@upandcomingweekly.com, Pub./
Adv. Mgr., Up & Coming Weekly, NC,
Fayetteville

Bowman, Bill
bbowman@dailyitem.com, Ed, The Compass,
NL, Carbonear
bbowman@dailyitem.com, Ed. City Editor, The
Daily Item, PA, Sunbury

Bowman, Brad
news@hclocal.com, Reporter, Henry County
Local, KY, Eminence

Bowman, Carolyn
cb@nebpress.com, Adv. Mgr., Nebr Press
Adv. Service, Nebraska Press Association/
Nebraska Press Advertising Service, NE,
Lincoln

Bowman, Donnie......................**(256) 235-9251**
dbowman@annistonstar.com, Circ. Mgr., The
Anniston Star, AL, Anniston

Bowman, Joseph......................**(216) 999-6643**
jbowman@plaind.com, VP of Operations, The
Plain Dealer, OH, Brooklyn

Bowman, Katherine
znewskbowman@verizon.net, Circ. Mgr,
Zephyrhills News, FL, Zephyrhills

Bowman, Kelsee......................**(800) 287-2295**
kelsee@easterngazette.com, Opns. Mgr.,
Eastern Gazette, ME, Dexter

Bowman, Ron F.
rosbacksales@qtm.net, Vice Pres., Sales/
Mktg., Rosback Co., MI, Saint Joseph

Bowman, Serena......................**(336) 506-3063**
sbowman@thetimesnews.com, Sales Mgr.,
Times-News, NC, Burlington

Bowman, Sharynn......................**ext. 202**
sharynn@gctelegram.com, Classifieds Mgr.,
The Garden City Telegram, KS, Garden City

Bown, John......................**(309) 343-7181 ext. 278**
jbowen@register-mail.com, Prodn. Mgr., The
Register-Mail, IL, Galesburg

Box, Dennis
dbox@courierherald.com, Ed., The Courier-
Herald, WA, Enumclaw
dbox@courierherald.com, Ed., The Enumclaw
Courier-Herald, WA, Enumclaw

Box, Dennis
dbox@maplevalleyreporter.com, Ed.,
Covington-Maple Valley-Black Diamond
Reporter, WA, Kent

Boyce, Flint......................**(318) 255-4353**
flint@rustonleader.com, Adv. Sales Exec.,
Ruston (LA) Daily Leader, LA, Ruston

Boyce, Lisa......................**(615) 384-3567**
lboyce@mtcngroup.com, Prod. Mgr., Robertson
County Times, TN, Clarksville

Boyce, Rod
editor@newsminer.com, Mng. Ed., Fairbanks
Daily News-Miner, AK, Fairbanks

Boyd, Ann......................**(563) 383-2483**
aboyd@qctimes.com, Adv. Mgr., Bettendorf
News, IA, Davenport
aboyd@qctimes.com, Adv. Sales Dir., Quad-
City Times, IA, Davenport

Boyd, Brenda
bboyd@pqbnews.com, Sales Mgr., Parksville
Qualicum Beach News, BC, Parksville

Boyd, Brian......................**(203) 245-1877 ext. 6136**
b.boyd@shorepublishing.com, Ed., East Haven
Courier, CT, Madison

Boyd, Brian......................**(203) 245-1877 ext. 6136**
b.boyd@shorepublishing.com, Ed., Valley
Courier, CT, Madison
b.boyd@shorepublishing.com, Managing Ed.,
Waterford Times, CT, New London

Boyd, Brian......................**(203) 245-1877 ext. 6136**
b.boyd@shorepublishing.com, Ed., North
Haven Courier, CT, Madison

Boyd, Brian......................**(203) 245-1877 ext 6136**
b.boyd@shorepublishing.com, Managing Ed.,
The Sound, CT, Madison

Boyd, Brian......................**(203) 245-1877 ext. 6136**
b.boyd@shorepublishing.com, Ed., Guilford
Courier, CT, Madison

Boyd, Brian......................**(203) 245-1877 ext. 6136**
b.boyd@shorepublishing.com, Managing
Editor, Harbor News, CT, Madison

Boyd, Brian......................**(203) 245-1877 ext. 6136**
b.boyd@shorepublishing.com, Mng. Ed.,
Source, CT, Madison
b.boyd@shorepublishing.com, Managing Ed.,
The Stonington Times, CT, New London

Boyd, David......................**(803) 644-2397**
dboyd@aikenstandard.com, System
Mgr., Evening Post Industries' Aiken
Communications, SC, Aiken

Boyd, Diane......................**(785) 421-5700**
times@ruraltel.net, Associate Editor, The Hill
City Times, KS, Hill City

Boyd, Heather
heather.boyd@thecanadianpress.com, Bureau
Chief, Canadian Press, The - Edmonton, AB,
AB, Edmonton

Boyd, Joshua......................**(978) 739-8512**
jboyd@wickedlocal.com, Sports Ed., Tri-Town
Transcript, MA, Danvers

Boyd, Judy
legals@omahadailyrecord.com, Legal Notice,
Daily Record, NE, Omaha

Boyd, K. Denise......................**(509) 335-7574**
boydenise@wsu.edu, Fiscal Officer,
Washington State University, Daily
Evergreen, WA, Pullman

Boyd, Kathy
kathyboyd@timesleader.net, Adv. Mgr., Times
Leader, KY, Princeton

Boyd, Kathy......................**(360) 629-8066 x2217**
kboyd@scnews.com, Gen. Mgr/ Ed., Stanwood
Camano News, WA, Stanwood
kboyd@scnews.com, Ed., The Argus, WA,
Mount Vernon

Boyd, Lea
lea@coastalview.com, Ed., Coastal View News,
CA, Carpinteria

Boyd, Lorraine
lorraine@omahadailyrecord.com, Editor, Daily
Record, NE, Omaha

Boyd, Pam......................**(970) 328-6656**

pboyd@eaglevalleyenterprise.com, Ed., The Eagle Valley Enterprise, CO, Gypsum

Boyd, R. Scott
maconbeacon@aol.com, Ed., Macon Beacon, MS, Macon

Boyd, Rick
rboyd@somdnews.com, Ed., The Enterprise, MD, California

Boyd, Robert..........................(785) 421-5700
times@ruraltel.net, Pub., The Hill City Times, KS, Hill City

Boyd, Vickey...........................(843) 958-7480
vboyd@moultrienews.com, Pub., Moultrie News, SC, Charleston

Boyea, Dave
sports@bloomeradvance.com, Sports Ed., Bloomer Advance, WI, Bloomer

Boyer, Gerald
gboy@maryville.edu, PhD, Maryville University, MO, Saint Louis

Boyer, Jeremy.........................(315) 282-2231
jeremy.boyer@lee.net, Exec. Ed. , The Citizen, Auburn, NY, Auburn

Boyer, Leroy...........................(570) 628-6026
lboyer@republicanherald.com, Sports Ed., The Republican-Herald, PA, Pottsville

Boyer, Meg.............................(970) 668-4638
mboyer@summitdaily.com, Pub., Sky-Hi News, CO, Granby

Boyer-Schwartz, Vern..........................ext. 125
vern@njparentweb.com, Adv. Mgr., Suburban Parent, NJ, North Brunswick

Boyett, Dick
dboyett@fww.com, Sales Mgr., Franklin Wire Works, Inc., IL, Belvidere

Boyett, Frank
fboyett@thegleaner.com, Religion Ed., The Gleaner, KY, Henderson

Boyett, Jessie Kelley
bernicebanner@oeccwildblue.com, Pub./Ed., The Bernice Banner, LA, Bernice

Boyett, Rosanne......................(505) 287-4411
rosanne@cibolabeacon.com, Senior Staff Writer, Cibola Beacon, NM, Grants

Boyette, John..........................(706) 823-3337
john.boyette@augustachronicle.com, Sports Editor, The Augusta Chronicle, GA, Augusta

Boykin, Debbie.......................(252) 265-7801
debbie@wilsontimes.com, Controller, The Wilson Times, NC, Wilson

Boyle, Alan
atboyle@gmail.com, Ed., Newsphere, WA, Bellevue

Boyle, Bob
r.boyle@mirachem.com, Sales Mgr., Mirachem Corp., AZ, Phoenix

Boyle, Jim.............................(763) 241-3670
editor.erstarnews@ecm-inc.com, Ed., Star News, MN, Elk River

Boyle, Joe
thereporter@comcast.net, Ed., The Reporter, IL, Palos Heights

Boyle, John.............................(937) 225-2395
john.boyle@coxinc.com, Sports Editor, Dayton Daily News, OH, Franklin

Boyle, Mike.............................(905) 664-8800
mboyle@thespec.com, Produ Mgr., Stoney Creek News, ON, Stoney Creek

Boyle, Mike.............................(905) 664-8800
mboyle@thespec.com, Produ Mgr., Dundas Star News, ON, Stoney Creek
mboyle@thespec.com, Production Manager, Hamilton Mountain News, ON, Stoney Creek

Boyle, Patrick C.
info@thederrick.com, Pres., The News-Herald/ The Derrick, PA, Oil City

Boyle, Paul.............................(571) 366-1150

paul.boyle@naa.org, SVP of Public Policy, News Media Alliance, VA, Arlington

Boyle, Sue.............................(618) 239-2664
sboyle@bnd.com, Features, Belleville News-Democrat, IL, Belleville

Boyle, Tom
tboyle@titusvilleherald.com, Reporter, The Titusville Herald, PA, Titusville

Boyles, Bonnie
bonnie@kchomes.com, Pub., Suburban North Homes Buyer's Guide, KS, Kansas City

Boyles, Bonnie
bonnie@kchomes.com, Pub., Jackson-Cass Homes, KS, Kansas City

Boyles, Bonnie
kansas@kchomes.com, Pub., Kansas Homes, KS, Kansas City

Boyles, Dana.....................................ext. 131
dboyles@cnhi.com, Adv. Mgr., The Duncan Banner, OK, Duncan

Boyles, Larry
lboyles@stanfordproductsllc.com, Sales Mgr., Stanford Products, IL, Salem

Boyles, Lisa
editor@chickasawjournal.com, Pub., Chickasaw Journal, MS, Houston

Boyles, Sam W.
sam@neiinc.com, Pres., Northeast Industries, Inc., AZ, Prescott

Boyll, Linda
holdregecitizenads@yahoo.com, Adv. Mgr., Holdrege Daily Citizen, NE, Holdrege

Boyne, Barb.....................................ext. 216
barb.boyne@sunmedia.ca, Circ. Mgr., The Stratford Beacon Herald, ON, Stratford

Boynton, Lois.........................(919) 843-8342
Assoc. Prof., University of North Carolina, NC, Chapel Hill

Boyum, Jana.........................(507) 765-2151
ads@fillmorecountyjournal.com, Creative Dir., Fillmore County Journal, MN, Preston

Bozarth, A.J..........................(620) 456-2232
ajprinting@havilandtelco.com, Pub/Ed, Norwich News, KS, Conway Springs
ajprinting@havilandtelco.com, Ed., The South Haven New Era, KS, Conway Springs

Bozarth, Mike.........................(816) 754-6462
news@stjtelegraph.org, Pub./Ed., Saint Joseph Telegraph, MO, Saint Joseph

Bozeman, Robert
courantpublisher@earthlink.net, Ed. / Pub. / Adv. Mgr., Evergreen Courant, AL, Evergreen

Bracamontes, Ramon................(915) 546-6142
rbracamontes@elpasotimes.com, Managing Editor, El Paso Times, TX, El Paso
rbracamontes@elpasotimes.com, Bus. Ed., El Paso y Mas, TX, El Paso

Bracchi, John
jbracchi@metroland.net, Art Dir., Metroland, NY, Albany

Bracic , Lynn.........................(440) 899-1222
Executive Administrator, The Press Club of CLEVELAND, OH, Cleveland

Brack, Dennis
president@rappnews.com, Pres., Rappahannock Times, VA, Tappahannock

Brack, Ric.............................(903) 237-7759
rbrack@news-journal.com, Ed. Dlr., Longview News-Journal, TX, Longview

Bracken, Matt.........................(410) 332-6674
mbracken@baltsun.com.., Dir. Audience/Dev. , The Baltimore Sun, MD, Baltimore

Bracken, Michael..................(800) 736-7350
Editor@Seniorific.com, Editor, Seniorific News, TX, Waco

Brackenbury, Mark....................(203) 789-5708
Exec. Ed., The Middletown Press, CT,

Middletown

Brackett, Ron.........................(727) 892-2395
rbrackett@tampabay.com, Deputy Managing Ed./tampabay.com, Presentation, Tampa Bay Times, FL, St Petersburg

Brackin, Elaine
ebrackin@dothanprogress.com, Ed., Dothan Progress, AL, Dothan

Bradbury, Dieter......................(207) 791-6329
dbradbury@pressherald.com, Deputy Managing Ed. , Portland Press Herald / Maine Sunday Telegram, ME, Portland

Bradbury, Emily
ebradbury@kspress.com, Director of Member Services, Kansas Press Association, KS, Topeka

Bradbury, Sarah
sarah@sonomawest.com, Assoc. Pub, Sonoma West Times and News, CA, Healdsburg
sarah@sonomawest.com, Assoc. Pub., The Windsor Times, CA, Healdsburg

Bradbury, Shonnie
sbradbury@times-standard.com, Adv. Dir., On The Market, CA, Eureka

Braddy, Joe.................(863) 294-7731 ext. 3045
news@newschief.com, Mng. Ed., Lake Wales Shopper, FL, Winter Haven

Braddy, Leigh................(770) 428-9411 ext. 454
Prodn. Mgr., Pre Press, Marietta Daily Journal, GA, Marietta

Braden, Lou
lbraden@chieftain.com, Adv. Dir., Pueblo West View, CO, Pueblo West

Braden, Michael
mbraden@loyola.edu, TV-Radio, Loyola College, MD, Baltimore

Braden, Stewart
ycn@sekansas.com, Ed., Yates Center News, KS, Yates Center

Braden, Susan
sbraden@ctcentral.com, Editor, Shoreline Times, CT, New Haven

Bradfield, Jeremy......................(952) 392-6841
jeremy.bradfield@ecm-inc.com, Adv. Dir., North Crow River News, MN, Osseo
jeremy.bradfield@ecm-inc.com, Adv. Mgr, South Crow River News, MN, Osseo
jeremy.bradfield@ecm-inc.com, Adv. Dir., Champlin-Dayton Press, MN, Osseo
jeremy.bradfield@ecm-inc.com, Adv. Dir., Press and News Publications, MN, Osseo
jeremy.bradfield@ecm-inc.com, Adv. Dir., Osseo-Maple Grove Press, MN, Osseo
jeremy.bradfield@ecm-inc.com, Adv Dir, Rockford Area News Leader, MN, Osseo

Bradford, Alissa.............................ext. 32
sicirc@heartlandpublications.com, Circ. Dir., The Sampson Independent, NC, Clinton

Bradford, Jeremy
jeremy.bradfield@ecm-inc.com, Adv. Mgr., Excelsior/Shorewood/Chanhassen Sun Sailor, MN, Eden Prairie

Bradford, Pat
pat@luminanews.com, Pub./Circ. Mgr., Lumina News, NC, Wilmington

Bradigan, Bret
bret@ojaivalleynews.com, Ed., Ojai Valley Shopper, CA, Ojai

Bradley, Brian.........................(816) 271-8508
brian.bradley@npgco.com, President, News-Press & Gazette Co., MO, Saint Joseph

Bradley, David.........................(816) 271-8502
david.bradley@newspressnow.com, Ed., Midland Express, MO, Saint Joseph
david.bradley@newspressnow.com, Pub., St. Joseph News-Press, MO, Saint Joseph

Bradley, David R.......................(816) 271-8502
david.bradley@npgco.com, Chief Executive Officer, News-Press & Gazette Co., MO, Saint Joseph

Bradley, Don...........................(618) 277-1796
dbradley@bnd.com, Prod. Dir, Belleville News-Democrat, IL, Belleville

Bradley, Harry..............(909) 337-6145 ext. 215
hbradley@mountain-news.com, Publisher, Mountain News & Crestline Courier-News, CA, Lake Arrowhead

Bradley, Joe............................(808) 242-6305
jbradley@mauinews.com, Pub., The Maui News, HI, Wailuku

Bradley, Lisa...........................(317) 472-5321
lbradley@ibj.com, Adv. Dir., Indianapolis Business Journal, IN, Indianapolis

Bradley, Melanie
mbradley@rvpublishing.com, Ed., Post Journal, IL, Machesney Park

Bradley, Meriel
mbradley@metroland.com, Adv. Mgr, Bracebridge Examiner, ON, Bracebridge
mbradley@metroland.com, Adv. Dir., Bloor West Villager, ON, Toronto
mbradley@metroland.com, Sales Dir, Annex Guardian, ON, Toronto
mbradley@metroland.com, Adv. Rep, Beach-Riverdale Mirror, ON, Toronto

Bradley, Michael......................(508) 563-2835
mbradley@capecod.net, Grimes, McGovern & Associates, NY, New York

Bradley, Shirley
sbradley@mtcngroup.com, Gen. Mgr., Cheatham County Money Saver, TN, Ashland City

Bradley, Stephanie
sbradley@thefranklinnewspost.com , Adv, The Franklin News-Post, VA, Rocky Mount

Bradley, Steve
sbradley@democratandchronicle.com, Content Strategist, Democrat and Chronicle, NY, Rochester

Bradley, Steve
sbradley@adirondackdailyenterprise.com, Prodn. Mgr., Adirondack Daily Enterprise, NY, Saranac Lake

Bradley, Tom.........................(608) 755-8344
tbradley@gazettextra.com, Director of Advertising Operations, The Gazette - gazettextra.com, WI, Janesville

Bradley, Tom
tbradley@gazettextra.com, Adv. Mgr., Retail, The Janesville Gazette - GazetteXtra, WI, Janesville

Bradley , Meriel
mbradley@metroland.com, Online Adv. , Markham Economist & Sun, ON, Markham

Bradner, Rebecca......................(520) 375-5766
rbradner@eacourier.com, Pub., Arizona Range News, AZ, Sierra Vista

Bradner, Rebecca
rbradner@gvnews.com, Pub., Green Valley News & Sahuarita Sn, AZ, Green Valley

Bradner, Rebecca......................(520) 547-9722
rbradner@svherald.com, Publisher, Sahuarita Sun, AZ, Green Valley

Bradow, Roxanne
editor@herald-publishing.com, Owner/Pub., Herald Publishing Co., AR, Hazen

Bradshaw, Ansel......................(936) 546-6707
news@messenger-news.com, Sales, The Messenger, TX, Grapeland

Bradshaw, Katherine
kabrads@bgsu.edu, Asst. Prof., Bowling Green State University, OH, Bowling Green

Bradshaw, Rusty
aznews@newszap.com, News Ed., Peoria Independent, AZ, Sun City
aznews@newszap.com, News Ed, Sun City West Independent, AZ, Sun City
aznews@newszap.com, Mng. Ed., Valley Times, OR, Milton-Freewater

Bradstreet, Brenda
bbradstreet@tompkinsvillenews.com,
Circulation mgr, Tompkinsville News, KY,
Tompkinsville

Bradwell, Mike ....(724) 222-2200
mbradwell@observer-reporter.com, Bus. Ed.,
Observer-Reporter, PA, Washington

Brady, Colleen.......................(928) 556-2279
cbrady@azdailysun.com, Ad Director, Arizona
Daily Sun, Flagstaff, AZ, Flagstaff

Brady, Dianne
dbrady@hcnonline.com, Eastex Advocate, TX,
Cleveland
dbrady@hcnonline.com, Adv. Dir., Cleveland
Advocate, TX, Conroe
dbrady@hcnonline.com, Adv. Dir., Dayton
News, TX, Conroe
dbrady@hcnonline.com, Adv. Dir., Eastex
Advocate, TX, Cleveland

Brady, Elaine ....(410) 641-0039
ebrady@baysidegazette.com, Pres./Pub.,
Bayside Gazette, MD, Berlin

Brady, Elaine
ebrady@oceancitytoday.net, Sales Manager,
Ocean City Today, MD, Ocean City

Brady, Joel
joel@fluidmotiontheaterfilm.org, Circ. Mgr.,
Daily Racing Form, NY, New York

Brady, John
contact@johnbrady.info, Pres., Brady & Paul
Communications, MA, Newburyport

Brady, Mark...........................(802) 388-6397
Gen. Mgr., The Eagle, VT, Middlebury
Gen. Mgr., Green Mountain Outlook, VT,
Middlebury

Brady, Shawn ....ext. 361
shawnb@hjnews.com, Adv. Dir., Quality Buys,
UT, Logan

Brady, Tim ....(978) 946-2161
Adv. Dir., The Haverhill Gazette, MA, North
Andover

Braeckel, Karen ....(317) 803-4772
kbraeckel@hspa.com, HSPA Foundation
Dir., Hoosier State Press Association, IN,
Indianapolis

Braga, Dave
editor@i-rule.net, Ed., Winterset Madisonian,
IA, Winterset

Bragdon, Ben ....(207) 621-5655
bbragdon@centralmaine.com, Editorial Page
Ed., Kennebec Journal, ME, Augusta
bbragdon@centralmaine.com, Editorial Page
Ed., Morning Sentinel, ME, Waterville

Bragdon, Ben ....(207) 854-2577 ext.177
bbragdon@keepmecurrent.com, Sun
Chronicle, ME, Westbrook
bbragdon@keepmecurrent.com, Mng. Ed. ,
Reporter, ME, Westbrook

Bragg, Dave
classified@thenickel.net, The Nickel-kelso,
WA, Kelso

Bragg, David.........................(256) 549-2084
david.bragg@gadsdentimes.com, Sales Mgr.,
Times2, AL, Gadsden

Bragg, Jeanine ....(734) 240-5027
jbragg@monroenews.com, Adv. Dir., Sales,
The Monroe News, MI, Monroe
jbragg@monroenews.com, Adv. Mgr./Retail,
Bedford Now, MI, Monroe

Brahaney, Mark ....(814) 368-3173
The Bradford Era, PA, Bradford

Brahney, Tim
tbrahney@cbaol.com, VP, Sales, Cba
Industries, NJ, Elmwood Park

Braima, Mahmoud
mahmoud_braima@cxs.subr.edu, Head,
Southern University and A&M College, LA,
Baton Rouge

Brais, Stephane

stephane.brais@monteregieweb.com,
Sales Dir., Le Journal Saint-francois, QC,
Salaberry-de-Valleyfield

Brake, Jon
jonbrake@kansas.net, Co-Pub., Manhattan
Free Press, KS, Blue Rapids

Braknis, Greg ....(419) 724-6198
gbraknis@theblade.com, Web News Ed., The
Blade, OH, Toledo

Brambila, Andrea ....(510) 658-9252
andrea@inman.com, Assoc. Ed., Inman News,
Emeryville

Bramble, Joy ....(410) 366-3900
jbramble@btimes.com, Pub., The Baltimore
Times, MD, Baltimore

Bramble, Joy ....(443) 831-8215
jbramble@btimes.com, Pub., The Annapolis
Times, MD, Baltimore

Bramble, Joy
jbramble@btimes.com, Mng. Ed., Prince
George's County Times, MD, Baltimore

Bramburger, Adam
gazette@bellnet.ca, Ed., The Picton Gazette,
ON, Picton

Brame, Richard
richard@oakwoodregister.com, Advertising
Sales, The Oakwood Register, OH, Dayton

Bramlett-Solomon, Sharon
bramlett@asu.edu, Class Manager, Arizona
State University, AZ, Tempe

Bramstedt, Linda A.
lindab@windomnews.com, Adv. Mgr., Windom
Shopper, MN, Windom

Brancaccio, Louis....................(360) 735-4505
lou.brancaccio@columbian.com, Ed., The
Columbian, WA, Vancouver

Brancato, Linda ....(212) 210-2069
lbrancato@nydailynews.com, VP Pres. Adv.,
New York Daily News, NY, New York

Brancato, Tom ....(800) 997-3600 ext. 2166
brancatot@graphline.com, Dir., Mktg.,
GraphLine, FL, Sunrise

Branch, Blake ....(318) 377-1866 ext. 106
blake@press-herald.com, Ed., Dakota County
Star, NE, Blair
blake@press-herald.com, Sports Writer,
Minden Press Herald, LA, Minden

Branch, Chuck
chuckb@cpimo.com, Gen. Mgr., Nixa News
Enterprise, MO, Nixa

Branch, Jana ....(205) 443-5612
jbranch@bizjournals.com, Business Mgr,
Birmingham Business Journal, AL,
Birmingham

Branch, Jay
jbranch@broadcastnews.ca, Saskatchewan
Correspondent, Broadcast News Limited,
SK, Regina

Branch, Kip ....(252) 335-3588
Elizabeth City State Univ., NC, Elizabeth City

Brand, Sandra
brand@osceolatimes.com, Ed., The Osceola
Times, AR, Osceola

Brandenburg, Cindy
nceeditor@centurylink.net, Mng. Ed, Brook
Reporter, IN, Kentland
nceeditor@centurylink.net, Morocco Courier,
IN, Kentland
nceeditor@centurylink.net, Staff Reporter, The
Newton County Enterprise, IN, Kentland

Brandenburg, Katrina
thorn@rose-hulman.edu, Editor-in-Chief, Rose-
Hulman Inst. of Technology, IN, Terre Haute

Brander, Don...........................(902) 629-6000
d.brander@theguardian.pe.ca, Pub., The
Guardian, PE, Charlottetown

Brandl, Tara.................(507) 537-1551 ext. 116
tbrandl@marshallindependent.com, Adv.

Mgr., Independent Shopper's Review, MN,
Marshall

Brandl, Tara.................(507) 537-1551 ext #116
tbrandl@marshallindependent.com, Adv. Mgr.,
Independent, MN, Marshall

Brandley, Sharon ....(765) 973-4442
sbrandle@richmond.gannett.com, Retail Adv.
Mgr., Palladium-Item, IN, Richmond

Brandner, Julie
info@lintonnd.com, Adv. Mgr., Emmons County
Record, ND, Linton
info@lintonnd.com, Adv. Dir., Prairie Pioneer,
SD, Pollock

Brandsasse, Kay ....(618) 253-7146 ext.223
kbrandsasse@dailyregister.com, Bus. Mgr.,
The Daily Register, IL, Harrisburg

Brandstetter, David
archcom@37.com, Pres., Arch
Communications, Inc., MO, Saint Louis

Brandt, Brenda
bbholent@chase3000.com, Pub./Adv. Mgr.,
Holyoke Enterprise, CO, Holyoke

Brandt, Dawn ....(303) 566-4073
dbrandt@coloradocommunitymedia.com, Adv.
Rep., The Englewood Herald, CO, Highlands
Ranch
dbrandt@coloradocommunitymedia.com, Adv.
Mgr., Centennial Citizen, CO, Highlands
Ranch
dbrandt@coloradocommunitymedia.com,
Adv. Rep., The Littleton Independent, CO,
Highlands Ranch

Brandt, Jane ....(701) 878-4494
hherald@westriv.com, Pub. / Ed. , Richardton
Merchant, ND, Hebron
hherald@westriv.com, Pub. / Ed., Hebron
Herald, ND, Hebron

Brandt, Jay.........................(541) 383-0370
jbrandt@bendbulletin.com, Adv. Dir., Central
Oregon Nickel Ads, OR, Bend

Brandt, Jay..........................(541) 383-0370
jbrandt@bendbulletin.com, Adv. Dir., The
Bulletin, OR, Bend

Brandt, Jay.........................(541) 382-1811
jbrandt@wescompapers.com, Adv. Dir.,
Western Communications, Inc., OR, Bend

Brandt, Kay
kbrandt@homemagonline.com, Creative Servs.
Mgr., Home Magazine, MN, Mankato

Branfcomb, Max ....(619) 482-6368
aaron.fenlason@sckans.edu, Southwestern
College, CA, Chula Vista

Branfman, David
dbranfman@branfman.com, Owner, Branfman
Law Group, P.C., CA, Oceanside

Branham, Lorraine
lbranham@syr.edu, Dean, Syracuse University,
NY, Syracuse

Brannan, Dianna
Dianna@allennewspaper.com, Pub./Ed, The
Allen Advocate, OK, Allen

Brannan, Patrick ....(410) 857-8554
Patrick.Brannan@carrollcountytimes.com,
Online Ed.
, Carroll County Times, MD, Westminster

Brannon, Genevieve
citadinc@bellsouth.net, Mng. Ed., Bourbon
County Citizen, KY, Paris

Brannon, James.......................(859) 987-1870
citadinc@bellsouth.net, Ed., The Citizen-
advertiser, KY, Paris

Brannon, Sue ....(386) 754-0419
sbrannon@lakecityreporter.com, Controller,
Lake City Reporter, FL, Lake City

Brannon Lawyer, Rebecca............(859) 987-1870
citadinc@bellsouth.net, Prodn. Mgr., Bourbon
County Citizen, KY, Paris

Branom, Edward

ebranom@boonecountyshopper.com, Pres./
Gen. Mgr., Boone County Shopper, IL,
Belvidere

Branom, Matthew
mbranom@boonecountyshopper.com, Sales
Mgr., Boone County Shopper, IL, Belvidere

Brant, Angie ....(301) 784-2526
abrant@times-news.com, Special Sections
Ed., The Cumberland Times-News, MD,
Cumberland

Brant, Christopher M. ....(203) 661-3344
President & COO, White Birch Paper, CT,
Greenwich

Brant, Joe ....(615) 596-6210
Managing Digital Editor, Out & About Nashville,
TN, Nashville

Brant, Lee................................(530) 477-4202
lbrandt@theunion.com, Prodn. Dir., The Union,
CA, Grass Valley

Brant, Patty ....(863) 657-6000
pbrant@newszap.com, Editor/Publisher,
Immokalee Bulletin, FL, Labelle

Brant, Peter M..........................(203) 661-3344
Chrmn./CEO, White Birch Paper, CT,
Greenwich

Brantley, Max
maxbrantley@arktimes.com, Ed., Arkansas
Times, AR, Little Rock

Branyon, S. Daniel
theobserver@embarqmail.com, Pub., The
Ware Shoals Observer, SC, Ware Shoals

Brasch, Walter ....(570) 784-2460
EDITOR@GREELEYANDSTONE.COM, Ed.
in Chief, Spectrum Features Syndicate,
Sacramento

Brasel, Jeff
jeffb@harrisondaily.com, Mng. Ed., Harrison
Daily Times, AR, Harrison

Brashear, Karen ....(904) 359-4435
karen.brashear@jacksonville.com, Mgr.,
Promo., The Florida Times-Union, FL,
Jacksonville

Brashear, Todd
todd_brashear@mccom.com, Vice President,
Creative Director, M/C/C, TX, Dallas

Brasher, Bill ....(618) 529-5454 ext. 5072
bill.brasher@TheSouthern.com, Prodn. Mgr.,
At Home With Flipside, IL, Carbondale

Brashier, Vanesa......................(936) 346-1051
vbrashier@hcnonline.com, Ed., Cleveland
Advocate, TX, Conroe
vbrashier@hcnonline.com, Ed., Eastex
Shopper, TX, Cleveland
vbrashier@hcnonline.com, Ed., Dayton News,
TX, Conroe
vbrashier@hcnonline.com, Ed., Eastex
Advocate, TX, Cleveland

Brasier, Deborah ....(563) 383-2452
Bus. Ed., Quad-City Times, IA, Davenport

Brassard , Donna ....(207) 761-8379 Ext. 327
dbrassard@mainebiz.biz, Pub., Mainebiz, ME,
Portland

Bratcher, Marsha.......................(601) 847-2525
countynews@bellsouth.net, Circ. Mgr.,
Simpson County News, MS, Magee

Bratich, Jack
jbratich@rutgers.edu, Asst. Prof., Rutgers
University, NJ, New Brunswick

Braton, David
david.braton@lee.net, Pub., Insider, IA,
Waterloo

Braton, David ....(319) 291-1500
David.Braton@wcfcourier.com, Pub., Lee Agri-
Media, Bismarck, ND
David.Braton@wcfcourier.com, Pub., The
Bismarck Tribune, ND, Bismarck

Bratt, Bill
bill.bratt@sunmedia.ca, Adv. Dir., The Toronto

Sun, ON, Toronto

Bratt, Calvin .... (360) 354-4444
editor@lyndentribune.com, Ed., Lynden Tribune, WA, Lynden

Bratton, Joanne .... (870) 508-8051
jobratton@baxterbulletin.com, Features ed., The Baxter Bulletin, AR, Mountain Home

Brauch, Kirk
kirkb@adstream.com, Business Mgr., Adstream America, NY, New York

Brauer, Angela .... (402) 444-1254
angela.brauer@owh.com, Dir., National & Major Accounts, Omaha World-Herald, NE, Omaha

Brauer, Rick
rick.brauer@ecm-inc.com, Adv., Carver County News, MN, Waconia
rick.brauer@ecm-inc.com, Adv. Mgr., Norwood Young America Times, MN, Waconia

Braun, Bob .... (215) 949-5708
bbraun@calkins.com, Production Director, Calkins Media, PA, Levittown

Braun, Bob .... (215) 345-3045
bbraun@phillyburbs.com, Prodn. Dir., The Intelligencer, PA, Doylestown

Braun, Chris
cbraun@therecorder.com, Pub., The Recorder, CA, San Francisco

Braun, Janna
jbraun@sdccd.edu, San Diego Mesa College, CA, San Diego

Braun, Kathy .... ext. 104
classifieds@pdsadnet.com, Classified Sales Mgr., Publishers Development Service, WI, Fond Du Lac
classifieds@pdsadnet.com, Classified Sales Mgr., Publishers Development Service, WI, Fond du Lac

Braun, Phyllis .... (520) 319-1112
pbraun@azjewishpost.com, Exec. Ed., Arizona Jewish Post, AZ, Tucson

Braun, Walter
wbraun@themercury.com, Editorial Page Ed., The Manhattan Mercury, KS, Manhattan

Braund, Jeff
jbraund@mykawartha.com, Regl. Dist. Mgr., Kawartha Lakes This Week, ON, Lindsay

Brauner, Cathy .... (781) 431-2003
cbrauner@wickedlocal.com, Ed., Wellesley Townsman, MA, Needham

Braunschweig, Joseph .... (210) 250-2010
JBraunschweig@express-news.net, VP of Circulation, San Antonio Express-News, TX, San Antonio

Braverman, Wayne .... (781) 433-7810
wbraverman@wickedlocal.com, Ed., Community Newspapers Co. Interactive Media Group, MA, Needham
wbraverman@wickedlocal.com, Mng. Ed., Dover-Sherborn Press, MA, Needham
wbraverman@wickedlocal.com, Mng. Ed., Sharon Advocate, MA, Needham

Brawdy, Bob .... (509) 582-1548
bbrawdy@tri-cityherald.com, Chief Photographer, Tri-City Herald, WA, Kennewick

Bray, Sean .... (613) 525-2020, ext.22
Sports Ed., The Glengarry News, ON, Alexandria

Bray, Tom .... (951) 368-9422
tbray@pe.com, Managing Ed., The Press-Enterprise, CA, Riverside

Bray, Tom
Tom. Bray@socalnewsgroup.com, Sr. Ed., Daily Breeze, CA, Torrance
Tom. Bray@socalnewsgroup.com, Sr. Ed., Press-Telegram, CA, Long Beach

Braymer, Donna
donnab@harrisondaily.com, Bus./Finance Ed.,

Harrison Daily Times, AR, Harrison

Brazee, Marie
mariebrazee@thewestfieldnewsgroup. com, Bus. Mgr., The Westfield News , MA, Westfield

Brazil, Everett
hollisnews@pldi.net, Ed., The Hollis News, OK, Hollis

Breakenridge, Dave
dave.breakenridge@sunmedia.ca, Ed, Edmonton Examiner, AB, Edmonton
dave.breakenridge@sunmedia.ca, Ed.-in-Chief, The Edmonton Sun, AB, Edmonton

Breakstone, Susan
susanb@jewishaz.com, Adv. Acc. Exec., Jewish News, AZ, Phoenix

Breashears, Vicki
vbreashears@ncronline.org, Adv. Sales/Prodn., National Catholic Reporter, MO, Kansas City

Breau, John
jbreau@rotadyne.com, Vice Pres. Graphic Sales, RotaDyne Corp., IL, Darien

Breazeale, Matthew .... (662) 834-1151
hcherald@gmail.com, Editor, Holmes County Herald, MS, Lexington

Brechenser, Jordan .... (413) 496-6308
jbrechenser@reformer.com, VP Adv., Brattleboro Reformer, VT, Brattleboro

Breck, Angela
abreck@somdnews.com, Ed., The Maryland Independent, MD, White Plains

Breckler, Adam .... (419) 784-5441
adamb@crescent-news.com, I.T. Director, Adams Publishing Group, LLC, MN, Virginia

Bredehoft, Thomas E. .... (719) 765-4466
Ed., Verison, CO, Flagler

Bredenberg, Al
ab@copywriter.com, Contact, Al Bredenberg Creative Services, CT, Danbury

Bredsten, Brielle .... (218) 927-3761
bbredsten@aitkinage.com, Ed., Aitkin Independent Age, MN, Aitkin

Breeden, Cheryl .... (507) 754-5486
Office Mgr., Meadow Area Shopper, MN, Grand Meadow

Breeding, Lucinda .... (940) 566-6884
cbreeding@dentonrc.com, Features Ed., Denton Record-Chronicle, TX, Denton

Breeding, Rob .... (307) 754-6444
Advisor, Northwest College, WY, Powell

Breeding, Ron
ron@kuar.org, Part-time Lectr., University of Arkansas at Little Rock, AR, Little Rock

Breedlove, Michael .... (336) 727-7256
mbreedlove@wsjournal.com, Monthly Magazine Editor, Winston-Salem Journal, NC, Winston Salem

Breedy, Gretchen .... (845) 346-3109
gbreedy@th-record.com, HR Dir., The Times Herald-Record, NY, Middletown

Brehl, Joan
joan.brehl@auditedmedia.com, VP/Gen. Mgr for AAM Canada, Alliance for Audited Media Canada, ON, Toronto

Brehm, Darryl .... (312) 421-0480
dbrehm@anovitz.com, Univ. of Illinois at Chicago, IL, Chicago

Brehm, Karen
karen.brehm@lubbockonline.com, Asst. Mng. Ed., News/Features, Lubbock Avalanche-Journal, TX, Lubbock

Brehm, Sharon .... (305) 628-6800
St. Thomas Univ., FL, Opa Locka

Brehm, William .... (858) 451-6200
billjr@brehmmail.com, Pres, Brehm Communications, Inc., CA, San Diego

Brehun, Deborah

echo@tribweb.com, Ed., The Ligonier Echo, PA, Ligonier

Breister, Peggy
pbreister@fdlreporter.com, Ed., Action Advertiser, WI, Fond Du Lac
pbreister@fdlreporter.com, Ed., Action Sunday, WI, Fond Du Lac

Breitenbach, Nancy
nancyb@businessreport.com, Greater Baton Rouge Business Report, LA, Baton Rouge

Breitenstein, Dave
dbreitenstein@news-press.com, Audience Analyst, The Commercial Appeal, TN, Memphis

Breitfelder, Kim
kbreitfelder@hotmail.com, Circ. Mgr., Southern Nebraska Register, NE, Lincoln

Bremmer, Rick .... (864) 562-7440
rick.bremmer@shj.com, Reg. Dir. of Finance, Herald-Journal, SC, Spartanburg

Brenden, Sarah .... (425) 336-4959
sbrenden@soundpublishing.com, Editor, Covington-Maple Valley-Black Diamond Reporter, WA, Kent

Brendergast, Nessa
nessa.brendergast@transcontinental.ca, Media Relations Dir., Transcontinental Media, ON, Montreal

Brendlinger, Brian .... (215) 619-7306
bbrendli@mc3.edu, Montgomery County Cmty. College, PA, Blue Bell

Brendlinger, Nancy
nbrendl@bgsu.edu, Assoc. Prof., Bowling Green State University, OH, Bowling Green

Brenk, Mary
mbrenk@dlnewspapers.com, Pub, Detroit Lakes Tribune, MN, Detroit Lakes

Brennan, Charles
cbrennan@chronicleonline.com, Ed., Citrus County Chronicle, FL, Crystal River

Brennan, Dan
editor@theweeklysentinel.com, Operations Mgr., Weekly Sentinel, ME, Wells

Brennan, Daniel .... (210) 250-2604
dbrennan@express-news.net, Exec. Sales Dir., San Antonio Express-News, TX, San Antonio

Brennan, David .... (502) 895-9770 ext. 208
dbrennan@southcomm.com, Publisher, Louisville Eccentric Observer (leo), KY, Louisville

Brennan, Neale
nealab@chronicleonline.com, Community Affairs Dir., Citrus County Chronicle, FL, Crystal River

Brennan, Patrick
pbrennan@ottawacitizen.com, VP Mftg. and Dist., The Ottawa Citizen, ON, Ottawa

Brennan, Shelia
sbrennan@timesleader.net, Photo tech/Online content, Times Leader, KY, Princeton

Brennan, Steve
International Ed., The Hollywood Reporter, CA, Los Angeles

Brennan, Timothy .... (407) 894-7300 ext. 223
rbma@rbma.com, Mgr., Mktg., Reed Brennan Media Associates, Inc., FL, Orlando

Brennan, Tom .... (419) 521-7340
tbrennan@gannett.com, Gen. Mgr./Ed., Telegraph-Forum, OH, Mansfield

Brennan, Tom
tbrennan@nncogannett.com, Pub., The Marion Star, OH, Marion

Brennan, Tom .... (419) 521-7340
tbrennan@nncogannett.com, Ed. , News Journal, OH, Mansfield

Brenner, Betsy
bbrenner@journalsentinel.com, Pub., Community Newspapers, Inc., WI, Waukesha

Brenner, Elizabeth .... (414) 224-2954
bbrenner@journalsentinel.com, Pres./Pub., Milwaukee Journal Sentinel, WI, Milwaukee

Brenner, Stuart
stu@skobrenner.com com, CEO, SKO Brenner American, NY, Baldwin

Brenning, Kim
kim@daily-jeff.com, Adv. Dir., The Daily Jeffersonian, OH, Cambridge

Brent, Justin
jbrent@presby.edu, Presbyterian College, SC, Clinton

Breslauer, Irwin J. .... (212) 580-8559
ijbnyc@aol.com, Ed., Journal Press Syndicate, New York

Breslin, Tom
dazzarello@corpemail.com, Pres., AEC, Inc., IL, Schaumburg

Bresnahan, Mary
bresnah1@msu.edu, Prof., Michigan State University, MI, East Lansing

Bressan, Nick .... (217) 788-1358
nick.bressan@sj-r.com, Adv. Supvr., Retail, The State Journal-Register, IL, Springfield

Bressers, Bonnie
bresser@ksu.edu, Assoc. Prof./Head, Journalism Digital Media Sequence, Kansas State University, KS, Manhattan

Breton, Claire
townline@fairpoint.net, Circulation Director, Town Line, ME, South China

Breton, Gail
gbreton@thereminder.com, Circ. Mgr., Springfield Reminder, MA, East Longmeadow

Breton, Patrick
patrick.breton@levoyageur.ca, Ed. in Chief, Journal Le Voyageur, ON, Sudbury

Brett, Lauri
essexfreepress@on.aibn.com, Pub., Essex Free Press, ON, Essex

Breuhl, Brad
bbreuhl@nola.com, Asst. Adv. Dir. , The Times-Picayune, LA, New Orleans

Breunig, Bri .... (608) 270-9470
sales@madtimes.com, Sales Manager, The Madison Times, WI, Madison

Brewer, Beth .... (315) 866-2220
news@timestelegram.com, Pub./Adv. Mgr. , The Herkimer Telegram, NY, Herkimer

Brewer, Catherine
cbrewer@ptleader.com, Adv. Dir., Port Townsend & Jefferson County Leader, WA, Port Townsend

Brewer, Chris
cbrewer@themailbox.com, New media director, News & Record, NC, Greensboro

Brewer, Colleen .... (512) 445-3715
cbrewer@statesman.com, Adv. Dir., Austin American-Statesman, TX, Austin

Brewer, Connie
business@haysfreepress.com, Bus. Mgr., Hays Free Press, TX, Kyle

Brewer, Dale .... ext. 211
dbrewer@heraldpalladium.com, Editorial Page Ed., The Herald-Palladium, MI, Saint Joseph

Brewer, Hamish
info@jda.com, CEO, JDA Software Group, Inc., AZ, Scottsdale

Brewer, John C. .... (360) 417-3500
jbrewer@peninsuladailynews.com, Publisher and Editor, Peninsula Daily News, WA, Port Angeles

Brewer, Kim
subscriptions@gonzalesinquirer.com, Office Mgr., The Gonzales Inquirer, TX, Gonzales

Brewer, Lani .... (208) 527-3038

arcoadv@aol.com, Office Mgr., Arco
Advertiser, ID, Arco

Brewer, Ray........................**(702) 990-2662**
ray.brewer@lasvegassun.com, Senior Editor/
Sports, Las Vegas Sun, NV, Henderson

Brewer-Tyson, Vanessa..............**(843) 672-2754**
vtyson@pagelandprogressive.com, Reporter,
Pageland Progressive-Journal, SC, Pageland

Brewerton, Gordon
gbrewerton@metroland.com, Gen. Mgr., The
Orangeville Banner, ON, Orangeville

Brewington, Sarah
vistaassociate@sandiego.edu, Associate Ed.,
Univ. of San Diego, CA, San Diego

Brewster, Deborah
deborah.brewster@wsj.com, Deputy Mng. Ed.,
The Wall Street Journal, NY, New York

Brewster, Kaylee
thepathfinder@lcmail.lcsc.edu, Lewis-Clark
State College, ID, Lewiston

Brewster, Murray
mbrewster@broadcastnews.ca, Legislative
Reporter, Broadcast News Limited, NS,
Halifax

Brey, Dave
dbrey@sooeveningnews.com, Composing
Mgr., Sault Ste. Marie Evening News, MI,
Sault Sainte Marie

Brezina, Ales........................**(416) 530-4222**
abe@satellite1-416.com, Pub., Satellite 1416,
ON, Toronto

Brezina, Mike........................**(903) 893-8181**
mbrezina@heralddemocrat.com, Circ. Dir.,
Herald Democrat, TX, Sherman

Brian, Chip
cbrian@comtexnews.net, Pres., Comtex News
Network, VA, Alexandria

Brian, Peggy
peg@newcastlepacer.com, Adv. Sales,
Newcastle Pacer, OK, Newcastle

Briar, John
jbriar@fujifilmgs.com, Reg'l Sales Mgr., Fujifilm
Graphic Systems USA, Inc., IL, Hanover Park

Bricault, Claude....................**(514) 721-4911**
journalstm@videotron.ca, Journal De St
Michel, QC, Montreal

Brichacek, Lisa....................**(402) 277-5500**
lisa.brichacek@wahoonewspaper.com, Exec.
Ed., The Ashland Gazette, NE, Ashland

Brichacek, Lisa
lisa.brichacek@wahoonewspaper.com, Exec.
Ed., The News, NE, Waverly

Brichacek, Lisa....................**(402) 443-4162**
lisa.brichacek@wahoonewspaper.com, Exec.
Ed. , The Waverly News, NE, Waverly
lisa.brichacek@wahoonewspaper.com,
Executive Editor, Wahoo Newspaper, NE,
Wahoo

Bricker, Don
dbricker@shawmedia.com, Pub., Batavia
Chronicle, IL, St Charles
dbricker@shawmedia.com, Pub., Kane County
Chronicle, IL, Saint Charles
dbricker@shawmedia.com, Pub., The
Midweek, IL, Dekalb

Brickley, Shari......................**(941) 361-4001**
shari.brickley@herladtribune.com, Adv. Dir.,
Sarasota Herald-Tribune, FL, Sarasota

Bricklin, Mark......................**(970) 748-2906**
mbricklin@vaildaily.com, Mktg. Dir., Vail Daily,
CO, Avon

Bridge, John........................**(402) 444-1407**
john.bridge@owh.com, Adv. Mgr., Ad.
Operations, Omaha World-Herald, NE,
Omaha

Bridge, Staci........................**(434) 808-0597**
staci.bridge@thecharlottegazette.com; staci.
bridge@kenbridgevictoriadispatch.com, Dir.

of Ops., The Charlotte Gazette, VA, Drakes
Branch
staci.bridge@thecharlottegazette.com; staci.
bridge@kenbridgevictoriadispatch.com, Dir.
of Ops., The Farmville Herald, VA, Farmville
staci.bridge@thecharlottegazette.com; staci.
bridge@kenbridgevictoriadispatch.com, Dir.
of Ops, The Kenbridge-Victoria Dispatch,
VA, Victoria

Bridge, Terry................**(519) 291-1660 ext. 111**
tbridge@northperth.com, Sports Ed., The
Listowel Banner, ON, Listowel

Bridge, Terry
tbridge@postmedia.com, The Stratford Beacon
Herald, ON, Stratford

Bridges, Deborah
dbridges@uh.edu, Clinical Asst. Prof.,
University of Houston, TX, Houston

Bridges, Denise......................**(757) 446-2000**
denise.bridges@pilotonline.com, Dir.,
Newsroom Ops., The Virginian-Pilot, VA,
Norfolk

Bridges, Janet A.....................**(936) 294-3651**
jabridges@shsu.edu, Chair/Prof., Sam
Houston State University, TX, Huntsville

Bridges, Johnna
johnna@azlenews.net, Adv. Mgr., Azle News,
TX, Azle

Bridges, Lamar W.
lamar_bridges@tamu-commerce.edu, Prof.,
Texas A&M University-Commerce, TX,
Commerce

Bridges, Pat......................**(541) 881-1209**
pbridges@nevadaappeal.com, Pub., The
Record-Courier, NV, Gardnerville

Bridges, Robert......................**(386) 754-0428**
Editor, Lake City Reporter, FL, Lake City

Bridges, Thomas......................**(540) 574-6241**
tbridges@dnronline.com, Circ. Dir., Daily
News-Record, VA, Harrisonburg

Bridges, Tommy......................**(540) 574-6241**
tbridges@dnronline.com, Circ. Mgr., The
Journal, VA, Harrisonburg

Bridges, Tommy......................**(540) 547-6241**
Circ. Mgr., The Valley Banner, VA, Elkton

Bridges, Vera......................**(601) 961-7098**
Circ. Mgr., The Clarion-Ledger, MS, Jackson

Bridgewater, Frank....................**(808) 529-4791**
fbridgewater@staradvertiser.com, VP/Ed.,
Honolulu Star-Advertiser, HI, Honolulu

Bridgman, Gary
garyb15@swbell.net, Gen Mgr., Arkansas
Weekly, AR, Batesville

Bridwell, Jay
ads@bridgeportindex.com, Ed., Bridgeport
Index, TX, Bridgeport
ads@bridgeportindex.com, Ed., Chico Texan,
TX, Bridgeport

Bridwell, Keith......................**(940) 683-4021**
bridwellk@bridgeportindex.com, Pub./Adv. Dir.,
Bridgeport Index, TX, Bridgeport

Bridwell, Keith......................**(940) 683-4021**
bridwellk@bridgeportindex.com, Pub./Adv. Dir.,
Chico Texan, TX, Bridgeport

Briere, Bob........................**(860) 701-4203**
b.briere@theday.com, Ad. Director, The
Thames River Times, CT, New London
b.briere@theday.com, Adv. Dir., New London
Times, CT, New London
b.briere@theday.com, Adv. Dir., The Stonington
Times, CT, New London
b.briere@theday.com, Adv. Dir., The Lyme
Times, CT, New London
b.briere@theday.com, Adv. Dir., The Montville
Times, CT, New London
b.briere@theday.com, Adv. Dir., Waterford
Times, CT, New London
b.briere@theday.com, Ad. Dir., The Groton
Times, CT, New London
b.briere@theday.com, Ad. Dir., The Mystic

Times, CT, New London
b.briere@theday.com, Adv. Dir., The
Housatonic Times (OOB), CT, Torrington
b.briere@theday.com, Adv. Mgr., The Day, CT,
New London

Brigandi, Ben
bbrigandi@sungazette.com, Other,
Williamsport Sun-Gazette/Lock Haven
Express, PA, South Williamsport

Briggs, Audria
audria@yanceypaper.com, Circ. Mgr., Yancey
Common Times Journal, NC, Burnsville

Briggs, Ben
bbriggs@state-journal.com, Circ. Mgr., The
State Journal, KY, Frankfort

Briggs, Cindy
cmbriggs@dailyiowegian.com, Bus. Mgr., Ad-
Express & Daily Iowegian, IA, Centerville

Briggs, Jerry........................**(304) 348-4895**
jerrybriggs@cnpapers.com, VP, Adv. Dir., The
Charleston Gazette-Mail, WV, Charleston

Briggs, John........................**(740) 413-0899**
jriggs@civitasmedia.com, Circ Mgr., Clear
Ridge Reporter (OOB), IL, Summit
jriggs@civitasmedia.com, Cir. Mgr., The
Delaware Gazette, OH, Delaware

Briggs, Josh
jbriggs@bentoncourier.com, Ed., The Saline
Courier, AR, Benton

Briggs, Paula
pbriggs@nsu.edu, Assoc. Prof., Norfolk State
University, VA, Norfolk

Briggs, Scott........................**(405) 475-3311**
sbriggs@opubco.com, VP, Admin., The
Oklahoman, OK, Oklahoma City

Briggs, Smokey
smokey@pecos.net, Pub., Pecos Enterprise,
TX, Pecos

Briggs, Stacy........................**(215) 345-3057**
Features Ed., The Intelligencer, PA, Doylestown

Briggs, Viktorija......................**(785) 675-3321**
thesheridansentinel@gmail.com, Owner/Ed/
Pub, The Sheridan Sentinel, KS, Hoxie

Briggs , James......**(740) 474-3131, Ext. 204**
jbriggs@circlevilleherald.com, Gen. Mgr., The
Circleville Herald, OH, Circleville

Brigham, Shannon....................**(843) 709-1906**
sbrigham@lowcountryparent.com, Ed.,
Lowcountry Parent Magazine, SC,
Charleston

Bright, Heather......................**(740) 681-4516**
hbright@gannett.com, Ops. Mgr., Eagle-
Gazette Media, OH, Lancaster

Bright, James
chickashaeditor@gmail.com, Ed. in Chief,
Chickasha News, OK, Chickasha

Bright, James
james@chickashanews.com, Publisher, The
Duncan Banner, OK, Duncan
james@chickashanews.com, Pub., The
Express-Star, OK, Chickasha

Bright, Ron........................**(800) 624-7355**
rbright@wickedlocal.com, Class. Adv. Mgr.,
Avon Messenger, MA, Brockton

Bright, Ron
rbright@wickedlocal.com, Adv. Mgr., Classified,
Belmont Citizen-Herald, MA, Lexington
rbright@wickedlocal.com, Classified Adv. Mgr.,
Arlington Advocate, MA, Lexington

Bright, Ron
rbright@cnc.com, Classified Adv. Mgr., Times &
Courier, MA, Concord

Brightbill, Earl
earlbrightbill@ldnews.com, Photo Ed., The
Lebanon Daily News, PA, Lebanon

Brignac, Gina........................**(504) 834-9292**
gina.brignac@nopg.com, Reg. Bus. Mgr. ,
Arizona Capitol Times, AZ, Phoenix

Brikowski, Steven....................**(717) 815-1312**
Advisor, York College of Pennsylvania, PA, York

Briley, Russ
RUSS@SIGNALSCU.COM, Exec VP , Santa
Clarita Valley Signal, CA, Santa Clarita
RUSS@SIGNALSCU.COM, Pub., Connect
SCV, CA, Santa Clarita
RUSS@SIGNALSCU.COM, Paladin Multi-
Media

Brill, James........................**(212) 210-2901**
jbrill@nydailynews.com, Sr. Vice Pres., Circ./
Distr., New York Daily News, NY, New York

Brill, Steven
brill@ldg.com, Co-Founder, Press+, NY, New
York

Brilliant, Ashleigh
ashleigh@ashleighbrilliant.com, Pres.,
Ashleigh Brilliant, Santa Barbara

Brilliant, Dorothy......................**(805) 682-0531**
ashleigh@ashleighbrilliant.com, Vice Pres.,
Ashleigh Brilliant, Santa Barbara

Brimhall, Wanda......................**(815) 561-2112**
rnlcirc@rochellenews-leader.com, Circ., The
Rochelle News Leader, IL, Rochelle

Brimo, Rene J.
rbrimo@faithexpressions.com, Pres., R.B.
Intermark, Inc., QC, Kirkland

Brincefield, Robert....................**(325) 641-3130**
bob.brincefield@brownwoodbulletin.com, Pub.,
The Brown County Post, TX, Brownwood

Bringle, Jerry........................**(812) 231-4270**
jerry.bingle@tribstar.com, Controller , The
Tribune Star, IN, Terre Haute

Brink, Diane
brink@us.ibm.com, Vice Pres., Worldwide
Integrated Mktg. Commun., IBM Corp., NY,
Armonk

Brinker, Shannon....................**(605) 394-8301**
shannon.brinker@lee.net, Publisher, Rapid City
Journal, SD, Rapid City

Brinker, Shannon....................**(605) 394-8301**
shannon.brinker@rapidcityjournal.com, Pub.,
Butte County Post, SD, Rapid City

Brinkman, Anna
collegian@gcc.edu, Grove City College, PA,
Grove City

Brinkman, Gail
gbrinkman@tribune.com, Atlanta Mgr., Tribune
365, GA, Atlanta

Brinkman, Gary......................**(928) 775-3804**
gbrinkman@prescottaz.com, Prodn. Dir., Smart
Shopper Ash Fork, AZ, Prescott
gbrinkman@prescottaz.com, Prodn. Dir., Smart
Shopper, AZ, Prescott
gbrinkman@prescottaz.com, Prodn. Dir., The
Daily Courier, AZ, Prescott

Brinkmeyer, Alsy......................**(775) 881-7326**
abrinkmeyer@sierranevadamedia.com, Class.
Adv. Mgr., Nevada Appeal, NV, Carson City

Brinks, Ryan
editor@livewireprinting.com, Ed., Jackson
County Pilot, MN, Jackson

Brinn, David
davidb@jpost.com, Managing Ed., The
Jerusalem Post Foreign Service, Jerusalem

Brinn, Nikki................**(203) 245-1877 ext. 6113**
n.brinn@shorepublishing.com, Acct. Manager,
The Sound, CT, Madison

Brinser, Diane
dianeb@pa-news.org, Pennsylvania
NewsMedia Association, PA, Harrisburg

Brinson, Maureen......................**(252) 335-8132**
mbrinson@dailyadvance.com, Financial/
Accounting Manager, The Daily Advance,
NC, Elizabeth City

Brinson, Susan
brinssl@auburn.edu, Prof., Auburn University,
AL, Auburn

Brinton, Greg
news@thercononline.com, Pub., The Record-Courier, OR, Baker City

Brinton, Scott
sbrinton@liherald.com, Ed., Merrick Herald, NY, Garden City

Briody, Linda
lbriody@cfl.rr.com, Ed., The News Leader, FL, Clermont

Briody, Linda
lbriody@cfl.rr.com, Pub., Sumter Shopper, FL, Clermont

Briscoe, Keith W. ....ext. 155
Exec. Ed., Beaver County Times, PA, Beaver

Brisebois, Dan
brbanner@outlook.com , Ed., Beaver River Banner, AB, cold lake

Brisendine, Lynn
publisher@brownfieldonline.com, Pub./Ed., Brownfield News, TX, Brownfield

Brisendine, Lynn
publisher@seminolesentinel.com, Pub., Seminole Sentinel, TX, Seminole

Brislin, Kevin
kbrislin@timesshamrock.com , Adv. Mgr., Northeast Pennsylvania Business Journal, PA, Scranton

Brislin, Kevin
kbrislin@timesshamrock.com, Gen. Mgr., The Pocono Shopper, PA, East Stroudsburg

Brisson, Annemarie ....(401) 680-4800
advertising@pbn.com, Adv. Dir., Newport Mercury, RI, Newport
advertising@pbn.com, Adv. Dir., Newport Navalog, RI, Newport
advertising@pbn.com, Dir of Sales & Mktg, Providence Business News, RI, Providence
advertising@pbn.com, Adv. Dir., The Independent, RI, Newport

Brisson, Luc
luc.brisson@journalhautecotenord.com, Pub., Journal Haute Cote-nord, QC, Forestville

Brisson, Paul ....(418) 589-9990
CGAGNON@EDITIONSNORDIQUES.COM, Manic, QC, Baie Comeau

Britt, Tammy ....(910) 416-5668
tbritt@civitasmedia.com, Circ. Dir. , The Robesonian, NC, Lumberton

Britten, Robert ....(304) 293-8710
bob.britten@mail.wvu.edu, Asst. Prof., West Virginia University, WV, Morgantown

Brittingham, Tamra
shelclen@newszap.com, Corp. Pres., Independent Newsmedia Inc. Usa, DE, Dover

Britton, Chuck ....(815) 547-9393
chuck@bobray.com, Pres., Bob Ray & Associates, Inc., IL, Belvidere

Britton, Dawn
dbritton@spotlightnews.net, Advt Sales, The South County Spotlight, OR, Scappoose

Britton, Phyllis ....(501) 375-2985
phyllis@arktimes.com, Adv. Mgr., Arkansas Times, AR, Little Rock

BroKar, Faith. ....(620) 659-2080
edcsentinel@hotmail.com, Editor, Edwards County Sentinel, KS, Kinsley

Broadbooks, Jon
jon.broadbooks@sj-r.com, Exec. Ed., Springfield Advertiser, IL, Springfield

Broadus, Stephan ....(412) 481-8302 ext. 129
sbroadus@newpittsburghcourier.com, Asst. to Pub., New Pittsburgh Courier, PA, Pittsburgh

Broadway, Rob ....(706) 290-5287
rbroadway@npco.com, Prodn. Mgr., Press, Rome News-Tribune, GA, Rome

Broadwell, Charles
cbwell@sayobserver.com, Pub., Carolina Trader Autos, NC, Fayetteville

Broadwell, Charles W. ....(910) 323-4848
cbwell@fayetteobserver.com, Pub., Fort Bragg Paraglide, NC, Fayetteville

Broadwell, Charles W. ....(910) 486-3501
cbwell@fayettevillenc.com, Pub., Carolina Flyer, NC, Fayetteville

Broadwell, Charles W. ....(910) 486-3501
broadwellc@fayobserver.com, Pres./Pub., Fayetteville Publishing Co., NC, Fayetteville

Broas, Steve ....(920) 996-7219
sbroas@gannett.com, Adv. Dir., Post-Crescent, WI, Appleton

Brocato, Mary
maryb@nsula.edu, Assoc. Prof., Northwestern State University of Louisiana, LA, Natchitoches

Brock, Aimee ....(606) 248-1010 Ext. 1122
abrock@civitasmedia.com, Business Development Specialist, Middlesboro Daily News, KY, Middlesboro

Brock, Ashley ....(910) 875-2121
ashley@thenews-journal.com, Office Manager, The News-Journal, NC, Raeford

Brock, Carly ....(606) 451-4906
Classified Adv. Rep., The Commonwealth-Journal, KY, Somerset

Brock, Fred
feb2@k-state.edu, Asst. Prof./R.M. Seaton Professinal Chair, Kansas State University, KS, Manhattan

Brock, Gordon ....(705) 647-6791 ext. 239
editorial@northernontario.ca, Ed., Temiskaming Speaker, ON, New Liskeard

Brock, Harvey ....(701) 456-1201
hbrock@thedickinsonpress.com, Pub. , Advertizer, ND, Dickinson
hbrock@thedickinsonpress.com, Publisher, The Dickinson Press, ND, Dickinson
hbrock@thedickinsonpress.com, President, North Dakota Newspaper Association, ND, Bismarck

Brock, Kristen
kristen@hubcityspokes.com, Adv. Mgr., The Petal News, MS, Hattiesburg
kristen@hubcityspokes.com, Adv. Mgr., The Hattiesburg Post, MS, Hattiesburg

Brock, Nadine
Nadine@postvilleherald.com, Circ. Mgr., Postville Herald, IA, Postville

Brock, Terry ....(731) 287-7244
tbrock@stategazette.com, Circ. Dir., State Gazette, TN, Dyersburg

Brock , John
news1@sapulpaheraldonline.com, Ed. , Sapulpa Daily Herald, OK, Sapulpa

Brockett, Jr., Beau
bsb13@albion.edu, Mng. Ed., Albion College, MI, Albion

Brockington, Wanda
wgbrockington@nsu.edu, Chair/Assoc. Prof., Norfolk State University, VA, Norfolk

Brod, Bill
bbrod@syracusenewtimes.com, Owner and publisher, Syracuse New Times, NY, Syracuse

Brod, William ....(315) 422-7011 x138
publisher@syracusenewtimes.com, Pub., Syracuse New Times, NY, Syracuse

Brodeen, Jackson S.
avonclarion@hotmail.com, Pub./Ed./Adv. Mgr., Avon Clarion, SD, Avon

Broderick, James
jbroderick@njcu.edu, New Jersey City Univ., NJ, Jersey City

Broderick, Jim
tabads@comcast.net, Circ. Mgr, Huntington County Tab, IN, Huntington

Broders, Betty

ghrads@iowatelecom.net, Adv. Sales Rep., Grinnell Herald-Register, IA, Grinnell

Brodeur, Chris
hub@hayriverhub.com, Pub., The Hub, NT, Hay River

Brodigan, Martin
dynamic.capture@ricoh-usa.com, Pres., Ricoh Corp., NJ, West Caldwell

Brodt, Jay ....(509) 526-8342
jaybrodt@wwub.com, Adv. Dir., Walla Walla Union-Bulletin, WA, Walla Walla

Brody, Ambrosia ....(949) 660-6150 ext. 226
ambrosia@thelog.com, Managing Ed., The Log Newspaper, CA, Fountain Valley

Brody, Jeff
jbrody@fullerton.edu, Prof., California State University, Fullerton, CA, Fullerton

Broeck, Tom
generalmanager@chieflandcitizen.com, Gen. Mgr., Chiefland Citizen, FL, Chiefland

Broemmer, Don
donald.broemmer@courierpost.com, Prod. Mgr, Hannibal Courier-Post, MO, Hannibal

Brogan, Cecile
sales@pennypowerads.com, Pub., Penny Power, PA, Coopersburg

Brogdon, Mike ....(317) 736-2782
mbrogdon@dailyjournal.net, IT mgr., Daily Journal, IN, Franklin

Brogoitti, Karrine ....(541) 963-3161
ads@lagrandeobserver.com, Advt Dir, The Observer, OR, La Grande

Brogoitti, Karrine ....(541) 963-3161
ads@bakercityherald.com, Advt Dir, Baker City Herald, OR, Baker City

Brohard, Mike
mbrohard@reporter-herald.com, Sports Ed., Loveland Reporter-Herald, CO, Loveland

Brokaw, Jill
jbrokaw@monticelloexpress.com, Prodn. Mgr., Monticello Shoppers' Guide, IA, Monticello

Bromley, Jeff ....(940) 569-2191
jeff@burknews.com, Ed., Burkburnett Informer Star, TX, Burkburnett

Bromley, Rebekah
echo@utc.edu, Assoc. Prof., University of Tennessee at Chattanooga, TN, Chattanooga

Bromley, Seth
sbromely@woonsocketcall.com, Ed. , The Call, RI, Woonsocket

Bronson, William
williambronson@daltoncitizen.com, Pub., The Daily Citizen, GA, Dalton

Bronstein, Richard
jewishfp@tellus.net, Pub., Jewish Free Press, AB, Calgary

Brook, Larry ....(205) 322-9002
editor@sjlmag.com, Ed/Pub., Southern Jewish Life, AL, Mountain Brk

Brook, Steve
steve@thestatesb.com, Mng. Ed., The State, SC, Columbia

Brooke, Jodee
jodee@bannerjournal.com, Ed., Shopper, WI, Black River Falls

Brooker, Vicki
vbrooker@stpaul.greatwest.ca, Ed., Elk Point Review, AB, Elk Point

Brookman, W. Joseph
support@mlog.com, Pres./CEO/Dir., Microlog Corp., MD, Gaithersburg

Brooks, Alex
news@eastwickpress.com, Pub., The Eastwick Press, NY, Cropseyville

Brooks, Alison ....(423) 623-6171
alison.brooks@newportplaintalk.com, Staff Writer, The Newport Plain Talk, TN, Newport

Brooks, Becky ....(419) 483-4190
news@gazettepublishingco.com, Editor, Gazette Extra, OH, Bellevue

Brooks, Carol ....(336) 841-4933
jtowneditor@northstate.net, Editor, Jamestown News, NC, Jamestown

Brooks, Dan ....(616) 632-2068
newsroom@aqsaint.com, Aquinas College, MI, Grand Rapids

Brooks, David ....(412) 765-2583
dbrooks@amm.com, Sen. Vice Pres./Ed in Chief, American Metal Market, NY, New York

Brooks, Debby ....(317) 477-3213
dbrooks@greenfieldreporter.com, Admin. Mgr., Daily Reporter, IN, Greenfield

Brooks, Diana ....(507) 553-3131
mirror.shoppe@gmail.com, Sales and Customer Service Representative, Wells Mirror, MN, Wells

Brooks, Erin
eebrooks@timesdispatch.com, Regional Sales Director, Richmond Times-Dispatch, VA, Richmond

Brooks, Hubby ....(229) 244-1880 Ext. 1262
hubby.brooks@gaflnews.com, VP Technology, Valdosta Daily Times, GA, Valdosta

Brooks, James ....(907) 486-3227 ext.622
editor@kodiakdailymirror.com, Editor, Kodiak Daily Mirror, AK, Kodiak

Brooks, Jason
jbrooks@newsrepublican.com, Ed., Boone News-Republican, IA, Boone

Brooks, Jason ....(505) 425-6796
jbrooks@lasvegasoptic.com, Editor, Las Vegas Optic, NM, LAS VEGAS

Brooks, John ....(605) 692-4300
advertising@sdna.com, Advertising Sales Director, South Dakota Newspaper Association, SD, Brookings

Brooks, Joni ....(405) 278-2815
joni.brooks@journalrecord.com, Pub., The Journal Record, OK, Oklahoma City

Brooks, Kelly
kelly@northfulton.com, Associate Pub., John's Creek Herald, GA, Alpharetta
kelly@northfulton.com, Associate Pub., The Revue & News, GA, Alpharetta
kelly@northfulton.com, Associate Pub., Milton Herald, GA, Alpharetta
kelly@northfulton.com, Associate Pub., The Forsyth Herald, GA, Alpharetta

Brooks, Kim
kbrooks@monticelloexpress.com, Ed., Monticello Shoppers' Guide, IA, Monticello

Brooks, Lee
lbrooks@newzgroup.com, Mgr., Missouri Press Clipping Bureau - Newz Group, MO, Columbia

Brooks, Linda
lbrooks@sacbee.com, Vice-President, Human Resources, Bee Niche Products, CA, Sacramento

Brooks, Linda ....(916) 321-1639
lbrooks@sacbee.com, Vice Pres., HR, The Sacramento Bee, CA, Sacramento

Brooks, Mary Lou
btymes@telus.net, Publisher/Advertising Manager, The Bassano Times, AB, Bassano

Brooks, Michael
michael.brooks@norfolk.gov, Circ. Mgr., Journal And Guide, VA, Norfolk

Brooks, Mimi
mbrooks@lds.com, Pres./CEO, Logical Design Solutions, Inc., NJ, Florham Park

Brooks, Ron ....(704) 797-4221
rbrooks@salisburypost.com, Circ. Dir., Salisbury Post, NC, Salisbury

Brooks, Roz

editor@kentuckynewera.com, Ed., Fort
Campbell Courier, KY, Hopkinsville

Brown, Jennifer
jbrown@bsnsports.com, Classified Dir., Dallas
Observer, TX, Dallas

Brown, Jennifer
htpress99@gmail.com, Gen. Mgr., Hometown
Press, TX, Winnie

Brown, Jennifer
jpbrown@kentuckynewera.com, Opinion Ed.,
Kentucky New Era, KY, Hopkinsville

Brown, Jennifer .... (225) 383-0656
jbrown@theadvocate.com, Exec. News Ed.,
The Advocate, LA, Baton Rouge

Brown, Jill
jbrown@multiad.com, Local Search
Association, IL, Peoria

Brown, Jill
jibrown@dmreg.com, Adv. Mgr., Grinnell
Pennysaver, IA, Grinnell

Brown, John .... (979) 732-2304
jbrown5246@aol.com, The Colorado County
Citizen, TX, Columbus

Brown, John Pat
mcourier@bellsouth.net, Ed., The Magee
Courier, MS, Magee

Brown, John R. .... (616) 642-9411
icsg@sbcglobal.net, Pub., Ionia County
Shoppers Guide, MI, Saranac

Brown, Johnny
jbrown@coastalcourier.com, Circ. Mgr., The
Coastal Courier, GA, Hinesville

Brown, Jon P. .... (208) 337-4681 ext.102
jon@owyheeavalanche.com, Mng. Ed., The
Owyhee Avalanche, ID, Homedale

Brown, Joseph
jbrown@catholictranscript.org, Graphic
Designer, The Catholic Transcript, CT,
Bloomfield

Brown, Joseph
jbrown@starherald.net, Ed./Pub. , The Star-
Herald, MS, Kosciusko

Brown, Josh .... ext. 116
jbrown@robdailynews.com, Sports Ed., Daily
News, IL, Robinson

Brown, Kara .... ext. 1335
Design Dir., Metro, CA, San Jose

Brown, Karen .... (706) 884-7311 Ext. 238
kbrown@civitasmedia.com, Piqua Daily Call,
OH, Piqua
kbrown@civitasmedia.com, Mktg. Dir., Auglaize
Merchandiser, OH, Wapakoneta

Brown, Karen
publisher@sidneyherald.com, Pub., Sidney
Herald, MT, Sidney

Brown, Kathryn B. .... (541) 276-2211
kbbrown@eastoregonian.com, Pub, East
Oregonian, OR, Pendleton

Brown, Kathy .... ext. 104
Sports Ed., The News-Record, WY, Gillette

Brown, Kelli .... (515) 284-8123
kkbrown@dmreg.com, Sr. News Dir. Digital,
The Des Moines Register, IA, Des Moines

Brown, Kelly .... (979) 731-4656
kelly.brown@theeagle.com, Exec. Ed., The
Eagle, TX, Bryan

Brown, Kellyn
editor@flatheadbeacon.com, Ed, Flathead
Beacon, MT, Kalispell

Brown, Ken
ken.brown@clarke.edu, City Ed., Telegraph
Herald, IA, Dubuque

Brown, Ken
kbrown@kjla.com, Asst. Ed., Investor's
Business Daily, CA, Los Angeles

Brown, Kendrick
kbrown@gadcotimes.com, Reporter, Gadsden

County Times, FL, Quincy

Brown, Kevin .... (425) 339-3474
brown@heraldnet.com, Sports Ed., The
Herald, WA, Everett

Brown, L.G.
lgbrown59@gmail.com, Pres., Brown's Web
Press Service & Machine Shop, MO, Mexico

Brown, Laura
laura.brown@thewinneradvocate.com, Adv.
Mgr., Winner Advocate, SD, Winner

Brown, Laurie Ezzell .... (806) 323-6461
laurie@canadianrecord.com, Pub./Ed., The
Canadian Record, TX, Canadian

Brown, LeAnn
ads@thesheridanheadlight.com, Adv. Dir./
Graphic Dsgn., Sheridan Headlight, AR,
Sheridan

Brown, Leah
lbrown@alonovus.com, Ed., Jewish Reporter,
NV, Las Vegas
lbrown@alonovus.com, Ed, The Bargain
Hunter - Holmes, OH, Millersburg

Brown, Lee
lbrown3@csulb.edu, Part-time Fac., California
State University, Long Beach, CA, Long
Beach

Brown, Lenny .... (212) 210-2089
lbrown@nydailynews.com, Dir. Class. Adv.
Sales
, New York Daily News, NY, New York

Brown, Linda Smith .... (309) 686-3106
lsmithbrown@timestoday.com, Gen. Sales
Mgr., Times News Group, IL, Pekin

Brown, Lynn .... (202) 747-2077 x8075
lbrown@washblade.com, Publisher,
Washington Blade, DC, Washington

Brown, M. Eileen .... (847) 427-4373
ebrown@dailyherald.com, Vice Pres./Director
Strategic Marketing and Innovation, Daily
Herald, IL, Arlington Heights

Brown, Malcolm .... ext. 255
mbrown@backemarketing.com, Sr. Vice Pres.,
Backe Difital Brand Marketing, PA, Radnor

Brown, Mandy .... (386) 754-0405
Circulation Director, Lake City Reporter, FL,
Lake City

Brown, Marci .... (712) 229-5492
aurstar@gmail.com, Owner/Ed., Aurelia Star,
IA, Aurelia

Brown, Mark A. .... (330) 747-1471 ext. 1204
markbrown@vindy.com, Gen. Mgr., The
Vindicator, OH, Youngstown

Brown, Martha
advertising@thedeal.com, Dir., Cor. Commun.,
The Daily Deal, NY, New York

Brown, Matt .... (707) 776-8458
matt.brown@arguscourier.com, Ed., Petaluma
Argus-Courier, CA, Petaluma

Brown, Matthew .... (410) 332-6491
matbrown@baltsun.com. , Enterprise Ed. , The
Baltimore Sun, MD, Baltimore

Brown, Meghan
meaghan.brown@sunmedia.ca, Sales, The
Whitecourt Star, AB, Whitecourt

Brown, Melissa .... (423) 837-6312
mcnews@marioncountynews.net, Pub.,
Sequatchie Valley Purchase, TN, South
Pittsburg

Brown, Michael .... (918) 968-2581
stroudamerican@brightok.net, Ed., Stroud
American, OK, Stroud

Brown, Michael
idcathreg@rcdb.org, Ed., Idaho Catholic
Register, ID, Boise

Brown, Michael .... (313) 222-1470
michael.brown@detroitnews.com,
Administrative Ed,, The Detroit News, MI,
Detroit

michael.brown@detroitnews.com, Asst.
Managing Editor, Detroit Free Press, MI,
Detroit

Brown, Michael .... (918) 622-4996
mikeb@commpub.com, Exec. Vice Pres.,
Community Publishers, Inc., AR, Bentonville

Brown, Michelle .... (810) 989-6249
mibrown@thetimesherald.com, Controller, The
Meadville Tribune, PA, Meadville
mibrown@thetimesherald.com, Office Mgr.,
Times Herald, MI, Port Huron
mibrown@thetimesherald.com, The Lebanon
Daily News, PA, Lebanon

Brown, Mike .... (918) 259-7500
mikeb@ok.neighbournews.com, Pub.,
Collinsville News, OK, Tulsa

Brown, Mike
mikeb@ok.neighbornews.com, Pub., Tulsa
Pennysaver, OK, Tulsa

Brown, Mike .... (918) 259-7500
mikeb@ok.neighbornews.com, Pub., Skiatook
Journal, OK, Skiatook

Brown, Mike .... (918) 259-7500
mikeb@ok.neighbournews.com, Pub., Owasso
Reporter, OK, Owasso

Brown, Mike .... (512) 446-5838
mike@rockdalereporter.com, Ed., Rockdale
Reporter, TX, Rockdale

Brown, Mike .... (918) 259-7500
mikeb@ok.neighbornews.com, Pub., Bixby
Bulletin - (OOB), OK, Bixby
mikeb@ok.neighbornews.com, Pub., Catoosa
Times, OK, Tulsa
mikeb@ok.neighbornews.com, Pub., Sand
Springs Leader, OK, Tulsa
mikeb@ok.neighbornews.com, Pub., South
County Leader - (OOB), OK, Bixby

Brown, Nancy
tppub@1starnet.com, Ed., Bogata News-Talco
Times, TX, Bogata

Brown, Nancy
nbrown@envoymortgage.com, Adv. Dir.,
Houston Business Journal, TX, Houston

Brown, Nancy .... (530) 741-2345
nbrown@appealdemocrat.com, Adv. Mgr.,
Classified, Appeal Democrat, CA, Marysville
nbrown@appealdemocrat.com, Classified
Adv. Mgr., Colusa County Sun-Herald, CA,
Marysville
nbrown@appealdemocrat.com, Classifieds
Adv. Mgr., Willows Journal (OOB), CA,
Willows

Brown, Neil .... (727) 893-8441
nbrown@tampabay.com, Ed. & VP, Tampa Bay
Times, FL, St Petersburg

Brown, Nick .... ext. 5704
nick@atomicimaging.com, Commun.
Consultant, Atomic Imaging, Inc., IL, Chicago

Brown, Oby .... (478) 744-4396
obrown@macontel.com, News Ed., The
Telegraph, GA, Macon

Brown, Pamela .... (780) 827-3539
pamnews@telus.net, Pub./Ed./GM, Grande
Cache Mountaineer, AB, Grande Cache

Brown, Pat
pdbrown@theindependent.com , Circ. Dir., The
Grand Island Independent, NE, Grand Island

Brown, Paul .... (740) 592-6612 Ext. 207
pbrown@athensmessenger.com, Cir. Dir., The
Athens Messenger, OH, Athens

Brown, Paul B.
mail@urnerbarry.com, Pres., Urner Barry's
Price-Current, NJ, Bayville

Brown, Phil
phil.brown@djc.com, Pub., Seattle Daily
Journal of Commerce, WA, Seattle

Brown, Randy
randy@dmprinters.com, Sr. Fellow, Wichita
State University, KS, Wichita

Brown, Randy .... (318) 747-7900 Ext. 111
rbrown@bossierpress.com, Pub, Bossier
Press-Tribune, LA, Bossier City

Brown, Renee .... (239) 574-1110
rbrown@breezenewspapers.com, Adv. Dir.,
Cape Coral Breeze, FL, Cape Coral

Brown, Renee .... (239) 425-8870
rbrown@breezenewspapers.com, Commerical
Print Manager, Lee County Shopper, FL,
Cape Coral

Brown, Richard .... (402) 444-1243
richard.brown@owh.com, Adv. Mgr., Digital
Products, Omaha World-Herald, NE, Omaha

Brown, Richard H.
digitalinfo@fujifilm.com, Chrmn./CEO, EDS
(Electronic Data Systems), TX, Plano
digitalinfo@fujifilm.com, Reg'l Sales Mgr.,
Fujifilm Graphic Systems USA, Inc., MO,
Kansas City

Brown, Rick
rick.brown@kearneyhub.com, Food/Women's
Ed., Kearney Hub, NE, Kearney

Brown, Rob
editor@dcdn.ca, Ed, The Mirror, BC, Dawson
Creek
editor@dcdn.ca, Ed, The Northern Horizon,
BC, Dawson Creek

Brown, Robert L. .... (775) 850-7676
rbrown@swiftcom.com, President & COO,
Swift Communications, Inc., NV, Carson City

Brown, Ron
ron.brown@mountaintimes.com, Adv./Gen.
Mgr, The Ashe Mountain Times, NC, West
Jefferson

Brown, Ron .... (336) 372-8999
manager@alleghanynews.com, Gen. Mgr./Adv.
Dir., The Alleghany News, NC, Sparta

Brown, Ross .... (509) 527-2971
Walla Walla College, WA, College Place

Brown, Ruth
rbrown15@unl.edu, Vstg. Assoc. Prof.,
University of Nebraska-Lincoln, NE, Lincoln

Brown, Samuel .... (305) 376-3163
sbrown@miamiherald.com, VP Advertising
, Miami Herald, FL, Doral

Brown, Sandra .... (732) 571-5712
sbrown@monmouth.edu, Office Coordinator,
Monmouth University, NJ, West Long Branch

Brown, Scott .... (330) 580-8343
scott.brown@cantonrep, Mng. Ed., The
Repository, OH, Canton
scott.brown@cantonrep.com, Part-time Fac.,
California State University, Northridge, CA,
Northridge

Brown, Scott .... (334) 365-6739
smbrown@gannett.com, Pub., Prattville
Progress, AL, Prattville

Brown, Scott .... (256) 340-2381
scott.brown@decaturdaily.com, Op. Dir., The
Decatur Daily, AL, Decatur

Brown, Scott .... (256) 340-2381
scott.brown@decaturdaily.com, Dir.,
Operations, The Decatur Daily, AL, Decatur

Brown, Scottie .... (334) 670-6323
scottie.brown@troymessenger.com, Staff
Writer, The Troy Messenger, AL, Troy

Brown, Sharon .... (903) 872-3931
sbrown@corsicanadailysun.com, Bus. Mgr.,
Corsicana Daily Sun, TX, Corsicana

Brown, Stacey .... (812) 277-7278
Prod. Mgr., The Times-Mail, IN, Bedford

Brown, Stephen
sbrown@chartis.com, Mng. Ed., Chicago Daily
Law Bulletin, IL, Chicago

Brown, Steve .... (503) 630-3241
sbrown@theoutlookonline.com, Pub/Ed, Sandy
Post, OR, Gresham

Brown, Steve

sbrown@phx.com, Associate Publisher, Providence Phoenix, RI, Providence

Brown, Steve N.
sjbrown@pressline.info, Pres., Pressline Services, Inc., IL, Dupo

Brown, Sue
sbrown@pleasantonexpress.com, Editor, Pleasanton Express, TX, Pleasanton

Brown, Susanne J.
editorial@gleaner-source.com, Ed., Les Hebdos Monteregiens, QC, Huntingdon

Brown, T.C.
tcbrown@blackchronicle.com, Adv. Rep., Black Chronicle, OK, Oklahoma City

Brown, Tara .... (405) 665-4333
info@wwgazette.news, Advertising Manager, Wynnewood Gazette, OK, Wynnewood

Brown, Tim
tim.brown@ucf.edu, Asst. Prof., University of Central Florida, FL, Orlando

Brown, Tom .... (843) 488-7234
tom.brown@myhorrynews.com, Adv. Dir., The Loris Scene, SC, Conway
tom.brown@myhorrynews.com, Adv. Dir., The Horry Independent, SC, Conway
tom.brown@myhorrynews.com, Adv. Dir., Myrtle Beach Herald, SC, Myrtle Beach

Brown, Tony
aaron.livingston@hamptonu.edu, Dean, Hampton University, VA, Hampton

Brown Minn, Lucy
lbrown@ucclocalmedia.com, CEO/President, United Communications Corporation, WI, Kenosha

Brownbridge, Alice
ebrownbridge@cowichanvalleycitizen.com, Prod. Mgr., Cowichan Valley Citizen, BC, Duncan

Browne, Alix .... (877) 203-2327
alix@afcp.org, Administrative Assistant, Association of Free Community Papers, NY, Liverpool

Browne, Denise
dbrowne@repub.com, NIE , The Republican, MA, Springfield

Browne, Donna
dbrowne@rmoutlook.com, Circ. Mgr, Rocky Mountain Outlook, AB, Canmore

Browne, Jason
ismgr@kdhnews.com, Coord., Telecommun., Killeen Daily Herald, TX, Killeen

Browne, Nancy
nbrowne@ncronline.org, Chief Advancement Officer, National Catholic Reporter, MO, Kansas City

Brownell, Cheryl .... (802) 865-1020 x 31
cheryl@sevendaysvt.com, Bus. Mgr., Seven Days, VT, Burlington

Browning, Amanda .... (812) 663-3111 x7004
amanda.browning@greensburgdailynews.com, Staff Writer , Greensburg Daily News, IN, Greensburg

Browning, Bruce .... (470) 729-3248
bbrowning@times-georgian.com, Managing Ed., Times-Georgian, GA, Carrollton

Browning, Bruce .... (770) 834-6631
bbrowning@times-georgian.com, Editor, West Georgia Weekly, GA, Carrollton

Browning, Donna
classified@snyderdailynews.com, Adv. Mgr., Classified, Snyder Daily News, TX, Snyder

Browning, George
gbrowning@gbpnews.com, Ed., The Banner-Gazette, IN, Pekin

Browning, Jeremy .... (435) 674-6200
jeremy@thespectrum.com, Adv. Mgr., The Spectrum, UT, Saint George

Browning, Mardi .... (831) 706-3265

Circ. Mgr., Santa Cruz Sentinel, CA, Scotts Valley

Browning, Pamela
pbrowning@postandcourier.com, Pub., The Post and Courier, SC, Charleston

Browning, Skylar
sbrowning@missoulanews.com, Ed., Missoula Independent, MT, Missoula

Brownlee, Patsy
thestar@socket.net, Pub., Cedar County Buyers Guide, MO, El Dorado Springs

Brownlee, Phillip .... (316) 268-6262
pbrownlee@wichitaeagle.com, Opinion editor, The Wichita Eagle, KS, Wichita

Brownlee, Steve .... (906) 228-2500 ext #252
sbrownlee@miningjournal.net, Sports Editor, The Mining Journal, MI, Marquette

Brownr, Jan .... (360) 384-1411
jan@ferndalerecord.com, Adv. Mgr., Ferndale Record, WA, Ferndale

Broyles, Alan .... (423) 929-3111
albroy@johnsoncitypress.com, Johnson City Press, TN, Johnson City

Broyles, Grace
jimnedjournal@taylortel.net, Adv. Dir., The Jim Ned Journal, TX, Tuscola

Broyles, Jane
biz@theleadernews.com, Circ. Mgr., The Leader, TX, Houston
biz@theleadernews.com, Circ. Mgr., Leader News, TX, Castroville

Broyles, Jim .... (334) 261-1571
jimbroyles@gannett.com, Adv. Dir., Montgomery Advertiser, AL, Montgomery

Broyles, Pam
pbroyles@snu.edu, Speech Commun. Dept., Southern Nazarene Univ., OK, Bethany

Broyles, Sheri
sbroyles@unt.edu, Assoc. Prof./Coord., Adv. seq., University of North Texas, TX, Denton

Brozs, John .... (203) 354-1093
jbrosz@thehour.com, VP Sales and marketing, The Wilton Villager, CT, Norwalk

Brubacher, Heidi .... (519) 537-2341 x515235
hbrubacher@postmedia.com, Classified sales, The Norwich Gazette, ON, Woodstock

Brubaker, Christine .... (706) 886-6831 ext. 5340
Toccoa Falls College, GA, Toccoa Falls

Brubaker, Drew
dbrubaker@newstribune.info, Circ. Mgr., Today's Shopper, WV, Keyser

Bruce, Colin J. .... (807) 343-6201
cbruce@chroniclejournal.com, Pub., The Chronicle-Journal, ON, Thunder Bay

Bruce, Layne
lbruce@mspress.org, Exec. Dir., Mississippi Press Association, MS, Jackson

Bruce, Layne
mpa@mspress.org, Exec. Dir., Mississippi Press Services, Inc., MS, Jackson

Bruck, Bob .... (270) 691-7306
bbruck@messenger-inquirer.com, City Ed., Messenger-Inquirer, KY, Owensboro

Bruck, Robert
bbruck@messenger-inquirer.com, Photo Ed., Messenger-Inquirer, KY, Owensboro

Brueckner, Rich
rbrueckner@devilslakejournal.com, Display Ad. Mgr., Devils Lake Journal, ND, Devils Lake

Brueggermann, Brian .... (618) 692-9487
bbrueggermann@bnd.com, Newsroom, Belleville News-Democrat, IL, Belleville

Bruess, Carol
cjbruess@stthomas.edu, Assoc. Prof., University of St. Thomas, MN, Saint Paul

Bruestle, Sara .... (425) 347-5634
editor@mukilteobeacon.com, Ed., Mukilteo

Beacon, WA, Mukilteo

Bruett, Raymond
rbruett@timesdispatch.com, Circ. Dir., Richmond Delivery Service, VA, Richmond

Bruffy, Kevin
bruffy.2@osu.edu, Ohio State Univ., OH, Columbus

Brugger, Patti
patti@tecumsehherald.com, Circ. Mgr., The Tecumseh Herald, MI, Tecumseh

Bruha, Carol .... (403) 577-3337
ads@consortenterprise.com, Circ. Mgr./Adv. Mgr., The Consort Enterprise, AB, Consort

Bruha, David
editor@consortenterprise.com, Ed., The Consort Enterprise, AB, Consort

Bruke, Sean
sean.bruke@rutlandherald.com, Adv. Mgr., Preferred Properties Real Estate Guide, VT, Rutland

Brum, Aiko .... (808) 656-3155
editor@hawaiiarmyweekly.com, Chief, Internal Communication, Hawaii Army Weekly, HI, Schofield Barracks

Brumbeloe, Katie
kbrumbeloe@press-citizen.com, News Dir., Iowa City Press-Citizen, IA, Iowa City

Brumby, Otis .... (770) 428-9411 x301
otis3@mdjonline.com, Pub., Cherokee Ledger-News, GA, Canton

Brumby, Otis .... (770) 428-9411 x 301
otis3@mdjonline.com, Pub., Kennesaw-Acworth Neighbor, GA, Marietta
otis3@mdjonline.com, Pub., Neighbor Newspapers, Inc., GA, Marietta
otis3@mdjonline.com, Pub. , South Cobb Neighbor, GA, Marietta

Brumby, Otis .... (770) 428-9411 x 301
otis3@mdjonline.com, CEO/Pub., Cherokee Tribune, GA, Canton

Brumby, Otis A.
obrumbyjr@neighbornewspapers.com, Pub., Henry Neighbor, GA, Forest Park

Brumby, Otis A.
smetro@neighbornewspapers.com, Gen. Mgr., South Fulton Neighbor, GA, Forest Park

Brumby, Otis A. .... ext. 301
paulding@neighbornewspapers.com, Pub., Paulding Neighbor, GA, Marietta

Brumby, Otis A.
bartow@neighbornewspapers.com, Pub., Bartow Neighbor, GA, Hiram

Brumby, Otis A.
douglas@neighbornewspapers.com, Pub., The Douglas Neighbor, GA, Hiram

Brumby, Otis A.
dekalb@neighbornewspapers.com, Pub., DeKalb Neighbor, GA, Roswell

Brumby, Otis A.
otis@mdjonline.com, Pub., Northside Neighbor, GA, Atlanta

Brumby, Otis A.
otis@mdjonline.com, CEO/Pub., Marietta Daily Journal, GA, Marietta
otis@mdjonline.com, Pub./CEO, North Cobb Neighbor, GA, Marietta

Brumby, Otis A. .... (770) 428-9411 x 301
otis3@mdjonline.com, Pub., East Cobb Neighbor, GA, Marietta

Brumby, Otis A. .... (770) 428-9411 ext. 301
oabjr@aol.com, Pub., Cherokee Tribune Plus, GA, Canton

Brumby Garrett, Lee
lgarrett@mdjonline.com, Gen. Mgr., Milton Neighbor, GA, Roswell
lgarrett@mdjonline.com, Gen. Mgr., Cherokee Ledger-News, GA, Canton
lgarrett@mdjonline.com, Gen. Mgr., Alpharetta

Neighbor, GA, Roswell
lgarrett@mdjonline.com, Gen. Mgr., Johns Creek Neighbor (OOB), GA, Roswell
lgarrett@mdjonline.com, Gen. Mgr., North Cobb Neighbor, GA, Marietta
lgarrett@mdjonline.com, Gen. Mgr., Roswell Neighbor, GA, Roswell
lgarrett@mdjonline.com, Gen. Mgr., DeKalb Neighbor, GA, Roswell
lgarrett@mdjonline.com, Gen. Mgr., Mid DeKalb Neighbor (OOB), GA, Roswell
lgarrett@mdjonline.com, Gen. Mgr., Paulding Neighbor, GA, Marietta
lgarrett@mdjonline.com, Gen. Mgr., Northside Neighbor, GA, Atlanta
lgarrett@mdjonline.com, Gen. Mgr., The Clayton Neighbor (OOB), GA, Marietta

Brumby III, Otis A. .... (770) 428-9411 x 301
otis3@mdjonline.com, Pub., Northside/Sandy Springs/Vinings/Brookhaven Neighbor, GA, Sandy Springs

Brumit, Colby
colby@outfrontonline.com, Art Dir., Out Front, CO, Denver

Brumleve, William .... (217) 379-2356
wbrumleve@paxtonrecord.net, Editor, Ford County Record, IL, Paxton

Brumley, Roger
rbrumley@jonesborosun.com, Production Manager, IT, The Jonesboro Sun, AR, Jonesboro

Brummer, Courtney
cbrummer@nonpareilonline.com, Asst. Mng. Ed., The Daily Nonpareil, IA, Council Bluffs

Brundy, Lacy
circulation@parkrecord.com, Circ. Mgr., Park Record, UT, Park City

Brunelle, Marco .... ext. 342
mbrunelle@groupejcl.com, Sports Ed., Le Groupe Jcl Inc., QC, Saint Eustache

Bruneman, Clay .... (224) 361-8300
clay.bruneman@gammerler.com, CEO, Gammerler (US) Corp., IL, Mt Prospect

Bruner, Andrea
andreab@guardonline.com, Mng. Ed., Batesville Daily Guard, AR, Batesville

Bruner, Leah .... (803) 532-6203
bltwincitynews@gmail.com, Editor, The Twin-City News, SC, Batesburg Leesville

Bruner III, Douglas .... (803) 924-3991
twincitynews@pbtcomm.net, Publisher, The Twin-City News, SC, Batesburg Leesville

Brunjes, Allendria .... (780) 675-9222 Ext. 22
abrunjes@athabasca.greatwest.ca, Pub., The Athabasca Advocate, AB, Athabasca

Brunjes, Bob .... (772) 221-4273
Pres./Pub., Jupiter Courier, FL, Stuart

Brunner, Al
ajb@glunz-jensen.com, Pres., Autologic Information International, CA, Thousand Oaks
ajb@glunz-jensen.com, Vice Pres., Sales, K & F International, Inc., IN, Granger

Brunner, Debra
dbrunner@post-journal.com, Adv. Dir., The Post-Journal, NY, Jamestown

Bruno, Kathy .... (716) 312-8088
info@polamjournal.com, Accounting, Polish American Journal, NY, North Boston

Bruns, Andy .... (814) 444-5944
abruns@dailyamerican.com, Pub., Daily American, PA, Somerset

Bruns, Penny .... (623) 876-2572
pbruns@yourwestvalley.com, Adv. Dir., Daily News-Sun, AZ, Sun City

Bruns, Tom
tomb@commpub.com, CFO, Community Publishers, Inc., AR, Bentonville

Brunson, Dennis .... (803) 774-1241
Dennis@theitem.com, Sports Ed., The Sumter

Item , SC, Sumter

Brush, Coral ....(705) 645-8771
ccunningham@metrolandnorthmedia.
com, Sales Coordinator, Muskoka District
Weekender, ON, Bracebridge

Brusic, Ken ....(714) 796-2226
kbrusic@ocregister.com, Ed., Fullerton News-
Tribune, CA, Santa Ana
kbrusic@ocregister.com, Ed., Laguna Niguel
News, CA, Santa Ana
kbrusic@ocregister.com, Ed., Brea-La Habra
Star-Progress, CA, Santa Ana
kbrusic@ocregister.com, Ed., Laguna Woods
Globe, CA, Santa Ana
kbrusic@ocregister.com, Ed., Saddleback
Valley News, CA, Santa Ana
kbrusic@ocregister.com, Ed., Orange City
News, CA, Santa Ana
kbrusic@ocregister.com, Ed., San Clemente
Sun Post, CA, Santa Ana
kbrusic@ocregister.com, Ed., Aliso Viejo News,
CA, Santa Ana
kbrusic@ocregister.com, Ed., Yorba Linda Star,
CA, Santa Ana
kbrusic@ocregister.com, Ed., Anaheim
Bulletin, CA, Santa Ana
kbrusic@ocregister.com, Ed., Rancho Canyon
News (OOB), CA, Santa Ana
kbrusic@ocregister.com, Ed., Capistrano Valley
News, CA, Santa Ana
kbrusic@ocregister.com, Ed., Current, CA,
Santa Ana
kbrusic@ocregister.com, Ed., Dana Point
News, CA, Santa Ana
kbrusic@ocregister.com, Ed., Fountain Valley
View, CA, Santa Ana
kbrusic@ocregister.com, Ed., Huntington
Beach Wave, CA, Santa Ana
kbrusic@ocregister.com, Ed., Irvine World
News, CA, Santa Ana
kbrusic@ocregister.com, Ed., Ladera Post
(OOB), CA, Santa Ana
kbrusic@ocregister.com, Ed., Laguna Beach
News Post, CA, Santa Ana
kbrusic@ocregister.com, Ed., Placentia News
Times, CA, Santa Ana
kbrusic@ocregister.com, Ed., Saddleback
Valley News - Mission Viejo, CA, Santa Ana
kbrusic@ocregister.com, Ed., The Tustin News,
CA, Santa Ana

Bruursema, L. Richard
editor@kcparent.com, Pub., Kansas City
Parent, NJ, Mountainside

Bruyns, Rosaline................................ext. 264
rbruyns@bowesnet.com, Sales Mgr., Oxford
Shopping News/review, ON, Woodstock

Bruyns, Rosaline............ (519) 537-2341 ext. 264
Adv. Mgr., Woodstock Sentinel-Review, ON,
Woodstock

Bryan, Harry ....(502) 582-4060
hbryan@courier-journal.com, Sports Ed., The
Courier-Journal, KY, Louisville

Bryan, Kathie
kbryan@keynoter.com, Financial Dir., Florida
Keys Keynoter, FL, Marathon

Bryan, Mark
mbryan@lmtribune.com, Circ. Dir., Northwest
Market, ID, Moscow

Bryan, Scott............................(386) 312-5231
sbryan@palatkadailynews.com, Ed., Palatka
Daily News, FL, Palatka

Bryan, Scott
sbryan@hickoryrecord.com, Editor, The
Hickory Daily Record, NC, Hickory

Bryan, Teresa...................(740) 947-2149 x 104
tbryan@newswatchman.com, Adv. Mgr., The
Pike County News Watchman, OH, Waverly

Bryan, Teresa
tbryan@timesjournal.com, Adv. Dir., The
Jackson County Times-Journal, OH, Jackson

Bryan, Tommy
tbryan@wilsonpost.com, Main Street Media ,
TN, Lebanon

Bryant, Bill
voicenews@inebraska.com, Ed., Voice News,
NE, Hickman

Bryant, Cal ....(252) 322-7207
cal.bryant@r-cnews.com, Ed., Roanoke-
Chowan News-Herald, NC, Ahoskie

Bryant, Cal
cal.bryant@roanoke-chowannewsherald.com,
Ed., The Chowan Herald, NC, Edenton
cal.bryant@roanoke-chowannewsherald.com,
Ed., Gates County Index, NC, Ahoskie

Bryant, Calvin
calvin.bryant@roanoke-chowannewsherald.
com, Ed., The Roanoke-chowan's Shopper
Weekly, NC, Ahoskie

Bryant, Cherie ....(661) 267-4127
cbryant@avpress.com, Vice Pres./Gen. Mgr.,
Antelope Valley Press, CA, Palmdale

Bryant, Cherie ....(661) 267-4127
cbryant@avpress.com, Vice Pres./Gen.
Mgr., Antelope Valley Press Express, CA,
Palmdale

Bryant, Jaime ....(563) 262-0543
adjutant@legionpost500.com, Adv. Mgr., The
Post, IA, Muscatine

Bryant, Jennings
jbryant@ua.edu, Prof./Reagan Chair, Assoc.
Dean, Grad. Studies, University of Alabama,
AL, Tuscaloosa

Bryant, Jim
jbryant@stopandshop.com, Online Mgr.,
Cleveland Daily Banner, TN, Cleveland

Bryant, Jonathan
jonathan.bryant@greenvilleadvocate.com ,
Mng. Ed. , The Greenville Advocate, AL,
Greenville

Bryant, Kevin ....(248) 615-7003 ext. 29
kevin@pridesource.com, Webmaster/IT Mgr.,
Between The Lines, MI, Livonia

Bryant, Kimberly ....ext. 16
kdb@atling.com, Prodn. Mgr., The Atlanta
Inquirer, GA, Atlanta

Bryant, Kristen ....(509) 662-1405
kristenb@targetmediapartners.com, Regional
Manager, Ncw Nickel Ads, WA, Wenatchee
kristenb@targetmediapartners.com, Regional
Manager, Nickel Nik - Spokane, WA,
Spokane
kristenb@targetmediapartners.com, Regional
Manager, Nickel Nik / Buyline - Tri Cities, WA,
Kennewick

Bryant, Matt ....(319) 385-3131
pub@mpnews.net, Publisher, Mt. Pleasant
News, IA, Mount Pleasant

Bryant, Matt ....(205) 780-0558
mbgoat207@gmail.com, Pub., New Hampton
Shopper, IA, New Hampton
mbgoat207@gmail.com, Pub., The Western
Star, AL, Bessemer

Bryant, Matt ....(319) 653-2191
sales@washjrnl.com, Publisher, Washington
County Shoppers Guide, IA, Washington
sales@washjrnl.com, Publisher, The
Washington Evening Journal, IA, Washington

Bryant, Patty ....(219) 326-3844
pbryant@heraldargus.com, Acct. Exec.,
Herald-Argus, IN, La Porte

Bryant, Paul ....(936) 564-8361
pbryant@dailysentinel.com, City Editor, The
Daily Sentinel, TX, Nacogdoches

Bryant, Paula
pbryant@gazettevirginian.com, Ed., The
Gazette-Virginian, VA, South Boston

Bryant, Sharon ....(423) 623-6171
sharon.bryant@newportplaintalk.com,
Advertising, The Newport Plain Talk, TN,
Newport

Bryant, Teri
tbryant@prescottaz.com, Classified Adv. Mgr.,
Chino Valley Review, AZ, Chino Valley

tbryant@prescottaz.com, Classified Coord.,
Prescott Valley Tribune, AZ, Chino Valley

Bryant, Thomas J.
tbryant@jtmchugh.com, Owner/CEO, J.
Thomas McHugh Co., Inc., IN, Fishers

Bryant, Tricia ....(540) 213-9199
tlbryant@newsleader.com, Adv. Mgr., The
News Leader, VA, Staunton

Bryce Young, Jessica
jyoung@orlandoweekly.com, Ed. in Cheif,
Orlando Weekly, FL, Orlando

Bryden, Maureen
mbryden@jcpgroup.com, Oshkosh Buyers
Guide, WI, Oshkosh

Brydon, Lucinda
brydonlm@delhi.edu, SUNY College of
Technology/Delhi, NY, Delhi

Brydson, David ....(212) 586-7773
brydmedia@aol.com, Pres., Brydson Global
Media Sales, NY, New York

Bryl, Annette.........................(307) 672-2431
circulation@thesheridanpress.com, Circ. Mgr.,
The Sheridan Press, WY, Sheridan

Bryson, Keith ....See General
Publisher, News Editor, Lamar Leader, AL,
Sulligent

Bublitz, Alan
print@livent.net, Production Mgr., The
Livingston Enterprise, MT, Livingston

Bublitz, Will
Editor@thelimonleader.com, Ed., The Limon
Leader, CO, Limon
Editor@thelimonleader.com, Ed., Eastern
Colorado Plainsman, CO, Limon

Buboltz, Catherine ....(507) 379-3427
catherine.buboltz@albertleatribune.com, Adv.
Dir., Albert Lea Tribune, MN, Albert Lea

Bucar, Angela.........................(508) 862-1198
abucar@capecodonline.com, Digital Sales
Mgr., Cape Cod Times, MA, Hyannis

Bucey, Tim ....(937) 328-0371
tbucey@coxohio.com, Bus. Ed., Springfield
News-Sun, OH, Springfield

Buch, Janki ....ext. 240
Circ. Mgr., Glastonbury Citizen, CT,
Glastonbury

Buchan, Cliff
editor.forestlaketimes@ecm-inc.com, Ed., St.
Croix Valley Peach, MN, Forest Lake

Buchan, Jim ....ext. 292
jbuchan@wwub.com, Sports Ed., Walla Walla
Union-Bulletin, WA, Walla Walla

Buchanan, Brad ....(573) 474-1000
geotelcorporation@hotmail.com, Pres., Newz
Group, MO, Columbia

Buchanan, Brad
bbuchanan@newzgroup.com, President/CEO,
Missouri Press Clipping Bureau - Newz
Group, MO, Columbia

Buchanan, Chris
chris@brantleyenterprise.com, Editor, The
Brantley Enterprise, GA, Nahunta

Buchanan, Diane ....(905) 727-3300
Adv. Sales, The Auroran, ON, Aurora

Buchanan, Ian
ibuchanan@newzgroup.com, Vice President,
Newz Group, MO, Columbia

Buchanan, Jim ....(401) 789-9744 Ext. 132
jbuchanan@ricentral.com, Art Dir., Kent County
Daily Times, RI, West Warwick

Buchanan, Ken ....(912) 816-2013
publisher@brantleyenterprise.com, Publisher,
The Brantley Enterprise, GA, Nahunta

Buchanan, Margaret
mbuchana@cincinna.gannett.com, Pres./Pub.,
Northwest Press, OH, Cincinnati
mbuchana@cincinna.gannett.com, Pres./Pub.,

Price Hill Press, OH, Cincinnati
mbuchana@cincinna.gannett.com, Pres./Pub.,
Hilltop Press, OH, Cincinnati
mbuchana@cincinna.gannett.com, Pres./Pub.,
Delhi Press, OH, Cincinnati
mbuchana@cincinna.gannett.com, Pres./Pub.,
Community Journal Clermont, OH, Cincinnati
mbuchana@cincinna.gannett.com, Pres./Pub.,
Western Hills Press, OH, Cincinnati
mbuchana@cincinna.gannett.com, Pres./Pub.,
Indian Hill Journal, OH, Loveland
mbuchana@cincinna.gannett.com, Pres./Pub.,
Loveland Herald, OH, Loveland
mbuchana@cincinna.gannett.com, Pres./Pub.,
Tri-County Press, OH, Cincinnati
mbuchana@cincinna.gannett.com, Pres./Pub.,
Northeast Suburban Life, OH, Loveland
mbuchana@cincinna.gannett.com, Pres./Pub.,
Milford-Miami Advertiser, OH, Cincinnati
mbuchana@cincinna.gannett.com, Pres./Pub.,
Bethel Journal, OH, Loveland
mbuchana@cincinna.gannett.com, Pres./Pub.,
Eastern Hills Journal, OH, Cincinnati
mbuchana@cincinna.gannett.com, Pres./Pub.,
Forest Hills Journal, OH, Cincinnati

Buchanan, Ryan............ (620) 694-5700 Ext. 349
rbuchanan@hutchnews.com, Online Ed., The
Hutchinson News, KS, Hutchinson

Buchanan, Scott.........................(573) 474-1000
sbuchanan@newzgroup.com, Vice Pres., Newz
Group, MO, Columbia

Buchanan, Taunya
circulation@advertisergleam.com, Circ. Mgr.,
The Advertiser-Gleam, AL, Guntersville

Buchanan, Tyler
tbuchanan@vintoncourier.com, Ed, The Vinton
County Courier, OH, Mc Arthur

Buchholz, Hans-Herbert
info@uniton.de, Mng. Dir., ELAPLAN Buchholz
GmbH & Co., Schonberg

Buchs, Merrily.........................(978) 961-3148
mbuchs@newburyportnews.com, Night Ed.,
The Daily News, MA, Newburyport

Buck, Maria............................(212) 621-1500
maria.buck@cuny.edu, Associated Press, The,
New York

Buck, Maynard
fps44615@yahoo.com, Pub., The Free Press
Standard, OH, Carrollton

Buck, Robert................ (309) 343-7181 ext. 259
rbuck@register-mail.com , Local News Ed.,
The Register-Mail, IL, Galesburg

Buck, Suzanne
sbuck@central.uh.edu, Clinical Asst. Prof.,
University of Houston, TX, Houston

Buckalew, Mindy.......................(770) 326-8801
mbuckelaw@ajc.com, General Manager,
MundoHispánico Newspaper, GA, Atlanta

Buckhalter, Deborah
dbuckhalter@jcfloridan.com, Reporter, Jackson
County Floridan, FL, Marianna

Buckingham, Lisa.....................(408) 920-5255
lbuckingham@bayareanewsgroup.com, Sr. VP/
CFO, The Mercury News, CA, San Jose

Buckley, Chloe
posttrib@airmail.net, Production Manager,
Dallas Post Tribune, TX, Dallas

Buckley, Dennis
dennis.buckley@lee.net, Ed., Neighborhood
Extra, NE, Lincoln

Buckley, Joshua
jbuckley@moodygardens.org, Sports Ed., The
Galveston County Daily News, TX, Galveston

Buckley, Karen ....(401) 334-9555 ext.127
kbuckley@valleybreeze.com, Adv. Dir., The
Valley Breeze - Cumberland/Lincoln, RI,
Lincoln
kbuckley@valleybreeze.com, Adv. Dir,, The
Valley Breeze & Observer, RI, Lincoln
kbuckley@valleybreeze.com, Adv. Dir., The
North Providence Breeze, RI, Lincoln

kbuckley@valleybreeze.com, Adv. Dir., The Valley Breeze - Woonsocket/North Smithfield, RI, Lincoln

kbuckley@valleybreeze.com, Adv. Dir., The Valley Breeze - Pawtucket, RI, Lincoln

Buckley, Ronnie L.
ronbuckley@bayspringstel.net, Pub., Impact Of Laurel, MS, Meridian

ronbuckley@bayspringstel.net, Pub., Impact Of Hattiesburg, MS, Hattiesburg

Buckley, Ronnie L.
bni@teleclipse.net, Pub., The Jasper County News, MS, Bay Springs

Buckmaster, Mike
mbuckmaster@dailyadvocate.com, News Ed., Weekend Advocate, OH, Greenville

Bucknam, Sandy .... (603) 594-1240
sbucknam@cabinet.com, The Milford Cabinet, NH, Milford

sbucknam@cabinet.com, Managing Ed. , Hollis Brookline Journal, NH, Milford

sbucknam@cabinet.com, Managing Ed. , Bedford Journal, NH, Milford

sbucknam@cabinet.com, Merrimack Journal, NH, Milford

sbucknam@cabinet.com, Wk Ed. & Comm. Ed., The Telegraph, NH, Nashua

Buckner, Dawn .... (586) 826-7310
DBUCKNER@DNPS.COM, Facilities Mgr., Detroit Free Press, MI, Detroit

Buckner, Heather .... (256) 304-0053
hbuckner@times-journal.com, Mang. Ed., Fort Payne Newspapers, Inc., AL, Fort Payne

Bucksbaum, Robert .... (310) 441-7400
robert@reelsource.com, Pres., Exhibitor Relations Co., Los Angeles

Buday, Ken
ken.buday@havenews.com, Ed./Gen. Mgr., The Havelock News, NC, Havelock

Buday, Ken .... (252) 444-1999
kbuday@freedomenc.com, Ed., Windsock, NC, Havelock

Budd, Bernadette S.
LettersCJ25A@aol.com, Ed., Community Journal, NY, Wading River

Budd, James
JJenkins@cninewspapers.com, Pub, The Graham Star, NC, Robbinsville

Budde, Neil .... (502) 582-4295
nbudde@courier-journal.com, Exec. Ed./VP, News, The Courier-Journal, KY, Louisville

Budig, Jennifer .... (212) 597-5896
jennifer.budig@wsj.com, Gen. Adv. , Sales Dir., The Wall Street Journal, NY, New York

Budman, Richard .... (661) 212-1589
richard@easyreadernews.com, Easy Reader, CA, Hermosa Beach

Budner, Marty .... (586) 826-7277
mbudner@hometownlife.com, Sports Ed. , Birmingham Eccentric, MI, Detroit

Budrick, Jerry
editor@calaverasenterprise.com, Ed., Calaveras Enterprise, CA, San Andreas

Budris, William .... ext. 223
bbudris@timesonline.com, Circ. Mgr., Home Delivery, Beaver County Times, PA, Beaver

Budzak, Gary .... (740) 413-0906
Managing Ed., The Sunbury News, OH, Delaware

Buechlein, Daniel Mark
criterion@archindy.org, Pub., The Criterion, IN, Indianapolis

Buechler, Zach .... (605) 823-4490
macnews@westriv.com, Ed.itor, Corson Sioux County News Messe, SD, Mc Laughlin

Buehler, Cheryl
news@thepolkcountynews.com, Pub., Polk County News/Citizen Advance, TN, Benton

Buendo, Christopher
cbuendo@thereminder.com, Pub., Reminder Metrowest / Chicopee Herald, MA, East Longmeadow

cbuendo@thereminder.com, Pub., The Reminder, MA, East Longmeadow

cbuendo@thereminder.com, Pub., Springfield Reminder, MA, East Longmeadow

Buendo, Christopher M.
news@thereminder.com, Pub., The Herald, MA, East Longmeadow

Buendo, Daniel
dbuendo@reminderpublications.com, Co-Pub., Reminder Metrowest / Chicopee Herald, MA, East Longmeadow

dbuendo@reminderpublications.com, Co-Pub., The Reminder, MA, East Longmeadow

dbuendo@reminderpublications.com, Co-Pub., Springfield Reminder, MA, East Longmeadow

Buendo, Daniel J. .... (413) 525-6661
dbuendo@reminderpublications.com, Pub., Prime Times, MA, East Longmeadow

Buenger, Paula
advertising@spencerdailyreporter.com, Pub., The Northwest Iowa Shopper Weekend, IA, Spencer

Buenger, Paula .... (712) 262-6610
pbuenger@spencerdailyreporter.com, Pub., The Daily Reporter, IA, Spencer

Buenger, Paula .... (712) 262-6610
pbuenger@spencerdailyreporter.com, Pub., Storm Lake Pilot Tribune, IA, Storm Lake

Buenker, Todd .... ext. 163
todd.buenker@effinghamdailynews.com, Circ. Mgr., Crossroads Supersaver, IL, Effingham

Buenker, Todd .... (217) 347-7151 ext. 163
todd.buenker@effinghamdailynews.com, Circ. Mgr., Effingham Daily News, IL, Effingham

Buenting, Kim .... (416) 292-5913 ext. 222
buenting@mirror-guardian.com, Circ. Mgr., The East York Mirror, ON, Willowdale

Buese, John .... (618) 239-2135
jbuese@bnd.com, Copy, Belleville News-Democrat, IL, Belleville

Buesing, Tony
tbuesing@mediaspace.com, Dir., Account Development, Mediaspace Solutions, MN, Hopkins

Buffalo, Mark
mbuffalo@cabotstarherald.com, Ed., Carlisle Independent, AR, Carlisle

Buffington, Mike .... (706) 367-5233
mike@mainstreetnews.com, Co-Publisher, Barrow News-journal, GA, Winder

Buffington, Mike .... (706) 367-2255
mike@mainstreetnews.com, Co-Pub., The Jackson Herald, GA, Jefferson

mike@mainstreetnews.com, Co-Pub., The Banks County News, GA, Jefferson

mike@mainstreetnews.com, Co-Pub., The Madison County Journal, GA, Jefferson

Buffington, Mike N. .... (706) 367-5233
scott@mainstreetnews.com, Co. Pub., The Commerce News, GA, Jefferson

Buffington, Scott .... (706) 367-2485
scott@mainstreetnews.com, Co-Pub., The Jackson Herald, GA, Jefferson

Buffington, Scott .... (706) 367-2485
scott@mainstreetnews.com, Co-Pub./Adv. Mgr., The Commerce News, GA, Jefferson

Buffington, Scott .... (706) 367-2485
ads@mainstreetnews.com, Co-Pub./Adv. Mgr., The Banks County News, GA, Jefferson

Buffington, Scott .... (706) 367-2485
ads@mainstreetnews.com, Co-Pub./Adv. Mgr., The Madison County Journal, GA, Jefferson

Buffington, Scott .... (706) 621-5685
scott@mainstreetnews.com, Co-Publisher, Barrow News-journal, GA, Winder

Buffington, Tracy .... (402) 941-1436
fremont.newsroom@lee.net, Exec. Ed., Fremont Tribune, NE, Fremont

Buffman, Stephanie .... (989) 426-9441
sbuffman@thegladwincountyrecord.com, Ed., Gladwin County Record, MI, Gladwin

Bufkin, Janice G.
reveille@bellsouth.net, Adv./Circ. Mgr., The Port Gibson Reveille, MS, Port Gibson

Buford, Floyd
gapost@pstel.net, President, The Georgia Post, GA, Roberta

Bugbee, Tom. .... (302) 741-8245
tbugbee@newszap.com, Printing Plant - Operations Manager, Delaware State News, DE, Dover

Bugge', Michael .... (267) 405-4000 ext. 210
mcb@glunz-jensen.com, VP Sales, Glunz & Jensen, Inc., PA, Quakertown

Buhlmann, Leona
leona.buhlmann@lexch.com, Cir. Mng., People Plus, NE, Lexington

Buhrman, Judy
jbuhrman@yourjournal.com, Suburban Journals of Greater St. Louis, MO, Town and Country

Buhrman, Kathy .... (402) 664-3198
rustlernews@gpcom.net, Reporter, Rustler Sentinel, NE, Scribner

Bui, Quan .... (717) 255-8100
qbui@pnco.com, Production Mgr., The Patriot-News, PA, Mechanicsburg

Buice, Jeff .... ext. 464
Prodn. Mgr., Paulding Neighbor, GA, Marietta

Buie, Dale .... (936) 598-3377
dbuie@lightandchampion.com, Pub., The Light & Champion, TX, Center

Bujese, David .... (860) 281-4747
dbujese@anocoil.com, Pres., Anocoil Corporation, CT, Vernon Rockville

Buker, Deb
editor@perrysburg.com, Ed., Perrysburg Messenger Journal, OH, Perrysburg

Bukovich, Carole .... (970) 328-6656
cbukovich@vaildaily.com, Display Adv. Rep., The Eagle Valley Enterprise, CO, Gypsum

Buksar, Cathy
cathyb@messengerpostmedia.com, Circ. Mgr, Community Shopping Guide - Canandaigua/Victor, NY, Canandaigua

cathyb@messengerpostmedia.com, Circ. Mgr., Lyons Clyde Savannah Shopper, NY, Canandaigua

cathyb@messengerpostmedia.com, Circ. Mgr., Sodus Williamson Pennysaver, NY, Canandaigua

Bukzin, Paul
paul@jewishweek.org, Circ. Mgr., Jewish Week, NY, New York

Bulington, Toni
tonib@intranix.com, Morocco Courier, IN, Kentland

Bulington, Tony
editor@sugardog.com, Adv. Mgr., Indiana Spirit, IN, Kentland

Bullard, Cheri .... (770) 205-8963
cboghos@forsythnews.com, Adv, Account Exec., Forsyth County News, GA, Cumming

Buller, Jon
jbuller@forumcomm.com, Dir. of Finance, Forum Communications Co., ND, Fargo

Bullett, Crystal .... (618) 932-2146
wfclass@dailyamericannews.com, Adv. Mgr., Classified, The Daily American, IL, West Frankfort

Bullette, Crystal
benclass@bentoneveningnews.com, Classified Mgr., Benton Evening News, IL, Benton

Bullington, Tena
tena.bullington@athens.edu, Athens State Univ., AL, Athens

Bullis, Judy
judy.bullis@sunmedia.ca, Senior Group Pub., Niagara Falls Review, ON, Niagara Falls

Bullis, Judy
jbullis@wellandtribune.ca, Senior Group Pub., Welland Tribune, ON, Welland

Bullock, Tammy .... (662) 365-3232
thebaldwynnews@dixie-net.com, Mng. Ed., Baldwyn News, MS, Baldwyn

Bulmer, Ben .... (819) 459-2222
ben@lowdownonline.com, Reporter, The Low Down To Hull And Back News, QC, Wakefield

Bulow, George M. .... (212) 580-5015
george.bulow@verizon.net, Pres., Interactive International, Inc., NY, New York

Bultemeier, Bruce .... (574) 658-4111
bruceb@the-papers.com, Commercial Printing Sales Rep, The Paper - Kosciusko Edition, IN, Milford

Bultena, Kelli .... (605) 647-2284
editor@lennoxnews.com, Co-Pub./Ed, The Lennox Independent, SD, Lennox

Bulwa, Demian
dbulwa@sfchronicle.com, Deputy Metro Ed, San Francisco Chronicle, CA, San Francisco

Bumba, Tracy .... (443) 524-8120
tracy.bumba@thedolancompany.com, Audience Dev. Dir., The Daily Record, MD, Baltimore

Bumgardner, Traci
tracibsales@gmail.com, Adv., The Leesville Daily Leader, LA, Leesville

Bummer, Jenny
journalads@crosbynd.com , Prod. , The Journal, ND, Crosby

Bump, Debbie
circulation@thedailyreview.com, Circulation Supervisor, The Daily Review, PA, Towanda

Bumpas, Gena .... (901) 853-2241
gbumpas@colliervilleherald.net, Office Manager, The Collierville Herald, TN, Collierville

Bunch, Beth
beth@hubcityspokes.com, Mng. Ed., The Lamar Times, MS, Hattiesburg

beth@hubcityspokes.com, Mng Ed., The Hattiesburg Post, MS, Hattiesburg

beth@hubcityspokes.com, Mng. Ed., The Petal News, MS, Hattiesburg

Bunch, Jeff .... (740) 592-6612 Ext. 209
jbunch@athensmessenger.com, Adv. Dir. , The Athens Messenger, OH, Athens

Buncher, Alan
ecledger@ellwoodcityledger.com, Pub., This Week, PA, Ellwood City

Bunde, Deb
dbunde@hastingstribune.com, Director of Marketing, Hastings Tribune, NE, Hastings

Bundy, Dave
dbundy@journalstar.com, Ed., Lincoln Journal Star, NE, Lincoln

Bundy, Deb
dbundy@skagitpublishing.com, Adv. Mgr., Display, Skagit Valley Herald, WA, Mount Vernon

Bundy, Sam .... (843) 317-7274
sbundy@florencenews.com, Sports Ed., Morning News, SC, Florence

Bunk, Matt .... (406) 293-4124
mbunk@thewesternnews.com, Publisher, The Western News, MT, Libby

Bunker, Matthew
mbunker@ua.edu, Phifer Prof., University of Alabama, AL, Tuscaloosa

Bunn, John R. .... (863) 647-1555
jbunn@bunntyco.com, Pres., B.H. Bunn Co.,

FL, Lakeland

Bunner, John D.
photostarnews@frontier.com, Co-Pub./Ed., Willshire Photo Star, OH, Willshire

Bunner, Judith
photostarnews@frontier.com, Pub./Ed., Willshire Photo Star, OH, Willshire

Bunt, Tiffany .... (205) 665-6231
bunttr@forum.montevallo.edu, Adviser, Univ. of Montevallo, AL, Montevallo

Bunten, Cindy
cindy.bunten@nonpareilonline.com, Adv. Mgr., Retail, The Daily Nonpareil, IA, Council Bluffs

Buntin, Margaret .... (662) 563-4591
margaretb@panolian.com, Advt Mgr, Graphic Designer, The Panolian, MS, Batesville

Bunyan, Clytie .... (405) 475-3311
cbunyan@opubco.com, Bus. Ed., The Oklahoman, OK, Oklahoma City

Bunzel, Tom .... (310) 286-0969
tombunzel@gmail.com, Pres., The Presentation Professor, CA, Los Angeles

Bur, Christy .... (231) 439-9329
cbur@petoskeynews.com, Adv. Mgr., Northern Michigan Review, MI, Petoskey

Burbach, Mike .... (651) 228-5544
mburbach@pioneerpress.com, Ed., St. Paul Pioneer Press, MN, Saint Paul

Burbidge, Sara .... (760) 744-1150 ext. 2450
Palomar College, CA, San Marcos

Burch, Ann .... (269) 782-1457
aburch@swmich.edu, Advisor, Southwestern Michigan College, MI, Dowagiac

Burch, Cathalena
cburch@tucson.com, Instr., University of Arizona, AZ, Tucson

Burch, Dillon
dburch@newsexaminer.com, Ad account texecutive, Connersville News-Examiner, IN, Connersville

Burch, Kerry
servicer3d@emphasys-software.com, Pres., Emphasys Software, CA, Poway

Burch, Teddy
tburch2@uco.edu, The Vista, OK, Edmond

Burcham, Jennifer .... (513) 483-5240
Jennifer.Burcham@coxinc.com, Editor, Today's Pulse, OH, Liberty Township
Jennifer.Burcham@coxinc.com, Editor, The Oxford Press, OH, Liberty Township

Burcham, Lucy
lburcham@logandaily.com, Bus. Mgr., Logan Daily News, OH, Logan

Burck, David
dburck@herald-zeitung.com, Adv. Dir., New Braunfels Herald-Zeitung, TX, New Braunfels

Burda, James
jburda@star-telegram.com, Majors/Nat'l Sales Dir., Fort Worth Star-Telegram, TX, Fort Worth

Burda, Jan .... (231) 933-1427
jburda@record-eagle.com, Single Copy Mgr., Traverse City Record-Eagle, MI, Traverse City

Burden, Ernesto
eburden@nnenews.com, VP/Digital, Newspapers of New England, NH, Concord

Burdett, Bruce
bburdett@eastbaynewspapers.com, Ed., Sakonnet Times, RI, Bristol

Burdett, Bruce
shorelines@eastbaynewspapers.com, Ed., Westport Shorelines, RI, Bristol

Burdette, Matthew .... (304) 636-2121 ext 120
mburdette@theintermountain.com, Exec. Ed., The Inter-Mountain, WV, Elkins

Burdorf, Jamie .... (641) 483-2120
midiaenterprise@partnercom.net, Ed., State

Center Mid Iowa Enterprise, IA, State Center

Burford, Brendan .... (212) 969-7575
bburford@hearst.com, Gen. Mgr., Syndication, North America Syndicate, New York
bburford@hearst.com, Gen. Mgr., Syndication, King Features Syndicate, NY, New York

Burford, Tom .... (218) 694-6265
farmpubads@gvtel.com, Ed.
, Farmers Independent, MN, Bagley

Burgamy, Debbie .... (770) 867-7557 ext. 223
debbie@barrowcountynews.com, Pub., Barrow News-journal, GA, Winder
debbie@barrowcountynews.com, Barrow County News, GA, Hinesville

Burgar, Mary
maryb@cablecomet.com, Pub, Lakeside Leader, AB, Slave Lake

Burgar, Mary
publisher@smokyriverexpress.com, Circ. Mgr., Smoky River Express, AB, Falher

Burgar, Mary
maryb@cablecomet.com, Pub., South Peace News, AB, High Prairie

Burgard, Allen .... (920) 453-5108
Transportation Supvr., The Sheboygan Press, WI, Sheboygan

Burgason, Verle .... (515) 232-2161 ext. 440
vburgason@amestrib.com, Chrmn., Iowa Newspapers, Inc., IA, Ames

Burge, Terry .... (713) 686-8494
publisher@leader-news.com, Pub., The Leader, TX, Houston

Burgen , Alice
classifieds@kystandard.com , Class Advt Mgr, Kentucky Standard, KY, Bardstown

Burger, Allison
aburger@edmondsun.com, Sales , The Edmond Sun, OK, Edmond

Burger, Anna
anna.burger@seiu.org, Sec./Treasurer, Service Employees International Union, CLC, DC, Washington

Burger, Brenda
bburger@cherokeeherald.com, Classified/ Legal, Cherokee County Herald, AL, Centre
bburger@cherokeeherald.com, VP. Adv., Chattooga Press (OOB), GA, Rome
bburger@cherokeeherald.com, VP, Ops., Walker County Messenger, GA, La Fayette
bburger@cherokeeherald.com, VP, Ops., The Polk County Standard Journal, GA, Cedartown
bburger@cherokeeherald.com, VP, Ops., Catoosa County News, GA, Ringgold

Burger, Jennifer .... (661) 654-6341
jburger1@csub.edu, Lecturer and Adviser to the Runner Student Media Center, California State University, Bakersfield, CA, Bakersfield

Burger, Mark .... (321) 283-5267
mburger@intersectmediasolutions.com, CFO, Intersect Media Solutions, FL, Lake Mary

Burger, Tom
Salestom@Lcom.net, GM/Adv. Mgr., West Liberty Index, IA, West Liberty
Salestom@Lcom.net, Adv. Mgr., West Branch Times, IA, West Branch

Burgess, Bill
bburgess.eph@lnpnews.com, Pres./Pub., The Ephrata Review, PA, Ephrata
bburgess.eph@lnpnews.com, President and publisher, Lancaster Farming, PA, Ephrata

Burgess, Carol .... (575) 437-7120 ext. 7102
cburgess@alamogordonews.com, GM, Alamogordo Daily News, NM, Alamogordo

Burgess, David
dburgess@vinitanews.com, Mng. Ed., The Vinita Daily Journal, OK, Vinita

Burgess, Dennis
djburgess@burgessind.com, Pres./CEO, Burgess Industries, Inc., MN, Brooklyn Park

Burgess, Landra .... (321) 242-3920
lburgess@floridatoday.com, Controller, Florida Today, FL, Melbourne

Burgess, Robert
lynnfieldvillager@rcn.com, Ed., The Lynnfield Villager, MA, Wakefield
lynnfieldvillager@rcn.com, Asst. Ed., Wakefield Daily Item, MA, Wakefield

Burgess, Robert ....(765) 459-3121 Ex. 8577
rob.burgess@kokomotribune.com, City Ed., Kokomo Tribune, IN, Kokomo

Burghardt, Joanne
jburghardt@durhamregion.com, Ed., Ajax-pickering News Advertiser, ON, Oshawa

Burghardt, Joanne
jburghardt@durhamregion.com, Ed. in Chief, Oshawa-whitby This Week, ON, Oshawa

Burghardt, Joanne
jhuffman@northumberlandnews.com, Ed. in Chief, Northumberland News, ON, Cobourg

Burghardt, Joanne
jburghardt@durhamregion.com, Ed. in Chief, Clarington This Week, ON, Oshawa

Burgin, Keith
kburgin@okpress.com, Digital Clipping Service Manager, Oklahoma Press Association, OK, Oklahoma City

Burk, CJ
cj@wnpa.com, Assistant Director, Washington Newspaper Publishers Association, Inc., WA, Port Townsend

Burk, Dan .... (520) 881-8101
Dir., Mktg., JupiterImages, AZ, Tucson

Burke, Allan C.
info@lintonnd.com, Pub. Emeritus, Emmons County Record, ND, Linton

Burke, Andrew
aburke0503@westfield.ma.edu, Editor-in-Chief, Westfield State University, MA, Westfield

Burke, Dale
dburke@hpu.edu, Instr., Hawaii Pacific University, HI, Honolulu

Burke, Daniel .... (202) 463-8777
daniel.burke@religionnews.com, Associate Editor, Religion News Service, Washington

Burke, Dyana .... (407) 420-5272
dburke@orlandosentinel.com, Compensation/ Commun. Mgr., Orlando Sentinel, FL, Orlando

Burke, Howard .... (763) 712-2409
howie.burke@ecm-inc.com, Online Servs. Dir., Anoka County Shopper, MN, Coon Rapids

Burke, Jeremy .... (530) 852-0200
CEO, Auburn Trader, CA, Auburn

Burke, Jeremy
publisher@southcountynewspapers.com, Pub., The Rustler, CA, King City

Burke, Judy .... (802) 748-8121
burkej@caledonian-record.com, Bookkeeper, The Caledonian-Record, VT, Saint Johnsbury

Burke, Laura
lburke@shawmedia.com, Adv. Dir., Addison Suburban Life, IL, Downers Grove

Burke, Leah
leah@lintonnd.com, NDNA Director, North Dakota Newspaper Association, ND, Bismarck

Burke, Leah P. .... (605) 889-2320
ppioner@valleytel.net, Pub., Prairie Pioneer, SD, Pollock

Burke, Leah P.
info@lintonnd.com, Publisher/Editor, Emmons County Record, ND, Linton

Burke, M.W. (Maury)
mwburke@aol.com, Pres./Chrmn., M.W. Burke & Associates, Inc., CA, Danville

Burke, Mike ....(301) 722-4600 ext. 2241

mburke@times-news.com, Sports Ed., The Cumberland Times-News, MD, Cumberland

Burke, Ron .... (202) 888-6835
rburke@washingtoninformer.com, Director of Advertising, Washington Informer, DC, Washington

Burke, Sean
newsroom@mpgnews.com, Pub., Marshfield Mariner, MA, Marshfield

Burke, Sean .... (508) 676-2524
sburke@heraldnews.com, Pub., Real Estate Guide, MA, Fall River

Burke, Sean .... (781) 433-6720
sburke@wickedlocal.com, President, Group Publisher, Sudbury Town Crier, MA, Framingham
sburke@wickedlocal.com, Publisher and Group President, The Patriot Ledger, MA, Quincy

Burke, Sharon .... (910) 276-2311 ext 18
sburke@civitasmedia.com, Circ. Mgr., The Laurinburg Exchange, NC, Laurinburg

Burke, Tim
tburke@pbpost.com, Pub., Palm Beach Newspapers, Inc., FL, West Palm Beach
tburke@pbpost.com, Pres., Palm Beach Daily News, FL, Palm Beach

Burke, Tom .... (817) 741-5284
tcburke@us.ibm.com, IBM Corp., NY, Armonk

Burke, Vince
camcanadian.editor@sunmedia.ca, Editor(online), The Camrose Canadian, AB, Camrose

Burke , Sean .... (802) 774-3010
sean.burke@rutlandherald.com, Adv. Exec., Times Argus Extra, VT, Barre

Burker, Renee
r.burke@22ndcenturymedia.com, Nat. Sales Dir., The Winnetka Current, IL, Northbrook
r.burke@22ndcenturymedia.com, Nat. Sales Dir., The Lake Forest Leader, IL, Northbrook
r.burke@22ndcenturymedia.com, Nat. Sales Dir., The Glencoe Anchor, IL, Northbrook
r.burke@22ndcenturymedia.com, Nat. Sales Dir., The Highland Park Landmark, IL, Northbrook

Burkert, Becky .... (269) 637-1104
bburkert@southhaventribune.com, Ed./Gen. Mgr., South Haven Tribune, MI, South Haven

Burket, Dave
publisher@thevoiceofpelham.ca, Pub., Fonthill Voice Of Pelham, ON, Fonthill

Burkett, Ken .... (419) 724-6233
kburkett@toledoblade.com, PrePress Mgr, The Blade, OH, Toledo

Burkett, Kevin .... (574) 732-5155
kevin.burkett@pharostribune.com, Editor, Pharos-Tribune, IN, Logansport

Burkhardt, Charles
charlesb@firstcapitalfcu.com, Data Processing Mgr., The York Dispatch, PA, York

Burkhart, Libby .... (563) 588-5719
lburkhart@wcinet.com, Business Manager, Telegraph Herald, IA, Dubuque

Burkhart-Fisher, Valerie
circulation@mtvernonlisbonsun.com, Circ. Mgr., The Sunlight, IA, Mount Vernon

Burkholder, Mike
editor@theeveningleader.com, Mng. Ed. , The Evening Leader, OH, Saint Marys

Burkman, Sarah .... (571) 366-1018
sarah.burkman@naa.org, VP of HRO, News Media Alliance, VA, Arlington

Burks, Jimmy
jburks@crossville-chronicle.com, Prodn. Mgr., Crossville Chronicle, TN, Crossville

Burks, John
jburks@sfsu.edu, Prof., San Francisco State University, CA, San Francisco

Burleigh, Dawn......................(409) 883-3571
news@orangeleader.com, Ed, The Orange
Leader, TX, Orange

Burleson, Barry
bburleson@southreporter.com, Ed., South
Reporter, MS, Holly Springs

Burleson, Cassy
cassy_burleson@baylor.edu, Instr., Baylor
University, TX, Waco

Burleson, Erica............(314) 961-2660 ext. 7523
review@webster.edu, Asst. Gen. Mgr., St. Louis
Journalism Review, MO, Saint Louis

Burleson, John
john@akronlegalnews.com, Pres., Daily Legal
News, OH, Youngstown

Burlew, Angie.................(814) 665-8291 Ext. 15
aburlew@thecorryjournal.com, Corry Journal,
PA, Corry

Burlison, David
dburlison@thevalleychronicle.com, Sales &
Adv, The Valley Chronicle, CA, Hemet

Burman, Rick
rburman@adirondackguide.com, Pressroom
Foreman, Adirondack Daily Enterprise, NY,
Saranac Lake

Burmeister, Tim
riverpress@live.com, Ed., The River Press, MT,
Fort Benton

Burn, Nicole
Nicole.burn@sungard.com, Vice Pres., Mktg.,
SunGard, PA, Wayne

Burner, Kim
kburner@lmtribune.com, Adv. Mgr., Lewiston
Morning Tribune, ID, Lewiston

Burnett, Dan..........................(570) 991-6114
dburnett@timesleader.com, News Editor,
Times Leader, PA, Wilkes Barre

Burnett, Dave.........................(416) 774-2230
dbarnett@insidetoronto.com, Dir., Prodn., The
Scarborough Mirror, ON, Toronto

Burnett, Gillian......................(604) 605-2158
gburnett@vancouversun.com, The Vancouver
Sun, BC, Vancouver

Burnett, Kathy
kburnett@therepublic.com, Adv. Ops. Mgr., The
Republic, IN, Columbus

Burnett, Mark
mburnett@apdi.net, Pres./CEO, APDI-
Application Programming & Development,
Inc., MD, Waldorf

Burnett, Wanda English
wburnett@ripleynews.com, Ed., Spotlight-
advertiser, IN, Versailles

Burnette, Joseph
Springhopeads@embarqmail.com, Circ. Mgr.,
Spring Hope Enterprise & The Bailey News,
NC, Spring Hope

Burney, Bobby
sportsed@ssecho.com, Sports Ed., Sulphur
Springs News-Telegram, TX, Sulphur Springs

Burney, Butch
butchb@ssecho.com, Gen. Mgr., Sulphur
Springs News-Telegram, TX, Sulphur Springs

Burney, Kenneth.....................(248) 641-9944
Sports Ed., Nordamerikaniche Wochenpost,
MI, Troy

Burney, Pam.................(478) 272 - 5522 ext. 235
advertising@courier-herald.com, Adv. Dir., The
Courier Herald, GA, Dublin

Burney, Wayne
advertising@snyderdailynews.com, Adv. Dir.,
Snyder Daily News, TX, Snyder

Burnham, Kevin...........(207) 633-4620, ext. 112
kevinburnham@boothbayregister.com, Ed.,
Wiscasset Newspaper, ME, Boothbay Harbor

Burnham, Kevin G.........(207) 633-4620, ext. 112
kevinburnham@boothbayregister.com, Editor,

Boothbay Register, ME, Boothbay Harbor

Burnham, Lola
laburnham@eiu.edu, Eastern Illinois Univ., IL,
Charleston

Burnham, Michael.....................(413) 746-1135
mburnham@masslive.com, Sales Mgr., The
Republican, MA, Springfield

Burnham Rousseau, Robyn (207) 282-1535 ext. 329
rburnham@journaltribune.com, City Ed.,
Journal-Tribune, ME, Biddeford

Burns, Bobby.........................(252) 329-9572
baburns@reflector.com, Exec. Ed., The Daily
Reflector, NC, Greenville

Burns, Bobby.........................(252) 329-9572
baburns@reflector.com, Editor, Cooke
Communications North Carolina, LLC, NC,
Greenville

Burns, Brenda.............(937) 652-1331 Ext. 1771
bburns@civitasmedia.com, Ed., Urbana Daily
Citizen, OH, Urbana

Burns, Brian...........................(813) 259-7711
bburns@tampatrib.com, Pub., Plant City
Courier & Tribune, FL, Tampa
bburns@tampatrib.com, Tampa Bay Times, FL,
St Petersburg

Burns, Christopher
cburns@bangordailynews.com, Copy Ed.,
Bangor Daily News, ME, Bangor

Burns, Dennis..............(763) 488-9910 ext. 101
dburns@innotek-ep.com, CEO President,
Innotek Corporation, MN, Maple Grove

Burns, Eddie...........................(512) 445-3552
eburns@statesman.com, Vice Pres./CFO,
Austin American-Statesman, TX, Austin

Burns, Howard
howard.burns@sunmedia.ca, News Ed., The
London Free Press, ON, London

Burns, Howard
hburns@bizjournals.com, Ed., Pittsburgh
Business Times, PA, Pittsburgh

Burns, John............................(707) 933-2711
john.burns@sonomanews.com, Pub., The
Sonoma Index-Tribune, CA, Sonoma

Burns, John............................(707) 776-8450
john.burns@arguscourier.com, Pub., Petaluma
Argus-Courier, CA, Petaluma

Burns, Judith M.
jburns@indexjournal.com, CEO/Pres./Pub.,
The Index-Journal, SC, Greenwood

Burns, Kelli
kburns@usf.edu, Asst. Prof., University of
South Florida, FL, Tampa

Burns, Lisa
lisa.burns@quinnipiac.edu, Asst. Prof.,
Quinnipiac University, CT, Hamden

Burns, Marcia.........................(573) 364-2468
mburns@therolladailynews.com, Adv. Dir.,
Rolla Daily News, MO, Rolla

Burns, Marcia.........................(800) 969-4464
ekrywucki@ingnews.com, Adv. Mgr., Newtown
Advance, PA, Lansdale

Burns, Mary
spiritofjefferson@gmail.com, Adv. Mgr., Spirit of
Jefferson, WV, Charles Town

Burns, Michael.......................(608) 791-8285
mike.burns@lee.net, Group Publisher, La
Crosse Tribune, WI, La Crosse

Burns, Mike
mike.burns@lee.net, Pub., The Dunn County
News, WI, Chippewa Falls

Burns, Mike...........................(503) 221-8563
mburns@oregonian.com, VP, Mktg., Beaverton
Leader, OR, Beaverton
mburns@oregonian.com, Chief Revenue
Officer, The Oregonian, OR, Portland

Burns, Mike
rusty.cunningham@lee.net, Group Publisher,

Winona Daily News, MN, Winona

Burns, Rick
rburns@delgazette.com, Asst. Mgr., The
Sunbury News, OH, Delaware

Burns, Roxanne
roxanne@indyschild.com, Circ. Mgr., Indy's
Child, IN, Indianapolis

Burns, Sarah..........................(702) 259-2330
sales@hintonvoice.ca, Mktg. Specialist, The
Hinton Voice, AB, Hinton

Burns, Shannon...................................(775)
842-6933
sburns@rgj.com, Assoc. Sales Mgr, Mason
Valley News/The Leader-Courier, NV,
Yerington

Burns, Tom
t.burns@carrollspaper.com, Adv. Mgr., Times
Herald Advertiser, IA, Carroll

Burns, Tony
sports@eldodradonews.com, Sports Ed., El
Dorado News-Times / Sunday News, AR,
El Dorado

Burns, Wes
wburns@timesrepublican.com, Copy Ed.,
Times-Republican, IA, Marshalltown

Burr, Brenda
publisher@aransaspassprogress.com, Pub./
Ed., The Ingleside Index, TX, Aransas Pass

Burr, Brenda
publisher@aransaspassprogress.com, Pub./
Ed./Adv. Dir., Aransas Pass Progress, TX,
Aransas Pass

Burr, Grant
gburr@thecarillon.com, Ed, The Carillon, MB,
Steinbach

Burress, Chuck.......................(276) 236-5178
news@galaxgazette.com, Pub., Gazette Plus,
VA, Galax

Burress, Chuck
news@galaxgazette.com, Pub., Galax Gazette,
VA, Galax

Burress, Dana........................(217) 477-5115
Adv., Commercial News, IL, Danville

Burris, Jeanne
jeanne.burris.braziltimes@gmail.com, Gen.
Mgr., The Brazil Times, IN, Brazil

Burriss, Andy..............(803) 329-4000 ext. 8380
aburriss@heraldonline.com, Photo Ed., The
Herald, SC, Rock Hill

Burrough, Rick
rburrough@viewnewspapers.net, Owner,
Grand Blanc View, MI, Davison

Burroughs, Park......................(724) 222-2200
pburroughs@observer-reporter.com, Mng. Ed.,
Observer-Reporter, PA, Washington

Burrows, Kenda......................(309) 757-4990
burrows@qconline.com, Editorial Page Ed.,
The Dispatch-Argus, IL, Moline

Burrows, Shannon
sburrows@metroland.com, Ed, Arthur
Enterprise News, ON, Mount Forest
sburrows@metroland.com, Ed, Minto Express, ON,
Palmerston

Burrows , Shannon.........(519) 291-1660 ext. 109
sburrows@metroland.com, Ed., The Fergus-
elora News Express, ON, Fergus

Burrus, Bill.........................(662) 581-7237
bburrus@gwcommonwealth.com, Sports
Ed., The Greenwood Commonwealth, MS,
Greenwood

Burse, Cathy
cburse@thespec.com, Circ. Mgr., Home
Delivery, The Hamilton Spectator, ON,
Hamilton

Burson, Paula
pburson@wehco.com, Business Office Mgr.,
El Dorado News-Times / Sunday News, AR,
El Dorado

Burstiner, Marcy
marcy.burstiner@humboldt.edu, Humboldt
State Univ., CA, Arcata

Burstiner, Marcy......................(707) 826-5935
marcy.burstiner@humboldt.edu, Asst. Prof.,
Humboldt State University, CA, Arcata

Burt, Bill..............................(978) 946-2227
bburt@eagletribune.com, Exec. Sports Ed.,
The Eagle-Tribune, MA, North Andover

Burt, Dan
ad@templecitystar.net, Office Mgr., Temple
City Star, AB, Cardston

Burt, Jim
info@burtmountain.com, Founder/Pres., Burt
Technologies, Inc., CO, Evergreen

Burt, Rich
richburt@burtmountain.com, CEO, Burt
Technologies, Inc., CO, Evergreen

Burtch, Jessica
jburtch@creators.com, Editor, Creators,
Hermosa Beach

Burtchaell, Carolyn
carolyn65@windstream.net, Bus. Mgr., Clinch
County News, GA, Homerville

Burtis, Robin
rburtis@gatehousemedia.com, Gen. Mgr.,
Neosho Daily News, MO, Neosho

Burton, April
advertising@adairprogress.com, Advt, Adair
Progress, KY, Columbia

Burton, Bobby
bobby@dailydata.com, Gen. Mgr., The Daily
Record, AR, Little Rock

Burton, Bonita........................(352) 753-1119
bonita.burton@thevillagesmedia.com, Vice
President for Editorial Operations, The
Villages Daily Sun, FL, The Villages
bonita.burton@thevillagesmedia.com, Assoc.
Mng. Ed., Photo/Design/Visuals, Orlando
Sentinel, FL, Orlando

Burton, Brian.........................(660) 747-8123
Advertising Director, The Daily Star-Journal,
MO, Warrensburg

Burton, Bruce.........................(530) 406-6236
bburton@dailydemocrat.com, Sports Ed., The
Daily Democrat, CA, Woodland

Burton, Darlene......................(951) 737-9784
SentinelWeekly@aol.com, Gen. Mgr., Perris
Progress, CA, Perris

Burton, David.........................(785) 832-7231
dburton@ljworld.com, Lawrence Journal-
World, KS, Lawrence

Burton, Gary
Gary_Burton@tamu-commerce.edu, Assoc.
Prof., Texas A&M University-Commerce, TX,
Commerce

Burton, Greg.........................(760) 778-4599
Greg.Burton@thedesertsun.com, Exec. Ed.,
The Desert Sun, CA, Palm Springs

Burton, Janice
editor@upandcomingweekly.com, Associate
Pub., Up & Coming Weekly, NC, Fayetteville

Burton, Josh.................(918) 272-1155 ext 402
news@tulsaworld.com, Ed, Collinsville News,
OK, Tulsa

Burton, Kathryn
kburton@thealpenanews.com, Business Office
Mgr., The Alpena News, MI, Alpena

Burton, Lucy
lburton@bnd.com, Belleville News-Democrat,
IL, Belleville

Burton, Mandy........................(307) 266-0526
mandy.burton@trib.com, Ed, Casper Star-
Tribune, WY, Casper

Burton, Michelle......................(785) 823-3209
michelle@buyersguide4u.com, Gen Mgr,
Country Roads (OOB) , KS, Salina
michelle@buyersguide4u.com, General

Manager, Buyer's Guide, KS, Salina

Burton, Rustan
rustan.burton@morris.com, Pub., Columbia
Daily Tribune, MO, Columbia

Burton, Sharon
snburton@duo-county.com, Pub./Ed., Adair
County Community Voice, KY, Columbia

Burton, Sue .... (785) 562-2317
sburton@marysvilleonline.net, Classified ad
sales, Marysville Advocate, KS, Marysville

Bury, Mary
bookkeeper@machiasnews.com, Bus. Mgr.,
Machias Valley News Observer, ME, Machias

Buryk, Alexis .... (212) 556-4104
Adv. Sr. Vice Pres., The New York Times, NY,
New York

Busby, Christy .... ext. 7236
cbusby@texarkanagazette.com, City Ed.,
Texarkana Gazette, AR, Texarkana

Buscaglia, Marco .... (312) 222-5964
mbuscaglia@tribune.com, Gen. Mgr., TMS
Specialty Products, IL, Chicago

Busch, Cassandra
cassandra.busch@loras.edu, Co-Exec. Ed.,
Loras College, IA, Dubuque

Buschmann, Bill
bill.buschmann@Greensboro.com, National
Adv. Dir, News & Record, NC, Greensboro

Buschmann, Bill .... (336) 373-7116
wbuschmann@wsjournal.com, Major &
National Manager, Winston-Salem Journal,
NC, Winston Salem

Buse, Dean .... (308) 233-9749
Audiotex Mgr., Kearney Hub, NE, Kearney

Bush, Adam .... (412) 263-1384
abush@post-gazette.com, Director of
Advertising & Digital Initiatives, Pittsburgh
Post-Gazette, PA, Clinton

Bush, Ann .... (303) 715-3121
dcrads@archden.org, Adv. Mgr., El Pueblo
Catolico, CO, Denver

Bush, Clara .... (574) 296-5920
cbush@elkharttruth.com, Copy Ed., Elkhart
Truth, IN, Elkhart

Bush, Dale A. .... (231) 722-3784
Pub., Buyers' Guide, MI, Muskegon

Bush, Jerry .... (865) 974-5178
beaconads@utk.edu, Dir. of Student Media,
UT Daily Beacon (University of Tennessee),
TN, Knoxville

Bush, Jerry ....ext. 229
deadvert@siu.edu, Southern Illinois Univ., IL,
Carbondale

Bush, Kent .... (405) 214-3921
kent.bush@news-star.com, Pub., Shawnee
News-Star, OK, Shawnee

Bush, Lee
lbush3@elon.edu, Asst. Prof., Elon University,
NC, Elon

Bush, Linda .... (620) 231-2600 ext. 100
lbush@morningsun.net, Classified Adv. Mgr.,
The Morning Sun, KS, Pittsburg

Bush, Lori .... (270) 831-8319
lbush@thegleaner.com, Circ. Mgr., The
Gleaner, KY, Henderson

Bush, Raymond .... (314) 935-4240
Ray.Bush@WUStL.edu, General Manager,
Washington Univ., MO, Saint Louis

Bush, Robert. .... (323) 633-07310
admogul@gmail.com, Sr. VP Sales
&Marketing, Wave Community Newspaper,
CA, Los Angeles

Bush, Sharmia
ads@thesentinel.com, Montgomery County
Sentinel, MD, Rockville

Bush, Terry .... (613) 966-2034 ext.510
tbush@theemc.ca, Mng. Ed., Campbellford/

northwest News Emc, ON, Belleville
tbush@theemc.ca, Mng. Ed., Stirling/northeast
News Emc, ON, Belleville

Bush, Toebe
tbush@newsmirror.net, Pub./VP, Yucaipa &
Calimesa News-Mirror, CA, Yucaipa

Bush, Toebe .... (909) 797-9101
tbush@centurygroup.com, President / CEO
/ Pub., Century Group Newspapers, CA,
Yucaipa

Bush-Reeves, Lillie M.
optic@mt-vernon.com, Ed., Mount Vernon
Optic-Herald, TX, Mount Vernon

Bushart, Julie .... (989) 774-6682
advertising@cm-life.com, Advertising Manager,
2013-2014, Central Michigan University, MI,
Mount Pleasant

Bushey, Edward
edward.bushey@newsday.com, Co-Pub. ,
amNew York, NY, New York
edward.bushey@newsday.com, Co-Pub.,
Newsday, NY, Melville

Bushey, Pat .... (541) 885-4479
pbushey@heraldandnews.com, Opinion Ed.,
Herald and News, OR, Klamath Falls

Bushman, Ed .... (815) 284-2224 Ext. 230
ebushman@saukvalley.com, Gen. Mgr., The
Telegraph, IL, Dixon

Bushnell, Michael
mbushnell@northeastnews.net, Pub./Adv. , The
Northeast News, MO, Kansas City

Bushorn, Chrystal ....(812) 663-3111 x7406
chrystal.bushorn@greensburgdailynews.com,
Acc. Exec. , Greensburg Daily News, IN,
Greensburg

Busing, JoAnne
jbusing@akronnewsreporter.com, Ed., Akron
News-Reporter, CO, Akron

Busis, Jim .... (412) 228-4690
jimb@thejewishchronicle.net, Interim CEO, The
Jewish Chronicle, PA, Pittsburgh

Busker, Cathy
cathyb@messengerpostmedia.com, Cir. Mgr.,
Daily Messenger, NY, Canandaigua

Buskirk, Eric
ebuskirk@verican.com, Pub., The Valley
Chronicle, CA, Hemet

Buss, Mark
news@clipper.mb.ca, Editor, The Clipper
Weekly & Lac Du Bonnet Clipper, MB,
Beausejour

Bussard, Pat .... (540) 964-2555
Southwest Virginia Cmty. College, VA,
Richlands

Busse, Richard .... ext. 6449
rbusse@jewishomaha.org, Mng. Ed., Jewish
Press, NE, Omaha

Busselle, Rick
busselle@wsu.edu, Assoc. Prof., Washington
State University, WA, Pullman

Bussey, Bill .... (864) 260-1240
bussey@independentmail.com, IT Mgr.,
Anderson Independent-Mail, SC, Anderson

Bussler, Rick
bptimes@frontiernet.net, Pub., Prairie Times,
MN, Blooming Prairie

Bustillos, Rodolfo. .... (214) 357-2186 ext. 205
Marketing Mgr, El Hispano News, TX, Dallas

Bustos, Aida .... (858) 490-8374
abustos@sdcatholic.org, Staff Writer (Spanish),
The Southern Cross, CA, San Diego

Bustos, Joseph .... (618) 239-2451
jbustos@bnd.com, Copy Editor, Belleville
News-Democrat, IL, Belleville

Butani, Kavita .... (757) 683-4773
advertising@maceandcrown.com, Advertising
& Business Manager, Old Dominion
University, VA, Norfolk

Butcher, Ashley. .... (386) 754-0417
Advertising Director, Lake City Reporter, FL,
Lake City

Butcher, Ashley. .... (828) 488-2189
publisher@thesmokymountaintimes.com,
Publisher, The Smoky Mountain Times, NC,
Bryson City

Butcher, Jim
editor@cj.kscoxmail.com, Coffeyville Journal,
KS, Coffeyville

Butcher, Steven .... (509) 525-3300
stevenbutcher@wwub.com, HR Mgr, Walla
Walla Union-Bulletin, WA, Walla Walla

Butcher, Stu
stu@chanute.com, Exec. Ed., The Chanute
Tribune, KS, Chanute

Buteux, Pat
info@fourpalms.com, Pres., Four Palms, Inc.,
VA, Reston

Buth, Keith .... (203) 876-3020
kbuth@journalregister.com, Adv. Dir., Elm City
Newspapers, CT, Milford

Butler, Al
sports@cortlandstandard.net, Sports Ed.,
Cortland Standard, NY, Cortland

Butler, Brian
brian.butler@lmh-na.com, Pres., Linde Lift
Truck Corp., SC, Summerville

Butler, Bruce .... (952) 944-9457
info@colorspan.com, Dir., Mktg., Hewlett-
Packard Co., MN, Minnetonka

Butler, Dave. .... (401) 277-7332
dbutler@providencejournal.com, Executive Ed.,
The Providence Journal, RI, Providence

Butler, David. .... (408) 920-5456
Ed./VP, The Cupertino Courier, CA, San Jose
Ed./VP, Saratoga News, CA, San Jose
Ed./VP, Campbell Reporter, CA, San Jose
Almaden Resident, CA, San Jose

Butler, Erica
managingeditor@gmail.com, Florida A&M
Univ., FL, Tallahassee

Butler, Frank E.
fbutler@proxios.com, Pres., Proxios, VA,
Richmond

Butler, Janice
lawcoadv@bellsouth.net, Adv. Mgr., Lawrence
County Advocate, TN, Lawrenceburg

Butler, Jeff
jbutler@simplyss.com, Assoc. Prof./Head, I/O,
University of Central Florida, FL, Orlando

Butler, Jennifer
jennifer@forestcitynews.com, Adv. Sales, The
Forest City News, PA, Forest City

Butler, Jeremy
jbutler@ua.edu, Prof., University of Alabama,
AL, Tuscaloosa

Butler, Jim .... (867) 667-4481
editorial@whitehorsestar.com, Editor,
Whitehorse Star, YT, Whitehorse

Butler, Jim .... (903) 885-8663
jimb@ssecho.com, Vice Pres., Sulphur Springs
News-Telegram, TX, Sulphur Springs

Butler, Jim
jimb@Cooperreview.com, Pub./Adv. Dir.,
Cooper Review, TX, Cooper

Butler, Kyle
kyle.butler@sunmedia.ca, Prod. Mgr.,
Brandtford Expositor, ON, Brantford

Butler, Laura. .... (208) 639-3528
lbutler@idahobusinessreview.com, Admin
Asst., Idaho Business Review, ID, Boise

Butler, Mary .... (580) 221-6511

mary.butler@ardmoreite.com, Cir. Dist. Mgr.,
The Ardmoreite, OK, Ardmore

Butler, Monica
advertise@oregonian.com, Adv. Sales, Forest
Grove Leader, OR, Portland

Butler, Monica .... (503) 648-1131
mbutler@hillsboroargus.com, Adv. Dir.,
Hillsboro Argus, OR, Portland

Butler, Pamela
pamela@mississippicatholic.com, Circ. Mgr.,
Mississippi Catholic, MS, Jackson

Butler, Patrick
religion@tylerpaper.com, Religion Ed., Tyler
Morning Telegraph, TX, Tyler

Butler, Patrick
pbutler@icfj.org, Vice Pres., Programs,
International Center for Journalists, DC,
Washington

Butler, Patti
pbutler@newsvirginian.com, Bus. Develop
sales Rep., The News Virginian, VA,
Waynesboro

Butler, Rhett .... (252) 329-9584
rbutler@reflector.com, Photo Ed., The Daily
Reflector, NC, Greenville

Butler, Seth .... (423) 623-6171
seth.butler@newportplaintalk.com, Pub. Ed.,
The Newport Plain Talk, TN, Newport

Butler, Shawn
sbutler@summitdaily.com, Circ. Dir. , Summit
Daily News, CO, Frisco

Butler, Sheryl .... (901) 521-9000 ext. 403
sheryl@memphisparent.com, Adv. Mgr.,
Memphis Parent, TN, Memphis

Butler, Will
hts@pacific.net, Gen. Mgr., Hometown
Shopper, CA, Ukiah

Butler , Dwayne
dbutler@conleynet.com, Ed., Greater
Milwaukee Jobs, WI, Waukesha

Butlet, Loren
lbutler@brantnews.com, Adv Mgr, Brant News,
ON, Brantford

Butner, Cindy .... (707) 526-8577
cindy.butner@pressdemocrat.com, Dir., Mktg.,
The Press Democrat, CA, Santa Rosa

Butner, Cindy .... (417) 836-1208
cbutner@news-leader.com, Dir., Market Devel.,
Springfield News-Leader, MO, Springfield

Butorac, Matt .... (719) 544-0166 ext. 310
circ@chieftain.com, Circ. Dir., The Pueblo
Chieftain, CO, Pueblo

Butters, Rita .... (607) 569-2622
ads@the-shopper.com, Pub., New York State's
Southern Tier Shopper, NY, Hammondsport

Butterworth, Candy .... (814) 231- 4612
cbutterworth@centredaily.com, Cir. Ops. Mgr. ,
Centre Daily Times, PA, State College

Buttice, Bobbi
business@malheurenterprise.com, Bus. Mgr.,
Malheur Enterprise, OR, Vale

Button, Bruce .... (518) 673-0104
bbutton@leepub.com, Ad. Sales, Country Folks
- East Zone, NY, Palatine Bridge

Button, Laura
editor@mountaineer.bz, Ed., The Mountaineer,
AB, Rocky Mountain House

Butts, David
dbutts@staradvertiser.com, Bus. Ed., Honolulu
Star-Advertiser, HI, Honolulu

Butts, Larry
lbutts@21st-centurymedia.com, Circ. Mgr.,
Main Line Suburban Life, PA, Ardmore

Butzer, Ann
sitmausa@sitma.com, Mktg. Mgr., SITMA USA,
Inc., MN, Saint Paul

Buum, Paul .... (605) 934-2640

info@ahenews.com, Pub./Ed., Alcester Union & Hudsonite, SD, Alcester

Buus, Holly ....(530) 283-0800
hbuus@plumasnews.com, Advertising Director, Feather Publishing Co., Inc., CA, Quincy

Buxton, Dianne
etgdirector@bentonrea.com, Adv. Mgr., PROSSER RECORD-BULLETIN, WA, Prosser

Buxton, Rodney
rodney.buxton@du.edu, Assoc. Prof./Dir., Communication Undergrad. Studies, University of Denver, CO, Denver

Buzine, Patti ....(215) 354-3021
pbuzine@bsmphilly.com, Adv. Sales Rep., Star Community Newsweekly, PA, Bensalem

Buzzard, Natalie ....(937) 538-4667
nbuzzard@civitasmedia.com, Gen. Mgr. / Med. Dir., The Sidney Daily News, OH, Sidney

Buzzard, Sandra.......................(304) 258-1800
news@hancocknews.us, Mgr Ed., The Hancock News, MD, Hancock

Buzzetta, John
vznews@aol.com, Pub., Van Banner, TX, Wills Point

Byars, Carey
cbyars@jbu.edu, Chair, John Brown Univ., AR, Siloam Springs

Byars, Greg
gbyars@sshopper.com, Sales Mgr., Southside Shopper, NC, Garner

Byars, Keely ....(402) 444-1110
keely.byars@owh.com, VP of Advertising, Omaha World-Herald, NE, Omaha

Byars, Robin
rbyars@messenger-inquirer.com, Circ. Mgr., Mktg., Messenger-Inquirer, KY, Owensboro

Bybee, Rick
circulation@cantondailyledger.com, Circ. Mgr., Fulton County Shopper, IL, Canton

Bybee, Rick
twatson@cantondailyledger.com, Circ. Mgr., Daily Ledger, IL, Canton

Byer, Garrett
gbyers@thedigitalcourier.com, Photographer, The Daily Courier, NC, Forest City

Byerly, Marina
mabyerly0@frostburg.edu, Editor-in-Chief, The Bottom Line, MD, Frostburg

Byers, Alex..............................(202) 994-1313
George Washington Univ., DC, Washington

Byers, Doug............................(541) 812-6052
doug.byers@lee.net, Controller, The Philomath Express, OR, Corvallis

Byers, Doug
doug.byers@lee.net , General manager, Corvallis Gazette-Times, OR, Corvallis

Byers, Ed
ed.byers@medmutual.com, President, Trustee, The Press Club of CLEVELAND, OH, Cleveland

Byers, Joshua .... ext. 18
jbyers@heartlandpublications.com, Pub., Floyd County Times, KY, Prestonsburg

Byers, Joshua ....(937) 552-2121
jbyers@civitasmedia.com, Pub., The Hazard Herald, KY, Hazard
jbyers@civitasmedia.com, Pub., Williamson Daily News, WV, Williamson
jbyers@civitasmedia.com, Pub. , Troy Daily News, OH, Troy

Byers, Karlyn ....(937) 642-6397
Marysville Journal-Tribune, OH, Marysville

Byers, Karma .... (620) 792-1211, ext. 219
kbyers@gbtribune.com, Prodn. Mgr., Pre Press, Great Bend Tribune, KS, Great Bend

Byers, LeeAnn.............. (620) 792-1211 ext. 215

circulation@gbtribune.com, Distributors Asst., Great Bend Tribune, KS, Great Bend

Byers, Paul
paul.byers@marymount.edu, Mass Commun. Coord., Marymount Univ., VA, Arlington

Bykofsky, Melissa......................(607) 777-2257
SUNY/Binghamton, NY, Binghamton

Bynum, Jennifer
jbynum@themexianews.com, Adv. Dir., The Mexia News, TX, Mexia

Bynum , Brad
reno@newsreview.com, Ass. Ed. , Reno News & Review, NV, Reno

Byrd, Dale
ngadvertising@comcast.net, Press Room Mgr., The News-Gazette, IN, Winchester

Byrd, Dennis
dbyrd@arkansasnews.com, Exec. Ed., Lonoke Democrat, AR, Lonoke
dbyrd@arkansasnews.com, Exec. Ed., Hot Springs Village Voice, AR, Hot Springs Village
dbyrd@arkansasnews.com, Exec. Ed., Carlisle Independent, AR, Carlisle

Byrd, Dennis M.
dbyrd@suntimes.com, Treasurer, Sun-Times Media Group Inc., IL, Chicago

Byrd, Ellie
ellie@elheraldonews.com, Adv. Mgr., El Heraldo News, TX, Dallas

Byrd, James
james.byrd@startribune.com, Director, Digital Yield
, Star Tribune, MN, Minneapolis

Byrd, Kay
newsandpost@florencenews.com, Adv. Dir., Marion County News Journal, SC, Marion

Byrd, Rachel
Rbyrd52ccp.edu, Associate Editor, Community College of Philadelphia, PA, Philadelphia

Byrd, Sherlynn
shbyrd@alcorn.edu, Chair, Alcorn State University, MS, Alcorn State

Byrd, Thomas W. ....(540) 667-3200
twbyrd@winchesterstar.com, Gen. Mgr., The Winchester Star, VA, Winchester

Byrd, Tina .... (419) 238-2285 ext. 230
tbyrd@timesbulletin.com, Mkt. Dev. Dir., The Times Bulletin, OH, Van Wert

Byrd, Tom ....(302) 741-8258
tbyrd@newszap.com, Publisher, Delaware State News, DE, Dover

Byrd, Warren
wbyrd@atu.edu, Asst. Prof., Arkansas Tech University, AR, Russellville

Byrd-Jenkins, Julie .... (603) 224-5301 ext. 325
Copy Ed., Concord Monitor, NH, Concord

Byrne, A.R. ....(215) 886-4900
ired@voicenet.com, Pub., Irish Edition, Inc., PA, Oreland

Byrne, Dean ....(435) 797-3754
Lectr., Utah State University, UT, Logan

Byrne, Ed..............................(920) 756-2222
edbyrne@thebrillionnews.com, Reporter, The Brillion News, WI, Brillion

Byrne, Penny ....(435) 797-3289
Assoc. Prof., Utah State University, UT, Logan

Byrne, Trapper
tbyrne@sfchronicle.com, Metro Editor, San Francisco Chronicle, CA, San Francisco

Byrnes, Jessica ....(727) 298-0341
jessica@competencesoftware.net, Asst. to CEO, Competence Software, CO, Dove Creek

Byrnes, Larry
larry@competencesw.com, Founder, Competence Software, CO, Dove Creek

Byron, Laurie
Lbyron@yourmvi.com, Adv. Mgr., The Mon Valley Independent, PA, Monessen

Byron, Spires
byron@havanaherald.net, Managing Editor, The Herald, FL, Havana

Bytwerk, Randall
bytw@calvin.edu, Chair, Dept. of Commun. Arts & Sciences, Calvin College, MI, Grand Rapids

Bywater, Pat .... (814) 724-6370 ext. 267
pbywater@meadvilletribune.com, Exec. Ed., The Meadville Tribune, PA, Meadville
pbywater@meadvilletribune.com, Exec. Ed., The Lebanon Daily News, PA, Lebanon

Bywater, Pat ....ext. 267
pbywater@meadvilletribune.com, Ed., Bravo Extra, PA, Meadville

Bélair, Francois
francois.belair@eap.on.ca, Adv. Mgr., Cie d'Edition Andre Paquette, Inc., ON, Hawkesbury

C

CM, Suma.............................(212) 293-8725
scm@unitedmedia.com, Exec. Ed., Newspaper Enterprise Association (Div. of United Media), NY, New York
scm@unitedmedia.com, Exec. Ed., United Feature Syndicate (Div. of United Media), New York

Caballero, Paloma
pekin@efe.com, Rep., EFE News Services - Beijing, China, Beijing

Caballero, Shelby
shelby.caballero@lubbockonline.com, Dir., HR, Lubbock Avalanche-Journal, TX, Lubbock

Cabana, Michelle ....(250) 588-2275
michelle.cabana@goldstreamgazette.com, Pub., Goldstream Gazette, BC, Victoria

Cable, Claudia
claudia.cable@nptelegraph.com, Dist. Mgr., Circ., The North Platte Telegraph, NE, North Platte

Cable, Darrell
darrell@cableprinting.com, Pub., Lindsay News, OK, Lindsay

Cable, Gina
gina@cableprinting.com, Ed., Lindsay News, OK, Lindsay

Cabral, Doug ....(508) 693-6100 ext. 20
Ed., The Martha's Vineyard Times, MA, Vineyard Haven

Cabral, Hector.........................(213) 237-3453
hcabral@hoyllc.com, Adv. Dir., Hoy Fin de Semana, CA, Los Angeles
hcabral@hoyllc.com, Adv. Dir., Hoy Los Angeles, CA, Los Angeles
hcabral@hoyllc.com, Sales Dir., Burbank Leader, CA, Los Angeles

Caddell, Scarlett
advertising@hartsvillenewsjournal.com, Advertising, The Hartsville News Journal, SC, Hartsville

Caddle, Sam ....(707) 521-5353
Production Dir., The Press Democrat, CA, Santa Rosa

Cadi, Thierry...............................4017-1780
thierry.cadin@dowjones.com, Reg'l Sales Mgr., Dow Jones Newswires - Paris, France, Paris

Cadieux, Diane
diane.cadieux@monteregieweb.com, Adv. Rep., Le Soleil Du St-laurent, QC, Chateauguay

Caesar, Lael ....(301) 680-6562
caesarl@gc.adventist.org, associate editor, Adventist Review, MD, Silver Spring

Caetano, Irieska D. ....(202) 281-2406

Caetano, Irieska D. ....(202) 281-2406
irieska@elpreg.org, Circ. Mgr., El Pregonero, MD, Hyattsville

Caetano, Irieska D. ....(202) 281-2406
irieska@elpreg.org, Circ. Mgr., Catholic Standard, DC, Washington

Cagala, Anthony
tcagala@coastnewsgroup.com, Managing Ed., Rancho Santa Fe News, CA, Encinitas

Cagala, Tony
tcagala@coastnewsgroup.com, Mng. Ed., The Coast News, CA, Encinitas

Cagle, Daryl
daryl@cagle.com, Pres./CEO, Cagle Cartoons, Inc., CA, Santa Barbara

Cagle, Joe
joe.cagle@advertisergleam.com, Reporter, The Advertiser-Gleam, AL, Guntersville

Cagle, Steve ....(252) 329-9576
scagle@reflector.com, Features Ed., The Daily Reflector, NC, Greenville

Cagnina, James ....(805) 642-5585
jim@inksoup.com, Pres., Coast Graphic Supply, CA, Ventura

Cahalane, Dan
info@americanroller.com, Pres., American Roller Co., WI, Union Grove

Cahir, Ashley
ashleigh@crestedbuttenews.com, Adv. Rep., Crested Butte News, CO, Crested Butte

Cahn, Martin
martin.cahn@farmvilleherald.com, Mng. Ed., The Farmville Herald, VA, Farmville

Cahoon, Susan ....(505) 986-3001
scahoon@sfnewmexican.com, HR Director, The Santa Fe New Mexican, NM, Santa Fe

Caimano, Kellie......................(315) 470-2221
kcaimano@advancemediany.com, Executive Assistant, The Post-Standard, NY, Syracuse

Cain, Brandon ....(815) 561-2152
sports@rochellenews-leader.com, Sports Ed. , The Rochelle News Leader, IL, Rochelle

Cain, Chad ....(413) 585-5238
ccain@gazettenet.com, Night Managing Ed. , Daily Hampshire Gazette, MA, Northampton

Cain, Debbie
debbie.cain@news-herald.net, Bus. Mgr., The Connection, TN, Lenoir City
debbie.cain@news-herald.net, Bus. Mgr., News-Herald, TN, Lenoir City

Cain, J. Damon.......................(303) 954-1826
dcain@denverpost.com, ME, Presentation, The Denver Post, CO, Denver

Cain, Jayme ....(815) 723-0325
jcain@thetimesweekly.com, Pres./Pub., The Times Weekly, IL, Joliet

Cain, Louise
rlinscott@atokaspeedynet.net, Pub., Atoka County Times, OK, Atoka

Cain, Stephanie ....(225) 771-2230
Southern Univ. A&M College, LA, Baton Rouge

Cain, Tim...............................(217) 421-6908
tcain@herald-review.com, Audience Engagement Ed. , Herald & Review, Decatur, IL, Decatur

Cains, Isis...............................(219) 326-3881
icains@heraldargus.com, Adv. Dir., Herald News Review, IL, Decatur
icains@heraldargus.com, Adv. Dir., News Dispatch, IN, Michigan City
icains@heraldargus.com, Adv. Dir., Harbor Country News, MI, New Buffalo
icains@heraldargus.com, Advertising Dir., Herald-Argus, IN, La Porte

Calabrese, Andrew
andrew.calabrese@colorado.edu, Prof./Assoc. Dean/Dir. Graduate Studies, University of Colorado, CO, Boulder

Calabro, Tim

publisher@ourherald.com, Ed & Pub, The
Herald of Randolph, VT, Randolph

Calantone, Jen .... (202) 885-1402
American Univ., DC, Washington

Calchi, Joseph .... (856) 563-5215
jcalchi@gannettnj.com, Pres. & Pub., The Daily
Journal, NJ, Vineland
jcalchi@gannettnj.com, Pres. & Pub., The
Courier-Post, NJ, Cherry Hill

Calcutt, William
circdirector@hammondstar.com, Circ. Dir., The
Daily Star, LA, Hammond

Caldara, Jon
jon@i2i.org, Pres., Independence Feature
Syndicate, Denver

Calder, Amy .... (207) 861-9247
acalder@centralmaine.com, Reporter, Morning
Sentinel, ME, Waterville

Calder, Chris .... (707) 964-5642 ex. 6091
editor@advocate-news.com, Editor
, Fort Bragg Advocate-News, CA, Fort Bragg

Calder, Chris .... (707) 964-5642
editor@advocate-news.com, Ed, The
Mendocino Beacon, CA, Fort Bragg

Calder, Pamela .... (978)
371-5723 ....
pcalder@wickedlocal.com, Adv. Mgr., Display,
Littleton Independent, MA, Concord

Calderon, R.A.
rcalderon@verican.com, Operations Dir., The
Valley Chronicle, CA, Hemet

Caldwell, Debbie .... (606) 248-1010 Ext. 1162
dcaldwell@civitasmedia.com, News Ed., The
Harlan Daily Enterprise, KY, Harlan

Caldwell, Debbie .... (606) 248-1010 Ext. 1123
dcaldwell@civitasmedia.com, Reg. Ed.,
Middlesboro Daily News, KY, Middlesboro

Caldwell, Donna .... (530) 336-6262
mtecho@shasta.com, Pub., The Mountain
Echo, CA, Fall River Mills

Caldwell, Doug
dcaldwell@petoskeynews.com, Pub.,
Charlevoix Courier, MI, Charlevoix

Caldwell, Doug .... (231) 347-2544
dcaldwell@petoskeynews.com, Pres./Pub.,
Petoskey News-Review, MI, Petoskey

Caldwell, Doug .... (559) 674-8134
Pres./Pub., The Madera Tribune, CA, Madera

Caldwell, Doug
petoskeynews@petoskeynews.com, Pub.,
Northern Michigan Review, MI, Petoskey

Caldwell, Joy
gcherald@lcs.net, Pub./Ed., Grundy County
Herald, TN, Tracy City

Caldwell, Matt .... (614) 738-2280
Adv. Contact, Capital Track Co., OH, Columbus

Caldwell, Michael
mike.caldwell@irontontribune.com, Pres./Pub.,
The Ironton Tribune, OH, Ironton

Caldwell, Patricia .... (318) 435-4521
patricia@franklinsun.com, Advertising, The
Franklin Sun, LA, Winnsboro

Calhoon, Jim
supprod@supportproducts.com, CEO, Support
Products, Inc., IL, Effingham

Calhoun, Ken
kcalhoun@elon.edu, Asst. Prof., Elon
University, NC, Elon

Calhoun, Scott
calhouns@cedarville.edu, Cedarville Univ.,
OH, Cedarville

Calhoun, Scott .... (256) 235-9290
scalhoun@annistonstar.com, Controller/
Treasurer, Consolidated Publishing Co., AL,
Anniston

Calhoun, Scott
scalhoun@annistonstar.com, Office Manager,

The Anniston Star, AL, Anniston

Cali, Jeff .... (580) 310-7526
jcali@theadanews.com, Sports Ed., The Ada
News , OK, Ada

Calibaba, Dave
davecalibaba@canwest.com, Gen. Mgr., The
Lakeshore News, ON, Tecumseh

Calibaba, Dave
wengland@shorelineweek.com, Pub.,
Shoreline Week, ON, Tecumseh

Calister, Scotta .... (541) 575-0710
editor@bmeagle.com, Ed., Blue Mountain
Eagle, OR, John Day

Calkins, Royal .... (831) 646-4381
rcalkins@montereyherald.com, Ed., Salinas
Valley Weekly, CA, Monterey
rcalkins@montereyherald.com, Political Ed.,
The Monterey County Herald, CA, Monterey

Call, Lloyd .... (435) 835-4241
ads@sanpetemessenger.co, Associate Pub
and Advt Mgr, Sanpete Messenger, UT, Manti

Callaghan , Brian
brian@tecumsehherald.com, Adv. Mgr., The
Tecumseh Herald, MI, Tecumseh

Callahan, Amy .... (978) 556-3397
acallahan@necc.mass.edu, Adv. Mgr.,
Northern Essex Community College, MA,
Haverhill

Callahan, Angie .... (760) 951-6288
acallahan@vvdailypress.com, Adv. Director,
Daily Press, CA, Victorville

Callahan, Christopher
ccallahan@asu.edu, Dean, Arizona State
University, AZ, Tempe

Callahan, M. Catherine .... (401) 380-2354
CityDesk@NewportRI.com, City Ed., The
Newport Daily News, RI, Newport

Callahan, Marybeth .... (978) 675-2720
mbcallahan@capeannmagazine.com,
Adv. Mgr., Gloucester Daily Times, MA,
Gloucester

Callahan, Robert .... (608) 822-3912
timeseditor@tds.net, Ed., Fennimore Times,
WI, Fennimore

Callahan, Sean .... (978) 262-9799
SCALLAHAN@EDGIL.COM, Dir., Sales, Edgil
Associates, Inc., MA, Danvers

Callahan, Shawn .... (724) 779-7149
scallahan@tribweb.com, Prodn. Dir., Trib Total
Media, Inc., PA, Pittsburgh

Callahan, Tom
tcallahan@iona.edu, Adj. Fac., Iona College,
NY, New Rochelle

Callaway, Kelley
thresher@rice.edu, Advisor, Rice Univ., TX,
Houston

Callaway, Wendi .... (903) 962-4275
wcallaway@grandsalinesun.com, Ed., Grand
Saline Sun, TX, Grand Saline

Calle, Brian
bcalle@ocregister.com, VP, Opinion Page Ed.,
The Orange County Register, CA, Santa Ana

Calle, Brian
bcalle@scng.com, Opinion Ed, Press-
Telegram, CA, Long Beach

Calle, Javier T. .... (213) 237-4388
jcalle@hoyllc.com, Editor Adjunto Hoy/ Los
Angeles, Hoy LLC, CA, Los Angeles

Calligas, Gary .... (318) 636-5510
gary.calligas@gmail.com, Publisher, The Best
of Times, LA, Shreveport

Callihan, Lisa .... (606) 326-2606
lcallihan@cnhi.com, Business Manager, The
Daily Independent, KY, Ashland

Callison, Coy
coy.callison@ttu.edu, Assoc. Prof./Chair, Dept.
of Public Relations, Texas Tech University,

TX, Lubbock

Callister, Scotta
scotta@malheurenterprise.com, Pub/Ed,
Malheur Enterprise, OR, Vale

Calloway, James
jcalloway@mcclatchyinteractive.com, Vice
President Strategic Development, McClatchy
Interactive, NC, Raleigh

Calloway, Melissa ....(217) 241-1700 x 286
mcalloway@illinoispress.org, Dig. Adv. Mgr.,
Illinois Press Association, IL, Springfield

Calloway, Nikki
nikki@photosys.com, Sales Mgr., Photo
Systems, Inc., MI, Dexter

Calloway, Susan
susan@ozona.com, Adv. Dir., Ozona
Stockman, TX, Ozona

Caltabiano-Ponce, Marcia
mponce@brownsvilleherald.com, Ed., The
Brownsville Herald, TX, Brownsville

Caluori, Paul
pcaluori@ap.org, Associated Press, The, New
York

Calvert, Brandy .... ext. 206
editor@middlesborodailynews.com, Mng. Ed.,
Cumberland Trading Post, KY, Middlesboro

Calvert, Ericka .... (646) 682-9466
ecalvert@newscom.com, Mktg. Dir.,
NewsCom, Salt Lake City

Camacho, George
pub@elpopularnews.com, President/Publisher,
El Popular, CA, Bakersfield

Camacho, Raul
raulcamacho@elpopularnews.com, Founding
Publisher/Editor, El Popular, CA, Bakersfield

Camacho, Vivian
vcamacho@hbu.edu, Adj. Prof., Houston
Baptist University, TX, Houston

Camara, Leah .... (401) 421-4111
lcamara@jfri.org, Prodn. Mgr., Jewish Voice of
Rhode Island, RI, Providence

Cameron, Michelle
mcameron@imediainc.com, Vice Pres./
Creative Dir., Interactive Media Associates,
NJ, Boonton

Cambell, Fred
president@wcai.com, Pres., Wireless
Communications Association International,
DC, Washington

Cambrel, Kelly
kcambrel@shepherdstownchronicle.com, Ed.
Assistant, The Shepherdstown Chronicle,
WV, Shepherdstown

Cambridge, Patricia .... (740) 593-0899
Asst. Prof., Ohio University, OH, Athens

Cambron, Tricia
mdareing@npco.com, Assistant Ed., The Polk
County Standard Journal, GA, Cedartown

Camden, Bridget
bkcamden@vcu.edu, Asst. Prof., Virginia
Commonwealth University, VA, Richmond

Camero, Holly .... (978) 371-5759
hcamero@wickedlocal.com, Ed., The Bolton
Common, MA, Concord

Camero, Holly .... (978) 371-5759
hcamero@wickedlocal.com, Regional Ed., The
Harvard Post, MA, Concord

Cameron, Brian .... (503) 842-7535
editor@northcoastcitizen.com, Managing
Editor, North Coast Citizen, OR, Manzanita

Cameron, Dan
distribution@gtrnews.com, Circ. Mgr, Owasso
Rambler, OK, Tulsa

Cameron, Forrest .... (918) 254-1515
fcameron@gtrnews.com, Pub./CEO, Owasso
Rambler, OK, Tulsa

Cameron, Gordon .... (905) 664-8800

gocameron@hamiltonnews.com, Mng Ed,
Ancaster News, ON, Stoney Creek

Cameron, Gordon .... (905) 664-8800
gocameron@hamiltonnews.com, Managing
Editor, Hamilton Mountain News, ON, Stoney
Creek

Cameron, Gordon .... (905) 664-8800
gocameron@hamiltonnews.com, Mng Ed,
Dundas Star News, ON, Stoney Creek

Cameron, Gordon .... (905) 664-8800
gocameron@hamiltonnews.com, Mng Ed.,
Stoney Creek News, ON, Stoney Creek

Cameron, Ian
ImagesAPI@ap.org, Vice Pres., AP Digital and
Commercial Services, New York

Cameron, Scott .... (312) 222-8697
jscameron@tronc.com, Dir., US Syndication
Sales, Tribune Content Agency, IL, Chicago

Cameron, Scotty
scotty@thepaper24-7.com, Managing Editor,
The Paper of Montgomery County, IN,
Crawfordsville

Cameron, Sharon
scameron@gtrnews.com, Adv. Dir., Owasso
Rambler, OK, Tulsa

Cammack, Charles L. .... (208) 527-3038
arcoadv@aol.com, Gen. Mgr., Arco Advertiser,
ID, Arco

Cammack, Holly
metigosh@utma.com, Bus. Mgr. , Lake
Metigoshe Mirror, ND, Rolla

Cammarata, Frank
frank@mediamonitors.com, VP, Sales, Media
Monitors, Inc., NY, White Plains

Cammock, Lorraine .... (305) 694-6210
lcammock@miamitimesonline.com, Operation
Manager, The Miami Times, FL, Miami

Camp, Ken
ken@baptiststandard.com, Mng. Ed., Baptist
Standard, TX, Plano

Camp, Mary
mcamp@thevermontstandard.com, Circ./
Bus. Columnist, The Vermont Standard, VT,
Woodstock

Camp, Paul A. .... (773) 728-8351
paul@contentthatworks.com, CEO, Content
That Works, Chicago
paul@contentthatworks.com, Gen. Mgr.,
Thomson Target Media, IL, Chicago

Camp,Sr., Phillip .... (802) 457-1313
pcamp@thevermontstandard.com, Pub., The
Vermont Standard, VT, Woodstock

Campagne , Henriette
henriette.campagne@lawyersweekly.com, Ed.,
Massachusetts Lawyers Weekly, MA, Boston
henriette.campagne@lawyersweekly.com, Ed.,
Rhode Island Lawyers Weekly, MA, Boston

Campanelli, Jimmy V.
pubital@biz.videotron.ca, Adv. Mgr., Corriere
Italiano, QC, Montreal

Campanini, James .... (978) 970-4621
jcampanini@lowellsun.com, Ed., The Sun,
MA, Lowell

Campanini, James .... (978) 970-4621
jcampanini@lowellsun.com, Ed., The Dispatch
News, MA, Lowell

Campanini, John .... (978) 970-4621
jcampanini@lowellsun.com, Ed., Broadcaster,
MA, Lowell

Campbell, Alan C.
alan@leelanaunews.com, Ed., The Leelanau
Enterprise, MI, Lake Leelanau

Campbell, Amber
acampbell@tcnewsnet.com, Sales, Centerville-
Washington Times (OOB), OH, Xenia
acampbell@tcnewsnet.com, Sales, Sugarcreek
Bellbrook Times, OH, Xenia

Campbell, Anthony .... (256) 582-3232

news@advertisergleam.com, Editor, The Advertiser-Gleam, AL, Guntersville

Campbell, Beau .... (913) 492-9050
bcampbell@inlandnews.com, Pres., Inland Newspaper Machinery LLC, KS, Olathe

Campbell, Ben .... (360) 735-4472
ben.campbell@columbian.com, Circulation Manager, The Columbian, WA, Vancouver

Campbell, Bob .... (321) 242-3554
bcampbell@floridatoday.com, Ops.Production Mgr., Florida Today, FL, Melbourne

Campbell, Bruce
news@pikepress.com, Pres./Pub., Campbell Publishing Co., Inc., IL, Jerseyville

Campbell, Candi .... (859) 236-2551 Ext. 355
ccampbell@amnews.com, NIE Coord., The Advocate-Messenger, KY, Danville

Campbell, Carol .... (540) 298-9444
vbads@comast.net, Adv. Mgr., The Valley Banner, VA, Elkton

Campbell, Carolyn
ccampbell@pnj.com, Nat'l Sales Coord., Pensacola News Journal, FL, Pensacola

Campbell, Catherine
ccampbell@argus-press.com, Adv. Dir., The Argus-Press, MI, Owosso

Campbell, Chad .... (508) 862-1225
ccampbell@capecodonline.com, Regional Circ. Dir. , The Standard-Times, MA, New Bedford

Campbell, Chad .... (508) 826-1225
ccampbell@capecodonline.com, Circ. Dir., Cape Cod Times, MA, Hyannis

Campbell, Charles .... (719) 544-3520 ext. 411
newsroom@chieftain.com, Editorial Page Ed., The Pueblo Chieftain, CO, Pueblo

Campbell, Christopher P.
christopher.campbell@usm.edu, Dir./Prof. School of Mass Commun. and Journ., University of Southerm Mississippi, MS, Hattiesburg

Campbell, Chuck
campbell@knoxnews.com, Entertainment Ed., Knoxville News Sentinel, TN, Knoxville

Campbell, Coleen .... (403) 328-4003
ccampbell@abnewsgroup.com, Publisher/GM, The Lethbridge Herald, AB, Lethbridge

Campbell, Coleen .... (403) 330-3699
ccampbell@abnewsgroup.com, Pub., Lethbridge Sun Times, AB, Lethrbidge

Campbell, Coleen
ccampbell@tabertimees.com, Pub., The 40-mile County Commentator, AB, Bow Island

Campbell, Dan
dcampbell@keysnews.com, Managing Ed., Florida Keys Free Press, FL, Tavernier

Campbell, David .... (406) 222-2000
circ@livent.net, Circ. Dir, The Livingston Enterprise, MT, Livingston

Campbell, David .... (812) 265-3641, ext. 231
dcampbell@madisoncourier.com, Sports Ed., Madison Courier, Inc., IN, Madison

Campbell, Deb
deb.campbell@sunmedia.ca, Prod. Mgr., The Simcoe Reformer, ON, Simcoe

Campbell, Debbie ....ext. 262
deb.campbell@sunmedia.ca, Prodn. Mgr., Woodstock Sentinel-Review, ON, Woodstock

Campbell, Debra
deb@leelanaunews.com, Adv. Mgr., The Leelanau Enterprise, MI, Lake Leelanau

Campbell, Dee Ann .... (251) 843-6397
choctawsun@millry.net, Editor, Choctaw Sun-Advocate, AL, Gilbertown

Campbell, Don .... (269) 429-2400 ext. 204
photos@thehp.com, Photo Ed., The Herald-Palladium, MI, Saint Joseph

Campbell, Don .... (867) 668-2002

don@whitehorsestar.com, Head Pressman, Whitehorse Star, YT, Whitehorse

Campbell, Emily
notices@thelegalrecord.net, Ed., Legal Record, KS, Olathe

Campbell, Emily
notices@wyandottecountylegalnews.com, Ed, Wyandotte County Business News, KS, Kansas City

Campbell, Freddie
fcampbell@hearstnp.com, Mgmt. Info Servs. Mgr., The Beaumont Enterprise, TX, Beaumont

Campbell, Frederick
fcampbell@colsdioc.org, Pub., The Catholic Times, OH, Columbus

Campbell, George .... (520) 573-4173
campbell@azstarnet.com, Copy Chief, Arizona Daily Star, AZ, Tucson

Campbell, Harry
harry@hot-promos.com, President, Hot Off the Press Promotions, INC., FL, New Smyrna Beach

Campbell, Jerry .... (618) 667-3111
sports@wisperhome.com, Sports Reporter, Troy Times-Tribune, IL, Troy

Campbell, Jessica .... (219) 326-3887
jcampbell@heraldargus.com, Reporter , Herald-Argus, IN, La Porte

Campbell, Jim .... (360) 792-9204
jcampbell@kitsapsun.com, Submitted Content Ed., Kitsap Sun, WA, Bremerton

Campbell, Jody .... (360) 735-4467
jody.campbell@columbian.com, Dir. of Community Outreach, The Columbian, WA, Vancouver

Campbell, Joel
joel_campbell@byu.edu, Asst. Prof., Brigham Young University, UT, Provo

Campbell, John .... (613) 392-6501 ext. 40
news@communitypress-online.com, News Ed., The Community Press, ON, Trenton

Campbell, June .... (785) 485-2290
Office Manager, Riley Countian, KS, Riley

Campbell, Keith .... (214) 977-8341
kcampbell@dallasnews.com, Deputy Managing Editor/News & Business, The Dallas Morning News, TX, Dallas

Campbell, Kev .... (406) 443-2850
campbell@mtnewspapers.com, Business Development Manager, Montana Newspaper Association, MT, Helena

Campbell, Laurie .... (203) 894-3322
lcampbell@hersamacorn.com, Account Executive, Ridgefield Press, CT, Ridgefield

Campbell, Linda .... (908) 647-1180
lcampbell@recodernewspapers.com, Prodn. Mgr., Chatham Courier, NJ, Bernardsville

Campbell, Linda .... (561) 820-4651
lcampbell@pbpost.com, Circ. Mgr., Admin. Servs., The Palm Beach Post, FL, West Palm Beach

Campbell, Linda .... (908) 766-3900
Prod. Mgr., Hunterdon Review, NJ, Whippany The Citizen, NJ, Bernardsville

Campbell, Linda .... (908) 766-3900 ext. 219
lcampbell@recordernewspapers.com, Prodn. Mgr., Bernardsville News, NJ, Bernardsville

Campbell, Lynne .... (618) 932-2146
lcampbell@gatehousemedia.com, Pub., Argus-Sentinel, IL, Galesburg
lcampbell@gatehousemedia.com, Group Pub., The Marion Daily Republican, IL, Marion
lcampbell@gatehousemedia.com, Pub., Du Quoin Evening Call, IL, Du Quoin
lcampbell@gatehousemedia.com, Pub., Benton Evening News, IL, Benton
lcampbell@gatehousemedia.com, Pres. Pub., The Daily Register, IL, Harrisburg

Campbell, Margie .... (580) 548-8129
margiec@enidnews.com, Major Acct. Rep., Enid News & Eagle, OK, Enid

Campbell, Mark
markcampbell@azlenews.net, Ed., Azle News, TX, Azle

Campbell, Mark .... (812) 265-3641 ext. 27
mcampbell@madisoncourier.com, Sports Ed., Madison Courier, Inc., IN, Madison

Campbell, Mark .... (817) 270-3340
Ed., Springtown Epigraph, TX, Springtown

Campbell, Melanie .... (717) 436-8206
mcampbell@juniata-sentinel.com, Adv., Juniata Sentinel, PA, Mifflintown

Campbell, Mike .... (304) 291-9451
mcampbell@dominionpost.com, Circ. Single Copy Sales Mgr., The Dominion Post, WV, Morgantown

Campbell, Myrna .... (580) 338-3355 Ext. 12
businessmanager@guymondailyherald.com, Off. Mgr., Guymon Daily Herald, OK, Guymon

Campbell, Paul .... (417) 345-2224
paulc@buffaloreflex.com, Ed./Gen. Mngr., Buffalo Reflex, MO, Buffalo

Campbell, Renee .... (970) 875-1788
rcampbell@craigdailypress.com, Pub., Craig Daily Press, CO, Craig

Campbell, Roland
rcampbell@azinformant.com, CEO, Arizona Informant, AZ, Phoenix
rcampbell@azinformant.com, Pub., Arizona Informant, AZ, Phoenix

Campbell, Sarah .... (770) 683-1729
sarah@newnan.com, Reporter, The Newnan Times-Herald, GA, Newnan

Campbell, Scott
scampbell@northscottpress.com, Ed., The North Scott Press, IA, Eldridge

Campbell, Scott .... (360) 735-4500
scott.campbell@columbian.com, Pub., The Columbian, WA, Vancouver

Campbell, Susan .... (931) 455-4545
tnedit@lcs.net, Editor, The Tullahoma News, TN, Tullahoma

Campbell, Suzie
suzie@countywidenews.com, Mktg. Dir., Countywide & Sun, OK, Tecumseh

Campbell, Thomas E. .... (989) 725-5136
tcampbell@argus-press.com, Pub., The Argus-Press, MI, Owosso

Campbell, Tina
composition@southern-sentinel.com, Asst. Pub., Southern Sentinel, MS, Ripley

Campbell, Tommy .... (251) 843-6397
tommy.campbell@therogersvillereview.com, Publisher/Advertising Manager, Choctaw Sun-Advocate, AL, Gilbertown
tommy.campbell@therogersvillereview.com, Pub./Ed., The Rogersville Review, TN, Rogersville

Campbell, Will
wcampbell@prescottaz.com, Adv. Mgr., Prescott Valley Tribune, AZ, Chino Valley

Campbell , Dot
dot@prpeak.com, Sales, Powell River Peak, BC, Powell River

Campbell , Paula .... (217) 477-5143
pcampbell@dancomnews.com, Business Mgr., Commercial News, IL, Danville

Camper, Laura .... (256) 463-2872
news@cleburnnews.com, Ed., The Cleburne News, AL, Heflin

Camping, Danielle .... (207) 990-8208
dcamping@bangordailynews.com, Sales Manager, Aroostook Republican and News, ME, Presque Isle

Campise, Amber
ads@bctribune.com, Ad. Director, Burleson

County Tribune, TX, Caldwell

Campomizzi-Clews, Kathryn .... (570) 628-6006
kclews@republicanherald.com, News Ed., The Republican-Herald, PA, Pottsville

Campos, Jennifer .... x 384
Jennifer.Campos@gjsentinel.com, Classified Manager, The Daily Sentinel, CO, Grand Junction

Campus, Steve
campuss@campusgroup.com, Owner, Interactive Conferencing Network, NY, Tuckahoe

Canaan, Don .... (352) 750-9420
dcanaan@israelfaxx.com, Contact, Israel Faxx, FL, The Villages

Canacci, Bill .... (732) 643-4218
bcanacci@thnt.com, Reg. Feat. Coord., Home News Tribune, NJ, Somerville

Canady, Hoyt
hoyt.canady@knews.com, Editorial Page Ed., Knoxville News Sentinel, TN, Knoxville

Canalis, John
john.canalis@latimes.com, Exec. Ed., Daily Pilot, CA, Costa Mesa

Canalis, John
bonnie.zone@latimes.com, Exec. Ed., Times Community News (TCN), CA, Los Angeles

Canalis, John
John.Canalis@latimes.com, Ed., Huntington Beach Independent (OOB), CA, Fountain Valley
John.Canalis@latimes.com, Part-time Fac., California State University, Long Beach, CA, Long Beach

Canaval, Tatiana .... (312) 870-7033
tatiana.canaval@laraza.com, Mktg. Mgr., La Raza Newspaper, IL, Chicago

Canazaro, Rich .... (717) 272-5611
rcanazaro@mediaonepa.com, Adv. Mgr., The Lebanon Daily News, PA, Lebanon

Canazaro, Rich
rcanazaro@mediaonepa.com, Advertising Manager, The Palm, PA, Lebanon

Candemeres, Michael .... (212) 803-8830
michael.candemeres@sourcemedia.com, Dist. Mgr., American Banker, NY, New York

Candiotti, Arleen .... (514) 223-3567
advertising@westmountindependent.com, Advt Consultant, The Westmount Independent, QC, Westmount

Caneles, Christopher .... (561) 820-4131
ccaneles@pbpost.com, Vice Pres./CIO, Cox Media Group, GA, Atlanta
ccaneles@pbpost.com, VP Operations , The Palm Beach Post, FL, West Palm Beach

Canfield, Michael .... (716) 649-4040 ext 222
News Editor, SUNY College/Buffalo, NY, Buffalo
Community Reporter, The Sun and Erie County Independent, NY, Hamburg

Canfield, Sandy .... (304) 788-3333
scanfield@newstribune.info, Staff, Mineral Daily News-Tribune, WV, Keyser

Canfield, William
moreinfo@talx.com, CEO, TALX Corp., MO, Saint Louis

Canine, Jamie
jamie@addsheet.com, Pub., The Add Sheet!, MO, Columbia

Cann, Mavis
mavis.cann@revelstokereview.com, Pub./Adv Mgr, Revelstoke Review, BC, Revelstoke

Cannada, Billy .... (864) 877-2076
Ed., The Greer Citizen, SC, Greer

Cannizzaro, Ben .... ext. 8282
gmntnews@gmnews.com, Pub., Tri-Town News, NJ, Manalapan

Cannizzaro, Ben

bcannizzaro@gmnews.com, Pub./Gen. Mgr., The Independent, NJ, Manalapan

Cannizzaro, Ben
ebsent@gmnews.com, Pub., Suburban, NJ, Manalapan

Cannon, Bill
bcannon@jconline.com, Regl. Digital Dir., Journal and Courier, IN, Lafayette

Cannon, Frank
sales@pdisaneck.com, Pres., PDI Plastics, OH, Westerville

Cannon, Frank
sales@pdisaneck.com, Pres., The Cannon Group, Inc., OH, Westerville

Cannon, Jonathan .... (903) 893-8181
jcannon@heralddemocrat.com, Ed., Herald Democrat, TX, Sherman

Cannon, K.M............................ (702) 387-5257
kcannon@reviewjournal.com, Asst. Dir. of Photo, Las Vegas Review-Journal, NV, Las Vegas

Cannon, Keith .... (704) 233-8161
cannon@wingate.edu, Wingate Univ., NC, Wingate

Cano, Carol .... (925) 600-0840, ext. 226
ccano@pleasantonweekly.com, Adv. Acct. Exec., Pleasanton Weekly, CA, Pleasanton

Cantatore, Felice .... (516) 284-3302
felice@longislandpress.com, Exec. VP & Adv., Long Island Press, NY, Syosset

Cantillo, Tatiana .... (305) 348-6993
Florida International Univ., FL, Miami

Cantin, Adrien
dg@apf.ca, Gen. Mgr, Association de la presse francophone, ON, Ottawa

Cantin, Caroline
communication@apf.ca, Deputy Dir. of Special Events, Development and Communications, Association de la presse francophone, ON, Ottawa

Cantin, Linda
lcantin@lequotidien.com, Dir. Sales & Mktg., Le Quotidien, QC, Saguenay

Cantin, Omer .... (705) 372-1234
ocantin@lenord.on.ca, Ed., Le Nord, ON, Hearst

Cantley, Rebeccah.................... (850) 599-2391
rcantley@tallahassee.com, Managing Ed., Tallahassee Democrat, FL, Tallahassee

Cantor, Lori .... (330) 72-0887
Kent State Univ., OH, Kent

Cantore, Mat........................... (518) 629-4998
Hudson Valley Cmty. College, NY, Troy

Cantrell, Jon
jon@opcfla.com, Pub., Clay Today, FL, Fleming Island
jon@opcfla.com, Publisher, Clay County Leader, FL, Fleming Island

Cantrell, Regina
rcantrell@thesuntimes.com, Adv. Mgr., The Sun-Times, AR, Heber Springs

Cantrell, Susan........................ (785) 295-1142
susan.cantrell@cjonline.com, VP of Sales/Mktg., The Topeka Capital-Journal, KS, Topeka

Cantu, Mariel
spubs@utpa.edu, Univ. of Texas Pan American, TX, Edinburg

Cantu-Gutierrez, Cristina .... (956) 565-2425
mercedesenterprise@sbcglobal.net, Office Manager, Mercedes Enterprise, TX, Mercedes

Cantu-Rodriguez, Ruben
news@ballingerledger.com, Ed., The Ballinger Ledger, TX, Ballinger

Cantua, Judith
laopinion@suddenlinkmail.com, La Opinion, TX, Jacksonville

Cao, Xiaoxia .... (414) 229-4436
xcao@uwm.edu, Assistant Professor, University of Wisconsin-Milwaukee / Department of Journalism, Advertising, and Media Studies (JAMS), WI, Milwaukee

Capasso, Lang
capasso@sun-herald.com, Adv. Mgr., The Sun Shopper, FL, Venice

Capdepon, Lesley
lesley@franklisun.com, Gen Mgr, The Franklin Sun, LA, Winnsboro

Capdepon, Lesley H.
Lesley@concordiasentinel.com, Mng. Ed., Concordia Sentinel, LA, Ferriday

Capellari, Reva .... ext. 127
rcapellari@fiftyplusadvocate.com, Sales Coord., Fifty Plus Advocate, MA, Worcester

Capellen, Rose
office@kemmerergazette.com, Office Mgr., The Kemmerer Gazette, WY, Kemmerer

Capitelli, Lisa
lisa@oceancitytoday.net, Managing Editor, Ocean City Today, MD, Ocean City

Caplan, Marc .... (503) 799-3274
mcaplan@pamplmedia.com, Public Notice, Forest Grove News-Times, OR, Forest Grove

Caplinger, Steve
cap@thenewsleaf.com, Pub, Newsleaf, KS, Effingham

Caporizzo, Maria...................... (401) 277-7647
mcaporiz@providencejournal.com, Assistant Managing Editor, Multi-platform, The Providence Journal, RI, Providence

Cappa, Dominic .... (614) 461-4040
dcappa@bizjournals.com, Ed., Columbus Business First, OH, Columbus

Capparelli, Rebecca
rcapparelli@gatehousemedia.com, VP of Sales Productivity, GateHouse Media, Inc., NY, Pittsford

Cappiello, Vin .... (307) 587-2231
vin@codyenterprise.com, Editor, The Cody Enterprise, WY, Cody

Cappola, Manuel
manuel.cappola@svherald.com, Pub., Wick Communications - Herald/Review, AZ, Sierra Vista

Cappon, Mary Ann
macappon@BeeNews.com, Adv. Sales Dir., Cheektowaga Bee, NY, Williamsville

Cappon, Mary Anne .... (716) 632-4700
macappon@beenews.com, Adv. Dir., Bee Group Newspapers, NY, Williamsville

Cappon, Mary Anne .... (716) 204-4937
macappon@beenews.com, Adv. Sales Dir., East Aurora Bee, NY, Williamsville

Cappon, Mary Anne .... (716)
macappon@beenews.com, Adv. Dir., Amherst Bee, NY, Williamsville
macappon@beenews.com, Adv. Mgr., Depew Bee, NY, Williamsville

Caputo, John .... (780) 990-9575
john.caputo@sunmedia.ca, Regional Vice-President Sales Prairie Region, Edmonton Journal, AB, Edmonton

Caputo, John .... (780) 468-0228
john.caputo@sunmedia.ca, Pub., The Edmonton Sun, AB, Edmonton

Caputo, John .... (780) 453-9001 ext. 7575
Pub, Edmonton Examiner, AB, Edmonton

Caputo, Roland A. .... (212) 556-7542
roland@nytimes.com, Sr. Vice Pres./CFO, The New York Times, NY, New York

Caraway , Kris........................... (870) 793-2383
photos@guardonline.com, Photo Ed., Batesville Daily Guard, AR, Batesville

Carbajal, Alfredo...................... (469) 977-3603
acarbajal@dallasnews.com, Ed. in Chief, Al Dia, TX, Dallas
acarbajal@dallasnews.com, Managing Editor, Al Dia, The Dallas Morning News, TX, Dallas

Carberry, Carrie .... (918) 775-4433
carrie@seqcotimes.com, Advertising Manager, Sequoyah County Times, OK, Sallisaw

Carberry, Carry
carrie@bigbasinllc.com, Adv. Mgr., Okmulgee Daily Times, OK, Okmulgee

Carbery, Thomas...................... (847) 227-9021
tcarbery@technotrans.com, Vice Pres., Technotrans America, Inc., IL, Mount Prospect

Card, Douglas M. .... (605) 448-2281
Pub./Ed., Langford Bugle, SD, Britton

Card, Douglas M.
journal@brittonsd.com, Pub./Ed., The Britton Journal, SD, Britton

Card, Irene C. .... (973) 492-2828
irenec@micinsurance.com, Pres./Author, MIC Insurance Services, Kinnelon

Carda, Carla .... (402) 461-1202
ccarda@hastingstribune.com, Mktg. Dir., Hastings Tribune, NE, Hastings

Cardamone, Linda .... (814) 368-3173
lindac@bradfordera.com, Commercial Printing, The Bradford Era, PA, Bradford

Cardamone, Linda .... (814) 368-3173
lindac@bradfordera.com, Prodn. Mgr., Bradford Era, PA, Bradford

Cardello, Frank
sales@thoughtequity.com, Vice Pres., Bus. Devel., Thought Equity Management, Inc., CO, Denver

Carden, Barry
bcarden@the-messenger.com, Circ. Dir., Messenger-Inquirer, KY, Owensboro
bcarden@the-messenger.com, Circ. Dir., The Messenger, KY, Madisonville

Carden, Curtis .... (423) 743-4112
ccarden@erwinrecord.net, Staff Writer/Sports Writer, The Erwin Record, TN, Erwin

Carden, Odie .... (956) 982-6684
ocarden@brownsvilleherald.com, IT Systems Manager, The Brownsville Herald, TX, Brownsville

Carden, Roger .... (205) 486-9461
nwaads@centurytel.net, Adv. Mgr., Northwest Alabamian, AL, Haleyville

Carden, Sandy
scarden@dailyhome.com, Adv. Mgr., Retail Sales, The Daily Home, AL, Talladega

Cardenas, Alfredo .... (361) 693-6603
acardenas@diocesecc.org, Editor, South Texas Catholic, TX, Corpus Christi

Cardenas, Carlos .... (956) 565-2425
mercedesenterprise@sbcglobal.net, Editor, Mercedes Enterprise, TX, Mercedes

Cardenas, Lucretia ....(260) 426-2640 Ext. 3311
lcardenas@kpcmedia.com, Editor, Greater Fort Wayne Business Weekly, IN, Fort Wayne

Carder, Doug
dcarder@ottawaherald.com, Mng. Ed., The Ottawa Herald, KS, Ottawa

Carderry, Mandy
circ@dauphinherald.com, Circ. Mgr., Dauphin Herald, MB, Dauphin

Cardon, Michele .... (714) 796-7016
mcardon@ocregister.com, Photography, Dir., The Orange County Register, CA, Santa Ana

Cardon, Odie .... (956) 982-6684
ocarden@brownsvilleherald.com, Prodn. Mgr., Systems, The Brownsville Herald, TX, Brownsville

Cardona-Maguigad, Adriana Maria . (773) 523-4416 Ext: 111

editor@thegatenewspaper.com, Editor, Kennedy-King College, IL, Chicago

Cardwell, Tracy
ad_director@kernersvillenews.com, Adv. Dir, Kernersville News, NC, Kernersville

Carew, Gerry
gcarew@thetelegram.com, Digital Dir., The Telegram, NL, Saint John's

Carey, Bob
bob.carey@lethbridgeherald.com, Gen. Mgr., The Southern Sun Times, AB, Lethbridge

Carey, Bob .... (403) 328-4003
bcarey@lethbridgeherald.com, Vice Pres./Gen. Mgr., Alta. Newspaper Group, Ltd, AB, Lethbridge

Carey, Caroline
carolinemcarey@thehudsonvalleynews.com, Pub., Hudson Valley News, NY, Hyde Park

Carey, George B. .... (765) 832-2443
gbcarey@mikes.com, Pres./Pub., The Daily Clintonian , IN, Clinton

Carey, James
jcarey@vnews.com, Circ. Dir., Valley News, NH, West Lebanon

Carey, James .... (925) 432-7246
james@onthehouse.com, Pres./Co-Host, On The House Syndication, Inc., Brentwood

Carey, Morris .... (925) 432-7246
morris@onthehouse.com, Vice Pres./Co-Host, On The House Syndication, Inc., Brentwood

Carey, Renee .... (724) 981-6100
rcarey@sharonherald.com, Ed., The Herald, PA, Sharon
rcarey@sharonherald.com, Editor, Goldsboro News-Argus, NC, Goldsboro

Carico, Kelli
kcarico@floridaweekly.com, Classifieds Mgr., Punta Gorda/Port Charlotte Florida Weekly, FL, Punta Gorda

Carifio, Eddie
ecarifio@shawmedia.com, Sports Ed., Daily Chronicle, IL, Dekalb

Carignan, Roland-Yves
rycarignan@ledevoir.com, Info. Mgr., Le Devoir, QC, Montreal

Carl, Carlton
carl@texasobserver.org, Exec. Pub., The Texas Observer, TX, Austin

Carl, Josephine .... (928) 871-1148
jo@navajotimes.com, Class/Legals Mgr, Navajo Times Publishing Company, Inc., AZ, Window Rock

Carletta, Dennis...................... (973) 392-1705
dcarletta@starledger.com, VP, Circ., Hunterdon County Democrat, NJ, Flemington
dcarletta@starledger.com, Circ. Dir., The Star-Ledger, NJ, Newark

Carley, Gord .... (705) 772-8282
gcarley@mediamergers.com, Sr. Assoc.-CANADA-Mag. & Newspapers, Grimes, McGovern & Associates, NY, New York

Carlin, Edward J. .... (717) 477-1521
Chair/Prof./electronic media, Shippensburg University/Communication/Journalism Department , PA, Shippensburg

Carlin, Matthew
mcarlin6141@westfield.ma.edu, Assistant Managing Editor, Westfield State University, MA, Westfield

Carlisle, John .... (586) 498-1059
jcarlisle@candnews.com, Ed., C & G Newspapers, MI, Warren

Carlisle, Terry...................................... ext. 231
tcarlisle@ellsworthamerican.com, Gen. Mgr., The Ellsworth American, ME, Ellsworth

Carlock, Mary Beth
mcarlock@cadizrecord.com, Gen. Mgr., The Cadiz Record, KY, Cadiz

Carls, Mindy
mcarls@oriongazette.com, Ed., Orion Gazette, IL, Orion

Carls, Mindy
mcarls@cambridgechron.com, Mng. Ed., Cambridge Chronicle IN ILLINOIS, IL, Cambridge

Carlsen, Jill ....(313) 343-5578
circulation@grossepointenews.com, Circ. Mgr., The Connection, MI, Grosse Pointe Woods

Carlsen, Randy
dci@kmtel.com, Ed., Dodge County Independent, MN, Kasson

Carlson, Ben.........................(502) 839-6906
bcarlson@theandersonnews.com, Ed./Pub., The Anderson News, KY, Lawrenceburg

Carlson, Bernadette
bcarlson@gaa.org, Exec. Dir., Gravure Association of America, NC, Denver

Carlson, Cliff
cliff@irishamericannews.com, publisher, Irish American News, IL, Zion

Carlson, D. Lee ....(717) 255-8272
lcarlson@pennlive.com, President, The Patriot-News, PA, Mechanicsburg

Carlson, Deb........................(574) 583-5121
dcarlson@thehj.com, Adv. Mgr., Herald Journal, IN, Monticello

Carlson, Fran
fran.carlson@revelstokereview.com, Office Mgr., Revelstoke Review, BC, Revelstoke

Carlson, Jan
miner@copperarea.com, Circ. Mgr., San Manuel Miner, AZ, Kearny

Carlson, John...............(847) 981-9399 ext. 275
carlsonj@corp.inxintl.com, Sr. Vice Pres.-Gen. Affairs/Admin., INX International Ink Co., IL, Schaumburg

Carlson, Ken.........................(209) 578-2321
kcarlson@modbee.com, Health/Medical Reporter, The Modesto Bee, CA, Modesto

Carlson, Lorie
editor@plamerican.com, Ed., Prior Lake American, MN, Savage

Carlson, Mary ....(262) 513-2629
mcarlson@conleynet.com, Automotive Ed., The Freeman, WI, Waukesha

Carlson, Michelle
mcarlson@spooneradvocate.com, Adv. Mgr., Spooner Advocate, WI, Spooner

Carlson, Mike ....(715) 830-5885
mike.carlson@ecpc.com, Circ. Dir., Leader-Telegram, WI, Eau Claire

Carlson, Mike ....(715) 830-5885
mike.carlson@ecpc.com, Circ. Dir., Entertainment Spotlight Saver, WI, Eau Claire

Carlson, Patti........................(651) 407-1214
wbpressad3@presspubs.com, Adv., Quad Community Press, MN, White Bear Lake

wbpressad3@presspubs.com, Adv. Consultant, Press Publications, Inc., MN, White Bear Lake

Carlson, Phil
pcarlson@whig.com, Photo Ed., The Quincy Herald-Whig, IL, Quincy

Carlson, Richard ....(574) 533-2151
Circ. Dir., The Goshen News, IN, Goshen

Carlson, Rick ....(574) 533-2151 ext. 346
rick.carlson@goshennews.com, Circ. Mgr., Extra, IN, Goshen

Carlson, Robert ....(617) 696-7758 X 101
robert.miltontimes@gmail.com, Circulation manager, Milton Times, MA, Milton

Carlson, Rod..........................(541) 957-4292
rcarlson@nrtoday.com, Prodn. Mgr., The News-Review, OR, Roseburg

Carlson, Ryan ....(620) 257-2368
Reporter, The Lyons News, KS, Lyons

Carlson, Susan
susancarlson@clca.org, Capitol News Service, Sacramento

Carlson, Vance
vcarlson@parkrapidsenterprise.com, Sports Editor, Park Rapids Enterprise Express, MN, Park Rapids

Carlton, Kat ....(812) 331-4351
Digital Content Mgr. , The Herald Times, IN, Bloomington

Carlton, Paul ....(615) 743-3430
pcarlto@scitn.org, Ed., Forward Focus, TN, Nashville

Carlucci, Paul V. ....(212) 597-5636
paul.carlucci@wsj.com, Greater N.Y. Sec., Sales Dir., The Wall Street Journal, NY, New York

Carman, Bill
sales@dccusa.com, Sales Rep., Dialogic Communications Corp., TN, Franklin

Carmichael, Thomas
fimsdean@uwo.ca, Dean, University of Western Ontario, ON, London

Carmier, Olga........................(954) 574-5375
ocarmier@tribune.com, Adv. Mgr., Eastsider, FL, Tamarac

Carnan, Azriane
sales.us@interactivedata.com, Mktg. Mgr., Interactive Data Real-Time Services, Inc., MA, Bedford

Carnes, Gayle
gcarnes@copperarea.com, Mng. Ed., San Manuel Miner, AZ, Kearny

Carnes, James
jamesc@copperarea.com, Pub., San Manuel Miner, AZ, Kearny

Carnes, Jennifer
jenniferc@copperarea.com, Mng. Ed., Copper Basin News, AZ, Kearny

Carnes, Michael
michaelc@copperarea.com, Adv. Prodn., Copper Basin News, AZ, Kearny

Carney, Connie ....(217) 532-3933
The Journal-News, IL, Hillsboro

Carney, Jeff ....(402) 444-1078
jeff.carney@owh.com, Dir., Digital Development, Omaha World-Herald, NE, Omaha

Carney, Jeffrey
jcarney@bhmginc.com, Corporate Director, BH Media Group, NE, Omaha

Carney, John I. ....ext. 216
jcarney@t-g.com, City Ed., Shelbyville Times-Gazette, TN, Shelbyville

Carney, Josh
jcarney@postindependent.com, Sports editor, Glenwood Springs Post Independent, CO, Glenwood Springs

Carnogursky, Paul
administrator@kanadskyslovak.ca, Webmaster, www.kanadskyslovak.ca, Kanadsky Slovak / The Canadian Slovak, ON, Mississauga

Carolus, Michelle
mcarolus@huntingdondailynews.com, The Huntingdon Daily News, PA, Huntingdon

Caron, Glen
gcaron@esthervillenews.net, Pub./Classified Adv. Mgr./Business Mgr., Estherville News, IA, Estherville

Caron, Jacqueline ....(978) 249-3535 ext. 615
jcaron@atholdailynews.com, Adv. Mgr., Athol Daily News, MA, Athol

Caron, Kevin................(705) 759-3030 ext. 268
Prodn. Mgr., The Sault Star, ON, Sault Sainte Marie

Carpenter, Bryant ....(203) 317-2204
bcarpenter@record-journal.com, Asst. Sports Ed., Record-Journal, CT, Meriden

Carpenter, Chris.......................(607) 777-2515
SUNY/Binghamton, NY, Binghamton

Carpenter, Greg ....(330) 580-8466
greg.carpenter@cantonrep.com, HR Dir., The Repository, OH, Canton

Carpenter, Hal ....(618) 539-3320
Hal@freeburgtribune.com, Vice President, The Freeburg Tribune, IL, Freeburg

Carpenter, Jeff
info@dtint.com, Pres./COO, Digital Technology International, UT, Springville

Carpenter, John
jcarpenter@rheamedical.org, Bryan College, TN, Dayton

Carpenter, Kathy ....(610) 377-2051
kcarpenter@tnonline.com, Circ. Mgr., Whitehall-Coplay Press, PA, Allentown

Carpenter, Kathy ....(610) 377-2051
kcarpenter@tnonline.com, Circ. Mgr., Times News, PA, Lehighton

Carpenter, Ken ....(407) 299-5000
ken.carpenter@kmcservicesinc.com, Valencia Cmty. College, FL, Orlando

Carpenter, Linda
lcarpenter@corbinnewsjournal.com, Production Mgr., News Journal, KY, Corbin

Carpenter, Lisa
parent@gazette.com, Ed., Pikes Peak Parent, CO, Colorado Springs

Carpenter, Melinda ....(217) 892-9613
circulation@rantoulpress.com, Circ. Mgr., Rantoul Press, IL, Rantoul

Carpenter, Melinda ....(217) 892-9613
Circ. Mgr., Piatt County Journal-Republican, IL, Monticello

Carpenter, Rick ....(803) 774-1201
Rick@theitem.com, Managing Ed., The Sumter Item , SC, Sumter

Carpenter, Steve ....(814) 946-7537
Scarpenter@Altoonamirror.Com, Assist. Managing Ed., Altoona Mirror, PA, Altoona

Carpenter, Sue ....(260) 925-2611 Ext. 2545 ....
scarpenter@kpcmedia.com, Ed. , The Garrett Clipper, IN, Auburn

Carpenter, Tina.............(620) 694-5700 Ext. 370
tcarpenter@hutchnews.com, News Clerk, The Hutchinson News, KS, Hutchinson

Carpenter, Todd
todd.carpenter@natchezdemocrat.com, Pub., Natchez Newspapers, Inc., MS, Natchez

Carr, Andrew
acarr@bedfordgazette.com, Ass. Ed. , The Bedford Gazette, PA, Bedford

Carr, Betty
metroland@insidetoronto.com, Pub., Bloor West Villager, ON, Toronto

Carr, Betty
etg@mirror-guardian.net, Pub., The York Guardian, ON, Toronto

Carr, Betty
carr@insidetoronto.com, Vice Pres./Grp. Pub., The Scarborough Mirror, ON, Toronto

Carr, Betty
bsrm@insidetoronto.com, Pub., Beach-Riverdale Mirror, ON, Toronto

Carr, Betty
eym@mirror-guardian.com, Pub., The East York Mirror, ON, Willowdale

Carr, Betty
etg@mirror-guardian.com, Pub., Etobicoke Guardian, ON, Etobicoke

Carr, Cindy ....(662) 678-1534

cindy.carr@djournal.com, Classified Adv. Mgr., Northeast Mississippi Daily Journal, MS, Tupelo

Carr, Dan ....ext. 141
dcarr@timesonline.com, Adv. Mgr., Sales, Beaver County Times, PA, Beaver

Carr, Gene..........................(952) 392-6851
gcarr@mnsun.com, CEO, American Community Newspapers LLC, MN, Osseo

Carr, Geoff ....(208) 769-3228
gtcarr@nic.edu, Advisor, North Idaho College, ID, Coeur D Alene

Carr, John
jcarr@gtowntimes.com, Pub., The Georgetown Times, SC, Georgetown

Carr, John
john.carr@suffolknewsherald.com, Pub., Suffolk News-Herald, VA, Suffolk

Carr, John
jcarr@gtowntimes.com, Pub., Georgetown Communications, Inc., SC, Georgetown

Carr, Kathy
kathy@carberrynews.ca, Gen. Mgr., Carberry News Express, MB, Carberry

Carr, Martha ....(504) 636-7401
mcarr@theadvocate.com, New Orleans Managing Ed., The Advocate, LA, Baton Rouge

Carr, Paul ....(254) 710-4693
Dir., Mktg. Information, Baylor University, TX, Waco

Carr, Scott............................(337) 289-6438
scarr2@mediaacadien.com, Adv. Sales Dir., Daily World, LA, Opelousas

Carr-Elsing, Debra
dcarrelsing@madison.com, Food Writer, The Capital Times, WI, Madison

Carranza, Rafael ....(305) 262-7575
rcarranza@efeamerica.com, Sales and Business Dev. Dir., EFE News Services - Washington, DC, Washington

Carre, Karen ....(518) 483-4720
kcarre@mtelegram.com, Adv. Mgr., The Malone Telegram, NY, Malone

Carreira, Chris ....(603) 352-1234 Ext. 1007
ccarreira@keenesentinel.com, IT Dir. , The Keene Sentinel, NH, Keene

Carrier, Wayne ....(251) 219-5305
Circ. Mgr., Home Delivery, Press-Register, AL, Mobile

Carriere, Chantal ....(705) 272-3344
chantal.carriere@sunmedia.ca, Sales Representative, print & digital, Cochrane Times-post, ON, Cochrane

Carrig, Toby...........................(573) 883-2222
tcarrig@stegenherald.com , Pub./Ed., Ste. Genevieve Herald, MO, Sainte Genevieve

Carrigan, Rob ....(719) 963-8831 x 111
robcarrigan@yourpeaknews.com, pub., The Tribune, CO, Monument

robcarrigan@yourpeaknews.com, Pub., The Pikes Peak Courier, CO, Woodland Park

Carrigg, David.......................(604) 605-2110
dcarrigg@postmedia.com, City Ed., The Province, BC, Vancouver

Carrillo, Carlos
ccarrillo@controlengineering.com, Engineering Mgr., Control Engineering Co., CA, Costa Mesa

Carrillo, Maria
maria.carrillo@chron.com, Senior Ed., Houston Chronicle, TX, Houston

Carrine, Jeremy
jc167@nyu.edu, NYU Stern School of Bus., NY, New York

Carrington, Ricky ....(830) 257-0302
ricky.carrington@dailytimes.com, Press Mgr., Kerrville Daily Times, TX, Kerrville

Carrol, Trish ....(410) 857-7885
tcarroll@carrollcountytimes.com, Sr. V.P. ,
Carroll County Times, MD, Westminster

Carroll, Brad............................(860) 801-5071
bcarroll@newbritainherald.com, Mng. Ed., New
Britain Herald, CT, New Britain

Carroll, Braxton ....(805) 739-2222
bcarroll@santamariatimes.com, IT/Web
Admin., The Lompoc Record, CA, Santa
Maria

Carroll, Braxton ....(805) 739-2222
bcarroll@santamariatimes.com, IT Admin.,
Times-Press-Recorder (OOB), CA, Santa
Maria
bcarroll@santamariatimes.com, Web Master,
Santa Maria Times, CA, Santa Maria

Carroll, Deborah
hottopics@comcast.net, Pres., Hot Topics
Publications, Inc., Wyncote

Carroll, Ellen ....(732) 775-3010
editor@thecoaster.net, Ed., Coaster, NJ,
Asbury Park

Carroll, Gary J.........................(412) 369-3590
gcarroll@denexinc.com, Pres., Denex, Inc.,
NC, Southern Pines

Carroll, Hillary
h.carroll@22ndcenturymedia.com, Circ. Mgr.,
The Mokena Messenger, IL, Orland Park
h.carroll@22ndcenturymedia.com, Circ. Mgr.,
The Homer Horizon, IL, Orland Park
h.carroll@22ndcenturymedia.com, Circ. Mgr.,
The Orland Park Prairie, IL, Orland Park
h.carroll@22ndcenturymedia.com, Circ. Mgr.,
The New Lenox Patriot, IL, Orland Park
h.carroll@22ndcenturymedia.com, Circ. Mgr.,
The Glenview Lantern, IL, Northbrook
h.carroll@22ndcenturymedia.com, Circ. Mgr.,
The Wilmette Beacon, IL, Northbrook
h.carroll@22ndcenturymedia.com, Circ. Mgr.,
The Malibu Surfside News, CA, Malibu
h.carroll@22ndcenturymedia.com, Circ. Mgr.,
The Tinley Junction, IL, Orland Park
h.carroll@22ndcenturymedia.com, Circ. Mgr.,
The Frankfort Station, IL, Orland Park
h.carroll@22ndcenturymedia.com, Circ. Mgr.,
The Lockport Legend, IL, Orland Park

Carroll, Mike ....(800) 408-4726 x 1
nhographics@nhonews.com, Prodn. Mgr.,
Navajo-Hopi Observer, AZ, Flagstaff

Carroll, Nick ....(304) 788-3333
ncarroll@newstribune.info, Sports Editor,
Mineral Daily News-Tribune, WV, Keyser

Carroll, Nicole
nicole.carroll@arizonarepublic.com, VP News
Executive Editor, Arizona Republic Digital
Media, AZ, Phoenix

Carroll, Nicole........................(602) 444-8797
ncarroll@republicmedia.com, VP, News Ed.,
The Arizona Republic, AZ, Phoenix

Carroll, Patricia ....(410) 332-6952
tcarroll@baltsun.com, SVP - targeted Media,
The Baltimore Sun, MD, Baltimore

Carroll, Rick ....(970) 429-9141
rcarroll@aspentimes.com, Mng. Ed.,
Snowmass Sun, CO, Aspen
rcarroll@aspentimes.com, Mng. Ed., The
Aspen Times, CO, Aspen

Carroll, Terry .... (519) 633-1640 ext.25
terry@theweeklynews.ca, Gen. Mgr., St.
Thomas/elgin Weekly News, ON, Saint
Thomas

Carroll, William........................(806) 296-1353
william.carroll@hearstnp.com, Ed, Plainview
Herald, TX, Plainview

Carroll , Nick ....(203) 317-2257
ncarroll@record-journal.com, News Editor, The
Southington Citizen, CT, Meriden

Carruth, Bob ....(701) 456-1220
bcarruth@thedickinsonpress.com, Adv. Dir, The
Dickinson Press, ND, Dickinson

Carruth, Bob ....(701) 456-1220

bcarruth@thedickinsonpress.com, Adv. Dir. ,
Advertizer, ND, Dickinson

Carruthers, Angela ....(416) 774-2244
acarruthers@insidetoronto.com, Sales Rep.,
North York Mirror, ON, Toronto

Carruthers, Muriel ....(613) 448-2321
therecord.editor@gmail.com, Editor, The
Chesterville Record/the Villager, ON,
Chesterville

Carry, Marty ....(217) 788-1350
Adv. Dir., Rochester Eccentric, MI, Birmingham
Dir., Adv. Sales, Lincoln Courier, IL, Lincoln

Carry, Marty ....(734) 953-2150
mcarry@oe.homecomm.net, Adv. Dir., South
Oakland Eccentric, MI, Detroit

Carry, Marty ....(734) 953-2150
mcarry@oe.homecomm.com, Adv. Dir.,
Westland Observer, MI, Detroit

Carry, Marty ....(734) 953-2150
mcorry@oe.homecomm.net, Adv. Dir.,
Plymouth Observer, MI, Detroit

Carson, Al
opllynnallred@earthlink.net, Ed., Oxford Public
Ledger, NC, Oxford

Carson, Ed
ed.carson@investors.com, To The Point Ed.,
Investor's Business Daily, CA, Los Angeles

Carson, Mary ....(414) 410-4173
Cardinal Stritch Univ., WI, Milwaukee

Carstens, Scott
scarstens@hastingstribune.com, Produ. Mgr.,
Hastings Tribune, NE, Hastings

Carstensen, Glenda
customerservice@pipestonestar.com, Circ.
Mgr., Free Star Shopper, MN, Pipestone

Carstensen , Norma
norma.carstensen@ecm-inc.com, Class. Adv.,
The Pioneer, MN, Waconia
norma.carstensen@ecm-inc.com, Class. Adv.,
The Laker, MN, Waconia

Carter, Alicia ....(270) 259-6061
acarter@graysonrecord.com, Circulation/office
manager, The Record, KY, Leitchfield

Carter, Carey
carey@athensnews-courier.com, Adv Sales,
The News-Courier, AL, Athens

Carter, Chris ....(212) 271-0715
chris.carter@auditedmedia.com, Dir., Admin.,
Watertown Public Opinion, SD, Watertown

Carter, Christine
ccarter@ara.com, Prodn. Mgr., Prime Time,
NM, Albuquerque

Carter, Cindy................. (770) 963 - 9205 x1160
cindy.carter@gwinnettdailypost.com, Adv. Mgr.,
Legal Notices, Gwinnett Daily Post, GA,
Lawrenceville

Carter, Danny............................(229) 888-9346
danny.carter@albanyherald.com, Managing
Editor, The Albany Herald, GA, Albany

Carter, Dave .... (519) 271-2220 ext. 250
dave.carter@sunmedia.ca, Pub./Adv. Mgr. ,
The Stratford Beacon Herald, ON, Stratford

Carter, Dave .... (519) 537-2341 ext 241
dcarter@postmedia.com, Group Director,
Media Sales, The Ingersoll Times, ON,
Woodstock

Carter, Dave ....(519) 537-2341 ext. 515241
dcarter@postmedia.com, Group Adv. Dir. , The
Norwich Gazette, ON, Woodstock

Carter, Debbie
ads@highcountrypress.com, Ad. Director, High
Country Press, NC, Boone

Carter, Denise ....(540) 932-3542
dcarter@newsvirginian.com, Bus. Mgr., The
News Virginian, VA, Waynesboro

Carter, Donnie ....(912) 283-2244
donnie.carter@wjhnews.com, Business/

General Manager, Waycross Journal-Herald,
GA, Waycross

Carter, Elizabeth
rdavis@triplicate.com, Circ District Mgr, The
Del Norte Triplicate, CA, Crescent City

Carter, Jennifer........................(563) 383-2485
jcarter@qctimes.com, Adv. Sales Mgr. , Quad-
City Times, IA, Davenport

Carter, John
jcarter@hearstcorp.com, managing editor,
Market News International, New York

Carter, Karen
editor@mebaneenterprise.com, Ed., The
Mebane Enterprise, NC, Mebane

Carter, Ken
kcarter@alaskadispatch.com, VP, Production,
Alaska Dispatch News, AK, Anchorage

Carter, Larry ....ext. 153
larry@slweekly.com, Circ. Mgr., Salt Lake City
Weekly, UT, Salt Lake City

Carter, Laura .... (519) 271-8002 ext. 221
admin@stratfordgazette.com, Front Office/
Distribution, Stratford Gazette, ON, Stratford

Carter, Lee
lcarter@standard.net, El Estandar, UT, Ogden

Carter, Lenora
lcarter@forwardtimes.com, Ed., Forward
Times, TX, Houston

Carter, Lenora
lcarter@forwardtimes.com, Mng. Ed., Houston
Metro Weekender, TX, Houston

Carter, M Scott ....(405) 682-1611
matthew.s.carter@occc.edu, Oklahoma City
Community College, OK, Oklahoma City

Carter, Rusty
rcarter@vagazette.com, Mng. Ed., The Virginia
Gazette, VA, Newport News

Carter, Ryan ....(740) 313-0351
ryancarter@civitasmedia.com, Ed., Record
Herald, OH, Washington Court House

Carter, Shelby ....(443) 524-8184
scarter@thedailyrecord.com, Admin. Asst. ,
The Daily Record, MD, Baltimore

Carter, Shelby ....(616) 331-2486
business@lanthorn.com, Business Manager,
Grand Valley State Univ., MI, Allendale

Carter, Sue
sucarter@msu.edu, Prof., Michigan State
University, MI, East Lansing

Carter, Tom
manager.mobile@americanclassifieds.com,
Adv. Mgr., South County Journal (OOB), MO,
Town and Country
manager.mobile@americanclassifieds.com,
Publisher, American Classifieds - Mobile,
AL, Mobile

Carter, Treca............................(918) 885-2101
hominynews2@gmail.com, Office Mgr, The
Hominy News-Progress, OK, Hominy

Carter, Ulish ....(412) 481-8302
ucarter@newpittsburghcourier.com, Managing
Editor, New Pittsburgh Courier, PA,
Pittsburgh

Carter, Van
van.carter@wjhnews.com, Adv. Mgr., Nat'l,
Waycross Journal-Herald, GA, Waycross

Carter, Wayne ....(410) 857-7878
wayne.carter@carrollcountytimes.com, Ed.,
Carroll County Times, MD, Westminster

Carthew, Renee ....(814) 532-5072
rcarthew@tribdem.com, Style Ed., The Tribune-
Democrat, PA, Johnstown

Cartledge, Ron ....(843) 937-4783
rcartledge@postandcourier.com, President of
Shared Services, The Post and Courier, SC,
Charleston

Cartmill, Bill................. (843) 546-4148 ext. 231

bcartmill@gtowntimes.com, Bus. Mgr.,
Georgetown Communications, Inc., SC,
Georgetown

Cartwright, Brian
briancartwright@boernestar.com, Pub./Ed.,
Boerne Star, TX, Boerne

Cartwright, Cathryn....................(662) 746-4911
cathryn@yazooherald.net, Staff Writer, The
Yazoo Herald, MS, Yazoo City

Carver, Lori ....(330) 996-3303
lcarver@thebeaconjournal.com, VP/
Advertising, Akron Beacon Journal, OH,
Akron

Carver, Thomas .... (620) 442-4200 ext. 120
webmaster@winfieldcourier.com, Webmaster,
Winfield Daily Courier, KS, Winfield

Carveth, Rod
carvethr@csusys.ctstateu.edu, Chair,
University of Bridgeport, CT, Bridgeport

Casale, Tony
acasale@imsworld.com, Chrmn./CEO,
American Opinion Research, NJ, Princeton

Casanova, Amanda ....(979) 845-3315
Texas A&M Univ., TX, College Station

Casanova de Toro, Dora ....(407) 767-0070
dora.toro@laprensaorlando.com, Pub./CEO, La
Prensa, FL, Longwood

Casari, Marissa
circulation@yourdailyglobe.com, Circulation
Supervisor, The Daily Globe, MI, Ironwood

Casas, Shannon........................(770) 718-3417
scasas@gainesvilletimes.com, Managing
Editor, The Times, GA, Gainesville

Casaus, Phill ....(505) 986-3033
pcasaus@sfnewmexican.com, Editor, The
Santa Fe New Mexican, NM, Santa Fe

Casciano, Debra
dcasciano@press-register.com, Sec., Southern
Circulation Managers Association, TN,
Kingsport

Cascioli, Terry........................(315) 792-5002
tcascioli@uticaod.com, Pub. , Mid York Weekly,
NY, Utica
tcascioli@uticaod.com, Pub., The Observer-
Dispatch, NY, Utica
tcascioli@uticaod.com, Pub. , Your Valley, NY,
Utica

Case, Carol
carol.case@bogalusadailynews.com, Adv. Dir.,
Bogalusa Daily News, LA, Bogalusa

Case, Chris
news@cubafreepress.com, Ed., The Cuba
Free Press, MO, Cuba
news@cubafreepress.com, Ed., Steelville Star-
Crawford Mirror, MO, Steelville

Case, Jerilyn ....(307) 787-3229
ads@bridgervalleypioneer.com, Adv., Bridger
Valley Pioneer, WY, Lyman

Case, Lloyd
lcase@forumcomm.com, Pres./COO, InForum,
ND, Fargo

Case, Nancy
nancycase8@hotmail.com, Gen. Mgr., The
People's Tribune, MO, Bowling Green

Casey, Aileen
acasey@repub.com, Sales/Retention Mgr., The
Republican, MA, Springfield

Casey, Ashley ....(315) 445-4542
dolphin@lemoyne.edu, Co-Executive Editor,
The Dolphin, NY, Syracuse

Casey, Betty
editor@tulsakids.com, Mng. Ed., Tulsa Kids,
NY, Mamaroneck

Casey, Caleb
caleb@crawfordcountyavalanche.com,
Managing Ed. , Crawford County Avalanche,
MI, Grayling

Casey, Carol

ccasey@hsvbg.org, Mktg. Mgr., The Huntsville Times, AL, Huntsville

Casey, J. C. .... (405) 574-1242
faccaseyjc@usao.edu, Faculty Advisor & Professor of Communication, Univ. of Science & Arts of Oklahoma, OK, Chickasha

Casey, Jane
advertising@manchesternewspapers.com, Prodc. Mgr & Ad., The Granville Sentinel, NY, Granville
advertising@manchesternewspapers.com, Prodc. Mgr. & Ad., The Whitehall Times, NY, Granville

Casey, Jean .... (301) 670-2650
jcasey@gazette.net, Circ. Dir., The Gazette - Damascus / Clarksburg, MD, Gaithersburg
jcasey@gazette.net, Circ. Dir., Business Gazette, MD, Gaithersburg
jcasey@gazette.net, Circ. Dir., The Gazette - Bethesda / Chevy Chase / Kensington (OOB), MD, Gaithersburg
jcasey@gazette.net, Circ. Dir., The Gazette - Gaithersburg / Mont. Village (OOB), MD, Gaithersburg
jcasey@gazette.net, Circ. Dir., The Gazette - Germantown / Poolsville / Boyds (OOB), MD, Gaithersburg
jcasey@gazette.net, Circ. Dir., The Gazette - North / Central Prince George Co. (OOB), MD, Gaithersburg
jcasey@gazette.net, Circ. Dir., The Gazette - Olney (OOB), MD, Gaithersburg
jcasey@gazette.net, Circ. Dir., The Gazette - Potomac / North Potomac, MD, Gaithersburg
jcasey@gazette.net, Circ. Dir., The Gazette - Rockville / Aspen Hill / Wheaton (OOB), MD, Gaithersburg
jcasey@gazette.net, Circ. Dir., The Gazette - Silver Spring / Takoma Park / Burtonsville (OOB), MD, Gaithersburg
jcasey@gazette.net, Circ. Dir., The Gazette - South / Central Prince George Co. (OOB), MD, Gaithersburg

Casey, Jean
jcasey@gazette.net, Circ. Mgr., Fort Detrick Standard, MD, Gaithersburg

Casey, Kevin .... (973) 210-6382
kcasey@lds.com, Vice Pres., Mktg., Logical Design Solutions, Inc., NJ, Florham Park

Casey, Mike
mikec@ndna.com, Adv. Dir., North Dakota Newspaper Association, ND, Bismarck

Casey, Pat
pcasey@theexaminernews.com, Ed., The White Plains Examiner, NY, Mount Kisco

Casey, Paula .... (602) 261-7655
p.casey@ananews.com, Exec. Dir., Arizona Newspapers Association, AZ, Phoenix

Casey, Paula .... (602) 261-7655 ext. 102
p.casey@ananews.com, Exec. Dir., ANA Advertising Services, Inc. (Arizona Newspaper Association), AZ, Phoenix

Casey, William .... (319) 335-5788
Univ. of Iowa, IA, Iowa City

Casey, Wilson .... (864) 621-7129
trivguy@bellsouth.net, wc@triviaguy.com, Trivia Guinness World Record Holder/ Syndicated Columnist, Trivia Guy by Guinness Holder, Spartanburg

Cash, John E. .... (423) 359-3165
john.cash@greenevillesun.com, Gen. Mgr., The Greeneville Sun, TN, Greeneville

Cash, John E. .... (423) 359-3165
john.cash@greenevillesun.com, Chief Revenue Officer of APG Media of TN/NC, and General Manager of The Greeneville Sun., APG Media of Tennessee/North Carolina, TN, Greeneville

Cash, Margene
clyderepublican@hotmail.com, Ed., Clyde Republican, KS, Clyde

Cashiola, Mary .... (901) 259-1724
mcashiola@bizjournals.com, Managing Editor,

Memphis Business Journal, TN, Memphis

Cashman, Ken
kencashman@thecornwalllocal.com, Ed., The Cornwall Local, NY, Cornwall

Casillas, Heather
heather@athensnews-courier.com, Adv Sales, The News-Courier, AL, Athens

Casimiro, Paulo
vision@eap.on.ca, Prodn. Mgr., Rockland Vision, ON, Rockland

Casler, Sheila .... (330) 580-8356
sheila.casler@cantonrep.com, Cir. Dir., The Independent, OH, Massillon

Cason, Ann
ann@graingertoday.com, Pub., Grainger Today, TN, Bean Station

Cason, Ben .... (740) 888-6050
bcason@thisweeknews.com, Exec. Ed., Consumer News Service Inc., OH, Lewis Center

Cason, Tammie
tcason@theblaksheartimes.com, Prodn. Mgr., The Blackshear Times, GA, Blackshear

Cass, Philip
philip.cass@zu.ac.ae, Asst. Prof., Zayed University, Al Ruwayyah

Cassady, Dave .... (503) 352-2701
cassadyd@pacificu.edu, Adviser, Pacific Univ., OR, Forest Grove

Cassady, Russ
editor@news-expressky.com, Ed., The Appalachian News-Express, KY, Pikeville

Cassan, Jean .... (740) 413-0893
jcassan@delgazette.com, Med. Sales Cons., The Delaware Gazette, OH, Delaware

Cassara, Catherine
ccassar@bgsu.edu, Assoc. Prof., Bowling Green State University, OH, Bowling Green

Cassell, Rebecca
editor@cknj.com, Ed., Central Kentucky News-Journal, KY, Campbellsville

Cassell, Regina
regina.cassell@washburn.edu, Lectr., Washburn University, KS, Topeka

Cassello, Mark
mcassello@ccsj.edu, Calumet College of St. Joseph, IN, Whiting

Casselton, Valerie .... (604) 605-2125
vcasselton@postmedia.com, Mng. Ed. , The Vancouver Sun, BC, Vancouver
vcasselton@postmedia.com, Managing Editor, The Province, BC, Vancouver

Cassidy, Bill
bcassidy@niu.edu, Asst. Prof./Journ. Area Coord., Northern Illinois University, IL, DeKalb

Cassidy, Dan
dcassidy@tribpub.com, Metro Ed., The Beacon News, IL, Chicago
dcassidy@tribpub.com, Ed., Glen-Ellyn Sun (OOB), IL, Aurora

Cassidy, Maggie
mcassidy@vnews.com, Web Editor, Valley News, NH, West Lebanon

Cassidy, Mckenzie
mcassidy@breezenewspapers.com , Editor, Captiva Current, FL, Sanibel
mcassidy@breezenewspapers.com , Editor, Sanibel-Captiva Islander, FL, Cape Coral

Cassidy, Naomi .... (315) 425-1255
nbelmar@humidity.com, Mktg. Coord., Walter Meier Climate (USA), Inc., NY, Ogdensburg

Cassidy, Neil .... (212) 803-8440
neil.cassidy@sourcemedia.com, Co-Chief, Copy Desk, American Banker, NY, New York

Cassidy, Tami
tcassidy@thepostnewspapers.com, Adv. Mgr, The Post Newspapers - Northern Wayne,

OH, Medina
tcassidy@thepostnewspapers.com, Adv. Mgr, The Post Newspapers - Eastern Medina, OH, Medina
tcassidy@thepostnewspapers.com, Adv. Mgr, The Post Newspapers - Medina, OH, Medina
tcassidy@thepostnewspapers.com, Adv. Mgr, The Post Newspapers - Brunswick, OH, Medina
tcassidy@thepostnewspapers.com, Adv. Mgr, The Post Newspapers - Southern Medina, OH, Medina
tcassidy@thepostnewspapers.com, Adv. Mgr, The Post Newspapers - Wadsworth, OH, Medina
tcassidy@thepostnewspapers.com, Adv. Mgr, The Post Newspapers - Strongsville, OH, Medina

Cassil, Ben
ben@fbcpasadena.com, Fuller Theological Seminary, CA, Pasadena

Casson, Edward A. .... (800) 638-7990
tcasson@slp.com, Chrmn./CEO, Southern Lithoplate, Inc., NC, Youngsville

Casson, Thomas J.
tom@superiorlihtoplate.com, Nat'l Sales Mgr., Superior Lithoplate of Indiana, Inc., IN, Rockville

Castagnier, Andre .... (450) 264-5364
Gen. Mgr., Les Hebdos Monteregiens, QC, Huntingdon

Castaneda, John .... (979) 968-3155
john@fayettecountyrecord.co , Prod. Mgr., The Fayette County Record, TX, La Grange

Castaneda, Leonardo .... (619) 594-4190
editor@thedailyaztec.com, San Diego State Univ., CA, San Diego

Castaneda, Michael
Michael.Castaneda@gmail.com, Editor-In-Chief, Community College of Philadelphia, PA, Philadelphia

Castaneda, Tara .... (719) 384-1427
tcastaneda@ljtdmail.com, Multimedia Sales Exec., Bent County Democrat, CO, Las Animas

Castano, Gregg
gregg.castano@businesswire.com, Co-Chief Opns., Business Wire - San Francisco, CA, San Francisco

Casteel, Shayleen
bpnews@sktc.net, Pub., The Belle Plaine News & The Oxford Register, KS, Belle Plaine

Castegnier, Pierre
marketing@elcorsy.com, Vice Pres., Mktg., Elcorsy Technology, Inc., QC, Saint-Laurent

Castelaz, Terri
tcastelaz@ironmountaindailynews.com, Lifestyles Ed., The Daily News, MI, Iron Mountain

Castellano, Cody .... (541) 758-9591
cody.castellano@lee.net, Director of Audience, Albany Democrat-Herald, OR, Albany

Castellano, Cody
cody.castellano@lee.net, Circ. Mgr., Corvallis Gazette-Times, OR, Corvallis

Castellaw, Debbie .... (706) 367-5233
debbie@mainstreetnews.com, Circ. Mgr., The Madison County Journal, GA, Jefferson

Castellaw, Debbie
debbie@mainstreetnews.com, Circ. Mgr., The Jackson Herald, GA, Jefferson

Castellaw, Debbie .... (706) 367-5233
debbie@mainstreetnews.com, Classified/Billing Mgr., The Commerce News, GA, Jefferson

Castello, Tom
tjcastello@cbaol.com, Market Mapping Specialist, Cba Industries, NJ, Elmwood Park

Castillo, Christina
ccastillo@valleystar.com, Adv. Dir. , Valley Morning Star, TX, Harlingen

Castillo, Cindy .... (210) 250-2327
ccastillo@express-news.net, Legal Coordinator, The Daily Commercial Recorder, TX, San Antonio

Castillo Jones , Lilia .... (956) 430-6250
lilia@valleystar.com , Pub./AD Dir., Valley Morning Star, TX, Harlingen

Castle, Joe .... (828) 232-5892
jcastle@citizen-times.com, Digital Prod., The Asheville Citizen-Times, NC, Asheville

Castle, Kirk
kirkcastle@mcgrann.com, Sr. VP, Sales, McGrann Paper Corp., NC, Charlotte

Castleberry, Randel
randel.castleberry@origincom.com, President, Origin Communications, Inc., CO, Colorado Springs

Castonguay, Bertrand .... (613) 632-0949
bertrand@eap.on.ca, Pres, Cie d'Edition Andre Paquette, Inc., ON, Hawkesbury

Castonguay, Bertrand .... (613) 632-4155
bertrand.castonguay@eap.on.ca, Pres., L'argenteuil, QC, Lachute
bertrand.castonguay@eap.on.ca, News, ON, Embrun
bertrand.castonguay@eap.on.ca, President, Tribune Express, ON, Hawkesbury

Castonguay, Bertrand .... (613) 632-4155
bertrand.castonguay@eap.on.ca, Pres., Le Carillon, ON, Hawkesbury

Castor, Gary .... (573) 761-0255
gary@newstribune.com, Mng. Ed., News Tribune, MO, Jefferson City

Castranio, Mary Anne
mcastranio@georgiabulletin.org, Exec. Ed., The Georgia Bulletin, GA, Smyrna

Castrejon, Aaron .... (909) 869-3530
The Poly Post, CA, Pomona

Castricone, Maria
maria@marionshopperscompass.com, Adv. Mgr., Marion County Shopper's Compass, OH, Marion

Castro, Greg .... (760) 322-8889 ext. 565
greg.castro@thedesertsun.com, Circ. Mgr., Homefinder, CA, Palm Springs

Castrodad, Elizabeth
elizabethc@lakevillejournal.com, Adv. Mgr., The Millerton News, NY, Millerton

Catalano, Larry .... (307) 633-3164
Controller, Wyoming Color Comic Group, Cheyenne

Catalano, Larry .... (307) 633-3164
larryc@wyomingnews.com, Controller, Wyoming Newspaper Group, WY, Cheyenne

Catalano, Patricia
thereminderads@comcast.net, Adv. Mgr, Cumberland Reminder, NJ, Millville

Catania Chiaramida, Lisa .... (519) 667-5480
lisa.catania@sunmedia.ca, Adv. Dir., The London Free Press, ON, London

Catarivas Corbett, Jimena .... (312) 870-7011
jimena.catarivas@laraza.com, Adv. Dir./Gen. Mgr., La Raza Newspaper, IL, Chicago

Catchatoorian, Latisha
latisha.catch@triangletribune.com, General Assignment Reporter, The Triangle Tribune, NC, Durham

Catchings, Billy
catchings@uindy.edu, Chair, University of Indianapolis, IN, Indianapolis

Catchings, Troy
tcatchings@pressregister.com, Photography Ed., The Clarksdale Press Register, MS, Clarksdale

Cater, Danielle .... (205) 631-8716
danielle@njeffersonnews.com, Gen. Mgr., North Jefferson News, AL, Gardendale

Caterina, Michael

michael@pdclarion.com, Presentation Ed., Princeton Daily Clarion, IN, Princeton

Caterson, Charlotte
charlette.caterson@mountaineagle.com, Office/Credit Mgr., Daily Mountain Eagle, AL, Jasper

Cates, Carl
ccates@valdosta.edu, Head, Valdosta State University, GA, Valdosta

Cates, Emily
Barbra@dailycommercialrecord.com, Ed., Collin County Commercial Record, TX, McKinney
Barbra@dailycommercialrecord.com, Ed., Daily Commercial Record, TX, Dallas

Cates Jr., E. Nuel
dcr@dailycommercialrecord.com, Pub., Daily Commercial Record, TX, Dallas

Cathcart, Bill
billc@southernstandard.com, Circ. Mgr., Southern Standard, TN, McMinnville

Cathey, Jeff P.
clthomes@attglobal.net, Pub., Homes & Land of Metro Charlotte, NC, Charlotte

Catlett, Vicki .... **(251) 219-5402**
Controller/Treasurer, Press-Register, AL, Mobile

Caton, Anthony
acaton@atu.edu, Asst. Prof., Arkansas Tech University, AR, Russellville

Caton, Cathy
ccaton@harrodsburgherald.com, Adv. Mgr., The Harrodsburg Herald, KY, Harrodsburg

Caton-Rosser, Mary .... **(605) 642-6422**
mary.catonrosser@bhsu.edu, Black Hills State Univ., SD, Spearfish

Caton-Rosser, Mary
marycatonrosser@bhsu.edu, Asst. Prof., Mass Commun., Black Hills State University, SD, Spearfish

Catrambone, Kathy .... **(847) 797-5101**
catrambone@pioneerlocal.com, Bureau Chief, Buffalo Grove Countryside, IL, Chicago

Catrambone, Kathy .... **(847) 797-5101**
catrambone@pioneerlocal.com, Bureau Chief, Arlington Heights Post, IL, Chicago

Catron, Derek
derek.catron@news-jrnl.com, Asst. Mng. Ed., Daytona Beach News-Journal, FL, Daytona Beach

Catsimatidis, John
helnctimes@aol.com, Pub., Hellenic Times, NY, New York

Caudell, Justin .... **(828) 226-7686**
jcaudell@westerncarolinian.com, Ed. in Chief, Western Carolina Univ., NC, Cullowhee

Caudill, Tom .... **(859) 231-3301**
tcaudill@herald-leader.com, Asst. Mng. Ed., Lexington Herald-Leader, KY, Lexington

Caughlin, Joe
j.coughlin@22ndcenturymedia.com, Pub., The Lake Forest Leader, IL, Northbrook
j.coughlin@22ndcenturymedia.com, Pub., The Glencoe Anchor, IL, Northbrook
j.coughlin@22ndcenturymedia.com, Pub., The Highland Park Landmark, IL, Northbrook

Caulkins, Ann .... **(704) 358-5000**
acaulkins@charlotteobserver.com, Pres./Pub., The Charlotte Observer, NC, Charlotte

Caulkins, Heather .... **(860) 495-8283**
hcaulkins@thewesterlysun.com, Digital Advertising Mgr, The Westerly Sun, CT, Pawcatuck

Caumartin, Richard
marketing@laction.ca, Sales Dir, Action (l'), ON, London

Caumartin, Richard
marketing@laction.ca, Sales Dir, Action

London Sarnia, ON, Brampton
marketing@laction.ca, Dir., sales, Le Rempart, ON, Windsor

Causey, Jade
circulation@hendersondailynews.com, Circ. Mgr., Henderson Daily News, TX, Henderson

Causman, Paul .... **(419) 724-0363**
paul@jewishtoledo.org, Marketing Manager and Editor, Toledo Jewish News, OH, Sylvania

Cauthen, Marita .... **(978) 343-8147**
editor@raivaaja.org, Ed., Raivaaja, MA, Fitchburg

Cauthorn, Robert .... **(702) 385-3111**
COO, Las Vegas Sun, NV, Henderson

Cavalier, Keyle .... **(318) 459-3407**
keyle.cavalier@shreveporttimes.com, Digital Sales Mgr., The Times, LA, Shreveport

Cavaliere, Phyllis .... **(212) 576-9504**
pcav@metrosn.com, Chairperson & CEO, Metro Newspaper Advertising Services, Inc., NY, New York

Cavallo, George
gcavallo@gilbaneco.com, Sr. Vice Pres./Mgr.-North East Reg., Gilbane Building Co., RI, Providence

Cavanagh, Paul .... **(216) 999-4388**
Dir Labor & Empl Relations, The Plain Dealer, OH, Brooklyn

Cavaretta, Andrew .... **(716) 965-2908**
webdesign@post-journal.com, The Post-Journal, NY, Jamestown

Cavazos, Daniel R.
rdcavazos@brownsvilleherald.com, Pub., The Brownsville Herald, TX, Brownsville

Cavazos, R. Daniel
rdaniel_cavazos@link.freedom.com, Pub., El Nuevo Heraldo, TX, Brownsville

Cave, Michele
mcave@parsonssun.com, Graphic Designer, Parsons Sun, KS, Parsons

Cavell, William C. .... **(613) 224-5755**
Pub, The Enterprise, ON, Iroquois Falls A

Cavender, Mike .... **(770) 622-7011**
mikec@rtdna.org, Exec. Dir., Radio Television Digital News Association, DC, Washington

Cavin, Nadja
ads@nomenugget.com, Adv. Mgr., The Nome Nugget, AK, Nome

Cavrich, J.D. .... **(814) 949-7037**
Jcavrich@Altoonamirror.Com, Photo Ed., Altoona Mirror, PA, Altoona

Cawley, Dennis
dcawley@norwoodrecord.com, Pub., West Roxbury/Rosindale Bulletin, MA, Hyde Park

Caya, Joel .... **(819) 762-4361 #227**
joel.caya@tc.tc, General manager, Citoyen Rouyn Noranda, QC, Rouyn-Noranda

Caylor, Matthew .... **(717) 703-3040**
matthewc@mansimedia.com, Dir., Interactive Media, MANSI Media, PA, Harrisburg

Caywood, Kurt .... **(904) 359-4438**
kurt.caywood@jacksonville.com , VP Audience Development, The Florida Times-Union, FL, Jacksonville

Cazalas, Mike .... **(850) 747-5094**
mmcazalas@pcnh.com, Eastern Ed., Halifax NW Florida Group, The News Herald, FL, Panama City

Ceaseretti, Jackie
jceaseretti@pdpost.com, Adv. Sales Mgr., Florida Pennysaver, FL, West Palm Beach

Cech, Lisa
Online Ed., editor@dln.com, The Daily Legal News and Cleveland Recorder, OH, Cleveland

Cecil, Mike .... **(309) 686-3117**

mcecil@pjstar.com, Metro Ed., Journal Star, IL, Peoria

Cederholm, Vicki .... **(719) 636-0307**
vicki.cederholm@gazette.com, Adv. Dir., Sales Opns., The Gazette, CO, Colorado Springs

Celeste, Eric .... **(404) 614-2509**
eric.celeste@creativeloafing.com, Editor in Chief, Creative Loafing Atlanta, GA, Atlanta

Celona, Thomas .... **(215) 648-1077**
tcelona@montgomerynews.com, Ed, Times Chronicle, PA, Fort Washington
tcelona@montgomerynews.com, Exec. Ed., Montgomery Life, PA, Fort Washington
tcelona@montgomerynews.com, Exec. Ed., Ambler Gazette, PA, Lansdale
tcelona@montgomerynews.com, Ed., Willow Grove Guide, PA, Fort Washington
tcelona@montgomerynews.com, Ed, The Globe, PA, Fort Washington
tcelona@montgomerynews.com, Ed., Perkasie News-Herald, PA, Fort Washington
tcelona@montgomerynews.com, Ed, Glenside News, PA, Fort Washington
tcelona@montgomerynews.com, Ed, Springfield Sun, PA, Fort Washington
tcelona@montgomerynews.com, North Penn Life, PA, Fort Washington
tcelona@montgomerynews.com, Ed, Public Spirit, PA, Fort Washington
tcelona@montgomerynews.com, Ed., The Colonial, PA, Fort Washington

Celona, Thomas
tcelona@montgomerynews.com, News Ed., Souderton Independent, PA, Fort Washington

Cembal, Darryl
kingston@theheritageemc.ca, Ed., The Heritage, ON, Kingston

Cembal, Darryl
heritagenews@bellnet.ca, Pub., The Frontenac Gazette, ON, Kingston

Centers, Joe .... **(419) 668-3771 Ext/ 1234**
jcenters@norwalkreflector.com, Mng. Ed., Norwalk Reflector, OH, Norwalk

Centofanti, Lou
corporate@perma-fix.com, Pres./CEO, Perma-Fix Environmental Services, GA, Atlanta

Cerasani, Monty
mpi@marketingplusinc.com, Pres./CEO, Marketing Plus, Inc., NJ, Woodbridge

Ceravolo, Tim
ceravot@bethelcollege.edu, Bethel College, IN, Mishawaka

Cerderberg, Jenna
editor@leaderadvertiser.com, Ed., Advertiser, MT, Polson

Cerfus, Daniel
daniel.cerfus@mines.sdsmt.edu, Business Manager, South Dakota School of Mines & Technology, SD, Rapid City

Cerny, Keith R. .... **(719) 589-2553 x120**
kcerny@alamosanews.com, Publisher, Valley Courier, CO, Alamosa

Cervantes, Sandra
cervantes@cervantespublishingcompany.com, Pub., Miniondas, CA, Tustin

Cerveny, Amanda
acerveny@postindependent.com, Advertising sales, Glenwood Springs Post Independent, CO, Glenwood Springs

Cervi, Joe .... **(719) 404-2769**
jcervi@chieftain.com, Sports Editor, The Pueblo Chieftain, CO, Pueblo

Cessna, Robert .... **(979) 731-4638**
robert.cessna@theeagle.com, Sports Ed., The Eagle, TX, Bryan

Cessna, Sara
classifieds@ssecho.com, Classified Sales, Sulphur Springs News-Telegram, TX, Sulphur Springs

Cetron, Ari .... **(425) 392-6434**

samrev@isspress.com, Ed., Sammamish Review, WA, Issaquah

Chabot, John
sales@miraclepress.com, Pres., Miracle Industries, Inc., CT, Winsted

Chacanaca, Mike
mike@claycountyleader.com, Ed., Clay County Leader, TX, Henrietta

Chadda, Kalyani
kchadha@jmail.umd.edu, Exec. Dir., Society for Features Journalism, MD, College Park

Chadderdon, Jesse
jesse.chadderdon@doverpost.com, Exec. Ed., Dover Post, DE, Dover
jesse.chadderdon@doverpost.com, Exec. Ed., The Middletown Transcript, DE, Middletown
jesse.chadderdon@doverpost.com, Exec. Ed., The Sussex Countian, DE, Dover
jesse.chadderdon@doverpost.com, Exec. Ed., Milford Beacon, DE, Dover
jesse.chadderdon@doverpost.com, Exec. Ed., Hockessin Community News, DE, Middletown

Chadwick, Melissa A. .... **(301) 670-2071**
mchadwick@gazette.net, Ed., The Gazette - Damascus / Clarksburg, MD, Gaithersburg
mchadwick@gazette.net, Ed., The Gazette - Rockville / Aspen Hill / Wheaton (OOB), MD, Gaithersburg
mchadwick@gazette.net, Ed., The Gazette - Silver Spring / Takoma Park / Burtonsville (OOB), MD, Gaithersburg
mchadwick@gazette.net, Ed., The Gazette - Olney (OOB), MD, Gaithersburg
mchadwick@gazette.net, Ed., The Gazette - Germantown / Poolsville / Boyds (OOB), MD, Gaithersburg
mchadwick@gazette.net, Ed., The Gazette - Bethesda / Chevy Chase / Kensington (OOB), MD, Gaithersburg
mchadwick@gazette.net, Ed., The Gazette - Gaithersburg / Mont. Village (OOB), MD, Gaithersburg
mchadwick@gazette.net, Ed., The Gazette - North / Central Prince George Co. (OOB), MD, Gaithersburg
mchadwick@gazette.net, Ed., The Gazette - South / Central Prince George Co. (OOB), MD, Gaithersburg
mchadwick@gazette.net, Ed., The Gazette - Potomac / North Potomac, MD, Gaithersburg

Chadwick, Sharon R.
davispaper@sbcglobal.net, Pub./Ed., The Davis News, OK, Davis

Chaffey, Joanne
pilotsales@optipress.ca, Adv. Mgr., The Pilot, NL, Lewisporte

Chaffier, Tim .... **(215) 854-2845**
mbroad@phillynews.com, Marketing, Strategy, Branding, Design & Leadership , Philadelphia Inquirer, Daily News & Philly.com, PA, Philadelphia

Chaffin, Andrea .... **(740) 852-1616 Ext. 1619**
achaffin@civitasmedia.com, Ed., The Madison Press, OH, London

Chagnon, Maritime
maritime.chagnon@canadafrancais.com, Mng. Ed., Granby Express, QC, Granby

Chagolla, Ray
ray_chagolla@dailyjournal.com, Circ. Mgr., Daily Commerce, CA, Los Angeles

Chagollan, Steve
steve.chagollan@variety.com, Sr. Ed., Special Reports, Daily Variety, CA, Los Angeles

Chaiken, Mike
mchaiken@bristolobserver.com, Edition Ed., The Observer, CT, Southington

Chaisson, Bill
bill@mclallenhouse.com, Mng. Ed., The Trumansburg Free Press, NY, Ithaca

Chaisson, Rebecca
jdneditor@bellsouth.net, News/Family/Living Ed., Jennings (LA) Daily News, LA, Jennings

Chaisson, Vicki......................(985) 693-7229
editor@tlgnewspaper.com, Ed./Adv. Mgr.,
LaFourche Gazette, LA, Larose

Chalabian, Steven H.
kjack@kjack.com, Vice Pres., Sales, K-Jack
Engineering Co., Inc., CA, Gardena

Chalat-Noaker, Nan
editor@parkrecord.com, Ed., Park Record, UT,
Park City

Chalifour, Michel ....(418) 862-1911
journal@infodimanche.com, Info Dimanche,
QC, Riviere-du-Loup
journal@infodimanche.com, Info Week-end,
QC, Edmundston

Chalker, Roy F.
rchalker@bellsouth.net, Ed./Pub., The True
Citizen, GA, Waynesboro

Chalmers, Christina
cchalmers@civitasmedia.com, Editor, Miami
County Advocate, OH, Troy

Chalmers, Christina ....(937) 569-4312
cchalmers@dailyadvocate.com, Ed., Daily
Advocate, OH, Greenville
cchalmers@dailyadvocate.com, Weekend
Advocate, OH, Greenville

Chalmers, John
jchalmers@postmedia.com, Ed., Airdrie Echo,
AB, Airdrie

Chalmers, Josh ....(403) 934-3021(ext 110)
josh.chalmers@sunmedia.ca, Ed, Strathmore
Standard, AB, Strathmore

Chaloner, Clayton
expos@mts.net, Ed., The Exponent, MB,
Grandview

Chalphin, Donald ....(215) 557-2359
dchalphin@alm.com, Associate Publisher, The
Legal Intelligencer, PA, Philadelphia

Chamberlain, Amanda ....(573) 324-2222
bgtcirc@lcs.net, Circulation, Bowling Green
Times, MO, Bowling Green

Chamberlain, Don ....(586) 323-8146
don.chamberlain@advisorsource.com, Assoc.
Ed., Adviser & Source, MI, New Baltimore

Chamberlain, Gwen
GwenChamberlain@Chronicle-Express.com,
Ed., The Chronicle-Express, NY, Penn Yan

Chamberlin, Lillie ....(616) 822-8981
lgchamberlin@knox.edu, Co-Editor-in-Chief,
Knox College, IL, Galesburg

Chamberlin, Tim ....(918) 581-8343
tim.chamberlin@tulsaworld.com, Presentation
editor, Tulsa World, OK, Tulsa

Chambers, Ashley
achambers@oaklandpostonline.com,
Associate Editor, Oakland Post, CA, Oakland
achambers@oaklandpostonline.com,
Associate Editor, Marin County Post, CA,
Oakland
achambers@oaklandpostonline.com,
Associate Editor, Richmond Post, CA,
Oakland

Chambers, Billie ....(217) 849-2000
tdnews@cell1net.net, Ed., Toledo Democrat,
IL, Toledo

Chambers, Cliff ....(541) 269-0310
cliff@scod.com, Ed., South Coast Shopper,
OR, Coos Bay

Chambers, Dianna...................(615) 254-5522
dchambers@TNLedger.com, Adv. Mgr.,
Nashville Ledger, TN, Nashville

Chambers, Doug L. ....(317) 888-3376
doug@indychallenger.com, Ed./Pub., The
Franklin Challenger, IN, Greenwood

Chambers, Doug L....................(317) 888-3376
doug@indychallenger.com, Pub./Ed.,
Greenwood and Southside Challenger, IN,
Greenwood

Chambers, Emily......................(404) 894-2831

emily.chambers@coxmediagroup.com, Georgia
Inst. of Technology, GA, Atlanta

Chambers, Gus
gus.chambers@mso.umt.edu, Adj. Instr., The
University of Montana, MT, Missoula

Chambers, Larry
lchambers@valink.com, Ed., Declaration, VA,
Independence

Chambers, Lynda ....(520) 547-9734
lchambers@gvnews.com, Business Manager,
Green Valley News & Sahuarita Sn, AZ,
Green Valley

Chambers, Marianne
mchambers@tdn.com, Business Mgr., The
Daily News, WA, Longview

Chambers, Mary
advertising@timesnewspapers.com, Adv. Mgr,
South County Times, MO, Saint Louis
advertising@timesnewspapers.com, Adv. Mgr,
West End Word, MO, Saint Louis
advertising@timesnewspapers.com, Adv. Mgr,
Webster-Kirkwood Times, Inc., MO, Saint
Louis

Chambers, Scott ....(313) 882-3500
schambers@grossepointenews.com, Pub.,
Grosse Pointe News, MI, Grosse Pointe
Woods

Chambers, Todd
todd.chambers@ttu.edu, Assoc. Prof./
Chair, Dept. Electronic Media, Texas Tech
University, TX, Lubbock

Chambliss, Alex
achambliss@timesfreepress.com, Region
Ed., Chattanooga Times Free Press, TN,
Chattanooga

Chambliss, Cathy ....(937) 878-3993 Ext. 2115
cchambliss@civitasmedia.com, Adv., Fairborn
Daily Herald, OH, Xenia

Chamney, Megan ....(306) 662-2100
mchamney@maplecreeknews.com, Office/
Circulation Manager, The Maple Creek News,
SK, Maple Creek

Champane, James
james.champane@hope.edu, Co-Editor-in-
Chief, Hope College, MI, Holland

Champion, Eric
eric@cambridge-chamber.com, Adv. Mgr.,
Isanti-Chisago County Star, MN, Cambridge

Champion, Lana ....(904) 359-4471
lana.champion@jacksonville.com , VP Sales,
The Florida Times-Union, FL, Jacksonville

Champion, Laurel
laurelchampion@mlive.com, Gen. Mgr., The
Jackson Citizen Patriot, MI, Jackson

Champion, Lea Ann...................(210) 821-4105
Sr. Exec. Vice Pres./CMO, AT&T, Inc., TX, San
Antonio

Champion, Lee
lee.champion@alexcityoutlook.com, Prodn.
Mgr., Alexander City Outlook, AL, Alexander
City

Champion, Scott ....(513) 732-2511
Owner, The Clermont Sun, OH, Batavia

Chan, Michael G. ....(212) 969-7578
mchan@hearst.com, Dir. of Tech., North
America Syndicate, New York

Chan-Olmsted, Sylvia ....(352) 392-6557
Prof./Assoc. Dean, Research/AI and
Effie Flanagan Prof. in Journalism &
Communications, University of Florida, FL,
Gainesville

Chan-Pool, Vera ....(206) 461-1346
QAMagNews@nwlink.com, Ed., Queen Anne &
Magnolia News, WA, Seattle

Chan-Pool, Vera ....(206) 461-1346
CityLivingEditor@nwlink.com, Ed., City Living
Seattle, WA, Seattle

Chance, Don

info@yale.com, Pres., Yale Materials Handling
Corp., NC, Greenville

Chance, John ....(432) 230-1131
jchance@jalrecord.net, Publisher/ Owner, The
Jal Record, NM, Jal

Chance, Lisa
lisaj@thetruecitizen.com, Gen. Mgr., The True
Citizen, GA, Waynesboro

Chancellor, Jennifer
jchancellor@okgazette.com, Ed, Okcbiz, OK,
Oklahoma City

Chancellor, Rhonda ....(830) 281-2341
rchancellor@pleasantonexpress.com, Business
Manager, Classifieds Manager, Pleasanton
Express, TX, Pleasanton

Chandler, Jerry
jchandler@jsu.edu, Asst. Prof./Internship
Coord., Jacksonville State University, AL,
Jacksonville

Chandler, Linda
lchandler@ripleynews.com, Pub., Spotlight-
advertiser, IN, Versailles

Chandler, Linda
lchandler@ripleynews.com, Pub./Adv. Mgr.,
Osgood Journal, IN, Versailles

Chandler, Linda
lchandler@ripleynews.com, Pub., Versailles
Republican, IN, Versailles

Chandler, Meghan ....(269) 387-2097
herald-editor@wmich.edu, Editor-in-chief,
Western Michigan Univ., MI, Kalamazoo

Chandler, Robert C.
robert.chandler@pepperdine.edu, Chair,
Pepperdine University, CA, Malibu

Chandler, Ross ....(252) 407-9942
Features Ed., Rocky Mount Telegram, NC,
Rocky Mount

Chandler, Tim
tchandler@roxboro-courier.com, Ed., The
Courier-Times, NC, Roxboro

Chaney, Jason
jchaney@centraloregonian.com, Ed., Central
Oregonian, OR, Prineville

Chaney, Jessica ....(410) 732-6618
jchaney@baltimoreguide.com, Acct. Exec.,
Baltimore Guide South, MD, Baltimore

Chaney, Kathy ....(312) 225-2400
Managing Editor, Chicago Defender, IL,
Chicago

Chaney, Ken
signred@lisco.com, Pub., The News-Review,
IA, Sigourney

Chaney, Paul
paul@webmarketingtoday.com, Ed., Practical
Ecommerce, Traverse City

Chaney, Robert L.......................(541) 863-5233
dcmail@dcmail.info, Pub./Ed., The Douglas
County Mail, OR, Myrtle Creek

Chang, Grant
grant@koreatimes.com, Gen. Mgr., Korea
Times, CA, Los Angeles

Chang, Jaemin
chyeon@koreatimes.com, Pub., The Korea
Times, NY, Long Island City

Chang, Julia
chang@rowan.edu, Assoc. Prof., Rowan Univ.,
NJ, Glassboro

Chang, Karrie
karrie@lloydminstersource.com, Prod. Mgr. ,
Lloydminster Source, SK, Lloydminster

Chang, Li-Jing
li-jing.a.chang@jsums.edu, Asst. Prof., Jackson
State University, MS, Jackson

Channell, Gina
gchannell@pleasantonweekly.com, Pres.,
Pleasanton Weekly, CA, Pleasanton

Chant, Cindy ....(902) 853-3320

cindy@peicanada.com, Ed., West Prince
Graphic, PE, Alberton

Chantry, Michelle ....(661) 395-7211
mchantry@bakersfield.com, Pres. & Chief
Exec. Officer, The Bakersfield Californian,
CA, Bakersfield

Chapdelaine, Ronald ....ext. 760
Adv. Mgr., Item Extra, MA, Clinton

Chapin, Josh......................(765) 973-4463
jchapin@pal-item.com, Sports Ed., Palladium-
Item, IN, Richmond

Chapline, Kent
k.chapline@tcu.edu, Adj. Fac., Texas Christian
University, TX, Fort Worth

Chapman, Bob ....(937) 651-2125
bchapman@examiner.org, Adv. Mgr.,
Bellefontaine Examiner, OH, Bellefontaine

Chapman, Caleb ....(254) 968-9056
cchapman@tarleton.edu, Dir., Tarleton State
University, TX, Stephenville

Chapman, Debbie
debbiec@marshfieldmail.com, Adv. Mgr., The
Marshfield Mail, MO, Marshfield

Chapman, Debra
debbiec@cpimo.com, Adv. Mgr., The Edge,
MO, Marshfield

Chapman, Don ....(808) 529-4869
dchapman@midweek.com, Editor-in-Chief,
MidWeek Oahu, HI, Honolulu

Chapman, Greg ....(972) 544-2369
greg@elliscountypress.com, Creative Director,
The Ellis County Press, TX, Ferris

Chapman, Jim......................(260) 461-8366
jchapman@jg.net, Assistant Metro Ed./day city
Ed., The Journal Gazette, IN, FORT WAYNE

Chapman, John ....(256) 549-2030
john.chapman@gadsdentimes.com, Circ. Mgr.,
Times2, AL, Gadsden

Chapman, John ....(256) 549-2030
john.chapman@gadsdentimes.com, Circ.
Director, The Gadsden Times, AL, Gadsden

Chapman, Josie ....(559) 784-5000 Ext. 1061
jchapman@portvillerecorder.com, Adv./Mktg.
Dir., The Porterville Recorder, CA, Porterville

Chapman, Laurie
lchapman@cullmantimes.com, Adv. Dir., The
Cullman Times, AL, Cullman

Chapman, Paul......................(604) 605-2078
pchapman@postmedia.com, Deputy Editor,
The Vancouver Sun, BC, Vancouver

Chapman, Paul......................(604) 605-2078
pchapman@postmedia.com, Prodn. Mgr., Post
Press, Nugget, ON, North Bay
pchapman@postmedia.com, Deputy Editor,
The Province, BC, Vancouver

Chapman, Randy
rchapman@postbulletin.com, Ed., The
Rochester Shopper, MN, Rochester

Chapman, Randy......................(507) 285-7602
news@postbulletin.com, Pub., Post-Bulletin,
MN, Rochester

Chapman, Sam.............(415) 383-4500 ext. 315
schapman@pacificsun.com, Pub., Pacific Sun,
CA, San Rafael

Chapman, Tricia
triciac@ccheadliner.com, Gen. Mgr., Christian
County Headliner News, MO, Ozark

Chapman, Vann ....(706) 846-3188
news2@star-mercury.com, Ed, Talbotton New
Era, GA, Manchester

Chapman, Yvonne ....(414) 390- 5769
yvonnec@milwaukeejewish.org, Production
Manager, The Wisconsin Jewish Chronicle,
WI, Milwaukee

Chapnick, Ben ....(212) 679-3288
ben@blackstar.com, Pres., Black Star
Publishing Co., Inc., NY, White Plains

Chapnick, John P.
john@blackstar.com, Vice Pres., Black Star Publishing Co., Inc., NY, White Plains

Chappell, Ginger .... (706) 367-2487
Prodn. Mgr., The Madison County Journal, GA, Jefferson

Chappell, Lisa
advertising@heraldbanner.com, Pub., Commerce Journal, TX, Greenville

Chappell, Lisa
publisher@heraldbanner.com, Pub., Herald-Banner, TX, Greenville
publisher@heraldbanner.com, Pub., Gainesville Daily Register, TX, Gainesville

Charbonneau, Louis
louis.charbonneau@thomsonreuters.com, 1st Vice Pres., United Nations Correspondents Association, NY, New York

Charland, Todd
mbanfield@thechronicle.com, Circ. Dir., The Chronicle, CT, Willimantic

Charles, Mickey 1215/947-5199
mcharles3848@verizon.net, Pres./CEO, The Sports Network, PA, Hatboro
mcharles3848@verizon.net, President & Founder, The Sports Network (OOB), PA, Hatboro

Charlet, Bob
bcharlet@bizjournals.com, Pub., Pacific Business News, HI, Honolulu

Charnosky, Christine
countryjournal@turley.com, Ed., Country Journal, MA, Huntington

Chartier, Benoit .... (450) 773-6028
bchartier@leclarion.qc.ca, Pub., Le Clairon Regional De Saint-hyacinthe, QC, Saint Hyacinthe
bchartier@leclarion.qc.ca, Ed., La Pensee De Bagot, QC, Acton Vale

Chartock, Alan .... (518) 465-5233 ext. 150
achartock@wamc.org, Pub., The Legislative Gazette, NY, Albany

Chase, Carla
cchase@chasemediagroup.com, Yorktown Pennysaver - Yorktown Somers, NY, Yorktown Heights
cchase@chasemediagroup.com, Yorktown Pennysaver - Mahopac, NY, Yorktown Heights
cchase@chasemediagroup.com, Yorktown Pennysaver - Carmel, NY, Yorktown Heights
cchase@chasemediagroup.com, Yorktown Pennysaver - Brewster - New Fairfield, NY, Yorktown Heights
cchase@chasemediagroup.com, Yorktown Pennysaver - Mt. Kisco - Katonah, NY, Yorktown Heights
cchase@chasemediagroup.com, Yorktown Pennysaver - Croton - Ossining, NY, Yorktown Heights
cchase@chasemediagroup.com, Yorktown Pennysaver - Pleasantville, NY, Yorktown Heights
cchase@chasemediagroup.com, Yorktown Pennysaver - Tarrytown, NY, Yorktown Heights
cchase@chasemediagroup.com, Yorktown Pennysaver - N White, NY, Yorktown Heights
cchase@chasemediagroup.com, Yorktown Pennysaver - Putnam Valley, NY, Yorktown Heights
cchase@chasemediagroup.com, Yorktown Pennysaver - Peekskill, NY, Yorktown Heights
cchase@chasemediagroup.com, Yorktown Pennysaver - Fishkill, NY, Yorktown Heights
cchase@chasemediagroup.com, Yorktown Pennysaver - Hopewell, NY, Yorktown Heights
cchase@chasemediagroup.com, Yorktown Pennysaver - Wappingers, NY, Yorktown Heights
cchase@chasemediagroup.com, Yorktown Pennysaver - Pawling, NY, Yorktown Heights

Chase, Carla
cchase@chasemediagroup.com, Owner/Pub., Pennysaver, NY, Yorktown Heights

Chase, Christy .... ext. 2246
cchase@durhamregion.com, Entertainment Ed., Oshawa-whitby This Week, ON, Oshawa

Chase, Debra .... (716) 250-6892
dchase@classifiedsplus.com, Client Partnerships, Media Sales Plus, Inc., NY, Williamsville

Chase, Denny .... (231) 933-1494
dchase@record-eagle.com, Sports Ed., Traverse City Record-Eagle, MI, Traverse City

Chase, MacKenzie .... (928) 556-2262
mchase@flaglive.com, Staff Writer, Flagstaff Live!, AZ, Flagstaff

Chase, Marc .... (219) 662-5330
marc.chase@nwi.com, Page Ed., Investigative Reporter, The Times of Northwest Indiana, IN, Munster

Chase, Neil .... (408) 920-5456
nchase@bayareanewsgroup.com, Exec. Ed., East Bay Times, CA, Walnut Creek

Chase, Sara .... (715) 685-4510
Reporter, The Ashland Daily Press, WI, Ashland

Chase, Sarah
bhgads@nd-bhginc.com, Ad. Mgr., McLean County Independent, ND, Garrison

Chase, Trevor
tchase@bfp.burlingtonfreepress.com, Dir., IT, The Burlington Free Press, VT, Burlington

Chasney, Susan .... (518) 828-1616 Ext. 2490
schasney@registerstar.com, Ed., Register-Star, NY, Hudson

Chastain, Rhesa .... (706) 635-4313
News@timescourier.com, Circ./Office Mgr., Times-Courier, GA, Ellijay

Chatelain, Stephen .... (308) 233-9700
Ed., Kearney Hub, NE, Kearney

Chater, John
johnc@captureddigital.com, Captured Digital, Inc., CA, Newbury Park

Chatham, Betty
bchatham@wehco.com, Pub., El Dorado News-Times / Sunday News, AR, El Dorado

Chattopadhyay, Sumana
sumana.chattopadhyay@marquette.edu, Asst. Prof., Marquette University, WI, Milwaukee

Chau, Katie
herald@cchc.org, Exec. Ed., The Herald Monthly, NY, Flushing

Chau, Katie
herald@cchc.org, Exec. Ed., Chinese Christian Herald Crusades, Inc., NY, New York

Chaulk, Joann
jchaulk@thetelegram.com, National Adv. Sales, The Telegram, NL, Saint John's

Chauvette, Ghislain .... (819) 758-6211
chauvetteg@transcontinental.ca, Ed., L'avenir De L'erable, QC, Plessisville
chauvetteg@transcontinental.ca, Director de l'information, La Nouvelle, QC, Victoriaville

Chauvin, Michael .... (843) 873-9424
mchauvin@journalscene.com, Pub., Summerville Journal-Scene, SC, Summerville

Chavern, David .... (571) 366-1100
david@newsmediaalliance.org, Pres. & CEO, News Media Alliance, VA, Arlington

Chaves, Susan
bridgeportnews@hersamacorn.com, Ed., Bridgeport News, CT, Shelton

Chavez, Adriana .... (915) 546-6117
chavezadr@gmail.com, El Paso Times, TX, El Paso

Chavez, Gene
gchavez@dallasnews.com, Circulation Director, The Dallas Morning News, TX, Dallas

Chavez, Stephen .... (301) 680-6569
chavezs@gc.adventlst.org, Mng. Ed., Adventist Review, MD, Silver Spring

Chciuk, Jennifer Cone
tribune.jenny@gmail.com, Pub., West Essex Tribune, NJ, Livingston

Cheak, Connie J.
janicep@nacms-c.com, Pub., The Daily Record, KY, Louisville

Cheatham, Brandi
bcheatham@kystandard.com, Advt Mgr, Kentucky Standard, KY, Bardstown

Cheavis, Patricia .... (985) 857-2250
patricia.cheavis@houmatoday.com, District Mgr., The Courier, LA, Houma

Checketts, Patrick
pchecketts@sewardindependent.com, Adv. Mgr., Seward County Independent, NE, Seward

Cheek, Kip
kip@mendotareporter.com, Pub., Mendota Reporter, IL, Mendota

Cheek, Mary Lou .... (252) 586-2700
Adv. Mgr., Lake Gaston Gazette-Observer, NC, Littleton

Cheek, Pat
pcheek@heartlandpublications.com, Adv. Dir., Claiborne Progress, TN, Tazewell

Cheek, Pat .... (606) 248-1010 Ext. 1124
pcheek@civitasmedia.com, Adv. Dir., Middlesboro Daily News, KY, Middlesboro
pcheek@civitasmedia.com, Rgl. Admin. Coord., The Harlan Daily Enterprise, KY, Harlan

Cheek, Pat .... ext. 223
advertising@middlesborodailynews.com, Adv. Mgr., Cumberland Trading Post, KY, Middlesboro

Cheek, Patricia .... (336) 694-4145
cmofficemanager@caswellmessenger.com, Office Mgr., Caswell Messenger, NC, Yanceyville

Cheffen, Jimmy .... (501) 370-5354
jcheffen@philander.edu, Philander Smith College, AR, Little Rock

Cheffey, Mark
editorial@palmyra-spectator.com, Pub., Palmyra Spectator, MO, Palmyra

Chelsea, Modglin
cmodglin@bannergraphic.com, Reporter, Banner-Graphic, IN, Greencastle

Chelstowski, Ray .... (212) 856-6380
rchelstowski@nnnlp.com, CEO, Newspaper National Network LP, NY, New York

Chelton, Mark .... ext. 121
Pub., Suburban Parent, NJ, North Brunswick

Chen, Danny .... (228) 283-3377 ext. 227
danny@ifallsjournal, Sports editor, The Journal, MN, International Falls

Chen, Hwei Ying
info@batonlockusa.com, Pres., Baton Lock & Hardware Co., Inc., CA, Garden Grove

Chen, Jade Z.
jchen@buffalospree.com, Prod. Dir., Forever Young, NY, Buffalo

Chen, Jay
info@asianfortune.com, Pres., Asian Fortune, VA, Haymarket

Chen, Joshua
sales@cybercon.com, Pres., Cybercon.com, MO, Saint Louis

Chen, Wei-Huan .... (781) 433-8244
wchen@wickedlocal.com, Reporter, Needham Times, MA, Needham

Chenault-Usher, Sherine R.
sherine.chenault@parenthood.com, Adv. Coord., New York Family, KS, Overland Park

Cheney, Lora .... (512) 756-6136
lora@burnetbulletin.com, Adv. Consultant, Burnet Bulletin, TX, Burnet

Cheng, Hong .... (740) 593-2619
Assoc. Prof., Ohio University, OH, Athens

Chermoore, Ed .... (636) 207-9880 ext. 4
echermoore@plainlabelpress.com, Vice Pres./Mng. Ed., Plain Label Press, Manchester

Chernivsky, Ben .... (618) 374-4748
Principia College, IL, Elsah

Chernoff, Amy
achernoff@pubgroup.com, Sr. Vice Pres./Grp. Pub., Relish - New York, NY, New York

Chernoff, Amy .... (212) 478-1900 ext. 102
achernoff@pubgroup.com, Sr. Vice Pres./Grp. Pub., American Profile - New York, NY, New York

Chernoff, Andrew
achernoff@seacoastonline.com, Seacoast Media Group, NH, Portsmouth
achernoff@seacoastonline.com, Ad Director, The Hampton Union, NH, Portsmouth
achernoff@seacoastonline.com, Ad. Dir., Portsmouth Herald, NH, Portsmouth

Cherry, Glenn .... (813) 267-7348
gcherry813@aol.com, Circ. Mgr., Daytona Times, FL, Tampa

Cherry, Stephany .... (704) 869-1731
scherry@gastongazette.com, Major accounts, The Gaston Gazette, NC, Gastonia

Cherubini, Vic .... (281) 363-3742
epic@epicsoftware.com, Pres., epic software group, Inc., TX, The Woodlands

Chessher, Melissa
mchesshe@syr.edu, Assoc. Prof., Syracuse University, NY, Syracuse

Chester, Britt
britt@yesweekly.com, Ed., Yes! Weekly, NC, Greensboro

Chester, Deborah
dchester@ou.edu, Prof., University of Oklahoma, OK, Norman

Chester, Kenneth J. .... (515) 986-1155
motornewsmedia@live.com, Pres./CEO, Motor News Media Corp., Grimes

Cheung, Ariel .... (513) 556-5912
chief.newsrecord@gmail.com, Editor-in-chief, The News Record, OH, Cincinnati

Cheung, Mandle
info@icescape.com, Pres./CEO, Computer Talk Technology, Inc., ON, Richmond Hill

Chew, Fiona
cmrfchew@syr.edu, Assoc. Prof., Syracuse University, NY, Syracuse

Chiaia, Nicholas .... (202) 898-8000
President, United Press International, Boca Raton

Chianca, Pete
pchianca@wickedlocal.com, Ed. in Chief, Tri-Town Transcript, MA, Danvers

Chianca, Pete
pchianca@wickedlocal.com, Ed. in Chief, North Andover Citizen, MA, Danvers

Chianca, Pete
pchianca@wickedlocal.com, Ed. in Chief, Stoneham Sun, MA, Somerville

Chianca, Pete
pchianca@wickedlocal.com, Ed. in Chief, Malden Observer, MA, Danvers

Chianca, Pete
pchianca@wickedlocal.com, Ed. in Chief, Saugus Advertiser, MA, Danvers

Chianca, Pete
pchianca@wickedlocal.com, Ed. in Chief, Medford Transcript, MA, Danvers

Chianca, Pete
pchianca@wickedlocal.com, Ed. in Chief,

Georgetown Record, MA, Danvers

Chianca, Pete
pchianca@wickedlocal.com, Ed.-in-Chief, Melrose Free Press, MA, Danvers
pchianca@wickedlocal.com, Ed.-in-Chief, Salem Gazette, MA, Danvers
pchianca@wickedlocal.com, Ed. in Chief , North Shore Sunday, MA, Danvers
pchianca@wickedlocal.com, Ed. in Chief, Swampscott Reporter, MA, Marblehead

Chianca, Pete
pchianca@wickedlocal.com, Ed. in Chief, Wakefield Observer, MA, Danvers

Chianca, Pete
pchianca@wickedlocal.com, Ed. in Chief, Hamilton-Wenham Chronicle, MA, Danvers

Chianca, Pete
pchianca@wickedlocal.com, Ed. in Chief, Newburyport Current, MA, Danvers

Chianca, Pete
pchianca@wickedlocal.com, Ed.-in-Chief, Amesbury News, MA, Danvers

Chianca, Pete
pchianca@wickedlocal.com, Ed. in Chief, Reading Advocate, MA, Danvers

Chianca, Pete
pchianca@wickedlocal.com, Ed. in Chief, Danvers Herald, MA, Danvers

Chianca, Peter
pchianca@wickedlocal.com, Ed. in Chief, Marblehead Reporter, MA, Marblehead

Chianca, Peter
pchianca@wickedlocal.com, Ed.-in-Chief, Cape Ann Beacon, MA, Danvers

Chiapetta, Leslie
office@thevoiceofpelham.ca, Office Mgr. , Fonthill Voice Of Pelham, ON, Fonthill

Chiappa, Jim ....(203) 402-2335
jchiappa@hersamacorn.com, Adv. Rep., Amity Observer (OOB), CT, Shelton
jchiappa@hersamacorn.com, Account Exec., Milford Mirror, CT, Shelton

Chiappa, Jim ....(203) 402-2335
jchiappa@hersamacorn.com, Account Exec., Stratford Star, CT, Shelton

Chiappetta, Delia ....(262) 656-6227
dchiappetta@kenoshanews.com, Prodn. Mgr., Opns., Kenosha News, WI, Kenosha

Chiaramonte, Vince ....(716) 849-4444
vchiaramonte@buffnews.com, Design Dir., The Buffalo News, NY, Buffalo

Chiasson, Gaetan
gaetan.chiasson@acadienouvelle.com, News Manager, L'Acadie Nouvelle, NB, Caraquet

Chiasson, Isabelle
nordest@hebdosquebecor.com, Dir., Nordest Plus, QC, Sept-Iles

Chiasson, Lloyd
lloyd.chiasson@nicholls.edu, Prof., Nicholls State University, LA, Thibodaux

Chiaviello, Anthony...................(713) 221-8520
chiaviello@uhd.edu, Univ. of Houston Downtown, TX, Houston

Chibbaro, Lou ....(202) 747-2077 x8079
lchibbaro@washblade.com, Sr. News Editor , Washington Blade, DC, Washington

Chichester, Duayne
dchichester@suncoastnews.com, Pub., The Suncoast News, FL, New Port Richey

Chiddister, Diane
dchiddister@ysnews.com, Ed., The Yellow Springs News, OH, Yellow Springs

Chieca, Susan ....(717) 255-88442
schieca@pennlive.com, VP of Sales, The Patriot-News, PA, Mechanicsburg

Chikie, Susan
vermilionvoice@gmail.com, Pub, Vermilion Voice, AB, Vermilion

Childers, Delia
delia.childers@oxfordeagle.com, Adv. Dir., The Oxford Eagle, MS, Oxford

Childers, Ken ....(405) 382-1100
news@seminoleproducer.com, The Seminole Producer, OK, Seminole

Childree, Zach ....(256) 782-5701
zach@jaxnews.com, Jacksonville State Univ., AL, Jacksonville

Childrey, Tom
ads@brunswicktimes-gazette.com, Acct. Exec., Brunswick Times-Gazette, VA, Lawrenceville

Childs, Ann ....(816) 583-2116
Circ. Mgr., The Hamilton Advocate, MO, Hamilton

Childs, Betty
betty@sterlingbulletin.com, Ed., Sterling Bulletin, KS, Sterling

Childs, Joe ....(727) 893-8328
childs@tampabay.com, Mng. Ed., Tampa Bay, Tampa Bay Times, FL, St Petersburg

Childs, Johnny ....(520) 460-9089
jchilds@tucson.com, Circ. Distrib. Spec, Arizona Daily Star, AZ, Tucson

Childs, Kevin
holdit@4asap.com, Consultant, Audio Service America Productions / FreeHold Division, NY, Albany

Chilinski, Frank
frank@salmonpress.com, Pub. , The Coos County Democrat, NH, Lancaster
frank@salmonpress.com, Pub., Meredith News, NH, Meredith
frank@salmonpress.com, Pub., Littleton Courier, NH, Littleton
frank@salmonpress.com, Pub., The Berlin Reporter, NH, Lancaster

Chilinski, Frank
frank@stonebridgepress.com, President & Publisher, Southbridge Evening News, MA, Southbridge

Chilinski, Frank
fchilinski@stonebridgepress.com, President & Publisher, The Webster Times, MA, Southbridge

Chilinski, Frank .... (603) 279-4516 ext. 125
frank@salmonpress.com, Pub., Granite State News, NH, Wolfeboro
frank@salmonpress.com, The Baysider, NH, Wolfeboro Falls
frank@salmonpress.com, The Record-Enterprise (OOB), NH, Meredith

Chilinski, Frank ....(508) 909-4101
frank@stonebridgepress.com, President & Publisher, Stonebridge Press, Inc., MA, Southbridge

Chilinski, Frank ....(603) 279-4516
frank@salmonpress.com, Pub., Winnisquam Echo, NH, Meredith
frank@salmonpress.com, Carroll County Independent, NH, Wolfeboro

Chilinski, Frank
frank@stonebridgepress.com, President & Publisher, Spencer New Leader, MA, Southbridge

Chilinski, Frank G. ....(508) 764-4325
frank@stonebridgepress.com, Publisher, Blackstone Valley Tribune, MA, Southbridge

Chilnski, Frank ....(603) 279-4516
Pub., The Gilford Steamer, NH, Meredith

Chilton, Mary ....(928) 645-8888
mchilton@lakepowellchronicle.com, Sales Rep., Lake Powell Chronicle, AZ, Page

Chin, Mary
marychin@aaca-boston.org, Exec. Dir., AACA, Sampan Newspaper, MA, Boston

Chin, Steven ....(415) 476-0910
steven.chin@ucsf.edu, Managing Editor, University of California, San Francisco, CA, San Francisco

Chinoy, Ira
ichinoy@umd.edu, Assoc. Prof., University of Maryland, MD, College Park

Chiodo, Daniel P.
emailads@joplinglobe.com, Pres., The Joplin Globe, MO, Joplin

Chiodo, Terri.......................(310) 448-6700
terri.chiodo@investors.com, Vice Pres./Nat'l Adv. Dir., Investor's Business Daily, CA, Los Angeles

Chionsini, Brandi
brandi.chionsini@granitepublications.com, CEO, Fenice Community Media, TX, Taylor

Chionsini, Jim
jchionsini@yahoo.com, Founder, Fenice Community Media, TX, Taylor

Chirpich, Randy
ads@fairmontphotopress.com, Adv./Sales, Fairmont Photo Press, MN, Fairmont

Chisenhall, Sherry
schisenhall@charlotteobser.com, Managing Ed., The Charlotte Observer, NC, Charlotte

Chisholm, Khristi ....(912) 356-0025
khristi@savannahherald.net, Co-Publisher, Savannah Herald, GA, Savannah

Chism, Billy ....(706) 865-4718
publisher@whitecountynews.net, Ed./Pub., White County News, GA, Cleveland

Chism, Susan
susan.chism@greenville.edu, Greenville College, IL, Greenville

Chittim, Linda ....(425) 347-5634
linda@mukilteobeacon.com, Gen. Mgr., Mukilteo Beacon, WA, Mukilteo

Chittim, Linda
gm@yourbeacon.net, Adv. Dir., Edmonds Beacon, WA, Mukilteo

Chitwood, Pat
pchitwood@ledger-enquirer.com, Circ. Dir., Columbus Ledger-Enquirer, GA, Columbus

Chitwood, Tim
tchitwood@ledger-enquirer.com, Columnist, Columbus Ledger-Enquirer, GA, Columbus

Chiuilicek, Dave
davec@communityshoppers.com, Prod. Mgr, Stateline News, WI, Elkhorn

Chivers, David.......................(515) 284-8502
dchivers@dmreg.com, Pub. & Pres., The Des Moines Register, IA, Des Moines

Chlovechok, Anne
news@journal-leader.com, Pub./Ed./Adv. Dir., The Journal & Noble County Leader, OH, Caldwell

Choate, Alan.......................(928) 753-6397
achoate@kdminer.com, News Ed., Kingman Daily Miner, AZ, Kingman

Choate, Ed ....(918) 684-2933
echoate@muskogeephoenix.com, Exec. Ed., Muskogee Phoenix, OK, Muskogee

Choate, Norene
monitorok@sbcglobal.net, Ed., Marietta Monitor, OK, Marietta

Choate, Willis
monitorok@sbcglobal.net, Pub., Marietta Monitor, OK, Marietta

Chodan, Lucinda ....(514) 987-2222
lchodan@montrealgazette.com, Editor, Montreal Gazette & Vice-President, Editorial, Eastern Region, Postmedia , Montreal Gazette, QC, Montreal

Choi, Jihyun
jchoi@estevanmercury.ca, Prod. Mgr., Estevan Mercury, SK, Estevan

Cholowsky, Leslie ....(780) 385-6693
news@thecommunitypress.com, Ed., The Weekly Review, AB, Viking
news@thecommunitypress.com, Editor, The Community Press, AB, Killam

Chomicki, Marie
dillsburgbanner@dillsburgbanner.net, Pres./ Pub./Ed., Dillsburg Banner, PA, Dillsburg

Chong, Shiao ....(905) 336-2920
schong@crcna.org, Editor in chief, The Banner, MI, Grand Rapids

Choo-Foo, Sean ....(306) 736-2535
thecitizen@sasktel.net, Sales Representative, Kipling Citizen, SK, Kipling

Choquette, Paul J.
accommodations@gilbaneco.com, Chrmn./ CEO, Gilbane Building Co., RI, Providence

Chorba, Frank
frank.chorba@washburn.edu, Prof., Washburn University, KS, Topeka

Chorney, Allison
achorney@airdrie.greatwest.ca, Ed, Airdrie City View, AB, Airdrie
achorney@airdrie.greatwest.ca, Ed, Rocky View Weekly, AB, Airdrie

Chottiner, Lee
leec@thejewishchronicle.net, Exec. Ed., The Jewish Chronicle, PA, Pittsburgh

Chou, Cecilia ....(630) 922-9381
cecilia.chou@gossinternational.com, Mktg. Mgr., Goss International Corporation, NH, Durham

Chou, Elizabeth
echou@egpnews.com, Prodn. Mgr., Eastside Sun, CA, Los Angeles
echou@egpnews.com, Prodn. Mgr., City Terrace Comet, CA, Los Angeles
echou@egpnews.com, Prodn. Mgr., Commerce Comet, CA, Los Angeles
echou@egpnews.com, Prodn. Mgr., Ela Brooklyn-Belvedere Comet, CA, Los Angeles
echou@egpnews.com, Prodn. Mgr., Mexican American Sun, CA, Los Angeles
echou@egpnews.com, Prodn. Mgr., Montebello Comet, CA, Los Angeles
echou@egpnews.com, Prodn. Mgr., Monterey Park Comet, CA, Los Angeles
echou@egpnews.com, Prodn. Mgr., Northeast Sun, CA, Los Angeles
echou@egpnews.com, Prodn. Mgr., Vernon Sun, CA, Los Angeles
echou@egpnews.com, Prodn. Mgr., Wyvernwood Chronicle, CA, Los Angeles
echou@egpnews.com, Prodn. Mgr., Bell Gardens Sun, CA, Los Angeles

Chouinard, Lucien
watpress@sk.sympatico.ca, Ed., Waterfront Press, SK, Lumsden

Chouinard, Michelle.................(905) 857-2378
mchouinard@maratek.com, Mktg. Mgr., Maratek Environmental Technologies, Inc., ON, Bolton

Chow, David
david.chow@hawaiipacifichealth.org, Social Media Tech, Hawaii Pacific University, HI, Honolulu

Chown, Amy ....(404) 526-7214
achown@ajc.com, VP, Marketing, Atlanta Journal-Constitution, GA, Atlanta

Chown, Jeff
jchown@niu.edu, Acting Chair, Northern Illinois University, IL, DeKalb

Chretien, Claire ....(888) 678-6008 x 946
cchretien@lifesitenews.com, Journalist, LifeSiteNews.com, VA, Front Royal

Chris, Ashley
editor@thetigernews.com, Clemson Univ., SC, Clemson

Chrisco, Carrie
cchrisco@mcneese.edu, Assoc. Prof., McNeese State University, LA, Lake Charles

Chriske, Pamela ....(406) 443-2850
pamela@mtnewspapers.com, Accounting Specialist, Montana Newspaper Association, MT, Helena

Chrisman, scott

spioneer@tcaexpress.net, Pub./Ed., Sanborn Pioneer, IA, Sanborn

Chriss, Holly ....**(905) 523-5800**
hollyc@hamiltonnews.com, Dir of Advt, Ancaster News, ON, Stoney Creek

Christ, Shelly ....**(507) 389-1079**
rachelle.christ@mnsu.edu, Advertising Sales Manager, Minnesota State Univ. Mankato, MN, Mankato

Christen, Cindy
cindy.christen@colostate.edu, Assoc. Prof., Colorado State University, CO, Fort Collins

Christensen, Bente ....**(828) 628-1994**
Bus. Mgr., Editor's Copy Syndicate, Sarasota

Christensen, Glen
acvisalia@yahoo.com, American Classifieds - Visalia, CA, Visalia

Christensen, Jill ....**(712) 563-2741**
News Reporter, Audubon County Advocate Journal, IA, Audubon

Christensen, John
jchristensen@osv.com, Strategic Mktg. Dir., Our Sunday Visitor, IN, Huntington

Christensen, Karen
info@thenickel.com, American Classifieds - Colorado Springs, CO, Colorado Springs

Christensen, Karen ....**(435) 835-4241**
karen@sanpetemessenger.com, Office Mgr, Sanpete Messenger, UT, Manti

Christensen, Layne
lchristensen@nsnews.com, Ed, North Shore News, BC, North Vancouver
lchristensen@nsnews.com, Ed, North/west Shore Outlook, BC, North Vancouver

Christensen, Nolan
nolan.christensen@mowercountyshopper. com, Acct. Rep., Mower County Shopper, MN, Austin

Christensen, Peter F.
editor@catholicherald.org, Publisher, Catholic Herald, WI, Superior

Christensen, Sandra
sandra@themountainmail.com, Circ. Direc., Mountain Guide, CO, Salida

Christensen, Sandra..........**(719) 539-6694 ext. 14**
sandra@themountainmail.com, Circ. Mgr., The Mountain Mail, CO, Salida

Christensen, Sarah J. ....**(503) 725-5691**
Portland State Univ., OR, Portland

Christensen, Terry ....**(515) 573-2141 ext. 434**
tchristensen@messengernews.net, Pub., Messenger Extra, IA, Fort Dodge

Christensen, Terry
tchristensen@messengernews.net, Publisher, The Messenger, IA, Fort Dodge

Christensen, Terry
tchristensen@freemanjournal.net, Gen. Mgr./ Pub, The Daily Freeman-Journal, IA, Webster City

Christenson, Jane Dunlap
nctimes@ritternet.com, Pub., The Newton County Times, AR, Jasper

Christenson, Jerome
jchristenson@winonadailynews.com, Online Ed., Winona Daily News, MN, Winona

Christer, Ryan ....**(620) 694-5700 Ext. 327**
ryanc@hutchnews.com, Page Designer, The Hutchinson News, KS, Hutchinson

Christian, Claudia
cchristian@pressreview.net, Adv. Mgr, University City Review, PA, Philadelphia
cchristian@pressreview.net, Adv. Mgr, Philadelphia Free Press, PA, Philadelphia

Christian, Gabe
editor@oitm.org, Out in the Mountains, VT, Benson

Christian, Robert ....**(215) 817-4576**

editor@pressreview.net, Pub./Ed., Philadelphia Free Press, PA, Philadelphia
editor@pressreview.net, Pub./Ed., University City Review, PA, Philadelphia

Christian, Scott
support@spanlink.com, CEO, Spanlink Communications, MN, Minneapolis

Christians, Lindsay
lchristians@capitalnewspapers.com, The Capital Times, WI, Madison

Christiansen, Anders
achristiansen@saxotech.com, CEO, SAXOTECH, Inc., FL, Tampa

Christiansen, Rew
america@americamagazine.org, Ed., America, NY, New York

Christiansen, Steve
comfreytimes@frontiernet.net, Ed., Comfrey Times, MN, Comfrey

Christiansen-Bullers, Anne
abullers@jccc.edu, Johnson County Cmty. College, KS, Overland Park

Christianson, Adam
adam.christianson@my.und.edu, Managing/ Opinion Editor, Univ. of North Dakota, ND, Grand Forks

Christianson, Cam
cchristanson@airdrie.greatwest.ca, Pub., Airdrie City View, AB, Airdrie

Christianson, Cameron
cchristianson@airdrie.greatwest.ca, Publisher, Rocky View Publishing, AB, Airdrie

Christianson, Cameron
cchristianson@airdrie.greatwest.ca, Pub., Rocky View Weekly, AB, Airdrie

Christie, Brett
bchrist2@mlive.com, Sr. Retail Dir., The Jackson Citizen Patriot, MI, Jackson

Christie, Gaye
AChristie@tampatrib.com, Tampa Bay Times, FL, St Petersburg

Christie, Rick ....**(561) 820-4476**
rchristie@pbpost.com, Editorial Page Ed., The Palm Beach Post, FL, West Palm Beach

Christie, Thomas
christie@uta.edu, Assoc. Prof., University of Texas at Arlington, TX, Arlington

Christine, Benavente
cbenavente@bakersfield.com, Prod. Dev. Director, The Bakersfield Californian, CA, Bakersfield

Christino, Scott......................**(804) 649-6437**
schristino@timesdispatch.com, Classified Adv. Mgr., Richmond Times-Dispatch, VA, Richmond

Christman, Michael J. ....**(260) 461-8324**
mchristman@fortwayne.com, CEO/Pres./Pub., The News-Sentinel, IN, Fort Wayne

Christman, Rebecca.................**(414) 647-4731**
Editor, Metroparent, WI, Milwaukee

Christner, Christi ....**(308) 394-5389**
breeze.editor@jpipapers.com, News Editor, The Wauneta Breeze, NE, Wauneta

Christofides, Aris T. ....**(614) 408-3865**
info@criticsinc.com, Pub./Ed., Critics, Inc., Dublin

Christofilopoulos, Holly..............**(905) 664-8800**
hollyc@hamiltonnews.com, Dir of Advt, Dundas Star News, ON, Stoney Creek

Christofilopoulos, Holly..............**(905) 664-8800**
hollyc@hamiltonnews.com, Director of Advertising, Hamilton Mountain News, ON, Stoney Creek

Christofilopoulos, Holly..............**(905) 664-8800**
hollyc@hamiltonnews.com, Adv. Dir., Stoney Creek News, ON, Stoney Creek

Christoph, N/A..........................**CEO**

World Association of Newspapers and News Publishers (WAN-IFRA)

Christopher, Angie
angiec@athensnews-courier.com, Adv Sales, The News-Courier, AL, Athens

Christopher, Joel.....................**(920) 993-1000**
jchristopher@postcrescent.com, Editor/Digital, Post-Crescent, WI, Appleton

Christopher, L. Carol ....**(510) 558-0150**
carol@jjcs.com, Principal Analyst, John Juliano Computer Services Co., GA, Decatur

Christy, Matt..........................**(219) 326-3870**
mchristy@heraldargus.com, News Ed., Herald-Argus, IN, La Porte

Chrysler, Rod ....**(908) 687-3225**
info@pscturn.com, Pres., PSC Flo-Turn, Inc., NJ, Union

Chrystie, Grace
seattle@allenspcb.com, Regional Manager, Allen's Press Clipping Bureau, WA, Seattle

Chu, Emerson
wealee@scdaily.com, Gen. Mgr., U.S. Asia News, TX, Houston

Chu, Michael ....**(212) 803-8313**
michael.chu@sourcemedia.com, Senior Art Director, American Banker, NY, New York

Chu, Yao
info@filestream.com, Chrmn./CEO, Filestream, Inc., NY, Glen Head

Chubb, Anne ....**(610) 371-5141**
achubb@readingeagle.com, Product Management & Research Director, Reading Eagle Company, PA, Reading

Chubb, Anne T. ....**(610) 371-5141**
achubb@readingeagle.com, COO, Reading Eagle, PA, Reading

Chuckray, Laura
lachuckray@davidson.edu, Davidson College, NC, Davidson

Chui, Vivian
newsroom@ominecaexpress.com, Ed, Vanderhoof Omineca Express, BC, Vanderhoof

Chumpolpakdee, Sammy
advertising@dailylobo.com, Sales Mgr., New Mexico Daily Lobo, NM, Albuquerque

Chung, Deborah
dchung@uky.edu, Asst. Prof., University of Kentucky, KY, Lexington

Chung, Hwiman
hchung@nmsu.edu, Assoc. Prof., New Mexico State University, NM, Las Cruces

Church, Beth
editor@rossford.com, Ed., Rossford Record Journal, OH, Rossford

Church, Debby
subs@journalpatriot.com, Circ. Mgr., The Wilkes Journal-Patriot, NC, North Wilkesboro

Church, Kathy
kathy@ycobserver.com, Pub./Ed., The Yankton County Observer, SD, Yankton

Churchill, David.....................**(218) 739-7012**
Pub./Pres., Weekender, MN, Fergus Falls

Churchill, Lisa
lisa_churchill@dailyjournal.com, Ed., Daily Commerce, CA, Los Angeles

Churchill, Penny ....**(519) 344-3641 Ext.502259**
pchurchill@postmedia.com, Distribution Mgr., Sarnia This Week, ON, Sarnia

Churm, Steve
schurm@freedom.com, Chief Revenue Officer, The Orange County Register, CA, Santa Ana

Churney, Dan
danc@mywebtimes.com, Other, The Times, IL, Ottawa

Chute, Michael ....**(731) 661-6594**
Union Univ., TN, Jackson

Chvilicex, Dave
davec@communityshoppers.com, Prod. Mgr, Walworth County Sunday, WI, Elkhorn

Chyz, Ken
kenchyz@yorktonnews.com, Adv. Mgr., Yorkton News Review, SK, Yorkton

Ciambrone, Ed ....**(785) 832-7260**
eciambrone@ljworld.com, Circulation Manager, Shawnee Dispatch, KS, Shawnee

Ciampi, Vince
vciampi@seacoastonline.com, Adv. Dir., Exeter News-Letter, NH, Portsmouth
vciampi@seacoastonline.com, Adv. Dir., York County Coast Star, NH, Portsmouth
vciampi@seacoastonline.com, The York Weekly, NH, Portsmouth

Cianci, Lisa ....**(407) 420-6229**
lcianci@orlandosentinel.com, City Ed., Orlando Sentinel, FL, Orlando

Ciastkowski, Artur ....**(250) 287-9227**
publisher@campbellrivermirror.com, Publisher, The Campbell River Mirror, BC, Campbell River

Cibart, Michael........................**(509) 525-3301**
mikecibart@wwub.com, Circ. Mgr., Walla Walla Union-Bulletin, WA, Walla Walla

Cibula, Matt ....**(608) 836-6660 Ext. 368**
cibula@newscurrents.com, Marketing Mgr., NewsCurrents, WI, Middleton

Cicalo, Lora............................**(619) 293-1376**
lora.cicalo@utsandiego.com, Managing Editor, Hoy San Diego - The San Diego Union Tribune, CA, San Diego
lora.cicalo@utsandiego.com, Man. Ed., San Diego State University, CA, San Diego

Cicalo, Lora............................**(619) 293-1376**
lora.cicalo@sduniontribune.com, Managing Editor, The San Diego Union-Tribune, CA, San Diego

Ciccantelli, Steve ....**(262) 670-1502**
sciccantelli@conleynet.com, Vice Pres., Sales/ Mktg., Conley Media LLC, WI, Beaver Dam

Ciccocioppo, Brittany ....**(717) 582-4305**
Circulation Manager, Perry County Times, PA, New Bloomfield
Circulation Manager, Duncannon Record, PA, New Bloomfield

Ciccocioppo, Brittany ....**(717) 582-4305**
circulation@perrycountytimes.com, Circulation Manager, The News-Sun, PA, New Bloomfield

Cichelli, Richard
cichelli@newspapersystems.com, Pres., Software Consulting Services, LLC, PA, Nazareth

Cichelli, Richard J.
scs@nscs.fast.net, Pres., Software Consulting Services, LLC, PA, Nazareth

Cichocki, Carol ....**(773) 358-3129**
display@hpherald.com, Adv. Mgr., Hyde Park Herald, IL, Chicago

Cichon, Joe ....**(913) 441-0139 ext. 109**
cichonj@corp.inxintl.com, Sr. Vice Pres., Product/Mfg. Technology, INX International Ink Co., IL, Schaumburg

Cidzikaite, Dalia
chief editor @ gmail.com , Ed. in Chief, Draugas, IL, Chicago

Ciechon, Sharon ....**(603) 668-4321**
sciechon@unionleader.com, VP HR, New Hampshire Union Leader/New Hampshire Sunday News, NH, Manchester

Ciliberti, Dino
editor@wayneindependent.com, Editor, The Wayne Independent, PA, Honesdale

Cimburek, James
james.cimburek@yankton.net, Sports Ed., Yankton Daily Press & Dakotan, SD, Yankton

Cimino, Matt...........................**(410) 332-6126**

mcimino@baltsun.com, Nat'l Adv & Majors Sales Mgr, Catonsville Times, MD, Baltimore

mcimino@baltsun.com, Nat'l Adv & Majors Sales Mgr, Owings Mills Times, MD, Baltimore

mcimino@baltsun.com, Nat'l Adv & Majors Sales Mgr, Columbia Flier, MD, Columbia

mcimino@baltsun.com, Nat'l Adv & Majors Sales Mgr, Baltimore Messenger-OOB, MD, BALTIMORE

mcimino@baltsun.com, Nat'l Adv & Majors Sales Mgr, Jeffersonian, MD, Towson

mcimino@baltsun.com, Nat'l Adv Majors/Sales Mgr., Arbutus Times, MD, Baltimore

mcimino@baltsun.com, Nat'l Adv & Majors, Sales Mgr., The Record, MD, Bel Air

mcimino@baltsun.com, Nat'l Adv & Majors Sales Mgr, Northeast Booster Reporter-OOB, MD, TOWSON

mcimino@baltsun.com, Nat'l Adv./Sales Mgr., Towson Times, MD, Baltimore

mcimino@baltsun.com, Nat'l Adv./Sales Mgr., The Weekender, MD, Bel Air

mcimino@baltsun.com, Nat'l Adv & Majors Sales Mgr, Howard County Times, MD, Columbia

Cimms, Karen
kcimms@tnonline.com, Lifestyle Ed., Times News, PA, Lehighton

Cinnamon, Lori
loric@jfssv.org, Adv. Mgr., Jewish Community News, CA, Los Gatos

Ciofalo, Andrew
aciofalo@loyola.edu, Journ., Loyola College, MD, Baltimore

CISNEROS, APRIL .... (806) 272-4536
circulation@muleshoejournal.com, CIRCULATON/BOOK KEEPING, Muleshoe Journal, TX, Muleshoe

Cisneros, Theresa
tcisneros@ocregister.com, City Ed., The Tustin News, CA, Santa Ana

Cisternino, Mark .... (631) 737-6020 x125
markc@flexography.org, Pres., Flexographic Technical Association, NY, Bohemia

Ciszczon, Erin .... (219) 769-9292
Advertising Representative, Northwest Indiana Catholic, IN, Merrillville

Ciuffo, Philip A. .... (212) 556-1234
Vice Pres., Internal Audit, The New York Times Co., NY, New York

Claar, Beth
bclaar@altoonamirror.com, Circ. Mgr., Office, Altoona Mirror, PA, Altoona

Clackley, Brandy .... (205) 755-5747, ext. 604
brandy.clackley@clantonadvertiser.com, Marketing Consultant, The Clanton Advertiser, AL, Clanton

Claggett, Rick
rick@watermarkonline.com, CFO, Watermark Media, FL, Orlando

Claiborne, Jamii .... (712) 749-1212
claiborne@bvu.edu, Buena Vista Univ., IA, Storm Lake

Claiborne, Mary Pam .... (518) 235-3455
claibornem@ipix.com, Contact, Interactive Pictures Corporation (IPIX), NY, Cohoes

Clair, Philippe ....(450) 441-5300 ext 4003
pclair@versants.com, Ed. , Le Journal De St-bruno, QC, Saint Bruno
pclair@versants.com, Ed., Concorde (OOB) , QC, Saint Eustache

Claire, Joy .... (815) 889-9930
milfordnews@netoptioninc.com, Adv. Mgr., Milford Herald-News, IL, Milford

Clakston, Derek .... (907) 486-3227 ext. 625
sports@kodiakdailymirror.com, Reporter, Kodiak Daily Mirror, AK, Kodiak

Clancy, Doug .... (201) 646-4481
Exec. Ed., Herald News, NJ, Rockaway

Clapham, Sue

sclapham@fiftyplusadvocate.com, Art Dir., Fifty Plus Advocate, MA, Worcester

Clapp, Jake .... (585) 244-3329 x25
jclapp@rochester-citynews.com, Arts & Entertainment Editor, City Newspaper, NY, Rochester

Clapper, Bryan
bryan.clapper@leaderpub.com, Adv. Mgr., The Leader, MI, Niles

Clapper, Frank H.
theherald@mac.com, Pub./Ed., The Louisville Herald, OH, Louisville

Clapper, Jackie
heraldads@mac.com, Adv. Mgr., The Louisville Herald, OH, Louisville

Clardy, Doris
dclardy@ptsi.net, Adv. Dir., Perryton Herald, TX, Perryton

Claridge, Alan
mail@citizen.on.ca, Pub, Caledon Citizen, ON, Bolton

Claridge, Alan M.
mail@citizen.on.ca, Pub., Orangeville Citizen, ON, Orangeville

Claridge, Thomas M.
editor@citizen.on.ca, Ed., Orangeville Citizen, ON, Orangeville

Clarin, Paul
pclarin@keysnews.com, Pub., Florida Keys Free Press, FL, Tavernier

Clarin, Paul .... (305) 292-7777
pclarin@keysnews.com, Pub., Key West Citizen, FL, Key West

Clark, Abbie
aclark@bcrnews.com, Circ. Mgr., Bureau County Republican, IL, Princeton

Clark, Alli
aclark@westondemocrat.com, Sports Reporter, Weston Democrat, WV, Weston

Clark, Amanda
news@nashvillegraphic.co, Mng. Ed., The Nashville Graphic, NC, Nashville

Clark, Andrew
amclark@uta.edu, Asst. Prof., University of Texas at Arlington, TX, Arlington

Clark, Angie
aclark@walkermessenger.com, Adv. Mgr., Walker County Messenger, GA, La Fayette

Clark, Anthony
anthony.clark@gvillesun.com, Bus. Ed., The Gainesville Sun, FL, Gainesville

Clark, Becky .... (951) 659-2145
nowatastar1@sbcglobal.net, Publisher-Editor, Idyllwild Town Crier, CA, Idyllwild
nowatastar1@sbcglobal.net, Ed, The American, OK, Fairland

Clark, Bob
bclark@bishamon.com, Vice Pres., Sales/Mktg., Bishamon Industries Corp., CA, Ontario

Clark, Brian
bclark@neighbornewspapers.com, Mng. Ed., North Cobb Neighbor, GA, Marietta
bclark@neighbornewspapers.com, Mng. Ed., Alpharetta Neighbor, GA, Roswell

Clark, Brian .... (209) 578-2362
bclark@modbee.com, Digital Ed., Merced Sun-Star, CA, Merced

Clark, Bruce
bgclark@ncat.edu, Instr., North Carolina A&T State University, NC, Greensboro

Clark, Carol
lanews@lamonitor.com, Pres., New Mexico Press Women, NM, Los Alamos

Clark, Chuck .... (270) 745-4206
chuck.clark@wku.edu, Dir of Student Publications, Western Kentucky University, KY, Bowling Green

Clark, Cliff
cclark@civitasmedia.com, Ed., Jefferson Post, NC, West Jefferson

Clark, Cliff .... (978) 516-2276
cclark@sentinelandenterprise.com , City Ed. , Sentinel & Enterprise, MA, Fitchburg

Clark, Cliff
cclark@elkintribune.com, Ed., Yadkin Valley Advertiser, NC, Elkin

Clark, Cris
cclark@theadvertiser.net, Sales Mgr., Pickaway County Advertiser, OH, Circleville

Clark, Darrin .... ext. 3051
dclark@staffordgroup.com, News Ed., The Daily News, MI, Greenville

Clark, David
ads@mainelymediallc.com, Adv. Mgr./Gen. Mgr., Biddeford Courier, ME, Biddeford
ads@mainelymediallc.com, Gen. Mgr./Adv. Mgr., Making It At Home, ME, Biddeford
ads@mainelymediallc.com, Gen. Mgr./Adv. Mgr., Register Gazette, ME, Biddeford
ads@mainelymediallc.com, Adv. Mgr., Scarborough Leader, ME, Biddeford
ads@mainelymediallc.com, Adv. Mgr./Gen. Mgr , South Portland-Cape/Elizabeth Sentry, ME, Biddeford

Clark, David .... (989) 774-3493
clark6da@cmich.edu, Director, Student Publications, Central Michigan University, MI, Mount Pleasant

Clark, David .... (207) 282-4337, ext. 214
ads@mainelymediallc.com, Gen. Mgr./Adv. Mgr., Kennebunk Post, ME, Biddeford

Clark, Debbie
debbie.clark@communitycare707.com, Pub Emeritus, The Willits News, CA, Willits

Clark, Diane
bdclark@frontiernet.net, Co-Pub., Tyler Tribute, MN, Tyler

Clark, Diane
crawfordclipper@gmail.com, Ed., Crawford Clipper/Harrison Sun LLC, NE, Crawford

Clark, Diane
hendrickspioneer@gmail.com, Co-Pub., The Hendricks Pioneer, MN, Hendricks

Clark, Diane .... (308) 665-2319
crawfordclipper@gmail.com, Reporter/Photographer, Crawford Clipper/Harrison Sun LLC, NE, Crawford

Clark, Diane
bdclark@frontiernet.net, Pub., Southwestern Peach, MN, Tyler

Clark, Doug .... ext. 39
Asst. Ed., The Sampson Independent, NC, Clinton

Clark, Erin
editor@thestandardnewspaper.net, Ed., The Standard, AZ, Kingman

Clark, Gail .... (870) 735-1010
Circ. Mgr., The Evening Times, AR, Marion

Clark, Gordon .... (604) 605-2008
gclark@postmedia.com, Editorial Page Editor, The Province, BC, Vancouver

Clark, Heidi .... (570) 704-3947
hclark@timesleaderonline.com, Adv Dir., The Times Leader, OH, Martins Ferry

Clark, James
editor@southernstandard.com, Ed., Southern Standard, TN, McMinnville

Clark, James
composing@lakevillejournal.com, Prodn. Coord., The Lakeville Journal, CT, Falls Village

Clark, Jeff .... (301) 784-2500
jclark@times-news.com, Circulation Manager, The Garrett County Weekender, MD, Cumberland

Clark, Jennifer
jennifer@okcfriday.com, Circ. Mgr., Oklahoma City Friday, OK, Oklahoma City

Clark, Jim .... (617) 666-4010
jimclark@thesomervillenews.com, Ed., The Somerville Times, MA, Somerville

Clark, Jim
apmontana@ap.org, Bureau Chief, Montana Associated Press Association, MT, Helena
apmontana@ap.org, Bureau Chief, Wyoming Associated Press, WY, Cheyenne

Clark, Jim
jim.clark@sunmedia.ca, Publisher(online), The Camrose Canadian, AB, Camrose

Clark, Jimmy
jclark@vicksburgpost.com, Gen. Mgr., The Vicksburg Post, MS, Vicksburg

Clark, Joe .... (717) 272-5611
jclark@ldnews.com, Circ. Mgr., The Lebanon Daily News, PA, Lebanon

Clark, Joe
jclark@ldnews.com, Circulation Manager, The Palm, PA, Lebanon

Clark, John .... (205) 602-2627
gwatchman@bellsouth.net, Greensboro Watchman, AL, Greensboro

Clark, John
jclark@pop.uky.edu, Asst. Prof., University of Kentucky, KY, Lexington

Clark, Jonathan .... (520) 415-1837
editorial@nogalesinternational.com, Mng. Ed., Nogales International, AZ, Nogales
editorial@nogalesinternational.com, Ed., The Weekly Bulletin, AZ, Nogales
editorial@nogalesinternational.com, Mng. Ed., Santa Cruz Valley Sun, AZ, Nogales

Clark, Joshua
jclark8517@westfield.ma.edu, Editor-in-Chief, Westfield State University, MA, Westfield

Clark, Jud
info@statenet.com, Pres., State Net, CA, Sacramento

Clark, Kaitlyn .... (905) 768-3111
kaitlyn@haldimandpress.com, Publisher, The Haldimand Press, ON, Hagersville

Clark, Karie
karie.clark@molawyersmedia.com, Public Notice Mgr, St. Charles County Business Record, MO, Saint Charles

Clark, Kim .... (928) 645-8888
kclark@lakepowellchronicle.com, Office Mgr., Lake Powell Chronicle, AZ, Page

Clark, Larry .... ext. 253
Interim Editor, The Hickory Daily Record, NC, Hickory
Opinion Page Ed., Pow, NC, Hickory

Clark, Laura
laura@sentinelnews.com, Sports Ed., Sentinel News Plus, KY, Shelbyville

Clark, Linda
lclark@astate.edu, Asst. Prof., Arkansas State University, AR, Jonesboro

Clark, Lori .... (847) 214-7475
lclark@elgin.edu, Faculty Advisor, Elgin Community College, IL, Elgin

Clark, Michael .... ext. 224
info@pageint.com, Pres., Page International, GA, Savannah

Clark, Michael
michael.clark@tkmus.com, Market Mgr., TKM United States, Inc., KY, Erlanger

Clark, Mike .... (904) 359-4307
mike.clark@jacksonville.com, Editorial Page Ed., The Florida Times-Union, FL, Jacksonville

Clark, Missy
bni@bayspringstel.net, Prodn. Mgr., The Jasper County News, MS, Bay Springs

Clark, Nathan
nclark@register-mail.com, Adv. Mgr., The Register-Mail, IL, Galesburg

Clark, Nicole...........................(907) 486-3227
sales@kodiakdailymirror.com, Advertising Sales , Kodiak Daily Mirror, AK, Kodiak

Clark, Pam.............................(712) 378-2770
recordkingsley@wiatel.net, Kingsley Office Mgr, The Record, IA, Moville

Clark, Pam
pclark@mfa-inc.com, Office Mgr., The Columbia Star, SC, Columbia

Clark, Patricia A........................(802) 496-5322
pat@valleyreporter.com, Pub., The Valley Reporter, VT, Waitsfield

Clark, Paul
paul@blackmountainnews.com, Ed., Black Mountain News, NC, Black Mountain

Clark, Paul...........................(828) 669-8727
pclark@ashevill.gannett.com, Ed., The Asheville Citizen-Times, NC, Asheville

Clark, Randy..........................(678) 466-4724
randyclark@clayton.edu, Clayton State Univ., GA, Morrow

Clark, Richard
rclark@johnsoncitypress.com, Sales/Mktg Dir., Johnson City Press, TN, Johnson City

Clark, Rob.............................(306) 691-1254
rob.clark@mjtimes.sk.ca, GM/Pub., The Moose Jaw Times-Herald, SK, Moose Jaw

Clark, Robert
bob.clark@mlb.com, COO, The Daily Deal, NY, New York

Clark, Ron
rclark@paducahsun.com, Farm/Agriculture Ed., The Paducah Sun, KY, Paducah

Clark, Sandra
sclark@phillynews.com, Deputy Managing Editor/ Feature & Inquire.com, Philadelphia Inquirer, Daily News & Philly.com, PA, Philadelphia

Clark, Sandra L.
clarks@shoppernewsnow.com, Ed., Halls Shopper News, TN, Knoxville

Clark, Stacy...............................x116
editor@catfishalleymag.com, Catfish Alley Ed., The Commercial Dispatch, MS, Columbus

Clark, Steve..........................(503) 546-0715
sclark@commnewspapers.com, Pres./Pub., Pamplin Media Group, OR, Portland

Clark, Stuart
info@westbranchtimes.com, Pub., West Branch Times, IA, West Branch

Clark, Stuart
WLIndex@Lcom.net, Pub., West Liberty Index, IA, West Liberty
WLIndex@Lcom.net, Ed., Tipton Conservative and Advertiser, IA, Tipton

Clark, Terry M.
tclark@ucok.edu, Chair, University of Central Oklahoma, OK, Edmond

Clark, Tiffany.........................(850) 762-4086
TiffWhy1@aol.com, Classified Coordinator, Community Papers of Florida, FL, Belleview

Clark, Todd
tclark@the-papers.com, Prod. Mgr., The Paper - Kosciusko Edition, IN, Milford

Clark, Tom...........................(304) 847-5828
websterecho@citlink.net, Ed., Webster Echo, WV, Webster Springs

Clark, Tom...........................(304) 847-5828
websterecho@citlink.net, Ed., Webster Republican, WV, Webster Springs

Clark, Tony..........................(252) 332-2123
tony.clark@tidewarternews.com, Pub, Gates County Index, NC, Ahoskie

Clark, Tony...307

tony.clark@tidewaternews.com, Assc. Pub., The Tidewater News, VA, Franklin

Clark, Vickie..........................(901) 433-9138
vickie.clark@journalinc.com, Sales Mgr, The Bartlett Express, TN, Bartlett

Clark, Vonnie........................(405) 366-3570
vjclark@cnhi.com, Circ. Dir., Chickasha News, OK, Chickasha
vjclark@cnhi.com, Circ. Mgr., The Express-Star, OK, Chickasha
vjclark@cnhi.com, Reg. Cir. Dir. , Norman Transcript, OK, Norman

Clark, Vonnie
vclark@normantranscript.com, Circ. Dir., Moore American, OK, Norman

Clark, William
bdclark@frontiernet.net, Pub., Southwestern Peach, MN, Tyler
bdclark@frontiernet.net, Co-Pub., The Hendricks Pioneer, MN, Hendricks

Clarke, Angie
angie@pressroomcleaners.com, Office Mgr., Pressroom Cleaners, Inc., NE, Omaha

Clarke, Brad..........................(812) 331-4272
bclarke@heraldt.com, Prodn. Dir., The Herald Times, IN, Bloomington

Clarke, Cheryl........................(570) 326-1551
cclarke@sungazette.com, Williamsport Sun-Gazette/Lock Haven Express, PA, South Williamsport

Clarke, Harry
hclarke@gulfcoastnewspapers.com, Adv. Mgr., The Islander, AL, Foley

Clarke, Jerry..........................(785) 798-2213
nessnews@gbta.net, Ed., Ness County News, KS, Ness City

Clarke, Jim............... (407) 894-7300 ext. 251
jclarke@hearstsc.com, Editorial Dir., King Feat. Weekly Service, King Features Syndicate, NY, New York

Clarke, Jim
jclarke@ap.org, Bureau Chief, Colorado Associated Press Editors and Reporters, CO, Denver
jclarke@ap.org, Bureau Chief, Utah-Idaho-Spokane Associated Press Association, UT, Salt Lake City

Clarke, Jim................. (800) 708-7311 Ext. 251
jclarke@hearstsc.com, Editorial Dir., King Feat. Weekly Service, North America Syndicate, New York

Clarke, Owen.........................(307) 670-8980
OwenClarke@Campbellcountyobserver.com , Advertising Design, The Campbell County Observer, WY, Rozet

Clarke, Sandra.......................(416) 364-0321
sandra.clarke@thecanadianpress.com, Broadcast News Limited, ON, Toronto

Clarkson, Maggie.............(830) 379-5441 x 205
maggie.clarkson@seguingazette.com, Business Manager, The Seguin Gazette, TX, Seguin

Clary, Gareth
msnews@themississippipress.com, Pub., The Mississippi Press, MS, Pascagoula

Clasen, Rachel
news@eurekaherald.com, Pub, The Eureka Herald, KS, Eureka

Clausen, Donita............ (620) 442-4200 ext. 120
photographer@arkcity.net, Photographer/ Videographer, The Arkansas City Traveler, KS, Arkansas City

Clausen, Ron..........................(336) 415-4681
Pub., The Yadkin Ripple, NC, Yadkinville
Pub., The Pilot, NC, Pilot Mountain
Pub., The Carroll News, VA, Hillsville
Pub., Jefferson Post, NC, West Jefferson
Pub., The Tribune, NC, Elkin
Pub., Mount Airy News, NC, Mount Airy

Claussen, Douglas...................(303) 622-9796
dclaussen@i-70scout.com, Ed., Eastern Colorado News, CO, Strasburg

Claussen, E. Neal
aab@bradley.edu, Prof. Emer., Bradley University, IL, Peoria

Claussen, Nick.......................(740) 245-7521
Univ. of Rio Grande, OH, Rio Grande

Clawson, Scott A.
sales@datafest.com, Pres., Datafest Technologies, Inc., UT, Salt Lake City

Claxton, Deb
thewedge@nelson-tel.net, Ed., The Courier-Wedge, WI, Durand

Claxton, Sharon
sclaxton@jacksonvilleprogress.com, Adv. Asst., Jacksonville Daily Progress, TX, Jacksonville

Clay, Neely............................(770) 683-1763
clay@newnan.com, Reporter, The Newnan Times-Herald, GA, Newnan

Claybaugh, Casey
casey@benewsjournal.com, Pub., Box Elder News Journal, UT, Brigham City

Claybaugh, Thomas..................(607) 798-1111
tclaybaugh@pressconnects.com, Pub., Press & Sun-Bulletin, NY, Binghamton

Claybaugh, Thomas..................(607) 798-1111
tclaybaugh@ithacajournal.com, Pres./Pub., The Ithaca Journal, NY, Ithaca
tclaybaugh@ithacajournal.com, Delmarva Media Group, MD

Claybaugh, Tom......................(410) 749-7171
tclaybau@dmg.gannett.com, Gen Mgr., The Delaware Wave, DE, Bethany Beach

Claybaugh, Tom......................(828) 232-5933
tclaybau@gannett.com, Pres. , The Asheville Citizen-Times, NC, Asheville

Claybourn, David........................ ext. 20
dclaybourn@heraldbanner.com, Sports Ed., Herald-Banner, TX, Greenville

Clayman, Arthur J....................(518) 395-3133
aclayman@dailygazette.net, Editorial Page Ed., The Daily Gazette, NY, Schenectady

Clayton, Brinn................ (336) 599-0162 ex 103
ctbrinn@roxboro-courier.com, Pub, The Courier-Times, NC, Roxboro

Clayton, Christina
cclayton@mainstreetmg.com, Circ. Mgr, Santa Cruz Good Times, CA, Santa Cruz

Clayton, Frank.......................(336) 727-7219
fclayton@wsjournal.com, Production Plant Manager, Winston-Salem Journal, NC, Winston Salem

Clayton, Reg.........................(807) 468-5555 ext.242
RClayton@postmedia.com, Reg. Managing Ed. , Lake Of The Woods Enterprise, ON, Kenora

Clayton, Richmond..................(423) 338-2818
polkadvertising@bellsouth.net, Ed., Polk County News/Citizen Advance, TN, Benton

Cleare, Ashley.......................(802) 864-5684
ashley@sevendaysvt.com, Classifieds & personals manager, Seven Days, VT, Burlington

Cleary, Joe
JCleary@tampatrib.com, Tampa Bay Times, FL, St Petersburg

Cleary, John.........................(765) 640-4875
john.cleary@heraldbulletin.com, Photo Ed., The Herald Bulletin, IN, Anderson

Cleary, Michael J.
farmersweekly@sbcglobal.net, Pub., Farmers Weekly Review, IL, Joliet

Cleaveland, Chris....................(860) 701-4461
c.cleaveland@theday.com, Dir. of IT, The Day Publishing Co., CT, New London
c.cleaveland@theday.com, Director of Information Technology, The Day, CT, New London

Cleckley, Laura............ (205) 755-5747, ext. 601
laura.cleckley@clantonadvertiser.com, Customer Service, The Clanton Advertiser, AL, Clanton

Cleesen, Bobbi
classified@journalpilot.com, Clas. Adv./Circ., Hancock County Journal-Pilot, IL, Carthage

Clegg, Chris
spn@cablecomet.com, Ed., South Peace News, AB, High Prairie

Cleland, Rob..........................(202) 334-5070
robert.cleland@washpost.com, Sr. Systems Admin., The Washington Post Writers Group, Washington

Cleland, Robert......................(202) 334-5070
robert.cleland@washpost.com, Senior Systems Administrator, Washington Post News Service with Bloomberg News, Washington

Clem, Darrell.........................(734) 972-0919
dclem@hometownlife.com, Reporter , Canton Observer, MI, Detroit

Clemens, Diane............... (765) 482-4650 ext. 102
diane.clemens@reporter.net, Circ. and Prod., The Reporter, IN, Lebanon

Clement, Chuck
Chuck@MadisonDailyLeader.com, City Reporter, The Madison Daily Leader, SD, Madison

Clement, Doug......................(860) 355-4121
editor@countytimes.com, Exec. Ed., Housatonic Publications, CT, New Milford

Clement, Douglas........... (860) 489-3121 ext. 364
dclement@ctcentral.com, Exec. Ed., West Hartford News, CT, New Haven
dclement@ctcentral.com, Ed., The Litchfield County Times, CT, Torrington

Clement, Sarah
sclement@idahocountyfreepress.com, Pub., Idaho County Free Press, ID, Grangeville

Clementi, Greg
gpclementi@yahoo.com, Sports Ed, Sonoma West Times and News, CA, Healdsburg

Clements, Jeff........................(434) 292-3019
clements@courier-record.com, Advertising Representative, Courier-Record, VA, Blackstone

Clements, Julie......................(316) 321-1120
jclements@butlercountytimesgazette.com, Managing Ed., The Butler County Times-Gazette, KS, Augusta

Clements, Julie......................(316) 321-1120
cjanney@butlercountytimesgazette.com, Managing Ed., Andover American, KS, Augusta

Clements, Melissa....................(217) 322-1010
melissa.clements@casscomm.com, General Manager, Star-gazette Extra, IL, Beardstown

Clements, Michael
info@dailycourtreview.com, Editor, Daily Court Review, TX, Houston

Clements, Thomas H........................ext. 207
thomas.clements@gaflnews.com, Circ. Dir., Thomasville Times-Enterprise, GA, Thomasville

Clemmensen, Jon
jlclemme@samford.edu, Samford Univ., AL, Birmingham

Clemons, Mike........................(904) 359-4393
mike.clemons@jacksonville.com, VP-Operations, The Florida Times-Union, FL, Jacksonville

Clendaniel, Sheila....................(302) 741-8259
shelclen@newszap.com, Exec. Asst., Independent Newsmedia Inc. Usa, DE, Dover

Clendenning, Richard...... (847) 981-9399 ext. 205
Pres./CEO, INX International Ink Co., IL, Schaumburg

Clermont, Lois ....(518) 565-4148
bgrady@pressrepublican.com, Editor, Press-
Republican, NY, Plattsburgh

Clermont-Anderson, Twyla ....(306) 781-5364
tclermont-anderson@leaderpost.canwest.com,
Mgr., HR, The Leader-Post, SK, Regina

Cleveland, Barry
advertising@carmitimes.com, Gen. Mgr., The
Carmi Times, IL, Carmi

Clevenson, Laurie
news@jewishworldnews.org, editor., The
Jewish World, NY, Schenectady

Cleworth, David ....(813) 929-6907
david.cleworth@sourcemedia.com, Adv.,
Southeast, American Banker, NY, New York

Click, J. William
clickw@winthrop.edu, Chair/Prof., Winthrop
University, SC, Rock Hill

Clifford, James M.
jimc@wdtimes.com, Ed., Watertown Daily
Times, WI, Watertown

Clifford, James M.
dcind@charterinternet.com, Pub., Dodge
County Independent-News, WI, Juneau

Clifford, John
butler@butlerautomatic.com, Vice Pres.,
Engineering, Butler Automatic, MA,
Middleboro

Clifford, Kevin
kevinc@wdtimes.com, Gen. Mgr., Watertown
Daily Times, WI, Watertown

Clifford, Neil
clinton.news@bowesnet.com, Pub., Clinton
News-record, ON, Clinton

Clifford, Neil
neil.clifford@sunmedia.ca, Adv. Dir. ,
Lakeshore Advance, ON, Grand Bend
neil.clifford@sunmedia.ca, Pub., The Huron
Expositor, ON, Seaforth

Clifford, Sara
sclifford@bcdemocrat.com, Ed., Brown County
Democrat, IN, Nashville

Clifford, Sara
sclifford@bcdemocrat.com, Ed., Marketplace,
IN, Nashville

Clift, Katie ....(530) 336-6513
mtecho@frontiernet.net, Adv. Mgr., The
Mountain Echo, CA, Fall River Mills

Clifton, Daniel
daniel@thepicayune.com, Ed., The Picayune,
TX, Marble Falls

Clifton, Orkke
americanclass834@suddenlinkmail.com,
American Classifieds - Alexandria, LA,
Alexandria

Clifton, Tammy ....(317) 477-3204
tclifton@greenfieldreporter.com, Adv. Mgr.,
Clas., Daily Reporter, IN, Greenfield

Clifton, Will
newsbooster@bellsouth.net, Ed., Catahoula
News Booster, LA, Jonesville

Cline, Todd ....(770) 963 - 9205 x1300
todd.cline@gwinnettdailypost.com, Ed.,
Gwinnett Daily Post, GA, Lawrenceville

Cline, Yevonne
classifieds@clearwatertimes.com, Admin
Coord./Sales Rep, North Thompson Times,
BC, Clearwater

Clinebell, Ken ....(941) 554-5000
kclinebell@vertical.com, CFO, Vertical
Communications, Inc., AZ, Phoenix

Clingingsmith, Mara ....(217) 221-3337
mclingingsmith@whig.com, Classified Mgr.,
Herald News, NJ, Rockaway

Clingingsmith, Mara ....(217) 221-3337
mclingingsmith@whig.com, Class. Mgr., New
Jersey Herald, NJ, Newton

Clinkscales, Kirk
kirk@goodnewspress.com, Adv. Mgr., Good
News, KS, Caney

Clinton, Kendall ....(334) 712-7954
kclinton@dothaneagle.com, Managing Ed., The
Dothan Eagle, AL, Dothan

Clinton, Pete
pclinton@mihomepaper.com, Adv. Mgr, Swartz
Creek View, MI, Davison
pclinton@mihomepaper.com, Adv. Mgr, Grand
Blanc View, MI, Davison
pclinton@mihomepaper.com, Adv. Mgr, LA
View, MI, Lapeer
pclinton@mihomepaper.com, Adv. Mgr, The
Brown City Banner, MI, Sandusky
pclinton@mihomepaper.com, Adv. Mgr, Flint
Township View, MI, Davison
pclinton@mihomepaper.com, Adv. Mgr,
Township View, MI, Chesaning
pclinton@mihomepaper.com, Adv. Mgr, The
Davison Index, MI, Davison
pclinton@mihomepaper.com, Adv. Mgr, Tri-
County Citizen, MI, Sandusky

Clinton, Sharon ....(662) 843-4241 ext. 43
sharon.clinton@bolivarcommercial.com, Prodn.
Mgr., The Bolivar Commercial, MS, Cleveland

Clinton Dunne, Tricia ....(256) 304-0050
tclinton@times-journal.com, Pres. and Pub,
Fort Payne Newspapers, Inc., AL, Fort Payne
tclinton@times-journal.com, Pres./Pub., The
Times-Journal, AL, Fort Payne

Clohessy, Craig
cclohessy@lmtribune.com, City Ed., Lewiston
Morning Tribune, ID, Lewiston

Clontz, Katie ....(765) 575-4651
editor@thecouriertimes.com, Editor, The
Courier-Times, IN, New Castle

Close, Jeannette
jeannette@pressbanner.com, Ad. Dir., Press
Banner, CA, Scotts Valley

Close, Jeannette
jclose@community-newspapers.com, Adv.
Mgr., Saratoga News, CA, San Jose
jclose@community-newspapers.com, Adv.
Mgr., The Sunnyvale Sun, CA, San Jose
jclose@community-newspapers.com, Adv.
Mgr., Campbell Reporter, CA, San Jose
jclose@community-newspapers.com, Adv.
Mgr., Almaden Resident, CA, San Jose

Clossey, Erin ....(781) 433-8334
eclossey@wickedlocal.com, News Ed.,
Brookline TAB, MA, Needham

Cloud, Barbara
barbara.cloud@unlv.edu, Prof. Emer.,
University of Nevada, Las Vegas, NV, Las
Vegas

Cloud, George W. ....(919) 962-4070
Assoc. Prof., University of North Carolina, NC,
Chapel Hill

Cloud, Robert
wpcompany@gmail.com, Ed., Waupaca
County Post, WI, Waupaca

Cloud, Scott
news@newkirkherald.com, Ed./Pub., The
Newkirk Herald Journal, OK, Newkirk

Clough, Bill
goliad@mysoutex.com, Ed, Goliad Advance-
Guard, TX, Goliad

Clough, Chris ....(920) 743-3321
cclough@gannett.com, Your Key to the Door
Weekly Editor, Door County Advocate, WI,
Sturgeon Bay

Clough, Jennifer ....(309) 690-5307
jclough@multiad.com, Business Development
Manager, Local Search Association, IL,
Peoria

Clouser, Jeff
jeffclouser@ldnews.com, Weekend Ed., The
Lebanon Daily News, PA, Lebanon

Clouston, Scott
sclouston@fujihuntusa.com, Vice Pres., Fujifilm

Hunt Chemicals U.S.A., Inc., NJ, Allendale

Cloutier, Don ....(508) 749-3164 x380
dcloutier@holdenlandmark.com, Prod. Mgr. ,
Worcester Magazine, MA, Worcester
dcloutier@holdenlandmark.com, Prod. Mgr,
Leominster Champion, MA, Leominster

Cloutier, Don
dcloutier@thelandmark.com, Prodn. Mgr., The
Landmark, MA, Holden

Cloutier, Maurice
maurice.cloutier@latribune.qc.ca, Ed.-in-Chief,
La Tribune, QC, Sherbrooke

Clow, Caitlin
cclow@postmedia.com, Ed, Pincher Creek
Echo, AB, Pincher Creek

Clubb, Angela ....(301) 650-1490
Montgomery College, MD, Takoma Park

Clubbs, Brooke
bclubbs@semo.edu, Adj. Fac., Southeast
Missouri State University, MO, Cape
Girardeau

Clucas, Matt
mclucas@pcgazette.com, Adv. Rep., The
Portage County Gazette, WI, Stevens Point

Cluett, Rick ....(902) 625-3300
rickc@porthawkesburyreporter.com, Pub., The
Scotia Sun, NS, Port Hawkesbury
rickc@porthawkesburyreporter.com, Pub, The
Reporter, NS, Port Hawkesbury

Cluett Pactol, Catherine ....(808) 552-2781
editor@themolokaidispatch.com, Ed. in Chief,
The Molokai Dispatch, HI, Kaunakakai

Cluff, Judy ....(204) 725-0209
jcluff@wheatcityjournal.ca, Admin Asst.,
Westman Journal, MB, Brandon

Cluff, Leon ....(204) 726-4022
distribution@wheatcityjournal.ca, Dist. Mgr.,
Westman Journal, MB, Brandon

Clugston, Patty
pclugston@chambers.gannett.com, Prodn.
Mgr., Composing/Camera, Public Opinion,
PA, Chambersburg

Clutter, Brian
bclutter@tylerstarnews.com, Pub., Tyler Star
News, WV, Sistersville

Clutter, Brian ....(304) 845-4050 ext. 210
bclutter@greentab.com, Publisher, Green Tab,
WV, Moundsville

Clutter, Brian
bclutter@wetzelchronicle.com, Pub., Wetzel
Chronicle, WV, New Martinsville

Clyde, Nelson ....(903) 596-6326
cnciv@tylerpaper.com, Pub. , Tyler Morning
Telegraph, TX, Tyler

Clyde, Thomas ....(903) 596-6239
tclyde@tylerpaper.com, CFO, Tyler Morning
Telegraph, TX, Tyler

Coady, Walter J.
insurance@walterry.com, Dir., Mktg., Walterry
Insurance Brokers, MD, Clinton

Coakley, Jeff
jcoakley@baywindows.com, Co-Pub., Bay
Windows, MA, Boston

Coakley, John ....(559) 441-6143
jcoakley@fresnobee.com, Adv. Sr. Vice Pres.,
Sales/Strategic Mktg., The Fresno Bee, CA,
Fresno

Coates, Chris ....(217) 421-8905
ccoates@herald-review.com, Editor, Fairview
Heights Journal (OOB) , IL, St. Louis
ccoates@herald-review.com, Ed., Herald &
Review, Decatur, IL, Decatur

Coates, Cindy
ccoates@bonnyville.greatwest.ca, Circ. Mgr.,
Bonnyville Nouvelle, AB, Bonnyville

Coates, Joe ....(601) 757-8960
publisher@copiahcountycourier.com,
Publisher, Marketing Director, Account Rep

Editor, Sports Director, Copiah County Courier,
MS, Hazlehurst

Coates, Ken ....(210) 250-3676
Ops. Dir., San Antonio Express-News, TX, San
Antonio

Coates, Rusty ....(813) 259-8353
Tampa Bay Times, FL, St Petersburg

Coats, Bill ....(518) 873-6368
bill@denpubs.com, Plant Operations Mgr, The
Valley News Sun, NY, Elizabethtown

Coats, Bill ....ext. 224
bill@denpubs.com, Prodn. Mgr., The
Adirondack Journal Sun, NY, Elizabethtown

Coats, Bill ....(518) 873-6368 ext. 225
bill@suncommunitynews.com, Prodn. Mgr., The
North Countryman Sun, NY, Elizabethtown

Coats, Edward ....(518) 873-6368
ed@suncommunitynews.com, Associate
Pub, The North Countryman Sun, NY,
Elizabethtown

Coats, Edward ....(802) 388-6397
ed@denpubs.com, Pres./Pub., The Adirondack
Journal Sun, NY, Elizabethtown

Coats, Edward ....(802) 388-6397
vermonttimes@gmail.com, Pres./Pub., Green
Mountain Outlook, VT, Middlebury

Coats, Edward ....(518) 873-6368
ed@denpubs.com, Assoc. Pub., The News
Enterprise Sun, NY, Elizabethtown
ed@denpubs.com, Assoc. Pub., The Times of
Ti Sun, NY, Elizabethtown

Coats, William ....(518) 873-6368
bill@denpubs.com, Plant Operations Mgr., The
Times of Ti Sun, NY, Elizabethtown
bill@denpubs.com, Plant Operations Mgr., The
News Enterprise Sun, NY, Elizabethtown

Coats, William ....(518) 873-6368
bill@suncommunitynews.com, Plant
Operations Mgr, Sun Community News,
Published by:Denton Publications, Inc., NY,
Elizabethtown

Cobb, Lana
lcobb@maryvilledailyforum.com, Business Mgr,
The Maryville Daily Forum, MO, Maryville

Cobb, Landon ....(405) 499-0022
lcobb@okpress.com, Sales Director, Oklahoma
Press Association, OK, Oklahoma City

Cobb, Lona D. ....(336) 750-8639
cobblo@wssu.edu, Advisor, Winston-Salem
State Univ., NC, Winston Salem

Cobb, Mark ....(205) 722-0201
mark.cobb@tuscaloosanews.com, Theater/
Music Ed., The Tuscaloosa News, AL,
Tuscaloosa

Cobb, Phil
pcobb@maryvilledailyforum.com, Pub., The
Maryville Daily Forum, MO, Maryville

Cobbs, Cherith
ccobbs@thegurdontimes.com, Reporter,
Nevada County Picayune, AR, Hope

Cobbs, Paul ....(510) 287-8200
info@postnewsgroup.com, Pub., Oakland Post,
CA, Oakland
info@postnewsgroup.com, Pub., Marin County
Post, CA, Oakland
info@postnewsgroup.com, Pub., Richmond
Post, CA, Oakland

Coblentz, Whitney
registerdisplay@gmail.com, Adv. Rep./Graphic
Designer, The Iola Register, KS, Iola

Cobler, Chris ....(361) 574-1222
ccobler@vicad.com, Ed., Victoria Advocate,
TX, Victoria

Coburn, Tom
wsrecord@comcast.net, Ed., West Springfield
Record, MA, West Springfield

Coccagna, Tony ....(724) 465-5555 ext. 266
tonyc@indianagazette.net, Sports Ed., The

Indiana Gazette, PA, Indiana

Cochran, Lee .... **(740) 888-6054**
lcochran@thisweeknews.com, Mng. Ed.,
ThisWeek West Side News, OH, Lewis
Center

lcochran@thisweeknews.com, Mng. Ed.,
ThisWeek Delaware News, OH, Lewis Center

lcochran@thisweeknews.com, Mng. Ed.,
ThisWeek Johnstown Independent, OH,
Lewis Center

lcochran@thisweeknews.com, Mng. Ed.,
ThisWeek Licking County News, OH, Lewis
Center

lcochran@thisweeknews.com, Mng. Ed.,
ThisWeek Marysville News, OH, Lewis
Center

lcochran@thisweeknews.com, Mng. Ed.,
ThisWeek Bexley News, OH, Lewis Center

lcochran@thisweeknews.com, Mng. Ed.,
ThisWeek The Canal Winchester Times, OH,
Lewis Center

lcochran@thisweeknews.com, Mng. Ed.,
ThisWeek Clintonville Booster, OH, Lewis
Center

lcochran@thisweeknews.com, Mng. Ed.,
ThisWeek Dublin Villager, OH, Lewis Center

lcochran@thisweeknews.com, Mng. Ed.,
ThisWeek Rocky Fork Enterprise, OH, Lewis
Center

lcochran@thisweeknews.com, Mng. Ed.,
ThisWeek German Village Gazette, OH,
Lewis Center

lcochran@thisweeknews.com, Mng. Ed.,
ThisWeek Tri-Village News, OH, Lewis
Center

lcochran@thisweeknews.com, Mng. Ed.,
ThisWeek Grove City Record, OH, Lewis
Center

lcochran@thisweeknews.com, Mng. Ed.,
ThisWeek Hilliard Northwest News, OH,
Lewis Center

lcochran@thisweeknews.com, Mng. Ed.,
ThisWeek New Albany News, OH, Lewis
Center

lcochran@thisweeknews.com, Mng. Ed.,
ThisWeek Northland News, OH, Lewis
Center

lcochran@thisweeknews.com, Mng. Ed.,
ThisWeek Northwest News, OH, Lewis
Center

lcochran@thisweeknews.com, Mng. Ed.,
ThisWeek Olentangy Valley News, OH, Lewis
Center

lcochran@thisweeknews.com, Mng. Ed.,
ThisWeek Pickerington Times-Sun, OH,
Lewis Center

lcochran@thisweeknews.com, Mng. Ed.,
ThisWeek Reynoldsburg News, OH, Lewis
Center

lcochran@thisweeknews.com, Mng. Ed.,
ThisWeek Upper Arlington News, OH, Lewis
Center

lcochran@thisweeknews.com, Mng. Ed.,
ThisWeek Westerville News & Public
Opinion, OH, Lewis Center

lcochran@thisweeknews.com, Mng. Ed.,
ThisWeek Whitehall News, OH, Lewis Center

lcochran@thisweeknews.com, Mng. Ed.,
ThisWeek Worthington News, OH, Lewis
Center

Cochran, Lee
lcochran@thisweeknews.com, Asst. Mng. Ed.,
Consumer News Service Inc., OH, Lewis
Center

Cochran, Richard
richardc@journalmultimedia.com, Assoc. Pub.,
Central Penn Parent, PA, Harrisburg

Cochran, Wendell
cochran@american.edu, Assoc. Prof.,
American University, DC, Washington

Cocker, Lexie
lexie@wyandottepublishing.com, Exec. Asst.,
Wyandotte Daily News Weekly Print Edition,
KS, Kansas City

Coday, Dennis .... **(816) 968-2230**
dcoday@ncronline.org, Editor, National
Catholic Reporter, MO, Kansas City

Coddington, Mindy .... **765/743-1111 ext. 109**
addirector@purdueexponent.org, Advertising
director, The Purdue Exponent, IN, West
Lafayette

Coddon, David
dcoddon@sdmesa.edu, Lectr., San Diego
State University, CA, San Diego

Coder, Darlene
dcoder@alltel.net, Pub., The Daily Press, PA,
Saint Marys

Coder, Darlene .... **(814) 773-3161**
ridgwayrecord@shop-right.com, Pub., Shop
Right, PA, Ridgway

Coder, Darlene
publisher3@zitomedia.net, Pub., Daily Press,
PA, Saint Marys

Codner, Mark A. .... **(580) 795-3355**
recordeditorial@sbcglobal.net, Ed., Madill
Record, OK, Madill

Cody, Karen Jones .... **(606) 785-5134**
kjones@troublesomecreektimes.com, Co-
Publisher/ Exec. Editor, Troublesome Creek
Times, KY, Hindman

Cody, Kevin
kevin@easyreadernews.com, Adv. Mgr., Easy
Reader, CA, Hermosa Beach

Cody, Phil .... **(229) 888-9304**
phil.cody@albanyherald.com, Adv. Accts. Rep.,
Nat'l/Major, The Albany Herald, GA, Albany

Cody, Theresa .... **(978) 249-3535 ext. 640**
production@atholdailynews.com, Prod. Mgr.,
Athol Daily News, MA, Athol

Cody, Tim .... **(606) 785-5134**
tcody@troublesomecreektimes.com,
Classifieds/Production, Troublesome Creek
Times, KY, Hindman

Coelho, Kaysi
kaysi@thebusinessjournal.com, Adv. Mgr., The
Business Journal, CA, Fresno

Coello, Henry .... **(830) 625-9144 ext. 301**
Prodn. Mgr., New Braunfels Herald-Zeitung,
TX, New Braunfels

Coen, Jeremy .... **(620) 694-5700 Ext. 700**
jcoen@hutchnews.com, Packaging/Distribution
Manager, The Hutchinson News, KS,
Hutchinson

Coester, Dana .... **(304) 293-6790**
dana.coester@mail.wvu.edu, Assistant
Professor, West Virginia University, WV,
Morgantown

Cofer, Donny .... **(405) 257-3341**
news@seminoleproducer.com, Mng. Ed.,
Wewoka Times, OK, Wewoka

Cofer, Kelly
KCofer@tbo.com, Tampa Bay Times, FL, St
Petersburg

Coffee, Christina
ccoffee@boonevilledemocrat.com, Circ. Mgr.,
Booneville Democrat, AR, Booneville

Coffey, Bural .... **(606) 451-4903**
Circ. Dir., The Commonwealth-Journal, KY,
Somerset

Coffey, Danielle .... **(571) 366-1153**
Danielle.Coffey@naa.org, VP of Public Policy,
News Media Alliance, VA, Arlington

Coffman, Debbie .... **(541) 383-0384**
debcoffman@bendbulletin.com, Sales
Specialist , Central Oregon Nickel Ads, OR,
Bend

Coffman, Frank .... **(815) 921-3307**
f.coffman@rockvalleycollege.edu, Rock Valley
College, IL, Rockford

Coffman, Steve
scoffman@jacksonsun.com, Exec. Ed., The
Jackson Sun, TN, Jackson

Cogbill, Nan
class@summerlandreview.com, Class./Circ
Mgr, Summerland Review, BC, Summerland

Coggins, Rudy .... **(919) 739-7856**
rcoggins@newsargus.com, Sports Ed.,
Goldsboro News-Argus, NC, Goldsboro

Cogley, Colette .... **(312) 981-1747**
ccogley@unitedmedia.com, Regl. Sales Mgr.,
Newspaper Enterprise Association (Div. of
United Media), NY, New York

ccogley@unitedmedia.com, Regl. Sales Mgr.,
United Feature Syndicate (Div. of United
Media), New York

Cogswell, George
gcogswell@commercialappeal.com, Memphis
Publishing Co., TN, Memphis

Cohea, David .... **(407) 894-7300 ext. 252**
dcohea@hearstsc.com, Gen. Mgr., King Feat.
Weekly Service
Inside Sales, King Features Syndicate, NY,
New York

dcohea@hearstsc.com, Gen. Mgr., King Feat.
Weekly Service, North America Syndicate,
New York

dcohea@hearstsc.com, King Features Weekly
Service, Reed Brennan Media Associates,
Inc., FL, Orlando

Cohen, Elizabeth
elizabeth-cohen@utulsa.edu, Business and
Advertising Manager, Univ. of Tulsa, OK,
Tulsa

Cohen, Hal
hcohen@alm.com, Publisher, The Legal
Intelligencer, PA, Philadelphia

Cohen, Irwin
irwinc@amtrealtyny.com, Daily Racing Form,
NY, New York

Cohen, Jeffrey
jcohen@teleperformance.com, COO,
Teleperformance Interactive, PA, Plymouth
Meeting

Cohen, Jennie
jpostopinion@gmail.com, Ed., National Jewish
Post & Opinion, IN, Indianapolis

Cohen, Jennie
jpostopinion@gmail.com, Ed., The Indiana
Jewish Post & Opinion, IN, Indianapolis

Cohen, Jeremy
jxc45@psu.edu, Prof./Assoc. Vice Pres./
Sr. Assoc. Dean, Undergrad. Educ., The
Pennsylvania State University, PA, University
Park

Cohen, Jess........................... **(812) 316-5419**
jcohen@suncommercial.com, Reporter ,
Vincennes Sun-Commercial, IN, Vincennes

Cohen, Julie .... **(781) 433-8384**
jcohen@wickedlocal.com, Ed. , West Roxbury
Transcript, MA, Needham
jcohen@wickedlocal.com, Ed., Allston-Brighton
TAB, MA, Needham

Cohen, Julie .... **(781) 433-8384**
jcohen@wickedlocal.com, Ed., Roslindale
Transcript, MA, Needham

Cohen, Larry........................... **(202) 434-1100**
lcohen@cwa-union.org, Pres.,
Communications Workers of America, DC,
Washington

Cohen, Larry
lcohen@cwa-union.org, Pres., Printing,
Publishing & Media Workers Sector-CWA,
DC, Washington

Cohen, Leon .... **(414) 390-5770**
leonc@milwaukeejewish.org, Editor, The
Wisconsin Jewish Chronicle, WI, Milwaukee

Cohen, Marc
mcohen@teleperformance.com, Pres.,
Teleperformance Interactive, PA, Plymouth
Meeting

Cohen, Mark .... **(781) 433-6950**
salesteam@wickedlocal.com, Pres.,
Pennsylvania NewsMedia Association, PA,
Harrisburg

Cohen, Mark

salesteam@wickedlocal.com, Vice Pres., Adv.,
Times & Courier, MA, Concord

Cohen, Mark .... **(781) 433-6950**
salesteam@wickedlocal.com, Vice Pres., Adv.,
Marshfield Mariner, MA, Marshfield

Cohen, Mark
mcohen@thebeaconjournal.com, Publisher,
Akron Beacon Journal, OH, Akron

Cohen, Mark .... **(781) 433-6950**
salesteam@wickedlocal.com, Vice Pres., Adv.,
Amesbury News, MA, Danvers

Cohen, Mark
salesteam@wickedlocal.com, Vice Pres., Adv.,
Arlington Advocate, MA, Lexington

Cohen, Mark
salesteam@wickedlocal.com, Vice Pres., Adv.,
Westford Eagle, MA, Concord

Cohen, Mark .... **(781) 433-6950**
salesteam@wickedlocal.com, VP., Adv.,
Weston Town Crier, MA, Framingham

Cohen, Michael
ads@villagevoice.com, Pub., The Village Voice,
NY, New York

Cohen, Mick .... **(415) 777-6450**
mcohen@sfchronicle.com, VP of Cir., San
Francisco Chronicle, CA, San Francisco

Cohen, Murray .... **(419) 695-0015 ext. 21**
murray@delphosherald.com, Pub., Delphos
Daily Herald, OH, Delphos

Cohen, Murray
murray@delphosherald.com, Pres., Delphos
Herald, Inc., OH, Delphos

Cohen, Murray
murray@delphosherald.com, Pub., The Dart,
OH, Delphos

Cohen, Rachelle .... **(617) 619-6105**
shelco@bostonherald.com, Editorial Page Ed. ,
Boston Herald, MA, Boston

Cohen, Robert L. .... **(646) 654-8411**
Pres./CEO, Scarborough Research, NY, New
York

Cohen, Roberta
rcohen@delphosherald.com, VP, Delphos
Herald, Inc., OH, Delphos

Cohen, Shelly .... **(617) 619-6105**
rachelle.cohen@bostonherald.com, Editorial
Page Ed., Boston Herald, MA, Boston

Cohrs, Daniel
dcohrs@ccu.edu, Colorado Christian Univ.,
CO, Lakewood

Coile, Norma .... **(520) 573-4102**
ncoile@azstarnet.com, Science/Technology
Ed., Arizona Daily Star, AZ, Tucson

Coish, Gladys
gcoish@amherstdaily.com, Adv. Mgr., The
Citizen-record, NS, Amherst

Coish, Gladys
gcoish@amherstdaily.com, Adv. Mgr., Amherst
Daily News, NS, Amherst

Cojocaru, Mihia
mcojocaru@polychem.com, Gen. Mgr., Sterling
Packaging Systems, OH, Mentor

Coker, Meg
meg@tunicatimes.com, Managing Editor, The
Tunica Times, MS, Tunica

Coker, Melanie
mcoker@aurorasentinel.com, Mktg. Dir., Aurora
Sentinel, CO, Aurora

Colacioppo, Lee Ann .... **(303) 954-1754**
lcolacioppo@denverpost.com, Ed., The Denver
Post, CO, Denver

Colandrea, Richard.................... **(973) 569-7810**
Colandrea@northjersey.com, Dir. Corporate &
National Adv., Herald News, NJ, Rockaway

Colber, Dianne .... **(812) 265-3641, ext. 228**
Inside Sales, Madison Courier, Inc., IN,
Madison

Colbert, Ethan .... (573) 324-2222
bgted@lcs.net, Editor, Bowling Green Times, MO, Bowling Green

Colburn, A. Loren
lcolburn@scotsmanpress.com, Pub., Onondaga Valley News, NY, Syracuse

Colburn, A. Loren .... (315) 472-7825
lcolburn@scotsmanpress.com, Pub., Scotsman Community Publication, NY, Syracuse

Colburn, Carrie .... (308) 381-9411
carrie.colburn@theindependent.com, New Media Dir., The Grand Island Independent, NE, Grand Island

Colburn, Carrie .... (402) 204-7001
carrie.colburn@yorknewstimes.com, Pub., York News-Times, NE, York

Colburn, Loren .... (877) 203-2327
loren@afcp.org, Executive Director, Association of Free Community Papers, NY, Liverpool

Colden, Rebecca .... (218) 386-3940
warroadpioneer@gmail.com, Pub., The Warroad Pioneer, MN, Warroad

Colden, Sue
suec@glencoenews.com, Adv. Mgr., The Glencoe Advertiser, MN, Glencoe

Cole, Arnold
acole@ourweekly.com, Circulation Manager, Our Weekly, CA, Los Angeles

Cole, Asa
pressreleases@ccnewspapers.com, Sales Mgr., Courier Extra, CO, Woodland Park

Cole, Bettyann .... (419) 724-6218
bcole@toledoblade.com, Sr. IT Manager, The Blade, OH, Toledo

Cole, Bob .... (763) 712-2403
bob.cole@ecm-inc.com, Mktg. Dir., Adams Publishing Group, LLC, MN, Virginia

Cole, Brian D. .... (304) 284-0303
bcole@dominionpost.com, Controller, The Dominion Post, WV, Morgantown

Cole, C.E.
saintjotribune@embarqmail.com, Co-Pub./Ed., The Saint Jo Tribune, TX, Saint Jo

Cole, Cindy .... (575) 763-3431
Circ. Dir., Eastern New Mexico News, NM, Clovis

Cole, Darell
darrell.cole@tc.tc, Ed, The Citizen-record, NS, Amherst

Cole, Darrell
darrell.cole@tc.tc, Sr. Ed., Amherst Daily News, NS, Amherst

Cole, Gail .... (541) 737-3191
Oregon State Univ., OR, Corvallis

Cole, Jacque .... (575) 356-4481 ext. 18
Off. Mgr., Eastern New Mexico News, NM, Clovis

Cole, James
cole.james@telegraphjournal.com, Prod. Mgr., New Brunswick Telegraph-Journal, NB, Saint John

Cole, Jason
jason.cole@startribune.com, Services Sales Supervisor
, Star Tribune, MN, Minneapolis

Cole, Jean
jean@athensnews-courier.com, Reporter, The News-Courier, AL, Athens

Cole, Karen
majoraccountsales@americanpress.com, National Desk/Sr. Acct. Exec. , American Press, LA, Lake Charles

Cole, Natalie
ncole@ourweekly.com, Publisher, Our Weekly, CA, Los Angeles

Cole, Preston J. .... (660) 748-3266
posttele@grm.net, Ed., Princeton Post-

Telegraph, MO, Princeton

Cole, Richard R. .... (919) 843-8289
Dean Emer./John Thomas Kerr Distinguished Prof., University of North Carolina, NC, Chapel Hill

Cole, Robert .... (212) 782-8160
rcole@newsamerica.com, News America FSI, GA, Atlanta
rcole@newsamerica.com, News America FSI, TX, Dallas
rcole@newsamerica.com, News America FSI, CA, Los Angeles
rcole@newsamerica.com, News America FSI, MN, Minneapolis
rcole@newsamerica.com, Sr. Vice President, News America FSI, NY, New York
rcole@newsamerica.com, Sr. Vice President, News America FSI, IL, Chicago
rcole@newsamerica.com, News America FSI, CT, Wilton

Colebank, Kristen
kcolebank@winchesterstar.com, Production Mgr, The Winchester Star, VA, Winchester

Coleburn, James .... (434) 292-3019
news@courier-record.com, Publisher, Courier-Record, VA, Blackstone

Coleburn, John .... (434) 292-3019
john@courier-record.com, Advertising Manager, Courier-Record, VA, Blackstone

Coleburn, William .... (434) 292-3019
news@courier-record.com, Editor, Courier-Record, VA, Blackstone

Colegrove, Wendy
sales@StIgnaceNews.com , Circ. Mgr., The St. Ignace News, MI, Saint Ignace

Coleman, Alice .... (804) 722-5110
acoleman@progress-index.com, Adv. Sales Asst., The Progress-Index, VA, Petersburg

Coleman, Daniel .... (617) 929-3094
d_coleman@globe.com, Prod. Ed. , The Boston Globe, MA, Boston

Coleman, Darrell
ashley.barnett@caller.com, Pub., Wichita Falls Times Record News, TX, Wichita Falls
ashley.barnett@caller.com, Pres./Pub., Corpus Christi Caller-Times, TX, Corpus Christi

Coleman, Dave .... (905) 454-4344 ext. 200
distribution@thebramptonguardian.com, Circ. Mgr., Brampton Guardian, ON, Mississauga

Coleman, Elizabeth
bcnews@mindspring.com, Pub./Ed., The Butner-Creedmoor News, NC, Creedmoor

Coleman, Elster
posttrib@airmail.net, Circulation Manager, Dallas Post Tribune, TX, Dallas

Coleman, Frances .... (251) 219-5607
fcoleman@press-register.com, Editorial Page Ed., Press-Register, AL, Mobile

Coleman, George
gcoleman@timesnews.net, VP, Nat'l Adv. , Kingsport Times-News, TN, Kingsport

Coleman, George .... (615) 444-3952
gcoleman@lebanonpublishing.com, Publisher, The Lebanon Democrat, TN, Lebanon

Coleman, J. Edward
info@unisys.com, Chrmn./CEO, Unisys Corp., PA, Blue Bell

Coleman, Joe
jcoleman@kcstar.com, Prod. Dev. Dir., The Kansas City Star, MO, Kansas City

Coleman, John .... (519) 255-5531
jcoleman@windsorstar.com, Editorial Page Ed., The Windsor Star, ON, Windsor

Coleman, Kathleen .... (509) 459-5060
kathleenc@spokesman.com, Dir., Sales and Mktg., The Spokesman-Review, WA, Spokane

Coleman, Keith
k.coleman@newsoforange.com, Adv./Gen.

Mgr, The News of Orange County, NC, Hillsborough

Coleman, Lynn .... (860) 423-8466
lynnc@thechronicle.com , Prodn. Mgr., The Chronicle, CT, Willimantic

Coleman, Mike .... (602) 444-8074
mcoleman@republicmedia.com, VP/Digital Media, The Arizona Republic, AZ, Phoenix

Coleman, Most Rev. George W. ..... (508) 675-7151
theanchor@anchornews.org, Pub., The Anchor, MA, Fall River

Coleman, Rachel
rcoleman@darnews.com, Bus. Mgr./Controller, Daily American Republic, MO, Poplar Bluff

Coleman, Scott .... (512) 259-4449
publisher@hillcountrynews.com, Pub., Hill Country News, TX, Cedar Park

Coleman, Terri
tcoleman@dddnews.com, Adv. Mgr., The Daily Dunklin Democrat, MO, Kennett
tcoleman@dddnews.com, Adv. Mgr., Daily Dunklin Democrat Extra, MO, Kennett

Coleman, Tom
tcoleman@lsnweb.com, Webmaster, The Daily Review, LA, Morgan City

Coleman, Yvonne
ycoleman@aol.com, Ed., The Louisville Defender, KY, Louisville

Coleman, Zack .... (361) 779-1580
zackncrp@gmail.com, Owner, Coleman Advertising, TX, Corpus Christi

Coles, Julia .... (905) 732-2411 ext. 281
julia.coles@sunmedia.ca, In Port News, ON, Port Colborne
julia.coles@sunmedia.ca, Adv. Dir., Welland Tribune, ON, Welland

Coles, Keri .... (250) 480-3239
reporter@oakbaynews.com, Multimedia Journalist, Oak Bay News, BC, Victoria

Coles, Michelle .... (907) 564-8297
Alaska Pacific Univ., AK, Anchorage

Coles, Nikki
echoads1@mrnews.ca, Advertising, The Echo-pioneer, AB, High Level

Coles, Tim .... ext. 221
tcoles@haltonsearch.com, Prodn. Mgr., The Milton Canadian Champion, ON, Milton

Coley, Chris .... (252) 265-7866
ccoley@wilsontimes.com, Circ Mngr, The Wilson Times, NC, Wilson

Coley, Ellen .... (661) 324-9466
observernews@gmail.com, Owner, Bakersfield News Observer, CA, Bakersfield

Coley, Jon .... (661) 324-9466
Observernews@gmail.com, Owner, Bakersfield News Observer, CA, Bakersfield

Coley, Joseph
joseph@observercop.com, Pub & Mng Partner, Bakersfield News Observer, CA, Bakersfield

Colip, Randy
rcolip@baldor.com, Vice Pres., Sales, Baldor Electric Co., AR, Fort Smith

Colistra, Rita .... (304) 293-6793
rita.colistra@mail.wvu.edu, Asst. Prof., West Virginia University, WV, Morgantown

Collar, Jim .... (920) 993-1000 x216
jcollar@gannett.com, Reporter/Fox Cities, Post-Crescent, WI, Appleton

Collazo, Manuel .... (310) 769-6900 x3555
mcollazo@cipsmarketing.com, President & CEO, Cips Marketing Group, Inc., CA, Los Angeles

Collazzi, John .... (718) 260-4596
Ed., Bronx Times Reporter, NY, Bronx

Collen, Bruce
bcollen@same-page.com, Pres., Same Page. com, FL, Sanibel

Collette, Kim
kcollette@timesleaderonline.com, Class. / Ins. Sales Mgr., The Times Leader, OH, Martins Ferry

Colley, Billy
billy@centrevillepress.com, Adv. Mgr., The Centreville Press, AL, Centreville

Colley, Jody
info@eastbayexpress.com, Pub., East Bay Express, CA, Oakland

Colley, Kay .... (817) 531-6525
kcolley@txwes.edu, Student Media Director, The Rambler, TX, Fort Worth

Colley, Tom
editor@bdtonline.com, Exec. Ed., Bluefield Daily Telegraph, WV, Bluefield

Collie, Doug
dcollie@olds.greatwest.ca, Ed, Olds Albertan, AB, Olds

Collier, Andy .... (662) 843-4241
sports@bolivarcommercial.com, Sports Ed., The Bolivar Commercial, MS, Cleveland

Collier, Carolyn
class@newsprogress.com, Class. Mgr. , News-Progress, IL, Sullivan

Collier, Christy .... (770) 478-5753
ccollier@news-daily.com, Adv. Dir., Clayton News Daily, GA, Jonesboro

Collier, D'Lorah .... (409) 683-5218
dlorah.collier@galvnews.com, Bus. Mgr., The Galveston County Daily News, TX, Galveston

Collier, Jana .... (937) 225-2388
jana.collier@coxinc.com, Editor in Chief, Dayton Daily News, OH, Franklin

Collier, Lyn .... (702) 383-0299
lcollier@businesspress.vegas, Editor, Las Vegas Business Press, NV, Las Vegas

Collier, Scott
classads@smokymountainnews.com, Circ. Mgr., Smoky Mountain News, NC, Waynesville

Collier , Grey .... (931) 296-5156
Greycollier@bellsouth.net , Ed., The News-Democrat, TN, Waverly

Colling, Ronald A.
manningmonitor@iowatelecom.net, Ed., Manning Monitor, IA, Manning

Colling, Todd .... (608) 364-9209 ext. 180
tcolling@beloitdailynews.com, Asst. Adv. Dir., My Stateline Shopper, WI, Beloit

Colling, Todd .... (608) 364-9236
tcolling@beloitdailynews.com, Director of Business Development, Beloit Daily News, WI, Beloit

Collinger, Tom
t-collinger@northwestern.edu, Assoc. Prof., Northwestern University, IL, Evanston

Collins, Allison
ttnews@tritownnews.com, Ed., Tri-Town News, NY, Sidney

Collins, Allison
alliedcollins@frontier.com, Ed., The Chenango American/Whitney Point Reporter/Oxford Review-Times, NY, Greene

Collins, Brandie .... (307) 334-2867
lhads@luskherald.com, Ed., The Lusk Herald, WY, Lusk

Collins, Calvin
calvincollinsjr@aol.com, The Orlando Times, FL, Orlando

Collins, Connie .... ext. 210
ccollins@ant-news.com, Southwest Iowa Shopper, IA, Atlantic

Collins, Cynthia .... (252) 265-7826
ccollings@wilsontimes.com, Ad Rep, The Wilson Times, NC, Wilson

Collins, David

david_collins@learningtree.com, Chrmn., Learning Tree International, CA, El Segundo

Collins, Dennis .... (231) 439-9358
dcollins@petoskeynews.com, Prodn. Mgr., Northern Michigan Review, MI, Petoskey

Collins, Dr. Calvin .... (407) 841-3052 ext.10
calvincollinsjr@aol.com, Pres./Pub., The Orlando Times, FL, Orlando

Collins, Erik .... (803) 777-7726
Univ. of South Carolina, SC, Columbia

Collins, Janay .... (360) 344-2938
ads@wnpa.com, Member Services Director, Washington Newspaper Publishers Association, Inc., WA, Port Townsend

Collins, Janice
jcollins@eiu.edu, Asst. Prof./Advisor, Broadcast, Eastern Illinois University, IL, Charleston

Collins, Jason
news@mysoutex.com, Ed., Beeville Bee-Picayune, TX, Beeville

Collins, Jennifer
jennifer.collins@latimes.com, VP, Digital Revenue Develop., Los Angeles Times, CA, Los Angeles

Collins, Kandi
kcollins@bannergraphic.com, Marketing Consultant, Banner-Graphic, IN, Greencastle

Collins, Kari
kcollins@iowaparkleader.com, Adv. Mgr., Iowa Park Leader, TX, Iowa Park

Collins, Lawrence .... (201) 703-0911
stepoutmag@aol.com, Publisher, Collins Communications, Fair Lawn

Collins, Leslie
lcollins@registerherald.com, Gen. Mgr., The Register-Herald, OH, Eaton

Collins, Lottie H.
news@orlando-times.com, Prodn. Mgr., The Orlando Times, FL, Orlando

Collins, Mary .... (847) 716-7000
mcollins@bccacredit.com, President & CEO, Media Financial Management Association, IL, Northfield

Collins, Michelle
quincysunads@verizon.net, Adv. Dir., The Quincy Sun, MA, Quincy
quincysunads@verizon.net, Classified Rep., Round Rock Leader, TX, Round Rock

Collins, Natalia .... (413) 732-3306
nfurjanc@masslive.com, HR Mgr., The Republican, MA, Springfield

Collins, Phyllis
pcollins@lewistonschools.net, Librarian, Lewiston Morning Tribune, ID, Lewiston

Collins, Rebekah .... (405) 366-3554
rebekah@normantranscript.com, Adv. Mgr., Norman Transcript, OK, Norman

Collins, Rob .... (580) 548-8163
editor@enidnews.com, Executive Editor, Enid News & Eagle, OK, Enid

Collins, Robyn .... (203) 245-1877 ext. 6142
collins@shorepublishing.com, Pub., Guilford Courier, CT, Madison

Collins, Robyn .... (203) 245-1877 ext 6142
collins@shorepublishing.com, Pub., North Haven Courier, CT, Madison

Collins, Robyn .... (203) 245-1877 ext. 6142
collins@shorepublishing.com, Pub., Harbor News, CT, Madison

Collins, Robyn .... (203) 245-1877 ext. 6142
collins@shorepublishing.com, Pub., The Sound, CT, Madison

Collins, Robyn
r.collins@shorepublishing.com, Adv. Mgr., Shore Publishing LLC, CT, Madison

Collins, Robyn .... (203) 245-1877 ext 6142

collins@shorepublishing.com, Pub., Valley Courier, CT, Madison

Collins, Robyn .... (203) 245-1877 ext. 6142
collins@shorepublishing.com, Pub., Source, CT, Madison

Collins, Robyn .... (203) 245-1877 ext 6142
collins@shorepublishing.com, Pub., East Haven Courier, CT, Madison

Collins, S. John
jcollins@bakercityherald.com, Photo Ed., Baker City Herald, OR, Baker City

Collins, Steve
steven.collins@ucf.edu, Asst. Prof., University of Central Florida, FL, Orlando

Collins, Steven .... (740) 474-3131
scollins@circlevilleherald.com, Reporter, The Circleville Herald, OH, Circleville

Collins, Susan .... (502) 477-2239 ext. 27
bookkeeping@spencermagnet.com, Circulation Manager, Spencer Magnet, KY, Taylorsville

Collins, Tammy
tcollins@keysnews.com, Adv. Mgr., Attica Hub, OH, Attica
tcollins@keysnews.com, Sales Consultant, Florida Keys Free Press, FL, Tavernier
tcollins@keysnews.com, Sales Consultant, The Free Press, FL, Tampa

Collins, Tracy .... (602) 444-8094
tracy.collins@pni.com, Deputy Ed., Presentation/Sports, The Arizona Republic, AZ, Phoenix

Collinsworth, Frank
fcollinsworth@brainworks.com, Business Development Manager, Brainworks Software Development Corp., NY, Sayville

Collver, Doug .... (541) 382-5643
dcollver@westernroller.com, Owner, Western Roller Corp., OR, Bend

Colman, Leigh
news@osrecord.com, Pub., Ocean Springs Record, MS, Ocean Springs

Colmenero, Lupita .... (214) 357-2186 ext 202
lupita@elhispanonews.com, Adv. Mgr., Nat'l, El Hispano News, TX, Dallas

Colmenero, Ruben .... (214) 357-2186 ext. 0
Circ. Mgr., El Hispano News, TX, Dallas

Colombo, Jim
jimc@barbertonherald.com, Adv. Dir., The Barberton Herald, OH, Barberton

Colombo, John A. .... (212) 450-7094
New York Sales Mgr., Metro Suburbia, Inc./ Newhouse Newspapers, NY, New York

Colombo, Mike .... (706) 290-5259
mcolombo@rn-t.com, Mng. Ed., Rome News-Tribune, GA, Rome

Colon, Milly .... (407) 767-0070
milly.colon@laprensaorlando.com, Sales, La Prensa, FL, Longwood

Colonna, Brenda .... ext. 249
brenda.colonna@lipennysaver.com, Prodn. Mgr., Pennysaver News, NY, Edgewood

Colosimo, Mark
mcolosimo@mysuburbanlife.com, Publisher, Suburban Life Publications, IL, Downers Grove

Colosimo, Stefan
scolosimo@mountainx.com, Techn. Mgr., Mountain Xpress, NC, Asheville

Colosky, Jill .... (701) 241-5437
jcolosky@forumcomm.com, Forum Communications Co., ND, Fargo

Colquhon, Dixie
adv@newkirkherald.com, Mktg. Dir., The Newkirk Herald Journal, OK, Newkirk

Colshan, Michelle
mcolshan@messengernews.net, Prodn Sup, The Messenger, IA, Fort Dodge

Coltam, Dede
sales@trftimes.com, Adv. Mgr., Northern Watch, MN, Thief River Falls

Coltharp, Richard .... (575) 524-8061
richard@lascrucesbulletin.com, Pub., The Las Cruces Bulletin, NM, Las Cruces

Coltharp, Tina
tcoltharp@bannergraphic.com, Office Mgr., Banner-Graphic, IN, Greencastle

Colton, Corey .... (920) 676-0495
ccolton@gannett.com, Advertising Executive, Lakes/forest Beacon, WI, Oconto

Colton, Corey .... (920) 676-0495
ccolton@gannett.com, Advertising Executive, Oconto County Beacon, WI, Oconto

Colton, Corey .... (920) 676-0495
ccolton@gannett.com, Advertising Executive, Lakes/forest Beacon, WI, Oconto

Colton, Mitch .... (614) 486-6677 ext. 1022
mcolton@adohio.net, Network Acct. Exec. & Digital Specialist, Ohio Newspaper Association, OH, Columbus

Colver, Adam
acolver@poststar.com, Online Ed., The Post-Star, NY, Glens Falls

Colville, Warren T. .... (716) 849-3426
wcolville@buffnews.com, Pres./Pub., The Buffalo News, NY, Buffalo

Colvin, Becky .... (970) 392-5646
bcolvin@greeleytribune.com, Acct. Mgr., Windsor Now, CO, Windsor

Colvin, Dick
dcolvin@gmail.com, Exec. Dir., TEXCAP, TX, Allen

Colvin, Dick
dick.colvin@hotmail.com, Exec. Dir., Texas Community Media LLC, TX, Allen

Combs, Sandra
scombs@astate.edu, Asst. Prof., Arkansas State University, AR, Jonesboro

Combs, Steven
scombs@hpu.edu, Dean/Prof., Hawaii Pacific University, HI, Honolulu

Combs, Tim
contact@fujifilmgs.com, Pres., Industrial Imaging Markets Grp., Fuji Photo Film USA/ Graphic Systems Div., IL, Hanover Park

Comcowich, William J.
comcowic@meds.com, Pres., UltiTech, Inc., CT, Stratford

Comden, David .... (310) 822-1629 x 120
david@argonautnews.com, Pub., The Argonaut, CA, Los Angeles

Comden, David .... (805) 648-2244 x 220
david@vcreporter.com, Pub., Ventura County Reporter, CA, Ventura

Comeau, Stacey
scomeau@prestoncitizen.com, Adv. Mgr., Preston Citizen, ID, Preston

Comer, Debbie .... (705) 286-1288
debbie@haliburtonpress.com, Circ., Classified, The Minden Times, ON, Minden

Comer, Hope .... (740) 353-3101 Ext. 1911
hcomer@civitasmedia.com, Pub., The Portsmouth Daily Times, OH, Portsmouth

Comer, Matt
editor@goqnotes.com, Ed., Q Notes, NC, Charlotte

Comer , Hope .... (740) 353-3101 ext. 1911
Pub. , The Community Common, OH, Portsmouth

Comey, Claire
claire.comey@richmond.edu, Editor in Chief, Univ. of Richmond, VA, Richmond

Comfort, Kim
kcomfort@sundre.greatwest.ca, Sales Mgr, Sundre Round-up, AB, Sundre

Comings, Peter
editor@westlifenews.com, Ed., West Life, OH, Rocky River

Comlinson, Bruce .... ext. 264
btomlinson@njherald.com, Exec. Ed., Shopper's Guide, NJ, Newton

Compere, Brian .... (410) 857-7891
bcompere@carrollcountytimes.com, Night Ed., Carroll County Times, MD, Westminster

Compston-Strough, Jennifer
jcompston@timesleaderonline.com, Mng. Ed., The Times Leader, OH, Martins Ferry

Compton, April
acompton@thenortheastgeorgian.com, Prodn. Mgr., The Northeast Georgian, GA, Cornelia

Compton, David .... (830) 625-9144 ext. 201
david.compton@herald-zeitung.com, Pub., New Braunfels Herald-Zeitung, TX, New Braunfels

Compton, David W. .... (203) 458-5777
dcompton@journalregister.com, Pub., Elm City Newspapers, CT, Milford

Compton, Jay .... ext. 219
sports@middlesborodailynews.com, Sports Ed., Cumberland Trading Post, KY, Middlesboro

Conaboy, Chelsea .... (207) 791-6362
cconaboy@pressherald.com, Features Ed. , Portland Press Herald / Maine Sunday Telegram, ME, Portland

Conaboy, Jack
jconaboy@lsj.com, Prod. Mgr, Portland Review & Observer, MI, Lansing
jconaboy@lsj.com, Prod. Mgr, Lansing City Community News, MI, Lansing
jconaboy@lsj.com, Prod. Mgr., Charlotte Shopping Guide, MI, Lansing
jconaboy@lsj.com, Prod. Mgr, Ingham County Community News, MI, Lansing
jconaboy@lsj.com, Prod. Mgr, Eaton Rapids Community News, MI, Lansing
jconaboy@lsj.com, Prod. Mgr, Delta Waverly Community News, MI, Lansing
jconaboy@lsj.com, Prod. Mgr, Dewitt Bath Review, MI, Lansing
jconaboy@lsj.com, Prod. Mgr, Grand Ledge Independent, MI, Lansing
jconaboy@lsj.com, Prod. Mgr, Lansing State Journal, MI, Lansing
jconaboy@lsj.com, Prod. Mgr, Williamston Enterprise, MI, Lansing
jconaboy@lsj.com, Prod. Mgr, Towne Courier, MI, Lansing

Conaghan, Jim .... (571) 366-1026
jim.conaghan@naa.org, VP, Research & Industry Analysis, News Media Alliance, VA, Arlington

Conant, Ben
bconant@ledgertranscript.com, Ed., Monadnock Ledger-Transcript, NH, Peterborough

Conard, Debra
debra@dumas-clarion.com, Prod. Mgr., Dumas Clarion, AR, Dumas

Conarro, Kathy .... ext. 106
kcc@csindy.com, Art Dir., Colorado Springs Independent, CO, Colorado Springs

Conboy, Jack
addesk@dotnews.com, Adv. Mgr., The Dorchester Reporter, MA, Dorchester
addesk@dotnews.com, Ad. Director, Mattapan Reporter, MA, Dorchester
addesk@dotnews.com, Ad. Director, Boston Irish Reporter, MA, Dorchester
addesk@dotnews.com, Ad. Director, Boston Haitian Reporter, MA, Dorchester

Concannon, Karmen
kconcannon@sentinel-tribune.com, Pub. / V.P., Sentinel-Tribune, OH, Bowling Green

Conchel, Anthony .... (740) 413-0900
aconchel@gannett.com, Ed., The Delaware Gazette, OH, Delaware

aconchel@gannett.com, Ed., Telegraph-Forum, OH, Mansfield

aconchel@gannett.com, Ed., The Morrow County Sentinel, OH, Mount Gilead

Condit, Elsa
news@kenmarend.com, Prod. Asst., The Kenmare News, ND, Kenmare

Condit, John .... (937) 259-2174
john.comdit@cmgohio.com, General Sales Manager - TV, Dayton Daily News, OH, Franklin

Condon, Brian
Brian@auditedmedia.com, EVP, Com. Dev., Alliance for Audited Media (AAM), IL, Arlington Heights

Condon, Kent .... (801) 236-6075
kcondon@deseretnews.com, Sports Ed., Deseret News, UT, Salt Lake City

Condon, Melinda
melindac@pa-news.org, Pennsylvania Newspaper Association, PA, Harrisburg

Condon, Michael .... (908) 766-3900, ext. 223
mcondon@recordernewspapers.com, Ed., Roxbury Register, NJ, Bernardsville

Condon, Michael .... (530) 283-0800
internet@plumasnews.com, Webmaster, Lassen County Times, CA, Susanville

Condon, Mike .... (908) 766-3900, ext. 223
mcondon@Newjerseyhills.com, Ed., The Citizen, NJ, Bernardsville

Condra, Edward
econdra@21st-centurymedia.com, Pub., Mercury Sampler, PA, Pottstown
econdra@21st-centurymedia.com, Adv. Dir., The Reporter, PA, Lansdale
econdra@21st-centurymedia.com, Pub., Daily Local News, PA, West Chester

Condra, Edward .... (610) 622-8857
econdra@21st-centurymedia.com, The Trentonian, NJ, Trenton
econdra@21st-centurymedia.com, Sr. Pub., Delaware County Daily Times, PA, Swarthmore

Condra, Edward
econdra@21st-centurymedia.com, Pub., Avon Grove Sun, PA, West Chester
econdra@21st-centurymedia.com, Pub., The Kennett Paper, PA, West Chester

Condreay, Debra J.
dcon@frontiernet.net, Gen. Mgr., The Advisor, NE, Albion

Cone, William .... (412) 471-1252 ext. 226
wcone@pittsburghcatholic.org, Ed., Pittsburgh Catholic, PA, Pittsburgh

Cone, Yvonne
yvonnec@harrisondaily.com, Fashion/Style Ed., Harrison Daily Times, AR, Harrison

Conger, Philip G.
rclipper@grm.net, Ed., Pony Express, MO, Bethany

Conger, Philip G.
rclipper@grm.net, Ed., Bethany Republican-Clipper, MO, Bethany

Conigliaro, James .... (414) 225-5011
james.conigliaro@jmg.com, Journal Media Group, Sr. Dir., Digital Tech.& Analytics, Milwaukee Journal Sentinel, WI, Milwaukee

Conkle, Patricia .... (614) 486-6677
pconkle@adohio.net, Advertising Coordinator, Ohio Newspaper Services, Inc., OH, Columbus

Conkle, Patricia .... (614) 486-6677 Ext. 1021
pconkle@adohio.net, Operations Manager, Ohio Newspaper Association, OH, Columbus

Conklin, Brad .... (570) 387-1234 Ext 1514
Prodn. Mgr., Press, Press Enterprise, PA, Bloomsburg

Conklin, Marty .... (607) 337-3034
General Manager Print Facility, The Evening

Sun, NY, Norwich

Conley, James
shr@inebraska.com, Pub., Southern Nebraska Register, NE, Lincoln

Conley, James E.
concept@conleynet.com, Pres., Conley Publishing Systems, WI, Beaver Dam

Conley, Michael
mike@trentonsun.net, Ed./Pub., The Trenton Sun, IL, Trenton

Conlon, Kevin
kconlon@cortlandstandard.net, Mng. Ed., Cortland Standard, NY, Cortland

Conlon, Kevin .... (607) 756-5665
kconlon@cortlandstandard.net, Man. Ed., Consumer News, NY, Cortland

Conn, Dave
ads@therconline.com, Adv. Mgr., The Record-Courier, OR, Baker City

Conn, Rebecca ....(606) 528-7898 Ext. 16
rconn@thetimestribune.com, Adv. Sales Asst., Times-Tribune, KY, Corbin

Connell, Mike
hhhomesmag@aol.com, Pub., Hallmark Homes, CT, Norwich

Connell, Mike
sales@balemaster.com, Sales Mgr., Balemaster, IN, Crown Point

Connelly, Allen
aconnelly@lagrangecounty.org, Prodn. Mgr., Countian, IN, Lagrange

Connelly, Bill .... (574) 825-9112
publisher@lagrangepublishing.com, Pub., The Middlebury Independent, IN, Middlebury

Connelly, Bryce .... (540) 213-9185
bconnelly@newsleader.com, Prodn. Dir., The News Leader, VA, Staunton

Connelly, Jill .... (818) 710-4235
Los Angeles Pierce College, CA, Woodland Hills

Connelly, John
jconnelly@transylvaniatimes.com, Adv. Exec., The Transylvania Times, NC, Brevard

Connelly, Mike .... (716) 849-4444
editor@buffnews.com, Ed., The Buffalo News, NY, Buffalo

Connelly, Ross .... (802) 472-6521
news@thehardwickgazette.com, Pub./Ed., The Hardwick Gazette, VT, Hardwick

Connelly, Tracy
tconnelly@metroparent.com, Office Mgr., Metro Parent Magazine, MI, Ferndale

Connelly, William .... (260) 463-2166
publisher@lagrangepublishing.com, Pub., Countian, IN, Lagrange
publisher@lagrangepublishing.com, Pub., LaGrange News, IN, Lagrange
publisher@lagrangepublishing.com, Pub., LaGrange Standard, IN, Lagrange

Connolly, Brian .... (716) 849-4444
bconnolly@buffnews.com, Mng. Ed., The Buffalo News, NY, Buffalo

Connolly, Connie .... (443) 786-1060
cconnolly@chespub.com , Reporter , The Star-Democrat, MD, Easton

Connolly, Craig .... (856) 317-7885
cconnolly@gannettnj.com, Dir., Info Servs., The Courier-Post, NJ, Cherry Hill

Connolly, Greg .... (208) 885-7825
Univ. of Idaho, ID, Moscow

Connolly, John .... Ext. 3577
jconnolly@pittsburghcatholic.org, Dir. of Adv., Pittsburgh Catholic, PA, Pittsburgh

Connolly, Keith .... (709) 748-0846
kconnolly@thetelegram.com, Interim Pub./Adv. Mgr., The Telegram, NL, Saint John's

Connolly, Matt .... (563) 588-3919
matt.connolly@thmedia.com, Interactive Media/Database Director, Telegraph Herald, IA, Dubuque

Connolly, Patrick .... (970) 748-2946
pconnolly@vaildaily.com, Adv. Dir., The Eagle Valley Enterprise, CO, Gypsum
pconnolly@vaildaily.com, Adv. Dir., Vail Daily, CO, Avon

Connor, Jessica
jconnor@umcsc.org, Editor, South Carolina United Methodist Advocate, SC, Columbia

Connor, Richard
sd@psdispatch.com, Pub., Sunday Dispatch, PA, Pittston

Connor, Richard L. .... (570) 829-7272
rconnor@timesleader.com, Ed., Nepa Shopper, PA, Wilkes Barre

Connor, Richard L. .... (570) 829-7272
rconnor@timesleader.com, Ed./Pub., Times Leader, PA, Wilkes Barre

Connor, Richard L.
rconnor@pressherald.com, Pub., Saving Source, ME, Portland

Connor, Richard L. .... (207) 791-6630
rconnor@centralmaine.mainetoday.com, Pres./Pub., Maine Today Media Inc., ME, Portland

Connor, Terry
tconnor@cullmantimes.com, Pub., The Cullman Times, AL, Cullman

Connors, Caroline
cconnors@beverlyreview.net, Ed., Beverly Review, IL, Chicago

Connors, Jack
jconnors@bizjournals.com, Pub. , Buffalo Business First, NY, Buffalo
jconnors@bizjournals.com, Pub., Business First of Buffalo, NY, Buffalo
jconnors@bizjournals.com, Pub., Buffalo Law Journal, NY, Buffalo

Connors, Jim
jim.connors@militarynews.com, Pub., RotoVue, NC, Jacksonville

Connors, Mary .... (773) 728-8351
mary@contentthatworks.com, Editorial Director, Content That Works, Chicago

Conover, Bob
bconover@smumn.edu, St. Marys Univ. of Minnesota, MN, Winona

Conover, Duke
dconover@paducahsun.com, Mng. Ed., The Paducah Sun, KY, Paducah

Conover, Mark
mconover@gannett.com, Circ. Mgr, Portland Review & Observer, MI, Lansing
mconover@gannett.com, Circ. Mgr, Dewitt Bath Review, MI, Lansing
mconover@gannett.com, Circ. Mgr, Grand Ledge Independent, MI, Lansing
mconover@gannett.com, Circ. Mgr, Lansing State Journal, MI, Lansing
mconover@gannett.com, Circ. Mgr, Lansing City Community News, MI, Lansing
mconover@gannett.com, Circ. Mgr, Ingham County Community News, MI, Lansing
mconover@gannett.com, Circ. Mgr, Eaton Rapids Community News, MI, Lansing
mconover@gannett.com, Circ. Mgr, Delta Waverly Community News, MI, Lansing
mconover@gannett.com, Circ. Mgr, Charlotte Shopping Guide, MI, Lansing
mconover@gannett.com, Circ. Mgr, Clinton County News, MI, Lansing
mconover@gannett.com, Circ. Mgr, Williamston Enterprise, MI, Lansing
mconover@gannett.com, Circ. Mgr, Towne Courier, MI, Lansing

Conoway, Elizabeth
heraldstar@consolidated.net, Pub., The Herald-Star, IL, Edinburg

Conquergood, Tom

tbads@my403.com, Adv. Mgr., The 40-mile County Commentator, AB, Bow Island

Conrad, Ashley .... (231) 779-4121
Inside Sales Leader, Cadillac News, MI, Cadillac

Conrad, Dave
ads@trurodaily.com, Prodn. Mgr., The Daily News, NS, Truro

Conrad, Dianne .... (360) 867-6078
The Evergreen State College, WA, Olympia

Conrad, Melissa .... (812) 663-3111 x7010
melissa.conrad@greensburgdailynews.com, Managing Ed., Greensburg Daily News, IN, Greensburg
melissa.conrad@greensburgdailynews.com, Managing Ed., The Greensburg Times, IN, Greensburg

Conrad, Shirleen .... (270) 783-3202
Office Asst., Daily News, KY, Bowling Green

Conradi, Peter
peter.conradi@sunmedia.ca, Mng. Ed., Niagara Falls Review, ON, Niagara Falls

Conradi, Peter .... (905) 684-7251 ext. 1169
peter.conradi@sunmedia.ca, Ed. in Chief , St. Catharines Standard, ON, Saint Catharine's

Conroy, Adam
westerng@frontiernet.net, Pub., The Western Guard, MN, Madison

Conroy, Paul .... (631) 287-1100 ext. 115
pconroy@pressnewsgroup.com, Sales Mgr., The Southampton Press, NY, Southampton

Conry, Holly .... (978) 516-2260
hconry@mediaonene.com, Adv. Admin., Sentinel & Enterprise, MA, Fitchburg

Consalvi, Aaron .... (402) 444-1422
aaron.consalvi@owh.com, Classified Employment Manager, Omaha World-Herald, NE, Omaha

Consenza, Lisa .... (949) 290-8123
lisa.cosenza@latimes.com, Los Angeles Times, CA, Los Angeles
lisa.cosenza@latimes.com, Dir. Adv. , News-Press, CA, Los Angeles

Consroe, Karla .... (843) 724-8375
Circ./Adv. Coord., The Catholic Miscellany, SC, Charleston

Constantine, Kermit
trsales2@htc.net, Pub., Republic-times Shopper, IL, Waterloo

Constantine, Kristie .... (406) 496-5554
kristie.constantine@mtstandard.com, Lead Copy Ed., The Montana Standard, MT, Butte

Constantine, Melissa
abenson@mountida.edu, Mount Ida College, MA, Newton Center

Consudado, Bernadine
swtdaily@yahoo.com, Multimedia Acct. Specialist, Southwest Daily News, LA, Sulphur

Conte, Henry .... (740) 328-8546
hconte@gannett.com, Sports Ed., The Marion Star, OH, Marion

Conte, Henry .... (740) 328-8546
hconte@gannett.com, Sports Ed., The News-Messenger, OH, Fremont

Conte, Henry .... (740) 328-8546
hconte@gannett.com, Sports Ed., Telegraph-Forum, OH, Mansfield

Contini, Nora .... (415) 263-7200
nora@jweekly.com, Publisher, J. The Jewish News Weekly of Northern Califonia, CA, San Francisco

Contreras, Art .... (310) 676-2806
Nat'l Sales Mgr., Dee-Paul Graphic Services, CA, South Gate

Contreras, John
sports@lamarledger.com, Sports Ed., The Lamar Ledger, CO, Lamar

Contreras, Mark........................(215) 949-4017
mcontreras@calkins.com, CEO, Calkins Media, PA, Levittown

Contreras, Yvonne
sabanews@centex.net, Adv. Dir., San Saba News & Star, TX, San Saba

Conway, Denise
dconway@squamishchief.com, Circ. Mgr., Squamish Chief, BC, Squamish

Conway, Kazia ....(254) 583-7811
rosebudnews@windstream.net, Gen Mgr., The Rosebud News, TX, Rosebud

Conway, Linda ....(781) 281-7648
l.conway@nenpa.com, Executive Director, NENPA Ad Network (New England Newspaper and Press Association), MA, Woburn

Conway, Maia ....(231) 933-1402
mconway@record-eagle.com, Mktg. Dir., Traverse City Record-Eagle, MI, Traverse City

Conway, Nancy ....(801) 204-6701
letters@sltrib.com, Ed., The Salt Lake Tribune, UT, Salt Lake City

Conway, Richard
richard.conway@ncc.edu, Nassau Cmty. College, NY, Garden City

Conwell, Rob
rob@opcfla.com, Circ. Mgr, Clay County Leader, FL, Fleming Island
rob@opcfla.com, Circ. Mgr., Clay Today, FL, Fleming Island

Conwell, Rob ....(904) 686-3936
rob@opcfla.com, Circ. Mgr., Ponte Vedra Recorder, FL, Ponte Vedra Beach

Conzett, Lance
lance@raventools.com, Belmont Univ., TN, Nashville

Conzola, Ej...........................(518) 483-2000
econzola@mtelegram.com, Ed., The Malone Telegram, NY, Malone

Cooch, Sandy
sandy@ourherald.com, Mgr Ed, The Herald of Randolph, VT, Randolph

Coody, Jen ....ext. 124
jenc@free-times.com, Gen. Mgr., Free Times, SC, Columbia

Cook, Amber
classman@arkcity.net, Classified Mgr., The Arkansas City Traveler, KS, Arkansas City

Cook, Andrew
andrew.cook@cmdg.com, Vice Pres./Pub., Daily Commercial News and Construction Record, ON, Markham

Cook, Angie
acook@jcfloridan.com, Reporter, Jackson County Floridan, FL, Marianna

Cook, Carey Orr ....(772) 492-9032
careycook@hotmail.com, Pres./Cartoon Ed., Sam Mantics Enterprises, Vero Beach

Cook, Chris R
chris.cook@peninsulanewsreview.com, The Peninsula News Review, BC, Sidney

Cook, Chuck ....(601) 266-4288
chuck.cook@usm.edu, News Content Adviser, Univ. of Southern Mississippi, MS, Hattiesburg

Cook, Corry ....(650) 690-1244
mrscorrycook@gmail.com, Senior Ed., Sam Mantics Enterprises, Vero Beach

Cook, Dan ....(803) 765-0707 ext. 133
editor@free-times.com, Ed., Free Times, SC, Columbia

Cook, Danny
eaglepub@sbcglobal.net, Adv. Mgr., The Eagle Democrat, AR, Warren

Cook, Dean
hdcook@sunherald.com, Prodn. Mgr., Pressroom, The Sun Herald, MS, Gulfport

Cook, Deb
sales@atticahub.com, Owner/Pub., Attica Hub, OH, Attica

Cook, Donna ....(828) 837-5122, Ext. 108
advertising@cherokeescout.com, Adv. Mgr., Cherokee Scout, NC, Murphy

Cook, Doris ....(440) 576-9125
dcook@gazettenews.com, Ed., The News, OH, Jefferson

Cook, Elizabeth G. ....(704) 797-4244
Ecook@salisburypost.com, Ed., Salisbury Post, NC, Salisbury

Cook, Ellen...........................(435) 257-5182
ellenc@tremontonleader.com, Editor, The Leader, UT, Tremonton

Cook, Gary
elytimes.gary@gmail.com, Ed. , The Eureka Sentinel, NV, Ely

Cook, Glenn...........................(702) 383-4647
gcook@reviewjournal.com, Mng. Ed., Las Vegas Review-Journal, NV, Las Vegas

Cook, Jennifer
optimes@mts.net, Gen. Mgr., Opasquia Times, MB, The Pas

Cook, John
john.a.cook@utb.edu, Program Coord., University of Texas at Brownsville, TX, Brownsville

Cook, John ....(814) 643-4040 x157
jcook@huntingdondailynews.com, VP & Gen Mgr., The Daily Herald, PA, Tyrone
jcook@huntingdondailynews.com, Pub, The Huntingdon Daily News, PA, Huntingdon
jcook@huntingdondailynews.com, Regional Vice President, The Daily News (OOB), PA, McKeesport

Cook, Khalida
kcook@mlive.com, Dir. of Automotive Sales, The Jackson Citizen Patriot, MI, Jackson

Cook, Kristen ....(520) 573-4194
kcook@azstarnet.com, Food/Home Ed., Arizona Daily Star, AZ, Tucson

Cook, Mary...........................(618) 239-2630
mcook@bnd.com, Adv., Belleville News-Democrat, IL, Belleville

Cook, Matthew
editor@harvardpress.com, Ed., The Harvard Press, MA, Harvard

Cook, Michelle
editorial@winnemuccapublishing.net, Ed. , Battle Mountain Bugle, NV, Winnemucca

Cook, Michelle
editorial@winnemuccapublishing.net , Ed. , Lovelock Review-Miner, NV, Winnemucca

Cook, Nancy ....(902) 426-2811 ext. 3003
ncook@herald.ca, Sales Dir., The Chronicle Herald, NS, Halifax

Cook, Nancy
cook.nancy@miramichileader.com, Pub., Miramichi Leader, NB, Miramichi

Cook, Pat
advertising@hopewellnews.com, Adv. Mgr., The Hopewell News, VA, Hopewell

Cook, Peter J. ....ext. 12
pcook@heartlandpublications.com, Gen. Mgr., Yadkin Valley Advertiser, NC, Elkin

Cook, Peter J.
pcook@parsonssun.com, Pub., Parsons Sun, KS, Parsons

Cook, Rocky ....(208) 639-3519
rcook@idahobusinessreview.com, Acct. Exec., Idaho Business Review, ID, Boise

Cook, Russell
rjcook@loyola.edu, Chair, Loyola College, MD, Baltimore

Cook, Ryan...........................(740) 328-8846
rcook@gannett.com, Cons. Exp. Dir., The Marion Star, OH, Marion

Cook, Ryan...........................(740) 328-8846
rcook@gannett.com, Cons. Expert. Dir., News Journal, OH, Mansfield

Cook, Shane ....(865) 475-2081
scook@standardbanner.com, Adv. Mgr., The Standard Banner, TN, Jefferson City

Cook, Steve ....(434) 978-7296
scook@dailyprogress.com, Regional Circulation Director, The Daily Progress, VA, Charlottesville

Cook-Snyder, Freda
classifieds@hopewellnews.com, Gen. Mgr., The Hopewell News, VA, Hopewell

Cooke, Gene
info@coldjet.com, Pres./CEO, Cold Jet, Inc., OH, Loveland

Cooke, Jay Jefferson ....(908) 243-6603
jcooke@gannettnj.com, Sen. Rep., Courier News, NJ, Somerville

Cooke, John ....(252) 329-9500
jcooke@reflector.com, Pub., The Daily Reflector, NC, Greenville
jcooke@reflector.com, The Bargain Sheet, PA, State College

Cooke, Nancy
ncooke@toledodiocese.org, Adv. Sales Rep., Catholic Chronicle, OH, Toledo

Cooke, Jr., John Kent ....(252) 329-9500
jcooke@reflector.com, President and Publisher, Cooke Communications North Carolina, LLC, NC, Greenville

Cooksey, Fred ....(413) 552-2538
fcooksey@hcc.edu, Holyoke Cmty. College, MA, Holyoke

Cookson, Matt
mcookson@entechnology.com, Opns. Mgr., En Technology Corp., NH, Newport

Cool, Kim ....(941) 207-1105
kcool@venicegondolier.com, Venice Gondolier Sun, FL, Venice

Coolbaugh, Janelle ....(717) 637-3736 ext. 176
chirko@eveningsun.com, Metro Ed., The Evening Sun, PA, Hanover

Cooley, Jeremy
jcooley@uvsj.com, Audience Dev. Dir., The Standard-Journal, ID, Rexburg

Cooley, Marga........................(805) 739-2143
mcooley@syvnews.com, Mng. Ed., Santa Ynez Valley News/Extra, CA, Solvang

Cooley, Mary ....(618) 239-2528
mcjones@bnd.com, Copy, Belleville News-Democrat, IL, Belleville

Coolman, Jeff ....(952) 392-6807
jeff.coolman@ecm-inc.com, Gen. Mgr., Mounds View/New Brighton Sun Focus, MN, Eden Prairie

Coombe, Tom..................(218) 365-3141 ext. 11
Mng. Ed., The Ely Echo, MN, Ely

Coombs, Stephanie...................(780) 429-5202
scoombs@edmontonjournal.com, Managing Editor, Edmonton Journal, AB, Edmonton

Coomes, Terry ....(518) 742-3211
tcoomes@poststar.com, Pub., The Post-Star, NY, Glens Falls

Coon, Debbie ....(850) 910-5316
dcoon@srpressgazette.com, Ad. Accounts Exec., Santa Rosa Press Gazette, FL, Milton

Coon, Jim
coon@wingate.edu, Chair, Wingate University, NC, Wingate

Cooney, Carol
carol.cooney@thesuburbanite.com, Adv. Mgr., The Suburbanite, OH, Akron

Cooney, Sarah
smorse@sfchronicle.com, VP Marketing, San Francisco Chronicle, CA, San Francisco

Cooney, Stephen

editor@hofstrachronicle.com, Hofstra Univ., NY, Hempstead

Cooper, Alex ....(250) 837-4667
alex.cooper@revelstokereview.com, Ed, Revelstoke Review, BC, Revelstoke

Cooper, Allison
acooper@messengerpostmedia.com, Mng. Ed./Content, Messenger Post Media, NY, Canandaigua

Cooper, Amanda
circulation@pdclarion.com, Circ. Clerk, Princeton Daily Clarion, IN, Princeton

Cooper, Ann
ann.cooper@alcoa.com, Prof., Columbia University, NY, New York

Cooper, Audrey ....(415) 777-7112
acooper@sfchronicle.com, Editor in Chief, San Francisco Chronicle, CA, San Francisco

Cooper, Becky
bcooper@vicad.com, Other, Victoria Advocate, TX, Victoria

Cooper, Brenda........................(435) 797-3253
bcooper@cc.usu.edu, Assoc. Prof., Utah State University, UT, Logan

Cooper, Brian ....(937) 225-2321
brian.cooper@coxinc.com, COO, Middletown Journal, OH, Liberty Township

Cooper, Brian ....(404) 526-5123
bcooper@ajc.com, Sr. VP, Finance & Business Op., Atlanta Journal-Constitution, GA, Atlanta

Cooper, Brian
bcooper@wcinet.com, Editorial Page Ed., Telegraph Herald, IA, Dubuque
bcooper@wcinet.com, COO, Springfield News-Sun, OH, Springfield

Cooper, Chris
ccooper@newsdemocratleader.com, Mng. Ed., The News Democrat & Leader, KY, Russellville

Cooper, Christopher ....(347) 549-5627
cjcooper@utica.edu, Editor-in-Chief, Utica College, NY, Utica

Cooper, Clint
ccooper@timesfreepress.com, Free Press Page Ed., Chattanooga Times Free Press, TN, Chattanooga

Cooper, Don...........................(254) 774-5203
dcooper@tdtnews.com, Graphic Artist, Berting Communications, IN, Indianapolis
dcooper@tdtnews.com, Gen. Mgr., Temple Daily Telegram, TX, Temple

Cooper, Donald........................(580) 654-1443
news@carnegieherald.com, Pub./Adv. Dir./Ed., Carnegie Herald, OK, Carnegie

Cooper, Donald
galvinnews@mchsi.com, Pub., Wrova Weekly Shopper, IL, Galva

Cooper, Douglas
scottd@journalmultimedia.com, Pub., Central Penn Business Journal, PA, Harrisburg

Cooper, Drew
drew@themiddletownnews.com, Co-Pub. , The Middletown News, IN, Middletown

Cooper, Emily
ecooper@umcsc.org, Ed., South Carolina United Methodist Advocate, SC, Columbia

Cooper, Jack
hs40231@windstream.net, Ed., Humboldt Standard, NE, Humboldt

Cooper, Jim
jcoop@thetimesrecord.net, Ed., The Times Record, WV, Spencer

Cooper, Jim
jcoop@thetimesrecord.net, Ed., Roane County Reporter, WV, Spencer

Cooper, Jo Anne ....(252) 459-7101
jcooper@nashvillegraphic.com, Pub./Adv. Mgr., The Nashville Graphic, NC, Nashville

Cooper, Joey
joey@themiddletownnews.com, Co-Pub., The Middletown News, IN, Middletown

Cooper, Julian
jcooper@plumtreecompany.com, Vice Pres., Sales, Plumtree Co., GA, Savannah

Cooper, Kara K. .... (520) 836-7461
kcooper@pinalcentral.com, Co-publisher, Adv. Dir., Casa Grande Valley Newspapers Inc., AZ, Casa Grande

Cooper, Kevin .... (601) 445-3539
kevin.cooper@natchezdemocrat.com, Pub., Miss-lou Buyers Guide, MS, Natchez

Cooper, Kevin .... (601) 445-3539
kevin.cooper@natchezdemocrat.com, Publisher, Natchez Newspapers, Inc., MS, Natchez
kevin.cooper@natchezdemocrat.com, VP, Boone Newspapers, Inc., AL, Northport

Cooper, Lori
lcooper@times-call.com, Pub./Adv. Dir./ Managing Ed., Carnegie Herald, OK, Carnegie
lcooper@times-call.com, Prod. Services Mgr., Longmont Times-Call, CO, Longmont

Cooper, Marie .... (954) 425-1045
macooper@sun-sentinel.com, Adv. Ops./ Admin., South Florida Sun-Sentinel, FL, Fort Lauderdale

Cooper, Michael
michael@themiddletownnews.com, Design Ed., The Middletown News, IN, Middletown

Cooper, Peter .... (615) 259-8063
pcooper@tennessean.com, Music Writer, The Tennessean, TN, Nashville
pcooper@tennessean.com, Music Writer, TN Media, TN, Nashville

Cooper, Robert
rcooper@elkodaily.com, Cir., Elko Daily Free Press, NV, Elko

Cooper, Sam
sportern@wythenews.com, Pub., Bland County Messenger, VA, Wytheville

Cooper, Sam
sam_cooper@wythenews.com, Pub., Enterprise Buyers Catalogue, VA, Wytheville

Cooper, Samuel
scooper@wythenews.com, Pub., The Floyd Press, VA, Floyd

Cooper, Scott
scooper@beltingindustries.com, Pres., Belting Industries Co., Inc., NJ, Kenilworth

Cooper, Shirley .... (662) 581-7246
scooper@gwcommonwealth.com, Circ. Mgr., The Greenwood Commonwealth, MS, Greenwood

Cooper, Steve .... (937) 328-0357
scooper@coxohio.com, Film/Theater Ed., Springfield News-Sun, OH, Springfield

Cooper, Sue
sue@themiddletownnews.com, Office Mgr./ Copy Ed., The Middletown News, IN, Middletown

Cooper, Tim
tsbcooper@msn.com, Pres., Plumtree Co., GA, Savannah

Cooper-Chen, Anne .... (740) 593-2598
cooper@ohiou.edu, Prof., Ohio University, OH, Athens

Cooper-Peters, Latasha .... (443) 260-3304
lxcooper@dmg.gannett.com, Sales Mgr., The Daily Times, MD, Salisbury

Coopwood, Scott
publisher@theclevelandcurrent.com, Pub., The Cleveland Current, MS, Cleveland

Coord., Reprint Rights .... (212) 293-8500
reprints@unitedmedia.com, Reprint Rights Sales, United Feature Syndicate (Div. of United Media), New York

Copass, Michelle .... (270) 678-5171 Ext. 240
mcopass@glasgowdailytimes.com, Special Accounts Mgr., Glasgow Daily Times, KY, Glasgow

Cope, Brenda .... (478) 744-4351
bcope@macon.com, HR Mgr, The Telegraph, GA, Macon

Cope, Jay .... (850) 665-6121
jay.cope@navy.mil, Ed., Whiting Tower, FL, Milton

Cope, Randy .... (214) 356-3227
rcope@cribb.com, Dir., Cribb, Greene & Cope LLC, MT, Helena

Cope, Randy .... (214) 356-3227
rcope@cribb.com, Director, Cribb, Greene & Cope, MT, Helena

Copelan, Howard
advocate@cut.net, Ed., High Desert Advocate, NV, Wendover

Copeland, Dave .... (816) 637-6155
circulation@leaderpress.com, Circulation Manager, Town & Country Leader, MO, Excelsior Springs

Copeland, David
dcopeland@elon.edu, Prof./Fletcher Chair/ Grad. Dir., Elon University, NC, Elon

Copeland, Denise .... (201) 217-2439
denise.copeland@jjournal.com, Oper. Dir., The Jersey Journal, NJ, Secaucus

Copeland, Eric .... (816) 637-6155
editor@leaderpress.com, Managing Editor, Town & Country Leader, MO, Excelsior Springs

Copeland, Gary
copeland@ua.edu, Prof./Chair, Telecommunication/Film, University of Alabama, AL, Tuscaloosa

Copeland, James
mgrcircu@eacourier.com, Circulation Manager, Eastern Arizona Courier, AZ, Safford

Copeland, Joe
editor@crosscut.com, Ed., Crosscut, WA, Seattle

Copeland, Julie .... (831) 429-2467
jcopeland@santacruzsentinel.com, Bus. Ed., Santa Cruz Sentinel, CA, Scotts Valley

Copeland, Mike
mcopeland@wacotrib.com, Bus./Finance Ed., Waco Tribune-Herald, TX, Waco

Copeland, Peter .... (202) 408-2756
copelandp@shns.com, Ed./Gen. Mgr., Scripps Howard News Service, Washington

Copelin, Nancy P.
journaltrib@mchsi.com, Pub., Waverly Journal, IL, Waverly

Copenhaver, David
dcopenhaver@lemarssentinel.com, Adv., Shoppers Guide, IA, Le Mars

Copic, Nancy
copic@up.edu, The Beacon/ Univ. of Portland, OR, Portland

Coplan, Alvin M.
advertising@syrianlebanesestar.net, Prodn. Mgr., The Syrian-Lebanese Star, FL, Jacksonville

Coplen, Debbie .... (318) 362-0204
Gen. Sales Mgr., The News-Star, LA, Monroe

Coplen, Kat .... (317) 254-2400
kcoplen@nuvo.net, Ed., Nuvo, IN, Indianapolis

Copler, Lori
loric@glencoenews.com, Ed., The McLeod County Chronicle, MN, Glencoe

Copley, Andrew
web.queries@computershare.com, Sr. Cor. Vice Pres., Kodak GCG, CT, Norwalk

Coplin, Lynn
lcoplin@trcle.com, Adv. Mgr., Classified,

Cleburne Times-Review, TX, Cleburne

Copper, Janett
janettec@joplinglobe.com, Ret'l Adv. Mgr., The Joplin Globe, MO, Joplin

Copple, Julie .... (618) 532-5604
Office Mgr., Morning Sentinel, IL, Centralia

Coppler, Jeff .... (419) 332-5511
jcoppler@nncogannett.com, Adv. Dir., The Marion Star, OH, Marion
jcoppler@nncogannett.com, Sales Mgr., The News-Messenger, OH, Fremont

Coppola, Manuel .... (520) 375-5766
publisher@nogalesinternational.com, Pub., The Weekly Bulletin, AZ, Nogales

Coppola, Manuel .... (520) 375-5766
publisher@nogalesinternational.com, Pub., Nogales International, AZ, Nogales
publisher@nogalesinternational.com, Pub., Santa Cruz Valley Sun, AZ, Nogales

Coppola, Maureen
sales@queenstribune.com, Adv. Admin., Queens Tribune, NY, Whitestone
sales@queenstribune.com, Adv. Admin., The Press of Southeast Queens, NY, Whitestone

Copsey, Jonathan
jcopsey@northfulton.com, Ed., Milton Herald, GA, Alpharetta
jcopsey@northfulton.com, Ed., The Forsyth Herald, GA, Alpharetta
jcopsey@northfulton.com, Ed., The Revue & News, GA, Alpharetta

Copus, Heather
fennimoretimes@tds.net, Office Mgr., Fennimore Times, WI, Fennimore

Coram, Shon .... (660) 332-4431
scoram.homepress@gmail.com, Pub., The Home Press, MO, La Plata

Corban, Jose .... (973) 569-7041
corban@northjersey.com, Gen. Mgr., Su Guia, NJ, Clifton

Corbett, Christie .... (803) 532-6203
christie.twincitynews@gmail.com, Advertising Account Executive, The Twin-City News, SC, Batesburg Leesville

Corbett, Christopher
ccorbet3@jhu.edu, Univ. of Maryland Baltimore County, MD, Baltimore

Corbett, Jenny .... (765) 724-4469
alextribune@elwoodpublishing.com, Managing Ed., Alexandria Times-Tribune, IN, Elwood

Corbett, Neil .... ext. 2063
Sports Ed., The Citizens' Voice, PA, Wilkes Barre

Corbin, David
dcorbin@goleader.com, Asst. Pub., The Times of Scotch Plains-Fanwood, NJ, Westfield

Corbin, Horace R.
press@goleader.com, Pub., The Times of Scotch Plains-Fanwood, NJ, Westfield

Corbin, Horace R. .... (908) 232-4407
press@goleader.com, Pub., The Westfield Leader, NJ, Westfield

Corcoran, Brian .... (518) 742-3355
bcorcoran@poststar.com, Controller, The Post-Star, NY, Glens Falls

Corcoran, Heather
hcorcoran@mccubbin.com, Ed., Upper East Side Resident, NY, New York

Corcoran, James
james.corcoran@simmons.edu, Adviser, Simmons College, MA, Boston

Corcoran, John C.
john.corcoran@usink.com, Vice Pres., Sales, US Ink, NJ, Carlstadt

Corcoran, Linda .... (508) 862-1178
lcorcoran@capecodonline.com, Managing Ed., Cape Cod Times, MA, Hyannis

Corcoran, Steve .... (617) 532-0120

steve.corcoran@metro.us, Assoc. Pub., Metro Boston, MA, Boston

Corcoran, Tim .... (416) 774-2321
tcorcoran@insidetoronto.com, Regl. Dir., Adv., The Scarborough Mirror, ON, Toronto

Corcoran Jr., David .... (304) 462-7309
Gen. Mgr., The Glenville Pathfinder, WV, Glenville
General Manager, The Glenville Democrat/ Pathfinder, WV, Glenville

Corcoran Sr., David H. .... (304) 462-4643
dhcorcoran@gmail.com, Pub./Sr. Ed./Owner, The Glenville Democrat/Pathfinder, WV, Glenville
dhcorcoran@gmail.com, Pub./Sr. Ed./Owner, The Glenville Pathfinder, WV, Glenville

Cord Taylor, Karen .... (617) 523-9490
ktaylor@backbaysun.com, Exec. Ed. & Pub., The Back Bay Sun, MA, Revere

Cord Taylor, Karen
ktaylor@charlestownbridge.com, Ed./Pub., The Charlestown Patriot-Bridge, MA, Charlestown

Cord Taylor, Karen .... (617) 241-8500
ktaylor@beaconhilltimes.com, Pub., The Revere Journal, MA, Revere

Cordeau, Louise
louise.cordeau@quebecormedia.com, Pub., Le Journal de Quebec, QC, Vanier

Cordeiro, Kathleen .... (978) 371-5736
kcordeiro@wickedlocal.com, Ed., Woburn Advocate, MA, Concord

Cordeiro, Kathleen .... (978) 371-5736
kcordeiro@wickedlocal.com, Ed. in Chief, The Bolton Common, MA, Concord

Cordeiro, Kathleen .... (978) 371-5736
kcordeiro@wickedlocal.com, Ed. in Chief, Wilmington Advocate, MA, Concord

Cordeiro, Kathleen .... (978) 371-5736
kcordeiro@wickedlocal.com, Ed.-in-Chief, Times & Courier, MA, Concord

Cordeiro, Kathleen .... (978) 371-5736
kcordeiro@wickedlocal.com, Ed. in Chief, Billerica Minuteman, MA, Concord
kcordeiro@wickedlocal.com, Chelmsford Independent, MA, Concord

Cordeiro, Kathy .... (978) 371-5736
kcordeiro@wickedlocal.com, Ed. in Chief, Winchester Star, MA, Lexington

Cordeiro, Kathy .... (978) 371-5736
kcordeiro@wickedlocal.com, Ed. in Chief, The Concord Journal, MA, Concord

Cordeiro, Kathy .... (978) 371-5736
kcordeiro@wickedlocal.com, Ed. in Chief, Tewksbury Advocate, MA, Concord

Cordeiro, Kathy .... (978) 371-5736
kcordeiro@wickedlocal.com, Ed. in Chief, Westford Eagle, MA, Concord

Cordeiro, Kathy .... (978) 371-5736
kcordeiro@wickedlocal.com, Ed. in Chief, The Harvard Post, MA, Concord

Cordeiro, Kathy .... (978) 371-5736
kcordeiro@wickedlocal.com, Ed. in Chief, The Beacon-Villager, MA, Concord

Cordeiro, Kathy .... (978) 371-5736
kcordeiro@wickedlocal.com, Ed. in Chief, Littleton Independent, MA, Concord

Cordeiro, Kathy .... (978) 371-5736
kcordeiro@wickedlocal.com, Ed. in Chief, Lincoln Journal, MA, Concord

Cordeiro, Monivette .... (407) 377-0400
mcordeiro@orlandoweekly.com, Staff Writer, Orlando Weekly, FL, Orlando

Corder, Charles .... (662) 581-7241
ccorder@gwcommonwealth.com, Mng. Ed., The Greenwood Commonwealth, MS, Greenwood

Cordes, Kim
kcordes@northwestsignal.net, Adv., Northwest

Signal, OH, Napoleon

Cordes, Wade ....(541) 823-4841
wadec@argusobserver.com, Prodn. Mgr.,
Independent-Enterprise, ID, Payette
wadec@argusobserver.com, Prodn. Mgr.,
Argus Observer, OR, Ontario

Cordiero, Kathleen ....(978) 371-5736
kcordeiro@wickedlocal.com, Ed. in Chief ,
Arlington Advocate, MA, Lexington

Coredine, Miguel
miguel@c-ville.com, Circ. Mgr., C-ville Weekly,
VA, Charlottesville

Corella, Hipolito R. ....(520) 4=573-4101
lcorella@tucson.com, Sr. Ed., Arizona Daily
Star, AZ, Tucson

Corey, Wes.............................(253) 597-8875
wes.corey@thenewstribune.com, Production
Manager, The News Tribune, WA, Tacoma

Corf, Cynthia...........................(660) 565-2555
halehorizons@cvalley.net, Publisher, Hale
Horizons, MO, Hale

Corio, Emily ....(304) 293-7007
emily.corio@mail.wvu.edu, Teaching Assistant
Professor, West Virginia University, WV,
Morgantown

Corison, Cynthia
corison@rowan.edu, Assoc. Prof., Rowan
Univ., NJ, Glassboro

Cormier, Jack
jcormier@tampatrib.com, Ed., South Shore
News, FL, Tampa

Cormier, John
JCormier@tampatrib.com, Tampa Bay Times,
FL, St Petersburg

Cormier, Kathy ....(337) 893-4223
kathy.cormier@vermiliontoday.com, Pub.,
Abbeville Meridional, LA, Abbeville

Corn, Brian............................(316) 268-6231
BCorn@wichitaeagle.com, Visuals Editor, The
Wichita Eagle, KS, Wichita

Corn, Henriette ....(415) 435-1190
hcorn@thearknewspaper.com, Dir. of Bus &
Adv., The Ark, CA, Tiburon

Corn, Mike
mcorn@dailynews.net, Special Projects
Coord., The Hays Daily News, KS, Hays

Corneli, Janet ....(334) 393-2969
circulation@southeastsun.com, Circulation
Manager, Qst Publications-(consolidated),
AL, Enterprise
circulation@southeastsun.com, Circ. Mgr,
Daleville Sun-courier, AL, Enterprise
circulation@southeastsun.com, Circ. Mgr,
Southeast Sun, AL, Enterprise

Cornejo, Azenett ....(956) 882-5142
azenett.cornejo@utb.edu, Advisor, University
of Texas at Brownsville, TX, Brownsville

Cornelius, Karen
info@vermilion-news.com, Ed./Gen. Mgr.,
Vermilion Photojournal, OH, Vermilion

Cornelius, Steve ....(606) 451-4925
scornelius@somerset-kentucky.com, Sports
Ed., The Commonwealth-Journal, KY,
Somerset

Cornell, Ann .... (215) 361-8820
acornell@21st-centurymedia.com, Ed., The
Reporter, PA, Lansdale

Cornell, Christopher
ccornell@timesshamrock.com, Ed., The Valley
Advantage, PA, Scranton

Cornell, Deanne........................(403) 854-3366
deanne.cornell@sunmedia.ca, Adv. Sales
Rep., Hanna Herald, AB, Hanna

Cornell, Jim
accounting@leaderherald.com, Prodn. Mgr.,
East, Katahdin Paper Company LLC, ME,
Millinocket
accounting@leaderherald.com, Accounting,

The Leader-Herald, NY, Gloversville

Cornell, Shawn........................(403) 473-0705
shawn.cornell@sunmedia.ca, Group Pub., The
High River Times, AB, High River
shawn.cornell@sunmedia.ca, Group Pub., The
Nanton News, AB, Nanton

Cornell, Shawn........................(403) 473-0705
shawn.cornell@sunmedia.ca, Pub, Hanna
Herald, AB, Hanna
shawn.cornell@sunmedia.ca, Publisher, Vulcan
Advocate, AB, Vulcan

Cornell, Shawn........................(403) 473-0705
shawn.cornell@sunmedia.ca, Pub, Bow Valley
Crag & Canyon, AB, Banff
shawn.cornell@sunmedia.ca, Publisher, Banff
Crag & Canyon OOB* (2013), AB, Banff
shawn.cornell@sunmedia.ca, Pub, Cochrane
Times, AB, Cochrane

Cornell, Tricia
tcornell@mnpubs.com, Ed., Good Age, MN,
Minneapolis

Cornely, Deborah ....(410) 288-6060
info@dundalkeagle.net, Pub., The Dundalk
Eagle, MD, Dundalk

Cornett, Johnna
advertise@mcrecordonline.com, Adv. Mgr., The
Madison County Record, AR, Huntsville

Cornette, Cindy
cindy.cornette@thefacts.com, Adv. Dir., The
Facts, TX, Clute

Cornwell, Bill...........................(979) 265-7411
bcornwell@thefacts.com, Pub./Ed., The Facts,
TX, Clute

Coronado, Diana
dcoronado@dddnews.com, News Ed., Daily
Dunklin Democrat Extra, MO, Kennett

Coronel, Sheila
ssc2136@columbia.edu, Prof., Columbia
University, NY, New York

Corpus, Sonny
lcorpus@bristolnews.com, Circ. Dir., Enterprise
Buyers Catalogue, VA, Wytheville

Corpus, Sonny
lcorpus@bristolnews.com, Circ. Dir.,
Washington County News, VA, Wytheville

Corpus, Sonny
lcorpus@wythenews.com, Circ. Mgr., Smyth
County News & Messenger, VA, Marion

Corrado, Kevin
kcorrado@nhregister.com, Pres./Pub., New
Haven Register, CT, New Haven

Corrales, Charles
adline@lavozcolorado.com, Prodn. Coord., La
Voz Newspaper, CO, Denver
adline@lavozcolorado.com, Prod. Coord., La
Voz Bilingue, CO, Thornton

Corrigan, Amy ....(402) 444-1061
amy.corrigan@owh.com, Production Control
Manager, Gretna Breeze, NE, Bellevue
amy.corrigan@owh.com, Production Control
Manager, Bellevue Leader, NE, Bellevue

Corrigan, Amy ....(402) 532-4854
Prodn. Mgr., Air Pulse, NE, Bellevue

Corrigan, Amy ....(402) 444-1061
amy.corrigan@owh.com, Creative Servs. Mgr.,
Papillion Times, NE, Bellevue

Corrigan, Don
corrigan@timesnewspapers.com, Ed., South
County Times, MO, Saint Louis

Corrigan, Don
corrigdh@webster.edu, Journ. Seq., Webster
Univ., MO, Saint Louis

Corrigan, Don
corrigan@timesnewspapers.com, Ed.,
Webster-Kirkwood Times, Inc., MO, Saint
Louis
corrigan@timesnewspapers.com, Ed., West
End Word, MO, Saint Louis

Corrigan, John
john.corrigan@latimes.com, Arts & Ent., Asst.
Managing Ed., Los Angeles Times, CA, Los
Angeles

Corrigan, Steve ....(912) 652-0312
steve.corrigan@savannahnow.com,
Community Ed., Savannah Morning News,
GA, Savannah

Corrinne-Harvey, Janet
jcorrinne@tribweb.com, Trib Total Media, Inc.,
PA, Pittsburgh

Corriveau, Nancy
nancy.corriveau@monjournalexpress.com,
Sales Coord., Granby Express, QC, Granby

Corsetti, Perry..........................(215) 355-9009
pcorsetti@bsmphilly.com , Pub., Northeast
Times, PA, Bensalem
pcorsetti@bsmphilly.com , Pub., Star
Community Newsweekly, PA, Bensalem
pcorsetti@bsmphilly.com , Pub., The Midweek
Wire, PA, Bensalem

Corsetti, Perry..........................(215) 354-3125
pcorsetti@bsmphilly.com, Pub., Baltimore
Guide South, MD, Baltimore
pcorsetti@bsmphilly.com, Pub. , The Baltimore
Guide, MD, Baltimore

Corsoe, Frank ....(419) 724-6115
fcorsoe@theblade.com, Sports Ed., The Blade,
OH, Toledo

Cortado, Myra ....(831) 818-6231
mcortado@calkins.com, Director of Corporate
Development & Strategic Partnerships,
Calkins Media, PA, Levittown

Cortes, Raul
montevideo@efe.com, Rep., EFE News
Services - Montevideo, Uruguay, Montevideo

Cortez, Ernie ....(956) 683-4515
ecortez@themonitor.com, Regional Production
Director, The Monitor, TX, McAllen

Cortez, Julie
jcortez@elhispanicnews.com, Ed., El Hispanic
News, OR, Portland

Cortez, Phillip ....(915) 546-6258
pcortez@elpasotimes.com, Mktg. Dir., El Paso
Times, TX, El Paso
pcortez@elpasotimes.com, Mktg. Dir., El Paso
y Mas, TX, El Paso

Cortina, Matt .... (949) 388-7700 ext. 114
mcortina@picketfencemedia.com, Grp. Mng.
Ed., San Clemente Times, CA, Capistrano
Beach
mcortina@picketfencemedia.com, Dana Point
Times, CA, Capistrano Beach
mcortina@picketfencemedia.com, The
Capistrano Dispatch, CA, Capistrano Beach

Corty, Andrew P. ....(727) 893-8204
acorty@tampabay.com, Vice Pres./Sec., Tampa
Bay Times, FL, St Petersburg

Cory, Matt
mcory@bemidjipioneer.com, Ed., The Bemidji
Pioneer, MN, Bemidji

Coryell, Janis
janis@cheboygantribune.com, Business Mgr.,
Cheboygan Daily Tribune, MI, Cheboygan

Cosby, James..........................(937) 259-2119
james.cosby@coxinc.com, VP of Sales, Dayton
Daily News, OH, Franklin

Cosby, Jason ....(770) 787-6397
jcosby@covnews.com, Digital Mgr., The
Covington News, GA, Covington

Cosby, Sylvester ....(312) 264-6273
scosby@ndigo.com, Administrator, N'digo, IL,
Chicago

Cosenza, Donna ....(203) 402-2327
dcosenza@hersamacorn.com, Account Exec.,
Easton Courier, CT, Ridgefield
dcosenza@hersamacorn.com, Account Exec.,
Fairfield Sun, CT, Shelton

Cosenza, Donna ....(203) 402-2327
dcosenza@hersamacorn.com, Account Exec.,

Monroe Courier, CT, Shelton

Cosenza, Donna ....(203) 402-2327
dcosenza@hersamacorn.com, Account Exec.,
Shelton Herald, CT, Shelton

Cosenza, Donna ....(203) 402-2327
dcosenza@hersamacorn.com, Account
Executive, Trumbull Times, CT, Shelton

Cosey, Jane
advertising@manchesternewspapers.com,
Prodn. Mgr./Adv. Mgr., The Weekender, NY,
Granville
advertising@manchesternewspapers.com,
Prodn. Mgr./Adv. Mgr., The North Country
Free Press, NY, Granville

Cosey, Jane
advertising@manchesternewspapers.com,
Prodn. Mgr., The Lakes Region Free Press,
NY, Granville

Cosgrove, David
cosgrove@aig.com, New York Univ., NY, New
York

Cosgrove, Mary
mcosgrove@mdjonline.com, Ed., South Fulton
Neighbor, GA, Forest Park
mcosgrove@mdjonline.com, Ed., Henry
Neighbor, GA, Forest Park
mcosgrove@mdjonline.com, Ed., The Clayton
Neighbor (OOB), GA, Marietta

Cosino, Ana
ads@navasotaexaminer.com, Adv. Dir., The
Navasota Examiner, TX, Navasota

Cosma, Eileen ....(631) 737-6020 x130
scox@flexography.org, Marketing Manager,
Flexographic Technical Association, NY,
Bohemia

Cosmides, John
john@barustors.com, Mktg. Dir., The Recorder,
CA, San Francisco

Cosner, Christina......................(317) 736-2750
ccosner@dailyjournal.net, Adv. Dir., Daily
Journal, IN, Franklin

Cossey, Mike
info@risi.com, CEO, RISI, Inc., MA, Bedford

Costa, Crystal ....(479) 571-6441
ccosta@nwadg.com, Adv./Mktg. Dir. ,
Northwest Arkansas Democrat-Gazette, AR,
Fayetteville
ccosta@nwadg.com, Pub., Times Record, AR,
Fort Smith

Costa, Denise ....(541) 383-0356
dcosta@bendbulletin.com, Associate editor,
The Bulletin, OR, Bend

Costa, John ....(541) 383-0337
jcosta@bendbulletin.com, Publisher, The
Bulletin, OR, Bend

Costa, Matthew
mcosta@nwaonline.com, Online Dir., WEHCO
Media, Inc., AR, Little Rock

Costa, Matthew ....(479) 571-6454
mcosta@arkansasonline.com, Online Dir.,
Arkansas Democrat-Gazette, AR, Little Rock

Costello, Carlita.........................(915) 546-6176
ccostello@elpasotimes.com, Design Ed., El
Paso Times, TX, El Paso
ccostello@elpasotimes.com, Design Ed., El
Paso y Mas, TX, El Paso

Costello, David W............................ext. 120
dcostello@sunjournal.com, Pres., The
Forecaster, ME, Falmouth

Costello, Gail...........................(217) 477-5137
Circ., Commercial News, IL, Danville

Costello, James
sports@thepilotnews.com, Sports Ed., Pilot
News, IN, Plymouth
sports@thepilotnews.com, Sports Ed., The
Shopper, IN, Plymouth

Costello, James R. ....(207) 784-5411
jcostello@sunjournal.com, Pres., Sun Media
Group, ME, Lewiston

Costello, James R. ....(207) 784-5411
jcostello@sunjournal.com, Pres., Livermore
Falls Advertiser, ME, Livermore Falls

Costello, Jay
jay.costello@yale.com, Vice Pres., Aftermarket
Sales, Yale Materials Handling Corp., NC,
Greenville

Costello, Jeremy.....................(316) 775-2218
jcostello@butlercountytimesgazette.com,
Sports Ed., The Butler County Times-
Gazette, KS, Augusta

Costello, John A.
jcostello@rotadyne.com, Vice Pres., OEM
Sales, RotaDyne Corp., IL, Darien

Costello, Stephen M..................(207) 689-2920
scostello@sunjournal.com, Vice Pres. Adv./
Mktg., Sun Journal, ME, Lewiston

Costello, Steve ....(207) 784-5411 ext. 1220
Vice Pres., Adv./Mktg., Sun Media Group, ME,
Lewiston

Costello, Steven
scostello@sunjournal.com, Dir., Adv., Maine
Daily Newspaper Publishers Association,
ME, Lewiston

Costello, Vic
vcostello@elon.edu, Assoc. Prof., Elon
University, NC, Elon

Cota, Elaine............................(480) 898-7926
ecota@ahwatukee.com, Class Mgr.,
Ahwatukee Foothills News, AZ, Tempe

Cote, Andre-Philippe
apcote@lesoleil.com, Cartoonist, Le Soleil,
QC, Quebec

Cote, Cassay
casey.cote@naplesnews.com, Prodn. Mgr.,
Pressroom, Naples Daily News, FL, Naples

Cote, Dave
lois.sills@honeywell.com, CEO, Honeywell,
Inc., NJ, Morristown

Cote, Elizabeth ....(203) 966-9541 ext 106
ecote@hersamacorn.com, Account Exec., New
Canaan Advertiser, CT, New Canaan

Cote, Mike ....(603) 206-7724
mcote@unionleader.com, Deputy Mng. Ed.,
Bus., New Hampshire Union Leader/New
Hampshire Sunday News, NH, Manchester

Cote, Monique.........................(819) 843-3500
monique.cote@tc.tc, CEO, Reflet Du Lac, QC,
Magog
monique.cote@tc.tc, Ed., Le Progres De
Coaticook, QC, Coaticook

Cote, Ralph
journal@letincelle.qc.ca, Ed. in Chief, Etincelle,
QC, Windsor

Cote, Sylvia
cotes2@transcontinental.ca, Ed., L'avenir De
L'erable, QC, Plessisville

Cote, Sylvie
cotes2@transcontinental.ca, Mng. Ed., La
Nouvelle, QC, Victoriaville

Cote, Therese ....(418) 686-3254
tcote@lesoleil.com, Supvr., Le Soleil, QC,
Quebec

Cotherman, Gen.......................(307) 265-3870
editor@casperjournal.com, Assistant Ed.,
Casper Journal, WY, Casper

Cotlar, Brian ....(207) 990-8152
bcotlar@bangordailynews.com, Sales and
Marketing Dir., Bangor Daily News, ME,
Bangor

Cotler, Bruce
president@nyppa.org, President, New York
Press Photographers Association, Inc., NY,
New York

Cott, Jeff
jeff@derbyinformer.com, Publisher/Owner,
Derby Informer, KS, Derby

Cotter, Barbara ....(719) 636-0194

barb.cotterClari@gazette.com, Business Editor,
The Gazette, CO, Colorado Springs

Cotter, Christina
ccotter@ugapress.uga.edu, Mng. Ed., Flagpole
Magazine, GA, Athens

Cotter, Dan
d.cotter@nenpa.com, Exec. Dir. NENPA,
NENPA Marketing & Advertising Council,
MA, Dedham

Cotter, Dan
d.cotter@nenpa.com, Exec. Dir., New
England Newspaper Advertising Executives
Association, MA, Dedham

Cotter, Tim 860/701-4372
t.cotter@theday.com, Ed, The Thames River
Times, CT, New London
t.cotter@theday.com, ed, The Groton Times,
CT, New London
t.cotter@theday.com, Ed, The Mystic Times,
CT, New London
t.cotter@theday.com, Ed, The Stonington
Times, CT, New London
t.cotter@theday.com, Ed, Waterford Times, CT,
New London
t.cotter@theday.com, Ed, The Lyme Times, CT,
New London
t.cotter@theday.com, Ed, East Haven Courier,
CT, Madison
t.cotter@theday.com, Managing Editor, The
Day, CT, New London

Cotter, William M. ....(412) 871-2304
bcotter@tribweb.com, Exec. Dir., Sales, Leader
Times, PA, Kittanning
bcotter@tribweb.com, Exec. Dir. Sales, Trib
Total Media, Inc., PA, Pittsburgh
bcotter@tribweb.com, Exec. Dir., Sales, The
Valley Independent (OOB), PA, Monessen
bcotter@tribweb.com, Exec. Dir., Sales,
Tribune-Review, PA, Greensburg

Cotters, Mary ....ext. 241
mcotters@timesonline.com, Circ. Mgr., Opns.,
Beaver County Times, PA, Beaver

Cottew, Mitch ....(320) 968-7220
Mitch.c@star-pub.com, Reporter, Benton
County News, MN, Foley

Cottingham, Mary
mcottingham@diocesecc.org, Associate Editor,
South Texas Catholic, TX, Corpus Christi

Cottingham, Rob ....(803) 359-7633
cottinghamrob@yahoo.com, News Editor,
Lexington County Chronicle & The Dispatch-
News, SC, Lexington

Cottle, Lee
sales@vicorp.com, COO, Vicorp.com, TX,
Plano

Cotton, Amy...........................(603) 504-3107
acotton@eagletimes.com, Social Med. Ed.,
Eagle Times, NH, Claremont

Cotton, Ben
ben.cotton@nytimes.com, Columbia Univ., NY,
New York

Cotton, Connie Jo ....(650) 223-6571
ccotton@embarcaderomediagroup.com, VP,
Sales/Mktg, Mountain View Voice, CA, Palo
Alto
ccotton@embarcaderomediagroup.com, Major
Accounts Sales Mgr., The Almanac, CA,
Menlo Park

Cotton, Eric ....(203) 317-2344
ecotton@record-journal.com, City Ed., Record-
Journal, CT, Meriden

Cottrell, Sally A.
TCADV@ROCHESTER.RR.COM , Ed., Tri-
county Advertiser, NY, Brockport

Cottrill, Pat
pcottrill@amestrib.com, Circ. Dir., Ames
Tribune, IA, Ames

Couch, Jeffry ....(618) 239-2551
jcouch@bnd.com, Ed., Command Post, IL,
Belleville

Couch, Yolanda ....(606) 528-7898 Ext. 18

ycouch@thetimestribune.com, Circ. District
Mgr. , Times-Tribune, KY, Corbin

Couch , Jeffrey ....(618) 239-2557
Jcouch@bnd.com, Editor/VP, Belleville News-
Democrat, IL, Belleville

Coughlan, Andy ....(409) 880-8103
editor@lamaruniversitypress.com, Lamar Univ.,
TX, Beaumont

Cougill, Deb
story@linncountynews.net, Reporter, The Linn
County News, KS, Pleasanton

Coulombe, Daniel
dcoulombe@sherbrookerecord.com , Ed. , The
Record, QC, Sherbrooke

Coulombe, Rita ....(207) 729-3315 ext. 3210
rcoulombe@timesrecord.com, Circ. Mgr.,
Church World, ME, Portland

Coulombe , Gary
advert@bellnet.ca, Adv. Rep., Manotick
Messenger, ON, Johnstown

Coulson, Joan ....(217) 285-5415
pikecountyexpressnews@yahoo.com, Pub.,
Pike County Express, IL, Pittsfield

Coulter, Alex
news@theeveningtimes.com, Pub., The
Evening Times, AR, Marion

Coulter, Barry.....................................ext. 210
barry.coulter@cranbrooktownsman.com, Ed.,
Cranbrook Daily Townsman, BC, Cranbrook

Coulter, RoGlenda
hermes10@pld.com, Co-Owner, The Hugoton
Hermes, KS, Hugoton

Counterman, Traci ....(641) 683-5371
t.counterman@ottumwacourier.com, Audience
Development Director, The Ottumwa Courier,
IA, Ottumwa

Countryman, Albert J.................(856) 456-1199
gcneditor@verizon.net, Pub./Ed., Gloucester
City News, NJ, Gloucester City

Countryman, Mike ....(785) 832-7137
mcountryman@ljworld.com, Shawnee
Dispatch, KS, Shawnee

Countryman, Toni ....(815) 455-8570
tcountryman@mchenry.edu, Advisor, McHenry
County College, IL, Crystal Lake

Counts, Donna.........................(256) 714-7152
Donna.Counts@theredstonerocket.com, Adv.
Rep., Redston Rocket, AL, Decatur

Courchesne, Martin ....(514) 504-2183
martin.courchesne@canoe.ca, Nat'l Dir., Sales,
Shopper's Market, ON, Belleville

Coursey, Barbara
ads@warrensentinel.com, Inside Adv. Sales,
Warren Sentinel, WY, Cheyenne

Courson, Mike.........................(620) 257-2368
Sports Reporter, The Lyons News, KS, Lyons

Courson, Sharon
scourson@gannett.com, Nat'l Sales Coord,
The Advocate, OH, Newark
scourson@gannett.com, Nat'l Sales Coord. ,
The Marion Star, OH, Marion
scourson@gannett.com, Nat'l Adv. Coord.,
Times Recorder, OH, Zanesville

Courter, Amanda ....(308) 882-4453
frontdesk@jpipapers.com, Office/Circ Mgr.
, Imperial Republican, NE, Imperial

Courtis, Chris ....(519) 490-1100
chris.courtis@sunmedia.ca, Marketing
Manager, Sarnia & Lambton County This
Week, ON, Sarnia

Courtney, Jamie
engineeringproductsco@gmail.com, Owner,
Engineering Products Co., Inc., IL, Genoa

Courtney, Kevin ....(707) 256-2217
kcourtney@napanews.com, City Ed., Napa
Valley Register, CA, Napa
kcourtney@napanews.com, Commun. Mgr.,
Sun-Sentinel Co., FL, Fort Lauderdale

Courtney, Misty ....(217) 283-5111
chronads@frontier.com, Advertising Executive,
The Chronicle, IL, Hoopeston

Coury, Marilyn..............(620) 442-4200 ext. 108
circulation@arkcity.net, Circulation Manager,
The Arkansas City Traveler, KS, Arkansas
City

Cousins, Bruce ....(250) 380-5274
bcousins@timescolonist.com, Circ. Mgr., Distr./
Mktg., Victoria Times Colonist, BC, Victoria

Cousins, Scott
scousins@ftimes.com, Ed., The Times, IN,
Frankfort

Couto, Dan ....(518) 454-5401
dcouto@timesunion.com, Vice President
Operations, Times Union, NY, Albany

Coutts, Kathy ....(807) 727-2888
classifieds@thenorthernsun.com, Gen Mgr. ,
The Northern Sun News, ON, Red Lake

Couture, Caroline ....(819) 762-4361
caroline.couture@hebdosquebecor.com,
Citoyen de l'Abitibi Ouest (OOB) , QC,
Rouyn-Noranda
caroline.couture@hebdosquebecor.com,
Citoyen De L'harricana, QC, Amos

Couture, Kenneth
classifieds@merritherald.com, Office Mgr.,
Merritt Herald, BC, Merritt

Couture, Marc
mcouture@jdeq.com, Circ. Mgr., Le Journal de
Quebec, QC, Vanier

Couturier, Brian
bcouturier@progress-index.com, Managing
Ed., The Progress-Index, VA, Petersburg

Covatch, Cindy ....(814) 938-8740
circulation@punxsutawneyspirit.com,
Circ. Mgr., The Punxsutawney Spirit, PA,
Punxsutawney

Cover, Susan ....(207) 621-5643
scover@centralmaine.com, City Ed., Kennebec
Journal, ME, Augusta

Covert, Tom ....ext. 667
Mgr., Computer Serv., New Castle News, PA,
New Castle

Covert, Judy ....(716) 532-2288
jcovert@metrowny.com, Off. Mgr. , Gowanda
News, NY, Buffalo

Covington, Jay
jay@theforumnews.com, Pub., The Forum, LA,
Shreveport

Covington, Peter ....(318) 377-1866 ext. 117
circulation@press-herald.com, Circ. Mgr.,
Minden Press Herald, LA, Minden

Cowan, Amanda.......................(360) 735-4461
amanda.cowan@columbian.com, Photo Editor,
The Columbian, WA, Vancouver

Cowan, Bruce...............(705) 472-3200 ext. 314
bruce.cowan@sunmedia.ca, Mng. Ed., Nugget,
ON, North Bay

Cowan, Bruce
bcowan@thesudburystar.com, Pub.,
Entertainment, ON, Sudbury

Cowan, Chris ....(734) 997-4872
chris.cowan@proquest.com, ProQuest LLC,
MI, Ann Arbor

Cowan, Geoffrey
gcowan@usc.edu, Prof./Dean, Annenberg
School for Communication, University of
Southern California, CA, Los Angeles

Cowan, Jennifer
publisher@castlegarnews.com, Ed, Rossland
News, BC, Castlegar

Cowan, Mike ....(815) 232-0177
mike.cowan@blackpress.ca, Pub, Victoria
News, BC, Victoria
mike.cowan@blackpress.ca, Sales Adv. Mgr.,
The Journal-Standard, IL, Freeport

Cowan, Ted ....(416) 869-4994

tcowan@torstar.com, Sales Representative
Torstar Syndication Services
GetStock.com, Torstar Syndication Services,
ON, Toronto

Coward, John
john-coward@utulsa.edu, Chair, University of
Tulsa, OK, Tulsa

Cowart, Ned
nedcowart@gmail.com, Pub., The News-
Herald/The Derrick, PA, Oil City

Cowell, Fuller .... (907) 459-7511
Pub., Fairbanks Daily News-Miner, AK,
Fairbanks

Cowenhoven, Virginia .... (661) 392-5735
vcowenhoven@bakersfield.com, Assoc. Pub.,
The Bakersfield Californian, CA, Bakersfield

Cowles, Roger .... (409) 721-2431
rcowles@panews.com, Editorial Page Ed., Port
Arthur News, TX, Port Arthur

Cowley, Ed .... (780) 942-2023
redwater@shaw.ca, Pub./Adv. Mgr./Owner, The
Review, AB, Redwater
redwater@shaw.ca, Pub./Owner/Adv. Mgr./ Ed.,
Farm 'n' Friends, AB, Redwater

Cowley, Ed .... (780) 939-3309
morinville@shaw.ca, Pub., The Free Press, AB,
Morinville

Cowling, Mark
mcowling@pinalcentral.com, Ed., Florence
Reminder & Blade-Tribune, AZ, Florence

Cowling, Mike
cowling@uwosh.edu, Chair/Prof., University of
Wisconsin-Oshkosh, WI, Oshkosh

Cowsert, Sandra .... (618) 683-3531
herald@shawneelink.net, Ed., Herald-
Enterprise, IL, Golconda

Cox, Bob
bob.cox@freepress.mb.ca, Chairman,
Canadian News Media Association, ON,
Toronto

Cox, Brandon .... (979) 479-3792
brandon.cox@baycitytribune.com, The Bay City
Tribune, TX, Bay City

Cox, Brandon .... (256) 259-1020
brandon.cox@thedailysentinel.com, Publisher
, The Daily Sentinel, AL, Scottsboro

Cox, Brian .... (617) 532-0120
brian.cox@metro.us, Associate Publisher/
Executive Sales Director , Metro Boston,
MA, Boston

Cox, Brian
bcox@legalnews.com, Detroit Legal News,
MI, Troy

Cox, Brian .... (617) 619-6183
Brian.Cox@bostonherald.com, Vice Pres./
Display Advertising, Boston Herald, MA,
Boston

Cox, Christine
ccox@bnd.com, Belleville News-Democrat, IL,
Belleville

Cox, Donna
circulation@wjhnews.com, Circ. Mgr.,
Waycross Journal-Herald, GA, Waycross

Cox, Eileen .... (302) 324-2558
Marketing Director, The News Journal, DE,
New Castle

Cox, Erin
ecox@timesbulletin.com, News Ed., The Times
Bulletin, OH, Van Wert

Cox, Greg
greg.cox@hearst.com, Director, Houston
Chronicle, TX, Houston

Cox, James A.
jimcox@tds.net, Ed., Clarke County Democrat,
AL, Grove Hill

Cox, James B.
elnewsrog@aol.com, Ed., East Lauderdale
News, AL, Rogersville

Cox, Jennifer
ads.newsshield@chibardun.net, Adv. Mgr.,
Barron News-Shield, WI, Barron

Cox, Jeremy
herald@valleytel.net, Pub./Ed., McPherson
County Herald, SD, Leola

Cox, Jerry
jcox@nacdl.org, Prodn. Foreman, Mailroom,
Washington Daily News, NC, Washington

Cox, Jim .... (251) 275-3375
jimcox@tds.net, Pub., Clarke County
Democrat, AL, Grove Hill

Cox, Jim
jcox@garrardcentralrecord.com, Pub., Garrard
Central Record, KY, Lancaster

Cox, John Ferrin
gvnews@wfeca.net, Pub., The Graceville
News, FL, Graceville

Cox, John Ferrin .... (334) 897-2823
clipper@alaweb.com, Pub., The Elba Clipper,
AL, Elba

Cox, Kevin
kevin.cox@galvnews.com, Galveston
Newspapers, Inc., TX, Galveston

Cox, Marc .... (217) 206-6397
journal@uis.edu, EIC, Univ. of Illinois/
Springfield, IL, Springfield

Cox, Mary .... (317) 710-6622
indyschild@indyschild.com, Pub., Indy's Child,
IN, Indianapolis

Cox, Melanie .... (651) 487-5778
mcox@anrinc.net, Regl. Sales Mgr.,
Minneapolis, American Newspaper
Representatives, MI, Troy

Cox, Melanie
mcox@anrinc.net, Sales Mgr., American
Newspaper Representatives, Inc., MN,
Roseville

Cox, Pattie
pcox@garrardcentralrecord.com, Mng. Ed.,
Garrard Central Record, KY, Lancaster

Cox, Peter
news@nafreepress.com, Ed., North Attleboro
Free Press, MA, North Attleboro

Cox, Phyllis D.
elnewsrog@aol.com, Co-Pub., East
Lauderdale News, AL, Rogersville

Cox, Randy .... (256) 773-6566
randy.cox@themadisonrecord.com, Pub.,
Hartselle Enquirer, AL, Hartselle
randy.cox@themadisonrecord.com, Pub., The
Madison Record, AL, Madison
randy.cox@themadisonrecord.com, Pub., The
Madison County Record, AR, Huntsville

Cox, Renita .... (859) 236-2551 Ext. 180
rcox@amnews.com, Controller, The Advocate-
Messenger, KY, Danville

Cox, Ron ....(434) 432-1654 ext. 31
rcox@womackpublishing.com, HR Mgr.,
Womack Publishing Co., VA, Lynchburg

Cox, Scott .... (613) 279-3150
info@frontenacnews.ca, Designer/bookeeper,
The Frontenac News, ON, Sharbot Lake

Cox, Stacy .... (765) 345-2292
scox@thebanneronline.com, General Manager,
Knightstown Banner, IN, Knightstown

Cox, Stephanie
bnews@sbcglobal.net, Adv. Dir., The Bowie
News, TX, Bowie

Cox, Trista .... (541) 575-0710
trista@bmeagle.com, Class./Circ., Blue
Mountain Eagle, OR, John Day

Cox, V. Marvin
mcox@boisestate.edu, Chrmn., Boise State
Univ., ID, Boise

Cox, Wendy
wendy.cox@thecanadianpress.com, Bureau
Chief, Canadian Press, The - Vancouver, BC,

BC, Vancouver

Coxon-Smith, Maria
mariacoxonsmith@tucsonsentinel.com, News/
Engagement Ed., TucsonSentinel.com, AZ,
Tuscon

Coxson, Doug .... (519) 763-3333 ext. 230
dcoxson@guelphmercurytribune.com, Ed.,
Guelph Tribune, ON, Guelph

Coxwell, Samantha .... (904) 879-2727
advertising@nassaucountyrecord.com,
Marketing Associate, Nassau County
Record, FL, Callahan

Coy, Sharon
coy@nckcn.com, Social Ed., Concordia Blade-
Empire, KS, Concordia

Coy, Stacy
stacy@burnettcountysentinel.com, Advertising
Agent, Burnett County Sentinel, WI,
Grantsburg

Coyla, Alice .... (508) 967-3505
acoyle@wickedlocal.com, Mng. Ed. , Easton
Journal, MA, Raynham

Coyle, Alice .... (508) 967-3505
acoyle@wickedlocal.com, Ed., Norton Mirror,
MA, Raynham

Coyle, Alice .... (508) 967-3505
acoyle@wickedlocal.com, Managing Ed.,
Bridgewater Independent, MA, Raynham

Coyle, Alice .... (508) 967-3505
acoyle@wickedlocal.com, Managing Ed.,
Canton Journal, MA, Raynham
acoyle@wickedlocal.com, Managing Ed.,
Randolph Herald, MA, Randolph
acoyle@wickedlocal.com, Managing Ed.,
Stoughton Journal, MA, Raynham
acoyle@wickedlocal.com, Ed., The Lakeville
Call, MA, Brockton
acoyle@wickedlocal.com, Ed., The Raynham
Call, MA, Taunton
acoyle@wickedlocal.com, GateHouse Media,
Inc., NY, Pittsford

Coyle, David
davecoyle@morning-times.com, Graphics/I.T.
Manager, Sample News Group LLC, PA,
Corry

Coyle, Elizabeth .... (814) 623-1151
ecoyle@bedfordgazette.com, Ed., Bedford
Gazette, PA, Bedford

Coyle, Elizabeth
ecoyle@bedfordgazette.com, Mng. Ed. , The
Bedford Gazette, PA, Bedford

Coyle, Mark
mark@fredoniapennysaver.com, Adv. Mgr.,
Dunkirk/fredonia/westfield Pennysaver, NY,
Fredonia

Coyne, Brian
bcoyne@journalinquirer.com, Executive Sports
Editor, Journal Inquirer, CT, Manchester

Coyne, Ryland .... (613) 283-3182 Ext.142
rcoyne@perfprint.ca, The Perth Courier Emc,
ON, Smith Falls
rcoyne@perfprint.ca, Reg. Ed. , The Carleton
Place-almonte Canadian Gazette Emc, ON,
Smith Falls
rcoyne@perfprint.ca, Ed., Smiths Falls Record
News Emc, ON, Smiths Falls

Cozak, Colleen
colleen.cozak@independentmail.com, Night
Ed., Anderson Independent-Mail, SC,
Anderson

Cozart, Gary .... (440) 329-7220
gcozart@chroniclet.com, Cir. Mgr., The Medina
County Gazette, OH, Medina

Cozart, Gary
gcozart@chroniclet.com, Circ. Mgr.,
Coverstory, OH, Elyria

Crabb, Cynthia .... (501) 505-1211
cynthia.crabb@thecabin.net, Group Controller,
HR
, Log Cabin Democrat, AR, Conway

Crabbe, Duane .... (701) 250-8288
duane.crabbe@bismarcktribune.com, Retail
Ad. Mgr., Sales Mgr., The Finder, The
Bismarck Tribune, ND, Bismarck

Crabbe, Nathan .... (352) 374-5075
nathan.crabbe@gvillesun.com, Editorial Page
Ed.
, The Gainesville Sun, FL, Gainesville

Crabtree, Peggy .... (765) 648-4203,
peggy.crabtree@indianamediagroup.com,
Accounting, The Herald Bulletin, IN,
Anderson

Crabtree, Scott
scrabtree@coxnews.com, Prodn. Foreman,
Pressroom, The Daily Sentinel, CO, Grand
Junction

Craft, Dan .... (309) 820-3259
dcraft@pantagraph.com, Entertainment Ed.,
The Pantagraph, IL, Bloomington

Craft, Kelli .... (541) 963-3161
kcraft@lagrandeobserver.com, Circ. Mgr., Jeff
Davis Ledger, GA, Hazlehurst
kcraft@lagrandeobserver.com, Circ. Mgr., The
Observer, OR, La Grande
kcraft@lagrandeobserver.com, Circ. Mgr., Baker
City Herald, OR, Baker City

Craft, Lisa
community@monett-times.com, Mktg. Dir.,
Cassville Democrat, MO, Cassville

Craft, Michael .... (318) 869-0115
jmichaelcraft@bellsouth.net, Sr. Newspaper
Consultant, The Austin Company, OH,
Cleveland

Craft, Tracy .... (407) 515-2605
tcraft@turnstilemediagroup.com, Pub., Winter
Park-Maitland Observer, FL, Orlando

Crager, Gary .... (260) 347-0400
gcrager@kpcmedia.com, Production Manager,
Smart Shopper, IN, Kendallville

Crager, Gary .... (260) 347-0400
gcrager@kpcmedia.com, Production Manager,
KPC Media Group, Inc., IN, Kendallville

Crager, Gary .... (260) 347-0400 Ext. 1148
gcrager@kpcmedia.com, Production Mgr., The
News Sun, IN, Kendallville

Crago, Brandon
online@laramieboomerang.com, Graphic
Design Mgr., Laramie Boomerang, WY,
Laramie

Cragwall, Glenn
gcragwall@cn.edu, Carson-Newman
University, TN, Jefferson City

Craig, Frank
fcraig@tribweb.com, Exec. Ed., The Herald,
PA, Aspinwall

Craig, Frank .... (412) 320-7816
fcraig@tribweb.com, Ed., North Journal, PA,
Monroeville
fcraig@tribweb.com, Exec. Ed., Plum Advance
Leader, PA, Pittsburgh
fcraig@tribweb.com, Ed., Sewickley Herald,
PA, Sewickley
fcraig@tribweb.com, Ed., Tribune-Review, PA,
Greensburg

Craig, H. .... (304) 772-3016
watchman2@earthlink.net, Ed., Monroe
Watchman, WV, Union

Craig, Jeremy .... (903) 897-2281
Photographer/Reporter, The Monitor, TX,
Naples

Craig, Joseph
jcraig@civitasmedia.com, Chief Revenue
Officer, Civitas Media, LLC-OOB, NC,
Davidson
jcraig@civitasmedia.com, Reg. Pub., Morning
News, SC, Florence

Craig, Kevin .... (951) 760-1115
kevin_craig@parade.com, Representative, Mid-
Atlantic Circulation Managers Association,
NC, Roanoke Rapids

Craig, Lloyd
lloyd@winfieldcourier.com, Pub., The Leader, KS, Winfield

Craig, Lloyd.............................(620) 221-1050
advertising@winfieldcourier.com, Publisher, Cedar Vale Lookout, KS, Winfield
advertising@winfieldcourier.com, Pub., Winfield Daily Courier, KS, Winfield

Craig, Richard..........................(408) 924-3270
San Jose State Univ., CA, San Jose

Craig, Richard
richard.craig@oclaro.com, Assoc. Prof., San Jose State University, CA, San Jose

Craig, Rick
rcraig@hcnews.com, Adv. Dir., Hood County News, TX, Granbury

Craig, Tim.....................(605) 224-7301 ext 120
tim.craig@capjournal.com, Adv. Dir., Reminder Plus, SD, Pierre

Craig, Tim
publisher@newsmontana.com, Pub., Carbon County News, MT, Red Lodge

Craig, Victoria
craig.victoria@kingscorecord.com, Pub./Ed, The Kings County Record, NB, Sussex

Craiger, Gary..........................(260) 347-0400
gcrager@kpcmedia.com, Production Manager, KPC Media Group, Inc., IN, Kendallville

Crain, Tracy..............................(501) 224-4256
tracy@arkanasfreepress.net, Publisher, Editor, Arkansas Free Press, AR, Little Rock

Craine, Patrick..............(888) 678-6008 ext 926
pcraine@lifesitenews.com, Editor / Journalist, LifeSiteNews.com, VA, Front Royal

Crake, Melinda
mcrake@caledonenterprise.com, Adv. Rep, Caledon Enterprise, ON, Bolton

Cram, Deb...............................(570) 724-2287
dcram.tiogapublishing@gmail.com, Adv., The Wellsboro Gazette, PA, Wellsboro

Cramer, George
gcramer@arglobal.com, Vice Pres., Commercial Devel., Adhesives Research, Inc., PA, Glen Rock

Cramer, Tim...........................(505) 428-7632
tcramer@sfnewmexican.com, Director of Production, The Santa Fe New Mexican, NM, Santa Fe

Crampton, Sarah
marketing@rogueriverpress.com, Adv, Rogue River Press, OR, Grants Pass

Crane, Ben
bcrane@ithaca.edu, Assoc. Prof., Ithaca College, NY, Ithaca

Crane, Joyce
jcrane@wickedlocal.com, Ed., Westford Eagle, MA, Concord

Crane, Joyce Pellino.................(978) 371-5729
jcrane@wickedlocal.com, News Ed. , Littleton Independent, MA, Concord

Crane, Kevin...........................(607) 352-2701
kcrane@pressconnects.com, Gen. Mgr., The Ithaca Journal, NY, Ithaca
kcrane@pressconnects.com, Gen. Mgr. / Gannett Pub. Serv. , Press & Sun-Bulletin, NY, Binghamton

Crane, Kevin...........................(607) 352-2701
kcrane@stargazette.com, Gen. Mgr. / Gannett Pub. Serv. , Star-Gazette, NY, Elmira

Cranmer, Jenetta
circulation@chillicothenews.com, Circ Mgr, Salt River Journal, MO, Hannibal

Cranshaw, William O.
bcranshaw@mpival.com, Vice Pres., Management Planning, Inc., CT, Simsbury

Cranston, Charles
charles.cranston@washburn.edu, Prof., Washburn University, KS, Topeka

Crary, Miki....................(315) 265-1000, ext. 3
Office Manager, North Country This Week, NY, Potsdam

Cravaritis, Rob........................(954) 425-1730
rcravaritis@sunsentinel.com, Vice President Sales/Advertising, South Florida Sun-Sentinel, FL, Fort Lauderdale

Cravaritis, Rob
rob.cravaritis@chron.com, Executive Vice President/Sales, Houston Chronicle, TX, Houston

Craven, JoAnn..............................ext. 224
circ@barrowcountynews.com, Circ. Mgr., Barrow News-journal, GA, Winder

Cravens, Beth..........................(731) 587-3144
advertising@wcpnews.com, Editorial Cartoonist
Graphic Design, Weakley County Press, TN, Martin

Cravens, Mona
cravens@usc.edu, Univ. of Southern California, CA, Los Angeles

Cravey, Eric
eric@opcfla.com, Editor, Clay Today, FL, Fleming Island

Crawford, Carolyn...................(215) 949-4017
ccrawford@calkins-media.com, Sec. to Pres., Calkins Media, PA, Levittown

Crawford, Cindy......................(205) 443-5631
ccrawford@bizjournals.com, Editor, Birmingham Business Journal, AL, Birmingham

Crawford, Colin
colin.crawford@latimes.com, Deputy Managing Ed.
, Los Angeles Times, CA, Los Angeles

Crawford, Dale
wymorearborstate@windstream.net, Ed., Wymore Arbor State, NE, Wymore

Crawford, Donald.....................(979) 731-4686
donald.crawford@theeagle.com, Mailroom Mgr., The Eagle, TX, Bryan

Crawford, Grant.......................(918) 456-8833
gcrawford@tahlequahdailypress.com, general assignment reporter, Tahlequah Daily Press, OK, Tahlequah

Crawford, Jessica
news@hpleader.com, News, The Leader & Times, KS, Liberal

Crawford, Jim
colbertcountyreporter@earthlink.net, Ed., Colbert County Reporter, AL, Tuscumbia
colbertcountyreporter@earthlink.net, Pub., Standard & Times, AL, Tuscumbia

Crawford, Karen......................(317) 477-3224
kcrawford@greenfieldreporter.com, Mng. Ed., Daily Reporter, IN, Greenfield

Crawford, Lyall
lyall.crawford@zu.ac.ae, Prof., Zayed University, Al Ruwayyah

Crawford, Michael
sacosagenews@centurytel.net, Ed., Humansville Star-Leader, MO, Humansville

Crawford, Michael
sacosagenews@centurytel.net, Pub., St. Clair Co. Courier, MO, Osceola

Crawford, Micheal
sacosagenews@centurytel.net, Pub., Rich Hill Mining Review, MO, Rich Hill

Crawford, Mike
mike_crawford@mccom.com, Pres., M/C/C, TX, Dallas

Crawford, Mike
sacosagenews@centurytel.net, Ed., Appleton City Journal, MO, Appleton City

Crawford, Paul.......................(509) 577-7692
pcrawford@yakimaherald.com, Digital Content Director, Yakima Herald-Republic, WA, Yakima

Crawford, Paul M.....................(502) 644-5650
paulc@technidyne.com, Bus. Dir., Technidyne Corp., IN, New Albany

Crawford, Richard...................(952) 345-6471
editor@chanvillager.com, Ed, Lakeshore Weekly News, MN, Wayzata
editor@chanvillager.com, Ed, Chanhassen Villager, MN, Chaska
editor@chanvillager.com, Ed. , Savage Pacer, MN, Savage

Crawford, Shawn
class@standard-democrat.com, Classified Mgr., Standard Democrat, MO, Sikeston

Crawford, Thomas
spectrum@technidyne.com, Vice Pres., Sales/Mktg., Technidyne Corp., IN, New Albany

Crawford, Tom........................(218) 894-1112
tcrawford@staplesworld.com, Ed., Sunday Square Shooter, MN, Staples

Crawford, Trish
belinda@countrypeddlerbg.com, Prod. Mgr., Country Peddler, KY, Bowling Green

Crawford-Muhammad, Naeem
law.commentator@nyu.edu, New York University School of Law, NY, New York

Crawley, LeeAnn
leeann.crawley@trib.com, Circ. Mgr., Casper Journal, WY, Casper

Crawley, Lori...........................(724) 731-0094
info@nsslife.org, Prodn. Mgr., Narodne Noviny, PA, McMurray

Creager, Ashley.....................(254) 559-5412
admgr@breckenridgeamerican.com, Adv. Mgr., Breckenridge American, TX, Breckenridge

Creamer, Dennis....................(336) 373-7188
dennis.creamer@news-record.com, Production manager, News & Record, NC, Greensboro

Creaney, Ronan..............(212) 684-3366 ext. 12
Adv. Mgr., Irish Voice, NY, New York

Creech, Ledeana
lcreech@tompkinsvillenews.com, Graphics, Tompkinsville News, KY, Tompkinsville

Creed, Becke...................(440) 576-9125 x102
beckecreed@gazettenews.com, Director of Operations/Adv. Mgr., Lake County Tribune, OH, Jefferson

Creed, Becke...................(440) 576-9125 x102
beckecreed@gazettenews.com, Director of Operations/Adv. Mgr., The News, OH, Jefferson

Creed, Becke...................(440) 576-9125 x102
beckecreed@gazettenews.com, Director of Operations/Advert. Man., The Courier, OH, Jefferson

Creed, Becke...................(440) 576-9125 x102
beckecreed@gazettenews.com, Director of Operations/Adv. Mgr., The Shores News, OH, Jefferson

Creed, Becke...................(440) 576-9125 x102
beckecreed@gazettenews.com, Director of operations/Adv. Mgr., The Gazette, OH, Jefferson

Creed, Becke.................(440) 576-9125 x 102
beckecreed@gazettenews.com, Director of Operations/Human Resources, The Gazette, OH, Jefferson

Creed, Bill
bcreed@gazettenews.com, The Gazette, OH, Jefferson

Creed, Kelly
kcreed@gazettenews.com, The Gazette, OH, Jefferson

Creed, William..............(440) 576-9125 ext. 103
bcreed@gazettenews.com, Pres./Pub., Lake County Tribune, OH, Jefferson
bcreed@gazettenews.com, Pres./Pub., Gazette Newspapers, Inc., OH, Jefferson

bcreed@gazettenews.com, Pres./Pub., The News, OH, Jefferson
bcreed@gazettenews.com, Adv. Mgr., The Sentinel, OH, Jefferson
bcreed@gazettenews.com, Pres./Pub., The Shores News, OH, Jefferson
bcreed@gazettenews.com, Pres./Pub., The Albion News (OOB), PA, Albion
bcreed@gazettenews.com, Pres./Pub., The Gazette, OH, Jefferson
bcreed@gazettenews.com, Adv. Mgr., The Valley News, OH, Andover
bcreed@gazettenews.com, Pres./Pub., The Courier, OH, Jefferson

Creel, Jean
jcreel@colopress.net, Office Man., Colorado Press Association, CO, Denver

Creer, J.D.
jdcreer@salemnews.net, Mng. Ed., Salem News, OH, Salem

Crees, Jim.............................(231) 592-8360
editor@pioneergroup.com, Ed., The Pioneer - Big Rapids, MI, Big Rapids

Crees, Jim
jcrees@pioneergroup.com, Ed., Herald Review, MI, Big Rapids

Cregar, Heather......................(302) 741-8210
hcregar@newszap.com, Promo. Mgr., Delaware State News, DE, Dover
hcregar@newszap.com, Promotions Manager, Dorchester Banner, MD, Cambridge
hcregar@newszap.com, Promotions Manager, Sussex Post, DE, Milford
hcregar@newszap.com, Adv./Promo Coord., Crisfield-Somerset County Times, MD, Crisfield
hcregar@newszap.com, Promotions Manager, Milford Chronicle, DE, Milford

Creger, Bonita..............(740) 532-1441 Ext. 204
bonita.creger@irontontribune.com, Class. Mktg. Rep. , The Ironton Tribune, OH, Ironton

Creighton, Bill.......................(202) 383-6058
bcreighton@newscom.com, Gen. Mgr., NewsCom, Salt Lake City

Crenshaw, Richard..................(662) 678-0550
richard.crenshaw@journalinc.com, Adv. & Marketing Dir., Northeast Mississippi Daily Journal, MS, Tupelo

Crepeau, Jean.................(819) 445-7000 ext.222
redaction_dr@tc.tc, Ed., Journal L'impact De Drummondville, QC, Drummondville

Creps, Marcela
mcreps@heraldt.com, Arts Ed., The Herald Times, IN, Bloomington

Creskey, Anne Marie
acreskey@hilltimes.com, Pub., The Hill Times, ON, Ottawa

Creskey, Jim.................(613) 232-5952 ext. 207
jcreskey@hilltimes.com, Pub., The Hill Times, ON, Ottawa

Crespi, Dan
information@goval.com, Natl. Accts./Equipment Mgr., Samuel, Son & Co., ON, Burlington

Crespo, Emilio
lisboa@efe.com, Rep., EFE News Services - Lisbon, Portugal, DC, Lisbon

Crespolini, Russ
rcrespolini@newjerseyhills.com, Sports Ed., Suburban News, NJ, New Providence
rcrespolini@newjerseyhills.com, Ed. , The Progress, NJ, Caldwell

Cressman, Dale
cressman@byu.edu, Asst. Prof., Brigham Young University, UT, Provo

Cressman, Mark....................1 (506) 343-3524
cressman.mark@brunswicknews.com, Head of Sales, New Brunswick Telegraph-Journal, NB, Saint John

Cressman, Mark...........(905) 684-7251 ext. 1100
mark.cressman@sunmedia.ca, Pub. , St.

Catharines Standard, ON, Saint Catharine's

Cressman, Michael ....(905) 358-5711 ext. 1111
michael.cressman@sunmedia.ca, Pub.,
Niagara Falls Review, ON, Niagara Falls

Crevier, Guy
gcrevier@lapresse.ca, Pub., La Presse, QC,
Montreal

Crevier, Nancy
editor@thebee.com, Ed., The Newtown Bee,
CT, Newtown

Crews, Doug ....(573) 449-4167
dcrews@socket.net, Exec. Dir., Missouri Press
Association, MO, Columbia
dcrews@socket.net, Exec. Dir., Missouri Press
Service, Inc., MO, Columbia

Cribb, John ....(406) 579-2925
jcribb@cribb.com, Managing Dir., Cribb,
Greene & Cope LLC, MT, Helena

Cribb, John T. ....(406) 586-6621
jcribb@cribb.com, Managing Dir., Cribb,
Greene & Cope, MT, Helena

Cribb, John Thomas ....(406) 570-5595
johnthomas@cribb.com, Associate, Cribb,
Greene & Cope, MT, Helena

Cribb, John Thomas ....(406) 570-5595
johnthomas@cribb.com, Assoc., Cribb, Greene
& Cope LLC, MT, Helena

Cribb, Vince ....(229) 219-0230 ext. 1202
vince.cribb@gaflnews.com, VP Prodn.,
Valdosta Daily Times, GA, Valdosta

Crichton, Howie
editor@review-mirror.com, Ed. , Rideau Valley
Mirror, ON, Westport

Criddle, Dean ....(618) 239-2665
dcriddle@bnd.com, Sports, Belleville News-
Democrat, IL, Belleville

Crider, Robert ....(509) 577-7701
bcrider@yakimaherald.com, Pub, Yakima
Herald-Republic, WA, Yakima

Crim, Don ....(217) 221-3361
dcrim@whig.com, Mng. Ed., The Quincy
Herald-Whig, IL, Quincy

Crimmins, Geoff
photo@dnews.com, Photo Ed., Moscow-
Pullman Daily News, ID, Moscow

Crine, Joe .... (229) 246-2827 x116
news@thepostsearchlight.com, Sports Ed.,
The Post-Searchlight, GA, Bainbridge

Crine, Joe .... (229) 246-2827 ext. 116
joe.crine@thepostsearchlight.com, Sports Ed.,
Post-searchlight Extra, GA, Bainbridge

Crisafulli, Jamie
rrnews@rangerreview.com, Pub., Glendive
Ranger-Review, MT, Glendive

Crisler, Emma F.
reveille@bellsouth.net, Pub./Ed., The Port
Gibson Reveille, MS, Port Gibson

Crisp, Cathy ....(605) 940-4650
cathy@sfshoppingnews.co0m, sales manager,
Sioux Falls Shopping News, SD, Sioux Falls

Crisp, John ....(419) 724-6491
srockwell@toledoblade.com, VP of New Media,
The Blade, OH, Toledo

Crisp, Ken
kcrisp@newswatchman.com, Circ. Mgr., The
Pike County News Watchman, OH, Waverly

Criss, Leslie ....(662) 678-1584
leslie.criss@journalinc.com, Lifestyles Ed.,
Northeast Mississippi Daily Journal, MS,
Tupelo

Crist, Bill ....(325) 573-5486
publisher@snyderdailynews.com, Pub., Snyder
Daily News, TX, Snyder

Criswell, Heidi
heidi@mifflinburgtelegraph.com, Ed.,
Mifflinburg Telegraph, PA, Mifflinburg

Criswell, Jeanne

jcriswell@uindy.edu, Univ. of Indianapolis, IN,
Indianapolis

Critcher, Charles
opl@earthlink.net, Pub., Oxford Public Ledger,
NC, Oxford

Critcher, Ronald
oplronnieadvertising@earthlink.net, Adv. Mgr.,
Oxford Public Ledger, NC, Oxford

Critchlow, David
dgc@ucmessenger.com, Pres./Pub., The
Messenger, TN, Union City

Crittenden, Jules ....(617) 619-6486
jules.crittenden@bostonherald.com, City Ed.,
Boston Herald, MA, Boston

Crivellone, Jim
jimcriv@cgipressparts.com, Pres., Central
Graphics, IL, Romeoville

Crochet, Sandy
jdnaccounting@bellsouth.net, Bookkeeping,
Jennings (LA) Daily News, LA, Jennings

Crockford, Dick ....(406) 683-2331
publisher@dillontribune.com, pUB., Dillon
Tribune, MT, Dillon

Crockwell, Dan ....(660) 327-4192
danielcrockwell@monroecountyappeal.com,
Pub, Monroe County Appeal, MO, Paris

Crockwell, Dan
dcrockwell@yourjournal.com, Circ. Mgr.,
Overland/St. Ann Journal-North Couny
Journal, MO, Hazelwood

Crockwell, Dan ....(314) 556-6403
Circ. Dir., Southwest County Journal, MO, Town
And Country

Crockwell, Dan
dcrockwell@yourjournal.com, Circ Dir, North
Side Journal, MO, Chesterfield

Crockwell, Dan
dcrockwell@yourjournal.com, Circ. Dir.,
Louisiana Press Journal, MO, Town And
Country
dcrockwell@yourjournal.com, Suburban
Journals of Greater St. Louis, MO, Town and
Country

Crockwell, Margie ....(660) 327-4192
margiecrockwell@monroecountyappeal.com,
Ad Design, Monroe County Appeal, MO,
Paris

Crofoot, Art ....(301) 848-0175
acrofoot@chespub.com, Pub, The Calvert
Recorder, MD, Prince Frederick

Croft, Charles ....(251) 434-8620
ccroft@mobileregister.com, Farm/Agriculture
Ed., Press-Register, AL, Mobile

Croft, Margaret ....(318) 362-0308
mcroft@thenewsstar.com, Photography Ed.,
The News-Star, LA, Monroe

Croft, Mary Lou ....(902) 426-1133
mcroft@herald.ca, Dir., Cor. Admin., The
Chronicle Herald, NS, Halifax

Croft, Tim ....(850) 227-7827
tcroft@starfl.com, Ed., The Apalachicola
Carrabelle Times, FL, Apalachicola

Croft, Tim ....(850) 227-7827
tcroft@starfl.com, Ed., The Star, FL, Port
Saint Joe

Crofton, Richard ....(906) 632-2235
richard@sooeveningnews.com, Ed., Sault Ste.
Marie Evening News, MI, Sault Sainte Marie

Crofton, Richard
rcrofton@cheboygantribune.com, Pub.,
Cheboygan Daily Tribune, MI, Cheboygan

Cromeens, Barton ....(325) 670-5221
Ed., Sound of Freedom, TX, Abilene

Cromeens, Barton ....(325) 670-5213
cromeensb@reporternews.com, Ed., Abilene
Reporter-News, TX, Abilene

Crompton, Brett

press1@press-times.com, Pub., Power County
Press, ID, American Falls

Crompton, Dave ....ext. 304
david.crompton@ok.bc.ca, Sports Ed.,
Penticton Herald, BC, Penticton

Crompton, Debbie
press3@press-times.com, Adv. Mgr., Power
County Press, ID, American Falls

Crompton, Kim ....(509) 344-1263
kimc@spokanejournal.com, Ed., Spokane
Journal of Business, WA, Spokane

Cronan, John
john.cronan@kantarmedia.com, Sales Director,
Southwest Region, SRDS, a Kantar Media
Company, IL, Des Plaines

Cronick, Scott ....(609) 272-7017
SCronick@pressofac.com, At The Shore Ed.
/ AC Weekly, The Press of Atlantic City, NJ,
Pleasantville

Cronin, Dan ....(515) 663-6908
dcronin@amestrib.com, Dir., Circ., Story
County Advertiser, IA, Ames

Cronin, Daniel .... (515) 232-2160 ext. 314
dcronin@amestrib.com, Circ. Dir., Iowa
Newspapers, Inc., IA, Ames

Cronin, Dennis ....(402) 444-1482
dennis.cronin@owh.com, Dir., Circulation,
Omaha World-Herald, NE, Omaha

Cronin, Jennifer ....(250) 423-4666
customerservice@thefreepress.ca, Adv, The
Free Press, BC, Fernie

Cronin, Joe ....(412) 263-1907
jcronin@post-gazette.com, Special Projects &
Senior IT Manager, Pittsburgh Post-Gazette,
PA, Clinton

Cronin, Steve ....(609) 272-7242
scronin@pressofac.com, Local Content
Producer/Features, The Press of Atlantic
City, NJ, Pleasantville

Cronk, Alan ....(336) 727-7406
acronk@wsjournal.com, Bus. Mgr., Spotlight,
Winston Salem

Cronk, Alan ....(336) 727-7406
Exec. Ed., Star Watch, Winston Salem

Cronk, Alan ....(336) 727-7339
acronk@wsjournal.com, Features Editor,
Travel, Winston-Salem Journal, NC, Winston
Salem

Cronk, Dale .... ext. 2388
dcronk@wdt.net, Prod. Mgr., Watertown Daily
Times, NY, Watertown

Cronk, Donna ....(765) 575-4657
dcronk@thecouriertimes.com, Neighbors Ed.,
The Courier-Times, IN, New Castle

Cronk, Dorothy ....(712) 868-3460
Editor, Armstrong Journal, IA, Armstrong

Cronk, Ryan .... (805) 466-2585 x113
news@pasoroblespress.com, Ed., Atascadero
News, CA, Atascadero
news@pasoroblespress.com, Ed., Paso Robles
Press, CA, Paso Robles

Cronsell, Carole
ccronsell@catholictranscript.org, Business
Manager, The Catholic Transcript, CT,
Bloomfield

Crook, David ....(212) 416-3375
david.crook@dowjones.com, Ed., The Wall
Street Journal Sunday, New York

Crook, Jordan
chronicle@dtnspeed.net, Reporter, The Extra,
IL, Hoopeston

Croom, Brenna ....(713) 280-2490
Brenna.Croom@houstonpress.com, Marketing
Director, Houston Press, TX, Houston

Croom, Larry ....(352) 753-1119
larry.croom@thevillagesmedia.com,
Ombudsman, The Villages Daily Sun, FL,
The Villages

Croom, Marvin
mcroom@chestercountyindependent.com,
Adv. Dir., Chester County Independent, TN,
Henderson

Croomes, Rebecca
rebecca@athensnews-courier.com, Lifestyles
Reporter, The News-Courier, AL, Athens

Cropley, Dan ....(610) 266-7069
aftermarket@mullermartinims.com, After
Market Sales/Services Manager, Muller
Martini Mailroom Systems, Inc., PA,
Allentown

Crosbie, Patrice
patricec@thechronicle.com , Pub., The
Chronicle, CT, Willimantic

Crosby, Bruce .... (308) 345-4500 ext 120
editor@mccookgazette.com, Ed., McCook
Daily Gazette, NE, Mc Cook

Crosby, Cherrill
ccrosby@statesmanjournal.com, Ed, Appeal
Tribune, OR, Salem
ccrosby@statesmanjournal.com, Ed, Stayton
Mail, OR, Salem
ccrosby@statesmanjournal.com, Sr. Dir., The
Arizona Republic, AZ, Phoenix

Crosby, Edward
therecord@odessaoffice.com, Co-Pub., The
Odessa Record, WA, Odessa

Crosby, Sarah ....(413) 585-5258
scrosby@gazettenet.com, Photographer , Daily
Hampshire Gazette, MA, Northampton

Crosby, Tom .... (785) 823-6363 Ext. 319
tcrosby@salina.com, Ops Mgr., The Salina
Journal, KS, Salina

Crosier, David ....(540) 962-2121
Online Mgr., Virginian Review, VA, Covington

Crosman, Penny ....(212) 803-8673
penny.crosman@sourcemedia.com, Ed.,
Technology, American Banker, NY, New York

Cross, Al
al.cross@uky.edu, Asst. Prof., University of
Kentucky, KY, Lexington

Cross, Cynthia
cynthia.cross@news-jrnl.com, Retail Adv. Mgr.,
Daytona Beach News-Journal, FL, Daytona
Beach

Cross, Danny
dcross@citybeat.com, Editor, Cincinnati
Citybeat, OH, Cincinnati

Cross, Jason ....(408) 920-5399
jcross@adtaxinetworks.com, Sr. VP/Digital
Adv., The Mercury News, CA, San Jose

Cross, John
john.cross@mnsu.edu, Adj. Fac., Minnesota
State University Mankato, MN, Mankato

Cross, Josh ....(615) 575-7115
jcross@mtcngroup.com, Gen. Mgr., Gallatin
News Examiner, TN, Gallatin

Cross, Leslie
crossl@lincolnu.edu, Part-time Fac., Lincoln
University, MO, Jefferson City

Cross, Nancy
class@bbherald.com , Adv. Mgr., New Lenox
Community Reporter, IL, Peotone
class@bbherald.com , Adv. Sales, The Herald/
Country Market, IL, Bourbonnais

Cross, Pete ....(561) 820-4466
pcross@pbpost.com, Asst. Mng. Ed., Photo,
The Palm Beach Post, FL, West Palm Beach

Cross, Stewart ....(770) 795-9195
stewart.cross@zane.com, Pres./COO, Zane
Publishing, Inc., GA, Woodstock

Cross, Sue
scross@ap.org, Reg'l Vice Pres. Newyork,
Associated Press/California-Nevada News
Executives, CA, Los Angeles

Cross, Tom ....(505) 986-3006
tcross@sfnewmexican.com, Pub., The Santa

Fe New Mexican, NM, Santa Fe

Crossley, Gay Lynn ....(317) 955-6397
Marian College, IN, Indianapolis

Crosten, Jason .... (330) 376-0917 ext. 202
jason@akronlegalnews.com, Gen. Mngr.,
Akron Legal News, OH, Akron

Crosthwaite, Fred.....................(530) 896-7751
fcrosthwaite@chicoer.com, Adv. Dir., Oroville
Mercury - Register, CA, Oroville
fcrosthwaite@chicoer.com, Adv. Dir., Chico
Enterprise-Record, CA, Chico

Croston, Stephanie
scinews@sewardindependent.com, Ed.,
Seward County Independent, NE, Seward

Croteau, Brian.........................(207) 689-2909
bcroteau@sunjournal.com, Acc. Exec., Sun
Journal, ME, Lewiston

Croteau, Maureen
maureen.croteau@uconn.edu, Prof./Head,
University of Connecticut, CT, Storrs

Crouch, William.........................(931) 552-1160
ads@e-peddler.com, Adv. Mgr., Peddler, TN,
Clarksville

Crouse, Katelyn ....(252) 328-9249
editor@theeastcarolinian.com, The East
Carolinian, NC, Greenville

Crouse-Dick, Christine ....(316) 284-5271
cecrouse-dick@bethelks.edu, Advisor, Bethel
College, KS, North Newton

Crovitz, Gordon
gordon.crovitz@wsj.com, Co-Founder, Press+,
NY, New York

Crow, Cecilia ....(706) 290-5220
CCrow@rn-t.com, Adv. Dir., Rome News-
Tribune, GA, Rome

Crow, Deserai
deserai.crow@colorado.edu, Asst. Prof./Assoc.
Dir., Ctr. for Environmental Journalism,
University of Colorado, CO, Boulder

Crow, Dianna
realestate@times-standard.com, Pub., On The
Market, CA, Eureka

Crowe, Craig
ccrowe@uh.edu, Clinical Asst. Prof., University
of Houston, TX, Houston

Crowe, J.D. ....(251) 219-5676
jdcrowe@al.com, Statewide Editorial
Cartoonist, AL.com & Alabama Media Group,
J.D. Crowe, Fairhope

Crowe, Joy G.
kvnews@kidsvillenews.com, Associate Pub.,
Up & Coming Weekly, NC, Fayetteville

Crowe, Richard L. ....(610) 915-2223
rcrowe@21st-centurymedia.com, Pub./Adv.
Dir., County Press, PA, Swarthmore
rcrowe@21st-centurymedia.com, Pub./Adv.
Mgr., News of Delaware County, Town Talk,
Garnet Valley Press, Springfield Press,
County PRess, PA, Swarthmore
rcrowe@21st-centurymedia.com, Adv. Mgr.,
Haverford Press, PA, Newtown Square
rcrowe@21st-centurymedia.com, Pub., Upper
Darby and Drexel Hill Press, PA, Newtown
Square
rcrowe@21st-centurymedia.com, Adv.
Mgr. , Delaware County Daily Times, PA,
Swarthmore
rcrowe@21st-centurymedia.com, Adv Mgr.,
Garnet Valley Press, PA, Swarthmore
rcrowe@21st-centurymedia.com, Adv. Mgr.,
Springfield Press, PA, Swarthmore
rcrowe@21st-centurymedia.com, Adv. Mgr.,
Town Talk Newspapers, PA, Swarthmore

Crowfoot, Simon
sales@iceni.com, Dir., Iceni Technology,
Norwich

Crowley, Andrea ....(515) 284-8228
acrowley@dmreg.com, Comm. Content
Specialist- Juice, The Des Moines Register,
IA, Des Moines

Crowley, Dan ....(413) 585-5239
dcrowley@gazettenet.com, Managing Ed. ,
Daily Hampshire Gazette, MA, Northampton

Crowley, Jean
records@arkcity.net, Society Ed., The
Arkansas City Traveler, KS, Arkansas City

Crowley, Moira
mcrowley@cheesereporter.com, Asst. Ed., The
Cheese Reporter, WI, Madison

Crowley, Peter.........................(518) 891-2600
pcrowley@adirondackdailyenterprise.com,
Mng. Ed. , Adirondack Daily Enterprise, NY,
Saranac Lake

Crown, Rosemond
rcrown8@stedwards.edu, Online EIC, St.
Edwards Univ., TX, Austin

Crowther-Barnes, Wendy .... (352) 753-1119
wendy.crowther-barnes@thevillagesmedia.
com, Customer Service Manager, The
Villages Daily Sun, FL, The Villages

Cruce, Joyce
joyce_cruce@link.freedom.com, HR Dir.,
Cannon Connection, NM, Clovis

Cruce, Joyce...........................(575) 763-3431
jcruce@cnjonline.com, Hum. Res. Dir., Eastern
New Mexico News, NM, Clovis

Cruden, Alex..........................(313) 223-4702
cruden@freepress.com, Copy Desk Chief,
Detroit Free Press, MI, Detroit

Cruger, Jack
theclintontopper@aol.com, Pub., The Clinton
Topper, WI, Clinton

Cruger, Jack
elkinde@elkhornindependent.com, Pub., The
Elkhorn Independent, WI, Elkhorn

Cruger, John
SLN@StandardPress.com, Pres./COO,
Southern Lakes Newspapers LLC, WI,
Burlington

Cruger, Peter
sln@StandardPress.com, Pub., Southern
Lakes Newspapers LLC, WI, Burlington

Cruger, Peter
info@rvpublishing.com, Pub., The Herald, IL,
Rockton

Cruickshank, John ....(416) 869-4775
jcruickshank@thestar.ca, Pub., Toronto Star,
ON, Toronto
jcruickshank@thestar.ca, Ed., The Northfield
News, VT, Northfield

Cruikshank, L. Alan
alan@fhtimes.com, Pub., The Fountain Hill
Times, AZ, Fountain Hills
alan@fhtimes.com, Pub., Let's Go, AZ,
Fountain Hills

Crum, Becky
info@bigsandynews.com, Adv. Mgr., The Big
Sandy News, KY, Louisa

Crum, Lynn............................(423) 623-6171
lynn.crum@newportplaintalk.com, District
Manager Circulation, The Newport Plain Talk,
TN, Newport

Crumb, Michael
mcrumb@amestrib.com, Managing Ed., Ames
Tribune, IA, Ames

Crumbaker, Richard ....(410) 968-1188
rcrumbacker@newszap.com, Ed./Gen Mgr.
, Crisfield-Somerset County Times, MD,
Crisfield

Crumbaugh, Lee
leepublish@aol.com, Pres., Forrest Consulting,
IL, Glen Ellyn

Crump, Stewart ....(306) 463-4611
Owner/publisher, The Rosetown Eagle, SK,
Rosetown

Crump, Stewart
editor.jamac@gmail.com, Pub., Kindersley
Clarion, SK, Kindersley

Crump, Stewart
eastonpress@sasktel.net, Pub., Eston-elrose
Press Review, SK, Eston

Crump, Stewart
jamacpublishing@sk.sympatico.ca, Pub., West
Central Crossroads, SK, Kindersley

Crump, Stewart
editor.jamac@gmail.com, Pub., Leader News,
SK, Kindersley

Crumpton, Kathy ....(434) 822-1800
Kathy@piedmontshopper.com, Pub., Piedmont
Shopper, VA, Danville

Crumrine, J.P.
jp@towncrier.com, Ed., Idyllwild Town Crier,
CA, Idyllwild

Crutchfield, Aaron ....(831) 385-4880
editor@southcountynewspapers.com, Ed.,
Soledad Bee, CA, King City

Crutchfield, Lisa
rpmeditor@richmondpublishing.com, Ed, Fifty
Plus, VA, Richmond

Cruz, Debra Renee....................(215) 849-9016
fashionnnb@aol.com, Fashion/Beauty/
Lifestyles Ed., National News Bureau,
Philadelphia

Cruz, Jose
jacruz@pww.org, Ed., Nuestro Mundo, NY,
New York

Cruz, Manny
manny@sandiegometro.com, Mng. Ed.,
Uptown San Diego Examiner, CA, San Diego

Cruz, Mike ....(909) 386-3880
mcruz@scng.com, City Editor, Inland Valley
Daily Bulletin, CA, Rancho Cucamonga

Cruzan, John
jcruzan@joplin.k12.mo.us, Online Mgr., The
Joplin Globe, MO, Joplin

Cryder, Chris
ccryder@daily-jeff.com, Cir. Dir., The Daily
Jeffersonian, OH, Cambridge

Cryder, Chris
ccryder@daily-jeff.com, Circ. Mgr., Jeffersonian
Advantage, OH, Cambridge

Crytzer, Barry W. ....(724) 543-6290
barryc16201@yahoo.com, Pub., Horse Trader,
PA, Kittanning

Cseke, Bianca .... N/A
chief.freepress@unlv.edu, Editor-in-Chief,
University of Nevada, Las Vegas, NV, Las
Vegas

Cseke, Bianca
chief.freepress@unlv.edu, Editor-in-Chief,
University of Nevada, Las Vegas, NV, Las
Vegas

Csukas, Diane
dcsukas@evansville-diocese.org, Sales
and Office Coordinator, The Message, IN,
Evansville

Cuaresma, Kea
kcuaresma@alaskadispatch.com, Advertising
Operations Director, Alaska Dispatch News,
AK, Anchorage

Cubbal, Kayleen ....ext. 617
Sports Ed., New Castle News, PA, New Castle

Cube, Christine
christine.cube@prnewswire.com, Audience
Relations Manager, PR Newswire, NY, New
York

Cubitt, Babette
bcubitt@prescottaz.com, Adv. Dir., Chino Valley
Review, AZ, Chino Valley
bcubitt@prescottaz.com, Adv. Dir., Prescott
Valley Tribune, AZ, Chino Valley
bcubitt@prescottaz.com, Adv./Graphics Dir.,
The Daily Courier, AZ, Prescott

Cuccoli, Rosarita
rcuccoli@press-iasn.org, Sec. Gen.,
International Association of Sports

Newspapers (IASN), Paris

Cucore, Addie
ahowell@jrpress.com, Composing Mgr.,
Journal Review, IN, Crawfordsville

Cuddihy, Dave ....(910) 343-2321
dave.cuddihy@starnewsonline.com, Adv. Dir.,
StarNews, NC, Wilmington

Cuddy, Bruce
bcuddy@gulfcoastnewspapers.com, Adv. Mgr.,
The Baldwin Times Independent, AL, Foley

Cuddy, Jim
jcuddy@tribweb.com, Mng. Ed., South Hills
Record, PA, Pittsburgh
jcuddy@tribweb.com, Mng. Ed., North Journal,
PA, Monroeville
jcuddy@tribweb.com, Mng. Ed., The Times
Express, PA, Pittsburgh

Cuddy Jr., Jim ....(412) 320-7830
jcuddy@tribweb.com, Managing Ed., Tribune-
Review, PA, Greensburg

Cuellar, Lori
lcuellar@kspress.com, Accountant, Kansas
Press Association, KS, Topeka

Cuenca, Nicolas.......................(617) 888-8939
Adv. Mgr., La Semana, MA, Boston

Cuenca, Peter N. ....(617) 541-2222
wcea2000@aol.com, Ed., La Semana, MA,
Boston

Cueto, Ruben ....(954) 752-7474
rcueto@tribune.com, Ed., The Forum - Sunrise
& Tamarac, FL, Davie

Cueto, Ruben ....(954) 752-7474
rcueto@tribune.com, Mng. Ed., The Forum -
Sunrise & Tamarac, FL, Davie

Cueva, Alma ....(479) 530-9313
acueva@nwaonline.com, Acct. Exec., La
Prensa Libre, AR, Fayetteville

Cuevas, Ernesto ....(617) 779-3789
ECuevas@pilotcatholicnews.com, Bus. Mgr.,
The Pilot, MA, Braintree

Cuevas, Jason ....(608) 847-7341
jcuevas@wiscnews.com, Weeklies Lead, Sauk
Prairie Eagle, WI, Baraboo

Cuevas, Jason ....(608) 547-3062
jcuevas@capitalnewspapers.com, Ed., Juneau
County Star-Times, WI, Mauston

Cuillier, David
cuillier@email.arizona.edu, Asst. Prof.,
University of Arizona, AZ, Tucson

Culbertson, Don
donc@standard-democrat.com, CEO, Standard
Democrat, MO, Sikeston

Culbertson, Kay
k.culbertson@mountvernonnews.com, Pub.,
Shopper's Mart, OH, Mount Vernon

Culbertson, Kay H.
kculbertson@mountvernonnews.com, Pub.,
Mount Vernon News, OH, Mount Vernon

Culian, Grigore L.
nymagazin@aol.com, Ed., New York Magazin,
NY, Middle Village

Cull, Jeffrey
jcull@floridaweekly.com, VP and Exec. Ed.,
Bonita Springs Florida Weekly, FL, Naples
jcull@floridaweekly.com, Ed., Fort Myers
Florida Weekly, FL, Fort Myers
jcull@floridaweekly.com, VP and Exec. Ed.,
Naples Florida Weekly, FL, Naples
jcull@floridaweekly.com, VP and Exec. Ed.,
Palm Beach Gardens Florida Weekly, FL,
Palm Beach Gardens
jcull@floridaweekly.com, VP and Exec. Ed.,
Punta Gorda/Port Charlotte Florida Weekly,
FL, Punta Gorda

Cull, Robin................. (812) 265-3641, ext. 238
rcull@madisoncourier.com, New Media Dir.,
Madison Courier, Inc., IN, Madison

Cullen, Jackie ....(608) 822-3262

Southwest Wisconsin Tech. College, WI, Fennimore

Cullen, John .... (712) 732-4991
news@stormlake.com, Publisher, The Storm Lake Times, IA, Storm Lake

Cullen, Kevin
kcullen@dol-in.org, Ed., The Catholic Moment, IN, Lafayette

Cullen, Laurie
lcullen@dol-in.org, Mng. Ed., The Catholic Moment, IN, Lafayette

Culley, Sara .... (831) 438-8408
sara.culley@sourcemedia.com, Adv., West, American Banker, NY, New York

Cullinan, Tom .... (559) 441-6060
tcullinan@fresnobee.com, Pres./Pub., The Fresno Bee, CA, Fresno
tcullinan@fresnobee.com, Pub./Pres., The Clovis Independent, CA, Fresno

Cullinan, Tom .... (559) 441-6060
tcullinan@thetribunenews.com, President / Publisher, The Tribune, CA, San Luis Obispo

Cullis, Christopher
cullis123@gmail.com, Chrmn./Pres./Pub., The Bryan Times, OH, Bryan

Cullis, Christopher .... (419) 636-1111
christopher@bryantimes.com, Pres./Pub., Northwest Signal, OH, Napoleon

Culp, Brian .... (765) 342-3311 ext. 215
bculp@reporttert.com, Mng. Ed., The Reporter Times, IN, Martinsville

Culver, Cathy
forestpress1@yahoo.com, Ed., Forest Press, PA, Tionesta

Culver, Roger
mtnnews@nntcwireless.com, Ed., San Miguel Basin Forum, CO, Nucla

Cumby, Alison
acumby@communitypress.com, Adv. Mgr., Community Journal Clermont, OH, Cincinnati
acumby@communitypress.com, Adv. Mgr., Northeast Suburban Life, OH, Loveland
acumby@communitypress.com, Adv. Mgr., Milford-Miami Advertiser, OH, Cincinnati
acumby@communitypress.com, Adv. Mgr., Bethel Journal, OH, Loveland
acumby@communitypress.com, Adv. Mgr., Eastern Hills Journal, OH, Cincinnati
acumby@communitypress.com, Adv. Mgr., Forest Hills Journal, OH, Cincinnati
acumby@communitypress.com, Adv. Mgr., Indian Hill Journal, OH, Loveland
acumby@communitypress.com, Adv. Mgr., Loveland Herald, OH, Loveland
acumby@communitypress.com, Adv. Mgr., Tri-County Press, OH, Cincinnati

Cumiskey, Gail .... (904) 819-3518
gail.cumiskey@staugustinerecord.com, Special Projects Dir., The St. Augustine Record, FL, Saint Augustine

Cumming, Don
dcumming@fortfrances.com, Prodn. Mgr., Fort Frances Daily Times, ON, Fort Frances

Cumming, Don
dcumming@fortfrances.com, Prod. Mgr., Fort Frances Times, ON, Fort Frances

Cumming, Doug
dcumming@wlu.edu, Asst. Prof., Washington and Lee University, VA, Lexington

Cumming, James R.
jcumming@fortfrances.com, Pub., Fort Frances Daily Times, ON, Fort Frances

Cumming, James R.
jcumming@fortfrances.com, Pub., Fort Frances Times, ON, Fort Frances

Cummings, Barbara .... (304) 824-5101
Adv. Mgr., The Lincoln Journal, WV, Hamlin

Cummings, Bill .... ext. 381
wcummings@heraldandtribune.com, Adv. Sales Mgr., Johnson City Press, TN, Johnson

City

Cummings, Kelly
kelly@sharonherald.com, Controller, The Herald, PA, Sharon

Cummings, Norm .... (860) 355-7323
ncummings@newmilford.com, Ed., New Milford Spectrum, CT, New Milford

Cummins, Glenn
glenn.cummins@ttu.edu, Asst. Prof., Texas Tech University, TX, Lubbock

Cummins, Gregg ....ext. 120
gcummins@robdailynews.com, Prodn. Foreman, Press, Daily News, IL, Robinson

Cummins, Kandy .... (928) 753-6397
KCUMMINS@KINGMANDAILYMINER.COM, Circ. Dir., Kingman Daily Miner, AZ, Kingman

Cummins, Michelle
advertising@malvern-online.com, Adv. Dir., Malvern Daily Record, AR, Malvern

Cunniff, Michael .... (617) 697-6704
Editor-in-Chief, St. John's University, NY, Jamaica

Cunniff, Peggy
pcunniff@pioneerlocal.com, Adv. Dir., Winnetka Talk, IL, Chicago

Cunningham, Alyson
acunningh@dmg.gannett.com, Beachcomber Ed., Beachcomber, DE, Bethany Beach
acunningh@dmg.gannett.com, Ed., Delaware Coast Press, DE, Bethany Beach
acunningh@dmg.gannett.com, Ed., The Delaware Wave, DE, Bethany Beach

Cunningham, Ben .... (256) 235-3541
bcunningham@annistonstar.com, Mng. Ed., The Anniston Star, AL, Anniston

Cunningham, Bill
sjdailycourier@sbcglobal.net, Pres./Pub., St. Joseph Daily Courier, MO, Saint Joseph

Cunningham, Craig .... (304) 348-1234
craigcunningham@dailymail.com, Chief Photographer, The Charleston Gazette-Mail, WV, Charleston

Cunningham, Cynthia
ccunningham@kentuckynewera.com, Classified Adv. Sales, Kentucky New Era, KY, Hopkinsville

Cunningham, Douglas .... (845) 265-2468
doug@pcnr.com, Pub. & Editor-in-Chief, The Putnam County Courier, NY, Cold Spring

Cunningham, Douglas .... (845) 265-2468
doug@pcnr.com, Pub, Putnam County News & Recorder, NY, Cold Spring

Cunningham, James .... (201) 347-9200 X5402
Publishers Circulation Fulfillment Inc., NY, Farmingdale

Cunningham, Jerry
jerry@outfrontonline.com, Pub., Out Front, CO, Denver

Cunningham, Joseph
sports@vermiliontoday.com, Sports Ed., Abbeville Meridional, LA, Abbeville

Cunningham, Julie
jcunningham@theblacksheartimes.com, Production Layout, The Blackshear Times, GA, Blackshear

Cunningham, Laura .... (561) 820-4939
lcunningham@pbpost.com, Dir., Mktg. Servs., The Palm Beach Post, FL, West Palm Beach

Cunningham, Lawrence
Lawrence.cunningham@iowastatedaily.com, General Manager of the Iowa State Daily Media Group, Iowa State University, IA, Ames

Cunningham, Linda Grist .... (815) 987-1355
lgrist@rockford.gannett.com, Exec. Ed., The Star Shopper, IL, Rockford

Cunningham, Lisa ....ext. 193
lcunning@steelcitymedia.com, Art Dir.,

Pittsburgh City Paper, PA, Pittsburgh

Cunningham, Rusty
rusty.cunningham@lee.net, Pub., La Crosse Foxxy Shopper, WI, La Crosse
rusty.cunningham@lee.net, Pub., Tri-county Foxxy Shopper, WI, La Crosse

Cunnison, Jennifer .... (757) 345-2399
jcunnison@dailypress.com, Advertising Manager, The Virginia Gazette, VA, Newport News

Cupertino, Diann
dcupertino@thecitizen.com, Major Accts. Mgr., The Citizen, GA, Fayetteville

Cupid, Jamila .... (717) 477-1521
Asst. Prof./public relations, Shippensburg University/Communication/Journalism Department , PA, Shippensburg

Cupo, Al .... (215) 256-6801
al.cupo@localmedia.org, Vice President - Director of R & D Services, Local Media Association, MI, Lake City

Cupp, Jasmine
editor@thebeacon.net, Ed., The Beacon, OH, Port Clinton

Curan, Tina
circulation@themonroetimes.com, Circulation Manager, The Monroe Times, WI, Monroe

Curbelo, Carlos .... (305) 346-6647
ccurbelo@alm.com, Director of Advertising, Miami Daily Business Review, FL, Miami

Curbelo, Carlos .... (305) 347-6647
ccurbelo@alm.com, Director of Advertising, Palm Beach Daily Business Review, FL, Miami

Curcuru, Nick .... (978) 675-2712
ncurcuru@gloucestertimes.com, Sports Ed., Gloucester Daily Times, MA, Gloucester

Curd, Bobbie .... (859) 236-2551 Ext. 133
bcurd@amnews.com, The Advocate-Messenger, KY, Danville

Curet, Monique .... (251) 434-8604
wrabb@mobileregister.com, Health/Medical Reporter, Press-Register, AL, Mobile

Curl, Glenda .... (334) 682-4422
progressiveera@mchsi.com, Editor/Publisher, Wilcox Progressive Era, AL, Camden

Curling, Greg .... (305) 376-2056
GCurling@miamiherald.com, CFO & VP of Finance, Miami Herald, FL, Doral
GCurling@miamiherald.com, Vice Pres., Finance/CFO, Herald Values, FL, Miami

Curnane, Joseph A.
everettleader@comcast.net, Pub., Everett Leader Herald News Gazette, MA, Everett

Curnock, Kevin 1 (506) 645-3285
curnock.kevin@brunswicknews.com, General Manager, New Brunswick Telegraph-Journal, NB, Saint John

Curran, Gary .... (860) 801-5073
gcurran@newbritainherald.com, Adv. Mgr. , The Bristol Press, CT, Bristol
gcurran@newbritainherald.com, Adv. Mgr. , New Britain Herald, CT, New Britain

Curran, Gary .... (860) 225-4601 ext 281
gcurran@centralctcommunications.com, Ad. Manager, Wethersfield Post (OOB), CT, New Britain
gcurran@centralctcommunications.com, Adv. Mgr., Valley News, CT, New Haven
gcurran@centralctcommunications.com, Ad. Manger, Newington Town Crier, CT, New Britain
gcurran@centralctcommunications.com, Ad. Manger, Rocky Hill Post (OOB), CT, New Britain

Curran, Sean
sean.curran@catalystpaper.com, SVP Sales & Marketing, Catalyst Paper (USA), Inc., WA, Seattle

Curran, Tom .... (973) 392-4003

tcurran@starledger.com, Assoc. Ed., The Star-Ledger, NJ, Newark

Currie, Don
currie@statesman.org, Bus./Finance Ed., Statesman Journal, OR, Salem

Currie, Keith .... (250) 334-4722
keith.currie@comoxvalleyecho.com, Publisher, Comox Valley Echo, BC, Courtenay

Currie, Rod
rod.currie@sunmedia.ca, Circ. Mgr., The Post, ON, Hanover

Currier, Craig .... (231) 439-9358
Asst. Ed. , Petoskey News-Review, MI, Petoskey

Currim, Luke .... (818) 237-6467
lcurrim@colgate.edu, Ed., Colgate Univ., NY, Hamilton

Currim, Saboohi
editor@southcoasteditorcom, Ed., South Coast Editor, CA, Irvine

Curry, Betsy .... (978) 946-2231
bcurry@eagletribune.com, Community News Ed., The Eagle-Tribune, MA, North Andover

Curry, Carrie .... (859) 624-6695
ccurry@richmondregister.com, Features Ed., The Richmond Register, KY, Richmond

Curry, Greg .... (334) 737-2502
gcurry@oanow.com, Creative Serv Mgr, Opelika-Auburn News, AL, Opelika

Curry, Jennifer
jcurry@bizjournals.com, Mng. Ed., Pittsburgh Business Times, PA, Pittsburgh

Curry, John .... (706) 208-2265
john.curry@onlineathens.com, Photo Dir., Athens Banner-Herald, GA, Athens

Curry, Travis
travis@spencereveningworld.com, Sports Ed., Panola Shopper, TX, Carthage
travis@spencereveningworld.com, Editor, The Ellettsville Journal, IN, Ellettsville
travis@spencereveningworld.com, Ed., The Owen Leader (OOB), IN, Spencer

Curtin, Caitlin
info@luminare.com, Pres., Luminare, CA, San Francisco

Curtin, Jack .... (407) 420-5270
jcurtin@orlandosentinel.com, Adv. Sr. Mgr., Delivery, Orlando Sentinel, FL, Orlando

Curtin, Josh .... (229) 931-2035
Georgia Southwestern State Univ., GA, Americus

Curtin, Mike .... (413) 302-2628
mcurtin@masslive.com, Sales Mgr., Worcester, The Republican, MA, Springfield

Curtis, Andy ....ext. 691
Prodn. Mgr., Bldg., The Jackson Sun, TN, Jackson

Curtis, Charlotte
frontdesk@wetmountaintribune.com, Graphic Dsgnr., Wet Mountain Tribune, CO, Westcliffe

Curtis, Dean .... (417) 836-1182
dcurtis@news-leader.com, Photo Ed., Springfield News-Leader, MO, Springfield

Curtis, Harry L.
hcurtis@mpival.com, Pres., Management Planning, Inc., NJ, Princeton

Curtis, Harry.L
hcurtis@mpival.com, Gen. Mgr., Management Planning, Inc., CT, Simsbury

Curtis, Jane
jcurtis@messengernews.net, Editor, The Messenger, IA, Fort Dodge

Curtis, Jasper .... (903) 596-6200
Adv. Mgr., Ops., Tyler Morning Telegraph, TX, Tyler

Curtis, John .... (217) 774-2161 ext.262
john.curtis@shelbyvilledailyunion.com, Sports

Editor, Dodge City Daily Globe, KS, Dodge City
john.curtis@shelbyvilledailyunion.com, Sports Ed., Daily Union, IL, Shelbyville

Curtis, Kyle
kcurtis@triplicate.com, Operations Manager , The Del Norte Triplicate, CA, Crescent City

Curtis, Kyle .... (707) 464-2141
kcurtis@triplicate.com, Ops. Mgr., The Del Norte Triplicate, CA, Crescent City

Curtis, Lisa
lcurtis@conleynet.com, Mng. Ed., News Graphic, WI, Cedarburg

Curtis, Opal .... (540) 374-5471
ocurtis@freelancestar.com, Classified Call Ctr. Sales Mgr., The Free Lance-Star, VA, Fredericksburg

Curtis, Penni .... (505) 564-4605
pcurtis@daily-times.com, Admin. Asst., The Daily Times, NM, Farmington

Curtis, Richard
rcurtis@thestate.com, Single Copy Mgr., The State, SC, Columbia

Curtis, Wayne .... (404) 419 - 2801
wcurtis@alm.com, Group Publisher, Fulton County Daily Report, GA, Atlanta
wcurtis@alm.com, Pub., Daily Report, GA, Atlanta

Curtiss, Brook
plainviewnews@nyecom.net, Pub., The Plainview News, NE, Plainview

Curtman, Randal
rcurtman@eldoradonews.com, Managing Ed., El Dorado News-Times / Sunday News, AR, El Dorado

Curtus, Claudine .... (740) 892-2771
uticaherald@earthlink.net, Ed., The Utica Herald, OH, Utica

Cusenza, Michael
michael@theforumnewsgroup.com, Editor-in-Chief, The Forum, NY, Howard Beach

Cushing, Marie
letters@jhunewsletter.com, The Johns Hopkins News-Letter, MD, Baltimore

Cushman, Erik
erik@mcweekly.com, Publisher, Monterey County Weekly, CA, Seaside

Cusick, Corey .... (470) 729-3249
ccusick@times-georgian.com, Sports Editor, West Georgia Weekly, GA, Carrollton

Cusick, Nick .... (563) 262-0533
Sports Editor, Muscatine Journal, IA, Muscatine

Cusick, Noah
Ncusick@PVTimes.com, Publisher, Pahrump Valley Times, NV, Pahrump

Cusick, Noah .... (423) 779-7936
ncusick@bouldercityreview.com, Publisher, Boulder City Review, NV, Boulder City

Cusimano, Leo .... ext. 114
cusimano@dallasvoice.com, Adv. Dir., Dallas Voice, TX, Dallas

Cuskey, Thomas C.
tcuskey@scotsmanpress.com, Adv. Mgr., Onondaga Valley News, NY, Syracuse
tcuskey@scotsmanpress.com, Adv. Mgr., Cortland Democrat Sunday (OOB), NY, Syracuse

Cuskey, Thomas C.
tcuskey@scotsmanpress.com, Assoc. Pub., Scotsman Community Publication, NY, Syracuse

Cuskey, Tom
tcuskey@fcpny.com, Sales & Training , Free Community Papers of New York, NY, Syracuse

Cuskey, Tom
tcuskey@fcpny.com, Sales & Training Director,

AdNetworkNY, NY, Syracuse

Custeau, Andre .... (819) 564-5465
andre.custeau@latribune.qc.ca, Nouvelle De Sherbrooke, QC, Sherbrooke
andre.custeau@latribune.qc.ca, Circ. Mgr., La Tribune, QC, Sherbrooke

Cutillo, Michael J. .... (315) 789-3333
mcutillo@fltimes.com, Exec. Ed., Finger Lakes Times, NY, Geneva

Cutler, Andrew .... (541) 963-3161
acutler@lagrandeobserver.com, Ed/Pub, The Observer, OR, La Grande

Cutri, Christopher
chris_cutri@byu.edu, Asst. Prof., Brigham Young University, UT, Provo

Cutright, Eric
eric@barbourdemocratwv.com, Owner, The Barbour Democrat, WV, Philippi

Cutright, Jane
observer@gcctv.com, Ed., The Petersburg Observer, IL, Petersburg

Cutright, Jane
observer@casscomm.com, Pub., Menard County Review, IL, Petersburg

Cutright, Jason .... same
same, The Petersburg Observer, IL, Petersburg

Cutright, Randy
rcutright@timesrepublican.com, Circ. Dir., Times-Republican, IA, Marshalltown

Cutshall, Brian .... (423) 359-3109
brian.cutshall@greenevillesun.com, Dir. Online Opp., The Greeneville Sun, TN, Greeneville

Cutshall, Carol A.
ccutshall@huntingdondailynews.com, Adv. Dir., The Huntingdon Daily News, PA, Huntingdon

Cymbalisty, Vasil
baspress@pathcom.com, Ed., Svitlo, ON, Toronto

Cyr, Eric
journal@diffusionfermont.ca, Ed., Le Trait D'union Du Nord, QC, Fermont

Cyr, Marcia .... (850) 521-1165
mcyr@flpress.com, Membership Coordinator, Florida Society of Newspaper Editors, FL, Tallahassee

Czajka, Mark .... ext. 479
mczajka@ags.com, Dir., New Technology, Automated Graphic Systems, MD, White Plains

Czaplicki, Jeff .... (212) 313-9683
jczaplicki@thefiscaltimes.com, Acct. Mgr., The Fiscal Times, NY, New York

Czaplinski, Kate
huntingtonherald@hersamacorn.com, Ed., The Huntington Herald, CT, Shelton
huntingtonherald@hersamacorn.com, Ed, Shelton Herald, CT, Shelton

Czech, Joe
news@nadignewspapers.com, Circ., Reporter Journal, IL, Chicago

Czoba, Lori
lori.czoba@sunmedia.ca, Sales (online), The Record-gazette, AB, Peace River

D

D'Adamo, Gene .... (602) 444-8078
gene.dadamo@pni.com, Vice Pres., Community Rel., The Arizona Republic, AZ, Phoenix

D'Agostino, John
jdagostino@observertoday.com, Pub., The Observer, NY, Dunkirk

D'Alessandro, Matt
matt@fnanews.com, Photo Bureau Chief, FNA News, Salt Lake City

D'Alessio, Lisa .... (270) 505-1426

ldalessio@thenewsenterprise.com, Business Mgr., The News-Enterprise, KY, Elizabethtown

D'Alessio, Marietta
marietta.dalessio@sunmedia.ca, Classified Mgr. , The Ottawa Sun, ON, Ottawa

D'Alio, Cindy .... (570) 628-6015
Special Sections Ed., The Republican-Herald, PA, Pottsville

D'Ambrosio, Paul .... (732) 643-4261
pdambrosio@gannettnj.com, News & Invest. Dir.
, Asbury Park Press, NJ, Neptune

D'Andrea, Nick .... (718) 281-7251
deignd@nytimes.com, The New York Times, NY, New York

D'Andrea, Niki .... (480) 898-5612
ndandrea@timespublications.com, Executive Editor, Lovin' Life After 50, AZ, Tempe

D'Angelo, Chris .... (610) 371-5215
cdangelo@readingeagle.com, Sr. Director of Production, Reading Eagle, PA, Reading

D'Armour, Mike
editor@lloydminstersource.com, Mng. Ed. , Lloydminster Source, SK, Lloydminster

D'Avignon, Jim .... (903) 534-1077
editorcet@excite.com, Ed., Catholic East Texas, TX, Tyler

D'Eramo, Dan .... (412) 263-1587
dderamo@post-gazette.com, Retail Adv. Mgr. - S.E. Territories, Pittsburgh Post-Gazette, PA, Clinton

D'Onofrio, John .... ext. 6247
Sports Ed., Lockport Union-Sun & Journal, NY, Lockport

D'Orlando, John
jdorlando@orlandosentinel.com, Adv. Vice Pres./Dir., Orlando Sentinel, FL, Orlando

D'Vari, Marisa
mdvari@deg.com, Pres./Writer, Deg Syndication, New York

D'onofrio, Ralph
rdonofrio@cnglocal.com, Vice Pres., Adv., Caribbean Life, NY, Brooklyn
rdonofrio@cnglocal.com, VP, Display Sales, Caribbean Life, NY, Brooklyn
rdonofrio@cnglocal.com, VP, Display Sales, Bay Ridge Courier, NY, Brooklyn

DAWSON, STEPHANIE
Stephanie Dawson <kpistephanie@gmail.com>, AD SALES, The Carlisle County News, KY, Paducah

DaSilva, Lourdes .... (508) 678-3844 ext. 16
editorial@ojornal.com, Mng. Ed., O Jornal, MA, Fall River

Daack, Jessica .... (563) 383-2352
jdaack@qctimes.com, Adv. Sales Mgr, Quad-City Times, IA, Davenport

Daar, Adina .... (904) 620-2727
Univ. of North Florida, FL, Jacksonville

Dabb, Holly P. .... (307) 324-3411
publisher@rocketminer.com, publisher, Rawlins Daily Times, WY, Rawlins

Dabovich, Chris
managingeditor@bensonnews-sun.com, Mng. Ed., San Pedro Valley News-Sun, AZ, Benson

Dadge, David
ipi@freemedia.at, Dir., International Press Institute, Vienna

Daffron, Renee
people@tjrcn.com, Prodn. Mgr., The Times Journal, KY, Russell Springs

Dagostino, Bob .... (216) 870-0904
bdagostino@plaind.com, Prod. Qual Assurance & Commercial Printing Coordinator, The Plain Dealer, OH, Brooklyn

Dahl, David

david_dahl@emerson.edu, Asst. Managing Ed., The Boston Globe, MA, Boston

Dahl, Kristina .... (859) 231-1481
kdahl@herald-leader.com, Commercial Printing Rep., Lexington Herald-Leader, KY, Lexington

Dahl, Kurt
kurtdahl@montenews.com, Montevideo Star Advisor, MN, Montevideo

Dahlberg, Eric .... (775) 316-2265
sparkstribune.eric@gmail.com, Ed., Sparks Tribune, NV, Sparks

Dahlem, Christene
cdahlem@gantdaily.com, Pres., Gant Daily, PA, Clearfield

Dahlia, John .... (304) 329-0090
Editor, The Preston County Journal, WV, Kingwood

Dahlman, Jim .... (423) 461-8995
Milligan College, TN, Milligan College

Dahlman, Ryan .... (403) 528-5769
rdahlman@prairiepost.com, Mng Ed., Prairie Post, AB, Medicine Hat

Dahlman, Simon J. .... (423) 461-8994
sjdahlman@milligan.edu, Chair, Milligan College, TN, Milligan College

Dahlstrom, Katie
kdahlstrom@shawmedia.com, Reporter, Daily Chronicle, IL, Dekalb

Dahm, Lisa
editor@northhawaiinews.net, Mgn. Ed., North Hawaii News, HI, Kamuela

Dahms, Betty
editor@northernsunprint.com, Ed., Northern-Sun Print, IA, Gladbrook

Dahms, Steven P. .... (614) 870-9444 ext. 1001
sdahms@msitarget.com, Vice Pres., Metals Recovery Service, OH, Columbus

Dahms Foster, Heidi .... (928) 445-3333 x 1020
hdfoster@prescottaz.com, Ed., Chino Valley Review, AZ, Chino Valley

Daigle, Cindy
class@newkirkherald.com, Class./Legal Dir., The Newkirk Herald Journal, OK, Newkirk

Daigle, John .... (806) 364-2030
sports@herefordbrand.com, Sports Ed., The Hereford Brand, TX, Hereford

Daigle, Susan
nambooks@comcast.net, Finance Officer, Newspaper Association Managers, Inc., MA, Beverly

Dail, Annette W. .... (919) 736-0447
dailadvertising@bellsouth.net, Nat'l Rep., Dail Advertising Service, NC, Goldsboro

Dailey, Al .... (301) 862-2111
adailey@somdnews.com, Adv. Dir., The Enterprise, MD, California

Dailey, Kelly .... (912) 489-9473
kdailey@statesboroherald.com, Print Adv. Mgr., Statesboro Herald, GA, Statesboro

Dailey, Marc .... (360) 694-2312
marc.dailey@columbian.com, Circ. and Prod. Dir., The Columbian, WA, Vancouver

Dailey, Marc .... (360) 694-3391
marc.dailey@columbian.com, Circ. Dir., The Columbian Alternate Delivery Service, WA, Vancouver

Dailey, Milo .... (605) 892-2528
bcpnews@rapidcityjournal.com, Reporter/Ed, Butte County Post, SD, Rapid City

Daintith, Stephen
stephen.daintith@dowjones.com, Exec. Vice Pres./CFO, Dow Jones & Company, NY, New York

Dakin, Dan .... (905) 732-2411 ext. 247
dan.dakin@sunmedia.ca, Mng. Ed., Welland Tribune, ON, Welland

Dakin, Ted...............................(780) 444-5450
ted.dakin@sunmedia.ca, Asst. Adv. Director
& Distribution, The Edmonton Sun, AB,
Edmonton

Dakin, Ted...............................(780) 444-5450
ted.dakin@sunmedia.ca, Adv. Dir, Edmonton
Examiner, AB, Edmonton

Dal Monte, Richard
newsroom@tricitynews.com, Ed., Tri-city News,
BC, Port Coquitlam

Dale, Jeff................................(203) 354-1050
cdale@thehour.com, News Editor, The Hour,
CT, Norwalk

Dale, Kevin.............................(303) 954-1213
kdale@denverpost.com, News Director, The
Denver Post, CO, Denver

Dalessandro, Joan
janen@trumatch.com, Office Mgr., Stock,
Fund, or ETF, NY, Water Mill

Daley, David
ddaley@ctmirror.org, Pub., The Connecticut
Mirror, CT, Hartford
ddaley@ctmirror.org, Pub., The Connecticut
News Project, Inc., CT, Hartford

Daley, Jim......................(518) 581-2480 x 209
jdaley@saratogapublishing.com, Ad., Saratoga
Today, NY, Saratoga Springs

Daley, Ray
rdaley@tribune.com, Adv. Mgr., Boca Raton
Forum, FL, Fort Lauderdale
rdaley@tribune.com, Adv. Mgr., Plantation/
Davie Forum, FL, Fort Lauderdale
rdaley@tribune.com, Adv. Mgr., Coral Springs
Focus (OOB), FL, Coral Springs
rdaley@tribune.com, Adv. Mgr., Oakland Park
Gazette (OOB), FL, Fort Lauderdale
rdaley@tribune.com, Adv. Mgr., South
Woodham Focus (OOB), FL, Fort Lauderdale
rdaley@tribune.com, Adv. Mgr., Weston
Gazette, FL, Fort Lauderdale
rdaley@tribune.com, Adv. Mgr., Shalom -
Broward, FL, Fort Lauderdale
rdaley@tribune.com, Adv. Mgr., Shalom - Palm
Beach, FL, Fort Lauderdale

Daley, Raymond.......................(954) 425-1730
rdaley@sun-sentinel.com, VP, Adv., South
Florida Sun-Sentinel, FL, Fort Lauderdale

Daley, Yvonne
ydaley@sfsu.edu, Prof., San Francisco State
University, CA, San Francisco

Dalgleish, Jim...............................ext. 219
jdalgleish@heraldpalladium.com, Asst. Local
News Ed., The Herald-Palladium, MI, Saint
Joseph

Dalglish, Lucy A.
rcfp@rcfp.org, Exec. Dir., Reporters Committee
for Freedom of the Press, VA, Arlington

Dall, Caroline
caroline.dall@lee.net, Adv. Rep., The
Plattsmouth Journal, NE, Plattsmouth

Dallas, Ann.............................(203) 789-5645
adallas@nhregister.com, Graphics Ed., New
Haven Register, CT, New Haven

Dallas, Rechelle
rdallas@northaugustastar.com, Account Exec.
Adv., The Star, SC, North Augusta

Dallons, Jon
jon@westernquartz.com, Pres., Western
Quartz Products, Inc., CA, Paso Robles

Dalman, Dennis
editor@thenewsleaders.com, Ed.-in-Chief, The
Newsleaders, MN, SAINT JOSEPH

Dalman, Dennis
editor@thenewsleaders.com, Editor, St. Joseph
Newsleader, MN, Saint Joseph
editor@thenewsleaders.com, Editor, Sartell
Newsleader, MN, Saint Joseph

Dalpiaz, Ryan
advertising@tritownnews.com, Sales and
Office Manager, Tri-Town News, NY, Sidney

Dalton, Dan.............................(909) 793-9890
dan@contentthatworks.com, Vice Pres., Sales,
Content That Works, Chicago

Dalton, Dick
dick@cannonfalls.com, Ed., Cannon Falls
Beacon, MN, Cannon Falls

Dalton, Eric
edalton@justnormlicht.com, Vice President,
Just Normlicht, Inc., PA, Langhorne

Dalton, G. Richard
beacon@cannonfalls.com, Ed., Cannon
Shopper, MN, Cannon Falls

Dalton, G. Richard..................(507) 263-3991
dick@cannonfalls.com, Pub., Cannon Falls
Beacon, MN, Cannon Falls

Dalton, Lisa
ldalton@nodawaynews.com, Adv. Mgr.,
Nodaway News Leader, MO, Maryville

Dalton, Margaret
mdalton@slis.ua.edu, Bristol-EBSCO Prof.,
University of Alabama, AL, Tuscaloosa

Dalton, Richard
alcalam@canoncitydailyrecord.com, Telecom
Mgr., Daily Record, WA, Ellensburg

Dalton, Robert.........................(864) 562-7293
bob.dalton@shj.com, Sports Ed., Herald-
Journal, SC, Spartanburg

Dalton, Tara
tara@gunkjournal.com, Sales & Marketing,
Shawangunk Journal, NY, Ellenville

Dalton, Tina..............................(888) 309-0639
Finance Representative, Miracom Computer
Corp., NY, Eastchester

Daly, Michael...........................(203) 330-6394
mdaly@ctpost.com, Editorial Page Ed.,
Connecticut Post, CT, Bridgeport

Daly, Nancy
ndaly@communitypress.com, Sr. Ed., The
Erlanger Recorder, KY, Fort Mitchell

Daly, Nancy
ndaly@communitypress.com, Sr. Ed., South
Kenton Recorder, KY, Fort Mitchell

Daly, Nancy
ndaly@communitypress.com, Sr. Ed, Union
Recorder, KY, Fort Mitchell

Daly, Nancy
ndaly@communitypress.com, Sr. Ed.,
Campbell County Recorder, KY, Fort Mitchell

Daly, Nancy.............................(859) 578-1059
ndaly@communitypress.com, Sr. Ed., Boone
Community Recorder, KY, Fort Mitchell

Daly, Nancy.............................(859) 578-1059
ndaly@communitypress.com, Community
Recorder Editor, Eastern Hills Journal, OH,
Cincinnati
ndaly@communitypress.com, Ed., Forest Hills
Journal, OH, Cincinnati
ndaly@communitypress.com, Ed., Indian Hill
Journal, OH, Loveland
ndaly@communitypress.com, Ed., Loveland
Herald, OH, Loveland
ndaly@communitypress.com, Ed., Northeast
Suburban Life, OH, Loveland
ndaly@communitypress.com, Ed., Tri-County
Press, OH, Cincinnati

Daly, Nancy
ndaly@communitypress.com, Sr. Ed., Fort
Thomas Recorder, KY, Fort Mitchell

Daly, Tim......................(770) 227 - 3276 x223
tim@griffindailynews.com, Mng. Ed., Griffin
Daily News, GA, Griffin

Daly, Trevor.............................(262) 656-6361
tdaly@kenoshanews.com, IT Manager,
Kenosha News, WI, Kenosha

Damarjian, Diane..........(413) 525-3247 ext. 109
circulation@reminderpublications.com, Circ.
Mgr., The Herald, MA, East Longmeadow

Damhuis, Hank
hank@lissomcorp.com, Lissom Corp. Inc., NY,
Bronxville

Damilano, Ken
kdamilano@recordnet.com, Tech Servs. Mgr.,
The Record, CA, Stockton

Damish, Steven.......................(508) 427-4023
sdamish@enterprisenews.com, Managing Ed.,
The Enterprise, MA, Brockton

Damlo, Chris
cdamlo@mnpubs.com, Gen. Mgr., Southwest
Journal, MN, Minneapolis

Damm, David
dammd@waldorf.edu, Waldorf College, IA,
Forest City

Dana, Stephen.........................(559) 441-6041
stephendana@fresnobee.com, V.P. of Digital
/ Audience development, The Fresno Bee,
CA, Fresno

Danbom, Patti
sciads@sewardindependent.com, Prodn. Mgr.,
Seward County Connection, NE, Seward

Dance, Leslie...........................(847) 523-2226
leslie.dance@motorola.com, Global Dir.,Media
Commun./Pub. Aff., Motorola Mobility, LLC.,
IL, Libertyville

Dancey, Rob
rdancey@shawmedia.com, Adv. Sales, Valley
Life, IL, Dekalb

Dandes, Rick
rdances@dailyitem.com, Reporter, The Daily
Item, PA, Sunbury

Danford, Bruce............(705) 749-3383 ext. 234
bdanford@mykawartha.com, Pub.,
Peterborough This Week, ON, Peterborough

Danford, Bruce
bdanford@mykawartha.com, Pub., Kawartha
Lakes This Week, ON, Lindsay

Danforth, David N.....................(970) 925-2221
ddanforth@aol.com, Owner, Aspen Daily
News, CO, Aspen

Danforth, Mike
mikedanforth@cfo.com, Adv. Sr. Mgr., The
Daily Deal, NY, New York

Daniel, Lori.............................(785) 765-3327
signal@embarqmail.com, Owner / Publisher
/ Editor, The Wabaunsee County Signal-
Enterprise, KS, Alma

Daniel, Richard J.....................(617) 383-2258
Pres., Boston Globe, The New York Times Co.,
NY, New York

Daniel, Ron.............................(470) 336-5224
ron@douglascountysentinel.com, Mng. Ed.,
Douglas County Sentinel, GA, Douglasville

Daniell, Diane.........................(803) 644-2369
ddaniell@aikenstandard.com, Sales and
Special Projects Man., Evening Post
Industries' Aiken Communications, SC, Aiken

Daniels, Ashley.......................(610) 996-9356
danielaj@eckerd.edu, Editor-in-Chief,
The Current - Eckerd College, FL, Saint
Petersburg

Daniels, Barbara
bdaniels@leavenworthtimes.com, Classifieds/
Circ. Dir., The Leavenworth Times, KS,
Leavenworth

Daniels, Carol.........................(931) 245-0213
caroldaniels@theleafchronicle.com, Sales/
Marketing Dir., The Leaf-Chronicle, TN,
Clarksville

Daniels, Cheri
cdaniels@call-post.com, Vice Pres., Opns.,
King Media Enterprises, OH, Columbus

Daniels, Dan...............................ext. 116
ddaniels@jcpgroup.com, Circ. Mgr., Wausau
Buyers Guide, WI, Wausau

Daniels, Doug.........................(618) 542-2133
dqsports@frontier.com, Sports Ed., Du Quoin
Evening Call, IL, Du Quoin

Daniels, Gretchen....................(641) 584-2770
thompsoncourier.rakeregister@gmail.com,
Editor, The Thompson Courier, IA, Thompson

Daniels, Jackie.......................(979) 968-3155
jackie@fayettecountyrecord.com, Classified
Mgr., The Fayette County Record, TX, La
Grange

Daniels, Johnnie.....................(843) 774-3311
jd@thedillonherald.com, Gen. Mgr./Adv. Mgr.,
The Dillon Herald, SC, Dillon

Daniels, Linda
ads@thedailyherald.net, Adv. Sales Mgr., The
Daily Herald, PA, Tyrone

Daniels, Peter.........................(715) 369-3331
pdaniels@mmclocal.com, Pub., Star Journal,
WI, Rhinelander
pdaniels@mmclocal.com, Gen. Mgr., Hodag
Buyer's Guide, WI, Rhinelander

Daniels, Richard J.
RDaniels@courant.com, Chief Operating
Officer, Community Newspaper Co. - South,
MA, Marshfield

Daniels, Rick...........................(781) 433-6720
Regional VP - New England, GateHouse
Media, Inc., NY, Pittsford

Daniels, Stephen......................(707) 526-8589
sandy.mcadler@pressdemocrat.com,
Controller, The Press Democrat, CA, Santa
Rosa

Daniels, Ted...............(419) 281-0581 ext. 211
tdaniels@times-gazette.com, Editor and
General Manager, Ashland Publishing Co.
LLC, OH, Ashland

Daniels, Terry
sales@accjournal.ca, Publisher, The Ashcroft-
cache Creek Journal, BC, Ashcroft

Danielson, Lynn
ldanielson@capitalnewspapers.com, Books
Ed., The Capital Times, WI, Madison

Daniloff, Nicholas
n.daniloff@neu.edu, Prof., Northeastern
University, MA, Boston

Danko, Dennis.........................(877) 658-2424
ddanko@hearst.com, Inside Sales Mgr., King
Features Syndicate, NY, New York
ddanko@hearst.com, Inside Sales Mgr., North
America Syndicate, New York

Dann, Michael...............(618) 253-7146 ext 231
mdann@dailyregister.com, Sports Ed, The
Daily Register, IL, Harrisburg

Danner, Dean W.
webmaster@etcia.com, Pres./CEO, Electronic
Tele-Communications, Inc., WI, Waukesha

Danner, Ed
sentinel@up.net, Pub., L'Anse Sentinel, MI,
Lanse

Danny, Strickland....................(912) 427-3757
drewd01@bellsouth.net, Press mgr., The
Press-Sentinel, GA, Jesup

Dantuono, Phyllis
phyllis.dantuono@businesswire.com, Vice
Pres., New York Reg., Business Wire - New
York, NY, NY, New York

Dao , James.............................(212) 556-1234
dao@nytimes.com, The New York Times, NY,
New York

Dapp, Sharon.........................(570) 584-2134
shopper@elsnonline.com, General Manager,
East Lycoming Shopper, PA, Hughesville

Darch, Melody
melody.darch@coxmediagroup.com, Vice
Pres./CFO, Cox Media Group, GA, Atlanta

Dardarian, Suki
sdardarian@seattletimes.com, Mng. Ed.,
Seattle Post-Intelligencer, WA, Seattle

Dardeau, Genevieve
gdardeau@usouthal.edu, Instr., University of
South Alabama, AL, Mobile

Darden, Sherri ....(267) 357-4456
Publisher, Scoop Usa, PA, Philadelphia

Dare, Chad..............................(217) 477-5151
Sports Ed., Commercial News, IL, Danville

Dare, Olatunji
ohdee@bradley.edu, Assoc. Prof., Bradley
University, IL, Peoria

Dargus, Laura
laura@weeklydig.com, Mng. Ed., Boston's
Weekly Dig, MA, Boston

Dark, Angela............................(319) 291-1573
Angela.Dark@wcfcourier.com, Mktg. Dir., The
Courier, IA, Waterloo

Darling, Ann
ann.darling@utah.edu, Chair, University of
Utah, UT, Salt Lake City

Darling, Ed
ed.darling@greenvilleadvocate.com, Pub.,
Bonus Express, AL, Luverne

Darling, Julie ....(601) 981-3060
jdarling@mspress.org, Marketing Manager,
Mississippi Press Services, Inc., MS,
Jackson

Darling, Mary
mary.darling@heraldobserver.com, Ed., The
Logan Herald-Observer, IA, Logan

Darling-Wolf, Fabienne
fabienne.darling-wolf@temple.edu, Assoc.
Prof., Temple University, PA, Philadelphia

Darmiento, Tammy
mburns@buckslocalnews.com, Adv. Mgr.,
Bristol Pilot, PA, Bristol

Darmiento, Tammy ....(267) 563-3030
tdarmiento@buckslocalnews.com, Adv. Mgr.,
Advance of Bucks County, PA, Lansdale

Darnall, Janet
ads@arkcity.net, Adv. Asst., The Arkansas City
Traveler, KS, Arkansas City

Darnay, Keith ....(701) 250-8287
keith.darnay@bismarcktribune.com, Online
Mgr., The Bismarck Tribune, ND, Bismarck

Darnell, Gwen
gs125@zoominternet.net, Adv. Mgr., Boardman
News, OH, Boardman

Darnell, Jack A.
bnews@zoominternet.net, Pub. Emeritus,
Boardman News, OH, Boardman

Darnell, Neil
lpjads@lcs.net, Adv. Mgr., The Louisiana
Press-Journal, MO, Bowling Green

Darnton, Jack
jdarnton@goanacortes.com, Pub./Ed.,
Anacortes American, WA, Anacortes

Darnton, Jack
jdarnton@goanacortes.com, Publisher, Fidalgo
This Week, WA, Anacortes

Darr, Ron..................................(203) 330-6528
rdarr@newstimes.com, Ops. Dir., The News-
Times, CT, Danbury

Darrow, Dennis.............(719) 544-3520 ext. 471
ddarrow@chieftain.com, Bus. Ed., The Pueblo
Chieftain, CO, Pueblo

Darrow, Joe.............................(607) 271-8302
jdarrow@gannett.com, Adv. Mgr., Star-Gazette,
NY, Elmira

Dart, Les
ldart@snu.edu, Broadcasting, Southern
Nazarene Univ., OK, Bethany

Dash, Max
newspaper@hsc.edu, Editor-in-Chief,
Hampden-Sydney College, VA, Hampden
Sydney

Dashnaw , Sandy ....(716) 592-4550 ext 21
Circ. Mgr. , Springville Journal, NY, Buffalo

Dasta, Jackie
info@syntellect.com, Contact, Syntellect, Inc.,
AZ, Phoenix

Daswani, Raju
ammnews@amm.com, American Metal
Market, NY, New York

Dater, Denice ....(620) 897-6234
themonitor@lrmutual.com, Co-Pub., Monitor-
Journal, KS, Little River

Datta, Frank ....(406) 796-2218
wibaux@midrivers.com, Ed., The Wibaux
Pioneer-Gazette, MT, Wibaux

Daubel, Philip F. .... (614) 272-5422 ext. 220
phildaubel@columbusmessenger.com, Pub./
Gen. Mgr., Madison Messenger, OH,
Columbus

Daubel, Philip F. .... (614) 272-5422 ext. 220
phildaubel@columbusmessenger.com, Pub./
Gen. Mgr., Eastside Messenger, OH,
Columbus

Daubel, Philip F. ....ext. 220
phildaubel@columbusmessenger.com, Pub./
Gen. Mgr., Southeast Messenger, OH,
Columbus

Daubel, Philip F.
phildaubel@columbusmessenger.com, Pub./
Gen. Mgr., Westside Messenger, OH,
Columbus

Daubel, Philip F.
phildaubel@columbusmessenger.com, Pub./
Gen. Mgr., Southwest Messenger, OH,
Columbus

Dauby, Cindy
circulation@perrycountynews.com, Adv. Mgr.,
Lincolnland Shopping Guide, IN, Tell City

Dauby, Joyce
circulation@perrycountynews.com, Circ. Mgr.,
Perry County News, IN, Tell City

Daugherty, Gretel .... x 227
Photo Editor, The Daily Sentinel, CO, Grand
Junction

Daugherty, Marla
editor@mybiglake.com, Ed., Big Lake Wildcat,
TX, Big Lake

Daugherty, Melissa
melissa@newsreview.com, Editor, Chico News
& Review, CA, Chico

Daugherty, Shirley
sdaugherty@forwardtimes.com, Prodn. Mgr.,
Houston Metro Weekender, TX, Houston

Daughtrey, Cathy
cathy.daughtrey@suffolknewsherald.com, Bus.
Mgr., Suffolk News-Herald, VA, Suffolk

Daughtrey, Cathy
cathy.daughtrey@suffolknewsherald.com, Circ.
Mgr, Suffolk News-Herald, VA, Suffolk

Dautel, Chris ....(574) 247-7265
Director of Strategic Planning and Corporate
Development, Schurz Communications Inc,
IN, Mishawaka

Dauzat, Karen ....(985) 857-2231
karen.dauzat@houmatoday.com, HR, The
Courier, LA, Houma

Davalos, Carlo ....(619) 427-3000 x 220
carlos@thestarnews.com, Ed., The Star-News,
CA, Chula Vista

Dave, Nirali
ndave@kdminer.com, Bus. Mgr., Kingman
Daily Miner, AZ, Kingman

Davenport, David
publisher@tjrcn.com, Pub., The Times Journal,
KY, Russell Springs

Davenport, Jane
jdavenport@thestar.ca, Mng. Ed., Toronto Star,
ON, Toronto

Davenport, Rob
rob@ifallsdailyjournal.com, Pub., The Journal,
MN, International Falls

Davey, Jeff ....(518) 873-6368
jeff@denpubs.com, Post Press Produ Mgr,
Sun Community News, Published by:Denton

Publications, Inc., NY, Elizabethtown

Davich, Jerry ....(219) 713-7237
jdavich@post-trib.com, Advisor, Post-Tribune,
IN, Crown Point

David, Arkin
darkin@gatehousemedia.com, Vice President,
Content and Audience, GateHouse Media,
Inc., NY, Pittsford

David, C.F.
bcnews@ptsi.net, Ed., The Boise City News,
OK, Boise City

David, Gabrielle
editor@cunews.info, Ed., Ajo Copper News,
AZ, Ajo

David, H.J.
hopd@cunews.info, Pub., Ajo Copper News,
AZ, Ajo

David, Irina
idavid@tribune.com, Dir., Mktg., Tribune 365,
NY, New York

David, Liza
elizabeth.david@richmond.edu, Managing
Editor, Univ. of Richmond, VA, Richmond

David, Marie
marie.david@sunmedia.ca, Grey Bruce Group
Pub., Owensound Sun Times, ON, Owen
Sound

David, Marie
chronicle.news@dc-uoit.ca , Pub., The Durham
Chronicle, ON, Durham

David, McHugh ....(225) 931-1012
editor@livingstonparishnews.com, Pub., The
Livingston Parish News, LA, Denham Springs

David, Ortego
dvdortego7@gmail.com, Pub., Ville Platte
Gazette, LA, Ville Platte

David, Reno ....(757) 446-2897
david.reno@pilotonline.com, Ops. Dir., The
Virginian-Pilot, VA, Norfolk

David, Reuben ....(612) 343-4727
rxdavid@northcentral.edu, North Central Univ.,
MN, Minneapolis

David D., N/A ....Pres./CEO
Tribune Media Services TV Log, IL, Chicago

David D., N/A ....Pres./CEO
Tribune Media Services TV Log - Chicago, IL,
Chicago

Davidson, Art ....(508) 626-4403
artd@wickedlocal.com, Metrowest Daily News,
MA, Framingham

Davidson, Art ....(508) 626-4403
artd@wickedlocal.com, Sports Ed., Milford
Daily News, MA, Milford

Davidson, Art ....(508) 626-4403
Artd@wickedlocal.com, Sports Ed. ,
Marlborough Enterprise, MA, Framingham

Davidson, Art ....(508) 626-4403
artd@wickedlocal.com, Sports Ed., Ashland
TAB, MA, Framingham

Davidson, Bob..........................(785) 822-1404
bdavidson@salina.com, Sports Ed., The Salina
Journal, KS, Salina

Davidson, Bruce ....(210) 250-3478
bdavidson@express-news.net, Editorial Page
Ed., San Antonio Express-News, TX, San
Antonio

Davidson, Donna..........................(941) 206-1164
Features Ed., Charlotte Sun, FL, Punta Gorda

Davidson, JD
jdavidson@theparisnews.com, Pub., The Paris
News, TX, Paris

Davidson, Jim ....(252) 639-2665
jdavidson@freedomenc.com, Adv. Sales, The
Shopper, NC, New Bern

Davidson, Stephanie ....(907) 335-1222
stephanie.davidson@peninsulaclarion.com,
Adv. Rep., Peninsula Clarion, AK, Kenai

Davidson, Todd.......................(812) 349-1415

davidson@heraldtimesonline.com, The
Reporter Times, IN, Martinsville
davidson@heraldtimesonline.com, Digital
Media Dir., The Times-Mail, IN, Bedford
davidson@heraldtimesonline.com, Online Mgr.,
The Herald Times, IN, Bloomington

Davies, Dave ....(530) 896-7779
ddavies@chicoer.com, Sports Ed., Chico
Enterprise-Record, CA, Chico

Davies, David ....(517) 377-1122
ddavies@michigan.com, Controller, Lansing
State Journal, MI, Lansing
ddavies@michigan.com, Reg. Controller, Times
Herald, MI, Port Huron

Davies, Joel
joeldavies@creighton.edu, Asst. Prof.,
Creighton Univ., NE, Omaha

Davies, Kathleen
kdavies@stpeterherald.com, Adv. Mgr., St.
Peter Herald, MN, Saint Peter

Davies, Sandy
sandy.davies@sunmedia.ca, Pub. and GM, The
Barrie Examiner, ON, Barrie

Davis, Alan ....(770) 282-3434
alan.davis@daily-tribune.com, Pub., The North
Bartow News, GA, Adairsville

Davis, Alan ....(770) 382-4545
Pub., The Daily Tribune News, GA, Cartersville

Davis, Alesia
eaglelakeheadlight@sbcglobal.net, Adv. Dir.,
Eagle Lake Headlight, TX, Eagle Lake

Davis, Alice
adavis@mdjonline.com, Classified Adv.
Supervisor, Northside Neighbor, GA, Atlanta
adavis@mdjonline.com, Credit Mgr., Marietta
Daily Journal, GA, Marietta

Davis, Andrew ....(904) 822-7224
Stetson Univ., FL, Deland

Davis, Andrew
ad15@uchicago.edu, Mng. Ed, Windy City
Times, IL, Chicago

Davis, Anita..........................(951) 368-9207
adavis@pe.com, Adv. Dir., The Press-
Enterprise, CA, Riverside

Davis, Anthony ....(575) 437-7120 ext. 7114
adavis@alamogordonews.com, Dist. Mgr.,
Alamogordo Daily News, NM, Alamogordo

Davis, Ashley ashley.davis@themadisonrecord.com
Mktg. Consult., The Madison Record, AL,
Madison

Davis, Beth ....(580) 875-3326
cottoncountylegals@sbcglobal.net, Ed. Adv./
Gen Mgr, Walters Herald, OK, Walters

Davis, Bill..........................(209) 954-5286
bdavis@deltacollege.edu, San Joaquin Delta
College, CA, Stockton

Davis, Bill...................(740) 397-5333 Ext. 247
bdavis@mountvernonnews.com, Sports Ed.,
Mount Vernon News, OH, Mount Vernon

Davis, Bill
bdavis@swpub.com, Grp. Pub., Southwest
Suburban Publishing, MN, Shakopee

Davis, Bill..........................(952) 345-6672
bdavis@swpub.com, Technical Dir., Interactive
Visuals, Inc. (OOB), IL, Chicago
bdavis@swpub.com, Pub./Gen. Mgr.,
Chanhassen Villager, MN, Chaska
bdavis@swpub.com, Gen. Mgr., Prior Lake
American, MN, Savage

Davis, Candi
candi.davis@natchezdemocrat.com, Sales
Mgr., Natchez Newspapers, Inc., MS,
Natchez

Davis, Catherine ....(540) 374-5453
catherined@freelancestar.com, Graphics/
Design Dir., The Free Lance-Star, VA,
Fredericksburg

Davis, Chris..........................(727) 893-8859

cdavis@tampabay.com, Deputy Managing Ed./ Investigations, Tampa Bay Times, FL, St Petersburg

Davis, Christine ....(641) 483-2120
midiaenterprise@partnercom.net, Pub., State Center Mid Iowa Enterprise, IA, State Center

Davis, Cindy
cindy@allennewspaper.com, Adv. Mgr, The Allen Advocate, OK, Allen

Davis, Clarke ....(785) 945-3257
vindicator@embarqmail.com, Pub/Ed, Valley Falls Vindicator, KS, Valley Falls

Davis, Clarke ....(785) 863-2520
Pub., Oskaloosa Independent, KS, Oskaloosa

Davis, Clinton ....(712) 868-3460
clint@armstrongjournal.com, Office Manager, Ringsted Dispatch, IA, Armstrong
clint@armstrongjournal.com, Office Manager, Armstrong Journal, IA, Armstrong

Davis, Cole
cdavis@kentuckynewera.com, Copy Ed., Kentucky New Era, KY, Hopkinsville

Davis, Connie
ohcirc@oskyherald.com, Circ. Mgr., Oskaloosa Herald, IA, Oskaloosa

Davis, Curtis..........................(217) 632-2236
observer@casscomm.com, The Petersburg Observer, IL, Petersburg

Davis, Dan .... (812) 523-7051 ext. 217
ddavis@tribtown.com, Ed., The Tribune, IN, Seymour

Davis, Debbie .... (530) 756-0800 ext. 254
ddavis@davisenterprise.net, Political/Gov't Ed., The Davis Enterprise, CA, DAVIS

Davis, Debra
circulation@nnsl.com, Circ. Mgr., Deh Cho Drum, NT, Yellowknife

Davis, Debra..........................(873) 873-4031
circulation@nnsl.com, Circ. Mgr., News/north, NT, Yellowknife

Davis, Debra
circulation@nnsl.com, Circ. Mgr., Yellowknifer, NT, Yellowknife

Davis, Debra
circulation@nnsl.com, Circ. Mgr., Inuvik Drum, NT, Yellowknife

Davis, Donna
ddavis@dominionpost.com, Nat'l Acct. Exec., The Dominion Post, WV, Morgantown

Davis, Doug
doug.davis@d2studios.net, Pres., D-Squared Studios, Inc., TX, Dallas

Davis, Douglas R.
doug.davis@news-jrnl.com, Circ. Dir., Daytona Beach News-Journal, FL, Daytona Beach

Davis, Drew..........................(912) 427-3757
drewd01@bellsouth.net, Ed., The Press-Sentinel, GA, Jesup

Davis, Dustin
ddavis@frostburg.edu, The Bottom Line, MD, Frostburg

Davis, Edd
Ed@athensnews-courier.com, Copy Editor, The News-Courier, AL, Athens

Davis, Elbra
enewspaper@aol.com, Mng. Ed./Adv. Dir., The Union News Leader, TN, Maynardville

Davis, Erik ....ext. 125
davise@maps.com, Dir., Education Mktg., Maps.com, CA, Santa Barbara

Davis, Gwen ....(252) 407-9900
gdavis@rmtelegram.com, Mgr., HR, Rocky Mount Telegram, NC, Rocky Mount

Davis, Harry ....(512) 445-3758
hdavis@statesman.com, Vice Pres., Fulfillment/Group Lead, Austin American-Statesman, TX, Austin

Davis, Imzadi
ldavis14@ccp.edu, Managing Editor, Community College of Philadelphia, PA, Philadelphia

Davis, Janis .... (270) 678-5171 Ext. 225
jdavis@glasgowdailytimes.com, Circ. Bookkeeper, Glasgow Daily Times, KY, Glasgow

Davis, Jay
jay.davis@selmatimesjournal.com, VP/Bus. Mgr., The Selma Times-Journal, AL, Selma

Davis, Jay..............................(605) 845-3646
sports@mobridgetribune.com, Sports Ed., Mobridge Tribune, SD, Mobridge

Davis, Jennifer........................(309) 686-3249
jdavis@pjstar.com, Lifestyles Ed., Journal Star, IL, Peoria

Davis, Jessica.........................(818) 713-0043
jessica.davis@langnews.com, Dig. News Dir., Los Angeles Daily News, CA, Woodland Hills

Davis, Jill ....(905) 632-4444
jdavis@burlingtonpost.com, Ed. in Chief, The Burlington Post, ON, Burlington

Davis, Jim ....(847) 608-2737
jdavis@dailyherald.com, Deputy Managing Editor / News, Daily Herald, IL, Arlington Heights

Davis, Jim ....(425) 339-3097
jdavis@heraldnet.com, Herald Business Journal Editor, The Herald, WA, Everett

Davis, Jim ....ext. 111
jimdavis@dnj.com, Chief Photographer, The Daily News Journal, TN, Murfreesboro

Davis, Joanie........................(270) 783-3205
jdavis@bgdailynews.com, Adv. Mgr., Nat'l, Daily News, KY, Bowling Green

Davis, K
sales@texasmetronews.com, Circulation Manager, Texas Metro News, TX, Dallas

Davis, K
sales@myimessenger.com, Circulation Manger, Garland Journal News, TX, Dallas

Davis, Kaire
kaire.davis@sunmedia.ca, Admin./Office Mgr., The High River Times, AB, High River

Davis, Karen
kdavis@corsicanadailysun.com, Adv. Dir., Corsicana Daily Sun, TX, Corsicana

Davis, Karen ....(860) 495-8223
kdavis@thewesterlysun.com, Classified Advertising, Mystic River Press, CT, Pawcatuck
kdavis@thewesterlysun.com, Class. Adv. Mgr., The Express, CT, Pawcatuck
kdavis@thewesterlysun.com, Classified Adv. Mgr, The Westerly Sun, CT, Pawcatuck

Davis, Kevin .... (209) 722-1812 ext. 402
kdavis@pspub.com, Vice Pres., Adv., Pacific Sierra Publishing, Inc., CA, Merced

Davis, Kimberly
circulation.plainsman@midconetwork.com, Gen. Mng. Oberlin Herald, The, KS, Oberlin
circulation.plainsman@midconetwork.com, Circ. Mgr./Marketing Mgr., The Daily Plainsman, SD, Huron

Davis, Kirk
kdavis@gatehousemedia.com, President & COO Gatehouse Media, Inc, The Patriot Ledger, MA, Quincy

Davis, Kirk
kdavis@gatehousemediane.com, Pres./CEO/ Pub., Community Newspaper Co.-North, MA, Beverly

Davis, Kirk
kdavis@gatehousemediane.com, Pres./CEO/ Pub., Community Newspaper Co.-West, MA, Framingham

Davis, Kirk
kdavis@gatehousemediane.com, Pres./CEO/

Pub., Community Newspaper Co. - South, MA, Marshfield

Davis, Kirk
kdavis@gatehousemediane.com, Pres./CEO/ Pub., Community Newspaper Co., MA, Framingham

Davis, Kirk ....(617) 786-7018
kdavis@gatehousemedia.com, Pres./COO, GateHouse Media, Inc., NY, Pittsford

Davis, Kirk
kdavis@gatehousemedia.com, CEO, Community Newspaper Co.-Metro, MA, Needham

Davis, Kirk A.
kdavis@thelandmark.com, Pres., The Landmark, MA, Holden

Davis, Larry..........................(423) 623-6171
larry.davis@newportplaintalk.com, Circulation Manager, The Newport Plain Talk, TN, Newport

Davis, Lisa ....(256) 235-3555
ldavis@annistonstar.com, Features Ed., The Anniston Star, AL, Anniston

Davis, Lisa....................(940) 627-5987 ext. 13
ldavis@wcmessenger.com, Adv. Mgr., Wise County Messenger, TX, Decatur

Davis, Lucas................ (620) 231-2600 ext. 139
ldavis@morningsun.net, Sports Editor, The Morning Sun, KS, Pittsburg

Davis, Maggie........................(904) 629-6020
AgeVentureNewsService@demko.com, Lifestyle & Fashion COR, AgeVenture News Service, Orange Park

Davis, Mark
medemail@aol.com, Pub./Adv. Dir., The Daily Plainsman, SD, Huron

Davis, Mark
editor.redpress@midconetwork.com, Pub., The Redfield Press, SD, Redfield

Davis, Mark..........................(605) 353-7414
medemail@aol.com, Pub, Pay Day, SD, Huron

Davis, Marty ....(859) 231-1434
madavis2@herald-leader.com, Adv. Sales Mgr., Auto. Adv., Lexington Herald-Leader, KY, Lexington

Davis, Marveta........................(785) 945-3257
vindicator@embarqmail.com, Society Ed, Valley Falls Vindicator, KS, Valley Falls

Davis, Meekahl
npnews@comcast.net, Pub., Nashville Pride, TN, Nashville

Davis, Meekahl
npnews@comcast.net, Pub., The Enlightener, TN, Nashville

Davis, Meekahl
npnews@comcast.net, Pub., Chattanooga Courier, TN, Nashville

Davis, Meekahl
npnews@comcast.net, Pub., Murfreesboro Vision, TN, Nashville

Davis, Michael ....(770) 775-3107 x 102
mdavis@myjpa.com, Ed., Jackson Progress-Argus, GA, Jackson

Davis, Michael
mdavis@syracusenewtimes.com, Photographer, Syracuse New Times, NY, Syracuse

Davis, Michael ....(503) 399-6712
mdavis4@statesmanjournal.com, Exec. Ed., Statesman Journal, OR, Salem

Davis, Michelle ....(806) 894-3121
levellandads@valornet.com, Adv. Mgr., Levelland & Hockley County News-Press, TX, Levelland

Davis, Mike
mdavis@murrayledger.com, Pub., The Murray Ledger & Times, KY, Murray

Davis, Mike
mdavis@news-expressky.com, Adv. Dir., The Mountain Bargain Hunter, KY, Pikeville

Davis, Mike
mdavis@marshallnews.com, Adv. Mgr., The Marshall Democrat-News, MO, Marshall

Davis, Mike
mdavis@hopewellnews.com, Pub., The Hopewell News, VA, Hopewell

Davis, Natalie ....(478) 453-1462
ndavis@unionrecorder.com, Ed., Lake Oconee Breeze, GA, Milledgeville

Davis, Natalie
ndavis@unionrecorder.com, Mng. Ed., The Union-Recorder, GA, Milledgeville

Davis, Nicole
ndavis@ss-times.com, Ed., Southside Times, IN, Indianapolis

Davis, O.K. ....(318) 255-4353
buddy@rustonleader.com, Sports Ed., Ruston (LA) Daily Leader, LA, Ruston

Davis, Paul ....(336) 852-9496
paul.davis@sourcemedia.com, Editor, Comm. Banking, American Banker, NY, New York

Davis, Peg ....(904) 261-3696
pdavis@fbnewsleader.com, Editor, News-Leader, FL, Fernandina Beach

Davis, Philip
pdavis@fiftyplusadvocate.com, Pub., Fifty Plus Advocate, MA, Worcester

Davis, Rachad........................(757) 401-5843
rachadcorey@gmail.com, Editor-in-Chief, Lynchburg College, VA, Lynchburg

Davis, Rachel
editor@njeffersonnews.com, Ed., North Jefferson News, AL, Gardendale

Davis, Ralph B. ....(606) 886-8506 ext. 17
web@floydcountytimes.com, Mng. Ed., Floyd County Times, KY, Prestonsburg

Davis, Rayma B.
lamardemocrat@tiadon.com, Ed., Lamar Democrat, MO, Lamar

Davis, Richard ....(281) 378-1042
rdavis@hcnonline.com, Pub., Sugar Land Sun, TX, Houston
rdavis@hcnonline.com, Pub./Adv. Dir., The Woodlands Villager, TX, Conroe
rdavis@hcnonline.com, Pub., Cypress Creek Mirror, TX, Houston
rdavis@hcnonline.com, Pub., Memorial Examiner, TX, Conroe
rdavis@hcnonline.com, Pub., River Oaks Examiner, TX, Houston
rdavis@hcnonline.com, Pub., Bellaire Examiner, TX, Houston
rdavis@hcnonline.com, Pub., Fort Bend Sun, TX, Conroe
rdavis@hcnonline.com, Pub., The Examiners, TX, Conroe
rdavis@hcnonline.com, Pub., Tomball Potpourri, TX, Conroe
rdavis@hcnonline.com, Pub./Adv. Dir., Spring Observer, TX, Conroe
rdavis@hcnonline.com, Pub., The Rancher, TX, Conroe

Davis, Richard ....(256) 549-2027
richard.davis@gasdentimes.com, Finance Dir, The Gadsden Times, AL, Gadsden

Davis, Rita ....(301) 696-3641
Hood College, MD, Frederick

Davis, Robin
robin.davis@scripps.com, VP, Strategic Planning & Development, E. W. Scripps Co., OH, Cincinnati

Davis, Ronaldo........................(717) 703-3057
ronaldod@MANSIMedia.com, Sr. Media Buyer, MANSI Media, PA, Harrisburg

Davis, Russ .... (435) 752-2121 ext. 380
rdavis@hjnews.com, Circ. Dir., Quality Buys, UT, Logan

Davis, Samuel ....(410) 332-6534
sam.davis@baltsun.com, Managing Ed., The
Baltimore Sun, MD, Baltimore

Davis, Sara ....(515) 989-0525
news@carlislecitizen.com, Ed., The Carlisle
Citizen, IA, Carlisle

Davis, Scott
scott.davis@caremark.com, Adv. Mgr.,
Nashville Pride, TN, Nashville

Davis, Shawn
sdavis@fiberweb.com, Area Mgr., Fiberweb,
SC, Simpsonville

Davis, Sheila ....(816) 254-8600
sheila.davis@examiner.net, Exec. Ed., The
Examiner / Examiner Weekend, MO,
Independence
sheila.davis@examiner.net, Ed., The Examiner
, MO, Independence

Davis, Shelley
sdavis@bryantimes.com, Adv., The Bryan
Times, OH, Bryan

Davis, Shelley
srdavis@tennessean.com, Director of Sales,
TN Media, TN, Nashville
srdavis@tennessean.com, Director of Sales,
The Tennessean, TN, Nashville

Davis, Sherri ....(928) 425-7121
sherri@silverbelt.com, Gen. Mgr., Arizona
Silver Belt, AZ, Globe

Davis, Stanley
northdistmgr@hammondstar.com, Circ. District
Mgr., The Daily Star, LA, Hammond

Davis, Stephania ....(860) 512-2694
sdavis@manchestercc.edu, Manchester
Community College, CT, Manchester

Davis, Stephen ....(646) 895-8424
stephen.davis@srds.com, President, SRDS, a
Kantar Media Company, IL, Des Plaines

Davis, Steve ....(207) 596-0055
admanager@freepressonline.com, Adv. Mgr.,
Free Press, ME, Rockland

Davis, Tim ....(434) 432-1654 ext. 18
tim.davis@womackpublishing.com, Editorial
Dir., Womack Publishing Co., VA, Lynchburg

Davis, Tom ....(260) 461-8240
tdavis@news-sentinel.com, Sports Ed., The
News-Sentinel, IN, Fort Wayne

Davis, Tom
tdavis@usa-800.com, Pres./CEO, USA 800,
Inc., MO, Raytown

Davis, Victoria
victoriad@indianapolisrecorder.com,
Newsroom Mgr., The Indianapolis Recorder,
IN, Indianapolis

Davis Bundy, Deb ....(360) 416-2126
dbundy@skagitpublishing.com, Display Adv.
Mgr., Anacortes American, WA, Anacortes

Davis-Guerra, Kimberly...............(713) 266-1885
Publisher, Houston Family Magazine, TX,
Houston

Davison, Matt ....(208) 465-8101
mdavison@idahopress.com, Publisher, Idaho
Press, ID, Nampa

Davison, Nick..........................(630) 942-2683
editor@cod.edu, Editor-in-chief, College of
DuPage, IL, Glen Ellyn

Davison, Pat...........................(919) 962-4073
Assoc. Prof., University of North Carolina, NC,
Chapel Hill

Daw, Sheila
dawsb@washpost.com, Account Manager,
National Retail, The Washington Post, DC,
Washington

Dawkins, Jim ....(727) 535-4400
jdawk43@aol.com, Adv. Mgr., Jewish Press of
Pinellas County, FL, Clearwater

Dawkins, Jim ....(727) 535-4400
jewishpress@aol.com, Pub., Jewish Press of

Tampa, FL, Largo

Dawkins, Stephen ....(205) 755-5747, ext. 610
stephen.dawkins@clantonadvertiser.com,
Managing Editor, The Clanton Advertiser,
AL, Clanton

Dawley, Wanda........................(613) 543-2987
leaderads@vianet.ca, Circ. Mgr., The
Morrisburg Leader, ON, Morrisburg

Dawn, Keith...........................(718) 816-8583
kdawn@siadvance.com, Publisher, Staten
Island Advance, NY, Staten Island

Dawson, Anastasia ....(813) 974-5190
Ed. in chief, Univ. of South Florida, FL, Tampa

Dawson, Cory
cynic@uvm.edu, Editor-in-Chief, University of
Vermont, VT, Burlington

Dawson, Ed ....(304) 526-2787
edawson@heralddispatch.com, Pub., The
Herald-Dispatch, WV, Huntington
edawson@heralddispatch.com, Pub./Ed. ,
Herald & Dispatch, WV, Huntington

Dawson, Fabian.......................(604) 605-2258
fdawson@postmedia.com, Deputy Editor, The
Province, BC, Vancouver

Dawson, Marianne ....(705) 645-8771 ext. 235
examiner@muskoka.com, Prodn. Coord., The
Muskokan, ON, Bracebridge

Dawson, Matt.........................(902) 563-3888
Circ. Mgr., Promotional, The Cape Breton Post,
NS, Sydney

Dawson, Stephanie A. ....(402) 678-2771
advance@gpcom.net, Ed., The St. Edward
Advance, NE, Saint Edward

Dawson Bartley, Cari ....(800) 696-7561
cari@cagle.com, Exec. Ed./Mktg. Dir., Cagle
Cartoons, Inc., Santa Barbara

Day, Beth Howell
smokesig@wamego.net, Ed, Wamego Smoke
Signal, KS, Wamego

Day, Bill
bday@magid.com, Frank N Magid Associates,
IA, Marion

Day, Chris
cday@dailyadvance.com, Asst. News Ed., The
Daily Advance, NC, Elizabeth City

Day, Chris
cday@examiner-enterprise.com, Ed, Pawhuska
Journal-Capital, OK, Pawhuska

Day, Christy...............(260) 925-2611 Ext. 2517
cday@kpcmedia.com, District Mgr., The Star,
IN, Auburn

Day, David
david@weeklydig.com, Arts/Music Ed.,
Boston's Weekly Dig, MA, Boston

Day, Janet
dayje@oneonta.edu, SUNY College/Oneonta,
NY, Oneonta

Day, Jerome ....(603) 656-6063
aguthrie@anselm.edu, St. Anselm College,
NH, Manchester

Day, Larry
press@fairmontphotopress.com, Pressman,
Fairmont Photo Press, MN, Fairmont

Day, Loretta
lday@registerpublications.com, Adv. Dir., The
Journal-Press, IN, Lawrenceburg

Day, Marshall
publisher@gatesvillemessenger.com, Pub.,
Gatesville Messenger and Star Forum, TX,
Gatesville

Day, Melanie
mel@milanmirrorexchange.com, Mng. Ed.,
Milan Mirror-Exchange, TN, Milan

Day, Peter............................(760) 956-7827
editor@hesperiastar.com, Ed., Hesperia Star,
CA, Victorville

Day, Stewart.............(615) 256-2158 ext. 3011

stewart@daycommedia.com, Pub., Nashville
Parent Magazine, TN, Nashville

Day, Stewart..........................(615) 256-2158
stewart@daycommedia.com, Adv. Mgr.,
Rutherford Parent, TN, Nashville

Day, Stormi
sbday@baxterbulletin.com, Ad. Acct.
Relationship Specialist, The Baxter Bulletin,
AR, Mountain Home

Day, Susan.............................. ext. 3001
susan@daycommail.com, Ed., Nashville Parent
Magazine, TN, Nashville

Day, Susan
susan@daycommail.com, Ed. in Chief.,
Rutherford Parent, TN, Nashville

Day, Susan ....(937) 512-2744
clarion@sinclair.edu , Advt Rep, Sinclair
Community College, OH, Dayton

Dayberry, John ....ext. 275
jdayberry@hickoryrecord.com, Bus. Ed., The
Hickory Daily Record, NC, Hickory
jdayberry@hickoryrecord.com, Bus. Ed., Pow,
NC, Hickory

Daye, Jan
adbargain@comcast.net, Ad Bargain, PA,
Smithmill

Daza, Roberto
editor@accionlatina.org, Ed., El Tecolote, CA,
San Francisco

De Armas, Lisa........................(843) 693-1116
lisa@elinformadornewspaper.com, Director, El
Informador Spanish Language Newspaper,
SC, Mount Pleasant

De Armas, Pedro ....(843) 817-2896
sales@elinformadornewspaper.com,
Publisher, El Informador Spanish Language
Newspaper, SC, Mount Pleasant

De Bruijn, Albert ....(916) 844-2437
albert.debruijn [at] miles33.com, VP Marketing
and Sales for Western USA, Tera Digital
Publishing, CT, Norwalk

De Bruijn, Albert ....(916) 844-2437
albert.debruijin@miles33.com, VP Marketing
and Western USA Sales, Miles 33, CT,
Norwalk

De Choiniere, Alain
alain.dechoiniere@transcontinental.ca, Gen.
Mgr., Courrier-ahuntsic, QC, Saint Laurent

De La Cruz, Jose ....(760) 776-5181
news@desertentertainer.com, Ed, Desert
Entertainer, CA, Palm Desert

De Laat, Candice ....(307) 670-8980
CandiceDeLaat@CampbellCountyObserver.
com, Owner/Manager, The Campbell County
Observer, WY, Rozet

De Laat, Nicholas.....................(370) 670-8980
NicholasDeLaat@CampbellCountyObserver.
com, Owner/Publisher/Editor, The Campbell
County Observer, WY, Rozet

De Laet, Steve
steve@partsriver.com, Chief Devel. Officer,
PartsRiver, Inc., CA, Fremont

De Lemos, Nancy ....(506) 225-80016
ndelemos@acan-efe.com, Director, EFE News
Services - San Jose, Costa Rica, San Jose

De Los Santos, Elise
ekdelossantos@redeyechicago.com, Exec.
Ed., RedEye, IL, Chicago

De Luca, Chris........................(312) 321-3000
cdeluca@suntimes.com, Deputy Managing
Ed., News/Sports, Chicago Sun-Times, IL,
Chicago

De Marco, Jim........................(262) 656-6216
jdemarco@kenoshanews.com, Cir. Mgr.,
Kenosha News, WI, Kenosha

De Palma, Frank ....(902) 426-2811
fdepalma@herald.ca, Asst. Dir., Newsroom,
The Chronicle Herald, NS, Halifax

De Rengifo, Martha...................(57 1) 623-5020
datanewsdj@hotmail.com, Sales Exec., Dow
Jones Newswires - Bogota, Colombia,
Bogota

De Ryk, Tara
davidsonleader@sasktel.net, Publisher,
Davidson Leader, SK, Davidson

De Silva, Indra
desilva@Xavier.edu, Chair, Xavier University,
OH, Cincinnati

De Souza, Priscila ....(650) 543-3786
priscila.desouza@menlo.edu, Dean of
Enrollment Management, Menlo College,
CA, Atherton

De Varenne, Maria ....(615) 259-8003
mdevarenne@tennessean.com, Director
of News & Editor, The Tennessean, TN,
Nashville
mdevarenne@tennessean.com, Director of
News & Editor, TN Media, TN, Nashville

De la Torre, Martha C. ....(323) 278-5310
mdelatorre@elclasificado.com, El Clasificado,
CA, Norwalk

De la Vega, Tamara ....ext. 237
News Ed., Huntsville Forester, ON, Huntsville

DeAmbrose, Faith (207) 374-2341, (207) 367-2200
news@pbp.me, Mng. Ed., Castine Patriot, ME,
Blue Hill

DeAmbrose, Faith ....(207) 374-2341
news@pbp.me, Managing Editor, The Weekly
Packet, ME, Blue Hill
news@pbp.me, Managing Ed., Island Ad-
Vantages, ME, Stonington

DeAmicis, Ruth ....(978) 297-0050
ruth@stonebridgepress.com, Ed./Adv Mgr.,
The Winchendon Courier, MA, Winchendon

DeAngelis, Bernard...................(215) 361-8803
bdeangelis@journalregister.com, Controller/
Purchasing Agent, The Reporter, PA,
Lansdale

DeAngelo, Debra
debra@wintersexpress.com, Ed., Winters
Express, CA, Winters
debra@wintersexpress.com, Ed., McNaughton
Newspapers, CA, Fairfield

DeAngelo, Tracey ....(412) 263-1460
tdeangelo@post-gazette.com, Director of
Marketing and Audience, Pittsburgh Post-
Gazette, PA, Clinton

DeArmond, Joe
bclingan@courier.com, Courier, IL, Washington

DeArmond, Joi ....(309) 444-3139 ext.12
Joi67@courierpapers.com, Ed., Woodford
Courier, IL, Washington

DeArmond, Joi ....(309) 444-3139 ext.12
Joi67@courierpapers.com, Ed., Courier, IL,
Washington

DeBacker, Emily ....(707) 526-8599
HR Dir., The Press Democrat, CA, Santa Rosa

DeBartolo, Mike
det_sales@parade.com, Vice Pres., Adv.,
Parade Publications, Inc. - Bloomfield Hills,
MI, Bloomfield Hills

DeBeer, Sandy........................(605) 692-4300
sandy@sdna.com, Advertising Placement
Coordinator, South Dakota Newspaper
Association, SD, Brookings

DeBono, Nili ....(212) 576-9505
debonon@metrosn.com, Sr. Vice Pres.,
Finance, Metro Newspaper Advertising
Services, Inc., NY, New York

DeBord, Derek
ahayes@iwanna.com, Gen. Mgr., Iwanna, NC,
Hickory

DeBord, John ....(828) 328-5296
Pub., Iwanna, NC, Hickory

DeBow, Matt..........................(541) 259-3126
matt.debow@lee.net, Ed., Lebanon Express,

OR, Lebanon

DeBrito, Sophie 7775-6248
sophie.debrito@ft.com, Synd. Mgr., Financial
Times, London

DeBruin, Rick...............(207) 282-1535 ext. 341
rdebruin@journaltribune.com, New Business
Development Dir., Journal-Tribune, ME,
Biddeford

DeBuse, Nikki ....(503) 357-3181
ndebuse@pamplinmedia.com, Publ., Forest
Grove News-Times, OR, Forest Grove

DeCanio, Lesley ....(305) 376-3163
ldecanio@miamiherald.com, VP of Advertising,
Miami Herald, FL, Doral

DeCesare, Donna
donna.decesare@austin.utexas.edu, Asst.
Prof., University of Texas at Austin, TX,
Austin

DeChantal, Rick......................(312) 222-4544
rdechantal@tronc.com, Sales Dir., Tribune
News Service, Chicago
rdechantal@tronc.com, Sales Dir., Tribune
Content Agency, IL, Chicago

DeCicco, Nick ....(707) 427-6966
ndecicco@dailyrepublic.net, Tailwind Ed., Daily
Republic, CA, Fairfield

DeClue, Emmaly ....(270) 259-6061
edeclue@graysonrecord.com, Advertising
representative, The Record, KY, Leitchfield

DeClue, Marlene
greenfieldvedettepublisher@mchsi.com, Ed.,
The Vedette, MO, Greenfield

DeCuir, Randy
avoyellesjournal@yahoo.com, Pub./Ed.,
Avoyelles Journal, LA, Marksville

DeCuir, Randy
avoyellesjournal@yahoo.com, Pub., The
Marksville Weekly News, LA, Marksville

DeDe, Cathy .... ext. 22
Mng. Ed., The Chronicle, NY, Glens Falls

DeFalco, Joseph
joseph.defalco@publicitas.com, CFO,
Publicitas North America, Inc., NY, New York

DeFrancesco, Jefferey ....(603) 279-4516 x 120
The Record-Enterprise (OOB), NH, Meredith
The Gilford Steamer, NH, Meredith

DeFranco, Robert J. ....(561) 630-2400
bdefranco@bankrate.com, Sr. Vice Pres.,
Finance/CFO, Bankrate.com, North Palm
Beach

DeFrangesco, Donna
donna@phillyareapapers.com, Acct. Supvr.,
Hitchings & Co., PA, Plymouth Meeting

DeGrado, Mari Jo...............................ext. 530
mdegrado@newtondailynews.com, Prodn.
Supvr., Composing Room, Newton Daily
News, IA, Newton

DeGrandpre, Andrew
adegrandpre@marinecorpstimes.com, Ed.,
Marine Corps Times, VA, Vienna

DeGrassa, Peg
pdegrassa@delconewsnetwork.com, Ed,
County Press, PA, Swarthmore
pdegrassa@delconewsnetwork.com, Ed,
Garnet Valley Press, PA, Swarthmore

DeGrasssa, Margaret ....(610) 915-2248
pdegrassa@delconewsnetwork.com, Ed., Town
Talk Newspapers, PA, Swarthmore

DeGrechie, Eric
eric@wilmettebeacon.com, Mng. Ed., The Lake
Forest Leader, IL, Northbrook
eric@wilmettebeacon.com, Mng. Ed., The
Glencoe Anchor, IL, Northbrook
eric@wilmettebeacon.com, Mng. Ed., The
Highland Park Landmark, IL, Northbrook

DeGrie, Elizabeth ....(318) 255-4353
elizabeth@rustonleader.com, News Ed.,
Ruston (LA) Daily Leader, LA, Ruston

DeHaan, Jeff
sales@stormlake.com, Advertising Manager,
The Storm Lake Times, IA, Storm Lake

DeHaan, Joy
jdehaan@madraspioneer.com, Adv. Dir., The
Madras Pioneer, OR, Madras

DeHaan, Lauren ....(616) 819-0011
Calvin College, MI, Grand Rapids

DeHaven, Dick ....(570) 970-7202
ddehaven@timesleader.com, Vice Pres., Circ.,
Nepa Shopper, PA, Wilkes Barre

DeJarnette, Stephanie
sdejarnette@neighbornewspapers.com, Adv.
Mgr., Northside Neighbor, GA, Atlanta

DeLapp, Bill ....(315) 422-7011 x126
editorial@syracusenewtimes.com, Ed.,
Syracuse New Times, NY, Syracuse
editorial@syracusenewtimes.com, Editor-in-
chief, Syracuse New Times, NY, Syracuse

DeLapp, Bill
bdelapp@syracusenewtimes.com, Managing
Editor
, Syracuse New Times, NY, Syracuse

DeLaurier, Trish ....(386) 760-1035
trish.delaurier@srds.com, VP, Information
Sales & Client Service, SRDS, a Kantar
Media Company, IL, Des Plaines

DeLoach, Jeff.........................(423) 757-6370
jdeloach@timesfreepress.com, Pres.,
Chattanooga Times Free Press, TN,
Chattanooga
jdeloach@timesfreepress.com, Pub./Adv. Dir. ,
San Angelo Standard-Times, TX, San Angelo

DeLong, Dan...............(425) 392-6434 ext. 229
admanager@isspress.com, Adv. Mgr.,
Sammamish Review, WA, Issaquah
admanager@isspress.com, Adv. Mgr.,
SnoValley Star, WA, Issaquah

DeLong, Michele
editor@centralstcroixnews.com, Gen. Mgr./EIC,
Central St. Croix News, WI, Roberts

DeLonge, David
ddelonge@triplicate.com, Production Mgr., The
Del Norte Triplicate, CA, Crescent City

DeLost, Bill ....(218) 363-2002
presscit@eot.com, Ed., Pine Cone Press
Citizen, MN, Longville

DeLuca, Joe ....(813) 226-3307
jdeluca@tampabay.com, VP / Tampa Pub.,
TampaBay.com Pub., Tampa Bay Times, FL,
St Petersburg

DeLuca, Matt ....(617) 552-2223
editor@bcheights.com, Boston College, MA,
Chestnut Hill

DeLuca, Suzanne ....(631) 286-0058 ext. 230
Art Dir., 50+ LifeStyles, NY, Bellport

DeLuna, Martha.....................(312) 870-7023
martha.deluna@impremedia.com, Nat'l Acct.
Exec., La Raza Newspaper, IL, Chicago

DeMaggio, Susan.....................(858) 875-5950
susandemaggio@lajollalight.com, Exec. Ed.,
La Jolla Light, CA, La Jolla

DeMasters, Carol
caroldemasters@yahoo.com, Exec. Dir.,
Association of Food Journalists, Inc., NM,
Santa Fe

DeMeer, Andrea......................(250) 499-2653
editor@similkameenspotlight.com, Ed/Assist.
Pub, Princeton Similkameen Spotlight, BC,
Princeton
editor@similkameenspotlight.com, Assoc.
Pub., Keremeos Review, BC, Keremeos

DeMola, Pete.........................(518) 873-6368
pete@suncommunitynews.com, Mgr Ed, The
North Countryman Sun, NY, Elizabethtown

DeMola, Pete ....(518) 873-6368
pete@suncommunitynews.com, Deputy Mng Ed,
Sun Community News, Published by:Denton
Publications, Inc., NY, Elizabethtown

DeMontis, Rita ....(416) 947-2247
rita.demontis@sunmedia.ca, Lifestyle/Food
Ed., The Toronto Sun, ON, Toronto

DeMorett, Pamela ....(507) 724-3475
pam.demorett@ecm-inc.com, Adv. Dir, The
Caledonia Argus, MN, Caledonia

DeNatale, Mary
mdenatale@21st-centurymedia.com, Class.
Supv., Daily Local News, PA, West Chester

DeNeal, Brian ....(618) 253-7146 ext.243
bdeneal@dailyregister.com, Ed., Gallatin
Democrat, IL, Shawneetown
bdeneal@dailyregister.com, Managing Editor,
The Daily Register, IL, Harrisburg

DeNeal, Brian
bdeneal@dailyregsiter.com, Prodn. Mgr.,
Eldorado Daily Journal, IL, Harrisburg

DeOilers, Taryn
opinion@theaggie.org, Opinion Editor,
University of California, Davis, CA, Davis

DePaolo, Wayne ....(860) 801-5076
wdepaolo@centralctcommunications.com,
Prepress Mgr., New Britain Herald, CT, New
Britain

DePaul, Jeanne
jdepaul@lmtribune.com, Garden Ed., Lewiston
Morning Tribune, ID, Lewiston

DePelsmaeker, Mary Jo ....(800) 461-3457
maryjo@oldautos.ca, Publisher, Old Autos,
ON, Bothwell

DePersis, Jenn
jenn@thereportergroup.org, Prodn. Coord.,
The Reporter, NY, Vestal

DePietto, Bud
bud.depietto@dtint.com, Exec. Vice Pres.,
Digital Technology International, MN, Saint
Paul

DePriest, Keaton
kdepriest@BeeNews.com, Ed., Amherst Bee,
NY, Williamsville

DePyssler, Dr. Bruce ....(919) 530-7116
North Carolina Central Univ., NC, Durham

DeRienzo, Matt.......................(860) 489-1877
mderienzo@registercitizen.com, Pub., The
Register Citizen, CT, Torrington
mderienzo@registercitizen.com, West Hartford
News, CT, New Haven
mderienzo@registercitizen.com, Sr. Content
Dir., The Housatonic Times (OOB), CT,
Torrington

DeRienzo, Matt............ (860) 489-3121, ext. 350
mderienzo@21st-centurymedia.com, Group
Ed., The Middletown Press, CT, Middletown

DeRoche, Jerry
news@ironcountyreporter.com, Ed., Reporter,
MI, Iron River

DeRoeck, Corky ....(906) 774-2772
cderoeck@ironmountaindailynews.com,
Publisher, The Daily News, MI, Iron Mountain

DeRose, Dena
dderose@mailtribune.com, Adv. Dir., The
Ashland Daily Tidings, OR, Medford
dderose@mailtribune.com, Adv. Dir., Mail
Tribune, OR, Medford

DeRossett, Dennis...................(217) 241-1400
dennis@nna.org, Exec. Dir., National
Newspaper Association Publishers' Auxiliary,
IL, Springfield

DeRossett, Dennis....................(217) 241-1400
dennis@nna.org, Chief Op.Officer, National
Newspaper Association, IL, Springfield

DeRossett, Dennis ....(217) 241-1300 ext 222
dderossett@illinoispress.org, Exec. Dir., Illinois
Press Association, IL, Springfield

DeRuiter, Shirley..............................ext. 103
shirley@scenepub.com, Asst. Pub., Senior
Times South Central Michigan, MI, Battle
Creek

DeRuyter, Ron
rderuyter@therecord.com, Bus. Ed., The
Record, ON, Kitchener

DeSchriver, Thomas J................(570) 420-4358
tdeschriver@poconorecord.com, Exec. Ed.,
Pocono Record, PA, Stroudsburg

DeSelm, Chala
chala.deselm@sandspringsleader.com, CSR,
Sand Springs Leader, OK, Tulsa

DeShazo, Jennifer ....(901) 853-2241
ads@colliervilleherald.net, Production/
Graphics, The Collierville Herald, TN,
Collierville

DeSisto, Lisa
lisa@sunjournal.com , Pub., Advertiser
Democrat, ME, Norway

DeSisto, Lisa ....(207) 791-6630
lisa@mainetoday.com, CEO/Publisher,
Portland Press Herald / Maine Sunday
Telegram, ME, Portland

DeVally, Adriana
adriana@lmtonline.com, Gen. Mgr., El Tiempo
de Laredo, TX, Laredo

DeVaul, Frank ....(360) 748-3335
fdevaul@myhome.net, Pub., Skamania County
Pioneer, WA, Stevenson
fdevaul@myhome.net, Co-Pub., The East
County Journal, WA, Morton
fdevaul@myhome.net, Pub., DeVaul Publishing Inc.,
WA, CHEHALIS

DeVaul, Frank
fdevaul@devaulpublishing.com, Pub., The
Tenino Independent, WA, Tenino

DeVaul, Judy
jdevaul@myhome.net, Pub., Skamania County
Pioneer, WA, Stevenson
jdevaul@myhome.net, Co-Pub./Adv. Vice Pres.,
The East County Journal, WA, Morton

DeVeau, Carol
bcdem@sbcglobal.net, Gen. Mgr., Bay County
Legal News, MI, Bay City

DeVon, Gary
gary@gazette-tribune.com, Pub./Ed.,
Okanogan Valley Gazette-Tribune, WA,
Oroville

DeWeese, Jeanne ....(740) 413-0896
jdeweese@delgazette.com, Off. Mgr., The
Delaware Gazette, OH, Delaware

DeWitt, Blake...............(928) 783-3311 ext. 103
bdewitt@westernnewspapers.com, Sr. Vice
Pres., Western News&Info., Inc., AZ, Yuma

DeWitt, Brian
bdewitt@chronohio.com, Assoc. Ed., Gay
People's Chronicle, OH, Cleveland

DeWitt, Carlton
messenger@dewittmedia.com, Pub./Ed., The
Colfax Messenger, WI, Colfax

DeWitt, Carlton
tribune@dewittmedia.com, Pub./Ed., Tribune
Press Reporter, WI, Glenwood City

DeWitt, Karen
kdewitt@reporter-times.com, Adv. Mgr., The
Reporter Times, IN, Martinsville

DeWitt, Michael
michael.dewitt@hamptoncountyguardian.
com, Pub., Hampton County Guardian, SC,
Hampton

DeYoung, Dirk........................(612) 288-2111
ddeyoung@bizjournals.com, Ed., The Business
Journal, MN, Minneapolis

DeYoung, Matt ....(616) 842-6400 ext. 232
mdeyoung@grandhaventribune.com, Content
Dir. & Audience Dev't. , Grand Haven Tribune,
MI, Grand Haven

DeZur, David
editor@oelweindailyregister.com, Editor,
Shopper's Reminder, IA, Oelwein

Deakin, Erika Stutzman ....(303) 473-1354

stutzmane@dailycamera.com, Features Ed., Daily Camera, CO, Boulder

Deal, Jason
jdeal@theblaersheartimes.com, Staff Writer, The Blackshear Times, GA, Blackshear

Deal, Jonathan
johnathan@athensnews-courier.com, Sports, The News-Courier, AL, Athens

Deal, Kent
sales@k-f.com, Gen. Mgr., K & F International, Inc., IN, Granger

Deam, Evan
evan@na-weekly.com, Adv. Mgr., Norwegian American Weekly, WA, Seattle

Dean, Allan
editor@ahherald.com, Pub. & Ed., Atlantic Highlands Herald, NJ, Atlantic Highlands

Dean, Irving ....(518) 395-3103
dean@dailygazette.net, City Ed., The Daily Gazette, NY, Schenectady

Dean, James
jdean@columbustelegram.com, Ed., Telegram Advantage, NE, Columbus

Dean, Jan
jdean@franklincountycitizen.com, Adv. Rep., Franklin County Citizen Leader, GA, Lavonia

Dean, Jim
jdean@columbustelegram.com, Pub., Telegram Advantage, NE, Columbus

Dean, Jim ....(770) 205-8978
jdean@forsythnews.com, Online Ed., Forsyth County News, GA, Cumming

Dean, Katie
kdean@capitalnewspapers.com, The Capital Times, WI, Madison

Dean, Kyle
kyle.dean@gaflnews.com, Sports Ed., Tifton Shopper, GA, Tifton

Dean, Lena
lena@stanlynewspress.com, Circ. Mgr., The Stanly News & Press, NC, Albemarle

Dean, Leslie ....(219) 326-3889
ldean@heraldargus.com , District Sales Mgr. , Herald-Argus, IN, La Porte

Dean, Matthew ....(212) 854-5833
deanm@coned.com, Columbia Univ. Law School, NY, New York

Dean, Suzanne ....(435) 835-4241
suzanne@sanpetemessenger.com, Pub., Sanpete Messenger, UT, Manti

Dean, Tammy K.
tdean@heartlandpublications.com, Adv. Sales Rep., The Thomaston Times, GA, Lagrange

Dean, Terry
tdean@cherokeeherald.com, Pub./Ed., Cherokee County Herald, AL, Centre

Dean, Terry
tdean@wjinc.com, Ed., Austin Weekly News, IL, Oak Park

Dean, Trey ....(559) 735-3230
tdean@gannett.com, Advert Mgr, Visalia Times-Delta, CA, Visalia

Dean, Walter ....(678) 947-8550
sales@deanmachinery.com, Pres., Dean Machinery International, Inc., GA, Alpharetta

Dean-Simmons, Barbara ....(709) 466-2243
editor@thepacket.ca, Ed., The Packet, NL, Clarenville

Deane, Dawn ....(870) 946-3933
manager@dewitt-ee.com, Manager/Ad Sales, De Witt Era-Enterprise, AR, De Witt

Dearman, Tim ....(704) 761-2925
tdearman@statesville.com, Pub., Statesville Record & Landmark, NC, Statesville

Dearman, Tim
tdearman@hickoryrecord.com, Reg. Pub., The Hickory Daily Record, NC, Hickory

tdearman@hickoryrecord.com, Reg. Pub., Pow, NC, Hickory

Deas, Tommy ....(205) 722-0224
tommy.deas@tuscaloosanews.com, Sports Ed, The Tuscaloosa News, AL, Tuscaloosa

Deaton, Dell ....(734) 668-2001
dd@divorcePeers.com, Divorce Mediator, Divorce Reality Group, Saline

Deaton, Tona ....(706) 290-5318
tdeaton@npco.com, Prodn. Dir., Dispatch, Rome News-Tribune, GA, Rome

Debatin, Bernhard ....(740) 593-9809
debatin@ohio.edu, Assoc. Prof./Dir. Studies, Honors Tutorial College, Ohio University, OH, Athens

Debilzen, James ....(608) 208-1679
couriereditor@hngnews.com, Mng. Ed., The Milton Courier, WI, Milton

Debilzen, James ....(608) 283-7623
james.debilzen@wnanews.com, Communications Dir., Wisconsin Newspaper Association, WI, Madison

Debilzen, James ....(920) 563-5553
jdebilzen@dailyunion.com, Grp. Circ. / Readership Dir., Daily Jefferson County Union, WI, Fort Atkinson

Deborah, Anderson ....(816) 234-4088
danderson@kcstar.com, Class. Mgr., The Olathe News, MO, Kansas City

Debruin, Natalie
nd208604@ohiou.edu, Ohio Univ., OH, Athens

Deburro, Joe ....(413) 788-1117
jdeburro@repub.com, Online, The Republican, MA, Springfield

Decherd, Robert W.
blc@belo.com, Chrmn. of the Bd./CEO, A.H. Belo Corporation, TX, Dallas

Deck, Cecilia ....(408) 864-8588
deckcecilia@deanza.edu, Journalism Chair, De Anza College, CA, Cupertino

Deckard, Stephen A. ....(812) 247-2828
steve@theshoalsnews.com, Editor and Publisher, The Shoals News, IN, Shoals

Decker, Bill
bdecker@daily-review.com, Managing Ed. , The Daily Review, LA, Morgan City

Decker, Bill
bill@acadiananow.com, The Daily Advertiser, LA, Lafayette

Decker, Caron ....(717) 264-6161
cdecker@publicopinionnews.com, Controller, Public Opinion, PA, Chambersburg

Decker, Cindy ....(217) 477-5105
cdecker@dancomnews.com, Adv. Sales. Mgr., Commercial News, IL, Danville

Decker, Danyel ....(765)
ddecker@muncie.gannett.com, Classified Sales Rep., The Star Press, IN, Muncie

Decker, Joe
joe@gutcheckfitness.com, Pres./Author, Get Fit with The World's Fittest Man, San Diego

Decker, Lori
ldecker@glasgowdailytimes.com, Acct. Exec., Glasgow Daily Times, KY, Glasgow

Decker, Shirley Pyne
shirley@dckr.com, Ed., County Shopper, NY, Delhi

Decoste, Francoise ....ext. 0
secretaire@leradar.qc.ca, Circ. Mgr., Le Radar, QC, Cap Aux Meules

Decota, Jennifer ....(985) 748-7156
business@tangilena.com, Business Mgr., Amite Tangi-Digest, LA, Amite

Deeds, Lacey
gbnews@pldi.net, Ed., Garber-Billings News, OK, Garber

Deegan, Jim ....(610) 258-7171 ext. 3535

jdeegan@lehighvalleylive.com, Ed., The US, PA, Easton
jdeegan@lehighvalleylive.com, Editor, The Express-Times, PA, Easton

Deegan, Joanne ....(978) 970-4634
jdeegan@lowellsun.com, Lifestyle Copy Ed., The Sun, MA, Lowell

Deegan, Suzanne ....(916) 321-1400
sdeegan@sacbee.com, Adv. Mgr., Nat'l, The Sacramento Bee, CA, Sacramento

Deeks, Gordon ....(780) 429-5577
gdeeks@thejournal.canwest.com, Adv. Mgr., Sales Planning/Nat'l Sales, Edmonton Journal, AB, Edmonton

Deeley, James ....(503) 294-0840 Ext. 16
salesinfo@portlandmercury.com, Adv. Dir., Portland Mercury, OR, Portland

Deere, Vicky
vdeere@enterprise-journal.com, Adv. Mgr., Enterprise-Journal, MS, McComb

Deflitch, Jerry
jdeflitch@tribweb.com, Ed, The Jeannette Spirit, PA, Greensburg

Defrang, Lindsie
ldefrang@ncppub.com, Ed. , Steele County Press, ND, Finley

Degenstien, Dave ....(306) 528-2020
editor@lastmountaintimes.ca, Owner/Pub Ed, Last Mountain Times, SK, Nokomis

Deggendorf, Steve
sdeggendorf@thehawkeye.com, Prodn. Mgr., Hawk Eye Shopper, IA, Burlington

Deggendorf, Steve
sdeggendorf@thehawkeye.com, Prodn. Mgr., The Hawk Eye, IA, Burlington

Degrood, MaryKay
maryk@homemagonline.com, Sales Mgr., Home Magazine, MN, Mankato

Dehlinger, Tom
tdehlinger@isthmus.com, Circ. Mgr., Isthmus, WI, Madison

Deibert, Kendra ....(605) 692-6271
registerdesign@brookingsregister.com, Mgr., Brookings Register, SD, Brookings

Deis, Bob
bob_deis@nela-usa.com, Mgr., Engineering, NELA, WI, River Falls

Deitiker, Kristi
kristi.deitiker@ttu.edu, Texas Tech University, TX, Lubbock

Deitrich, Jessica ....(574) 732-5123
jessica.deitrich@pharostribune.com, HR/ Finance, Pharos-Tribune, IN, Logansport

Deitz, Harry J. ....(610) 371-5004
hdeitz@readingeagle.com, Associate Pub/Ed., Reading Eagle, PA, Reading

Dejoie-Hall, Renette
rdh@louisianaweekly.com, Exec. Ed., Louisiana Weekly, LA, New Orleans

Del Toro, Jesus
jesus.deltoro@impremedia.com, EIC, La Prensa, FL, Longwood

Del-Riccio, Ana 4314-8788
ana.del-riccio@dowjones.com, Sales Exec., Dow Jones Newswires - Buenos Aires, Argentina, Buenos Aires

DelBello, Dee
dee@westfairinc.com, Pub., Fairfield County Business Journal, NY, White Plains
dee@westfairinc.com, Pub., Westchester County Business Journal, NY, White Plains

DelMauro, John
john.delmauro@sourcemedia.com, SVP, Conferences, American Banker, NY, New York

Delamater, Mary ....(207) 689-2825
mdelamater@sunjournal.com, Copy Ed., Sun Journal, ME, Lewiston

Delaney, Leigh Ann ....(318) 757-3646
leighann@concordiasentinel.com, Advertising, Concordia Sentinel, LA, Ferriday

Delaney, Michael ....(401) 277-7220
mdelaney@providencejournal.com, Mang. Ed. Visuals, The Providence Journal, RI, Providence

Delaney, Robert ....(850) 747-5000
rdelaney@pcnh.com, Rgl.Controller, The News Herald, FL, Panama City
rdelaney@pcnh.com, Rgl. Controller , Halifax Media, FL, Daytona Beach

Delaney, Steve ....(319) 758-8110
sdelaney@thehawkeye.com, Pub./Ed., The Hawk Eye, IA, Burlington

Delaney, Steve
sdelaney@thehawkeye.com, Ed., Hawk Eye Shopper, IA, Burlington

Delaney, Tim ....(361) 526-2397
refugiocountypress@mysoutex.com, Ed., Refugio County Press, TX, Refugio

Delano, Norman
fobnews@aol.com, Pub., Four Oaks-Benson News in Review, NC, Benson

Delano Brown, Jane ....(919) 962-4089
Prof./James L. Knight, University of North Carolina, NC, Chapel Hill

Delany, Patrick
pdelany@yorkdispatch.com, Editorial Page Ed., The York Dispatch, PA, York

Delasho, Kenneth
info@industrialacoustics.com, Pres., Industrial Acoustics Co., NY, Bronx

Delatore, Denise
ddelatore@heraldstaronline.com, Adv. Dir., Herald-Star, OH, Steubenville

Delatore, Denise ....(740) 283-4711 ext. 317
ddelatore@heraldstaronline.com, Adv. Dir., Weirton Daily Times, OH, Steubenville

Delazzer, Anita
adelazzer@cbpost.com, Pub., The Cape Breton Post, NS, Sydney

Delcorto, Elysa ....(239) 263-4726
Editor, The Banner, FL, Naples

Deleon, Nick
ndeleon@thedalleschronicle.com, Class. Mgr., The Dalles Daily Chronicle, OR, The Dalles

Delhaye, Vicki ....(217) 443-8484
indnews@news-gazette.com, Editor/office manager, Independent News, IL, Danville

Delhotal, Tim
tdelhotal@martinautomatic.com, Contract Admin., Martin Automatic, Inc., IL, Rockford

Delinski, Rachel
rdelinski@mysanfordherald.com, Ed., Sanford Herald, FL, Sanford

Dell, Cheryl
cdell@sacbee.com, Pres./Pub., The Sacramento Bee, CA, Sacramento

Dell, Cheryl
cdell@sacbee.com, Chairman, Inland Press Association, IL, Des Plaines

Dell'Aquila, Johanna ....(201) 459-2836
Admin, Advance Internet, Inc., NJ, Jersey City

Dellavecchia, Mike ....(609) 272-7343
MDellavecchia@pressofac.com, Digital Mgr., The Press of Atlantic City, NJ, Pleasantville

Delli Carpini, Domenico ....(201) 358-6692
ddellicarp@aol.com, Vice President , America Oggi, NJ, Norwood

Dellinger, Sara
sdellinger@seattleweekly.com, Ad Director, Seattle Weekly, WA, Seattle

Dellinger, Timothy O. ....(910) 323-0349
tim@newspaperconsultants.com, President, Advantage Newspaper Consultants, NC, Fayetteville

Deloach, Harris
harris.deloach@sonoco.com, Pres., Sonoco Products Co., SC, Hartsville

Delperdang, Judy
judy.delperdang@globegazette.com, Librarian, Globe Gazette, Mason City, IA, Mason City

Delso, Nick .... **(318) 362-0234**
Asst. Mng. Ed., Online/Sports, The News-Star, LA, Monroe

Deluca, Dean
dean.deluca@pittsburghpennysaver.com, Gen. Mgr., Pennysaver, PA, Pittsburgh

Delventhal, William
w.delventhal@antonnews.com, Gen. Mgr., Anton Community Newspapers, NY, Mineola

Demarco, Marisa .... **ext. 245**
marisademarco@kunm.org, News Ed., Weekly Alibi, NM, Albuquerque

Demarest, Dusti .... **(253) 274-7380**
ddemarest@theolympian.com, Features Ed., The Olympian, WA, Olympia

Demas, Carol
cdemas@timesshamrock.com, Nat'l. Adv. Mgr., The Times-Tribune, PA, Scranton

Dembski, Jeff .... **(847) 498-4520**
jeffrey.dembski@sourcemedia.com, Adv., Midwest, American Banker, NY, New York

Demeer, Andrea
ademeer@bowesnet.com, Pub., Oxford Shopping News/review, ON, Woodstock

Demeer, Andrea
classifieds@brantfordpennysaver.com, Pub., Brantford Pennysaver, ON, Brantford

Demeer, Andrea .... **(519) 537-2341ext. 241**
andrea.demeer@sunmedia.ca, Pub., Woodstock Sentinel-Review, ON, Woodstock
andrea.demeer@sunmedia.ca, Princeton Similkameen Spotlight, BC, Princeton

Demeer, Andrea
classifieds@kitchenerpennysaver.com, Pub./ Gen. Mgr., Pennysaver, ON, Kitchener

Demeer, Andrea
g-pennysaver@on.albn.com, Gen. Mgr., Guelph Pennysaver, ON, Guelph

Demers, David
ddemers@candgnews.com, Circ. Mgr, Farmington Press, MI, Warren
ddemers@candgnews.com, Circ. Mgr, West Bloomfield Beacon, MI, Warren
ddemers@candgnews.com, Circ. Mgr, Rochester Post, MI, Warren
ddemers@candgnews.com, Circ. Mgr, Royal Oak Review, MI, Warren
ddemers@candgnews.com, Circ. Mgr, Southfield Sun, MI, Warren
ddemers@candgnews.com, Circ. Mgr, St. Clair Shores Sentinel, MI, Warren
ddemers@candgnews.com, Circ. Mgr, Madison-Park News, MI, Warren
ddemers@candgnews.com, Circ. Mgr, Birmingham-Bloomfield Eagle, MI, Warren
ddemers@candgnews.com, Circ. Mgr, Woodward Talk, MI, Warren
ddemers@candgnews.com, Circ. Mgr, Warren Weekly, MI, Warren
ddemers@candgnews.com, Circ. Mgr, The Eastsider, MI, Warren
ddemers@candgnews.com, Circ. Mgr, Macomb Chronicle, MI, Warren
ddemers@candgnews.com, Circ. Mgr, Fraser-Clinton Chronicle, MI, Warren
ddemers@candgnews.com, Circ. Mgr, Sterling Heights Sentry, MI, Warren
ddemers@candgnews.com, Circ. Mgr, Grosse Pointe Times, MI, Warren
ddemers@candgnews.com, Circ. Mgr, Advertiser Times, MI, Warren
ddemers@candgnews.com, Circ. Mgr, Shelby-Utica News, MI, Warren
ddemers@candgnews.com, Circ. Mgr, Journal, MI, Warren
ddemers@candgnews.com, Assoc. Prof., Washington State University, WA, Pullman

Demers, Gregg
gdemers@candnews.com, Ed., Macomb Chronicle, MI, Warren

Demers, Gregg .... **(586) 498-1042**
jdemers@candgnews.com, Owner, Advertiser Times, MI, Warren

Demers, Gregg .... **(586) 498-1042**
gdemers@candgnews.com, Editorial Dir., C & G Newspapers, MI, Warren

Demers, Gregg
gdemers@candgnews.com, Ed., Birmingham-Bloomfield Eagle, MI, Warren

Demers, Gregg .... **(586) 498-1042**
gdemers@candgnews.com, Ed. Dir., Woodward Talk, MI, Warren

Demers, Jeff
jdemers@candgnews.com, Circ. Mgr., Troy Times, MI, Warren

Demers, Jeff
jdemers@candgnews.com, Adv. Mgr., Advertiser Times, MI, Warren

Demers, Jeff
jdemers@candgnews.com, Adv. Mgr., Madison-Park News, MI, Warren

Demers, Jeff
jdemers@candgnews.com, Adv. Mgr., Grosse Pointe Times, MI, Warren

Demers, Jeff .... **(586) 498-1031**
jdemers@candgnews.com, Adv. Sales Mgr., Macomb Chronicle, MI, Warren

Demers, Jeff
jdemers@candgnews.com, Pub., Warren Weekly, MI, Warren

Demers, Jeff .... **(586) 498-1031**
jdemers@candgnews.com, Adv. Sales Mgr., Birmingham-Bloomfield Eagle, MI, Warren

Demers, Jeff .... **(586) 291-1874**
jdemers@candgnews.com, Adv. Mgr., Fraser-Clinton Chronicle, MI, Warren

Demers, Jeff .... **(586) 498-8000**
jdemers@candgnews.com, Dir of Sales, Farmington Press, MI, Warren
jdemers@candgnews.com, Pub., Journal, MI, Warren
jdemers@candgnews.com, Dir of Sales, Royal Oak Review, MI, Warren
jdemers@candgnews.com, Pub., The Eastsider, MI, Warren
jdemers@candgnews.com, Dir of Sales, Southfield Sun, MI, Warren
jdemers@candgnews.com, Pub., St. Clair Shores Sentinel, MI, Warren
jdemers@candgnews.com, Adv. Dir., C & G Newspapers, MI, Warren

Demers, Jeff .... **(586) 291-1874**
jdemers@candgnews.com, Pub., Sterling Heights Sentry, MI, Warren

Demers, Jeff .... **(586) 498-1031**
jdemers@candgnews.com, Dir of Sales, Rochester Post, MI, Warren
jdemers@candgnews.com, Pub., West Bloomfield Beacon, MI, Warren

Demers, Lisa A.
newsroom@pioneertribune.com, Pub., Pioneer Tribune, MI, Manistique

Demers, Matt .... **(518) 561-7408**
mattdemers@primhall.com, Mktg. Coord., Prim Hall Enterprises, Inc., NY, Plattsburgh

Demidov, Yuri .... **(973) 569-7744**
Demidov@northjersey.com, VP Internet Technology, Herald News, NJ, Rockaway

Demjanik, Daniel .... **(888) 942-3253**
Regl. Mgr., Church Rickards, Whitlock & Co., Inc., IL, Westchester

Demko, David J. .... **(904) 629-6020**
AgeVentureNewsService@demko.com, Ed.-in-Chief, AgeVenture News Service, Orange Park

Demming, Brenda

sunweekly@aol.com, Circulation Mgr, Shreveport Sun, LA, Shreveport

Demola, Pete .... **(518) 873-6368**
pete@suncommunitynews.com, Asst Mgr Ed, The Valley News Sun, NY, Elizabethtown

Demola, Pete .... **(518) 873-6368 x213**
pete@suncommunitynews.com, Asst Mgr Ed, The North Countryman Sun, NY, Elizabethtown

Demont-Heinrich, Christof
christof.demont-heinrich@du.edu, Asst. Prof., University of Denver, CO, Denver

Demory, Kim
egeagle@goldfieldaccess.net, Ed., Eagle Grove Eagle, IA, Eagle Grove

Dempsey, Jeff .... **(415) 944-4561**
jdempsey@thearknewspaper.com, Prod ed & youth reporter, The Ark, CA, Tiburon

Dempsey, John
sports@h-ponline.com, Sports Ed., Huntington Herald-Press, IN, Huntington

Dempsey, John Mark
John_Dempsey@tamu-commerce.edu, Assoc. Prof., Texas A&M University-Commerce, TX, Commerce

Dempsey, Joy-Ann .... **(514) 636-7314**
joyann.dempsey@tc.tc, Sales Support Supervisor, The Chronicle, QC, Dorval

Dempsey, Joy-Ann .... **(514) 636-7314**
joyann.dempsey@tc.tc, Sales Support Supervisor, Cites Nouvelles, QC, Dorval

Dempsey, Mary .... **(518) 828-1616, ext. 2533**
mdempsey@registerstar.com, Executive Editor, The Daily Mail, NY, Hudson

Demuth, Gary .... **(785) 822-1405 ext. 109**
sjgdemuth@saljournal.com, Society Ed., The Salina Journal, KS, Salina

Denault, Sylvain
sylvain.denault@latribune.qc.ca, Adv. Dir., La Tribune, QC, Sherbrooke

Dendurent, Mike
mdendurent@themercury.com, Wire Ed., The Manhattan Mercury, KS, Manhattan

Deneault, Benoit .... **bdeneault@hilltimes.com**
bdeneault@hilltimes.com, Prod. Mgr., The Hill Times, ON, Ottawa

Denesha, Sherry .... **(416) 756-2213**
sherryd@taylorenterprises.com, Operations Manager, RTDNA - Canada (Radio Television Digital News Association), ON, Markham

Dengler, John .... **(417) 836-1206**
jdengler@news-leader.com, Graphics Ed., Springfield News-Leader, MO, Springfield

Denham, Janice
denham3@sbcglobal.net, treasurer, Missouri Press Women, MO, Kirkwood

Denison, Georgi
georgi@creemore.com, Office Mgr., Creemore Echo, ON, Creemore

Denk, Jon .... **(608) 745-3571**
jdenk@capitalnewspapers.com, General Manager, Sauk Prairie Eagle, WI, Baraboo
jdenk@capitalnewspapers.com, Adv. Dir., Daily Register, WI, Portage

Denk, Jon .... **(608) 745-3571**
GM, Badgerland Values Columbia County, WI, Portage

Denk, Jon .... **(608) 745-3571**
jdenk@capitalnewspapers.com, General Manager, Reedsburg Times-Press, WI, Baraboo
jdenk@capitalnewspapers.com, Gen. Mgr., Wisconsin Dells Events, WI, Portage
jdenk@capitalnewspapers.com, Adv. Dir., Baraboo News Republic, WI, Baraboo

Denke, Kevin .... **ext. 225**
kdenke@metrowestnewspapers.com, Ed., Fort Lupton Press, CO, Brighton

kdenke@metrowestnewspapers.com, Ed., Commerce City Sentinel Express, CO, Brighton

Dennan, John F.
jdennan@starledger.com, Gen. Mgr., The Star-Ledger, NJ, Newark

Dennehy, Sharon .... **(214) 785-7661**
Paris Junior College, TX, Paris

Denney, Ken .... **(470) 729-3254**
ken@times-georgian.com, Ed., The Villa Rican, GA, Carrollton

Denning, W. Mitchel
mitch.denning@jacksonville.com, Controller, Div., The Florida Times-Union, FL, Jacksonville

Dennis, Abigail
editor@madisoniannews.com, News Ed., The Madisonian, MT, Ennis

Dennis, Andy .... **(270) 783-3235**
adennis@bgdailynews.com, Managing Ed., Daily News, KY, Bowling Green

Dennis, Bruce .... **(970) 392-4429**
bdennis@greeleytribune.com, Sales Mgr., Windsor Now, CO, Windsor

Dennis, Carolyn
classifieds@citizen.on.ca, Classifieds , Orangeville Citizen, ON, Orangeville

Dennis, Howie
Howie.Dennis@CrowleyToday.com, Ed., The Crowley Post-Signal, LA, Crowley

Dennis, Joan
sales@alliance-rubber.com, Director Sales & Marketing, Alliance Rubber Co., AR, Hot Springs

Dennis, Kathy
kdennis@parkrapidsenterprise.com, Circ. Mgr, Park Rapids Enterprise, MN, Park Rapids

Dennis, Larry
larry@mansfieldmirror.com, Ed./Pub., The Mansfield Mirror/Wright Co. Republican, MO, Mansfield

Dennis, Laura .... **(432) 333-7740**
ldennis@oaoa.com, Editor, Odessa American, TX, Odessa

Dennis, Pete .... **(740) 592-6612 Ext. 212**
pdennis@athensmessenger.com, APG Media Adv. Dir. , The Athens Messenger, OH, Athens

Dennis, Rob .... **(510) 659-6074**
rdennis@ohlone.edu, Adviser, Ohlone College, CA, Fremont

Dennis, Sarah .... **(902) 426-3345**
sdennis@herald.ca, Pub./CEO/Vice Pres., The Chronicle Herald, NS, Halifax

Dennis, Tom
tdennis@gfherald.com, Editorial Page Ed., Grand Forks Herald, ND, Grand Forks

Dennison, Brad .... **(630) 368-1100**
Senior Vice Pres., Content/News Opns., GateHouse Media, Inc., NY, Pittsford

Denny, Debbie
ddenny@bastropadvertiser.com, Adv. Dir., The Bastrop Advertiser, TX, Bastrop

Denny, Kevin
kdenny@oregonian.com, VP and General Manager, The Oregonian, OR, Portland

Denny, Liz .... **(859) 623-1669 Ext. 6708**
lshort@richmondregister.com, Page Designer, The Richmond Register, KY, Richmond

Denny, Shannie .... **(937) 547-0851 ext. 215**
sdenny@earlybirdpaper.com, Prod. Mgr., The Early Bird, OH, Greenville

Denny, Vickie .... **(918) 885-2101**
hominynews2@gmail.com, Pub./Ed., Pawnee Chief, OK, Pawnee
hominynews2@gmail.com, Gen Mgr, The Hominy News-Progress, OK, Hominy

Denny-Bailey, Tracy
tracy@nashvilleleader.com, The Nashville News-Leader, AR, Nashville

Deno, Chris ....(765) 420-5277
cdeno@journalandcourier.com, Controller, Journal and Courier, IN, Lafayette

Densmore, Greg ....(281) 391-3141
news@katytimes.com, Mgr. Ed., The Katy Times, TX, Katy

Denson, Donna
ddenson@semissourian.com, Adv. Dir., Southeast Missourian Plus, MO, Cape Girardeau

Denson, Sandy ....(281) 425-8003
sunnews@baytownsun.com, Business Manager/HR, The Baytown Sun, TX, Baytown

Denton, David
ddenton@iwanna.com, Prodn. Mgr., Iwanna, SC, Greenville

Denton, Frank ....(904) 359-4197
frank.denton@jacksonville.com, Ed., The Florida Times-Union, FL, Jacksonville

Denty, Eric ....(912) 427-3757
edenty@bellsouth.net, Pub., The Press-Sentinel, GA, Jesup

Denty, Eric
edenty@thetelfairenterprise.com, Pub., The Telfair Enterprise, GA, Mc Rae

Depies, Lisa
editor@geneseorepublic.com, Ed., Geneseo Republic, IL, Geneseo

Deppe, Jackie F.
commnews@communitypapers.net, Pub./Gen. Mgr./Adv. Mgr., West Side Community News & West Indianapolis Community News, IN, Indianapolis

Deptula, Tom ....(212) 594-2266 ext. 113
td@dziennik.com, Commentator, Nowy Dziennik, NJ, Garfield

Depuoz, Thomas
thomas.depuoz@corbis.com, Office Mgr., Corbis, New York

Deramus, Hallee
ads@mccurtain.com, Adv. Dir., Broken Bow News, OK, Idabel
ads@mccurtain.com, Adv. Dir., McCurtain Daily Gazette, OK, Idabel

Derby, Bill ....(423) 979-1300
bderby@jcnewsandneighbor.com, Pub./Ed., Johnson City News & Neighbor, TN, Johnson City

Derby, Jeff ....(423) 979-1300
jderby@jcnewsandneighbor.com, Assoc. Publisher, Johnson City News & Neighbor, TN, Johnson City

Deremer, Charles
cd@ogdennews.com, Controller, The Intelligencer, WV, Wheeling

Derksen, Jeremy
publisher@fitzhugh.ca, Pub., The Fitzhugh, AB, Jasper

Dermody, Tom
cathpost@mcleodusa.net, Ed., The Catholic Post, IL, Peoria

Dermont, Stacy
stacy@danspapers.com, Sr. Ed. , Dan's Papers LLC, NY, Southampton

Dernosek, Jessica
jessicaashley@theweeklyrecorder.com, Owner/Pub./Ed., The Weekly Recorder, PA, Eighty Four

Derocher, Anna
aderocher@rrstar.com, Mng. Ed., The Journal-Standard, IL, Freeport

Derocher, Anna.......................(815) 987-1431
aderocher@rrstar.com, Asst. Mng. Ed., Rockford Register Star, IL, Rockford

Deroeck, Corky ....(906) 786-2021
cderoeck@dailypress.net, Publisher, Daily Press, MI, Escanaba

Derr, John ....(717) 291-8821
jderr@lnpnews.com, VP of Client Solutions, LNP Media Group, Inc., PA, Lancaster

Derraugh, Annette
annette@simcoeyorkprinting.com, The Times Of New Tecumseth, ON, Beeton

Derrer, Nancy
info@shieldmedia.ca, Ed., Havelock Citizen, ON, Marmora

Derringer, Alan
aderringer@detroitnews.com, Auto Editor, Detroit Free Press, MI, Detroit

Dershowitz, Toby
toby@ajpa.org, Exec. Dir., American Jewish Press Association, DC, Washington

Derstine, Steven P.
info@mediasupply.com, Sales Mgr., Media Supply, Inc., PA, Exton

Dertinger, Jeff ....(519) 756-2020 ext. 2219
jeff.dertinger@sunmedia.ca, Mng. Ed. , Brandtford Expositor, ON, Brantford

DesJardins, Marc ....(831) 566-3920
mdesjardins@santacruzsentinel.com, Feat. Ed., Santa Cruz Sentinel, CA, Scotts Valley

Desai, Jigsha ....(239) 403-6146
jigsh.desai@naplesnews.com, Digital Content Director, Naples Daily News, FL, Naples

Desalvo, Joe ....(904) 359-4366
joe.desalvo@jacksonville.com, Managing Ed., Sports, Features and Specialty Publications, The Florida Times-Union, FL, Jacksonville

Desch, Larry ....(920) 683-4731
Univ. of Wisconsin Center, WI, Manitowoc

Deschamps, Laurent C. ....(410) 263-8593
info@sparusa.com, Pres., Spar Associates, Inc., MD, Annapolis

Descoteaux, Bernard
bdescoteaux@ledevoir.com, Pub., Le Devoir, QC, Montreal

Deselms, Jen.......................(361) 886-3627
deselmsj@caller.com, News Ed., Corpus Christi Caller-Times, TX, Corpus Christi

Desilets, Lorna
circ@hayriverhub.com, Circ. Mgr., The Hub, NT, Hay River

Desjardins, Claude ....ext. 338
Ed. in Chief, Le Groupe Jcl Inc., QC, Saint Eustache

Desjardins, Stephane ....(514) 899-5888
bradettes@transcontinental.ca, Flambeau, QC, Montreal

Desjardins, Stephane .... ext. 2203
sdesjardins@transcontinental.ca, Journal De Rosemont / Petite Patrie, QC, Montreal
sdesjardins@transcontinental.ca, Nouvelles Hochelaga Maisonneuve, QC, Montreal
sdesjardins@transcontinental.ca, Plateau, QC, Montreal
sdesjardins@transcontinental.ca, publisher, Transcontinental Medias, QC, Montreal

Desmarteau, Charles.................(514) 926-2354
c.desmarteau@videotron.ca, Ed. & Gen. Mgr., La Reléve, QC, Boucherville

Desmarteau, Charles ....(450) 641-4844
c.desmarteau@videotron.ca, Pub. , La Seigneurie, QC, Boucherville

Desmond, Kevin ....(612) 673-8710
kevin.desmond@startribune.com, Sr. VP, Op., Star Tribune, MN, Minneapolis

Desmond, Mackenzie ....(518) 861-4026
Adv representative, The Altamont Enterprise & Albany County Post, NY, Altamont

Desmond, Pat ....(617) 696-7758 X 106
pat@miltontimes.com, Publisher, Milton Times, MA, Milton

Despeaux, Bryant ....(202) 334-8365
bryant.despeaux@washpost.com, Division Manager Commercial Sales $ Deli, The Washington Post, DC, Washington

Desrochers, Ariane
ariane.desrochers@monteregieweb.com, Ed., L'information, QC, Sainte Julie

Desroches, Jacques ....(770) 421-7700
Gen. Mgr., Markem-Imaje, GA, Kennesaw

Desroches, Patty
pdesroches@valleyadvocate.com, Adv. Dir., Valley Advocate, MA, Northampton

Desrosiers, Francis
francis.desrosiers @ hebdosquebecor.com, Dir. Gen., L'avant-poste Gaspesien, QC, Amqui

Desrosiers, Francis
journalinformation@globetrotter.net, Le Information, QC, Mont-Joli
journalinformation@globetrotter.net, Ed., L'information, QC, Riviere-du-Loup

Desrosiers, Rich ....(330) 580-8310
rich.desrosiers@cantonrep.com, Exec. Ed., The Repository, OH, Canton

Detjen, Jim
detjen@msu.edu, Prof./Dir., Knight Ctr., Michigan State University, MI, East Lansing

Deutsch, Glenn
Pleiadh@albion.edu, Albion College, MI, Albion

Deutsch, Kevin
scourier@sbtc.net, Pub./Ed., Sisseton Courier, SD, Sisseton

Deutsch, Ted
publisher@americanisraelite.com, Pub., The American Israelite, OH, Cincinnati

Devall, Cheryl ....(337) 943-7032
cdevall@gannett.com, City Ed., Daily World, LA, Opelousas

Devally, Adriana ....(956) 728-2511
adriana@lmtonline.com, Adv. Dir., Laredo Morning Times, TX, Laredo

Devincenzi, Robert J.
rdevincenzi@themilpitaspost.com, Ed., Fremont Bulletin, CA, Milpitas

Devine, Jacqueline ....(575) 437-7120 ext. 7123
jadevine@alamogordonews.com, Hollogram Ed., Alamogordo Daily News, NM, Alamogordo

Devine, Kevin ....(734) 487-1026
kdevine@emich.edu, Student Media Dir., Eastern Michigan University, MI, Ypsilanti

Devitt, Phil
pdevitt@hathawaypublishing.com, Gen. Mgr., The Chronicle, MA, New Bedford

Devlin, Michelle
mdevlin@highpoint.edu, Admin. Asst., High Point Univ., NC, High Point

Devlin, Sean.........................(715) 463-2341
editor@burnettcountysentinel.com, Editor, Burnett County Sentinel, WI, Grantsburg

Devlin, Shawna ....(239) 435-3473
shawna.devlin@naplesnews.com, Advertising Director, Naples Daily News, FL, Naples

Devore, Lenore ....(863) 802-7501
lenore.devore@theledger.com, Ed., The Ledger, KS, Hesston
lenore.devore@theledger.com, Ed., The Ledger, FL, Lakeland

Devore-Mitchell, Ophelia
columbustimes@knology.net, Pub., The Columbus Times, GA, Columbus

Dew, Megan ....(919) 789-2087
megan@ncpress.com, Media Director , North Carolina Press Association, NC, Raleigh

Dewaele, Lou.........................(406) 791-6543
ldewaele@greatfallstribune.com, Circ. Sales and Retention Mgr., Great Falls Tribune, MT, Great Falls

Dewall, Tricia
tdewall@iowacity.gannett.com, Asst. Ed., Iowa City Press-Citizen, IA, Iowa City

Dewalt, Gregg ....(256) 740-5748
gregg.dewalt@timesdaily.com, Sports Ed., Times Daily, AL, Florence

Dewar, Tim ....(805) 646-1476
publisher@ojaivalleynews.com, Pub., Ojai Valley News, CA, Ojai

Dewitt, Larry
info@creweb.com, Pres., Commodity Resource & Environment, CA, Burbank

Dews Jr., Warren C.
wdews@berkshireeagle.com, CCSEO, New England Newspapers Inc, MA, Pittsfield
wdews@berkshireeagle.com, VP, Audience Development, Sales, Mktg, The Berkshire Eagle, MA, Pittsfield

Dey, Jim.........................(217) 351-5369
jdey@news-gazette.com, Opinions Page Ed., The News-Gazette, IL, Champaign

Deyo, Amber
publisher@springfieldtimes.net, Pub., Springfield Times, OR, Springfield

Dezort, Jeff ....(870) 446-2645
jeffd@newtoncountytimes.com, Editor, The Newton County Times, AR, Jasper

Dhillon, Paul ....(604) 880-3463
editorpd@hotmail.com, Ed., The Link, BC, Surrey

Dhondt, Melodie Susan.......................ext. 130
Sr. Ed., Suburban Parent, NJ, North Brunswick

Di Carlo, John ....(215) 204-5888
john.dicarlo@temple.edu, Temple University, PA, Philadelphia

Di Pietro, Sylvia.......................(212) 255-4059
femalelitigator@yahoo.com, Self-Syndicator, Sylvia Di Pietro, New York

Di Salvo, Andrea
editor@rapidserve.net, Ed., Heppner Gazette-Times, OR, Heppner

DiBagno, Nathan
ndibagno@civitasmedia.com, Rgl. Local Bus. Develop. Mgr., Mount Airy News, NC, Mount Airy

DiBiasio, Rachel
countykids@news-herald.com, Gen. Mgr., Lake County Kids, OH, Willoughby

DiDomenico, Tracy ....(216) 342-5184
tdidomenico@cjn.org, Controller, Cleveland Jewish News, OH, Beachwood

DiLeo, John ....(203) 680-9924
jdileo@newhavenregister.com, Advt Dir, The Dolphin, CT, Groton

DiMambro, John ....(402) 563-7503
jdimambro@columbustelegram.com, Interim Pub., The Columbus Telegram, NE, Columbus

DiMarzio, Bishop Nicholas
thetablet@aol.com, Pub., The Tablet, NY, Brooklyn

DiMauro, Sharon.............(707) 964-5642 ext. 14
sdimauro@advocate-news.com, Pub., Fort Bragg Advocate-News, CA, Fort Bragg

DiMauro, Sharon.......................(707) 964-5642
sdimauro@mcn.org, Adv. Mgr., The Mendocino Beacon, CA, Fort Bragg

DiMenna, Hernan 4309-7216
hdimenna@clarin-contenidos.com.ar, Ed., Clarin Contenidos, CA, Buenos Aires

DiMiceli, Vince.......................(718) 260-4508
VDiMiceli@CNGLocal.com, EIC, Bay News, NY, Brooklyn

DiModica, Paul.......................(617) 325-1500
pdimodica@bulletinnewspapers.com, Pub., West Roxbury/Rosindale Bulletin, MA, Hyde Park

DiModica, Paul.........................(617) 325-1500
news@jamaicaplainbulletin.com, Pub., The
Boston Bulletin, MA, Hyde Park

DiModica, Paul.........................(617) 361-8400
pdimodica@bulletinnewspapers.com, Pub.,
Hyde Park Bulletin, MA, Norwood

DiNardo, Daniel
tch@archgh.org, Pub., The Texas Catholic
Herald, TX, Houston

DiNicola, Tony
tdinicola@gazettextra, Graphics Ed./Art
Dir., The Janesville Gazette - GazetteXtra,
WI, Janesville

DiPaolo, Roger......................(330) 298-2023
editor@recordpub.com, Ed., Record-Courier,
OH, Kent

DiSandro, Deb.........................(815) 439-1172
deb@slightlyoff.com, Author/Owner, Slightly
Off!, Plainfield

DiSanto, Laura
laura@thetriangle.org, Staff Mgr, Drexel Univ.,
PA, Philadelphia

DiVenere, Leslie
ldivenere@catholictranscript.org, Graphic
Designer, The Catholic Transcript, CT,
Bloomfield

DiVincenzo, Leslie....................(800) 399-4294
leslie@bob-weber.com, Director of Marketing,
Bob Weber, Inc., OH, Cleveland

Diaczuk, Doug
ddiaczuk@dougallmedia.com, Reporter,
Thunder Bay Source, ON, Thunder Bay

Diamataris, Anthony H.
publisher@thenationalherald.com, Ed., The
National Herald, NY, Long Island City

Diamataris, Victoria........ (718) 784-5255 ext. 101
advertising.athens@ekirikas.com, Asst. to
Pub., The National Herald, NY, Long Island
City

Diamond, Arlen
arlendiamond@missouristate.edu, Prof.,
Missouri State University, MO, Springfield

Dianda, Mario.........................(650) 391-1342
mdianda@dailynewsgroup.com, Exec. Ed.,
Palo Alto Daily News, CA, Menlo Park

Dianda, Mario
mdianda@mercurynews.com, Editor, Silicon
Valley Community Newspapers, CA, San
Jose

Diane, Shannon
dshannon@farragutpress.com, Adverstising
Sales, Farragut Press, TN, Farragut

Diaz, Doris.........................(909) 862-1771
ddiaz@highlandnews.net, Gen. Mgr., Highland
Community News, CA, Highland

Diaz, Fernando
fernando.diaz@wellsfargo.com, Managing
Editor, Hoy LLC, CA, Los Angeles
fernando.diaz@wellsfargo.com, Mng. Ed.,
Digital, San Francisco Chronicle, CA, San
Francisco

Diaz, Iris.........................(469) 977-3723
idiaz@aldiatx.com, Mktg. Exec., Al Dia, TX,
Dallas

Diaz, John
jdiaz@sfchronicle.com, Editorial Page Ed, San
Francisco Chronicle, CA, San Francisco

Diaz, Julio.........................(850) 435-8699
jdiaz@pnj.com, Community Content Editor,
Pensacola News Journal, FL, Pensacola

Diaz, Margarita
margarita.diaz@quinnipiac.edu, Asst. Prof.,
Quinnipiac University, CT, Hamden

Diaz, Mauro.........................(469) 977-3677
mdiaz@aldiatx.com, Sports Ed., Al Dia, TX,
Dallas

Dibiase, Carol
cdibiase@franklinshopper.com, Sales

Manager, The Franklin Shopper, PA,
Chambersburg

Dick, Brad
bdick@sunprintinginc.com, Norwich
Pennysaver, NY, Norwich
bdick@sunprintinginc.com, Circ. Mgr., Sidney
Pennysaver, NY, Norwich

Dick, Brad
bdick@evesun.com, Circ. Mgr., Wharton Valley
Pennysaver, NY, Norwich

Dick, Clint
clintondick@ottawaherald.com, Sports
Reporter, The Ottawa Herald, KS, Ottawa

Dick, Marie
marie@wheatstate.net, Asst. Prof., St. Cloud
State University, MN, Saint Cloud

Dick, Steve
steve.dick@heraldbulletin.com, Ed., Madison
County Direct, IN, Anderson
steve.dick@heraldbulletin.com, Asst. Ed., The
Herald Bulletin, IN, Anderson

Dickelman, Craig.......... (740) 592-6612 Ext. 230
cdickelman@athensmessenger.com, Bus. Mgr.,
The Athens Messenger, OH, Athens

Dickens, David.........................(270) 505-1494
ddickens@thenewsenterprise.com,
Production Mgr., The News-Enterprise, KY,
Elizabethtown

Dickens, Julie.........................(270) 783-3225
jdickens@bgdailynews.com, Adv. Mgr.,
Classified, Daily News, KY, Bowling Green

Dickerman, Morgan..................(252) 265-7802
mpd@wilsontimes.com, Pub, The Wilson
Times, NC, Wilson

Dickerman, Morgan Paul.............(252) 265-7802
mpd@wilsontimes.com, Pres./Pub., The Wilson
Times, NC, Wilson

Dickerson, Becky
becky@communitycurrentnewspaper.com,
Pub./Ed., The Community Current, WA,
Saint John

Dickerson, Brian.........................(309) 690-5306
bdickerson@multiad.com, VP Prod. Dev., Local
Search Association, IL, Peoria

Dickerson, Cindy
healdtonherald@att.net , Ed, The Healdton
Herald, OK, Healdton

Dickerson, Cindy
healdtonherald@att.net, Ed., Wilson Post-
Democrat, OK, Healdton

Dickerson, Jim.........................(402) 395-2115
albnnuz@frontiernet.net, VP and Creative Dir.,
Naples Florida Weekly, FL, Naples
albnnuz@frontiernet.net, co-publisher,
Petersburg Press, NE, Albion
albnnuz@frontiernet.net, Ed and co-pub,
Albion News, NE, Albion
albnnuz@frontiernet.net, Creative Dir., Punta
Gorda/Port Charlotte Florida Weekly, FL,
Punta Gorda
albnnuz@frontiernet.net, VP and Creative Dir.,
Bonita Springs Florida Weekly, FL, Naples
albnnuz@frontiernet.net, Ed., Petersburg
Press, NE, Petersburg
albnnuz@frontiernet.net, VP and Creative Dir.,
Fort Myers Florida Weekly, FL, Fort Myers
albnnuz@frontiernet.net, VP and Creative Dir.,
Palm Beach Gardens Florida Weekly, FL,
Palm Beach Gardens

Dickerson, Molly.........................(409) 787-2172
screporter@yahoo.com, Reporter, The Sabine
County Reporter, TX, Hemphill

Dickey, Arden.........................(612) 673-4156
arden.dickey@startribune.com, Vice Pres.,
Circ., Knight Ridder, CA, San Jose
arden.dickey@startribune.com, Sr. VP, Cir.,
Star Tribune, MN, Minneapolis

Dickey, Chris.........................(970) 641-1414
publisher@gunnisontimes.com, Pub./Own.,
Gunnison Country Times, CO, Gunnison

Dickey, Donna
ddickey@miamiherald.com, Vice Pres./Broward
Bus. Mgr., Herald Values, FL, Miami

Dickinson, Betty
legals@clintoncountyleader.com, Gen. Mgr,
The Clinton County Leader, MO, Plattsburg

Dickinson, Jon.........................(603) 673-6600
jon@cnicorp.com, Pres., CNI Corp., NH,
Milford

Dickinson, Karen
kdickinson@cmcherald.com, Adv. Sales, Cape
May County Herald Times, NJ, Rio Grande

Dickson, Bonnie
bdickson@lcsnw.org, Ed., Senior Scene, WA,
Tacoma

Dickson, Charles.........................(819) 647-2204
charles.dickson@theequity.ca, Pub, The Equity,
QC, Shawville

Dickson, Ross.........................(613) 232-5952
rdickson@hilltimes.com, Pub., The Hill Times,
ON, Ottawa

Dickson , Tod
editor@mvtelegraph.com, Ed., Mountain View
Telegraph, NM, Moriarty

Dicroce, Albert
production@lipennysaver.com, Office Mgr.,
Pennysaver/town Crier, NY, Hicksville

Didier, Barbara
advertising@hclocal.com, Adv Sales, Henry
County Local, KY, Eminence

Diebel, Craig
cdiebel@star-telegram.com, VP, Fort Worth
Star-Telegram, TX, Fort Worth

Dieckman, Tracy.........................(920) 533-8338
sales@thecampbellsportnews.com, Adv.,
Campbellsport News, WI, Campbellsport

Diedrich, Allan.........................(406) 271-5561
ioreporter@theindependentobserver.com,
Reporter, Independent Observer, MT, Conrad

Dieffenbacher, Amy..................(315) 445-4542
dolphin@lemoyne.edu, The Dolphin, NY,
Syracuse

Diehl, Becky.........................(573) 882-6288
diehlb@missouri.edu, Univ. of Missouri, MO,
Columbia

Diehl, Caleb.........................(435) 659-9184
csdiehl@lclark.edu, Editor-in-Chief, Lewis &
Clark College, OR, Portland

Diehl, Dan.........................(785) 336-3475
ctseneca@nvsc.com, Pub., The Courier-
Tribune, KS, Seneca

Diehl, Helen
gm@catskillshopperonline.com, Pub./Gen.
Mgr., Catskill Shopper - Western Sullivan
County (OOB), NY, Liberty
gm@catskillshopperonline.com, Pub./Gen.
Mgr., Catskill Shopper - Eastern Sullivan
County, NY, Liberty
gm@catskillshopperonline.com, Pub./Gen.
Mgr., Catskill Shopper - Ulster County, NY,
Liberty

Diehl, Mark W.
em@douthittcorp.com, Int'l Sales, Douthitt
Corp., MI, Detroit

Diels, Sarah.........................(920) 885-7800
sdiels@conleynet.com, Commun. Coord.,
Conley Media LLC, WI, Beaver Dam

Diem, Caroline.........................(906) 293-8401
nbybusiness@jamadots.com, Bus. Mgr., The
Newberry News, MI, Newberry

Diem, James
nbynews@att.net, Ed., The Newberry News,
MI, Newberry

Dienhart, Rebecca..................(815) 526-4401
rdienhart@shawmedia.com, Major Sales
Coord., Kane County Chronicle, IL, Saint
Charles
rdienhart@shawmedia.com, Major/Nat'l Sales

Coord., Northwest Herald, IL, Crystal Lake

Dieter, Sue.........................(320) 589-2525
sdieter@morrissuntribune.com, Pub., Morris
Sun Tribune, MN, Morris

Dieter, Sue
kerdman@hancockrecord.com, Pub., The
Hancock Record, MN, Morris

Dieterich, Sean.............(928) 537-5721 x 228
sdieterich@wmicentral.com, Ed., White
Mountain Independent, AZ, Show Low

Dietl, J.G..........................(507) 752-7181
lambnews@centurylink.net, Ed., Lamberton
News, MN, Lamberton

Dietrich, Kim.........................(262) 306-5030
kdietrich@conleynet.com, Circulation Dierector,
Weekend Post, WI, West Bend

Dietrich, Shawn
extra@ncppub.com, Adv. Sales, The FM Extra,
MN, Moorhead

Dietterle, Paul.............(603) 742-4455 ext. 2939
pdietterle@fosters.com, Ed. Rep., Foster's
Daily Democrat, NH, Dover

Dietz, Phyllis
somdcirc@somdnews.com, Circ. Exec., The
Enterprise, MD, California
somdcirc@somdnews.com, Circ. Mgr., The
Maryland Independent, MD, White Plains

Diffey, Steve.........................(662) 472-9068
sdiffey@holmescc.edu, District Director of
Communications, Holmes Cmty. College, MS,
Goodman

Diggs, Angel.........................(203) 789-5642
library@nhregister.com, Librarian, New Haven
Register, CT, New Haven

Digmon, Sherry
myrna@atmorenews.com, Co-Pub., Atmore
News, AL, Atmore

Dika, Rebecca.........................(780) 354-2980
rebecca@nextchapterpublishing.ca, Pub., Town
& Country News, AB, Beaverlodge

Dillabough, Lorraine..................(204) 725-0209
Graphic Design - Production, Westman
Journal, MB, Brandon

Dillard, Bob.........................(915) 756-2090
Pub./Ed., Martin County Messenger, TX,
Stanton

Dillard, Bob.........................(915) 426-3077
dispatch@mztv.net, Ed., Jeff Davis County Mt.
Dispatch, TX, Fort Davis

Dillard, Bob.........................(432) 756-2090
mcmessanger@crcom.net, Pub., Greenwood
Ranger, TX, Midland

Dillard, Gabriel
gabriel@thebusinessjournal.com, Mng. Ed.,
The Business Journal, CA, Fresno

Dillaway, Warren............ (440) 998-2323 Ext. 127
warren@starbeacon.com, Staff Writ. / Photo. ,
Star Beacon, OH, Ashtabula

Dillback, Beverly......................(317) 477-3239
bdillback@greenfieldreporter.com, Sales Mgr.,
Daily Reporter, IN, Greenfield

Dillehay, George
george.dillehay@incisivemedia.com, Pub., New
York Law Journal, NY, New York

Dillingham, Bill
bdillingham@heritage.com, Mktg. Dir., Press &
Guide, MI, Southgate

Dillingham, Russell..................(207) 689-2855
rdillingham@sunjournal.com, Chief
Photographer, Sun Journal, ME, Lewiston

Dillingham, Scott N...................(270) 797-3271
progress@vci.net, Mng. Ed., The Dawson
Springs Progress, KY, Dawson Springs

Dillingham, Tina
tdillingham@the-messenger.com, Retail Acct.
Exec., The Messenger, KY, Madisonville

Dillmore, John.........................(918) 341-1101

jdilmore@claremoreprogress.com, Ed. /
Pub., The Claremore Daily Progress, OK,
Claremore

jdilmore@claremoreprogress.com, Pub.,
Decatur Herald (merged with Westside Eagle
Observer), AR, Decatur

Dillon, Carolyn .... (601) 876-5112
tylertowntimes@bellsouth.net, Owner/Ed./Pub.,
The Tylertown Times, MS, Tylertown

Dillon, Greg
gdillon@sheboygansun.com, Publisher, The
Sheboygan Sun, WI, Sheboygan

Dillon, Hannah
hannah.dillon@albertleatribune.com, Special
Sections Ed., Albert Lea Tribune, MN, Albert
Lea

Dillon, John
john.dillon@murraystate.edu, Prof., Murray
State University, KY, Murray

Dillon, John .... (541) 889-5387
johnd@argusobserver.com, Pub./Adv. Dir.,
Argus Observer, OR, Ontario

johnd@argusobserver.com, Pub., Independent-
Enterprise, ID, Payette

Dillon, John .... (541) 823-4830
johnd@argusobserver.com, Pub., Treasure
Valley Reminder, OR, Ontario

Dillon, Karen .... (804) 649-6242
kdillon@timesdispatch.com, Mgr., Pre Press
Design Servs., Richmond Times-Dispatch,
VA, Richmond

Dillon, Peggy
peggy.dillon@salemstate.edu, Salem State
College, MA, Salem

Dillon, Roger
cwave128@gmail.com, Ed., Current Wave
LLC, MO, Eminence

Dilmore, John
jdilmore@nwaonline.com, Pub., Neighbor
Shopper, AR, Siloam Springs

Dimare, Dario .... (508) 877-4444
dario@dariodesigns.com, Pres., Dario
Designs, Inc., MA, Northborough

Dimauro, Lauren
winstedjournal@sbcglobal.net, Office Mgr., The
Winsted Journal, CT, Winsted

Dimecili, Vincent
vdimiceli@cnglocal.com, Ed., New York
Parenting - Brooklyn Family/Manhattan
Family/Queens Family/Bronx-Riverdale
Family/Westchester Family, NY, Brooklyn

Dimesio, Rose ....ext. 294
rose.dimesio@morton.edu, Morton College,
IL, Cicero

Dimichele, Amie
editor@etownian.edu, Elizabethtown College,
PA, Elizabethtown

Dimmick, John
dimmick.1@osu.edu, Assoc. Prof., Ohio State
University, OH, Columbus

Dimmitt, Craig ....(559) 784-5000 Ext. 1011
cdimmitt@portervillerecorder.com, Bus. Mgr.,
The Porterville Recorder, CA, Porterville

Dimock, Donna .... (805) 737-1031
Bus. Mgr., The Lompoc Record, CA, Santa
Maria

Dimond, Jack
dimond@missouristate.edu, Lectr., Missouri
State University, MO, Springfield

Dinan, Stephen
sdinan@washingtontimes.com, Politics Ed.,
The Washington Times, DC, Washington

Dinapoli, Joann .... (212) 210-2355
jdinapoli@nydailynews.com, Retail Adv. Dir.,
New York Daily News, NY, New York

Dinar, Nancy B.
tribuneeditorial@verizon.net, Ed., West Essex
Tribune, NJ, Livingston

Dingman, Judy
editor@auroraadvertiser.net, Gen. Mgr., Aurora
Advertiser, MO, Aurora

Dinkel, John .... (410) 454-0522
jdinkel@bizjournals.com, President &
Publisher, Baltimore Business Journal, MD,
Baltimore

Dinnebier, Kent
kent.dinnebier@clarindaherald.com, Ed., The
Clarinda Herald-Journal, IA, Clarinda

Dinse, Bruce
bdinse@ncbj.net, Circ. Mgr., The Beacon, OH,
Port Clinton

Dinsmore , Pam......................(916) 321-1024
pdinsmore@sacbee.com , Director Community
affairs , The Sacramento Bee, CA,
Sacramento

Dion, Jill .... (203) 402-2315
Ed., Milford Mirror, CT, Shelton

Dionisio, Lori .... (480) 898-6309
ldionisio@timespublications.com, Adv. Admin.,
Ahwatukee Foothills News, AZ, Tempe

ldionisio@timespublications.com, Adv. Mgr.,
East Valley Tribune, AZ, Tempe

Dionne, Jamie
jamie.dionne@mlive.com, Regional Sales Dir.
of Grand Rapids & Muskegon, The Jackson
Citizen Patriot, MI, Jackson

Dionne, Nick
ndionne@mlive.com, Sr. Strategy Dir., The Bay
City Times, MI, Bay City

Dionne, Tracy......................(603) 594-1260
news@nashuatelegraph.com, Events Prod.,
The Telegraph, NH, Nashua

Diotte, Lise .... (450) 655-5556
lisediotte@hebdos.net, Controller, Les Hebdos
Monteregiens, QC, Boucherville

Dippo, Brooklyn
vistaeditor@sandiego.edu, EIC, Univ. of San
Diego, CA, San Diego

Dirks, Kacie...........................(620) 826-3311
bucklinbanner@ucom.net, Editor, Bucklin
Banner, KS, Cimarron

Dirks, Michael.......................(828) 694-7863
michael.dirks@blueridgenow.com,
Chief Photographer, Times-News, NC,
Hendersonville

Dirks, Nicole...........................(620) 408-9919
ndirks@dodgeglobe.com, Retail Adv. Mgr.,
Dodge City Daily Globe, KS, Dodge City

Discoe, Connie Jo ....(308) 345-4500 ext. 113
regionalnews@mccookgazette.com, Regional
Ed., McCook Daily Gazette, NE, Mc Cook

Dish, Jim
jdishman@roswell-record.com, Cir. Dir.,
Roswell Daily Record, NM, Roswell

Dishman, Matthew .... (276) 638-8801, ext. 248
mdishman@martinsvillebulletin.com, Circ. Mgr.,
Martinsville Bulletin, VA, Martinsville

Dishmon, Banks
bdishmon@sentinel-tribune.com, Adv. Dir.,
Sentinel-Tribune, OH, Bowling Green

Disney, Lisa
ldisney@diobr.org, Circulation, The Catholic
Commentator, LA, Baton Rouge

Distelhorst, Mike .(252) 635-5629; (910) 343-2209;
(910) 219-8400
mike.distelhorst@newbernsj.com; mike.
distelhorst@starnewsonline.com, Pub.,
StarNews, NC, Wilmington

mike.distelhorst@newbernsj.com; mike.
distelhorst@starnewsonline.com, Pub., The
Sun Journal, NC, New Bern

mike.distelhorst@newbernsj.com; mike.
distelhorst@starnewsonline.com, Pub., The
Kinston Free Press, NC, Kinston

mike.distelhorst@newbernsj.com; mike.
distelhorst@starnewsonline.com, The Daily
News, NC, Jacksonville

Distelhorst, Mike
mike.distelhorst@amarillo.com, Adv. Dir.,
Amarillo Globe-News, TX, Amarillo

Diver, Debbie
assistant@mcrecordonline.com, Ed. Asst., The
Madison County Record, AR, Huntsville

Dix, Andrew
asdix@dixcom.com, Pub., New Concord Area
Leader, OH, Cambridge

Dix, Andrew
asdix@dixcom.com, Pub., Barnesville
Enterprise, OH, Barnesville

Dix, Andrew S. .... (419) 281-0581
asdix@dixcom.com, Publisher, Ashland Times-
Gazette, OH, Ashland

Dix, Andrew S. .... (330) 287-1601
asdix@dixcom.com, Publisher, Jeffersonian
Advantage, OH, Cambridge

Dix, Andrew S. .... (330) 287-1601
asdix@dixcom.com, Pub. , The Daily Record,
OH, Wooster

asdix@dixcom.com, Pub., The Daily
Jeffersonian, OH, Cambridge

Dix, David.............................. (330) 541-9400
dedix@dixcom.com, Pub., Record Publishing
Company, LLC, OH, Kent

Dix, David E.................(330) 296-9657 ext. 1280
Pub., Hudson Hub-Times, OH, Kent

Dix, David E.................(330) 296-9657 ext. 1280
Pub., Cuyahoga Falls News-Press, OH, Kent

Dix, David E.................(330) 298-2000
dedix@dixcom.com, Pub., Record-Courier,
OH, Kent

Dix, David E.................(330) 296-9657 ext. 1280
Pub., Aurora Advocate, OH, Kent

Dix, David E.................(330) 296-9657 ext. 1280
Pub., Nordonia Hills News Leader, OH, Kent

Dix, David E.................(330) 296-9657 ext. 1280
Pub., Tallmadge Express, OH, Kent

Dix, David E.................(330) 541-9400 Ext. 4101
dedix@dixcom.com, Pub., Stow Sentry, OH,
Kent

Dix, Deb
stkpaper@ruraltel.net, News Ed, Stockton
Sentinel, KS, Stockton

Dix, G. Charles
GCDixll@the-review.com, Pub., The Press-
News, OH, Minerva

Dix, G. Charles
gcdixii@the-reviewcom, Pub., The Review,
OH, Alliance

Dix, G. Charles
GCDixll@the-review.com, Pub., The News
Leader, OH, Minerva

Dix, G. Charles
gcdixii@dixcom.com, Pub., Alliance Publishing
Co. LLC, OH, Alliance

Dix, Troy.....................(419) 281-0581 ext. 212
tadix@dixcom.com, Publisher, Ashland
Publishing Co. LLC, OH, Ashland

Dix, Troy
tdix@dixcom.com, Manager of Mergers &
Acquisitions, Ashland Times-Gazette, OH,
Ashland

Dix Maenza, Ann
admaenza@state-journal.com, Publisher,
Frankfort Publishing Co., KY, Frankfort

Dixie, Patricia
pdixie@evtrib.com, Nat'l Acct. Coord., Marana
News, AZ, Tucson

pdixie@evtrib.com, Nat'l Acct. Coord., East
Valley Tribune, AZ, Tempe

Dixon, Chris .... (419) 448-3207
cdixon@advertiser-tribune.com, Pub. , The
Advertiser-Tribune, OH, Tiffin

Dixon, David.......................... (330) 471-8212
Malone College, OH, Canton

Dixon, David...........................(270) 831-8333
ddixon@thegleaner.com, Ed., The Gleaner, KY,
Henderson

Dixon, Doug .... (740) 888-6007
ddixon@thisweeknews.com, Adv. Dir.,
ThisWeek Bexley News, OH, Lewis Center

ddixon@thisweeknews.com, Adv. Dir.,
ThisWeek Clintonville Booster, OH, Lewis
Center

ddixon@thisweeknews.com, Adv. Dir.,
ThisWeek Delaware News, OH, Lewis Center

ddixon@thisweeknews.com, Adv. Dir.,
ThisWeek Dublin Villager, OH, Lewis Center

ddixon@thisweeknews.com, Adv. Dir.,
ThisWeek German Village Gazette, OH,
Lewis Center

ddixon@thisweeknews.com, Adv. Dir.,
ThisWeek Grove City Record, OH, Lewis
Center

ddixon@thisweeknews.com, Adv. Dir.,
ThisWeek Hilliard Northwest News, OH,
Lewis Center

ddixon@thisweeknews.com, Adv. Dir.,
ThisWeek Johnstown Independent, OH,
Lewis Center

ddixon@thisweeknews.com, Adv. Dir.,
ThisWeek Licking County News, OH, Lewis
Center

ddixon@thisweeknews.com, Adv. Dir.,
ThisWeek Marysville News, OH, Lewis
Center

ddixon@thisweeknews.com, Adv. Dir.,
ThisWeek New Albany News, OH, Lewis
Center

ddixon@thisweeknews.com, Adv. Dir.,
ThisWeek Northland News, OH, Lewis
Center

ddixon@thisweeknews.com, Adv. Dir.,
ThisWeek Northwest News, OH, Lewis
Center

ddixon@thisweeknews.com, Adv. Dir.,
ThisWeek Olentangy Valley News, OH, Lewis
Center

ddixon@thisweeknews.com, Adv. Dir.,
ThisWeek Pickerington Times-Sun, OH,
Lewis Center

ddixon@thisweeknews.com, Adv. Dir.,
ThisWeek Reynoldsburg News, OH, Lewis
Center

ddixon@thisweeknews.com, Adv. Dir.,
ThisWeek Rocky Fork Enterprise, OH, Lewis
Center

ddixon@thisweeknews.com, Adv. Dir.,
ThisWeek The Canal Winchester Times, OH,
Lewis Center

ddixon@thisweeknews.com, Adv. Dir.,
ThisWeek Tri-Village News, OH, Lewis
Center

ddixon@thisweeknews.com, Adv. Dir.,
ThisWeek Upper Arlington News, OH, Lewis
Center

ddixon@thisweeknews.com, Adv. Dir.,
ThisWeek West Side News, OH, Lewis
Center

ddixon@thisweeknews.com, Adv. Dir.,
ThisWeek Westerville News & Public
Opinion, OH, Lewis Center

ddixon@thisweeknews.com, Adv. Dir.,
ThisWeek Whitehall News, OH, Lewis Center

ddixon@thisweeknews.com, Adv. Dir.,
ThisWeek Worthington News, OH, Lewis
Center

Dixon, Doug .... (740) 888-6007
ddixon@thisweeknews.com, Sales Mgr.,
Consumer News Service Inc., OH, Lewis
Center

Dixon, Michael
miked@spokesman.com, Director of
Advertising, The Spokesman-Review, WA,
Spokane

Dixon, Nicole
ndixon@dougallmedia.com, Content editor,
Thunder Bay Source, ON, Thunder Bay

Dixon, Rev. Al
adixon711@aol.com, Ed., Montgomery/
tuskegee Times, AL, Montgomery

Dixon, Rod
rdixon@chillicothenews.com, Pub., Linn

County Leader, MO, Brookfield

Dixon, Rod ....(660) 646-2411
ctnews@chillicothenews.com, Pub., The Moberly Monitor-Index, MO, Moberly
ctnews@chillicothenews.com, Pub./Purchasing Agent, Constitution-Tribune, MO, Chillicothe

Dixon, Sam .... (276) 679-1101, ext. 234
sdixon@coalfield.com, Sports Ed., The Coalfield Progress, VA, Norton
sdixon@coalfield.com, Sports Ed., The Post, VA, Big Stone Gap
sdixon@coalfield.com, Sports Ed., The Dickenson Star, VA, Clintwood

Dlugos, Courtney ....(304) 284-0307
promo@dominionpost.com, Mktg. Assistant, The Dominion Post, WV, Morgantown

Do, Hai ....(914) 694-5055
Photo Ed., The Journal News, NY, White Plains

Doak, Griffin
griffin@whitingtech.com, Sr. Engineer, Whiting Technologies, IL, La Grange

Doane, Brian
bdoane@chespub.com, Adv. Dir., The Avenue News, MD, Dundalk

Doane, Brian ....(585) 337-4276
bdoane@messengerpostmedia.com, Ad Group - Lyons Shopping Guide, NY, Canandaigua
bdoane@messengerpostmedia.com, Pres./Pub, Ad Group - Newark Pennysaver, NY, Canandaigua
bdoane@messengerpostmedia.com, Ad Group - Sodus Pennysaver, NY, Canandaigua
bdoane@messengerpostmedia.com, Exe. Ed., Messenger Post Media, NY, Canandaigua

Doane, Brian ....(585) 337-4276
bdoane@messengerpostmedia.com, Pres./Pub. , Greece Post, NY, Canandaigua

Doane, Brian ....(585) 337-4276
bdoane@messengerpostmedia.com, Pub., Lyons Clyde Savannah Shopper, NY, Canandaigua
bdoane@messengerpostmedia.com, Pub. , Messenger Post Media, NY, Canandaigua
bdoane@messengerpostmedia.com, Pub., Sodus Williamson Pennysaver, NY, Canandaigua
bdoane@messengerpostmedia.com, Pres./Pub., Timesaver, NY, Canandaigua
bdoane@messengerpostmedia.com, Irondequoit Post, NY, Canandaigua
bdoane@messengerpostmedia.com, Penfield Post, NY, Canandaigua
bdoane@messengerpostmedia.com, Pub., Rush-Henrietta Post, NY, Canandaigua
bdoane@messengerpostmedia.com, Pres./Pub., Victor Post, NY, Canandaigua
bdoane@messengerpostmedia.com, Pres./Pub., Webster Post, NY, Canandaigua
bdoane@messengerpostmedia.com, Pres./Pub., Wayne Post, NY, Canandaigua

Doane, Brian ....(585) 337-4276
bdoane@messengerpostmedia.com, Pres. / Pub., Daily Messenger, NY, Canandaigua

Doane, Patrick ....(717) 240-7123
pdoane@cumberlink.com, Prodn. Mgr., The Sentinel, PA, Carlisle

Dobberstein, Kim
kdobberstein@eotfocus.com, Adv. Mgr., Perham Focus, MN, Perham

Dobbs, G. Michael......... (413) 525-3247 ext. 103
mdobbs@ReminderPublications.com, Ed., The Herald, MA, East Longmeadow

Dobbs, G.Michael .... (413) 525-3247 ext. 103
news@reminderpublications.com, Mng. Ed., Prime Times, MA, East Longmeadow

Dobbs, Michael ....ext. 103
mdobbs@ReminderPublications.com, Editorial Mgr., Reminder Metrowest / Chicopee Herald, MA, East Longmeadow
mdobbs@ReminderPublications.com, Editorial Mgr., The Reminder, MA, East Longmeadow
mdobbs@ReminderPublications.com, Editorial Mgr., Springfield Reminder, MA, East Longmeadow

Dobie, Mark ....(360) 416-2128
mdobie@skagitpublishing.com, Adv. Dir., Skagit Valley Herald, WA, Mount Vernon
mdobie@skagitpublishing.com, Pres./Pub., Herald and News, OR, Klamath Falls

Doblin, Alfred ....(973) 569-7084
doblin@northjersey.com, Editorial Ed., Herald News, NJ, Rockaway

Dobrowolski, Tony
tdobrowolski@berkshireeagle.com, Bus. Ed., The Berkshire Eagle, MA, Pittsfield

Dobson, Byron.........................(850) 599-2256
bdobson@tallahassee.com, Metro Ed., Tallahassee Democrat, FL, Tallahassee

Dobson, Jana...........................(512) 912-2525
jdobson@statesman.com, Circ. Dir., Austin American-Statesman, TX, Austin

Dobson, Larry ....(507) 374-6531
hayfieldherald@kmtel.com, Adv. Mgr., Byron Review, MN, Byron

Dobson, Larry
communitynewscorp@kmtel.com, Pub., Dodge Center Star-Herald, MN, Dodge Center

Dobson, Patricia ....(575) 562-2130
patricia.dobson@enmu.edu, Advisor (dept. chair, associate prof of communication, graduate coordinator), Eastern New Mexico Univ., NM, Portales

Dobson, Stewart
sdobson@oceancitytoday.net, Ed./Pub., Ocean City Today, MD, Ocean City

Dockendorf, Randy
randy.dockendorf@yankton.net, Regional Ed., Yankton Daily Press & Dakotan, SD, Yankton

Dockery, Georgina
newsdesk@octimesnews.com, Community Ed., The Ohio County Times, KY, Hartford

Dockham, Janice ....(306) 781-5378
jdockham@leaderpost.canwest.com, Ed. in Chief, The Leader-Post, SK, Regina

Dockstader, Dan........................(307) 885-5727
svidan@silverstar.com, Pub., Star Valley Independent, WY, Afton

Dockter, Betty Jean
turtle@westriv.com, Ad. Mgr. , McLean County Journal, ND, McClusky

Dockter, Betty Jean....................(701) 363-2492
gazette@westriv.com, Ad Manager, McClusky Gazette, ND, McClusky

Dodd, Donald...........................(573) 729-4126
salemnews@thesalemnewsonline.com, Pub., The Salem News, MO, Salem

Dodd, Donald
donald@thelickingnews.com, Pub., The Licking News, MO, Licking

Dodd, J. Edward
heraldrnews@centurytel.net, Ed., Abbeville Herald, AL, Abbeville

Dodd, Julie
jdodd@jou.ufl.edu, Prof., University of Florida, FL, Gainesville

Dodd, Michael.........................(201) 935-8666
mike.dodd@usink.com, President, US Ink, NJ, Carlstadt

Dodds, Kim ....(580) 585-5044
kdodds@swoknews.com, Adv. Dir., The Lawton Constitution, OK, Lawton

Dodds, Michael ....(888) 309-0639
mdodds@miracomcomputer.com, Project Engineer, Miracom Computer Corp., NY, Eastchester

Dodge, Rusty
rusty.dodge@bellinghamherald.com, General Manager and Vice President of Advertising, The Bellingham Herald, WA, Bellingham

Dodge, Tara
taradodge@aledger.net, Ad, The Albany Ledger, MO, Albany

Dodson, Richard ....(865) 981-1146
News Ed., The Daily Times, TN, Maryville

Dodson, Sandy ....(423) 447-2996
valleypbuinc@bledsoe.net, Ed./Adv. Mgr., The Bledsonian-Banner, TN, Pikeville

Dodson, Sandy ....(423) 447-2996
valleypbuinc@bledsoe.net, Mng. Ed./Adv. Mgr., The Dunlap Tribune, TN, Dunlap

Dodson, Sandy ....(423) 447-2996
valleypubinc@bledsoe.net, Publisher, Sequatchie Valley Shopper, TN, Pikeville

Dodson, Tammie.......................(256) 963-6739
tammie.dodson@adtran.com, PR Dir., ADTRAN, AL, Huntsville

Dodson Tyler, Selma ....(713) 663-6996
selma@defendermediagroup.com, Adv. & Marketing Dir., Houston Defender Media Group, Formerly Houston Defender, TX, Houston

Doeden, Dennis........................(218) 751-3740
ddoeden@bemidjipioneer.com, Pub., Buyline, MN, Bemidji

Doeden, Dennis........................(218) 333-9771
ddoeden@bemidjipioneer.com, Pub., The Bemidji Pioneer, MN, Bemidji
ddoeden@bemidjipioneer.com, Forum Communications Co., ND, Fargo

Doeden, Dennis........................(218) 333-9771
bldknews@blackduckamerican.com, Pub., The American, MN, Bemidji

Doege, Cindy ....(612) 673-4142
Cindy.Doege@startribune.com, Circ. Vice Pres., Star Tribune, MN, Minneapolis

Doege, Jack
jd@centuryinteractive.com, COO, CenturyTel Interactive, TX, Dallas

Doell, Lorelei
lorelei.doell@sunmedia.ca+, Circ. Mgr., The Nanton News, AB, Nanton

Doench, Debbie ....ext. 5635
doencde@hobartbrothers.com, Adv./Commun. Mgr., ITW Hobart Brothers Co., OH, Troy

Doerschner, Kristen
kdoerschner@timesonline.com, Asst. Mng. Ed. , Beaver County Times, PA, Beaver

Doheny, Connie
theobsnews@verizon.net, Ed., The Observer, NJ, Hasbrouck Heights

Doherty, Brad..........................(956) 982-6626
brad_doherty@link.freedom.com, Photo Ed., El Nuevo Heraldo, TX, Brownsville

Doherty, Brad..........................(956) 982-6626
Photo Dept. Mgr., The Brownsville Herald, TX, Brownsville

Doherty, Donna........................(203) 789-5672
ddoherty@nhregister.com, Arts/Travel Ed., New Haven Register, CT, New Haven

Doherty, Joanne...........(815) 625-3600 ext. 5240
jdoherty@saukvalley.com, Finance Dir., Daily Gazette, IL, Sterling

Doherty, Lyonel ....(250) 498-3711
editor@oliverchronicle.com, Ed., Oliver Chronicle, BC, Oliver

Doherty, Phil...........................(312) 222-3117
pdoherty@tribune.com, Vice Pres., Finance/CFO, Chicago Tribune, IL, Chicago

Doherty, Scott
sdoherty@sackvilletribunepost.com, Ed., The Sackville Tribune-post, NB, Sackville

Doherty, Terrence
tdoherty1@ccc.edu, Wilbur Wright College, IL, Chicago

Dohrer, Stephanie
madillrecord@sbcglobal.net, Adv. Rep, Madill Record, OK, Madill

Doig, Becky
newsoptimist.editor@sasktel.net, Ed., Battlefords News-optimist, SK, North Battleford

Doig, Becky ....(306) 445-7261
newsoptimist.editor@sasktel.net, Ed., Northwest Neighbors, SK, North Battleford
newsoptimist.editor@sasktel.net, Ed, Regional Optimist, SK, North Battleford

Doiron, Moe
mdoiron@globeandmail.com, Photo Ed., The Globe and Mail, ON, Toronto

Dolan, Carrie ....(708) 946-2208
cdolan@gmail.com, Administration, Hamilton Circulation Supplies Co., IL, Beecher

Dolan, Jennifer C. ....(212) 556-1234
Vice Pres., Forest Pdct., The New York Times Co., NY, New York

Dolan, Leah............................(936) 598-3377
ldolan@lightandchampion.com, Managing editor, The Light & Champion, TX, Center

Dolan, Mary ....(914) 694-5070
mdolan@lohud.com, Lifestyles Ed., The Journal News, NY, White Plains

Dolch, Janet
office@winfieldcourier.com, Office Mgr. , Winfield Daily Courier, KS, Winfield

Dold, R. Bruce
editor@chicagotribune.com, Pub./Ed.-in-Chief, Evanston Review, IL, Chicago
editor@chicagotribune.com, Pub., Forest Leaves, IL, Chicago
editor@chicagotribune.com, Pub./Ed.-in-Chief, The Naperville Sun, IL, Chicago
editor@chicagotribune.com, Pub./Ed.-in-Chief, Franklin Park Herald-Journal, IL, Chicago
editor@chicagotribune.com, Pub./Ed.-in-Chief, The Doings – La Grange, IL, Chicago
editor@chicagotribune.com, Pub./Ed.-in-Chief, The Doings – Hinsdale, IL, Chicago
editor@chicagotribune.com, Pub./Ed.-in-Chief, The Doings – Clarendon Hills, IL, Chicago
editor@chicagotribune.com, Pub./Ed.-in-Chief, The Doings Weekly – Burr Ridge, IL, Chicago
editor@chicagotribune.com, Pub./Ed.-in-Chief, Crown Point Star, IL, Chicago
editor@chicagotribune.com, Pub./Ed.-in-Chief, The Doings – Western Springs, IL, Chicago
editor@chicagotribune.com, Pub./Ed.-in-Chief, The Doings – Oak Brook and Elmhurst, IL, Chicago
editor@chicagotribune.com, Pub./Ed.-in-Chief, Buffalo Grove Countryside, IL, Chicago
editor@chicagotribune.com, Pub./Ed.-in-Chief, Elmwood Park Leaves, IL, Chicago
editor@chicagotribune.com, Pub./Ed.-in-Chief, Deerfield Review, IL, Chicago
editor@chicagotribune.com, Pub./Ed.-in-Chief, Chicago Tribune, IL, Chicago
editor@chicagotribune.com, Pub./Ed.-in-Chief, Glencoe News, IL, Chicago
editor@chicagotribune.com, Pub./Ed.-in-Chief, Glenview Announcements, IL, Chicago
editor@chicagotribune.com, Pub./Ed.-in-Chief, Highland Park News, IL, Chicago
editor@chicagotribune.com, Pub./Ed.-in-Chief, Arlington Heights Post, IL, Glenview
editor@chicagotribune.com, Pub./Ed.-in-Chief, Lake Forester, IL, Chicago
editor@chicagotribune.com, Pub./Ed.-in-Chief, Lake Zurich Courier, IL, Chicago
editor@chicagotribune.com, Pub./Ed.-in-Chief, Libertyville Review, IL, Chicago
editor@chicagotribune.com, Pub./Ed.-in-Chief, Lincolnshire Review, IL, Chicago
editor@chicagotribune.com, Pub./Ed.-in-Chief, Lincolnwood Review, IL, Chicago
editor@chicagotribune.com, Pub./Ed.-in-Chief, Morton Grove Champion, IL, Chicago
editor@chicagotribune.com, Pub./Ed.-in-Chief, Mundelein Review, IL, Chicago
editor@chicagotribune.com, Pub./Ed.-in-Chief, Niles Herald-Spectator, IL, Chicago
editor@chicagotribune.com, Pub./Ed.-in-Chief, Norridge-Harwood Heights News, IL, Chicago
editor@chicagotribune.com, Pub./Ed.-in-Chief,

Northbrook Star, IL, Chicago
editor@chicagotribune.com, Pub./Ed.-in-Chief, Oak Leaves, IL, Chicago
editor@chicagotribune.com, Pub./Ed.-in-Chief, Park Ridge Herald Advocate, IL, Chicago
editor@chicagotribune.com, Pub./Ed.-in-Chief, Skokie Review, IL, Chicago
editor@chicagotribune.com, Pub./Ed.-in-Chief, Vernon Hills Review, IL, Chicago
editor@chicagotribune.com, Pub./Ed.-in-Chief, Wilmette Life, IL, Chicago
editor@chicagotribune.com, Pub./Ed.-in-Chief, Winnetka Talk, IL, Chicago
editor@chicagotribune.com, Pub./Ed.-in-Chief, Barrington Courier-Review, IL, Glenview

Dolejs, Mark .... (252) 436-2842
Photographer, Daily Dispatch, NC, Henderson

Dolgov, Anna
adolgov@riverdalepress.com, Ed. , The Riverdale Press, NY, Bronx

Doll, Dennis
press@natchitochestimes.com, Systems Mgr., Natchitoches Times, LA, Natchitoches

Dollar, Linda
Sales@menastar.com, Advertising Director, The Mena Star, AR, Mena

Dolle, A.J. .... (325) 869-5717
edenecho@wcc.net, Pub./Ed./Adv. Dir., The Eden Echo, TX, Eden

Dolliver, Courtney................... (310) 694-3254
courtney_dolliver@bhimpact.com, B/HI, CA, Los Angeles

Dolowitz, Annetta .... (205) 870-7889
annetta@sjlmag.com, Advertising, Southern Jewish Life, AL, Mountain Brk

Dolzenko, Aleks .... (703) 318-1386
adolzenko@insidenova.com, Ed., InsideNoVa/Prince William, VA, Woodbridge

Dolzenko, Aleks ....
, InsideNoVa/North Stafford, VA, Woodbridge

Domalick, Scott
sdomalic@greenbay.gannett.com, Circ. Mgr., Door County Advocate, WI, Sturgeon Bay
sdomalic@greenbay.gannett.com, Circ. Mgr., Kewaunee County Star-News, WI, Kewaunee

Dombek, Lynn .... (201) 307-9900
sjames@ap.org, Associated Press, The, New York

Dombrouskis, Aigar ....(312) 649-1800 ext. 5720
aigar@atomicimaging.com, Producer, Atomic Imaging, Inc., IL, Chicago

Domina, Alex .... (802) 524-9771
Press Mgr., St. Albans Messenger, VT, Saint Albans

Dominguez, Catherine
cdominguez@hcnonline.com, Mng. Ed., The Woodlands Villager, TX, Conroe
cdominguez@hcnonline.com, Mng. Ed., Spring Observer, TX, Conroe

Dominguez, David
advertising@douglasdispatch.com, Adv. Mgr., The Douglas Dispatch, AZ, Douglas

Dominowski, Wayne .... (712) 943-2583
advocate@longlines.com, Pblr/Editor, The Sergeant Bluff Advocate, IA, Sergeant Bluff

Domis, Ray .... (954) 722-3000
azizs@graphline.com, Exec. Vice Pres./CFO, GraphLine, FL, Sunrise

Domke, Keith ....(830) 625-9144 ext. 220
keith.domke@herald-zeitung.com, Managing Editor, New Braunfels Herald-Zeitung, TX, New Braunfels

Donahoe, Jane .... (901) 528-8625
jdonahoe@memphisdailynews.com, Managing Ed., The Memphis News, TN, Memphis

Donahoe, Patrick R.
pdonahoe@email.usps.gov, Deputy Postmaster General, United States Postal Service, DC, Washington

Donahue, Crystal
cdonahue@umhb.edu, Univ. of Mary Hardin-Baylor, TX, Belton

Donahue, Jill .... (763) 712-3532
jill.donahue@ecm-inc.com, Bus. Mgr., Anoka County Union Herald, MN, Coon Rapids

Donahue, Kathlene
kathlene.donahue@telegram.com, Human Resources Director, Telegram & Gazette, MA, Worcester

Donahue, Patrick .... (912) 826-5012
pdonahue@effinghamherald.net, Mng. Ed., Effingham Herald, GA, Rincon

Donald, Elizabeth
edonald@bnd.com, Belleville News-Democrat, IL, Belleville

Donaldson, Jim .... (360) 715-2288
jim.donaldson@bellinghamherald.com, Sr. Ed./Audiene, The Bellingham Herald, WA, Bellingham

Donaldson, John
nsa@newspubinc.com , Mng. Ed., Spring Green Home News, WI, Spring Green

Donaldson, John
nsa@newspubinc.com, New Glarus Sugar River Shopper, WI, New Glarus
nsa@newspubinc.com, Mng. Ed., News-Sickle-Arrow, WI, Black Earth

Donat, Brenda
brenda.donat@goshennews.com, Accounting, The Goshen News, IN, Goshen

Donato, Andrew .... (416) 947-2253
andy.donato@sunmedia.ca, Cartoonist, The Toronto Sun, ON, Toronto

Donavan, Bill .... (505) 863-6811 ext. 223
cops@gallupindependent.com, Cops/courts, Gallup Independent, NM, Gallup

Donavan, Thomas ....(732) 922-6000 ext. 4110
Pres. & Pub., Asbury Park Press, NJ, Neptune

Donde, David
dave.donde@simonmiller.com, Vice Pres., Mktg., Simon Miller Sales Co., PA, Philadelphia

Doner, Dawn
springportsignal@springcom.com, Ed., Springport Signal, MI, Springport

Dones, M. Ofelia
continews@aol.com, Pres., Continental Newspaper, NJ, Union City

Dong, Qingwen........................ (209) 946-2505
qdong@uop.edu, Chair, University of the Pacific, CA, Stockton

Doniger, Nancy
ndoniger@hersamacorn.com, Mng. Ed., Bridgeport News, CT, Shelton

Doniger, Nancy........................ (203) 894-3343
ndoniger@hersamacorn.com, Ed., Easton Courier, CT, Ridgefield
ndoniger@hersamacorn.com, Ed., Fairfield Sun, CT, Shelton

Donley, Lynche ....(260) 647-0400 Ext. 3305
ldonley@kpcmedia.com, Adv. Dir., Churubusco News, IN, Churubusco

Donley, Lynette ....(260) 347-0400 Ext. 3305
ldonley@kpcmedia.com, Adv. Dir., The Star, IN, Auburn
ldonley@kpcmedia.com, Adv. Dir., The Herald Republican, IN, Angola
ldonley@kpcmedia.com, Adv. Dir., The News Sun, IN, Kendallville

Donley, Paul E. .... (417) 548-3311
fstop@centurytel.net, Ed., Pierce City Leader-Journal, MO, Sarcoxie

Donley, Paul E.
fstop@centurytel.net, Pub., The Sarcoxie Record, MO, Sarcoxie

Donmyer, Gwen
donmyer@sturgisjournal.com, Bus. Mgr.,

Sturgis Journal, MI, Sturgis

Donnellan, LaRae
larae.donnellan@famu.edu, Prof., Florida A&M University, FL, Tallahassee

Donnelly, Ben
donnellybt@wssu.edu, Staff, Winston-Salem State University, NC, Winston-Salem

Donnelly, Hal
hal@phillyvoice.com, VP of Sales/Mktg., PhillyVoice.com, PA, Philadelphia

Donnelly, Jerry
jerryd@mail.nwmissouri.edu, Chair, Northwest Missouri State University, MO, Maryville

Donnelly, Kelly .... (207) 990-8021
kdonnelly@bangordailynews.com, Events and Brand Coord., Bangor Daily News, ME, Bangor

Donnelly, Kimberly .... (203) 894-3328
editor@thewestonforum.com, Ed., Weston Forum, CT, Ridgefield

Donnelly, Michael J. .... (724) 465-5555 ext. 202
mjd@indianagazette.net, Pres./Pub., The Indiana Gazette, PA, Indiana

Donnelly, Timothy .... (518) 261-7030
donnelly@vdata.com, Sales Mgr, Vision Data Equipment Corp., NY, Rensselaer

Donoghue, Dennis .... (518) 395-3055
ddonoghue@dailygazette.net, Circulation Mgr/Mailroom, The Daily Gazette, NY, Schenectady

Donoghue, James
spotnews@priority.dowjones.com, Vice Pres., Sales/Mktg., Dow Jones Newswires - New York, NY, New York

Donoghue, Mike .... (802) 654-2442
mdonoghue@smcvt.edu, Executive Director, Vermont Press Association, VT, Colchester

Donohue, Andrea
adonohue@springfieldmed.org, Court Reporter, The Daily Events, MO, Springfield

Donohue, Colin
cdonohue@elon.edu, Advisor, Elon University, NC, Elon

Donohue, Thomas
aa4vb@hscmail.mcc.virginia.edu, Prof., Virginia Commonwealth University, VA, Richmond

Donovan, Dana
dana@houstonfamilymagazine.com, Adv. Mgr., Houston Family Magazine, TX, Houston

Donovan, Donna .... (315) 792-5002
ddonovan@uticaod.com, Utica Pennysaver, NY, Utica

Donovan, Fran
fdonovan@jjournal.com, Exec. Asst. to Pub. , The Jersey Journal, NJ, Secaucus

Donovan, Heather .... (315) 829-8356
hdonovan@indiancountry.com, Sales Mgr., Indian Country Today, NY, Canastota

Donovan, Mark .... (919) 419-6655
mdonovan@heraldsun,com, Metro Ed., The Herald-Sun, NC, Durham

Donovan, Thomas
tdonovan@app.com, Pub., Tuckerton Beacon, NJ, Neptune

Donovan, Thomas M. .... (732) 643-4110
tdonovan@gannettnj.com, President/Publisher, Courier News, NJ, Somerville

Donovan, Thomas M. .... (732) 643-4110
tdonovan@gannettnj.com, President/Publisher, Home News Tribune, NJ, Somerville

Donovan, Thomas M.
observer@app.com, Pub., Toms River Observer-Reporter, NJ, Neptune

Donovan, Tom ....(800) 822-9770 ext. 4110
tdonovan@njpressmedia.com, Pres./Pub., Beach Haven Times, NJ, Neptune

Donovan, Tom
tbeacon@app.com, Pub., The Lacey Beacon, NJ, Neptune

Dooley, Ellen
edooley@njnpublishing.com, Ed., Suburban News, NJ, New Providence

Dooley, Patricia
padooley@wichita.edu, Assoc. Prof., Wichita State University, KS, Wichita

Dooley, Ty
tdooley@cninewspapers.com, Adv. Rep., The Toccoa Record, GA, Toccoa

Doolittle, John
john.doolittle@redcross.org, Assoc. Prof., American University, DC, Washington

Doolittle, Will
will@poststar.com, Projects Dir., The Post-Star, NY, Glens Falls

Doornenbal, Bob
bobd@peterboroughexaminer.com, Adv. Dir., The Examiner, ON, Peterborough

Dopf, Martina.......................... (250) 395-2219
publisher@100milefreepress.net, Publisher, 100 Mile House Free Press, BC, 100 Mile House

Dopf, Norman
buhlherald@cableone.net, Ed., The Upper Country News-Reporter, ID, Cambridge

Dopfner, Mathias
info@asv.de, Chrmn., Axel Springer Verlag AG, Hamburg

Doppelt, Jack
j-doppelt@northwestern.edu, Prof., Northwestern University, IL, Evanston

Dorais, Jean-Francois
jfdorais@lapensee.qc.ca, Adv. Rep., La Pensee De Bagot, QC, Acton Vale

Dorais, Yolaine
yolaine.dorais@monteregieweb.com, Adv. Rep., Le Soleil Du St-laurent, QC, Chateauguay

Doran, Emily .... (616) 331-2464
editorial@lanthorn.com, Editor-and-Chief, Grand Valley State Univ., MI, Allendale

Doran, Maxine .... (320) 398-5000
news@tricountynews.mn, Office Asst, Tri-County News, MN, Kimball

Dore, David
editor@leominsterchamp.com, Ed., Leominster Champion, MA, Leominster

Doreen, Stewart
sdoreen@mrt.com, Ed., Midland Reporter-Telegram, TX, Midland

Doren, Tracy .... (480) 966-0837
tracy.doren@wranglernews.com, Pub., Wrangler News, AZ, Tempe

Dorger, Samanda .... (707) 864-7000 x 4363
samanda.dorger@solano.edu, Journalism Adviser, Solano Community College, CA, Fairfield

Doria, Cathie .... (219) 326-3831
cdoria@heraldargus.com , Acc. Exec. , Herald-Argus, IN, La Porte

Dorksen, Aaron.............................. ext. 1621
adorksen@the-daily-record.com, Sports Ed., The Daily Record, OH, Wooster

Dorman, Bill
bill.dorman@millersville.edu, Chair, Millersville University, PA, Millersville

Dorman, David
dcdorman@hfri.net, Lead Independent Dir. of the Board, Motorola Solutions, Inc., IL, Schaumburg

Dormann, Henry O.
sipa@sipausa.com, Chrmn./Ed. in Chief, Sipa News Service, New York

Dorn, Alicia

dorna@uapb.edu, Editor, University of Arkansas at Pine Bluff, AR, Pine Bluff

Dorn, Lisa .... (706) 823-3702
lisa.dorn@augustamagazine.com, Advertising Director, AUGUSTA Magazine, The Augusta Chronicle, GA, Augusta

Dorn, Vicki
mccmess@wctel.net, Gen. Mgr., McCormick Messenger, SC, Mc Cormick

Dorr, Adriane
adriane.dorr@lcms.org, Executive Editor, Reporter, MO, Saint Louis

Dorrance, Bob
bdorrance@chronotype.com, Nat'l Adv. Mgr., Rice Lake Chronotype, WI, Rice Lake

Dorrance, Warren .... (715) 790-1555
publish1@chronotype.com, Publisher, The Early Bird, WI, Rice Lake
publish1@chronotype.com, Pub., Rice Lake Chronotype, WI, Rice Lake

Dorries, Bruce .... (540) 887-7112
bdorries@mbc.edu, Chair, Mary Baldwin College, VA, Staunton
bdorries@mbc.edu, Mary Baldwin College, VA, Staunton

Dorsch, Vicki
vdorsch@bentoncourier.com, Bus. Mgr., The Saline Courier TMC, Benton

Dorschner, Larry .... (330) 424-9541
ldorschner@mojonews.com, Pub., Morning Journal, OH, Lisbon

Dorsett, Dale
ddorsett@van.net, Circ. Mgr, The Record, BC, Burnaby
ddorsett@van.net, Circ. Mgr., North/west Shore Outlook, BC, North Vancouver
ddorsett@van.net, Circ Mgr, New Westminster Record, BC, New Westminster

Dorsey, Nancy .... (308) 784-3644
news@tricitytrib.com, Pub., The Tri-City Tribune, NE, Cozad

Dorsey, Patrick E. .... (850) 599-2124
Pub., Sarasota Herald-Tribune, FL, Sarasota
Pres./Pub., Tallahassee Democrat, FL, Tallahassee

Dorsey, Tom .... (785) 822-1406 ext. 123
sjphoto@saljournal.com, Chief Photograher, The Salina Journal, KS, Salina

Dortch, Sebastian .... (727) 893-8084
sdortch@tampabay.com, HR Dir., Tampa Bay Times, FL, St Petersburg

Dosa, Don .... (360) 792-8569
ddosa@kitsapsun.com, Nat'l Adv. Mgr., Kitsap Sun, WA, Bremerton

Doskocil, Lori
ldoskocil@uta.edu, Bus Mgr, University of Texas at Arlington, TX, Arlington

Doss, Rod .... (412) 481-8302
newsroom@newpittsburghcourier.com, Editor & Publisher, New Pittsburgh Courier, PA, Pittsburgh

Doto, Pam .... (954) 574-5358
pdoto@tribune.com, VP/Exec. Ed., Live Wellington, FL, Fort Lauderdale
pdoto@tribune.com, VP/ Exec. Ed., Lake Worth Forum, FL, Fort Lauderdale
pdoto@tribune.com, VP/Exec. Ed., West Boca Forum, FL, Fort Lauderdale

Doto, Pam .... (954) 698-6397
pdoto@tribune.com, Exec. Ed., Eastsider, FL, Tamarac

Doto, Pam
pdoto@tribune.com, VP/Exec. Ed., Hi-Riser - Broward, FL, Pompano Beach

Doto, Pam .... (954) 698-6397
PDoto@tribune.com, VP/Exec. Ed., Deerfield and Pompano Forum, FL, Fort Lauderdale

Doto, Pam .... (954) 574-5358
PDoto@tribune.com, VP/Exec. Ed., Deerfield

and Pompano Forum, FL, Fort Lauderdale

Doto, Pamela .... (954) 596-5690
VP/Editorial, Forum Publishing Group, FL, Deerfield Beach

Dotson, Judith
cascadecourier@mcn.net, Ed., Cascade Courier, MT, Cascade

Dotson-Newton, Amy .... (302) 346-5449
amy.dotsonnewton@doverpost.com, Pub. & Adv. Dir., Dover Post, DE, Dover

Doty, Clayton
editor@rensselaerrepublican.com, Morocco Courier, IN, Kentland

Doty-Lloyd, Sue .... (570) 296-6641
Suedotylloyd@gmail.com, Pub., Pike County Dispatch, PA, Milford

Dotzler, Sharon .... (218) 927-3761
sdotzler@aitkinage.com, Circulation Manager, Bargain Hunter, MN, Isle

Doucet, Charles F. .... (434) 978-7296
cdoucet@dailyprogress.com, Circ. Dir., The Daily Progress, VA, Charlottesville

Doucet, Dany
dany.doucet@quebecormedia.com, Ed.-in-Chief, Le Journal de Montreal, QC, Montreal

Doucet, Janet
Advertising@CrowleyToday.com, Adv. Mgr., The Crowley Post-Signal, LA, Crowley

Doucett, Susan .... (603) 224-5301 ext. 324
Comm. Ed., Concord Monitor, NH, Concord

Doucette, Erin .... (260) 347-0400 Ext. 1175
edoucette@kpcmedia.com, Presentation Ed., The News Sun, IN, Kendallville

Doucette, Mary Ann
madoucette@ksliga.ca, President, Slovak Canadian Publishing Company, Kanadsky Slovak / The Canadian Slovak, ON, Mississauga

Doucette, Mike .... (810) 989-6214
mdoucette@thetimesherald.com, Distribution Manager, Times Herald, MI, Port Huron

Doud, Charles P. .... (559) 674-8134
Ed., The Madera Tribune, CA, Madera

Dougal, Kirk .... (419) 238-2285 ext. 210
kdougal@timesbulletin.com, Pub., The Times Bulletin, OH, Van Wert

Dougal, Kirk .... (419) 238-2285
kdougal@timesbulletin.com, Publisher, West Central Ohio Shopping Guide, OH, Van Wert

Dougherty, Patrick
pdougherty@skagitpublishing.com, Interactive Media Mgr., Skagit Valley Herald, WA, Mount Vernon

Doughton, James E.
jim.doughton@gvillesun.com, Pub., The Gainesville Sun, FL, Gainesville

Doughton, Jim .... (352) 374-5001
jim.doughton@gvillesun.com, Pub., Ocala Star-Banner, FL, Ocala

Doughty, Pat
p.doughty@mirachem.com, COO, Mirachem Corp., AZ, Phoenix

Douglas, Beth
bdouglas@21st-centurymedia.com, Adv. Mgr., Perkasie News-Herald, PA, Fort Washington
bdouglas@21st-centurymedia.com, Adv. Mgr., Times Chronicle, PA, Fort Washington
bdouglas@21st-centurymedia.com, Adv. Mgr., The Colonial, PA, Fort Washington
bdouglas@21st-centurymedia.com, Adv. Mgr., Springfield Sun, PA, Fort Washington
bdouglas@21st-centurymedia.com, Adv. Mgr., Ambler Gazette, PA, Lansdale
bdouglas@21st-centurymedia.com, Adv. Mgr., North Penn Life, PA, Fort Washington
bdouglas@21st-centurymedia.com, Adv. Mgr., Glenside News, PA, Fort Washington
bdouglas@21st-centurymedia.com, Adv. Mgr., Montgomery Life, PA, Fort Washington

bdouglas@21st-centurymedia.com, Adv. Mgr., Willow Grove Guide, PA, Fort Washington
bdouglas@21st-centurymedia.com, Adv. Mgr., The Globe, PA, Fort Washington
bdouglas@21st-centurymedia.com, Adv. Mgr., Public Spirit, PA, Fort Washington

Douglas, Brian .... (650) 704-3236
brian@autoeditor.com, Ed./Pub., Autoeditor Syndication, Half Moon Bay

Douglas, Bruce .... (216) 368-2916
Case Western Reserve Univ., OH, Cleveland

Douglas, Christine
ads@ahobserver.com, Adv, Rep, The Agassiz-harrison Observer, BC, Agassiz

Douglas, Dan 615/881-7104
ddouglas@gannett.com, Regional Sales Manager, The Tennessean, TN, Nashville

Douglas, Donnie .... (910) 416-5649
ddouglas@civitasmedia.com, Ed., The Robesonian, NC, Lumberton

Douglas, Karen .... (541) 383-0332
kdouglas@bendbulletin.com, The Bulletin, OR, Bend

Douglas, Sherrie .... (239) 940-7884
sdouglas@fortmyer.gannett.com, Acct. Exec., Lehigh Acres News-Star, FL, Fort Myers

Douglas, Tim
tdouglass@pctribune.com, Pub, The Starbuck Times, MN, Glenwood

Douglas, William
wdouglas@uh.edu, Prof., University of Houston, TX, Houston

Douglass, John
jdougla@american.edu, Assoc. Prof., American University, DC, Washington

Douglass, Tim
tdouglass@pctribune.com, Pub./Ed., Pope County Tribune, MN, Glenwood

Doumar, Karim
editor@dailycal.org, Editor in Chief and President, Univ. of California, Berkeley, CA, Berkeley

Douthit, H. Kenneth .... (419) 625-5825
Pres., Douthit Communications, Inc., OH, Sandusky

Douthit, Hal
info@homes-illustrated.com, Pub., ColSouthern Colorado Homes Illustrated, CO, Colorado Springs

Douthit, Harold K.
hkdiii@hqdci.com, Pub., The Press, OH, Millbury

Douthit, Harold K. .... (419) 625-5825
Pub., North Ridgeville Press, OH, Avon Lake

Douthit III, H. Kenneth
editor@chagrinvalleytimes.com, Pub., Geauga Courier, OH, Chagrin Falls

Dove, Andrew
dove@paper.net, Vice Pres., Pulse Research, Inc., OR, Portland

Dove, Jim .... (915) 494-0041
jdove@elpasotimes.com, VP of Circulation, El Paso Times, TX, El Paso
jdove@elpasotimes.com, Circ. Dir., El Paso y Mas, TX, El Paso

Dow, Evelyn .... (585) 352-3411 x127
editor@westsidenewsny.com, Editor, Hamlin Clarkson Herald, NY, Spencerport

Dow, Evelyn .... (585) 352-3411 ext. 127
editor@westsidenewsny.com, Editor, Suburban News West, NY, Spencerport

Dow, Evelyn .... (585) 352-3411 ext. 127
editor@westsidenewsny.com, Editor, Suburban News South, NY, Spencerport

Dow, Evelyn .... (585) 352-3411 x127
editor@westsidenewsny.com, Editor, Suburban News North, NY, Spencerport

Dowaliby, Chazy .... (617) 786-7022
cdowaliby@ledger.com, Ed., The Patriot Ledger, MA, Quincy

Dowaliby, Chazy
cdowaliby@ledger.com, Ed., The Enterprise, MA, Brockton

Dowd, Joe .... (631) 913-4238
joe.dowd@libn.com, Bus. Mgr., Long Island Business News, NY, Ronkonkoma
joe.dowd@libn.com, West Texas A&M Univ., TX, Canyon

Dowd, Kevin .... (206) 543-2700
Univ. of Washington, WA, Seattle

Dowd, Micheal J. .... (207) 990-8238
mdowd@bangordailynews.com, Metro/Standards Ed., Bangor Daily News, ME, Bangor

Dowd, Michelle
michelle.dowd@chaffey.edu, Adviser, Chaffey College, CA, Rancho Cucamonga

Dowd, Mike .... (207) 990-8000
mdowd@bangordailynews.com, Mngr., The Piscataquis Observer, ME, Dover Foxcroft

Dowd, Mike .... (207) 990-8000
mdowd@bangordailynews.com, Manager, The Piscataquis Observer, ME, Dover Foxcroft

Dowd , Michael .... (315) 282-2234
michael.dowd@lee.net, Mng. Ed. , The Citizen, Auburn, NY, Auburn

Dowdell, Ken .... (262) 656-6249
kdowdell@kenoshanews.com, Pub., Bargaineer, WI, Kenosha

Dowding, Ian .... (519) 631-2790 x532242
idowding@postmedia.com, Group Director, Media Sales, The Norwich Gazette, ON, Woodstock

Dowding, Ian .... (519) 631-2790 x532242
idowding@postmedia.com, Group Dir., Media Sales, The Ingersoll Times, ON, Woodstock

Dowdy, Tommy .... (540) 981-3162
tommy.dowdy@roanoke.com, Circulation Director, The Roanoke Times, VA, Roanoke

Dowdy-Sue, Hannah
classifieds@dailylobo.com, Class. Mgr., New Mexico Daily Lobo, NM, Albuquerque

Dowell, Amber .... (276) 728-7311
adowell@civitasmedia.com, Class./Circ., The Carroll News, VA, Hillsville

Dowell, Cassandra
cdowell@shawmedia.com, Sr. Reporter, Lake County Journal, IL, Grayslake

Dowling, Denise
denise.dowling@umontana.edu, Assoc. Prof., The University of Montana, MT, Missoula

Dowling, Mary
mdowling@nnlp.com, Sales Dir., Newspaper National Network LP, NY, New York

Dowling, Matt .... (609) 989-5684
mdowling@njtimes.com, News Ed., The Times, NJ, Trenton

Down, Michael
fshopper@twcny.rr.com, Circ. Mgr., Suburban Cortland-ithaca Shopper, NY, Freeville

Down, William .... (717) 318-9407
GateHouse Media, Inc., NY, Pittsford

Downer, Ellie
edowner@turley.com, Ed., Barre Gazette, MA, Barre

Downes, Patrick
pdownes@rcchawaii.org, Ed., Hawaii Catholic Herald, HI, Honolulu

Downes, Robert
info@northernexpress.com, Ed., Northern Express, MI, Traverse City

Downey, Debra .... (905) 664-8800
ddowney@hamiltonnews.com, Ed, Dundas Star News, ON, Stoney Creek

Downey, Debra .... (905) 664-8800
ddowney@hamiltonnews.com, News Ed.,
Ancaster News, ON, Stoney Creek

Downey, Jim
jdowney@suburbanpublishing.com, Circ. Mgr.,
Weekly News, MA, Peabody

Downing, John
jdowning@siu.edu, Prof./Dir. Global media
Research Ctr., Southern Illinois University
Carbondale, IL, Carbondale

Downing, Margaret .... (713) 280-2470
margaret.downing@houstonpress.com, Ed.,
Houston Press, TX, Houston

Downing, Ross .... (620) 842-5129
anthonyrepublican@att.net, Editor, Anthony
Republican, KS, Anthony

Downs, Donna
echo@taylor.edu, Ed. in Chief, Taylor Univ.,
IN, Upland

Downs, Jere .... (502) 582-4669
jdowns@courier-journal.com, Food/
Restaurants Editor, The Courier-Journal, KY,
Louisville

Downs, Morgan .... (254) 965-3124
mdowns@gatehousemedia.com, Digital Dir.,
Cherokee County News-Advocate, KS,
Columbus

Downs, Scott .... (717) 272-5611
sdowns@ldnews.com, Pub., Lebanon Valley
Review, PA, Lebanon

Downs, Scott .... (717) 272-5611
sdowns@ldnews.com, Lebanon Daily News,
PA, York
sdowns@ldnews.com, Pub., The Lebanon
Daily News, PA, Lebanon

Downs, Scott .... (717) 272-5611 ext. 102
sdowns@ldnews.com, Publisher, The Palm,
PA, Lebanon

Downs, Sue
sdowns@bowesnet.com, Adv. Mgr., Times-
reformer, ON, Simcoe

Downs, Sue .... (519) 426-5710 ext. 118
sue.downs@sunmedia.ca, Adv. Mgr. , The
Simcoe Reformer, ON, Simcoe

Dowty, JoAnn .... (618) 936-2212
editor@sumnerpress.com, Ed., The Sumner
Press, IL, Sumner

Doxee, Sharon .... ext. 343
CFO, The Pioneer - Big Rapids, MI, Big Rapids

Doyle, Danette .... (231) 592-8359
advertising@pioneergroup.com, Adv. Mgr.,
Pioneer East, MI, Big Rapids
advertising@pioneergroup.com, Adv., The
Pioneer - Big Rapids, MI, Big Rapids

Doyle, Jim .... (503) 221-8329
jdoyle@oregonian.com, Dir. Categories, The
Oregonian, OR, Portland

Doyle, Kenneth
kendoyle@umn.edu, Assoc. Prof., University of
Minnesota, MN, Minneapolis

Doyle, Kevin
kdoyle@pnj.com, Pub./Pres., Pensacola News
Journal, FL, Pensacola

Doyle, Laurie
ldoyle@sharonherald.com, Adv. Mgr. , The
Herald, PA, Sharon

Doyle, Michael B.
aawaibarber@astate.edu, Instr., Arkansas
State University, AR, Jonesboro

Doyle, Rick .... (509) 525-3300 ext. 249
rdoyle@ubnet.com, Ed., Walla Walla Union-
Bulletin, WA, Walla Walla

Doyle, Steve .... (336) 373-7012
steven.doyle@news-record.com, Managing
Ed., News & Record, NC, Greensboro

Doyle, Steve
sdoyle@sentinelnews.com, Ed., Sentinel News
Plus, KY, Shelbyville

Doyle-Kimball, Mary .... (561) 391-3599
madkimba@aol.com, Executive Director,
National Association of Real Estate Editors
(NAREE), FL, Boca Raton

Doyon, Dan
dan.doyon@sjvalley-times.com, Press Mgr., St.
John Valley Times, ME, Madawaska

Dozier, Van .... (334) 826-6847
van@circulationsolutions.com, Pres.,
Circulation Solutions, Inc., AL, Auburn

Dozier, Walt .... (614) 486-6677 ext. 1020
wdozier@adohio.net, Acting Director of
Advertising, Ohio Newspaper Services, Inc.,
OH, Columbus
wdozier@adohio.net, Adv. Dir., Ohio
Newspaper Association, OH, Columbus

Drafall, Lisa
ldrafall@redwoodfallsgazette.com, Gen Mgr,
The Redwood Falls Gazette, MN, Redwood
Falls

Drage, Gerry .... (705) 745-4641 ext. 239
gerry.drage@sunmedia.ca, Adv. Mgr. , The
Peterborough Examiner, ON, Peterborough

Drage, Gerry
gerry.drage@sunmedia.ca, Adv. Dir., The
Community Press, ON, Belleville
gerry.drage@sunmedia.ca, Adv. Dir., Colborne
Chronicle, ON, Colborne

Drager, Michael
mwdrag@ship.edu, Shippensburg
University:The Slate, PA, Shippensburg

Drager, Michael W. .... (717) 477-1521
mwdrag@ship.edu, Assoc. Prof./print&
online media, Shippensburg University/
Communication/Journalism Department , PA,
Shippensburg

Dragin, Burt .... (510) 464-3459
bdragin@peralta.edu, Laney College, CA,
Oakland

Drahn, Sharon
sharon@postvilleherald.com, Ed., Postville
Herald, IA, Postville

Drain, Christina .... (850) 484-1374
Pensacola Junior College, FL, Pensacola

Drake, Carolyn .... (902) 629-6000 (ext. 6036)
lifestyles@theguardian.pe.ca, Features Ed.,
The Guardian, PE, Charlottetown

Drake, Cecelia .... (916) 288-6011
cecelia@cnpa.com, Director of Advertising ,
California News Publishers Association, CA,
Sacramento

Drake, Cecil .... (214) 206-3333
CDrake@DrakeCommunications.com, Pres.,
Drake Communications, Inc., TX, Krum

Drake, Chris .... (608) 729-4709
cdrake@hngnews.com, Business Manager,
The Lake Mills Leader, WI, Lake Mills

Drake, Chris .... (608) 729-4709
cdrake@hngnews.com, Bus. Mgr., DeForest
Times-Tribune, WI, Windsor

Drake, Chris .... (608) 729-4709
cdrake@hngnews.com, Business Manager,
Lodi Enterprise & Poynette Press, WI, Lodi

Drake, Monica
monica.drake@oakpress.com, Community
Engagement Ed., The Oakland Press, MI,
Pontiac

Drake, Shelly .... (316) 283-1500 x106
sdrake@gatehousemedia.com, Controller/
Business Dir., The Newton Kansan, KS,
Newton

Drake, Terri .... (509) 783-5455
drake@giantnickel.com, Gen. Mgr., The Giant
Nickel, WA, Kennewick

Drane, Amanda .... (413) 585-5230
adrane@gazettenet.com, Reporter/Sunday Ed.
, Daily Hampshire Gazette, MA, Northampton

Dranginis, Lisa .... (248) 437-2011

ldranginis@gannett.com, Adv. Mgr., South Lyon
Herald, MI, Detroit

Draper, Alison .... (214) 977-8419
alison.draper@belomediagroup.com,
President, BMG, The Dallas Morning News,
TX, Dallas

Draper, Bill
bill.draper@lee.net, Dir. of Ops., Lebanon
Express, OR, Lebanon

Draper, Bill .... (541) 926-2211
bill.draper@lee.net, Dir., Mgmt. Info Servs.,
Albany Democrat-Herald, OR, Albany

Draper, Chris .... (732) 219-5788 ext. 209
trtproduction@aol.com, Prodn. Mgr., The Two
River Times, NJ, Red Bank

Draper, John C. .... (507) 825-3333
jdraper@pipestonestar.com, Pub., Free Star
Shopper, MN, Pipestone

Draper, John C.
pipepub@pipestonestar.com, Publisher,
Pipestone County Star, MN, Pipestone

Draper, Whit
portland@allenspcb.com, Office Mgr., Allen's
Press Clipping Bureau, OR, Portland

Draughn, Kim .... (843) 792-4107
Medical Univ. of South Carolina, SC,
Charleston

Draut, Sam .... (502) 222-7183
sports@oldhamer.com, Sports Ed., Oldham
Era, KY, La Grange

Dreasler, Brady
bdreasler@qni.biz, Dir., Facilities/Capital
Project/Broadcast Engineering, Quincy
Media, Inc., IL, Quincy

Dreckman, Jessi .... (417) 679-4641
jessi@ozarkcountytimes.com, Online manager/
reporter, Ozark County Times, MO,
Gainesville

Dreeszen, Dave .... (712) 293-4211
ddreeszen@siouxcityjournal.com, Managing
Editor/News, Sioux City Journal, IA, Sioux
City

Dregni, Eric
dregni@csp.edu, Concordia Univ. at St. Paul,
MN, Saint Paul

Dreher, Dan
dan.dreher@eammosca.com, Pres., EAM-
Mosca Corp., PA, Hazle Township

Dreibelbis, Curt .... (717) 582-4305
cdreibelbis@perrycountytimes.com, Pub.,
Duncannon Record, PA, New Bloomfield

Dreibelbis, Curt .... (717) 582-4305
cdreibelbis@perrycountytimes.com, Pub.,
Perry County Times, PA, New Bloomfield
cdreibelbis@perrycountytimes.com, Publisher,
The News-Sun, PA, New Bloomfield

Dreibelbis, Curt .... (717) 436-8206
cdreibelbis@perrycountytimes.com, Pub.,
Juniata Sentinel, PA, Mifflintown

Dreisenga, Marilyn .... (616) 669-5210
Prodn. Mgr., South Advance, MI, Jenison

Drendel, Jamie
freemontnews@wyoming.com, Copy Editor
, The Riverton Ranger, WY, Riverton

Drescher, John .... (919) 829-4515
drescher@newsobserver.com, Managing Ed.,
The News & Observer, NC, Raleigh

Dressler, Tom .... (631) 270-3133
tom.dressler@pcfcorp.com, VP of Growth
and Development, Publishers Circulation
Fulfillment Inc., NY, Farmingdale

Drew, Adam
adrew@uta.edu, Production Mgr., University of
Texas at Arlington, TX, Arlington

Drew, Diann .... (320) 763-1214
ddrew@echopress.com, Bus. Mgr., Echo-
Press, MN, Alexandria

Drew, Duchesne .... (612) 673-7111
ddrew@startribune.com, Managing Editor,
Operations, Star Tribune, MN, Minneapolis

Drewry, Dan .... (406) 826-3402
Pub., Clark Fork Valley Press, MT, Plains

Drewsen, Alan
info@inta.org, Exec. Dir., International
Trademark Association, NY, New York

Drexel, Robert C. .... (610) 371-5216
rdrexel@readingeagle.com, Building Supvr.,
Reading Eagle, PA, Reading

Dreyer, Steve .... ext. 207
editor@pomeradonews.com, Ed., Poway News
Chieftain, CA, Poway

Dreyer, Steve .... ext. 207
editor@pomeradonews.com, Exec. Ed.,
Rancho Bernardo News-Journal, CA, Poway

Drilingas, Randy
ads@timesnewspapers.com, Prod. Mgr., West
End Word, MO, Saint Louis
ads@timesnewspapers.com, Prod. Mgr., South
County Times, MO, Saint Louis
ads@timesnewspapers.com, Prod. Mgr.,
Webster-Kirkwood Times, Inc., MO, Saint
Louis

Drillen, Ron
rdrillen@kingstonthisweek.com, Gen. Mgr.,
Kingston This Week, ON, Kingston

Dring, Neil
sachem@sachem.on.ca, Ed., The Grand River
Sachem, ON, Caledonia

Driscoll, George .... ext. 204
gdriscoll@swbooster.com, Prodn. Mgr., The
Southwest Booster, SK, Swift Current

Driscoll, Jodi
rtr@mncable.net, Pub., Roseau Times-Region,
MN, Roseau

Driscoll, Jody
rtr@mncable.net, Pub., Borderline, MN,
Roseau

Driscoll, Lori .... (810) 985-7171 ext. 236
advdirector@thetimesherald.com, General
Manager/Director of Advertising, Blue Water
Shopper, MI, Port Huron

Driver, Mark
mtd@tidbitsfun.com, Tidbits Of The Blue
Mountain Region, WA, Walla Walla

Driver, Michael J. .... (850) 456-3121
escambiasunpress@aol.com, Owner/Publisher,
Escambia Sun Press, FL, Pensacola

Driver, R. Sonny .... 215=232=5974
scoopus@aol.com, editor/publisher, Scoop
Usa, PA, Philadelphia

Droege, LuAnn .... (618) 532-5601
ldroege@morningsentinel.com, Sr. Ed.,
Morning Sentinel, IL, Centralia

Droege, luAnn .... (618) 532-5601
ldroege@morningsentinel.com, editor, Crier/
schrol,rlc Clocktoweer, IL, Centralia

Droge, Mitchell-Ann .... (225) 344 - 9309 x107
mitch@lapress.com, Dir. of Ops., Louisiana
Press Association, LA, Baton Rouge

Drogin, Bob
bob.drogin@latimes.com, Deputy Bureau
Chief, Washington D.C. , Los Angeles Times,
CA, Los Angeles

Drogomatz, Mariella .... (250) 567-9258
office@ominecaexpress.com, Circ., Caledonia
Courier, BC, Fort St. James

Drolet, Jamie .... (843) 937-5904
jdrolet@postandcourier.com, Retail Advert.,
The Post and Courier, SC, Charleston

Drolet, Kevin
kevind@metrosuburbia.com, Adv. Sales Mgr.,
Metro Suburbia, Inc./Newhouse Newspapers,
NY, New York

Drucker, Irwin
drucker@us.ibm.com, Program Dir., GLBT

Supplier Rel./Procurement, IBM Corp., NY, Armonk

Drudge, Mark............(970) 375-4517
mdrudge@cortezjournal.com, Adv. Dir., Dolores Star, CO, Cortez
mdrudge@cortezjournal.com, Adv. Mgr., Cortez Journal, CO, Cortez
mdrudge@cortezjournal.com, Dir., Adv./Mktg., Durango Herald, CO, Durango

Drummond, Mike
clearcreekrancher@yahoo.com, Author/Self-Syndicator/Pub., Clear Creek Features, Grass Valley

Drummond, Paul...........(705) 645-8771 ext. 229
examsales@muskoka.com, Adv. Sales Mgr., The Muskokan, ON, Bracebridge

Drummond, Rod
roddrummond@hudsonsharp.com, CEO, Hudson-Sharp, WI, Green Bay

Drumond, Rosana....................(408) 509-3455
rossana@alianzanews.com, Pub., Alianza Metropolitan News, CA, San Jose

Drury, Sarah.....................(443) 205-2539
sdrury@chespub.com , Reporter, The Star-Democrat, MD, Easton

Dryden, Brian...............(613) 933-3160 ext. 225
brian.dryden@sunmedia.ca, Ed., Standard-Freeholder, ON, Cornwall

Dryden, Lee..........................(248) 745-4641
lee.dryden@oakpress.com, Metro Ed., The Oakland Press, MI, Pontiac

Dryden, Shelby.............(620) 694-5700 Ext. 211
sdryden@hutchnews.com, Marketing Consultant, The Hutchinson News, KS, Hutchinson

Drye, B.J.
bj@stanlynewspress.com, Editor, The Stanly News & Press, NC, Albemarle

Dryer, Carolyn.........................(623) 847-4604
cdryer@star-times.com, Mng. Ed., The Glendale Star, AZ, Glendale

Dryer, Carolyn.........................(623) 847-4604
cdryer@star-times.com, Ed., Peoria Times, AZ, Glendale

Drysdale, M. Dickey
mdd@quest-net.com, Editor Emeritus, The Herald of Randolph, VT, Randolph

Drzewiecka, Jolanta
jolanta@wsu.edu, Assoc. Prof./Head, Comm. Studies seq., Washington State University, WA, Pullman

Drzewiecki, James....................(860) 973-1804
jDrzewiecki@bristolpress.com, Associate editor, The Bristol Press, CT, Bristol

DuBois, Andy..........................(936) 521-3418
adubois@hcnonline.com, Exec. Ed. , The Courier of Montgomery County, TX, Conroe

DuBois, Andy
adubois@hcnonline.com, Exec. Ed., Spring Observer, TX, Conroe
adubois@hcnonline.com, Exec. Ed., The Woodlands Villager, TX, Conroe

DuBois , Denise......................(334) 664-0152
ddubois@citizenea.com, Executive Editor , The Citizen of East Alabama, AL, Phenix City

DuFour, Susan
sdufour@themountaineer.com, Adv. Dir., The Mountaineer, NC, Waynesville

DuPree, Stella
SDupree@The-Leader.com, Ed. , Steuben Courier-Advocate, NY, Bath
SDupree@The-Leader.com, Online Ed., Horseheads Shopper, NY, Corning
SDupree@The-Leader.com, Online Ed., The Leader, NY, Corning

Duane, Christy
cduane@okgazette.com, Adv. Dir., Okcbiz, OK, Oklahoma City

Duarte, Jesse..........................(707) 967-6803
jduarte@sthelenastar.com, Staff writer, St Helena Star, CA, Saint Helena

Duarte, Mario.........................(612) 312-1760
news@laprensa-mn.com, Pub., La Prensa de Minnesota, MN, Minneapolis

Dubail, Jean.........................(203) 731-3361
jdubail@newstimes.com, Managing Editor, The News-Times, CT, Danbury

Dubensky, Morgan
mdubensky@gantdaily.com, Bus. Dev't. Mgr., Gant Daily, PA, Clearfield

Dubois, Susan
sdubois@ctcentral.com, Circ. Mgr., Housatonic Publications, CT, New Milford

Dubois, Susan
sdubois@ctcentral.com, Circ. Asst., The Litchfield County Times, CT, Torrington

Dubois, Tessie
tessie.dubois@sjvalley-times.com, Pub./Ed., St. John Valley Times, ME, Madawaska

Dubyk, Craig
copychief@dailylobo.com, Copy Chief, New Mexico Daily Lobo, NM, Albuquerque

Duchemin, Bob.......................(902) 563-3886
b.duchemin@cbpost.com, Sports Ed., The Cape Breton Post, NS, Sydney

Duchene, Seth
sethduchene@napaneebeaver.com, Ed., The Napanee Beaver, ON, Napanee

Duchesne, Drew.....................(612) 673-7111
ddrew@startribune.com, Star Tribune, MN, Minneapolis

Duchin, Susan........................(410) 332-6793
sduchin@baltsun.com, Dir. Nat'l Adv & Majors, Columbia Flier, MD, Columbia
sduchin@baltsun.com, Dir Nat'l Adv & Majors, Catonsville Times, MD, Baltimore
sduchin@baltsun.com, Dir. Nat'l Adv & Majors, Baltimore Messenger-OOB, MD, BALTIMORE
sduchin@baltsun.com, Dir. Nat'l Adv., Northeast Booster Reporter-OOB, MD, TOWSON
sduchin@baltsun.com, Dir. Nat'l Adv & Majors, The Record, MD, Bel Air
sduchin@baltsun.com, Dir. Nat'l Adv & Majors, Owings Mills Times, MD, Baltimore
sduchin@baltsun.com, Dir. Nat'l Adv & Majors, The Aegis, MD, Baltimore
sduchin@baltsun.com, Dir. Nat'l Adv., Arbutus Times, MD, Baltimore
sduchin@baltsun.com, Dir. Nat'l Adv & Majors, Howard County Times, MD, Columbia
sduchin@baltsun.com, Dir. Nat'l Adv., The Weekender, MD, Bel Air
sduchin@baltsun.com, Dir. Nat'l Adv & Majors, Jeffersonian, MD, Towson
sduchin@baltsun.com, Dir. Nat'l Adv & Majors, Towson Times, MD, Baltimore
sduchin@baltsun.com, Adv. Dir., The Baltimore Sun, MD, Baltimore

Duckett, Sean.......................(514) 987-2222
sduckett@montrealgazette.com, Manager, Advertising Sales, Montreal Gazette, QC, Montreal

Duckworth, Carroll
cduckworth@timesfreepress.com, Circ. Dir., Chattanooga Times Free Press, TN, Chattanooga

Duckworth, Keeley....................(336) 373-7360
keeley.duckworth@Greensboro.com, Advertising Department Manager, News & Record, NC, Greensboro

Ducote, Amy
ads@avoyelles.com, Adv. Mgr., Avoyelles Journal, LA, Marksville

Dudajek, Dave
ddudajek@uticaod.com, Opinion Page Ed., The Observer-Dispatch, NY, Utica

Dudden, Katie.........................(417) 256-9191
Web Services, Pagination, Digital Print, West Plains Daily Quill, MO, West Plains

Dudek, Shaun
dudeks@wwstout.edu, University of Wisconsin-Stout, WI, Menomonie

Dudgeon, Thom.....................(251) 434-8478
tdudgeon@mobileregister.com, Graphics Ed., Press-Register, AL, Mobile

Dudinksie, Scott
sdudinskie@dailyitem.com, Sports Reporter, The Daily Item, PA, Sunbury

Dudka, Donna.........................(514) 987-2222
ddudka@montrealgazette.com, Mgr, Admin–Eastern Region, Montreal Gazette, QC, Montreal

Dudley, Darla
darladudley@windstream.net, Owner/Pub., Grandview Tribune, TX, Grandview

Dudley, Gary D.
journal@journalherald.com, Pub., Journal Herald, IA, Manson

Dudley, Gary D.
gddudley@calhouncountyreminder.com, Tri-county Special, IA, Auburn
gddudley@calhouncountyreminder.com, Adv. Mgr., Calhoun County Reminder, IA, Rockwell City

Dudley, Lynette........................(843) 626-0289
ldudley@thesunnews.com, Op. Mgr., The Sun News, SC, Myrtle Beach

Dudley, Mary
secretary@wtpa.org, Secretary-Treasurer, West Texas Press Association, TX, Perryton

Dudley, Mary H.
mhdudley@ptsi.net, Ed., Perryton Herald, TX, Perryton
mhdudley@ptsi.net, Ed., The Perryton Herald, TX, Perryton

Duenas, Mario G.
editorial@semananews.com, Pub., Semana News, TX, Houston

Duenas, Raul
raul.duenas@newspan.net, Prodn. Mgr., Semana News, TX, Houston

Duerr, Sandra.........................(805) 781-7901
sduerr@thetribunenews.com, VP/Exec. Ed., The Tribune, CA, San Luis Obispo

Duerr, Sandra.................(805) 927-8652, ext. 12
VP/Exec Ed, The Cambrian, CA, Cambria

Dufek, Lee Anne.....................(605) 793-2293
Pub., Estelline Journal, SD, Estelline

Dufek, LeeAnne......................(605) 793-2293
hcp@itctel.com, Pub., Hamlin County Republican, SD, Castlewood

Duffield, Ginny
gduffield@vernonpublishing.com, Ed., Miller County Autogram Sentinel, MO, Eldon

Duffy, Jim...........................(973) 627-2427
jduffy@fulcoinc.com, Owner/Pres., Fulco, Inc., NJ, Denville

Duffy, Lynn...........................(845) 265-2468
ads@pcnr.com, Adv Mgr, Putnam County News & Recorder, NY, Cold Spring

Duffy, Shana..........................(262) 513-2618
sduffy@conleynet.com, Editorial Page Ed., The Freeman, WI, Waukesha

Duffy, Terry
dispatch@wnypapers.com, Mng. Ed., Island Dispatch, NY, Grand Island

Duffy, Terry............................(716) 773-7676
nfpnews@c1mail.com, Mng. Ed., Niagara-Wheatfield Tribune, NY, Grand Island

Duffy, Terry
sentinel@wnypapers.com, Mng. Ed., Lewiston-Porter Sentinel, NY, Grand Island

Duffy, Tim.............................(613) 636-0539
info@mflo.com, Vice Pres., Opns., Master Flo Technology, ON, Hawkesbury

Dufresne, Marcel
marcel.dufresne@uconn.edu, Assoc. Prof., University of Connecticut, CT, Storrs

Dugan, Chris...............(724) 222-2200 ext. 2431
dugan@observer-reporter.com, Sports Ed., Observer-Reporter, PA, Washington

Dugan, Niko..........................(217) 351-5212
ndugan@news-gazette.com, Online Ed., The News-Gazette, IL, Champaign

Dugar, Michael-Shawn...............(208) 883-4629
mdugar@dnews.com, Sports Editor, Moscow-Pullman Daily News, ID, Moscow

Dugay, Juan Martinez
jmdugay@towmar.net, Pres., Towmar Representaciones S.A., FL, Mexico City

Duggal, Rakesh
rduggal@deloitte.com, NYU Stern School of Bus., NY, New York

Duggan, Brian.........................(775) 327-6761
bduggan@rgj.com, Key Topics Ed., Reno Gazette-Journal, NV, Reno

Dugger, Victoria
vdugger@sentinel-tribune.com, Ed., Sentinel-Tribune, OH, Bowling Green

Duhe, Ken..............................(225) 388-0656
kduhe@theadvocate.com, Online News Editor, The Advocate, LA, Baton Rouge

Duhon, Christine
circulation@banner-tribune.com, Franklin Banner-Tribune, LA, Franklin

Duignan, Wayne
sales@horizonsig.com, Vice Pres., Mktg., Horizons, Inc., OH, Cleveland

Dukate, Jake
ads@theleadernews.com, Prod. Mgr., The Leader, TX, Houston

Duke, Biddle
biddleduke@stowereporter.com, Pres./Owner, Waterbury Record, VT, Stowe

Duke, Carla
wsn@mesh.net, Publisher, Wedgwood Shopping News, TX, Fort Worth

Duke, Dan..............................(757) 446-2000
dan.duke@pilotonline.com, Production Ed., The Virginian-Pilot, VA, Norfolk

Duke, Kevin
newsguardeditor@countrymedia.net, Ed., The News Guard, OR, Lincoln City

Duke, Oak..............................(585) 593-5300
oakduke@wellsvilledaily.com, General Manager - Wellsville, Pennesaverplus, NY, Hornell

Duke, Oak
publisher@wellsvilledaily.com, Adv. Mgr., Allegany County Pennysaver, NY, Wellsville

Duke, Oak..............................(585) 593-5300
publisher@wellsvilledaily.com, Adv. Dir., Wellsville Daily Reporter, NY, Wellsville

Duke, Ricky.............................(318) 307-7588
rduke@monroe.gannett.com, News Planning Ed., The Times, LA, Shreveport

Dukes, Seth
editor@octimesnews.com, Ed., The Ohio County Times, KY, Hartford

Duley, Joe..............................(304) 291-9457
nie@dominionpost.com, Newspaper In Education Coordinator, The Dominion Post, WV, Morgantown

Duley, Joseph.........................(304) 291-9457
circulation@dominionpost.com, Circ. Operations Mgr., The Dominion Post, WV, Morgantown

Dulin, Ed
ed0783@aol.com, CEO/President, Delaware State News, DE, Dover

Dulin, Ed.............................(623) 445-2800

valleyoffc@aol.com, Pres., Independent
Newspapers, Inc. (Arizona), AZ, Phoenix

Dulin, Ed .... **(302) 674-3600**
ed0783@aol.com, Pres., Opns., Independent
Newsmedia Inc. Usa, DE, Dover

Dulin, Ed .... **(302) 674-3600**
newsroom@newszap.com, Pres., Opns.,
Independent Newspapers, Inc. (Delmarva),
DE, Dover

Dulley, James T. .... **(513) 231-6034**
dulley@dulley.com, Pres., Starcott Media
Services, Inc., Cincinnati

Dumas, Carol .... **(508) 247-3255**
cdumas@wickedlocal.com, Editor, The Cape
Codder, MA, Orleans

Dumas, Carol
cdumas@wickedlocal.com, Senior Managing
Ed., Sandwich Broadsider, MA, Yarmouth
Port

Dumas, Maurice
mdumas@lesoleil.com, Sports Dir., Le Soleil,
QC, Quebec

Dumas, Rob .... **(514) 459-0200 ext. 23**
robd@isd.ca, Director of Sales and Marketing,
Innovative Systems Design, Inc., QC, Pointe-
Claire

Dumont, Diane
diane.dumont@monteregieweb.com, Pub./Dir.,
Le Journal Saint-francois, QC, Salaberry-de-
Valleyfield

Dumont, Mickey
mickey.dumont@sunmedia.ca, Editorial ,
Brooks & County Chronicle (OOB), AB,
Brooks
mickey.dumont@sunmedia.ca, Ed, Central
Plains Herald Leader, MB, Portage La Prairie

Dumont, Mickey
mdmont@postmedia.com, Ed., The Daily
Graphic, MB, Portage la Prairie

Dump, Rob
randolph@cedarcountynews.net, The
Randolph Times, NE, Randolph
randolph@cedarcountynews.net, Ed., The
Wausa Gazette, NE, Wausa

Dump, Rob
ccnews@hartel.net, Pub., Northeast Nebraska
News Co., NE, Hartington

Dump, Rob .... **(402) 748-3666**
osmondnews@abbnebraska.com, Pub., The
Osmond Republican, NE, Osmond

Dunagan, Christopher .... **(360) 792-9207**
cdunagan@kitsapsun.com, Environmental/
Tech. Writer, Kitsap Sun, WA, Bremerton

Dunaief, Leah S. .... **ext. 116**
pub@tbrnewspapers.com, Pub., The Village
Times Herald, NY, Setauket

Dunbar, Cheyenne
cheyenne.dunbar@stvincent.edu, Business
Manager, Saint Vincent College, PA, Latrobe

Dunbar, Heather .... **(519) 763-3494 Ext. 240**
hdunbar@guelphmercurytribune.com, Adv.
Mgr., New Hamburg Independent, ON, New
Hamburg

Dunbar, Heather .... **(519) 763-3333 ext. 240**
hdunbar@guelphmercurytribune.com, Sales
Mgr., Guelph Tribune, ON, Guelph

Dunbar, Steve .... **(319) 653-2191**
prod@washjrnl.com, Prodn. Mgr., The
Washington Evening Journal, IA, Washington

Duncan, Amy
aduncan@dmreg.com, Pub., Record-Herald
and Indianola Tribune, IA, Indianola

Duncan, Amy
aduncan@dmreg.com, Pub., Extra, IA,
Indianola

Duncan, Barbara
barbara@oldhamera.com, Advertising
Representative, Oldham Era, KY, La Grange

Duncan, Craig .... **(931) 388-6464**
cduncan@c-dh.net, Adv. Dir., Columbia Daily
Herald, TN, Columbia

Duncan, Dan .... **(606) 784-4116**
dduncan@journal-times.com, Adv. Mgr., Olive
Hill Times, KY, Olive Hill

Duncan, Dan
dduncan@themoreheadnews.com, Adv. Dir.,
The Morehead News, KY, Morehead

Duncan, Dan
dduncan@journal-times.com, Adv. Dir.,
Grayson Journal-Enquirer, KY, Grayson

Duncan, Dustin
dustin.duncan@thesouthern.com, Ed.,
Carbondale Times, IL, Carbondale

Duncan, Greg
info@qcna.qc.ca, Exec. Dir., Quebec
Community Newspapers Association, QC,
Ile Perrot

Duncan, Kat
kduncan@sfchronicle.com, Photo Ed, San
Francisco Chronicle, CA, San Francisco

Duncan, Kathy
Kathy.Duncan@CrowleyToday.com, Production
Mgr., The Crowley Post-Signal, LA, Crowley

Duncan, Lisa
duncan@knews.com, Mktg. Dir., Knoxville
News Sentinel, TN, Knoxville

Duncan, Melanie
mduncan@the-messenger.com, Retail Acct.
Exec., The Messenger, KY, Madisonville

Duncan, Sean .... **(812) 277-7283**
Sports Ed., The Times-Mail, IN, Bedford

Duncan, Susan .... **(812) 231-4333**
susan.duncan@tribstar.com, News Ed., The
Tribune Star, IN, Terre Haute

Duncan, Susan .... **(812) 206-2130**
Ed., Tribune, IN, New Albany

Duncan, Susan
circulation@iafalls.com, Circ. Mgr., Times-
citizen, IA, Iowa Falls

Dundas, Tim
tdundas@niagaracommunitynewspapers.com,
Pub., The Niagara Advance, ON, Virgil

Dundas, Tim
tdundas@rannie.com, Pub., Niagara Shopping
News, ON, Niagara Falls

Dundon, Eric
eric.dundon@courierpost.com, Ed., Salt River
Journal, MO, Hannibal

Dungen, Maridel
nuent@industrynet.com, Pub., The New Ulm
Enterprise, TX, New Ulm

Dungey, Diane .... **(847) 427-4515**
ddungey@dailyherald.com, Senior Deputy
Managing Editor, Daily Herald, IL, Arlington
Heights

Dunham, Amy
cteditor@uah.edu, Managing Editor, Univ. of
Alabama Huntsville, AL, Huntsville

Dunham, Melanie
editor2003@austinfamily.com, Ed., Austin
Family, TX, Round Rock

Dunhill, Candy .... **(561) 910-6424**
candy@dunhillintl.com, Vice Pres., Dunhill
International List Co., Inc., FL, Boca Raton

Dunhill, Cindy .... **(561) 910-6422**
cindy@dunhillintl.com, Vice Pres., Dunhill
International List Co., Inc., FL, Boca Raton

Dunhill, Robert .... **(561) 910-6427**
robert@dunhillintl.com, Pres., Dunhill
International List Co., Inc., FL, Boca Raton

Dunick, Leith .... **(807) 346-2650**
ldunick@dougallmedia.com, Mng. Ed., Thunder
Bay Source, ON, Thunder Bay

Dunigan, Matt

mdunigan@gazette.net, Gen. Mgr., The Bolling
Aviator, MD, Gaithersburg

Dunigan, Matt
mdunigan@gazette.net, Gen. Mgr., The NNMC
Journal, MD, Gaithersburg

Dunkel, Bob .... **(202) 253-3899**
dunkelratings@msn.com, Co-Ed./Co-Owner,
Dunkel Sports Research Service, Mount
Vernon

Dunkerley, William .... **(860) 827-8896**
wdpc@publishinghelp.com, Principal, William
Dunkerley Publishing Consultant, CT, New
Britain

Dunkle, Daniel
news@villagesoup.com, Ed., The Republican
Journal, ME, Belfast

Dunkle, Dirk .... **(573) 815-1608**
ddunkle@columbiatribune.com, Circ. Dir.,
Columbia Daily Tribune, MO, Columbia

Dunlap, Anne .... **(407) 420-5671**
Arts/Entertainment Ed., Orlando Sentinel, FL,
Orlando

Dunlap, Charles .... **(660) 463-7522**
concordianreporter@centurytel.net, Staff
Writer, The Concordian, MO, Concordia

Dunlap, Joe .... **(309) 686-3127**
jdunlap@pjstar.com, Credit Mgr., Journal Star,
IL, Peoria

Dunlap, LeAnna .... **(704) 562-9067**
ldunlap@mooresvilletribune.com, Adv.
Dir., Statesville Record & Landmark, NC,
Statesville

Dunlap, LeAnna .... **(704) 696-2950**
ldunlap@mooresvilletribune.com, Adv. Mgr.,
Mooresville Tribune, NC, Mooresville

Dunn, Adrianne
adunn@baxterbulletin.com, Adv. Dir., The
Baxter Bulletin, AR, Mountain Home

Dunn, Anita .... **(330) 580-8365**
anita.dunn@cantonrep.com, Cir. Dir., The
Repository, OH, Canton

Dunn, Bill
bdunn@theindependent.com, Ed., Ad/venture,
NE, Grand Island

Dunn, Brad
bdunn@parade.com, Executive Editor, Parade,
New York

Dunn, Dennis .... **(256) 235-9250**
ddunn@annistonstar.com, Circ. Mgr., The
Anniston Star, AL, Anniston

Dunn, Ian
iand@leavenworthecho.com, Ed., The
Leavenworth Echo, WA, Leavenworth

Dunn, Jeanette
jeanette@greenepublishing.com, Ad., Madison
County Carrier, FL, Madison
jeanette@greenepublishing.com, Ad., Madison
Enterprise-Recorder, FL, Madison

Dunn, Jim .... **(989) 739-2054**
publisher@iosconews.com, Pub., Oscoda
Press, MI, Oscoda

Dunn, Kathryn
editor@claremont-courier.com, Ed., Claremont
Courier, CA, Claremont

Dunn, Larry .... **(620) 842-5129**
anthonyrepublican@att.net, Pub, Anthony
Republican, KS, Anthony

Dunn, Ryan
dunn@uga.edu, Ohio Univ., OH, Athens

Dunn, Sharon
dunn@greeleytrib.com, City Ed., Greeley Daily
Tribune, CO, Greeley

Dunn, Tammy
tdunn@montgomeryherald.com, Publisher,
Montgomery Herald, NC, Troy
tdunn@montgomeryherald.com, NCPA
Secretary/Treasurer, North Carolina Press
Association, NC, Raleigh

Dunn-Rankin, David .... **(941) 206-1003**
DAVIDDR@SUN-HERALD.COM, President/
CEO/COO, Sun Coast Media Group Inc, FL,
Punta Gorda

Dunn-Rankin, David .... **(941) 206-1003**
daviddr@sun-herald.com, Pres., Charlotte Sun,
FL, Punta Gorda
daviddr@sun-herald.com, Southern
Newspaper Publishers Association, GA,
Atlanta
daviddr@sun-herald.com, Pres., Arcadian, FL,
Arcadia

Dunn-Rankin, Debbie .... **(941) 206-1500**
debbiedr@sun-herald.com, VP of Marketing,
Charlotte Sun, FL, Punta Gorda

Dunnavant, Bob .... **(931) 424-2845**
bob@pulaskicitizen.com, Advt Mgr, Pulaski
Citizen, TN, Pulaski

Dunnavant, Trea .... **(931) 363-3544 ext. 133**
trea.dunnavant@pulaskicitizen.com, Staff
Writer/Photographer, Pulaski Citizen, TN,
Pulaski

Dunne , Tricia .... **(256) 845-2550**
tclinton@times-journal.com , Publisher , Sand
Mountain Shopper's Guide, AL, Fort Payne

Dunning, Ernie
ernie@dunningphoto.com, Pres., Dunning
Photo Equipment, Inc., OK, Bixby

Dunning, Joe
jdunning@the-leader.com, Mng. Ed.,
Horseheads Shopper, NY, Corning

Dunsford, Deborah
dj-king@tamu.edu, Program Coord., Texas
A&M University, TX, College Station

Dunsky, Ron
rondunsky@passur.com, Media, Megadata
Corp., CT, Stamford

Dunsmore, Cynthia .... **(604) 575-2323**
cynthia.dunsmore@cloverdalereporter.com,
Sales Representative, Cloverdale Reporter,
BC, Surrey

Dunson, Doug
sports@dequeenbee.com, Sports Ed.,
DeQueen Bee, AR, De Queen

Dunstan, Allen
allen.dunstan@coxinc.com, Vice Pres., Eastern
Reg., Newspapers First, Inc., NY, New York
allen.dunstan@coxinc.com, Sr. Dir., Nat'l
Accts., Atlanta Journal-Constitution, GA,
Atlanta

Dunwoody, Sharon
dunwoody@wisc.edu, Evjue-Bascom Prof.,
University of Wisconsin-Madison, WI,
Madison

Duplantie, Roger .... **(613) 632-4155**
roger@eap.on.ca, Gen. Mgr., Le Carillon, ON,
Hawkesbury

Duplantie, Roger
roger@eap.on.ca, Gen. Mgr., Tribune Express,
ON, Hawkesbury

Duplantie, Roger
info@lereflet.com, Gen. Dir. , Journal Le Reflet,
ON, Embrun
info@lereflet.com, Dir. Gen., L'argenteuil, QC,
Lachute

Duplantie, Roger .... **(613) 632-4155**
roger@eap.on.ca, Gen. Mgr., Cie d'Edition
Andre Paquette, Inc., ON, Hawkesbury

Dupont, Michel .... **(418) 275-2911**
michel.dupont@transcontinental.ca, Regional
Publisher, L'etoile Du Lac, QC, Roberval

Dupont, Michelle
redaction_alma@transcontinental.ca, Gen.
Mgr., Le Lac St. Jean, QC, Alma

Dupont, Ron .... **(941) 207-1101**
rdupont@venicegondolier.com, Ed., Venice
Gondolier Sun, FL, Venice

Dupre, Crystal
publisher@theeagle.com, Pub., The Eagle,

TX, Bryan

Dupre, Farn .... (908) 232-2913 ext. 103
farn.dupre@njfamily.com, Ed., Union County
Family, NJ, Mountainside

Dupre, Farn .... (908) 232-2913 ext. 103
farn.dupre@njfamily.com, Ed., Morris County
Family, NJ, Mountainside

Dupre, Farn .... (908) 232-2913 ext. 103
farn.dupre@njfamily.com, Ed., New Jersey
Family, NJ, Summit

Dupree, Cheryl
cheryldk@aol.com, Ed., International Photo
News, West Palm Beach

Dupree, Danielle .... (903) 636-4351
BSHjournal@aol.com, Mgr., Big Sandy-
Hawkins Journal, TX, Big Sandy

Duprez, Mike
mike.duprez@the-dispatch.com, Sports Ed.,
The Dispatch, NC, Lexington

Dupuy, Benjamin...................... (718) 434-8100
editor@haiti-progres.com, Pub., Haiti Progres,
NY, Brooklyn

Dura, Gary
gdura@wcinet.com, Copy Ed., Telegraph
Herald, IA, Dubuque

Duran, Charlene
charlene.duran@trinidadstate.edu, Trinidad
State Junior College, CO, Trinidad

Duran, Tino
tinoduran@laprensa.com, Pub., La Prensa De
San Antonio, TX, San Antonio

Durante, John
jdurante@cbaol.com, Senior VP, Sales, Cba
Industries, NJ, Elmwood Park

Durawa, Gary
gdurawa@metrowny.com, Pub., Niagara Falls /
Wheatfield Metro Retailer (OOB), NY, Buffalo
gdurawa@metrowny.com, Pub., Arcade
Pennysaver, NY, Arcade
gdurawa@metrowny.com, Pub., Blasdell /
Lackawanna (OOB), NY, Buffalo
gdurawa@metrowny.com, Pub., Hamburg
Pennysaver, NY, Hamburg
gdurawa@metrowny.com, Pub., Lockport
Retailer, NY, Buffalo
gdurawa@metrowny.com, Pub., Tonawanda
Source, NY, Buffalo
gdurawa@metrowny.com, Pub., South
Cheektowaga Source, NY, Buffalo
gdurawa@metrowny.com, Pub., Kenmore /
Tonawanda Source, NY, Buffalo
gdurawa@metrowny.com, Pub., Eggertsville /
Snyder Smart Shopper, NY, Buffalo
gdurawa@metrowny.com, Pub., North
Tonawanda Source, NY, Buffalo
gdurawa@metrowny.com, Pub., North
Cheektowaga Source, NY, Buffalo
gdurawa@metrowny.com, Pub., South Buffalo
Metro Source, NY, Buffalo
gdurawa@metrowny.com, Pub., Depew Metro
Source, NY, Buffalo
gdurawa@metrowny.com, Pub., Lancaster
Source, NY, Buffalo
gdurawa@metrowny.com, Pub., Clarence
Metro Source, NY, Buffalo
gdurawa@metrowny.com, Pub., Amherst
/ Tonawanda Metro Source (OOB) , NY,
Buffalo
gdurawa@metrowny.com, Pub., Springville
Journal, NY, Buffalo
gdurawa@metrowny.com, Pub./Prod. Mgr,
Alden Metro Source, NY, Buffalo
gdurawa@metrowny.com, Pub., Williamsville
Smart Shopper, NY, Buffalo
gdurawa@metrowny.com, Pub./Prod. Mgr,
Amherst / Getzville Smart Shopper, NY,
Buffalo
gdurawa@metrowny.com, Pub., North Buffalo
Smart Shopper, NY, Buffalo
gdurawa@metrowny.com, Pub., Gowanda
News, NY, Buffalo

Durawa, Gary........................... (585) 343-8000
gdurawa@batavianews.com, Advt Dir, The
Livingston County News, NY, Geneseo

Durawa, Gary .... (585) 815-1454
gdurawa@batavianews.com, Circulation
Director, The Daily News, NY, Batavia

Duray, Christopher.................... (860) 486-6141
Univ. of Connecticut, CT, Storrs

Durazo, Armando V. .... (915) 546-6124
adurazo@elpasotimes.com, City/Metro Ed., El
Paso Times, TX, El Paso
adurazo@elpasotimes.com, City/Metro Ed., El
Paso y Mas, TX, El Paso

Durbin, Debra .... (918) 421-2021
composing@mcalesternews.com, Prod. Mgr.,
McAlester News-Capital, OK, McAlester

Durch, Lana
ads@bloomeradvance.com, Adv. Production.,
Bloomer Advance, WI, Bloomer

Duren, Ashlee .... (706) 823-3714
ashlee.duren@augustamagazine.com,
Publisher, AUGUSTA MAGAZINE, The
Augusta Chronicle, GA, Augusta

Duren, Diane
diane.duren@advpubtech.com, Online Product
Mgr., Advanced Publishing Technology, CA,
Burbank

Durfey, James
ads@livent.net, Adv. Dir., The Livingston
Enterprise, MT, Livingston

Durgin, Brittany .... (508) 749-3166 x321
bdurgin@worcestermag.com, Ed., Worcester
Magazine, MA, Worcester

Durham, Cindy
cindy@snpa.org, Asst ED, Southern
Newspaper Publishers Association, GA,
Atlanta

Durham, Darrell...................... (520) 573-4412
ddurham@tucson.com, Mrktg. Dir. , Arizona
Daily Star, AZ, Tucson

Durham, Judy
jdurham@npes.org, Dir., Commun., NPES,
VA, Reston

Durham, Pam
pdurham@reidsvillereview.com, Adv. Dir., The
Eden News, NC, Reidsville
pdurham@reidsvillereview.com, Ad. Dir, The
Reidsville Review, NC, Reidsville
pdurham@reidsvillereview.com, Retail Adv.
Dir., The Eden Daily News, NC, Reidsville

Durham, Pam
pdurham@reidsvillereview.com, Adv. Dir., The
Messenger, NC, Reidsville

Durham, Paul.......................... (252) 265-7808
paul@wilsontimes.com, Sports Ed., The Wilson
Times, NC, Wilson

Durham, Renee .... (870) 338-9181
rdurham@stuttgartdailyleader.com, Gen. Mgr.,
The Helena Arkansas Daily World, AR,
HELENA

Durham, Rob
editor@breckenridgeamerican.com, Ed.,
Breckenridge American, TX, Breckenridge

Durham, Tony.......................... (419) 724-6062
tdurham@theblade.com, News Ed., The Blade,
OH, Toledo

Durheim, Duane .... (507) 794-3511
ddurheim@stjamesnews.com, GM, Sleepy Eye
Herald-Dispatch, MN, Sleepy Eye

Durheim, Duane "Doc" .... (507) 794-3511
ddurheim@stjamesnews.com, General
Manager, Brown County Reminder, MN,
Sleepy Eye

Durheim, Duane (Doc)
ddurheim@redwoodfallsgazette.com, General
Manager, The Redwood Falls Gazette, MN,
Redwood Falls

Durheim, Duane (Doc) .... (507) 375-3161
ddurheim@stjamesnews.com, Gen. Mgr., Town
& Country Shopper, MN, Saint James
ddurheim@stjamesnews.com, Gen. Mgr./Adv.
Mgr., St James Plaindealer, MN, Saint James

Duriga, Joyce
mail@catholicnewworld.com, Ed., The Catholic
New World, IL, Chicago

Durkee, Matt
mdurkee@triplicate.com, Ed., The Del Norte
Triplicate, CA, Crescent City

Durkee, Steve
sdurkee@mvgazette.com, Prodn. Mgr.,
Vineyard Gazette, MA, Edgartown

Durnin, Valerie
publisher@thereminder.ca, Pub, Flin Flon
Reminder, MB, Flin Flon

Durocher, Jean-Yves
jy.durocher@stanstead-journal.com, Sales
Mgr., The Stanstead Journal, QC, Stanstead

Durrell, Brad........................... (203) 402-2332
Ed., Shelton Herald, CT, Shelton

Durrell, Brad
eastoncourier@hersamacorn.com, Ed, Monroe
Courier, CT, Shelton

Durreman, Beth .... (573) 547-4567
bethd@perryvillenews.com, Pub., The Perry
County Republic-Monitor, MO, Perryville

Durso, Ken
kdurso@multigroup.com, Owner, Multimedia
Resource Group, CA, Sunnyvale

Durst, Susan.......................... (715) 693-2300
motimes@mtc.net, Publisher and Editor,
Mosinee Times, WI, Mosinee

Duscher, Whitney
whitneyd@dailynews.net, Customer Service
Rep., The Hays Daily News, KS, Hays

Dussault, Sarah .... (408) 806-9287
sdussault@bayareanewsgroup.com, AME,
Visual Journalism, East Bay Times, CA,
Walnut Creek

Dustin, Jim
jcstar@yahoo.com, Contrib. Ed., Jackson
County Star, CO, Walden

Duthler, Gaelle
gaelle.duthler@zu.ac.ae, Asst. Prof., Zayed
University, Al Ruwayyah

Dutson, Lewis .... (435) 864-2400
lewis@millardccp.com, Co-Publisher, Millard
County Chronicle Progress, UT, Delta

Dutton, Josh
sports@andalusiastarnews.com, Sports Ed.,
Andalusia Star-News, AL, Andalusia

Duval, Denise
dduval@redmondspokesman.com, Adv. Mgr.,
The Redmond Spokesman, OR, Redmond

Duval, Diane........................... (613) 678-3327
accounts@thereview.ca, Accounts, The
Review, ON, Vankleek Hill

Duval, Lynn
bne@fcpne.com, Admin., Free Community
Papers of New England, CT, Concord
bne@fcpne.com, Admin., Free Community
Papers of New England, CT, Willimantic

Duvall, Crystal
ads@murrayledger.com, Adv. Rep., The Murray
Ledger & Times, KY, Murray

Duvoisin, Marc
marc.duvoisin@latimes.com, Managing Ed.,
Los Angeles Times, CA, Los Angeles

Dwinell, Joseph .... (617) 619-6493
City Desk Ed., Boston Herald, MA, Boston

Dwyer, Karen
kdwyer@1stcomp.com, Reilly Prof./Basic
Course Dir., University of Nebraska at
Omaha, NE, Omaha

Dwyer, Terry
tdwyer@messengernews.net, Editorial Page
Ed., The Messenger, IA, Fort Dodge

Dwyer, Timothy .... (860) 701-4379
t.dwyer@theday.com, Exec. Ed., New London
Times, CT, New London

t.dwyer@theday.com, Exec. Ed., The Montville
Times, CT, New London
t.dwyer@theday.com, Executive Ed., The
Thames River Times, CT, New London
t.dwyer@theday.com, Exec. Ed., Waterford
Times, CT, New London
t.dwyer@theday.com, Exec. Ed., The Groton
Times, CT, New London
t.dwyer@theday.com, Exec. Ed., The Mystic
Times, CT, New London
t.dwyer@theday.com, Exec. Ed., The
Stonington Times, CT, New London
t.dwyer@theday.com, Exec. Ed., The Lyme
Times, CT, New London

Dwyer Ryan, Christa
cryan@villagevoice.com, Assoc. Pub., The
Village Voice, NY, New York

Dyck, Kristin
mznnews1@mrnews.ca, Ed, Banner Post, AB,
Grimshaw

Dyck, Matt
matt.dyck@zu.ac.ae, Asst. Prof., Zayed
University, Al Ruwayyah

Dye, Keith
keith.dye@trelleborg.com, CEO, Reeves
Brothers, Inc., SC, Spartanburg

Dye, Robert
rdye@examiner-enterprise.com, Cir. Mgr.,
Examiner-Enterprise, OK, Bartlesville
rdye@examiner-enterprise.com, Circ. Mgr,
Pawhuska Journal-Capital, OK, Pawhuska

Dyer, Andrew
Editor@TheDailyAztec.com , San Diego State
Univ., CA, San Diego

Dyer, Deidre .... (702) 383-0493
ddyer@reviewjournal.com, Div. Sales Mgr.,
Nifty Nickel, NV, Las Vegas

Dyer, Diane .... (270) 526-5946
diane@beechtreenews.com, Beech Tree News,
KY, Benton

Dyer, Jennifer .... (618) 656-4700 x32
jdyer@edwpub.net, Adv. Design Mgr. ,
Edwardsville Intelligencer, IL, Edwardsville

Dyer, Ray T.
rdyer@elrenotribune.com, Pub., El Reno
Tribune, OK, El Reno

Dyer, Richard
rrdyer@newszap.com, Mng. Ed., Apache
Junction/Gold Canyon Independent, AZ,
Phoenix

Dyer, Richard
rdyer@newszap.com, Mng. Ed., East
Mesa Independent (OOB), AZ, APACHE
JUNCTION
rdyer@newszap.com, Mng. Ed., Queen Creek
Independent, AZ, Apache Junction

Dyer, Tom
tom@watermarkonline.com, Pub., Watermark
Media, FL, Orlando

Dyer Fry, Kelly .... (405) 475-3247
kfry@opubco.com, Dir. Multimedia, The
Oklahoman, OK, Oklahoma City

Dyke, Justin .... (850) 561-1606
jdyke@fsview.com, Content Supervisor,
FSView & Florida Flambeau, FL, Tallahassee

Dykes, David .... (864) 298-4273
ddykes@greenvillenews.com, Reporter, The
Greenville News, SC, Greenville

Dykes, Mark .... (308) 762-3060 ext. 22
schools@alliancetimes.com, Asst. Mng. Ed.,
Alliance Times-Herald, NE, Alliance

Dykes, Valerie.......................... (717) 307-2431
valerie.dykes@mercersburgjournal.com, Office
Mgr, Mercersburg Journal, PA, Mercersburg

Dykstra, Dave .... (250) 364-1416 ext 203
d.dykstra@trailtimes.ca, sales, Trail Daily
Times, BC, Trail

Dykstra, Diane .... (920) 356-6772
ddykstra@capitalnewspapers.com, Gen. Mgr.,
Columbus Journal, WI, Beaver Dam

Dylong, Geoff .... **(518) 843-1100 Ext. 131**
geoff@recordernews.com, Associate Pub.,
Sacandaga Express, NY, Amsterdam
geoff@recordernews.com, Associate Pub.,
Mohawk Valley Express, NY, Amsterdam
geoff@recordernews.com, Assoc. Pub.,
Courier Standard Enterprise, NY, Amsterdam
geoff@recordernews.com, Assoc. Pub. , The
Recorder, NY, Amsterdam

Dzaran, John .... **(253) 597-8487**
john.dzaran@thenewstribune.com, VP
Advertising, The News Tribune, WA, Tacoma

Dzaran, John .... **(253) 597-8625**
john.dzaran@thenewstribune.com, Adv. Dir.,
The Olympian, WA, Olympia

Dzubay, Steve
sdzubay@rivertowns.net, Pub., Pierce County
Herald, WI, Ellsworth

Dzubay, Steve
SDzubay@rivertowns.net, Publisher, Hot Sheet
Shopper, WI, River Falls

Dzwonchyk, Melanie .... **(410) 332-6594**
mdzwonchyk@baltsun.com, Ed., Laurel
Leader, MD, Baltimore

Dzwonkowski, Ron .... **(313) 222-6583**
letters@freepress.com, Editorial Page Ed.,
Detroit Free Press, MI, Detroit

E

Eagle, Kathy 937-259- 2069
kathy.eagle@cmgohio.com, General Sales
Manager - Radio, Dayton Daily News, OH,
Franklin

Eagles, Dana .... **(407) 420-5427**
deagles@orlandosentinel.com, Ed.,
Recruitment/Staff Devel., Orlando Sentinel,
FL, Orlando

Eakin, Chris
chris.eakin@sunmedia.ca, Ed., Fairview Post,
AB, Fairview

Eakins, Paul .... **(714) 796-6853**
peakins@ocregister.com , Comm. News Ed.,
The Orange County Register, CA, Santa Ana

Eanes, Gary .... **(336) 727-7362**
geanes@wsjournal.com, IT Systems Manager,
Winston-Salem Journal, NC, Winston Salem

Earhart, Karen .... **(303) 566-4091**
kearhart@coloradocommunitymedia.com,
Golden Transcript, CO, Golden
kearhart@coloradocommunitymedia.com,
Wheat Ridge Transcript, CO, Golden
kearhart@coloradocommunitymedia.com, The
Englewood Herald, CO, Highlands Ranch
kearhart@coloradocommunitymedia.com,
Class. Sales, Centennial Citizen, CO,
Highlands Ranch
kearhart@coloradocommunitymedia.com,
Class. Sales, Castle Rock News Press, CO,
HIGHLANDS RANCH
kearhart@coloradocommunitymedia.com,
Class. Sales, Highlands Ranch Herald, CO,
Highlands Ranch
kearhart@coloradocommunitymedia.
com, Northglenn-Thornton Sentinel, CO,
Westminster
kearhart@coloradocommunitymedia.com,
Class. Sales Mgr., Lakewood Sentinel, CO,
Golden
kearhart@coloradocommunitymedia.com,
Class. Sales, Elbert County News, CO,
Highlands Ranch
kearhart@coloradocommunitymedia.com,
Class. Sales, Lone Tree Voice, CO, Highlands
Ranch
kearhart@coloradocommunitymedia.com,
Class. Sales, Douglas County News Press,
CO, Highlands Ranch
kearhart@coloradocommunitymedia.com,
Class. Sales, Arvada Press, CO, Golden
kearhart@coloradocommunitymedia.
com, Class. Sales, Parker Chronicle, CO,
Highlands Ranch
kearhart@coloradocommunitymedia.com,

Class. Sales, The Littleton Independent, CO,
Highlands Ranch

Earl, Carl
cearl@dailyastorian.com, Corporate Systems
Manager, The Daily Astorian, OR, Astoria

Earle, Jenny
salesvp@ky-leadernews.com, Sales, Central
City Leader News, KY, Central City

Earley, Brenda .... **(937) 393-3456 Ext. 1675**
bearley@civitasmedia.com, Circ. Mgr.,
Hillsboro Times-Gazette, OH, Hillsboro

Earls, Lynn
tristateconnection@netcommander.com, Tri-
state Connection, TN, Harrogate

Earls, Paula
editor@californiademocrat.com, Ed.,
California Democrat, MO, California

Early, Bob .... **(956) 683-4141**
bearly@themonitor.com, Advertising Director,
The Monitor, TX, McAllen

Early, Kristen .... **(423) 359 - 3138**
kristen.early@greenevillesun.com, Assoc. Ed.,
The Greeneville Sun, TN, Greeneville

Early, Linda
LEarly@mcdowellnews.com, Adv. Asst./Circ. ,
The McDowell News, NC, Marion

Earnheardt, Mary Beth .... **(330) 742-3095**
Youngstown State Univ., OH, Youngstown

Eason, David
deason@mtsu.edu, Prof., Middle Tennessee
State University, TN, Murfreesboro

Eason, Jeff
office@blowingrocket.com, Ed., The Blowing
Rocket, NC, Blowing Rock

Eason, Tom .... **(518) 454-5332**
teason@timesunion.com, Vice President
Advertising, Times Union, NY, Albany

East, Cindy .... **(731) 692-3506**
ceast@tricityreporter.net, Mng. Ed., The Tri-City
Reporter, TN, Dyer

Easterbrook, Cathryn
ceasterbrook@thespec.com, Adv. Mgr., Class.,
The Hamilton Spectator, ON, Hamilton

Easterday, Conrad .... **(620) 388-4257**
ceasterday@dodgeglobe.com, Pub., Kiowa
County Signal, KS, Pratt

Easterday, Conrad .... **(620) 672-5511**
editor@pratttribune.com, Gen. Mgr., The Pratt
Tribune, KS, Pratt

Easterday, Conrad .... **(620) 408-9918**
ceasterday@dodgeglobe.com, Gen. Mgr.,
Dodge City Daily Globe, KS, Dodge City

Easterling, Chris
chris.easterling@indeonline.com, Sports Ed.,
The Independent, OH, Massillon

Easterling, Mike .... **(970) 252-7030**
mikee@montrosepress.com, Managing Editor,
The Montrose Daily Press, CO, Montrose

Easterly, Jim .... **(530) 852-0224**
jime@goldcountrymedia.com, Auburn Journal,
CA, Auburn

Eastin, Dawn
dawn@downtownnews.com, Gen. Mgr., Los
Angeles Downtown News, CA, Los Angeles

Easton, Mark J. .... **(561) 585-9381**
lwherald@bellsouth.net, Editor/Publisher,
Coastal/Greenacres Observer, FL, Lake
Worth
lwherald@bellsouth.net, Editor/Publisher, The
Lake Worth Herald, FL, Lake Worth

Easttom, Holly .... **(405) 878-2236**
holly.easttom@okbu.edu, Oklahoma Baptist
Univ., OK, Shawnee

Eastway, Chris
ceastway@cadillacnews.com, IT Dir., Cadillac
News, MI, Cadillac

Eaton, Brad

beaton@qni.biz, VP/CFO, Quincy Media, Inc.,
IL, Quincy

Eaton, Bryan .... **(978) 978-961 ext. 3153**
beaton@newburyportnews.com, Photo Ed.,
The Daily News, MA, Newburyport

Eaton, Eddie .... **(731) 989-6000**
Freed-Hardeman Univ., TN, Henderson

Eaton, Susan
susane@waynecojournalbanner.com, Adv.
Mgr., Wayne County Journal-Banner, MO,
Piedmont

Ebbert, David A. .... **(216) 769-4528**
debbert@chronohio.com, Adv. Mgr., Gay
People's Chronicle, OH, Cleveland

Ebel, Jim .... **(304) 293-7005**
jim.ebel@mail.wvu.edu, Harrison/Omnicom
Chair, Visiting Assistant Professor, West
Virginia University, WV, Morgantown

Ebelhack, Nick
Micour@wiu.edu, Editor-in-Chief, Western
Illinois University, IL, Macomb

Ebeling, Eric .... **(724) 465-5555 ext. 269**
eebeling@indianagazette.net, Exec. Ed., The
Indiana Gazette, PA, Indiana

Eben, Barb
classifieds@bighorncountynews.com, Sub/
Classifieds, Big Horn County News, MT,
Hardin

Ebenal, Dan
editor@saanichnews.com, Ed, Saanich News,
BC, Victoria

Eberhardt, Eric P. .... **(215) 345-3124**
eeberhardt@phillyburbs.com, Mktg. Dir., The
Intelligencer, PA, Doylestown

Ebert, Karl .... **(920) 431-8321**
kebert@pressgazettemedia.com, Content
Coash, Green Bay Press-Gazette, WI, Green
Bay

Ebert, Pam .... **(202) 659-1921**
Ed., Global Horizons, Washington

Ebrahim, Nick
mail@communitydigest.ca, Adv. Mgr.,
Community Digest, BC, N. Vancouver

Eby, John .... **(217) 351-2278**
jeby@parkland.edu, Parkland College, IL,
Champaign

Eby, John .... **(269) 782-1457**
jeby02@swmich.edu, Senior Writer
and Coordinator of Media Relations,
Southwestern Michigan College, MI,
Dowagiac

Echchaibi, Nabil
nabil.echchaibi@colorado.edu, Asst. Prof.,
University of Colorado, CO, Boulder

Echo, Spartan .... **(757) 823-8200**
seopfer@nsu.edu, Norfolk State University,
VA, Norfolk

Eck, Elizabeth .... **(410) 332-6463**
eeck@baltsun.com, AME, Community News,
Baltimore Sun Media Group, Towson Times,
MD, Baltimore

Eckard, Nancy
neckard@freedomenc.com, Pub., The
Shopper, NC, New Bern
neckard@freedomenc.com, The Shopper -
New Bern, NC, New Bern

Eckard, Nancy
neckard@freedomenc.com, The Shopper -
Havelock / Cherry Point, NC, New Bern

Eckels, Gayla .... **(530) 737-5044**
geckels@redbluffdailynews.com , Multi-Media
Acc. Exec., Daily News, CA, Red Bluff

Eckenrode, Ray .... **(814) 946-7463**
reckenrode@altoonamirror.com, Gen. Mgr.
Adv., Altoona Mirror, PA, Altoona

Eckenroth, Dean .... **(619) 429-5555 x 11**
publisher@eaglenewsca.com, Pub./Ed.,
Imperial Beach Eagle & Times, CA,
Coronado

Eckenroth, Dean .... **(619) 437-8800 x 11**
publisher@eaglenewsca.com, Pub., Coronado
Eagle & Journal, CA, Coronado

Eckenroth, Jr., Dean .... **(619) 437-8800**
editor@eaglenewsca.com, Assoc. Pub.,
Coronado Eagle & Journal, CA, Coronado

Eckersley, Lorne
publisher@crestonvalleyadvance.ca, Pub.,
Creston Valley Advance, BC, Creston

Eckert, Eric
eric.eckert@yorknewstimes.com, Online Ed.,
York News-Times, NE, York

Eckert, Michael .... **(810) 989-6264**
meckert@thetimesherald.com, Ed., Times
Herald, MI, Port Huron

Eckert, Susan
seckert@post-dispatch.com, Director of Major
& National Adv.
, St. Louis Post-Dispatch, MO, Saint Louis

Eckhardt, Edgar
eckhardt@rowan.edu, Assoc. Prof., Rowan
Univ., NJ, Glassboro

Eckl, Glenn .... **(417) 866-0841**
glenn@dioscg.org, Production/Web, The Mirror,
MO, Springfield

Eckstrom, Jim .... **(716) 372-3121 Ext. 223**
jeckstrom@oleantimesherald.com, Mng. Ed.,
Olean Times Herald, NY, Olean

Eckstrom, Jim .... **(814) 362-6531**
jeckstrom@oleantimesherald.com, Grp Ed.,
The Bradford Era, PA, Bradford

Eckstrom, Kevin .... **(202) 463-8777**
kevin.eckstrom@religionnews.com, Editor-in-
Chief, Religion News Service, Washington

Eddleman, Mike
mike@themexianews.com, Pub., The Mexia
News, TX, Mexia

Eddy, Ruth .... **(717) 248-6741**
reddy@lewistownsentinel.com, Pub., The
Sentinel, PA, Lewistown

Edelen, Ashlee .... **(706) 823-3886**
ashlee.edelen@augustachronicle.com,
Marketing Director, The Augusta Chronicle,
GA, Augusta

Edelman, Andy .... **(215) 849-9016**
nnbfeature@aol.com, Features Ed., National
News Bureau, Philadelphia

Edelman, Harvey
hedelman@holdcom.com, CEO, Holdcom, NJ,
Glen Rock

Eden, Ami
aeden@jta.org, Mng. Ed., Jewish Telegraphic
Agency Daily News Bulletin, NY, New York

Eden, Mark
maeden@stcloudstate.edu, Asst. Prof., St.
Cloud State University, MN, Saint Cloud

Edenborg, Kate .... **(651) 246-5358**
edenborgk@uwstout.edu, Advisor, University of
Wisconsin-Stout, WI, Menomonie

Edenloff, Al .... **(320) 763-3251236**
aedenloff@echopress.com, News Ed./Opinion
Page Ed., Echo-Press, MN, Alexandria

Edey, Noel
editor@cochranetimes.com, Ed, Cochrane
Times, AB, Cochrane

Edgar , Doug
doug.edgar@sunmedia.ca, Mng. Ed.,
Owensound Sun Times, ON, Owen Sound

Edge, Lisa
ledge@thelafayettesun.com, Gen. Mgr.,
LaFayette Sun, AL, Lafayette

Edgecombe, Jan .... **(402) 723-5861**
servpress@mainstaycomm.net, Pub., The
Henderson News, NE, Henderson

Edgecombe, Jim
mindencourier@gtmc.net, Adv. Mgr., The

Minden Courier, NE, Minden

Edgecombe, Mike
hebronjr@alltel.net, Ed., Hebron Journal-
Register, NE, Hebron

Edgeman, Alycia
walkercountymessenger@walkermessenger.
com, Adv. Rep., Walker County Plus, GA,
La Fayette

Edgren, Charlie .... (915) 546-6121
cedgren@elpasotimes.com, Editorial Page Ed.,
El Paso y Mas, TX, El Paso

Edie, Johnnie
jedie@4bca.com, Adv. Mgr., Barry County
Advertiser, MO, Cassville

Ediger, Karen .... (405) 341-2121 x 122
kediger@edmondsun.com, Pub., The Edmond
Sun, OK, Edmond

Edler Knoll, Lisa
lisa@bayweekly.com, Mktg. Dir., Passwords,
MD, Annapolis

Edmisten, Jason .... (423) 359-3149
jason.edmisten@jonesmedia.biz, CFO, Jones
Media, Inc., The Greeneville Sun, TN,
Greeneville

Edmo-Suppah, Lori .... (208) 478-3701
shobnews@ida.net, Ed., Sho-Ban News, ID,
Fort Hall

Edmonds, Eve
eedmonds@richmond-news.com, Ed,
Richmond News, BC, Richmond

Edmonds, Kenneth W.
thecarolinatimes@cs.com, Pub., The Carolina
Times, NC, Durham

Edmondson, Aimee .... (740) 597-3336
Asst. Prof., Ohio University, OH, Athens

Edmondson, Melissa
medmondson@nwkansas.com, Office Mgr.,
Colby Free Press, KS, Colby

Edmonson, John H.
homenewseditor@aol.com, Pub., The Home
News, NC, Marshville

Edney, Hazel Trice
Hazel@nnpa.org, Interim Exec. Ed., National
Newspaper Publishers Association Black
Press of America, DC, Washington

Edney, Wanda .... (828) 694-7897
wanda.edney@blueridgenow.com, Adv. Mgr.,
Times-News, NC, Hendersonville

Edshaw, Robert .... (902) 563-3846
Adv. Serv., The Cape Breton Post, NS,
Sydney

Edu, Martin O.
edum@gram.edu, Acting Head, Grambling
State University, LA, Grambling

Edwards, Betsy .... (804) 521-7584
betsye@vpa.net, Executive Director, Virginia
Press Association, Inc., VA, Glen Allen

Edwards, Bob .... (815) 526-4474
BEdwards@ShawMedia.com, Senior
Circulation Director, Northwest Herald, IL,
Crystal Lake

Edwards, Brian .... (616) 608-6170
bedwards@mibiz.com, Pub, MiBiz, MI, Grand
Rapids

Edwards, Carol
carol.edwards@cuny.edu, Vice Pres., Sales,
Advertiser/Agency Servs., The Arbitron Co.,
NY, New York

Edwards, Chris .... (319) 398-8205
chris.edwards@thegazettecompany.com, Adv.
Dir, Penny Saver, IA, Cedar Rapids
chris.edwards@thegazettecompany.com, VP
Sales & Marketing, The Gazette Company,
IA, Cedar Rapids
chris.edwards@thegazettecompany.com, VP,
Adv., The Gazette, IA, Cedar Rapids

Edwards, Chuck
cedwards@dailyadvance.com, Circ. Mgr., The

Daily Advance, NC, Elizabeth City

Edwards, Danny .... (661) 395-4344
Advisor, Bakersfield College, CA, Bakersfield

Edwards, Doug .... (402) 462-2131
douge@hastingstribune.com, Webmaster,
Hastings Tribune, NE, Hastings

Edwards, Florence
ap@thepicayune.com, Prodn. Mgr., The
Picayune, TX, Marble Falls

Edwards, Glenn .... (901) 529-2201
glenn.edwards@commercialappeal.com,
Executive Administrator, The Commercial
Appeal, TN, Memphis

Edwards, Jay
jedwards@dailydata.com, Adv./Mktg. Dir., The
Daily Record, AR, Little Rock

Edwards, Jeff
jeff@moultonadvertiser.com, Staff Writer, The
Moulton Advertiser, AL, Moulton

Edwards, Jerry .... (864) 882-3272
jerry@edwgroupinc.com, Owner, Daily Journal/
Messenger, SC, Seneca

Edwards, Jim
jime@camdenarknews.com, Mng. Ed.,
Camden News, AR, Camden

Edwards, John
je@punchin.com, Contributing Writer, Punch
In Travel, Food, Wine & Entertainment News
Syndicate, New York

Edwards, Kevin .... (570) 253-3055 ext. 314
kedwards@wayneindependent.com, Group
Sports Editor, The Wayne Independent, PA,
Honesdale

Edwards, Kim
kedwards@scmginc.com, Adv. Dir., The Polk
County News and Democrat, FL, Winter
Haven

Edwards, Lisa
lisaedwards@ddtonline.com, Asst. Adv. Dir.,
Delta Democrat Times, MS, Greenville

Edwards, Madolin
madolin@dailyamerican.com, Lifestyles Ed.,
Daily American, PA, Somerset

Edwards, Melissa
medwards@middlesexcc.edu, Middlesex
County College, NJ, Edison

Edwards, Nancy .... (360) 577-2544
nedwards@tdn.com, Regl. Ed., The Daily
News, WA, Longview

Edwards, Natalie
natalie.edwards@edelman.com, School of the
Art Institute, IL, Chicago

Edwards, Patricia Speziale .... (828) 236-8991
pspezial@gannett.com, Representative, Mid-
Atlantic Circulation Managers Association,
NC, Roanoke Rapids

Edwards, Paul .... (801) 237-2194
pedwards@deseretnews.com, Ed. / Pub.,
Deseret News, UT, Salt Lake City

Edwards, Richard
edwards@xtn.net, Mng. Ed., The Daily Post-
Athenian, TN, Athens

Edwards, Robert
robert.edwards@morningstar.com, Circ. Dir.,
Sales, Chicago Sun-Times, IL, Chicago

Edwards, Ross
redwards@sentinelandenterprise.com, Sports
Ed., Sentinel & Enterprise, MA, Fitchburg

Edwards, Sara
sedwards@santamariatimes.com, Retail Mgr.,
Santa Maria Times, CA, Santa Maria

Edwards, Thomas
thomas@thepicayune.com, Ed., The Picayune,
TX, Marble Falls

Edwards, Tim .... (631) 286-0058 ext. 11
tedwards@50pluslifestylesny.com, Exec. Ed.,
50+ LifeStyles, NY, Bellport

Edwards, Todd .... 1-(870) 741-2325
preston edwards <todde@harrisondaily.com>,
Advertising Manager, The Newton County
Times, AR, Jasper

Edwards, Todd
todde@phillipsmedia.com, Advertising
Manager, Harrison Daily Times, AR, Harrison

Edwards, Tom
recorder@bellnet.ca, Pub., The Mattawa
Recorder, ON, Mattawa

Edwards, Vanya .... (212) 727-8170
vanya@sovfoto.com, President, Sovfoto/
Eastfoto, New York

Eerola, Anna
anna.eerola@voicenews.com, Adv. Asst., The
Armada Times, MI, Clinton Township

Effenberger, Pat .... (651) 228-5016
peffenberger@pioneerpress.com, Commun.
Mgr., St. Paul Pioneer Press, MN, Saint Paul

Efune, Dovid
defune@gjcf.com, Dir., Algemeiner Journal,
NY, Brooklyn

Egan, Cathie .... (315) 661-2434
cegan@wdt.net, Asst. Feat. Ed., Watertown
Daily Times, NY, Watertown

Egan, Lori
lori.egan@thebayonet.com, Ed., The Bayonet,
GA, Fort Benning

Egan, Thomas A.
tegan@mpival.com, Sr. Vice Pres.,
Management Planning, Inc., NJ, Princeton

Egdish, Len
len.egdish@naplesnews.com, Nat'l Adv. Mgr.,
Naples Daily News, FL, Naples

Egenberger, Deb
deb.egenberger@nptelegraph.com, Asst. Mng.
Ed., The North Platte Telegraph, NE, North
Platte

Egenolf, James
egenolfma@gmail.com, Pres., Egenolf
Machine, Inc. (Egenolf Contracting &
Rigging), IN, Indianapolis

Eger, John
john.eger@sdsu.edu, Lectr./Van Deerlin Prof.
of Commun. & Pub. Policy, San Diego State
University, CA, San Diego

Eggen, Daniel
danielegg@goldcountrymedia.com, IT Mgr.,
Coverstory, CA, Auburn

Eggen, Marnie
meggen@geneseorepublic.com, Circ. Mgr.,
Geneseo Republic, IL, Geneseo

Eggenberger, Andrew .... (651) 345-3316
andrew@lakecitygraphic.com, editor, Lake City
Shopper, MN, Lake City

Eggenberger, Andrew .... (651) 345-3316
andrew@lakecitygraphic.com, Editor, The Lake
City Graphic, MN, Lake City

Eggensperger, Tom .... (406) 827-3421
ledgerclassads@blackfoot.net, Off. Mgr./
Classifieds, Sanders County Ledger, MT,
Thompson Falls

Egger, Jim
dsnews@europa.com, Pub., Daily Shipping
News, WA, Vancouver

Egger, Terrance C.Z. .... (215) 854-2000
tegger@philly.com, Publisher and CEO,
Philadelphia Inquirer, Daily News & Philly.
com, PA, Philadelphia

Eggers, David .... ext. 234
deggers@hickoryrecord.com, Circ. Dir., The
Hickory Daily Record, NC, Hickory
deggers@hickoryrecord.com, Circ. Dir., Pow,
NC, Hickory

Eggers, Tom .... (541) 957-4220
teggers@nrtoday.com, Sports Ed., The News-
Review, OR, Roseburg

Eggert, Don .... (802) 865-1020 x 20

don@sevendaysvt.com, Creative Dir./Assoc.
Pub., Seven Days, VT, Burlington

Egyir, Willie .... (212) 213-8585
newyorkbeacon@yahoo.com, Mng. Ed., New
York Beacon, NY, New York

Ehde, Lori
editor@star-herald.com, Ed., The Rock County
Star Herald, MN, Luverne

Ehde, Lori
editor@star-herald.com, Ed., Luverne
Announcer, MN, Luverne

Ehde, Lori
editor@star-herald.com, Ed., Hills Crescent,
MN, Luverne

Ehl, Dan .... (319) 656-2273
News Editor, The Kalona News, IA, Kalona

Ehler, Scott E.
advance@santel.net, Pub., The Parkston
Advance, SD, Parkston

Ehlers, Kim .... (605) 249-2420
info@auroracountynews.net, Owner, The
Stickney Argus, SD, White Lake

Ehli, Nick .... (406) 582-2647
nehli@dailychronicle.com, Mng. Ed., Bozeman
Daily Chronicle, MT, Bozeman

Ehrenberg, Leslie
editor@appletonpress.com, Ed., The Appleton
Press, MN, Appleton

Ehrenfeld, Charles .... (806) 894-9611 x 2448
Advisor, South Plains College, TX, Levelland

Ehrhardt, David
dehrhardt@dariodesigns.com, VP, Dario
Designs, Inc., MA, Northborough

Ehrke, Petra .... (867) 766-8264
advertising@nnsl.com, Adv. Mgr., Deh Cho
Drum, NT, Yellowknife

Ehrke, Petra .... (867) 766-8264
advertising@nnsl.com, Adv., Yellowknifer, NT,
Yellowknife

Ehrke, Petra
advertising@nnsl.com, Adv. Mgr., Inuvik Drum,
NT, Yellowknife

Ehrke, Petra .... (867) 766-8264
advertising@nnsl.com, Adv. Mgr., News/north,
NT, Yellowknife

Ehrlich, Doug .... (201) 741-8901
dehrlich@imagezone.com, MD, Image Zone,
Inc., NY, New York

Ehrlich, Fred .... (314) 558-3221
fred.ehrlich@molawyersmedia.com, Ed, St.
Charles County Business Record, MO, Saint
Charles

Ehrlick, Darrell .... (406) 657-1289
dehrlick@billingsgazette.com, Ed., Billings
Gazette, MT, Billings

Eich, Karen .... (312) 222-4501
keich@tronc.com, Director of Operations,
Tribune Content Agency, IL, Chicago

Eichenberger, Bob .... (406) 582-2606
beichenberger@dailychronicle.com, Bus. Mgr.,
Bozeman Daily Chronicle, MT, Bozeman

Eicher, Bob .... ext. 239
bob.eicher@gjsentinel.com, Mgr., Mgmt.
Info Servs., The Daily Sentinel, CO, Grand
Junction

Eichorn, Jennifer .... (941) 361-4404
jennifer.eichorn@heraldtribune.com, Circ. Mgr.,
Sarasota Herald-Tribune, FL, Sarasota

Eickhoff, Chris .... (678) 996-2411
ceickhoff@eeausa.com, CM, COO, Ewert
America Electronics Ltd., GA, Marietta

Eide, Rachel
rachel.eide@dailyleader.com, Ed. / Gen. Mgr.,
Daily Leader, MS, Brookhaven

Eidson, Leslie .... (417) 866-0841
leidson@dioscg.org, Ed., The Mirror, MO,
Springfield

Eikenberry, Kent
keikenberry@nwaonline.net, Adv. Dir., The
Free Weekly, AR, Fayetteville

Eikenberry, Kent .... (479) 571-6420
keikenberry@nwadg.com, Adv. Mgr., Northwest
Arkansas Democrat-Gazette, AR, Fayetteville

Eiland, Randy .... (806) 793-2500
randy@lubbocktnol.com, Thrifty Nickel -
Columbus, GA, Columbus
randy@lubbocktnol.com, Thrifty Nickel -
Lubbock, TX, Lubbock

Eilola, Gale .... (906) 524-6194
sentinel1886@gmail.com, Production. Mgr.,
L'Anse Sentinel, MI, Lanse

Eiman, Mark .... (559) 583-2458
meiman@HanfordSentinel.com, City Ed., The
Sentinel, CA, Hanford

Eimer, Debi
deimer@jcpgroup.com, Mng. Ed., Milwaukee
Journal Sentinel, WI, Milwaukee

Einselen, Sarah ....(574) 722-5000 Ext. 5151
Sarah.Einselen@pharostribune.com, News
Ed., Pharos-Tribune, IN, Logansport

Einstein, Donald
deinstein@stny.rr.com, Pub. & Ad., The
Country Courier, NY, Conklin

Einstein, Donald .... (607) 427-0143
deinstein@stny.rr.com, Pub., Vestal Town Crier,
NY, Conklin

Einstein, Donald .... (607) 775-0472
deinstein@stny.rr.com, Adv. Mgr., The Windsor
Standard, NY, Conklin

Einstein, Donald .... (607) 427-0143
deinstein@stny.rr.com, Pub and Adv. Mgr., The
Windsor Standard, NY, Conklin

Eisele, Joe 8282
Jeisele@newspapermediagroup.com, Pub.,
Examiner, NJ, Manalapan

Eisele , Joe .... (609) 874-2125
jeisele@centraljersey.com, Pub., Hopewell
Valley News, NJ, Princeton
jeisele@centraljersey.com, Pub., South
Brunswick Post, NJ, Princeton
jeisele@centraljersey.com, Pub., Cranbury
Press, NJ, Princeton
jeisele@centraljersey.com, Pub. , Register-
News, NJ, Princeton
jeisele@centraljersey.com, Pub. , The Beacon,
NJ, Princeton

Eisenberg, Beth .... (603) 594-1244
news@nashuatelegraph.com, Sr. Des., The
Telegraph, NH, Nashua

Eisenberg, Luke ....(815) 625-3600, Ext. 5613
leisenberg@oglecountynews.com, Adv. Sales
Mgr., Tri-County Press, IL, Dixon
leisenberg@oglecountynews.com, Adv. Mgr.,
Ogle County Life, IL, Oregon

Eisenberg, Paul
peisenberg@tribpub.com, News Ed., Daily
Southtown, IL, Aurora

Eisenbraun, Tyler ....(402) 371-1020 ext. 248
tylere@norfolkdailynews.com, Prod. Mgr.,
Norfolk Daily News, NE, Norfolk

Eisenhardt, Benjamin .... (412) 263-1424
beisenhardt@post-gazette.com, Customer
Service Supervisor, Pittsburgh Post-Gazette,
PA, Clinton

Eismont, Fred
feismont@durhamregion.com, Adv. Mgr.,
Oshawa-whitby This Week, ON, Oshawa

Eismont, Fred .... (905) 215-0440 ext.2207
feismont@durhamregion.com, Dir. Adv. ,
Canadian Statesman, ON, Oshawa

Eismont, Fred
feismont@durhamregion.com, Adv. Dir.,
Clarington This Week, ON, Oshawa

Eisner, Bill .... (414) 425-8800
bille@nonbox.com, Exec. Dir., Intermarket
Agency Network, WI, Hales Corners

Eisner, Jane
eisner@forward.com, Ed. in Chief, The
Forward, NY, New York
eisner@forward.com, Ed., Forward Newspaper,
NY, New York

Eisner, Samantha
samantha.eisner@icann.org, Loyola
Marymount Univ., CA, Los Angeles

Eiss, Frances .... (973) 392-1824
feiss@starledger.com, The Star-Ledger, NJ,
Newark

Eitreim, Dan .... (605) 759-6687
EIC, South Dakota School of Mines &
Technology, SD, Rapid City

Ek, John
jek@bizjournals.com, Pub, Wichita Business
Journal, KS, Wichita

Eke, Ocek
oeke@elon.edu, Asst. Prof., Elon University,
NC, Elon

Eko, Lyombe
lyombe.eko@umit.maine.edu, Asst. Prof.,
University of Maine, ME, Orono

Ekstam, Fred
fredek@mst.edu, Missouri Univ. of Science &
Technology, MO, Rolla

El Nabli, Dina
editor@njfamily.com, Editorial Director, New
Jersey Family, NJ, Summit

Elam, Angela
elama@umkc.edu, Instr., Radio, University of
Missouri-Kansas City, MO, Kansas City

Elam, Danny
delam@garrardcentralrecord.com, Sports Ed.,
Garrard Central Record, KY, Lancaster

Elam, Mark
melam@tompkinsvillenews.com, Gen. Mgr.,
Tompkinsville News, KY, Tompkinsville

Elam, Ronda
relam@tompkinsvillenews.com, Ed.,
Tompkinsville News, KY, Tompkinsville

Elbakyan, Anush .... (617) 929-7411
anush.elbakyan@globe.com, Sr. Ed./Video,
The Boston Globe, MA, Boston

Elbel, Gus .... (830) 625-5232
Pressroom Supvr., New Braunfels Herald-
Zeitung, TX, New Braunfels

Elder, Dave .... (407) 420-5149
delder@orlandosentinel.com, Circ. Mgr.,
Subscriber Servs., Orlando Sentinel, FL,
Orlando

Elder, Kevin
kelder@shawsuburban.com, VP/Production,
Northwest Herald, IL, Crystal Lake

Elder, Peggy
peggye@valleystar.com, Adv. Ops. Mgr., Valley
Morning Star, TX, Harlingen

Elder, Rob .... (609) 339-1220
Rtelder@gmail.com, Adv. Mgr., Cape May Star
and Wave, NJ, West Cape May

Eldredge, Charles
heraldpressonline@yahoo.com, Pub., The
Herald-Press, ND, Harvey

Eldridge, Dave .... (859) 623-1669
deldridge@richmondregister.com, Publisher,
The Richmond Register, KY, Richmond

Eldridge, Dave
news@spencercountyjournal.com, Pub,
Spencer County Journal-Democrat, IN,
Rockport
news@spencercountyjournal.com, Pub., Perry
County News, IN, Tell City

Elges, Nick .... (360) 354-4444
sports@lyndentribune.com, Sports Ed., Lynden
Tribune, WA, Lynden

Elhart, Maurice .... (303) 776-2244 ext. 304
melhart@lehmancomm.com, Circ. Dir., Cor.,
Longmont Times-Call, CO, Longmont

Eli, Jack C.
jack.eli@angelo.edu, Prof./Head, Angelo State
University, TX, San Angelo

Elias, LeAnn .... (702) 385-3111
Designer, Las Vegas Sun, NV, Henderson

Elig, Jenny .... (812) 379-5671
jelig@therepublic.com, Lifestyle Ed., The
Republic, IN, Columbus

Elizabeth, Jane
jane.elizabeth@pressinstitute.org, Senior
Research Project Manager, American Press
Institute, VA, Arlington

Elizondo, Daniel .... (409) 385-5278
editor@silsbeebee.com, Ed., Silsbee Bee, TX,
Silsbee

Elkins, Arron .... (202) 994-7079
George Washington Univ., DC, Washington

Elkins, Katie ....(304) 752-6950 ext 1727
kfarmer@civitasmedia.com, Circ Rep , The
Logan Banner, WV, Logan

Elkins, Rick ....(559) 784-5000 Ext 1040
relkins@portervillerecorder.com, Pub./Ed., The
Porterville Recorder, CA, Porterville

Ell, Wendi ....(715) 365-6397 ext.382
wendi@rivernewsonline.com, Gen. Mgr. , The
Northwoods River News , WI, Rhinelander
wendi@rivernewsonline.com, Gen. Mgr. ,
Northwoods Super Shopper, WI, Rhinelander

Eller, David
davide@mwicorp.com, Publisher, Observer
Newspaper, FL, Deerfield Beach

Ellerbach, Susan .... (918) 581-8329
susan.ellerbach@tulsaworld.com, Exec. Ed.,
Tulsa World, OK, Tulsa

Ellerbee, Jacob .... (501) 941-9322
jjellerbee@ualr.edu, Exec. Ed., The Forum,
University of Arkansas at Little Rock, AR,
Little Rock

Ellerbee, Terrie
tellerbee@thedahloneganugget.com, Ed., The
Dahlonega Nugget, GA, Dahlonega

Ellerman, Jean
gftemail@aol.com, Pub., Taylor County Value
Guide, WV, Grafton

Ellestad, Barbara .... (702) 346-6397
barb@bjellestad.com, Ed, Mesquite Local
News, NV, Mesquite

Elling, Debbie .... (618) 532-5604
dellin@morningsentinel.com, Advertising
Manager, Crier/schrol,rlc Clocktoweer, IL,
Centralia

Ellinghouse, Brenda
brendae@waynecojournalbanner.com, Ed./
Bus. Mgr., Wayne County Journal-Banner,
MO, Piedmont

Ellinghouse, Harold T. .... (573) 223-7122
harold@waynecojournalbanner.com, Pub,
Wayne County Journal-Banner, MO,
Piedmont

Ellingson, Marlys .... (763) 241-3677
marlys.ellingson@ecm-inc.com, Adv. Dir, Star
News, MN, Elk River

Ellington, Amanda .... (770) 787-6397
aellington@covnews.com, Circ. Mgr., The
Covington News, GA, Covington

Ellington, Coke
cellington@alasu.edu, Instr., Alabama State
Univ., AL, Montgomery

Elliott, Bo .... (740) 532-1441 Ext. 215
bo.elliott@irontontribune.com, Prod. Mgr. /
Pres. Fore., The Ironton Tribune, OH, Ironton

Elliott, Brian
brianelliott@reviewatlas.com, Circ. Mgr., Daily
Review Atlas, IL, Monmouth

Elliott, Chuck
celliott@bignickel.com, Gen. Mgr., Big Nickel,
MO, Joplin

Elliott, Darrell .... (912) 489-9425
delliott@statesboroherald.com, Circ. Mgr.,
Statesboro Herald, GA, Statesboro

Elliott, Dylan .... (918) 542-5533
delliott@gatehousemedia.com, Circ. Mgr,
Grove Sun, OK, Grove
delliott@gatehousemedia.com, Circ. Mgr.,
Delaware County Journal, OK, Jay

Elliott, Eric .... (250) 341-6299
eric@columbiavalleypioneer.com, Reporter,
The Columbia Valley Pioneer, BC, Invermere

Elliott, Gary .... (518) 673-0143
cfeditor@leepub.com, Ed., Country Folks -
East Zone, NY, Palatine Bridge

Elliott, James W.
jim@elliott-publishing.com, Pres., Camp Point
Journal, IL, Camp Point

Elliott, James W.
jim@elliott-publishing.com, Pub., The Liberty
Bee-Times, IL, Liberty

Elliott, James W.
jim@elliott-publishing.com, Pub., Golden-
Clayton New Era, IL, Camp Point

Elliott, Jerrie
trbusiness@centurytel.net, Gen. Mgr., The
Times-Record, AL, Fayette

Elliott, Jim
jim@elliott-publishing.com, Pub., Mendon
Dispatch-Times, IL, Camp Point

Elliott, John
ads@wyodaily.com, Prodn. Supt., Northern
Wyoming Daily News, WY, Worland

Elliott, John
qlpj5qk713lkdss@marketplace.amazon.com,
IT Dir., Seattle Daily Journal of Commerce,
WA, Seattle

Elliott, John T.
gstar@colint.com, Ed., The Gilman Star, IL,
Gilman

Elliott, Julia.................................... ext. 120
jelliott@metroparent.com, Ed., Metro Parent
Magazine, MI, Ferndale

Elliott, Marcia .... (217) 593-6515
cpjournal@adams.net, Gen. Mgr., Camp Point
Journal, IL, Camp Point

Elliott, Marcia
marcia@elliott-publishing.com, Ed., Golden-
Clayton New Era, IL, Camp Point

Elliott, Marcia
marcia@elliott-publishing.com, Adv. Mgr., Elliott
Publishing, Inc., IL, Camp Point

Elliott, Marcia
cpjournal@adams.net, Ed., Mendon Dispatch-
Times, IL, Camp Point

Elliott, Mark .... (765) 640-2312
mark.elliott@heraldbulletin.com, Adv. Dir., The
Herald Bulletin, IN, Anderson
mark.elliott@heraldbulletin.com, Adv. Mgr.,
Madison County Direct, IN, Anderson

Elliott, Murray
melliott@olds.greatwest.ca, Grp. Pub./Gen.
Mgr., Mountain View Gazette, AB, Olds

Elliott, Murray .... (403) 556-7510
melliott@olds.greatwest.ca, Pub, Olds
Albertan, AB, Olds

Elliott, Murray
melliott@greatwest.ca, Grp. Pub./Gen. Mgr.,
Mountain View Publishing, AB, Olds
melliott@greatwest.ca, Senior Group Publisher,
Great West Newspapers LP, AB, St. Albert

Elliott, Nancy .... (217) 337-8300
nelliott@illinimedia.com, Adv. Dir., Univ. of
Illinois, IL, Champaign

Elliott, Scarlet
scarlet@milanmirrorexchange.com, Adv. Mgr.,
Milan Mirror-Exchange, TN, Milan

Elliott, Shannon
shannon.elliott@wetumpkaherald.com,

Classified Adv. Mgr., Eclectic Observer, AL, Wetumpka

shannon.elliott@wetumpkaherald.com, Classifieds Adv. Mgr., The Wetumpka Herald, AL, Alexander City

Elliott, Sonny
sonnye@baxterbulletin.com, Managing Editor, The Baxter Bulletin, AR, Mountain Home

Elliott, Teresa
teresa@thenewsprogress.com, Adv. Rep., Super Shopper (OOB), VA, Clarksville
teresa@thenewsprogress.com, Acct. Exec., Mecklenburg Reporter, VA, South Hill

Elliott, Tess
editor@ptreyeslight.com, Ed., Point Reyes Light, CA, Inverness

Ellis, Adam .... (508) 591-6625
aellis@wickedlocal.com, Sports Ed., Carver Reporter, MA, Plymouth

Ellis, Alan ....ext. 117
Prodn. Mgr., Harbor News, CT, Madison

Ellis, Alan .... (203) 245-1877 ext. 117
Prodn. Mgr., Guilford Courier, CT, Madison

Ellis, April
aellis@harrodsburgherald.com, Owner/Gen. Mgr, The Harrodsburg Herald, KY, Harrodsburg

Ellis, Connie .... (269) 673-5534
accounting@allegannews.com, Office Mgr., The Commercial Record, MI, Saugatuck

Ellis, Dave
classifieds@shorepublishing.com, Classified Adv. Mgr., The Mystic Times, CT, New London
classifieds@shorepublishing.com, Classifieds Adv. Mgr., The Lyme Times, CT, New London
classifieds@shorepublishing.com, Classified Adv. Mgr., The Montville Times, CT, New London
classifieds@shorepublishing.com, Classified Adv. Mgr., Guilford Courier, CT, Madison

Ellis, Dennis
dellis@ocpnews.com, Ed., Paoli News-Republican, IN, Paoli

Ellis, Dorris
info@houstonsun.com, Houston Sun, TX, Houston

Ellis, Elizabeth S. .... (860) 646-0500
eellis@journalinquirer.com, Publisher, Journal Inquirer, CT, Manchester

Ellis, Gene .... (717) 871-2102
Millersville Univ. of Pennsylvania, PA, Millersville

Ellis, Hughes
sports@hendersondailynews.com, Sports Ed., Henderson Daily News, TX, Henderson

Ellis, Jennifer
jellis@sbtinfo.com, INTHEBEND.COM Ed., South Bend Tribune, IN, South Bend

Ellis, Jennifer
jellis@catholicsun.org, Adv. Rep., The Catholic Sun, AZ, Phoenix
jellis@catholicsun.org, Prod. Mgr., Forever Young, NY, Buffalo

Ellis, Jim
jim.ellis@miaminewsrecord.com, Sports Ed., Miami News-Record, OK, Miami

Ellis, Jim ....(918) 542-5533
jellis@miaminewsrecord.com, Sports Editor, Miami News-record, OK, Miami

Ellis, John..........................(970) 375-4528
jellis@durangoherald.com, Circ. Mgr., Durango Herald, CO, Durango

Ellis, Kae .... (307) 789-6560 ext. 105
kellis@uintacountyherald.com, Prodn. Mgr., Uinta County Herald, WY, Evanston

Ellis, Kevin ....(704) 869-1823
kellis@gastongazette.com, Managing Editor, The Gaston Gazette, NC, Gastonia

Ellis, Leanna ....(402) 426-2121
online@enterprisepub.com, Editor, Arlington Citizen, NE, Blair

Ellis, Lisa .... (217) 753-2226 ext.137
lellis@illinoistimes.com, Assoc. Pub., Illinois Times, IL, Springfield

Ellis, Lorraine ....(603) 352-1234 ext. 1202
lellis@keenesentinel.com, Adv. Mgr., Classified, The Keene Sentinel, NH, Keene

Ellis, Marilyn
marilyne@cpimo.com, Adv. Mgr., Cedar County Republican/Stockton Journal, MO, Stockton

Ellis, Michael .... (580) 765-3311
mdellis@poncacitynews.com, Controller, The Ponca City News, OK, Ponca City

Ellis, Milton..............................ext. 229
publisher@standard-freeholder.com, Pub./Gen. Mgr., Standard-freeholder Complimentary, ON, Cornwall

Ellis, Reggie .... (559) 592-3171
editor@thesungazette.com, Pub., The Foothills Sun-Gazette, CA, Exeter

Ellis, Sandra
sandra.ellis@uwrf.edu, Chair, University of Wisconsin-River Falls, WI, River Falls

Ellis, Sheryl
sellis@kentuckynewera.com, Bus. Mgr., Fort Campbell Courier, KY, Hopkinsville

Ellis, Sheryl
sellis@kentuckynewera.com, VP and Gen. Mgr. , Kentucky New Era, KY, Hopkinsville

Ellis, Stan
sellis@calkins.com, VP/Director, Calkins Media, PA, Levittown

Ellis, Stanley M. .... (609) 871-8020
sellis@phillyburbs.com, Calkins Media, PA, Levittown

Ellis, Susan
ellis@memphisflyer.com, Mng. Ed., Memphis Flyer, TN, Memphis

Ellis, Tavi..............................(870) 423-6636
ccnsports@cox-internet.com, Photograher, Carroll County News, AR, Berryville

Ellison, Fred .... (901) 529-2345
fellison@prescottaz.com, Adv. Mgr., Chino Valley Review, AZ, Chino Valley

Ellison, Julie .... (662) 834-1151
submit legals to: heraldlegals@gmail.com, General Manager, Holmes County Herald, MS, Lexington

Ellison-Rider, Elaine
elaine@bhpnc.com, Co-Pub./Ed., The Belton & Honea Path News-Chronicle, SC, Belton

Ellyson, Tyler .... (402) 352-2424
tellyson@columbustelegram.com, Interim Ed., The Columbus Telegram, NE, Columbus
tellyson@columbustelegram.com, Interim Ed., The Schuyler Sun, NE, Schuyler

Elmatti, Heather .... (352) 323-3652
Lake Sumter Cmty. College, FL, Leesburg

Elmes, Nicholas
nelmes@civitasmedia.com, Adv. Mgr., Yadkin Valley Advertiser, NC, Elkin

Elmes, Nicholas
nelmes@civitasmedia.com, Ed, The Weekly Independent, NC, Walnut Cove

Elmore, Allen..........................(505) 686-3831
Allen@AmClass.us, Sales Mgr., American Classifieds - Farmington - Four Corners, NM, Farmington

Elmore, Allen .... (505) 686-3831
Allen@AmClass.us, Sales Manager, Four Corners American Classifieds (thrifty Nickel), NM, Farmington

Elmore, Robert .... (505) 564-2535
Robert@AmClass.us, Pres., American Classifieds - Farmington - Four Corners, NM, Farmington

Elmore, Robert .... (505) 564-2535
Robert@AmClass.us, President, Four Corners American Classifieds (thrifty Nickel), NM, Farmington

Elmore, Ross
rosse@dandydime.com, Gen. Mgr., Dandy Dime Classifieds, AZ, Tucson

Elmore, Spencer
Spencer@AmClass.us, Circ. Mgr., Four Corners American Classifieds (thrifty Nickel), NM, Farmington

Elpers, Scott .... (316) 978-6918
Wichita State Univ., KS, Wichita

Elsberry, Chris..........................(203) 400-4765
celsberry@ctpost.com, Sports Ed., Fairfield Citizen, CT, Bridgeport

Elsen, Fran..........................(859) 231-3323
felsen@herald-leader.com, Adv. Sales Mgr., Local Adv., Lexington Herald-Leader, KY, Lexington

Elsken, Katrina
kelsken@newszap.com, Exec. Ed. , Caloosa Belle, FL, Labelle
kelsken@newszap.com, Ed., Okeechobee News, FL, Okeechobee

Elson, Mary .... (312) 222-4423
melson@Tribpub.com, Mng. Ed., TMS Specialty Products, IL, Chicago

Elson, Tracey .... (419) 334-1012
telson@gannett.com, Sales Mgr., News Herald, OH, Fremont

Elstein, Dara..........................(858) 875-5941
Darad@lajollalight.com, Circ. Mgr., La Jolla Light, CA, La Jolla

Elstein, Dara
darad@lajollalight.com, Circ. Mgr., Carmel Valley News, CA, Solana Beach
darad@lajollalight.com, Circ. Mgr., Del Mar Times, CA, Solana Beach
darad@lajollalight.com, Circ. Mgr., Rancho Santa Fe Review, CA, Solana Beach
darad@lajollalight.com, Circ. Mgr., San Diego Suburban News (OOB), CA, La Jolla

Elston, Christina .... (818) 264-2222, ext 226
Christina.Elston@laparent.com, Ed, LA Parent Magazine, CA, Woodland Hills

Elston, Mark
mark@mendotareporter.com, Gen. Mgr., Mendota Reporter, IL, Mendota

Elswick, Jon
jon.elswick@whnpa.org, Treasurer, White House News Photographers Association, Inc., DC, Washington

Elswick, Mike..........................(972) 563-6476
publisher@terrelltribune.com, Publisher, Terrell Tribune Update, TX, Terrell

Elswick, Stephanie .... (972) 563-6476
selswick@terrelltribune.com, Advertising Director, Terrell Tribune Update, TX, Terrell

Eltantawy, Nahed
neltante@highpoint.edu, Asst. Prof., High Point Univ., NC, High Point

Elton, Al
Al@euro-knivesusa.com, Owner, Euro-Knives USA, KS, Overland Park

Elton, Rob
Rob@euro-knivesusa.com, Sales Mgr., Euro-Knives USA, KS, Overland Park

Elwell, Patty
calendar@news-banner.com, Classified Mgr., News-Banner, IN, Bluffton

Elznic, Jason
jason@northeastcollege.com, Northeast Cmty. College, NE, Norfolk

Emanuel, Dr. Juliet .... (212) 406-3972
Borough of Manhattan Cmty. College, NY, New York

Emanuel, Rick .... (607) 936-9231

remanuel@the-leader.com, Regional Publisher, Pennesaverplus, NY, Hornell
remanuel@the-leader.com, Reg. Pub., The Evening Tribune, NY, Hornell

Emanuel, Rick..........................(607) 936-9231
remanuel@the-leader.com, Regional Publisher, Genesee Country Express, NY, Dansville

Emberger, Edward E. .... (215) 949-4021
eemberger@calkins-media.com, Dir., Information Servs., Calkins Media, PA, Levittown

Embick, Tracy..........................(570) 923-1500
clintoncountyrecord@comcast.net, Billing/Subscriptions, The Record, PA, Renovo

Embree, Jessie
jembree@moberlymonitor.com, The Moberly Monitor-Index, MO, Moberly

Embry, Eugene .... (270) 783-3241
eembry@bgdailynews.com, Copy Ed., Messenger-Inquirer, KY, Owensboro
eembry@bgdailynews.com, Weekend Ed., Daily News, KY, Bowling Green

Embry, John .... (270) 526-7945
jwe@beechtreenews.com, Beech Tree News, KY, Aberdeen

Embry, Scott .... (843) 937-5405
sembry@postandcourier.com, Adv. Dir., The Post and Courier, SC, Charleston

Embs, MerriLee .... (937) 878-3993
Membs@civitasmedia.com, Managing Ed., Fairborn Daily Herald, OH, Xenia

Embs, Merrilee............(937) 372-4444 Ext. 2120
membs@xeniagazette.com, Mng. Ed. , Xenia Daily Gazette, OH, Xenia

Emden, Christie .... (212) 450-7049
mediarelations@parade.com, Vice Pres., Commun., Parade, New York

Emens, Diane
diane.emens@rheaheraldnews.com, Gen. Mgr., The Herald-News, TN, Dayton

Emerson, Ellen
Ellen@FauquierNow.com, Pub., Fauquier Now, VA, Warrenton

Emerson, Gloria
news@chicotnewspaper.com, Circ. Mgr., Chicot Spectator, AR, Lake Village

Emerson, Jason .... (315) 434-8889 ext. 338
editor@cazenoviarepublican.com, Ed., Cazenovia Republican, NY, Syracuse

Emerson, Lawrence
LKE@FauquierNow.com, Ed., Fauquier Now, VA, Warrenton

Emerson, Mike
memerson@thoughtequity.com, Vice Pres., Mktg., Thought Equity Management, Inc., CO, Denver

Emerson, Teresa
taesun@philasun.com, Mng. Ed., Philadelphia Sunday Sun, PA, Philadelphia

Emhoff, Laurena
emhoffl@nytimes.com, Vice Pres./Treasurer, The New York Times Co., NY, New York

Emigh, Anita .... (812) 523-7062
AEmigh@TribTown.com, Sales Rep., The Tribune, IN, Seymour

Emirdjiin, Lala
manager@hairenik.com, Adv. Mgr., Armenian Weekly, MA, Watertown

Emirdjiin, Lala
manager@hairenik.com, Adv. Mgr., Hairenik Weekly, MA, Watertown

Emma, Leslie..........................(302) 324-2520
lemma@gannettnj.com, Asst. Cont., The Courier-Post, NJ, Cherry Hill

Emmelhainz, Nicole
nicole.emmelhainz@cnu.edu, Faculty advisor, Christopher Newport Univ., VA, Newport News

Emmerich, J. Wyatt .... (601) 957-1122 ext. 992
wyatt@northsidesun.com, Pres./CEO,
Emmerich Newspapers, Inc., MS, Jackson

Emmerich, J. Wyatt
wyatt@northsidesun.com, Pub./Adv. Mgr.,
Northside Sun, MS, Jackson

Emmons, Laura .... (281) 485-7501
drdaviddavis@yahoo.com, Pub. / Exec. Ed.,
Pearland Reporter News, TX, Pearland

Emmons, Laura
laurae3009@yahoo.com, Adv. Mgr.,
Friendswood Reporter News, TX, Pearland

Emmons, Randy
laurae3009@yahoo.com, Circ. Mgr.,
Friendswood Reporter News, TX, Pearland

Emmons, Susan
mail@carlislemosquito.org, Gen. Mgr., Carlisle
Mosquito, MA, Carlisle

Emmons, Tim........................... (903) 796-7133
temmons@casscoutynow.com, Sports Editor,
Atlanta Citizens Journal, TX, Atlanta

Emory, Marcy
marcy.emory@pagecooperative.com, Accnt.
Supervisor, PAGE Cooperative, VA, Vienna

Emrick, Corky
emrick@sturgisjournal.com, Sports Ed., Sturgis
Journal, MI, Sturgis

Encow, Danny .... (501) 623-4404
thriftynickel22@gmail.com, Pub., Thrifty Nickel
Want Ads, AR, Hot Springs

Enderle, Marvin .... (470) 729-3234
publisher@douglascountysentinel.com, Pub.,
Douglas County Sentinel, GA, Douglasville

Enderle, Marvin .... (770) 834-6631
publisher@times-georgian.com, Pub., Times-
Georgian, GA, Carrollton

Endter, Dave
homemag@earthlink.net, Gen. Mgr., The
Homes Magazine, CA, Alta Loma

Eng, Jess
jeng@PlantCityObserver.com, Asst. Ed., Plant
City Observer, FL, Plant City

Eng, Michael
meng@PlantCityObserver.com, Mng. Ed./Gen.
Mgr., Plant City Observer, FL, Plant City

Engberg, M.D., Karen M.
kengbergmd@aol.com, Self-Syndicator, Karen
M. Engberg, M.D., Goleta

Engbrock, Chad .... (972) 442-5515 x29
cengbrock@csmediatexas.com, Pub./Ed./Adv.
Mgr., Farmersville Times, TX, Farmersville

Engbrock, Chad .... (974) 442-5515 ext. 29
cengbrock@csmediatexas.com, Pub./Ed./Adv.
Dir., Princeton Herald, TX, Farmersville

Engbrock, Chad B. .... (972) 442-5515
cengbrock@wylienews.com, Pub./Ed./Adv. Dir.,
Murphy Monitor, TX, Wylie
cengbrock@wylienews.com, Pub./Ed./Adv. Dir.,
Sachse News, TX, Wylie
cengbrock@wylienews.com, Pub., The Wylie
News, TX, Wylie

Engel, Bob 615/259-8377
rengel@gannett.com, Regional Finance
Director, The Tennessean, TN, Nashville
rengel@gannett.com, VP, Finance, TN Media,
TN, Nashville

Engel, Mary
rcnmary@gbta.net, Pub, Rush County News,
KS, La Crosse

Engel, Paul
mcherald@hbch.com, Ed., The Minden City
Herald, MI, Minden City

Engel, Tim
rcn@gbta.net, Ed, Rush County News, KS,
La Crosse

Engel, William
william_engel@guardianlife.com, Chrmm/
CEO, Simmons Market Research Bureau,

NY, New York

Engelgau, Gail .... (321) 266-0096
gailengelgau@gmail.com, Publisher, Thrifty
Nickel Want Ads, TX, Odessa

Engelhardt, Elizabeth ....(830) 379-5441 x 207
elizabeth.engelhardt@seguingazette.com,
Advertising Director, The Seguin Gazette,
TX, Seguin

Engelhart, Steve
sengelhart@rivertowns.net, Advertising
Director, River Falls Journal, WI, River Falls
sengelhart@rivertowns.net, Adv. Dir., The
Hudson Star-Observer, WI, River Falls

Engelhart, Steve
sengelhart@woodburybulletin.com, Adv. Dir,
Woodbury Bulletin, MN, Hastings
sengelhart@woodburybulletin.com, Adv. Dir,
Farmington Rosemount Independent Town
Pages, MN, Hastings
sengelhart@woodburybulletin.com, Adv. Dir,
Hastings Star Gazette, MN, Hastings

Engelman, Kenneth................... (541) 822-3358
rivref@aol.com, Pub., McKenzie River
Reflections, OR, McKenzie Bridge

Engelman, Ralph .... (718) 488-1009
engelman@liu.edu, Dept. Chair, Long Island
University - The Brooklyn Campus, NY,
Brooklyn

Engh, Jeri
DAISY@photosource.com, Editorial Dir.,
PhotoSource International, Osceola

Engh, Rohn .... (715) 248-3800
info@photosource.com, Pub., PhotoSource
International, WI, Osceola

England, Barb
barb@threeriversnews.com, Gen. Mgr., Three
Rivers Commercial-News, MI, Three Rivers

England, Robyn
wdn@wdnonline.com, Mktg. Rep., Weatherford
Daily News, OK, Weatherford

England, Tim
england@txstate.edu, Assoc. Profs./Coord.,
Electronic Media, Texas State University-San
Marcos, TX, San Marcos

England, William .... ext. 30
Ed., Shoreline Week, ON, Tecumseh

Engle, Charles A.
jhemperly@engleonline.com, CEO/Pres./
Pub., Engle - York Community Courier West
Edition, PA, Mount Joy
jhemperly@engleonline.com, CEO/Pres./
Pub., Engle - York Community Courier South
Edition, PA, Mount Joy
jhemperly@engleonline.com, CEO/Pres./Pub.,
Engle - York Community Courier East Edition,
PA, Mount Joy
jhemperly@engleonline.com, CEO/Pres./Pub.,
Engle - Willow Street Strasburg Advertiser,
PA, Mount Joy
jhemperly@engleonline.com, CEO/Pres./Pub.,
Engle - West Chester Community Courier,
PA, Mount Joy
jhemperly@engleonline.com, CEO/Pres./Pub.,
Engle - Quarryville Advertiser, PA, Mount Joy
jhemperly@engleonline.com, CEO/Pres./
Pub., Engle - New Holland Pennysaver, PA,
Mount Joy
jhemperly@engleonline.com, CEO/Pres./
Pub., Engle - Morgantown / Honey Brook
Community Courier, PA, Mount Joy
jhemperly@engleonline.com, CEO/Pres./Pub.,
Engle - Millersville Advertiser, PA, Mount Joy
jhemperly@engleonline.com, CEO/Pres./Pub.,
Engle - Middletown Shopper, PA, Mount Joy
jhemperly@engleonline.com, CEO/Pres./Pub.,
Engle - Manheim Township Merchandiser,
PA, Mount Joy
jhemperly@engleonline.com, CEO/Pres./Pub.,
Engle - Manheim / Lititz Merchandiser, PA,
Mount Joy
jhemperly@engleonline.com, CEO/Pres./Pub.,
Engle - Hershey / Hummelstown / Palmyra
Community Courier, PA, Mount Joy
jhemperly@engleonline.com, CEO/Pres./Pub.,

Engle - Hempfield / Mountville Merchandiser,
PA, Mount Joy
jhemperly@engleonline.com, CEO/Pres./Pub.,
Engle - Gap / Oxford Community Courier, PA,
Mount Joy
jhemperly@engleonline.com, CEO/Pres./
Pub., Engle - Elizabethtown / Mount Joy
Merchandiser, PA, Mount Joy
jhemperly@engleonline.com, CEO/Pres./Pub.,
Engle - Downingtown / Exton / Community
Courier, PA, Mount Joy
jhemperly@engleonline.com, CEO/Pres./Pub.,
Engle - Conestoga Valley / Pequea Valley
Penny Saver, PA, Mount Joy
jhemperly@engleonline.com, CEO/Pres./
Pub., Engle - Columbia / Wrightsville
Merchandiser, PA, Mount Joy

Engle, Charles A. .... (717) 492-2502
charlie_engle@engleonline.com, Pres./Pub.,
Shopper, PA, Mount Joy

Engle, Jeremy
jpengle@engleonline.com, Prodn. Mgr.,
Shopper, PA, Mount Joy

Engle, Jeremy
jpengle@engleonline.com, VP Operations,
Chester County Community Courier, PA,
Mount Joy

Engle, Jeremy
jpengle@engleonline.com, Prod. Mgr., Engle
- Columbia / Wrightsville Merchandiser, PA,
Mount Joy
jpengle@engleonline.com, Prod. Mgr., Engle
- Conestoga Valley / Pequea Valley Penny
Saver, PA, Mount Joy
jpengle@engleonline.com, Prod. Mgr., Engle -
Downingtown / Exton / Community Courier,
PA, Mount Joy
jpengle@engleonline.com, Prod. Mgr., Engle
- Elizabethtown / Mount Joy Merchandiser,
PA, Mount Joy
jpengle@engleonline.com, Prod. Mgr., Engle
- Gap / Oxford Community Courier, PA,
Mount Joy
jpengle@engleonline.com, Prod. Mgr., Engle
- Hempfield / Mountville Merchandiser, PA,
Mount Joy
jpengle@engleonline.com, Prod. Mgr.,
Engle - Hershey / Hummelstown / Palmyra
Community Courier, PA, Mount Joy
jpengle@engleonline.com, Prod. Mgr., Engle
- Manheim / Lititz Merchandiser, PA, Mount
Joy
jpengle@engleonline.com, Prod. Mgr., Engle
- Manheim Township Merchandiser, PA,
Mount Joy
jpengle@engleonline.com, Prod. Mgr., Engle -
Middletown Shopper, PA, Mount Joy
jpengle@engleonline.com, Prod. Mgr., Engle -
Millersville Advertiser, PA, Mount Joy
jpengle@engleonline.com, Prod. Mgr., Engle
- Morgantown / Honey Brook Community
Courier, PA, Mount Joy
jpengle@engleonline.com, Prod. Mgr., Engle -
New Holland Pennysaver, PA, Mount Joy
jpengle@engleonline.com, Prod. Mgr., Engle -
Quarryville Advertiser, PA, Mount Joy
jpengle@engleonline.com, Prod. Mgr., Engle
- West Chester Community Courier, PA,
Mount Joy
jpengle@engleonline.com, Prod. Mgr., Engle
- Willow Street Strasburg Advertiser, PA,
Mount Joy
jpengle@engleonline.com, Prod. Mgr., Engle
- York Community Courier East Edition, PA,
Mount Joy
jpengle@engleonline.com, Prod. Mgr., Engle -
York Community Courier South Edition, PA,
Mount Joy
jpengle@engleonline.com, Prod. Mgr., Engle
- York Community Courier West Edition, PA,
Mount Joy

Engle, Susan
cembree@lmtribune.com, Health/Medical Ed.,
Lewiston Morning Tribune, ID, Lewiston

Engler, Dan .... (928) 634-2241 x 6032
dengler@verdenews.com, Ed., Camp Verde
Bugle, AZ, Camp Verde
dengler@verdenews.com, Ed., The Verde

Independent, AZ, Cottonwood
dengler@verdenews.com, Editor, Kudos, AZ,
Cottonwood
dengler@verdenews.com, Editor, Smart
Shopper, AZ, Cottonwood

Engler, Edward .... (603) 737-2015
ed@laconiadailysun.com, Pres, The Laconia
Daily Sun, NH, Laconia

Engles, Shannon .... (928) 453-4237
Bus. Mgr., Today's News-Herald, AZ, Lake
Havasu City

English, Alan .... (413) 496-6370
aenglish@benningtonbanner.com, Pub.,
Brattleboro Reformer, VT, Brattleboro
aenglish@benningtonbanner.com, Pub.,
Manchester Journal, VT, Manchester Center
aenglish@benningtonbanner.com, Pub.,
Bennington Banner, VT, Bennington
aenglish@benningtonbanner.com, Publisher,
The Berkshire Eagle, MA, Pittsfield

English, Brad
brad@alabamapress.org, Adv. Mgr., Alabama
Newspaper Advertising Service, Inc., AL,
Birmingham

English, Brad
brad@alabamapress.org, Adv. Mgr., Alabama
Press Association, AL, Birmingham

English, Dewey........................(251) 219-5612
denglish@press-register.com, Mng. Ed., Press-
Register, AL, Mobile

English, Susan .... (509) 313-3899
english@gonzaga.edu, Adviser, Gonzaga
University, WA, Spokane

English, Tom .... (618) 351-5070
tom.english@thesouthern.com, Exec. Ed., The
Southern Illinoisan, IL, Carbondale

Englram, Paul
penglram@beksystems.com, Pres., BEK
Systems, Inc., IL, Addison

Engstrom, Candace .... (701) 642-8585
ads@wahpetondailynews.com, Prod. Mgr., The
Daily News, ND, Wahpeton

Engstrom, Candace .... (701) 642-8585
ads@wahpetondailynews.com, Prod. Mgr., The
Daily News, ND, Wahpeton

Engstrom, Jennifer .... (406) 988-7985
accounts@dillontribune.com, Office Mgr., Dillon
Tribune, MT, Dillon

Engstrom, Tim........................(507) 379-3433
tim.engstrom@albertleatribune.com, Ed.,
Albert Lea Tribune, MN, Albert Lea

Engstrom, Tim
tim.engstrom@albertleatribune.com, Mng. Ed.,
Tribune Shopping News, MN, Albert Lea

Enlow, Linda
tulsa.americanclassifieds@yahoo.com, Pub.,
American Classifieds, OK, Tulsa

Enlow, Roger
editor@hcnews.com, Ed., Hood County News,
TX, Granbury

Enman, Marcia .... (902) 436-6005
marcia.enman@lavoixacadienne.com, Dir.
Gen., La Voix Acadienne, PE, Summerside

Ennis, Ron
ron.ennis@transcontinental.ca, Ed., The
Advertiser, NL, Grand Falls

Enoch, David .... (706) 823-3321
david.enoch@augustachronicle.com, VP of
Circulation, The Augusta Chronicle, GA,
Augusta

Enrietto, John .... ext. 241
jenrietto@butlereagle.com, Sports Ed., Butler
Eagle, PA, Butler

Enright, Jeff R. .... (651) 748-7857
Co-Pub., Lillie Suburban Newspapers, MN,
North Saint Paul
Co-Pub., New Brighton Bulletin, MN, North
St Paul

Enright, Jeffery R. .... (651) 748-7857
Co-Pub., East Side Review, MN, North St Paul

Enright, Jeffery R.
news@lillienews.com, Pub., Woodbury-South
Maplewood Review, MN, North Saint Paul
news@lillienews.com, Co-Pub., Shoreview
Bulletin, MN, North Saint Paul

Enrique, Antonio .... (617) 779-3781
aenrique@pilotcatholicnews.com, Ed., The
Pilot, MA, Braintree

Ens, Devyn
newsroom@northernsentinel.com, Editor/
Reporter, Northern Sentinel - Kitimat, BC,
Kitimat

Ens, Rhonda J.
herbertherald@sasktel.net, Ed., The Herald,
SK, Herbert

Ensley, Debbie .... (507) 444-1561
densley@owatonna.com, Adv. Dir., Owatonna
People's Press, MN, Owatonna

Ensley, Ron .... (507) 444-2367
rensley@owatonna.com, Sr. Vice Pres.,
Mainstream Publications LLC, MI, Traverse
City

Ensley, Ron .... (507) 444-2367
rensley@owatonna.com, Senior VP, Faribault
Daily News, MN, Faribault

Ensley, Ronald .... (507) 444-2367
rensley@owatonna.com, Pub./Ed., Owatonna
People's Press, MN, Owatonna

Enstad, David .... (608) 845-9559
david.enstad@wcinet.com, Gen. Mgr., The
Verona Press, WI, Verona

Enstad, David .... (608) 845-9559
david.enstad@wcinet.com, Gen. Mgr.,
Stoughton Courier Hub, WI, Stoughton

Enstad, David .... (608) 845-9559
david.enstad@wcinet.com, Gen. Mgr., Oregon
Observer, WI, Oregon

Enstad, David .... (608) 845-9559
david.enstad@wcinet.com, General Manager,
Unified Newspaper Group, WI, Verona

Entler, Patty .... (580) 585-5106
pentler@swoknews.com, Nat'l Adv. Mgr., The
Lawton Constitution, OK, Lawton

Entwistle, Graham .... (978) 368-0176, ext. 4797
Sports Ed., The Item, MA, Clinton

Enwald, Nathanael
pcgazette@g2a.net , Managing Ed., The
Portage County Gazette, WI, Stevens Point

Ephraim, Michelle
ephraim@wpi.edu, Worcester Polytechnic
Institute, MA, Worcester

Epp, Dan M. .... (620) 376-4264
newspaper@sunflowertelco.com, Ed., Greeley
County Republican, KS, Tribune

Epp, Jeff .... (306) 781-5281
jepp@leaderpost.com, Dir., Reader Sales &
Service, The Leader-Post, SK, Regina

Epp, Peter .... (519) 351-7331 ext.502269
pepp@postmedia.com, Managing Ed.,
Chatham This Week, ON, Chatham

Epperly, Darin .... (402) 371-1020 ext. 230
depperly@norfolkdailynews.com, Photo Chief,
Norfolk Daily News, NE, Norfolk

Eppley, Jonathan
jeppley@pioneergroup.com, News Ed., The
Pioneer - Big Rapids, MI, Big Rapids

Epps, Richard
repps@detroitnews.com, Presentation Editor,
Detroit Free Press, MI, Detroit

Epstein, Rick .... (908) 782-4747 ext. 649
repstein@hcdemocrat.com, Mng. Ed.,
Hunterdon County Democrat, NJ, Flemington

Epstein, Rick
news@hcdemocrat.com, Mng. Ed., Hunterdon
Observer, NJ, Flemington

Epstein-Shepherd, Dr. Bee .... (831) 625-3188
drbeemm@aol.com, Mental Skills Coach/
Writer, Dr. Bee Epstein-Shepherd, Carmel

Erb, Kris
kris.erb@goshennews.com, Accounting, The
Goshen News, IN, Goshen

Erb-Miller, Fannie
ferbmiller@thebudgetnewspaper.com, National
Edition Ed., The Budget, OH, Sugarcreek

Erdahl, Jason .... (612) 673-7889
jason.erdahl@startribune.com, Exec. Dir.,
Digital, Star Tribune, MN, Minneapolis

Erdelt, Paul
sop@bektel.com, Ed. / Pub. , Steele Ozone
and Kidder County Press, ND, Steele
sop@bektel.com, Ed., The Steele Ozone-
Press, ND, Steele
sop@bektel.com, NDNA Director, North Dakota
Newspaper Association, ND, Bismarck

Erdmann, Devan .... (715) 799-5167
DErdmann@mitw.org, Ed., Menominee Nation
News, WI, Keshena

Erdner, Lisa
lerdner@printing.org, Mktg. Mgr., Printing
Industries of America, PA, Sewickley

Eric, Mustafa
editor@bashawstar.com, Ed., The Bashaw
Star, AB, Ponoka

Eric, Mustafa .... (403) 742-2395
editor@castoradvance.com , Ed., Castor
Advance, AB, Castor

Ericksen-Mendoza, Carlos
charlie@hispaniclink.org, Pub., Hispanic Link
News Service, Washington

Ericksen-Mendoza, Charles
charles1@hispaniclink.org, Pub., Hispanic Link
Weekly Report, DC, Washington

Erickson, Amy
aerickson@lemarssentinel.com, Staff Writer,
Le Mars Daily Sentinel, IA, Le Mars

Erickson, Anna
aerickson@parkrapidsenterprise.com, Editor,
Park Rapids Enterprise Express, MN, Park
Rapids

Erickson, Beth
submissions@thecantoncitizen.com, Ed./Pub.,
Canton Citizen, MA, Canton

Erickson, Elizabeth
elizabeth.e.erickson@my.und.edu, Sports
Editor, Univ. of North Dakota, ND, Grand
Forks

Erickson, Jill .... (816) 234-4420
JErickson@wichitaeagle.com, News Editor,
The Wichita Eagle, KS, Wichita

Erickson, John .... (937) 225-2266
john.erickson@coxinc.com, Senior Editor,
Dayton Daily News, OH, Franklin

Erickson, Kristen
kerickson@ironmountaindailynews.com,
Accounting Mgr., The Daily News, MI, Iron
Mountain

Erickson, Kristin .... (608) 831-2131
kerickson@ericksonpublishing.com, Pres./
Pub., Dane County Kids, WI, Mc Farland

Erickson, Kurt .... (217) 782-1249
kerickson@springnet1.com, Capitol Bureau
Chief, The Pantagraph, IL, Bloomington

Erickson, LaVonne L. .... (701) 756-6363
rcf1@ndak.net, Ed., Renville County Farmer,
ND, Mohall

Erickson, Mary
merickson@citypages.com, Editor, City Pages,
MN, Minneapolis

Erickson, Matt
matt.erickson@brainerddispatch.com, Ed.,
Brainerd Dispatch, MN, Brainerd

Erickson, Mike
merickson@mnsun.com, Prod. Mgr.,
Minnetonka/Deephaven/Hopkins Sun Sailor,
MN, Eden Prairie

Erickson, Mike
merickson@mnsun.com, Prod. Mgr., Richfield
Sun-Current, MN, Eden Prairie

Erickson, Randy .... (608) 791-8219
Ed., Onalaska Holmen Courier-Life, WI, La
Crosse

Erickson, Randy .... (608) 791-8219
rerickson@couleenews.com, Ed., Coulee
News, WI, La Crosse

Erickson, Randy
news@nadignewspapers.com, Ed., Chicago's
Northwest Side Press, IL, Chicago

Erickson, Randy
news@nadignewspapers.com, Ed., Reporter
Journal, IL, Chicago

Erickson, Taag
taag_erickson@nela-usa.com, Pdct. Mgr., Web
& Sheetfed, NELA, WI, River Falls

Erickson, Tony .... (800) 959-1566 ext. 408
tony@seniormedia.com, Nat'l/Regl. Sales,
Lovin' Life After 50, AZ, Tempe

Ericson, Paul
pericson@rbj.net, VP & Editor, Rochester
Business Journal, NY, Rochester

Ericson, William
advertising@southpasadenareview.com,
Pub., South Pasadena Review, CA, South
Pasadena

Erikson, Max .... (509) 773-3777
Max@GoldendaleSentinel.com, Reporter,
Goldendale Sentinel, WA, Goldendale

Erin, Meyer
emeyer1@mlive.com, Mktg. Analyst , The Ann
Arbor News, MI, Ann Arbor

Erlacher, Brandon .... (574) 296-5845
berlacher@etruth.com, Pub., Standard-
Examiner, UT, Ogden

Erlandson, Greg R. .... (260) 356-8400
gerlandson@osv.com, Pres./Pub., Our Sunday
Visitor, IN, Huntington

Ermen, Don
donald.ermen@sunmedia.ca, Mng. Ed. , The
Ottawa Sun, ON, Ottawa

Ernesti, Colleen .... ext. 2412
Circ. Mgr., West Point News, NE, West Point

Ernewein, Bruce
bernewein@sungazette.com, Operations
Manager, Williamsport Sun-Gazette/Lock
Haven Express, PA, South Williamsport

Ernsberger, Carol .... (260) 347-0400 Ext. 1139
cernsberger@kpcmedia.com, Desk Ed., The
News Sun, IN, Kendallville

Ernst, Anne .... (707) 942-4035
editor@weeklycalistogan.com, Ed., The Weekly
Calistogan, CA, Calistoga

Ernst, Charles A. S. .... (716) 649-7900 ext. 315
cernst@hilbert.edu, Hilbert College, NY,
Hamburg

Ernst, Trent .... (250) 242-5597
editor@tumblerridgenews.com, Pub/Ed.,
Tumbler Ridge News, BC, Tumbler Ridge

Ertz, Michele .... (712) 654-2911
manillatimesads@fmctc.com, Graphic Des,
Tech Supp, Manilla Times, IA, Manilla

Ervin, Cynthia L. .... (217) 692-2323
bmleader1@yahoo.com, Pub./Ed., Blue Mound
Leader, IL, Blue Mound

Ervin, Jim .... (913) 367-0583 ext. 20405
jim.ervin@npgco.com, Adv. Rep., Atchison
Globe, KS, Atchison

Ervin, Kenneth Scott
shrecnew@netins.net, Ed., South Hamilton
Record-News, IA, Jewell

Ervin, Scott
stratfordcourier@globalccs.net, Ed., Stratford
Courier, IA, Stratford

Erwin, Greg .... (916) 498-1234, ext 1317
grege@newsreview.com, Distribution
Mgr, Sacramento News & Review, CA,
Sacramento

Erwin, Mike .... (423) 569-8351
scn@highland.net, Pub., Scott County News,
TN, Oneida

Erwin, Terry .... (918) 647-3188
publisher@poteaudailynews.com, Pub., The
Shoppers Guide, OK, Poteau

Escabar, Mimi .... (530) 344-5070
mescabar@mtdemocrat.net, Lifestyle Ed.,
Mountain Democrat, CA, Placerville

Escarilla, Gary
gary@balita.com, Sales Mgr., Weekend Balita/
Midweek Balita, CA, Glendale

Eschliman, Bob
beschliman@newtondailynews.com, Ed.,
Newton Daily News, IA, Newton

Eschman, Todd .... (618) 239-2540
teschman@bnd.com, Group Manager,
Command Post, IL, Belleville

Eschman, Todd .... (613) 239-2540
teschman@bnd.com, Sports Ed., O'Fallon
Progress, IL, Belleville

Escobar Coakley, Nell .... (781) 393-1826
ncoakley@wickedlocal.com, Mng. Ed. , Saugus
Advertiser, MA, Danvers

Escobar Coakley, Nell .... (781) 393-1826
ncoakley@wickedlocal.com, Mng. Ed. ,
Wakefield Observer, MA, Danvers

Escobar Coakley, Nell .... (978) 739-1318
mswitzer@cnc.com, Mng. Ed. , Melrose Free
Press, MA, Danvers

Escobar Coakley , Nell .... (781) 393-1826
ncoakley@wickedlocal.com, Ed., Malden
Observer, MA, Danvers

Escobar-Coakley, Nell .... (781) 393-1826
ncoakley@wickedlocal.com, Ed., Medford
Transcript, MA, Danvers

Escobedo, Eddie
elchiefo@aol.com, Pub./Founder, El Mundo,
NV, Las Vegas

Escobedo, Frank .... (956) 982-6646
fescobedo@brownsvilleherald.com, Pub., The
Brownsville Herald, TX, Brownsville

Escobedo, Frank .... (951) 368-9913
fescobedo@pe.com, Gen. Mgr./Hispanic
Media, The Press-Enterprise, CA, Riverside

Eshleman, Bill .... (403) 235-7419
beshleman@calgaryherald.com, Adv. Sales
& Operations Mgr., Calgary Herald, AB,
Calgary

Eshleman, Jim
ads@bighorncountynews.com, Gen. Mngr., Big
Horn County News, MT, Hardin

Eskelsen, Rich
advertising@mtvernonlisbonsun.com, Adv.
Mgr., The Sunlight, IA, Mount Vernon

Esken, Wanda .... (937) 222-8855 ext. 212
publisher@daytoncitypaper.com, Publisher,
Dayton City Paper, OH, Dayton

Eskil, Rick .... ext. 271
reskil@wwub.com, Editorial Page Ed., Walla
Walla Union-Bulletin, WA, Walla Walla

Eskridge, Larry
leskridge@cantondailyledger.com, Reporter,
Daily Ledger, IL, Canton

Eskridge, Theresa
teskridge@soundpublishing.com, Nat'l/Rgl
Acct. Mgr., The Whidbey Examiner, WA,
Coupeville
teskridge@soundpublishing.com, Nat'l/Rgl
Acct. Mgr., Bainbridge Island Review, WA,
Bainbridge Island

Esley, Karla .... (585) 232-6921

karla.esley@nydailyrecord.com, Admin. / Class., The Daily Record, NY, Rochester

Esovoloff, Christine
sales@rosslandnews.com, Sales, Rossland News, BC, Castlegar

Esper, Mark
editor@silverrtonstandard.com, Ed., Silverton Standard and The Miner, CO, Silverton

Espetia, Tony .... (305) 376-3543
tespetia@miamiherald.com, Dir., Int'l Edition, Herald Values, FL, Miami

Espey, Bruce .... (416) 774-2370
kespey@insidetoronto.com, Dir., Bus. Admin., The Scarborough Mirror, ON, Toronto

Espino, Judy .... (320) 616-1905
judy.espino@mcrecord.com, Bus. Mgr., Morrison County Record, MN, Little Falls

Espinosa Solis, Suzanne
sespinosa@sfchronicle.com, Assist. Metro Ed, San Francisco Chronicle, CA, San Francisco

Espinoza, Elvira .... (602) 444-3800
elvira.ortiz@lavozarizona.com, Publisher, La Voz, AZ, Phoenix

Espinoza, Josh .... (970) 392-9327
Univ. of Northern Colorado, CO, Greeley

Espinoza, Leon
lespinoza@seattletimes.com, Exec. News Ed., Seattle Post-Intelligencer, WA, Seattle

Espinoza, Leon .... (206) 464-8212
lespinoza@seattletimes.com, Assistant Managing Ed., Visuals, The Seattle Times, WA, Seattle

Espiritu, John B. .... (650) 872-3000
info@philippinenews.com, Chrmn., Philippine News, CA, Burlingame

Espitia, Rick .... (512) 756-6640
cgazette@tstar.net, Ed./Pub./Adv. Dir., Citizens Gazette, TX, Burnet

Esposito, Carl .... (865) 981-1137
carl.esposito@thedailytimes.com, Publisher, The Daily Times, TN, Maryville
carl.esposito@thedailytimes.com, Pres., Adams Publishing Group, LLC, MN, Virginia

Esposito, Carl
carl.esposito@thedailytimes.com, President of APG Media of TN/NC and Publisher of The Daily Times, APG Media of Tennessee/North Carolina, TN, Greeneville

Esposito, Danny
danny@espositocommunications.com, Adv. Mgr., Lake Travis View, TX, Austin

Esposito, Martha .... (609) 871-8143
mesposito@calkins.com, Feat. Ed., Burlington County Times, NJ, Willingboro

Esposito, Richard .... (530) 344-5055
resposito@mtdemocrat.net, Pub., Village Life, CA, Placerville

Esposito, Richard B .... (530) 344-5055
resposito@mtdemocrat.net, Pub., Mountain Democrat, CA, Placerville

Esposito, Robert .... (215) 679-5060
TownAndCountry@UPVNews.com, Graphics Editor, Town and Country, PA, Pennsburg

Espy, Winston Eugene .... (706) 857-2494
sumnews@aol.com, Ed., The Summerville News, GA, Summerville

Esquivel Long, Lisa .... (260) 461-8244
lesquivel@news-sentinel.com, Asst. Metro/ Bus. Ed.
, The News-Sentinel, IN, Fort Wayne

Essary, Sharon .... (417) 256-9191
Customer Service Representative, West Plains Daily Quill, MO, West Plains

Esserman, Eddie .... (912) 634-6575
edwesser@bellsouth.com, Assoc., Media Services Group, Inc., FL, Ponte Vedra

Essex, Randy .... (970) 384-9110
ressex@postindependent.com, Pub./Ed., Citizen Telegram, CO, Glenwood Springs
ressex@postindependent.com, Publisher and Editor, Glenwood Springs Post Independent, CO, Glenwood Springs
ressex@postindependent.com, Bus. Ed., Detroit Free Press, MI, Detroit

Estabrooks, Joshua
publisher@thevalleysentinel.com, Pub., The Valley Sentinel, BC, Valemount

Estadt, Brian
b.estadt@gatewaynewspapers.com, Ed., Penn-Trafford Star, PA, Pittsburgh

Estadt, Brian
murrysville.star@gatewaynewspapers.com, Ed., Murrysville Star, PA, Pittsburgh

Esteban, Lia
lia@islandernews.com, Ad. Dir., Islander News, FL, Key Biscayne

Esten Cooke, Ken .... (830) 997-2155
ken@fredericksburgstandard.com, Pub., Fredericksburg Standard-Radio Post, TX, Fredericksburg

Estep, Don
destep@corbinnewsjournal.com, Publisher, News Journal, KY, Corbin

Estes, Carolyn .... (918) 443-2428 ext. 26.
Carolyn.Estes@sbcglobal.net, Mktg. Dir., Oologah Lake Leader, OK, Oologah

Estes, Charlea .... (417) 847-4475
editor@4bca.com, Editor, Barry County Advertiser, MO, Cassville

Estes, Crystal
htpress99@windstream.net, Adv. Mgr., Hometown Press, TX, Winnie

Estes, Dale .... (870) 453-3731
estesd@flippinonline.com, Adv. Mgr., The Mountaineer Echo, AR, Flippin

Estes, Jane .... (870) 448-3321
mmw@windstream.net, Publisher/Editor, Marshall Mountain Wave, AR, Marshall

Estes, Jim
jim@wescographics.com, Pres., Wesco Graphics, CA, Tracy

Estes, Lindsey .... (410) 838-3018
lindsey.l.estes@localmedia.org, Sales & Marketing Manager
, Local Media Association, MI, Lake City

Estes, Robert .... (269) 429-2400 ext. 296
restes@paxtonmedia.com, Controller, The Herald-Palladium, MI, Saint Joseph

Estes, Tracy
wjr@centurytel.net, Ed., Journal Record, AL, Haleyville

Estes-Jones, Isaac .... (417) 723-5248
screditor@centurylink.net, Ed, Crane Chronicle/Stone County Republican, MO, Crane

Estey, Jon
jestey@thevermontstandard.com, Gen. Mgr., The Vermont Standard, VT, Woodstock

Estlack, Roger A. .... (806) 874-2259
publisher@clarendonlive.com, Pub./Ed., Clarendon Enterprise, TX, Clarendon

Estrada, George
ge2@humboldt.edu, Assoc. Prof., Humboldt State University, CA, Arcata

Estrada, Juan .... (707) 521-5342
Adv. Mgr., La Prensa Sonoma, CA, Santa Rosa

Estrada, Patricia
pattyestrada@semananews.com, Univ. of Houston, TX, Houston

Etchey, Donna .... (360) 779-4464
publisher@northkitsapherald.com, Pub., North Kitsap Herald, WA, Poulsbo

Etchey, Donna
publisher@bainbridgereview.com, Pub., Bainbridge Island Review, WA, Bainbridge Island

Etchey, Donna .... (360) 779-4464
publisher@kingstoncommunitynews.com, Pub., Kingston Community News, WA, Poulsbo

Etheridge, Kellie .... (502) 624-2098
kellie.etheridge@us.army.mil, Leisure Ed., Turret, KY, Fort Knox

Ethier, Marc
marc@carquinezreview.com, Ed., Benicia Herald, CA, Benicia

Ethier, Nick .... (508) 909-4133
sports@stonebridgepress.com, Sports Ed. , Southbridge Evening News, MA, Southbridge

Ethridge, Patrick .... (402) 223-5233
pethridge@beatricedailysun.com, Regl. Pub., Beatrice Daily Sun, NE, Beatrice

Ethridge, Tim
tethridge@courierpress.com, Exec. Ed., Evansville Courier & Press, IN, Evansville

Etienne, Larry .... (402) 444-1408
larry.etienne@owh.com, VP of Advertising, Omaha World-Herald, NE, Omaha

Etling, Bert
betling@dailytidings.com, Ed., The Ashland Daily Tidings, OR, Medford

Etten, Doug .... (715) 479-4421
douge@vcnewsreview.com, Assit. Editor, Vilas County News-Review, WI, Eagle River

Etten, Doug .... (715) 479-4421
douge@vcnewsreview.com, Assist. Editor, Three Lakes News, WI, Eagle River

Ettenhofer, Connie .... (906) 786-2021
cettenhofer@dailypress.net, Bus. Mgr., Daily Press, MI, Escanaba

Etter, Gerald
jwishtimes@aol.com, Mng. Ed., Jewish Times, NJ, Pleasantville

Etzel, Nancy .... (952) 392-6855
nancy.etzel@ecm-inc.com, Adv. Sales, Bloomington Sun-Current, MN, Eden Prairie

Eubank, Gayle
geubank@yorkdispatch.com, City Ed., The York Dispatch, PA, York

Eubank , Stephanie
seubank@newsadvance.com, Circ. Dir. , The News & Advance, VA, Lynchburg

Eubanks, Johnny
jbe@gtcom.net, Pub., The Calhoun Liberty Journal, FL, Bristol

Eugene, N/A .... Adv. Mgr., Design Herald-Standard, PA, Uniontown

Eure, Julian
jeure@dailyadvance.com, News Ed., The Daily Advance, NC, Elizabeth City

Eure, Julian
jeure@dailyadvance.com, Mng Ed., Perquimans Weekly, NC, Hertford

Evan, Corey
cevan@thevalleychronicle.com, The Valley Chronicle, CA, Hemet

Evans, Akwasi
akwasievans@gmail.com, Ed., Nokoa-the Observer, TX, Austin

Evans, Andrea .... (620) 241-2422
aevans@mcphersonsentinel.com, Multi-media Sales Executive, McPherson Sentinel, KS, McPherson

Evans, Angie
advertise2@yelmonline.com, Adv. Mgr., Nisqually Valley Shopper, WA, Yelm

Evans, Angie
advertise@yelmonline.com, Adv. Mgr., Nisqually Valley News, WA, Yelm

Evans, Barry .... (704) 243-4725
barry.evans@wrh-global-americas.com, VP, WRH Global Americas, NJ, Somerset

Evans, Barry .... (856) 842-0600
barry.evans@wrh-global-americas.com, WRH Global Americas, NJ, Somerset

Evans, Brandon A. .... (317) 236-1577
bevans@archindy.org, Online Ed., The Criterion, IN, Indianapolis

Evans, Cari .... (850) 599-2189
clevans@tallahassee.com, Adv. Dir., Tallahassee Democrat, FL, Tallahassee

Evans, Carrie .... (850) 599-2189
clevans@tallahassee.com, Adv. Dir., Tallahassee Democrat, FL, Tallahassee

Evans, Chris .... (802) 656-2060
crevans@uvm.edu, Adv., University of Vermont, VT, Burlington

Evans, Chris .... (270) 965-3191
evans@the-press.com, Pub., The Crittenden Press, KY, Marion

Evans, Cindy .... (870) 642-2111
cindye@dequeenbee.com, Advertising, DeQueen Bee, AR, De Queen

Evans, Dan .... (818) 637-3234
Dan.Evans@latimes.com, Editor, Times Community News (TCN), CA, Los Angeles

Evans, Dan .... (818) 637-3234
Dan.Evans@latimes.com, Ed., Burbank Leader, CA, Los Angeles

Evans, Dan .... (507) 754-5486
evans@frontiernet.net, Pub., Meadow Area Shopper, MN, Grand Meadow

Evans, Dan
Dan.Evans@latimes.com, Los Angeles Times, CA, Los Angeles
Dan.Evans@latimes.com, Ed., News-Press, CA, Los Angeles

Evans, Daniel
daniel.evans@selmatimesjournal.com, News Ed., The Selma Times-Journal, AL, Selma

Evans, Daniel
recorder@omnitelcom.com, Pub., Riceville Recorder, IA, Riceville

Evans, Daniel F.
devans@sunmulti.com, Pub., The Houston Home Journal, GA, Perry

Evans, Dee
devans@gatehousemedia.com, Pub., Orion Gazette, IL, Orion

Evans, Dee
mindycarls1957@gmail.com, Pub., Cambridge Chronicle IN ILLINOIS, IL, Cambridge

Evans, Dietra .... (309) 852-2181
devans@gatehousemedia.com, Pub., Star-Courier, IL, Kewanee

Evans, Gail
citizennewspaper@midconetwork.com, Circ. Mgr., Clearwater Tribune, MN, Big Lake
citizennewspaper@midconetwork.com, Circ. Mgr, West Sherburne Tribune, MN, Big Lake

Evans, Helen
ccpress@qwestoffice.net, Gen. Mgr., Colfax County Press, NE, Clarkson

Evans, Jason
jevans@reportalaska.com, Pub., The Arctic Sounder, AK, Anchorage
jevans@reportalaska.com, Pub., The Bristol Bay Times, AK, Anchorage
jevans@reportalaska.com, Pub., The Dutch Harbor Fisherman, AK, Anchorage

Evans, John
john.evans@tctmail.com, Bus Mgr, Tri-County Times, MI, Fenton

Evans, John J. .... (716) 632-4700 ext. 214
jevans@beenews.com, Exec. Vice Pres., Bee Group Newspapers, NY, Williamsville

Evans, Justin
justin@wesellvegas.net, Sales/Mktg. Mgr., The Beehive, NV, Las Vegas

Evans, Malissa .... (918) 465-2321

lcntclassifieds@att.net, Class./Legals, Latimer County News-Tribune, OK, Wilburton

Evans, Mark
marke@emergecenter.org, Instr., University of Arizona, AZ, Tucson

Evans, Mark
mevans@azbiz.com, Ed., Inside Tucson Business, AZ, Tucson

Evans, May
mevans@grantky.com, Assistant Sales to Mr. Stone, Grant County News and Express, KY, Williamstown

Evans, Mike..............................(847) 427-4616
mevans@dailyherald.com, Director of Local Advertising, Daily Herald, IL, Arlington Heights

Evans, Molly
molly.evans@dowjones.com, Senior Vice President, Advertising Sales , Dow Jones Local Media Group, NY, Middletown

Evans, Molly............................(508) 862-1377
mevans@capecodonline.com, Adv. Dir., Cape Cod Times, MA, Hyannis

Evans, Molly............................(508) 862-1377
mevans@capecodonline.com, Adv. Dir. , The Standard-Times, MA, New Bedford

Evans, Molly
molly.evans@dowjones.com, Senior VP, Advertising Sales, Dow Jones Local Media Group, NY, Middletown

Evans, Perry
pevans@aptas.com, CEO, Aptas, CO, Denver

Evans, Richard
sports@hometownclinton.com, Sports ed., The Courier News, TN, Clinton

Evans, Sean
sevans@idahopress.com, Advertising Director , Idaho Press-Tribune, ID, Nampa

Evans, Stan ....(716) 849-4444
sevans@buffnews.com, Deputy Mng. Ed., The Buffalo News, NY, Buffalo

Evans, T.A.
ccpress@megavision.com, Ed., Colfax County Press, NE, Clarkson

Evans, Tatum ....(715) 453-2151
sales@tomahawkleader.com, Sales Consultant, Tomahawk Leader, WI, Tomahawk

Evans, Thomas
tevans@nccu.edu, Associate Professor, North Carolina Central Univ., NC, Durham

Evans, Tim
tevans@news-gazette.com, Gen. Mgr., News Gazette Community News, IL, Rantoul

Evans, Tim ....(217) 840-8704
tevans@news-gazette.com, Gen. Mgr., Rantoul Press, IL, Rantoul

Evans, Tim ....(217) 840-8704
tevans@news-gazette.com, Vice Pres./Gen. Mgr., Piatt County Journal-Republican, IL, Monticello

Evans, Tim ....(217) 840-8704
tevans@news-gazette.com, General Manager, Rantoul Press, IL, Rantoul

Evans, Tim ....(217) 892-9613
tevans@news-gazette.com, Gen. Mgr., Independent News, IL, Danville

Evans, Todd ....(908) 232-2021
todd@rivendellmedia.com, Pres., Rivendell Media, Inc., NJ, Mountainside

Evans, Tom ....(917) 368-8600
tevans@bankrate.com, President & CEO (Former), Bankrate, North Palm Beach

Evans, William
wevans@uab.edu, Prof./Dir., Institute for Comm. & Information Research, University of Alabama, AL, Tuscaloosa

Evans-Helle, Annette ....(907) 335-1260
annette.evanshelle@peninsulaclarion.com, Classified Adv., Peninsula Clarion, AK, Kenai

Evavold, Ross ....(715) 738-1606
ross.evavold@lee.net; news@chippewa.com, Editor, The Chippewa Herald, WI, Chippewa Falls

Evavold, Ross
ross.evavold@lee.net, Ed., Your Family Shopper, WI, Chippewa Falls

Eveland, William
william_eveland@fc.uhaul.com, Assoc. Prof., Ohio State University, OH, Columbus

Eveld, Jo ....(479) 667-2136
Ed., The Spectator, AR, Ozark

Even, Jan...............................(541) 617-7849
jeven@bendbulletin.com, New Media Dir., Western Communications, Inc., OR, Bend

Evenson, Kathy
kevenson@willistonherald.com, Circ. Mgr., Williston Daily Herald, ND, Williston

Everbach, Tracy
everbach@po7.cas.unt.edu, Asst. Prof./NT Daily Advisor, University of North Texas, TX, Denton

Everberg, Steve ....(904) 819-3521
steve.everberg@staugustinerecord.com, Prodn. Dir., The St. Augustine Record, FL, Saint Augustine

Everett, Manny
manny@strathmoretimes.com, Office Mgr., Strathmore Times, AB, Strathmore

Everett, Mark ....(850) 435-8626
Circ. Direc., Pensacola News Journal, FL, Pensacola

Everhart, Bill
weverhart@berkshireeagle.com, Editorial Page Ed., The Berkshire Eagle, MA, Pittsfield

Everidge, Frank ....(541) 963-3161
feveridge@lagrandeobserver.com, Gen Mgr, Operations, The Observer, OR, La Grande

Everidge, Frank ....(541) 963-3161
feveridge@lagrandeobserver.com, Prodn. Mgr., Baker City Herald, OR, Baker City

Everitt, Kelly ....(208) 587-3331
keveritt@mountainhomenews.com, Ed., Mountain Home Patriot, ID, Mountain Home

Everitt, Tammy ....(765) 648-4242
tammy.everitt@heraldbulletin.com, Editorial Asst., The Herald Bulletin, IN, Anderson

Everly, Lori ....(570) 628-6036
leverly@republicanherald.com, Bus. Office Mgr., The Republican-Herald, PA, Pottsville

Evers, Byron
bevers@mesastate.edu, Dir., Mesa State College, CO, Grand Junction

Everson, Chad
Ceverson@theet.com, Digital Director, The Exponent Telegram, WV, Clarksburg

Everson, Diane ....(608) 884-3367
ereport@ticon.net, Publisher and Editor, Edgerton Reporter, WI, Edgerton

Everson, Helen V.
ereport@ticon.net, Ed., Edgerton Reporter, WI, Edgerton

Everson, Michael ....(509) 661-6381
everson@wenatcheeworld.com, Director of Technology and Communications, The Wenatchee World, WA, Wenatchee

Eveslage, Thomas
eveslage@temple.edu, Prof., Temple University, PA, Philadelphia

Evins, Darla...........................(417) 256-9191
Customer Service Representative, West Plains Daily Quill, MO, West Plains

Evjen, Doug..........................(403) 528-5650
devjen@abnewsgroup.com, Director of Sales

and Marketing, Prairie Post, SK, Swift Current

Ewald, Mel
mewald@championnewspapers.com, Mng. Ed., Chino Champion, CA, Chino
mewald@championnewspapers.com, Mng. Ed., Chino Hills Champion, CA, Chino

Ewers, Mary ....(417) 256-9191
General Assignment Reporter, West Plains Daily Quill, MO, West Plains

Ewert, Jim ....(916) 288-6015
jim@cnpa.com, Gen. Counsel, California News Publishers Association, CA, Sacramento

Ewing, Thomas M..........(603) 352-1234 ext. 1001
tewing@keenesentinel.com , Own & Pub., The Keene Sentinel, NH, Keene

Ewing, Tommy.......................(901) 529-2317
tommy.ewing@commercialappeal.com, Advertising Sales Director, The Commercial Appeal, TN, Memphis

Ewing, Wendy
ewing@essexreporter.com, Adv. Dir., The Colchester Sun, VT, Colchester
ewing@essexreporter.com, Adv. Man., The Essex Reporter, VT, Saint Albans

Ewing, Wendy ....(802) 985-3091
wendy@sheburnenews.com, Adv. Dir., Shelburne News, VT, Shelburne

Ewing, Zach............................(661) 395-7324
tlacava@bakersfield.com, Sports Ed., The Bakersfield Californian, CA, Bakersfield

Ewoldt, John
jewoldt@startribune.com, Ed., Star Tribune Buyer's Edge, MN, Minneapolis

Exline, Carol...........................(717) 328-3223
carol.exline@mercersburgjournal.com, Office Mgr., Mercersburg Journal, PA, Mercersburg

Exner, Rhonda ....(306) 781-5293
rexner@postmedia.com, Prod. Mgr., The Leader-Post, SK, Regina

Exum, Jonna
theberrienpress@windstream.net, Gen. Mgr., The Berrien Press, GA, Nashville

Exum, Ken ....(309) 343-7181 ext. 253
kexum@register-mail.com, Website Mgr., Pennysaver, IL, Monmouth

Ey, Craig
cey@bizjournals.com, Ed., Philadelphia Business Journal, PA, Philadelphia

Eyer, Jen
jeyer@mlive.com, Dir. of Community Engagement, The Jackson Citizen Patriot, MI, Jackson

Eyerly, Brandon R.....................(570) 784-2121
Pub., Around The House, PA, Bloomsburg

Eyerly, Brandon R...........(570) 387-1234 Ext 1611
brandon.eyerly@pressenterprise.net, Pub., Press Enterprise, PA, Bloomsburg

Eyerly, Paul R. ....(570) 387-1234 ext 1616
paul.eyerly@pressenterprise.net, Pres., Press Enterprise, PA, Bloomsburg

Eymann, Kent D. ....(608) 364-9211
keymann@beloitdailynews.com, Pub., Beloit Daily News, WI, Beloit

Eymann, Kent D. ....(608) 364-9211
keymann@beloitdailynews.com, Pub., My Stateline Shopper, WI, Beloit

Eymard, Chad ....(318) 362-0208
ceymard@gannett.com., Multi-media Acc. Exec. , The News-Star, LA, Monroe

Eyre, Jan
jeyre@leducrep.com, Circ. Mgr., Leduc Representative, AB, Leduc

Ezell, Jon..............................(931) 372-3063
jezell@tntech.edu, Advisor / Assistant Professor, Tennessee Technological Univ., TN, Cookeville

F

F, Darlene ....(928) 539-6829
nationals@yumasun.com, Nationals Account Manager, Yuma Sun, AZ, Yuma

Faase, Michael........................(262) 512-8456
njfranz@ra.rockwell.com, Mktg. Commun. Specialist, Rockwell Automation, WI, Milwaukee

Faber, Ronald
a-digr@umn.edu, Prof., University of Minnesota, MN, Minneapolis

Fabian, Doug
doug@reminderpublications.com, Adv. Mgr., Hebron Columbia, CT, Vernon
doug@reminderpublications.com, Adv. Dir., Springfield Reminder, MA, East Longmeadow

Fabisiak, Lori
lori@weinrichadv.com, Pres., League of Advertising Agencies, Inc., NY, New York

Fabris, Hans H.
FABRIS@EDVZ.SBG.AC.AT, Chair, University of Salzburg, A-5010 Salzburg

Fabrizio, Rick ....(603) 610-1193
rfabrizio@seacoastonline.com , Mng. Ed., Portsmouth Herald, NH, Portsmouth

Facemire, Mike ....(520) 573-4456
mfacemire@tucson.com, Dir. IT, Arizona Daily Star, AZ, Tucson

Fackhourie, Abe
afackhourie@durhamregion.com, Circ. Mgr., Ajax-pickering News Advertiser, ON, Oshawa

Faddis, Jim ....(308) 381-9413
jim.faddis@theindependent.com, Mng. Ed., The Grand Island Independent, NE, Grand Island

Fadojutimi, Joycelyne
joycelyne@easttexasreview.com, Publisher/ General Manager, East Texas Review, TX, Longview

Fagan, Cathy ....ext. 202
cfagan@hickoryrecord.com, Adv. Dir., Pow, NC, Hickory

Fagan, Shannon
sfagan@cherokeeherald.com, Sports Ed, Cherokee County Herald, AL, Centre

Fahey, Pam ....(985) 857-2271
pam.fahey@houmatoday.com, Adv. Sales, The Courier, LA, Houma

Fahey, Pam
art@yourneighborhoodnews.com, Prodn. Mgr., Goffstown News, NH, Manchester

Fahrenbacher, C.J.
burkegaz@gwtc.net, Pub./Ed., The Burke Gazette, SD, Burke

Fahsholtz, Tammy ....(509) 577-6163
tfahsholtz@yakimaherald.com, Senior Circulation Manager, Yakima Herald-Republic, WA, Yakima

Faigin, Doug..........................(310) 481-0401
Pres., City News Service, Inc. - Los Angeles, CA, Los Angeles

Faimon, Catherine
cfaimon@yahoo.com, Pub., The Osage County Herald-Chronicle, KS, Osage City

Faimon, Chris
chrisfaimon@yahoo.com, Pub., Coffey County Republican, KS, Burlington

Fain, Terry ....(206) 461-1322
PPCsales@nwlink.com, Adv. Mgr., City Living Seattle, WA, Seattle

Fain, Terry ....(206) 461-1322
PPCsales@nwlink.com, Sales Mgr., Queen Anne & Magnolia News, WA, Seattle

Fair, Charles
fair@umco.edu, Chair, University of Central Missouri, MO, Warrensburg

Fair, Debbie
dfair@vernonpublishing.com, Ad Sales, Miller County Autogram Sentinel, MO, Eldon

Fairbanks, Stephanie
sfairbanks@poconorecord.com, Print and Digital ad Manager, Pocono Record, PA, Stroudsburg

Fairgrieve, Stewart
theobserver@nb.aibn.com, Gen. Mgr., The Observer, NB, Hartland

Fajardo, Sara .... (575) 622-7710
sfajardo@rdrnews.com, General Manager, Roswell Daily Record, NM, Roswell

Fakazis, Liz
lfakazis@uwsp.edu, Univ. of Wisconsin Stevens Point, WI, Stevens Point

Falandys, Donna
sales@cubapatriot.com, Ad. Sales, Cuba Patriot & Free Press, NY, Cuba

Faldalen, Crystal
classifieds@havredailynews.com, Classified Adv. Mgr., The Havre Daily News, MT, Havre

Falduto, Anthony .... (609) 365-6184
anthony.falduto@catamaranmedia.com, Gen. Mgr. , Shore News Today, NJ, Marmora

Falk, April
april@gbpnews.com, Adv. Mgr, The Giveaway, IN, Scottsburg
april@gbpnews.com, Adv. Mgr, The Scott Co. Journal & Chronicle, IN, Scottsburg

Falk, April
april@gbpnews.com, Sales Mgr., The Leader, IN, Charlestown

Falk, April
april@gbpnews.com, Adv. Mgr., The Washington County Edition, IN, Salem

Falk, April
april@gbpnews.com, Adv. Mgr., The Banner-Gazette, IN, Pekin

Falkenhein, John .... (618) 497-8272
cjournal@egyptian.net, Adv. Mgr., County Journal, IL, Percy

Falkjar, Eric 1 (506) 645-3313
falkjar.eric@brunswicknews.com, Director of IT, New Brunswick Telegraph-Journal, NB, Saint John

Falkner, Mark .... (519) 255-5769
falkner@windsorstar.com, Sports Ed., The Windsor Star, ON, Windsor

Fallati, Donald .... (203) 381-7000
Sr. Vice Pres., Mktg./Strategic Planning, Nuance Communications, Inc., MA, Burlington

Fallon, Helen
hfallon@pointpark.edu, Chair/Prof., Point Park University, PA, Pittsburgh

Fallon, Jim
jfallon@itw.com, Dir., Mktg. Commun., Signode Corp., IL, Glenview

Falsone, Nick .... (610) 258-7171 ext. 3638
nfalsone@express-times.com, Mng. Ed, The Express-Times, PA, Easton

Faltz, Mary .... (608) 297-2424
marquettetribune@newspubinc.com, Prodn. Mgr., The Marquette County Tribune, WI, Montello

Falzone, Mike .... (603) 880-1516
mike@areanewsgroup.com, customer service, Salem Community Patriot, NH, Hudson

Fancher, Don .... (901) 528-5283
dfancher@memphisdailynews.com, Public Notice Adv., Nashville Ledger, TN, Nashville

Fancher, Johnnie .... (903) 927-5986
jfancher@marshallnewsmessenger.com, Adv. Sales Exec., Marshall News Messenger, TX, Marshall

Fanlund, Paul .... (608) 252-6210
pfanlund@madison.com, Ed., Capital

Newspapers, WI, Madison

Fanlund, Paul .... (608) 252-6210
pfanlund@madison.com, Editor, The Capital Times, WI, Madison

Fannin, Mike
publiceditor@kcstar.com, Ed., The Kansas City Star, MO, Kansas City

Fanning, Paul
cashtonrecord@centurytel.net, Pub., The Cashton Record, WI, Cashton

Fanning, Ray
ray.fanning@mso.umt.edu, Asst. Prof., The University of Montana, MT, Missoula

Fant, Janette
circulation@weatherforddemocrat.com, Circ. Mgr., The Weatherford Democrat, TX, Weatherford

Fantle, David
david.fantle@gmail.com, Creator/Writer, Reel to Real Celebrity Profiles, Milwaukee

Farago, Peter
peter@faragoassoc.com, President, Farago & Associates, MI, Southfield

Faram, Monica
editor@trcle.com, News Editor, Cleburne Times-Review, TX, Cleburne

Faranzetti, John
nr2003@austinfamily.com, Art Dir., Austin Family, TX, Round Rock

Farber, Jared
jared.farber@washpost.com, Director of Digital Marketing, The Washington Post, DC, Washington

Farber, Keith
kfarber@renmedia.us, Adv. Mgr., The Detroit Jewish News, MI, Southfield

Fares, Nabil E.
info@admarketintl.com, Pres./CEO, Admarket International (Div. of Marcom International, Inc.), CT, Southport

Fariman, Julie .... (702) 298-6090
lntedit@cmaaccess.com, Ed., Laughlin Nevada Times, AZ, Bullhead City

Farina, Robert .... (920) 453-5190
rfarina@sheboygan.gannett.com, Presentation Ed., The Sheboygan Press, WI, Sheboygan

Farkas, Kim .... (507) 452-1262 ext. 111
farkas@winonapost.com, Adv. Mgr, Winona Post, MN, Winona

Farkas, Tammy .... (936) 348-3505
tammy.farkas@madisonvillemeteor.com, Advertising Manager, Madisonville Meteor, TX, Madisonville

Farkas, Tim .... (315) 661-2363
tfarkas@wdt.net, Editor, VP of News Operations
, Johnson Newspaper Corp., NY, Watertown
tfarkas@wdt.net, VP News Ops., Watertown Daily Times, NY, Watertown

Farkas, Tony .... (936) 348-3505
publisher@madisonvillemeteor.com, Ed./Pub., Madisonville Meteor, TX, Madisonville

Farley, Don
dfarley@citypaper.com, Pub., City Paper, MD, Baltimore

Farley, Tom .... (262) 631-1723
tfarley@journaltimes.com, News Ed., The Journal Times, WI, Racine

Farmer, Doug
dfarmer@turley.com, Ed., The Journal Register, MA, Palmer

Farmer, Lisa .... (910) 230-2028
lfarmer@mydailyrecord.com, Executive Ed., The Angier Independent (OOB), NC, Angier
lfarmer@mydailyrecord.com, Online Ed., The Daily Record, NC, Dunn

Farmer, Mary Jane .... (903) 564-3565
news@whitesboronews.com, Reporter,

Whitesboro News-Record, TX, Whitesboro

Farmer, Nancy .... (270) 259-6061
nfarmer@thenewsenterprise.com, Advertising representative, The Record, KY, Leitchfield

Farmer, Paul .... (707) 425-4646 ext. 264
pfarmer@dailyrepublic.net, Sports Ed., Daily Republic, CA, Fairfield

Farmer, William C.
amail@rpt.coop, Ed., Atchison County Mail, MO, Rock Port

Farmer , Judy .... (252) 332-7217
judy.farmer@r-cnews.com, Mktg. Consult., Roanoke-Chowan News-Herald, NC, Ahoskie
judy.farmer@r-cnews.com, Sales Coord., The Chowan Herald, NC, Edenton

Farnham, Michelle
mfarnham@thepostnewspapers.com, Mng. Ed., The Post Newspapers - Brunswick, OH, Medina
mfarnham@thepostnewspapers.com, Mng. Ed., The Post Newspapers - Eastern Medina, OH, Medina
mfarnham@thepostnewspapers.com, Managing Editor, The Post Newspapers - Medina, OH, Medina
mfarnham@thepostnewspapers.com, Mng. Ed., The Post Newspapers - Northern Wayne, OH, Medina
mfarnham@thepostnewspapers.com, Mng. Ed., The Post Newspapers - Norton, OH, Medina
mfarnham@thepostnewspapers.com, Mng. Ed., The Post Newspapers - Southern Medina, OH, Medina
mfarnham@thepostnewspapers.com, Mng. Ed., The Post Newspapers - Strongsville, OH, Medina
mfarnham@thepostnewspapers.com, Mng. Ed., The Post Newspapers - Wadsworth, OH, Medina

Farnsworth, Joshua
jfarnsworth@millburysutton.com, Ed., Millbury-Sutton Chronicle, MA, Worcester

Farnsworth, Robert .... (603) 352-1234 Ext. 1803
rfarnsworth@keenesentinel.com , Graph. & Prod. Mgr., The Keene Sentinel, NH, Keene

Farquharson, Lisa
lisa@blackpress.ca, Pub, Langley Advance, BC, Langley
lisa@blackpress.ca, Pub, Langley Times, BC, Langley
lisa@blackpress.ca, Pub, The Aldergrove Star, BC, Aldergrove

Farrah, Bret .... (734) 913-8080
bfarrah@xitron.com, Executive Vice President, Xitron, MI, Ann Arbor

Farrell, Bill .... (845) 437-4738
farrellb@poughkee.gannett.com, Circ. Mgr., Poughkeepsie Journal, NY, Poughkeepsie

Farrell, Bill .... (845) 437-4738
farrellb@poughkee.gannett.com, Board Member, New York State Circulation Managers Association, NY, Poughkeepsie

Farrell, Edward
farrell.edward@thebugle.ca, Circ. Mgr., The Bugle-observer, NB, Woodstock

Farrell, John
stclaircountycourier@gmail.com, Reporter, St. Clair Co. Courier, MO, Osceola

Farrell, John
jfarrell@brodiesystem.com, Prodn. Mgr., Opns., Brodie System, Inc., NJ, Linden

Farrell, John R. .... (908) 709-7550
Vice Pres., Union County College, NJ, Cranford

Farrell, Kathleen
farrelk@slu.edu, Chair/Prof., Saint Louis University, MO, Saint Louis

Farrell, Kevin
texascatholic@msn.com, Pub., The Texas Catholic, TX, Dallas

Farrell, Paul .... (563) 383-2100

paul.farrell@lee.net, Dir. Corp. Sales, Framingham TAB, MA, Framingham
paul.farrell@lee.net, VP, Digital Sales, Lee Enterprises, Inc., IA, Davenport

Farrell, Peter
pgfarrell@newjerseyhills.com, Advertising Sales Representative, New Jersey Hills Media Group, NJ, Whippany

Farrell, Terry .... (778) 225-0029
editor@comoxvalleyrecord.com, Ed., Comox Valley Record, BC, Courtenay

Farrell, Terry
editor@comoxvalleyrecord.com, Ed, North Island Midweek, BC, Courtenay
editor@comoxvalleyrecord.com, Sports Ed., Daily Herald-Tribune, AB, Grande Prairie

Farren, Jeff .... (630) 553-7034
news@kendallcountyrecord.com, Pub., Sandwich Record, IL, Yorkville

Farren, Jeffery A.
news@kendallcountyrecord.com, Pub., Plano Record, IL, Yorkville

Farren, Jeffrey A. .... (630) 553-7034
jfarren@kendallcountyrecord.com, Pub., Kendall County Record, Oswego Ledger, Sandwich Record, Plano Record, IL, Yorkville

Farren, Jeffrey A.
ledgersentinel@sbcglobal.net, Pub., Ledger-Sentinel, IL, Yorkville

Farren, Kathleen M. .... (630) 553-7034
kfarren@kendallcountyrecord.com, Ed., Kendall County Record, Oswego Ledger, Sandwich Record, Plano Record, IL, Yorkville

Farrer, Alex .... (706) 629-2231
AFarrer@calhountimes.com, Sports Ed., Calhoun Times and Gordon County News, GA, Calhoun

Farrer, Fran
publisher@countynews4you.com, Pub., County News, NC, Statesville

Farrey, Patrick
pfarrey@marketing.org, Exec. Dir., Business Marketing Association, IL, Naperville

Farrin, Bruce .... (207) 364-7893 ext 5208
editor@rumfordfallstimes.com, Mng. Ed., Rumford Falls Times, ME, Rumford

Farris, Cathy .... (606) 528-7898 Ext. 45
cfarris@thetimestribune.com, Circ. Mgr., Times-Tribune, KY, Corbin

Farris, Patricia
newsreview@lwvisp.com, Pub., The News Review, CA, Ridgecrest

Farros, Royal
sales@imsisoft.com, Chrmn./CEO, IMSI, CA, Novato

Farrow, Kaye
towncrier@centurytel.net, Ed., The Town Crier, AR, Manila

Farrow, Mandy .... (601) 267-4501
mandy@thecarthaginian.com, advertising director, The Carthaginian, MS, Carthage

Farrugia, Gary .... (860) 701-4202
g.farrugia@theday.com, Pub., The Groton Times, CT, New London
g.farrugia@theday.com, Pub, New London Times, CT, New London
g.farrugia@theday.com, Pub, The Day, CT, New London

Farrugia, Gary .... (860) 701-4202
g.farrugia@theday.com, Pub., The Mystic Times, CT, New London

Farwell, Melodie
mail@cubapatriot.com, Managing Ed., Cuba Patriot & Free Press, NY, Cuba

Fasnacht, Andrew
afasnacht.eph@lnpnews.com, Ed., The Ephrata Review, PA, Ephrata
afasnacht.eph@lnpnews.com, Ed., Lititz Record Express, PA, Ephrata

Fasol, Tara .... **(618) 985-3741**
John A. Logan College, IL, Carterville

Fasselin, Jenni
ads@ecprogress.com, Adv. Dir., Emery County
Progress, UT, Castle Dale

Fasselin, Jenni
jenni.fasselin@sunad.com, Adv. Dir., Sun
Advocate, UT, Price

Fassnacht, Jon
jfassnacht@readingeagle.com, Reading Eagle
Company, PA, Reading

Fastow, Gershon
gershon@jewishweek.org, Adv. Coord., Jewish
Week, NY, New York

Fattahinia, Bahram
bahram.fattahinia@parentingoc.com, Art Dir.,
Parenting Magazine of Orange County, CA,
Orange

Fauci, Jennifer
smosco@antonmediagroup.com, Ed.,
Massapequan Observer, NY, Mineola

Fauci, Jennifer
jfauci@antonmediagroup.com, Ed., Levittown
Tribune, NY, Mineola

Faughender, Jeff .... **(502) 582-4981**
jfau@courier-journal.com, Online Production
Mgr.
, The Courier-Journal, KY, Louisville

Faught, Karen
sabanews@centex.net, Pub./Ed., San Saba
News & Star, TX, San Saba

Faught, Tonya
tfaught@timesjournal.com, Acct Exec, The
Vinton County Courier, OH, Mc Arthur

Faulkner, Alan .... **(931) 363-3544 ext. 118**
alan.faulkner@pulaskicitizen.com, Advertising
Rep, Pulaski Citizen, TN, Pulaski

Faulkner, Beth .... **(519) 537-2341 x515237**
bfaulkner@postmedia.com, Circ., The Norwich
Gazette, ON, Woodstock

Faulkner, J. .... **(860) 576-0291**
james.faulkner@fujifilm.com, Newspaper
Acct. Mgr., NE Reg., Fujifilm North America
Corporation, IL, Hanover Park

Faulkner, Jeramiah .... **(740) 474-3131 Ext. 222**
jfaulkner@circlevilleherald.com, Cir. Mgr., The
Circleville Herald, OH, Circleville

Faulkner, Kari
karifaulkner@thecourier.com, Adv. Mgr., The
Courier, OH, Findlay

Faulkner, Lisa
lfaulkner@lacrossetribune.com, Adv. Mgr., Tri-
county Foxxy Shopper, WI, La Crosse
lfaulkner@lacrossetribune.com, Adv. Mgr., La
Crosse Foxxy Shopper, WI, La Crosse

Faulmann, Bruce .... **(727) 893-8984**
bfaulmann@tampabay.com, VP / Sales
& Marketing, Tampa Bay Times, FL, St
Petersburg

Faust, Lisa
lfaust@theadvertiser.com, Mng. Ed., Times Of
Acadiana, LA, Lafayette

Faust, Ray .... **(612) 673-4899**
ray.faust@startribune.com, VP, National &
Emerging Media
, Star Tribune, MN, Minneapolis

Fausz, Linda
linda@villagenewsonline.com, Pub., Village
News, VA, Chester

Favale, Susanne
sfavale@legalnews.com, Pub., Detroit Legal
News, MI, Troy

Favela, Olivia
info@iptech.com, Vice Pres., Sales/Mktg.,
Information Presentation Tech., CA, San
Luis Obispo

Fawcett, Nicole
nicolefawcett@porthawkesburyreporter.com,

Adv, The Reporter, NS, Port Hawkesbury

Fawkes, Jennifer .... **(707) 256-2244**
jfawkes@napanews.com, Circulation &
Classified Advertising Director, Distinctive
Properties, CA, Napa

Fawley-Martin, Pam
pfawley@journal-news.net, Retail Adv. Mgr.,
The Journal, WV, Martinsburg

Fayander, Fred
ffayander@thevanguard.ca, Pub, The Advance,
NS, Liverpool

Fayander, Fred
ffaynder@transcontinental.ca, Pub., The Coast
Guard, NS, Shelburne

Fazio, Brian .... **(770) 787-6397**
bfazio@covnews.com, Ed., The Covington
News, GA, Covington

Fazzini, Elizabeth
efazzini@dioceseofgreensburg.org, Assistant
Editor, The Catholic Accent, The Catholic
Accent, PA, Greensburg

Feagan, Kent
production@barrieadvance.com, Prodn. Dir.,
Collingwood Connection, ON, Collingwood

Feagans, John .... **(858) 875-5942**
johnf@lajollalight.com, Graphics Mgr., La Jolla
Light, CA, La Jolla

Feagin, Terry .... **(559) 784-5000 Ext. 1015**
tfeagin@portervillerecorder.com, Asst.
Circ. Mgr., The Porterville Recorder, CA,
Porterville

Fears, Lillie
lfears@astate.edu, Assoc. Prof., Arkansas
State University, AR, Jonesboro

Fecco, Patty
fecco@shoppernewsnow.com, Adv. Sales Mgr.,
Halls Shopper News, TN, Knoxville

Fedak, Brenda .... **(618) 239-2550**
bfedak@bnd.com, Adv., Belleville News-
Democrat, IL, Belleville

Feddema, Kristen
mznnews1@mrnews.ca, Ed., The Mile Zero
News, AB, High Level

Fedder, Diane .... **(570) 326-1551**
dfedder@sungazette.com, Nat'l Adv. Mgr.
, Williamsport Sun-Gazette/Lock Haven
Express, PA, South Williamsport

Federoff, Shawna
shawna.federoff@inlandnewspapers.com,
Marketing Dir, The Sun, CA, San Bernardino

Fedor-Cunningham, John
editor@oitm.org, Out in the Mountains, VT,
Benson

Fedoroff, Vince .... **(867) 668-2060**
vince@whitehorsestar.com, Photo Ed.,
Whitehorse Star, YT, Whitehorse

Fedrick, Bill
citydesk@dailychronicle.com, Circ. Mgr., Penny
Pincher, MT, Bozeman

Fedrigon, Dan
inbox@beckart.com, Mgr., Mktg./Sales,
Beckart Environmental, Inc., WI, Kenosha

Fedrigon, Thomas M. ...... **(262) 656-7680 ext. 115**
tfedrigon@beckart.com, Pres., Beckart
Environmental, Inc., WI, Kenosha

Fedrizzi, Nina
editor@otherpapersbvt.com, Mng. Ed., The
Other Paper, VT, South Burlington

Fee, Frank .... **(919) 962-4071**
Assoc. Prof., University of North Carolina, NC,
Chapel Hill

Fee, John .... **(973) 210-6393**
jfee@lds.com, Vice Pres., Sales, Logical
Design Solutions, Inc., NJ, Florham Park

Fee, John
mstar@bigriver.net, Pub., The Bluejacket, TN,
Millington

Feeney, Caroline
caroline@inman.com, Assoc. Ed., Inman
News, Emeryville

Feeney, Chris
chris@memphisdemocrat.com, Ed., Memphis
Democrat, MO, Memphis

Feeney, Joe .... **(336) 888-3537**
jfeeney@hpenews.com, City Editor, High Point
Enterprise, NC, High Point

Feeney, Tom .... **(352) 563-3275**
tfeeney@chronicleonline.com, Prodn. Mgr.,
Citrus County Chronicle, FL, Crystal River

Fegley, Mariel
news@rcleader.com, Ed., Rock County Leader,
NE, Bassett

Feher, James .... **(610) 778-2277**
james.feher@mcall.com, Vice Pres., Direct
Marketing Distribution, PA, Allentown

Feher, Jim .... **(610) 778-2212**
james.feher@mcall.com, VP, Adv., The Morning
Call, PA, Allentown

Fehlinger, Will .... **(765) 825-0588 ext. 232**
wfehlinger@newsexaminer.com, Reporter,
Connersville News-Examiner, IN,
Connersville

Fehlinger, Will .... **(812) 934-4343**
sports@batesvilleheraldtribune.com, sports
writer, The Herald-Tribune, IN, Batesville

Fehr, Janice .... **(780) 429-5159**
Digital Ad. Delivery Tech., Edmonton Journal,
AB, Edmonton

Feider, Gary
editor@thesounder.com, Ed., The Sounder, WI,
Random Lake

Feiler, Missy .... **(608) 478-2517**
mfeiler@hngnews.com, Adv Mgr, The Star, WI,
Sun Prairie

Feiler, Missy .... **(608) 478-2517**
mfeiler@hngnews.com, Advertising Manager,
Lodi Enterprise & Poynette Press, WI, Lodi

Feiler, Missy .... **(608) 478-2517**
mfeiler@hngnews.com, Advertising Manager,
The Lake Mills Leader, WI, Lake Mills

Feiler, Missy .... **(608) 478-2517**
mfeiler@hngnews.com, Advertising Manager,
The Waterloo/Marshall Courier, WI, Waterloo

Fein, Chris
cfein@rochester-citynews.com, News Editor,
City Newspaper, NY, Rochester

Feinberg, Terry
editorial@elsoln1.com, Gen. Mgr., El Sol, CA,
Salinas

Feinblatt, Rick
gmntnews@gmnews.com, Pub., News
Transcript, NJ, Manalapan

Feineman, Carol
carolf@goldcountrymedia.com, Pub., Colfax
Record, CA, Colfax

Feineman, Carol .... **(916) 774-7972**
carolf@goldcountrymedia.com, Ed, Lincoln
News Messenger, CA, Lincoln

Feisal, Marcia
mfeisal@snu.edu, Yearbook, Southern
Nazarene Univ., OK, Bethany

Feiss, Kristi .... **(816) 380-3228**
kfeiss@demo-mo.com, Ad Manager, Cass
County Democrat-Missourian, MO,
Harrisonville

Feit, Laura .... **(608) 755-9433**
lfeit@gazettextra.com, Director of Digital
Advertising, The Gazette - gazettextra.com,
WI, Janesville

Feitl, Steve .... **(732) 643-4227**
sfeitl@gannettnj.com, Sports Ed., Home News
Tribune, NJ, Somerville

Feld, Karen .... **(202) 337-2044**
karen@karenfeld.com, Owner/Editor, Capital

Connections, Washington

Feld, Terry .... **(505) 823-3834**
tfeld@abqjournal.com, Bus. Edit. Asst.,
Albuquerque Journal, NM, Albuquerque

Feldman, Aliya
afeldman@arkansasleader.com, Ed., The
Leader, AR, Jacksonville

Feldman, Brad
studios@nypost.com, Post Studios & Creative
Services, New York Post, NY, New York

Feldman, David
aaldrich@projects.sdsu.edu, Lectr., San Diego
State University, CA, San Diego

Feldman, Eileen
efeldman@arkansasleader.com, Exec. Ed.,
The Leader, AR, Jacksonville

Feldman, Garrick .... **(501) 982-9421**
gfeldman@arkansasleader.com, Ed. / Pub.,
The Leader, AR, Jacksonville

Feldman, Jeremy .... **(520) 515-4640**
jeremy.feldman@svherald.com, Circ. Mgr.,
Sierra Vista Herald - Sunday Bravo Shopper,
AZ, Sierra Vista

Feldman, Joseph .... **(773) 927-0025**
JRBridgeportNews@aol.com, Pub., Bridgeport
News, IL, Chicago

Feldman, Steve
support@mlog.com, Exec. Vice Pres.,
Worldwide Sales, Microlog Corp., MD,
Gaithersburg

Feliciano, Arnold . **(352) 374-5055 - Call in results:**
(352) 374-5074
felicia@gvillesun.com, Sports Ed., The
Gainesville Sun, FL, Gainesville

Felicissimo, Paul
pfelicissimo@gatehousemedia.com, VP
Circulation/Consumer Marketing, GateHouse
Media, Inc., NY, Pittsford

Felix, Debbie .... **(812) 523-7054**
DFelix@TribTown.com, Business Office, The
Tribune, IN, Seymour

Felkins, Jared .... **(615) 444-3952**
jfelkins@lebanondemocrat.com, Editor, The
Lebanon Democrat, TN, Lebanon

Fell, Chris .... **(519) 538-1421**
newsroom@simcoe.com, Community Events,
Express, ON, Meaford

Fellers, Kent
arrow@arrowprintco.com, Pres., Arrow Printing
Co., KS, Salina

Fellone, Frank
ffellone@arkansasonline.com, Part-time Lectr.,
University of Arkansas at Little Rock, AR,
Little Rock

Fellows, Betsy
ahathcock@metropolisplanet.com, Gen. Mgr.,
Metropolis Planet, IL, Metropolis

Fellows, Jody
jfellows@fcnp.com, Mng. Ed., Falls Church
News-Press, VA, Falls Church

Felsberg, Jay
news@genevareaper.com, Ed., Geneva
County Reaper, AL, Geneva
news@genevareaper.com, Ed., Hartford News-
Herald, AL, Geneva
news@genevareaper.com, Ed., Samson
Ledger, AL, Geneva

Felten, Bob
bfelten@sierracapital.net, Asst. Prof., University
of Nevada-Reno, NV, Reno

Felten, Ralph
rfelten@asltg2.com, Mgr., Atlas Specialty
Lighting, FL, Tampa

Feltes, Mike .... **(815) 561-2124**
mike@oglecountylife.com, Gen. Mgr., Ashton
Gazette, IL, Ashton
mike@oglecountylife.com, Prodn. Mgr.,
Pressroom, The Latrobe Bulletin, PA, Latrobe

Feltman, Betty..........................(701) 780-1161
bfeltman@gfherald.com, Adv. Mgr., Grand
Forks Herald, ND, Grand Forks

Felton, Cortney
cfelton@muncie.gannett.com, Account Mgr.,
The Star Press, IN, Muncie

Felton, Patrick
feltonpa@wvstateu.edu, West Virginia State
Univ., WV, Institute

Felts, Laura
laura@pioneernews.net, Adv. Sales Rep.,
Pioneer News, KY, Shepherdsville
laura@pioneernews.net, Pioneer News, KY,
Shepherdsville

Felts, Todd
mfelts@unr.edu, Asst. Prof., University of
Nevada-Reno, NV, Reno

Felts, Tommy
tfelts@ottawaherald.com, Ed./Pub., The Ottawa
Herald, KS, Ottawa

Fennell, Dan..........................(724) 223-2633
dfennell@observer-reporter.com, Systems
Mgr., Observer-Reporter, PA, Washington

Fennell, Greg
gfennell@vnews.com, Sports Ed., Valley News,
NH, West Lebanon

Fennell, Ian..........................(208) 232-4161
ifennell@journalnet.com, Mng. Ed., Portneuf
Valley Trader, ID, Pocatello

Fennicks, Annmarie
adservices2@dailygazette.net, Adv. Suprv.,
The Daily Gazette, NY, Schenectady

Fenske, Bruce..............(507) 359-2911 ext. 130
bfenske@nujournal.com, Pub., The Journal,
MN, New Ulm

Fenske, Sarah..........................(314) 754-6407
sarah.fenske@riverfronttimes.com, Editor in
Chief, The Riverfront Times, MO, Saint Louis

Fenstermaker, Susan
susan@newspapersystems.com, VP of
Finance and HR, Software Consulting
Services, LLC, PA, Nazareth

Fenter, Nancy..........................(903) 473-2653
subscription@rainscountyleader.com, Circ.
Mgr., Rains County Leader, TX, Emory

Fenton, Angie
angie@voice-tribune.com, Ed., The Voice-
Tribune, KY, Louisville

Fenton, Kevin
kfenton@reviewonline.com, Cir. Mgr., The
Review, OH, East Liverpool

Fenton, Lois..........................(914) 698-0721)
lois.fenton@prodigy.net, Columnist/Advice,
Men's Business & Social Dress Consultant/
Men's Personal Shopper, Blogger, Male Call,
Mamaroneck

Feorino, Lu R...........................(413) 788-1216
lfeorino@repub.com, City Ed., Night, The
Republican, MA, Springfield

Fera, Brett..........................(520) 621-1714
bfera@email.arizona.edu, Asst. Dir., Univ. of
Arizona, AZ, Tucson

Ferdon, Douglas
doug_ferdon@baylor.edu, Assoc. Prof., Baylor
University, TX, Waco

Ferencak, Dawn..........................(708) 613-3329
dawn@oakpark.com, Advertising Manager,
Landmark, IL, Oak Park

Fergusen, Keith..........................(508) 921-1857
keith@walpoletimes.com, Ed., The Walpole
Times, MA, Walpole

Ferguson, Carly
publisher@theprogress.com, Pub., The
Agassiz-harrison Observer, BC, Agassiz

Ferguson, Carly..........................(604) 869-2421
publisher@hopestandard.com, Pub., Hope
Standard, BC, Hope

Ferguson, Carly
carly.ferguson@blackpress.ca, Pub, Mission
City Record, BC, Mission
carly.ferguson@blackpress.ca, Pub, The
Abbotsford News, BC, Abbotsford

Ferguson, Carly
publisher@theprogress.com, Pub., The
Chilliwack Progress, BC, Chilliwack

Ferguson, Carol
cferguson@heraldbanner.com, Features Ed.,
Herald-Banner, TX, Greenville

Ferguson, Carole..........................(530) 225-8232
cferguson@redding.com, Mng. Ed., Record
Searchlight, CA, Redding

Ferguson, Catherine
cferguson@express-news.net, VP of Marketing,
San Antonio Express-News, TX, San Antonio

Ferguson, Chad..........................(979) 732-6243
bannercolumbus@sbcglobal.net, Pub./Ed.,
The Banner Press Newspaper, TX, Columbus

Ferguson, Denise P.
denise.ferguson@indwes.edu, Chair, Indiana
Wesleyan University, IN, Marion

Ferguson, Gary..........................(606) 337-2333
news@pinevillesun.net, Ed., Pineville Sun, KY,
Pineville

Ferguson, Jason
custernews@gwtc.net, Gen. Mgr., Western
Trader, SD, Custer

Ferguson, Jason
custernews@gwtc.net, Gen. Mgr., Custer
County Chronicle, SD, Custer

Ferguson, John
john.ferguson@baledger.com, Ed, Broken
Arrow Ledger, OK, Tulsa

Ferguson, Karen..........................(317) 444-4000
k.ferguson@indystar.com, Pres./Pub., The
Indianapolis Star, IN, Indianapolis

Ferguson, London..........................(979) 732-6243
london1214@sbcglobal.net, Classified Sales,
The Banner Press Newspaper, TX, Columbus

Ferguson, Lucy
orchardnews@juno.com, Prodn. Mgr., The
Orchard News, NE, Orchard

Ferguson, Mary
mferguson@chespub.com, Circ. Mgr., The
Avenue News, MD, Dundalk

Ferguson, Ramona..........................(979) 732-6243
banneroffice@sbcglobal.net, Bookkeeper, The
Banner Press Newspaper, TX, Columbus

Ferguson, Rusty..........................(918) 358-2553
news@theclevelandamerican.com, Pub./Ed.,
The Cleveland American, OK, Cleveland

Ferguson, Samantha
samantha.ferguson@sandspringsleader.com,
Mktg., Sand Springs Leader, OK, Tulsa

Ferguson , Sarag............(905) 871-3100 ext. 207
sarah.ferguson@sunmedia.ca, Ed., The Fort
Erie Times, ON, Fort Erie

Ferlazzo, Don
dferlazzo@nynpa.com, Dir. of Adv. &
Event Mgmt., New York News Publishers
Association, NY, Albany

Ferlet-Helton, Kristy
kferlet@wacotrib.com, Nat'l Sales Rep., Waco
Tribune-Herald, TX, Waco

Fern, Matthew..........................(207) 942-2901
msfern@themaineedge.com, Adv./Ops. Mgr.,
The Maine Edge, ME, Bangor

Fern, Michael..........................(207) 942-2901
mfern@themaineedge.com, Pub., The Maine
Edge, ME, Bangor

Fernandes, Gregg
gregg.fernandes@washpost.com, Vice
President, The Washington Post, DC,
Washington

Fernandez, Carolyn

carolyn@northcoastjournal.com, Circ. Mgr,
North Coast Journal, CA, Eureka

Fernandez, Franco..........................(202) 898-8000
ffernandez@upi.com, Business Manager,
United Press International, Boca Raton

Fernandez, Frank
frank.fernandez@news-jrnl.com, Mng. Ed./
Bureau Chief, Daytona Beach News-Journal,
FL, Daytona Beach

Fernandez, Joe
jfernandez@mdjonline.com, VP, Productions,
Cherokee Tribune, GA, Canton

Fernandez, Luis
lfernandez@readingeagle.com, Reading Eagle
Company, PA, Reading

Fernandez, Lynne..........................(209) 588-4573
lfernandez@uniondemocrat.com, Bus. Mgr.,
The Union Democrat, CA, Sonora

Fernandez, Phil..........................(941) 206-1168
pfernandez@sun-herald.com, Ed., Charlotte
Sun, FL, Punta Gorda

Fernandez, Willie..........................(954) 356-4178
WFernandez@sun-sentinel.com, Managing
Ed., South Florida Sun-Sentinel, FL, Fort
Lauderdale

Ferolie, James..........................(608) 845-9559
veronapress@wcinet.com, Group Ed., The
Verona Press, WI, Verona

Ferolie, Jim..........................(608) 845-9559
stoughtoneditor@wcinet.com, Group Ed.,
Stoughton Courier Hub, WI, Stoughton

Ferolie, Jim
stoughtoneditor@wcinet.com, Ed., The
Fitchburg Star, WI, Verona

Ferolie, Jim..........................(608) 845-9559
ungeditor@wcinet.com, Group Ed., Oregon
Observer, WI, Oregon

Ferrand Bullock, Cathy..............(435) 797-1412
Assoc. Prof., Utah State University, UT, Logan

Ferrara, Geri..........................(304) 291-9447
editor@dominionpost.com, Editor, The
Dominion Post, WV, Morgantown

Ferrari, Jerrod..........................(203) 330-6582
jferrari@hearstmediact.com, Ed., Darien News,
CT, Bridgeport
jferrari@hearstmediact.com, Ed., Fairfield
Citizen, CT, Bridgeport
jferrari@hearstmediact.com, Ed., Westport
News, CT, Bridgeport
jferrari@hearstmediact.com, Ed., New Canaan
News, CT, Bridgeport

Ferrari, Steven
editor@queenstribune.com, Ed., The Press of
Southeast Queens, NY, Whitestone

Ferrell, Jennifer..........................(202) 334-5042
jennifer.ferrell@washpost.com, Sales Rep.,
North America, The Washington Post Writers
Group, Washington

Ferrell , Scott..........................(318) 459-3299
sferrell@gannett.com, Sports Planning Ed. ,
The Times, LA, Shreveport

Ferrello, Sherry
sferrello@express-times.com, HR, The
Express-Times, PA, Easton

Ferri, John
mitch@thestar.com, Asst. Mng. Ed.,
Entertainment/Life, Toronto Star, ON, Toronto

Ferriell, Stephanie..........................(812) 883-3281
stephanie@salemleader.com, Senior Editor,
The Salem Democrat, IN, Salem

Ferris, Tim..........................(315) 282-2270
Tim.Ferris@lee.net, The Citizen, Auburn, NY,
Auburn

Ferro, Dave..........................(517) 437-7351
david.ferro@hillsdale.net, general manager,
Tip-off Shopping Guide, MI, Hillsdale

Ferro, David
david.ferro@hillsdale.net, Pub./ Gen. Mgr.,

Hillsdale Daily News, MI, Hillsdale

Ferro, David..........................(517) 278-2318
dferro@thedailyreporter.com, Pub., Register-
Tribune, MI, Coldwater

Ferrotta, Mauro
mferrott@lohud.com, Circ. Mgr., Single Copy,
The Journal News, NY, White Plains

Ferrucci, Patrick..........................(203) 789-5678
news@nhregister.com, Entertainment Ed.,
New Haven Register, CT, New Haven

Ferrufino, Gabriella..........................(202) 334-4512
gabriella.ferrufino@washpost.com, Marketing
Representative/Midwest & West, Washington
Post News Service with Bloomberg News,
Washington

Ferry, John
jferry@mtexpress.com, Adv. Dir., Idaho
Mountain Express, ID, Ketchum

Ferstel, Vicki..........................(225) 388-0641
vferstel@theadvocate.com, Night Metro Editor,
The Advocate, LA, Baton Rouge

Fertal, Bridget..........................(717) 669-0703
bridget.fertal@stvincent.edu, Editor-in-Chief,
Saint Vincent College, PA, Latrobe

Ferugean, Carmen..........................(215) 354-3075
cferugean@bsmphilly.com, Adv. Sales Rep.,
Star Community Newsweekly, PA, Bensalem

Fessard, Olya..........................(478) 471-7393
olyafessard@gmail.com, Ed. in Chief, Georgia
Family Magazine, GA, Macon

Festi, Rick
rfesti@alonovus.com, Circ. Mgr., Tuscarawas
Bargain Hunter, OH, Millersburg
rfesti@alonovus.com, Circulation Mgr, The
Bargain Hunter - Holmes, OH, Millersburg
rfesti@alonovus.com, Circulation Mgr,
The Bargain Hunter - Tuscarawas, OH,
Millersburg
rfesti@alonovus.com, Circ. Mgr., Wooster
Weekly News, OH, Millersburg

Festo, Chris
ads@willistonpioneer.com, Graphic Designer,
Williston Pioneer Sun News, FL, Williston

Fett, Samantha..................(515) 244-2145 x 126
sfett@cnaads.com, Inside Sales Mgr., Iowa
Newspaper Association, Inc., IA, Des Moines

Fetter, Donnie..........................(706) 208-2227
donnie.fetter@onlineathens.com, Managing
Ed., Athens Banner-Herald, GA, Athens

Fetter, Mark
mfetter@richmondpublishing.com, Pub., Fifty
Plus, VA, Richmond

Fetter, William
william.fetter@hexagonmetrology.com, Adv.
Mgr., Hexagon Metrology, Inc., RI, North
Kingstown

Fetterhoff, Charlie..........................(870) 777-8841
Asst. Circ. Mgr., Arkadelphia Siftings Herald,
AR, Arkadelphia

Fetterolf, Judy..........................(717) 273-8127
judyf@aboutfamiliespa.com, Publication
Coord., About Families Parenting
Newspaper, PA, Lebanon

Fettin, Carol..........................(308) 233-9727
Religion Ed., Kearney Hub, NE, Kearney

Feuer, Dan..........................(501) 884-6012
editor@lakeareaweekly.com, Mng. Ed., Lake
Area Weekly, AR, Fairfield Bay

Feuerherd, Joe
jfeuerherd@ncronline.org, Ed. in Chief,
National Catholic Reporter, MO, Kansas City

Feuling, Dan..........................(641) 394-2111
nhpublisher@mchsi.com, Pub., New Hampton
Shopper, IA, New Hampton

Feumba, Angeline..........................(306) 347-0481
adjoint@myaccess.ca, Administrative
Assistant, Eau Vive (l'), SK, Regina

Feusse, Carl..........................(989) 275-5911

KFEUSSE@HOTMAIL.COM, Copy Ed., Detroit Free Press, MI, Detroit

Fevola, Nannette
nannette.fevola@am-ny.com, National Sales Mktg Dir.
, amNew York, NY, New York

Few, Jenel .... (912) 652-0345
jenel.few@savannah.com, Educ. Reporter, Savannah Morning News, GA, Savannah

Fey, J.T. .... (605) 886-6901
Online Mgr., Watertown Public Opinion, SD, Watertown

Feyerabend, Debbie
debbie.feyerabend@latimes.com, Bus. Mgr., Times Community News (TCN), CA, Los Angeles

Fiander, Fred
fred.fiander@tc.tc, Pub, The Vanguard, NS, Yarmouth

Fiander, Fred
ffiander@thevanguard.com, Pub., Register, NS, Kentville

Fiander, Fred
info@annapolisspectator.ca, Pub., The Spectator, NS, Middleton

Fiander, Fred
ffiander@thevanguard.ca, Pub., The Advertiser, NS, Kentville

Ficarra, Mark .... (619) 293-1110
mark.ficarra@sduniontribune.com, Sr. VP, The San Diego Union-Tribune, CA, San Diego

Ficarro, Charles .... (570) 853-3134
susqtran@epix.net, Ed., Susquehanna County Transcript, PA, Susquehanna

Ficcaglia, Jennifer
newsroom@catholiccourier.com, Asst. Ed., Catholic Courier, NY, Rochester

Fichaud, Robert
robert.fichaud@monteregieweb.com, Pub./Dir., Le Reflet, QC, Delson
robert.fichaud@monteregieweb.com, Le Soleil Du Mercredi, QC, Chateauguay

Fichter, Jack
Cmstarwave@comcast.net, Ed., Cape May Star and Wave, NJ, West Cape May

Fichter, Robin .... (973) 383-1170
rfichter@njherald.com, HR & Admin. Ass., New Jersey Herald, NJ, Newton

Fickling, Phyllis
pfickling@tri-statedefender.com, Gen. Mgr., Tri State Defender, TN, Memphis

Fidel, Steve .... (801) 422-2958
steve.fidel@byu.edu, Director, Brigham Young University, UT, Provo

Fideldy, Rachelle .... (620) 694-5700 Ext. 232
rfideldy@hutchnews.com, Inside Sales Mgr., The Hutchinson News, KS, Hutchinson

Fidler, Chris .... (308) 882-4453
Prodn. Mgr., Imperial Republican, NE, Imperial

Fidler, Eric J. .... ext. 247
Southern Illinois Univ., IL, Carbondale

Fiedler, David .... ext. 5039
david.fiedler@TheSouthern.com, MIS Mgr., At Home With Flipside, IL, Carbondale

Fiege, Robert .... (904) 261-3696
rfiege@fbnewsleader.com, Prodn. Dir., News-Leader, FL, Fernandina Beach

Fiege, Robert
rfiege@nassaucountyrecord.com, Prodn. Dir., Nassau County Record, FL, Callahan

Fiegle, Doug .... (716) 773-7634
sales@nrdinc.com, Pres./CEO, NRD LLC, NY, Grand Island

Field, Angie .... (815) 244-2411
afield@grics.net, Reporter/Adv. Rep., Carroll County Mirror-Democrat, IL, Mount Carroll

Field, Malena .... (915) 546-6254

mfield@elpasotimes.com, Dir., HR, El Paso Times, TX, El Paso
mfield@elpasotimes.com, Dir., HR, El Paso y Mas, TX, El Paso

Field, Mike
mfield@amisun.com, Publisher, Editor, Anna Maria Island Sun, FL, Anna Maria

Fielder, Jeff
sports@starherald.com, Ed. , Gering Courier, NE, Scottsbluff
sports@starherald.com, Sports Ed., Star-Herald, NE, Scottsbluff

Fields, Becky
office@heraldledger.com, Office Mgr., The Herald-Ledger, KY, Eddyville

Fields, Connie .... (703) 303-8713
cfields@insidenova.com, Sales Mgr., Northern Virginia Media Services, VA, Leesburg
cfields@insidenova.com, Adv. Mgr., InsideNoVa/Prince William, VA, Woodbridge

Fields, Marlene
mrfields@pcwan.net, Pub./Adv. Dir./Managing Ed., Shidler Review, OK, Shidler

Fields, Rhonda
rhonda@auburnvillager.com, Accts. Mgr., Auburn Villager, AL, Auburn

Fields, Tonya .... (703) 771-8831
tfields@insidenova.com, Class. Sales Mgr., Northern Virginia Media Services, VA, Leesburg

Fien, Karen .... (585) 352-3411 ext. 128
info@westsidenewsny, Production manager, Suburban News South, NY, Spencerport

Fien, Karen .... (585) 352-3411 ext. 128
info@westsidenewsny, Production manager, Suburban News West, NY, Spencerport

Fien, Karen .... (585) 352-3411 x128
info@westsidenewsny, Production manager, Suburban News North, NY, Spencerport

Fien, Karen .... (585) 352-3411 x128
info@westsidenewsny, Ad. & Production Manager, Hamlin Clarkson Herald, NY, Spencerport

Fienup, Jim .... (918) 962-3531
spirographic@sbcglobal.net, Pub., Spiro Graphic, OK, Spiro

Fierstine, Terri
tfierstine@pilotindependent.com, Gen. Mgr., The Pilot-Independent, MN, Walker

Figeat, Jean .... (780) 998-7070
jean.figeat@sunmedia.ca, Pub., The Fort Saskatchewan Record, AB, Fort Saskatchewan

Figeat, Jean .... (780) 929-6632
jean.figeat@sunmedia.ca, Adv. Dir., La Nouvelle Beaumont News, AB, Beaumont

Figeat, Jean .... (780) 468-0343
jean.figeat@sunmedia.ca, Retail Adv. Mgr., The Edmonton Sun, AB, Edmonton

Figeat, Jean .... (780) 990-9516
jfigeat@postmedia.com, Adv. Dir., Sherwood Park/strathcona County News, AB, Sherwood Park
jfigeat@postmedia.com, Adv. Dir, Devon Dispatch News, AB, Devon

Figueira, Matt .... (780) 852-4888
advertising@fitzhugh.ca, Sales, The Fitzhugh, AB, Jasper

Figueroa, Maria Laura .... (786) 286-8787
patrianews@aol.com, Gen. Mgr., El Nuevo PATRIA, FL, Miami

Fike, Brenda
bfike@socket.net, News Ed., Mexico Ledger, MO, Mexico

Fike, David .... (410) 770-4040
dfike@chespub.com, Vice. Pres./Pub., The

Avenue News, MD, Dundalk

Fike, David
dfike@chespub.com, Pub., Queen Anne's Record Observer, MD, Centreville
dfike@chespub.com, VP/Pub., Kent County News, MD, Chestertown

Fike, David .... (443) 245-5054
dfike@chespub.com, Pub., Cecil Whig, MD, Elkton

Fike, David .... (410) 770-4040
dfike@chespub.com, VP/Pub, The Bay Times, MD, Chester

Fike, David .... (410) 770-4040
stardem@chespub.com, Pres./Pub., The Star-Democrat, MD, Easton

Fike, David .... (410) 770-4040
dfike@chespub.com, Pres. & Pub., Adams Publishing Group, LLC, MN, Virginia

Fike, Kevin A. .... (410) 770-4113
kfike@chespub.com, Circ. Dir., The Star-Democrat, MD, Easton

Filby, Marc
mfilby@townnews.com, Sr. Tech. Sales Rep., TownNews.com, IL, Moline

Filipek, Kori .... (562) 938-4284
Long Beach City College, CA, Long Beach

Filliat, Arnaud
afilliat@mymail.mines.edu, Copy Editor, Colorado School of Mines, CO, Golden

Fillmore, Ken .... (260) 665-3117 Ext. 2143
kfillmore@kpcmedia.com, Sports Ed., The Herald Republican, IN, Angola

Filloramo, Charlotte Ann .... (256) 740-5763
charlotte-ann.filloramo@timesdaily.com, Controller, Times Daily, AL, Florence

Fils, Manny .... (770) 483-7108 ext. 238
manny.fils@newtoncitizen.com, Sports Ed., The Rockdale Citizen, GA, Conyers

Finazzo, Sam
newsroom@chronotype.com, Managing Ed., Rice Lake Chronotype, WI, Rice Lake

Finch, Bill .... (251) 434-8535
bfinch@mobileregister.com, Growth/Environmental Ed., Press-Register, AL, Mobile

Finch, Nicholas
nicholas.finch@demopolistimes.com, Sports Ed. & Staff Writer, Blackbelt Gazette, AL, Demopolis

Finch, Rhonda .... (434) 394-0403
rhonda.finch@farmvilleherald.com; rhonda.finch@kenbridgevictoriadispatch.com, Circ. Mgr., The Farmville Herald, VA, Farmville
rhonda.finch@farmvilleherald.com; rhonda.finch@kenbridgevictoriadispatch.com, Circ. Dir., The Charlotte Gazette, VA, Drakes Branch
rhonda.finch@farmvilleherald.com; rhonda.finch@kenbridgevictoriadispatch.com, Circ. Dir., The Kenbridge-Victoria Dispatch, VA, Victoria

Finch, Tony .... (662) 720-7304
tfinch@nemcc.edu, Northeast Mississippi Community College, MS, Booneville

Fincher, Brenda .... (208) 587-3331
bfincher@mountainhomenews.com, Business Manager, Mountain Home Patriot, ID, Mountain Home

Fincher, Brenda
bfincher@mountainhomenews.com, Publisher, Mountain Home News, ID, Mountain Home

Finder, Christian
finder@ppimedia.de, Sales Mgr., ppi Media GmbH, Hamburg

Findley, Jeff .... (229) 246-2827 x110
jeff.findley@thepostsearchlight.com, Pub., The Post-Searchlight, GA, Bainbridge

Findley, Jeff .... (229) 246-2827 ext. 110

jeff.findley@thepostsearchlight.com, Adv. Mgr., Post-searchlight Extra, GA, Bainbridge

Fine, M.J. .... (856) 486-2418
mjfine@gannettnj.com, Regional Comm. Ed., The Courier-Post, NJ, Cherry Hill

Fine, Neal .... (650) 223-6583
nfine@embarcaderomediagroup.com, Real Estate Sales Manager, The Almanac, CA, Menlo Park

Finefrock, Ray .... (540) 351-0487
rfinefrock@timespapers.com, Virginia New Group, VA, Leesburg

Finger, Tom .... (608) 767-3655 ext. 234
tfinger@newspubinc.com, CFO/Controller, Spring Green Home News, WI, Spring Green
tfinger@newspubinc.com, Controller/CFO, News Publishing, Co., Inc., WI, Black Earth

Fingeroot, Randy .... (850) 599-2141
rfingeroot@tallahassee.com, Prepress, Postpress, IT Mgr, Tallahassee Democrat, FL, Tallahassee

Fink, Beverly .... (419) 739-3501
circulation@wapakwdn.com, Circ. Mgr., Auglaize Merchandiser, OH, Wapakoneta

Fink, Katherine
kfink@pace.edu, Pace Univ., NY, Pleasantville

Fink, Tom .... (918) 341-0220
tfink@claremoreprogress.com, Staff Writer, The Claremore Daily Progress, OK, Claremore

Finke, Kris .... (520) 836-7461
kfinke@pinalcentral.com, Circulation Manager, Casa Grande Valley Newspapers Inc., AZ, Casa Grande

Finke, Rainer 49 40 4113-32310
finke.rainer@dpa.com, English Correspondent International Marketing and Sales Head, Deutsche Presse-Agentur (dpa), New York

Finkelstein, Ed .... (314) 535-9660
ed@labortribune.com, Publisher, St. Louis/Southern Illinois Labor Tribune, MO, Saint Louis

Finken, Zach .... (312) 527-8756
zfinken@tronc.com, Assoc. Ed., Tribune News Service, Chicago

Finkle, Phil
pfinkle@registerstar.com, Data Processing Mgr., The Daily Mail, NY, Hudson

Finklea, Betsy .... ext. 11
bf@thedillonherald.com, Pub./Ed., The Dillon Herald, SC, Dillon

Finley, Denis .... (802) 651-4853
dfinley@freepressmedia.com, Executive Editor, The Burlington Free Press, VT, Burlington

Finley, Laurie .... (204) 697-7164
laurie.finley@freepress.mb.ca, Pub/Gen. Mgr., The Carillon, MB, Steinbach
laurie.finley@freepress.mb.ca, VP Sales and Marketing, Winnipeg Free Press, MB, Winnipeg

Finley, Maris .... (520) 319-1112, ext. 136
maris@azjewishpost.com, Account Executive, Arizona Jewish Post, AZ, Tucson

Finley, Nolan .... (313) 222-2064
nfinley@detroitnews.com, Editorial Pg. Ed., The Detroit News, MI, Detroit
nfinley@detroitnews.com, Editorial Page Editor, Detroit Free Press, MI, Detroit

Finley, Ryan
rfinley@azstarnet.com, High School Sports Ed., Arizona Daily Star, AZ, Tucson

Finley, Skip
sfinley@mvgazette.com, Director of Sales and Marketing, Vineyard Gazette, MA, Edgartown

Finley, Stephani
sfinley@crestonnews.com, Mng. Ed, Southwest Iowa Advertiser, IA, Creston

Finn, Jeff
jfinn@esoft.com, CEO/Pres., eSoft, CO,

Capital-Journal, KS, Topeka

Fitch, Cynthia
cfitch@lasvegasoptic.com, Advertising Manager
, Las Vegas Optic, NM, LAS VEGAS

Fitch, Kim
kfitch@advertisergleam.com, Gen. Mgr, The Advertiser-Gleam, AL, Guntersville

Fitton, Mark .... **ext. 5807**
mark.fitton@thesouthern.com, Mng. Ed., At Home With Flipside, IL, Carbondale

FitzPatrick, Joel
fitz@greercitizen.com, Ed., The Greer Citizen, SC, Greer

Fitzgerald, Debra
editor@pipestonestar.com, Ed., Pipestone County Star, MN, Pipestone

Fitzgerald, Mark
mfitzgerald@inlandpress.org, Ed., Inland Press Association, IL, Des Plaines

Fitzgerald, Megan
alumni@medaille.edu, Medaille College, NY, Buffalo

Fitzgerald, Mike .... **(618) 239-2533**
mfitzgerald@bnd.com, Newsroom, Belleville News-Democrat, IL, Belleville

Fitzgerald, Pat
pfitzgerald@greene-news.com, Ed., The Greene County Record, VA, Stanardsville

Fitzgerald, Shane
sfitzgerald@thebct.com, Executive Editor, Burlington County Times, NJ, Willingboro

Fitzgerald, Shane .... **(361) 886-3688**
fitzgeralds@caller.com, Ed., Corpus Christi Caller-Times, TX, Corpus Christi

Fitzgerald, Suzanne
sparks@rowan.edu, Assoc. Prof., Rowan Univ., NJ, Glassboro

Fitzhenry, James
jfitzhen@oshkosh.gannett.com, Post-Crescent, WI, Appleton

Fitzhenry, Jim .... **(920) 426-6672**
Mng. Ed., Oshkosh Northwestern, WI, Oshkosh

Fitzmorris, Dave
dfitzmorris@chasemediagroup.com, Vice President & COO, Pennysaver, NY, Yorktown Heights

Fitzpatrick, Alexis ....**(765) 342-3311 ext. 4412**
afitzpatrick@reporter-times.com, Managing Ed., The Mooresville-Decatur Times, IN, Martinsville
afitzpatrick@reporter-times.com, News Ed., Reporter, The Reporter Times, IN, Martinsville

Fitzpatrick, Brent
pub@sasktel.net, Pub., The Tisdale Recorder, SK, Tisdale
pub@sasktel.net, Group Publisher, East Central Trader, SK, Humboldt

Fitzpatrick, Brent
pub@southcal.net, Ed., Parkland Review, SK, Tisdale

Fitzpatrick, Debbie
dfitzpatrick@moberlymonitor.com, Office Mgr., The Moberly Monitor-Index, MO, Moberly

Fitzpatrick, Tim.........................**(801) 257-8726**
fitz@sltrib.com, Administration - Deputy Editor, Editorial Page Editor, The Salt Lake Tribune, UT, Salt Lake City

Fitzsimmons, Cal .... **(509) 665-1176**
fitzsimmons@wenatcheeworld.com, Ed., The Wenatchee World, WA, Wenatchee

Fitzsimmons, Marcus .... **(865) 981-1141**
marcusf@thedailytimes.com, Sports Ed., The Daily Times, TN, Maryville

Fitzsimmons, Sylvia .... **(763) 425-3323**
sylvia.fitzsimmons@ecm-inc.com, Circ. Mgr, Press and News Publications, MN, Osseo

sylvia.fitzsimmons@ecm-inc.com, Circ. Mgr, Monticello Times, MN, Monticello

Fitzsimons, Michael
mfitz@desknetinc.com, Co-CEO, DeskNet, Inc., NJ, Jersey City

Fix, Bridget
advertising@kootenayadvertiser.com, Prod. Mgr., Kootenay Advertiser, BC, Cranbrook

Fix, Cece
cfix@thedalleschronicle.com, Office Mgr./ Bookkeeper, The Dalles Daily Chronicle, OR, The Dalles

Fix, Wanda.............................. **(434) 696-5550**
wanda.fix@kenbridgevictoriadispatch.com, Community Ed., The Kenbridge-Victoria Dispatch, VA, Victoria

Fladung, Bonnie
corporateemail@xrite.com, Dir.-Mktg., Monaco Systems, Inc., MA, Andover

Fladung, Ranee .... **(319) 646-2712**
wellnews@netins.net, Pub, Wellman Advance, IA, Wellman

Fladwood, Dee .... **(262) 728-3411, ext. 135**
karend@standardpress.com, Adv. Mgr., Waterford Post, WI, Burlington
karend@standardpress.com, Adv. Dir., Paddock Lake Report, WI, Delavan
karend@standardpress.com, Asst. Adv. Dir., Lake Geneva Times, WI, Delavan

Flagg, James .... **ext. 3547**
letters@express-times.com, Editorial Page Ed., The Express-Times, PA, Easton

Flagg, Linda ....**(603) 352-1234 ext. 1601**
lflagg@keenesentinel.com, Bus. & HR Mgr., The Keene Sentinel, NH, Keene

Flagstad, Tim .... **(208) 239-3124**
Sports Ed., Idaho State Journal, ID, Pocatello

Flahavin, Kathy
kflahavin@nuvo.net, Circ. Mgr., Nuvo, IN, Indianapolis

Flaherty, Erika
eflaherty@scity.com, Inside Sales Representative, Steel City Corp., OH, Ashland

Flaherty, Sean.........................**(509) 582-1460**
sflaherty@tricityherald.com, Adv. Dir., Tri-City Herald, WA, Kennewick

Flaig, Michael .... **(860) 701-4234**
m.flaig@theday.com, DayDirect & Specialty Products Manager, The Day Publishing Co., CT, New London
m.flaig@theday.com, Commercial Print Sales Manager, The Day, CT, New London

Flake, Nancy
nflake@hcnonline.com, City Ed., The Courier of Montgomery County, TX, Conroe

Flanagan, Jacque .... **(660) 543-4050**
muleskinner@ucmo.edu, Managing Editor, University of Central Missouri, MO, Warrensburg

Flanagan, Maria .... **(405) 214-3941**
maria.flanagan@news-star.com, Adv. Sales Asst., Shawnee News-Star, OK, Shawnee

Flanagan, Mark .... **(508) 236-0331**
opinion@thesunchronicle.com, Editorial Page Ed., The Sun Chronicle, MA, Attleboro

Flanagan, Terry .... **(630) 388-6901**
tflanagan@copia.com, VP, Eng., Copia International Ltd., IL, Roselle

Flanders, Colin
sports@essexreporter.com, The Colchester Sun, VT, Colchester
sports@essexreporter.com, Sports Ed., The Essex Reporter, VT, Saint Albans

Flanigan, Meg
meg@accufastpps.com, Mgr., ACCUFAST Package Printing Systems, NY, Troy

Flank, Steve .... **(610) 371-5121**

sflank@readingeagle.com, General Sales Director, Reading Eagle, PA, Reading

Flannery, Mary Ann
mflannery@jcu.edu, Chair/Assoc. Prof., John Carroll University, OH, University Heights

Flatow, Tom .... **(262) 763-3330, ext. 158**
tflatow@standardpress.com, Circ. Mgr., Westosha Report, WI, Twin Lakes
tflatow@standardpress.com, Circ. Mgr, Paddock Lake Report, WI, Delavan
tflatow@standardpress.com, Circ. Mgr, Lake Geneva Times, WI, Delavan

Flattau, Edward .... **(202) 363-1270**
edflattau@msn.com, Pres., Global Horizons, Washington

Flaviano, Ron .... **(330) 424-9541**
ronflaviano@mac.com, Mgmt. Info Servs. Mgr. , Morning Journal, OH, Lisbon

Flax, Kyle .... **(620) 694-5700 Ext. 212**
kflax@hutchnews.com, Marketing Consultant, The Hutchinson News, KS, Hutchinson

Fleck, Bob Fleck .... **(608) 791-8420**
Publisher, The Dunn County News, WI, Chippewa Falls

Fleck, Robert .... **(312) 222-6691**
rfleck@tribune.com, Adv. Sr. Vice Pres., Chicago Tribune, IL, Chicago

Fleece, Michelle .... **(570) 253-3055 ext. 301**
mfleece@wayneindependent.com, Pres./Pub/ Adv. Sales Mgr., Carbondale News, PA, Honesdale

Fleece, Michelle .... **(570) 253-3055 x301**
mfleece@wayneindependent.com, Pres./ Pub./Adv. Dir., The Moscow Villager, PA, Honesdale
mfleece@wayneindependent.com, Pub./Adv. Dir., The Wayne Independent, PA, Honesdale

Fleee, Michelle ....**(570) 253-3055 et. 301**
mhessling@wayneindependent.com, Pub., The News Eagle, PA, Honesdale

Fleener, Brenna
bjf32@georgetown.edu, McDonough Bus. School/Georgetown Univ., DC, Washington

Fleener, Keith L. .... **(812) 988-2221**
kfleener@bcdemocrat.com, Adv. Mgr., Brown County Democrat, IN, Nashville

Fleener, Keith L.
kfleener@bcdemocrat.com, Adv. Mgr., Marketplace, IN, Nashville

Fleet, Bob .... **(405) 523-2000**
bob.fleet@af-group.com, Div. Mktg. Mgr., American Fidelity Assurance Co., OK, Oklahoma City

Fleischaker, Ted....................**(317) 632-8840**
ted@midwestword.com, Word Publications, IN, INDIANAPOLIS
ted@midwestword.com, Publisher, The Word, IN, Indianapolis

Fleischer, Marilyn
mfleischer@saladovillagevoice.com , Pub./Adv. Mgr. , Salado Village Voice, TX, Salado

Fleischer, Richard .... **(401) 732-3100**
RichardF@rhodybeat.com, General Manager, Beacon Communications, Inc, RI, Warwick

Fleischer, Richard G. .... **(401) 732-3100 ext. 222**
richardf@rhodybeat.com, Gen. Mgr., Cranston Herald, RI, Warwick
richardf@rhodybeat.com, Gen. Mgr., Johnston Sun Rise, RI, Warwick

Fleischer, Richard G. .... **(401) 732-3100 ext. 222**
richardf@warwickonline.com, Gen. Mgr., Rhody Beat, RI, Warwick
richardf@warwickonline.com, Gen. Mgr., Warwick Beacon, RI, Warwick

Fleischer, Richard G. .... **(401) 732-3100 ext. 222**
richardf@warwickonline.com, Gen. Mgr., Pennysaver, RI, Warwick

Fleischer, Tim .... **(254) 947-5321**
tfleischer@saladovillagevoice.com, Pub./Ed.,

Salado Village Voice, TX, Salado

Fleisig, Dr. Wayne .... **(205) 969-2963**
wfleisig@hotmail.com, Writer/Self-Syndicator, Healthy Minds, Mountain Brk

Fleming, Christina .... **(416) 947-3170**
christina.fleming@sunmedia.ca, Executive Assistant to the Publisher, The Toronto Sun, ON, Toronto

Fleming, Derek
dfleming@thespec.com, Vice Pres., Bus. Admin., The Hamilton Spectator, ON, Hamilton

Fleming, Jeff .... **(949) 660-6150**
jeff@duncanmcintoshco.com, Editor-in-Chief, Editor & Publisher Magazine, CA, Fountain Valley
jeff@duncanmcintoshco.com, Associate Ed./ Associate Pub., The Log Newspaper, CA, Fountain Valley

Fleming, Jeff M.
jeff@flemingenterprises.net, Owner, Fleming Enterprises, TX, Fort Worth

Fleming, Jennifer
aabbott@csulb.edu, Asst. Prof., California State University, Long Beach, CA, Long Beach

Fleming, Lisa..........................**(406) 755-7000**
Collections, Daily Inter Lake, MT, Kalispell

Fleming, Patrick .... **(817) 232-9575**
patrick@flemingenterprises.net, Office Manager, Fleming Enterprises, TX, Fort Worth

Fleming, Sharrie Lynn ..... **(905) 372-0131 ext. 331**
sharielynn.fleming@sunmedia.ca, Mng. Ed., Northumberland Today, ON, Cobourg

Fleming Leonard, Suzy .... **(321) 242-3614**
sleonard@floridatoday.com, Lifestyles Ed., Florida Today, FL, Melbourne

Flemmer, Kevin
kflemmer@mitchellrepublic.com, Adv. Mgr., The Advisor Advantage, SD, Mitchell

Flemming, Paul .... **(850) 671-6550**
pflemming@tallahassee.com, State Editor, Tallahassee Democrat, FL, Tallahassee

Flenders, Joe
jflenders@21st-centurymedia.com, Circ. Dir., North Penn Life, PA, Fort Washington
jflenders@21st-centurymedia.com, Circ. Mgr, Willow Grove Guide, PA, Fort Washington
jflenders@21st-centurymedia.com, Circ. Mgr., The Globe, PA, Fort Washington
jflenders@21st-centurymedia.com, Circ. Mgr, Glenside News, PA, Fort Washington
jflenders@21st-centurymedia.com, Circ. Mgr, Springfield Sun, PA, Fort Washington
jflenders@21st-centurymedia.com, Circ. Mgr., Public Spirit, PA, Fort Washington
jflenders@21st-centurymedia.com, Circ. Mgr., Ambler Gazette, PA, Lansdale
jflenders@21st-centurymedia.com, Circ. Mgr., Times Chronicle, PA, Fort Washington
jflenders@21st-centurymedia.com, Circ. Mgr., The Colonial, PA, Fort Washington
jflenders@21st-centurymedia.com, Circ. Mgr, Montgomery Life, PA, Fort Washington
jflenders@21st-centurymedia.com, Circ. Mgr., Perkasie News-Herald, PA, Fort Washington

Flerschauer, Eric .... **(256) 340-2435**
eric@decaturdaily.com, Bus. Writer, The Decatur Daily, AL, Decatur

Fletcher, Carlton .... **(229) 888-9360**
carlton.fletcher@albanyherald.com, Metro Editor, The Albany Herald, GA, Albany

Fletcher, Danny .... **(575) 628-5502**
dfletcher@currentargus.com, Gen. Mgr., Current-Argus, NM, Carlsbad

Fletcher, Don .... **(251) 294-3564**
don@atmorenews.com, Staff Writer, Atmore News, AL, Atmore

Fletcher, Douglas .... **(212) 210-1913**
dfletcher@nydailynews.com, Acct. Mgr. Sup.,

New York Daily News, NY, New York

Fletcher, Duncan
dfletcher@durhamregion.com, Adv. Mgr., Ajax-pickering News Advertiser, ON, Oshawa

Fletcher, Gloria.........................(405) 880-6153
Regional VP - Midwest, GateHouse Media, Inc., NY, Pittsford

Fletcher, Gloria
gfletcher@soundpublishing.com, President, Sound Publishing, Inc., WA, Poulsbo

Fletcher, Jim
jfletcher@srpressgazette.com, Pub., Santa Rosa Press Gazette, FL, Milton

Fletcher, Joel.........................(217) 421-7959
jfletcher@herald-review.com, Gen. Mgr., Herald & Review, Decatur, IL, Decatur
jfletcher@herald-review.com, Adv. Dir., The Pantagraph, IL, Bloomington

Fletcher, Lynne.........................ext. 114
lfletcher@samessenger.com, Prodn. Mgr., St. Albans Messenger, VT, Saint Albans

Fletcher, Nancy
nfletcher@oaaa.org, Pres. & CEO, Outdoor Advertising Association of America (OAAA), DC, Washington
nfletcher@oaaa.org, Pres. & CEO, The 4 A's, NY, New York

Fletcher, Stephen.........................(251) 633-4300
Pres./COO, Konica Minolta Business Solutions, AL, Mobile

Fletcher, Sue
sfletcher@cninewspapers.com, Adv. Rep., The Toccoa Record, GA, Toccoa

Fliger, Jerry
jfliger@tfc.edu, Dir., Toccoa Falls College, GA, Toccoa Falls

Flink, Kevin.........................(715) 223-2342 ext. 24
tpprint@pcpros.net, Prodn. Mgr., Central Wisconsin Shopper, WI, Abbotsford

Flinn, Keith.........................(973) 383-1010
kflinn@njherald.com, Pub., New Jersey Herald, NJ, Newton

Flint, Connie.........................ext. 12
officemgr@themonroetimes.com, Office Mgr., The Monroe Times, WI, Monroe

Flint, Leslie
ads@elburnherald.com, Adv. Mgr., The Elburn Herald, IL, St Charles

Flippen, Charles
cflippen@towson.edu, Chair, Towson University, MD, Towson

Flippin, William S..........................(610) 371-5000
wflippin@readingeagle.com, Chairman, Publisher, Reading Eagle, PA, Reading

Flom, Erik
erik@elfworks.com, Owner, ELFWorks 3D Construction Co., CA, Alameda

Flood, Pat.........................ext. 296
Photo Dept. Mgr., The Fond du Lac Reporter, WI, Fond Du Lac

Florek, Geri R.
geri@waheagle.com, Adv. Mgr./Prod. Mgr., Wahkiakum County Eagle, WA, Cathlamet

Florence, David.........................(978) 516-2259
dflorence@mediaonene.com, Adv. Mgr., Sentinel & Enterprise, MA, Fitchburg

Flores, Adam.........................(757) 683-3452
editorinchief@maceandcrown.com, Editor-in-Chief, Old Dominion University, VA, Norfolk

Flores, Kathleen.........................(915) 747-7436
kmrogers@utep.edu, Dir, Univ. of Texas El Paso, TX, El Paso

Flores, Kevin.........................(863) 386-5808
kevin.flores@newssun.com, Circ. Dir., Highlands News-Sun, FL, Sebring

Flores, Manuel
manuel.c.flores@tamuk.edu, Advisor, Texas

A&M Univ. Kingsville, TX, Kingsville

Flores, Michael
indysales@chartermi.net, Pub., Sunday Independent, MI, Owosso

Flores, Michael
indysales@chartermi.net, Pub., Durand Independent, MI, Owosso

Flores, Michael
indysales@chartermi.net, Pub., The Perry Independent, MI, Owosso

Flores, Rick
rflores@hcnonline.com, Cypress Creek Champions (OOB), TX, Houston
rflores@hcnonline.com, Circ. Mgr, Fort Bend Sun, TX, Conroe
rflores@hcnonline.com, Circ. Mgr, Friendswood Journal, TX, Conroe
rflores@hcnonline.com, Circ. Mgr, Memorial Examiner, TX, Conroe
rflores@hcnonline.com, Circ. Mgr, The Examiners, TX, Conroe
rflores@hcnonline.com, Circ. Mgr, The Rancher, TX, Conroe
rflores@hcnonline.com, Circ. Mgr, Atascocita Observer, TX, Conroe
rflores@hcnonline.com, Circ. Mgr, Cleveland Advocate, TX, Conroe
rflores@hcnonline.com, Circ. Mgr, Humble Observer, TX, Conroe
rflores@hcnonline.com, Circ. Mgr, Kingwood Observer, TX, Conroe
rflores@hcnonline.com, Circ. Mgr, Magnolia Potpourri, TX, Conroe
rflores@hcnonline.com, Circ. Mgr, Pearland Journal, TX, Conroe
rflores@hcnonline.com, Circ. Mgr, Spring Observer, TX, Conroe
rflores@hcnonline.com, Circ. Mgr, The Woodlands Villager, TX, Conroe
rflores@hcnonline.com, Circ. Mgr, Tomball Potpourri, TX, Conroe
rflores@hcnonline.com, Circ. Mgr, Dayton News, TX, Conroe
rflores@hcnonline.com, Circ. Mgr, Lake Houston Observer, TX, Conroe

Flores-Panlagua, Veronica.........(713) 362-6317
veronica.flores@chron.com, Outlook Editor, Houston Chronicle, TX, Houston

Florez, Sergio.........................(212) 556-1658
florez@nytimes.com, Managing Editor, Images, The New York Times News Service & Syndicate, New York

Florez, Sergio.........................(212) 556-1658
florez@nytimes.com, Managing Editor, Images, The New York Times News Service & Syndicate, New York

Florez, Sergio.........................(212) 556-4204
florez@nytimes.com, Managing Editor/Images, The NYT News Service/Syndicate - Photos & Graphics, New York
florez@nytimes.com, Managing Editor/Images, The New York Times News Service/Syndicate, New York

Florman, Katherine.........................(719) 636-0308
kflorman@freedom.com, Regional Director HR, The Gazette, CO, Colorado Springs

Floro, Charles D.
earthskyweb@cs.com, Prodn. Mgr., Sisseton-Wahpeton Sioux Tribe, SD, Wilmot

Flory, Tonya.........................(541) 506-4607
tflory@thedalleschronicle.com, Adv. Dir. , The Dalles Daily Chronicle, OR, The Dalles

Floss, Dennis.........................(585) 258-2242
dfloss@democratandchronicle.com, Gen. Mgr., Specialty Publications, Democrat and Chronicle, NY, Rochester

Flower, Kathy
news@mteagle.com, Ed., Mountaintop Eagle, PA, Mountain Top

Flowers, Darryl.........................(406) 467-2334
suntimes@3rivers.net, Ed., Pub., Propr., Fairfield Sun Times, MT, Fairfield

Flowers, Debbie

deb.flowers@starherald.com, Dir., Bus./Personnel Servs., Star-Herald, NE, Scottsbluff

Flowers, John
john.flowers@galvnews.com, Ad. Director, The Galveston County Daily News, TX, Galveston

Flowers, Laurie
lflowers@salemnews.net, Class., Salem News, OH, Salem

Floyd, Carla.........................(813) 657-4505
cfloyd@mediageneral.com, Pub., South Tampa News & Tribune, FL, Saint Petersburg

Floyd, Carla.........................(813) 657-4505
cfloyd@mediageneral.com, Pub., Thunderbolt, FL, Tampa

Floyd, Jesse.........................(781) 433-8325
jfloyd@wickedlocal.com, Ed. in Chief, Roslindale Transcript, MA, Needham

Floyd, Jesse
jfloyd@wickedlocal.com, Ed.-in-Chief, Wellesley Townsman, MA, Needham

Floyd, Jesse.........................(781) 433-8325
jfloyd@wickedlocal.com, Ed. in Chief, Watertown TAB, MA, Needham

Floyd, Jesse.........................(781) 433-8325.
jfloyd@wickedlocal.com, Ed. in Chief, Westwood Press, MA, Needham

Floyd, Jesse.........................(781) 433-8325
jfloyd@wickedlocal.com, Ed. in Chief, Somerville Journal, MA, Somerville

Floyd, Jesse.........................(781) 433-8325
jfloyd@wickedlocal.com, Ed. in Chief, Allston-Brighton TAB, MA, Needham
jfloyd@wickedlocal.com, Ed. in Chief, Dover-Sherborn Press, MA, Needham

Floyd, Jesse.........................(978) 618-7583
jfloyd@wickedlocal.com, GateHouse Media, Inc., NY, Pittsford

Floyd, Jesse
jfloyd@wickedlocal.com, Ed. in Chief, Sharon Advocate, MA, Needham

Floyd, Jesse.........................(781) 433-8325
jfloyd@wickedlocal.com, Ed. in Chief, The Walpole Times, MA, Walpole

Floyd, Lewis.........................(850) 532-9466
lfloydmedia@gmail.com, Senior Associate-Southern States, Grimes, McGovern & Associates, NY, New York
lfloydmedia@gmail.com, Consulting Services, Lewis Floyd- Grimes, W.B. & Co., AL, Gulf Shores
lfloydmedia@gmail.com, Sr. Associate-South/Southwest, W.B. Grimes & Company, MD, Gaithersburg

Floyd, Mike.........................(662) 328-2424 ext.158
mfloyd@cdispatch.com, Circ. & Production Mgr., The Commercial Dispatch, MS, Columbus

Floyd, Shannon.........................(719) 346-5381
brecordadvertising@plainstel.com, Advt Dir, The Plainsdealer, CO, Burlington
brecordadvertising@plainstel.com, Adv. Mgr., Burlington Record, CO, Burlington

Fluker, Cassandra.........................(313) 845-9838
crfluker@hfcc.edu, Henry Ford Cmty. College, MI, Dearborn

Fluker, Laurie
lf04@txstate.edu, Assoc. Prof./Assoc. dean, Texas State University-San Marcos, TX, San Marcos

Flynn, Adrianne
aflynn@jmail.umd.edu, Sec., Regional Reporters Association, DC, Washington

Flynn, Carmon.........................(570) 253-3055 x306
cflynn@wayneindependent.com, Adv. Mgr., The Moscow Villager, PA, Honesdale

Flynn, Janie.........................(870) 895-3207
news@areawidenews.com, Pub., South Missourian-News, MO, Thayer

Flynn, Jennifer
jflynn@ironmountaindailynews.com, Cir. Dir., The Daily News, MI, Iron Mountain

Flynn, Mary Ann.........................(606) 451-4928
Adv. Rep., The Commonwealth-Journal, KY, Somerset

Flynn, Robert
rflynn@ct-innovations.com, Pres., C-T Innovations, KY, Louisville

Flynn, Tillie
tflynn@lakecountyexam.com, Ed., Lake County Examiner, OR, Lakeview

Flynn, Tina.........................ext. 2260
tinaf@newsreview.com, Prodn. Mgr., Chico News & Review, CA, Chico

Flyte, Rebecca.........................(814) 444-5900
beckyf@dailyamerican.com, Gen. Mgr., Daily American, PA, Somerset

Flzone, Mike.........................(603) 880-1516
sales@areanewsgroup.com, Sales, Pelham/Windham News, NH, Hudson

Fobes, Jeff.........................(828) 251-1333 ext. 109
publisher@mountainx.com, Pub., Mountain Xpress, NC, Asheville

Fodnes, Lyle
lfodnes@bbc.net, Adv. Mgr., The Ledger, NE, Hemingford

Foerster, Trey.........................(715) 258-1332
trey.foerster@jrn.com, Pub., Wisconsin State Farmer, WI, Waupaca

Foery, Raymond
raymond.foery@quinnipiac.edu, Prof., Quinnipiac University, CT, Hamden

Fogel, Delinda.........................(904) 819-3421
delinda.fogel@staugustine.com, Publisher, The St. Augustine Record, FL, Saint Augustine

Fogel, Tammara.........................(316) 942-5385
tammara@theactivage.com, Business and media manager, The Active Age, KS, Wichita

Fogg, Ethan.........................(315) 789-3333
efogg@fltimes.com, Circ. Mktg. Dir., Finger Lakes Times, NY, Geneva

Foglio, Maria.........................(410) 245-5045
mfoglio@chespub.com, Adv. Dir., Cecil Whig, MD, Elkton

Foisy, Janice
janice.foisy@sunmedia.ca, Pub., Edson Leader, AB, Edson

Fojud, Nick
photoeditor@dailylobo.com, Photo Ed., New Mexico Daily Lobo, NM, Albuquerque

Folb, Stuart
stuart.folb@houstonpress.com, Pub., Houston Press, TX, Houston

Foley, Dana
kschief@carsoncomm.com, Ed., The Kansas Chief, KS, Wathena

Foley, Dana
headlight@carsoncomm.com, Pub., Horton Headlight, KS, Horton

Foley, Ivan
news@plattecountylandmark.com ... , Ed., The Landmark, MO, Platte City

Foley, Jack.........................(408) 847-7037
jfoley@newsvmedia.com, Editor, The Gilroy Dispatch, CA, Gilroy

Foley, Karen M.
karen@flsentry.com, Pub., The Sentry, FL, Pompano Beach

Foley, Larry
lfoley@ledger-enquirer.com, News Ed., Columbus Ledger-Enquirer, GA, Columbus

Foley, Lisa
lisa.foley@albertleatribune.com, Acct. Mgr., Albert Lea Tribune, MN, Albert Lea

Foley, Pat.........................(814) 444-5910
patf@dailyamerican.com, Adv. Mgr., Classified,

Daily American, PA, Somerset

Folkerts, Jean
jfolk@email.unc.edu, Dean/Alumni
Distinguished Prof., University of North
Carolina, NC, Chapel Hill

Folkner, Brent .... **(260) 347-0400**
bfolkner@kpcmedia.com, IT Manager, KPC
Media Group, Inc., IN, Kendallville

Folkner, Brent .... **(765) 671-2239**
bfolkner@chronicle-tribune.com, IT Manager,
The Current Bargain, IN, Marion

Folkner, Brent **260-0347-0400**
bfolkner@kpcmedia.com, IT Manager, KPC
Media Group, Inc., IN, Kendallville

Follo, James
james.follo@nytimes.com, CFO, New England
Newspaper Group, NY, New York

Folsom, Geoff .... **(541) 548-2186**
gfolsom@redmondspokesman.com, Senior
Reporter, The Redmond Spokesman, OR,
Redmond

Fonda, Bill .... **(781) 682-4850**
bfonda@wickedlocal.com, Ed., Braintree
Forum, MA, Randolph

Fonda, Bill .... **(781) 837-4562**
bfonda@wickedlocal.com, News Ed.,
Marshfield Mariner, MA, Marshfield

Fonda, Bill .... **(781) 682-4850**
bfonda@wickedlocal.com, Ed., Weymouth
News, MA, Randolph

Fonda, Tim
tfonda@leaderherald.com, Editorial Page Ed.,
The Leader-Herald, NY, Gloversville

Fondren, Belinda
classified@leesvilledailyleader.com, Circ., The
Leesville Daily Leader, LA, Leesville

Fondriest, Steve .... **(800) 399-4294**
sfondriest@bob-weber.com, Senior Technician,
Bob Weber, Inc., OH, Cleveland

Fong, David A.
sacgazette@aol.com, Ed., Sacramento
Gazette, CA, Sacramento

Fontaine, Sandra .... **(418) 833-3113**
sandrafontaine@journaldelevis.com, Journal
De Levis, QC, Levis

Fontenot, Amy .... **(970) 875-1785**
circulation@craigdailypress.com, Circ. Mgr.,
Craig Daily Press, CO, Craig

Fontenot, Karen
kfontenot@selu.edu, Head/Assoc. Prof.,
Southeastern Louisiana University, LA,
Hammond

Fonteyn, Frank
ffonteyn@cheshireherald.com, Adv. Dir., The
Cheshire Herald, CT, Cheshire

Fonticiella, Nelson
nfonticiella@herald-leader.com, Circ. Dir.,
Lexington Herald-Leader, KY, Lexington

Foor, Heather .... **(419) 724-6382**
hfoor@toledoblade.com, Advertising Dir., The
Blade, OH, Toledo

Foos, Bob .... **(417) 673-2421**
news@webbcity.net, Ed., Webb City Sentinel,
MO, Webb City

Foote, Joe .... **(405) 325-5997**
jfoote@ou.edu, Dean/Prof., University of
Oklahoma, OK, Norman

Foote, Kevin
kfoote@theadvertiser.com, Sports Ed., The
Daily Advertiser, LA, Lafayette

Foote, Russ .... **(607) 336-7318**
Adv. Mgr., Sidney Pennysaver, NY, Norwich

Foran, Mike
mforan@arcinternational.com, Pres., ARC
International, NC, Charlotte

Forber, Greg .... **(802) 985-3091**

greg@windridgepublishing.com, Pub.,
Shelburne News, VT, Shelburne

Forberg, Rick
info@stmi.com, Vice Pres., Mktg., STM
Networks, CA, Irvine

Forbes, Amy
idacourier@frontiernet.net, Bus. Mgr.,
Reminder, IA, Ida Grove

Forbes, Amy
idacourier@frontiernet.net, Business Mgr., Ida
County Courier, IA, Ida Grove

Forbes, David
dforbes@turley.com, Sports Ed., Barre
Gazette, MA, Barre

Forbes, Ed
eforbes@lohud.com, Digital Team Leader, The
Journal News, NY, White Plains

Forbes, Ed
eforbes@lohud.com, Adv. Dir., Putnam
Express, NY, White Plains
eforbes@lohud.com, Consumer Exper. Dir
, Northern Westchester Express, NY, White
Plains
eforbes@lohud.com, Adv. Mgr., Rockland
County Express, NY, White Plains
eforbes@lohud.com, Review Press (OOB), NY,
White Plains

Forbes, Inez .... **(902) 928-3522**
inezforbes@ngnews.ca, Sales Mgr., The News,
NS, New Glasgow

Forbes, Sylvia .... **(660) 248-3455**
sylvia@forbesfreelance.com, Administrative
Assistant, Midwest Travel Writers
Association, IL, St. Charles

Forcey, Rob .... **(315) 282-2201**
robert.forcey@lee.net, Pub., This Week, NY,
Auburn

Forcey, Robert .... **(518) 792-3131**
RForcey@poststar.com, Pub., The Post-Star,
NY, Glens Falls
RForcey@poststar.com, Pres./Pub., The
Citizen, Auburn, NY, Auburn

Forcier, George
gforcier@recorder.com, Ed. in chief , The
Recorder, MA, Greenfield
gforcier@recorder.com, Mng. Ed., The
Recorder, CA, San Francisco

Ford, Amber .... **(208) 467-8656**
Northwest Nazarene Univ., ID, Nampa

Ford, Bobby
bford@winchesterstar.com, Online Ed., The
Winchester Star, VA, Winchester

Ford, Chris
ford@pulaskijournal.com, Adv. Rep., The
Pulaski County Journal, IN, Winamac

Ford, Christine .... **(574) 946-6628**
ford@pulaskijournal.com, Advertising Director,
The Independent, IN, Winamac

Ford, Cristena
cford@mountainhomenews.com, Bus Mgr,
Mountain Home News, ID, Mountain Home

Ford, Don .... **(905) 632-4444**
dford@burlingtonpost.com, Mng. Ed., The
Burlington Post, ON, Burlington

Ford, George
george.ford@gazettecommunications.com, The
Gazette, IA, Cedar Rapids

Ford, Imelda
iford@capita.com, Exec. Vice Pres., Techn./
Opns., Capita Technologies, CA, Irvine

Ford, Jana .... **(603) 224-5301 ext. 327**
Day Ed., Concord Monitor, NH, Concord

Ford, Loyd
news@thelakenews.com, Ed./Pub., The Lake
News, KY, Calvert City

Ford, Mary .... **(781) 741-2933**
mford@wickedlocal.com, Ed., Cohasset
Mariner, MA, Hingham

Ford, Nicole
subscriptions@westprint.com, Circ. Mgr., West
Prince Graphic, PE, Alberton

Ford, Paul .... **(270) 783-3278, Ext. 319**
pford@bgdailynews.com, Single Copy Mgr.,
Daily News, KY, Bowling Green

Ford, Rob
rob@gonzalesinquirer.com, Reporter, The
Gonzales Inquirer, TX, Gonzales

Ford, Ronda
rondaf@pld.com, Ed., Johnson Pioneer, KS,
Johnson

Ford, Terry
sales@pamarcoinc.com, Pres./CEO, Pamarco
Global Graphics, NJ, Roselle

Ford, Tony
tony.ford@alfactp.com, President, alfa CTP
Systems Inc., MA, Tewksbury

Ford, Walter .... **(530) 477-4232**
wford@theunion.com, Sports Ed., The Union,
CA, Grass Valley

Ford, Wayne .... **(706) 208-2218**
wayne.ford@onlineathens.com, Oconee Ed.,
Athens Banner-Herald, GA, Athens

Ford , Robert .... **(916) 321-1747**
rford@sacbee.com, Production Director , The
Sacramento Bee, CA, Sacramento

Forde, John
jforde@comm.msstate.edu, Assoc. Prof./Head,
Mississippi State University, MS, Mississippi
State

Foreman, Belinda .... **(702) 895-4803**
belinda.foreman@unlv.edu, Bus. Mgr.,
University of Nevada, Las Vegas, NV, Las
Vegas

Foreman, Joe
news@opinion-tribune.com, Ed., Opinion-
Tribune, IA, Glenwood

Foreman, John .... **(217) 351-5225**
jforeman@news-gazette.com, Pub., Mahomet
Citizen, IL, Mahomet

Foreman, John .... **(217) 351-5225**
jforeman@news-gazette.com, Pub., The
Leader, IL, Saint Joseph

Foreman, John .... **(217) 351-5225**
jforeman@news-gazette.com, President,
Rantoul Press, IL, Rantoul
jforeman@news-gazette.com, Pub., Rantoul
Press, IL, Rantoul

Foreman, John .... **(217) 351-5225**
jforeman@news-gazette.com, Pub.,
Independent News, IL, Danville

Foreman, John
jforeman@news-gazette.com, Pub., Ford
County Record, IL, Paxton
jforeman@news-gazette.com, Pres., The
News-Gazette, IL, Champaign

Foreman, John .... **(217) 357-5225**
jforeman@news-gazette.com, Pub., Piatt
County Journal-Republican, IL, Monticello

Foreman, Shari
shari@familyflyer.com, Pub./Owner,
Community Papers of Indiana, IN, Crown
Point

Foreman, Steve .... **ext. 240**
sforeman@independentfreepress.com, Gen.
Mgr., Independent & Free Press, ON,
Georgetown

Foreman, Tamara .... **(209) 249-3504**
tforeman@mantecabulletin.com, Business
Manager, Manteca Bulletin, CA, Manteca

Foreman-Plaisance, Amy.. **(225) 292-0032 ext. 951**
amy@brparents.com, Pub., Baton Rouge
Parents Magazine, LA, Baton Rouge

Forest, Nancy
news@bethelcitizen.com, Prodn. Mgr., The
Bethel Citizen, ME, Bethel

Forhan, Bill .... **(509) 548-5286**

record@cashmerevalleyrecord.com, CEO/Pub.,
Cashmere Valley Record, WA, Cashmere

Forhan, Bill .... **(509) 548-5286**
publisher@leavenworthecho.com, Pub/CEO
, Lake Chelan Mirror, WA, Chelan

Forhan, Bill
publisher@leavenworthecho.com, Pub., The
Leavenworth Echo, WA, Leavenworth

Forhan, Carol .... **(509) 548-5286**
carol@leavenworthecho.com, Adv. Dir., The
Leavenworth Echo, WA, Leavenworth
carol@leavenworthecho.com, VP, Adv., Lake
Chelan Mirror, WA, Chelan

Forhan, Carol .... **(509) 548-5286**
carol@leavenworthecho.com, Adv. Mgr.,
Cashmere Valley Record, WA, Cashmere

Forhan, Carol .... **(509) 548-5286**
carol@leavenworthecho.com, Pub./Adv. Mgr.,
Quad City Herald, WA, Chelan

Forman, Elaine
starcity@midrivers.com, News Ed., Miles City
Star, MT, Miles City

Formanek, Barb .... **(608) 786-6827**
barb.formanek@lee.net, Adv. Mgr., The Westby
Times, WI, Westby

Forness, Roger .... **(808) 529-4312**
rforness@staradvertiser.com, VP/Tech,
Honolulu Star-Advertiser, HI, Honolulu

Forney, Don
publisher@rrv.net, Pub., The Shopper, MN,
Halstad

Forney, Don
publisher@rrv.net, The Shopper, MN, Halstad

Forney, Rahn
rahnforney@ldnews.com, Editorial Page Ed.,
The Lebanon Daily News, PA, Lebanon

Forney, Rahn .... **(717) 272-5611**
rahnforney@ldnews.com, News Ed., Lebanon
Valley Review, PA, Lebanon

Fornof, David .... **(928) 539-6988**
dfornof@yumasun.com, Production Dir., Yuma
Sun, AZ, Yuma

Forrest, Denise .... **(203) 245-1877 ext. 6131**
d.forrest@shorepublishing.com, Acct. Manager,
Source, CT, Madison

Forrest, Matthew .... **(731) 253-6666**
matthew@lakecountybanner.com, Ed.,
Typesetting, Photo./Reporter, Adv., The Lake
County Banner, TN, Tiptonville

Forrest, Tim .... **(731) 642-1162**
circulation@parispi.net, Circ. Mgr., The Paris
Post-Intelligencer, TN, Paris

Forrey, Edward
eforry@dotnews.com, Pub. , Mattapan
Reporter, MA, Dorchester
eforry@dotnews.com, Pub. , Boston Irish
Reporter, MA, Dorchester
eforry@dotnews.com, Pub. , Boston Haitian
Reporter, MA, Dorchester

Forry, Edward W.
eforry@dotnews.com, Pub., The Dorchester
Reporter, MA, Dorchester

Forry, William
bforry@dotnews.com, Ed., Mattapan Reporter,
MA, Dorchester
bforry@dotnews.com, Ed., Boston Irish
Reporter, MA, Dorchester
bforry@dotnews.com, Ed., Boston Haitian
Reporter, MA, Dorchester
bforry@dotnews.com, Mng. Ed., The
Dorchester Reporter, MA, Dorchester

Forsberg, Bob
robert.forsberg@sappi.com, Vice Pres., Sales,
Sappi Fine Paper North America, MA, Boston

Forst, Joseph
jforst@pottsmerc.com, Cir. Dir., Delaware
County Daily Times, PA, Swarthmore
jforst@pottsmerc.com, Cir. Dir., Daily Local
News, PA, West Chester

Forster, Cathy
cforster@lfpress.com, Gen. Mgr., Pennysaver, ON, London

Forsythe, Dana ....(781) 433-8331
dforsythe@wickedlocal.com, Ed., Watertown TAB, MA, Needham

Forsythe, Jamie ....(618) 239-2562
jforsythe1@bnd.com, Ed., The Journal-Messenger (OOB), IL, Sparta
jforsythe1@bnd.com, Newsroom, Belleville News-Democrat, IL, Belleville

Fort, Frankie ....(912) 652-0261
frankie.fort@savannahnow.com, HR Dir., Savannah Morning News, GA, Savannah

Fortine, Nick ....(614) 220-5476
nfortine@bizjournals.com, Pres./Pub., Columbus Business First, OH, Columbus

Fortis, Louis
louisf@shepherd-express.com, Ed., Shepherd Express Weekly News, WI, Milwaukee

Fortkamp, Ashley ....(402) 371-1020 ext. 236
afortkamp@norfolkdailynews.com, Ed. Asst., Norfolk Daily News, NE, Norfolk

Fortman, Mike ....(563) 588-5740
mike.fortman@wcinet.com, Group Dir. of Adv., Telegraph Herald, IA, Dubuque

Fortner, Cari ....(912) 599-0332
chfortner@windstream.net, Advertising Sales Rep, Clinch County News, GA, Homerville

Fortunato, Buddy
bfsicilily@gmail.com, Pub., Italian Tribune, NJ, Montclair

Fortune, Cornelius ....ext. 247
tcabell@michronicle.com, Mng. Ed., Michigan Chronicle, MI, Detroit

Fortune, Kari ....(850) 227-7847
kfortune@starfl.com, Ad. Rep., The Star, FL, Port Saint Joe

Foscolos, Toula
toula.foscolos@transcontinental.ca, Ed. in Chief, The Monitor, QC, West Mill

Fosdick, Scott
scott.fosdick@sjsu.edu, Assoc. Prof., San Jose State University, CA, San Jose

Foshee, Charles ....(918) 582-8504
publisher@tulsakids.com, Publisher, Designer, Tulsa Kids, NY, Mamaroneck

Fosset, Christine ....(360) 807-8242
cfossett@chronline.com, Pub., Etc!, WA, Centralia

Fossett, Christine ....(360) 807-8242
cfossett@chronline.com, Mktg. Mgr., Etc!, WA, Centralia

Fossett, Christine ....(360) 807-8200
cfossett@chronline.com, Marketing Director, Laframboise Communications, Inc., WA, Centralia
cfossett@chronline.com, Pub., The Chronicle, WA, Centralia

Fossett, Christine ....(360) 687-5151
christine@thereflector.com, Pub., The Reflector, WA, Battle Ground

Fosso, Tracey ....(808) 329-3111
tfosso@westhawaiitoday.com, Adv. Mgr. / Pub., North Hawaii News, HI, Kamuela

Foster, Andrea ....(519) 756-2020 ext. 2295
andrea.foster@sunmedia.ca, Circ. Dir., Brandtford Expositor, ON, Brantford

Foster, Bernie
info@theskanner.com, Pub., The Skanner, OR, Portland

Foster, Clay ....(662) 678-1505
clay.foster@journalinc.com, Pub./CEO, Northeast Mississippi Daily Journal, MS, Tupelo

Foster, Clay ....(662) 842-2611
clay.foster@journalinc.com, CEO/Publisher/President, Journal Publishing Company, MS, Tupelo

Foster, Crystal
trnews@centurytel.com, Ed., The Times-Record, AL, Fayette

Foster, Debbie ....(662) 328-2424 ext.119
dfoster@cdispatch.com, Acct. Clerk, The Commercial Dispatch, MS, Columbus

Foster, Greg ....(847) 427-4351
gfoster@dailyherald.com, Financial Ops Mgr., Daily Herald, IL, Arlington Heights

Foster, Heidi Dahms
hdfoster@prescottaz.com, Ed. Mgr., Prescott Valley Tribune, AZ, Chino Valley

Foster, Jean
scpioneer@gorge.net, Office Mgr./Sports Ed., Skamania County Pioneer, WA, Stevenson

Foster, Jeanne 483-3126
response@gambitweekly.com, Publisher, Gambit, LA, New Orleans

Foster, Jeffrey
info@dailycourt.com, Pres./Pub., Daily Court Reporter, OH, Dayton

Foster, Jerry
jerry@theskanner.com, Circ. Mgr., The Skanner, OR, Portland

Foster, Kasie ....(317) 862-1774
ftinformer@sbcglobal.net, Editor, Franklin Township Informer, IN, Indianapolis

Foster, Keri ....(207) 990-8057
kfoster@bangordailynews.com, Sales, The Piscataquis Observer, ME, Dover Foxcroft

Foster, Keri ....(207) 990-8057
kfoster@bangordailynews.com, Sales, The Piscataquis Observer, ME, Dover Foxcroft

Foster, Laura ....(806) 364-2030
class@herefordbrand.com, Classifieds/Circulation, The Hereford Brand, TX, Hereford

Foster, Linda ....ext. 224
lindafoster@rrdailyherald.com, Adv. Dir., The Revue, NC, Roanoke Rapids

Foster, Linda ....(252) 537-2505 ext. 224
Adv. Mgr., Classified, Daily Herald, NC, Roanoke Rapids

Foster, Lisa
miltonvalerecord@twinvalley.net, Co-Pub, Miltonvale Record, KS, Miltonvale

Foster, Mark
elmertimes@hotmail.com, Pub., Elmer Times, NJ, Elmer

Foster, Marta ....(312) 217-6611
ehnews@comcast.net, Adv. Mgr., El Heraldo, IL, Chicago

Foster, Michael ....(360) 452-2346, ext 5064
mfoster@peninsuladailynews.com, Managing Editor, Peninsula Daily News, WA, Port Angeles

Foster, Randy ....(252) 635-5663
randy.foster@newbernsj.com, Ed., StarNews, NC, Wilmington
randy.foster@newbernsj.com, Ed., The Sun Journal, NC, New Bern

Foster, Ron
miltonvalerecord@twinvalley.net, Co-Pub, Miltonvale Record, KS, Miltonvale

Foster, Tom ....(513) 587-2944
tfoster@gmti.gannett.com, Vice Pres., Celebro Opns., Celebro, OH, Cincinnati

Fosu, Ignatius
ifosu@uark.edu, Asst. Prof., University of Arkansas, AR, Fayetteville

Fouch, Bill ....(304) 257-1844
news@grantcountypress.com, Ed., Grant County Press, WV, Petersburg

Foulds, Chris ....(250) 374-7467
publisher@kamloopsthisweek.com, Pub & Ed, Kamloops This Week, BC, Kamloops

Fountain, Charles
c.fountain@neu.edu, Assoc. Prof., Northeastern University, MA, Boston

Fourney, Dennis
dnf@capegazette.com, Pub./Adv. Dir., Cape Gazette, DE, Lewes

Fournier, Danielle
sales@recordbulletin.com, Pub., PROSSER RECORD-BULLETIN, WA, Prosser

Fournier, Della
dfournier@maplecreeknews.com, Advertising Sales, Maple Creek & Southwest Advance Times, SK, Maple Creek

Foust, James
jfoust@bgnet.bgsu.edu, Assoc. Prof., Bowling Green State University, OH, Bowling Green

Fouts, Lisa ....(712) 873-3141
lisa@wiatel.net, Office/Circu/Bus Mgr, The Record, IA, Moville

Foutz, Keith ....(937) 548-3330
kcfoutz@earlybirdpaper.com, Pres./Pub., The Early Bird, OH, Greenville

Foutz, Keith ....(541) 382-0977
ads@conickelads.com, Pub., Central Oregon Nickel Ads, OR, Bend

Fowkes, Kate
kfowkes@highpoint.edu, Prof., High Point Univ., NC, High Point

Fowler, Blain ....(780) 672-3142 ext. 102
mcfoul@cable-lynx.net, Publisher, The Camrose Booster, AB, Camrose

Fowler, Darran ....(402) 461-1203
dfowler@hastingstribune.com, Pub., Hastings Tribune, NE, Hastings

Fowler, Darran
dfowler@hastingstribune.com, Mng. Ed., Encore, NE, Hastings

Fowler, Ed ....(256) 235-9203
efowler@annistonstar.com, Pub., The Saint Clair Times, AL, Pell City

Fowler, Frances
jbgpress@windstream.net, Ed., The Johnsonburg Press, PA, Johnsonburg

Fowler, Gene
gfowler@coxnc.com, Pub., The Avery Journal-Times, NC, Newland

Fowler, Gene
gene.fowler@mountaintimes.com, Pub., The Blowing Rocket, NC, Blowing Rock
gene.fowler@mountaintimes.com, The Watauga Mountain Times, NC, Boone

Fowler, Gene ....(252) 202-1462
gfowler@mountaintimes.com, Pub., Watauga Democrat, NC, Boone

Fowler, Jeff ....(830) 379-5441 x 206
jeff.fowler@seguingazette.com, President, Editor & Publisher, The Seguin Gazette, TX, Seguin

Fowler, Jeff
jeff@camrosebooster.com, Sales Rep., The Camrose Booster, AB, Camrose

Fowler, Kari ....(970) 242-5555
Sales Mgr., The Nickel, CO, Grand Junction

Fowler, Karl A. ....(315) 232-4586
jcjesfucn@citlink.net, Ed., Jefferson County Journal, NY, Adams

Fowler, Kim ....(770) 479-1441
kfowler@cherokeetribune.com, Adv. Mgr., Cherokee Tribune Plus, GA, Canton

Fowler, Kim
kforlwer@cherokeetribune.com, Adv. Mgr., Cherokee Tribune, GA, Canton

Fowler, Kirby ....ext. 121
ads@camrosebooster.com, Production Manager, The Camrose Booster, AB, Camrose

Fowler, Sadie
editor@t-g.com, Ed., Shelbyville Times-Gazette, TN, Shelbyville

Fowler, Wade
atateditor@perrycountytimes.com, Editorial Consultant, Duncannon Record, PA, New Bloomfield
atateditor@perrycountytimes.com, Editorial Consultant, Perry County Times, PA, New Bloomfield
atateditor@perrycountytimes.com, Editorial Consultant, The News-Sun, PA, New Bloomfield

Fowlks, Deb ....(309) 462-3785
abingdonargus@gmail.com, Ed., Argus-Sentinel, IL, Galesburg

Fox, Angela
afox@clackamasreview.com, Pub., The Clackamas Review, OR, Portland

Fox, Angela
afox@clackamasreview.com, Pub., Oregon City News, OR, Portland

Fox, Bill ....(864) 298-4284
bfox@greenvillenews.com, News Dir., Tribune-Times, SC, Greenville
bfox@greenvillenews.com, Mng. Ed., The Greenville News, SC, Greenville

Fox, Bucky
bucky.fox@investors.com, Leaders Ed., Investor's Business Daily, CA, Los Angeles

Fox, Carey
redwood17257@yahoo.com, Sports Ed., The Brazil Times, IN, Brazil

Fox, Carolyn ....(818) 990-5945
editor@newscalendar.com, Ed. in Chief, Hollywood News Service, Sherman Oaks

Fox, Christine
cfox@michigannewspapers.com, Circ. Mgr., Northeastern Shopper South, MI, Tawas City
cfox@michigannewspapers.com, Circ. Mgr., Northeastern Shopper North, MI, Tawas City
cfox@michigannewspapers.com, Circ. Mgr., Ogemaw/Oscoda County Star, MI, West Branch
cfox@michigannewspapers.com, Circ. Mgr., Mt. Pleasant Buyers Guide, MI, Mount Pleasant
cfox@michigannewspapers.com, Circ. Mgr., Alma Reminder, MI, Alma
cfox@michigannewspapers.com, Circ. Mgr., Grand Traverse Insider, MI, Traverse City
cfox@michigannewspapers.com, Circ. Mgr., Gladwin Buyers Guide, MI, Gladwin
cfox@michigannewspapers.com, Circ. Mgr., Clare County Buyer's Guide, MI, Mount Pleasant
cfox@michigannewspapers.com, Circ. Mgr., Alpena Star, MI, Alpena

Fox, Deanna ....(215) 949-4111
dfox@calkins.com, Dir. of Adv., The Intelligencer, PA, Doylestown

Fox, Jason
news@theberlinjournal.com, Ed., Markesan Regional Reporter, WI, Berlin
news@theberlinjournal.com, Ed., Omro Herald, WI, Berlin
news@theberlinjournal.com, Ed., Princeton Times-Republic, WI, Berlin
news@theberlinjournal.com, Ed., The Fox Lake Representative, WI, Berlin
news@theberlinjournal.com, Ed., Green Lake Reporter, WI, Berlin
news@theberlinjournal.com, Ed., Berlin Journal, WI, Berlin

Fox, Kathryn
kfox@coastalcourier.com, Gen. Mgr., Tri-county Pennysaver, GA, Hinesville

Fox, Kathryn
kfox@coastalcourier.com, Gen. Mgr., The Coastal Courier, GA, Hinesville

Fox, Kym
kfox@txstate.edu, Lectr./Coord., Print, Texas State University-San Marcos, TX, San Marcos

Fox, Laurie ....(817) 272-3188

laurie.fox@uta.edu, Newsroom advisor, University of Texas at Arlington, TX, Arlington

Fox, Marjorie
foxm@uc.edu, Journalism Coord., University of Cincinnati, OH, Cincinnati

Fox, Shawn
sfox@dnps.com, Director, Retail Sales , Detroit Free Press, MI, Detroit

Fox, Steve .... **(231) 591-2529**
StevenFox@ferris.edu, Ferris State Torch., MI, Big Rapids

Fox, Sue .... **(847) 635-1678**
Oakton Cmty. College, IL, Des Plaines

Fox, Tom .... tfox@ncronline.org
Ed., National Catholic Reporter, MO, Kansas City

Fox, Vicki .... **(228) 435-0720**
Production Mgr., Biloxi-D'Iberville Press, MS, Biloxi

Fox-Arnott, Julie .... **(814) 532-5010**
jfox@tribdem.com, Circ. Dir., The Tribune-Democrat, PA, Johnstown

Fox-Smith, Ashley
ashley@countryroadsmag.com, Associate Pub. , Country Roads Magazine, LA, Baton Rouge

Foy, Robert .... **(912) 238-2040 ext. 143**
rfoy@morrisnews.com, Circ. Mgr., Savannah Pennysaver, GA, Savannah

Fracchia, Gilda .... **(408) 399-4842 ext. 14**
gilda.fracchia@parenthood.com, Adv. Mgr., Bay Area Parent, CA, Campbell

Fracker, Lisa
lfracker@richmondpublishing.com, Office Mgr., Fifty Plus, VA, Richmond

Fradellin, Marc
redaction.mirabel@hebdosquebecor.com, Pub., Le Mirabel, QC, Saint Jerome

Fraembs, Laura .... **(309) 757-4943**
lfraembs@qconline.com, Associate Managing Editor, The Dispatch-Argus, IL, Moline

Fragetti, Jerry
gfragetti@nnnlp.com, Sr. Vice Pres., Media/Opns., Newspaper National Network LP, NY, New York

Fragnito, Tony
tfragnito@lillienews.com, Adv. Dir., Shoreview Arden Hills Bulletin, MN, North Saint Paul
tfragnito@lillienews.com, Adv. Dir., New Brighton Bulletin, MN, North St Paul

Fragnito, Tony .... **(651) 748-7860**
tfragnito@lillienews.com, Adv. Dir., Oakdale Lake Elmo Review, MN, North Saint Paul

Fragnito, Tony
tfragnito@lillienews.com, Adv. Dir., Review Perspectives, MN, North Saint Paul

Fragnito, Tony
tfragnito@lillienews.com, Adv. Dir., St. Anthony Bulletin, MN, North Saint Paul

Fragnito, Tony
tfragnito@lillienews.com, Adv. Dir, Roseville Review, MN, North Saint Paul

Fragnito, Tony .... **(651) 748-7860**
tfragnito@lillienews.com, Adv. Dir., Ramsey County Review, MN, North Saint Paul

Fragnito, Tony
tfragnito@lillienews.com, Adv. Mgr., Maplewood Review, MN, North Saint Paul
tfragnito@lillienews.com, Adv. Dir., New Brighton-Mounds View Bulletin, MN, North Saint Paul

Fragnito, Tony .... **(651) 748-7860**
tfragnito@lillienews.com, Adv. Dir., South-West Review, MN, North Saint Paul

Fragnito, Tony .... **(651) 748-7860**
tfragnito@lillienews.com, Adv. Dir., East Side Review, MN, North St Paul

Fragnito, Tony .... **(651) 748-7860**

tfragnito@lillienews.com, Adv. Dir., South St. Paul - South West Review, MN, North St Paul

Frajkor, George
gfrajkor@ksliga.ca, Editorial Page, Kanadsky Slovak / The Canadian Slovak, ON, Mississauga

Fraley, Rory .... **ext. 124**
rfraley@southernlakesnewspapers.com, Sales Mgr., Wisconsin Hi-liter, WI, Burlington
rfraley@southernlakesnewspapers.com, Sales Mgr., Illinois Hi-liter, WI, Burlington

Frampton, Pam .... **(709) 748-0858**
pframpton@thetelegram.com, Assoc. Ed., The Telegram, NL, Saint John's

Francas, Mark
mark.francas@tnsglobal.com, Sales Rep., TNS Global, NY, New York

Francesco, Beth .... **(817) 272-3188**
bfrances@uta.edu, Dir. of Student Pubs., University of Texas at Arlington, TX, Arlington

Francis, Amy .... **(812) 231-4228**
amy.francis@tribstar.com, Marketing Mgr., The Tribune Star, IN, Terre Haute

Francis, Barbara
bfrancis@religiousherald.org, Adv. Mgr., The Religious Herald, VA, Richmond

Francis, Charles
wrcnews@centurytel.net, Pub., White River Current, AR, Calico Rock

Francis, David .... **(504) 826-3176**
tpdfrancis@gmail.com, Vice Pres./Bus. Mgr., The Times-Picayune, LA, New Orleans

Francis, Dennis .... **(808) 529-4700**
dfrancis@enterprisehonolulu.com, Pres., Street Pulse, HI, Honolulu

Francis, Dennis .... **(808) 529-4700**
dfrancis@staradvertiser.com, Pres., Kauai Midweek, HI, Honolulu
dfrancis@staradvertiser.com, Pres., MidWeek Oahu, HI, Honolulu

Francis, Dennis .... **(808) 529-4700**
dfrancis@staradvertiser.com, Pres. & Pub., Honolulu Star-Advertiser, HI, Honolulu
dfrancis@staradvertiser.com, President, West Hawaii Today, HI, Kailua Kona
dfrancis@staradvertiser.com, President, Hawaii Tribune-Herald, HI, Hilo

Francis, Dennis .... **(808) 529-4700**
dfrancis@thegardenisland.com, Pres., The Garden Island, Kauai, HI, Lihue

Francis, Dennis .... **(808) 529-4700**
dfrancis@staradvertiser.com, Pres. & Pub., USA Today Hawaii Edition , HI, Honolulu

Francis, John
info@tobermorypress.com, Pub. , The Bruce Peninsula Press, ON, Tobermory

Francis, Lee
wmneditor@lcs.net, Ed., Westmoreland News, VA, Montross

Francis, Matthew .... **(270) 691-7292**
mfrancis@messenger-inquirer.com, Mng. Ed., Messenger-Inquirer, KY, Owensboro

Francis, Rob .... **(616) 842-6400 ext. 241**
rfrancis@grandhaventribune.com, Dir. of Rev. Dev., Grand Haven Tribune, MI, Grand Haven

Francis, Robert .... **(817) 336-8300**
rfrancis@bizpress.net, Ed., Fort Worth Business Press, TX, Fort Worth

Franck, Kurt .... **(419) 724-6163**
kfranck@theblade.com', Executive Editor, The Blade, OH, Toledo

Franco, Elise .... **(704) 669-3337**
efranco@shelbystar.com, Sr. Reporter, The Star, NC, Shelby

Franco, Jose .... **(864) 562-7223**
jose.franco@shj.com, Ent. Writer, Herald-Journal, SC, Spartanburg

Franco, Melecio C. .... **(281) 378-1062**

mfranco@hcnonline.com, Ed., Humble Observer, TX, Conroe
mfranco@hcnonline.com, Ed., Kingwood Observer, TX, Conroe

Frandsen, M. Olaf .... **(785) 823-6363**
ofrandsen@salina.com, Pub., The Salina Journal, KS, Salina

Frandsen, Olaf .... **ext. 140**
ofrandsen@salina.com, Ed., The Hays Daily News Extra, KS, Hays

Frandsen, Olaf .... **(785) 628-1081**
ofrandsen@salina.com, Pub. , The Hays Daily News, KS, Hays

Frangia, Michal .... **(301) 627-0900**
pgpost@gmail.com, Ed., Prince George's Post, MD, Upper Marlboro

Frangoulis, Theresa .... **(800) 657-2110**
theresa@pressroomcleaners.com, Pres., Pressroom Cleaners, Inc., NE, Omaha

Frank, Bernd .... **ext. 263**
Bernd.Franke@sunmedia.ca, Sports Ed., Welland Tribune, ON, Welland

Frank, Buck .... **(814) 946-7461**
Bfrank@Altoonamirror.Com, Sports Ed., Altoona Mirror, PA, Altoona

Frank, Eric .... **(469) 532-8040**
eric.frank@kba.com, Vice Pres., Mktg., KBA North America, Inc. (Koenig & Bauer AG), TX, Dallas

Frank, Kevin
kevin.frank@stowewoodward.com, Vice Pres., Sales, Xerium Technologies Inc., NC, Youngsville

Frank, Martin .... **ext. 231**
mfrank@vnews.com, Editor, Valley News, NH, West Lebanon

Frank, Peter .... **(920) 431-8301**
pfrank@greenbaypressgazette.com, News Ed., Green Bay Press-Gazette, WI, Green Bay

Frank, Peter .... **(920) 431-8321**
pfrank@greenbaypressgazette.com, Community Engagement Editor, Green Bay Press-Gazette, WI, Green Bay

Frank, Robert .... **(425) 339-3426**
frank@heraldnet.com, City Ed., The Herald, WA, Everett

Frank, Robert L.
bfrank@berry.edu, Chair, Berry College, GA, Mount Berry

Frank, Rudy .... **(608) 755-8213**
rfrank@gazettextra.com, Director of Circulation , The Gazette - gazettextra.com, WI, Janesville

Frank, Russell
rbf5@psu.edu, Assoc. Prof., The Pennsylvania State University, PA, University Park

Frank, Scott
editor@marysvilleglobe.com, Mng. Ed., The Arlington Times, WA, Marysville

Frank, Suzanna
suzanna.frank@lee.net, VP, Audience, Lee Enterprises, Inc., IA, Davenport

Frank , Geoff
gfrank@diocesefwsb.org, Accounting/Circulation, Today's Catholic, TX, San Antonio

Frankel, Mike .... **(408) 920-5746**
Asst. Mng. Ed. – Reg., The Berkeley Voice, CA, Richmond

Franken, Denise .... **(330) 305-6960**
dfranken@presteligence.com, Dir. of Mktg., Presteligence, OH, North Canton

Franklin, Barry N.
barry@cityshopperonline.com, Adv. Mgr., City Shopper, MA, Boston

Franklin, Bruce .... **(318) 377-1866 ext. 126**
bruce@press-herald.com, Ed., Minden Press Herald, LA, Minden

Franklin, Carolyn
franklinc@courierpress.com, Mgr., Mktg. Servs., Evansville Courier & Press, IN, Evansville

Franklin, Cheryl .... **(918) 786-2228**
cfranklin@gatehousemedia.com, Pub., Grove Sun, OK, Grove
cfranklin@gatehousemedia.com, Publisher, Miami News-record, OK, Miami
cfranklin@gatehousemedia.com, Pub, Delaware County Journal, OK, Jay

Franklin, Cheryl .... **(620) 429-2773**
tnewberry@sekvoice.com, Pub., Cherokee County News-Advocate, KS, Columbus

Franklin, Debbie
debbie.franklin@lakesunonline.com, Bus. Mgr., Lake Sun Leader, MO, Camdenton

Franklin, Doug
doug.franklin@coxenterprises.com, Director of Online Strategy, Cox Media Group, GA, Atlanta
doug.franklin@coxenterprises.com, CEO, The Boston Globe, MA, Boston

Franklin, Douglas
Doug.Franklin@coxinc.com, Exec. Vice. Pres., Cox Media Group, GA, Atlanta

Franklin, Ellen
ellenfranklin@timesleader.net, Gen. Mgr., Times Leader, KY, Princeton

Franklin, Janice .... **(864) 833-1900**
janice@clintonchronicle.net, Office Mgr. , The Clinton Chronicle, SC, Clinton

Franklin, Karen .... **(305) 694-6210**
kfranklin@miamitimesonline.com, Assistant To The Publisher , The Miami Times, FL, Miami

Franklin, Larry .... **(864) 833-1900**
lfranklin@clintonchronicle.net, Pub., The Clinton Chronicle, SC, Clinton

Franklin, Mark
mfranklin@yorkdispatch.com, Mng. Ed., The York Dispatch, PA, York

Franklin, Sammy .... **(318) 992-4121**
editor@thejenatimes.net, Pub., Ed., The Jena-Times/Olla-Tullos-Urania Signal, LA, Jena

Franklin, Teryl .... **(608) 252-6117**
tfranklin@madison.com, Managing Ed., Wisconsin State Journal, Madison, WI, Madison

Franklin, Tim
hinckleynews@scicable.com, Pub., Hinckley News, MN, Hinckley

Franklin, Tom
lexprogress@bellsouth.net, Pub., Lexington Progress, TN, Lexington

Franko, Todd .... **(330) 747-1471 Ext. 1253**
Tfranko@vindy.com , Ed. , The Vindicator, OH, Youngstown

Franks, Bob .... **(541) 957-4245**
rfranks@nrtoday.com, Circ. Dir., The News-Review, OR, Roseburg

Franks, Erik .... **(208) 465-8148**
efranks@idahopress.com, Advertising Manager, Idaho Press-Tribune, ID, Nampa

Franscell, Ann
publisher@gillettenewsrecord.com, Editorial Page Ed., The News-Record, WY, Gillette

Frantz, Janice .... **(815) 741-2001**
janice@kskjlife.com, Ed., English, KSKJ Voice, IL, Joliet

Frantz, Jen Perkins .... **(410) 833-6347**
jengaf@jpfdesign.com, Prodn. Mgr., Baltimore's Child, PA, Philadelphia

Frantz, Todd .... **(573) 761-0237**
tfrantz@newstribune.com, Gen Mgr, Central Missouri Newspapers Inc., MO, Jefferson City

Frantz, Todd .... **(530) 852-0200**
toddf@goldcountrymedia.com, Publisher,

Auburn Journal, CA, Auburn

Franz, Karen M. .... (585) 529-9530
info@catholiccourier.com, GM/Editor, Catholic
Courier, NY, Rochester

Franz, Maximilian .... (443) 524-8171
mfranz@thedailyrecord.com, Sr. Photographer,
The Daily Record, MD, Baltimore

Franz, Todd
tfrantz@gatehousemedia.com, Gen. Mgr., Glen
Rose Reporter, TX, Stephenville

Franzene, Jessica .... (262) 248-4444
jaf@lakegenevanews.net, Prod. Mgr., Lake
Geneva Times, WI, Delavan

Frappier, Stephen
stephane.frappier@lenouvelliste.qc.ca, Ed.-in-
Chief, Le Nouvelliste, QC, Trois-Rivieres

Frasca, Ralph
ralph.frasca@marymount.edu, Mass Commun.
Coord., Marymount Univ., VA, Arlington

Fraser, Andrew
aptrenton@ap.org, Deputy Bureau Chief, New
Jersey Associated Press Managing Editors
Association, NJ, Trenton

Fraser, James R. .... (870) 269-3841
leader@mvtel.net, Pub., Owner, Stone County
Leader, AR, Mountain View

Fraser, Judith C. .... (413) 788-1026
jfraser@repub.com, Dir., HR, The Republican,
MA, Springfield

Fraser, Rick .... (306) 657-6214
rfraser@postmedia.com, VP., Adv. Sales,
Saskatoon StarPhoenix, SK, Saskatoon

Fraser, Rick .... (306) 657-6214
rfraser@postmedia.com, VP, Mktg., The
Leader-Post, SK, Regina

Fraser, Susan O'Connor
susan@tamcom.com, Pres./CEO, Tam
Communications, CA, Scotts Valley

Fraser, Wendy
editor@lillooetnews.net, Ed., Bridge River
Lillooet News, BC, Lillooet

Frasz, Krista .... (250) 470-0761
krista.frasz@ok.bc.ca, Adv. Dir., The Daily
Courier, BC, Kelowna

Frattura, Al .... (760) 955-5345
afrattura@vvdailypress.com, Pub., Desert
Dispatch, CA, Victorville

Frattura, Al .... (989) 779-6000
afrattura@journalregister.com, Grand Traverse
Insider, MI, Traverse City
afrattura@journalregister.com, Northeastern
Shopper South, MI, Mount Pleasant
afrattura@journalregister.com, Ed., Clare
County Buyer's Guide, MI, Mount Pleasant

Frattura, Al .... (989) 779-6001
afrattura@michigannewspapers.com, Pub.,
Northern Michigan Real Estate Marketplace,
MI, Mount Pleasant

Frattura, Al .... (989) 779-6001
afrattura@michigannewspapers.com, Pub., Mt.
Pleasant Buyers Guide, MI, Mount Pleasant

Frausto, Michelle
currentads@att.net, Adv. Dir., Frio-Nueces
Current, TX, Pearsall

Frazier, Cassidy
cassidy@austinchronicle.com, Sales Dir,
Austin Chronicle, TX, Austin

Frazier, Jan
jfrazier@bradley.edu, Instr., Bradley University,
IL, Peoria

Frazier, Julie .... (507) 837-5442
jfrazier@wasecacountynews.com, Publisher,
Waseca Area Shopper, MN, Waseca

Frazier, Julie .... (507) 837-5442
jfrazier@wasecacountynews.com, Pub.,
Janesville Argus, MN, Janesville

Frazier, Julie .... (507) 444-2376

jfrazier@owatonna.com, Pub, Owatonna Area
Shopper, MN, Owatonna

Frazier, Julie .... (507) 444-2367
jfrazier@owatonna.com, Publisher, Owatonna
People's Press, MN, Owatonna

Frazier, Julie .... (507) 444-2367
jfrazier@owatonna.com, Reg. Pub., Adams
Publishing Group, LLC, MN, Virginia

Frazier, Mary .... (417) 256-9191
printing@wpdailyquill.net, Production Manager
/ Digital Services, West Plains Daily Quill,
MO, West Plains

Frebault, Phil .... (651) 319-4510
pfrebault@rivertowns.net, Advertising Director,
Eagle Extra, MN, Red Wing

Frebault, Phil .... (715) 426-1052
pfrebault@rivertowns.net, Adv. Dir., Pierce
County Herald, WI, Ellsworth

Frechette, Aaron
afrechette@heraldnews.com, Editorial Page
Ed., The Herald News, MA, Fall River

Fredeking, Carole .... (618) 239-2622
cfredeking@bnd.com, Adv., Belleville News-
Democrat, IL, Belleville

Fredendall, Erick .... (810) 989-5786
ejfredendall@gmail.com, Editor-in-Chief, St.
Clair County Community College, MI, Port
Huron

Frederick, Amy
times@gpcom.net, Co-Pub., Hayes Center
Times Republican, NE, Hayes Center

Frederick, Bill .... (406) 582-2650
frederick@dailychronicle.com, Circ. Dir.,
Bozeman Daily Chronicle, MT, Bozeman

Frederick, Sharon .... (231) 592-8365
sharon@pioneergroup.net, Adv. Dir., Pioneer
Group, MI, Big Rapids

Frederick, Sharon .... ext. 265
Adv. Mgr., The Pioneer - Big Rapids, MI, Big
Rapids

Frederick, Sharon
sharon@pioneergroup.net, Sales Mgr., River
Valley News Shopper, MI, Howard City

Frederick, Sherman
shermfrederick@gmail.com, Pub. , Ely Times,
NV, Ely

Frederick, Sherman .... (702) 525-2440
shermfrederick@gmail.com, Owner/Publisher,
Marinscope Community Newspapers, CA,
Novato

Frederick, Sherman .... (702) 525-2440
cmikkelson@dailysparkstribune.com, Pub. ,
Sparks Tribune, NV, Sparks

Frederick, Sherman .... (415) 892-1516 x 12
shermfrederick@gmail.com, Pub., Novato
Advance, CA, Novato

Frederick, Stanton .... (845) 346-3050
fstanton@th-record.com, Commercial Printing,
The Times Herald-Record, NY, Middletown

Frederick, Steve
steve.frederick@starherald.com, Ed., Star-
Herald, NE, Scottsbluff

Frederick, Steve .... (308) 632-9055
sfrederick@starherald.com, Ed., Twin City
Weekly, NE, Scottsbluff

Frederick, Todd .... (410) 808-9633
frederick@chespub.com, Gen. Mgr., The
Bargainer, MD, Aberdeen

Fredericks, Scott
sfredericks@beverlyreview.net, Sports Editor,
Beverly Review, IL, Chicago

Fredericksen, Angie .... (419) 724-6076
angief@toledoblade.com, IT Support Mgr, The
Blade, OH, Toledo

Frederickson, Dave
dfrederickson@pacific.edu, Univ. of the Pacific,
CA, Stockton

Fredrick, Amy
bpost@bwtelcom.net, Pub., The Benkelman
Post and News-Chronicle, NE, Benkelman

Fredrick, Trici .... (757) 221-3254
pafredrick@wm.edu, College of William and
Mary, VA, Williamsburg

Fredricks, Dave
dave@newtucsonshopper.com, Tucson
Shopper - Week A, AZ, Tucson
dave@newtucsonshopper.com, Tucson
Shopper - Week B, AZ, Tucson

Fredricks, Jim
jfredricks@hcnonline.com, Grp. Pub., The
Courier of Montgomery County, TX, Conroe

Fredrickson, Amy
afredrickson@forumcomm.com, Adv. Dir. ,
InForum, ND, Fargo

Fredrickson, Keli .... (706) 635-7002
graphicart@timescourier.com, Prod. Mgr.,
Times-Courier, GA, Ellijay

Free, Cheryl .... (309) 343-7181 ext. 272
cfree@gatehousemedia.com, Bus. Mgr.,
Pennysaver, IL, Monmouth

Free, Ginny
classifieds@swbell.net, Class. Rep., The Pryor
Times, OK, Claremore

Freeberg, Tina
tfreeberg@parsonssun.com, Circ. Clerk,
Parsons Sun, KS, Parsons

Freeborn, Anita .... (360) 807-8243
afreeborn@chronline.com, Circ. Mgr., The
Chronicle, WA, Centralia

Freed, Doug
doug.freed@nickads.com, Gen. Mgr., The
Nickel, CO, Grand Junction

Freedman, Ken
Kfreedman@mediaspangroup.com, Vice Pres.,
Sales & Mktg., MediaSpan, MI, Ann Arbor

Freedman, Ken .... (508) 369-4693
ken.freedman@newscycle.com, Vice President
of Market Development, Newscycle
Solutions, MN, Bloomington

Freedman, Richard .... (707) 553-6820
rfreedman@timesheraldonline.com,
Community Ed., Vallejo Times-Herald, CA,
Vallejo

Freel, Daniel .... (973) 383-1157
dfreel@njherald.com, Senior Photo., New
Jersey Herald, NJ, Newton

Freels, Larry .... (660) 665-2808
kvdaily@sbcglobal.net, Pub., Kirksville Crier,
MO, Kirksville

Freels, Larry W. .... (660) 665-2808
kvnews@sbcglobal.net, Pub./Bus. Mgr.,
Kirksville Daily Express, MO, Kirksville

Freeman, Brett .... (845) 208-8151
freeman@halstonmedia.com, Pub., Mahopac
News, NY, Somers

Freeman, Brett .... (845) 208-8151
freeman@halstonmedia.com, Pub., Yorktown
News, Mahopac News, The Somers Record,
North Salem News, NY, Somers

Freeman, Eric
efreeman@bnd.com, Belleville News-
Democrat, IL, Belleville

Freeman, Heather .... (225) 771-5819
heather_freeman@subr.edu, Student Media
Director, Southern University, LA, Baton
Rouge

Freeman, Henry .... (914) 694-5002
hfreeman@lohud.com, Ed., Lohud Express,
NY, White Plains

Freeman, Henry .... (914) 694-5002
letters@thejournalnews.com, Vice Pres./Exec.
News Ed., The Journal News, NY, White
Plains

Freeman, Jenny
jenny@theprogressortimes.com, Circ. Mgr.,

The Mohawk Leader, OH, Carey
jenny@theprogressortimes.com, Circ. Mgr.,
The Progressor Times, OH, Carey

Freeman, Joanne .... (785) 378-3191
jcr@nckcn.com, Office Manager, Jewell County
Record, KS, Mankato

Freeman, Julie
jfreeman@iabc.com, Pres./CEO, International
Association of Business Communicators
(IABC), CA, San Francisco

Freeman, Julie .... (254) 710-3683
julie_freeman@baylor.edu, Asst. Media
Adviser, Baylor University, TX, Waco

Freeman, Justin
jfreeman@jcpgroup.com, Prod. Mgr, Clay
Today, FL, Fleming Island

Freeman, Karen Wynn
kfreeman@nabj.org, Exec. Dir., National
Association of Black Journalists, MD, College
Park

Freeman, Mary .... (806) 364-2303
news@herefordbrand.com, Staff News Writer,
The Hereford Brand, TX, Hereford

Freeman, Rachael .... (417) 847-4475
events@4bca.com, Office Manager, Barry
County Advertiser, MO, Cassville

Freeman, Randy
info@quadtechworld.com, Vice Pres., Bus.
Devel., QuadTech, WI, Sussex

Freeman, Sally
info@boiseweekly.com, Pub., Boise Weekly,
ID, Boise

Freemyer, Jordan .... (970) 392-9341
Univ. of Northern Colorado, CO, Greeley

Freeze, Lori
lori@stonecountyleader.com, Mng. Ed., Stone
County Leader, AR, Mountain View

Fregonas, Michele
mfregonas@stonewallcolumbus.org, Adv. Mgr.,
Stonewall Columbus, OH, Columbus

Frehner, Stephanie .... (702) 346-6397
sfrehner@mesquitelocalnews.com, Class
Sales Exec, Mesquite Local News, NV,
Mesquite

Freiberger, Brian .... (269) 749-7622
bfreiberger@olivetcollege.edu, Editor, Olivet
College, MI, Olivet

Freimanis, Kate
kfreimanis@forumcomm.com, HR Dir.,
InForum, ND, Fargo

Freireich, Elliott
publisher@westvalleyview.com, Pub., West
Valley View, AZ, Goodyear

Freisberg, June
editor@goodnewspress.com, Ed., Good News,
KS, Caney

Freisinger, Judi
jfreisinger@currentargus.com, Cir. Dist. Mgr.,
Current-Argus, NM, Carlsbad

Freivogel, William
wfreivog@siu.edu, Assoc. Prof./Dir., Journ.,
Southern Illinois University Carbondale, IL,
Carbondale

French, Audrey M.
creativeprinters@gpcom.net, Pub., Stapleton
Enterprise, NE, Stapleton

French, Barry
barryfrench@yahoo.com, Pres., French, Barry,
MA, Assonet

French, Barry
barryfrench@yahoo.com, Owner, Barry French,
MA, Assonet

French, Janice
news@thedawsonnews.com, Secretary,
Bookkeeper, The Dawson News, GA,
Dawson

French, Jill

pixel@theforumnews.com, Prod. Mgr, The Forum, LA, Shreveport

French, John P. ....(480) 834-4884
Pres./COO, BurrellesLuce, NJ, Florham Park

French, Mark ....(413) 788-1108
mfrench@repub.com, Adv. Dir., The Republican, MA, Springfield

French, Robbie
french@memphisflyer.com, Circ. Mgr., Memphis Flyer, TN, Memphis

French, Tania
tfrench@plwave.com, Pub./Ed., Port Lavaca Wave, TX, Port Lavaca

French, Terry
art@mdcoastdispatch.com, VP, Sales, Maryland Coast Dispatch, MD, Berlin

French, Virginia ....(310) 914-2064
Grp. Vice Pres., The New York Times, NY, New York

French-Parker, Jami
jami@crossroadsnews.com, Circ. Mgr, CrossRoadsNews, GA, Decatur

Frenette, Claude
cfrenette@letincelle.qc.ca, Ed., Etincelle, QC, Windsor

Freshour, Sandy ....(423) 623-6171
sandy.freshour@newportplaintalk.com, Classifieds Manager, The Newport Plain Talk, TN, Newport

Fret, Angel ....(787) 794-2000
arf@elexpresso.com, Publisher, El Expresso De Puerto Rico, PR, Dorado

Freud, Chris ....(970) 748-2934
cfreud@vaildaily.com, Sports Ed., Vail Daily, CO, Avon

Freudensprung, Kelly ....(870) 508-8075
kfreudensprung@bentoncourier.com, Pub., The Saline Courier, AR, Benton

Frey, Chad .... (316) 283-1500 x105
cfrey@thekansan.com, Mng. Ed., The Newton Kansan, KS, Newton

Frey, Kristen
kfrey@leavenworthtimes.com, Adv. Acct. Exec., The Leavenworth Times, KS, Leavenworth

Frey, Mike ....(805) 937-3343
mfrey@daily-journal.com, Ed, The Daily Journal, IL, Kankakee

Frey, Mike ....(815) 937-3343
Editor at Large, Small Newspaper Group, IL, Kankakee

Frey, Russell
info@bbscomputing.co.uk, Pres., BBS Computing, NY, Rochester

Frick, Kelly
kfrick@mlive.com, Sr. Dir. for Journalism and Engagement, The Jackson Citizen Patriot, MI, Jackson

Frick, Kelly
kfrick@bc-times.com, Sr. Dir. for Journalism and Engagement, The Bay City Times, MI, Bay City

Friday, Rufus ....(859) 231-3248
rfriday@herald-leader.com, Pres. & Pub., Lexington Herald-Leader, KY, Lexington

Friddell, Guy
rusty.friddell@dominionenterprises.com, Exec. Vice Pres./Sec./Gen. Counsel, Landmark Communications, Inc., VA, Norfolk

Fried, Jeff ....(305) 347-6615
jfried@alm.com, Associate Publisher/Chief Financial Officer , Miami Daily Business Review, FL, Miami

Fried, Jeff ....(305) 347-6615
jfried@alm.com, Associate Publisher/Chief Financial Officer , Palm Beach Daily Business Review, FL, Miami

Friedel, Harve ....(306) 734-2313

craiknews@sasktel.net, Ed., Craik Weekly News, SK, Craik

Frieden, Julie
jfrieden@thepaperofwabash.com, Sales Rep., The Paper, IN, Wabash

Frieden, Sam
sfrieden@thepaperofwabash.com, Opns. Mgr., The Paper, IN, Wabash

Friedes, Sharon ....(409) 838-2836
sfriedes@beaumontenterprise.com, Adv. Dir., Jasper Newsboy, TX, Jasper

Friedland, Joanne
ads@jewishlasvegas.com, Adv. Sales Dir., Jewish Reporter, NV, Las Vegas

Friedlander, David
editor@quchronicle.com, Editor-in-Chief, Quinnipiac University, CT, Hamden

Friedlander, Sharon ....(325) 236-6677
publisher@sweetwaterreporter.com, Pub., Sweetwater Reporter, TX, Sweetwater
publisher@sweetwaterreporter.com, Pub., Nolan County Shopper, TX, Sweetwater

Friedlander, Sharon ....(785) 462-3963
sfriedlander@nwkansas.com, Pub., Country Advocate, KS, Colby

Friedlander, Sharon ....(785) 462-3963
sfriedlander@nwkansas.com, Pub., Colby Free Press, KS, Colby

Friedman, Aron ....(718) 797-3900
adv@deryid.org, Ed., Der Yid, NY, Brooklyn

Friedman, Corey ....(910) 997-3111, ext. 13
cfriedman@civitasmedia.com, Ed./Content Manager, Richmond County Daily Journal, NC, Rockingham

Friedman, Corey ....(704) 694-2161
cfriedman@civitasmedia.com, Ed., The Anson Record, NC, Wadesboro

Friedman, Dan
dfriedman@forward.com, Managing Ed., Forward Newspaper, NY, New York

Friedman, Dan ....(229) 244-3400 ext. 1375
Controller, Valdosta Daily Times, GA, Valdosta

Friedman, David
david@telephonedoctor.com, Gen. Mgr./Vice Pres., Telephone Doctor Customer Service Training, MO, Bridgeton

Friedman, Donn ....(505) 823-3874
dfriedman@abqjournal.com, Asst. Mng. Ed., Online, Albuquerque Journal, NM, Albuquerque

Friedman, Herman
herman@shopharmony.com, Gen. Mgr., Der Yid, NY, Brooklyn

Friedman, Janice ....(973) 569-7272
friedmanj@northjersey.com, Pub., Twin-Boro News, NJ, Cresskill

Friedman, Janice
suburbannews@northjersey.com, Vice Pres./Pub., Midland Park Suburban News, NJ, Ridgewood

Friedman, Janice
FriedmanJ@northjersey.com, Pub., Glen Rock Gazette, NJ, Ridgewood

Friedman, Janice
communitynews@northjersey.com, Pub. , Community News, NJ, Fair Lawn
communitynews@northjersey.com, Pub., The Gazette, NJ, Fair Lawn

Friedman, Janice ....(973) 569-7272
FriedmanJ@northjersey.com, VP/Pub., North Jersey Community Newspapers, NJ, Woodland Park
FriedmanJ@northjersey.com, VP/Pub., North Jersey Deals, NJ, Woodland Park

Friedman, Melissa
melissa@thevalleypress.net, Ad. Director, The Valley Press, CT, Simsbury
melissa@thevalleypress.net, Ad. Director, The

West Hartford Press, CT, Simsbury

Friedman, Richard H.
info@weatherline.com, Pres., Weatherline, Inc., MO, Saint Louis

Frielich, Craig ....(315) 265-1000, ext. 24
News Editor, North Country This Week, NY, Potsdam

Frieling, Sarah ....(573) 474-1000
sfrieling@newzgroup.com, Director of Customer Service, Kansas Press Clipping Service, KS, Topeka

Frieling, Sarah ....(573) 474-1000
sfrieling@newzgroup.com, Director of Customer Service, South Carolina Press Clipping Bureau, SC, Columbia

Frieling, Sarah ....(573) 474-1000
sfrieling@newzgroup.com, Director of Customer Service, Iowa Press Clipping Bureau, IA, Des Moines

Friend, Cecilia
cfriend@utica.edu, Dir./Prof., Utica College of Syracuse University, NY, Utica

Friend, Christopher ....(413) 206-9319
Publisher, Amherst College, MA, Amherst

Friend, Diane
editor@senecanewsdispatch.com, Ed., Seneca News-Dispatch, MO, Seneca

Frierick, Joyce
joyce@saukherald.com, Bus. Mgr., Sauk Centre Herald, MN, Sauk Centre

Fries, Jacob
jacobf@inlander.com, Editor, The Pacific Northwest Inlander, WA, Spokane

Friesz, Jill
gcn@westriv.com, Ed., Carson Press, ND, Elgin

Friesz, Jill
gcn@westriv.com, Ed., The Grant County News, ND, Elgin

Frink, Clayton ....(608) 252-6402
cfrink@madison.com, Publisher, The Capital Times, WI, Madison

Frink, Clayton
c.frink@madison.com, Pub., Coverstory, WI, Madison

Frink, Clayton ....(608) 252-6402
cfrink@madison.com, Pres./Pub., Capital Newspapers, WI, Madison

Frisbee , Leslie ....(702) 380-4574
lfrisbee@luxurylv.com, Ed. , Luxury Las Vegas magazine, NV, Las Vegas

Frisch, Debbie
dfrisch@timesleader.net, Business Manager, Times Leader, KY, Princeton

Frisch, Kevin
kfrisch@messengerpostmedia.com, Mng. Ed./Presentation, Messenger Post Media, NY, Canandaigua

Frischling, Michael
mfrisch@steelcity.com, Pub., Pittsburgh City Paper, PA, Pittsburgh

Frisina, Jeanette ....(516) 997-7909
jeanette@marketplacepublications.com, Publ., Market Place Publications, NY, Carle Place

Fritch, April ....1-(812) 537-0063
afritch@registerpublications.com, Gen. Mgr., Harrison Press, IN, Lawrenceburg

Fritch, John
john.fritch@uni.edu, Dept. Chair, University of Northern Iowa, IA, Cedar Falls

Fritchen, Karl ....(414) 566-7500
info@qtiworld.com, Pres., Quad Tech, WI, Sussex

Fritchen, Karl ....(414) 566-7500
karl.fritchen@quadtechworld.com, Pres., QuadTech, WI, Sussex

Frith, Cary ....(740) 593-9581

Asst. Prof., Ohio University, OH, Athens

Frith, Katherine
kfrith@siu.edu, Assoc. Prof., Southern Illinois University Carbondale, IL, Carbondale

Frith, Stefanie ....(818) 719-6492
frithsa@piercecollege.edu, Adviser to the Roundup newspaper, Los Angeles Pierce College, CA, Woodland Hills

Frith, Stefanie
sfrith@elcamino.edu, Adviser, El Camino College, CA, Torrance

Fritsche, Lydia ....(920) 356-6720
lfritsche@conleynet.com, Employment Manager, Conley Media LLC, WI, Beaver Dam

Fritz, David ....(540) 213-9116
dfritz@newsleader.com, Exec. Ed., The News Leader, VA, Staunton

Fritz, Marsha ....ext. 240
marsha.fritz@lee.net, Circ. Mgr., The Advertiser, KY, Maysville

Fritz, Ron ....(410) 332-6421
ron.fritz@baltsun.com ...., Sr. Ed. sports, The Baltimore Sun, MD, Baltimore

Fritz, Shannon ....(785) 456-2602
office@wamegonews.com, Co-Managing Editor, The Wamego Times, KS, Wamego

Fritz, Theresa ....(613) 221-6261
theresa.fritz@metroland.com, Ed. , Ottawa East Emc, ON, Ottawa
theresa.fritz@metroland.com, Ed., West Carleton Review, ON, Arnprior
theresa.fritz@metroland.com, Ed. , Ottawa West Emc, ON, Ottawa
theresa.fritz@metroland.com, Ed, Arnprior Chronicle Guide Emc, ON, Arnprior
theresa.fritz@metroland.com, Ed., Orleans News Emc, ON, Ottawa
theresa.fritz@metroland.com, Ed. , Manotick News Emc, ON, Ottawa
theresa.fritz@metroland.com, Ed., Nepean-barrhaven News Emc, ON, Ottawa
theresa.fritz@metroland.com, Ed. , Ottawa South Emc, ON, Ottawa
theresa.fritz@metroland.com, Ed., Kanata Kourier-standard Emc, ON, Ottawa
theresa.fritz@metroland.com, Ed., The Renfrew Mercury Emc, ON, Renfrew
theresa.fritz@metroland.com, Ed, Belleville News Emc, ON, Belleville

Frizzell, Kathy ....(207) 633-4620, ext. 107
kathyfrizzell@boothbayregister.com, Adv. Mgr., Boothbay Register, ME, Boothbay Harbor

Frizzell, Kathy ....(207) 633-4620, ext. 107
kathyfrizzell@boothbayregister.com, Adv. Mgr., Wiscasset Newspaper, ME, Boothbay Harbor

Frizzelle, Christopher
frizzelle@thestranger.com, Mng. Ed., The Stranger, WA, Seattle

Frobe, Bill ....(607) 778-5110
Broome Cmty. College, NY, Binghamton

Froelich, Mark
mfroelich@crescent-news.com, Features Ed., The Crescent-News, OH, Defiance

Frogg, Randy
ledg@mtelco.net, Ed, Ledger (Moundridge), KS, Moundridge

Fromson, H.A.
ajohnston@anocoil.com, CEO, Anocoil Corporation, CT, Vernon Rockville

Fromson, Timothy A. ....(860) 657-9015
tfromson@anocoil.com, Vice Pres., Anocoil, Anocoil Corporation, CT, Vernon Rockville

Fronick., April M.
april@thepeoplestribune.com, Ed., The People's Tribune, MO, Bowling Green

Frontani, Michael
mfrontani@elon.edu, Assoc. Prof., Elon University, NC, Elon

Froschl, Joanna

jfroschl@indyeastend.com, Adv. Sales, The
Independent, NY, East Hampton

Froseth, Fay
news@kenmarend.com, Cir. Mgr., The
Kenmare News, ND, Kenmare

Froseth, Glen
news@kenmarend.com, Pub. Emeritus, The
Kenmare News, ND, Kenmare

Froseth, Terry
news@kenmarend.com, Pub. / Ed., The
Kenmare News, ND, Kenmare

Frosgren, Rich ....(814) 870-1694
CTO, Erie Times-News, PA, Erie

Frost, Chris
editor@lamarledger.com, Gen. Mgr./Ed., The
Lamar Ledger, CO, Lamar

Frost, Chris ....(920) 648-2334
leadereditor@hngnews.com, Managing Editor,
The Lake Mills Leader, WI, Lake Mills

Frost, Mark ....ext. 21
thechronicle@loneoak.com, Owner/Pub., The
Chronicle, NY, Glens Falls

Frtiz, John........................(702) 990-2657
john.fritz@lasvegassun.com, Deputy Managing
Editor/Digital, Las Vegas Sun, NV, Henderson

Fruchter, Jonah........................(206) 382-6137
jonah.fruchter@crosscut.com, Acc. Mgr.,
Crosscut, WA, Seattle

Fruge, Nicole
NFruge@sfchronicle.com, Photo Ed, San
Francisco Chronicle, CA, San Francisco

Fruit, Jeff........................(330) 672-0890
jfruit@kent.edu, P, Kent State University,
Kappa Tau Alpha National Honor Society for
Journalism & Mass Communication, MO,
Columbia

Frusciano, Dylan
dylan@gutcheckit.com, Vice Pres., Business
Wire - Denver, CO, Denver

Fry, Ben
ben@klre.org, Part-time Lectr., University of
Arkansas at Little Rock, AR, Little Rock

Fry, Douglas
info@sapatoday.com, Exec. Dir., Southeastern
Advertising Publishers Association, TN,
Columbia

Fry, Ken ....(479) 474-5215
kfry@pressargus.com, Ed., Alma Journal, AR,
Van Buren

Fry, Matt........................(352) 753-1119
matt.fry@thevillagesmedia.com, Managing
Editor, The Villages Daily Sun, FL, The
Villages

Fry, Sonya........................(212) 626-9220
sonya@opcofamerica.org, Exec. Dir., Overseas
Press Club of America, NY, New York

Fry, Tori ....(806) 402-0120
penhappyhippie@gmail.com, Reporter/
Photographer, Briscoe County News, TX,
Silverton

Frye, Nancy
nfrye@icfj.org, Vice Pres., Finance,
International Center for Journalists, DC,
Washington

Frye, Roger
rogerf@commpub.com, Community Publishers,
Inc., AR, Bentonville

Frye, Stephen
steve.frye@oakpress.com, Online Ed., The
Oakland Press, MI, Pontiac

Frye, Tucker ....(540) 473-2741
tfrye@ourvalley.org, Advertising, The Fincastle
Herald, VA, Fincastle

Fryer, Melissa
editor@nanaimobulletin.com, Ed., Nanaimo
News Bulletin, BC, Nanaimo

Fryhling, Risa ....(605) 845-3646

ads@mobridgetribune.com, Sales Mgr,
Mobridge Tribune, SD, Mobridge

Fryling, Risa........................(605) 845-3646
risa@mobridgetribune.com, Sales Mgr,
Monday Reminder, SD, Mobridge

Fuchs, Rose Kruger........................ext. 339
scvdesk@aol.com, Adv. Mgr., St. Cloud Visitor,
MN, Saint Cloud

Fuellenbach, Mark
reaperpub@richfieldreaper.com, Pub., Gull
Communications, UT, Richfield

Fuemmeler, Vince
vince@imssecure.com, Vice Pres., Sales/
Mktg., Continental Products, MO, Mexico

Fuentes, Manuel 5545 8256
redaccion@agenciaefe.tie.cl, Rep., EFE News
Services - Santiago, Chile, Santiago
redaccion@agenciaefe.tie.cl, Rep., EFE News
Services - Mexico City, Mexico, Mexico City

Fuentes, Monica ....(713) 280-2490
monica.fuentes@houstonpress.com, Art Dir.,
Houston Press, TX, Houston

Fugarino, Paul
pfugarino@theadvocate.com, Distr. Mgr., The
Advocate Newspaper, LA, Baton Rouge

Fugate, James David
info@jacksontimesky.com, Gen. Mgr., Jackson
Times-Voice, KY, Jackson

Fugleberg, Patty ....(701) 642-8585
pattya@wahpetondailynews.com, Business
Office Manager, The Daily News, ND,
Wahpeton

Fuguitt, Gayle
gayle.fuguitt@thearf.org, CEO & Pres., The
Advertising Research Foundation (ARF), NY,
New York

Fuhrmann, Henry
henry.fuhrmann@latimes.com, Multiplatform./
Copy Desk & Standards, Asst. Managing Ed.,
Los Angeles Times, CA, Los Angeles

Fujimoto, Troy ....(808) 695-6322
tfujimoto@staradvertiser.com, VP/Digital
Media, Street Pulse, HI, Honolulu

Fujimoto, Troy ....(808) 695-6322
tfujimoto@staradvertiser.com, VP/Digital
Media, Honolulu Star-Advertiser, HI,
Honolulu
tfujimoto@staradvertiser.com, VP/Digital
Media, West Hawaii Today, HI, Kailua Kona
tfujimoto@staradvertiser.com, VP/Digital
Media, Kauai Midweek, HI, Honolulu
tfujimoto@staradvertiser.com, VP/Digital
Media, Hawaii Tribune-Herald, HI, Hilo
tfujimoto@staradvertiser.com, VP/Digital
Media, MidWeek Oahu, HI, Honolulu

Fulbright, Jon
jon@pecos.net, Ed., Pecos Enterprise, TX,
Pecos

Fulcher, Albert
editor@eccalifornian.com, Ed., The East
County Californian, CA, El Cajon

Fulcher, Kat
webmaster@thevermontstandard.com,
Webmaster/Calendar/eEdition, The Vermont
Standard, VT, Woodstock

Fuld, Charles L. ....(858) 490-8279
cfuld@diocese-sdiego.org, Mng. Ed., The
Southern Cross, CA, San Diego

Fulgieri, Stacey
sfulgieri@floridamariner.com, Ed., Florida
Mariner/Gulf Mariner, FL, North Port

Fulginiti, Anthony
fulginiti@rowan.edu, Prof., Rowan Univ., NJ,
Glassboro

Fulham, Denise ....(631) 843-2492
denise.fulham@newsday.com, VP Local Retail
Sales, Newsday Hometown Shopper, NY,
Melville

Fulk, Scott ....(219) 980-6792

sfulk@iun.edu, Indiana Univ. Northwest, IN,
Gary

Fullam, Peter
peter.fullam@inlandnewspapers.com, The
Whittier Daily News, CA, Monrovia

Fuller, Bruce........................(269) 945-9554
circulation@j-adgraphics.com, Circulation Mgr,
Maple Valley News, MI, Hastings

Fuller, Doug........................(440) 266-1705
doug.fuller@investors.com, Circ. Vice Pres.,
Investor's Business Daily, CA, Los Angeles

Fuller, Douglas .... (800) 94-PAPER Ext. 612
dfuller@morningjournal.com, Cir. Dir., The
Morning Journal, OH, Lorain
dfuller@morningjournal.com, Cir. Dir., The
News-Herald, OH, Willoughby

Fuller, Dustin ....(307) 347-3241
adsales@wyodaily.com, Adv. Mgr., Northern
Wyoming Daily News, WY, Worland

Fuller, George ....(717) 262-4731
gfuller@publicopinionnews.com, Circ. Dir.,
Public Opinion, PA, Chambersburg

Fuller, Richard ....(419) 724-6314
dfuller@toledoblade.com, Circ. Dir., The Blade,
OH, Toledo

Fuller, Robert G.
bob@rgcreations.com, Owner, RG Creations,
Inc., CA, San Carlos

Fullerton, Doug .... (956) 683-40602
dfullerton@aimmediatx.com, Regional Director
of Information Technology, The Monitor, TX,
McAllen

Fullerton, Jackie
jfullerton@wellingtondailynews.com,
Classifieds, Wellington Daily News, KS,
Wellington

Fullerton, Jami
jami.fullerton@okstate.edu, Assoc. Prof.,
Oklahoma State University, OK, Stillwater

Fullerton Powell, Wendy
wfullerton@news-press.com, News Dir., The
Commercial Appeal, TN, Memphis

Fullylove, BJ
sales@texasmetronews.com, Advertising
Manager, Texas Metro News, TX, Dallas

Fullylove, BJ
sales@myimessenger.com, Advertising
Manger, Garland Journal News, TX, Dallas

Fulton, Sean
sean@gcnpublishing.com, Vice Pres.,
Technology, GCN Publishing, CT, Norwalk

Funabiki, Jon
funabiki@sfsu.edu, Assoc. Dept. Chair/Prof.,
San Francisco State University, CA, San
Francisco

Fung, Brian ....(802) 443-4827
Middlebury College, VT, Middlebury

Funk, Debbie ....(703) 778-9444
dfunk@connectionnewspapers.com, Adv. Dir.,
Alexandria Gazette Packet, VA, Alexandria
dfunk@connectionnewspapers.com, Nat'l Adv.
Sales, Arlington Connection, VA, Alexandria
dfunk@connectionnewspapers.com, Adv. Dir.,
Burke Connection, VA, Alexandria
dfunk@connectionnewspapers.com, Adv. Dir.,
Centre View, VA, Alexandria
dfunk@connectionnewspapers.com, Adv. Dir.,
Fairfax Connection, VA, Alexandria
dfunk@connectionnewspapers.com, Adv. Dir.,
Fairfax Station/Clifton/Lorton Connection, VA,
Alexandria
dfunk@connectionnewspapers.com, Adv. Dir.,
Great Falls Connection, VA, Alexandria
dfunk@connectionnewspapers.com, Adv. Dir.,
McLean Connection, VA, Alexandria
dfunk@connectionnewspapers.com, Adv. Dir.,
Potomac Almanac, VA, Alexandria
dfunk@connectionnewspapers.com, Adv. Dir.,
Reston Connection, VA, Alexandria
dfunk@connectionnewspapers.com, Adv. Dir.,
Vienna/Oakton Connection, VA, Alexandria

dfunk@connectionnewspapers.com, Adv. Dir.,
Oak Hill/Herndon Connection, VA, Alexandria
dfunk@connectionnewspapers.com, Adv. Dir.,
Mount Vernon Gazette, VA, Alexandria
dfunk@connectionnewspapers.com, Adv. Dir.,
Springfield Connection, VA, Alexandria

Funk, Deborah........................(703) 518-4631
corpconnection@erols.com, Dir., Cor.,
Connection Publishing, Inc., VA, Alexandria

Funk, Jeff........................(580) 548-8135
publisher@enidnews.com, Pres./Pub., Enid
News & Eagle, OK, Enid

Funk, Jerry........................(740) 452-3601
jfunk@adjustoveyor.com, Purchasing Manager,
Stewart Glapat Corp., OH, Zanesville

Funk, Loraine........................(250) 242-5343
mail@tumblerridgenews.com, Owner, Tumbler
Ridge News, BC, Tumbler Ridge

Funk, Michael
bfelsman@qni.biz, IT Mgr., Quincy Media, Inc.,
IL, Quincy

Funk, Robert........................(210) 831-5996
rfunk@tnolsa.com, Publisher, Thrifty Nickel,
TX, San Antonio

Funk, Sharon
sfunk@nwkansas.com, Adv. Rep., Colby Free
Press, KS, Colby

Funk, Steve
sfunk@wnit.org, Gen. Mgr., Market Place, IN,
South Bend

Funke, Becky........................(316) 942-5385
bfunke@activeaginonline.com, Kansas
Professional Communicators, KS, Americus

Funnell, Lee
sales@sccmediaserver.com, Vice Pres.,
The Software Construction Co. (SCC), GA,
Alpharetta

Fuqua, Brad ....(503) 480-6919
brad.fuqua@lee.net, Ed. , The Philomath
Express, OR, Corvallis

Furchner, Julie .... (605) 224-7301 x123
julie.furchner@capjournal.com, Adv. Consultant
, Capital Journal, SD, Pierre

Furio, Brian
bfurio@ycp.edu, Chair, York College of
Pennsylvania, PA, York

Furlong, Teresa .... (270) 678-5171 Ext. 222
tfurlong@glasgowdailytimes.com, Glasgow
Daily Times, KY, Glasgow

Furry, Lucy........................(310) 306-6100
Vice Pres., Syndication, The Science Advice
Goddess-Amy Alkon, Santa Monica

Furu, Marcia
advisor_circ@j-adgraphics.com, Circ. Mgr, Ad-
Visor and Chronicle, MI, Marshall

Fuschetti, Steve........................(513) 587-2934
sfuschetti@gmti.gannett.com, Pres./CEO,
Gannett Media Technologies International
(GMTI), OH, Cincinnati

Fuschetti, Steve
info@celebro.com, Pres./CEO, Celebro, OH,
Cincinnati

Futch, Jennifer
jfutch@npco.com, Adv. Mgr., The Polk County
Standard Journal, GA, Cedartown

Futhey, Paul ....(416) 774-2256
pfuthey@insidetoronto.com, Mng. Ed., The York
Guardian, ON, Toronto

Futhey, Paul ....(416) 774-2256
pfuthey@insidetoronto.com, Mng. Ed., North
York Mirror, ON, Toronto

Futrell, Al ....(502) 852-6976
Al@louisville.edu, Chair, University of
Louisville, KY, Louisville

Futrell, Ashley B. ....(252) 946-9797
news@wdnweb.com, Pres./Pub., Washington
Daily News, NC, Washington

Fyffe, Tony
editor@bigsandynews.com, Mng. Ed., The Big Sandy News, KY, Louisa

Fyffe, Tony ....(606) 638-4581
editor@bigsandynews.com, Ed., The Tri-Rivers Advertiser, KY, Louisa

Fyke, Corey ....(860) 495-8245
cfyke@thewesterlysun.com, News & Digital Editor, The Westerly Sun, CT, Pawcatuck

G

Gable, Erik ....(419) 530-7788
egable@independentcollegian.com, Adviser, University of Toledo, OH, Toledo

Gable, Paul ....(317) 398-1277
pgable@shelbynews.com, Ed., The Shelbyville News, IN, Shelbyville

Gabor, Elena
egabor@bradley.edu, Asst. Prof., Bradley University, IL, Peoria

Gackle, Jill Denning
jilldg@restel.net, Second Vice President, North Dakota Newspaper Association, ND, Bismarck

Gackle, Michael W.
nsads@srt.com, Pub., The Northern Sentry, ND, Minot

Gackle, Mike
coalnews@westriv.com, Pub., Owner, Beulah Beacon, ND, Beulah

Gackle, Mike
mgackle@nd-bhginc.com, Pub., McLean County Independent, ND, Garrison

Gaddis, J. Pason.....................(239) 333-2135
pgaddis@floridaweekly.com, Pres./Pub., Bonita Springs Florida Weekly, FL, Naples
pgaddis@floridaweekly.com, Pres./Pub., Fort Myers Florida Weekly, FL, Fort Myers
pgaddis@floridaweekly.com, President and Group Publisher, Palm Beach Gardens Florida Weekly, FL, Palm Beach Gardens
pgaddis@floridaweekly.com, Pres./Grp. Pub., Naples Florida Weekly, FL, Naples
pgaddis@floridaweekly.com, Pres./Grp. Pub., Punta Gorda/Port Charlotte Florida Weekly, FL, Punta Gorda
pgaddis@floridaweekly.com, Pub., Florida Today, FL, Melbourne

Gaddy, John ....(904) 261-3696
jgaddy@fbnewsleader.com, Circulation Manager, Nassau County Record, FL, Callahan

Gaddy, John ....904 261_-3696
jgaddy@fbnewsleader.com, Circulation/ Distribution Manager, News-Leader, FL, Fernandina Beach

Gaddy, Joy ....(770) 227 - 3276 x202
advertising@griffindailynews.com, Pub./Adv. Dir., Griffin Daily News, GA, Griffin

Gaden-Flanagan, Dorothy ....(630) 388-6903
dorothy@copia.com, Vice Pres., Mktg., Copia International Ltd., IL, Roselle

Gadson, Catina
catina.gadson@morris.com, Adv. Sales, Hampton County Guardian, SC, Hampton

Gaebel, Gerald
lithco@lithcoinc.com, Pres., Lithco Inc., CA, Culver City

Gaedert, Cindy ....(517) 543-1099 ext 225
cgwing@county-journal.com, Pub./Sales/ Owner, Flashes Advertising & News, MI, Charlotte

Gaedert, Cindy ....(269) 209-3532
cgwing@county-journal.com, Owner, Pub. & Sales, The County Journal, MI, Charlotte

Gaeser, Jeffrey ....(407) 834-8787
news@orlandoheritage.com, Ed., Heritage Florida Jewish News, FL, Fern Park

Gaffney, Michael ....(978) 739-1395
saugus@wickedlocal.com, Ed., Saugus Advertiser, MA, Danvers

Gage, Bob ....(361) 886-3730
gageb@caller.com, Circ. Opns. Mgr., Corpus Christi Caller-Times, TX, Corpus Christi

Gage, Donald ....(519) 326-4434
gagerom@bowesnet.com, Pub., Leamington Shopper, ON, Leamington

Gage, Gwen...........................(617) 619-6272
gwen.gage@bostonherald.com, VP/Promotion, Boston Herald, MA, Boston

Gage, Linda
lgage@bowesnet.com, Adv. Mgr., Leamington Shopper, ON, Leamington

Gage, Ralph
rgage@ljworld.com, Lawrence Journal-World, KS, Lawrence

Gage, Ralph D.
rgage@ljworld.com, Cor. Sec., WorldWest LLC, KS, Lawrence

Gagliano, John ....(218) 855-5810
JOHN.GAGLIANO@BRAINERDDISPATCH.COM, Circ. Dir., Brainerd Dispatch, MN, Brainerd

Gagliardi, Robert
robert.gagliardi@abc-amega.com, Regional Account Manager, NEW YORK MEDIA CREDIT GROUP, NY, Buffalo

Gagne, Carole
carole.gagne@monteregieweb.com, Ed., Le Soleil Du St-laurent, QC, Chateauguay

Gagne, Gary
ggagne@mr-llc.net, Maine Daily Newspaper Publishers Association, ME, Cape Elizabeth

Gagnon, Claude
cgagnon@lesoleil.com, Pub./Pres. & Ed., Le Soleil, QC, Quebec

Gagnon, Jean
jgagnon@ledroit.com, Mng. Ed., Le Droit, ON, Ottawa

Gagnon, Jean..........................(418) 562-4040
jean.gagnon@quebecormedia.com, Avant Poste, QC, Matane
jean.gagnon@quebecormedia.com, Ed., Le Riverain, QC, Matane
jean.gagnon@quebecormedia.com, Voix De La Matanie, QC, Matane

Gagnon, Jean ....(418) 562-4040
jean.gagnon@quebecormedia.com, (Ed.), La Voix Gaspesienne, QC, Matane

Gagnon, John.........................(352) 753-1119
john.gagnon@thevillagesmedia.com, Circ. Dir., The Villages Daily Sun, FL, The Villages

Gagnon, Maurice
montage@leplacoteux.com, Ed. , Le Placoteux, QC, Saint Pascal

Gahagan, Jack
glmsconf@comcast.net, Bus. Mgr./Sec./ Treasurer, Great Lakes/Midstates Newspaper Conference, Inc., OH, Colombus

Gahan, Terry
tgahan@mnpubs.com, Co-Pub., Good Age, MN, Minneapolis

Gahan, Terry
tgahan@mnpubs.com, Adv. Mgr., The Downtown Journal, MN, Minneapolis

Gaier, Paul ....(815) 987-1451
pgaier@rrstar.com, Publisher, Rockford Register Star, IL, Rockford
pgaier@rrstar.com, Pub., The Journal-Standard, IL, Freeport

Gaike, Vita
latvija.amerika@gmail.com, Ed., Latvija-Amerika, ON, Toronto

Gail, Richard
cnews@frontiernet.net, Pub, Canby News, MN, Canby

Gainer, Vickie ....(850) 315-4413
vgainer@pcnh.com, Regional Business Development and Marketing Director, Northwest Florida Daily News, FL, Fort Walton Beach

Gaines, Eric.....................................ext. 128
Adv. Mgr., New Pittsburgh Courier, PA, Pittsburgh

Gaines, John
jgaines@thehawkeye.com, Photo Dept. Mgr., The Hawk Eye, IA, Burlington

Gaines, Mary ....(270) 783-3206
mgaines@bgdailynews.com, Co-Owner, Daily News, KY, Bowling Green

Gaines, Pipes ....(270) 781-1700
pgaines@bgdailynews.com, Pub./Pres., Daily News, KY, Bowling Green

Gaines, Scott ....(270) 781-1700
sgaines@bgdailynews.com, Co-Pub. , Daily News, KY, Bowling Green

Gaines, Steve ....(270) 783-3269
sgaines@bgdailynews.com, Editorial Page Ed., Daily News, KY, Bowling Green

Gainor, Mike
editor@pinecitymn.com, Ed., Pine County Courier, MN, Pine City
editor@pinecitymn.com, Ed., Pine City Pioneer, MN, Pine City

Gairdner, Janet......................(250) 480-3251
jgairdner@blackpress.ca, Pub., Oak Bay News, BC, Victoria

Gaiter, Cristy
classifieds@olneydailymail.com, Adv. Mgr., The Advantage, IL, Olney

Galant, Richard ....(631) 843-3274
Mng. Ed., News, Newsday, NY, Melville

Galantis, James
jgalantis@meadvilletribune.com, Pub., The Meadville Tribune, PA, Meadville

Galati, Gerry Lynn ....(508) 428-8700
L.printing@comcast.net, Graphic Manager, Otis Notice, MA, Cotuit

Galbraith, Deb.........................(610) 740-0944
dgalbraith@tnonline.com, Ed., Salisbury Press, PA, Allentown

Galbraith, Debra ....(610) 740-0944
dgalbraith@tnonline.com, Ed., East Penn Press, PA, Allentown

Galbraith, Judy ....(602) 690-2912
judy.galbraith@pvc.maricopa.edu, Paradise Valley Cmty. College, AZ, Phoenix

Gale, Jim ....(202) 650-6406
jgale@cq.com, Sr. Vice Pres., Sales, Congressional Quarterly, Inc., DC, Washington

Gale, Kendra
kendra.gale@colorado.edu, Asst. Prof., University of Colorado, CO, Boulder

Galer, John M.
journal@consolidated.net, Pub., Gazette-News, IL, Bunker Hill

Galer, John M.
thejournal-news@consolidated.net, Publisher, M & M Journal, IL, Hillsboro

Galer, John M.
chronicl@madisontelco.com, Pub., Madison County Chronicle, IL, Worden
chronicl@madisontelco.com, Pub., Southwestern Journal, IL, Brighton

Galetano, James J.
jgaletano@dailyherald.com, Sr. Vice. Pres./ Director of Circulation, Daily Herald, IL, Arlington Heights

Galician, Mary-Lou
drfun@asu.edu, Assoc. Prof., Arizona State University, AZ, Tempe

Galindo, Amanda
amanda@alvareviewcourier.net, Ad Rep, Alva Review-Courier, OK, Alva

Galindo, Judy
jgalindo@norsanmultimedia.com, Hola Noticias, NC, Charlotte

Gall, Robert.............................(315) 792-5056
rgall@uticaod.com, Cir. Dir., The Herkimer Telegram, NY, Herkimer
rgall@uticaod.com, Circ. Dir. , The Observer-Dispatch, NY, Utica

Gall, Robert
rgall@uticaod.com, Circ. Mgr, Your Valley, NY, Utica

Gall, Steve ....(715) 426-1052
sgall@republican-eagle.com, Gen. Mgr., The Farmington Independent, MN, Farmington
sgall@republican-eagle.com, Adv. Dir., Republican Eagle, MN, Red Wing

Gall, Steven ....(651) 253-3049
gallboy58@gmail.com, Cut Bank Pioneer Press, MT, Cut Bank

Gallabrese, Ross
rgallabrese@heraldstaronline.com, Mng. Ed., Herald-Star, OH, Steubenville

Gallacher, John .... (860) 347-3331, Ext. 156
jgallacher@registercitizen.com, Adv. Dir. , The Middletown Press, CT, Middletown
jgallacher@registercitizen.com, Adv. Mgr., The Register Citizen, CT, Torrington

Gallagher, Amanda
agallagher3@elon.edu, Asst. Prof., Elon University, NC, Elon

Gallagher, Cindy
cgallagher@breezenewspapers.com, Adv. Mgr, North Fort Myers Neighbor, FL, Cape Coral
cgallagher@breezenewspapers.com, Adv. Mgr, Sanibel-Captiva Islander, FL, Cape Coral
cgallagher@breezenewspapers.com, Adv. Mgr, Fort Myers Beach Observer, FL, Fort Myers Beach

Gallagher, Cynthia
cgallagher@breezenewspapers.com, Adv. Dir., The Pine Island Eagle, FL, Bokeelia

Gallagher, Dana........................(505) 286-1212
jeannette@lobo.net, Adv. Sales Rep, The Independent, NM, Edgewood

Gallagher, Dave
dave@cardinnguyen.com, Business Ed., The Bellingham Herald, WA, Bellingham

Gallagher, Lisa
lgallagher@iwanna.com, Prodn. Mgr., Iwanna, NC, Asheville

Gallagher, Michael
mike.gallagher@camaspostrecord.com, Adv. Mgr., At Your Leisure, WA, Camas

Gallagher, Michael S.
mgallagher@sunshinepaper.com, Vice Pres., Sales/Mktg., SunShine Paper Co., CO, Aurora

Gallagher, Mike
mike.gallagher@camaspostrecord.com, Pub./ Adv. Mgr., Camas-Washougal Post Record, WA, Camas

Gallagher, Ronnie ....(704) 797-4287
rgallagher@salisburypost.com, Sports Ed., Salisbury Post, NC, Salisbury

Gallagher, Steven..........(905) 358-5711 Ext. 1129
steven.gallagher@sunmedia.ca, Ed. in Chief, Niagara Falls Review, ON, Niagara Falls

Gallagher, Tim
tgallagher@siouxcityjournal.com, Society/ Women's Ed., Sioux City Journal, IA, Sioux City

Gallant, Andre ....(706) 208-2230
andre.gallant@onlineathens.com, Arts/ Entertainment Ed., Athens Banner-Herald, GA, Athens

Gallant, James
gallantj@elms.edu, Elms College, MA, Chicopee

Gallant, Jean-Charles
jc.gallant@acadiemedia.com, Dir. of Sales, L'Acadie Nouvelle, NB, Caraquet

Gallant, Sharon .... **(709) 896-3341**
sgallant@thelabradorian.ca, Adv, The Labradorian, NL, Happy Valley

Gallardo, Margaret .... **(915) 546-6166**
mgallardo@elpasotimes.com, Sports Editor , El Paso Times, TX, El Paso
mgallardo@elpasotimes.com, Sports Editor , El Paso y Mas, TX, El Paso

Gallardo, Marti .... **(212) 597-5619**
marti.gallardo@wsj.com, Class. Adv., VP Vertical Markets, The Wall Street Journal, NY, New York

Gallatin, Dianne .... **(307) 755-3304**
gallatin@laramieboomerang.com, Bus. Office Mgr., Laramie Boomerang, WY, Laramie

Gallaty, Conan .... **(501) 378-3441**
cgallaty@arkansasonline.com, Online Dir., Arkansas Democrat-Gazette, AR, Little Rock

Galle, Roger
rgalle@hillsbororeporter.com, Pub./Adv. Dir., Hillsboro Reporter, TX, Hillsboro

Galle, Shelley
advantage005@centurytel.net, Office Mgr., The Warroad Pioneer, MN, Warroad

Gallego, Nicole
marketing.freepress@unlv.edu, Director of Marketing & Sales, University of Nevada, Las Vegas, NV, Las Vegas

Gallego, Nicole
marketing.freepress@unlv.edu, Director of Marketing & Sales, University of Nevada, Las Vegas, NV, Las Vegas

Gallegos, Jason .... **(719) 384-1430**
jgallegos@ljtdmail.com, Multimedia Sales Exec., The Fowler Tribune, CO, Fowler
jgallegos@ljtdmail.com, Multimedia Sales Exec., Ag Journal, CO, La Junta
jgallegos@ljtdmail.com, Multimedia Sales Exec., Bent County Democrat, CO, Las Animas

Gallegos, Jason .... **(719) 384-1430**
jason@ljtdmail.com, Adv. Dir. , La Junta Tribune-Democrat, CO, La Junta

Gallegos, Mary
mgallegos@pleasantonexpress.com, Adv. Dir., Pleasanton Express, TX, Pleasanton

Galli, Linda
linda.galli@njfamily.com, Dir., Adv., New Jersey Family, NJ, Summit

Galli, Linda
linda.galli@njfamily.com, Dir., Adv., Union County Family, NJ, Mountainside

Galli, Linda
linda.galli@njfamily.com, Dir., Adv., Morris County Family, NJ, Mountainside

Gallian, Wally
wally@mynwmo.com, Publisher, Cameron Shopper, MO, Cameron
wally@mynwmo.com, Pub., The Citizen Observer, MO, Cameron

Gallimore, Joe .... **(863) 494-0300**
jgallimore@sun-herald.com, Pub., Arcadian, FL, Arcadia

Gallimore, Joe .... **(863) 494-2434**
jgallimore@sun-herald.com, Publisher, Arcadian, Sun Coast Media Group Inc, FL, Punta Gorda

Gallman, Vanessa .... **(859) 231-1393**
vgallman@herald-leader.com, Editorial Page Ed., Lexington Herald-Leader, KY, Lexington

Gallo, Andrea
andreaelizabeth.gallo@gmail.com, Editor in Chief, Louisiana State University, LA, Baton Rouge

Gallo, John C. .... **(215) 336-2500**
jgallo@southphillyreview.com, Pub./COO,

South Philly Review, NJ, Cherry Hill
jgallo@southphillyreview.com, Pub., Philadelphia Weekly, NJ, Cherry Hill

Gallo, Michelle
mgallo@hammondstar.com, Adv. Dir., The Daily Star, LA, Hammond

Galloway, Debra .... **(850) 599-2292**
dgalloway@tallahassee.com, News Ass't, Tallahassee Democrat, FL, Tallahassee

Galloway, Justin .... **(713) 487-6566**
justin@houstonvoice.org, Publisher, Houston Voice, TX, Houston

Galloway, Robert .... **(775) 788-6702**
rgalloway@rgj.com, Key Accnt. Sales Mgr., Reno Gazette-Journal, NV, Reno

Gallup, Larry .... **(920) 993-1000**
lgallup@appleton.gannett.com, Aud. Analyst, News-Record, WI, Appleton
lgallup@appleton.gannett.com, Editor/Opinion, Post-Crescent, WI, Appleton

Galvin, Michael .... **(334) 261-1582**
mgalvin@gannett.com, Pres., Montgomery Advertiser, AL, Montgomery

Gambardella, Ed .... **(262) 656-6243**
egambardella@kenoshanews.com, Adv. Dir., Bargaineer, WI, Kenosha

Gambardella, Ed .... **(262) 656-6243**
ejgambardella@kenoshanews.com, Adv. Dir., Kenosha News, WI, Kenosha

Gambell, Julie .... **(505) 564-4531**
jgambell@daily-times.com, Dist. Cir. Sup., The Daily Times, NM, Farmington

Gambill, Angie
editor@thetomahawk.com, Ed., The Tomahawk, TN, Mountain City

Gamble, Danielle .... **(419) 530-7788**
editor@independentcollegian.com, Editor-in-Chief, University of Toledo, OH, Toledo

Gamble, DeRay .... **(620) 694-5700 Ext. 252**
dgamble@hutchnews.com, Graphic Designer, The Hutchinson News, KS, Hutchinson

Gamble, Phonda .... **(937) 225-0550**
phonda.gamble@coxinc.com, Sr. Director, Product Delivery, Dayton Daily News, OH, Franklin

Gamble, Vicki .... **(208) 397-4440**
times1@dcdi.net, Editor, Aberdeen Times, ID, Aberdeen

Gambles, Sarah
sgambles@dvtnv.com, Reporter, Desert Valley Times, NV, Mesquite

Gamboa, Jonathan
designdirector@dailylobo.com, Design Dir., New Mexico Daily Lobo, NM, Albuquerque

Gambrell, Mandy
mgambrell@coxohio.com, Lifestyle Ed., JournalNews, OH, Hamilton

Gambrell, Sudie .... **(251) 947-7712**
SUDIE@GULFCOASTNEWSPAPERS.COM, Gulf Coast Newspapers, AL, Fairhope

Gambrell, Sudie .... **(251) 943-2151**
sudie@gulfcoastnewspapers.com, Pub., The Baldwin Times Independent, AL, Foley
sudie@gulfcoastnewspapers.com, Pub., The Islander, AL, Foley

Gamel, Gerry
mcnnews@hctc.net, Ed., Mason County News, TX, Mason

Gammon, Suzanne .... **(705) 753-2930**
tribune@westnipissing.com, Ed., The Tribune, ON, Sturgeon Falls

Gammons, Bob
schaefer01@snet.net, Pres., Schaefer Machine Co., Inc., CT, Deep River

Ganak, Steve
adreps1@yahoo.com, Pres., Ad Reps, MA, Boston

Gandy, Terry E.
tgandy@kdhnews.com, Gen. Mgr., Killeen Daily Herald, TX, Killeen

Gang, Duane
dgang@tennessean.com, Content Strategist, TN Media, TN, Nashville
dgang@tennessean.com, Content Strategist, The Tennessean, TN, Nashville

Ganje, Lucy
lucy.ganje@und.edu, Assoc. Prof., University of North Dakota, ND, Grand Forks

Gannaway, Glen
ggannaway@coalfield.com, News Ed., The Post, VA, Big Stone Gap

Gannon, Richard
rgannon@kspress.com, Dir., Gov't Affairs, Kansas Press Association, KS, Topeka

Gans, Felicia
editor@dailyfreepress.com, Managing Ed., Boston Univ., MA, Boston

Gant, Michael .... **ext. 1348**
Arts Ed., Metro, CA, San Jose

Ganz, Tom .... **(708) 524-4400**
ganz@pioneerlocal.com, Bureau Chief, Niles Herald-Spectator, IL, Chicago

Gao, May
mgao@kennesaw.edu, Asst. Prof., Kennesaw State University, GA, Kennesaw

Garay, Matt .... **(978) 632-8000 ext. 22**
mgaray@thegardnernews.com, Managing Ed. , The Gardner News, MA, Gardner

Garber, Mark .... **(503) 546-9853**
mgarber@theoutlookonline.com, Pres., Sustainable Life, OR, Portland
mgarber@theoutlookonline.com, Pres., The Portland Tribune, OR, Portland
mgarber@theoutlookonline.com, Pres., Estacada News, OR, Estacada
mgarber@theoutlookonline.com, Pres./Pub., Pamplin Media Group, OR, Portland
mgarber@theoutlookonline.com, Pres., Sandy Post, OR, Gresham
mgarber@theoutlookonline.com, Pub., The Beaverton Valley Times, OR, Portland

Garber, Phil
pgarber@recordernewspapers.com, Ed., Mount Olive Chronicle, NJ, Bernardsville

Garber, William E. .... **(269) 473-3103**
bill@ilsw.com, Founder, Interlink, MI, Berrien Springs

Garceau, Viviane
viviane.garceau@enpa.be, Office Mgr., European Newspaper Publishers' Association, 1050 Bruxelles

Garcia, Arnold .... **(512) 445-3667**
agarcia@statesman.com, Editorial Page Ed., Austin American-Statesman, TX, Austin

Garcia, Astrid .... **(563) 383-2100**
astrid.garcia@lee.net, VP, HR, Lee Enterprises, Inc., IA, Davenport

Garcia, Astrid .... **(314) 340-8045**
AGARCIA@POST-DISPATCH.COM, St. Louis Post-Dispatch, MO, Saint Louis

Garcia, Carlos
carlos.garcia@dallasobserver.com, Circ. Dir., Dallas Observer, TX, Dallas

Garcia, Carmen Sara
cgarcia@sagrado.edu, Dir., University of the Sacred Heart, PR, San Juan

Garcia, Clara .... **(505) 864-4472**
Ed., Valencia County News-Bulletin, NM, Belen

Garcia, Claudia .... **(956) 682-2423**
claudia@valleytowncrier.com, Majors/Nationals Representative, Edinburg Review, TX, McAllen

Garcia, Daniel .... **(908) 352-6654**
lavoznj@aol.com, Adv. Mgr., La Voz, NJ, Elizabeth

Garcia, Deborah .... **(408) 842-1546**
dgarcia@newsvmedia.com, Adv. Dir., The Gilroy Dispatch, CA, Gilroy

Garcia, Deborah
dgarcia@newspress.com, NYU Stern School of Bus., NY, New York
dgarcia@newspress.com, Ed. in chief, Santa Barbara News-Press, CA, Santa Barbara

Garcia, Dennis
dgarcia@courier-tribune.com, Sports Ed., The Courier-Tribune, NC, Asheboro

Garcia, Guillermo .... **(305) 347-6658**
ggarcia@alm.com, Director of Operations & MIS, Miami Daily Business Review, FL, Miami

Garcia, Hermie
philreporter@gmail.com, Ed., Philippine Reporter, ON, Toronto

Garcia, Javier
javiergarcia@efe.com, Rep., EFE News Services - Algiers, Algeria, Algiers

Garcia, Jessica .... **(603) 352-1234 Ext. 1701**
jgarcia@keenesentinel.com, Inter. Media Dir., The Keene Sentinel, NH, Keene

Garcia, Jodie
jgarcia@ottawaherald.com, Reader Engagement Ed., The Ottawa Herald, KS, Ottawa

Garcia, Jose M.
sales@laguiafamiliar.net, Pub., La Guia Familiar, CA, Van Nuys

Garcia, Josie .... **(830) 775-1551**
josie.garcia@delrionewsherald.com, AR rep , Del Rio News-Herald, TX, Del Rio

Garcia, Kay .... **(209) 249-3549**
kgarcia@mantecabulletin.com, Composing Mgr., Manteca Bulletin, CA, Manteca

Garcia, Manny
manny.garcia@rightthisminute.com, Pres., Prensa Hispana, AZ, Phoenix

Garcia, Manny .... **(239) 263-4863**
manny.garcia@naplesnews.com, Editor, Naples Daily News, FL, Naples

Garcia, Manuel
mgarcia@oakvillebeaver.com, Prodn. Mgr., Oakville Beaver, ON, Oakville

Garcia, Marcela
editor@elplaneta.com, Ed., El Planeta Publishing, MA, Boston

Garcia, Maria
rgsunads@cybermesa.com, General Manager, Rio Grande Sun, NM, Espanola

Garcia, Maria Lopez
rgsun@cybermesa.com, Adv./Mktg., Rio Grande Sun, NM, Espanola

Garcia, Martha .... **(530) 346-2232**
marthag@goldcountrymedia.com , Ed., Colfax Record, CA, Colfax

Garcia, Meghann
mgarcia@uvaldeleadernews.com, Managing Ed., Uvalde Leader-News, TX, Uvalde

Garcia, Petina
pgarcia@wilsontimes.com, Ad Sales Asst., The Wilson Times, NC, Wilson

Garcia, Ralph .... **(786) 286-8787**
patrianews@aol.com, Book Editor, El Nuevo PATRIA, FL, Miami

Garcia, Robert .... **ext. 226**
Graphics Ed./Art Dir., The Daily Sentinel, CO, Grand Junction

Garcia, Vanessa .... **(505) 287-4411**
vgarcia@cibolabeacon.com, Adv. Acct. Mgr., Cibola Beacon, NM, Grants

Garcia , Jennifer
rgsun@cybermesa.com, News Ed., Rio Grande Sun, NM, Espanola

Garcia , Paz .... **(915) 546-6387**

pgarcia@elpasotimes.com, Information Technology Dir., El Paso Times, TX, El Paso

pgarcia@elpasotimes.com, Information Technology Dir., El Paso y Mas, TX, El Paso

Garcia Marble, Jessie.................(414) 229-4436
marble@uwm.edu, Associate Lecturer, University of Wisconsin-Milwaukee / Department of Journalism, Advertising, and Media Studies (JAMS), WI, Milwaukee

Gard, Jeff...ext. 330
jeff.gard@sunmedia.ca, Ed., Northumberland Today, ON, Cobourg

Gard, Richard
richard.gard@molawersmedia.com, Pub., The St. Louis Countian, MO, Saint Louis

Gardiner, Wyatt ....(360) 577-2570
Circ. Mgr., Tahoe Daily Tribune, CA, South Lake Tahoe

Gardiner, Wyatt ....(509) 664-7120
gardiner@wenatcheeworld.com, Circulation and Production Director, The Wenatchee World, WA, Wenatchee

Gardner, Adam ....(913) 367-0583 ext. 20414
adam.gardner@npgco.com, Sports Ed., Atchison Globe, KS, Atchison

Gardner, Furman ....ext. 200
Mktg. Dir., Paulding Neighbor, GA, Marietta

Gardner, Jim............................(415) 288-4955
jgardner@bizjournals.com, Mng. Ed., East Bay Business Times, CA, San Francisco

Gardner, Joseph
circulation@olneydailymail.com, Circ. Mgr., The Advantage, IL, Olney

Gardner, Karie............................(801) 625-4394
Adv. Supvr., Classified Telephone Sales, Standard-Examiner, UT, Ogden

Gardner, Kathy
danamclass@gmail.com, Vice Pres., Integrated Research Div., CanWest Media Sales, ON, Toronto

danamclass@gmail.com, Prod. Mgr., American Classifieds - Alexandria, LA, Alexandria

Gardner, Mark
mark.gardner@sappi.com, Pres./CEO, Sappi Fine Paper North America, MA, Boston

Gardner, Matt
leadereditor@hngnews.com, Managing Ed., The Lake Mills Leader, WI, Lake Mills

Gardner, Matt........................(912) 496-3585
editor@charltonherald.com, Ed., Charlton County Herald, GA, Folkston

Gardner, Robert ....(530) 896-7703
rgardner@chicoer.com, Controller, Chico Enterprise-Record, CA, Chico

Gardner Aarons, Ginger ....(205) 443-5616
gaarons@bizjournals.com, Audience Dev Dir, Birmingham Business Journal, AL, Birmingham

Gardyne, Marilyn
advertising@newportvermontdailyexpress.com, Adv. Dir., The Newport Daily Express, VT, Newport

Gareau, Chris
editor@interior-news.com, Ed, The Smithers Interior News, BC, Smithers

Gareau, Michel
info-nord@sympatico.ca, Adv. Mgr., Information Du Nord Mont Tremblant, QC, Mont-Tremblant

Garey, Ashley
agarey@trcle.com, Graphics Ed./Art Dir., Cleburne Times-Review, TX, Cleburne

Garfinkel, Laura
laura@bradley.edu, Lectr., Bradley University, IL, Peoria

Gargano, James
independent@humboldtnews.com, Pub./Gen. Mgr., Humboldt Independent, IA, Humboldt

Garick, David
dgarick@colsdioc.org, Ed., The Catholic Times, OH, Columbus

Gariepy, Peter
peterg@mrbeer.com, Pres., JupiterImages, AZ, Tucson

Garland, Frank ....(814) 871-5808
garland003@gannon.edu, Gannon Univ., PA, Erie

Garland, Steve ....(828) 632-2532
sgarland@taylorsvilletimes.com, Adv. Mgr., The Taylorsville Times, NC, Taylorsville

Garman, Gloria.........................(785) 378-3191
jcrecord@alltel.net, Office Mgr., Jewell County Record, KS, Mankato

Garman, Mont
magnuson@hagadone.com, CFO, Hagadone Corporation, ID, Coeur D Alene

Garman, Shannon ....(717) 255-8205
sgarman@pennlive.com, National Adv. Sales, The Patriot-News, PA, Mechanicsburg

Garmendia, Marco..................(719) 589-2553
mgarmendia@alamosanews.com, Adv. sales, Valley Courier, CO, Alamosa

Garmo, Morgan
mrg13@albion.edu, Opinions editor, Albion College, MI, Albion

Garmon, Ryan ....(770) 205 - 8960
rgarmon@forsythnews.com, Adv. Dir., Forsyth County News, GA, Cumming

Garner, Andrew........................(251) 368-2123
andrew.garner@atmoreadvance.com, Editor, Atmore Advance, AL, Atmore

Garner, Brooks
brooks.garner@okstate.edu, Assoc. Prof., Oklahoma State University, OK, Stillwater

Garner, Gary ....(254) 778-4444
garyg@tdtnews.com, Retail Adv. Mgr., Temple Daily Telegram, TX, Temple

Garner, J. Ken ....(703) 836-9200
info@epicomm.org, President & CEO, Epicomm, VA, Alexandria

Garner, Ron ....(501) 505-1219
ron.garner@thecabin.net, Circulation Operations Mgr, Log Cabin Democrat, AR, Conway

Garnett, Craig
cgarnett@uvaldeleadernews.com, Pub./Ed., Uvalde Leader-News, TX, Uvalde

Garnett, Craig
cgarnett@uvaldeleadernews.com, Pub., Frio-Nueces Current, TX, Pearsall

Garnica, Jenna ....(316) 283-1500 x101
jgarnica@thekansan.com, Classifieds Adv/, The Newton Kansan, KS, Newton

Garrahan, John........................(856) 563-5248
jgarrahan@gannettnj.com, Plan. Ed., The Daily Journal, NJ, Vineland

Garreck, Robin
production@hintonvoice.ca, Prodn./Distrib. Mgr., The Hinton Voice, AB, Hinton

Garren, Linda
linda@edwgroupinc.com, Office Mgr., Daily Journal/Messenger, SC, Seneca

Garret, Wayne
GARRETT_K@students.lynchburg.edu, Copy Desk Chief, Lynchburg College, VA, Lynchburg

Garrett, Alyssa ....(949) 388-7700 ext. 100
agarrett@picketfencemedia.com, The Capistrano Dispatch, CA, Capistrano Beach
agarrett@picketfencemedia.com, Bus. Ops. Mgr., Dana Point Times, CA, Capistrano Beach

Garrett, Dana
danagarrett@post-register.com, Pub., Lockhart Post-Register, TX, Lockhart

Garrett, Deborah
dgarrett@mycarrollnews.com, Adv. Sales, River City Trading Post, KY, Carrollton
dgarrett@mycarrollnews.com, Adv. Sales Consult., Trimble Banner, KY, Bedford

Garrett, Grady ....(928) 539-6882
jseverson@yumasun.com, Sports Ed., Yuma Sun, AZ, Yuma

Garrett, John
jgarrett@cuny.edu, Dir., Classified, The New York Sun, NY, New York

Garrett, Kathy
cmorgan@colliervilleherald.net, Adv. Mgr., The Collierville Herald, TN, Collierville

Garrett, Lee ....(770) 428-9411 ext. 301
lgarrett@mdjonline.com, Gen. Mgr., Marietta Daily Journal, GA, Marietta

Garrett, Lee ....(770) 428-9411 x 301
lgarrett@mdjonline.com, Gen. Mgr., East Cobb Neighbor, GA, Marietta
lgarrett@mdjonline.com, Gen. Mgr., Northside/Sandy Springs/Vinings/Brookhaven Neighbor, GA, Sandy Springs
lgarrett@mdjonline.com, Gen. Mgr., South Cobb Neighbor, GA, Marietta
lgarrett@mdjonline.com, Gen. Mgr., Kennesaw-Acworth Neighbor, GA, Marietta
lgarrett@mdjonline.com, Gen. Mgr., Cherokee Tribune, GA, Canton

Garrett, Norb
ngarrett@picketfencemedia.com, The Capistrano Dispatch, CA, Capistrano Beach
ngarrett@picketfencemedia.com, CEO/pUB., San Clemente Times, CA, Capistrano Beach
ngarrett@picketfencemedia.com, Dana Point Times, CA, Capistrano Beach

Garrett, Thomas........................(870) 508-8053
sgarrett@baxterbulletin.com, Editorial page Ed., The Baxter Bulletin, AR, Mountain Home

Garrick, Rick
rickg@wataway.on.ca, Reporter, Wawatay News, ON, Sioux Lookout

Garris, Kevin ....(651) 228-2028
kgarris@pioneerpress.com, VP, Production, St. Paul Pioneer Press, MN, Saint Paul

Garrison, Homer ....(580) 326-3311
homer@hugonews.com, Prodn. Mgr., Hugo News, OK, Hugo

Garrison, John
johng@hendersondailynews.com, Circ. Mgr., Henderson Daily News, TX, Henderson

Garrison, Mary ....(419) 448-2003
mgarriso@heidelberg.edu, Visiting Assistant Professor of Communication, Heidelberg University, OH, Tiffin

Garrison, Matt ....(618) 985-2828 ext. 8387
John A. Logan College, IL, Carterville

Garrison, Ron ....(859) 231-1601
rgarrison@herald-leader.com, Visual Ed., Lexington Herald-Leader, KY, Lexington

Garrison, Teresa ....(903) 237-7787
Bindery Mgr., Longview News-Journal, TX, Longview

Garrity, Maureen......................(530) 896-7752
mgarrity@chicoer.com, Dir., HR, Chico Enterprise-Record, CA, Chico

Garske, Monica
monica@flashnews.com, Sr. Ed., Wireless Flash News, Inc., San Diego

Garson, Arnold ....(502) 582-4295
publisher@courier-journal.com, Pres./Pub., The Courier-Journal, KY, Louisville

Garstin, Michaela
michaela@squamishchief.com, Ed, Squamish Chief, BC, Squamish

Garth, Shelly
classifieds@guardonline.com, Classified Adv. Mgr, Batesville Daily Guard, AR, Batesville

Garth, William

wgarth34@yahoo.com, CEO/Pub., Chicago Citizen Newspapers, IL, Chicago
wgarth34@yahoo.com, Pub., South Suburban Citizen, IL, Chicago
wgarth34@yahoo.com, Pub., Southend Citizen, IL, Chicago
wgarth34@yahoo.com, Pub., Hyde Park Citizen, IL, Chicago

Garver, Ben
bgarver@berkshireeagle.com, Photo Ed., The Berkshire Eagle, MA, Pittsfield

Garvey, Megan
megan.garvey@latimes.com, Digital, Deputy Managing Ed., Los Angeles Times, CA, Los Angeles

Garvey, Tim
garvey@valassis.com, VP, Integrated Media Sales
, Valassis, MI, Livonia

Garvie, Glenn
garvie@northjersey.com, Vice Pres., Prodn., Glen Rock Gazette, NJ, Ridgewood

Garvie, Glenn........................(973) 569-7027
garvie@northjersey.com, Vice Pres., Prodn., Su Guia, NJ, Clifton

Garvie, Glenn.........................(973) 569-7027
garvie@northjersey.com, Vice Pres., Prodn., Twin-Boro News, NJ, Cresskill

Garvin, Felecia........................(903) 813-2296
Austin College, TX, Sherman

Garwood, Elizabeth.........(620) 694-5700 Ext. 115
egarwood@hutchnews.com, Single Copy Mgr., The Hutchinson News, KS, Hutchinson

Garwood, Eric ....(321) 242-3759
egarwood@floridatoday.com, Delivery News Editor, Florida Today, FL, Melbourne

Garwood, Mona ....(319) 472-3303
mona@vintonnewspapers.com, Gen. Mgr., Vinton Livewire, IA, Vinton

Gary, Angela.............................(706) 367-2490
angieeditor@aol.com, Ed., The Banks County News, GA, Jefferson

Gary, Tim.................................(302) 741-8222
adsales@newszap.com, Major Accts. Adv. Mgr., Dorchester Banner, MD, Cambridge
adsales@newszap.com, Major Accts. Adv. Mgr., Crisfield-Somerset County Times, MD, Crisfield
adsales@newszap.com, Major Accts. Adv. Mgr., Milford Chronicle, DE, Milford
adsales@newszap.com, Major Accounts Advertising Manager, Delaware State News, DE, Dover

Garyantes, Michael................(651) 772-4902
MGARYANTES@PIONEERPRESS.COM, St. Paul Pioneer Press, MN, Saint Paul

Garza, Joseph ....(812) 231-4206
joe.garza@tribstar.com, Chief Photographer, The Tribune Star, IN, Terre Haute

Garzilli, Anthony ....(843) 726-6161
news@jaspercountysun.com, Ed., Jasper County Sun, SC, Ridgeland

Gasaway, Angel ....(256) 356-2148
rbaynews@gmail.com, Advertising Manager, The Red Bay News, AL, Red Bay

Gaskins, Brad ....(731) 587-3144
wcpeditor@frontiernet.net, Ed., Weakley County Press, TN, Martin

Gaskins, Frederick A.
fgaskins@rrecord.com, Pub., Southside Sentinel, VA, Urbanna

Gasper, Joe ....(330) 541-9400 Ext. 4114
jgasper@recordpub.com, Adv. Sales Mgr., Twinsburg Bulletin, OH, Kent

Gasper, Robert ....(540) 659-4171
rgasper@all.org, Editor, ALL News, VA, Stafford

Gasper, Terry
graphic@wctatel.net, Pub., Lake Mills Graphic,

IA, Lake Mills

Gast, Dorothy
dot@gonzalescannon.com, The Gonzales
Cannon, TX, Gonzales

Gastle, Leta...............(519) 662-1240
Admin/Circulation, New Hamburg Independent,
ON, New Hamburg

Gaston, Robert
bgaston@theet.com, Operations Director, The
Exponent Telegram, WV, Clarksburg

Gate, Leigh ....(705) 527-5500 ext. 226
themirror@simcoe.com, Gen. Mgr., The Mirror,
ON, Midland

Gates, Dominic
dgates@seattletimes.com, Aerospace/Boeing
Reporter, Seattle Post-Intelligencer, WA,
Seattle

Gates, Susie
susieg@shannoncountycurrentwave.com,
Office Mgr., Current Wave LLC, MO,
Eminence

Gathe-Barr, Barbara
news@altnewsban.com, Pub., The Altamont
News, IL, Altamont

Gatta, Michael ....(631) 843-3926
mike.gatta@newsday.com, MGR Information
Systems, Newsday, NY, Melville

Gatti, Maria ....(202) 334-4466
maria.gatti@washpost.com, Dir., Sales &
Mktg., The Washington Post Writers Group,
Washington

Gatti, Maria............................(202) 334-4466
maria.gatti@washpost.com, Dir., Int. Sales &
Marketing, Washington Post News Service
with Bloomberg News, Washington

Gatto, Patricia
patricia.gatto@dowjones.com, Vice Pres.,
Human Resources, Dow Jones Local Media
Group, NY, Middletown

Gatz, Nick
ngatz@fcnp.com, Adv. Sales, Falls Church
News-Press, VA, Falls Church

Gaub, Adam
agaub@pinalcentral.com, Editor, Eloy
Enterprise, AZ, Florence
agaub@pinalcentral.com, County Team Ed.,
Coolidge Examiner, AZ, Coolidge

Gaudet, Pierre
gaudetp@transcontinental.ca, Dir., Sales,
L'avenir De L'erable, QC, Plessisville

Gaudet, Pierre ....(819) 758-6211
gaudetp@transcontinental.ca, Sales Dir., La
Nouvelle, QC, Victoriaville

Gaudet, Simone......................(306) 882-4348
The Rosetown Eagle, SK, Rosetown

Gauger, Dave ....(360) 942-3560
dave@gaugermedia.com, Pres/Broker, Gauger
Media Service, Inc., WA, Raymond

Gauger, Jeff ....(336) 373-7051
jeff.gauger@Greensboro.com, Executive
Editor and Publisher, News & Record, NC,
Greensboro

Gauger, Jeff............................(318) 459-3530
jeff.gauger@shreveporttimes.com, Exec. Ed. ,
The Times, LA, Shreveport

Gauger, Jeff............................(815) 987-1358
jgauger@rockford.gannett.com, Mng. Ed., The
Star Shopper, IL, Rockford

Gauger, Jeff............................(336) 373-7051
jeff.gauger@greensboro.com, Pub.,
Rockingham Now, NC, Reidsville

Gault, Tony
aarellan@du.edu, Assoc. Prof., University of
Denver, CO, Denver

Gaunt, Philip
philip.gaunt@wichita.edu, Prof., Wichita State
University, KS, Wichita

Gauthier, Debbie ....(734) 591-7392
gauthierd@valassis.com, Valassis, MI, Livonia

Gauthier, Dolores ....(248) 336-7300
dgauthier@rangerdata.com, National
Dir. of Sales & Marketing, Ranger Data
Technologies Inc., MI, Troy

Gauthier, Michel
gauthierm@transcontinental.ca, Pub., La
Nouvelle, QC, Victoriaville

Gauthier, Tom ....(978) 970-4867
tgauthier@lowellsun.com, Circ. Mgr., Systems,
The Sun, MA, Lowell

Gautreau, Brenda
bgautreau@weeklycitizen.com, Classified Adv.
Mgr., Gonzales Weekly Citizen, LA, Gonzales

Gautreau, Darcy
graphics@conwaydailysun.com, Graphics Mgr.,
The Conway Daily Sun, NH, North Conway

Gautreau, Michelle
michelle.gautreau@sths.org, Univ. of St.
Thomas, TX, Houston

Gauvreau, Clare
cgauvreau@greatwest.ca, Pub./Adv. Mgr., Elk
Point Review, AB, Elk Point

Gave, Keith ....(734) 677-5405
kgave@wccnet.edu, Advisor, Washtenaw
Community College, MI, Ann Arbor

Gavin, Brian ....(810) 989-6214
bgavin@usatoday.com, Distribution Director,
Blue Water Shopper, MI, Port Huron

Gavin, christoph.riess@wan-ifra.com..........Pres.
World Association of Newspapers and News
Publishers (WAN-IFRA)

Gavlock, Lynn ....(570) 923-1500
clintoncountyrecord@comcast.net, Editor, The
Record, PA, Renovo

Gay, Brian
bgmfcp@mchsi.com, Exec. Dir., Midwest Free
Community Papers, IA, Iowa City

Gay, Cheryl ....(478) 272-5522 ext. 204
tchcirculation@gmail.com, Circ. Mgr., The
Courier Herald, GA, Dublin

Gay, Gregory...........................ext. 2377
ggay@wdt.net, Sports Ed., Watertown Daily
Times, NY, Watertown

Gay, Sheila
sgay@cnhi.com, Pub. / Ad Mgr. , Woodward
News, OK, Woodward

Gaydos, Bishop John R.
cathmoed@diojeffcity.org, Pub., The Catholic
Missourian, MO, Jefferson City

Gaydou, Dan
dan.gaydou@gr-press.com, Pres., The Grand
Rapids Press, MI, Grand Rapids

Gaye, Jeff ....(780) 840-8000 ext. 7854
Jeff.Gaye@forces.gc.ca, Ed, The Courier, AB,
Cold Lake

Gayeski, Diane
diane@dgayeski.com, Prof., Ithaca College,
NY, Ithaca

Gayheart, Tina
tgayheart@news-expressky.com, Prodn. Mgr.,
The Mountain Bargain Hunter, KY, Pikeville

Gayle, Barbara Mae
gayle@uofport.edu, Chair, University of
Portland, OR, Portland

Gayle, Gina
gina.gayle@usm.edu, Professor of Practice,
University of Southern Mississippi, MS,
Hattiesburg

Gaynor, Joseph.......................(630) 755-9330
joe.gaynor@gossinternational.com, CFO, Goss
International Corporation, NH, Durham

Gaynor, Liz
elizabeth_gaynor@mlive.com, Business Mgr.,
The Advance, MI, Blissfield

Gazzolo, Jim...........................(337) 494-4069
jgazzolo@americanpress.com, Managing Ed.,
American Press, LA, Lake Charles

Geaney, Keven ....(559) 591-4632
sports@thedinubasentinel.com, Sports Writer,
The Dinuba Sentinel, CA, Dinuba

Geary, Joseph L. ....(724) 465-5555 ext. 240
jgeary@indianagazette.net, Gen. Mgr., The
Indiana Gazette, PA, Indiana

Geary, Ray ....(419) 695-0015 Ext. 120
rgeary@delphosherald.com, Gen. Mgr.,
Delphos Daily Herald, OH, Delphos

Geary, Ray ....
rgeary@delphosherald.com, Bus. Mgr.,
Delphos Herald, Inc., OH, Delphos

Gebelein, Michael
editor@lincolntimesnews.com, Mng. Ed.,
Lincoln Times-News, NC, Lincolnton

Gebhard, Rick ....(715) 735-7500 Ext. 162
photographer, EagleHerald - ehextra.com, WI,
Marinette

Gebhardt, Heidi
hgebhardt@meadvilletribune.com, Adv. Dir.,
The Meadville Tribune, PA, Meadville

Gebhart, Mike
mike.gebhart@gwinnettdailypost.com,
Publisher, Gwinnett Daily Post, GA,
Lawrenceville

Gebis, Wayne S. ....(847) 427-4335
wgebis@dailyherald.com, Circ. Mgr., New Bus.,
Daily Herald, IL, Arlington Heights

Gebruck, Lisa
lgabruk@irricana.greatwest.ca, Circ. Mgr.,
Rocky View Weekly, AB, Airdrie

Geddings, Jerry
jasper@mountaineagle.com, Adv. Dir., Daily
Mountain Eagle, AL, Jasper

Gee, Andy ....(716) 487-1111
agee@post-journal.com, Circ. Dir., The Post-
Journal, NY, Jamestown
agee@post-journal.com, Post Journal, IL,
Machesney Park

Gee, Jenifer ....(530) 852-0231
jeniferg@goldcountrymedia.com, Auburn
Journal, CA, Auburn

Geeraerts, Dirk 285-0151
dirk.geeraerts@dowjones.com, Acct. Mgr.,
Dow Jones Newswires - Brussels, Belgium,
Brussels

Geerdes, Lauren
lgeerdes@vcu.edu, Virginia Commonwealth
Univ., VA, Richmond

Geers, George
george@nenews.org, Ed., New England
Society of Newspaper Editors, MA, Dedham

Geffert, Karen ....(203) 330-6445
kgeffert@hearstmediact.com, Director of
Human Resources, The News-Times, CT,
Danbury

Geffre, Anita ....(701) 780-1156
ageffre@gfherald.com, Cont., Grand Forks
Herald, ND, Grand Forks

Geffs, Tolman
tolman@jegi.com, Mng. Dir., Jordan,
Edmiston Group, Inc., NY, New York

Gehl, Robert ....(602) 677-2831
rgehl@asu.edu, Editor-in-chief, West News,
AZ, Glendale

Gehrt, Amy
agehrt@pekintimes.com, Ed., Pekin Daily
Times, IL, Pekin

Geibel, Evan ....(607) 756-5665
egeibel@cortlandstandardnews.net, Publisher,
Consumer News, NY, Cortland

Geibel, Evan ....(607) 756-5665 x 168
egeibel@cortlandstandard.net, Publisher,
Cortland Standard, NY, Cortland

Geibel, Kim
kgeibel@newsandsentinel.com, Nat'l Adv.
Mgr., Parkersburg News & Sentinel, WV,
Parkersburg

Geier, Leslie ....(618) 393-2931
accounting@olneydailymail.com, Office Mgr.,
Olney Daily Mail, IL, Olney

Geiger, Bob ....(813) 259-7494
Tampa Bay Times, FL, St Petersburg

Geiger, Jo Ann
jgeiger@rbj.net, Rochester Business Journal,
NY, Rochester

Geiger, Matt ....(608) 512-6420
mgeieger@newspubinc.com, Mng Ed.,
Middleton Times-Tribune, WI, Black Earth

Geiger, Walter
news@barnesville.com, Pub., Pike County
Journal and Reporter, GA, Zebulon

Geis, Amber
ads@thermopir.com, Advertising Sales ,
Thermopolis Independent Record, WY,
Thermopolis

Geisler, Heidi...................(515) 244-2145 x 136
hgeisler@cnaads.com, Media Dir., Iowa
Newspaper Association, Inc., IA, Des Moines

Geissler, Kyle...........................(262) 472-1426
geisslek@uww.edu, Adviser, Univ. of Wisconsin
Whitewater, WI, Whitewater

Geissler, Nancy ....ext. 228
distribution@independentfreepress.com,
Circ. Mgr., Independent & Free Press, ON,
Georgetown

Gelber, Alex
nyoffice@strausnews.com, Ed.-in-Chief, The
Westsider, NY, New York

Gelbman, Michael ....(916) 498-1234, ext 1321
michaelg@newsreview.com, Sales Manager,
Sacramento News & Review, CA,
Sacramento

Gelbman, Michael ....(606) 326-2611
mgelbman@dailyindependent.com, Advertising
Director, The Daily Independent, KY, Ashland

Gele, Jason ....(225) 388-0672
JGELE@THEADVOCATE.COM, Online Adv.
Coord.
, The Advocate, LA, Baton Rouge

Gelestor, Judy ....(304) 263-8931 ext. 110
jgelestor@journal-news.net, Adv. Dir., The
Journal, WV, Martinsburg

Gelfand, Jeff
jeff.gelfand@us.abb.com, Nat'l Sales/Mktg. Dir.,
ABB Inc., TX, Dallas

Gelfand, Jeffrey ....(214) 328-1202
jeff.gelfand@us.abb.com, Nat'l Sales/Mktg.
Dir.-Printing Systems, ABB, Inc. (Printing
Systems), WI, New Berlin

Gelfius, Ann...........................(317) 444-6707
Ann.Gelfius@indystar.com, Client Services
Director, The Indianapolis Star, IN,
Indianapolis

Gell, Alan
alangell@ix.netcom.com, Ed., Gold Sheet
Shopper, TX, Red Oak

Gellar, David 860/701-4291
d.gellar@theday.com, Sales Development
Manager, The Day, CT, New London

Gelman, Bernard
bernardgelman@aol.com, Owner/Ed., The
Gelman Feature Syndicate, Roscoe

Geloff, Peter ....(360) 735-4625
peter.geloff@columbian.com, Circ. Mgr., Single
Copy, The Columbian, WA, Vancouver

Gelvin, Trudy...........................ext. 201
tgelvin@comcast.net, Circ. Mgr., Fulton County
News, PA, Mc Connellsburg

Gemmet, Andrea ....(650) 223-6537
agemmet@mv-voice.com, Ed., Mountain View
Voice, CA, Palo Alto

Gemmett, Richard P.
rpgemmett@aol.com, Ed., Shopper, SC, North Charleston

Gemmill, Michelle .... (702) 201-1940
mgemmill@bouldercityreview.com, Office Coordinator, Boulder City Review, NV, Boulder City

Gemmiti, Jamie
jamieg@mountwashingtonvalley.com, Photography Ed., The Conway Daily Sun, NH, North Conway

Gemondo, Kim
newsandjournal@yahoo.com, Pub., Shinnston News & Harrison County Journal, WV, Lewisburg

Gendes Shact, Barb
info@communitechservices.com, Vice Pres., CommuniTech Services Inc., IL, Arlington Heights

Gendron, Jodi
ihwnews@sasktel.net, Pub., Indian Head-wolseley News, SK, Indian Head

Gendron, Louis
lgendron@lesoleil.com, VP, Adv., Le Soleil, QC, Quebec

Gendron, Marc
marc.gendron@lavoixdelest.ca, Info. Mgr., La Voix De L'est Plus, QC, Granby

Genenbacher, Joe
jgenenbacher@quincyrecycle.com, Prodn. Dir., Opns., The Quincy Herald-Whig, IL, Quincy

Generali, Philippe
philippe@rcsworks.com, Pres., Media Monitors, Inc., NY, White Plains

Genest, Lyne .... (418) 220-0222
info@journaldebeauce.com, Journal De La Beauce, QC, Saint Georges

Genier, Sylvie .... (705) 335-2283
sylvie.genier@sunmedia.ca, Senior Sales Representative, The Northern Times, ON, Kapuskasing
sylvie.genier@sunmedia.ca, Senior Sales Representative, The Weekender, ON, Kapuskasing

Gennario, Chris .... (631) 843-4744
Adv. Administrator, Newsday.com Bus., Newsday, NY, Melville

Gensiorek, Michelle .... (204) 759-2644 ext. 1
smpclassified@mymts.net, Classified/Accounting, South Mountain Press, MB, Shoal Lake

Genslorek, Michelle .... (204) 759-2644 ext. 1
ctwclassified@mymts.net, Classified/Accounting, Crossroads This Week, MB, Shoal Lake

Genter, Jamie .... (702) 259-4074
Copy Ed., Las Vegas Sun, NV, Henderson

Gentile, Jennifer .... (919) 718-1221
jgentile@sanfordherald.com, News Ed., Herald-Sanford, NC, Sanford

Gentile, Robyn .... (865) 584-5761, Ext. 105
rgentile@tnpress.com, Member Services Manager, Tennessee Press Association, Inc., TN, Knoxville

Gentili, Mark .... (705) 673-5667 Ext. 337
mgentili@sudbury.com, Managing Ed., Northern Life, ON, Sudbury

Gentle, Irene
city@thestar.ca, Managing Ed. , Toronto Star, ON, Toronto

Gentry, Andrew
eagle_record@bellsouth.net, Pub./Ed., The Eagle-Record, SC, Saint George

Gentry, Bradley G. .... (417) 967-2000
news@houstonherald.com, Publisher, Houston Herald, MO, Houston

Gentry, Dale
news@standardbanner.com, Pub./Ed., The Standard Banner, TN, Jefferson City

Gentry, Dave .... (865) 475-2081
davegentry@standardbanner.com, Sports Ed., The Standard Banner, TN, Jefferson City

Gentry, James K. .... (785) 864-4755
jschool@ku.edu, Prof., University of Kansas, KS, Lawrence

Gentry, Jim .... (252) 329-9594
jgentry@reflector.com, Sports Ed., The Daily Reflector, NC, Greenville

Gentry, Robert
news@sabineindex.net, Pub., The Sabine Index, LA, Many

Genzale, Louisa
publisher@northernsentinel.com, Publisher, Northern Sentinel - Kitimat, BC, Kitimat

Geoghegan, Martha
mgeoghegan@bizjournals.com, Adv. Mgr., Puget Sound Business Journal, WA, Seattle

Geoghegan, William .... (401) 380-2370
sports@independentri.com, Sports Editor, The Independent, RI, Newport

George, Amiso
a.george@tcu.edu, Assoc. Prof., Texas Christian University, TX, Fort Worth

George, Amy .... (217) 373-7453
ageorge@news-gazette.com, Dir. of Market Dev., The News-Gazette, IL, Champaign

George, Beverly .... ext. 130
bgeorge@nvdaily.com, Preprint Adv., Northern Virginia Daily, VA, Strasburg

George, Charles
sales@midamericagraphics.com, Pres., Mid-America Graphics, Inc., MO, Harrisonville

George, Karen
ewines@sanmarcosrecord.com, Circ. Dir., San Marcos Daily Record, TX, San Marcos

George, Kari
classifieds@themadisonrecord.com, Class. Consult., The Madison Record, AL, Madison

George, Karrisa
karissa@pacindex.com, Managing editor, Pacific Univ., OR, Forest Grove

George, Laura
lgeorge@emich.edu, Head, Eastern Michigan University, MI, Ypsilanti

George, Sharon
sgeorge@weatherforddemocrat.com, Bus. Mgr., The Weatherford Democrat, TX, Weatherford

George, Tom .... (304) 272-3433
publisher@waynecountynews.com, Consultant, HD Media Company LLC, WV, Huntington

George-Bealer, Cindy .... (517) 368-0365
jhite@gannett.com, Pub., Farmers Advance, MI, Camden

George-Palilonis, Jennifer
aahoward@bsu.edu, Asst. Prof./Coord., Journ. Graphics, Ball State University, IN, Muncie

Georges, John
jdgeorges@theadvocate.com, Pub./CEO, The Advocate, LA, Baton Rouge

Geosits, Stephanie .... (617) 495-5969
Harvard Univ./JFK School of Gov't, MA, Cambridge

Gerace, Steve .... (530) 926-5215
sgerace@mtshastanews.com, Ed., Weed Press, CA, Mount Shasta

Gerace, Steve .... (530) 926-5215
news@mtshastanews.com, Ed., Voice Of The Mountain, CA, Mount Shasta

Gerace, Steve
sgerace@mtshastanews.com, Ed., Dunsmuir News, CA, Mount Shasta
sgerace@mtshastanews.com, Ed., Mt. Shasta Herald, CA, Mount Shasta

Geracie, Bud .... (408) 920-5389
sports@mercurynews.com, Sports Editor, Palo Alto Daily News, CA, Menlo Park

Geraghty, Pat .... (651) 322-6342
Nat'l Sales Mgr./Newspaper Handling Systems, Cannon Equipment, MN, Rosemount

Gerard, Gary
ggerard@timesuniononline.com, Gen. Mgr., Times-Union, IN, Warsaw

Gerard-Flynn, Anne
aflynn@repub.com, Asst. Managing Ed., Lifestyles, The Republican, MA, Springfield

Gerardi, Charles .... (561) 820-4125
cgerardi@pbpost.com, Vice Pres./Gen. Mgr., The Palm Beach Post, FL, West Palm Beach

Gerber, Alison .... (423) 757-6408
agerber@timesfreepress.com, Ed. & Dir of Content , Chattanooga Times Free Press, TN, Chattanooga

Gerber, Amber .... (608) 579-0425
agerber@hngnews.com, Managing Ed., McFarland Thistle, WI, Cottage Grove

Gerding, Barry .... (250) 979-7302
newsroom@lakecountrynews.net, Ed., Lake Country Calendar, BC, Kelowna

Gerding, Lisa
lgerding@sngnews.com, Majors/Nat'l Accts. Mgr., The Times, IL, Ottawa

Gereau, John .... ext. 214
johng@denpubs.com, Ed., The Adirondack Journal Sun, NY, Elizabethtown

Gereau, John .... (518) 873-6368
johng@denpubs.com, Mng. Ed., The Valley News Sun, NY, Elizabethtown

Gereau, John .... (518) 873-6368
johng@denpubs.com, Mng. Ed., The Times of Ti Sun, NY, Elizabethtown
johng@denpubs.com, Mng. Ed., The News Enterprise Sun, NY, Elizabethtown

Gereau, John .... (518) 873-6368 ext. 214
johng@suncommunitynews.com, Managing Ed., The Burgh Sun, NY, Elizabethtown
johng@suncommunitynews.com, Mng Ed, Sun Community News, Published by:Denton Publications, Inc., NY, Elizabethtown

Gerhard, Corey ....(916) 498-1234, ext. 1321
coreyg@newsreview.com, Dir of Adv, Sacramento News & Review, CA, Sacramento

Gerhart, Lori E. .... (610) 371-5103
lgerhart@readingeagle.com, Newspaper Sales Manager, Reading Eagle, PA, Reading

Gerik, Nick .... (785) 832-7185
ngerik@ljworld.com, Digital Ed., Lawrence Journal-World, KS, Lawrence

Gerke, Julie .... (309) 820-3256
jgerke@pantagraph.com, Enterprise Ed., The Pantagraph, IL, Bloomington

Gerl, Ellen .... (740) 597-3136
gerl@ohio.edu, Asst. Prof., Ohio University, OH, Athens

Gerlach, Michele
michele.gerlach@andalusiastarnews.com, Pub./Ed, Andalusia Star-News, AL, Andalusia

Gerlich, Jessica .... (219) 798-8824
jngerlich@gmail.com, Editor-in-Chief, Purdue University Calumet, IN, Hammond

Germain, Jeanne-d'Arc .... (450) 692-8552
info@informationchateauguay.qc.ca, Le Soleil Du Mercredi, QC, Chateauguay
info@informationchateauguay.qc.ca, Soleil Du Samedi, QC, Chateauguay

German, Greg
info@martinyale.com, Pres., Martin Yale, Inc., IN, Wabash

Germann, Chris .... (941) 206-1435
cgermann@suncoastpress.com, Press Room Mgr., Charlotte Sun, FL, Punta Gorda

Germond, Tom .... (727) 397-5563

Germond, Tom
tgermond@tbnweekly.com, Executive Editor, Tampa Bay Newspapers, Inc., FL, Seminole

Gerreira, Natalie
nferreira@breezenewspapers.com, Nat'l Acct. Mgr., The Pine Island Eagle, FL, Bokeelia

Gerry, Kristy .... (402) 444-3129
kristy.gerry@owh.com, Dir., Production, Omaha World-Herald, NE, Omaha

Gertin, Lesile
lgertin@gbpnews.com, Distribution Manager, The Giveaway, IN, Scottsburg

Gertin, Leslie
lgertin@gbpnews.com, Circ. Mgr., The Banner-Gazette, IN, Pekin

Gertin, Leslie
lgertin@gbpnews.com, Dist. Mgr., The Leader, IN, Charlestown

Gertjegerdes, Helmut
helmut@columbustimes.com, Mng. Ed., The Columbus Times, GA, Columbus

Gervais, Mike .... (760) 934-3929 x 1
mgervais@mammothtimes.com, Managing Ed., Mammoth Times, CA, Mammoth Lakes

Gervin, Jake .... (843) 626-0226
jgervin@thesunnews.com, Audience Dev. Dir., The Sun News, SC, Myrtle Beach

Gerzanics, Janine .... (408) 741-4073
gerzanics@westvalley.edu, West Valley College, CA, Saratoga

Geskie, Pam .... (518) 943-2100
Adv. Dir., The Daily Mail, NY, Hudson

Gesler, Josh .... ext. 237
Systems Specialist, Walla Walla Union-Bulletin, WA, Walla Walla

Gess, Joe .... (813) 259-7447
jgess@tampatrib.com, Dir, Nat'l Sales, Plant City Courier & Tribune, FL, Tampa
jgess@tampatrib.com, Tampa Bay Times, FL, St Petersburg

Gess, Joseph
jgess@tampatrib.com, Tampa Bay Times, FL, St Petersburg

Gessel, Chris
chris.gessel@investors.com, Exec. Ed., Investor's Business Daily, CA, Los Angeles

Gessner, John .... (952) 846-2031
john.gessner@ecm-inc.com, Ed., Sun Thisweek Lakeville, MN, Apple Valley
john.gessner@ecm-inc.com, Ed., Thisweek Newspapers, MN, Apple Valley
john.gessner@ecm-inc.com, Ed., Thisweek Burnsville-Eagan Sun, MN, Apple Valley

Getler, Al .... (978) 946-2110
agetler@eagletribune.com, Pub., The Haverhill Gazette, MA, North Andover

Gett, Sam
sgett@faribault.com, Ed./Pub., Faribault Daily News, MN, Faribault

Gett, Sam .... (507) 645-1112
sgett@northfieldnews.com, Vice Pres., Mainstream Publications LLC, MI, Traverse City

Gett, Sam .... (507) 333-3105
sgett@faribault.com, Pub., Faribault Area Shopper, MN, Faribault

Gett, Sam .... (507) 645-1102
sgett@northfieldnews.com, Pub., Northfield News, MN, Northfield

Gett, Sam .... (507) 333-3105
sgett@faribault.com, Reg. Pub., Adams Publishing Group, LLC, MN, Virginia

Gettman, Tracy .... ext. 241
tracy.gettman@gjsentinel.com, Circ. Mgr., The Daily Sentinel, CO, Grand Junction

Geurts, Jimmy .... (813) 974-5190
Univ. of South Florida, FL, Tampa

Ghanem, Salma

Hillsboro Times-Gazette, OH, Hillsboro

Gilliland, Lew .... (256) 304-0053
lgilliland@times-journal.com, Ed., The Times-Journal, AL, Fort Payne

Gilliland, Norman .... (740) 286-2187 ext. 301
ngilliland@timesjournal.com, Pub., The Jackson County Times-Journal, OH, Jackson

Gilliland, Norman .... (740) 941-0089
ngilliland@newswatchman.com, Pub., The Pike County News Watchman, OH, Waverly

Gilliland, Randy
council@hampton.gov, Pres., MAXX Material Handling LLC, VA, Hampton

Gillis, Heather .... (416) 847-2092
hgillis@bbm.ca, Exec. Asst., BBM Canada, ON, Toronto

Gillis, Kerrie .... (212) 556-7194
kerrie@nytimes.com, VP, Adv. & Sales Op., The New York Times, NY, New York

Gillis, Len .... ext. 27
lgillis@timminstimes.com; len.gillis@sunmedia.ca, Ed., Timmins Times, ON, Timmins

Gillis, Tamara L.
GILLISTL@etown.edu, Chair/Assoc. Prof., Elizabethtown College, PA, Elizabethtown

Gillispie, Jay .... (973) 383-1047
jgillispie@njherald.com, Cir. Dir., New Jersey Herald, NJ, Newton

Gillispie, Mike .... (410) 454-0533
mgillispie@bizjournals.com, Production Director, Baltimore Business Journal, MD, Baltimore

Gillette, Aaron
agillette@townnews.com, Dir. Mktg., TownNews.com, IL, Moline

Gillmly, C.W.
sales@comtexnews.net, Chrmn./Interim CEO, Comtex News Network, VA, Alexandria

Gillon, Chris .... ext. 236
Contact, College Publisher, Inc., MA, Boston

Gills, Sandy .... (843) 706-8160 ext. 8160
sgillis@islandpacket.com, Adv. Dir., The Island Packet, SC, Bluffton

Gilman, David Mr. .... (401) 364-6061
dave@motterstitch.com, Chief Engineer, Motterstitch Company, Inc., RI, Carolina

Gilmartin, David
dgilmartin@phillyburbs.com, The Intelligencer, PA, Doylestown

Gilmer, Monica
mgilmer@mspress.org, Member Services Mgr., Mississippi Press Association, MS, Jackson

Gilmer, Monica .... (601) 981-3060
mgilmer@mspress.org, Member Services Manager, Mississippi Press Services, Inc., MS, Jackson

Gilmore, Guy .... (651) 228-5448
bregal@pioneerpress.com, Publisher, St. Paul Pioneer Press, MN, Saint Paul

Gilmore, Kendra
kgilmore@thelafayettesun.com, Adv. Mgr., LaFayette Sun, AL, Lafayette

Gilmore, Lee .... (248) 519-9200
bbinfo@bbfurnitureadvertising.com, Pres., B&B - Banker & Brisebois Advertising, MI, Troy

Gilmore, Linda
publisher@picayuneitem.com, Publisher, The Poplarville Democrat, MS, Poplarville
publisher@picayuneitem.com, Pub., Picayune Item, MS, Picayune

Gilreath, Ben
bgilreath@annistonstar.com, Pro. Mgr., The Anniston Star, AL, Anniston

Gilreath, Eric .... (479) 571-6484
egilreath@arkansasonline.com, Info. Systems Mgr., Arkansas Democrat-Gazette, AR, Little Rock

Gilroy, Brian T. .... (204) 734-3858
brian@starandtimes.ca, Adv. Mgr., Publ., Gen. Mgr., Owner, Swan Valley Star & Times, MB, Swan River

Gilroy, Robert F.
dherald@mts.net, Pub./Owner, Dauphin Herald, MB, Dauphin

Gilson, Lora .... (303) 823-6625
editor@lyonsrecorder.com, Pub., The Lyons Recorder, CO, Lyons

Gilson, Robert
ralph@aim-okc.com, Pres., Applied Industrial Machinery, OK, Oklahoma City

Ginader, Emma
eginader@dailyitem.com, Reporter, The Daily Item, PA, Sunbury

Gindlesperger, Linda A. .... (814) 634-8321
lagindy@tnrnewspaper.com, Pub./Gen. Mgr., The New Republic, PA, Meyersdale

Ginfrida, Kimberly .... (843) 317-7285
kginfrida@florencenews.com, News Ed., Morning News, SC, Florence

Gingell, Kim
kimgingell@columbianprogress.com, Adv. Mgr., The Columbian-Progress, MS, Columbia

Gingold, Lester .... (901) 458-2911 ext. 1
lgingold@thesbesttimes.com, publisher emeritus, The Best Times, TN, Memphis

Gingras, Helene
helene.gingras@monteregieweb.com, Ed., Le Reflet, QC, Delson

Gingrich, Joyce .... (620) 241-2422
jgingrich@mcphersonsentinel.com, Office Manager, McPherson Sentinel, KS, McPherson

Ginsbach, Pam
anwclub@comcast.net, Pres., American News Women's Club, Inc., DC, Washington

Ginsburg, Ned
sales@mbmcorp.com, Pres., MBM Corp., SC, North Charleston

Gintzler, Ariella
agintzler@postindependent.com, Glenwood Springs Post Independent, CO, Glenwood Springs

Ginyard, Tiffaney
editor@afro.com, Mng. Ed., The Afro American Newspaper-baltimore, MD, Baltimore

Giofu, Ron
mail@rivertowntimes.com, Ed., River Town Times, ON, Amherstburg

Gioioso, Joseph
jgioioso@njnpublishing.com, Pres./Pub., Hunterdon County Democrat, NJ, Flemington

Giordana, Gino .... (920) 759-2000
sales@timesvillager.com, Account Representative, The Times-Villager, WI, Kaukauna

Giordano, Basilio
journal@cittadinocanadese.com, Prodn. Mgr., La Voz de Montreal, QC, Montreal

Giorgianni, Michelle
giorgianni@poststar.com ...., Circ. Dir. , The Post-Star, NY, Glens Falls

Giorgis, Virginia .... (307) 787-3229
news@bridgervalleypioneer.com, Ed., Bridger Valley Pioneer, WY, Lyman

Giovingo, Mary Ann
mgiovingo@hammondstar.com, Mailroom Mgr., The Daily Star, LA, Hammond

Gipe, Alison
publisher@guymondailyherald.com, Adv. Dir. / Gen. Mgr., Guymon Daily Herald, OK, Guymon

Gipson, Michelle
advertising@atlantadailyworld.com, Adv. Dir., Atlanta Daily World, GA, Atlanta

Giradin, Lina .... (785) 295-1223
linda.girardin@cjonline.com, The Topeka Capital-Journal, KS, Topeka

Girard, Matthew
editor@beltonjournal.com, Ed., The Belton Journal, TX, Belton

Girard, P.A. .... (610) 259-4141
mail@presspublishing.org, Mng. Ed., Ridley Press, PA, Drexel Hill

Girard, Philippe A. .... (610) 259-4141
mail@presspublishing.org, Ed., Upper Darby Press, PA, Drexel Hill

Girard, Philippe A.
mail@presspublishing.org, Ed., The Yeadon Times, PA, Drexel Hill

Giroir, Chris .... (256) 740-4716
chris.giroir@timesdaily.com, Dir., ITS/Pre Press Serv., Times Daily, AL, Florence

Girouard, Scott .... (863) 802-7400
scott.girouard@theledger.com, Dig. Dir., The Ledger, FL, Lakeland
scott.girouard@theledger.com, Digital Adv. Mgr., News Chief, FL, Winter Haven

Girsdansky, Gwen .... (928) 453-4237
ggirsdansky@havasunews.com, Copy Ed, Today's News-Herald, AZ, Lake Havasu City

Girsdansky, Gwendolyn
gwendolyn.girsdansky@recordernews.com, Ed., Hamilton County Express, NY, Speculator

Gisclair, Jessica
jgisclair@elon.edu, Assoc. Prof., Elon University, NC, Elon

Gish, Thomas
bengish@bellsouth.net, Pub., The Mountain Eagle, KY, Whitesburg

Gittens, Jim .... ext. 2053
Editorial Page Ed., The Citizens' Voice, PA, Wilkes Barre

Gitter, Emily
emily.gitter@wsj.com, Features Ed., The New York Sun, NY, New York

Gitto, Joseph A.
jgitto@mpival.com, Vice Pres., Management Planning, Inc., FL, Orlando

Giuliani, Diane .... (218) 624-3344
journal@proctormn.com, Gen. Mgr., Proctor Journal, MN, Proctor

Giunta, Carol .... (215) 625-8501
carol@epgn.com, Executive Assistant to Publisher, Philadelphia Gay News, PA, Philadelphia

Giusti, Andrea
agiusti@news-graphic.com, Ed., The Scott Shopper, KY, Georgetown

Giusti, Michael .... (504) 865-3295
mdgiusti@loyno.edu, Advisor, Loyola University New Orleans, LA, New Orleans

Giustiniani, John .... (718) 816-3942
johng@siadvance.com, Production Director, Staten Island Advance, NY, Staten Island

Given, Ed .... (304) 765-5193
editor@bcn-news.com, Pub/Ed., Braxton Citizens' News, WV, Sutton

Givens, C. Josh .... (270) 526-4151
Editor, The Butler County Banner-Republican, KY, Morgantown

Giza, Jan .... (405) 366-3501
jan@normantranscript.com, Class. Sales Exec. , Norman Transcript, OK, Norman

Giza, Joanne .... (410) 542-4166
joanne@baltimoreschild.com, Pub., Baltimore's Child, PA, Philadelphia

Giza, Roger .... (847) 274-4231
rgiza@burnishine.com, President, Burnishine Products, IL, Lake Villa

Gjurich, Louis .... (814) 532-5110

lgjurich@tribdem.com, Controller, The Tribune-Democrat, PA, Johnstown

Gladding, Sheri .... (519) 655-2341
tavistockgazette@rogers.com, Circulation Manager, Tavistock Gazette, ON, Tavistock

Gladding, William J.
gazette@tavistock.on.ca, Ed., Tavistock Gazette, ON, Tavistock

Glaeser, Paul
glaeserp@gnnewspapers.com, Circ. Mgr., Niagara Gazette, NY, Niagara Falls

Glantz, Beth
subscribe@winfieldcourier.com, Circ. Mgr., Winfield Daily Courier, KS, Winfield

Glaser, Al .... (780) 460-5500
aglaser@greatwest.ca, Adv. Mgr., St. Albert Gazette, AB, St. Albert

Glaser, Sarah .... (508) 591-6629
sglaser@wickedlocal.com, Ed., The Sentinel, MA, Plymouth

Glass, David
daveglass@findlayoh.com, Vice President. Broadcast, Findlay Publishing Co., OH, Findlay

Glass, Doug
dglass@ap.org, News Ed., Minnesota Associated Press Association, MN, Minneapolis

Glass, Faye
njprogresslog@aol.com, News Ed., North Jackson Progress, AL, Stevenson

Glass, Jamie
ads@altavistajournal.com, Adv. Mgr., Altavista Journal, VA, Altavista
ads@altavistajournal.com, Adv. Mgr., The Journal (OOB), VA, KING GEORGE

Glass, Jeanne
jeanne.glass@demopolistimes.com, Adv. and Mktg. Rep., Blackbelt Gazette, AL, Demopolis

Glass, Larry O. .... (256) 437-2395
njprogresslog@aol.com, Ed. / Pub., North Jackson Progress, AL, Stevenson

Glass, Sarah .... (913) 530-0854
saglass@mnu.edu, Editor-in-Chief, MidAmerica Nazarene University, KS, Olathe

Glass, Tesa .... (618) 242-0114 Ext. 209
tesa.Glass@register-news.com, Mng. Ed., Register-News, IL, Effingham

Glasscock, Lisa
circ@boonvilledailynews.com, Circ. Mgr., The Weekly, MO, Boonville

Glasser, Jeff
jeff.glasser@latimes.com, Senior Counsel , Los Angeles Times, CA, Los Angeles

Glassman, Anthony
tglassman@chronohio.com, Circ. Mgr., Gay People's Chronicle, OH, Cleveland

Glassner, Greg
gglassner@herald-progress.com, Ed., Herald-Progress, VA, Ashland

Glasspoole, Donna .... (613) 546-8885 ext.211
dglasspoole@theemc.ca, Gen. Mgr. , Kingston Heritage Emc, ON, Kingston
dglasspoole@theemc.ca, Classified Dir., Osprey Media Group, ON, Markham

Glastris, Paul .... (202) 955-9010
pglastris@washingtonmonthly.com, Ed. in Chief, Washington Monthly LLC, Washington

Glazier, Becky
graphics@fairmontphotopress.com, Graphics Designer, Fairmont Photo Press, MN, Fairmont

Glazier, Jacy .... (605) 673-2217
reporter@gwtc.net, Reporter, Custer County Chronicle, SD, Custer

Gleason, Brian .... (941) 206-1133
Viewpoint Ed., Charlotte Sun, FL, Punta Gorda

Gleason, Timothy W. ....(541) 346-3739
tgleason@uoregon@edu., Dean, University of
Oregon, OR, Eugene

Gledhill, Jeff............................(559) 441-6076
jgledhill@fresnobee.com, West Reg VP
Production, The Fresno Bee, CA, Fresno

Gleeson, John
editor@coastreporter.net, Ed./Assoc. Pub.,
Coast Reporter, BC, Sechelt

Gleim, Jim ....(707) 453-8189
jgleim@bayareanewsgroup.com, Pub., The
Reporter, CA, Vacaville

Gleim, Jim
jgleim@bayareanewsgroup.com, Pub., The
Daily Democrat, CA, Woodland
jgleim@bayareanewsgroup.com, Pub., Chico
Enterprise-Record, CA, Chico

Gleim, Jim ....(707) 453-8189
jgleim@bayareanewsgroup.com , Pub., Vallejo
Times-Herald, CA, Vallejo

Glen, Dale
mail@petcorolls.com, Sales Mgr., Petco Roller
Co., IL, Lake Forest

Glencross, Dorothy ....(406) 758-4450
dorothyg@dailyinterlake.com, Bus. Mgr., Daily
Inter Lake, MT, Kalispell

Glende, Phil ....(608) 252-6117
pglende@madison, City Ed., Wisconsin
State Journal, Madison, WI, Madison

Glendenning, Laura ....(970) 429-9120
lglendenning@aspentimes.com, Ed.,
Snowmass Sun, CO, Aspen

Glenen, Dave ....(902) 928-2511
dglenen@ngnews.ca, Ed, The Digby County
Courier, NS, Digby
dglenen@ngnews.ca, Ed., The News, NS, New
Glasgow

Glenetske, McKenzie
mckenzie@advertisewis.com, Pub./Gen. Mgr.,
The Antigo Area Shopper, WI, Antigo

Glenn, Amy
ecn@att.net, Ed., Eastland Telegram, TX,
Eastland

Glenn, Barry ....(407) 420-5497
bglenn@orlandosentinel.com, Lifestyles Ed.,
Orlando Sentinel, FL, Orlando

Glenn, Jason
jglenn@valleynewstoday.com, Sports Ed.,
Valley News Today, IA, Shenandoah

Glenn, Steven L.
info@clipperpubco.com, Pub., The Gibbon
Reporter, NE, Shelton
info@clipperpubco.com, Pub., The Wood River
Sunbeam, NE, Shelton

Glenn, Steven L. ....(308) 647-5158
Ed., Shelton Clipper, NE, Shelton

Glennie, Rich
richg@glencoenews.com, Mng. Ed., The
Glencoe Advertiser, MN, Glencoe

Glennon, Amy ....(404) 526-7237
aglennon@ajc.com, Pub., Atlanta Journal-
Constitution, GA, Atlanta

Glennon, Gary
gglennon@pcgazette.com, Gen. Mgr., The
Portage County Gazette, WI, Stevens Point

Glick, Brian ....(260) 347-0400 Ext. 1187
bglick@kpcmedia.com, IT Mgr., The Herald
Republican, IN, Angola

Glickman, Caroline ....(434) 385-5552
cglickman@newsadvance.com, Managing
Editor, The News & Advance, VA, Lynchburg

Glickman, Rhonda .... (516) 569-4000 x250
Adv. Mgr., Lynbrook/East Rockaway Herald,
NY, Garden City

Glickman, Rhonda .... (516) 569-4000 ext. 250
Adv. Mgr., Baldwin Herald, NY, Garden City

Glickman, Rhonda .... (516) 569-4000 x250

rglickman@liherald.com, Adv. Mgr., Franklin
Square/Elmont Herald, NY, Garden City

Glickman, Rhonda ....ext. 250
rglickman@liherald.com, Adv. Mgr., Primetime,
NY, Garden City

Glickman, Rhonda .... (516) 569-4000 ext. 250
rglickman@liherald.com, Vice Pres., Sales,
Richner Communications, Inc., NY, Garden
City

Glickman, Rhonda ....ext. 250
rglickman@liherald.com, Adv. Mgr., Rockville
Centre Herald, NY, Garden
City

Glickman, Rhonda ....ext. 250
Adv. Mgr., Rockville Centre Herald, NY, Garden
City

Glickman, Rhonda ....ext. 250
Adv. Mgr., Long Beach Herald, NY, Garden City

Glickman, Rhonda .... (516) 569-4000 ext. 250
rglickman@liherald.com, Ad. Mgr., Oyster Bay
Guardian, NY, Garden City
rglickman@liherald.com, Adv. Mgr., Malverne/
West Hempstead Herald, NY, Garden City

Glickman, Rhonda ....ext. 250
Adv. Mgr., Merrick Herald, NY, Garden City

Glidewell, Jim..............(434) 432-1654 ext. 11
jglidewell@womackpublishing.com, Accounting
Mgr., Womack Publishing Co., VA, Lynchburg

Glincher, Amanda......................(408) 358-3033
amanda@jvalley.org, Ed., Jewish Community
News, CA, Los Gatos

Glines, Sara ....(717) 767-3490
sglines@mediaonepa.com, Publisher, York
Daily Record/York Sunday News, PA, York

Glines, Sara ....(919) 829-4659
Pub., Southwest Wake News, NC, Cary

Glines, Sara
sglines@mediaonespa.com, Pres.,
MediaOnePA
sglines@mediaonespa.com, Pub., Public
Opinion, PA, Chambersburg

Glink, Ilyce R. ....(847) 242-0550
ilyce@thinkglink.com, Pub., Think Glink Inc.,
Glencoe

Glisky, Bill ....(613) 962-9171 ext. 624
bill.glisky@sunmedia.ca, Mng. Ed.,
Intelligencer, ON, Belleville

Globokar, Becky
becky_globokar@jewishaz.com, Prodn. Mgr.,
Jewish News, AZ, Phoenix

Gloe, Jerry ....(651) 464-4601
jerry.gloe@ecm-inc.com, Adv. Dir., Princeton
Union-Eagle, MN, Princeton
jerry.gloe@ecm-inc.com, Adv. Dir., Forest Lake
Times, MN, Forest Lake
jerry.gloe@ecm-inc.com, Adv. Dir., Mille Lacs
County Times, MN, Princeton
jerry.gloe@ecm-inc.com, Adv. Dir., St. Croix
Valley Peach, MN, Forest Lake

Glover, Barbara ....Adv. Mgr.
The Oakley Graphic, KS, Oakley

Glynn, Carroll J.
glynn.14@osu.edu, Dir./Prof., Ohio State
University, OH, Columbus

Glynn, John ....(716) 773-7634 Ext. 339
jglynn@nrdllc.com, Director of Sales and
Marketing, NRD LLC, NY, Grand Island

Glynn, Patrick ....ext. 161
pglynn@flashnews.com, Mng. Ed., Wireless
Flash News, Inc., San Diego

Glynn, Sara
sglynn@norwichbulletin.com, Mktg. Dir., The
Bulletin, CT, Norwich

Gnadt, Paul
keenestar@thestargroup.com, Ed., Keene Star,
TX, Burleson

Gneiser, Jon ....(920) 787-3334
argusjon@wausharaargus.com, Publisher,
Waushara Argus, WI, Wautoma

Gnuechtel, Herman...................(847) 477-6323
mark.krueger@baldwintech.com, Product
Line Leader WPC, Web Printing Controls, a

Baldwin Company, IL, Arlington Heights

Gochenour, Mike
mgochenour@nvdaily.com, Pub./Gen Mgr. ,
Northern Virginia Daily, VA, Strasburg

Godbey, John .... (256) 340-2374
photos@decaturdaily.com, Photo Dept. Ed.,
The Decatur Daily, AL, Decatur

Godbey, Todd
todd@nancyhall.net, Pub./Adv. Mgr., Livin' Out
Loud, NC, Wilmington

Godbout, Neil.........................(250) 562-9201
ngodbout@pgcitizen.ca, Ed., The Prince
George Citizen, BC, Prince George

Goddard, Debbie ....(334) 261-1580
dgoddard@gannett.com, Exec/ Asst.,
Montgomery Advertiser, AL, Montgomery

Goddard, Wendy
wendy@northfulton.com, Sr. Acct. Exec., Milton
Herald, GA, Alpharetta

Godfredsen, Chris
rvbee@mtcnet.net, Pub., Rock Valley Bee, IA,
Rock Valley

Godfredsen, Chris
gtnews@nethtc.net, Pub., Osceola County
Gazette-Tribune, IA, Sibley

Godfrey, Gary
production@woh.rr.com, Secreatary/Treasurer,
OHIAD, OH, Covington
production@woh.rr.com, Secreatary/Treasurer,
OHIAD, OH, Covington

Godfrey, Gary L.
garyg@arenpub.com, Publisher, Stillwater
Valley Advertiser, OH, Covington

Godfrey, Gary L.
production@woh.rr.com, Adv. Mgr., Penny
Saver, OH, Covington

Godfrey, Kathy..........................(540) 351-1162
kgodfrey@virginianewsgroup.com, Piedmont
Adv. Supervisor, Fauquier Times, VA,
Warrenton

Godfrey, Nick
ngodfrey@highlands.edu, Georgia Highlands
College, GA, Rome

Godinho, Amy
admin@theeveningleader.com, Bus. Mgr., The
Evening Leader, OH, Saint Marys

Godlow, Diane
publish@metins.net, Pub., Iowa County
Advertiser, IA, Marengo

Godoy, Dr. Ramon ....(806) 371-7084
editor@elmensajero-ama.com, Ed., El
Mensajero, TX, Amarillo

Godsey, John
jgodsey@kentuckynewera.com, Webmaster,
Kentucky New Era, KY, Hopkinsville

Goebel, Jenn ....(508) 520-1714
jenn@contentthatworks.com, COO, Content
That Works, Chicago

Goebel, Jil ....(719) 785-9900
jil.goebel@origincom.com, Acct. Servs./Media
Dir., Origin Communications, Inc., CO,
Colorado Springs

Goecks, Tricia
bdrnews@rvpublishing.com, Ed., The Belvidere
Daily Republican, IL, Belvidere

Goehring, Preston
sports@cseagle.com, Sports Ed, Chadron
State College, NE, Chadron

Goeller, Annie ....(317) 736-2718
Asst. Managing Ed., News, Daily Journal, IN,
Franklin

Goelzhaeufer, Nicola
nicola@mpimedia.com, Contact, MPI Media
Group, IL, Orland Park

Goer, Mahlon
Advertising@thehudsonvalleynews.com, Adv.
Dir., Hudson Valley News, NY, Hyde Park

Goetz, Dan
dgoetz@newtondailynews.com, Jasper County
Advertiser, IA, Newton

Goetz, Dan ....(641) 792-3121 ext. 612
dgoetz@newtondailynews.com, Pub., Newton
Daily News, IA, Newton

Goetz, Devon P. ....(805) 781-7805
dgoetz@thetribunenews.com, General
Manager, The Tribune, CA, San Luis Obispo

Goetz, Nick.............................(780) 352-2231
nick.goetz@sunmedia.ca, Pub., Wetaskiwin
Times, AB, Wetaskiwin

Goetz, Nick.............................(780) 362-0019
nick.goetz@sunmedia.ca, Publisher, The
Camrose Canadian, AB, Camrose

Goetz, Nick.............................(403) 782-3498
nick.goetz@sunmedia.ca, Adv. Dir, Lacombe
Globe, AB, Lacombe
nick.goetz@sunmedia.ca, Adv. Dir., Leduc
Representative, AB, Leduc

Goetz, Nicki ....(780) 672-4421 ext. 706020
ngoetz@postmedia.com, Dir. of Adv., Vermilion
Standard, AB, Vermilion

Goetz, Paul
pgoetz@themountainmail.com, Mng. Ed., The
Mountain Mail, CO, Salida

Goff, Mike
goffmk@bv.com, Vice Pres., Cor. Mktg., Sprint
Nextel Corp., KS, Overland Park

Goff, Nixie
ngoff@blackwelljournaltribune.net, News Ed.,
Blackwell Journal-Tribune, OK, Blackwell

Goff, Victoria ....(920) 544-1376
Univ. of Wisconsin Green Bay, WI, Green Bay

Goffinet, Larry
sports@perrycountynews.com, Sports Ed.,
Perry County News, IN, Tell City

Goforth, Martha
matha.goforth@sunmedia.ca, Office Mgr,
Pincher Creek Echo, AB, Pincher Creek

Goforth, Toni ....(580) 822-4401
bcpub@pldi.net, Managing Editor, Okeene
Record, OK, Okeene

Gofus, Nancy B. ....(703) 206-5600
info@mci.com, Sr. Vice Pres., Mktg./CMO,
MCI, VA, Ashburn

Goggin, Julie
julie_goggin@jewishaz.com, Adv. Coord.,
Jewish News, AZ, Phoenix

Goggins, Walter.......................(256) 740-5784
walter.goggins@timesdaily.com, TVPCO circ
mgr, Times Daily, AL, Florence

Gogick, John...........................(706) 823-3450
john.gogick@augustachronicle.com, Executive
Editor, The Augusta Chronicle, GA, Augusta

Goheen, Mike ....(937) 225-2219
mike.goheen@coxinc.com, Director, Copy
Desks, Dayton Daily News, OH, Franklin

Goings, Linda
lgoings@pbdailynews.com, Adv. Dir., Palm
Beach Daily News, FL, Palm Beach

Goins, Anita ....(575) 541-5420
agoins@lcsun-news.com, Adv. Mgr., Las
Cruces Sun-News, NM, Las Cruces

Gokyu, Nobuyoshi
nikoninstruments@nikon.net, Pres./CEO,
Nikon, Inc., NY, Melville

Golan, Ari
ari@atomicimaging.com, Pres., Atomic
Imaging, Inc., IL, Chicago

Golas, Matt
dmartin@mydallaspost.com, Ed., The Dallas
Post, PA, Wilkes Barre

Golbeare, Glenn ....(781) 334-6319
lynnfieldvillager@rcn.com, Pub./Ed., The
Lynnfield Villager, MA, Wakefield

Gold, Anita ....(773) 267-9773

thecapecod@aol.com, Author/Creator/Owner, Antiques & Collectible Self-Syndicated Column, Chicago

Gold, Jackie
jackie.gold@sunmedia.ca, Mng. Ed., Hanna Herald, AB, Hanna

Gold, James
jgold@aurorasentinel.com, Pub., Aurora Sentinel, CO, Aurora
jgold@aurorasentinel.com, Vice Pres./CMO, The New York Times Reg'l Newspaper Group, FL, Tampa

Gold, Jim
jim.gold@albertleatribune.com, Circ. Mgr., Tribune Shopping News, MN, Albert Lea

Gold, Jon
jgold@metrosuburbia.com, Adv. Sales Mgr., Metro Suburbia, Inc./Newhouse Newspapers, NY, New York

Gold, Paul.....................(404) 250-0100
gold@transpconsult.com, Pres., Transportation Consultants, Inc., GA, Atlanta

Goldbaum, Howard
goldbaum@unr.edu, Assoc. Prof., University of Nevada-Reno, NV, Reno

Goldberg, Howard
info@ap.org, Bureau Chief, New York State Associated Press Association, NY, Albany

Goldberg, J.J......................(212) 453-9432
Ed., The Forward, NY, New York

Goldberg, Jeffrey
goldberg@contemporary-media.com, Adv. Dir., Memphis Flyer, TN, Memphis

Goldberg, Larry
info@betascreen.com, Contact, Beta Screen Corp., NJ, Carlstadt

Goldberg, Miriam
email@ijn.com, Ed., Intermountain Jewish News, CO, Denver

Goldberg, Nicholas
nicholas.goldberg@latimes.com, Ed. of the Editorial Pages, Los Angeles Times, CA, Los Angeles

Goldberg, Stan
sales@printwarellc.com, Pres., Printware, MN, Saint Paul

Goldberger, Herman I.
hebwat@bellsouth.net, Ed., Hebrew Watchman, TN, Memphis

Goldberger, Richard.................(801) 355-3336
richard@fnanews.com, Mng. Ed., FNA News, Salt Lake City

Goldblum, Robert
robert@jewishweek.org, Mng. Ed., Jewish Week, NY, New York

Goldblum, Robert.....................(212) 921-7822
robert@jewishweek.org, Mng. Ed., The Queens Jewish Week, NY, New York

Goldblum, Robert.....................(212) 921-7822
robert@jewishweek.org, Mng. Ed., The Jewish Week, NY, New York

Goldblum, Robert...............(212) 921-7822 x213
robert@jewishweek.org, Managing Ed., Manhattan/Westchester Jewish Week, NY, New York
robert@jewishweek.org, Mng. Ed., The Westchester Jewish Week, NY, New York

Goldblum, Robert.....................(212) 921-7822
robert@jewishweek.org, Mng. Ed., The Long Island Jewish Week, NY, New York

Golde, Tammy.....................(906) 524-6194
sentinel1886@gmail.com, Composition/Photo Editor, L'Anse Sentinel, MI, Lanse

Golden, Amanda.....................(415) 246-3072
agolden@colgate.edu, Exec. Ed., Colgate Univ., NY, Hamilton

Golden, Jill.............(814) 765-7813 ext. 234
news@theprogressnews.com, Ed., The Progress, PA, Clearfield

Golden, Kim
kgolden@enterprise-journal.com, Business Mgr., Enterprise-Journal, MS, McComb

Golden, Marc.....................(256) 549-2069
marc.golden@gasdentimes.com, Photo Dept. Mgr., The Gadsden Times, AL, Gadsden

Golden, Michael
info@wan-ifra.org, WAN-IFRA President, World Association of Newspapers and News Publishers (WAN-IFRA), Frankfurt am Main

Golden, Michael.....................(212) 556-1234
michael.golden@nytimes.com, Vice Chrmn., New England Newspaper Group, NY, New York
michael.golden@nytimes.com, Vice Chrmn., The New York Times Co./Pub., International Herald Tribune, The New York Times Co., NY, New York
michael.golden@nytimes.com, Vice Chairman, The New York Times, NY, New York

Golden, Mike.....................(605) 331-2258
mgolden@argusleader.com, IT Manager, Argus Leader, SD, Sioux Falls

Golden, Sloane
Sloane@TheIslandReporter.com, Ed., The Island Reporter, FL, South Pasadena

Golden, Todd.....................(812) 231-4272
todd.golden@tribstar.com, Sports Ed., The Tribune Star, IN, Terre Haute

Goldfarb, Bob
goldfarb@forward.com, Mktg. Dir., Forward Newspaper, NY, New York

Goldfarb, Deborah
dgoldfarb@jewishlongbeach.org, CEO, Jewish Community Chronicle, CA, Long Beach

Golding, Chuck.....................(951) 244-1966
chuck@goldingpublications.com, Pub., The Friday Flyer, CA, Canyon Lake

Golding, Greg.....................(951) 244-1966
greg@goldingpublications.com, Adv. Mgr., The Friday Flyer, CA, Canyon Lake

Golding, Jeff.....................(306) 657-6463
jgolding@thestarphoenix.com, Prod. Mgr. , Saskatoon StarPhoenix, SK, Saskatoon

Golding, Mark.....................(770) 834-6631
markgolding@times-georgian.com, Cir. Dir., Times-Georgian, GA, Carrollton

Golding, Mark.............(770) 227 - 3276 x203
mark@griffindailynews.com, Circ. Dir., Griffin Daily News, GA, Griffin

Golding, Mark.....................ext. 301
markgolding@forsythnews.com, Forsyth County News, GA, Cumming

Golding, Mark.....................(470) 729-3241
markgolding@times-georgian.com, Cir. Mgr., Douglas County Sentinel, GA, Douglasville

Goldman, Ari
agoldman@storagedeluxe.com, Prof., Columbia University, NY, New York

Goldman, Irvin
goldman@uwindsor.ca, Chair, University of Windsor, ON, Windsor

Goldman , Jenna.....................(904) 304-8765
editor@lawweekly.org, Editor-in-Chief, Univ. of Virginia School of Law, VA, Charlottesville

Goldsby, Shawn.....................(317) 803-4772
sgoldsby@hspa.com, Nat'l Adv. Mgr./ Classifieds Adv. Mgr., Greenwood and Southside Challenger, IN, Greenwood
sgoldsby@hspa.com, Nat'l Adv. Mgr./ Classifieds Adv. Mgr., The Franklin Challenger, IN, Greenwood
sgoldsby@hspa.com, Adv. Coord., Hoosier State Press Association, IN, Indianapolis

Goldstein, Lorrie.....................(416) 947-2212
lorrie.goldstein@sunmedia.ca, Sr. Assoc. Ed., The Toronto Sun, ON, Toronto

Goldstein, Terrie
publisher@excitingread.com, Pub., Hudson Valley Parent, NY, Newburgh

Goldsworthy, Jim..........(301) 722-4600 ext. 2240
jgoldsworthy@times-news.com, Editorial page editor, The Cumberland Times-News, MD, Cumberland

Goldthwaite, Carmen
a.a.laws@tcu.edu, Adj. Fac., Texas Christian University, TX, Fort Worth

Goldy, Andrea.....................(518) 395-3008
agoldy@dailygazette.net, Credit Mgr., The Daily Gazette, NY, Schenectady

Goldy, Mary.....................(606) 326-2656
mgoldy@dailyindependent.com, Website Creative/Adv., The Daily Independent, KY, Ashland

Golightly, Amy.....................(307) 739-9542
amy@jhnewsandguide.com, Director of Business Development, Jackson Hole News&Guide, WY, Jackson

Gollob, Michelle
michelleg@goplastics.com, Adv. Customer Info Serv., Go Plastics/StreetSmart LLC, GA, Canton

Golnick, Linda
linda@crawfordcountyavalanche.com, Gen. Mgr., Crawford County Avalanche, MI, Grayling

Golombisky, Kim
kgolombi@cas.usf.edu, Assoc. Prof., University of South Florida, FL, Tampa

Gomes, Julio.....................(807) 343-6204
jgomes@chroniclejournal.com, Mng. Ed., The Chronicle-Journal, ON, Thunder Bay

Gomez, Adrian.....................(505) 823-3921
agomez@abqjournal.com, Journal Arts & Entertain. Editor, Albuquerque Journal, NM, Albuquerque

Gomez, Justin.....................(336) 727-7293
jgomez@wsjournal.com, Marketing Director, Winston-Salem Journal, NC, Winston Salem

Gomez, Sloan
sloan@sdcnn.com, Art Dir., Gay & Lesbian Times, CA, San Diego

Gonders, Susan
sgonders@semo.edu, Prof., Southeast Missouri State University, MO, Cape Girardeau

Goni, Rosanna.....................(303) 715-3219
Ed., El Pueblo Catolico, CO, Denver

Gonsalves, Ann Marie.................(610) 838-2066
valleyvoice@verizon.net, Pub./Adv. Mgr., The Valley Voice, PA, Hellertown

Gonyaw, Michael
gonyawm@caledonian-record.com, Adv. Dir./ Online Mgr., The Caledonian-Record, VT, Saint Johnsbury

Gonyo, Tyler
news@theberlinjournal.com, Pub./Gen. Mgr., Markesan Regional Reporter, WI, Berlin
news@theberlinjournal.com, Pub./Gen. Mgr., Omro Herald, WI, Berlin
news@theberlinjournal.com, Pub./Gen. Mgr., Princeton Times-Republic, WI, Berlin
news@theberlinjournal.com, Pub./Gen. Mgr., The Fox Lake Representative, WI, Berlin
news@theberlinjournal.com, Pub./Gen. Mgr., Green Lake Reporter, WI, Berlin
news@theberlinjournal.com, Pub./Gen. Mgr., Berlin Journal, WI, Berlin

Gonzales, Chris
cgonzales@ruidosonews.com, Circ. Mgr., The Ruidoso News, NM, Ruidoso

Gonzales, Harold
haroldgonzalesjr@yahoo.com, Gen. Mgr., The Crowley Post-Signal, LA, Crowley

Gonzales, Juan.....................(415) 239-3446
Accionjg@aim.com, City College of San Francisco, CA, San Francisco

Gonzales, Kimberly.....................(207) 990-8122
kgonzales@bangordailynews.com, Finance Dir., Bangor Daily News, ME, Bangor

Gonzales, Raymond.....................(806) 364-2030
retail@herefordbrand.com, Adv. Dir., The Hereford Brand, TX, Hereford

Gonzales, Sandra.....................(408) 920-5778
(408) 920-5778, City Ed., The Mercury News, CA, San Jose

Gonzales, Scott P.
gctimes@netins.net, Ed., Guthrie Center Times, IA, Guthrie Center

Gonzales, Shelly
shelly.gonzales@lubbockonline.com, Features Ed., Lubbock Avalanche-Journal, TX, Lubbock

Gonzales, Victor.....................(650) 508-3677
Notre Dame De Namur University, CA, Belmont

Gonzales, Viola.....................(575) 763-3431
sadair@cnjonline.com, Ad. Director, Quay County Sun, NM, Tucumcari

Gonzales, Viola.............(575) 763-3431 Ext. 210
Eastern New Mexico News, NM, Clovis

Gonzalez, Abe
abeg@brownsvilleherald.com, Circ. Dir., El Nuevo Heraldo, TX, Brownsville

Gonzalez, Amanda.....................(956) 283-6057
Managing Editor, St. Edwards Univ., TX, Austin

Gonzalez, Bertha Alicia
ahoranow2008@hotmail.com, Ed., Ahora Now, CA, San Ysidro

Gonzalez, Hugo.............(620) 792-1211 ext 223
hgonzalez@gbtribune.com, Digital Media/ Innovative Projects Coord., Great Bend Tribune, KS, Great Bend

Gonzalez, Keilani.....................(903) 645-3948
beenewspaper@etcnonline.com, Adv. Dir., The Bee, TX, Daingerfield

Gonzalez, Robert.....................(903) 683-2257
rgonzalez@mediactr.com, Adv. Dir., Cherokeean Herald, TX, Rusk

Gonzalez, Sarah
classifieds@iolaregister.com, Classified Adv., The Iola Register, KS, Iola

Gonzalez, Terrie.....................(903) 683-2257
herald@mediactr.com, Ed., Cherokeean Herald, TX, Rusk

Gonzalez, Veronica.....................(915) 747-7434
vegonzalez@utep.edu, Asst. Adv. Dir., Univ. of Texas El Paso, TX, El Paso

Gonzalez, Yadira.....................(214) 977-7214
ygonzalez@aldiatx.com, Cliente Serv. Coord., Al Dia, TX, Dallas

Gonzalo, Mar.....................(305) 262-7575
mgonzalo@efe.com, Bureau Chief-Miami, EFE News Services - Washington, DC, Washington

Gonzenbach, William
gonzenbach@apr.ua.edu, Prof., University of Alabama, AL, Tuscaloosa

Gooch, Bonita.....................(316) 681-1155
gooch@tcvpub.com, Editor-in-Chief, The Community Voice, KS, Wichita

Gooch, Bonita
ttimes@tcvpub.com, Ed., Tanker Times, KS, Wichita

Gooch, Cheryl R.
cgooch@claflin.edu, Chair/Prof., Claflin University, SC, Orangeburg

Good, David.....................(630) 427-6270
dgood@shawmedia.com , Ed., Elmhurst Suburban Life, IL, Downers Grove
dgood@shawmedia.com , Ed., Hinsdale Suburban Life, IL, Downers Grove
dgood@shawmedia.com , Ed., Villa Park Suburban Life, IL, Downers Grove
dgood@shawmedia.com , Ed., Lombard Suburban Life, IL, Downers Grove

Good, Deborah
dgood@mymail.mines.edu, Editor-in-Chief, Colorado School of Mines, CO, Golden

Good, Duane E.
dgood@sentinelnow.com, Ed., Upper Dauphin Sentinel, PA, Millersburg

Good, Jake .... (705) 645-8771 ext. 238
jakegood@metrolandnorthmedia.com, Editorial Coord., The Muskokan, ON, Bracebridge

Good, Jean
jgood@torringtontelegram.com, Office Mgr., The Torrington Telegram, WY, Torrington

Good, Jeff
jgood@gazettenet.com, Exec Editor, Amherst Bulletin, MA, Northampton

Good, Linda
goodl@msu.edu, Prof., Michigan State University, MI, East Lansing

Goodbar, Gay Lea
advertsing@thenews-gazette.com, Adv. Coord., The News-Gazette, VA, Lexington

Gooden, Carolyn
cgooden@capgaznews.com, Classified Adv. Mgr., The Maryland Gazette, MD, Annapolis

Goodhand, Mark .... (780) 429-5201
mgoodhand@edmontonjournal.com, Ed.-in-Chief, Edmonton Journal, AB, Edmonton

Goodhue, David
dgoodhue@keysreporter.com, Ed., The Reporter, FL, Tavernier

Gooding, Amber............................... ext. 3978
amber.gooding@forces.gc.ca, Asst. Ed., Wing Commander, ON, Astra

Gooding, Stace........................(701) 355-8800
stace.gooding@bismarcktribune.com, Systems Admin., The Bismarck Tribune, ND, Bismarck

Goodlin, Lisa
lgoodlin@sfparenting.com, Pub., South Florida Parenting Magazine, NC, Durham

Goodlin, Lisa .... (954) 574-5393
lgoodlin@tribune.com, Pres, Jewish Journal - Miami Dade, FL, Pompano Beach
lgoodlin@tribune.com, Boynton Forum, FL, Fort Lauderdale
lgoodlin@tribune.com, Delray Beach Forum, FL, Fort Lauderdale
lgoodlin@tribune.com, East Side Forum, FL, Fort Lauderdale
lgoodlin@tribune.com, Teenlink, FL, Fort Lauderdale
lgoodlin@tribune.com, Jewish Journal - Palm Beach Central, FL, Pompano Beach

Goodlow, Diane
dgoodlow@dmreg.com, Gen. Mgr., Grinnell Pennysaver, IA, Grinnell
dgoodlow@dmreg.com, Pub., Journal Tribune, IA, Williamsburg

Goodman, Bridgette
bridgette@hilites.net, Seneca County Area Shopper, NY, Ovid
bridgette@hilites.net, Hi Lites, NY, Watkins Glen

Goodman, Diana
dgoodman@thearknewspaper.com, Copy ed. & calendar ed., The Ark, CA, Tiburon

Goodman, Hays .... (262) 670-1521
hgoodman@conleynet.com, Online/Mgmt. Info Servs. Mgr., The Freeman, WI, Waukesha

Goodman, Jennifer ....ext. 445
Circ. Mgr., Carrier News, NY, Bohemia

Goodman, Jennifer ....ext. 445
jenn.goodman@lipennysaver.com, Circ. Mgr., Pennysaver News, NY, Edgewood

Goodman, Jerri ....(912) 685-6566
jgoodman@metteradvertiser.com, Ed., The Metter Advertiser, GA, Metter

Goodman, Jim
jgoodman@highpoint.edu, Asst. Prof., High Point Univ., NC, High Point

Goodman, Michael
mgoodman@dailyadvance.com, Pub., Perquimans Weekly, NC, Hertford

Goodman, Mike .... (252) 335-8110
mgoodman@dailyadvance.com, Editor/ Editorial Page Editor, The Daily Advance, NC, Elizabeth City

Goodman, Mike .... (252) 335-8107
mgoodman@dailyadvance.com, Publisher, The Daily Advance, Cooke Communications North Carolina, LLC, NC, Greenville

Goodman, Peter
peter.goodman@hofstra.edu, Hofstra Univ., NY, Hempstead

Goodman, Robyn
fgoodman@alfred.edu, Alfred Univ., NY, Alfred

Goodman, Shane .... (515) 953-4822 x305
shane@dmcityview.com, Publisher, Cityview, IA, Johnston

Goodman, Zac
zac.goodman@trader.ca, Prodn. Mgr., Buy & Sell, BC, Burnaby

Goodrich, Charles
cgoodrich@wickedlocal.com, Pub. , Brookline TAB, MA, Needham

Goodrich, Charles
cgoodrich@wickedlocal.com, Pub., Medford Transcript, MA, Danvers

Goodrich, Charles
cgoodrich@wickedlocal.com, Pub., Danvers Herald, MA, Danvers

Goodrich, Charles
cgoodrich@wickedlocal.com, Pub., Marblehead Reporter, MA, Marblehead

Goodrich, Charles
cgoodrich@wickedlocal.com, Pub., Malden Observer, MA, Danvers

Goodrich, Charles
cgoodrich@wickedlocal.com, Pub., Georgetown Record, MA, Danvers

Goodrich, Charles
cgoodrich@wickedlocal.com, Pub., Hamilton-Wenham Chronicle, MA, Danvers

Goodrich, Charles
cgoodrich@wickedlocal.com, Pub., Ipswich Chronicle, MA, Danvers

Goodrich, Charles .... (978) 739-1301
cgoodrich@wickedlocal.com, GateHouse Media, Inc., NY, Pittsford

Goodrich, Charles
cgoodrich@wickedlocal.com, Pub., Swampscott Reporter, MA, Marblehead

Goodrich, Dan
news@heraldnews.com, Pub., Classified Plus, MA, Fall River

Goodrich, Teresa..................... (248) 745-4526
tgoodrich@digitalfirstmedia.com, Rgl VP, Sales, The Oakland Press, MI, Pontiac
tgoodrich@digitalfirstmedia.com, VP, The Voice, MI, Clinton Township

Goodrich, Teresa
tgoodrich@digitalfirstmedia.com, VP, The Chelsea Standard, MI, Southgate
tgoodrich@digitalfirstmedia.com, Rgl. VP, Sales, The Daily Tribune, MI, Clinton Township
tgoodrich@digitalfirstmedia.com, Rgl. VP, Sales, The Macomb Daily, MI, Clinton Township

Goodrich , Chuck..................... (508) 626-3850
cgoodrich@wickedlocal.com, Pub., Amesbury News, MA, Danvers
cgoodrich@wickedlocal.com, Pub., The Walpole Times, MA, Walpole
cgoodrich@wickedlocal.com, Pub., Roslindale Transcript, MA, Needham
cgoodrich@wickedlocal.com, Pub., Somerville Journal, MA, Somerville
cgoodrich@wickedlocal.com, Pub., Belmont Citizen-Herald, MA, Lexington

cgoodrich@wickedlocal.com, Pub., Norwood Transcript & Bulletin, MA, Needham
cgoodrich@wickedlocal.com, Pub., Needham Times, MA, Needham
cgoodrich@wickedlocal.com, Pub., North Shore Sunday, MA, Danvers
cgoodrich@wickedlocal.com, Pub., Medfield Press, MA, Needham
cgoodrich@wickedlocal.com, Pub., Watertown TAB, MA, Needham
cgoodrich@wickedlocal.com, Pub., Hudson Sun, MA, Framingham
cgoodrich@wickedlocal.com, Pub., Melrose Free Press, MA, Danvers
cgoodrich@wickedlocal.com, Pub., Chelmsford Independent, MA, Concord
cgoodrich@wickedlocal.com, Pub., Swampscott Reporter, MA, Marblehead
cgoodrich@wickedlocal.com, Pub., Wilmington Advocate, MA, Concord
cgoodrich@wickedlocal.com, Pub., North Andover Citizen, MA, Danvers
cgoodrich@wickedlocal.com, Sr. Acct. Exec., USA WEEKEND - New York, NY (OOB), NY, New York
cgoodrich@wickedlocal.com, Pub., Reading Advocate, MA, Danvers
cgoodrich@wickedlocal.com, Pub., The Concord Journal, MA, Concord
cgoodrich@wickedlocal.com, Pub., The Beacon-Villager, MA, Concord
cgoodrich@wickedlocal.com, Pub., Wakefield Observer, MA, Danvers
cgoodrich@wickedlocal.com, Publisher, Bedford Minuteman, MA, Concord
cgoodrich@wickedlocal.com, Pub., Lexington Minuteman, MA, Lexington
cgoodrich@wickedlocal.com, Pub., Arlington Advocate, MA, Lexington
cgoodrich@wickedlocal.com, Pub., Saugus Advertiser, MA, Danvers
cgoodrich@wickedlocal.com, Pub., Newburyport Current, MA, Danvers
cgoodrich@wickedlocal.com, Pub., Times & Courier, MA, Concord
cgoodrich@wickedlocal.com, Pub., Lincoln Journal, MA, Concord
cgoodrich@wickedlocal.com, Pub., The Harvard Post, MA, Concord
cgoodrich@wickedlocal.com, Pub., Burlington Union, MA, Concord
cgoodrich@wickedlocal.com, Pub., The Bolton Common, MA, Concord
cgoodrich@wickedlocal.com, Pub. , Beverly Citizen, MA, Danvers
cgoodrich@wickedlocal.com, Pub., Tewksbury Advocate, MA, Concord
cgoodrich@wickedlocal.com, Pub. , Tri-Town Transcript, MA, Danvers
cgoodrich@wickedlocal.com, Pub., Winchester Star, MA, Lexington
cgoodrich@wickedlocal.com, Pub., Billerica Minuteman, MA, Concord
cgoodrich@wickedlocal.com, Pub., Westford Eagle, MA, Concord
cgoodrich@wickedlocal.com, Pub. , Dover-Sherborn Press, MA, Needham
cgoodrich@wickedlocal.com, Pub., Littleton Independent, MA, Concord
cgoodrich@wickedlocal.com, Pub., Newton Tab, MA, Needham
cgoodrich@wickedlocal.com, Pub., Wellesley Townsman, MA, Needham
cgoodrich@wickedlocal.com, Pub., Sharon Advocate, MA, Needham
cgoodrich@wickedlocal.com, Pub., Westwood Press, MA, Needham
cgoodrich@wickedlocal.com, Pub. , Stoneham Sun, MA, Somerville
cgoodrich@wickedlocal.com, Pub. , The Dedham Transcript, MA, Needham
cgoodrich@wickedlocal.com, Pub., Woburn Advocate, MA, Concord
cgoodrich@wickedlocal.com, Pub., Allston-Brighton TAB, MA, Needham

Goodson, Donna
dgoodson@news-daily.com, Bus. Mgr., Clayton News Daily, GA, Jonesboro

Goodstein, Jennifer ....(212) 229-1890 ext. 2506
ads@chelseanow.com, Publisher, Gay City

News, NY, New York
ads@chelseanow.com, Pub., Chelsea Now, NY, New York
ads@chelseanow.com, The Downtown Express, NY, New York
ads@chelseanow.com, East Villager and Lower East Sider, NY, Brooklyn
ads@chelseanow.com, The Villager, NY, Brooklyn

Goodwin, Andrew .... (415) 422-6680
goodwina@usfca.edu, Chair, University of San Francisco, CA, San Francisco

Goodwin, Brooke......................(309) 438-5929
Illinois State University, IL, Normal

Goodwin, Dave .... (305) 865-0158
davegoodwi@aol.com, Author/Owner, Dave Goodwin & Associates, Miami Beach

Goodwin, David
david.goodwin@theeclecticobserver.com, Ed., Eclectic Observer, AL, Wetumpka

Goodwin, James O.
news@theoklahomaeagle.net, Pub., The Oklahoma Eagle, OK, Tulsa

Goodwin, Jerry .... (918) 595-7388
jgoodwin@tulsacc.edu, Tulsa Cmty. College, OK, Tulsa

Goodwin, Karen
rsgazette@sbcglobal.net, Ed., The Rush Springs Gazette, OK, Rush Springs

Goodwin, Lucy .... (870) 533-4708
lcpress@sbcglobal.net, Pub., Lafayette County Press, AR, Stamps

Goodwin, Melissa
melissa.goodwin@albertleatribune.com, Circ. Rep., Albert Lea Tribune, MN, Albert Lea

Goodwin, Tina
tina.goodwin@yale.com, Dir., Financial Servs., Yale Materials Handling Corp., NC, Greenville

Goodwin-Garcia, Brenda
bgoodwin@metrosuburbia.com, Adv. Sales Mgr., Metro Suburbia, Inc./Newhouse Newspapers, NY, New York

Goodyear, Dan
mexpress@n-connect.net, Co-Pub., The Monticello Express, IA, Monticello

Goodyear, Dan
dgoodyear@monticelloexpress.com, Co-Pub., Monticello Shoppers' Guide, IA, Monticello

Goossen, John
jgoossen@amestrib.com, Pres., Iowa Newspapers, Inc., IA, Ames

Goossen, John .... (515) 663-6943
jgoossen@amestrib.com, Pub., Story County Advertiser, IA, Ames

Gopwani, Jewel
jgopwani@freepress.com, Asst. Ed., Opinion , Detroit Free Press, MI, Detroit

Goralski, John
jgoralski@southingtonobserver.com, Sports Ed., The Observer, CT, Southington

Gorby, Marshall .... (937) 328-0340
mgorby@coxohio.com, Photo Ed., Springfield News-Sun, OH, Springfield

Gordanier, Derek........................... ext. 500107
derek.gordanier@sunmedia.ca, Managing Ed., The Brockville Recorder and Times, ON, Brockville

Gorder, Eric
egorder@uark.edu, Instr., University of Arkansas, AR, Fayetteville

Gordon, Barbara A.
metrocourier@comcast.net, Ed., The Metro Courier, GA, Augusta

Gordon, Dan .... (541) 347-2423
dgordon@theworldlink.com, Prod. Supv., The World, OR, Coos Bay
dgordon@theworldlink.com, Prod. Supv.,

Bandon Western World, OR, Bandon

Gordon, Donna .... (704) 358-5280
drgordon@charlotteobserver.com, Dir. of National Adv., The Charlotte Observer, NC, Charlotte

Gordon, Emily .... (419) 724-0363
emilyg@jewishtoledo.org, Staff writer, Marketing Associate, Toledo Jewish News, OH, Sylvania

Gordon, Grant .... (818) 637-3225
Grant.Gordon@latimes.com, Sports Ed., News-Press, CA, Los Angeles

Gordon, Jean
jgordon@thedigitalcourier.com, Ed., The Daily Courier, NC, Forest City

Gordon, Joye
gordon@ksu.edu, Assoc. Prof., Kansas State University, KS, Manhattan

Gordon, Kim
kim.gordon@roswell-record.com, Adv. Dir., Vincennes Sun-Commercial, IN, Vincennes
kim.gordon@roswell-record.com, Adv. Dir., Roswell Daily Record, NM, Roswell

Gordon, Mark .... (941) 362-4848 x303
mgordon@BusinessObserverFL.com, Ed., Business Observer, FL, Sarasota

Gordon, Mark
ads@brookvillestar.net, Adv. Mgr./Circ. Mgr., Brookville Star, OH, Brookville

Gordon, Rich
richgor@northwestern.edu, Assoc. Prof., Northwestern University, IL, Evanston

Gordon, Tracy .... (502) 419-0919
tracy.gordon@religionnews.com, Editorial/ Publishing Consultant, Religion News Service, Washington

Gordon, Veronica .... (812) 316-5383
vgordon@suncommercial.com, Acct. Exec., Vincennes Sun-Commercial, IN, Vincennes

Gordon, William
gordonw@lafayette.edu, EIC, Lafayette College, PA, Easton

Gordon, Yanela
yanela.gordon@famu.edu, Asst. Prof./Vstg. Dir., Career Devel. Servs., Florida A&M University, FL, Tallahassee

Gordon-Broome, Danielle
editor@starandtimes.ca, Ed., Swan Valley Star & Times, MB, Swan River

Gore, Don
don.gore@sonoco.com, Division Vice Pres., Sales, Sonoco Products Co., SC, Hartsville

Gore, Fred
fredgore@thewestfieldnewsgroup.com, Chief Photographer, The Westfield News , MA, Westfield

Gore, Jim .... (314) 682-3808
jpgore@presslineservices.com, Pres., Pressline Services, Inc., IL, Dupo

Gore, Kevin .... (936) 564-8361
kgore@dailysentinel.com, Sports, The Daily Sentinel, TX, Nacogdoches

Gore, Lynn .... (540) 825-0771 ext. 102
Adv. Mgr. , Culpeper Star-Exponent, VA, Culpeper

Gorin, Walter C.
news@record-herald.com, Adv. Mgr., Greensburg Record-Herald, KY, Greensburg

Gorman, Doug .... (770) 683-1781
doug@newnan.com, Sports Editor, The Newnan Times-Herald, GA, Newnan

Gorman, Fred
fgorman@reddeeradvocate.com, Pub., Red Deer Advocate, AB, Red Deer

Gorman, James M. .... (412) 263-1735
jgorman@post-gazette.com, Regional Operations Manager/AOZ, Pittsburgh Post-Gazette, PA, Clinton

Gorman, Mary .... (603) 594-1210
getclassifieds@nashuatelegraph.com, Retail adv. - S. Nashua, The Telegraph, NH, Nashua

Gorman, Michael .... (713) 362-6585
michael.gorman@chron.com, Vice President, Consumer Sales & Services, Houston Chronicle, TX, Houston

Gorman, Mike .... (985) 448-7612
mike.gorman@houmatoday.com, Op. Ed. , Daily Comet, LA, Thibodaux

Gorman, Ted C.
vpolk@i-rule.net, Pub., Winterset Madisonian, IA, Winterset

Gormley, Mike .... (937) 376-6491
Central State Univ., OH, Wilberforce

Gors, Mike
mgors@siouxcityjournal.com, Opinion Ed., Sioux City Journal, IA, Sioux City

Gorske, Elizabeth
liz@ogemawherald.com, Pub. , Arenac County Independent, MI, Standish

Gorske, Liz
liz@ogemawherald.com, Pub., Ogemaw County Herald, MI, West Branch

Gorski, Steve
info@alarcorp.com, Sales Mgr., Alar Engineering Corporation, IL, Mokena

Gorven, Kelly
k.gorven@ocna.org, Member Services Coordinator, Member Services Coordinator, ON, Toronto

Goss, Catherine .... (519) 843-5410 ext. 527
circulation@wellingtonadvertiser.com, Circ. Mgr., The Wellington Advertiser, ON, Fergus

Goss, Cathy
cgoss@eagletribune.com, Adv. Dir., Andover Townsman, MA, Andover

Goss, Cathy
cgoss@northofboston.com, Adv. Dir., Derry News, NH, Derry

Goss, Dick .... (815) 729-6040
dgoss@scnl.com, Sports Ed., The Herald News, IL, Chicago

Goss, Nathan R. .... (770) 534-6162
Brenau Univ., GA, Gainesville

Goss, Rex .... (336) 835-1513
rgoss@civitasmedia.com, Gen. Mgr., The Tribune, NC, Elkin

Gosse, Leo
lgosse@thetelegram.com, Reader Sales and Mktg. Mgr., The Telegram, NL, Saint John's

Gosser, Dale
dgosser@trcle.com, Managing Editor, Cleburne Times-Review, TX, Cleburne

Gosser, Trisha
tgosser@republicmedia.com, VP, Finance, The Arizona Republic, AZ, Phoenix

Gossert, Shirley
classified@therecordherald.com, Adv. Mgr., Classified, The Record Herald, PA, Waynesboro

Gossett, Dave .... (478) 744-4210
dgossett@macon.com, Circ. Mgr., Cherokee Tribune, GA, Canton

Gossett, Debra .... (606) 451-4905
Classified Adv. Dir., The Commonwealth-Journal, KY, Somerset

Gostisa, Leticia
info@quipp.com, Mktg. Mgr., Quipp System, Inc., FL, Miami Lakes

Gotchell, Margaret ....(330) 541-9400 ex. 4103
mgotschall@recordpub.com, Circ. Mgr., Nordonia Hills News Leader, OH, Kent

Gotcher, Mike
gotcherm@apsu.edu, Chair, Austin Peay State University, TN, Clarksville

Gotschall, Margaret ....(330) 541-9400 Ext. 4103

Gotschall, Margaret ....
mgotschall@recordpub.com, Circ. Mgr., Streetsboro Gateway News (OOB), OH, Kent
mgotschall@recordpub.com, Cir. Mgr., Twinsburg Bulletin, OH, Kent

Gottesman, Jan .... (978) 368-0176 ext. 790
Mng. Ed., The Banner, MA, Clinton

Gottesman, Jan .... ext. 4790
clintonitem@yahoo.com, Ed., The Item, MA, Clinton

Gottlieb, Martin .... (973) 569-7118
Gottlieb@northjersey.com, VP Ed., Herald News, NJ, Rockaway

Gottlieb, Paul ....(360) 452-2345, ext 5060
pgottlieb@peninsuladailynews.com, Letters to Editors/Commentary, Peninsula Daily News, WA, Port Angeles

Gottschall, Margaret .... (330) 541-9400 x 4103
mgotschall@recordpub.net, Cir. Mgr., Stow Sentry, OH, Kent

Gottshall, Cynthia
gottshall_cm@mercer.edu, Broadcast/Film, Mercer University at Macon, GA, Macon

Gottus, Tina .... (863) 386-5811
tgottus@highlandstoday.com, Highlands News-Sun, FL, Sebring

Gotwals, Ed .... (717) 262-4755
egotwals@publicopinionnews.com, Sports Ed., Public Opinion, PA, Chambersburg

Goudreau, Paula
pgoudreau@gannett.com, El Sol - Visalia, CA, Visalia
pgoudreau@gannett.com, Pres./Pub., Tulare Advance-Register, CA, Visalia

Goudreau, Paula
pgoudreau@gannett.com, Pres./Pub., Visalia Times-Delta, CA, Visalia

Goudreau, Paula .... (831) 754-4100
pgoudreau@thecalifornian.com, Publisher & President, The Salinas Californian, CA, Salinas

Goudswaard, Ken
editorial@chilliwacktimes.com, Ed., Chilliwack Times, BC, Chilliwack

Goudy, Olivia .... (724) 984-6521
gou4055@setonhill.edu, Editor-in-Chief, Seton Hill University, PA, Greensburg

Gouge, Michael
mgouge@unca.edu, Univ. of North Carolina, NC, Asheville

Gougeon, Lori .... (810) 989-6215
lgougeon@timesherald.com, Adv. Mgr., Times Herald, MI, Port Huron

Gould, Alexander .... (601) 693-1551 ext.3202
Pub. , The Meridian Star, MS, Meridian

Gould, Dave .... (615) 444-6008
news@wilsonpost.com, Pres./Pub., The Wilson Post, TN, Lebanon

Gould, Gary .... (810) 452-2650
ggould@mihomepaper.com, Ed, The Davison Index, MI, Davison

Gould, Jedd .... (860) 379-9602
jgould@mediabids.com, President, Mediabids, Inc., CT, Winsted

Gould, Les .... (250) 729-4223
lgould@nanaimodailynews.com, Circ. Dir., Nanaimo Daily News, BC, Nanaimo
lgould@nanaimodailynews.com, Circ. Mgr., Harbour City Star (OOB), BC, Nanaimo

Gould, Linda R.
lgould@timesrepublican.com, Adv. Dir., Times-Republican, IA, Marshalltown

Gould, Lisa
gcnews@telus.net, Sales, Grande Cache Mountaineer, AB, Grande Cache

Gould, Scott
scott@waynegouldpuzzles.com, Mgr., Pappocom, Glen

Gould, Wayne .... (603) 383-6729
wayne.gould@sudoku.com, Dir., Pappocom, Glen

Goulding, Waren .... (250) 748-2666 x229
warren.goulding@blackpress.ca, Pub., The Lake Cowichan Gazette, BC, Duncan

Gouldstone, Barbara
sales@nwgraphic.com, Pres., Northern Graphic Supply, NV, Sparks

Goulet, Christian .... (514) 985-3357
production@ledevoir.com, Prodn. Dir., Le Devoir, QC, Montreal

Gounley, Thomas .... (417) 836-1213
tgounley@news-leader.com, Bus. Watchdog Rep., Springfield News-Leader, MO, Springfield

Gourd, Sheri .... (918) 456-8833
sgourd@tahlequahdailypress.com, Mult. Media Ed., Tahlequah Daily Press, OK, Tahlequah

Gourley, Vicki
vicki@okcfriday.com, CEO/Pub, Oklahoma City Friday, OK, Oklahoma City

Gouvellis, Jim
gouvellis@heartlandnewspapers.com, The Polk County News and Democrat, FL, Winter Haven

Gouvellis, Jim .... (863) 533-4183
gouvellis@heartlandnewspapers.com, VP/Polk Operations
Publisher/Heartland Newspapers, Sun Coast Media Group Inc, FL, Punta Gorda

Gouvellis, Jim .... (941) 206-1136
jgouvellis@sun-herald.com, Exec. Ed., Arcadian, FL, Arcadia
jgouvellis@sun-herald.com, Exec. Ed., Charlotte Sun, FL, Punta Gorda

Gouvion, Michael .... (608) 208-1678
couriersports@hngnews.com, Sports Ed., The Milton Courier, WI, Milton

Govang, Don
govangd@lincolnu.edu, Dept. Head/Assoc. Prof., Lincoln University, MO, Jefferson City

Gove, Kim
classifieds@rockportpilot.com, Adv. Dir., The Rockport Pilot, TX, Rockport

Gove, Scott
globe@sdgnewsgroup.com, Pub., New London Record, OH, New London
globe@sdgnewsgroup.com, Pub., Firelands Farmer, OH, New London

Gove, Scott M. .... (419) 342-4276
globe@sdgnewsgroup.com, Pres./Pub., Daily Globe, OH, Shelby

Gover , Keith .... (709) 748-0812
keith.gover@thetelegram.com, Controller, The Telegram, NL, Saint John's

Govi, Rose
rgovi@dioceseofgreensburg.org, Adv. Mgr., The Catholic Accent, PA, Greensburg

Gowan, Sharon .... (707) 205-1538
Sharon@family-life.us , Publisher/Editor , Family-Life Magazine, CA, Santa Rosa

Gowan, Sharon
sharon@family-life.us, Ed., Sonoma Family-Life Magazine, CA, Rohnert Park

Gower, Ron
rgower@tnonline.com, Entertainment Ed., Times News, PA, Lehighton

Gowing, Dale
dgowing@mooresvilletribune.com, Ed, Mooresville Tribune, NC, Mooresville

Goza, Tracy
tracy@hughescountytimes.com, Pub., The Hughes County Times, OK, Wetumka

Gozzi, Raymond
gozzi@ithaca.edu, Assoc. Prof., Ithaca College, NY, Ithaca

Gozzo, Frank

fgozzo@bowebellhowell.com, Exec. Vice Pres., Bowe Bell + Howell, NC, Durham

Graaskamp, Dan ....(715) 830-5821
dan.graaskamp@ecpc.com, Sales Dir., Entertainment Spotlight Saver, WI, Eau Claire

Graaskamp, Daniel ....(715) 830-5821
dan.graaskamp@ecpc.com, VP, Leader-Telegram, WI, Eau Claire

Graaskamp, Pieter..................... ext. 3277
pieter.graaskamp@ecpc.com, Pres./CEO, Leader-Telegram, WI, Eau Claire

Graaskamp, Pieter
pieter.graaskamp@ecpc.com, Pub., Entertainment Spotlight Saver, WI, Eau Claire

Graber, Roy
courier@winfieldcourier.com, Mng. Ed., The Leader, KS, Winfield

Grabin, Heather
mdiamond@windstream.net, Adv. Mgr., Murfreesboro Diamond, AR, Murfreesboro

Grabinoski, Kristin..................(712) 868-3460
krisg@armstrongjournal.com, Publisher, Armstrong Journal, IA, Armstrong

Grable, Bettye
bettye.grable@famu.edu, Assoc. Prof., Florida A&M University, FL, Tallahassee

Grabowski, Christine
cgrabowski@citypaper.com, Circ. Mgr., City Paper, MD, Baltimore

Grabowski, Gerard.........(716) 668-5223 ext. 8001
info@metrowny.com, Pub., Metro Community News, NY, Cheektowaga

Grabowski, Gerry
ggrabowski@metrowny.com, Pub., Pennysaver, NY, Hamburg
ggrabowski@metrowny.com, Arcade Pennysaver, NY, Arcade
ggrabowski@metrowny.com, Blasdell / Lackawanna (OOB), NY, Buffalo
ggrabowski@metrowny.com, Gowanda PennySaver News (OOB), NY, Buffalo
ggrabowski@metrowny.com, Hamburg Pennysaver, NY, Hamburg
ggrabowski@metrowny.com, Springville Pennysaver, NY, Springville

Grace, Beth ....(919) 789-2090
beth@ncpress.com, Publisher, North Carolina Press Association, NC, Raleigh

Grace, Beth ....(919) 789-2090
beth@ncpress.com, Exec. Dir., North Carolina Press Service, Inc., NC, Raleigh

Grace, Cyndi ....(574) 583-5121
cgrace@thehj.com, Circ. Dir., Herald Journal, IN, Monticello

Grace, Cyndi
cgrace@thehj.com, Circ. , The Hoopeston Chronicle, IL, Hoopeston
cgrace@thehj.com, Circ., Rensselaer Republican, IN, Rensselaer

Grace, Cyndi
cgrace@thehj.com, Circ., Kankakee Valley Post-News, IN, Demotte

Grace, Cyndi
cgrace@thehj.com, Circ. , The Review Republican, IN, Attica

Grace, David
photo@timesnews.net, Photo Dept. Mgr., Kingsport Times-News, TN, Kingsport

Grace, Jo-Ann W.
news@metnews.com, Co-Pub., Metropolitan News-Enterprise, CA, Los Angeles

Grace, Melissa
ringlingeagle@sbcglobal.net, Pub./Ed., The Ringling Eagle, OK, Ringling

Grace, Rob
rgmax99@yahoo.com, Pres./Ed., Arkansas Weekly, AR, Batesville

Grace-Kellogg, Lisa
lisa@thecomptonbulletin.com, Pub., Compton Bulletin, CA, East Rancho Dominguez

Gracyzk, Mark
mgraczyk@batavianews.com, Ed., Drummer Pennysaver, NY, Batavia

Grad, Shelby
shelby.grad@latimes.com, Local & CA., Asst. Managing Ed., Los Angeles Times, CA, Los Angeles

Gradi, Cyndi
heraldads@roadrunner.com, Ad. Mgr., Arcade Herald, NY, Arcade

Grady, Don
gradyd@elon.edu, Assoc. Prof./Dept. Chair, Elon University, NC, Elon

Grady, Gary
advertising@leesvilledailyleader.com, Adv., The Leesville Daily Leader, LA, Leesville

Grady, Jaclyn ....(518) 290-3897
jgrady@digitalfirstmedia.com, Multi Media Account Exec., The Saratogian, NY, Saratoga Springs

Grady, James..................(615) 596-6210
jgrady@outandaboutnashville.com, Managing Print Editor, Out & About Nashville, TN, Nashville

Graf, Darla ....(620) 257-2368
Office Asst,, The Lyons News, KS, Lyons

Graf, Randy ....(937) 382-2574 x 2501
rgraf@civitasmedia.com, Pub., Wilmington News Journal, OH, Wilmington

Graf, Randy
rgraf@civitasmedia.com, Pub., Fairborn Daily Herald, OH, Xenia

Graf, Randy ....(937) 382-2574 x2501
rgraf@civitasmedia.com, Pub., News Journal Star, OH, Wilmington

Grafe, Mike ....(406) 791-6516
mgrafe@greatfal.gannett.com, Production Operations Dir., Great Falls Tribune, MT, Great Falls

Graff, Diane..................(920) 478-2188
dgraff@hngnews.com, Managing Editor, The Waterloo/Marshall Courier, WI, Waterloo

Graff, Tim J. ....(509) 837-4500
tgraff@sunnewspapers.com, Pub., Daily Sun News, WA, Sunnyside

Graham, Chris
cgraham@beenews.com, Ed. , Orchard Park Bee, NY, Williamsville
cgraham@beenews.com, Ed. , Lancaster Bee, NY, Williamsville

Graham, Gary ....(705) 259-5811
Prodn. Foreman, Pressroom, The Sault Star, ON, Sault Sainte Marie

Graham, Gary ....(509) 459-5405
garyg@spokesman.com, Editor, The Spokesman-Review, WA, Spokane

Graham, Ian ....(204) 677-4534
editor@thompsoncitizen.net, Ed., Thompson Citizen/nickel Belt News, MB, Thompson

Graham, Janene
grahamja@valassis.com, Senior Newspaper Specialist
, Valassis, MI, Livonia

Graham, Jarrod ....(661) 395-7478
jgraham@bakersfield.com, Design Ed., The Bakersfield Californian, CA, Bakersfield

Graham, Jay
news@frankstoncitizen.com, Ed., Frankston Citizen, TX, Frankston

Graham, Jaynell ....(304) 799-4973
Editor, The Pocahontas Times, WV, Marlinton

Graham, Jeff
jgraham@burnstimesherald.info, Circ. Mgr., Burns Times-Herald, OR, Burns

Graham, John
dcpress@midtech.net, Pub., Denver City Press, TX, Denver City

Graham, John ....(847) 427-4382
jgraham@dailyherald.com, Audience Analytics/ Digital Ad Operations Manager, Daily Herald, IL, Arlington Heights

Graham, John
leader@leaconet.com, Ed./Pub., Lovington Leader, NM, Lovington

Graham, Karen ....(705) 932-8815
kgraham@nexicom.net, Pub., Millbrook Times, ON, Fraserville

Graham, Keith.............. (724) 282-8000 ext. 204
kgraham@butlereagle.com, Retail Sales Manager, Butler Eagle, PA, Butler

Graham, Keith ....(724) 282-8000
kgraham@butlereagle.com, Director of advertising, Eagle Printing Co., PA, Butler

Graham, Lara ....(604) 444-3030
lgraham@burnabynow.com, Pub., Burnaby Now, BC, Burnaby

Graham, Lara
lgraham@burnabynow.com, Pub, New Westminster Record, BC, New Westminster
lgraham@burnabynow.com, Pub, The Record, BC, Burnaby

Graham, Larry ....(501) 918-4537
lgraham@arkansasonline.com, V.P./Circulation, Arkansas Democrat-Gazette, AR, Little Rock

Graham, Luke
lgraham@sync2media.com, Business Development Specialist , SYNC2 Media, CO, Denver

Graham, Mark
mgraham@iwanna.com, Circ. Mgr., Iwanna, NC, Asheville

Graham, Martin ....(740) 313-0351
mgraham@civitasmedia.com, Cont. Prod., Record Herald, OH, Washington Court House

Graham, Michele
circulation@pqbnews.com, Circ. Mgr., Parksville Qualicum Beach News, BC, Parksville

Graham, Mike ....(772) 215-7447
mike.graham@tcpalm.com, Indian River Press Journal, FL, Vero Beach
mike.graham@tcpalm.com, Sports Ed. , St. Lucie News Tribune, FL, Port Saint Lucie
mike.graham@tcpalm.com, Sports Ed., The Stuart News, FL, Stuart

Graham, Patrick ....(770) 267-2443
patrick.graham@waltontribune.com, Pub./Ed., The Walton Tribune, GA, Monroe

Graham, Renee
reneegraham@bellsouth.net, Adv. Mgr., The West Carroll Gazette, LA, Oak Grove

Graham, Rhonda ....(910) 486-3510
grahamr@fayobserver.com , Chief Financial Officer, Fayetteville Publishing Co., NC, Fayetteville

Graham, Robert
rgraham@co.hinds.ms.us, Regional Sales Dir. of Flint, Saginaw and Bay City, The Jackson Citizen Patriot, MI, Jackson

Graham, Robin ....(416) 528-6930
rgraham.cssi@gmail.com, International Sales Consultant, North America Syndicate, New York

Graham, Robin ....(416) 869-4993
rgraham@thestar.com, Managing Director, Torstar Syndication Services, ON, Toronto

Graham, Robin ....(416) 528-6930
rgraham.cssi@gmail.com, International Sales Consultant, King Features Syndicate, NY, New York

Graham, Rusty ....(281) 378-1911
rgraham@hcnonline.com, Ed., Sugar Land

Sun, TX, Houston
rgraham@hcnonline.com, Ed., Memorial Examiner, TX, Conroe
rgraham@hcnonline.com, Ed., River Oaks Examiner, TX, Houston
rgraham@hcnonline.com, Ed., Fort Bend Sun, TX, Conroe
rgraham@hcnonline.com, Ed., The Examiners, TX, Conroe
rgraham@hcnonline.com, Ed., The Rancher, TX, Conroe

Graham, Sammy
sgraham@afro.com, Circ. Mgr., The Afro American Newspaper-baltimore, MD, Baltimore

Graham, Sandy............(580) 482-1221 Ext. 2073
skgraham@civitasmedia.com, Cir. Mgr., Altus Times, OK, Altus

Graham, Scott
Ed. in Chief, The Recorder, CA, San Francisco

Graham, Stephanie
info@thecanadianpress.com, Correspondent, Canadian Press, The - Regina, SK, SK, Regina

Graham, Tom ....(812) 316-5431
tgraham@suncommercial.com, Sports, Vincennes Sun-Commercial, IN, Vincennes

Grahan, Mark
grahan@iwanna.com, Circ. Mgr., Iwanna, SC, Greenville

Grainger, Steven
frankenmuthnews@airadvantage.net, Pub., Frankenmuth News, MI, Frankenmuth

Gralish, Jen
jgralish@bellevuereporter.com, Adv. Mgr., Bellevue Reporter, WA, Bellevue

Gramling, Sue..................(309) 757-4996
sueg@qconline.com, Data Processing Mgr., The Dispatch-Argus, IL, Moline

Grammens, Bob
grammens@wavecom.net, The Country Bounty, WY, Sheridan

Grams, John A.
a.a.arkadan@marquette.edu, Assoc. Prof., Marquette University, WI, Milwaukee

Granberg, Susan ....(778) 225-0024
production@comoxvalleyrecord.com, Prod. Mgr., North Island Midweek, BC, Courtenay
production@comoxvalleyrecord.com, Prodn. Mgr., Comox Valley Record, BC, Courtenay

Grandbois, Will
will@postindependent.com, Outdoors and entertainment editor, Glenwood Springs Post Independent, CO, Glenwood Springs

Grandcolas, Jack ....(415) 713-6568
jgrandcolas@nnnlp.com, Sales Dir., Newspaper National Network LP, NY, New York

Grande, Maggie..................(973) 569-7543
Grande@northjersey.com, Dir. Marketing, Herald News, NJ, Rockaway

Grande, Maggie..................(973) 569-7543
grande@northjersey.com, Dir. of Marketing, The Record, NJ, Woodland Park

Grandguillot, August
recorder3@sasktel.net, Ad., The Tisdale Recorder, SK, Tisdale

Grandstaff, Mark ....(540) 351-1634
mgrandstaff@virginianewsgroup.com, Managing Ed., Fauquier Times, VA, Warrenton

Grandstaff, Mike
dchubb@axcess.net, Gen. Mgr., Pennysaver/ pennywise, NY, Syracuse

Grandy, James ....(518) 395-3094
jgrandy@dailygazette.com, Prodn. Mgr., The Daily Gazette, NY, Schenectady

Granger, David ....(256) 234-4281
david.granger@tallasseetribune.com,

Managing Editor, The Tallassee Tribune, AL, Tallassee

Granger, David ....(334) 567-7811
david.granger@thewetumpkaherald.com, Managing Editor, The Wetumpka Herald, AL, Alexander City

Granger, Randy.........................(251) 219-5370
rgranger@press-register.com, Dir., Mktg./ Promo., Press-Register, AL, Mobile

Granier, Frank ....(208) 664-8176 ext. 1008
fgranier@cdapress.com, Bus. Mgr./Purchasing Agent, Coeur d'Alene Press, ID, Coeur D Alene

Granillo, Gabriel ....(928) 913-8669
ggranillo@flaglive.com, Staff Writer, Flagstaff Live!, AZ, Flagstaff

Graning, Stacy ....(334) 566-4270
stacy.graning@troymessenger.com, Pub., The Troy Messenger, AL, Troy

Grant, Carolyn.........................(250) 427-5333
carolyn.grant@kimberleybulletin.com, Ed., The Kimberley Daily Bulletin, BC, Kimberley

Grant, Chandra ....(707) 938-1783
chandra@winecountrythisweek.com, Ed., Wine Country This Week, CA, Sonoma

Grant, Craig
craig@easyrealtysites.com, Online Sales Mgr., The Gainesville Sun, FL, Gainesville

Grant, Debbie ....(956) 683-4021
dgrant@aimmediatx.com, Dir., Finance & Controller, The Monitor, TX, McAllen

Grant, Jeff
editor@iowainformation.com, Ed., The Golden Shopper, IA, Sheldon

Grant, Jeff
editor@iowainformation.com, Ed., N'West Iowa Review, IA, Sheldon

Grant, Mischelle ....(317) 444-4000
mischelle.grant@indystar.com, Dir. Local Sales, The Indianapolis Star, IN, Indianapolis

Grant, Mischelle
mgrant@alm.com, Adv. Dir., Daily Report, GA, Atlanta

Grant, Sandra
sandra.grant@mwsu.edu, Asst. Prof., Midwestern State University, TX, Wichita Falls

Grant, Sheryl
sgrant@herald.ca, Adv. Media Dir., Cole Harbour Weekly, NS, Halifax
sgrant@herald.ca, Adv. Media Dir., Bedford - Sackville Weekly News, NS, Halifax
sgrant@herald.ca, Adv. Media Dir., Halifax West-clayton Park Weekly News, NS, Halifax

Grant, Thomas ....(803) 359-7633
chroniclesports@yahoo.com, Sports Editor, Lexington County Chronicle & The Dispatch-News, SC, Lexington

Grantham, John ....(360) 705-4585
john@noteads.com, President, NoteAds.com, Inc./Post-it Note Advertising, WA, Olympia

Granville, Charles
sales@capita.com, CEO, Capita Technologies, CA, Irvine

Grap, John
jgrap@battlecreekenquirer.com, Photo Ed., Battle Creek Enquirer, MI, Battle Creek

Grapperhaus, Mae ....(618) 667-3111
dazemae1@juno.com, Reporter, Troy Times-Tribune, IL, Troy

Graser, Tom
tgraser@ogd.com, Ed., Ogdensburg Journal/ Advance News, NY, Ogdensburg

Graslie, Serri
editor@hamlineoracle.com, Hamline Univ., MN, Saint Paul

Grasseschi, Wendi.................(760) 934-3929 x 2
wendilyn@mammothtimes.com, Staff Writer,

Mammoth Times, CA, Mammoth Lakes

Grasska, Denis ....(858) 490-8267
dgrasska@diocese-sdiego.org, Asst. Ed., The Southern Cross, CA, San Diego

Grasso, Frank
frank@metrosn.com, New Ventures Development, Metro Newspaper Advertising Services, Inc., NY, New York

Grasso, Frank P.
fgrasso@nnnlp.com, Vice Pres., Newspaper Rel., Newspaper National Network LP, NY, New York

Graupman, Dustin
dgraupman@ags.com, Pres., Automated Graphic Systems, MD, White Plains

Graustein, Jennifer ....(734) 794-1315
jgraustein@xitron.com, Marketing Coordinator, Xitron, MI, Ann Arbor

Gravel, Martin.........................(450) 932-4782
danielle.patry@hebdosquebecor.com, Echo De Repentigny, QC, Repentigny

Graveland, Bill ....(403) 543-7238
bill.graveland@thecanadianpress.com, National Correspondent, Canadian Press, The - Calgary, AB, AB, Calgary

Graves, Andrea.........................(660) 646-2411
AGRAVES@CHILLICOTHENEWS.COM, Adv. Dir., Constitution-Tribune, MO, Chillicothe

Graves, Brian
auroraproduction@ns.aliantzinc.ca, Graphics designer, The Aurora, NS, Greenwood

Graves, Christy
cgraves@advertisergleam.com, Advert. Sales, The Advertiser-Gleam, AL, Guntersville

Graves, Courtney
yournews@srt.com, Ed., Velva Area Voice, ND, Velva

Graves, Ed
egraves@gatehousemedia.com, Sr. Grp. Pub., White Hall Journal, AR, White Hall
egraves@gatehousemedia.com, Sr. Vice Pres., Newspaper Rel., USA WEEKEND - New York, NY (OOB), NY, New York
egraves@gatehousemedia.com, Sr. Grp. Pub., The Sun-Times, AR, Heber Springs
egraves@gatehousemedia.com, Pub., Pine Bluff Commercial, AR, Pine Bluff
egraves@gatehousemedia.com, Sr. Group Pub., Arkadelphia Siftings Herald, AR, Arkadelphia
egraves@gatehousemedia.com, Sr. Group Publisher, Nevada County Picayune, AR, Hope

Graves, Jane
louie@nashvilleleader.com, Co-Pub, The Nashville News-Leader, AR, Nashville

Graves, Jeanna ....(662) 263-5352
Wood College, MS, Mathiston

Graves, Kandace
kandaceg@gambitweekly.com, Managing Editor, Gambit, LA, New Orleans

Graves, Karen ....ext. 104
karen@dckr.com, Circ. Mgr., County Shopper, NY, Delhi

Graves, Keven R.
yelmnews@yelmonline.com, Ed., Nisqually Valley Shopper, WA, Yelm
yelmnews@yelmonline.com, Pub./Ed., Nisqually Valley News, WA, Yelm

Graves, Lawrence
montcnews2@alltel.net, Pub., Montgomery County News, AR, Mount Ida

Graves, Louie
louie@nashvilleleader.com, Co-Pub., The Nashville News-Leader, AR, Nashville

Graves, Lyle ....(615) 254-5522
lgraves@TNLedger.com, Pub./Ed., Nashville Ledger, TN, Nashville

Graves, Michelle......................(231) 398-3106

mgraves@pioneergroup.com, Managing Ed., Manistee News Advocate, MI, Manistee

Graves, Mike ....(870) 845-2010
gwherald@alltel.net, Pub., Glenwood Herald, AR, Glenwood

Graves, Mike ....(870) 845-2010
gpcceo@nashvillenews.org, The Nashville News-Leader, AR, Nashville

Graves, Randy
rgraves@darnews.com, Prodn. Foreman, Pressroom, Daily American Republic, MO, Poplar Bluff

Graves, Scott ....(541) 469-3123
sgraves@currypilot.com, Ed., Curry Coastal Pilot, OR, Brookings

Graves, Tom
anaheimbulletin@ocregister.com, Ed., Brea-La Habra Star-Progress, CA, Santa Ana

Graves-McRae, Sharon ....(613) 678-3327
websitedesign@thereview.ca, Website Designer, The Review, ON, Vankleek Hill

Gravois, John.........................(817) 390-7734
grav@star-telegram.com, Asst. Mng. Ed., Gov't Affairs, Fort Worth Star-Telegram, TX, Fort Worth

Grawunder, Angie
bvtimes@sbcglobal.net, Adv. Dir., The Bellville Times, TX, Bellville

Graxiola, Mike ....(830) 257-0330
mike.graxiola@dailytimes.com, Pub./Ed., Kerrville Daily Times, TX, Kerrville

Gray, Alex ....(888) 309-0639
agray@miracomcomputer.com, Application Developer, Miracom Computer Corp., NY, Eastchester

Gray, Alison
akern@thearknewspaper.com, Owner-publisher, The Ark, CA, Tiburon

Gray, Andy ....ext. 752
grayareas@tribtoday.com, Ent. /Amusements Reporter, The Tribune Chronicle, OH, Warren

Gray, Bill ....(319) 986-5186
pub@mpnews.net, Editor & Publisher, Mt. Pleasant News, IA, Mount Pleasant

Gray, Bill
wgray01@wgray.com, Ed., Tradewinds Publishing, NC, Davidson

Gray, Bill ....(319) 931-1026
pub@mpnews.net, Publisher/Ad Director, Mt. Pleasant Shopper, IA, Mt Pleasant

Gray, Bob
rgray@starledger.com, Dir. Adv. , The Star-Ledger, NJ, Newark

Gray, Brian ....(252) 335-8097
bgray@dailyadvance.com, Creative Services Manager, The Daily Advance, NC, Elizabeth City

Gray, Casey ....(912) 520-0397
cwgray1979@gmail.com, Adv. Rep., Clinch County News, GA, Homerville

Gray, Dana
grayd@caledonian-record.com, Exec. Ed., The Caledonian-Record, VT, Saint Johnsbury

Gray, Donna
quincysunsubs@gmail.com, Circ. Mgr., The Quincy Sun, MA, Quincy

Gray, Genevieve ....(819) 845-2705
journal@letincelle.qc.ca, Etincelle, QC, Windsor

Gray, Heather
hgray@bluffcountrynews.com, Ed., Spring Grove Herald, MN, Spring Grove

Gray, Jana
jana.gray@austindailyherald.com, Pub., Austin Daily Herald, MN, Austin

Gray, Janie............................(281) 425-8000
janie.gray@baytownsun.com, Ed. / Pub., The

Baytown Sun, TX, Baytown

Gray, Joel
joelg@charlescitypress.com, Adv. Mgr., Northeast Iowa Shopper, IA, Charles City

Gray, Kathy
kgray@thedalleschronicle.com, Managing Ed., The Dalles Daily Chronicle, OR, The Dalles

Gray, Kristie.................(606) 528-7898 Ext. 31
kgray@thetimestribune.com, Business Mgr., Times-Tribune, KY, Corbin

Gray, Linda
blackmesapub@yahoo.com, Adv. Mgr, The Boise City News, OK, Boise City

Gray, Lisa ....ext. 220
lgray@heartlandpubllications.com, Circ. Mgr., Cumberland Trading Post, KY, Middlesboro

Gray, Lisa ....(202) 636-3379
lgray@washingtontimes.com, Circ. Mgr., Systems, The Washington Times, DC, Washington

Gray, Lloyd ....(662) 678-1579
lloyd.gray@journalinc.com, Exec. Ed., Northeast Mississippi Daily Journal, MS, Tupelo

Gray, Margo
margo@thesylvaherald.com, Adv. Mgr., The Sylva Herald & Ruralite, NC, Sylva

Gray, Michael
michael.gray@sotech.com, Mng. Ed., Enterprise, San Francisco Chronicle, CA, San Francisco

Gray, Michelle
michelle.stainback@tidewaternews.com, Office Mgr., The Tidewater News, VA, Franklin

Gray, Nancy
nanogray@bullitt.net, Adv. Sales Rep., Pioneer News, KY, Shepherdsville

Gray, Rhonda ....(251) 866-5998
callnews@belltsouth.net, Office Mgr., Call News, AL, Citronelle

Gray, Robert J. ....(207) 262-2773
irregular.classifieds@tds.net, Ed., Original Irregular, ME, Kingfield

Gray, Sally ....(785) 562-2317
sgray@mvleadvocate.com, News editor, Marysville Advocate, KS, Marysville

Gray, Steven B.
sbg@thesylvaherald.com, Pub., The Sylva Herald & Ruralite, NC, Sylva

Gray, TC ....(808) 529-4832
tgray@staradvertiser.com, VP/Controller, Honolulu Star-Advertiser, HI, Honolulu

Gray, Tom ....(574) 473-6641
tgray@perutribune.com, Pub., Peru Tribune, IN, Peru

Gray, William
williamgray@thecallnews.com, Adv. Mgr., Call News, AL, Citronelle

Gray, Willie
williegray@thecallnews.com, Pub., Call News, AL, Citronelle
williegray@thecallnews.com, Pub., Washington County News, AL, Citronelle

Grayson, David.........................(585) 768-2201
editor@leroyny.com, Pub./Ed., Le Roy Pennysaver & News, NY, Le Roy

Grayson, David J.
editor@leroyny.com, Pub., Leroy Pennysaver, NY, Le Roy

Grayson, Mark
markgrayson@me.com, Ed., Levisa Lazer, KY, Louisa

Grayson, Regina
regina.grayson@luvernejournal.com, The Luverne Journal, AL, Luverne

Graziadei, Jason ....(508) 228-0001 x 19
jgraziadei@inkym.com, The Inquirer and Mirror,

MA, Nantucket

Graziano, Amy
aveeditorial@chespub.com, Ed., The Avenue News, MD, Dundalk

Graziano, Dan ....**(860) 425-4322**
dgraziano@norwichbulletin.com, Advertising Director, The Bulletin, CT, Norwich

Graziano, Dan ....**(860) 489-3121 ext. 350**
dgraziano@21st-centurymedia.com, Sales Dir., The Litchfield County Times, CT, Torrington

Graziano, Jim
jimgraziano@skobrenner.com, Sr. Vice Pres., SKO Brenner American, NY, Baldwin

Grazier, Steven
steven.grazier@indeonline.com, Reporter, The Independent, OH, Massillon

Grear, Kathy
kgrear@greaterdiversity.com, Pub., Greater Diversity News, NC, Wilmington

Grear, Mark ....**(254) 932-6450**
vmprogress@windstream.net, Pub./Ed./Adv. Dir., Valley Mills Progress, TX, Valley Mills

Grear, Peter
pgrear@greaterdiversity.com, Pub., Greater Diversity News, NC, Wilmington

Greathead, Jamie S.
jgreathead@comcast.net, Pub. / Adv. Mgr, Fulton County News, PA, Mc Connellsburg

Greaves, David Mark ....**(718) 599-6828**
editors@ourtimepress.com, Ed., Our Time Press, NY, Brooklyn

Greco, Marcus...........................**(321) 242-3512**
mgreco@floridatoday.com, Packaging Center Mgr., Florida Today, FL, Melbourne

Greco, christine ....**(978) 462-6666**
Home Delivery Mgr., The Daily News, MA, Newburyport

Green, Agnes ...... **(718) 240-4554; (347) 816-7408**
agreen@springcreektowers.com, Ed., Spring Creek Sun, NY, Brooklyn

Green, Alice
agreen@echo-pilot.com, Adv. Mgr, The Echo-Pilot, PA, Greencastle

Green, Andi
addirector@athensreview.com, Adv. Dir., The Star, TX, Athens

Green, Andrew ....**(410) 332-6227**
andrew.green@baltsun.com, Editorial Page Ed. , The Baltimore Sun, MD, Baltimore

Green, Ann
anngreen@sterlingbenefits.net, Westminster College, UT, Salt Lake City

Green, Barbara Beckwith ....**(940) 872-2247**
bnews@sbcglobal.net, Ed., The Bowie News, TX, Bowie

Green, Bill ....**(540) 665-4945**
bgreen@winchesterstar.com, Circ. Mgr., The Winchester Star, VA, Winchester

Green, Bill ....**(719) 540-0220**
bill@hispanianews.com, Circ. Mgr., Hispania News, CO, Colorado Springs

Green, Brian ....**(785) 822-1432**
bgreen@salina.com, Marketing Consultant, The Salina Journal, KS, Salina

Green, Carla
cgreen@mediapsansoftware.com, Vice Pres., Customer Servs., MediaSpan, MI, Ann Arbor

Green, Cindy.................**(270) 678-5171 Ext. 248**
cgreen@glasgowdailytimes.com, Business Mgr., Glasgow Daily Times, KY, Glasgow

Green, Colleen
production-standard@powergate.ca, Gen. Mgr., The Standard Newspaper, ON, Port Perry

Green, David G.
editor@statelineobserver.com, Ed., State Line Observer, MI, Morenci

Green, Doug ....**(760) 297-2900 ext. 5457**
Editor, Times-Advocate, CA, Escondido

Green, Erica ....**(785) 822-1458**
egreen@salina.com, New Media Sales Rep., The Salina Journal, KS, Salina

Green, J. Steven
editor@mdcoastdispatch.comv, Ed., Maryland Coast Dispatch, MD, Berlin

Green, James ....**(563) 383-2100**
james.green@lee.net, VP, Digital, Lee Enterprises, Inc., IA, Davenport

Green, Jamie ....**(318) 747-7900**
legals@bossierpress.com, Legals/Classifieds Manager, Bossier Press-Tribune, LA, Bossier City

Green, Jason ....**(650) 391-1337**
jgreen@dailynewsgroup.com, City Ed., Palo Alto Daily News, CA, Menlo Park

Green, Jeff ....**(613) 279-3150**
nfnews@frontenac.net, Publisher/Editor, The Frontenac News, ON, Sharbot Lake

Green, Jeff
g.jeff@stonesource.com, Nat'l Sales Dir., VNU eMedia, NY, New York

Green, Jennifer
jgreen@bnd.com, Belleville News-Democrat, IL, Belleville

Green, Jenny ....**(317) 444-6245**
jenny.green@indystar.com, Sports Director, The Indianapolis Star, IN, Indianapolis

Green, Joe ....**(812) 967-3176 ext. 242**
paperman@gbpnews.com, Pub., Green Banner Publications, Inc., IN, Pekin

Green, Joe
paperman@gbpnews.com, Pub., The Washington County Edition, IN, Salem

Green, Joe
paperman@gbpnews.com, Pub., The Leader, IN, Charlestown

Green, Joe ....**(812) 967-3176**
Pub., R-J Delivery Systems, Inc., IN, Pekin

Green, Joe
paperman@gbpnews.com, Pub., The Banner-Gazette, IN, Pekin

Green, Joe ....**(812) 967-3176**
paperman@gbpnews.com, Publisher, The Giveaway, IN, Scottsburg

Green, John.................**(620) 694-5700 ext. 311**
jgreen@hutchnews.com, Business Editor, The Hutchinson News, KS, Hutchinson

Green, Katie ....**(724) 949-1190**
kgreen@thealmanac.net, Ed., The Almanac, PA, Pittsburgh

Green, Kevin...........................**(903) 237-7792**
kgreen@coxnews.com, Chief Photographer, Longview News-Journal, TX, Longview

Green, Larry
lgreen@pioneerlocal.com, Pres., Pioneer Press, IL, Glenview

Green, Lee ....**(205) 322-9002**
lee@sjlmag.com, Adv. Mgr., Southern Jewish Life, AL, Mountain Brk

Green, Leslie
lgreen@detroitnews.com, Digital Ed./News Ed., The Courier-Tribune, NC, Asheboro

Green, Linda
lgreen@hanfordsentinel.com, Editor, The Sentinel, CA, Hanford

Green, Marcia ....**(401) 334-9555 ext. 122**
mgreen@valleybreeze.com, Ed., The Valley Breeze - Cumberland/Lincoln, RI, Lincoln
mgreen@valleybreeze.com, Ed.-in-Chief, The Valley Breeze & Observer, RI, Lincoln
mgreen@valleybreeze.com, Ed.-in-Chief, The North Providence Breeze, RI, Lincoln
mgreen@valleybreeze.com, Ed.-in-Chief, The Valley Breeze - Woonsocket/North Smithfield, RI, Lincoln

mgreen@valleybreeze.com, Ed.-in-Chief, The Valley Breeze - Pawtucket, RI, Lincoln

Green, Marianne ....**(802) 651-4817**
mgreen@gannett.com, Media Specialist - National Sales, The Burlington Free Press, VT, Burlington

Green, Michael
chf@chffoto.com, Co-Owner, CHF Foto Supply, NJ, South Hackensack

Green, Michelle
michelle@shoppernews.com, Asst. Pub./Ed., Monadnock Shopper News, NH, Keene
michelle@shoppernews.com, Ed., Monadnock Shopper News, NH, Keene

Green, Mike
mgreen@flintgrp.com, Vice Pres./Gen. Mgr., News Ink/Pub. Div., Flint Group, MI, Plymouth

Green, Randy
rgreen@nncogannett.com, Adv. Mgr., Newark-licking Advertiser, OH, Newark

Green, Ray
ray@vervewireless.com, Vice President, Publisher Services, Verve Mobile, CA, Carlsbad

Green, Richard
richard.green@oracle.com, Exec. Vice Pres., Sun Software, Oracle & Sun Microsystems, Inc., CA, Redwood City

Green, Rick
green@northjersey.com, Ed. , Englewood Suburbanite, NJ, Cresskill
green@northjersey.com, Ed. , Edgewater View, NJ, Cresskill
green@northjersey.com, Ed. , Argus, NJ, Butler
green@northjersey.com, Ed. , Passaic Valley Today, NJ, Woodland Park
green@northjersey.com, Ed. , Aim West Milford, NJ, Butler
green@northjersey.com, Ed. , Aim Jefferson, NJ, Rockaway
green@northjersey.com, Ed. , Belleville Times, NJ, Nutley
green@northjersey.com, Ed. , Ramsey Suburban News, NJ, Ridgewood
green@northjersey.com, Ed. , Neighbor News, NJ, Rockaway
green@northjersey.com, Ed. , Northern Valley Suburbanite, NJ, Cresskill
green@northjersey.com, Ed. , Windsor-Hights Herald, NJ, Princeton
green@northjersey.com, Ed. , Suburban News, NJ, Ridgewood
green@northjersey.com, Town News, NJ, Ridgewood
green@northjersey.com, Ed. , Tenafly Suburbanite, NJ, Cresskill
green@northjersey.com, Ed. , Bayonne Journal (OOB) , NJ, Secaucus
green@northjersey.com, Ed., Suburban Trends, NJ, Butler
green@northjersey.com, Ed., The Item of Millburn and Short Hills, NJ, Millburn
green@northjersey.com, Ed. , Pascack Valley Community Life, NJ, Westwood
green@northjersey.com, Ed. , Wayne Today, NJ, Woodland Park
green@northjersey.com, Ed. , Glen Ridge Voice, NJ, Woodland Park
green@northjersey.com, Ed. , Clifton Journal, NJ, Clifton
green@northjersey.com, Ed. , The Montclair Times, NJ, Montclair
green@northjersey.com, Ed. , The Ridgewood News, NJ, Woodland Park
green@northjersey.com, Ed. , Franklin Lakes/Oakland Suburban News, NJ, Ridgewood
green@northjersey.com, Ed. , Waldwick Suburban News, NJ, Ridgewood
green@northjersey.com, Ed. , Bloomfield Life, NJ, Woodland Park
green@northjersey.com, Ed. , South Bergenite, NJ, Little Falls
green@northjersey.com, Ed. , Verona-Cedar Grove Times, NJ, Montclair
green@northjersey.com, Ed. , Midland Park Suburban News, NJ, Ridgewood
green@northjersey.com, Ed. , Town Journal,

NJ, Ridgewood
green@northjersey.com, Ed. , Teaneck Suburbanite, NJ, Cresskill
green@northjersey.com, Ed. , Parsippany Life, NJ, Rockaway
green@northjersey.com, Ed. , Wyckoff Suburban News, NJ, Ridgewood
green@northjersey.com, Ed. , Aim Vernon, NJ, Butler
green@northjersey.com, Ed. , Bogota Bulletin, NJ, Cresskill
green@northjersey.com, Ed., Cliffside Park Citizen, NJ, Cresskill
green@northjersey.com, Ed. , Fort Lee Suburbanite, NJ, Cresskill
green@northjersey.com, Ed. , Hackensack Chronicle, NJ, Cresskill
green@northjersey.com, Ed. , Leonia Life, NJ, Cresskill
green@northjersey.com, Ed. , Little Ferry Local, NJ, Cresskill
green@northjersey.com, Ed. , Ridgefield Park Patriot, NJ, Cresskill
green@northjersey.com, Ed. , Nutley Sun, NJ, Woodland Park
green@northjersey.com, Ed. , Mahwah Suburban News, NJ, Ridgewood
green@northjersey.com, Ed. , Glen Rock Gazette, NJ, Ridgewood

Green, Russ
sports@richmond-dailynews.com, Sports Ed., Richmond News, MO, Richmond

Green, Ryan
circulation@decaturdailydemocrat.com, Circ. Mgr., Berne Shopping News, IN, Decatur

Green, Sean
sean@bossierpress.com, Mng. Ed., Bossier Press-Tribune, LA, Bossier City

Green, Stephen
record@sctelcom.net, Pub, The Record, KS, Turon

Green, Steve...........................**(714) 796-7714**
sgreen@ocregister.com, Op., Asst. Managing Ed., The Orange County Register, CA, Santa Ana

Green, Steven
editor@mdcoastdispatch.com, Pub., Maryland Coast Dispatch, MD, Berlin

Green, Stuart
sgreen@wickedlocal.com, News Ed., Canton Journal, MA, Raynham

Green, Stuart ....**(508) 967-3515**
sgreen@wickedlocal.com, Ed., Stoughton Journal, MA, Raynham

Green, Susan ....**(843) 706-8201**
sgreen@islandpacket.com, Adv. Mgr., Classified, The Island Packet, SC, Bluffton

Green, Tammy
tgreen@examiner-enterprise.com, Office Mgr., Pawhuska Journal-Capital, OK, Pawhuska
tgreen@examiner-enterprise.com, Off. Mgr., Examiner-Enterprise, OK, Bartlesville

Green, Tom
tomsavoy@apt-4-rent.com, Pub., Apartments, MA, Springfield

Green, William B. ....**(956) 728-2501**
bill@lmtonline.com, Pub., El Tiempo de Laredo, TX, Laredo
bill@lmtonline.com, Pub., Laredo Morning Times, TX, Laredo

Green Jr., Harry .... **(603) 224-5301 ext. 352**
Press/Camera Mgr., Concord Monitor, NH, Concord

Greenberg, Bernie .... **(215) 441-8444**
bgreenberg@sportsnetwork.com, Sales Associate, The Sports Network, PA, Hatboro

Greenberg, David
davidg@rutgers.edu, Asst. Prof., Rutgers University, NJ, New Brunswick

Greenberg, Heywood
greenberg_h@mail.lynchburg.edu, Dena/Prof., Journ., Lynchburg College, VA, Lynchburg

Greenberg, Julianne
jgreenberg@bocabeacon.com, Ad. Rep., Boca
Beacon, FL, Boca Grande

Greenberg, Matthew
neiuindependent@gmail.com, Managing Editor,
Northeastern Illinois University, IL, Chicago

Greenberg, Terry
terry.greenberg@lubbockonline.com, Ed.,
Lubbock Avalanche-Journal, TX, Lubbock

Greene, Aaron .... (260) 481-6584
contact@ipfwcommunicator.org, Indiana-
Purdue Univ., IN, Fort Wayne

Greene, Coreen
ads@oceansidestar.com, Adv. Mgr., The
Oceanside Star, BC, Parksville

Greene, David
dagreene@usfca.edu, Lectr., San Francisco
State University, CA, San Francisco

Greene, Donna .... ext. 205
dgreene@middlesborodailynews.com,
Lifestyle Ed., Cumberland Trading Post, KY,
Middlesboro

Greene, Emerald
emerald@greenepublishing.com, Publisher,
Madison Enterprise-Recorder, FL, Madison

Greene, Emerald
emerald@greenepublishing.com, Pub.,
Monticello News, FL, Monticello

Greene, Emerald
emeraldk@greenepublishing.com, Pub.,
Madison County Carrier, FL, Madison

Greene, Gary .... (434) 227-0952
ggreene@cribb.com, MD., Cribb, Greene &
Cope, MT, Helena
ggreene@cribb.com, Managing Dir., Cribb,
Greene & Cope LLC, MT, Helena

Greene, Glenda .... (575) 542-8705
Adv. Mgr., Hidalgo County Herald, NM,
Lordsburg

Greene, Jonathan .... (859) 623-1669
Editor, The Richmond Register, KY, Richmond

Greene, Joshua .... (229) 924-2751 ext 1519
joshua.greene@gaflnews.com, Ad Sales,
Americus Times-Recorder, GA, Americus

Greene, Karen H. .... (202) 334-4511
karen.greene@washpost.com, Ops. Mgr., The
Washington Post Writers Group, Washington

Greene, Michael .... (719) 636-0301
michael.greene@gazette.com, Political
advertising, The Gazette, CO, Colorado
Springs

Greene, Nancy
subscriptions@alleghanynews.com, Circ. Mgr.,
The Alleghany News, NC, Sparta

Greene, Richard
rgreene@postsignal.com, Mng. Ed., Pilot Point
Post Signal, TX, Pilot Point

Greene, Rustin
greenerp@jmu.edu, Prof., James Madison
University, VA, Harrisonburg

Greene, Sherry .... (901) 458-2911 ext. 7
sgreene@thebesttimes.com, Assistant
Publisher, The Best Times, TN, Memphis

Greene, Tom
tgreene@michigannewspapers.com, Adv. Mgr.,
Alpena Star, MI, Alpena

Greene, Tom
alpena@michigannewspapers.com, Gen. Mgr.,
Presque Isle Star, MI, Alpena

Greene, Wayne .... (918) 581-8308
wayne.greene@tulsaworld.com, Senior writer,
Tulsa World, OK, Tulsa

Greene, William R.
gilmermirror@gmail.com, Pub., Gilmer Mirror,
TX, Gilmer

Greenfield, Tonja
tgreenfield@amboynews.com, Gen. Mgr./ Adv.

Dir., The Amboy News, IL, Amboy
tgreenfield@amboynews.com, General
Manager/Editor, Marana News, AZ, Tucson

Greening, John
j-greening@northwestern.edu, Assoc. Prof.,
Northwestern University, IL, Evanston

Greening, Nikki
nikki.greening@sunmedia.ca, Sales, The
Whitecourt Star, AB, Whitecourt

Greenlee, David .... (209) 546-8361
dgreenlee@recordnet.com, Press Manager,
The Record, CA, Stockton

Greenlee, Steve .... (207) 791-6301
sgreenlee@pressherald.com, Managing Ed.,
Portland Press Herald / Maine Sunday
Telegram, ME, Portland

Greenlund, Michael .... (646) 274-6242
mgreenlund@amm.com, American Metal
Market, NY, New York

Greenspon, Susan
sgreenspon@mainlinemedianews.com, Mng.
Ed., King of Prussia Courier, PA, Wayne

Greenspon, Susan
sgreenspon@mainlinemedianews.com, Mng.
Ed., Main Line Times, PA, Ardmore
sgreenspon@mainlinemedianews.com, Ed.,
Main Line Suburban Life, PA, Ardmore

Greenspun, Brian .... (702) 385-3111
brain.greenspun@gmgvegas.com, Pub./Ed.,
Boulder City News, NV, Henderson
brain.greenspun@gmgvegas.com, CEO/Pub./
Ed., Las Vegas Sun, NV, Henderson

Greenstreet, Robert
bgrnst@ecok.edu, Chair, East Central
University (Oklahoma), OK, Ada

Greenwald, Jerry
jgreenwald@jewishpress.com, Mng. Ed., The
Jewish Press, NY, Brooklyn

Greenwald, Marilyn .... (740) 593-4387
greenwal@ohiou.edu, Prof., Ohio University,
OH, Athens

Greenway, Betsy .... (803) 895-2018
Adv. Mgr., The Shaw News, SC, Camden

Greenway, Betsy
bgreenway@chronicle-independent.com, Adv.
Mgr., Chronicle-Independent, SC, Camden
bgreenway@chronicle-independent.com, Adv.
Mgr., West Wateree Chronicle, SC, Camden

Greenwell, Charles .... (410) 263-8593
info@sparusa.com, Vice Pres., Opns., Spar
Associates, Inc., MD, Annapolis

Greenwood, Alan .... (603) 594-6427
agreenwood@nashuatelegraph.com, Sports
Ed., The Telegraph, NH, Nashua

Greenwood, Penny
penny.greenwood@awp.ch, Sr. Acct. Mgr.,
Dow Jones Newswires - Zurich, Switzerland,
Zurich

Greenwood, Tim .... (715) 735-7500 Ext. 152
tgreenwood@eagleherald.com, associate
night editor, EagleHerald - ehextra.com, WI,
Marinette

Greer, Bill .... (561) 820-4530
bgreer@pbpost.com, Asst. Mng. Ed., Projects,
The Palm Beach Post, FL, West Palm Beach

Greer, Carolyn .... (502) 498-1961
cgreer@bizjournals.com , Mng. Ed., Louisville
Business First, KY, Louisville

Greer, Dennis
cranenews@apex2000.net, Pub./Ed., Crane
News, TX, Crane

Greer, Frederick .... (701) 241-5447
fgreer@forumcomm.com, Forum
Communications Co., ND, Fargo

Greer, Park .... (859) 622-1489
Eastern Kentucky Univ., KY, Richmond

Greer, Tom .... (270) 691-7255
tgreer@messenger-inquirer.com, HOME

DELIVERY MGR., Messenger-Inquirer, KY,
Owensboro

Greever, Amanda .... (865) 981-1161
amanda.greever@thedailytimes.com, Asst.
Mng. Ed., The Daily Times, TN, Maryville

Grefe, Richard .... ext. 3100
grefe@aiga.org, Exec. Dir., AIGA, the
professional association for design, NY,
New York

Greg, Evans .... (608) 269-3186
Pub., Monroe County Herald, WI, Sparta

Gregerson, Austen .... (904) 819-3492
austen.gregerson@staugustine.com, Sports
writer, The St. Augustine Record, FL, Saint
Augustine

Gregg, Jessica .... (443) 524-8155
jgregg@thedailyrecord.com, Special Products
Ed. , The Daily Record, MD, Baltimore

Gregg, John .... (603) 298-8711
newseditor@vnews.com, News Editor, Valley
News, NH, West Lebanon

Gregg, Judy
jgregg@timesshamrock.com , Adv. Exec.,
Northeast Pennsylvania Business Journal,
PA, Scranton

Gregg, Randa
news@oracleandleader.com, Gen. Mgr.,
Pleasants County Leader, WV, Saint Marys

Gregoire, Joanne
jgregoire@theshaunavonstandard.com,
Adv. Sales, The Shaunavon Standard, SK,
Shaunavon

Gregorio, John
jgregorio@chicagotribune.com, Director
of Major Accounts, Chicago Tribune, IL,
Chicago

Gregorson, Rhonda
circulation@prestoncitizen.com, Circ. Mgr.,
Preston Citizen, ID, Preston

Gregory, April
april.gregory@greenvilleadvocate.com, Mktg.
Coord., The Greenville Advocate, AL,
Greenville

Gregory, Dawn .... (212) 293-8603
dgregory@unitedmedia.com, Customer Serv.
Rep, United Feature Syndicate (Div. of United
Media), New York

Gregory, Italia .... (434) 568-3341
italia.gregory@thecharlottegazette.com,
Community Ed., The Charlotte Gazette, VA,
Drakes Branch

Gregory, Jim
njgdesign@att.net, NASJA East, NY, Latham

Gregory, Mark
mark@hotsr.com, Online Ed., The Sentinel-
Record, AR, Hot Springs National Park

Gregory, Mark
mark@wilsongregory.com, Vice Pres., Opns.,
Wilson Gregory Agency, Inc., PA, Camp Hill

Gregory, Orvena .... (405) 214-3903
orvena.gregory@news-star.com, Multi-Med.
Exec. , Shawnee News-Star, OK, Shawnee

Gregory, Pam
pgregory@pcnh.com, Adv. Dir., Gulf Defender,
FL, Panama City

Gregory, Rich .... (203) 731-3379
rgregory@newstimes.com, Sports Editor, The
News-Times, CT, Danbury

Gregory, Sarah .... (423) 359-3156
sarah.gregory@greenevillesun.com, Lifestyle
Ed., The Greeneville Sun, TN, Greeneville

Gregory, Ted .... (717) 901-0758
ted@wilsongregory.com, Chrmn./CEO, Wilson
Gregory Agency, Inc., PA, Camp Hill

Gregory, Thom 615/259-8881
tgregory@tennessean.com, Gen. Mgr. GPS
Production Nashville, The Tennessean, TN,
Nashville

tgregory@tennessean.com, Gen. Mgr. GPS
Production Nashville, TN Media, TN,
Nashville

Gregory, Todd .... (717) 901-0757
todd@wilsongregory.com, Vice Pres., Wilson
Gregory Agency, Inc., PA, Camp Hill

Gregory, Wendy
wgregory@dunndailyrecord.com, Prodn. Mgr.,
Post Press, The Daily Record, NC, Dunn

Greider, John .... ext. 36
johng@mvtcnews.com, Pub., The Mid-Valley
Town Crier, TX, Weslaco

Greiner, Vickie K.
trutrib1@frontiernet.net, Ed., Truman Tribune,
MN, Truman

Gremillion, Robert .... (954) 356-4000 ext. 4305
Pres., Sun-Sentinel Co., FL, Fort Lauderdale

Grenier, Corey .... (802) 865-1020 x 36
corey@sevendaysvt.com, Marketing Dir.,
Seven Days, VT, Burlington

Grenier, Sandy
publisher@northislandgazette.com, Pub, North
Island Gazette, BC, Port Hardy

Grennier, Nancy .... (908) 668-0010
spobserver@comcast.net, Pub., South
Plainfield Observer, NJ, South Plainfield

Grenzow, Mary Jane .... ext. 22
editor@themonroetimes.com, Editorial Page
Ed., The Monroe Times, WI, Monroe

Gresenberg, Ana 3842-1151
ana.gresenberg@dowjones.com, Sales Exec.,
Dow Jones Newswires - Sao Paulo, Brazil,
Sao Paulo

Greser, Kathy
kgresey@shawmedia.com, Ed., Kane County
Chronicle, IL, Saint Charles

Gresey, Kathy
kgresey@shawmedia.com, Geneva Chronicle,
IL, St Charles

Gresham, Lane
lgresham@thenortheastgeorgian.com, Ed.,
The Northeast Georgian, GA, Cornelia

Gresham, Michael
mgresham@kaufmanherald.com, Kaufman
Shopper, TX, Kaufman

Gresham, Michael
mgresham@kaufmanherald.com, Ed.,
Shopping Guide, TX, Kaufman

Gresham, Patricia
pgresham@pres-outlook.org, Bus. Mgr., The
Presbyterian Outlook, VA, Richmond

Gress, Karol
karolgress@ldnews.com, City Ed., The
Lebanon Daily News, PA, Lebanon

Gressette, Felicia
FELICIA.GRESSETTE@NEWSOBSERVER.
COM, Pub., The Durham News, NC, Chapel
Hill

Grether, Ryan
pathfinderbusmgr@lcmail.lcsc.edu, Business
Manager, Lewis-Clark State College, ID,
Lewiston

Gretschmann, Kelly .... (260) 225-4664
kgretschmann@wabashplaindealer.com,
General Sales Manager, Wabash Plain
Dealer, IN, Wabash

Greve, Megan .... (260) 356-6700 ext. 163
mgreve@h-ponline.com, Ed., Huntington
Herald-Press, IN, Huntington

Greving, John
jgreving@amestrib.com, Adv. Dir., Ames
Tribune, IA, Ames
jgreving@amestrib.com, Adv. Dir., The Story
City Herald, IA, Ames

Greving, John .... (515) 663-6947
jgreving@amestrib.com, Dir., Adv., Story
County Advertiser, IA, Ames

Greving, John
john.greving@amestrib.com, Adv. Mgr., The Tri-County Times, IA, Ames

Greyowl, Wendy
editor@dailyevents.com, Editor, The Daily Events, MO, Springfield

Greyshock, Tricia ....(717) 703-3070
triciag@pa-news.org, Vice President, Association Services, Pennsylvania NewsMedia Association, PA, Harrisburg

Grezlak, Hank
hgrezlak@alm.com, Editor-in-Chief, New Jersey Law Journal, NJ, Newark

Gribbin, William
wgribbin@Liberty.edu, Dean, School of Commun., Liberty Univ., VA, Lynchburg

Grice, Jennifer ....(580) 335-2188
jgrice@civitasmedia.com, Adv. Mgr., Frederick Press-Leader, OK, Frederick

Grider, Randy........................(903) 796-7133
randy@casscountynow.com, Pub, The Cass County Sun, TX, Linden

Griep, John ....(410) 770-4093
jgriep@chespub.com, Exec. Ed. , The Star-Democrat, MD, Easton

Griep, Josh............................(410) 770-4093
jgriep@stardem.com, Ed., Eastern Shore Bargaineer, MD, Easton

Grieve, Simon
sgrieve@gazettes.com, Pub./Adv. Mgr., Downtown Gazette, CA, Long Beach
sgrieve@gazettes.com, Pub./Adv. Mgr., Grunion Gazette, CA, Long Beach
sgrieve@gazettes.com, Pub./Adv. Mgr., Georgetown Gazette, CA, Georgetown

Grieve, Simon
sgrieve@gazettes.com, Pub., Uptown Gazette, CA, Long Beach

Griffen, Sherri
sherrig@tnwa.org, Adv. Mgr., Thrifty Nickel Want Ads, ID, Idaho Falls

Griffey, Jan
jan.griffey@vicksburgpost.com, Ed., The Vicksburg Post, MS, Vicksburg

Griffin, Alaine
agriffin@courant.com, Towns Ed., Courant Community - West Hartford, CT, Hartford
agriffin@courant.com, Towns Ed., Courant Community - Wethersfield, CT, Hartford

Griffin, Andrea
officemgr@mustangnews.info, Office Mgr., The Mustang News, OK, Mustang

Griffin, Candace ....(504) 615-3411
candace@plaqueminesgazette.com, Reporter, Plaquemines Gazette, LA, Belle Chasse

Griffin, Candace ....(504) 616-3411
candace@thestbernardvoice.com, Reporter, The St. Bernard Voice, LA, Arabi

Griffin, Candi
cgriffin@carolinaparent.com, Sales Team Leader, Carolina Parent, NY, White Plains

Griffin, Carol ....(252) 586-2700
Office Mgr., Lake Gaston Gazette-Observer, NC, Littleton

Griffin, Cary L.
messengernews@sbcglobal.net, Pub., Forney Messenger, TX, Forney

Griffin, George
ggriffin@times-news.com, Circ. Mgr., The Garrett County Weekender, MD, Cumberland

Griffin, Howard
hlgriffin@gannett.com, VP, Gannett National Sales, USCP, Gannett News Service - Albany, NY, Albany

Griffin, J. Frank
homereporter@aol.com, Pub., Home Reporter and Sunset News, NY, Brooklyn

Griffin, Jacob

jgriffin@breezecourier.com, News, Breeze Courier, IL, Taylorville

Griffin, Joanie
joanie@wallisnews.com, Pub./Adv. Dir., Wallis News-Review, TX, Wallis

Griffin, Johnnie........................(601) 445-3609
Prodn. Mgr., Miss-lou Buyers Guide, MS, Natchez

Griffin, Johnny
johnny@wallisnews.com, Ed., Wallis News-Review, TX, Wallis

Griffin, Judy
messengernews@sbcglobal.net, Ed., Forney Messenger, TX, Forney

Griffin, Kenna
kgriffin@okcu.edu, Advisor, Oklahoma City University, OK, Oklahoma City

Griffin, Leah ....(817) 257-6274
leah.griffin@tcu.edu, Manager of Student Media Sales and Marketing, Texas Christian University, TX, Fort Worth

Griffin, Mark
mgriffin@coastalcourier.com, Pub., The Frontline, GA, Hinesville

Griffin, Mark
mgriffin@coastalcourier.com, Pub., Barrow County News, GA, Hinesville

Griffin, Marshall
mgriffin@coastalcourier.com, Pub., The Coastal Courier, GA, Hinesville

Griffin, Marshall ....(912) 756-2757
mgriffin@bryancountynews.net, Pub., Bryan County News, GA, Richmond Hill

Griffin, Marshall ....(912) 876-0156 ext. 12
mgriffin@coastalcourier.com, Pub., Tri-county Pennysaver, GA, Hinesville

Griffin, Peter
pgriffin@epg-inc.com, Pres., Essex Products Group, CT, Centerbrook

Griffin, Rhonda
officemgr@louisvilleherald.com, Office Manager, The Louisville Herald, OH, Louisville

Griffin, Robin
couriereditorial@vineyardpress.biz, Mng. Ed., Courier-Leader, MI, Paw Paw

Griffin, Stephanie
editor@dawsonnews.com, Ed., Dawson County News, GA, Dawsonville

Griffin, Susan........................(904) 686-3938
susan@opcfla.com, Publisher , Ponte Vedra Recorder, FL, Ponte Vedra Beach

Griffin, Teresa ....(314) 340-8909
tgriffin@post-dispatch.com, Digital Sales Dir. , St. Louis Post-Dispatch, MO, Saint Louis

Griffin, Todd........................(270) 365-5588
toddgriffin@timesleader.net, Sports Ed, Times Leader, KY, Princeton

Griffing, Jeff ....(612) 673-4901
jeff.griffing@startribune.com, Chief Revenue Officer, Star Tribune, MN, Minneapolis

Griffis, Tammy ....(405) 366-3591
tjgriffis@normantranscript.com, Bus. Mgr., Moore American, OK, Norman
tjgriffis@normantranscript.com, Bus. Mgr., Norman Transcript, OK, Norman

Griffith, Cathy..............(217) 347-7151 ext. 136
editor@effinghamdailynews.com, Mng. Ed., Effingham Daily News, IL, Effingham

Griffith, Ira
igriffith@gainsvilletimes.com, Major Accounts Manager, The Times, GA, Gainesville

Griffith, Laura ....(618) 463-2556
Online Ed., The Telegraph, IL, Alton

Griffith, Lynn........................(308) 728-3261
quizpub@frontiernet.net, Pub./Adv. Mgr., The Ord Quiz, NE, Ord

Griffith, Matt
mgriffith@brainworks.com, Business Development Manager, Brainworks Software Development Corp., NY, Sayville

Griffith, Michelle ....(316) 321-1120
mgriffith@butlercountytimesgazette.com, Business Mgr. , The Pratt Tribune, KS, Pratt
mgriffith@butlercountytimesgazette.com, Business Office, Wellington Daily News, KS, Wellington
mgriffith@butlercountytimesgazette.com, Business Mgr. , The Butler County Times-Gazette, KS, Augusta

Griffith, Steve..........................(712) 224-6277
steve.griffith@lee.net, Gen. Mgr., Shopper's Guide, IA, Sioux City

Griffith, Teri ....(785) 295-1278
teri.griffith@cjonline.com, Asst. Controller, The Topeka Capital-Journal, KS, Topeka

Griffith, Todd................(940) 627-5987 ext. 19
tgriffith@wcmessenger.com, Prod. Mgr., Wise County Messenger, TX, Decatur

Griffith, Traci
tgriffith@smcvt.edu, Asst. Prof., St. Michael's College, VT, Colchester

Griffiths, Natasha
sales@northislandgazette.com, Sales Rep, North Island Gazette, BC, Port Hardy

Griffy Seeton, Melissa ....(330) 364-8318
melissa.griffy@TimesReporter.com, Ed., The Times-Reporter, OH, New Philadelphia

Grigg, Mike
mgrigg@cnjonline.com, Circ. Dir., Cannon Connection, NM, Clovis

Griggs, Susan
susan.griggs.1@us.af.mil, Ed., Keesler News, MS, Gulfport

Grillo, Gina
gina@theadvertisingclub.org, Exec. Dir., Advertising Club of Greater New York, NY, New York

Grills, Lisa ....(613) 962-9171 ext. 611
lisa.grills@sunmedia.ca, Adv. Dir., Intelligencer, ON, Belleville

Grim, Hubert............................(540) 213-9131
hgrimiii@newsleader.com, Sports Ed., The News Leader, VA, Staunton

Grimes, Ann
agrimes@stanford.edu, Vstg. Prof., Stanford University, CA, Stanford

Grimes, Charlotte
cgrimes@syr.edu, Prof., Syracuse University, NY, Syracuse

Grimes, David ....(941) 957-5209
david.grimes@heraldtribune.com, Columnist, Sarasota Herald-Tribune, FL, Sarasota

Grimes, Gwin..........................(432) 837-3334
publisher@alpineavalanche.com, Publisher and editor, Alpine Avalanche, TX, Alpine

Grimes, Jacob
jacob@carthaginian.com, News-sports, The Carthaginian, MS, Carthage

Grimes, Larry..........................(301) 253-5016
lgrimes@mediamergers.com, Chmn., Grimes, McGovern & Associates, NY, New York
lgrimes@mediamergers.com, Pres., W.B. Grimes & Company, MD, Gaithersburg
lgrimes@mediamergers.com, President, Lewis Floyd- Grimes, W.B. & Co., AL, Gulf Shores

Grimes, Lorraine........................(850) 747-5002
lgrimes@pcnh.com, Rgl HR Dir., The News Herald, FL, Panama City

Grimes, Lydia ....(251) 867-4876, Ext. 113
lydia.grimes@brewtonstandard.com, Features Report., The Brewton Standard, AL, Brewton

Grimes, Mary Anne ....(212) 293-8626
magrimes@unitedmedia.com, Exec. Dir., Pub. Rel., Newspaper Enterprise Association (Div. of United Media), NY, New York

magrimes@unitedmedia.com, Exec. Dir., Pub. Rel., United Feature Syndicate (Div. of United Media), New York

Grimes, Millard
starmercury@earthlink.net, Owner/CEO, Star-Mercury Publishing Co., GA, Manchester

Grimes, Sheryl ....(605) 745-4170
Sheryl.Grimes@lee.net, Prod. Mgr., Hot Springs Star, SD, Hot Springs

Grimes, Tom
grimes@txstate.edu, Prof., Texas State University-San Marcos, TX, San Marcos

Grimm, Heidi
hgrimm@mojonews.com, Circ. Dir., Morning Journal, OH, Lisbon

Grimm, Julie Ann ....(505) 988-5541 ext. 1215
editor@sfreporter.com, Pub./Ed., Santa Fe Reporter, NM, Santa Fe

Grimm, Nathan ....(618) 208-6456
ngrimm@civitasmedia.com, Mng. Ed., The Telegraph, IL, Alton

Grimmelt, Kristjanna
news@prrecordgazette.com, Mng. Ed., The Record-gazette, AB, Peace River

Grimmett, James
james.grimmett@lubbockonline.com, Circ. Dir. , Lubbock Avalanche-Journal, TX, Lubbock

Grimminck, Jerry ....(616) 842-6400 ext. 250
Press Foreman/Supvr., Grand Haven Tribune, MI, Grand Haven

Grimsrud, Matthew
news@zumbrota.com, Ed., News-Record, MN, Zumbrota

Grindinger, Shannon ....(816) 221-2552
shannon@pulselegal.com, Pub., St. Charles County Journal, MO, Saint Charles

Grindle, Russ..........................(260) 356-1107
tabads@comcast.net, Adv. Mgr., Huntington County Tab, IN, Huntington

Grindstaff, Robb ....(920) 563-5553
rgrindstaff@dailyunion.com, Gen Mgr, The Star, WI, Sun Prairie

Grindstaff, Robb ....(920) 563-5553
rgrindstaff@dailyunion.com, Advertising/ Business Manager, Union Extra, WI, Fort Atkinson
rgrindstaff@dailyunion.com, Gen. Mgr., Waunakee Tribune, WI, Waunakee

Grindstaff, Robb ....(920) 563-5553
Rgrindstaff@dailyunion.com, Adv. Mgr./ Business Mgr., Daily Jefferson County Union, WI, Fort Atkinson

Grindstaff, Robb ....(920) 563-5553
rgrindstaff@dailyunion.com, General Manager, The Lake Mills Leader, WI, Lake Mills

Grindstaff, Robb ....(920) 563-5553
rgrindstaff@dailyunion.com, General Manager, The Waterloo/Marshall Courier, WI, Waterloo

Grindstaff, Robb ....(920) 563-5553
rgrindstaff@dailyunion.com, General Manager, Lodi Enterprise & Poynette Press, WI, Lodi

Grinstead, Jeanne ....(727) 893-8769
grinstead@tampabay.com, Deputy Managing Ed./Features, Lifestyles, Tampa Bay Times, FL, St Petersburg

Grinsteinner, Kelly
kgrinsteinner@hibbingdailytribune.net, Pub., Hibbing Daily Tribune, MN, Hibbing

Grissom, Angie........................(214) 977-8381
agrissom@dallasnews.com, Sr. Dir., Audience Development, The Dallas Morning News, TX, Dallas

Grissom, Garry
garry.grissom@resolutefp.com, Rgl. Mgr., Resolute Forest Products, QC, Montreal

Grist, Stephanie
advertising@henryettanewspaper.com, Adv. Dir., Henryetta Free-Lance, OK, Henryetta

Griswold, Charlann
cgriswold@turley.com, Circ. Mgr., Barre Gazette, MA, Barre
cgriswold@turley.com, Circulation Director, The Sentinel, MA, Belchertown

Griswold, Matthew L. .... (240) 912-3202
mgriswold@merchmag.com, CEO/Publisher, The Merchandiser Magazine, MD, Germantown

Grittner, Karen.......................... (320) 632-2271
karen.grittner@mcrecord.com, Circ. Mgr., Morrison County Record, MN, Little Falls

Gritzan, Mike
mike.gritzan@trader.ca, Circ. Mgr., Super Shopper, Buy, Trade & Sell, ON, Barrie

Grizzard, Mike.......................... (252) 329-9580
mgrizzard@reflector.com, Bus. Ed., The Daily Reflector, NC, Greenville

Grnak, Robert
bgrnak@mihomepaper.com, Gen Mgr., Township View, MI, Chesaning

Grnak, Robert
bgrnak@mihomepaper.com, Pub., Tri-County Citizen, MI, Sandusky

Groce, Kathy....................................... ext. 10
elkcirculation@elkintribune.com, Circ., Yadkin Valley Advertiser, NC, Elkin

Groeneveld , Carla
CGroeneveld@avtimes.net, Circ. Mgr., Alberni Valley Times, BC, Port Alberni

Groessel, Paul
paul.wahl@ecm-inc.com, Mng. Ed., Excelsior/ Shorewood/Chanhassen Sun Sailor, MN, Eden Prairie

Grondin, Claude........................ (418) 387-1205
administration@journaldebeaucenord.com, Edition Beauce Nord, QC, Sainte Marie-de-Beauce

Gronemeyer, Maria-Elena
mgronemeyer@puc.cl, Dir., Pontificia Universidad Catolica de Chile, Santiago

Gronenthal, Greig
starmail@frontiernet.net, Owners, The Madison Star-Mail, NE, Madison

Gronenthal, Niko
starmail@frontiernet.net, Pub., Adv. Mgr., Ed., The Madison Star-Mail, NE, Madison

Grones, John .... (218) 768-3405
vpofmg@frontiernet.net, Pub., The Voyageur Press of McGregor, MN, McGregor
vpofmg@frontiernet.net, Pub, Portage News, MN, Floodwood

Groppe, Christine
advertising@putnampresstimes.com, Adv. Mgr./Graphic Designer, Putnam County Times, NY, Mahopac
advertising@putnampresstimes.com, Adv. Mgr., Putnam County Press, NY, Mahopac

Grosam, Steve
sgrosam@nujournal.com, Circ. Mgr., The Journal, MN, New Ulm

Grose, Paula
pgrose@leesburgtoday.com, Classified Adv. Dir., InsideNoVa/Prince William, VA, Woodbridge
pgrose@leesburgtoday.com, Classified Adv. Mgr., Sun Gazette, VA, Mc Lean

Groser, Fred
publisher@newsday.com, Sr. VP, Sales & Marketing, Philadelphia Media Network Inc., PA, Philadelphia

Groshart, Craig
cgroshart@bellevuereporter.com, Ed., Issaquah/Sammamish Reporter, WA, Bellevue

Groskreutz, Stuart .... (651) 796-1107
stuart.groskreutz@ecm-inc.com, Sports Ed., Stillwater Gazette, MN, Stillwater

Gross, Adam.......................... (212) 754-0710

---

adamg@jegi.com, Vice Pres., Mktg., Jordan, Edmiston Group, Inc., NY, New York

Gross, Josh
josh@bhweekly.com, Pub. Mgr, Beverly Hills Weekly, CA, Beverly Hills

Grosse, Randy
ragrosse@archomaha.org, Adv. Mgr., The Catholic Voice, NE, Omaha

Grossman, Andrew .... (757) 220-3076
andrew@cartoonresource.com, Creative Dir., Cartoon Resource, Grand Rapids

Grossman, Gary
publisher@dailyitem.com, Pub., Scrapbook, PA, Sunbury
publisher@dailyitem.com, Pub., The Daily Item, MA, Lynn

Grossman, Jay .... (586) 826-7030
jgrossma@hometownlife.com, Reporter , Birmingham Eccentric, MI, Detroit

Grossman, Kay
chreview@fedtel.net, Pub., Chokio Review, MN, Chokio

Grossman, Nancy
office@salemleader.com, Pub., Your Advantage, IN, Salem

Grossman, Nancy
gm@salemleader.com, Gen. Mgr., The Salem Leader, IN, Salem

Grossmith, JT .... (613) 525-2020 ext.23
The Glengarry News, ON, Alexandria

Grosso, Tom
tgrosso@nydailynews.com, Pressroom, New York Daily News, NY, New York

Grosswiler, Paul
paul_grosswiler@umit.maine.edu, Assoc. Prof., University of Maine, ME, Orono

Grote, Galen .... (712) 662-7161
sacsun1@frontiernet.net, Advt Sales, The Sac Sun, IA, Sac City

Grote, Tom .... (208) 634-2123
starnews@frontier.com, Ed./Pub., The Star-News, ID, McCall

Groth, Debbie
dgroth@bluffcountrynews.com, Circ. Mgr., Spring Valley Tribune, MN, Spring Valley

Groth, Debby
dgroth@bluffcountrynews.com, Circ. Mgr., Bluff Country Reader, MN, Spring Valley

Grotloh, Ingrid........................ (248) 641-9944
Gen. Mgr., Nordamerikaniche Wochenpost, MI, Troy

Grou, Claude .... (514) 733-8211
ndumas@osj.qc.ca, Oratoire, QC, Montreal

Grove, Elaine
egrove@farragutpress.com, Adv. Mgr., Farragut Press, TN, Farragut

Grove, John
jgrove@bnd.com, Circ. Dir., Command Post, IL, Belleville

Grover, Carol
signalads@telus.net, Circ. Mgr., Rycroft Central Peace Signal, AB, Rycroft

Groves, Christy
news@aledger.net, Pub./Graphic Artist, The Albany Ledger, MO, Albany

Groves, Dick
dgroves@cheesereporter.com, Pub./Ed., The Cheese Reporter, WI, Madison

Groves, Don .... (641) 322-3161
publisher@acfreepress.com, Publisher, Adams County Free Press, IA, Corning

Groves, Jason .... (575) 541-5459
jgroves@lcsun-news.com, Sports Ed., Las Cruces Sun-News, NM, Las Cruces

Groves, Roberta
robertag@classicstock.com, Vice Pres., Creative, ClassicStock / Robertstock,

---

Philadelphia

Grow, Christopher
cgrow@jrn.com, Majors Nat'l Acct. Dir., Milwaukee Journal Sentinel, WI, Milwaukee

Growden, Sherri
sgrownden@befordgazette.com, Adv. Dir., The Bedford Gazette, PA, Bedford

Grubb, Chalo .... (520) 797-4384 ext. 32
chelo@tucsonlocalmedia.com, Prod. Mgr., Tucson Weekly, AZ, Tucson

Grubb, Chelo .... (520) 797-4384 ext. 32
chelo@tucsonlocalmedia.com, Web Ed., Explorer, AZ, Tucson

Grubb, Jere .... (425) 339-3411
grubb@heraldnet.com, Circ. Opns. Mgr., The Herald, WA, Everett

Grubb, Patrick J.
pgrubb@pointrobertspress.com, Pub./Mng. Ed., The Northern Light, WA, Blaine

Grubbs, Jimmy .... (901) 458-2911 ext. 8
jgrubbs@thebesttimes.com, Publisher, The Best Times, TN, Memphis

Grubbs, Paula
pgrubbs@butlereagle.com, Ed, The Cranberry Eagle, PA, Cranberry Township

Gruber, Chuck
info@cannonequipment.com, Pres., Cannon Equipment, MN, Rosemount

Gruber, Jurgen .... (972) 310-0685
jgruber@fujifilm.com, Newspaper Acct. Mgr., SW Reg., Fujifilm North America Corporation, IL, Hanover Park

Gruber, Jurgen
jurgen_gruber@nela-usa.com, Sales Dir., NELA, WI, River Falls

Gruber, Katharina...................... (651) 407-4863
katharina_gruber@nela-usa.com, Mktg. Mgr., NELA, WI, River Falls

Gruber, Robert
bob.gruber@starnewsonline.com, Publisher, The Fayetteville Observer, NC, Fayetteville

Gruber, Russel ....(361) 664-6588 x 217
rgruber@aliceechonews.com, National/Major acciunts, Alice Echo-News Journal, TX, Alice

Gruber Nelson, Tess.................. (712) 246-3097
editorial@valleynewstoday.com, Managing Editor, Sidney Argus-Herald, IA, Sidney

Gruber Nelson, Tess
tgruber@valleynewstoday.com, Ed., Valley News Today, IA, Shenandoah

Gruber-Nelson, Tess
tgruber@valleynewstoday.com, Ed., Essex Independent, IA, Shenandoah

Grubert, Stephanie
steffie@ptd.net, Pub., Mountaintop Eagle, PA, Mountain Top

Gruenberg, Mark J.................... (202) 898-4825
press_associates@yahoo.com, Ed. in Chief, Press Associates, Inc., Washington

Grundman, Jerry
jerry@messengerpostmedia.com, Adv. Mgr., Community News, NY, Canandaigua

Grundmann, Mike
grundmmj@jmu.edu, Asst. Prof., James Madison University, VA, Harrisonburg

Grunewald, Paula.................... (218) 739-3308
paula@themidweekpublications.com, Production Manager, This Week's Shopping News, MN, Fergus Falls

Grunow, Randy
rgrunow@mediaspace.com, Chief Operating Officer, Mediaspace Solutions, MN, Hopkins

Gruss, Jean .... (239) 275-2230
jgruss@BusinessObserverFL.com, Ed., Business Observer-Lee, FL, Sarasota
jgruss@BusinessObserverFL.com, Ed., Business Observer-Collier, FL, Naples

---

Gryn, Nir
nir.gryn@xtivia.com, CEO, Xtivia, CO, Colorado Springs

Grzegorek, Vince
vgrzegorek@clevescene.com, Ed., Metro Times, MI, Ferndale

Grzegorek, Vince
vgrzegorek@clevescene.com, Ed., Cleveland Scene, OH, Cleveland

Grzella, Paul.......................... (908) 243-6601
pgrzella@gannett.com, General Manager/ Editor, Home News Tribune, NJ, Somerville

Grzella, Paul.......................... (908) 243-6601
pgrzella@gannett.com, Gen. Mgr./Ed., Courier News, NJ, Somerville

Guab, Adam .... (520) 568-4198
agaub@copamonitor.com, Mng. Ed., Maricopa Monitor, AZ, Maricopa

Guaracao, Gaby .... (215) 789-6959
gabrielag@aldiainc.com, Strategy & Operations, Al Dia, PA, Philadelphia

Guaracao, Hernan .... (215) 569-4666
Hernan@aldianews.com, Founder & CEO, Al Dia, PA, Philadelphia

Guarasi, Karen .... (732) 922-6000 ext. 3644
kguarasi@njpressmedia.com, Regional VP/ Adv., Asbury Park Press, NJ, Neptune

Guarasi, Karen .... (732) 643-3644
kguarasi@gannettnj.com, Reg. VP Adv., Daily Record, NJ, Parsippany

Guarnieri, Damion.......... (770) 428-9411 ext. 231
Photo Dept. Mgr., Marietta Daily Journal, GA, Marietta

Guastaferro, Denny.........(716) 668-5223 ext 8118
dguastaferro@metrowny.com, Pub., Amherst / Tonawanda Metro Source (OOB) , NY, Buffalo
dguastaferro@metrowny.com, Pub. , Springville Journal, NY, Buffalo
dguastaferro@metrowny.com, Pub., Alden Metro Source, NY, Buffalo
dguastaferro@metrowny.com, Lewiston / Youngstown Metro Retailer, NY, Buffalo
dguastaferro@metrowny.com, Niagara Falls / Wheatfield Metro Retailer (OOB), NY, Buffalo
dguastaferro@metrowny.com, Niagara Falls City Metro Retailer (OOB), NY, Buffalo
dguastaferro@metrowny.com, Tonawanda Source, NY, Buffalo
dguastaferro@metrowny.com, Lockport Metro Retailer, NY, Buffalo
dguastaferro@metrowny.com, Pub., Williamsville Smart Shopper, NY, Buffalo
dguastaferro@metrowny.com, Pub., Amherst / Getzville Smart Shopper, NY, Buffalo
dguastaferro@metrowny.com, Pub., North Buffalo Smart Shopper, NY, Buffalo
dguastaferro@metrowny.com, Pub., South Cheektowaga Source, NY, Buffalo
dguastaferro@metrowny.com, Pub., Kenmore / Tonawanda Source, NY, Buffalo
dguastaferro@metrowny.com, Pub., Eggertsville / Snyder Smart Shopper, NY, Buffalo
dguastaferro@metrowny.com, Pub., North Tonawanda Source, NY, Buffalo
dguastaferro@metrowny.com, Pub., North Cheektowaga Source, NY, Buffalo
dguastaferro@metrowny.com, Pub., South Buffalo Metro Source, NY, Buffalo
dguastaferro@metrowny.com, Pub., Depew Metro Source, NY, Buffalo
dguastaferro@metrowny.com, Pub., Lancaster Source, NY, Buffalo
dguastaferro@metrowny.com, Pub., Clarence Metro Source, NY, Buffalo
dguastaferro@metrowny.com, Pub, The Sun and Erie County Independent, NY, Hamburg

Guay, David
daveg@commpub.com, Community Publishers, Inc., AR, Bentonville

Guay, David
dguay@rustcom.com, Vice President of Production, Rust Communications, MO,

Cape Girardeau
dguay@rustcom.com, Southeast Missourian, MO, Cape Girardeau

Guay, Gilles
gilles.guay@transcontinental.ca, Ed., L'hebdo Mekinac/des Chenaux, QC, Shawinigan

Guay, Gilles.....................................ext. 224
gilles.guay@transcontinental.ca, Adv. Mgr., Hebdo Du St. Maurice, QC, Shawinigan

Gubanc, Susanne
sgubanc@coe.edu, Coe College, IA, Cedar Rapids

Guckeen, Angela
ads@banner-tribune.com, Adv. Rep., Franklin Banner-Tribune, LA, Franklin

Gudat, Sandra
info@customer.com, Pres., Customer Communications Group, CO, Lakewood

Gudde, Emily
egudde@parsonssun.com, Graphic Desgner, Parsons Sun, KS, Parsons

Guenther, Jerry..............(402) 371-1020 ext. 234
jguenther@norfolkdailynews.com, Reg. Ed., Norfolk Daily News, NE, Norfolk

Guenther, Steve
steve.guenther@auditedmedia.com, VP, Digital Auditing Services, Alliance for Audited Media, IL, Arlington Heights

Guerin, Joe
jguerin@kpbs.org, Ed. in Chief, The Daily Transcript, CA, San Diego

Guerke, Gwen
mc@newszap.com, Sr. Ed., Milford Chronicle, DE, Milford

Guernsey, Dean ....(541) 419-8057
dguernsey@bendbulletin.com, Photo Ed., The Bulletin, OR, Bend

Guerra, Danielle
dguerra@shawmedia.com, Photo Ed., Daily Chronicle, IL, Dekalb

Guerrero, Debbie
dmarez@eaglenewspapers.com, Circ. Mgr., Daily Sun News, WA, Sunnyside

Guerrero, Maribel
enterprise78361@aol.com, Adv. Dir., Jim Hogg County Enterprise, TX, Hebbronville

Guerrero, Mariel
mguerrero1@live.ndm.edu, Editor-in-Chief, Notre Dame of Maryland University, MD, Baltimore

Guerriero, Laura ....(718) 260-4593
LGuerriero@CNGLocal.com, Pub., Bronx Times Reporter, NY, Bronx

Guerringue, Mark.....................(603) 733-5800
mark@conwaydailysun.com, Pub., The Berlin Daily Sun, NH, BERLIN

Guerringue, Mark
Mark@conwaydailysun.com, Pub., The Conway Daily Sun, NH, North Conway

Guess, Rhonda
guessrd@lacitycollege.edu, Los Angeles City College, CA, Los Angeles

Guevara, Melissa
sales@vri.com, Customer Service Rep., Voice Retrieval & Information Services, Inc., TX, Carrollton

Gugliociello, Steve
sgugliociello@ellwoodcityledger.com, Ed., Ellwood City Ledger, PA, Ellwood City

Gugliotti, Elio.................(203) 729-2228 ext. 20
editor@mycitizensnews.com, Ed., Citizen's News, CT, Waterbury

Gugliotto, Mike
mgugliotto@pioneernewsgroup.com, Pres., Pioneer Newspapers Inc, WA, Seattle
mgugliotto@pioneernewsgroup.com, Assoc. Pres., Inland Press Association, IL, Des Plaines

Guidarelli, Audrey ....(847) 929-1909
aguidarelli@thermalcare.com, Mktg. Servs. Mgr., AWS, A Thermal Care Division, IL, Niles

Guidry, Darrin ....(985) 876-3008, ext. 25
darrin@tri-parishtimes.com, Pub, Tri-Parish Times & Business News, LA, Houma

Guidry, Dianne ....(225) 388-0283
dguidry@theadvocate.com, Exec. Asst., The Advocate, LA, Baton Rouge

Guidry, Jaunita
juanitag@lasmag.com, Office Mgr., St. Charles Herald-Guide, LA, Boutte

Guidry, Joe..............................(813) 259-7673
jjguidry@tampatrib.com, Tampa Bay Times, FL, St Petersburg

Guilford, Terry
terry@leroyny.com, Prod. Mgr, Le Roy Pennysaver & News, NY, Le Roy

Guilfoyle, Christine
christine_guilfoyle@condenast.com, Pub., Women's Wear Daily, NY, New York

Guillemette, Andre
andre.guillemette@hebdosquebecor.com, Gen. Mgr., Le Mirabel, QC, Saint Jerome

Guillemette, Andre ....(819) 623-3112
andre.guillemetee@hebdosquebecor.com, Ed., L'echo Du Nord, QC, Saint Jerome
andre.guillemetee@hebdosquebecor.com, Journal Le Choix D'antoine Labelle, QC, Mont-Laurier
andre.guillemetee@hebdosquebecor.com, Journal Le Pays D'en Haut La Vallee, QC, Saint Sauveur-des-Monts

Guillen, Gloria
gguillen@themilpitaspost.com, Bus. Mgr., Fremont Bulletin, CA, Milpitas

Guillory, Angela ....(903) 756-7396
aguillory@casscountynow.com, Ad Mgr, The Cass County Sun, TX, Linden

Guillory, Darrell ....(337) 266-2154
dguillory@phihelico.com, COO, LSN Publishing Company LLC, LA, Lafayette

Guillory, Darrell ....(337) 457-3061
darrell.guillory@eunicetoday.com, COO/Pub., The Eunice News, LA, Eunice

Guimarin, Kimberly ....(909) 386-3991
kimberly.guimarin@inlandnewspapers.com, Asst. Managing Ed., Los Angeles Daily News, CA, Woodland Hills

Guimarin, Kimberly ....(909) 386-3991
kguimarin@scng.com, Sr. Ed., The Sun, CA, San Bernardino
kguimarin@scng.com, Senior Editor, Inland Valley Daily Bulletin, CA, Rancho Cucamonga
kguimarin@scng.com, Sr. Ed., The Press-Enterprise, CA, Riverside

Guin, Tanya
tanya@corridormessenger.com, Mng. Ed., The Corridor Messenger, AL, Jasper

Guiniven, John
guinivje@jmu.edu, Assoc. Prof., James Madison University, VA, Harrisonburg

Guinn, Rick ....(253) 620-4747
Rickg@webpressllc.com, Operations Manager, WebPress, LLC, WA, Tacoma

Guinta, Peter ....(904) 819-3493
peter.guints@staugustinerecord.com, Senior Writer, The St. Augustine Record, FL, Saint Augustine

Guiot, Shanna
shanna@chanute.com, Bus. Mgr., Parsons Sun, KS, Parsons

Guiot, Shanna
shanna@chanute.com, Pub./Bus. Mgr., The Chanute Tribune, KS, Chanute

Guisinger, Tracie..........(937) 393-3456 Ext. 1674
tguisinger@civitasmedia.com, Med. Sales

Cons., Hillsboro Times-Gazette, OH, Hillsboro

Gulbrandsen, Eric
bnewsads@roadrunner.com, Adv., The Bridgton News, ME, Bridgton

Gulbranson, Sheryl .... (815) 625-3600 Ext. 300
sgulbranson@saukvalley.com, Circ. Mgr., The Telegraph, IL, Dixon

Gulbranson, Sheryl ....(815) 625-3500 ext. 5300
sgulbranson@saukvalley.com, Circ. Dir., Daily Gazette, IL, Sterling

Guldan, Dennis
publisher@Bird-dog-news.com, Pub., Bird Dog & Retriever News, MN, Saint Paul

Gulig, Joe ....(920) 453-5191
jgulig@sheboygan.gannett.com, Editorial Page Ed., The Sheboygan Press, WI, Sheboygan

Gulli, Amy
amys@cpbj.com, Mng. Ed., Central Penn Business Journal, PA, Harrisburg

Gullifor, Paul
pfg@bradley.edu, Chair/Prof., Bradley University, IL, Peoria

Gullixson, Paul.........................(707) 526-8651
paul.gullixson@pressdemocrat.com, Editorial Page Ed., The Press Democrat, CA, Santa Rosa

Gumprecht, Blake
news@claytonrecord.com, Ed./Pub., Clayton Record, AL, Clayton

Gumz, F. Mark
info@olympusamerica.com, Pres./COO, Olympus America, Inc., PA, Center Valley

Gun, Milton J. ....(857) 231-6054
nenewsnow@yahoo.com, Pub./Ed., Travel & Leisure Features, MA, Newton
nenewsnow@yahoo.com, Bureau Chief, New England News Service, Inc., Newton

Gunaratne, Shelton
gunarat@mnstate.edu, Prof., Minnesota State University, Moorehead, MN, Moorhead

Gundersen, Dave ....(612) 673-4819
David.Gundersen@startribune.com, Dir., Sales Mktg./Research, Star Tribune, MN, Minneapolis

Gunderson, Ed
egunderson@indexjournal.com, Advertising Director, The Index-Journal, SC, Greenwood

Guniss, Carolyn ....(305) 694-6210
cguniss@miamitimesonline.com, Executive Editor, The Miami Times, FL, Miami

Gunkel, Dawn ....(937) 556-5763
dgunkel@civitasmedia.com, Cir. Mgr, Wilmington News Journal, OH, Wilmington

Gunn, Drew ....(205) 348-8995
Univ. of Alabama, AL, Tuscaloosa

Gunn, James
sales@arcoengineering.com, Pres., Arco Engineering, Inc. (Newspaper Div.), KY, Louisville

Gunn, Steve
sgunn@capgaznews.com, Ed., Crofton-West County Gazette, MD, Annapolis

Gunn, Steve............................(757) 446-2000
steve.gunn@pilotonline.com, Exec. Ed., The Virginian-Pilot, VA, Norfolk

Gunner, Bob
bobgunner@gmail.com, Pub./Ed., The Paper, TX, Spring

Gunst, Carla
cgunst@jcpgroup.com, Ed., Wisconsin State Farmer, WI, Waupaca

Gunter, Julie
jgunter@farragutpress.com, Advertising Sales, Farragut Press, TN, Farragut

Guo, Henry.............................(647) 705-3194
henry.guo@epochtimes.com, Sales Dir., The

Epoch Times, ON, Toronto

Gupta, Shardul Vikram
patnaaj@gmail.com, Ed., AJ, Patna, Bihar

Guptill, Janet F. ....(406) 557-2337
tradwind@midrivers.com, Pub., Tradewind, MT, Jordan

Gurdian, Alvaro ....ext. 104
agurdian@lanoticia.com, Circ. Mgr., La Noticia, NC, Charlotte

Gurdian, Hilda..............(704) 568-6966 ext. 106
hgurdian@lanoticia.com, Pub., La Noticia, NC, Charlotte

Gurevich, Guily
reklama2000@yahoo.com, Adv. Mgr., Russkaya Reklama, NY, Brooklyn

Gurley, Georgia ....(919) 739-7811
ggurley@newsargus.com, Adv. Mgr., Nat'l, Goldsboro News-Argus, NC, Goldsboro

Gursha, Rob ....(612) 673-4040
rob.gursha@startribune.com, VP, Consumer Marketing, Star Tribune, MN, Minneapolis

Guscott, Lindsay
mineradvertising@povn.com, Adv. Mgr., Newport Miner, WA, Newport

Gushard, Keith
kgushard@meadvilletribune.com, Bus. Ed., The Meadville Tribune, PA, Meadville

Gusmano, Nicholas
nick.gusmano@startribune.com, Retail Marketing Analyst, Star Tribune, MN, Minneapolis

Gustafson, David
david@hubcityspokes.com, Ed./Pub., The Lamar Times, MS, Hattiesburg

Gustafson, David
david@hubcityspokes.com, Ed./Pub., The Hattiesburg Post, MS, Hattiesburg

Gustafson, David
david@hubcityspokes.com, Editor/Publisher, The Petal News, MS, Hattiesburg

Gustafson, Denese
northernstar@mchsi.com, Adv. Mgr., Northern Star, MN, Clinton

Gustafson, Donald ....(630) 238-4817
donald.gustafson@baldwintech.com , Vice President, Baldwin Americas Sales & Marketing, Baldwin Technology Company, Inc., IL, Downers Grove

Gustafson, Kim ....(877) 235-7714
kimg@digiconow.com, CEO, DigiConnect, AR, Rogers

Gustin, Kristin ....(800) 309-7502
sales@noteads.com, Sales, NoteAds, Inc./Post-it Note Advertising, WA, Olympia

Guterman, Rebecca
rguterman@uchicago.edu, Editor-in-Chief, Univ. of Chicago, IL, Chicago

Guthard, Lori ....(308) 233-9701
lori.guthard@kearneyhub.com, Adv. Mgr., Shopping Link, NE, Kearney

Guthard, Lori ....(308) 233-9701
lori.guthard@kearneyhub.com , Adv. Mgr., Sales, Kearney Hub, NE, Kearney

Guthrie, Lisa
lisa@twptimes.com, Gen. Mgr., The Township Times, MI, Breckenridge

Guthrie, Matt
mguthrie@gatehousemedia.com, Pub., Dunsmuir News, CA, Mount Shasta
mguthrie@gatehousemedia.com, Pub., Mt. Shasta Herald, CA, Mount Shasta
mguthrie@gatehousemedia.com, Pub., Weed Press, CA, Mount Shasta
mguthrie@gatehousemedia.com, Pub., The Carthage Press, MO, Carthage

Guthrie, Matt ....(530) 842-5777
publisher@siskiyoudaily.com, Pub., Siskiyou Daily News, CA, Yreka

bulletin@drtel.net, Pub. , Enderlin Independent, ND, Enderlin

bulletin@drtel.net, Pub. , Tri County News, ND, Gackle

bulletin@drtel.net, Pub., Kulm Messenger, ND, Kulm

bulletin@drtel.net, Pub., The Litchville Bulletin, ND, Litchville

Hagedorn, Christopher G.
bronxnews@gmail.com, Pub., Parkchester News, NY, Bronx

Hagedorn, Christopher G.
bronxnews@gmail.com, Pub., The Bronx News, NY, Bronx

Hagedorn, Christopher G.
bronxnews@gmail.com, Pub., Co-op City News, NY, Bronx

Hagel, Roger .... (309) 444-3139
hagelnews@aol.com, Pub., Courier, IL, Washington

hagelnews@aol.com, Pub., Woodford Courier, IL, Washington

Hageman, Kathy
kathy.hageman@abilenetx.com, Interim News Ed., Abilene Reflector-Chronicle, KS, Abilene

Hagen, Jeff
jeff@fairmontphotopress.com, Mgr., Fairmont Photo Press, MN, Fairmont

Hagen, Michael .... (256) 340-2423
michael.hagen@decaturdaily.com, Ad Sale Exec, The Decatur Daily, AL, Decatur

Hagenbuch, Julie
hagenjk@bgsu.edu, Instr., Bowling Green State University, OH, Bowling Green

Hager, Kevin
kevin.hager@wichita.edu, Assoc. Prof., Wichita State University, KS, Wichita

Hagerman, Scott .... (270) 691-7317
shagerman@messenger-inquirer.com, News Ed., Messenger-Inquirer, KY, Owensboro

Hagert, Mary
mlhagert@lillienews.com, Ed., South St. Paul - South West Review, MN, North St Paul

mlhagert@lillienews.com, Ed., New Brighton Bulletin, MN, North St Paul

Hagert, Mary Lee .... (651) 748-7820
Mng. Ed., East Side Review, MN, North St Paul

Hagert, Mary Lee .... (651) 748-7820
mlhagert@lillienews.com, Mng. Ed., St. Anthony Bulletin, MN, North Saint Paul

Hagert, Mary Lee
mlhagert@lillienews.com, Exec. Ed., Ramsey County Review, MN, North Saint Paul

Hagert, Mary Lee
mlhagert@lillienews.com, Exec. Ed., New Brighton-Mounds View Bulletin, MN, North Saint Paul

Haggard, Kim .... (317) 398-1253
F, Customer Service Rep., The Shelbyville News, IN, Shelbyville

Haggard, Shannon .... (250) 490-0880 EXT 309
shannon.huggard@pentictonherald.ca , Circ. Mgr., Penticton Herald, BC, Penticton

Haggarty, Peter
office@yourtowncrier.com, Pub., Town Crier, MA, Woburn

Haggerty, James
news@woburnonline.com, Nat'l Ed., Daily Times Chronicle, MA, Woburn

Haggerty, James D.
news@woburnonline.com, News Ed., Daily Times Chronicle, MA, Woburn

Haggerty, Jay M. .... (781) 933-3700
Prodn. Mgr., The Stoneham Independent, MA, Stoneham

Haggerty, Mark
news@stonehamindependent.com, Mgr., Promo., Daily Times Chronicle, MA, Woburn

Haggerty, Mark J. .... (781) 933-3700
mark.haggerty@dailytimesinc.com, Business Manager, The Stoneham Independent, MA, Stoneham

Haggerty, Mathew E.
mhaggerty@timesshamrock.com, Pub., The Times-Tribune, PA, Scranton

Haggerty, Peter M. .... (781) 933-3700
Pub., The Stoneham Independent, MA, Stoneham

Haggerty, Sandra .... (740) 593-2604
Assoc. Prof., Ohio University, OH, Athens

Haggerty, Stacy
sales@newslj.com, Adv. Sales Mgr., News Letter Journal, WY, Newcastle

Haglund, Alex
ahaglund@mail.com, Ed., The Nashville News, IL, Nashville

Hague, Bill .... (847) 922-0418
bhague@magid.com, Exec. Vice Pres., Frank N Magid Associates, IA, Marion

Hague, Susan
shague@dcc.edu, Delgado Community College, LA, New Orleans

Hahn, Arthur
arthur@brenhambanner.com, Editor, Brenham Banner-Press, TX, Brenham

Hahn, Carol
chahn@enquirer.com, Adv. VP, Western Hills Press, OH, Cincinnati

chahn@enquirer.com, Adv. VP, Price Hill Press, OH, Cincinnati

chahn@enquirer.com, Adv. VP, Hilltop Press, OH, Cincinnati

chahn@enquirer.com, Adv. VP, Delhi Press, OH, Cincinnati

Hahn, Erin .... (270) 505-1409
ehahn@thenewsenterprise.com, Adv. Dir., The News-Enterprise, KY, Elizabethtown

Hahn, Erin .... (410) 857-7888
erin.hahn@carrollcountytimes.com, Advertising Director, Mason-dixon Marketplace, MD, Westminster

Hahn, Mark .... (847) 818-1100
mark.hahn@aaapress.com, Vice Pres., Sales/Mktg., AAA Press International, IL, Arlington Heights

Hahn, Shannon
office@mcrecordonline.com, Office Mgr., The Madison County Record, AR, Huntsville

Hahn, Terri .... (308) 381-9463
terri.hahn@theindependent.com, Women's Ed., The Grand Island Independent, NE, Grand Island

Haider, Halima
hhaider@thevalleychronicle.com, Journalist, The Valley Chronicle, CA, Hemet

Haidet, Doug .... (419) 281-0581 ext. 245
dhaidet@times-gazette.com, Sports Editor, Ashland Publishing Co. LLC, OH, Ashland

Haile, Mike .... (217) 351-5349
mitm@news-gazette.com, VP/Gen. Mgr. Radio, The News-Gazette, IL, Champaign

Haimer, Darren
dhaimer@bradenton.com, VP, Adv., Bradenton Herald, FL, Bradenton

Hain, Rich .... (402) 426-2121 x113
distribute@enterprisepub.com, Distribution Manager, Washington County Enterprise, NE, Blair

Hain, Rich
distribute@enterprisepub.com, Circ. Mgr., The Pilot Tribune / Enterprise, NE, Blair

Haines, John
merchanteer@aol.com, Ed., The Local Merchanteer, NY, Brooklyn

Haines, Rebecca .... (417) 358-2191
rhaines@carthagepress.com, Reporter/

designer, The Carthage Press, MO, Carthage

Haines, Rosalee .... (330) 877-9345
knowlespress@sbcglobal.net, Ed., The Hartville News, OH, Hartville

Haines, Tom .... (215) 949-4201
thaines@calkins.com, Life Ed., Bucks County Courier Times, PA, Levittown

Haire, Clarke
clarke@ccchronicle.net, Pub., Cass City Chronicle, MI, Cass City

Haire, Melissa .... (828) 610-8727
mhaire@newstopicnews.com, District Mgr. , News-Topic, NC, Lenoir

Hairlson, Gary .... (314) 340-8279
ghairlson@post-dispatch.com, Multimedia Dir., St. Louis Post-Dispatch, MO, Saint Louis

Hairston, Stacey
shairston@thefranklinnewspost.com, Staff Writer, The Franklin News-Post, VA, Rocky Mount

Haish, Jessi
jhaish@shawmedia.com, Reporter, Daily Chronicle, IL, Dekalb

Haitz III, Henry B. .... (203) 337-4890
hhaitz@hearstmediact.com, Group Publisher and President, Greenwich Time, CT, Old Greenwich

Hajian, David
david@nextcom.net, Opns. Mgr., Nextcom, CA, Los Angeles

Hajiantoni, Pete .... (410) 332-6298
phajiantoni@baltsun.com, Strategic Information Mgr., The Prince George's Sentinel, MD, Seabrook

phajiantoni@baltsun.com, Strategic Information Mgr., Montgomery County Sentinel, MD, Rockville

Hajostek, John .... (701) 235-7311 ext. 5499
CFO, Forum Communications Co., ND, Fargo

Hajostek, John
jhajostek@forumcomm.com, CFO, InForum, ND, Fargo

Hakala, Bruce .... (260) 347-0400
bhakala@kpcmedia.com, KPC Media Group, Inc., IN, Kendallville

Hakala, Bruce
bhakala@kpcnews.net, Circ. Dir., Smart Shopper, IN, Angola

Hakala, Bruce .... (260) 347-0400 Ext. 1172
bhakala@kpcmedia.com, Circ. Dir., The News Sun, IN, Kendallville

Hakala, Bruce .... (260) 426-2640
Circ. Dir., The Advance Leader, IN, Kendallville

Hakanson, David .... (317) 444-8218
david.hakanson@indystar.com, Director of Key Accounts , The Indianapolis Star, IN, Indianapolis

Hakes, David .... (970) 748-2976
dhakes@vaildaily.com, Circ. Mgr., The Eagle Valley Enterprise, CO, Gypsum

Halbfoerster, William J.
editorial@homenewspa.com, Ed., The Home News, PA, Walnutport

Halbreich, Jeremy
halbreich@amercomm.com, Foundation VP, Inland Press Association, IL, Des Plaines

Halcomb, Tracy
halcombt@flagler.edu, Chair/Assoc. Prof., Flagler College, FL, Saint Augustine

Halcombe, Jason .... (478) 272-5522 ext. 211
jhalcombe@courier-herald.com, Managing Ed., The Courier Herald, GA, Dublin

Haldane, Neal
nhaldane@madonna.edu, Dir., Madonna University, MI, Livonia

Haldeman, Rita
addirector@heraldbanner.com, Adv. Dir.,

Commerce Journal, TX, Greenville

Haldeman, Rita .... (936) 295-5407
rhaldeman@itemonline.com, Pub./Adv. Dir., The Huntsville Item, TX, Huntsville

Hale, Amy
addept@thnews.com, Adv. Mgr. , Times-Herald, AR, Forrest City

Hale, Amy Sue .... (423) 447-2996
valleypubinc@bledsoe.net, Pub., The Bledsonian-Banner, TN, Pikeville

Hale, Amy Sue .... (423) 447-2996
valleypubinc@bledsoe.net, Publisher, Sequatchie Valley Shopper, TN, Pikeville

Hale, Angie .... (765) 659-4622
aharden@nola.com, Classified/Retail Inside Sales, The Times, IN, Frankfort

Hale, Caitlin .... (205) 328-9249
Editor, The East Carolinian, NC, Greenville

Hale, David
dhale@swoknews.com, Managing Ed., The Lawton Constitution, OK, Lawton

Hale, John
jhale@heraldstaronline.com, Circ. Dir., Herald-Star, OH, Steubenville

Hale, Marjie
mphale@bigsandynews.com, Pub., The Tri-Rivers Advertiser, KY, Louisa

Hale, Monte .... (615) 869-0800
mhale@mainstreetmediatn.com, Sports Ed, The Murfreesboro Post, TN, Murfreesboro

Hale, Randy
rhale@bigsandynews.com, Adv. Mgr., The Tri-Rivers Advertiser, KY, Louisa

Hale, Sarah
svisarah@silverstar.com, Managing Ed., Star Valley Independent, WY, Afton

Hale, Terri .... (304) 327-2802
thale@bdtonline.com, Adv. Dir., Bluefield Daily Telegraph, WV, Bluefield

thale@bdtonline.com, Adv. Dir., Princeton Times, WV, Princeton

Hale-Spencer, Melissa .... (518) 861-5005
MHale-Spencer@AltamontEnterprise.com, Ed co-pub, The Altamont Enterprise & Albany County Post, NY, Altamont

Hales, Mike
mike.hales@scripps.com, VP, Finance & Administration, E. W. Scripps Co., OH, Cincinnati

Hales, Ryan
halesr@byui.edu, Advisor, Brigham Young Univ. Idaho, ID, Rexburg

Hales, Sean
editor@benewsjournal.com, Ed., Box Elder News Journal, UT, Brigham City

Haley, Ann
ann.haley@latimes.com, Online Ed., Daily Pilot, CA, Costa Mesa

Haley, Dan .... (708) 386-5555
dhaley@wjinc.com, Pub., Chicago Parent, IL, Oak Park

Haley, Dan
dhaley@wjinc.com, Pub., Wednesday Journal of Oak Park & River Forest, IL, Oak Park

Haley, Dan
dhaley@wjinc.com, Pub., Forest Park Review, IL, Oak Park

Haley, Dan .... (708) 524-8300
dhaley@wjinc.com, Pub., Austin Weekly News, IL, Oak Park

Haley, John
haley@pulaskijournal.com, Pub./Exec. Ed., The Pulaski County Journal, IN, Winamac

haley@pulaskijournal.com, Publisher/Owner, The Independent, IN, Winamac

Halfman, Linda
linda.halfman@globegazette.com, Financial

Mgr., Globe Gazette, Mason City, IA, Mason City

Hall, Ameen
ahall@claflin.edu, Prodn. Specialist, Claflin University, SC, Orangeburg

Hall, Andy
ahall@palatkadailynews.com, Sports Ed., Palatka Daily News, FL, Palatka

Hall, Arthur R ....(609) 886-8600 ext. 45
ahall@cmcherald.com, Pub., Cape May County Herald Times, NJ, Rio Grande

Hall, Bennie ....(318) 872-4120
enterprise@wnonline.net, Gen. Mgr., The Enterprise & Interstate Progress, LA, Mansfield

Hall, Brad ....(606) 528-7898 Ext. 36
bhall@thetimestribune.com, Nighttime/Religion Page Ed., Times-Tribune, KY, Corbin

Hall, Camey ....(731) 986-2253
camey@newsleaderonline.com, Circulation Mgr, Carroll County News-Leader, TN, Huntingdon

Hall, Carla
chall@timesanddemocrat.com, Mktg./Promo., The Times and Democrat, SC, Orangeburg

Hall, Charlene ....(905) 632-4444
charlenehall@metroland.com, Circ. Mgr., The Flamborough Review, ON, Waterdown

Hall, Charlotte H. ....(407) 420-5195
editor@orlandosentinel.com, Ed., Orlando Sentinel, FL, Orlando

Hall, Christine
chall@scni.com, Ed., Stamford Advocate, CT, Stamford
chall@scni.com, Ed., The Advocate, CT, Stamford

Hall, Christopher ....(641) 228-3211
christopherhall@charlescitypress.com, Owner, Charles City Press, IA, Charles City

Hall, Christopher
christopher.hall@libertymutual.com, Vice Pres., HR, The Boston Globe, MA, Boston

Hall, Christopher Hall
christopherhall@charlescitypress.com, Pub., Northeast Iowa Shopper, IA, Charles City

Hall, David E. ....ext. 112
davehall@primhall.com, Vice Pres., Prim Hall Enterprises, Inc., NY, Plattsburgh

Hall, Debbie
manager.kansascity@americanclassifieds. com, Thrifty Nickel - Kansas City - Kansas, MO, Kansas City

Hall, Debbie
deborah.hall@hrblock.com, Gen. Mgr., American Classifieds, MO, Kansas City

Hall, Don ....(845) 628-8400
legals@putnampresstimes.com, Pub., Putnam County Times, NY, Mahopac

Hall, Don ....(914) 628-8400
Pub., Putnam County Press, NY, Mahopac

Hall, Donna
dhall@tnonline.com, Adv. Nat'l. Rep., Times News, PA, Lehighton

Hall, Emily
emily@hubcityspokes.com, Art Dir., The Lamar Times, MS, Hattiesburg

Hall, Fred
hall@mid-valleypublishing.com, Pub., Herald Advertiser, CA, Reedley
hall@mid-valleypublishing.com, Publisher, The Reedley Exponent, CA, Reedley

Hall, Gene
gene@charlescitypress.com, Pub., The Extra, IA, Charles City

Hall, Janis
jhall@mnpubs.com, Pub., The Downtown Journal, MN, Minneapolis

Hall, Janis
jhall@mnpubs.com, Pub., Good Age, MN, Minneapolis

Hall, Jim
jhall@americanclassifieds.com, Thrifty Nickel - Evansville, IN, Evansville

Hall, John
jhall@forsythnews.com, Pub./Mktg. Dir., Dawson County News, GA, Dawsonville

Hall, Jordan Thomas ....(606) 785-5134
jhall@troublesomecreektimes.com, Asst. Gen. Mgr./Photographer, Troublesome Creek Times, KY, Hindman

Hall, Julia
fn.editor@udayton.edu, Print-Ed., Univ. of Dayton, OH, Dayton

Hall, Julie ....ext. 321
julie.hall@sunmedia.ca, Class. Adv. Mgr. , Northumberland Today, ON, Cobourg

Hall, Karen
khall@marshalltribune.com, Ed., Marshall County Tribune, TN, Lewisburg

Hall, Katie
living@cortlandstandard.net, Society/Women's Ed., Cortland Standard, NY, Cortland

Hall, Mark ....(217) 238-7987
mhall@herald-review.com, Oper. Dir., Journal Gazette & Times-Courier, IL, Mattoon

Hall, Mark ....(770) 718-3456
mhall@gainesvilletimes.com, Prodn. Dir., The Times, GA, Gainesville

Hall, Mark
mhall@herald-review.com, Circulation Operations Manager, Herald & Review, Decatur, IL, Decatur

Hall, Mary ....(815) 937-3391
mhall@daily-journal.com, Life Ed., The Daily Journal, IL, Kankakee

Hall, Matt
currycountyreporter@gmail.com, Co-Pub., Curry County Reporter, OR, Gold Beach

Hall, Matt
portorfordnews@gmail.com, Pub., Port Orford News, OR, Port Orford

Hall, Matthew ....(619) 293-1335
matthew.hall@sduniontribune.com, Editorial & Opinion Director, The San Diego Union-Tribune, CA, San Diego

Hall, Melanie
mhall.valleyherald@yahoo.com, Circ. Mgr, Valley Herald, OR, Milton Freewater

Hall, Michael
editor@mapleridgenews.com, Ed., The Maple Ridge News, BC, Maple Ridge

Hall, Mike ....(325) 670-5245
hallm@reporternews.com, Prodn. Dir., Opns., Abilene Reporter-News, TX, Abilene

Hall, Mike
mhall@abilenetx.com, Opns Dir., Sound of Freedom, TX, Abilene

Hall, Philippe ....(847) 427-4615
phall@dailyherald.com, Manager of Digital Technology, Daily Herald, IL, Arlington Heights

Hall, Rebecca
rebecca@okcfriday.com, Class./Legal Mgr., Oklahoma City Friday, OK, Oklahoma City

Hall, Robert
rhall@amongstmen.org, Publisher, Philadelphia Inquirer, Daily News & Philly. com, PA, Philadelphia

Hall, Robert G.
press.h@news-net.ca, Ed., The Haldimand Press, ON, Hagersville

Hall, Rusty
rustyh@valleystar.com, Circ. Dir., Valley Morning Star, TX, Harlingen

Hall, Sharon Kay ....(606) 788-5134
shall@troublesomecreektimes.com, Co-Pub. , Troublesome Creek Times, KY, Hindman

Hall, Sherrie ....(256) 840-3000 ext 122
shall@sandmountainreporter.com, Account Executive, Sand Mountain Reporter, AL, Albertville

Hall, Stan
knobnosteritem@sbcglobal.net, Ed., Knob Noster Item, MO, Knob Noster

Hall, Steve ....(251) 219-5503
shall@press-register.com, Adv. Mgr., Retail, Press-Register, AL, Mobile

Hall, Sue
shall@jcpgroup.com, Gen. Mgr., Living - Kettle Moraine Sunday, WI, Mukwonago

Hall, Sue ....(920) 674-2679
shall@jcpgroup.com, Pub./Gen. Mgr., Jefferson County Living, WI, Watertown
shall@jcpgroup.com, Pub./Gen. Mgr., Living Jefferson County Advertiser-north, WI, Watertown
shall@jcpgroup.com, Pub./Gen. Mgr., Living Jefferson County Advertiser-south, WI, Watertown

Hall, Terry ....(804) 649-6030
thall@timesdispatch.com, Telephone Sales Mgr., Richmond Times-Dispatch, VA, Richmond

Hall, Tommy Curtis ....(606) 785-5134
ads@troublesomecreektimes.com, Advertising Sales, Troublesome Creek Times, KY, Hindman

Hall, Tony
ahall@alaskanewspapers.com, Mng. Ed., The Cordova Times, AK, Cordova

Hallahan, Gene ....(606) 326-2636
ghallahan@dailyindependent.com, Composing Mgr., The Daily Independent, KY, Ashland

Hallahan, Kirk
kirk.hallahan@colostate.edu, Prof., Colorado State University, CO, Fort Collins

Hallam, Suzanne
paper@haysfreepress.com, Circ. Dir., The News-Dispatch, TX, Driftwood
paper@haysfreepress.com, Circ. Mgr., Hays Free Press, TX, Kyle

Hallas, James .... (860) 633-4691 ext. 226
citizen@snet.net, Ed. & Pub., Glastonbury Citizen, CT, Glastonbury

Hallas, James .... (860) 633-4691 ext. 226
citizen@snet.net, Pub., Rivereast News Bulletin, CT, Glastonbury

Hallbauer, Holm
nxinfo@net-linx.com, Pres., net-linx AG, Dresden

Hallee , Roland
townline@fairpoint.net , Mng. Ed., Town Line, ME, South China

Hallford, Scott
scott.hallford@navy.mil, Ed., Gosport, FL, Pensacola

Hallgren, Elaine
fashionshowroom@yahoo.com, Ed., Fashion Syndicate Press, Woodstock

Hallier, Brad .... (620) 694-5700 Ext. 350
bhallier@hutchnews.com, Sports Ed., The Hutchinson News, KS, Hutchinson

Hallion, Kathleen ....(518) 454-5568
khallion@timesunion.com, Adv. Vice Pres., Times Union, NY, Albany

Hallisey, Michael .... (518) 439-4949 ext 416
halliseym@spotlightnews.com, Mng. Ed., Colonie/Loudonville Spotlight, NY, Delmar

Hallisey, Michael ....(518) 439-4949
halliseym@spotlightnews.com, Ed., The Spotlight, NY, Delmar

Hallman, Wallace

wallace@eseco-speedmaster.com, Pres., Electronic Systems Engineering Co., OK, Cushing

Hallmark, Herrel ....(806) 872-2177
editor@pressreporter.com, Ed., Lamesa Press Reporter, TX, Lamesa

Hallock, Steve
shallock@pointpark.edu, Point Park College, PA, Pittsburgh

Halm, Paula
news@paintsvilleherald.com, Pub., The Paintsville Herald, KY, Paintsville

Halmo, Bruce ....(920) 453-5131
bhalmo@sheboygan.gannett.com, Photo Lab, The Sheboygan Press, WI, Sheboygan

Halpern, Kevin ....ext. 304
online@dnj.com, Online Servs. Dir., The Daily News Journal, TN, Murfreesboro

Halpern, Robert L. ....(432) 729-4342
editor@bigbendnow.com, Ed., The Presidio International, TX, Presidio
editor@bigbendnow.com, Pub./Ed., The Presidio International, TX, Presidio

Halpern, Robert L. ....(432) 729-4342
editor@bigbendsentinel.com, Pub./Ed., The Big Bend Sentinel, TX, Marfa

Halpin, Dale
dhalpin@dailyhome.com, Adv. Sales, The Saint Clair Times, AL, Pell City

Halstead, Scott ....(617) 929-2582
scott.halstead@globe.com, Dir. Event Mktg. , The Boston Globe, MA, Boston

Halsted, Lyla
lyhalsted@davidson.edu, Davidson College, NC, Davidson

Halston, Anne
ahalston@tribpub.com, Ed., The Beacon News, IL, Chicago
ahalston@tribpub.com, Ed., The Courier-News, IL, Aurora

Halterman, Chris ....(304) 291-9479
productdir@dominionpost.com, Prodn. Dir., Pre Press/Systems, The Dominion Post, WV, Morgantown

Halverson, Jeff E.
jhalverson@bemidjipioneer.com, Adv. Mgr., Buyline, MN, Bemidji

Halverson, John
regnews@lakegenevanews.net, Gen. Mgr./ Ed., Lake Geneva Regional News, WI, Lake Geneva

Halverson, Steve
info@haskell.com, Pres., The Haskell Co., FL, Jacksonville

Halvorsen, Melodie .... (574) 296-5804
mhalvorsen@elkharttruth.com, Assistant to the Publisher, Elkhart Truth, IN, Elkhart

Halvorson, Brenda ....(218) 894-1112
info@staplesworld.com, Devlin Newspapers, Inc., MN
info@staplesworld.com, Gen. Mgr., Staples World, MN, Staples

Halvorson, Brenda
info@staplesworld.com, Gen. Mgr., Sunday Square Shooter, MN, Staples

Ham, Jeff ....(800) 799-6008
mainepressmail@gmail.com, Exec. Dir., Maine Press Association, ME, Cape Elizabeth

Hama, Carla ....(440) 329-7216
chama@chronclet.com, Adv. Sales Mgr. , Chronicle-Telegram, OH, Elyria

Hamacher, Lawrence ....(267) 907-2522
ithacanads@ithaca.edu, Advertising Sales Manager, Ithaca College, NY, Ithaca

Hamar, Bob ....(308) 381-9417
bob.hamar@theindependent.com, Sports Ed., The Grand Island Independent, NE, Grand Island

Hamberg, Terry
terry@nkctribune.com, Pub., Northern Kittitas County Tribune, WA, Cle Elum

Hamblen, Carrie
chamblen@nmsu.edu, Instr., New Mexico State University, NM, Las Cruces

Hamel, John
johnhamel@nckcn.com, Bus. Mgr., Concordia Blade-Empire, KS, Concordia

Hamel, Kerri .... (403) 528-5692
khamel@medicinehatnews.com, City Ed., Medicine Hat News, AB, Medicine Hat

Hamilton, Bob
stkpaper@ruraltel.net, Pub, Stockton Sentinel, KS, Stockton

Hamilton, Brian .... (530) 477-4249
brianh@theunion.com, Ed., The Union, CA, Grass Valley

Hamilton, Bryan
bmhamilton@bizjournals.com, Pub., Triangle Business Journal, NC, Raleigh

Hamilton, Clarissa
clarissahamilton@whiteville.com, The News Reporter, NC, Whiteville

Hamilton, Dave
dhamilton@delta-optimist.com, Gen Mgr, Delta Optimist, BC, Delta

Hamilton, Dave
dhamilton@delta-optimist.com, Gen Mgr/Adv. Sales, South Delta Leader, BC, Ladner

Hamilton, David
publisher@campbellrivermirror.com, Pub, The Campbell River Courier-islander, BC, Campbell River
publisher@campbellrivermirror.com, Production Director, The Herald-Dispatch, WV, Huntington

Hamilton, David .... 1(205) 204-2720
publisher@campbellrivermirror.com, Pub., The Campbell River Mirror, BC, Campbell River

Hamilton, Devin .... (814) 371-4200
sunday@thecourierexpress.com, Pub., The Leader-Vindicator, PA, New Bethlehem
sunday@thecourierexpress.com, Pub., Tri-County Sunday, PA, Du Bois

Hamilton, Devin .... (814) 503-8860
publisher@eagletimes.com, Pub., Eagle Times, NH, Claremont

Hamilton, Dolores
dhamilton@iowaparkleader.com, Ed./Pub., Iowa Park Leader, TX, Iowa Park

Hamilton, Ed
elwoodsports@elwoodpublishing.com, Sports Ed., The Elwood Call-Leader, IN, Elwood

Hamilton, Grant M.
granthamilton@eastaurorany.com, Pub., Arcade Herald, NY, Arcade
granthamilton@eastaurorany.com, Pub., Warsaw's Country Courier, NY, Warsaw
granthamilton@eastaurorany.com, Pub., Elma Review, NY, East Aurora

Hamilton, Jared .... (575) 546-2611 ext. 2601
jhamilton@scsun-news.com, Gen. Mgr., Silver City Sun-News, NM, Silver City

Hamilton, Jared .... (575) 546-2611 ext. 2601
jhamilton@scsun-news.com, Gen. Mgr., Deming Headlight, NM, Deming

Hamilton, John
manager@pittnews.com, Univ. of Pittsburgh, PA, Pittsburgh

Hamilton, Kevin
khamilton@iowaparkleader.com, Sports Ed., Iowa Park Leader, TX, Iowa Park

Hamilton, Lynn .... (501) 378-3400
lhamilton@arkansasonline.com, Pres./Gen. Mgr., Arkansas Democrat-Gazette, AR, Little Rock

Hamilton, Mark H.

markhh@iafalls.com, Pub., Times-citizen, IA, Iowa Falls

Hamilton, Martin B.
editor@johnstownbreeze.com, Ed., The Johnstown Breeze, CO, Johnstown

Hamilton, Matthew .... (518) 454-5449
mhamilton@timesunion.com, President, Legislative Correspondents Association of NYS, NY, Albany

Hamilton, Misty .... (502) 238-2778
mhamilton@jewishlouisville.org, Graphic Artist, Jewish Louisville Community, KY, Louisville

Hamilton, Phillip .... (806) 285-7766
oltonenterprise@hotmail, Pub./Ed., Hale Center American, TX, Hale Center

Hamilton, Phillip .... (806) 285-7766
oltonenterprise@hotmail, Pub./Ed., The Olton Enterprise, TX, Olton

Hamilton, Rob
roberthamilton@civitasmedia.com, Sports Ed., The Morrow County Sentinel, OH, Mount Gilead

Hamilton, Sharon
shamilton@northvernon.com, Sports Ed., The North Vernon Sun, IN, North Vernon

Hamilton, Sharon
shamilton@northvernon.com, Sports Ed., North Vernon Plain Dealer & Sun, Inc., IN, North Vernon

Hamilton, Thomas P.
thamilton@hamiltoncirculation.com, Vice Pres., Hamilton Circulation Supplies Co., IL, Beecher

Hamilton, Todd .... (250) 559-4680
publisher@thenorthernview.com, Pub./Ed., Haida Gwaii Observer, BC, Queen Charlotte

Hamke, Judy
cccc@mikes.net, The Daily Clintonian , IN, Clinton

Hamlan, Sheila
sheila@trinidadchroniclenews.com, Prodn. Mgr., The Chronicle-News, CO, Trinidad

Hamlet, Marvin
editor@timesvirginian.com, Ed./Gen. Mgr., Times-Virginian, VA, Appomattox

Hamlett, Marvin
editor@timesvirginian.com, Pub., The Union Star, VA, Brookneal

Hamlin, Kimberly
bookkeeping@oldhamera.com, Bookkeeper, Oldham Era, KY, La Grange

Hamm, Benjy .... (502) 649-8822
BHAMM@LCNI.COM, Landmark Community Newspapers, LLC, KY, Shelbyville

Hamm, Colleen .... (262) 544-5252
colleen@newsfinder.com, Account Manager, Newsfinder, Waukesha

Hamm, Liz
liz.hamm@langnews.com, Dir., Mktg. Research, Los Angeles Daily News, CA, Woodland Hills

Hamm, Mark
mark.hamm@sunmedia.ca, Ed. in Chief, The Winnipeg Sun, MB, Winnipeg

Hamm, Sandy .... (262) 544-5252
nf-support@newsfinder.com, Gen. Mgr., Newsfinder, Waukesha

Hammel, Cathy .... (318) 678-6000
Bossier Parish Cmty. College, LA, Bossier City

Hammell, Rick
rhammell@gapress.org, Sales & Marketing Director, Georgia Press Association, GA, Atlanta

Hammer, Hoby
editor@fairviewrepublican.com, Ed., Fairview Republican, OK, Fairview
editor@fairviewrepublican.com, Pub, The Cherokee Messenger & Republican, OK, Cherokee

Hammer, Jo
ads@fairviewrepublican.com, Adv. Mgr., Fairview Republican, OK, Fairview

Hammer, Pam
phammer@gosanangelo.com, Adv. Dir., San Angelo Standard-Times, TX, San Angelo

Hammerback, John
jhammerb@csuhayward.edu, Interim Chair, California State University, Hayward, CA, Hayward

Hammers, Christine
chammers@havasunews.com, Adv. Dir., Today's News-Herald, AZ, Lake Havasu City

Hammers, Christine
chammers@havasunews.com, Adv. Mgr., The Parker Pioneer, AZ, Parker

Hammes, Daniel H.
dan@smgazette.com, Pub., Saint Maries Gazette-Record, ID, Saint Maries

Hammett, Laura .... (614) 461-5240
lhammett@dispatch.com, Class. Sales Mgr., The Columbus Dispatch, OH, Columbus

Hammett, Laura
lhammett@dispatch.com, Retail Sales Mgr., Suburban News Publications, OH, Columbus

Hammill, John .... (705) 325-1355 ext. 244
john.hammill@sunmedia.ca, Publisher/General Manager, Orillia Packet, ON, Orillia

Hammitt, Sylvia
shammitt@bnd.com, Belleville News-Democrat, IL, Belleville

Hammock, Will .... (770) 963 - 9205 x1310
will.hammock@gwinnettdailypost.com, Sports Ed., Gwinnett Daily Post, GA, Lawrenceville

Hammond, Bill
bhammond@observertoday.com, Regl. News Ed., The Observer, NY, Dunkirk

Hammond, Jeri
jhammond@pacesetterusa.com, Exec. Vice Pres., Pacesetter Graphic Service Corp., GA, Acworth

Hammond, Kathy
khammond@messengerpostmedia.com, Pub., Community News, NY, Canandaigua

Hammond, Kathy
kathyhammond@gvpennysaver.com, Controller, Genesee Valley Pennysaver, NY, Avon

Hammond, Marisa .... (301) 784-2528
News Editor, The Cumberland Times-News, MD, Cumberland

Hammond, Matt .... (937) 651-1122
mhammond@examiner.org, Sports Ed., Bellefontaine Examiner, OH, Bellefontaine

Hammond, Robert
bhammond@wyosports.net, Sports Ed., Laramie Boomerang, WY, Laramie

Hammond, Robert
hammore@nytimes.com, Pres., American Newspaper Layout Managers Association (ANLOMA), FL, Fort Myers

Hammond, Sandra
skelly@dentonrc.com, Ad. Director, Denton Record-Chronicle, TX, Denton

Hammond, Teresa .... (209) 847-3021 x 8131
thammond@oakdaleleader.com, Circ. Mgr., The Riverbank News, CA, Oakdale
thammond@oakdaleleader.com, Circ. Mgr., Oakdale Leader, CA, Oakdale
thammond@oakdaleleader.com, Circ. Mgr., Escalon Times, CA, Oakdale

Hammonds, Michelle .... (304) 636-2127
mhammonds@theintermountain.com, Adv. Dir., The Inter-Mountain, WV, Elkins

Hammons, Dean
dean.hammons@mountvernonnews.com, Prodn. Mgr., Shopper's Mart, OH, Mount Vernon

Hammons, Michelle .... (847) 490-6000 x208
michelleh@usspi.com, Executive Vice President, McNaughton Newspapers, IL, Schaumburg

Hamon, Kristie .... (859) 622-1572
Eastern Kentucky Univ., KY, Richmond

Hamp, Bryan .... (989) 366-5341
bryan.hamp@houghtonlakeresorter.com, Prodn. Mgr., The Houghton Lake Resorter, MI, Houghton Lake

Hamp, Eric M. .... (989) 366-5341
eric.hamp@houghtonlakeresorter.com, Mng. Ed., The Houghton Lake Resorter, MI, Houghton Lake

Hamp, Marcia
ads@pokyrd.com, Adv. Mgr., Pocahontas Record-Democrat, IA, Pocahontas

Hamp, Thomas W. .... (989) 366-5341
tom.hamp@houghtonlakeresorter.com, Pub./Ed., The Houghton Lake Resorter, MI, Houghton Lake

Hampden Daley, Jane .... (414) 229-4436
jhampden@uwm.edu, Senior Lecturer, University of Wisconsin-Milwaukee / Department of Journalism, Advertising, and Media Studies (JAMS), WI, Milwaukee

Hample, Dale
dhample@umd.edu, Assoc. Prof., Argumentation/Interpersonal Commun., University of Maryland, MD, College Park

Hampshire, Angie
ahampshire@bonnyville.greatwest.ca, Pub, Bonnyville Nouvelle, AB, Bonnyville

Hampton, Arthur
svh@bluemarble.net, Ed., Springs Valley Herald, IN, French Lick

Hampton, Arthur
ocpninc@ocpnews.com, Pub., Orange Countian, IN, Paoli
ocpninc@ocpnews.com, Pub., Paoli News-Republican, IN, Paoli

Hampton, Daniel
newseditor@students.clark.edu, Clark College, WA, Vancouver

Hampton, Jackie
publisher@mississippilink.com, Pub., Mississippi Link, MS, Jackson

Hampton, Megan .... (815) 526-4480
Advertising Operations Director, Northwest Herald, IL, Crystal Lake

Hampton, Rob
rob.hampton@nptelegraph.com, Prod. Mgr., The North Platte Telegraph, NE, North Platte

Hampton, Rusty .... (570) 771-2039
rhampton@sungazette.com, Production Director, Williamsport Sun-Gazette/Lock Haven Express, PA, South Williamsport

Hampton, Talon
creative@oldhamera.com, Graphic Designer, Oldham Era, KY, La Grange

Hamrick, Ken .... (719) 384-1425
sports@ljtdmail.com, Sports Ed., Ag Journal, CO, La Junta
sports@ljtdmail.com, Sports Ed., The Fowler Tribune, CO, Fowler
sports@ljtdmail.com, Sports Ed., Bent County Democrat, CO, Las Animas

Hamrlik, Rose .... (403) 934-5589
rose@strathmoretimes.com, Adv Mgr, Strathmore Times, AB, Strathmore

Hamstead, Scott .... (865) 675-6397
scott.hamstead@farragutpress.com, Sales, Farragut Press, TN, Farragut

Hanafin, John C.
lfdnews@litchfieldil.com, Pub., News-Herald, IL, Litchfield

Hanahan, Brad .... (815) 526-4439

bhanahan@shawmedia.com, Class Advt Mgr,
Bensenville Press, IL, Downers Grove
bhanahan@shawmedia.com, Class Advt Mgr,
Roselle Itasca Press, IL, Downers Grove

Hanahan, Brad ....(877) 264-2527
bhanahan@shawmedia.com, Group Classified
Dir. , St. Charles Chronicle, IL, St Charles

Hanahan, Brad ....(815) 526-4439
BHanahan@shawmedia.com, Group Classified
Director, Northwest Herald, IL, Crystal Lake

Hanauer, Joe F.
corporateinfo@move.com, Chrmn., Move, Inc.,
Westlake Village

Hanbury, Sophie 020 7931 1010
sophie.hanbury@telegraph.co.uk, Content
Partnerships Director , Telegraph Media
Group, London

Hanc, John
jhanc@nyit.edu, New York Institute of
Technology, NY, Old Westbury

Hancock, Brian ....(403) 380-7585
bhancock@lethbridgeherald.com, Retail Sales
Mgr., The Lethbridge Herald, AB, Lethbridge

Hancock, Caitlin ....(812) 237-4344
Indiana State Univ., IN, Terre Haute

Hancock, Donna........................(270) 384-6471
donna@adairprogress.com , Pub., Adair
Progress, KY, Columbia

Hancock, Eric...............(803) 765-0707 ext. 129
erich@free-times.com, Pub., Free Times, SC,
Columbia

Hancock, Greg
ghancock@cleansource.com, Acct. Dir.,
Parade Publications, Inc. - Los Angeles, CA,
Los Angeles

Hancock, Joan..............(520) 458-9440 ext. 660
photos@myheraldreview.com, Data Processing
Mgr., Sierra Vista Herald - Sunday Bravo
Shopper, AZ, Sierra Vista
photos@myheraldreview.com, Bus. Mgr., Wick
Communications - Herald/Review, AZ, Sierra
Vista

Hancock, Joan........................(520) 586-3382
accounting@bensonnews-sun.com, Bus. Mgr.,
San Pedro Valley News-Sun, AZ, Benson

Hand, Fay
fhand@nassaucountyrecord.com, Adv. Mgr.,
Nassau County Record, FL, Callahan

Hand, Jeff...............................(505) 646-6397
New Mexico State Univ., NM, Las Cruces

Hand, Michael D.
mhand@thelafayettesun.com, Ed. / Pub.,
LaFayette Sun, AL, Lafayette

Handelman, Jay........................(941) 361-4931
jay.handelman@heraldtribune.com, Critic,
Theater/Television, Sarasota Herald-Tribune,
FL, Sarasota

Handfield, Mike
mhandfield@therecord.com, Mailroom Mgr. ,
The Record, ON, Kitchener

Handforth, Laurel
laurel@upandcomingweekly.com, Circ. Mgr, Up
& Coming Weekly, NC, Fayetteville

Handgraaf, Brie ....(252) 265-7821
bhandgraaf@wilsontimes.com, Staff Writer ,
The Wilson Times, NC, Wilson

Handleman, Allan .... ext. 6451
ads@jewishpress.com, Adv. Mgr., Jewish
Press, NE, Omaha

Handley, Allen
ahandley@mycouriernews.com, Pub., The
Courier News, TN, Clinton

Handloff, Rich ....(202) 334-6000
rich.handloff@washpost.com, Director,
Consumer Marketing, The Washington Post,
DC, London

Haneal, Lon...............................(608) 754-3311
lonh@gazettextra.com, Director of Circulation,

The Janesville Gazette - GazetteXtra, WI,
Janesville

Hanel, Rachael
rachael.hanel@mnsu.edu, Adj. Fac., Minnesota
State University Mankato, MN, Mankato

Hanes, Karen E.........................(850) 747-5001
khanes@pcnh.com, Pub./Reg'l Vice Pres., Gulf
Defender, FL, Panama City

Haney, Joseph........................(540) 967-0368
jhaney@thecentralvirginian.com, Reporter, The
Central Virginian, VA, Louisa

Haney, Mark
catholictimes@sbcglobal.net, Ed., The Catholic
Times, MI, Saginaw

Haney, Roger
roger.haney@murraystate.edu, Prof., Murray
State University, KY, Murray

Hankey, Lee
lhankey@emersonct.com, Sales Mgr., Printing,
Fincor Automation, Inc., PA, York

Hankin, Larry
larry@ijn.com, Mng. Ed., Intermountain Jewish
News, CO, Denver

Hankins, Linette
maryac@iowatelecom.net, make-up, Dunlap
Reporter, IA, Dunlap

Hankins, Mike ....(964) 261-3676
mhankins@fbnewsleader.com, Adv. Dir., News-
Leader, FL, Fernandina Beach

Hankins, Mike
mhankins@nassaucountyrecord.com, Adv. Dir.,
Nassau County Record, FL, Callahan

Hankinson, John ....ext. 265
advertising@alibi.com, Sales Dir., Weekly Alibi,
NM, Albuquerque

Hanley, Christopher
chanley@iuoe.org, Gen. Sec./Treasurer,
International Union of Operating Engineers,
DC, Washington

Hanley, Michael
mmajournal@mmaglobal.com, Asst. Prof./
Coord. Advertising, Ball State University, IN,
Muncie

Hanlon, Andrew ....(920) 759-2000
sports@timesvillager.com, Sports Editor, The
Times-Villager, WI, Kaukauna

Hanlon, Katie
mainlinenews@verizon.net, Adv. Mgr., The
Star-Courier, PA, Northern Cambria

Hann, Kerry ....(709) 748-0824
khann@thetelegram.com, Mng. Ed. , The
Telegram, NL, Saint John's

Hann, Kevin
kevin.hann@sunmedia.ca, Deputy Editor, The
Toronto Sun, ON, Toronto

Hanna, Amy
ahanna@altoonamirror.com, Marketing Mgr.,
Altoona Mirror, PA, Altoona

Hanna, Bill
bhanna@mesabidailynews.net, Exec. Ed.,
Mesabi Daily News, MN, Virginia

Hanna, Melissa
mhanna@aikenstandard.com, Editor, Evening
Post Industries' Aiken Communications, SC,
Aiken

Hanna, Melissa
mhanna@aikenstandard.com, Exec. Ed., The
Star, SC, North Augusta

Hanna, Rodger ....(613) 478-2017
info@thetweednews.ca, Ed./Pub., The Tweed
News, ON, Tweed

Hanna, Sam
samhannajr@hannapublishing.com, Publisher,
The Ouachita Citizen, LA, West Monroe

Hanna Jr., Sam
samhannajr@samhannajr.com, Ed, The
Franklin Sun, LA, Winnsboro

Hanna Jr., Sam
samhannajr@samhannajr.com, Ed
, Concordia Sentinel, LA, Ferriday

Hannagan, Ana
ana@hispanosnews.com, Pub., Hispanos
Unidos, CA, Escondido

Hannah, Brittney ....(256) 840-3000
bhannah@sandmountainreporter.com, Staff
Photographer, Sand Mountain Reporter, AL,
Albertville

Hannah, Pam ....(402) 563-7522
pam.hannah@lee.net, Adv. Mgr., Columbus
Area Choice, NE, Columbus

Hannell, Nancy........................(530) 747-8032
nhannell@davisenterprise.net, Adv. Dir., The
Davis Enterprise, CA, DAVIS

Hanneman, Doug
hanneman@hutchinsonleader.com, Ed.,
Hutchinson Leader And Leader Shopper,
MN, Hutchinson
hanneman@hutchinsonleader.com, Ed.,
Hutchinson Leader, MN, Hutchinson

Hanner, Gary
ghanner@thestclairtimes.com, Assoc. Ed., The
Saint Clair Times, AL, Pell City

Hanner, Richard............(209) 369-7035 ext. 215
richardh@lodinews.com, Ed., Sentinel
Express, CA, Lodi

Hanner, Richard
richardh@lodinews.com, Ed., Lodi News-
Sentinel , CA, Lodi

Hanners, John
john_hanners@tamu-commerce.edu, Head/
Prof., Texas A&M University-Commerce, TX,
Commerce

Hanners, Rick
editor@whitefishpilot.com, Ed., The Whitefish
Pilot, MT, Whitefish

Hanning, Ida........................(419) 521-7297
ihanning@gannett.com, Cir. Mgr., Telegraph-
Forum, OH, Mansfield
ihanning@gannett.com, Cir. Mgr., News
Journal, OH, Mansfield

Hanning, Ida........................(419) 521-7297
ihanning@gannett.com, Dis. Mgr., The Marion
Star, OH, Marion

Hannum, Beverly
beverly@webstercountycitizen.com, Prod. Mgr.,
Webster County Citizen, MO, Seymour

Hannum, Beverly
beverly@webstercountycitizen.com, Prodn.
Mgr., Webster County Advertiser, MO,
Seymour

Hansen, Amy
ahansen@osceolaiowa.com, News Ed.,
Osceola Sentinel-Tribune, IA, Osceola

Hansen, Bill
info@elo[...]osceolastar.com, Ed., El Osceola Star,
FL, Kissimmee

Hansen, Bob........................(765) 575-4650
bhansen@thecouriertimes.com, Pub., The
Courier-Times, IN, New Castle

Hansen, Brandon ....(509) 935-8422
brandon@chewelahindependent.com,
Managing Editor, The Independent, WA,
Chewelah

Hansen, Dave
sales@accraply.com, Vice Pres., Sales,
Accraply, Inc., MN, Minneapolis

Hansen, Deb........................(412) 263-1655
dhansen@post-gazette.com, Classified Real
Estate Mgr., Pittsburgh Post-Gazette, PA,
Clinton

Hansen, Geoff ....(603) 727-3230
ghansen@vnews.com, Photo Ed., Valley News,
NH, West Lebanon

Hansen, Glenn ....ext. 2801
ghansen@bpaww.com, Pres./CEO, BPA

Worldwide, CT, Shelton
ghansen@bpaww.com, Pres./CEO, BPA
Worldwide, CT, Shelton

Hansen, Greg
greg_hansen@mccom.com, Vice Pres.,
Creative Servs., M/C/C, TX, Dallas

Hansen, Helge
helge.hansen@kba.com, Pres., Koenig &
Bauer Aktiengesellschaft (KBA), Wuerzburg

Hansen, Jeff ....(307) 266-0506
jeff.hansen@trib.com, Controller, Casper Star-
Tribune, WY, Casper

Hansen, Joe
jhansen@idahopress.com, IT Dir., Idaho Press,
ID, Nampa

Hansen, Kara
khansen@shawsuburban.com, Circ. Dir.,
Northwest Citizen Shopper, IL, Crystal Lake

Hansen, Karen ....(309) 820-3236
khansen@pantagraph.com, Bus. Ed., The
Pantagraph, IL, Bloomington

Hansen, Karen ....(202) 536-8356
karenh@rtdna.org, Manager of Membership
and Programs, Radio Television Digital News
Association, DC, Washington

Hansen, Kathleen
hanso041@umn.edu, Prof./Dir., Minnesota
Journalism Ctr., University of Minnesota, MN,
Minneapolis

Hansen, Kathy
khansen@wjinc.com, Circ. Mgr., Chicago
Parent, IL, Oak Park

Hansen, Keith ....(918) 456-8833 Ext. 12
khansen@tahlequahdailypress.com, Pub.,
Mineral Wells Index, TX, Mineral Wells
khansen@tahlequahdailypress.com, Pub., The
Weatherford Democrat, TX, Weatherford

Hansen, Keith
khansen@countystar.com, Pub., Isanti-
Chisago County Star, MN, Cambridge

Hansen, Keith ....(308) 254-2818
publisher@suntelegraph.com, Pub., Sidney Sun-
Telegraph, NE, Sidney

Hansen, Lauren
lhansen@carthage.edu, Carthage College,
WI, Kenosha

Hansen, Lynette...............(402) 426-2121 x114
lhansen@enterprisepub.com, Sales Manager,
Arlington Citizen, NE, Blair

Hansen, Lynette ....(402) 426-2121 Ext. 114
lhansen@enterprisepub.com, Adv. Mgr., Hi-
Line Enterprise, NE, Curtis
lhansen@enterprisepub.com, Sales Mgr., The
Clipper, NE, Blair

Hansen, Lynette ....(402) 426-2121 x114
lhansen@enterprisepub.com, Sales Manager,
Washington County Enterprise, NE, Blair

Hansen, Lynette...............(402) 426-2121 x114
lhansen@enterprisepub.com, Adv. Mgr., The
Pilot Tribune / Enterprise, NE, Blair

Hansen, Marcia A.........................(866) 664-4432
marcia@motivateROI.com, Prtnr. , Motivate,
Inc., CA, San Diego

Hansen, Megan
mhansen@whidbeynewsgroup.com, Ed.,
Whidbey News Times, WA, Coupeville

Hansen, Nathan
NHansen@farmingtonindependent.com, Pub.,
Farmington Rosemount Independent Town
Pages, MN, Hastings
NHansen@farmingtonindependent.com,
Ed., The Rosemount Town Pages, MN,
Farmington

Hansen, Nathan
nhansen@rosemounttownpages.com, Ed., The
Farmington Independent, MN, Farmington

Hansen, Teri ....(620) 241-2422
thansen@mcphersonsentinel.com, Editor,

McPherson Sentinel, KS, McPherson

Hansen, Travis
thansen@prestoncitizen.com, Gen. Mgr.,
Preston Citizen, ID, Preston

Hansen, Trevor ....(858) 272-9023
trevor@epmg360.com, CEO, Motivate, Inc.,
CA, San Diego

Hansen Abler, Andrea ....(920) 533-8338
editor@thecampbellsportnews.com, Ed.,
Campbellsport News, WI, Campbellsport

Hansen-Maffet, Ryan.................(530) 752-9877
University of California, Davis, CA, Davis

Hanshaw, Emily
ehanshaw4380@westfield.ma.edu, Managing
Editor, Westfield State University, MA,
Westfield

Hansmith, Amy........................(707) 900-2010
ahansmith@record-bee.com, Adv. Asst., Lake
County Record-Bee, CA, Lakeport

Hanson, Aaron .... (701) 572-2165 ext. 132
ahanson@willistonherald.com, Comp. Dir.,
Williston Daily Herald, ND, Williston

Hanson, Alex ....(603) 727-3219
ahanson@vnews.com, Feat., Ed., Valley News,
NH, West Lebanon

Hanson, Aprille ....(501) 664-0125
ahanson@dolr.org, associate editor, Arkansas
Catholic, AR, Little Rock

Hanson, Bill ....(812) 206-2134
bhanson@cnhi.com, Pub., News and Tribune,
IN, Jeffersonville
bhanson@cnhi.com, Pub., Tribune, IN, New
Albany
bhanson@cnhi.com, Pub., Glasgow Daily
Times, KY, Glasgow

Hanson, Bob ....(414) 297-7824
hansonjr@matc.edu, Faculty Adviser,
Milwaukee Area Tech. College, WI,
Milwaukee

Hanson, Carmela
carmela@focus-news.com, Ad. Director, Focus
Daily News, TX, Desoto

Hanson, Debra ....(203) 354-1012
dhanson@thehour.com, Adv. Dir., The Wilton
Villager, CT, Norwalk

Hanson, Doug
winnews@means.net, Pub., The Winthrop
News, MN, Winthrop

Hanson, Frank
fhanson@blackpress.ca, VP Finance, Black
Press Group Ltd., BC, Surrey

Hanson, Jody
news@theosakisreview.com, Pub., Osakis
Review, MN, Alexandria

Hanson, Jody ....(320) 763-1222
jhanson@echopress.com, Pub., Echo-Press,
MN, Alexandria

Hanson, Jody
echo@echopress.com, Adv. Mgr., Lakeland
Shopping Guide, MN, Alexandria

Hanson, Jolene ....(515) 238-2334
jhanson@dmreg.com, Account Executive,
Ankeny Register & Press Citizen, IA, Des
Moines

Hanson, Kevin
khanson@courierherald.com, Ed./Sr. Writer,
The Enumclaw Courier-Herald, WA,
Enumclaw

Hanson, Marlon ....(972) 223-9175
focusnews@wans.net, Pub., Focus Daily News,
TX, Desoto

Hanson, Merridee ....(360) 735-4527
merridee.hanson@columbian.com, News
Editor, The Columbian, WA, Vancouver

Hanson, Mike........................(215) 822-5519
Engineering, ICANON Associates, Inc., PA,
Hatfield

Hanson, Rachel
rhanson@fanzz.com, Univ. of Utah, UT, Salt
Lake City

Hanson, Rhonda
rhonda@valleybreeze.com, Circ. Mgr, The
Valley Breeze - Cumberland/Lincoln, RI,
Lincoln

Hanson, Shelley
shanson@timesleaderonline.com, Staff Writer/
Lifestyles, The Times Leader, OH, Martins
Ferry

Hanus, Jerome
dbqcwo@arch.pvt.k12.ia.us, Pub., The
Witness, IA, Dubuque

Hapney, Terry..........................(740) 351-4778
Shawnee State Univ., OH, Portsmouth

Happ, Michael
happ.michael@gmail.com, Ed., The Beacon-
Observer, NE, Elm Creek

Happner, Asia
asia@junctioneagle.com, Admin. Assistant,
The Junction Eagle, TX, Junction

Harakawa, Ann
aharakawa@twotwelve.com, Principal, Two
Twelve, NY, New York

Harbert, Tom..........................(530) 477-4257
tomh@theunion.com, Mgmt. Info Servs./Online
Mgr., The Union, CA, Grass Valley

Harbin, Jennifer
fchb.editor@yahoo.com, Ed., Floyd County
Hesperian-Beacon, TX, Floydada

Harbin, Norm
info@na.flintgrp.com, Vice Pres., Bus./
Technical Devel., Flint Group, MI, Plymouth

Harbison, Glenn
glenn@thenewsobserver.com, Pub., The
News-Observer, GA, Blue Ridge

Harbison, Steven K. ....(423) 359-3110
sharbison@xtn.net, Vice Pres., Special
Projects, APG Media of Tennessee/North
Carolina, TN, Greeneville

Harbison, Steven K. ....(423) 359-3110
steve.harbison@greenevillesun.com, Gen.
Mgr., The Greeneville Sun, TN, Greeneville

Harbor, Kingsley O...................(256) 782-5300
kharbor@jsu.edu, Chair/Prof., Jacksonville
State University, AL, Jacksonville

Harbour, Alison.................................ext. 141
Photographer, The Sentinel-Record, AR, Hot
Springs National Park

Harbrecht, Gene ....(714) 796-5037
gharbrecht@ocregister.com, National &
Foreign Rep., Senior Ed., The Orange
County Register, CA, Santa Ana

Harbron, Chris..........................(306) 781-5228
editorial@leaderpost.canwest.com, News
Coord., The Leader-Post, SK, Regina

Harbuck, Tina..........................(850) 654-8440
tharbuck@thedestinlog.com, Managing Ed. ,
The Destin Log, FL, Destin

Harcourt, Patricia
tofmerc@telus.net, Ed, Tofield Mercury, AB,
Tofield

Hardalo, Andrea ....(631) 790-4382
andrea@theknightnews.com, Editor-In-Chief,
Queens College/CUNY, NY, Flushing

Harden, Randy
r4rrpub@aol.com, Pub., Buy A Home, TN,
Chattanooga

Harden, Randy ....(423) 855-1831
Prodn. Mgr., Real Estate Guide, TN,
Chattanooga

Harden, Tammy ....(423) 855-1831
r4rrpub@aol.com, Adv. Mgr., Real Estate
Review, TN, Chattanooga

Harden, Tammy ....(423) 855-1831
Adv. Mgr., Buy A Home, TN, Chattanooga

Harder, Joe
oherald@bluevalley.net, Pub., Onaga Herald,
KS, Onaga

Hardick, Dan
dhardick@austinchronicle.com, Circ. Mgr.,
Austin Chronicle, TX, Austin

Hardie, Chris
chris.hardie@lee.net, Pub., Vernon County
Broadcaster, WI, Viroqua

Hardie, Chris ....(608) 786-1950
chardie@couleenews.com, Pub., Coulee News,
WI, La Crosse

Hardie, Chris
chardie@rivervalleynewspapers.com, Pub.,
Jackson County Chronicle, WI, Black River
Falls

Hardie, Chris
chris.hardie@lee.net, Winona Foxxy Shopper,
WI, La Crosse

Hardie, Chris
chardie@rivervalleynewspapers.com, Pub.,
The Tomah Journal, WI, Tomah

Hardie, Chris
chardie@rivervalleynewspapers.com, Pub.,
Houston County News, WI, La Crosse

Hardie, Chris ....(608) 791-8223
chardie@rivervalleynewspapers.com, Pub.,
The Westby Times, WI, Westby

Hardin, Amber
mail@colemannews.com, Ed./Adv. Dir.,
Chronicle & Democrat-Voice, TX, Coleman

Hardin, Betty
info@jacksontimesky.com, Ed., Jackson Times-
Voice, KY, Jackson

Hardin, John Thomas
editor@ssentinel.com, Ed., Southside Sentinel,
VA, Urbanna

Hardin, Rozella
rhardin@starhq.com, Ed., Elizabethton Star,
TN, Elizabethton

Hardin, Scott ....(812) 379-5653
shardin@therepublic.com, Digital Media Dir.,
The Republic, IN, Columbus

Hardina, Bruce .... (207) 282-1535 ext. 332
bhardina@journaltribune.com, Pub., Journal-
Tribune, ME, Biddeford

Hardina, Bruce ....(207) 386-5226
bhardina@coastaljournal.com, Ed./Pub. ,
Coastal Journal, ME, Bath

Harding, Cathie ....(580) 310-5250
East Central University, OK, Ada

Harding, Gail M.
mail@theenterprise.net, Pub., The Enterprise,
VA, Stuart

Harding, John ....(250) 905-0019
editor@pqbnews.com, Ed., Parksville Qualicum
Beach News, BC, Parksville

Harding, Sally ....(212) 431-2851
sally.harding@nyls.edu, New York Law School,
NY, New York

Harding, Stephen ....ext. 229
sharding@tek-tools.com, Dir., Mktg., Tek-Tools,
Inc., TX, Dallas

Harding, Tracy
lmtleader@gmail.com, Sales & Prod., The
Lamont Leader, AB, Lamont

Hardt, James ....(425) 387-1551
james.hardt@catalystpaper.com, Sales
Director, Catalyst Paper (USA), Inc., WA,
Seattle

Hardwick, John H.
jhardwick@mpival.com, Reg'l Dir.,
Management Planning, Inc., NY, New York

Hardwig, Greg
greg.hardwig@naplesnews.com, Sports Ed.,
Naples Daily News, FL, Naples

Hardy, Darlene ....(901) 529-5885

Hardy, Darlene
darlene.hardy@commercialappeal.com, Adv.
Sales Manager, The Commercial Appeal,
TN, Memphis

Hardy, Jeanette ....(315) 661-2318
jhardy@wdt.net, HR VP, The Daily News, NY,
Batavia
jhardy@wdt.net, HR VP, Carthage Republican
Tribune, NY, LOWVILLE

Hardy, Jeanette ....(315) 661-2318
jhardy@wdt.net, HR VP, Daily Courier-
Observer/Advance News, NY, Massena

Hardy, Katrice ....(864) 298-4165
khardy1@greenvillenews.com, Exec. Ed., The
Greenville News, SC, Greenville

Hardy, Kevin
khardy@tnonline.com, Rgl. Adv. Mgr., Times
News, PA, Lehighton

Hardy, Larry
lhardy@timesanddemocrat.com, Photographer,
The Times and Democrat, SC, Orangeburg

Hardy, Sandra ....(215) 949-4017
shardy@calkins.com, Director, Calkins Media,
PA, Levittown

Hardy, Sandra C...................................Sec.
Herald-Standard, PA, Uniontown

Hardy, Shawn..........................(717) 762-2151
shawnh@therecordherald.com, Ed., The
Record Herald, PA, Waynesboro

Hardy, Wayne
whardy@theblacksheartimes.com, Mng. Ed./
Gen. Mgr., The Blackshear Times, GA,
Blackshear

Hare, Andrew..........................(603) 738-8485
andy@shoppersguideinc.com, Marketing
and Sales, Shopper's Guide, MA, Great
Barrington

Harff, Jayne..........................(320) 398-5000
news@tricountynews.MN, Office Mgr, Tri-
County News, MN, Kimball

Hargenrader, Rhonda ....(704) 789-9107
rhargenrader@hickoryrecord.com, Bus Mgr,
Independent Tribune, NC, Concord

Hargenrader, Rhonda
rhargenrader@morganton.com, Bus. Mgr., The
News Herald, NC, Morganton

Hargett, Malea ....(501) 664-0125
mhargett@dolr.org, Ed., Arkansas Catholic,
AR, Little Rock

Hargis, Teresa........................(765) 348-0110
ngadvertising@comcast.net, Adv. Conslt. ,
News Times, IN, Hartford City

Hargrave, Hank
publisher@texasbb.com, Pub./Ed./Adv. Dir.,
The Normangee Star, TX, Normangee

Hargrave, Hank ....(254) 883-2554
publisher@marlindemocrat.com , Pub., The
Rosebud News, TX, Rosebud

Hargreaves, Meg ....(202) 650-6680
meghargreaves@cqrollcall.com, SVP,
legislative services and publisher,
Congressional Quarterly, Inc., DC,
Washington

Hargus, Marsha
mhargus@moberlymonitor.com, General Mgr./
Adv. Dir., The Moberly Monitor-Index, MO,
Moberly

Harjo, Jeff
harjo@naja.com, Interim. Dir., Native American
Journalists Association, OK, Norman

Harker, John
info@infocus.com, Pres./CEO, Infocus Corp.,
OR, Portland

Harkey, Manda
manda@stanlynewspress.com, Ad. Director,
The Stanly News & Press, NC, Albemarle

Harkey, Sanya
subsriptions@gonzalescannon.com, The
Gonzales Cannon, TX, Gonzales

Harkins, Joe .... (201) 985-2105
joe@travelthenet.com, Self-Syndicator, Joe
Harkins, Jersey City

Harknett, Rich .... (212) 210-2271
rharknett@nydailynews.com, Circ. Vice Pres.,
New York Daily News, NY, New York

Harley, Bill .... (888) 309-0639 x83
bharley@miracomcomputer.com, Vice
President, Miracom Computer Corp., NY,
Eastchester

Harley, Richard
esther.simard@hebdosquebecor.com, Mng.
Ed., Plein Jour De Charlevoix, QC, La
Malbaie

Harm, Christopher
charm@thegardenisland.com, Circ., The
Garden Island, Kauai, HI, Lihue

Harman, Donna
sybil_lair@afandpa.org, Pres./CEO, American
Forest & Paper Association, Inc., DC,
Washington

Harman, Greg
hgarman@sacurrent.com, Advertising Director,
San Antonio Current, TX, San Antonio

Harmon, Brad
bharmon@gatehousemedia.com, VP
Publishing - Community East, GateHouse
Media, Inc., NY, Pittsford

Harmon, Brad .... (585) 298-0030
Vice Pres., Sales & Marketing, GateHouse
Media, Inc., NY, Pittsford

Harmon, Bradley .... (614) 461-5586
bharmon@dispatch.com, Pub., ThisWeek West
Side News, OH, Lewis Center
bharmon@dispatch.com, Pub., ThisWeek
Delaware News, OH, Lewis Center
bharmon@dispatch.com, Pub., ThisWeek
Johnstown Independent, OH, Lewis Center
bharmon@dispatch.com, Pub., ThisWeek
Licking County News, OH, Lewis Center
bharmon@dispatch.com, Pub., ThisWeek
Marysville News, OH, Lewis Center
bharmon@dispatch.com, Pres./Pub. ,
ThisWeek Bexley News, OH, Lewis Center
bharmon@dispatch.com, Pub., ThisWeek The
Canal Winchester Times, OH, Lewis Center
bharmon@dispatch.com, Pub., ThisWeek
Clintonville Booster, OH, Lewis Center
bharmon@dispatch.com, Pub., ThisWeek
Dublin Villager, OH, Lewis Center
bharmon@dispatch.com, Pub., ThisWeek
Rocky Fork Enterprise, OH, Lewis Center
bharmon@dispatch.com, Pub., ThisWeek
German Village Gazette, OH, Lewis Center
bharmon@dispatch.com, Pub., ThisWeek Tri-
Village News, OH, Lewis Center
bharmon@dispatch.com, Pub., ThisWeek
Grove City Record, OH, Lewis Center
bharmon@dispatch.com, Pub., ThisWeek
Hilliard Northwest News, OH, Lewis Center
bharmon@dispatch.com, Pub., ThisWeek New
Albany News, OH, Lewis Center
bharmon@dispatch.com, Pub., ThisWeek
Northland News, OH, Lewis Center
bharmon@dispatch.com, Pub., ThisWeek
Northwest News, OH, Lewis Center
bharmon@dispatch.com, Pub., ThisWeek
Olentangy Valley News, OH, Lewis Center
bharmon@dispatch.com, Pub., ThisWeek
Pickerington Times-Sun, OH, Lewis Center
bharmon@dispatch.com, Pub., ThisWeek
Reynoldsburg News, OH, Lewis Center
bharmon@dispatch.com, Pub., ThisWeek
Upper Arlington News, OH, Lewis Center
bharmon@dispatch.com, Pub., ThisWeek
Westerville News & Public Opinion, OH,
Lewis Center
bharmon@dispatch.com, Pub., ThisWeek
Whitehall News, OH, Lewis Center
bharmon@dispatch.com, Pub., ThisWeek
Worthington News, OH, Lewis Center

Harmon, Joseph .... (970) 224-7718
Digital Sales Mgr., The Coloradoan, CO, Fort
Collins

Harmon, Karlie

kharmon@okcu.edu, Chair, Oklahoma City
University, OK, Oklahoma City

Harmon, Kathy
kathy.harmon@savannahnow.com, Nat'l
Acct. Rep., Savannah Morning News, GA,
Savannah

Harmon, Tracy .... (706) 769-5175 x 21
adsales@oconeeenterprise.com, Adv. Rep.,
Oconee Enterprise, GA, Watkinsville

Harmonson, Todd .... (714) 796-2428
tharmonson@ocregister.com, Sen. Ed., Santa
Ana Register (OOB), CA, Santa Ana
tharmonson@ocregister.com, Sr. Ed., Anaheim
Bulletin, CA, Santa Ana
tharmonson@ocregister.com, Sr. Ed., The
Orange County Register, CA, Santa Ana

Harms, Bridget .... (712) 662-7161
sacsun2@frontiernet.net, Office Mgr/Billing,
The Sac Sun, IA, Sac City

Harms, Janet
jharms@beatricedailysun.com, Adv. Mgr.,
Beatrice Daily Sun, NE, Beatrice

Harms, Joni
jharms@dglobe.com, Pub., The Bulletin, MN,
Worthington

Harms, Joni .... ext. 208
jharms@dglobe.com, Pub., Worthington Daily
Globe, MN, Worthington

Harms, Shari .... (843) 626-3131
Advertising Director, The Loris Scene, SC,
Conway

Harms, Shari .... (843) 626-3131
shari.harms@myhorrynews.com, Advertising
Directo, Myrtle Beach Herald, SC, Myrtle
Beach

Harms, Shari .... (843) 626-3131
shari.harms@myhorrynews.com, Advertising
Director, Carolina Forest Chronicle, SC,
Myrtle Beach

Harn, Jay .... (661) 857-4595
jayharn@gmail.com, Senior Associate-Western
States, Lewis Floyd- Grimes, W.B. & Co., AL,
Gulf Shores

Harnack, Roger .... (509) 826-1110
rharnack@omakchronicle.com, Publisher and
editor, Omak-Okanogan County Chronicle,
WA, Omak

Harne, Angela .... (252) 524-4376
timesleader@ncweeklies.com, Ed., The Times-
Leader, NC, Grifton

Harness, Brad .... (519) 293-1095
editor@banner.on.ca, Pub./Ed., The Middlesex
Banner, ON, Ailsa Craig

Harney, Mary
sentinel@ticz.com, Pub., Parke County
Sentinel, IN, Rockville

Harnice, Milinda
mharnice@paxtonmedia.com, Asst., Paxton
Media Group, LLC, KY, Paducah

Harnitchek, Steffanie
sharnitchek@star-telegram.com, Adv. Mgr.,
The Keller Citizen, TX, Fort Worth

Harold, Marion
hmarion@timesshamrock.com, Managing Dir.,
Scranton Times Co., PA, Scranton

Harold, Rich
ssystems@bellsouth.net, Pres., Shreve
Systems, LA, Shreveport

Harp, Willie
contact@cenlafocus.com, Pub. , Cenla Focus
Magazine, LA, Alexandria

Harper, Christopher
charper@temple.edu, Assoc. Prof., Temple
University, PA, Philadelphia

Harper, Ed .... ext. 109
eharper@stateportpilot.com, Ed./Pub., The
State Port Pilot, NC, Southport

Harper, Jo Anne Hartley .... (620) 325-3000
thederrick@cableone.net, Ed., Neodesha
Derrick, KS, Neodesha

Harper, Mary
maryharper@rogerspublishing.com,
Proofreader, The Winneconne News, WI,
Winneconne

Harper, Morgan
morgan@stateportpilot.com, The State Port
Pilot, NC, Southport

Harper, Pam .... (440) 998-2323 Ext. 117
pharper@starbeacon.com, CS Mgr., Star
Beacon, OH, Ashtabula

Harper, Rita
info@rotadyne.com, Mgr., Customer Serv., Day
International, GA, Covington

Harper, Robin .... (574) 722-5000 Ext. 5179
robin.harper@indianamediagroup.com, Reg.
Circ. Dir. , Kokomo Tribune, IN, Kokomo
robin.harper@indianamediagroup.com,
Regional Director Audience Developement,
Pharos-Tribune, IN, Logansport

Harper, Stephanie
sharper@skagitpublshing.com, Adv. Mgr.,
Majors/Natl. Accts., Skagit Valley Herald, WA,
Mount Vernon

Harper, Susan
sharper@indyweek.com, Pub., Indy Week,
NC, Durham

Harpine, William
williamh@usca.edu, Chair, University of South
Carolina, Aiken, SC, Aiken

Harpke, Mark
digitalinfo@fujifilm.com, Reg'l Sales Mgr.,
Fujifilm Graphic Systems USA, Inc., WI,
New Berlin

Harr, Brian
brian.harr@dailynews.com, Exec News Ed, Los
Angeles Daily News, CA, Woodland Hills

Harr, Gregg .... (561) 820-4647
gharr@pbpost.com, Adv. Dir., Opns., The Palm
Beach Post, FL, West Palm Beach

Harr, Jane
mgr@sspmt.com, Office Mgr., Silver State
Post, MT, Deer Lodge

Harrau, Sharon .... (617) 367-9100
SharonH@TheJewishAdvocate.com,
Administrator, The Jewish Advocate, MA,
Boston

Harreld, J. Bruce .... (914) 499-5433
harreld@us.ibm.com, Sr. Vice Pres., Strategy,
IBM Corp., NY, Armonk

Harrell, Al
sales@uspetrolon.com, Regl. Distributor, U.S.
Petrolon Industrial, NE, Omaha

Harrell, Meredith
editor@kernersvillenews.com, Assist. Pub/Ed,
Kernersville News, NC, Kernersville

Harrell, Scott
publisher@brunswickbeacon.com, Rgl. Pub.,
Bastrop Daily Enterprise, LA, Bastrop
publisher@brunswickbeacon.com, Pub., The
Brunswick Beacon, NC, Shallotte
publisher@brunswickbeacon.com, Reg. Pub.,
GateHouse Media, Inc., NY, Pittsford

Harres, Victoria
victoria.harres@prnewswire.com, VP, Strategic
Communications & Content, PR Newswire,
NY, New York

Harrier, Karen .... (320) 523-2032
oclassifieds@rencopub.com, Circ. Mgr.,
Renville County Register, MN, Renville

Harrigan, Karen .... (603) 237-5501
editor@colebrooknewsandsentinel.com, Editor
and Publisher, The News and Sentinel, NH,
Colebrook

Harriger, Ginny .... (717) 262-4710
gharriger@mediaonepa.com, Adv. Dir., Public
Opinion, PA, Chambersburg

Harrill, Rob
rob.harrill@edcc.edu, Edmonds Cmty. College,
WA, Lynnwood

Harriman, Dwight
dharriman@livent.net, News Ed., The
Livingston Enterprise, MT, Livingston

Harriman, Leota .... (505) 286-1212
leota@lobo.net, Editor & Publisher, The
Independent, NM, Edgewood

Harring, Valarie .... (239) 574-1110 x119
vharring@breezenewspapers.com, Exec. Ed.,
The Pine Island Eagle, FL, Bokeelia
vharring@breezenewspapers.com, Executive
Editor, Sanibel-Captiva Islander, FL, Cape
Coral
vharring@breezenewspapers.com, Ed., North
Fort Myers Neighbor, FL, Cape Coral
vharring@breezenewspapers.com, Executive
ed., Cape Coral Breeze, FL, Cape Coral

Harrington, Craig .... (530) 725-0925
craig@northstate.news, Pres./Pub., The
Intermountain News, CA, Burney

Harrington, Craig .... (530) 225-4929
charrington@shastacollege.edu, Shasta
College, CA, Redding

Harrington, Erica
erica.harrington@mountaintimes.info, Bus.
Mgr., The Mountain Times, VT, Killington

Harrington, Graham
gsh@gvnews.com, Production Mgr., Green
Valley News & Sahuarita Sn, AZ, Green
Valley

Harrington, Gregory .... (907) 335-1225
gregory.harrington@peninsulaclarion.com, Adv.
Rep, Peninsula Clarion, AK, Kenai

Harrington, John
jharrington@aps-web.com, Layout Ed., The
Boston Globe, MA, Boston

Harrington, Katie .... (530) 725-0925
katie@northstate.news, Mgr., The
Intermountain News, CA, Burney

Harrington, Kimberly .... (843) 672-3002
kharrington@pagelandprogressive.com, Editor,
Pageland Progressive-Journal, SC, Pageland

Harrington, Mike .... (810) 686-3840
publisher@myherald.net, Pub., Genesee
County Herald, Inc., MI, Clio

Harris, Amy
aharris@bizjournals.com, Adv. Dir., Nashville
Business Journal, TN, Nashville

Harris, Ardua .... (316) 268-6246
AHarris@wichitaeagle.com, Features Editor,
The Wichita Eagle, KS, Wichita

Harris, Bill
bharris@miningjournal.net, Ed., The Lakeshore
News, ON, Tecumseh

Harris, Chad
chad@cerc.net, Lectr., San Diego State
University, CA, San Diego

Harris, Charlene
charlene.harris@lubbockonline.com, Div.
Controller, Lubbock Avalanche-Journal, TX,
Lubbock

Harris, Cheri .... (850) 627-7649
editor@gadcotimes.com, Mng. Ed., Gadsden
County Times, FL, Quincy

Harris, Christy .... (405) 238-6464
charris@pvdemocrat.com, Class./Legal , Pauls
Valley Democrat, OK, Pauls Valley

Harris, Claudine .... (423) 623-6171
claudine.harris@newportplaintalk.com,
Business Manager, The Newport Plain Talk,
TN, Newport

Harris, Clifton
samerisam1@earthlink.net, Co-Pub., The San
Bernardino American News, CA, Victorville

Harris, Clint .... (807) 343-6219
charris@chroniclejournal.com, Pub./GM, The

Chronicle-Journal, ON, Thunder Bay

Harris, Dean
dharris@mattosnews.com, Ed., Tuesday Review, CA, Newman

Harris, Dean .... **(209) 243-8104**
dharris@mattosnews.com, Ed., MATTOS NEWSPAPERS, INC., CA, Newman

Harris, Dorothy .... **(904) 629-6020**
AgeVentureNewsService@demko.com, Arts & Education COR, AgeVenture News Service, Orange Park

Harris, Ed
eharris@southingtonobserver.com, Ed., The Observer, CT, Southington

Harris, Frank .... **(203) 392-5804**
harrisf1@southernct.edu, Southern Connecticut State Univ., CT, New Haven

Harris, Franklin .... **(256) 340-2394**
franklin@decaturdaily.com, Asst. Metro Ed., The Decatur Daily, AL, Decatur

Harris, Gail
gharris@carolinaparent.com, General Manager, Carolina Parent, NY, White Plains

Harris, Heather
hharris@yrmg.com, Circ Mgr, Blue Mountains Courier-herald, ON, Meaford
hharris@yrmg.com, Distr. Mgr., The Barrie Advance, ON, Barrie

Harris, Ike
info@daige.com, Pres., Daige Products, Inc., NY, Albertson

Harris, Jacqueline
jharris@backbaysun.com, Mng. Dir., The Back Bay Sun, MA, Revere

Harris, Jennifer
editor@warrenrecord.com, Ed./Gen. Mgr., Warren Record, NC, Warrenton

Harris, Joe .... **(805) 237-6060 x124**
jharris@pasoroblespress.com, Adv. Mgr., Paso Robles Press, CA, Paso Robles

Harris, John
harrisj@wwu.edu, Asst. Prof., Western Washington University, WA, Bellingham

Harris, Kandace L.
klharris@jcsu.edu, Interim Dept. Chair, Johnson C. Smith University, NC, Charlotte

Harris, Karen .... **(540) 368-5006**
kharris@printinnovators.com, Bus. Mgr., The Free Lance-Star, VA, Fredericksburg

Harris, Karen
advertising@olneyenterprise.com, Adv. Mgr., The Olney Enterprise, TX, Olney

Harris, Kathryn .... **(402) 371-1020 ext. 242**
kharris@norfolkdailynews.com, Online News Ed., Norfolk Daily News, NE, Norfolk

Harris, Kevin
kharris@inwapgames.com, Prodn. Mgr., American Classifieds, IN, Indianapolis

Harris, Mark .... **(301) 784-2539**
mharris@times-news.com, City Editor , The Cumberland Times-News, MD, Cumberland

Harris, Mary
samerisam1@earthlink.net, Pub., The San Bernardino American News, CA, Victorville

Harris, Michael
mharris@news-press.com, Planning Ed., Digital Print, The Commercial Appeal, TN, Memphis

Harris, Michelle...................... **(479) 968-5252**
michelle@couriernews.com, Adv. Dir., The Courier, AR, Russellville

Harris, Mike .... **(803) 644-2364**
mharris@aikenstandard.com, Man ed., Evening Post Industries' Aiken Communications, SC, Aiken

Harris, Nancy
nharris@hendersondailynews.com,

Accountant, Henderson Daily News, TX, Henderson

Harris, Pam............................**(616) 628-5122**
vbcadvertiser@yahoo.com, Pub., Michigan Printing/van Buren County Advertiser, MI, Gobles

Harris, Patricia G.
editor@chronohio.com, Ed./Mng. Ed., Gay People's Chronicle, OH, Cleveland

Harris, Patti
editor@chronohio.com, Pub., Gay People's Chronicle, OH, Cleveland

Harris, Paul
pharris@saxotech.com, Vice Pres., Cor. Mktg., SAXOTECH, Inc., FL, Tampa

Harris, Richard..............**(904) 486-3088 ext.640**
rharris@kodiakdailymirror.com, Publisher, Kodiak Daily Mirror, AK, Kodiak

Harris, Ron
rharris@edwpub.net, Mgmt. Info Servs. Mgr., Edwardsville Intelligencer, IL, Edwardsville

Harris, Susan..........................**(252) 335-8077**
sharris@dailyadvance.com, Customer Service/ Classified Mgr., The Daily Advance, NC, Elizabeth City

Harris, Tammy.........................**(304) 255-4487**
tharris@register-herald.com, Adv. Dir., The Register Herald, WV, Beckley

Harris, Tess
tess@leader-press.com, Print/Dig Media Consultant, Richmond News, MO, Richmond

Harris, Willie ....**(618) 239-2657**
wharris@bnd.com, Adv., Belleville News-Democrat, IL, Belleville

Harris , Bethany
bethany@sacramentopress.com, Editor, Sacramento Press, CA, Citrus Heights

Harris , Grant
publisher@interior-news.com, Pub/Sales Mgr, The Smithers Interior News, BC, Smithers

Harris Lipschultz, Jeremy
jlipschultz@mail.unomaha.edu, Dir./Prof., University of Nebraska at Omaha, NE, Omaha

Harris-Lockwood, Cassandra
uticaphoenix@gmail.com, Pub., Utica Phoenix, NY, Utica

Harrison, Anna
anna@readthehook.com, Circulation, The Hook, VA, Charlottesville

Harrison, Brenda
bharrison@florencenewsjournal.com, Ed., The Florence News Journal, SC, Florence

Harrison, Carla
carla@waldronnews.com, Prodn. Dir., The Citizen, AR, Waldron

Harrison, Caroline D ....**(718) 981-1234**
harrison@siadvance.com, Pub., Staten Island Advance, NY, Staten Island

Harrison, Chad ....**(434) 369-6688**
chadjourn@gmail.com, Pub., Altavista Journal, VA, Altavista
chadjourn@gmail.com, Pub., Brunswick Times-Gazette, VA, Lawrenceville
chadjourn@gmail.com, Pub., The Journal (OOB), VA, KING GEORGE
chadjourn@gmail.com, Pub., Star-Tribune, VA, Chatham
chadjourn@gmail.com, Pub., Times-Virginian, VA, Appomattox

Harrison, Christine
maxwell.dispatch@maxwell.af.mil, Ed., Maxwell-Gunter Dispatch, AL, Maxwell Afb

Harrison, Colleen
colleen.harrison@albertleatribune.com, Community Ed., Albert Lea Tribune, MN, Albert Lea

Harrison, David ....**(502) 582-4607**

dharrison@courier-journal.com, Photo Dir., The Courier-Journal, KY, Louisville

Harrison, J. Stephen
steveharrison@gvpennysaver.com, Ed., Genesee Valley Pennysaver, NY, Avon

Harrison, Jeff
sports@daily-jeff.com, Sports Ed., The Daily Jeffersonian, OH, Cambridge

Harrison, Jeff
editor@tuttletimes.com, Ed., The Tuttle Times, OK, Mustang

Harrison, Jennifer
advertising@winfieldcourier.com, Adv. Sales, Winfield Daily Courier, KS, Winfield

Harrison, Lisa ....(606) 528-7898 Ext. 41
lharrison@thetimestribune.com, Adv. Rep., Times-Tribune, KY, Corbin

Harrison, Lucinda
lucinda@barnstablepatriot.com, Adv. Rep., Barnstable Patriot, MA, Hyannis

Harrison, Marcie ....(204) 759-2644 ext. 6
smpnews@mymts.net, Editor, Nesbitt Publishing Ltd., MB, Shoal Lake

Harrison, Marcie ....(204) 759-2644 ext. 6
smpnews@mymts.net, Editor, South Mountain Press, MB, Shoal Lake
smpnews@mymts.net, News Reporter, Crossroads This Week, MB, Shoal Lake

Harrison, Michael
mharison@fortmilltimes.com, Ed., Fort Mill Times, SC, Rock Hill

Harrison, Randy.......................(505) 823-3907
rharrison@abqjournal.com, Journal Sports Ed., Albuquerque Journal, NM, Albuquerque

Harrison, Shawn
sharrison@hjnews.com, Sports Ed., The Herald Journal, UT, Logan

Harrison, Steve
steveharrison@gvpennysaver.com, Genesee Valley Penny Saver - Batavia, NY, Avon
steveharrison@gvpennysaver.com, President, Genesee Valley Penny Saver - Canandaigua, NY, Canandaigua
steveharrison@gvpennysaver.com, Genesee Valley Penny Saver - Eastway, NY, Avon
steveharrison@gvpennysaver.com, Genesee Valley Penny Saver - Fairport, NY, Avon
steveharrison@gvpennysaver.com, Genesee Valley Penny Saver - Livingston, NY, Avon
steveharrison@gvpennysaver.com, Genesee Valley Penny Saver - Oatka, NY, Avon
steveharrison@gvpennysaver.com, Genesee Valley Penny Saver - Pittsford / E Rochester, NY, Avon
steveharrison@gvpennysaver.com, Genesee Valley Penny Saver - Rush / Henrietta, NY, Avon
steveharrison@gvpennysaver.com, Genesee Valley Penny Saver - Tri-county Advertiser, NY, Avon
steveharrison@gvpennysaver.com, Genesee Valley Penny Saver - Dansville Wayland, NY, Avon
steveharrison@gvpennysaver.com, Pub./Pres., Genesee Valley Penny Saver - Webster - Ontario - Walworth, NY, Avon

Harrison, Susan ....(903) 887-4511
publisher@themonitor.net, Gen. Mgr., Lake Area Leader, TX, Mabank

Harrison, Susan ....(903) 887-4511
publisher@themonitor.net, Gen. Mgr., Media One, TX, Mabank

Harrison, Susan ....(903) 887-4511
publisher@themonitor.net, General Manager, Lake Area Leader, TX, Mabank

Harrison, Vicki ....(828) 232-5993
vharriso@gannett.com, Operations Mgr., The Asheville Citizen-Times, NC, Asheville

Harrow, Richard
rharrow@msn.com, Vice Pres., League of Advertising Agencies, Inc., NY, New York

Harry, Felicia
felicia.harry@nicholls.edu, Instr., Nicholls State University, LA, Thibodaux

Hart, Adrian.................(719) 384-4475 Ext. 1437
Circ. Mgr., Bent County Democrat, CO, Las Animas

Hart, Bill .... (585) 258-2520
bhart@democratandchronicle.com, VP Fin. , Democrat and Chronicle, NY, Rochester

Hart, Clare
clare.hart@wsj.com, Exec. Vice Pres., Enterprise Media Grp., Dow Jones & Company, NY, New York

Hart, Heather .... (914) 381-7474
heather.hart@parenthood.com, Sr. Ed., New York Family, KS, Overland Park

Hart, Heather .... (516) 227-0270
longislandparenting@unitedad.com, Ed., Connecticut Family, NY, Mamaroneck

Hart, Jim
jhart@criernewspapers.com, Nat'l/Retail Adv. Dir., Dunwoody Crier, GA, Dunwoody

Hart, Jim .... (701) 857-1959
jhart@minotdailynews.com, Adv. Dir., The Trading Post, ND, Minot

Hart, John
johnh@wdtimes.com, Photo Ed., Watertown Daily Times, WI, Watertown

Hart, Josh........................... (903) 237-7765
jhart@news-journal.com, Circ. Dir., Longview News-Journal, TX, Longview
jhart@news-journal.com, Circ. Dir., Marshall News Messenger, TX, Marshall

Hart, Michael .... (760) 765-2231
publisher@juliannews.com, Pub/ Produc Mgr., Julian News, CA, Julian

Hart, Patricia
psh@uidaho.edu, Asst. Prof., University of Idaho, ID, Moscow

Hart, Paul
circ@greenfieldreporter.com, Circ. Dir., Daily Reporter, IN, Greenfield

Hart, Paul .... (812) 523-7058
phart@hnenewspapers.com, Circ. Dir., The Tribune, IN, Seymour

Hart, Ross .... (847) 682-8296
rhart@smithpressroomproducts.com, VP, Smith Pressroom Products, Inc., KS, Overland Park

Hart, Shelley .... (801) 626-6359
shelleyhart@weber.edu, Advt Mgr, Weber State Univ., UT, Ogden

Hart, Tina
thart@bnd.com, Belleville News-Democrat, IL, Belleville

Hart, Wayne .... (208) 462-3487
publisher@idahoworld.com, Adv. Mgr., Idaho World, ID, Idaho City

Hart, Wendy
winnipegpressclub@outlook.com, VP, Winnipeg Press Club, MB, Winnipeg

Harta, Pearl...........................(215) 355-9009
pharta@phillynews.com, Circ. Mgr., Northeast Times, PA, Bensalem

Harta, Pearl
pharta@bsmphilly.com, Circ. Mgr, The Midweek Wire, PA, Bensalem
pharta@bsmphilly.com, Circ. Mgr, Star Community Newsweekly, PA, Bensalem

Harte, C.J. ....ext. 212
charte@middlesborodailynews.com, Correspondent, Cumberland Trading Post, KY, Middlesboro

Harte, Ellen Q.
tribunebeancounter@verizon.net, Bus. Mgr., West Essex Tribune, NJ, Livingston

Hartenstein, Eddy
eddy.hartenstein@latimes.com, CEO/Pub., Los Angeles Times, CA, Los Angeles

Harter, Lee
lharter@timesanddemocrat.com, Editorial Page Ed., The Times and Democrat, SC, Orangeburg

Harter, Lee .... (803) 533-5520
lharter@timesanddemocrat.com, Claflin University, SC, Orangeburg

Harter, Lorie .... (417) 667-3344
lharter@nevadadailymail.com, Pub./Adv. Mgr., Nevada Herald, MO, Nevada
lharter@nevadadailymail.com, Adv. Dir., The Nevada Daily Mail, MO, Nevada
lharter@nevadadailymail.com, Pub./Dir. of Adv., The Fort Scott Tribune, KS, Fort Scott

Harter, Shana .... (417) 723-5248
scrlegal@centurylink.net, Legals, Crane Chronicle/Stone County Republican, MO, Crane

Hartgrave, Greg .... (360) 735-4603
greg.hartgrave@columbian.com, Circ.Systems Admin., The Columbian, WA, Vancouver

Hartgrove, Rhett .... ext. 671
rhett.hartgrove@svherald.com, Prodn. Foreman, Press/Camera, Sierra Vista Herald - Sunday Bravo Shopper, AZ, Sierra Vista

Hartley, David .... (860) 236-9998 ext. 130
dhartley@HartfordBusiness.com, Senior Acct. Mgr., Hartford Business Journal, CT, Hartford

Hartley, Karol
billing@titusvilleherald.com, Office Mgr., The Titusville Herald, PA, Titusville

Hartley, Tom
thartley@pnj.com, Dir., Finance, Pensacola News Journal, FL, Pensacola

Hartman, Fred B. .... (281) 342-8691
Vice Chairman, Hartman Newspapers LP, TX, Rosenberg

Hartman, Greg
ghartman@catholiccincinnati.org, Circ. Mgr., The Catholic Telegraph, OH, Cincinnati

Hartman, Harry .... (717) 253-9403
hhartman@gburgtimes.com, Pub., Gettysburg Times, PA, Gettysburg

Hartman, Hermene D.
hhartman@ndigo.com, Pub., N'digo, IL, Chicago

Hartman, Holly
hhartman@berkshireeagle.com, Circ. Office. Mgr., The Berkshire Eagle, MA, Pittsfield

Hartman, Julie .... (801) 625-4329
Adv. Mgr., Major/Nat'l, Standard-Examiner, UT, Ogden

Hartman, Kathy
khartman@farragutpress.com, Advertising Sales, Farragut Press, TN, Farragut

Hartman, Laurie .... (952) 345-6878
hartmann@swpub.com, Pub., Shakopee Valley News, MN, Savage

Hartman, Lee
leehart@fbherald.com, Gen. Mgr., Fort Bend Herald, TX, Rosenberg

Hartman, Mark .... ext. 137
ads@franklinshopper.com, Art Dir., The Franklin Shopper, PA, Chambersburg

Hartman, Melissa
melissahartman@thewestfieldnewsgroup. com, Circ. Mgr., The Westfield News , MA, Westfield

Hartman, Michelle .... (740) 397-5333 Ext. 241
mhartman@mountvernonnews.com, Coor., Mount Vernon News, OH, Mount Vernon

Hartman, Olivia
ohartman@vagazette.com, Adv. Mgr., The Virginia Gazette, VA, Newport News

Hartman, Bruce .... (865) 342-6920
hartmann@scripps.com, Knoxville News Sentinel, TN, Knoxville

Hartmann, Laurie

lhartmann@swpub.com, Op. Dir., Savage Pacer, MN, Savage
lhartmann@swpub.com, Ops. Dir., Red Wing Publishing Co., MN, Red Wing

Hartmann, Laurie
hartmann@swpub.com, Op. Dir., Prior Lake American, MN, Savage

Hartmann, Laurie
lhartmann@swpub.com, Pub., Jordan Independent, MN, Jordan
lhartmann@swpub.com, Op. Dir., Lakeshore Weekly News, MN, Wayzata

Hartmann, R.L.B.
rlb@wombania.com, Ed., Wombania, ON, Hamilton

Hartmann, Yvonne .... (830) 997-2155
fbgnews@fredericksburgstandard.com, Mng Ed., Fredericksburg Standard-Radio Post, TX, Fredericksburg

Hartmayer, Gregory J. .... (912) 201-4100
Publisher, Southern Cross, GA, Savannah

Hartranft, Mike
mhartranft@rrobserver.com, Managing Ed., The Rio Rancho Observer, NM, Rio Rancho

Hartsock, Steve
stevesads@nwcable.net, Adv. Mgr., The Prairie Post, IL, Albion

Hartsough, Jane .... (609) 406-0600 x27
jhartsough@njpa.org, Accounting Coordinator, New Jersey Press Association, NJ, Ewing

Hartung, Raymond .... (412) 380-5612
rhartung@tribweb.com, Sr. Vice. Pres./ CFO, Tribune-Review Publishing Co., PA, Greensburg

Hartwell, Jay .... (808) 956-3217
hartwell@hawaii.edu, Ed. Advisor, University of Hawaii Manoa, HI, Honolulu

Harty, Ken .... (701) 642-8585
kenh@wahpetondailynews.com, Pub., Southern Valley Shopper, ND, Wahpeton

Harty, Ken
kenh@wahpetondailynews.com, Pub., News-Monitor, ND, Wahpeton

Harty, Tim .... ext. 204
Tim.Harty@gjsentinel.com, Sports Editor, The Daily Sentinel, CO, Grand Junction

Harvey, Alyssa .... (270) 783-3257
aharvey@bgdailynews.com, Features Ed., Daily News, KY, Bowling Green

Harvey, Carol .... (507) 444-1561
charvey@owatonna.com, Circ. Mgr., Owatonna Area Shopper, MN, Owatonna

Harvey, Carol .... (507) 444-1561
charvey@owatonna.com, Circ. Mgr., Owatonna People's Press, MN, Owatonna

Harvey, Christine Lynn .... (631) 751-8819
charvey@newliving.com, Pub./Ed. in Chief, New Living Syndicate, Patchogue

Harvey, Craig
charvey@observertoday.com, News editor, The Observer, NY, Dunkirk

Harvey, David
dharvey@metroland.com, Regional General Manager, The Milton Canadian Champion, ON, Milton

Harvey, Faye
f_harvey@hotmail.com, Broker, Harvey, Faye, MO, Lebanon

Harvey, James
fdvs_info@firstdatacorp.com, Vice Pres., Devel., First Data Voice Services, NE, Omaha

Harvey, Julie
jharvey@dmreg.com, VP, Finance, The Des Moines Register, IA, Des Moines

Harvey, Michele
editor@juliannews.com, Ed/Columnist, Julian News, CA, Julian

Harvey, Norman
norman.harvey@transcontinental.ca, Sales Rep., L'action, QC, Joliette

Harvey, Pam
pharvey@jacksonconews.com, Adv. Dir., Jackson County Herald-Tribune, TX, Edna

Harvey, Ryan .... (641) 456-2585 ext. 118
ryanharvey@iowaconnect.com, President/ CEO/Publisher, The Leader, IA, Garner

Harvey, Ryan
egeagle@goldfieldaccess.net, Pub., Wright County Shopper's Guide, IA, Eagle Grove

Harvey, Tom .... (801) 257-8767
tharvey@sltrib.com, Government - Courts reporter, The Salt Lake Tribune, UT, Salt Lake City

Harvieux, Gerry .... (519) 809-4347
gharvieux@tilburytimes.com, Ed., The Tilbury Times, ON, Tilbury

Harvill, Jerry
jharvill@timesanddemocrat.com, Mgmt. Info Servs. Mgr., The Times and Democrat, SC, Orangeburg

Harville, Brian .... (615) 444-6008
bharville@mainstreetmediatn.com, Ed, Mature Lifestyles of Tennessee, TN, Lebanon

Harvin, Audrey
aharvin@thebct.com, Managing Editor, Burlington County Times, NJ, Willingboro

Harwell, Donna .... (870) 845-2010
business@nashvillenews.org, Comptroller, Glenwood Herald, AR, Glenwood

Hasaan, Eddie
ehasaan@stlouisargus.com, Pub., St. Louis Argus, MO, Saint Louis

Hasamear, Angie
ahasamear@bnd.com, Belleville News-Democrat, IL, Belleville

Hasein, Margaret
tip@sasktel.net, Pub., The Independent, SK, Biggar

Hasek, Robert
advert@ysnews.com, Adv. Mgr., The Yellow Springs News, OH, Yellow Springs

Haselden, Barry
haseldenb@valassis.com, VP Media Services , Valassis, MI, Livonia

Haselden, Mark .... (843) 317-7271
mhaselden@florencenews.com, Asst. Sports Ed., Morning News, SC, Florence

Hasen, Lorie .... (605) 996-5514
lhasen@mitchellrepublic.com, Adv. Dir., The Daily Republic, SD, Mitchell

Hasenaver, Christine .... (806) 376-8663
amarillo@americanclassifieds.com, Prodn. Mgr., American Classifieds, TX, Amarillo

Haserick, Patricia
thereminderbeth@comcast.net, Pub., Cumberland Reminder, NJ, Millville

Hash, Arlie .... (502) 348-9003
ahash@kystandard.com , Circulation Manager , Kentucky Standard, KY, Bardstown

Hashem, Mahboub
mhashem@aus.edu, Chair/Prof., The American University of Sharjah, Sharjah

Hashimoto, Serena
shashimoto@hpu.edu, Asst. Prof., Hawaii Pacific University, HI, Honolulu

Haskell, Bonni
bonni@statesmanexaminer.com, Adv. Mgr., Statesman Examiner, WA, Colville

Haskell, Robert H.
info@martinsvillebulletin.com, Pres./Pub., Martinsville Bulletin, VA, Martinsville

Haskins, Linda
lhaskins@thephillipsbee.com, Circ. Mgr., The Bee, WI, Phillips

lhaskins@thephillipsbee.com, Circ. Mgr., Park Falls Herald, WI, Phillips

Haslag, Jane .... (573) 761-0270
jane@newstribune.com, Adv. Mgr., News Tribune, MO, Jefferson City

Haslam, Wendy
wendy@ominecaexpress.com, Prod., Caledonia Courier, BC, Fort St. James

Hasley, Jane
abingdonargus@gmail.com, Adv. Mgr, Argus-Sentinel, IL, Galesburg

Hasquin, Linda
moherald1880@yahoo.com, Ed., Mount Olive Herald, IL, Mount Olive

Hass, Gary .... (802) 479-2582
ghass@vt-world.com, Co-Pub./owner, The World, VT, Barre

Hass, Paul .... (205) 722-0120
paul.haas@tuscaloosanews.com, Opns. Dir., The Tuscaloosa News, AL, Tuscaloosa

Hasse, Ron .... (818) 713-3883
rhasse@scng.com, Pres. & Pub., Press-Telegram, CA, Long Beach

Hasse, Ron .... (818) 713-3883
ron.hasse@langnews.com, Pres. & Pub., Los Angeles Daily News, CA, Woodland Hills

Hasse, Ron .... (818) 713-3883
rhasse@scng.com, Pres. & Pub., Southern California News Group, CA, Woodland Hills

Hasse, Ron .... (818) 713-3883
rhasse@scng.com, Pres./Pub., Inland Valley Daily Bulletin, CA, Rancho Cucamonga

Hasse, Ron .... (818) 713-3883
ron.hasse@langnews.com, Pres./Pub., The Sun, CA, San Bernardino

Hasse, Ron .... (818) 713-3883
rhasse@scng.com , Pres. & Pub., Daily Breeze, CA, Torrance
rhasse@scng.com , Pres./Pub., Pasadena Star-News, CA, Torrance
rhasse@scng.com , Pres./Pub., The Facts (Redlands), CA, Redlands

Hasse, Ron
rhasse@ocregister.com, Pub. & CEO, The Orange County Register, CA, Santa Ana

Hasse, Ron .... (818) 713-3101
ron.hasse@langnews.com, Pres./Pub., Azusa Herald Highlander, CA, Monrovia
ron.hasse@langnews.com, Pres./Pub., La Puente Highlander, CA, Monrovia
ron.hasse@langnews.com, Pres./Pub., Rowland Heights Highlander, CA, Monrovia
ron.hasse@langnews.com, Pres./Pub., Glendora Press Highlander, CA, Monrovia
ron.hasse@langnews.com, Pres./Pub., The Highlander - Rowland Heights Edition, CA, Monrovia
ron.hasse@langnews.com, Pres./Pub., West Covina Highlander, CA, West Covina

Hassing, Geoff .... (253) 503-7573
geofftoons@comcast.net, Cartoonist, Travelin' Light, Muncie

Hassinger, Scott
scott@threeriversnews.com, Sports Ed., Three Rivers Commercial-News, MI, Three Rivers

Hassler, Violet .... (580) 548-8152
violeth@enidnews.com, Digital Director, Enid News & Eagle, OK, Enid

Hasslinger, Tom .... (808) 930-8600
thasslinger@westhawaiitoday.com, Ed., West Hawaii Today, HI, Kailua Kona

Hasten, Mike .... (225) 342-7333
mhasten@gannett.com, Bureau Chief, Gannett News Service - Baton Rouge, LA, Baton Rouge

Hastings, Catherine .... (570) 372-4298
hastings@susqu.edu, Susquehanna Univ., PA, Selinsgrove

Hastings, Cecily .... (916) 203-8528

publisher@insidepublications.com, Pub., Inside Publications, CA, Sacramento

publisher@insidepublications.com, Pub., Inside East Sacramento, CA, Sacramento

publisher@insidepublications.com, Pub., Inside Land Park, CA, Sacramento

publisher@insidepublications.com, Pub., Inside Pocket, CA, Sacramento

Hastings, Connie ....(301) 662-1177
chastings@newspost.com, Adv. Mgr., The Frederick News-Post, MD, Frederick

Hastings, Doug ....(781) 674-7724
lexington.sports@wickedlocal.com, Sports Ed., Belmont Citizen-Herald, MA, Lexington

Hastings, Doug
burlington.sports@wickedlocal.com, Sports Ed., Burlington Union, MA, Concord

Hastings, Doug
lexington.sports@wickedlocal.com, Sports Ed., Billerica Minuteman, MA, Concord

Hastings, Mark L. ....(620) 365-2111
registerdisplay@gmail.com, Adv. Mgr., The Iola Register, KS, Iola

Hastings, Michael
mhastings@wsjournal.com, Food Ed., Winston-Salem Journal, NC, Winston Salem

Hasty, Dozier ....(718) 422-7400
jdh@brooklyneagle.com, Pub., Brooklyn Heights Press & Cobble Hill News, NY, Brooklyn

Hasty, J.D. ....(718) 858-2300
publisher@BrooklynEagle.com, Pub., The Phoenix, NY, Brooklyn

Hasty, J.D.
publisher@brooklyneagle.net, Pub., Brooklyn Daily Eagle & Daily Bulletin, NY, Brooklyn

Hatch, Addy ....(509) 459-3805
addyh@spokesman.com, City Editor, The Spokesman-Review, WA, Spokane

Hatch, Danielle ....(309) 686-3262
dhatch@pjstar.com, Entertainment Ed., Journal Star, IL, Peoria

Hatch, Jim
marketing@v-studios.com, Dir., Mktg./Sales, V! Studios, VA, Vienna

Hatcher, Anthony
ahatcher@elon.edu, Assoc. Prof., Elon University, NC, Elon

Hatcher, Craig ....(256) 260-2515
craig.hatcher@decaturdaily.com, Ad. Dir., The Decatur Daily, AL, Decatur

Hatcher, Craig ....(409) 838-2838
Chief Revenue Officer, The Beaumont Enterprise, TX, Beaumont

Hatfield, Abby ....(618) 529-5454 ext. 5024
abby.hatfield@TheSouthern.com, Opns. Mgr., At Home With Flipside, IL, Carbondale

Hatfield, David ....(520) 295-4237
dhatfield@azbiz.com, Ed., The Daily Territorial, AZ, Tucson

Hatfield, Fred ....(902) 742-7111
info@thevanguard.ca, Ed, The Vanguard, NS, Yarmouth

Hatfield Jr., Charles D. ....(972) 544-2369
charles@elliscountypress.com, Pub./Ed., Red Oak Record, TX, Ferris

Hatfield Jr., Charles D. ....(972) 544-2369
charles@elliscountypress.com, Pub./Owner/Ed., The Ellis County Press, TX, Ferris

Hatfield-Barger, Teresa ....(606) 723-5161
teresa@hatfieldnewspapers.com, Adv. Mgr., Citizen Voice & Times, KY, Irvine

teresa@hatfieldnewspapers.com, Publisher, The Clay City Times, KY, Clay City

Hathaway, Cindy ....(574) 658-4111
chathaway@the-papers.com, Advertising Representative, The Paper - Kosciusko Edition, IN, Milford

Hathaway, Warren A.
editor@advocatenewsonline.com, Pub., The Advocate, MA, Fairhaven

Hathcock, Areia ....(618) 524-2141
ahathcock@metropolisplanet.com, Gen. Mgr., Metropolis Planet, IL, Metropolis

Hathcock, Chuck
news@grenadastar.com, Sports Ed., Grenada Star, MS, Grenada

Hathcock, Joyce ....(903) 569-2442
publishe@rwoodcountymonitor.com, Pub., Wood County Monitor, TX, Mineola

Hatmaker, Cristie
cristie@myspartanews.com, Gen. Mgr., The Expositor, TN, Sparta

Hatten, Justin
sports@olneydailymail.com, Sports Ed., The Advantage, IL, Olney

Hattock, Sandy ....(913) 682-1334
ftlvlamp@sbcglobal.net, Adv. Mgr., Fort Leavenworth Lamp, KS, Fort Leavenworth

Hattock, Sandy
shattock@leavenworthtimes.com, Gen. Mgr./Adv. Dir., The Leavenworth Times, KS, Leavenworth

Hatton, Terah ....(859) 355-1208
thatton@winchestersun.com, Pre-Press Mgr., The Winchester Sun, KY, Winchester

Hauck, Stefanie
shauck@thisweeknews.com, Sr. Web. Producer, The Bag, OH, Lewis Center

Hauer, Mark ....(262) 673-2900
ads@booster-ads.com, President, West Bend Booster, WI, Hartford

Haufe, Melodie ....(410) 770-4020
mhaufe@chespub.com, Rgl. Controller, The Star-Democrat, MD, Easton

Haufe, William ....(410) 310-9011
bhaufe@chespub.com, Sports Ed., The Star-Democrat, MD, Easton

Haug, Glenn ....(306) 691-1277
glenn.haug@mjtimes.sk.ca, Adv. Mgr., The Moose Jaw Times-Herald, SK, Moose Jaw

Haug, Heidi
housatonicart@ctcentral.com, Classified Mgr., Housatonic Publications, CT, New Milford

Haug, Kaydee ....(316) 942-5385
kaydee@theactiveage.com, Business, Media Manager, The Active Age, KS, Wichita

Hauge, Alan
advsales@midrivers.com, Adv. Mgr., Miles City Star, MT, Miles City

Hauge, Amber ....(208) 345-9929
amber@rischpisca.com, Dir., Newspaper Association of Idaho, ID, Boise

Haugen, Janet Brutschea
janet.haugen@unisys.com, Sr. Vice Pres./CFO, Unisys Corp., PA, Blue Bell

Haught, Jerry Staas ....(856) 317-7828
jhaught@gannettnj.com, Cont. Strategist, The Courier-Post, NJ, Cherry Hill

Haught, Steven ....(215) 886-5662 ext. 261
shaught@maned.com, Vice Pres., Worldwide Newspaper Sales, Managing Editor, Inc., PA, Jenkintown

Haughton, Louise
lhaughton@review-mirror.com, Circ. Mgr., Rideau Valley Mirror, ON, Westport

Hauk, Joyce
jhauk@coveleaderpress.com, Adv. Dir., Copperas Cove Leader-Press, TX, Copperas Cove

Hauk, Larry
lhauk@coveleaderpress.com, Pub., Copperas Cove Leader-Press, TX, Copperas Cove

Hauk, Larry
lhauk@aol.com, Pub., The Mart Messenger, TX, Mart

Haulman, Denny
dennyh@montrosepress.com, Prodn. Mgr., Mailroom, The Montrose Daily Press, CO, Montrose

Haun, Brian ....(253) 620-4747
Brianh@webpressllc.com, President, WebPress, LLC, WA, Tacoma

Haun, Sarah ....(212) 254-6670
shaun@twotwelve.com, CMO, Two Twelve, NY, New York

Haupert, Craig ....(269) 687-7720
craig.haupert@leaderpub.com, Community Editor, Niles Daily Star, MI, Niles

Haupt, Wyatt
whaupt@newportnewstimes.com, Ed., News-Times, OR, Newport

Hauptman, Robert
rhauptman@gannett.com, Account Executive, Gannett News Service - Albany, NY, Albany

Haus, Keith
khaus@gfherald.com, Prodn. Mgr., Pressroom, Grand Forks Herald, ND, Grand Forks

Hausch, Mary
hausch@unlv.nevada.edu, Asst. Prof., University of Nevada, Las Vegas, NV, Las Vegas

Hauser, Linda ....(262) 673-2900
LH@booster-ads.com, Pub., West Bend Booster, WI, Hartford

LH@booster-ads.com, Publisher, Hartford Booster, WI, Hartford

Hausfeld, Kevin
advertising@lanthorn.com, Grand Valley State Univ., MI, Allendale

Hausman, Carl
hausman@rowan.edu, Assoc. Prof., Rowan Univ., NJ, Glassboro

Haut, Lou ....(410) 749-7171 ext 399
lhaut@dmg.gannett.com, The Daily Times, MD, Salisbury

lhaut@dmg.gannett.com, Circ. Mgr., Delaware Coast Press, DE, Bethany Beach

Hautecoeur, Emma ....(780) 465-6581
direction@lefranco.ab.ca, Ed., Le Franco, AB, Edmonton

Havard, Josh
jhavard@lufkindailynews.com, Sports Ed., The Lufkin Daily News, TX, Lufkin

Haver, Sharon
information@focusonstyle.com, Syndicated Columnist, Newspaper/Online, Focus On Style, New York

Haverstick, Amanda ....(219) 326-3894
ahaverstick@heraldargus.com, Lead News Ed., Herald-Argus, IN, La Porte

Havranek, Sharon
publisher@piedmontparent.com, Pub., Piedmont Parent, NC, King

Havranek, Sharon
shavranek@charlotteparent.com, Publisher, Charlotte Parent, NC, Charlotte

Hawes, Steve ....(425) 339-3051
shawes@redmonspokesman.com, Pub., The Redmond Spokesman, OR, Redmond

Hawes, William
william.hawes@elpaso.com, Prof., University of Houston, TX, Houston

Hawk, David
dhawk@thenewsdispatch.com, Mng. Ed., Herald News Review, IL, Decatur

Hawk, Jason
news@theoberlinnews.com, Ed., Wellington Enterprise, OH, Oberlin

news@theoberlinnews.com, Ed., Amherst News-Times, OH, Oberlin

Hawk, Jim
jhawk@lincolnindustrial.com, Vice Pres., Sales/Mktg., Lincoln Industrial, MO, Saint Louis

Hawk, Linda
linda.hawk@globegazette.com, Sales Rep., The Mason City Shopper, IA, Mason City

Hawken, Kevin
sales@theflashes.com, Pub., Flashes Shopping Guide, FL, Stuart

Hawkenson, Kim ....(320) 354-2945
lakesareareview@tds.net, Pub., Lakes Area Review, MN, New London

Hawker, Ross
ross@greenerecorder.com, Pub., Greene Recorder, IA, Greene

Hawkins, Carol Lee ....(703) 264-7211
clhawkins@nes.org, Asst. Dir., Membership, Graphic Communications Council, VA, Reston

Hawkins, Dave ....(905) 688-2444 ext. 233
dhawkins@niagarathisweek.com, Adv., Fort Erie Post, ON, Thorold

Hawkins, Dave ....(905) 688-2444 ext. 233
dhawkins@niagarathisweek.com, Newspaper/Online Adv. , Niagara This Week, ON, Thorold

Hawkins, James E.
james.hawkins@famu.edu, Dean, Florida A&M University, FL, Tallahassee

Hawkins, John
WLIndex@Lcom.net, Circ., West Liberty Index, IA, West Liberty

Hawkins, Lesa
ngcomp@comcast.net, Prod. Mgr., The News-Gazette, IN, Winchester

Hawkins, Michael ....(830) 995-3634
dukecomfort@hctc.net, Co-Pub./Ed., The Comfort News, TX, Comfort

Hawkins, Nick ....(519) 667-4660
nhawkins@lfpress.com, Sales Rep., Pennysaver, ON, London

Hawkins, Scott
schawkins@sunherald.com, Features Ed., The Sun Herald, MS, Gulfport

Hawkins, Taylor
taylor@yazooherald.net, Sports Ed., The Yazoo Herald, MS, Yazoo City

Hawkins, Terry
thawkins@centurytel.net, Treasurer, Arkansas Press Women Association, Inc., AR, Little Rock

Hawkins, Terry G. ....(870) 382-4915
thawkins@dumas-clarion.com, Pub., Delta Advertiser, AR, Dumas

thawkins@dumas-clarion.com, Pub., Dumas Clarion, AR, Dumas

Hawkins, Tom ....(937) 328-0343
thawkins@coxohio.com, Graphics Ed./Art Dir., Springfield News-Sun, OH, Springfield

Hawkinson, Karen
printing@midrivers.com, Mgr., Commercial Printing, Miles City Star, MT, Miles City

Hawley, Chuck .... ext. 16
reaperpub@richfieldreaper.com, Pub., The Richfield Shopper, UT, Richfield

Hawley, Jason
jason.hawley@sunmedia.ca, Circ Mgr, The Community Press, ON, Belleville

jason.hawley@sunmedia.ca, Dist. Mgr., Intelligencer, ON, Belleville

Hawley, Sarah ....(740) 992-2155 Ext. 2555
shawley@civitasmedia.com, Mng. Ed., The Daily Sentinel, OH, Pomeroy

Hawley-Jerome, Jessica
jessica@banderabulletin.com, Pub./Ed., Bandera Bulletin, TX, Bandera

Hawn, Sherrie ....(859) 624-6683
shawn@richmondregister.com, Rgl. Sales Mgr., The Richmond Register, KY, Richmond

Haws, Lynn .... ext. 32
Prodn. Mgr., Chino Champion, CA, Chino
Prodn. Mgr., Chino Hills Champion, CA, Chino

Hay, Alan .... **(202) 281-2424**
alan@cathstan.org, Dir., Sales/Mktg., Catholic
Standard, DC, Washington

Hay, Gerald .... **(913) 715-0736**
gerald.hay@jocogov.org, Editor, The Best
Times, KS, Olathe

Hay, Shannon
shay@pubgroup.com, Adv. Dir., American
Profile - New York, NY, New York

Hay, Shannon
shay@pubgroup.com, Adv. Dir., Relish - New
York, NY, New York

Haydel, Sheila
shaydel@oanow.com, Adv. Dir, Opelika-Auburn
News, AL, Opelika

Hayden, Jani .... **(248) 408-9501**
cawhite1@hometownlife.com, Dir. Adv.,
Farmington Observer, MI, Detroit
cawhite1@hometownlife.com, Dir. Adv. ,
Garden City Observer, MI, Detroit
cawhite1@hometownlife.com, Dir. Adv. ,
Observer & Eccentric Media, MI, Detroit
cawhite1@hometownlife.com, Dir. Adv. ,
Northville Record, MI, Detroit
cawhite1@hometownlife.com, Dir. Adv., Milford
Times, MI, Detroit
cawhite1@hometownlife.com, Adv. Dir. , South
Lyon Herald, MI, Detroit
cawhite1@hometownlife.com, Dir. Adv. , Novi
News, MI, Detroit
cawhite1@hometownlife.com, Dir. Adv. ,
Redford Observer, MI, Detroit
cawhite1@hometownlife.com, Adv. Dir. , South
Oakland Eccentric, MI, Detroit

Hayden, Jeff
pennysavererie@gmail.com, Pub./Gen. Mgr.,
Erie Penny Saver, PA, Erie

Hayden, Joe .... **(830) 625-9144 ext. 228**
jhayden@herald-zeitung.com, Circ. Dir., New
Braunfels Herald-Zeitung, TX, New Braunfels

Hayden, Kathy .... **(715) 833-7420**
kathy.hayden@ecpc.com, Sales Dir., Leader-
Telegram, WI, Eau Claire

Hayden, Tim .... **(812) 464-7640**
haydent@courierpress.com, VP of Sales,
Evansville Courier & Press, IN, Evansville

Hayden, Vicky
vhayden@airadv.net, Adv. Mgr., Frankenmuth
News, MI, Frankenmuth

Haydon, Kim
business@tjrcn.com, Bus. Mgr., The Times
Journal, KY, Russell Springs

Hayduk, Cathy .... ext. 13
graphics@tradersguide.com, Prodn. Mgr.,
Pennysaver, PA, Ebensburg

Hayes, Alex .... **(717) 253-9413**
ahayes@gburgtimes.com, Mng. Ed.,
Gettysburg Times, PA, Gettysburg

Hayes, Ben .... **(727) 893-6716**
bhayes@tampabay.com, Op. Dir., Tampa Bay
Times, FL, St Petersburg

Hayes, Billie Jo .... **(605) 583-4419**
Circ., Scotland Journal, SD, Scotland

Hayes, Bob
bhayes@artbeats.com, Dir., Tech.,
ArtbeatsEXPRESS, OR, Myrtle Creek

Hayes, Daniel K. .... **(563) 383-2100**
dan.hayes@lee.net, VP, Commun., Lee
Enterprises, Inc., IA, Davenport

Hayes, Debbi .... **(812) 883-3281**
am@salemleader.com, Sales and Marketing
Mgr., The Salem Democrat, IN, Salem

Hayes, Debbie .... **(812) 883-3281**
am@salemleader.com, Adv. Mgr., The Salem
Leader, IN, Salem

Hayes, Donna

voice9696@comcast.net, Pub./Ed., Voice of the
Valley, WA, Maple Valley

Hayes, Gwen
ghayes@flsentinel.com, Ed., Florida Sentinel-
bulletin, FL, Tampa

Hayes, Holly .... **(936) 348-3505**
ads@madisonvillemeteor.com, Adv. Exec.,
Madisonville Meteor, TX, Madisonville

Hayes, James
jhayes@bangordailynews.com, Sr. Adv. Circ.,
Bangor Daily News, ME, Bangor

Hayes, Jennifer
jennifer.hayes@doverpost.com, News Ed.,
Dover Post, DE, Dover
jennifer.hayes@doverpost.com, Ed., The
Sussex Countian, DE, Dover
jennifer.hayes@doverpost.com, News Ed.,
Milford Beacon, DE, Dover

Hayes, Jeremy
jhayes@navinet.net, Suffolk Univ., MA, Boston

Hayes, Jock
jock@eastbaynewspapers.com, Prodn. Mgr.,
Westport Shorelines, RI, Bristol

Hayes, Jock .... **(401) 253-6000 ext. 133**
jock@eastbaynewspapers.com, Prodn. Mgr.,
East Bay Newspapers, RI, Bristol

Hayes, Jock
jock@eastbaynewspapers.com, Prodn. Mgr.,
Warren Times-Gazette, RI, Bristol

Hayes, Kristi
circmgr@ssecho.com, Circ. Mgr., Sulphur
Springs News-Telegram, TX, Sulphur Springs

Hayes, Kristie .... **(580) 765-3311**
news@poncacitynews.com, Mng. Ed, The
Ponca City News, OK, Ponca City

Hayes, Lise .... **(765) 285-8256**
lhayes2@bsu.edu, Advertising Manager, Ball
State University, IN, Muncie

Hayes, Mary .... **(310) 372-4689**
mary@intellivisiongames.com, Office Manager,
Making It Productions, Hermosa Beach

Hayes, Matthew D.
matthayes@eastbaynewspapers.com, Pub.,
Sakonnet Times, RI, Bristol

Hayes, Matthew D.
matthayes@eastbaynewspapers.com, Pub.,
Barrington Times, RI, Bristol

Hayes, Matthew D. .... **(401) 253-6000**
mhayes@eastbaynewspapers.com, Pub.,
Warren Times-Gazette, RI, Bristol

Hayes, Matthew D. .... **(401) 253-6000 ext. 140**
mhayes@eastbaynewspapers.com, Pub./ Adv.
Mgr., East Bay Newspapers, RI, Bristol

Hayes, Matthew D.
matthayes@eastbaynewspapers.com, Pub.,
Bristol Phoenix, RI, Bristol

Hayes, Matthew D.
matthayes@eastbaynewspapers.com, Pub.,
Westport Shorelines, RI, Bristol

Hayes, Matthew D. .... **(401) 253-6000**
mhayes@eastbaynewspapers.com, Pub., The
Post, RI, Bristol

Hayes, Reggie
rhayes@news-sentinel.com, The News-
Sentinel, IN, Fort Wayne

Hayes, Rockford
theobserver@rrobserver.com, Pub., The Rio
Rancho Observer, NM, Rio Rancho

Hayes, Sharon
sharonhayes@kingsporthousing.org, Real
Estate Ed., Kingsport Times-News, TN,
Kingsport

Hayes, Taylor Wood .... **(270) 886-4444**
twhayes@kentuckynewera.com, Pub.,
Kentucky New Era, KY, Hopkinsville

Hayes, Taylor Wood
twhayes@hopkinsville.net, Pub., Fort Campbell

Courier, KY, Hopkinsville

Hayes, Ted
thayes@eastbaynewspapers.com, Ed., Warren
Times-Gazette, RI, Bristol

Hayley, Randy
randy.hayley@sunmedia.ca, Dist. Dir., The
Ottawa Sun, ON, Ottawa

Hayman, Amber
ahayman@nrtoday.com, Nat'l/Major Accts.
Mgr., The News-Review, OR, Roseburg

Haymes, Baker
jaramos@laestrelladigital.com, Adv. Mgr., La
Estrella, TX, Fort Worth

Haynes, Cynthia
c.haynes@nwkansas.com, Co-Owner, The
Norton Telegram, KS, Norton

Haynes, Dana
dhaynes@pamplinmedia.com, Ed., The Times
(Tigard/Tualatin Times), OR, Portland
dhaynes@pamplinmedia.com, Ed., The
Beaverton Valley Times, OR, Portland

Haynes, Dave .... x 202
News Editor, The Daily Sentinel, CO, Grand
Junction

Haynes, Dayna .... **(409) 267-6131**
theprogress@theanahuacprogress.com, Mng.
Ed./Gen. Mgr., The Anahuac Progress, TX,
Anahuac

Haynes, Jennifer
jhaynes@tidewaterreview.com, Adv. Mgr., The
Tidewater Review, VA, West Point

Haynes, Jill
jill@sullivanstclair.com, Lectr., University of
South Alabama, AL, Mobile

Haynes, Lori .... **(805) 781-7818**
lhaynes@thetribunenews.com, Advert. Opt.
Mgr., The Tribune, CA, San Luis Obispo

Haynes, Reagan
REAGHAY@GMAIL.COM, Soundings, VA,
Norfolk

Haynes, Stephen .... **(845) 437-4826**
shaynes@poughkeepsiejournal.com, Sports
Reporter, Poughkeepsie Journal, NY,
Poughkeepsie

Haynes, Stephen C. .... **(785) 475-2206**
s.haynes@nwkansas.com, Pres., Haynes
Publishing Co., KS, Oberlin

Haynes, Steve
steve.haynes@nwkansas.com, Ed., Oberlin
Herald, The, KS, Oberlin

Haynes, Steven .... **(785) 877-3361**
oberlinherald@nwkansas.com, Co-Owner, The
Norton Telegram, KS, Norton

Hays, David
dhays@timesuniononline.com, IT Dir./Circ.
Mgr., Times-Union, IN, Warsaw

Hays, Debbie
dhays@timesonline.com, Credit Mgr., Beaver
County Times, PA, Beaver

Hays, Jean .... **(316) 268-6557**
JHays@wichitaeagle.com, Investigations Ed.,
The Wichita Eagle, KS, Wichita

Hays, Norm
nhays@memphis.edu, Instr., University of
Memphis, TN, Memphis

Hays, Rob .... **(610) 861-4159**
rhays@northampton.edu, Advisor,
Northampton Cmty. College, PA, Bethlehem

Hayt, Teri
thayt@asne.org, Exec. Dir., American Society
of News Editors, MO, Columbia

Hayter, Bill
bill.hayter@starbanner.com, Circ. Mgr., Ocala
Star-Banner, FL, Ocala

Hayter, Dale .... **(519) 294-6262**
gazette@execulink.com, Circ. Mgr., The
Parkhill Gazette, ON, Parkhill

Hayter, Dale
guideadvocate@execulink.com, Pub., Hayter
Walden Publications Inc., ON, Forrest

Hayter, Dale
standard@xcelco.on.ca, Pub., Forest Standard,
ON, Forest

Hayter, Dale
guideadvocate@execulink.com, Pub., Watford
Guide-advocate, ON, Watford

Hayward, Jill .... **(250) 672-5611**
news@starjournal.net, Ed., Barriere Star
Journal, BC, Barriere

Haywood, Josh ....**(760) 934-3929 x 0**
sales@mammothtimes.com, Classifieds/Circ,
Mammoth Times, CA, Mammoth Lakes

Hazard, Glenda .... **(508) 490-7454**
ghazard@wickedlocal.com, Ed., The Villager,
MA, Framingham

Hazard, Glenda .... **(508) 490-7454**
ghazard@wickedlocal.com, Ed., Shrewsbury
Chronicle, MA, Framingham

Hazarian, Tommy
auburnjournal@goldcountrymedia.com, Auburn
Journal, CA, Auburn

Hazarian, Tony
tonyh@goldcountrymedia.com, Pub., Placer
Community Newspapers, Inc., CA, Roseville

Hazarian, Tony
tonyh@goldcountrymedia.com, Auburn
Journal, CA, Auburn

Hazel, Donna .... **(269) 969-1091**
dhazel@j-adgraphics.com, Adv. Mgr., Battle
Creek Shopper News, MI, Battle Creek

Hazelwood, Mary .... **(530) 852-0251**
maryh@goldcountrymedia.com, Auburn
Journal, CA, Auburn

Heacock, Lesa .... **(419) 674-4066 EXT 226**
lheacock@kentontimes.com, Adv. Sales Mgr.,
The Kenton Times, OH, Kenton

Head, Caleb .... **(918) 358-2553**
advertising@theclevelandamerican.com, Adv.
Dir, The Cleveland American, OK, Cleveland

Head, Pat .... **(270) 691-7265**
phead@messenger-inquirer.com , Press Mgr.,
Messenger-Inquirer, KY, Owensboro

Headlee, Cathy
cathy.headlee@kearneyhub.com, Circ. Mgr.,
Shopping Link, NE, Kearney
cathy.headlee@kearneyhub.com, Kearney
Hub, NE, Kearney

Headlee, Terry .... **(301) 662-1177**
theadlee@newspost.com, Managing Ed. , The
Herald-Mail, MD, Hagerstown
theadlee@newspost.com, Mng. Ed., The
Frederick News-Post, MD, Frederick

Headley, Jeff
newsboy@ogallalakcnews.com, Pub., Keith
County News, NE, Ogallala

Headley, R.B.
colby.sports@nwkansas.com, Sports Ed.,
Colby Free Press, KS, Colby

Headley, Rich
sports@fmtimes.com, Sports Ed., Fort Morgan
Times, CO, Fort Morgan

Headrick, Doug
dheadrick@xtn.net, Editorial Writer, The Daily
Post-Athenian, TN, Athens

Heady, Toni .... **(304) 342-1011**
theady@wvpress.org, Adv. Dir., West Virginia
Press Association, Inc., WV, Charleston

Heady , Toni
theady@kystandard.com , Bus Office Mgr,
Kentucky Standard, KY, Bardstown

Healey, Gerard .... **(303) 566-4076**
jhealey@ourcoloradonews.com, Pub.,
Colorado Community Media, CO, Highlands
Ranch

Healey, Jerry ....**(303) 566-4076**
jhealey@coloradocommunitymedia.com, Pres. / Pub., Arvada Press, CO, Golden

jhealey@coloradocommunitymedia.com, Pres./ Pub., Northglenn-Thornton Sentinel, CO, Westminster

jhealey@coloradocommunitymedia.com, Pres./ Pub., Lakewood Sentinel, CO, Golden

jhealey@coloradocommunitymedia.com, Pub., Centennial Citizen, CO, Highlands Ranch

jhealey@coloradocommunitymedia.com, Pub., Golden Transcript, CO, Golden

jhealey@coloradocommunitymedia.com, Pres./ Pub., Wheat Ridge Transcript, CO, Golden

jhealey@coloradocommunitymedia.com, Pub., Elbert County News, CO, Highlands Ranch

jhealey@coloradocommunitymedia.com, Pub., Parker Chronicle, CO, Highlands Ranch

jhealey@coloradocommunitymedia.com, The Littleton Independent, CO, Highlands Ranch

jhealey@coloradocommunitymedia.com, Pub., Douglas County News Press, CO, Highlands Ranch

jhealey@coloradocommunitymedia.com, Pub., Highlands Ranch Herald, CO, Highlands Ranch

Healey, Jerry ....**(303) 566-4076**
jhealey@coloradocommunitymedia.com, Pres/ Pub., Castle Rock News Press, CO, HIGHLANDS RANCH

Healey, Mark ....**(718) 634-4000**
editor@rockawave.com, Managing Editor., The Wave, NY, Rockaway Beach

Healey, Mike
mike.healey@sunmedia.ca, Ntn'l Sales , The Kingston Whig-Standard, ON, Kingston

Healing, Dan ....**(403) 543-7237**
dan.healing@thecanadianpress.com, Business reporter, Canadian Press, The - Calgary, AB, AB, Calgary

Healy, James ....**(912) 489-9402**
jhealy@statesboroherald.com, Pub., Statesboro Herald, GA, Statesboro

Healy, Jean ....**(605) 331-2369**
jhealy@argusleader.com, Principal HR Business Partner, Argus Leader, SD, Sioux Falls

Healy, Jim ....**(912) 489-9402**
jhealy@statesboroherald.com, Operations Manager, Statesboro Herald, GA, Statesboro

Healy , Sheila
go_cubs_win@yahoo.com, Wenona Index, IL, Henry

Heard, Carol ....**(229) 246-2827 ext. 114**
carol.heard@thepostsearchlight.com, Mng. Ed., Post-searchlight Extra, GA, Bainbridge

Hearen, Shaun
shaun.hearen@vermiliontoday.com, News Ed., Abbeville Meridional, LA, Abbeville

Hearing, Carl ....**(608) 328-4202 ext. 15**
chearing@themonroetimes.com, Pub., Stateline Buyers'guide, WI, Monroe

Hearing, Carl ....**(608) 328-4202**
chearing@themonroetimes.com, Pub./Gen. Mgr., Monroe Shopping News, WI, Monroe

Hearing, Carl C. ....**(608) 328-4202 ext. 15**
chearing@themonroetimes.com, Vice Pres./ Gen. Mgr., The Monroe Times, WI, Monroe

Hearne, Stephanie
shearne@texaspress.com, Controller, Texas Press Association, TX, Austin

Hearst, George R. ....**(518) 454-5555**
ghearst@timesunion.com, Pub./CEO, Times Union, NY, Albany

Heastings, David ....**ext. 266**
dheastings@butlereagle.com, News Ed., Butler Eagle, PA, Butler

Heaston, John
johnh@thereader.com, Publisher, The Reader, NE, Omaha

Heaston, Sally

sheaston@bryantimes.com, Gen. Mgr., The Bryan Times, OH, Bryan

Heaston, Sally
sally@northwestsignal.net, VP, Adv./Mktg. Dir./ Gen. Mgr., Northwest Signal, OH, Napoleon

Heater, Jay ....**(812) 379-5632**
jheater@therepublic.com, Sports Ed., The Republic, IN, Columbus

Heath, Cheryl
clinton.news@bowesnet.com, Ed., Clinton News-record, ON, Clinton

Heath, Jay
voicet@bellsouth.net, Ed., The Lauderdale Voice, TN, Ripley

Heath, Mary ....**(906) 228-2500 ext #247**
mheath@miningjournal.net, News Editor, The Mining Journal, MI, Marquette

Heath, Mary ....**(304) 263-8931**
mheath@journal-news.net, Editor, The Journal, WV, Martinsburg

Heath, Will
wheath@thestclairtimes.com, Ed., The Saint Clair Times, AL, Pell City

Heatherly, Chase ....**(864) 622-1712**
chase.heatherly@independentmail.com, Mktg. Mgr., Anderson Independent-Mail, SC, Anderson

Heatherly, Chase ....**(803) 765-0707 x129**
publisher@free-times.com, Publisher & Advertising Director, Free Times, SC, Columbia

Heatherly, Roy
rheatherly@wichitaeagle.com, Pub./Pres., The Jackson Sun, TN, Jackson

rheatherly@wichitaeagle.com, President and Publisher, The Wichita Eagle, KS, Wichita

Heaton, Lauren
lheaton@ysnews.com, Assc. Ed., The Yellow Springs News, OH, Yellow Springs

Heaven, Jim
jim.heaven@sunmedia.ca, Adv. Mgr., Digital, The London Free Press, ON, London

Heberlig, Dale
nceditor@gmail.com, Mng. Ed., The Valley Times-Star, PA, Shippensburg

nceditor@gmail.com, Mng. Ed., The Shippensburg News-Chronicle, PA, Shippensburg

Hebert, Alysa ....**(985) 857-2277**
alysa.hebert@houmatoday.com, Digital Sales, Daily Comet, LA, Thibodaux

Hebert, Brady
bhebert@cheboygantribune.com, Managing Ed. , Mackinaw Journal, MI, Cheboygan

Hebert, David ....**(989) 893-6507**
dbhebert1@charter.net, Pub., The Valley Farmer, MI, Bay City

Hebert, Emeral
jessica.meaux@vermiliontoday.com, Adv. Sales Rep., Abbeville Meridional, LA, Abbeville

Hebert, Karine
Pub@cinnfm.com, Graphic Designer , Le Nord, ON, Hearst

Hecht, Brian K.
info@treehouse1.com, Contact, Treehouse One Interactive, TX, Magnolia

Heck, Amanda ....**(641) 842-2155**
composing@journalexpress.net, Head Expeditor, Marion County Reminder, IA, Knoxville

Heck, Matt ....**(770) 428-9411 ext. 406**
mheck@mdjonline.com, Circ. Dir., Cherokee Tribune Plus, GA, Canton

Heck, Matt ....**(770) 428-9411 ext. 406**
mheck@mdjonline.com, Circ. Mgr., Cherokee Tribune, GA, Canton

Heck, Matt ....**(770) 428 - 9411 ext. 406**
mjheck@mdjonline.com, Circ. Dir., Marietta

Daily Journal, GA, Marietta

Heckel, Dan
dheckel@messenger-inquirer.com, Ed., Messenger-Inquirer, KY, Owensboro

Heckel, Sherri
sheckel@messenger-inquirer.com, Librarian, Messenger-Inquirer, KY, Owensboro

Heckler, Sharon ....**(850) 747-5049**
sheckler@flafreedom.com, Rgl. Circ. Dir., The News Herald, FL, Panama City

Heckman, Cecelia
ceceliaheckman@gmail.com, Cabrini University Loquitur, PA, Radnor

Heckman, Rick
manager@franklinshopper.com, General Manager, The Franklin Shopper, PA, Chambersburg

Hedes, Ed
ehedes@tnonline.com, Sports Ed., Times News, PA, Lehighton

Hedge, Dave
hedged@reporternews.com, Ad. Director, Abilene Reporter-News, TX, Abilene

Hedges, Annie ....**(304) 927-2360**
sales@thetimesrecod.net, Sales Mgr., Roane County Reporter, WV, Spencer

Hedges, Annie ....**(304) 927-2360**
sales@thetimesrecord.net, Sales Mgr, The Times Record, WV, Spencer

Hedges, David J. ....**(304) 927-2360**
Pub., Roane County Reporter, WV, Spencer
Pub./VP, Sales & Mktg, Abilene Reporter-News, TX, Abilene

Hedges, David J.
dhedges@thetimesrecord.net, Pub., The Times Record, WV, Spencer

Hedges, Joe
joe.hedges@murraystate.edu, Lectr., Murray State University, KY, Murray

Hedges, Rebecca
rhedges@logandaily.com, Media Rep., The Pike County News Watchman, OH, Waverly

Hedrick, Bonnie ....**(907) 766-2688**
cvn@chilkatvalleynews.com, Pub., CHILKAT VALLEY NEWS, AK, Haines

Hedrick, Jeffrey
jhedrick@jsu.edu, Asst. Prof., Jacksonville State University, AL, Jacksonville

Hedrick, Nick
nick@thebanner.com, Ed, The Jackson County Banner, IN, Brownstown

Hedstrom, P.C.
aps@newulmtel.net, Pub., Springfield Advance-Press, MN, Springfield

Heekin-Canedy, Scott ....**(212) 556-1234**
Pres., New York Times, The New York Times Co., NY, New York

Heemer, Dave ....**(570) 321-4315**
heemer@lycoming.edu, Advisor, Lycoming College, PA, Williamsport

Heeschen, Paula C. ....**(570) 420-4348**
pheeschen@poconorecord.com, Editorial Page Ed., Pocono Record, PA, Stroudsburg

Heeter, Carrie J.
aaustin@msu.edu, Prof., Michigan State University, MI, East Lansing

Heffernan, Thomas ....**(973) 569-7304**
Heffernan@northjersey.com, CEO, Herald News, NJ, Rockaway

Hefflinger, Bruce ....**(419) 784-5441 ext. 226**
hefflinger@crescent-news.com, Sports Ed., Adams Publishing Group, LLC, MN, Virginia

Hefflinger, Bruce ....**(419) 784-5441 ext 226**
bhefflinger@crescent-news.com, Sports Ed., The Crescent-News, OH, Defiance

Hefner, Jay ....**(910) 649-4104 ext. 260**

jayhefner@newsreporter.biz, Ops. Dir., The News Reporter, NC, Whiteville

Hegarty, Erin ....**(847) 951-8018**
ehegarty@vikings.northpark.edu, Editor-In-Chief, North Park Univ., IL, Chicago

Hegg, Melissa
Melissa@MadisonDailyLeader.com, Marketing Mgr., The Madison Daily Leader, SD, Madison

Heglund, Eric
hopper@crosbyironton.net, Adv. Mgr, News Hopper, MN, Brainerd

Heglund, Laura ....**(218) 772-0300**
hopper@crosbyironton.net, Owner, News Hopper, MN, Brainerd

Hehir, Scott ....**(715) 845-0654**
shehir@wdhprint.com, Adv. Dir., The Wausau Daily Herald, WI, Wausau

Heichel, Steve ....**(814) 765-5581 ext. 224**
shop@theprogressnews.com, Prodn. Supt., Plant, The Progress, PA, Clearfield

Heidbreder, Paul ....**(231) 933-1403**
pheidbreder@record-eagle.com, Pub. , Traverse City Record-Eagle, MI, Traverse City

pheidbreder@record-eagle.com, Publisher, North Coast, MI, Traverse City

Heide, Ruth ....**(719) 589-2553, x109**
rheide@alamosanews.com, Editor, Valley Courier, CO, Alamosa

Heidel, Jesse ....**(618) 282-3803**
incnews@htc.net, Advertising Manager, North County News, IL, Red Bud

Heidel, Joel ....**(618) 282-3803**
nccomp@htc.net, Classifieds/Composition, North County News, IL, Red Bud

Heidman, Bruce ....**(705) 674-5271 ext. 269**
bruce.heidman@sunmedia.ca, Sports Ed., The Sudbury Star, ON, Sudbury

Heifner, Barry ....**(505) 863-6811 Ext. 213**
barryheifner@yahoo.com, Mng. Ed., Gallup Independent, NM, Gallup

Heighton, Sharon
subscribe@guysboroughjournal.ca, Office/ Circ. Mgr, Guysborough Journal, NS, Guysborough

Heike, Grace ....**(520) 797-4384 ext. 21**
editor@tucsonlocalmedia.com, Sales Admin, Inside Tucson Business, AZ, Tucson

Heikkila, Cory ....**(210) 250-3161**
cheikkila@mysa.com, Executive Digital Media Producer, San Antonio Express-News, TX, San Antonio

Heilman, Dan
dheilman@computeruser.com, Ed., ComputerUser, Minneapolis

Heilman, Hunter ....**(704) 687-7148**
editor@ninertimes.com, EIC, Univ. of North Carolina at Charlotte, NC, Charlotte

Heim, Delores
tct@pageone-inc.com, Pub., Tri-City Times, MI, Imlay City

Heim, Kyle ....**(717) 477-1521**
Asst. Prof./print & online media, Shippensburg University/Communication/Journalism Department , PA, Shippensburg

Heim, Mike ....**(620) 694-5700 Ext. 820**
mheim@hutchnews.com, Press Manager, The Hutchinson News, KS, Hutchinson

Heimbaugh, Mona ....**(605) 892-2528**
mona.heimbaugh@rapidcityjournal.com, Gen Mgr, Butte County Post, SD, Rapid City

Heimes, Heather
heather.heimes@plaintalk.net, Vermillion Plain Talk, SD, Vermillion

Heimgartner, Janna ....**(541) 966-0822**
jheimgartner@eastoregonian.com, Business Office Manager, East Oregonian, OR, Pendleton

Heimlich, Richard .... (760) 804-1641
rheimlich@hearst.com, Sales Mgr., W. Reg., King Features Syndicate, NY, New York
rheimlich@hearst.com, Sales Mgr., Western Reg., North America Syndicate, New York

Hein, Sue
publisher@thegoldenstar.net, Classified Mgr., Golden Star, BC, Golden

Heinen, Meg
mheinen@tetonvalleynews.net, Adv. Mgr., Teton Valley News, ID, Driggs

Heiner, Steve
sheiner@nikon.net, Gen. Mgr., Mktg. Pro Pdcts./Digital SLR Systems/Speedlights, Nikon, Inc., NY, Melville

Heinrich, Lisa
lheinrich@stcloudstate.edu, Assoc. Prof., St. Cloud State University, MN, Saint Cloud

Heinrichs, Timothy .... (661) 395-7350
theinrichs@bakersfield.com, Copy/Layout Ed., The Bakersfield Californian, CA, Bakersfield

Heintz, Paul
paul@sevendaysvt.com, Political Ed., Seven Days, VT, Burlington

Heintzelman, Andrew .... ext. 241
andy_h@newsitem.com, Exec. Ed., The News-Item, PA, Shamokin

Heintzelman, Mark .... (406) 523-5201
publisher@ravallirepublic.com, Pub., Ravalli Republic, MT, Hamilton

Heinz, Eric .... (970) 392-9341
Univ. of Northern Colorado, CO, Greeley

Heinz, Lisa .... (803) 765-0707 ext. 121
webmaster@free-times.com, Prodn. Mgr., Free Times, SC, Columbia

Heinzer, Jerry .... (530) 344-5074
lkane@mtdemocrat.net, Sports Ed., Mountain Democrat, CA, Placerville

Heirtzler, Bill
bill.heirtzler@daily-iberian.com, Adv. Dir., The Daily Iberian, LA, New Iberia

Heisel, John
john.heisel@frontrange.edu, Front Range Cmty. College, CO, Westminster

Heiser, Christine
cheiser@yourneighborhoodnews.com, Exec. Ed., Goffstown News, NH, Manchester

Heiser, Christine .... (603) 668-4321 x166
cheiser@yourneighborhoodnews.com, Exec. Ed., Salem Observer(OOB), NH, Manchester
cheiser@yourneighborhoodnews.com, Exec. Ed., Bedford Bulletin, NH, Manchester

Heiser, Steve
sheiser@yorkdispatch.com, Sports Ed., The York Dispatch, PA, York

Heisse, Bob .... (219) 933-3327
Bob.Heisse@nwi.com, Ed., The Times of Northwest Indiana, IN, Munster

Heithaus, Harriet Howard
harriet.heithaus@naplesnews.com, Homes/Ambience Ed., Naples Daily News, FL, Naples

Heitman, Danny .... (225) 388-0295
dheitman@theadvocate.com, Editorial Page Ed., The Advocate, LA, Baton Rouge

Heitshusen, Chris .... (402) 654-2218
sentinel@midlands.net, Managing Editor, Rustler Sentinel, NE, Scribner

Heitz, Tammy .... (304) 626-1413
Theitz@theet.com, Advertising Director, The Exponent Telegram, WV, Clarksburg

Helberg, Todd
thelberg@crescent-news.com, Political/Gov. Ed., The Crescent-News, OH, Defiance

Held, Jon .... (602) 444-8566
jon.held@pni.com, Exec. Vice Pres./CFO, The Arizona Republic, AZ, Phoenix

Heldman, Julie
julie@fostoriafocus.com, Adv. Mgr, The Fostoria Focus, OH, Fostoria

Helems, Jerry
jhelems@poncacitynews.com, Prodn. Mgr., The Ponca City News, OK, Ponca City

Helicke, James .... (724) 222-2200
pressroom@observer-reporter.com, Prodn. Mgr./Foreman, Pressroom, Observer-Reporter, PA, Washington

Hellegaard, Deanna .... (406) 765-2190
scnews@nemont.net, Business Manager, Sheridan County News, MT, Plentywood

Heller, Josh
jheller@thealbanydevils.com, Execu Ed, College of St. Rose, NY, Albany

Helliker, Kevin .... (312) 750-4124
kevin.helliker@wsj.com, Bureau Chief, The Wall Street Journal, NY, New York

Helling, Thomas .... (212) 556-4164
Adv. Vice Pres., The New York Times, NY, New York

Hellman, Rick .... (913) 385-6083
chronicle@sunpublications.com, Ed., The Kansas City Jewish Chronicle, KS, Fairway

Hellner, Oren .... (212) 944-1060
editor@featurephoto.com, Pres./CEO, Feature Photo Service, Inc., New York

Helm, Tammy
thelm@fstribune.com, Mng. Ed., The Fort Scott Tribune, KS, Fort Scott

Helmberger, Marshall .... (218) 753-2950
marshall@timberjay.com, Pub., Ely Timberjay, MN, Tower

Helmberger, Marshall .... (218) 753-2950
marshall@timberjay.com, Pub., Timberjay, MN, Tower

Helmchen, Scott .... (815) 459-4122
scotthelmchen@nwherald.com, Features Ed., Northwest Herald, IL, Crystal Lake

Helmchen, Scott
scotthelmchen@shawsuburban.com, Features Ed., Northwest Citizen Shopper, IL, Crystal Lake

Helmer, Mark .... (800) 533-1635 ext. 112
mark@helmerprinting.com, Adv. Mgr., Hiawatha Valley Shopper, WI, Beldenville
mark@helmerprinting.com, Adv. Mgr., Hiawatha Valley Shopper, MN, Red Wing

Helmer, Mark .... (715) 273-4601 ext. 112
mark@helmerprinting.com, Adv. Mgr., Helmer Printing, Inc., WI, Beldenville

Helmer, Mark .... (800) 533-1635 ext. 112
Adv. Mgr., Free Press, WI, Beldenville

Helmer, Mark .... (800) 533-1635 ext. 112
mark@helmerprinting.com, The Ellsworth Shopper, WI, Beldenville
mark@helmerprinting.com, The Hastings Free Press, WI, Beldenville
mark@helmerprinting.com, The Hudson Free Press, WI, Beldenville
mark@helmerprinting.com, The Miss-croix Shopper, WI, Beldenville
mark@helmerprinting.com, The River Falls Shopper, WI, Beldenville
mark@helmerprinting.com, Adv. Mgr., Baldwin Shopper, WI, Baldwin

Helmer, Mark .... (715) 273-4601 ext. 112
mark@helmerprinting.com, Adv. Mgr., Shopper, WI, Beldenville

Helmer, Mark
mark@helmerprinting.com, The Baldwin Shopper, WI, Beldenville

Helmer, Scott
info@helmerprinting.com, Pub., Shopper, WI, Beldenville

Helmer, Scott
info@helmerprinting.com, Pub., Free Press, WI, Beldenville

Helmer, Scott A.
info@helmerprinting.com, Co-Pub., Helmer Printing, Inc., WI, Beldenville

Helmer, Scott A.
info@helmerprinting.com, Prodn. Mgr., Baldwin Shopper, WI, Baldwin

Helms, Kay
khelms@trcle.com, Pub./ Adv. Dir., Cleburne Times-Review, TX, Cleburne

Helms, Patrick .... (423) 623-6171 ext. 3128
pat.helms@newportplaintalk.com, Circ. Mgr., The Newport Plain Talk, TN, Newport

Helmstetter, Cassandra
news@spencervillenews.com, Manager, The Journal News, OH, Spencerville

Helper, Lee .... (310) 473-4147
lee_helper@bhimpact.com, Pres., B/HI, CA, Los Angeles

Hembree, Jason
jason@pdclarion.com, Graphic Designer, Princeton Daily Clarion, IN, Princeton

Hembree, Larry
larryhembree@hembreeconsulting.com, Pub./Ed., The Loogootee Tribune, IN, Loogootee

Hemery, Kevin
kevinh@abbynews.com, Circ. Mgr., The Abbotsford News, BC, Abbotsford

Hemig, Jim .... (530) 477-4299
jhemig@theunion.com, Prod. Mgr., Press, Vail Daily, CO, Avon

Heminger, Karl L. .... (419) 427-8081
karlheminger@thecourier.com, Pub., The Courier AdVantage, OH, Findlay

Heminger, Karl L. .... (419) 427-8081
karlheminger@thecourier.com, Pres./Pub., The Courier, OH, Findlay

Heminger, Karl L. .... (419) 427-8081
karlheminger@thecourier.com, Pres., The Review Times, OH, Fostoria

Heminger, Karl L. .... (419) 427-8081
karlheminger@thecourier.com, Pres./Publisher, Findlay Publishing Co., OH, Findlay

Heminger, Kurt F.
kurtheminger@findlayoh.com, Vice Pres/Treasurer, Findlay Publishing Co., OH, Findlay

Hemmerich, Stephanie .... (305) 347-6623
shemmerich@alm.com, Director of Client Development, Palm Beach Daily Business Review, FL, Miami

Hemmila, Soren .... (415) 892-1516 x 31
shemmila@marinscope.com, Ed., Sausalito Marinscope, CA, Novato
shemmila@marinscope.com, Ed., Mill Valley Herald, CA, Novato
shemmila@marinscope.com, Southern Marin Editor, Novato Advance, CA, Novato

Hempel, Carlene
c.hempel@neu.edu, Lectr., Northeastern University, MA, Boston

Hempel, Tricia
ctadvertising@catholiccincinnati.org, Ed., The Catholic Telegraph, OH, Cincinnati

Hemperly, John .... (717) 492-2514
jhemperly@engleonline.com, Sales Manager, Chester County Community Courier, PA, Mount Joy

Hemperly, John .... (717) 492-2518
jhemperly@engleonline.com, Adv. Mgr., Engle Printing & Publishing Co., Inc., PA, Mount Joy

Hemperly, John .... (717) 492-2514
jhemperly@engleonline.com, General Sales Manager, Hershey Community Courier, PA, Mount Joy

Hemperly, John .... (717) 492-2514
jhemperly@engleonline.com, General Sales Manager, Merchandiser-lancaster County, WI, Beldenville

Hemperly, John .... (717) 492-2514
jhemperly@engleonline.com, Sales Manager, Pennysaver, PA, Mount Joy

Hemperly, John .... (717) 492-2514
jhemperly@engleonline.com, Sales Mgr., Engle - York Community Courier West Edition, PA, Mount Joy
jhemperly@engleonline.com, Sales Mgr., Engle - Columbia / Wrightsville Merchandiser, PA, Mount Joy
jhemperly@engleonline.com, Sales Mgr., Engle - Conestoga Valley / Pequea Valley Penny Saver, PA, Mount Joy
jhemperly@engleonline.com, Sales Mgr., Engle - Downingtown / Exton / Community Courier, PA, Mount Joy
jhemperly@engleonline.com, Sales Mgr., Engle - Elizabethtown / Mount Joy Merchandiser, PA, Mount Joy
jhemperly@engleonline.com, Sales Mgr., Engle - Gap / Oxford Community Courier, PA, Mount Joy
jhemperly@engleonline.com, Sales Mgr., Engle - Hempfield / Mountville Merchandiser, PA, Mount Joy
jhemperly@engleonline.com, Sales Mgr., Engle - Hershey / Hummelstown / Palmyra Community Courier, PA, Mount Joy
jhemperly@engleonline.com, Sales Mgr., Engle - Manheim / Lititz Merchandiser, PA, Mount Joy
jhemperly@engleonline.com, Sales Mgr., Engle - Manheim Township Merchandiser, PA, Mount Joy
jhemperly@engleonline.com, Sales Mgr., Engle - Middletown Shopper, PA, Mount Joy
jhemperly@engleonline.com, Sales Mgr., Engle - Millersville Advertiser, PA, Mount Joy
jhemperly@engleonline.com, Sales Mgr., Engle - Morgantown / Honey Brook Community Courier, PA, Mount Joy
jhemperly@engleonline.com, Sales Mgr., Engle - New Holland Pennysaver, PA, Mount Joy
jhemperly@engleonline.com, Sales Mgr., Engle - Quarryville Advertiser, PA, Mount Joy
jhemperly@engleonline.com, Sales Mgr., Engle - West Chester Community Courier, PA, Mount Joy
jhemperly@engleonline.com, Sales Mgr., Engle - Willow Street Strasburg Advertiser, PA, Mount Joy
jhemperly@engleonline.com, Sales Mgr., Engle - York Community Courier East Edition, PA, Mount Joy
jhemperly@engleonline.com, Sales Mgr., Engle - York Community Courier South Edition, PA, Mount Joy

Hemphill, Della
dhemphill@starlocalmedia.com, Classifieds, Plano Star-Courier, TX, Plano
dhemphill@starlocalmedia.com, Classifieds, Flower Mound Leader, TX, Plano
dhemphill@starlocalmedia.com, Classifieds, Sunnyvale View, TX, Plano
dhemphill@starlocalmedia.com, Cklassifieds, The Colony Courier Leader, TX, Plano
dhemphill@starlocalmedia.com, Classifieds, Rowlett Lakeshore Times, TX, Plano
dhemphill@starlocalmedia.com, Classifieds, Mesquite News, TX, Plano
dhemphill@starlocalmedia.com, Classifieds, Lewisville Leader, TX, Plano
dhemphill@starlocalmedia.com, Classified Adv. Mgr., Carrollton Leader, TX, Plano
dhemphill@starlocalmedia.com, Classified Adv. Mgr., Coppell Gazette, TX, Plano
dhemphill@starlocalmedia.com, Classifieds, McKinney Courier-Gazette, TX, Plano
dhemphill@starlocalmedia.com, Classified Adv. Mgr., Frisco Enterprise, TX, Plano
dhemphill@starlocalmedia.com, Celina Record, TX, Plano

Henard, Tim
timhenard@daycommail.com, Prodn. Mgr., Rutherford Parent, TN, Nashville

Henard, Tim .... ext. 3004
timhenard@daycommail.com, Prodn. Mgr., Nashville Parent Magazine, TN, Nashville

Fort Worth

Hensley, Jim
jhensley@ncppub.com, Pub./COO, Lyon County Reporter, IA, Rock Rapids
jhensley@ncppub.com, Pub./COO, The Northwest Iowa Extra, IA, Rock Rapids

Hensley, Jim
jhensley@ncppub.com, CEO, West Lyon Herald, IA, Inwood

Hensley, Larry .... **(859) 469-6500**
larry.hensley@theinteriorjournal.com, Pres./Pub./Ed., The Winchester Sun, KY, Winchester
larry.hensley@theinteriorjournal.com, Pres./Pub./Ed., The Advocate-Messenger, KY, Danville
larry.hensley@theinteriorjournal.com, Pub., The Interior Journal, KY, Stanford
larry.hensley@theinteriorjournal.com, CFO, Petoskey News-Review, MI, Petoskey

Hensley, Mike .... **(334) 670-6315**
mike.hensley@troymessenger.com, Sports Writer, The Troy Messenger, AL, Troy

Hensley, Phil .... **ext. 310**
phensley@johnsoncitypress.com, Circ. Dir., Johnson City Press, TN, Johnson City

Henson, John .... **(606) 573-4510 Ext. 1163**
jhenson@civitasmedia.com, Sports Ed., The Harlan Daily Enterprise, KY, Harlan

Henson, Pamela .... **(920) 996-7202**
pdhenson@gannett.com, Pres. / Pub., News-Record, WI, Appleton
pdhenson@gannett.com, Post-Crescent, WI, Appleton

Henson, Steve .... **(719) 544-3520 ext. 410**
shenson@chieftain.com, Mng. Ed., News, The Pueblo Chieftain, CO, Pueblo

Henson, Tony .... **(270) 887-3284**
thenson@kentuckynewera.com, Circ. Dir., Kentucky New Era, KY, Hopkinsville

Henton, Nicole
nhenton@ncppub.com, Off. Mgr. , Griggs County Courier, ND, Cooperstown

Hentzelman, Andy
andy_h@newsitem.com, Ed., The News Item, Shamokin

Henwood, Carolyn
carolyn@shelbyinfo.com, Prod. Mgr, Shelby Shopper & Info, NC, Shelby

Henz, Katie .... **(920) 743-3321**
khenz@doorcountyadvocate.com, Account Executive, Door County Real Estate Guide, WI, Sturgeon Bay

Hepperla, Rick
rick.hepperla@abb.com, Vice Pres.-Paper Drives Systems/Printing, ABB, Inc. (Printing Systems), WI, New Berlin

Heptig, Kathy
kheptig@leavenworthtimes.com, Av. Acct. Exec., The Leavenworth Times, KS, Leavenworth

Heraldson, Tina
omahane@ap.org, Bureau Chief, Nebraska Associated Press Association, NE, Lincoln

Herbert, Rosemary
amesbury@wickedlocal.com, Ed., Amesbury News, MA, Danvers

Herbig, Donna .... **(309) 757-4920**
dherbig@qconline.com, HR Mgr., The Dispatch-Argus, IL, Moline

Herbst, Rob
rherbst@bgdailynews.com, Sports Ed., Daily News, KY, Bowling Green

Herburger, David .... **(209) 745-1551**
dherburger@herburger.net, Pub., Galt Shopper, CA, Galt
dherburger@herburger.net, Pub., The Galt Herald, CA, Galt

Herburger, David .... **(916) 685-5533**

dherburger@herburger.net, Grp. Pub./Gen. Mgr., Herburger Publications, Inc., CA, Galt

Herburger, David .... **(209) 745-7551**
dherburger@herburger.net, Pub., River Valley Times, CA, Galt

Herburger, David .... **(209) 745-1551**
dherburger@herburger.net, Pub., Laguna Citizen, CA, Galt

Herburger, David
dherburger@herburger.net, Gen. Mgr., Elk Grove Citizen, CA, Elk Grove

Herburger, Roy
rherburger@herburger.net, Pres./CEO, Herburger Publications, Inc., CA, Galt
rherburger@herburger.net, Pub., Elk Grove Citizen, CA, Elk Grove

Heredia, Arthur
arthur@icatholic.org, Circ. Mgr., Intermountain Catholic, UT, Salt Lake City

Heredia, Rosario .... **(469) 977-2816**
rheredia@aldiatx.com, Circ. Dir., Al Dia, TX, Dallas

Herhoogen , Therese
tverhoogen@charlestownbridge.com, Adv. Mgr., The Charlestown Patriot-Bridge, MA, Charlestown

Hering, Hasso .... **(541) 812-6097**
hasso.hering@lee.net, Editorial Page Ed., Albany Democrat-Herald, OR, Albany

Herkimer, Mary
mary_herkimer@jewishakron.org, Circ. Mgr., Akron Jewish News, OH, Akron

Herl, Barbara .... **(620) 241-2422, Ext. 12**
bherl@mcphersonsentinel.com, Circ. Mgr., McPherson Sentinel, KS, McPherson

Herlinger, Darrell .... **(757) 345-2304**
dherlinger@vagazette.com, The Virginia Gazette, VA, Newport News

Herman, Dan
dherman@ydr.com, York Daily Record/York Sunday News, PA, York

Herman, Gail
gail@warsawpennysaver.com, Display Adv. Mgr., Warsaw Penny Saver, NY, Warsaw

Herman, Steven .... **(845) 469-4000**
CFO, Orange County Marketplace,ltd., NY, Chester

Hermann, Marc .... **(917) 407-9180**
historian@nyppa.org, Secretary - Historian, New York Press Photographers Association, Inc., NY, New York

Hermen, Steph .... **(563) 422-5410**
shermen@fayettepublishing.com, Adv. Exec., Fayette Leader, IA, West Union
shermen@fayettepublishing.com, Adv. Dir., Ossian Bee, IA, West Union
shermen@fayettepublishing.com, Acc. Exec., The Elgin Echo, IA, West Union

Hermes, Diana .... **(701) 642-8585**
dianah@wahpetondailynews.com, Multi-Media Sales Rep, The Daily News, ND, Wahpeton

Hermes, Sharon
sharon@durangoherald.com, Mktg/Promos, Durango Herald, CO, Durango

Hermiston, Taylor .... **(780) 672-4421**
thermiston@postmedia.com, Reg. Mng. Ed. ext.4, Vermilion Standard, AB, Vermilion

Hermsen, Julie
ads@norfolkareashopper.com, Adv. Mgr., Norfolk Area Shopper, NE, Norfolk

Hernandez, Elissa
tdchamp@vvm.com, Adv. Dir., Thorndale Champion, TX, Cameron
tdchamp@vvm.com, Adv. Mgr., The Cameron Herald, TX, Cameron

Hernandez, Jesus
jhernandez@kendallmitsubishi.com, Data Processing Mgr., Diario Las Americas, FL,

Miami

Hernandez, John .... **(305) 347-6642**
jhernandez@alm.com, Web Administrator, Palm Beach Daily Business Review, FL, Miami

Hernandez, John .... **(305) 347-6642**
jhernandez@alm.com, Web Adminstrator, Miami Daily Business Review, FL, Miami

Hernandez, Karla .... **(540) 981-3278**
karla.hernandez@roanoke.com, Regional H/R Director, The Roanoke Times, VA, Roanoke

Hernandez, Lashay .... **(307) 634-3361**
Adv. Mgr., Classified, Wyoming Tribune-Eagle, WY, Cheyenne

Hernandez, Pat
path@copperarea.com, Adv. Mgr., San Manuel Miner, AZ, Kearny

Hernandez, Patsy .... **(915) 546-6182**
phernandez@elpasotimes.com, VP of Production, El Paso y Mas, TX, El Paso
phernandez@elpasotimes.com, VP of Production, El Paso Times, TX, El Paso

Hernandez, Poncho
enterprise78361@aol.com, Ed., Jim Hogg County Enterprise, TX, Hebbronville

Hernandez, Salvador .... **(915) 546-6250**
shernandez@elpasotimes.com, Sales Director, El Paso Times, TX, El Paso

Hernandez, Sonja
shernandez@lsjournal.com, Adv. Sales Mgr., Lee's Summit Journal, MO, Kansas City
shernandez@lsjournal.com, Advertising Sales Manager, Lee's Summit Advertising Extra, MO, Lees Summit

Hernandez, Tony
composing@bigspringherald.com, Prodn. Mgr., Big Spring Herald, TX, Big Spring

Heroff, Todd .... **(507) 285-7676**
circulation@agrinews.com, Circ. Mgr., Agri News, MN, Rochester

Heronumus, Mike .... **(785) 263-1000**
arc.editor@abilene-rc.com, Editor, Abilene Reflector-Chronicle, KS, Abilene

Herpin, Freddie .... **(337) 943-7030**
fherpin@gannett.com, Photographer, Daily World, LA, Opelousas

Herpst, Scott
sherpst@walkermessenger.com, Sports Ed., Walker County Plus, GA, La Fayette

Herra, Dana .... **(815) 756-4841 ext.2233**
dherra@shawsuburban.com, Ed., The MidWeek, IL, Dekalb

Herratti, Jay
contactus@citysearch.com, CEO, citysearch. com, CA, West Hollywood

Herren, Rebecca
rherren@dailyastorian.com, Office Coord., Seaside Signal, OR, Seaside

Herrera, Dan .... **(505) 823-3810**
dherrera@abqjournal.com, Ed. Pg. Ed., Albuquerque Journal, NM, Albuquerque

Herrera, Ricardo
rherrera@bgco.org, Art Director, Baptist Messenger, OK, Oklahoma City

Herreras, Mari .... **(520) 797-4384 ext. 36**
mari@tucsonlocalmedia.com, Ed., Explorer, AZ, Tucson
mari@tucsonlocalmedia.com, Mng Ed, Tucson Weekly, AZ, Tucson
mari@tucsonlocalmedia.com, Ed., Inside Tucson Business, AZ, Tucson

Herres, Dan
dherres@postandcourier.com, Pres., Evening Post Community Publications Grp., Evening Post Publishing Newspaper Group, SC, Charleston

Herrig, Nicole .... **(605) 692-4300**
nicole@sdna.com, Business Manager,

South Dakota Newspaper Association, SD, Brookings

Herriges, Allen .... **(503) 538-2181**
aherriges@newberggraphic.com, Pub, The Newberg Graphic, OR, Newberg

Herriges, Allen
thegraphic@eaglenewspapers.com, Pub., Valley Classifieds, OR, Newberg

Herriges , Al
Aherriges@pamplinmedia.com, Pub., Woodburn Independent, OR, Woodburn

Herrin, Janie .... **(931) 433-6151**
evtadmgr@lcs.net, Advertising Manager, The Elk Valley Times, TN, Fayetteville

Herrin, Jeff .... **(252) 407-9943**
jherrin@rmtelegram.com, Editor, Rocky Mount Telegram, NC, Rocky Mount

Herring, Dal M.
dherring@usi.edu, Prof. Emer., University of Southern Indiana, IN, Evansville

Herring, Jane .... **(217) 347-7151 ext. 111**
jane.herring@effinghamdailynews.com, Bus. Mgr., Effingham Daily News, IL, Effingham

Herring, Mike
publisher@maryvilledailyforum.com, Pub., Gentry County Shopper, MO, Albany

Herrmann, Jonathan ..... **(865) 986-6581, ext. 1309**
jonathan.herrmann@news-herald.net, News Editor, News-Herald, TN, Lenoir City

Herrmann, Jonathan ..... **(865) 986-6581, ext. 1309**
jonathan.herrmann@news-herald.net, News Ed., The Connection, TN, Lenoir City
jonathan.herrmann@news-herald.net, News Ed., News-Herald, TN, Lenoir City

Herrmann, Julie .... **(907) 486-3227**
jherrmann@kodiakdailymirror.com, Reporter, Kodiak Daily Mirror, AK, Kodiak

Herrmann, Tess
therrmann@therecorder.com, Prodn. Mgr./Art Dir., The Recorder, CA, San Francisco

Herron, Bud
bherron@therepublic.com, Pub., Republic Extra, IN, Columbus

Herron, Connie .... **(901) 333-5380**
pworthy@southwest.tn.edu, Coorindator, Southwest Tennessee Cmty. College, TN, Memphis

Herron, Mike .... **(757) 222-3991**
mike.herron@insidebiz.com, Pub., Inside Business, The Hampton Roads Business Journal, VA, Norfolk

Herron, Steve
sherron@leaderherald.com, Pub., The Leader-Herald, NY, Gloversville

Hersam, Martin V.
mvh@hersamacorn.com, CEO & Publisher, HAN Network, CT, Ridgefield

Hersam, Martin V. .... **(203) 438-1183 ext. 118**
COO, Wilton Bulletin, CT, Ridgefield

Hersam, Mary Anne .... **(203) 966-9541**
mahersam@ncadvertiser.com, VP of Sales, Wilton Bulletin, CT, Ridgefield

Hersam, Mary Anne
mahersam@hersamacorn.com, VP of Sales, Ridgefield Press, CT, Ridgefield

Hersam, Mary Anne .... **(203) 438-1183 Ext. 123**
mahersam@ucadvertiser.com, VP of Sales, Monroe Courier, CT, Shelton

Hersam, Mary Anne .... **(203) 438-1183 Ext. 123**
mahersam@ucadvertiser.com, VP of Sales, Stratford Star, CT, Shelton

Hersam, Mary Anne
mahersam@hersamacorn.com, VP of Sales, Redding Pilot, CT, Ridgefield

Hersam, Mary Anne
mahersam@ncadvertiser.com, Adv. Mgr, Easton Courier, CT, Ridgefield

mahersam@ncadvertiser.com, Adv. Sales, Fairfield Sun, CT, Shelton

Hersam, Mary Anne
mahersam@ucadvertiser.com, VP of Sales, Shelton Herald, CT, Shelton

Hersam, Mary Anne
mahersam@ucadvertiser.com, VP of Sales, Trumbull Times, CT, Shelton

Hersam, Mary Anne .... (203) 438-1183 Ext. 123
mahersam@ucadvetiser.com, VP of Sales, Weston Forum, CT, Ridgefield
mahersam@ucadvertiser.com, VP, Sales, Milford Mirror, CT, Shelton

Hersam, Mary Anne .... (203) 438-1183 Ext. 123
mahersam@hersamacorn.com, VP of Sales, New Canaan Advertiser, CT, New Canaan

Hersam, V. Donald .... ext. 108
dhersam@ncadvertiser.com, Pub., New Canaan Advertiser, CT, New Canaan

Herscovitz, Heloiza
hherscov@csulb.edu, Asst. Prof., California State University, Long Beach, CA, Long Beach

Hersee, Steve .... (630) 388-6901
shersee@copia.com, Pres., Copia International Ltd., IL, Roselle

Hershoff, Sara .... (705) 466-9906
info@creemore.com, Pub., Creemore Echo, ON, Creemore

Herskowitz, Mickey
mlh008@shsu.edu, Philip J. Warner Chair in Journ., Sam Houston State University, TX, Huntsville

Hersom, Terry
terryhersom@siouxcityjournal.com, Sports Ed., Sioux City Journal, IA, Sioux City

Herter Warren, Christine
Burlington@wickedlocal.com, Ed., Times & Courier, MA, Concord
Burlington@wickedlocal.com, Ed., Burlington Union, MA, Concord

Hertz, Kelly
kelly.hertz@yankton.net, Mng. Ed., Yankton Daily Press & Dakotan, SD, Yankton

Hertz, Leba
lhertz@sfchronicle.com, Arts/Entertain. Ed., San Francisco Chronicle, CA, San Francisco

Hertz, Michael .... (403) 527-1101 ext. 675
mhertz@abnewsgroup.com, Pub., Medicine Hat News, AB, Medicine Hat

Hertz, Mike
mhertz@labnewsgroup.com, Senior VP & Group Pub., The Lethbridge Herald, AB, Lethbridge

Hertzberg, Mark .... (262) 631-1719
mhertzberg@journaltimes.com, Photo Dir., The Journal Times, WI, Racine

Herum, Jandell
jherum@sbtinfo.com, Adv. Vice Pres., Milwaukee Journal Sentinel, WI, Milwaukee

Herzfeld, James
barnold@journalsentinel.com, Vice Pres., Info Technologies/CIO, Milwaukee Journal Sentinel, WI, Milwaukee

Herzog, Garry .... (908) 766-3900, ext. 240
gherzog@newjerseyhills.com, Ed., Madison Eagle, NJ, Bernardsville

Herzog, Karen .... (701) 250-8267
karen.herzog@bismarcktribune.com, Religion Reporter, The Bismarck Tribune, ND, Bismarck

Hesket Sahlfeld, Sharon .... (785) 738-3537
beloitcall@nckcn.com, Ed., Beloit Call, KS, Beloit

Heslet, Joe
jheslet@isspress.com, Gen. Mgr., SnoValley Star, WA, Issaquah

Hess, Abby R .... (417) 256-9191

news@wpdailyquill.net, Editorial Assistant, Senior Reporter, West Plains Daily Quill, MO, West Plains

Hess, Angie
ectartdept@comcast.net, Art. Dir., East County Times, MD, Baltimore

Hess, Shelly .... (205) 486-9461
nwanews@centurytel.net, Mng. Ed., Northwest Alabamian, AL, Haleyville

Hessdorfer, Pat.......................... (918) 421-2015
business@mcalesternews.com, Bus. Mgr., McAlester News-Capital, OK, McAlester

Hesse, Herb .... (952) 392-6835
hhesse@acnpapers.com, Circ. Mgr., Robbinsdale/Crystal/New Hope/Golden Valley Sun-Post, MN, Eden Prairie

Hesse, Herb .... (952) 392-6835
hhesse@mnsun.com, Circ. Mgr., Wayzata/Orono/Plymouth/Long Lake Sun Sailor, MN, Eden Prairie

Hessel, Kevin
editor@thearknewspaper.com, Executive editor, The Ark, CA, Tiburon

Hesselberg, Erik .... (203) 458-5786
ehesselberg@ctcentral.com, Exec. Ed., Elm City Newspapers, CT, Milford

Hessler, Michelle .... (402) 444-1440
michelle.hessler@owh.com, Mgr., Real Estate Sales, Omaha World-Herald, NE, Omaha

Hessling, Kate
khessling@hearstnp.com, Ed., Huron Daily Tribune, MI, Bad Axe

Hesson, Gary .... (432) 333-7635
ghesson@oaoa.com, Prod. Foreman, Mail room, Odessa American, TX, Odessa

Hester, Ashton
keoweecourier@bellsouth.net, Ed., Keowee Courier, SC, Walhalla

Hester, Jamie
sales1@benewsjournal.com, Advertising Manager, Box Elder News Journal, UT, Brigham City

Hester, Wes .... (434) 978-7283
weshester@dailyprogress.com, Ed., The Daily Progress, VA, Charlottesville

Hestor, Wes .... (434) 978-7283
whester@dailyprogress.com, Editor, The Daily Progress, VA, Charlottesville

Heth, Ginny
standard@srt.com, Ed., Westhope Standard, ND, Westhope

Hetherington, Angela .... (780) 594-5206
thecourier@telus.net, Admin, The Courier, AB, Cold Lake

Hetland, Caitlin
chetland@ncppub.com, Ed., Griggs County Courier, ND, Cooperstown

Hetrick, Margaret
ecn@att.net, Ed., Ranger Times, TX, Eastland

Hettig, Rose
rproduction@rencopub.com, Publisher, Renville County Register, MN, Renville

Hettinga, Don.......................... (616) 526-6520
Prof., Dept. of English, Calvin College, MI, Grand Rapids

Hetzel, Dennis.......................... (614) 486-6677, Ext. 1016
dhetzel@ohionews.org, Exec. Dir., Ohio Newspaper Association, OH, Columbus

Hetzel, Dennis.......................... (614) 486-6677
dhetzel@ohionews.org, Executive Director Ohio Newspaper Association, Ohio Newspaper Services, Inc., OH, Columbus

Hetzel, Joey
ads@pcgazette.com, Adv. Rep., The Portage County Gazette, WI, Stevens Point

Hetzler, Byron .... (618) 351-5031
byron.hetzler@thesouthern.com, Photo Ed.,

The Southern Illinoisan, IL, Carbondale

Hetzler, John.......................... (252) 638-8101
jhetzler@freedomenc.com, Adv. Dir., Windsock, NC, Havelock

Heuel, Diane
diane_heuel@dailyjournal.com, Pub., The Record Reporter, AZ, Phoenix

Heuring, Frank .... (812) 354-8500
editor@pressdispatch.net, Pres./Pub., The Press-Dispatch, IN, Petersburg

Heuring, Frank
editor@sgstartimes.com, Pres./Pub., South Gibson Star Times, IN, Fort Branch

Heuring, John .... (812) 354-8500
ads@pressdispatch.net, Adv. Mgr., The Press-Dispatch, IN, Petersburg

Heuring, John
jheuring@pressdispatch.net, Adv. Mgr., South Gibson Star Times, IN, Fort Branch

Heuther, Bill
bhuether@metroland.com, Gen. Mgr., Minto Express, ON, Palmerston

Hewes-Casler, Lee.............. (207) 854-2577 x192
leehews@maine.rr.com, Pub., The Lakes Region Weekly, ME, Westbrook

Hewitt, John .... (404) 373-7779 ext. 110
johnh@dekalbchamp.com, COO/Gen. Mgr., The Champion, GA, Decatur

Hewitt, R. Cress
lawsonreview@juno.com, Pub., The Lawson Review, MO, Lawson

Hews, Lee.................. (207) 854-2577 ext. 192
leehews@maine.rr.com, Pres./Pub. , Reporter, ME, Westbrook

Hews, Mark .... (207) 854-2577
mhews@keepmecurrent.com, Circ. Mgr., The Lakes Region Weekly, ME, Westbrook
mhews@keepmecurrent.com, Circ. Mgr., American Journal, ME, Falmouth
mhews@keepmecurrent.com, Advertising/Circulation Director, Reporter, ME, Westbrook
mhews@keepmecurrent.com, Sun Chronicle, ME, Westbrook
mhews@keepmecurrent.com, Ad. Dir., Weekly Observer, ME, Westbrook
mhews@keepmecurrent.com, Ad. Director, The Current, ME, Westbrook
mhews@keepmecurrent.com, Ad. Dir., Tri-Town Weekly, ME, Westbrook

Hey, Lisa
lvandehey@gridleyherald.com, Pub./Ed., The Gridley Herald, CA, Gridley

Heyens, Jim
jim@southpointsun.ca, Pub. , Southpoint Sun, ON, Wheatley
jim@southpointsun.ca, Pub., Wheatley Journal, ON, Leamington

Heymen, Anne.......................... (904) 819-3486
anne.heymen@staugustinerecord.com, Features Ed., The St. Augustine Record, FL, Saint Augustine

Heyser, Holly
editor@statehornet.com, Sacramento State, CA, Sacramento

Heywood, Steven
editor@peninsulanewsreview.com, The Peninsula News Review, BC, Sidney

Hiassen, Rob .... (410) 280-5931
rhiassen@capgaznews.com, Managing Editor, The Capital, MD, Annapolis

Hiatt, Stephanie
stephanieh@lodinews.com, Bookkeeper, Lodi News-Sentinel , CA, Lodi

Hibbard, Janice
jhibbard@thetd.com, Adv. Mgr., The Times Dispatch, AR, Walnut Ridge

Hibbert, Andrew.......................... (519) 782-4563
andrew@lebeacon.ca, Editor/Publisher, Lake

Erie Beacon (oob), ON, Port Stanley

Hibbert, Heidi .... (252) 407-9902
Cir. Mgr., Rocky Mount Telegram, NC, Rocky Mount

Hibbert, Linda .... (519) 782-4563
linda@lebeacon.ca, Sales Manager, Lake Erie Beacon (oob), ON, Port Stanley

Hibbison, Roberta
citizenlegals@midconetwork.com, Circ. Mgr, Sherburne County Citizen, MN, Becker

Hibbs, Eddi
news@erierecord.com, Pub., Erie Record, KS, Erie

Hibbs, Robert.......................... (727) 815-1064
rhibbs@suncoastnews.com, Ed., The Suncoast News, FL, New Port Richey

Hibert, Michael
mhibert@gmti.gannett.com, Dir., Implementation Servs., Celebro, OH, Cincinnati

Hichborn, Michael .... (540) 659-4171
mhichborn@all.org, Contributing Author, ALL News, VA, Stafford

Hicka, Gail .... (516) 307-1045 Ext. 209
ghicka@theislandnow.com, Acct Exc, Williston Times, NY, Williston Park

Hickerson, Jerry L.
jerry@thepeoplestribune.com, Pub., The People's Tribune, MO, Bowling Green

Hickey , Lori .... (620) 342-4841 Ext. 233
sales13@emporiagazette.com, Adv. Mgr., St. Marys Star, KS, Saint Marys
sales13@emporiagazette.com, The Emporia Gazette, KS, Emporia

Hicklin, Kim .... (580) 875-3326
waltersheraldads@sbcglobal.net, Adv. Mgr./Circ. Mgr., Walters Herald, OK, Walters

Hickman, Anitra
robert@arktimes.com, Circ. Mgr., Arkansas Times, AR, Little Rock

Hickman, Charles
sales@nationwideadvertising.com, Pres., Network Newspaper Advertising, Inc., OH, Cleveland

Hickman, Gerald .... (724) 222-2200
mailroom@observer-reporter.com, Prodn. Mgr., Mailroom, Observer-Reporter, PA, Washington

Hickman, Matt.......................... ext. 619
sports@svherald.com, Sports Ed., Sierra Vista Herald - Sunday Bravo Shopper, AZ, Sierra Vista

Hicks, Allen
ahicks@wisconsinrapidstribune.com, Exec. Ed., Daily Tribune, WI, Wisconsin Rapids

Hicks, Angela
ahicks@hcnonline.com, Cypress Creek Champions (OOB), TX, Houston
ahicks@hcnonline.com, Prod. Mgr, Dayton News, TX, Conroe
ahicks@hcnonline.com, Prod. Mgr, Lake Houston Observer, TX, Conroe
ahicks@hcnonline.com, Prod. Mgr, Kingwood Observer, TX, Conroe
ahicks@hcnonline.com, Prod. Mgr, Spring Observer, TX, Conroe
ahicks@hcnonline.com, Prod. Mgr, Humble Observer, TX, Conroe
ahicks@hcnonline.com, Prod. Mgr, Cleveland Advocate, TX, Conroe
ahicks@hcnonline.com, Prod. Mgr, Atascocita Observer, TX, Conroe

Hicks, Arty .... (620) 442-4200 ext. 103
arty@arkcity.net, Ad Director, The Arkansas City Traveler, KS, Arkansas City

Hicks, Carol.......................... (701) 764-5312
dcherald@countrymedia.net, Office Mgr, Dunn County Herald, ND, Killdeer

Hicks, Catherine .... ext. 270
cjhicks@wwub.com, Wire Ed., Walla Walla

Union-Bulletin, WA, Walla Walla

Hicks, Judy .... (309) 686-3109
jhicks@pjstar.com, Head Librarian, Journal
Star, IL, Peoria

Hicks, Julie .... (816) 380-3228
Jhicks@demo-mo.com, General Sales
Assistant, Cass County Democrat-
Missourian, MO, Harrisonville

Hicks, Karen .... (906) 774-3708
khicks@ironmountainadvertiser.com, Gen Mgr,
Advertiser, MI, Iron Mountain

Hicks, Lynn .... (515) 284-8290
lhicks@dmreg.com, Engagement/Opinion Ed.,
The Des Moines Register, IA, Des Moines

Hicks, Phil
phicks@tylerpaper.com, Sports Ed., Tyler
Morning Telegraph, TX, Tyler

Hicks, Robert .... (307) 684-2223
robb@buffalobulletin.com, Pub., Buffalo
Bulletin, WY, Buffalo

Hicks, Sue .... (601) 981-3060
shicks@mspress.org, Business Development
Manager, Mississippi Press Services, Inc.,
MS, Jackson

Hickson, Fern .... (780) 513-3985
fhickson@bowesnet.com, Adv. Mgr., Nat'l,
Daily Herald-Tribune, AB, Grande Prairie

Hidook, Kevin .... (518) 565-4118
khidook@pressrepublican.com, Press
Room Supervisor, Press-Republican, NY,
Plattsburgh

Hiduk, Rick
rocket@epix.net, Ed., The Rocket-Courier, PA,
Wyalusing

Hieb, Gene .... (406) 791-1499
Production Mgr., Mailroom, Great Falls Tribune,
MT, Great Falls

Hieb, Laurie .... (503) 624-6397 ext 25
laurie@orenews.com, Exec. Dir., Oregon
Newspaper Publishers Association, OR,
Lake Oswego

Hiemstra, Doug .... (402) 444-1172
doug.hiemstra@bhmginc.com, Exec VP,
Omaha World-Herald, NE, Omaha
doug.hiemstra@bhmginc.com, SR. VICE
PRESIDENT, COO, BH Media Group, NE,
Omaha
doug.hiemstra@bhmginc.com, Assoc. Pres.-
Elect, Inland Press Association, IL, Des
Plaines

Higa, Jay .... (808) 529-4712
jhiga@staradvertiser.com, VP/Bus. Dev. & Reg.
Sales, Honolulu Star-Advertiser, HI, Honolulu

Higa, Jay .... (808) 529-4712
jhiga@staradvertiser.com, Adv. Dir., The
Garden Island, Kauai, HI, Lihue
jhiga@staradvertiser.com, VP Business
Development & Regional Sales, Hawaii
Tribune-Herald, HI, Hilo
jhiga@staradvertiser.com, VP Regional Sales,
West Hawaii Today, HI, Kailua Kona
jhiga@staradvertiser.com, VP Bus.
Development/Regional Sales, Metro HNL
(OOB), HI, Honolulu
jhiga@staradvertiser.com, VP/Bus.
Development & Regional Sales, MidWeek
Oahu, HI, Honolulu

Higa, Jay .... (808) 529-4712
jhiga@staradvertiser.com, VP Business
Development/Regional Sales, USA Today
Hawaii Edition , HI, Honolulu

Higa, Jay .... (808) 529-4712
jhiga@thegardenisland.com, VP Regional
Sales, Kauai Midweek, HI, Honolulu

Higgin, Byron .... (715) 431-0321
byron@minneotamascot.com, Pub., Minnesota
Mascot, MN, Minneota

Higgins, Cathy
cathy.higgins@alexcityoutlook.com, Ed., The
Onlooker, AL, Foley

cathy.higgins@alexcityoutlook.com, Sports Ed.,
Dadeville Record, AL, Alexander City
cathy.higgins@alexcityoutlook.com, Sports Ed.,
Alexander City Outlook, AL, Alexander City

Higgins, Cathy
timeseditor@gulfcoastnewspapers.com, News
Ed., The Baldwin Times Independent, AL,
Foley

Higgins, Damaris .... (423) 743-4112
dh@erwinrecord.net, Advertising Director, The
Erwin Record, TN, Erwin

Higgins, Jack
jhiggins@suntimes.com, Editorial Cartoonist,
Chicago Sun-Times, IL, Chicago

Higgins, Jody
jody@yanceypaper.com, Pub./Ed., Yancey
Common Times Journal, NC, Burnsville

Higgins, Joe .... (740) 592-6612 Ext. 224
jhiggins@athensmessenger.com, Ed., The
Athens Messenger, OH, Athens

Higgins, Kevin
info@ganderbeacon.ca, Gen. Mgr., The
Gander Beacon, NL, Gander

Higgins, Lynn
news@thepenobscottimes.com, Pub.,
Penobscot Times, ME, Old Town

Higgins, Polly
polly.higgins@amny.com, Ed. in Chief, amNew
York, NY, New York

Higgins, Sandra .... (618) 262-5144
skhpiglet@mtcarmelregister.com, Advertising
Sales Manager, Mount Carmel Register, IL,
Mount Carmel

Higgins, Shaun .... (509) 459-5060
shaunh@spokesman.com, CEO, New Media
Venture, WA, Spokane

Higgins, Shelly
shiggins@theintelligencer.net, Adv. Mgr.,
Classified, The Intelligencer, WV, Wheeling

Higgins, Tucker .... (818) 919-1039
jthiggins@email.wm.edu, Editor-in-
chief, College of William and Mary, VA,
Williamsburg

Higgs, Chuck .... (209) 249-3505
higgs@mantecabulletin.com, Advertising
Director, Bulletin Extra, CA, Manteca

Higgs, Chuck .... (209) 249-3505
higgs@mantecabulletin.com, Advertising
Director, Manteca Bulletin, CA, Manteca

Higgs, Larry .... (575) 538-5893 Ext. 5806
lhiggs@scsun-news.com, Cir. Mgr., Silver City
Sun-News, NM, Silver City
lhiggs@scsun-news.com, Circ. Mgr., Deming
Headlight, NM, Deming

High, Brooke
brooke@northerncomfortinc.com, Bus. Mgr.,
The Free Press, MN, Mankato

High, James C. .... (910) 642-4104 ext. 222
jimhigh@nrcolumbus.com, Pub/owner, The
News Reporter, NC, Whiteville

High, Les
postnews@thependerpost.com, Pub., Pender-
Topsail Post & Voice, NC, Burgaw

High, Les
leshigh@whiteville.com, Ed, The News
Reporter, NC, Whiteville
leshigh@whiteville.com, Immediate Past
President, North Carolina Press Association,
NC, Raleigh

Highfill, Bob
bhighfill@recordnet.com, Sports Editor, The
Record, CA, Stockton

Highland, Debi .... (270) 783-3243
dhighland@bgdailynews.com, News Ed., Daily
News, KY, Bowling Green

Hightower, Kathryn H.
Guardian-Journal@ClaiborneOne.com, Co-
Owner, Homer Guardian-Journal, LA, Homer

Hightower, Mary
mhightower@uaex.edu, President, Arkansas
Press Women Association, Inc., AR, Little
Rock

Hightower, Sam .... (804) 649-6603
shightower@timesdispatch.com; shightower@
worldmediaenterprise.com, Hand over
production plant, Richmond Times-Dispatch,
VA, Richmond

Higley, Michelle .... (208) 847-0552
newseditor@news-examiner.net, Ed./ Gen.
Mgr., The News-Examiner, ID, Montpelier

Hilario, Arturo .... (408) 938-1700
a_j_hilario@yahoo.com, Managing Editor, El
Observador, CA, San Jose

Hilario, Arturo .... (408) 457-1055
arturo@el-observador.com, Ed., El
Observador, CA, San Jose

Hilchey, Scott L.
info@sourcelink.com, Vice Pres., Interactive
Servs., SourceLink, IL, Itasca

Hildebrand, Greg
ghildebrand@thepilotnews.com, Prodn. Mgr.,
The Bremen Enquirer, IN, Bremen

Hildebrand, Greg
editor@thepilotnews.com, Managing Ed., Pilot
News, IN, Plymouth
editor@thepilotnews.com, Prodn. Foreman,
Composing, The Shopper, IN, Plymouth

Hildebrand, Greg
ghildebrand@thepilotnews.com, Prodn. Mgr.,
The Culver Citizen, IN, Plymouth

Hildebrand, Joe
joe.hildebrand@oakpress.com, Promotions
Mgr., The Oakland Press, MI, Pontiac

Hildebrand, Kurt
khildebrand@recordcourier.com, Ed., The
Record-Courier, NV, Gardnerville

Hildebrand, Nick .... (724) 458-2155
nahildebrand@gcc.edu, Adviser, Grove City
College, PA, Grove City

Hilder, Ann
publisher@manchesternewspapers.com, Circ.
Mgr, The North Country Free Press, NY,
Granville
publisher@manchesternewspapers.com, Circ.
Mgr, Northshire Free Press, NY, Granville
publisher@manchesternewspapers.com, Circ.
Mgr, The Weekender, NY, Granville
publisher@manchesternewspapers.com, Circ.
Mgr, The Lakes Region Free Press, NY,
Granville

Hildreth, Chris .... (812) 320-0144
Indiana Univ. Kelley School of Bus., IN,
Bloomington

Hilfrink, Michael B .... (217) 221-3333
mhilfrink@whig.com , Gen. Mgr./Exec. Ed, The
Quincy Herald-Whig, IL, Quincy

Hilgier, Jacek .... (715) 345-0744
pointpub@sbcglobal.net, Ed. in Chief, Gwiazda
Polarna, WI, Stevens Point

Hill, Allyson
enterprise@iw.net, Pub./Gen. Mgr., Viborg
Enterprise/Hurley Leader, SD, Viborg

Hill, Andrew .... (906) 364-4255
news@wnbpa.net, Ed., Wakefield News/
Bessemer Pick & Axe, MI, Wakefield

Hill, Bonnie
bonnie.hill@bulletinreview.com, Prodn. Mgr.,
Denison Bulletin & Review, IA, Denison

Hill, Bradley .... (269) 473-3103
brad@ilsw.com, President, Interlink, MI,
Berrien Springs

Hill, Candi .... (719) 384-4475
publisher@ljtdmail.com, Ed., La Junta Tribune-
Democrat, CO, La Junta

Hill, Candi .... (719) 384-1435
publisher@ljtdmail.com, Pub., The Fowler
Tribune, CO, Fowler

publisher@ljtdmail.com, Pub., Bent County
Democrat, CO, Las Animas

Hill, Candy .... (719) 384-4475
publisher@ljtdmail.com, Pub./Ed., Ag Journal,
CO, La Junta

Hill, Chris .... (505) 564-4583
chill@daily-times.com, Adv. Coord., The Daily
Times, NM, Farmington

Hill, Chrissy .... (540) 667-3200
chill@winchesterstar.com, Adv. Manager, The
Winchester Star, VA, Winchester

Hill, Dale
dhill@kaskaskia.edu, Kaskaskia College, IL,
Centralia

Hill, Dave
dhill@trftimes.com, Ed., Northern Watch, MN,
Thief River Falls

Hill, Dave
dhill@trftimes.com, Ed., Thief River Falls
Times, MN, Thief River Falls

Hill, Debbie
dhill@innisfail.greatwest.ca, Circ. Mgr., Innisfail
Province, AB, Innisfail

Hill, Dennis .... (919) 739-7834
dhill@newsargus.com, Mng. Ed., Goldsboro
News-Argus, NC, Goldsboro

Hill, Earl, III .... (903) 473-2653
Trey.Hill@RainsCountyLeader.com, Ed., Rains
County Leader, TX, Emory

Hill, Erin .... (850) 627-7649
ehill@gadcotimes.com, Reporter, Gadsden
County Times, FL, Quincy

Hill, Gary .... (585) 589-5641 ext. 15
ads@lakecountrypennysaver.com, Ed., Lake
Country Pennysaver, NY, Albion

Hill, Holly
hhill@thereporteronline.com, Nat'l. Adv. Coord.,
The Reporter, PA, Lansdale

Hill, Janet .... (563) 383-2396
jhill@qctimes.com, Ed., Bettendorf News, IA,
Davenport

Hill, Jen
jen@theheraldtimes.com, Rangely
Correspondent, The Rio Blanco Herald
Times, CO, Meeker

Hill, John .... (919) 508-2214
john.hill@dhhs.nc.gov, Peace College, NC,
Raleigh

Hill, John .... (360) 735-4452
john.hill@columbian.com, Metro Team Editor,
The Columbian, WA, Vancouver

Hill, Julie .... (541) 863-4429 ext. 304
jhill@artbeats.com, Adv./Mktg. Mgr.,
ArtbeatsEXPRESS, OR, Myrtle Creek

Hill, Karen .... (250) 763-3212
khill@kelownacapnews.com, Pub. , Kelowna
Capital News, BC, Kelowna

Hill, Levi .... (575) 391-5438
managingeditor@hobbsnews.com, Mng. Ed.,
Hobbs News-Sun, NM, Hobbs

Hill, Linda
circulation@emmetsburgnews.com, Circ Mgr,
Brant News, ON, Brantford
circulation@emmetsburgnews.com, Circ. Mgr.,
The Emmetsburg Reporter, IA, Emmetsburg
circulation@emmetsburgnews.com, Circ.,
Reporter-Democrat, IA, Emmetsburg
circulation@emmetsburgnews.com, Circ. Mgr.,
The Democrat, IA, Emmetsburg

Hill, Lisa .... (256) 232-2720
lisa@athensnews-courier.com, Customer
Service Specialist, The News-Courier, AL,
Athens

Hill, Mary .... (814) 827-3634
mhill@titusvilleherald.com, Reporter, The
Titusville Herald, PA, Titusville

Hill, Melody
mhill@ahnfsj.ca, Sales, The Northerner, BC,

Fort Saint John

Hill, Mike ....(985) 448-7614
mike.hill@houmatoday.com, City Ed., Daily
Comet, LA, Thibodaux
mike.hill@houmatoday.com, Night City Ed.,
The Courier, LA, Houma

Hill, Nessie
hill@essex.edu, Advisor, Essex County
College, NJ, Newark

Hill, Pamela
phill@jsu.edu, Adj. Fac., Jacksonville State
University, AL, Jacksonville

Hill, Peter ....(519) 823-6035
phill@guelphmercury.com, Circ. Mgr., The
Guelph Mercury Tribune, ON, Guelph

Hill, Rachel
rachel.hill@nisd.net, Univ. of Texas, TX, San
Antonio

Hill, Robert
hill.robert@mayo.edu, Ed., Post-Bulletin, MN,
Rochester

Hill, Robin
robin@dailydata.com, Comptroller, The Daily
Record, AR, Little Rock

Hill, Shane
sestar@iw.net, Pub., Star Publishing Co., SD,
Beresford

Hill, Stacey ....(816) 271-8503
nadine.pinzino@newspressnow.com, Dir of
Adv/Sales, St. Joseph News-Press, MO,
Saint Joseph

Hill, Stacey ....(816) 236-6205
stacey.hill@npgco.com, Exec. Vice-President,
COO- Newspapers, News-Press & Gazette
Co., MO, Saint Joseph

Hill, Susanne
s.hill@madisoniannews.com, Owner/Dir.,
Sales/Mktg, The Madisonian, MT, Ennis

Hill, Vernon
vhill@repub.com, Asst. Managing Ed., Sports,
The Republican, MA, Springfield

Hillard, David
dhillard@dailyitemcom, Managing Ed./Online
News, The Daily Item, PA, Sunbury

Hillebrand, Melissa ....(402) 280-4058
editor@creightonian.com, Creighton Univ.,
NE, Omaha

Hilliard, Bruce ....(617) 939-6870
bruce@yourtowncrier.com, Advertising Rep,
Town Crier, MA, Woburn

Hilliard, David
dhilliard@dailyitem.com, Mng. Ed., Scrapbook,
PA, Sunbury

Hilliard, David R. ....(570) 988-5484
dhilliard@dailyitem.com, Managing Ed., The
Daily Item, MA, Lynn

Hillis, Doug ....(419) 334-1083
rhillis@gannett.com, Cir. Dist. Mgr., The News-
Messenger, OH, Fremont
rhillis@gannett.com, Dist. Mgr., News Herald,
OH, Fremont

Hillmer, Samantha
orders@fairmontphotopress.com, Graphics
Designer, Fairmont Photo Press, MN,
Fairmont

Hills, Curt ....(352) 753-1119
curt.hills@thevillagesmedia.com, Managing
Editor of Projects, The Villages Daily Sun,
FL, The Villages

Hills, Lisa ....(612) 278-0222
lisa@mna.org, Executive Director, Minnesota
Newspaper Association, MN, Minneapolis

Hillyer, Gregg
ghillyer@progressivefarmer.com, Ed.-in-
Chief, DTN/The Progressive Farmer, AL,
Birmingham

Hilsabeck, Sandi
shilsabeck@newsrepublican.com, Circ. Mgr.,

Boone News-Republican, IA, Boone

Hilse, Mark
nuz4u@fidnet.com, Adv. Mgr., Sullivan
Independent News, MO, Sullivan

Hilsendager, Brian ....(253) 620-4747
Bhilsendager@webpressllc.com, Customer
Service/Parts, WebPress, LLC, WA, Tacoma

Hilson, Gwen
gwen@grandcoulee.com, Prod. Mgr., The Star,
WA, Grand Coulee

Hilson, Gwen
gwen@grandcoulee.com, Prodn. Coord., Star
Buyer's Guide, WA, Grand Coulee

Hilt, Michael
mhilt@unomaha.edu, Prof./Asst. Dean,
University of Nebraska at Omaha, NE,
Omaha

Hilton, Fred
sports@poncacitynews.com, Sports Ed., The
Ponca City News, OK, Ponca City

Hilton, Ken ....(251) 947-7712
khilton@gulfcoastnewspapers.com, Pub., The
Independent (OOB) , AL, Robertsdale
khilton@gulfcoastnewspapers.com, Prod. Dir.,
The Baldwin Times Independent, AL, Foley

Hilton, Spud
shilton@sfchronicle.com, Travel Ed, San
Francisco Chronicle, CA, San Francisco

Hilton-Morrow, Wendy
wendyhilton-morrow@augustana.edu, Chair,
Augustana College, IL, Rock Island

Hilts, Rod ....(519) 354-2000 ext. 324
rod.hilts@sunmedia.ca, Mng. Ed. , The
Chatham Daily News, ON, Chatham

Hilts, Rod ....(519) 344-3641 ext. 2341
rod.hilts@sunmedia.ca, Mng. Ed., The
Observer, ON, Sarnia

Hiltunen, Jen ....(952) 345-6670
jhiltunen@swpub.com, Adv. Dir., Lakeshore
Weekly News, MN, Wayzata
jhiltunen@swpub.com, Adv. Dir, Chanhassen
Villager, MN, Chaska
jhiltunen@swpub.com, Adv. Mgr., Jordan
Independent, MN, Jordan

Himler, Jeffrey
jhimler@tribweb.com, Ed., Blairsville Dispatch,
PA, Blairsville

Himsel, Don ....(603) 594-6590
news@nashuatelegraph.com, Photo Ed. / Staff
Wtr., The Telegraph, NH, Nashua

Hincks, Jean
publisher@chilliwacktimes.com, Pub.,
Chilliwack Times, BC, Chilliwack

Hind, Travis ....(250) 782-4888 ext 125
Prodn. Mgr., Pre Press, Dawson Creek Mirror,
BC, Dawson Creek

Hinde, Tom ....(806) 273-5611
publisher@borgernewsherald.com, Publisher,
Borger News-Herald, TX, Borger

Hinde, Tom ....ext. 229
thinde@columbiabasinherald.com, Circ. Dir.,
Columbia Basin Herald, WA, Moses Lake

Hindle, Isaac ....(816) 234-4914
ihindle@kcstar.com, Marketing Analyst, The
Kansas City Star, MO, Kansas City

Hindmon, Randy
rhindmon@dddnews.com, CIrc. Mgr., Daily
Dunklin Democrat Extra, MO, Kennett

Hinds, Derrick ....(202) 495-8730
derrickh@rtdna.org, Digital, Communications
and Marketing Manager, Radio Television
Digital News Association, DC, Washington

Hinds, John
info@ccna.com, Pres., News Media Canada,
ON, Toronto

Hinds, John ....(416) 923-0858
jhinds@ccna.ca, Pres., Canadian Media
Circulation Audit, ON, Toronto

Hinds, Olga
ohinds@mercedes.k12.tx.us, Pub., Mercedes
Enterprise, TX, Mercedes

Hine, Kristi ....(605) 539-1281
kristi@truedakotan.com, Editor/Publisher, True
Dakotan, SD, Wessington Springs

Hine, Richard ....(650) 223-6525
editor@almanacnews.com, Editor, The
Almanac, CA, Menlo Park

Hiner, John
jhiner@mlive.com, VP of Content, The Jackson
Citizen Patriot, MI, Jackson

Hines, Alice
hines@hendrix.edu, Hendrix College, AR,
Conway

Hines, Cary
news1@westvalleyview.com, Mng. Ed., West
Valley View, AZ, Goodyear

Hines, Doug
doug.hines@wcfcourier.com, Asst. News Ed.,
The Courier, IA, Waterloo

Hines, Elena
elena@threeriversnews.com, Managing Ed.,
Three Rivers Commercial-News, MI, Three
Rivers

Hines, Larry
l.hines@blmachinedesign.com, Pres., B & L
Machine & Design, IL, Effingham

Hines, Peter ....(518) 339-5334
Peter.hines@nasja.org, Pres., NASJA East,
NY, Latham

Hines, Ryan
sports@dailystandard.com, Sports Ed., The
Daily Standard, OH, Celina

Hines, Theresa
wheadlight@bellsouth.net, Pub., The
Wrightsville Headlight, GA, Wrightsville

Hinestrosa, Marina ....(408) 920-5843
mhinestrosa@mercurynews.com, Ed., Nuevo
Mundo, CA, San Jose

Hinick, Walter ....(406) 496-5509
walter.hinick@mtstandard.com, Photo Ed., The
Montana Standard, MT, Butte

Hink-Wagner, Sheri ....(308) 394-5389
waunetabreeze@bwtelcom.net, Managing
Editor, The Wauneta Breeze, NE, Wauneta

Hinkle, April ....(512) 716-8634
ahinkle@texastribune.org, CRO & Advertising,
The Texas Tribune, TX, Austin

Hinkle, Don ....(573) 636-0400, ext. 312
dhinkle@mobaptist.org, Editor, The Pathway,
MO, Jefferson City

Hinkle, Kurt ....(970) 392-9286
khinkle@uncmirror.com, Univ. of Northern
Colorado, CO, Greeley

Hinojosa, III, C.A. ....(956) 565-2425
mercedesenterprise@sbcglobal.net, Sales/
Owner, Mercedes Enterprise, TX, Mercedes

Hinshaw, Horace ....(650) 359-6666
hhinshaw@bayareanewsgroup.com, Ed./Pub.,
Pacifica Tribune, CA, Novato

Hinshaw, Joe
hinshamj@jmu.edu, Assoc. Prof., James
Madison University, VA, Harrisonburg

Hinshaw, Wayne ....(704) 797-4296
wayne@hinshawphoto.com, Photo Dept. Mgr.,
Salisbury Post, NC, Salisbury

Hinske, Sue
sue@lakegenevanews.net, Office Mgr., Lake
Geneva Regional News, WI, Lake Geneva

Hinson, Karen
editor@machiasnews.com, Ed./Pub., Machias
Valley News Observer, ME, Machias

Hinton, Dave
dhinton@news-gazette.com, Ed. in Chief,
Rantoul Press, IL, Rantoul

Hinton, Earleen

ehinton@oglecountynews.com, Gen. Mgr.,
Forreston Journal, IL, Dixon

Hinton, Earleen ....(815) 732-6166, Ext. 5902
ehinton@oglecountynews.com, Pub., The
Exchange (OOB), IL, Oregon
ehinton@oglecountynews.com, Gen. Mgr.,
Ogle County Life, IL, Oregon

Hinton, Earleen
ehinton@shawnews.com, Gen. Mgr, Mt. Morris
Times, IL, Dixon

Hinton, Earleen ....(815) 732-6166, Ext. 5902
ehinton@shawnews.com, Gen. Mgr., Tri-County
Press, IL, Dixon

Hinton, Leslie
les.hinton@dowjones.com, CEO, Dow Jones &
Company, NY, New York

Hinton, Lonnie
viennatimes@frontier.com, Ed., The Vienna
Times, IL, Vienna

Hinton, Lonnie ....(618) 995-9445
gorevillegazette@frontier.com, Pub., Goreville
Gazette, IL, Goreville

Hinton, Mike ....(740) 452-3601
mhinton@adjustoveyor.com , Director of
Engineering, Stewart Glapat Corp., OH,
Zanesville

Hintze, Lynnette ....(406) 758-4421
lhintze@dailyinterlake.com, Features Ed., Daily
Inter Lake, MT, Kalispell

Hiott, Debbie ....(512) 912-2937
dhiott@statesman.com, Ed., Austin American-
Statesman, TX, Austin

Hipp, Kim
tbcads@otelco.net, Advert. Dir, The Blount
Countian, AL, Oneonta

Hirata, Hugh
hugh.hirata@kitsapsun.com, Circ. Dir., Kitsap
Sun, WA, Bremerton

Hire, Pat
ads_pat@cretenews.net, Adv. Mgr., The Crete
News, NE, Crete

Hires, Sheila ....(912) 427-3757
thepress@bellsouth.net, Prodn. Mgr., The
Press-Sentinel, GA, Jesup

Hirko, Cathy ....(717) 771-2027
chirko@ydr.com, Bus. Ed. and Weekly/Web
Editor, York Daily Record/York Sunday News,
PA, York

Hiro, Erin ....(760) 744-1150
ehiro@palomar.edu, Palomar College, CA,
San Marcos

Hirsch, Rick ....(305) 376-3504
rhirsch@miamiherald.com, Mng. Ed.,
Multimedia, Herald Values, FL, Miami
rhirsch@miamiherald.com, Managing Editor
, Miami Herald, FL, Doral

Hirshan, Adam ....(603) 737-2011
adam@laconiadailysun.com, Pub. , The
Laconia Daily Sun, NH, Laconia

Hirshan, Adam ....(603) 737-2011
adam@laconiadailysun.com, Publisher , The
Laconia Daily Sun, NH, Laconia

Hirshan, Elaine ....(603) 737-2014
elaine@laconiadailysun.com, Advertising
Manager, The Laconia Daily Sun, NH,
Laconia

Hirten, Mickey ....(517) 377-1076
mhirten@lsj.com, Exec. Ed., The Source
Sampler, MI, Lansing

Hirten, Mickey
mickey@lansingcitypulse.com, Exec. Ed.,
Lansing State Journal, MI, Lansing

Hiruko, Ashley ....(360) 354-4444
ashley@lyndentribune.com, Reporter, Lynden
Tribune, WA, Lynden

Hiruko, Ashley ....(360) 384-1411
ashley@lyndentribune.com, Reporter, Social
Media editor, Ferndale Record, WA, Ferndale

Hisayasu, Staci
busmgr@pacificcitizen.org, Business Manager, Japanese American Citizens League, CA, Los Angeles

Hischar, Mark ....(469) 532-8000
mark.hischar@kba.com, Pres./CEO, KBA North America, Inc. (Koenig & Bauer AG), TX, Dallas

Histed, William M.
mulberrypress@juno.com, Owner, Pub. & Ed., Polk County Press, FL, Mulberry

Hitchcock, Melanie ....(603) 413-5157
mhitchcock@parentingnh.com, Ed., Parenting New Hampshire, NH, Manchester

Hitchings, Brian
brian@phillyareapapers.com, Pres., Hitchings & Co., PA, Plymouth Meeting

Hitchings, Brian ....(717) 703-3049
brianh@mansimedia.com, Director, Client Solutions, MANSI Media, PA, Harrisburg

Hitchings, R. Brian
brian@phillyareapapers.com, Pres., Philadelphia Area Newspapers, PA, Plymouth Meeting

Hitchner, Melody
melody.hitchner@bellinghamherald.com, Adv. Sales Coord., The Bellingham Herald, WA, Bellingham

Hite, Sandy
sandyhite@pressregister.com, Office Mgr., The Clarksdale Press Register, MS, Clarksdale

Hite, Tom ....(405) 475-3311
thite@opubco.com, Adv. Mgr., Classified, The Oklahoman, OK, Oklahoma City

Hitsky, Alan ....ext. 248
ahitsky@thejewishnews.com, Assoc. Ed., The Detroit Jewish News, MI, Southfield

Hittle, Todd
info@abmmail.com, Exec. Dir., American Business Media Agricultural Council, NY, New York

Hittmeier, Cayla ....(217) 421-6994
chittmeier@herald-review.com, Dig. Adv. Sales Mgr., Herald & Review, Decatur, IL, Decatur

Hitzig, Bill
billh@jegi.com, COO, Jordan, Edmiston Group, Inc., NY, New York

Hively, Richard ....(717) 901-0770
rick@wilsongregory.com, Pres., Wilson Gregory Agency, Inc., PA, Camp Hill

Hixson, Rachel ....(620) 694-5700 Ext. 254
rhixson@hutchnews.com, Graphic Designer, The Hutchinson News, KS, Hutchinson

Hjellming, Chad........................(507) 645-1110
chjellming@northfieldnews.com, Reg Gen Mgr, Le Sueur News-Herald, MN, Le Center

Hjellming, Chad........................(507) 645-1110
chjellming@northfieldnews.com, Pub., Northfield News, MN, Northfield

Hjellming, Chad
chjellming@wasecacountynews.com, Gen. Mgr, Waseca County News, MN, Waseca

Hjellming, Chad........................(507) 645-1110
chjellming@northfieldnews.com, Pub, Northfield Weekender, MN, Northfield

Hjellming, Chad ....(507) 298-0327
chjellming@northfieldnews.com, Gen. Mgr., St. Peter Herald, MN, Saint Peter
chjellming@northfieldnews.com, Reg. Pub., Adams Publishing Group, LLC, MN, Virginia

Hladun, Carol
chladun@njnpublishing.com, Adv. Dir., Suburban News, NJ, New Providence

Ho, Hwee-Kun ....(65) 6415-4200
hweekun.ho@dowjones.com, Regl. Sales Mgr., Dow Jones Newswires - Singapore, Singapore, Singapore

Hoag, Mary ....(402) 371-1020 ext. 235

mhoag@norfolkdailynews.com, Agriculture/Youth Ed., Norfolk Daily News, NE, Norfolk

Hoagland, Will ....(270) 745-6285
william.hoagland@wku.edu, Advt Adviser and Sales Mgr, Western Kentucky University, KY, Bowling Green

Hoar, William H.
neacesecretary@aol.com, Sec., New England Association of Circulation Executives, MA, Chelmsford

Hoare, Eva ....(902) 426-3088
ehoare@herald.ca, Assignment Ed., Night, The Chronicle Herald, NS, Halifax

Hoban, Bill..............................(707) 933-2731
managingeditor@sonomanews.com, Mng. Ed., The Sonoma Index-Tribune, CA, Sonoma

Hobbs, Brian
bhobbs@bgco.org, Editor, Baptist Messenger, OK, Oklahoma City

Hobbs, Chris..................................ext. 245
chobbs@hickoryrecord.com, Sports Ed., The Hickory Daily Record, NC, Hickory
chobbs@hickoryrecord.com, Sports Ed., Pow, NC, Hickory

Hobbs, Jyl
news@westok.net, Co-Pub., The Mountain View News, OK, Mountain View

Hobbs, Lynn ....(706) 485-3501
editor@msgr.com, Associate Editor, The Eatonton Messenger, GA, Eatonton

Hobbs, Scooter........................(337) 494-4075
shobbs@americanpress.com, Sports Ed., American Press, LA, Lake Charles

Hobbs, Shelley
shobbs@floridaweekly.com, Nat'l Adv. Mgr., Bonita Springs Florida Weekly, FL, Naples
shobbs@floridaweekly.com, Nat'l Adv. Mgr., Naples Florida Weekly, FL, Naples
shobbs@floridaweekly.com, Nat'l Adv. Mgr., Punta Gorda/Port Charlotte Florida Weekly, FL, Punta Gorda

Hobbs, Tim..............................(785) 762-5000
t.hobbs@thedailyunion.net, Pub., Wamego Smoke Signal, KS, Wamego

Hobin, Keith
keith@thetriangle.org, Mng Ed, Drexel Univ., PA, Philadelphia

Hobson, Gene
ghobson@beltingindustries.com, COO, Belting Industries Co., Inc., NJ, Kenilworth

Hobson, Grace ....(816) 234-7738
ghobson@olathenews.com, Ed, The Olathe News, MO, Kansas City

Hobson, Tammy
tammy-courierads@roadrunner.com, Ad. Director, Warsaw's Country Courier, NY, Warsaw

Hochberg, Joseph ....ext. 243
Circ. Mgr., The Jewish Press, NY, Brooklyn

Hochberger, Larry ....(215) 248-8817
larry@chestnuthilllocal.com, Assc. Pub., Chestnut Hill Local, PA, Philadelphia

Hochheimer, John
hoch@siu.edu, Prof., Southern Illinois University Carbondale, IL, Carbondale

Hochstein, Marc ....(212) 803-8887
marc.Hochstein@sourcemedia.com, Ed.-in-chief, American Banker, NY, New York

Hochstrasser, Jeff
hochstrasserj@byui.edu, Brigham Young Univ. Idaho, ID, Rexburg

Hochswender, Cynthia
cynthiah@lakevillejournal.com, Exec. Ed., The Lakeville Journal, CT, Falls Village

Hock, Liz ....(540) 981-3198
liz.hock@roanoke.com, Editor I, The Roanoke Times, VA, Roanoke

Hockett, Brandi.............(706) 884-7311 ext. 2146

brandi.hockett@lagrangenews.com, Classified Ads, LaGrange Daily News, GA, Lagrange

Hockin, Sharon........................(416) 364-0321
info@thecanadianpress.com, Office Mgr., Canadian Press, The - Toronto, ON, ON, Toronto

Hocking, Julie
jhocking@ptd.net, Ed., The Shopping News of Lancaster County, PA, Ephrata

Hocklander, Sony
shocklander@news-leader.com, Engagement Ed, Springfield News-Leader, MO, Springfield

Hodgden, Ken ....(920) 833-0420
ken@adcommnews.com, Pub./Owner, Advertiser Community News, WI, Seymour
ken.h@adcommnews.com, Circ. Mgr., Advertiser Community News, WI, Seymour

Hodge, Alan
alan.bannernews@gmail.com, Ed., Banner News, NC, Belmont

Hodge, Dorothy ....(613) 678-3327
dhodge@thereview.ca, Graphic Designer, The Review, ON, Vankleek Hill

Hodge, Eddy
pjch@suddenlinkmail.com, Perry County Petit Jean Country Headlight, AR, Morrilton

Hodge, Kelly...................................ext. 340
khodge@johnsoncitypres.com, Sports Ed., Johnson City Press, TN, Johnson City

Hodge, Linda
clipperace@alaweb.com, Ed., The Elba Clipper, AL, Elba

Hodge, Raymond
kburdi@heralddemocrat.com, Mailroom Supvr., Herald Democrat, TX, Sherman

Hodge, Walter
whodge@wsj.com, District Sales Mgr., The Wall Street Journal, NY, New York

Hodges, Dave ....(850) 599-2321
dhodges@tallahassee.com, Bus. Ed., Tallahassee Democrat, FL, Tallahassee

Hodges, Felicia ....(845) 562-3606
editor@excitingread.com, Editor, Hudson Valley Parent, NY, Newburgh

Hodges, Fr. Mark ....(888) 678-6008 x 940
mhodges@lifesitenews.com, Journalist, LifeSiteNews.com, VA, Front Royal

Hodges, John........................(701) 456-1225
jhodges@thedickinsonpress.com, Cir. Mgr, The Dickinson Press, ND, Dickinson

Hodges, John ....(701) 456-1225
jhodges@thedickinsonpress.com, Cir. Mgr. , Advertizer, ND, Dickinson

Hodges, Katie
khodges@jackson.gannett.com, Sales Dir., Madison County Herald, MS, Ridgeland

Hodges, Kristen
graphics1@monticellonews.net, Graphics Designer, Advance-Monticellonian, AR, Monticello

Hodges, Mary Pat
mphodges@gapress.org, Member Services Director , Georgia Press Association, GA, Atlanta

Hodges, Michael A.
lpc@louisacomm.net, Pub., New London Journal, IA, New London

Hodges, Michael A.
lpc@louisescomm.net, Pres./Pub., Louisa Publishing Co. Ltd., IA, Wapello

Hodges, Michael A.
lpc@louisacomm.net, Pub., Des Moines County News, IA, West Burlington

Hodges, Micheal....................(512) 477-6755
mhodges@texaspress.com, Exec. Dir., Texas Press Association, TX, Austin

Hodges, Staci

shodges@brookshirebros.com, Nacogdoches Adv. Mgr., The Lufkin Daily News, TX, Lufkin

Hodgson, Alison
ahodgson@nycedc.com, Barnard College, NY, New York

Hodgson, Donna
freedomcall@pldi.net, Ed., The Freedom Call, OK, Freedom

Hodgson, Jack
jack.hodgson@okstate.edu, Assoc. Prof., Oklahoma State University, OK, Stillwater

Hodgson, Judy ....(707) 826-2000
judy@northcoastjournal.com, Pub. Mgr, North Coast Journal, CA, Eureka

Hodson, Thomas ....(740) 593-2550
aac@ohiou.edu, Dir./Assoc. Prof., Ohio University, OH, Athens

Hoeft, John
john.hoeft@startribune.com, Associate VP, Digital Sales, Star Tribune, MN, Minneapolis

Hoeft, Randy ....(928) 539-6869
rhoeft@yumasun.com, Special Content Ed., Yuma Sun, AZ, Yuma

Hoegl, Katherine
thebeaconnews5@aol.com, Pub., West Hempstead Beacon, NY, Hempstead

Hoegl, Kathleen
thebeaconnews5@aol.com, Pub., The Merrick Beacon, NY, Hempstead

Hoegl, Kathleen
thebeaconnews5@aol.com, Pub., East Meadow Beacon, NY, Hempstead

Hoegl, Kathleen
thebeaconnews5@aol.com, Pub., The Hempstead Beacon, NY, Hempstead

Hoegl, Kathleen
thebeaconnews5@aol.com, Pub., The Uniondale Beacon, NY, Hempstead

Hoegl, Kathleen
thebeaconnews5@aol.com, Pub., Nassau County Publications, NY, Hempstead

Hoekstra, Paula
phoekstra@pbdailynews.com, Nat'l Acct. Exec., Palm Beach Daily News, FL, Palm Beach

Hoel, Arne L. ....(775) 850-2281
Pres./CEO, Swift Communications, Inc., NV, Carson City

Hoel, Debbie ....(760) 922-3181 ext. 102
dwhite@paloverdevalleytimes.com, Pub., Palo Verde Valley Times, CA, Blythe
dwhite@paloverdevalleytimes.com, Publisher, Quartzsite Times, CA, Blythe
dwhite@paloverdevalleytimes.com, Publisher, Desert Shopper, CA, Blythe

Hoelter, Larry............................(956) 271-4500
southtexasreporter@ymail.com, Chief Ed., South Texas Reporter, TX, Roma

Hoemann, Darrell....................(217) 351-5603
dhoemann@news-gazette.com, Photo Ed., The News-Gazette, IL, Champaign

Hofacre, Amy
ahofacre@scity.com, Inside Sales Representative, Steel City Corp., OH, Ashland

Hofer, James ....ext. 117
Adv. Dir., Eagle Herald Sunday, WI, Marinette

Hoff, Barry
editor@bloomeradvance.com, Ed./Gen. Mgr., Bloomer Advance, WI, Bloomer

Hoff, Beth ....(205) 443-5611
bhoff@bizjournals.com, Credit Mgr, Birmingham Business Journal, AL, Birmingham

Hoffacker, Muriel
mhoffacker@salemnews.com, Community Ed., The Salem News, MA, Beverly

Hoffer, Michael......................(207) 781-3661
mhoffer@theforecaster.net, Sports Ed., The
Forecaster, ME, Falmouth

Hoffland, Darcie......................(307) 755-3313
advmgr@laramieboomerang.com, Adv. Mgr.,
Laramie Boomerang, WY, Laramie

Hoffman, Ace
rhoffman@animatedsoftware.com, Owner/
Chief Programmer, Animated Software Co.,
CA, Carlsbad

Hoffman, Brooke......................(856) 308-9022
bhoffma1@gccnj.edu, Advisor, Gloucester
County College, NJ, Sewell

Hoffman, Bruce
bhoffman@whitegatefeatures.com, Sr. Vice
Pres./Mgr., Mid Atlantic, Gilbane Building
Co., RI, Providence

Hoffman, Charles
Publisher@thelimonleader.com, Co-Pub.,
Eastern Colorado Plainsman, CO, Limon

Hoffman, Dana......................(610) 236-4744
dhoffman@readingeagle.com, Mktg. Cord.,
Reading Eagle Company, PA, Reading

Hoffman, Debbie...........(620) 694-5700 Ext. 247
dhoffman@hutchnews.com, Sales Asst., The
Hutchinson News, KS, Hutchinson

Hoffman, Ed
ehoffman@baltimoreguide.com, Adv. Mgr.,
Newark Post, MD, Elkton
ehoffman@baltimoreguide.com, Pub., The
Baltimore Guide, MD, Baltimore

Hoffman, George..................(406) 388-5101 x10
ghoffman@belgrade-news.com, Adv. Dir.,
Belgrade News, MT, Belgrade

Hoffman, Gilbert
nenewsroom@aol.com, Pub./Gen. Mgr./Adv.
Mgr., Northeast News, TX, Houston

Hoffman, Jessica
Advertising@thelimonleader.com, Co-Pub.,
Eastern Colorado Plainsman, CO, Limon

Hoffman, Jim
news@brookvillestar.net, Pub./Ed., Brookville
Star, OH, Brookville

Hoffman, Kevin
khoffman@braunintertec.com, Ed. in Chief,
City Pages, MN, Minneapolis

Hoffman, Kurt......................(212) 453-9477
hoffman@forward.com, Prodn. Mgr., The
Forward, NY, New York

Hoffman, Marsha......................(712) 325-5730
mhoffman@nonpareilonline.com, Internet
Coord./New Media Ed., The Daily Nonpareil,
IA, Council Bluffs

Hoffman, Natalie
natalie@hillsborofreepress.com, Adv. Mgr.,
Hillsboro Free Press, KS, Hillsboro
natalie@hillsborofreepress.com, Adv. Mgr.,
Buyer's Edge Of South Central Kansas, KS,
Newton

Hoffman, Nick......................(814) 371-4200
nhoffman@thecourierexpress.com, Mng. Ed.,
The Courier Express, PA, Du Bois

Hoffman, Paul......................(317) 736-2701
Special Publications Ed., Daily Journal, IN,
Franklin

Hoffman, Roxane
Sdnadvertising@aol.com, Ad., Southern
Dutchess News, NY, Wappingers Falls

Hoffman, Roxane
Sdnadvertising@aol.com, Ad., Beacon Free
Press, NY, Wappingers Falls

Hoffman, Steve
shoffman@inlandpress.org, Accounting Mgr.,
Inland Press Association, IL, Des Plaines

Hoffman, Steve
editor@chestercounty.com, Ed., Chester
County Press, PA, West Grove

Hoffman, Wayne......................(212) 453-9417
whoffman@forward.com, Mng. Ed., The
Forward, NY, New York

Hoffman, Greg......................(973) 586-8290
Hoffmann@northjersey.com, Dir. Information
Technology, Herald News, NJ, Rockaway

Hoffmann, Pauline
hoffmann@sbu.edu, Asst. Prof., St.
Bonaventure University, NY, Saint
Bonaventure

Hoffmann, Stephen......................(228) 377-3163
stephen.hoffmann.ctr@us.af.mil, Editor,
Keesler News, MS, Gulfport

Hoffmann, Steve......................(541) 383-0380
shoffmann@bendbulletin.com, IT Director, The
Bulletin, OR, Bend

Hoffpauir, Saja
lifestyles@CrowleyToday.com, Lifestyles Ed.,
The Crowley Post-Signal, LA, Crowley

Hofmann, Lisa......................(330) 869-2424
lisa_hofmann@jewishakron.org, Adv. Mgr.,
Akron Jewish News, OH, Akron

Hogan, Colin......................(315) 598-6397
colin@fultonvalleynews.com, Ed. , The Valley
News, NY, Fulton

Hogan, Francis
fhogan@diocesefwsb.org, Page Designer ,
Today's Catholic, TX, San Antonio

Hogan, Jeff
editor@mihomepaper.com, Ed., The County
Press, MI, Lapeer

Hogan, Joseph
media.relations@ch.abb.com, CEO, ABB Ltd.,
Zurich

Hogan, Kathy......................(530) 737-5047
circ@redbluffdailynews.com, Circ. Mgr., Daily
News, CA, Red Bluff

Hogan, Mark
mhogan@maxxmh.com, Vice Pres., MAXX
Material Handling LLC, VA, Hampton

Hogan, Randy
editorial@helena-arkansas.com, Mng. Ed., The
Helena Arkansas Daily World, AR, HELENA

Hogan, Robert......................ext. 12
rhogan@irishvoice.com, Adv. Dir., Irish Voice,
NY, New York

Hogan, Tara......................(806) 874-2259
ads@clarendonlive.com, Adv. Dir., Clarendon
Enterprise, TX, Clarendon

Hogarth, Debora
dhogarth@masonvalleyws.com, Adv. Mgr.,
Mason Valley News/The Leader-Courier, NV,
Yerington

Hogerty, Dianne............(913) 722-0055 ext. 234
dhogerty@familyfeatures.com, Owner, Family
Features Editorial Syndicate, Inc., KS,
Mission

Hogg, Dale................(620) 792-1211, ext. 226
dhogg@gbtribune.com, Mng. Ed., Great Bend
Tribune, KS, Great Bend

Hoggatt, Dolan
hoggatt@hometownnewsol.com, Circ. Mgr.,
Hometown News, FL, Fort Pierce

Hoggatt, Dutch
dhoggatt@harding.edu, Assoc. Prof., Harding
University, AR, Searcy

Hoglund, Louis
louish@eot.com, Ed., Enterprise Bulletin, MN,
Perham

Hogshead, Nancy
nancy.hogshead@shj.com, Classified manager,
The Gaston Gazette, NC, Gastonia

Hogue, Glen......................(479) 785-7860
ghogue@swtimes.com, Circ. Mgr., Times
Record, AR, Fort Smith

Hogue-Heiby, Claire........(740) 373-2121 Ext. 537
chogue@mariettatimes.com, Copy Ed., The

Marietta Times, OH, Marietta

Hohlt, Adam......................(318) 255-4353
adam@rustonleader.com, Asst. Adv. Mgr.,
Ruston (LA) Daily Leader, LA, Ruston

Hohlt, Rick......................(318) 255-4353
rick@rustonleader.com, Pub./Ed. , Ruston (LA)
Daily Leader, LA, Ruston

Hohmann, Kellan......................(580) 548-8101
bizmgr@enidnews.com, Business manager,
Enid News & Eagle, OK, Enid

Hoilman, Josie......................(404) 471-6000
Agnes Scott College, GA, Decatur

Hoisington, Mary..........(620) 792-1211, ext. 201
mhoisington@gbtribune.com, Pub., Great Bend
Tribune, KS, Great Bend

Hojnacki, Stan......................(704) 261-2220
shojnacki@theej.com, Mng. Ed., The Enquirer-
Journal, NC, Monroe

Hoke, Patti
patti@theheraldtimes.com, Front Office, The
Rio Blanco Herald Times, CO, Meeker

Holbrook, Aaron
aholbrook@capitalnewspapers.com, Ed.,
Monday-mini, WI, Beaver Dam

Holbrook, Andrea......................(978) 675-2713
aholbrook@gloucestertimes.com, Managing
Ed., Gloucester Daily Times, MA, Gloucester

Holbrook, Antoinette..................(318) 362-0325
aholbrook@gannett.com, Classified Inside
Sales, The News-Star, LA, Monroe

Holbrook, Betty......................NA
NA, Perry County Petit Jean Country Headlight,
AR, Morrilton

Holbrook, Matt
matt.holbrook@kinston.com, Adv. Dir, The
Kinston Free Press, NC, Kinston

Holbrook, Vickie Schaffeld...........(208) 465-8111
vholbrook@idahopress.com, Ed., Idaho Press,
ID, Nampa

Holcher, Molly......................(308) 381-9435
molly.holcher@theindependent.com, HR Mgr.,
The Grand Island Independent, NE, Grand
Island

Holcomb, Anna
aholcomb@civitasmedia.com, Office Mgr., The
Stokes News, NC, King

Holcomb, Jody......................(818) 677-3140
California State University, Northridge, CA,
Northridge

Holcombe, Larry
lholcombe@yourdailyglobe.com, Mng. Ed., The
Daily Globe, MI, Ironwood

Holden, Mary Ellen..................(212) 856-6335
meholden@nnnlp.com, Sr. Vice Pres., Mktg.,
Newspaper National Network LP, NY, New
York

Holden, Tom
tom.holden@dailytimes.com, Photographer,
Kerrville Daily Times, TX, Kerrville

Holder, Bill
bholder@atcnonline.com, Pub., Panola
Shopper, TX, Carthage

Holder, Bill......................(903) 693-7888
news@panolawatch.com, Pub./Adv. Dir., The
Panola Watchman, TX, Carthage

Holder, Timothy......................(601) 485-1212
tholder@themeridianstar.com, Publisher,
Skyline, MS, Meridian

Holdrup, Pam
sales@wtsinc.com, Sales, Agility, TX, Houston

Holdway, Neil......................(847) 427-4573
nholdway@dailyherald.com, Assistant
Managing Editor / Copy Desk, Daily Herald,
IL, Arlington Heights

Hole, Leslie......................ext. 106
leslie@wwthayne.com, Adv. Mgr., Senior Times
South Central Michigan, MI, Battle Creek

Hole, Robert
echonews@gvtel.com, Ed., The Erskine Echo,
MN, Erskine

Holecek, Russell
rholecek@tampatrib.com, Ed., Carrollwood
News & Tribune, FL, Tampa

Holeton, Marcy..................(908) 277-1919x110
Marcy@njfamily.cpm, Advertising Director, New
Jersey Family, NJ, Summit

Holeva, Larry..............(570) 821-2064 ext. 2064
lholeva@citizensvoice.com, Executive Editor,
The Citizens' Voice, PA, Wilkes Barre

Hoffman, Christina
ads@pikedispatch.com, Prod. Mgr., Pike
County Dispatch, PA, Milford

Holgate, David
dholgate@theh-p.com, Pub., The Herald-
Palladium, MI, Saint Joseph

Holguin, Sergio......................(805) 781-7880
sholguin@thetribunenews.com, Digital
Development Director, The Tribune, CA, San
Luis Obispo

HolINS, Deb......................(605) 347-2503
deb.holland@rapidcityjournal.com, NH Editor,
Butte County Post, SD, Rapid City

Holland, Becky......................(903) 849-3333
editor@c-bstatesman.com, Editor, Chandler &
Brownsboro Statesman, TX, Chandler

Holland, Don......................(760) 951-6270
dholland@vvdailypress.com, Ed., Review, CA,
Victorville

Holland, Gunter......................96050
druck@schnitzer-azmod.de, Proprietor,
ALLGAUER ZEITUNG, Marktoberdorf

Holland, Jim
jim.holland@starherald.com, Pub., Twin City
Weekly, NE, Scottsbluff

Holland, Joel...............(616) 669-2700 ext. 101
joelch@advancenespapers.com, Pub./Mktg.
Dir./Adv. Mgr., South Advance, MI, Jenison

Holland, Katrina
katrina@bigbasinllc.com, Class., Okmulgee
Daily Times, OK, Okmulgee

Holland, Kurt
kholland@polkio.com, Ed., The Polk County
Itemizer-Observer, OR, Dallas

Holland, Liz......................(410) 651-1600
lholland@dmg.gannett.com, Ed., Somerset
Herald, MD, Salisbury

Holland, Makenzie..................(260) 225-4663
mholland@wabashplaindealer.com, Reporter,
Wabash Plain Dealer, IN, Wabash

Holland, Pam
accountsreceivables@iolaregister.com, Adv.
Mgr., Classified, The Iola Register, KS, Iola

Holland, Scott
sholland@mcdonoughvoice.com, Sports Ed.,
The McDonough County Voice, IL, Macomb

Holland, Stephanie..................(951) 222-8495
Riverside Cmty. College, CA, Riverside

Hollander, Brian
wtedit@gmail.com, Ed., Woodstock Times, NY,
Kingston

Hollander, Brian
saugertiestimes@gmail.com, Ed. , Saugerties
Times, NY, Kingston
saugertiestimes@gmail.com, Pub., Kingston
Times, NY, Kingston

Hollands, Jaclyn......................(701) 451-5661
jhollands@forumcomm.com, Multi-Media Sales
Mgr., InForum, ND, Fargo

Holle, Sheila
sholle@ottawaherald.com, Graphic Design
Coordinator, The Ottawa Herald, KS, Ottawa

Hollerbach, Karie
khollerbach@semo.edu, Asst. Prof., Southeast
Missouri State University, MO, Cape

Girardeau

Hollett, Michael
michaelh@nowtoronto.com, Pub., Now, ON, Toronto

Hollett, Paul
phollett@lightfantasticstudios.com, Pres./ Creative Dir., Light Fantastic Studios, Inc., NY, North Baldwin

Holley, Alvin
polknews@livingston.net, Pub., San Jacinto News-Times, TX, Livingston

Holley, Alvin
polknews@livingston.net, Pres./Pub., Polk County Publishing Co., TX, Livingston

Holley, Alvin
trinitystandard@valornet.com, Pub., The Trinity Standard, TX, Trinity

Holley, Alvin
grovetonnews@gmail.com, Pub./Adv. Dir., Groveton News, TX, Groveton

Holley, Alvin ....(936) 327-4357
polknews@livingston.net, Pub., Polk County Enterprise, TX, Livingston

Holley, Alvin
news@houstoncountycourier.com, Owner, Houston County Courier, TX, Crockett

Holley, Linda ....(936) 327-4357
enterprise@easttexasnews.com, Adv. Mgr., Polk County Enterprise, TX, Livingston

Holley, Linda ....(936) 398-2535
polknews@livingston.net, Adv. Dir., Corrigan Times, TX, Corrigan
polknews@livingston.net, Adv. Dir., San Jacinto News-Times, TX, Livingston

Holliday, Guy D ....(212) 556-8090
Adv. Vice Pres., Sales, The New York Times, NY, New York

Holliday, Susan
sholliday@rbj.net, President & Pub., Rochester Business Journal, NY, Rochester

Hollifield, Laura
lhollifield@artbeats.com, COO, ArtbeatsEXPRESS, OR, Myrtle Creek

Hollifield, Scott ....(828) 559-4051
rhollifield@mcdowellnews.com, Ed., The McDowell News, NC, Marion

Hollinger, Bernadette
wpeters@bluelinemediaholdings.com, Group Controller, BlueLine Media Holdings, WI, Neenah

Hollinger, Berni ....(715) 526 - 7003
bhollinger@shawanoleader.com, Group Controller, Shawano Leader, WI, Shawano

Hollinger, Kendra
info@activedatax.com, COO, Active Data Exchange, PA, Bethlehem

Hollingshead, Amy
publisher@atlantathriftynickel.com, Thrifty Nickel - South Metro, GA, Marietta
publisher@atlantathriftynickel.com, Publisher, Thrifty Nickel - Marietta North, GA, Marietta

Hollingsworth, Laura..................(615) 259-8303
lhollingsworth@tennessean.com, Pub., Robertson County Times, TN, Clarksville
lhollingsworth@tennessean.com, Pres./Pub., Fairview Observer, TN, Fairview
lhollingsworth@tennessean.com, Pres./Pub., The Hendersonville Star News, TN, Gallatin
lhollingsworth@tennessean.com, Pres./Pub., The Tennessean, TN, Nashville
lhollingsworth@tennessean.com, Pres./Pub., TN Media, TN, Nashville

Hollingsworth, Laura..................(615) 259-8303
lhollingsworth@tennessean.com, Pres./Pub., The Dickson Herald, TN, Dickson

Hollins, Kacey..........................(870) 895-3207
Adv. Exec. , The News, AR, Salem

Hollinshead, Matt

mhollinshead@currentargus.com, Sports Editor, Current-Argus, NM, Carlsbad

Hollis, Chris
rshepherd@kentuckynewera.com, Prodn. Mgr., Fort Campbell Courier, KY, Hopkinsville

Hollis, Chris
chollis@kentuckynewera.com, Prod. Mgr., Kentucky New Era, KY, Hopkinsville

Hollis, Donnie
dhollis@hopestar.com, Circ. Dir., Hope Star, AR, Hope

Hollis, Donnie ....(870) 777-8841
Circ. Mgr., The Gurdon Times, AR, Arkadelphia

Hollis, Gareth ....(479) 872-3035
ghollis@nwaonline.net, Display Adv. Mgr., The Free Weekly, AR, Fayetteville

Hollon, Jay..............................ext. 297
jhollon@monroenews.com, CFO, The Monroe News, MI, Monroe
jhollon@monroenews.com, C.F.O. , Bedford Now, MI, Monroe

Holloway, David
office@thetomahawk.com, Office Manager, The Tomahawk, TN, Mountain City

Holloway, Jane
record1@modocrecord.com, Ed., The Modoc County Record, CA, Alturas

Holloway, Rachel L.
rhollowa@vt.edu, Head, Virginia Polytechnic Institute and State University, VA, Blacksburg

Holloway, Rick
record1@modocrecord.com, Ed., The Modoc County Record, CA, Alturas

Holloway, Vicky
vicky@oakwoodregister.com, Advertising Sales, The Oakwood Register, OH, Dayton

Hollyfield, Amy........................(727) 893-8491
ahollyfield@tampabay.com, Deputy Managing Ed./Politics, Business , Tampa Bay Times, FL, St Petersburg

Holm, A J................................(916) 340-4793
aj@insidepublications.com, Acc. Rep., Inside Land Park, CA, Sacramento

Holm, Cheryl
cholm@thepiercecountytribune.com, Adv. Acct. Exec., Pierce County Tribune, ND, Rugby

Holman, Jeffrey .... (217) 241-1700 ext 248
jholman@illinoispress.org, Adv. Dir., Illinois Press Association, IL, Springfield

Holman, Jim
jholman@sdreader.com, Publisher and editor, San Diego Reader, CA, San Diego

Holman, Marvin......................(217) 477-5210
Sports, Commercial News, IL, Danville

Holmdahl, Teresa
sales@osceolasun.com, Ad. Sales, Messenger, MN, Scandia

Holmes, Adrian
a.holmes@projectsinknowledge.com, Vice Pres., Design Servs., Projects In Knowledge, Inc., NJ, Livingston

Holmes, Anita J ....(507) 376-7307
aholmes@dglobe.com, Business Mgr., Worthington Daily Globe, MN, Worthington

Holmes, Barbara......................(352) 347-3384
CPFDisplayAds@aol.com, Administrative Asst., Community Papers of Florida, FL, Belleview

Holmes, Barbara
FreePaperINK@aol.com, Production Manager, Association of Free Community Papers, NY, Liverpool

Holmes, Bonnell ....(229) 263-4615
quitmanpress@windstream.net, Editor, Quitman Free Press, GA, Quitman

Holmes, Bruce ....(613) 739-5152
bruce.holmes@sunmedia.ca, Adv. Sales Dir.,

The Ottawa Sun, ON, Ottawa

Holmes, Christina
cholmes@boonevilledemocrat.com, Office Mgr. , Booneville Democrat, AR, Booneville

Holmes, Dan..........................(315) 472-6007
dholmes@fcpny.com, Exec. Dir., AdNetworkNY, NY, Syracuse

Holmes, Dan
ads@fcpny.com, Exec. Dir., Community Papers Advertising Network, NY, Syracuse

Holmes, Dan
ads@fcpny.com, Executive Director, Free Community Papers of New York, NY, Syracuse

Holmes, James ....(706) 823-3400
james.holmes@augustachronicle.com, VP of Sales, The Augusta Chronicle, GA, Augusta

Holmes, Jennifer ....(207) 990-8216
jholmes@bangordailynews.com, Vice President, Bangor Daily News, ME, Bangor

Holmes, Keith
kholmes@republicmedia.com, The Arizona Republic, AZ, Phoenix

Holmes, Kris..........................(202) 334-9100
kris@eltiempolatino.com, Office Mgr., El Tiempo Latino, DC, Washington

Holmes, Mark ....ext. 304
mark.holmes@sunmedia.ca, Pub./Adv. Dir. , Northumberland Today, ON, Cobourg

Holmes, Mark ....(919) 789-2096
mark@ncpress.com, Director of Sales, North Carolina Press Service, Inc., NC, Raleigh

Holmes, Michael ....(402) 444-1073
michael.holmes@owh.com, Editorial Page Editor, Omaha World-Herald, NE, Omaha

Holmes, Michelle....................(205) 325-2160
mholmes@al.com, VP, Content, The Birmingham News, AL, Birmingham

Holmes, Monica
monica.holmes@goshennews.com, Adv. Sales Rep., The Goshen News, IN, Goshen

Holmes, Patrick
pholmes@lenoir.k12.nc.us, Exec. Ed., The Kinston Free Press, NC, Kinston

Holmes, Penny ....(910) 653-7444
tribpenny@tabor-loris.com, Advertising Manager, Tabor-Loris Tribune, NC, Tabor City

Holmes, Richard C. ....(780) 753-2564
rcholmes@agt.net, Ed., The Provost News, AB, Provost

Holmes, Rick ....(508) 626-3932
rholmes@wickedlocal.com, Opinion Ed., Milford Daily News, MA, Milford

Holmes, Roger ....(780) 842-4465
roger@starpress.ca, Publisher, Wainwright Star (OOB), AB, Wainwright
roger@starpress.ca, Pub., Wainwright Star Edge, AB, Wainwright

Holmes, Ron........................... 403- 526-5937
holmesprinting@inter.ab.ca, Pres., Holmes Publishing Co. Ltd., AB, Medicine Hat

Holmes, Ronald E.
oyenecho@telusplanet.net, Pub., Oyen Echo, AB, Oyen

Holmes, Sarah ....(250) 247-9337
sarah@soundernews.com, Pub., Gabriola Sounder, BC, Gabriola Island

Holmes, Tim
tholmes@timeshamrock.com, Adv. Mgr., The Valley Advantage, PA, Scranton

Holmlund, Susanne ....(780) 980-7480
susanne.holmlund@sunmedia.casholmlund@ leducrep.com, Pub., Leduc Representative, AB, Leduc

Holmlund, Susanne ....(780) 987-3488
susanne.holmlund@sunmedia.ca, Pub., Devon Dispatch News, AB, Devon

Holmlund, Susanne ....(780) 542-5380
susanne.holmlund@sunmedia.ca, Pub., Drayton Valley Western Review, AB, Drayton Valley

Holoman, Tammy ....(336) 727-7363
tholoman@wsjournal.com, Custom Publishing Manager, Winston-Salem Journal, NC, Winston Salem

Holota, Andrew
aholota@blackpress.ca, Mng. Ed., The Abbotsford News, BC, Abbotsford

Holschuh, Jeff
jholschuh@newtondailynews.com, Adv. Mgr., Newton Daily News, IA, Newton

Holski, Marty
angela@smartshopperusa.com, Circ. Mgr., Smart Shopper, ON, Ottawa

Holstein, Judah ....(888) 309-0639
judah@miracomcomputer.com, CEO, Miracom Computer Corp., NY, Eastchester

Holt, J. Tim ....(252) 329-9510
tholt@reflector.com, Chief Operating Officer, The Daily Reflector, NC, Greenville

Holt, Jim
jimh@signalscv.com, Senior Writer, Santa Clarita Valley Signal, CA, Santa Clarita
jimh@signalscv.com, Senior Writer, Connect SCV, CA, Santa Clarita

Holt, John ....(252) 436-2840
kholtzman@hendersondispatch.com, Sports Editor, Daily Dispatch, NC, Henderson

Holt, Kristi
kristi.holt@lubbockonline.com, Production Dir., Lubbock Avalanche-Journal, TX, Lubbock

Holt, Liz Sprague
lholt@carolinaparent.com, Circ. Mgr., Carolina Parent, NY, White Plains

Holt, Marcy
mholt@sanmarcosrecord.com, Adv. Dir., San Marcos Daily Record, TX, San Marcos

Holt, Newell
npta@gonpta.com, Pres., National Paper Trade Association, Inc., IL, Chicago

Holt, Pamela ....(850) 623-2120
pholt@srpressgazette.com, Editor, Santa Rosa Press Gazette, FL, Milton

Holt, Randy
inserts@reddeeradvocate.com, Insert Mgr., Red Deer Advocate, AB, Red Deer

Holt, Randy ....(403) 887-2331
publisher@sylvanlakenews.com, Pub, Sylvan Lake News, AB, Sylvan Lake

Holt, Randy ....(403) 887-2331
publisher@sylvanlakenews.com, Pub, Eckville Echo, AB, Sylvan Lake

Holt, Terri ....(618) 664-4566
Ed., Bond And Fayette County Shopper, IL, Greenville

Holt, Tim ....(252) 329-9510
tholt@reflector.com, Chief Operating Officer, Cooke Communications North Carolina, LLC, NC, Greenville

Holtan, Sarah
sarahholdon@cuw.edu, Concordia Univ. of Wisconsin, WI, Mequon

Holtkamp, Michele ....(317) 736-2774
mholtkamp@dailyjournal.net, Ed. , Daily Journal, IN, Franklin

Holtmann, Derik ....(618) 239-2470
dholtmann@bnd.com, Photo, Belleville News-Democrat, IL, Belleville

Holtsoi, Willie..........................(928) 871-1154
willie@navajotimes.com, Press Foreman, Navajo Times Publishing Company, Inc., AZ, Window Rock

Holtzclaw, Barry
barry@pressbanner.com, Editor, Press Banner, CA, Scotts Valley

Horton, Andrea ....(250) 423-4666
publisher@thefreepress.ca, Pub, The Free Press, BC, Fernie

Horton, Anita
sales@crestonvalleyadvance.ca, Sales Coord., Creston Valley Advance, BC, Creston

Horton, Barbara
bhorton@darnews.com, News Ed., Daily American Republic, MO, Poplar Bluff

Horton, Charles
chorton@standard.net, Pres./Pub., Kitsap Sun, WA, Bremerton

Horton, Jay
jhorton@scrippsweb.com, Director of Digital Sales, Newspapers, E. W. Scripps Co., OH, Cincinnati

Horton, Kevin
mail@goldcoastgazette.net, Ed./Pub., Gold Coast Gazette, NY, Glen Cove

Horton, Lee ....(360) 417-3525
lhorton@peninsuladailynews.com, Sports Editor, Peninsula Daily News, WA, Port Angeles

Horton, Pat
ads@camrosebooster.com, Art Director, The Camrose Booster, AB, Camrose

Horton, Rick ....(317) 736-2704
Prodn. Mgr., Pressroom, Columbia Basin Herald, WA, Moses Lake

Horton, Susan ....(213) 361-0932
sue.horton@latimes.com, Los Angeles Times, CA, Los Angeles

Horton , Sue
sue.horton@latimes.com, Ed., Op-Ed and Sunday Opinion, Los Angeles Times, CA, Los Angeles

Horton Gay, Gale ....(404) 284-4010 ext. 102
Gale@dekalbchamp.com, Mng. Ed., The Champion, GA, Decatur

Horvath, Laura ....(520) 797-4384 ext. 17
Laura@TucsonLocalMedia.com, Circ. Mgr. / Special Events Mgr., Tucson Weekly, AZ, Tucson

Horvath, Laura ....ext. 17
Laura@tucsonlocalmedia.com, Circ., Inside Tucson Business, AZ, Tucson
Laura@tucsonlocalmedia.com, Circ. Dir., The Daily Territorial, AZ, Tucson
Laura@tucsonlocalmedia.com, Circ. Mgr., Foothills News, AZ, Tucson

Horvath, Laura ....(520) 797-4384 ext. 17
Laura@TucsonLocalMedia.com, Circulation Manager, Explorer, AZ, Tucson

Horvit, Beverly ....(573) 882-7685
umcjourkta!missouri.edu, Exec. Dir./Treasurer, Kappa Tau Alpha National Honor Society for Journalism & Mass Communication, MO, Columbia

Horvit, Mark
mark@ire.org, Exec. Dir., Investigative Reporters and Editors (IRE), MO, Columbia

Horwitz, Arthur ....(248) 354-6060
ahorwitz@renmedia.us, Pub., The Detroit Jewish News, MI, Southfield

Hose, Matthew ....(415) 944-4627
mhose@thearknewspaper.com, Belvedere & public safety reporter, The Ark, CA, Tiburon

Hoskins, Greg
tribune@cbnstl.comt, Pub., Fairview Heights Tribune, IL, Mascoutah

Hoskins, Greg ....(618) 566-8282
ghoskins@heraldpubs.com, Pub., Clinton County News, IL, Mascoutah

Hoskins, Greg ....(618) 566-8282
mascherald@heraldpubs.com, Pub., The Mascoutah Herald, IL, Mascoutah
mascherald@heraldpubs.com, Pub., Scott AFB Flier, IL, Mascoutah

Hoskins, Greg
altnewsban@frontiernet.net, Owner, The Altamont News, IL, Altamont

Hoskins, Greg
heraldpubs@cbnstl.com, Pub., Scott Flier, IL, Mascoutah

Hoskinson, Kim ....(620) 694-5700 Ext. 240
khoskinson@hutchnews.com, Graphic Designer, The Hutchinson News, KS, Hutchinson

Hosman, Jen ....(616) 842-6400 ext. 221
jhosman@grandhaventribune.com, Business Services Supervisor , Grand Haven Tribune, MI, Grand Haven

Hostein, Lisa ....(215) 832-0744
Ed., Jewish Exponent, PA, Philadelphia

Hostetler, David ....(602) 308-6542
dhostetler@bizjournals.com, Prod. Dir., The Business Journal, AZ, Phoenix

Hostetler, Susan
s.hostetler@projectsinknowledge.com, Sr. Vice Pres., Projects In Knowledge, Inc., NJ, Livingston

Hotaling, Lynn
lynn@thesylvaherald.com, Ed., The Sylva Herald & Ruralite, NC, Sylva

Hotaling, Richard
rkhot@nycap.rr.com, Member Services Mgr., New York Press Association, NY, Cohoes

Hotchkiss, Jordyn ....(570) 321-4315
hotjord@lycoming.edu, Editor-in-Chief, Lycoming College, PA, Williamsport

Hothi, Dal
dal.hothi@thenownewspaper.com, Sales Mgr, The Now Newspaper, BC, Surrey

Hott, Jessie
publisher@gonzalesinquirer.com, Adv. Mgr., The Gonzales Inquirer, TX, Gonzales

Hotvet, Owen ....(605) 331-2240
ohotvet@argusleader.com, Circulation Director, Argus Leader, SD, Sioux Falls

Houchin, Rick ....(402) 756-2077
bluehillleader@gtmc.net, Editor, Blue Hill Leader, NE, Blue Hill

Houck, Jim ....(559) 735-3276
news@visaliatimesdelta.com, City Ed., Visalia Times-Delta, CA, Visalia

Houdeshell, Jordan
eic@mainecampus.com, Ed. in Chief, University of Maine, ME, Orono

Hough, Bill ....(508) 548-4700 ext.214
bhough@capenews.net, Ed./Pub., The Bourne Enterprise, MA, Falmouth
bhough@capenews.net, Pub./Ed., The Falmouth Enterprise, MA, Falmouth
bhough@capenews.net, Ed./Pub. , The Sandwich Enterprise, MA, Falmouth

Hough, William Henry
hough@capenews.net, Pub., Enterprise, MA, Falmouth

Houghton, Donald M. ....(207) 469-6722
theenterpr@aol.com, Ed., The Bucksport Enterprise, ME, Bucksport

Houghton, Howard ....(505) 986-3015
hhoughton@sfnewmexican.com, City Ed., The Santa Fe New Mexican, NM, Santa Fe

Houk, Keith
khouk@uh.edu, Clinical Asst. Prof., University of Houston, TX, Houston

Houk, Robert ....ext. 325
rhouk@johnsoncitypress.com, Editorial Page Ed., Johnson City Press, TN, Johnson City

Houk, Suzanne
bookkeeping@cknj.com, Prodn. Mgr., Central Kentucky News-Journal, KY, Campbellsville

Hould, Kelly ....(904) 686-3943
kelly@opcfla.com, Ed., Ponte Vedra Recorder, FL, Ponte Vedra Beach

Houlne, Rose ....(215) 832-0756
Circ. Mgr., Jewish Exponent, PA, Philadelphia

Houlton, Elizabeth ....(973) 569-7133
Houlton@northjersey.com, Dir. News & Production, Herald News, NJ, Rockaway

House, Brenda ....(606) 528-7898 Ext. 46
bhouse@thetimestribune.com, Accounting Clerk, Times-Tribune, KY, Corbin

House, Denis
sports@sentinel-echo.com, Sports Ed., The Sentinel-Echo, KY, London

House, Ginger ....(816) 234-4247
ghouse@kcstar.com, Circ, The Olathe News, MO, Kansas City

House, Kipper ....(606) 248-1010 Ext. 1129
dhouse@civitasmedia.com, Rgl. Delivery Mgr., The Harlan Daily Enterprise, KY, Harlan

House, Michael A.
mhouse@chicagodefender.com, Pres./COO, Chicago Defender, IL, Chicago

House, Tammy ....(870) 508-8034
thouse@baxterbulletin.com, Composing Supervisor, The Baxter Bulletin, AR, Mountain Home

House, Terri
terri@pagosasun.com, Owner/Pub./Ed., The Pagosa Springs Sun, CO, Pagosa Springs

Householder, Grace ....(260) 347-0738
ghousholder@kpcmedia.com, KPC Media Group, Inc., IN, Kendallville

Householder, Lorri
lhouseholder@jonesborosun.com, Circ. Director, The Jonesboro Sun, AR, Jonesboro

Householder, Max
mhouseholder@civitasmedia.com, Sports Ed., Swanton Enterprise, OH, Wauseon
mhouseholder@civitasmedia.com, Sports Ed., Fulton County Expositor, OH, Wauseon

Householder, Terry ....(260) 347-0400 Ext. 1176 ....
thousholder@kpcmedia.com, Pres./Pub., Northwest News, IN, Huntertown

Householder, Terry ......(260) 426-2640 Ext. 1176
thousholder@kpcmedia.com, Pres., Greater Fort Wayne Business Weekly, IN, Fort Wayne

Houseman, Alex ....(616) 331-2486
business@lanthorn.com, Grand Valley State Univ., MI, Allendale

Houser, Amanda
amanda@wellandshoppingnews.com, Adv. Mgr., Welland Shopping News, ON, Welland

Housholder, Terry
thousholder@kpcmedia.com, Pres./CEO/Pub., The Herald Republican, IN, Angola

Housholder, Terry ....(260) 347-0400 Ext. 1176
thousholder@kpcmedia.com, Pres./Pub./CEO, The Star, IN, Auburn
thousholder@kpcmedia.com, President, KPC Media Group, Inc., IN, Kendallville

Housholder, Terry ....(260) 347-0400 Ext. 1176 ....
thousholder@kpcmedia.com, Pres./CEO, The Butler Bulletin, IN, Auburn
thousholder@kpcmedia.com, Pres./Pub. , The Garrett Clipper, IN, Auburn

Housholder, Terry ....(260) 347-0400 ext. 176
TERRYH@KPCNEWS.NET, Pres./CEO/Pub., The News Sun, IN, Kendallville

Housholder, Terry ....(260) 347-0400, ext. 176
thousholder@kpcmedia.com, CEO, Smart Shopper, IN, Kendallville
thousholder@kpcmedia.com, Pres./CEO, Smart Shopper, IN, Angola

Housholder, Terry ....(260) 347-0400 Ext. 1176
thousholder@kpcmedia.com, Pub. , The Advance Leader, IN, Kendallville

Houslet, Travis ....(608) 745-3518
thouslet@capitalnewspapers.com, Sports Ed.,

Wisconsin Dells Events, WI, Portage
thouslet@capitalnewspapers.com, Sports Ed., Daily Register, WI, Portage

Houston, Angela` ....(903) 882-8880
classifieds@lindalnews-times.com, Office Mgr., The Lindale News & Times, TX, Lindale

Houston, Brant
houstonb@ad.uiuc.edu, Knight Chair Prof., University of Illinois, IL, Urbana

Houston, Brant
brant@ire.org, Prof., University of Missouri, MO, Columbia

Houston, Delores ....(337) 321-6744
classifieds@daily-iberian.com , Classified Adv. Supv. , The Daily Iberian, LA, New Iberia

Houston, Jeri ....(432) 687-8894
jhouston@mrt.com, Adv. Dir., Midland Reporter-Telegram, TX, Midland

Houston, Lorraine E.
editor@therecorder.ca, Ed., The Boissevain Recorder, MB, Boissevain

Houston, Maureen
mhouston@bnd.com, Belleville News-Democrat, IL, Belleville

Houston-Logan, Pat ....(325) 944-7653
sanangelo@thriftynickelads.com, Ed., American Classifieds, TX, San Angelo

Houtman, Jenny ....(740) 373-2121 Ext. 500
jhoutman@mariettatimes.com, Pub., The Marietta Times, OH, Marietta

Hovland, Roxanne
rhovland@utk.edu, Prof., The University of Tennessee, TN, Knoxville

Howald, Eric ....(519) 396-3111
indepen@bmts.com, Ed., The Independent, ON, Kincardine

Howald, Eric A. ....(503) 390-1051
editor@keizertimes.com, News Ed., Keizertimes, OR, Keizer

Howard, Alisha ....(770) 421-7700 ext. 174
ahoward@markem-imaje.com, Mgr., Mktg., Markem-Imaje, GA, Kennesaw

Howard, Bonnie ....(502) 223-8821
bfhoward@kypress.com, Controller, Kentucky Press Association, Inc., KY, Frankfort

Howard, Bonnie
bfhoward@kypress.com, Controller, Kentucky Press Service, Inc., KY, Frankfort

Howard, Brad ....(970) 384-9101
bhoward@postindependent.com, Assoc. Prof., Western Washington University, WA, Bellingham
bhoward@postindependent.com, Adv. Dir., Citizen Telegram, CO, Glenwood Springs

Howard, Brad
bhoward@postindependent.com, Advertising Director, Glenwood Springs Post Independent, CO, Glenwood Springs

Howard, Camille ....(304) 257-1844
choward@grantcountypress.com, Managing Editor, Grant County Press, WV, Petersburg

Howard, Dana
dhoward@brownpublishing.com, Adv. Dir., Times Community Newspapers, OH, Kettering

Howard, Diane ....(908) 766-3900
dhoward@newjerseyhills.com, Gen. Office Mgr., Today in Hunterdon (OOB), NJ, Bernardsville
dhoward@newjerseyhills.com, Hunterdon Review, NJ, Whippany
dhoward@newjerseyhills.com, The Citizen, NJ, Bernardsville

Howard, Diane ....(908) 766-3900
dhoward@recordernewspapers.com, Gen. Office Mgr., New Jersey Hills Media Group, NJ, Whippany

Howard, Diane ....(908) 766-3900 ext. 253

dhoward@newjerseyhills.com, Gen. Off. Mgr, Bernardsville News, NJ, Bernardsville

Howard, Elaine
ehoward@atpco.com, Pres./Pub., Navy Times, VA, Springfield

Howard, Freddie .... ext. 3029
Prodn. Mgr., The Baltimore Times, MD, Baltimore

Howard, James
james.howard@creativeloafing.com, Pub., Creative Loafing Tampa Bay, FL, Tampa

Howard, Jennifer .... (251) 867-4876, Ext 110
jennifer.howard@brewtonstandard.com, Circ Mgr, The Brewton Standard, AL, Brewton

Howard, Jon
jhoward@dailynews.net, IT Dir., The Hays Daily News, KS, Hays

Howard, Katie .... (717) 244-6753
info@igsknives.com, Corporate Sec, IGS Knives, Inc., PA, Red Lion

Howard, Linda .... (706) 208-235
linda.howard@onlineathens.com, Circ. Dir., Athens Banner-Herald, GA, Athens

Howard, Mari .... (401) 274-2149
webmaster@whitegatefeatures.com, Office Mgr., Whitegate Features Syndicate, Providence

Howard, Pat .... (814) 870-1721
pat.howard@timesnews.com , Mng. Ed., Erie Times-News, PA, Erie

Howard, Patterson .... (216) 999-4058
Controller, The Plain Dealer, OH, Brooklyn

Howard, Sallie Pope .... ext. 16
seph@atling.com, Adv. Mgr., The Atlanta Inquirer, GA, Atlanta

Howard, Stan .... (765) 671-2230
showard@chronicle-tribune.com, Advertising Director, The Current Bargain, IN, Marion

Howard, Stan .... (765) 671-2230
showard@chronicle-tribune.com, Adv. Dir., Chronicle-Tribune, IN, Marion

Howard, Tommy
thoward@gtowntimes.com, Ed., The Georgetown Times, SC, Georgetown

Howard , Steve .... (916) 321-1469
showard@sacbee.com, National/Key Account Manager , The Sacramento Bee, CA, Sacramento

Howard-Glaspie, Regina .... (336) 506-3020
rglaspie@thetimesnews.com, President, North Carolina Press Association, NC, Raleigh
rglaspie@thetimesnews.com, Audience Development Director, Times-News, NC, Burlington

Howarth, Dawn
dfournier@scansoft.com, Vice Pres., HR, Nuance Communications Inc., MA, Burlington

Howarth, Sue
sueh@warwickonline.com, Classified Adv. Mgr., Johnston Sun Rise, RI, Warwick

Howat, Amy .... (304) 526-2820
akerr@heralddispatch.com, Adv. Dir./Mktg. Dir., The Herald-Dispatch, WV, Huntington
akerr@heralddispatch.com, Adv. Dir., Putnam Herald, WV, Huntington

Howe, Andrea .... (812) 385-2525
ahowe@mtcarmelregister.com, Editor, Mount Carmel Register, IL, Mount Carmel
ahowe@mtcarmelregister.com, Ed. , Wabash And Edwards Today, IN, Princeton
ahowe@mtcarmelregister.com, Editor, Oakland City Journal, IN, Princeton
ahowe@mtcarmelregister.com, Ed., Princeton Publishing Co., Inc., IN, Princeton
ahowe@mtcarmelregister.com, Ed., Princeton Daily Clarion, IN, Princeton

Howe, Gary .... (608) 326-2441
howeads@mhtc.net, Publisher, North Iowa

Times, IA, Mc Gregor

Howe, Gary
ccrnews@alpinecom.net, Pub., The Clayton County Register, IA, Elkader

Howe, Hilary .... (248) 643-7766
American Newspaper Representatives, MI, Troy

Howe, Roberta .... (408) 374-9700
info@campbellexpress.com, Co Ed., Campbell Express, CA, Campbell

Howe, Stephanie
alabamian@montevallo.edu, Business Manager, Univ. of Montevallo, AL, Montevallo

Howe, Victoria
vhowe@rivertown.net, Gen. Mgr., Pierce County Herald, WI, Ellsworth

Howell, Amanda .... (325) 597-2959
newseditor@bradystandard.com, News Ed., Brady Standard-Herald, TX, Brady

Howell, Andy .... (520) 423-8614
ahowell@pinalcentral.com, Editor, Eloy Enterprise, AZ, Florence

Howell, Andy .... (801) 625-4288
cityed@standard.net, Graphics Ed., Standard-Examiner, UT, Ogden

Howell, Brenda .... (601) 267-4501
brendah@thecarthaginian.com, Office manager, The Carthaginian, MS, Carthage

Howell, David
southernreporter@bellsouth.net, Ed., The Southern Reporter, MS, Sardis

Howell, Haney
howellh@exchange.winthrop.edu, Assoc. Prof., Winthrop University, SC, Rock Hill

Howell, John .... (401) 732-3100
JohnH@rhodybeat.com, Publisher, Beacon Communications, Inc, RI, Warwick

Howell, John .... (662) 563-4591
publisher@panolian.com, Pub., The Panolian, MS, Batesville

Howell, John
johnh@rhodybeat.com, Pub./Beacon Ed., Rhody Beat, RI, Warwick

Howell, John I. .... (401) 732-3100 x226
johnh@rhodybeat.com, Pub., Cranston Herald, RI, Warwick
johnh@rhodybeat.com, Pub./Ed., Johnston Sun Rise, RI, Warwick

Howell, John I. .... ext. 226
johnh@rhodybeat.com, Pub., Pennysaver, RI, Warwick

Howell, John I. .... (401) 732-3100 ext. 226
johnh@rhodybeat.com, Pub./Ed., Warwick Beacon, RI, Warwick

Howell, Julie .... (740) 313-0350
jhowe@civitasmedia.com, Adv. Sales Coor., Record Herald, OH, Washington Court House
jhowe@civitasmedia.com, Adv. Sales Coord., Herald-Star, OH, Steubenville

Howell, Kathi .... (360) 795-3391
kathi@waheagle.com, Adv. Account Mgr., Wahkiakum County Eagle, WA, Cathlamet

Howell, Lizzie
ehowell5@emory.edu, Managing Ed., Emory Univ., GA, Atlanta

Howell, Michael .... (406) 777-3928
editor@bitterrootstar.com, Ed., Bitterroot Star, MT, Stevensville

Howell, Nancy .... (620) 231-2600 ext. 108
nhowell@morningsun.net, Adv. Rep., The Morning Sun, KS, Pittsburg

Howell, Penda .... (212) 932-7498
penda.howell@amsterdamnews.com, Vice President, Advertising, Sales, Partnerships., New York Amsterdam News, NY, New York

Howell, Rita W.
rita@panolian.com, News Ed., The Panolian,

MS, Batesville

Howell, Rupert
rupert@panolian.com, Mng. Ed., The Panolian, MS, Batesville

Howell, Scott .... (209) 369-7035 ext. 221
scotth@lodinews.com, Newsroom Ed, Lodi News-Sentinel , CA, Lodi

Howell, Wanda .... (706) 571-8626
whowell@ledger-enquirer.com, HR Manager, Columbus Ledger-Enquirer, GA, Columbus

Howell, Wendy
wendy.howell@thedailysentinel.com, Business Mgr., The Daily Sentinel, AL, Scottsboro

Hower, Kevin
joel@hillsborofreepress.com, Prod. Mgr., Hillsboro Free Press, KS, Hillsboro
joel@hillsborofreepress.com, Prod. Mgr., Buyer's Edge Of South Central Kansas, KS, Newton

Hower, Kurt .... (717) 255-8434
khower@acspa.com, Director of Operations, The Patriot-News, PA, Mechanicsburg

Howes, Adam .... (44-20) 78429550
adam.howes@dowjones.com, Regl. Sales Mgr., Dow Jones Newswires - London, United Kingdom, London

Howett, Grant
thewesterncanadian@gmail.com, Ed., The Western Canadian, MB, Manitou

Howitt, John .... (902) 426-0478
jhowitt@herald.ca, Asst. Dir., Design, The Chronicle Herald, NS, Halifax

Howsare, Timothy
editor@thepampanews.com, Ed., The Pampa News, TX, Pampa
editor@thepampanews.com, Community News Ed., Hernando Today (OOB), FL, SAINT PETERSBURG

Howse, Robert .... (902) 426-3098
bhowse@herald.ca, Editorial Page Ed., The Chronicle Herald, NS, Halifax

Howze, Lenora .... (410) 554-8271
lhowze@afro.com, Adv. Dir., The Afro American Newspaper-baltimore, MD, Baltimore
lhowze@afro.com, Adv. Dir., Afro American, MD, Baltimore

Hoying, Dave .... (419) 586-2371 ext. 235
business@dailystandard.com, Bus. Mgr., The Daily Standard, OH, Celina

Hoyos, Jorge M. De .... (316) 978-6908
Wichita State Univ., KS, Wichita

Hoyt, Katie
khoyt@mediaonepa.com, Adv. & Marketing Dir., The Evening Sun, PA, Hanover

Hozjan, Martin
info@mahmachine.com, Pres., MAH Machine Co., Inc., IL, Cicero

Hrabanek, Vickie .... (402) 371-1020 ext. 259
vhrabanek@norfolkdailynews.com, Adv. Dir., Norfolk Daily News, NE, Norfolk

Hrebicek, Brett .... (432) 687-8842
bhrebicek@hearstnp.com, IT Dir., Midland Reporter-Telegram, TX, Midland

Hreno, Cheryl .... (765) 825-0581 ext. 245
chreno@newsexaminer.com, Adv. Rep, Connersville News-Examiner, IN, Connersville

Hruby, Trish .... (973) 383-1500 ext. 214
thruby@njherald.com, Adv. Dir., Shopper's Guide, NJ, Newton

Hrycko, Mike
mhrycko@theworldlink.com, Cir. Dir., The World, OR, Coos Bay

Hsieh, Jeremy
jeremy@ktoo.org, Univ. of Alaska Southeast, AK, Juneau

Huang, Tom .... (214) 977-8635
thuang@dallasnews.com, Assistant Managing

Editor/Features & Community Engagement, The Dallas Morning News, TX, Dallas

Hubartt, Kerry .... (260) 461-8471
khubartt@news-sentinel.com, Sr. Ed., The News-Sentinel, IN, Fort Wayne

Hubbarb , TJ .... (937) 651-1114
tjhubbard@examiner.org, Asst. Gen. Mgr. , Bellefontaine Examiner, OH, Bellefontaine

Hubbard, Charles G.
chubbard@baldor.com, Cor. Commun. Dir., Baldor Electric Co., AR, Fort Smith

Hubbard, Dana .... (434) 978-7288
dhubbard@dailyprogress.com, Classified Coord, The Daily Progress, VA, Charlottesville

Hubbard, Edward
ehubbard@miles33.com, VP, Business Development, Miles 33, CT, Norwalk

Hubbard, J.C.
wjpjule@wilkes.net, Pub., The Wilkes Journal-Patriot, NC, North Wilkesboro

Hubbard, Jon B.
news@examiner.org, Vice Pres., Bellefontaine Examiner, OH, Bellefontaine

Hubbard, Todd .... (757) 247-4843
thubbard@dailypress.com, Circ. Mgr., Daily Press, VA, Newport News

Hubbell, Amy
amy@leelanaunews.com, Mng. Ed., The Leelanau Enterprise, MI, Lake Leelanau

Hubbell, Anne
ahubbell@ad.nmsu.edu, Interim Head, New Mexico State University, NM, Las Cruces

Hubbell, Linda
linda_hubbell@dailyjournal.com, Ed., San Francisco Daily Journal, CA, San Francisco

Hubble, Melissa .... (580) 235-1456
East Central University, OK, Ada

Hubele, Don .... (601) 968-8702
Belhaven College, MS, Jackson

Huber, Beth .... ext. 22
bhuber@cmcherald.com, Adv. Mgr., Cape May County Herald Times, NJ, Rio Grande

Huber, David R.
info@hotwax.com, Owner, Hotwax Multimedia, Inc., NJ, Ramsey

Huber, Ed
customerservice@simcomail.com, Customer Serv. Mgr., Simco Industrial Static Control Products, PA, Hatfield

Huber, Mary .... (419) 445-4466
Adv. Dir., Archbold Buckeye, OH, Archbold

Huber, Sandra
forttimes@sasktel.net, Pub., Fort Qu'appelle Times, SK, Fort Qu'Appelle

Huberdeau, Jennifer
jhuberdeau@berkshireeagle.com, Asst. Editor-Berkshire Eagle, New England Newspapers Inc, MA, Pittsfield
jhuberdeau@berkshireeagle.com, Online Ed., The Berkshire Eagle, MA, Pittsfield

Hubert, Achilles .... (418) 986-2345 ext. 3
editeur@leradar.qc.ca, Ed., Le Radar, QC, Cap Aux Meules

Hubin, Aaron .... (320) 848-2248
newsmir@hcctel.net, Adv. Mgr., The News Mirror, MN, Hector

Hubin, John
newsmir@hcctel.net, Ed., The News Mirror, MN, Hector

Hubin, John N.
newsmir@hcctel.net, Pub., Bird Island Union, MN, Bird Island

Hubner, Larry
lhubner@mediaonene.com, Pub., Harvard Hillside, MA, Devens
lhubner@mediaonene.com, Pub. , Pepperell

Free Press, MA, Devens

Hubrecht, Steve
steve@cv-pioneer.com, Reporter, The Columbia Valley Pioneer, BC, Invermere

Huchel, Brian............................(217) 477-5173
Newsroom, Commercial News, IL, Danville

Huck, Bill..................................(212) 576-9510
billh@metrosn.com, Sr. Vice Pres., Eastern Adv., Metro Newspaper Advertising Services, Inc., NY, New York

Huck, William...........................(212) 576-9510
billh@metrosn.com, Sr. Vice Pres./Eastern Region, Metro Newspaper Advertising Services, Inc., NY, New York

Huckle, Christopher...................(231) 775-6565
huckle@cadillacnews.com, Pub., Cadillac News, MI, Cadillac
huckle@cadillacnews.com, Pub./Gen. Mgr., Northern Michigan News, MI, Cadillac

Huckle, James E.......................(231) 929-3571
jhuckle@charter.net, Chrmn., Mainstream Publications LLC, MI, Traverse City

Huckle Mittelstaedt, Renee..........(231) 929-3365
rhmittelstaedt@charter.net, Pres., Mainstream Publications LLC, MI, Traverse City

Huculak, Ed............................(403) 973-0310
ed.huculak@sunmedia.ca, Pub., Airdrie Echo, AB, Airdrie
ed.huculak@sunmedia.ca, Pub./Adv. Dir., The Calgary Sun, AB, Calgary

Huculak, Ed............................(403) 235-7175
ehuculak@postmedia.com, Dir. of Sales, Calgary Herald, AB, Calgary

Hudder, Christine
christine@thevalleygazette.ca, Ed, Barry's Bay This Week, ON, Barry's Bay

Huddleston, Patricia
huddles2@msu.edu, Prof., Michigan State University, MI, East Lansing

Hudgin, Melissa
mhudgins@metroland.com, Adv, Belleville News, ON, Belleville

Hudgin, Melissa............(613) 966-2034 ext. 504
mhudgins@metroland.com, Sales, Rainy River Record, ON, Rainy River

Hudler, Rol..............................(719) 346-5381
rolhudler@plainstel.com, Pub., The Plainsdealer, CO, Burlington

Hudler, Rol
brecordadvertising@plainstel.com, Pub., Burlington Record, CO, Burlington

Hudnutt, Arthur
ect@ohio.net, Pub., Coverstory, OH, Elyria

Hudnutt, George D....................(330) 721-4040
ghudnutt@medina-gazette.com, Pub., The Medina County Gazette, OH, Medina

Hudson, Bob...............(719) 544-3520 ext. 511
bhudson@chieftain.com, Adv. Mgr., Display, The Pueblo Chieftain, CO, Pueblo

Hudson, Bonnie
bonniehudson@columbianprogress.com, Office Mgr., The Columbian-Progress, MS, Columbia

Hudson, Cindy
chudson@lsj.com, News Ed., Lansing State Journal, MI, Lansing

Hudson, David..........................(651) 523-2893
dhudson@hamline.edu, Hamline Univ., MN, Saint Paul

Hudson, Don............................(256) 340-2431
dhudson@decaturdaily.com, Exec. Ed., The Decatur Daily, AL, Decatur

Hudson, Gerald
gerald.hudson@seiu.org, Int'l Vice Pres., Service Employees International Union, CLC, DC, Washington

Hudson, Jeff............................(530) 747-8055

jhudson@davisenterprise.net, Educ./Schools Ed., The Davis Enterprise, CA, DAVIS

Hudson, Jerry C.
jerry.hudson@ttu.edu, Dean/Prof., Texas Tech University, TX, Lubbock

Hudson, Jim
jhudson@ptfi.net, Pub., The Perryton Herald, TX, Perryton
jhudson@ptfi.net, Pub., Perryton Herald, TX, Perryton

Hudson, Lou.........................(225) 388-0245
lhudson@theadvocate.com, Retail Sales Dir., The Advocate, LA, Baton Rouge

Hudson, Lugene..............................ext. 620
lhudson@ncnewsonline.com, Educ. Rep., New Castle News, PA, New Castle

Hudson, Phil............................(203) 789-5359
phudson@21st-centurymedia.com, Circ. Dir., The Middletown Press, CT, Middletown

Hudson, Phil
phudson@21st-centurymedia.com, Production Mgr., The Oneida Daily Dispatch, NY, Oneida
phudson@21st-centurymedia.com, Circ. Dir., The Times Herald-Record, NY, Middletown

Hudson, Robert
robert.hudson@alexcityoutlook.com, Sports Ed., Alexander City Outlook, AL, Alexander City

Hudson, Stacey.......................(706) 721-4410
smcgowen@georgiahealth.edu, Communications Coordinator Editor, The Connection (formerly the Beeper), Georgia Health Sciences University (formerly Medical College of Georgia), GA

Hudson, Tim
keyesa@mail.ecu.edu, Dir., East Carolina University, NC, Greenville

Hudsonc, Melissa
advertising@corbinnewsjournal.com, Adv. Mgr., News Journal, KY, Corbin

Huebert, Ellen
ellen.huebert@thecanadianpress.com, News Editor, Broadcast News Limited, ON, Toronto
ellen.huebert@thecanadianpress.com, News Editor, Canadian Press, The - Toronto, ON, ON, Toronto

Huebscher, Don............(715) 833-9216 ext. 3216
don.huebscher@ecpc.com, Ed., Leader-Telegram, WI, Eau Claire

Huebscher, Don.......................(715) 833-9216
don.huebscher@ecpc.com, Ed., Entertainment Spotlight Saver, WI, Eau Claire

Huelseman, Patricia...................1-(513) 367-4582...
phuelseman@registerpublications.com, Harrison Press, IN, Lawrenceburg

Huerta, Graciela
production@easyreader.info, Prodn. Dir., Easy Reader, CA, Hermosa Beach

Huesca, Robert
rhuesca@trinity.edu, Prof., Trinity University, TX, San Antonio

Hueston, John
info@aylmerexpress.ca, Ed., The Aylmer Express, ON, Aylmer

Huether, Bill.................(519) 291-1660 ext. 103
bhuether@northperth.com, Gen. Mgr., The Listowel Banner, ON, Listowel

Huether, Jordan.......................(308) 282-0118
jordan.scjs@gmail.com, Managing Editor, Sheridan County Journal Star, NE, Gordon

Huether, Tim...........................(605) 685-6866
booster@gwtc.net, Pub./Ed., Bennett County Booster II, SD, Martin

Huff, John..................(603) 742-4455 ext. 2945
jhuff@fosters.com, Chief Photo., Foster's Daily Democrat, NH, Dover

Huff, Lisa.....................(812) 663-3111 x7002

lisa.huff@indianamediagroup.com, Dir. Audience Dev., Greensburg Daily News, IN, Greensburg

Huff, Lisa.......................(812) 663-3111 x7002
lisa.huff@indianamediagroup.com, Regl. Circ. Mgr., Rushville Republican, IN, Rushville

Huff, Lisa.....................(812) 663-3111 ext 7002
lisa.huff@indianamediagroup.com, Reg Dir of Audience Development, The Herald-Tribune, IN, Batesville

Huff, Pierce...........................(504) 636-7426
phuff@theadvocate.com, Online Sports Editor, The Advocate, LA, Baton Rouge

Huffaker, Sheryl..............................x 293
Chief Financial Officer, The Daily Sentinel, CO, Grand Junction

Huffington, Arianna
Arianna@HuffingtonPost.com, Pres., The Huffington Post, NY, New York

Huffman, Faith
faith@ssecho.com, News Ed., Sulphur Springs News-Telegram, TX, Sulphur Springs

Huffman, Kristi
dispatch@mztv.net, Adv. Dir., Jeff Davis County Mt. Dispatch, TX, Fort Davis

Huffman, Lee
lhuffman@peoplesdefender.com, Pub./Ed., The People's Defender, OH, West Union

Huffman, Suzanne
s.huffman@tcu.edu, Prof./Grad. Advisor, News, Chair, Div., Journalism, Texas Christian University, TX, Fort Worth

Hug, Charles...........................(518) 454-5070
chug@timesunion.com, Pub, Pennysaver/moneysaver/advertiser, NY, Albany

Hug, Gerald............................(509) 582-1499
jhug@tri-cityherald.com, Controller, Tri-City Herald, WA, Kennewick

Hug, T.J...................................(618) 262-5144
tjhug@mtcarmelregister.com, Sports Editor/General Reporter, Mount Carmel Register, IL, Mount Carmel

Hug, Tj
gatoreditor@nwcable.net, Ed., The Prairie Post, IL, Albion

Huggins, Heather.....................(901) 433-9138
heather.huggins@journalinc.com, Advt Sales Consultant, The Bartlett Express, TN, Bartlett

Hugh, Rachel
rhugh@theweekender.com, Gen. Mgr., Weekender, PA, Wilkes Barre

Hughes, Autumn
autumnh@xtn.net, Lifestyles Ed., The Daily Post-Athenian, TN, Athens

Hughes, Bayne........................(256) 340-2432
bhughes@decaturdaily.com, Educ. Writer, The Decatur Daily, AL, Decatur

Hughes, Bill...............(570) 387-1234 ext 1325
Photo Ed., Press Enterprise, PA, Bloomsburg

Hughes, Buddy
bhughes@thebrunswicknews.com, City Ed., The Brunswick News, GA, Brunswick

Hughes, Cathy C.
chughes@timesanddemocrat.com, Pub./Adv. Dir., The Times and Democrat, SC, Orangeburg

Hughes, Connie......................(256) 304-0066
circulation@times-journal.com, Fort Payne Newspapers, Inc., AL, Fort Payne
circulation@times-journal.com, Circ. Mgr, The Times-Journal, AL, Fort Payne

Hughes, Dick
dahughes@statesmanjournal.com, Editorial Page Ed., Statesman Journal, OR, Salem

Hughes, Don
don.hughes@kobie.com, CIO, Kobie Marketing, Inc., FL, Saint Petersburg

Hughes, Jennifer
jhughes@timesjournal.com, Mng. Ed., The Jackson County Times-Journal, OH, Jackson

Hughes, Joe
joe.hughes@lubbockonline.com, Editorial Page Ed., Lubbock Avalanche-Journal, TX, Lubbock

Hughes, Julie
jhughes@pioneernewsgroup.com, Information & Circulation Systems Mgr., Pioneer Newspapers Inc, WA, Seattle

Hughes, Kat
khughes@businessobserverfl.com, Mng. Ed., Business Observer-Hillsborough-Pasco, FL, Sarasota
khughes@businessobserverfl.com, Exec. Ed., Business Observer, FL, Sarasota

Hughes, Kathy
hugheska@jmu.edu, Asst. Prof., James Madison University, VA, Harrisonburg

Hughes, Laura......................(608) 328-4202
lhughes@themonroetimes.com, Adv. Mgr., Monroe Shopping News, WI, Monroe

Hughes, Laura......................(608) 328-4202
Sales Mgr., Freeport Shopping News, IL, Freeport

Hughes, Laura..................................ext. 24
lhughes@themonroetimes.com, Adv. Mgr., Retail, The Monroe Times, WI, Monroe

Hughes, Laura..............(608) 328-4202 ext. 24
lhughes@themonroetimes.com, Adv. Dir., Stateline Buyers'guide, WI, Monroe

Hughes, Lynn..............................ext. 130
lhughes@innotek-ep.com, Vice Pres., Sales, Innotek Corporation, MN, Maple Grove

Hughes, Mariann.....................(306) 697-2722
sunnews@sasktel.net, Sales Associate, Broadview Express, SK, Grenfell

Hughes, Matt
matt.hughes@citizensbank.com, News Ed., The Journal Enterprise, KY, Providence

Hughes, Michael
mehughes@vcu.edu, Asst. Dir., Devel., Virginia Commonwealth University, VA, Richmond

Hughes, Pat...........................(765) 348-0110
newstimes@comcast.net, Ed., News Times, IN, Hartford City

Hughes, Peggy......................(304) 257-4833
bookkeeping@grantcountypress.com, Business Manager, Grant County Press, WV, Petersburg

Hughes, Sharon...........(937) 393-3456 Ext. 1673
shughes@civitasmedia.com, Med. Sales Mgr., Hillsboro Times-Gazette, OH, Hillsboro

Hughes, Tracy.......................(250) 832-2131
newsroom@saobserver.net, Senior Ed., Salmon Arm Observer, BC, Salmon Arm
newsroom@saobserver.net, Ed., Shuswap Market News, BC, Salmon Arm

Hughes, Will
will.hughes@aic.edu, American International College, MA, Springfield

Hughes, William.....................(718) 262-2492
whughes@york.cuny.edu, York College of CUNY, NY, Jamaica

Hugill, Bruce
bruce.hugill@skiatookjournal.com, Mktg., Skiatook Journal, OK, Skiatook

Huh, Jisu
jhuh@umn.edu, Asst. Prof., University of Minnesota, MN, Minneapolis

Hukel, Danny
danny@brenhambanner.com, Gen. Mgr., Banner Extra, TX, Brenham

Hukel, Danny
danny@brenhambanner.com, Gen. Mgr., Brenham Banner-Press, TX, Brenham

Hulbert, Jodi.................(515) 244-2145 ext 133

jhulbert@inanews.com, Comm. Dir., Iowa Newspaper Association, Inc., IA, Des Moines

Hulen, David..............................**ext. 596**
dhulen@alaskadispatch.com, Executive Ed., Alaska Dispatch News, AK, Anchorage

Hulings, Cindy
krcirculation@zitomedia.net, Circulation/ Business Manager , The Kane Republican, PA, Kane

Hulinsky, Jordyn
editor@csceagle.com, Mgr Ed, Chadron State College, NE, Chadron

Hull, Cindy
onecirculation@observernewsonline.com, Circ. Dir., The Observer News Enterprise, NC, Newton

Hull, Jeff
aakriti.kothiwal@umontana.edu, Adj. Instr., The University of Montana, MT, Missoula

Hull, Kelli....................**(386) 677-4262 ext. 2255**
daytona.pennysaver@psavers.com, Gen. Mgr., Volusia Pennysaver, Inc., FL, Ormond Beach

Hull, Kelli
kelli.hull@psavers.com, Gen. Mgr., Daytona Pennysaver, FL, Ormond Beach

Hull, Kelli
flagleri@psavers.com, Bus. Mgr., Flagler Pennysaver, FL, Bunnell

Hullett, Karen
kcraig@warricknews.com, Adv., Warrick County Today, IN, Boonville

Hulne, Rocky
rocky.hulne@austindailyherald.com, Sports Ed., Austin Daily Herald, MN, Austin

Hulsey, Randy
bhiwshopper@windstream.net, Circ. Mgr., Ben Hill Irwin Wilcox Shopper, GA, Fitzgerald

Hulstein, Robert
pluimpub@orangecitycomm.net, Pres., Advisor, IA, Orange City

Hultgren, Randy
randy@trftimes.com, Pub., Thief River Falls Times, MN, Thief River Falls

Hults, Beth...................**(607) 324-1425 Ext. 231**
bethhults@eveningtribune.com, Class. Adv., The Evening Tribune, NY, Hornell

Humayun, Hira
hhumayun@smith.edu, EIC, Smith College, MA, Northampton

Humble, Rhonda
submissions@gardnernews.com, Pub., Spring Hill New Era, KS, Gardner

Humble, Susan
busmgr@punxsutawneyspirit.com, Business Mgr., The Punxsutawney Spirit, PA, Punxsutawney

Humblot, Leslie......................**(514) 522-6142**
info@fpjq.org, Adv. Rep., Federation professionnelle des journalistes du Quebec, QC, Montreal (Quebec)

Hume, Mike
mhume@fcnp.com, Sports Ed., Falls Church News-Press, VA, Falls Church

Hume, Tim
thume@chronicleonline.com, Nat'l Acct. Exec., Citrus County Chronicle, FL, Crystal River

Humenik, John
jhumenik@azstarnet.com, Pub., Tucson Newspapers/TMC, AZ, Tucson

Humenik, John......................**(608) 252-6101**
jhumenik@madison.com, Pub, Wisconsin State Journal, Madison, WI, Madison

Humes, Jennifer T.....................**(860) 241-3669**
jhumes@courant.com, Dir. of Marketing and Communications, The Hartford Courant, CT, Hartford

Hummel, Todd

thummel@dailyitem.com, Sports Reporter, The Daily Item, PA, Sunbury

Hummels, Jill.........................**(785) 864-2934**
Univ. of Kansas Engineering School, KS, Lawrence

Humphrey, Brian
circulation@countrymedia.net, Circ. Mgr., Headlight-Herald, OR, Tillamook
circulation@countrymedia.net, Circ. Mgr., The News Guard, OR, Lincoln City

Humphrey, Janice
jhumphrey@bowesnet.com, Credit Mgr., The Stratford Beacon Herald, ON, Stratford

Humphrey, Lindsay
humphrey@uhcl.edu, Univ. of Houston Clear Lake, TX, Houston

Humphrey, Patricia...........**(606) 528-7898 Ext. 33**
thumphrey@thetimestribune.com, Adv. Clerk, Times-Tribune, KY, Corbin

Humphrey, Sean
shumphrey@globeandmail.com, VP, Mktg., The Globe and Mail, ON, Toronto

Humphrey, Steve
news@portlandmercury.com, Ed., Portland Mercury, OR, Portland

Hundsdorfer, Beth....................**(618) 239-2570**
bhundsdorfer@bnd.com, Newsroom, Belleville News-Democrat, IL, Belleville

Hundt, David..........................**(508) 862-1132**
dhundt@capecodonline.com, Controller, Cape Cod Times, MA, Hyannis
dhundt@capecodonline.com, Controller, The Standard-Times, MA, New Bedford

Hungarter, Jane......................**(717) 703-3000**
janeh@pa-news.org, Marketing Dir., MANSI Media, PA, Harrisburg

Hungerford, Steve
steve@countrymedia.net, Pres., Country Media Inc., OR, Portland

Hunley, Sara.........................**(618) 245-6216**
farinanews@yahoo.com, Ed./Pub., Farina News, IL, Farina

Hunn, Andy
andy.hunn@anygraaf.fi, Managing Dir., Anygraaf USA, MD, Owings Mills

Hunn, David
dhunn@post-dispatch.com, St. Louis Post-Dispatch, MO, Saint Louis

Hunshikatti, Nikhil
NHunshikatti@dispatch.com, Mktg. Dir. , The Columbus Dispatch, OH, Columbus

Hunsicker, Jason......................**(660) 665-2808**
dailyexpresseditor@gmail.com, Ed., Kirksville Daily Express, MO, Kirksville

Hunsinger, Karen......................**(478) 986-3929**
karen@jcnews.com, Adv. Rep., The Jones County News, GA, Gray

Hunt, Alanda..........................**(309) 690-5391**
ahunt@multiad.com, Business Development Manager, Local Search Association, IL, Peoria

Hunt, Bob..........................**(406) 257-9220**
hunt@flatheadbeacon.com, Adv. Dir., Flathead Beacon, MT, Kalispell

Hunt, Brian..........................**(509) 526-8331**
robblethen@wwub.com, Publisher, Walla Walla Union-Bulletin, WA, Walla Walla

Hunt, Bud...................**(740) 446-2342 Ext. 2108**
bhunt@civitasmedia.com, Pub., The Daily Sentinel, OH, Pomeroy

Hunt, Bud...................**(740) 446-2342 ext 2108**
bhunt@civitasmedia.com, Pub., Gallipolis Daily Tribune, OH, Gallipolis
bhunt@civitasmedia.com, Reg. Dir., Point Pleasant Register, WV, Point Pleasant

Hunt, Bud
bhunt@dddnews.com, Pub., The North-Stoddard Countian, MO, Dexter

Hunt, Bud
bhunt@dddnews.com, Pub., Daily Dunklin Democrat Extra, MO, Kennett

Hunt, Bud.................**(740) 446-2342, Ext. 2108**
bhunt@civitasmedia.com, Pub. , Sunday Times-Sentinel, OH, Gallipolis

Hunt, Christine..........................**ext. 109**
christine@sdsinc.com, Vice Pres., Opns., Sales Development Services, OH, Westerville

Hunt, Chuck..........................**(507) 247-5502**
brgazette@woodstocktel.net, Pub., Buffalo Ridge Newspapers, MN, Ruthton

Hunt, Clayton
editor@thecoasterr.ca, Ed., Harbour Breton Coaster, NL, Harbour Breton

Hunt, Fallon.................**(662) 287-6111 ext.339**
admanager@dailycorinthian.com, Adv. Mgr. , The Daily Corinthian, MS, Corinth

Hunt, Fay
fhunt@c-dh.net, IT Dir., Columbia Basin Herald, WA, Moses Lake
fhunt@c-dh.net, IT Dir., Columbia Daily Herald, TN, Columbia

Hunt, Gerri
ghunt@caswellmessenger.com, Ed, Rockingham Now, NC, Reidsville

Hunt, Gloria
gloria.hunt@tc.tc, Sales Mgr., The Western Star, NL, Corner Brook

Hunt, Gretchen
ghunt@thetd.com, Mng. Ed., The Times Dispatch, AR, Walnut Ridge

Hunt, Holly..........................**(870) 972-3135**
hollyhall@astate.edu, VP, Arkansas State, Kappa Tau Alpha National Honor Society for Journalism & Mass Communication, MO, Columbia

Hunt, Jill...................**(405) 372-5000 ext. 264**
advmgr@stwnewspress.com , Adv. Mgr., Stillwater News Press, OK, Stillwater

Hunt, Marcia
mhunt@hopestar.com, Bus. Mgr., Nevada County Picayune, AR, Hope
mhunt@hopestar.com, Bus. Mgr., Arkadelphia Siftings Herald, AR, Arkadelphia

Hunt, Marsha
mhunt@hopestar.com, Bus. Mgr., Hope Star, AR, Hope

Hunt, Peggy
phunt@fcgov.com, Prodn. Mgr., Senior Voice, CO, Fort Collins

Hunt, Steve.................**(626) 962-8811 ext. 2125**
steve.hunt@sgvn.com, Mng. Ed., The Whittier Daily News, CA, Monrovia

Hunt, Steve..........................**(760) 951-6270**
Ed., Desert Dispatch, CA, Victorville

Hunt, Steve..........................**(760) 951-6270**
shunt@vvdailypress.com, Ed., Daily Press, CA, Victorville

Hunt, Steve..........................**(626) 544-0811**
steve.hunt@sgvn.com, Sen. Ed., Covina Press Courier Highlander, CA, Monrovia
steve.hunt@sgvn.com, Sen. Ed., The Highlander - Glendora Edition, CA, Monrovia
steve.hunt@sgvn.com, Sen. Ed., Diamond Bar Highlander, CA, Monrovia
steve.hunt@sgvn.com, Sen. Ed., The Highlander - La Puente Edition, CA, Monrovia
steve.hunt@sgvn.com, Senior Ed., San Gabriel Valley Tribune, CA, Monrovia

Hunt, Tim
thunt@sshopper.com, Circulation Mgr., Southside Shopper, NC, Garner

Hunt, Wayne
wayne@inlander.com, Prodn. Mgr., The Pacific Northwest Inlander, WA, Spokane

Hunter, Alicia...............**(519) 291-1660 ext. 115**

ahunter@northperth.com, Adv. Mgr., The Listowel Banner, ON, Listowel

Hunter, Carol..........................**(515) 284-8545**
chunter@dmreg.com, Int. Exec. Ed., The Des Moines Register, IA, Des Moines

Hunter, Christopher
alexandra.froebe@mdbuyline.com, Prodn. Mgr., Buy Line, MI, Greenville

Hunter, Eddie........................**(580) 221-6513**
eddie.hunter@ardmoreite.com, Adv. Dir., The Ardmoreite, OK, Ardmore

Hunter, Eric..........................**(580) 323-5151**
Prodn. Supv., The Clinton Daily News, OK, Clinton

Hunter, Jay..........................**(330) 996-3184**
jhunter@thebeaconjournal.com, HR and Labor Relations Director, Akron Beacon Journal, OH, Akron

Hunter, Jill
jhunteradsales@gmail.com, Adv. Dir., Blanco County News, TX, Blanco

Hunter, Joan..........................**(814) 532-5120**
jhunter@tribdem.com, Personnel Mgr., The Tribune-Democrat, PA, Johnstown

Hunter, Jon M.
Jon@MadisonDailyLeader.com, Pub., The Madison Daily Leader, SD, Madison

Hunter, Julia..........................**(608) 283-7622**
Julia.Hunter@WNAnews.com, Member Services Dir., Wisconsin Newspaper Association, WI, Madison

Hunter, Kylee
khunter@nwkansas.com, Classified/ Adv. Graphic Designer, Colby Free Press, KS, Colby

Hunter, Ofelia................**(361) 664-6588 ext. 216**
ohunter@aliceechonews.com, Ed., Alice Echo-News Journal, TX, Alice
ohunter@aliceechonews.com, Ed., Freer Press, TX, Alice

Hunter, Rachel
gouvtribunepress@gmail.com, Ed., The Gouverneur Tribune-Press, NY, Gouverneur

Hunter, Scott
scott@grandcoulee.com, Ed./Pub., The Star, WA, Grand Coulee

Hunter, Scott B.
shunter@aikenstandard.com, Pub., Aiken Communications, Inc., SC, Aiken

Hunter, Scott W.
scott@grandcoulee.com, Ed., Star Buyer's Guide, WA, Grand Coulee

Hunter, Tippy
tippy.hunter@alexcityoutlook.com, Dir of Advert, Alexander City Outlook, AL, Alexander City

Hunter, Tippy
tippy.hunter@alexcityoutlook.com, Adv. Rep., Dadeville Record, AL, Alexander City

Hunter, Tippy..........................**(256) 234-4281**
tippy.hunter@alexcityoutlook.com, Advertising Director, Tallapoosa Publishers, Inc., AL, Alexander City

Hunter, Tippy..........................**(256) 234-4281**
tippy.hunter@alexcityoutlook.com, Advertising Director, The Wetumpka Herald, AL, Alexander City

Hunter, Tippy..........................**(256) 234-4281**
tippy.hunter@alexcityoutlook.com, Advertising Director, The Tallassee Tribune, AL, Tallassee

Hunter, Viv..........................**(406) 791-1415**
vhunter@greatfallstribune.com, Acct. Mgr., Great Falls Tribune, MT, Great Falls

Huntingford, Guy......................**(403) 235-7456**
ghuntingford@calgaryherald.com, Publisher, Calgary Herald, AB, Calgary

Huntington, Linn Ann..............**(785) 628-4018**
lhunting@fhsu.edu, Dir., Fort Hays State

University, KS, Hays

Huntzicker, Bill
behuntzicker@stcloudstate.edu, Asst. Prof., St. Cloud State University, MN, Saint Cloud

Hurd, Don
dongo75@aol.com, Pub., Times-Republic, IL, Watseka

Hurd, Don .... (765) 884-1902
bentonreviewads@gmail.com, Morocco Courier, IN, Kentland
bentonreviewads@gmail.com, Pub., The Benton Review, IN, Fowler

Hurd, Don .... (765) 884-1902
bentonreviewads@gmail.com, Pub., News & Review, IN, Monticello

Hurd, Hatcher
hhurd@northfulton.com, Exec. Ed./ Ed., John's Creek Herald, GA, Alpharetta
hhurd@northfulton.com, Exec. Ed., Milton Herald, GA, Alpharetta
hhurd@northfulton.com, Exec. Ed., The Forsyth Herald, GA, Alpharetta
hhurd@northfulton.com, Exec. Ed., The Revue & News, GA, Alpharetta

Hurd, Mark
mhead@hp.com, Chrmn./Pres./CEO, Hewlett-Packard Co., CA, Palo Alto

Hurdle, Lisa .... (434) 207-0229
lisa@fluvannareview.com, Adv. Mgr., Fluvanna Review, VA, Palmyra

Hurley, Chris .... (978) 739-8515
churley@wickedlocal.com, Sports Ed., Malden Observer, MA, Danvers

Hurley, Chris .... (978) 739-8515
churley@wickedlocal.com, Sports Ed., Medford Transcript, MA, Danvers

Hurley, Deborah C.
hurleyd@mscd.edu, Chair, Metropolitan State College of Denver, CO, Denver

Hurley, Morgan .... (619) 961-1960
morgan@sdcnn.com, Ed., GAY San Diego, CA, San Diego

Hurley, Sandra .... (336) 415-4635
shurley@civitasmedia.com, Regional Publisher, Mount Airy News, NC, Mount Airy
shurley@civitasmedia.com, Civitas Media, LLC-OOB, NC, Davidson

Hurley, Sandy
shurley@mtairynews.com, Publisher, The Tribune, NC, Elkin

Hurluy, Craig
viewpoints@chron.com, Adv. Sales Mgr., La Voz de Houston, TX, Houston

Hurm, Lisa .... (412) 263-2708
lhurm@post-gazette.com, General Manager, Pittsburgh Post-Gazette, PA, Clinton

Hurst, Gary .... (330) 298-2020
ghurst@recordpub.com, Cir. Mgr., Record-Courier, OH, Kent

Hurst, Gary .... (330) 298-2020
ghurst@recordpub.com, Cir. Dir., Twinsburg Bulletin, OH, Kent

Hurst, Leslie
publisher@clarionledger.com, Pres./Pub., Madison County Herald, MS, Ridgeland

Hurst, Lynn .... (540) 389-9355
lhurst@ourvalley.org, General Manager, The Fincastle Herald, VA, Fincastle

Hurst, Lynn .... (540) 389-9355
lhurst@ourvalley.org, General Manager, Salem Times-Register, VA, Salem

Hurt, Jeff .... (325) 735-2278
editor@dmchronicle.com, Editor, Double Mountain Chronicle, TX, Rotan

Husband, Bert
bwhusband@terracestandard.com, Sales, The Terrace Standard, BC, Terrace

Huschka, Robert
rmhuschka@freepress.com, Exec. Ed., Detroit Free Press, MI, Detroit

Huse, Jerry
jhuse@norfolkdailynews.com, Pub., Daily News Plus, NE, Norfolk

Huse, Jerry .... (402) 371-1020
Pres./Pub., Norfolk Daily News, NE, Norfolk

Husick , Phil
phusick@the-leader.com, Pub. , The Leader, NY, Corning
phusick@the-leader.com, Pub. , Horseheads Shopper, NY, Corning

Huskey, Stan .... ext. 215
shuskey@timesherald.com, Ed., The Times Herald, PA, Lansdale

Huss, Mary .... (419) 448-3205
mhuss@advertiser-tribune.com, Pub., East Bay Business Times, CA, San Francisco
mhuss@advertiser-tribune.com, Bus. Mgr., The Advertiser-Tribune, OH, Tiffin

Hussey, John
jphuss2@uky.edu, Mktg. Dir., University Press of Kentucky, KY, Lexington

Hussey, Mike
mhussey@butler.edu, Adv. Mgr., Indy's Child, IN, Indianapolis

Hussman, Walter .... (501) 378-3402
weh@arkansasonline.com, Pub.
, Arkansas Democrat-Gazette, AR, Little Rock

Hussman, Walter E.
news@arkansasonline.com, Owner/Pub., NAN LLC, MO, Little Rock

Hust, Charles
chust@journalenterprise.com, Ed, The Journal Enterprise, KY, Providence

Hust, Stacey
sjhust@wsu.edu, Asst. Prof., Washington State University, WA, Pullman

Husted, Amy
ahusted@wescompapers.com, Circ. Mgr., The Redmond Spokesman, OR, Redmond

Huston, Ashley
Ashley.Huston@dowjones.com, Head of Corporate Communication, The Wall Street Journal, NY, New York

Huston, Aubrey .... (609) 874-2182
ahuston@centraljersey.com, Ed, Hamilton-Robbinsville Observer, NJ, Princeton
ahuston@centraljersey.com, Ed., The Messenger Press (OOB), NJ, Cream Ridge

Huston, Aubrey .... (609) 874-2182
ahuston@centraljersey.com, Ed., Register-News, NJ, Princeton

Huston , Aubrey .... (609) 874-2182 .....
ahuston@centraljersey.com, Ed. , The Lawrence Ledger, NJ, Princeton
ahuston@centraljersey.com, Ed. , The Princeton Packet, NJ, Princeton
ahuston@centraljersey.com, Ed. , The Beacon, NJ, Princeton
ahuston@centraljersey.com, Ed. , Newspaper Media Group, NJ, Cherry Hill
ahuston@centraljersey.com, Ed. , Hopewell Valley News, NJ, Princeton
ahuston@centraljersey.com, Ed., Cranbury Press, NJ, Princeton

Husty, Mary Ann
mhusty@news-press.com, Asst. to the Exec. Ed., The Commercial Appeal, TN, Memphis

Hut, Margaret
contactus@washingtonparent.net, Ed., Washington Parent Magazine, MD, Bethesda

Hutchens, Mike
mhutch@ucmessenger.com, Sports Ed., The Messenger, TN, Union City

Hutcheson, Chip .... (270) 365-5588
chiphutcheson@timesleader.net, Pub., Times Leader, KY, Princeton

Hutcheson, Jack .... (317) 398-1273
jhutcheson@shelbynews.com, Circ. Dir., The Shelbyville News, IN, Shelbyville
jhutcheson@shelbynews.com, Circ. Mgr., Pharos-Tribune, IN, Logansport

Hutcheson, Linda .... (503) 624-6397 ext 22
linda@orenews.com, Advertising Services Manager, Oregon Newspaper Publishers Association, OR, Lake Oswego

Hutcheson, Paul .... (415) 892-1516 x 12
phutcheson@marinscope.com, Publisher, Marinscope Community Newspapers, CA, Novato
phutcheson@marinscope.com, Pub., Ross Valley Reporter, CA, Novato
phutcheson@marinscope.com, Pub., Ross Valley Reporter, CA, Sausalito
phutcheson@marinscope.com, Pub., San Rafael News Pointer, CA, Novato
phutcheson@marinscope.com, Pub./Adv. Mgr., Sausalito Marinscope, CA, Novato
phutcheson@marinscope.com, Pub., Twin Cities Times, CA, Novato

Hutcheson, Rick
convergent@convergent.com, Vice Pres., Mktg., Convergent Media Systems, GA, Alpharetta

Hutchins, Amber
ahutch13@kennesaw.edu, Asst. Prof., Kennesaw State University, GA, Kennesaw

Hutchins, Sally .... (207) 667-2576
Acct Mgr, The Ellsworth American, ME, Ellsworth

Hutchinson, Beth .... (716) 204-4919 ext. 4919
bhutchinson@beenews.com, Copy Ed., East Aurora Bee, NY, Williamsville

Hutchinson, Don .... ext. 103
hutch@cable-lynx.net, Comptroller, The Camrose Booster, AB, Camrose

Hutchinson, Jeff
jhutchinson@heralddispatch.com, Operations manager, The Herald-Dispatch, WV, Huntington

Hutchinson, Jeff
jhutchinson@bnd.com, Belleville News-Democrat, IL, Belleville

Hutchinson, Jerry
hutch@thisishutchinson.com, Pres., Hutchinson Associates, Inc., IL, Oak Park

Hutchinson, Karla
americanclassifieds@abilene.com, Owner, American Classifieds, TX, Abilene

Hutchinson, Rebecca
gctribune@consolidated.net, Ed., The Gulf Coast Tribune, TX, Needville

Hutchinson, Susan
susan@piquenewsmagazine.com, Sales Mgr, Pique Newsmagazine, BC, Whistler
susan@piquenewsmagazine.com, Sales Mgr, The Whistler Question, BC, Whistler
susan@piquenewsmagazine.com, Advertising Manager, Mountain Xpress, NC, Asheville

Hutchison, Darlene Kinsey
kinsey@shoppernewsnow.com, Adv. Sales, Halls Shopper News, TN, Knoxville

Hutchison, Earl R.
ehutch@tntech.edu, Dir., Tennessee Technological University, TN, Cookeville

Hutchison, Frank W.
ads@weeklybargainbulletin.com, Adv. Mgr., Weekly Bargain Bulletin, PA, New Castle

Hutchison, Mindy
info@nppa.org, Membership Dir., National Press Photographers Association, Inc., NC, Durham

Hutchison, Nathan .... (859) 624-6692
nhutchinson@richmondregister.com, Sports Ed., The Richmond Register, KY, Richmond

Hutchison, Patricia .... (780) 498-5743
phutchinson@thejournal.canwest.com,

Vice Pres., Mktg., Edmonton Journal, AB, Edmonton

Hutmire, Deb
news@perrytribune.com, Ed., Tribune Shopping News, OH, New Lexington

Hutmire, Deb
news@perrytribune.com, Ed., Perry County Tribune, OH, New Lexington

Hutner, Gary .... (978) 368-0176 ext. 4750
ghutner@telegram.com, Pub., The Banner, MA, Clinton

Hutner, Gary .... (978) 368-0176 ext. 750
ghutner@telegram.com, Pub., The Item, MA, Clinton

Hutner, Gary .... (978) 368-0176 ext. 750
ghutner@telegram.com, Pub., Item Extra, MA, Clinton

Hutson, Brenda .... (806) 352-2371
brenda.briscoenews@gmail.com, Mng. Ed., Briscoe County News, TX, Silverton

Hutson, Kaylea .... (918) 786-2228
news@grovesun.com, Mng. Ed., Grove Sun, OK, Grove

Hutson, Martin
martin.hudson@sunmedia.ca, Mng. Ed., The Calgary Sun, AB, Calgary

Hutson, Tom
thutson@civitasmedia.com, Reg. Rev. Dir., Amherst News-Times, OH, Oberlin
thutson@civitasmedia.com, Pub./Reg. Rev. Dir., Oberlin News-Tribune, OH, Oberlin
thutson@civitasmedia.com, Reg. Rev. Dir., Wellington Enterprise, OH, Oberlin

Hutson-Miller, Kaylea
khutson@grovesun.com, Ed, Grove Sun, OK, Grove
khutson@grovesun.com, Ed, Delaware County Journal, OK, Jay

Hutt, Marc .... (707) 453-8138
mhutt@thereporter.com , Adv. Dir., The Reporter, CA, Vacaville

Hutto, Carrie
chutto@dailyhome.com, Classified Mgr., The Daily Home, AL, Talladega

Hutto, Missy
mhutto@timesanddemocrat.com, Nat'l Adv. Mgr., The Times and Democrat, SC, Orangeburg

Hutton, Jeff .... ext. 255
jhutton@timesrepublican.com, Ed., Times-Republican, IA, Marshalltown

Hutton, Matt .... (440) 998-2323 Ext. 120
mhutton@starbeacon.com, Ed., Pennysaver, IL, Monmouth
mhutton@starbeacon.com, Ed., Star Beacon, OH, Ashtabula

Hutzell, Rick .... (410) 280-5938
rhutzell@capgaznews.com, Editor, The Capital, MD, Annapolis

Hutzell, Rick
rhutzell@capgaznews.com, Ed., The Maryland Gazette, MD, Annapolis

Huxley, Fred .... (519) 268-7337
signpost@on.aibn.com, Pub. , The Signpost, ON, Dorchester

Huxley, Lyndsay .... (519) 268-7337
signpost@rogers.com, Gen. Mgr. , The Signpost, ON, Dorchester

Huxman, Susan
susan.huxman@wichita.edu, Assoc. Prof./Dir., Wichita State University, KS, Wichita

Huybers, Johanna .... (775) 327-6736
jhuybers@rgj.com, Sports Ed., Reno Gazette-Journal, NV, Reno

Hwa-Yang, Kim
hykim@kyeongin.com, Ed. in Chief, KYEONGIN ILBO, Suwon

Hyatt, Beth .... (334) 335-3541

beth.hyatt@luvernejournal.com, Ed., The Luverne Journal, AL, Luverne

beth.hyatt@luvernejournal.com, Luverne Journal Ed., The Greenville Advocate, AL, Greenville

Hyatt, Ken
khyatt@tribune.com, Account Executive, Tribune Media Services Entertainment Products, Queensbury

khyatt@tribune.com, Account Executive, Tribune Media Services, NY, Glens Falls

Hyatt, Vicki
news@themountaineer.com, Mng. Ed, The Mountaineer, NC, Waynesville

Hyde, Deneane
deneane.hyde@examiner.net, Bus. Mgr., The Examiner / Examiner Weekend, MO, Independence

Hyde, Jon
jhyde@smcvt.edu, Assoc. Prof., St. Michael's College, VT, Colchester

Hyde, Peggy .... (256) 332-1881, ext.19
peggy.hyde@franklincountytimes.com, Adv. Mgr., Franklin County Times, AL, Russellville

Hyde, Rollie .... (405) 788-5597
rhyde@att.net, Southwest/Mountain States Assoc., Grimes, W.B. & Co., OK, Oklahoma City

rhyde@att.net, Senior Associate-Southwest/ Plains/West, Lewis Floyd- Grimes, W.B. & Co., AL, Gulf Shores

Hyde, Scotty .... (270) 783-3244
shyde@bgdailynews.com, Copy Ed., Daily News, KY, Bowling Green

Hyland, John
john.hyland@centro.net, VP, Pub. Solutions, Centro Inc., IL, Chicago

Hymovitz, Craig .... (831) 754-4133
chymovitz@thecalifornian.com, Adv. Sales Mgr., The Salinas Californian, CA, Salinas

Hynds, Mark
markhynds@hartcom.net, Ed., The Hartwell Sun, GA, Hartwell

Hynds, Tim
thynds@siouxcityjournal.com, Photo Dept. Mgr., Sioux City Journal, IA, Sioux City

Hynes, Terry .... (352) 392-0466
thynes@jou.ufl.edu, Dean Emerita/Prof., University of Florida, FL, Gainesville

Hypes, Eleanor .... (850) 315-4303
ehypes@nwfdailynews.com, Regional Human Resource Dir, Northwest Florida Daily News, FL, Fort Walton Beach

Hyslop, Noreen
nhyslop@dailystateman.com, Gen/Manag Ed, The Daily Statesman, MO, Dexter

Hyson, Bernadine
bhyson@trurodaily.com, Office Mgr., The Daily News, NS, Truro

Hytry, Janie ....(715) 345-2284
Adv. Services Mgr., Stevens Point Journal, WI, Stevens Point

Hyvonen, Cheryl
admin@sylvanlakenews.com, Admin, Eckville Echo, AB, Sylvan Lake

admin@sylvanlakenews.com, Admin, Sylvan Lake News, AB, Sylvan Lake

I

I'Anson, Steve ....(519) 733-2211 Ext 30
si'anson@postmedia.com, Associate News Editor, The Kingsville Reporter, ON, Kingsville

Iaia, Marcello ....(518) 861-4026
miaia@altamontenterprise.com, digital ed, co-pub, The Altamont Enterprise & Albany County Post, NY, Altamont

Ialacci, John J. ....(609) 844-7576

pia@new-proimage.com, President/CEO, ProImage America, Inc., NJ, Princeton

Iannucci, Maria .... (863) 802-7256
maria.iannucci@ledgermediagroup.com, Sales & Mktg. Mgr., The Ledger, FL, Lakeland

Iannuzzi, Mike
info@businesswire.com, Mgr., Southwest Reg., Business Wire - Los Angeles, CA, Los Angeles

Ibach, Dave ....(704) 761-2926
dibach@statesville.com, Ed., Statesville Record & Landmark, NC, Statesville

Ibanez, Enrique
redacquito@efe.com, Rep., EFE News Services - Quito, Ecuador, Quito

Ibanez, Gloria ....(509) 249-6184
gibanez@yakimaherald.com, Editor, El Sol de Yakima, Yakima Herald-Republic, WA, Yakima

Ibarra, Ricardo
ricardo.ibarra@pressdemocrat.com, La Prensa Sonoma, CA, Santa Rosa

Ibarria, Antonio
anthony@elespecial.com, Adv. Mgr., El Especialito, NJ, Union City

Ibarria, John
john@elespecial.com, VP, El Especialito, NJ, Union City

Iberson, Jodi
ntsales@nd-bhginc.com, Adv. Mgr., Mountrail County Record, ND, New Town

Icart, Melodye Hecht
namegameco@aol.com, Pres., The Name Game International, Inc., Plantation

Iceman, Deborah ....(419) 281-0581
diceman@times-gazette.com, Composing Manager, Ashland Publishing Co. LLC, OH, Ashland

Icenogle, Alan
editor@rushvilletimes.com, Ed./Owner, The Rushville Times, IL, Rushville

Ickes, Dave .... (304) 636-2121, ext. 121
dickes@theintermountain.com, Prod. Supervisor, The Inter-Mountain, WV, Elkins

Ida, Aileen
editor@etown.edu, EIC, Elizabethtown College, PA, Elizabethtown

Ifcic, Michael
mifcic@covnigtondiocese.org, Adv. Mgr., The Messenger, KY, Covington

Ifft, Bill
times@davenport-wa.com, Pub., Davenport Times, WA, Davenport

Ihator, Augustine
aihator@jsu.edu, Prof., Jacksonville State University, AL, Jacksonville

Iler, Betsy
betsy.iler@alexcityoutlook.com, Magazine Manag. Ed, Alexander City Outlook, AL, Alexander City

Iles, Stephen
ldlsports@gmail.com, Sports Ed., The Leesville Daily Leader, LA, Leesville

Iles, Steven
bdnsports@gmail.com, Sports Ed., Beauregard Daily News, LA, Deridder

Illman, Art ....(508) 626-3875
aillman@wickedlocal.com, Chief Photographer, Milford Daily News, MA, Milford

aillman@wickedlocal.com, Photo Dept. Mgr., Metrowest Daily News, MA, Framingham

Imada, Lee
leeimada@mauinews.com, News Ed., The Maui News, HI, Wailuku

Imada, Sarah
mgr@signalamerican.org, Gen. Mgr., Weiser Signal American, ID, Weiser

Imel, Joe .... (270) 783-3292

jimel@bgdailynews.com, Asst. Mgr./Photo Editor, Daily News, KY, Bowling Green

Imes, Birney .... (662) 328-2424 x163
birney@cdispatch.com, Pub., The Commercial Dispatch, MS, Columbus

Imes, Peter x118
pimes@cdispatch.com, Gen. Mgr., The Commercial Dispatch, MS, Columbus

Imm, Kim
kimm@northwestsignal.net, Asst. Pub. / Asst. Gen. Mgr., Northwest Signal, OH, Napoleon

Immroth, Norma ....(620) 659-2080
edcsentinel@hotmail.com, Ed, Edwards County Sentinel, KS, Kinsley

edcsentinel@hotmail.com, Bucklin Banner, KS, Cimarron

Ince, Bob
bob@auroran.com, Gen. Mgr./Adv. Mgr., The Auroran, ON, Aurora

Indig, Patrice ....(540) 675-3338
patrice@rappnews.com, Adv. Dir., Rappahannock Times, VA, Tappahannock

Infinger, Steven ....(352) 753-1119
steve.infinger@thevillagesmedia.com, Director of Operations, The Villages Daily Sun, FL, The Villages

Ingebrand, Lisa
ads@newpraguetimes.com, Adv. Mgr., Lake Region Life, MN, New Prague

Ingebritsen, John
tcpnews@yousq.net, Pub., Tri-County Press, WI, Cuba City

Ingebritsen, John
tcpnews@pcii.net, Pub., Round-up Shopper, WI, Cuba City

Ingebritsen, John
timeseditor@tds.net, Pub., Fennimore Times, WI, Fennimore

Ingebritsen, John ....(608) 723-2151
jinge@tds.com, Publisher, The Platteville Journal, WI, Platteville

Ingebritsen, John
lannews@tds.net, Pub., Reminder Shopper, WI, Lancaster

Ingebritsen, John
sentry@mwt.net, Reg. Pub., Hillsboro Sentry-Enterprise, WI, Hillsboro

Ingegneri, Paul ....(310) 543-6634
paul.ingegneri@langnews.com, V. Pres. Adv., Vida Latina - The San Diego Union Tribune, CA, San Diego

Ingle, Jamin .... (318) 377-1866 ext. 100
classifieds@press-herald.com, Classifieds, Minden Press Herald, LA, Minden

Ingles, Jo
joingles@owu.edu, Media Adviser, Ohio Wesleyan University, OH, Delaware

Ingmire, Dennis ....(719) 685-9690
dennis@pikespeakpublishing.com, Pub., Life After 50, CO, Manitou Springs

Ingold, Charles
charles.ingold@unco.edu, Prof./Chair, University of Northern Colorado, CO, Greeley

Ingold, Russell
ringold@fontanaheraldnews.com, Ed., Fontana Herald News, CA, Fontana

Ingram, Brenda ....(601) 782-4358
ads@smithcountyreformer.net, Gen. Mgr./ Marketing, Smith County Reformer, MS, Raleigh

Ingram, Denise
denise@therecordherald.com, Adv. Mng., The Record Herald, PA, Waynesboro

Ingram, Linda ....(940) 569-2191
linda@burknews.com, Adv. Mgr., Burkburnett Informer Star, TX, Burkburnett

Ingram, Silver ....(620) 257-2368

Distribution, The Lyons News, KS, Lyons

Ingram, Tom
ingram@uta.edu, Assoc. Prof., University of Texas at Arlington, TX, Arlington

Ingram, Wayne
wingram@cableone.net, Adv. Mgr., Bingham County Bargains, ID, Blackfoot

Ingrassia, Lawrence
lawrence.ingrassia@latimes.com, Managing Ed., Los Angeles Times, CA, Los Angeles

Inman, Laura
laura.inman@ajcmediasolutions.com, Dir., Mktg. Devel., Atlanta Journal-Constitution, GA, Atlanta

Inskeep, Julie ....(260) 461-8490
jinskeep@jg.net, Pres./Pub., The Journal Gazette, IN, FORT WAYNE

Insley, David ....(410) 770-4095
dinsley@stardem.com , Staff Writer , The Star-Democrat, MD, Easton

Iori, Amy .... (620) 231-2600 ext. 148
aiori@morningsun.net, Asst. Bookkeeper, The Morning Sun, KS, Pittsburg

Iorio, Sharon
sharon.iorio@wichita.edu, Prof., Wichita State University, KS, Wichita

Iovacchini, Nikki ....(410) 845-4622
niovacchini@dmg.gannett.com, Exec. Asst., The Daily Times, MD, Salisbury

Iovino, Jim ....(412) 263-3566
jiovino@post-gazette.com, Deputy Managing Editor, Pittsburgh Post-Gazette, PA, Clinton

Ipsan, Matthew ....(334) 293-5800
mipsan@cnhi.com, Chief Digital Officer/VP, Community Newspaper Holdings, Inc., AL, Montgomery

Iraci, Ray .... (203) 775-9122 ext. 232
ray@ctpennysaver.com, Sales. Mgr., Yankee Pennysaver, CT, Brookfield

Ireland, Jeff
jireland@statesgraphic.com, Sports Ed., Brownsville States-Graphic, TN, Brownsville

Ireland, Joe
envoyeditor@gmail.com, Hunter College/ CUNY, NY, New York

Ireland, Robert
rireland@lakegenevanews.net, Mng. Ed., Lake Geneva Regional News, WI, Lake Geneva

Ireland, Sean
sireland@gapress.org, Publications Editor , Georgia Press Association, GA, Atlanta

Iriwn, Aimee
aimee@vervewireless.com, SVP Publisher & Advertising Operations, Verve Mobile, CA, Carlsbad

Irmen, Debbie
dirmen@eotfocus.com, Ed., Perham Focus, MN, Perham

dirmen@eotfocus.com, Assistant Ed., The Fergus Falls Daily Journal, MN, Fergus Falls

Iroku, Tammy
tammy@thegreenmconsulting.com, Webmaster and Graphics Specialist, Heart Tones, Lumberton

Irsik, Jody .... (303) 659-2522 ext. 221
jirsik@metrowestnewspapers.com, Prodn. Mgr., Commerce City Express, CO, Brighton

jirsik@metrowestnewspapers.com, Graphics, Commerce City Sentinel Express, CO, Brighton

jirsik@metrowestnewspapers.com, Prod. Supvr., Fort Lupton Press, CO, Brighton

Irvine, Dale
nice@galaxynet.com, Sec./Treasurer, Northwest International Circulation Executives, WA, La Conner

Irvine, Donald K. ....ext. 110
Chrmn., Accuracy in Media, Bethesda

Njacob@the-tidings.com, Gen. Mgr., The Tidings, CA, Los Angeles

Jacobs, Ben ....**(585) 232-6922**
bjacobs@nydailyrecord.com, Ed. , The Daily Record, NY, Rochester
bjacobs@nydailyrecord.com, Planning Editor, Democrat and Chronicle, NY, Rochester

Jacobs, Bob
jacobs@bradley.edu, Prof., Bradley University, IL, Peoria

Jacobs, Cindy ....**ext. 280**
cindy.jacobs@sunmedia.ca, Class. , The Peterborough Examiner, ON, Peterborough

Jacobs, Collette
cjacobs@toledocitypaper.com, Ed. in Chief, Ann Arbor Family Press, OH, Toledo

Jacobs, Collette ....**(419) 244-9859 ext. 101**
cjacobs@adamsstreetpublishing.com, Publisher, The Toledo City Paper, OH, Toledo

Jacobs, Collette ....**(419) 244-9859 ext. 101**
cjacobs@toledocitypaper.com, Pub., Toledo Area Parent News, OH, Toledo

Jacobs, Curt ....**(812) 265-3641**
cjacobs@madisoncourier.com, Pub., Madison Courier, Inc., IN, Madison

Jacobs, Danny ....**(443) 524-8159**
djacobs@thedailyrecord.com, Legal Ed. , The Daily Record, MD, Baltimore

Jacobs, Eric ....**(215) 422-4640 ext. 1**
jacobs@theDP.com, The Daily Pennsylvanian, PA, Philadelphia

Jacobs, Fred ....**(269) 945-9554**
fred@j-adgraphics.com, Pub., Battle Creek Shopper News, MI, Battle Creek

Jacobs, Fred ....**(269) 945-9554**
fred@j-adgraphics.com, CEO, J-Ad Graphics, MI, Hastings

Jacobs, Fred
news@j-adgraphics.com, Pub., Sun & News, MI, Hastings

Jacobs, Fred
fred@j-adgraphics.com, Pub./Adv. Mgr., Reminder, MI, Hastings

Jacobs, Fred ....**(269) 945-9554**
Fred@j-adgraphics.com, Pub., Maple Valley News, MI, Hastings

Jacobs, George
gjacobs@cynthianademocrat.com, Pub., Harrison Shopper, KY, Cynthiana

Jacobs, Heather ....**(601) 384-2484**
advocate@telepak.net, Pub./Ed., Franklin Advocate, MS, Meadville

Jacobs, Helen ....**(615) 259-8306**
hjacobs@gannett.com, Sr. HR Business Partner, The Tennessean, TN, Nashville
hjacobs@gannett.com, Sr. HR Business Partner, TN Media, TN, Nashville

Jacobs, Janice ....**(312) 222-2122**
jjacobs@tribune.com, Vice Pres., HR, Chicago Tribune, IL, Chicago

Jacobs, John
chronicle@jasnetworks.net, Pres./Pub., The Hastings Banner, MI, Hastings

Jacobs, John
advisor_circ@j-adgraphics.com, Owner, Ad-Visor and Chronicle, MI, Marshall

Jacobs, Karen
karen@hcindependent.com, Ed, Harvey County Independent, KS, Halstead

Jacobs, Kevin
kjacobs@octimesherald.com, Adv. Mgr, Bonus, WI, Oconto Falls

Jacobs, Mark
mjacobs@toledocitypaper.com, Adv. Dir., The Toledo City Paper, OH, Toledo

Jacobs, Mark
mjacobs@kmnewspaper.com, Pres., K & M

Newspaper Services, Inc., NY, Monroe

Jacobs, Michael ....**(404) 883-2130 x 104**
mjacobs@atljewishtimes.com, Ed., Atlanta Jewish Times, GA, Atlanta

Jacobs, Micki ....**(800) 828-0242**
info@kmnewspaper.com, Controller, K & M Newspaper Services, Inc., NY, Monroe

Jacobs, Phil
phil.jacobs@laureate.net, Ed., Jewish Times, MD, Baltimore

Jacobs, Phil ....**(410) 723-6397**
pjacobs@oceancitytoday.net, Ocean City Today, MD, Ocean City

Jacobs, Sherry ....**(610) 371-5103**
lgerhart@readingeagle.com, Classified Mgr, Reading Eagle, PA, Reading

Jacobs, Susan ....**(978) 745-4111**
editor@jewishjournal.org, Editor, North Shore Jewish Press, MA, Salem

Jacobs, Susan
sjacobs@tribune.com, Ed., Shoplocal, IL, Oak Brook

Jacobs, Wanda ....**(228) 934-1417**
wjacobs@press-register.com, Adv. Mgr., Nat'l, Press-Register, AL, Mobile

Jacobs, Wanda Heary
whjmsps@aol.com, Pub., The Mississippi Press, MS, Pascagoula

Jacobsen, Leanne
sales@jewishindependent.ca, Adv. Mgr., Jewish Independent, BC, Vancouver

Jacobsen, Sally
sjacobsen@ap.org, Gen. Mgr., Associated Press Managing Editors Association, NY, New York

Jacobsen, Vaughn ....**(801) 625-4410**
vjacobsen@standard.net, Circ. Mgr., Hilltop Times, UT, Ogden

Jacobson, Andy
andyjacobson61@gmail.com, Adv. Dir., Southwest Daily News, LA, Sulphur

Jacobson, Anne
ajacobson@republican-eagle.com, News Ed., Republican Eagle, MN, Red Wing

Jacobson, Anne
ajacobson@republican-eagle.com, Ed., Eagle Extra, MN, Red Wing

Jacobson, Anne
ajacobson@rivertowns.net, Editor, River Falls Journal, WI, River Falls

Jacobson, Bryce ....**(970) 875-1788**
bjacobson@craigdailypress.com, Publisher - Craig Daily Press, WorldWest LLC, KS, Lawrence

Jacobson, Jeff
Jeff.Jacobson@xerox.com, Corporate Executive Vice President President, Xerox Technology , Xerox Corp., CT, Norwalk

Jacobson, John
john_jacobson@nac.net, Pres., American Graphic Arts, Inc., NJ, Elizabeth

Jacobson, Judie
editorial@jewishledger.com, Mng. Ed., Connecticut Jewish Ledger, CT, West Hartford

Jacobson, Kristi
mail.midlandpress@midconetwork.com, Prodn. Mgr., Midland Shopper, SD, Aberdeen

Jacobson, Lynn ....**(206) 464-2714**
ljacobson@seattletimes.com, Deputy Mng. Ed., The Seattle Times, WA, Seattle

Jacobson, Michael ....**(320) 243-3772**
editor@paynesvillepress.com, Central Minnesota Lakes Area Shopper, MN, Paynesville
editor@paynesvillepress.com, Ed., Paynesville Press, MN, Paynesville

Jacobson, Peyton ....**(720) 274-7176**
pjacobson@sync2media.com , Account Executive, SYNC2 Media, CO, Denver

Jacobson, Seth ....**(781) 837-4558**
sjacobson@wickedlocal.com, Ed., Rockland Standard, MA, Marshfield

Jacobson, Seth ....**(781) 837-4558**
sjacobson@wickedlocal.com, Ed., Abington Mariner, MA, Marshfield

Jacobson, Simon
editor@algemeiner.com, Pub., Algemeiner Journal, NY, Brooklyn

Jacobson, Susan
aagelan@temple.edu, Asst. Prof., Temple University, PA, Philadelphia

Jacobson-Hines, Julie ....**(248) 745-4632**
julie.jacobson@oakpress.com, Local News Ed., The Oakland Press, MI, Pontiac

Jacoby, Barbara
bjacoby@cherokeetribune.com, Ed., Cherokee Tribune, GA, Canton

Jacoby, Barbara
bjacoby@cherokeetribune.com, Ed., Cherokee Tribune Plus, GA, Canton

Jacoby, Cathy
cathy.jacoby@bulletinreview.com, Circ. Mgr., Today's Action, IA, Denison
cathy.jacoby@bulletinreview.com, Office Mgr., Denison Bulletin & Review, IA, Denison

Jacoby, Jay ....**(818) 595-1122**
jay@flipyourlid.com, Pres./CEO, Flip Your Lid, CA, Tarzana

Jacoby, Jayson ....**(541) 523-3673**
jjacoby@bakercityherald.com, Ed, Baker City Herald, OR, Baker City

Jacquart, Paul ....**(902) 426-2873**
pjacquart@herald.ca, Adv. Mgr., Retail Sales, The Chronicle Herald, NS, Halifax

Jaeckle, Michael
michael@beacononlinenews.com, Ad-Design Mgr., The West Volusia Beacon, FL, Deland

Jaeger, Jan
jjaeger@thehawkeye.com, Mgr., HR, The Hawk Eye, IA, Burlington

Jaeger, Jan
jjaeger@thehawkeye.com, HR Mgr., Hawk Eye Shopper, IA, Burlington

Jaeger, Lowell
ljaeger@fvcc.edu, Flathead Valley Cmty. College out of business, MT, Kalispell

Jaffe, Chuck A. ....**(781) 383-6688**
jfeatures@aol.com, Columnist, J Features, Cohasset

Jaffe, Maayan
mjaffe@jewishtimes.com, Pub., Jewish Times, MD, Baltimore

Jagler, Steve ....**(414) 336-7116**
steve.jagler@biztimes.com, Exec. Ed., Milwaukee Business Journal, WI, Milwaukee

Jagnow, Betty H. Brown ..**(330) 747-1471 ext. 1203**
bjagnow@vindy.com, Pub., The Vindicator, OH, Youngstown

Jahn, Steve
steve.jahn@finance-commerce.com, Vice Pres./Pub., Finance and Commerce, MN, Minneapolis

Jahng, Rosie
jahng@hope.edu, Hope College, MI, Holland

Jahns, Kathy ....**(713) 417-7615**
getinfony@metrosn.com, Mgr., Metro Newspaper Advertising Services, Inc., CA, San Francisco

Jakiela, Lori ....**(724) 836-7481**
Univ. of Pittsburgh/Greensburg, PA, Greensburg

Jakubiak, Jane ....**(765) 213-5702**
jjakubiak@muncie.gannett.com, HR Coord./

Exec. Asst., The Star Press, IN, Muncie

Jakubisyn, Joseph J.
news@cheshireherald.com, Pres./Pub., The Cheshire Herald, CT, Cheshire

Jalbert, Jody ....**(207) 689-2913**
jjalbert@sunjournal.com, Adv. Mgr., Sun Journal, ME, Lewiston

Jalsevac, John ....**(888) 678-6008 ext 922**
jjalsevac@lifesitenews.com, Managing Ed., LifeSiteNews.com, VA, Front Royal

Jalsevac, Steve ....**(888) 678-6008 ext 921**
sjalsevac@lifesitenews.com, Managing Director, LifeSiteNews.com, VA, Front Royal

Jamerson, Terry ....**(540) 981-3326**
terry.jamerson@roanoke.com, Publisher, The Roanoke Times, VA, Roanoke

James, Alfred
recordnews@optonline. net, Pres./Pub., The Amityville Record, NY, Amityville

James, Alfred ....**(631) 264-0077**
recordnews@optonline.net, Pub., The Beacon, NY, Babylon

James, Alfred
acjnews@rcn.com, Pub., Massapequa Post, NY, Amityville

James, Danny ....**(972) 398-4472**
djames@starlocalmedia.com, National Adv. Dir., Allen American, TX, Plano
djames@starlocalmedia.com, National Adv. Dir., Carrollton Leader, TX, Plano
djames@starlocalmedia.com, National Adv. Dir., Celina Record, TX, Plano
djames@starlocalmedia.com, National Adv. Dir., Coppell Gazette, TX, Plano
djames@starlocalmedia.com, Nat'l Adv. Mgr., Flower Mound Leader, TX, Plano
djames@starlocalmedia.com, National Adv. Dir., Frisco Enterprise, TX, Plano
djames@starlocalmedia.com, National Adv. Dir., Lewisville Leader, TX, Plano
djames@starlocalmedia.com, National Adv. Dir., Little Elm Journal, TX, Plano
djames@starlocalmedia.com, National Adv. Dir., McKinney Courier-Gazette, TX, Plano
djames@starlocalmedia.com, National Adv. Dir., Mesquite News, TX, Plano
djames@starlocalmedia.com, National Adv. Dir., Plano Star-Courier, TX, Plano
djames@starlocalmedia.com, National Adv. Dir., Rowlett Lakeshore Times, TX, Plano
djames@starlocalmedia.com, National Adv. Dir., Sunnyvale View, TX, Plano
djames@starlocalmedia.com, National Adv. Dir., The Colony Courier Leader, TX, Plano

James, Gary
garyjames111@hotmail.com, Feature Interviewer/ Investigative Journalist, Gary James, East Syracuse

James, John ....**(802) 865-1020 x 44**
john@sevendaysvt.com, Prodn. Mgr., Seven Days, VT, Burlington

James, Josie ....**(765) 213-5775**
jjames@muncie.gannett.com, Legal Adv. Clerk, The Star Press, IN, Muncie

James, Karen ....**(240) 215-8617**
community@newspost.com , Community News, The Frederick News-Post, MD, Frederick

James, Kathy
circulation@ecdailynews.com, Circ. Mgr., Elk City Daily News, OK, Elk City

James, Michael ....**(205) 722-0205**
michael.james@tuscaloosanews.com, VP, Adv./Mktg., The Enterprise, IL, Plainfield
michael.james@tuscaloosanews.com, Gen. Mgr./VP Adv./Mktg, The Bugle, IL, Plainfield
michael.james@tuscaloosanews.com, Exec. Ed., The Tuscaloosa News, AL, Tuscaloosa

James, Michael L.
james@harding.edu, Dean/Prof., Harding University, AR, Searcy

James, Mike
mike.james@voya.com, Int'l Sales Mgr., MicroVoice Applications, Inc., MN, Minneapolis

James, Moroney .... (214) 977-8866
jmoroney@dallasnews.com, Publisher and CEO, The Dallas Morning News, TX, Dallas

James, Pam .... (740) 450-6751
psjames@gannett.com, Ed., Times Recorder, OH, Zanesville

James, Pam .... (740) 295-3420
psjames@gannett.com, Ed., The Coshocton Tribune, OH, Coshocton

James, Rob .... (402) 476-2851
rj@nebpress.com, Adv. Sales Dir., Nebraska Press Advertising Service, NE, Lincoln

James, Rob
rj@nebpress.com, Sales Mgr., Nebr Press Adv. Service , Nebraska Press Association/ Nebraska Press Advertising Service, NE, Lincoln

James, Shirley .... (912) 233-6128
sharon@savannahtribune.com, Ed., The Savannah Tribune, GA, Savannah

James, Susan .... (515) 244-2145 x 129
sjames@cnaads.com, Tech. & Digital Dev. Mgr., Iowa Newspaper Association, Inc., IA, Des Moines

James, Susan
sjames@steinseniorcenter.org, Associated Press, The, New York

James-Gilboe, Lynda
lynda.james-gilboe@il.proquest.com, Sr. Vice Pres., Mktg., ProQuest LLC, MI, Ann Arbor

Jameson, Dana .... (806) 250-2211
frionastar@wtrt.net, Mng Ed., The Friona Star, TX, Friona

Jameson, Michael .... (215) 949-4067
mjameson@calkins.com, VP of Publishing/ President and Publisher, Calkins Media, PA, Levittown

Jameson, Stephanie L.
sjameson@americanhometownpublishing.com, Vice President HR, American Hometown Publishing, TN, Franklin

Jameson, Steve .... (563) 262-0552
Editor / Publisher, Muscatine Journal, IA, Muscatine

Jamison, Duff .... (780) 460-5500
djamison@greastwest.ca, Pres., Great West Newspapers LP, AB, St. Albert

Jamison, Evan .... (780) 460-5534
ejamison@greatwest.ca, Plant Mgr., Great West Newspapers LP, AB, St. Albert

Janaszek, Amanda .... (717) 291-8883
ajanaszek@lnpnews.com, Sr. Client Solutions Manager, LNP, PA, Lancaster
ajanaszek@lnpnews.com, Sr. Client Solutions Manager, LNP Media Group, Inc., PA, Lancaster

Jane Pitt, Mary
newsofthehighlands@gmail.com, Ed., The News of the Highlands, NY, Cornwall

Janendo, Janice .... (212) 626-7685
janice.janendo@investors.com, Adv. Mgr., Opns. (E. Coast), Investor's Business Daily, CA, Los Angeles

Janensch, Paul
edit@ctpost.com, Assoc. Prof., Quinnipiac University, CT, Hamden

Janet, Jona .... (806) 892-2233
beacon@windstream.net, Pub./Ed./Adv. Dir., Idalou Beacon, TX, Idalou

Jang, Chyng-Yang
cyjang@uta.edu, Asst. Prof., University of Texas at Arlington, TX, Arlington

Jangula, Dennis .... (604) 730-7080
d_jangula@straight.com, IT Director , Georgia

Straight, BC, Vancouver

Janik, Melinda A. .... (585) 598-0030
Sr. Vice Pres./CFO, GateHouse Media, Inc., NY, Pittsford

Janner, Wayne
editor@kokomoherald.com, President./ Ed./ Pub., Kokomo Herald, IN, Kokomo

Janney, Cristina .... (316) 321-1120
cjanney@butlercountytimesgazette.com, Pub., The Butler County Times-Gazette, KS, Augusta
cjanney@butlercountytimesgazette.com, Pub., Wellington Daily News, KS, Wellington

Janoff, James .... (201) 837-8818
jljcomm@aol.com, Pub., Jewish Standard, NJ, Teaneck

Janos, John G. .... (847) 427-4332
jjanos@dailyherald.com, Circulation Manager, Daily Herald, IL, Arlington Heights

Jansen, Shawn .... (320) 838-3151
askovamerican@scicable.net, Editor, Askov American, MN, Askov

Janssen, Roger .... (605) 997-3725
mce3@mcisweb.com, Gen. Mgr., Moody County Enterprise, SD, Flandreau

Janssen, Terry
ementerprise@triotel.net, Mng. Ed., The Alexandria Herald, SD, Alexandria

Janz, Tom .... (907) 335-1230
tom.janz@peninsulaclarion.com, Circ.Mgr, Peninsula Clarion, AK, Kenai

Janzaruk, Rich .... (812) 277-7277
Photo Ed., The Times-Mail, IN, Bedford

Janzen, Jared
jareddjanzen@tabor.edu, Editor-in-Chief, Tabor College, KS, Hillsboro

Janzen, Matt .... (316) 283-1500 x115
mjanzen@thekansan.com, Creative Design, The Newton Kansan, KS, Newton

Jaque, Don .... (867) 872-3000
don@norj.ca, Ed., Northern Journal, NT, Fort Smith

Jaque, Sandra .... (867) 872-3000
sandra@norj.ca, Mgr, Northern Journal, NT, Fort Smith

Jaquins, Stephanie .... (815) 431-4087
stephanies@mywebtimes.com, Digital Editor, The Times, IL, Ottawa

Jaramillo, Alaina .... (505) 287-4411
ajaramillo@cibolabeacon.com, Adv. Acct. Mgr., Cibola Beacon, NM, Grants

Jaramillo, Donald .... (505) 287-4411
djaramillo@cibolabeacon.com, Gen. Mgr., Cibola Beacon, NM, Grants

Jaramillo, Donald
djaramillo@cibolabeacon.com, Ed., Beacon Mid-week, NM, Grants

Jaraway, Gayle
advertise@ecareview.com, Adv. Rep, East Central Alberta Review, AB, Coronation

Jarchow, Bill
bill.jarchow@indianamediagroup.com, Adv. Dir., The Weekend Flyer, IN, Avon

Jardine, Glen .... (802) 748-8121
jardineg@caledonian-record.com, Dig. Services Dir., The Caledonian-Record, VT, Saint Johnsbury

Jardine, Jackie
editor@pictouadvocate.com, Ed, The Pictou Advocate, NS, Pictou

Jardis, Adam .... 1-(630) 860-5959
adam@jardis.coom, Gen. Mgr., Jardis Industries, Inc., IL, Itasca

Jardis, Alan W. .... 1-(630) 860-5959
ajardis@jardis.com, Pres., Jardis Industries, Inc., IL, Itasca

Jaroff, Rebecca

grizzly@ursinus.edu, Ursinus College, PA, Collegeville

Jarosh, Andrew .... (239) 335-0299
ajarosh@fortmyer.gannett.com, Planning Ed., Targeted Products, The Commercial Appeal, TN, Memphis

Jarrach, Robert
bjarrach@njtimes.com, The Star-Ledger, NJ, Newark

Jarrell, Rosemary .... (662) 678-1515
rosemary.jarrell@journalinc.com, Finance Dir., Northeast Mississippi Daily Journal, MS, Tupelo

Jarret, Pam .... (561) 439-8064
Palm Beach Cmty. College, FL, Lake Worth

Jarrett, Linda
write4you@sbcglobal.net, co-president, Missouri Press Women, MO, Kirkwood

Jarvis, Brian
Bjarvis@theet.com, President, The Exponent Telegram, WV, Clarksburg

Jarvis, Charles .... (330) 841-1600
cjarvis@tribtoday.com, Pub., The Tribune Chronicle, OH, Warren

Jarvis, Elena .... (386) 804-7103
jarvise@daytonastate.edu, Advisor, Daytona State College, FL, Daytona Beach

Jasey, Darren .... (734) 953-2212
djasey@oe.homecomm.net, IT Mgr., Lake Orion Eccentric, MI, Detroit

Jasiek, Gary
gjasiek@jcpgroup.com, Pub., Lake Country Buyers Guide, WI, Hartland

Jasinowski, Alex
west@kimototech.com , Sales Supvr., Kimoto Tech, IL, Elk Grove Village

Jasinski-Herbert, T. Ron .... (773) 763-1646
editor@poloniatoday.com, Ed., Polonia Today, IL, Chicago

Jasnica, Rick .... (630) 530-2203
rjasnica@guk-vijuk.com, Op. Mgr., G&K-Vijuk International, IL, Elmhurst

Jasperson, Dorothy
dorothy.jasperson@lee.net, Ed., The Westby Times, WI, Westby

Jastrzebski, Joe .... (224) 361-8300
joe.jastrzebski@gammerler.com, Managing Director, Gammerler (US) Corp., IL, Mt Prospect

Jatczak, Ted
tjatczak@kentuckynewera.com, Sales/Mktg. Dir., Fort Campbell Courier, KY, Hopkinsville

Jatczak, Ted
tjatczak@kentuckynewera.com, Adv./Mktg. Mgr., Kentucky New Era, KY, Hopkinsville

Jaworski, Randy .... (530) 852-0255
randyj@goldcountrymedia.com, Auburn Journal, CA, Auburn

Jay, Lowell .... (785) 243-2424
jaylowell@nckcn.com, Advertising Mgr, Advertiser, KS, Concordia

Jayne, Greg .... (360) 735-4531
greg.jayne@columbian.com, Editorial Page Editor, The Columbian, WA, Vancouver

Jayne, Sidney
sidney@pendantpublishing.com, Acct Exec, Beacon Senior Newspaper, CO, Grand Junction

Jayyusi, Lena
lena.jayyusi@zu.ac.ae, Assoc. Prof., Zayed University, Al Ruwayyah

Jean, Patrick .... ext. 237
City Ed., The Hickory Daily Record, NC, Hickory
City Ed., Pow, NC, Hickory

Jeanroy, Amy .... (207) 454-0779
editorcalais@gmail.com, Managing Ed., The

Calais Advertiser, ME, Calais

Jebailey, Heissam .... (407) 447-4555 ext. 102
Univ. of Central Florida, FL, Orlando

Jech, Krista .... (952) 392-6835
krista.jech@ecm-inc.com, Mktg. Mgr., Columbia Heights/Fridley Sun Focus, MN, Eden Prairie
krista.jech@ecm-inc.com, Mktg. Mgr., Richfield Sun-Current, MN, Eden Prairie
krista.jech@ecm-inc.com, Mktg. Mgr., Eden Prairie Sun-Current, MN, Eden Prairie
krista.jech@ecm-inc.com, Mktg. Mgr., Excelsior/Shorewood/Chanhassen Sun Sailor, MN, Eden Prairie

Jefcoats, Kathy .... (770) 957-9161
kjefcoats@henryherald.com, Editor, Henry Daily Herald, GA, McDonough

Jeffcoat, David
djeffcoat@triplicate.com, Circ. Dir., The Del Norte Triplicate, CA, Crescent City

Jefferies, Brenda .... (905) 698-4841
editor@flamboroughreview.com, Ed., The Flamborough Review, ON, Waterdown

Jefferson, Donna .... (410) 263-1641
dj@chesapeakefamily.com, Adv. Mgr., Chesapeake Family Life, MD, Annapolis

Jefferson, Letitia .... (803) 644-2344
ljefferson@aikenstandard.com, Customer Serv. /classifieds Mgr., Evening Post Industries' Aiken Communications, SC, Aiken

Jeffries, Jina .... ext. 27
jjeffries@stategazette.com, Bus. Mgr., State Gazette, TN, Dyersburg

Jeffries, Mary L.
marketing@polaroid.com, CEO, Polaroid Holding Co., MA, Concord

Jekel, Tom .... (812) 379-5665
tjekel@therepublic.com, Ed., The Republic, IN, Columbus

Jelinek, Martin
martin@martinigear.com, Online Mgr., The Jackson Sun, TN, Jackson

Jelks, Lo .... (404) 523-6136
lojelks@aol.com, Atlanta University Center, GA, Atlanta

Jemison, Larrie
larrie@tnol.com, American Classifieds - Tallahassee, FL, Tallahassee

Jendli, Adel
adel.jendli@zu.ac.ae, Assoc. Prof., Zayed University, Al Ruwayyah

Jenereaux, Joyce
jjenereaux@dnps.com, Pub. , Detroit Free Press, MI, Detroit

Jenkins, Brad .... (540) 568-8084
jenkinbd@jmu.edu, Advisor, James Madison University, VA, Harrisonburg

Jenkins, Brandy .... (602) 258-6400
brandy@freedomdelivers.com, Sr. Sales Coord., Freedom Marketing Corporation, AZ, Tempe

Jenkins, Dennis
chicago@e-sbco.com, Sales Contact, Schermerhorn Bros. Co., IL, Lombard

Jenkins, James
jcj@oh-pc.com, Pub., The Logan Banner, WV, Logan

Jenkins, Jamey .... (704) 869-1741
jjenkins@gastongazette.com, Digital Sales Mgr., The Star, NC, Shelby

Jenkins, Jay
jjenkins@ncweeklies.com, Pub., Bertie Ledger-Advance, NC, Windsor
jjenkins@ncweeklies.com, Gen. Mgr., Enterprise & Weekly Herald, NC, Williamston

Jenkins, Jim
jimjenkins@siouxcityjournal.com, News Ed., Night, Sioux City Journal, IA, Sioux City

Jenkins, Joel
jjenkins@cninewspapers.com, Corp. Mktg. Dir., The Graham Star, NC, Robbinsville
jjenkins@cninewspapers.com, Corp. Mktg. Dir., The News-Observer, GA, Blue Ridge
jjenkins@cninewspapers.com, Corp. Mktg. Dir., The Cheraw Chronicle, SC, Cheraw
jjenkins@cninewspapers.com, Mktg. Dir., Mitchell News-Journal, NC, Spruce Pine
jjenkins@cninewspapers.com, Corp. Mktg. Dir., The Dahlonega Nugget, GA, Dahlonega
jjenkins@cninewspapers.com, Corporate Marketing Director / Major Account Manager, Community Newspapers, Inc., GA, Athens
jjenkins@cninewspapers.com, Corp. Mktg. Dir., The Elberton Star, GA, Elberton
jjenkins@cninewspapers.com, Corp. Mktg. Dir., The Hartwell Sun, GA, Hartwell
jjenkins@cninewspapers.com, Mktg. Dir., The Highlander, NC, Highlands
jjenkins@cninewspapers.com, Corp. Mktg. Dir., Clay County Progress, NC, Hayesville
jjenkins@cninewspapers.com, Corp. Mktg. Dir., The Franklin Press, NC, Franklin
jjenkins@cninewspapers.com, Corp. Mktg. Dir., Dawson News & Advertiser (OOB), GA, Dawsonville
jjenkins@cninewspapers.com, Corp. Mktg. Dir., The Toccoa Record, GA, Toccoa
jjenkins@cninewspapers.com, Corp. Mktg. Dir., The Northeast Georgian, GA, Cornelia
jjenkins@cninewspapers.com, Corp. Mktg. Dir., The Sylva Herald & Ruralite, NC, Sylva
jjenkins@cninewspapers.com, Corp. Mktg. Dir., The Telfair Enterprise, GA, Mc Rae
jjenkins@cninewspapers.com, Corp. Mktg. Dir., Tribune & Georgian, GA, Saint Marys
jjenkins@cninewspapers.com, Corp. Mktg. Dir., The Press-Sentinel, GA, Jesup
jjenkins@cninewspapers.com, Corp. Mktg. Dir., News-Leader, FL, Fernandina Beach
jjenkins@cninewspapers.com, Corp. Mktg. Dir., Nassau County Record, FL, Callahan

Jenkins, Judy .... (270) 831-8339 ext. 8339
jjenkins@thegleaner.com, Health/Medical Ed., The Gleaner, KY, Henderson

Jenkins, Kimberly
Ads@WatongaRepublican.com, Adv Rep, Geary Star, OK, Geary
Ads@WatongaRepublican.com, Adv. Rep, Hinton Record, OK, Hinton
Ads@WatongaRepublican.com, Adv, The Watonga Republican, OK, Watonga

Jenkins, Marty .... (417) 847-4475
lithoprinters@yahoo.com, Prodn. Mgr., Barry County Advertiser, MO, Cassville

Jenkins, Patricia
pjenkins@cynthiandemocrat.com, Gen. Mgr., Cynthiana Democrat, KY, Cynthiana

Jenkins, Patricia
pjenkins@cynthianademocrat.com, Adv. Mgr., Harrison Shopper, KY, Cynthiana

Jenkins, Phil .... (540) 374-5422
Pjenkins@freelancestar.com, Editor, The Free Lance-Star, VA, Fredericksburg

Jenkins, Roy
circulation@jcnewsandneighbor.com, Circ. Mgr., Johnson City News & Neighbor, TN, Johnson City

Jenkins, Tom
info@opentext.com, CEO, Open Text Corp., ON, Waterloo

Jenkinson, Mike .... (780) 468-0226
mike.jenkinson@edm.sunpub.com, Editorial Page Ed., The Edmonton Sun, AB, Edmonton

Jenkkins, Cheryl
cjenkins@wallowa.com, Class/Circ. Mgr., Wallowa County Chieftain, OR, Enterprise

Jenks, Jennifer .... (541) 573-2022
jjenks@burnstimesherald.inco, Ed., Burns Times-Herald, OR, Burns

Jenky, Bishop Daniel R. .... (309) 671-1550
cathpost@cdop.org, Pub., The Catholic Post,

IL, Peoria

Jenne, Wendy
wjenne@thevermontstandard.com, Adv. Rep., The Vermont Standard, VT, Woodstock

Jennex, Ken .... (902) 426-2886
kjennex@herald.ca, Purchasing, The Chronicle Herald, NS, Halifax

Jenney, Rob
robjenney@thecourier.com, Circ. Dir., The Review Times, OH, Fostoria

Jenney, Rob
robjenney@thecourier.com, Circ. Mgr., The Courier, OH, Findlay

Jennings, Ben .... (316) 268-6383
bjennings@wichitaeagle.com, Marketing Director, The Wichita Eagle, KS, Wichita

Jennings, Brad .... (717) 771-2061
bjennings@ydr.com, AME - Visual and MultiMedia, York Daily Record/York Sunday News, PA, York

Jennings, Glenn .... (502) 222-7183
GlenJennings@oldhamera.com, Reporter, Oldham Era, KY, La Grange

Jennings, Joel
Joel@goldendalesentinel.com, Bookkeeper, Goldendale Sentinel, WA, Goldendale

Jennings, Robert
editor@mountainstatesman.com, Ed., Mountain Statesman, WV, Grafton

Jennings, Stacy .... (912) 652-0236
stacy.jennings@savannahnow.com, Dir., Mktg./ Promo., Savannah Morning News, GA, Savannah

Jennings, Tina .... ext. 229
cmushynski@durhamregion.com, Adv. Coord., Oshawa-whitby This Week, ON, Oshawa

Jensen, Alissa
alissa@strathmoretimes.com, Prod./Class. Mgr, Strathmore Times, AB, Strathmore

Jensen, Amy
amy@parsonssun.com, Circ. Mgr., Parsons Sun, KS, Parsons

Jensen, Amy
amy@chanute.com, Circ. Mgr., The Chanute Tribune, KS, Chanute

Jensen, Bret
bjensen@vancott.com, Cor. Sales, XMission, UT, Salt Lake City

Jensen, Carsten Boe
cje@ccieurope.com, President, CCI US, CCI Europe, Inc., GA, Kennesaw

Jensen, Cherie
cheriej@sdna.com, Asst. Mgr., South Dakota Newspaper Association, SD, Brookings

Jensen, Chris
chris@obsentinel.com, Adv. Mgr., Outer Banks Sentinel, NC, Nags Head

Jensen, Cyndi .... (262) 728-3411, ext. 111
cjensen@rvpublishing.com, Gen. Mgr., Waterford Post, WI, Burlington

Jensen, Cyndi
cjensen@rvpublishing.com, Gen. Mgr., Palmyra Enterprise, WI, Delavan

Jensen, Cyndi .... (262) 728-3411, ext. 111
cjensen@rvpublishing.com, Pub./Gen. Mgr., Lake Geneva Times, WI, Delavan
cjensen@rvpublishing.com, Pub./Gen. Mgr., Paddock Lake Report, WI, Delavan
cjensen@rvpublishing.com, Weekend Hi-liter, WI, Delavan

Jensen, Gert .... (847) 558-5039
gli@schur.com, Technical Sales Dir., Schur Packaging Systems, Inc., IL, Schaumburg

Jensen, Ian .... (250) 550-7906
publisher@vernonmorningstar.com, Pub., The Morning Star, BC, Vernon

Jensen, Jessica

jjensen@ncppub.com, Ed, Westbrook Sentinel Tribune, MN, Westbrook
jjensen@ncppub.com, Ed., Lyon County Reporter, IA, Rock Rapids
jjensen@ncppub.com, Ed., The Northwest Iowa Extra, IA, Rock Rapids

Jensen, Jodi .... (307) 789-6560 ext. 101
circulation@uintacountyherald.com, Circ. Mgr., Uinta County Herald, WY, Evanston

Jensen, John
eclipse@midamericapub.com, Mgr Ed, Parkersburg Eclipse-News-Review, IA, Parkersburg

Jensen, Karen
kjensen@printronix.com, Dir., Mktg., Tally Genicom, CA, Irvine

Jensen, Kolby
kjensen@minotdailynews.com, Minot Daily News, ND, Minot

Jensen, Michael L.
mrpublisher@yahoo.com, Pub., Standard Democrat, MO, Sikeston

Jensen, Mike .... (541) 215-0824
mjensen@eastoregonian.com, Production Manager, East Oregonian, OR, Pendleton

Jensen, Randy
randy.jensen@lethbridgeherald.com, News Desk Ed., The Lethbridge Herald, AB, Lethbridge

Jensen, Robert
rjensen@allentek.com, Assoc. Prof., University of Texas at Austin, TX, Austin

Jensen, Robert M.
jensenpub@hamilton.net, Ed., Republican-Nonpareil, NE, Central City

Jenson, James
jjensen@parsonssun.com, Production Mgr., Parsons Sun, KS, Parsons

Jenson, Terry .... (306) 668-0575
tjenson@ccgazette.ca, Publisher, Clark's Crossing Gazette, SK, Warman

Jepsen, John
jjepsen@gotoanr.com, Pres., American Newspaper Representatives, Inc., MI, Troy

Jernagan, Jared
jjernagan@bannergraphic.com, Asst. Ed., Banner-Graphic, IN, Greencastle

Jernigan, Floyd
fjernigan@fstribune.com, Pub., The Fort Scott Tribune, KS, Fort Scott

Jernigan, Janet
jjernigan@fiftyforward.org, Pub., Forward Focus, TN, Nashville

Jernigan-Glenn, Carolyn... (404) 373-7779 ext. 100
cfjglenn@hotmail.com, Pub., The Champion, GA, Decatur

Jerricks, Terelle .... (310) 519-1442
editor@randomlengthsnews.com, Mng Ed, Los Angeles Harbor College, CA, San Pedro

Jervay, Paul R.
thecarolinian@bellsouth.net, Pub., The Carolinian, NC, Raleigh

Jerzyk, Emma .... (630) 743-3381
ejerzyk@gmail.com, Editor-in-chief and president, The Brown Daily Herald, RI, Providence

Jesionowski, Kendrick ..... (419) 674-4066 Ext. 230
ktsports@kentontimes.com, Staff Writ. , The Kenton Times, OH, Kenton

Jeske, Jeff .... (336) 316-2216
jjeske@guilford.edu, Guilford College, NC, Greensboro

Jeskey, Rebecca
rebecca.jeskey@laroche.edu, La Roche College, PA, Pittsburgh

Jetchick, Mike .... (952) 846-2019
mike.jetchick@ecm-inc.com, Sales Mgr., Sun Thisweek Apple Valley, MN, Apple Valley

Jetchick, Mike .... (952) 846-2019
Gen Mgr., Dakota County Tribune, MN, Apple Valley

Jeter, Phillip
jeterph@wssu.edu, Chair/Prof., Winston-Salem State University, NC, Winston-Salem

Jewell, Janice .... (410) 337-2400
owingsmillstimes@patuxent.com, Ed., Owings Mills Times, MD, Baltimore

Jewell, Jason
jason@okcfriday.com, Prod. Mgr, Oklahoma City Friday, OK, Oklahoma City

Jewell, Steve .... ext. 229
sjewell@heraldpalladium.com, News Ed., The Herald-Palladium, MI, Saint Joseph

Jewett, Jeanne
jjewett@hermistonherald.com, Adv. Sales, The Hermiston Herald, OR, Hermiston

Jeyachandran, Tanya
tanya@blackpressused.ca, Class. Adv, The Agassiz-harrison Observer, BC, Agassiz

Jha, Sonora
sonora@seattleu.edu, Seattle University, WA, Seattle

Jill, Miller .... (316) 841-8927
jilldm@swbell.net, Kansas Professional Communicators, KS, Americus

Jimenez, Ralph .... (603) 224-5301
rjimenez@cmonitor.com, Opinion Ed., Concord Monitor, NH, Concord

Jimenez, Robyn .... (214) 941-3100
news@dallasexaminer.com, The Dallas Examiner, TX, Dallas

Jimenez, Sergio
photoeditor@dailylobo.com, Photo Ed., New Mexico Daily Lobo, NM, Albuquerque

Jimenez, Sharon .... (704) 261-2205
sjimenez@theej.com, Adv. Mgr., The Enquirer-Journal, NC, Monroe

Jimmar, Renita .... (256) 740-5815
renita.jimmar@timesdaily.com, Adv. Mgr., Display, Times Daily, AL, Florence

Jimmy, Moore
jimmy@carthaginian.com, Circulation Director, The Carthaginian, MS, Carthage

Jin, Yan
yji@vcu.edu, Asst. Prof., Virginia Commonwealth University, VA, Richmond

Jipp, Sherry .... (641) 472-4130
adv@ffledger.com, Advt Mgr, Fairfield Town Crier, IA, Fairfield

Jiranek, Rob .... (434) 978-7211
rjiranek@dailyprogress.com, Pub., The Daily Progress, VA, Charlottesville

Jiron, Stephen .... (719) 589-2553
sjiron@alamosanews.com, Sports Editor, Valley Courier, CO, Alamosa

Jo, Mary
maryjo@oldautos.ca , Office Mgr., Old Autos, ON, Bothwell

Joan, Graff
joan.graff@pagecooperative.com, Director, PAGE Cooperative, VA, Vienna

Joanisse, Madeleine .... (613) 744-4800
production_orleans@transcontinental.ca, Express D'orleans, ON, Gloucester
production_orleans@transcontinental.ca, Nouvelle, ON, Embrun

Joaquin, Jessica .... (480) 362-7362
jessica.joaquin@srpmic-nsn.gov, Ad Sales, Au-Authm Action News, AZ, Scottsdale

Joas, Kari .... (920) 582-4541
karijoas@rogerspublishing.com, Adv. Mgr., The Winneconne News, WI, Winneconne

Jobe, Jeff .... (270) 487-8666
Pub., The Monroe County Citizen, KY, Tompkinsville

Jobe, Jeff S.
print@jpinews.com, CEO, Hart County News
Herald, KY, Horse Cave

Jobe, Jeffrey...............................(270) 590-6625
Jobe@jobeinc.com, Pub./Owner, The
Edmonton Herald-News, KY, Edmonton

Jobe, Jeffrey
Jobe@jobeinc.com, Pub./Pres., The Butler
County Banner-Republican, KY, Morgantown

Jobe, Larry
ljobe@thenewsenterprise.com, Advertising
Director, Central Kentucky Homes Real
Estate, KY, Elizabethtown

Jobe, Larry............................(903) 237-7727
ljobe@news-journal.com, The Gold Standard,
KY, Fort Knox
ljobe@news-journal.com, Adv. Dir., Longview
News-Journal, TX, Longview

Jobe, Susan
susanjobe@logantele.com, The Butler County
Banner-Republican, KY, Morgantown

Jobin, Benoit
bjobin@lesoleil.com, VP, Circ., Le Soleil, QC,
Quebec

Jocol, Elvis...........................(617) 522-5060
elvis@elmundoboston.com, CMO, El Mundo,
MA, Boston

Joe, Rhonda.........................(928) 871-1149
circulation@navajotimes.com, Circulation Mgr,
Navajo Times Publishing Company, Inc., AZ,
Window Rock

Joey, Bennett
jbennett@bannergraphic.com, Sports Editor,
Banner-Graphic, IN, Greencastle

Joffe, Mark J.
info@jta.org, Pub., Jewish Telegraphic Agency
Daily News Bulletin, NY, New York

Johal, Hardip...........................(604) 605-2047
hjohal@postmedia.com, Weekend Editor, The
Province, BC, Vancouver

Johanek, John
johanek@publicationdesign.com, Partner,
Ayers/Johanek Publication Design, Inc., PA,
Zionsville

Johannes, Kelly.......................(309) 757-5013
kjohannes@qconline.com, Adv. Dir., Moline/
Rock Island/Quad City Metro Unit, Moline

Johannes, Kelly.......................(309) 757-5013
kjohannes@qconline.com, MM AD DIR, Ad
Extra, IL, Moline
kjohannes@qconline.com, Multi-Media
Advertising Director, The Dispatch-Argus,
IL, Moline

Johannesen, Kirk.......................(812) 379-5639
johannesen@therepublic.com, Asst. Managing
Ed., The Republic, IN, Columbus

Johanning, Heather...................(785) 295-1218
heather.johanning@cjonline.com, Dir., HR, The
Topeka Capital-Journal, KS, Topeka

Johansen, Bruce
bjohansen@unomaha.edu, Prof./Kayser Prof.,
University of Nebraska at Omaha, NE,
Omaha

Johansen, Karsten
karsten.johansen@sunmedia.ca, General
Manager, The Standard, ON, Elliot Lake

Johansen, Karsten......................... ext. 505250
karsten.johansen@sunmedia.ca, Publisher /
Ad Director, The Sudbury Star, ON, Sudbury

Johansen, Karsten
karsten.johansen@sunmedia.ca, General
Manager, Marketplace, ON, Elliot Lake

Johanson, Barry S. ....(920) 893-6411 ext. 125
Pub., The Sheboygan Falls News, WI,
Plymouth

Johanson, Barry S.
reply@plymouth-review.com, Pub., The
Review, WI, Plymouth

Johanson, Ian ....(920) 893-6411 ext. 130
Assoc. Pub., The Sheboygan Falls News, WI,
Plymouth

Johanson, M. Christine .... (920) 893-6411 ext. 124
reply@plymouth-review.com, Pub., The
Sheboygan Falls News, WI, Plymouth

John, Gary ....(530) 852-0203
Circ. Dir., Coverstory, CA, Auburn

John, India
johni@beloit.edu, Co Editor-in-Chief , Beloit
College, WI, Beloit

John, James
jcjohn@sulphurtimes.com, Ed., Sulphur Times-
Democrat, OK, Sulphur

John, Moush
editor@stettlerindependent.com, Ed, Stettler
Independent, AB, Stettler

John, Open inch rate $25.20 ....Pub.
The Daily Journal, CO, Denver

John, Sierra
puxpress@sbcglobal.net, Ed., Puxico Press,
MO, Puxico

Johns, Amy ....(580) 310-7525
ajohns@theadanews.com, Pub., McAlester
News-Capital, OK, McAlester
ajohns@theadanews.com, Pub., The Ada
News , OK, Ada

Johns, Britney ....(574) 722-5000 Ext. 5114
britney.johns@pharostribune.com , Customer
Service Rep., Pharos-Tribune, IN,
Logansport

Johns, Kim.............................(419) 724-6216
kjohns@toledoblade.com, Asst. to Pres., The
Blade, OH, Toledo

Johns, L. Wayne
wayne.johns@greensboro.edu, Advisor,
Greensboro College, NC, Greensboro

Johns, Michael.......................(573) 761-0261
mjohns@newstribune.com, Circ. Mgr. , News
Tribune, MO, Jefferson City

Johns, Mike.........................(573) 636-3132
mjohns@newstribune.com, Circ. Mgr, The Lake
Today OOB, MO, Lake Ozark
mjohns@newstribune.com, Circ. Mgr., News
Tribune, MO, Jefferson City

Johns, Ron.........................(315) 792-5008
rjohns@uticaod.com, Managing Ed., The
Observer-Dispatch, NY, Utica

Johnson, Alec
johnsoal@dickinson.edu, Dickinson College,
PA, Carlisle

Johnson, Allen ....(336) 373-7010
ajohnson@News-Record.com, Editorial Page
Ed., News & Record, NC, Greensboro

Johnson, Amy
ajohnson@countrymedia.net, Editor,
Springview Herald, NE, Springview
ajohnson@countrymedia.net, Adv. Sales, The
Chronicle, OR, Saint Helens

Johnson, Amy ....(651) 407-1226
news@presspubs.com, Circ. Mgr., Quad
Community Press, MN, White Bear Lake
news@presspubs.com, Circulation Manager,
Vadnais Heights Press, MN, White Bear Lake
news@presspubs.com, News Clerk, Press
Publications, Inc., MN, White Bear Lake

Johnson, Andrea
ajohnson@heilicherjds.org, Minneapolis Cmty.
& Tech. College, MN, Minneapolis

Johnson, Andrew
johnson@dodgecountypionier.com, Pub.,
Campbellsport News, WI, Campbellsport

Johnson, Andrew ....(920) 387-2211
johnson@dodgecountypionier.com, Pub., The
Dodge County Pioneer, WI, Mayville

Johnson, Angie ....(202) 561-4100 ext 104
ajohnson@washingtoninformer.com, circulation
manager, Washington Informer, DC,
Washington

Johnson, Ann-Marie...................(901) 529-2662
ann-marie.johnson@commercialappeal.com,
Advertising Sales Director, Automotive, The
Commercial Appeal, TN, Memphis

Johnson, Ashley ....(229) 246-2827 x114
ashley.johnson@thepostsearchlight.com, Mng.
Ed., The Post-Searchlight, GA, Bainbridge

Johnson, Becky
bjohnson@madraspioneer.com, Comp. Supv.,
The Madras Pioneer, OR, Madras

Johnson, Becky ....(334) 624-8323
gwatchman@bellsouth.net, Pub., Greensboro
Watchman, AL, Greensboro

Johnson, Benjamin ....(888) 678-6008 ext 932
bjohnson@lifesitenews.com, US Bureau Chief,
LifeSiteNews.com, VA, Front Royal

Johnson, Bernard ....(418) 368-3242 ext. 223
bernard.johnson@quebecormedia.com, Pub.,
L'echo De La Baie, QC, New Richmond

Johnson, Bernard
bernard.johnson@hebdosquebecor.com, A
Gaspesie (OOB) , QC, Gaspe
bernard.johnson@hebdosquebecor.com,
Havre, QC, Gaspe
bernard.johnson@hebdosquebecor.com, Mng.
Ed., Le Pharillon, QC, Gaspe

Johnson, Beth
gleaner@invisimax.com, Pub., The Gleaner,
ND, Northwood

Johnson, Beverly
bjohnson@lawdailyrecord.com, Gen. Mgr.,
Lawrence County News, IL, Lawrenceville

Johnson, Beverly
bjohnson@lawdailyrecord.com, Layout Mgr.,
Daily Record, IL, Lawrenceville

Johnson, Bill
bjohnson@paweekely.com, Pub., Palo Alto
Weekly, CA, Palo Alto

Johnson, Bill
bjohnson@fhsaa.org, Co-Owner, Community
Features, Gainesville

Johnson, Bob
bob.johnson@thecharlottepost.com, Gen. Mgr.,
Charlotte Post, NC, Charlotte

Johnson, Bob
w.advance@sasktel.net, Ed., The Advance/
gazette, SK, Wynyard

Johnson, Bob ....(306) 795-2412
news.ituna@sasktel.net, Prodn. Mgr., The Ituna
News, SK, Ituna

Johnson, Bob
bobjohnsonregister@yahoo.com, City Ed., The
Iola Register, KS, Iola

Johnson, Brian ....(712) 873-3141
brianrecord@wiatel.net, Composition Mgr, The
Record, IA, Moville

Johnson, Brian ....(908) 766-3900
bjohnson@newjerseyhills.com, Advert. Sales
Rep., New Jersey Hills Media Group, NJ,
Whippany

Johnson, Brian K.
bkj@bkjproductions.com, Pres., BKJ
Productions, MA, Melrose

Johnson, Bridget.......................(319) 462-3511
advertising@journal-eureka.com, Asst Pub, Ad
Sales, Anamosa Publications, IA, Anamosa

Johnson, Brooke ....(417) 256-9191
Production, Web, Print Services, West Plains
Daily Quill, MO, West Plains

Johnson, Carleen ....(618) 239-2527
cjohnson@bnd.com, Adv., Belleville News-
Democrat, IL, Belleville

Johnson, Carter ....(651) 407-1200
ppinfo@presspubs.com, The Lowdown - St.
Croix Valley Area, MN, White Bear Lake

Johnson, Carter ....(651) 407-1200

ppinfo@presspubs.com, Pub., The Lowdown -
Forest Lake Area, MN, White Bear Lake

Johnson, Carter ....(651) 407-1200
ppinfo@presspubs.com, Pub., Forest Lake
Lowdown, MN, White Bear Lake

Johnson, Carter ....(651) 407-1251
ppinfo@presspubs.com, Pub, The Hugo
Citizen, MN, White Bear Lake

Johnson, Carter ....(651) 407-1200
Pub., Vadnais Heights Press, MN, White Bear
Lake
Pub., White Bear Press, MN, White Bear Lake
Pub, The Lowdown - St. Croix Valley Area, MN,
White Bear Lake

Johnson, Cedric.......................(321) 242-3856
cjohnson@floridatoday.com, Distribution Ops.
Mgr., Florida Today, FL, Melbourne

Johnson, Chad
cjohnson@metrosuburbia.com, Adv. Sales
Mgr., Metro Suburbia, Inc./Newhouse
Newspapers, NY, New York

Johnson, Charles R.
charles.johnson@crjtrust.com, Pres./CEO,
Superior Publishing Company, NE, Superior

Johnson, Chelsea
cjohns25@gustavus.edu, Editor In Chief
2013-14, Gustavus Adolphus College, MN,
Saint Peter

Johnson, Chris ....(830) 672-7100
reporter@gonzalescannon.com, Reporter, The
Gonzales Cannon, TX, Gonzales

Johnson, Chris ....(815) 732-6166 ext. 22
cjohnson@oglecountynews.com, Reporter,
Forreston Journal, IL, Dixon

Johnson, Chris
editor@mycameronnews.com, Editor, Cameron
Shopper, MO, Cameron

Johnson, Chrissy
cjohnson@nickelsworth.com, Ed., Nickels
Worth, ID, Coeur D Alene

Johnson, Colleen
colleen_johnson@tnc.org, Office Mgr., The
Brunswicker, MO, Brunswick

Johnson, Connie
sales@rimbeyreview.com, Sales, Rimbey
Review, AB, Rimbey

Johnson, D.J. .... (928) 783-3311 ext. 105
djjohnson@westernnewspapers.com, Vice
Pres./Dir., HR, Western News&Info, Inc.,
AZ, Yuma

Johnson, Dan ....(705) 475-2192
dan.johnson@sunmedia.ca, Pub., Nugget, ON,
North Bay

Johnson, Darren
editor@campus-news.org, New York Metro
Community Colleges, NY, Greenwich

Johnson, Dave
djohnson@harborcountry-news.com, Ed.,
Harbor Country News, MI, New Buffalo

Johnson, David.........................(518) 290-3946
djohnson@digitalfirstmedia.com, Sports Ed.,
The Saratogian, NY, Saratoga Springs

Johnson, David
editor@newalbanygazette.com, Managing Ed.,
New Albany Gazette, MS, New Albany

Johnson, David.........................(317) 272-5800
david.johnson@flyergroup.com, Adv. Dir.,
Westside Flyer, IN, Avon
david.johnson@flyergroup.com, Adv. Dir., The
Weekend Flyer, IN, Avon

Johnson, David.........................(843) 317-7301
djohnson@florencenews.com, Circ. Dir.,
Morning News, SC, Florence

Johnson, David.........................(202) 408-2717
johnsond@shns.com, Chief Tech. Officer/
Webmaster, Scripps Howard News Service,
Washington

Johnson, David

djohnson@florencenews.com, Circ. Mgr., News & Post, SC, Lake City

Johnson, David .... (617) 696-7758, X 112
david@miltontimes.com, Editor, Milton Times, MA, Milton

Johnson, Deb .... (507) 537-1551 ext #144
dkjohnson@marshallindependent.com, Creative Servs. Mgr., Independent Shopper's Review, MN, Marshall

Johnson, Deb .... (507) 537-1551 ext #144
dkjohnson@marshallindependent.com, Creative Services Mgr, Independent, MN, Marshall

Johnson, Debe
alicek@hotsr.com, Adv. Dir., The Sentinel-Record, AR, Hot Springs National Park

Johnson, Diane
ads@lcmoneysaver.com, Publication Mgr., Moneysaver-lewis Clark Edition, ID, Lewiston

Johnson, Diane
ads@lcmoneysaver.com, Mgr., Moneysaver-palouse Edition, ID, Lewiston

Johnson, Ed .... (505) 823-3933
ejohnson@abqjournal.com, Journal Asst. Sports Ed., Albuquerque Journal, NM, Albuquerque

Johnson, Ed .... (904) 686-3940
ed@opcfla.com, Sr. Acct. Exec., Ponte Vedra Recorder, FL, Ponte Vedra Beach

Johnson, Elizabeth
ejohnson@antonmediagroup.com, Ed., Manhasset Press, NY, Mineola

Johnson, Elizabeth
PortWashington@antonmediagroup.com, Ed., Port Washington News, NY, Port Washington

Johnson, Ephel
generalmanager@theweeklychallenger.com, Pub., Weekly Challenger, FL, Saint Petersburg

Johnson, Erick
Ejohnson@chicagocrusader.com, Ed., Chicago Crusader, IL, Chicago

Johnson, Eugene .... (651) 407-1200
kjohn12623@aol.com, Pres, White Bear Press, MN, White Bear Lake

Johnson, Eugene D.
news@presspubs.com, Pub., Quad Community Press, MN, White Bear Lake

Johnson, Frank
fjohnson@ourgazette.com, Ed., The Gazette, SC, Summerville

Johnson, Fred .... (785) 295-1282
fred.johnson@cjonline.com, Opinion Page Ed., The Topeka Capital-Journal, KS, Topeka

Johnson, Gary
edit@mspmag.com, Pres., MSP Communications, MN, Minneapolis

Johnson, Gary .... (715) 833-9211
gary.johnson@ecpc.com, Local News Ed., Leader-Telegram, WI, Eau Claire

Johnson, George
johnsogc@jmu.edu, Prof., James Madison University, VA, Harrisonburg

Johnson, Gerald
publisher@triangletribune.com, CEO/Pub., The Triangle Tribune, NC, Durham

Johnson, Gerald .... (507) 425-2303
ncreview@myclearwave.net, Pub., Nobles County Review, MN, Adrian

Johnson, Gerald D.
tcnews@mysmbs.com, Pub., Tri County News, MN, Heron Lake

Johnson, Gerald D. .... (507) 836-8929
mcnews@frontiernet.net, Pub., Murray County News, MN, Slayton

Johnson, Gerald D. .... (507) 360-2384
text@fuldafreepress.net, Publisher, Murray

County Advantage, MN, Fulda
text@fuldafreepress.net, Ed., Fulda Free Press, MN, Fulda

Johnson, Gerald O.
publisher@thecharlottepost.com, Pub., Charlotte Post, NC, Charlotte

Johnson, Glenn
galjohns@wsu.edu, Prof./Cable 8 News Exec. Producer, Washington State University, WA, Pullman

Johnson, Greg .... (715) 588-9272
news@lacduflambeautribe.com, Ed., Our Voice Newspaper, WI, Lac Du Flambeau

Johnson, Greg
news@seniormessenger.org, Ed., Senior Messenger, WA, Vancouver

Johnson, Harold .... (315) 661-2472
hbj@wdt.net, Pres. / Co-Pub., Daily Courier-Observer/Advance News, NY, Massena
hbj@wdt.net, Pres. / Co-Pub., Carthage Republican Tribune, NY, LOWVILLE
hbj@wdt.net, Pres. / Co-Pub., Ogdensburg Journal/Advance News, NY, Ogdensburg
hbj@wdt.net, Pres. & Co-publisher, Watertown Daily Times, NY, Watertown

Johnson, Harold B. .... (315) 661-2472
hbj@wdt.net, Pres./COO, Johnson Newspaper Corp., NY, Watertown
hbj@wdt.net, Pres. , The Daily News, NY, Batavia

Johnson, Haynes
hjohnson@umd.edu, Prof./Knight Chair in Journalism, University of Maryland, MD, College Park

Johnson, Henry
hjohnson@journalnet.com, Bus. Mgr., Idaho State Journal, ID, Pocatello

Johnson, Holly .... (802) 985-3091
publisher@windridgepublishing.com, Pub., Shelburne News, VT, Shelburne

Johnson, Jamie
jamjohnson@klcorp.com, Pub./Gen. Mgr., The Portland Leader, TN, Portland

Johnson, Jamie S.
jjohnson@franklinfavorite.com, Gen. Mgr., Franklin Favorite, KY, Franklin

Johnson, Jane
jane_johnston@marioncity.k12.oh.us, Office manager, Marion County Record, KS, Marion

Johnson, Janet .... (307) 266-0500
janet.johnson@trib.com, Adv. Sales, Casper Journal, WY, Casper
janet.johnson@trib.com, Ad Dir, Casper Star-Tribune, WY, Casper

Johnson, Jason
jjoseph@hcnonline.com, Pub., The Rancher, TX, Conroe

Johnson, Jeanie
addirector@register-pajaronian.com, Pub., Register-Pajaronian, CA, Watsonville

Johnson, Jeff .... (858) 451-6200
JeffJ@BrehmMail.com, Controller, Brehm Communications, Inc., CA, San Diego

Johnson, Jeff
SFC_JeffJohnson-communications@sfchronicle.com, Pub, San Francisco Chronicle, CA, San Francisco

Johnson, Joann .... (212) 947-5100
jjohnson@alixpartners.com, Metro Editorial Services, NY, New York

Johnson, John .... (315) 661-2304
jbj@wdt.net, Chief Exec. Off. / Co-Pub., Daily Courier-Observer/Advance News, NY, Massena
jbj@wdt.net, CEO / Co-Pub. , The Daily News, NY, Batavia
jbj@wdt.net, Chief Exec. Off. / Co-Pub., Carthage Republican Tribune, NY, LOWVILLE
jbj@wdt.net, CEO / Co-Pub., Ogdensburg

Journal/Advance News, NY, Ogdensburg

Johnson, John
jajohnson@hurleyandassociates.com, Instr., Eastern Illinois University, IL, Charleston

Johnson, John .... (316) 782-1000
jbj@wdt.net, CEO & Co-Pub., Watertown Daily Times, NY, Watertown

Johnson, John B.
jbjjr@wdt.net, Chrmn. of the Bd./CEO, Johnson Newspaper Corp., NY, Watertown

Johnson, Jon .... (906) 341-4204
info@manistiquepapers.com, Gen. Mgr., Manistique Papers, Inc., MI, Manistique

Johnson, Jon .... (334) 712-7965
jjohnson@dothaneagle.com, Sports Ed., The Dothan Eagle, AL, Dothan

Johnson, Josh
josh@libertylakesplash.com, Pub./Ed., Liberty Lake Splash, WA, Liberty Lake

Johnson, Joshua
focusnews@wans.net, Ed., Focus Daily News, TX, Desoto

Johnson, Julie .... (203) 245-1877
j.johnson@shorepublishing.com, Prod. Mgr, Source, CT, Madison
j.johnson@shorepublishing.com, Prod. Mgr, The Sound, CT, Madison
j.johnson@shorepublishing.com, Prod. Mgr., Guilford Courier, CT, Madison
j.johnson@shorepublishing.com, Prod. Mgr, North Haven Courier, CT, Madison
j.johnson@shorepublishing.com, Prod. Mgr, East Haven Courier, CT, Madison
j.johnson@shorepublishing.com, Prod. Mgr, Harbor News, CT, Madison

Johnson, Julie
juliejohnson@columbianprogress.com, Pub., The Columbian-Progress, MS, Columbia

Johnson, Karen .... (719) 382-5612
karen@epcan.com, General Manager, El Paso County Advertiser & News, CO, Fountain

Johnson, Kathleen
kjohnson@ljworld.com
, Advertising Manager, Lawrence Journal-World, KS, Lawrence

Johnson, Kathleen
kjohnson@ljworld.com, Advertising Manager, Shawnee Dispatch, KS, Shawnee

Johnson, Kathy
johnsonk@dailycamera.com, Creative Dir., Albert Lea Tribune, MN, Albert Lea
johnsonk@dailycamera.com, Nat'l Adv. Rep., Colorado Daily, CO, Boulder
johnsonk@dailycamera.com, Major/Nat'l Acct. Rep., Longmont Times-Call, CO, Longmont

Johnson, Kathy
tcnews@sairpoint.net, Mng. Ed., Twin City News, FL, Chattahoochee

Johnson, Ken .... (978) 946-2237
kjohnson@eagletribune.com, Metro Ed., The Eagle-Tribune, MA, North Andover

Johnson, Ken .... (617) 786-7052
kjohnson@ledger.com, Online Ed., The Enterprise, MA, Brockton

Johnson, Ken .... (617) 786-7052
kjohnson@ledger.com, Online Ed., The Patriot Ledger, MA, Quincy

Johnson, Ken .... (617) 786-7052
kjohnson@ledger.com, Managing editor, The Patriot Ledger, MA, Quincy

Johnson, Kent .... (602) 889-7129
kjohnson@azcapitoltimes.com, Pub., Arizona Capitol Times, AZ, Phoenix

Johnson, Kent
kjohnson@dailyherald.com, Sr. Vice Pres./CFO/Treasurer/Secretary, Daily Herald, IL, Arlington Heights

Johnson, Kerry
kjohnson@sentinelnews.com, Pub., Sentinel

News Plus, KY, Shelbyville

Johnson, Kevin .... (954) 985-5701, ext. 10715
kevinjohnson@semtribe.com, Senior Ed, The Seminole Tribune, FL, Hollywood

Johnson, Kevin
johnsonk@obrien.com, Pres., Platform Products/Servs. Div., Microsoft Corp., WA, Redmond

Johnson, Kevin .... (515) 471-3505
krjohnson@dmreg.com, GM, Production Ops., The Des Moines Register, IA, Des Moines

Johnson, Kirsten
johnsonka@etown.edu, Lectr./Dir., Stud. Pubs., Elizabethtown College, PA, Elizabethtown

Johnson, Kris
kjohnson@faribault.com, Circ. Mgr., Lonsdale Area News-Review, MN, Lonsdale
kjohnson@faribault.com, Circ. Mgr., Faribault Daily News, MN, Faribault
kjohnson@faribault.com, Circ. Mgr., Kenyon Leader, MN, Kenyon

Johnson, Kristin .... (765) 454-6720
kristin.johnson@kokomotribune.com, Reg. Digital Mgr. , Kokomo Tribune, IN, Kokomo

Johnson, Kurt .... (402) 694-2131
newsregister@hamilton.net, Pub., Aurora News-Register, NE, Aurora

Johnson, Kyle
kj@parenttoparent.com, Personal Assistant Assistant Editor, Parent to Parent, Wildwood

Johnson, Laura
ljohnson@annistonstar.com, News Ed., Piedmont Journal, AL, Anniston

Johnson, Lawrence
bwtrib@tribune2000.com, Ed., The Burwell Tribune, NE, Burwell

Johnson, Lawrence
bwtrib@tribune2000.com, Pub., Sargent Leader, NE, Burwell

Johnson, Leanne
ljohnston@postmedia.com, Adv. Dir., Lloydminster Meridian Booster, AB, Lloydminster
ljohnston@postmedia.com, Adv Mgr, Cold Lake Sun, AB, Cold Lake

Johnson, Leigh
leigh@alternet.org, Bus. Mgr., AlterNet, San Francisco

Johnson, Linda
ljohnson@bonnersferryherald.com, Office Mgr., Bonners Ferry Herald, ID, Bonners Ferry

Johnson, Liz .... (816) 637-6155
liz@leaderpress.com, Production Manager, Town & Country Leader, MO, Excelsior Springs

Johnson, Lonnie .... (301) 306-9500
lonnie@thesentinel.com, Adv. Dir., The Prince George's Sentinel, MD, Seabrook

Johnson, Lonnie .... (301) 306-9500
lonnie@thesentinel.com, Adv. Mgr., Montgomery County Sentinel, MD, Rockville

Johnson, Lorretta
ljohnson@aft.org, Exec. Vice Pres., American Federation of Teachers, Washington

Johnson, Lowell
ljohnso2@gannett.com, Adv. Dir. , Herald Times Reporter, WI, Manitowoc
ljohnso2@gannett.com, Pub., Lakeshore Chronicle, WI, Manitowoc

Johnson, Malcolm .... (239) 220-2754
mjohnson@breezenewspapers.com , Ad. Sales, North Fort Myers Neighbor, FL, Cape Coral

Johnson, Marcus
tribads@otelco.net, VP/OPs, The Arab Tribune, AL, Arab

Johnson, Marda .... (765) 482-4650 Ext. 131
marda.johnson@reporter.net, Mng. Ed., The

Reporter, IN, Lebanon

Johnson, Margy
margy@alaskadispatch.com, Executive Vice President, Alaska Dispatch News, AK, Anchorage

Johnson, Marilou
johnsomx@jmu.edu, Prof., James Madison University, VA, Harrisonburg

Johnson, Mark
mwjohnson@gannett.com, Distribution Director, Post-Crescent, WI, Appleton

Johnson, Mark
mwjohnso@appleton.gannett.com, Circ. Mgr, News-Record, WI, Appleton

Johnson, Marlo
mjohnson@mnpubs.com, Dist. Mgr., Good Age, MN, Minneapolis

Johnson, Marsha
mjohnson@gfherald.com, Administrative Assistant, Grand Forks Herald, ND, Grand Forks

Johnson, Mary Jo .... (715) 345-2051
Adv. Dir., Stevens Point Journal, WI, Stevens Point

Johnson, Matt .... (608) 328-4202
mjohnson@themonroetimes.com, Publisher, Monroe Shopping News, WI, Monroe

Johnson, Matt .... (870) 793-4196,
mattjohnson21@swbell.net, Sales Mgr., Arkansas Weekly, AR, Batesville

Johnson, Matt
matt.johnson@lee.net, Mng. Ed., Vernon County Broadcaster, WI, Viroqua

Johnson, Michael .... (740) 446-2342 ext 2102
michaeljohnson@civitasmedia.com, Ed., Gallipolis Daily Tribune, OH, Gallipolis
michaeljohnson@civitasmedia.com, Ed., Point Pleasant Register, WV, Point Pleasant

Johnson, Michael .... (740) 446-2342 Ext. 2102
michaeljohnson@civitasmedia.com, Ed., The Daily Sentinel, OH, Pomeroy

Johnson, Michael J. .... (912) 201-4054
mjjohnson@diosav.org, Editor, Southern Cross, GA, Savannah

Johnson, Mike
gazette@mts.net, Ed./Pub/Adv, Gazette, MB, Glenboro

Johnson, Mike .... (763) 712-3524
mike.johnson@ecm-inc.com, Adv. Mgr., Anoka County Shopper, MN, Coon Rapids

Johnson, Nancy
nancy.johnson@tc.tc, Pub., The Moose Jaw Times-Herald, SK, Moose Jaw

Johnson, Nate
njohnson@rustconsulting.com, Univ. of Minnesota Inst. of Tech, MN, Minneapolis

Johnson, Nikie .... (951) 368-9556
njohnson@pe.com, Ed., The Press-Enterprise, CA, Riverside

Johnson, Pat .... (608) 839-7047
pjohnson@hngnews.com, Adv. Mgr., McFarland Thistle, WI, Cottage Grove

Johnson, Pat
pjohnson@gulfcoastnewspapers.com, Adv. Mgr., The Fairhope Courier, AL, Fairhope

Johnson, Patrick
pat@zumapress.com, CTO, ZUMA Press, Inc., San Clemente

Johnson, Paul
pjohnson@hpe.com, Politics/business/general, High Point Enterprise, NC, High Point

Johnson, Phylis
phylis@selmaware.com, Interim Chair, Radio-Television/Prof., Southern Illinois University Carbondale, IL, Carbondale

Johnson, Polly .... (936) 295-5407
pjohnson@itemonline.com, Director of

Audience Development, The Huntsville Item, TX, Huntsville

Johnson, Randall
rjohnson@rvpublishing.com, Gen. Mgr., The Herald, IL, Machesney Park

Johnson, Randall .... ext. 18
Gen. Mgr., The Gazette, IL, Pecatonica

Johnson, Randall
info@rvpublishing.com, Gen. Mgr., Post Journal, IL, Machesney Park

Johnson, Randy .... (815) 877-4044 ext. 54
rjohnson@rvpublishing.com, Gen. Mgr., The Belvidere Daily Republican, IL, Belvidere

Johnson, Randy
rjohnson@rvpublishing.com, Pub., Senior Courier, IL, Machesney Park

Johnson, Randy .... (715) 395-5031
rjohnson@superiortelegram.com, Pub./Gen. Mgr., The Independent Register, WI, Brodhead

Johnson, Randy
rjohnson@rvpublishing.com, Gen. Mgr., Rock Valley Publishing LLC, IL, Machesney Park

Johnson, Randy
rjohnson@rvpublishing.com, The Elmhurst Independent, IL, Machesney Park
rjohnson@rvpublishing.com, Gen. Mgr., The Tempo, IL, Byron

Johnson, Rebecca .... (814) 765-5581
Asst. Pub./Bus. Mgr., The Progress, PA, Clearfield

Johnson, Reed
reed.johnson@rheaheraldnews.com, Ed., The Herald-News, TN, Dayton

Johnson, Ric
bac@bloapco.com, Mgr., Sales, Blower Application Co., Inc., WI, Germantown

Johnson, Rob
rjohnson@pnj.com, Content Coach/Watchdog, Pensacola News Journal, FL, Pensacola

Johnson, Robert .... (573) 563-5014
guidoneditor@myguidon.com, Ed., Guidon, MO, Saint Robert

Johnson, Roijon .... (806) 296-1320
rjohnson@hearstnp.com, Class. Acct. Exec., Plainview Herald, TX, Plainview

Johnson, Roxanne .... (361) 786-3022
progressads@mysoutex.com, Office Manager, The Progress, TX, Three Rivers

Johnson, Ruth .... (406) 243-6646
ruth.johnson@umontana.edu, Office manager, University of Montana, MT, Missoula

Johnson, Ryan .... (701) 231-8994
The Kearney Courier, MO, Kearney

Johnson, Sally .... (906) 497-5652
sjohnson@powersprinting.net, Prodn. Mgr., Mailroom, The Daily News, MI, Iron Mountain

Johnson, Sandi .... (209) 546-8240
sjohnson@recordnet.com, HR Director, The Record, CA, Stockton

Johnson, Scott
sejohnso@greenbay.gannett.com, Pub., Kewaunee County Star-News, WI, Kewaunee
sejohnso@greenbay.gannett.com, Pub, Herald Times Reporter, WI, Manitowoc

Johnson, Scott
sejohnso@baycominc.com, Pres./Pub., Oconto County Reporter, WI, Oconto
sejohnso@baycominc.com, Pres./Pub., De Pere Journal, WI, Green Bay

Johnson, Scott .... (570) 748-6791
sjohnson@lockhaven.com, Pub., Door County Advocate, WI, Sturgeon Bay

Johnson, Scott .... (920) 431-8502
sejohnso@gannett.com, President & Publisher, Green Bay Press-Gazette, WI, Green Bay

Johnson, Sheila .... (405) 238-6464

sjohnson@pvdemocrat.com, Circ., Pauls Valley Democrat, OK, Pauls Valley

Johnson, Stan
ctmaned@lcs.net, Features Ed., Citizen Tribune, TN, Morristown

Johnson, Stephen .... (256) 340-2379
art@decaturdaily.com, Art Dept Mgr., The Decatur Daily, AL, Decatur

Johnson, Stephen .... (419) 233-3622
sjohnson@the419.com, Pub. & CEO, the419, OH, Lima

Johnson, Steve & Gail .... (402) 447-6012
editor@ngreporter.com, Owners/Publishers, Newman Grove Reporter, NE, Newman Grove

Johnson, Tad .... (952) 846-2033
editor.thisweek@ecm-inc.com, Ed., Dakota County Tribune, MN, Apple Valley
editor.thisweek@ecm-inc.com, Ed., Thisweek Newspapers, MN, Apple Valley
editor.thisweek@ecm-inc.com, Ed., Thisweek Burnsville-Eagan Sun, MN, Apple Valley

Johnson, Tad .... (952) 846-2033
tad.johnson@ecm-inc.com, Mng. Ed., Sun Thisweek Lakeville, MN, Apple Valley

Johnson, Tad .... (952) 846-2033
tad.johnson@ecm-inc.com, Mng. Ed., Sun Thisweek Apple Valley, MN, Apple Valley

Johnson, Tamara .... (870) 633-3131
tamjohns@thnews.com, Mng. Ed., East Arkansas Advertiser, AR, Forrest City

Johnson, Tamara
tamjohns@thnews.com, Pub., Times-Herald, AR, Forrest City

Johnson, Taylor
tjohnson@the419.com, Brand Mgr., the419, OH, Lima

Johnson, Ted
ted.johnson@variety.com, Mng. Ed., Daily Variety, CA, Los Angeles

Johnson, Tee .... (603) 326-610
bds@berlindailysun.com, Adv. Rep., The Berlin Daily Sun, NH, BERLIN

Johnson, Tiffany .... (937) 775-5534
Wright State Univ., OH, Dayton

Johnson, Tom
tjohnson@mediaspace.com, Director Media Planning, Mediaspace Solutions, MN, Hopkins

Johnson, Tom
bleader@latimes.com, Gen. Mgr., Times Community News (TCN), CA, Los Angeles

Johnson, Tom
tom.johnson@metavante.com, Creator/Writer, Reel to Real Celebrity Profiles, Milwaukee

Johnson, Travis
gazette2@mts.net, Ed./Pub/Adv, Gazette, MB, Glenboro

Johnson, Tricia .... (800) 543-9913 ext. 509
tjohnson@cn.homecomm.net, Gen. Mgr., Clinton County News, MI, Lansing
tjohnson@cn.homecomm.net, Gen. Mgr., Community Newspapers, Inc., MI, Charlotte
tjohnson@cn.homecomm.net, Gen. Mgr., Towne Courier, MI, Lansing
tjohnson@cn.homecomm.net, Gen. Mgr., Williamston Enterprise, MI, Lansing
tjohnson@cn.homecomm.net, Pub., Club Fifty (OOB), MI, Charlotte
tjohnson@cn.homecomm.net, Gen. Mgr., DeWitt-Bath Review, MI, Saint Johns

Johnson, Trudy .... (870) 255-4538
Circulation, Herald Publishing Co., AR, Hazen

Johnson, Tyana
editor@mandan-news.com, Mandan News Ed./Reporter, Mandan News, ND, Mandan

Johnson, Vicki .... (417) 256-9191
ads@wpdailyquill.net, Advertising Manager, West Plains Daily Quill, MO, West Plains

Johnson, Vince
distribution@greentab.com, Distribution Manager, Green Tab, WV, Moundsville

Johnson, Vince .... (770) 205-8945
vjohnson@forsythnews.com, Pub., Forsyth County News, GA, Cumming

Johnson, W. James .... (319) 462-3511
publisher@journal-eureka.com, Pub, Anamosa Publications, IA, Anamosa
publisher@journal-eureka.com, Anamosa Publications, IA, Anamosa

Johnson, W. James .... (319) 462-3511
Publisher@AnamosaJE.com, Publisher, Journal-eureka And Town Crier, IA, Anamosa

Johnson, Waymon
gwatchman@bellsouth.net, Adv. Dir., Greensboro Watchman, AL, Greensboro

Johnson, Will .... (936) 687-2424
wjohnson@messenger-news.com, Reporter, The Messenger, TX, Grapeland

Johnson, William W.
avalanche@rpt.com, Ed., The Tarkio Avalanche, MO, Tarkio

Johnsrud, Mathew
math.johnsrud@journaltimes.com, Circ. Mgr., The Journal Times, WI, Racine

Johnston, Amanda
amanda.johnston@doverpost.com, Sales Mgr., Hockessin Community News, DE, Middletown
amanda.johnston@doverpost.com, Adv. Sales Mgr., The Middletown Transcript, DE, Middletown
amanda.johnston@doverpost.com, Adv. Mgr., Smyrna/Clayton Sun-Times, DE, Middletown
amanda.johnston@doverpost.com, Adv. Sales Mgr., Dover Post, DE, Dover
amanda.johnston@doverpost.com, Adv. Mgr., The Sussex Countian, DE, Dover
amanda.johnston@doverpost.com, Adv. Mgr., Milford Beacon, DE, Dover

Johnston, Anne .... (919) 962-4286
Prof./Assoc. Dean for Grad. Studies, University of North Carolina, NC, Chapel Hill

Johnston, April .... (304) 293-8609
april.johnston@mail.wvu.edu, Teaching Assistant Professor, West Virginia University, WV, Morgantown

Johnston, Bill .... (306) 743-2617
fourtown@sk.sympatico.ca, Editor/Publisher, Langenburg Four-town Journal, SK, Langenburg

Johnston, Ellen .... (407) 846-7600 ext. 124
Prodn. Mgr., Osceola News-gazette, FL, Kissimmee

Johnston, Ellen .... (407) 846-7600 ext. 124
Prodn. Mgr., Osceola Homefinder, FL, Kissimmee

Johnston, Ellen
ejohnston@osceolanewsgazette.com, Prodn. Mgr., Osceola News-Gazette, FL, Kissimmee

Johnston, Eric
eric@soundfootprint.com, Pioneer Newspapers Inc, WA, Seattle

Johnston, Jennifer .... (563) 383-2296
jjohnston@qctimes.com, Exec. Admin. Asst., Quad-City Times, IA, Davenport

Johnston, Jonathan .... (715) 329-0673
jjohnston@ashlanddailypress.net, Bayfield County Journal, WI, Ashland

Johnston, Mike .... (905) 215-1499
mjohnston@durhamregion.com, Mng. Ed., Oshawa-whitby This Week, ON, Oshawa
mjohnston@durhamregion.com, Managing Ed., Canadian Statesman, ON, Oshawa

Johnston, Mike .... (905) 215-0462
mjohnston@durhamregion.com, Mng. Ed., Clarington This Week, ON, Oshawa

Johnston, Patrick .... (334) 737-2541
pjohnston@oanow.com, Mng. Ed., Opelika-

Auburn News, AL, Opelika

Johnston, Rebecca .... (770) 479-1441
rjohnston@cherokeetribune.com, Ed.,
Cherokee Ledger-News, GA, Canton

Johnston, Robin
kfr.ads.robin@gmail.com, Ad Mng., The
Kingfisher Times & Free Press, OK,
Kingfisher

Johnston, Scott
scottwjohnston01@gmail.com, Advertising
manager, The Picton Gazette, ON, Picton

Johnston, Tricia
tjohnston@dailylocal.com, Adv., The Kennett
Paper, PA, West Chester

Johnston, Tricia
tricia.johnston@hollandsentinel.com, Publisher,
West Michigan Senior Times, MI, Holland

Johnston, Wendy
ads@killarneyguide.ca, Adv. Mgr., Killarney
Guide, MB, Killarney

Johnstone, Bruce .... (306) 781-5304
bjohnstone@leaderpost.canwest.com, Finance
Ed., The Leader-Post, SK, Regina

Joiner, Al
wayxshop@atc.cc, Pub., Waycross Shopper,
GA, Waycross

Joiner, Gail .... (830) 796-9799
bccourier@sbcglobal.net, Pub., Bandera
County Courier, TX, Bandera

Joiner, Justin
justinj@montrosepress.com, Managing Ed.,
The Montrose Daily Press, CO, Montrose

Joines, Angela .... (803) 329-4042
ajoines@heraldonline.com, Gen Mgr, Advt,
Fort Mill Times, SC, Rock Hill

Jollet, Robert .... (514) 337-1974 ext. 270
rjollet@elconsy.com, Sales Rep., Elcorsy
Technology, Inc., QC, Saint-Laurent

Jolley, Susan M. .... (910) 323-0349
susan@newspaperconsultants.com, General
Mgr., Advantage Newspaper Consultants,
NC, Fayetteville

Jolliffe, Lee
lee.jolliffe@drake.edu, Assoc. Prof., Drake
University, IA, Des Moines

Jollymore, Cynthia
cynthia@mcgown.com, Vice Pres., Sales,
Publicitas McGown Inc., QC, Montreal

Joly, Don
djoly@ottawacitizen.com, Prod. Mgr., The
Ottawa Citizen, ON, Ottawa

Joly, Yvan .... (613) 632-4155
yvan@eap.on.ca, Newspaper manager,
Tribune Express, ON, Hawkesbury

Jon, Jimison .... (336) 727-7287
jjimison@wsjournal.com, Weekend Editor,
Winston-Salem Journal, NC, Winston Salem

Jonaitis, Ramune
tevzib@rogers.com, Mng. Ed., Teviskes
Ziburiai, ON, Mississauga

Joncas, Tim .... (814) 665-8291 Ext.22
tim@thecorryjournal.com, Adv. Sales Mgr.,
Corry Journal, PA, Corry

Jones, Alan
ajones@hcnonline.com, Tomball Potpourri,
TX, Conroe

Jones, Alex .... (212) 210-1585
ajones@nydailynews.com, Mng. Ed. , New York
Daily News, NY, New York

Jones, Alexandra
alexandra.jones@thetriangle.org, EIC, Drexel
Univ., PA, Philadelphia

Jones, Allen
ajones@cwlp.com, Pres., The Baxter Bulletin,
AR, Mountain Home
ajones@cwlp.com, Pres., Springfield News-

Leader, MO, Springfield

Jones, Amy
ajones@billingsleyco.com, Pub., Dallas
Observer, TX, Dallas

Jones, Beth
bjones@fbnewsleader.com, Sports Ed., News-
Leader, FL, Fernandina Beach

Jones, Bob
bob@jwcycles.com, Desk Ed., Scripps Howard
News Service, Washington

Jones, Brian
bjones@pantex.doe.gov, Circ. Mgr., The
Midlothian Mirror, TX, Waxahachie

Jones, Brook
bjones@postmedia.com, Ed, The Stonewall
Argus & Teulon Times, MB, Stonewall
bjones@postmedia.com, Ed, Selkirk Journal,
MB, Selkirk
bjones@postmedia.com, Ed, The Interlake
Spectator, MB, Stonewall

Jones, Bryan .... (573) 378-5441
bjones@vernonpublishing.com, Ed, The
Versailles Leader-Statesman, MO, Versailles

Jones, Carlton
cj@jones2.net, Pub. / Mgn. Ed. / Adv. mgr.,
Coosa County News, AL, Rockford

Jones, Celeste .... (515) 953-4822 ext. 313
celeste@dmcityview.com, Art Director,
Cityview, IA, Johnston

Jones, Charles
taylor2039@aol.com, Production Manager, The
San Antonio Observer, TX, San Antonio

Jones, Chris
editor@pikedispatch.com, Ed., Pike County
Dispatch, PA, Milford

Jones, Chris .... (417) 667-3344 ext. 20
Prod. Mgr., Nevada Herald, MO, Nevada
Prodn. Mgr., The Nevada Daily Mail, MO,
Nevada

Jones, Chris
cjones@cajonesinc.com, Exec. Vice Pres.,
Solutions/Servs., Descartes Systems Group,
ON, Waterloo

Jones, Christopher .... (225) 771-2464
cjones@communitycoffee.com, Southern Univ.
A&M College, LA, Baton Rouge

Jones, Chuck .... ext. 292
cjones@thenewsenterprise.com, Sports Ed.,
The News-Enterprise, KY, Elizabethtown

Jones, Chuck .... (205) 722-0240
chuck.jones@tuscaloosanews.com, Prepress/
Commercial Print Manager, The Tuscaloosa
News, AL, Tuscaloosa

Jones, Clayton .... (575) 391-5431
Sports Ed., Hobbs News-Sun, NM, Hobbs

Jones, Connie
circulation@sapulpaheraldonline.com, Cir.
Mgr., Sapulpa Daily Herald, OK, Sapulpa
circulation@sapulpaheraldonline.com,
Classified Ads Mgr., Constitution-Tribune,
MO, Chillicothe

Jones, Dan
djones@crain.com, Editorial Asst., Crain
News Service (includes Automotive News
Syndicate), Detroit

Jones, Daniel .... (318) 256-3495
news@sabineindex.net, The Sabine Index,
LA, Many

Jones, David .... (919) 419-6704
djones@heraldsun.com, Adv. Dir., The Herald-
Sun, NC, Durham

Jones, Deidre .... (903) 675-6397
dbjones@tvcc.edu, Media Instructor/Adviser,
Trinity Valley Cmty. College, TX, Athens

Jones, Doug
doug.jones@regions.com, Adv. Mgr.,
Birmingham Times, AL, Birmingham

Jones, Earl .... (757) 934-9607

Adv. Dir., Suffolk News-Herald, VA, Suffolk

Jones, Elizabeth
ejones@marthaobryan.org, Art Dir., Nashville
Scene, TN, Nashville

Jones, Elvyn J. .... (913) 845-2222
editor@baldwincity.com, Ed., Eudora News
(OOB), KS, Lawrence
editor@baldwincity.com, Ed., The Baldwin City
Signal, KS, Baldwin City

Jones, Ernest
ernest.jones@famu.edu, Instr./Mgr., FAMU-TV
20, Florida A&M University, FL, Tallahassee

Jones, Evan .... (804) 733-8636
evan@dinwiddie-monitor.com, Pub., Dinwiddie
Monitor, VA, Sutherland
evan@dinwiddie-monitor.com, Pub., The
Sussex-Surry Dispatch, VA, Wakefield

Jones, Fred
fjones@semo.edu, Asst. Prof., Southeast
Missouri State University, MO, Cape
Girardeau

Jones, Gary
starexaminer@elberton.com, Pub., The
Elberton Star, GA, Elberton

Jones, Gary .... (706) 272-7709
jeffmutter@daltoncitizen.com, Adv. Dir., The
Daily Citizen, GA, Dalton

Jones, Greg
hudsongazette@videotron.ca, Pub., Hudson
Gazette, QC, Hudson

Jones, Gregg .... (636) 239-7701
Asst. Mgr. Editor, Washington Missourian, MO,
Washington

Jones, Gregg K. .... (423) 359-3122
gregg.jones@adamspg.com, President of APG
East and Publisher of The Greeneville Sun
, APG Media of Tennessee/North Carolina,
TN, Greeneville

Jones, Gregg K. .... (423) 359-3122
gregg.jones@adampg.com, Pub., The
Greeneville Sun, TN, Greeneville

Jones, Howard
hjones@news-banner.com, Prodn. Supt.,
News-Banner, IN, Bluffton

Jones, Hugh
hjones@t-g.com, Pub., Shelbyville Times-
Gazette, TN, Shelbyville

Jones, Hugh
news@ltrib-gaz.com, Pub., Marshall County
Tribune, TN, Lewisburg

Jones, J. Ross
ross@guardonline.com, Online Mgr., Batesville
Daily Guard, AR, Batesville

Jones, Jacob .... (509) 335-7191
cadviser@dailyevergreen.com, Content
Adviser, Washington State University, Daily
Evergreen, WA, Pullman

Jones, Jacqueline
jjones@apexanalytix.com, Instr., North
Carolina A&T State University, NC,
Greensboro

Jones, Jana .... (727) 893-8634
jljones@tampabay.com, VP / CFO, Tampa Bay
Times, FL, St Petersburg

Jones, Jason
jjones@timesshamrock.com, Univ. of
Massachusetts, MA, North Dartmouth
jjones@timesshamrock.com, Adv. Mgr., The
Times-Tribune, PA, Scranton

Jones, Jay
jay.jones@rockdalecitizen.com, Mng. Ed., The
Rockdale Citizen, GA, Conyers

Jones, Jeff
jjones@modelelectric.com, Prodn. Foreman,
Pressroom, Norfolk Daily News, NE, Norfolk

Jones, Jerrel .... (414) 449-4860
milwaukeecourier@aol.com, Pub, The
Milwaukee Courier, WI, Milwaukee

Jones, Jerry .... (615) 596-6210
publisher@outandaboutnashville.com, Pub.,
Out & About Nashville, TN, Nashville

Jones, Juanell .... (806) 561-4888
LCNjuanell@poka.com, Pub, Lynn County
News, TX, Tahoka

Jones, Kathy
kjones@sentinel-echo.com, Adv. Mgr., The
Sentinel-Echo, KY, London

Jones, Kathy .... (606) 528-7898 Ext. 27
kjones@thetimestribune.com, Adv. Mgr.,
Times-Tribune, KY, Corbin

Jones, Kenneth
kenneth.jones@famu.edu, Assoc. Prof., Florida
A&M University, FL, Tallahassee

Jones, Kevin .... (314) 289-5418
kjones@stlamerican.com, COO/Adv. Dir., St.
Louis American, MO, Saint Louis

Jones, Kimberley .... (512) 453-4280
kj@austinchronicle.com, Ed, Austin Chronicle,
TX, Austin

Jones, Lesa
lesa.jones@tulsabusiness.com, Editor , Tulsa
Business & Legal News, OK, Tulsa

Jones, Leween .... (321) 242-3541
ljones3@floridatoday.com, Retail Sales Mgr.,
Florida Today, FL, Melbourne

Jones, Lilia
lcjones@elpasotimes.com , President, El Paso
Times, TX, El Paso

Jones, Linda
linda.jones@bankerslife.com, Chair, Roosevelt
University, IL, Chicago

Jones, Lloyd
lloyd@conwaydailysun.com, Sports Ed., The
Conway Daily Sun, NH, North Conway

Jones, Lou Elliott
editor@chieflandcitizen.com, Ed., Chiefland
Citizen, FL, Chiefland

Jones, Lyzz .... (717) 771-2058
ejones@ydr.com, Assistant Managing Editor
for Sports, York Daily Record/York Sunday
News, PA, York

Jones, Mark .... (423) 757-6505
mjones@timesfreepress.com, Dir. of Strategic
Marketing & Audience Dev., Chattanooga
Times Free Press, TN, Chattanooga

Jones, Max .... (812) 231-4336
max.jones@tribstar.com, Ed., Tribune-Star
Publishing Co., Inc., IN, Terre Haute
max.jones@tribstar.com, Ed., The Tribune Star,
IN, Terre Haute

Jones, Melissa
melissaj@clackamas.edu, Clackamas Cmty.
College, OR, Oregon City

Jones, Michael
mjones@floridamariner.com, Publisher, Florida
Mariner/Gulf Mariner, FL, North Port

Jones, Mike
mjones@norfolkdailynews.com, Prodn. Mgr.,
Daily News Plus, NE, Norfolk

Jones, Mike
alarson@norfolkdailynews.com, Prodn. Mgr.,
Norfolk Daily News, NE, Norfolk

Jones, Mike
mjones@hcnonline.com, Sports Ed., The
Courier of Montgomery County, TX, Conroe

Jones, Molly
molly@na-weekly.com, Ed. Asst., Norwegian
American Weekly, WA, Seattle

Jones, Nathan
nj1655@aol.com, Adv. Mgr., Virden Recorder,
IL, Virden

Jones, Nathan
nj1655@aol.com, Gen. Mgr., Gold Nugget
Publications, Inc., IL, Virden

Jones, Nathan .... (217) 965-3355

nj331@royell.net, Adv. Mgr., The Girard Gazette, IL, Girard

Jones, Nathan
nj1655@aol.com, Gen. Mgr., Gold Nugget Express, IL, Virden

Jones, Nathan .... **(217) 965-3355**
nj331@royell.net, Adv. Mgr., The Panhandle Press, IL, Raymond

Jones, Nathan E. .... **(217) 725-0175**
nj1655@aol.com, Adv. Mgr., Northwestern News, IL, Palmyra

Jones, Pat
news@guardonline.com, Gen. Mgr., Batesville Daily Guard, AR, Batesville

Jones, Paula .... **(606) 451-4901**
Accounting/HR Mgr., The Commonwealth-Journal, KY, Somerset

Jones, Pete .... **(217) 351-5327**
pjones@news-gazette.com, Circ. Dir., The News-Gazette, IL, Champaign

Jones, Rich
rich.jones@detroitnews.com, IT Mgr., Westland Observer, MI, Detroit

Jones, Richard
rljones@dmnmedia.com, Gen. Mgr., Proven Performance Media, The Dallas Morning News, TX, Dallas

Jones, Richard
rljones@tribune.com, Dir., Western Reg., Tribune Media Network, CA, Los Angeles

Jones, Roger
roger@jonesprint.com, Pub./Adv. Dir., Riesel Rustler, TX, Waco

Jones, Samantha
ccnews@cox-internet.com, Associate Ed, Lovely County Citizen, AR, Eureka Springs

Jones, Sherrie .... **(770) 535-6304**
sjones@gainesvilletimes.com, Adv. Dir., The Times, GA, Gainesville

Jones, Shirley .... **(563) 488-2281**
midtimes@netins.net, Pub., Wyoming Midland Times, IA, Wyoming

Jones, Sue
scurry@douglascountyherald.com, Douglas County Herald, MO, Ava

Jones, Sue .... **(412) 320-7946**
sjones@tribweb.com, News Ed., Pittsburgh, Tribune-Review, PA, Greensburg

Jones, Tami .... **(601) 364-1011**
tami.jones@msbusiness.com, Associate Publisher, Mississippi Business Journal, MS, Jackson

Jones, Tammy .... **(276) 638-8801, ext. 249**
tjones@martinsvillebulletin.com, Adv. Mgr., Martinsville Bulletin, VA, Martinsville

Jones, Terry
terry.jones@investors.com, Assoc. Ed., Investor's Business Daily, CA, Los Angeles

Jones, Terry B. .... **(504) 821-7421**
terrybjones@bellsouth.net, Pub., New Orleans Data News Weekly, LA, New Orleans

Jones, Thurman R.
publisher@northdallasgazette.com, Pub., North Dallas Gazette, TX, Plano

Jones, Tia
tia.jones@mountaineagle.com, Circ. Dir., Daily Mountain Eagle, AL, Jasper

Jones, Tim
tjones@ashwoth.com, Mktg. Mgr., Ashworth Brothers, Inc., VA, Winchester

Jones, Tom .... **(336) 506-3040**
tjones@thetimesnews.com, City Ed., Times-News, NC, Burlington

Jones , Bob
bjones@kystandard.co , Circu Mgr, Kentucky Standard, KY, Bardstown

Jons, Doreen

djamerpork@win-4-u.net, Office Mgr., Westside Observer, IA, Westside

Jonson, Kerry
kjonson@sentinelnews.com, Pub., The Sentinel-News, KY, Shelbyville

Jordache, Costin .... **(301) 680-6564**
JordacheC.2gc.adventist.org, Communication Director and News Editor, Adventist Review, MD, Silver Spring

Jordan, Annette .... **(336) 626-6140**
ajordan@courier-tribune.com, Ed., The Courier-Tribune, NC, Asheboro

Jordan, Carolyn
cjordan@tompkinsvillenews.com, Office Mgr., Bookkeeping, Tompkinsville News, KY, Tompkinsville

Jordan, Choya .... **(248) 926-2203**
cbjordan@hometownlife.com, Mktg. Mgr., Plymouth Observer, MI, Detroit

Jordan, David .... **(406) 782-3820**
publisher@butteweekly.com, Pub, The Butte Weekly, MT, Butte

Jordan, David .... **(603) 594-1200**
customercare@nashuatelegraph.com, Aud. Dev. Mgr. , The Telegraph, NH, Nashua

Jordan, Hugo .... **(312) 870-7025**
hugo.jordan@laraza.com, Sr. Account Mgr., Local Sales, La Raza Newspaper, IL, Chicago

Jordan, Jessica .... **(603) 594-6438**
news@nashuatelegraph.com, NH.com Ed., The Telegraph, NH, Nashua

Jordan, Jodie .... **(402) 374-2226**
jodie.jordan@lee.net, Circ. Mgr., Burt County Plaindealer, NE, Tekamah

Jordan, Klonie .... **(864) 489-1131**
klonie@bellsouth.net, Ed., The Gaffney Ledger, SC, Gaffney

Jordan, Mark
mjordan@wcmessenger.com, Gen. Mgr./VP, Adv., Wise County Messenger, TX, Decatur

Jordan, Pat .... **(580) 765-3311**
ads@poncacitynews.com, Adv. Mgr., The Ponca City News, OK, Ponca City

Jordan, Patsy
patsyj@hometown-shopper.com, Prodn. Mgr., Hometown Shopper, CA, Ukiah

Jordan, Phil .... **(309) 686-3026**
pjordan@pjstar.com, Mgr., Mktg./Pub. Affairs, Journal Star, IL, Peoria

Jordan, Robert A.
bjordan@themediaaudit.com, Pres., International Demographics/The Media Audit, TX, Houston

Jordan, Sharon
Sharon.Jordan@wcfcourier.com, Adv. Dir., Insider, IA, Waterloo

Jordan, Susan ....(585) 244-9030 ext. 12
susanj@gayalliance.org, Ed., Gay Alliance, NY, Rochester

Jordan, Tammy .... **(217) 238-6835**
tjordan@jg-tc.com, Adv. Dir., Journal Gazette & Times-Courier, IL, Mattoon

Jordan, Tom .... **(901) 458-2911 ext. 2**
tjordan@thebesttimes.com, managing editor, The Best Times, TN, Memphis

Jordan, Wilma
wilmaj@jegi.com, CEO, Jordan, Edmiston Group, Inc., NY, New York

Jordan III, George .... **(413) 637-2250**
george@berkshirebeacon.com, Ed./Pub. , Berkshire Beacon, MA, Lenox Dale

Jorde, Paul
pjorde@perretta.com, Serv. Mgr., Perretta Graphics Corp., NY, Poughkeepsie

Jordon, Denise .... **(816) 531-5253**
kcglobe@swbell.net, Prodn. Mgr., Kansas City

Globe, MO, Kansas City

Jordon, Marion
kcglobe@swbell.net, Ed., Kansas City Globe, MO, Kansas City

Jorgensen, Ben
progress@clearwaterprogress.com, Ed., The Clearwater Progress, ID, Kamiah

Jorgensen, Jeanie
jjorgensen@appliedart.com, Media Mgr., Applied Art & Technology, IA, Des Moines

Jorgenson, Todd .... **(972) 563-6476**
sports@terrelltribune.com, Managing Editor, Terrell Tribune Update, TX, Terrell

Jorrey, Kyle
tonewstip@theacorn.com, Ed., Thousand Oaks Acorn, CA, Agoura Hills

Jose Torres, Maria
maria-jose.torres@publicitas.com, Sales Mktg. Mgr., Charney/Palacios & Co., FL, Miami

Joseph, Adam
adam@mcweekly.com, Editorial Department , Monterey County Weekly, CA, Seaside

Joseph, Jason .... **(520) 797-4384**
jjoseph@azlocalmedia.com, Pres.?Pub., Foothills News, AZ, Tucson
jjoseph@azlocalmedia.com, Pres./Pub., Inside Tucson Business, AZ, Tucson
jjoseph@azlocalmedia.com, Pres./Pub., Marana News, AZ, Tucson
jjoseph@azlocalmedia.com, Pres./Pub., Explorer, AZ, Tucson

Joseph, Jason
clee@hcnonline.com, Pub., The Courier of Montgomery County, TX, Conroe

Joseph, Jason
jjoseph@hcnonline.com, Pub., The Examiners, TX, Conroe
jjoseph@hcnonline.com, Pub., Memorial Examiner, TX, Conroe
jjoseph@hcnonline.com, Pub., Fort Bend Sun, TX, Conroe
jjoseph@hcnonline.com, Pub., The Woodlands Villager, TX, Conroe
jjoseph@hcnonline.com, Pub., Friendswood Journal, TX, Conroe
jjoseph@hcnonline.com, Pub., Humble Observer, TX, Conroe
jjoseph@hcnonline.com, Pub. , Kingwood Observer, TX, Conroe
jjoseph@hcnonline.com, Pub., Atascocita Observer, TX, Conroe
jjoseph@hcnonline.com, Pub., Cleveland Advocate, TX, Conroe
jjoseph@hcnonline.com, Pub. , Pearland Journal, TX, Conroe
jjoseph@hcnonline.com, Pub., Magnolia Potpourri, TX, Conroe
jjoseph@hcnonline.com, Pub. , Spring Observer, TX, Conroe
jjoseph@hcnonline.com, Pub., Tomball Potpourri, TX, Conroe
jjoseph@hcnonline.com, Pub., Dayton News, TX, Conroe
jjoseph@hcnonline.com, Pub., Lake Houston Observer, TX, Conroe

Joseph, Jason .... **(520) 797-4384**
jjosph@azlocalmedia.com, Pres/Pub, Tucson Weekly, AZ, Tucson

Joseph, Stephane............................ext. 226
stephane.joseph@transcontinental.ca, Sales Mgr., Hebdo Rive Nord, QC, Repentigny

Joseph, Whitney
editor@millertonnews.com, Ed., The Millerton News, NY, Millerton

Josephson, Kelly....................... **(901) 853-2241**
editor@collervilleherald.net, Editor, The Collierville Herald, TN, Collierville

Joshi, Rahul
rahul.joshi@timesgroup.com, Exec. Ed., THE ECONOMIC TIMES, Mumbai, Maharashtra

Joss, Molly .... **(484) 206-4233**
contact@thejossgroup.com, Publisher, Editor,

Owner, The Seybold Report, PA, Trappe

Jost, Monte .... **(712) 546-7031 ext. 31**
mjost@lemarscomm.net, Mktg. Dir., Le Mars Daily Sentinel, IA, Le Mars

Jost, Monte
mjost@lemarscomm.net, Mktg. Dir., Shoppers Guide, IA, Le Mars

Jost, Shannon .... **(712) 546-7031 ext. 16**
sjost@lemarssentinel.com, Account manager-Advertising, Le Mars Daily Sentinel, IA, Le Mars

Joubert, Tony **613- 933-3160 x258**
readersales@standard-freeholder.com, Circulation Sales And Inserts, Standard-freeholder Complimentary, ON, Cornwall

Joudy, Rich .... **(203) 731-3407**
rjoudy@newstimes.com, IT Help Desk, The News-Times, CT, Danbury

Jovanovic, Bojan
cws@cartoonweb.com, Assoc. Ed., Cartoonists & Writers Syndicate/Cartoon Arts International - Rancho Palos Verdes, CA, Rancho Palos Verdes

Jowett, Garth
gjowett@uh.edu, Prof., University of Houston, TX, Houston

Joy, Bonner .... **(941) 778-7978**
news@islander.org, Ed./Pub., The Islander, FL, Holmes Beach

Joy, Bonniesue .... **(319) 988-3855**
Ed, Pub, Hudson Herald, IA, Hudson

Joy, Lisa .... **(403) 307-3398**
contact@ECAreview.com, Marketing Rep/ Reporter Photographer, East Central Alberta Review, AB, Coronation

Joyce, Beverly.......................... **(765) 640-2307**
beverly.joyce@heraldbulletin.com, Pub., The Herald Bulletin, IN, Anderson

Joyce, Cecil
cjoyce@mtcngroup.com, Sports Ed., Gallatin News Examiner, TN, Gallatin

Joyce, Denise
djoyce@tribune.com, Pres., Society for Features Journalism, MD, College Park

Joyce, Gary P. .... **(631) 286-0058 ext. 250**
Ed., 50+ LifeStyles, NY, Bellport

Joyce, Janet .... **(570) 628-6145**
jjoyce@republicanherald.com, Dir., Mktg./ Community Serv., The Republican-Herald, PA, Pottsville

Joyce, Jason
jjoyce@madison.com, The Capital Times, WI, Madison

Joyce, John
joycemed@pacbell.net, Pub., Acton-Agua Dulce News, CA, Acton

Joyce, Marion
marion.joyce@verizon.net, Pres., Marion Joyce, Bronxville

Joyce, Michael A....................... **(570) 628-6049**
mjoyce@republicanherald.com, Adv. Dir., The Republican-Herald, PA, Pottsville

Juarez, Alfonso
info@sipiapa.org, Librarian, Inter American Press Association, FL, Miami

Juarez, Melva .... **(956) 982-6650**
mjuarez@brownsvilleherald.com, Business Manager, The Brownsville Herald, TX, Brownsville

Judd, Don ....ext. 677
it@svherald.com, IT Mgr., Sierra Vista Herald - Sunday Bravo Shopper, AZ, Sierra Vista

Judd, Heather .... **(918) 653-2425**
heavenerledger@windstream.net, Mktg Rep, The Heavener Ledger, OK, Heavener

Judd, Patsy .... **(270) 864-3891**
ccn@burkesville.com, Pub., Cumberland

County News, KY, Burkesville

Judge, Bernie ....**(312) 644-7800**
displayads@lbpc.com, Consultant , Chicago
Daily Law Bulletin, IL, Chicago

Judge, Betsy .... **(7(527) 361-4730**
info@theislandreporter.com, Pub./Ed., The
Island Reporter, FL, South Pasadena
info@theislandreporter.com, Island Reporter,
FL, Sanibel

Judge, Jay ....**(410) 468-2622**
jay.judge@baltsun.com....., Sr. Ed. visuals, The
Baltimore Sun, MD, Baltimore

Judge, Lee
ljudge@kcstar.com, Cartoonist, The Kansas
City Star, MO, Kansas City

Judie, Natealine ....**(805) 437-0333**
natealine.judie@vcstar.com, VP Adv., Ventura
County Star, CA, Camarillo

Judith, Burton ....**(615) 384-3567**
jaburton@mtcngroup.com, Adv. Rep.,
Robertson County Times, TN, Clarksville

Judson, Mark ....**(850) 682-6524**
mjudson@crestviewbulletin.com, Reporter,
Crestview News Bulletin, FL, Crestview

Judson, Mary ....**(361) 749-5131**
southjetty@centurytel.net, Co-Pub./Ed., Port
Aransas South Jetty, TX, Port Aransas

Judy, Kristin
kjudy@bannergraphic.com, Accounting,
Banner-Graphic, IN, Greencastle

Juedes, Jan ....**(715) 365-6397 ext. 364**
advertising@rivernewsonline.com, Classifieds/
Adv. Dir., Northwoods Super Shopper, WI,
Rhinelander
advertising@rivernewsonline.com, Adv.
Dir., The Northwoods River News , WI,
Rhinelander

Jugan, Irene
straz@pnu.org, Ed., Straz, PA, Scranton

Jugenheimer, Don
a.heuman@ttu.edu, Prof./Chair, Dept. of
Advertising, Texas Tech University, TX,
Lubbock

Juha, Jonathan
jjuha@postmedia.com, Reporter, The Stratford
Beacon Herald, ON, Stratford

Juhasz, Andrea
andrea.juhasz@zu.ac.ae, Administrative
Officer, Zayed University, Al Ruwayyah

Jule, Koch.............................**(613) 279-3150**
info@frontenacnews.ca, Managing Editor, The
Frontenac News, ON, Sharbot Lake

Julian, William.......................**(250) 262-7437**
wj@ahnfsj.ca, Reg. Mgr., The Mirror, BC,
Dawson Creek
wj@ahnfsj.ca, Pub, North Peace Express, BC,
Fort Saint John
wj@ahnfsj.ca, Pub, The Northern Horizon, BC,
Dawson Creek
wj@ahnfsj.ca, Reg. Mgr. , Alaska Highway
News, BC, Fort Saint John
wj@ahnfsj.ca, Reg. Mgr., Dawson Creek Mirror,
BC, Dawson Creek
wj@ahnfsj.ca, Pub., The Northerner, BC, Fort
Saint John

Juliano, John
john@jjcs.com, Pres., John Juliano Computer
Services Co., GA, Decatur

Juliano, Jon
john.juliano@miles33.com, VP, Business
Development, Miles 33, CT, Norwalk

Julien, Andrew S.......................**(860) 241-3997**
ajulien@courant.com, Pub./Ed.-in-Chief,
Courant Community - West Hartford, CT,
Hartford
ajulien@courant.com, Pub., Courant
Community - Wethersfield, CT, Hartford
ajulien@courant.com, Publisher & Editor-in-
Chief, The Hartford Courant, CT, Hartford

ajulien@courant.com, Pub./Ed.-in-Chief,
Courant Community - Windsor Locks, CT,
Hartford
ajulien@courant.com, Pub./Ed.-in-Chief,
Courant Community - Windsor, CT, Hartford
ajulien@courant.com, Pub./Ed.-in-Chief,
Courant Community - Windham, CT, Hartford
ajulien@courant.com, Pub./Ed.-in-Chief,
Courant Community - Vernon, CT, Hartford
ajulien@courant.com, Pub./Ed.-in-Chief,
Courant Community - Valley, CT, Hartford
ajulien@courant.com, Pub./Ed.-in-Chief,
Courant Community - Stafford, CT, Hartford
ajulien@courant.com, Pub./Ed.-in-Chief,
Courant Community - South Windsor, CT,
Hartford
ajulien@courant.com, Pub./Ed.-in-Chief,
Courant Community - Putnam, CT, Hartford
ajulien@courant.com, Pub./Ed.-in-Chief,
Courant Community - Manchester, CT,
Hartford
ajulien@courant.com, Pub./Ed.-in-Chief,
Courant Community - Killingly, CT, Hartford
ajulien@courant.com, Pub./Ed.-in-Chief,
Courant Community - Hebron, CT, Hartford
ajulien@courant.com, Pub./Ed.-in-Chief,
Courant Community - Glastonbury, CT,
Hartford
ajulien@courant.com, Pub.Pub./Ed.-in-Chief,
Courant Community - Enfield, CT, Hartford
ajulien@courant.com, Pub., Courant
Community - East Hartford, CT, Hartford
ajulien@courant.com, Pub., Courant
Community - Colchester, CT, Hartford

Julius, Tom ....**(440) 930-0050**
tjulius@hallcontractingservices.com, Vice
President of Operations, Hall Contracting
Services, Inc., OH, Avon Lake

Juma, M.
The False Creek News, Adv. Sales, The False
Creek News, BC, Vancouver

Jump, Jason
jjump@kcnonline.com, Pub., Kingman Leader-
Courier, KS, Kingman

Jump, Stephanie ....**(620) 532-3151**
sjump@kcnonline.com, Bus. Mgr., Kingman
Leader-Courier, KS, Kingman

Junck, Mary
mary.junck@lee.net, Exec. Chairman, Lee
Enterprises, Inc., IA, Davenport

Junek, Greg
gjunek@tylerpaper.com, Bus. Ed., Tyler
Morning Telegraph, TX, Tyler

Jung, Chris
cjung@kentuckynewera.com, Sports Editor,
Kentucky New Era, KY, Hopkinsville

Jung, Kimberly
kim@fredericksburgstandard.com, Adv. Dir.,
Fredericksburg Standard-Radio Post, TX,
Fredericksburg

Jung, Michael
mjung@news-press.com, Pres. & Pub., The
Commercial Appeal, TN, Memphis

Jung, Mike ....**(901) 529-2201**
mike.jung@commercialappeal.com, President,
The Commercial Appeal, TN, Memphis

Jungels, Allen ....**(605) 331-2399**
ajungels@argusleader.com, Production
Manager, Argus Leader, SD, Sioux Falls

Junger, Dr. Richard
richard.junger@wmich.edu, Prog. Dir., Western
Michigan University, MI, Kalamazoo

Junger, Richard ....**(269) 387-2110**
herald-general-manager@wmich.edu, General
Manager, Western Michigan Univ., MI,
Kalamazoo

Jurado, Jay
info@midwestdigital.com, CEO, Midwest Digital
Communications, WI, Madison

Juranovich, Tyler ....**(765) 671-1266**
tjuranovich@chronicle-tribune.com, Managing
Ed., Chronicle-Tribune, IN, Marion

Jurczyk, Rita............................**(619) 293-1424**
rita.jurczyk@sduniontribune.com, Director,
National Sales, The San Diego Union-
Tribune, CA, San Diego

Jurden, Janice ....**(580) 795-3355**
madillrecord@sbcglobal.net, Advertising Sales,
Madill Record, OK, Madill

Jurek, Rachael ....**(414) 229-4436**
jurek@uwm.edu, Lecturer, University of
Wisconsin-Milwaukee / Department of
Journalism, Advertising, and Media Studies
(JAMS), WI, Milwaukee

Jurewicz, Ron
rjurewicz@hfwindustries.com, Manufacturing
Manager, HFW Industries, NY, Buffalo

Jurica, Gaby ....**(702) 477-3845**
gjurica@reviewjournal.com, Advertising
Manager, El Tiempo, NV, Las Vegas

Jurik, Phil
jbiesk@tribpub.com, Ed., Franklin Park Herald-
Journal, IL, Chicago
jbiesk@tribpub.com, Ed., The Doings –
Western Springs, IL, Chicago
jbiesk@tribpub.com, Ed., The Doings – Oak
Brook and Elmhurst, IL, Chicago
jbiesk@tribpub.com, Ed., The Doings – La
Grange, IL, Chicago
jbiesk@tribpub.com, Pub., The Doings –
Clarendon Hills, IL, Chicago
jbiesk@tribpub.com, Ed., The Doings Weekly –
Burr Ridge, IL, Chicago
jbiesk@tribpub.com, Ed., The Doings –
Hinsdale, IL, Chicago
jbiesk@tribpub.com, Ed., The Naperville Sun,
IL, Chicago
jbiesk@tribpub.com, Ed., Forest Leaves, IL,
Chicago
jbiesk@tribpub.com, Exec. Ed., The Beacon
News, IL, Chicago
jbiesk@tribpub.com, Ed., Evanston Review,
IL, Chicago
jbiesk@tribpub.com, Exec. Ed., The Courier-
News, IL, Aurora
jbiesk@tribpub.com, Exec. Ed., Lake County
News-Sun, IL, Gurnee
jbiesk@tribpub.com, Exec. Ed., Post-Tribune,
IN, Crown Point
jbiesk@tribpub.com, Ed., Park Ridge Herald
Advocate, IL, Chicago
jbiesk@tribpub.com, Ed., Buffalo Grove
Countryside, IL, Chicago
jbiesk@tribpub.com, Ed., Crown Point Star,
IL, Chicago
jbiesk@tribpub.com, Ed., Deerfield Review,
IL, Chicago
jbiesk@tribpub.com, Ed., Elmwood Park
Leaves, IL, Chicago
jbiesk@tribpub.com, Ed., Glencoe News, IL,
Chicago
jbiesk@tribpub.com, Ed., Glenview
Announcements, IL, Chicago
jbiesk@tribpub.com, Ed., Highland Park News,
IL, Chicago
jbiesk@tribpub.com, Ed., Arlington Heights
Post, IL, Glenview
jbiesk@tribpub.com, Ed., Lake Forester, IL,
Chicago
jbiesk@tribpub.com, Ed., Lake Zurich Courier,
IL, Chicago
jbiesk@tribpub.com, Ed., Libertyville Review,
IL, Chicago
jbiesk@tribpub.com, Ed., Lincolnshire Review,
IL, Chicago
jbiesk@tribpub.com, Ed., Lincolnwood Review,
IL, Chicago
jbiesk@tribpub.com, Ed., Morton Grove
Champion, IL, Chicago
jbiesk@tribpub.com, Ed., Mundelein Review,
IL, Chicago
jbiesk@tribpub.com, Ed., Niles Herald-
Spectator, IL, Chicago
jbiesk@tribpub.com, Ed., Norridge-Harwood
Heights News, IL, Chicago
jbiesk@tribpub.com, Ed., Northbrook Star, IL,
Chicago
jbiesk@tribpub.com, Ed., Oak Leaves, IL,
Chicago
jbiesk@tribpub.com, Ed., Skokie Review, IL,
Chicago

jbiesk@tribpub.com, Ed., Vernon Hills Review,
IL, Chicago
jbiesk@tribpub.com, Ed., Wilmette Life, IL,
Chicago
jbiesk@tribpub.com, Ed., Winnetka Talk, IL,
Chicago
jbiesk@tribpub.com, Ed., Barrington Courier-
Review, IL, Glenview

Jurkowitz, Mark ....**(252) 480-2234**
mark@obsentinel.com, Pub., Outer Banks
Sentinel, NC, Nags Head

Jurney, Larry
larry.jurney@oc.edu, Chair, Oklahoma
Christian University, OK, Edmond

Juruzel, Jo Ann
billing@houghtonlakeresorter.com, Office Mgr.,
The Houghton Lake Resorter, MI, Houghton
Lake

Just, Cameron.........................**(306) 651-6307**
Tech. Officer, Saskatchewan Weekly
Newspapers Association, SK, Saskatoon

Justesen, DeAnn ....**(805) 437-0207**
dajustesen@vcstar.com, Asst. Mng. Ed.,
Ventura County Star, CA, Camarillo

Justice, Candy
candyjustice@dailyhelmsman.com, Asst. Prof.,
University of Memphis, TN, Memphis

Justice, Heather
hjustice@newsdemocratleader.com, Adv. Sales
Rep., The News Democrat & Leader, KY,
Russellville

Justice, Jennifer ....**(719) 384-1439**
bcd@ljtdmail.com, Asst. Ed. , La Junta Tribune-
Democrat, CO, La Junta

Justice, Keith
kjustice@unionrecorder.com, Prodn. Dir., The
Union-Recorder, GA, Milledgeville

Justice, Phyllis Dolan
gcreview@itcmilbank.com, Pub./Ed., Grant
County Review, SD, Milbank

Justin, Heela ....**(212) 790-0283**
Cardozo School of Law/Yeshiva, NY, New York

Justine Lanyon, Mary ...... **(909) 337-6145 ext. 221**
editor@mountain-news.com, Ed., Mountain
News & Crestline Courier-News, CA, Lake
Arrowhead

Juteau, Rob..........................**(315) 866-2220**
rjuteau@timestelegram.com, Mng. Ed. , The
Herkimer Telegram, NY, Herkimer

Juul, Torben
tj@ccieurope.com, Vice Pres., Mktg., CCI
Europe, Inc., GA, Kennesaw

K

K A , Lesnar............................**(605) 274-2659**
klesnar@siouxfallsshoppingnews.com, ceo/
president, Sioux Falls Shopping News, SD,
Sioux Falls

Kaas, Delair
fforum@loretel.net, Gen. Mgr., Frazee-Vergas
Forum, MN, Frazee

Kaas, Gale ....**(218) 334-3566**
fforum@loretel.net, Ed., Frazee-Vergas Forum,
MN, Frazee

Kabat, Susan
susan_kabat@jewishaz.com, Adv. Acc. Exec.,
Jewish News, AZ, Phoenix

Kabler, Jane .... **(606) 564-9091 ext. 278**
Jane.Kabler@lee.net, The Mayfield Messenger,
KY, Mayfield

Kachala, Jay Sivin
jsivinkachala@iesdinc.com, Vice Pres.,
Interactive Educational Systems Design, Inc.,
NY, New York

Kacich, Tom............................**(217) 351-5221**
tkacich@news-gazette.com, Columnist, The
News-Gazette, IL, Champaign

Kaczynski, James .... (412) 965-9183
info@polamjournal.com, Advertising Sales,
Polish American Journal, NY, North Boston

Kadrmas, Jeremy .... (701) 456-1230
jkadrmas@thedickinsonpress.com, Prod. Mgr,
The Dickinson Press, ND, Dickinson

Kaechele, Cheryl..................... (269) 673-5534
publisher@allegancountynews.com, Pub, The
Commercial Record, MI, Saugatuck

Kaechele, Cheryl..................... (269) 673-5534
publisher@allegannews.com, Pub., Allegan
County News, MI, Allegan

Kaechele, Cheryl A. .... (269) 673-5534
publisher@allegannews.com, Pub., Union
Enterprise, MI, Allegan

Kaercher, Sue
northernstar@mchsi.com, Pub., Northern Star,
MN, Clinton

Kaerh, Jennifer
businessmanager@decaturdailydemocrat.com,
Office/Bus. Mgr., Decatur Daily Democrat,
IN, Decatur
businessmanager@decaturdailydemocrat.
com, Bus. Mgr., Berne Shopping News, IN,
Decatur

Kafentzis, John .... (509) 313-3896
kafentzis@gonzaga.edu, Adviser, Gonzaga
University, WA, Spokane

Kaggwa, Lawrence .... (202) 806-9401
lkaggwa@howard.edu, Publisher, District
Chronicles, DC, Washington
lkaggwa@howard.edu, Prof., Howard
University, DC, Washington

Kahan, Jonathan
jonathan.kahan@dowjones.com, CFO, Dow
Jones Local Media Group, NY, Middletown

Kahana, Leslie .... (423) 757-6514
lkahana@timesfreepress.com, Advertising
Director, Chattanooga Times Free Press, TN,
Chattanooga

Kahlau, Susan
advertising@timesleader.com, Adv. Dir., The
Dallas Post, PA, Wilkes Barre

Kahn, A. David
kahn@artistmarket.com, CEO/Ed.,
ArtistMarket.com, Farmington Hills

Kahn, Dean
dean.kahn@bellinghamherald.com, Whatcom
Magazine Ed., The Bellingham Herald, WA,
Bellingham

Kahn, Joseph
joekahn@nytimes.com, Mng. Ed., The New
York Times, NY, New York

Kahn, Larry
lkahn@keynoter.com, Ed., Florida Keys
Keynoter, FL, Marathon

Kahnt, Joann
ppost@tctelco.net, Ed., The Prairie Post, KS,
White City

Kaible, Jay .... (631) 737-6020 x120
jkaible@flexography.org, Membership & Buss.
Dev. Dir., Flexographic Technical Association,
NY, Bohemia

Kaim, Wayne
wayne@kaiminc.com, Pres., Kaim &
Associates International Marketing, Inc.,
WI, Lodi

Kain, Chris
newsdesk@currentnewspapers.com, Mgn. Ed.,
Dupont Current, DC, Washington
newsdesk@currentnewspapers.com, Mgn. Ed.,
Foggy Bottom Current, DC, Washington
newsdesk@currentnewspapers.com,
Georgetown Current, DC, Washington
newsdesk@currentnewspapers.com, Mgn. Ed.,
Northwest Current, DC, Washington

Kain, Donald..................... (507) 462-3321
MLTRIB@BEVCOMM.NET, Pub., Minnesota
Lake Tribune, MN, Minnesota Lake

Kaiser, Gidal .... (605) 224-7301 x134
gidal.kaiser@capjournal.com, Sports Ed,
Capital Journal, SD, Pierre

Kaiser, Gina .... (321) 242-3740
gkaiser@floridatoday.com, Strategic Marketing
Solutions Dir., Florida Today, FL, Melbourne

Kaiser, Glenn .... (780) 468-0259
glenn.kaiser@edm.sunpub.com, Info. Serv.
Mgr., The Edmonton Sun, AB, Edmonton

Kaiser, Howard
enpub@sooeveningnews.com, Adv. Mgr., Tri-
county Buyer's Guide, MI, Sault Sainte Marie

Kaiser, Rob .... (716) 439-9222 ext. 2253
rob.kaiser@lockportjournal.com; matt.
winterhalter@niagara-gazette.com, Exec.
Ed., Lockport Union-Sun & Journal, NY,
Lockport
rob.kaiser@lockportjournal.com; matt.
winterhalter@niagara-gazette.com, Exec Ed.,
Niagara Gazette, NY, Niagara Falls

Kalantzis, Dimitrios 815/802-5144
dkalantzis@daily-journal.com, Managing
Editor, The Daily Journal, IL, Kankakee

Kalenak, JoeAnn
hcnsyndicate@hcnsyndicate.org, Syndicate
Representative, High Country News, Paonia

Kaleta, Kenneth
kaleta@rowan.edu, Prof., Rowan Univ., NJ,
Glassboro

Kalich, Kevin .... (361) 575-6400
Ed., American Classifieds, TX, Victoria

Kalich, Rhonda
rhonda.victoria@americanclassifieds.com,
Prodn. Mgr., American Classifieds, TX,
Victoria

Kalich, Tim..................... (662) 581-7243
tkalich@gwcommonwealth.com, Pub./Ed., The
Greenwood Commonwealth, MS, Greenwood

Kalina, David .... ext. 320
dkalina@innotek-ep.com, Vice Pres., Finance,
Innotek Corporation, MN, Maple Grove

Kalinowski, Linda..................... (262) 544-5252
kalinowski@newsfinder.com, Acct. Mgr.,
Newsfinder, Waukesha

Kalita , S. Mitra
mitra.kalita@latimes.com, Managing Ed., Los
Angeles Times, CA, Los Angeles

Kalkbrenner, Ashley
advertising@universitychronicle.net, St. Cloud
State Univ., MN, Saint Cloud

Kallan, Richard A.
rakallan@csupomona.edu, Chair, California
State Polytechnic University, Pomona, CA,
Pomona

Kallas, Tracy
classifieds@theberlinjournal.com, Circ. Mgr.,
Berlin Journal, WI, Berlin
classifieds@theberlinjournal.com, Circ. Mgr.,
Markesan Regional Reporter, WI, Berlin
classifieds@theberlinjournal.com, Circ. Mgr.,
Omro Herald, WI, Berlin
classifieds@theberlinjournal.com, Circ. Mgr.,
Princeton Times-Republic, WI, Berlin
classifieds@theberlinjournal.com, Circ. Mgr.,
The Fox Lake Representative, WI, Berlin
classifieds@theberlinjournal.com, Circ. Mgr.,
Green Lake Reporter, WI, Berlin

Kallemeyn, Arlo..................... (708) 271-8967
arlok@excelprintmail.com, Pub., The Shopper,
IL, South Holland

Kallman, Greg..................... (414) 566-7500
greg.kallman@quadtechworld.com, Regional
Sales Manager, QuadTech, WI, Sussex

Kalman, Sean
skalman@inkym.com, Prodn. Dir., The Inquirer
and Mirror, MA, Nantucket

Kalmer, Karen
staffordcourier@sbcglobal.net, Ed., The
Stafford Courier, KS, Stafford

Kalyango, Yusuf..................... (740) 597-3335
Advisor, Lincoln Univ., MO, Jefferson City
Asst. Prof./Dir., Inst. for Int'l Journalism, Ohio
University, OH, Athens

Kam, Karl .... (212) 557-1133 ext. 13
karl.kam@iaaglobal.org, Mgr. IT., International
Advertising Association, Inc., NY, New York

Kamen, Kevin Brian .... (516) 379-2797
info@kamengroup.com, Pres./CEO, Kamen &
Co. Group Services, NY, Uniondale
info@kamengroup.com, Pres., Kevin Brian
Kamen & Co. (Kamen & Co. Group Services),
NY, Baldwin
info@kamengroup.com, Pres./CEO, Kevin
Brian Kamen & Co. (Kamen & Co. Group
Services), NY, Uniondale

Kamerick, Marcia
mkamerick@ottumwacourier.com, Business
Manager, The Ottumwa Courier, IA, Ottumwa

Kamins, Charles
editor@rereader.com, Mng. Ed., Wine Country
Weekly Real Estate Reader, CA, Napa

Kaminski, John
chicago@rotadyne.com, Vice Pres. Industrial
Sales, RotaDyne Corp., IL, Darien

Kaminski, Robert .... ext. 208
Press. Mgr., The Pioneer - Big Rapids, MI, Big
Rapids

Kammers, Bryce
bgkammers@lcsc.edu, Lewis-Clark State
College, ID, Lewiston

Kamowski, Kim
kkamowski@cumberlink.com, Mktg. Dir., The
Sentinel, PA, Carlisle

Kampman, Kevin..................... (330) 580-8451
Regional VP - Great Lakes, GateHouse Media,
Inc., NY, Pittsford

Kampman , Kevin .... (336) 727-7349
KKampman@wsjournal.com, Publisher & V.P.
Northern Region , Winston-Salem Journal,
NC, Winston Salem

Kanaly, Drew
kanaly@kanaly.com, Chairman/CEO, Kanaly
Trust Co., TX, Houston

Kane, Charles
ckane@buschusa.com, Pres., Busch, Inc., VA,
Virginia Beach

Kane, Coleman
ckane@pti.com, Pres./CEO, PTI Marketing
Technologies, Inc., CA, Solana Beach

Kane, Keith .... (518) 565-4124
kkane@pressrepublican.com, Sports Editor,
Press-Republican, NY, Plattsburgh

Kane, Michael..................... (978) 368-0176 ext. 4790
clintonitem@yahoo.com, Ed., The Banner,
MA, Clinton

Kane, Tim
tkane@turley.com, Ed., Quaboag Current,
MA, Ware
tkane@turley.com, Ed., Southwick Suffield
News, MA, Feeding Hills
tkane@turley.com, Ed., Ware River News,
MA, Ware

Kane, Tim
tkane@turley.com, Ed. , The Tantasqua Town
Common, MA, Palmer

Kane, Tom..................... (618) 253-7146 ext 230
tkane@dailyregister.com, Reporter, The Daily
Register, IL, Harrisburg

Kaneva, Nadia
nadia.kaneva@du.edu, Asst. Prof., University
of Denver, CO, Denver

Kang, Seok
skang@atu.edu, Assoc. Prof., Arkansas Tech
University, AR, Russellville

Kanick, Robert W. .... (724) 465-5555 ext. 200
rwkanick@indianagazette.net, Controller, The
Indiana Gazette, PA, Indiana

Kannberg, Daryl .... (216) 999-4865
dkannberg@plaind.com, Publications Director,
The Plain Dealer, OH, Brooklyn

Kanner, Matt
news@stowereporter.com, Ed., Waterbury
Record, VT, Stowe

Kanniard, Ken .... (347) 802-7732
kkanniard@dailygazette.net, Production Dir.,
The Daily Gazette, NY, Schenectady

Kannon, Steve .... (519) 669-5790 ext 103
skannon@woolwichobserver.com, Ed., The
Observer, ON, Elmira

Kantor, Gregory
weeklyeditor@gmail.com, Editor in Chief,
Muhlenberg College, PA, Allentown

Kao, JoAnne .... (212) 803-8325
joanne.kao@sourcemedia.com, Assoc. Dir.
of Classified Sales, American Banker, NY,
New York

Kapiloff, Lynn
lynn@thesentinel.com, CEO, Montgomery
County Sentinel, MD, Rockville

Kapiloff, Lynn
lynn@thesentinel.com, CEO, The Prince
George's Sentinel, MD, Seabrook

Kaplan, Adam .... (305) 347-6680
akaplan@alm.com, Audience Development
Manager, Palm Beach Daily Business
Review, FL, Miami

Kaplan, Jackie .... (305) 376-2398
JKaplan@MiamiHerald.com, Dir. Interactive
Sales, Miami Herald, FL, Doral
JKaplan@MiamiHerald.com, Interactive Sales
Mgr., Herald Values, FL, Miami

Kaplan, Jeff
reviewads@alliancelink.com, Adv. Mgr., Mr.
Thrifty, OH, Alliance

Kaplan, Jeff
jkaplan@the-review.com, Adv. Dir., The News
Leader, OH, Minerva
jkaplan@the-review.com, Adv. Dir., The Press-
News, OH, Minerva

Kaplan, John
jkaplan@ufl.edu, Prof./UF Res. Foundation
Prof., University of Florida, FL, Gainesville

Kaplan, Pam
pamk@actionunlimited.com, Adv. Mgr, Action
Unlimited, MA, Concord

Kaplan, Thomas
editor@yaledailynews.com, Yale Univ., CT,
New Haven

Kappel, Joanne ....(864) 370-1800 ext. 2738
Bob Jones University, SC, Greenville

Kappes, Keith .... (606) 784-4116
kkappes@journal-times.com, Publisher and
Editor, Grayson Journal-Enquirer, KY,
Grayson

Kappes, Keith .... (800) 247-6142
kkappes@journal-times.com, Publisher and
Editor, Olive Hill Times, KY, Olive Hill

Kapral, Robert
bkapral@timesleaderonline.com, Exec. Sports
Ed., The Times Leader, OH, Martins Ferry

Kapur, Jyotsna
jkapur@siu.edu, Assoc. Prof., Southern Illinois
University Carbondale, IL, Carbondale

Kara, Stevens .... (519) 284-2440
kstevens@stmarys.com, Sales Supervisor, St.
Mary's Journal Argus, ON, St Marys

Karaffa, Eric
chi_sales@parade.com, Vice Pres./Mid-
Western Mgr., Parade Publications, Inc. -
Chicago, IL, Chicago

Karametros, Chrysoula
production@thenationalherald.com, Prodn.
Mgr., The National Herald, NY, Long Island
City

Karbonit, Judy

jkarbonit@register-herald.com, Vice Special Editions Ed., The Register Herald, WV, Beckley

Kardoes, Lanita
bctrib@wctatel.net, Pub., Buffalo Center Tribune, IA, Buffalo Center

Kardos, Thomas J........... (207) 773-6471 ext. 133
tkardos@portlanddiocese.net, Ed., Church World, ME, Portland

Karelf, Trisha
trishak@glencoenews.com, Circ. Mgr., The Glencoe Advertiser, MN, Glencoe

Karen, Brian .... (301) 838-0788
editor-mc@thesentinel.com, Ed., Montgomery County Sentinel, MD, Rockville

Karen, Hayes .... (308) 882-4453
imperialads@jpipapers.com, Production Mgr., Imperial Republican, NE, Imperial

Karimabadi, Wilona
karimabadiw@gc.adventist.org, assistant editor, Adventist Review, MD, Silver Spring

Kark-Wren, Joan .... (518) 673-0141
jkarkwren@leepub.com, Ed. , Country Folks - East Zone, NY, Palatine Bridge

Karl, Heidi
heidik@hollistercreative.com, Art Dir., Hollister Kids, Bryn Mawr

Karlic, Alicja
alicjakarlic@gmail.com, Ed, in Chief Publisher, Altad, Inc., MI, Rochester

Karlovec, John .... (440) 285-2013
jdk@dln.com, Ed., Geauga County Maple Leaf, OH, Chardon

Karlovec, Richard
rickkarlovec@dln.com, The Daily Legal News and Cleveland Recorder, OH, Cleveland

Karlson, Bruce .... (937) 225-2249
bruce.karlson@coxinc.com, Cox Media Group, GA, Atlanta

Karlson, Bruce .... (937) 225-2249
bruce.karlson@coxinc.com, Nat'l Dir., Middletown Journal, OH, Liberty Township
bruce.karlson@coxinc.com, Sales Manager - National/Major, Dayton Daily News, OH, Franklin

Karlson, Douglas .... (508) 274-3265
Ed., Harwich Oracle, MA, Orleans

Karlsson, Lotta .... (212) 457-7938
lotta.karlsson@metro.us, Chief Digital Officer, Metro New York, NY, New York

Karmel, Terese
terese.karmel@uconn.edu, Lectr., University of Connecticut, CT, Storrs

Karol, Susan .... (847) 486-7320
karol@pioneerlocal.com, Vice Pres., Adv., Morton Grove Champion, IL, Chicago

Karolyi, Anne
akarolyi@rep-am.com, Managing Editor , Republican-American, CT, Waterbury

Karpen, Jim .... (641) 472-0778
jkarpen@mum.edu, Maharishi Univ. of Mgmt., IA, Fairfield

Karst, Mary .... (785) 628-1081
maryk_ads@dailynews.net, Adv. Dir., The Hays Daily News Extra, KS, Hays

Karst, Mary
maryk.ads@dailynews.net, Adv. Dir., The Hays Daily News, KS, Hays

Karstedt, Theresia .... (979) 968-3155
theresia@fayettecountyrecord.com, Circ. Mgr., The Fayette County Record, TX, La Grange

Karsten, Linda
lkarsten@rny.com, Production Mgr., Daily Sentinel, NY, Rome

Kartis, Ray
rkartis@scnl.com, Circ. Mgr., Regl., The Herald News, IL, Chicago

Karununean, Lilian 885-0288
Lilian.Karununean@dowjones.com, Correspondent, Dow Jones Newswires - Manila, Philippines, Manila

Kasbohm, Paul .... (612) 673-7207
paul.kasbohm@startribune.com, CFO, Star Tribune, MN, Minneapolis

Kasch, Chris
ckasch@bradley.edu, Assoc. Prof., Bradley University, IL, Peoria

Kaselis Tzouvelis , Joanna .... (781) 674-7723
jtzouvelis@wickedlocal.com, Ed., Belmont Citizen-Herald, MA, Lexington

Kashner, Dean .... ext. 1305
dean.k@pe-online.com, Mng. Ed., Around The House, PA, Bloomsburg

Kashner, Dean ....(570) 387-1234 Ext 1305
Mng. Ed., News, Press Enterprise, PA, Bloomsburg

Kasik, Matt
mkasik@journalstar.com, Pkg. Mgr., Lincoln Journal Star, NE, Lincoln

Kaskan, Mary .... ext. 2397
mkaskan@wdt.net, Sunday Ed., Watertown Daily Times, NY, Watertown

Kaskovich, Steve .... (817) 390-7773
skaskovich@star-telegram.com, Asst. Mng. Ed., Bus., Fort Worth Star-Telegram, TX, Fort Worth

Kasper, Dr. Jeffrey S. ....(925) 798-0896 ext. 15
jk@service-quality.com, Pres., ServiceQuality. US, Concord

Kasper, Valerie .... (352) 588-7424
valerie.kasper@saintleo.edu, Saint Leo University, FL, Saint Leo

Kasperek, Kenneth B.
advertising@akronbugle.com, Adv. Mgr., Akron Bugle, NY, Akron

Kasperek, Marilyn J.
editor@akronbugle.com, Pub., Akron Bugle, NY, Akron

Kaspryzk, Joseph ....ext. 244
dsybert@butlereagle.com, Editorial Writer., Butler Eagle, PA, Butler

Kass, Mark
mkass@mmsd.com, Ed. in Chief, Milwaukee Business Journal, WI, Milwaukee

Kast, Eileen
ekast@ogd.com, HR/Purch. , Ogdensburg Journal/Advance News, NY, Ogdensburg

Kasten, Judy
jkasten@strato.net, Adv. Dir., Okeechobee News, FL, Okeechobee

Kasten, Krista
kkasten@journal-advocate.com, Circ., Journal-Advocate, CO, Sterling

Kastrup, Thom......................... (402) 444-1429
thom.kastrup@owh.com, Chief Revenue Officer, Omaha World-Herald, NE, Omaha

Kastrup, Thomas .... (402) 444-1429
THOM.KASTRUP@BHMGINC.COM, BH Media Group, NE, Omaha

Katches, Mark .... (503) 221-8393
mkatches@oregonian.com, Ed, Hillsboro Argus, OR, Portland
mkatches@oregonian.com, Ed., VP of Content, The Oregonian, OR, Portland

Katchur, Mark
mkatchur@standardspeaker.com, Ed., Hazleton Standard-Speaker, PA, Hazleton

Kathy, Neumeister .... (608) 845-9559
kathy.neumeister@wcinet.com, Sales Mgr, Great Dane Shopping News, WI, Verona

Kato, Gerald
gkato@hawaii.edu, Chair/Assoc. Prof., University of Hawaii at Manoa, HI, Honolulu

Kato, Nicole

nkato@hpu.edu, Copy Editor, Hawaii Pacific University, HI, Honolulu

Katz, Bernard .... (302) 658-6945
telesonics@aol.com, Pres., Telesonic Packaging Corp., Ames Engineering Div., DE, Wilmington

Katz, Harry Jay .... (215) 849-9016
hjaykatz@aol.com, Pub./Ed. in Chief, National News Bureau, Philadelphia

Katz, Janice................. (207) 594-4401 ext. 243
jkatz@courierpub.com, Controller, Courier Publications, LLC, ME, Rockland

Katz, Linda
marketing@buschinc.com, Mktg. Specialist, Busch, Inc., VA, Virginia Beach

Katzeff, Dottie .... (415) 338-3133
San Francisco State University, CA, San Francisco

Katzinger, Harald
hka@teufelberger.com, Mgr., Mktg./Sales Agriculture, Teufelberger GmbH, Wels

Katzman, Carol .... (402) 334-6450
ckatzman@jewishomaha.org, Ed., Jewish Press, NE, Omaha

Kauck, Eliane
eliane.kauck@penton.com, Comm. Mgr., Penton Media, NY, New York

Kaufer, Anton .... (318) 459-3310
anton.kaufer@shreveporttimes.com, Adv. Dir., The Times, LA, Shreveport

Kauffman, Bette J.
kauffman@ulm.edu, Dept. Head/Assoc. Prof., University of Louisiana at Monroe, LA, Monroe

Kauffman, Corrine .... (410) 857-7892
jkauffman@carrollcountytimes.com, Adv. Asst. , Carroll County Times, MD, Westminster

Kauffman, Dan .... (301) 791-7520
dkauffman@herald-mail.com, Asst. Sports Ed. , The Herald-Mail, MD, Hagerstown

Kauffman, Diane .... (916) 278-6583
Sacramento State, CA, Sacramento

Kauffman, Kermit .... (813) 259-7700
Tampa Bay Times, FL, St Petersburg

Kauffold, Kathleen
dodgecriterion@gpcom.net, Editor, Dodge Criterion, NE, Dodge

Kauffold, Ken H.
dodgecriterion@gpcom.net, Ed., Dodge Criterion, NE, Dodge

Kaufman, Dirk .... (412) 380-5631
dkaufman@tribweb.com, Systems Ed., Tribune-Review, PA, Greensburg

Kaufman, Kathy
kkaufman@ncnewspress.com, Penny Press 1, NE, Nebraska City
kkaufman@ncnewspress.com, Publications Director, Penny Press, NE, Syracuse

Kaufman, Kevin
kaufmank@dailycamera.com, Exec. Ed., Daily Camera, CO, Boulder

Kaufman, Sam
sam@basinbroadband.com, Ed., Andrews County News, TX, Andrews

Kaus, Adam .... (605) 996-5514
akaus@mitchellrepublic.com, Circ. Mgr., The Daily Republic, SD, Mitchell

Kauten, Sandra .... (541) 683-7452
sandy@oregonfamily.com, Owner/Pub, Oregon Family Magazine, OR, Eugene

Kavanagh, Brian .... (406) 338-2090
glacrptr@3rivers.net, Pub., Glacier Reporter, MT, Browning

Kavanagh, Brian
cbpress@bresnan.net, Pub., Cut Bank Pioneer Press, MT, Cut Bank

Kavanagh, Brian .... (406) 873-2201

presspix@bresnan.net, Pub., The Shelby Promoter, MT, Shelby

Kavanagh, Leanne................... (406) 873-2201
valierian@bresnan.net, Pub., The Shelby Promoter, MT, Shelby

Kawamoto, Jon......................... (510) 748-1658
jkawamoto@bayareanewsgroup.com, Hills Ed., The Montclarion, CA, Alameda

Kawasaki, Bryan .... (760) 951-6235
bkawasaki@vvdailypress.com, Online Coordinator, Daily Press, CA, Victorville

Kay, Angela
akay@lmtribune.com, Adv. Dir., Northwest Market, ID, Moscow

Kay, Beverly
beverly@observernews.net, Circ. Mgr., Observer News, FL, Ruskin

Kay, Connie .... (204) 759-2644 ext. 2
smpdisplay@mymts.net, Advertising, Nesbitt Publishing Ltd., MB, Shoal Lake

Kay, Connie .... (204) 759-2644 ext. 2
smpdisplay@mymts.net, Advertising Manager, Crossroads This Week, MB, Shoal Lake
smpdisplay@mymts.net, Advertising, South Mountain Press, MB, Shoal Lake

Kay, Mary
bjpc@breespub.com, Circ. Mgr., The Breese Journal, IL, Breese

Kay, Richard .... (850) 599-2204
rkay@tallahassee.com, Distribution Director, Tallahassee Democrat, FL, Tallahassee

Kaye, Daniel
dkaye@montgomerynews.com, Ed., South Jersey Parents Express, PA, Fort Washington

Kaye, Daniel Sean
dk@montgomerynews.com, Ed., Parents' Express, PA, Fort Washington

Kaylor, Steve .... (434) 791-7910
skaylor@registerbee.com, Pub., Danville Register & Bee, VA, Danville

Kaylor, Steven K.
skaylor@reidsvillereview.com, Pub., The Reidsville Review, NC, Reidsville

Kaylor, Steven W...................... (434) 791-7910
skaylor@reidsvillereview.com, The Reidsville Review, NC, Reidsville
skaylor@reidsvillereview.com, Ed, The Messenger, NC, Reidsville
skaylor@reidsvillereview.com, Pub., The Eden News, NC, Reidsville

Kays, Mike .... (918) 684-2904
mkays@muskogeephoenix.com, Sports Ed., Muskogee Phoenix, OK, Muskogee

Kazakoff, Lois
lkazakoff@sfchronicle.com, Deputy Editorial Ed, San Francisco Chronicle, CA, San Francisco

Kazarian-Hodder, Louise ....(519) 372-4344
louise.kazarian@sunmedia.ca, Adv. Dir., Owensound Sun Times, ON, Owen Sound

Kazlauskas, Chris
chrisk@mansimedia.com, MANSI Media, PA, Harrisburg

Kazoleas, Dean
dkazoleas@fullerton.edu, Assoc. Prof., California State University, Fullerton, CA, Fullerton

Kealing, Jonathan .... (785) 832-7221
jkealing@ljworld.com, Lawrence Journal-World, KS, Lawrence

Keane, Connie......................... (302) 998-1650
keane@motormatters.biz, Pres., AutoWriters Associates, Inc. (Motor Matters), Wilmington

Keane, Jeff
crowsegal@crowsegal.com, Pres., National Cartoonists Society, FL, Maitland

Keane, Paul .... (601) 735-4341
publisher@thewaynecountynews.com, Pub,

The Wayne County News, MS, Waynesboro

Keane, Robert .... (631) 843-2781
Vice Pres./Mng. Ed., Newsday, NY, Melville

Kearney, Jan Michele
sesh@fuse.net, Pub., Cincinnati Herald, OH, Cincinnati

Kearney, Tom
tkearney@stowereporter.com, Ed., Stowe Reporter, VT, Stowe
tkearney@stowereporter.com, Ed., Waterbury Record, VT, Stowe

Kearns, Alana
akearns@catholicsun.org, Adv. Sales, The Catholic Sun, AZ, Phoenix

Kearns, John .... (613) 966-2034 ext.570
jkearns@theemc.ca, Pub., Belleville News Emc, ON, Belleville
jkearns@theemc.ca, Pub., Campbellford/northwest News Emc, ON, Belleville
jkearns@theemc.ca, Pub., Stirling/northeast News Emc, ON, Belleville
jkearns@theemc.ca, Publisher, The Brighton Independent, ON, Brighton
jkearns@theemc.ca, Pub. , Quinte West Emc, ON, Belleville

Kearns, Judy
judy@otherpapersbvt.com, Pub./Adv. Mgr., The Other Paper, VT, South Burlington

Kearns, Marry Ann .... (606) 564-9091 ext. 270
Mary.Kearns@lee.net, Managing Ed., The Mayfield Messenger, KY, Mayfield

Kearns, Mary Ann ....ext. 270
mary.kearns@lee.net, Mng. Ed., The Advertiser, KY, Maysville

Kearsey, David .... (709) 637-4670
dkearsey@thewesternstar.com, Sports Ed., The Western Star, NL, Corner Brook

Keary, Polly
comp@monroemonitor.com, Pub./Ed., The Monroe Monitor & Valley News, WA, Seattle

Keathley, Dawn .... (580) 310-7518
circulation@theadanews.com, Cir. Mgr., The Ada News , OK, Ada

Keathley, Hank .... (330) 364-8343
hank.keathley@TimesReporter.com, Local News Ed., The Times-Reporter, OH, New Philadelphia

Keating, Chris
ckeating@clevescene.com, Pub., Metro Times, MI, Ferndale

Keating, Chris .... (216) 802-7250
ckeating@clevescene.com, Pub., Cleveland Scene, OH, Cleveland

Keating, Jessica .... (909) 386-3810
City Editor, The Facts (Redlands), CA, Redlands

Keating, Jessica .... (909) 386-3810
jessica.keating@langnews.com, Opinion Ed., Los Angeles Daily News, CA, Woodland Hills

Keating, Patrick
pkeating@trinity.edu, Asst. Prof., Trinity University, TX, San Antonio

Keating, Terry ....ext. 265
tkeating@peterboroughexaminer.com, Prodn. Mgr., The Examiner, ON, Peterborough

Kebbati, Lora
advertising@inkym.com, Adv. Mgr., The Inquirer and Mirror, MA, Nantucket

Kechichian , Mike
mike.kechichian@latimes.com, VP, Adv. Marketing , Los Angeles Times, CA, Los Angeles

Keck, Randy
randy@community-news.com, Pub./Ed., The Community News, TX, Aledo

Keck, Tim .... (206) 323-7101
tim@thestranger.com, Publisher, The Stranger, WA, Seattle

Keckeisen, Kevin .... (951) 827-3460
Mgr Ed., Univ. of California, Riverside, CA, Riverside

Keddy, Sara .... (902) 765-1494
auroraeditor@ns.aliantzinc.ca, Mgr. Ed., The Aurora, NS, Greenwood

Kedinger, Paul
raynenews@cox-internet.com, Mng. Ed., The Rayne-Acadian Tribune, LA, Rayne

Kedrowicz, Tammy .... (936) 631-2630
tkedrowicz@lufkindailynews.com, Adv. Dir., The Lufkin Daily News, TX, Lufkin

Kedzierski, Ryan .... (503) 399-6648
rkedziersk@statesmanjournal.com, Pub., The Examiner / Examiner Weekend, MO, Independence
rkedziersk@statesmanjournal.com, Adv. Dir., Statesman Journal, OR, Salem
rkedziersk@statesmanjournal.com, Pres., Reno Gazette-Journal, NV, Reno

Kedzierski, Ryan .... (503) 399-6648
rkedziersk@statesmanjournal.com, Pres., Stayton Mail, OR, Salem
rkedziersk@statesmanjournal.com, Pres., Appeal Tribune, OR, Salem

Keebaugh, Reid
reid@lloydminstersource.com, Publisher, Lloydminster Source, SK, Lloydminster

Keeble, Jim .... (337) 289-6399
jkeeble@gannett.com, Circ. Distribution Dir., Daily World, LA, Opelousas

Keech, Sharon .... (410) 719-9342
sharon@baltimoreschild.com, Mng. Ed., Baltimore's Child, PA, Philadelphia

Keefe, Patrick M. .... (785) 762-5000 ext. 180
Adv. Mgr., Fort Riley Post, KS, Junction City

Keefer, Lindsay
Lkeefer@woodburnindependent.com, Ed., Woodburn Independent, OR, Woodburn

Keegan, Tom .... (785) 832-7147
tkeegan@ljworld.com, Sports Ed., Lawrence Journal-World, KS, Lawrence

Keel, Vernon
vekeel@wichita.edu, Prof., Wichita State University, KS, Wichita

Keeler, Doug
editor@bak.rr.com, Ed., Bargain Hunter, CA, Taft

Keem, Dennis .... (708) 824-9600
mccainbind@earthlink.net, Vice Pres./Gen. Mgr., McCain Bindery Systems, IL, New Lenox

Keena, Brian .... (813) 259-7438
Tampa Bay Times, FL, St Petersburg

Keenan, Cheryl
ckeenan@register-herald.com, Ed., The Fayette Tribune, WV, Oak Hill

Keenan, Cheryl
ckeenan@register-herald.com, Ed., Montgomery Herald, WV, Oak Hill

Keenan, Debra B.
debbi@keenangroup.com, Vice Pres., Sales/Mktg., The Keenan Group, Inc., TN, Pleasant View

Keenan, Robert P. .... (615) 945-5698
Pres., The Keenan Group, Inc., TN, Pleasant View

Keener, Kyle .... (574) 732-5152
keener@pharostribune.com, Photo Ed., Pharos-Tribune, IN, Logansport

Keener, Laura
lkeener@covingtondiocese.org, Asst. Ed., The Messenger, KY, Covington

Keep, Paul
pkeep@mlive.com, Exec. Ed. of Print, The Jackson Citizen Patriot, MI, Jackson

Keep, Paul
pkeep@mlive.com, Exec. Editor of Print, The

Flint Journal, MI, Flint

Keep, Paul
kkoziel@boothmidmichigan.com, Exec. Ed. of Print, The Bay City Times, MI, Bay City

Keese, Pat .... (985) 850-3132
pkeese@htdiocese.org, Sec., The Bayou Catholic, LA, Schriever

Keeton, Michael
michael.keeton@mountaineagle.com, Prod. Mgr, Daily Mountain Eagle, AL, Jasper

Keever, Matthew
matthew.keever@argusmedia.com, Univ. of Houston, TX, Houston

Keever, Paul .... (305) 453-5456
pkaic@aol.com, Pres./CEO, American International Communications, Inc., FL, Key Largo

Keffaber, Barb
barbk@thepaperofwabash.com, Sales Rep., The Paper, IN, Wabash

Kegley, Randy .... (276) 236-5178 ext. 218
Adv. Mgr., Gazette Plus, VA, Galax

Kegley, Randy
rkegley@galaxgazette.com, Adv. Mgr., Galax Gazette, VA, Galax

Kehias, Jonell .... (309) 820-3350
jkehias@pantagraph.com, Mktg. Servs. Mgr., The Pantagraph, IL, Bloomington

Kehl, Lisa .... (740) 373-2121 Ext. 328
lkehl@mariettatimes.com, Class., The Marietta Times, OH, Marietta

Kehne , Betsy
bkehne@bayweekly.com, Prod. Mgr., Passwords, MD, Annapolis

Kehrer, Geoff
gkehrer@mediaspangroup.com, Technical Sales and Marketing Dir., MediaSpan, MI, Ann Arbor

Kehrer, Geoff .... (734) 887-4400
geoff.kehrer@newscycle.com, Sales Engineer, Newscycle Solutions, MN, Bloomington

Kehrl, Brian .... (508) 548-4700 x228
kehrl@capenews.net, Mng. Ed. , The Mashpee Enterprise, MA, Falmouth

Keiffner, Patricia .... (317) 472-5354
pkeiffner@ibj.com, Prodn. Mgr., Indianapolis Prime Times, IN
pkeiffner@ibj.com, Prod. Dir., Indianapolis Business Journal, IN, Indianapolis

Keilers, Regina .... (979) 968-3155
regina@fayettecountyrecord.com, Pub., The Fayette County Record, TX, La Grange

Keim, David
keimdm@ornl.gov, Bus. Ed., Knoxville News Sentinel, TN, Knoxville

Keim, Henry
hkeim@breezenewspapers.com, Prodn. Mgr., Press, Cape Coral Breeze, FL, Cape Coral

Keirsey, Karen .... (856) 825-8811
keirs1@comcast.net, Pub., Cumberland Reminder, NJ, Millville

Keirsey, Karen L.
thereminderkaren@comcast.net, Pub., Cumberland Reminder, NJ, Millville

Keiser, Gretchen R. .... (404) 877-5500
taisthorpe@georgiabulletin.org, Ed., The Georgia Bulletin, GA, Smyrna

Keiser, Kristin
ads@lakecountyexam.com, Adv., Lake County Examiner, OR, Lakeview

Keisman, David
david.keisman@moodys.com, Pub., The Bronx Free Press, NY, New York

Keith, David
dkeith@uca.edu, University of Central Arkansas, AR, Conway

Keith, Debbie .... (409) 683-5240

debbie.keith@galvnews.com, Adv. Mgr., Retail, The Galveston County Daily News, TX, Galveston

Keith, James
lfdnews@litchfieldil.com, Prodn. Supt., News-Herald, IL, Litchfield

Keith, Jamie
jkeith@appealdemocrat.com, nat'l Adv. Mgr., Colusa County Sun-Herald, CA, Marysville
jkeith@appealdemocrat.com, Nat'l Adv. Mgr., Corning Observer, CA, Marysville
jkeith@appealdemocrat.com, Nat'l Adv. Mgr., Willows Journal (OOB), CA, Willows

Keith, Janice
jkeith@dailyhome.com, Assoc. Ed., The Daily Home, AL, Talladega

Keith, Madeline .... (928) 635-4426 ext 3606
mkeith@williamsnews.com, Pub., Williams-Grand Canyon News, AZ, Williams

Keith, Susan
skeith@rutgers.edu, Asst. Prof., Rutgers University, NJ, New Brunswick

Keitlen, Matthew
info@spectrumhr.com, Exec. Vice Pres., SPECTRUM Human Resource Systems Corp., CO, Denver

Keitner, Liz .... (902) 402-7822
liz@newspapersatlantic.ca, Value Advertising Manager, Newspapers Atlantic, NS, Halifax

Keleer, Walter
wkleer@bowesnet.com, Adv. Mgr., Delhi News-record, ON, Delhi

Kelk, Gillan
publisher.sdt@gmail.com, Pub. , The Sullivan Daily Times, IN, Sullivan

Kelk, Gillian
ads2.sdt@gmail.com, Adv. Rep., The Sullivan Daily Times, IN, Sullivan

Kell, Kim .... (541) 575-0710
kim@bmeagle.com, Adv. Rep, Blue Mountain Eagle, OR, John Day

Kellagher, Robert R. .... (215) 269-5054
bkellagher@phillyburbs.com, Dir., Interactive Media, Calkins Media, PA, Levittown

Kellam, Gary .... (909) 888-6511
San Bernardino Valley College, CA, San Bernardino

Kellam, Mark .... (818) 495-4016
mark.kellam@latimes.com, Los Angeles Times, CA, Los Angeles
mark.kellam@latimes.com, City Ed., News-Press, CA, Los Angeles

Kellar, Liz .... (530) 477-4229
lkellar@theunion.com, City Editor, The Union, CA, Grass Valley

Kellar, Patrick
pkellar@thenewsdispatch.com, Pub., Herald News Review, IL, Decatur

Kellenburger, Tim
sabethaherald@sbcglobal.net, Pub., The Sabetha Herald, KS, Sabetha

Keller, Bill
keller@nytimes.com, Exec. Ed., New England Newspaper Group, NY, New York

Keller, Brenda .... (870) 239-8562
bkeller@paragoulddailypress.com, General Manager, Paragould Daily Press, AR, Paragould

Keller, Christopher
christopherk@cameron.edu, Cameron Univ., OK, Lawton

Keller, David .... (740) 962-3377
dkeller@mchnews.com, General Manager, Morgan County Herald, OH, McConnelsville

Keller, Debbie .... (520) 415-1831
dkeller@gvnews.com, Adv. Mgr., Nogales International, AZ, Nogales
dkeller@gvnews.com, Adv. Mgr., Santa Cruz

Valley Sun, AZ, Nogales

Keller, Don .... (740) 962-3377
dwkeller@mchnews.com, Ed., Morgan County
Herald, OH, McConnelsville

Keller, Judy
publisher@marlowreview.com, Pub., The
Marlow Review, OK, Marlow

Keller, Karri
info@kunamelba.com, Gen Mgr., Kuna Melba
News, ID, Kuna

Keller, Lexi .... (618) 667-3111
troy.il.news@gmail.com, Reporter, Troy Times-
Tribune, IL, Troy

Keller, Mandy .... (785) 562-2317
mkeller@marysvilleonline.net, Ad sales,
Marysville Advocate, KS, Marysville

Keller, Mark .... (815) 965-0882
sales@a-americanpressparts.com, Pres.,
A-American Machine & Assembly (Press
Parts Div.), IL, Rockford

Keller, Mark J.
mkeller@bryantimes.com, Cir. Mgr., The Bryan
Times, OH, Bryan

Keller, Melissa
mkeller@news-expresssky.com, Adv. Dir, The
Appalachian News-Express, KY, Pikeville

Keller, Neel
neel@obsentinel.com, Ed., Outer Banks
Sentinel, NC, Nags Head

Keller, Rebecca
rkeller@dispatch.com, Gen. Mgr., The Bag,
OH, Lewis Center

Keller, Teresa
tkeller@ehc.edu, Chair, Emory and Henry
College, VA, Emory

Kelley, Bryan
bkelley@shipleyenergy.com, VP, Sales/
Marketing, The York Dispatch, PA, York

Kelley, Jami .... (606) 326-2655
jkelley@dailyindependent.com, News Clerk,
The Daily Independent, KY, Ashland

Kelley, Kevin
kkelley2@smcvt.edu, Instr., St. Michael's
College, VT, Colchester

Kelley, Michael
news@scarboroughleader.com, Mainely
Media, LLC, ME, Biddeford

Kelley, Reed
reed@theheraldtimes.com, Meeker
Correspondent, The Rio Blanco Herald
Times, CO, Meeker

Kelley, Richard .... (304) 255-4462
rkelley@register-herald.com, Ed., The Register
Herald, WV, Beckley

Kelley, Sarah
sarah.kelley@lubbockonline.com, Adv. Mgr.,
Classified Sales, Lubbock Avalanche-
Journal, TX, Lubbock

Kelley, Sarah .... (502) 895-9770 ext. 204
skelley@leoweekly.com, Editor, Louisville
Eccentric Observer (leo), KY, Louisville

Kelley, Sean
editor.plainsman@midconetwork.com, Ed., The
Daily Plainsman, SD, Huron

Kelley, Sherry
skelley@thegurdontimes.com, Reporter, The
Gurdon Times, AR, Arkadelphia

Kelley, Stuart
info.jp@acscapital.co.th, Contact, ACS Capital,
TX, North Richland Hills

Kelley, Susan
skelley@thephillipsbee.com, Adv. Dir., The
Bee, WI, Phillips
skelley@thephillipsbee.com, Adv. Dir., Park
Falls Herald, WI, Phillips

Kelley, Thomas .... (507) 453-3561
tom.kelley@lee.net, Ret'l Adv. Mgr., Winona

Daily News, MN, Winona

Kelley, Tim .... (608) 252-6115
tkelley@madison.com, Online Director,
Wisconsin State Journal, Madison, WI,
Madison

Kelley, Tracy .... (209) 369-2761
TracyK@lodinews.com, Ad Director, Sentinel
Express, CA, Lodi

Kelley, Verdena
vkelly@ncppub.com, Associate Ed., West Lyon
Herald, IA, Inwood

Kelley-Hellenthal, Brendan .... (907) 644-5417
bjk@anchoragepresss.com, Editor, Anchorage
Press, AK, Anchorage

Kelling, Patrick .... (970) 521-6671
Northeastern Junior College, CO, Sterling

Kelling, Tom .... (217) 231-3464
tkelling@whig.com, Adv. Dir., The Quincy
Herald-Whig, IL, Quincy

Kellison, Kimberly
kkellison@valleynewstoday.com, Circ. Mgr.,
Weekly Times, IA, Shenandoah

Kellner, Mark
mkellner@washingtontimes.com, News Ed.,
Adventist Review, MD, Silver Spring

Kellogg, Rachel
nfulton@neighbornewspapers.com, Ed,
Alpharetta Neighbor, GA, Roswell
nfulton@neighbornewspapers.com, Ed, Johns
Creek Neighbor (OOB), GA, Roswell
nfulton@neighbornewspapers.com, Ed, Milton
Neighbor, GA, Roswell
nfulton@neighbornewspapers.com, Ed.,
Roswell Neighbor, GA, Roswell

Kelly, Aeletha .... (802) 479-2582
sales@vt-world.com, Circ., The World, VT,
Barre

Kelly, Albert F.
info@neclease.com, Gen. Mgr., NEC
Corporation of America, TX, Irving

Kelly, Brad
brad.kelly@nielsen.com, Gen. Mgr./Domestic
Radio, The Arbitron Co., NY, New York

Kelly, Brian
editor@bainbridgereview.com, Ed., Bainbridge
Island Review, WA, Bainbridge Island

Kelly, Brian
customer.service@schlenkboth.com, Pres.,
Schlenk-Both Industries, MA, Ashland

Kelly, Catherine
editor@michigancitizen.com, Pub., Michigan
Citizen, MI, Detroit

Kelly, Catherine .... (604) 249-3500
ckelly@bbm.ca, Vice Pres., Western Servs.,
BBM Canada, ON, Toronto

Kelly, Charles
ckelly@paramountjournal.org, Ed., The
Paramount Journal, CA, Paramount

Kelly, Charles W.
journal@ogd.com, Ed., Advance News, NY,
Ogdensburg

Kelly, Cheryl
info@thescteller.com, Co-pub., The Sargent
County Teller, ND, Milnor

Kelly, Cheryl
info@rcgazette.com, Adv. Mgr., The Ransom
County Gazette, ND, Lisbon

Kelly, Cheryl
hbanner@rrv.net, Pub., Hillsboro Banner, ND,
Hillsboro

Kelly, Connor .... (770) 205-8964
ckelly@forsythnews.com, Adv. Acct Exec.,
Forsyth County News, GA, Cumming

Kelly, Debora
dkelly@yrmg.com, Ed. in Chief, The
Newmarket Era-banner, ON, Newmarket

Kelly, Debora

dkelly@yrmg.com, Ed. in Chief, The Georgina
Advocate, ON, Keswick

Kelly, Debora
dkelly@yrmg.com, Ed. in Chief, The Richmond
Hill Liberal, ON, Markham

Kelly, Duffy .... (916) 224-1604
dk@insidepublications.com, Acc. Rep., Inside
Publications, CA, Sacramento

Kelly, Eric
ekelly@overlandstorage.com, Pres, Overland
Storage, Inc., CA, San Diego

Kelly, Hattie
ppages2@sbcglobal.net, Advertising Manager,
The Power Pages News, TX, Farmersville

Kelly, Jacques .... (410) 332-6570
jacques.kelly@baltsun.com ...., Columnist, The
Baltimore Sun, MD, Baltimore

Kelly, Jamie
editor@willistonherald.com, Managing Editor,
The Plains Reporter, ND, Williston
editor@willistonherald.com, Managing Ed.,
Williston Daily Herald, ND, Williston

Kelly, Jim .... (863) 773-3255
Ed. & Pub., The Herald-Advocate, FL,
Wauchula

Kelly, Jim
jim.kelly.rhdu@statefarm.com, Assoc. Prof.,
Indiana University, IN, Bloomington
jim.kelly.rhdu@statefarm.com, Adv. Rep., The
Vermont Standard, VT, Woodstock

Kelly, Joe .... (315) 942-4449
boonherald@aol.com, Pub. & Sr. Ed., Boonville
Herald & Adirondack Tourist, NY, Boonville

Kelly, John W. .... (804) 649-6136
jwk7@aol.com, VP, Revenue & Business
Development, Richmond Times-Dispatch,
VA, Richmond

Kelly, Kathleen
kskelly@jou.ufl.edu, Prof., University of Florida,
FL, Gainesville

Kelly, Laurie .... (306) 463-4611
ads.jamac@gmail.com, Salesperson,
Kindersley Clarion, SK, Kindersley

Kelly, Leslie .... (360) 779-4464
editor@kitsapveteranslife.com, Ed., Veterans'
Life-OOB, WA, Silverdale
editor@kitsapveteranslife.com, Ed., Central
Kitsap Reporter, WA, Poulsbo

Kelly, Lisa
lkelly@slarc.org, Circulation Verification
Council, MO, Saint Louis

Kelly, Lynne
kelly@hartford.edu, Dir., University of Hartford,
CT, West Hartford

Kelly, Marguerite .... (202) 544-5698
margueriketly@gmail.com, Columnist of Family
Almanac, WA Post and other papers, Family
Almanac, Washington

Kelly, Maria .... (433) 524-8111
maria.kelly@thedailyrecord.com, Comptroller ,
The Daily Record, MD, Baltimore

Kelly, Mary .... (617) 929-2146
mary.kelly@globe.com, Dir. Adv. Sales, The
Boston Globe, MA, Boston

Kelly, Maryann .... (207) 791-6535
mkelly@mainetoday.com, VP/Labor &
Employee Relations, Portland Press Herald /
Maine Sunday Telegram, ME, Portland

Kelly, Meghan .... (508) 626-3858
mkelly@wickedlocal.com, Digital Ed. ,
Marlborough Enterprise, MA, Framingham
mkelly@wickedlocal.com, Digital Ed., Milford
Daily News, MA, Milford
mkelly@wickedlocal.com, Dig. Ed., Metrowest
Daily News, MA, Framingham

Kelly, Michael
makelly@oceansidestar.com, Circ. Mgr., The
Oceanside Star, BC, Parksville

Kelly, Michael J.
ipeditors@njnpublishing.com, Pub.,
Independent Press, NJ, New Providence

Kelly, Paul
midvalleypub@aol.com, Ed., Waterford News,
CA, Waterford

Kelly, Ray .... (413) 788-1291
rkelly@repub.com, Asst. Managing Ed., Ent.,
The Republican, MA, Springfield

Kelly, Ron .... (902) 629-6031
ronkelly@theguardian.pe.ca, Bus. Mgr., The
Guardian, PE, Charlottetown

Kelly, Ruthie .... (619) 594-3906
San Diego State Univ., CA, San Diego

Kelly, Ryan .... (434) 978-7278
rkelly@dailyprogress.com, Photojournalist, The
Daily Progress, VA, Charlottesville

Kelly, Sandra
ppages2@sbcglobal.net, Publisher, The Power
Pages News, TX, Farmersville

Kelly, Scott B.
ppages2@sbcglobal.net, Production Manager,
The Power Pages News, TX, Farmersville

Kelly, Sean
info@thescteller.com, Pub. / Ed. , The Sargent
County Teller, ND, Milnor

Kelly, Sean W. .... (701) 683-4128
Pub./Ed., Cass County Reporter, ND,
Casselton

Kelly, Sean W.
info@rcgazette.com, Ed., The Ransom County
Gazette, ND, Lisbon

Kelly, Shawn
hbanner@rrv.net, Pub., Hillsboro Banner, ND,
Hillsboro

Kelly, Teresa
teresa@michigancitizen.com, Ed., Michigan
Citizen, MI, Detroit

Kelly, Tim .... ext. 2336
tkelly@durhamregion.com, Copy Ed., Oshawa-
whitby This Week, ON, Oshawa

Kelly, Timothy M.
tkelly@hearstnp.com, Ed., Jasper Newsboy,
TX, Jasper

Kelly, Tom .... (818) 713-3110
tom.kelly@langnews.com , Chief Rev. Officer,
Los Angeles Daily News, CA, Woodland Hills

Kelly, Tom
newspub@cableone.net, Pub., Elkhorn Valley
Shopper, NE, West Point

Kelly, Tom
tkelly@ocregister.com, VP, Sales, The Orange
County Register, CA, Santa Ana

Kelly, Tom
wisnews@gpcom.net, Pub., Wisner News-
Chronicle, NE, Wisner

Kelly, Tom .... (818) 713-3110
tkelly@scng.com, Chief Revenue Officer,
Southern California News Group, CA,
Woodland Hills
tkelly@scng.com, Chief Revenue Officer,
Press-Telegram, CA, Long Beach

Kelly, Tom .... (402) 372-2461
tknewspub@gmail.com, Pub./Gen. Mgr., West
Point News, NE, West Point

Kelly, Vicki .... (870) 367-5325
advertising@monticellonews.net, Ad Manager,
Advance-Monticellonian, AR, Monticello

Kelly-Gilbert, Susan .... (864) 260-1279
skelly-gilbert@independentmail.com, Pub.
& CRO, Anderson Independent-Mail, SC,
Anderson

Kelly-Goss, Robert
rkelly-goss@dailyadvance.com, Albemarle Life
Ed., The Daily Advance, NC, Elizabeth City

Kelsay, Linda .... (765) 671-2200
lkelsay@chronicle-tribune.com, President &

Pub., Chronicle-Tribune, IN, Marion
lkelsay@chronicle-tribune.com, Publisher, The Current Bargain, IN, Marion

Kelsey, Kim .... **(402) 342-4426**
omaha@amclassifieds.com, Prodn. Mgr., American Classifieds, NE, Omaha

Kelsey, Stephen .... **(801) 344-2912**
skelsey@heraldextra.com, Circ. Dir., Daily Herald, UT, Provo

Kelsh, James
jkelsh@capitalnewspapers.com, Pub., Monday-mini, WI, Beaver Dam

Kelsh, James
jkelsh@capitalnewspapers.com, Pub., Tri-county, WI, Beaver Dam

Kelsh, James .... **(920) 356-6750**
jkelsh@madison.com, Pub., Shopping Reminder, WI, Columbus

Kelsh, James
jkelsh@capitolnewspapers.com, Pub., Daily Citizen, Beaver Dam, WI, Beaver Dam
jkelsh@capitolnewspapers.com, Pub., Beaver Dam - Monday Mini, WI, Beaver Dam
jkelsh@capitolnewspapers.com, Pub., Beaver Dam - Tri County, WI, Beaver Dam

Kelso, Travis
tkelso@mail.bradley.edu, Adv. Mgr., Bradley University, IL, Peoria

Kemby, Don
rfccompany@aol.com, Pres., RFC Wire Forms, CA, Ontario

Kemmeter, John
sports@pcgazette.com, Sports Ed., The Portage County Gazette, WI, Stevens Point

Kemmis, Mary
mkemmis@reddeeradvocate.com, Pub, Central Alberta Life, AB, Red Deer

Kemmis, Mary .... **(403) 314-4311**
mary.kemmis@blackpress.ca, Pres., Ponoka News, AB, Ponoka

Kemmis, Mary .... **(403) 314-4311**
mkemmis@blackpress.ca, Pub Red Deer Advocate; Pres Prarie/ East Kootenay Division Black Press, Friday Forward, AB, Red Deer

Kemp, Denise .... **(641) 753-6611**
Marketing Director, Pennysaver, IA, Marshalltown

Kemp, Louis .... **ext. 233**
Dir., Sales, Le Groupe Jcl Inc., QC, Saint Eustache

Kemp, Nancy
poinsettdteditor@centurytel.net, ccd@centurytel.net, Co-Pub., Co-Ed., Clay County Times-Democrat, AR, Piggott

Kemp, Ron
ronkemp@centurytel.net, Pub., The Daily Dunklin Democrat, MO, Kennett

Kemp, Ron
ronkemp@centurytel.net, Co-Pub., Co-Ed., Clay County Times-Democrat, AR, Piggott
ronkemp@centurytel.net, Pub., Poinsett County Democrate Tribune, AR, Trumann

Kemp, Sandi .... **(850) 939-8040**
skemp@navarrepress.com, Pub., Navarre Press, FL, Navarre

Kempen, Roberta
watsekasales@intranix.com, Adv. Dir., Times-Republic, IL, Watseka

Kemper, Alice .... **(561) 482-8801**
akemper@salestrainingconsultants.com, Pres., Sales Training Consultants, Inc., FL, Boca Raton

Kemper, Betty
calendar2003@austinfamily.com, Calendar Ed., Austin Family, TX, Round Rock

Kemper, Dan .... **(847) 558-5040**
dmk@schur.com, President, Schur Packaging

Systems, Inc., IL, Schaumburg

Kemper, Kaye .... **(512) 773-0038**
kaye2003@austinfamily.com, Pub., Austin Family, TX, Round Rock

Kemper, Kristie
kkemper@highlands.edu, Georgia Highlands College, GA, Rome

Ken, Gerould
editor@chicagotribune.com, SVP Ed., Chicago Tribune, IL, Chicago

Kendall, Don .... **(205) 492-0444**
dkendall@blackpress.ca, Pub., Keremeos Review, BC, Keremeos
dkendall@blackpress.ca, Pub, Princeton Similkameen Spotlight, BC, Princeton

Kendall, Jason
jkendall@shawneedispatch.com, Ed, Shawnee Dispatch, KS, Shawnee

Kendall, Jeanette .... **(309) 346-1111 ext. 660**
jkendall@timestoday.com, Chillicothe Times-Bulletin, IL, Peoria
jkendall@timestoday.com, Exec. Ed., Times News Group, IL, Pekin
jkendall@timestoday.com, Exec. Ed., Morton Pumpkin Advertiser, IL, Peoria

Kendall, Jeanette
jkendall@timestoday.com, Exec. Ed., Woodford Times, IL, Pekin
jkendall@timestoday.com, Exec. Ed., Washington Times Reporter, IL, Pekin
jkendall@timestoday.com, Executive Ed, Morton Times-News, IL, Pekin

Kendall, Justin .... **(816) 218-6778**
justin.kendall@pitch.com, Managing Editor, The Pitch, MO, Kansas City

Kendall, Paul
kendallpw@yahoo.com, Ed., Merchant's Directory, KS, Mullinville

Kendall, Peter
pkendall@chicagotribune.com, Mng. Ed., Chicago Tribune, IL, Chicago
pkendall@chicagotribune.com, Mng. Ed., The Doings – Western Springs, IL, Chicago
pkendall@chicagotribune.com, Mng. Ed., Franklin Park Herald-Journal, IL, Chicago
pkendall@chicagotribune.com, Mng. Ed., The Doings Weekly – Burr Ridge, IL, Chicago
pkendall@chicagotribune.com, Mng. Ed., The Doings – Clarendon Hills, IL, Chicago
pkendall@chicagotribune.com, Mng. Ed., The Doings – Hinsdale, IL, Chicago
pkendall@chicagotribune.com, Mng. Ed., The Doings – La Grange, IL, Chicago
pkendall@chicagotribune.com, Mng. Ed., The Doings – Oak Brook and Elmhurst, IL, Chicago
pkendall@chicagotribune.com, Mng. Ed., Forest Leaves, IL, Chicago
pkendall@chicagotribune.com, Mng. Ed., Evanston Review, IL, Chicago
pkendall@chicagotribune.com, Mng. Ed., The Naperville Sun, IL, Chicago
pkendall@chicagotribune.com, Mng. Ed., Crown Point Star, IL, Chicago
pkendall@chicagotribune.com, Mng. Ed., Park Ridge Herald Advocate, IL, Chicago
pkendall@chicagotribune.com, Mng. Ed., Deerfield Review, IL, Chicago
pkendall@chicagotribune.com, Mng. Ed., Elmwood Park Leaves, IL, Chicago
pkendall@chicagotribune.com, Mng. Ed., Buffalo Grove Countryside, IL, Chicago
pkendall@chicagotribune.com, Mng. Ed., Glencoe News, IL, Chicago
pkendall@chicagotribune.com, Mng. Ed., Glenview Announcements, IL, Chicago
pkendall@chicagotribune.com, Mng. Ed., Highland Park News, IL, Chicago
pkendall@chicagotribune.com, Mng. Ed., Arlington Heights Post, IL, Glenview
pkendall@chicagotribune.com, Mng. Ed., Lake Forester, IL, Chicago
pkendall@chicagotribune.com, Mng. Ed., Lake Zurich Courier, IL, Chicago
pkendall@chicagotribune.com, Mng. Ed., Libertyville Review, IL, Chicago

pkendall@chicagotribune.com, Mng. Ed., Lincolnshire Review, IL, Chicago
pkendall@chicagotribune.com, Mng. Ed., Lincolnwood Review, IL, Chicago
pkendall@chicagotribune.com, Mng. Ed., Morton Grove Champion, IL, Chicago
pkendall@chicagotribune.com, Mng. Ed., Mundelein Review, IL, Chicago
pkendall@chicagotribune.com, Mng. Ed., Niles Herald-Spectator, IL, Chicago
pkendall@chicagotribune.com, Mng. Ed., Norridge-Harwood Heights News, IL, Chicago
pkendall@chicagotribune.com, Mng. Ed., Northbrook Star, IL, Chicago
pkendall@chicagotribune.com, Mng. Ed., Oak Leaves, IL, Chicago
pkendall@chicagotribune.com, Mng. Ed., Skokie Review, IL, Chicago
pkendall@chicagotribune.com, Mng. Ed., Vernon Hills Review, IL, Chicago
pkendall@chicagotribune.com, Mng. Ed., Wilmette Life, IL, Chicago
pkendall@chicagotribune.com, Mng. Ed., Winnetka Talk, IL, Chicago
pkendall@chicagotribune.com, Mng. Ed., Barrington Courier-Review, IL, Glenview

Kendle, John .... **(204) 697-7093**
john.kendle@canstarnews.com, Managing Editor, The Sou'wester, MB, Winnipeg
john.kendle@canstarnews.com, Mng. Ed., The Metro, MB, Winnipeg

Kendle, John .... **(204) 697-7093**
john.kendel@canstarnews.com, Managing Editor, The Headliner, MB, Winnipeg
john.kendel@canstarnews.com, Mng. Ed., The Times, MB, Winnipeg

Kendle, John .... **(204) 697-7093**
john.kendle@canstarnews.com, Managing Editor, The Lance, MB, Winnipeg

Kendle, John
john.kendle@uptownmag.com, Mng. Ed., The Herald, MB, Winnipeg

Kendrick, David .... **(256) 234-4281 ext. 13**
david.kendrick@alexcityoutlook.com, Circ.Mgr, Alexander City Outlook, AL, Alexander City
david.kendrick@alexcityoutlook.com, Dadeville Record, AL, Alexander City

Kendrick, Larry .... **(928) 763-2505 Ext.7122**
Larry@nwppub.com, Operations Director, Mohave Valley Daily News, AZ, Bullhead City

Kendrick, Sid
sid.kendrick@advpubtech.com, Cir. Prod. Mgr., Advanced Publishing Technology, CA, Burbank

Kendrick, Stephanie .... **(808) 529-4329**
skendrick@staradvertiser.com, News Ed., Honolulu Star-Advertiser, HI, Honolulu

Kendrick, Tracey .... **(479) 667-2136**
Adv. Mgr., The Spectator, AR, Ozark

Kendrick-holmes, Dimon .... **(706) 571-8560**
dkholmes@ledger-enquirer.com, Exec. Ed., Columbus Ledger-Enquirer, GA, Columbus

Kenedy, Beverly
circulation@vernonrecord.com, Circ. Coord., The Vernon Daily Record, TX, Vernon

Kenfield, Benjamin .... **(541) 885-4410**
bkenfield@heraldandnews.com, Adv. Dir. , Herald and News, OR, Klamath Falls

Kennedy, Aaron
sports.sdt@gmail.com, Sports Ed., The Sullivan Daily Times, IN, Sullivan

Kennedy, Chris .... **(217) 351-5272**
ckennedy@shawanoleader.com, Regional Advertising Director, Shawano Leader, WI, Shawano

Kennedy, Christine
perryshopper@frontiernet.net, Pub., Perry Shopper, NY, Perry

Kennedy, Colleen
colleen@warsawpennysaver.com, Treasurer Co-owner, Warsaw Pennysaver, NY, Warsaw

Kennedy, Cristie .... **(719) 395-8621 x11**
ckennedy@chaffeecountytimes.com, Advertising director, The Chaffee County Times, CO, Buena Vista

Kennedy, Daniel
dkennedy@springfieldcollege.edu, Vstg. Prof., Northeastern University, MA, Boston

Kennedy, Dave .... **(808) 529-4818**
dkennedy@staradvertiser.com, Chief Revenue Officer, Honolulu Star-Advertiser, HI, Honolulu
dkennedy@staradvertiser.com, Chief Revenue Officer, West Hawaii Today, HI, Kailua Kona
dkennedy@staradvertiser.com, Chief Revenue Officer, Hawaii Tribune-Herald, HI, Hilo

Kennedy, Dave .... **(808) 529-4818**
dkennedy@thegardenisland.com, CRO, The Garden Island, Kauai, HI, Lihue

Kennedy, Dave .... **(808) 529-4818**
dkennedy@staradvertiser.com, CRO, USA Today Hawaii Edition , HI, Honolulu

Kennedy, Dave .... **(808) 529-4818**
dkennedy@staradvertiser.com, Chief Revenue Officer, Kauai Midweek, HI, Honolulu
dkennedy@staradvertiser.com, Chief Revenue Officer, MidWeek Oahu, HI, Honolulu

Kennedy, Dave .... **(808) 529-4818**
dkennedy@staradvertiser.com, Chief Revenue Officer, Street Pulse, HI, Honolulu

Kennedy, David
ads@theweeklysentinel.com, Acct. Mgr. , Weekly Sentinel, ME, Wells

Kennedy, Diane
dianenynpa@aol.com, Pres., New York News Publishers Association, NY, Albany

Kennedy, Diane
diane@nynpa.com, Pres., New York News Publishers Association, NY, Albany

Kennedy, Ed
ekennedy@theguardian.pe.ca, Circ. Dir., The Journal Pioneer, PE, Summerside

Kennedy, Grace .... **(604) 575-5319**
grace.kennedy@cloverdalereporter.com, Reporter, Cloverdale Reporter, BC, Surrey

Kennedy, Jason
jkennedy@times-standard.com, Prodn. Mgr., On The Market, CA, Eureka

Kennedy, Jim
jimk@mo.neighbornews.com, Circ. Mgr, Harrison Daily Times, AR, Harrison

Kennedy, Jim
jkennedy@cvcaudit.com, VP Audit Services, Circulation Verification Council, MO, Saint Louis

Kennedy, Joyce Lain .... **(760) 652-5302**
jlk@sunfeatures.com, Pres., Sun Features, Encinitas

Kennedy, Larry .... **(254) 865-5212**
editor@gatesvillemessenger.com, Ed., Gatesville Messenger and Star Forum, TX, Gatesville

Kennedy, Linda
news@metropolisplanet.com, News Ed., Metropolis Planet, IL, Metropolis

Kennedy, Matt .... **(412) 263-1982**
mkennedy@post-gazette.com, Asst. Mng. Ed., Content, Pittsburgh Post-Gazette, PA, Clinton

Kennedy, Michael D. .... **(308) 432-6047**
Advisor, Chadron State College, NE, Chadron

Kennedy, Michelle .... **ext. 235**
Retail Sales Rep., The Barrie Examiner, ON, Barrie

Kennedy, Mike .... **(705) 759-5816**
mike.kennedy@sunmedia.ca, Adv. Mgr., The Sault Star, ON, Sault Sainte Marie

Kennedy, Natalie .... **(570) 724-2287**
nkennedy@tiogapublishing.com, Ed., Free Press-Courier, PA, Wellsboro

Kennedy, Paul .... (904) 819-3444
PAUL.KENNEDY@STAUGUSTINE.COM, Circ.
Mgr., The St. Augustine Record, FL, Saint
Augustine

Kennedy, Sam
advocateeditor@bellsouth.net , Pub., Lawrence
County Advocate, TN, Lawrenceburg

Kennedy, Tim
timkennedy@advancemediany.com, President
, The Post-Standard, NY, Syracuse

Kennedy, William T.
william.kennedy@dowjones.com, Chief
Operating Officer, Dow Jones Local Media
Group, NY, Middletown

Kennedy , Davis
newsdesk@currentnewspapers.com, Pub./Ed.,
Dupont Current, DC, Washington
newsdesk@currentnewspapers.com, Pub./Ed.,
Foggy Bottom Current, DC, Washington
newsdesk@currentnewspapers.com, Pub./Ed.,
Georgetown Current, DC, Washington
newsdesk@currentnewspapers.com, Pub./Ed.,
Northwest Current, DC, Washington

Kennedy , Ed .... (250) 490-0880 ext. 120
ed.kennedy@ok.bc.ca, Sales Mgr., Penticton
Herald, BC, Penticton

Kennedy , Eileen .... (781) 674-7726
ekennedy@wickedlocal.com, Ed., Arlington
Advocate, MA, Lexington

Kennedy-Till, Christine
chris@warsawpennysaver.com, President
Co-owner, Warsaw Pennysaver, NY, Warsaw

Kennedy-Till, Christine
chris@warsawpennysaver.com, Prodn. Mgr.,
Warsaw Penny Saver, NY, Warsaw

Kennedy-Turner, Ann
aturner@gillettenewsrecord.net, Pub./Ed., The
News-Record, WY, Gillette

Kenner, Natasha
nkenner@sla.org, Dir., Exec. Office Relations,
Special Libraries Association, News Division,
VA, Alexandria

Kenney, Erica
ekenney@ottumwacourier.com, Classified
Supervisor, The Ottumwa Courier, IA,
Ottumwa

Kenney, Jeff .... (574) 216-0075 (news)
culvercitizen@gmail.com, Ed., The Culver
Citizen, IN, Plymouth

Kenney, Trevor
trevor.kenney@lethbridgeherald.com, Sports
Ed., The Lethbridge Herald, AB, Lethbridge

Kenny, Justin
jkenny@news-sentinel.com, Multimedia
Specialist, The News-Sentinel, IN, Fort
Wayne

Kenny, Margaret .... (716) 849-4444
mkenny@buffnews.com, Asst. Mng. Ed., The
Buffalo News, NY, Buffalo

Kenny, Michael .... (574) 224-5314
mkenny@rochsent.com, Photo Dept. Mgr., The
Rochester Sentinel, IN, Rochester

Kenny, Thane .... ext. 252
thane@alibi.com, Circ. Dir., Weekly Alibi, NM,
Albuquerque

Kenoly, Deitra .... (209) 546-8238
Adv. Dir., The Record, CA, Stockton

Kent, Beverly
bkent@lnpnews.com, Adv. Mgr, Lititz Record
Express, PA, Ephrata

Kent, Beverly
bkent@lnpnews.com, Adv. Mgr., The Ephrata
Review, PA, Ephrata

Kent, Douglas
production@ladysmithchronicle.net, Prodn.
Mgr., The Ladysmith Chronicle, BC,
Ladysmith

Kent, Heather
hkent@gannett.com, Adv. Mgr., The Daily
News Journal, TN, Murfreesboro

Kent, Norm
norm.kent@sfgn.com, Publisher, South Florida
Gay News, FL, Wilton Manors

Kent, Roy .... (281) 378-1087
rkent@hcnonline.com, Ed., Tomball Potpourri,
TX, Conroe
rkent@hcnonline.com, Ed., Magnolia Potpourri,
TX, Conroe
rkent@hcnonline.com, Ed., Cypress Creek
Mirror, TX, Houston
rkent@hcnonline.com, Publisher, Cypress
Creek Champions (OOB), TX, Houston

Kent, Roy .... (281) 378-1087
rkent@hcnonline.com, Ed, West University
Examiner, TX, Houston

Kent, Sandra .... (617) 619-6315
sandra.kent@bostonherald.com, Deputy Mgr.
Ed., Features, Boston Herald, MA, Boston

Kent, Stephen .... (850) 678-1080
info@baybeacon.com, Ed. & Pub., The Bay
Beacon, FL, Niceville

Kentch, Carrie .... (402) 444-1448
carrie.kentch@owh.com, Adv. Mgr., Custom
Pub., Omaha World-Herald, NE, Omaha

Kentling, Fran .... (316) 942-5385
fran@theactiveage.com, Editor/Publisher, The
Active Age, KS, Wichita

Kenworthy, George
gkenworthy@andersonvalleypost.com, Adv.
Sales Supvr., Senior Scene, WA, Tacoma

Kenyon, Donna
dkenyon@gmnews.com, Exec. Ed., Newspaper
Media Group, NJ, Cherry Hill

Kenyon, Judith A. .... (250) 776-2357
editorial@fortnelsonnews.ca, Ed & Pub, The
Fort Nelson News, BC, Fort Nelson

Kepka, Juanita .... (785) 472-5085
indy@eaglecom.net, Bus. Mgr., The Ellsworth
County Independent-Reporter, KS, Ellsworth

Keplar, Kevin
kevin.keplar@wichita.edu, Instr., Wichita State
University, KS, Wichita

Keplinger, Teresa .... (360) 735-4470
teresa.keplinger@columbian.com, Adv. Dir.,
The Columbian, WA, Vancouver

Kerbaugh, Jim
jlkerbau@ic.edu, Chair, English, Illinois
College, IL, Jacksonville

Kerber, Scott .... (417) 468-2013
Scottk@marshfieldmail.com, Gen. Mgr/Ed.,
The Marshfield Mail, MO, Marshfield

Kerber, Scott
scottk@marshfieldmail.com, Ed./GM, South
County Mail, MO, Rogersville

Keren, Phil .... (330) 688-0088
pkeren@recordpub.com, Ed., Cuyahoga Falls
News-Press, OH, Kent

Kerley, Coye .... (432) 333-7603
ckerley@oaoa.com, Director of Advertising &
Marketing, Odessa American, TX, Odessa

Kerlin, Charles
kerlin@saintjoe.edu, St. Joseph's College, IN,
Rensselaer

Kerluke, Georgia
class@minnedosatribune.com, Office Mgr/
Class., Minnedosa Tribune, MB, Minnedosa

Kermoade, Brian
bkermoade@dailyrepublic.net, Adv. Mgr., Nat'l,
Daily Republic, CA, Fairfield

Kern, Arthur
akern@thearknewspaper.com, Owner/pub.,
The Ark, CA, Tiburon

Kern, Barkley .... (202) 650-6414
bkern@cq.com, Vice President and Publisher,
advocacy, state and transcripts
, Congressional Quarterly, Inc., DC,
Washington

Kern, Frank
frankkern@us.ibm.com, Sr. Vice Pres./Grp.
Exec., Sales, IBM Corp., NY, Armonk

Kern, Kirk
bbm.kirk@gmail.com, COO, Mineral County
Independent News, NV, Hawthorne

Kerner, Water
info@lati2d.com, CCO, L@it2'd (Latitude), CA,
Los Angeles

Kerns, Mary Ann .... ext. 270
mary.kearns@lee.net, Ed., The Ledger
Independent, KY, Maysville

Kerns, Richard
rkerns@solnaweb.com, Pres., Solna Web USA,
Inc., KS, Lenexa

Kerr, Alan .... (215) 345-3049
Editorial Page Ed., The Intelligencer, PA,
Doylestown

Kerr, Alec
alec@mountwashingtonvalley.com, Wire/
Entertainment Ed., The Conway Daily Sun,
NH, North Conway

Kerr, Frank E.
triftynickels@home.com, Pub., Thrifty Nickel
Publications, Llc, FL, Panama City

Kerr, George "Buddy" .... (813) 259-7896
Tampa Bay Times, FL, St Petersburg

Kerr, Jaime .... (973) 383-1306
jkerr@njherald.com, Tech Mgr., New Jersey
Herald, NJ, Newton

Kerr, John .... (951) 368-5191
jkerr@pe.com, Dir. Multimedia Sales Dev., The
Press-Enterprise, CA, Riverside

Kerr, Kaye .... (901) 528-8624
kayekerr@memphisdailynews.com, Circ.
Coordinator, The Memphis News, TN,
Memphis

Kerr, Pauline .... (519) 291-1660 ext. 109
pkerr@northperth.com, Ed., The Listowel
Banner, ON, Listowel

Kerr, Robert
rkerr@ou.edu, Asst. Prof., University of
Oklahoma, OK, Norman

Kerr, Robert .... (913) 684-1722
editor@ftleavenworthlamp.com, Ed., Fort
Leavenworth Lamp, KS, Fort Leavenworth

Kerr, Susan .... (860) 241-3730
skerr@courant.com, Circ. Dir., The Hartford
Courant, CT, Hartford

Kerrigan, Pat .... (608) 796-3041
Viterbo College, WI, La Crosse

Kersch, Elaine .... (914) 696-8511
ekirsch@lohud.com, Circ. Dir., Lohud Express,
NY, White Plains

Kerschinske, Rebecca
mascinfo@masclabels.com, Vice Pres. Mktg.,
Lauterbach Group, WI, Sussex

Kersey, Kate .... (540) 574-6276
kkersey@dnronline.com, Ed., The Journal, VA,
Harrisonburg

Kershaw, Lisa
kershawl@valassis.com, Client Liason
Manager, Valassis, MI, Livonia

Kershner, James ....(508) 362-2131 ext. 4734
jkershner@capecod.edu, Cape Cod Cmty.
College, MA, West Barnstable

Kerton, Megan .... (780) 743-8186 ext. 232
megan.kerton@sunmedia.ca, Adv. Mgr., Fort
McMurray Today, AB, Fort McMurray

Kerworuka, Karen .... (207) 689-2841
kkreworuka@sunjournal.com, Copy Desk
Chief, Sun Journal, ME, Lewiston

Kesel, Beth .... (585) 337-4217
bkesel@messengerpostmedia.com,
Irondequoit Post, NY, Canandaigua
bkesel@messengerpostmedia.com, Gen. Mgr./

Adv. Dir., Webster Post, NY, Canandaigua
bkesel@messengerpostmedia.com,
Pres./Pub., Brighton-Pittsford Post, NY,
Canandaigua
bkesel@messengerpostmedia.com, Adv. Mgr
Community Shopping Guide - Canandaigua/
Victor, NY, Canandaigua
bkesel@messengerpostmedia.com, Gen.
Mng./Adv. Dir., Daily Messenger, NY,
Canandaigua
bkesel@messengerpostmedia.com, Pres./
Pub., East Rochester-Fairport Post, NY,
Canandaigua
bkesel@messengerpostmedia.com, Pres./Pub.
, Gates-Chili Post, NY, Canandaigua
bkesel@messengerpostmedia.com, Adv.
Mgr., Lyons Clyde Savannah Shopper, NY,
Canandaigua
bkesel@messengerpostmedia.com, Adv.
Mgr., Sodus Williamson Pennysaver, NY,
Canandaigua
bkesel@messengerpostmedia.com, Adv. Mgr.,
Timesaver, NY, Canandaigua
bkesel@messengerpostmedia.com, Gen. Mgr./
Adv. Dir., Wayne Post, NY, Canandaigua
bkesel@messengerpostmedia.com, Gen. Mgr./
Adv. Dir., Greece Post, NY, Canandaigua
bkesel@messengerpostmedia.com, Penfield
Post, NY, Canandaigua
bkesel@messengerpostmedia.com, Rush-
Henrietta Post, NY, Canandaigua
bkesel@messengerpostmedia.com, General
Mgr./Adv. Director , Victor Post, NY,
Canandaigua
bkesel@messengerpostmedia.com, Adv. Dir. ,
Messenger Post Media, NY, Canandaigua

Kessinger, Sarah .... (785) 562-2317
skessinger@marysvilleonline.net, Editor,
publisher, owner, Marysville Advocate, KS,
Marysville

Kessinger, Sharon
skessinger@marysvilleonline.net, Editor
emeritus, Marysville Advocate, KS,
Marysville

Kessler, Christi .... (541) 484-0434
christi@oregonfamily.com, Advt Acct Mgr,
Oregon Family Magazine, OR, Eugene

Kessler, J.R.
kesslerj@acu.edu, Instr., Abilene Christian
University, TX, Abilene

Kessler, Rick
rick.kessler@oakpress.com, Mng. Ed. , News-
Herald, MI, Southgate

Kester, Mitze
mitze@lyndentribune.com, Adv. Mgr., Lynden
Tribune, WA, Lynden

Kesterson, Janelle
opinion@csceagle.com, Opinion Ed, Chadron
State College, NE, Chadron

Kestner, Laura
laura@deleonfreepress.com, Ed., De Leon
Free Press, TX, De Leon

Ketchie, Ken
ken@highcountrypress.com, Pub./Ed., High
Country Press, NC, Boone

Ketchum, Mark
sports@alleghanynews.com, Sports Ed., The
Alleghany News, NC, Sparta

Ketring, Teresa .... (937) 569-4301
tketring@dailyadvocate.com, Cust. Sales /
Serv. Rep., Daily Advocate, OH, Greenville

Ketterer, Michelle
michelle@ncpublish.com, Adv. Mgr., Harbor
Light, MI, Harbor Springs

Ketterer, Stan
kstan@okstate.edu, Assoc. Prof., Oklahoma
State University, OK, Stillwater

Ketterling, Theresa .... (613) 678-3327
tketterling@thereview.ca, Reporters/
Photographer, The Review, ON, Vankleek Hill

Kettler, C.J. .... (212) 969-7540
cj.kettler@hearst.com, President, King
Features Syndicate, NY, New York

amanda.kingsbury@indystar.com, News
Director, The Indianapolis Star, IN,
Indianapolis

Kingsbury, Kathleen .... **(617) 929-2059**
katie.kingsbury@globe.com, Managing Ed./
Digital , The Boston Globe, MA, Boston

Kinion, Storm
skinion@kdminer.com, Circ. Mgr., Kingman
Daily Miner, AZ, Kingman

Kinison, Paul J.
billwhitham@aerotechnews.com, Pub.,
Aerotech News & Review, CA, Lancaster

Kinnaird, Jamie .... **(540) 981-3145**
jamie.kinnaird@roanoke.com, VP of
Advertising, The Roanoke Times, VA,
Roanoke

Kinnaird, Karen
kkinnaird@bgco.org, Account Manager, Baptist
Messenger, OK, Oklahoma City

Kinnaird, Keith
kkinnaird@bonnercountydailybee.com, News
Ed., Bonner County Daily Bee, ID, Sandpoint

Kinnaman, Mandy
archernews@yahoo.com, Assistant Editor,
Archer County News, TX, Archer City

Kinney, Bill .... **(770) 428-9411 ext. 516**
bkinney@mdjonline.com, Columnist, Marietta
Daily Journal, GA, Marietta

Kinney, Bob .... **(303) 954-1941**
kinney@denverpost.com, VP, Info. Tech. & Pre-
Pub., The Denver Post, CO, Denver

Kinney, J.D.
mediagraphics@devkinney.com, Pres., Dev.
Kinney/MediaGraphics, Inc., TN, Memphis

Kinney, James .... **(413) 788-1298**
Bus. Ed., The Republican, MA, Springfield

Kinney, Pat .... **(319) 291-1426**
Pat.Kinney@wcfcourier.com, News Ed., The
Courier, IA, Waterloo

Kinney, Pat .... **(903) 237-7706**
pkinney@news-journal.com, HR Dir., Longview
News-Journal, TX, Longview

Kinney, Sarah
sarah.kinney@nexage.com, Advisor
Editor
, Simmons College, MA, Boston

Kinos, Lydia .... **(905) 732-2411 ext. 244.**
lkinos@wellandtribune.ca, Prod. Mgr., Welland
Tribune, ON, Welland

Kinsella, Jim
kinsella@capenews.net, Ed., The Mashpee
Enterprise, MA, Falmouth

Kinser, Melody
mkinser@mechlocal.com, Mechanicsville
Local, VA, Mechanicsville
mkinser@mechlocal.com, Managing Ed.,
Goochland Gazette, VA, Mechanicsville
mkinser@mechlocal.com, Ed., Powhatan
Today, VA, Powhatan

Kinsey, Linda
linda@sunnews.com, Exec. Ed., Sun
Newspapers, OH, Cleveland

Kinsey, Linda
lkinsey@sunnews.com, Exec. Ed., Sun News,
OH, Cleveland

Kinsler, Chris
ckinsler@journal-news.net, Editor, The Journal,
WV, Martinsburg

Kinter, Hastie D.
hastie@indianagazette.net, News In Edu.
Coordinator, The Indiana Gazette, PA,
Indiana

Kinter, Scott .... **(319) 291-1501**
scott.kinter@wcfcourier.com, Circ. Mgr., Insider,
IA, Waterloo
scott.kinter@wcfcourier.com, Circ. Mgr./Ops.
Dir., The Courier, IA, Waterloo

Kinzer, Jessica .... **(937) 652-1331**

jkinzer@civitasmedia.com, Retail Adv. Rep.,
The Mechanicsburg Telegram, OH, Urbana

Kinzler, Ron
urep@nemr.net, Pub., Princeton Post-
Telegraph, MO, Princeton

Kirby, Ian .... **(709) 748-0834**
ikirby@thetelegram.com, Prod. Mgr. , The
Telegram, NL, Saint John's

Kirby, Joe .... **(505) 823-3804**
jkirby@abqjournal.com, Asst. Mng. Ed.,
Albuquerque Journal, NM, Albuquerque

Kirby, Kenton .... **(718) 260-8318**
KKirby@CNGLocal.com, Ed., Caribbean Life,
NY, Brooklyn

Kirby, Mike .... **(508) 236-0335**
mkirby@thesunchronicle.com, Ed., The Sun
Chronicle, MA, Attleboro

Kirby, Nancy .... **(630) 637-5283**
North Central College, IL, Naperville

Kirby, Tim .... **(386) 754-0421**
tkirby@lakecityreporter.com, Sports Ed., Lake
City Reporter, FL, Lake City

Kirchner, James .... **(502) 582-4180**
jkirchner@courier-journal.com, Op. News Mgr.,
The Courier-Journal, KY, Louisville

Kirchoff, Aaron .... **(765) 932-2222**
aaron.kirchoff@rushvillerepublican.com,
Managing Ed., Rushville Republican, IN,
Rushville

Kirk, Thomas .... **(858) 451-6200**
TomK@BrehmMail.com, VP-Sales and Mktg,
Brehm Communications, Inc., CA, San Diego

Kirk, Bill
bkirk@andovertownsman.com, Ed., Andover
Townsman, MA, Andover

Kirk, Billy
bkirk@timesnews.net, Display Mgr., Kingsport
Times-News, TN, Kingsport

Kirk, Douglas .... **(830) 237-7313**
dougkirk@gvtc.com, Ed., Canyon Lake Week,
TX, Canyon Lake
dougkirk@gvtc.com, Pub./Ed., Comal County
Beacon, TX, Canyon Lake

Kirk, Douglas .... **(830) 899-3137**
dougkirk@gvtc.com, Pub./Ed., Bulverde
Standard, TX, Canyon Lake

Kirk, Jim **312-321-257**
jkirk@suntimes.com, Pub. / Ed. in Chief,
Chicago Sun-Times, IL, Chicago

Kirk, Mike .... **(402) 444-1589**
mike.kirk@owh.com, Finance Dir./Controller,
Omaha World-Herald, NE, Omaha

Kirk, Nan
nan@observernews.net, Adv. Mgr., Observer
News, FL, Ruskin

Kirk, Ray .... **(530) 896-7782**
rkirk@chicoer.com, Systems Mgr., Chico
Enterprise-Record, CA, Chico

Kirk, Rebecca .... **(918) 542-8441**
Northeastern Oklahoma A&M College, OK,
Miami

Kirk, Roger .... **(606) 248-1010 Ext. 1130**
rkirk@civitasmedia.com, Prod. mgr.,
Middlesboro Daily News, KY, Middlesboro

Kirk, Thomas
woburnads@rcn.com, Adv. Dir., Daily Times
Chronicle, MA, Woburn

Kirk, Violet
sales@nebpress.com, Adv. Sales Asst.,
Nebr. Press Adv. Service, Nebraska Press
Association/Nebraska Press Advertising
Service, NE, Lincoln

Kirkendall, Criss
crissk@journalpub.com, Circ. Dir., Central
Penn Parent, PA, Harrisburg

Kirkendoll, Kip
kip@fhtimes.com, Bus. Mgr., The Fountain Hill

Times, AZ, Fountain Hills

Kirkland, Don
don.kirkland@wranglernews.com, Wrangler
News, AZ, Tempe

Kirkland, Don .... **(864) 232-8736**
don@baptistcourier.com, Ed., The Baptist
Courier, SC, Greenville

Kirkman, David B. .... **(804) 775-2702**
dkirkman@timesdispatch.com, Vice Pres.,
Circ., Richmond Times-Dispatch, VA,
Richmond

Kirkman, Larry
larry@american.edu, Prof./Dean, American
University, DC, Washington

Kirkman, Lesa
lpkirma@valassis.com, Sales Director,
Valassis, MI, Livonia

Kirkpatrick, Kyle
kkirkpatrick@mountainx.com, Webmaster,
Mountain Xpress, NC, Asheville

Kirkpatrick, Tara .... **(613) 678-3327**
tara@thereview.ca, Advertising Sales, The
Review, ON, Vankleek Hill

Kirkwood, R. Cort .... **(540) 574-6289**
kirkwood@dnronline.com, Mng. Ed., Daily
News-Record, VA, Harrisonburg

Kirkwood, Sam .... **(205) 722-0239**
sam.kirkwood@tuscaloosanews.com, Creative
Serv Dir., The Tuscaloosa News, AL,
Tuscaloosa

Kirsch, Bernard
bernardkirsch@mac.com, Editor, Silurian
News, Society of the Silurians, NY, New York

Kirsch, Nancy
info@kona-kohala.com, Ed., Jewish Voice of
Rhode Island, RI, Providence

Kirsh, Julie .... **(416) 947-2257**
julie.kirsh@sunmedia.ca, News Research
Dept., The Toronto Sun, ON, Toronto

Kirsten, Dichiappari
kirsten@onebradford.com, MANAGING
DIRECTOR, ONE BRADFORD, East Bay
Newspapers, RI, Bristol

Kirtley, Jane
kirtl001@umn.edu, Silha Prof./Dir., Silha Ctr.,
University of Minnesota, MN, Minneapolis

Kirtley, Matthew .... **(503) 725-5686**
Portland State Univ., OR, Portland

Kirtz, William
w.kirtz@neu.edu, Assoc. Prof., Northeastern
University, MA, Boston

Kirwan, Donna .... **(401) 767-8525**
Asst. Ed., The Times, RI, Pawtucket

Kirzner, Ellie .... **ext. 333**
ellie@nowtoronto.com, Sr. News Ed., Now,
ON, Toronto

Kish, Laura
thecitizen@sasktel.net, Gen. Mgr., Kipling
Citizen, SK, Kipling

Kish, Peter .... **(203) 354-1028**
pkish@thehour.com, Bus. Systems Mgr., The
Hour, CT, Norwalk

Kish, Rebecca .... **(812) 488-2221**
crescentadvertising@evansville.edu, Marketing
& Sales Director, Univ. of Evansville, IN,
Evansville

Kislingbury, Graham .... **(541) 812-6111**
graham.kislingbury@lee.net, Online Ed.,
Albany Democrat-Herald, OR, Albany

Kiss, Andrew .... **ext. 113**
andrew.kiss@sunmedia.ca, Circ. Mgr. , The
Simcoe Reformer, ON, Simcoe

Kissel, Mary
mkissel@messenger-inquirer.com, Copy Ed.,
Messenger-Inquirer, KY, Owensboro

Kissler, Donald L.
dkissler@hastingstribune.com, Bus. Mgr./Credit

Mgr., Hastings Tribune, NE, Hastings

Kita, Leslie .... **(501) 664-0125**
lkita@dolr.org, Adv. Mgr., Arkansas Catholic,
AR, Little Rock

Kitch, Carolyn
ckitch@temple.edu, Assoc. Prof., Temple
University, PA, Philadelphia

Kitchens, Deborah .... **(706) 554-2111**
deborahk@thetruecitizen.com, Adv. Mgr., The
Signal, GA, Waynesboro

Kitchings, Kristy
kristy@theclevelandcurrent.com, Ads., The
Cleveland Current, MS, Cleveland

Kitkowski, Dan .... **(715) 735-7500 Ext. 155**
dkitkowski@eagleherald.com, Editor,
EagleHerald - ehextra.com, WI, Marinette

Kitner, Scott .... **(219) 933-3210**
scott.kinter@nwi.com, Reg. Circ. Dir., The
Times of Northwest Indiana, IN, Munster

Kitsch, LeDonna .... **(319) 758-8114**
lkitsch@thehawkeye.com, Bus. Mgr., The Hawk
Eye, IA, Burlington

Kittey, Steve
steve@scalise.com, Ed., The Latrobe Bulletin,
PA, Latrobe

Kittrell, Catherine .... **(319) 291-1462**
Catherine.kittrell@wcfcourier.com, Community
Desk Ed., The Courier, IA, Waterloo

Kitzmann, Richard
richardk@raksystems.com, Pres., RAK
Systems, Inc., AL, Theodore

Kizzia, Kevin .... **(918) 684-2960**
kkizzia@muskogeephoenix.com, Dis. Mgr.,
Muskogee Phoenix, OK, Muskogee

Kizzias, Steven .... **(405) 376-6688**
mustangpublisher@sbcglobal.net, Pub., The
Tuttle Times, OK, Mustang

Klaas, Mark
mklaas@kentreporter.com, Reg. Ed., Kent
Reporter, WA, Kent

Klaassen, Joel
joel@hillsborofreepress.com, Pub., Hillsboro
Free Press, KS, Hillsboro
joel@hillsborofreepress.com, Founding
Publisher, Buyer's Edge Of South Central
Kansas, KS, Newton

Klaassen, Virginia .... **(712) 479-2270**
vksc@mtcnet.net, Pub., Little Rock Free Lance,
IA, Little Rock

Klaimon, Bill
rbm2@frontiernet.net, Pub., Dawson Sentinel,
MN, Dawson

Klamo, Lynne .... **(812) 375-2801**
Circ. Mgr., Republic Extra, IN, Columbus

Klasne, Nick .... **(386) 283-4944**
nick.klasne@news-jrnl.com, Assistant
Managing Editor/Team Leader, Daytona
Beach News-Journal, FL, Daytona Beach

Klass, Irene
editor@jewishpress.com, Pub., The Jewish
Press, NY, Brooklyn

Klassen, Kelsey
editor@westender.com, Ed, We Vancouver
Weekly, BC, Vancouver
editor@westender.com, Ed, The Westender,
BC, Vancouver

Klausing, Denny .... **(419) 695-0015 Ext. 102**
dklausing@eagleprint.net, Prod. Mgr., Delphos
Daily Herald, OH, Delphos

Klauss, Nicole .... **(907) 486-3227 ext.627**
nklauss@kodiakdailymirror.com, Reporter,
Kodiak Daily Mirror, AK, Kodiak

Klawinski, Gary
gklawinski@jardis.com, Mgr., Graphic System
Services, Inc., IL, Itasca

Kleba, Kim .... **(262) 306-5030**
kkleba@conleynet.com, Circ. Dir., Times Press,

WI, Hartford
kkleba@conleynet.com, Circ. Mgr., The Daily News, WI, West Bend
kkleba@conleynet.com, Circ. Mgr, The Hartford Times Press, WI, West Bend

Kleba, Kim .... (262) 306-5030
kkleba@conleynet.com, Circulation Dir, Washington County Post, WI, West Bend

Kleban, Monika
mkleban@yourjournal.com, Mng. Ed., Citizen Journal, MO, Town And Country

Kleban, Monika .... (314) 821-2462
mkleban@yourjournal.com, Mng. Ed., Louisiana Press Journal, MO, Town And Country

Kleber, Leah-Ann
lkleber@willistonherald.com, Ret. Sales Mgr., Williston Daily Herald, ND, Williston

Kleczewski, Linda .... (815) 223-3200 ext. 140
ntnews@newstrib.com, Ed., Illinois Valley Shopper, IL, La Salle

Kleefeld, Gail .... (306) 682-1772
pm.circulation@stpeters.sk.ca, Adv. Mgr., Order Of St. Benedict, SK, Muenster

Kleen, Barton .... (937) 512-4577
clarion@sinclair,edu, Mng Ed, Sinclair Community College, OH, Dayton

Klein, Al .... (507) 764-6681
mcstar@frontiernet.net, Ed., The Martin County Star, MN, Sherburn

Klein, Alice .... ext. 335
alice@nowtoronto.com, Ed., Now, ON, Toronto

Klein, Dee
dee.klein@nptelegraph.com, Dir., Sales (NPC), The North Platte Telegraph, NE, North Platte

Klein, Helen .... (718) 238-6600
hklein@brooklynreporter.com, EIC, The Brooklyn Spectator, NY, Brooklyn

Klein, Jason E. .... (212) 856-6380
jklein@nnnlp.com, President & CEO, Newspaper National Network LP, NY, New York

Klein, Karen .... (925) 600-0840, ext. 122
kklein@pleasantonweekly.com, Adv. Acct. Exec., Pleasanton Weekly, CA, Pleasanton

Klein, Kevin .... (807) 468-5555 ext 231
kevin.klein@sunmedia.ca, Publisher/Director of Sales, The Winnipeg Sun, MB, Winnipeg

Klein, Margaret A.
maggieklein@pelhamweekly.com, Ed., The Pelhams-PLUS, NY, Pelham

Klein, Patrick .... (808) 529-4842
pklein@staradvertiser.com, VP Advertising, Metro HNL (OOB), HI, Honolulu
pklein@staradvertiser.com, VP/Advertising, Street Pulse, HI, Honolulu

Klein, Patrick .... (808) 529-4842
pklein@staradvertiser.com, VP/Advertising, Honolulu Star-Advertiser, HI, Honolulu

Klein, Patrick .... (808) 529-4842
pklein@staradvertiser.com, VP of Advertising, USA Today Hawaii Edition , HI, Honolulu

Klein, Patrick .... (808) 529-4842
pklein@staradvertiser.com, VP/Advertising, MidWeek Oahu, HI, Honolulu

Klein, Steven
carlislecitizen@mchsi.com, Pub., The Carlisle Citizen, IA, Carlisle

Klein, Steven .... (515) 981-0406
Pub., North Warren Town and County News, IA, Norwalk

Klein, Steven .... (515) 848-5614
Pub., Marion County News, IA, Pleasantville

Kleine, Ben
starj@starj.com, Reporter, Hillsboro Star-Journal, KS, Hillsboro

Kleine, Kevin .... (706) 236-2294

Berry College, GA, Mount Berry

Kleiner, Dan
publisher@elgincourier.com, Publisher, Elgin Courier, TX, Elgin

Kleinerman, Ellen
editor@chagrinvalleytimes.com, Editor , Solon Times, OH, Chagrin Falls

Kleinerman, Ellen
editor@chagrinvalleytimes.com, Ed. , Geauga Courier, OH, Chagrin Falls

Kleinerman, Ellen J
editor@chagrinvalleytimes.com, Ed., Chagrin Valley Times, OH, Chagrin Falls

Kleinklaus, Sherry
sherryk@journalpub.com, Adv. Mgr., Central Penn Parent, PA, Harrisburg

Kleinknecht, John
jkleinknecht@civitasmedia.com, Sports Ed., Galion Inquirer, OH, Galion

Kleinsmith, Lori .... (610) 562-2267
Display@WindsorPress.com, Assistant Display Advertising Manager, Northern Berks Merchandiser, PA, Hamburg
Display@WindsorPress.com, Assistant Display Advertising Manager, East Penn Valley Merchandiser, PA, Hamburg

Klemann, Mackenzi .... (260) 225-4665
mklemann@wabashplaindealer.com, Reporter, Wabash Plain Dealer, IN, Wabash

Klenz, Mark
catholicsun@yahoo.com, Ad. Director, The Catholic Sun, NY, Syracuse

Klepac, Patti .... (618) 239-2572
pklepac@bnd.com, Adv., Belleville News-Democrat, IL, Belleville

Kless, Richard F. .... (401) 865-2214
Providence College, RI, Providence

Klevorn, Patti .... (231) 845-5181
patti@ludingtondailynews.com, Editor, Ludington Shopper's Edition, MI, Ludington

Klevorn, Patti .... (231) 845-5182 ext. 341
patti@ludingtondailynews.com, Managing Ed. , Ludington Daily News, MI, Ludington

Klimek, David .... (514) 987-2222
dklimek@montrealgazette.com, Research Manager, Montreal Gazette, QC, Montreal

Kline, Alan .... (571) 403-3846
alan.kline@sourcemedia.com, Ed., News, American Banker, NY, New York

Kline, Bill .... (610) 807-9619
billk@lvb.com, Editor, Lehigh Valley Business, PA, Bethlehem

Kline, Daniel .... (860) 584-0501, ext. 7257
dkline@centralctcommunications.com, Managing Editor, Newington Town Crier, CT, New Britain
dkline@centralctcommunications.com, Managing Editor, Wethersfield Post (OOB), CT, New Britain

Kline, Dave .... (610) 371-5200
dkline@readingeagle.com, Exec. Dir of Circ & Promotions, Reading Eagle, PA, Reading

Kline, Karen E.
kkline@lhup.edu, Chair, Lock Haven University, PA, Lock Haven

Kline, Kevin
kevin.klein@sunmedia.ca, Pub./Dir of Sales, The Daily Graphic, MB, Portage la Prairie

Kline, Ron .... (217) 241-1300 x 239
rkline@illinoispress.org, Tech & Online Coord., Illinois Press Association, IL, Springfield

Kline, Susan
kline.48@osu.edu, Assoc. Prof., Ohio State University, OH, Columbus

Klinebriel, Michelle .... (740) 474-3131 Ext. 218
mklinebriel@circlevilleherald.com, Acct. Exec. , The Circleville Herald, OH, Circleville

Klingbeil, Gerald
klingbeilg@gc.adventist.org, associate editor, Adventist Review, MD, Silver Spring

Klingensmith, Michael .... (612) 673-7576
michael.klingensmith@startribune.com, Pub./CEO, Star Tribune, MN, Minneapolis

Klinger, Carolyn
cklinger@intersectmediasolutions.com, Acct. Mgr., Intersect Media Solutions, FL, Lake Mary

Klinger, Carolyn .... (321) 283-5262
cklinger@mediagenius.com, VP, Strategy, Florida Press Association, FL, Lake Mary

Klinger, Stephen .... (505) 524-0122
sklinger@zignet.com, Grimes, McGovern & Associates, NY, New York

Klinger, Teresa .... (608) 745-3565
tklinger@capitalnewspapers.com, Circ. Mgr., Wisconsin Dells Events, WI, Portage

Klinger, Teresa .... (608) 745-3565
tklinger@capitalnewspapers.com, Circ. Dir, Daily Register, WI, Portage

Klinger, Teresa .... (608) 745-3565
tklinger@capitalnewspapers.com, Circ. Dir., Monday-mini, WI, Beaver Dam

Klinger, Teresa .... (608) 745-3565
tklinger@capitalnewspapers.com, Circ. Dir., Tri-county, WI, Beaver Dam

Klingman, Amanda
amanda@bendsource.com, Adv. Dir., Source Weekly, OR, Bend

Klingsporn, Katie
editor@telluridedailyplanet.com, Ed., Telluride Daily Planet; the Watch; The Norwood Post, CO, Telluride

Klink, Luke .... (715) 532-5591
editor@ladysmithnews.com, Editor, Ladysmith News, WI, Ladysmith

Klinker, Carol .... (406) 346-7067
cklinker@rangeweb.net, Ed., Hysham Echo, MT, Forsyth

Klinsky, Terri
terri@windycitymediagroup.com, Adv. Mgr., Black Lines, IL, Chicago

Klipper, Leslie .... (858) 536-7000
lklipper@sdccd.edu, San Diego Miramar College, CA, San Diego

Klocke, Mike .... (209) 546-8250
mklocke@recordnet.com, Editor, The Record, CA, Stockton

Kloman, Harry
kloman@pitt.edu, Univ. of Pittsburgh, PA, Pittsburgh

Klomp, Noelle .... (586) 469-4510
nklomp@21st-centurymedia.com, Classifieds, The Macomb Daily, MI, Clinton Township
nklomp@21st-centurymedia.com, Classifieds Dir., The Daily Tribune, MI, Clinton Township
nklomp@21st-centurymedia.com, Classifieds Dir., The Oakland Press, MI, Pontiac
nklomp@21st-centurymedia.com, Adv. Dir., Daily Tribune, WI, Wisconsin Rapids

Klopfenstein, Suzanne .... (937) 225-9870
suzanne.klopfenstein@coxinc.com, Senior Director, Local & Major Accounts, Dayton Daily News, OH, Franklin

Klostreich, Tara .... (701) 642-8585
tarak@wahpetondailynews.com, Pub., The Daily News, ND, Wahpeton
tarak@wahpetondailynews.com, Pub., Williston Daily Herald, ND, Williston

Klostreich, Tara .... (701) 642-8585
tarak@wahpetondailynews.com, Adv. Mgr., News-Monitor, ND, Wahpeton

Klostreich, Tara .... (701) 642-8585
tarak@wahpetondailynews.com, Advt Mgr, Southern Valley Shopper, ND, Wahpeton

Klostreich, Tara .... (701) 642-8585

tarak@wahpetondailynews.com, Gen. Mgr., The Daily News, ND, Wahpeton

Kluetzmann, Judy A.
judyk@wdtimes.com, Adv. Dir., Retail/Nat'l, Watertown Daily Times, WI, Watertown

Klumpp, Teresa
tklumpp@fstribune.com, Adv. Mgr./Office Mgr., The Fort Scott Tribune, KS, Fort Scott

Kluttz, Lee
lkluttz@harperimage.com, VP of Operations, Harper Corporation of America, NC, Charlotte

Klyde-Silverstein, Lynn
lynn.klyde@unco.edu, Asst. Prof., University of Northern Colorado, CO, Greeley

Klyne, Marty
mklyne@leaderpost.canwest.com, Pub., The Leader-Post, SK, Regina

Klypchak, Carrie Lee
Carrie_klypchak@tamu-commerce.edu, Asst. prof., Texas A&M University-Commerce, TX, Commerce

Klypka, Richard
rklypka@gmnews.com, Circ. Dir., North/South Brunswick Sentinel, NJ, Manalapan

Kmiec, Lynn
lkmiec@hearstnp.com, Mgr., Info Systems, Midland Reporter-Telegram, TX, Midland

Knaak, Mike
mknaak@stcloudtimes.com, Adj. Prof., St. Cloud State University, MN, Saint Cloud

Knapek, Kurt .... (843) 937-5746
kknapek@postandcourier.com, Dir., Audience Development, The Post and Courier, SC, Charleston

Knapp, Amy
amy.knapp@IndeOnline.com, Reporter, The Independent, OH, Massillon

Knapp, Brian
knap@paper.net, Vice Pres., Pulse Research, Inc., OR, Portland

Knapp, Connie .... (218) 739-7014
connie.knapp@fergusfallsjournal.com, Circ. Mgr., Weekender, MN, Fergus Falls

Knapp, Kim
kim@tribune-courier.com, Adv. Mgr., Tribune Courier & Madison Tribune, OH, Ontario

Knapp, Lee .... (850) 747-5000
Pub., The News Herald, FL, Panama City

Knarr, Glenn .... ext. 245
nisysmgr@ptd.net, Systems Mgr., The News-Item, PA, Shamokin

Knarr, Glenn .... (570) 504-8217
gknarr@timesshamrock.com, Times-Shamrock Communications, PA, Scranton

Knarr, Glenn A. .... ext. 7
omar_k@newsitem.com, Prodn. Foreman, Composing, The News-Item, PA, Shamokin

Knaus, Mary .... (320) 398-5000
marketing.tricounty@gmail.com, Mktg and Advt Sales, Tri-County News, MN, Kimball

Knecht, William K.
news@southschuylkill.net, Pub./Ed./Adv. Dir., South Schuylkill News, PA, Schuylkill Haven

Knechtel, Jamie .... (724) 537-3351 ext. 14
Office Mgr., The Latrobe Bulletin, PA, Latrobe

Kneer, Mark .... ext. 120
mkneer@semissourian.com, Circ. Dir., Southeast Missourian Plus, MO, Cape Girardeau

Kneer, Mark .... (573) 335-6611 ext. 120
mkneer@semissourian.com, Gen. Mgr., Southeast Missourian, MO, Cape Girardeau

Knepp, Collette .... (574) 658-4111
cknepp@the-papers.com, Bus. Mgr., Senior Life (OOB), IN, Milford
cknepp@the-papers.com, Business Manager,

Advocate, MN, Henning

Koenen, Danielle
danielle@henningadvocate.com, Citizen's
Advocate, MN, Henning

Koenen , Chad
chad@henningadvocate.com, Co-Pub., New
York Mills Herald, MN, New York Mills

Koenen , Dani
news@henningadvocate.com, Co-Pub., New
York Mills Herald, MN, New York Mills

Koenig, Jerome .... (212) 453-9426
advertising@forward.com, Adv. Mgr., The
Forward, NY, New York

Koenig, Jerry
koenig@forward.com, Adv. Mgr., The Forward,
NY, New York

Koenig, Marcia
mkoenig@post-dispatch.com, Newsroom
Admin., St. Louis Post-Dispatch, MO, Saint
Louis

Koenig, Roman .... (619) 388-3880
rkoenig@sdccd.edu, San Diego City College,
CA, San Diego

Koenigs, Joel .... (651) 286-6700
jkoenigs@risdall.com, Vice Pres./Dir. Web Dev.,
Risdall Marketing Group, MN, New Brighton

Koenigsfeld, Stephen
stephen.koenigsfeld@iowastatedaily.com, Ed.,
Iowa State Daily, IA, Ames

Koerner, Doug .... (419) 724-6183
dkoerner@theblade.com, News Editor -
Sunday/Projects, The Blade, OH, Toledo

Koerner, Jane
jane.koerner@usu.edu, Adj. Instr., Utah State
University, UT, Logan

Koerselman, Cheryl .... (712) 475-3351
lyonconews@siebring.com, Ed., Lyon County
News, IA, George

Koesema, Michelle .... (361) 886-3601
koesemam@caller.com, CFO, Corpus Christi
Caller-Times, TX, Corpus Christi

Koester, Mary .... (618) 282-3803
ncnews@htc.net, Managing Ed., North County
News, IL, Red Bud

Kogler, David .... (507) 933-7636
Gustavus Adolphus College, MN, Saint Peter

Kohan, Mark A. .... (716) 312-8088
info@polamjournal.com, Ed., Polish American
Journal, NY, North Boston

Kohatsu, Gary .... (310) 329-6351 x 121
gvneditorial@gardenavalleynews.org, Ed.,
Gardena Valley News, CA, Gardena

Kohl Kremer, Deborah .... (502) 227-0053
Assistant Editor, Kentucky Monthly, KY,
Frankfort

Kohler, Christy .... (785) 823-6363 Ext. 347
ckohler@salina.com, Customer Service Mgr.,
The Salina Journal, KS, Salina

Kohls, Katherine
katherine.kohls@startribune.com, Preprint
Sales Mgr., Star Tribune, MN, Minneapolis

Kohlsaat, Ernie .... (603) 727-3302
ekohlsaat@vnews.com, Sunday and Bus.
News Ed., Valley News, NH, West Lebanon

Kohn, Eva
etkohn@cbaol.com, Executive VP, Cba
Industries, NJ, Elmwood Park

Kohntopp, Greg .... (330) 580-8397
greg.kohntopp@thesuburbanite.com, Ed., The
Suburbanite, OH, Akron

Kohoutova, Vera .... (416) 439-4354
office@masaryktown.ca, Editor, Novy domov
(New Homeland), ON, Toronto

Kohut, Carleen C.
kohutc@nrf.com, CFO, National Retail
Federation, DC, Washington

Kokmeyer, Pamela .... (508) 548-4700 x234
kokmeyer@capenews.net, Ed., Cape Cod
Shopper, MA, Falmouth
kokmeyer@capenews.net, Ed., The Falmouth
Enterprise, MA, Falmouth

Kolarik, Kim .... (502) 582-4683
kkolarik@courier-journal.com, Community
Engagement Dir., The Courier-Journal, KY,
Louisville

Kolb, Layton .... (972) 248-0451 x 235
Lkolb@willowbend.com, Cust Sup Mgr, Willow
Bend Communications, Inc., TX, Dallas

Kolbe, Carla
carla@sacandagaexpress.com, Ed.,
Sacandaga Express, NY, Amsterdam

Kolbe, Mike
mike@harlanonline.com, Adv. Mgr./Mktg. Dir.,
News-Advertiser, IA, Harlan

Kole, William
apboston@ap.org, News Ed., Associated
Press, MA, Boston
apboston@ap.org, Bureau Chief, New
England Associated Press News Executives
Association, MA, Boston

Kolenc, Victor .... (915) 546-6117
vkolenc@elpasotimes.com, El Paso Times,
TX, El Paso

Koller, Sheryl .... (501) 262-8190
skoller@alliance-rubber.com, Alliance Rubber
Co., AR, Hot Springs

Kolness, John .... (218) 596-8813
theunionnews@aol.com, Ed., Clay County
Union, MN, Ulen

Kolodny, Aaron .... (480) 898-5641
customercare@ahwatukee.com, Circ. Dir.,
Ahwatukee Foothills News, AZ, Tempe

Kolody, Tracy
tkolody@tribune.com, Mng. Ed., Boca Raton
Forum, FL, Fort Lauderdale
tkolody@tribune.com, Plantation/Davie Forum,
FL, Fort Lauderdale
tkolody@tribune.com, Mng. Ed., Coral Springs
Focus (OOB), FL, Coral Springs
tkolody@tribune.com, Mng. Ed., Oakland Park
Gazette (OOB), FL, Fort Lauderdale
tkolody@tribune.com, Mng. Ed., South
Woodham Focus (OOB), FL, Fort Lauderdale
tkolody@tribune.com, Mng. Ed., Weston
Gazette, FL, Fort Lauderdale
tkolody@tribune.com, Mng. Ed., Shalom -
Broward, FL, Fort Lauderdale
tkolody@tribune.com, Mng. Ed., Shalom - Palm
Beach, FL, Fort Lauderdale

Kolodziej, Elaine .... (830) 216-4519
editor@wcn-online.com, Publisher, La Vernia
News, TX, La Vernia

Kolodziej, Elaine .... (830) 216-4519
elaine@wcn-online.com, Publisher, Wilson
County News, TX, Floresville

Kolodziej, Tim .... ext. 614
Television/Film Ed., New Castle News, PA,
New Castle

Komai, Michael .... (213) 629-2231
Publisher, The Rafu Shimpo, CA, Los Angeles

Komai, Michael
info@rafu.com, Pub., The Rafu Shimpo, CA,
Los Angeles

Komidar, Travis .... (585) 258-9900
tkomidar@gannett.com, GM/Ops Gannett
Pub. Serv., Democrat and Chronicle, NY,
Rochester

Kominicki, John
jkominicki@longislandpress.com, Pub, Long
Island Press, NY, Syosset

Komives, Stephen
skomives@snd.org, Exec. Dir., Society for
News Design, Inc., FL, Orlando

Komives, Stephen .... (912) 652-0316
skomives@savannahnows.com, News
Planning Ed., Savannah Morning News, GA,
Savannah

Komlanc, Anthony M. .... ext. 25
sentinel@whitesidesentinel.com, Owner/Mng.
Ed., Whiteside News Sentinel, IL, Morrison

Komlanc, Tony
echo@whitesidesentinel.com, Owner/Ed.,
Prophetstown Echo, IL, Prophetstown

Kompf, Colleen .... (315) 422-8048
ctkompf@yahoo.com, Adv. Sales, Syracuse
Parent, NY, Syracuse

Kondik, Lisa .... (440) 998-2323 Ext. 139
lkondik@starbeacon.com, Bus. Mgr., Star
Beacon, OH, Ashtabula

Konecny, Jerry
jkonecny@breze.com, Vice Pres., Breze, Inc.,
NJ, Hamilton

Konig, Bob .... (973) 586-8117
Konig@northjersey.com, VP Operations,
Herald News, NJ, Rockaway

Konig, Jim .... (239) 574-1110
jkonig@breezenewspapers.com, Advertising
Director, Lee County Shopper, FL, Cape
Coral

Konig, Jim .... (239) 574-1110
jkonig@breezenewspapers.com, Adv. Dir.,
Fort Myers Beach Observer, FL, Fort Myers
Beach
jkonig@breezenewspapers.com, Advertisng
Director, Cape Coral Breeze, FL, Cape Coral

Konig, Jim .... (603) 882-2741
news@nashuatelegraph.com, Pub., The
Telegraph, NH, Nashua

Konig, Robert .... (973) 586-8117
konig@northjersey.com, VP / Cir. & Mfg., The
Record, NJ, Woodland Park
konig@northjersey.com, VP of Operations,
North Jersey Media Group Inc., NJ,
Woodland Park

Konrad, Jim .... (860) 425-4201
jkonrad@norwichbulletin.com, Exec. Editor,
The Bulletin, CT, Norwich

Konradi, Mark .... (214) 977-8983
mkonradi@dallasnews.com, Director of News
Operations, The Dallas Morning News, TX,
Dallas

Konter, Kathy .... (281) 378-1902
kkonter@hcnonline.com, Advt Sales Mgr, West
University Examiner, TX, Houston

Kontrelos, Tracy
tracy.kontrelos@westword.com, Assoc. Pub.,
Denver Westword, CO, Denver

Konz, Michael .... (308) 233-9720
mike.konz@kearneyhub.com, Mng. Ed.,
Shopping Link, NE, Kearney

Konz, Michael .... (308) 233-9720
mkonz@kearneyhub.com, Managing Ed.,
Kearney Hub, NE, Kearney

Koob, Michael
enterpub@hickorytech.net, Pub., Maple River
Messenger, MN, Mapleton

Koob, Michael
publisher@prairiepublishingmn.com, Pub.,
Madelia Times-Messenger, MN, Madelia

Koob, Michael
publisher@prairiepublishingmn.com, Pub,
Lafayette Nicollet Ledger, MN, Lafayette

Koob, Mike
tm@prairiepublishingmn.com, Ed., Pure Gold,
MN, Madelia

Koolen, Robert
robert.koolen@savantisgroup.com, Pres.,
Scala, Inc., PA, Exton

Koon, Bob
bkoon@usatoday.com, Distribution Mgr., Times
Herald, MI, Port Huron

Koon, Scott .... (574) 583-5121
skoon@thehj.com, Publisher, The News
Reminder, IN, Monticello

Koonce, Brian .... ext. 235
bkoonce@mobaptist.org, News Writer, The
Pathway, MO, Jefferson City

Koonce, Jill
kooncej@fayettevillenc.com, Credit Mgr., The
Fayetteville Observer, NC, Fayetteville

Koones, Charles C.
ckoones@variety.cahners.com, Grp. Vice Pres./
Pub., Daily Variety, CA, Los Angeles

Kopas, Ken .... (203) 789-5484
kkopas@westportminuteman.com, Ad.
Director, Westport Minuteman, CT, New
Haven
kkopas@westportminuteman.com, Ad. Dir.,
Shoreline Times, CT, New Haven
kkopas@westportminuteman.com, Adv. Dir.,
Fairfield Minuteman, CT, New Haven

Kopec, John .... (973) 383-1017
jkopec@njherald.com, Auto. Category Mgr.,
New Jersey Herald, NJ, Newton

Koperski, Ron
chipol@bradley.edu, Assoc. Prof., Bradley
University, IL, Peoria

Kopit Levien, Meredith .... (212) 556-7777
mlevien@nytimes.com, Chief Rev. Officer, The
New York Times, NY, New York

Kopitsky, Alan
dn@democratnewsonline.com, General
Manager, Democrat News, MO,
Fredericktown

Kopp, Darrell .... (856) 825-8811
Pub., Cumberland Reminder, NJ, Millville

Kopp, Linda
lkopp@simbainformation.com, Pub., Simba
Information, CT, Stamford

Koppejan, Debbi
dkoppejan@niagarathisweek.com, Adv. Mgr.,
Niagara This Week, ON, Thorold

Koppejan, Debbi
dkoppejan@burlingtonpost.com, Advertising
Director, The Flamborough Review, ON,
Waterdown

Koppejan, Debbi .... (905) 632-4444 ext. 224
dkoppejan@burlingtonpost.com, Advertising
Director, The Burlington Post, ON, Burlington

Koppel, Andrew W.
naps@napsys.com, Retail Sales Mgr., North
Atlantic Publishing Systems, Inc., MA,
Concord

Koppenhofer, Tom .... (814) 444-5922
tomk@dailyamerican.com, Adv. Mgr., Daily
American, PA, Somerset

Kopshever, Kathy .... (618) 542-2133
duquoin@frontier.com, News Ed., Du Quoin
Evening Call, IL, Du Quoin

Koralewski, Don
editor@bryantimes.com, Ed. , The Bryan
Times, OH, Bryan

Koran, Nicole .... (250) 426-5201
nicole.koran@kimberleybulletin.com, Adv.
Sales Mgr., Cranbrook Daily Townsman, BC,
Cranbrook
nicole.koran@kimberleybulletin.com, The
Kimberley Daily Bulletin, BC, Kimberley

Korbel, Bill .... (630) 427-6230
bkorbel@shawmedia.com, Local Sales Mgr,
Roselle Itasca Press, IL, Downers Grove

Korbelik, Jeff
jkorbelik@journalstar.com, Features Editor,
Lincoln Journal Star, NE, Lincoln

Korch, Jody .... (715) 735-7500 Ext. 153
jkorch@eagleherald.com, Sports Ed.,
EagleHerald - ehextra.com, WI, Marinette

Koren, Michael
a-kornroller@a-kornroller.com, Pres., A-Korn
Roller, Inc., IL, Chicago

Koren, Michael J.
mkoren@medianewsgroup.com, CFO, Digital

First Media, CO, Denver

Korff, Grand Rabbi Y. A. .... (617) 227-8200
rebbe@rebbe.org, Pub., The Jewish Advocate, MA, Boston

Koriakin, Nicholas .... (561) 370-3336
Nick.Koriakin@ePublish4me.com, Senior Account Executive, ePublish4me, FL, Boynton Beach

Korman, Chris .... (812) 331-4353
ckorman@heraldt.com, Sports Ed., The Herald Times, IN, Bloomington

Kornblit, Heshy .... (718) 330-1100
heshy@jewishpress.com, Display Dept. Mgr., The Jewish Press, NY, Brooklyn

Kornmiller, Debbie .... (520) 573-4127
dkornmiller@tucson.com, Sr. Editor, Arizona Daily Star, AZ, Tucson

Korosec, Libby .... (513) 768-8109
ekorosec@gannett.com, Client Strategy Director, The Cincinnati Enquirer, OH, Cincinnati

Korporal , Heather .... (765) 671-6905
hkorporal@chronicle-tribune.com, Circ. Mgr. , Chronicle-Tribune, IN, Marion

Kortus, Diane .... (813) 503-5213
dkortus@lakerlutznews.com, Pres./Pub., Land O Lakes Laker, FL, Land O Lakes
dkortus@lakerlutznews.com, Pres./Pub./Adv., The Lutz News, FL, Land O Lakes
dkortus@lakerlutznews.com, Pres./Pub., Wesley Chapel Laker, FL, Land O Lakes
dkortus@lakerlutznews.com, Pres./Pub., Zephyrhills Laker, FL, Land O Lakes

Kosanke, Bernie .... (305) 376-4727
BKosanke@MiamiHerald.com, Regional Dir. of Audience Development (Circulation), Miami Herald, FL, Doral
BKosanke@MiamiHerald.com, Circ. Vice Pres., Herald Values, FL, Miami

Kosel, Paul Irvin .... (605) 397-2352
paperpaul@grotonsd.net, Pub., Groton Independent, SD, Groton

Kosel, Tina .... (605) 397-2352
Office Mgr., Groton Independent, SD, Groton

Koshan, Aseem
mail@omaid.com, Adv. Mgr., Omaid Weekly, VA, Alexandria

Kosicki, Gerald
kosicki.1@osu.edu, Assoc. Prof., Ohio State University, OH, Columbus

Kosloff, David
dkosloff@rooseveltpaper.com, Pres., Roosevelt Paper, NJ, Mount Laurel

Kosmicki, Kollin .... (831) 637-5566
kkosmicki@freelancenews.com, Ed., Hollister Free Lance, CA, Hollister

Kosmoski, Kristi .... (315) 841-4105
displayads@citlink.net, Adv. Mgr., The Waterville Times, NY, Waterville

Kosnac, Erin .... (601) 584-3070
ejkosnac@hattiesburgamerican.com, News Dir., Hattiesburg American, MS, Hattiesburg

Kostecka, Norma .... (707) 256-2228
nkostecka@napanews.com, Disp. Dir., American Canyon Eagle, CA, Napa
nkostecka@napanews.com, Adv. Dir., Napa Valley Register, CA, Napa

Kostich, Drago
dkostich@eldiariolaprensa.com, Prodn. Dir., El Diario La Prensa, NY, Brooklyn

Kostiuk, Mary-Ann .... (780) 214-9847
mary-ann.kostiuk@sunmedia.ca, Publisher, Vermilion Standard, AB, Vermilion
mary-ann.kostiuk@sunmedia.ca, Pub, Lloydminster Meridian Booster, AB, Lloydminster

Kostiuk, Mary-Ann .... ((780) 214-9847
mary-ann.kostiuk@sunmedia.ca, Pub Cold Lake Sun, AB, Cold Lake

mary-ann.kostiuk@sunmedia.ca, Circ. Mgr., The Stony Plain Reporter, AB, Spruce Grove

Kostiuk, Mary-Ann .... (780) 743-8186
mary-ann.kostiuk@sunmedia.ca, Pub., Fort McMurray Today, AB, Fort McMurray

Kostolansky, Dave
dkost@srds.com, Vice Pres., Mktg./Bus. Devel., SRDS, a Kantar Media Company, IL, Des Plaines

Kostrzewa, John .... (401) 277-7330
jkostrze@providencejournal.com, Asst. Managing Ed. Commerce & Consumer Des k , The Providence Journal, RI, Providence

Kosuowei, Richard O.
aac_eca@shsu.edu, Lectr., Sam Houston State University, TX, Huntsville

Kotarek, Aaron .... (808) 695-6318
akotarek@staradvertiser.com, Pres., Cal Western Circulation Managers' Association, CA, Novato

Kotarek, Aaron .... (808) 695-6318
akotarek@staradvertiser.com, VP, Circ., The Garden Island, Kauai, HI, Lihue
akotarek@staradvertiser.com, VP/Circ., Honolulu Star-Advertiser, HI, Honolulu

Kotecki, Stacy
slkotecki@cpapersmi.com, Office Mgr., Community Papers of Michigan, Inc., MI, East Lansing

Kotellnikof, Mark .... (306) 657-6382
mkotelnikoff@thestarphoenix.com, Circ. Dir. , Saskatoon StarPhoenix, SK, Saskatoon

Kotfila, Dave
dkotfila@repub.com, Digital Adv. Sales Mgr., The Republican, MA, Springfield

Kotrotsios, Linda
linda@hellenicnews.com, Circ. Mgr., Hellenic News of America, PA, Concordville

Kotrotsios, Paul
info@hellenicnews.com, Adv. Mgr., Hellenic News of America, PA, Concordville

Kott, Doug .... (605) 692-6271
dkott@brookingsregister.com, News Ed., Brookings Register, SD, Brookings

Kottke, Penny .... (920) 356-6739
pkottke@conleynet.com, CFO, Conley Media LLC, WI, Beaver Dam

Kotwasinski, Bob .... (602) 444-8211
VP/Production, The Arizona Republic, AZ, Phoenix

Kotz, Geri .... (941) 429-3108
gkotz@sun-herald.com, Class/Telmktg Mgr., Charlotte Sun, FL, Punta Gorda

Kourajian, Chad
chad.kourajian@bismarcktribune.com, HR Mgr., The Bismarck Tribune, ND, Bismarck

Kourpanidis, Wanda
wKourpanidis@mysanfordherald.com, Circ. Mgr., Sanford Herald, FL, Sanford

Kovach, Carol .... (216) 986-6060
ckovach@sunnews.com, Mng. Ed., Sun News, OH, Cleveland

Kovach, John
jkovach@hersamacorn.com, Ed, Fairfield Sun, CT, Shelton

Kovacs, Peter .... (225) 388-0277
pkovacs@theadvocate.com, Editor, The Advocate, LA, Baton Rouge

Kovacs, Sue
circulation@pentictonwesternnews.com, Circ. Mgr., Penticton Western News, BC, Penticton

Kovaleski, Jeff .... (765) 459-3121 Ex. 8590
jeff.kovaleski@kokomotribune.com, Ed./Op. Page Ed., Kokomo Tribune, IN, Kokomo

Kovar, Dale .... (320) 485-2535
hj@heraldjournal.com, Gen. Mgr., Herald Journal Classifieds & Going Out, MN,

Winsted

Kovar, Dale
dale@heraldjournal.com, Gen. Mgr., Herald Journal, MN, Winsted

Kovener, Curt
ctimes@crothersville.net, Ed., Crothersville Times, IN, Crothersville

Kowalczyk, Melissa .... (715) 735-7500 Ext. 143
Page designer, EagleHerald - ehextra.com, WI, Marinette

Kowalski, Tom
tom@hi-lites.com, Circ. Mgr., Hi-lites Shoppers Guide, MI, Fremont

Koyama, Ken .... (519) 756-2020 ext. 2200
ken.koyama@sunmedia.ca, Pub., Paris Star, ON, Paris
ken.koyama@sunmedia.ca, Pub., Brandtford Expositor, ON, Brantford

Koyano, Keith .... (909) 624-1887
Claremont Colleges, CA, Claremont

Koyoma, Ken .... (519) 756-2200 ext. 2200
ken.koyama@sunmedia.ca, Pub., The Simcoe Reformer, ON, Simcoe

Koyoma, Ken .... (519) 756-2020
ken.koyama@sunmedia.ca, Pub., Delhi News-record, ON, Delhi

Koziatek, Michael .... (618) 239-2500
mkoziatek@bnd.com, Asst. City Ed., Belleville News-Democrat, IL, Belleville

Kozlowski, Dan
dkozlows@slu.edu, Asst. Prof., Saint Louis University, MO, Saint Louis

Kozlowski, Ginger .... (603) 524-0156
ginger@laconiadailysun.com, Managing Ed., The Laconia Daily Sun, NH, Laconia

Kozlowski, Jennifer .... (575) 541-5403
jkozlowski@lcsun-news.com, Off. Admin., Las Cruces Sun-News, NM, Las Cruces

Kraai, David
kraai@advpubtech.com, Pres., Advanced Publishing Technology, CA, Burbank

Krabben, Gail
production@mountaineer.bz, Prodn. Mgr., The Mountaineer, AB, Rocky Mountain House

Krabel, Charlie .... (518) 290-3905
ckraebel@digitalfirstmedia.com, Managing Ed. , The Record, NY, Troy

Krabel, Charlie .... (518) 290-3905
ckraebel@digitalfirstmedia.com, Ed., Greenbush Life, NY, Troy
ckraebel@digitalfirstmedia.com, Ed., Latham Life, NY, Troy
ckraebel@digitalfirstmedia.com, Ed., The Record, NY, Troy

Kraebel, Charlie .... (518) 290-3905
ckraebel@digitalfirstmedia.com, Mng. Ed., Community News, NY, Saratoga Springs
ckraebel@digitalfirstmedia.com, Managing Ed., The Saratogian, NY, Saratoga Springs

Kraemer, Gini
gkraemer@commnewspapers.com, Circ. Mgr., The Lake Oswego Review, OR, Lake Oswego

Kraft, Kent ....ext. 202
kent.kraft@masthead.net, Bus. Devel. Mgr., Masthead International, Inc., AZ, Phoenix

Krahn, Iris
info@killarneyguide.ca, Circ Mgr, Killarney Guide, MB, Killarney

Kraiselburd, Raul
editor@eldia.com, Ed., El Dia, Gualeguaychu, Provincia de Entre Rios

Kraker, Mark .... (419) 281-0581 Ext. 224
mkraker@times-gazette.com, Adv. Mgr., Ashland Times-Gazette, OH, Ashland

Kraker, Mark .... (419) 281-0581 ext. 224
mkraker@times-gazette.com, Advertising Director, Ashland Publishing Co. LLC, OH,

Ashland

Kram, Jerry
nteditor@bhgnews.com, Editor, New Town News, ND, New Town
nteditor@bhgnews.com, Ed. , Mountrail County Record, ND, New Town

Kramer, Cecil V.
cvkramer@liberty.edu, Jr. Assoc. Dean, Liberty Univ., VA, Lynchburg

Kramer, Diana .... (206) 543-7666
dianakramer@dailyuw.com, Dir., Student Publications, Univ. of Washington, WA, Seattle

Kramer, Jack
jkramer@centralctcommunications.com, Chair, Hastings College, NE, Hastings

Kramer, Jack .... (203) 789-5601
jkramer@nhregister.com , Ed., New Haven Register, CT, New Haven

Kramer, Joann
info@beacononlinenews.com, Co-Owner/Co-Pub., The West Volusia Beacon, FL, Deland

Kramer, Kieron
news@eastwickpress.com, Ed., The Eastwick Press, NY, Cropseyville

Kramer, Nancy
subscriptions@pcgazette.com, Circ./Classifieds, The Portage County Gazette, WI, Stevens Point

Kramer Jr., Donovan .... (520) 423-8611
DKRAMERJR@PINALCENTRAL.COM, Co-Pub., Mng. Ed., Casa Grande Valley Newspapers Inc., AZ, Casa Grande
DKRAMERJR@PINALCENTRAL.COM, Co-Pub./Managing Ed., Casa Grande Dispatch, AZ, Casa Grande

Krantz, Laura
lkra@tjc.edu, Tyler Junior College, TX, Tyler

Kranz, Patricia .... (212) 626-9220
patricia@opcofamerica.org, Exec. Dir., Overseas Press Club of America, NY, New York

Krasne, Robert
rkrasne@lnpnews.com, Publisher and Chairman, LNP Media Group, Inc., PA, Lancaster
rkrasne@lnpnews.com, Publisher and Chairman, LNP, PA, Lancaster

Kraszyk, Tish .... (201) 798-7800
tishk@hudsonreporter.com, Advertising Manager, West New York/Union City Reporter, NJ, Hoboken

Kraszyk, Tish .... (201) 798-7800
tishk@hudsonreporter.com, Advt Mgr, Mr., NJ, Bayonne

Kraszyk, Tish .... (201) 798-7800
tishk@hudsonreporter.com, Adv. Mgr., The Weehawken Reporter, NJ, Bayonne

Kratky, Carmen
milezeronews@mrnews.ca, Office/Advertising, The Mile Zero News, AB, High Level

Kratzer, Al .... (908) 782-4747
Akratzer@express-times.com, Adv. Dir., Hunterdon County Democrat, NJ, Flemington

Kratzer, Brian .... (573) 884-0693
kratzerb@missouri.edu, Photo Dir., Columbia Missourian, MO, Columbia

Kratzer, Brian
kratzerb@missouri.edu, Director of Photography, Assistant Professor, Kappa Alpha Mu Honorary Society in Photo Journalism, MO, Columbia

Kraus, Ann S. .... (212) 556-1234
Vice Pres., Compensation/Benefits, The New York Times Co., NY, New York

Kraus, Jay
jkraus@seattleweekly.com, Circ. Mgr., Seattle Weekly, WA, Seattle

Kraus, Lindsey ....(406) 622-3311
riverpress@live.com, Adv. Mgr., The River
Press, MT, Fort Benton

Krause, Axel
axelkrause@wanadoo.fr, Sec. Gen., Anglo-
American Press Association of Paris, Paris

Krause, Ken
archie333@aol.com, Pub., Joint Forces
Journal, CA, Oakland

Krause, Lauren.............(905) 688-4332 ext. 1128
lauren.krause@sunmedia.ca, Advertising,
Thorold Niagara News, ON, Saint Catharine's

Krause, Marla ....(847) 612-1509
mkrause1@depaul.edu, DePaul University, IL,
Chicago

Krause, Mike
mike@i2i.org, Media/Publications Mgr.,
Independence Feature Syndicate, Denver

Krause, Troy
tkrause@redwoodfallsgazette.com, Ed., The
Redwood Falls Gazette, MN, Redwood Falls

Kravetz, Jay N. ....(561) 683-9090
jay@jaykravetz.com, Ed., International Photo
News, West Palm Beach

Krawczak, Katie ....ext. 225
kkrawczak@thehp.com, Features Ed., The
Herald-Palladium, MI, Saint Joseph

Krawitz, Jan
krawitz@leland.stanford.edu, Courtesy
Appointments, Stanford University, CA,
Stanford

Kreager, Tom ....(615) 278-5168
tkreager@dnj.com, Sports Ed., The Daily News
Journal, TN, Murfreesboro

Krebs, Margaret........................(814) 765-5581
Pres., The Progress, PA, Clearfield

Krebs, Randy ....(320) 255-8762
rkrebs@stcloud.gannett.com, Ed. Page Ed., St.
Cloud Times, MN, Saint Cloud

Krecklow, Robb ....(940) 549-7800
publisher@grahamleader.com, Group Pub.,
The Olney Enterprise, TX, Olney

Krecklow, Robb ....(940) 549-7800 ext. 306
publisher@grahamleader.com, Vice President /
Group Publisher
Graham Newspapers, Inc., Lake Country
Shopper, TX, Graham

Krecklow, Robert
editor@theindependent.com, Pub., Ad/venture,
NE, Grand Island

Kreher, Kristin
kkreher@mail.bradley.edu, Managing Ed.,
Bradley University, IL, Peoria

Kreiser, Mike ....(951) 782-7782
mkreiser@pe.com, Circ. Mgr., Home Del., The
Press-Enterprise, CA, Riverside

Krell, Tracy
longview@americanclassifieds.com, Prodn.
Mgr., American Classifieds, TX, Longview

Kremer, Lyn
lkremer@bizjournals.com, Pub., Philadelphia
Business Journal, PA, Philadelphia

Kremer, Mary Beth
hsoads@rivertowns.net, Adv. Mgr., Hot Sheet
Shopper, WI, River Falls

Kremer, Michael P.
wgazette@frontiernet.net, Mng. Ed., Wheaton
Gazette, MN, Wheaton

Krenek, Debby
publisher@newsday.com, Co-Pub., amNew
York, NY, New York
publisher@newsday.com, Co-Pub., Newsday,
NY, Melville

Krenik, Kyle
kyle@tctrib.com, Bus. Mgr., Tri-County News,
OR, Junction City

Kreppert, Mike ....(815) 987-1463

mkreppert@rrstar.com, Prodn. Dir., Rockford
Register Star, IL, Rockford

Kreppert, Mike ....(217) 788-1492
mike.kreppert@sj-r.com, Director of
Operations, Springfield Advertiser, IL,
Springfield

Kreps, Rick
publisher@thepostandmail.com, Pub., The
Post and Mail (Tuesday), IN, Columbia City

Kreps, Rick
publisher@thepostandmail.com, Pub., The
Post & Mail, IN, Columbia City

Kreps, Rick A.
rkreps@thepilotnews.com, Pub., The Shopper,
IN, Plymouth

Kresl, Lisa ....(214) 977-8807
lkresl@dallasnews.com, Deputy Mng. Ed.,
Lifestyle, The Dallas Morning News, TX,
Dallas

Kress, James
motimes@mtc.net, Pub., Mosinee Times, WI,
Mosinee

Kreten, Peter ....(773) 298-3375
pkreten@sxu.edu , Asst. Dir, Saint Xavier
University, IL, Chicago

Kretschmer, Mark ....(262) 656-6211
Circ. Asst. Mgr., Delivery/Collections, Kenosha
News, WI, Kenosha

Kretser, Rich ....(518) 843-1100 Ext. 117
rkretser@recordernews.com, Circ. , The
Recorder, NY, Amsterdam

Krey, Mike
mike.krey@investors.com, Technology Bureau
Chief, Silicon Valley, Investor's Business
Daily, CA, Los Angeles

Krick, Melinda
progress@progressnewspaper.org, Ed., The
Paulding Progress, OH, Paulding

Kridelbaugh, John ....(740) 439-3531
jkridelbaugh@dixcom.com, General Manager,
Jeffersonian Advantage, OH, Cambridge

Krien, Karen
sfherald@nwkansas.com, Publisher, St.
Francis Herald, KS, Saint Francis

Kriener, Zak
zkriener@fayettepublishing.com, News Writer /
Sports Writer, Ossian Bee, IA, West Union
zkriener@fayettepublishing.com, News Writer /
Sports Writer, Fayette Leader, IA, West Union
zkriener@fayettepublishing.com, News Writer
/ Sports Writer, The Elgin Echo, IA, West
Union

Krier, Chuck........................(785) 483-2116
russel@mainstreetmedia.us, Pub., The Russell
County News, KS, Russell

Krier, Chuck ....(785) 483-2116
russel@mainstreetmedia.us, Pub., Main Street
Media, Inc., KS, Russell

Krier, Jack
frcochron@gtmc.net, Pub., Franklin County
Chronicle, NE, Franklin

Krier, Jack........................(660) 542-0881
democrat@carollnet.com, Pres., Main Street
Media, Inc., MO, Carrollton

Krier, Jack
ospubco@ruraltel.net, Pub., Osborne County
Farmer, KS, Osborne

Krier, Jack
downsnews@ruraltel.net, Pub., Downs News
and Times, KS, Downs

Krier, Jack
review@gbta.net, Pub., The Ellis Review, KS,
Ellis

Krier, Jack
jack@mainstreetmedia.us, Chrmn., Main Street
Media, Inc., KS, Russell

Krier, Timothy ....(540) 374-5481
tkrier@freelancestar.com, Circulation Director,

The Free Lance-Star, VA, Fredericksburg

Krier, Wendy........................(209) 883-9215
Wendyk@midvalleypub.com , Chief Ed./Sales/
Mktg., Hughson Chronicle-Denair Dispatch,
CA, Hughson

Krift, Bro ....(334) 261-1509
bkrift@montgomeryadvertiser.com, Exec. Ed.,
Montgomery Advertiser, AL, Montgomery

Krikac, Bill
courier@itctel.com, Pub./Ed., Clark County
Courier, SD, Clark

Krimm, Cecile ....(701) 664-2222
cecilew@crosbynd.com, Pub., Tioga Tribune,
ND, Tioga

Krimm, Cecile ....(701) 664-2222
cecilew@crosbynd.com, Pub. / Ed. , The
Journal, ND, Crosby

Krishnamurthy, Priyanka
pkrish4@emory.edu, Ed., Emory Univ., GA,
Atlanta

Krisiak, Todd
spe-news@madison.com, Ed., Sauk Prairie
Eagle, WI, Baraboo

Krist, Annette
akrist@moraminn.com, Adv. Mgr., Advertiser,
MN, Mora
akrist@moraminn.com, Adv. Mgr., Kanabec
County Times, MN, Mora
akrist@moraminn.com, Pub., Pine City
Pioneer, MN, Pine City

Krist, Annette
akrist@moraminn.com, Pub., Pine County
Courier, MN, Pine City

Krob, Jake
WLIndex@Lcom.net, Ed., The Sunlight, IA,
Mount Vernon
WLIndex@Lcom.net, Pub., West Liberty Index,
IA, West Liberty

Krob, Jake
info@westbranchtimes.com, Pub., West Branch
Times, IA, West Branch

Krob, Jake
publisher@mtvernonlisbonsun.com, Pub.,
Mount Vernon-Lisbon Sun, IA, Mount Vernon

Krochmal, Dan ....(610) 282-4808
circ@pennypowerads.com, Circulation/Preprint
Manager, Penny Power, PA, Coopersburg

Kroeger, Terry J. ....(402) 444-1179
terry.kroeger@owh.com, Pres. & CEO, Pub.,
Omaha World-Herald, NE, Omaha

Kroemer, Jim ....(574) 533-2151 ext. 301
jim.kroemer@goshennews.com, Pub., Extra,
IN, Goshen

Kroeplin, Jane................(715) 223-2342 ext. 22
classsub@tpprinting.com, Circ. Mgr., Central
Wisconsin Shopper, WI, Abbotsford

Krohn, Brian
briankrohn@adirondackexpress.com, Mktg. Dir,
Hamilton County Express, NY, Speculator

Krohn, Brian ....(518) 843-1100 Ext. 125
briankrohn@recordernews.com, Gen. Mgr.,
The Recorder, NY, Amsterdam
briankrohn@recordernews.com, Ad. Director,
Mohawk Valley Express, NY, Amsterdam
briankrohn@recordernews.com, Ad. Director,
Courier Standard Enterprise, NY, Amsterdam
briankrohn@recordernews.com, Ad. Director,
Sacandaga Express, NY, Amsterdam

Krohn, Tim
tkrohn@mankatofreepress.com, Adj. Fac.,
Minnesota State University Mankato, MN,
Mankato

Krokos, Mike
mkrokos@archindy.org, Ed., The Criterion, IN,
Indianapolis

Krokson, Janet I.........................(715) 635-2181
jkrokson@spooneradvocate.com, Pub./Ed./
Gen. Mgr., Spooner Advocate, WI, Spooner

Krolak, Barbara
Barb@monroenews.com, City Ed., The Monroe
News, MI, Monroe

Kronman, Alex
alex.kronman@coloradocollege.edu, Colorado
College, CO, Colorado Springs

Kroon, Birgit ....(248) 641-9944
birgit@wochenpostusa.com, Ed.,
Nordamerikaniche Wochenpost, MI, Troy

Kropff, Megan
mkropff@kansa.com, Kansa Technology, LLC,
KS, Emporia

Kroshus, Brian
brian.kroshus@bismarcktribune.com, Pub.,
Finder, ND, Bismarck

Krosnick, Jon
krosnick@stanford.edu, Frederic O. Glover
Prof., Stanford University, CA, Stanford

Krost, Maggie ....(205) 325-3344
mkrost@greenvillenews.com, Marketing VP,
Tribune-Times, SC, Greenville

Krpalek, Michele........................(616) 471-3385
Andrews Univ., MI, Berrien Springs

Krueger, Gloria
gkrueger@actionprinting.com, Adv. Mgr.,
Maturity Times, WI, Fond Du Lac

Krueger, Kurt
kurtk@vcnewsreview.com, Publisher, North
Woods Trader, WI, Eagle River

Krueger, Kurt
kurtk@vcnewsreview.com, Pub., Vilas County
News-Review, WI, Eagle River
kurtk@vcnewsreview.com, Pub., Three Lakes
News, WI, Eagle River

Krueger, Margaret A.
marg@wdtimes.com, Sec., Watertown Daily
Times, WI, Watertown

Krueger, Mark ....1-(847) 477-6323
mark.krueger@baldwintech.com, Director
Of Sales; WPC, Web Printing Controls, a
Baldwin Company, IL, Arlington Heights

Krueger, Ralph H.
ralphk@wdtimes.com, Treasurer/Bus. Mgr.,
Watertown Daily Times, WI, Watertown

Krueger, Ray ....(212) 556-1927
krueger@nytimes.com, Managing Ed, News
Services, The New York Times News Service
& Syndicate, New York

Krueger, Ray........................(212) 556-1927
krueger@nytimes.com, Managing Editor, News
Service, The New York Times News Service
& Syndicate, New York

Krueger , Mark
mark.krueger@baldwintech.com, Prodn. Mgr.,
Press Servs., WPC Machinery Corp., IL,
West Chicago

Kruemmer, Carol........................(734) 246-0800
Adv. Dir., Heritage Newspapers, Inc., MI,
Southgate

Krug, Chris
ckrug@nwherald.com, Vice Pres./Exec. Ed.,
Northwest Citizen Shopper, IL, Crystal Lake

Krugel, Lauren ....(403) 543-7235
lauren.krugel@thecanadianpress.com,
National Business Correspondent, Canadian
Press, The - Calgary, AB, AB, Calgary

Kruger, David ....(603) 413-5154
dkruger@parentingnh.com, Adv. Dir., Parenting
New Hampshire, NH, Manchester

Kruger, Ed ....(814) 946-7411
ekruger@altoonamirror.com, Pub., Altoona
Mirror, PA, Altoona

Kruger, Leann ....(712) 475-3351
lyonconews@mtcnet.net, Ad Sales/Graphic
Artist, Lyon County News, IA, George

Kruger, Peg
peg.kruger@nptelegraph.com, Dist. Mgr., Circ.,
The North Platte Telegraph, NE, North Platte

Krugler, Philip H. ....ext. 201
general@pencoproducts.com, Mktg. Mgr.,
Penco Products, NC, Greenville

Kruithof, Doug ....(801) 575-7003
doug@slweekly.com, Retail Sales Mgr., Salt
Lake City Weekly, UT, Salt Lake City

Kruithof, Susan ....ext. 148
susan@slweekly.com, Prodn. Mgr., Salt Lake
City Weekly, UT, Salt Lake City

Krull, Andrew
editor.sdt@gmail.com, Ed., The Sullivan Daily
Times, IN, Sullivan

Krull, Maria ....(815) 753-0707
mkrull@niu.edu, Northern Illinois Univ., IL,
Dekalb

Krumel, Jim ....(567) 242-0391
jkrumel@limanews.com, Ed., The Lima News,
OH, Lima

Krummy, Catherine
ckrummey@berkshirebeacon.com, Copy Ed.,
Berkshire Beacon, MA, Lenox Dale

Kruse, C David ....(519) 823-6010
dkruse@guelphmercury.com, Adv. Dir./Gen.
Mgr., The Guelph Mercury Tribune, ON,
Guelph

Kruse, Christina ....(920) 834-4242
ckruse@OcontoCountyReporter.com, Account
Executive, Oconto County Beacon, WI,
Oconto

Kruse, Christina ....(920) 834-4242
ckruse@ocontocountyreporter.com, Account
executive, Oconto County Reporter, WI,
Oconto

Kruse, Christina ....(920) 834-4242
ckruse@OcontoCountyReporter.com, Account
Executive, Lakes/forest Beacon, WI, Oconto

Kruse, Hans-Joachim
hjkruse@mediaphone.de, Mng. Dir., MPS
Media Phone Service KG, Duesseldorf

Kruse, Jorg
joerg.kruse@ppimedia.de, Product Mgr., ppi
Media GmbH, Hamburg

Kruse, Wayne ....(785) 562-2317
wkruse@marysvilleonline.net, Advertising
director, Marysville Advocate, KS, Marysville

Krycia, Felice ....(716) 649-4040 ext 239
Assoc. Ed., The Sun and Erie County
Independent, NY, Hamburg

Krygiel, Chris ....(416) 947-2057
chris.krygiel@sunmedia.ca, Cor. Dir., HR, The
Toronto Sun, ON, Toronto

Kryscio, Jesse ....(973) 383-1202
jkryscio@njherald.com, Copy Ed., New Jersey
Herald, NJ, Newton

Krysiak, Todd ....(608) 356-4808
tkrysiak@capitalnewspapers.com, Editor,
Reedsburg Times-Press, WI, Baraboo
tkrysiak@capitalnewspapers.com, Ed.,
Baraboo News Republic, WI, Baraboo

Ksycki, Michael
m.ksycki@22ndcm.com, Circ. Dir., The
Winnetka Current, IL, Northbrook
m.ksycki@22ndcm.com, Circ. Dir., The Lake
Forest Leader, IL, Northbrook
m.ksycki@22ndcm.com, Circ. Dir., The
Glencoe Anchor, IL, Northbrook
m.ksycki@22ndcm.com, Circ. Dir., The
Highland Park Landmark, IL, Northbrook

Kubera, Nanette
nkubera@verafast.com, Vice Pres., Mktg./
Devel., Ver-A-Fast Corporation, OH, Rocky
River

Kubey, Robert
kubey@rutgers.edu, Prof., Rutgers University,
NJ, New Brunswick

Kubik, John M.
kubikjohn@fotopressnews.org, Opns. Dir.,
Fotopress Independent News Service
International, ON, Peterborough

Kubilius, Ausra
a.kubilius@snhu.edu, Chair, Southern New
Hampshire University, NH, Manchester

Kubinski, Chris
chris.kubinski@sunmedia.ca, Adv. Mgr., Auto/
Real Estate, The London Free Press, ON,
London

Kubosiak, Ed ....(413) 731-2478
ekubosia@masslive.com, Ed. in Chief, The
Republican, MA, Springfield

Kubus, Jim ....(412) 320-7846
jkubus@tribweb.com, Deputy Managing Ed.,
Tribune-Review, PA, Greensburg

Kuchenberg, Alfred
info@grenzecho.be, MD, GRENZ-ECHO, Saint
Vith, Liege

Kuchera, Tom ....(712) 293-4286
t.kuchera@siouxcityjournal.com, Gen. Mgr.,
Leader, ND, Grand Forks AFB
t.kuchera@siouxcityjournal.com, Retail Adv.
Dir., Sioux City Journal, IA, Sioux City

Kuczynski, Matt
msk002@aquinas.edu, Editor in Chief, Aquinas
College, MI, Grand Rapids

Kuehl, Breezy ....(605) 845-3646
circulation@mobridgetribune.com, Circulation
Mgr., Mobridge Tribune, SD, Mobridge

Kuehl, Mark D.
markk@wdtimes.com, Circ. Dir., Watertown
Daily Times, WI, Watertown

Kuehl, Michael ....(901) 433-9138
michael.kuehl@journalinc.com, Advt Sales
Consultant, The Bartlett Express, TN, Bartlett

Kuehneman, Ed ....(928) 425-0355
ed@coppercountrynews.com, Ed., Copper
Country News, AZ, Globe

Kuehner, Elmer
ekuehner@infoblvd.net, Circ. Dir., Horseheads
Shopper, NY, Corning
ekuehner@infoblvd.net, Circ. Dir., The Leader,
NY, Corning

Kueker, Jana ....(618) 282-3803
jncnews@hotmail.com, Circ. Mgr./Asst. Ed.,
North County News, IL, Red Bud

Kueter, Maricarrol ....(605) 331-2332
mkueter@argusleader.com, Executive Editor,
Argus Leader, SD, Sioux Falls

Kuhle, Caren
kuhle@poststar.com, Production Dir., The Post-
Star, NY, Glens Falls

Kuhlman, Erin
erin.kuhlman@parsons.com, Corporate Vice
President, Marketing & Communications,
Parsons Corporation, CA, Pasadena

Kuhlman, Steve
info@agfamonotype.com, Mgr., Sales/Mktg.,
Agfa Monotype Corporation, IL, Elk Grove
Village

Kuhn, Angie
angiek@indyrecorder.com, Circ. Mgr.,
Indianapolis Recorder, IN, Indianapolis

Kuhns, Denise
mcnews@swko.net, Editor & Publisher, Clark
County Gazette, KS, Minneola
mcnews@swko.net, Ed., Meade County News,
KS, Meade

Kuhns, John
jkuhns@cmonitor.com, Chrmn., Newspapers of
New England, NH, Concord

Kuhns, Michael D. ....(570) 420-4389
mkuhns@poconorecord.com, Executive Editor,
Pocono Record, PA, Stroudsburg

Kuhr, Peggy
peggy.kuhr@umontana.edu, Dean, The
University of Montana, MT, Missoula

Kuiperij, Jon
sports@oakvillebeaver.com, Sports Ed.,
Oakville Beaver, ON, Oakville

Kujawa, Dawn
dkujawa@thestate.com, Asst. Metro Ed., The
State, SC, Columbia

Kujichagulia, Kamau ....(609) 989-0285
nubiannews@nubiannews.com, Adv. Mgr.,
Nubian News, NJ, Trenton

Kukis, Kelly ....(916) 789-2699
Sierra College, CA, Rocklin

Kukle, Terry ....(905) 279-0440 x250
tkukle@metroland.com, VP, Business
Development & Acquisitions, Metroland
Media Group Ltd., ON, Mississauga

Kukuka, Josephine
jkukuka@jewishexponent.com, Prodn. Mgr.,
Jewish Exponent, PA, Philadelphia

Kulavich, Christie ....(334) 712-7964
Ckulavich@dothaneagle.com, News Ed., The
Dothan Eagle, AL, Dothan

Kulczar, Angie
angie.kulczar@goshennews.com, Classified
Mgr., The Goshen News, IN, Goshen

Kulhanek, Elaine
ekulhanek@lsj.com, Content Strategist
, Lansing State Journal, MI, Lansing

Kulhanek, Shelly
skulhanek@journalstar.com, Asst. City Ed.,
Lincoln Journal Star, NE, Lincoln

Kullen, Michael
mkullen@merlinone.com, Dir., Cust. Support,
MerlinOne, Inc., MA, Quincy

Kullgren, Ian ....(517) 432-3071
editorinchief@statenews.com, Editor in chief,
The State News/Michigan State University,
MI, East Lansing

Kulseth, Gene Anne
pioneerinfo@countrymedia.net, Off. Mgr.,
Bowman County Pioneer, ND, Bowman

Kumar, Ravindra ....(913) 371-071700
rk.statesman@gmail.com, Mng. Dir., THE
STATESMAN, Kolkata, West Bengal

Kumba, Sherman L.
editor@fairmontphotopress.com, Ed./Circ.,
Fairmont Photo Press, MN, Fairmont

Kunasch, Mary ....(920) 787-3334
argusmary@waushaaargus.com, Senior
Publisher, Waushara Argus, WI, Wautoma

Kundanis, Rose
rkundani@keene.edu, Prof., Keene State
College of the University System of New
Hampshire, NH, Keene

Kunerth, Bill
bkunerth@journalnet.com, Pub., Portneuf
Valley Trader, ID, Pocatello

Kunkel, Alix ....(785) 762-5000
m.editor@thedailyunion.net, Managing Editor,
The Daily Union, KS, Junction City

Kunkel, Linda ....(989) 779-6008
lkunkel@michigannewspapers.com,
Administrative Asst., Morning Star, MI, Mount
Pleasant

Kunken, Darrell ....(916) 321-1594
dkunken@sacbee.com, Adv. Mgr., Market
Analysis, The Sacramento Bee, CA,
Sacramento

Kunkle, Alix
news@leesvilledailyleader.com, Ed., The
Leesville Daily Leader, LA, Leesville
news@beauregarddailynews.net, Ed.,
Beauregard Daily News, LA, Deridder

Kunkle, Deb
news@oelweindailyregister.com, City Ed., The
Oelwein Daily Register, IA, Oelwein

Kuntzelman, Becky ....(308) 882-4453
Reporter, Imperial Republican, NE, Imperial

Kuper, Kelly
sales@mcpress.com, Adv. Sales Mgr., Town &
Country Shopper, IA, Osage

Kuperstock, Steve ....(985) 839-9077
steve@era-leader.com, Pub., The Era-Leader,
LA, Franklinton

Kupetz, John
jkupetz@clcillinois.edu, College of Lake
County, IL, Grayslake

Kupferer, Anna Mae
advertising@lakevillejournal.com, Adv. Dir., The
Winsted Journal, CT, Winsted

Kupiecki, Anna ....(414) 229-4436
kupiecki@uwm.edu, Academic Department
Associate, University of Wisconsin-
Milwaukee / Department of Journalism,
Advertising, and Media Studies (JAMS), WI,
Milwaukee

Kupris, Kim
billing@citlink.net, Office Mgr., The Waterville
Times, NY, Waterville

Kurata, Osamu
o_kurata@tks-net.co.jp, Sales Chief Officer,
TKS Ltd., Tokyo

Kurazawa, Kathy ....(912) 233-1281
kathyk@morrismultimedia.com, Asst. to
President , Morris Multimedia, Inc., GA,
Savannah

Kurdi, Habeab
hkurdi@statesman.com, Sports Ed., Westlake
Picayune, TX, Austin

Kuritz, Theresia ....(574) 722-5000 Ext. 5145
theresia.kuritz@pharostribune.com, Circ.
Supervisor., Pharos-Tribune, IN, Logansport

Kurtz, Bill ....(570) 265-2151
Bill_K@newsitem.com, Circulation Director,
Morning Times, PA, Sayre

Kurtz, Bruce ....(805) 685-3100 ext. 136
kurtzb@maps.com, Dir., Mktg., Maps.com, CA,
Santa Barbara

Kurtz, Dave ....(260) 347-0400 Ext. 2546
dkurtz@kpcmedia.com, Exec. Ed. , Northwest
News, IN, Huntertown
dkurtz@kpcmedia.com, Exec. Ed., The Star,
IN, Auburn

Kurtz, Dave ....(260) 347-0400 Ext. 2546
dkurtz@kpcmedia.com, Exec. Ed., Albion New
Era, IN, Albion

Kurtz, Laura
lkurtz@gvnews.com, Ops./Circ Dir., Green
Valley News & Sahuarita Sn, AZ, Green
Valley

Kurtz, Robert ....(330) 651-5411
advertising@forparentsonline.com, Adv. Sales,
Mahoning Valley Parent Magazine, OH,
Warren

Kurtzke, Kristina
kkurtzke@nikon.net, Communications
Coordinator, Nikon, Inc., NY, Melville

Kurz, Jeffery ....(203) 317-2213
jkurz@record-journal.com, Sr. Writer, Record-
Journal, CT, Meriden

Kurzen, Andy ....(260) 745-0552
fwfrostads@gmail.com, Layout & Production
Manager, Frost Illustrated, IN, Fort Wayne

Kus, Denise ....(847) 966-0606
denisecjn@aol.com, Production Manager,
Chicago Jewish News, IL, Skokie

Kuser, James K. ....(419) 592-5055
jamiek@northwestsignal.net, Prodn. Mgr.,
Spotlite, OH, Napoleon

Kush, Ken ....(402) 204-7015
ken.kush@yorknewstimes.com, Sports Ed.,
York News-Times, NE, York

Kushner, Aaron ....(714) 796-7705
nfoltz@ocregister.com, Pub., Aliso Viejo News,
CA, Santa Ana
nfoltz@ocregister.com, Pub., Laguna Niguel
News, CA, Santa Ana
nfoltz@ocregister.com, Pub., Fullerton News-
Tribune, CA, Santa Ana
nfoltz@ocregister.com, Pub., Brea-La Habra

Star-Progress, CA, Santa Ana
nfoltz@ocregister.com, Pub., Laguna Woods Globe, CA, Santa Ana
nfoltz@ocregister.com, Pub., Saddleback Valley News, CA, Santa Ana
nfoltz@ocregister.com, Pub., Orange City News, CA, Santa Ana
nfoltz@ocregister.com, Pub., The Tustin News, CA, Santa Ana
nfoltz@ocregister.com, Ed., Yorba Linda Star, CA, Santa Ana
nfoltz@ocregister.com, Anaheim Bulletin, CA, Santa Ana
nfoltz@ocregister.com, Pub., Rancho Canyon News (OOB), CA, Santa Ana
nfoltz@ocregister.com, Pub., Capistrano Valley News, CA, Santa Ana
nfoltz@ocregister.com, Pub., Current, CA, Santa Ana
nfoltz@ocregister.com, Pub., Dana Point News, CA, Santa Ana
nfoltz@ocregister.com, Pub., Fountain Valley View, CA, Santa Ana
nfoltz@ocregister.com, Pub., Huntington Beach Wave, CA, Santa Ana
nfoltz@ocregister.com, Pub., Irvine World News, CA, Santa Ana
nfoltz@ocregister.com, Pub., Ladera Post (OOB), CA, Santa Ana
nfoltz@ocregister.com, Pub., Laguna Beach News Post, CA, Santa Ana
nfoltz@ocregister.com, Pub., Placentia News Times, CA, Santa Ana
nfoltz@ocregister.com, Pub., Saddleback Valley News - Mission Viejo, CA, Santa Ana
nfoltz@ocregister.com, Pub., San Clemente Sun Post, CA, Santa Ana

Kushner, Melissa
mkushner@racc.edu, Reading Area Cmty. College, PA, Reading

Kushnier, Joanne .... (807) 343-6215
joanne.kushnier@chroniclejournal.com, News Ed., The Chronicle-Journal, ON, Thunder Bay

Kusic, Galen
rveditor@citlink.net, Ed., The River News-Herald & Isleton Journal, CA, Rio Vista

Kutcher , Scott .... (609) 406-0600 x 12
Business Manager, Business Manager, New Jersey Press Association, NJ, Ewing

Kutka, Cyndy .... (559) 441-6477
ckutka@fresnobee.com, Asst. to VP & Dir of Audience Devel, The Fresno Bee, CA, Fresno

Kutschke, Carol
leader@nrtco.net, Circ. Mgr., The Eganville Leader, ON, Eganville

Kutz-Gemmett, Lynn
lgemmett@aol.com, Adv. Mgr., Shopper, SC, North Charleston

Kuykendall, John
news@star-mercury.com, Pub., Meriwether Vindicator, GA, Manchester

Kuykendall, John
customerservice@smalltownpapers.com. , Pub., Talbotton New Era, GA, Manchester

Kuzmak, Pam
sales@eammosca.com, Sales Admin., EAM-Mosca Corp., PA, Hazle Township

Kvarnstrom, Peter .... (604) 788-6252
publisher@coastreporter.net, Pub., Coast Reporter, BC, Sechelt
publisher@coastreporter.net, Pub., Bowen Island Undercurrent, BC, Bowen Island

Kvarnstrom, Peter
pkvarnstrom@glaciermedia.ca, Pub, North/west Shore Outlook, BC, North Vancouver
pkvarnstrom@glaciermedia.ca, Pres., Comm. Media, Glacier Media Group, BC, Vancouver

Kwiatkowski, Jim .... (613) 732-3691 ext 223
jim.kwiatkowski@sunmedia.ca, Pub./Adv. Mgr., The Daily Observer, ON, Pembroke

Kwon, Ki
kjkwon@koreatimes.com, Ed., Korea Times, CA, Los Angeles

Kydd, Chris
advertising@coastnewsgroup.com, Adv. Mgr./Assc. Pub., Rancho Santa Fe News, CA, Encinitas

Kydd, James .... (760) 436-9737 ext. 108
jkydd@coastnewsgroup.com, Pub./Own., The Coast News, CA, Encinitas

Kyle, Louis
info@francetoday.com, Pub., Journal Francais, CA, San Francisco

Kyse, Bruce .... (209) 500-6182
publisher@calaverasenterprise.com, Pub., Calaveras Enterprise, CA, San Andreas

Kyzer, Ann Marie
annemariek@thetruecitizen.com, Staff Reporter, The True Citizen, GA, Waynesboro

L

L'Ecluse, Kathleen .... (707) 427-6933
Online/Projects Ed., Daily Republic, CA, Fairfield

L. Grady, Mary .... (206) 232-1215
editor@mi-reporter.com, Ed., Mercer Island Reporter, WA, Bellevue

L. West, Carleton
cwest@state-journal.com, Ed., Buyer's Guide, KY, Frankfort

LANGRELL, ROB
rlangrell@cnjonline.com, PUBLISHER, Eastern New Mexico News, NM, Clovis
rlangrell@cnjonline.com, PUBLISHER, Quay County Sun, NM, Tucumcari

LUNDY, LORIE .... (807) 221-4252
lorie@drydenobserver.ca, Adv. Mgr., Dryden Observer, ON, Dryden

La Barth, Len .... (831) 427-2411
llabarth@santacruzsentinel.com, City Desk, Santa Cruz Sentinel, CA, Scotts Valley

La Pean, Gary A.
lapean@evergreencountryshopper.com, Pub., North Country Sun, MI, Ironwood

La Prade , Darel .... (443) 235-4704
dlaprade@newszap.com, Sr. VP/Pub, The Harrington Journal, DE, Milford

La Prade, Darel .... (443) 235-4704
dlaprade@newszap.com, Publisher, Milford Chronicle, DE, Milford

La Prade, Darel .... (443) 235-4704
dlaprade@newszap.com, Publisher, Salisbury Independent, MD, Salisbury

La Rocque, Doug .... (518) 491-1613
news@eastwickpress.com, Publisher, editor, The Eastwick Press, NY, Cropseyville

LaBarca, Joanne ....(631) 475-1000 ext. 27
jlb@longislandadvance.net, Gen. Mgr., Suffolk County News, NY, Patchogue

LaBarca, Joanne ....(631) 475-1000 x27
Gen. Mgr., Islip Bulletin, NY, Patchogue

LaBell, Dave .... (727) 893-8523
dlabell@tampabay.com, Community/Events Mgr., Tampa Bay Times, FL, St Petersburg

LaBine, Brian
blabine@manugraphdgmusa.com, Pres., Manugraph DGM, Inc., PA, Millersburg

LaBombarda, Anita
anita.labombarda@parenthood.com, Circ. Mgr., Bay Area Parent, CA, Campbell

LaBonia, Michael C. .... (713) 362-6495
mlabonia@hearst.com, Executive VP/Multi-Market Advertising, Houston Chronicle, TX, Houston

LaBorde, Lori .... (218) 546-5029
courier@crosbyironton.net, Gen. Mgr., Crosby-Ironton Courier, MN, Crosby

LaBuff, Mike .... ext. 3325
mlabuff@thedailymail.com, Sports Ed., The

Daily Mail, NY, Hudson

LaChall, Chris .... (856) 486-2452
clachall@gannettnj.com, Photo/Video, The Courier-Post, NJ, Cherry Hill

LaCour, Mary
pcbanner@bellsouth.net, Pub., The Pointe Coupee Banner, LA, New Roads

LaCroix, Dustin .... (250) 442-2191
production2@grandforksgazette.ca, Graphic Artist, The Grand Forks Gazette, BC, Grand Forks

LaCroix , Sharon .... (613) 966-2034 ext. 560
slacroix@perfprint.ca, Community, Quinte West Emc, ON, Belleville
slacroix@perfprint.ca, Ed. , Rainy River Record, ON, Rainy River

LaDue, Becky
beckyladue@rogerspublishing.com, Ed., The Winneconne News, WI, Winneconne

LaFauci, Doris .... (219) 769-9292
Page and graphic designer, Northwest Indiana Catholic, IN, Merrillville

LaFavers, Carol .... (606) 451-4927
Circ. Clerk, The Commonwealth-Journal, KY, Somerset

LaFleur, Becky
Classifieds@CrowleyToday.com, Classifieds Adv., The Crowley Post-Signal, LA, Crowley

LaFontaine, Eric
elafontaine@columbiabasinherald.com, Publisher, Columbia Basin Herald, WA, Moses Lake

LaFontaine, Josh
jlafontaine@hickoryrecord.com, Editor, The Hickory Daily Record, NC, Hickory
jlafontaine@hickoryrecord.com, Lifestyle Ed., Pow, NC, Hickory

LaForge, Ron
ron@newscolor.com, Mng. Dir., Newscolor, LLC, OR, Silverton

LaFromboise, Alvin
metigosh@utma.com, Cir. Mgr. , Lake Metigoshe Mirror, ND, Rolla

LaFuria, Scott .... (850) 599-2130
slafuria@tallahassee.com, Controller, Tallahassee Democrat, FL, Tallahassee

LaGasse, Mark J. .... (715) 669-5525
thropcourier@centurytel.net, Pub./Ed., Thorp Courier, WI, Thorp

LaMorte, Timothy ....(914) 478-2787 x11
tlamorte@rivertownsenterprise.net, Ed., The Rivertowns Enterprise, NY, Dobbs Ferry

LaMorte, Valerie
vlamo@srds.com, Vice Pres., HR, SRDS, a Kantar Media Company, IL, Des Plaines

LaOrange, Monte
bhansen@postregister.com, Asst. Mng. Ed., Post Register, ID, Idaho Falls

LaPean, Gary A. ....(715) 682-8131 ext. 16
ads@evergreencountryshopper.com, Owner/Pub., Evergreen Country Shopper, WI, Ashland

LaPierre, Jim ....(902) 426-2811 ext. 2472
jlapierre@herald.ca, Dir., Dist. and Log., The Chronicle Herald, NS, Halifax

LaPointe, Kirk .... (604) 353-6228
klapointe@newsombudsmen.org, Executive Director, Organization of News Ombudsmen, BC, Vancouver

LaPorte, David .... (715) 685-4510
lservinsky@ashlanddailypress.net, Managing Editor, The Ashland Daily Press, WI, Ashland

LaPrade, Darel .... (443) 235-4704
dlaprade@newszap.com, Pub., Dorchester Banner, MD, Cambridge

LaPrade, Darel .... (443) 235-4704
dlaprade@newszap.com, Pub., Sussex Post, DE, Milford

dlaprade@newszap.com, Sr. VP New Media, Delaware State News, DE, Dover

LaPrade, Darel .... (443) 235-4704
dlaprade@newszap.com, Vice Pres., Adv., Independent Newsmedia Inc. Usa, DE, Dover

LaPrade, Konrad
klaprade@chespub.com, Reg. Dir., Adv., The Avenue News, MD, Dundalk

LaPrade , Konrad .... (704) 869-1725
klaprade@gastongazette.com , Adv. Dir., The Gaston Gazette, NC, Gastonia
klaprade@gastongazette.com , Adv. Dir., The Bay Times, MD, Chester
klaprade@gastongazette.com , Adv. Dir. , The Star, NC, Shelby

LaRochelle, Jacques
jacques.larochelle@tc.tc, Journalist, Journal Le Coup D'oeil, QC, Napierville

LaRose, Greg
greg.larose@nopg.com, Ed., New Orleans City Business, LA, Metairie

LaRose, Teddy
ladana@easttexasreview.com, Circulation Manager, East Texas Review, TX, Longview

LaRue, Coby
news@alleghanynews.com, Ed., The Alleghany News, NC, Sparta

LaSalle, Mitzi ....(318) 274-2866
lasallem@gram.edu, Interim Director of University Communications, Marketing, and Media Relations , Grambling State University, LA, Grambling

LaSota, Andrew
alasota@fstribune.com, Adv. Consultant, The Fort Scott Tribune, KS, Fort Scott

LaTorre, Christine ....(718) 238-6600
clatorre@brooklynreporter.com, VP, S&O, The Brooklyn Spectator, NY, Brooklyn

Labalme, Jenny ....(317) 701-1130
jlabalme.indypress@att.net, Executive Director, Indianapolis Press Club Foundation, IN, Indianapolis

Labat, Russell D. .... (507) 537-1551 ext. 107
rlabat@marshallindependent.com, Pub., Independent Shopper's Review, MN, Marshall

Labat, Russell D. .... (507) 537-1551 ext. 107
rlabat@marshallindependent.com, Pub., Independent, MN, Marshall

Labbe, Monique
monique.labbe@sjvalley-times.com, Reporter, St. John Valley Times, ME, Madawaska

Labelle, Matt ....(703) 282-5491
mrlabelle@radford.edu, Radford Univ., VA, Radford

Labovitz, Peter C.
info@connectionnewspapers.com, CEO/Pub., Fairfax Connection, VA, Alexandria
info@connectionnewspapers.com, Pres./CEO, Fairfax Station/Clifton/Lorton Connection, VA, Alexandria
info@connectionnewspapers.com, Pres./CEO, Great Falls Connection, VA, Alexandria
info@connectionnewspapers.com, Pres./CEO, McLean Connection, VA, Alexandria
info@connectionnewspapers.com, Pres./CEO, Mount Vernon Gazette, VA, Alexandria
info@connectionnewspapers.com, Pres./CEO, Oak Hill/Herndon Connection, VA, Alexandria
info@connectionnewspapers.com, Pres./CEO, Potomac Almanac, VA, Alexandria
info@connectionnewspapers.com, Pres./CEO, Reston Connection, VA, Alexandria
info@connectionnewspapers.com, CEO/Pres., Springfield Connection, VA, Alexandria
info@connectionnewspapers.com, Pres./CEO, Vienna/Oakton Connection, VA, Alexandria
info@connectionnewspapers.com, CEO/Pres., Arlington Connection, VA, Alexandria
info@connectionnewspapers.com, Pres./CEO, Burke Connection, VA, Alexandria
info@connectionnewspapers.com, Pres./CEO,

Centre View, VA, Alexandria

Labovitz, Peter C. ....(703) 821-5050
Founder/Prinicpal/Pres./CEO, Connection
Publishing, Inc., VA, Alexandria

Laboy, Vincent ....(402) 941-1422
vincent.laboy@lee.net, Pub., Fremont Area
Shopper, NE, Fremont

Labozan, Christine
labozanc@dailycamera.com, Adv. Dir.,
Longmont Times-Call, CO, Longmont

Labrador, Jorge ....(702) 895-3889
jorge.labrador@unlv.edu, Ed. in Chief,
University of Nevada, Las Vegas, NV, Las
Vegas

Labunski, Richard
labunski@uky.edu, Prof., University of
Kentucky, KY, Lexington

Lacasse, Lionel
letemiscamien@sympatico.ca, Ed., Le Journal
Temiscamien, QC, Ville-Marie

Lacey, Heather
hlacey@bizjournals.com, Controller, Boston
Business Journal, MA, Boston

Lacey, Keith
editor@osoyoostimes.com, Ed, Osoyoos
Times, BC, Osoyoos

Lacey, Mike
mlacey@mykawartha.com, News Ed.,
Peterborough This Week, ON, Peterborough

Lacey, Robert
rlacey@gciu.org, Vice Pres., Graphic
Communications International, DC,
Washington

Lacey, Ryan.........................(203) 337-4876
rlacey@bcnnew.com, Sports Ed., Westport
News, CT, Bridgeport

Lachambre, Ray ....(403) 638-3577
roundup@sundre.greatwest.ca, Pub., Sundre
Round-up, AB, Sundre

Lachance, Janice R.
janice@sla.org, CEO, Special Libraries
Association, News Division, VA, Alexandria

Lachance, Lucyl.......................(418) 338-5181
info@courrierfrontenac.com, Courrier
Frontenac, QC, Thetford Mines

Lacher, Doug ....(651) 796-1114
doug.lacher@ecm-inc.com, Adv. Acct. Exec.,
Stillwater Gazette, MN, Stillwater

Lachniet, Dale.........................(540) 735-1940
dlachniet@bhmginc.com, Vice President, BH
Media Group, NE, Omaha

Lachniet, Dale.........................540/735-1940
dlachniet@freelancestar.com, Pub., The Free
Lance-Star, VA, Fredericksburg

Laciura, Phil
placiura@detroitnews.com, Sports Editor,
Detroit Free Press, MI, Detroit

Lackey, Brad.........................(318) 362-0214
Adv. Dir., The News-Star, LA, Monroe

Lackey, James
james.lackey@gsa.gov, Web Editor, Catholic
News Service, Washington

Lacombe, Danielle ....(775) 788-6464
dlacombe@rgj.com, Bus. Dev. Sales Mgr.,
Reno Gazette-Journal, NV, Reno

Lacourcière, Denise..................(819) 449-1725
redaction@lagatineau.com, Executive Director
, Le Gatineau, QC, Egan South

Lacroixe, Sonya............(780) 743-8186 ext. 230
Circ. Mgr., Fort McMurray Today, AB, Fort
McMurray

Lacy, Drew ....(321) 987-5989
lacyd2010@my.fit.edu, Editor-in-Chief, Florida
Institute of Technology, FL, Melbourne

Lacy, Ed
ed.lacy@beatleygravitt.com, Pres./Dir.,
Mktg., Beatley Gravitt Communications, VA,

Richmond

Lacy-Trostle, Diane.........(620) 792-1211 ext. 210
dlacy@gbtribune.com, Advertising Director,
Great Bend Tribune, KS, Great Bend

Ladd, Doug
dladd@hippopress.com, Circulation, The
Hippo, NH, Manchester

Ladd, Karen............................(603) 237-5501
karenhladd@colebrooknewsandsentinel.com,
Ed., The News and Sentinel, NH, Colebrook

Ladd, Susan
susan.ladd@News-Record.com, Columnist,
News & Record, NC, Greensboro

Ladinsky, Kaylene ....(404) 883-2130 x100
kaylene@atljewishtimes.com, Assoc. Pub.,
Atlanta Jewish Times, GA, Atlanta

Ladson, Cynthia............(210) 349-6667 ext. 215
cynthia.ladson@parenthood.com, Ed., Our
Kids San Antonio, TX, San Antonio

Ladwig, Boris.................(812) 663-3111 x7401
boris.ladwig@greensburgdailynews.com,
Staff Writer , Greensburg Daily News, IN,
Greensburg

Laethem, Shawna
slaethem@nwfdailynews.com, Northwest
Florida Daily News, FL, Fort Walton Beach

Laferriere, Anne
anne.laferriere@sunmedia.ca, Adv. Mgr., The
Timmins Daily Press, ON, Timmins

Laferrière, François ....(514) 866-3131
francois.laferriere@tc.tc, General Manager,
Reseau Select/Select Network, QC, Montreal

Laffe, Alison
alaffe@jrn.com, Milwaukee Journal Sentinel,
WI, Milwaukee

Lafond, Richard
rlafond@thericatholic.com, Display Advertising
Manager, Rhode Island Catholic, RI,
Providence

Lagasse, Jeff ....(207) 282-1535 ext. 319
jlagasse@journaltribune.com, Photo Ed.,
Journal-Tribune, ME, Biddeford

Lage, Wally
wlage@semissourian.com, Vice Pres./COO,
Rust Communications, MO, Cape Girardeau

Lago, Amy ....(202) 334-6510
amy.lago@washpost.com, Comics Ed., The
Washington Post Writers Group, Washington

Lahde, Jim ....(989) 779-6061
nschneider@michigannewspapers.com, Sports
Ed., Morning Sun, MI, Alma

Lahmeyer, Debi ....(360) 683-3311 Ext. 1050
dlahmeyer@sequimgazette.com, Gen. Mgr./
Adv. Mgr., The Sequim Gazette, WA, Sequim

Lahodny, Denise
deniselah@nckcn.com, Class. Adv. Mgr.,
Advertiser, KS, Concordia
deniselah@nckcn.com, Classified Adv.,
Concordia Blade-Empire, KS, Concordia

Lahr, Steve ....(309) 820-3343
steve.lahr@lee.net, Nat'l Adv. Mgr., Journal
Gazette & Times-Courier, IL, Mattoon
steve.lahr@lee.net, Adv. Mgr., Majors/Nat'l, The
Pantagraph, IL, Bloomington

Lahr-Smith, Diane ....(315) 789-3333 ext 261
dlahr@fltimes.com, Business Mgr., Finger
Lakes Times, NY, Geneva

Lai, Sidney................(718) 746-8889 ext. 6207
Circ. Mgr., World Journal, NY, Whitestone

Lai, Steven.............................(323) 782-8763
tj@mail.gio.gov.tw, Ed., Taiwan Journal, CA,
Los Angeles

Laidlaw, Dawn ....(989) 426-9411
dlaidlaw@thegladwincountyrecord.com, Office
Mgr., Gladwin County Record, MI, Gladwin

Laigo, Rhony
rhony@balita.com, Ed. in Chief, Weekend

Balita/Midweek Balita, CA, Glendale

Laine, Burton
editor@harborcenters.org, Ed., The Senior
Reporter, MN, Duluth

Laird, Cynthia
c.laird@ebar.com, Ed., Bay Area Reporter, CA,
San Francisco

Laird, Jean
jlaird@perretta.com, Sales Mgr., Perretta
Graphics Corp., NY, Poughkeepsie

Laitman, Judith ....(608) 661-5666
csis@newscurrents.com, President,
Knowledge Unlimited, INC, WI, Middleton

Lajara, Ivan ....(845) 331-5000 Ext. 01214
ilajara@freemanonline.com, Life. Ed. , Daily
Freeman, NY, Kingston

Lake, Chris..............................(408) 842-6400
clake@mainstreetmg.com, COO, CFO &
General Counsel, Mainstreet Media Group,
LLC, CA, Gilroy

Lake, David
david@pcworld.com, Mgr. Bus Devl, PC World,
CA, San Francisco

Lake, Kari ....(218) 855-5807
kari.lake@brainerddispatch.com, Controller/HR
Dir., Brainerd Dispatch, MN, Brainerd

Lakeidra, Chavis......................(907) 474-5508
editor@uafsunstar.com, Editor-in-Chief, Univ.
of Alaska Fairbanks, AK, Fairbanks

Laker, Andrew ....(812) 379-5688
alaker@therepublic.com, Chief Photographer,
The Republic, IN, Columbus

Lakey, Jon ....(704) 797-4202
Jlakey@salisburypost.com, Salisbury Post, NC,
Salisbury

Lakhani, Faizel
info@ss8.com, President & COO, SS8
Networks, CA, Milpitas

Laksham, Nikhil
editorial@indiaabroad.com, Ed., India Abroad,
NY, New York

Lalanne, Tara.........................(604) 730-7068
t_lalanne@straight.com, Sales Director,
Georgia Straight, BC, Vancouver

Laliberte, Kevin
sreeditor@telus.net, EIC, Smoky River
Express, AB, Falher

Lalime, Christopher ....+52 55 5658 5681
clalime@nytimes.com, Regional Director, Latin
America, Mexico & the Caribbean, The New
York Times News Service & Syndicate, New
York

Lalime, Christopher ....+52 55 5658 5681
clalime@nytimes.com, Regional Director, Latin
America, Mexico & the Caribbean, The New
York Times News Service & Syndicate, New
York

Laline, Brian............................(718) 816-3167
laline@siadvance.com , Ed., Staten Island
Advance, NY, Staten Island

Lalley, Patrick ....(605) 331-2291
plalley@argusleader.com, Managing Editor,
Argus Leader, SD, Sioux Falls

Lally, Michael ....ext. 14
L.printing@comcast.net, Pub., Otis Notice,
MA, Cotuit

Lamb, Brenda ....ext. 618
Bus. Mgr., Newton Daily News, IA, Newton

Lamb, Carol ....(705) 444-1875 Ext.24
clamb@simcoe.com, General Mgr.,
Collingwood Connection, ON, Collingwood

Lamb, Diane
diane.lamb@News-Record.com, Librarian,
News & Record, NC, Greensboro

Lamb, John
jlamb@forumcomm.com, Features Ed.,
InForum, ND, Fargo

Lamb, Laura ....(517) 437-7351
laura.lamb@tipoffonline.com, Prodn. Mgr., Tip-
off Shopping Guide, MI, Hillsdale

Lamb, Richard W.
editor@piadvance.com, Pub, Presque Isle
County Advance, MI, Rogers City

Lamb, Teresa ....(434) 975-7437
tlamb@dailyprogress.com, Adv. Mgr, The Daily
Progress, VA, Charlottesville

Lambdin, William
thevoice@frii.com, Pub., Senior Voice, CO,
Fort Collins

Lamberg, Gary
gary@cheboygantribune.com, Pub.,
Cheboygan Daily Tribune, MI, Cheboygan

Lambert, Brad
blambert@highpoint.edu, Asst. Prof., High
Point Univ., NC, High Point

Lambert, Clay ....(650) 726-4424 x 304
clay@hmbreview.com, Ed., Half Moon Bay
Review, CA, Half Moon Bay

Lambert, Cynthia Royle..............(914) 694-5099
Sr. Mng. Ed., The Journal News, NY, White
Plains

Lambert, Dale
dlambert@gtowntimes.com, Sales Mgr., The
Georgetown Times, SC, Georgetown

Lambert, Dale ....(843) 546-4148 ext. 239
dlambert@gtowntimes.com, Sales Mgr.,
Georgetown Communications, Inc., SC,
Georgetown

Lambert, Deborah.............................ex. 108
deb@aim.org, Special Projects Dir., Accuracy
in Media, Bethesda

Lambert, Gina ....(808) 529-4706
glambert@staradvertiser.com, Art Director,
Kauai Midweek, HI, Honolulu

Lambert, Jeff
jlambert@theneighbornewspapers.com,
Pub./Adv. Dir., South Bay's Neighbor, NY,
Farmingdale
jlambert@theneighbornewspapers.com, Pub./
Adv. Dir., The Neighbor Newspapers, NY,
Farmingdale

Lambert, Julie
jlambert@mcclatchy.com, National Sales Mgr.,
The McClatchy Company, CA, Sacramento

Lambert, Linda
lambert@dumas-clarion.com, Ed., Dumas
Clarion, AR, Dumas

Lambert, Lynn Rees ....(613) 544-5000 ext. 116
lynnlambert@kingstonthisweek.com, News
Ed., Kingston This Week, ON, Kingston

Lambert, M. Brice ....(406) 775-6245
ekeagle@midrivers.com, Ed., The Ekalaka
Eagle, MT, Ekalaka

Lambert, Melissa
melissa.lambert@baledger.com, Mktg., Broken
Arrow Ledger, OK, Tulsa

Lambert, Michelle
michelle.westernstarnews@gmail.com, Office
Mgr., The Western Star, AL, Bessemer

Lambert, Mike.........................(828) 610-8726
mlambert@newstopicnews.com, Circ. Mgr. ,
News-Topic, NC, Lenoir

Lambert, Mike
mlambert@newstopic.net, Circ. Dir., Caldwell
Weekly, NC, Lenoir

Lambert, Steve
slambert@broadcastnews.ca, Manitoba
Correspondent, Broadcast News Limited,
MB, Winnipeg
slambert@broadcastnews.ca, Manitoba
Correspondent, Canadian Press, The -
Winnipeg, MB, MB, Winnipeg

Lambert, Stéphanie
slambert@poste21.ca, Prod. Mgr. , Le Journal
De St-bruno, QC, Saint Bruno

Lambeth, Michael
advertising@monroejournal.com, Adv. Mgr.,
The Monroe Journal, AL, Monroeville

Lamburg, Gary
gary@cheboygantribune.com, Pub., Shoppers
Fair, MI, Cheboygan

Lamdin, Courtney
courtney@miltonindependent.com, Ed., Milton
Independent, VT, Milton

Lamers, Kelli
klamers@txwes.edu, The Rambler, TX, Fort
Worth

Lamm, Holly ....(336) 835-1513
hlamm@civitasmedia.com, Sr. Ad. Rep, The
Tribune, NC, Elkin

Lamm, Holly
hlamm@civitasmedia.com, Gen. Mgr., The
Yadkin Ripple, NC, Yadkinville

Lamm, Mike
mike@decaturdailydemocrat.com, Reporter,
Decatur Daily Democrat, IN, Decatur

Lamonoff, Marty ....(717) 232-6279
lammie@aol.com, Editor, Community Review,
PA, Harrisburg

Lamont, Ray ....(978) 675-2705
rlamont@gloucestertimes.com, City Issues
Reporter, Gloucester Daily Times, MA,
Gloucester

Lampert, Dan
service@dlc2.com, Pres., Daniel Lampert
Communications Corp., FL, Altamonte
Springs

Lampinen, John
jlampinen@dailyherald.com, Sr. Vice Pres./
Editor, Daily Herald, IL, Arlington Heights

Lamplet, Kerry ....(931) 296-2426
Kerrylampley@bellsouth.net, Adv. Mgr., The
News-Democrat, TN, Waverly

Lampos, Maria ....(301) 864-1558
mlampos@gazette.net, Adv. Coord., The
Gazette - Damascus / Clarksburg, MD,
Gaithersburg
mlampos@gazette.net, Adv. Coord., The
Gazette - Rockville / Aspen Hill / Wheaton
(OOB), MD, Gaithersburg
mlampos@gazette.net, Adv. Coord., The
Gazette - Silver Spring / Takoma Park /
Burtonsville (OOB), MD, Gaithersburg
mlampos@gazette.net, Adv. Coord., The
Gazette - Olney (OOB), MD, Gaithersburg
mlampos@gazette.net, Adv. Coord., The
Gazette - Germantown / Poolsville / Boyds
(OOB), MD, Gaithersburg
mlampos@gazette.net, Adv. Coord., The
Gazette - Bethesda / Chevy Chase /
Kensington (OOB), MD, Gaithersburg
mlampos@gazette.net, Adv. Coord., The
Gazette - Gaithersburg / Mont. Village (OOB),
MD, Gaithersburg
mlampos@gazette.net, Adv. Coord., The
Gazette - North / Central Prince George Co.
(OOB), MD, Gaithersburg
mlampos@gazette.net, Adv. Coord., The
Gazette - South / Central Prince George Co.
(OOB), MD, Gaithersburg
mlampos@gazette.net, Adv. Coord., The
Gazette - Potomac / North Potomac, MD,
Gaithersburg

Lampton, Luke
magnoliagazette@telepak.net, Ed., The
Magnolia Gazette, MS, Magnolia

Lamy, André ....ext. 222
andre.lamy@transcontinental.ca, Dir., L'echo
De Maskinonge, QC, Louisville

Lamy, Francis
flamy@x-rite.com, CTO, X-Rite Inc., MI, Grand
Rapids

Lan, Leah ....(416) 986-3525
leah@epochtimes.com, Senior Director of
Sales Development, The Epoch Times, ON,
Toronto

Lancaster, Charles W.
mschuver@lminews.com, Pres., Lancaster
Management, Inc., AL, Gadsden

Lancaster, Cory
cory.lancaster@news-jrnl.com, Mng. Ed.,
Daytona Beach News-Journal, FL, Daytona
Beach

Lancaster, Mark
mark.lancaster@transcontinental.com, Gen.
Mgr., Optipress Print, NS, Dartmouth

Lancaster, Michele
michele@easterngazette.com, Gen. Mgr. ,
Eastern Gazette, ME, Dexter

Lance, Eddie
eddie.lance@oxfordeagle.com, Head
Pressman, The Oxford Eagle, MS, Oxford

Lance, Howard L.
dkingcol@harris.com, Pres./CEO/Chrmn.,
Harris Corp., FL, Melbourne

Lance, Lynne ....(217) 241-1300
llance@illinoispress.org, Dir. of Member
Relations, Illinois Press Association, IL,
Springfield

Lance, Lynne ....(217) 241-1400 ext. 300
lynne@nna.org, Chief Operating Officer,
National Newspaper Association, IL,
Springfield

Lance, Lynne ....(217) 241-1400, ext. 300
Chief Operating Officer, National Newspaper
Association Publishers' Auxiliary, IL,
Springfield

Lancione, Anisa ....(416) 929-0011 ext. 5
anisa.lancione@thebulletin.ca, Mng Ed., The
Bulletin - Journal Of Downtown Toronto, ON,
Toronto

Land, Lisa
lfdnews@litchfieldil.com, Admin. Exec. Asst. to
Pub., News-Herald, IL, Litchfield

Land, Mary Jean
maryjean.land@gcsu.edu, Chair/Prof., Georgia
College & State University, GA, Milledgeville

Land, Robin ....(903) 596-6244
Adv. Mgr., Nat'l, Tyler Morning Telegraph, TX,
Tyler

Landaluce, Joy ....(907) 424-7181
cdvtimes@alaskanewspapers.com, News Ed.,
The Cordova Times, AK, Cordova

Landau, George ....(636) 537-8548
george@newsengin.com, Pres., NewsEngin,
Inc., MO, Chesterfield

Landegent, Magdalene
dseditor@frontiernet.net, Ed., Shoppers Guide,
IA, Le Mars

Landers, Bettye ....(361) 729-1828
theherald@the-i.net, Prodn. Mgr., The Coastal
Bend Herald, TX, Portland

Landers, James
james.landers@colostate.edu, Assoc. Prof.,
Colorado State University, CO, Fort Collins

Landers, Mary ....(912) 652-0337
mary.landers@savannahnow.com,
Environmental Reporter, Savannah Morning
News, GA, Savannah

Landes, Mary ....(785) 822-1491
mlandes@salina.com, Interactive Services Dir.,
The Salina Journal, KS, Salina

Landholm, Rhea
crenews@gpcom.net, Ed., Creighton News,
NE, Creighton

Landis, Debra ....(217) 206-7717 (office)
dland2@uis.edu, Faculty Advisor, Univ. of
Illinois/Springfield, IL, Springfield

Landis, Mike ....(309) 852-2181
mlandis@starcourier.com, Ed., Star-Courier,
IL, Kewanee

Landis, Tim ....(217) 788-1536
tim.landis@sj-r.com, Bus. Ed., The State
Journal-Register, IL, Springfield

Landry, Brian
photo@theaggie.org, Photo Director, University
of California, Davis, CA, Davis

Landry, Cathy
cathy@gaylordheraldtimes.com, Ed.,
Marketplace Upnorth, MI, Gaylord

Landry, Chris
chris.landry@daily-iberian.com, Sports Ed.,
The Daily Iberian, LA, New Iberia

Landry, Greg ....(902) 661-5429
glandry@amherstdaily.com, Ops. Mgr.,
Amherst Daily News, NS, Amherst

Landry, JP
dcpress@midtech.net, Ed., Denver City Press,
TX, Denver City

Landry, Kim
kiml@hollistercreative.com, Pres., Hollister
Kids, Bryn Mawr

Landry, Peter ....(877) 643-5437
peterl@hollistercreative.com, Vice Pres.,
Hollister Kids, Bryn Mawr

Landry, Serge ....(450) 649-0719
serge.landry@quebecormedia.com, L'oeil
Regional, QC, Beloeil
serge.landry@quebecormedia.com,
Information De Ste Julie, QC, Saint Julie
serge.landry@quebecormedia.com, Ed.,
L'information, QC, Sainte Julie

Landry, Sonya C. ....(318) 631-6222
sunweekly@aol.com, Ed., Shreveport Sun, LA,
Shreveport

Landry, Tammy
waprint@vianet.ca, Ed., The Algoma News
Review, ON, Wawa

Landsberg, David A.
dlandsberg@miamiherald.com, Pres./Pub.,
Herald Values, FL, Miami

Lane, Brian ....(812) 231-4216
brian.lane@tribstar.com, Prod. Dir., The Tribune
Star, IN, Terre Haute

Lane, Debbie ....(615) 783-0770
debbie.Lane@dioceseofnashville.com, Prodn.
Mgr., Tennessee Register, TN, Nashville

Lane, Frank ....(912) 265-1104 x 363
flane@thebrunswicknews.com, Circulation
Director, The Brunswick News, GA,
Brunswick

Lane, Kelly
Kelly.Sivley@theredstonerocket.com, Copy
Ed., Redston Rocket, AL, Decatur

Lane, Laura
llane@oysterbayguardian.com, Ed., Oyster Bay
Guardian, NY, Garden City

Lane, Nancy ....(312) 631-3270
nancy.lane@localmedia.org, President, Local
Media Association, MI, Lake City

Lane, Rose
rose@okcfriday.com, Ed/Co-Pub., Oklahoma
City Friday, OK, Oklahoma City

Lane, Tonya ....(870) 247-4700
tlane@whitehalljournal.com, Gen. Mgr. Adv.,
White Hall Journal, AR, White Hall

Laney, Nina
nlaney@wapakwdn.com, Prodn. Mgr.,
Composing/Printing, Auglaize Merchandiser,
OH, Wapakoneta

Laney, William ....(419) 739-3515
blaney@wapakwdn.com, Exec. Ed., Auglaize
Merchandiser, OH, Wapakoneta

Lang, Ada
classified@willistonpioneer.com, Classifieds/
Circ, Mgr., Williston Pioneer Sun News, FL,
Williston

Lang, Betty
blang@blockislandtimes.com, Co-Pub./Adv.
Dir., The Block Island Times, RI, Block Island

Lang, Craig
cl1951@hotmail.com, Sports Ed., Prairie

Advocate, IL, Lanark

Lang, Elizabeth
lizzie3158@hotmail.com, Circ. Mgr., Prairie
Advocate, IL, Lanark

Lang, Fernando
fernando.lang@impremedia.com, Director, Ad
Rev/Operations, El Diario La Prensa, NY,
Brooklyn

Lang, Fraser
flang@blockislandtimes.com, Co-Pub., The
Block Island Times, RI, Block Island

Lang, Mike ....(941) 361-4845
mike.lang@heraldtribune.com, Photo Dir.,
Sarasota Herald-Tribune, FL, Sarasota

Lang, Sandra ....(860) 435-9873, x301
accounting@lakevillejournal.com, Controller,
The Lakeville Journal, CT, Falls Village

Lang, Stacey ....(701) 250-8201
stacey.lang@bismarcktribune.com, Mktg. Mgr.,
The Bismarck Tribune, ND, Bismarck

Langan, Jim
jimlangan@thehudsonvalleynews.com, Exec.
Ed., Hudson Valley News, NY, Hyde Park

Langdon, Craig D.
lucaspc@wtciweb.com, Prodn. Mgr., Lucas-
Sylvan News, KS, Lucas

Langdon, Helen
helen@coalgaterecordregister.com, Adv. Mgr.,
The Coalgate Record-Register, OK, Coalgate

Lange, Ryan ....(610) 568-1557
ryan.lange@alvernia.edu, Faculty Advisor,
Alvernia University, PA, Reading

Lange, Sue
ad@standardpress.com, Prod. Mgr, Paddock
Lake Report, WI, Delavan

Lange, Sue Z. ....(262) 728-3411, ext. 114
suez@standardpress.com, Creative Dept. Dir.,
Westosha Report, WI, Twin Lakes

Lange, Tasha
tlange@ncppub.com, Circ. Mgr, The FM Extra,
MN, Moorhead
tlange@ncppub.com, Circ. Mgr, The Extra, IA,
Charles City

Langford, Gale ....(989) 843-6242
mayvillemonitor@hotmail.com, Editor &
Publisher, Mayville Monitor, MI, Mayville

Langford, Julia ....(662) 325-7907
jlangford@reflector.msstate.edu, Mississippi
State Univ., MS, Mississippi State

Langis, Barbara
Barbie@dotnews.com, Prodn. Mgr., The
Dorchester Reporter, MA, Dorchester
Barbie@dotnews.com, Prod. Mgr., Mattapan
Reporter, MA, Dorchester
Barbie@dotnews.com, Prod. Mgr., Boston Irish
Reporter, MA, Dorchester
Barbie@dotnews.com, Prod. Mgr., Boston
Haitian Reporter, MA, Dorchester

Langkopp, Bill
pressclub_no@hotmail.com, Exec. Dir., New
Orleans Press Club, LA, New Orleans

Langley, Catherine ....(609) 406-0600 x17
clangley@njpa.org, Communications Manager,
New Jersey Press Association, NJ, Ewing

Langley, Jay ....(908) 782-4747 ext. 659
jaylan@hcdemocrat.com, Ed., Hunterdon
County Democrat, NJ, Flemington

Langley, Michael
mlangley@tracypress.com, Ed., Tracy Press,
CA, Tracy

Langlois, Norman ....(450) 491-1410
Circ. Mgr., Le Groupe Jcl Inc., QC, Saint
Eustache

Langlois, Robert ....(514) 878-9711
rlanglois@bbm.ca, Vice Pres., Quebec Servs.,
BBM Canada, ON, Toronto

Langlois, Serge ....(450) 472-3440
redactionnordinfo@groupejcl.com, Eveil, QC,

Saint Eustache
redactionnordinfo@groupejcl.com, Voix Des Mille Iles, QC, Sainte Therese

Langlois, Serge ....ext. 322
serge@groupejcl.com, Dir., Dist., Le Groupe Jcl Inc., QC, Saint Eustache

Langman, William......................860/701-4283
b.langman@theday.com, Director of Operations, The Day, CT, New London

Langmann, Kurt
newsroom@aldergrovestar.com, Ed., The Aldergrove Star, BC, Aldergrove

Langston, Scott
vpolicy@roadrunner.com, Pub./Ed./Adv. Mgr., Versailles Policy, OH, Versailles

Langton, Trent..........................(734) 240-5789
trent@monroenews.com, Ops. Mgr. , Bedford Now, MI, Monroe
trent@monroenews.com, Opns. Dir., Systems, The Monroe News, MI, Monroe

Lanier, David ....(603) 352-1234 ext. 1411
dlanier@keenesentinel.com, Sports Ed., The Keene Sentinel, NH, Keene

Lanier, John
jlanier@transylvaniatimes.com, Ed., The Transylvania Times, NC, Brevard

Lanka, Benjamin......................(740) 328-8576
blanka@gannett.com, Enterprise Ed., The Marion Star, OH, Marion

Lankford, Jennifer ....(970) 542-3170
Morgan Cmty. College, CO, Fort Morgan

Lankton, Robin ....(239) 263-4893
robin.lankton@naplesnews.com, Director of Marketing, Naples Daily News, FL, Naples

Lankton, Robin
rlankton@tampatrib.com, Tampa Bay Times, FL, St Petersburg

Lankton, Stella ....(620) 221-1050
composing1@ctnewsonline.com, Composition, Winfield Daily Courier, KS, Winfield

Lanman, Patrick
planman@vevaynewspapers.com, Pub, Vevay Reveille-Enterprise, IN, Vevay

Lanman, Patrick
planman@vevaynewspapers.com, Pub., The Switzerland Democrat, IN, Vevay

Lannan, Anne.....................................ext. 228
a.lannan@ocna.org, Executive Director, Ontario Community Newspapers Association, ON, Burlington

Lannan, Anne
a.lannan@ocna.org, Executive Director, Member Services Coordinator, ON, Toronto

Lansden, Joe ....(580) 625-3241
cowchipnews@gmail.com, Co-pub., The Herald-Democrat, OK, Beaver
cowchipnews@gmail.com, Ed., The Herald-Democrat, OK, Beaver

Lansing, Jeff
jlansing@postbulletin.com, Prodn. Mgr., The Rochester Shopper, MN, Rochester

Lansing, Jeffrey
jrl6166@rit.edu, Prodn. Dir., Opns., Post-Bulletin, MN, Rochester

Lanthier, Maggie
mlanthier@ironmountaindailynews.com, Online Mgr., The Daily News, MI, Iron Mountain

Lanthier, Marguerite
mlanthier@ironmountaindailynews.com, Ent. Ed., The Daily News, MI, Iron Mountain

Lantrip, Terry
terry@sunnewspapers.com, Pub./Ed., Lake Cities Sun, TX, Plano

Lantz, Dianne
Ads@FarmlandNews.com, Pub/Adv. Mgr., Farmland News, OH, Archbold

Lantz, Joey

jlantz@madraspioneer.com, Circ. Dir, The Madras Pioneer, OR, Madras

Lantz, Susie .... (949) 388-7700 ext. 111
slantz@picketfencemedia.com, Sales Associate, San Clemente Times, CA, Capistrano Beach

Lantz, Zak................................(814) 938-8740
zlantz@punxsutawneyspirit.com, Ed., Jefferson County Neighbors, PA, Punxsutawney
zlantz@punxsutawneyspirit.com, Editor, The Punxsutawney Spirit, PA, Punxsutawney

Lanyon, Mary-Justine .... (909) 337-6145 x221
editor@mountain-news.com, Mountain News & Crestline Courier-News, CA, Lake Arrowhead

Lanzetta, Giancarlo....................(514) 987-2222
glanzetta@montrealgazette.com, Dir., Integrated Adv., Montreal Gazette, QC, Montreal

Lapidos, Juliet
juliet.lapidos@latimes.com, Op-Ed Ed., Los Angeles Times, CA, Los Angeles

Lapinskie, Pete
peter.lapinskie@sunmedia.ca, Gen. Mgr., Barry's Bay This Week, ON, Barry's Bay

Lapointe, Michele ....(205) 344-5251
advertising@thegoldenstar.net, Pub., Golden Star, BC, Golden

Lapointe, Mychel
editeur@journallenord.com, Ed., Journal Le Nord, QC, Saint Jerome

Lapp, Susan ....(267) 663-6300
slapp@buxmontmedia.com, Pub., Courier News Weekly, PA, Souderton

Lapping, Kelly..........................(613) 584-4161
NRT@magma.ca, Pub, The North Renfrew Times, ON, Deep River

Laprad, David
dlaprad@hamiltoncountyherald.com, Ed., Hamilton County Herald, TN, Chattanooga

Laprise, Lilianne......................(418) 686-3036
admin_quebec@transcontinental.ca, Autre Voix, QC, Beaupre
admin_quebec@transcontinental.ca, Pub./Ed., Quebec Express, QC, Quebec
admin_quebec@transcontinental.ca, Ed., Journal L'actuel, QC, Quebec

Laprise, Lilianne
production_quebec@transcontinental.ca, Ed., Charlesbourg Express, QC, Quebec

Laraway, Cindy........................(757) 247-7466
claraway@dailypress.com, Admin./Planning Mgr., Daily Press, VA, Newport News

Lareau, Denise
denise.lareau@quebecormedia.com, VP, Comm. & Promo., Le Journal de Montreal, QC, Montreal

Larenas, Patrick
blarenas2@yahoo.com, Ed., El Hispano, CA, Sacramento

Large, Suzette........................(660) 529-2249
Receptionist, Slater Main Street News, MO, Slater

Largever, Jason
nyitc@55broadst.com, Dir.-Info Serv., NY Information Technology Center, NY, New York

Larimer, Tom ....(501) 374-1500
tom@arkansaspress.org, Exec. Dir., Arkansas Press Services, AR, Little Rock

Larimore, Melissa ....(270) 797-3271
melissa@dawsonspringsprogress.com, Managing editor, The Dawson Springs Progress, KY, Dawson Springs

Larison, Dennis ....(717) 721-4425
dlarison.eph@lnpnews.com, Editor, Lancaster Farming, PA, Ephrata

Larivee, Rita............................(816) 531-0538
rlarivee@ncronline.org, Gen. Superior, National Catholic Reporter, MO, Kansas City

Larivi, Natalie ....(514) 392-9000
Pres., Trancontinental Media Inc., Transcontinental Media, ON, Montreal

Larkin, Janette ....(515) 288-3336
janettelarkin@bpcdm.com, Pub., Des Moines Business Record, IA, Des Moines
janettelarkin@bpcdm.com, Publisher, Business Publications Corporation Inc., IA

Larkin, Joe ....(602) 229-8452
joe.larkin@voicemediagroup.com, SVP Sale & Operations, Ruxton Group/VMG Advertising, AZ, Phoenix

Larkin, Joe
joe.larkin@voicemediagroup.com, Sr. Vice Pres. Sales , Voice Media Group, CO, Denver

Larkin, Will
wlarkin@saukvalley.com, Sports Ed., The Telegraph, IL, Dixon

Larmer, Paul
paul@hcn.org, Exec. Dir., High Country News, Paonia

Larocque , Cory
nfr.citydesk@sunmedia.ca, Mng. Ed., Niagara Falls Review, ON, Niagara Falls

Larose, Greg
greg.larose@nopg.com, Managing Editor, Daily Journal of Commerce, LA, Metairie

Larose, Patrick ....(613) 933-0014
patrick.larose@tc.tc, Media Strategy Manager, Seaway News, ON, Cornwall

Larrabee, Debra ....(207) 367-2200
billing@pbp.me, Financial Manager, Castine Patriot, ME, Blue Hill

Larrinaga, Amanda ....(406) 994-2224
editor@exponent.montana.edu, Montana State Univ. Bozeman, MT, Bozeman

Larry, N/A ....Dir., Commun.
Kilman, World Association of Newspapers and News Publishers (WAN-IFRA)

Larsen, Belinda ....(316) 775-2218
blarsen@butlercountytimesgazette.com, Augusta City Ed., The Butler County Times-Gazette, KS, Augusta

Larsen, Dana ....(712) 762-4158
danalarsen407@yahoo.com, Ed., Anita Tribune, IA, Anita

Larsen, Dana
dlarsen@stormlakepilottribune.com, Mng. Ed., Pilot Tribune, IA, Storm Lake

Larsen, DeWayne ....ext. 280
dlarsen@ellsworthamerican.com, Prodn. Mgr., The Ellsworth American, ME, Ellsworth

Larsen, Jim
editor@whidbeynewstimes.com, Ed., The Whidbey Classifieds, WA, Coupeville

Larsen, Linda
llarsen@reporter-herald.com, Mgr., Mktg./ Promo., Loveland Reporter-Herald, CO, Loveland

Larsen, Tom
tlarsen@skagitpublishing.com, Prodn. Dir., Skagit Valley Herald, WA, Mount Vernon

Larson, Alex .... (559) 784-5000 Ext. 1039ext. 1039
alarson@portervillerecorder.com, Circ. Dir., The Porterville Recorder, CA, Porterville

Larson, Brad
blarson@startribune.com, Star Tribune, MN, Minneapolis

Larson, Brad..........................(250) 726-7029
bradley.larson@westerlynews.ca, Adv/Office/ Circ, Westerly News, BC, Ucluelet

Larson, Brenda
blarson@carolinaparent.com, Publisher, Carolina Parent, NY, White Plains

Larson, Carrie
office@osceolasun.com, Circ. Mgr., Messenger, MN, Scandia

Larson, Dale
dlarson@press-citizen.com, Gen. Mgr./Adv. Dir., Iowa City Press-Citizen, IA, Iowa City

Larson, Darren
dlarson@newspapersfirst.com, Vice Pres./ Sales Mgr., Newspapers First, Inc., TX, Dallas
dlarson@newspapersfirst.com, Vice Pres., Southern Reg., Newspapers First, Inc., NY, New York

Larson, David ....(815) 544-4430
dlarson@boonecountyjournal.com, Owner/Pub. , Boone County Journal, IL, Belvidere

Larson, Debbie
debbie.larson@missoulian.com, Co-op Adv. Coord., Missoulian, MT, Missoula

Larson, Gary
gary.larson@unlv.edu, Asst. Prof./Prog. Undergrad. Coord., University of Nevada, Las Vegas, NV, Las Vegas

Larson, Gwen
glarson1@emporia.edu, Mng. Ed., The Emporia Gazette, KS, Emporia

Larson, Jayson ....(909) 675-5626
editor@athensreview.com, Ed., Athens Daily Review, TX, Athens

Larson, Jayson
sportseditor@athensreview.com, Sports Ed., The Star, TX, Athens

Larson, Kathy
kathy.larson@yorknewstimes.com, Adv. Sales Mgr., York News-Times, NE, York

Larson, Kathy
kathy.larson@yorknewstimes.com, Adv. Mgr., Advantage, NE, York

Larson, Kyle
klarson@larsonnewspapers.com, Adv. Dir, The Camp Verde Journal, AZ, Camp Verde
klarson@larsonnewspapers.com, Adv. Dir, Sedona Red Rock News, AZ, Sedona

Larson, LeAnn ....(563) 422-5410
lanews@fayettepublishing.com, Pub., Fayette County Union, IA, West Union
lanews@fayettepublishing.com, Pub., The Elgin Echo, IA, West Union
lanews@fayettepublishing.com, Pub., Fayette Leader, IA, West Union
lanews@fayettepublishing.com, Pub., Ossian Bee, IA, West Union

Larson, Rahn
rahnl@windomnews.com, Ed., Windom Shopper, MN, Windom

Larson, Rahn
rahnl@windomnews.com, Ed., Cottonwood County Citizen, MN, Windom

Larson, Richard K.
dlarson@swiftcom.com, Chrmn., Bd., Swift Communications, Inc., NV, Carson City

Larson, Robert
bob@redrocknews.com, Pub., Cottonwood Journal Extra, AZ, Cottonwood
bob@redrocknews.com, Pub., Sedona Red Rock News, AZ, Sedona

Lascer, Nannette
Editor@GrenadaStar.com, Managing Ed., Grenada Star, MS, Grenada

Lash, Jarrod .... (724) 465-5555 ext 206
jlash@indianagazette.net, Adv. / Mrkt. Dir. , The Indiana Gazette, PA, Indiana

Lashaway, Alana ....(317) 477-3246
alashaway@greenfieldreporter.com, Adv. Rep., Clas., Daily Reporter, IN, Greenfield

Laska, Virginia
stkpaper@ruraltel.net, Editorial Writer, Stockton Sentinel, KS, Stockton

Laskowski, Mark ....(843) 667-6647
mlaskowski@bellsouth.net, Senior Associate-Southeast, Lewis Floyd- Grimes, W.B. & Co., AL, Gulf Shores

dlawson@thestate.com, Info Systems Site Mgr., The State, SC, Columbia

Lawson, Eric .... (250) 505-3671
eric.lawson@blackpress.ca, Group Publisher, Trail Daily Times, BC, Trail

Lawson, Eric .... (506) 458-6435
eric.lawson@brunswicknews.com, Co-Pub., Brunswick News, Inc., GA, Brusnswick

Lawson, Eric
eric.lawson@blackpress.ca, Pub., Arrow Lakes News, BC, Nakusp

Lawson, Eric .... (250) 365-6397
eric.lawson@blackpress.ca, Pub., Rossland News, BC, Castlegar

Lawson, Eric .... (250) 365-6397
eric.lawson@blackpress.ca, Pub., The Castlegar News, BC, Castlegar

Lawson, Eric .... (204) 571-7401
elawson@brandonsun.com, Publisher, Brandon Sun, MB, Brandon

Lawson, Eric 1 (877) 365-6397
eric.lawson@blackpress.ca, Publisher, Nelson Star, BC, Nelson

Lawson, George
obsrev@gmail.com, Pres. and Pub., The Observer, NY, Penn Yan

Lawson, George
obsrev@gmail.com, Pres. and Pub., The Watkins Review & Express, NY, Watkins Glen

Lawson, George
lawsong@unk.edu, Chair, University of Nebraska-Kearney, NE, Kearney

Lawson, Jeff .... ext. 500251
jeff.lawson@sunmedia.ca, Pub./Adv. Dir., The Brockville Recorder and Times, ON, Brockville

Lawson, Jeff .... (513) 768-8128
jlawson@enquirer.com, Market Sales & Distribution Director, The Cincinnati Enquirer, OH, Cincinnati

Lawson, Jonathan
ads4web@blackpress.ca, Trafficking Coordinator, Lake Country Calendar, BC, Kelowna

Lawson, Kayleigh .... (620) 442-4200 ext. 111
online@arkcity.net, Online Ed., The Arkansas City Traveler, KS, Arkansas City

Lawson, Kelly
klawson@hcnonline.com, Asst. Opns. Mgr., The Courier of Montgomery County, TX, Conroe

Lawson, Michael .... (973) 569-7221
LawsonM@northjersey.com, VP/Pub., North Jersey Deals, NJ, Woodland Park
LawsonM@northjersey.com, VP/Pub., North Jersey Community Newspapers, NJ, Woodland Park

Lawson, Mike .... ext. 234
Circ. Dir., Shopper's Guide, NJ, Newton

Lawson, Mike .... (973) 569-7221
lawsonm@northjersey.com, Vice Pres./Pub., Su Guia, NJ, Clifton

Lawson, Rhonda .... (606) 528-7898 Ext. 12
rlawson@thetimestribune.com, Adv. Classified Clerk, Times-Tribune, KY, Corbin

Lawson, Robin
rlawson@tidewaterreview.com, Gen. Mgr./Ed., The Tidewater Review, VA, West Point

Lawson, Sandra
sandra.lawson@mountaineagle.com, Classified Ad Mgr., Daily Mountain Eagle, AL, Jasper

Lawson, Steve
slawson@wellmarkco.com, VP Sales/Mktg., The Wellmark Company, OK, Oklahoma City

Lawson, Tammy
tlawson@leavenworthtimes.com, Adv. Acct. Exec., The Leavenworth Times, KS, Leavenworth

Lawton, David M. ....(603) 366-8463 x 317
dlawton@weirs.com, Pub., The Cocheco Times, NH, Laconia
dlawton@weirs.com, Managing Ed. , The Weirs Times, NH, Laconia

Lawton, Starr
sales@weirs.com, Off. Mgr., The Cocheco Times, NH, Laconia

Laxineta, Stephen C. ....(310) 372-0388
Pres., National Media, Inc., CA, Rancho Palos Verdes

Lay, Lydia .... (901) 435-1309
lydia_lay@loc.edu, LeMoyne-Owen College, TN, Memphis

Laye, Basya
editor@jewishindependent.ca, editor, Jewish Independent, BC, Vancouver

Layng Rosner, Terre
trosner@stfrancis.edu, Chair, University of St. Francis, IL, Joliet

Layton, John .... (860) 495-8265
jlayton@thewesterlysun.com, VP and Advertising director, The Westerly Sun, CT, Pawcatuck

Layton, John .... (860) 495-8265
jlayton@thewesterlysun.com, Adv, Mystic River Press, CT, Pawcatuck

Layton, Les
llayton@whitneyworld.com, CEO, Whitney Worldwide, Inc., MN, Saint Paul

Layton, Robin .... (928) 445-3333
rlayton@prescottaz.com, Editor, The Daily Courier, AZ, Prescott

Lazar, Kim .... (989) 723-1118
kim@owossoindependent.com, Adv. Mgr.`, Sunday Independent, MI, Owosso

Lazarczyk, Travis .... (207) 621-5621
tbarrett@centralmaine.com, Sports/ Copy Ed. , Kennebec Journal, ME, Augusta

Lazarus, Paul
plazarus@miami.edu, Prof., University of Miami, FL, Coral Gables

Lazcano, Maria .... (316) 804-7725
mlazcano@gatehousemedia.com, Recruitment , The Newton Kansan, KS, Newton

Lazenby, David ....(334) 524-7555 (cell)
david@corridormessenger.com, Pub./Ed., The Corridor Messenger, AL, Jasper

Lazurko, Robert
rlazurko@yrmg.com, Bus. Mgr., The Richmond Hill Liberal, ON, Markham

Lazurko, Robert
rlazurko@yrmg.com, Bus. Mgr., The Georgina Advocate, ON, Keswick

Lazzuri, Brian
editor@thecasket.ca, Gen Mgr/Mng Ed/Adv Mgr, The Casket, NS, Antigonish

Le Gal, Stéphane .... (514) 987-2222
slegal@montrealgazette.com, Regional Vice-President, Advertising - Eastern Canada , Montreal Gazette, QC, Montreal

LeBeau, Maggie
info@dexone.com, Sr. Vice Pres./CMO, Dex One Corp., TX, Dallas

LeBeau, Nancy ....(937) 372-4444 Ext. 2114
nlebeau@civitasmedia.com, Adv. Mgr., Xenia Daily Gazette, OH, Xenia

LeBeau, Wade .... (815) 937-3315
wlebeau@daily-journal.com, Dir., Network Operations, The Daily Journal, IL, Kankakee

LeBeau, Wade .... (815) 937-3315
Network Operations Director, Small Newspaper Group, IL, Kankakee

LeBlanc, Linda .... (519) 474-5371
linda.leblanc@sunmedia.ca, Pub./Adv. Mgr., St. Thomas Times-Journal, ON, Saint Thomas

LeBlanc, Linda

linda.leblanc@sunmedia.ca, Publisher, Londoner, ON, London
linda.leblanc@sunmedia.ca, Pub., Sarnia This Week, ON, Sarnia
linda.leblanc@sunmedia.ca, Pub., The Petrolia Topic, ON, Sarnia

LeBlanc, Norman F. .... ext. 145
nleblanc@portlanddiocese.net, Adv. Mgr., Church World, ME, Portland

LeBlanc, Stephanie
productions@lecourrier,, Prod. Mgr., Le Courrier De La Nouvelle-ecosse, NS, Comeauville

LeBlanc, Steve
sleblanc@miltoncanadianchampion.com, News/Sports Ed., The Milton Canadian Champion, ON, Milton

LeBlanc, Theresa
znewstleblanc@verizon.net, Adv. Sales Mgr., Zephyrhills News, FL, Zephyrhills

LeBoeuf, Bob
bleboeuf@dispatch.com, Gen. Mgr., The Columbus Dispatch, OH, Columbus

LeBoeuf, Michael ....(315) 343-3800 ext. 2239
mleboeuf@palltimes.com, Sports Ed., The Palladium-Times, NY, Oswego

LeClerc, Brian
brianl@wcrecord.com, Adv. Sales Rep., The Walsh County Record, ND, Grafton

LeGrand, Gera .... ext. 109
banpress@hotmail.com, Pub., The Banner-Press, MO, Marble Hill

LeJeune, Darrel B.
thebasileweekly@hotmail.com, Ed., The Basile Weekly, LA, Basile

LeJeune, Jeannine
Jeannine.LeJeune@CrowleyToday.com, Online Ed., The Crowley Post-Signal, LA, Crowley

LeMaster, Steve .... ext. 22
sports@floydcountytimes.com, Sports Ed., Floyd County Times, KY, Prestonsburg

LeMay, Melissa
V.P. Sales and Marketing, V.P. Sales and Marketing, The Express, NY, Mechanicville

LeMiere, Ann Marie .... (617) 262-2489
annmarie@cityshopperonline.com, Office Mgr., City Shopper, MA, Boston

LeMoine, Julie
julie@thechetekalert.com, Sales Mgr., The Chetek Alert, WI, Chetek

LeNeave, Greg ....(270) 442-7389 Headquarters
greg007@ky-news.com, Publisher, The Huntingburg Press, IN, Huntingburg
greg007@ky-news.com, Pub., Twin City Journal-Reporter, IN, Gas City

LePage, Alain
alain.lepage@transcontinental.ca, Gen. Mgr., Charlesbourg Express, QC, Quebec

LePage, Alain
production_quebec@transcontinental.ca, Dir., Journal l'actuel, QC, Quebec

LePorin, Eliza .... (850) 561-1600
eleporin@fsview.com, General Manager, FSView & Florida Flambeau, FL, Tallahassee

LeRoy, Angelina
napressweekly@aol.com, Pub., New American Weekly, FL, Pensacola

LeRoy, Jeff ....(620) 792-1211 ext.220
jleroy@gbtribune.com, Graphic Designer, Great Bend Tribune, KS, Great Bend

Lea, Nat
nlea@arkansasonline.com, NAN LLC, MO, Little Rock

Leach, Don
don.leach@latimes.com, Photo Ed., Daily Pilot, CA, Costa Mesa

Leach, Leah .... (36) 417-3530
lleach@peninsuladailynews.com, Executive

Editor, Peninsula Daily News, WA, Port Angeles

Leader, Matt .... (585) 243-0296
matt@livingstonnews.com, Reporter, The Livingston County News, NY, Geneseo

Leahy, Jim
cdna@djstrat.com, Connecticut Daily Newspapers Association, CT, Hartford

Leahy, Leah .... (812) 277-7762
lleahy@heraldt.com, Classified Ad. Mgr., The Times-Mail, IN, Bedford
lleahy@heraldt.com, Classified Sales Mgr., The Herald Times, IN, Bloomington

Leake, Tara .... (519) 537-2341 x515269
tleake@postmedia.com, Media sales, The Norwich Gazette, ON, Woodstock

Leal, Jennifer .... (830) 625-9144 ext. 202
jennifer.leal@herald-zeitung.com, Bus. Mgr., New Braunfels Herald-Zeitung, TX, New Braunfels

Leaming, Dave .... (207) 861-9255
dleaming@centralmaine.com, Photographers , Morning Sentinel, ME, Waterville

Lear, Amy .... (609) 281-5257
aclear@njpa.org, Adv. Dir., New Jersey Newsmedia Network (NJNN), NJ, Ewing

Lear, Amy C. ....(609) 406-0600, ext. 15
aclear@njpa.org, NJNN Director, New Jersey Press Association, NJ, Ewing

Learn, Rob .... (705) 382-9996 ext. 32
editor@almaguinnews.com, News Ed., Almaguin News, ON, Burks Falls

Leary, Michael .... (210) 250-3111
mleary@express-news.net, Sr. VP/Editor, San Antonio Express-News, TX, San Antonio
mleary@express-news.net, Ed., Brooks Discovery News, TX, San Antonio

Leary, Nadine .... (617) 696-7758
ads@miltontimes.com, Ad. Director, Milton Times, MA, Milton

Lease, Denise .... (630) 920-3574
denise.lease@manroland-web.com, Marketing Manager, Manroland Web Systems Inc., IL, Lisle

Leasor, Lydia .... (270) 505-1487
lleasor@thenewsenterprise.com, Graphic Design/IT Mgr., The News-Enterprise, KY, Elizabethtown

Leasure, Dan
americanclassifieds@emadisonriver.com, American Classifieds - Greensboro, NC, Greensboro

Leath, Susan D. .... (814) 238-5000
sleath@delawareonline.com, President & Publisher, The News Journal, DE, New Castle

Leau, Janet .... (65) 6415-4200
janet.leau@dowjones.com, Acct. Mgr., Dow Jones Newswires - Kuala Lumpur, Malaysia, Kuala Lumpur

Leavell, Dorothy R. .... (773) 752-2500
crusaderil@aol.com, Ed., Chicago Crusader, IL, Chicago

Leavell, Dorothy R. .... (773) 752-2500
crusaderil@aol.com, Ed., Gary Crusader, IN, Gary

Leavell, Gary .... (214) 977-8987
gleavell@dallasnews.com, Assistant Managing Editor/Sports, The Dallas Morning News, TX, Dallas

Leavenworth, Stuart .... (916) 321-1185
sleavenworth@sacbee.com, Editorial Pages Editor , The Sacramento Bee, CA, Sacramento

Leavitt, Barry .... (612) 436-4690
barry@lavendermagazine.com, Adv. Sales Dir., Lavender, MN, Edina

Leavitt, Betty

tlee@swpub.com, Adv. Rep., Shakopee Valley News, MN, Savage

Lee, Theodore
posttrib@airmail.net, Publisher, Dallas Post Tribune, TX, Dallas

Lee, Thomas............................**(520) 294-1200**
editorial@azbiz.com, Pub., The Daily Territorial, AZ, Tucson

Lee, Tom
info@sfadvertiser.com, Pub., The Advertiser, CA, San Francisco

Lee, Vincent
graphics@city-sentinel.com, Creative. Dir., The City Sentinel, OK, Oklahoma City

Lee, W. Douglas
sales@bargainbrowser.com, Pub., Bargain Browser, TN, White House

Lee, Wea H.
wealee@scdaily.com, Pub., Southern Chinese Daily News, TX, Houston

Lee, William
weyrelee@uga.edu, Prof., University of Georgia, GA, Athens

Lee, William H.
observer@concourse.net, Pub., Observer Group, CA, Sacramento

Leebrick, Kristal
editor@parkbugle.org, Ed, The Park Bugle, MN, Saint Paul

Leech, Carol
advertising@fayettenews.com, The Fayette Advertiser, MO, Fayette
advertising@fayettenews.com, Fayette Advertiser, MO, Fayette

Leeds, Larry
Sports@MadisonDailyLeader.com, Sports Ed., The Madison Daily Leader, SD, Madison

Leeds, Tim
tleeds@havredailynews.com, The Havre Daily News, MT, Havre

Leedy, Jerry G..........................**(704) 735-3031**
jerryleedy@lincolntimesnews.com, Pub., Lincoln Times-News, NC, Lincolnton
jerryleedy@lincolntimesnews.com, Publisher, The Lincoln Times, WV, Hamlin

Leedy, Nancy
Nancy.leedy@theinteriorjournal.com, Sports Editor, The Interior Journal, KY, Stanford

Leeman, Tommy
classified@olneyenterprise.com, Circ. Mgr., The Olney Enterprise, TX, Olney

Leer, June
circulation@bannergraphic.com, Circ./NIE Asst., Banner-Graphic, IN, Greencastle

Lees, Ross......................**(613) 392-6501 ext. 41**
editor@communitypress-online.com, Mng. Ed., The Community Press, ON, Trenton

Leese, Vernon.........................**(717) 485-3162**
Bus. Mgr., Mercersburg Journal, PA, Mercersburg

Leeser, John.........................**(570) 325-1551**
Adv. Dir., Williamsport Sun-Gazette/Lock Haven Express, PA, South Williamsport

Leff, Donna
d-leff@northwestern.edu, Prof., Northwestern University, IL, Evanston

Leff, Laurel
l.leff@northeastern.edu, Assoc. Prof., Northeastern University, MA, Boston

Leff, Tammy
tammyleff@sewardindependent.com, Circ. Mgr., Seward County Connection, NE, Seward

Leff, Tammy
tammyleff@sewardindependent.com, Bookkeeper, Seward County Independent, NE, Seward

Leffel, Tara
tleffel@thepostnewspapers.com, Adv. Mgr., The Post Newspapers - Brunswick, OH, Medina
tleffel@thepostnewspapers.com, Adv. Mgr., The Post Newspapers - Eastern Medina, OH, Medina
tleffel@thepostnewspapers.com, Adv. Mgr., The Post Newspapers - Medina, OH, Medina
tleffel@thepostnewspapers.com, Adv. Mgr., The Post Newspapers - Northern Wayne, OH, Medina
tleffel@thepostnewspapers.com, Adv. Mgr., The Post Newspapers - Norton, OH, Medina
tleffel@thepostnewspapers.com, Adv. Mgr., The Post Newspapers - Southern Medina, OH, Medina
tleffel@thepostnewspapers.com, Adv. Mgr., The Post Newspapers - Strongsville, OH, Medina
tleffel@thepostnewspapers.com, Adv. Mgr., The Post Newspapers - Wadsworth, OH, Medina

Leffler, Charlie
cleffler@mechlocal.com, Sports Ed., Goochland Gazette, VA, Mechanicsville

Lefort, Debora
dlefort@pnj.com, Adv. Mgr., Inside Sales, Pensacola News Journal, FL, Pensacola

Leftridge, Danny............**(870) 862-6610 ext. 152**
dleftridge@eldoradonew.com, Circ. Mgr., El Dorado News-Times / Sunday News, AR, El Dorado

Lega, Stephen
slega@lebanonenterprise.com, Other, Lebanon Enterprise, KY, Lebanon

Legaspi, Winnie............**(416) 923-3567 ext. 323**
wlegaspi@newspaperscanada.ca, CMCA Manager, Canadian Media Circulation Audit, ON, Toronto

Legault, François.....................**(613) 443-2741**
francois.legault@eap.on.ca, Chief Ed., Le Carillon, ON, Hawkesbury

Legault, Tracey
tracey.legault@ott.sunpub.com, Prodn. Mgr., The Ottawa Sun, ON, Ottawa

Legendre, Addy.....................**(985) 693-7229**
addy@viscom.net, Publisher, LaFourche Gazette, LA, Larose

Leger, Dan...................................**ext. 3340**
dleger@herald.ca, Dir., News Content, The Chronicle Herald, NS, Halifax

Legg, Sue
slegg@johnsoncitypress.com, Johnson City Press, TN, Johnson City

Legg, Tom
tlegg@hcnonline.com, Major Sr. Acct. Mgr., Bellaire Examiner, TX, Houston
tlegg@hcnonline.com, Dir, Nat'l Accts., Surprise Today, AZ, Sun City
tlegg@hcnonline.com, Dir., Nat'l Sales, Marana News, AZ, Tucson
tlegg@hcnonline.com, Major Sr. Acct. Mgr., River Oaks Examiner, TX, Houston
tlegg@hcnonline.com, Major Sr. Acct. Mgr., Cypress Creek Mirror, TX, Houston
tlegg@hcnonline.com, Majors Sr. Acct. Mgr., Sugar Land Sun, TX, Houston
tlegg@hcnonline.com, Dir., Nat'l Accts., East Valley Tribune, AZ, Tempe
tlegg@hcnonline.com, Major Sr. Acct. Mgr., Magnolia Potpourri, TX, Conroe
tlegg@hcnonline.com, Major Sr. Acct. Mgr., The Examiners, TX, Conroe
tlegg@hcnonline.com, Major Sr. Acct. Mgr., Memorial Examiner, TX, Conroe
tlegg@hcnonline.com, Major Sr. Acct. Mgr., Pearland Journal, TX, Conroe
tlegg@hcnonline.com, Major Sr. Acct. Mgr., The Woodlands Villager, TX, Conroe
tlegg@hcnonline.com, Major Sr. Acct. Mgr., Tomball Potpourri, TX, Conroe
tlegg@hcnonline.com, Majors Sr. Acct. Mgr., Spring Observer, TX, Conroe
tlegg@hcnonline.com, Major/Nat'l Sr. Acct. Mgr., The Courier of Montgomery County, TX, Conroe

Legler, Phil.........................**(515) 284-8385**
plegler@dmreg.com, VP, Info. Tech., The Des Moines Register, IA, Des Moines

Lego, Pamela.........................**(812) 350-7711**
plego@hspa.com, Adv. Dir., Hoosier State Press Association, IN, Indianapolis
plego@hspa.com, Mktg. Mgr./Adv. Dir., The Franklin Challenger, IN, Greenwood
plego@hspa.com, Mktg. Mgr/Adv. Dir., Greenwood and Southside Challenger, IN, Greenwood

Legree, Brian.................................**ext. 2243**
blegree@durhamregion.com, Sports Ed., Oshawa-whitby This Week, ON, Oshawa

Lehman, Dean
dlehman@times-call.com, Pub., Colorado Hometown Weekly, CO, Boulder

Lehman, Fred
flehman@philly.com, Philadelphia Media Network Inc., PA, Philadelphia
flehman@philly.com, Philadelphia Inquirer, Daily News & Philly.com, PA, Philadelphia

Lehman, Jacquelynn.................**(717) 703-3021**
jacquelynnl@mansimedia.com, Mgr. Collections, MANSI Media, PA, Harrisburg

Lehman, Sandra.....................**(530) 532-1714**
slehman@orovillemr.com, Adv, Exec., Oroville Mercury - Register, CA, Oroville

Lehmert, Amanda
alehmert@reidsvillereview.com, Ed., The Eden Daily News, NC, Reidsville

Lehmert, Amanda K.................**(336) 373-7075**
alehmert@reidsvillereview.com, Ed., The Reidsville Review, NC, Reidsville
alehmert@reidsvillereview.com, Group Ed., The Eden News, NC, Reidsville
alehmert@reidsvillereview.com, Office Mgr., The Messenger, NC, Reidsville
alehmert@reidsvillereview.com, Grp. Ed., The Eden Daily News, NC, Reidsville

Lehmkuhl, Lynn.....................**(212) 856-6329**
llehmkuhl@nnnlp.com, SVP, Sales, Newspaper National Network LP, NY, New York

Lehmkuhl, Lynn A......................**(212) 856-6329**
llehmkuhl@nnnlp.com, Sr. Vice Pres., Sales, Newspaper National Network LP, NY, New York

Lehnen, Carol
carol.lehnen@ecm-inc.com, Adv. Mgr., St. Croix Valley Peach, MN, Forest Lake

Lehrke, Terry
terry@littlefalls.net, Asst. Sec./Treasurer, Minnesota Free Paper Association, MN, Little Falls

Lehrke, Terry.........................**(320) 616-1917**
terry.lehrke@mcrecord.com, News Ed., Morrison County Record, MN, Little Falls

Leibold, Kelly.........................**(530) 852-0201**
kellyl@goldcountrymedia.com, GCM Circulation Director, The Press-Tribune, CA, Roseville

Leibold, Kelly.........................**(530) 852-0201**
kellyl@goldcountrymedia.com, Brehm Communications, Inc.
Director of Circulations , Auburn Journal, CA, Auburn

Leibold, Kelly.........................**(530) 852-0201**
kellyl@goldcountrymedia.com, Circulation Mgr, Loomis News, CA, Loomis

Leibrock, Rachel..........**(916) 498-1234, ext. 1363**
rachell@newsreview.com, Ed, Sacramento News & Review, CA, Sacramento

Leibson, Mark.........................**(337) 738-5642**
kindernews@centurytel.net, Mng. Ed., Kinder Courier News, LA, Kinder

Leidemann, Michael.................**(808) 227-5922**
leideman@hawaii.edu, Adviser, Asst Professor of Journalism, Honolulu Cmty. College Univ. of Hawaii, HI, Honolulu

Leidholdt, Alex
leidhoas@jmu.edu, Prof., James Madison University, VA, Harrisonburg

Leidy, Karen.........................**(903) 389-6397**
news@freestonecountytimes.com, Ed., Freestone County Times, TX, Fairfield

Leifeste, Terri.........................**(501) 315-8228**
tleifeste@ricentral.com, Publisher, The Saline Courier TMC, Benton

Leifeste, Terri.........................**(573) 761-0237**
terril@newstribune.com, Pub., The Lake Today OOB, MO, Lake Ozark
terril@newstribune.com, Gen. Mgr., News Tribune, MO, Jefferson City

Leighton, Susan
sleighton@newhavenadvocate.com, Adv. Dir., New Haven Advocate, CT, New Haven
sleighton@newhavenadvocate.com, Adv. Dir., Hartford Advocate, CT, Hartford
sleighton@newhavenadvocate.com, Adv. Dir., Hartford Courant, CT, Hartford

Leiman, Jennifer
jenny.leiman@cranbrooktownsman.com, Office Mgr., Cranbrook Daily Townsman, BC, Cranbrook

Lein, Dave.........................**(231) 486-0073**
dlein@michigannewspapers.com, Ed., The Leader and The Kalkaskian, MI, Traverse City

Lein, Pam.........................**(231) 486-0072**
plein@michigannewspapers.com, Adv. Mgr., The Leader and The Kalkaskian, MI, Traverse City

Leinbach, Richard
rich.leinbach@goshennews.com, IT Dir., The Goshen News, IN, Goshen

Leinen, Kathleen.....................**(701) 642-8585**
editor@wahpetondailynews.com, Mng. Ed., The Daily News, ND, Wahpeton

Leinen, Kathy.........................**(701) 642-8585**
editor@wahpetondailynews.com, Mng. Ed., The Daily News, ND, Wahpeton

Leinhart, Ken
editor@hometownclinton.com, Ed., The Courier News, TN, Clinton

Leininger, Kevin
kleininger@news-sentinel.com, Reporter/columnist, The News-Sentinel, IN, Fort Wayne

Leischner, Molly.....................**(360) 384-1411**
advertising@ferndalerecord.com, Office Mgr./Graphic Designer, Ferndale Record, WA, Ferndale

Leiser, Mark
maleiser@hammingtonnews.com, Exec. Ed., Atlantic County Record, NJ, Hammonton

Leishman, Chuck
chuck@northcoastjournal.com, Adv. Mgr, North Coast Journal, CA, Eureka

Leist, Katie
katie@fdlac.com, Marian University, WI, Fond Du Lac

Leister, Mark.........................**(215) 886-5662**
mleister@maned.com, Managing Director, Managing Editor, Inc., PA, Jenkintown

Leistikow, Chad.........................**(515) 284-8321**
cleistikow@dmreg.com, Univ. of Iowa Reporter, The Des Moines Register, IA, Des Moines

Leitgeb, Susan
susan.leitgeb@gvillesun.com, Adv. Dir., Ocala Star-Banner, FL, Ocala

Leithauser , Debra.........................**(208) 377-6301**
publisher@idahostatesman.com, Pres./Pub., Idaho Statesman, ID, Boise

Leitner, Jim
jleitner@wcinet.com, Sports Ed., Telegraph Herald, IA, Dubuque

Leitzke, Amy

aleitzke@appleton.gannett.com, Sr. Dir., News-Record, WI, Appleton

aleitzke@appleton.gannett.com, Appleton Fox Cities Bargain Bulletin, WI, Appleton

Leitzke, Amy ....(920) 996-7235
aleitzke@gannett.com, Senior Director/Distribution-Wisconsin, Post-Crescent, WI, Appleton

Lekarczyk, Joseph ....(303) 823-6625
editor@lyonsrecorder.com, Ed., The Lyons Recorder, CO, Lyons

Lekocevic, Melanie
Melanie@thedailymail.net, Ed., The Ravena News-Herald, NY, Ravena

Lekoski, Lauren ....(212) 947-5100
llekoski@metro-email.com, Mktg. Mgr., Metro Editorial Services, NY, New York

Lem, Nancy
artdept@southpasadenareview.com, Adv. Mgr., South Pasadena Review, CA, South Pasadena

Lemaster, Milton ....(972) 931-0711
milton@ghosting.com, Pres., AirSystems, Inc., TX, Addison

Lemay, Stacy ....ext. 128
slemay@fiftyplusadvocate.com, Circ. Mgr., Fifty Plus Advocate, MA, Worcester

Lembcke, Denise .... (509) 765-4561 ext. 213
dlembcke@columbiabasinherald.com, Bus. Mgr., Columbia Basin Herald, WA, Moses Lake

Lemelin, Tina
tina.lemelin @ transcontinental.ca, Adv. Mgr., Lachine Messenger, QC, Dorval

Lemery, Dave ....(630) 427-6250
dlemery@shawmedia.com, Ed, Bensenville Press, IL, Downers Grove
dlemery@shawmedia.com, Ed, Roselle Itasca Press, IL, Downers Grove

Lemery, David ....(630) 427-6250
dlemery@shawmedia.com, Ed., Glen Ellyn Suburban Life, IL, Downers Grove

Lemieux, Peter H.
support@cyways.com, Pres., Cyways, Inc., MA, Newton

Leming, Mary Kate
editor@thecoastalstar.com, Ed., The Coastal Star, FL, Ocean Ridge

Lemire, Don ....(585) 258-2207
dlemire@gannett.com, Democrat and Chronicle, NY, Rochester

Lemke, Paula
plemke@gw.stcdio.org, Circ. Mgr., St. Cloud Visitor, MN, Saint Cloud

Lemke, Stephanie
stephanie.lemke@advertisergleam.com, Advert. Sales, The Advertiser-Gleam, AL, Guntersville

Lemmer, James
observer@belgradearea.com, Pub./Ed./Adv. Mgr., The Belgrade Observer, MN, Belgrade

Lenardson, Bill ....(608) 782-9710
Circ Dir, The Chippewa Herald, WI, Chippewa Falls
Cir. Dir., La Crosse Tribune, WI, La Crosse

Lendennie, Gary ....(909) 657-1810
perriscitynews@aol.com, Ed., Perris Progress, CA, Perris

Lene, Jared ....(580) 482-1221 Ext. 2083
jlene@civitasmedia.com, Cir. Dir., Altus Times, OK, Altus

Leneave, Greg.........................(270) 628-5490
greg007@ky-news.com, Pub., The Carlisle County News, KY, Paducah

Leng, Lynda
lleng@barrhead.greatwest.ca, Pub, Barrhead Leader, AB, Barrhead

Lenhard, Robin M.

rlenhard@buffalospree.com, Dir., Circ., Forever Young, NY, Buffalo

Lenhart, Wendell ....(660) 359-2212
rtimes@lyn.net, Pub., Trenton Republican-Times, MO, Trenton

Lenhoff, Alyssa
alenhoff@ysu.edu, Dir., Journalism, Youngstown State University, OH, Youngstown

Lenihan, Kevin ....(845) 437-4834
klenihan@poughkee.gannett.com, City Ed., Poughkeepsie Journal, NY, Poughkeepsie

Lenkersdorfer, Jay ....(208) 678-6643
jay@theweeklymailer.com, Pub., Weekly Mailer, ID, Burley

Lennon, Gene ....(732) 358-5200 ext. 8210
Dir., Prodn., News Transcript, NJ, Manalapan

Lennon, Gene .... ext. 8210
glennon@gmnews.com, Prodn./System Mgr., Tri-Town News, NJ, Manalapan

Lennox, Sandra
slennox@thespec.com, Class. Mgr., The Record, ON, Kitchener

Lenoard , Brenda ....(517) 417-2004
dsanchez@lenconnect.com, Dir. Adv. Operations , The Daily Telegram, MI, Adrian

Lent, Jim ....(908) 766-3900, ext. 245
jlent@newjerseyhills.com, Ed., Morris News-Bee, NJ, Bernardsville

Lent, Jim
jlent@recordernewspapers.com, Ed., Hanover Eagle, NJ, Bernardsville

Lenton, Garry
glenton@readingeagle.com, Reading Eagle Company, PA, Reading

Lentz, Betty ....ext. 231
blentz@crescent-news.com, Circ. Mgr., Adams Publishing Group, LLC, MN, Virginia

Lenz, Mark ....(517) 417-2022
editor@lenconnect.com, Ed., The Daily Telegram, MI, Adrian

Lenz, Ryan
rlenz@thenorthwestern.com, Circ. Dir., Oshkosh Northwestern, WI, Oshkosh

Lenz, Terri.........................(507) 333-3148
tlenz@thekenyonleader.com, Ed./Pub., Kenyon Leader, MN, Kenyon

Leo, Jacqueline
info@thefiscaltimes.com, Ed.-in-Chief, The Fiscal Times, NY, New York

Leon, Gustavo ....(617) 619-6330
gustavo.leon@bostonherald.com, Art Dir., Boston Herald, MA, Boston

Leon, Kayla
kathleen@apopkachief.fdn.com, Adv. Rep., Apopka Chief (The), FL, Apopka

Leon, Skip ....(806) 296-1355
skip.leon@hearstnp.com, Sports Ed, Plainview Herald, TX, Plainview

Leon, Stephen ....(518) 463-2500
sleon@metroland.net, Pub., Metroland, NY, Albany

Leonard, Alison ....(609) 727-7118
ALeonard@pressofac.com, Adv. Sys. Mgr., The Press of Atlantic City, NJ, Pleasantville

Leonard, Angie ....(802) 362-3535
aleonard@hersamacornvt.com, General Manager, Vermont News Guide, VT, Manchester Center

Leonard, Christina
christina.leonard@arizonarepublic.com, The Arizona Republic, AZ, Phoenix

Leonard, Christine
christine.leonard@hebdosquebecor.com, Prodn. Dir., Le Mirabel, QC, Saint Jerome

Leonard, Erin

ads@madisoniannews.com, Owner/Adv. Dir., The Madisonian, MT, Ennis

Leonard, Gladys
advertising@thewesternstar.com, Bus. Mgr./Accountant, The Western Star, NL, Corner Brook

Leonard, Kurt
karlheminger@thecourier.com, City Ed., The Courier, OH, Findlay

Leonard, Kyle ....(847) 486-7285
leonard@pioneerlocal.com, Mgr., Niche Publications, Morton Grove Champion, IL, Chicago

Leonard, Michael
mleonard@TheClaytonTribune.com , Pub., The Clayton Tribune, GA, Clayton

Leonard, Suzy ....(321) 242-3614
sleonard@floridatoday.com, Custom Content Editor, Florida Today, FL, Melbourne

Leonard, Terry
tleonard@wcinet.com, Bus. Mgr., Unified Newspaper Group, WI, Verona

Leonard, Trisha ....(530) 542-8006
editor@tahoedailytribune.com, Ed., Tahoe Daily Tribune, CA, South Lake Tahoe

Leonard-Tackett, Jackie ....(414) 229-4436
leonardjm@uwm.edu, Lecturer, University of Wisconsin-Milwaukee / Department of Journalism, Advertising, and Media Studies (JAMS), WI, Milwaukee

Leones, Sonia
sonia@chestnuthillocal.com, Adv. Mgr., Chestnut Hill Local, PA, Philadelphia

Leos III, Moses.........................(512) 268-7862
moses@haysfreepress.com, Ed., Hays Free Press, TX, Kyle

Lepage, Audette
alepage@cowishanvalleycitizen.com, Circ. Mgr., Cowichan Valley Citizen, BC, Duncan

Lepage, Bernard
bernard.lepage@transcontinental.ca, Dir., Information, L'hebdo Mekinac/des Chenaux, QC, Shawinigan

Lepage, Bernard ....ext. 227
bernard.lepage@transcontinental.ca, Ed./Dir., Information, Hebdo Du St. Maurice, QC, Shawinigan

Leposky, George ....(305) 285-2200
amprsnd@aol.com, Ed., Ampersand Communications, Miami

Leposky, Rosalie E.
amprsnd@aol.com, Mng. Partner, Ampersand Communications, Miami

Leppin, Heidi
hleppin@polkio.com, Adv. Leader, The Polk County Itemizer-Observer, OR, Dallas

Lerch, Steven...................(972) 248-0451 x 230
slerch@willowbend.com, Chief Software Engineer, Willow Bend Communications, Inc., TX, Dallas

Lerner, Diane
diane@startreatment.com, Pub., La Guia Familiar, CA, Van Nuys

Lerner, John
jlerner@vnuemedia.com, Vice Pres., eMedia, VNU eMedia, NY, New York

Leroux-Lanthier, Sylvie ....(613) 933-3160
sylvie.leroux-lanthier@sunmedia.ca, Office Mgr., Standard-Freeholder, ON, Cornwall

Lerseth, Lisa ....(707) 553-6853
llerseth@timesheraldonline.com, Pre Press Mgr., Vallejo Times-Herald, CA, Vallejo

Lerseth, Michael
mlerseth@sfchronicle.com, Asst. Sports Ed, San Francisco Chronicle, CA, San Francisco

Lesar, Dean
news@trgnews.com, Ed., The Tribune-Phonograph, WI, Loyal

news@trgnews.com, Ed., The Tribune Record-Gleaner, WI, Loyal

Lescelius, Terri..ext. 155
Ed., Eagle Herald Sunday, WI, Marinette

Lesco, Deana ....(979) 265-7411
deana.lesco@thefacts.com, Retail Mgr., Buyer's Express, TX, Clute

Lesko, Cathy
clesko@bannergraphic.com, Receptionist/Typist, Banner-Graphic, IN, Greencastle

Lesko, Robert
sales@amergraph.com, Pres., Amergraph Corporation, NJ, Sparta

Leslie, Joey
jleslie@outandaboutnewspaper.com, Creative Dir., Out & About Nashville, TN, Nashville

Leslie, Kathy
ads@maplecreeknews.com, Adv. Mgr., The Maple Creek News, SK, Maple Creek

Leslie, Keith ....(416) 325-7843
keith.leslie@thecanadianpress.com, Legislature Correspondent, Canadian Press, The - Toronto, ON, ON, Toronto

Leslie, Melissa
melissa_leslie@mcgraw-hill.com, Ed., The Daily Journal, CO, Denver

Leslie, Tammy ....(780) 849-4380
lsleader@telusplanet.net, Circulation Mgr/Primary Ad Contact, Lakeside Leader, AB, Slave Lake

Lesnick, Dave ....(406) 758-4426
dlesnick@dailyinterlake.com, Sports Ed., Daily Inter Lake, MT, Kalispell

Lesnikowski, Danuta ....(401) 272-1010
dlesnikowski@thericatholic.com, Circulation Manager, Rhode Island Catholic, RI, Providence

Lessard, Dean .... (705) 268-5050 ext. 247
dean.lessard@sunmedia.ca, Circ. Mgr., The Timmins Daily Press, ON, Timmins

Lessard, Isabelle ....(613) 488-2651
redaction@journalagricom.ca, Ed, Agricom, ON, Clarence Creek

Lessard, Martyne
martyne.lessard@lavoixdelest.ca, Adv. Mgr., La Voix De L'est Plus, QC, Granby

Lessard, Paul.........................(418) 304-2080
paul.lessard@quebecormedia.com, Journal Le Peuple, QC, Levis
paul.lessard@quebecormedia.com, Ed., Beauport Express, QC, Beauport
paul.lessard@quebecormedia.com, Peuple De Lotbiniere, QC, Levis

Lessard, Richard.........................(819) 569-9981
Prodn. Mgr., Brome County News, QC, Knowlton

Lessersohn, James C. ....(212) 556-1234
Vice Pres., Finance/Cor. Devel., The New York Times Co., NY, New York

Lessley, Chris ....(918) 653-2425
heavenerledgerchris@windstream.net, Classified, The Heavener Ledger, OK, Heavener

Lessman, Justin
justinl@livewireprinting.com, Pub., Jackson County Pilot, MN, Jackson

Lessman, Justin R.
justin.lessman@livewireprinting.com, Pub., Jackson County Livewire, MN, Jackson

Lester, Jeff..ext. 235
jlester@coalfield.com, News Ed., The Coalfield Progress, VA, Norton

Lester, Lorna ....(905) 664-8800
llester@hamiltonnews.com, Office Mgr., Dundas Star News, ON, Stoney Creek

Lester, Lorna .... (905) 664-8800 ext. 225
llester@hamiltonnews.com, Office Mgr., Ancaster News, ON, Stoney Creek

Lester, Michelle .... (570) 970-7147
mlester@timesleader.com, Vice Pres., Classified Adv., Nepa Shopper, PA, Wilkes Barre

Lester, Michelle
mlester@fosters.com, Adv. Mgr., Saving Source, ME, Portland
mlester@fosters.com, VP, Adv., Sanford News, ME, Sanford

Lester , Corrinne
clester@carriagetownenews.com, Prod. Mgr. , Carriage Towne News, NH, Kingston

Leszczynski, Emily
popmail@insnet.com, Gen. Mgr., Dziennik Zwaizkowy, IL, Chicago

Letheby, Pete .... (308) 381-9468
pete.letheby@theindependent.com, Assoc. Ed., The Grand Island Independent, NE, Grand Island

Leto, Frank .... (575) 541-5401
fleto@lcsun-news.com, Business Consultant, Ruidoso Free Press (OOB) , NM, Ruidoso
fleto@lcsun-news.com, Adv. Dir., The Ruidoso News, NM, Ruidoso

Leto, Frank
fleto@dailyitem.com, Pub, The Danville News, PA, Danville
fleto@dailyitem.com, Pub., The Daily Item, PA, Sunbury

Lett, Mark
mark@thestatesb.com, VP/Exec. Ed., The State, SC, Columbia

Lette, Chad .... (608) 755-9493
clette@gazettextra.com, Director of Technical Services & Facilities, The Gazette - gazettextra.com, WI, Janesville

Letteney, Larry
larry.letteney@creo.com, Pres., Creo Americas, Creo, MA, Billerica

Lettera, Larry
larry@nycphoto.com, Adv. Mgr., Wagner International Photos, Inc., New York

Letterman, Amanda
aletterman@theunionstar.com, Adv. Mgr., The Union Star, VA, Brookneal

Letterman, Gretchen .... (727) 892-2203
letterman@tampabay.com, Dir., Editorial/ Creative, Times Targeted Media, Tampa Bay Times, FL, St Petersburg

Leu, Jon
jleu@nonpareilonline.com, Editorial Page Ed., The Daily Nonpareil, IA, Council Bluffs

Leu, Ken
harperadvocate@sbcglobal.net, Pub., Harper Advocate, KS, Harper

Leukam, Diane
diane@saukherald.com, Ed., Sauk Centre Herald, MN, Sauk Centre

Lev, Deborah .... (908) 852-1400 x2243
levd@centenarycollege.edu, Advisor, Centenary College, NJ, Hackettstown

Levan, Jason .... (724) 465-5555 ext. 270
jlevan@indianagazette.net , News Ed., The Indiana Gazette, PA, Indiana

Levant, Lilyan .... (217) 337-8300
levant@illinimedia.com, Advisor, Univ. of Illinois, IL, Champaign

Levasseur, Rick .... (207) 990-8000
rlevasseur@bangordailynews.com, Editor, Houlton Pioneer Times, ME, Houlton

Levasseur, Rick .... (207) 990-8000
rlevasseur@bangordailynews.com, Editor, Aroostook Republican and News, ME, Presque Isle

Levasseur, Rick .... (207) 990-8123
rlevasseur@bangordailynews.com, State Ed., Bangor Daily News, ME, Bangor

Levasseur, Yves .... (514) 987-2309

ylevasseur@montrealgazette.com, Montreal Gazette, QC, Montreal

Leveille, Georges
georges.leveille@quebecormedia.com, Circ. Mgr., Le Journal de Quebec, QC, Vanier

Levene, Steve .... (404) 917-2200, ext. 111
stevelevene@reporternewspapers.net, Fouder & Publisher, Reporter Newspapers, GA, Atlanta

Levensalor, William C. .... (678) 341-2600
bill@beltcorp.com, Pres., Belt Corporation of America, GA, Cumming

Levenstein, Alan .... (757) 446-2000
alan.levenstein@pilotonline.com, Business Develop. Mgr., The Virginian-Pilot, VA, Norfolk

Leverenz, Harvey .... (608) 489-2264
sentry@mwt.net, Managing Editor, Hillsboro Sentry-Enterprise, WI, Hillsboro

Leveritt, Alan .... (501) 375-2985
alan@arktimes.com, Pub., Arkansas Times, AR, Little Rock

Levesque, Gilles
gilles.levesque@canadafrancais.com, Ed., Le Canada Francais, QC, Sainte Jean sur Richelieu

Levesque, Gino .... (418) 960-2090
journal@lenord-cotier.com, Nord Cotier, QC, Sept-Iles

Levesque, Joyce M. .... (603) 668-4321 ext. 401
jlevesque@unionleader.com, VP Finance, New Hampshire Union Leader/New Hampshire Sunday News, NH, Manchester

Levesque, Lucy-Rose
lucie-rose.levesque @ hebdosquebecor.com, Ed., L'avant-poste Gaspesien, QC, Amqui

Levesque, Pierre
pierre.levesque@hebdosquebecor.com, Ed., Le Saint-laurent Portage, QC, Riviere-du-Loup

Levesque, Sidney
sidney@abilenecac.org, Editorial Page Ed., Abilene Reporter-News, TX, Abilene

Levey, Brian
ecmarketing@datacolor.com, Vice Pres. Mktg./ Sales, ColorVision, Inc., NJ, Lawrenceville

Levin, Becky
blevin@postindependent.com, Advertising sales, Glenwood Springs Post Independent, CO, Glenwood Springs

Levin, Deborah
deblevin@aol.com, Pres., Levin Represents, Santa Monica

Levin, Larry .... (314) 743-3672
llevin@thejewishlight.com, CEO/Pub., Saint Louis Jewish Light, MO, Saint Louis
llevin@thejewishlight.com, Publisher/CEO, St. Louis Jewish Light, MO, Saint Louis

Levin, Linda
lllevin@uri.edu, Secretary, Rhode Island Press Association, RI, Kingston

Levine, Charisse .... (704) 463-1360
Pfeiffer Univ., NC, Misenheimer

Levine, Elana .... (414) 229-4436
ehlevine@uwm.edu, Associate Professor, University of Wisconsin-Milwaukee / Department of Journalism, Advertising, and Media Studies (JAMS), WI, Milwaukee

Levine, Jacki
levinej@gvillesun.com, Mng. Ed., The Gainesville Sun, FL, Gainesville

Levine, Jeff
info@logopremiums.com, Project Mgr., LOGOpremiums.com, NY, Mount Kisco

Levine, Jeremy .... (516) 512-3878
jeremyalanlevine@gmail.com, Editor-In-Chief, Clark University, MA, Worcester

Levine, Jonathan
jonathan@pittsfieldgazette.com, Ed., The

Pittsfield Gazette, MA, Pittsfield

Levinsohn, Peter
info@autotypeamerica.com, Pres., Mac Dermid Autotype Inc., IL, Rolling Meadows

Levinson, Paul
paullevinson1@cs.com, Chair, Fordham University, NY, Bronx

Levinson, Warren
wlevinson@ap.org, Producer, Associated Press, The, New York

Levit, Henri C.
info@simonmiller.com, COO, Simon Miller Sales Co., PA, Philadelphia

Levit, Joseph
info@simonmiller.com, Pres., Simon Miller Sales Co., PA, Philadelphia

Levit, Mark
mark@partnerslevit.com, Treasurer, League of Advertising Agencies, Inc., NY, New York

Levite, Laurence A.
llevite@buffalospree.com, Pub., Forever Young, NY, Buffalo

Levitt, Ed .... (914) 592-5222 ext. 276
Circ. Mgr., Pennysaver, NY, Elmsford
Circ. Mgr., Pennysaver, NY, Nanuet

Levitt, Leon
leon.levitt@cmgdigital.com, Vice Pres., Digital Media, Cox Media Group, GA, Atlanta

Levrier, Robert .... (956) 683-4322
rlevrier@themonitor.com, Circ. Dir. , The Monitor, TX, McAllen

Levy, Alan .... (415) 461-6006, ext. 213
alevy@verifiedaudit.com, VP Marketing and Sales, Verified Audit Circulation (VAC), CA, San Rafael

Levy, Danny
dlevy@jewishlongbeach.org, Director of Development, Jewish Community Chronicle, CA, Long Beach

Levy, Janice
jlevy@ithaca.edu, Assoc. Prof./Cinema & Photography Chair, Ithaca College, NY, Ithaca

Levy, Jay R. .... (212) 686-6850
news@blackradionetwork.com, Pres., Black Press Service, Inc., New York

Levy, June .... (847) 375-5183
june.levy@srds.com, Director, Data Services, SRDS, a Kantar Media Company, IL, Des Plaines

Levy, Michael
info@arpac.com, Pres., Arpac Group, IL, Schiller Park

Lewchuk, Ken .... (306) 563-5131
k.lewchuk@sasktel.net, Publisher, The Kamsack Times, SK, Canora
k.lewchuk@sasktel.net, Gen. Mgr., Norquay North Star (OOB) , SK, Canora
k.lewchuk@sasktel.net, Preeceville Progress, SK, Canora

Lewey, Weston McCollum .... (870) 633-3131
wlewey@thnews.com, Pub., East Arkansas Advertiser, AR, Forrest City

Lewin, Chantelle
clewin@amisun.com, Advertisement, Anna Maria Island Sun, FL, Anna Maria

Lewin, Jim
jlewin@shepherd.edu, Shepherd University, WV, Shepherdstown

Lewinski, Joe .... (215) 822-5519
lewinski@icanon.com, Pres., ICANON Associates, Inc., PA, Hatfield

Lewis, Ashley .... (705) 272-3344
ashley.lewis@sunmedia.ca, Reporter, Cochrane Times-post, ON, Cochrane

Lewis, Barry .... (845) 346-3178
blewis@th-record.com, Ed., The Times Herald-Record, NY, Middletown

Lewis, Beth
beth@acrobatrecruiting.com, Malcolm X College, IL, Chicago

Lewis, Brian .... (212) 803-8442
brian.lewis@sourcemedia.com, Asst. Ed., American Banker Online, American Banker, NY, New York

Lewis, Brian .... (319) 961-0448
brian@cvsaver.com, Pub., Cedar Valley Saver, IA, Waterloo

Lewis, Cammy
ads@gonzalesinquirer.com, Classifieds Adv. Sales, The Gonzales Inquirer, TX, Gonzales

Lewis, Charles
charles.lewis@mnsu.edu, Chair/Prof., Minnesota State University Mankato, MN, Mankato

Lewis, Chris .... (229) 273 - 2277 x1603
chris.lewis@gaflnews.com, Gen. Mngr./Adv. Mngr., Cordele Dispatch, GA, Cordele

Lewis, Dal .... (403) 250-5220
dal.lewis@sunmedia.ca, Asst. Dir. of Sales, The Calgary Sun, AB, Calgary

Lewis, Darrell .... (217) 347-7151 ext.112
darrell.lewis@effinghamdailynews.com, Pub./Adv. Dir., Effingham Daily News, IL, Effingham
darrell.lewis@effinghamdailynews.com, Pub., Register-News, IL, Effingham
darrell.lewis@effinghamdailynews.com, Pub., The Times-Leader, IL, Mc Leansboro
darrell.lewis@effinghamdailynews.com, Pub., Daily Union, IL, Shelbyville

Lewis, David .... (940) 686-2169
editor@postsignal.com, Pub./Ed., Pilot Point Post Signal, TX, Pilot Point

Lewis, Deanna .... (207) 384-5022
deanna.lewis@localmedia.org, Classified Avenue Director of Sales, Local Media Association, MI, Lake City

Lewis, Diane .... (937) 651-1132
classifieds@examiner.org, Class., Bellefontaine Examiner, OH, Bellefontaine

Lewis, Elise R. .... (601) 888-4293
lililewis@bellsouth.net, Adv. Mgr., The Woodville Republican, MS, Woodville

Lewis, Eric .... (248) 628-4801 ext. 20
shermanpub@aol.com, Adv. Mgr., The Lake Orion Review, MI, Lake Orion

Lewis, Eric
eric@shermanpublications.org, Adv. Mgr., Oxford Leader, MI, Oxford

Lewis, Holly .... (317) 477-3240
hlewis@greenfieldreporter.com, Circ. Clerk, Daily Reporter, IN, Greenfield

Lewis, Hugh .... (903) 665-2462
generalmanager@jimplecute.com, Gen. Mgr., Jefferson Jimplecute, TX, Jefferson

Lewis, James
james.lewis@scc-adventist.org, Prodn. Mgr., Nashville Pride, TN, Nashville

Lewis, James E.
jlewis@birminghamtimes.com, Pub., Birmingham Times, AL, Birmingham

Lewis, Jennifer .... (912) 489-9439
jlewis@morrismultimedia.com, Regl. Controller, Statesboro Herald, GA, Statesboro

Lewis, John .... (405) 382-1100
news@seminoleproducer.com, Prod. / Cir. Dir., The Seminole Producer, OK, Seminole

Lewis, John
jlewis@thelegalrecord.net, Pub., Legal Record, KS, Olathe

Lewis, Julie .... (607) 441-7212
jlewis@thedailystar.com, Photo Dept. Mgr., The Daily Star, NY, Oneonta

Lewis, Kathleen
news@robdailynews.com, Pub., Lewis

(Real Estate), Los Angeles Times, CA, Los Angeles

Linden, Brian ....ext. 220
brian.l@crawfordthomas.com, Univ. of Central Florida, FL, Orlando

Linden, Thomas R. ....(919) 962-4078
Glaxo Wellcome Distinguished Prof. of Medical Journalism, University of North Carolina, NC, Chapel Hill

Lindenberg, Scott
sclinden@mailbox.sc.edu, Univ. of South Carolina, SC, Columbia

Linder, Doug
hybrid@southslope.net, Pub., The Solon Economist, IA, Solon

Linder, Peter
linderpeter@nmhu.edu, Chair, New Mexico Highlands University, NM, Las Vegas

Lindley, Doug ....(208) 239-3138
douglind@journalnet.com, Photo Ed., Idaho State Journal, ID, Pocatello

Lindley, Kevin
klindley@crestonnews.com, Prodn. Mgr., Southwest Iowa Advertiser, IA, Creston

Lindley, Kevin
klindley@crestonnews.com, Prodn. Mgr., Creston News Advertiser, IA, Creston

Lindner, Doug ....(319) 624-2233
hybrid@southslope.net, Pub., North Liberty Leader, IA, North Liberty

Lindquist, Brent ....(360) 384-1411
news@ferndalerecord.com, News Editor, Ferndale Record, WA, Ferndale

Lindquist, Brent ....(360) 354-4444
brent@lyndentribune.com, Assistant Ed., Lynden Tribune, WA, Lynden

Lindquist, Dizey ....(941) 320-7972
dizey@bocabeacon.com, Adv. Rep., Boca Beacon, FL, Boca Grande

Lindquist, Peter ....(717) 721-4414
plindquist.eph@lnpnews.com, Vice Pres./Asst. Gen. Mgr., Lititz Record Express, PA, Ephrata
plindquist.eph@lnpnews.com, Vice Pres./Asst. Gen. Mgr., The Ephrata Review, PA, Ephrata
plindquist.eph@lnpnews.com, Vice President, Lancaster Farming, PA, Ephrata

Lindsay, Alvie ....(317) 444-8218
alvie.lindsay@indystar.com, News Director , The Indianapolis Star, IN, Indianapolis

Lindsay, Carol
meta@kwnews.com, Admin., Keister Williams Newspaper Services, Inc., VA, Charlottesville

Lindsay, Debbie ....(858) 451-6200
debbiel@brehmmail.com, Execu Asst, Brehm Communications, Inc., CA, San Diego

Lindsay, Jason ....(712) 336-1211
jlindsay@dickinsoncountynews.com, Adv. Mgr., Storm Lake Pilot Tribune, IA, Storm Lake

Lindsay, John
john.d.lindsay@nasa.gov, Sports Ed., Scripps Howard News Service, Washington

Lindsay, Molly......................ext. 257
cheryl@desert.net, Controller, Weekly Alibi, NM, Albuquerque

Lindsay, Ted ...... (905) 632-4444 ext. 272
tlindsay@burlingtonpost.com, Adv. Mgr., The Flamborough Review, ON, Waterdown

Lindsay, Walton
ky@kwnews.com, Pres., Keister Williams Newspaper Services, Inc., VA, Charlottesville

Lindsay, Walton C.
ky@kwnews.com, Pres., Keister-Williams Newspaper Services, Inc., VA, Charlottesville

Lindsay, Walton C. (Ky)
ky@kwnews.com, Pres./Treasurer, Keister Williams Newspaper Services, Inc., VA, Charlottesville

Lindsey, Amy
alindsey@republicmedia.com, Dir., Territory Sales, The Arizona Republic, AZ, Phoenix

Lindsey, Breonna ....(937) 538-4828
blindsey@civitasmedia.com, Dist. Cir. Mgr., The Sidney Daily News, OH, Sidney

Lindsey, Cindy
adrep@mitchellnews.com, Adv. Mgr., Mitchell News-Journal, NC, Spruce Pine

Lindsey, Corey R.
jrnews@grm.net, Pub., The Leon Journal-Reporter, IA, Leon

Lindsey, Jerry .... Ext. 1024
Editor, Whiteside News Sentinel, IL, Morrison

Lindsey, Patricia ....(314) 831-4645
independentnws@aol.com., Assistant editor-Entertainment, Independent News, MO, Florissant

Lindsey, Robert ....(314) 831-4645
independentnws@aol.com, Editor-Publisher, Independent News, MO, Florissant

Lindsley, Gary ....(972) 563-6476
news@terrelltribune.com, News Ed, The Terrell Tribune, TX, Terrell

Lindus, Cheryl ....(765) 213-5701
clindus@muncie.gannett.com, Gen. Mgr./Adv. Dir., The Star Press, IN, Muncie

Lindus, Linda ....(562) 499-1422
linda.lindus@presstelegram.com, Publisher, Press-Telegram Publications, Inc., CA, Long Beach

Linebarger, Les
Leslinebarger@hendersondailynews.com, Pub., Overton News, TX, Henderson

Linebarger, Les
leslinebarger@hendersondailynews.com, Pub./Nat'l Adv. Mgr., Henderson Daily News, TX, Henderson

Lineman, Thomas
juniatanews@comcast.net, Pub./Ed., Juniata News, PA, Philadelphia

Linenberger, Shawn
slinenberger@theworldco.info, News Ed, The Mirror, KS, Tonganoxie

Linens, Janina ....(828) 437-2161
jlinens@morganton.com, Sales Leader, The News Herald, NC, Morganton

Linens, Nina
jlinens@morganton.com, Adv. Dir. , The McDowell News, NC, Marion

Linert, Brenda ....(330) 841-1768
blinert@tribtoday.com, Ed., The Tribune Chronicle, OH, Warren

Linette, Jim ....(239) 574-1110
jlinette@breezenewspapers.com, Ed., Island Reporter, FL, Sanibel
jlinette@breezenewspapers.com, Sports Ed., Cape Coral Breeze, FL, Cape Coral

Linex, Raymond
rlinex@corsicanadailysun.com, Pub., Star Shopper, TX, Corsicana

Liney, Kathy
kathyliney@issisvs.com, Sales, Insurance Specialties Services, Inc., PA, New Britain

Lingenfelter, Tom
tlingenfelter@thehawkeye.com, Prodn. Supt., The Hawk Eye, IA, Burlington

Link, John ....(918) 273-2446
nowatastar@sbcglobal.net, Gen. Mgr., The Nowata Star, OK, Nowata

Link, John
pdjnews@sbcglobal.net, Gen Mgr., The American, OK, Fairland

Linker, Erich ....(212) 807-4791
erich.linker@impremedia.com, Sr. Vice Pres., Sales, impreMedia LLC, NY, Brooklyn

Linn, Betty E. ....(559) 683-4464

blinn@sierrastar.com, Pub., Sierra Star, CA, Oakhurst
blinn@sierrastar.com, Publisher/Sierra Star, The Fresno Bee, CA, Fresno

Linn, Maureen ....(605) 886-6901
Circ. Mgr., Watertown Public Opinion, SD, Watertown

Linn, Sarah ....(805) 781-7907
Ticket Ed., The Tribune, CA, San Luis Obispo

Linnehan, Helen .... (508) 749-3166 x333
hlinnehan@worcestermag.com, Sales Mgr. , Worcester Magazine, MA, Worcester

Linnell, Laura ....(403) 235-7214
llinnell@calgaryherald.com, Adv. Sales Mgr., Calgary Herald, AB, Calgary

Linneman, Janice...................(856) 486-2421
jlinneman@gannettnj.com, Admin Assist., The Courier-Post, NJ, Cherry Hill

Linscott, Ron ....(580) 889-3319
rlinscott@atokaspeedynet.net, Adv. Mgr., Atoka County Times, OK, Atoka

Linscott, Tim
wilberrepublican@windstream.net, Ed., Wilber Republican, NE, Wilber

Linscott, Tim
Timothylinscott1@gmail.com, Pub./Owner, Fairbury Journal-News, NE, Fairbury

Linsey, Herbert
subs@atling.com, Circ. Mgr., The Atlanta Inquirer, GA, Atlanta

Linsner, Dawn ....(804) 947-4299
Randolph-Macon Woman's College, VA, Lynchburg

Lint, Bea ....(760) 256-4140
blint@desertdispatch.com, Adv. Dir., Desert Dispatch, CA, Victorville

Linton, David ....(843) 537-2791
countysh@bellsouth.net, Gen. Mgr., Chesterfield County Shopper, SC, Cheraw

Linton, Kathy ....ext. 134
kathy.linton@flyergroup.com, Mng. Ed., Westside Flyer, IN, Avon

Linton, Kathy ....ext. 134
kathy.linton@flyergroup.com, Ed., The Weekend Flyer, IN, Avon

Linton, Kathy .... (317) 272-5800 ext. 134
kathy.linton@flyergroup.com, Ed., Hendricks County Flyer, IN, Avon

Linville, Danny
thezephyrhillsnews@gmail.com, Pub., Zephyrhills News, FL, Zephyrhills

Linville, Jan
thezephyrhillsnews@gmail.com, Pub., Zephyrhills News, FL, Zephyrhills

Linville, Jeff
jlinville@mtairynews.com, Assistant Editor, Mount Airy News, NC, Mount Airy

Linz, Marguerite
mlinz1@live.ndm.edu, Lead Writer/ Managing Editor, Notre Dame of Maryland University, MD, Baltimore

Liot, Alex...................(902) 426-2811 ext. 3039
aliot@herald.ca, Mgr., Bus. Devel., The Chronicle Herald, NS, Halifax

Lipez, Jeannine ....(570) 858-5688
jlipez2@yahoo.com, Advertising, The Record, PA, Renovo

Lipez, John ....(570) 858-5688
jlipez@yahoo.com, Publisher, The Record, PA, Renovo

Lippincott, John
lippincott@case.org, Pres., Council for Advancement and Support of Education, DC, Washington

Lippincott, Judy ....(608) 208-1676
milton@hngnews.com, Office Clerk, The Milton Courier, WI, Milton

Lippman, Jerome W. ....(516) 829-4000
lijworld@aol.com, Ed., Manhattan Jewish Sentinel, NY, Far Rockaway

Lippman, Jerome W. ....(516) 829-4000
lijworld@aol.com, Mng. Ed., Long Island Jewish World, NY, Far Rockaway

Lippman, Jerome W. ....(516) 829-4000
lijworld@aol.com, Mng. Ed., Jewish Tribune of Rockland County, NY, Far Rockaway

Lipps, Shelley .... (440) 998-2323 Ext. 108
slipps@starbeacon.com, Adv. Acct. Exec. , Star Beacon, OH, Ashtabula

Lipschutz, Neal
neal.lipschutz@dowjones.com, Mng. Ed., Dow Jones Newswire Americas, Dow Jones Newswires - New York, NY, New York

Lipshetz, Terry ....(920) 993-7198
tlipshet@appleton.gannett.com, Consumer Experience Director, Post-Crescent, WI, Appleton

Lipsky, Seth......................ext. 688
lipsky@nysun.com, Ed., The New York Sun, NY, New York

Liptak, Cindy ....(815) 937-3310
Business Manager, Small Newspaper Group, IL, Kankakee

Liptak, Cindy ....(815) 937-3310
cliptak@daily-journal.com, Bus. Mgr., The Daily Journal, IL, Kankakee

Liptak, Cindy ....(815) 431-4055
cindyl@mywebtimes.com, Bus. Mgr., The Times, IL, Ottawa

Lipton, Gary ....ext. 107
gary@napsnet.com, Vice Pres., Media Rel., North American Precis Syndicate, Inc., NY, New York

Lira, Norma ....(760) 337-3443
nlira@ivpressonline.com, Sales Mgr, Imperial Valley Press, CA, El Centro

Liroff, Bruce
liroffb@prisco.com, Pres., Printers' Service/ Prisco/PriscoDigital, NJ, Newark

Lisa, Newell ....(217) 593-6515
lisa@elliott-publishing.com, Advertising, Camp Point Journal, IL, Camp Point

Lisagor, Nancy .... (215) 291-5560 ext. 109
nlisagor@metrokids.com, Ed. in Chief, Metrokids Magazine, TX, Addison

Lisagor, Nancy ....ext. 109
nlisagor@metrokids.com, Ed. in Chief, MetroKids Delaware, PA, Philadelphia

Lisagor, Nancy ....ext. 109
nlisagor@metrokids.com, Ed. in Chief, Metrokids South Jersey, PA, Philadelphia

Lisby, Addie ....(704) 599-4630
sozbusiness@yahoo.com, Editor and Publisher, The Star Of Zion, NC, Charlotte

Lisi, Clemente ....(646) 930-0617
clisi@tkc.edu, Assistant Affiliate Professor of Journalism, The Empire State Tribune, NY, New York

Lisk, Sue ....(202) 414 -0555
sue.lisk@afp.com, Senior Account Manager, Agence France-Presse - Washington, DC, Washington

List, Karen
klist@journ.umass.edu, Dir., University of Massachusetts, MA, Amherst

List, Randy
rlist22@gmail.com, Pub., Kingsley News-Times, IA, Kingsley

Lister, Fred...................(719) 541-2288
limonleader@netecin.net, Co-Pub., Ranchland News, CO, Simla
limonleader@netecin.net, Pub, The Limon Leader, CO, Limon

Lister, Letitia
letti@bhpioneer.com, Pub., Weekly Prospector,

SD, Spearfish

Lister, Letitia .... (605) 642-2761
letti@bhpioneer.com, Pub., Black Hills Pioneer,
SD, Spearfish

Lister, Letitia
Letti@bhpioneer.com, Pub., Nation's Center
News, SD, Buffalo

Lister, Nancy .... (905) 985-6985
standardnancy@powergate.ca, Adv. Rep. , The
Standard Newspaper, ON, Port Perry

Lister, Scott .... (605) 642-2761
scott@bhpioneer.com, Circ. Mgr., Black Hills
Pioneer, SD, Spearfish

Liston, Roz .... ext. 136
timesledgernews@cnglocal.com, Ed., Astoria
Times, NY, Bayside

Liston, Roz .... (718) 260-4545
timesledgernews@cnglocal.com, Ed., Forest
Hills Ledger, NY, Bayside

Liston, Roz .... (718) 260-4545
timesledgernews@cnglocal.com, Mng. Ed.,
Flushing Times, NY, Bayside

Liston, Roz .... (718) 260-4545
timesledgernews@cnglocal.com, Ed., Bayside
Times, NY, Bayside

Liston, Roz .... (718) 260-4545
timesledgernews@cnglocal.com, Ed., The
Little Neck Ledger, NY, Bayside

Liston, Roz .... (718) 260-4545
timesledgernews@cnglocal.com, Ed., Fresh
Meadows Times, NY, Bayside
timesledgernews@cnglocal.com, Ed., Jackson
Heights Times, NY, Bayside
timesledgernews@cnglocal.com, Ed.,
Laurelton Times, NY, Bayside
timesledgernews@cnglocal.com, Mng. Ed.,
Ridgewood Ledger, NY, Bayside
timesledgernews@cnglocal.com, Mng. Ed.,
Jamaica Times, NY, Bayside

Liston, Roz .... (718) 229-0300 ext. 111
liston@timesledger.com, Mng. Ed., The
Whitestone Times, NY, Bayside

Listopad, Steve .... (870) 230-5075
listops@hsu.edu, Advisor, Henderson State
Univ., AR, Arkadelphia

Listopad, Steve .... (701) 252-3467
Jamestown College, ND, Jamestown

Liter, Hannah .... (208) 885-5780
Univ. of Idaho, ID, Moscow

Litowitz, Patrick
plitowitz@ncnewsonline.com, News Ed., New
Castle News, PA, New Castle

Litteral, Ed .... (740) 353-3101 Ext. 1925
elitteral@civitasmedia.com, Cir. Mgr., The
Portsmouth Daily Times, OH, Portsmouth

Little, Blair
frontdesk@wetmountaintribune.com, Admin.
Asst., Wet Mountain Tribune, CO, Westcliffe

Little, Greg .... (570) 253-3055 x301
glittle@wayneindependent.com, Group Ed.,
The Wayne Independent, PA, Honesdale

Little, Heather .... (618) 932-2146
sicirc@sitraders.com, Office/Circ. Mgr., The
Daily American, IL, West Frankfort

Little, James A.
editor@wetmountaintribune.com, Ed./Pub., Wet
Mountain Tribune, CO, Westcliffe

Little, Wendy
wendy@qctonline.com, Circulation Manager,
Quebec Chronicle-telegraph, QC, Quebec

Littlefield, Susan .... (574) 658-4111
slittlefield@the-papers.com, Advertising
Representative, The Paper - Kosciusko
Edition, IN, Milford

Littlejohn, Lila .... (661) 287-5520
llittlejohn@signalscv.com, Editorial Ed., Santa
Clarita Valley Signal, CA, Santa Clarita
llittlejohn@signalscv.com, Connect SCV, CA,

Santa Clarita

Littlepage, Deborah
dlittlepage@the-messenger.com, Adv. Dir., The
Messenger, KY, Madisonville

Littlewood, Philip
info@airloc.com, Engineering Mgr., AirLoc
LLC, MA, Franklin

Litty, Jamie
jamie.litty@uncp.edu, Chair, University of North
Carolina at Pembroke, NC, Pembroke

Liu, Dejun
dejun_liu@pvamu.edu, Head, Prairie View
A&M University, TX, Prairie View

Liu, Don
Don.Liu@xerox.com, Corporate Executive Vice
President
General Counsel and Secretary , Xerox Corp.,
CT, Norwalk

Liu, George
george@nwasianweekly.com, Circ. Mgr.,
Seattle Chinese Post, WA, Seattle

Liu, William W.
bill@cdtechnology.com, Pres., CD Technology,
CA, Santa Clara

Liulamaga, David
dliulamaga@newportnewstimes.com, Circ.
Mgr., News-Times, OR, Newport

Lively, Kristina .... (716) 645-0170
klively@buffalo.edu, Webmaster, University at
Buffalo School of Law, NY, Amherst

Liverett, Suzanne .... (706) 868-1222
suzanne.liverett@augustachronicle.com, Office
Mgr., The Columbia County News-Times,
GA, Evans

Liveris, Andrew
dowmedia.relations@dow.com, Chrmn./Pres./
CEO, The Dow Chemical Co., MI, Midland

Livermore, Ann
ann_livermore@hp.com, Exec. Vice Pres.,
Enterprise Bus., Hewlett-Packard Co., CA,
Palo Alto

Livingston, Cynde .... same
same, News Reporter, Balaton Press Tribune,
MN, Balaton

Livingston, Sharon
sharon.livingston@advocateanddemocrat.com,
Adv. Mgr., The Advocate & Democrat, TN,
Sweetwater

Livingston, Tom .... ext. 102
editor@metrokids.com, Exec. Ed., Metrokids
South Jersey, PA, Philadelphia

Livingston, Tom .... ext. 102
editor@metrokids.com, Exec. Ed., MetroKids
Delaware, PA, Philadelphia

Livingston, Tom .... (314) 340-8000
TLIVINGSTON@STLDIST.COM, Pres., St.
Louis Post-Dispatch, MO, Saint Louis

Lix, Doug
doug.lix@mjtimes.sk.ca, Circ. Mgr., The Moose
Jaw Times-Herald, SK, Moose Jaw

Ljungaeus, Diana
diana@lapressclub.org, Exec. Dir., Los Angeles
Press Club, CA, Los Angeles

Llevada, Vicky .... (407) 767-0070 Ext. 142
vicky.llevada@laprensaorlando.com, Calssified
/ Display Classifieds, La Prensa, FL,
Longwood

Llewelyn, Lisa .... (801) 344-2957
lllewelyn@heraldextra.com, Adv. Cord., Daily
Herald, UT, Provo

Lloyd, Betty
advertising@coastalview.com, Adv. Mgr.,
Coastal View News, CA, Carpinteria

Lloyd, Caitlin .... (212) 930-5753
clloyd@nypost.com, Advertising, New York
Post, NY, New York

Lloyd, Eddy

elloyd@chathamstartribune.com, Sports Ed.,
Star-Tribune, VA, Chatham

Lloyd, Jared .... (801) 344-2555
jllloyd@heraldextra.com, Sports Editor, Daily
Herald, UT, Provo

Lloyd, Lynn
lynn.lloyd@mtstandard.com, Gen. Mgr. , The
Montana Standard, MT, Butte

Lloyd, Nicholas .... ext. 16
nlloyd@brodiesystem.com, Eng., Brodie
System, Inc., NJ, Linden

Lloyd, Robin .... (914) 592-5222 ext. 208
rlloyd@nysaver.com, Prodn. Mgr., Pennysaver,
NY, Elmsford
rlloyd@nysaver.com, Prodn. Mgr., Pennysaver,
NY, Nanuet

Lloyd, Ruth .... (250) 996-8482
newsroom@caledoniacourier.com, Ed.,
Caledonia Courier, BC, Fort St. James

Lo, Jenny
jlo@wesleyan.edu, Wesleyan University, CT,
Middletown

Lo Sapio, Camille ....(610) 258-7171, ext. 3530
closapio@express-times.com, Adv Sales
Manager, The Express-Times, PA, Easton

LoBasso, Randy
RLoBasso@ccp.edu, Faculty Advisor,
Community College of Philadelphia, PA,
Philadelphia

LoCascio, Chris .... (951) 827-2105
EIC, Univ. of California, Riverside, CA,
Riverside

LoCoco, Renee .... (574) 722-5000 Ext. 5136
renee.lococo@pharostribune.com, Marketing
Exec., Pharos-Tribune, IN, Logansport

LoPilato, Joseph .... (617) 619-6121
joseph.lopilato@bostonherald.com, Vice Pres./
Classified Advt., Boston Herald, MA, Boston

Loader, Marcia .... (517) 486-2400
advance@cass.net, Ed., The Advance, MI,
Blissfield

Lobanov, Igor .... (858) 270-9002
Travel Ed., Mature Life Features, San Diego

Lobb, Bill .... (610) 371-5158
blobb@readingeagle.com, Director of
Circulation Sales, Reading Eagle Company,
PA, Reading

Lobb, Karyn .... (409) 379-2416
newtonnews@valornet.com, Office Mgr./
Classifieds, Newton County News, TX,
Newton

Lobb, William J. .... (610) 371-5158
blobb@readingeagle.com, Circulation Sales
Director, Reading Eagle, PA, Reading

Lobeck, Linda
lobeck@ironmountaindailynews.com, Business
Ed., The Daily News, MI, Iron Mountain

Lobecker, William B. .... (215) 345-3034
blobecker@phillyburbs.com, Circ. Dir., The
Intelligencer, PA, Doylestown

Loberstein, Adam .... (530) 752-9887
University of California, Davis, CA, Davis

Lobianco, David
davidl@mansimedia.com , Dir. Order
Fulfillment, MANSI Media, PA, Harrisburg

Lobsinger, Caroline
clobsinger@bonnercountydailybee.com, News
Room Ed., Bonner County Daily Bee, ID,
Sandpoint

Locher, Caroline .... (514) 522-6142
caroline.locher@fpjq.org , Exec. Dir, Federation
professionnelle des journalistes du Quebec,
QC, Montreal (Quebec)

Lochte, Kate
kate.lochte@murraystate.edu, Adj., Murray
State University, KY, Murray

Lockart, Lovetta .... ext. 223

llockart@leaderunion.com, Office Mgr., The
Leader-union Publishing Co., IL, Vandalia

Lockart, Lovetta .... (618) 283-3374
llockart@leaderunion.com, Office Mgr., The
Leader-Union, IL, Vandalia

Locke, Kerth
Keith.locke@rheaheraldnews.com, Adv. Mgr.,
The Herald-News, TN, Dayton

Locke, Sara Jane
sarajane.locke@rheaheraldnews.com, Pub.,
The Herald-News, TN, Dayton

Locke, Susan
circulation@iolaregister.com, Circ. Mgr., The
Iola Register, KS, Iola

Locke, Susan B. .... (718) 634-4000
sbl@rockawave.com, Pub., The Wave, NY,
Rockaway Beach

Lockhart, Greg .... ext. 340
gregl@nowtoronto.com, Prodn. Mgr., Now, ON,
Toronto

Lockhart, Jhaneel
jlockhart@expandedschools.org, Baruch
College/CUNY, NY, New York

Lockhart, Lee
leel@wyodaily.com, Pub., Northern Wyoming
Daily News, WY, Worland

Lockhart, Susan
susanl@wyodaily.com, Special Projects Ed.,
Northern Wyoming Daily News, WY, Worland

Locklear, Brenda
blocklear@sctnews.com, Circ. Mgr., Sumter
County Times, FL, Bushnell

Lockwood, John .... (978) 739-8506
newburyport@wickedlocal.com, Ed.,
Newburyport Current, MA, Danvers

Lockwood, Nicole
nlockwood@AntonMediaGroup.com, Ed.,
Syosset/Jericho Tribune, NY, Mineola

Lockwood , John .... (978) 739-8506
amesbury@wickedlocal.com, Ed., Amesbury
News, MA, Danvers

Lockyer, Shane
slockyer@mykawartha.com, Adv. Mgr.,
Kawartha Lakes This Week, ON, Lindsay

Locorriere, Judith
judy.locorriere@jjournal.com, Ed., The Jersey
Journal, NJ, Secaucus

Lodge, Kristen .... (970) 557-6030 ext. 19600
klodge@skyhidailynews.com, Gen. Mgr., Sky-
Hi News, CO, Granby

Lodge, Richard
rlodge@wickedlocal.com, Ed. in Chief, The
Westborough News, MA, Framingham

Lodge, Richard .... (508) 626-3871
rlodge@wickedlocal.com, Ed. in Chief, Natick
Bulletin & TAB, MA, Framingham

Lodge, Richard .... (508) 626-3871
rlodge@wickedlocal.com, Ed. in Chief,
Marlborough Enterprise, MA, Framingham

Lodge, Richard .... (508) 626-3871
rlodge@wickedlocal.com, Ed. in Chief,
Shrewsbury Chronicle, MA, Framingham

Lodge, Richard .... (508) 626-3871
rlodge@wickedlocal.com, Ed. in Chief, The
Country Gazette, MA, Milford

Lodge, Richard .... (508) 626-3871
rlodge@wickedlocal.com , Ed. in Chief,
Framingham TAB, MA, Framingham

Lodge, Richard .... (508) 626-3871
Ed. in Chief, Hopkinton Crier, MA, Framingham

Lodge, Richard .... (508) 626-3871
rlodge@wickedlocal.com, Ed. in Chief, Ashland
TAB, MA, Framingham

Lodge, Richard .... (508) 626-3871
Ed. in Chief, Hudson Sun, MA, Framingham

Lodge, Richard

rlodge@wickedlocal.com, Ed.-in-Chief, Newton Tab, MA, Needham

rlodge@wickedlocal.com, Ed. in Chief, Wayland Town Crier, MA, Framingham

Lodge, Richard
rlodge@wickedlocal.com, Ed. in Chief, Weston Town Crier, MA, Framingham

Lodge, Richard
rlodge@wickedlocal.com, Ed. in Chief , The Villager, MA, Framingham

Lodge, Richard ....**(978) 961-3155**
awhite@newburyportnews.com, Managing Ed. , The Daily News, MA, Newburyport

Lodl, Kathy..............................**(402) 664-3198**
rustlersentinel@gpcom.net, Pub, Rustler Sentinel, NE, Scribner

Lodwick, Gary
trehernetimes@mts.net, Ed., Times, MB, Treherne

Loeb, Daniel ....**(610) 649-1454**
publisher@pjvoice.com, Pub, Philadelphia Jewish Voice, PA, Bala Cynwyd

Loeb, Jake ....**(518) 290-3908**
jloeb@digitalfirstmedia.com, Regional Digital Dir, The Saratogian, NY, Saratoga Springs

Loehr, Aileen ....**(979) 968-3155**
aileen@fayettecountyrecord.com, Office Mgr., The Fayette County Record, TX, La Grange

Loehr, Mandy.......................**(937) 651- 1116**
mloehr@examiner.org, Staff Writ. , Bellefontaine Examiner, OH, Bellefontaine

Loeks, Maunette
maunette.loeks@starherald.com, New Med. Dir., Star-Herald, NE, Scottsbluff

Loera, Juan Esparza
jesparza@vidaenelvalle.com, Ed., Vida en el Valle, CA, Fresno

Loerzel, Robert.......................**(847) 797-5103**
loerzel@pioneerlocal.com, Ed., Arlington Heights Post, IL, Chicago

Loesch, Ron
wrgsent@gci.net, Co-Owner/Pub./Ed., Wrangell Sentinel, AK, Wrangell

Loesch, Ronald J. ....**(907) 772-9393**
captainron389@yahoo.com, Co-Owner/Pub./ Ed., Petersburg Pilot, AK, Petersburg

Loesing, John
newstip@theacorn.com, Ed., The Acorn, CA, Agoura Hills

Loewen, Jeanne
montepress@ucom.net, Ed, Montezuma Press, KS, Montezuma

Loewen, Rudolph
montepress@ucom.net, Pub, Montezuma Press, KS, Montezuma

Lofdahl, Duane ....**(404) 564-3968**
duane.lofdahl@theaustin.com, Vice Pres., Planning/Design, The Austin Company, OH, Cleveland

Loftis, Scott..........................**(870) 423-6636**
carrollcountynews@cox-internet.com, Mng Ed, Carroll County News, AR, Berryville

Loftis, Scott ....**(479) 981-9419**
carrollcountynews@cox-internet.com, Mng Ed, Lovely County Citizen, AR, Eureka Springs

Lofton, Joy
editor.newsledger@tangilena.com, Ed., The Kentwood News-Ledger, LA, Kentwood

Logan, Casey ....**(239) 344-4721**
clogan@lehighnewsstar.com, Editorial, Lehigh Acres News-Star, FL, Fort Myers

Logan, Debbie
dlogan@fortfrances.com, Adv. Mgr., Fort Frances Daily Times, ON, Fort Frances

Logan, Donna
dlogan@interchange.ubc.ca, Dir./Prof., University of British Columbia, BC, Vancouver

Logan, Fern
flogan@siu.edu, Assoc. Prof., Southern Illinois University Carbondale, IL, Carbondale

Logan, Rita
RLogan@tampatrib.com, Tampa Bay Times, FL, St Petersburg

Logan, Samuel ....**ext. 236**
slogan@michronicle.com, Pub., Michigan Chronicle, MI, Detroit

Logan, Sherry
taylor2039@aol.com, The San Antonio Register, TX, San Antonio

taylor2039@aol.com, Publisher, The San Antonio Observer, TX, San Antonio

taylor2039@aol.com, Adv. Mgr., San Antonio Observer, TX, San Antonio

Loger, Deb
dloger@idacountycourier.com, Reporter, Ida County Courier, IA, Ida Grove

Loggins, Debbie
debbie.loggins@voicenews.com, Gen. Mgr., Blue Water Voice, MI, Clinton Township

debbie.loggins@voicenews.com, Gen. Mgr., The Bay Voice, MI, Clinton Township

Loggins, Debbie
debbie.loggins@voicenews.com , Adv., The North Macomb Voice, MI, Clinton Township

Loggins, Debra
debbie@voicenews.com, Gen. Mgr., The Armada Times, MI, Clinton Township

Loggins, Debra
editor@voicenews.com, Gen. Mgr., The Macomb Voice, MI, Clinton Township

Loggins, Debra
editor@voicenews.com, Gen. Mgr., Downriver Voice, MI, Clinton Township

Logsdon, Kullen.......................**(989) 779-6065**
klogsdon@digitalfirstmedia.com, Community Ed. , Morning Sun, MI, Alma

Loh, Sharon...........................**(203) 576-4382**
Univ. of Bridgeport, CT, Bridgeport

Lohman, Eric ....**(414) 229-4436**
erlohman@uwm.edu, Lecturer, University of Wisconsin-Milwaukee / Department of Journalism, Advertising, and Media Studies (JAMS), WI, Milwaukee

Lohr, Cheryl
clohr@mediamonitors.com, National Account Manager, Media Monitors, Inc., NY, White Plains

Lohrenz, Randy ....**(704) 261-2200**
rlohrenz@theej.com, Pub., The Enquirer-Journal, NC, Monroe

Lohrey, James.........................**(717) 477-1521**
Assit. Prof./electronic media, Shippensburg University/Communication/Journalism Department , PA, Shippensburg

Loker, Kevin
kevin.loker@pressinstitute.org, Program Coordinator, American Press Institute, VA, Arlington

Lokey, Jenny
jenny.lokey@capital-democrat.com, Ed., Johnston County Capital-Democrat, OK, Tishomingo

Lokey, Ray
ray.lokey@capital-democrat.com, Pub, Johnston County Capital-Democrat, OK, Tishomingo

Lolwing, Mark ....**(520) 573-4536**
mlolwing@tucson.com, Dir. Circ & Consumer Innovation, Arizona Daily Star, AZ, Tucson

Loman, Christine
cloman@ydr.com, York Daily Record/York Sunday News, PA, York

Lomax, Stephen
slomax@simtechinc.com, Asst. News Ed., The Huntsville Times, AL, Huntsville

Lombardo, Antonio
ilpensiero@charter.net, Pub., Il Pensiero, MO, Saint Louis

Lombardo, Barbara
blombardo@21st-centurymedia.com, Mng. Ed., The Saratogian, NY, Saratoga Springs

Lomenick, Rick
sports@thejournalok.com, Sports Ed., Perkins Journal, OK, Perkins

London, Aaron........................**(386) 437-2492**
aaron.london@news-jrnl.com, Asst. Bureau Chief, Daytona Beach News-Journal, FL, Daytona Beach

London, Cindy .... **(602) 261-7655 ext. 112**
c.meaux@ananews.com, Ad Placement Manager, Arizona Newspapers Association, AZ, Phoenix

c.meaux@ananews.com, Media Buyer, ANA Advertising Services, Inc. (Arizona Newspaper Association), AZ, Phoenix

Londono, Jorge ....**(401) 767-8508**
jlondono@pawtuckettimes.com, Dist. Mgr., The Call, RI, Woonsocket

Lonergan, Patricia
patricia.lonergan@transcontinental.ca, Ed., Weekly Journal, ON, Orleans

patricia.lonergan@transcontinental.ca, Ed, Brampton Guardian, ON, Mississauga

Lonergan, Patricia
patricia.lonergan@transcontinental.ca, Ed., The Star, ON, Ottawa

Long, Amanda
amanda.long@hope.edu, Co-Editor-in-Chief, Hope College, MI, Holland

Long, Amber
along@pontiacdailyleader.com, Advertising Executive, Livingston Shopping News, IL, Pontiac

Long, Becky
beckyl@claycountyprogress.com, Pub., Clay County Progress, NC, Hayesville

Long, Betty
ncelegals@centurylink.net, Classifieds/Legal Notice, The Newton County Enterprise, IN, Kentland

ncelegals@centurylink.net, Office Admin, Brook Reporter, IN, Kentland

ncelegals@centurylink.net, Morocco Courier, IN, Kentland

Long, Dale ....**(423) 359-3151**
dale.long@greenevillesun.com, Circ/Prod. Mgr., The Greeneville Sun, TN, Greeneville

Long, Gary ....**(956) 982-6674**
gary_long@link.freedom.com, News Ed., El Nuevo Heraldo, TX, Brownsville

Long, Hank
editor@woodburybulletin.com, Ed., Woodbury Bulletin, MN, Hastings

Long, Heather ....**(858) 270-3103 x 115**
heather@sdnews.com, Ad Manager, Peninsula Beacon, CA, San Diego

Long, Ita Mari
classified@decaturdailydemocrat.com, Adv. Mgr., Classified, Berne Shopping News, IN, Decatur

Long, Jeff ....**(217) 347-7151 x129**
jeff.long@shelbyvilledailyunion.com, Ed., Daily Union, IL, Shelbyville

jeff.long@shelbyvilledailyunion.com, Ed., Effingham Daily News, IL, Effingham

Long, Joel..............................**(402) 444-1493**
joel.long@owh.com, Dir., Communications, Omaha World-Herald, NE, Omaha

Long, Judy ....**(207) 990-8194**
jlong@bangordailynews.com, Universal Desk Ed., Bangor Daily News, ME, Bangor

Long, Katherine
klong@thecatholicsun.com, Ed., The Catholic Sun, NY, Syracuse

klong@thecatholicsun.com, Ed. in Chief, Catholic Sun, NY, Syracuse

Long, Kenneth W. ....**(417) 876-3841**
Ed., El Dorado Springs Sun, MO, El Dorado Springs

Long, Kimball S.
sunnews@socket.net, Pub., El Dorado Springs Sun, MO, El Dorado Springs

Long, Marian ....**(985) 857-2291**
marian.long@houmatoday.com, Adv. Dir., Daily Comet, LA, Thibodaux

Long, Marian
marian@rushing-media.com, Adv. Mgr, The Weekly Want Ads, LA, Houma

Long, Marian ....**(985) 857-2291**
marian.long@houmatoday.com, Adv. Dir., The Courier, LA, Houma

Long, Marilee
malong@lamar.colostate.edu, Prof., Colorado State University, CO, Fort Collins

Long, Matt ....**(916) 351-3749**
mattl@goldcountrymedia.com , Sports Ed., El Dorado Hills Telegraph, CA, Roseville

Long, Matt ....**(919) 836-5670**
mlong@newsobserver.com, Adv. Prod. Mgr., The News & Observer, NC, Raleigh

Long, Michele
michele.long@lincolncourier.com, Pub., Logan County Shopper, IL, Lincoln

Long, Nat
nlong@neighbornewspapers.com, Adv. Mgr., Henry Neighbor, GA, Forest Park

Long, Rhett
rlong@thespectrum.com, Pres./Pub. , The Spectrum, UT, Saint George

rlong@thespectrum.com, Pub., Daily Herald, UT, Provo

Long, Robert
rlong@delawareonline.com, Consumer Experience Director , The News Journal, DE, New Castle

Long, Sherry
slong@farragutpress.com, Advertising Sales, Farragut Press, TN, Farragut

Long, Steven ....**(806) 291-1084**
longs@wbu.edu, Wayland Baptist Univ., TX, Plainview

Long, Summer
summer@stiglernews.com, Asst. Pub./Adv. Mgr., Stigler News-Sentinel, OK, Stigler

Long, Tammy ....**(870) 633-3131**
addept@thnews.com, ad sales, East Arkansas Advertiser, AR, Forrest City

Long, Tonya
starheraldads@yahoo.com, Adv. Mgr., Pocahontas Star Herald, AR, Pocahontas

Long, Travis
vbnews@comcast.net, Ed., The Valley Banner, VA, Elkton

Longacre, Mark ....**(215) 822-4489**
mark.longacre@jbtc.com, Mktg. Mgr., JBT Corporation (formerly FMC Technologies), PA, Chalfont

Longchamps, Lesley ...**(613) 342-4441, ext 500263**
lesley.longchamps@sunmedia.ca, Dist. Mgr., The Brockville Recorder and Times, ON, Brockville

Longest, Geanie
glongest@ssentinel.com, Customer Acct. Mgr., Southside Sentinel, VA, Urbanna

Longley, Rob ....**(540) 932-3556**
rlongley@newsvirginian.com, Mng. Ed., The News Virginian, VA, Waynesboro

Longman, Ellen West ....**(712) 374-2251**
staff@argusherald.com, Owner, Sidney Argus-Herald, IA, Sidney

Crescent, WI, Appleton

Lovett, Griffin
eagle@nlamerica.com, Pub., The Wheeler County Eagle, GA, Dublin

Lovett, Griffin .... (478) 272-5522
press@courier-herald.com, Pub., The Courier Herald, GA, Dublin

Lovett, Griffin
monitor@nlamerica.com, Pub., The Montgomery Monitor, GA, Soperton

Lovett, Kristi .... (785) 366-6186
editor@heringtontimes.com, Office Manager, The Herington Times, KS, Herington

Lovin, Claudia
clovin@newsrepublican.com, Boone County Shopping News, IA, Boone

Loving, Bill
lovibill@isu.edu, Chair, Idaho State University, ID, Pocatello

Loving, Lindsey .... (571) 366-1009
lindsey.loving@naa.org, Comm. Mgr., News Media Alliance, VA, Arlington

Lovins, David
dlovins@thewarrengroup.com, Pres./COO, Banker & Tradesman, MA, Boston

Lovoie-Murray, Nathalie
hintonparklander.classifieds@sunmedia.ca, Nationals & Classified Booking, The Hinton Parklander, AB, Hinton

Lovoy, Jason
jason@infomedia.com, President, InfoMedia, Inc., AL, Vestavia Hills

Low, Andrew .... ext. 242
andrew.low@sunmedia.ca, News Ed., The Sudbury Star, ON, Sudbury

Lowder, Russel .... (203) 661-3344
Sr. Vice Pres., Sales, White Birch Paper, CT, Greenwich

Lowe, David
davidlowe@yourpeaknews.com, Adv. Rep., The Pikes Peak Courier, CO, Woodland Park
davidlowe@yourpeaknews.com, Advertising Rep., The Tribune, CO, Monument

Lowe, James
jlowe@lampasas.com, Co-Pub./Ed., Lampasas Dispatch Record, TX, Lampasas

Lowe, Kelsey
klowe@okgazette.com, Mktg. Mgr., Okcbiz, OK, Oklahoma City

Lowe, Tiffany
tiffany.lowe@staugustine.com, Nat'l Coord., The St. Augustine Record, FL, Saint Augustine

Lowell, Abby
abby.lowell@juneauempire.com, Director of Audience, Juneau Empire, AK, Juneau

Lowell, Brad
bladeempire@prapevine.net, Ed., Advertiser, KS, Concordia

Lowell, Brad
jbrad@nckcn.com, Ed./Pub., Concordia Blade-Empire, KS, Concordia

Lowell, Daphne
dlowell@gannett.com, TN Media, TN, Nashville
dlowell@gannett.com, The Tennessean, TN, Nashville

Lowell, Jay
jaylowell@nckcn.com, Online Ed./Photographer/Adv. Sales, Concordia Blade-Empire, KS, Concordia

Lowell, Jim
bladeempire@nckcn.com, Sports Ed./Managing Ed., Concordia Blade-Empire, KS, Concordia

Lowenstein, Adam .... (321) 242-3654
alowenst@floridatoday.com, Business Editor, Florida Today, FL, Melbourne

Lowenthal, Marla .... (650) 688-3840
Chair, Menlo College, CA, Atherton

Lower, Jerry .... (561) 337-1553
publisher@thecoastalstar.com, Publlisher, The Coastal Star, FL, Ocean Ridge

Lower, Ron .... (785) 543-2349
theadvocate@ruraltel.net, Pub, Advocate of Phillips County, KS, Phillipsburg

Lowers, Ehren .... (901) 529-2415
ehren.lowers@commercialappeal.com, Sr. Manager, Newspaper Production, The Commercial Appeal, TN, Memphis

Lowery, Debbie
dlowery@moberlymonitor.com, Bus. Mgr., The Moberly Monitor-Index, MO, Moberly

Lowery, Steve
editor@lebanonenterprise.com, Ed., Lebanon Enterprise, KY, Lebanon

Lowery, Stevie
editor@lebanonenterprise.com, Gen. Mgr., Lebanon Enterprise, KY, Lebanon

Lowman, Polly .... (843) 249-3525 ext. 10
nmbtimes@sc.rr.com, Pub./Ed., North Myrtle Beach Times, SC, North Myrtle Beach

Lowman, Wayne
wayne.lowman@baltsun.com, Classified Adv. Dir., Towson Times, MD, Baltimore
wayne.lowman@baltsun.com, Dir, Classified Adv. , Arbutus Times, MD, Baltimore
wayne.lowman@baltsun.com, Classified Adv. Dir., The Record, MD, Bel Air
wayne.lowman@baltsun.com, Classified Adv. Dir., The Weekender, MD, Bel Air

Lown, Wayne .... (312) 222-4673
wlown@tronc.com, VP Sales, Tribune News Service, Chicago
wlown@tronc.com, VP Sales, Tribune Content Agency, IL, Chicago

Lowrey, Nick .... (605) 224-7301 x136
nick.lowrey@capjournal.com, Asst. Managing Ed., Capital Journal, SD, Pierre

Lowry Arrington, Willie Jean
gwatchman@bellsouth.net, Ed., Greensboro Watchman, AL, Greensboro

Loy, Lynn
lynn.loy@thedailysentinel.com, Classified Sales, The Daily Sentinel, AL, Scottsboro

Loynes, Lauralyn .... (949) 388-7700 ext. 102
lloynes@picketfencemedia.com, The Capistrano Dispatch, CA, Capistrano Beach
lloynes@picketfencemedia.com, Assoc. Pub., San Clemente Times, CA, Capistrano Beach
lloynes@picketfencemedia.com, Dana Point Times, CA, Capistrano Beach

Loza, Josie .... (402) 554-2470
Univ. of Nebraska at Omaha, NE, Omaha

Lozano, Jose .... (212) 807-4770
jose.lozano@impremedia.com, Vice Chrmn., impreMedia LLC, NY, Brooklyn

Lozano, Monica .... (213) 896-2153
monica.lozano@laopinion.com, CEO/Pub., La Opinion, CA, Los Angeles

Lozano, Monica .... (213) 896-2153
monica.lozano@laopinion.com, CEO & Pub./CEO, La Opinion, impreMedia LLC, NY, Brooklyn

Lozano-Harper, Ana
alharper@wacotrib.com, Adv. Sales Mgr., Waco Tribune-Herald, TX, Waco

Lozeau, Louise .... (780) 429-5449
llozeau@edmontonjournal.com, Special Feat., Edmonton Journal, AB, Edmonton

Lozier, Kurt
kurt.lozier@dowjones.com, Senior Vice President, Product Marketing , Dow Jones Local Media Group, NY, Middletown

Lozinski, Peter
plozinski@postmedia.com, Ed, Cold Lake Sun,

AB, Cold Lake

Lubbers, Rick
rlubbers@duluthnews.com, Editor, Duluth News Tribune, MN, Duluth

Lubbers, Rick
rlubbers@lcnewschronicle.com, Ed., Lake County News-Chronicle, MN, Two Harbors

Lubbes, Sara .... (314) 889-4550
Fontbonne College, MO, Clayton

Lube, Mark
sportseditor@gonzalescannon.com, The Gonzales Cannon, TX, Gonzales

Luca, Raymond .... (703) 912-7745
loge@starpower.net, Pres., LogEtronics Corp., VA, Falls Church

Lucas, David .... (717) 362-3243 ext. 301
dlucas@dauphingraphic.com, Mgr., Inside Sales/Mktg., Manugraph DGM, Inc., PA, Millersburg

Lucas, Donnie
dlucas@thealbanynews.net, Pub., Albany News, TX, Albany

Lucas, Guy
guylucas@newstopic.net, Ed., Caldwell Weekly, NC, Lenoir

Lucas, Guy .... (828) 758-7381
guylucas@newstopic.net, Ed., News-Topic, NC, Lenoir

Lucas, Kelly
klucas@ibj.com, Ed./Pub., Court & Commercial Record, IN, Indianapolis

Lucas, Kim .... (519) 323-1550
klucas@mountforest.com, Sales , The Mount Forest Confederate, ON, Mount Forest

Lucas, Kim .... (316) 321-1120
klucas@butlercountytimesgazette.com, Classifieds Adv., The Butler County Times-Gazette, KS, Augusta

Lucas, Linda .... (850) 640-0855
llucas@baybullet.com, Pub., Bay County Bullet, FL, Panama City

Lucas, Marvin .... (702) 990-8197
marvin.lucas@gmgvegas.com, Designer, Las Vegas Sun, NV, Henderson

Lucas, Matt .... (740) 947-2149
mlucas@newswatchman.com, Ed., The Pike County News Watchman, OH, Waverly

Lucas, Melinda
melinda@thealbanynews.net, Ed., Albany News, TX, Albany

Lucas, Mitch
sports@kilgorenewsherald.com, Sports Ed., Kilgore News Herald, TX, Kilgore

Lucas, Phil .... (850) 624-6169
plucas@baybullet.com, Editor, Bay County Bullet, FL, Panama City

Lucas, Roger S.
roger@grandcoulee.com, Reporter, Star Buyer's Guide, WA, Grand Coulee

Lucas, Tom
TomL@milehighnews.com, Gen. Mgr., Milehigh Newspapers, CO, Golden

Luce, Jeri
jluce@paradisepost.com, Prodn. Mgr., Paradise Post, CA, Paradise

Lucenti, Randy .... ext. 249
randy.lucenti@sunmedia.ca, Mng. Ed. , Orillia Packet, ON, Orillia

Lucero, Leanne
copy@dailylobo.com, Copy Ed., New Mexico Daily Lobo, NM, Albuquerque

Lucey, William F. .... (401) 380-2302
lucey@newportri.com, Pub., Newport Mercury, RI, Newport
lucey@newportri.com, Pub., Newport Navalog, RI, Newport
lucey@newportri.com, Pub., The Independent,

RI, Newport
lucey@newportri.com, Gen. Mgr., Newport Navalog, RI, Newport
lucey@newportri.com, Publisher, The Newport Daily News, RI, Newport

Luchene, Annette
annette.luchene@sappi.com, Vice Pres., Finance/CFO, Sappi Fine Paper North America, MA, Boston

Luchetta, Kerry .... (765) 482-4650 ext. 132
kerry.luchetta@reporter.net, Office Mgr., The Reporter, IN, Lebanon

Luchsinger, Danielle
dluchsinger@fayettepublishing.com, Graphic Designer, The Elgin Echo, IA, West Union

Luchsinger, Rene ....(856) 842-0600 x 112
rene.luchsinger@wrh-global-americas.com, CEO, WRH Global Americas, NJ, Somerset

Luciani, Kim .... (706) 823-3829
kim.luciani@augustachronicle.com, Digital Product Development Director, The Augusta Chronicle, GA, Augusta

Lucid, Mary
mary.lucid@njfamily.com, Bus. Mgr., New Jersey Family, NJ, Summit

Luck, Jessica .... (916) 551-1776
editor@c-ville.com, Ed, C-VILLE Holdings LLC, VA, Charlottesville

Luck, Josh .... (415) 461-6006, ext. 208
jluck@verifiedaudit.com, Field Verification Mgr., Verified Audit Circulation (VAC), CA, San Rafael

Luck Newton, Sheby .... (336) 373-7383
slucknewton@news-record.com, Human Resources Generalist, News & Record, NC, Greensboro

Luckeroth, Kylee
bfarrell@courier-tribune.com, Ad Director, The Courier-Tribune, KS, Seneca

Luckey, James
jamesluckey@thenewsobserver.net, Circ. Mgr., Bakersfield News Observer, CA, Bakersfield

Lucus, Roselie .... (517) 372-2424 x 10
roselie@michiganpress.org, Growth & Operations Manager, Michigan Press Association, MI, Lansing

Lucy, Darlene
dlucy@cvcaudit.com, Buss. Mgr., Circulation Verification Council, MO, Saint Louis

Ludina, Kristine .... (416) 466-1514
latvija.amerika@gmail.com, admin, Latvija-Amerika, ON, Toronto

Ludlow, Cindy
cludlow@sourcenews.com, Editor, The Daily Reporter, OH, Columbus

Ludovici, Lisa
lludovici@reviewonline.com, Adv. Dir., The Review, OH, East Liverpool

Ludwig, Craig
cludwig@republicmedia.com, Dir., Adv. Op., The Arizona Republic, AZ, Phoenix

Ludwig, Jack
jack.ludwig@aaapress.com, Pres., AAA Press International, IL, Arlington Heights

Ludwig, Jessica
ads@russellbanner.com, Adv, Banner, MB, Russell

Ludwig, Robert D.
bob.ludwig@htimes.com, Pres./Pub., The Huntsville Times, AL, Huntsville

Luebrecht, Linda .... (573) 324-2222
bgtpub@lcs.net, Pub., Bowling Green Times, MO, Bowling Green

Lueck, Colin .... (715) 842-4424
Ed., Foto News, WI, Merrill
Ed., Wausau Times / Buyers' Guide, WI, Merrill

Lueck, Nicki
strattonspotlight@yahoo.com, Owner/Ed.,

Stratton Spotlight, CO, Stratton

Luecke, Joey .... **(618) 262-5144**
jluecke@mtcarmelregister.com, Advertising
Consultant/Digital Director, Mount Carmel
Register, IL, Mount Carmel

Luecke, John
jluecke@highpoint.edu, Assoc. Prof., High
Point Univ., NC, High Point

Luecke, Vince
editor@spencercountyjournal.com, Ed.,
Lincoln's Country Shopper, IN, Rockport

Luelo, Donna
dluelo@metroland.com, Pub, Cambridge
Times, ON, Cambridge
dluelo@metroland.com, Dir. Adv. & Circ., The
Record, ON, Kitchener

Luelo, Donna .... **(519) 895-5500**
dluelo@therecord.com, Pub., New Hamburg
Independent, ON, New Hamburg

Luetjen, Jeanne .... **(207) 990-8066**
jluetjen@bangordailynews.com, Exec. Asst.,
Bangor Daily News, ME, Bangor

Luhmann, Dallas
dallasl@livewireprinting.com, Adv. Sales Rep.,
Jackson County Pilot, MN, Jackson

Lujan, Tomas
cultureassistant@dailylobo.com, Asst.
Culture Ed., New Mexico Daily Lobo, NM,
Albuquerque

Lukaszewski, Paul .... **(203) 256-2304**
paul.lukaszewski@storaenso.com, Mgr., Mktg.,
StoraEnso, CT, Stamford

Luke, Tony
tony.luke@newspressnow.com, Adv. Dir.,
Raytown Tribune, MO, Raytown
tony.luke@newspressnow.com, Retail Adv.
Mgr., St. Joseph News-Press, MO, Saint
Joseph

Luken, Marianne
lmarianne@hpu.edu, Instr., Hawaii Pacific
University, HI, Honolulu

Luken, Richard
rluken@iolaregister.com, Sports Ed., The Iola
Register, KS, Iola

Luker, Randall
vidorian1@sbcglobal.net, Ed./Adv. Dir., Vidor
Vidorian, TX, Vidor

Luksan, Don
dluksan@lemarssentinel.com, Prodn. Mgr.,
Shoppers Guide, IA, Le Mars

Lule, Jack .... **(610) 758-4177**
jack.lule@lehigh.edu, Ed. in Chief, Lehigh
Univ., PA, Bethlehem

Lum, Deb
editorial@scotsmanpress.com, Ed., Cortland
Democrat Sunday (OOB), NY, Syracuse
editorial@scotsmanpress.com, Ed., Onondaga
Valley News, NY, Syracuse

Luma, Lori
lluma@parsonssun.com, Circ. Clerk, Parsons
Sun, KS, Parsons

Lumanog, Jack
jlumanog@ncronline.org, Sales Account Rep.,
National Catholic Reporter, MO, Kansas City

Lumpkin, John .... **(817) 257-7908**
j.lumpkin@tcu.edu, Texas Christian University,
TX, Fort Worth

Lumpkins, Crystal
clumpkins@kumc.edu, Asst. Prof., University of
Kansas, KS, Lawrence

Luna, Christina
recorderads01@gmail.com, Adv. Mgr., The
Weekly Recorder, PA, Eighty Four

Luna, Diego
vistamanaging@sandiego.edu, Mgr Ed., Univ. of
San Diego, CA, San Diego

Luna, Frances .... **(575) 894-3088**
frances@gpkmedia.com, Pub. , Sierra County

Sentinel, NM, Truth Or Consequences

Lund, Brian
rjpub@centurytel.net, Pub., Republican
Journal, WI, Darlington

Lund, Jean .... **(916) 774-7971**
jeanl@goldcountrymedia.com, Pub., Lincoln
News Messenger, CA, Lincoln

Lund, Ron .... **(902) 629-6005**
rlund@theguardian.pe.ca, Dir., Reader Sales &
Dist., The Guardian, PE, Charlottetown

Lund, Ron .... **(902) 629-6005**
rlund@theguardian.pe.ca, Dir., Reader Sales/
Serv., The Journal Pioneer, PE, Summerside

Lund, Steve .... **(262) 656-6283**
slund@kenoshanews.com, Editorial Page Ed.,
Kenosha News, WI, Kenosha

Lunde, Anne .... **(708) 524-4440**
Ed., Niles Herald-Spectator, IL, Chicago

Lundgren, John .... **(520) 573-4469**
jlunmdgren@tucson.com, Dir. Print Ops.,
Arizona Daily Star, AZ, Tucson

Lundgren, Mark
mlundgren@sfchronicle.com, Asst. Metro Ed,
San Francisco Chronicle, CA, San Francisco

Lundmark, Jodi
jlundmark@dougallmedia.com, Reporter,
Thunder Bay Source, ON, Thunder Bay

Lundquist, Derek
kross@amm.com, Pricing Dir., American Metal
Market, NY, New York

Lundquist, Jeff .... **(712) 243-2624**
Jrlund@ant-news.com, Pub./Gen Mgr., Atlantic
News Telegraph, IA, Atlantic

Lundry, Lillie .... **(417) 256-9191**
lillie@wpdailyquill.net, General Manager, West
Plains Daily Quill, MO, West Plains

Lundsford, Kaci .... **(319) 385-3131**
adv@mpnews.net, Advertising Manager, Mt.
Pleasant News, IA, Mount Pleasant

Lundstrom, Chris .... **(361) 782-3547**
clundstrom@jacksoncnews.com, Publisher,
Jackson County Herald-Tribune, TX, Edna

Lundstrom, Mack
aaron.friedman@sjsu.edu, Lectr., San Jose
State University, CA, San Jose

Lundy, Ashley
ashley@junctioneagle.com, Adv. Director, The
Junction Eagle, TX, Junction

Lundy, Jeff .... **(613) 544-5000 ext. 215**
jlundy@thewhig.com, Regional Dir., Circ. &
Dist., The Kingston Whig-Standard, ON,
Kingston

Lunn, Alice .... **(724) 421-2200**
alunn@butlereagle.com, Circulation Director,
Eagle Printing Co., PA, Butler

Lunn, Alice .... **(724) 431-2200 ext. 231**
alunn@butlereagle.com, Circ. Dir., The
Cranberry Eagle, PA, Cranberry Township
alunn@butlereagle.com, Cir. Dir., Butler Eagle,
PA, Butler

Lunn, Jon R.
collect@skobrenner.com, COO, SKO Brenner
American, NY, Baldwin

Lunneborg, Susan
slunneborg@wctrib.com, News Ed., West
Central Tribune, MN, Willmar

Lunsford, Danielle .... **(641) 683-5360**
dlunsford@ottumwacourier.com, Reporter, The
Ottumwa Courier, IA, Ottumwa

Lunzer, Bernard .... **(202) 434-7175**
bernielunzer@gmail.com, President, The
NewsGuild-CWA, DC, Washington

Lunzer, Laurie .... **(509) 459-5222**
lauriel@spokesman.com, Dir. Production/IT,
The Spokesman-Review, WA, Spokane

Luparello, Gail
gail@alachuatoday.com, Associate Publisher,

Alachua County Today, FL, Alachua

Lupton, Sean .... **(615) 259-8000**
slupton@gannett.com, National Adv. Mgr., The
Hendersonville Star News, TN, Gallatin
slupton@gannett.com, National Adv. Mgr., The
Dickson Herald, TN, Dickson
slupton@gannett.com, Nat'l Adv. Mgr., The
Daily News Journal, TN, Murfreesboro
slupton@gannett.com, Manager, National/
Major Accounts, The Tennessean, TN,
Nashville
slupton@gannett.com, Manager, National/
Major Accounts, TN Media, TN, Nashville

Lurgio, Jeremy
jeremy.lurgio@umontana.edu, Asst. Prof., The
University of Montana, MT, Missoula

Lurie, Joshua
josh@jcnews.com, Pub., The Jones County
News, GA, Gray

Lurie-Smith, Debbie
debsmith@jcnews.com, Ed., The Jones County
News, GA, Gray

Luscombe, Shawn .... **(575) 763-3431**
sluscombe@thenews.email, Creative Services
Director, Eastern New Mexico News, NM,
Clovis

Lushina, Lori
lori.peoria@americanclassifieds.com,
American Classifieds - Peoria, IL, Peoria

Lusk, Eric .... **ext. 16**
elusk@elkintribune.com, Sports. Ed., Yadkin
Valley Advertiser, NC, Elkin

Lusk, John
jlusk@sc4.edu, St. Clair County Community
College, MI, Port Huron

Lusk, Julie .... **(321) 242-3753**
jlusk@floridatoday.com, VP/South Region, HR
Business Partner Team, Florida Today, FL,
Melbourne

Lusk, Mitzi
mitzi.lusk@tidewaternews.com, Adv. Dir., The
Tidewater News, VA, Franklin

Lussier, Cherie .... **(518) 861-4026**
CLussier@Altamontenterprise.com, Adv. Mgr.,
The Altamont Enterprise & Albany County
Post, NY, Altamont

Lussier, John H. .... **(608) 252-6403**
Chrmn., Board, Capital Newspapers, WI,
Madison

Lussier, Sylviane .... **ext. 217**
sylviane.lussier@transcontinental.ca, Pub.,
L'hebdo Journal, QC, Trois-Rivieres

Luste Maran, Kimberly
marank@gc.adventist.org, Asst. Ed., Adventist
Review, MD, Silver Spring

Luster, Clifford
cluster@cnglocal.com, Pub., Brooklyn Courier,
NY, Brooklyn
cluster@cnglocal.com, Pub./Bus. Mgr., New
York Parenting - Brooklyn Family/Manhattan
Family/Queens Family/Bronx-Riverdale
Family/Westchester Family, NY, Brooklyn

Luster, Clifford
clifford@courierlife.com, Grp. Co-Pub., Courier
Life Publications, Inc., NY, Brooklyn

Luster, Clifford .... **(718) 615-2500**
Editorial@CNGLocal.com , Pub., Bay Ridge
Courier, NY, Brooklyn

Luster, Clifford .... **(718) 260-2500**
cluster@cnglocal.com, Pub., Caribbean Life,
NY, Brooklyn
cluster@cnglocal.com, The Brooklyn Papers,
NY, Brooklyn

Lutgen, Beth .... **(563) 875-7131**
blutgen@wcinet.com, Managing Editor,
Dyersville Commercial, IA, Dyersville

Lutgen, Beth .... **(563) 875-7131**
blutgen@wcinet.com, Managing Editor,
Eastern Iowa Shopping News, IA, Dyersville

Lutgens, Jim .... **(507) 463-8112**
news@newrichlandstar.com, Ed., Star Eagle,
MN, New Richland

Luther, Catherine A.
a.armsworth@utk.edu, Assoc. Prof., The
University of Tennessee, TN, Knoxville

Luther, Kirk
kirk@2020publications.com, Owner/Pub., The
Lake Murray News, SC, Irmo

Luther, Luanne
luanne@dailyranger.com, Classifieds Adv.
Mgr., The Riverton Ranger, WY, Riverton

Lutter, Hillary
sanjournal@santel.net, Pub./Ed., Sanborn
Weekly Journal, SD, Woonsocket

Lutterschmidt, Kelly
klutterschmidt@tnonline.com, Ed, Whitehall-
Coplay Press, PA, Allentown

Lutwick, Elizabeth .... **ext. 224**
lutwick@mountvernonnews.com, Asst. Pub.,
Mount Vernon News, OH, Mount Vernon

Luty, Peggy
pluty@modbee.com, Nat'l Sales Coord., The
Modesto Bee, CA, Modesto

Lutz, Ashley
al164906@ohiou.edu, Ohio Univ., OH, Athens

Lutz, Jeanne
cr.ads@comcast.net, Adv. Mgr., The Circulator,
IN, Portland

Luvison, Kirk
kirk@morning-times.com, Production manager,
Morning Times, PA, Sayre

Lwery, Llana .... **(602) 308-6513**
Ed.-in-Chief, The Business Journal, AZ,
Phoenix

Lyden, Megan .... **(303) 954-1896**
mlyden@denverpost.com, Senior Ed. for
Photography & Multimedia, The Denver Post,
CO, Denver

Lyerla, Crystal .... **(573) 547-4567**
Ed., The Perry County Republic-Monitor, MO,
Perryville

Lyke, Tim
TimL@riponprinters.com, Pub., Ripon
Commonwealth Press, WI, Ripon
TimL@riponprinters.com, Pub., The
Commonwealth Express, WI, Ripon

Lykins, Chris .... **(830) 625-9144 ext 220**
chrislykins@herald-zeitung.com, Managing
Ed., New Braunfels Herald-Zeitung, TX, New
Braunfels

Lyle, David F. .... **(724) 229-2200**
dlyle@observer-reporter.com, CFO, Observer-
Reporter, PA, Washington

Lyles, Steve
styles@jcpgroup.com, Pub./Adv. Dir./Gen. Mgr.,
Kettle Moraine Index, WI, Hartland
styles@jcpgroup.com, Pub./Adv. Dir./Gen. Mgr.,
Lake Country Reporter, WI, Hartland
styles@jcpgroup.com, Pub./Adv. Dir./Gen. Mgr.,
Oconomowoc Focus, WI, Hartland
styles@jcpgroup.com, Pub./Adv. Dir./Gen. Mgr.,
Sussex Sun, WI, Hartland

Lyles, Steve
styles@jcpgroup.com, Pub./Gen. Mgr./Adv. Dir.,
Milwaukee Journal Sentinel, WI, Milwaukee

Lyles, Steve
styles@jcpgroup.com, Pub., Lake County
Publications, WI, Hartland

Lyman, Mary
marylyman.boone@alexcityoutlook.com,
Bookkeeper, Dadeville Record, AL,
Alexander City

Lyman, Shelby .... **(607) 775-0587**
slyman@tds.net, Pres., Basic Chess Features,
Windsor

Lynas, Sarah
designdirector@dailylobo.com, Design Dir.,

New Mexico Daily Lobo, NM, Albuquerque

Lynch, David
news@dailylobo.com, News Ed., New Mexico Daily Lobo, NM, Albuquerque

Lynch, Ed .... (808) 529-4758
elynch@staradvertiser.com, Managing Ed., Honolulu Star-Advertiser, HI, Honolulu

Lynch, Emma
attractions@lavozcolorado.com, Entertainment Ed., La Voz Newspaper, CO, Denver

Lynch, Greg
glynch@coxohio.com, Photo Ed., JournalNews, OH, Hamilton

Lynch, John
john@lexingtonfamily.com, Ed., Lexington Family Magazine, KY, Lexington

Lynch, Judy
jlynch@paducahsun.com, Circ. Mgr., The Paducah Sun, KY, Paducah

Lynch, Lloyd
llynch@state-journal.com, Adv. Dir., The State Journal, KY, Frankfort

Lynch, Lloyd
llynch@state-journal.com, Adv. Dir., Buyer's Guide, KY, Frankfort

Lynch, Michael
autonomyinfo@hp.com, CEO, Autonomy, Inc., CA, San Francisco

Lynch, Michael
info@cipsmarketing.com, Pres., Association of Alternate Postal Systems, OK, Oklahoma City

Lynch, Michael
mlynch@amestrib.com, Circulation Sales/Ops manager, Ames Tribune, IA, Ames

Lynch, Nathan .... (207) 730-0322
nlynch@colgate.edu, Freelance Artist/Writer, Journal-Tribune, ME, Biddeford

Lynch, Peter
lynchp@caledonian-record.com, Picture Ed., The Caledonian-Record, VT, Saint Johnsbury

Lynch, Richard
richard.lynch@miaminewtimes.com, Circ. Mgr., Miami New Times, FL, Miami

Lynch, Shawna
shawna_lynch@bhimpact.com, Sr. Vice Pres., B/HI, CA, Los Angeles

Lynch, Stefanie ....ext. 204
stefanie.lynch@sunmedia.ca, Buss. Mgr. , The Peterborough Examiner, ON, Peterborough

Lynch, Tara .... (479) 785-7731
tlynch@swtimes.com, Dig. Sales Mgr., Times Record, AR, Fort Smith

Lynch, Tara .... (479) 785-7700 ext 1312
tlynch@swtimes.com, Dig. Mgr., Times Record, AR, Fort Smith

Lynch, Valerie .... (217) 234-5270
vlynch@lakeland.cc.il.us, Dir of Student Life, Lake Land College, IL, Mattoon

Lynch, Zena .... (828) 743-5101
ads@CrossroadsChronicle.com, Graphic Designer, Crossroads Chronicle, NC, Cashiers

Lynch Pape, Susan .... (210) 250-3811
spape@express-news.net, Publisher, San Antonio Express-News, TX, San Antonio

Lynch-Hudson, Regina .... (770) 998-9911
thewritepublicist@earthlink.net, Creator/Writer, Doing Biz In, Roswell

Lyness, Jennifer .... (706) 265-3384
jlyness@dawsonnews.com, Adv. Dir., Dawson County News, GA, Dawsonville

Lynett, George .... (570) 348-9107
glynett@timesshamrock.com, Pub., Scranton Times Co., PA, Scranton

Lynett, W. Scott .... (570) 821-2064 ext. 2095
slynett@citizensvoice.com, Pub., The Citizens'

Voice, PA, Wilkes Barre

Lynett, William R. .... (570) 348-9100
wlynett@timesshamrock.com, Pub., Times-Shamrock Communications, PA, Scranton

Lynett Jr, George .... (570) 348-9100
glynettjr@timesshamrock.com, CEO, Times-Shamrock Communications, PA, Scranton

Lynn, Angelo
ewing@colchestersun.com, Co-Pub., The Colchester Sun, VT, Colchester
ewing@colchestersun.com, Co-Pub., The Essex Reporter, VT, Saint Albans

Lynn, Angelo S.
angelo@addisonindependent.com, Ed./Pub., Addison County Independent, VT, Middlebury

Lynn, Chris .... (615) 384-3567
cdlynn@mtcngroup.com, Sports Ed., Robertson County Times, TN, Clarksville

Lynn, Christy
christy@addisonindependent.com, Adv. Mgr., Addison County Independent, VT, Middlebury

Lynn, Emerson ....ext. 108
emerson@samessenger.com, Pub., Extra, VT, Saint Albans

Lynn, Emerson
emersonlynn@iolaregister.com, Assoc. Ed., Iola-register Shopper, KS, Iola

Lynn, Emerson
news@samessenger.com, Pub., St. Albans Messenger, VT, Saint Albans

Lynn, Emerson
emerson@samessenger.com, Pub., Milton Independent, VT, Milton
emerson@samessenger.com, Co-Pub., The Colchester Sun, VT, Colchester
emerson@samessenger.com, Co-Pub., The Essex Reporter, VT, Saint Albans

Lynn, Gina
tradvertising@centurytel.net, Adv. Mgr., The Times-Record, AL, Fayette

Lynn, Jodie .... (636) 236-6236
editor@parenttoparent.com, Owner, Parent to Parent, Wildwood

Lynn, Lisa .... (870) 243-2039
llynn@jonesborosun.com, Adv. Dir., The Jonesboro Sun, AR, Jonesboro

Lynn, Michelle .... (360) 417-3510
mlynn@peninsuladailynews.com, Director of Circulation , Peninsula Daily News, WA, Port Angeles

Lynn, Polly
editor@mountaintimes.info, Pub./Ed., The Mountain Times, VT, Killington

Lynn, Rice .... (912) 427-3757
lsrice@bellsouth.net, Office mgr., The Press-Sentinel, GA, Jesup

Lynn, Susan
susanlynnks@yahoo.com, Ed., Iola-register Shopper, KS, Iola

Lynn, Susan
editorial@iolaregister.com, Pub./Ed., The Iola Register, KS, Iola

Lynn, Suzanne ....ext. 106
suzanne@samessenger.com, Gen. Mgr., St. Albans Messenger, VT, Saint Albans

Lyon, Allen
alyon@meadvilletribune.com, Prodn. Mgr., Mailroom, The Meadville Tribune, PA, Meadville

Lyon, Barb
barb.lyon@lee.net, Ed., Dunn County Reminder, WI, Menomonie

Lyon, Barb
barb.lyon@lee.net, Ed., Dunn County Big Buck, WI, Chippewa Falls

Lyon, Barbara .... (715) 738-1619
editor@dunnconnect.com, Ed., The Dunn County News, WI, Chippewa Falls

Lyon, Frank
advertising@sedaliademocrat.com, Pub., Free Plainsman, MO, Sedalia

Lyon, Jason
jlyon@outlook.greatwest.ca, Pub/Adv. Mgr, Rocky Mountain Outlook, AB, Canmore

Lyon, Jeff .... (312) 369-8902
jlyon@colum.edu, Columbia College Chicago, IL, Chicago

Lyon, Jeff .... (312) 369-8903
jlyon@colum.edu, Faculty advisor, Columbia College, IL, Chicago

Lyon, Ray .... (505) 473-1775
info@lyonenterprises.com, Pres., Lyon Enterprises, NM, Santa Fe

Lyon, Steve
scoop@signalamerican.org, Ed., Weiser Signal American, ID, Weiser

Lyon, Toni
toni@islander.org, Adv. Dir., The Islander, FL, Holmes Beach

Lyons, Angie .... (309) 686-3174
alyons@pjstar.com, Journal Star, IL, Peoria

Lyons, Christy .... (231) 838-9949
clyons@petoskeynews.com, Adv. Dir., Petoskey News-Review, MI, Petoskey
clyons@petoskeynews.com, Adv. Dir., Charlevoix Courier, MI, Charlevoix

Lyons, David .... (305) 347-6694
dlyons@alm.com, Editor-in-Chief, Miami Daily Business Review, FL, Miami

Lyons, David .... (305) 347-6694
dlyons@alm.com, Editor-in-Chief, Palm Beach Daily Business Review, FL, Miami

Lyons, Paul
paul@theweeklymailer.com, Circ. Mgr., Weekly Mailer, ID, Burley

Lyons, Robert .... (618) 498-1234
regional editori, Calhoun News-Herald, IL, Hardin

Lyons, Robert .... (618) 498-1234
regional editor, Greene Prairie Press, IL, Carrollton

Lyons, Rod
lyonsrj@lavc.edu, Los Angeles Valley College, CA, Valley Glen

Lyons, Susan .... (302) 539-1788
susan.lyons@coastalpoint.com, Pub., Coastal Point, DE, Ocean View

Lyons, Tammy
talemail@aol.com, Pub., The Record Delta, WV, Buckhannon

Lyons, Tom .... (941) 957-5367
tom.lyons@heraldtribune.com, Columnist, Sarasota Herald-Tribune, FL, Sarasota

Lysen, Luicinda
spressnews@aol.com, Pub./Co-owners, Beverly News, IL, Midlothian

Lysen, Margaret
spressnews@aol.com, Pub., Palos Citizen, IL, Midlothian

Lysen, Margaret .... (708) 388-2425
spressnews@aol.com, Pub., Hickory Hills Citizen, IL, Midlothian

Lysen, Margaret
spressnews@aol.com, Pub., Chicago Ridge Citizen, IL, Midlothian

Lysen, Margaret
spressnews@aol.com, Pub., Southwest Messenger Press, Inc., IL, Midlothian

Lysen, Margaret
spressnews@aol.com, Pub., Burbank-Stickney Independent - Scottsdale Edition, IL, Midlothian

Lysen, Margaret
spressnews@aol.com, Pub., Oak Lawn Independent, IL, Midlothian

Lysen, Margaret D.
spressnews@aol.com, Ed., Bridgeview Independent, IL, Midlothian

Lysen, Margaret D.
spressnews@aol.com, Pub., Orland Township Messenger, IL, Midlothian

Lyster, Cridalyn
clyster@eomediagroup.com, Digital Development Director, The Daily Astorian, OR, Astoria

Lyter, Nikki
nikki.lyter@brainerddispatch.com, Marketing Coord., Brainerd Dispatch, MN, Brainerd

Lytle, Denise .... (903) 237-7702
dlytle@news-journal.com, Chief Financial Officer, Longview News-Journal, TX, Longview

Lytle, Gary .... (252) 329-9620
glytle@reflector.com, Director of Information Systems, Cooke Communications North Carolina, LLC, NC, Greenville

Lytle, Regina .... (252) 329-9643
rlytle@reflector.com, Pre-Press Mgr., The Daily Reflector, NC, Greenville

Lytle, Regina .... (252) 329-9643
rlytle@reflector.com, Production Director, Cooke Communications North Carolina, LLC, NC, Greenville

Lytle, William H. .... (913) 498-0040
billlytle8@cs.com, Dir., Media Services Group, Inc., FL, Ponte Vedra

M

M. Galligan, Teresa .... (707) 258-6150
teresa@rereader.com, Pub., Wine Country Weekly Real Estate Reader, CA, Napa

MARCHAND, CHRIS .... (807) 221-4259
chrism@drydenobserver.ca, Ed., Dryden Observer, ON, Dryden

MCDOWELL, SUZIE .... (785) 421-5700
times@ruraltel.net, Associate Editor, The Hill City Times, KS, Hill City

MCorkle, Jamie .... (928) 763-2505
Sales Manager, Mohave Valley Daily News, AZ, Bullhead City

MESSERSMITH, Alysia
messersmithaj@gmail.com, Hayes Center Times Republican, NE, Hayes Center

Maagad, Clare
cmaagad@lifesitnews.com, Adv. Mgr., LifeSiteNews.com, VA, Front Royal

Maas, Duke .... (813) 259-7753
Tampa Bay Times, FL, St Petersburg

Maas, Julie .... (612) 965-1965
julie.maas@newscycle.com, Sales Director, Newscycle Solutions, MN, Bloomington

Maassen, Mark .... (573) 449-4167
mmaassen@kcstar.com, Missouri Press Association, MO, Columbia

Maberry, Nora .... (217) 469-0045
nmaberry@news-gazette.com, Ed., The Leader, IL, Saint Joseph

Mabry, Marcus .... (212) 626-9220
patricia@opcofamerica.org, Pres., Overseas Press Club of America, NY, New York

Mabry, Seth
onenews@observernewsonline.com, Pub./Ed., The Observer News Enterprise, NC, Newton

Mac Leod, Jim .... (416) 847-2001
jmacleod@bbm.ca, Pres./CEO, BBM Canada, ON, Toronto

MacAfee, Michelle
michelle.macafee@thecanadianpress.com, Correspondent, Canadian Press, The - Saint John's, NL, NL, Saint John's

MacAulay, Kim

macaulay@clipper.mb.ca, Publisher, The
Clipper Weekly & Lac Du Bonnet Clipper,
MB, Beausejour

MacCallum, Alex
alex.maccallum@nytimes.com, Audience
Expansion and Engagement Editor, The New
York Times, NY, New York

MacClaren, Joel ....(203) 483-1700
joel.macclaren@ctparent.com, Ed./Pub.,
Connecticut Parent Magazine, CT, Branford

MacCormack, Bruce ....(902) 426-2811 ext. 2847
bmaccormack@herald.ca, Vice Pres., Bus.
Devel., The Chronicle Herald, NS, Halifax

MacCoy, Helen
hmaccoy@cbpost.com, Dir., Reader Sales and
Dist., The Cape Breton Post, NS, Sydney

MacDonald, Don .... (705) 674-5271 ext. 232
don.macdonald@sunmedia.ca, City Ed., The
Sudbury Star, ON, Sudbury

MacDonald, Doug
doug.macdonald@eurorscg.com, Newspaper
National Network LP, NY, New York

MacDonald, Gail
gail.macdonald@uconn.edu, Lectr., University
of Connecticut, CT, Storrs

MacDonald, Gregg ....(571) 323-6224
gmacdonald@fairfaxtimes.com, Exec. Ed,
Fairfax County Times, VA, Sterling

MacDonald, Joanne ....(416) 869-4989
jmacdon@torstar.com, Sales Asst., Torstar
Syndication Services, ON, Toronto

MacDonald, Ken
ken@thenews-journal.com, Ed., The News-
Journal, NC, Raeford

MacDonald, Mark......................(250) 729-4240
mamacdonald@nanaimodailynews.com, Mng.
Ed., Nanaimo Daily News, BC, Nanaimo

MacDonald, Paul ....(902) 928-3506
pmacdonald@ngnews.ca, Circ. Mgr., The Daily
News, NS, Truro

MacDonald, Paul
pmacdonald@ngnews.ca, Circ. Dir., The News,
NS, New Glasgow

MacDonald, Rankin
editor@oran.ca, Ed., The Inverness Oran, NS,
Inverness

MacDonald, Tom
tom@gcherald.com, Pub., Gratiot County
Herald, MI, Ithaca

MacDonald, Wendy...................(913) 461-3721
wendy@afcp.org, Marketing Representative,
Association of Free Community Papers, NY,
Liverpool

MacDougall, Gary J. .... (902) 629-6039
gmacdougall@theguardian.pe.ca, Mng. Ed.,
The Guardian, PE, Charlottetown

MacDuff, Cassie ....(951) 368-9470
dbernstein@pe.com, Columnist, The Press-
Enterprise, CA, Riverside

MacEachen, Matthew
matthew.maceachen@sunmedia.ca, Adv. Mgr.,
The Grove Examiner, AB, Spruce Grove

MacGregor, James
jmacgregor@bizjournals.com, Pub., San Jose
Business Journal, CA, San Jose

MacInnes, Chuck
cmacinnes@amherstdaily.com, Circ. Mgr.,
Amherst Daily News, NS, Amherst

MacKay, Bonnie
lombardian@sbcglobal.net, Ed./Pub., Villa Park
Review, IL, Lombard

MacKay, Brian........................(360) 735-4447
brian.mackay@columbian.com, IT Mgr., The
Columbian, WA, Vancouver

MacKay, Margaret ....(902) 426-1143
mmackay@herald.ca, Lifestyle Ed., The
Chronicle Herald, NS, Halifax

MacKay, Scott D.
lombardian@sbcglobal.net, Co-Pub.,
Lombardian, IL, Lombard

MacKenzie, Cecil
harnews@mnsi.net, Ed., Harrow News, ON,
Harrow

MacKenzie, Dick ....(807) 737-3209
bulletin@siouxbulletin.com, Ed., The Bulletin,
ON, Sioux Lookout

MacKenzie, Heather
webmaster@cbpost.com, Online Mgr., The
Cape Breton Post, NS, Sydney

MacKinney, Cheri
cmackinney@smartshopperad.com, Smart
Shopper, MA, Webster

MacKinnon, Doyle
dmackinnon@lethbridgeherald.com, Mng. Ed.,
The Lethbridge Herald, AB, Lethbridge

MacKintosh, Roxanne ....(403) 605-3872
rmackintosh@postmedia.com, Adv. Dir,
Strathmore Standard, AB, Strathmore
rmackintosh@postmedia.com, Reg. Dir. of
Adv., Vulcan Advocate, AB, Vulcan
rmackintosh@postmedia.com, Adv Dir,
Cochrane Times, AB, Cochrane

MacLaren, Mike
mike@michiganpress.org, Executive Director,
MNI, MI, Lansing

MacLean, April .... ext. 32
amaclean@theenterprisebulletin.com,
Circ. Mgr., The Enterprise-bulletin, ON,
Collingwood

MacLennan, Bruce
pub@lillooetnews.net, Publisher, Bridge River
Lillooet News, BC, Lillooet

MacLeod, Sandy ....(416) 869-4654
smacleod@thestar.ca, Vice Pres., Mktg.,
Toronto Star, ON, Toronto

MacMahon, M<itchell ....(805) 683-1115;(805) 403-4251cell
mimcmahon@westmont.edu, Editor-in-Chief,
Randy VanderMey, CA, Santa Barbara

MacMillan, Kevin .... (775) 831-4666, ext. 19311
kmacmillan@sierrasun.com, Ed., North Lake
Tahoe Bonanza, NV, Incline Village
kmacmillan@sierrasun.com, Co-Gen. Mgr.,
Sierra Sun, CA, Truckee

MacNaull, Steve
steve.macnaull@ok.bc.ca, Bus. Ed., The Daily
Courier, BC, Kelowna

MacNealy, Jane
jane@washingtonparent.com, Prodn. Mgr.,
Washington Parent Magazine, MD, Bethesda

MacNeil, Paul
standard@theshaunavonstandard.com, Ed.,
The Shaunavon Standard, SK, Shaunavon

MacNeill, Jan .... (902) 838-2515 ext. 203
jan@peicanada.com, Adv. Mgr., The Eastern
Graphic, PE, Montague
jan@peicanada.com, Atlantic Post Calls, PE,
Montague

MacNeill, Jan ....(902) 838-2515 ext. 12
janmacneill@islandpress.pe.ca, Adv. Mgr.,
West Prince Graphic, PE, Alberton

MacNeill, Paul ....(902) 838-2515 ext. 13
paul@peicanada.com, Pub., West Prince
Graphic, PE, Alberton

MacNeill, Paul .... (902) 838-2515 ext. 201
paul@peicanada.com, Atlantic Post Calls, PE,
Montague
paul@peicanada.com, Pub., The Eastern
Graphic, PE, Montague

MacNeille, Jeanette
sales@eclipseservices.com, President, Eclipse
Services (Div. of Quadrivium, Inc.), PA,
Wyndmoor

MacPherson, Robert ....(540) 981-3273
bob.macpherson@roanoke.com, Regional
Controller, The Roanoke Times, VA, Roanoke

MacQuarrie, Scott
smacquarrie@cbpost.com, Retail Sales Mgr.,
The Cape Breton Post, NS, Sydney

MacVicar, George
editor@southerngazette.ca, Ed., The Southern
Gazette, NL, Marystown

MacWilliams, Randi ....(440) 236-8982
Graphic Artist/News Ed, The Rural-Urban
Record, OH, Columbia Station

Macbeth, Adrienne
adriennem@redhillstudios.com, Dir. Business
Development, Red Hill Studios, CA, San
Rafael

Maccini, Robert J. ....(401) 454-3130
rmaccini@cox.net, Dir., Media Services Group,
Inc., FL, Ponte Vedra

Macdonald, Cameron
cameronjmacdonald@gmail.com, News Ed.,
Elk Grove Citizen, CA, Elk Grove

Mace, Ben
ben.mace@doverpost.com, Ed., The
Middletown Transcript, DE, Middletown
ben.mace@doverpost.com, Ed., Smyrna/
Clayton Sun-Times, DE, Middletown

Mace, Tony..............................(212) 669-6400
tony@marketnews.com, Mng. Ed., Market
News International, New York

Macfarlane, Bill ....(413) 496-6280
bmacfarlane@berkshireeagle.com, Systems
Director, The Berkshire Eagle, MA, Pittsfield

Machado, Colleen
cmachado@kdminer.com, Adv. Dir., Kingman
Daily Miner, AZ, Kingman

Machan, Randy ....(419) 352-4421
rmachan@sentinel-tribune.com, Cir. Mgr.,
Sentinel-Tribune, OH, Bowling Green

Machesic, Dale ....(215) 345-3018
dmachesic@phillyburbs.com, Adv. Mgr.,
Classified/Retail, The Intelligencer, PA,
Doylestown

Machesic, Len
lmachesic@dailyitem.com, Controller, The
Danville News, PA, Danville
lmachesic@dailyitem.com, Controller, HR, The
Daily Item, MA, Lynn

Maciejewski, Jeffrey
jeffm@creighton.edu, Assoc. Prof., Creighton
Univ., NE, Omaha

Maciel, Alejandro ....(213) 237-3374
amaciel@hoyllc.com, Director Editorial Hoy/
Los Angeles, Hoy LLC, CA, Los Angeles

Macinga, Carol........................(219) 769-9292
cmacinga@dcgary.org, Circulation/
Administrative Assistant/Accounts
Receivable, Northwest Indiana Catholic, IN,
Merrillville

Macingosh, Peter
news@thebugle.ca, Gen Mgr., The Bugle-
observer, NB, Woodstock

Macintosh, John ....(519) 537-2341 x515244
jmacintosh@postmedia.com, Media sales, The
Norwich Gazette, ON, Woodstock

Macisaac, Chantelle
chantelle.macisaac@gulfnews.ca, Ed, The Gulf
News, NL, Port aux Basques

Mack, Lloyd
Lloyd.Mack@sunmedia.ca, Ed., Kenora Daily
Miner & News, ON, Kenora

Mack, Richard
rich@buffaloreview.com, Ed., Riverside Review,
NY, Buffalo

Mack, Tracy
tracy@haysfreepress.com, Adv./Mktg. Dir., The
News-Dispatch, TX, Driftwood
tracy@haysfreepress.com, Adv. Mgr., Hays
Free Press, TX, Kyle

Mack, Tyler ....(541) 338-2291
tyler.mack@registerguard.com, Dir. of Dig.

Solutions, The Register-Guard, OR, Eugene

Mackay Smith, Janet
amesbury@cnc.com, News Ed., Amesbury
News, MA, Danvers

Mackay-Smith, Janet..................(978) 739-1347
jmackays@wickedlocal.com , ed., Newburyport
Current, MA, Danvers

Mackay-Smith, Janet
jmackays@wickedlocal.com, Managing Ed.,
Hamilton-Wenham Chronicle, MA, Danvers
jmackays@wickedlocal.com, Managing Ed.,
Cape Ann Beacon, MA, Danvers
jmackays@wickedlocal.com, Mng. Ed. , North
Shore Sunday, MA, Danvers

Mackay-Smith, Janet..................(978) 739-1347
jmackays@wickedlocal.com , Senior Ed.,
Swampscott Reporter, MA, Marblehead

Mackay-Smith, Janet..................(978) 739-1347
jmackays@wickedlocal.com, Managing Ed.,
Salem Gazette, MA, Danvers

Macke, Rich ....(805) 739-2147
Circ. Dir., The Lompoc Record, CA, Santa
Maria

Macke, Rich ....(409) 721-2445
rich.macke@panews.com, Publisher, Port
Arthur News, TX, Port Arthur

Macke, Rick
rmacke@santamariatimes.com, Circ. Dir.,
Santa Maria Times, CA, Santa Maria

Mackenzie, Linda ....(204) 697-7021
linda.mackenzie@canstarnews.com, Executive
Assistant, The Lance, MB, Winnipeg

Mackenzie, Linda ....(204) 697-7021
linda.mackenzie@canstarnews.com, Exec
Asst, The Metro, MB, Winnipeg

Mackey, Jim
jmackey@reviewonline.com, Ed., The Review,
OH, East Liverpool

Mackie, Dan
dmackie@vnews.com, Editorial Page Ed.,
Valley News, NH, West Lebanon

Mackin, James
jim@indyeastend.com, Pub., The Independent,
NY, East Hampton

Mackin, Randy
brreview@tds.net, Ed., Buffalo River Review,
TN, Linden

Mackintoch, Roxanne
rmackintosh@postmedia.com, Adv. Dir,
Pincher Creek Echo, AB, Pincher Creek

Mackintosh, Roxanne ....(403) 605-3872
rmackintosh@postmedia.com, Adv. Dir, Bow
Valley Crag & Canyon, AB, Banff
rmackintosh@postmedia.com, Adv. Dir, Airdrie
Echo, AB, Airdrie
rmackintosh@postmedia.com, Reg. Adv. Dir.,
The High River Times, AB, High River
rmackintosh@postmedia.com, Reg. Adv. Dir.,
The Nanton News, AB, Nanton

Mackowski, Christopher
cmackowski@sbu.edu, Assoc. Prof.,
St. Bonaventure University, NY, Saint
Bonaventure

Macks, Barbara E.
bmack@buffalospree.com, Dir., Sales, Forever
Young, NY, Buffalo

Maclearie, Cathleen...........................ext. 19
cathleen@jbnc.com, Art Dir., J. The Jewish
News Weekly of Northern Califonia, CA, San
Francisco

Macomber, Aletha ....(360) 650-3171
Western Washington Univ., WA, Bellingham

Macy, Kandi
kmacy@dailyhome.com, Circ. Mgr., The Daily
Home, AL, Talladega

Madalena, Chris
chris@creativeloafing.com, Adv. Dir., Creative
Loafing Tampa Bay, FL, Tampa

Journal, OH, Perrysburg

Maisel, Todd
toddphoto@aol.com, Vice President, New York
Press Photographers Association, Inc., NY,
New York

Maitland, Gary ....(256) 740-5721
gary.maitland@timesdaily.com, Exec. Ed.,
Times Daily, AL, Florence

Majeski, Kelsey ....(605) 845-3646
kelsey@mobrigetribune.com, Bus. Mgr.,
Mobridge Tribune, SD, Mobridge

Major, Dwight ....(248) 745-4540
dwight.major@oakpress.com, Circ. Mgr., The
Oakland Press, MI, Pontiac

Major, Mark
mmajor@cninewspapers.com, CFO,
Community Newspapers, Inc., GA, Athens

Major, Phil
news@wcmessenger.com, The Community
News, TX, Aledo

Major, Phil
publisher@cameronherald.com, Pub./Ed., The
Cameron Herald, TX, Cameron
publisher@cameronherald.com, Pub./Ed.,
Thorndale Champion, TX, Cameron

Major, Rick
weyburnthisweek@sasktel.net, Pub., Weyburn
This Week, SK, WEYBURN

Major, Rick
rmajor@avtimes.net, Pub., Alberni Valley
Times, BC, Port Alberni

Major, Wayne................(705) 335-2283 ext.229
wayne.major@sunmedia.ca, Pub., Cochrane
Times-post, ON, Cochrane
wayne.major@sunmedia.ca, Pub., The
Northern Times, ON, Kapuskasing
wayne.major@sunmedia.ca, Pub., The
Weekender, ON, Kapuskasing
wayne.major@sunmedia.ca, Pub., Timmins
Times, ON, Timmins

Major , Rick
production@weyburnreview.com, Pub.,
Weyburn Review, SK, Weyburn

Majors, Kendra
kendra.majors@andalusiastarnews.com,
Principal Designer/Magazine Ed, Andalusia
Star-News, AL, Andalusia

Makaroff, Angela ....(705) 435-6228 ext. 222
amakaroff@simcoe.com, Sales Mgr., The
Alliston Herald, ON, Alliston

Makemson, Harlen
hmakemson@elon.edu, Assoc. Prof., Elon
University, NC, Elon

Makings, Vicki ....(303) 954-1691
vmakings@denverpost.com, Editorial Librarian,
The Denver Post, CO, Denver

Makintosh, Peter
tribune@tribunenb.ca, Pub./Ed, The Tribune,
NB, Campbellton

Makley, Bill ....(561) 923-5000
billmakley@tycoint.com, Media Rel., Siemens
Communications Group, FL, Boca Raton

Maksl, Adam ....(812) 941-2892
amaksl@ius.edu, Adviser, Indiana Univ.
Southeast, IN, New Albany

Malan, Sarah ....(760) 335-4641
smalan@ivpressonline.com, Copy Editor,
Imperial Valley Press, CA, El Centro

Malarchik, Debra
debra@kenlynews.com, Adv. Dir., Kenly News,
NC, Kenly

Malarski, Amy.......................(816) 218-6702
amy.malarski@pitch.com, Pub., The Pitch, MO,
Kansas City

Malat, Adam ....(410) 857-7888
amalat@carrollcountytimes.com, Adv. Dir.,
Carroll County Times, MD, Westminster

Malatesta, Shiela

smalatesta@chespub.com, Adv. Mgr., The
Avenue News, MD, Dundalk

Malato, Lucha ....(201) 798-7800 ext. 216
dunger@hudsonreporter.com, Co-Pub./Gen.
Mgr., Hudson Reporter Associates, Lp, NJ,
Bayonne

Malato, Lucha
lmalato@hudsonreporter.com, Co-Pub.,
Bayonne Community News, NJ, Bayonne

Malato, Lucha
editorial@hudsonreporter.com, Co-Pub.,
Secaucus Reporter, NJ, Bayonne

Malato, Lucha M.
lmalato@hudsonreporter.com, Pub., Mr., NJ,
Bayonne

Malato, Lucha M.
editorial@hudsonreporter.com, Pub., The
North Bergen Reporter, NJ, Bayonne

Malato, Lucha M.
editorial@hudsonreporter.com, Pub., The
Hoboken Reporter, NJ, Bayonne

Malato, Lucha M.
lmalato@hudsonreporter.com, Co-Pub., The
Weehawken Reporter, NJ, Bayonne

Malato, Lucha M.
lmalato@hudsonreporter.com, Pub., West New
York/Union City Reporter, NJ, Hoboken

Maldonado, Michelle
michelle@russellcountynewspapers.com,
Office Mgr, The Russell County News-
Register, KY, Russell Springs

Maldonaldo, Crystal ....(203) 317-2449
news@theplainvillecitizen.com, Mng. Ed., The
Plainville Citizen, CT, Meriden

Maldre, Matt........................(312) 222-4249
mmaldre@tronc.com, Marketing Manager,
Tribune Content Agency, IL, Chicago

Malek, Terri....................(814) 665-8291 Ext. 19
circulation@thecorryjournal.com, Cir. Mgr.,
Corry Journal, PA, Corry

Males, Jon
news@recordnews.com, Pub, Kansas City
Record, KS, Basehor

Malette, Chris
chris.malette@metroland.com, Ed, Belleville
News, ON, Belleville

Maley, Mark ....(574) 296-5939
mmaley@elkharttruth.com, Managing Editor,
Elkhart Truth, IN, Elkhart

Malfitano, Ricardo
aaron_miller@praxair.com, Exec. Vice Pres.,
Praxair, Inc., CT, Danbury

Malhotra, Jawahar
indoamericannews@yahoo.com, Indo
American News, TX, Houston

Malinee, Patty
dqcir@frontier.com, Circ. Mgr., Du Quoin
Evening Call, IL, Du Quoin

Malinowski, Mark (Scoop) ....(201) 833-2350
mrbiofile@aol.com, Ed., Biofile, Teaneck

Malkin, James
john.delmauro@sourcemedia.com, CEO,
American Banker, NY, New York

Mallais, Alina ....(780) 594-5206
thecourier@telus.net, Produc Coord, The
Courier, AB, Cold Lake

Mallard, Teretha ....(414) 265-5300
teretha@yahoo.com, PRODN. MGR.
, Milwaukee Community Journal, WI,
Milwaukee

Mallett, Linda ....(306) 365-2010
laniganadvisor@sasktel.net, Publisher/Editor,
Lanigan Advisor, SK, Lanigan

Mallette, Karl
wa@csolve.net, Ed., The Woodbridge
Advertiser, ON, Beeton

Mallin, Linda

lmallin@marinscope.com, Circ. Mgr., Sausalito
Marinscope, CA, Novato
lmallin@marinscope.com, Circ. Mgr., Twin
Cities Times, CA, Novato

Mallon, Shelly
circulation@star-herald.com, Circ. Mgr,
Luverne Announcer, MN, Luverne

Mallonee, Chris ....(219) 548-4327
chris.mallonee@nwi.com, Digital Operations
Manager, The Times of Northwest Indiana,
IN, Munster

Mallory, Kevin................(530) 283-0800 ext. 30
kmallory@plumasnews.com, Asst. to the Pub.,
I-T Director, Feather Publishing Co., Inc.,
CA, Quincy

Malloy, Jason ....(902) 629-6000 (ext. 6106)
jmalloy@theguardian.pe.ca , Sports Ed., The
Guardian, PE, Charlottetown

Malloy, Kate .... (613) 232-5952 ext. 202
kmalloy@hilltimes.com, Ed. , The Hill Times,
ON, Ottawa

Malloy, Lawrence J.
lmalloy@newspapersfirst.com, Vice Pres./
Sales Mgr., Newspapers First, Inc, FL,
Hollywood

Malloy, Mark
mmalloy@engleonline.com, Circ. Mgr., Engle
- York Community Courier West Edition, PA,
Mount Joy
mmalloy@engleonline.com, Circ. Mgr., Engle
- Columbia / Wrightsville Merchandiser, PA,
Mount Joy
mmalloy@engleonline.com, Circ. Mgr., Engle
- Conestoga Valley / Pequea Valley Penny
Saver, PA, Mount Joy
mmalloy@engleonline.com, Circ. Mgr., Engle
- Downingtown / Exton / Community Courier,
PA, Mount Joy
mmalloy@engleonline.com, Circ. Mgr., Engle
- Elizabethtown / Mount Joy Merchandiser,
PA, Mount Joy
mmalloy@engleonline.com, Circ. Mgr., Engle
- Gap / Oxford Community Courier, PA,
Mount Joy
mmalloy@engleonline.com, Circ. Mgr., Engle
- Hempfield / Mountville Merchandiser, PA,
Mount Joy
mmalloy@engleonline.com, Circ. Mgr.,
Engle - Hershey / Hummelstown / Palmyra
Community Courier, PA, Mount Joy
mmalloy@engleonline.com, Circ. Mgr., Engle
- Manheim / Lititz Merchandiser, PA, Mount
Joy
mmalloy@engleonline.com, Circ. Mgr., Engle
- Manheim Township Merchandiser, PA,
Mount Joy
mmalloy@engleonline.com, Circ. Mgr., Engle -
Middletown Shopper, PA, Mount Joy
mmalloy@engleonline.com, Circ. Mgr., Engle -
Millersville Advertiser, PA, Mount Joy
mmalloy@engleonline.com, Circ. Mgr., Engle
- Morgantown / Honey Brook Community
Courier, PA, Mount Joy
mmalloy@engleonline.com, Circ. Mgr., Engle -
New Holland Pennysaver, PA, Mount Joy
mmalloy@engleonline.com, Circ. Mgr., Engle -
Quarryville Advertiser, PA, Mount Joy
mmalloy@engleonline.com, Circ. Mgr., Engle
- West Chester Community Courier, PA,
Mount Joy
mmalloy@engleonline.com, Circ. Mgr., Engle
- Willow Street Strasburg Advertiser, PA,
Mount Joy
mmalloy@engleonline.com, Circ. Mgr., Engle
- York Community Courier East Edition, PA,
Mount Joy
mmalloy@engleonline.com, Circ. Mgr., Engle -
York Community Courier South Edition, PA,
Mount Joy

Malloy, Mark ....(717) 892-6004
mmalloy@engleonline.com, Circ. Mgr., Chester
County Community Courier, PA, Mount Joy

Malloy, Mark
mmalloy@engleonline.com, Circ. Mgr.,
Merchandiser-lancaster County, PA, Mount
Joy

Malloy, Mark
mwmalloy@engleonline.com, Circ. Mgr.,
Shopper, PA, Mount Joy

Malloy, Mark
mmalloy@engleonline.com, Circ. Mgr.,
Pennysaver, PA, Mount Joy

Mallya, Vijay
mscope@marinscope.com, Owner, Marinscope
Community Newspapers, CA, Novato

Malm, Kathy ....(785) 822-1453
kmalm@salina.com, Adv. Mgr., The Salina
Journal, KS, Salina

Malmberg, John ....(307) 587-2231
jt@codyenterprise.com, Publisher, The Cody
Enterprise, WY, Cody

Malo, Christian
christian.malo@lavoixdelest.ca, Circ. Dir., La
Voix De L'est Plus, QC, Granby

Malone, Cary Jane ....(931) 424-2831
cary.malone@pulaskicitizen.com, EIC, Pulaski
Citizen, TN, Pulaski

Malone, Jeffrey ....(412) 263-1743
jmalone@post-gazette.com, Home Delivery
Distribution Opns. Mgr., Pittsburgh Post-
Gazette, PA, Clinton

Malone, Josh ....(716) 773-7676
Lewiston-Porter Sentinel, NY, Grand Island

Malone, Rick
rickm@kis-kiosk.com, Pres., Kiosk Information
Systems, CO, Louisville

Malone, Tim ....(865) 981-1136
tim.malone@thedailytimes.com, IT Director,
The Daily Times, TN, Maryville

Maloney, E. Mayer.....................(812) 331-4251
mmaloney@heraldt.com, Pub., The Herald
Times, IN, Bloomington

Maloney, Josh........................(716) 773-7676
josh@wnypapers.com, editor, Island Dispatch,
NY, Grand Island

Maloney, Richard ....(513) 248-7134
rmaloney@communitypress.com, Ed., Bethel
Journal, OH, Loveland
rmaloney@communitypress.com, Ed., Milford-
Miami Advertiser, OH, Cincinnati
rmaloney@communitypress.com, Ed.,
Northeast Suburban Life, OH, Loveland
rmaloney@communitypress.com, Editor,
Community Journal Clermont, OH, Cincinnati
rmaloney@communitypress.com, Mng. Ed.,
Western Hills Press, OH, Cincinnati
rmaloney@communitypress.com, Editor, Delhi
Press, OH, Cincinnati
rmaloney@communitypress.com, Mng. Ed.,
Hilltop Press, OH, Cincinnati
rmaloney@communitypress.com, Mng. Ed.,
Price Hill Press, OH, Cincinnati

Maloney, Ron..........................(707) 441-0518
rmaloney@times-standard.com, System
Admin., On The Market, CA, Eureka

Malonson, Roy Douglas
news@aframnews.com, Pub., African
American News & Issues, TX, Houston

Malott, Mike
mmalotte@gannett.com, Managing Ed., The
Livingston County Daily Press & Argus, MI,
Howell
mmalotte@gannett.com, Ed., Green Sheet,
MI, Howell

Maloy, Foy
fmaloy@nassaucountyrecord.com, Pub.,
Nassau County Record, FL, Callahan

Maloy, Foy R...........................(904) 261-3696
fmaloy@fbnewsleader.com, Pub., News-
Leader, FL, Fernandina Beach

Maltais, Mike
sports@methowvalleynews.com, Vice
President, Washington Press Association,
WA, Renton

Maltezos, Nick ....(973) 569-7751
maltezos@northjersey.com, Dig. Ad. Ops. Mgr.,

Herald News, NJ, Rockaway

Maltsberger, Merlin
merlinm@bannergraphic.com, Adv. Mgr.,
Banner-Graphic, IN, Greencastle

Malviney, Pat
sadtad@centurytel.net, Ed., The Sparta
Herald, WI, Sparta

Mamis, Josh
jmamis@newmassmedia.com, Grp. Pub., New
Mass Media, Inc., CT, Hartford

Mamis, Joshua .... (203) 838-1825 ext. 101
editor@newhavenadvocate.com, Pub., Hartford
Advocate, CT, Hartford
editor@newhavenadvocate.com, Pub., New
Haven Advocate, CT, New Haven
editor@newhavenadvocate.com, Pub., Hartford
Courant, CT, Hartford

Mammen, Larry
lmammen@dailyrepublic.net, Prodn. Foreman,
Pressroom, Daily Republic, CA, Fairfield

Manchester, John
publisher@manchesternewspapers.com, Pub./
Nat'l Adv. Mgr., The Lakes Region Free
Press, NY, Granville

Manchester, John MacArthur .... (518) 642-1234
publisher@manchesternewspapers.com, Pres.,
Manchester Newspapers, Inc., NY, Granville

Manchester, John MacArthur
publisher@manchesternewspapers.com, Ed.,
The Whitehall Times, NY, Granville

Manchester, John MacArthur
publisher@manchesternewspapers.com, Pub.,
The Granville Sentinel, NY, Granville

Manchester, John MacArthur
publisher@manchesternewspapers.com, Pub./
Nat'l Adv. Mgr., Northshire Free Press, NY,
Granville
publisher@manchesternewspapers.com, Pub.,
The Weekender, NY, Granville
publisher@manchesternewspapers.com, Pub.,
The North Country Free Press, NY, Granville

Mancino, Michael .... (718) 263-6930
mmancino@hearst.com, Sales Mgr., New
Media Inside Sales, King Features Syndicate,
NY, New York
mmancino@hearst.com, Sales Mgr., New
Media Inside Sales Rep, North America
Syndicate, New York

Mancuso, Dan .... (541) 592-2541
dan@illinois-valley-news.com, Pub, Illinois
Valley News, OR, Cave Junction

Mancuso, Steve
Steve@hartindus.com, Pres., Hart Industries,
CT, East Haven

Mancuso, Theresa .... (315) 797-2417
uticaphoenix@gmail.com, Office and
Distribution Manager, Online Editor, Utica
Phoenix, NY, Utica

Mancuso, Tony .... (217) 351-5219
tmancuso@news-gazette.com, Features Ed.,
The News-Gazette, IL, Champaign

Mandarion, Jamie
kmelvage@schawk.com, Sales Mgr., Schawk,
IL, Chicago

Mandell, Adam .... (216) 342-5191
amandell@cjn.org, VP of Sales, Cleveland
Jewish News, OH, Beachwood

Mandeville, Nicole
nmandeville@freedomforum.org, Sr. Vice Pres.,
Finance, Freedom Forum, DC, Washington

Mandl, Donna .... (717) 771-2065
dmandl@ydr.com, Exec. Asst. to Pub., York
Daily Record/York Sunday News, PA, York

Mandou, Ashmar
ashmar.mandou@lawndalenews.com, Ed.,
The Lawndale News/Su Noticiero Bilingue,
IL, Cicero

Mandracchia, Kathryn .... ext. 118
kjm@tbrnewspapers.com, Adv. Dir., The Village

Times Herald, NY, Setauket

Mandracchia, Kathryn ...... (631) 751-7744 ext. 118
kjm@tbrnewspapers.com, Adv. Mgr., The Port
Times-Record, NY, Setauket

Mandrake, Tina
tina@jacksonnewspapers.com, Sales Rep.,
The Star-herald, WV, Ripley

Mandrell, Patty
pmandrell@mercedsun-star.com, Mng. Ed.,
The Chowchilla News, CA, Merced

Mandros, Athena
sales@dialogic.com, Contact, Dialogic Corp.,
NJ, Parsippany

Mangalonzo, John .... (360) 715-2280
john.mangalonzo@bellinghamherald.com,
Sr. Ed./News, The Bellingham Herald, WA,
Bellingham

Mangan, Kevin
irvce@aol.com, Circ. Mgr., Irish Voice, NY,
New York

Mangano, Julianne
jmangano@njpa.org, Marketing Specialist,
New Jersey Press Association, NJ, Ewing

Manges, Dawn
dawn@aspendailynews.com, Bus. Mgr., Aspen
Daily News, CO, Aspen

Mangini, Melissa .... (518) 640-6835
mmangini@bizjournals.com, Mgn. Editor,
Albany Business Review, NY, Latham

Mangus, Kathryn
kmangus@gmu.edu, George Mason University,
VA, Fairfax

Manikis, Christos
info@bhma.net, Ed., Greek Canadian Tribune,
QC, Montreal

Manikis, Peter
info@bhma.net, Adv. Mgr., Greek Canadian
Tribune, QC, Montreal

Manilla, Kathy .... (312) 222-2499
kmanilla@tribune.com, Adv. Dir., Devel.,
Chicago Tribune, IL, Chicago

Manion, B.C. .... (813) 909-2800
bcmanion@lakerlutznews.com, Ed, The Lutz
News, FL, Land O Lakes

Manion, B.C. .... (813) 909-2800
bcmanion@lakerlutznews.com, Ed, Zephyrhills
Laker, FL, Land O Lakes

Manion, B.C. .... (813) 909-2800
bcmanion@lakerlutznews.com, Ed, Wesley
Chapel Laker, FL, Land O Lakes

Manion, B.C. .... (813) 909-2800
bcmanion@lakerlutznews.com, Ed, Land O
Lakes Laker, FL, Land O Lakes

Manion, Kirt
kmanion@ncnewspress.com, Sports Ed.,
Nebraska City News-Press, NE, Nebraska
City

Mankin, Kathy
kathy@myeldorado.net, Gen. Mgr./Adv. Dir,
Eldorado Success, TX, Eldorado

Mankin, Randy .... (325) 853-3125
success@myeldorado.net, Pub., Eldorado
Success, TX, Eldorado

Manko, Janet
publisher@lakevillejournal.com, Pub. & Ed. in
Chief, The Winsted Journal, CT, Winsted

Manko, Janet
publisher@lakevillejournal.com, Pub./EIC, The
Lakeville Journal, CT, Falls Village

Manko, Janet
publisher@lakevillejournal.com, Pub./Ed.-in-
Chief, The Millerton News, NY, Millerton

Manly, Gary .... (541) 942-3325
gmanly@cgsentinel.com, Gen. Mgr., Cottage
Grove Sentinel, OR, Cottage Grove

Mann, Chris
Chris.mann@gaflnews.com, Adv. Mgr., Buyers

Guide, GA, Cordele

Mann, Cody .... (503) 728-3350
cmann@countrymedia.net, Ed, The Chief, OR,
Clatskanie

Mann, Dave
mann@texasobserver.org, Assoc. Ed., The
Texas Observer, TX, Austin

Mann, Jeff
jeff@greenpointnews.com, Ed. & Pub., The
Greenpoint Gazette, NY, Brooklyn

Mann, Les
lmann@norfolkdailynews.com, Gen. Mgr.,
Norfolk Daily News, NE, Norfolk

Mann, Les
lmann@norfolkdailynews.com, Gen. Mgr., Daily
News Plus, NE, Norfolk

Mann, Mark .... (724) 282-8000
mmann@butlereagle.com, Managing Editor,
Eagle Printing Co., PA, Butler

Mann, Merlin
mannm@acu.edu, Assoc. Prof./Dir., Journ.,
Abilene Christian University, TX, Abilene

Mann, Richard
storeystories@gmail.com, Pub., Comstock
Chronicle, NV, Virginia City

Mann, Rick
rmann@starlocalnews.com, Mng. Ed.,
Sunnyvale View, TX, Plano
rmann@starlocalnews.com, Mng. Ed.,
Carrollton Leader, TX, Plano
rmann@starlocalnews.com, Mng. Ed., Coppell
Gazette, TX, Plano
rmann@starlocalnews.com, Mng. Ed., Flower
Mound Leader, TX, Plano
rmann@starlocalnews.com, Mng. Ed., The
Colony Courier Leader, TX, Plano
rmann@starlocalnews.com, Mng. Ed., Plano
Star-Courier, TX, Plano
rmann@starlocalnews.com, Mng. Ed., Allen
American, TX, Plano
rmann@starlocalnews.com, Mng. Ed., Rowlett
Lakeshore Times, TX, Plano
rmann@starlocalnews.com, Mng. Ed.,
Mesquite News, TX, Plano
rmann@starlocalnews.com, Mng. Ed., Celina
Record, TX, Plano
rmann@starlocalnews.com, Mng. Ed., Little
Elm Journal, TX, Plano
rmann@starlocalnews.com, Mng. Ed., Frisco
Enterprise, TX, Plano
rmann@starlocalnews.com, Mng. Ed.,
Lewisville Leader, TX, Plano

Mann, Sarah
smann@conleynet.com, Ed., The Hartford
Times Press, WI, West Bend

Manna, John K. ....ext. 624
Political Ed., New Castle News, PA, New Castle

Mannarino, James .... (301) 670-2648
jmannarino@gazette.net, Pub., The Gazette -
Damascus / Clarksburg, MD, Gaithersburg
jmannarino@gazette.net, Pub., The Gazette
- Bethesda / Chevy Chase / Kensington
(OOB), MD, Gaithersburg
jmannarino@gazette.net, Pub., The Gazette
- Gaithersburg / Mont. Village (OOB), MD,
Gaithersburg
jmannarino@gazette.net, Pub., The Gazette -
Germantown / Poolsville / Boyds (OOB), MD,
Gaithersburg
jmannarino@gazette.net, Pub., The Gazette
- North / Central Prince George Co. (OOB),
MD, Gaithersburg
jmannarino@gazette.net, Pub., The Gazette -
Olney (OOB), MD, Gaithersburg
jmannarino@gazette.net, Pub., The Gazette -
Potomac / North Potomac, MD, Gaithersburg
jmannarino@gazette.net, Pub., The Gazette -
Rockville / Aspen Hill / Wheaton (OOB), MD,
Gaithersburg
jmannarino@gazette.net, Pub., The Gazette
- Silver Spring / Takoma Park / Burtonsville
(OOB), MD, Gaithersburg
jmannarino@gazette.net, Pub., The Gazette
- South / Central Prince George Co. (OOB),

MD, Gaithersburg

Manney, Todd .... (218) 312-1716
tpmanney@mx3.com, Pub., The Chisholm
Tribune Press, MN, Chisholm

Manning, Amanda .... (502) 222-7183
editor@oldhamera.com, Oldham Era, KY, La
Grange

Manning, Barry S.
news@gotowncrier.com, Pub./Adv. Mgr., The
Town Crier, FL, Wellington

Manning, Carl
carl@dailyranger.com, Circ. Mgr., Wind River
News, WY, Riverton

Manning, Jason
jason.manning@asu.edu, Arizona State Univ.,
AZ, Tempe

Manning, Mark .... (949) 731-4671
mark.manning@theeagle.com, Prod. Dir., The
Eagle, TX, Bryan

Manning, Sharon
advertising@msadvocate.com, Adv. Mgr., The
Advertiser, KY, Mount Sterling

Manning, Stacey
editor@brunswickbeacon.com, Ed., The
Brunswick Beacon, NC, Shallotte

Manning, Stefanie .... (207) 791-6201
smanning@mainetoday.com, VP/Circ. &
Marketing , Portland Press Herald / Maine
Sunday Telegram, ME, Portland

Manning, Tamara
amasis@amasis.com, Head Designer, Amasis,
IL, Chicago

Manning, Tammy .... (276) 236-5178
ads@galaxgazette.com, Circulation Manager,
Gazette Plus, VA, Galax

Manning, Taylor
taylor.manning@conferenceamerica.com,
Auburn Univ., AL, Montgomery

Manning, Thomas
info@mesacorp.com, Vice Pres.-Sales/Mktg.,
Mesa Corp., NE, Lincoln

Manning, Timothy .... (563) 588-7954
timothy.manning@loras.edu, Advisor, Loras
College, IA, Dubuque

Manning, Vern
circulation@canyoncourier.com, Pub./Ed., The
Canyon Courier, CO, Evergreen

Manning-Jacobs, Mary .... (352) 365-8287
mary.manning-jacobs@dailycommercial.com,
Director of Sales and Marketing, The Daily
Commercial, FL, Leesburg

Manning-Miller, Carmen
cmanning@olemiss.edu, Assoc. Prof./Grad.
Coord., University of Mississippi, MS,
University

Mannino, Fran .... (314) 968-2699
editor@westendword.com, Managing Editor,
West End Word, MO, Saint Louis

Mannis, David .... (619) 961-1951
david@sdcnn.com, Pub./Circ. Mgr, GAY San
Diego, CA, San Diego

Mannis, David .... (619) 961-1951
david@sdcnn.com, Pub./Circ. Mgr., San Diego
Uptown News, CA, San Diego

Manon-Rossi, Moises O.
atiempo@comcast.net, Ed., Acento Hispano
News, PA, Reading

Manoni, Douglas
rona@rdcdinc.com, CEO, SourceMedia,
American Banker, NY, New York

Manring, Liz .... (520) 515-4618
liz.manring@svherald.com, Mng. Ed., Wick
Communications - Herald/Review, AZ, Sierra
Vista

Mansch, Scott .... (406) 791-1481
tribsports@greatfallstribune.com, Sports Editor,
Great Falls Tribune, MT, Great Falls

Mansell, Archbishop Henry J. ....**(860) 286-2828**
info@catholictranscript.org, Pub., The Catholic Transcript, CT, Bloomfield

Manser, James M.
publisher@starnewsgroup.com, Pub., The Coast Star, NJ, Manasquan

Manser Ertl, Alison ....**(732) 223-0076, Ext. 38**
gm@starnewsgroup.com, General Manager, The Coast Star, NJ, Manasquan

Mansfield, Jim
mcmsales@bbtel.com, Ed, The Meade County Messenger, KY, Brandenburg

Mansfield, Mark.......................**(404) 645-4031**
mark.mansfield@@cox.com, Pres., Cox Media Group, GA, Atlanta
mark.mansfield@@cox.com, Vice Pres., Newsprint Supply, Cox Media Group, GA, Atlanta

Mansfield, Melissa
mmansfield@sooeveningnews.com, Circulation Manager, Sault Ste. Marie Evening News, MI, Sault Sainte Marie

Mansfield, Rebecca ....**(971) 204-7757**
rmansfield@pamplinmedia.com, Clas. Adv., Forest Grove News-Times, OR, Forest Grove

Manship, David
david.manship@theadvocate.com, Pres., Louisiana Press Women, Inc., LA, Baton Rouge

Mansoor, Sabih ....**(905) 337-3030**
sabih@mansoor.com, Mng. Ed., The South Asian Voice, ON, Oakville

Mansoor, Sabih
pakeeza@mansoor.com, Prodn. Mgr., Pakeeza International, ON, Oakville

Manteiga, Angie
amanteiga@lagacetanewspaper.com, Prodn. Mgr., La Gaceta, FL, Tampa

Manteiga, Patrick
pmanteiga@lagacetanewspaper.com, Ed., La Gaceta, FL, Tampa

Mantell, Nikki ....**(819) 459-2222**
nmantell@lowdownonline.com, Pub./Owner, The Low Down To Hull And Back News, QC, Wakefield

Mantineo, Andrea.....................**(201) 358-6697**
americoggi@aol.com, President/Ed., America Oggi, NJ, Norwood

Mantione, Russ
mantioner@prisco.com, CFO, Printers' Service/ Prisco/PriscoDigital, NJ, Newark

Mantle, Stacy
smantle@havredailynews.com, Pub./Adv. Mgr., The Hi-line Shopper, MT, Havre

Mantle, Stacy
smantle@havredailynews.com, Pub./Adv. Mgr., The Havre Daily News, MT, Havre

Manuel, Dodie ....**(480) 362-7731**
Dodie.Manuel@srpmic-nsn.gov, Mng. Ed., Au-Authm Action News, AZ, Scottsdale

Manuel, Donnie
dmanuel@btimes.com, Adv. Sales Mgr., Prince George's County Times, MD, Baltimore

Manuel, Donnie
dmanuel@btimes.com, Sales Mgr., The Baltimore Times, MD, Baltimore

Manuel, Julia
julia@newspapersatlantic.ca, Advertising Coordinator, Newspapers Atlantic, NS, Halifax

Manzano, Alexandra
alexandria.manzano@latimes.com, Audience Eng., Dir., Los Angeles Times, CA, Los Angeles

Manzano, Esther H.
elmexicalo@sbcglobal.net, Pub., El Mexicalo, CA, Bakersfield

Manzi, Al

manzia@dailycamera.com, Pub., Daily Camera, CO, Boulder

Manzi, Albert
manzia@dailycamera.com, Pres. and CEO, Prairie Mountain Publishing, CO, Boulder
manzia@dailycamera.com, Pub., Longmont Times-Call, CO, Longmont

Manzi, Albert
manzia@dailycamera.com, Pub., Broomfield Enterprise, CO, Boulder

Manzi, Jonh.................**(313) 584-4000 ext. 200**
Adv. Mgr., Dearborn Times-Herald, MI, Dearborn

Maoz, Jason ....**ext. 271**
jmaoz@jewishpress.com, Sr. Ed., The Jewish Press, NY, Brooklyn

Mara, Jamie
jmara@postcrescent.com, Mng. Ed., News-Record, WI, Appleton

Marabella, Gianni
gjmarabella@willamette.edu, Ed. in Chief, Willamette Univ., OR, Salem

Maraccini, Terry
tmaraccini@kenohsanews.com, Web Servs. Supvr., Kenosha News, WI, Kenosha

Marachlian, Kevork
armenmirr@aol.com, Gen. Mgr., Armenian Mirror-Spectator, MA, Watertown

Maragoudakis, Debbie.........................**ext. 123**
dmaragoudakis@certifiedaudit.com, Audit Mgr., Certified Audit of Circulations, Inc., NJ, Wayne

Marano, Jodi
jodimarano@cfl.rr.com, Adv. Dir., The News Leader, FL, Clermont

Marathe, Jack
sales@uts.us.com, Pres., Universal Technical Systems, Inc., IL, Rockford

Maravalli, Marc
editor@thetowncommon.com, Pub./Ed., The Town Common, MA, Rowley

Marble, Rhonda
rmarble@breezenewspapers.com, Prod. Mgr., Fort Myers Beach Observer, FL, Fort Myers Beach

Marcano, Cara ....**(609) 933-1400**
Caramarcano@reportehispano.com, Pub., Reporte Hispano, NJ, Princeton

Marceau, Johanne ....**(819) 478-8171**
johanne.marceau@transcontinental.ca, Ed., La Parole, QC, Drummondville

Marceau, Johanne ....**(819) 478-8171**
johanne.marceau@transcontinental.ca, Ed., L'express, QC, Drummondville

Marcel, Amanda ....**(765) 659-4622**
amarcel@ftimes.com, Circ. Dir., The Times, IN, Frankfort

Marcelo, Marvin
a-gonzalez@vancouver.wsu.edu, Asst. Prof./Dir., Murrow Symposium/Cable 8 Productions, Washington State University, WA, Pullman

March, Greg ....**(717) 278-1509**
gmarch@engleonline.com, Advertising Sales Manager, Pennysaver, PA, Mount Joy

March, Nancy
nmarch@pottsmerc.com, Ed., The Mercury, PA, Pottstown

March, Nancy
letters@pottsmerc.com, Ed., Mercury Sampler, PA, Pottstown

Marchand, Karen ....**(225) 388-0603**
kmarchand@theadvocate.com, Adv. Asst., The Advocate, LA, Baton Rouge

Marchek, Mike
mmarchek@timesbulletin.com, Cir. Mgr., The Times Bulletin, OH, Van Wert

Marchese, Mary Gay ....**(949) 756-5100**
pr@markzware.com, Public Relations, Markzware Software, Inc., CA, Santa Ana

Marchese, Patrick
sales@markzwarwe.com, Pres./CEO, Markzware Software, Inc., CA, Santa Ana

Marchi, Regina
rmarchi@rutgers.edu, Asst. Prof., Rutgers University, NJ, New Brunswick

Marchitto, Kristina.....................**(201) 236-4399**
Konica Minolta Business Solutions USA Inc., NJ, Ramsey

Marciano, Michael
winstedjournal@sbcglobal.net, Ed., The Winsted Journal, CT, Winsted

Marciano, Michael
mmcarciano@centralctcommunications.com, Editor, The Bristol Press, CT, Bristol

Marciano, Vincent ....**(513) 977-3949**
vincent.marciano@scripps.com, General Manager, United Media, United Media/EW Scripps, Cincinnati
vincent.marciano@scripps.com, United Feature Syndicate (Div. of United Media), New York

Marcil, William C. ....**(701) 235-0731**
wmarcil@forumcomm.com, Pub., Forum Communications Co., ND, Fargo

Marcil, William C. ....**(701) 235-7311**
bmarcil@forumcomm.com, Publisher/COO/ Executive Vice President, InForum, ND, Fargo

Marcil Jr., Bill ....**1-701—235-7322**
bmarcil@forumcomm.com, President & CEO, Forum Communications Co., ND, Fargo

Marcink, Robert.......................**(815) 280-2607**
rmarcink@jjc.edu, Advisor, Joliet Junior College, IL, Joliet

Marciocchi, Alan
entertainereditor@gmail.com, Ed., Laughlin Entertainer, AZ, Bullhead City

Marciochi, Alan ....**(928) 763-2505 Ext. 7232**
entertainereditor@gmail.com, Entertainment Ed., Mohave Valley Daily News, AZ, Bullhead City

Marcon, Tony
info@prolinedigital.com, Pres., Proline Digital, CO, Denver

Marcone, Matt
echonews2@mrnews.ca, Ed, The Echo-pioneer, AB, High Level

Marcotte, Michele ....**(318) 313-7176**
mmarcotte@gannett.com, Features Content Strategist, The Times, LA, Shreveport

Marcoux Prevost, Angele ....**(450) 455-6111**
nouvelles@hebdosdusuroit.com, Etoile De L'outaouais St Laurent, QC, Vaudreuil-Dorion

Marcum, Kim ....**(407) 420-5082**
kmarcum@orlandosentinel.com, Assoc. Mng. Ed., Features, Orlando Sentinel, FL, Orlando

Marcus, Aaron
aaron.marcus@bamanda.com, Principal, Aaron Marcus and Associates., CA, Berkeley

Marcus, Joel
manassyparts@yahoo.com, Pres., Manassy Sales Inc., NY, Forest Hills

Mardekian, Richard
communitynews@northjersey.com, Ed., Community News, NJ, Fair Lawn

Mardekian, Richard
thegazette@northjersey.com, Ed., The Gazette, NJ, Fair Lawn

Marek, Cynthia M.
cindym@wyomingnews.com, Adv. Mgr., Nat'l, Wyoming Tribune-Eagle, WY, Cheyenne

Marek, Joseph M. ....**(847) 427-4505**
jmarek@dailyherald.com, Circulation Manager, Single Copy Sales, Daily Herald, IL, Arlington

Heights

Marek, Patrick.........................**(507) 452-1262**
winpost@winonapost.com, VP/Pub., Winona Post, MN, Winona

Mares, Patrick.........................**(920) 522-3043**
editor@chiltontimesjournal.com, Ed, Chilton Times-Journal, WI, Chilton

Margolis, David G. ....**(508) 668-2150**
davidmargolis@synadinc.com, Pres., Syndicated Ad Features, Inc., MA, Walpole

Margolis, John
nu-qadmissions@northwestern.edu, Dean, Northwestern University in Qatar, Doha

Margoreeth, Jeanine ....**(250) 368-8551 ext 204**
nationals@trailtimes.ca, classifieds, Trail Daily Times, BC, Trail

Marian, Marc
publisher@silverbelt.com, Pub., Gile County Advantage, AZ, Globe

Mariano, Andrea ....**(212) 556-5162**
andrea.mariano@nytimes.com, Marketing Manager, The New York Times News Service & Syndicate, New York

Mariano, Andrea ....**(212) 556-5162**
andrea.mariano@nytimes.com, Mkt Mgr., The New York Times News Service & Syndicate, New York

Mariano, Fernando
info@multimediausa.com, Pres., Multimedia, Inc., FL, Orlando

Marietta, Roger ....**(912) 430-6808**
rmarietta@albany.ga.us, Darton College, GA, Albany

Marin, Mar
redaccion@efe.com.ar, Rep., EFE News Services - Havana, Cuba, Havana
redaccion@efe.com.ar, Rep., EFE News Services - Buenos Aires, Argentina, Buenos Aires

Marin, Marc
publisher@silverbelt.com, Pub., San Carlos Apache Moccasin, AZ, Globe

Marinacci, Peter ....**(905) 544-6174**
pdm@wombania.com, Owner/Cartoonist, Wombania, ON, Hamilton

Marine, Jake ....**(970) 384-9148**
jmarine@postindependent.com, Circ. Dir., Citizen Telegram, CO, Glenwood Springs

Maring, Brent
bmaring@nwherald.com, Mktg. Dir., Northwest Citizen Shopper, IL, Crystal Lake

Marino, Marie ....**(703) 854-5866**
mmarino@gns.gannett.com, Office Mgr., Gannett News Service - McLean, VA, Mc Lean

Marino, Mike ....**(315) 265-1000, ext. 29**
thisweek@northcountrynow.com, Circulation Supervisor, North Country This Week, NY, Potsdam

Marino, Rob ....**(352) 854-2322 ext. 1364**
marinor@cf.edu, Central Florida Cmty. College, FL, Ocala

Marjara, Jaswinder
jazz@CanIndia.com, Pres./Pub., Can-India News, ON, Mississauga

Mark, Blum ....**(609) 272-7110**
MBlum@pressofac.com, Pub, The Press of Atlantic City, NJ, Pleasantville

Mark, Liz ....**(919) 829-4771**
emark@newsobserver.com, VP, HR, The News & Observer, NC, Raleigh

Mark, Patricia
pmark@usouthal.edu, Asst. Prof., University of South Alabama, AL, Mobile

Mark, Sheridan........................**(812) 663-3111**
Mark.Sheridan@indianamediagroup.com, sales director, The Herald-Tribune, IN, Batesville

Markevicz, George....................(251) 219-5300
gmarkevicz@press-register.com, Circ. Dir.,
Press-Register, AL, Mobile

Markham, Bonnie....................(618) 208-6427
Advertising Director, The Telegraph, IL, Alton

Markham, Bonnie
bmarkham@civitasmedia.com, Local Business
Develop. Mgr., The Telegraph, IL, Alton

Markham, Matt....................(608) 755-8423
mmarkham@gazettextra.com, Dir of
Advertising & Audience, The Gazette -
gazettextra.com, WI, Janesville

Markham, William
wmarkham@avpress.com, Pub., Antelope
Valley Press Express, CA, Palmdale

Markham, William C..................(661) 273-2700
Pub., Antelope Valley Press, CA, Palmdale

Markle, Gary.............. (215) 822-5519 ext. 103
gmarkle@icanon.com, Dir., Mktg., ICANON
Associates, Inc., PA, Hatfield

Markley, Lance
lance@farmtalknewspaper.com, Co-Pub./Adv.
Mgr. , Farm Talk, KS, Parsons

Marko, Bob
bmarko@mcgrann.com, Sales Rep., McGrann
Paper Corp., NC, Charlotte

Markoe, Lauren....................(202) 463-8777
lauren.markoe@religionnews.com, National
Correspondent, Religion News Service,
Washington

Markon, John
jmarkon@tdn.com, Managing Ed., The Daily
News, WA, Longview

Markou, Mary.............. (416) 922-6678 ext. 236
mmarkou@retailcouncil.org, Manager, Special
Projects, Flyer Distribution Standards
Association, ON, Toronto

Markowski, Denise....................(920) 431-8268
dmarkows@gannett.com, Prod. Mgr, Door
County Advocate, WI, Sturgeon Bay

Markowski, Steve
sdm12@albion.edu, Mng. Ed., Albion College,
MI, Albion

Marks, Andy....................(352) 867-4143
eric.barnes@starbanner.com, Sports Ed.,
Ocala Star-Banner, FL, Ocala

Marks, Ellen....................(505) 823-3842
emarks@abqjournal.com, Asst. Bus. Ed.,
Albuquerque Journal, NM, Albuquerque

Marks, John....................(803) 831-8166
jmarks@fortmilltimes.com, Reporter, Fort Mill
Times, SC, Rock Hill

Marks, Melinda
mmarks@therecord.com, Mng. Ed. , The
Record, ON, Kitchener

Marks, Sherwin....................508 37-62001
sales@craftsmenmachinery.com, Pres./Chief
Exec. Officer, Craftsmen Machinery Co., Inc.,
MA, Framingham

Marks, Ted....................(207) 389-2620
tmarks@mfamedia.com, Pres., Marks &
Frederick Assoc., LLC, Kent

Markward, Loretta
lmarkward@timesbulletin.com, Bus. Off., The
Times Bulletin, OH, Van Wert

Marla, Lavonne
thefactsnewspaper@excite.com, Ed., Facts
News, WA, Seattle

Marlett, Matt....................(262) 542-2501
mmarlett@conleynet.com, VP of Media
Operations, Conley Media LLC, WI, Beaver
Dam

Marlette, Shauna....................(605) 624-4429
shauna.marlette@plaintalk.net, Ed., Vermillion
Plain Talk, SD, Vermillion

Marling, John
marling@pulseresearch.com, Pres., Pulse

Research, OR, Portland

Marling, John W.
marling@paper.net, PRESIDENT, Pulse
Research, Inc., OR, Portland

Marlman, Heather
graphics@gbpnews.com, Prodn. Mgr., The
Washington County Edition, IN, Salem

Marlman, Heather
graphics@gbpnews.com, Prodn. Mgr., The
Banner-Gazette, IN, Pekin

Marlman, Heather
graphics@gbpnews.com, Prodn. Mgr., The
Leader, IN, Charlestown

Marlman, Heather
graphics@gbpnews.com, Production Manager,
The Giveaway, IN, Scottsburg

Marlow, Kim....................(936) 336-3611
ads@thevindicator.com, Adv. Mgr., The
Vindicator, TX, Liberty

Marlow, Mike....................(828) 248-1408
mike@cfmedia.info, Advertising Manager,
Shelby Shopper & Info, NC, Shelby

Marlow, Mike....................(828) 248-1408
mike@rutherfordweekly.com, Gen. Mgr.,
Rutherford Weekly, NC, Forest City

Marlow, Sam
editor@grahamstar.com, Ed, The Graham Star,
NC, Robbinsville

Marlow, Tim
tmarlow@stormlakepilottribune.com, Prodn.
Mgr., Advertising Guide, IA, Storm Lake

Marlowe, David
davidK@tnwa.org, Gen. Mgr., Thrifty Nickel
Want Ads, ID, Idaho Falls

Marlowe, Michelle....................(843) 294-8424
amarlowe@wbtw.com, Adv. Mgr., Interactive
Sales, Morning News, SC, Florence

Marmon, Travis....................(248) 343-2023
tmarmon14@wooster.edu, College of Wooster,
OH, Wooster

Marois, Mario
jpdh@hebdosquebecor.com, Pub., Le Journal
Des Pays D'en Haut Le Vallee, QC, Sainte
Adele

Marotta, Eric....................(440) 232-4055
Ed., Nordonia Hills News Leader, OH, Kent

Marousky, Robert
composing@thedailysentinel.com, Graphic
Design, The Daily Sentinel, AL, Scottsboro

Marples, Krisi
editor@stcroixcourier.ca, Ed, St. Croix Courier,
NB, Saint Stephen

Marquard, Jennifer
ppinews@me.com, Pub., The Parkers Prairie
Independent, LLC, MN, Parkers Prairie

Marquardt, Kathy
kathy@inhnews.com, Ed., The Verndale Sun,
MN, Verndale

Marques Gonzalez , Aminda.........(305) 376-3429
amarques@MiamiHerald.com, Executive
Editor, Miami Herald, FL, Doral
amarques@MiamiHerald.com, Vice Pres./Exec.
Ed., Herald Values, FL, Miami

Marquez, Anthony
amarquez@ap.org, Bureau Chief, Los Angeles,
Associated Press/California-Nevada News
Executives, CA, Los Angeles

Marquez, JC
jc@thedenmarknews.com, Adv. Mgr., The
Denmark News, WI, Denmark

Marquez, Myriam....................(305) 376-3618
mmarquez@elnuevoherald.com, Exec Ed, El
Nuevo Herald, FL, Doral

Marquis, Michele
mmarquis@norwichbulletin.com, Circ. Mgr.,
The Bulletin, CT, Norwich

Marr, Heather

heather@northwestsignal.net, Adv., Northwest
Signal, OH, Napoleon

Marra, David.............(716) 282-2311 ext. 2242
marrad@gnnewspaper.com, Graphics Ed.,
Niagara Gazette, NY, Niagara Falls

Marran, David....................(262) 656-6294
dmarran@kenoshanews.com, Sports Ed.,
Kenosha News, WI, Kenosha

Marsala, Robert....................(203) 354-1076
Production Director, The Hour, CT, Norwalk

Marsala, Robert....................(203) 354-1076
Prodn. Dir., The Wilton Villager, CT, Norwalk

Marsan, Bruce
bmarsan@bentoneveningnews.com, Sports
Ed., Benton Evening News, IL, Benton

Marsch, Charlotte
dasp@cpimo.com, Ed., Bolivar Herald-Free
Press, MO, Bolivar

Marsden, David....................(403) 235-7592
dmarsden@calgaryherald.com, Editorial Page
Ed., Calgary Herald, AB, Calgary

Marsh, Cathy
cmarsh@neweraprogress.com, Classified Adv.
Mgr., Nelson County Times, VA, Amherst

Marsh, Elizabeth
elizabeth.marsh@fiu.edu, Asst. Prof., Florida
International University, FL, North Miami

Marsh, Pete....................(978) 590-7400
peter.marsh@newscycle.com, Vice President
of Marketing, Newscycle Solutions, MN,
Bloomington

Marsh, Peter....................(781) 266-1616
pmarsh@atex.com, Sr. Vice Pres./Chief
Integration Officer, Atex, Reading

Marsh, Steven
smarsh@thefranklinnewspost.com, The
Franklin News-Post, VA, Rocky Mount

Marshak, William
tricityvoice@aol.com, Pub., Tri-City Voice, CA,
Fremont

Marshal, Rick
rick@kirkrudy.com, Pres., Kirk-Rudy, Inc., GA,
Woodstock

Marshall, Alex.............. (740) 283-4711 Ext. 327
amarshall@heraldstaronline.com, Pub.,
Weirton Daily Times, OH, Steubenville

Marshall, Alex
amarshall@heraldstaronline.com, Pub., Herald-
Star, OH, Steubenville

Marshall, Ben
bmarshall31@cox.net, Pub., Sterling Bulletin,
KS, Sterling

Marshall, Bill
bmarshall@metrowny.com, Dist. Mgr., Metro
Community News, NY, Cheektowaga
bmarshall@metrowny.com, Circ. Mgr., Lockport
Retailer, NY, Buffalo
bmarshall@metrowny.com, Circ. Mgr. Arcade
Pennysaver, NY, Arcade
bmarshall@metrowny.com, Circ. Mgr, Blasdell /
Lackawanna (OOB), NY, Buffalo
bmarshall@metrowny.com, Circ. Mgr, Hamburg
Pennysaver, NY, Hamburg
bmarshall@metrowny.com, Circ. Mgr, Niagara
Falls / Wheatfield Metro Retailer (OOB), NY,
Buffalo
bmarshall@metrowny.com, Circ. Mgr, Amherst
/ Tonawanda Metro Source (OOB) , NY,
Buffalo
bmarshall@metrowny.com, Circ. Mgr, Alden
Metro Source, NY, Buffalo
bmarshall@metrowny.com, Circ. Mgr.
Tonawanda Source, NY, Buffalo
bmarshall@metrowny.com, Circ. Mgr,
Lancaster Source, NY, Buffalo
bmarshall@metrowny.com, Circ. Mgr, Clarence
Metro Source, NY, Buffalo
bmarshall@metrowny.com, Circ. Mgr,
Williamsville Smart Shopper, NY, Buffalo
bmarshall@metrowny.com, Circ. Mgr, Amherst
/ Getzville Smart Shopper, NY, Buffalo

bmarshall@metrowny.com, Circ. Mgr, North
Buffalo Smart Shopper, NY, Buffalo
bmarshall@metrowny.com, Circ. Mgr, South
Cheektowaga Source, NY, Buffalo
bmarshall@metrowny.com, Circ. Mgr, Kenmore
/ Tonawanda Source, NY, Buffalo
bmarshall@metrowny.com, Circ. Mgr,
Eggertsville / Snyder Smart Shopper, NY,
Buffalo
bmarshall@metrowny.com, Circ. Mgr, North
Tonawanda Source, NY, Buffalo
bmarshall@metrowny.com, Circ. Mgr, North
Cheektowaga Source, NY, Buffalo
bmarshall@metrowny.com, Circ. Mgr, South
Buffalo Metro Source, NY, Buffalo
bmarshall@metrowny.com, Circ. Mgr, Depew
Metro Source, NY, Buffalo
bmarshall@metrowny.com, Circ. Mgr,
Springville Journal, NY, Buffalo
bmarshall@metrowny.com, Circ. Mgr, Gowanda
News, NY, Buffalo

Marshall, Brad....................(217) 421-6955
Tech. Servs. Mgr., Herald & Review, Decatur,
IL, Decatur

Marshall, Cathy....................(207) 374-2341
subscriptions@pbp.me, Circ. Mgr., Island Ad-
Vantages, ME, Stonington

Marshall, Cathy....................(207) 374-2341
subscriptions@pbp.me, Circulation Mgr,
Castine Patriot, ME, Blue Hill

Marshall, Cathy....................(207) 374-2341
subscriptions@pbp.me, Circ. Mgr., The Weekly
Packet, ME, Blue Hill

Marshall, David....................(780) 429-5144
dmarshall@thejournal.canwest.com, Credit
Mgr., Edmonton Journal, AB, Edmonton

Marshall, Howard....................(202) 994-7079
hmarshall@ucp.org, George Washington Univ.,
DC, Washington

Marshall, Jennifer.........(606) 564-9091 ext. 240
misty.maynard@lee.net, Cir. Mgr., The Ledger
Independent, KY, Maysville

Marshall, Jennifer.........(606) 564-9091 ext. 221
Jennifer.Marshall@lee.net, Front Desk, The
Mayfield Messenger, KY, Mayfield

Marshall, John
info@utilimaster.com, Sr. Vice Pres., Sales/
Mktg., Utilimaster, IN, Wakarusa

Marshall, Kristine....................(574) 457-3666
syracuse@the-papers.com, Syracuse Office
Manager, The Paper - Kosciusko Edition,
IN, Milford

Marshall, Lorne
edit@metrowny.com, Ed., Metro Group, Inc.,
NY, Cheektowaga

Marshall, Marilyn....................(713) 663-6996
marilyn@defendermediagroup.com, Print Ed.,
Houston Defender Media Group, Formerly
Houston Defender, TX, Houston

Marshall, Marlon....................(306) 781-5241
mmarshall@leaderpost.canwest.com, Assoc.
Ed., The Leader-Post, SK, Regina

Marshall, Marti....................(304) 647-5724
Pub./Ed., Clay County Free Press, WV, Clay

Marshall, Michael....................(251) 219-5674
mmarshall@press-register.com, Vice Pres.,
News/Ed., Press-Register, AL, Mobile

Marshall, Pluria
addvalue@att.net, Pub., Wave Community
Newspaper, CA, Los Angeles

Marshall, Pluria....................ext. 129
Pub., Los Angeles Wave, CA, Los Angeles

Marshall, Rhonda
rmarshall@rvpublishing.com, Adv. Mgr., The
Gazette, IL, Pecatonica
rmarshall@rvpublishing.com, Adv. Mgr., The
Tempo, IL, Byron

Marshall, Scott
editor@nelsoncountytimes.com, Ed., Nelson
County Times, VA, Amherst

editor@nelsoncountytimes.com, Ed., Amherst New Era-Progress, VA, Amherst

Marshall, Sherrie .... (478) 744-4340
smarshall@macon.com, Exec. Ed., The Telegraph, GA, Macon

Marshall, Steve
smarshall@bcdemocrat.com, Gen. Mgr., Brown County Democrat, IN, Nashville

Marshall, Sue .... (306) 781-5234
Librarian, The Leader-Post, SK, Regina

Marshall, Susan
susanmarshall@berthel.com, Reporter, Marion County Record, KS, Marion

Marshall, Susan
susan@peabodykansas.com, Ed., Peabody Gazette-Bulletin, KS, Peabody

Marshall, Terry .... (778) 225-0031
circulation@comoxvalleyrecord.com, Circ. Mgr., Comox Valley Record, BC, Courtenay
circulation@comoxvalleyrecord.com, Circ Mgr., North Island Midweek, BC, Courtenay

Marshall, Tom
tmarshall@mtsterlingadvocate.com, Staff Writer, Mt. Sterling Advocate, KY, Mount Sterling

Marshall, Woody .... (478) 744-4233
wmarshall@macontel.com, Chief, Photography, The Telegraph, GA, Macon

Marshalsea, Cheryl
cmarshalsea@4freepress.com, Ed., The Free Press, FL, Tampa

Marshman, Barbara .... (408) 920-5542
bmarshman@bayareanewsgroup.com, Editorial Ed. , The Mercury News, CA, San Jose

Marster Sr., Scott .... (903) 389-6397
news@freestonecountytimes.com, Pub./Adv. Dir., Freestone County Times, TX, Fairfield

Marsters, Dave .... (443) 482-3146
dmarsters@capgaznews.com, Digital Editor, The Capital, MD, Annapolis

Mart, Sharon
siles@yourdouglasshopper.com, Office Mgr., Douglas Shopper, GA, Douglas

Martell, Sherry
sherry.martell@tc.tc, Newsroom Mgr., The Daily News, NS, Truro

Martens, Jeff
jmartens@northscottpress.com, Adv. Mgr., The North Scott Press, IA, Eldridge

Martens, Jeff .... (563) 285-8111
adsales@northscottpress.com, Advertising Mgr., Eastern Iowa Bizzzy Bee, IA, Eldridge

Martey, Rosa
rosa.martey@colostate.edu, Asst. Prof., Colorado State University, CO, Fort Collins

Martilla, Jenna
jmartilla@yourdailyglobe.com, Exec. Asst. , The Daily Globe, MI, Ironwood

Martin, Andre .... (250) 492-4002 ext. 120
andre.martin@pentichonherald.ca, GM, Penticton Herald, BC, Penticton

Martin, Annalisa .... (406) 523-5206
annalisa.martin@lee.net, Marketing Mgr., Missoulian, MT, Missoula

Martin, Ashley
amartin@morganton.com, Mgr., Pre Press, The News Herald, NC, Morganton

Martin, Bill
bmartin@gaa.org, Pres./CEO, Gravure Association of America, NC, Denver

Martin, Bob .... (859) 355-1237
bmartin@winchestersun.com, Commercial Printing Mgr./Ops. Mgr., The Winchester Sun, KY, Winchester

Martin, Bobby .... (928) 871-1152
bobbymartin@thenavajotimes.com, Production Mgr, Navajo Times Publishing Company, Inc.,
AZ, Window Rock

Martin, Brian
bmartin@texpac.com, Classified Adv. Dir., Fort Worth Weekly, TX, Fort Worth

Martin, Bryce
bmartin@countrymedia.net, Ed. , Bowman County Pioneer, ND, Bowman

Martin, Cal .... (306) 781-5219
cmartin@leaderpost.canwest.com, Prodn. Foreman, Pre Press, The Leader-Post, SK, Regina

Martin, Catherine .... (418) 962-9441 poste 232
catherine.martin@quebecormedia.com, Ed., Le Port Cartois, QC, Sept-Iles

Martin, Craig
craig.martin@sunmedia.ca, VP of Operations, Western Canada, The Edmonton Sun, AB, Edmonton

Martin, David .... (307) 875-3103
editor@greenriverstar.com, Editor, Green River Star, WY, Green River

Martin, Debbie
dmartin@sungazette.net, Adv. Mgr., Sun Gazette, VA, Mc Lean

Martin, Debbie .... (706) 864-1468
North Georgia College, GA, Dahlonega

Martin, Deborah
deborah@centrevillepress.com, Reporter, The Centreville Press, AL, Centreville

Martin, Debra
echo@comoxvalleyecho.com, Mng. Ed., Comox Valley Echo, BC, Courtenay

Martin, Denise .... (651) 257-5115
cpeditor@frontier.com, Ed., Search Shopper, MN, Lindstrom

Martin, Derek
sports@crookstontimes.com, Sports Ed., Crookston Daily Times, MN, Crookston

Martin, Diane ....ext. 254
d.martin@theday.com, Adv. Mgr., Retail, The Day, CT, New London

Martin, Dotty .... (570) 704-3982
dmartin@timesleader.com, Ed. , Abington Journal, PA, Clarks Summit
dmartin@timesleader.com, Ed., Sunday Dispatch, PA, Pittston

Martin, Doug
dmartin@benderus.com, Acct. Mgr., Bender Machine, Inc., CA, Vernon

Martin, Ed .... (304) 752-6950
emartin@civitasmedia.com., Asst Dir, The Logan Banner, WV, Logan

Martin, Edward
edward.martin@eammosca.com, VP, Sales, EAM-Mosca Corp., PA, Hazle Township

Martin, Fred
fredmartin@jvrhomes.com, Adv. Mgr., Clay County Courier, AR, Corning

Martin, Gary
gmartin@fbherald.com, Sports Ed., Fort Bend Herald, TX, Rosenberg

Martin, Gregory
gsmartin@stcloudstate.edu, Assoc. Prof./ Coord., Broadcast, St. Cloud State University, MN, Saint Cloud

Martin, Harold
hmartin@messenger-inquirer.com, Sports Copy Ed., Messenger-Inquirer, KY, Owensboro

Martin, Hernan
panama@acan-efe.com, Rep., EFE News Services - Panama City, Panama, Panama City

Martin, Holly .... (620) 227-1806
hmartin@hpj.com, Ed, High Plains Journal, KS, Dodge City

Martin, Jackie .... (217) 351-5275

jmartin@news-gazette.com, Adv. Sales Mgr. & National Sales, The News-Gazette, IL, Champaign

Martin, Jeff .... (434) 292-3019
ads@courier-record.com, Advertising Department / Graphic Designer, Courier-Record, VA, Blackstone

Martin, Jeff .... (901) 458-2911 ext. 5
jmartin@thebesttimes.com, Publisher's representative, The Best Times, TN, Memphis

Martin, Jo
martin@iafalls.com, Gen. Mgr., Times-citizen, IA, Iowa Falls

Martin, JoAnna
jmartin@lightandchampion.com, Publisher, The Merchandiser, TX, Center

Martin, Jodi
editor@diocesefwsb.org, Editor, Today's Catholic, TX, San Antonio

Martin, Josh .... (717) 339-2070
jmartin@gburgtimes.com, Sports Ed., Gettysburg Times, PA, Gettysburg

Martin, Karen .... (255) 388-0378
kmartin@theadvocate.com, Features Ed., The Advocate, LA, Baton Rouge

Martin, Kate
kmartin@perryvillenews.com, Pub., The Republic-monitor Shopping Guide, MO, Perryville

Martin, Kelli .... (478) 714-3688
kelli@jcnews.com, Adv. Rep., The Jones County News, GA, Gray

Martin, Kelly .... (336) 727-4065
kmartin@wsjournal.com, Digital Sales Manager, Winston-Salem Journal, NC, Winston Salem

Martin, Kelly .... (573) 635-4127 ext. 238
cathads@diojeffcity.org, Adv. Dir., The Catholic Missourian, MO, Jefferson City

Martin, Laira
editor@ucsdguardian.org, Editor in Chief, University of California San Diego, CA, La Jolla

Martin, Leonard C.
publisher@cableone.net, Pub., Bingham County Bargains, ID, Blackfoot

Martin, Linda
linda@enterprisepublications.com, Classified Adv. Mgr., The Bugle, IL, Plainfield

Martin, Lisa
lmartin@picayune-times.com, Class. Mgr., Nevada County Picayune, AR, Hope

Martin, Lori
lmartin@pdclarion.com, Adv. Mgr., Princeton Daily Clarion, IN, Princeton

Martin, Lori
lmartin@simcoe.com, Ed, Blue Mountains Courier-herald, ON, Meaford
lmartin@simcoe.com, Mng. Ed., The Mirror, ON, Midland

Martin, Marc .... (928) 425-0355
publisher@coppercountrynews.com, Pub., Copper Country News, AZ, Globe

Martin, Maria .... (816) 803-4449
rmoore@lsjournal.com , Ed., Lee's Summit Journal, MO, Kansas City
rmoore@lsjournal.com , Publisher, Editor, Lee's Summit Advertising Extra, MO, Lees Summit

Martin, Marione .... (580) 327-2202
marione@alvareviewcourier.net, Ed, Alva Review-Courier, OK, Alva

Martin, Mary .... (419) 448-3210
mmartin@advertiser-tribune.com, Cir. CS, The Advertiser-Tribune, OH, Tiffin

Martin, Matt .... (814) 870-1704
matt.martin@timesnews.com, Online News

Ed., Erie Times-News, PA, Erie

Martin, Matt 667-2576
mmartin@ellsworthamerican.com, Production Manager, The Ellsworth American, ME, Ellsworth

Martin, Millie .... (765) 973-4468
mmartin@pal-item.com, Special Content Ed., Palladium-Item, IN, Richmond

Martin, Misty
mmartin@catoosanews.com, Sports Ed., Catoosa County News, GA, Ringgold

Martin, Patricia
pat.martin@peoplenewspapers.com, Pub., Park Cities People, TX, Dallas

Martin, Patricia .... (214) 523-5242
pat.martin@peoplenewspapers.com, Pub., Oak Cliff People (OOB), TX, Dallas
pat.martin@peoplenewspapers.com, Pub., Preston Hollow People, TX, Dallas

Martin, Patrick
martinp@telspan.com, COO, TelSpan, Inc., IN, Indianapolis

Martin, Paul .... (440) 329-7101
pmartin@chroniclet.com, Pres. , Chronicle-Telegram, OH, Elyria
pmartin@chroniclet.com, President and CEO, Lorain County Printing & Publishing Co., OH, Elyria

Martin, Ralph
rmartin@steinmancommunications.com, Executive Vice President, LNP, PA, Lancaster
rmartin@steinmancommunications.com, Executive Vice President, LNP Media Group, Inc., PA, Lancaster

Martin, Ralph .... (412) 320-7977
rmartin@tribweb.com, Pres./CEO, Trib Total Media, Inc., PA, Pittsburgh
rmartin@tribweb.com, Pres., Tribune-Review, PA, Greensburg
rmartin@tribweb.com, Chrmn./Pres., Tribune-Review Publishing Co., PA, Greensburg
rmartin@tribweb.com, Pub., Woodland Area Progress, PA, Monroeville
rmartin@tribweb.com, CEO, Civitas Media, LLC-OOB, NC, Davidson

Martin, Robert .... (623) 876-2578
rmartin@yourwestvalley.com, Circulation. Dir., Daily News-Sun, AZ, Sun City

Martin, Robert L.
fultondemocrat@att.net, Pub., Fulton Democrat, IL, Canton

Martin, Robert L.
mcdemo@havanaprint.com, Pub., Mason County Democrat, IL, Havana

Martin, Robin .... (505) 986-3002
robinm@sfnewmexican.com, Owner, The Santa Fe New Mexican, NM, Santa Fe

Martin, Ron
rmartin@michigannewspapers.com, Prod. Mgr., Ogemaw/Oscoda County Star, MI, West Branch
rmartin@michigannewspapers.com, Prod. Mgr., Northeastern Shopper South, MI, Tawas City
rmartin@michigannewspapers.com, Prod. Mgr., Northeastern Shopper North, MI, Tawas City
rmartin@michigannewspapers.com, Prod. Mgr, Alma Reminder, MI, Alma
rmartin@michigannewspapers.com, Prod. Mgr, Grand Traverse Insider, MI, Traverse City
rmartin@michigannewspapers.com, Prod. Mgr, Mt. Pleasant Buyers Guide, MI, Mount Pleasant
rmartin@michigannewspapers.com, Prod. Mgr, Gladwin Buyers Guide, MI, Gladwin
rmartin@michigannewspapers.com, Prod. Mgr, Clare County Buyer's Guide, MI, Mount Pleasant
rmartin@michigannewspapers.com, Prod. Mgr, Alpena Star, MI, Alpena

Martin, Ross .... (816) 271-8553
Sports Ed., St. Joseph News-Press, MO, Saint

Joseph

Martin, Ruby
bcpress@frontier.com, Circ. Mgr, The Brown County Press, OH, Mount Orab

Martin, Sandra
editor@bayweekly.com, Ed./Pub., Passwords, MD, Annapolis

Martin, Shannon
smartin@jaxnews.com, Adv. Dir., Piedmont Journal, AL, Anniston
smartin@jaxnews.com, Adv. Mgr., The Jacksonville News, AL, Anniston

Martin, Sheila
sheila@gaebel.com, Office Mgr., Lithco Inc., CA, Culver City

Martin, Steve
steve.martin@starbanner.com, Adv. Mgr., Retail, Ocala Star-Banner, FL, Ocala

Martin, Susan .... (717) 771-2039
smartin@ydr.com, Asst. Mng. Ed., Metro, York Daily Record/York Sunday News, PA, York

Martin, Susan 641-28-3882
advertising@pellachronicle.com, Marketing Consultant, Marion County Reminder, IA, Knoxville

Martin, Terry .... (575) 374-2587
ucleader@plateautel.net, Ed./Pub., Union County Leader, NM, Clayton

Martin, Tim .... (701) 352-0640
advertising@wcrecord.com, Adv. Mgr., The Walsh County Record, ND, Grafton

Martin, Todd .... (502) 633-2526
tmartin@sentinelnews.com, Ed., The Sentinel-News, KY, Shelbyville

Martin, Tom
martine@princeton.edu, Mng. Ed., Illinois Valley Shopping News, IL, Princeton

Martin, Tom .... (309) 343-7181 ext. 250
tmartin@register-mail.com , Ed., The Register-Mail, IL, Galesburg

Martin, Tom
tmartin@register-mail.com, Knox College, IL, Galesburg

Martin, Tony .... (906) 341-4234
tony.martin@manistiquepapers.com, Prodn. Mgr., Manistique Papers, Inc., MI, Manistique

Martin, Vincent
vincent@lawattstimes.com, Bus. Mgr., La Watts Times, CA, Los Angeles

Martin, Wendy .... (478) 744-4443
wmartin@macon.com, Events and Engagement, The Telegraph, GA, Macon

Martin-Stewart, Shannon .... (915) 964-2426
hcherald@dellcity.com, Ed, Hudspeth County Herald, TX, Dell City

Martina, Alyssa
amartina@metroparent.com, Pub., Metro Parent Magazine, MI, Ferndale

Martindale, Carolyn .... (403) 314-4326
cmartindale@stalbert.greatwest.ca, Ed, St. Albert Gazette, AB, St. Albert

Martinek, Marcia .... (719) 486-0641 x 10
editor@leadvilleherald.com, Ed., Herald Democrat, CO, Leadville

Martinelli, Kathleen
kathleen.martinelli@sjsu.edu, Assoc. Prof., San Jose State University, CA, San Jose

Martinelli, Kevin
kmartinelli@republicmedia.com, Dir., Key Account Sales, The Arizona Republic, AZ, Phoenix

Martines, Blake .... (760) 934-3929 x 3
blake@mammothtimes.com, Sales Rep, Mammoth Times, CA, Mammoth Lakes

Martinette, Tony
tmartinette@lcni.com, Adv. Dir., Landmark Community Newspapers, LLC, KY,

Shelbyville

Martinez, Annette .... (305) 347-6670
amarinez@alm.com, Group Subscriptions Manager, Palm Beach Daily Business Review, FL, Miami

Martinez, Armando .... (956) 683-4090
amartinez@aimmediatx.com, Rgl. HR Dir., The Monitor, TX, McAllen

Martinez, Carlos .... (956) 689-2421
carlos@raymondvillechroniclenews.com, Adv. Dir., Raymondville Chronicle & Willacy County News, TX, Raymondville

Martinez, Cindy .... (806) 872-2177
accounting@pressreporter.com, Bookkeeper, Lamesa Press Reporter, TX, Lamesa

Martinez, Clarissa
mercedesenterprise@sbcglobal.net, Ed., Mercedes Enterprise, TX, Mercedes

Martinez, Denise
denmartinez@sanduskyregister.com, Staff Acct., Sandusky Register, OH, Sandusky

Martinez, Emilio
esm@buenasuerte.com, Periodico Buena Suerte - Austin, TX, Austin
esm@buenasuerte.com, Periodico Buena Suerte - Dallas, TX, Dallas
esm@buenasuerte.com, Periodico Buena Suerte - Houston, TX, Houston
esm@buenasuerte.com, Periodico Buena Suerte - San Antonio, TX, San Antonio

Martinez, Gina .... ext. 33
Prodn. Mgr., The Rio Rancho Observer, NM, Rio Rancho

Martinez, Jose
jose.martinez@myspace.com, Loyola Marymount Univ., CA, Los Angeles

Martinez, Joseph .... (800) 526-0827
joem@dynaric.com, Pres., Dynaric, Inc., VA, Virginia Beach

Martinez, Joseph .... (800) 446-8240
joem@dynaric.com, Pres., DYC Supply Co., VA, Virginia Beach

Martinez, Judith .... (770) 416-7570 ext. 109
editor@atlantalatino.com, Ed. in Chief, Atlanta Latino, GA, Atlanta

Martinez, Marco .... (509) 664-7149
martinez@wenatcheeworld.com, Features Ed., The Wenatchee World, WA, Wenatchee

Martinez, Max .... (302) 530-6007
martinpm@eckerd.edu, Managing Editor, The Current - Eckerd College, FL, Saint Petersburg

Martinez, Melissa .... (915) 546-6345
mmartinez@elpasotimes.com, Features Ed., El Paso y Mas, TX, El Paso

Martinez, Mike .... (847) 486-7278
mmartinez@pioneerlocal.com, Mng. Ed., Morton Grove Champion, IL, Chicago

Martinez, Norma
normamartinez@wildblue.net, Ed., Bird City Times, KS, Saint Francis

Martinez, Peggy
circulation@guymondailyherald.com, Cir. Mgr., Guymon Daily Herald, OK, Guymon

Martinez, Philadelphus
nicaragua@acan-efe.com, Rep., EFE News Services - Managua, Nicaragua, Managua

Martinez, Rodrigo .... (954) 766-4492
Director, El Noticiero, FL, Fort Lauderdale

Martinez, Rudy .... (325) 576-3606
pipernews@sbcglobal.net, Owner, Hamlin Herald, TX, Hamlin

Martinez, Theresa .... (925) 952-5097
tmartinez@bayareanewsgroup.com, Exec. Asst. to the Ed., East Bay Times, CA, Walnut Creek

Martinez, Thomas .... (970) 875-1790
tmartinez@craigdailypress.com, Ed., Morgan

Times Review, CO, Fort Morgan
tmartinez@craigdailypress.com, Ed., Craig Daily Press, CO, Craig

Martinez Dugay, Juan .... (525) 553-955888
jmdugay@towmar.net, Pres., Towmar Representaciones S.A., FL, Mexico City

Martinez-Smit, Julia
julianewhorizons@yahoo.com, Panorama De Nuevos Horizontes, TX, Fort Worth

Martino, Carmine
southbendlathe@att.net, Pres., South Bend Lathe Corp., IN, South Bend

Martino, Sam .... (262) 472-5100
martinos@uww.edu, Univ. of Wisconsin Whitewater, WI, Whitewater

Martino Dahlia, Gina .... (304) 293-5739
gina.dahlia@mail.wvu.edu, Teaching Associate Professor, West Virginia University, WV, Morgantown

Martins, Andrew .... (609) 874-2163
amartins@centraljersey.com, Mgr Ed., Hillsborough Beacon, NJ, Hillsborough

Martinsen, Melody .... (406) 466-2403
tetonads@3rivers.net, Ed., Choteau Acantha, MT, Choteau

Marton, Adam .... (410) 332-6024
adam.marton@baltsun.com, Sr. Ed. Interactive Design , The Baltimore Sun, MD, Baltimore

Marton, George
george.marton@bowebellhowell.com, Pres., Bell & Howell Scanners, IL, Wheeling

Marton, Lisa .... (307) 672-2431
lisa@thesheridanpress.com, advertising sales manager, The Sheridan Press, WY, Sheridan

Marts, Kent
kmarts@nwaonline.com, Pub., The Herald-Leader, AR, Siloam Springs
kmarts@nwaonline.com, Weeklies Ed. & Gen. Mgr., The Times of Northeast Benton County, AR, Pea Ridge

Marturello, Michael ....(260) 665-3117 Ext. 2140
mmarturello@kpcmedia.com, Ed., The Herald Republican, IN, Angola

Marturello, Mike
mikem@kpcnews.net, Ed., Smart Shopper, IN, Angola

Marty, Carolyn
cmarty@yourjournal.com, Pub., North Side Journal, MO, Chesterfield

Marty, Carolyn
cmarty@yourjournal.com, Pub., Overland/St. Ann Journal-North Couny Journal, MO, Hazelwood

Marty, Michael .... (608) 781-1606
info@lptnow.com, Pres., Laser Products Technologies, WI, Holmen

Martyniak, Shoshana
shoshana@shalomdel.org, Editor, The Jewish Federation of Delaware, DE, Wilmington

Martz, Linda .... (419) 521-7229
lmartz@nncogannett.com, Watchdog Rep., News Journal, OH, Mansfield

Martínez, Raúl .... (310) 543-6130
raul.martinez@impactousa.com, Dsgn. Mgr., Impacto USA, CA, Torrance

Martínez, Thomas
tmartinez@corsicanadailysun.com, Ed., Palestine Herald-Press, TX, Palestine
tmartinez@corsicanadailysun.com, Ed., Corsicana Daily Sun, TX, Corsicana

Marubashi, Rachel
subscriptions@gridleyherald.com, Circ. Mgr., The Gridley Shopping News, CA, Gridley

Marucci, Rick
rick.marucci@swcc.com, CEO, The Software Construction Co. (SCC), GA, Alpharetta

Marx, John .... (309) 757-8388
johnny@qconline.com, Columnist, The

Dispatch-Argus, IL, Moline

Marx, R.J.
rmarx@seasidesignal.com, Ed, Seaside Signal, OR, Seaside

Mary Lou, N/A ....Ed.
Kilian, North Country Catholic, NY, Ogdensburg

Mascareno, Katharina
ads.times@att.net, Advertising manager, The Herington Times, KS, Herington

Maschak, Monica
mmaschak@shawmedia.com, Photographer, Daily Chronicle, IL, Dekalb

Masciadrelli, Flora
floram@thewestfieldnewsgroup.com, Classifieds Sales Mgr., The Westfield News , MA, Westfield

Mascorro, Yvonne .... (409) 683-5264
yvonne.mascorro@galvnews.com, Circ. Mgr., The Galveston County Daily News, TX, Galveston

Masengill, Brenda .... (575) 541-5439
bmasengill@lcsun-news.com, Feat. Ed. , Las Cruces Sun-News, NM, Las Cruces

Masenheimer, Scott .... (610) 377-2051
smasenheimer@tnonline.com, Gen. Mgr., Catasauqua Press, PA, Allentown

Masenheimer, Scott .... (610) 377-2051
smasenheimer@tnonline.com, Gen. Mgr., Whitehall-Coplay Press, PA, Allentown

Masenheimer, Scott .... (610) 377-2051
smasenheimer@tnonline.com, Gen. Mgr., Northampton Press, PA, Allentown

Masenheimer, Scott A. .... (610) 377-2051
smasenheimer@tnonline.com, VP, Ops., Times News, PA, Lehighton

Mason, Andy .... (301) 791-6049
andrewm@herald-mail.com, Sports Ed., The Herald-Mail, MD, Hagerstown

Mason, Bill .... (203) 330-6506
bmason@hearstmediact.com, Assoc. Pub., Upper West Side Resident, NY, New York
bmason@hearstmediact.com, Circ. Dir., Westport News, CT, Bridgeport
bmason@hearstmediact.com, Circ. Dir., Darien News, CT, Bridgeport
bmason@hearstmediact.com, Circ. Dir., Fairfield Citizen, CT, Bridgeport

Mason, Bob .... (213) 896-2153
bob.mason@laopinion.com, Dir. IT, La Opinion, CA, Los Angeles

Mason, Charles
c.mason@uaf.edu, Chair, University of Alaska at Fairbanks, AK, Fairbanks

Mason, Daniel .... (570) 662-4986
Mansfield Univ. of Pennsylvania, PA, Mansfield

Mason, Felicia
felicia@alabamapress.org, Exec. Dir., Alabama Press Association, AL, Birmingham

Mason, Felicia
felicia@alabamapress.org, Exec. Dir., Alabama Newspaper Advertising Service, Inc., AL, Birmingham

Mason, Joan .... (609) 989-5476
jmason@njadvancemedia.com, Pub., The Times, NJ, Trenton

Mason, Julie
julie@zumapress.com, CFO, ZUMA Press, Inc., San Clemente

Mason, Lynette .... (502) 477-2239 ext. 25
lmason@spencermagnet.com, Publisher, Spencer Magnet, KY, Taylorsville

Mason, Melissa
mmason@bnd.com, Adv. Dir., Command Post, IL, Belleville

Mason, Paty
pmason@houstonianonline.com, Business Manager, Sam Houston State University, TX, Huntsville

Mason, Rachel
rmason@nanaimodailynews.com, Bus. Mgr., Nanaimo Daily News, BC, Nanaimo

Mason, Ron .... (765) 973-4549
rmason3@pal-item.com, District Mgr., Palladium-Item, IN, Richmond

Mason, Shelagh .... (615) 444-3952
smason@lebanondemocrat.com, Mgr., Accounting, The Lebanon Democrat, TN, Lebanon

Mason, Tammy .... (620) 792-1211, ext. 209
tmason@gbtribune.com, Marketing Consultant, Great Bend Tribune, KS, Great Bend

Mason, Teresa .... (501) 370-8309
tmason@cabotstarherald.com, Retail Adv. Mgr., Cabot Star-Herald, AR, Cabot

Mason, Vickie .... (423) 623-6171
vickie.mason@newportplaintalk.com, Advertising, The Newport Plain Talk, TN, Newport

Mason , Melissa .... (618) 239-2541
mmason@bnd.com, VP Adv., O'Fallon Progress, IL, Belleville
mmason@bnd.com, VP Adv. , Belleville News-Democrat, IL, Belleville

Masonbrink, Gayle
retailadv@wapakwdn.com, Adv. Dir., Auglaize Merchandiser, OH, Wapakoneta

Masonbrink, Gayle
publisher@theeveningleader.com, Pub./Mktg. Mgr., The Evening Leader, OH, Saint Marys

Masonbrink, Gayle .... (419) 394-7414
publisher@theeveningleader.com, Adv. Mgr., Wapakoneta Daily News, OH, Wapakoneta

Masotta, Richard .... (617) 929-2279
masotta@globe.com, Adv. Dir., Opns., The Boston Globe, MA, Boston

Massa, Jeffrey P. .... (703) 548-3300
info@yellowbrix.com, Founder/Pres./CEO, YellowBrix, VA, Arlington

Massaro, Cheryl
circulation@chestnuthilllocal.com, Circ. Mgr., Chestnut Hill Local, PA, Philadelphia

Massawe, Catherine .... (985) 254-7850
northdistmgr@hammondstar.com, Circ. District Mgr. , The Daily Star, LA, Hammond

Masse, Lucie
direction@courrierdusud.com, Pub., Le Courrier Du Sud/south Shore Courier, QC, Longueuil

Masse, Lucie .... (450) 646-3333
Gen. Mgr. , Magazine De Saint Lambert, QC, Longueuil

Masse, Lucie .... (450) 616-8080
lucie.masse@quebecormedia.com, Ed., Brossard Eclair, QC, Longueuil

Massek, Mike .... (812) 206-2107
mike.massek@newsandtribune.com, Dir. of Aud. Dev. , News and Tribune, IN, Jeffersonville
mike.massek@newsandtribune.com, Circ. Mgr., Tribune, IN, New Albany

Massey, Cal
cal.massey@news-jrnl.com, Deputy Mng. Ed., News, Daytona Beach News-Journal, FL, Daytona Beach

Massey, Ron
rmassey@archindy.org, Exec. Asst., The Criterion, IN, Indianapolis

Massey, Steve
teaguechronicle@sbcglobal.net, Pub./Ed., Teague Chronicle, TX, Teague

Massicotte, Andrea
ads@mackenzietimes.com, Adv Mgr, The Times, BC, Mackenzie

Massoth, Michele .... (815) 987-1320
mmassoth@rockford.gannett.com, Adv. Dir., The Star Shopper, IL, Rockford

Massoth, Michele .... (815) 232-0121
michele.massoth@journalstandard.com, Gen. Mgr, The Journal-Standard, IL, Freeport

Mast, Greg
gmast@ottowaherald.com, Sr. Writer, The Ottawa Herald, KS, Ottawa

Mast, Michael .... (330) 674-2300
mlmast@alonovus.com, Pres, Tuscarawas Bargain Hunter, OH, Millersburg
mlmast@alonovus.com, Pres, The Bargain Hunter - Tuscarawas, OH, Millersburg
mlmast@alonovus.com, Pres, The Bargain Hunter - Wayne, OH, Millersburg
mlmast@alonovus.com, Pres., Wooster Weekly News, OH, Millersburg
mlmast@alonovus.com, Pres., Holmes County Journal, OH, Millersburg

Mast, Michael
mlmast@alonovus.com, Pres., The Bargain Hunter - Holmes, OH, Millersburg

Masters, Christine
cmasters@townnews.com, Dir./Product Mgmt., TownNews.com, IL, Moline

Masters, Jeff
jmasters@cnhi.com, Adv. VP, Valdosta Daily Times, GA, Valdosta

Masters, Linda .... (870) 508-8058
lmasters@baxterbulletin.com, Online Ed. / Food Ed., The Baxter Bulletin, AR, Mountain Home

Masters, Troy .... (646) 452-2501
troy@gaycitynews.com, Assoc. Pub., Gay City News, NY, New York

Mastin, Dan .... (252) 329-9654
dmastin@reflector.com, Dir., Ops., The Daily Reflector, NC, Greenville

Masuda, Hiroshi
hiroshi.masuda@jijiusa.com, Pres., Jiji Press America Ltd., New York

Maszk, Mary .... (815) 244-2411
mmaszk@grics.net, Office/Circ. Mgr., Carroll County Mirror-Democrat, IL, Mount Carroll

Matassa Flores, Michele .... (206) 464-2292
mflores@seattletimes.com, Managing Ed., The Seattle Times, WA, Seattle

Matassa Flores, Michele .... (206) 464-2292
mflores@seattletimes.com, Mng Ed, The Seattle Times, WA, Seattle

Matchett, Brenda
brenda@minerjournal.com, Adv. Mgr., The Esterhazy Miner-journal, SK, Esterhazy

Matczak, Melissa .... (402) 444-1088
melissa.matczak, Executive Editor, Omaha World-Herald, NE, Omaha

Matera, Jerry
matera@scrtc.com, Ed., Hart County News Herald, KY, Horse Cave

Materi, Francis
wishekstar@gmail.com, Editorial Dir., The Wishek Star, ND, Wishek

Matheis, Brenda .... (217) 753-2226 ext. 137
bmatheis@illinoistimes.com, Circ. Mgr., Illinois Times, IL, Springfield

Matheny, Susan
smatheny@madraspioneer.com, Ed., The Madras Pioneer, OR, Madras

Mather, Tim
tmather@inlandpress.org, Financial Studies Mgr., Inland Press Association, IL, Des Plaines

Mathes, Joe
joe@deltapublications.com, Vice Pres., Sales, Tempo, WI, Kiel

Mathes, Mike E.
mike@deltapublications.com, Pub., Tempo, WI, Kiel

Matheson, Jason
jmatheson@journalpioneer.com, Prod.

Supervisor, The Journal Pioneer, PE, Summerside

Matheson, Keith .... ext. 265
Prodn. Mgr., Mailroom, St. Catharines Standard, ON, Saint Catharine's

Mathews, Colin
customerservice@eisinc.com, CEO/Pres., readMedia, NY, Albany

Mathews, Gregory .... (417) 836-1195
gmatthews@news-leader.com, Online Ed., Springfield News-Leader, MO, Springfield

Mathews, Guy
gmathews@thecarbondalenews.com, Other, The Wayne Independent, PA, Honesdale

Mathews, Ricky
publisher@nola.com, Pub., The Times-Picayune, LA, New Orleans

Mathews, Thomas
news@waycopress.com, Pub./Gen. Mgr., Wayne County Press, IL, Fairfield

Mathewson, Bob
rm@vnews.com , Operations, Valley News, NH, West Lebanon

Mathewson, Kim .... (616) 527-2100
kim.mathewson@sentinel-standard.com, Business Office Mgr., Ionia Sentinel-Standard, MI, Ionia

Mathewson, Melanie .... (321) 283-5259
mmathewson@intersectmediasolutions.com, VP/CSO, Intersect Media Solutions, FL, Lake Mary

Mathis, Dee Dee
dmathis@cnhi.com, Vice Pres., Digital Sales, Community Newspaper Holdings, Inc., AL, Montgomery

Mathis, Dee Dee .... (205) 325-2450
dmathis@cnhi.com, VP, Digital Solutions, The Birmingham News, AL, Birmingham

Mathis, Gregory .... (781) 837-4560
gmathis@wickedlocal.com, Ed. in Chief, Weymouth News, MA, Randolph

Mathis, Gregory .... (781) 837-4560
gmathis@wickedlocal.com, Ed. in Chief, Kingston Reporter, MA, Plymouth

Mathis, Gregory .... (781) 837-4560
gmathis@wickedlocal.com, Ed. in Chief, Braintree Forum, MA, Randolph

Mathis, Gregory .... (781) 837-4560
gmathis@wickedlocal.com, Ed. in Chief, Norwell Mariner, MA, Marshfield

Mathis, Gregory .... (781) 837-4560
gmathis@wickedlocal.com, Ed. in Chief, Cohasset Mariner, MA, Hingham

Mathis, Gregory
gmathis@cnc.com, Ed.-in-Chief, Halifax-Plympton Reporter, MA, Marshfield
gmathis@cnc.com, Sr. Mng. Ed., Hanover Mariner, MA, Marshfield

Mathis, Gregory .... (781) 837-4560
gmathis@wickedlocal.com, Ed. in Chief, Old Colony Memorial, MA, Plymouth

Mathis, Gregory 781- 837-4560
gmathis@wickedlocal.com, Ed. in Chief, Rockland Standard, MA, Marshfield

Mathis, Gregory .... (781) 837-4560
gmathis@wickedlocal.com, Ed. in Chief, The Sentinel, MA, Plymouth

Mathis, Gregory .... (781) 837-4560
gmathis@wickedlocal.com, Ed. In Chief, Abington Mariner, MA, Marshfield

Mathis, Gregory .... (781) 837-4560
gmathis@wickedlocal.com, Ed. in Chief, Scituate Mariner, MA, Marshfield

Mathis, Kandy .... (256) 232-2720
kandy@athensnews-courier.com, Classified Sales Consultant, The News-Courier, AL, Athens

Mathis, Keith
sun@sunnews.com, Pres./CEO, Sun Newspapers, OH, Cleveland

Mathis, P. Dawn
dawnlcnchandler@sbcglobal.net, Gen. Mgr., Lincoln County News, OK, Chandler
dawnlcnchandler@sbcglobal.net, office Mgr./ Adv. Mgr., Lincoln County News, NM, Carrizozo

Mathis, Scott .... (217) 477-5187
Circ. Dir., Commercial News, IL, Danville

Mathison, Mike
mmathison@heraldstaronline.com, Sports. Ed., Herald-Star, OH, Steubenville

Mathison, Teresa
tmathison@yrmg.com, Distribution Coord., The Newmarket Era-banner, ON, Newmarket

Matics, Greg .... (304) 372-4222
gmatics@jacksonnewspapers.com, Ed/Gen Mgr, Jackson Herald, WV, Ravenswood

Matics, Gregory .... (304) 372-4222
gmatics@jacksonnewspapers.com, Ed/ Gen Mgr, The Jackson Star News, WV, Ravenswood

Matics, Gregory
editor@jacksonnewspapers.com, News Ed., The Star-herald, WV, Ripley

Matinho, A.S.
lusoamerican@earthlink.net, Ed. in Chief, Luso Americano, NJ, Newark

Matinho, Paul
pmatinho@lusoamericano.com, Opns. Dir., Luso Americano, NJ, Newark

Matire, Kitie
guymondailyeditor@gmail.com, Mng. Ed., Guymon Daily Herald, OK, Guymon

Matlock, Staci .... (575) 758-2241
editor@taosnews.com, Editor , The Taos News, NM, Taos

Maton, Leeann
phoenixnews@luc.edu, Loyola Univ., IL, Chicago

Matos, Joao Santos
news@24horasnewspaper.com, News Ed., 24 Horas, NJ, Newark

Matoushek, Jean
jean@forestcitynews.com, Office Mgr., The Forest City News, PA, Forest City

Matrazzo, Steve
editor@dundalkeagle.net, Editor, The Dundalk Eagle, MD, Dundalk

Matsui, Sandy .... (808) 956-7146
matsuis@hawaii.edu, Dir, University of Hawaii Manoa, HI, Honolulu

Matsuzawa, M. .... (847) 981-9399 ext. 210
info@inxintl.com, Chrmn., INX International Ink Co., IL, Schaumburg

Matta, Cris .... (360) 735-4423
cris.matta@columbian.com, Production Manager, The Columbian, WA, Vancouver

Matta-Caro, Cristina
mcmatta@reviewjournal.com, Reporter, El Tiempo, NV, Las Vegas

Matta-Caro, Maria Cristina .... (702) 477-3845
mariamattac@reviewjournal.com, Pub./Ed. , El Tiempo, NV, Las Vegas

Matteau, Michel
michel.matteau@transcontinental.ca, Pub., L'hebdo Mekinac/des Chenaux, QC, Shawinigan

Matteau, Michel .... ext. 225
michel.matteau@transcontinental.ca, Pub., Hebdo Du St. Maurice, QC, Shawinigan

Mattern, Jody
matternj@mnstate.edu, Asst. Prof., Minnesota State University, Moorhead, MN, Moorhead

Matthew, Pellegrino .... (850) 932-8986 ext. 111

news@gulfbreezenews.com, Editor, Gulf Breeze News, FL, Gulf Breeze

Matthew, Scott .... (434) 292-3019
scott@courier-record.com, Advertising Representative, Courier-Record, VA, Blackstone

Matthews, Betsy .... (585) 244-3329 x27
bmatthews@rochester-citynews.com, New Business Director, City Newspaper, NY, Rochester

Matthews, Carl
cmatthews@call-post.com, Circ. Mgr., King Media Enterprises, OH, Columbus

Matthews, Denise
fccitizen@windstream.net, Ed., The News Leader, GA, Lavonia

Matthews, Denise
dmatthews@franklincountycitizen.com, Mng. Ed., Franklin County Citizen Leader, GA, Lavonia

Matthews, Lisa
lisamatthews@lincolntimesnews.com, Adv. Mgr., Lincoln Times-News, NC, Lincolnton

Matthews, Robert
news@pattersonirrigator.com, Pub., Patterson Irrigator, CA, Patterson

Matthews, Sherry .... (910) 249-4612
Publisher/Editor, The Sampson Independent, NC, Clinton

Matthews, Travis
Ads@thesouthalabamian.com, Adv. Mgr., The South Alabamian, AL, Jackson

Matthies, Steve
smatthies@heraldandnews.com, Oregon Institute of Technology, OR, Klamath Falls

Mattiace, Peter
petermattiace@thecourier.com, Ed., The Courier, OH, Findlay

Mattiace, Peter
petermattiace@thecourier.com, Ed., The Courier AdVantage, OH, Findlay

Mattice, Gerry .... (519) 886-2830 ext. 230
sales@waterloochronicle.ca, Adv. Mgr., Retail Sales, Waterloo Chronicle, ON, Waterloo

Mattice, Ken .... ext. 214
boosterads@swbooster.com, Circ. Mgr., The Southwest Booster, SK, Swift Current

Mattingly, Elizabeth .... (937) 382-2574 Ext. 2505
emattingly@civitasmedia.com, Adv. Mgr., Wilmington News Journal, OH, Wilmington

Mattingly, Mary
mmattingly@ripleynews.com, Ed., Versailles Republican, IN, Versailles

Mattingly, Steve .... (800) 638-7990
smattingly@slp.com, Sr. VP, Southern Lithoplate, Inc., NC, Youngsville

Mattison, Michael
winthropnews@gmail.com, Ed., The Winthrop News, MN, Winthrop

Mattos, Susan .... (209) 243-8101
smattos@mattosnews.com, Pub., MATTOS NEWSPAPERS, INC., CA, Newman

Mattress, Willie .... (864) 260-1274
mattresswm@independentmail.com, Ed., HomeTown People, Anderson Independent-Mail, SC, Anderson

Mattrick, Don
don@xbox.com, Sr. Vice Pres., Interactive Entertainment Bus., Microsoft Corp., WA, Redmond

Matts-Sprague, Jennifer
jmatts-sprague@theolympian.com, VP Finance, The Olympian, WA, Olympia

Matts-Sprague, Jennifer .... (704) 358-5844
jmatts-sprague@charlotteobserver.com, VP of Finance, The Charlotte Observer, NC, Charlotte

Mattson, Eric N.
warrensheaf@mncable.net, Ed., Warren Sheaf, MN, Warren

Mattson, Sophie
editor@thesantaclara.org, Santa Clara University, CA, Santa Clara

Matua, Jean .... (320) 398-5000
editor@tricountynews.mn, Owner/Pub./Ed., Tri-County News, MN, Kimball

Matuella, Dan .... (402) 444-1485
dan.matuella@owh.com, Adv. Mgr., Papillion Times, NE, Bellevue

Matulaitis, Barry .... (207) 778-2075
bmatulaitis@thefranklinjournal.com, Editor, Franklin Journal, ME, Farmington

Matulionis, A.V. .... (216) 531-8150
dirva@ix.netcom.com, Pres of Viltis Inc. Pub of Dirva, Dirva, OH, Cleveland

Matuszak, Donna
tribnews@otelco.net, Sports Ed, The Arab Tribune, AL, Arab

Matya, Erica
ematya@valleynewstoday.com, Acct. Exec., Valley News Today, IA, Shenandoah

Matzner, Caren
cmatzner@hudsonreporter.com, Ed., Mr., NJ, Bayonne

Matzner, Caren .... (201) 798-7800 ext. 211
editorial@hudsonreporter.com, Ed., Secaucus Reporter, NJ, Bayonne

Matzner, Harold .... (760) 320-7404
hbmatzner@cbaol.com, Chrmn., Cba Industries, NJ, Elmwood Park

Maulden, Ron .... (912) 265-8320 x 326
rmaulden@thebrunswicknews.com, Vice President/General Manager, The Brunswick News, GA, Brunswick

Mauldin, Charles
charliem@immediatesfa.com, VP, Solutions, Media Marketing, Inc., CO, Westminster

Maulucci, Lou .... (705) 759-5810
lou.maulucci@sunmedia.ca, Pres./Pub., The Sault Star, ON, Sault Sainte Marie

Maulucci, Lou
lou.maulucci@sunmedia.ca, Pub. , Sault Ste. Marie This Week, ON, Sault Sainte Marie

Maune, Dietrich
maunedx@jmu.edu, Asst. Dir./Prof., James Madison University, VA, Harrisonburg

Mauney, Paul .... (336) 506-3002
pmauney@thetimesnews.com, President, North Carolina Press Association, NC, Raleigh

Maurer, Jerry .... (937) 328-0387
jmaurer@coxohio.com, Prodn. Suprvr., Bldg., Springfield News-Sun, OH, Springfield

Maurer, Jim
jmaurer@scng.com, Adv. VP, Inland Valley Daily Bulletin, CA, Rancho Cucamonga

Maurer, Mary
mary@StIgnaceNews.com, Bus. Mgr., The St. Ignace News, MI, Saint Ignace

Maurer, Patricia
info@clarecountyreview.com, Owner/Pub., The Clare County Review, MI, Clare

Maurer, Wesley H. Jr.
wes@stignacenews.com, Pub, The St. Ignace News, MI, Saint Ignace

Maury, David .... (310) 908-5927
david@mauryres.com, The Argonaut, CA, Los Angeles

Mauser, Ken .... (309) 686-3005

kmauser@pjstar.com, Pub., Times News Group, IL, Pekin
kmauser@pjstar.com, Pub., Woodford Times, IL, Pekin
kmauser@pjstar.com, Pub. , Journal Star, IL, Peoria
kmauser@pjstar.com, Pub., Washington Times Reporter, IL, Pekin

Maver, Ron
rmaver@bizjournals.com, Adv. Mgr., Philadelphia Business Journal, PA, Philadelphia

Mawyer, Carol
carol@abc.state.va.us, Asst. Dir., Student Services/Scholastic Journ., Virginia Commonwealth University, VA, Richmond

Max, Ben
bmax@gothamgazette.com, Exec. Ed., Gotham Gazette, NY, New York

Maxedon, Becky
editor@havasunews.com, Ed., River Extra, AZ, Lake Havasu City
editor@havasunews.com, Ed., Smart Buyer, AZ, Lake Havasu City

Maxey, Brian .... (559) 278-5732
California State Univ., CA, Fresno

Maxfield, Dennis C .... (585) 396-0027
tns@fats-and-oils.com, Sr. Ed., Trade News Service (Fats And Oils), Canandaigua

Maxim, Lori........................... (206) 855-4205
lmaxim@soundpublishing.com, Vice Pres., Sound Publishing, Inc., WA, Poulsbo

Maxwell, Becky
iowegan@lisco.com, Publisher, Ad Express, IA, Centerville

Maxwell, Becky .... (641) 895-0768
publisher@journalexpress.net, Publisher, Marion County Reminder, IA, Knoxville

Maxwell, Becky .... (641) 856-6336
bmaxwell@dailyiowegian.com, Circ. Mgr., Ad-Express & Daily Iowegian, IA, Centerville

Maxwell, Brenda...................... (937) 644-9111
Marysville Journal-Tribune, OH, Marysville

Maxwell, Rebecca
jepublisher@iowatelecom.net, Pub., Marion County Reminder, IA, Knoxville

Maxwell, Rebecca .... (641) 842-2155
publisher@journalexpress.net, Publisher, The Knoxville Journal-Express, IA, Knoxville

Maxwell, Scotty .... (270) 678-5171
smaxwell@glasgowdailytimes, General Manager, Glasgow Daily Times, KY, Glasgow

Maxwell, Sherrie .... (478) 744-4292
smarshall@macon.com, Exec. Ed., The Telegraph, GA, Macon

Maxwell, Shirley
smaxwell@currentargus.com, Acct. Crk., Current-Argus, NM, Carlsbad

May, Allen
amay@niu.edu, Supportive Professional Staff/Gen. Mgr., Broadcast News, Northern Illinois University, IL, DeKalb

May, Colin
cmay@mediaspace.com, Director of Media Development , Mediaspace Solutions, MN, Hopkins

May, David .... ext. 3416
editor@mineralwellsindex.com, Mng. Ed., Mineral Wells Index, TX, Mineral Wells

May, David
editor@mineralwellsindex.com, General Manager & Editor, Mineral Wells Index, TX, Mineral Wells

May, Derek
derek.may@morris.com, Pres., Morris Communications Co. LLC, GA, Augusta

May, Diane
dmay@tylerpaper.com, Librarian, Tyler Morning Telegraph, TX, Tyler

May, Emily
emay@warricknews.com, Managing Ed. , Warrick County Today, IN, Boonville

May, Emily .... (812) 897-2330
emay@warricknews.com, Mgr Ed, The Standard, IN, Boonville

May, Gary .... (813) 627-1309
Tampa Bay Times, FL, St Petersburg

May, Isaiah .... (402) 371-1020 ext. 244
imay@norfolkdailynews.com, News Ed., Norfolk Daily News, NE, Norfolk

May, Joey .... (785) 742-2111
joeymay@npgco.com, Managing Ed., Hiawatha World, KS, Hiawatha
joeymay@npgco.com, Lady A Ed., Atchison Globe, KS, Atchison

May, Michael
mmay@publicitas.com, Branch Dir., Publicitas North America, Inc., MI, Troy

May, Molly .... (501) 505-1267
molly.may@thecabin.net, Mktg. Dir. , Log Cabin Democrat, AR, Conway

May, Pamela .... ext. 139
pmay@designmedia.com, Pres./CEO, Design Media, Inc., CA, San Francisco

May, Roy .... (228) 934-1412
rmay@themississippipress.com, Adv. Mgr., The Mississippi Press, MS, Pascagoula

May-Faulkner, Kari
advertising@thecourier.com, Adv. Mgr., The Courier AdVantage, OH, Findlay

Mayberry, Bobby
advanceyeoman@gmail.com, Ed., The Advance Yeoman, KY, Paducah

Mayberry, Eric...................... (217) 788-1350
eric.mayberry@sj-r.com , VP of Adv., The State Journal-Register, IL, Springfield

Mayborn, Sue .... (254) 778-4444
Pub., Fort Hood Sentinel, TX, Fort Hood

Mayborn, Sue .... (254) 778-4444
edla@tdtnews.com, Pres., Frank Mayborn Enterprises, Inc., TX, Temple
edla@tdtnews.com, Editor and Publisher, Temple Daily Telegram, TX, Temple

Maybury, Susan .... (330) 376-0917 ext. 210
subscribe@bedfordgazette.com, Ed., Akron Legal News, OH, Akron
subscribe@bedfordgazette.com, Cir., The Bedford Gazette, PA, Bedford

Mayer, Bryce
bmayer@northvernon.com, Ed., North Vernon Plain Dealer & Sun, Inc., IN, North Vernon

Mayer, Diane
diane.mayer@monteregieweb.com, Adv. Rep., Le Soleil Du St-laurent, QC, Salaberry-de-Valleyfield

Mayer, Kurt .... (401) 277-7826
kmayer@providencejournal.com, Managing Ed. Ops, The Providence Journal, RI, Providence

Mayer, Larry .... (406) 657-1391
lmayer@billingsgazette.com, Photo Chief, Billings Gazette, MT, Billings

Mayer, Michael
mmayer@dallasnews.com or mmayer@dmnmedia.com, General Manager, Recruitment, Real Estate, General Classifieds, Southwest Classified Advertising Managers Association, TX, Dallas
mmayer@dallasnews.com or mmayer@dmnmedia.com, Gen. Mgr. Recruitment, Real Estate & Gen. Classifieds, The Dallas Morning News, TX, Dallas

Mayer, Mitch
mmayer@njherald.com, Adv.Dir., Shopper's Guide, NJ, Newton

Mayer, Robert .... (860) 282-5720
Mng. Ed., Berlin Citizen, CT, Meriden

Mayer, Russ
mayerr@merrimack.edu, Merrimack College, MA, North Andover

Mayer, Tom .... (386) 754-0428
Ed., Lake City Reporter, FL, Lake City

Mayes, Malcolm .... (780) 471-6112
mmayes@artizans.com, Pres., Artizans.com Syndicate, AB, Edmonton

Mayes, Warren
wmayes@bnd.com, Belleville News-Democrat, IL, Belleville

Mayfield, Trevis .... (815) 625-3600 ext. 230
tmayfield@svnmail.com, Pub., Forreston Journal, IL, Dixon

Mayle, Ric
rmayle@imcamerica.com, Vice Pres., Sales./Mktg., Metso Paper, PA, York

Maynard, Brett .... (517) 552-2822
bbmaynard@gannett.com, Digital Specialist , The Livingston County Daily Press & Argus, MI, Howell

Maynard, Clayton
clayton@buffalobulletin.com, Adv. Sales Rep., Buffalo Bulletin, WY, Buffalo

Maynard, Julie
citizen@mip.net, Ed., The Valley Citizen, MD, Brunswick

Maynard, Leigh Ann .... (803) 460-4811
leighmaynard30@gmail.com, Pub., The Manning Times, SC, Manning

Maynard, Mark .... (606) 326-2648
mmaynard@dailyindependent.com, Editor, The Daily Independent, KY, Ashland

Maynard, Teresa .... (740) 474-3131 Ext. 204
tmaynard@circlevilleherald.com, Pub., The Circleville Herald, OH, Circleville

Mayne Davis, Laurena ..... (970) 242-5050 ext. 256
Laurena.Davis@gjsentinel.com, Mktg. Dir., The Daily Sentinel, CO, Grand Junction

Maynes, Jean
jmaynes@thevermontstandard.com, Bus. Mgr., The Vermont Standard, VT, Woodstock

Maynor, Rex .... (334) 737-2558
rmaynor@oanow.com, Pub, Opelika-Auburn News, AL, Opelika

Maynor, Sarah
events@alleghanynews.com, Ed Assit., The Alleghany News, NC, Sparta

Mayo, Aida .... (818) 340-5300
AidaMayo@mayocommunications.com, CEO & President, Mayo Communications, CA, West Hills

Mayo, James
jimmayo@seqcotimes.com, Publisher, Sequoyah County Times, OK, Sallisaw

Mayo, Jeff .... (918) 775-4433
jeff@bigbasinllc.com, Gen. Mgr. /Assoc. Pub., Sequoyah County Times, OK, Sallisaw
jeff@bigbasinllc.com, Pub., Okmulgee Daily Times, OK, Okmulgee

Mayo, Jeremy .... (715) 365-6397 ext. 375
jeremy@rivernewsonline.com, Sports Ed., The Northwoods River News , WI, Rhinelander
jeremy@rivernewsonline.com, Sports Ed., Northwoods Super Shopper, WI, Rhinelander

Mayo, Tracy .... (912) 384-2323
dougent@alltel.net, Pub./Ed., The Douglas Enterprise, GA, Douglas

Mays, Carolene
leroyl@indyrecorder.com, Pub., Indianapolis Recorder, IN, Indianapolis

Mays, Curtis .... (318) 377-1866 ext. 125
advertising@press-herald.com, Adv. Exec., Minden Press Herald, LA, Minden

Mays, Deirdre C.
deirdre@catholic-doc.org, Ed., The Catholic Miscellany, SC, Charleston

Mays, Mary .... (815) 857-2311
mmays@amboynews.com, Circ. Mgr., The Amboy News, IL, Amboy

Mays, Nancy .... (913) 715-0730
Nancy.Mays@jocogov.org, Editor, The Best Times, KS, Olathe

Mays, Shelley
smays@tennessean.com, Photographer, TN Media, TN, Nashville
smays@tennessean.com, Photographer, The Tennessean, TN, Nashville

Mays, William
wgmays@mayschem.com, Pub., The Indianapolis Recorder, IN, Indianapolis

Mazanec, Greg .... (651) 228-5315
gmazanec@pioneerpress.com, Vice Pres., Adv., St. Paul Pioneer Press, MN, Saint Paul

Mazare, Jean
express@lexpress.to, Pub., L'express, ON, Toronto

Mazenauer, A. Skip .... (716) 773-7676
skip@wnypapers.com, PubCEO, Lewiston-Porter Sentinel, NY, Grand Island

Mazenauer, A. Skip
skip@wnypapers.com, Pub., Niagara-Wheatfield Tribune, NY, Grand Island

Mazenauer, A. Skip .... (716) 773-7676
skip@wnypapers.com, Pub., Island Dispatch, NY, Grand Island

Mazenauer, Skip .... (716) 773-7676
skip@wnypapers.com, Publisher and CEO, Grand Island Pennysaver, NY, Grand Island

Mazuka, Ruben Carrillo .... (830) 773-8610
elgram@hilconet.com, Pub., The News Gram/The Gram, TX, Eagle Pass

Mazur, Melanie Brubaker
prt@pinerivertimes.com, Ed., Pine River Times, CO, Bayfield

Mazur, Robert .... (970) 884-2331
Adv. Dir., Pine River Times, CO, Bayfield

Mazza, Glen
publish@mountaineer.bz, Pub., The Mountaineer, AB, Rocky Mountain House

Mazzaccaro, Peter
pete@chestnuthilllocal.com, Ed., Chestnut Hill Local, PA, Philadelphia

Mazzara, Sam .... (256) 734-2131 ext. 238
smazzara@cullmantimes.com, Dir. of Audience Develp, The Cullman Times, AL, Cullman

Mazzio, Mike
MMazzio@pinejournal.com, Adv. Dir, The Pine Journal, MN, Duluth

Mazzone, Karen
karen-m@cm-media.com, Bus. Mgr., Suburban News Publications, OH, Columbus

Mazzotta, Gary
gmazzotta@tribweb.com, Trib Total Media, Inc., PA, Pittsburgh

Mazzulli, John
jmazzulli@repub.com, Major Accts. Mgr., The Republican, MA, Springfield

Mc Corkle, Mary .... (805) 546-3288
Cuesta College, CA, San Luis Obispo

Mc Corthy, Jean
jean.mccorthy@broadvision.com, Dir., BroadVision, CA, Redwood City

McAbee, Michelle .... (203) 316-2044
michelle.mcabee@scni.com, Pub., Greenwich Time, CT, Old Greenwich

McAbee, Michelle
michelle.mcabee@scni.com, Pub., The Advocate, CT, Stamford

McAdams, Jerry .... (254) 796-4325
hiconews@gmail.com, Pub., Hico News Review, TX, Hico

McAden, Fitz .... (843) 706-8110 ext. 8105
fmcaden@islandpacket.com, Exec. Ed., The Island Packet, SC, Bluffton

McAfee, Paul .... (951) 368-5160
pmcafee@pe.com, Interactive Dev. Dir., The Press-Enterprise, CA, Riverside

McAferty, Wade .... (702) 259-2303
wade.mcaferty@lasvegassun.com, Web Ed., Las Vegas Sun, NV, Henderson

McAlister, Allison
ecteditorial@comcast.net, Ed., East County Times, MD, Baltimore

McAlister, Bonnie
optic@mt-vernon.com, Adv. Dir., Mount Vernon Optic-Herald, TX, Mount Vernon

McAlister, Gail .... (707) 380-1134
udjgail@ukiahdj.com , Lake Mendo Group Dig. Dir., The Ukiah Daily Journal, CA, Ukiah

McAlister, Jim
jmcalister@corbinnewsjournal.com, Sports Ed., News Journal, KY, Corbin

McAllister, Debbie .... (563) 383-2348
dmcallister@qctimes.com, Nat'l Adv. Coord., Quad-City Times, IA, Davenport

McAllister, Marcia
mmcallister@ledger-enquirer.com, Assoc. Ed., Columbus Ledger-Enquirer, GA, Columbus

McAllister, Marnie
mmcallister@archlou.org, Editor, The Record, KY, Louisville

McAllister, Natha
nert@grm.net, Ed., Tri-County Weekly, MO, Jamesport

McAnally, Neil
Neil.mcanally@latimes.com, Opns. Mgr., Times Community News (TCN), CA, Los Angeles

McAndrew, John .... (570) 348-9119
jmcandrew@timesshamrock.com, Production Director, The Times-Tribune, PA, Scranton

McAnelly, Pam
pam@nashvilleleader.com, Office Mgr., The Nashville News-Leader, AR, Nashville

McAree, Jayson .... (603) 581-1965
jmcaree@citizen.com, Pub., The Dallas Post, PA, Wilkes Barre
jmcaree@citizen.com, Sports Reporter, Citizen (OOB), NH, Laconia

McArthur, Dana .... (780) 723-5787
anchorwk@telusplanet.net, Pub./Adv. Dir., The Weekly Anchor, AB, Edson

McBain, Jeremy .... (231) 439-9316
Exec. Ed. , Petoskey News-Review, MI, Petoskey

McBee, Becky
bmcbee@t-g.com, Bus. Mgr., Shelbyville Times-Gazette, TN, Shelbyville

McBrayne, Sheila
sheila@southpointsun.ca, Ed., Southpoint Sun, ON, Wheatley

McBride, Brian .... (321) 402-0436
bmcbride@osceolanewsgazette.com, Editor, Osceola News-gazette, FL, Kissimmee

McBride, Carolyn N.
dailynews@netride.net, Pub., The Anadarko Daily News, OK, Anadarko

McBride, Dara .... (410) 245-5028
dmcbride@cecilwhig.com, Features Ed., Cecil Whig, MD, Elkton

McBride, Doug .... (908) 766-3900
dmcbride@recordernewspapers.com, Adv. Dir., Chatham Courier, NJ, Bernardsville

McBride, Jason
rmcbride@newsadvance.com, Pub., American Classifieds, TX, River Oaks
rmcbride@newsadvance.com, Adv. Dir. , The Burg, VA, Lynchburg

McBride, Jessica .... (414) 229-4436
mcbridej@uwm.edu, Senior Lecturer, University of Wisconsin-Milwaukee / Department of Journalism, Advertising, and Media Studies (JAMS), WI, Milwaukee

McBride, Joe W. .... (405) 247-3331
Ed., The Anadarko Daily News, OK, Anadarko

McBride, Michael .... (208) 743-9600 ext. 220
mcbride@lmtribune.com, Circ. Dir., Lewiston Morning Tribune, ID, Lewiston

McBride, Mike
mcbride@lmtribune.com, Circ. Mgr., Moscow-Pullman Daily News, ID, Moscow

McBride, Mikkel .... (208) 239-3142
mmcbride@journalnet.com, Adv. Asst., Portneuf Valley Trader, ID, Pocatello

McBride, Nadine .... (860) 425-4351
nmcbride@norwichbulletin.com, Controller/Director of Operations/Pub., The Bulletin, CT, Norwich

McBride, Roland .... (618) 993-1711
rmcbride@horizonpublicationsinc.com, Exec. Vice Pres./CFO, Horizon Publications Inc., IL, Marion

McBride, Ronald
rmcbride@newsadvance.com, Adv. Dir. , The News & Advance, VA, Lynchburg

McBride, Susy
susy@lagrandenickel.com, The Nickel - La Grande, OR, La Grande

McBride-Brown, Dana .... (850) 627-7649
dmcbride@gadcotimes.com, Advertising Sales Representative, Gadsden County Times, FL, Quincy

McCabe, Jenny .... (312) 527-8077
advertisingredeye@tribpub.com, Adv., RedEye, IL, Chicago

McCadams, Steve
dwilliams@parispi.net, Outdoors Ed., The Paris Post-Intelligencer, TN, Paris

McCaffrey, Scott .... (703) 738-2532
smccaffrey@sun-gazette.com, Ed., Sun Gazette, VA, Mc Lean

McCain, Dan
dmccain@emmetsburgnews.com, Pub./Adv. Mgr., Reporter-Democrat, IA, Emmetsburg

McCain, Dan
dmccain@emmetsburgnews.com, Pub./Gen. Mgr., The Emmetsburg Reporter, IA, Emmetsburg

McCain, Dan
advertising@emmetsburgnews.com, Adv. Mgr., The Democrat, IA, Emmetsburg

McCain, Joseph .... (662) 773-6241
newsroom@winstoncountyjournal.com, Ed., Winston County Journal, MS, Louisville

McCain, Joseph
newsroom@winstoncountyjournal.com, Ed., Louisville Shopper's Guide, MS, Louisville

McCain, Joseph
ads@websterprogresstimes.com, Pub., Webster Progress-Times, MS, Eupora

McCain, Maire .... (760) 778-4719
Marie.McCain@DesertSun.com, Prod., The Desert Sun, CA, Palm Springs

McCain, Pennie .... (740) 474-3131
Advertising Executive, The Circleville Herald, OH, Circleville

McCain, Sherri
sherri@hattiesburgamerican.com, Mgr., Bus. Systems, Hattiesburg American, MS, Hattiesburg

McCaleb, Dan
dmccaleb@nwherald.com, Ed., Northwest Citizen Shopper, IL, Crystal Lake

McCaleb, Dan .... (815) 526-4603
DMcCaleb@shawmedia.com, Executive Group Editor , Northwest Herald, IL, Crystal Lake

McCall, Alison .... (508) 490-7459

amccall@wickedlocal.com, Ed., Hopkinton Crier, MA, Framingham

McCall, Jean
info@solarsystems.com, CFO, Solar Systems, WA, Preston

McCall, Jeffrey M.
jeffmccall@depauw.edu, Professor of media studies, DePauw University, IN, Greencastle

McCall, John
jmccall@lsjournal.com, Circ. Mgr., Lee's Summit Journal, MO, Kansas City
jmccall@lsjournal.com, Circ. Mgr., Lee's Summit Advertising Extra, MO, Lees Summit

McCallen, Tiffany
McCallen@RNA.org, Chief Ops. Officer, Religion News Association, MO, Columbia

McCallum, Ian .... (519) 631-2790 ext. 248
ian.mccallum@sunmedia.ca, Reg. Managing Ed. , Chronicle, ON, West Lorne
ian.mccallum@sunmedia.ca, Page Ed., St. Thomas Times-Journal, ON, Saint Thomas

McCann, Andrea
andrea.mccann@timessentinel.com, Editor, Zionsville Times Sentinel, IN, Zionsville

McCann, Charlotte
mccann@texasobserver.org, Pub., The Texas Observer, TX, Austin

McCann, Darin
darin.mccann@coastalpoint.com, Ed., Coastal Point, DE, Ocean View

McCann, Pat .... (850) 747-5068
pmccann@pcnh.com, Sports Ed., The News Herald, FL, Panama City

McCann, Rick
rmccann@heralddispatch.com, Sports Ed., The Herald-Dispatch, WV, Huntington

McCants, Dee .... (580) 548-8105
addirector1@enidnews.com, Adv. Dir., Enid News & Eagle, OK, Enid

McCarren, William
wmccarren@press.org, Exec. Dir., National Press Club, DC, Washington

McCarron, Heather .... (508) 634-7584
hmccarron@wickedlocal.com, Ed., The Country Gazette, MA, Milford

McCarry, Lori .... (403) 250-4242
lori.mccarry@sunmedia.ca, Exec. Asst. , The Calgary Sun, AB, Calgary

McCarter, Michael .... (513) 768-8374
mmccarter@enquirer.com, Interim Editor , The Cincinnati Enquirer, OH, Cincinnati

McCarthy, Carol 860/701-4352
c.mccarthy@theday.com, Pub., The Day Publishing Co., CT, New London
c.mccarthy@theday.com, Deputy Managing Editor/News Operations, The Day, CT, New London

McCarthy, Dan
dmccarthy@yourwestvalley.com, Exec. Ed., Surprise Today, AZ, Sun City

McCarthy, Dan .... (623) 876-2534
dmccarthy@yourwestvalley.com, Exec. Ed., Glendale Today, AZ, Sun City

McCarthy, Dan .... (623) 876-2534
dmccarthy@yourwestvalley.com, Editor, Glendale-peoria Today, AZ, Sun City
dmccarthy@yourwestvalley.com, Exec. Ed., Daily News-Sun, AZ, Sun City

McCarthy, Desmond
dmccart@frc.mass.edu, Framingham State University - The Gatepost, MA, Framingham

McCarthy, Heather .... (207) 689-2895
hmccarthy@sunjournal.com, Sr. Design, Sun Journal, ME, Lewiston

McCarthy, John .... (321) 752-5018
jmccarthy@floridatoday.com, Enterprise Editor/ county, state, Florida Today, FL, Melbourne

McCarthy, John P.
cinemansyndicate@verizon.net, Pub./Ed./Co-Owner, Cineman Syndicate, NY, Rye

McCarthy, Julia
jmccarthy-consultant@scholastic.com, New York Univ., NY, New York

McCarthy, Michael .... (540) 654-1033
Advisor, University of Mary Washington, VA, Fredericksburg

McCarthy, Mick
info@process.com, Vice Pres., Sales, Process Software, MA, Framingham

McCarthy, Patrick
patrick.a.mccarthy@marsh.com, Chrmn./ Editorial Dir., Women's Wear Daily, NY, New York

McCarthy, Patsy .... (705) 444-1875 Ext.27
pmccarthy@simcoe.com, Sales Mgr. , Collingwood Connection, ON, Collingwood

McCarthy, Peter .... (240) 215-8628
pmccarthy@newspost.com, City Ed. , The Frederick News-Post, MD, Frederick

McCarthy, Randy .... (253) 597-8277
randy.mccarthy@thenewstribune.com, Crime/ Breaking News Team Leader, The News Tribune, WA, Tacoma

McCarthy, Tim .... (978) 739-1331
tmccarthy@wickedlocal.com, Ed., North Andover Citizen, MA, Danvers

McCarthy, Tim .... (978) 739-1331
tmccarthy@wickedlocal.com, Ed., Georgetown Record, MA, Danvers

McCarthy, Will
william.mccarthy@zu.ac.ae, Asst. Prof., Zayed University, Al Ruwayyah

McCartney, Diane .... (316) 268-6593
DMcCartney@wichitaeagle.com, News Editor, The Wichita Eagle, KS, Wichita

McCartney, Jeanie .... (318) 255-4353
jeanie@rustonleader.com, Adv. Mgr., Ruston (LA) Daily Leader, LA, Ruston

McCartney, Rob
accounting@stormlake.com, Circulation Manager, The Storm Lake Times, IA, Storm Lake

McCarty, Jeff .... (513) 403-4198
jeffmccarty@hadronics.com, VP., Sales, Hadronics, OH, Cincinnati

McCarty, John .... (847) 427-4378
jmccarty@dailyherald.com, Build. Maint. Sup., Daily Herald, IL, Arlington Heights

McCarty, Lisa .... (276) 386-6300
lisa@virginiastar.org, Pub./Ed., Scott County Virginia Star, VA, Gate City

McCarty, Rex .... (423) 360-2947
rexmccarty@rexmccarty.com, Advt Dir, Scott County Virginia Star, VA, Gate City

McCaul, Edward
mccaul.1@osu.edu, Ohio State Univ. College of Engineering, OH, Columbus

McChesney, Rashah .... (907) 335-1238
rashah.mcchesney@peninsulaclarion.com, Reporter, Peninsula Clarion, AK, Kenai

McChesney , Deb .... (402) 444-1448
deb.cavalier@owh.com, Director of Classified Advertising, Omaha World-Herald, NE, Omaha

McClain, Millie
millie@thesheridanheadlight.com, Mng. Ed., Sheridan Headlight, AR, Sheridan

McClanahan, Jenny
jmcclanahan@coxohio.com, Prodn. Mgr., Pre Press, Middletown Journal, OH, Liberty Township

McClary, Kevin .... (518) 843-1100
kevin@recordernews.com, Pub., Hamilton County Express, NY, Speculator

McClary, Kevin
office@adirondackexpress.com, Pub., The Adirondack Express, NY, Old Forge

McClary, Kevin .... (518) 843-1100
kevin@recordernews.com, Pub., The Recorder, NY, Amsterdam

McClary, Kevin
news@recordernews.com, Pub., Courier Standard Enterprise, NY, Amsterdam

McClay, Ginger
agrimes@eprisenow.com, Receptionist, The Enterprise Ledger, AL, Enterprise

McCleary, Mike .... (701) 250-8265
mike.mccleary@bismarcktribune.com, Photographer, The Bismarck Tribune, ND, Bismarck

McCleerey, Ruth E.
bulletin@drtel.net, Ed. , The Litchville Bulletin, ND, Litchville

McClellan, Bill
editor@bigspringherald.com, News Ed., Big Spring Herald, TX, Big Spring

McClelland, Art .... (903) 596-6269
amcclelland@tylerpaper.com, Vice Pres., Sales/Mktg., Tyler Morning Telegraph, TX, Tyler

McClelland, Judy
tlfreepress@yahoo.com, Gen. Mgr./Adv. Mgr., Tupper Lake Free Press, NY, Tupper Lake

McClelland, M. Dan
tlfreepress@yahoo.com, Pub., Tupper Lake Free Press, NY, Tupper Lake

McClelland, M. Dan
Gouvtribunepress@gmail.com, Pub., The Gouverneur Tribune-Press, NY, Gouverneur

McClesky, Pat .... (770) 428-9411 ext. 401
Prodn. Mgr., Mailroom, Marietta Daily Journal, GA, Marietta

McCloat, Keith .... (212) 969-7595
kmccloat@hearst.com, Vice Pres./Gen. Mgr., North America Syndicate, New York
kmccloat@hearst.com, VP., Gen. Mgr., King Features Syndicate, NY, New York

McClory, Daniel D.
dmcclory@vnews.com , Pub. , Valley News, NH, West Lebanon

McCloskey, Brian .... (440) 951-0000 ext. 611
Prodn. Mgr., Chatter, OH, Willoughby

McCloskey, Robyn .... (574) 732-5133
robyn.mccloskey@indianamediagroup.com, Regional Publisher/ Senior VP Operations CNHI, Pharos-Tribune, IN, Logansport

McCloskey, Robyn .... (765) 459-3121 ext. 8563
robyn.mccloskey@kokomotribune.com, Pub., Kokomo Tribune, IN, Kokomo
robyn.mccloskey@kokomotribune.com, Senior Vice President, Community Newspaper Holdings, Inc., AL, Montgomery

McCloud, Carol .... (734) 953-2020
cmccloud@oe.homecomm.net, Mktg./ Research Mgr., Lake Orion Eccentric, MI, Detroit

McCloud, Ken .... (901) 529-2654
ken.mccloud@commercialappeal.com, Circulation Director, The Commercial Appeal, TN, Memphis

McCloud, Kenneth
kmccloud@news-press.com, Dist. Dir., The Commercial Appeal, TN, Memphis

McClure, Beverly .... ext. 136
distribution@franklinshopper.com, Dist. Mgr., The Franklin Shopper, PA, Chambersburg

McClure, C. Arnold
news@thevalleylog.net, Pub., The Valley Log, PA, Huntingdon

McClure, James .... (717) 771-2011
jem@ydr.com, Editor, York Daily Record/York Sunday News, PA, York

McClure, John .... (336) 888-3545
jmcclure@hpenews.com, Adv. Dir., High Point Enterprise, NC, High Point

McClure, John
jmcclure@hpenews.com, Regl. Pub., Tribune-Gazette, WI, Clintonville
jmcclure@hpenews.com, Adv. Dir., Archdale Trinity News, NC, High Point

McClure, John
jmcclure@jcpgroup.com, Waupaca County Post, WI, Waupaca

McClure, Julie .... (812) 379-5631
jmcclure@therepublic.com, Asst. Managing Ed., The Republic, IN, Columbus

McClure, Mike
mike.mcclure@colorwebprinters.com, Chairman, Central States Circulation Managers Association, IL, Moline

McClure, Natalie
nataliem@randb.com, General Manager, Univ. of Georgia, GA, Athens

McCoach, ShaunJude .... (717) 236-4300
shaunm@cpbj.com, Sales Mgr., Central Penn Business Journal, PA, Harrisburg

McCollom, Mike .... (606) 451-4911
mmccollom@somerset-kentucky.com, Adv, McCreary County Record (OOB), KY, Whitley City
mmccollom@somerset-kentucky.com, Adv. Rep., The Commonwealth-Journal, KY, Somerset

McCollough, Rob .... (606) 451-4900
Pub., The Commonwealth-Journal, KY, Somerset

McCollum, Bonner .... (870) 633-3131
thpub@yahoo.com, Pub., East Arkansas Advertiser, AR, Forrest City
thpub@yahoo.com, Pub. Emer., Times-Herald, AR, Forrest City

McCollum, Charles
cmccollum@hjnews.com, Managing Ed., Quality Buys, UT, Logan
cmccollum@hjnews.com, Managing Ed., The Herald Journal, UT, Logan

McCollum, Jimmy
jimmy.mccollum@lipscomb.edu, Lipscomb Univ., TN, Nashville

McCollum, Thad
tmccollum@orlandoweekly.com, Cal. Ed., Orlando Weekly, FL, Orlando

McCombs, Allen .... (909) 628-5501
AMcCombs@ChampionNewspapers.com, Pub. Emeritus, Chino Champion, CA, Chino
AMcCombs@ChampionNewspapers.com, Pub. Emeritus, Chino Hills Champion, CA, Chino

McCombs, Tisha .... (970) 252-7080
tisham@montrosepress.com ... , Circ. Dir., The Montrose Daily Press, CO, Montrose

McCommons, Pete
mail@flagpole.com, Ed., Flagpole Magazine, GA, Athens

McConiga, Rimsie
rmcconiga@leavenworthtimes.com, News Ed., The Leavenworth Times, KS, Leavenworth

McConkey, Bill
ads@nunatsiaqonline.ca, Adv. Mgr., Nunatsiaq News, NU, Iqaluit

McConnel, Joe .... (978) 739-1324
jmcconnell@wickedlocal.com, Sports Ed., North Andover Citizen, MA, Danvers

McConnell, Catherine .... (250) 995-4426
cmcconnell@timescolonist.com, Dir., Finance, Victoria Times Colonist, BC, Victoria

McConnell, Gregg .... (509) 582-1443
gmcconnell@tricityherald.com, Pub., Paradise Post, CA, Paradise
gmcconnell@tricityherald.com, Publisher, Tri-City Herald, WA, Kennewick

McConnell, Jane

jmcdermott@tribpub.com, VP of Adv., Lake County Suburban Life, IL, Grayslake

jmcdermott@tribpub.com, VP of Adv., Lincolnshire Review, IL, Chicago

jmcdermott@tribpub.com, VP of Adv., Post-Tribune, IN, Crown Point

jmcdermott@tribpub.com, VP of Adv., The Beacon News, IL, Chicago

jmcdermott@tribpub.com, VP of Adv., The Doings – Western Springs, IL, Chicago

jmcdermott@tribpub.com, VP of Adv., Lake County News-Sun, IL, Gurnee

jmcdermott@tribpub.com, VP of Adv., The Courier-News, IL, Aurora

jmcdermott@tribpub.com, VP of Adv., The Doings Weekly – Burr Ridge, IL, Chicago

jmcdermott@tribpub.com, VP of Adv., Buffalo Grove Countryside, IL, Chicago

jmcdermott@tribpub.com, VP of Adv., The Doings – Clarendon Hills, IL, Chicago

jmcdermott@tribpub.com, VP of Adv., The Doings – Hinsdale, IL, Chicago

jmcdermott@tribpub.com, VP of Adv., The Doings – La Grange, IL, Chicago

jmcdermott@tribpub.com, VP of Adv., The Doings – Oak Brook and Elmhurst, IL, Chicago

jmcdermott@tribpub.com, VP of Adv., Crown Point Star, IL, Chicago

jmcdermott@tribpub.com, VP of Adv., Elmwood Park Leaves, IL, Chicago

jmcdermott@tribpub.com, VP of Adv., Evanston Review, IL, Chicago

jmcdermott@tribpub.com, VP of Adv., Forest Leaves, IL, Chicago

jmcdermott@tribpub.com, VP of Adv., Franklin Park Herald-Journal, IL, Chicago

jmcdermott@tribpub.com, VP of Adv., Glencoe News, IL, Chicago

jmcdermott@tribpub.com, VP of Adv., Glenview Announcements, IL, Chicago

jmcdermott@tribpub.com, VP of Adv., Highland Park News, IL, Chicago

jmcdermott@tribpub.com, VP of Adv., Arlington Heights Post, IL, Glenview

jmcdermott@tribpub.com, VP of Adv., Lake Forester, IL, Chicago

jmcdermott@tribpub.com, VP of Adv., Lake Zurich Courier, IL, Chicago

jmcdermott@tribpub.com, VP of Adv., Libertyville Review, IL, Chicago

jmcdermott@tribpub.com, VP of Adv., Lincolnwood Review, IL, Chicago

jmcdermott@tribpub.com, VP of Adv., Morton Grove Champion, IL, Chicago

jmcdermott@tribpub.com, VP of Adv., Mundelein Review, IL, Chicago

jmcdermott@tribpub.com, VP of Adv., Niles Herald-Spectator, IL, Chicago

jmcdermott@tribpub.com, VP of Adv., Norridge-Harwood Heights News, IL, Chicago

jmcdermott@tribpub.com, VP of Adv., Northbrook Star, IL, Chicago

jmcdermott@tribpub.com, VP of Adv., Oak Leaves, IL, Chicago

jmcdermott@tribpub.com, VP of Adv., Park Ridge Herald Advocate, IL, Chicago

jmcdermott@tribpub.com, VP of Adv., Skokie Review, IL, Chicago

jmcdermott@tribpub.com, VP of Adv., Wilmette Life, IL, Chicago

jmcdermott@tribpub.com, VP of Adv., Winnetka Talk, IL, Chicago

jmcdermott@tribpub.com, VP of Adv., Barrington Courier-Review, IL, Glenview

McDermott, John .... (843) 937-5572
jmcdermott@postandcourier.com, Bus. and Tech. Ed., The Post and Courier, SC, Charleston

McDermott, Kaitie .... (386) 801-9546
Lipscomb Univ., TN, Nashville

McDermott, Mark
mark@easyreader.info, News Ed., Easy Reader, CA, Hermosa Beach

McDermott, Michael .... (401) 277-7126
mmcdermott@providencejournal.com, Sports Ed., The Providence Journal, RI, Providence

McDermott, Russell

rmcdermott@texarkanagazette.com, Editorial Page Ed., Texarkana Gazette, AR, Texarkana

McDevitt, Donna
donna@ipa.org, Exec. Asst., Idealliance, VA, Alexandria

McDevitt, Michael
mike.mcdevitt@colorado.edu, Assoc. Prof., University of Colorado, CO, Boulder

McDevitt, Michelle .... (215) 354-3128
mmcdevitt@bsmphilly.com, Adv. Sales Mgr., Star Community Newsweekly, PA, Bensalem

McDivitt, Krista .... (812) 464-7680
mcdivittk@courierpress.com, I.T. Director, Evansville Courier & Press, IN, Evansville

McDonald, Aaron .... (405) 598-3793
aaron@countywidenews.com, Advertising Executive, Countywide & Sun, OK, Tecumseh

McDonald, Anita .... (519) 235-1331x104
amcdonald@southhuron.com, Business Manager, St. Mary's Journal Argus, ON, St Marys

McDonald, Autumn
editor@quesnelobserver.com, Ed., Quesnel Cariboo Observer, BC, Quesnel

McDonald, Connor
comcdona@mymail.mines.edu, Webmaster, Colorado School of Mines, CO, Golden

McDonald, Craig
cmmcdonald@newarkadvocate.com, Mng. Ed., The Granville Sentinel, OH, Newark
cmmcdonald@newarkadvocate.com, Mng. Ed., The Pataskala Standard, OH, Newark

McDonald, Dan .... (701) 857-1912
dmcdonald@minotdailynews.com, Publisher, Minot Daily News, ND, Minot

McDonald, Dan .... (906) 786-2021 ext 101
dmcdonald@dailypress.net, Pub./Ed., Daily Press, MI, Escanaba
dmcdonald@dailypress.net, Pub., Minot Daily News, ND, Minot

McDonald, Dan
cheboygan@michigannewspapers.com, Gen. Mgr., Straits Area Star, MI, Cheboygan

McDonald, Dan .... (906) 786-2021 ext. 101
tbelongie@upaction.com, Pub., Up Action News, MI, Escanaba

McDonald, Dan .... (701) 875-1912
dmcdonald@minotdailynews.com, Publisher, The Trading Post, ND, Minot

McDonald, Daniel
mcdonald.221@osu.edu, Prof., Ohio State University, OH, Columbus

McDonald, Darlinda
globeleaderparrish@gmail.com, Mng. Ed., The Globe Leader, PA, New Wilmington

McDonald, David
info@worldpressinstitute.org, Exec. Dir., World Press Institute, MN, Saint Paul

McDonald, Jack
jmcdonald@morpace.com, Pres., Morpace International, MI, Farmington Hills

McDonald, Jim
jlmcd1492@aol.com, Pres., ADI/PDM Trade Group, NC, High Point

McDonald, Jonathan .... (604) 605-2261
jmcdonald@postmedia.com, Sports Editor, The Province, BC, Vancouver

McDonald, Michael
mmcdonald@cecoconcrete.com, Asst. Prof., University of Missouri-Kansas City, MO, Kansas City

McDonald, Nancy .... (212) 597-5642
nancy.mcdonald@wsj.com, Gen. Adv., Sales Dir., The Wall Street Journal, NY, New York

McDonald, Sean .... (360) 876-4414 ext. 1050
publisher@portorchardindependent.com, Pub., Port Orchard Independent, WA, Port Orchard

McDonald, Sean
publisher@centralkitsapreporter.com, Pub., Central Kitsap Reporter, WA, Poulsbo

McDonald, Tom .... (505) 425-6796
optic@lasvegasoptic.com, Ed., Las Vegas Optic, NM, LAS VEGAS

McDonnell, James P.
thedrummer@ibm.net, Pub., The Drummer, MN, Buffalo

McDonnell, James P.
ads@thedummer.com, Ed., Wright County Journal-Press, MN, Buffalo

McDonough, Dan
info@siregister.com, Pub., Staten Island Pennysaver, NY, Staten Island

McDonough, Doug .... (806) 296-1350
dmcdonough@hearstnp.com, Ed., Plainview Herald, TX, Plainview

McDonough, Gary .... (812) 523-7058
gmcdonough@tribtown.com, Ops. Mgr., The Tribune, IN, Seymour

McDonough, Jeffrey J. .... (401) 423-3200
jmcdonough@jamestownpress.com, Pub., The Jamestown Press, RI, Jamestown

McDonough , Kathy .... (207) 386-5232
kmcdonough@coastaljournal.com, Adv. Rep, greater Brunswick , Coastal Journal, ME, Bath

McDougal, Audrey
editorinchief@clarknews.org, Clark College, WA, Vancouver

McDougal, Linda .... (940) 549-7800
controller@grahamleader.com, Controller, The Graham Leader, TX, Graham

McDougall, Bruce
bmcdougall@acorn-online.com, Circ. Mgr., Darien Times, CT, Darien

McDougall, Bruce
bmcdougall@acorn-online.com, Circ. Mgr., The Lewisboro Ledger (OOB), CT, Ridgefield
bmcdougall@acorn-online.com, Circ. Mgr., The Valley Gazette (OOB), CT, Shelton
bmcdougall@acorn-online.com, Circ. Mgr., Fairfield Sun, CT, Shelton
bmcdougall@acorn-online.com, Circ. Mgr., Monroe Courier, CT, Shelton
bmcdougall@acorn-online.com, Circ. Mgr., Trumbull Times, CT, Shelton
bmcdougall@acorn-online.com, Circ. Mgr., Milford Mirror, CT, Shelton
bmcdougall@acorn-online.com, Circ. Mgr., New Canaan Advertiser, CT, New Canaan
bmcdougall@acorn-online.com, Circ. Mgr., Redding Pilot, CT, Ridgefield
bmcdougall@acorn-online.com, Circ. Mgr., Shelton Herald, CT, Shelton
bmcdougall@acorn-online.com, Circ. Mgr., Weston Forum, CT, Ridgefield
bmcdougall@acorn-online.com, Circ. Mgr., Wilton Bulletin, CT, Ridgefield

McDougall, Tim
adavis@medina-gazette.com, Publisher, The Gazette, IA, Cedar Rapids

McDowell, Brian .... (315) 684-6169
mcdowebl@morrisville.edu, Morrisville State College, NY, Morrisville

McDowell, Elsa .... (843) 937-5543
elsa@postandcourier.com, Assoc. Ed., The Post and Courier, SC, Charleston

McDowell, Katie
katie.mcdowell@shelbycountyreporter.com, General Manager, Shelby County Newspapers, Inc, AL, Columbiana

McDowell, Raymond .... (804) 649-6240
rmcdowell@timesdispatch.com, Controller, Richmond Times-Dispatch, VA, Richmond

McDuffie, Ross
rmcduffie@ledger-enquirer.com, VP of Ads., Columbus Ledger-Enquirer, GA, Columbus

McEathron, Jennifer .... (705) 457-1037

jenniferm@haliburtonpress.com, Sales, The Minden Times, ON, Minden

McEldowney, Kevin .... (630) 783-8900
kevin.mceldowney@samuel.com, U.S. Manager of Inside Sales and Administration, Samuel, Son & Co., ON, Burlington

McElhinny, Brad .... (304) 348-5124
bradmc@wvgazettemail.com, Co-Editor, The Charleston Gazette-Mail, WV, Charleston

McElhinny, Dave
DMcElhinny@tribweb.com, Ed., Pine Creek Journal, PA, Warrendale

McElligott, Donna
editor@newenglandshowcase.com, Marketing Mgr., New England Showcase, VT, Brattleboro

McElroy, Becky .... (276) 679-1101, ext. 224
bmcelroy@coalfield.com, Circ., The Coalfield Progress, VA, Norton
bmcelroy@coalfield.com, Circ. Mgr., The Post, VA, Big Stone Gap
bmcelroy@coalfield.com, Circ., The Dickenson Star, VA, Clintwood

McElroy, Jack .... (865) 342-6300
Ed., Knoxville News Sentinel, TN, Knoxville

McElroy, Quindelda .... (937) 225-6905
quindelda.mcelroy@coxinc.com, Senior Director, Digital, Dayton Daily News, OH, Franklin

McElvy, Jonathan .... (713) 686-8494
jonathan@theleadernews.com, Pub., The Leader, TX, Houston

McElwain, Karen
karenm@lwsbnews.com, Adv. Sales, Leisure World Golden Rain News, CA, Seal Beach

McElwee, John .... (843) 317-7203
jmcelwee@florencenews.com, Controller, Morning News, SC, Florence

McElwee, Pat
pmcelwee@philly.com, Philadelphia Inquirer, Daily News & Philly.com, PA, Philadelphia

McElyea, Angie
angie@athensnews-courier.com, Adv Sales, The News-Courier, AL, Athens

McEnery, Brian .... (860) 241-6219
BMcEnery@courant.com, Circ., Courant Community - Vernon, CT, Hartford
BMcEnery@courant.com, Circ. Mgr, Courant Community - East Hartford, CT, Hartford
BMcEnery@courant.com, Circ., Courant Community - Colchester, CT, Hartford
BMcEnery@courant.com, Circ., Courant Community - Killingly, CT, Hartford
BMcEnery@courant.com, Circ., Courant Community - Enfield, CT, Hartford
BMcEnery@courant.com, Circ., Courant Community - Glastonbury, CT, Hartford
BMcEnery@courant.com, Circ., Courant Community - Hebron, CT, Hartford
BMcEnery@courant.com, Circ., Courant Community - Valley, CT, Hartford
BMcEnery@courant.com, Circ., Courant Community - Manchester, CT, Hartford
BMcEnery@courant.com, Circ., Courant Community - Putnam, CT, Hartford
BMcEnery@courant.com, Circ., Courant Community - South Windsor, CT, Hartford
BMcEnery@courant.com, Circ., Courant Community - Stafford, CT, Hartford
BMcEnery@courant.com, Circ., Courant Community - Windham, CT, Hartford
BMcEnery@courant.com, Circ., Courant Community - Windsor, CT, Hartford
BMcEnery@courant.com, Circ., Courant Community - Windsor Locks, CT, Hartford
BMcEnery@courant.com, Circ. Ops. Dir., The Hartford Courant, CT, Hartford

McEntire, Mac .... (978) 371-5744
tewksbury@wickedlocal.com, Ed., Tewksbury Advocate, MA, Concord

McEntire, Mac .... (978) 371-5744
wilmington@wickedlocal.com, Ed., Wilmington Advocate, MA, Concord

McGuigan, Marc ....(973) 569-7852
mcguigan@northjersey.com, Director of
Internet Sales, Herald News, NJ, Rockaway

McGuigan, Patrick ....(405) 740-8687@
news@city-sentinel.com, Pub./Ed., The City
Sentinel, OK, Oklahoma City

McGuiness, Debbie....................(231) 439-9353
Goodlife Ed., Petoskey News-Review, MI,
Petoskey

McGuire, Bill ....(902) 629-6000 (ext. 6051)
bmcguire@theguardian.pe.ca, Editorial Page
Ed., The Guardian, PE, Charlottetown

McGuire, Dennis
dmcguire@maned.com, President, Managing
Editor, Inc., PA, Jenkintown

McGuire, John
john.mcguire@okstate.edu, Asst. Prof.,
Oklahoma State University, OK, Stillwater

McGuire, Lanette ....(260) 347-0400 Ext. 1154
legals@kpcmedia.com, Legal Adv. Clerk,
Albion New Era, IN, Albion

McGuire, Nancy L.....................(907) 443-5323
nancym@nomenugget.com, Ed./Pub., The
Nome Nugget, AK, Nome

McGuire, Tegan ....(207) 367-2200
classifieds@pbp.me, events@pbp.me,
Classifieds & Coming Events Manager,
Castine Patriot, ME, Blue Hill

McGunagle, Michelle
mmcgunagle@atlantaparent.com, Asst. Pub.,
Atlanta Parent, GA, Atlanta

McGurgan, Diane
diane@nasw.org, Admin., Council for the
Advancement of Science Writing, Inc., WV,
Hedgesville

McGurgan, Diane
diane@nasw.org, Admin., Council for the
Advancement and Support of Education, DC,
Washington

McGurk, John...................................ext. 2017
aluke@citizensvoice.com, Prodn. Mgr.,
Mailroom, The Citizens' Voice, PA, Wilkes
Barre

McGurk, Tom ....(856) 486-2420
tmcgurk@gannettnj.com, Reg. Sports
Strategist/Editor, The Courier-Post, NJ,
Cherry Hill

McHam, David ....(713) 661-8339
dmcham@aol.com, Clinical Prof., University of
Houston, TX, Houston

McHaney, Stephen ....(903) 237-7700
snmchaney@news-journal.com, Pub.,
Longview News-Journal, TX, Longview

McHardy, Tom
mchardtj@jmu.edu, Assoc. Prof., James
Madison University, VA, Harrisonburg

McHenry, Melissa
mmchenry@orlandoweekly.com, Art Dir.,
Orlando Weekly, FL, Orlando

McHugh, Brien ....(800) 740-3683
bmchugh@stfrancis.edu, Univ. of St. Francis,
IL, Joliet

McHughes, Pat
pmchughes@paris-express.com, Ed., Paris
Express, AR, Paris

McIlveen, Claire ....(902) 426-2811 ext. 3077
cmcilveen@herald.ca, Ed., The Chronicle
Herald, NS, Halifax

McInally, Mike
mike.mcinally@lee.net, Ed., Corvallis Gazette-
Times, OR, Corvallis

McInally, Mike
mike.mcinally@lee.net, Gen. Mngr., The
Philomath Express, OR, Corvallis

McInally, Mike
mike.mcinally@lee.net, Pub./Ed., Albany
Democrat-Herald, OR, Albany

McInnes, Garry R.
mmpl@onlink.net, Adv. Mgr., The Marathon
Mercury, ON, Marathon

McInnes, Ian
ian.mcinnes@sunmedia.ca, Ed., Edson
Leader, AB, Edson

McInnis, Steve
Direction@cinnfm.com, Gen. Mgr. , Le Nord,
ON, Hearst

McIntee, Sophie
smcintee@whig.com, Classified Adv. Mgr., The
Quincy Herald-Whig, IL, Quincy

McIntire, Carol ....(330) 627-5591
fps44615@yahoo.com, Ed., The Free Press
Standard, OH, Carrollton

McIntire, Janice
jmcintire@eldoradonews.com, Features Ed.,
El Dorado News-Times / Sunday News, AR,
El Dorado

McIntosh, Amanda....................(606) 451-4911
jilllawson@sekypub.com, Adv. Rep., The
Commonwealth-Journal, KY, Somerset

McIntosh, Bill
dciadvertising@aol.com, Dir., Bus. Devel.,
America Online Digital City, Inc., VA, Dulles

McIntosh, Duncan ....(949) 660-6150
duncan@thelog.com, Publisher, Editor &
Publisher Magazine, CA, Fountain Valley
duncan@thelog.com, Pub., The Log
Newspaper, CA, Fountain Valley

McIntosh, Ed..........................(941) 206-1446
emcintosh@sun-herald.com, Systems Mgr.,
Charlotte Sun, FL, Punta Gorda

McIntosh, Scott ....(208) 465-8110
smcintosh@idahopress.com, Mng. Ed., Idaho
Press-Tribune, ID, Nampa
smcintosh@idahopress.com, Ed.,
Independent-Enterprise, ID, Payette
smcintosh@idahopress.com, Ed., Argus
Observer, OR, Ontario

McIntosh, Tammie
tmcintosh@reviewonline.com, Pub., The
Review, OH, East Liverpool

McIntyre, Bill ....(515) 576-2571
mcintyre@iowacentral.edu, Iowa Central Cmty.
College, IA, Fort Dodge

McIntyre, Jeff.........................(256) 740-5737
jeff.mcintyre@timesdaily.com, Asst. Sports Ed.,
Times Daily, AL, Florence

McIntyre, John
mcintyrej@spotlightnews.com, Pub., Spotlight
Newspapers, NY, Delmar

McIntyre, John ....(518) 439-4949 x 420
mcintyrej@spotlightnews.com, Pub., The
Spotlight, NY, Delmar

McIntyre, John ....(518) 439-4944 Ext. 420
mcintyrej@spotlightnews.com, Pub., Colonie/
Loudonville Spotlight, NY, Delmar

McIntyre, Lisa ....(412) 263-1191
lmcintyre@post-gazette.com, Auto Mgr.,
Pittsburgh Post-Gazette, PA, Clinton

McIntyre, Sarah ....(304) 696-2360
Sarah.mcintyre@marshall.edu, Program
Assistant, Marshall University, WV,
Huntington

McIver, Rose...........................(215) 949-4207
rmciver@calkins.com, Mng. Ed., Bucks County
Courier Times, PA, Levittown

McJunkins, James
olafjames@earthlink.net, Chair, Clark Atlanta
University, GA, Atlanta

McJunkins, James................(770) 941-7089
jamesolaf@comcast.net, Advisor, Clark Atlanta
Univ., GA, Atlanta

McKay, Amy ....(402) 537-4840
amy.mckay@nonpareilonline.com, Gen Man,
Ralston Recorder, NE, Bellevue

McKay, Amy ....(402) 537-4840

amy.mckay@nonpareilonline.com, Gen Man,
Gretna Breeze, NE, Bellevue
amy.mckay@nonpareilonline.com, Gen Man,
Bellevue Leader, NE, Bellevue

McKay, Amy ....(712) 325-5664
amckay@nonpareilonline.com, General
Manager, Wahoo Newspaper, NE, Wahoo

McKay, Amy ....(402) 537-4840
amy.mckay@nonpareilonline.com, General
Manager, Papillion Times, NE, Bellevue

McKay, Amy ....(712) 325-5664
amy.mckay@nonpareilonline.com, General
Mgr Central Weeklies Group, Market Weekly,
NE, Wahoo

McKean, Matthew T. ....(256) 740-5753
matt.mckean@timesdaily.com, Photo Ed.,
Times Daily, AL, Florence

McKean, Patrick ....(562) 938-4282
Long Beach City College, CA, Long Beach

McKean, Tracy
sales@parentspress.com, Pub., Parents'
Press, CA, Alameda

McKeand, Bret ....(623) 972-6101
azpublisher@newszap.com, Pub., Apache
Junction/Gold Canyon Independent, AZ,
Phoenix
azpublisher@newszap.com, VP, Sun City
Independent, AZ, Sun City
azpublisher@newszap.com, VP, The Verde
Independent, AZ, Cottonwood
azpublisher@newszap.com, VP, White
Mountain Independent, AZ, Show Low
azpublisher@newszap.com, Vice Pres., Opns.,
Chandler/Sun Lakes Independent, AZ,
Chandler
azpublisher@newszap.com, Pub., East
Mesa Independent (OOB), AZ, APACHE
JUNCTION

McKeand, Bret ....(623) 445-2867
azpublisher@newszap.com, VP, Gilbert
Independent (OOB) , AZ, Apache Junction
azpublisher@newszap.com, Pub., Queen
Creek Independent, AZ, Apache Junction

McKeand, Bret ....(623) 445-2867
azpublisher@newszap.com, VP, Independent
Newspapers, Inc. (Arizona), AZ, Phoenix

McKeand, Bret ....(623) 445-2867
azpublisher@newszap.com, Publisher/
President, Scottsdale Independent, AZ,
Phoenix

McKeand, Bret ....(623) 445-2867
azpublisher@newszap.com, VP, Town of
Paradise Valley Independent, AZ, Phoenix

McKeand, Bret ....(623) 972-6101
scibret@aol.com, VP., Opns., Surprise
Independent, AZ, Sun City

McKechnie, Ralph ....(541) 826-7700
editor@urindependent.com, Owner/Ed, Upper
Rogue Independent, OR, Eagle Point

McKee, Chris ....(913) 845-1139
chris.mckee@newscycle.com, Sales Director,
Newscycle Solutions, MN, Bloomington

McKee, Kim..........................(936) 348-3505
kim.mckee@madisonvillemeteor.com,
Office Manager, Madisonville Meteor, TX,
Madisonville

McKee, Mark .... (812) 265-3641, ext. 242
Nt'l. Acc. and Job Listings , Madison Courier,
Inc., IN, Madison

McKee, Rick ....(706) 823-3369
graphix@augustachronicle.com, Editorial
Cartoonist, The Augusta Chronicle, GA,
Augusta

McKee, Roger
editor@islandgazette.net, Pub., The Island
Gazette, NC, Carolina Beach

McKee, Russ
ads2@brownfieldonline.com, Adv. Dir.,
Brownfield News, TX, Brownfield

McKee, Sally ....(309) 686-3157
smckee@pjstar.com, Asst. Mng. Ed., Sunday
Features/Servs., Journal Star, IL, Peoria

McKeel, Jim ....(251) 219-5351
Circ. Mgr., Single Copy, Press-Register, AL,
Mobile

McKeeman, Shelley
shelley@stcroixcourier.ca, Gen. Mgr., St. Croix
Courier, NB, Saint Stephen

McKeen, William ....(352) 392-0500
Prof./Chair, Dept. of Journalism, University of
Florida, FL, Gainesville

McKeever, Jim
jmckeever@thewestfieldnewsgroup.com,
Content Dir., The Westfield News , MA,
Westfield

McKeighan, Tammy ....(402) 941-1433
fremont.newsroom@lee.net, News Ed.,
Fremont Tribune, NE, Fremont

McKeithan, Diane
diane@stateportpilot.com, The State Port Pilot,
NC, Southport

McKenna, Frank.......................(413) 496-6309
fmckenna@berkshireeagle.com, CFO, The
Berkshire Eagle, MA, Pittsfield

McKenna, John.............(203) 245-1877 ext. 6123
j.mckenna@shorepublishing.com, Acct.
Manager, East Haven Courier, CT, Madison

McKenna, John.............(203) 245-1877 ext. 6123
j.mckenna@shorepublishing.com, Acct.
Manager, North Haven Courier, CT, Madison

McKenna, Marsha ....(330) 541-9400 Ext. 4178
mmckenna@recordpub.com, Sr. Ed., Stow
Sentry, OH, Kent

McKenna, Michael ....(508) 663-1920
mmckenna@burrellesluce.com, National Sales
Manager, New England Newsclip Agency,
Inc., NJ, Florham Park

McKenna, Sean ....(978) 946-2161
smckenna@eagletribune.com, Retail Adv. Dir.,
The Eagle-Tribune, MA, North Andover
smckenna@eagletribune.com, Adv. Dir.,
Concord Monitor, NH, Concord

McKenna, Trina
trobba@comcast.net, Ed., Icon Magazine, PA,
New Hope

McKenney, Janene
finance@newsmontana.com, Finance, Big
Horn County News, MT, Hardin

McKennon, Teresa ....(575) 763-3431
tmckennon@cnjonline.com, Bus. Mgr., Eastern
New Mexico News, NM, Clovis

McKennon, Teresa .... (575) 763-3431 ext. 510
Eastern New Mexico News, NM, Clovis

McKenzie, Amy
subscriptions@pcgazette.com, Circ./
Classifieds, The Portage County Gazette, WI,
Stevens Point

McKenzie, Deedie
deedie.mckenzie@morris.com, Capital City
Weekly, AK, Juneau
deedie.mckenzie@morris.com, Interim Pub.,
Juneau Empire, AK, Juneau

McKenzie, Laura J.
laura.mckenzie@morris.com, Pub., The
People-Sentinel, SC, Barnwell

McKenzie, Mack
sales@west.com, Vice Pres., Sales/Mktg.,
West Interactive Corp., NE, Omaha

McKenzie, Margaret ....(603) 733-5801
Margaret@conwaydailysun.com, Mng. Ed. ,
The Conway Daily Sun, NH, North Conway

McKenzie, Sarah ....(612) 436-4371
smckenzie@mnpubs.com, Ed., The Downtown
Journal, MN, Minneapolis

McKenzie, Sarah ....(612) 436-4371
smckenzie@mnpubs.com , Ed., Southwest
Journal, MN, Minneapolis

Metroland Media Group Ltd., ON, Mississauga

McLeod, Katie
agulizia@globe.com, Features Ed., The Boston Globe, MA, Boston

McLeod, Scott
info@smokymountainnews.com, Pub., Smoky Mountain News, NC, Waynesville
info@smokymountainnews.com, Ed., The Enterprise Mountaineer (OOB), NC, Canton

McLeod, Tommie .... (336) 727-7445
tmcleod@wsjournal.com, Circulation Manager, Winston-Salem Journal, NC, Winston Salem

McLeod, Tommie .... (813) 259-7435
tmcleod@tampatrib.com, Tampa Bay Times, FL, St Petersburg

McLeod, Waldo L.
scott@donalsonvillenews.com, Ed., Donalsonville News, GA, Donalsonville

McLister, Steven K.
smclister@minotdailynews.com, Pub., The Trading Post, ND, Minot

McLoone, John
therepublican@charterinternet.com, Pub./Ed., The Stanley Republican, WI, Stanley

McLoughlin, Stephanie .... (321) 242-3927
smcloughlin@floridatoday.com, Ad. Dir., Best - South, FL, Melbourne
smcloughlin@floridatoday.com, Ad. Director, Best - North, FL, Melbourne
smcloughlin@floridatoday.com, Ad. Dir. - Central, FL, Melbourne
smcloughlin@floridatoday.com, Adv. Dir., Florida Today, FL, Melbourne

McMacken, William .... (605) 692-6271
registeradvertising@brookingsregister.com, Adv. Dir., Brookings Register, SD, Brookings

McMacken, William
bmcmacken@brookingsregister.com, Adv. Dir., Profile, SD, Brookings

McMahan, Johnny
editor@woodwardnews.net, Ed. / Sports Ed. , Woodward News, OK, Woodward

McMahon, Bill .... (814) 231-4606
wmcmahon@centredaily.com, Aud. Dev. & Prod. Dir. , Centre Daily Times, PA, State College

McMahon, Bryan T. .... (985) 386-2877
editor@ponchatoula.com, Pub./Ed., The Ponchatoula Times, LA, Ponchatoula

McMahon, Colin
cmcmahon@chicagotribune.com, Assoc. Ed., Chicago Tribune, IL, Chicago

McMahon, Martie
mcmahonm@archspm.org, Acct. Supvr., The Catholic Spirit, MN, Saint Paul

McMahon, Renee
rmcmahon@messenger-index.com, Adv. Assoc., Messenger-Index, ID, Emmett

McManamon, Joe
joem@ppsi.co.uk, Pres., Printing Press Services, Inc., Preston Lancs

McManamon, Stephen
stephenm@ppsi.co.uk, Mng. Dir.-Press Division, Printing Press Services, Inc., Preston Lancs

McManis, Charlie .... (310) 265-8076
director@cwcma.com, Exec. Dir., Cal Western Circulation Managers Association, CA, Hemet

McManus, Dan
dmcmanus@sunjournal.com, Acc. Exec., Sun Journal, ME, Lewiston

McManus, Doyle
doyle.mcmanus@latimes.com, Los Angeles Times, CA, Los Angeles

McMeans, Alison
editor@ahnfsj.ca, Mng. Ed. , Alaska Highway

News, BC, Fort Saint John

McMeans, Alison .... (250) 782-4888 ext.120
editor@dcdn.ca, Mng. Ed., Dawson Creek Mirror, BC, Dawson Creek

McMenemy, Cheryl
cmcmenemy@owensoundsuntimes.com, Pub. , Owensound Sun Times, ON, Owen Sound

McMenimen, Rachel
rmcmenimen@multiad.com, Local Search Association, IL, Peoria

McMichael, Pate
pmcmichael@gcsu.edu, Instr., Georgia College & State University, GA, Milledgeville

McMillan, Agnes .... (819) 459-2222
Circ. Mgr., The Low Down To Hull And Back News, QC, Wakefield

McMillan, Betty .... (423) 623-6171 ext. 3104
betty.mcmillian@newportplaintalk.com, Adv. Mgr., The Newport Plain Talk, TN, Newport

McMillan, Brian .... (386) 447-9723
bmcmillan@palmcoastobserver.com, Managing Ed., Palm Coast Observer, FL, Palm Coast

McMillan, Lonnie .... (419) 294-2332 Ext. 30
lmcmillan@dailychiefunion.com, Sports Ed., The Daily Chief-Union, OH, Upper Sandusky

McMillan, Matt
mcmillan@hutchinsonleader.com, Pub., Hutchinson Leader, MN, Hutchinson

McMillan, Matt
mmcmillan@forumcom.com, NDNA Director, North Dakota Newspaper Association, ND, Bismarck

McMillan, Tina .... (320) 432-4141
news@hutchinsonleader.com, Adv. Mgr., Hutchinson Leader, MN, Hutchinson

McMillen, Bill .... (800) 571-3835 x 5144
bmcmillen@mohavedailynews.com, News Ed., Bullhead City Booster, AZ, Bullhead City
bmcmillen@mohavedailynews.com, City Editor, Mohave Valley Daily News, AZ, Bullhead City

McMillen, Terri .... (507) 357-2233
mcmillen752@gmail.com, Adv. Mgr., The Le Center Leader, MN, Le Center

McMillin, Sue .... (719) 636-0251
sue.mcmillin@gazette.com, Local News Editor, The Gazette, CO, Colorado Springs

McMinn, Teresa .... (301) 784-2519
tmcminn@times-news.com, Digital Ed. , The Cumberland Times-News, MD, Cumberland

McMullen, Arthur .... (724) 838-5165
amcmullen@tribweb.com, Gen. Mgr., Westmoreland, Tribune-Review, PA, Greensburg

McMullen, Cathy .... (218) 299-3994
mcmullen@cord.edu, Concordia College, MN, Moorhead

McMullen, Paul
pmcmullen@catholicreview.org, Managing Ed., The Catholic Review, MD, Baltimore

McMullian, Bo .... (850) 526-1501
bo.jctimes@gmail.com, Advertising, Jackson County Times, FL, Marianna

McMullin, Mike .... (661) 940-5352
mmcmullin@avpress.com, Classified Adv. Dir., Antelope Valley Press, CA, Palmdale

McMurray, Paul .... (608) 208-1683
courierads@hngnews.com, Adv. Mgr., The Milton Courier, WI, Milton

McMurtrie, Rhonda
rmcmurtrie@idahopress.com, Bus. Mgr., Idaho Press-Tribune, ID, Nampa

McNab, Andrew
amcnab@idahocountyfreepress.com, The Shopper, ID, Grangeville

McNair, Emily
emcnair@mymail.mines.edu, Managing Editor, Colorado School of Mines, CO, Golden

McNair, William .... (352) 753-1119
william.mcnair@thevillagesmedia.com, Printing & Distribution Manager, The Villages Daily Sun, FL, The Villages

McNall, Carole
cmcnall@sbu.edu, Faculty Advisor, St. Bonaventure Univ., NY, Saint Bonaventure

McNally, Kevin
kmcna@srds.com, CFO, SRDS, a Kantar Media Company, IL, Des Plaines

McNamara, Katelyn
kmcnamara@mediaonene.com, Multimedia Retail Adv. Mgr., The Sun, MA, Lowell

McNamara, Tom .... (215) 854-2549
tmcnamara@phillynews.com, Deputy Mng. Ed., Sunday, Philadelphia Inquirer, Daily News & Philly.com, PA, Philadelphia

McNamee, Chris .... (203) 625-4425
chris.mcnamee@scni.com, Sports Editor, Greenwich Time, CT, Old Greenwich

McNamee, Tom .... (312) 321-3000
tmcnamee@suntimes.com, Editorial Page Ed., Chicago Sun-Times, IL, Chicago

McNaughton, A. J. .... (770) 442-3278 ext.129
Prod. Mgr., John's Creek Herald, GA, Alpharetta
Prod. Mgr., The Forsyth Herald, GA, Alpharetta
Prod. Mgr., Milton Herald, GA, Alpharetta

McNaughton, Burt .... (530) 747-8030
bmcnaughton@davisenterprise.net, Pub./Vice Pres./Sec., The Davis Enterprise, CA, DAVIS

McNaughton, Foy .... (707) 425-4646
fmcnaughton@dailyrepublic.net, Pres./CEO/Pub., Daily Republic, CA, Fairfield
fmcnaughton@dailyrepublic.net, Pres./CEO, McNaughton Newspapers, CA, Fairfield

McNaughton, Marimar
marimar@luminanews.com, Ed., Lumina News, NC, Wilmington

McNaughton, R. .... (530) 756-0800
bmcnaughton@davisenterprise.net, Vice Pres., McNaughton Newspapers, CA, Fairfield

McNeal, Craig A.
cgnews@cgtelco.net, Pub./Ed., Council Grove Republican, KS, Council Grove

McNeal, Jake
jmcneal@spotlightnews.net, Sports Ed, The South County Spotlight, OR, Scappoose

McNeal, Quasha .... (252) 407-9961
qmcneal@rmtelegram.com, Classified Adv. Mgr., Rocky Mount Telegram, NC, Rocky Mount

McNealy, Scott G.
info@sun.com, Chrmn., Oracle & Sun Microsystems, Inc., CA, Redwood City

McNeece, Joel
joelmcneece@gmail.com, Pub., The Calhoun County Journal, MS, Bruce

McNeeley, Kathy
kmcneeley@thevalleychronicle.com, Sales & Adv, The Valley Chronicle, CA, Hemet

McNeely, Jason .... (435) 752-2128 ext 380
jmneely@hjnews.com, Circ. Mgr., The Herald Journal, UT, Logan

McNeely, Paula
paula@claxtonenterprise.com, Vice Pres., Opns./Adv., Claxton Enterprise, GA, Claxton

McNeil, Bryce .... (404) 413-1592
bmcneil1@gsu.edu, Advisor, Georgia State Univ., GA, Atlanta

McNeil, Dan .... (800) 736-7350 ext 101
Dan@Seniorific.com, Pub., Seniorific News, TX, Waco

McNeil, Donovan .... (800) 736-7350 ext 102
Donovan@Seniorific.com, COO, Seniorific News, TX, Waco

McNeil, Helen
helenm@islandfamilymagazine.com, Ed., Island Family, HI, Honolulu

McNeil, Judy .... (919) 718-1224
news@sanfordherald.com, News Clerk, Herald-Sanford, NC, Sanford

McNeil, Michele
michele@opdfla.com, Production, Clay Today, FL, Fleming Island

McNeill, Amy .... (910) 506-3021
amyjohnson@civitasmedia.com, Classified, The Laurinburg Exchange, NC, Laurinburg

McNeill, Keith .... (250) 674-3343
newsroom@clearwatertimes.com, Ed., North Thompson Times, BC, Clearwater

McNeir, Kevin .... (202) 561-4100
mcneirdk@washingtoninformer.com, Editor, Washington Informer, DC, Washington

McNichols, Michael P. .... (740) 397-5333
csplain@mountvernonnews.com, MIDS Mgr., Marketing Information Distribution Service, OH, Mount Vernon

McNickle, Colin .... (412) 320-7836
cmcnickle@tribweb.com, Editorial Page Ed., Tribune-Review, PA, Greensburg

McNiel, Dan .... (843) 479-3815
dmcniel@heraldadvocate.com, Ed., Herald-Advocate, SC, Bennettsville

McNiel, Elizabeth
ekmcniel@haroldadvocate.com, Pub., Herald-Advocate, SC, Bennettsville

McNiell, Jeff
jmcniell@houstonherald.com, Ed., Houston Herald, MO, Houston

McNiff, Tom .... (352) 867-4010
tom.mcniff@starbanner.com, Dir Edit, Ocala Star-Banner, FL, Ocala

McNulty, Aidan .... (212) 556-4015
mcnulaj@nytimes.com, Regional Director, US & Canada, The New York Times News Service & Syndicate, New York
mcnulaj@nytimes.com, The New York Times, NY, New York

McNulty, Aidan .... (212) 556-4015
mcnulaj@nytimes.com, Regional Director, US & Canada, The New York Times News Service & Syndicate, New York

McNulty, Diane
diane.mcnulty@nytimes.com, Dir., Community Affairs, The New York Times, NY, New York

McNulty, Gerald
gerald.mcnulty@marist.edu, Dir., Internship Prog., Marist College, NY, Poughkeepsie

McNutt, Fred
mcmeganutt@aol.com, Pres., Megasys International, Inc., CT, Tolland

McPeek, Gerald
gerald.mcpeek@thriftynickelads.com, Thrifty Nickel Want Ads - St. Louis, MO, Saint Peters

McPhaul, F. Steve .... (334) 293-5800
smcphaul@cnhi.com, Executive VP/COO, Community Newspaper Holdings, Inc., AL, Montgomery

McPherson, Beth .... (816) 640-2251
wcnews@embarqmail.com, Ed. & Pub., Weston Chronicle, MO, Weston

McPherson, Connie
press@kiowacountypress.com, Ed., Kiowa County Press, CO, Eads

McPherson, Darryl
frontpagegroupinc@gmail.com, Ex Ed, South Buffalo News, NY, Lackawanna

McPherson, Jamie .... (615) 259-8822
jmcpherson@tnmedia.com, VP of Advertising, Robertson County Times, TN, Clarksville

McPherson, Jeanne
jmcpherson@usouthal.edu, Asst. Prof., University of South Alabama, AL, Mobile

McPherson, Jim
jmcpherson@whitworth.edu, Whitworth University, WA, Spokane

McPherson, Jim......................(816) 640-2251
Wcads@embarqmail.com, Adv. & Sports, Weston Chronicle, MO, Weston

McQuaid, Brendan....................(603) 668-4321
bmcquaid@unionleader.com, President, New Hampshire Union Leader/New Hampshire Sunday News, NH, Manchester

McQuaid, Joseph..........(603) 668-4321 ext. 200
publisher@unionleader.com , Publisher, New Hampshire Union Leader/New Hampshire Sunday News, NH, Manchester

McQuaide, Carol....................(724) 465-5555
cmcquaide@indianagazette.net, Mktg. Dir., Indiana Printing & Publishing Co., PA, Indiana

McQuaide, Christine
cmcquaide@ccac.edu, Cmty. College Allegheny County, PA, Pittsburgh

McQueen, Mariann....................(252) 329-9550
mmcqueen@reflector.com, CFO, Cooke Communications North Carolina, LLC, NC, Greenville

McQueen, Mariann....................(252) 329-9550
mmcqueen@reflector.com, CFO, The Daily Reflector, NC, Greenville

McQueen, Nick
nmcqueen@dailynews.net, Sports Ed., The Hays Daily News, KS, Hays

McQueen, Sarah
smcqueen@pcgazette.com, Assoc. Ed., The Portage County Gazette, WI, Stevens Point

McQuillen, William
william_mcquillen@nps.gov, Catholic Univ. of America, DC, Washington

McRae, Barbara
bmcrae@franklin-press.com, Ed., The Franklin Press, NC, Franklin

McRea, Heather....................(714) 796-7932
hmcrea@ocregister.com, City Ed., Anaheim Bulletin, CA, Santa Ana
hmcrea@ocregister.com, Ed., Yorba Linda Star, CA, Santa Ana

McRoy, Eric....................(618) 463-0612
ericmcroy@advantagenews.com , VP, Rex Encore, AdVantage News, IL, Godfrey
ericmcroy@advantagenews.com , VP, AdVantage News - Granite City, IL, Godfrey

McRoy, Sharon....................(618) 463-0612
semcroy@aol.com, President, AdVantage News - Edwardsville, IL, Alton

McSheffrey, Kevin
kevin.mcsheffrey@sunmedia.ca, Managing Editor, Marketplace, ON, Elliot Lake

McSheffrey, Kevin
kevin.mcsheffrey@sunmedia.ca, Managing Editor, The Mid-north Monitor, ON, Elliot Lake

McSheffrey, Kevin
news@elliotlakestandard.ca, Man. Ed., The Standard, ON, Elliot Lake

McSwain, Amy....................(904) 359-4459
amy.mcswain@jacksonville.com, VP-Circulation/Marketing, The Florida Times-Union, FL, Jacksonville

McSweeney, Sarah
smcsweeney@oakvillebeaver.com, Circ. Mgr., Oakville Beaver, ON, Oakville

McTighe, Emily
tmgsales@telus.net, Adv. Mgr., The Macleod Gazette, AB, Fort Macleod

McTighe, Frank....................(403) 553-3391
ftmgazet@telus.net, Pub./Ed., The Macleod Gazette, AB, Fort Macleod

McTigue, Marlene
mmctigue@columbiagreenemedia.com, Multi-Media Consultant, The Ravena News-Herald, NY, Ravena

McVay, MJ....................(419) 448-3248
mjmcvay@advertiser-tribune.com, Ed. , The Advertiser-Tribune, OH, Tiffin

McVeigh, J.T.............(705) 726-6537 Ext. 525225
JMcVeigh@postmedia.com, Ed., The Enterprise-bulletin, ON, Collingwood

McVeigh, Jody
jody.mcveigh@advisorsource.com, Ed., Adviser & Source, MI, New Baltimore

McVey, Kathy....................(620) 355-6162
indpndt@pld.com, Ed., The Lakin Independent, KS, Lakin

McVicar, Brice
brice.mcvicar@sunmedia.ca, Ed, The Community Press, ON, Belleville

McVoy, Tom
momoney@momoney.com, Mktg. Mgr., Mo-Money Associates, Inc., FL, Pensacola

McWebb, Chris
cmcwebb@runge.net, Regl. Pub., Runge Newspapers, Inc., ON, Renfrew

McWilliams, Avery....................(432) 552-2659
mesajournal@utpb.edu, Editor, Univ. of Texas Permian Basin, TX, Odessa

McWilliams, Joe
lsleader@telusplanet.net, Ed, Lakeside Leader, AB, Slave Lake

Mcbrayne, Shelia....................(519) 674-5205
ridgeind@netrover.com, Editor in Chief, The Ridgetown Independent News, ON, Ridgetown

Mccann, Deb
dmccann1@bellnet.ca, Bus. Mgr., The Napanee Beaver, ON, Napanee

Mccarthy, Sharron....................(603) 413-5117
smccarthy@nh.com, Pub., Parenting New Hampshire, NH, Manchester

Mccaw, Wendy
wmccaw@newspress.com, Co-Pub., Santa Barbara News-Press, CA, Santa Barbara

Mcchesney, Mary....................(757) 446-2000
mary.mcchesney@pilotonline.com, Acquisition Manager, The Virginian-Pilot, VA, Norfolk

Mcclure, John
jmcclure@jcpgroup.com, Adv. Dir., Hometown, IN, Terre Haute

Mccoy, Helen....................(902) 563-3845
Adv. Mgr., Classified, The Cape Breton Post, NS, Sydney

Mccully, Sharon
outletjournal@sympatico.ca , Pub. , The Record, QC, Sherbrooke

Mcdhail, Nusete
advertising@grenadastar.com, Adv. Mgr, Grenada Lake Herald, MS, Grenada

Mcfadden, Susan
susan@sitkasentinel.com, Adv. Mgr., Daily Sitka Sentinel, AK, Sitka

Mcfall, Michael
mmcfall@sltrib.com, Univ. of Utah, UT, Salt Lake City

Mcfarland, Jodi....................(989) 776-9678
editor@thesaginawnews.com, Ed, Saginaw Press, MI, Saginaw

Mcfarlane, Anthony....................(845) 346-3016
amcfarlane@recordonline.com, regional Ad Direcor, The Times Herald-Record, NY, Middletown

Mcgill, Jenny....................(559) 896-1976 x 1013
jmcgill@kingsburgrecorder.com, Ed., The Selma Enterprise, CA, Hanford

Mcginity, Megan
mcginity@unc.edu, Univ. of North Carolina - The Daily Tar Heel, NC, Chapel Hill

Mcintosh, Duncan
letters@ocweekly.com, Pres./CEO., Oc Weekly, CA, Fountain Valley

Mckelvey, Walter
wmckelvey@gilbaneco.com, Sr. Vice Pres./ Mgr.-Central Reg., Gilbane Building Co., RI, Providence

Mckeon, John....................(214) 977-8467
jmckeon@dallasnews.com, President and General Manager, Southwest Classified Advertising Managers Association, TX, Dallas

Mckibben, Julie
julie.mckibbin@gazettes.com, Circ. Mgr, Downtown Gazette, CA, Long Beach
julie.mckibbin@gazettes.com, Circ. Mgr, Grunion Gazette, CA, Long Beach

Mctuire, Bill
info@brocksolutions.com, Project Mgr., Brock Solutions U.S. Inc., TX, Irving

Mctyiere, Issac
melanie@lawattstimes.com, Dist. Mgr., La Watts Times, CA, Los Angeles

Mead, Richard
richardm@jegi.com, Mng. Dir., Jordan, Edmiston Group, Inc., NY, New York

Meade, Angie..............(419) 281-0581 ext. 222
ameade@times-gazette.com, Business Office, Ashland Publishing Co. LLC, OH, Ashland

Meade, Angie..............(419) 281-0581 Ext. 222
ameade@times-gazette.com, Bus. Mgr., Ashland Times-Gazette, OH, Ashland

Meade, Angie........................(608) 364-9220
ameade@beloitdailynews.com, Business Manager, Beloit Daily News, WI, Beloit

Meade, Darcy........................(616) 527-2100
darcy.meade@sentinel-standard.com, News Editor, Ionia Sentinel-Standard, MI, Ionia

Meade, David C.
editor@thejournalonline.com, Mng. Ed., The Journal, SC, Williamston

Meador, Cherie........................(312) 935-4217
Robert Morris College, IL, Chicago

Meadowcroft, Ted
tmeadowcroft@njnpublishing.com, Circ. Mgr., Suburban News, NJ, New Providence

Meadows, Angie
srads@dtccom.net, Pub./Gen. Mgr./Adv. Dir., Smithville Review, TN, Smithville

Meadows, David
dmeadows@couriernews.com, Pub., The Courier, AR, Russellville

Meadows, David
postdispatch@centurytel.net, Pub., Dardanelle Post-Dispatch, AR, Dardanelle

Meadows, James
news@theunionstar.com, Ed., The Union Star, VA, Brookneal

Meadows, KC
udjkcm@ukiahdj.com , Ed., The Willits News, CA, Willits

Meadows, Rashelle....................(530) 257-5321
rmeadows@lassennews.com, Class, Lassen County Times, CA, Susanville

Meadows, Sheila....................(252) 635-5635
Sheila.Meadows@newbernsj.com, Circ. Dir., StarNews, NC, Wilmington
Sheila.Meadows@newbernsj.com, Circ. Dir., The Sun Journal, NC, New Bern

Meadows, Steve....................(865) 986-6581
steve.meadows@news-herald.net, Pub./Ed., The Connection, TN, Lenoir City
steve.meadows@news-herald.net, Pub./Ed., News-Herald, TN, Lenoir City

Mealing, Travis....................(705) 527-5500
mirror@simcoe.com, Ed., The Mirror, ON, Midland

Meaney, Karen
kmeaney@marketresearch.com, Ed., Simba Information, CT, Stamford

Means, Greg........................(231) 894-5356
gmeans@whitelakebeacon.com, Ed., White Lake Beacon, MI, Whitehall

Mears, Jim........................(479) 872-5011
sporter@nwaonline.net, Classified Adv. Mgr., The Free Weekly, AR, Fayetteville

Measer, Michael..........(716) 204-4950 ext. 4950
mmeaser@beenews.com, Exec. Vice Pres., East Aurora Bee, NY, Williamsville

Measer, Michael................................ext. 214
jevans@beenews.com, Exec. Vice Pres., Cheektowaga Bee, NY, Williamsville

Measer, Michael
mmeaser@beenews.com, Exec. Vice Pres., West Seneca Bee, NY, Williamsville

Measer, Michael....................(716) 204-4950
mmeaser@beenews.com, Exec. Vice Pres, Amherst Bee, NY, Williamsville

Measer, Michael
mmeaser@beenews.com, Vice Pres., Depew Bee, NY, Williamsville

Measer, Trey............................(716) 204-4900
tmeaser@beenews.com, Pub., Amherst Bee, NY, Williamsville
tmeaser@beenews.com, Pres./Pub., Bee Group Newspapers, NY, Williamsville
tmeaser@beenews.com, Pub./Pres., East Aurora Bee, NY, Williamsville
tmeaser@beenews.com, Pub., Cheektowaga Bee, NY, Williamsville
tmeaser@beenews.com, Pub, Lancaster Bee, NY, Williamsville
tmeaser@beenews.com, Pub., Clarence Bee, NY, Williamsville
tmeaser@beenews.com, Pub., West Seneca Bee, NY, Williamsville
tmeaser@beenews.com, Pub., Depew Bee, NY, Williamsville
tmeaser@beenews.com, Pub., Ken-Ton Bee, NY, Williamsville

Measer, Trey
read@beenews.com, Pub., Orchard Park Bee, NY, Williamsville

Meaux, Jessica
jessica.meaux@vermiliontoday.com, Adv. Sales Rep., Abbeville Meridional, LA, Abbeville

Mebane, William deBerniere
bmebane@crescentsc.com, Pres./CEO, Crescent Publishing Company LLC, SC, Greenville

Mechanic, Barry
bmechanic@woonsocketcall.com, Pub., Woonsocket Neighbour, RI, Woonsocket

Mechanic, Barry M.....................(401) 767-8572
publisher@woonsocketcall.com, Pub., Cumberland Lincoln Neighbors, RI, Woonsocket

Medici, Mark........................(404) 526-2804
mark.medici@ajc.com, Sr. VP, Audience & Group Lead for CMG Newspapers, Atlanta Journal-Constitution, GA, Atlanta

Medina, Carlos........................(936) 294-1495
Advertising Manager, Sam Houston State University, TX, Huntsville

Medina, Daniel
daniel.medina@fiu.edu, Credit Mgr., Diario Las Americas, FL, Miami

Medina, Dom................................ext. 32
domm@flynnburner.com, Vice Pres., Flynn Burner Corp., NY, New Rochelle

Medina, Eliseo
eliseo.medina@seiu.org, Int'l Exec. Vice Pres., Service Employees International Union, CLC, DC, Washington

Medina, Felix
felix.medina@newspan.net, Semana News, TX, Houston

Medina, Jim............................(805) 437-0201
jmedina@vcstar.com, Bus. Ed., Ventura County Star, CA, Camarillo

Medina, Lupe........................(661) 325-7725
lupe@elpopularnews.com, Associate Editor, El Popular, CA, Bakersfield

KurtM@arlingtonmnnews.com, Ed., Arlington Enterprise, MN, Arlington

Menser, Stacey
staceym@timesleader.net, Lifestyles/Features, Times Leader, KY, Princeton

Mentzer, Marie ....**(904) 629-6020**
AgeVentureNewsService@demko.com, Health & Science COR, AgeVenture News Service, Orange Park

Menu, Gavin
gmenu@sagharboronline.com, Ad. Dir., Sag Harbor Express, NY, Sag Harbor

Menu, Kathryn..........................**(631) 725-1700**
kmenu@sagharboronline.com, Ed, Sag Harbor Express, NY, Sag Harbor

Menz, Alexa
amenz@westerncarolinian.com, Editor-in-Chief, Western Carolina Univ., NC, Cullowhee

Menzies, Mishelle
production@fitzhugh.ca, Prod., The Fitzhugh, AB, Jasper

Mercadel, Chric
datanewsad@bellsouth.net, Circ. Mgr., New Orleans Data News Weekly, LA, New Orleans

Mercer, Frank
news@windsornews.net, Pub., The Windsor Review, MO, Windsor

Mercer, Frank
higvladv@ctcis.net, Pub, Higginsville Advance, MO, Higginsville

Mercer, Frank
bluehillleader@gtmc.net, Publisher, Blue Hill Leader, NE, Blue Hill

Mercer, Frank
safetnews@yahoo.com, Pub., The Santa Fe Times, MO, Alma

Mercer, Frank..........................**(785) 483-2116**
Pub., Franklin County Chronicle, NE, Franklin

Mercer, Frank
glasgow@mcmsys.com, Pub., Glasgow Missourian, MO, Glasgow

Mercer, Frank
cdemocrat@yahoo.com, Ed., Norborne Democrat-Leader, MO, Norborne

Mercer, Frank
pvtimes@ruraltel.net, Pub., Plainville Times, KS, Plainville

Mercer, Frank W.
democrat@carolnet.com, Pub., Main Street Media, Inc., MO, Carrollton
democrat@carolnet.com, Pub., The Lafayette County Shopper, MO, Higginsville
democrat@carolnet.com, Pub., The Lexington News, MO, Lexington

Mercer, Michael L. ....**(210) 829-6069**
mercer@uiwtx.edu, Advisor, University of the Incarnate Word, TX, San Antonio

Mercer, Robert ....**(714) 484-7267**
rmercer@cypresscollege.edu, Cypress College Chronicle, CA, Cypress

Mercer, Robert ....**(937) 328-0240**
rmercer@coxohio.com, Adv. Dir., Springfield News-Sun, OH, Springfield

Merchant, Jim..........................**(941) 206-1117**
jmerchant@sun-herald.com, Systems Ed., Charlotte Sun, FL, Punta Gorda

Mercier, Guylaine
guylaine.mercier@monteregieweb.com, Adv. Rep., Le Soleil Du St-laurent, QC, Chateauguay

Mercier, Larry ....**(250) 492-3636**
larry@pentictonwesternnews.com, Sales Mgr., Penticton Western News, BC, Penticton

Mercier, Louis
mercierl@transcontinental.ca, Ed., La Voix Populaire, QC, Lasalle

Mercier, Sunnie ....**(715) 453-2151**
sales@tomahawkleader.com, Adv. Mgr., Tomahawk Leader, WI, Tomahawk

Merck, Mark
mmerck@forumcomm.com, Page Des., InForum, ND, Fargo

Merckx, Cindy ....**(856) 694-1600**
Owner/Ed., The Sentinel of Gloucester County, NJ, Malaga

Mercure, Philipe
phillipe.mercure@thecanadianpress.com, Exec. Dir., Canadian Press, The - Toronto, ON, ON, Toronto

Mercurio, Sherry
sherry.mercurio@franklin.edu, Ed., Franklin University, OH, Columbus

Meredith, Rick ....**ext. 5324**
rmeredith@texarkanagazette.com, Adv. Sales Mgr., Texarkana Gazette, AR, Texarkana

Merek, Jim ....**(253) 620-4747**
Jmarek@webpressllc.com, Sales, WebPress, LLC, WA, Tacoma

Merendino, Jon
jmerendino@scng.com, VP Operations, Southern California News Group, CA, Woodland Hills

Merendino, Jon
jmerendino@ocregister.com, VP, Op., The Orange County Register, CA, Santa Ana

Merfeld, Scarlette ....**(518) 873-6368**
ads@suncommunitynews.com, Southern Adirondacks Publishing Group Mgr, Sun Community News, Published by:Denton Publications, Inc., NY, Elizabethtown

Merfeld, Scarlette ....**(518) 585-9173**
ads@suncommunitynews.com, Southern Adirondacks Publishing Group Mgr/Ad. Mgr , The Times of Ti Sun, NY, Elizabethtown
ads@suncommunitynews.com, Ad. Mgr, The Valley News Sun, NY, Elizabethtown
ads@suncommunitynews.com, Adv. Mgr, The Adirondack Journal Sun, NY, Elizabethtown
ads@suncommunitynews.com, Ad. Mgr, The Burgh Sun, NY, Elizabethtown
ads@suncommunitynews.com, Southern Adirondacks Publishing Group Manager , The News Enterprise Sun, NY, Elizabethtown
ads@suncommunitynews.com, Adv. Mgr, The North Countryman Sun, NY, Elizabethtown

Merhi, Lisa ....**(301) 670-7129**
lmerhi@gazette.net, Prodn. Mgr., The Gazette - Damascus / Clarksburg, MD, Gaithersburg
lmerhi@gazette.net, Prodn. Mgr., The Gazette - Rockville / Aspen Hill / Wheaton (OOB), MD, Gaithersburg
lmerhi@gazette.net, Prodn. Mgr., The Gazette - Silver Spring / Takoma Park / Burtonsville (OOB), MD, Gaithersburg
lmerhi@gazette.net, Prodn. Mgr., The Gazette - Olney (OOB), MD, Gaithersburg
lmerhi@gazette.net, Prodn. Mgr., The Gazette - Germantown / Poolsville / Boyds (OOB), MD, Gaithersburg
lmerhi@gazette.net, Prodn. Mgr., The Gazette - Bethesda / Chevy Chase / Kensington (OOB), MD, Gaithersburg
lmerhi@gazette.net, Prodn. Mgr., The Gazette - Gaithersburg / Mont. Village (OOB), MD, Gaithersburg
lmerhi@gazette.net, Prodn. Mgr., The Gazette - North / Central Prince George Co. (OOB), MD, Gaithersburg
lmerhi@gazette.net, Prodn. Mgr., The Gazette - South / Central Prince George Co. (OOB), MD, Gaithersburg
lmerhi@gazette.net, Prodn. Mgr., The Gazette - Potomac / North Potomac, MD, Gaithersburg

Merit, Jocelyn
admin@osoyoostimes.com, Office Mgr., Osoyoos Times, BC, Osoyoos

Merkel, Ralph ....**(502) 852-6727**
rmerkel@louisvillecardinal.com, Adviser,

University of Louisville, KY, Louisville

Merkel, Thomas G. ....**(815) 539-7476**
msg1@tsf.net, Ed., Mendota Shopping Guide, IL, Mendota

Merkes, Betty
bmerkes@cheesereporter.com, Subscriptions, The Cheese Reporter, WI, Madison

Merlihan, Joe ....**(519) 669-5790 ext. 107**
jmerlihan@woolwichobserver.com, Pub., The Observer, ON, Elmira

Merlin, Tim
deldridge@richmondregister.com, The Madison County Advertiser, KY, Richmond

Mermer, Noel ....**(843) 577-5304 ext. 113**
publisher@charlestoncitypaper.com, Pub., The Charleston City Paper, SC, Charleston

Merrell, Dennis ....**(780) 989-4900**
dennis@awna.com, Exec. Dir., Alberta Weekly Newspapers Association, AB, Edmonton

Merrett, Tammy ....**(618) 650-3597**
tmerret@siue.edu, Advisor, Southern Illinois University Edwardsville, IL, Edwardsville

Merriam, Kiera
kmerriam@bowesnet.com, Gen. Mgr., Shoreline Beacon, ON, Port Elgin

Merriam, Kiera.................**(519) 832-9001 x106**
kiera.merriam@sunmedia.ca, Adv. Mgr., The Post, ON, Hanover

Merriam, Roger ....**(605) 886-6901**
rogerm@thepublicopinion.com, Sports Ed., Watertown Public Opinion, SD, Watertown

Merrick, Rick ....**(805) 564-5171**
rmerrick@newspress.com, MIS Mgr., Santa Barbara News-Press, CA, Santa Barbara

Merrifield, Denny
americanclassified@swbell.net, Pub., American Classifieds, IL, Champaign

Merrill, Barry..........................**(919) 658-9456**
publisher@mountolivetribune.com, Pub, Mount Olive Tribune, NC, Mount Olive

Merrill, Brian
brian@amclass1.com, American Classifieds - Birmingham, AL, Pelham

Merrill, Gregory..........................**(435) 753-8090**
gmerrill@mediaservicesgroup.com, Dir., Media Services Group, Inc., FL, Ponte Vedra

Merrill, Tina
tina@bkrstudio.com, Office Mgr., BKR Studio, Inc., IN, South Bend

Merrit, Mary Gelling
MERRITTM@CAYUGA-CC.EDU, Cayuga Community College, NY, Auburn

Merritt, Al
al@wakeweekly.com, Prod. Mgr., The Wake Weekly, NC, Wake Forest

Merritt, Mimi ....**(276) 326-3682**
mmerritt@bluefield.edu, Bluefield College, VA, Bluefield

Merritt, Paula ....**(601) 693-1551 ext. 3304**
pmerritt@themeridianstar.com, Photo Dept. Mgr., The Meridian Star, MS, Meridian

Merritt, Sage
sage.merritt@nptelegraph.com, News Ed., The North Platte Telegraph, NE, North Platte

Merriweather, Frances J.
criterion@apollo3.com, Ed., Buffalo Criterion, NY, Buffalo

Merriweather, John....................**(740) 328-8594**
jlmerriw@gannett.com, Ops. Mgr., The Advocate, OH, Newark
jlmerriw@gannett.com, Ops. Dir., The Coshocton Tribune, OH, Coshocton
jlmerriw@gannett.com, Cir. Ops. Mgr., Times Recorder, OH, Zanesville

Merry, Annie ....**(207) 386-5231**
amerry@coastaljournal.com, Adv. Rep., greater Bath , Coastal Journal, ME, Bath

Merry, Nikki M.
editor@centralpennparent.com, Ed., Central Penn Parent, PA, Harrisburg

Merry, Stu
editors@nd-bhginc.com, Ed., McLean County Independent, ND, Garrison

Mersch, Ben
ben.mersch@miamivalleynewspapers.com, Ed., The Germantown Press, OH, Miamisburg

Mertes, Chris ....**(608) 478-2521**
spedit@hometownnews.com, Mng. Ed., The Star, WI, Sun Prairie

Merves, Jared ....**(214) 977-8532**
jmerves@dmnmedia.com, General Manager: Digital Sales, The Dallas Morning News, TX, Dallas

Mesher, Arthur
info@descartes.com, CEO, Descartes Systems Group, ON, Waterloo

Meske, Melissa
jcjnews@campbellpublications.net, Reg. Ed., Jesey County Journal, IL, Jerseyville
jcjnews@campbellpublications.net, Reg. Ed., Calhoun News-Herald, IL, Hardin
jcjnews@campbellpublications.net, Reg. Ed., Greene Prairie Press, IL, Carrollton

Mesler, Linda
advertising@noconanews.net, Co-Pub./Adv. Dir., Nocona News, TX, Nocona

Mesler, Tracy
news@noconanews.net, Co-Pub./Ed., Nocona News, TX, Nocona

Messa, Chris ....**(337) 289-6382**
chris.messa@timesofacadiana.com, Adv. Mgr., Times Of Acadiana, LA, Lafayette

Messenger, Jane......................**(612) 673-7327**
Jane.Messenger@startribune.com, Creative Director, Star Tribune, MN, Minneapolis

Messerly, Michael ....**(518) 343-8000**
ttowner@batavianews.com, BNC Pub. / JNC Dig. Dir., The Daily News, NY, Batavia
ttowner@batavianews.com, Pub., The Drummer Pennysaver, NY, Batavia
ttowner@batavianews.com, Gen. Mgr./Ed., Spiro Graphic, OK, Spiro

Messiah-Jiles, Sonceria
ceo@defendermediagroup.com, Pub. & CEO, Houston Defender Media Group, Formerly Houston Defender, TX, Houston

Messick, Allen ....**(303) 659-2522 ext. 204**
amessick@metrowestnewspapers.com, Pub., Fort Lupton Press, CO, Brighton

Messick, Allen
amessick@metrowestnewspapers.com, Pub., Adam County Advertiser, CO, Brighton
amessick@metrowestnewspapers.com, Pub., Commerce City Sentinel Express, CO, Brighton

Messick, David........................**(757) 247-4940**
dmessick@dailypress.com, Dir., Consumer Mktg., Daily Press, VA, Newport News

Messick, Steve
smessick@republican-eagle.com, Pub., Republican Eagle, MN, Red Wing

Messick, Steve
smessick@republican-eagle.com, Pub., Eagle Extra, MN, Red Wing

Messick, Steven R.
smessick@hastingsstargazette.com, Pub., Trade Winds Shopping Guide, MN, Hastings

Messick, Steven R.
news@hastingsstargazette.com, Pub., Hastings Star Gazette, MN, Hastings

Messina, Charles ....**(416) 507-2021**
charles.messina@thecanadianpress.com, Sales/Mktg. Dir., Broadcast News Limited, ON, Toronto

Messinger, Kelly ....**(614) 236-6567**

Capital Univ., OH, Columbus

Messner, Anne
amessner@intouchhealth.com, Vice Pres.,
Finance/Admin., Maps.com, CA, Santa
Barbara

Messner, Marcus
mmessner@vcu.edu, Asst. Prof., Virginia
Commonwealth University, VA, Richmond

Meszoros, Mark
mmeszoros@news-herald.com, Asst. Mng. Ed.
/ Feat., The News-Herald, OH, Willoughby

Metcalf, Chris .... (585) 243-0296
sports@livingstonnews.com, Sports Ed, The
Livingston County News, NY, Geneseo

Metcalf, Kathy
kmetcalf@dailyrepublicannews.com, Adv.
Sales. , The Marion Daily Republican, IL,
Marion

Metcalf, Sandra
subscriptions@bloomeradvance.com, Circ.
Mgr., Bloomer Advance, WI, Bloomer

Metcalfe, Jim .... ext. 33
jmetcalfe@delphosherald.com, Sports Ed.,
Delphos Daily Herald, OH, Delphos

Metcalfe, Wendy 1 (506) 345-3255
metcalfe.wendy@brunswicknews.com, Editor
in Chief, New Brunswick Telegraph-Journal,
NB, Saint John

Mete, Georgia
classified@sachem.ca, Adv. Mgr., Classified,
The Grand River Sachem, ON, Caledonia

Methvin, Cynthia .... (940) 497-5900
cmethvin@scarborough.com, Scarborough
Research, NY, New York

Metrick, Gene .... (252) 407-9944
gmetrick@rmtelegram.com, Online/Print Ed.,
Rocky Mount Telegram, NC, Rocky Mount

Metro, Gary .... ext. 5033
gary.metro@thesouthern.com, Ed., At Home
With Flipside, IL, Carbondale

Metz, Henry
editor@yourneighborhoodnews.com, Ed.,
Hooksett Banner, NH, Manchester

Metz, Jean .... (304) 265-3333
jmeemail@aol.com, Pub., Mountain
Statesman, WV, Grafton

Metz, Jenn .... (574) 631-4542
Univ. of Notre Dame, IN, Notre Dame

Metz, Philip
pmetz@trentonian.com, Cir. Dir., The
Trentonian, NJ, Trenton

Metzer, Steve
smetzer@swoknews.com, City Ed., The Lawton
Constitution, OK, Lawton

Metzgar, Dusty .... (304) 269-1600, ext. 106
dmetzgar@westondemocrat.com, Reporter,
Weston Democrat, WV, Weston

Metzger, Joel .... (209) 498-2052
jmetzger@calaverasenterprise.com, Ed./Pres.,
Calaveras Californian, CA, San Andreas

Metzger, Melissa .... (646) 223-4000
m.metzger@thomsonreuters.com, Publishing
Solutions Specialist, Reuters Media, NY,
New York

Metzger, Michelle
mmetzger@smu.edu, Pub. Rel. Mgr., M/C/C,
TX, Dallas

Metzler, Amy
amy@alabamapress.org, Sales/Mktg Exec,
Alabama Press Association, AL, Birmingham

Metzler, John J.
jjmcolumn@earthlink.net, Editor, Worldwatch/
Foreign Affairs Syndicate, Jamaica

Meurer, Brandy .... (409) 787-2172
screporter@yahoo.com, Ed., The Sabine
County Reporter, TX, Hemphill

Meyer, Adam .... (307) 739-9538

adam@jhnewsandguide.com, Adv. Dir.,
Jackson Hole News&Guide, WY, Jackson

Meyer, Annell
bkp@brenhambanner.com, Office Mgr.,
Brenham Banner-Press, TX, Brenham

Meyer, Avis
meyerae@slu.edu, Prof./Dir., Political Journ.,
Saint Louis University, MO, Saint Louis

Meyer, Betsy .... (765) 285-1200
ecmeyer@bsu.edu, Business Manager, Ball
State University, IN, Muncie

Meyer, Carmen .... (320) 632-2345
carmen.meyer@mcrecord.com, Adv. Dir.,
Dairyland Peach, MN, Sauk Centre
carmen.meyer@mcrecord.com, General
Manager, Morrison County Record, MN,
Little Falls

Meyer, Christina
christina.meyer.braziltimes@gmail.com, Ad.
rep, The Brazil Times, IN, Brazil

Meyer, Dan .... (414) 336-7114
dan.meyer@biztimes.com, Pub., Milwaukee
Business Journal, WI, Milwaukee

Meyer, Debbie
dmeyer@times-news.com, Special Projects
Editor, The Cumberland Times-News, MD,
Cumberland

Meyer, Dennis .... (402) 371-1020 ext. 230
pics@norfolkdailynews.com, Photo Mgr./Online
Ed., Norfolk Daily News, NE, Norfolk

Meyer, Erica .... (828) 202-2924
emeyer@thedigitalcourier.com, Adv. Mgr., The
Daily Courier, NC, Forest City

Meyer, Gary W. .... (763) 263-3602
editor@westsherburnetribune.net, Pub., West
Sherburne Tribune, MN, Big Lake
editor@westsherburnetribune.net, Pub.,
Sherburne County Citizen, MN, Becker
editor@westsherburnetribune.net, Ed. / Pub,
Clearwater Tribune, MN, Big Lake

Meyer, Ida .... (218) 262-1011
imeyer@hibbingdailytribune.net, Circ. Dir.,
Manney's Shopper, MN, Hibbing

Meyer, Jason
jason@postvilleherald.com, Pub., Postville
Herald, IA, Postville

Meyer, Jeff
adsprpress@loretel.net, Adv. Mgr., Pelican
Rapids Press, MN, Pelican Rapids

Meyer, Joel .... (954) 425-1230
jmeyer@sunsentinel.com, Manufacturing
Director, South Florida Sun-Sentinel, FL, Fort
Lauderdale

Meyer, Joseph
jmeyer@metlife.com, Pub., The New York
Observer, NY, New York

Meyer, Judith .... (207) 689-2902
jmeyer@sunjournal.com, Mng. Ed., Day, Sun
Journal, ME, Lewiston

Meyer, Julie
jeffprpress@loretel.net, Pub., Pelican Rapids
Press, MN, Pelican Rapids

Meyer, Karl
karl@actionunlimited.com, Prod. Mgr., Action
Unlimited, MA, Concord

Meyer, Kim .... (515) 885-2531
bancroftregister@yahoo.com, Editor, The
Bancroft Register, IA, Bancroft

Meyer, Linda .... (805) 893-7601
linda.meyer@sa.ucsb.edu, Adv. Mgr., Univ.
of California, Santa Barbara, CA, Santa
Barbara

Meyer, Linda .... (605) 845-3646
linda@mobridgetribune.com, Gen Mgr.,
Monday Reminder, SD, Mobridge

Meyer, Linda .... (605) 845-3646
linda@mobridgetribune.com, Gen. Mgr.,
Mobridge Tribune, SD, Mobridge

Meyer, Mary
mmeyer@conleynet.com, Adv. Mgr., The
Hartford Times Press, WI, West Bend

Meyer, Nancy
nmeyer@courant.com, Pres. , The Record, NJ,
Woodland Park

Meyer, Neal
neal@thetrumantribune.com, Adv. Mgr.,
Truman Tribune, MN, Truman

Meyer, Nicole
thetrumantribune@gmail.com, Pub, Truman
Tribune, MN, Truman

Meyer, Peter .... (508) 862-1111
pmeyer@capecodonline.com, Pres./Pub., The
Standard-Times, MA, New Bedford

Meyer, Peter D. .... (508) 862-1111
pmeyer@capecodonline.com, President &
Publisher, Cape Cod Times, MA, Hyannis
pmeyer@capecodonline.com, New England
Reg. Pub., GateHouse Media, Inc., NY,
Pittsford

Meyer, Rebecca .... (815) 937-3353
rmeyer@daily-journal.com, CIRCULATION
AND AUDIENCE DIRECTOR, Small
Newspaper Group, IL, Kankakee
rmeyer@daily-journal.com, Circulation &
Audience Director, The Daily Journal, IL,
Kankakee

Meyer, Rolf G.
design@austrianpublications.com, Pub.,
Deutsche Presse, ON, Toronto

Meyer, Sharon
sharon@deltapublications.com, Office Mgr.,
Tempo, WI, Kiel

Meyer, Suzy .... (970) 564-6040
smeyer@cortezjournal.com, Pub., Mancos
Times, CO, Cortez

Meyer, Suzy .... (970) 564-6040
smeyer@cortezjournal.com, Pub./Ed., Dolores
Star, CO, Cortez

Meyer, Suzy .... (970) 564-6040
smeyer@cortezjournal.com, Pub./Ed., Cortez
Journal, CO, Cortez

Meyer, Thomas
info@interknife.com, Pres./CEO, IKS
Klingelnberg GmbH

Meyerhoffer, Peter .... (780) 532-1110 ext. 274
kentk@bowesnet.com, Publisher/Plant
Manager, Daily Herald-Tribune, AB, Grande
Prairie

Meyerhoffer, Peter .... (780) 978-3369
peter.meyerhoffer@sunmedia.ca, Adv. Dir,
Fairview Post, AB, Fairview
peter.meyerhoffer@sunmedia.ca, reg. Adv. Dir.,
The Record-gazette, AB, Peace River

Meyering, Carl E.
cmeyering@ameritech.net, Ed., Business
Newsfeatures, Grosse Pointe Farms

Meyers, Bob .... ext. 101
bob@nationalpress.org, President and COO,
National Press Foundation, DC, Washington

Meyers, Greg .... (419) 784-5441 ext 231
gmeyers@crescent-news.com, Circ. Mgr, The
Crescent-News, OH, Defiance

Meyers, Greg
gregm@crescent-news.com, Circulation Mgr.,
Crescent Extra, OH, Defiance

Meyers, Matt .... (608) 745-3571
mmeyers@madison.com, Badgerland Values
Columbia County, WI, Portage
mmeyers@madison.com, Pub., Baraboo News
Republic, WI, Baraboo

Meyers, Matt .... (608) 745-3571
mmeyers@madison.com, Pub., Daily Register,
WI, Portage

Meyers, Matt
mmeyers@capitalnewspapers.com, Gen. Mgr.,
Juneau County Star-Times, WI, Mauston

Meyers, Roy H.
rmeyers@mpival.com, Sr. Vice Pres.,
Management Planning, Inc., NJ, Princeton

Mezera, Cathy .... (304) 293-3505
catherine.mezera@mail.wvu.edu, Teaching
Assistant Professor, West Virginia University,
WV, Morgantown

Mezera, Chad .... (304) 293-5903
chad.mezera@mail.wvu.edu, Director of Online
Programs, West Virginia University, WV,
Morgantown

Mgrditchian, Khajag
hairenik@compuserve.com, Ed., Hairenik
Weekly, MA, Watertown

Micale, Anthony .... (781) 239-4229
Babson College, MA, Babson Park

Micco, Jerry .... (412) 263-3052
jmicco@post-gazette.com, Sr. Managing
Editor/NewsSlide, Pittsburgh Post-Gazette,
PA, Clinton

Micco, Lisa
lmicco@times online.com, Exec. Ed., Ellwood
City Ledger, PA, Ellwood City

Miceli, Karen
miltoned@haltonsearch.com, Ed., The Milton
Canadian Champion, ON, Milton

Michael, Branyon .... (770) 834-6631
pressroom@times-georgian.com, Press Mgr.,
Times-Georgian, GA, Carrollton

Michael, N/A .... Sports Ed.
Herald-Standard, PA, Uniontown

Michaels, Bruce
bmichaels@sportsnetwork.com, Dir., Technical
Opns., The Sports Network, PA, Hatboro

Michalski, Patty
pmichalski@usatoday.com, Editor in Chief,
USA TODAY, VA, Mc Lean

Michaud, Kimberly
kmichaud@tribune.com, Account Director,
Tribune 365, NY, New York

Micheli, Grace
info@elargentino.com, Adv. Mgr., El Argentino
Newspaper, FL, Miami

Michelich, Connie .... (217) 438-6155
southco@royell.org, Adv. Mgr., Pawnee Post,
IL, Auburn

Michelich, Connie
southco@royell.org, Adv. Mgr., South County
Publications, IL, Auburn

Michelich, Connie .... (217) 438-6155
southco@royell.org, Adv. Mgr., Pleasant Plains
Press, IL, Auburn

Michelich, Joseph
southco@royell.org, Pub., South County
Express, IL, Auburn

Michelich, Joseph .... (217) 438-6155
southco@royell.org, Pub., New Berlin Bee, IL,
Auburn

Michelich, Joseph M.
southco@royell.org, Ed., Pawnee Post, IL,
Auburn
southco@royell.org, Ed., Pleasant Plains
Press, IL, Auburn
southco@royell.org, Ed., Rochester Times,
IL, Auburn

Michelich, Joseph M.
southco@royell.org, Pub., South County
Publications, IL, Auburn

Michelle, Van Meter
class.antlers.amer@sbcglobal.net, Class/Legal
Clerk, Antlers American, OK, Antlers

Michner, Mike
mmischner@ci-camden.com, Pub., Kershaw
Co. Extra, SC, Camden

Mick-Evans, Allison
allison@the-press.com, Adv. Mgr., The
Crittenden Press, KY, Marion

Mickelow, Deanna
ads@valley-sentinel.com , Ad Sales, The Valley Sentinel, BC, Valemount

Mickelson, Joe
jmickelson@numberninemediainc.com, Pub, Valencia County News-Bulletin, NM, Belen

Mickelson, Marc
marc@newspubinc.com, Adv. Mgr., News-Sickle-Arrow, WI, Black Earth

Mickey, Kathy ....(203) 325-8193
kmickey@simbainformation.com, Mng. Ed., Simba Information, CT, Stamford

Micklow, James T..........(570) 387-1234 ext 1600
Treasurer, Press Enterprise, PA, Bloomsburg

Midani, Sarah ....+1 (518) 588-4603
s16mida@siena.edu, Editor-in-Chief, Siena College, NY, Loudonville

Middlebrook, Walter ....(313) 222-2429
wmiddlebrook@detroitnews.com, Asst. Managing Ed., I-Team , The Detroit News, MI, Detroit
wmiddlebrook@detroitnews.com, Asst. Managing Editor, Detroit Free Press, MI, Detroit

Middlemus, Jackie ....(941) 708-7733
The Telegraph, GA, Macon

Middleton, James
jasmiddleton@gmail.com, Ed., Boone County Journal, IL, Belvidere

Middleton, Kent
kentm@uga.edu, Prof./Head, Journalism Dept., University of Georgia, GA, Athens

Middleton, Marg ....(416) 774-2302
mmiddleton@insidetoronto.com, Gen. Mgr., The Scarborough Mirror, ON, Toronto

Middleton, Marg ....(416) 774-2302
mmiddleton@insidetoronto.com, Gen. Mgr., North York Mirror, ON, Toronto

Middleton, Marg
mmiddleton@mirror-guardian.com, Gen. Mgr., The East York Mirror, ON, Willowdale

Middleton, Nancy ....(403) 601-0015
nancy.middleton@sunmedia.ca, Pub, Pincher Creek Echo, AB, Pincher Creek

Middleton, Nancy
nancy@bowesnet.com, Pub., The Nanton News, AB, Nanton

Middleton, Nancy
nancy@highrivertimes.com, Pub., The High River Times, AB, High River

Middleton, Victoria
victoria@newcastlepacer.com, Mng. Ed., Early Bird Express, OK, Newcastle

Middleton, Victoria ....(405) 376-4571
vmiddleton@mustangnews.info, Ed, The Mustang News, OK, Mustang

Mider, Nick
nick.mider@richmond.edu, Univ. of Richmond, VA, Richmond

Midgorden, Sarah
smidgorden@themercury.com, Photographer, The Manhattan Mercury, KS, Manhattan

Midkiff, Tammy.......................(701) 377-2626
tribune@nccray.net, Reporter, Burke County Tribune, ND, Bowbells

Midstokke, Lisa
lmidstokke@ncppub.com, Cir. Mgr., Steele County Press, ND, Finley

Midyette, Dean..............(250) 341-6299 ext.107
publisher@invermerevalleyecho.com, Pub., Invermere Valley Echo, BC, Invermere
publisher@invermerevalleyecho.com, Pub., Advertising Sales, The Columbia Valley Pioneer, BC, Invermere

Mielcarek, Sandy
sandy@sturgisjournal.com, Prepress Mgr., Sturgis Journal, MI, Sturgis

Miele, Frank ....(406) 758-4447
edit@dailyinterlake.com, Managing Ed., Daily Inter Lake, MT, Kalispell

Mielke, Treena
editor@rimbeyreview.com, Ed, Rimbey Review, AB, Rimbey

Mienk, Jake...........................(903) 729-0281
jmienk@corsicanadailysun.com, Publisher, Palestine Herald-Press, TX, Palestine
jmienk@corsicanadailysun.com, Publisher , Corsicana Daily Sun, TX, Corsicana

Migneault, Daniel
daniel.migneault@transcontinental.ca, Ed. in Chief, L'etoile Du Lac, QC, Roberval

Miguel, Dawne
advmgr@mauinews.com, Adv. Mgr., Retail, The Maui News, HI, Wailuku

Mihaly, Tom
publisher@mrnews.ca, Pub./Mng. Ed., The Echo-pioneer, AB, High Level
publisher@mrnews.ca, Pub., The Mile Zero News, AB, High Level

Mihaly, Tom
publisher@mrnews.ca, Pub/Ed, Banner Post, AB, Grimshaw

Mihaly, Tom
echohl@mackreport.ab.ca, The Echo-pioneer, AB, High Level

Mike, Devon
mike.devon@resolutefp.com, VP, Sales-Southern Market, Resolute Forest Products, QC, Montreal

Mike, Frankel........................(408) 920-5746
mfrankel@bayareanewsgroup.com, Asst. Mng. Ed., Alameda Journal, CA, Alameda
mfrankel@bayareanewsgroup.com, Asst. Mng. Ed. – Reg., Piedmonter, CA, Alameda

Mikel, Emalee.......................(800) 592-7606
adv@taylornews.org, Adv. Dir., Labette Avenue, KS, Oswego

Mikells, Kathryn
Kathryn.Mikells@xerox.com, Corporate Executive Vice President
Chief Financial Officer , Xerox Corp., CT, Norwalk

Mikels, April
circulation@thenews-gazette.com, Circ. Mgr., The News-Gazette, VA, Lexington

Mikenas, Diane
diane@starcourier.com, Sales Mgr., Star-Courier, IL, Kewanee

Miko, Robert J.......................(203) 378-2803
bmiko@pacificdialogue.com, Ed., Miko's Pacific News Service, Solon

Mikolajczak, Joanna ....(972) 273-3057
jmikolajczak@dcccd.edu, Photography Editor, North Lake College, TX, Irving

Mikolajczyk, Mark
publisher@floridatoday.com, Florida Today, FL, Melbourne

Mikolajczyk, Mark ....(321) 242-3777
publisher@floridatoday.com, Pub., Missileer, FL, Melbourne

Mikoletic, Cheryl
ruralurban@windstream.net, Circ. Mgr., The Rural-Urban Record, OH, Columbia Station

Miksis, Lisa ....(203) 245-1877 ext. ext 6134
l.miksis@shorepublishing.com, Pub., Shore Publishing LLC, CT, Madison

Miksis, Lisa..................(203) 245-1877 ext 6134
miksis@shorepublishing.com, Pub., The Lyme Times, CT, New London
miksis@shorepublishing.com, Pub./Circ. Mgr., The Groton Times, CT, New London

Miksis, Lisa...........................(860) 701-4202
l.miksis@shorepublishing.com, Pub., The Montville Times, CT, New London
l.miksis@shorepublishing.com, Pub., The Thames River Times, CT, New London

l.miksis@shorepublishing.com, Pub./Ed., The Day, CT, New London

Miksis, Lisa...........................(860) 701-4202
l.miksis@shorepublishing.com, Pub., New London Times, CT, New London

Miksis, Lisa
l.miksis@shorepublishing.com, Pub., The Stonington Times, CT, New London

Miksis, Lisa...........................(860) 701-4202
l.miksis@shorepublishing.com, Pub., Waterford Times, CT, New London

Mikula, Jason
jason@mountaintimes.info, Sales Mgr., The Mountain Times, VT, Killington

Mikus, Kim ....(847) 287-9838
kmikus@dailyherald.com, Business Editor, Daily Herald Business Products, Daily Herald, IL, Arlington Heights

Milano, Tracy ....(509) 335-4573
tmilano@wsu.edu, Program Coord., Washington State University, Daily Evergreen, WA, Pullman

Milburn, Jodi
jmilburn@tcnewsnet.com, Ed., Centerville-Washington Times (OOB), OH, Xenia
jmilburn@tcnewsnet.com, Ed., Sugarcreek Bellbrook Times, OH, Xenia

Milburn, Sandra............(620) 694-5700 Ext. 360
smilburn@hutchnews.com, Photo Ed., The Hutchinson News, KS, Hutchinson

Miles, Duane ....(970) 522-1990
DMILES@JOURNAL-ADVOCATE.COM, Pre-press Mgr., Journal-Advocate, CO, Sterling

Miles, Elizabeth ....(330) 264-1125 Ext. 2224
bmiles@the-daily-record.com, Off. Mgr., The Daily Record, OH, Wooster

Miles, Gary ....(313) 222-2594
gmiles@detroitnews.com, Managing Ed., The Detroit News, MI, Detroit
gmiles@detroitnews.com, Deputy Managing Editor, Detroit Free Press, MI, Detroit

Miles, George A.
editor@holtindependent.com, Ed., Holt County Independent, NE, O' Neill

Miles, Jacqueline......................(850) 434-6963
jmiles@pensacolavoice.com, Ed., Pensacola Voice, FL, Pensacola

Miles, James T.
news@holtindependent.com, Publisher, Holt County Independent, NE, O' Neill

Miles, Jordan........................(434) 808-0622
jordan.miles@kenbridgevictoriadispatch.com, Mng. Ed., The Kenbridge-Victoria Dispatch, VA, Victoria

Miles, Joyce ....(716) 439-9222 Ext. 6238
joyce.miles@lockportjournal.com, Mng. Ed., Lockport Union-Sun & Journal, NY, Lockport

Miles, Mandy ....(330) 841-1600
mmiles@tribtoday.com, Ad Prod. Mgr., The Tribune Chronicle, OH, Warren

Miles, Rachel
remiles@presby.edu, Co-Editor, Presbyterian College, SC, Clinton

Milheiser, Pam
pmilheiser@gazetteextra.com, Sec., The Janesville Gazette - GazetteXtra, WI, Janesville

Milhoan, Denise ....(330) 364-8319
denise.milhoan@TimesReporter.com, Cir. Dir., The Times-Reporter, OH, New Philadelphia

Milici, Bob ....(732) 574-1200
bob@njtoday.net, Assc. Pub./Dir. Sales Ops., NJTODAY.NET, NJ, Rahway

Milks, Gary ....(530) 852-0250
garym@goldcountrymedia.com, Publisher, The Press-Tribune, CA, Roseville

Milks, Gary ....(928) 763-2505 ext. 2109
publisher@nwppub.com, Pub., Laughlin

Nevada Times, AZ, Bullhead City

Milks, Gary ....(928) 763-2505 Ext. 2109
publisher@nwpub.com, Publisher, Mohave Valley Daily News, AZ, Bullhead City
publisher@nwppub.com, Pub, Needles Desert Star, CA, Needles

Milks, Gary ....(928) 763-2505
publisher@nwppub.com, Pub., Bullhead City Booster, AZ, Bullhead City

Millan, Jamie
jmillan@islandernews.com, Art Dir., Islander News, FL, Key Biscayne

Millar, Lindsey ....(501) 375-2985 ext353
lindseymillar@arktimes.com, Editor, Arkansas Times, AR, Little Rock

Millar, Quin ....(416) 593-2035
qmillar@canwest.com, Dir., Newspaper Sales, TVtimes, ON, Toronto

Millard, Hal
halmillard@gmail.com, Metro Editor, Lexington County Chronicle & The Dispatch-News, SC, Lexington

Millard, Janet
janet@otzman.com, Belleville-Area Independent, MI, Belleville

Millen, Lainey
production@goqnotes.com, Prodn. Mgr., Q Notes, NC, Charlotte

Millener, George ....(707) 521-5244
gmillener@pressdemocrat.com, Sr. Ed., Presentation, The Press Democrat, CA, Santa Rosa

Miller, Alan
millerad@denison.edu, Denison Univ., OH, Granville

Miller, Alan ....(614) 461-5500
amiller@dispatch.com, Ed., The Columbus Dispatch, OH, Columbus

Miller, Amy
accounts@fairmontsentinel.com, Office Mgr., Sentinel, MN, Fairmont

Miller, Andrea ....ext. 100
info@metrokids.com, Circ. Mgr., Metrokids South Jersey, PA, Philadelphia

Miller, Andria
advertising@journalpilot.com, Adv. Dir., Hancock County Journal-Pilot, IL, Carthage

Miller, Angela
angela@merrittsearchgroup.com, Adv. Mgr., Ohio Jewish Chronicle, OH, Columbus

Miller, Angelina
angmariemiller@gmail.com, EIC, Cabrini University Loquitur, PA, Radnor

Miller, Angelina
angmariemiller@gmail.com, Ed., Cabrini University Loquitur, PA, Radnor

Miller, Anita ....(512) 392-2458
amiller@sanmarcosrecord.com, News Ed., San Marcos Daily Record, TX, San Marcos

Miller, Ashley...........................(316) 283-1500
amiller@mphersonsentinel.com, Prod. Mgr., McPherson Sentinel, KS, McPherson

Miller, Audrey
audrey_miller@dailyjournal.com, Adv. Dir., The Los Angeles Daily Journal, CA, Los Angeles

Miller, Beckham
b.miller@carrollspaper.com, Prodn. Mgr., Times Herald Advertiser, IA, Carroll

Miller, Beth
bmiller@flexco.com, Pdct. Mgr., Clipper Belt Lacer Co., IL, Downers Grove

Miller, Betsy ....(843) 937-5576
bmiller@postandcourier.com, News Prod. Ed., The Post and Courier, SC, Charleston

Miller, Bill
billmiller@emissourian.com, Ed., Washington Missourian, MO, Washington

Miller, Bill..............................(214) 361-2276
bill.miller@flintgrp.com, Pres., North Amer.,
Flint Group, MI, Plymouth

Miller, Bill..............................(905) 645-2086
bmiller@quickwire.com, Gen. Mgr., Quickwire
Labs, MB, Winnipeg

Miller, Bob..............................(573) 388-3625
bmiller@semissourian.com, Ed., Southeast
Missourian, MO, Cape Girardeau

Miller, Bob..............................(610) 377-2051
bmiller@tnonline.com, Dir. of Pre-Press
Operations, Times News, PA, Lehighton

Miller, Brian............................(814) 425-7272
Prodn. Mgr., Area Shopper, PA, Cochranton

Miller, Bruce
bmiller@siouxcityjournal.com, Music Ed., Sioux
City Journal, IA, Sioux City

Miller, Chuck ....(937) 393-3456 Ext. 1672
cmiller@civitasmedia.com, Med. Sales Cons. ,
Hillsboro Times-Gazette, OH, Hillsboro

Miller, Crystal
chrystal.miller@albertleatribune.com, Adv.
Mgr., Tribune Shopping News, MN, Albert
Lea

Miller, Crystal ....(507) 379-3420
crystal.miller@albertleatribune.com, Pub.,
Albert Lea Tribune, MN, Albert Lea

Miller, Curt..............................(949) 451-9050
curt.miller@theaustin.com, Gen. Mgr., The
Austin Company, OH, Cleveland

Miller, Cynthia..........................(505) 986-3095
cmiller@sfnewmexican.com, News Ed./Copy
Chief, The Santa Fe New Mexican, NM,
Santa Fe

Miller, Cynthia.............(260) 347-0400 Ext. 1137
cmiller@kpcmedia.com, Acct. Exec., The News
Sun, IN, Kendallville

Miller, Darice...........................(443) 524-8141
ddixon@thedailyrecord.com, Acc. Mgr., The
Daily Record, MD, Baltimore

Miller, Darlene
dmiller@pontiacdailyleader.com, Creative
Designer, Livingston Shopping News, IL,
Pontiac

Miller, Dave..............................(231) 933-1441
dmiller@record-eagle.com, Editorial Page Ed.,
Traverse City Record-Eagle, MI, Traverse City

Miller, Dave
dmiller@claritas.com, Sr. VP, Claritas, CA,
San Diego

Miller, David............................(646) 736-3618
dmiller@davlermedia.com, CEO, NY Metro
Parents, NY, New York

Miller, David............................(580) 765-3311
sports@poncacitynews.com, Sports reporter,
The Ponca City News, OK, Ponca City

Miller, David
dmiller@ourweekly.com, Advertising Manager,
Our Weekly, CA, Los Angeles

Miller, David............................(254) 501-7543
Asst. Mng. Ed., Killeen Daily Herald, TX, Killeen

Miller, David
info@davlermedia.com, Pub., Westchester
Parent, NY, Briarcliff Manor

Miller, David
dave@diggernews.com, Publisher, The Digger
& Shopper News, CA, Oroville

Miller, David.......................(618) 374-4415
Principia College, IL, Elsah

Miller, Debbie
dmiller@cullmantimes.com, Classifieds, The
Cullman Times, AL, Cullman

Miller, Dendra ....(304) 462-7309
News Ed., The Glenville Pathfinder, WV,
Glenville

Miller, Dennis
dpmiller54@yahoo.com, Prodn. Mgr., The

Salem Leader, IN, Salem

Miller, Dennis
dennis.w.miller@das.state.or.us, Prodn. Mgr.,
Your Advantage, IN, Salem

Miller, Dennis ....(812) 883-3281
dpmiller54@gmail.com, Production Manager,
The Salem Democrat, IN, Salem

Miller, Don..............................(831) 706-3265
dmiller@santacruzsentinel.com, Ed., Santa
Cruz Sentinel, CA, Scotts Valley

Miller, Donald
news@miamivalleynewspapers.com, Pub./
Adv. Mgr., The Germantown Press, OH,
Miamisburg

Miller, Donna ....(507) 829-1040
Accounting, Balaton Press Tribune, MN,
Balaton

Miller, Doris
dmiller@mycarrollnews.com, Office Mgr., River
City Trading Post, KY, Carrollton

Miller, Eric..............................(616) 384-3567
ebmiller@mtcngroup.com, Ed., Robertson
County Times, TN, Clarksville

Miller, Fanny
fanny@ellatino.net, Pub./Pres., El Latino, CA,
Chula Vista

Miller, Fort..............................(815) 220-6952
FMILLER@NEWSTRIB.COM, Mailroom Mgr.,
Illinois Valley Shopper, IL, La Salle

Miller, Gary
gary.miller@tangilena.com, Pub, St. Helena
Echo, LA, Greensburg

Miller, Gary
gary.miller@tangilena.com, Pub, The Zachary
Plainsman-News, LA, Baton Rouge

Miller, Gary
gm@lawndalenews.com, Adv. Mgr., The
Lawndale News/Su Noticiero Bilingue, IL,
Cicero

Miller, George
george@lansultants.com, Asst. Prof., Temple
University, PA, Philadelphia

Miller, Gina
rmiller@civitasmedia.com, Adv. Mgr., Ottawa
County Exponent, OH, Bellevue

Miller, Grant ....(305) 669-7355
grant@communitynewspapers.com, Pres./Pub.,
Miller Publishing, FL, South Miami

Miller, Grant ....(305) 669-7355
grant@communitynewspapers.com, Co-Pub.,
Kendall Gazette, FL, South Miami

Miller, Grant ....(305) 669-7355
grant@communitynewspapers.com, Pub.,
Miami's Community Newspapers, FL, South
Miami

Miller, Grant ....(305) 669-7355
michael@communitynewspapers.com, Co-
Pub., South Miami News, FL, South Miami

Miller, Grant ....(305) 669-7355
grant@communitynewspapers.com, Co-Pub,
Palmetto Bay News, FL, South Miami

Miller, Heather
hmiller@lfs.com, Adv. Mgr., RotoVue, NC,
Jacksonville

Miller, Jackie ....(410) 732-6600 ext 1
jmiller@baltimoreguide.com, Office Mgr.,
Baltimore Guide South, MD, Baltimore

Miller, Jaimi
jaimi.miller@nonpareilonline.com, Adv. Mgr.,
Classified, The Daily Nonpareil, IA, Council
Bluffs

Miller, James.........................(770) 795-8556
jimmym@pamarcoglobal.com, Vice Pres., Mfg.,
Pamarco Global Graphics, GA, Marietta

Miller, Jason
jmiller@perhamfocus.com, Publisher, Perham
Focus, MN, Perham

Miller, Jay

jamiller@smu.edu, Exec. Dir./Editorial Advisor,
Southern Methodist Univ., TX, Dallas

Miller, Jay K.
jmiller@ursinus.edu, Chair, Ursinus College,
PA, Collegeville

Miller, Jayne.................... (978) 658-2346 x100
Jayne@yourtowncrier.com, News Editor, Town
Crier, MA, Woburn

Miller, Jean Ann .... (217) 732-2101 ext. 333
jeanann.miller@lincolncourier.com, Mng. Ed.,
Lincoln Courier, IL, Lincoln

Miller, Jeannette
electrastarnews@electratel.net, Ed., Electra
Star-News, TX, Electra

Miller, Jefferey ....(714) 796-7866
jsmiller@ocregister.com, Feat., Asst. Managing
Ed., The Orange County Register, CA, Santa
Ana

Miller, Jeffrey ....(605) 274-5431
miller@augie.edu, Advisor, Augustana
University, SD, Sioux Falls

Miller, Jen ....(617) 619-6495
jennifer.miller@bostonherald.com, Exec. City
Ed., Boston Herald, MA, Boston

Miller, Jim
jemiller@harding.edu, Asst. Prof., Harding
University, AR, Searcy

Miller, Joanna
jmiller@moorparkcollege.edu, Moorpark
College, CA, Moorpark

Miller, Jodie
jodie@ojaivalleynews.com, Gen. Mgr., Ojai
Valley Shopper, CA, Ojai

Miller, Jody
jody@houstonvoice.org, Political Editor,
Houston Voice, TX, Houston

Miller, Joe
jmiller@aamva.org, Circ. Mgr., Arlington
Catholic Herald, VA, Arlington

Miller, John..............................(304) 626-1473
Jmiller@theet.com, Executive Editor, The
Exponent Telegram, WV, Clarksburg

Miller, John
telegraf@atlantic.net, Mng. Ed., Union County
Times, FL, Starke

Miller, John..............................(828) 304-6909
jmiller@hickoryrecord.com, Mng. Ed. , Pow,
NC, Hickory

jmiller@hickoryrecord.com, Mng. Ed. , The
Hickory Daily Record, NC, Hickory

Miller, John
editor@bctelegraph.com, Pub., Bradford
County Telegraph, FL, Starke

Miller, Jolene.........................(308) 697-3326
clarion@cambridgeclarion.com, Oxford
Standard, NE, Oxford

clarion@cambridgeclarion.com, Ed.,
Cambridge Clarion, NE, Cambridge

Miller, Joseph
millerj@buffalostate.edu, Sales Dir., Voice
Technologies Group, Inc., NY, Getzville

Miller, Joyce
joyce.miller@lakesunonline.com, Ed. Dir., Lake
Sun Leader, MO, Camdenton

Miller, Judy
editor@fostoriafocus.com, Pub., The Fostoria
Focus, OH, Fostoria

Miller, Julie
edgewood.reminder@yahoo.com, Owner/Ed.,
Edgewood Reminder, IA, Edgewood

Miller, Justin ....(937) 652-1331
jmiller@civitasmedia.com, Ed., The
Mechanicsburg Telegram, OH, Urbana

Miller, Katherine
katherine@athensnews-courier.com, Gen.
Mgr., The News-Courier, AL, Athens

Miller, Kathy

krmiller@ottowaherald.com, Data Processing
Mgr., The Ottawa Herald, KS, Ottawa

Miller, Kathy ....(269) 781-5444
kathymiller@jasnetworks.net, Adv., Ad-Visor
and Chronicle, MI, Marshall

Miller, Kelly..............................(304) 788-3333
kmiller@newstribune.info, Pub., Today's
Shopper, WV, Keyser

Miller, Kelly..............................(304) 367-2503
kmiller@timeswv.com, Publisher, Times West
Virginian, WV, Fairmont

Miller, Kelly.................. (304) 788-3333 ext. 116
kmiller@newstribune.info, Pub, Mineral Daily
News-Tribune, WV, Keyser

Miller, Kenneth
kmiller@thehamiltonherald-news.com, Pub./
Ed./Adv. Dir., Hamilton Herald-News, TX,
Hamilton

Miller, Kimberly
kmiller@buckeyeranch.org, Grove City College,
PA, Grove City

Miller, Larry
pjch@fuddenlinkmail.com, Ed., Conway County
Petit Jean Country Headlight, AR, Morrilton

Miller, Larry ....(803) 774-1277
lmiller@theitem.com, CEO, The Sumter Item ,
SC, Sumter

Miller, Lary
pjch@suddenlinkmail.com, Ed., Perry County
Petit Jean Country Headlight, AR, Morrilton

Miller, Leslie
lmiller@coastalcourier.com, Prodn. Mgr., The
Coastal Courier, GA, Hinesville

Miller, Leslie
lmiller@coastalcourier.com, Prodn. Mgr., Tri-
county Pennysaver, GA, Hinesville

Miller, Lisa..............................(603) 862-0251
lc.miller@unh.edu, Dir., University of New
Hampshire, NH, Durham

Miller, Lisa
lmiller@ncppub.com, Pub., The Extra, IA,
Charles City

lmiller@ncppub.com, Gen. Mgr., Lyon County
Reporter, IA, Rock Rapids

lmiller@ncppub.com, Pub., The FM Extra, MN,
Moorhead

lmiller@ncppub.com, Gen. Mgr., The Northwest
Iowa Extra, IA, Rock Rapids

Miller, Lisa
lmiller@thechronicle.ms, Circ. Mgr., The Laurel
Chronicle, MS, Laurel

Miller, Lisa..............................(712) 472-3846
lmiller@ncppub.com, General Manager, New
Century Press, IA, Rock Rapids

Miller, Liza..............................(814) 765-7813
news@theprogressnews.com, Assistant Editor,
The Progress, PA, Clearfield

Miller, Lowell
ccullen@dailyprogress.com, Regional Adv. Dir.
, The Daily Progress, VA, Charlottesville

Miller, Mark
email@news-banner.com, Ed., The Ossian
Journal, IN, Ossian

Miller, Mark..............................(254) 501-7563
markm@kdhnews.com, Sports Ed., Killeen
Daily Herald, TX, Killeen

Miller, Mark F..........................(260) 824-0224
miller@news-banner.com, Vice President,
Opinion Page Editor, News-Banner, IN,
Bluffton

Miller, Marsha.........................(580) 221-6529
marsha.miller@ardmoreite.com, News Ed., The
Ardmoreite, OK, Ardmore

Miller, Mary ....(417) 837-1353
mfmiller@news-leader.com, Prodn. Mgr.,
Distr. Ctr., Springfield News-Leader, MO,
Springfield

Miller, Matt ....(707) 453-8148

rmiller@thereporter.com, Managing Ed., The Reporter, CA, Vacaville

Miller, Matt ....(707) 553-6811
mattmiller@bayareanewsgroup.com , Adv. Dir., Vallejo Times-Herald, CA, Vallejo

Miller, Matt ....(724) 225-2073
mtmiller@observer-reporter.com, Adv. Dir., Observer-Reporter, PA, Washington

Miller, Maureen
mkmiller@cnhi.com, Pub., Pella Chronicle, IA, Pella

Miller, Maureen
publisher@journalexpress.net, Pub., The Knoxville Journal-Express, IA, Knoxville

Miller, Meghan.................(317) 444-4000
meghan.miller@indystar.com, V.P. / Finance, The Indianapolis Star, IN, Indianapolis

Miller, Melanie
ayork@the-messenger.com, Bus. Office, The Messenger, KY, Madisonville

Miller, Melissa ....(270) 783-3204
melissm@bgsu.edu, Office Mgr., Daily News, KY, Bowling Green

Miller, Michael ....(305) 669-7030
michaelmiller@communitynewspapers.com, Ed., Miami's Community Newspapers, FL, South Miami

Miller, Michael ....(305) 669-7355 Ext. 249
michael@communitynewspapers.com, Co-Pub., Kendall Gazette, FL, South Miami
michael@communitynewspapers.com, Co-Pub., South Miami News, FL, South Miami

Miller, Michael ....(305) 669-7030
michaelmiller@communitynewspapers.com, Ed., Miller Publishing, FL, South Miami

Miller, Michael
michaelm@menznerhardwoods.com, Adv Director, The Newton County Appeal, MS, Union

Miller, Michael
millerm@hsu.edu, Chair, Henderson State University, AR, Arkadelphia

Miller, Michael ....(305) 669-7355 Ext. 249
michael@communitynewspapers.com, Co-Pub., Palmetto Bay News, FL, South Miami

Miller, Michael H ....(662) 720-7421
mhmiller@nemcc.edu, Advisor, Northeast Mississippi Community College, MS, Booneville

Miller, Michele...............(716) 836-3486
michele@wnyfamilymagazine.com, Editor & Publisher, Western New York Family, NY, Buffalo

Miller, Mike
cirdir@newstrib.com, Circ. Dir., News-Tribune, IL, La Salle

Miller, Mike
mmiller@starlocalnews.com, Group Pub., Lewisville Leader, TX, Plano
mmiller@starlocalnews.com, Group Pub., McKinney Courier-Gazette, TX, Plano
mmiller@starlocalnews.com, Group Pub., Sunnyvale View, TX, Plano
mmiller@starlocalnews.com, Group Pub., Carrollton Leader, TX, Plano
mmiller@starlocalnews.com, Group Pub., Coppell Gazette, TX, Plano
mmiller@starlocalnews.com, Group Pub., Flower Mound Leader, TX, Plano
mmiller@starlocalnews.com, Group Pub., The Colony Courier Leader, TX, Plano
mmiller@starlocalnews.com, Group Pub., Plano Star-Courier, TX, Plano
mmiller@starlocalnews.com, Group Pub., Allen American, TX, Plano
mmiller@starlocalnews.com, Group Pub., Rowlett Lakeshore Times, TX, Plano
mmiller@starlocalnews.com, Group Pub., Mesquite News, TX, Plano
mmiller@starlocalnews.com, Group Pub., Celina Record, TX, Plano

mmiller@starlocalnews.com, Group Pub., Little Elm Journal, TX, Plano
mmiller@starlocalnews.com, Group Pub., Frisco Enterprise, TX, Plano
mmiller@starlocalnews.com, Pub., Lake Cities Sun, TX, Plano

Miller, Mike...........................(815) 220-6970
cirdir@newstrib.com, Circ. Mgr., Illinois Valley Shopper, IL, La Salle

Miller, Missy.....................(303) 954-2746
mmiller@denverpost.com, Senior VP Pres., HR, Labor Relations, The Denver Post, CO, Denver

Miller, Morgan ....(863) 386-5810
cmiller@highlandstoday.com, Highlands News-Sun, FL, Sebring

Miller, Nate
miller@greeleytrib.com, Sports Ed., Greeley Daily Tribune, CO, Greeley

Miller, Pam
pmiller@acnpapers.com, Adv. Mgr., Minnetonka/Deephaven/Hopkins Sun Sailor, MN, Eden Prairie

Miller, Pam ....(952) 392-6862
pmiller@acnpapers.com, Class. Adv. Mgr., Robbinsdale/Crystal/New Hope/Golden Valley Sun-Post, MN, Eden Prairie

Miller, Pam
pmiller@acnpapers.com, Adv. Mgr., Edina Sun-Current, MN, Eden Prairie

Miller, Pam ....(928) 634-2241 x 6019
pmiller@westernnews.com, Pub., Camp Verde Bugle, AZ, Camp Verde
pmiller@westernnews.com, Publisher, Kudos, AZ, Cottonwood
pmiller@westernnews.com, Publisher, Smart Shopper, AZ, Cottonwood
pmiller@westernnews.com, Adv. Mgr., Blaine/Spring Lake Park Sun Focus, MN, Eden Prairie

Miller, Pam
pam.miller@ecm-inc.com, Class. Adv. Mgr., Excelsior/Shorewood/Chanhassen Sun Sailor, MN, Eden Prairie

Miller, Patricia ....(317) 444-7189
patricia.miller@indystar.com, President, Gannett Indiana, The Indianapolis Star, IN, Indianapolis

Miller, Patricia ....(314) 421-8326
tmiller@bizjournals.com, Ed., St. Louis Business Journal, MO, Saint Louis

Miller, Paul
pmiller@keenesentinel.com, Executive Editor, The Keene Sentinel, NH, Keene

Miller, Paul A...............(603) 352-1234 ext. 1401
pmiller@keenesentinel.com, Exec. Ed., The Keene Sentinel, NH, Keene

Miller, Phil
pmiller@usspi.com, CEO, USSPI Media, IL, Schaumburg

Miller, Philip......................(616) 662-6420
pmiller@usspi.com, CEO, McNaughton Newspapers, IL, Schaumburg

Miller, Rachel
news@brunswick-nc.net, Ed., Brunswick County News, NC, Shallotte

Miller, Randy ....(717) 273-8127
randym@themerchandiser.com, General Sales Manager, Kapp Advertising Service, Inc., PA, Lebanon

Miller, Randy
randymiller@usf.edu, Assoc. Prof./Head, Journalism seq., University of South Florida, FL, Tampa

Miller, Randy
randym@aboutfamiliespa.com, Sales Manager, Merchandiser, PA, Lebanon

Miller, Randy
rmiller@thehawkeye.com, News Ed., The Hawk Eye, IA, Burlington

Miller, Randy
miller.randy@mac.com, Pres., Times Media Group, NV, Reno

Miller, Rich ....(407) 420-5706
rmiller@oriontechnologies.com, Adv. Mgr., Bus., Orlando Sentinel, FL, Orlando

Miller, Richard
rmiller@romecitygov.com, Community Ed., Daily Sentinel, NY, Rome

Miller, Richard ....(509) 335-5138
millerr@wsu.edu, Dir of Student Media, Washington State University, Daily Evergreen, WA, Pullman

Miller, Rick
rmiller@civitasmedia.com, Ed., Ottawa County Exponent, OH, Bellevue

Miller, Robert
rmiller@semissourian.com, Ed., Southeast Missourian Plus, MO, Cape Girardeau

Miller, Robert........................(330) 364-8321
robert.miller@TimesReporter.com, Adv. Dir., The Tribune Star, IN, Terre Haute
robert.miller@TimesReporter.com, Adv. Mgr., The Times-Reporter, OH, New Philadelphia

Miller, Robin
rmiller@thefranklinnewspost.com, Classifeids, The Franklin News-Post, VA, Rocky Mount

Miller, Robin.................(863) 583-1202 ext 355
rmiller@sunpubfla.com, Commercial Print Manager, Sun Publications of Fla., FL, Lakeland

Miller, Rudy.................(610) 258-7171 ext. 3612
rmiller@express-times.com, Lehigh Valley Editor, The Express-Times, PA, Easton

Miller, Ruth
ruth.miller@globegazette.com, Mktg. Mgr., Globe Gazette, Mason City, IA, Mason City

Miller, Ryan
rmiller@etnainteractive.com, Exec Ed., New Times, CA, San Luis Obispo
rmiller@etnainteractive.com, Exec Ed., The Santa Maria Sun, CA, Santa Maria

Miller, Sandra
jdn_subscribe@bellsouth.net, Circ. Mgr., Jennings (LA) Daily News, LA, Jennings

Miller, Sarah
sarah.miller@wustl.edu, St. Louis Post-Dispatch, MO, Saint Louis

Miller, Scott.........................(970) 748-2930
smiller@vaildaily.com, Bus. Ed., Vail Daily, CO, Avon

Miller, Scott
webmaster@yorkdispatch.com, Mgmt. Info Servs./Online Mgr., The York Dispatch, PA, York

Miller, Shan.................(220) 244-3400 ext. 1291
shan.miller@gaflnews.com, Business Mgr., Valdosta Daily Times, GA, Valdosta

Miller, Shane
smiller@queensledger.com, Ed., Queens Ledger, NY, Maspeth

Miller, Sheena
lzeilstra@oquawka-current.com, Adv. Dir., Oquawka Current, IL, Oquawka

Miller, Shawn..........................(707) 427-6958
News Ed., Daily Republic, CA, Fairfield

Miller, Steve ....(530) 749-4767
smiller@appealdemocrat.com, Ed., Colusa County Sun-Herald, CA, Marysville
smiller@appealdemocrat.com, Ed., Corning Observer, CA, Marysville
smiller@appealdemocrat.com, Editor, Appeal Democrat, CA, Marysville

Miller, Susan ....(305) 283-9335
susan@communitynewspapers.com, Sales, Palmetto Bay News, FL, South Miami
susan@communitynewspapers.com, Sales, Kendall Gazette, FL, South Miami
susan@communitynewspapers.com, Sales,

South Miami News, FL, South Miami

Miller, Susan ....(725) 775-3200 ext. 119
smiller@timesonline.com, Exec. Sec., Beaver County Times, PA, Beaver

Miller, Terry
news@ketchikandailynews.com, Mng. Ed., Ketchikan Daily News, AK, Ketchikan

Miller, Thaddeus............(209) 826-3831 ext. 562
tmiller@losbanosenterprise.com, Reporter, Los Banos Enterprise, CA, Los Banos

Miller, Thomas
thomas.miller@sunmedia.ca, CARDonline(10/31/14), The Stony Plain Reporter, AB, Spruce Grove

Miller, Tim ....(937) 642-6397
Marysville Journal-Tribune, OH, Marysville

Miller, Tom............................(509) 313-6748
Advisor, Gonzaga University, WA, Spokane

Miller, Tony
tmiller@thehawkeye.com, Prodn. Mgr., Systems, The Hawk Eye, IA, Burlington

Miller, Tony
tmiller@thehawkeye.com, Systems Mgr., Hawk Eye Shopper, IA, Burlington

Miller, Trina
trina.miller@austindailyherald.com, Home Delivery Mgr., Austin Daily Herald, MN, Austin

Miller, Tyler............................(406) 447-4002
tyler.miller@mtstandard.com, Publisher, The Montana Standard, MT, Butte

Miller, Victor
victormiller@daltoncitizen.com, Online Mgr., The Daily Citizen, GA, Dalton

Miller, Warren
warren@telecompute.com, Pres., Telecompute Corp., DC, Washington

Miller, Wendy ....(480) 982-7799
qcnews@newszap.com, Ed., Queen Creek Independent, AZ, Apache Junction

Miller, William L.
bmillerjr@emissourian.com, Pub., Warren County Record, MO, Warrenton

Miller, William L.
billmillerjr@emissourian.com, Gen. Mgr., Washington Missourian/missourian Publishing Co, MO, Washington

Miller, Yawu
yawu@bannerpub.com, Bay State Banner, MA, Dorchester

Miller , Ric............................(419) 609-5892
ricmiller@sanduskyregister.com, Foreman, Sandusky Register, OH, Sandusky

Miller Cressman, Scott ......(519) 662-1082 ext. 31
editor@newhamburgindependent.ca, Ed, New Hamburg Independent, ON, New Hamburg
editor@newhamburgindependent.ca, Metroland Media Group Ltd., ON, Mississauga

Miller III, William
williameomiller@aol.com, Assoc. Pub., Tennessee Tribune, TN, Nashville

Miller Warden, Susan.................(636) 390-3041
millers@emissourian.com, Asst. Mgr Ed, Washington Missourian, MO, Washington

Miller-Carl, Michelle ....(530) 852-0235
michellem@goldcountrymedia.com, Auburn Journal, CA, Auburn

Miller-Fergerson, Brenda............(281) 378-1950
bmiller-fergerson@hcnonline.com, Pub., Atascocita Observer, TX, Conroe
bmiller-fergerson@hcnonline.com, Pub, Deer Park Broadcaster, TX, Webster
bmiller-fergerson@hcnonline.com, Pub., Bay Area Citizen, TX, Webster
bmiller-fergerson@hcnonline.com, Pub., Cleveland Advocate, TX, Conroe
bmiller-fergerson@hcnonline.com, Pub.,

Dayton News, TX, Conroe
bmiller-fergerson@hcnonline.com, Pub., East
Montgomery County Observer, TX, Humble
bmiller-fergerson@hcnonline.com, Pub.,
Eastex Advocate, TX, Cleveland
bmiller-fergerson@hcnonline.com, Pub.,
Friendswood Journal, TX, Conroe
bmiller-fergerson@hcnonline.com, Pub.,
Humble Observer, TX, Conroe
bmiller-fergerson@hcnonline.com, Pub.,
Kingwood Observer, TX, Conroe
bmiller-fergerson@hcnonline.com, Pub., Lake
Houston Observer, TX, Conroe
bmiller-fergerson@hcnonline.com, Pub.,
Pasadena Citizen, TX, Webster
bmiller-fergerson@hcnonline.com, Pub.,
Pearland Journal, TX, Conroe
bmiller-fergerson@hcnonline.com, Pub., The
Courier of Montgomery County, TX, Conroe
bmiller-fergerson@hcnonline.com, Hearst
Communications, Inc., NY, New York

Millerjames, James .... (250) 470-0741
james.millerjames@pentictonhead.ca, Mng.
Ed., Penticton Herald, BC, Penticton

Millett, Jennifer .... (913) 647-0934
jmillet@familyfeatures.com, Media Manager,
Family Features Editorial Syndicate, Inc.,
KS, Mission

Millett, Kristeen .... (360) 735-4472
kristeen.millett@columbian.com, Digital
Marketing Manager, The Columbian, WA,
Vancouver

Millette, Lise .... (514) 985-3324
lmillette@ledevoir.com, VP, Adv. Sales, Le
Devoir, QC, Montreal

Millican, Mark .... (706) 635-4313
markmillican@timescourier.com, News Ed.,
Times-Courier, GA, Ellijay

Milligan, Adam
amilligan@mykawartha.com, Adv. Mgr.,
Peterborough This Week, ON, Peterborough

Milligan, Barbara
barbaramilligan@whiteville.com, The News
Reporter, NC, Whiteville

Milligan, Benjie
bmilligan@theeasleyprogress.com, Grp. Pub.,
Easley Publications, SC, Easley

Milliken, Maureen .... (207) 621-5732
mmilliken@centralmaine.com, News Ed.,
Kennebec Journal, ME, Augusta
mmilliken@centralmaine.com, News Ed.,
Morning Sentinel, ME, Waterville

Millikin, David
david.millikin@afp.com, Executive Director
North America, Agence France-Presse -
Washington, DC, Washington

Milliman, Dirk
publisher@threeriversnews.com, Pub., Three
Rivers Commercial-News, MI, Three Rivers

Milliman, Richard L. .... (269) 279-7488
publisher@threeriversnews.com, Pub., Penny
Saver, MI, Three Rivers

Milliman, Theresa
theresa.milliman@vermiliontoday.com,
Business Mgr., Abbeville Meridional, LA,
Abbeville

Milling, Matt
mmilling@tylerpaper.com, Prod. & Dist. Dir. ,
Tyler Morning Telegraph, TX, Tyler

Milliren, Patrick
patrick@media-md.net, Adv. Mng., Tri-County
News, WI, Mondovi

Millman, Stephanie
mktg@maxcessintl.com, Dir., Mktg./Sales,
Maxcess, OK, Oklahoma City

Millrood, Gary
sales@click2learn.com, Vice Pres., Worldwide
Sales/Alliances, Sumtotal System Inc., WA,
Bellevue

Mills, Belinda
bmills@ivpressonline.com, Pub., Imperial

Valley Press, CA, El Centro

Mills, Carrie .... (615) 354-1699
carrie@nashvillejcc.org, Adv. Mgr., The Jewish
Observer, TN, Nashville

Mills, Carson
carsonm@bowesnet.com, Ed., The Grove
Examiner, AB, Spruce Grove

Mills, Carson
carsonm@bowesnet.com, Ed., The Stony Plain
Reporter, AB, Spruce Grove

Mills, Karlene
kmills@sooeveningnews.com, Sales Manager,
Sault Ste. Marie Evening News, MI, Sault
Sainte Marie

Mills, Kevin
kevin.mills@missioncityrecord.com, Ed,
Mission City Record, BC, Mission

Mills, Kris
sports@thehj.com, Sports Ed., Herald Journal,
IN, Monticello

Mills, LaVale
rbaynews@gmail.com, Publisher Emeritus, The
Red Bay News, AL, Red Bay

Mills, Mark
mlmills@stcloudstate.edu, Prof., St. Cloud
State University, MN, Saint Cloud

Mills, Mike .... (202) 650-6535
mikemills@cqrollcall.com, Editorial Director,
Congressional Quarterly, Inc., DC,
Washington

Mills, Rick .... (989) 779-6003
rmills@michigannewspapers.com, Exec. Ed.,
Northern Michigan Real Estate Marketplace,
MI, Mount Pleasant

Mills, Rick .... (989) 779-6003
rmills@michigannewspapers.com, Ed.,
Morning Sun, MI, Alma

Mills, Susan
ads@carlislemosquito.org, Adv. Mgr., Carlisle
Mosquito, MA, Carlisle

Millsap, Mark .... (405) 366-3590
publisher@normantranscript.com, Pub, Moore
American, OK, Norman

Millsap, Susan
smillsap@otterbein.edu, Chair, Otterbein
College, OH, Westerville

Millsaps, Eric
emillsaps@statesville.com, Statesville Record
& Landmark, NC, Statesville

Millsaps, Eric .... ext. 388
emillsaps@hickoryrecord.com, Pub., Pow, NC,
Hickory

Millsaps, Tommy
editor@advocateanddemocrat.com, Ed., The
Advocate & Democrat, TN, Sweetwater

Millspaugh, Jaye
jaye.millspaugh.2@my.und.edu, Multimedia
Editor, Univ. of North Dakota, ND, Grand
Forks

Milne, Judy .... (219) 933-4178
judy.milne@nwi.com, Dir. Finance, The Times
of Northwest Indiana, IN, Munster

Milner, Martha .... (334) 644-5587
Classified Manager, The Valley Times-News,
AL, Lanett

Milner, Michelle .... (918) 273-2446
nowatastar@sbcglobal.net, Advertising rep,
The Nowata Star, OK, Nowata
nowatastar@sbcglobal.net, Adv., The Vinita
Daily Journal, OK, Vinita

Milo, Miller .... (330) 852-4634
mmiller@thebudgetnewspaper.com, Adv. Dir.,
The Budget, OH, Sugarcreek

Milochnikov, Michael
kurier@optonline.net, Gen. Mgr., Kurier, NY,
Brooklyn

Milone, Steve .... (978) 946-2200

smilone@eagletribune.com, Circ. Dir., The
Eagle-Tribune, MA, North Andover

Milone, Steve .... (978) 946-2350
smilone@eagletribune.com, Circ. Dir., The
Haverhill Gazette, MA, North Andover

Milone, Steve
smilone@eagletribune.com, Circ. Mgr., Derry
News, NH, Derry

Milstead, Leta .... (256) 740-5773
leta.milstead@timesdaily.com, Office Mgr,
Times Daily, AL, Florence

Milt, Victor .... (561) 483-7734
vicmilt@victormilt.com, Creative Dir.,
interActive Publishing Corp., FL, Boca Raton

Milton, Patsy .... (785) 295-1294
patsy.milton@cjonline.com, Front Desk Clerk,
The Topeka Capital-Journal, KS, Topeka

Milton, Paul
pmilton@tribune.com, Executive Editor,
Patuxent Publishing Co., MD, Columbia
pmilton@tribune.com, Exec. Ed., Baltimore
Messenger-OOB, MD, BALTIMORE
pmilton@tribune.com, The Carroll Eagle, MD,
Baltimore

Milton, Paul
pmilton@patuxent.com, Exec. Ed., Maryland
Family Magazine, MD, Towson

Milton, Tanya
tanya@savannahtribune.com, Adv. Mgr., The
Savannah Tribune, GA, Savannah

Milwit, Lily .... (504) 865-5657
lmilwit@tulane.edu, Editor In-Chief, Tulane
University, LA, New Orleans

Mims, Bruce
bmims@semo.edu, Prof., Southeast Missouri
State University, MO, Cape Girardeau

Mims, Jerry
jmims@laurinburgexchange.com, Circ. Mgr.,
Community News Advertiser, NC, Laurinburg

Mims, Scott .... ext. 28
scott.mims@clantonadvertiser.com, Mailroom
mgr, The Clanton Advertiser, AL, Clanton

Mindus, Angie
editor@wltribune.com, Ed, The Williams Lake
Tribune, BC, Williams Lake

Minelli, Pat .... (952) 345-6680
editor@shakopeenews.com, Ed., Shakopee
Valley News, MN, Savage

Mineroff, Samantha
quadeic@wcupa.edu, EIC, West Chester
University, PA, West Chester

Minford, Chris
cminford@mauinews.com, Circ. Mgr., The Maui
News, HI, Wailuku

Minger, John
addenver@aol.com, Treasurer, Yankee Peddler
Postal Service, CO, Englewood

Mingos , Adam
amingos@the-leader.com, Adv. Mgr.,
Horseheads Shopper, NY, Corning
amingos@the-leader.com, Adv. Mgr., The
Leader, NY, Corning

Miniard, Wylene .... (606) 573-4510 Ext. 1169
wminiard@civitasmedia.com, Inside Sales
Rep., The Harlan Daily Enterprise, KY,
Harlan

Minick, Tori
mctribune@gmail.com, Ed, Motley County
Tribune, TX, Turkey

Mininger, Brian .... (215) 997-3447
bmininger@simcomail.com, Technical Rep.,
Simco Industrial Static Control Products, PA,
Hatfield

Minnich, Michael
mminnich@newstribune.info, Mineral Daily
News-Tribune, WV, Keyser

Minopoli, Kim .... (301) 764-2800
kminopoli@somdnews.com, Adv. Dir., The

Maryland Independent, MD, White Plains

Minor, Adam .... (508) 909-4130
aminor@stonebridgepress.com, Ed.,
Southbridge Evening News, MA, Southbridge

Minor, Adam .... (860) 928-1818
aminor@villagernewspapers.com, Ed., Killingly
Villager, CT, Woodstock
aminor@villagernewspapers.com, Ed., Auburn
News, MA, Southbridge
aminor@villagernewspapers.com, Ed.,
Blackstone Valley Tribune, MA, Southbridge
aminor@villagernewspapers.com, Ed., The
Webster Times, MA, Southbridge

Minor, Adam .... (508) 909-4130
Aminor@stonebridgepress.com , Ed.,
Sturbridge Villager, MA, Southbridge

Minor, Adam .... (508) 909-4130
aminor@villagernewspapers.com, Ed.,
Charlton Villager, MA, Southbridge

Minor, Les .... (903) 794-3311
lminor@texarkanagazette.com, Ed., Texarkana
Gazette, AR, Texarkana

Minor, Robyn .... (270) 783-3249
rminor@bgdailynews.com, City Ed., Daily
News, KY, Bowling Green

Minor, Stephanie
lamarleader@yahoo.com, Ed., Lamar Leader,
AL, Sulligent

Minor , BJ .... (254) 771-2777
minorranch@gmail.com, Pub., American
Classifieds, TX, Temple

Minton, Brenda .... (813) 259-7705
brenda.minton@mountaintimes.com, Class
Adv. Mgr., The Blowing Rocket, NC, Blowing
Rock
brenda.minton@mountaintimes.com, Class
Adv. Mgr., The Avery Journal-Times, NC,
Newland
brenda.minton@mountaintimes.com, Tampa
Bay Times, FL, St Petersburg

Minton, Tammy
bizoffice@jacksonvilleprogress.com, Office
Mgr., Jacksonville Daily Progress, TX,
Jacksonville

Minty, Dawn
dminty@ledger-enquirer.com, Features Ed.,
Columbus Ledger-Enquirer, GA, Columbus

Mintz, Yvonne
yvonne.mintz@thefacts.com, Mng. Ed., Buyer's
Express, TX, Clute

Mintz, Yvonne .... (979) 265-7411
yvonne.mintz@thefacts.com, Managing Ed.,
The Facts, TX, Clute

Miramontes, Rosaura
rmiramontes@mercurynews.com, Adv. Mgr.,
Natl' Sales, Nuevo Mundo, CA, San Jose

Miranda, Luis
lmiranda@sbsnewyork.com, Pub., The Bronx
Free Press, NY, New York

Mirando, Lillian K. .... (985) 254-7834
editor@hammondstar.com, Exec. Ed., The
Daily Star, LA, Hammond

Mirelli, Rich
rich.mirelli@albertleatribune.com, Mailroom
Mgr., Albert Lea Tribune, MN, Albert Lea

Mirman, Richard .... (951) 782-7782
nfoltz@ocregister.com, Pub., The Long Beach
Register (OOB), CA, Santa Ana
nfoltz@ocregister.com, Pub., The Press-
Enterprise, CA, Riverside

Mironovich, Cindy ..... (908) 232-2913 ext. 105
cindy.mironovich@njfamily.com, Co-Pub., New
Jersey Family, NJ, Summit

Mironovich, Cindy .... (908) 232-2913 ext. 105
cindy.mironovich@njfamily.com, Pub., Morris
County Family, NJ, Mountainside

Mironovich, Cindy .... (908) 232-2913 ext. 105
cindy.mironovich@njfamily.com, Pub., Union
County Family, NJ, Mountainside

Mirrington, Andrew .... (970) 728-9788 ext.22
publisher@telluridenews.com, Pub., Telluride Daily Planet; the Watch; The Norwood Post, CO, Telluride
publisher@telluridenews.com, Pub., The Norwood Post, CO, Telluride

Mirt, Kelly ....(704) 358-5333
kmirt@charlotteobserver.com, VP, Adv., The Charlotte Observer, NC, Charlotte
kmirt@charlotteobserver.com, Pub. & V.P. of Adv., The Wichita Eagle, KS, Wichita

Misarski, Michael ....(203) 317-2241
mmisarski@record-journal.com, News Ed., Record-Journal, CT, Meriden

Mischel, Marie
marie@icatholic.org, Ed., Intermountain Catholic, UT, Salt Lake City

Mischke, Michael ....(651) 699-1462
vci@myvillager.com, Pub, Villager, MN, Saint Paul

Mischner, Michael ....(803) 432-6157
mmischner@ci-camden.com, Pub., Fort Jackson Leader, SC, Camden

Mischner, Michael
observer@sc.rr.com, Pub., Lee County Observer, SC, Bishopville

Mischner, Michael ....(803) 432-6157
mmischner@ci-camden.com, Pub., Chronicle-Independent, SC, Camden
mmischner@ci-camden.com, Pub., West Wateree Chronicle, SC, Camden

Mischner, Michael
mmischner@ci-camden.com, Pub., The Shaw News, SC, Camden

Misener, Jacob ....(308) 235-3631
editor@westernnebraskaobserver.net, Editor & Publisher, Western Nebraska Observer, NE, Kimball

Miske, Michael
info@vegra.com, Vice Pres., Sales, Vegra USA, IL, Chicago

Miske, Michael T.
admin@bblocks.net, Pres., Litho Research, Inc., IL, Chicago

Misner, John ....(602) 444-123
jmisner@kpnx.com, Pres./Gen. Mgr., The Arizona Republic, AZ, Phoenix

Missal, Maureen ....(570) 674-5600
mmissal@outsourcingsua.net, VP Business Development, Outsourcing USA, PA, Dallas

Missen, Randy ....(416) 289-6566
rmissen@bbm.ca, Vice Pres., Meter Servs., BBM Canada, ON, Toronto

Missit, Jim
johnb@navycompass.com, Adv. Mgr., Compass, CA, San Diego

Missler, Sherry
smissler@timesbulletin.com, Obit., The Times Bulletin, OH, Van Wert

Misterek, Matt ....(253) 597-8639
matt.misterek@thenewstribune.com, Editorial Page Editor, The News Tribune, WA, Tacoma

Misty, Johnsen ....(250) 632-6144
classifieds@northernsentinel.com, Circulation, Northern Sentinel - Kitimat, BC, Kitimat

Misureli, Frank M.
fmisureli@kenoshanews.com, Adv. Mgr., Bargaineer, IL, Zion

Misureli, Frank M. ....(262) 656-6260
Pub., Zion Benton News, IL, Zion

Mitcham, Marq
mmitcham@bastropenterprise.com, Sports Ed., Bastrop Daily Enterprise, LA, Bastrop

Mitcham, Zach ....(706) 795-2567
madisonjournal@alltel.net, Ed., The Madison County Journal, GA, Jefferson

Mitchel, Barbara
bmitchel@mcclatchy.com, Gen. Mgr., The

Press Democrat, CA, Santa Rosa

Mitchell, Anthony
sports@banner-tribune.com, Sports Ed., Franklin Banner-Tribune, LA, Franklin

Mitchell, Beckie
bmitchell@leavenworthtimes.com, Bus. Mgr., The Leavenworth Times, KS, Leavenworth

Mitchell, Billy .... (770) 428-9411 ext. 207
bmitchell@mdjonline.com, Mng. Ed., Marietta Daily Journal, GA, Marietta

Mitchell, Billy ....(770) 428-9411 x 207
bmitchell@mdjonline.com, Mng. Ed., East Cobb Neighbor, GA, Marietta
bmitchell@mdjonline.com, Mng. Ed., South Cobb Neighbor, GA, Marietta
bmitchell@mdjonline.com, Mng. Ed., Kennesaw-Acworth Neighbor, GA, Marietta

Mitchell, Charles D. .... (601) 636-4545 ext. 123
post@vicksburg.com, Exec. Ed., The Vicksburg Post, MS, Vicksburg

Mitchell, Colleen ....(770) 683-1707
colleen@newnan.com, Sales & Marketing Dir., The Newnan Times-Herald, GA, Newnan

Mitchell, Cynthia
gnlnews@yahoo.com, Adv. Mgr., The Cadiz Record, KY, Cadiz

Mitchell, Dennis ....(970) 256-4270
dennis.mitchell@gjsentinel.com, Adv. Dir., The Daily Sentinel, CO, Grand Junction

Mitchell, Dick
dmitchell@mcduffieprogress.com, Pub, Dollar Saver, GA, Thomson

Mitchell, Elena
elena.mitchell@savannahnow.com, Acct. Mgr., Savannah Morning News, GA, Savannah

Mitchell, Glenn
glenn@vernonmorningstar.com, Mng. Ed., The Morning Star, BC, Vernon

Mitchell, Jack ....(209) 223-8771
jmitchell@ledger-dispatch.com, Pub., Amador Ledger-Dispatch, CA, Jackson

Mitchell, Jason ....ext. 294
pwallner@heraldpalladium.com, Sports Ed., The Herald-Palladium, MI, Saint Joseph

Mitchell, Jeff
jmitchell@pomeradonews.com, The Monterey County Herald, CA, Monterey

Mitchell, Jeff
jmitchell@gtweekly.com, Publisher, Santa Cruz Good Times, CA, Santa Cruz

Mitchell, Jeff
jmtchell@newsvmedia.com, Publisher, Hollister Free Lance, CA, Hollister

Mitchell, Jeff
jmitchell@newsvmedia.com, Publisher, Morgan Hill Times, CA, Morgan Hill

Mitchell, Josh
news@columbianprogress.com, Mng. Ed., The Columbian-Progress, MS, Columbia

Mitchell, Karen
eastcentral@sk.sympatico.ca, Pub./Gen. Mgr., Naicam News, SK, Watson

Mitchell, Kathy
kmitchell@turley.com, Ed., The Chicopee Register, MA, Chicopee

Mitchell, Kathy .... (404) 373-7779 Ext. 104
kathy@dekalbchamp.com, Ed., The Champion, GA, Decatur

Mitchell, Kenny ....(903) 628-5801
kmitchell@bowiecountynow.com, Gen. Mgr., Bowie County Citizen Tribune, TX, New Boston

Mitchell, Kim ....(317) 444-6269
kim.mitchell@indystar.com, Exec. Admin. Asst., The Indianapolis Star, IN, Indianapolis

Mitchell, Linda ....ext. 520
lmitchell@reporter-herald.com, Librarian,

Loveland Reporter-Herald, CO, Loveland

Mitchell, Lisa
lmitchell@berksmontnews.com, Ed., The Kutztown Area Patriot, PA, Pottstown

Mitchell, Lisa ....(610) 850-0269
lmitchell@berksmontnews.com, Ed., The Community Connection, PA, Pottstown

Mitchell, Michelle ....(727) 893-8363
mmitchell@tampabay.com, Adv. Mgr., Classified, Tampa Bay Times, FL, St Petersburg

Mitchell, Nancy
ndmitche@unlnotes.unl.edu, Prof., University of Nebraska-Lincoln, NE, Lincoln

Mitchell, Pamela ....(225) 344 - 9309 x108
pam@lapress.com, Exec. Dir., Louisiana Press Association, LA, Baton Rouge

Mitchell, Paul
pmitchell@metroland.com, Circ Mgr, Belleville News, ON, Belleville

Mitchell, R. John ....(802) 747-6121 ext. 2202
Pub., Preferred Properties Real Estate Guide, VT, Rutland

Mitchell, R. John ....(802) 479-4039 ext. 1133
news@timesargus.com, Pres./Pub., Times Argus Extra, VT, Barre

Mitchell, Randy ....(580) 310-7521
rmitchell@theadanews.com, Mng. Ed., The Ada News , OK, Ada

Mitchell, Randy ....(620) 672-5511
randy.mitchell@mcphersonsentinel.com, Publisher, Sunflower Shopper's Guide, KS, Pratt

Mitchell, Randy ....(260) 347-0400
randymitchell@kpcmedia.com, CEO, The Star, IN, Auburn

Mitchell, Randy ....(260) 347-0400
randymitchell@kpcmedia.com, CEO, KPC Media Group, Inc., IN, Kendallville

Mitchell, Randy ....(316) 283-1500
rmitchell@gatehousemedia.com, Pub., The Pratt Tribune, KS, Pratt

Mitchell, Rick ....(260) 347-7210
rickmitchell@kpcmedia.com, CFO, KPC Media Group, Inc., IN, Kendallville

Mitchell, Ron
ron@scod.com, Sales Mgr., South Coast Shopper, OR, Coos Bay

Mitchell, Russ
rmitchell@dickinsoncountynews.com, Editor, Dickinson County News, IA, Spirit Lake

Mitchell, Sara ....(661) 763-3171
editor@bay.rr.com, Sports Ed., Daily Midway Driller, CA, Taft

Mitchell, Shannon
smitchell@tricitynews.com, Pub, Tri-city News, BC, Port Coquitlam

Mitchell, Sheila
smitchell@drummerpennysaver.com, Adv Mgr, Drummer Pennysaver, NY, Batavia

Mitchell, Sue
tlfreepress@yahoo.com, Ed., Tupper Lake Free Press, NY, Tupper Lake

Mitchell, T. Wayne ....(662) 534-6321
wayne.mitchell@journalinc.com, Pub., New Albany Gazette, MS, New Albany

Mitchell, Wendy .... (606) 564-9091 ext. 276
Wendy.Mitchell@lee.net, Newsroom, The Mayfield Messenger, KY, Mayfield

Mitchell, William
wmitchell@t-g.com, Gen. Mgr., Shelbyville Times-Gazette, TN, Shelbyville

Mitchelson, Chrissy ....(315) 343-3800 ext. 2222
circulation@palltimes.com, Circ. Mgr., The Palladium-Times, NY, Oswego

Mitchin, Joe
joe.mitchin@indeonline.com, Sports Writer,

The Independent, OH, Massillon

Mitchum, William
wmitchum@thebesttimes.com, Social Media Specialist, The Best Times, TN, Memphis

Mithcell, Toni ....(937) 225-0502
toni.mitchell@coxinc.com, Director of Human Resources, Dayton Daily News, OH, Franklin

Mittag, Craig
cmittag@crestonnews.com, Adv. Mgr., Creston News Advertiser, IA, Creston

Mittag, Craig
cmittag@crestonnews.com, Adv.Mgr., Southwest Iowa Advertiser, IA, Creston

Mitten, Alyse
alyse.mitten@gmail.com, Exec. Dir., MACNET, PA, Hamburg
alyse.mitten@gmail.com, Exec. Dir., MACNET, Bernville

Mitten, Alyse ....(610) 914-0142
alyse.mitten@gmail.com, Exec. Dir., Mid-Atlantic Community Papers Association, PA, Hamburg

Mitten, George T.
george@windsorpress.com, Prodn. Mgr., Northern Berks Merchandiser, PA, Hamburg

Mitten, George T. ....(610) 562-2267
george@windsorpress.com, Prodn. Mgr., East Penn Valley Merchandiser, PA, Hamburg

Miyasaki, Gail
gmiyasaki@rafu.com, Circ. Mgr.; advertising, The Rafu Shimpo, CA, Los Angeles

Mize, Mark ....(931) 424-2834
mark.mize@pulaskicitizen.com, Sports Ed, Pulaski Citizen, TN, Pulaski

Mizell, Sue ....(906) 932-2211
smizell@yourdailyglobe.co, publisher, Range Source, MI, Ironwood

Mizell, Sue
smizell@yourdailyglobe.com, Pub., The Daily Globe, MI, Ironwood

Mizener, Todd ....(309) 757-4993
tmizener@qconline.com, Information Editor/ Photography & Multimedia, The Dispatch-Argus, IL, Moline

Mlodecki, Rena ....(760) 873-3535 x 222
rena@inyoregister.com, Publisher, Inyo Register, CA, Bishop

Mlodecki , Rena ....(760) 873-3535
rena@inyoregister.com, Publisher, Inyo Register, CA, Bishop

Mlot, Samantha
samantha@hubcityspokes.com, Adv. Mgr., The Lamar Times, MS, Hattiesburg

Moar, Kim
newsroom@herald.ca, Mng. Ed., Bedford - Sackville Weekly News, NS, Halifax
newsroom@herald.ca, Mng. Ed., Halifax West-clayton Park Weekly News, NS, Halifax

Moates, Ron
ron.moates@theledger.com, Nat'l Adv. Mgr., News Chief, FL, Winter Haven
ron.moates@theledger.com, nat'l adv. mgr., The Ledger, FL, Lakeland

Moats, Cecilia ....(307) 635-3905
wyopress@wyopress.org, Deputy Dir., Wyoming Press Association, WY, Cheyenne

Moberg, Jeff
jeff@sundancetimes.com, Adv. Mgr./Ed., The Sundance Times, WY, Sundance

Mobley, Chris ....(305) 347-6612
cmobley@alm.com, Group Publisher, FL/GA/ TX, Miami Daily Business Review, FL, Miami

Mobley, Chris ....(305) 347-6612
cmobley@alm.com, Group Publisher, FL/GA/ TX, Palm Beach Daily Business Review, FL, Miami

Mobley-Martinez, Tracy ....(719) 476-1602
tracy@coloradosprings.com, A&E Editor, The

Gazette, CO, Colorado Springs

Mock, Gloria Wyly
gloria@indyweek.com, Adv. Mgr., The Independent Weekly, NC, Durham

Mock, Justin .... (303) 473-1500
mockj@dailycamera.com, VP of Finance for PMP, Daily Camera, CO, Boulder

Modarelli, Vince .... (259) 213-5373
vmodarelli@naplesnews.com, Ad. Dir., Marco Eagle, FL, Naples
vmodarelli@naplesnews.com, Adv. Dir., The Collier Citizen, FL, Naples
vmodarelli@naplesnews.com, Ad. Director, The Banner, FL, Naples

Modestino, Lou
lmodestino@hotmail.com, Author, TV Times/ New England Motorsports Syndication, Brockton

Modrack, Barb
editor@fentonpress.com, Ed., The Fenton Press, MI, Flint

Mody, Bella
bella.mody@colorado.edu, Prof./James E. de Castro Chair in Global Media Studies, University of Colorado, CO, Boulder

Modzeleski, Julian
julianm@flynnburner.com, Pres., Flynn Burner Corp., NY, New Rochelle

Moehnke, Sharon
starnews@stewiestar.com, Circ. Mgr., Stewartville Star, MN, Stewartville

Moelis, Gary
garym@microfilmproducts.com, Pres., Microfilm Products Co., NY, Nanuet

Moeller, Dan
dmoeller@indreg.com, Ed., The Independent Register, WI, Brodhead

Moeller, Susan
smoeller@capecodonline.com, Assoc. Prof., University of Maryland, MD, College Park

Moeller, Wanda .... (641) 683-5365
wmoeller@timesrepublican.com, Pub./Ed., The Ottumwa Courier, IA, Ottumwa

Moen, Daryl
moend@missouri.edu, Prof., University of Missouri, MO, Columbia

Moen, Sue
pmreditor@newspubinc.com, Ed., Post Messenger Recorder, WI, New Glarus

Moen, Todd
todd.moen@ecm-inc.com, Mng. Ed., The Gold Miner, MN, Waconia

Moeur, John ....ext. 233
johnmoeur@rrdailyherald.com, Mng. Ed., The Revue, NC, Roanoke Rapids

Moffatt, Jim .... (901) 458-2911 ext. 5
jmoffatt@thebesttimes.com, advertising manager, The Best Times, TN, Memphis

Moffett, Robbie .... (402) 444-1417
robbie.moffett@owh.com, Mgr., Consumer Classifieds, Omaha World-Herald, NE, Omaha

Moffitt, Chandra
cmoffitt@bnd.com, Adv. Sales , Republic-times Shopper, IL, Waterloo
cmoffitt@bnd.com, Adv, Belleville News-Democrat, IL, Belleville

Mogensen, Mark .... (207) 689-2805
mmogensen@sunjournal.com, Business, News Ed., Sun Journal, ME, Lewiston

Mohar, Shannon .... (717) 703-3053
shannonm@mansimedia.com, Account Manager, MANSI Media, PA, Harrisburg

Mohler, Dale .... (304) 772-3016
watchman2@earthlink.net, Pub./Gen. Mgr., Monroe Watchman, WV, Union

Mohler, Titus .... (434) 808-0618
titus.mohler@farmvilleherald.com;.

mohler@kenbridgevictoriadispatch.com, Sports Ed., The Farmville Herald, VA, Farmville
titus.mohler@farmvilleherald.com; titus. mohler@kenbridgevictoriadispatch.com, Sports Ed., The Kenbridge-Victoria Dispatch, VA, Victoria

Mohr, Pam
circulation@decaturdailydemocrat.com, Circ. Mgr., Decatur Daily Democrat, IN, Decatur

Mohr, Victor L. .... (618) 282-3803
Publisher, North County News, IL, Red Bud

Mohrey, Tina
info@visitANF.com, Adv. Mgr., Forest Press, PA, Tionesta

Mohs, Pete
pete.mohs@pequotlakesecho.com, Pub., Lake Country Echo, MN, Pequot Lakes
pete.mohs@pequotlakesecho.com, Pub., Echo Journal, MN, Pequot Lakes

Mohs, Pete .... (218) 855-5855
pete.mohs@brainerddispatch.com, Publisher, Echoland - Piper Shopper, MN, Brainerd
pete.mohs@brainerddispatch.com, Pub., pineandlakes Echo Journal, MN, Brainerd
pete.mohs@brainerddispatch.com, Pub., Echoland Shopper, MN, Brainerd

Moisan, Lucie .... (418) 722-0205
avantage@cgocable.ca, Avantage Votre Journal, QC, Rimouski

Moise, Grant
gmoise@dmnmedia.com, SVP/Business Development & Niche Products, The Dallas Morning News, TX, Dallas

Moise, Grant
gmoise@dallasnews.com, Southwestern Regl. Sales Dir., Tribune Media Network, TX, Dallas

Mok, Andrew .... (651) 228-5149
amok@pioneerpress.com, Vice Pres., Circ., St. Paul Pioneer Press, MN, Saint Paul

Moldaschel, Deb
dmoldaschel@sleepyeyenews.com, Ed., Sleepy Eye Herald-Dispatch, MN, Sleepy Eye

Molen, Logan
logan.molen@registerguard.com, Pub./CEO, The Register-Guard, OR, Eugene

Molenaar, Ruth .... (201) 863-3310
smolenaar@aol.com, Pub., La Tribuna Publication, NJ, Union City

Moler, Lance
lmoler@edmondsun.com, Pub., Oklahoma County Newspapers, Inc., OK, Midwest City
lmoler@edmondsun.com, Gen. Mgr., The Edmond Sun, OK, Edmond

Moliatu, Dana
smoliatu@readingeagle.com, CFO, Reading Eagle Company, PA, Reading

Moliatu, Shawn .... (610) 371-5204
smoliatu@readingeagle.com, CFO, Reading Eagle, PA, Reading

Molina, Andy ....ext. 116
Adv. Sales Mgr., La Noticia, NC, Charlotte

Molina, Sandra
sandra.molina@sgvn.com, Reporter, The Whittier Daily News, CA, Monrovia

Molinaro, Geena
molin22g@mtholyoke.edu, Editor-in-Chief, Mount Holyoke College, MA, South Hadley

Moll, Randy . (479) 524-5144 or (479) 233-0081 cell
rmoll@nwadg.com or eagleobserver@nwadg. com, Mng. Ed., Westside Eagle Observer, AR, Siloam Springs
rmoll@nwadg.com or eagleobserver@nwadg. com, Mng. Ed., Gentry Courier-Journal (merged - now Westside Eagle Observer), AR, Gentry

Molldrem, Todd
tmolldrem@startribune.com, Star Tribune, MN, Minneapolis

Molley, John
jmolley@johnsoncitypress.com, Mng. Ed., Johnson City Press, TN, Johnson City

Mollohan, Melissa
mmollohan@kentuckynewera.com, Features Ed., Kentucky New Era, KY, Hopkinsville

Molloy, Andy .... (207) 621-5619
amolloy@centralmaine.com, Photographer, Kennebec Journal, ME, Augusta

Molloy, Fiona .... (617) 619-6494
fiona.molloy@bostonherald.com, Sunday Editor, Boston Herald, MA, Boston

Molnar-Strejcek, Tony
tony@outpub.com, Co-Pub., Out, PA, Pittsburgh

Molone, Mark ....(815) 942-3221 ext. 2057
Assoc. Ed., Morris Herald-News, IL, MORRIS

Molony, Jim .... (281) 378-1930
jmolony@hcnonline.com, Ed., Bay Area Citizen, TX, Webster
jmolony@hcnonline.com, Ed., Friendswood Journal, TX, Conroe
jmolony@hcnonline.com, Ed., Pasadena Citizen, TX, Webster
jmolony@hcnonline.com, Ed., Pearland Journal, TX, Conroe

Momot, Kevin
kevin.momot@nydailyrecord.com, Vice Pres./ Pub., The Daily Record, NY, Rochester

Monaco, James .... (631) 725-9513
jmonaco@unet2.net, Pres., UNET 2 Corporation, NY, Sag Harbor

Monahan, Brian .... (503) 630-3241
BMonihan@lakeosworeview.com, VP, Estacada News, OR, Estacada

Monahan, Geri
bch@tc3net.com, Bi-county Herald, MI, Hudson

Monahan, John W.
bch@tc3net.com, Pub., Bi-county Herald, MI, Hudson

Monahan, Ron
advertising@times-news.com, Pub., The Garrett County Weekender, MD, Cumberland

Moncrief, Don
donm@hhjnews.com, d., The Houston Home Journal, GA, Perry

Moncrief, Robert
rmoncrief@kearneyhub.com, Business Mgr., Kearney Hub, NE, Kearney

Mondioch, Tara .... (715) 384-3131 x303
tmondioch@gannett.com, Adv Mgr, Marshfield News-Herald Media, WI, Marshfield

Mondt, Dave .... (702) 259-4086
dave.mondt@lasvegassun.com, The Sunday Managing Ed., Las Vegas Sun, NV, Henderson

Monette, Rejean
courtemanchen@transcontinental.ca, Regl. Dir., Courrier-laval, QC, Laval

Money, David
editor@alvinsun.net, Ed., Alvin Sun-Advertiser, TX, Alvin

Money, Robert
rmoney@civitasmedia.com, Sports Ed., The Stokes News, NC, King

Money, Sarah
sarah.money@dowjones.com, Sales Mgr., Dow Jones Newswires - London, United Kingdom, London

Monfiletto, Jonathan .... (315) 283-1615
jonathan.monfiletto@lee.net, Ed., This Week, NY, Auburn

Monge, Lorena .... (912) 373-1206
lorena.monge@cc.cdom.org, Ads and subscriptions, The West Tennessee Catholic, TN, Memphis

Monico, Nick .... (614) 403-7501

Regional VP - Western, GateHouse Media, Inc., NY, Pittsford

Monico, Nickolas
nick.monico@wickcommunications.com, COO, Wick Communications, AZ, Sierra Vista

Monico, Nickolas F.
nmonico@tribweb.com, COO, Tribune-Review Publishing Co., PA, Greensburg

Monihan, Brian .... (503) 546-0784
bmonihan@portlandtribune.com, Gen. Mgr., Pamplin Media Group, OR, Portland

Monihan, Brian
BMonihan@PamplinMedia.com, Pub., Southwest Community Connection, OR, Lake Oswego

Monihan, J. Brian .... (503) 546-0784
bmonihan@westlintidings.com, Pub., Wilsonville Spokesman, OR, Lake Oswego
bmonihan@westlintidings.com, Pub, West Linn Tidings, OR, Lake Oswego
bmonihan@westlintidings.com, Pub., The Bee, OR, Portland

Monihan, J. Brian .... (503) 546-0784
bmonihan@lakeoswegoreview.com, Pub, The Lake Oswego Review, OR, Lake Oswego

Monihan, J. Brian
bmonihan@lakeoswegoreview.com, VP, The Outlook, OR, Gresham

Moniz, Tracey
Tmoniz@capenews.net, Circ. Mgr., Enterprise, MA, Falmouth

Monk, Devin
devinmonk@lakeway-tx.gov, Lake Travis View, TX, Austin

Monke, Dustin .... (701) 456-1205
dmonke@thedickinsonpress.com, Mng. Ed. , Advertizer, ND, Dickinson
dmonke@thedickinsonpress.com, Mng. Ed., The Dickinson Press, ND, Dickinson

Monopoli, Joy
jmonopoli@worldmediaenterprise.com, Pub., Goochland Gazette, VA, Mechanicsville

Monreal, Leo
lmonreal@thevalleychronicle.com, Sales & Adv., The Valley Chronicle, CA, Hemet

Monroe, Colleen
cmonroe@goodnewsetc.com, Adv. Mgr., Good News, Etc., CA, Vista

Monroe, Marilyn
sdneditorial@yahoo.com, Newsroom Mgr., Southwest Daily News, LA, Sulphur

Monroe, Myrna .... (251) 368-6397
myrna@atmorenews.com, Co-owner., Atmore News, AL, Atmore

Monroe, Rick
goodnewseditor@cox.net, Ed., Good News, Etc., CA, Vista

Monroe, Scott .... (207) 621-5692
smonroe@centralmaine.com, Managing Ed., Morning Sentinel, ME, Waterville
smonroe@centralmaine.com, Asst. Sports Ed. , Kennebec Journal, ME, Augusta

Monserud, Scott .... (303) 954-1243
smonserud@denverpost.com, Asst. Managing Ed. Sports, The Denver Post, CO, Denver

Monsivais, Josephina
circulation@fmtimes.com , Circ. Mgr., Fort Morgan Times, CO, Fort Morgan

Monsivias, Josephina
circulation@fmtimes.com, Circ. Mgr., Morgan Times Review, CO, Fort Morgan

Monson, Eric John
editor@trinidadchroniclenews.com, Editor, The Chronicle-News, CO, Trinidad

Monson, Kristi .... (218) 477-2110
monson@mnstate.edu, Minnesota State Univ. Moorhead, MN, Moorhead

Monson, Ralph

tinker.takeoff@tinker.af.mil, Chief of Pub. Aff., Tinker Take Off, OK, Oklahoma City

Montagna, Diane ....(888) 678-6008 x 942
dmontagna@lifesitenews.com, Rome Correspondent, LifeSiteNews.com, VA, Front Royal

Montague, Brad ....(306) 781-5260
bmontague@leaderpost.canwest.com, Prodn. Mgr., Bldg., The Leader-Post, SK, Regina

Montague, Kelly
kmontague@thespec.com, Adv. Vice Pres., The Hamilton Spectator, ON, Hamilton

Montague, Sharon ....(785) 822-1411
smontague@salina.com, Exec. Ed., The Salina Journal, KS, Salina

Montalbano, Nick ....(732) 780-7474
nick@homeimprovementguides.com, Circ. Mgr., Home Improvement Guide, NJ, Colts Neck

Montalto, Mike .... (908) 766-3900, ext. 244
mmontalto@newjerseyhills.com, Ed., The Randolph Reporter, NJ, Bernardsville

Montana, Carol
editor@sc-democrat.com, Ed, Sullivan County Democrat, NY, Callicoon

Montana, Rob ....(207) 504-8209
rmontana@timesrecord.com, Mng. Ed., Ithaca Times, NY, Ithaca

Montano, Daniel
news@dailylobo.com, News Ed., New Mexico Daily Lobo, NM, Albuquerque

Montano, Ernie.........................(719) 544-4752
ernie@acpueblo.com, Pres., American Classifieds - Pueblo, CO, Pueblo

Montaya, Gustazo
gustazo@elmundous.com, Ed., El Mundo, WA, Wenatchee

Montaño, Ramona ....(505) 287-4411
composing@cibolabeacon.com, Composing Supervisor, Cibola Beacon, NM, Grants

Monteith, Dori
theqcn@gmail.com, Ad. Mgr. , Queen Central News, NY, Camden

Monteleone, Robert
rmonteleone@digitalfirstmedia.com, EVP & Chief Human Resources Officer, Digital First Media, CO, Denver

Montell, Gabriella ....(617) 349-8501
Lesley University, MA, Cambridge

Montemer, TJ....................(310) 310-2637 x 104
tj@smmirror.com , President/Publisher , Westside Today, CA, Santa Monica
tj@smmirror.com , President/Publisher , Santa Monica Mirror, CA, Santa Monica
tj@smmirror.com , President/Publisher , Brentwood News, CA, Santa Monica
tj@smmirror.com , President/Publisher , Yo Venice, CA, Santa Monica
tj@smmirror.com , President/Publisher , Century City News, CA, Santa Monica
tj@smmirror.com , President/Publisher , LA Pride, CA, Santa Monica

Montemurro, Ronald J. ....(262) 656-6301
rmontemurro@kenoshanews.com, CFO , Kenosha News, WI, Kenosha

Montenegro, Esmeralda
emontenegro@gavilan.edu, Faculty Advisor, Gavilan College, CA, Gilroy

Monter, Mike
mike.monter@new-proimage.com, Vice President, Operations, ProImage America, Inc., NJ, Princeton

Montero, Elena
clientes@efe.es, Bureau Chief, EFE News Services - WASHINGTON, D.C, Washington Post

Montes, Zeke ....(708) 466-6666
zekemontes@aol.com, Tele Guia de Chicago, IL, Cicero

Montgomery, Billy
bmontgom@roosevelt.edu, Roosevelt Univ., IL, Chicago

Montgomery, Brenda ....(815) 937-3319
bmontgomery@daily-journal.com, HR Asst.- Personnel Dev., The Daily Journal, IL, Kankakee

Montgomery, David........ (928) 783-3311 ext. 109
Vice Pres./CFO, Western News&Info, Inc., AZ, Yuma

Montgomery, Jessica
editor@claudenews.com, Co-Pub./Ed./Adv. Dir., The Claude News, TX, Claude

Montgomery, John
jmontgomery@townnews.com, Regional Sales Manager, TownNews.com, IL, Moline

Montgomery, John.......... (620) 694-5700 Ext. 400
jmont@hutchnews.com, Ed./Pub., The Hutchinson News, KS, Hutchinson

Montgomery, Kirby
kmontgomery@clearleap.com, College of St. Scholastica, MN, Duluth

Montgomery, Maria
mmontgomery@winchesterstar.com, Mng. Ed., The Winchester Star, VA, Winchester

Montgomery, Mark ....(916) 321-1648
mmontgomery@sacbee.com, Audience Admin & Operations Manager , The Sacramento Bee, CA, Sacramento

Montgomery, Mary Lou ....(573) 248-2750
marylou.montgomery@courierpost.com, Ed., Hannibal Courier-Post, MO, Hannibal

Montgomery, Paul ....(603) 668-4321 Ext.320
pmontgomery@unionleader.com, Sunday Editor, New Hampshire Union Leader/New Hampshire Sunday News, NH, Manchester

Montgomery, Shelagh
support@qualitytech.com, Gen. Mgr., Globix Corp., NJ, Jersey City

Montgomery, Tom
tom@ccchronicle.net, Ed., Cass City Chronicle, MI, Cass City

Montgomery , Matt
ads@OKCTribune.com, Ed/Adv, The Bethany Tribune, OK, Bethany

Montoni, Amy ....(704) 944-6765
amontoni@shalomcharlotte.org, Ed., Charlotte Jewish News, NC, Charlotte

Montoy, Kim ....(616) 427-7474
reminder@lotusnet.com, Pub., Reminder Shopping Guide, MI, Bangor

Montoya, Jan
laads@lamonitor.com, Adv. Dir., Los Alamos Monitor, NM, Los Alamos

Montoya, Martha
martha@elmundous.com, El Mundo - WA, WA, Kirkland

Montoya, Stephen
culture@dailylobo.com, Culture Ed., New Mexico Daily Lobo, NM, Albuquerque

Montreuil, Pierre
pierre.montreuil@monteregieweb.com, Sales Dir., Le Soleil Du St-laurent, QC, Salaberry-de-Valleyfield

Monty, Lynn............................(802) 985-3091
lynn@windridgepublishing.com, Ed., Shelburne News, VT, Shelburne

Montérégie, Réseau
redactionvalleyfieldexpress@tc.tc, Pub., Valleyfield Express, QC, Salaberry-de-Valleyfield

Monzon, Eduardo ....(561) 835-4913
eduardo@ellatino.com, Adv. Mgr., El Latino Newspaper, FL, West Palm Beach

Moody, Linda ....(937) 569-4315
lmoody@dailyadvocate.com, Asst. Ed., Weekend Advocate, OH, Greenville
lmoody@dailyadvocate.com, Rep., Daily

Advocate, OH, Greenville

Moon, Amy
amoon@orlandosentinel.com, Orlando Sentinel, FL, Orlando

Moon, Craig
cmoon@reviewjournal.com, Pub., Reno Gazette-Journal, NV, Reno
cmoon@reviewjournal.com, Pub., Las Vegas Review-Journal, NV, Las Vegas

Moon, Eileen
trtredbank@aol.com, Ed., The Two River Times, NJ, Red Bank

Moon, Lane ....(937) 652-1331 Ext. 1783
lmoon@civitasmedia.com, Pub./Adv. Dir., Urbana Daily Citizen, OH, Urbana
lmoon@civitasmedia.com, Pub., The Madison Press, OH, London

Moon, Lane
lmoon@aimmediamidwest.com, Publisher, Macon County Times, TN, Lafayette

Moon, Lynn
lfletcherherald@aol.com, Owner/Pub, Fletcher Herald, OK, Fletcher

Moon, Steve
steve.moon@newscyclesolutions.com, Rgl. Sales Dir., Newscycle Solutions, MN, Bloomington

Moon, Vicky ....(540) 687-6059
info@middleburglife.com, Advertising, Middleburg Life, VA, Middleburg

Mooney, Andre
a.mooney@lesoleil.qc.ca, Pub., Soleil De Valleyfield, QC, Salaberry-de-Valleyfield

Mooney, Andre
andre.mooney@monteregieweb.com, Dir., Le Soleil Du St-laurent, QC, Salaberry-de-Valleyfield

Mooney, Andrea G. ....(713) 362-7245
andrea.mooney@chron.com, Executive Producer/Director, Digital Content, Houston Chronicle, TX, Houston

Mooney, Burgett H. ....(706) 291-6397
bmooney@npco.com, Pub., Chattooga Press (OOB), GA, Rome
bmooney@npco.com, Pub., Rome News-Tribune, GA, Rome

Mooney, Charles
bonnie@mcgregormirror.com, Co-Pub./Ed., McGregor Mirror & Crawford Sun, TX, Mc Gregor

Mooney, Dick................(603) 472-5825 ext. 11
dick.mooney@ckp.com, Mng. Partner/CFO, Saxotech, NH, Bedford

Mooney, Donna
mooneyd@uapb.edu, University of Arkansas at Pine Bluff, AR, Pine Bluff

Mooney, Gail
tribune@tctribune.net, Graph. Des. / Adv. , Traill County Tribune, ND, Mayville

Mooney, James
james.mooney@ckp.com, Vice Pres., Opns., Saxotech, NH, Bedford

Mooney, Marysue....................(413) 788-1220
mmooney@repub.com, Adv. Mgr., Classified, The Republican, MA, Springfield

Mooneyham, Scott
smooneyh@ncinsider.com, Mgr., Capitol Press Association, NC, Raleigh

Moore, Anita
classified@klamathfallsnickel.com, Adv. Mgr., The Nickel, OR, Klamath Falls

Moore, Ann ....(903) 962-4275
amoore@grandsalinesun.com, Adv. Dir./Bus. Mgr., Grand Saline Sun, TX, Grand Saline

Moore, Ashley
Ashley@vineyardpress.biz, Adv., Courier-Leader, MI, Paw Paw
Ashley@vineyardpress.biz, Adv. Dir., Morning

Times, PA, Sayre

Moore, Barbara
bmoore@newportnewstimes.com, Adv. Dir., News-Times, OR, Newport

Moore, Bethany ....(606) 248-1010 Ext. 1164
bmoore@civitasmedia.com, Editorial Clerk, The Harlan Daily Enterprise, KY, Harlan
bmoore@civitasmedia.com, Editorial Clerk, Middlesboro Daily News, KY, Middlesboro

Moore, Bob ....(970) 224-7755
robertmoore@coloradoan.com, Exec. Ed., Colorado Connection, CO, Fort Collins

Moore, Bob ....(870) 423-6636 ext. 25
b.moore@cox-internet.com, Pub./Adv. Dir., Lovely County Citizen, AR, Eureka Springs
b.moore@cox-internet.com, Pub., Carroll County News, AR, Berryville

Moore, C.A. ....(660) 679-6127
Pub./Editor, News-Xpress, MO, Butler

Moore, Carol
cymoore@sun-herald.com, Pub., Englewood Sun, FL, Englewood
cymoore@sun-herald.com, General Manager, North Port Sun, FL, North Port

Moore, Catherine ....(518) 891-2600
cmoore@adirondackdailyenterprise.com, Pub. , Adirondack Daily Enterprise, NY, Saranac Lake

Moore, Catherine ....(518) 891-2600
cmoore@adirondackenterprise.com, Pub., The Lake Placid News, NY, Lake Placid

Moore, Chad ....(403) 235-8646
cmoore@postmedia.com, Adv. Mgr., Classified, Calgary Herald, AB, Calgary

Moore, Charlie ....(505) 823-3847
cmoore@abqjournal.com, Bus. Ed., Albuquerque Journal, NM, Albuquerque

Moore, Chris
kemoore@mckendree.edu, Associate Editor, McKendree University, IL, Lebanon

Moore, Christine ....(971) 204 7771
cmoore@pamplinmedia.com, Pub., Regal Courier, OR, Lake Oswego

Moore, Christine
cmoore@commnewspapers.com, Adv Dir, The Lake Oswego Review, OR, Lake Oswego

Moore, Christine ....(503) 546-0771
cmoore@commnewspapers.com, Adv. Dir., Southwest Community Connection, OR, Lake Oswego
cmoore@commnewspapers.com, Adv. Dir., Wilsonville Spokesman, OR, Lake Oswego
cmoore@commnewspapers.com, Adv. Dir., West Linn Tidings, OR, Lake Oswego
cmoore@commnewspapers.com, Retail Adv Dir, Pamplin Media Group, OR, Portland
cmoore@commnewspapers.com, Adv. Dir., Boom! Boomers and Beyond, OR, Gresham

Moore, Christine ....(503) 546-0771
cmoore@commnewspapers.com, Adv. Dir, The Times (Tigard/Tualatin Times), OR, Portland

Moore, Christine ....(503) 684-0360
cmoore@commnewspapers.com, Adv. Dir, The Beaverton Valley Times, OR, Portland

Moore, Christine
cmoore@commnewspapers.com, Adv. Dir., Sustainable Life, OR, Portland
cmoore@commnewspapers.com, Adv. Dir., The Portland Tribune, OR, Portland

Moore, Dan
publisher@alvinsun.net, Pub./Adv. Dir., Alvin Sun-Advertiser, TX, Alvin

Moore, Dan ....(903) 962-4275
dmoore@grandsalinesun.com, Pub., Grand Saline Sun, TX, Grand Saline

Moore, Daniel ....(208) 226-5294
press2@press-times.com, Staff Writer, Power County Press, ID, American Falls

Moore, Debra.........................(530) 283-0800

dmoore@plumasnews.com, Ed, Chester Progressive, CA, Chester

Moore, Debra..........................(530) 283-0800
dmoore@plumasnews.com, Mng Ed, Feather River Bulletin, CA, Quincy

Moore, Debra..........................(530) 283-0800
dmoore@plumasnews.com, Mng Ed, Portola Reporter, CA, Portola

Moore, Debra..........................(530) 283-0800
dmoore@plumasnews.com, Mng. Ed., Indian Valley Record, CA, Greenville

Moore, Debra..........................(530) 283-0800
dmoore@plumasnews.com, Mng Ed, Feather Publishing Co., Inc., CA, Quincy

Moore, Don
dmoore@highpoint.edu, Opns. Mgr., High Point Univ., NC, High Point

Moore, Don
dmoore@sanmarcosrecord.com, Pub., San Marcos Daily Record, TX, San Marcos

Moore, Eric ....(501) 337-7523 ext 213
sports@malvern-online.com, Sports Ed., Malvern Daily Record, AR, Malvern

Moore, Ernest
icm@ironcountyminer.com, Pub./Ed., Iron County Miner, WI, Hurley

Moore, Eva......................(803) 765-0707 x136
editor@free-times.com, Executive Editor, Free Times, SC, Columbia

Moore, Gatha.................(618) 253-7146 ext.235
gmoore@dailyregister.com, Prodn. Mgr., The Daily Register, IL, Harrisburg

Moore, Heather ....(902) 838-2515 ext. 207
editor@peicanada.com, Ed., The Eastern Graphic, PE, Montague

Moore, Horace ....(205) 486-9461
nwanews@centurytel.net, Editor/Publisher, Northwest Alabamian, AL, Haleyville

Moore, Horace
trnews@centurytel.net, Pub., The Times-Record, AL, Fayette

Moore, Horace
jrpaper@centurytel.net, Pub., Journal Record, AL, Haleyville

Moore, Ivy ....(803) 774-1221
ivym@theitem.com, Feat. Ed., The Sumter Item , SC, Sumter

Moore, Jeff
jmoore@mytrimblenews.com, Pub., Trimble Banner, KY, Bedford

Moore, Jeff
jmoore@mycarrollnews.com, Pub., River City Trading Post, KY, Carrollton

Moore, Jeff
jmoore@mycarrollnews.com, Pub./Ed., Carrollton News-Democrat, KY, Carrollton

Moore, Jennie
jmoore@fdba-tx.com, Adv. Dir., Forney Messenger, TX, Forney

Moore, John ....(805) 437-0200
jmoore@vcstar.com, Mng. Ed., Ventura County Star, CA, Camarillo

Moore, John ....(207) 791-6631
jmoore@mainetoday.com, Dir. Digital Products, Portland Press Herald / Maine Sunday Telegram, ME, Portland

Moore, Julie C.
julie@bguide.net, Ed., The Buyer's Guide, VA, Springfield

Moore, Karleigh
general@tech.mit.edu, Chairman, Massachusetts Inst. of Technology, MA, Cambridge

Moore, Keith..........................(417) 683-4181
keith@douglascountyherald.com, Ed., Douglas County Herald, MO, Ava

Moore, Kimberly
kmoore@bellpartnersinc.com, Adj. Asst. Prof., North Carolina A&T State University, NC, Greensboro

Moore, LaDana
ladana@easttexasreview.com, Advertising Manager, East Texas Review, TX, Longview

Moore, Laura
l_moore@straight.com, Dir. of Adv./Mktg., Georgia Straight, BC, Vancouver

Moore, Makayla ....(307) 266-0509
Reporter, Casper Journal, WY, Casper

Moore, Marcia
mmoore@dailyitem.com, Reporter, The Daily Item, PA, Sunbury

Moore, Michael ....(218) 779-7858
mdmoore@gvtel.com, Pub., The Thirteen Towns, MN, Fosston

Moore, Michael
mmoore@newsvmedia.com, Editor, Morgan Hill Times, CA, Morgan Hill

Moore, Michael ....(360) 377-3711
mmoore@kitsapsun.com, Entertainment Writer, Kitsap Sun, WA, Bremerton

Moore, Mike
moorem@hkywater.org, Graphics Ed./Art Dir., The Gleaner, KY, Henderson

Moore, Mike ....(205) 486-9461
nwamoore@centurytel.net, Gen. Mgr., Northwest Alabamian, AL, Haleyville

Moore, Neil
nmoore@yrmg.com, Adv. Mgr., The Georgina Advocate, ON, Keswick

Moore, Patricia ....(606) 564-9091 Ext. 280
patty.moore@lee.net, Adv. Mgr., The Ledger Independent, KY, Maysville

Moore, Patty ....(606) 564-9091
patty.moore@lee.net, Adv. Mgr., The Advertiser, KY, Maysville

Moore, Paulette ....(336) 722-8624 Ext 100
plewis@wschronicle.com, Office Mgr., The Chronicle, NC, Winston Salem

Moore, Peter J.
graphics@agfa.com, Pres., Pitman Co., NJ, Elmwood Park

Moore, Phyllis..........................(919) 739-7828
pmoore@newsargus.com, Educ./Health Ed., Goldsboro News-Argus, NC, Goldsboro

Moore, Richard 643-4947
news@ritchiecountynews.com, Editor, The Pennsboro News, WV, Harrisville

Moore, Richard
richard.moore@richlandone.org, Assoc. Prof., University of South Carolina, SC, Columbia

Moore, Robert................................ext. 126
info@icescape.com, Mktg. Dir., Computer Talk Technology, Inc., ON, Richmond Hill

Moore, Robert............. (214) 754-8710 ext. 112
robertmoore@dallasvoice.com, Pub., Dallas Voice, TX, Dallas

Moore, Robert ....(915) 546-6149
bmoore@elpasotimes.com, Ed., El Paso y Mas, TX, El Paso
bmoore@elpasotimes.com, Executive Editor , El Paso Times, TX, El Paso

Moore, Rochelle
rmoore@newsargus.com, Reporter, Goldsboro News-Argus, NC, Goldsboro

Moore, Roxanne ....(803) 359-7633
roxanne.chronicle@gmail.com, Advertising Representative, Lexington County Chronicle & The Dispatch-News, SC, Lexington

Moore, Sharon
smoore@newspress.com, Prodn. Mgr., Publishing Servs., Santa Barbara News-Press, CA, Santa Barbara

Moore, Shirley

moore_sw@tsu.edu, Chair, Texas Southern University, TX, Houston

Moore, Stacy
editor@hidesertstar.com, Mng. Ed., Hi-Desert Star, CA, Yucca Valley

Moore, Suzanne......................(518) 565-4131
smoore@pressrepublican.com, News Editor, Press-Republican, NY, Plattsburgh

Moore, Tammy
news@smithvilletimes.com, Vice Pres., The Smithville Times, TX, Bastrop

Moore, Tom ....(831) 212-2391
tom.moore@scng.com, Exec Sports Ed, Press-Telegram, CA, Long Beach

Moore, Tom ....(831) 212-2391
tom.moore@langnews.com, Exec. Sports Ed., Los Angeles Daily News, CA, Woodland Hills

Moore, Tom ....(626) 544-6678
tmoore2@scng.com, Prodn. Facilities, The Gloucester County Times, NJ, Woodbury
tmoore2@scng.com, Exec. Sports Ed., The Facts (Redlands), CA, Redlands
tmoore2@scng.com, Exec. Sports Ed., Pasadena Star-News, CA, Torrance

Moore, Tom ....(831) 212-2391
tmoore@langnews.com, Exec. Sports Ed., Daily Breeze, CA, Torrance

Moore, Trent
tmoore@cullmantimes.com, Digital Ed., The Cullman Times, AL, Cullman

Moore, Wendy......................(403) 314-4322
wmoore@reddeeradvocate.com, Advt Mgr, Friday Forward, AB, Red Deer

Moore, Wendy
wmoore@reddeeradvocate.com, Adv. Mgr., Central Alberta Life, AB, Red Deer

Moore , Greg ....(864) 489-1131
greg@gaffneyledger.com, Advt Mgr, The Gaffney Ledger, SC, Gaffney

Moore-Black, Wilma ....(316) 978-6113
wilma.black@wichita.edu, Kansas Professional Communicators, KS, Americus

Moore-Yount, Jeanne
tribune@meadvilletribune.com, Pub., Bravo Extra, PA, Meadville

Mooree, David
dmoore@the-tidings.com, Pub., The Tidings, CA, Los Angeles

Mooreland, Tom
tmooreland@sjmercury.com, Dir., Mercury Center, Mercury Center, CA, San Jose

Moorhead, Ron C.
glenmoorent@yahoo.com, Gen. Mgr., Glenmoor Enterprise Media Group, Willits

Moorhouse, Ginger F.
ginger@bakersfield.com, Chrmn. of the Board/Pub., The Bakersfield Californian, CA, Bakersfield

Moorman, J.R.
moorman-j@mail.mssc.edu, Head, Missouri Southern University, MO, Joplin

Moormann, David D.
editor@decaturrepublican.com, Ed., Decatur Republican, MI, Decatur

Moormann, Ramona
editor@marcellusnews.com, Ed., Marcellus News, MI, Marcellus

Mooty, Kyle ....(334) 687-3506 Ext. 111
kmooty@eprisenow.com, Gen. Mgr., Eufaula Tribune, AL, Eufaula
kmooty@eprisenow.com, Gen. Mgr./Editor, The Enterprise Ledger, AL, Enterprise

Mooty, Lee
mooty@hometownnewsol.com, Pub / Gen. Mgr., Hometown News, FL, Fort Pierce

Mooy, Rob ....(613) 544-5000 ext. 114
robmooy@kingstonthisweek.com, Photo Ed., Kingston This Week, ON, Kingston

Mora, Al ....(562) 841-6672
almora@olec.com, Sales Mgr., OLEC, CA, Santa Ana

Morace, Cora
Cora@concordiasentinel.com, Circ. Mgr., Concordia Sentinel, LA, Ferriday

Moraflores, Giovanna
gmoraflores@newszap.com, Copy Ed., Glades County Democrat, FL, Okeechobee

Morah, Tanya
tmorah@wilberforce.edu, Wilberforce Univ., OH, Wilberforce

Morales, Chuck ....(480) 898-5690
chuck@timespublications.com, Ops. Mgr., Ahwatukee Foothills News, AZ, Tempe

Morales, Ed
ed.morales@onlineathens.com, Univ. of Georgia, GA, Athens

Morales, Hilbert ....(408) 938-1700
ejr_morales@yahoo.com, hmorales@el-observador.com, Pub., El Observador, CA, San Jose

Morales, Kasey ....(360) 834-5756
kmorales@maxcessintl.com, Brand Manager, Maxcess, OK, Oklahoma City

Morales, Kasey
tidland@tidland.com, Media Mgr., Tidland Corp., WA, Camas

Morales, Melinda......................(559) 735-3278
Daily Ed., Visalia Times-Delta, CA, Visalia

Moran, Becky..........................(615) 560-2200
bmoran@tennessean.com, Gen. Mgr., Fairview Observer, TN, Fairview

Moran, Becky
news@dicksonherald.com, Gen. Mgr., The Dickson Herald, TN, Dickson

Moran, Becky
bmoran@mtcngroup.com, Gen. Mgr., Dickson Shopper, TN, Dickson

Moran, Brendan
bmoran@keepmecurrent.com, Ed., The Lakes Region Weekly, ME, Westbrook

Moran, Dan
danmoran@tribpub.com, News Ed., Lake County News-Sun, IL, Gurnee

Moran, Eric ....(404) 614-1228
eric.moran@creativeloafing.com, Advertising Director, Creative Loafing Atlanta, GA, Atlanta

Moran, James ....(920) 418-1777
moranpublishing@gmail.com, Pub., Chilton Times-Journal, WI, Chilton

Moran, Julio ....(818) 989-7764
juliomoran@ccnma.org, Executive Director, CCNMA: Latino Journalists of California, CA, Santa Monica

Moran, Kevin
kmoran@berkshireeagle.com, Rgl. Pub., The Berkshire Eagle, MA, Pittsfield

Moran, Mark
mmoran@citizensvoice.com, Photo Ed., The Citizens' Voice, PA, Wilkes Barre

Moran, Matt ....(580) 482-1221 Ext. 2071
mmoran@civitasmedia.com, Pub. , Altus Times, OK, Altus

Moran, Mike ....(413) 585-5247
mmoran@gazettenet.com, Sports Ed., Daily Hampshire Gazette, MA, Northampton

Moran, Roaldo ....(213) 237-4361
rmaoran@hoyllc.com, General Manager Hoy Los Angeles, Hoy LLC, CA, Los Angeles

Moran, Robert ....(631) 737-6020 x117
rmoran@flexography.org, Pub., FLEXO Mag., Flexographic Technical Association, NY, Bohemia

Moran, Tom
tmoran@starledger.com, Editorial Page Ed.,

The Star-Ledger, NJ, Newark

Morano, John...........................(732) 571-4424
morano@monmouth.edu, Professor of
Journalism, Monmouth University, NJ, West
Long Branch

Morava, Kim.............................(405) 214-3922
kimberly.morava@news-star.com, Ed.,
Shawnee News-Star, OK, Shawnee

Moravec, Amanda
chronicleclassifieds@countrymedia.net, Gen.
Mgr, The Chronicle, OR, Saint Helens

Mordhorst, Todd.....................(530) 852-0240
atoddm@goldcountrymedia.com, Auburn
Journal, CA, Auburn

Moreau, Michael.....................(818) 551-5214
mmoreau@glendale.edu, Glendale Cmty.
College, CA, Glendale

Moreau, Norman
nmoreau@sunjournal.com, Acc. Exec., Sun
Journal, ME, Lewiston

Morefield, Lilly
kpikate@gmail.com, Ed.
, The Carlisle County News, KY, Paducah

Moreland, David
dmoreland@dauphingraphic.com, Vice Pres.,
Sales/Mktg., Manugraph DGM, Inc., PA,
Millersburg

Moreland, Jeff
publisher@cknj.com, Pub/Ed, Central Kentucky
News-Journal, KY, Campbellsville

Morelli, Chris
cmorelli@butlereagle.com, Mng. Ed., Eagle
Media, PA, Butler
cmorelli@butlereagle.com, Mng. Ed. , Butler
Eagle, PA, Butler

Morelli, Joe............................(410) 617-2867
Loyola College, MD, Baltimore

Morello, Peter
morellop@umkc.edu, Assoc. Prof., University
of Missouri-Kansas City, MO, Kansas City

Moreno, Anthony
amoreno@tremorvideo.com, Circ. Mgr.,
Tazewell County Shopper, IL, Pekin
amoreno@tremorvideo.com, Newspaper
National Network LP, NY, New York

Moreno, Elena........................(212) 867-5757
efenyc@efeamerica.com , Bureau Chief- New
York, EFE News Services - Washington, DC,
Washington

Moreno, John
publisher@thestarnews.com, Pub., The Star-
News, CA, Chula Vista

Moreno, Julie.........................(850) 599-2126
jmoreno@tallahassee.com, Pub., The
Examiner / Examiner Weekend, MO,
Independence

Mores, Alan...........................(712) 755-3111
news2@harlanonline.com, Co-Pub., News-
Advertiser, IA, Harlan

Mores, Steven
news2@harlanonline.com, Pub., Pennysaver,
IA, Harlan

Moretti, Anthony
amoretti@pointpark.edu, Asst. Prof., Point Park
University, PA, Pittsburgh

Moretz, Brian
bmoretz@equipto.com, Mktg. Lead,
Consolidated Storage Cos., PA, Tatamy

Morey, Jed
jmorey@longislandpress.com, Pub., Long
Island Press, NY, Syosset

Morf, Marianne
marianne@clreporter.com, Ed., Clear Lake
Mirror Reporter, IA, Clear Lake

Morford, Mary Ann
hiherald@venturecomm.net, Pub./Ed.,
Highmore Herald, SD, Highmore

Morgan, Alicia........................(812) 231-4298
alicia.morgan@tribstar.com, News/Digital Ed. ,
The Tribune Star, IN, Terre Haute

Morgan, Andy
amorgan@postandcourier.com, Sales and
Mktg. Mgr, The Post and Courier, SC,
Charleston

Morgan, Barry
ads@newsprogress.com, Adv. Mgr., News-
Progress, IL, Sullivan

Morgan, Bill
newsroom@njeffersonnews.com, Pub., North
Jefferson News, AL, Gardendale

Morgan, David
dmorgan@novetta.com, The Hollywood
Reporter, CA, Los Angeles
dmorgan@novetta.com, Pres, Sports Media
Group, USA TODAY, VA, Mc Lean

Morgan, Heather.....................(403) 652-6849
hmorgan@postmedia.com, Advertising
Manager, The High River Times, AB, High
River

Morgan, James
abrinkmeyer@sierranevadamedia.com, Swift
Communications, Inc., NV, Carson City

Morgan, Jerry
jmorgan@dothaneagle.com, Regional Sales
Dir, The Dothan Eagle, AL, Dothan

Morgan, Jerry
jmorgan@dothaneagle.com, Regl. Sales Mgr.,
Dothan Progress, AL, Dothan

Morgan, Judith A............(908) 782-4747 ext. 693
Circ. Mgr., Hunterdon County Democrat, NJ,
Flemington

Morgan, Judy
jmorgan@hcdemocrat.com, Circ. Mgr.,
Hunterdon Observer, NJ, Flemington

Morgan, Karen........................(757) 247-4757
kmorgan@dailypress.com, Features Ed., Daily
Press, VA, Newport News

Morgan, Karen........................(856) 486-2478
karmorgan@gannettnj.com, Regional Prod,
The Courier-Post, NJ, Cherry Hill

Morgan, Lovina
lovina@okcfriday.com, Adv. Sales Rep.,
Wewoka Times, OK, Wewoka
lovina@okcfriday.com, Adv. Sales, Oklahoma
City Friday, OK, Oklahoma City

Morgan, McKayla....................(867) 668-2060
Advertising Rep., Whitehorse Star, YT,
Whitehorse

Morgan, Nicholas....................(541) 776-4411
news@mailtribune.com, Mail Tribune, OR,
Medford

Morgan, Nicole.......................(318) 368-9632
nicole@fgazette.com, Circulation manager, The
Gazette, LA, Farmerville

Morgan, Pam
pam.morgan@mwsu.edu, Adj. Fac.,
Midwestern State University, TX, Wichita
Falls

Morgan, Patricia
billing.sullivandailytimes@gmail.com, Bus.
Mgr., The Sullivan Daily Times, IN, Sullivan

Morgan, Patrick
theman@italiancc.org, Gen. Mgr., Italian
Times, WI, Milwaukee

Morgan, Richard......................(859) 231-1495
rmorgan@herald-leader.com, Asst. Mng. Ed.,
The Daily Deal, NY, New York
rmorgan@herald-leader.com, Audience
Operations Manager, Lexington Herald-
Leader, KY, Lexington

Morgan, Rick
rick@springfieldtimes.net, Ed, Springfield
Times, OR, Springfield

Morgan, Robert......................(412) 263-1353
rmorgan@post-gazette.com, Retail Advertising

Manager, Pittsburgh Post-Gazette, PA,
Clinton

Morgan, Shannon
editor@arbiteronline.com, Boise State Univ.,
ID, Boise

Morgan, Veda........................(502) 582-4215
vmorgan@courier-journal.com, News Dir., The
Courier-Journal, KY, Louisville

Morgan, William C.
hughescountytimes@sbcglobal.net, Ed., The
Hughes County Times, OK, Wetumka
hughescountytimes@sbcglobal.net, Ed./Mng.
Ed., The Weleetkan, OK, Weleetka

Morgan-Prager, Karole
karole@mcclatchy.com, VP/Sec./Gen. Counsel,
The McClatchy Company, CA, Sacramento

Morgante, Michelle
mmorgante@ap.org, Mng. Ed., Merced Sun-
Star, CA, Merced

Morganthaler, Jim
sales@stats.com, Gen. Mgr., STATS, LLC., IL,
Northbrook

Morgenstern, Barbara
bmorgenstern@ithaca.edu, Assoc. Prof., Ithaca
College, NY, Ithaca

Morgenstern, Barbara G.............(585) 427-2434
Ed., The Jewish Ledger, NY, Rochester

Morgenstern, George.................(585) 427-2468
info@thejewishleger.com, Gen. Mgr., The
Jewish Ledger, NY, Rochester

Morgnanesi, Lanny....................(215) 345-3075
lmorganesi@phillyburbs.com, Exec. Ed., The
Intelligencer, PA, Doylestown

Morgret, RoxAnne
roxanne.morgret@hillsdale.net, Circ. Mgr.,
Hillsdale Daily News, MI, Hillsdale

Mori, Michael.........................(419) 724-6000
mmori@toledoblade.com, Sales Dir., The
Blade, OH, Toledo

Moriarty, Dan
danmoriarty@thewestfieldnews.com, Ed., The
Westfield News , MA, Westfield

Morice, Sandy
smorice@cubafreepress.com, Advertising, The
Cuba Free Press, MO, Cuba

Morilak, Mark
mmorilak@sunnews.com, Ed., Sun News, OH,
Cleveland

Morin, Bob
rmorin@benningtonbanner.com, Adv. Mgr.,
Bennington Banner, VT, Bennington

Morin, Ed
sales@nwnexus.com, Pres., WinStar/
Northwest Nexus, Inc., WA, Bellevue

Morin, Phil.............................(612) 278-0242
phil@mna.org, Advertising Account Manager,
Minnesota Newspaper Association, MN,
Minneapolis

Morin, Sarah
smorin@heraldt.com, The Herald Times, IN,
Bloomington

Morin, Tom
editor@dailycourtreview.com, Pub., Daily Court
Review, TX, Houston

Morissette, Dove.....................(978) 338-2677
dmorissette@salemnews.com, Night Ed., The
Salem News, MA, Beverly

Moritz, James........................(605) 598-6525
info@faulkcountyrecord.com, Pub./Ed., Faulk
County Record, SD, Faulkton

Morley, Sam..........................(850) 521-1199
smorley@flpress.com, Gen. Counsel, Florida
Press Association, FL, Lake Mary

Morley, Sam..........................(321) 283-5353
smorley@flpress.com, General Counsel,
Intersect Media Solutions, FL, Lake Mary

Morlino, Robert

info@madisoncatholicherald.org, Pub., Catholic
Herald Newspaper, WI, Madison

Moroni, Kelly.........................(813) 739-4843
kelly.moroni@creativeloafing.com, Ad. Sales,
Creative Loafing Tampa Bay, FL, Tampa

Moroz, Patrick
patrick@starnews.ca, Adv. Mgr., Wainwright
Star (OOB), AB, Wainwright
patrick@starnews.ca, Adv. Sales, Wainwright
Star Edge, AB, Wainwright

Morrell, Mary.........................(609) 403-7135
mmorre@dioceseoftrenton.org, Mng Ed., The
Monitor, NJ, Trenton

Morrill, Dean
dmorrill@pilotindependent.com, Ed., The Pilot-
Independent, MN, Walker

Morrill, Dean
dean.morill@mx3.com, Ed., Co-pilot, MN,
Walker

Morris, Aly
alymorris@redeyechicago.com, Dsgn. Dir.,
RedEye, IL, Chicago

Morris, Bekki
bekki@ameliamonitor.com, Adv. Mgr., The
Amelia Bulletin Monitor, VA, Amelia Court
House

Morris, Beth
beth@winchesterpress.on.ca, Owner/Pres.,
Winchester Press, ON, Winchester

Morris, Beth
bmorris@slpprint.ca, Pub., The Prescott
Journal, ON, Prescott

Morris, Billy...........................(706) 823-3299
wsmiii@morris.com, CEO, Morris
Communications Co. LLC, GA, Augusta

Morris, Bob...........................(620) 532-3151
bmorris@kcnonline.com, Education and Sports
Ed., Kingman Leader-Courier, KS, Kingman

Morris, Bob...........................(270) 691-7210
bmorris@messenger-inquirer.com, Pub.,
Messenger-Inquirer, KY, Owensboro

Morris, Bob
bmorris@mccleannews.com, Pub., McLean
County News, KY, Calhoun

Morris, Bonnie........................(815) 539-9396
bmorris@mendotareporter.com, Ed., The
Amboy News, IL, Amboy

Morris, Bonnie
editor@mendotareporter.com, Ed., Mendota
Reporter, IL, Mendota

Morris, Brad.................(740) 474-3131 Ext. 211
sports@circlevilleherald.com, Sports Ed. , The
Circleville Herald, OH, Circleville

Morris, Brent.........................(616) 546-4259
Brent.morris@hollandsentinel.com, Pres. and
Pub., The Holland Sentinel, MI, Holland

Morris, Charles H.....................(912) 233-1281
chm@morrismultimedia.com, Chrmn./CEO,
Morris Multimedia, Inc., GA, Savannah
chm@morrismultimedia.com, Pub., The
Covington News, GA, Covington
chm@morrismultimedia.com, Southern
Newspaper Publishers Association, GA,
Atlanta

Morris, Chris
cmorris@newsadvance.com, Sports Ed., The
News & Advance, VA, Lynchburg
cmorris@newsadvance.com, Travel Ed., The
Boston Globe, MA, Boston

Morris, Chris.........................(812) 206-2155
chris.morris@newsandtribune.com, Asst. Ed.,
Tribune, IN, New Albany
chris.morris@newsandtribune.com, Asst. Ed.,
News and Tribune, IN, Jeffersonville

Morris, Darcie
Darcie.Morris@sunmedia.ca, Adv Dir, Morden
Times, MB, Morden
Darcie.Morris@sunmedia.ca, Adv Dir, Winkler
Times, MB, Winkler

Darcie.Morris@sunmedia.ca, Adv Dir, The Valley Leader, MB, Carman
Darcie.Morris@sunmedia.ca, Adv Dir, The Red River Valley Echo, MB, Altona

Morris, Daryn..........................**(712) 647-2821**
news@woodbinetwiner.com, The Woodbine Twiner, IA, Woodbine

Morris, Debbie Wachter ....**ext. 631**
Reporter, New Castle News, PA, New Castle

Morris, Edwin C.
thecalhountimes@windstream.net, Pub., The Calhoun Times, SC, Saint Matthews

Morris, Greg ....**(317) 472-5320**
gmorris@ibj.com, Pub., Indianapolis Business Journal, IN, Indianapolis

Morris, Hal..................**(859) 236-2551 Ext. 137**
hmorris@amnews.com, Asst. Sports Ed., The Advocate-Messenger, KY, Danville

Morris, Helen..........................**(304) 354-6917**
contact@calhounchronicle.com, Pub., The Calhoun Chronicle, WV, Grantsville

Morris, Jack ....**(785) 827-5541 ext. 5227**
jmorris@kwu.edu, Kansas Wesleyan Univ., KS, Salina

Morris, Jeff ....**(613) 692-6000**
newsfile@bellnet.ca, Pub., Manotick Messenger, ON, Johnstown

Morris, Jeff
editor@prescottjournal.com, Prodn. Mgr., The Daily News, MI, Greenville

Morris, Karen
morrisr@uwec.edu, Sr. Lectr./Dir., Forensics, University of Wisconsin-Eau Claire, WI, Eau Claire

Morris, Karen
chroniclenews1@rochester.rr.com, Pub., Chronicle Ad-viser, NY, Penn Yan

Morris, Karen
News@Chronicle-Express.com, Pub., The Chronicle-Express, NY, Penn Yan

Morris, Kim
kmorris.times@att.net, Bookkeeper, The Herington Times, KS, Herington

Morris, Kim Taylor....................**(509) 837-4500**
lmorris@eaglenewspapers.com, Adv. Sales, Daily Sun News, WA, Sunnyside

Morris, Larry
lbmorris@amclasstyler.com, American Classifieds - Tyler, TX, Tyler

Morris, Leo ....**(260) 461-8298**
lmorris@news-sentinel.com, Editorial Page Ed., The News-Sentinel, IN, Fort Wayne

Morris, Mary Ann
mmorris@thevalleychronicle.com, Ed., The Valley Chronicle, CA, Hemet

Morris, Matt
matt.morris@mhfi.com, Sales Contact, BMC Group, Inc., NY, New York

Morris, Merrill ....**(678) 717-3906**
mmorris@gsc.edu, Gainesville College, GA, Oakwood

Morris, Michelle
newnews@grm.net, Business Manager, Lamoni Chronicle, IA, Lamoni

Morris, Pam
publisher@mtexpress.com, Pub., Idaho Mountain Express, ID, Ketchum

Morris, Paul ....**(519) 583-0112**
news@portdovermapleleaf.com, Ed., Port Dover Maple Leaf, ON, Port Dover

Morris, Rebecca ....**(270) 259-6061**
rmorris@graysonrecord.com, General Manager/Editor, The Record, KY, Leitchfield

Morris, Richard
rmorris@dailystandard.com, Adv. Mgr., The Daily Standard, OH, Celina

Morris, Robert

rmorris@bizjournals.com, Ed, Charlotte Business Journal, NC, Charlotte

Morris, Robin R.
record@storm.ca, Pub., The Chesterville Record, ON, Chesterville

Morris, Sarah..........................**(252) 332-7215**
sarah.morris@r-cnews.com, Production Mgr., Roanoke-Chowan News-Herald, NC, Ahoskie
sarah.morris@r-cnews.com, Prod. Mgr., The Chowan Herald, NC, Edenton

Morris, Scott...........................**(256) 765-4426**
smorris4@una.edu, Student Media Advisor, Univ. of North Alabama, AL, Florence

Morris, Stan ....**(519) 583-0112**
stan@portdovermapleleaf.com, Ed., Port Dover Maple Leaf, ON, Port Dover

Morris, Steve
smorris@francevoiles.com, Pres., The Arbitron Co., NY, New York

Morris, Steve ....**(800) 451-9753**
smorris606@aol.com, President and CEO, Bellatrix Systems, Inc., OR, Bend

Morris, Tawnja
circulation@hclocal.com, Circulation manager, Oldham Era, KY, La Grange
circulation@hclocal.com, Circ Mgr, Henry County Local, KY, Eminence

Morris, Tony
tony.morris@armstrong.edu, Armstrong Atlantic State Univ., GA, Savannah

Morris , Michael ....**(404) 883-2130**
michael@atljewishtimes.com, Pub., Atlanta Jewish Times, GA, Atlanta

Morris III, William S. ....**(706) 823-3299**
Publisher, The Augusta Chronicle, GA, Augusta

Morris-Salster, Ann B.
ann@ameliamonitor.com, Pub., The Amelia Bulletin Monitor, VA, Amelia Court House

Morrison, Angye ....**ext. 1903**
angye.morrison@gaflnews.com, Mng. Ed., The Tifton Gazette, GA, Tifton

Morrison, Ellen
emorrison@rentonreporter.com, Pub./Adv. Mgr., Renton Reporter, WA, Kent

Morrison, Eric ....**(416) 364-0321**
eric.morrison@thecanadianpress.com, Pres., Canadian Press, The - Montreal, QC, QC, Montreal
eric.morrison@thecanadianpress.com, Pres., Canadian Press, The - Toronto, ON, ON, Toronto

Morrison, Jean
jmorr@napaneebeaver.com, Pub., Friday Regional Beaver, ON, Napanee

Morrison, Jean M.
beaver@bellnet.ca, Pub., The Napanee Beaver, ON, Napanee

Morrison, Jean M.
gazette@bellnet.ca, Pub., The Picton Gazette, ON, Picton

Morrison, Josh ....**(740) 532-1441 Ext. 211**
josh.morrison@irontontribune.com, Gen. Mgr. / Circ. Dir., The Ironton Tribune, OH, Ironton

Morrison, Kenn
kmorrison@morcor.com, Pres., Morcor Solutions, Inc., ON, Napanee

Morrison, Lindsay ....**(800) 851-7737 ext. 5123**
lmorr@srds.com, VP Marketing Communications, SRDS, a Kantar Media Company, IL, Des Plaines

Morrison, Mike........................**(518) 565-4179**
mmorrison@pressrepublican.com, Advertising Sales Manager, Press-Republican, NY, Plattsburgh

Morrissey, Andy ....**(336) 727-7389**
amorrissey@wsjournal.com, Managing Editor, Winston-Salem Journal, NC, Winston Salem

Morrissey, Scott

scot.morrissey@onlineathens.com, Pub., Athens Banner-Herald, GA, Athens

Morrone, AnnaMaria ....**(613) 232-5689**
annamaria@loradiottawa.com, Client Services, L'ora Di Ottawa, ON, Ottawa

Morrow, Andrew ....**(613) 232-5952 ext. 215**
amorrow@hilltimes.com, Gen. Mgr., The Hill Times, ON, Ottawa

Morrow, Derek ....**(205) 443-5629**
derekmorrow@bizjournals.com, Prod. Dir, Birmingham Business Journal, AL, Birmingham

Morrow, Mark ....**(617) 929-7129**
m_morrow@globe.com, Sr. Deputy Managing Ed., The Boston Globe, MA, Boston

Morrow, Pat...................**(660) 886-2233 ext. 13**
circmanager@socket.net, Circ. Mgr., Saline County Citizen, MO, Marshall

Morrow, Pat..........................**(660) 886-2233**
pmorrow@marshallnews.com, Circ. Mgr., The Marshall Democrat-News, MO, Marshall

Morrow, Richae ....**(785) 822-1412**
rmorrow@salina.com, Graphic Designer, The Salina Journal, KS, Salina

Morrow, Teresa
teresamorrow@miconews.com, Adv. Mgr., The Miami County Republic, KS, Paola

Morrow, Will...........................**(907) 335-1251**
will.morrow@peninsulaclarion.com, Mng. Ed., Peninsula Clarion, AK, Kenai

Morse, Deborah
deborah.morse@rutlandherald.com, Bus. Office Mgr., Rutland Herald, VT, Rutland
deborah.morse@rutlandherald.com, Pub., The Times Argus, VT, Barre

Morse, Ian
morsei@lafayette.edu, Mgr Ed, Lafayette College, PA, Easton

Morse, Jamie........................**(217) 832-4201**
vgads@mediacombb.net, Southern Champaign Co. Today, IL, Villa Grove
vgads@mediacombb.net, Advertising Representative, Villa Grove News, IL, Villa Grove

Morse, Kim
kim.morse@alexcityoutlook.com, Market. Consultant, Alexander City Outlook, AL, Alexander City

Morse, Melissa
mmorse@fcnp.com, Adv. Sales, Falls Church News-Press, VA, Falls Church

Morse, Robin
robin.morse@lubbockonline.com, Adv. Sales, Lubbock Avalanche-Journal, TX, Lubbock

Mort, Linda
lmort@idahocountyfreepress.com, Circ. Mgr., Idaho County Free Press, ID, Grangeville

Mortensen, Camilla ....**(541) 484-0519**
editor@eugeneweekly.com, Ed., Eugene Weekly, OR, Eugene

Mortensen, Hal........................**(801) 204-6151**
hmortensen@mediaoneutah.com, Vice President Circulation Operations, Media One of Utah, UT, West Valley City

Mortensen, Sarah....................**(860) 928-1818**
sarah@villagernewspapers.com, Ad. Director, Killingly Villager, CT, Woodstock
sarah@villagernewspapers.com, Adv. Dir., Sturbridge Villager, MA, Southbridge

Mortensen, Tammy
tmortensen@yourjournal.com, Adv. Mgr., Overland/St. Ann Journal-North Couny Journal, MO, Hazelwood

Mortenson, Brian ....**(541) 582-1707**
Brian@RogueRiverPress.com, Sports Ed., Rogue River Press, OR, Grants Pass

Morternsen, Ellen....................**(308) 537-7554**
news@gothenburgtimes.com, GM, Gothenburg

Times, NE, Gothenburg

Mortimore, Jim
jim.mortimore@starherald.com, Online Mgr., Star-Herald, NE, Scottsbluff

Mortimore, Rob
rmort@torringtontelegram.com, Gen. Mgr./Adv. Mgr., The Torrington Telegram, WY, Torrington
rmort@torringtontelegram.com, Gen. Mgr., The Lusk Herald, WY, Lusk

Morton, Dana
dmorton@marshallnewsmessenger.com, Bus. Mgr., Marshall News Messenger, TX, Marshall

Morton, Jerry
sales@tiltlock.com, Sales Mgr., Tilt-Lock, MN, Saint Michael

Mosbrucker , Mark....................**(563) 383-2303**
mmosbrucker@qctimes.com, Ops. Mgr., Quad-City Times, IA, Davenport

Mosby, Ray
deercreekpilot@bellsouth.net, Ed., Deer Creek Pilot, MS, Rolling Fork

Moscatelli, Liz ....**(651) 796-1116**
liz.moscatelli@ecm-inc.com, Multimedia Sales Dir, Star News, MN, Elk River

Mosco, Steve
smosco@antonmediagroup.com, Ed., Oyster Bay Enterprise Pilot, NY, Mineola

Mosconi, Toni
tmosconi@leaderherald.com, Circ. Dir., The Leader-Herald, NY, Gloversville

Moseley, Carol ....**ext. 251**
carolmoseley@rrdailyherald.com, Circ. Mgr., The Revue, NC, Roanoke Rapids

Moseley, Carol
carolmosely@rrdailyherald.com, Sec./Treasurer, Mid-Atlantic Circulation Managers Association, NC, Roanoke Rapids

Moseley, Davy
davy@ssecho.com, MIS Mgr./Websmaster, Sulphur Springs News-Telegram, TX, Sulphur Springs

Moseley, Kim
kim@thenewstimes.com, Adv. Dir., Carteret County News-Times, NC, Morehead City

Moseley, Paula........................**(503) 390-1051**
advertising@keizertimes.com, Adv. Acc. Rep., Keizertimes, OR, Keizer

Moseley, Steve ....**(402) 204-7019**
steve.moseley@yorknewstimes.com, Ed., York News-Times, NE, York

Moseley, Willie ....**(334) 283-6568**
willie.moseley@tallasseetribune.com, News Editor, The Tallassee Tribune, AL, Tallassee

Moser, Charles
cmoser@brenhambanner.com, Moser Community Media, LLC, TX

Moser, Christine ....**(303) 954-1133**
cmoser@denverpost.com, VP of Adv., The Denver Post, CO, Denver

Moser, David
david.moser@bc3.edu, Butler County Cmty. College, PA, Butler

Moser, Megan
news@themercury.com, Exec. Ed., The Manhattan Mercury, KS, Manhattan

Moser, Mike
mmoser@crossville-chronicle.com, Ed., Crossville Chronicle, TN, Crossville

Moser, Sayde
sayde@tctrib.com, Mng. Editor, Tri-County News, OR, Junction City

Moses, Betty..........................**(843) 488-7259**
betty.moses@myhorrynews.com, Prod. Mgr., Carolina Forest Chronicle, SC, Myrtle Beach

Moses, Donna ....**(765) 825-0581 ext. 244**
dmoses@newsexaminer.com, Adv. Rep.,

Connersville News-Examiner, IN, Connersville

Moses, George J. ....(810) 227-1575
gmoses@georgemosesco.com, Publisher, President, Advertising Director, Marketeer, MI, Brighton

Moses, Jamie
jamie@artvoice.com, Pub., Art Voice, NY, Buffalo

Moses, John ....(307) 732-7063
john@jhnewsandguide.com, Editor, Jackson Hole News&Guide, WY, Jackson

Moses, Karen..........................(505) 823-3803
kmoses@abqjournal.com, Mng. Ed., Albuquerque Journal, NM, Albuquerque

Moses, Lori ....(585) 292-3122
lmoses@monroecc.edu, Monroe Cmty. College, NY, Rochester

Moses, Melanie ....(810) 227-1575
melanie@georgemosesco.com, Publisher, CFO, Marketeer, MI, Brighton

Moses, Paul ....(718) 951-5302
CUNY/Brooklyn College, NY, Brooklyn

Mosesso, David
dmosesso@jonesborosun.com, Pub., The Jonesboro Sun, AR, Jonesboro

Moshavi, Sharon
smoshavi@icfj.org, Vice Pres., New Initiatives, International Center for Journalists, DC, Washington

Mosher, Mary
mary@omahadailyrecord.com, Legal Editor/Legal Notices, Daily Record, NE, Omaha

Mosier , Jeff ....(702) 224-5524
jmosier@viewnews.com, Ed. , View Neighborhood Newspapers, NV, Las Vegas

Moskal, Alan ....(310) 437-4401
gvnads@gardenavalleynews.org, Pub., Gardena Valley News, CA, Gardena

Mosley, Jim
jim@newsengin.com, CEO, NewsEngin, Inc., MO, Chesterfield

Mosley, Kyla
kmosley@simcoe.ca, Circ. Mgr., The Mirror, ON, Midland

Moss, Bill
billmoss@hendersonvillelightning.com, NCPS Secretary/Treasurer, North Carolina Press Association, NC, Raleigh

Moss, Dick ....(585) 258-2549
dmoss@democratandchronicle.com, News Ed., Democrat and Chronicle, NY, Rochester

Moss, Doug ....(203) 854-5559 ext. 106
doug@emagazine.com, Pub./Exec. Ed., Earth Talk: Questions & Answers About Our Environment, Norwalk

Moss, Joe ....(510) 642-7480
Univ. of California Bus. School, CA, Berkeley

Moss, Joe ....(574) 967-4135
comet@carrollcountycomet.com, Adv. Mgr., Carroll County Comet, IN, Flora

Moss, Loreta ....(719) 456-1333
lmoss@ljtdmail.com, Office Mgr., Bent County Democrat, CO, Las Animas

Moss, Robin ....(972) 239-8866
robin@ribit.com, Pres./Founder, Ribit, Inc., TX, Addison

Mossbarger, Jerry
jmossbarger@jcbiradio.com, Gen. Mgr., The Telegram, OH, Jackson

Mosser, Tami
tmosser@alonovus.com, Ed., Holmes County Journal, OH, Millersburg

Mosser, Tami
tmosser@alonovus.com, Ed, The Bargain Hunter - Wayne, OH, Millersburg

Mossiah, Karen ....(310) 243-1060

kmossiah@csudh.edu, California State Univ. Dominguez, CA, Carson

Mossman, Bill ....(808) 529-4863
Executive Editor, MidWeek Oahu, HI, Honolulu

Mossman, Bill ....(808) 529-4863
Executive Editor, MidWeek Oahu, HI, Honolulu

Mossman, Bill ....(808) 245-0457
bmossman@staradvertiser.com, The Garden Island, Lihue, HI, Lihue
bmossman@staradvertiser.com, Ed., The Garden Island, Kauai, HI, Lihue
bmossman@staradvertiser.com, Executive Editor, Kauai Midweek, HI, Honolulu

Mossman, Michael ....(765) 336-4454
mmossman@fujifilm.com, Newspaper Support Specialist, Fujifilm North America Corporation, IL, Hanover Park

Mote, Ryan
rmote@sacbee.com, VP, Adv., The Sacramento Bee, CA, Sacramento

Motley, Lorne........................(403) 235-7546
lmotley@calgaryherald.com, Ed. in Chief, Calgary Herald, AB, Calgary

Motsch, Gunther
gmotsch@edmsun.com, Controller, The Edmonton Sun, AB, Edmonton

Mott, Glenn ....(212) 969-7597
gmott@hearst.com, Ed./Pub. Dir., News, Feat., Books, North America Syndicate, New York

Mott, Patrick..........................(714) 282-3126
pmott@rcbo.org, Editor, Orange County Catholic, CA, Garden Grove

Motta, Bernardo......................(540) 828-5758
bmotta@bridgewater.edu, Assistant Professor of Communication Studies, Bridgewater College, VA, Bridgewater

Motter, Amy ....(316) 775-2218
amotter@butlercountytimesgazette.com, Adv. Exec., The Butler County Times-Gazette, KS, Augusta

Motz, Bonnie ....(812) 934-4343
bonnie.motz@batesvilleheraldtribune.com, advertising representative, The Herald-Tribune, IN, Batesville

Mouchard, Andre ....(714) 796-7926
amouchard@ocregister.com, Page One, Asst. Managing Ed., The Orange County Register, CA, Santa Ana

Moulton, Jordyn ....(518) 290-3927
moulton@digitalfirstmedia.com, Multi-Media Account Exec., The Saratogian, NY, Saratoga Springs

Mounsdon, Lynn ....(320) 763-1218
lmounsdon@echopress.com, Circ. Mgr., Echo-Press, MN, Alexandria

Mount, Tristan
tmount@newportindependent.com, Reporter, Newport Independent, AR, Newport

Mountain, Archie ....(603) 504-3182
archiemountain@gmail.com, Argus Champion Ed., Eagle Times, NH, Claremont

Mounts, Andrea
andrea.mounts@nclawyersweekly.com, Adv. Dir., The Mecklenburg Times, NC, Charlotte
andrea.mounts@nclawyersweekly.com, Ad. Dir, North Carolina Lawyers Weekly, NC, Charlotte

Mounts, Travis
graphicsdept@tsnews.com, Pub, Haysville Sun-Times, KS, Haysville

Mouser, Charles......................(800) 448-8595
cm@mouserinstitute.com, Pres., Mouser Institute School of Advertising, VA, Nottoway

Mouser, Shelly
smouser@logandaily.com, Bus. Mgr., Logan Daily News, OH, Logan

Mouton, Wanda
wmouton@sfasu.edu, Interim Chair, Stephen F.

Austin State University, TX, Nacogdoches

Mowat, Jamie
jmowat@niagaracommunitynewspaper.com, Adv. Mgr., St. Catherines Shopping News, ON, Saint Catharine's

Mowbray, Kevin ....(563) 383-2100
kevin.mowbray@lee.net, Chairman/Pres./CEO, Lee Enterprises, Inc., IA, Davenport

Mowe, Cliff
cliff@momoney.com, Pres., Mo-Money Associates, Inc., FL, Pensacola

Mowers, Carolyn
cmowers@bangordailynews.com, Chair, Board of Dir., Bangor Daily News, ME, Bangor

Mowery, David ....(610) 371-5011
dmowery@readingeagle.com, Mng. Ed., Reading Eagle, PA, Reading

Mowery-Denning, Linda ....(785) 472-5085
indy@eaglecom.net, Pub/Ed, The Ellsworth County Independent-Reporter, KS, Ellsworth

Mowrey, Deborah ....(228) 702-2127
dmowrey@biloxidiocese.org, Circ. Mgr., Gulf Pine Catholic, MS, Biloxi

Moya, Jesse ....(575) 546-2611 Ext. 2608
jmoya@demingheadlight.com, Rep., Deming Headlight, NM, Deming

Moyer, Amy ....(570) 644-6397 ext. 1316
amym@standard-journal.com, General manager, The News-Item, PA, Shamokin

Moyer, Amy ....(570) 742-9671
amym@standard-journal.com, Adv. Mgr., The Standard-Journal, PA, Milton

Moyer, J. Keith ....(702) 387-2906
kmoyer@reviewjournal.com, Ed. in Chief, Las Vegas Review-Journal, NV, Las Vegas

Moyer, Keith
kmoyer@reviewjournal.com, Ed., Reno Gazette-Journal, NV, Reno

Moyer, Michael........................(814) 472-8600
michaelmo@tradersguide.com, Circulation Manager, Traders Guide, PA, Ebensburg

Moyers, Gary ....(859) 236-2551 Ext. 205
gmoyers@amnews.com, Web Developer, The Winchester Sun, KY, Winchester
gmoyers@amnews.com, The Advocate-Messenger, KY, Danville

Moyet, Tera
sundaysunads@yahoo.com, Adv., Philadelphia Sunday Sun, PA, Philadelphia

Moyo, Debayo ....(662) 252-8000 ext. 4553
dmoyo@rustcollege.edu, Rust College, MS, Holly Springs

Moyo, Debayo R. ....(662) 252-8000 x4553
dmoyo@rustcollege.edu, Department Chair, Department of Mass Communications, Rust College, MS, Holly Springs

Mozingo, Regina
editor@wpdailyquill.net, News Editor, West Plains Daily Quill, MO, West Plains

Mracky, Ronald ....(818) 762-4020
africantimes-usa@mindspring.com, Mktg. Dir., The African Times/USA, CA, Hawthorne

Mrazek, Brenda ....(830) 379-5441 x 215
brenda.mrazek@seguingazette.com, Circulation Director, The Seguin Gazette, TX, Seguin

Mrok, Linda K.
ectartdept@comcast.net, Adv. Mgr., East County Times, MD, Baltimore

Muchmore, Kelly
kelly.muchmore@lee.net, Sales Exec., The Columbus Telegram, NE, Columbus

Muchmore, Tom........................(580) 765-3311
tmuch@poncacitynews.com, Ed. / Pub., The Ponca City News, OK, Ponca City

Muck, Rob ....ext. 245
Prodn. Mgr., Worthington Daily Globe, MN,

Worthington

Muckelbauer, Dan ....(262) 513-2626
dmuck@conleynet.com, Ed. , Milwaukee Post, WI, Milwaukee

Mudd, Angeline
amudd@nassaucountyrecord.com, Bus. Office Mgr., Nassau County Record, FL, Callahan

Mudd, Angeline ....(904) 261-3696
amudd@fbnewsleader.com, Regional Business Office Manager, News-Leader, FL, Fernandina Beach

Mudd, Kathy
editor@themonticellonews.com, Ed., The Monticello News, GA, Monticello

Mudge, Bob
bmudge@venicegondolier.com, Ed., The Sun Shopper, FL, Venice

Mudge, Chris
cmudge@cnaads.com, Exec. Dir., Customized Newspaper Advertising (Iowa), IA, Des Moines

Mueck, Michael
mmueck@brenhambanner.com, Ed., Banner Extra, TX, Brenham

Mueller, Becky
becky.m@adcommnews.com, Circ. Mgr, Advertiser Community News, WI, Seymour

Mueller, Debbie ....(920) 893-6411 ext. 128
Circ. Mgr., The Sheboygan Falls News, WI, Plymouth

Mueller, Felix
info@heidelberg.com , Senior Vice President, Equipment, Heidelberg USA, GA, Kennesaw

Mueller, Gary
gmueller@staplesworld.com, Adv. Mgr., Staples World, MN, Staples

Mueller, Gary........................(218) 894-1112
gmueller@staplesworld.com, Adv. Mgr., Sunday Square Shooter, MN, Staples

Mueller, James
james.mueller@unt.edu, Asst. Prof./Coord., News-Editorial seq., University of North Texas, TX, Denton

Mueller, Jeffrey ....ext. 310
jeff@towntooter.com, Gen. Mgr., Town Tooter, NC, Hendersonville

Muench, Glen
gmuench@pdpost.com, Display Mgr., Florida Pennysaver, FL, West Palm Beach

Muessig, Ben
bmeussig@sfchronicle.com, Business and Tech Ed, San Francisco Chronicle, CA, San Francisco

Mugar, Louise H.
louisemugar@thenorthernlight.com, Adv. Mgr., The Northern Light, WA, Blaine

Muharrem, Dean
deanm@bowesnet.com, Pub./Gen. Mgr., Chatham Pennysaver, ON, Chatham

Muharrem, Dean ....(519) 598-4700
dean.muharrem@sunmedia.ca, Chatham This Week, ON, Chatham
dean.muharrem@sunmedia.ca, Pub./Adv. Mgr. , The Chatham Daily News, ON, Chatham

Muharrem, Dean
DEAN.MUHARREM@SUNMEDIA.CA, Pub., Courier Press, ON, Chatham

Muhleman, Ron ....(360) 792-3355
rmuhleman@kitsapsun.com, Opns. Dir., Kitsap Sun, WA, Bremerton

Muilenburg, Robert....................361/698-1939
rmuilenburg@delmar.edu, Advisor, Del Mar College Foghorn, TX, Corpus Christi

Muilleoir , Mairtin O
momuilleoir@irishecho.com, Pub., Irish Echo, NY, New York

Muir, Nigel

info@praxair.com, Vice Pres., Commun./Pub. Rel., Praxair, Inc., CT, Danbury

Muir, Sandy
smuir@thestar.ca, VP, Adv., Toronto Star, ON, Toronto

Mukes, Arvid
arvid.mukes@famu.edu, Prof./Assoc. Dean./ Dir., Div. of Graphic Communication, Florida A&M University, FL, Tallahassee

Mulcahy, J.P.
siebert123@msn.com, Pres., Siebert, Inc., IL, Lyons

Mulcahy, James.......................(814) 781-7535
Sports Ed., The Daily Press, PA, Saint Marys

Mulder, Ron
newyork@magid.com, Pres., Minnesota Opinion Research, Inc. (MORI), MN, Minneapolis

Mulder, Ronald
rmulder@scarborough.com, VP, Analytics and Insights, Scarborough Research, NY, New York

Muldoon, Brian.......................(608) 744-2107
tcpads@yousq.net, Adv. Mgr., Tri-County Press, WI, Cuba City

Mulkey, Jack.........................(310) 660-3329
elcounionads000@yahoo.com, Adv. Mgr., El Camino College, CA, Torrance

Mullen, J. Louis.....................(307) 875-3103
Publisher , Green River Star, WY, Green River

Mullen, Jennifer
jen.mullen@colostate-pueblo.edu, Chair, Colorado State University, Pueblo, CO, Pueblo

Mullen, Jesse
publisher@statesmanexaminer.com , Regional Publisher, Statesman Examiner, WA, Colville

Mullen, Jimmy.............(601) 636-4545 ext. 148
jimmy.mullen@vicksburgpost.com, Prod. Mgr, The Vicksburg Post, MS, Vicksburg

Mullen, John
theislander@gulfcoastnewspapers.com, Ed., The Islander, AL, Foley

Mullen, Lawrence
lawrence.mullen@unlv.edu, Assoc. Prof./Prog. Grad. Coord., University of Nevada, Las Vegas, NV, Las Vegas

Mullen, Neil..........................(651) 228-5132
nmullen@pioneerpress.com, CFO, St. Paul Pioneer Press, MN, Saint Paul

Mullen, Norine.......................(253) 274-7344
norine.mullen@thenewstribune.com, HR Dir., The Olympian, WA, Olympia

Mullen, Rodger
mullenr@fayettevillenc.com, Columnist, The Fayetteville Observer, NC, Fayetteville

Mullen, Tom..........................(360) 426-4412
publisher@masoncounty.com, Pub., Pikes Peak Parent, CO, Colorado Springs
publisher@masoncounty.com, Pub., Shelton-Mason County Journal, WA, Shelton

Mullen, William
wmullen@Liberty.edu, Chrmn., Liberty Univ., VA, Lynchburg

Mullenax, Sherri
thechrismanleader@outlook.com, Pub., Chrisman Leader, IL, Chrisman

Mullens, Bonnie
bonnie@mcgregormirror.com, Co-Pub./Adv. Mgr., McGregor Mirror & Crawford Sun, TX, Mc Gregor

Mullens, Jeff........................(775) 748-2707
editor@elkodaily.com, Ed., Elko Daily Free Press, NV, Elko

Muller, Judy
jmmuller@usc.edu, Assoc. Prof., University of Southern California, CA, Los Angeles

Muller, Rich
news@barbertonherald.com, Ed., The Barberton Herald, OH, Barberton

Muller, Seth...........................(928) 913-8668
sethm@flaglive.com, Gen. Mgr., Flagstaff Live!, AZ, Flagstaff

Muller-Wharton, Leanne
lmuller-wharton@blackpearl.org, Adv. Sr. Acct. Exec., Chicago Defender, IL, Chicago

Mullholland, Curt...........(419) 674-4066 Ext. 238
cmullholand@kentontimes.com, Prod. Mgr. / Web. Admin. , The Kenton Times, OH, Kenton

Mulligan, Charles J.
jeanne@mulliganprinting.com, Mulligan Town & Country Shopper - N Wayne County, PA, Tunkhannock
jeanne@mulliganprinting.com, Mulligan's Penny - Wyoming County, PA, Tunkhannock
jeanne@mulliganprinting.com, Mulligan's Shopper - Lackauanna County, PA, Tunkhannock
jeanne@mulliganprinting.com, Mulligan's Shopping Guide - Susquehanna County, PA, Tunkhannock
jeanne@mulliganprinting.com, Adv. Sales Mgr., Town & Country Shopper (OOB), PA, Honesdale

Mulligan, Gerard.....................(352) 563-3222
gmulligan@chronicleonline.com, Pub., Sumter County Times, FL, Bushnell

Mulligan, Gerry......................(352) 563-6363
gmulligan@chronicleonline.com, Pub., Citrus County Chronicle, FL, Crystal River
gmulligan@chronicleonline.com, Pub., Riverland News, FL, Dunnellon

Mulligan, Holly.............(413) 525-3247 ext. 109
Circulation@ReminderPublications.com, Circ. Mgr., The Herald, MA, East Longmeadow

Mulligan, Holly
HollyM@TheReminder.com, Circ. Mgr., Reminder Metrowest / Chicopee Herald, MA, East Longmeadow
HollyM@TheReminder.com, Circ. Mgr., The Reminder, MA, East Longmeadow

Mullin, Beckie
bm@bulbtronics.com, Mgr., Mktg., Bulbtronics, NY, Farmingdale

Mullin, Deborah.......................(561) 820-2069
dmullin@alm.com, Vice President/Broward & Palm Beach Legals, Palm Beach Daily Business Review, FL, Miami

Mulliner, Michelle....................(231) 933-1492
mmulliner@record-eagle.com, Prodn. Dir., Traverse City Record-Eagle, MI, Traverse City

Mullinix, Heather....................(931) 484-5145
hmullinix@crossville-chronicle.com, Asst. Ed., Crossville Chronicle, TN, Crossville

Mullins, Angela
angela.mullins@alexcityoutlook.com, Bus. Mgr., Tallapoosa Publishers, Inc., AL, Alexander City

Mullins, Jack.........................(480) 461-7270
jackm@mesacc.edu, Advisor, Mesa Community College, AZ, Mesa

Mullins, Mike
mmullins@guhsdaz.org, Glendale Cmty. College, AZ, Glendale

Mullins, Penny.............(715) 735-7500 Ext. 157
pmullins@eagleherald.com, news and online editor, EagleHerald - ehextra.com, WI, Marinette

Mullins, Wes
wes@observernews.net, Pub. Mgr, Observer News, FL, Ruskin

Mullowney, Sheila L...................(401) 380-2351
editor@newportri.com, Exec. Ed., Newport Navalog, RI, Newport

Mulock, Greg
mulock.greg@thenorthernlight.ca, Ed., The Northern Light, NB, Bathurst

Mulvena, Debbie
dvena@thevalleychronicle.com, Adv. Mgr., Northumberland Echo, VA, Warsaw
dvena@thevalleychronicle.com, Journalist, The Valley Chronicle, CA, Hemet

Mulvey, Maxine
copy@theaggie.org, Copy Chief, University of California, Davis, CA, Davis

Mumert, Tommy.......................(501) 968-0284
tmumert@atu.edu, Arkansas Tech. Univ., AR, Russellville

Mummaw, Tracey
tracey.mummaw@npgco.com, Adv. Dir., Liberty Tribune, MO, Liberty

Munday, Patrick......................(406) 496-4461
Montana Tech. Univ., MT, Butte

Mundy, Becky
bmjones@sshopper.com, Office Mgr., Southside Shopper, NC, Garner

Mundy, David W.
dmundy@sshopper.com, Pub., Southside Shopper, NC, Garner

Munford, Roger......................(512) 259-4449
sales@hillcountrynews.com, Adv., Hill Country News, TX, Cedar Park

Munich, Chip.........................(812) 537-0063
cmunich@registerpublications.com, Adv. Rep. , The Dearborn County Register, IN, Lawrenceburg

Munk, Melanie.......................(425) 339-3430
munk@heraldnet.com, Features/Food Ed., The Herald, WA, Everett

Munn, Cindy
cindy.munn@zacharytoday.com, Classified Mgr, The Zachary Plainsman-News, LA, Baton Rouge

Munn, Pam
pmunn@fortfrances.com, Circ. Mgr., Fort Frances Daily Times, ON, Fort Frances

Munoz, Doris.........................(910) 630-7022
dmunoz@methodist.edu, Director of Student Life, Methodist University, NC, Fayetteville

Munoz, Julio
jmunoz@sipiapa.org, Exec. Dir., Inter American Press Association, FL, Miami

Munoz, Susan
smunoz@theclintonjournal.com, Sales Rep., Clinton Journal, IL, Clinton

Munoz, Veronica
web@dailylobo.com, Web Ed., New Mexico Daily Lobo, NM, Albuquerque

Munro, Harold......................(604) 605-2185
hmunro@postmedia.com, Ed. in Chief , The Vancouver Sun, BC, Vancouver
hmunro@postmedia.com, Editor-in-Chief, The Province, BC, Vancouver

Munro, Jenee
metigosh@utma.com, Adv. Mgr. , Lake Metigoshe Mirror, ND, Rolla

Munroe, Patrick
pmunroe@calpoly.edu, Prof., California Polytechnic State Universtiy, CA, San Luis Obispo

Munson, Beverly.....................(562) 985-5736
California State Univ. Long Beach, CA, Long Beach

Munson, Jim..........................(323) 343-4220
jmunson@cslanet.calstatela.edu, Business, Advt. Mgr., California State Univ., CA, Los Angeles

Munter, Ilene
ilene@midweek-pioneer.com, Circ. Mgr., The Metro Weekly, ND, Fargo

Munuzum, Scott
smunuzum@fstribune.com, Ed., Countryside, KS, Fort Scott

Muradian, Vago
vmuradian@defensenews.com, Ed., Defense

News, VA, Springfield

Muranaka, Gwen
gmuranaka@rafu.com, Ed., English, The Rafu Shimpo, CA, Los Angeles

Murarka, Bina A.......................(510) 383-1141
Ed., India-West, CA, San Leandro

Murarka, Ramesh P...................(510) 383-1151
editor@indiawest.com, Pub., India-West, CA, San Leandro

Muraro, Caroline
cmuraro@steinmancommunications.com, Chief Information Officer, LNP, PA, Lancaster
cmuraro@steinmancommunications.com, Chief Information Officer, LNP Media Group, Inc., PA, Lancaster

Murawski, Katie.......................(336) 316-1231
katie@yesweekly.com, News Ed., Yes! Weekly, NC, Greensboro

Murch, Steve
smurch@thealpenanews.com, Managing Ed., The Alpena News, MI, Alpena

Murciano, Vivian.....................(828) 232-6007
vmurciano@ashevill.gannett.com, Dir. Adv. , The Asheville Citizen-Times, NC, Asheville

Murcko, Mary
mmurcko@gannett.com, President of Sales, Gannett News Service - Albany, NY, Albany

Murdock, Aafke
amurdock@cdapress.com, National Ad. Director, Coeur d'Alene Press, ID, Coeur D Alene

Murdock, Kerry.......................(231) 946-0606
kmurdock@practicalecommerce.com, Pub and Ed, Practical Ecommerce, Traverse City

Murdock, Mark............(260) 347-0400 Ext. 1130
mmurdock@kpcmedia.com, Night Ed., The News Sun, IN, Kendallville

Murph, Jean..........................(972) 462-8192
citizensadvocate2000@yahoo.com, Pub./Ed., Citizens' Advocate, TX, Coppell

Murphy, Allan
publisher@guysboroughjournal.ca, Pub, Guysborough Journal, NS, Guysborough

Murphy, Anita
anita@starheraldnews.com, Editor, Pocahontas Star Herald, AR, Pocahontas

Murphy, Bill
bmurphy@pldi.net, Pub., Frederick Press-Leader, OK, Frederick

Murphy, Brien
brien.murphy@sj-r.com, Features Ed., Springfield Advertiser, IL, Springfield

Murphy, Carole
kvdaily@sbcglobal.net, Classified Ads. Mgr., Kirksville Daily Express, MO, Kirksville

Murphy, Cassidy.....................(617) 896-5313
editorial@thewarrengroup.com, Ed Dir, Banker & Tradesman, MA, Boston

Murphy, Cat...........................(615) 869-0800
cmurphy@mainstreetmediatn.com, Asst News Ed, The Murfreesboro Post, TN, Murfreesboro

Murphy, Charles
charles@wokc.com, Sports Ed., Okeechobee News, FL, Okeechobee

Murphy, Chris
cmurphy@capitalnewspapers.com, The Capital Times, WI, Madison

Murphy, Dan
sports@siskiyoudaily.com, Sports Ed., Siskiyou Daily News, CA, Yreka

Murphy, Daniel
danmurphy@starledger.com, Deputy Editorial Page Ed., The Star-Ledger, NJ, Newark

Murphy, Daniel
dmurphy@risingmediagroup.com, Ed. in Chief, Yonkers Rising, NY, Yonkers

Operations Manager, Daily Herald, IL, Arlington Heights

Music, Zoran ....(315) 792-4910
zmusic@uticaod.com, Prod. Mgr, Your Valley, NY, Utica

Musil, Connie ....(785) 292-4726
fan@bluevalley.net, Ed., Frankfort Area News, KS, Frankfort

Mustafaa, Ayesha ....(601) 896-0084
editor@mississippilink.com, Ed., Mississippi Link, MS, Jackson

Muszak, Susan ....(519) 667-4625
susan.muszak@sunmedia.ca, Pub./CEO, Digital & Print, The London Free Press, ON, London

Muthart, Phoebe ....(574) 658-4111
pmuthart@the-papers.com, Associate Editor, The Paper - Kosciusko Edition, IN, Milford

Muturi, Nancy
nmuturi@k-state.edu, Asst. Prof., Kansas State University, KS, Manhattan

Myczckowiak, Mark A.
catholicweekly@sbcglobal.net, Gen. Mgr./Adv. Mgr., The Catholic Weekly, MI, Saginaw

Myczckowiak, Mark A.
bissellnewman@newmanparishec.com, Pub., The Catholic Times, MI, Saginaw

Myers, Cory ....(605) 331-2389
ctmyers@argusleader.com, Consumer Exp. Dir./News, Argus Leader, SD, Sioux Falls

Myers, Dave ....(717) 262-4781
Production Dir., Public Opinion, PA, Chambersburg

Myers, David ....(620) 227-1519
skregister@dcdiocese.org, Ed, The Southwest Kansas Catholic, KS, Dodge City

Myers, Debbie
dmyers@neshobademocrat.com, Mng. Ed., The Neshoba Democrat, MS, Philadelphia

Myers, Elaine...........................(586) 218-5012
emyers@candgnews.com, Adv. Mgr., C & G Newspapers, MI, Warren

emyers@candgnews.com, Adv. Mgr, Farmington Press, MI, Warren

emyers@candgnews.com, Ad. Mgr, Rochester Post, MI, Warren

emyers@candgnews.com, Adv. Mgr, West Bloomfield Beacon, MI, Warren

emyers@candgnews.com, Adv. Mgr, Royal Oak Review, MI, Warren

emyers@candgnews.com, Ad. Mgr, Southfield Sun, MI, Warren

emyers@candgnews.com, Adv. Mgr, St. Clair Shores Sentinel, MI, Warren

emyers@candgnews.com, Adv. Mgr, Madison-Park News, MI, Warren

emyers@candgnews.com, Adv. Mgr, Warren Weekly, MI, Warren

emyers@candgnews.com, Adv. Mgr, Woodward Talk, MI, Warren

emyers@candgnews.com, Adv. Mgr, Birmingham-Bloomfield Eagle, MI, Warren

emyers@candgnews.com, Adv. Mgr, The Eastsider, MI, Warren

emyers@candgnews.com, Adv. Mgr, Macomb Chronicle, MI, Warren

emyers@candgnews.com, Adv. Mgr, Fraser-Clinton Chronicle, MI, Warren

emyers@candgnews.com, Adv. Mgr, Troy Times, MI, Warren

emyers@candgnews.com, Adv. Mgr, Sterling Heights Sentry, MI, Warren

emyers@candgnews.com, Adv. Mgr, Grosse Pointe Times, MI, Warren

emyers@candgnews.com, Adv. Mgr, Advertiser Times, MI, Warren

emyers@candgnews.com, Adv. Mgr, Shelby-Utica News, MI, Warren

emyers@candgnews.com, Adv. Mgr, Journal, MI, Warren

Myers, Eric...............................(404)526-578
eric.myers@ajc.com, VP, Adv. Sales, Atlanta Journal-Constitution, GA, Atlanta

Myers, Gary
gmyers@thespec.com, VP, Circ. & Mktg., The Hamilton Spectator, ON, Hamilton

Myers, Jack...........................(309) 757-5032
jmyers@qconline.com, Post Press/Facilities Manager, The Dispatch-Argus, IL, Moline

Myers, Jeff
jmeyers@republicmedia.com, The Arizona Republic, AZ, Phoenix

Myers, Jeff.............................(585) 244-8640
jeffm@gayalliance.org, Gay Alliance, NY, Rochester

Myers, John
john.meyers@latimes.com, Sacramento Bureau Chief, Los Angeles Times, CA, Los Angeles

Myers, John L.
journal@rtccom.net, Ed., The Odon Journal, IN, Odon

Myers, Joseph...............(215) 336-2500 ext 124
jmyers@southphillyreview.com, Ed., South Philly Review, NJ, Cherry Hill

Myers, Kathy ....(540) 213-9140
kmyers@newsleader.com, Circ. Dir., The News Leader, VA, Staunton

Myers, Kelly
admanager@langleytimes.com, Sales Mgr., Langley Times, BC, Langley

Myers, Ken..........................(215) 460-6395
myers@pjvoice.org, VP, Philadelphia Jewish Voice, PA, Bala Cynwyd

Myers, Linda Sue
subscriptions@pioneernews.net, Circ. Mgr., Pioneer News, KY, Shepherdsville

Myers, Rick ....(317) 300-8782
rickm@ss-times.com, The Southside Times, Southside Times, IN, Indianapolis

Myers, Robbin........................(620) 408-9920
classifieds@dodgeglobe.com, Classified Adv. Mgr., Dodge City Daily Globe, KS, Dodge City

Myers, Sherry ....(859) 422-6400
brianbutler@clarkmhc.com, Dir., HR, Clark Material Handling Co., KY, Lexington

Myers, Tamar.......................(608) 592-3261
tmyers@hngnews.com, Managing Editor, Lodi Enterprise & Poynette Press, WI, Lodi

Myers, Teresa ....(509) 826-1110
tmyers@omakchronicle.com, Advertising Manager, Omak-Okanogan County Chronicle, WA, Omak

Myers, Terri................(260) 347-0400 Ext. 1120
tmyers@kpcmedia.com, Acct. Exec., The News Sun, IN, Kendallville

Myers, Terry ....(613) 584-4161
NRT@magma.ca, Editor, The North Renfrew Times, ON, Deep River

Myers, Theodore W.
info@sihs.com, Chrmn., Paragon Technologies Inc., PA, Easton

Myers, Tony.........................(360) 735-4618
tony.myers@columbian.com, Home Delivery Mgr., The Columbian, WA, Vancouver

Myers-Sortland, Lisa.................(403) 578-4111
ads@ECAreview.com, Graphic Artist, East Central Alberta Review, AB, Coronation

Myftiu, Matt
matt.myftiu@oakpress.com, News Ed., The Oakland Press, MI, Pontiac

Myhre, Joel ....(218) 739-7023
joel.myhre@fergusfallsjournal.com, Gen. Mgr., Weekender, MN, Fergus Falls

Myhre, Joel
joel.myhre@fergusfallsjournal.com, Ed., The Fergus Falls Daily Journal, MN, Fergus Falls

Mykytiw, Christine ....(403) 223-2266
chrissales@tabertimes.com, Adv. Consult., The Taber Times, AB, Taber

Myler, Colin
voicers@nydailynews.com, Pres., Editor-in-chief, New York Daily News, NY, New York

Myrick, Kevin
KMyrick@npco.com, Ed./Pub., The Polk County Standard Journal, GA, Cedartown

Mysliwiec, Audrey
nsc@enescee.com, Pres., North Shore Consultants, Inc., IL, Chicago

N

Naab, Jerry
pressroom@gctelegram.com, Prodn. Mgr., Shopmate, KS, Garden City

Nabors, Nancy........................(865) 342-6454
nabors@knews.com, Adv. Mgr., Retail, Knoxville News Sentinel, TN, Knoxville

Nace, Dorothea
cpima@sympatico.ca, Exec. Dir./Sec./ Treasurer, Canadian Printing Ink Manufacturers Association, ON, Grimby

Nachtigall, Brett ....(605) 745-4170
Brett.Nachtigall@lee.net, Pub., Hot Springs Star, SD, Hot Springs

Nadeau, Anne-Marie
annemarie.nadeau@monteregieweb.com, Adv. Rep., Journal La Voix, QC, Sorel

Nadeau, Brandy .... (978) 249-3535 ext. 620
circulation@atholdailynews.com, Circ. Mgr., Athol Daily News, MA, Athol

Nadeau, Sebastien ....ext. 222
nadeaus@transcontinental.ca, Regl. Mgr., Hebdo Rive Nord, QC, Repentigny

Nadel, Natasha
natasha@ajpa.org, Assoc. Dir., American Jewish Press Association, DC, Washington

Nader, Christine...............(517) 265-5111 x2064
cnader@lenconnect.net, Controller , The Daily Telegram, MI, Adrian

Nadig, Brian ....(773) 286-6100
nadignewspapers@aol.com, Pub., Chicago's Northwest Side Press, IL, Chicago

Nadig, Brian
news@nadignewspapers.com, Pub., Reporter Journal, IL, Chicago

Nadig, Glenn
nadignewspapers@aol.com, Pub., Reporter Journal, IL, Chicago

Nadig, Glenn ....(773) 286-6100
nadignewspapers@aol.com, Pub., Chicago's Northwest Side Press, IL, Chicago

Nading, Brad
nading@gctelegram.com, Photo Dept. Mgr., The Garden City Telegram, KS, Garden City

Nadolski, Ed
enadolski@southernlakesnewspapers.com, Ed. in Chief, Waterford Post, WI, Burlington

Nadolski, Edward .... (262) 728-3411, ext. 126
enadolski@standardpress.com, Ed. in Chief, Paddock Lake Report, WI, Delavan

enadolski@standardpress.com, Ed. in Chief, Lake Geneva Times, WI, Delavan

Nadolski, Edward .... (262) 728-3411, ext. 126
enadolski@standardpress.com, Ed., Westosha Report, WI, Twin Lakes

Naegeli, Weiner.......................(631) 380-4343
info@mullermartiniusa.com, Vice-President, Muller Martini Corp., NY, Hauppauge

Nafed, Emad
allam@idirect.com, Ed., Arc Arabic Journal, ON, Toronto

Naff, Kevin ....(202) 747-2077 x8088
knaff@washblade.com, Editor, Washington Blade, DC, Washington

Naftel, Dale

sales@peninsulanewsreview.com, The Peninsula News Review, BC, Sidney

Naftolin, Marvin.......................(314) 535-9660
mnaftolin@labortribune.com, Gen. Mgr., St. Louis/Southern Illinois Labor Tribune, MO, Saint Louis

Nagasawa, Ron ....(808) 529-4849
rnagasawa@midweek.com, Pub., Street Pulse, HI, Honolulu

Nagasawa, Ron ....(808) 529-4849
rnagasawa@midweek.com, Pub., MidWeek Oahu, HI, Honolulu

rnagasawa@midweek.com, Publisher, Metro HNL (OOB), HI, Honolulu

Nagata, Pam...........................(858) 284-7317
info@sandiegoparent.com, Coord, The Parent Connection/Scripps Memorial Hospital, CA, San Diego

Nagel, Bill
bill.nagel@latimes.com, Exec. Vice Pres., Bus. Servs., Los Angeles Times, CA, Los Angeles

Nagel, Kevin...........................(905) 632-4444
knagel@burlingtonpost.com, Sports Ed., The Burlington Post, ON, Burlington

Nagel-Doughtie, Heather
heather.nagel@morris.com, Chief Marketing Officer
, Morris Communications Co. LLC, GA, Augusta

Nagle, Margaret
nagle@maine.edu, Instr., University of Maine, ME, Orono

Nagler, Melissa
lsncol@aol.com, Ed., Caldwell Watchman, LA, Columbia

Nagraj, Neil...........................(212) 930-8271
nnagraj@nypost.com, Ed., New York Post, NY, New York

Nagy, Chris
CNagy@gannett.com, Niche Products Ed., The Livingston County Daily Press & Argus, MI, Howell

Nagy, Christine ....(530) 365-2797
cnagy@andersonvalleypost.com, Gen. Mgr., Senior Scene, WA, Tacoma

Nagy, John
john@thepilot.com, Ed., The Pilot, NC, Southern Pines

Nagy, John ....(807) 343-6285
john.nagy@chroniclejournal.com, Sports Ed., The Chronicle-Journal, ON, Thunder Bay

Nagy, Steve ....(618) 692-9481
snagy@bnd.com, Photo, Belleville News-Democrat, IL, Belleville

Nahan, David
oc-ads@comcast.net, Editor and Publisher, Ocean City Sentinel, NJ, Ocean City

Nahan, David ....(609) 399-5411
Samplemedia@comcast.net, Pub., Cape May Star and Wave, NJ, West Cape May

Nahed, Aldo
Aldo@northfulton.com, Mng. Ed./ Bus. Ed., John's Creek Herald, GA, Alpharetta

Aldo@northfulton.com, Mng. Ed./ Bus. Ed., Milton Herald, GA, Alpharetta

Aldo@northfulton.com, Mng. Ed./ Bus. Ed., The Forsyth Herald, GA, Alpharetta

Aldo@northfulton.com, Mng. Ed./ Bus. Ed., The Revue & News, GA, Alpharetta

Naidu, Jack
jnaidu@oaklandpostonline.com, Production Manager, Oakland Post, CA, Oakland

jnaidu@oaklandpostonline.com, Production Manager, Marin County Post, CA, Oakland

jnaidu@oaklandpostonline.com, Production Manager, Richmond Post, CA, Oakland

Najacht, Charles W. ....(605) 673-2217
custerchronicle@gwtc.net, Pub./Adv. Mgr., Custer County Chronicle, SD, Custer

custerchronicle@gwtc.net, Pub., Hill City Prevailer-News, SD, Hill City
custerchronicle@gwtc.net, Pub., Western Trader, SD, Custer

Najacht, Norma G.
custerchronicle@gwtc.net, Ed., Custer County Chronicle, SD, Custer

Najacht, Norma G.
custerchronicle@gwtc.net, Ed., Western Trader, SD, Custer

Najar, Humberto
humberto.najar@publicitas.com, Mgr., Publicitas North America, Inc., CA, San Anselmo

Najera, Laura
laura@latinoprintnetwork.com, Vice Pres., Media Servs., Latino 247 Media Group, CA, Carlsbad

Nakakura, Darin .... (808) 529-4726
dnakakura@staradvertiser.com, Dir. of Advertising, Street Pulse, HI, Honolulu

Nakhle, Joseph .... (514) 747-0000
journal@almustakbal.com, Pub., L'Avenir/Al-Moustakbal, QC, Montreal

Nakoneczny, Laura .... (919) 789-2093
laura@ncpress.com, Editor, North Carolina Press Association, NC, Raleigh
laura@ncpress.com, Member Services Director, North Carolina Press Service, Inc., NC, Raleigh

Nally, Tracy .... (217) 351-5375
tnally@news-gazette.com, VP/Dir. HR, The News-Gazette, IL, Champaign

Namanny, David
editor@mcpress.com, Ed., Town & Country Shopper, IA, Osage

Namanny, David
editor@mcpress.com, Mng. Ed., Mitchell County Press-News, IA, Osage

Namanny, David
dnamanny@bellevueheraldleader.com, Ed., Bellevue Herald-Leader, IA, Bellevue

Nan, Xiaoli
nan@umd.edu, Asst. Prof., Persuasion & Social Influence/Health Commun., University of Maryland, MD, College Park

Nanna, Anthony V. .... (704) 369-8217
tnanna@mcgrann.com, Partner, McGrann Paper Corporation, CA, Rancho Cucamonga

Nanney, Robert
rnanney@utm.edu, Chair, University of Tennessee at Martin, TN, Martin

Naparstek, Donn ....(860) 489-3121 x 322
Adv. Dir., The Register Citizen, CT, Torrington

Nape, Jessica
jnape@sync2media.com, Business Development Specialist, SYNC2 Media, CO, Denver

Napora, Kathy .... (402) 342-4426
omaha@amclassifieds.com, President/ Publisher, American Classifieds, NE, Omaha

Nappi, Ralph
rnappi@gasc.org, Pres., NPES, VA, Reston

Naquin, Rebecca
becky.naquin@nopg.com, Asst. Data Ed., Daily Journal of Commerce, LA, Metairie

Narbut, Laura
narbut@valassis.com, Senior Buyer , Valassis, MI, Livonia

Nardi, Glen .... (228) 896-2420
gnardi@sunherald.com, Publisher, Keesler News, MS, Gulfport

Nardo, Perry A.
pnardo@theintelligencer.net, Gen. Mgr., The Intelligencer, WV, Wheeling

Nardone, Philip .... (908) 766-3900 ext. 220
pnardone@newjerseyhills.com, The Citizen, NJ, Bernardsville

pnardone@newjerseyhills.com, Ass. Exec. Ed. , Hunterdon Review, NJ, Whippany
pnardone@newjerseyhills.com, Ed. , Chatham Courier, NJ, Bernardsville
pnardone@newjerseyhills.com, Ass. Exec. Ed. , Bernardsville News, NJ, Bernardsville

Narrai, Andy
anarrai@reinhartlaw.com, Adv. Dir., Display, Milwaukee Journal Sentinel, WI, Milwaukee

Narvaez, Vivi
vivign@homes.illustrated.com, Gen. Mgr., Southern Colorado Homes Illustrated, CO, Colorado Springs

Nascimento, Mary
mnascimento@eastbaynewspapers.com, Ad Rep, The Post, RI, Bristol

Nase, Dan .... (740) 681-4333
dnase@gannett.com, Ad Manager, Hocking Valley Advertiser, OH, Lancaster

Nash, Andrew .... (620) 231-2600 ext. 140
anash@morningsun.net, Managing Ed., The Morning Sun, KS, Pittsburg

Nash, Bob
elpub@elwoodpublishing.com, Pub., Elwood Publishing Co., Inc., IN, Elwood

Nash, Daniel .... (253) 692-4813
nashd@uw.edu, Publications Manager, The University of Washington Tacoma Ledger Student Newspaper, WA, Tacoma

Nash, John .... (203) 354-1051
johnnash@thehour.com, Sports Ed., The Wilton Villager, CT, Norwalk

Nash, John .... (203) 354-1051
johnnash@thestamfordtimes.com, Managing Sports Editor, The Hour, CT, Norwalk

Nash, Lola
lnash@newsdemocratleader.com, Adv. Mgr., The News Democrat & Leader, KY, Russellville

Nash, Robert
tiptontri@netscape.net, Pub., Leader-Tribune Review West, IN, Tipton
tiptontri@netscape.net, Pub., Leader-Tribune Review East, IN, Tipton

Nash, Robert .... (765) 552-3355
elpub@elwoodpublishing.com, Pub., Alexandria Times-Tribune, IN, Elwood

Nash, Robert L.
tiptontribune@elwoodpublishing.com, Pub., Tipton County Tribune, IN, Tipton

Nash, Steve
snash@richmond.edu, Journ. Chair, University of Richmond, VA, Richmond

Nash, Thomas
tbnash@hersamacorn.com, Pub. Mgr, Easton Courier, CT, Ridgefield
tbnash@hersamacorn.com, Pub. Mgr, Fairfield Sun, CT, Shelton

Nash, Thomas
tbnash@hersamacorn.com, Pub., Monroe Courier, CT, Shelton

Nash, Thomas
tbnash@hersamacorn.com, Pub., Trumbull Times, CT, Shelton

Nash, Thomas B.
tbnash@hersamacorn.com, Pub., Shelton Herald, CT, Shelton

Nash, Thomas B. .... (203) 438-1183 Ext. 158
tbnash@hersamacorn.com, Pub., Stratford Star, CT, Shelton
tbnash@hersamacorn.com, Pub., Greenwich-Post, CT, Darien

Nash, Thomas B. .... (203) 438-1183 ext. 158
tbnash@acorn-online.com, Pub., Wilton Bulletin, CT, Ridgefield

Nash, Thomas B. .... (203) 894-3331
tbnash@acorn-online.com, Pub., Redding Pilot, CT, Ridgefield

Nash, Thomas B. .... (203) 544-9990
editor@thewesternforum.com, Pub., Weston Forum, CT, Ridgefield

Nash, Thomas B. .... (203) 894-3350
newsroom@acorn-online.com, Pub., Ridgefield Press, CT, Ridgefield

Nash, Tom
rburkhart@jpcgroup.com, Pub., Bridgeport News, CT, Shelton

Nash, Jr., Clarence .... (318) 342-5453
ulmhawkeyead@gmail.com, Advertising Director, Univ. of Louisiana at Monroe, LA, Monroe

Naso, Jon .... (973) 569-7141
Naso@northjersey.com, Dir. Photography, Herald News, NJ, Rockaway

Nason, Amanda .... (250) 341-6299 ext. 103
advertising@invermerevalleyecho.com, Adv. Sales, Invermere Valley Echo, BC, Invermere

Natale, Carl .... (207) 689-2972
cnatale@sunjournal.com, Web Ed., Sun Journal, ME, Lewiston

Nathaniel, Lea
nwlea@wehco.com, President, WEHCO Media, Inc., AR, Little Rock

Naughton, John .... (928) 474-5251
jnaughton@payson.com, Publisher - Payson Roundup, WorldWest LLC, KS, Lawrence

Nauman, Lori .... (507) 526-7324
lnauman@faribaultcountyregister.com, Pub./ Gen. Mgr., Town Crier Shopper, MN, Blue Earth

Nauman, Lori .... (507) 526-7324
lnauman@faribaultcountyregister.com, Pub./ Gen. Mng., Faribault County Register, MN, Blue Earth

Nauss-Redden, Pam .... (902) 426-1134
pnauss@herald.ca, Mktg. Mgr., The Chronicle Herald, NS, Halifax

Nava, Antonio .... (213) 291-9986
antonio@agenciapi.com, Ed., Agencia Prensa Internacional Inc., Los Angeles

Navarro, Julio .... (760) 337-3443
Dist. Mgr., Adelante Valle, CA, El Centro

Navasky, Victor
vnavasky@thenation.com, Prof., Columbia University, NY, New York

Nave, Shirley
snave@starhq.com, Adv. Mgr., Elizabethton Star, TN, Elizabethton

Navid, Venusse
venusse.navid@sgvn.com, Clerk, The Whittier Daily News, CA, Monrovia

Nay, Meta L.
meta@kwnews.com, Vice Pres., Mktg., Keister Williams Newspaper Services, Inc., VA, Charlottesville

Nayder, Tom ....ext. 232
tom@alibi.com, Prodn. Mgr., Weekly Alibi, NM, Albuquerque

Naylor, Dave
dave.naylor@sunmedia.ca, City Ed., The Calgary Sun, AB, Calgary

Naylor, Jonathon
news@thereminder.ca, Ed, Flin Flon Reminder, MB, Flin Flon

Nazem, Ali .... (415) 293-8464
ali@metrosn.com, Sr. Vice Pres., Metro Newspaper Advertising Services, Inc., CA, San Francisco

NeSmith, Alan
anesmith@thenortheastgeorgian.com, Reg. Pub., Dawson News & Advertiser (OOB), GA, Dawsonville
anesmith@thenortheastgeorgian.com, Reg. Pub., The Northeast Georgian, GA, Cornelia

NeSmith, Eric
enesmith@cninewspapers.com, Community

Newspapers, Inc., GA, Athens

NeSmith, William H. Dink
dnesmith@cninewspapers.com, Pres., Community Newspapers, Inc., GA, Athens

Neabel, R. Nicholas .... (315) 789-3333 ext 263
nneabel@fltimes.com, Adv. Dir., Finger Lakes Times, NY, Geneva

Neabling, Luann .... (608) 807-5251
lneabling@hngnews.com, Circ. Mgr., McFarland Thistle, WI, Cottage Grove

Neal, Adam .... (772) 978-2319
adam.neal@tcpalm.com, Editor, Indian River Press Journal, FL, Vero Beach
adam.neal@tcpalm.com, Editor, St. Lucie News Tribune, FL, Port Saint Lucie
adam.neal@tcpalm.com, Mng. Ed., The Stuart News, FL, Stuart
adam.neal@tcpalm.com, Managing Ed., Jupiter Courier, FL, Stuart

Neal, Amy
amyneal@npgco.com, Ed., Gladstone Dispatch, MO, Liberty
amyneal@npgco.com, Managing Editor, Liberty Tribune, MO, Liberty
amyneal@npgco.com, Ed., The Smithville Herald, MO, Smithville

Neal, Debi
business@warricknews.com, TSM Sales Coord., Warrick County Today, IN, Boonville

Neal, Gary .... (812) 897-2330
gwneal@aol.com, Pub., The Standard, IN, Boonville

Neal, Ida
ineal@btimes.com, Circ. Mgr, The Annapolis Times, MD, Baltimore
ineal@btimes.com, Circ. Mgr, The Baltimore Times, MD, Baltimore

Neal, Jeff .... (606) 451-4920
jneal@somerset-kentucky.com, News Ed., The Commonwealth-Journal, KY, Somerset

Neale, Barrett
barrett.neale@richmond.edu, Univ. of Richmond, VA, Richmond

Neale, Darrell
Westville Reporter@yahoo.com, Reporter, Stilwell Democrat Journal, OK, Stilwell

Neale, Keith .... (918) 696-2228
stilwelldj@windstream.net, Ed./Adv., Stilwell Democrat Journal, OK, Stilwell
stilwelldj@windstream.net, Ed., Westville Reporter, OK, Westville

Nealy-Brown, Jounice .... (727) 893-8289
nealybrown@tampabay.com, Communications Dir., Tampa Bay Times, FL, St Petersburg

Neault, Yves
yves.neault@lenouvelliste.qc.ca, Adv. Dir., Le Nouvelliste, QC, Trois-Rivieres

Nedbalek, Wayne .... (979) 731-4684
wayne.nedbalek@theeagle.com, Dir. Mail Mgr., The Eagle, TX, Bryan

Nedeljkovich, Misha
mihajlo@ou.edu, Assoc. Prof., University of Oklahoma, OK, Norman

Nedved, Marissa
mknedved0@frostburg.edu, Business Manager, The Bottom Line, MD, Frostburg

Nee, Eshin ....(718) 746-8889 ext. 6340
Sales. Mgr., World Journal, NY, Whitestone

Needham, Dawn .... (313) 222-1881
dneedham@detroitnews.com, Digital News Ed., The Detroit News, MI, Detroit

Needham, Kathie .... (401) 767-8525
kneedham@woonsocketcall.com, Controller, The Call, RI, Woonsocket

Needham, Marian .... (202) 434-7177
mneedham@cwa-union.org, Exec. VP, The NewsGuild-CWA, DC, Washington

Neel, Lindsey

info@charlestonexpress.com, Multi-Media Sales Exec., Charleston Express, AR, Greenwood

Neeley, Richard
rneely@timesdispatch.com, Sales Mgr., Richmond Delivery Service, VA, Richmond

Neese, Courtney
courtney.neese@greenvilleadvocate.com, Mktg. Consult., The Greenville Advocate, AL, Greenville

Neese, Jo
jneese@publicitas.com, Branch Dir., Publicitas North America, Inc., TX, Dallas

Negus, Don .... (989) 779-6118
dnegus@michigannewspapers.com, Adv. Dir., Northern Michigan Real Estate Marketplace, MI, Mount Pleasant

Negus, Don
dnegus@michigannewspapers.com, Gen. Mgr., Midland Buyers Guide, MI, Midland

Neher, Megan
mneher@pinedaleroundup.com, Ed., The Pinedale Roundup, WY, Pinedale

Nehrenz, Teri .... (702) 346-6397
terin.bbm@gmail.com, Office/Writer/Calendar, Mesquite Local News, NV, Mesquite

Neiber, Paul
contact@best-testproducts.com, Pres., Union Rubber, Inc., NJ, Trenton

Neidlinger, Debbie .... (912) 826-5012
dneidlinger@effinghamherald.net, Adv. Acct. Exec., Effingham Herald, GA, Rincon

Neil, Peter
bcbeditor@mihomepaper.com, Pub., Banner, MI, Brown City

Neill, Kenneth
mphsparent@contemporary-media.com, Pub., Memphis Parent, TN, Memphis

Neill, Kenneth
kneil@memphisflyer.com, Pub., Memphis Flyer, TN, Memphis

Neill, Peter .... (734) 891-3008
peter.neill@comcast.net, Sr. Associate-Lower Midwest/South, W.B. Grimes & Company, MD, Gaithersburg

Neill, Peter .... (734) 953-2252
pneill@hometownlife.com, Gen. Mgr., South Oakland Eccentric, MI, Detroit

Neill, Peter .... (734) 953-2252
pneill@hometownlife.com, Gen. Mgr., Westland Observer, MI, Detroit

Neilson, Stu
stu@yourtowncrier.com, Mng. Ed., Town Crier, MA, Woburn

Neiman, Chris
chris.neiman@azparenting.com, Circ. Mgr., Arizona Parenting, AZ, Scottsdale

Neiman, Kendall
kendall@anewspaper.net, Pub., Nemaha County Herald, NE, Auburn

Neiss, James
james.neiss@niagara-gazette.com, Web Ed., Niagara Gazette, NY, Niagara Falls

Neitz, Dean A. .... (406) 563-5283
leadernews@anacondaleader.com, Owner, Anaconda Leader, MT, Anaconda

Neknez, Jason .... (631) 843-3603
Jneknez@newsday.com, Class., amNew York, NY, New York

Neligh, Ian .... (303) 567-4491
couranteditor@evergreenco.com, Ed., Clear Creek Courant, CO, Idaho Springs

Nellessen-Lara, Lisa
news@stevenspointjournal.com, Editorial Page Ed., Stevens Point Journal, WI, Stevens Point

Nelon, Mindy
mnelon@coloradocommunitymedia.com, Adv.

Mgr., Golden Transcript, CO, Golden
mnelon@coloradocommunitymedia.com, Adv. Mgr., Wheat Ridge Transcript, CO, Golden
mnelon@coloradocommunitymedia.com, Adv. Mgr., Lakewood Sentinel, CO, Golden

Nelsen, Karen
karen@thedenmarknews.com, Office Mgr., The Denmark News, WI, Denmark

Nelson, Alan .... (541) 383-0346
ANELSON@BENDBULLETIN.COM, Prodn. Supvr., The Bulletin, OR, Bend

Nelson, Arden .... (605) 845-3646
asi@mobridgetribune.com, Adv. Specialties/Printing Mgr., Mobridge Tribune, SD, Mobridge

Nelson, Arden .... (605) 845-3646
arden@mobridgetribune.com, ASI/Printing Manager, Monday Reminder, SD, Mobridge

Nelson, Belinda .... (307) 633-3193
bnelson@wyomingbusinessreport.com, Pub. Dir of Sals, Wyoming Business Report, WY, Cheyenne

Nelson, Catherine
catherine.nelson@rutlandherald.com, Gen. Mgr., Preferred Properties Real Estate Guide, VT, Rutland

Nelson, Cindy
cinelson@dmreg.com, Sr. Acct. Exec., Record-Herald and Indianola Tribune, IA, Indianola

Nelson, Clay
bgchief@isu.edu, Idaho State Univ., ID, Pocatello

Nelson, Cyndi .... (256) 549-2062
cyndi.nelson@gadsentimes.com, Travel/Women's Ed., The Gadsden Times, AL, Gadsden

Nelson, Dave
dnelson@recordernewspapers.com, Circ. Mgr., Observer Tribune, NJ, Bernardsville

Nelson, David
gstimes@kans.com, Pub, Galena Sentinel-Times, KS, Galena

Nelson, David
david.nelson@northern.edu, Circ. Dir., Aberdeen American News, SD, Aberdeen

Nelson, David .... (908) 766-6960
dnelson@recordernewspapers.com, Circ. Dir., Chatham Courier, NJ, Bernardsville

Nelson, David .... (360) 377-3711
dnelson@kitsapsun.com, Ed., Kitsap Sun, WA, Bremerton

Nelson, DeAnna .... (573) 471-1137
dnelson@standard-democrat.com, Gen. Mgr., Standard Democrat, MO, Sikeston

Nelson, Dean
deannelson@pointloma.edu, Journalism Dir., Point Loma Nazarene Univ., CA, San Diego

Nelson, Debbie .... (785) 822-1440
dnelson@salina.com, Classified Consultant, The Salina Journal, KS, Salina

Nelson, Don .... (706) 208-2214
don.nelson@onlineathens.com, Bus./Finance Ed., Athens Banner-Herald, GA, Athens

Nelson, Don .... (509) 997-7011
editor@methowvalleynews.com, Pub./Ed., Methow Valley News, WA, Twisp

Nelson, Don
editor@skagitvalleyherald.com, Ed., Skagit Valley Herald, WA, Mount Vernon

Nelson, DuWayne .... ext. 602
dnelson@ncnewsonline.com, Circ. Mgr., New Castle News, PA, New Castle

Nelson, Greg
greg@gcherald.com, Ed., Gratiot County Herald, MI, Ithaca

Nelson, Greg
nelson@hosports.com, Sr. Vice Pres./Gen. Mgr., MSN Int'l, Microsoft Corp., WA,

Redmond

Nelson, Holly
editor1@oscodapress.com, Ed., Iosco County News Herald, MI, East Tawas
editor1@oscodapress.com, Ed., Oscoda Press, MI, Oscoda

Nelson, Jackie
jackie@hesstonrecord.com, Ed., Hesston Record, KS, Hesston

Nelson, Jared
jnelson@timesleader.net, Editor & General Manager, Times Leader, KY, Princeton

Nelson, John ....
jnelson@lcni.com, Editorial Director, Landmark Community Newspapers, LLC, KY, Shelbyville

Nelson, John
johnn@amnews.com, Exec. Ed. , The Winchester Sun, KY, Winchester

Nelson, John .... (859) 236-2551 Ext. 351
johnn@amnews.com, Exec. Ed., The Advocate-Messenger, KY, Danville

Nelson, John .... (502) 513-1157
jnelson@lcni.com, Editorial Director, Landmark Community Newspapers, LLC, KY, Shelbyville

Nelson, Judy .... (509) 750-2983
bbjagnews@basinbusinessjournal.com , Pub., Basin Business Journal Farm News, WA, Moses Lake

Nelson, Laura
lnelson@beauregarddailynews.net, Editor / General Manager, The Big Timber Pioneer, MT, Big Timber
lnelson@beauregarddailynews.net, Adv. Sales Rep., Beauregard Daily News, LA, Deridder

Nelson, Leah .... (770) 535-6330
lnelson@gainesvilletimes.com, Ad. Director, The Times, GA, Gainesville

Nelson, Liza
liza.nelson@sunmedia.ca, Pub./Adv. Dir. , The Kingston Whig-Standard, ON, Kingston
liza.nelson@sunmedia.ca, Group Adv. Dir., Napanee Guide, ON, Napanee
liza.nelson@sunmedia.ca, Kingston This Week, ON, Kingston

Nelson, Lori
lnelson@pantagraph.com, Adv. Dept., The Pantagraph, IL, Bloomington

Nelson, Margaret
mnelson@alaskanewspapers.com, Pub./Pres., The Cordova Times, AK, Cordova

Nelson, Marietta
nelson@pdclarion.com, Bus. Mgr., Princeton Daily Clarion, IN, Princeton

Nelson, Mark
mnelson@faribault.com, Adv. Team Leader, Faribault Daily News, MN, Faribault

Nelson, Maurisa .... (580) 310-7502
mnelson@theadanews.com, Adv. Mgr., The Ada News , OK, Ada

Nelson, Melanie
news@csceagle.com, News Ed, Chadron State College, NE, Chadron

Nelson, Mike .... (213) 637-7543
mnelson@the-tidings.com, Ed., The Tidings, CA, Los Angeles

Nelson, Miriam .... (715) 253-2737
mnelson@wolfrivermedia.com, Pub./Ed., The Wittenberg Enterprise & Birnamwood News, WI, Wittenberg

Nelson, Patricia .... (260) 563-2131
Bus. Mgr., Peru Tribune, IN, Peru

Nelson, Paul E.
paul.nelson.1@ndsu.edu, Prof./Head, North Dakota State University, ND, Fargo

Nelson, Penny
pnelson@wehco.com, Digital Media Sales

Mgr., WEHCO Media, Inc., AR, Little Rock

Nelson, Piper .... (512) 477-0746
nelson@texasobserver.org, Publisher, The Texas Observer, TX, Austin

Nelson, Rachel
Micour@wiu.edu, Advertising Manager, Western Illinois University, IL, Macomb

Nelson, Rick .... (843) 937-5701
rnelson@postandcourier.com, Managing Ed., The Post and Courier, SC, Charleston

Nelson, Rick
ernelson@teleport.com, Pub./Ed., Wahkiakum County Eagle, WA, Cathlamet

Nelson, Sandy
sandy.nelson@npgco.com, Pub., The Kearney Courier, MO, Kearney
sandy.nelson@npgco.com, Pub., Gladstone Dispatch, MO, Liberty
sandy.nelson@npgco.com, Pub., Liberty Tribune, MO, Liberty

Nelson, Sandy
sandynelson@miconews.com, Pub., The Smithville Herald, MO, Smithville
sandynelson@miconews.com, Pub, Kansas City Nursing News, KS, Paola

Nelson, Sandy .... (816) 616-4301
sandynelson@npgco.com., Group Pub., The Miami County Republic, KS, Paola

Nelson, Shelley .... (715) 395-5022
snelson@superiortelegram.com, Editor, Superior Telegram, WI, Superior

Nelson, Stanley
Stanley@concordiasentinel.com, Ed., Concordia Sentinel, LA, Ferriday

Nelson, Stephanie .... (251) 867-4876, Ext. 122
stephanie.nelson@brewtonstandard.com, Publisher, The Brewton Standard, AL, Brewton

Nelson, Susan
snelson@coastalcourier.com, Digital Sales Manager, The Coastal Courier, GA, Hinesville

Nelson, Suzi
suzi.nelson@ashland-gazette.com, Ed., The Ashland Gazette, NE, Ashland

Nelson, Theresa
nelson@townnews.com, Dir./Buss. Dev., TownNews.com, IL, Moline

Nelson, Todd .... (479) 571-6405
tnelson@nwadg.com, Pres., Northwest Arkansas Democrat-Gazette, AR, Fayetteville

Nelson, Tom
tnelson@lmu.edu, Loyola Marymount Univ., CA, Los Angeles

Nelson, Tom
nelsont@elon.edu, Assoc. Prof., Elon University, NC, Elon

Nelson, Wayne
wnelson@gfherald.com, Sports Ed., Grand Forks Herald, ND, Grand Forks

Nemec, Lisa .... (410) 732-6616
lnemec@baltimoreguide.com, Acct. Exec., Baltimore Guide South, MD, Baltimore

Nemerowski, John .... (617) 619-6188
john.nemerowski@bostonherald.com, Dir. of Display Adv., Boston Herald, MA, Boston

Nemirow, Mark
mnemirow@readingeagle.com, Editorial Page Ed., Reading Eagle, PA, Reading

Nenni, Pete .... (847) 680-5510
pnenni@dailyherald.com, Deputy Managing Editor / News, Daily Herald, IL, Arlington Heights

Nesbitt, Darrell .... (204) 759-2644 ext. 5
ctwdistrict@mymts.net, News Reporter, Crossroads This Week, MB, Shoal Lake
ctwdistrict@mymts.net, Reporter/Photographer, South Mountain Press, MB, Shoal Lake

Nesbitt, Gregory .... (204) 759-2644 ext. 4

gnesbitt@mymts.net, Chief Executive Officer, Nesbitt Publishing Ltd., MB, Shoal Lake

Nesbitt, Jamie........................(403) 362-5571
editor@brooksbulletin.com, Ed., The Brooks Bulletin, AB, Brooks

Nesbitt, Ryan ....(204) 759-2644 ext. 3
ctwdisplay@mymts.net, Publisher, Nesbitt Publishing Ltd., MB, Shoal Lake

Nesbitt, Ryan ....(204) 759-2644 ext. 3
ctwdisplay@mymts.net, Publisher, South Mountain Press, MB, Shoal Lake
ctwdisplay@mymts.net, Publisher, Crossroads This Week, MB, Shoal Lake

Nesmith, Eric
news@hilandsnews.com, Pub., The Highlander, NC, Highlands

Nesmith, Robert
robert.nesmith@gtri.gatech.edu, Prodn. Mgr., Northside Neighbor, GA, Atlanta

Ness, Gunnard
gunnard@cableone.net, Pub., Edmore Herald, ND, Fordville

Ness, Gunnard
gunnard@cableone.net, Pub., Leader-Tribune, ND, Fordville

Ness, Truman
nesspres@polarcomm.com, Ad. / Cir. , Aneta Star, ND, Fordville

Ness, Truman
nesspres@polarcomm.com, Ed., Edmore Herald, ND, Fordville
nesspres@polarcomm.com, Ad. / Cir. Mgr., McVille Messenger, ND, Fordville
nesspres@polarcomm.com, Ed., Nelson County Arena, ND, Fordville
nesspres@polarcomm.com, Ed., Hatton Free Press, ND, Fordville
nesspres@polarcomm.com, Ad. / Cir. Mgr. , Pembina New Era, ND, Fordville
nesspres@polarcomm.com, Ed., Fordville Tri-County Sun, ND, Fordville
nesspres@polarcomm.com, Ed., Leader-Tribune, ND, Fordville

Nessel, Lee ....(321) 242-3640
lnessel@floridatoday.com, Enterprise Editor/ breaking news, military, religion, Florida Today, FL, Melbourne

Nesseler, Marc ....(309) 757-4972
mnesseler@qconline.com, Information Editor/ Sports & Recreation, The Dispatch-Argus, IL, Moline

Nester, Melissa ....(304) 436-3144, ext. 31
Publisher, Mullens Advocate, WV, Mullens

Nester, Robert........................(734) 649-9776
rnester@charter.net, Owner/Pub., The Sun Times News, MI, Pinckney

Netcher, Lisa ....(212) 210-1998
lnetcher@nydailynews.com, Adv. Dir., Ed., Health & Hosp., New York Daily News, NY, New York

Nethercutt, Judy ....(501) 378-3430
jnethercutt@wehco.com, WEHCO Media, Inc., AR, Little Rock
jnethercutt@wehco.com, Bus. Mgr., Northwest Arkansas Newspapers LLC, AR, Little Rock

Nettland, Paul
pnettland@gannett.com, Circ. Dir., Appeal Tribune, OR, Salem
pnettland@gannett.com, Circ. Dir., Stayton Mail, OR, Salem

Neuenfeldt, Ernie
eneuenfeldt@mmlocal.com, Prod. Mgr, Star Journal, WI, Rhinelander

Neufeld, Johanna
jneufeld@therecord.com, Librarian, The Record, ON, Kitchener

Neugebauer, Mary
globe@siouxvalley.net, Pub./Ed./Adv. Mgr., The Corsica Globe, SD, Corsica

Neuharth, Dave ....(352) 347-4470
djneuharth@aol.com, Editor, Association of Free Community Papers, NY, Liverpool

Neuharth, Dave ....(352) 362-7350
djneuharth@aol.com, Executve Director, Community Papers of Florida, FL, Belleview

Neuman, Tim ....(989) 839-4277
tneuman@hearstnp.com, Gen. Mgr., Huron Daily Tribune, MI, Bad Axe

Neumann-Rea, Kirby
kneumann-rea@hoodrivernews.com, Ed., Hood River News, OR, Hood River

Neumeister, Kathy ....(608) 778-2515
kathy.neumeister@wcinet.com, Advertising & Marketing Manager, The Fitchburg Star, WI, Verona

Neutkens, Debra ....(651) 407-1230
reporter@presspubs.com, Mng. Ed., Press Publications, Inc., MN, White Bear Lake

Neuzil, Mark
mrneuzil@stthomas.edu, Prof., University of St. Thomas, MN, Saint Paul

Nevarez, Manny
mnevarez@skagitpublishing.com, Circ. Dir., Skagit Valley Herald, WA, Mount Vernon

Nevels-Haun, Jill ....(734) 240-5748
jnevels-haun@monroenews.com, Editor, The Monroe News, MI, Monroe

Nevers, Thomas
jbeckley@thechronicle.com, Adv. Dir., The Chronicle, CT, Willimantic

Neves, Christine ....(860) 870-3012
cneves@courant.com, Community Sales Mgr., Courant Community - West Hartford, CT, Hartford
cneves@courant.com, Community Sales Mgr., Courant Community - Wethersfield, CT, Hartford
cneves@courant.com, Community Sales Mgr., Courant Community - Colchester, CT, Hartford
cneves@courant.com, Community Sales Mgr., Courant Community - East Hartford, CT, Hartford
cneves@courant.com, Community Sales Mgr., Courant Community - Enfield, CT, Hartford
cneves@courant.com, Community Sales Mgr., Courant Community - Glastonbury, CT, Hartford
cneves@courant.com, Community Sales Mgr., Courant Community - Hebron, CT, Hartford
cneves@courant.com, Community Sales Mgr., Courant Community - Killingly, CT, Hartford
cneves@courant.com, Community Sales Mgr., Courant Community - Manchester, CT, Hartford
cneves@courant.com, Community Sales Mgr., Courant Community - Putnam, CT, Hartford
cneves@courant.com, Community Sales Mgr., Courant Community - South Windsor, CT, Hartford
cneves@courant.com, Community Sales Mgr., Courant Community - Stafford, CT, Hartford
cneves@courant.com, Community Sales Mgr., Courant Community - Valley, CT, Hartford
cneves@courant.com, Community Sales Mgr., Courant Community - Vernon, CT, Hartford
cneves@courant.com, Community Sales Mgr., Courant Community - Windham, CT, Hartford
cneves@courant.com, Community Sales Mgr., Courant Community - Windsor, CT, Hartford
cneves@courant.com, Community Sales Mgr., Courant Community - Windsor Locks, CT, Hartford

Neville, Abigail ....(250) 775-1710
Mgr, The Fort Nelson News, BC, Fort Nelson

Neville, Bill ....(205) 934-6691
Univ. of Alabama at Birmingham, AL, Birmingham

Neville, Hugh C.
hugh.neville@richmond-graphic.com, CEO, Richmond/Graphic Products, Inc., RI, Smithfield

Neville, John .... (716) 849-4444
jneville@buffnews.com, Editorial Page Ed., The Buffalo News, NY, Buffalo

Nevious, Kristen
neviousk@franklinpierce.edu, Franklin Pierce College, NH, Rindge

Nevitt, Heather D ....(214) 744-7746
hnevitt@alm.com, Ed. in Chief, Texas Lawyer, TX, Dallas

Newby, John ....(918) 684-2875
JNewby@muskogeephoenix.com, Pub., The Times, IL, Ottawa
JNewby@muskogeephoenix.com, Pub., Muskogee Phoenix, OK, Muskogee

Newby, John
jnewby@tahlequahdailypress.com, Pub. , Tahlequah Daily Press, OK, Tahlequah

Newcomb, Annette ....(262) 877-4566
annette@westoshareport.com, Southern Lakes Newspapers LLC, WI, Burlington

Newcomb, Hillary....................(318) 368-9732
Advertising sales
, The Gazette, LA, Farmerville

Newcomb, Lori
lnewcomb@eaglenewsonline.com, Gen. Mgr, Eagle Bulletin, NY, Syracuse

Newcomb, Lori ....(315) 434-8889 ext. 333
lnewcomb@eaglenewsonline.com, Circ. Mgr, Cazenovia Republican, NY, Syracuse

Newcomb, Lori
lnewcomb@eaglenewsonline.com, Prodn. Mgr., Skaneateles Press, NY, Syracuse

Newell, Ben..........................(202) 319-5779
editor@cuatower.com, Catholic Univ. of America, DC, Washington

Newell, Bob.................(850) 932-8986 ext. 104
bob@gulfbreezenews.com, Ad Sales, Gulf Breeze News, FL, Gulf Breeze

Newell, Lisa ....(217) 593-6515
lisa@elliott-publishing.com, Graphics, Mendon Dispatch-Times, IL, Camp Point

Newell, Lisa ....(217) 593-6515
lisa@elliott-publishing.com, Graphics, Golden-Clayton New Era, IL, Camp Point

Newell, Lisa ....(850) 932-8986 ext. 101
lisa@gulfbreezenews.com, Pub., Gulf Breeze News, FL, Gulf Breeze

Newfield, Amanda ....(909) 869-3530
The Poly Post, CA, Pomona

Newgate, J. Baxter
megalomedia@lawtv.com, Pres., Megalo Media, New York

Newhagen, John
newhagen@umd.edu, Assoc. Prof., University of Maryland, MD, College Park

Newham, Jennifer ....(386) 362-1734 x121
jennifer.newham@gaflnews.com, Circulation, Suwannee Democrat, FL, Live Oak

Newhoff, Doug ....(319) 291-1467
Doug.Newhoff@wcfcourier.com, Sports Ed., The Courier, IA, Waterloo

Newhoff, Nancy ....(319) 291-1445
Nancy.Newhoff@wcfcourier.com, Ed., Insider, IA, Waterloo
Nancy.Newhoff@wcfcourier.com, The Courier, IA, Waterloo

Newhouse, Mark ....(212) 286-5247
marknewhouse@condenast.com, Executive VP, Advance Publications, Inc., NY, Staten Island

Newhouse, Mary ....(530) 283-0800
mnewhouse@plumasnews.com, HR Dir/Office Mgr, Feather Publishing Co., Inc., CA, Quincy

Newhouse, Mary ....(530) 283-0800
mnewhouse@plumasnews.com, Classified and Circ. Mgr., Indian Valley Record, CA, Greenville

Newhouse, Steven
steven.newhouse@jjournal.com, Ed. in Chief, The Jersey Journal, NJ, Secaucus

Newland, Melissa ....(906) 524-6194
sentinel1886@gmail.com, Reporter, L'Anse Sentinel, MI, Lanse

Newland, Mike ....(563) 588-5629
mnewland@wcinet.com, Circ. Mgr., Telegraph Herald, IA, Dubuque

Newman, Arthur E.
arthur.newman@healthstream.com, Sr. Vice Pres., Finance, HealthStream, TN, Nashville

Newman, Bob ....(615) 885-6556
Adv. Mgr., Forward Focus, TN, Nashville

Newman, Brant........................(724) 222-2200
bnewman@observer-reporter.com, Asst. News Ed., Observer-Reporter, PA, Washington

Newman, Bruce
bruce.newman@oxfordeagle.com, Photo Ed., The Oxford Eagle, MS, Oxford

Newman, Dan ....(734) 764-0558
Univ. of Michigan, MI, Ann Arbor

Newman, David ....(801) 625-4374
dnewman@standard.net, Adv. Mgr., Classified, Standard-Examiner, UT, Ogden

Newman, Denton
denton.newman@brainerddispatch.com, Online Ed., Brainerd Dispatch, MN, Brainerd

Newman, Dolly
quincysunsubs@gmail.com, Asst. Mgr., The Quincy Sun, MA, Quincy

Newman, Harry ....ext. 3109
Adv. Mgr., Hudson Hub-Times, OH, Kent

Newman, Harry ....(330) 541-9400
hnewman@recordpub.com, Marketing Director, The Advantage, OH, Kent

Newman, Harry ....ext. 3109
Adv. Mgr., Aurora Advocate, OH, Kent

Newman, Ian ....(780) 429-5575
inewman@thejournal.canwest.com, Adv. Mgr., Retail Multi-Market Sales, Edmonton Journal, AB, Edmonton

Newman, Jackie ....(434) 808-0614
jackie.newman@kenbridgevictoriadispatch. com; jackie.newman@farmvilleherald. com; jackie.newman@thecharlottegazette. com, Adv. Mgr. , The Farmville Herald, VA, Farmville
jackie.newman@kenbridgevictoriadispatch. com; jackie.newman@farmvilleherald.com; jackie.newman@thecharlottegazette.com, Adv. Dir., The Charlotte Gazette, VA, Drakes Branch
jackie.newman@kenbridgevictoriadispatch. com; jackie.newman@farmvilleherald.com; jackie.newman@thecharlottegazette.com, Adv. Dir., The Kenbridge-Victoria Dispatch, VA, Victoria

Newman, John
jnewman@sfbrgenetics.org, Owner, Newman Brothers, TX, San Antonio

Newman, John T.
j.newman@att.net, Pres., Newman International, LLC, KS, Prairie Village

Newman, Joy ....(260) 347-0400
jnewman@kpcmedia.com, Regional Advertising Director, KPC Media Group, Inc., IN, Kendallville

Newman, Joy ....(260) 347-0400 Ext. 1002
mswann@kpcmedia.com, Adv. Dir., The Advance Leader, IN, Kendallville

Newman, Joy ....(260) 347-0400
jnewman@kpcmedia.com, Regional Advertising Director, KPC Media Group, Inc., IN, Kendallville

Newman, Joy .... (260) 347-0400 Ext. 1002 ....
jnewman@kpcmedia.com, Adv. Dir., The Garrett Clipper, IN, Auburn

Newman, Julie .... (479) 785-7704
jnewman@swtimes.com, Outside Sales Mgr.,
Times Record, AR, Fort Smith

Newman, Karen .... (712) 373-5571
recordsiouxvalley@ruralwaves.us, Sioux Valley
News Mgr, The Record, IA, Moville

Newman, Lily
lily.newman@jhunewsletter.com, The Johns
Hopkins News-Letter, MD, Baltimore

Newman, Marc .... (972) 392-0888
marc@wieck.com, Sr. VP, Wieck, Richardson

Newman, Matt .... (262) 446-6616
mnewman@cninow.com, Design/Interactive
Content Dir., Germantown NOW, WI,
Waukesha

mnewman@cninow.com, Design/Interactive
Content Dir., Brookfield-Elm Grove NOW, WI,
Waukesha

mnewman@cninow.com, Design/Interactive
Content Dir., Cudahy NOW, WI, Waukesha

mnewman@cninow.com, Design/Interactive
Content Dir., Fox Point NOW, WI, Waukesha

mnewman@cninow.com, Design/Interactive
Content Dir., Oak Creek-Franklin-Greendale-
Hales Corners NOW, WI, Waukesha

mnewman@cninow.com, Design/Interactive
Content Dir., Greenfield-West Allis NOW, WI,
Waukesha

mnewman@cninow.com, Design/Interactive
Content Dir., Mequon NOW, WI, Waukesha

mnewman@cninow.com, Design/Interactive
Content Dir., New Berlin NOW, WI,
Waukesha

mnewman@cninow.com, Design/Interactive
Content Dir., Muskego-New Berlin NOW, WI,
Waukesha

mnewman@cninow.com, Design/Interactive
Content Dir., Glendale NOW, WI, Waukesha

mnewman@cninow.com, Design/Interactive
Content Dir., West Allis NOW, WI, Waukesha

mnewman@cninow.com, Design/Interactive
Content Dir., Wauwatosa NOW, WI,
Waukesha

mnewman@cninow.com, Design/Interactive
Content Dir., St. Francis NOW, WI, Waukesha

mnewman@cninow.com, Design/Interactive
Content Dir., Bay View NOW, WI, Waukesha

mnewman@cninow.com, Design/Interactive
Content Dir., Elm Grove NOW, WI, Waukesha

mnewman@cninow.com, Design/Interactive
Content Dir., South Milwaukee NOW, WI,
Waukesha

mnewman@cninow.com, Design/Interactive
Content Dir., Franklin NOW, WI, Waukesha

mnewman@cninow.com, Design/Interactive
Content Dir., Hales Corners NOW, WI,
Waukesha

mnewman@cninow.com, Design/Interactive
Content Dir., Menomonee Falls-Germantown
NOW, WI, Waukesha

mnewman@cninow.com, Design/Interactive
Content Dir., Oak Creek NOW, WI, Waukesha

mnewman@cninow.com, Design/Interactive
Content Dir., North Shore NOW, WI,
Waukesha

Newman, Michael .... (414) 229-4436
mznewman@uwm.edu, Associate Professor
and Department Chair, University of
Wisconsin-Milwaukee / Department of
Journalism, Advertising, and Media Studies
(JAMS), WI, Milwaukee

Newman, Mildred
mildred.newman@thebogalusadailynews.com,
Business Office Mgr., Bogalusa Daily News,
LA, Bogalusa

Newman, Mitchell
menewman@mitchellsny.com, Owner,
Mitchell's, NY, New York

Newman, Robin .... (406) 296-2514
robin.newman22@icloud.com, Mng. Ed.,
Tobacco Valley News, MT, Eureka

Newman, Ruth
ruth@mainstreetmedia.us, Gen. Mgr., The
Russell County News, KS, Russell

Newman, Stanley
snpuzz@aol.com, Pres./Ed. in Chief, American

Crossword Federation, Massapequa Park

Newman, Steve
grizpaperboy@me.com, Ed., Tobacco Valley
News, MT, Eureka

Newman, Tim .... (989) 839-4277
tneuman@hearstnp.com, Gen. Mgr., Midland
Daily News, MI, Midland

Newman, Tom .... ext. 3043
Prodn. Foreman, Pressroom, The Intelligencer,
PA, Doylestown

Newman, Wendy
Wendy.Newman@CrowleyToday.com,
Bookkeeping, The Crowley Post-Signal, LA,
Crowley

Newquist, Michael
michael.newquist@fwweekly.com, Adv. Dir.,
Fort Worth Weekly, TX, Fort Worth

Newsom, Colleen
colleen@communityjournal.net, Adv. Mgr.,
Milwaukee Community Journal, WI,
Milwaukee

Newsome, Christy
enewsome@tampatrib.com, Tampa Bay Times,
FL, St Petersburg

Newsome, Mary
mary@wilkespublishing.com, Mng. Ed., The
News-Reporter, GA, Washington

Newsome, Sparky .... (706) 678-2636
editor@news-reporter.com, Ed./Pub., The
News-Reporter, GA, Washington

Newsome, Sparky
journal@nu-z.net, Ed./Pub., The Lincoln
Journal, GA, Lincolnton

Newton, Alison
alison.newton@independentmail.com, Content
Editor , Anderson Independent-Mail, SC,
Anderson

Newton, Christel .... (843) 958-7481
cnewton@moultrienews.com, Waccamaw
Times, SC, Georgetown

cnewton@moultrienews.com, Bus. Mgr., The
Georgetown Times, SC, Georgetown

Newton, Dawn .... (252) 329-9601
dnewton@reflector.com, Creative Servs. Mgr.,
The Daily Reflector, NC, Greenville

Newton, Georgia .... (503) 266-6831
Gnewton@CanbyHerald.com, Pub., The Canby
Herald, OR, Canby

Newton, Georgia
gnewton@molallapioneer.com, Pub, Molalla
Pioneer, OR, Molalla

Newton, Jim
jim.newton@latimes.com, Editor at Large, Los
Angeles Times, CA, Los Angeles

Newton, Linda .... (907) 350-3993
lnewton@thecordovatimes.com, Adv. Mgr., The
Cordova Times, AK, Cordova

Newton, Russ
russ.newton@latimes.com, Sr. Vice Pres., Op.,
Los Angeles Times, CA, Los Angeles

Newton, Steven .... (757) 547-5400
info@newtonmedia.com, Pres., Newton Media
Associates, Inc., VA, Chesapeake

Newton, Thomas .... (916) 288-6015
tom@cnpa.com, Exec. Dir., California News
Publishers Association, CA, Sacramento

Newton, Tracy .... (270) 745-2653
tracy.newton@wku.edu, Office Associate,
Western Kentucky University, KY, Bowling
Green

Newvine, Tari
tari@twptimes.com, Sales Assoc., The
Township Times, MI, Breckenridge

Ney, William .... (419) 609-5823
billney@sanduskyregister.com, Circ. Dir. ,
Sandusky Register, OH, Sandusky

billney@sanduskyregister.com, Circ. Mgr., Tsr
Express, OH, Sandusky

Ng, Assunta
info@nwasianweekly.com, Pub., Seattle
Chinese Post, WA, Seattle

Ng, Assunta
info@nwasianweekly.com, Pub., Northwest
Asian Weekly, WA, Seattle

Ng, Jeffrey
djnews.hk@dowjones.com, Correspondent,
Dow Jones Newswires - Hong Kong, Hong
Kong, Hong Kong

Ng, Peter
editor@estevanmercury.ca, Pub., Trader
Express, SK, Estevan

Ngo, Jenny
jenngo@cisco.com, San Jose State Univ., CA,
San Jose

Nguyen, Jeannie .... (212) 803-8324
jeannie.nguyen@sourcemedia.com, Mktg. Dir.,
American Banker, NY, New York

Nguyen, Kristie
nguyen@dioceseofvenice.org, Ed., The Florida
Catholic, FL, Venice

Ni, Lan
lni@uh.edu, Asst. Prof., University of Houston,
TX, Houston

NiCastro, Dom
amesbury@cnc.com, Sports Ed., Amesbury
News, MA, Danvers

Nibert, Angie
anibert@heralddispatch.com, Nat'l Sales, The
Herald-Dispatch, WV, Huntington

Niblett, Jason
newseditor@laurelleadercall.com, Ed./Pub.,
The Laurel Chronicle, MS, Laurel

Nice, Jennifer
classifieds@blackwelljournaltribune.net,
Class. Adv., Blackwell Journal-Tribune, OK,
Blackwell

Nichol-Caddy, Josh .... (573) 876-7133
jnichol@stephens.edu, Stephens Life Adviser,
Stephens College, MO, Columbia

Nicholas, Cynthia
cynthia.nicholas@vermiliontoday.com,
Managing Ed., Abbeville Meridional, LA,
Abbeville

Nicholas, Janey
janey.nicholas@iowastatedaily.com, Business
Manager, Iowa State University, IA, Ames

Nicholas, Jess
jnicholas@gannett.com, Ed., Prattville
Progress, AL, Prattville

Nicholas, Jim .... (580) 225-3000
jim@ecdailynews.com, Elk City Daily News,
OK, Elk City

Nicholas, Tim .... (601) 925-3462
Mississippi College, MS, Clinton

Nichols, Alexis .... (601) 928-4802
classifieds@stonecountyenterprise.com,
Classified Clerk, Stone County Enterprise,
MS, Wiggins

Nichols, Brianne .... (802) 525-3531
ads@bartonchronicle.com, Production Mgr.,
The Chronicle, VT, Barton

Nichols, Dan
dnichols@morningsentinel.com, Adv. Mgr.,
Crier/schrol,rlc Clocktoweer, IL, Centralia

Nichols, Daniel
news@morningsentinel.com, Adv. Mgr.,
Morning Sentinel, IL, Centralia

Nichols, Dave
nbfdavid@sbcglobal.net, Mgr., Opns., NB
Finishing, Inc., IL, Schaumburg

Nichols, Debi
bradfordjournal@excite.com, Ed., Bradford
Journal-Miner, PA, Bradford

Nichols, Denice
info@pulsesearch.com, Vice Pres., Sales,

Pulse Research, Inc., OR, Portland

Nichols, Dona
dona.nichols@sjsu.edu, Lectr., San Jose State
University, CA, San Jose

Nichols, John
jnichols@capitalnewspapers.com, The Capital
Times, WI, Madison

Nichols, Kimberly .... (951) 652-6529
knichols@thevalleychronicle.com, Acct. Exec.,
Valley Roadrunner, CA, Valley Center

Nichols, Nanalee .... (903) 652-4205
tppub@1starnet.com, Pub., Detroit Weekly,
TX, Deport

Nichols, Nanalee .... (903) 652-4205
nnichols@1starnet.com, Pub., Bogata News-
Talco Times, TX, Bogata

Nichols, Nanalee
nnichols@1starnet.com, Pub./Ed., Deport
Times-Blossom Times, TX, Deport

Nichols, Nanalee
tppub@1starnet.com, Owner/Pub., Thunder
Prairie Publishing, TX, Deport

Nichols, Newton
nnichols@calhounchronicle.com, Ed., The
Calhoun Chronicle, WV, Grantsville

Nichols, Peggy
pnichols@artbeats.com, Global Dist. Mgr.,
ArtbeatsEXPRESS, OR, Myrtle Creek

Nichols, Rick .... (785) 863-2520
independent@centurylink.net, Ed., Oskaloosa
Independent, KS, Oskaloosa

Nichols, Stefani
circclasspdjnews@yahoo.com, Class. / Cir.,
The Perry Daily Journal, OK, Perry

Nichols, Teresa
teresa.nichols@chickasawjournal.com, Office
Mgr., The Shopper Plus, MS, Houston

Nichols, Thomas .... (903) 905-3886 cell
thomas@1sstarnet.com, Adv. Dir., Bogata
News-Talco Times, TX, Bogata

Nichols, Thomas
tppub@1starnet.com, Adv. Mgr., Deport Times-
Blossom Times, TX, Deport

Nicholson, Amanda
amanda@weeklydig.com, Gen. Mgr., Boston's
Weekly Dig, MA, Boston

Nicholson, Bart
bart@yukonreview.net, Gen. Mgr., The Yukon
Review, OK, Yukon

Nicholson, Braden .... (317) 965-6405
bnicholson@nuvo.net, Gen. Mgr., Nuvo, IN,
Indianapolis

Nicholson, David
dnicholson@tampatrib.com, Mng. Ed., Plant
City Courier & Tribune, FL, Tampa

Nicholson, Ed .... (727) 893-8703
enicholson@tampabay.com, Chief Info. Officer ,
Tampa Bay Times, FL, St Petersburg

Nicholson, June
jnichols@vcu.edu, Assoc. Prof./Assoc. Dir.,
Virginia Commonwealth University, VA,
Richmond

Nicholson, Shane .... (815) 964-9767
shane.nicholson@rockrivertimes.com,
Managing Ed., The Rock River Times, IL,
Rockford

Nicholson, Tom
tnicholson@sprinklr.com, CEO, IconNicholson,
NY, New York

Nicholson, Virginia .... (304) 873-1600
theheraldrecord1@gmail.com, Pub./Ed., The
Herald Record, WV, West Union

Nicholson , Hugh .... (250) 729-4257
hnicholson@glaciermedia.com, Pub., Alberni
Valley Times, BC, Port Alberni

hnicholson@glaciermedia.com, Pub., Harbour
City Star (OOB), BC, Nanaimo

hnicholson@glaciermedia.com, Pub., Nanaimo Daily News, BC, Nanaimo

hnicholson@glaciermedia.com, Pub., The Prince George Citizen, BC, Prince George

hnicholson@glaciermedia.com, Pub., The Oceanside Star, BC, Parksville

Nickel, Abbey
pulse@findlay.edu, Editor, The University of Findlay, OH, Findlay

Nickel, Holly-Jaide
holly-jaide.nickel@thecarillon.com, Circ Mgr., The Carillon, MB, Steinbach

Nickel, Lori ....(507) 744-2551
lnickel@lonsdalenewsreview.com, Lonsdale News - Review, MN, Lonsdale
lnickel@lonsdalenewsreview.com, Ed./Pub., Lonsdale Area News-Review, MN, Lonsdale

Nickels, Scott
scott@edwgroupinc.com, Circ. Dir., Daily Journal/Messenger, SC, Seneca

Nickens, Tim.........................(727) 893-8532
tnickens@tampabay.com, Ed. of Editorials, Tampa Bay Times, FL, St Petersburg

Nickerson, Angela
advertising@capitolhilltimes.com, Designer/ Adv. Mgr., The Capitol Hill Times, WA, Seattle

Nickerson, Glen ....(863) 386-5624
glen.nickerson@newssun.com, Pub., Highlands News-Sun, FL, Sebring
glen.nickerson@newssun.com, President/ News-Sun & Highlands Sun, Sun Coast Media Group Inc, FL, Punta Gorda

Nickerson, Kathryn
kathryn.nickerson@juneauempire.com, Advertising Manager, Juneau Empire, AK, Juneau

Nickerson, Tracy ....(508) 366-5500 ext. 10
calendar@communityadvocate.com, Office Mgr., Community Advocate, MA, Westborough

Nickles, Alicia
alicia@flagpole.com, Adv. Mgr., Flagpole Magazine, GA, Athens

Nicklin, Madeleine ....(505) 986-3096
mnicklin@sfnewmexican.com, Asst. Ed., The Santa Fe New Mexican, NM, Santa Fe

Nicklin, Walter
publisher@rappnews.com, Pub./Chairman, Rappahannock Times, VA, Tappahannock

Nicks, Andrew
a.nicks@22ndcenturymedia.com, Adv. Dir., The Highland Park Landmark, IL, Northbrook
a.nicks@22ndcenturymedia.com, Adv. Dir., The Lake Forest Leader, IL, Northbrook
a.nicks@22ndcenturymedia.com, Adv. Dir., The Glencoe Anchor, IL, Northbrook
a.nicks@22ndcenturymedia.com, Classified Adv. Mgr., The Mokena Messenger, IL, Orland Park
a.nicks@22ndcenturymedia.com, Classified Adv. Mgr., The New Lenox Patriot, IL, Orland Park
a.nicks@22ndcenturymedia.com, Adv. Dir., The Glenview Lantern, IL, Northbrook
a.nicks@22ndcenturymedia.com, Classified Adv. Mgr., The Orland Park Prairie, IL, Orland Park
a.nicks@22ndcenturymedia.com, Adv. Dir., The Malibu Surfside News, CA, Malibu
a.nicks@22ndcenturymedia.com, Classified Adv. Mgr., The Homer Horizon, IL, Orland Park
a.nicks@22ndcenturymedia.com, Classified Adv. Mgr., The Tinley Junction, IL, Orland Park
a.nicks@22ndcenturymedia.com, Adv. Dir., The Wilmette Beacon, IL, Northbrook
a.nicks@22ndcenturymedia.com, Classified Adv. Mgr., The Frankfort Station, IL, Orland Park
a.nicks@22ndcenturymedia.com, Classified Adv. Mgr., The Lockport Legend, IL, Orland Park
a.nicks@22ndcenturymedia.com, Adv. Dir., The

Winnetka Current, IL, Northbrook

Nickson, Mark ....(203) 924-7000 ext. 4374
mnickson@dacsystems.com, Pres., DAC Systems, CT, Shelton
mnickson@dacsystems.com, Pres., DAC Systems, CT, Shelton

Nicol, Tom ....(936) 687-2424
nicolpc@aol.com, Pub., The Messenger, TX, Grapeland

Nicolanti, Diana............. (440) 247-5335 ext. 224
myad@chagrinvalleytimes.com, Classifieds Mgr., Solon Times, OH, Chagrin Falls

Nicoletti, Lindsay
lnicoletti@aurorasentinel.com, Mktg. Mgr., Aurora Sentinel, CO, Aurora

Niebes, Joylyn
publisher@dfwchild.com, Pub., Fort Worth Child Magazine, FL, Tamarac

Niebes, Joylyn ....(972) 447-9188
Joy@dfwchild.com, Pub., DallasChild, CO, Fort Collins

Niebes, Joylyn ....(972) 447-9188
joy@dfwchild.com, Publisher, DallasChild, TX, Addison

Niebes, Lauren
Lauren@dfwchild.com, Creative Director, DallasChild, CO, Fort Collins

Niebes-Piccirillo, Lauren............ (214) 707-6174
lauren@dfwchild.com, Creative & Content Director, DallasChild, TX, Addison

Niebling, Luann ....(608) 837-2521
lneabling@hngnews.com, Circ. Mgr., The Lake Mills Leader, WI, Lake Mills

Niebrugge, Linda
linda.niebrugge@effinghamdailynews.com, Composing Suprv., Effingham Daily News, IL, Effingham

Niedhammer, Mark
classifieds@lakevillejournal.com, Class Adv. Mgr., The Lakeville Journal, CT, Falls Village

Niekamp, Ray
rn10@txstate.edu, Asst. Prof., Texas State University-San Marcos, TX, San Marcos

Nield, Paula
svipaula@silverstar.com, Circ. Mgr., Star Valley Independent, WY, Afton

Nielsen, Alvin
alvin@thesheridanpress.com, Prodn. Mgr., Systems, The Sheridan Press, WY, Sheridan

Nielsen, Roger ....(706) 208-2225
roger.nielsen@onlineathens.com, Metro Ed., Athens Banner-Herald, GA, Athens

Nielsen, Thomas W.
tnielsen@brodiesystem.com, Pres., Brodie System, Inc., NJ, Linden

Nieman, Jim
jnieman@standardpub.com, Mng. Ed., Christian Standard, OH, Cincinnati

Niemetz, Agnes ....(212) 328-9555
aginiemetz@aol.com, Member, Foreign Press Association, NY, New York

Niemeyer, Cherry .... ext. 11
cherry@richfieldreaper.com, Office Mgr., The Richfield Shopper, UT, Richfield
cherry@richfieldreaper.com, Office Mgr., Richfield Reaper, UT, Richfield

Nienow, Flavio ....(250) 692-7526
newsroom@ldnews.net, Editor, Burns Lakes District News, BC, Burns Lake

Nieporte, Monica
mnieporte@athensmessenger.com, Pub., Messenger Consumer Services, OH, Athens

Nieporte, Monica ....(740) 592-6612 Ext. 242
mnieporte@athensmessenger.com, Pub./ APG Media Pres. , The Athens Messenger, OH, Athens

Nieporte, Monica

mnieporte@athensmessenger.com, Pub., The Vinton County Courier, OH, Mc Arthur

Nies, Jay ....(573) 635-9127 ext. 235
cathmoed@diojeffcity.org, Ed., The Catholic Missourian, MO, Jefferson City

Niester, Patty
pniester@cheboygantribune.com, Composition Mgr. , Cheboygan Daily Tribune, MI, Cheboygan

Nietert, Lacey ....(479) 474-5215
lnietert@pressargus.com , Multi-Media Account Executive, Alma Journal, AR, Van Buren

Nigh, Bob
bnigh@bgco.org, Managing Editor, Baptist Messenger, OK, Oklahoma City

Nighswonger, Todd ....(417) 451-1520
editor@neoshodailynews.com, Editor, Neosho Daily News, MO, Neosho

Nigro, Richard..........................(516) 485-6655
info@rollemusa.com, Vice Pres., Sales, Rollem Corp. of America, NY, Hempstead

Nigro, Vic ....(717) 291-8786
vnigro@steinmancommunications.com, IT Manager, LNP, PA, Lancaster
vnigro@steinmancommunications.com, IT Manager, LNP Media Group, Inc., PA, Lancaster

Nihles, Jason
journalsports@centurytel.net, Sports Ed., The Platteville Journal, WI, Platteville

Niiranen, Valtteri
valtteri.niiranen@enpa.be, Dir., European Newspaper Publishers' Association, 1050 Bruxelles

Nikic, Joe ....(516) 307-1045 Ext. 203
jnikic@theislandnow.com, Reporter, Great Neck News, NY, Williston Park

Nilan, Steve
steve.nilan@newscyclesolutions.com, Vice president, marketing, Digital Technology International, MN, Saint Paul

Niland, Michael
mniland@heraldnews.com, Prodn. Mgr., Classified Plus, MA, Fall River

Niland, Mike...........................(508) 676-2593
Prodn. Mgr., Real Estate Guide, MA, Fall River

Niles, Galen ....(361) 980-0008
Pub., American Classifieds, TX, Corpus Christi

Nimmo, Claudio
cnimmo@chespub.com, Gen, Mgr., The Avenue News, MD, Dundalk

Nimocks, Amber
amber.nimocks@nclawyersweekly.com, Ed, North Carolina Lawyers Weekly, NC, Charlotte

Nimz, Connie
ncesales@centurylink.net, Adv. Mgr., The Newton County Enterprise, IN, Kentland
ncesales@centurylink.net, Adv, Brook Reporter, IN, Kentland
ncesales@centurylink.net, Morocco Courier, IN, Kentland

Ningen, Amber
amber.ningen@hemingfordledger.com, Ed., The Ledger, NE, Hemingford

Nintzel, Jim...................(520) 797-4384 ext. 38
jimn@tucsonlocalmedia.com, News Ed., Explorer, AZ, Tucson
jimn@tucsonlocalmedia.com, News Ed., Tucson Weekly, AZ, Tucson

Nisenholtz, Martin A....................(212) 556-1234
Sr. Vice Pres., Digital Opns., The New York Times Co., NY, New York

Niser, Ed...ext. 239
eniser@nashobapub.com, Sports Ed., Pepperell Free Press, MA, Devens

Niser, Ed...ext. 239
eniser@nashobapub.com, Sports Ed., Shirley

Oracle, MA, Devens

Niser, Ed...x239
eniser@nashobapub.com ...., Sports Ed., Harvard Hillside, MA, Devens

Nishimura , Aki........................(248) 553-1000
info@daifukuna.com, Daifuku North America Holding
Company President and CEO, Jervis B. Webb Co., MI, Farmington Hills

Niswander, Peggy
pniswander@peoplesdefender.com, Bus. Mgr., The People's Defender, OH, West Union

Nitz, Steve
snitz@shawmedia.com, Sports Reporter, Daily Chronicle, IL, Dekalb

Niven, Deuce ....(910) 653-3153
tribdeuce@tabor-loris.com, Gen. Mgr./Ed., Tabor-Loris Tribune, NC, Tabor City

Nix, Charles D. ....(870) 578-2121
modernnews@pcsii.com, Ed., The Modern News, AR, Harrisburg

Nixdorf, Perry
pnixdorf@globeandmail.com, VP, Operations, The Globe and Mail, ON, Toronto

Nixon, Charity ....(912) 226-1621
Thomas College, GA, Thomasville

Nixon, Charles
coonrapidsenterprise@crmu.net, Editor, Coon Rapids Enterprise, IA, Coon Rapids

Nixon, Lance ....(605) 224-7301 x30
lance.nixon@capjournal.com, Managing Ed., Capital Journal, SD, Pierre

Nixon, Scott
snixon@carouselindustries.com, Editor, Times Advocate, ON, Exeter

Nixon, Steve ....(306) 651-6301
swna@swna.com, Exec. Dir., Saskatchewan Weekly Newspapers Association, SK, Saskatoon

Nizami, Zia ....(618) 239-2470
znizami@bnd.com, Photo, Belleville News-Democrat, IL, Belleville

Noah, Cathy
andrew.b.moore2.civ@mail.mil, Features Ed., Mail Tribune, OR, Medford

Noah, Paul .... (937) 222-8855, ext. 202
ceo@daytoncitymedia.com, CEO, Dayton City Media, Dayton City Paper, OH, Dayton

Noble, Gina
councilornoble@stillwater.org, Vstg. Asst. Prof., Oklahoma State University, OK, Stillwater

Noble, Kim
knoble@calkins-media.com, Dir., Adv./Mktg., Calkins Media, PA, Levittown

Noble, Kim...........................(215) 345-3088
knoble@phillyburbs.com, Adv. Dir., The Intelligencer, PA, Doylestown

Noble, Randy ....(407) 440-3056
rnoble@hearst.com, SE Sales, King Features Syndicate, NY, New York

Noble, Randy ....(407) 440-3056
rnoble@hearst.com, SE Sales, North America Syndicate, New York

Noble Jr, Jim
info@noblesystems.com, Pres./CEO, Noble System Corporation, GA, Atlanta

Nobles, Doug ....(318) 362-0238
dnobles@thenewsstar.com, Prodn. Dir., The News-Star, LA, Monroe

Noblitt, John F. ....(812) 865-3242
jnoblitt@blueriver.net, Ed., The Progress Examiner, IN, Orleans

Noce, Dorena ....(416) 847-2013
dnoce@bbm.ca, Corp. Scrvs., BBM Canada, ON, Toronto

Nocito, Marge
atlanticcapereview9@gmail.com, Atlantic Cape

Cmty. College, NJ, Mays Landing

Noda, Debbie .... (209) 578-2322
dnoda@modbee.com, Chief Photographer, The Modesto Bee, CA, Modesto

Noe, Kim
kim@newcastlepacer.com, Adv. Dir., Early Bird Express, OK, Newcastle

Noel, Alyssa
editor@whistlerquestion.com, Ed, The Whistler Question, BC, Whistler

Noel, Sarah .... (402) 371-1020 ext. 289
snoel@norfolkdailynews.com, E-Media Sales Mgr., Norfolk Daily News, NE, Norfolk

Noel, Sharrye .... (270) 783-3265
Mgr., Educ. Serv., Daily News, KY, Bowling Green

Noffsinger, Beth .... (270) 691-7233
bnoffsinger@messenger-inquirer.com, Special Publications Ed., Messenger-Inquirer, KY, Owensboro

Noiseux, Daniel
info@journaldechambly.com, Mng. Ed., Journal De Chambly, QC, Chambly

Nolan, Diane
dnolan@appleton.gannet.com, Prod. Mgr, Kewaunee County Star-News, WI, Kewaunee

Nolan, Jay .... (606) 546-9225
jnolan@mountainadvocate.com, Pub, The Mountain Advocate, KY, Barbourville

Nolan, Jeff
nolan@crestedbuttenews.com, Adv. Rep., Crested Butte News, CO, Crested Butte

Nolan, Jim .... (212) 969-7599
jdnolan@hearst.com, Sunday Comics Mgr., North America Syndicate, New York

Nolan, Sandi
sales@keremeosreview.com, Adv Mgr., Princeton Similkameen Spotlight, BC, Princeton
sales@keremeosreview.com, Adv. Rep., Keremeos Review, BC, Keremeos

Nolan, William .... (419) 724-6207
bnolan@toledoblade.com, Dir. of HR., The Blade, OH, Toledo

Nolan-Partnow, Maia
maia@alaskadispatch.com, Director, Sales & Special Content, Alaska Dispatch News, AK, Anchorage

Noland, Kevin J.
knoland@cyberlodg.com, Pub., The Gyp Hill Premiere, KS, Medicine Lodge

Nolda, Harry L.
pressj@iowatelecom.net, Pub., Strawberry Pt. Press Journal, IA, Strawberry Point

Noll, Robert T. .... (216) 397-4373
rnoll@jcu.edu, John Carroll University, OH, University Heights

Nolting, Ray
rnolting@parsonssun.com, Mng. Ed., Parsons Sun, KS, Parsons

Noneman, Mary Lou
news@woodbinetwiner.com, Prodn. Sup., The Woodbine Twiner, IA, Woodbine

Noon, Timothy .... (860) 646-0500
tnoon@journalinquirer.com, Vice President for Production, Journal Inquirer, CT, Manchester

Noonan, Colleen
cnoonan@nydailynews.com, VP, Mktg, New York Daily News, NY, New York

Noonan, James .... (336) 773-1595
thriftynickel@emadisonriver.com, Adv. Mgr., Thrifty Nickel Want Ads, NC, Winston Salem

Norbury, Angel
anorbury@michigannewspapers.com, Mktg. Cood., The Real Estate Review, MI, Mount Pleasant

Norcross, Lexie

lexie@phillyvoice.com, Exec. Dir, PhillyVoice. com, PA, Philadelphia
lexie@phillyvoice.com, Mng. Dir., WWB Holdings, LLC, PA, Philadelphia

Nordby, David .... (920) 756-2222
editor@thebrillionnews.com, Ed., The Brillion News, WI, Brillion

Norden, Kevin .... (815) 929-2135
knorden@daily-journal.com, Gen. Mgr, The Daily Journal, IL, Kankakee

Norden, Kevin .... (815) 929-2135
General Manager/Production Director, Small Newspaper Group, IL, Kankakee

Norder, Lois
lnorder@star-telegram.com, Mng. Ed., Investigations, Fort Worth Star-Telegram, TX, Fort Worth

Nordine, Julie M.
norstar@wiktel.com, Ed., North Star News, MN, Karlstad

Nordmark, Jason
tcrecordherald@stellarnet.com, Pub., Towner County Record Herald, ND, Cando
tcrecordherald@stellarnet.com, Pub., Lake Metigoshe Mirror, ND, Rolla

Nordmark, Jason .... (701) 422-6495
Pub., Billings County Pioneer, ND, Beach

Nordmark, Jason
tcrecordherald@gondtc.com, Ed., Towner County Record-Herald, ND, Cando

Nordmark, Jason
tmstar@utma.com, Pub. / Ed. , Turtle Mountain Star, ND, Rolla

Nordmark, Jason
tmstar@utma.com, Pub., Nordmark Publishing, ND, Rolla

Nordmark, Jason
wcpress@polarcomm.com, Pub., The Walsh County Press, ND, Park River

Nordmark, Jason
msrvrjnl@ndak.net, Pub., The Mouse River Journal, ND, Towner

Nordmark, Jason
tmstar@utma.com, Pub., Dickey County Leader, ND, Ellendale

Nordrum, Teresa
office@burnettcountysentinel.com, Office Mgr., Burnett County Sentinel, WI, Grantsburg

Nordstrom, Eric
webbads@webbweekly.com, Prod. Mgr, Webb Weekly, PA, South Williamsport

Norfleet, Gregory .... (319) 643-3725
info@westbranchtimes.com, Editor, West Branch Times, IA, West Branch

Norich, Samuel
norich@forward.com, CEO/Pub., Forward Newspaper, NY, New York

Norlock , George
george.norlock@sunmedia.ca, Circ. Dir., The Ottawa Sun, ON, Ottawa

Norman, Byron
circ@starkvilledailynews.com, Circ. Mgr., Starkville Daily News, MS, Starkville
circ@starkvilledailynews.com, Circ. Mgr., Bulldog Beat, MS, Starkville
circ@starkvilledailynews.com, Circ. Mgr., Daily Times Leader, MS, West Point

Norman, Dean .... (216) 251-1389
dnorman@bge.net, Artist/Owner, Beaver Creek Features, Cleveland

Norman, Diane .... (828) 694-7876
diane.norman@blueridgenow.com, Executive Editor, Times-News, NC, Hendersonville

Norman, Don .... (662) 323-1642
sdnpub@bellsouth.net, Pub., Bulldog Beat, MS, Starkville
sdnpub@bellsouth.net, Pub., Starkville Daily News, MS, Starkville

Norman, Don .... (662) 323-1642
sdnpub@bellsouth.net, Pub., Daily Times Leader, MS, West Point

Norman, Janice .... (231) 839-8651
janice.norman@localmedia.org, Accounting & Finance Director, Local Media Association, MI, Lake City

Norman, Jean .... (801) 626-7526
jeannorman@weber.edu, Signpost Adviser, Weber State Univ., UT, Ogden

Norman, Jeremy
sports@southwesttimes.com, Sports Ed., The Southwest Times (Pulaski, VA), VA, Pulaski

Norman, Rudy .... (709) 252-2954
editor@thenorwester.ca, Ed., The Nor'wester, NL, Springdale

Normand, Gilles .... (613) 632-4151
gilles.normand@eap.on.ca, Circ. Mgr., Le Carillon, ON, Hawkesbury

Normand, Gilles .... (613) 632-4151
gilles.normand@eap.on.ca, Circ. Mgr., Tribune Express, ON, Hawkesbury

Normandin, James .... (603) 668-4321 Ext. 240
jnormandin@unionleader.com, Chief Operating Officer, New Hampshire Union Leader/New Hampshire Sunday News, NH, Manchester

Normile, Trevor
tnormile@ncweeklies.com, Editor, Duplin Times, NC, Kenansville

Norrie, Gordon .... (780) 410-1010
gordon.norrie@sunmedia.ca, Pub., The Edmonton Sun, AB, Edmonton

Norris, Bob .... (865) 981-1143
City/Metro Ed., The Daily Times, TN, Maryville

Norris, Greg .... (603) 750-6864
GREG.NORRIS@GOSSINTERNATIONAL. COM, Goss International Corporation, NH, Durham

Norris, Marcus .... (337) 738-5642
kindernews@yahoo.com, Adv. Mgr., Kinder Courier News, LA, Kinder

Norris, Margaret .... (516) 931-0012
editor@gcnews.com, Pres./Pub., Litmor Publishing, NY, Garden City

Norris, Meg Morgan
editor@gcnews.com, Ed./Pub., Garden City News, NY, Garden City

Norris, Meg Morgan
editor@gcnews.com, Pub., Hicksville Mid-Island Times, NY, Garden City

Norris, Meg Morgan
editor@gcnews.com, Ed., Jericho News Journal, NY, Garden City

Norris, Michael
mnorris@marketresearch.com, Sr. Ed., Simba Information, CT, Stamford

Norselli, Daniel .... (585) 258-2226
dnorselli@democratandchronicle.com, Pres., Democrat and Chronicle, NY, Rochester

Northcraft , Lisa
lnorthcraft@wetzelchronicle.com, Adv. Mgr., Wetzel Chronicle, WV, New Martinsville
lnorthcraft@wetzelchronicle.com, Adv. Mgr., Tyler Star News, WV, Sistersville

Northrop, Cary
cnnorthrop@southwestdistribution.com, Pres., American Association of Independent News Distributors, DC, Washington

Northrop, Lucy S. .... (724) 222-2200
lnorthrop@observer-reporter.com, Director of News, Observer-Reporter, PA, Washington

Northrop, Thomas P. .... (724) 223-2626
tnorthrop@observer-reporter.com, Pres./Pub., Observer-Reporter, PA, Washington

Northsea, Michele .... (352) 489-2731
Advertising sales, Riverland News, FL, Dunnellon

Northup, Adam Mr. .... (401) 364-6061
adam@motterstitch.com, Office Assist., Motterstitch Company, Inc., RI, Carolina

Northup, Brent
bnorthup@carroll.edu, Carroll College, MT, Helena

Northup, David .... (401) 364-6061
david@motterstitch.com, Sales VP, Motterstitch Company, Inc., RI, Carolina

Northup, Linda .... (401) 364-6061
linda@motterstitch.com, Office Admin., Motterstitch Company, Inc., RI, Carolina

Northup, Thomas .... (401) 364-6061
tom@motterstitch.com, President, Motterstitch Company, Inc., RI, Carolina

Norton, Brian
brian.norton@douglascounty-ne.gov, Lectr., Creighton Univ., NE, Omaha

Norton, Buddie
bnorton@cherokeeherald.com, Layout Ed, Cherokee County Herald, AL, Centre

Norton, Carol
circulation@yourbeacon.net, Circ. Mgr., Edmonds Beacon, WA, Mukilteo
circulation@yourbeacon.net, Circ. Mgr., Mukilteo Beacon, WA, Mukilteo

Norton, David S.
davenorton@themcdonoughdemocrat.com, Ed., McDonough-Democrat, IL, Bushnell

Norton, Diane .... (207) 236-8511
chads@courierpub.com, Adv. Dir., Steppin' Out, ME, Rockland
chads@courierpub.com, Exec. Dir., Maine Press Association, ME, Cape Elizabeth

Norton, John
jnorton@pioneergroup.com, Pub., Herald Review, MI, Big Rapids
jnorton@pioneergroup.com, Pioneer East Shopper, MI, Big Rapids
jnorton@pioneergroup.com, River Valley Shopper, MI, Big Rapids
jnorton@pioneergroup.com, West Shore Shopper, MI, Big Rapids
jnorton@pioneergroup.com, Pub., The Benzie County Record-Patriot, MI, Frankfort

Norton, John
jnorton@pioneergroup.com, Pub., The Pioneer - Big Rapids, MI, Big Rapids

Norton, John .... (231) 592-8352
jnorton@pioneergroup.net, Pub., Tri-county Shoppers Guide, MI, Big Rapids

Norton, John .... (231) 937-4740
jnorton@pioneergroup.net, Pub., River Valley News Shopper, MI, Howard City

Norton, John
jnorton@pionneergroup.net, Pub., Pioneer Group, MI, Big Rapids

Norton, John S. .... (231) 796-4831 ext.352
jnorton@pioneergroup.com, Pub., Lake County Star, MI, Baldwin

Norton, Todd
tmnorton@wsu.edu, Asst. Prof., Washington State University, WA, Pullman

Norton, Will
wnorton1@unl.edu, Dean/Prof., University of Nebraska-Lincoln, NE, Lincoln

Nortz, Mark
marknortz@winthropalumni.com, Instr., Winthrop University, SC, Rock Hill

Norvell, Catherine .... (580) 221-6540
catherine.norvell@ardmoreite.com, Class. Sales, The Ardmoreite, OK, Ardmore

Norwood, Eric .... (202) 491-1685
enorwood@southcomm.com, Washington City Paper, DC, Washington

Norwood, Jody
jnorwood@heraldledger.com, Ed., The Herald-Ledger, KY, Eddyville

Norwood, Joy ....(814) 371-4200
newspaper@thecourierexpress.com, Ed., Tri-County Sunday, PA, Du Bois
newspaper@thecourierexpress.com, Sunday Ed., The Courier Express, PA, Du Bois

Noseworthy, Caroline ....(403) 235-7167
cnoseworthy@calgaryherald.com, Adv. Exec. Asst., Calgary Herald, AB, Calgary

Nossa, Jill
jnossa@antonmediagroup.com, Ed., Glen Cove Record-Pilot, NY, Mineola

Noth, Robin ....(608) 791-8331
robin.noth@lee.net, Circ. Mgr., Tri-county Foxxy Shopper, WI, La Crosse
robin.noth@lee.net, Circ. Mgr., La Crosse Foxxy Shopper, WI, La Crosse
robin.noth@lee.net, La Crosse Tribune, WI, La Crosse

Nothaft, Keira ....(602) 444-4850
keira.nothaft@arizonarepublic.com, Deputy Mng. Ed., Page One, The Arizona Republic, AZ, Phoenix

Nott, Gerry
gnott@ottawacitizen.com, Pub. & Ed.-in-Chief, The Ottawa Citizen, ON, Ottawa

Novack, Adriana ....(805) 466-2585 x115
anovack@atascaderonews.com, Ad. Mgr., Atascadero News, CA, Atascadero

Novak, Kim ....(519) 426-5710 ext. 143
kim.novak@sunmedia.ca, Mng. Ed. , The Simcoe Reformer, ON, Simcoe

Novak, Kim ....(519) 426-5710 ext. 143
knovak@bowesnet.com, Ed., Delhi News-record, ON, Delhi

Novak, Scott ....(269) 687-7702
scott.novak@leaderpub.com, Sports Ed., Niles Daily Star, MI, Niles

Novak, Scott
scott.novak@leaderpub.com, Community ed., Cassopolis Vigilant, MI, Niles

Novak, Scott
scott.novak@leaderpub.com, Community Ed., Edwardsburg Argus, MI, Niles

Novecosky, Peter
pm.editor@stpeters.sk.ca, Ed., Order Of St. Benedict, SK, Muenster

Novey, Madeline
madelinenovey@coloradoan.com, Colorado State Univ., CO, Fort Collins

Novotny, Jeff ....(603) 224-5301 ext. 338
Asst. Sports Ed., Concord Monitor, NH, Concord

Nowak, Chris
circ-dist@alliancetimes.com, Distr. Mgr., Alliance Times-Herald, NE, Alliance

Nowak, Judy ....(920) 834-4242
jmnowak@gannett.com, News Clerk, Lakes/forest Beacon, WI, Oconto

Nowak, Judy ....(920) 834-4242
jmnowak@gannett.com, News Clerk, Lakes/forest Beacon, WI, Oconto

Nowell, Joyce
news@echo-pilot.com, Ed., The Echo-Pilot, PA, Greencastle

Nowicki, Helen
retail@brenhambanner.com, Adv. Director, Brenham Banner-Press, TX, Brenham

Nowicki, Helen ....(979) 836-7956
retail@brenhambanner.com, Retail Adv. Mgr., Banner Extra, TX, Brenham

Nowicki, Jackie
shermanpub@aol.com, Adv. Mgr, Ortonville Citizen, MI, Ortonville

Nowling, Jada ....(907) 275-2154
jada.nowling@morris.com, Adv. Media Consultant, Alaska Star, AK, Eagle River

Nowotnik, Jacklyn
neiuindependent@gmail.com, Editor-in-Chief,

Northeastern Illinois University, IL, Chicago

Nugent, Gail ....(604) 606-8678
gnugent@westender.com, Pub, We Vancouver Weekly, BC, Vancouver
gnugent@westender.com, Pub, The Westender, BC, Vancouver

Nugent, Ken
knugent@metroland.com, Vice Pres., Metroland Media Group Ltd., ON, Mississauga

Nugent, Ken
eadvocate@sentex.ca, Pub., The Erin Advocate, ON, Erin

Null, Casey ....(614) 486-6677
cnull@adohio.net, Advertising Account Executive, Ohio Newspaper Services, Inc., OH, Columbus

Nulph, Brad ....(580) 548-8112
circmgr@enidnews.com, Director of Audience Development
(circulation), Enid News & Eagle, OK, Enid

Nun, Hal
hal@thenews-journal.com, Adv. Mgr., The News-Journal, NC, Raeford

Nunez, Louis
pressgripper@earthlink.net, Owner, G.T. Specialties, NM, Albuquerque

Nunez, Rick
advertising@bigspringherald.com, Adv. Mgr., Retail, Big Spring Herald, TX, Big Spring
advertising@bigspringherald.com, Ad Dir., Sweetwater Reporter, TX, Sweetwater

Nunn, Chuck ....Ext. 325
cnunn@hjnews.com, News Editor, The Herald Journal, UT, Logan

Nunn, Jayson ....(765) 575-4643
jnunn@thecouriertimes.com, Adv. Sales. Exec., The Courier-Times, IN, New Castle

Nunn, Teresa S.
tnunn@glasgowdailytimes.com, Glasgow Daily Times, KY, Glasgow

Nunnari, Ron ....(937) 684-9124
Rnunnari@civitasmedia.com, Mng. Ed., Vandalia Drummer News, OH, Vandalia
Rnunnari@civitasmedia.com, Mng. Ed., Englewood Independent, OH, Vandalia
Rnunnari@civitasmedia.com, Mng. Ed., Huber Heights Courier, OH, Vandalia

Nuno, Andres
andres@coastalview.com, Prodn. Mgr., Coastal View News, CA, Carpinteria

Nusbaum, Mark ....(904) 359-4349
mark.nusbaum@jacksonville.com, Pres., The Florida Times-Union, FL, Jacksonville

Nussbaum, Jake
thechronicle.business@gmail.com, Business Manager, Hofstra University, NY, Hempstead

Nussbaum, Kim
hedged@reporternews.com, Pub., Sound of Freedom, TX, Abilene

Nussbaum, Kim ....(916) 321-1956
knussbaum@mcclatchy.com, VP of Adv., The McClatchy Company, CA, Sacramento

Nussbaum, Michael
mnussbaum@queenstribune.com, Pub., Queens Tribune, NY, Whitestone

Nusser, Nancy
nussernl@jmu.edu, Asst. Prof., James Madison University, VA, Harrisonburg

Nusz, Nancy ....(530) 406-6224
Pre Press Mgr., The Daily Democrat, CA, Woodland

Nuti-De Biasi, Alex
editor@jonews.com, Mng. Ed., Journal Opinion, VT, Bradford

Nuttall, Toni
tnuttall@eastbaynewspapers.com, Adv. Dir., Sakonnet Times, RI, Bristol

tnuttall@eastbaynewspapers.com, Adv. Dir., Westport Shorelines, RI, Bristol
tnuttall@eastbaynewspapers.com, Adv. Dir., Barrington Times, RI, Bristol
tnuttall@eastbaynewspapers.com, Adv. Dir., Bristol Phoenix, RI, Bristol
tnuttall@eastbaynewspapers.com, Adv. Dir., Warren Times-Gazette, RI, Bristol

Nuttall, Toni ....(401) 253-6000 ext. 103
tnuttall@eastbaynewspapers.com, Advertising Dir., East Bay Newspapers, RI, Bristol

Nutter, Doug
dnutter@progressnewspaper.org, Pub./Adv. Mgr., The Paulding Progress, OH, Paulding

Nutter, Doug
dnutter@progressnewspaper.org, Pub., Weekly Reminder, OH, Paulding

Nutter, Jim
nutter@metrotimes.com, Sr. Acct. Exec., Metro Times, MI, Ferndale

Nutter, Pam
pnutter@greenwooddemocrat.com, Adv. Mgr., Greenwood Democrat, AR, Greenwood

Nutting, G. Ogden ....(304) 233-0100
ONUTTING@OGDENNEWS.COM, Publisher, Ogden Newspapers Inc., WV, Wheeling

Nutting, William O ....(304) 233-0100
wnutting@ogdennews.com, Vice Pres., Ogden Newspapers Inc., WV, Wheeling

Nuzum, Scott
snuzum@fstribune.com, Sports Ed., The Fort Scott Tribune, KS, Fort Scott

Nuzzo, Irene
irene@newsandcitizen.com, Display Adv. Mgr., News & Citizen, VT, Morrisville
irene@newsandcitizen.com, Display Adv. Mgr., The Transcript, VT, Morrisville

Nyberg, Amy
amy.nyberg@shu.edu, Seton Hall University, NJ, South Orange

Nyberg, Karen
knyberg@tcmhs.org, Dir., Finance, Sun Media Group, ME, Lewiston

Nyberg, Liz ....same
Liznyberg@gmail.com, HR Dir, Los Altos Town Crier, CA, Los Altos

Nyberg, Paul ....ext. 311
pauln@latc.com, Pub., Los Altos Town Crier, CA, Los Altos

Nyce, Henry H. ....(570) 621-3388
hnyce@republicanherald.com, Pub., The Republican-Herald, PA, Pottsville

Nyestvold, Renne
news@claycountyunion.net, Adv, Clay County Union, MN, Ulen

Nyhus, Craig
cnyhus@lonestaroutdoornews.com, Exec. Ed., Lone Star Outdoor News, TX, Dallas

Nylin, Peter ....(845) 437-4957
pnylin@poughkeepsiejournal.com, Adv. Mgr., Retail, Poughkeepsie Journal, NY, Poughkeepsie

Nylund, Debbie
info@mcink.com, Pres., Miller-Cooper Co., KS, Merriam

Nyquist, Peter
p.nyquist@antonnews.com, Circ. Mgr., Floral Park Dispatch, NY, Mineola

Nystrom, Andy
anystrom@bothell-reporter.com, Ed., Redmond Reporter, WA, Kirkland

Nystrom, Sue
sue.icsg@sbcglobal.net, Adv. Sales, Ionia County Shoppers Guide, MI, Saranac

O

O"Neal, John ....(336) 727-4097

joneal@wsjournal.com, Digital Platform Director, Winston-Salem Journal, NC, Winston Salem

O'Bannon, Jonathan
ctimberlake@corydondemocrat.com, Pub., Clarion News, IN, Corydon

O'Bannon, Jonathan
ctimberlake@corydondemocrat.com, Pres./Pub., The Corydon Democrat, IN, Corydon

O'Bannon, Jonathan
ctimberlake@corydondemocrat.com, Pres./Pub., Shopper, IN, Corydon

O'Brian, Sean
sobrien@dailyadvance.com, Ad. Dir, Perquimans Weekly, NC, Hertford

O'Briant, Tim ....(803) 644-2380
tobriant@aikenstandard.com, Audience Development Dir., Evening Post Industries' Aiken Communications, SC, Aiken

O'Brien, Annie ....(313) 202-8049
annieo@metrotimes.com, Circ. Mgr., Metro Times, MI, Ferndale

O'Brien, Art
editor@licatholic.org, Adv. Mgr., The Long Island Catholic, NY, Roosevelt

O'Brien, Beth ....(530) 852-0225
betho@goldcountrymedia.com, Advert Direct., Auburn Journal, CA, Auburn

O'Brien, Dan
dan.obrien@techimage.com, Blog Ed., Tech Image Ltd., IL, Buffalo Grove

O'Brien, Dan ....(978) 970-4642
dobrien@lowellsun.com, Bus. Ed., The Sun, MA, Lowell

O'Brien, Don
dobrien@whig.com, Sports Ed., The Quincy Herald-Whig, IL, Quincy

O'Brien, Felicia ....(406) 468-9231
cascadecourier@mcn.net, Pub./Ed., Cascade Courier, MT, Cascade

O'Brien, Gerry ....(541) 885-4437
gobrien@heraldandnews.com, Editor, Herald and News, OR, Klamath Falls

O'Brien, Houston V. ....(254) 629-1707
ecn@att.net, Pub., Rising Star, TX, Eastland

O'Brien, Houston V.
ecn@att.net, Pub., Ranger Times, TX, Eastland
ecn@att.net, Pub., Eastland Telegram, TX, Eastland

O'Brien, Houston V. ....(254) 629-1707
ecn@att.net, Pres./Co-Pub., Eastland County Newspapers, TX, Eastland

O'Brien, Houston V. ....(915) 629-1707
thebairdstar@yahoo.com, Pub./Ed., Callahan County Star, TX, Eastland

O'Brien, J.L. ....(307) 778-1368
jobrien@lccc.wy.edu, Advisor, Laramie County Cmty. College, WY, Cheyenne

O'Brien, Jeffrey
jobrien@newsadvance.com, Adv. Mgr. , Nelson County Times, VA, Amherst

O'Brien, John J. ....(609) 406-0600, ext. 13
jjobrien@njpa.org, Foundation Director, New Jersey Press Association, NJ, Ewing

O'Brien, Joseph
jwobrien@stetson.edu, Stetson Univ., FL, Deland

O'Brien, Kathryn ....(978) 739-1393
tritown@wickedlocal.com, Ed., Tri-Town Transcript, MA, Danvers

O'Brien, Kevin ....(212) 210-2162
kobrien@nydailynews.com, Dir., Nat. Adv., New York Daily News, NY, New York

O'Brien, Neal ....(570) 628-6117
Home Delivery Mgr., The Republican-Herald, PA, Pottsville

O'Brien, Peggy

O'Quinn, Vernon
voquinn@cbpost.com, IT/Systems Mgr., The Cape Breton Post, NS, Sydney

O'Reilly, Kerry..........................(727) 893-8411
koreilly@tampabay.com, Marketing Dir., Tampa Bay Times, FL, St Petersburg

O'Rourke, James.......................(617) 224-2344
Regional VP - Atlantic, GateHouse Media, Inc., NY, Pittsford

O'Rourke, Jennie ....(518) 445-7200
Albany College of Pharmacy, NY, Albany

O'Rourke, Jim
jorourke@digitalfirstmedia.com, Pub., Alma Reminder, MI, Alma
jorourke@digitalfirstmedia.com, Pub., Gladwin Buyers Guide, MI, Gladwin
jorourke@digitalfirstmedia.com, Pub. , Grand Traverse Insider, MI, Traverse City
jorourke@digitalfirstmedia.com, Pub., Alpena Star, MI, Alpena
jorourke@digitalfirstmedia.com, Pub., Mt. Pleasant Buyers Guide, MI, Mount Pleasant

O'Rourke, Jim
jorourke@digitalfirstmedia.com, Pub., Clare County Buyer's Guide, MI, Mount Pleasant

O'Rourke, Jim..........................(248) 284-1433
jorourke@21st-centurymedia.com, Pub., The Macomb Daily, MI, Clinton Township
jorourke@21st-centurymedia.com, Pub., Greater Detroit Ads, MI, Pontiac

O'Rourke, Michael..........(610) 807-9619 ext. 112
mikeor@lvb.com, Pub., Lehigh Valley Business, PA, Bethlehem

O'Rourke, Tim
torourke@sfchronicle.com, Asst. Mng. Ed., San Francisco Chronicle, CA, San Francisco

O'Rourke, Tim..........................(780) 790-6627
tim@starnews.ca, Publisher/Sales Manager, Connect, AB, Fort McMurray

O'Shaughnessy, Anne
circulation@northfulton.com, Circ. Mgr., The Revue & News, GA, Alpharetta
circulation@northfulton.com, Circ. Mgr., The Forsyth Herald, GA, Alpharetta
circulation@northfulton.com, Circ. Mgr., Milton Herald, GA, Alpharetta

O'Shea, Patrick
po'shea@timesonline.com, Mng. Ed. , Beaver County Times, PA, Beaver

O'Sullivan, Megan
mosullivan@hcnonline.com, Mktg. Mgr., River Oaks Examiner, TX, Houston
mosullivan@hcnonline.com, Mktg. Mgr., Cypress Creek Mirror, TX, Houston
mosullivan@hcnonline.com, Mktg. Mgr., Sugar Land Sun, TX, Houston
mosullivan@hcnonline.com, Mktg. Mgr., Tomball Potpourri, TX, Conroe
mosullivan@hcnonline.com, Mktg. Mgr., The Woodlands Villager, TX, Conroe
mosullivan@hcnonline.com, Mktg. Mgr., Memorial Examiner, TX, Conroe
mosullivan@hcnonline.com, Mktg. Mgr., The Examiners, TX, Conroe
mosullivan@hcnonline.com, Mktg. Mgr., Magnolia Potpourri, TX, Conroe
mosullivan@hcnonline.com, Mktg. Mgr., Spring Observer, TX, Conroe
mosullivan@hcnonline.com, Mktg. Mgr., Pearland Journal, TX, Conroe

O'Sullivan, Michael ....(518) 584-4242 ext.201
mosullivan@21st-centurymedia.com, Pub., Community News, NY, Saratoga Springs
mosullivan@21st-centurymedia.com, Pub., Latham Life, NY, Troy
mosullivan@21st-centurymedia.com, Pub., Greenbush Life, NY, Troy

O'Sullivan, Michael F.
mosullivan@21st-centurymedia.com, Pub., The Saratogian, NY, Saratoga Springs

O'Sullivan, Mike
fffnews@hotmail.com, Troy Publishing Co., Inc., NY, Troy

O'Toole, Kent ....(270) 781-1700
kotoole@bgdailynews.com, Gen. Mgr., Daily News, KY, Bowling Green

O'Toole, Thomas J.
traveljournalists@hotmail.com, Journalist/ Photographer, Tom & Joanne O'Toole, Travel Journalists/Photographers, Willoughby

O'Toole, Tom ....(630) 789-8666
tom@tomotoole.com, Pres., Tom O'Toole Communication, Inc., IL, Burr Ridge

Oakes, Kevin ....(847) 680-7022 x 104
koakes@hurletron.com, Asst. Gen. Mgr./Dir.of Sales, Hurletron, Inc., IL, Libertyville

Oakes, Zachery
editorial@adairprogress.com, Ed., Adair Progress, KY, Columbia

Oakley, Mitchell
farmvilleed@nccox.com, Pub., The Farmville Enterprise, NC, Farmville

Oalmann, David ....(540) 981-3290
david.oalmann@roanoke.com, Production Dir., The Roanoke Times, VA, Roanoke

Oates, Sean..........................(973) 569-7159
Oates@northjersey.com, Web Ed., Herald News, NJ, Rockaway

Obee, Dave ....(250) 380-5201
dobee@timescolonist.com , Ed. in Chief, Victoria Times Colonist, BC, Victoria

Oberdorf, Max ....(570) 444-9850
thevalleytrader@yahoo.com, Owner and Founder, The Valley Trader, PA, Lewisburg

Oberfest, Barbara.............(508) 693-6100 ext 17
mvt@mvtimes.com, Pub., The Martha's Vineyard Times, MA, Vineyard Haven

Oberfest, Peter ....(508) 693-6100 ext. 17
peter.oberfest@mvtimes.com, Pub., The Martha's Vineyard Times, MA, Vineyard Haven

Oberlin, Amy ....(260) 665-3117 Ext. 2142
aoberlin@kpcmedia.com, News Ed., The Herald Republican, IN, Angola

Oberlin, Debbie ....(250) 785-5631
circulation@ahnfsj.ca, Circ. Mgr., North Peace Express, BC, Fort Saint John
circulation@ahnfsj.ca, Circ., The Northerner, BC, Fort Saint John

Obermaier, Dan ....(847) 866-5250
Ed., Morton Grove Champion, IL, Chicago

Obermeier, Ron
actiont@evansville.net, Adv. Mgr., Retail Sales, Evansville Courier & Press, IN, Evansville

Oberski, Dena
jcfloridancirculation@jcfloridan.com, Circ. Mgr., Jackson County Floridan, FL, Marianna

Obley, Pat............................(941) 206-1122
pobley@sun-herald.com, Exec. Sports Ed., Charlotte Sun, FL, Punta Gorda

Oborne, Blair
nipigongazette@shaw.ca, Pub., Terrace Bay Schreiber News, ON, Terrace Bay

Oborne, Blair
nipigongazette@shaw.ca, Pub., Nipigon-red Rock Gazette, ON, Nipigon

Ochinero, Mark......................(559) 441-6280
dgrady@fresnobee.com, Human Resources Dir, The Fresno Bee, CA, Fresno

Ocker, Kyle..........................(641) 856-6336
kocker@dailyiowegian.com, Editor, Ad-Express & Daily Iowegian, IA, Centerville

Ockerman, Stephanie ....(606) 784-4116
tmnews@moreheadnewsgroup.com, Mng. Ed., Menifee County News, KY, Morehead

Ockerman, Stephanie ....(606) 784-4116
sockerman@themoreheadnews.com, Mng. Ed., Shopping News, KY, Morehead

Ockermann, Stephanie
sockerman@themoreheadnews.com, Ed., The Morehead News, KY, Morehead

Odden, Kathy
kodden@eot.com, Circ. Mgr., Staples World, MN, Staples

Oddy, Peg
peg@opcfla.com, Clay County Leader, FL, Fleming Island
peg@opcfla.com, Adv. Mgr., Clay Today, FL, Fleming Island

Odefey, Chad ....(203) 876-3002
codefey@ctcentral.com, Mng. Ed., Elm City Newspapers, CT, Milford

Oden, Jim
billwesa@circulation.net, Pres., Circulation Development, Inc., MO, Wentzville

Odette, Preston
podette@cn.homecomm.net, Pub., Clinton County News, MI, Lansing

Odom, Kelsey ....(806) 872-2177
adsales@pressreporter.com, ad manager, Lamesa Press Reporter, TX, Lamesa

Odom, Maida
mcodom@temple.edu, Asst. Prof./Internship Dir., Temple University, PA, Philadelphia

Odom, Marianne ....(210) 486-1786
modom@alamo.edu, Advisor, San Antonio College, TX, San Antonio

Odom, Mike
courier@gulfcoastnewspapers.com, Ed., The Fairhope Courier, AL, Fairhope

Odson, Bruce ....(605) 356-2632
leader2@iw.net, Pub., Southern Union County Leader-Courier, SD, Elk Point
leader2@iw.net, Area Wide Ad-vertiser, IA, Hawarden

Odson, Susan
leader1@iw.net, Gen. Mgr., Southern Union County Leader-Courier, SD, Elk Point

Oelrich, Cathy ....(715) 369-9284
coelrich@mmclocal.com, Circ. Mgr., Star Journal, WI, Rhinelander
coelrich@mmclocal.com, Circ. Mgr., Hodag Buyer's Guide, WI, Rhinelander

Oelrich, Stacey ....(715) 389-6545
unitedway.stacey@tznet.com, Univ. of Wisconsin Marshfield, WI, Marshfield

Oelschlagel, Kristen
koelschlagel@bonnyville.greatwest.ca, Ed, Bonnyville Nouvelle, AB, Bonnyville

Oetzel, John
joetzel@unm.edu, Chair, University of New Mexico, NM, Albuquerque

Offer, Luan
shermanpub@aol.com, Circ. Mgr, Ortonville Citizen, MI, Ortonville

Office, PNAWAN......................(509) 922-3456
Ads@PNAWAN.org, Pacific Northwest Association of Want Ad Newspapers (PNAWAN) & Western Regional Advertising Program (WRAP), WA, Spokane

Offill, Bill............................(386) 681-2276
bill.offill@news-jrnl.com, New Smyrna Pennysaver, FL, New Smyrna Beach
bill.offill@news-jrnl.com, Publisher, Daytona Beach News-Journal, FL, Daytona Beach

Offredi, Angel
aoffredi@digitalfirstmedia.com, Digital Dir. , The Oakland Press, MI, Pontiac

Ogas, Sue ....(910) 875-2121
sue@thenews-journal.com, Sales Manager, The News-Journal, NC, Raeford

Ogden, Roger
roger.ogden@gmail.com, Board Member, E. W. Scripps Co., OH, Cincinnati

Ogea, Rebekah ....(337) 738-5642
kindernews@yahoo.com, Office Mgr., Kinder Courier News, LA, Kinder

Ogg, Heather ....(615) 384-3567

Morehead News, KY, Morehead

hogg@mtcngroup.com, Adv. Rep., Robertson County Times, TN, Clarksville

Ogilvie, Clare
edit@piquenewsmagazine.com, Ed., Pique Newsmagazine, BC, Whistler

Ogle, Mark ....(541) 338-2513
mark.ogle@registerguard.com, Circ. Dir., The Register-Guard, OR, Eugene

Ogles, Jennifer
jjogles@fortmyer.gannett.com, Targeted Products Asst., The Commercial Appeal, TN, Memphis

Oglesby, William ....(804) 827-2785
boglesby@vcu.edu, Asst. Prof., Virginia Commonwealth University, VA, Richmond

Ogletree, Marla ....(912) 496-3585
ads@charltonherald.com, Advertising, Charlton County Herald, GA, Folkston

Ogram, Sheila
sogram@caledonenterprise.com, Circ Mgr, Caledon Enterprise, ON, Bolton

Ogrodnek, Vernon....................(609) 272-7222
VOgrodnek@pressofac.com, Multi. Media Ed., The Press of Atlantic City, NJ, Pleasantville

Ohl, Danielle
dohldbk@gmail.com, EIC, University of Maryland, MD, College Park

Ohler, Debbie ....(505) 281-3671
independent@lobo.net, Business Manager, The Independent, NM, Edgewood

Ohlig, Don ....(714) 258-5600
dohlig@olec.com, Mng. Dir., OLEC, CA, Santa Ana

Ohs, Jennifer
johs@slu.edu, Asst. Prof., Saint Louis University, MO, Saint Louis

Oiler, Sandra ....(740) 852-1616 Ext. 1620
soiler@civitasmedia.com, Cir. Mgr., The Madison Press, OH, London

Oitker, Robin..........................(217) 285-5415
Publisher, Brown County Democrat Message, IL, Mt Sterling

Oitker, Robin..........................(217) 285-5415
pikecountyexpressnews@yahoo.com, Publisher/Owner, Pike County Express, IL, Pittsfield

Ojeda, Rita............................(719) 384-1429
rojeda@ljtdmail.com, Class. Adv. , La Junta Tribune-Democrat, CO, La Junta
rojeda@ljtdmail.com, Class. Adv. Mgr., Ag Journal, CO, La Junta
rojeda@ljtdmail.com, Class. Adv., The Fowler Tribune, CO, Fowler

Oke, Babafunmilayo..................(212) 237-8308
John Jay College of Criminal Justice, NY, New York

Okeowo, David ....(334) 229-4493
dokeowo@asunet.alasu.edu, Prof./Chair, Alabama State Univ., AL, Montgomery

Oksenhorn, Stewart ....(970) 429-9151
stewart@aspentimes.com, Arts Ed., The Aspen Times, CO, Aspen

Olarte, Pauline
accounts@russellbanner.com, Circ, Banner, MB, Russell

Old, Joe
elconquistador@epcc.edu, El Paso Cmty. College, TX, El Paso

Oldenburg, Sam......................(270) 745-3055
samual.oldenburg@wku.edu, Talisman adviser, Western Kentucky University, KY, Bowling Green

Oldenquist, Emily
theprattler@gmail.com, Pratt Institute, NY, Brooklyn

Older, Mary
circulation@dailydem.com, Bus. Mgr., Fort Madison Daily Democrat, IA, Fort Madison

marketing@dtint.com, Vice Pres., Opns., Digital Technology International, MN, Saint Paul

Olson, Michael .... (801) 465-9221
thepaysonchronicle@msn.com, Pub./Ed., The Payson Chronicle, UT, Payson

Olson, Rose .... (701) 642-8585
circulation@wahpetondailynews.com, Circ. Mgr., The Daily News, ND, Wahpeton

Olson, Rosemary Mackay .... (707) 527-1200
rolson@bohemian.com, Pub., North Bay Bohemian, CA, Santa Rosa

Olson, Scott .... (541) 895-2197
publisher@springfieldtimes.net, Pub., The Creswell Chronicle, OR, Creswell

Olson, Tina
js@jamestownsun.com, Prodn. Mgr., Prairie Post, ND, Jamestown

Olson, Tina
trdesign@times-online.com, Prod. Mgr., Valley City Times-Record, ND, Valley City

Olsson, Doug .... (567) 242-0463
dolsson@civitasmedia.com, Pub., The Lima News, OH, Lima

Olsthoorn, Ana .... (641) 923-2684
glads@qwestoffice.net, Office and Production Manager, The Leader, IA, Garner

Olszak, Mitch .... ext. 628
Mng. Ed., New Castle News, PA, New Castle

Olszewski, Brian .... (414) 769-3466
olszewskib@archmil.org, Gen. Mgr., Catholic Herald, WI, Saint Francis

Olszewski, Gary
gary.olszewski@latimes.com, VP, Consumer Sales, Los Angeles Times, CA, Los Angeles

Olszewski, Jon
sales@bbherald.com, Gen. Mgr., The Herald/ Country Market, IL, Bourbonnais

Olszewski, Robert
bobo@beverlyreview.net, Adv. Mgr., Beverly Review, IL, Chicago

Olszewski, Susan
beverlyreview@earthlink.net, Beverly Review, IL, Chicago

Olszewski, Toby
news@bbherald.com, Ed., The Herald/Country Market, IL, Bourbonnais

Olvera, Patricia
pati@abilene.com, Owner, Abilene Hispanic Guide, TX, Abilene

Olvido, Gloria .... (412) 871-2335
golvido@tribweb.com, Major/Nat'l. Sales Exec., The Valley Independent (OOB), PA, Monessen
golvido@tribweb.com, Major/Nat'l Sales Exec., Tribune-Review, PA, Greensburg

Omachonu, John
john.omachonu@mtsu.edu, Assoc. Dean/ Prof., Middle Tennessee State University, TN, Murfreesboro

Omalza, Lennie
lennieo@islandfamilymagazine.com., Adv. Mgr., Island Family, HI, Honolulu

Omeig, Jennie
joemig@wickedlocal.com, News Ed., Hamilton-Wenham Chronicle, MA, Danvers

Omernick, Gary
gomernick@montereyherald.com, Pub., The Monterey County Herald, CA, Monterey

Omernick, Gary
gomernick@santacruzsentinel.com, Pub., Santa Cruz Sentinel, CA, Scotts Valley

Ommati, Marcos
marco@laureti.com, Ed. in Chief, Florida Review, FL, Miami

Ommen, Scott .... (269) 945-9554
sommen@j-adgraphics.com, Adv. Mgr., Maple

Valley News, MI, Hastings

Ommen, Scott
sommen@j-adgraphics.com, Adv. Mgr., Reminder, MI, Hastings

Omnerick, Gary .... (831) 648-1192
gomernick@montereyherald.com, Pub., Salinas Valley Weekly, CA, Monterey

Omoto, Loren .... (813) 259-8048
Tampa Bay Times, FL, St Petersburg

Ondesko, Matthew .... (716) 668-5223 ext. 8007
mondesko@metrowny.com, Ed., Alden Metro Source, NY, Buffalo
mondesko@metrowny.com, Managing Editor, Tonawanda Source, NY, Buffalo
mondesko@metrowny.com, Ed., Williamsville Smart Shopper, NY, Buffalo
mondesko@metrowny.com, Ed., Amherst / Getzville Smart Shopper, NY, Buffalo
mondesko@metrowny.com, Ed., North Buffalo Smart Shopper, NY, Buffalo
mondesko@metrowny.com, Ed., South Cheektowaga Source, NY, Buffalo
mondesko@metrowny.com, Ed., Kenmore / Tonawanda Source, NY, Buffalo
mondesko@metrowny.com, Ed., Eggertsville / Snyder Smart Shopper, NY, Buffalo
mondesko@metrowny.com, Ed., North Tonawanda Source, NY, Buffalo
mondesko@metrowny.com, Ed., North Cheektowaga Source, NY, Buffalo
mondesko@metrowny.com, Ed., South Buffalo Metro Source, NY, Buffalo
mondesko@metrowny.com, Ed., Depew Metro Source, NY, Buffalo
mondesko@metrowny.com, Ed., Lancaster Source, NY, Buffalo
mondesko@metrowny.com, Ed., Clarence Metro Source, NY, Buffalo
mondesko@metrowny.com, Ed., Amherst / Tonawanda Metro Source (OOB) , NY, Buffalo

Onellion, Tony
bargainsplusnow@gmail.com, Pub., Bargains Plus!, LA, Slidell

Ongkeko, Tina .... ext. 25
MD, Canadian Media Circulation Audit, ON, Toronto

Onorio, Joe
jonorio@devry.edu, Devry University, IL, Chicago

Onsurez, Jessica .... (575) 628-5531
jonsurez@currentargus.com, Mng. Ed. , Current-Argus, NM, Carlsbad

Ontiveros, Mario .... (915) 546-6178
montiveros@elpasotimes.com, Online Sales Mgr., El Paso y Mas, TX, El Paso

Onyschuk, Connie .... (780) 349-3033 Ext. 2
conyschuk@westlock.greatwest.ca, Adv., The Westlock News, AB, Westlock

Onze, George
gonze@ctpost.com, Prodn. Mgr., Connecticut Post, CT, Bridgeport

Opatz, Jarred .... (419) 281-0581 Ext. 256
jopatz@times-gazette.com, Sp. Proj. Ed. , Ashland Times-Gazette, OH, Ashland

Opatz, Jarred .... (419) 281-0581 ext. 256
jopatz@times-gazette.com, Special Projects Editor, Ashland Publishing Co. LLC, OH, Ashland

Opel, Paula .... (518) 395-3058
popel@dailygazette.net, Bus. Mgr., The Daily Gazette, NY, Schenectady

Opfer, Steven E. .... (757) 823-2444
seopfer@nsu.edu, Advisor, Norfolk State University, VA, Norfolk

Opitz, Becky
bopitz@neighbornewspapers.com, Adv. Mgr., North Cobb Neighbor, GA, Marietta

Oplinger, Doug .... (330) 996-3750
doplinger@thebeaconjournal.com, Mng. Ed., Akron Beacon Journal, OH, Akron

Oppe, Elizabeth .... (304) 293-6773
elizabeth.oppe@mail.wvu.edu, Teaching Assistant Professor, West Virginia University, WV, Morgantown

Oppenheim, JR
managingeditor@dailylobo.com, Managing Ed., New Mexico Daily Lobo, NM, Albuquerque

Opperman, Nathaniel .... (612) 336-9231
nopperman@keypromedia.com, Vice Pres., Publishing, ComputerUser, Minneapolis

Oppmann, Andrew .... (615) 893-5860
aoppmann@dnj.com, Pres./Pub., The Daily News Journal, TN, Murfreesboro

Oravec, Bernard .... (570) 326-1551
boravec@sungazette.com, Publisher, Williamsport Sun-Gazette/Lock Haven Express, PA, South Williamsport

Oravec, Bernard
boravec@sungazette.com, Pub., The Luminary, PA, Hughesville

Oravecz, John .... (412) 320-7882
joravecz@tribweb.com, Bus. Ed., Tribune-Review, PA, Greensburg

Orban, Brian
borban@mountainhomenews.com, Ed, Mountain Home News, ID, Mountain Home

Orban, Cathie .... (416) 774-2271
corban@insidetoronto.com, Sales Rep., The Scarborough Mirror, ON, Toronto

Ordiway, Daniell .... (419) 521-7343
dordiway@gannett.com, Sales Mgr. , News Journal, OH, Mansfield

Ordonez, Liza .... (407) 767-0070
liza.ordonez@laprensaorlando.com, Sales, La Prensa, FL, Longwood

Ordway, Chris .... (270) 505-1466
cordway@thenewsenterprise.com, Pub., The Gold Standard, KY, Fort Knox
cordway@thenewsenterprise.com, Pub., The News-Enterprise, KY, Elizabethtown

Ordway, Chris
cordway@thenewsenterprise.com, Pub., Central Kentucky Homes Real Estate, KY, Elizabethtown

Orf, Steve
steveo@allsystemscolour.com, Gen. Mgr., All Systems Color, Inc., OH, West Carrollton

Orlando, Joyce .... (704) 669-3341
jorlando@shelbystar.com, reporter, The Star, NC, Shelby

Orlando, Staci .... (530) 852-0257
stacio@goldcountrymedia.com, Auburn Journal, CA, Auburn

Orme, Terry .... (801) 257-8727
orme@sltrib.com, Administration - Editor and Publisher, The Salt Lake Tribune, UT, Salt Lake City

Orndoff, Debi .... (717) 339-2063
class@gettysburgtimes.com, Class., Gettysburg Times, PA, Gettysburg

Orr, Cynthia
corr@civitasmedia.com, Pub., Cumberland Trading Post, KY, Middlesboro

Orr, Cynthia .... (606) 302-9086
corr@civitasmedia.com, Pub., Middlesboro Daily News, KY, Middlesboro
corr@civitasmedia.com, Publisher , Claiborne Progress, TN, Tazewell
corr@civitasmedia.com, Publisher , The Harlan Daily Enterprise, KY, Harlan

Orr, Erin
erin.orr@sj-r.com, Mng. Ed., Springfield Advertiser, IL, Springfield

Orr, Jerry .... (800) 655-1411
jorr@wythenewscom, Sports Ed., Smyth County News & Messenger, VA, Marion

Orr, Jim
publisher@glasgowcourier.com, Publisher, The

Glasgow Courier, MT, Glasgow

Orr, Jimmy
jimmy.orr@latimes.com, Managing Ed., Digital , Los Angeles Times, CA, Los Angeles

Orr, Leith
leith@advocatemediainc.com , Pub, Fall River Laker, NS, Enfield

Orr, Leith .... (902) 422-4990
courier@nb.aibn.com, Pub., St. Croix Courier, NB, Saint Stephen
courier@nb.aibn.com, Pub, Enfield Weekly Press, NS, Enfield

Orr, Leith
leith@advocatemediainc.com, Pub, The Light, NS, Tatamagouche
leith@advocatemediainc.com, Pub., The Pictou Advocate, NS, Pictou

Orsi, Jennifer .... (727) 893-8245
jorsi@tampabay.com, Managing Ed., Tampa Bay Times, FL, St Petersburg

Orsi, Lucy
lorsi@mymail.mines.edu, Editor-in-Chief, Colorado School of Mines, CO, Golden

Ortblad, Clare
cortblad@soundpublishing.com, Market Develop. Admin., Bellevue Reporter, WA, Bellevue
cortblad@soundpublishing.com, Market Develop. Admin., Bainbridge Island Review, WA, Bainbridge Island

Ortega, Ashley .... (505) 425-6796
Circulation Coordinator, Las Vegas Optic, NM, LAS VEGAS

Ortega, Carmen
cortega@hearstnp.com, Adv. Dir., Plainview Herald, TX, Plainview

Ortega, Daniel .... (713) 280-2433
Daniel.Ortega@houstonpress.com, Production Manager, Houston Press, TX, Houston

Ortega, Jaime
jortega@efe.com, Rep., EFE News Services - Rio de Janeiro, Brazil, AL, Rio de Janeiro

Ortega, Manuel .... (202) 745 76 92
info@efeamerica.com, Business Development Director, EFE News Services - WASHINGTON, D.C, Washington Post

Ortega, Wendy .... (505) 995-3892
wortega@sfnewmexican.com, Advertising AE, HomelSanta Fe Real Estate Guide, NM, Santa Fe

Ortego, David
oakdalejournal@bellsouth.net, Pub., The Oakdale Journal, LA, Oakdale

Ortego, David .... (337) 363-3939
kindernews@centurytel.net, Pub., Kinder Courier News, LA, Kinder

Ortego, David L. .... (337) 363-3939
publisher.vp@centurytel.net, Pub., The Mamou Acadian Press, LA, Ville Platte

Orth, Don .... (928) 763-2505
Don@nwppub.com, Circulation Mgr, Needles Desert Star, CA, Needles
Don@nwppub.com, Circ. Mgr./Classifieds, Mohave Valley Daily News, AZ, Bullhead City

Orth, Larry .... (319) 291-1407
Larry.Orth@wcfcourier.com, IT Dir., The Courier, IA, Waterloo

Ortiz, Anthony
daortiz@currentargus.com, Class. Rep., Current-Argus, NM, Carlsbad

Ortiz, Bert
bortiz@orlandosentinel.com, Circ. Vice Pres., Orlando Sentinel, FL, Orlando

Ortiz, Elda .... (361) 225-8701
eoritz@adsack.com, General Manager, Ad Sack, TX, Corpus Christi

Ortiz, Elizabeth .... (610) 437-4471 ext. 3429
Cedar Crest College, PA, Allentown

Ortiz, Esteban ....(760) 337-3431
eortiz@ivpressonline.com, Copy Ed, Imperial
Valley Press, CA, El Centro

Ortiz, Luis Manuel
luismanuel@lavozpublishing.com, Ed., La Voz,
AZ, Phoenix

Ortiz, Manuel ....(650) 678-9657
manuel@alianzanews.com, Ed., Alianza
Metropolitan News, CA, San Jose

Ortiz, Marco ....(847) 427-1171
mor@reflejos.com, Editor / Reflejos Bilingual
Hispanic Journal, Daily Herald, IL, Arlington
Heights

Ortiz, Marco
marco.ortiz@reflejos.com, Asst. Mng. Ed.,
Reflejos Bilingual Publications, IL, Arlington
Heights

Ortiz, Toni-Ann
taortiz@ncronline.org, Art Dir., National
Catholic Reporter, MO, Kansas City

Ortiz-Sanchez, Leyda.................(203) 317-2337
lsanchez@record-journal.com, Adv. Mgr.,
Tiempo, CT, Meriden

Orty, Patti ....(315) 498-2278
Onondaga Cmty. College, NY, Syracuse

Orwig, Christy ....(605) 622-2250
corwig@aberdeennews.com, Adv. Dir, Farm
Forum, SD, Aberdeen

Orwig, Christy ....ext. 250
corwig@aberdeennews.com, Adv. Dir.,
Aberdeen American News, SD, Aberdeen

Osborn, Mia
mia.osborn@alexcityoutlook.com, Asst. Mag.
Ed, Alexander City Outlook, AL, Alexander
City

Osborne, Agnes ....(703) 777-1111
aosborne@timespapers.com, Bus. Mng.,
Virginia New Group, VA, Leesburg

Osborne, Cary
cosborne@the-signal.com, Asst. Mng. Ed./
Sports Ed., Connect SCV, CA, Santa Clarita

Osborne, Erika ....(502) 452-8157
Bellarmine College, KY, Louisville

Osborne, Leslie
leslie.osborne@metroland.com, Adv. Sales,
Belleville News Emc, ON, Belleville

Osborne, Matthew ....(828) 837-5122, Ext. 109
editor@cherokeescout.com, Ed., Cherokee
Scout, NC, Murphy

Osborne, Matthew ....(828) 321-4271
editor@myandrewsjournal.com, Ed., Andrews
Journal, NC, Andrews

Osborne, Paul ....(217) 422-9702
decaturtribune@aol.com, Ed./Pub., Decatur
Tribune, IL, Decatur

Osborne, Rodney
osborne@cherokee@nsuok.ed, Chair,
Northeastern State University (Oklahoma),
OK, Tahlequah

Osborne, Tammy ....(859) 231-3181
tosborne@herald-leader.com, Adv. Sales Mgr.,
Nat. & Retail Adv., Lexington Herald-Leader,
KY, Lexington

Osborne, Tammy...................................ext. 228
tosborne@thefloridacatholic.org, Circ. Mgr.,
Florida Catholic, FL, Orlando

Osis, Dianne Elizabeth...............(417) 831-4461
delizabeth@sbj.net, Pres., Springfield Business
Journal, MO, Springfield

Oskam, Judy
oskam@txstate.edu, Assoc. Prof./Assoc. Dir.
RRHEC, Texas State University-San Marcos,
TX, San Marcos

Oslovsky, Gay Lynn
gaylynn@seguingazette.com, Retail Sales
Manager, The Seguin Gazette, TX, Seguin

Oslund, Eric...........................(763) 241-3654

eric.oslund@ecm-inc.com, Sports Reporter,
Star News, MN, Elk River

Osmundson, Paul ....(803) 329-4061
posmundson@heraldonline.com, Ed., The
Herald, SC, Rock Hill

Osowski, Zach
news@oldhamera.com, Reporter/
Photographer, Oldham Era, KY, La Grange

Ospiguy, Claudette
costiguy@lavoixdelest.qc.ca, Prodn. Mgr., Pre
Press, La Voix De L'est Plus, QC, Granby

Osteen, Graham
graham@theitem.com, Co-Pres., The Sumter
Item , SC, Sumter

Osteen, Hubert D.
hubert@theitem.com, Chairman, The Sumter
Item , SC, Sumter

Osteen, Jack..........................(803) 774-1238
jack@theitem.com, Ed. & Pub./VP, The Sumter
Item , SC, Sumter

Osteen, Jim ....(352) 374-5035
Executive Editor, Ocala Star-Banner, FL, Ocala

Osteen, Kyle ....(803) 774-1254
kosteen@theitem.com, Co-Pres., The Sumter
Item , SC, Sumter

Osteen, Sandy ....(813) 220-4402
sandy@fname.org, Exec. Dir., Florida
Newspaper Advertising & Marketing
Executives, FL, Lake Mary

Osten, Albert M.
newsplace@aol.com, Pub., Beacon Free
Press, NY, Wappingers Falls

Osten, Albert M.
newsplace@aol.com, Pub., Southern Dutchess
News, NY, Wappingers Falls
newsplace@aol.com, Pub., Northern Dutchess
News, NY, Wappingers Falls

Ostendorf, Bill..........................(401) 455-1555
bill@creativecirclemedia.com, Pres & founder,
Creative Circle Media Solutions, RI, East
Providence

Ostendorf, Bill ....(401) 455-1555
bill@creativecirclemedia.com, Pres., Creative
Circle Media Syndication, East Providence

Ostendorf, Fran
fostendorf@jewishallianceri.org, Exec. Ed, The
Jewish Voice, RI, Providence
fostendorf@jewishallianceri.org, Treasurer,
Rhode Island Press Association, RI, Kingston

Osterman, Logan ....(208) 377-6305
losterman@idahostatesman.com, Adv. Dir.,
Idaho Statesman, ID, Boise

Ostermann, Miriam...................(403) 934-5589
Associate Editor, Strathmore Times, AB,
Strathmore

Ostermeier, Joe ....(618) 239-2512
jostermeier@bnd.com, Online Ed., Belleville
News-Democrat, IL, Belleville

Osting, Leila..........................(567) 242-0423
losting@civitasmedia.com, Dir., HR, The Lima
News, OH, Lima

Ostner, Heidi E.
ayrnews@golden.net, Circ. Mgr., Ayr News,
ON, Ayr

Ostrenga, Greg
gostrenga@miningjournal.net, Press Foreman,
The Mining Journal, MI, Marquette

Ostroff, David..........................(352) 392-2081
Prof./Chair, Dept. of Telecommunication,
University of Florida, FL, Gainesville

Ostroff, Michael
ostroffm@graphline.com, Pres./CEO,
GraphLine, FL, Sunrise

Ostroff, Ron ....(732) 393-0023
ron.ostroff@verizon.net, Ed., The Speaker, NJ,
Highland Park

Ostroff, Ron...........................(732) 393-0023

jewish@castle.net, Ed., Jewish Journal -
Ocean County, NJ, Jackson

Osuna, Karen ....(909) 866-3456
business@bigbeargrizzly.net, Business
Manager, Grizzly Weekender, CA, Big Bear
Lake

Osuna-Sharamitaro, Karen ...(909) 866-3456 x 125
business@bigbeargrizzly.net, Business
Manager , Big Bear Grizzly, CA, Big Bear
Lake

Oswald, John
joswald@ctcentral.com, Prodn. Dir., Housatonic
Publications, CT, New Milford

Oswald, Robert
roswald@tribpub.com, Metro Ed., The Courier-
News, IL, Aurora

Ota, Daisuke
kni@kyodonews.com, Sales Mgr., Kyodo News
International, Inc., New York

Otazu, Javier
lima@efe.com, Rep., EFE News Services -
Lima, Peru, Lima

Otolski, Greg A. ....(317) 236-1579
gotolski@archindy.org, Asst. Pub., The
Criterion, IN, Indianapolis

Ott, Marie
ads@elgincourier.com, Adv. Mgr., Elgin
Courier, TX, Elgin

Ott, Nicole ....(260) 625-3879 ext. 202
editor@thepostandmail.com, Ed. , The Post
and Mail (Tuesday), IN, Columbia City
editor@thepostandmail.com, Ed., The Post &
Mail, IN, Columbia City

Ott, Nicole
nicole.ott@trib.com, Marketing & Digital Dir,
Casper Star-Tribune, WY, Casper

Ottati, Leonardo
ecuanews@inch.com, Business Rep., Ecuador
News, NY, Woodside

Otte, Donna
edinasentinel@att.net, Circ. Mgr., The Edina
Sentinel, MO, Edina

Otterbein, Jeff
jotterbein@courant.com, Sports Ed., Courant
Community - West Hartford, CT, Hartford
jotterbein@courant.com, Sports Ed., Courant
Community - Wethersfield, CT, Hartford

Otto, Laura
mmu-arches@mtmary.edu, Mount Mary
College, WI, Milwaukee

Otzman, James
james@otzman.com, Prodn. Mgr., Belleville-
Area Independent, MI, Belleville

Otzman, Rosemary
rotzman@ameritech.net , Ed., The Belleville
Enterprise, MI, Belleville

Otzman, Rosemary K..................(734) 699-9020
rotzman@ameritech.net, PUB., Belleville-Area
Independent, MI, Belleville

Ouderkirk, Susie
susie@lascrucesbulletin.com, News Ed., The
Las Cruces Bulletin, NM, Las Cruces

Ouellett, Martin
mouellett@ntr.ca, Correspondent, Broadcast
News Limited, QC, Quebec City

Ougler, Jeff
j.ougler@sunmedia.ca, City Ed., The Sault
Star, ON, Sault Sainte Marie

Ova, Masaki ....(701) 952-8451
mova@jamestownsun.com, Asst. Ed., The
Jamestown Sun, ND, Jamestown

Ovalle, Nathan ....(518) 565-4142
novalle@pressrepublican.com, Feat. Ed.,
Press-Republican, NY, Plattsburgh

Ovans, Susan
hulltimes@aol.com, Ed., The Hull Times, MA,
Hull

Overbay, Ally
arts@theaggie.org, Arts and Culture Editor,
University of California, Davis, CA, Davis

Overby, Rhonda ....(803) 644-2345
roverbey@aikenstandard.com, Evening Post
Industries' Aiken Communications, SC, Aiken

Overduin, Henry
hover@mcneese.edu, Head/Prof., McNeese
State University, LA, Lake Charles

Overholser, Geneva
genevao@usc.edu, Dir./Annenberg Family
Chair in Commun. Leadership/Univ. Prof.,
University of Southern California, CA, Los
Angeles

Overlie, Paul ....(406) 759-5355
lctimes@itstriangle.com, Pub., Liberty County
Times, MT, Chester

Overman, Jason
jasono@harrisondaily.com, Gen. Mgr., Harrison
Daily Times, AR, Harrison
jasono@harrisondaily.com, Gen. Mgr., The
Newton County Times, AR, Jasper
jasono@harrisondaily.com, Adv. Mgr., Newton
County News, MO, Neosho

Overman, Tammy ....(256) 772-6677
tammy.overman@themadisonrecord.com,
Customer Service Rep., The Madison
Record, AL, Madison

Overmann, Mike
Mike@dcpostgazette.com, Pub. , The Douglas
County Post Gazette, NE, Elkhorn

Overmann, Penny
pennydcpostgazette.com, Co-Pub., The
Douglas County Post Gazette, NE, Elkhorn

Overstreet, Cheryl
cheryl@ecdailynews.com, Community Ed., Elk
City Daily News, OK, Elk City

Overstreet, James
joverstreet@memphisdailynews.com,
Associate Publisher/Exec. Ed., The Daily
News, TN, Memphis

Overstreet, Karen ....(310) 372-4689
Archivist, Making It Productions, Hermosa
Beach

Overton, Mac .... (903) 843-2503 ext. 204
gilmermirror@aol.com, Mng. Ed., Gilmer Mirror,
TX, Gilmer

Overton, Tom ....(229) 924-2751 ext. 1516
tom.overton@gaflnews.com, Pub./Adv. Dir.,
Americus Times-Recorder, GA, Americus

Overturf, Daniel
dvo0201@siu.edu, Assoc. Prof., Southern
Illinois University Carbondale, IL, Carbondale

Oviatt, Tim ....(605) 886-6901
tim.oviatt@thepubliccopinion.com, Sales &
Marketing Mgr., Watertown Public Opinion,
SD, Watertown

Oviatt, Tim
tim.oviatt@thepubliccopinion.com, Mktg. Mgr.,
Coteau Shopper, SD, Watertown

Owaisi, L.
lowaisi@rogers.com, Pub., Al-Hilal, ON,
Willowdale

Owczarz, Brandi......................(706) 629-2231
BOwczarz@NPCo.com, Editor, Calhoun Times
and Gordon County News, GA, Calhoun

Owen, Brittany ....(405) 273-4200 "0"
brittney.owen@news-star.com, CSR / Rec. ,
Shawnee News-Star, OK, Shawnee

Owen, Gary ....(610) 266-7000
g5owen@pplweb.com, Vice Pres., Sales/Mktg.,
Muller Martini Mailroom Systems, Inc., PA,
Allentown

Owen, Larry
larry@bigbasinllc.com, Sports Ed., Okmulgee
Daily Times, OK, Okmulgee

Owen, Shaylan ....(812) 349-1400
sowen@heraldt.com, Marketing Mgr., The

Herald Times, IN, Bloomington

Owen, Sherry
gnp-production@kscable.com, Prodn. Mgr., Good News, KS, Caney

Owens, Alexandra
director@asja.org, Exec. Dir., American Society of Journalists and Authors, NY, New York

Owens, Alisha .... (520) 573-4415
aowens@tucson.com, VP Adv. Sales & Mktg., Arizona Daily Star, AZ, Tucson

Owens, Billie
billie@thebatavian.com, Ed., The Batavian, NY, Batavia

Owens, Brad
brad_owens@baylor.edu, Instr., Baylor University, TX, Waco

Owens, David .... (870) 238-2375
news@wynneprogressinc.com, Wynne Progress, AR, Wynne

Owens, Debbie
debbie.owens@murraystate.edu, Assoc. Prof., Murray State University, KY, Murray

Owens, Howard
howard@thebatavian.com, Pub, The Batavian, NY, Batavia

Owens, J.W. .... (863) 763-2205
Ed., Real Estate Preview, FL, Okeechobee

Owens, Jake .... (410) 245-5043
jowens@cecilwhig.com, News Ed., Cecil Whig, MD, Elkton

Owens, Janet .... (903) 237-7773
jowen@news-journal.com, Prodn. Mgr., Longview News-Journal, TX, Longview

Owens, Joan .... (206) 323-3070
mediumnews@aol.com, Co-Pub., Tacoma True-citizen, WA, Seattle

Owens, Joan .... (206) 323-3070
mediumnews@aol.com, Co-Pub., Seattle Medium, WA, Seattle

Owens, Margot .... (250) 782-4888 ext 104
circulation@dcdn.ca, Circ. Mgr., Dawson Creek Mirror, BC, Dawson Creek
circulation@dcdn.ca, Circ Mgr, The Mirror, BC, Dawson Creek
circulation@dcdn.ca, Circ. Mgr, The Northern Horizon, BC, Dawson Creek

Owens, Michelle .... (704) 669-3333
michelle.owens@shelbystar.com, Newsroom Clerk, The Star, NC, Shelby

Owens, Reina .... (918) 421-2006
rowens@mcalesternews.com, Adv. Dir., McAlester News-Capital, OK, McAlester

Owens, Steve .... (805) 546-0609
slojournal@fix.net, Pub., Journal Plus Magazine, CA, San Luis Obispo

Owens, Sue .... (845) 887-5200 ext. 102
sowens@sc-democrat.com, Business Manager, Sullivan County Democrat, NY, Callicoon

Owens, Tiffeny
towens@cullmantimes.com, Staff Writer, The Cullman Times, AL, Cullman

Owensby, Connie
businessmanager@kernersvillenews.com, Vice Pres./Bus. Mgr, Kernersville News, NC, Kernersville

Owensby, John
publisher@kernersvillenews.com, Ed., Kernersville News, NC, Kernersville

Owensby, Mike
mowensby@lawton-constitution.com, Gen. Mgr., The Lawton Constitution, OK, Lawton

Owensby, Zack .... (615) 444-6008
zowensby@mainstreetmediatn.com, Ed, The Murfreesboro Post, TN, Murfreesboro

Owings, Mark
mark.owings@bellinghamherald.com, Pub.,

The Bellingham Herald, WA, Bellingham

Owings, Wanda .... (864) 298-4277
wowings@greenvillenews.com, Food Ed., The Greenville News, SC, Greenville

Oxendine, Ashley
aoxendine@civitasmedia.com, Adv, The Red Springs Citizen, NC, Red Springs

Oyhamburu, Terry .... (406) 791-1434
toyhambu@greatfal.gannett.com, Dir. of Business Development & Marketing , Great Falls Tribune, MT, Great Falls

Ozaeta, Cristina
redacpr@efe.com, Head of Puerto Ricos Bureau, EFE News Services - Santurce, Puerto Rico, PR, San Juan

Ozanich, Paul .... (906) 341-2424
advisor@chartermi.net, Pub., The Advisor, MI, Manistique

Ozee, Cheri
watsekasales@intranix.com, Gen. Mgr., The Chronicle, IL, Hoopeston
watsekasales@intranix.com, Classifieds Mgr., Macoupin County Journal, IL, Hillsboro

Ozier, Dona
donao@robinsonnews.com, Adv. Mgr., Westside Seattle, WA, Seattle
donao@robinsonnews.com, Adv. Mgr., Federal Way News, WA, Burien
donao@robinsonnews.com, Adv. Mgr., Ballard News-Tribune, WA, Seattle
donao@robinsonnews.com, Adv. Mgr., Highline Times, WA, Burien

O'Bannon, Cheri
cheri.obannon@ecm-inc.com, Adv. Dir., St. Louis Park Sun Sailor, MN, Osseo
cheri.obannon@ecm-inc.com, Adv. Dir., Brooklyn Center/Brooklyn Park Sun-Post, MN, Osseo

P

Pace, Eli
editor@kentuckynewera.com, Ed., Kentucky New Era, KY, Hopkinsville

Pace, Fred
fpace@civitasmedia.com, Pub./Ed., Coal Valley News, WV, Madison
fpace@civitasmedia.com, Pub./Ed., The Independent Herald, WV, Pineville

Pace, Jane .... (859) 231-3538
jpace@herald-leader.com, Adv. Sales Mgr., Marketing, Lipstick & Other Special Sections, Lexington Herald-Leader, KY, Lexington

Pace, Jane Ashley .... (502) 222-7183
publisher@oldhamera.com, Pub., Oldham Era, KY, La Grange

Pacenti, Charlene .... (202) 898-8000
cpacenti@upi.com, Chief Content Officer, United Press International, Boca Raton

Pacer, Megan .... (907) 235-7767
megan.pacer@homernews.com, Reporter, homer News, AK, Homer

Pacheco, Michelle
Pacheco@cunews.info, Off. Mgr., Ajo Copper News, AZ, Ajo

Pacio, Sarah
sunnews@sasktel.com, Office Manager, Grenfell Sun, SK, Grenfell

Pacitto, John .... (519) 667-4604
john.pacitto@sunmedia.ca, Dir., Operations, The London Free Press, ON, London

Pack, Kevin .... (865) 342-6070
kpack@metropulse.com, Dir. of Sales, Metro Pulse, TN, Knoxville

Pack, Paul
paul.pack@lexch.com, Sports Ed. & Photo., Lexington Clipper-Herald, NE, Lexington

Packard, Breanne
bpackard@mediaonepa.com, Nat'l Sales, The

Evening Sun, PA, Hanover

Packard, Linda .... (580) 326-3311
linda@hugonews.com, Adv. Dir., Hugo News, OK, Hugo

Packer, Kari .... (208) 664-0215
kpacker@cdapress.com, Sales Manager, Coeur d'Alene Press, ID, Coeur D Alene

Pacquett, Dave .... ext. 273
dave.paquette@sunmedia.ca, Circ. Mgr., The Sudbury Star, ON, Sudbury

Padbury, Peter .... (613) 933-3160 ext. 246
peter.padbury@sunmedia.ca, Pub. & Adv. Mgr., Standard-Freeholder, ON, Cornwall

Padbury, Peter
peter.padbury@sunmedia.ca, Adv. Mgr., Standard-freeholder Complimentary, ON, Cornwall

Padden, Martin .... (443) 482-3154
mpadden@capgaznews.com, Adv. Dir., The Capital, MD, Annapolis

Padden, Marty .... (443) 482-3154
mpadden@capgaznews.com, Adv. Dir. , Crofton-West County Gazette, MD, Annapolis

Padden, Marty .... (443) 482-3154
mpadden@capgaznews.com, Adv. Dir., The Maryland Gazette, MD, Annapolis

Paddock, Robert Y.
rpaddockjr@dailyherald.com, Vice Chairman/ Exec. Vice Pres./Administration, Daily Herald, IL, Arlington Heights

Paddock, Stuart .... (847) 427-4328
spaddock@dailyherald.com, Sr. Vice Pres./Director of Digital and Information Technologies, Daily Herald, IL, Arlington Heights

Paden, Ken
hometownnews@frontiernet.net, Pub., The Chenango American/Whitney Point Reporter/ Oxford Review-Times, NY, Greene

Padgett, Anita
anita@rensselaerrepublican.com, Adv. Acct. Rep. , Rensselaer Republican, IN, Rensselaer

Padgett, Beth .... (864) 298-4321
bpadgett@greenvillenews.com, Editorial Page Ed., The Greenville News, SC, Greenville

Padgett, George
padgettg@elon.edu, Assoc. Prof., Elon University, NC, Elon

Padgett, John .... (828) 884-8134
padgettjb@brevard.edu, Advisor, Brevard College, NC, Brevard

Padgett, Kelsey .... (252) 265-8117
kpadgett@wilsontimes.com, Paginator, The Wilson Times, NC, Wilson

Padgett, Pamela
pamela.padgett@harris.com, Vice Pres., Investor Rel., Harris Corp., FL, Melbourne

Padilla, Cecilio
padillc4@imail.losrios.edu, Sacramento City College, CA, Sacramento

Padilla, Edward R. .... (609) 773-0401
epadilla@globalpressmanagement.com, CEO, Global Press Management Services, LLC., NJ, Lambertville

Padro, Charles David .... (212) 740-4400
winnet@panix.com, Exec. Producer, Multimedia, World Interactive Network, NY, New York

Padrta, Gary .... (218) 983-3285 ext. 206
today@whiteearth.com, Ed., Anishinaabeg Today, MN, White Earth

Pagan, Leigh .... (415) 435-2652
lpagan@thearknewspaper.com, Accounts mgr, The Ark, CA, Tiburon

Page, Bill
bill.page@atusa.com, Exec. Vice Pres., Advanced Technical Solutions, Inc., MA,

Maynard

Page, Dave .... (651) 450-8563
Inver Hills Cmty. College, MN, Inver Grove Heights

Page, Denice .... (801) 257-8576
denice@utahpress.com, Advertising Coordinator, Utah Press Association, Inc., UT, Sandy

Page, Janice .... (617) 929-7071
JPage@globe.com, Deputy Managing Ed., Features, The Boston Globe, MA, Boston

Page, JoAnn .... (903) 378-3558
hgwcnews@sbcglobal.net, Adv. Dir., The Weekly Gazette, TX, Honey Grove

Page, Kevin
kpage@benedictine.edu, Benedictine College, KS, Atchison

Page, Lorrie .... (903) 227-6453
hgwgnews@yahoo.com, Pub./Ed., The Weekly Gazette, TX, Honey Grove

Page, Phil .... (262) 387-4830
ppaige@conleynet.com, Grp. Pub., Conley Media LLC, WI, Beaver Dam

Page, Steve .... (317) 831-0280 ext. 335
spage@md-times.com, Sports Ed., The Reporter Times, IN, Martinsville

Page, Steve .... (705) 475-2183
steve.page@sunmedia.ca, Adv. Dir., Nugget, ON, North Bay

Page-Kirby, Kristen
editor@chesapeakefamily.com, Ed., Chesapeake Family Life, MD, Annapolis

Pagel, Angie
Angie.pagel@baycitytribune.com, Pub./Retail Adv. Mgr., The Bay City Tribune, TX, Bay City

Pagel, Betty
bpagel@mihomepaper.com, Prodn. Mgr., Sanilac Buyer's Guide, MI, Sandusky

Pagel, Wayne
wayne@usarollerandsupply.com, Pres./Sales Mgr., Kepes, Inc., WI, Kenosha

Paige, Bob
rpaige@culver.edu, Interpersonal Head, Culver-Stockton College, MO, Canton

Paige, Phil
ppaige@conleynet.com, Ozaukee County Guide, WI, Cedarburg

Paine, Dawn
dawn.paine@cmich.edu, Instr., Central Michigan University, MI, Mount Pleasant

Painter, Byron
southcountypub@att.net, Ed, Tri-City Register, IL, Riverton

Painter, Laurie
billing@keizertimes.com, Legal Notices, Keizertimes, OR, Keizer

Painter, Vickie .... (972) 563-6476
accounting@terrelltribune.com, Bus Mgr/Circu/ Inserts, The Terrell Tribune, TX, Terrell

Palacios, Grace .... (828) 963-9731
grace.palacios@publicitas.com, CEO, Charney/ Palacios & Co., FL, Miami

Palacios, Juan
salesinfo@pakon.com, Sales/Mktg. Mgr., Impak (A Div. of Pakon, Inc.), MN, Minnetonka

Palacios, Neris Ramon
n.siglo@verizon.net, Pub., Nuevo Siglo, FL, Tampa

Palange, Paul .... (401) 767-8500
ppalange@woonsocketcall.com, Gen. Mgr., The Call, RI, Woonsocket

Palen, John
john.a.palen@cmich.edu, Prof., Central Michigan University, MI, Mount Pleasant

Palermo, Angelo
apalermo@wayuga.com, Pub., Shopper, NY, Red Creek

Palermo, Angelo
agpalermo@wayuga.com, The Wayuga Shopper, NY, Red Creek

Palermo, Charles
star@wayuga.com, Pub. & Adv. Mgr., Post-Herald, NY, Red Creek

Palesano, Lindsey
lindsey@chickashanews.com, Adv. Mgr, Chickasha News, OK, Chickasha

Paley, Jennifer .... (631) 265-2100
ads@smithtownnews.com, Pres., The Smithtown News, NY, Smithtown

Palfy, Nicole .... (250) 782-4888 ext 101
npalfy@dcdn.ca , Adv. Dir./Assoc. Pub., Dawson Creek Mirror, BC, Dawson Creek
npalfy@dcdn.ca , Assoc. Pub., The Northern Horizon, BC, Dawson Creek
npalfy@dcdn.ca , Assoc. Pub., The Mirror, BC, Dawson Creek

Pallini, Sam
spallini@mail.bradley.edu, Ed., Bradley University, IL, Peoria

Palm, Rory
rpalm@parkrapidsenterprise.com, Pub., Park Rapids Enterprise, MN, Park Rapids
rpalm@parkrapidsenterprise.com, Publisher, Park Rapids Enterprise Express, MN, Park Rapids

Palm, Tabitha
tpalm@mcdonoughvoice.com, Prodn. Mgr., The McDonough County Voice, IL, Macomb

Palmer, Bob .... (903) 665-2462
Pub., Jefferson Jimplecute, TX, Jefferson

Palmer, Bob
bob.palmer@ibuyibs.com, Mgr. Online News, Sun Newspapers, OH, Cleveland

Palmer, Dan .... (305) 284-7387
dan@communitynewspapers.com, Editor, South Miami News, FL, South Miami
dan@communitynewspapers.com, Editor, Kendall Gazette, FL, South Miami
dan@communitynewspapers.com, Editor, Palmetto Bay News, FL, South Miami

Palmer, Denise .... (813) 259-7424
dpalmer@tampatrib.com, Pub., Carrollwood News & Tribune, FL, Tampa

Palmer, Dennis .... (334) 875-2110
dennis.palmer@selmatimesjournal.com, Pub., The Selma Times-Journal, AL, Selma

Palmer, Dennis M.
dennis.palmer@selmatimesjournal.com, Vice Pres., Boone Newspapers, Inc., AL, Northport

Palmer, John .... (617) 619-6227
john.palmer@bostonherald.com, Circ. Mgr., Single Copy Sales, Boston Herald, MA, Boston

Palmer, Kathleen .... (603) 594-1255
news@nashuatelegraph.com, Encore Ed., Sunday Feat., The Telegraph, NH, Nashua

Palmer, Lane .... (636) 346-3074
lpalmer@fujifilm.com, VP Corp. Accounts & Newspapers, Fujifilm North America Corporation, IL, Hanover Park

Palmer, Mark .... (931) 388-6464
mpalmer@c-dh.net, Publisher, Columbia Daily Herald, TN, Columbia
mpalmer@c-dh.net, The Daily Herald, PA, Tyrone

Palmer, Michael
michael.palmer@cushwake.com, Pres., Adstream America, NY, New York

Palmer, Richard
rpalmer@scansoft.com, Sr. Vice Pres., Cor. Devel., Nuance Communications Inc., MA, Burlington

Palmer, Roger
kimberlypalmer@yahoo.com, Pub./Adv. Dir., Whitewright Sun, TX, Whitewright

Palmer, Shawn
spalmer@thewesterlysun.com, Sr. Vice Pres., The Westerly Sun, CT, Pawcatuck

Palmer, Shawn .... (203) 731-3401
spalmer@newstimes.com, Pub., New Milford Spectrum, CT, New Milford
spalmer@newstimes.com, Pub., The News-Times, CT, Danbury

Palmer, Shawn
spalmer@myrecordjournal.com, Senior VP and CRO, The Record-Journal Publishing Co., CT, Meriden

Palmer, Shawn E. .... ext. 264
s.palmer@theday.com, Adv. Dir., The Day, CT, New London

Palmersheim, Joseph .... (763) 424-7352
Joseph.palmersheim@ecm-inc.com, Mng. Ed., Bloomington Sun-Current, MN, Eden Prairie

Palmieri, Debbie .... (610) 740-0944
dpalmieri@tnonline.com, Ed, Northwestern Press, PA, Allentown
dpalmieri@tnonline.com, Ed., Parkland Press, PA, Allentown

Palmiero, Kimberly .... (412) 856-7400 x8607
kpalmiero@tribweb.com, Mng. Ed., Cranberry Journal, PA, Warrendale

Palmintier, Erin .... (225) 344 - 9309 x111
erin@LaPress.com, Adv. Dir., Louisiana Press Association, LA, Baton Rouge

Palmlund, Donna .... (605) 847-4421
mail@lakeprestontimes.net, Editor, Lake Preston Times, SD, Lake Preston

Paloian, John R.
info@rrd.com, COO, R.R. Donnelley & Sons Co., IL, Chicago

Palokangas, Brian
brian.palokangas@manneys.com, Zone Mgr., Manney's Shopper, MN, Hibbing

Palsgrove, Rick
southeast@columbusmessenger.com, Ed., Madison Messenger, OH, Columbus

Paluck, Patrick
ppaluck@lesoleil.com, Prod. Mgr., Le Soleil, QC, Quebec

Paluzzi, Jennifer .... (978) 970-4662
jpaluzzi@nashobavalleyvoice.com, Ed., Ayer Public Spirit, MA, Devens

Palzkill, Brian
mttsales@newspubinc.com, Adv. Sales, Middleton Times-Tribune, WI, Black Earth

Pamplin, Paula .... (870) 543-1478
ppamplin@pbcommercial.com, Class. Mgr., Pine Bluff Commercial, AR, Pine Bluff

Panek, Doug .... (715) 468-2314
news@wcregisternewsroom.com, Pub./Gen. Mgr., Washburn County Register, WI, Shell Lake
news@wcregisternewsroom.com, Inter-county Coop, WI, Frederic

Panek, Doug
dpanek@centurytel.net, Indianhead Advertiser, WI, Frederic

Panek, Doug
dpanek@centurytel.net, Tri-county North Advertiser, WI, Frederic

Panek, Douglas
dougpanek@centurytel.net, Manager, Inter-County Leader, WI, Frederic

Panek, Douglas
dougpanek@centurytel.net, Pub., Advertiser, WI, Frederic
dougpanek@centurytel.net, Tri-county South Advertiser, WI, Frederic
dougpanek@centurytel.net, Mgr., Wild Rivers North Advertiser, WI, Frederic

Panian, A.J.
apanian@tribweb.com, Ed., The Mount Pleasant Journal, PA, Mount Pleasant

Panichkul, Victor
vpanichkul@statesmanjournal.com, Senior Ed., Statesman Journal, OR, Salem

Pankake, Ellen
epankake@somdnews.com, Prodn. Mgr., The Maryland Independent, MD, White Plains

Pankey, Denise
dpankey@morrisdailyherald.com, Adv. Mgr., Herald Life, IL, Morris

Pankey, Denise .... (815) 280-4100
news@morrisherald-news.com, Morris Herald-News, IL, MORRIS

Pankonin, Lori .... (308) 882-4453
waunetabreeze@bwtelcom.net, Accounting, Holyoke Enterprise, CO, Holyoke
waunetabreeze@bwtelcom.net, Co-Publisher, Imperial Republican, NE, Imperial

Pankonin, Russ .... (308) 882-4453
pank@jpipapers.com, Co-Publisher, The Wauneta Breeze, NE, Wauneta

Pankonin, Russ .... (308) 394-5389
waunetabreeze@bwtelcom.net, Co-Publisher, The Wauneta Breeze, NE, Wauneta

Pankonin, Russ .... (308) 882-6946
pank@chase3000.com, Co-Publisher , Imperial Republican, NE, Imperial

Pankow , Mary .... (716) 532-2288 x104
mpankow@cpowny.com, Ed. , Gowanda News, NY, Buffalo

Pankratz, Kerri .... (402) 204-7017
kerri.pankratz@yorknewstimes.com, Copy Ed./Layout/Obits., York News-Times, NE, York

Pankratz, Pat
ppankratz@htrnews.com, Ed., Lakeshore Chronicle, WI, Manitowoc

Pantages, Lawrence .... (330) 721-4065
lpantages@medina-gazette.com, Mng. Ed., The Medina County Gazette, OH, Medina

Pantaleo, Diane
dpantaleo@theadvertiser.com, Copy Ed., The Daily Advertiser, LA, Lafayette

Pantenburg, Leon .... (541) 383-7249
lpantenburg@cocc.edu, advisor, Central Oregon Community College, OR, Bend

Paolella, Alissa .... (419) 294-2332 Ext. 28
apaolella@dailychiefunion.com, City Ed. , The Daily Chief-Union, OH, Upper Sandusky

Paolino, Tammy .... (856) 486-2477
tpaolino@gannettnj.com, Reg. Engagement Ed., The Courier-Post, NJ, Cherry Hill

Paolucci, Gord
gpaolucci@yrmg.com, Dir., Adv./Prodn./Distribution, The Newmarket Era-banner, ON, Newmarket

Paolucci, Gordon .... (905) 727-0819
gpaolucci@yrmg.com, Metroland Media Group Ltd., ON, Mississauga

Paolucci, Shauna .... (416) 774-2236
spaolucci@insidetoronto.com, Sales Rep., The Scarborough Mirror, ON, Toronto

Papacharissi, Zizi
zizi@uic.edu, Head, University of Illinois-Chicago, IL, Chicago

Papadopoulos, Greg
greg.papadopoulos@sun.com, Exec. Vice Pres./CTO, SunLabs, Oracle & Sun Microsystems, Inc., CA, Redwood City

Pape, Christine
cpape@lemarssentinel.com, Circ. Mgr., Shoppers Guide, IA, Le Mars

Pape, Richard
info@allsysgo.com, Pres., All Systems Go, MA, Woburn

Pape II, William J. .... (203) 574-3636
Publisher, Republican-American, CT, Waterbury

Paper, Sharon .... (307) 367-3203

spape@sublitteexamienr.com, Gen. Mgr./Adv. Dir, Sublette Examiner, WY, Pinedale

Papineau, Claude
claude.papineau@thecanadianpress.com, Vice Pres.-French Serv., Canadian Press, The - Montreal, QC, QC, Montreal

Papineau, Jeremiah .... (315) 493-1270
jpapineau@lowville.com, Managing Editor, Carthage Republican Tribune, NY, LOWVILLE

Papineau, Jeremiah .... (315) 376-6851
jpapineau@lowville.com, Managing Editor, Journal and Republican, NY, Lowville

Papoi, Danielle .... (239) 472-5185
dpapoi@breezenewspapers.com, Ad. Sales, Captiva Current, FL, Sanibel
dpapoi@breezenewspapers.com, Adv. Sales, Island Reporter, FL, Sanibel
dpapoi@breezenewspapers.com, Ad. Sales, Sanibel-Captiva Islander, FL, Cape Coral

Papp, Jozsef
gaeditor@georgiasouthern.edu, Exec. Ed., Georgia Southern Univ., GA, Statesboro

Pappas, Nick .... (505) 823-3841
npappas@abqjournal.com, City Ed., Albuquerque Journal, NM, Albuquerque

Pappas, Steven
steven.pappas@timesargus.com, Ed., Times Argus Extra, VT, Barre
steven.pappas@timesargus.com, Ed., The Times Argus, VT, Barre

Paprocki, Gayle
gpapr@srds.com, Vice Pres., Pdct. Opns., SRDS, a Kantar Media Company, IL, Des Plaines

Paproski, Pat .... (604) 885-4811 ext. 233
pat@coastreporter.net, Sales Mgr., Coast Reporter, BC, Sechelt

Paquet, Pierre
courier@voir.ca, Adv. Mgr., Le Journal Voir, QC, Montreal

Paquet, Pierre
listings@hour.ca, Pub., Hour, QC, Montreal

Paquette, Cameron .... (603) 504-3101
cameronp@eagletimes.com, Ed., Eagle Times, NH, Claremont

Paquette, Gilber .... (514) 861-2088 ext. 23
gpaquette@hebdos.com, Exec. Dir., Hebdos Quebec, QC, Laval

Paquette, Marie-France .... (514) 484-5610
marie-france.paquette@tc.tc, Assistant publisher, The Westmount Examiner, QC, Westmount

Paquette, Mercedes
mpaquette@hometownnewsol.com, Prod. Mgr, Hometown News, FL, Fort Pierce

Paquin, Ellen
news@SaintIgnaceNews.com, Ed. , The St. Ignace News, MI, Saint Ignace

Paradis, Hal J.
customer.service@desertshoppers.net, Pub., Green Sheet, CA, Redlands

Paradis, John .... (508) 548-4700
paradise@capenews.net, Mng Ed, Enterprise, MA, Falmouth

Paradis, Nadia .... (819) 684-4755
classifieds@bulletinaylmer.com, Classifieds manager, Le Bulletin D'aylmer, QC, Gatineau

Paradis, Nadia .... (819) 684-4755
classifieds@bulletinaylmer.com, Classified and subscription manager, The West-quebec Post, QC, Gatineau

Paradis, Robert
robert@canadafrancais.com, Ed., Le Canada Francais, QC, Sainte Jean sur Richelieu

Paradis, Robert
robert.paradis@canadafrancais.com, Ed., Le Group Canada Francais, QC, Saint Jean

Paradis, Scott ....(807) 346-2527
sparadis@dougallmedia.com, News Ed.,
Thunder Bay Source, ON, Thunder Bay

Paradise, John ....(508) 548-4700 x221
paradise@capenews.net, Managing Ed., The
Bourne Enterprise, MA, Falmouth
paradise@capenews.net, Ed., The Sandwich
Enterprise, MA, Falmouth

Paradiso, Diane
sales@wpafilmlibrary.com, Dir., Sales, WPA
Film Library, IL, Orland Park

Pare, Dave ....(203) 317-2407
dpare@record-journal.com, Circ Dir, The
Westerly Sun, CT, Pawcatuck

Pare, David ....(203) 317-2366
dpare@record-journal.com, Circ. Dir., Record-
Journal, CT, Meriden

Pare, Steve ....(603) 668-4321
spare@unionleader.com, Adv. Sales Mgr.,
Salem Observer(OOB), NH, Manchester
spare@unionleader.com, Adv Sales Mgr, New
Hampshire Union Leader/New Hampshire
Sunday News, NH, Manchester

Paregoris, Demetrios
circulation@thenationalherald.com, Circ. Mgr.,
The National Herald, NY, Long Island City

Parelli, Anthony........................(203) 337-4879
aparelli@bcnnew.com, Sports Ed., New
Canaan News, CT, Bridgeport
aparelli@bcnnew.com, Sports Ed., Darien
News, CT, Bridgeport

Parent, Jeanine
MiPublisher@digitalfirstmedia.com, Pub. , The
Daily Tribune, MI, Clinton Township

Parent, Jeannie
MiPublisher@digitalfirstmedia.com, Pub., The
Voice, MI, Clinton Township
MiPublisher@digitalfirstmedia.com, Pub., The
Chelsea Standard, MI, Southgate

Parent, Jeannie
MiPublisher@digitalfirstmedia.com, Pub., The
Ogemaw/Oscoda County Star, MI, West
Branch
MiPublisher@digitalfirstmedia.com, Pub., The
Oakland Press, MI, Pontiac
MiPublisher@digitalfirstmedia.com, Pub. ,
News-Herald, MI, Southgate

Parent, Jeannie
MiPublisher@digitalfirstmedia.com, Pub., The
Homes for Sale, MI, Pontiac

Parent, John
sports@timesbulletin.com, Sports Ed., The
Times Bulletin, OH, Van Wert

Parent, Kurt
kurt.parent@globe.com, Telegram & Gazette,
MA, Worcester
kurt.parent@globe.com, Bangor Daily News,
ME, Bangor

Parent, Lorrie ....(952) 936-5000
lorrie.parent@polaroid.com, Media Rel.,
Polaroid Holding Co., MA, Concord

Parent, Michelle
michelle@weatherline.com, Exec. Vice Pres.,
Weatherline, Inc., MO, Saint Louis

Parent, Rob ....(610) 622-8884
rparent@delcotimes.com, Sports Ed.,
Delaware County Daily Times, PA,
Swarthmore

Parette, Colleen........................(613) 933-0014
colleen.parette@tc.tc, Production Coordinator,
Seaway News, ON, Cornwall

Parham, Kim
kparham@philly.com, VP, National Print
Advertising Sales, Philadelphia Inquirer, Daily
News & Philly.com, PA, Philadelphia

Parham, Maria
mparham@azstarnet.com, Editorial Page Ed.,
Arizona Daily Star, AZ, Tucson

Parham, Wayne ....(706) 595-1601
wparham@mcduffieprogress.com, Pub./Ed.,

The McDuffie Progress, GA, Thomson

Paris, Daniel ....(208) 465-8152 ext. 135
dparis@idahopress.com, Prodn. Dir., Press,
Idaho Press-Tribune, ID, Nampa

Parisi, Christina........................(978) 675-2707
cparisi@gloucestertimes.com, Community
News Ed., Gloucester Daily Times, MA,
Gloucester

Parisi, Mark ....(781) 665-4442
markparisi@aol.com, Pres., Atlantic Feature
Syndicate, Melrose

Park, Colleen
colleenp@ndna.com, Adv./Public Notice
Coord., North Dakota Newspaper
Association, ND, Bismarck

Park, David
david.park@fiu.edu, Florida International
University, FL, North Miami

Park, Jackie ....(517) 417-2068
jpark@lenconnect.com, VP Adv., The Daily
Telegram, MI, Adrian

Park, Josh...................(614) 486-6677 ext. 1025
jpark@ohionews.org, Program Support Asst.,
Ohio Newspaper Association, OH, Columbus

Park, Norm
normpark@estevanmercury.ca, Ed. , Southeast
Lifestyles, SK, Estevan

Park, Norm
normpark@estevanmercury.ca, Ed., Estevan
Mercury, SK, Estevan

Park, Ron
ron@newsleaderonline.com, Sports Ed, Carroll
County News-Leader, TN, Huntingdon

Parke, Beth ....(215) 884-8178
bparke@sej.org, Exec. Dir., Society of
Environmental Journalists (SEJ), PA,
Jenkintown

Parker, Alana ....(618) 242-0114 Ext. 150
alana.parker@register-news.com, Adv. Mgr.,
Register-News, IL, Effingham

Parker, Barb
bparker@conleynet.com, Circulation Manager,
Oconomowoc Enterprise, WI, Waukesha

Parker, Bill
bparker@thedailycourier.com, Purchasing
Agent, Daily Courier, OR, Grants Pass

Parker, Brad
parkerb@fayettvillenc.com, Weekly Sales Mgr.,
Carolina Flyer, NC, Fayetteville

Parker, Brad ....ext. 726
parkerb@fayetteobserver.com, Mgr., Adv.
Sales, Fort Bragg Paraglide, NC, Fayetteville

Parker, Caitlyn........................(402) 204-7016
caitlyn.parker@yorknewstimes.com, Copy Ed./
Layout, York News-Times, NE, York

Parker, Chuck........................(613) 392-6501
Gen. Mgr, The Community Press, ON, Trenton

Parker, Clint
editor@weavervilletribune.com, Pub./Ed., The
Weaverville Tribune, NC, Weaverville

Parker, Curtis................(404) 284-1888 Ext. 25
cparker@crossroadsnews.com, Prod. Mgr,
CrossRoadsNews, GA, Decatur

Parker, Dennis
dparker@timesfreepress.com, Major &
National Account Executive
, Chattanooga Times Free Press, TN,
Chattanooga

Parker, Elizabeth ....(908) 647-1187
eparker@recordernewspapers.com, Pub.,
Chatham Courier, NJ, Bernardsville

Parker, Elizabeth K. ....(908) 647-1187
eparker@recordernewspapers.com, Co-Pub.,
Bernardsville News, NJ, Bernardsville

Parker, Elizabeth K.
eparker@recordernewspapers.com, Pub.,
Madison Eagle, NJ, Bernardsville

Parker, Elizabeth K. .... (908) 766-3900, ext. 241
eparker@newjerseyhills.com, Pub./Ed. ,
Echoes-Sentinel, NJ, Bernardsville

Parker, Elizabeth K. ....(908) 647-1187
eparker@newjerseyhills.com, Pub., Today in
Hunterdon (OOB), NJ, Bernardsville
eparker@newjerseyhills.com, The Citizen, NJ,
Bernardsville

Parker, Elizabeth K. .... (908) 766-3900 ext. 241
eparker@recordernewspapers.com, Co-Pub./
Exec Editor, New Jersey Hills Media Group,
NJ, Whippany

Parker, Elizabeth K.
eparker@recordernewspapers.com, Pub.,
Florham Park Eagle, NJ, Bernardsville

Parker, Elliott
elliott.s.parker@cmich.edu, Assoc. Prof.,
Central Michigan University, MI, Mount
Pleasant

Parker, Glen ....(204) 571-7424
gparker@brandonsun.com, Sales and
Marketing Manager, Brandon Sun, MB,
Brandon

Parker, Greg
greg.parker@theeagle.com, Circ. Dir., The
Eagle, TX, Bryan

Parker, Jack............................(830) 896-7000
jack.parker@dailytimes.com, Circ. Dir., Kerrville
Daily Times, TX, Kerrville

Parker, Jackie
jparker@diocesefwsb.org, Adv. Mgr., The New
Hope Gazette, PA, New Hope
jparker@diocesefwsb.org, Advertising Sales ,
Today's Catholic, TX, San Antonio

Parker, Jennifer ....(404) 284-1888 Ext. 22
jennifer@crossroadsnews.com, Ed./Pub.,
CrossRoadsNews, GA, Decatur
jennifer@crossroadsnews.com, Adv. Mgr.,
Classified, Herald Democrat, TX, Sherman

Parker, Jo Alyson
jparker@sju.edu, Chair, Saint Joseph's
University, PA, Philadelphia

Parker, Kayla ....(406) 988-7983
ads@dillontribune.com, Advertising Mgr., Dillon
Tribune, MT, Dillon

Parker, Kelvin
kparker@th-record.com, Circulation Director,
Dow Jones Local Media Group, NY,
Middletown

Parker, Kristi............................(316) 652-7737
editor@libertypress.net, Ed., Liberty Press,
KS, Wichita

Parker, Megan.........................(606) 723-5161
cvtads@windstream.net, Ad Composition
Classified, Citizen Voice & Times, KY, Irvine

Parker, Mel
mel.parker@theparisnews.com, Adv. Dir., The
Paris News, TX, Paris

Parker, Melody ....(319) 291-1429
Melody.Parker@wcfcourier.com, Lifestyles Ed.,
The Courier, IA, Waterloo

Parker, Paige
pparker@theblacksheartimes.com, Adv./Sales
Mgr., The Blackshear Times, GA, Blackshear

Parker, Preston........................(435) 797-3259
preston.parker@usu.edu, Lectr., Utah State
University, UT, Logan

Parker, Randy ....(717) 771-2012
rparker@ydr.com, Mng. Ed., York Daily Record/
York Sunday News, PA, York

Parker, Stephanie....................(850) 526-1501
stephanie@jacksoncountytimes.net, Pub./Adv.
Mgr., Jackson County Times, FL, Marianna

Parker, Stephen
sparker@newjerseyhills.com, Pub., The
Citizen, NJ, Bernardsville
sparker@newjerseyhills.com, Pub., Hunterdon
Review, NJ, Whippany
sparker@newjerseyhills.com, Co-Pub., Mount

Olive Chronicle, NJ, Bernardsville
sparker@newjerseyhills.com, Co-Pub.,
Observer Tribune, NJ, Bernardsville

Parker, Stephen
sparker@recordernewspapers.com, Pub., The
Randolph Reporter, NJ, Bernardsville

Parker, Stephen W.
sparker@recordernewspapers.com, Pub.,
Hanover Eagle, NJ, Bernardsville

Parker, Stephen W. ....(908) 766-3900
sparker@recordernewspapers.com, Co-Pub.,
Bernardsville News, NJ, Bernardsville

Parker, Stephen W. .... (908) 766-3900 ext. 215
sparker@recordernewspapers.com, Co-Pub./
Bus. Mgr., New Jersey Hills Media Group,
NJ, Whippany

Parker, Stephen W. ....(908) 766-3900
sparker@recordernewspapers.com, Pub.,
Chatham Courier, NJ, Bernardsville

Parker, Stephen W.
sparker@newjerseyhills.com, Pub., Roxbury
Register, NJ, Bernardsville

Parker, Steve ....(314) 340-8290
sparker@post-dispatch.com, Prod. Mgr., The
Park Bugle, MN, Saint Paul

Parker, Wayne
parker@amplified.com, Pres., Amplified.com,
Inc., GA, Atlanta

Parkey, Keeli ....(423) 743-4112
kparkey@erwinrecord.net, Managing Editor,
The Erwin Record, TN, Erwin

Parkhouse, Adam
aparkhouse@thenewsdispatch.com, Sports
Ed., Herald News Review, IL, Decatur

Parkhouse, Adam ....(219) 214-4210
aparkhouse@thenewsdispatch.com, Managing
Ed., News Dispatch, IN, Michigan City

Parkhouse, Adam ....(219) 326-3858
aparkhouse@heraldargus.com, Managing Ed.,
Herald-Argus, IN, La Porte

Parkhurst, Cheri........................(603) 504-3167
cheri@eagletimes.com, Adv. Rep., Eagle
Times, NH, Claremont

Parkin, Marlene
production@northislandgazette.com, Prodn.
Mgr., North Island Gazette, BC, Port Hardy

Parkins, Victor
victor@milanmirrorexchange.com, Ed., Milan
Mirror-Exchange, TN, Milan

Parkinson, Debra ....(306) 425-3344
ads.northerner@sasktel.net, Office Mgr./Circ.,
The Northerner, SK, La Ronge

Parkinson, Michael
michael.parkinson@ttu.edu, Prof./Associate
Dean for graduate studies, Texas Tech
University, TX, Lubbock

Parkinson, Tim ....(419) 625-5500 ext. 5830
Pub., Tsr Express, OH, Sandusky

Parkman, Katie
kparkman@jackson.gannett.com, Adv. Sales
Mgr., Madison County Herald, MS, Ridgeland

Parkman, Katie........................(601) 961-7242
kparkman@jackson.gannett.com, Advertising
Sales Manager, The Clarion-Ledger, MS,
Jackson

Parks, Candy
cparks@parkrapidsenterprise.com, Adv. Mgr.,
Park Rapids Enterprise, MN, Park Rapids
cparks@parkrapidsenterprise.com, Adv. Mgr.,
Park Rapids Enterprise Express, MN, Park
Rapids

Parks, David ....(203) 731-3474
dparks@newstimes.com, Circ. Mgr., The News-
Times, CT, Danbury

Parks, Don ....(858) 875-5954
donp@rsfreview.com, VP of Sales, Ramona
Sentinel, CA, Ramona

john.paton@impremedia.com, Chrmn./CEO, impreMedia LLC, NY, Brooklyn

Patrick, John E. .... **(614) 659-7253**
jepatri@us.ibm.com, Gen. Mgr., Internet Application Servs., IBM Corp., NY, Armonk

Patrick, Judy .... **(518) 395-3101**
jpatrick@dailygazette.net, Ed., The Daily Gazette, NY, Schenectady

Patrick, Mike .... **(208) 664-0227**
mpatrick@cdapress.com, Ed., Coeur d'Alene Press, ID, Coeur D Alene

Patrick, Scott .... **(406) 657-1217**
spatrick@billingsgazette.com, Controller, Billings Gazette, MT, Billings

Patrick, Sharon
patrick@southernstandard.com, Adv. Mgr., Southern Standard, TN, McMinnville

Patrick, Tammy........................ **(937) 552-2298**
tpatrick@civitasmedia.com, Cir. Mgr., Troy Daily News, OH, Troy
tpatrick@civitasmedia.com, Dist. Mgr., Piqua Daily Call, OH, Piqua

Patrusky, Ben
bpatrusky@aol.com, Exec. Dir., Council for Advancement and Support of Education, DC, Washington

Patten, Brian .... **(202) 334-4546**
brian.patten@washpost.com, Sales Mgr./North America, Washington Post News Service with Bloomberg News, Washington

Patten, Brian .... **(202) 334-4546**
brian.patten@washpost.com, Sales Mgr., The Washington Post Writers Group, Washington

Patten, Sharon
sharon@bryantimes.com, Soc. Ed., The Bryan Times, OH, Bryan

Patten, Sue .... **(815) 772-7244**
wnssentinel@gmail.com, Pub., Fulton Journal, IL, Fulton
wnssentinel@gmail.com, Pub./Adv. Mgr., Whiteside News Sentinel, IL, Morrison
wnssentinel@gmail.com, Prophetstown Echo, IL, Prophetstown

Patterson, Amy........................ **(573) 324-2222**
bgted@lcs.net, Advertising, Bowling Green Times, MO, Bowling Green

Patterson, Ben
bpatterson@selectmedicalcorp.com, Co-Owner, American Classifieds, TN, Knoxville

Patterson, Bill .... **(940) 566-6808**
bpatterson@dentonrc.com, Pub., Denton Record-Chronicle, TX, Denton

Patterson, David .... **(705) 368-2744**
expositor@manitoulin.ca, Production Manager, Manitoulin Expositor, ON, Little Current

Patterson, Dee Ann
dpatterson@swoknews.com, News Ed., The Lawton Constitution, OK, Lawton

Patterson, Dewayne
dewayne.patterson@thedailysentinel.com, Mng. Ed., The Daily Sentinel, AL, Scottsboro

Patterson, Don
dpatterson@countrymedia.net, Pub./Ed., The Chronicle, OR, Saint Helens

Patterson, Don
dpatterson@okotoks.greatwest.ca, Ed, Okotoks Western Wheel, AB, Okotoks

Patterson, Doug.............. **(256) 234-4281 ext. 14**
doug.patterson@alexcityoutlook.com, National Accts., Alexander City Outlook, AL, Alexander City

Patterson, Georgie .... **(254) 883-2554**
bookkeeper@marlindemocrat.com, Office Mgr., The Marlin Democrat, TX, Marlin

Patterson, Jami
jpatterson@bradenton.com, Display Advertising Manager, Bradenton Herald, FL, Bradenton

Patterson, Jeffrey
jpatterson@woodburybulletin.com, Gen. Mgr., South Washington County Bulletin, MN, Hastings

Patterson, Jeremy
jeremy@calvary.com, Prod. Mgr., Publishing Systems, The Monterey County Herald, CA, Monterey

Patterson, Jessica .... **(256) 840-3000 ext 134**
jpatterson@sandmountainreporter.com, Account Executive, Sand Mountain Reporter, AL, Albertville

Patterson, Jessie
jessie@thefairhopecourier.com, Pub., The Fairhope Courier, AL, Fairhope

Patterson, Keesha .... **(856) 468-5000**
Gloucester County College, NJ, Sewell

Patterson, Kris
kpatterson@avtimes.net, Sales Mgr., Alberni Valley Times, BC, Port Alberni

Patterson, Lolene .... **(705) 848-7195**
lolene.patterson@sunmedia.ca, Circ. Mgr., The Mid-north Monitor, ON, Elliot Lake

Patterson, Lolene
lolene.patterson@sunmedia.ca, Circ. Mgr., Marketplace, ON, Elliot Lake

Patterson, Lolene
lolene.patterson@sunmedia.ca, Circulation Manager, The Standard, ON, Elliot Lake

Patterson, Melanie .... **(205) 631-8716**
editor@njeffersonnews.com, Ed., North Jefferson News, AL, Gardendale

Patterson, Michael .... **(260) 745-0552**
fwfrostnews@gmail.com, Managing Ed., Frost Illustrated, IN, Fort Wayne

Patterson, Missy
circulation@ptreyeslight.com, Circ. Mgr., Point Reyes Light, CA, Inverness

Patterson, Nichole.......... **(870) 862-6611 Ext. 155**
npatterson2@eldoradonews.com, Adv. Dir., El Dorado News-Times / Sunday News, AR, El Dorado

Patterson, Oscar
opatters@unf.edu, Chair, University of North Florida, FL, Jacksonville

Patterson, Pat .... **(717) 762-2151**
ppatterson@therecordherald.com, Pub., The Record Herald, PA, Waynesboro

Patterson, Pat .... **(814) 503-8860**
ppatterson@thecourierexpress.com, Pub, Jeffersonian Democrat, PA, Brookville
ppatterson@thecourierexpress.com, Pub., The Courier Express, PA, Du Bois

Patterson, Philip
philip.patterson@oc.edu, Oklahoma Christian Univ., OK, Oklahoma City

Patterson, Robin
bookkeeping@moorenews.com, Bus. Mgr., The Moore County News-Press, TX, Dumas

Patterson, Sally .... **(508) 943-8784**
spatterson@yankeeshopper.net, Production Manager, The Yankee Xpress, MA, Webster

Patterson, Scott .... **(716) 204-4930**
spatterson@beenews.com, Adv. Sales, East Aurora Bee, NY, Williamsville

Patterson, Shana .... **(770) 205-8948**
Classifieds@forsythnews.com, Classified Adv., Forsyth County News, GA, Cumming

Patterson, Suzanne
gilmermirror@gmail.com, Adv. Mgr., Gilmer Mirror, TX, Gilmer

Patterson, Troy .... **(519) 396-2963 ext. 104**
tpatterson@postmedia.com, Ed., The Lucknow Sentinel, ON, Lucknow

Patterson Frank, Susan
customerservice@press-citizen.com, Pub., Add Sheet, IA, Iowa City

Patterson Plank, Susan .... **(515) 284-8261**
splank@dmreg.com, Sales & Mktg. Dir., Iowa Newspaper Association, Inc., IA, Des Moines

Patti-Bisson, Charlene .... **(623) 445-2823**
cbisson@newszap.com, Publisher, Surprise Independent, AZ, Sun City

Pattillo, Patricia O. .... **(414) 265-5300**
editorial@communityjournal.net, Pub., Milwaukee Community Journal, WI, Milwaukee

Pattison, Ian .... **(807) 343-6203**
ian.pattison@chroniclejournal.com, Editorial Page Ed., The Chronicle-Journal, ON, Thunder Bay

Pattison, Neal .... **(425) 339-3480**
npattison@heraldnet.com, The Daily Herald, PA, Tyrone
npattison@heraldnet.com, Exec. Ed., The Herald, WA, Everett

Patton, Beth
bpatton@islandpacket.com, Mktg. Dir., The Island Packet, SC, Bluffton

Patton, Geoff .... **(215) 361-8825**
gpatton@thereporteronline.com, Online Ed., The Reporter, PA, Lansdale

Patton, John
jpatton@standardspeaker.com, Ops. Mgr., Hazleton Standard-Speaker, PA, Hazleton

Patton, Kristi
kpatton@pentictonwesternnews.com, Ed, Penticton Western News, BC, Penticton

Patton, Meredith V.
mvpatton@observertoday.com, Adv. Dir., The Observer, NY, Dunkirk

Patton, Patti .... **(740) 373-2121 Ext. 316**
ppatton@mariettatimes.com, Office Mgr., The Marietta Times, OH, Marietta

Patton, Paula .... **(707) 441-0584**
ppatton@times-standard.com, Pub., Colusa County Sun-Herald, CA, Marysville
ppatton@times-standard.com, Pub., Corning Observer, CA, Marysville

Patton, Paula .... **(707) 441-0584**
ppatton@times-standard.com, Pub., Tri-City Weekly, CA, Eureka

Patton, Stephanie..................... **(662) 686-5700**
editor@thelelandprogress.com, Publisher/Editor, Leland Progress, MS, Leland

Patton, Tyler .... **(940) 549-7800**
publisher@grahamleader.com, Publisher, The Graham Leader, TX, Graham

Patton, Tyler .... **(940) 549-7800**
publisher@grahamleader.com, Publisher, Lake Country Shopper, TX, Graham

Patton, Tyler .... **(940) 549-7800**
publisher@grahamleader.com, Publisher, Breckenridge American, TX, Breckenridge

Patton, Victor.......................... **(209) 385-2431**
vpatton@mercedsunstar.com, Managing. Ed., Los Banos Enterprise, CA, Los Banos

Patty, Ranft .... **(502) 227-0053**
patty@kentuckymonthly.com, Executive Editor, Kentucky Monthly, KY, Frankfort

Patwardhan, Padmini
patwardhanp@winthrop.edu, Asst. Prof., Winthrop University, SC, Rock Hill

Paugh, Kelli .... **(419) 294-2332 Ext. 22**
dcucirc@dailychiefunion.com, Cir. Mgr. , The Daily Chief-Union, OH, Upper Sandusky

Paul, Anne
apaul@standard.net, Exec. Asst. to the Pub., Standard-Examiner, UT, Ogden

Paul, Chris
cpaul@nutpub.net, Art Dir., Londonderry Times, NH, Londonderry
cpaul@nutpub.net, Art Dir., Tri-Town Times, NH, Londonderry
cpaul@nutpub.net, Art Dir., Nutfield News, NH, Londonderry

Paul, Debra
dpaul@nutpub.net, Publisher, Nutfield News, NH, Londonderry
dpaul@nutpub.net, Pub., Londonderry Times, NH, Londonderry
dpaul@nutpub.net, Pub., Tri-Town Times, NH, Londonderry

Paul, Ellen
ellenpaul@buckleynewspapers.com, Circ. Mgr., The Jasper County News, MS, Bay Springs
ellenpaul@buckleynewspapers.com, Circ. Mgr, Impact Of Hattiesburg, MS, Hattiesburg
ellenpaul@buckleynewspapers.com, Circ. Mgr, Impact Of Laurel, MS, Meridian

Paul, Hallie
hpaul@express-news.net, Asst. Mng. Ed., Graphics/Design/Photo, Bulverde News, TX, San Antonio
hpaul@express-news.net, Asst. Mng. Ed., Graphics/Design/Photo, Fort Sam News Leader, TX, San Antonio
hpaul@express-news.net, Asst. Mng. Ed., Graphics/Design/Photo, Kelly Observer, TX, San Antonio
hpaul@express-news.net, Asst. Mng. Ed., Graphics/Design/Photo, Lackland Talespinner, TX, San Antonio
hpaul@express-news.net, Asst. Mng. Ed., Graphics/Design/Photo, Medical Patriot, TX, San Antonio
hpaul@express-news.net, Asst. Mng. Ed., Graphics/Design/Photo, North Central News, TX, San Antonio
hpaul@express-news.net, Asst. Mng. Ed., Graphics/Design/Photo, Northeast Herald, TX, San Antonio
hpaul@express-news.net, Asst. Mng. Ed., Graphics/Design/Photo, Randolph Wingspread, TX, San Antonio
hpaul@express-news.net, Asst. Mng. Ed., Graphics/Design/Photo, Northwest Weekly, TX, San Antonio

Paul, Jennifer .... **(765) 342-3311 ext. 221**
jpaul@reportert.com, Finance Mgr., The Reporter Times, IN, Martinsville

Paul, Nathanael....................... **(305) 626-3102**
Florida Memorial College, FL, Miami Gardens

Paul, Patricia
ppaul@journalregister.com, Pub., La Voz, PA, Boyertown

Paul, Patricia............... **(610) 367-6041 ext. 243**
ppaul@21st-centurymedia.com, Pub., The Phoenix Reporter & Item, PA, Pottstown

Paul, Patti
ppaul@journalregister.com, Pub., Berks-Mont Newspapers, Inc., PA, Boyertown

Paul, Patti.................... **(610) 367-6041 Ext. 243**
ppaul@21st-centurymedia.com, Pub., The Boyertown Area Times, PA, Pottstown
ppaul@21st-centurymedia.com, Pub., The Kutztown Area Patriot, PA, Pottstown

Paul, Patti
ppaul@journalregister.com, Pub., Tri-County Record, PA, Pottstown
ppaul@journalregister.com, Gen. Mgr., Berksmont News, PA, Pottstown

Paul, Sandra........................... **(705) 759-5825**
sandra.paul@sunmedia.ca, Ed., Sault Ste. Marie This Week, ON, Sault Sainte Marie

Paul, Wanda............... **(606) 248-1010 Ext. 1131**
wpaul@civitasmedia.com, Business Development Specialist, Middlesboro Daily News, KY, Middlesboro

Paulsen, Rich
cappublisher@osceolaiowa.com, Pub., Southwest Iowa Advertiser, IA, Creston
cappublisher@osceolaiowa.com, The Advertiser, IA, Osceola

Paulsen, Sasha
spaulsen@napanews.com, Features Ed., Napa Valley Register, CA, Napa

Paulson, Adam .... **(218) 683-8733**

adam.paulson@northlandcollege.edu, Northland Cmty. & Tech. College, MN, Thief River Falls

Paulson, Jill .... (605) 668-1293
jpaulson@mtmc.edu, Mt. Marty College, SD, Yankton

Paulson, Jon
mcgavin_l@utpb.edu, Area Coord., University of Texas of the Permian Basin, TX, Odessa

Paulson, Stephanie
info@stephenz.com, Vice Pres., Creative Servs., The Stephenz Group, CA, San Jose

Paulu, Tom............................ (360) 577-2540
tpaulu@tdn.com, Features Reporter, The Daily News, WA, Longview

Paulus, Shawn
spaulus@observertoday.com, Circ. Mgr., The Observer, NY, Dunkirk

Paupore, Jason .... (219) 464-5271
jason.paupore@valpo.edu, Valparaiso University, IN, Valparaiso

Pava, David
dpava@marcole.com, Vice Pres., Sales & Marketing, MarCole Enterprises, Inc., CA, Walnut Creek

Pavelek, Mace .... (724) 776-4270 ext. 118
macepavelek@butlereagle.com, Gen. Mgr., The Cranberry Eagle, PA, Cranberry Township

Paveto, Suzzane
swdailyadvertising@yahoo.com, Pub., Fort Folk Guardian, LA, Sulphur

Pavilons, Mark
editor@kingsentinel.com, Editor, King Weekly Sentinel, ON, Bolton

Paviluk, Susan .... (732) 747-7007
sue@themonmouthjournal.com, Gen. Mgr., The Monmouth Journal, NJ, Red Bank

Pavlik, John
jpavlik@rutgers.edu, Chair/Prof., Rutgers University, NJ, New Brunswick

Pavlik, Zach
advertising@dailylobo.com, Ad. Mgr., New Mexico Daily Lobo, NM, Albuquerque

Pavoncello, Bianca .... (401) 767-8558
editor@pawtuckettimes.com, Exec. Ed., The Times, RI, Pawtucket

Pavone, Michael
mpavone@ustensor.com, Chief Operating Officer and V. P. of Sales, Tensor International LLC, IL, Woodridge

Pawlaczyk, George .... (618) 239-2625
gpawlacyzk@bnd.com, Newsroom, Belleville News-Democrat, IL, Belleville

Pawlenty, Michele
publisher@maplelakemessenger.com, Pub., Maple Lake Messenger, MN, Maple Lake

Pawley, Maeghan.................... (706) 208-2318
maeghan.pawley@onlineathens.com, Director of Mktg. , Athens Banner-Herald, GA, Athens

Paxson, Doug
info@mediacy.com, Pres., Media Cybernetics LP, MD, Rockville

Paxton, Andrew .... (520) 206-6901
apaxton1@pima.edu, Business manager, Pima Community College, AZ, Tucson

Paxton, Casey
mangumnews@gmail.com, Ed., The Mangum Star-News, OK, Mangum

Paxton, David A.
charnews@charitonleader.com, Pub., Chariton Herald-Patriot, IA, Chariton

Paxton, David A.
brian@albianews.com, Ed., Monroe County News, IA, Albia

Paxton, David A.
dave@albianews.com, Ed., Albia Union-

Republican, IA, Albia

Paxton, Matthew .... (540) 463-3113
publisher@thenews-gazette.com, publisher, The News-Gazette, VA, Lexington

Paylor, Shirley....................................ext. 0
spaylor@franklinshopper.com, Office Mgr., The Franklin Shopper, PA, Chambersburg

Payment, Julie ....ext. 336
jpayment@ludingtondailynews.com, Circ. Mgr., Ludington Shopper's Edition, MI, Ludington

Payment, Theresa Dold ....ext. 956
theresa@brparents.com, Sales Mgr., Baton Rouge Parents Magazine, LA, Baton Rouge

Payne, David L.
editor@dixontribune.com, Pub., Dixon Tribune, CA, Dixon

Payne, David L.
gazette_ads@yahoo.com, Ed. in Chief, Martinez News-Gazette, CA, Martinez

Payne, Debbie
dpayne@news-leader.com, HR Dir., Springfield News-Leader, MO, Springfield

Payne, Eliza
sales@lillooetnews.net, Sales Associate, Bridge River Lillooet News, BC, Lillooet

Payne, Francie
franciepayne@cableone.net, Ed./Gen. Mgr., The Tribune-News, AZ, Holbrook
franciepayne@cableone.net, Ed./Gen. Mgr., Silver Creek Herald, AZ, Holbrook

Payne, Jeff
jeff.payne@voicenews.com, Ed., Blue Water Voice, MI, Clinton Township
jeff.payne@voicenews.com, Ed., The Bay Voice, MI, Clinton Township

Payne, Jeff
jeff.payne@voicenews.com, Ed., Downriver Voice, MI, Clinton Township

Payne, Jeff
jeff.payne@voicenews.com, Ed., The North Macomb Voice, MI, Clinton Township

Payne, Jeff
jeff.payne@voicenews.com, Ed., The Macomb Voice, MI, Clinton Township
jeff.payne@voicenews.com, Ed., The Armada Times, MI, Clinton Township
jeff.payne@voicenews.com, Managing Ed., The Macomb Daily, MI, Clinton Township
jeff.payne@voicenews.com, Ed., The Voice, MI, Clinton Township

Payne, Karen
ads@richmond-dailynews.com, Prod. Mgr., Richmond News, MO, Richmond

Payne, Pat .... (785) 295-5635
patricia.payne@cjonline.com, Payroll/Benefits Mgr., The Topeka Capital-Journal, KS, Topeka

Payne, Robert .... (813) 314-2413
Director of Marketing, SAXOTECH, Inc., FL, Tampa

Payne, Tammy
tpayne@hqdci.com, Prod. Mgr, The Press, OH, Millbury

Payne, Vince ....ext. 116
vince@colterpeterson.com, Vice President, Colter Peterson, NJ, Paterson

Payne, Wendy
wpayne@ssentinel.com, Adv. Dir., Southside Sentinel, VA, Urbanna

Payomo Jr, Daniel
daniel.payomo@parenthood.com, Group Publisher, Bay Area Parent, CA, Campbell

Payson, David
dpayson@keene.edu, Assoc. Prof., Keene State College of the University System of New Hampshire, NH, Keene

Payton, Brandy
ucleader@plateautel.net, Ed., Union County

Leader, NM, Clayton

Pazniokas, Mark
mpazniokas@ctmirror.org, Capital Bur. Chief, The Connecticut Mirror, CT, Hartford

Peabody, Jane........................ (812) 379-5633
jpeabody@therepublic.com, Newsroom Coord., The Republic, IN, Columbus

Peace, Mitchell E.
mpeace@claxtonenterprise.com, Pub., Claxton Enterprise, GA, Claxton

Peace, Pamela A.
papeace@claxtonenterprise.com, Pub., Claxton Enterprise, GA, Claxton

Peach, Nicki
classified@murrayledger.com, Classified Mgr., The Murray Ledger & Times, KY, Murray

Peacock, Grace
gpeacock@insidetoronto.com, Ed, Annex Guardian, ON, Toronto
gpeacock@insidetoronto.com, Ed, Bloor West Villager, ON, Toronto
gpeacock@insidetoronto.com, Mng. Ed., Etobicoke Guardian, ON, Etobicoke

Peake, Jason
jpeake@parsonssun.com, Sports Ed., Parsons Sun, KS, Parsons

Pearce, David .... (812) 459-4206
dpearce263@aol.com, Owner/Pub., The Posey County News, IN, New Harmony

Pearce, Donna
ijdemolegals@bigbasinllc.com, Ed., Indian Journal, OK, Eufaula

Pearce, Jennifer
jennifer@tidelandnews.com, Adv. Mgr., Tideland News, NC, Swansboro

Pearce, Joyce ....(519) 733-2211 Ext 10
JOPearce@postmedia.com, Reception, The Kingsville Reporter, ON, Kingsville

Pearce, Raymond.................... (212) 556-8912
pearcr@nytimes.com, VP, Circulation & Reader Applications, The New York Times, NY, New York

Pearcey, Kevin
editor@greenvilleadvocate.com, Ed., Butler County News, AL, Greenville

Pearse, Jo .... (770) 963-9205
jo.pearse@gwinnettdailypost.com, General Sales Manger, Gwinnett Daily Post, GA, Lawrenceville

Pearson, Bruce
bpearson@trurodaily.com, Adv. Mgr., The Daily News, NS, Truro

Pearson, Dianna .... (423) 585-6816
Walters State Cmty. College, TN, Morristown

Pearson, Elaine
epearson@the-papers.com, Circ. Mgr., Shopping Guide News, IN, Rochester
epearson@the-papers.com, Circ. Mgr., The Paper - Kosciusko Edition, IN, Milford

Pearson, Jean .... (651) 228-5306
jpearson@pioneerpress.com, Dir., Market Research/Info., St. Paul Pioneer Press, MN, Saint Paul

Pearson, Jeri
editor@menastar.com, Editor, The Mena Star, AR, Mena

Pearson, Jeri .... (318) 377-1866 ext. 105
jeri@press-herald.com, Reporter, Minden Press Herald, LA, Minden

Pearson, Jonna
jonna.pearson@colostate.edu, Asst. Prof., Colorado State University, CO, Fort Collins

Pearson, Lisa........................(252) 265-7827
lpearson@wilsontimes.com, Ad Rep, The Wilson Times, NC, Wilson

Pearson, Margo .... (291) 298-1010 ext. 103
margo@intercom-interactive.com, Gen. Mgr., InterCom, TX, The Woodlands

Pearson, Mark
mpearson@staff.bond.edu.au, Prof., Bond University, Gold Coast

Pearson, Michael .... (905) 664-8800
mpearson@hamiltonnews.com, Ed., Stoney Creek News, ON, Stoney Creek

Pearson, Michelle
mpearson@gapress.org, Business Development Manager, Georgia Press Association, GA, Atlanta

Pearson, Tammy
tpearson@ncnewspress.com, Exec. Ed., Syracuse Journal-Democrat, NE, Syracuse

Pearson, Tim .... (402) 371-1020 ext. 232
tpearson@norfolkdailynews.com, News Ed., Norfolk Daily News, NE, Norfolk

Pearson, Travis
tpearson@torringtontelegram.com, Ed., The Torrington Telegram, WY, Torrington

Pease, Edward C. .... (435) 797-3293
Prof./Grad. Coord., Utah State University, UT, Logan

Pease, Tom
info@corporatecopy.com, Pres., e/Doc Systems, TN, Memphis

Pebley, Leslie
production@sdjewishtimes.com, Prodn. Mgr., San Diego Jewish Times, CA, La Mesa

Pecha, Tanya
tpecha@tnonline.com, Marketing Assistant, Times News, PA, Lehighton

Pechek, Jay .... (512) 349-1333
jayp@buffalotech.com, PR, Buffalo Technology Inc., TX, Austin

Pechous, Barb .... (605) 384-5616
announcer@hcinet.net, Pub./Ed., The Wagner Post, SD, Wagner
announcer@hcinet.net, Pub./Ed., Lake Andes Wave, SD, Wagner

Peck, Allysen .... (816) 218-6779
peck.allysen@pitch.com, Art Director, The Pitch, MO, Kansas City

Peck, Barb .... (315) 661-2328
pennysaver@wdt.net, Adv. Mgr., Jefferson County Pennysaver, NY, Watertown

Peck, Bryan
bpeck@newsdemocrat.com, Ed., The News Democrat, OH, Georgetown

Peck, Bryan
bpeck@ripleybee.com, Ed., The Ripley Bee, OH, Georgetown

Peck, Chris
fremontnews@wyoming.com, Assistant Ed., Wind River News, WY, Riverton

Peck, Dana............................ (850) 201-8035
peckd@tcc.fl.edu, Advisor, Tallahassee Cmty. College, FL, Tallahassee

Peck, Greg
gpeck@gazetteextra.com, Editorial Page Ed., The Janesville Gazette - GazetteXtra, WI, Janesville

Peck, Janice
janice.peck@colorado.edu, Assoc. Prof., University of Colorado, CO, Boulder

Peck, Rick............................(417) 223-4378
rpeck@nwaonline.net, Sports Ed., The Anderson Graphic, MO, Pineville

Peck, Rick
rpeck@nwaonline.com, Ed., The Goodman News-Dispatch, MO, Pineville

Peck, Rick............................(417) 223-4378
Ed., The Southwest City Republic, MO, Pineville

Peck, Rick............................(417) 223-4378
Mng. Ed., McDonald County News-Gazette, MO, Pineville

Peck, Rick............................(417) 223-4378

mcpress@nwaonline.com, Ed., McDonald County Press, MO, Pineville

Peck, Steve
fremontnews@wyoming.com, Pub., Lander Journal, WY, Lander

Peck, Steve ....(307) 332-2323
steve@dailyranger.com, Pub./Ed., Wind River News, WY, Riverton

Peck, Steven R.
ranger@wyoming.com, Ed./Pub., The Riverton Ranger, WY, Riverton

Peck, Thomas H....................(212) 210-1810
tpeck@nydailynews.com, CFO, New York Daily News, NY, New York

Peck, Tony ....(805) 564-5200
avw@newspress.com, Editorial Page Assistant, Santa Barbara News-Press, CA, Santa Barbara

Pecquex, Linda
circulation@connectionnewspapers.com, Circ. Mgr., Alexandria Gazette Packet, VA, Alexandria
circulation@connectionnewspapers.com, Circ. Mgr., Arlington Connection, VA, Alexandria
circulation@connectionnewspapers.com, Circ. Mgr., Burke Connection, VA, Alexandria
circulation@connectionnewspapers.com, Circ. Mgr., Centre View, VA, Alexandria
circulation@connectionnewspapers.com, Circ. Mgr, Springfield Connection, VA, Alexandria
circulation@connectionnewspapers.com, Circ. Mgr., Fairfax Station/Clifton/Lorton Connection, VA, Alexandria
circulation@connectionnewspapers.com, Circ. Mgr, Great Falls Connection, VA, Alexandria
circulation@connectionnewspapers.com, Circ. Mgr, Potomac Almanac, VA, Alexandria
circulation@connectionnewspapers.com, Circ. Mgr., Vienna/Oakton Connection, VA, Alexandria
circulation@connectionnewspapers.com, Circ. Mgr., Mount Vernon Gazette, VA, Alexandria
circulation@connectionnewspapers.com, Circ. Mgr., Fairfax Connection, VA, Alexandria
circulation@connectionnewspapers.com, Circ. Mgr, McLean Connection, VA, Alexandria
circulation@connectionnewspapers.com, Circ. Mgr, Oak Hill/Herndon Connection, VA, Alexandria
circulation@connectionnewspapers.com, Circ. Mgr, Reston Connection, VA, Alexandria

Pedersen, Erik
epedersen@hollywoodreporter.com, News Ed, The Hollywood Reporter, CA, Los Angeles

Pedersen, Sue.........................(541) 573-2022
addrop@burnstimesherald.info, Gen. Mgr., Burns Times-Herald, OR, Burns

Pederson, Jeff
fallsnews@excel.net, Ed., The Sheboygan Falls News, WI, Plymouth

Pederson, Katie
pmr@newspubinc.com, Classifieds/ Subscriptions, Post Messenger Recorder, WI, New Glarus

Pederson, Laurie
admanager@theaggie.org, Business Development Manager, University of California, Davis, CA, Davis

Pederson, Miranda ....(270) 783-3270
photo@bgdailynews.com, Chief Photographer, Daily News, KY, Bowling Green

Pedigo, Bill ....(425) 339-3046
pedigo@heraldnet.com, Librarian/TV Ed., The Herald, WA, Everett

Pedroso, Raul ....(305) 634-8820
rp@solo-photography.com, Pres., Solo Photography, Inc., FL, Miami

Peek, Dewain
dewain.peek@overtoncountynews.com, Ed., Overton County News, TN, Livingston

Peel, Tom ....(724) 465-5555 ext. 275
tpeel@indianagazette.net, Chief Photo., The

Indiana Gazette, PA, Indiana

Peeler, Jodie ....(803) 321-5225
jodie.peeler@newberry.edu, Newberry College, SC, Newberry

Peeling, Michael..........(519) 756-2020 ext. 2223
michael.peeling@sunmedia.ca, Ed., Paris Star, ON, Paris

Peeples, Curtis
curtis.peeples@motion-ind.com, Circ. Mgr., Delta Democrat Times, MS, Greenville

Peeples, Michael ....(618) 437-5321
Rend Lake College, IL, Ina

Peerman, Lucas.......................(575) 541-5446
lpeerman@lcsun-news.com, News Dir., Las Cruces Sun-News, NM, Las Cruces

Peery, Mark
mark-peery@sandhills.com, Coord./Mgr., PC Today Magazine, NE, Lincoln

Pehler, Paul............................(715) 738-1644
paul.pehler@lee.net, Advertising Director, Dunn County Big Buck, WI, Chippewa Falls

Pehora, Jason ....(905) 664-8800
jpehora@hamiltonnews.com, Gen. Mgr., Ancaster News, ON, Stoney Creek

Pehora, Jason ....(905) 664-8800
jpehora@hamiltonnews.com, Gen. Mgr., Hamilton Mountain News, ON, Stoney Creek

Pehora, Jason ....(905) 664-8800
jpehora@hamiltonnews.com, Gen. Mgr., Stoney Creek News, ON, Stoney Creek

Pehora, Jason ....(905) 664-8800
jpehora@hamiltonnews.com, Gen. Mgr., Dundas Star News, ON, Stoney Creek

Pehowic, Eric
epehowic@dailyitem.com, News Ed./ Weekend Ed., The Daily Item, PA, Sunbury

Pehrson, Greg
greg.pehrson@lee.net, Circ. Mgr., Telegram Advantage, NE, Columbus

Pehrson, Greg
greg.pherson@lee.net, Circ. Dir., The Columbus Telegram, NE, Columbus

Pehrson, Greg ....(402) 941-1402
greg.pehrson@lee.net, Circ. Mgr., Fremont Area Shopper, NE, Fremont

Peifer, Emily...........................(570) 372-4298
crusader@susqu.edu, Editor in chief, Susquehanna Univ., PA, Selinsgrove

Peiffer, Susan ....(215) 717-2695
susan.peiffer@metro.us, Correspondent, Dow Jones Newswires - Milano, Italy, Milano
susan.peiffer@metro.us, Assoc. Pub., Metro Philadelphia, PA, Philadelphia

Peirce, Brian
techhelp@peirce.com, Pres., Peirce-Phelps, Inc., PA, Philadelphia

Peirce, Larry
lpeirce@thebanner-press.com, Editor, The Banner-Press, NE, David City

Pejman, Peyman
peyman.pejman@zu.ac.ae, Assoc. Prof., Zayed University, Al Ruwayyah

Pelayo, Libertito
bpelayo@aol.com, Ed., The Filipino Reporter, NY, New York

Pelchar, Joseph ....(610) 371-5156
jpelchar@readingeagle.com, Circ. Mgr., Home Delivery, Reading Eagle, PA, Reading

Pelczynski, Kate
katep@beenews.com, Ed., East Aurora Bee, NY, Williamsville

Pelfrey, Sue...........................(740) 353-3101
dtimes@zoomnet.net, Adv. Mgr., Focus, OH, Portsmouth

Pelisson, Maureen
maureen@telluridedailyplanet.com, Adv. Mgr., Telluride Daily Planet; the Watch; The

Norwood Post, CO, Telluride

Pelky, Sharon..........................(830) 693-4367
sharon.pelky@highlandernews.com, Bus. Mgr., Burnet Bulletin, TX, Burnet

Pell, Nicole ....(256) 332-1881
nicole.pell@franklincountytimes.com, General Manager, Franklin County Times, AL, Russellville

Pellegrene Jr., Tom ....(260) 461-8377
tpellegrene@jg.net, News Technology Mgr., The Journal Gazette, IN, FORT WAYNE

Pellegrini, Jim ....(219) 548-4339
james.pellegrini@nwi.com, Marketing Mgr, The Times of Northwest Indiana, IN, Munster

Pellegrino, Joe ....(973) 696-8008
joe@lifeandleisurenj.com, Pub./Adv. Mgr./Circ. Mgr., Life & Leisure, NJ, Lincoln Park

Pellerin, Carole ....(819) 879-6681 #232
carole.pellerin@quebecormedia.com, Éditrice, Les Actualites, QC, Asbestos

Pellerin, Rebecca.........................ext. 223
rpellerin@nashobapub.com, Office Coord., Shirley Oracle, MA, Devens

Pellerin, Rebecca.........................ext. 223
rpellerin@nashobapub.com, Office Coord., Pepperell Free Press, MA, Devens

Pellerin, Rebecca.........................ext. 223
rpellerin@nashobapub.com, Office Coord., Townsend Times, MA, Devens

Pelletier, Daniel ....(315) 282-2216
daniel.pelletier@lee.net, Adv. Dir., This Week, NY, Auburn

Pelletier, Justin ....(207) 689-2894
jpelletier@sunjournal.com, Sports Ed., Sun Journal, ME, Lewiston

Pelletier, Pierre .... (250) 287-7464 ext. 238
ppelletier@richmond-news.com, Pub, Richmond News, BC, Richmond

Pellman, Mark
baumfolder@baumfolder.com, Dir., Sales/ Mktg., Baumfolder Corp., OH, Sidney

Peloquin, Danielle
hilltops@hartwick.edu, Hartwick College, NY, Oneonta

Peloza, Brian
sports@ftimes.com, Mng. Ed., The Times, IN, Frankfort

Pelt, J.T.
jtpelt@thepiercecountytribune.com, Ed. / Mgr., Pierce County Tribune, ND, Rugby

Pelzer, Abigail
apelzer@newtondailynews.com, Editor, Newton Daily News, IA, Newton

Pemberton, Kim.......................(706) 407-2664
kim.pemberton@lagrangenews.com, Graphic Designer, LaGrange Daily News, GA, Lagrange

Pemble, Amannda
nhads2@mchsi.com, Adv. Mgr., New Hampton Shopper, IA, New Hampton

Pena, Arelis
apena@providenceenespanol.com, Ed., Providence En Espanol, RI, North Providence

Pena, Denny ....(212) 807-4618
dpena@eldiariolaprensa.com, Circ. Dir., El Diario La Prensa, NY, Brooklyn

Pena, Hilda ....(936) 254-3618
ttnews@ttnewsinc.com, Ed./Pub., Timpson & Tenaha News, TX, Timpson

Pena, Rudy
sanbenitonews@sbcglobal.net, Adv. Dir./Circ. Mgr., San Benito News, TX, San Benito

Pena, Tracy
cjmaher@king-ranch.com, Ad. Director, Kingsville Record & Bishop News, TX, Kingsville

Pence, Melissa
mpence@gatehousemedia.com, Nat'l Adv. Rep., Rolla Daily News, MO, Rolla

Pendergast, Thomas F. ....(903) 342-5247
Pub./Ed., The Winnsboro News, TX, Winnsboro

Pengelly, Robbi ....(707) 933-2738
robbi.pengelly@sonomanews.com, Photo Ed, The Sonoma Index-Tribune, CA, Sonoma

Penn, Michael
michael.penn@juneauempire.com, Photographer, Juneau Empire, AK, Juneau

Pennell, Debbie M....................(919) 739-7905
dpennell@newsargus.com, Mgr., HR, Goldsboro News-Argus, NC, Goldsboro

Penney, John
jpenney@poughkeepsiejournal.com, Editorial Page Ed., Poughkeepsie Journal, NY, Poughkeepsie

Pennington, Andy ....(208) 232-4161
apennington@journalnet.com, Pub., Idaho State Journal, ID, Pocatello

Pennington, Andy
apennington@journalnet.com, Pub., Teton Valley News, ID, Driggs

Pennington, Kathleen ....(218) 723-5212
kpennington@duluthbudgeteer.com, Sales Mgr., Duluth Budgeteer News, MN, Duluth

Penny, Mark
jmpenny@hempsteadco.com, Mng. Dir., Hempstead & Co., Inc., NJ, Haddonfield

Penny, Shelii ....ext. 100
shelii@wwthayne.com, Circ. Mgr., Senior Times South Central Michigan, MI, Battle Creek

Penny, Trent
tpenny@annistonstar.com, Photo Ed., The Anniston Star, AL, Anniston

Penrod, Diane
penrod@rowan.edu, Assoc. Prof., Rowan Univ., NJ, Glassboro

Penrose, Kathryn ....(830) 672-7100
news@gonzalescannon.com, News Editor, The Gonzales Cannon, TX, Gonzales

Pensiero, F. James ....(609) 520-7487
Vice Pres., News Projects, The Wall Street Journal, NY, New York

Penticuff, David ....(765) 671-2250
dpenticuff@chronicle-tribune.com, Ed., Chronicle-Tribune, IN, Marion

Penuel, Glenn
theweeklygazette@embarqmail.com, Ed., Weekly Gazette, NC, La Grange

Penwell, Kim ....(740) 313-0347
kpenwell@civitasmedia.com, Med. Sales Cons., Record Herald, OH, Washington Court House

Pepin, David............................(401) 767-8562
editor@pawtuckettimes.com, Managing Ed./ News Ed., The Times, RI, Pawtucket

Pepin, Matt ....(617) 929-7368
matt.pepin@globe.com, Sports Ed., The Boston Globe, MA, Boston

Peppas, Jeremy.......................(501) 370-8318
jpeppas@nlrtimes.com, Ed., Jacksonville Patriot, AR, North Little Rock
jpeppas@nlrtimes.com, Ed., Sherwood Voice, AR, North Little Rock
jpeppas@nlrtimes.com, Ed., The North Little Rock Times, AR, North Little Rock
jpeppas@nlrtimes.com, Ed., Lonoke Democrat, AR, Lonoke

Pepper, C.J.
chnews@shelbrookchronicle.com, Pub., Shellbrook Chronicle, SK, Shellbrook

Pepper, C.J.
cpepper@shellbrookchronicle.com, Pub., Shopper Chronicle, SK, Shellbrook

Pepper, Clark J ....(306) 747-2442
clark@sbchron.com, Publisher, Spiritwood

Herald, SK, Shellbrook

Peppers, Tina
tina.peppers@gadsdentimes.com, National Sales-Retail, The Gadsden Times, AL, Gadsden

Peppler-Moyer, Lonnie.........................ext. 221
lpepplermoyer@monroenews.com, Publisher, The Monroe News, MI, Monroe

Peppler-Moyer, Lonnie ....(734) 240-5795
lonnie@monroenews.com, Pub., Bedford Now, MI, Monroe

Peragallo, Wayne..........(732) 922-6000 ext. 2510
wperagallo@app.com, VP, Information Systems, Asbury Park Press, NJ, Neptune

Peragallo, Wayne L. ....(732) 643-2510
Sr. Dir. IT, Home News Tribune, NJ, Somerville

Perce, Lynn
info@rooseveltpaper.com, Mktg. Dir., Roosevelt Paper, NJ, Mount Laurel

Percefull, Gary
publisher@tulsacountynews.info, Pub., Tulsa County News, OK, Tulsa

Perdigao, John ....(713) 362-7622
john.perdigao@chron.com, Chief Financial Officer, Houston Chronicle, TX, Houston

Perdue, Beth..........................(508) 979-4430
bperdue@s-t.com, Editor, The Standard-Times, MA, New Bedford

Perdue, Michelle ....(361) 729-1828
theherald@the-i.net, Adv. Mgr., The Coastal Bend Herald, TX, Portland

Perdue, Suvanah...........(620) 442-4200 ext. 116
suvanah@arkcity.net, Assistant Ad Director , The Arkansas City Traveler, KS, Arkansas City

Perea, Frank
publisher@newsmontana.com, Pub., Big Horn County News, MT, Hardin

Perea, Frank............................(701) 567-2424
frankperea@countrymedia.net, Director, North Dakota Newspaper Association, ND, Bismarck

Perea II, Frank ....(701) 523-5623
frankperea@countrymedia.net, Pub., Bowman County Pioneer, ND, Bowman

Perea II, Frank
publisher@newsmontana.com, Pub., The Stillwater County News, MT, Columbus

Perel, Erica ....(919) 962-4215
Univ. of North Carolina - The Daily Tar Heel, NC, Chapel Hill

Perenchio, Matthew
Matthew.Perenchio@lee.net, Exec. Ed., The Tomah Journal, WI, Tomah
Matthew.Perenchio@lee.net, Exec. Ed., Jackson County Chronicle, WI, Black River Falls

Peretti, Greg..........................(505) 823-3888
gperetti@abqjournal.com, Web Devel., Prod., Albuquerque Journal, NM, Albuquerque

Perez, Carol ....(517) 417-2011
classifieds@lenconnect.com, Classified Mgr. , The Daily Telegram, MI, Adrian

Perez, Demetrio............ (305) 643-2947 ext. 226
djp@libreonline.com, Pub., Libre, FL, Miami

Perez, Eduardo
sales@lasubasta.com, Sales Manager, La Subasta De Dallas, TX, Dallas

Perez, Linda ....(909) 869-5483
linda@thepolypost.com, The Poly Post, CA, Pomona

Perez, Sylvia
perezs@caller.com, Exec. Sec., Corpus Christi Caller-Times, TX, Corpus Christi

Perfecto, Elizabeth ....(218) 681-0819
Northland Cmty. & Tech. College, MN, Thief River Falls

Perham, David ....(847) 486-7275
perham@pioneerlocal.com, Circ. Dir., Arlington Heights Post, IL, Chicago

Perham, David ....(847) 486-7275
perham@pioneerlocal.com, Circ. Dir., Morton Grove Champion, IL, Chicago

Perham, David ....(847) 486-7275
perham@pioneerlocal.com, Circ. Dir., Buffalo Grove Countryside, IL, Chicago

Perini, Bob............................ (715) 526 - 7002
rperini@shawanoleader.com, vice president production, Shawano Leader, WI, Shawano

Perkes, Allison
aperkes@dailydemocrat.com, Adv. Dir., The Daily Democrat, CA, Woodland

Perkins, Dan..........................(718) 768-2522
tomtomorrow@ix.netcom.com, Creator, This Modern World, Brooklyn

Perkins, David
dperkins@civitasmedia.com, Nat'l Acct. Mgr., Mount Airy News, NC, Mount Airy
dperkins@civitasmedia.com, Adv. Dir., Bladen Journal, NC, Elizabethtown

Perkins, Karla ....(920) 787-3334
arguskarlap@wausharaargus.com, Sales, Waushara Argus, WI, Wautoma

Perkins, Martha
mperkins@vancourier.com, Ed, The Vancouver Courier, BC, Vancouver

Perkins, Martha
editor@bowenislandundercurrent.com, Ed., Bowen Island Undercurrent, BC, Bowen Island

Perkins, Mary ....(419) 836-2221
mperkins@presspublications.com, General Manager, The Press, OH, Millbury

Perkins, Penny ....(518) 244-2016
perkip@sage.edu, Russell Sage College, NY, Troy

Perkins, William ....(334) 712-7901
bperkins@dothaneagle.com, Editorial Page Ed., The Dothan Eagle, AL, Dothan

Perkins, William H.
missibaptistrecord@mbcb.org, Ed., The Baptist Record, MS, Jackson

Perkinson, Elizabeth ....(580) 225-3000
elizabeth@ecdailynews.com, Owner/Pres./Pub., Elk City Daily News, OK, Elk City

Perkinson, Jennine ....(509) 577-7735
jperkinson@yakimaherald.com, Adv. Dir., Yakima Herald-Republic, WA, Yakima
jperkinson@yakimaherald.com, Adv. Dir., East Oregonian, OR, Pendleton

Perl, Mimi
office.jfec@gmail.com, Ed., The Jewish Leader, CT, New London

Perlberg, Rich
rperlberg@livingstondaily.com, Gen. Mgr., Hometown Newspapers, Inc., MI, Howell

Perlberg, Richard
rperlberg@gannett.com, Pub., Green Sheet, MI, Howell

Perloff, Richard
r.perloff@csuohio.edu, School Dir., Cleveland State University, OH, Cleveland

Permar, Matthew
ssislander@bellsouth.net, Pub., The Islander, GA, Brunswick

Perner, Melissa
melissa@ozona.com, Pub./Ed., Ozona Stockman, TX, Ozona

Pero, David ....(503) 325-3211
dpero@dailyastorian.com, Publisher and Editor, The Daily Astorian, OR, Astoria

Perpich, David
generalmgr@nytimes.com, Senior VP, Product, The New York Times, NY, New York

Perretta, Christopher ...... (845) 473-0550 ext. 836
cperretta@perretta.com, Pres., Perretta Graphics Corp., NY, Poughkeepsie

Perriman, Scott
scottp@milehighnews.com, Pub., Milehigh Newspapers, CO, Golden

Perriman, Scott D.
scottperriman@metronorthnews.com, Owner/Pres./Pub., Jackalope Publishing, CO, Thornton

Perrini, Ralph
ralph.perrini@investors.com, Vice Pres., Mktg., Investor's Business Daily, CA, Los Angeles

Perritano, Fran
fperrita@uticaod.com, Sports Ed., The Observer-Dispatch, NY, Utica

Perrone, Barbara
bxpp@aol.com, Pub./Gen. Mgr., The Bronx Penny Pincher, NY, Bronx

Perrota, Michael ....(914) 674-7422
mperrota@mercy.edu, Mercy College, NY, Dobbs Ferry

Perrotto, Greg
gperrotto@rensselaerrepublican.com, Gen. Mgr., Rensselaer Republican, IN, Rensselaer

Perrotto, Greg
gperrotto@rensselaerrepublican.com, Gen. Mgr., Kankakee Valley Post-News, IN, Demotte

Perrotto, Greg ....(574) 583-5121
perrotto_21@hotmail.com, Circ. Dir., Herald Journal, IN, Monticello

Perrotto, Larry J. .... (618) 937-6412 ext. 102
Chrmn./Pres./CEO, Community Media Group, IL, West Frankfort

Perry, Barbara.............. (413) 525-6661 ext. 135
bperry@reminderpublications.com, Adv. Mgr., Reminder Metrowest / Chicopee Herald, MA, East Longmeadow
bperry@reminderpublications.com, VP, Sales, The Reminder, MA, East Longmeadow

Perry, Barbara
bperry@reminderpublications.com, Adv. Mgr., The Herald, MA, East Longmeadow

Perry, Bernadean
bperry@heartlandpublications.com, Circ. Mgr., Williamson Daily News, WV, Williamson

Perry, Bobby .... ext. 6306
Circ. Mgr., Texarkana Gazette, AR, Texarkana

Perry, Brenda
newsroom@winstoncountyjournal.com, Circ. Mgr., The Choctaw Plaindealer, MS, Ackerman

Perry, Brenda
bperry@winstoncountyjournal.com, Circ. Mgr., Winston County Journal, MS, Louisville

Perry, Brian
bperry@mauinews.com, City Ed., The Maui News, HI, Wailuku

Perry, Bruce
info@bendermachine.com, Mktg. Mgr., Bender Machine, Inc., CA, Vernon

Perry, Captain Christopher ....(540) 464-7326
Virginia Military Institute, VA, Lexington

Perry, Carol
carol_perry@baylor.edu, Instr., Baylor University, TX, Waco

Perry, Dave ....(303) 750-7555
dlperry@aurorasentinel.com, Ed., Aurora Sentinel, CO, Aurora

Perry, Devon........................(812) 331-4253
dperry@heraldt.com, HR Dir., The Reporter Times, IN, Martinsville
dperry@heraldt.com, HR. Dir., The Herald Times, IN, Bloomington

Perry, Grace ....(248) 349-1700
gperry@gannett.com, Gen. Mgr., Novi News, MI, Detroit

Perry, Grace
gperry@hometownlife.com, Advertising Director, Westland Observer, MI, Detroit

Perry, Helayne ....(714) 796-6940
hperry@ocregister.com, Visuals, Asst. Managing Ed., The Orange County Register, CA, Santa Ana

Perry, Jack
jack.perry@syncbak.com, Pres./CEO, Decisionmark Corp., IA, Cedar Rapids

Perry, Jim.............................(940) 665-05511
jperry@ntin.net, Pub., Gainesville Daily Register, TX, Gainesville

Perry, Jim..............................(417) 256-9191
jimp@phillipsmedia.com, Publisher, West Plains Daily Quill, MO, West Plains

Perry, Jim ....(918) 285-5555
editor@cushingcitizen.com, Ed., Cushing Citizen, OK, Cushing

Perry, Jim .... 1-(870) 741-2325
Jim Perry <jimp@phillipsmedia.com>, Publisher, The Newton County Times, AR, Jasper

Perry, Jim
jim@phillipsmedia.com, Pub., Harrison Daily Times, AR, Harrison

Perry, John............................(503) 364-4431
jsperry@eomediagroup.com, Chief Operating Officer, EO Media Group, OR, Salem

Perry, Julie ....(785) 562-2317
sports@marysvilleonline.net, Sports writer, Marysville Advocate, KS, Marysville

Perry, Kelvin W................................. ext. 13
kelvin.perry@ne-corp.com, Pres., Newspaper Electronics Corp., MO, Kansas City

Perry, Lois ....(705) 647-6791 Ext. 224
loisperry@northernontario.ca, Gen. Mgr. , Speaker Weekender, ON, New Liskeard
loisperry@northernontario.ca, Gen. Mgr. , Temiskaming Speaker, ON, New Liskeard

Perry, Lorie
lorieperry@thewestfieldnewsgroup.com, Art Room Dir., The Westfield News , MA, Westfield

Perry, Nichole
classified@decaturdailydemocrat.com, Classified Mgr., Decatur Daily Democrat, IN, Decatur

Perry, Peary ....(512) 653-8545
pperry@pearyperry.com, Self-Syndicator/Columnist
Local & National Publications
www.pearyperry.com
, Peary Perry Enterprises, Richmond

Perry, Rita
jfreepress@aol.com, Pub., Jacksonville Free Press, FL, Jacksonville

Perry, Rosetta Miller ....(615) 509-3181
lperry8049@aol.com, Pub., Tennessee Tribune, TN, Nashville

Perry, Russell M.
tcbrown@blackchronicle.com, Ed., Black Chronicle, OK, Oklahoma City

Perry, Scott ....(217) 421-7976
sperry@herald-review.com, Managing. Ed./Print, Herald & Review, IL, Decatur

Perry, Steve ....(360) 417-3540
sperry@peninsuladailynews.com, Advertising Director, Peninsula Daily News, WA, Port Angeles

Perry, Steven
info@tsa.com, Sales Mgr., TSA, TX, Houston

Perry, Teresa
perry.teresa@kingscorecord.com, Circ. Mgr., The Kings County Record, NB, Sussex

Perry, Thomas.............. (705) 268-5050 ext. 228
thomas.perry@sunmedia.ca, Mng. Ed. , The Timmins Daily Press, ON, Timmins

Perry, Tina .... (662) 328-2424 ext.140
tinap@cdispatch.com, Prepress Mgr., The
Commercial Dispatch, MS, Columbus

Perry, charles .... (843) 248-6671
charles.perry@myhorrynews.com, Editor,
Carolina Forest Chronicle, SC, Myrtle Beach

Perryman, Don
dperryman@the-messenger.com, Ed., The
Messenger, KY, Madisonville

Perryman, Jennifer .... (805) 927-8652
jperryman@thetribunenews.com, Local Media
Consultant/Office Mgr, The Cambrian, CA,
Cambria

Persac, Nicholas
npersac@catholichigh.org, Louisiana State
University, LA, Baton Rouge

Persico, Joanne
info@gcnpublishing.com, Creative Dir., GCN
Publishing, CT, Norwalk

Persinger, Joanne .... ext. 219
jpersinger@tribtown.com, Commun./Copy Ed.,
The Tribune, IN, Seymour

Persons, David
dpersons@eptrail.com, News Ed., Estes Park
Trail-Gazette, CO, Estes Park

Persson, Heather .... (306) 657-6402
hpersson@thestarphoenix.com, Ed, Saskatoon
StarPhoenix, SK, Saskatoon

Perzo, Andrew
informer@americanpress.com, Copy Ed.,
American Press, LA, Lake Charles

Pescaia, Linn A.
westnews@sbcglobal.net, Pub., The West
News, TX, West

Peschka, Darrin .... (805) 437-0222
dpeschka@vcstar.com, News Ed., Ventura
County Star, CA, Camarillo

Peschka, Pat .... (620) 694-5700 Ext. 330
ppeschka@hutchnews.com, News Clerk, The
Hutchinson News, KS, Hutchinson

Petak, Ron .... (402) 505-3620
ron.petak@bellevueleader.com, Exec. Ed.,
Gretna Breeze, NE, Bellevue
ron.petak@bellevueleader.com, Exec. Ed.,
Bellevue Leader, NE, Bellevue

Petak, Ron .... (402) 505-3620
ron.petak@papilliontimes.com, Exec. Ed.,
Ralston Recorder, NE, Bellevue

Petak, Ron .... (402) 505-3620
ron.petak@owh.com, Exec. Ed., Papillion
Times, NE, Bellevue

Petcher, Robert
rpetcher@breezenewspapers.com, Ed., Fort
Myers Beach Bulletin, FL, Fort Myers Beach

Peter, Conti .... (804) 360-9434
peter.conti@localmedia.org, Sales and
Marketing Director, Local Media Association,
MI, Lake City

Peter, Haggert
phaggert@insidetoronto.com, Editor-In-
Chief, Metroland Media Group Ltd., ON,
Mississauga

Peter, Lynda St.
lstpeter@inkym.com, Office Mgr., The Inquirer
and Mirror, MA, Nantucket

Peter, Rebecca .... (641) 923-2684
gleadernews@qwestoffice.net, News Editor,
The Leader, IA, Garner

Petermann, Eric .... (520) 515-4610
eric.petermann@myheraldreview.com,
Opinions Ed., Wick Communications -
Herald/Review, AZ, Sierra Vista
eric.petermann@myheraldreview.com,
Managing Editor, Sierra Vista Herald -
Sunday Bravo Shopper, AZ, Sierra Vista

Petermann, Kassie .... (763) 424-7372
kassie.petermann@ecm-inc.com, Ed.,
Columbia Heights/Fridley Sun Focus, MN,

Eden Prairie

Peters, Annette .... (315) 430-6287
apeters@advancemediany.com, VP Marketing,
The Post-Standard, NY, Syracuse

Peters, Carl .... (856) 583-6147
cpeters@catholicstarherald.org, Ed., Catholic
Star Herald, NJ, Camden

Peters, Charles
charles.o.peters@faa.gov, Founding Ed.,
Washington Monthly LLC, Washington

Peters, Chuck .... (319) 398-8211
chuck.peters@gazettecommunications.com,
CEO/Pres., The Gazette, IA, Cedar Rapids

Peters, Chuck .... (319) 368-8878
chuck.peters@gazcomm.com, President and
CEO, The Gazette Company, IA, Cedar
Rapids

Peters, Debbie .... (620) 257-2368
Distribution, The Lyons News, KS, Lyons

Peters, Harvey B. .... (401) 380-2376
Peters@NewportRI.com, News Ed., The
Newport Daily News, RI, Newport

Peters, John .... (336) 719-1931
jpeters@heartlandpublications.com , Ed.,
Mount Airy News, NC, Mount Airy

Peters, John
jpeters@mediadatatech.com, Pres., Media
Data Technology, Inc. (MDTI), MA, South
Hadley

Peters, Keith E. .... (207) 582-8486
ads@comadvertiser.com, Ed., Community
Advertiser, ME, Farmingdale

Peters, Lisa .... (615) 452-4940
lpeters@mainstreetmediatn.com, Class Mgr,
The Murfreesboro Post, TN, Murfreesboro

Peters, Michael .... (918) 581-8348
michael.peters@tulsaworld.com, Sports editor,
Tulsa World, OK, Tulsa

Peters, Peg .... (712) 364-3131 ext. 101
Circ. Mgr., Ida County Courier, IA, Ida Grove

Peters, Scott
scottp@jegi.com, Mng. Dir., Jordan, Edmiston
Group, Inc., NY, New York

Peters, Susan .... (812) 663-3111 x7014
susan.peters@greensburgdailynews.com,
Graphic Arts Dir., Rushville Republican, IN,
Rushville

Peters, Susan .... (812) 663-3111 x7014
susan.peters@greensburgdailynews.com,
Expeditor, Greensburg Daily News, IN,
Greensburg

Peters, Tim .... (765) 482-4650 ext. 107
tim.peters@reporter.net, Adv. Rep., The
Reporter, IN, Lebanon

Petersen, Candace
capetersen@cu-portland.edu, Vice Pres.,
Mktg./Strategy, Infocus Corp., OR, Portland

Petersen, Carl
letters@alibi.com, Pub./Gen. Mgr., Weekly
Alibi, NM, Albuquerque

Petersen, Debra .... (315) 661-2502
dpeters@ogd.com, Class. , Ogdensburg
Journal/Advance News, NY, Ogdensburg
dpeters@ogd.com, Assoc. Prof., University of
St. Thomas, MN, Saint Paul

Petersen, Grace .... (402) 371-1020 ext. 265
gpetersen@norfolkdailynews.com, City Ed.,
Norfolk Daily News, NE, Norfolk

Petersen, Jeanna .... (541) 902-3529
jpetersen@thesiuslawnews.com, Sales person,
Siuslaw News, OR, Florence

Petersen, Justin .... (605) 845-3646
photo@mobridgetribune.com, Webmaster/
Photoshop, Mobridge Tribune, SD, Mobridge

Petersen, Mark .... (206) 303-9484
mark.petersen@catalystpaper.com, VP
International Sales, Catalyst Paper (USA),

Inc., WA, Seattle

Petersen, Matt .... (402) 371-1020 ext. 254
mpetersen@norfolkdailynews.com, Systems
Mgr., Norfolk Daily News, NE, Norfolk

Petersen, Scott
speterson@jcpgroup.com, Ed., Lake Country
Buyers Guide, WI, Hartland

Petersen, Ted
tpetersen@fit.edu, Adviser, Florida Institute of
Technology, FL, Melbourne

Peterson, Amanda .... (205) 348-6144
Univ. of Alabama, AL, Tuscaloosa

Peterson, Anne .... (307) 299-4662
AnnePeterson@CampbellCountyObserver.com
, Advertising Sales Manager, The Campbell
County Observer, WY, Rozet

Peterson, Charlene
cpeterson@messengernews.net, Adv. Mgr.,
Consumer News, IA, Fort Dodge

Peterson, Cheryl L. .... (989) 724-6384
editor@alconareview.com, Pub./Ed. , Alcona
County Review, MI, Harrisville

Peterson, Chuck .... (641) 713-4541
staej@iowatelecom.net, Ed., St. Ansgar
Enterprise Journal, IA, Saint Ansgar

Peterson, Craig .... (702) 259-4134
craig.peterson@lasvegassun.com, Special
Pub. V. Las Vegas Sun, NV, Henderson

Peterson, Craig .... (906) 483-2210
cpeterson@mininggazette.com, Mng. Ed., The
Daily Mining Gazette, MI, Houghton

Peterson, Donna
dpeters@atpco.com, Vice Pres., Adv., Defense
News, VA, Springfield

Peterson, Erica ....(330) 688-0088 ext. 3103
Exec. Ed., Tallmadge Express, OH, Kent

Peterson, Erick
epeterson@yvpub.com, Ed., Review
Independent, WA, Toppenish
epeterson@yvpub.com, Ed., Yakima Valley
Business Times, WA, Yakima

Peterson, Jana .... (218) 879-1950
Jpeterson@pinejournal.com, Ed, The Pine
Journal, MN, Duluth

Peterson, Jeff .... (508) 236-0314
jpeterson@thesunchronicle.com, Pub., The
Sun Chronicle, MA, Attleboro

Peterson, Jodi .... (608) 647-2911
jpeterson@wcinet.com, Prod. Mgr./Sales Team
Lead, Richland Center Shopping News, WI,
Richland Center

Peterson, Josh .... (931) 728-7577 ext. 106
jpeterson@manchestertimes.com, Pub.,
Manchester Times, TN, Manchester

Peterson, June .... (860) 379-9602
jpeterson@mediabids.com, Director, Media
Relations, Mediabids, Inc., CT, Winsted

Peterson, Karen .... (253) 597-8434
karen.peterson@thenewstribune.com, Exec.
Ed., The News Tribune, WA, Tacoma

Peterson, Kerri
kjohnston@stonebridgepress.com, Circ. Mgr.,
The Winchendon Courier, MA, Winchendon

Peterson, Kerri .... (508) 909-4103
kjohnston@stonebridgepress.com, Circc. ,
Southbridge Evening News, MA, Southbridge

Peterson, Kerri .... (508) 909-4115
kjohnston@stonebridgepress.com, Circulation
Director, Blackstone Valley Tribune, MA,
Southbridge

Peterson, Kevin
kevin@wayneherald.com, Pub., The Wayne
Herald, NE, Wayne
kevin@wayneherald.com, Morning Shopper,
NE, Wayne

Peterson, Laure
chisago@citlink.net, Prodn. Mgr., Search

Shopper, MN, Lindstrom

Peterson, Lori
ccr@utma.com, Cir. Mgr., Cavalier County
Republican, ND, Langdon

Peterson, Mark
stareditor@stewiestar.com, Ed., Stewartville
Star, MN, Stewartville

Peterson, Michael .... (724) 465-5555 ext. 271
mepetersen@indianagazette.net, Editorial
Page Ed., The Indiana Gazette, PA, Indiana

Peterson, Norma
therald@ndsupernet.com, Pub., The Herald,
ND, New England

Peterson, Patricia
ppeterson@projectsinknowledge.com, Sr.
Vice Pres., Projects In Knowledge, Inc., NJ,
Livingston

Peterson, Patrick
ppeterson@petersonmarineinc.com, Prince
Georges Cmty. College, MD, Largo

Peterson, Patti Jo .... ext. 112
pattijo.peterson@lee.net, Ed., The Plattsmouth
Journal, NE, Plattsmouth

Peterson, Paul .... (641) 422-4304
peterpau@niacc.edu, North Iowa Area Cmty.
College, IA, Mason City

Peterson, Per .... (507) 537-1551 ext. 126
phpeterson@marshallindependent.com,
Ed., Independent Shopper's Review, MN,
Marshall

Peterson, Per .... (507) 537-1551 ext #126
phpeterson@marshallindependent.com, News
Ed., Independent, MN, Marshall
phpeterson@marshallindependent.com, Ed.,
Tracy Headlight-Herald, MN, Tracy

Peterson, Rick
rick@star-herald.com, Gen. Mgr., The Rock
County Star Herald, MN, Luverne
rick@star-herald.com, Gen. Mgr., Hills
Crescent, MN, Luverne

Peterson, Rick
rick@star-herald.com, Adv. Mgr., Luverne
Announcer, MN, Luverne

Peterson, Rick .... (507) 283-2333
rickr@star-herald.com, General manager, Hills
Crescent, MN, Luverne

Peterson, Robert
robert.peterson2@usda.gov, Vice Pres./
Treasurer, United States Postal Service, DC,
Washington

Peterson, Ron .... (712) 293-4250
ron.peterson@lee.net, Pub., Sioux City
Journal, IA, Sioux City

Peterson, Scott .... (262) 446-6630
scott.peterson@jmg.com, Chief Ed.,
Germantown NOW, WI, Waukesha
scott.peterson@jmg.com, Chief Ed.,
Brookfield-Elm Grove NOW, WI, Waukesha
scott.peterson@jmg.com, Chief Ed., Cudahy
NOW, WI, Waukesha
scott.peterson@jmg.com, Chief Ed., Fox Point
NOW, WI, Waukesha
scott.peterson@jmg.com, Chief Ed., Oak
Creek-Franklin-Greendale-Hales Corners
NOW, WI, Waukesha
scott.peterson@jmg.com, Chief Ed.,
Greenfield-West Allis NOW, WI, Waukesha
scott.peterson@jmg.com, Chief Ed., Mequon
NOW, WI, Waukesha
scott.peterson@jmg.com, Chief Ed., New
Berlin NOW, WI, Waukesha
scott.peterson@jmg.com, Chief Ed., Muskego-
New Berlin NOW, WI, Waukesha
scott.peterson@jmg.com, Chief Ed., Glendale
NOW, WI, Waukesha
scott.peterson@jmg.com, Chief Ed., West Allis
NOW, WI, Waukesha
scott.peterson@jmg.com, Chief Ed.,
Wauwatosa NOW, WI, Waukesha
scott.peterson@jmg.com, Chief Ed., St. Francis
NOW, WI, Waukesha
scott.peterson@jmg.com, Chief Ed., Bay View

NOW, WI, Waukesha
scott.peterson@jmg.com, Chief Ed., Elm Grove NOW, WI, Waukesha
scott.peterson@jmg.com, Chief Ed., South Milwaukee NOW, WI, Waukesha
scott.peterson@jmg.com, Chief Ed., Franklin NOW, WI, Waukesha
scott.peterson@jmg.com, Chief Ed., Hales Corners NOW, WI, Waukesha
scott.peterson@jmg.com, Chief Ed., Menomonee Falls-Germantown NOW, WI, Waukesha
scott.peterson@jmg.com, Ed., Oak Creek NOW, WI, Waukesha
scott.peterson@jmg.com, Chief Ed., North Shore NOW, WI, Waukesha

Peterson, Scott
speterson@jcpgroup.com, Ed. in Chief, Milwaukee Journal Sentinel, WI, Milwaukee

Peterson, Scott.........................ext. 123
speterson@jcpgroup.com, Mng. Ed., Kettle Moraine Index, WI, Hartland
speterson@jcpgroup.com, Mng. Ed., Lake Country Reporter, WI, Hartland
speterson@jcpgroup.com, Mng. Ed., Oconomowoc Focus, WI, Hartland
speterson@jcpgroup.com, Mng. Ed., Sussex Sun, WI, Hartland

Peterson, Scott
speterson@jcpgroup.com, Ed. in Chief., Mukwonago Publications, WI, Mukwonago

Peterson, Shari
sharip@ndna.com, Office Coord./Adv. Assist., North Dakota Newspaper Association, ND, Bismarck

Peterson, Sharon ....(618) 239-2478
speterson@bnd.com, Adv., Belleville News-Democrat, IL, Belleville

Peterson, Stephen ....(717) 240-7169
speterson@cumberlink.com, Cont., The Sentinel, PA, Carlisle

Peterson, Steve ....(479) 785-7748
speterson@swtimes.com, Feat. Ed., Times Record, AR, Fort Smith

Peterson, Susan ....(806) 742-3388
s.peterson@ttu.edu, Student Media Dir., Texas Tech University, TX, Lubbock

Peterson, Susan
sentinel@mymts.net , Ed., The Sentinel Courier, MB, Pilot Mound

Peterson, Todd ....(518) 454-5703
tpeterson@timesunion.com, Vice President Circulation, Times Union, NY, Albany

Peterson, Tom
tpeterson@medicinehatnews.com, Prod. Mgr., Medicine Hat News, AB, Medicine Hat

Peterson, Willie J. ....(906) 387-3282
munisingnews@jamadots.com, Pub., The Munising News, MI, Munising

Peterson, Willie J. ....(906) 387-3282
Adv. Mgr., Alger County Shopper, MI, Munising

Peterson Arnold, Mary
mary.arnold@sdstate.edu, Head, South Dakota State University, SD, Brookings

Peth, Leslee ....(941) 206-1000
lpeth@sun-herald.com, Ad Director/PGH, Sun Coast Media Group Inc, FL, Punta Gorda

Pethel, Tina
tina.pethel@gwinnettdailypost.com, Controller, Gwinnett Daily Post, GA, Lawrenceville

Petitjean, Heather ....(859) 624-6613
hpetitjean@richmondregister.com, Circ. Mgr., The Richmond Register, KY, Richmond

Petrak, Michael
mpetrak@gatehousemedia.com, VP of Sales and Digital Services, GateHouse Media, Inc., NY, Pittsford

Petrassi, Mary.........................(773) 358-3127
busmgrhp@hpherald.com, Bus. Mgr., Hyde Park Herald, IL, Chicago

Petretti, Ken
ken@kenpetretti.com, Producer, Ken Petretti Productions, LLC, NJ, Maywood

Petrich, Bernie ....(813) 259-8056
Tampa Bay Times, FL, St Petersburg

Petrich, Wade ....(218) 727-0419
wpetrich@hermantownstar.com, Pub., Hermantown Star, MN, Hermantown

Petrie, Bob ....(920) 453-5143
bpetrie@sheboygan.gannett.com, City Gov't, The Sheboygan Press, WI, Sheboygan

Petrie, Matt
mpetrie@journalnet.com, Adv. Dir., Portneuf Valley Trader, ID, Pocatello

Petrie, Teri ....(906) 293-8401
nbyads@jamadots.com, Adv. Mgr., The Newberry News, MI, Newberry

Petrik, Randall ....(630) 830-4145
staff@examinerpublications.com, Pres., Pub., Examiner Publications, Inc., IL, Bartlett
staff@examinerpublications.com, Pres, Pub, The Examiner of Campton Hills (OOB), IL, Bartlett
staff@examinerpublications.com, Pres./Pub., The Examiner of Carol Stream, IL, Bartlett
staff@examinerpublications.com, Pres, Pub, The Examiner of St. Charles (OOB), IL, Bartlett
staff@examinerpublications.com, Pres./Pub., The Examiner of Streamwood, IL, Bartlett
staff@examinerpublications.com, Pres./Pub., The Examiner of South Elgin, IL, Bartlett

Petrik, Randall ....(630) 830-4145
news@examinerpublications.com, Pres./Pub., The Examiner of Wayne, IL, Bartlett

Petrik, Randall ....(630) 830-4145
staff@examinerpublications.com, Pres, Pub., The Examiner of Hanover Park, IL, Bartlett

Petrik, Randall 1 (630) 830-4145
randy@examinerpublications.com, Examiner Publications, Inc., IL, Bartlett

Petrillo, Carlo ....(781) 433-8238
cpetrillo@wickedlocal.com, Adv. Sales Rep., The Walpole Times, MA, Walpole
cpetrillo@wickedlocal.com, Retail Adv. , The Dedham Transcript, MA, Needham

Petro, Matt
mpetro@news-press.com, VP Finance, The Commercial Appeal, TN, Memphis

Petro, Michael ....(716) 649-4040 ext 236
Sports Ed, The Sun and Erie County Independent, NY, Hamburg

Petroff, Karen
kspetroff@punxsutawneyspirit.com, Prodn. Supvr., Composing, Jefferson County Neighbors, PA, Punxsutawney
kspetroff@punxsutawneyspirit.com, Prodn. Supvr., Composing, The Punxsutawney Spirit, PA, Punxsutawney

Petroski, Jessica
JPetroski@tampatrib.com, Tampa Bay Times, FL, St Petersburg

Petroski, Morgan ....(505) 823-3991
mpetroski@abqjournal.com, Photo Ed., Albuquerque Journal, NM, Albuquerque

Petrovits, Nicholas ....(414) 277-7255
Milwaukee School of Engineering, WI, Milwaukee

Petroziello, Guy ....(215) 949-4162
gpetroziello@calkins.com, Editorial Ed., Bucks County Courier Times, PA, Levittown

Petruska, David ....(617) 262-0444 ext. 1
dpetruska@wicketlocal.com, Pub., Boston Homes, MA, Needham

Petshow, Joe
jpetshow@hoodrivernews.com, Pub., Hood River News, OR, Hood River

Pett, Joel ....(859) 231-3443
jpett@herald-leader.com, Cartoonist, Lexington Herald-Leader, KY, Lexington

Pettengil, Linda ....(650) 726-4424 x 319
linda@hmbreview.com, Adv. Mgr., Half Moon Bay Review, CA, Half Moon Bay

Pettengill, Carol
cpettengill@staffordgroup.com, Circ. Mgr., Buy Line, MI, Greenville

Pettengill, Carol
cpettengill@staffordgroup.com, Circ. Dir, The Daily News, MI, Greenville

Pettiford, Johnathan
l.burris@chathamstartribune.com, Account Exec., Star-Tribune, VA, Chatham

Pettiford, Jonathan ....(336) 694-4145
ads@caswellmessenger.com, Acc. Exec., Caswell Messenger, NC, Yanceyville

Pettigrew, Andy
posteditor@thependerpost.com, Ed., Pender-Topsail Post & Voice, NC, Burgaw

Pettigrew, Jane ....(732) 922-6000 ext. 2580
jpettigrew@app.com, VP/Circ., Asbury Park Press, NJ, Neptune

Pettit, Leann ....(610) 933-8926 ext. 627
lpettit@phoenixvillenews.com, Ed., The Phoenix Reporter & Item, PA, Pottstown

Pettus, Mark
mark.pettus@prioritynews.net, Pub., The Herald, FL, Havana

Pettus, Mary
mpettus@heraldonline.com, Adv. Dir., The Enquirer-Herald, SC, York
mpettus@heraldonline.com, Advertising Director, The Herald, SC, Rock Hill

Petty, Allison ....(217) 421-6986
apetty@herald-review.com, Managing Ed./Digital, Herald & Review, Decatur, IL, Decatur

Petty, Charlotte
pettyc@umsl.edu, Univ. of Missouri, MO, Saint Louis

Petty, David B. ....(318) 362-0345
dpetty@thenewsstar.com, Pres./Pub., The News-Star, LA, Monroe

Petty, Tonya
circulation@southwesttimes.com, Circ. Mgr., The Southwest Times (Pulaski, VA), VA, Pulaski

Petykiewicz, Sandra
sandra@citpat.com, Pub., The Zone, MI, Jackson

Peveto-Nelson, Suzanne
speveto@gatehousemedia.com, Rgl. Pub., Southwest Daily News, LA, Sulphur
speveto@gatehousemedia.com, Pub., Beauregard Daily News, LA, Deridder
speveto@gatehousemedia.com, Pub., Vinton News, LA, Sulphur
speveto@gatehousemedia.com, Pub., The Leesville Daily Leader, LA, Leesville

Pevonka, Dave
dpevonka@rivertowns.net, Circulation Director Production Director, River Falls Journal, WI, River Falls

Pexa, Kristi
kristi.pexa@ecm-inc.com, Adv. Mgr., The Laker, MN, Waconia
kristi.pexa@ecm-inc.com, Adv. Mgr., The Gold Miner, MN, Waconia
kristi.pexa@ecm-inc.com, Adv. Mgr., The Pioneer, MN, Waconia
kristi.pexa@ecm-inc.com, Adv. Mgr., The Waconia Patriot, MN, Waconia

Pexton, Patrick
ppexton@newspost.com, Ed., The Frederick News-Post, MD, Frederick

Peyrègne, Vincent
vincent.peyregne@wan-ifra.org, CEO, World Association of Newspapers and News Publishers (WAN-IFRA), Frankfurt

Peyrègne, Vincent
vincent.peyregne@wan-ifra.org, WAN-IFRA CEO, World Association of Newspapers and

News Publishers (WAN-IFRA), Frankfurt am Main

Pezzullo, Rick
rpezzullo@theexaminernews.com, Ed., The Northern Westchester Examiner, NY, Mount Kisco

Peña, Denny
denny.pena@eldiariony.com, Circ. Dir., El Diario La Prensa, NY, Brooklyn

Pfaffenberger, Denette ....(513) 768-8132
dpfaffen@enquirer.com, Group Dir/Home Delivery , The Cincinnati Enquirer, OH, Cincinnati

Pfeffer, Ray ....(605) 224-7301 x140
ray.pfeffer@capjournal.com, Productions Mgr., Capital Journal, SD, Pierre

Pfeifer, Brian ....(973) 392-4141
bpfeifer@starledger.com, National Advertising Manager, The Star-Ledger, NJ, Newark

Pfeifer, Lisa
sales@fakebrains.com, VP/Sales Dir., Fake Brains, Inc., CO, Littleton

Pfeiffer, Jeff. ....(440) 329-7215
jpfeiffer@chroniclet.com, Lorain County Printing & Publishing Co., OH, Elyria

Pfeiffer, Jeff. ....(440) 329-7216
jpfeiffer@chroniclet.com, Adv. Mgr. /N'tl Sales, Chronicle-Telegram, OH, Elyria

Pfeiffer, Phyllis.......................(858) 875-5940
ppfeiffer@lajollalight.com, Pub., Carmel Valley Leader (OOB), CA, Del Mar
ppfeiffer@lajollalight.com, Pub., Carmel Valley News, CA, Solana Beach
ppfeiffer@lajollalight.com, President and General Manager, Hoy San Diego - The San Diego Union Tribune, CA, San Diego
ppfeiffer@lajollalight.com, Pres. & Gen. Mgr., Vida Latina - The San Diego Union Tribune, CA, San Diego
ppfeiffer@lajollalight.com, VP, Adv., Poway News Chieftain, CA, Poway

Pfeiffer, Phyllis.......................(858) 875-5940
ppfeiffer@lajollalight.com, Pub., Del Mar Times, CA, Solana Beach
ppfeiffer@lajollalight.com, VP, Adv., Rancho Bernardo News-Journal, CA, Poway

Pfeiffer, Phyllis.......................(858) 875-5940
ppfeiffer@lajollalight.com, Pub., Solana Beach Sun, CA, Solana Beach

Pfeiffer, Phyllis.......................(858) 875-5940
ppfeiffer@lajollalight.com, President/Gen Mgr, La Jolla Light, CA, La Jolla
ppfeiffer@lajollalight.com, VP/Gen. Mgr., Rancho Santa Fe Review, CA, Solana Beach

Pfeiffer, Phyllis
ppfeiffer@lajollalight.com, Pub. Mgr, Santa Cruz Good Times, CA, Santa Cruz

Pfeiffer, Phyllis ....(858) 875-5940
ppfeiffer@lajollalight.com, Pub., San Diego Suburban News (OOB), CA, La Jolla
ppfeiffer@lajollalight.com, President and General Manager, Encinitas Advocate, CA, Solana Beach

Pfieffer, Dick
sales@wellmarkco.com , Pres., The Wellmark Company, OK, Oklahoma City

Pfister, Julie ....(308) 432-5511
julie.pfister@lee.net, Adv. Mgr., The Chadron Record, NE, Chadron

Pfund, Ross
nci@loretl.net, Pub., Norman County Index, MN, Ada

Phair, Kelvin ....(250) 642-5752
sales@sookenewsmirror.com, Advertising Sales, The Sooke News Mirror, BC, Sooke

Phaneuf, Andre
andre.phaneuf@quebecormedia.com, Dir., Research & Mktg., Le Journal de Montreal, QC, Montreal

Phaneuf, Wayne E. ....(413) 788-1315

wphaneuf@repub.com,, Exec. Ed., The Republican, MA, Springfield

Phares, Brett
brett.phares@marist.edu, Instr., Marist College, NY, Poughkeepsie

Phares, Doug .... (419) 502-2180
dougphares@sanduskynewspapers.com, President and COO, Sandusky Newspapers, Inc., SC, Hilton Head Island

Phares, Doug
dougphares@sanduskynewspapers.com, Foundation Pres., Inland Press Association, IL, Des Plaines

Phelan, Missy
classads@pagosasun.com, Class. Adv., The Pagosa Springs Sun, CO, Pagosa Springs

Phelan, Peter .... (207) 689-2826
pphelan@sunjournal.com, Mng. Ed., Night, Sun Journal, ME, Lewiston

Phelps, Candice .... (269) 651-5407
cphelps@sturgisjournal.com, Ed./Website Mgr., Sturgis Journal, MI, Sturgis

Phelps, Dale .... (253) 597-8681
dale.phelps@thenewstribune.com, Mng. Ed., The News Tribune, WA, Tacoma

Phelps, Dan .... (978) 970-4640
dphelps@Lowellsun.com, Columnist/Copy Ed., The Sun, MA, Lowell

Phelps, Joseph
phelps@apr.ua.edu, Prof./Phifer Prof., University of Alabama, AL, Tuscaloosa

Phelps, Louise .... (912) 220-2759
phelpscutler@aol.com, Managing Partner, Phelps, Cutler & Associates, GA, Savannah

Phelps, Louise D. .... (912) 220-2759
phelpscutler@aol.com, Pres., Phelps, Cutler & Associates, GA, Savannah

Phelps, Matt
editor@bothell-reporter.com, Reg. Ed., Bothell/Kenmore Reporter, WA, Kirkland

Phelps, Matt
editor@kirklandreporter.com, Reg Ed, Kirkland Reporter, WA, Kirkland

Phenicie, Jeff .... (910) 233-0200
jeff@adpakweekly.com, Partner, Ad Pak, NC, Wilmington

Philbin, Larry
lawrence.philbin@my.und.edu, News Editor, Univ. of North Dakota, ND, Grand Forks

Phillip, Sue
subscribe@trftimes.com, Circ. Mgr., Northern Watch, MN, Thief River Falls

Phillipi, Karen
kphillippi@jewishcanton.org, Ed., Stark Jewish News, OH, Canton

Phillips, Autumn .... (563) 383-2264
aphillips@qctimes.com, Ed., Quad-City Times, IA, Davenport
aphillips@qctimes.com, News Ed., New Braunfels Herald-Zeitung, TX, New Braunfels

Phillips, Barbara .... (940) 733-7418
archernews@yahoo.com, Pres./Ed./Adv. Dir., Archer County News, TX, Archer City

Phillips, Bruce .... (978) 970-4638
bphillips@lowellsun.com, Copy Ed., The Sun, MA, Lowell

Phillips, Carron .... (219) 214-4206
cphillips@thenewsdispatch.com, Asst. Sports Ed., News Dispatch, IN, Michigan City

Phillips, Chad
chad@pdclarion.com, Graphic Designer, Princeton Daily Clarion, IN, Princeton

Phillips, Cheryl .... (405) 382-1100
ads@seminoleproducer.com, Entertainment/Amusements Ed., The Seminole Producer, OK, Seminole

Phillips, Cody .... (405) 382-1100
news@seminoleproducer.com, Teen-Age/Youth Ed., The Seminole Producer, OK, Seminole

Phillips, Dale
dphillips@mihomepaper.com, Circ. Mgr, Swartz Creek View, MI, Davison
dphillips@mihomepaper.com, Circ. Mgr, Grand Blanc View, MI, Davison
dphillips@mihomepaper.com, Circ. Mgr, Flint Township View, MI, Davison
dphillips@mihomepaper.com, Circ. Mgr, Township View, MI, Chesaning
dphillips@mihomepaper.com, Circ. Mgr, LA View, MI, Lapeer
dphillips@mihomepaper.com, Circ. Mgr, The Brown City Banner, MI, Sandusky
dphillips@mihomepaper.com, Circ. Mgr, The Davison Index, MI, Davison
dphillips@mihomepaper.com, Circ. Mgr, Tri-County Citizen, MI, Sandusky

Phillips, Dan .... (208) 664-0220 ext. 5001
dphillips@cdapress.com, Circ. Dir., Coeur d'Alene Press, ID, Coeur D Alene

Phillips, Dave .... (507) 346-7365
dphillips@bluffcountrynews.com, Pres., Bluff Country Newspaper Group, MN, Spring Valley
dphillips@bluffcountrynews.com, Pub., Johnson County Plainsman (OOB), MO, Sedalia
dphillips@bluffcountrynews.com, Pub, The Concordian, MO, Concordia
dphillips@bluffcountrynews.com, Pub., The Marshall Democrat-News, MO, Marshall
dphillips@bluffcountrynews.com, Pres., Phillips Publishing, Inc., MN, Spring Valley
dphillips@bluffcountrynews.com, Ed., The Chatfield News, MN, Chatfield
dphillips@bluffcountrynews.com, Pub., Spring Grove Herald, MN, Spring Grove
dphillips@bluffcountrynews.com, Pub., Spring Valley Tribune, MN, Spring Valley

Phillips, David
dphillips@bluffcountrynews.com, Pub., Bluff Country Reader, MN, Spring Valley
dphillips@bluffcountrynews.com, Publisher, Mabel/Harmony News-Record, MN, Harmony

Phillips, David .... (507) 765-2752
dphillips@bluffcountrynews.com, Pub., Fillmore County News Leader, MN, Preston

Phillips, David .... (507) 346-7365
dphillips@bluffcountrynews.com, Publisher, Tri-County Record, MN, Rushford

Phillips, Dean .... ext. 5084
phillde@hobartbrothers.com, Welding Equip. Mgr., ITW Hobart Brothers Co., OH, Troy

Phillips, Deborah .... (802) 479-2582
dphillips@vt-world.com, Co-Pub./owner, The World, VT, Barre

Phillips, Dennis .... (979) 279-3411
dennis@robconews.com, Bus./Finance Ed., The Post-Journal, NY, Jamestown
dennis@robconews.com, Publisher, Franklin Advocate, TX, Hearne

Phillips, Dennis .... (979) 279-3411
dennis@robconews.com, Publisher, The Marlin Democrat, TX, Marlin

Phillips, Fred .... (318) 362-0256
fred.phillips@centurylink.com, Multimedia Ed., The News-Star, LA, Monroe

Phillips, James .... (205) 221-2840
james.phillips@mountaineagle.com, Ed./Pub., Daily Mountain Eagle, AL, Jasper

Phillips, Jason
mcnews@mtintouch.net, Ed., The Meagher County News, MT, White Sulphur Springs

Phillips, Jim .... (570) 348-9112
jphillips@timesshamrock.com, Circ. Dir., The Times-Tribune, PA, Scranton

Phillips, Judy
jphillips@lagrangenews.com, Bus./Office Mgr., La Grange Shopper, GA, Lagrange

Phillips, Kathleen

ka-phillips@tamu.edu, Exec. Sec./Treasurer, North American Agricultural Journalists, TX, Bryan

Phillips, Larissa
larissa.phillips@parenthood.com, Ed., New York Family, KS, Overland Park

Phillips, Lockwood .... (252) 726-7081
lockwood@thenewstimes.com, Pub., Carteret County News-Times, NC, Morehead City

Phillips, Mandy .... (757) 286-0594
writethefirsttime@live.com, Grundy County Herald, TN, Tracy City

Phillips, Mary
ads@pokyrd.com, Classified Mgr., Pocahontas Record-Democrat, IA, Pocahontas

Phillips, Mike .... (609) 276-2115
mphillips@slp.com, Dir. North American Sales, Southern Lithoplate, Inc., NC, Youngsville

Phillips, Robert
brphillips@civitasmedia.com, Adv. Sales Rep., The Tribune, NC, Elkin

Phillips, Ryan .... (205) 443-5625
rphillips@bizjournals.com, Digital Prod., Birmingham Business Journal, AL, Birmingham

Phillips, Samantha .... (570) 372-4298
crusader@susqu.edu, Adv. Mgr., Susquehanna Univ., PA, Selinsgrove

Phillips, Sandy
reapered@richfieldreaper.com, Ed., Richfield Reaper, UT, Richfield

Phillips, Sandy .... ext. 21
reapered@richfieldreaper.com, Ed., The Richfield Shopper, UT, Richfield

Phillips, Scott .... (229) 924-2751 ext 1527
Scott.phillips@gaflnews.com, Sports Ed., Americus Times-Recorder, GA, Americus

Phillips, Stu
konawaleader@sbcglobal.net, Pub., Konawa Leader, OK, Konawa

Phillips, Stu
stu@seminoleoklahoma.com, Pub., Wewoka Times, OK, Wewoka
stu@seminoleoklahoma.com, Ed. / Pub. , The Seminole Producer, OK, Seminole

Phillips, Taylor .... (209) 634-9141 ext. 2013
tphillips@turlockjournal.com, Adv. Mgr., Turlock Journal, CA, Turlock
tphillips@turlockjournal.com, Sales Mgr., The Journal Shopping News, CA, Turlock

Phillips, Teak
slreview@stlouisreview.com, Ed., St. Louis Review, MO, Saint Louis

Phillips, Teresa .... (979) 279-3411
teresa@robconews.com, Adv. Dir., Robertson County News, TX, Hearne

Phillips, Thomas J.
pananews@consolidated.net, Pub., Pana News-Palladium, IL, Pana

Phillips, Walter
walter@thenewstimes.com, Pub., Tideland News, NC, Swansboro

Phillips, Walter D.
newstimes@aol.com, Ed., Carteret County News-Times, NC, Morehead City

Phillips, Ward .... (931) 296-2426
Wardphillips@bellsouth.net, Pub., The News-Democrat, TN, Waverly

Phillpp, Sue
subscribe@trftimes.com, Circ. Mgr., Thief River Falls Times, MN, Thief River Falls

Philpott, Tom .... (703) 830-6863
tomphilpott@militaryupdate.com, Self-Syndicator, Military Update, Centreville

Philpott-Sanders, Shannon
ssanders147@stlcc.edu, St. Louis Cmty. College Meramec, MO, Kirkwood

Phinney, Barbara .... (401) 334-9555 ext. 128
accounting@valleybreeze.com, Accounting/HR, The North Providence Breeze, RI, Lincoln
accounting@valleybreeze.com, Acounting/HR, The Valley Breeze - Woonsocket/North Smithfield, RI, Lincoln
accounting@valleybreeze.com, Accounting/HR, The Valley Breeze - Pawtucket, RI, Lincoln
accounting@valleybreeze.com, Accounting/HR, The Valley Breeze & Observer, RI, Lincoln

Phyrillas, Tony .... (610) 323-3000
tphyrillas@pottsmerc.com, ity Editor/Opinion Page Editor/Columnist/Blogger, The Mercury, PA, Pottstown

Piatt, Rich .... (603) 279-4516 ext. 125
publisher@salmonpress.com, Pub., Salmon Press, NH, Meredith

Picard, Cindy .... (228) 435-0720
publisher@biloxi-diberville-press.com, Pub., Biloxi-D'Iberville Press, MS, Biloxi

Picard, Jean-Pierre .... (306) 347-0481
direction@myaccess.ca, Publisher, Eau Vive (l'), SK, Regina

Piccone, Filippo
filippo.piccone@archden.org, Prodn. Mgr., El Pueblo Catolico, CO, Denver

Piche, Mylene .... ext. 251
mpiche@stanstead-journal.com, Prodn. Mgr., The Stanstead Journal, QC, Stanstead

Picht, Randy
rpicht@ap.org, Bureau Chief, Kansas Associated Press Managing Editors Association, MO, Kansas City
rpicht@ap.org, Bureau Chief, Missouri Associated Press Managing Editors, MO, Kansas City

Pickard, John E. .... (210) 658-0614
techenergy@techenergy.com, Pres., Tech-Energy Co., TX, Cibolo

Pickens, Jim .... (270) 691-7314
jpickens@messenger-inquirer.com, Sports Ed., Messenger-Inquirer, KY, Owensboro

Pickens, Kristen .... (419) 523-5709 ext. 1225
kpickens@putnamsentinel.com, Adv. Mgr., The Ada Herald, OH, Ada

Pickering, Mark .... (309) 820-3252
mpickering@pantagraph.com, Ed., Woodford County Journal Roanoke-Minonk Edition, IL, Roanoke

Pickering, Mark .... (309) 820-3252
mpickering@pantagraph.com, Ed., The Pantagraph, IL, Bloomington

Pickering, Scott
spickering@eastbaynewspapers.com, Mng. Ed., Westport Shorelines, RI, Bristol

Pickering, Scott .... (401) 253-6000 ext. 115
spickering@eastbaynewspapers.com, Mng. Ed., East Bay Newspapers, RI, Bristol

Pickering, Scott
spickering@eastbaynewspapers.com, Mng. Ed., Warren Times-Gazette, RI, Bristol

Pickett, Britt .... (251) 219-5003
bpickett@press-register.com, Adv. Mgr., Classified, Press-Register, AL, Mobile

Pickett, James
jpickett@flagler.edu, Asst. Prof., Flagler College, FL, Saint Augustine

Pickett, Scott
scotp@vertical.com, CTO, Vertical Communications, Inc., AZ, Phoenix

Pico, Kelli .... (209) 722-1812 ext. 506
kellis@pspub.com, Controller, Pacific Sierra Publishing, Inc., CA, Merced

Picone, Iris
ipicone@antonnews.com, Adv. Mgr., Glen Cove Record-Pilot, NY, Mineola

Piecowye, James
james.piecowye@zu.ac.ae, Assoc. Prof., Zayed University, Al Ruwayyah

Piecuch, Suzanne .... (207) 689-2804
spiecuch@theforecaster.net, Production Mgr., The Forecaster, ME, Falmouth

Piehl, Saran .... (262) 367-5303 ext. 12
saran@50plusnewsmag.com, Adv. Mgr., 50 Plus, WI, Hartland

Piel, Jock .... (209) 754-3733
jock@calaverasenterprise.com, Adv. Mgr., Calaveras Enterprise, CA, San Andreas

Piemonte, Gabriel .... (773) 358-3140
g.piemo@hpherald.com, Ed., Hyde Park Herald, IL, Chicago

Pieper, Laura
lpieper@theperrychief.com, Managing Editor, Chiefland Shopper, IA, Perry

Pierce, Bill .... (416) 947-2270
bill.pierce@sunmedia.ca, Sports Ed., The Toronto Sun, ON, Toronto

Pierce, Carol .... (703) 237-9802
carol@nna.org, Executive Director, National Federation of Press Women, VA, Falls Church
carol@nna.org, Managing Dir., National Newspaper Association, IL, Springfield

Pierce, Carol .... (937) 538-4656
cpierce@civitasmedia.com, Exec. Dir., American Court & Commercial Newspapers, Inc., MI, Pontiac
cpierce@civitasmedia.com, Med. Sales Cons., The Sidney Daily News, OH, Sidney

Pierce, Christina .... (318) 487-6409
Christina.pierce@thetowntalk.com, Gen. Mgr./ Adv. Dir., The Town Talk, LA, Alexandria

Pierce, Christina .... (337) 321-6747
christina.pierce@daily-iberian.com, Pub., The Daily Iberian, LA, New Iberia

Pierce, Christy
cpierce@darnews.com, Advertising Director, Daily American Republic, MO, Poplar Bluff

Pierce, Clark
jaxairnews@comcast.net, Ed., Jax Air News, FL, Jacksonville

Pierce, Ed .... (207) 282-1535 ext. 326
Editor@journaltribune.com, Executive Editor , Journal-Tribune, ME, Biddeford

Pierce, Jackie .... (867) 668-2063
jackie@whitehorsestar.com, Pub., Whitehorse Star, YT, Whitehorse

Pierce, Jerry
pierce@nsula.edu, Asst. Prof., Northwestern State University of Louisiana, LA, Natchitoches

Pierce, Joni .... (867) 667-4774
circulation@whitehorsestar.com, Circulation Assistant, Whitehorse Star, YT, Whitehorse

Pierce, Kelly
kpierce@newsexaminer.com, Gen. Mgr., Shopper Stopper, IN, Connersville

Pierce, Michael G. .... (440) 544-2607
mike.pierce@theaustin.com, Sr. Vice Pres., Sales/Mktg. Gen. Mgr., The Austin Company, OH, Cleveland

Pierce, Michele .... (867) 668-2060
advertising@whitehorsestar.com, Adv./Sales Mgr., Whitehorse Star, YT, Whitehorse

Pierce, Randi
randi@pagosasun.com, Asst. Ed., The Pagosa Springs Sun, CO, Pagosa Springs

Pierce, Robert
rpierce@johnsoncitypress.com, Religion Ed., Johnson City Press, TN, Johnson City

Pierce, Sean
sean.pierce@freshfields.com, Mktg./Promos. Dir., The Village Voice, NY, New York

Pierce, Shari

shari@pagosasun.com, Adv. Mgr., The Pagosa Springs Sun, CO, Pagosa Springs

Pierce, Tracy Davis .... (802) 525-3531
tracy@bartonchronicle.com, Pub., The Chronicle, VT, Barton

Pierik, Dave .... (360) 426-4412
dave@masoncounty.com, Adv. Mgr., Shelton-Mason County Journal, WA, Shelton

Pieronek, Cathy .... (574) 631-4385
Univ. of Notre Dame Engineering School, IN, Notre Dame

Pierquet, Chelly .... (920) 468-5477
cmp@advancesystems.com, Office Mgr., Advance Systems, Inc., WI, Green Bay

Piersol, Dick
dpiersol@journalstar.com, Bus. Editor, Lincoln Journal Star, NE, Lincoln

Pierzga, Kasia
news@whidbeyexaminer.com, Ed./Pub., The Whidbey Examiner, WA, Coupeville

Pieters Mayfield, Nancy
nmayfield@smwc.edu, Chair, Saint Mary-of-the-Woods College, IN, Saint Mary-of-the-Woods

Pietrafesa, Nora .... (845) 437-4758
join@poughkee.gannett.com, HR partner, Poughkeepsie Journal, NY, Poughkeepsie

Pietraszewski, Jason
jason.p@ecm-inc.com, Rgl Adv. Dir., Blaine-Spring Lake Park Life, MN, Coon Rapids

Pietrowicz, Peggy
ppietrowicz@uniondemocrat.com, Adv. Mgr., The Union Democrat, CA, Sonora

Pietsch, Eric
editor@thetimesstar.ca, Ed., Geraldton-longlac Times Star, ON, Geraldton

Pigden, Richard 873-3671
photosynd@ft.com, Picture Synd., Financial Times, London

Pignolet, Don .... (215) 625-8501 ext 200
don@epgn.com, Officer Manager, Philadelphia Gay News, PA, Philadelphia

Pike, Daniel .... (270) 678-5171 Ext. 234
dpike@glasgowdailytimes.com, Gen. Mgr., Glasgow Daily Times, KY, Glasgow
dpike@glasgowdailytimes.com, City Ed., Daily News, KY, Bowling Green

Pike, Doug .... (720) 648-5022
towntalk@coloradohometown.com, Mng. Ed., Colorado Hometown Weekly, CO, Boulder

Pike, Mary .... (270) 678-5171 Ext. 242
mpike@glasgowdailytimes.com, Circ. Dir., Glasgow Daily Times, KY, Glasgow

Pike, Megan
mpike@yrmg.com, Circ. Mgr., The Newmarket Era-banner, ON, Newmarket

Pike, Tracie .... (770) 205-8986
tpike@forsythnews.com, Production Mgr., Forsyth County News, GA, Cumming

Pikelny, Phil
ppikelny@dispatch.com, Vice Pres./New Media, The Columbus Dispatch, OH, Columbus

Pilcher, Craig .... (219) 696-7711
Prodn. Mgr., Lowell Tribune, IN, Lowell

Pilcher, Gary A. .... (219) 696-7711
Adv. Mgr., Lowell Tribune, IN, Lowell

Pilcher, Gary A. .... (219) 696-7711
Adv. Mgr., Cedar Lake Journal, IN, Lowell

Pilcher, Mary Jeanette
pilcherpubco@comcast.net, Pub., Cedar Lake Journal, IN, Lowell

Pilcher, Matt
mattpilcher@pilcherpublishing.com, Prodn. Mgr., Cedar Lake Journal, IN, Lowell

Pilcher, Matt
mattpilcher@pilcherpublishing.com, Pub.,

Lowell Tribune, IN, Lowell

Pilger, Ronald .... ext. 109
rpilger@cable-lynx.net, Associate Publisher / Sales Manager, The Camrose Booster, AB, Camrose

Pilkey , Jerry
jerry.pilkey@sunmedia.ca, Adv. Mgr., Retail, The London Free Press, ON, London

Pilkington, Tony .... (254) 559-5412
editor@breckenridgeamerican.com, Managing Editor, Breckenridge American, TX, Breckenridge

Piller, Cindy .... (303) 776-2244 ext. 338
cpiller@times-call.com, NIE Coord., Longmont Times-Call, CO, Longmont

Pilolla, Ed .... (310) 904-6037
ed.pilolla@pvnews.com, Ed.in Chief, Palos Verdes Peninsula News, CA, Rolling Hills Estates

Pilon, Nicole .... (613) 632-4155
nicole.pilon@eap.on.ca, sales secretary, national, display, Tribune Express, ON, Hawkesbury

Pilon, Sherry
postreview2@sasktel.ca, Mgr., Hudson Bay Post-review, SK, Hudson Bay

Pilotte, Josee .... (450) 227-7999
mjgladu@journalacces.ca, Journal Acces, QC, Piedmont

Piltz, Ken
kpiltz@gcnews.com, Adv. Dir., Jericho News Journal, NY, Garden City
kpiltz@gcnews.com, Adv. Sales, Garden City News, NY, Garden City
kpiltz@gcnews.com, Adv. Mgr., Hicksville Mid-Island Times, NY, Garden City

Pinarski, Bob .... (724) 439-7500
Pub., Herald-Standard, PA, Uniontown

Pincoee, Doug
anews@onlink.net, Sales Mgr., Omega Forester, ON, Burks Falls

Pindel, Angela .... (847) 427-4627
apindel@dailyherald.com, Exec Asst to Exec VP/Vice Chairman, Daily Herald, IL, Arlington Heights

Pinder, Herb
hpinder@thejournalnews.com, Editorial Page Ed., The Journal News, NY, White Plains

Pinder, Susan .... (352) 867-4060
susan.pinder@gvillesun.com, Advertising Director, Ocala Star-Banner, FL, Ocala

Pine, Frank .... (909) 483-9360
frank.pine@langnews.com , Exec. Ed., Los Angeles Daily News, CA, Woodland Hills

Pine, Frank .... (909) 483-9360
fpine@scng.com, SVP & Exec Ed, Southern California News Group, CA, Woodland Hills

Pine, Frank
fpine@scng.com, The Highlander - Rowland Heights Edition, CA, Monrovia

Pine, Frank
fpine@ocregister.com, Exec. Ed., The Orange County Register, CA, Santa Ana

Pine, Frank .... (909) 483-9360
fpine@scng.com, Executive Editor, The Facts (Redlands), CA, Redlands

Pine, Frank .... (909) 386-3841
frank.pine@inlandnewspapers.com, Exec. Ed., The Sun, CA, San Bernardino

Pine, Frank .... (909) 483-9360
fpine@scng.com, Exec. Ed., Press-Telegram, CA, Long Beach

Pine, Frank .... (909) 483-9360
fpine@scng.com , Exec. Ed., Inland Valley Daily Bulletin, CA, Rancho Cucamonga
fpine@scng.com , Ex. Ed., Santa Ana Register (OOB), CA, Santa Ana
fpine@scng.com , Exec. Ed., Anaheim Bulletin,

CA, Santa Ana
fpine@scng.com , Pasadena Star-News, CA, Torrance

Pine, Frank .... (909) 483-9360
frank.pine@langnews.com, Exec. Ed., Daily Breeze, CA, Torrance

Pinel, Yannick .... (514) 899-5888
bradettes@transcontinental.ca, Guide De Montreal-nord, QC, Montreal
bradettes@transcontinental.ca, Informateur De Riviere Des Prairies, QC, Montreal
bradettes@transcontinental.ca, Progres Saint-leonard, QC, Saint Leonard

Pinel, Yannick
web@journalmetro.com, Ed., Saint-laurent News, QC, Saint Laurent

Ping, Paul .... (618) 667-3111
timestribune@whisperhome.com, Adv. Mgr., Troy Times-Tribune, IL, Troy

Pingleton, Montica
mpingleton@bannergraphic.com, Marketing Consultant, Banner-Graphic, IN, Greencastle

Pingree, Suzanne
spingree@wisc.edu, Prof., University of Wisconsin-Madison, WI, Madison

Pinkerton, Christy .... (907) 352-2251
Circ. Mgr., Frontiersman, AK, Wasilla

Pinkleton, Bruce
pink@wsu.edu, Prof./Head, PR seq., Washington State University, WA, Pullman

Pinkowski, Scott
ads@theshoppersweekly.com, Prodn. Mgr., The Shoppers Weekly Papers, IL, Centralia

Pinnell, Ivan
ipinnell@wvu.edu, Assoc. Prof., West Virginia University, WV, Morgantown

Pinner, Karla
karla.pinner@lee.net, Pub., Thrifty Nickel, IA, Davenport
karla.pinner@lee.net, Pub., Muscatine Journal, IA, Muscatine

Pinnock, Geoff .... (509) 459-5592
geoffp@spokesman.com, Senior Editor, The Spokesman-Review, WA, Spokane

Pino, Abigail
abigail.pino@enmu.edu, Advisor, Eastern New Mexico Univ., NM, Portales

Pinon, Michelle
lamontnews@gmail.com, Ed., The Lamont Leader, AB, Lamont

Pinsky, Stephen
seniortimes@insight.rr.com, Pub., Senior Times, OH, New Albany

Pinson, Mark
mpinson@highlandstoday.com, Highlands News-Sun, FL, Sebring

Pinson, Matt .... (304) 654-0087
Pub./Owner, HuntingtonNews.net, WV, Huntington

Pinto, Juliet
juliet.gill@fiu.edu, Florida International University, FL, North Miami

Pintor, Juan
jpintor@ark-group.com, Wilbur Wright College, IL, Chicago

Piper, Chad
jtaylor1@caprock-spur.com, Mng. Ed., Paducah Post, TX, Paducah

Piper, Morley .... (978) 338-2555
mlpiper52@comcast.net, Exec. Dir., Newspaper Association Managers, Inc., MA, Beverly
mlpiper52@comcast.net, Exec. Dir., Newspaper Association Managers, Inc., MA, Essex

Piper, Morley L.
mlp@nenews.org, Exec. Dir., New England Newspaper Association, Inc., MA, Salem

Piper, Winnie ....ext. 119
wpiper@robdailynews.com, Adv. Mgr., Daily
News, IL, Robinson
wpiper@robdailynews.com, Nat'l Adv. Mgr.,
The Robinson Constitution, IL, Robinson

Pirtle, Kay
wsn@mesh.net, Editor, Wedgwood Shopping
News, TX, Fort Worth

Pisarik, Kris ....(978) 970-4637
kpisarik@lowellsun.com, Asst. Mng. Ed., Local
News, The Sun, MA, Lowell

Pisarik, Kris ....(978) 970-4637
kpisarik@lowellsun.com , Mng. Ed., The
Dispatch News, MA, Lowell

Pisarski, Dorothy
dorothy.pisarski@drake.edu, Asst. Prof., Drake
University, IA, Des Moines

Pisch, Tina
ads@squamishchief.com, Mktg. Coord.,
Squamish Chief, BC, Squamish

Piscia, Jason ....(217) 788-1525
jason.piscia@sj-r.com, Digital Mang. Ed.
, The State Journal-Register, IL, Springfield

Pistella, Michael ....(239) 574-1110
mpistella@breezenewspapers.com, Photo
Dept. Mgr., Cape Coral Breeze, FL, Cape
Coral

Pitcher, Michelle .... (510) 548-8300 ext 410
editor@dailycal.org, EIC and Pres, Univ. of
California, Berkeley, CA, Berkeley

Pitchford, Robert Burns
ctimes@nctc.com, Pub., The Citizen-Times,
KY, Scottsville

Pitlo, Stan
pitlo@alaska.net, Pub., Southeastern
Newspapers, Inc., AK, Kenai

Pitluck, Steven
office@ponyexpress.net, CEO, Brown
Mannschreck Business System, MO, Saint
Joseph

Pitman, Scott .... (404) 419 - 2890
spitman@alm.com, Systems Director, Fulton
County Daily Report, GA, Atlanta

Pitocchelli, Steve
spitocchelli@eastbaynewspapers.com,
Classified Mgr., Bristol Phoenix, RI, Bristol
spitocchelli@eastbaynewspapers.com,
Classified Mgr., Sakonnet Times, RI, Bristol
spitocchelli@eastbaynewspapers.com,
Classified Mgr., Barrington Times, RI, Bristol

Pitre, Mario
mario.pitre@monteregieweb.com, Ed., Le
Soleil Du St-laurent, QC, Salaberry-de-
Valleyfield

Pitre, Raymond
raymond.pitre@lenouvelliste.qc.ca, Prodn.
Mgr., Le Nouvelliste, QC, Trois-Rivieres

Pitt, Elaine
elpitt@wschronicle.com, Gen. Mgr., The
Chronicle, NC, Winston Salem

Pitt, Ernest H. ....(336) 723-8428
news@wschronicle.com, Co-Founder/Pub.,
The Chronicle, NC, Winston Salem

Pitt, Joe ....(509) 663-5161
pitt@wenatcheeworld.com, The Wenatchee
World, WA, Wenatchee

Pitt, Joe ....(509) 664-7143
pitt@wenatcheeworld.com, Pub., Douglas
County Empire Press, WA, East Wenatchee

Pitt , Elaine .... (336) 722-8624 Ext 103
elpitt@wschronicle.com, Bus. Mgr. , The
Chronicle, NC, Winston Salem

Pittari, Jeremy
jeremy.pittari@picayuneitem.com, Assoc. Pub./
Ed. , Picayune Item, MS, Picayune

Pittman, Angie
angie@phpublishingllc.com, Dir. of Marketing &
Adv., DeSoto Times-Tribune, MS, Hernando

Pittman, Chris
cpittman@annistonstar.com, Social Media
Consultant, Consolidated Publishing Co.,
AL, Anniston
cpittman@annistonstar.com, Online Dir, The
Anniston Star, AL, Anniston

Pittman, Colleen
cpittman@lcimedia.com, Vice Pres., Finance,
Landmark Communications, Inc., VA, Norfolk

Pittman, Daniel ....(336) 888-3651
dpittman@hpe.com, Circ. Dir., High Point
Enterprise, NC, High Point

Pittman, Erin ....(315) 792-5103
epittman@uticaod.com, Ad. Dir, Your Valley,
NY, Utica

Pittman, Erin ....(315) 792-5103
epittman@uticaod.com, Adv. Dir., The
Observer-Dispatch, NY, Utica

Pittman, Garth
pittman@sou.edu, Chair, Southern Oregon
University, OR, Ashland

Pittman, Jim ....(503) 842-7116
shopper1@gorge.net, Pub., Tillamook County
Shopper Llc, OR, Tillamook

Pittman, John S. ....(864) 298-4165
jpittman@greenvillenews.com, Exec. Ed.,
Tribune-Times, SC, Greenville

Pittman, Ronald ....(740) 593-2612
Assoc. Prof., Ohio University, OH, Athens

Pitts, Ashley .... (419) 668-3771 Ext. 231
ashleypitts@norwalkreflector.com, Adv. Traffic
Coor., Norwalk Reflector, OH, Norwalk

Pitts, Gary ....(916) 321-1418
gpitts@sacbee.com, New Business &
Operations Manager , The Sacramento Bee,
CA, Sacramento

Pitts, Jessica ....(321) 283-5266
jpitts@intersectmediasolutions.com, Media
Mgr., Intersect Media Solutions, FL, Lake
Mary

Pitts, Kevin
kpitts@bizjournals.com, Pres/Pub, Charlotte
Business Journal, NC, Charlotte

Pitts, Mac ....(404) 894-7732
Georgia Inst. of Technology, GA, Atlanta

Place, Missy
mplace@benningtonbanner.com, Adv. Sales
Coord., Bennington Banner, VT, Bennington

Place, Rich
rplacesp@gmail.com, Gen Mgr./Mng. Ed., The
Salamanca Press, NY, Salamanca

Plachy, Jenelle
jp@nebpress.com, Office Mgr., Nebraska
Press Association/Nebraska Press
Advertising Service, NE, Lincoln

Plageman, Mary ....(614) 461-5500
mplageman@dispatch.com, Managing Ed.
/ Features, The Columbus Dispatch, OH,
Columbus

Plagens, Sheila
coloradorecord@yahoo.com, Pub., Colorado
City Record, TX, Colorado City

Plagg, Kala
office@guthrienewsleader.net, Office Mgr,
Guthrie News Leader, OK, Guthrie

Plaisance, Patrick
patrick.plaisance@colostate.edu, Assoc. Prof.,
Colorado State University, CO, Fort Collins

Plaisance, Susan ....(802) 733-8827
splaisance@manchesterjournal.com, Adv.
Sales Mgr., Manchester Journal, VT,
Manchester Center
splaisance@manchesterjournal.com, Adv.
Sales Mgr., Bennington Banner, VT,
Bennington

Planakis, Beth ....(561) 630-2400
bplanakis@bankrate.com, Mktg. Dir., Bankrate.
com, North Palm Beach

Plank, Nancy
nplank@sachem.ca, Adv. Mgr., The Grand
River Sachem, ON, Caledonia

Plantz, Kyle
editor@dailyfreepress.com, Ed., Boston Univ.,
MA, Boston

Plath, Debra ....(319) 335-5786
Univ. of Iowa, IA, Iowa City

Platt, Eric ....(517) 750-1200
Spring Arbor Univ., MI, Spring Arbor

Platt, Eric
eplatt@kbfgeneral.com, New York Univ., NY,
New York

Plaxton, Charity
cplaxton@mlive.com, VP of Sales, The
Saginaw News, MI, Saginaw

Plaxton, Charity
cplaxton@mlive.com, Adv. Vice Pres., Greater
Detroit Ads, MI, Pontiac

Plaxton, Charity
charity.plaxton@mlivemediagroup.com, Chief
Revenue Officer, The Grand Rapids Press,
MI, Grand Rapids

Plemmons, Mark
mplemmons@independenttribune.com, Ed.,
Independent Tribune, NC, Concord

Plenke, Mark ....(952) 358-8716
mark.plenke@normandale.edu, Advisor,
Normandale Community College, MN,
Bloomington

Pless, Diane
dpless@windstream.net, Ed., The Ocilla Star,
GA, Ocilla

Pletcher, James .... Bus. Ed.
Herald-Standard, PA, Uniontown

Pletsch, Karen
kpletsch@shawmedia.com, Pub., Daily
Chronicle, IL, Dekalb

Pletsch, Karen
kpletsch@shawmedia.com, Advertising
Director, The Midweek, IL, Dekalb

Plett, Rowena
rowena@marionrecord.com, Reporter, Marion
County Record, KS, Marion

Pleus, Doug ....(727) 815-1032
dpleus@suncoastnews.com, Ad. Sales
Manager, The Suncoast News, FL, New Port
Richey

Pleus, Doug
DPleus@tampatrib.com, Tampa Bay Times, FL,
St Petersburg

Plewka, Dana
dplewka@denverpost.com, The Denver Post,
CO, Denver

Plocha, Matt ....(321) 402-0407
mplocha@osceolanewsgazette.com, Pub. Mgr.
Osceola News-Gazette, FL, Kissimmee

Plocha, Matt ....(407) 846-7600
mplocha@osceolanewsgazette.com, Publisher,
Osceola News-gazette, FL, Kissimmee

Ploessl, Adam
rjads@centurytel.net, Adv. Mgr., Republican
Journal, WI, Darlington

Ploner, Mike
mike@camrosebooster.com, Sales Rep., The
Camrose Booster, AB, Camrose

Plooster, Matthew ....(208) 239-3140
ploomatt@isu.edu, Circ. Mgr., Newspapers
in Educ./Sales, Idaho State Journal, ID,
Pocatello

Plothow, Roger ....(208) 500-1800
rplothow@postregister.com, Pub./Ed., Post
Register, ID, Idaho Falls

Plotkin, Jay
jplotkin@ltview.com, Pub., Lake Travis View,
TX, Austin

Plotkin, Paul H.

stichtco@aol.com, Pres., Herman H. Sticht Co.,
Inc., NY, Brooklyn

Ploudre, Kurt ....(480) 248-4198
keploudre@aol.com, Sound Publishing, Inc.,
WA, Poulsbo

Pluim, Dale H.
pluimpub@orangecitycomm.net, Pub., Sioux
County Capital-Democrat, IA, Orange City

Plum, Sara
lamerican@polarcomm.com, Ed., Lakota
American, ND, Lakota

Plum, Sara J.
farmerspress@gondtc.com, Ed., Benson
County Farmers Press, ND, Minnewaukan

Plum, Sara J.
farmerspress@gondtc.com, Past President,
North Dakota Newspaper Association, ND,
Bismarck

Plumb, Stacia ....(508) 862-1224
splumb@capecodonline.com, Mgr., HR, Cape
Cod Times, MA, Hyannis
splumb@capecodonline.com, HR, The
Standard-Times, MA, New Bedford

Plumley, Monique ....(864) 599-4124
mplumlwy@lg.com, Contact, Ch2MHill
Lockwood Greene, CO, Englewood

Plummer, Eric ....(780) 865-3115
eric.plummer@sunmedia.ca, Ed., The Hinton
Parklander, AB, Hinton

Plummer, Erin
mnews@salmonpress.com, Ed. , Meredith
News, NH, Meredith

Plummer, Mike
mplummer@thepaperofwabash.com, Prodn.
Mgr., The Paper, IN, Wabash

Plumridge, Linda
lplumridge@fortfrances.com, Office Mgr., Fort
Frances Times, ON, Fort Frances

Plunkett, Chuck ....(303) 954-2567
cplunkett@denverpost.com, Editorial Ed., The
Denver Post, CO, Denver

Plutchak, Dan
dplutchak@communityshoppers.com, Ed.,
Walworth County Sunday, WI, Elkhorn

Plutt, J.P. ....(406) 988-7986
editor@dillontribune.com, Managing Ed., Dillon
Tribune, MT, Dillon

Pluymert, Katie
horizon@westmont.edu, Editor-in-Chief, Randy
VanderMey, CA, Santa Barbara

Podgorniak, Jane
anchor@northwoodanchor.net, Publisher, Nora
Springs Rockford Register, IA, Northwood
anchor@northwoodanchor.net, Northwood
Anchor, IA, Northwood
anchor@northwoodanchor.net, Pub., Manly
Junction Signal, IA, Northwood

Podro, Robert
info@ipcb.co.uk, Sr. Partner/Gen. Mgr.,
International Press Cutting Bureau, ENG,
London

Poe, Dani
dani@northsidesun.com, Circ. Mgr., Northside
Sun, MS, Jackson

Poehlman, Jamie
jpoehlman@thespec.com, Dir., HR, The
Hamilton Spectator, ON, Hamilton

Poertner, Andrew
editor@roswell-record.com, Ed., Roswell Daily
Record, NM, Roswell

Pogemiller, Doug
austin@bizjournals.com, Adv. Dir., Austin
Business Journal, TX, Austin

Pogoda, Dianne
dianne_pogoda@fairchildfashion.com, Mng.
Ed., Special Reports, Women's Wear Daily,
NY, New York

Pogorzelski, Craig ....(915) 546-6452

cpogorzelski@elpasotimes.com, Circ. Mgr., City Home Delivery, El Paso y Mas, TX, El Paso

Pogue, George
gp@press-info.com, Pub., The Southwest City Republic, MO, Pineville
gp@press-info.com, Pub., McDonald County News-Gazette, MO, Pineville
gp@press-info.com, Pub., The Goodman News-Dispatch, MO, Pineville
gp@press-info.com, Pub., McDonald County Press, MO, Pineville
gp@press-info.com, Pub., The Anderson Graphic, MO, Pineville

Pohly, George .... (586) 783-0270
george.pohly@dailytribune.com, Sports Ed., The Daily Tribune, MI, Clinton Township

Pohly, George
george.pohly@macombdaily.com, Sports Ed., The Macomb Daily, MI, Clinton Township

Poindexter, Kim .... (918) 456-8833
kpoindexter@cnhi.com, Exec. Ed., Tahlequah Daily Press, OK, Tahlequah

Point, Flora
fpoint@sunherald.com, CFO, The Sun Herald, MS, Gulfport

Pointer, Misty .... (256) 463-2872
mpointer@cleburnenews.com, Adv. Mgr., The Cleburne News, AL, Heflin

Poirier, Denis .... (905) 790-3229
info@lemetropolitain.com, Ed, Action (l'), ON, London
info@lemetropolitain.com, Ed, Action London Sarnia, ON, Brampton
info@lemetropolitain.com, Ed. , Metropolitain (le), ON, Brampton

Poirier, Dennis
rempart@netcore.ca, Pub., Le Rempart, ON, Windsor

Poirier, JP .... (337) 321-6759
jp.poirier@daily-iberian.com, Circ. Mgr., The Daily Iberian, LA, New Iberia

Poirier, Kevin
kpoirier@kenoshanews.com, Chief Photographer, Kenosha News, WI, Kenosha

Poirier, Merle
poirierm@gc.adventist.org, Tech. Pjcts. Coord., Adventist Review, MD, Silver Spring

Pokorzynski, Ken
circulation@thealpenanews.com, Circ. Mgr., The Alpena News, MI, Alpena

Polachek, Neal
tkg@kelseygroup.com, CEO, BIAKelsey, VA, Chantilly

Polasik, George .... (847) 981-9399
polasikg@corp.inxintl.com, Sr. Vice Pres.- Offset Div./COO, INX International Ink Co., IL, Schaumburg

Polden, Adam .... (608) 791-8302
(608) 791-8302, Circ. District Mgr., The Chippewa Herald, WI, Chippewa Falls

Poletto, John
john.poletto@nielsen.com, Client Manager , Claritas, CA, San Diego

Polgreen, Lydia
lydia.polgreen@nytimes.com, Ed.-in-Chief, The Huffington Post, NY, New York

Poling, Haley .... (443) 524-8161
hpoling@thedailyrecord.com, Mktg. and Event Coord. , The Daily Record, MD, Baltimore

Poling, Martha
mpoling@news-banner.com, Bus. Mgr., News- Banner, IN, Bluffton

Polisse, Ken .... (315) 829-8343
kpolisse@indiancountry.com, Mng. Ed., Indian Country Today, NY, Canastota

Polito, Joseph
crestlineadvocate@yahoo.com, Pub./Gen. Mgr., The Crestline Advocate, OH, Crestline

Polizano, John .... (212) 210-2071
jpolizano@nydailynews.com, Sr. VP, Adv Dir., New York Daily News, NY, New York

Polk, Chris .... (410) 770-4108
cpolk@stardem.com , Staff Writer , The Star- Democrat, MD, Easton

Polk, Melanie .... (213) 251-5700 ext. 212
melanie@lawattstimes.com, Pub., La Watts Times, CA, Los Angeles

Pollack, Helene
hp@shorelinepub.com, Ed. in Chief, wsn2day. com, NY, Pelham

Pollack, Helene .... (914) 738-7869
hp@shorelinepub.com, Editor and Publisher, Westchester Jewish Life, NY, Pelham

Pollak, Sam .... (607) 441-7208
spollak@thedailystar.com, Ed., The Daily Star, NY, Oneonta

Pollak, William L.
cservice@nylj.com, Pres./CEO, New York Law Journal, NY, New York

Pollard, Becky .... (580) 634-2156
bpollard@civitasmedia.com, Class., Durant Daily Democrat, OK, Durant

Pollard, Francis
francis@times-georgian.com, Office Mgr., The Haralson County Gateway Beacon, GA, Carrollton

Pollard, Pamela .... (912) 489-9420
ppollard@statesboroherald.com, Adv. Mgr., Classified, Statesboro Herald, GA, Statesboro

Pollard, Patricia
norwaynews@hotmail.com, Ed., The Current, MI, Ann Arbor

Pollard, Robert
rpollard@stategazette.com, Pressroom Mgr., State Gazette, TN, Dyersburg

Pollert, Johannah .... (812) 379-5708
jpollert@therepublic.com, Ed., Republic Extra, IN, Columbus

Pollet, Tracie
tapollet@valassis.com, Senior Client Marketing Mgr. , Valassis, MI, Livonia

Polley, Robert
wlsvcirc@hotmail.com, Circ. Mgr., Allegany County Pennysaver, NY, Wellsville

Pollock, Arthur .... (617) 619-6498
arthur.pollock@bostonherald.com, Asst.t Photo Ed., Boston Herald, MA, Boston

Pollock, Chuck .... (716) 372-3121 Ext. 275
cpollock@oleantimesherald.com, Sports Ed., Olean Times Herald, NY, Olean

Pollock, Cindy
cpollock@jadeinc.com, Gen. Mgr., Guernsey Noble Advertiser, OH, Cambridge

Pollock, Sarah .... (510) 482-3203
sarah.pollock@me.com, Mills College, CA, Oakland

Polo, Samuel F.
polov13@aol.com, Pub., The Currents, LA, Gretna

Polodna, Duane .... (402) 444-1480
duane.polodna@owh.com, CFO/Sr. Vice Pres., Omaha World-Herald, NE, Omaha

Polodna, Taylor
tpolodna@mymail.mines.edu, Design Editor, Colorado School of Mines, CO, Golden

Polster, Susan .... (434) 613-5213
Susan.polster@usu.edu, Adviser, Utah state university eastern, UT, Price

Polston, Pamela .... (802) 865-1020 x 11
pamela@sevendaysvt.com, Assoc. Pub./Ed., Seven Days, VT, Burlington

Poltenson, Norman .... (315) 579-3916
npoltenson@cnybj.com, Pub., The Central New

York Business Journal, NY, Syracuse

Pomareda, Fabiola .... (312) 870-7043
fabiola.pomareda@laraza.com, Managing d., La Raza Newspaper, IL, Chicago

Pomeroy, Courtney .... (706) 208-2215
Features Ed., Athens Banner-Herald, GA, Athens

Pompe, Scott
scott.pompe@latimes.com, Pub., Burbank Leader, CA, Los Angeles
scott.pompe@latimes.com, Gen. Mgr., Direct Mktg., Milwaukee Journal Sentinel, WI, Milwaukee

Pomper, Rob
tribune@plateautel.net, Pub./Ed./Adv. Dir., The State Line Tribune, TX, Farwell

Ponce, Hernan .... (415) 777-6826
hponce@bayareanewsgroup.com, VP, Sales, Vallejo Times-Herald, CA, Vallejo
hponce@bayareanewsgroup.com, VP, Sales, Tri-Valley Herald/San Ramon Valley Herald (OOB), CA, PLEASANTON

Ponce, Marci
marci@brownsvilleherald.com, Ed., El Nuevo Heraldo, TX, Brownsville

Poncet, Dell
dponcet@bizjournals.com, Mng. Ed., Philadelphia Business Journal, PA, Philadelphia

Pond, Brian .... (217) 245-6121
bpond@civitasmedia.com, Circulation director, Jacksonville Journal-Courier, IL, Jacksonville

Pond, Jerry
jpond@cheboygantribune.com, Prod. Mgr., Pressroom, Cheboygan Daily Tribune, MI, Cheboygan

Pond, Jerry
jpond@cheboygantribune.com, Prodn. Mgr., Shoppers Fair, MI, Cheboygan

Ponder, Brian .... (828) 232-5859
BPonder@CITIZEN-TIMES.com, Writing Coach, The Asheville Citizen-Times, NC, Asheville

Ponder, Doug .... (270) 358-3118
editor@laruecountyherald.com, Ed, LaRue County Herald News, KY, Hodgenville

Ponder, James Randy .... (228) 467-5474
rponder@seacoastecho.com, Pub./Ed., Sea Coast Echo, MS, Bay Saint Louis

Ponds, Eddie .... (985) 386-7955
Ed., The Drum, LA, Ponchatoula

Ponte, Mary
mponte@gsptoday.com, Controller, GSP, Inc., RI, Westerly

Ponte, Teresa
teresa.ponte@fiu.edu, Assoc. Prof./Interim Chair, Dept. of Journ./Broadcasting, Florida International University, FL, North Miami

Pontious, Susie .... ext. 221
spontious@leaderunion.com, Circ. Mgr., The Leader-union Publishing Co., IL, Vandalia
spontious@leaderunion.com, Class Adv. mgr., The Leader-Union, IL, Vandalia

Ponton, Bev .... (519) 631-2790
bev.ponton@sunmedia.ca, Chronicle, ON, West Lorne
bev.ponton@sunmedia.ca, Pub., The Strathroy Age Dispatch, ON, Strathroy
bev.ponton@sunmedia.ca, Pub./Adv. Mgr., St. Thomas Times-Journal, ON, Saint Thomas

Ponton, Bev
bevponton@bowesnet.com, Gen. Mgr., Elgin County Market, ON, Saint Thomas

Pool, Colton .... (701) 456-1213
cpool@thedickinsonpress.com, Sports Ed., The Dickinson Press, ND, Dickinson

Pool, Yvonne .... (620) 343-1303
emporiashopper@cableone.net, Pub., The Shopper, KS, Emporia

Poole, Andrew .... (315) 343-3800 ext. 2245
apoole@palltimes.com, Ad. Mgr., The Palladium-Times, NY, Fulton

Poole, James
tjournalnews@yahoo.com, Pub., Times- Journal, NY, Cobleskill

Poole, Jeff .... (540) 672-1266 #23
jpoole@orangenews.com, Managing Editor, Madison County Eagle, VA, Madison

Poole, Mary .... (808) 529-4748
mpoole@staradvertiser.com, Weekend Ed., Honolulu Star-Advertiser, HI, Honolulu

Poon, Hilda
hilda@scdaily.com, Adv. Mgr., Southern Chinese Daily News, TX, Houston

Poor, Sharon
circulation@poteaudailynews.com, Cir. Dir., Poteau Daily News, OK, Poteau

Poore, Chris
c.poore@kykernel.com, Univ. of Kentucky, KY, Lexington

Poore, Stacey
stacey.poore@doverpost.com, Circ. Mgr, Hockessin Community News, DE, Middletown
stacey.poore@doverpost.com, Circ. Mgr, Smyrna/Clayton Sun-Times, DE, Middletown
stacey.poore@doverpost.com, Circ. Mgr, Dover Post, DE, Dover
stacey.poore@doverpost.com, Circ. Mgr, The Middletown Transcript, DE, Middletown
stacey.poore@doverpost.com, Circ. Mgr, The Sussex Countian, DE, Dover
stacey.poore@doverpost.com, Circ. Mgr, Milford Beacon, DE, Dover

Poorman, Kyle
kyle.poorman@tribstar.com, Circ. Mgr., Single Copy, The Tribune Star, IN, Terre Haute

Poorman, Michelle .... (812) 231-4360
michelle.poorman@tribstar.com, Customer Service Mgr., The Tribune Star, IN, Terre Haute

Poorte, Kimberly
kpoorte@ledgertranscript.com, Circ. Mgr., Monadnock Ledger-Transcript, NH, Peterborough

Popa, Greg
gpopa@stowereporter.com, Publisher, Stowe Reporter, VT, Stowe
gpopa@stowereporter.com, Pub., Waterbury Record, VT, Stowe

Pope, Colin .... (512) 494-2521
cpope@bizjournals.com, Ed., Austin Business Journal, TX, Austin

Pope, Jeffrey .... (978) 739-1378
jpope@wickedlocal.com, Ed., Danvers Herald, MA, Danvers

Pope, Mark .... (229) 246-2827 x127
mark.pope@thepostsearchlight.com, Gen. Mgr., The Post-Searchlight, GA, Bainbridge

Pope, Steve .... (520) 797-4384
spope@azlocalmedia.com, Pub, Tucson Weekly, AZ, Tucson

Pope, Steven
spope@evtrib.com, Pub. Mgr, East Valley Tribune, AZ, Tempe

Pope Robbins, Laura .... (631) 244-5023
Dowling College, NY, Oakdale

Popejoy, Richard
rpopejoy@mitchellrepublic.com, Prod. Foreman, Press-room, The Daily Republic, SD, Mitchell

Popham, Kim .... (936) 398-2535
polknews@livingston.net, Ed., Corrigan Times, TX, Corrigan

Popp, Richard .... (414) 229-4436
popp@uwm.edu, Associate Professor and Director of Undergraduate Studies, University of Wisconsin-Milwaukee / Department of Journalism, Advertising, and Media Studies

Powell, Larry .... (937) 743-6701
larry.powell@coxinc.com, Senior Director,
Production & Operations, Dayton Daily News,
OH, Franklin

Powell, Lawrence
editor@annapolisspectator.ca, Ed., The
Spectator, NS, Middleton

Powell, Lisa
lisa@parkrecord.com, Production Mgr., Park
Record, UT, Park City

Powell, Michael
michael.cherryvilleeagle@gmail.com, Ed., The
Cherryville Eagle, NC, Cherryville

Powell, Rebecca .... (970) 416-3969
RebeccaPowell@coloradoan.com, Sr. Ed. for
Platforms, The Coloradoan, CO, Fort Collins

Powell, Russell H. ....ext. 400
Circ. Mgr., Paulding Neighbor, GA, Marietta

Powell, Sherry .... (270) 678-5171 Ext. 223
classified@glasgowdailytimes.com, Classified
Sales Exec., Glasgow Daily Times, KY,
Glasgow

Powell, Stacey .... (306) 773-8260
spowell@prairiepost.com, Advertising, Prairie
Post, SK, Swift Current

Powell, Steve .... (360) 654-4157
spowell@marysvilleglobe.com, Managing Ed.,
The Marysville Globe, WA, Marysville

Power, Brandin
bpower@mediaonene.com, Digital Sales Mgr.,
The Sun, MA, Lowell

Power, Ed .... (757) 222-5354
ed.power@insidebiz.com, Pub., Inside
Business, The Hampton Roads Business
Journal, VA, Norfolk
ed.power@insidebiz.com, Gen. Mgr., Port Folio
Weekly, VA, Norfolk

Power, Mike .... (416) 947-8357
mike.power@sunmedia.ca, Pub., The Toronto
Sun, ON, Toronto

Power, Ted
tpower@theadvertiser.com, Pub., Times Of
Acadiana, LA, Lafayette

Power-Drutis, Tamara
tamara.powerdrutis@crosscut.com, Exec. Dir.,
Crosscut, WA, Seattle

Powers, Amy
apowers@dailypress.com, VP, Adv., Daily
Press, VA, Newport News

Powers, Brent
bpowers@joplinglobe.com, Adv. Dir., The Joplin
Globe, MO, Joplin

Powers, Ethan
epowers@beenews.com, Ed. , Clarence Bee,
NY, Williamsville

Powers, Helen..................................ext. 252
hpowers@meadvilletribune.com, Adv. Mgr.,
Bravo Extra, PA, Meadville

Powers, John
powersj@hssu.edu, Vice Pres., Machinery
Division, Western LithoTech, MO, Saint Louis

Powers, John
info@chemetron.com, Mgr., Chemetron Fire
Systems, IL, Burr Ridge

Powers, Kate .... (859) 231-1315
kpowers@herald-leader.com, Dig. Sales Mgr.,
Lexington Herald-Leader, KY, Lexington

Powers, Keith .... (901) 529-2239
keith.powers@commercialappeal.com,
Consumer Sales Manager, The Commercial
Appeal, TN, Memphis

Powers, Kevin .... (314) 754-6471
kevin.powers@riverfronttimes.com, Circ. Mgr.,
The Riverfront Times, MO, Saint Louis

Powers' Kim .... (770) 267-8371
kim.powers@waltontribune.com, Business
Office Mgr., The Walton Tribune, GA, Monroe

Powers, Sandi
spowers@civitasmedia.com, Class., The
Madison Press, OH, London

Powls, David M.
holtonrecorder@embarqmail.com, Ed., The
Holton Recorder, KS, Holton

Poynter, Rebecca .... (517) 377-1001
rpoynter@michigan.com, President, Lansing
State Journal, MI, Lansing

Poynter, Rebecca .... (517) 377-1001
rpoynter@michigan.com, Pres. , Times Herald,
MI, Port Huron

Pozarycki, Robert
rpozarycki@qns.com, Editor-in-chief, The
Queens Courier, NY, Bayside

Pozdrowski, Alex
alexp@simcoeyorkprinting.com, Adv., The
Scope Of Innisfil, ON, Beeton

Pracht, Adam
prachta@mcpherson.edu, Adviser, McPherson
College, KS, McPherson

Prashad, Tack .... (212) 576-9547
prashadt@metrosn.com, SVP Client Services,
Metro Newspaper Advertising Services, Inc.,
NY, New York
prashadt@metrosn.com, EVP Client Services,
Metro-Puck Comics Network - New York,
Yonkers

Prass, Paul
info@homenewspa.com, Pub., The Home
News, PA, Walnutport

Prast, Rhonda .... (208) 377-6403
rprast@idahostatesman.com, Ed./VP, Idaho
Statesman, ID, Boise

Prater, Kristi
kprater@monroenews.com, Classifieds, The
Monroe News, MI, Monroe

Prather, Waid
waid@carthaginian.com, Ed./Pub., The
Carthaginian, MS, Carthage

Pratt, Bonnie ....(770) 478-5753 x 245
bpratt@myjpa.com, Gen. Sales Mgr., Jackson
Progress-Argus, GA, Jackson

Pratt, Bonnie ....ext. 245
bpratt@news-daily.com, Pub., Henry Daily
Herald, GA, McDonough

Pratt, Carrie .... (270) 745-4591
Carrie.Pratt@wku.edu, Herald Adviser,
Multiplatform News Adviser, Western
Kentucky University, KY, Bowling Green

Pratt, Eric
epratt@messengernews.net, Sports Ed., The
Messenger, IA, Fort Dodge

Pratt, Jeff .... (717) 240-7112
jpratt@cumberlink.com, Ed., The Sentinel, PA,
Carlisle

Pratt, Milka
mpratt@amuniversal.com, Mng. Dir., Latin
America, Universal Uclick International
Divison, Kansas City

Pratt, Tara..............................(304) 257-1844
ads@grantcountypress.com, Advertising
Manager, Grant County Press, WV,
Petersburg

Pratt, Travis..........................(240) 215-8642
tpratt@newspost.com , Web Ed. , The
Frederick News-Post, MD, Frederick

Prattini, Amber........................(504) 279-7488
amber@thestbernardvoice.com, Reporter, The
St. Bernard Voice, LA, Arabi

Prauner, Jay .... (402) 371-1020 ext. 233
sports@norfolkdailynews.com, Sports Ed.,
Norfolk Daily News, NE, Norfolk

Prause, Diane .... (979) 743-3450
stickerads@cmaaccess.com, Ed., The
Schulenburg Sticker, TX, Schulenburg

Prause, Paul A. .... (361) 865-3510
newspaper@flatoniaargus.com, Pub./Ed./Adv.

Dir., The Flatonia Argus, TX, Flatonia

Praz, Bill
bpraz@newsday.com, Cir. Dir, amNew York,
NY, New York

Prazma, Michael
mprazma@bangordailynews.com, Dir. of
Circu., Bangor Daily News, ME, Bangor

Prazma, Michael......................(815) 987-1420
mprazma@rockford.gannett.com, Circ. Mgr.,
The Star Shopper, IL, Rockford

Preciado, Bianca
advertise@egpnews.com, Advertising/Office
Manager, Eastside Sun, CA, Los Angeles

Precourt, Jeff
jeff.precourt@lee.net, Publisher, Corvallis
Gazette-Times, OR, Corvallis

Preece, Melany
ads@stillwatercountynews.com, Adv, The
Stillwater County News, MT, Columbus

Preikschat, Orton ....(515) 777-7032
opreiksc@dmreg.com, Sr. Distribution Dir., The
Des Moines Register, IA, Des Moines

Prejean, Bob..........................(225) 473-3101
bprejean@donaldsonvillechief.com,
Multi Media Sales Representative, The
Donaldsonville Chief, LA, Donaldsonville

Prell, Marla .... (406) 234-0450
mceditor@midrivers.com, Ed., Miles City Star,
MT, Miles City

Premo-Rake, Kara ....(920) 356-6772
Kpremo-rake@capitalnewspapers.com, Adv.
Mgr., Columbus Journal, WI, Beaver Dam

Prescott, Diane......................(631) 287-8239
Southampton College, NY, Southampton

Press, Aric
apress@amlaw.com, Editorial Dir., ALM, New
York

Press, Ness
nesspres@polarcomm.com, Pub. / Ed. ,
Fordville Tri-County Sun, ND, Fordville
nesspres@polarcomm.com, Pub. / Ed. ,
Pembina New Era, ND, Fordville
nesspres@polarcomm.com, Pub. / Ed. , Hatton
Free Press, ND, Fordville
nesspres@polarcomm.com, Pub. / Ed. , McVille
Messenger, ND, Fordville
nesspres@polarcomm.com, Pub. / Ed. , Nelson
County Arena, ND, Fordville
nesspres@polarcomm.com, Pub. / Ed. , Aneta
Star, ND, Fordville

Pressly, Stephanie
spressly@dailychronicle.com, Pub., Belgrade
News, MT, Belgrade
spressly@dailychronicle.com, Pub., Penny
Pincher, MT, Bozeman

Pressly, Stephanie....................(406) 582-2626
spressly@dailychronicle.com, Pub./Pres.,
Bozeman Daily Chronicle, MT, Bozeman

Prestegard, Steve......................(608) 348-3006
journaleditor@centurytel.net, Ed., The
Platteville Journal, WI, Platteville

Preston, John............... (859) 236-2551 ext. 226
jpreston@amnews.com, Digital Mgr./Audience
Relations Mgr., The Winchester Sun, KY,
Winchester

Preston, John............... (859) 236-2551 Ext. 226
jpreston@amnews.com, Digital Mgr., The
Advocate-Messenger, KY, Danville

Preston, Renee........................(715) 695-3401
addelite@triwest.net, The Ad-delite, WI, Strum

Preuss, Sam .... (979) 567-3286
ads@bctribune.com, Pub., Burleson County
Tribune, TX, Caldwell

Prevatt, Jessica
advertising@bakercountypress.com, Ad. Dir.,
The Baker County Press, FL, Macclenny

Previs, Carl
eagle_editor@belvoir.army.mil, Ed., Belvoir

Eagle, VA, Fort Belvoir

Prewitt, Denise
denise.prewitt@kba.com, Digital Sales and
Marketing Specialist, KBA North America,
Inc. (Koenig & Bauer AG), TX, Dallas

Pribanic, Ian
Ian@WatongaRepublican.com, News Ed, The
Watonga Republican, OK, Watonga

Pribbeno, Jana .... (308) 882-4453
adrep@jpipapers.com, Ad Rep, Imperial
Republican, NE, Imperial

Pribble, Randall .... (573) 546-3917
randy@myironcountynews.com, Ed/Pub/owner,
The Mountain Echo, MO, Ironton

Pribble, Sue .... (806) 669-2525
circulation@thepampanews.com, Circ. Mgr.,
The Pampa News, TX, Pampa

Pribble, Susan .... (573) 546-3917
sue@myironcountynews.com, Off. Mgr/Owner,
The Mountain Echo, MO, Ironton

Price, Angela .... (410) 643-7770
baytimes@kibaytimes.com, Ed., The Bay
Times, MD, Chester

Price, Charlie
charlie.price@mountaintimes.com, Adv. Dir.,
The Daily Post-Athenian, TN, Athens

Price, Charlie
charlie.price@mountaintimes.com, Adv. Mgr.,
The Avery Journal-Times, NC, Newland

Price, Charlie
charlie.price@mountaintimes.com, Adv. Mgr./
Mktg. Dir., The Blowing Rocket, NC, Blowing
Rock
charlie.price@mountaintimes.com, Adv. Dir.,
Watauga Democrat, NC, Boone
charlie.price@mountaintimes.com, Adv. Dir.,
The Watauga Mountain Times, NC, Boone

Price, Dan
dprice@alonovus.com, Fulfillment Mgr, The
Bargain Hunter - Holmes, OH, Millersburg
dprice@alonovus.com, Fulfillment Mgr,
The Bargain Hunter - Tuscarawas, OH,
Millersburg
dprice@alonovus.com, Fulfillment Mgr, The
Bargain Hunter - Wayne, OH, Millersburg

Price, David .... (519) 935-4537
indie@westmountindependent.com, Pub, The
Westmount Independent, QC, Westmount

Price, Debra .... (803) 644-2377
dprice@aikenstandard.com, Adv. Mgr., Major
Accts./Nat'l/Co-op, Evening Post Industries'
Aiken Communications, SC, Aiken

Price, Derek
editor@heraldbanner.com, Ed., Commerce
Journal, TX, Greenville
editor@heraldbanner.com, Ed., Herald-Banner, TX,
Greenville

Price, Gil
gprice@call-post.com, Mng. Ed., King Media
Enterprises, OH, Columbus

Price, Greg..............................(403) 223-9659
gprice@tabertimes.com, Ed., Vauxhall
Advance, AB, Vauxhall
gprice@tabertimes.com, Ed., The Taber Times,
AB, Taber

Price, Heather
priceh@knoxnews.com, Senior Director,
Circulation Sales, Knoxville News Sentinel,
TN, Knoxville

Price, Hugh .... (202) 334-6763
priceh@washpost.com, Dir. of Operations
& Planning, The Washington Post, DC,
Washington

Price, James .... (707) 453-8173
jprice@thereporter.com, Internet Mgr., The
Daily Democrat, CA, Woodland

Price, Jeff
pricej@valassis.com, FSI Project Mgr.
, Valassis, MI, Livonia

Price, Jessica .... **(620) 694-5700 Ext. 250**
jprice@hutchnews.com, Prodn. Mgr., Weekly News, MA, Peabody

Price, Jordan .... **(731) 253-6666**
banner@lakecountybanner.com, Office Mgr/Circ., The Lake County Banner, TN, Tiptonville

Price, Kelly .... **(815) 561-2125**
kelly@rochellenews-leader.com, Adv. Mgr, The Rochelle News Leader, IL, Rochelle

Price, Kevin
kprice@ledger-enquirer.com, Sports Ed., Columbus Ledger-Enquirer, GA, Columbus

Price, Kim
kim.price@thewetumpkaherald.com, Pub./ Pres., The Wetumpka Herald, AL, Alexander City

Price, Kim
kim.price@thewetumpkaherald.com, Pub., Eclectic Observer, AL, Wetumpka

Price, Prudence .... **(478) 272-5522 x 203**
tchnewspaper@gmail.com, Classified, The Courier Herald, GA, Dublin

Price, Richard .... **(508) 839-2259**
editor@thegraftonnews.com, Editor, The Grafton Villager, MA, South Grafton

Price, Robert .... **(661) 395-7399**
rprice@bakersfield.com, Exec. Ed., The Bakersfield Californian, CA, Bakersfield

Price, Shona .... **(321) 242-3774**
sprice@floridatoday.com, Editor, Best - South, FL, Melbourne
sprice@floridatoday.com, Editor, Best - North, FL, Melbourne
sprice@floridatoday.com, Editor, Best - Central, FL, Melbourne

Price Arden, Allison
publisher@adage.com, Pub., Advertising Age, NY, New York

Prichard, Dr. Robert
rprichard@torstar.ca, Pres./CEO, Torstar, ON, Toronto

Prichard, Janice
janicep@nacms-c.com, Mng. Ed., The Daily Record, KY, Louisville

Prichard, Jennifer
editor@stamfordamerican.net, Ed., The New Stamford American, TX, Stamford

Prickett, Jerry .... **(254) 778-4444**
jprickett@tdtnews.com, Assistant Managing Editor, Temple Daily Telegram, TX, Temple

Prickett, Jordan .... **(413) 585-5292**
jprickett@gazettenet.com, Commercial Printing Mgr. , Daily Hampshire Gazette, MA, Northampton

Prickett, Quincey .... **(281) 391-3141**
katycirculation@katytimes.com, Circulation, The Katy Times, TX, Katy

Priddy, Michaela .... **(270) 259-6061**
mpriddy@graysonrecord.com, Advertising representative, The Record, KY, Leitchfield

Priddy, Michaela .... **(270) 259-6061**
mpriddy@graysonrecord.com, Advertising representative, The Record, KY, Leitchfield

Priddy, Tom .... **(864) 562-7292**
tom.priddy@shj.com, Asst. Managing Ed./Dig., Herald-Journal, SC, Spartanburg

Priddy, Tommy
sports@parispi.net, Sports Ed., The Paris Post-Intelligencer, TN, Paris

Pride, Corey .... **(209) 826-3831 ext. 563**
cpride@losbanosenterprise.com, Reporter, Los Banos Enterprise, CA, Los Banos

Pride, Linnie .... **(540) 981-3210**
linnie.pride@roanoke.com, Regional Circulation Director, The Roanoke Times, VA, Roanoke

Pride, Linwood .... **(334) 293-5812**

lpride@cnhi.com, Senior VP, Audience Development, Community Newspaper Holdings, Inc., AL, Montgomery

Pride, Tina .... **(620) 442-4200 ext. 118**
adrep@arkcity.net, Adv. Consultant , The Arkansas City Traveler, KS, Arkansas City

Pridemore, Donna .... **(434) 292-3019**
frontoffice@courier-record.com, Office Manager, Courier-Record, VA, Blackstone

Priebe, Melissa
watertown.editor@ecm-inc.com, Comm. Ed., Carver County News, MN, Waconia

Priest, Ellen
epriest@jounalscene.com, Pub., The Gazette, SC, Summerville

Priest, Ellen
editor@berkeleyind.com, Pub., Berkeley Independent, SC, Summerville

Priest, Ellen
epriest@journalscene.com, Grp. Pub., Summerville Communications, Inc., SC, Summerville

Priest, Ellen C. .... **(803) 644-2345**
epriest@aikenstandard.com, Pub., Evening Post Industries' Aiken Communications, SC, Aiken

Priester, Brian
bpriester@lsj.com, Pub, Portland Review & Observer, MI, Lansing
bpriester@lsj.com, Pub., Charlotte Shopping Guide, MI, Lansing
bpriester@lsj.com, Pub., Clinton County News, MI, Lansing
bpriester@lsj.com, Pub., Lansing City Community News, MI, Lansing
bpriester@lsj.com, Pres./Pub., Lansing State Journal, MI, Lansing
bpriester@lsj.com, Pub. , Ingham County Community News, MI, Lansing
bpriester@lsj.com, Pub., Eaton Rapids Community News, MI, Lansing
bpriester@lsj.com, Pub., Delta Waverly Community News, MI, Lansing
bpriester@lsj.com, Pub., Dewitt Bath Review, MI, Lansing
bpriester@lsj.com, Pub. , Grand Ledge Independent, MI, Lansing
bpriester@lsj.com, Pub., Lansing State Journal, MI, Lansing
bpriester@lsj.com, Pub., Williamston Enterprise, MI, Lansing
bpriester@lsj.com, Pub., Towne Courier, MI, Lansing

Priester, Jonna Spelbring
editor@hclocal.com, Pub., Henry County Local, KY, Eminence

Prieto, Martha
classifieds@heraldpublications.com, Classified Adv. Mgr., El Segundo Herald, CA, El Segundo

Prieto, Patricia .... **(231) 896-2308**
patricia.prieto@laopinion.com, Adv. Dir., La Opinion - Contigo, CA, Los Angeles

Prieto, Rafael
sales@quepasamedia.com, Mi Gente, NC, Charlotte

Prieto, Yizzar .... **(574) 584-2770**
design@webelpuente.com, Production Director.
Marketing., El Puente, IN, Goshen

Prieto, Zulma
zulma@webelpuente.com, Editor, El Puente, IN, Goshen

Prikker, Scott
sprikker@mykawartha.com, Prodn. Mgr., Peterborough This Week, ON, Peterborough

Prikker, Scott
sprikker@mykawartha.com, Prodn. Mgr., Kawartha Lakes This Week, ON, Lindsay

Priller, Trish
trish.priller@naplesnews.com, Asst. Pub.,

Naples Daily News, FL, Naples

Prim, Eugene
ads@hawleyherald.net, Pub., Lake Park Journal, MN, Hawley

Prim, Eugene A.
newsrecordreview@bvillemn.net , Ed., Barnesville Record Review, MN, Barnesville

Prim, John E. .... **(518) 561-7408**
johnprim@primhall.com, Pres., Prim Hall Enterprises, Inc., NY, Plattsburgh

Prince, Charles
charlesprince@buckeyelakebeacon.net, Pub./ Ed./Adv. Mgr., The Buckeye Lake Beacon, OH, Buckeye Lake

Prince, Dean .... **(763) 218-0033**
dean@realbits.com, OWNER PUBLISHER, Tidbits Of The North Metro, MT, Bozeman

Prince, Jay .... **(501) 505-1251**
jay.prince@thecabin.net, Adv. Production, Log Cabin Democrat, AR, Conway

Prince, Jim
jprince@onlinemadison.com, Ed., Madison County Journal, MS, Ridgeland

Prince, Jim
jprince@neshobademocrat.com, Ed., The Neshoba Democrat, MS, Philadelphia

Prince, Jim
messenger@meshobademocrate.com, Pub., Kemper County Messenger, MS, De Kalb

Prince, Michael
mprince@olympic.edu, Olympic College, WA, Bremerton

Prince, Tim .... **(205) 755-5747 ext. 609**
tim.prince@clantonadvertiser.com, Pres/ Publisher, The Clanton Advertiser, AL, Clanton
tim.prince@clantonadvertiser.com, Ed., Alabaster Reporter, AL, Columbiana
tim.prince@clantonadvertiser.com, Ed., Pelham Reporter, AL, Columbiana
tim.prince@clantonadvertiser.com, Ed., Shelby County Reporter, AL, Columbiana
tim.prince@clantonadvertiser.com, Vice Pres., Boone Newspapers, Inc., AL, Northport

Principato, Richard .... **(610) 253-6206**
rick@towerproducts.com, Pres./CEO, Tower Products, Inc., PA, Easton

Principe, Darleen
simi@theacorn.com, Ed., Simi Valley Acorn, CA, Agoura Hills

Pringle, Evan .... **(802) 447-7567, ext. 106**
espringle@benningtonbanner.com, Circ. Mgr., Manchester Journal, VT, Manchester Center

Pringle, Rhonda .... **rpringle@bizjournals.com**
rpringle@republicmedia.com, Adv. Dir., The Business Journal, AZ, Phoenix

Prinsen, Steven .... **(320) 274-3052**
advocate@lakedalelink.net, Pub., Annandale Advocate, MN, Annandale

Prinsen, Steven
ads@annandaleadvocate.com., Pub., Advantage, MN, Annandale

Prioe, Angelique .... **(321) 402-0425**
apriore@osceolanewsgazette.com, Production Manager, Osceola News-gazette, FL, Kissimmee

Prioleau, Monique .... **(407) 894-7300 Ext. 261**
mprioleau@hearstsc.com, Sales Coordinator, North America Syndicate, New York

Prioleau, Monique .... **(407) 894-7300 Ext. 261**
mprioleau@hearstsc.com, Sales Coordinator, King Features Syndicate, NY, New York

Prior, Mark
mprior@harding.edu, Adj., Harding University, AR, Searcy

Prisendorf, Anthony
berkrec@bcn.net, Pub., The Berkshire Record, MA, Great Barrington

Pritchard, Andrew .... **(701) 231-8221**
andrew.pritchard@my.ndsu.edu, North Dakota State Univ., ND, Fargo

Pritchard, David .... **(414) 229-4436**
pritchar@uwm.edu, Professor, University of Wisconsin-Milwaukee / Department of Journalism, Advertising, and Media Studies (JAMS), WI, Milwaukee

Pritchard, Griffin .... **(334) 283-6568**
editor@tallasseetribune.com, Managing Editor, The Tallassee Tribune, AL, Tallassee

Pritchett, Joe .... **(217) 483-2614**
chathamclarion@royell.org, Ed., Chatham Clarion, IL, Chatham

Pritt, Nancy .... **(717) 253-9402**
npritt@gettysburgtimes.com, Sales Mgr., Gettysburg Times, PA, Gettysburg

Pritt, Tina
tpritt@tribdem.com, Major/Nat'l. Sales, The Tribune-Democrat, PA, Johnstown

Pritts, Ronald .... **(814) 444-5926**
ronp@dailyamerican.com, Sports Ed., Daily American, PA, Somerset

Prizler, Nancy
nancy.pitlever@mowercountyshopper.com, Circ. Mgr., Mower County Shopper, MN, Austin

Probst, Caroline
weekly@gustavus.edu, Editor-in-Chief, Gustavus Adolphus College, MN, Saint Peter

Probst, Jason .... **(620) 694-5700 Ext. 313**
jprobst@hutchnews.com, Opinion/Weekend Editor, The Hutchinson News, KS, Hutchinson

Prociv, Theodore M.
info@versar.com, Pres./CEO, Versar Inc., VA, Springfield

Proctor, Colleen **860/701-4241**
c.proctor@theday.com, Product Manager, The Day, CT, New London

Proctor, Cynthia
cynthia@auroran.com, Prod. Mgr., The Auroran, ON, Aurora

Proctor, David
timesjournal@centurytel.net, Ed., Clay Times-Journal, AL, Lineville

Proctor, J.Christopher .... **(214) 491-0180**
jchristopher-proctor@utulsa.edu, Editor-in-Chief, Univ. of Tulsa, OK, Tulsa

Proffit, Kim
class2@yelmonline.com, Office Mgr., Nisqually Valley News, WA, Yelm

Proffitt, Beth **x137**
bproffitt@cdispatch.com, Adv. Dir., The Commercial Dispatch, MS, Columbus

Proffitt, Jennifer .... **(989) 284-5109**
Univ. of Michigan, MI, Flint

Pronovost, Jacques
jpronovost@ledroit.com, Pres., Ed., Le Droit, ON, Ottawa

Pronovost, Paul .... **(508) 862-1166**
ppronovost@capecodonline.com, Ed., Cape Cod Times, MA, Hyannis

Prophet, Lisa
publisher@mapleridgenews.com, Pub, The Maple Ridge News, BC, Maple Ridge

Propp, Lyn .... **(780) 429-5264**
lpropp@edmontonjournal.com, Adv. Services & Digital Mgr., Edmonton Journal, AB, Edmonton

Propper, David
dpropper@theexaminernews.com, Ed., The Putnam Examiner, NY, Mount Kisco

Propst, Jason .... **(828) 559-4045**
jpropst@morganton.com, The News Herald, NC, Morganton

Propst, Jason .... **(828) 304-6941**

jpropst@hickoryrecord.com, Adv. Dir., Pow, NC, Hickory

Proskuryakova, Mariya .... (907) 786-4690
Univ. of Alaska Anchorage, AK, Anchorage

Prososki, Norene
norene@ozarkcountytimes.com, Pub., Ozark County Times, MO, Gainesville

Pross, Dave .... (203) 402-2329
dpross@hersamacorn.com, Account Exec., Weston Forum, CT, Ridgefield

Prosser, Matthew
Mprosser@hendersondailynews.com, Ed., Overton News, TX, Henderson

Prosser, Matthew
Mprosser@hendersondailynews.com , Ed., Henderson Daily News, TX, Henderson

Prosser, Stacie
sprosser@bizjournals.com, Pub., Kansas City Business Journal, MO, Kansas City

Prostko, Veronica
vprostko@PlantCityObserver.com, Adv. Mgr., Plant City Observer, FL, Plant City

Protz, Brenda .... (217) 786-2589
brenda.protz@llcc.edu, Lincoln Land Cmty. College, IL, Springfield

Proudfit, Theresa
tpeterson@ironmountaindailynews.com, Photo Ed., The Daily News, MI, Iron Mountain

Proudfoot, Ian
newsroom@erabanner.com, Pub., The Newmarket Era-banner, ON, Newmarket

Proudfoot, Ian
iproudfoot@yrmg.com, Pub., The Richmond Hill Liberal, ON, Markham

Proudfoot, Ian .... (905) 294-2200
iproudfoot@yrmg.com, Pub., Markham Economist & Sun, ON, Markham

Proudfoot, Ian
iproudfoot@yrmg.com, Vice Pres./Reg. Pub., Vaughan Citizen, ON, Vaughan

Proudfoot, Ian
iproudfoot@yrmg.com, Pub., The Georgina Advocate, ON, Keswick

Proudfoot, Ian
iproudfoot@metroland.com, Vice Pres., Metroland Media Group Ltd., ON, Mississauga
iproudfoot@metroland.com, Ed., The Barrie Advance, ON, Barrie

Proulx, Ben
bproulx@postmedia.com, Ed, Sherwood Park/strathcona county news, AB, Sherwood Park
bproulx@postmedia.com, Ed., The Fort Saskatchewan Record, AB, Fort Saskatchewan

Proulx, Chantal
proulxc@transcontinental.ca, Prodn. Mgr., Hebdo Rive Nord, QC, Repentigny

Proulx, Serge
serge.proulx@monteregieweb.com, Adv. Rep., Le Soleil Du St-laurent, QC, Salaberry-de-Valleyfield

Prout, Teresa
teresa.prout@News-Record.com, Local content editor, News & Record, NC, Greensboro

Prouty, Tim..ext. 215
support@verifiedaudit.com, CEO, Verified Audit Circulation (VAC), CA, San Rafael

Provance, Jim .... (614) 221-0496
jprovance@theblade.com, Columbus Bureau Chief, The Blade, OH, Toledo

Provencher, Ron
swjpc@bellsouth.net, Mng. Ed., Stewart-Webster Journal, GA, Richland

Provencher, Ron T. .... (122) 932-14453
swjpc@bellsouth.net, Adv. Mgr., Stewart-Webster Journal, GA, Richland

Provost, John .... (352) 563-3240
jprovost@chronicleonline.com, Adv. Dir., Citrus County Chronicle, FL, Crystal River
jprovost@chronicleonline.com, Gen. Mgr., Riverland News, FL, Dunnellon

Provost, Paul
paul.provost@telegram.com, Pub., Telegram & Gazette, MA, Worcester

Provost, Robert C. .... (973) 392-1892
rprovost@starledger.com, Director of Marketing., The Star-Ledger, NJ, Newark

Provost, Roger .... (817) 390-7185
rprovost@star-telegram.com, Vice Pres./CFO, Fort Worth Star-Telegram, TX, Fort Worth

Provost, Steve .... (805) 927-8896
sprovost@thetribunenews.com, Mng Ed, The Cambrian, CA, Cambria

Proznick, Rick .... (250) 832-2131
publisher@saobserver.net, Pub., Salmon Arm Observer, BC, Salmon Arm

Proznick, Rick .... (250) 832-2131
publisher@saobserver.net, Pub., Shuswap Market News, BC, Salmon Arm

Pruett, Chris .... (812) 384-5765
cpruett79@gmail.com, Publisher, Greene County Daily World, IN, Linton

Pruett, Chris
cpruett79@gmail.com, Pub., The Brazil Times, IN, Brazil

Pruett, Chris
cpruett79@gmail.com, Pub., Banner-Graphic, IN, Greencastle

Pruitt, Gary
gpruitt@ap.org, Pres. & CEO, Associated Press, MA, Boston
gpruitt@ap.org, President and CEO, Associated Press, The, New York

Pruitt, James
editor@ypsilanticourier.com, Ed, Ypsilanti Courier, MI, Saline

Pruitt, Kerri
starbusiness@elberton.net, Office Mgr., The Elberton Star, GA, Elberton

Pruitt, Randy
randy.pruitt@mwsu.edu, Asst. Prof./Advisor, The Wichitan, Midwestern State University, TX, Wichita Falls

Pruneau, Ed
pruneaue@emissourian.com, Managing Editor, Washington Missourian/missourian Publishing Co, MO, Washington

Pruneau, Ed
pruneaue@emissourian.com, Mgr Ed., Washington Missourian, MO, Washington

Prunty, Donna
legals@westondemocrat.com, Production Assistant, Weston Democrat, WV, Weston

Prusina, Mario
mario@strathmoretimes.com, Pub/Ed, Strathmore Times, AB, Strathmore

Prutsok, Andy
andy.prutsok@suffolknewsherald.com, Ed., Tidewater Shopper, VA, Suffolk

Prutsok, Andy.............. (419) 668-3771 Ext. 1223
aprutsok@norwalkreflector.com, Pub., Norwalk Reflector, OH, Norwalk

Pryke, Raymond
valleywide@valleywidenews.com, Pub., Hesperia Resorter, CA, Hesperia

Pryke, Raymond
vwn@compu-ad.net, Ed., Apple Valley News, CA, Hesperia

Pryor, Christina
cpryor@aepaper.com, Ed., The Daily Herald, PA, Tyrone

Pryor, Rob
rpryor@capitalgazette.com, Circ. Dir., The Maryland Gazette, MD, Annapolis

Pryor, Rob.................(410) 268-5000 ext. 3322
rpryor@capitalgazette.com, Circ. Dir., Bowie Blade-News, MD, Annapolis

Pryor, Travis .... (303) 684-5212
tpryor@times-call.com, Longmont Times-Call, CO, Longmont

Publisher, Cory .... (812) 331-4251
Pub., The Reporter Times, IN, Martinsville

Pucci, Amanda .... (716) 6140-6259
Niagara County Cmty. College, NY, Sanborn

Puchek, Joe............................ (312) 321-2102
jpuchek@post-trib.com, Web Content Ed., Post-Tribune, IN, Crown Point

Puckett, Ann
apuckett@helena-arkansas.com, Gen. Mgr./Display Adv. Mgr., The Helena Arkansas Daily World, AR, HELENA

Puckett, Jeffrey .... (502) 582-4160
jpuckett@courier-journal.com, Music Critic, The Courier-Journal, KY, Louisville

Puckett, Lori
theclarksvilletimes@gmail.com, Adv. Dir., Clarksville Times, TX, Clarksville

Puckett, Nicole .... (770) 963 - 9205 x1320
nicole.puckett@gwinnettdailypost.com, Graphics Ed., Gwinnett Daily Post, GA, Lawrenceville

Puckey, Tara .... (317) 618-0581
tpuckey@spj.org, Interim Executive Director, Society of Professional Journalists, IN, Indianapolis

Puello, Carmen .... (212) 293-8602
cpuello@unitedmedia.com, Sales/Admin. Mgr., Newspaper Enterprise Association (Div. of United Media), NY, New York
cpuello@unitedmedia.com, Sales/Admin. Mgr., United Feature Syndicate (Div. of United Media), New York

Puerto, Sergio........................... (214) 770-6693
editorial@novedadesnews.com, Mktg. Dir., Novedades News, TX, Dallas

Puerto Sr., Sergio..................... (214) 770-6693
spuerto@novedadesnews.com, Pres./CEO, Novedades News, TX, Dallas

Pugh, Ed................................ (706) 407-2654
ed.pugh@lagrangenews.com, Circ. Mgr, LaGrange Daily News, GA, Lagrange

Pugh, Kari
kpugh@princewilliamtoday.com, Sr. Ed., InsideNoVa/Prince William, VA, Woodbridge
kpugh@princewilliamtoday.com, Sr. Ed., Northern Virginia Media Services, VA, Leesburg

Pugh, Mitch.......................... (712) 293-4201
Ed., Sioux City Journal, IA, Sioux City

Pugh, Mitch .... (843) 937-5534
mpugh@postandcourier.com, Executive Editor, The Post and Courier, SC, Charleston

Pugh, Roger
piedmontgazette@sbcglobal.net, Pub., The Piedmont-Surrey Gazette, OK, Piedmont

Pugh, Roger
editor@piedmontnewsonline.com, Pub., Chieftain, OK, Piedmont

Puglia, Chris
cpuglia@cochrane.greatwest.ca, Ed, Cochrane Eagle, AB, Cochrane

Pugliese, Rudy
rrpgsl@rit.edu, Rochester Inst. of Technology, NY, Rochester

Puglisi, Connie
cpuglisi@cadizrecord.com, Adv. Exec., The Cadiz Record, KY, Cadiz

Puhalla, Bev
news@tecumsehchieftain.com, Owner, Pub, The Tecumseh Chieftain, NE, Tecumseh

Puhalla, Beverly J. .... (402) 852-2575
news@pawneenews.com, Pub., The Pawnee Republican, NE, Pawnee City

Puit, Glenn .... (580) 310-7550
gpuit@theadanews.com, Exec. Ed., The Ada News , OK, Ada
gpuit@theadanews.com, Exec. Ed., McAlester News-Capital, OK, McAlester

Pujol, Brenda
brenda@genevareaper.com, Pub., Hartford News-Herald, AL, Geneva

Pujol, Brenda
brenda@genevareaper.com, Pub., Geneva County Reaper, AL, Geneva
brenda@genevareaper.com, Pub., Samson Ledger, AL, Geneva

Pujol, Moe
opppublisher@centurytel.net, Pub., The Opp News, AL, Opp

Pukas, John
john.pukas@newscyclesolutions.com, VP., Business Relations
, Newscycle Solutions, MN, Bloomington

Pulcrano, Dan .... ext. 1302
letters@metronews.com, Pub., Metro, CA, San Jose

Pulcrano, Dan .... ext. 1301
press@metronews.com, Pres., Metro Newspaper, CA, San Jose

Puleo, Sam .... (312) 915-7898
Loyola Univ. Law School, IL, Chicago

Pulis, Joanne
jpulis@keynoter.com, Florida Keys Keynoter, FL, Marathon
jpulis@keynoter.com, Class/Web Mgr., The Reporter, FL, Tavernier

Pullano, Kathy........................ (269) 473-5421
thejournalera@yahoo.com, Ed., The Journal Era, MI, Berrien Springs

Pullen, Rick
rpullen@fullerton.edu, Prof./Dean, California State University, Fullerton, CA, Fullerton

Pulliam, Patricia .... (616) 245-8737
staff@grtimes.com, Ed., The Grand Rapids Times, MI, Grand Rapids

Pullins, Wayne E.
waynepullins@earthlink.met, Pres., Distribution Unlimited, Inc., OH, Springfield

Punch, Jennifer .... (902) 426-2811 ext. 3073
jpunch@herald.ca, Senior Mktg. Mgr., The Chronicle Herald, NS, Halifax

Puntney, Linda
jea@spub.ksu.edu, Asst. Prof./Dir., Student Publications Inc./Exec. Dir., Journalism Educ. Assn., Kansas State University, KS, Manhattan

Purcell, Kathryn
kpurcell@wisc.edu, Mng. Ed., Morgan County Citizen, GA, Madison

Purcell, Nicki
npurcell@dallasnews.com, Chief Digital Officer/SVP, The Dallas Morning News, TX, Dallas

Purcell, Patrick........................ (617) 619-6200
patrick.purcell@bostonherald.com, Pres./Pub., Boston Herald, MA, Boston

Purcelley , Joann
springfieldtimesbookkeeping, Office Mgr., Springfield Times, OR, Springfield

Purdum, Pat
ppurdum@smgpo.gannett.com, Gen. Mgr., Beachcomber, DE, Bethany Beach
ppurdum@smgpo.gannett.com, Sales Mgr., Delaware Coast Press, DE, Bethany Beach
ppurdum@smgpo.gannett.com, Sales Mgr., The Delaware Wave, DE, Bethany Beach

Purdy, Michael
mpurdy@govst.edu, Emeritus Professor, Governors State Univ., IL, University Park

Puren, Candi........................... (402) 277-5500
candice.puren@wahoonewspaper.com,

Advertising Manager, Market Weekly, NE, Wahoo
candice.puren@wahoonewspaper.com, Advertising Manager, Wahoo Newspaper, NE, Wahoo

Purfield, Tom
tpurfield@chieftain.com, City Ed., The Pueblo Chieftain, CO, Pueblo

Puri, Shamlal ....+44 (330) 606-1438
info@adlinkinternational.com, Mng. Dir., ADLINK-INTERNATIONAL LTD, London

Purington, Rob ....(507) 537-1551 ext #117
rpurrington@marshallindependent.com, Circulation Manager, Independent, MN, Marshall

Purrier, Kim
kim.purrier@albanyherald.com, Circ. Mgr., The Albany Herald, GA, Albany

Purrington, Rob ....(507) 537-1551 ext #117
rpurrington@marshallindependent.com, Circu Mgr, Independent Shopper's Review, MN, Marshall

Purser, Thomas H.
news@jdledger.com, Ed., Jeff Davis Ledger, GA, Hazlehurst

Pursinger, Geoff ....(503) 357-3181
gpursinger@hillsborotribune.com, Editor, The Hillsboro Tribune, OR, Forest Grove

Puryear, James ....(919) 829-4727
jpuryear@newsobserver.com, Vice Pres., Circ., The News & Observer, NC, Raleigh

Puskar, Tom .... (419) 281-0581 Ext. 251
tpuskar@times-gazette.com, Chief Photo., Ashland Times-Gazette, OH, Ashland

Puskar, Tom .... (419) 281-0581 ext. 251
tpuskar@times-gazette.com, Chief Photographer, Ashland Publishing Co. LLC, OH, Ashland

Pustaver, Jennifer
jpustaver@cnhi.com, Chief Financial Officer, Community Newspaper Holdings, Inc., AL, Montgomery

Putnam, Eliot
mbayley@gatehousemedia.com, National Acct. Sales Mgr., GateHouse Media, Inc., NY, Pittsford

Putnam, Mark ....(207) 764-4471
Mng. Ed., Aroostook Republican and News, ME, Presque Isle

Putnam, Mark ....(207) 764-4471
observer@nepublish.com, Mng. Ed., The Piscataquis Observer, ME, Dover Foxcroft

Putnam, Mark ....(207) 764-4471
editor@nepublish.com, Managing Ed. , Presque Isle Star-Herald, ME, Presque Isle

Putt, Judy ....(662) 678-1594
judy.putt@journalinc.com, Radio/Television Ed., Northeast Mississippi Daily Journal, MS, Tupelo

Putterman, Bruce ....(860) 218-6380
bputterman@ctmirror.org, CEO and Publisher, The Connecticut News Project, Inc., CT, Hartford

Putterman, Bruce ....(860) 218-6380
bputterman@ctmirror.org, CEO / Publisher, The Connecticut Mirror, CT, Hartford

Putz, Andrew
aputz@minnpost.com, Editor, MinnPost, MN, Minneapolis

Putz, Chris
chrisputz@thewestfieldnews.com, Sports Ed., The Westfield News , MA, Westfield

Py, Chip
chippy@currentnewspapers.com, Acct. Exec., Dupont Current, DC, Washington
chippy@currentnewspapers.com, Acct. Exec., Foggy Bottom Current, DC, Washington
chippy@currentnewspapers.com, Acct. Exec., Georgetown Current, DC, Washington

chippy@currentnewspapers.com, Acct. Exec., Northwest Current, DC, Washington

Pyane, Richard
rpayne@fujifilmgs.com, Reg'l Sales Mgr., Fujifilm Graphic Systems USA, Inc., AZ, Tempe

Pye, Jana
editor@newsandpressonline.com, Ed., The News & Press, SC, Darlington

Pye, Jerry ....(903) 927-5977
jpye@marshallnewsmessenger.com, Reg. Pub., Longview News-Journal, TX, Longview

Pyfer, Dan
danp@communityshoppers.com, Gen. Mgr., Stateline News, WI, Elkhorn
danp@communityshoppers.com, Walworth County Shopper Advertiser, WI, Elkhorn
danp@communityshoppers.com, Gen. Mgr., Walworth County Sunday, WI, Elkhorn

Pyle, Melanie ....(903) 628-5801
mpyle@bowiecountynow.com, Adv. Dir., Bowie County Citizen Tribune, TX, New Boston

Pérez Cintrón, Héctor .... (787) 505-1426
President, Overseas Press de Puerto Rico, Overseas Press Club of Puerto Rico (Established 1968), PR, San Juan

Q

Quaife, Steve ....(360) 577-2559
squaife@tdn.com, Adv. Mgr., Retail, The Daily News, WA, Longview

Quaintance, John ....(567) 242-0452
jquaintance@civitasmedia.com, Cir. Dir., The Lima News, OH, Lima

Qualls, Lori ....(989) 839-4237
lqualls@mdn.net, Accent Ed., Midland Daily News, MI, Midland

Quam, Paula ....(218) 844-1466
pquam@dlnewspapers.com, Editor, Detroit Lakes Tribune, MN, Detroit Lakes

Quam, Paula
editorial@wadenapj.com, Ed., Wadena Pioneer Journal, MN, Wadena

Quan, Annie
aquan@slweekly.com, Mktg. Mgr., Salt Lake City Weekly, UT, Salt Lake City

Quan, Lyn
lyn.quan@oakbaynews.com, Prod., Oak Bay News, BC, Victoria

Quaranta, Anthony
meaganr@qgroupltd.com, Muller Martini Corp., NY, Hauppauge

Quaranto, Nicole ....(516) 474-5563
nquaranto.student@mountsaintvincent.edu, EIC, College of Mt. St. Vincent, NY, Bronx

Quast, Travis ....(208) 735-3345
tquast@elkodaily.com, Pub., Elko Daily Free Press, NV, Elko
tquast@elkodaily.com, Pub., The Times-News, ID, Twin Falls

Quattlebaum, Caroline ....(334) 393-2969
publisher@southeastsun.com, Co-publisher, Qst Publications-(consolidated), AL, Enterprise

Quattlebaum, Russell ....(334) 393-2969
rquattlebaum@southeastsun.com, Co-publisher, Qst Publications-(consolidated), AL, Enterprise
rquattlebaum@southeastsun.com, Adv. Mgr., Daleville Sun-courier, AL, Enterprise

Quattlebaum, Russell ....(334) 393-2969
sales@southeastsun.com, Adv. Mgr., Southeast Sun, AL, Enterprise

Quattrone, Tami
classifiedads@easyreader.info, Classifieds, Easy Reader, CA, Hermosa Beach

Quattrucci, John ....(508) 967-3517

sweinstein@wickedlocal.com, Sports Ed., Easton Journal, MA, Raynham

Quebedeaux, Chris
Chris.Quebedeaux@CrowleyToday.com, Sports Ed., The Crowley Post-Signal, LA, Crowley

Queen, Alice
alice.queen@rockdalecitizen.com, Ed., The Rockdale Citizen, GA, Conyers

Queen, Alice .... (770) 483 - 7108 x 226
alice.queen@newtoncitizen.com, Ed., The Newton Citizen, GA, Conyers

Queen, Caroline
caqueen@davidson.edu, Davidson College, NC, Davidson

Queenan, Jan
jqueenan@wctrib.com, Adv. Mgr., Sunday Reminder, MN, Willmar

Quelch, Judy ....(720) 274-7172
jquelch@colopress.net, Advertising , Colorado Press Association, CO, Denver

Quelch, Judy ....(720) 274-7172
jquelch@sync2media.com , Account Executive, SYNC2 Media, CO, Denver

Query, Dare ....(757) 446-2000
dare.query@pilotonline.com, Sales Exec., The Virginian-Pilot, VA, Norfolk

Query, Howard
howard.query@globegazette.com, The Mason City Shopper, IA, Mason City
howard.query@globegazette.com, The Winnebago, IA, Forest City
howard.query@globegazette.com, Pub./Gen. Mgr., Mitchell County Press-News, IA, Osage

Quezada, Cleiri ....(956) 882-5143
collegian@utb.edu, Editor, University of Texas at Brownsville, TX, Brownsville

Quick, Alee ....(618) 351-5807
alee.quick@thesouthern.com, Digital Editor, The Southern Illinoisan, IL, Carbondale

Quiding, Lisa ....(250) 672-5611
(250) 672-9900, Adv./Office/Production, Barriere Star Journal, BC, Barriere

Quiggle, James
sales@desertnews.com, Co-Pub./Ed., Mojave Desert News, CA, California City

Quigley, Buck
buck@artvoice.com, Managing editor, Artvoice, NY, Buffalo

Quigley, Kathryn ....(856) 256-4713
quigleyk@rowan.edu, Rowan Univ., NJ, Glassboro

Quigley, Katy
advertising@waynesvilledailyguide.com, Ads Rep., Daily Guide, MO, Waynesville

Quigley, Michelle ....(561) 820-4958
ref@pbpost.com, Data interactive editor, The Palm Beach Post, FL, West Palm Beach

Quigley, Stephen
editor@everettindependent.com, Pres., Everett Independent, MA, Revere

Quigley, Stephen
editor@revereindependent.com, Prodn. Mgr., Chelsea Record, MA, Revere

Quillchini, Gayle
gayle.quillchini@sunmedia.ca, Prod. Mgr., The Calgary Sun, AB, Calgary

Quillen, Yochanan ....(209) 532-7151
RQuillen@uniondemocrat.com, Prodn. Mgr., Opns./Press, The Union Democrat, CA, Sonora

Quilliam, Bruce
bquilliamjr@perretta.com, Bus. Mgr., Int'l Sales, Perretta Graphics Corp., NY, Poughkeepsie

Quilliam, Bruce L.
bquilliam@perretta.com, Vice Pres., Sales/ Mktg., Perretta Graphics Corp., NY, Poughkeepsie

Quillion, Robin ....(301) 784-2514
rquillion@times-news.com, Pub., The Garrett County Weekender, MD, Cumberland

Quillon, Robin ....(814) 532-5000
rquillon@tribdem.com, Pub., The Tribune-Democrat, PA, Johnstown

Quimby, Jim ....(410) 788-4500
dsturm@patuxent.com, Pub., Arbutus Times, MD, Baltimore

Quinell, Scott ....(315) 386-7315
quinells@canton.edu, SUNY College of Technology/Canton, NY, Canton

Quinlan, Mary Kay
mquinlan2@unl.edu, Assoc. Prof., University of Nebraska-Lincoln, NE, Lincoln

Quinlan, Tom ....(847) 427-4455
tquinlan@dailyherald.com, Assistant Managing Editor / Sports, Daily Herald, IL, Arlington Heights

Quinn, Gordon ....(949) 300-4800
gquinn@olec.com, Vice Pres.,Electronics Sales, OLEC, CA, Santa Ana

Quinn, James E. .... (401) 334-9555 ext. 129
jquinn@valleybreeze.com, Prodn. Mgr., The Valley Breeze - Cumberland/Lincoln, RI, Lincoln

Quinn, Jamie .... (401) 334-9555 ext.129
jquinn@valleybreeze.com, Dep. Pub., The North Providence Breeze, RI, Lincoln
jquinn@valleybreeze.com, Dep. Pub., The Valley Breeze - Woonsocket/North Smithfield, RI, Lincoln
jquinn@valleybreeze.com, Deputy Pub., The Valley Breeze & Observer, RI, Lincoln
jquinn@valleybreeze.com, Dep. Pub., The Valley Breeze - Pawtucket, RI, Lincoln

Quinn, Kevin
kquinn@frycomm.com, VP Sales, Fry Communications, Inc., PA, Mechanicsburg

Quinn, Michael E. ....(928) 453-4237
quinn@havasunews.com, Pub., Smart Buyer, AZ, Lake Havasu City
quinn@havasunews.com, Pub., The Parker Pioneer, AZ, Parker
quinn@havasunews.com, Pres/Pub, Today's News-Herald, AZ, Lake Havasu City
quinn@havasunews.com, Pub., River Extra, AZ, Lake Havasu City

Quinn, Paris ....(416) 774-2239
pquinn@insidetoronto.com, Sales Rep., The East York Mirror, ON, Willowdale

Quinn, Sally ....(412) 320-7885
squinn@tribweb.com, Deputy Mng. Ed., Features, Tribune-Review, PA, Greensburg

Quinn, Susan ....(414) 225-1844
squinn@dailyreporter.com, Advertising Director, The Daily Reporter, WI, Milwaukee

Quinn, Susan
editor@albernivalleynews.com, Ed., Alberni Valley News, BC, Port Alberni

Quinn, Tomari ....(785) 295-1212
tomari.quinn@cjonline.com, Ed. and VP audience , The Topeka Capital-Journal, KS, Topeka

Quintana, Shasta .... (719) 589-2553, x101
squintana@alamosanews.com, Circ. Mgr., Valley Courier, CO, Alamosa

Quirin, Liz ....(618) 235-9601
cathnews@bellevillemessenger.org, Ed., The Messenger, IL, Belleville

Quirion, Chantal
chantal.quirion@eap.on.ca, Ed., Tribune Express, ON, Hawkesbury

Quiroga, Ray ....(956) 399-2436
publisher@sbnewspaper.com, Publisher, San Benito News, TX, San Benito

Quiroga, Ray ....(956) 953-5545
rayq@portisabelsouthpadre.com, Pub./Ed., Port Isabel-South Padre Press, TX, Port Isabel

Quiros, Kristi
kquiros@tlu.edu, Texas Lutheran Univ., TX, Seguin

Quraishi, Ilayas
ilayasq@newsindia-times.com, Sales Exec., News India-Times, NY, New York

R

Raab, Gerald
gerald.raab@flashespublishers.com, Prodn. Mgr., Midwest Independent Postal, MI, Allegan

Raab, Gerard
gerard.raab@flashespublishers.com, Prodn. Mgr., Flashes Publishers, MI, Allegan

Raab, Jerry
brent.morris@hollandsentinel.com, Prodn. Mgr., Pre Press, The Holland Sentinel, MI, Holland

Rabago, Joaquin
efelondon@btclick.com, Rep., EFE News Services - London, United Kingdom, London

Rabalais, Sterling
strabalais@theadvocate.com, VP of Production, The Advocate, LA, Baton Rouge

Rabel, Bridget
rabelb@valassis.com, Senior Buyer , Valassis, MI, Livonia

Rabiroff, Jon
jrabiroff@tribpub.com, Mng. Ed., Lake County News-Sun, IL, Gurnee
jrabiroff@tribpub.com, Metro Ed., The Gainesville Sun, FL, Gainesville

Raby, Eric .... (618) 826-2385
eraby@randolphcountyheraldtribune.com, Multi-Media Sales, Randolph County Herald Tribune, IL, Du Quoin

Racette, Pat
sports@waverlynewspapers.com, Sports Ed., Bremer-butler Super Shopper, IA, Waverly

Racette, Steven A.
steve@vineyardpress.biz, Gen. Mgr., Courier-Leader, MI, Paw Paw

Racicot, Louise Gregoire
louise.gregoireracicot@monteregieweb.com, Ed., Les 2 Rives, QC, Sorel-Tracy

Racine, Claire .... (203) 330-6582
cracine@hearstmediact.com, Ed., New Canaan News, CT, Bridgeport

Rackers, Tom .... (573) 761-0256
trackers@newstribune.com, Sports Ed., News Tribune, MO, Jefferson City

Radbourne, Brent .... (519) 376-4303
bradbourne@owensoundtimes.com, Circ. Mgr., Owensound Sun Times, ON, Owen Sound

Radcliff, Carrie
cradcliff@heraldnet.com, Retail Adv. Mgr., The Herald, WA, Everett

Radcliff, Nancy .... (740) 474-3131,
nradcliff@circlevilleherald.com, Photographer, The Circleville Herald, OH, Circleville

Radde, Theodore .... (605) 269-3186
sadtad@centurytel.net, Pub., Monroe County Herald, WI, Sparta

Rade, John A.
info@imany.com, Pres./CEO, I-many, Inc., PA, Philadelphia

Radermacher, Lance
lance@auburnvillager.com, Advert. Mgr., Auburn Villager, AL, Auburn

Radetsky, Jane .... (407) 373-0085
jradetsky@thefloridacatholic.org, Web Adv., Florida Catholic, FL, Orlando

Radigan, Emily .... (347) 407-0081
e07radi@siena.edu, Editor-in-Chief, Siena College, NY, Loudonville

Radtke, Samantha .... (651) 228-5276
SRADTKE@PIONEERPRESS.COM, Cut Bank Pioneer Press, MT, Cut Bank

Radue, Ryan
ryan@thedenmarknews.com, Pub., The Denmark News, WI, Denmark

Radziewicz, Bob .... (305) 284-3709
bobr@miami.edu, Sr. Advisor, Univ. of Miami, FL, Coral Gables

Rae, Andy
info@heidelberg.com, Sr. VP, Equipment & Marketing, Heidelberg USA, GA, Kennesaw

Rae, Charles
kidderpress@worldnet.att.net, Pres., Kidder, Inc., MA, Agawam

Rae, Geoff .... (519) 633-1640 x227
geoff@theweeklynews.ca, Office/Sales Manager, St. Thomas/elgin Weekly News, ON, Saint Thomas

Raehal, Jerry .... (303) 571-5117
jraehal@colopress.net, CEO, Colorado Press Association, CO, Denver

Raehal, Jerry
jraehal@colopress.net, CEO, SYNC2 Media, CO, Denver

Raese, David A. .... (304) 291-9400
darraese@dominionpost.com, Owner/Pub., The Dominion Post, WV, Morgantown

Raffa, Kate
news@ourtownnews.com, Mng. Ed. , Our Town Eastside, NY, Pearl River

Rafferdy, Charlie
sales@voxware.com, Vice Pres., Sales/Bus. Devel., Voxware, Inc., NJ, Hamilton

Rafferty, Renata J.
rrafferty@raffertyconsulting.com, Pres., Rafferty Consulting Group, Indian Wells

Raffety, Gina
cashbook@mvp.net, Pub., Cash-Book Journal/ The Weekender, MO, Jackson

Ragazzo, Frank .... (908) 658-5992
frank@richmond-graphic.com, Vice Pres., Sales/Mktg., Richmond/Graphic Products, Inc., RI, Smithfield

Rager, Mark .... (740) 681-4333
mrager@gannett.com, Adv. Dir., Chillicothe Gazette, OH, Chillicothe
mrager@gannett.com, Sales. Mgr., Eagle-Gazette Media, OH, Lancaster

Ragin, Lee
leeragin@blackvoicenews.com, Circ. Mgr., Black Voice News, CA, Riverside

Ragland, Mealand
mragland@dnj.com, News Dir., The Daily News Journal, TN, Murfreesboro

Ragland-Hudgins, Mealand .... (615) 575-7161
mragland@gannett.com, Ed., Gallatin News Examiner, TN, Gallatin

Ragle, Jodie
argus@kkspc.com, Circ. Mgr., The Astoria South Fulton Argus, IL, Astoria

Ragle, Krystal .... (812) 277-7264
Managing Ed., The Times-Mail, IN, Bedford

Ragle, Laurie .... (812) 331-4291
lragle@hoosiertimes.com, Adv. Dir., The Times-Mail, IN, Bedford

Ragle, Laurie .... (812) 331-4291
lragle@heraldt.com, Adv. Dir., The Mooresville-Decatur Times, IN, Martinsville
lragle@heraldt.com, The Reporter Times, IN, Martinsville
lragle@heraldt.com, Adv. Dir., The Herald Times, IN, Bloomington

Raglin, Bonnie
braglin@themercury.com, Circ. Mgr., The Manhattan Mercury, KS, Manhattan

Ragsdale, Heather
aluttrell@recorder.com, Adv. Coord., Display,

The Recorder, CA, San Francisco

Ragsdale, Jaden
therald@countrymedia.net, Off. Mgr, The Herald, ND, New England

Ragsdale, Jayden
adamscountyrecord@countrymedia.net, Off. Mgr., Adams County Record, ND, Hettinger

Ragsdale, Kathie .... (978) 371-5742
kragsdale@wickedlocal.com, Ed., Lincoln Journal, MA, Concord

Ragsdale, Kathie
kragsdale@wickedlocal.com, Ed., The Concord Journal, MA, Concord

Ragsdale, Sally .... (202) 334-4557
sally.ragsdale@washpost.com, Marketing Representative/Midwest, Washington Post News Service with Bloomberg News, Washington

Raher, Michael .... (775) 881-7326
mraher@sierranevadamedia.com, Dir. of Sales, Nevada Appeal, NV, Carson City

Rahlf, Rona
pyramid@avpro.com, Pub., Pyramid Shopper, UT, Mount Pleasant

Rahman, Nadia
nadia.rahman@zu.ac.ae, Asst. Prof., Zayed University, Al Ruwayyah

Rahn, Karey
wpnewsadv@cableone.net, Adv. Mgr., West Point News, NE, West Point

Rahn, Sherri
srahn@randolphcountyheraldtribune.com, Office Mgr., Randolph County Herald Tribune, IL, Du Quoin
srahn@randolphcountyheraldtribune.com, Office Mgr., Steeleville Ledger, IL, Du Quoin

Raia, James .... (916) 508-5122
james@jamesraia.com, Self-Syndicator, James Raia, Sacramento

Raiche, Lynda
publicite@journaltdn.ca, Graphic & Adv. Consultant, Le Trait D'union Du Nord, QC, Fermont

Raifstanger, Eunice .... (413) 528-1651
info@shoppersguide-inc.com, Pub., Shopper's Guide, MA, Great Barrington

Raike, Mike
mraike@homesmagazine.com, Pub., Central Coast Homes Magazine, CA, Atascadero

Railey, John .... (336) 727-7357
jrailey@wsjournal.com, Editoral, Winston-Salem Journal, NC, Winston Salem

Raimondo, Lois .... (304) 293-8708
lois.raimondo@mail.wvu.edu, Shott Chair in Journalism, Asst. Prof., West Virginia University, WV, Morgantown

Raines, Ben .... (251) 439-7159
braines@mobileregister.com, Environmental Reporter, Press-Register, AL, Mobile

Raines, Elaine .... (520) 573-4164
eraines@azstarnet.com, News/Research Servs. Dir., Arizona Daily Star, AZ, Tucson

Raines, Rennie .... (334) 670-6300
Distrb. Mgr, The Troy Messenger, AL, Troy

Rainey, Lisa
lisa.pickron@andalusiastarnews.com, Office Mgr, Andalusia Star-News, AL, Andalusia

Rainey, Neva M. E.
thetimes@utma.com, Circ. Mgr., Turtle Mountain Times, ND, Belcourt

Rainey , Jim .... (205) 722-0115
jim.rainey@tuscaloosanews.com, Pub., The Tuscaloosa News, AL, Tuscaloosa

Rainone, Heather .... (330) 298-1124
hrainone@recordpub.com, Mng. Ed., Record-Courier, OH, Kent

Rains, Philly .... (870) 338-9181

Adv. Exec., The Helena Arkansas Daily World, AR, HELENA

Rainville, Marcel
marcel.rainville@tc.tc, Gen. Mgr. , Les 2 Rives, QC, Sorel-Tracy

Rainwater, Mark .... (318) 368-9732
Editor, The Gazette, LA, Farmerville

Rainwater, Todd
news@mcduffiemirror.com, Ed., The McDuffie Mirror, GA, Thomson

Rajtar, Steve
steve.rajtar@ecm-inc.com, Mgr., St. Croix Valley Peach, MN, Forest Lake

Rakow, Lana
lana.rakow@und.edu, Prof., University of North Dakota, ND, Grand Forks

Raleigh, Jill
jraleigh@yourobserver.com, Adv. Dir., Siesta Key Observer, FL, Sarasota
jraleigh@yourobserver.com, Ad. Dir., Longboat Observer, FL, Sarasota
jraleigh@yourobserver.com, Adv. Dir., East County Observer, FL, Sarasota
jraleigh@yourobserver.com, Adv. Dir., Plant City Observer, FL, Plant City

Ramdass, Dianne 516-569-400
dramdass@liherald.com, Circulation Director, Richner Communications, Inc., NY, Garden City

Ramer, Nancy
nramer@publicopinionnews.com, Circ. Asst. Mgr., Public Opinion, PA, Chambersburg

Ramey, Troy
t.ramey@technologyintegrators.net, Sales Engineer, Technology Integrators, IL, Effingham

Ramige, William .... (320) 328-4444
chronicle@glencoenews.com, Pub., The McLeod County Chronicle, MN, Glencoe

Ramige, William C.
chronicle@glencoenews.com, Pub., The Glencoe Advertiser, MN, Glencoe

Ramirez, Deborah .... (505) 863-6811 ext. 235
Adv., Gallup Independent, NM, Gallup

Ramirez, Maryann .... ext. 124
maryannramirez@lukeslocker.com, Circ. Mgr., Dallas Voice, TX, Dallas

Ramirez, Orlando .... (909) 806-3201
oramirez@pe.com, Ed., La Prensa, CA, Riverside
oramirez@pe.com, Pub., Excelsior Los Angeles, CA, Los Angeles

Ramirez, Roberto
roberto.ramirez@protravelinc.com, Pub., The Bronx Free Press, NY, New York

Ramm, Cindi
cindi@thetechnologyagency.com, Chief Brand Strategist, Kinetic Corporation, KY, Louisville

Ramos, George .... (805) 756-2508
Chair/Prof., California Polytechnic State Universtiy, CA, San Luis Obispo

Ramos, Laurie
lramos@leaderadvertiser.com, Adv. Dir./Gen. Mgr., Lake County Leader, MT, Polson
lramos@leaderadvertiser.com, Adv. Mgr., Mineral Independent, MT, Plains

Ramp, Tammy .... (309) 690-5382
tlramp@multiad.com, Business Development Manager, Local Search Association, IL, Peoria

Ramsay, Alan
aramsay@pgcitizen.ca, Circ. Mgr., The Prince George Citizen, BC, Prince George

Ramsay, Paul .... (902) 432-8238
pramsay@journalpioneer.com, Adv. Mgr., The Journal Pioneer, PE, Summerside

Ramsdell, Heather
hramsdell@dailyastorian.com, Circulation

Manager, The Daily Astorian, OR, Astoria

Ramseier, Anna
annar@fresnobee.com, Prodn. Mgr., Vida en el Valle, CA, Fresno

Ramsey, Austin ....(270) 691-7296
news@mcleannews.com, Editor, McLean County News, KY, Calhoun

Ramsey, Belinda
bramsey@blackwelljournaltribune.net, Pub./ Ed., Blackwell Journal-Tribune, OK, Blackwell

Ramsey, Betty ....(434) 808-0636
betty.ramsey@thecharlottegazette.com; betty.ramsey@kenbridgevictoriadispatch.com, Pub., The Charlotte Gazette, VA, Drakes Branch
betty.ramsey@thecharlottegazette.com; betty.ramsey@kenbridgevictoriadispatch.com, Pub., The Kenbridge-Victoria Dispatch, VA, Victoria

Ramsey, Carrie.........................(501) 745-5175
cramsey@vanburencountydem.com, Office Mgr., Van Buren County Democrat, AR, Clinton

Ramsey, Gwen
gramsey@jjournal.com, Prodn. Mgr., Pre Press, The Jersey Journal, NJ, Secaucus

Ramsey, Marshall
mramsey@jackson.gannett.com, Editorial Cartoonist, The Clarion-Ledger, MS, Jackson

Ramsey, Polly T. ....(205) 884-3400
Classified Adv. Sales, The Saint Clair Times, AL, Pell City

Ramsey, Ross ....(512) 716-8611
rramsey@texastribune.org, Exec. Editor, The Texas Tribune, TX, Austin

Ramsey, Stacey ....(269) 429-2400
sramsey@TheHP.com, Adv. Dir., South Haven Tribune, MI, South Haven

Ramshaw, Emily ....(512) 716-8619
eramshaw@texastribune.org, Ed.-in-Chief, The Texas Tribune, TX, Austin

Rancourt, Steve
steeve.rancourt@latribune.qc.ca, Asst. Prod. Mgr., La Tribune, QC, Sherbrooke

Rand, Jamie ....(541) 265-8571
publisher@newportnewstimes.com, Pub, News-Times, OR, Newport

Rand, Michael.............. (815) 562-2061 ext. 132
Controller, News Media Corp., IL, Rochelle

Randall, Christie ....(937) 569-4303
crandall@dailyadvocate.com, Adv. Mgr., Weekend Advocate, OH, Greenville
crandall@dailyadvocate.com, Adv. Mgr., Daily Advocate, OH, Greenville

Randall, Clinton.......................(937) 548-3330
crandall@earlybirdpaper.com, webmaster, The Early Bird, OH, Greenville

Randall, Debbie.......................(703) 986-0171
debrandall68@gmail.com, Exec. Dir., World Images News Service, Centreville

Randall, Jaclyn
editor2@pvvt.com, Assoc. Ed., Palo Verde Valley Times, CA, Blythe
editor2@pvvt.com, Mng. Ed., Quartzsite Times, CA, Blythe
editor2@pvvt.com, Mng. Ed., Desert Shopper, CA, Blythe

Randall, Judson
randallj@pdx.edu, Portland State Univ., OR, Portland

Randall, Keith ....(408) 271-3747
rkeith@bayareanewsgroup.com, Mng. Ed., East Bay Times, CA, Walnut Creek

Randall, Melanie
melanierandall@dailycommercial.com, Major/ Nat'l Accts. Mgr., The Daily Commercial, FL, Leesburg
melanierandall@dailycommercial.com, New Majors/Nat'l Acct. Rep., South Lake Press,

FL, Leesburg

Randall, Myron W.
mrandall@newspost.com, Pres., The Frederick News-Post, MD, Frederick

Randall, Sean ....(508) 548-4700 ext.205
randall@capenews.net, Ad. Director, The Bourne Enterprise, MA, Falmouth
randall@capenews.net, Ad. Director, Cape Cod Shopper, MA, Falmouth

Randall, Sean ....(508) 548-4700 x205
srandall@capenews.net, Ad. Director, The Mashpee Enterprise, MA, Falmouth
srandall@capenews.net, Ad. Director, The Sandwich Enterprise, MA, Falmouth
srandall@capenews.net, Ad. Director, The Falmouth Enterprise, MA, Falmouth

Randall, Shirley.......................(606) 451-4916
Compositor, The Commonwealth-Journal, KY, Somerset

Randall, Thom ....(518) 356-0795
ThomRand@aol.com, Ed., The Adirondack Journal Sun, NY, Elizabethtown

Randall, Will
wrandall@newspost.com, CEO, The Frederick News-Post, MD, Frederick

Randazzo, Joe
chicago@theonion.com, The Onion, IL, Chicago

Randell, Adam
arandell@northernpen.ca, Ed, Northern Pen, NL, Saint Anthony

Randles, Mr. Kary ....(580) 548-8191
krandles@enidnews.com, Prepress Mgr, Enid News & Eagle, OK, Enid

Randles, Shelli
harlotmf@mtintouch.net, Adv. Mgr., The Times Clarion, MT, Harlowton

Randolph, Brittany....................(704) 669-3349
brandolph@shelbystar.com, photographer, The Star, NC, Shelby

Randolph, Kathy ....(859) 654-3332
billing@falmouthoutlook.com, Receptionist/ Bookkeeper, The Shopper's Outlook (free Shopper), KY, Falmouth

Randolph, Pat
pat@yanceypaper.com, Pub./Adv. Dir., Yancey Common Times Journal, NC, Burnsville

Randolph, Shawn ....(740) 532-1441 Ext. 216
shawn.randolph@irontontribune.com, Mktg. / Adv. Dir., The Ironton Tribune, OH, Ironton

Ranes, Marji ....(623) 876-2591
mranes@yourwestvalley.com, Pub., Surprise Today, AZ, Sun City
mranes@yourwestvalley.com, Pub., Daily News-Sun, AZ, Sun City

Ranes, Marji ....(623) 876-2591
mranes@yourwestvalley.com, Pub., Glendale Today, AZ, Sun City

Ranes, Mark ....ext. 245
mranes@putnamsentinel.com, Circ. Mgr., Putnam County Sentinel, OH, Ottawa

Raney, Carolyn
craney@paducahsun.com, Adv. Dir. , The Paducah Sun, KY, Paducah

Raney, Rachael ....(317) 398-1276
rraney@shelbynews.com, Pub., The Shelbyville News, IN, Shelbyville

Rank, Dave ....(262) 306-5095
drank@conleynet.com, Conley Media LLC, WI, Beaver Dam

Rankin, Chase ....(520) 807-7760
crankin@tucson.com, Pub., Arizona Daily Star, AZ, Tucson

Rankin, Chase.........................(520) 573-4415
crankin@tucson.com, VP of Advertising, Tucson Newspapers/TMC, AZ, Tucson

Rankin, Chase
crankin@republicmedia.com, VP Pres., Adv.,

The Arizona Republic, AZ, Phoenix

Rankin, Chase ....(520) 573-4216
cjhorness@tucson.com, Pub, Arizona Daily Star, AZ, Tucson

Rankin, Flo
flo.rankin@gaflnews.com, Mng. Ed., Tifton Shopper, GA, Tifton

Rankin, John
RankinJ@monroenews.com, District Mgr., The Monroe News, MI, Monroe

Ranney, Arthur ....(608) 342-1627
ranneya@uwplatt.edu, Univ. of Wisconsin Platteville, WI, Platteville

Ransdell, Ty
news@newberryobserver.com, Pub., The Newberry Observer, SC, Newberry

Ransick, Chris
aspeditor@arapahoe.edu, Arapahoe Cmty. College, CO, Littleton

Ransom, Dale ....(508) 236-0348
dransom@thesunchronicle.com, Sports Ed., The Sun Chronicle, MA, Attleboro

Ranson, Steve ....(775) 423-6041
sranson@lahontanvalleynews.com, Ed. , Lahontan Valley News & Fallon Eagle Standard, NV, Fallon

Rao, Sandhya
sr02@txstate.edu, Prof./Assoc. Dir., Grad. Studies, Texas State University-San Marcos, TX, San Marcos

Rapone, Shari L.
sharirapone@gvpennysaver.com, Circ. Mgr., Genesee Valley Pennysaver, NY, Avon

Rapp , Bob ....(419) 609-5844
bobrapp@sanduskyregister.com, Ntnl Sales Mgr , Sandusky Register, OH, Sandusky

Rappleye, Christine
rappleye@deseretnews.com, Features Editor, Deseret News, UT, Salt Lake City

Rapson, Jeff ....(603) 650-1119
jeff.rapson@ckp.com, Dir., Sales, Saxotech, NH, Bedford

Rasbach, David
david.rasbach@bellinghamherald.com, Senior Editor Sports and Features, The Bellingham Herald, WA, Bellingham

Rasey, Dennis
drasey@j-adgraphics.com, Circ. Mgr., The Hastings Banner, MI, Hastings
drasey@j-adgraphics.com, Circ. Mgr, Reminder, MI, Hastings

Rasheed, Tahir .... (718) 229-0300 ext. 135
rasheed@timesledger.com, Acct. Mgr., TimesLedger Newspapers, NY, Bayside

Rasmussen, Al ....ext. 120
Gen. Mgr., Green Bay Real Estate Guide, WI, Green Bay

Rasmussen, Al .... (920) 432-2941 ext. 120
chronicle@itol.com, Vice Pres., Green Bay Community News (East/West), WI, Green Bay

Rasmussen, Al
chronicle@gogreenbay.com, Adv. Mgr., Weekend Open House Magazine, WI, Green Bay

Rasmussen, Eric N. ....(406) 323-1105
rrtnews@midrivers.com, Prodn. Mgr., The Roundup Record-Tribune/Winnett Times, MT, Roundup

Rasmussen, Kari ....(715) 845-5171
kari@thecitypages.com, Advt/Circu Mgr, City Pages, WI, Wausau

Rasmussen, Tim ....(303) 954-1896
trasmussen@denverpost.com, AME-Photography, The Denver Post, CO, Denver

Rasor, Rob ....(405) 366-3588
rrasor@normantranscript.com, Prod. Mgr., Moore American, OK, Norman

Ratajek, Bonnie L. ....(715) 395-5725
bonnie.ratajek@mx3.com, HR Mgr., Superior Publishing Company, NE, Superior

Ratcliff, Mary
editor@sfbayview.com, Ed., San Francisco Bay View, CA, San Francisco

Ratcliff, Willie
publisher@sfbayview.com, Pub., San Francisco Bay View, CA, San Francisco

Rath, Tim
trath@argus-press.com, Weekend Ed. , The Argus-Press, MI, Owosso

Rathke, Eric
ericr_ads@dailynews.net, Sales Associate, The Hays Daily News, KS, Hays

Rathsack, Richie ....(203) 317-2227
rrathsack@record-journal.com, Digital Content Editor, Record-Journal, CT, Meriden

Ratkovich, Tom.................(303) 296-9966 ext. 11
ter@astech-intermedia.com, Pres./CEO, ASTech InterMedia, CO, Denver

Ratliff, Chris
cratliff@salisburypost.com, Dir., Sales/Mktg., Salisbury Post, NC, Salisbury

Ratliff, Gregg ....(309) 346-1111 ext. 230
editor@pekintimes.com, Pub., Tazewell County Shopper, IL, Pekin

Ratliff, Jeffrey
jeffr@northwestsignal.net, Sports Ed., Northwest Signal, OH, Napoleon

Ratliff, Pat
editor@edmondsbeacon.com, Beacon Publishing Inc., WA

Ratliff, Stacie
classifieds@sidneyherald.com, Classified Sales, Sidney Herald, MT, Sidney

Rattiner, Dan
dan@danspapers.com, Pres./ Ed., Dan's Papers LLC, NY, Southampton

Rattray, David E.
editor@easthamptonstar.com, Ed., The East Hampton Star, NY, East Hampton

Rattray, Helen S........................(631) 838-4381
hsr@easthamptonstar.com, Pub., The East Hampton Star, NY, East Hampton

Ratza, Stephanie
sratza@descartes.com, CFO, Descartes Systems Group, ON, Waterloo

Ratzky, Harlan
harlan.ratzy@investors.com, Vice Pres., Internet Mktg., Investor's Business Daily, CA, Los Angeles

Ratzlaff, Don
donratz@hillsborofreepress.com, Ed., Hillsboro Free Press, KS, Hillsboro
donratz@hillsborofreepress.com, Ed., Buyer's Edge Of South Central Kansas, KS, Newton

Ratzmann, Bianka ....(212) 210-2194
bratzmann@nydailynews.com, Sales Mgr., New York Daily News, NY, New York

Rau, David ....(843) 842-9162
davidarau@aol.com, Chrmn/CEO, Sandusky Newspapers, Inc., SC, Hilton Head Island

Rauch, John
vci@myvillager.com, CEO, Villager, MN, Saint Paul

Rauh, Tracey.........................(978) 946-2242
trauh@eagletribune.com, Mng. Ed. , The Eagle-Tribune, MA, North Andover

Rausch, Brooke ....(810) 766-6326
brausch@flintjournal.com, Mng. Ed., The Swartz Creek News, MI, Flint

Rausch, Chris
chrisr@capegazette.com, Sales Manager, Cape Gazette, DE, Lewes

Rausch, Patricia ....(403) 314-4373
prausch@reddeeradvocate.com, National

Rep & Major Acct Asst, Friday Forward, AB, Red Deer

Rausch, Stacy
srausch@catholicherald.com, Prodn. Coord., Arlington Catholic Herald, VA, Arlington

Rausch, Tim .... (706) 823-3352
timothy.rausch@augusatchronicle.com, Business Editor, The Augusta Chronicle, GA, Augusta

Ravellette, Don
press@kadokatelco.com, Pub., Kadoka Press, SD, Kadoka

Ravellette, Don
don@pioneer-review.com, Pub., The Pioneer-Review, SD, Philip

Ravellette, Don
faithind@faithsd.com, Pub./Ed., The Faith Independent, SD, Faith

Ravellette, Don .... (605) 859-2516
Pub., Murdo Coyote, SD, Murdo

Ravellette, Don
courier@sdplains.com, Pub., The Bison Courier, SD, Bison

Raven, William
wraven@bellatrix.com, Sr. Vice Pres., Sales/Mktg., Bellatrix Systems, Inc., OR, Bend

Raver, Diane .... (812) 934-4343
Diane.Raver@batesvilleheraldtribune.com, assistant editor, The Herald-Tribune, IN, Batesville

Ravera, Maria .... (209) 578-2120
mravera@modbee.com, VP Audience Dev, Merced Sun-Star, CA, Merced

Ravera , Maria .... (916) 321-1615
mravera@sacbee.com, VP Audience Development, The Sacramento Bee, CA, Sacramento

Ravin, Kristen .... (802) 865-1020 x 47
calendar@sevendaysvt.com, Calendar Ed., Seven Days, VT, Burlington

Ravsten, Helen
enterprisenews@atcnet.net, Office Mgr., Idaho Enterprise, ID, Malad City

Rawley, Kate
srawley@trinity.edu, Instr./Dir., Devl., Trinity University, TX, San Antonio

Rawlings, Robert H.
pueblo@chieftain.com, Pub./Ed. , The Pueblo Chieftain, CO, Pueblo

Ray, David
dray@sbtinfo.com, Pub., Market Place, IN, South Bend

Ray, Deanna
deanna.ray@midwestproducer.com, Adv. Mgr., Midwest Messenger, NE, Tekamah

Ray, Douglas K. .... (847) 427-4510
dray@dailyherald.com, Chairman/Publisher/CEO, Daily Herald, IL, Arlington Heights
dray@dailyherald.com, Exec Ed/Gen Mgr, Ocala Star-Banner, FL, Ocala
dray@dailyherald.com, Gen Mgr, The Gainesville Sun, FL, Gainesville

Ray, Eddie .... (662) 581-7222
eray@gwcommonwealth.com, Bus. Mgr., The Greenwood Commonwealth, MS, Greenwood

Ray, Geri .... (859) 936-0350
gprice@amnews.com, Adv. Mgr., The Advocate-Messenger, KY, Danville

Ray, Karen
kray@sanmarcosrecord.com, Prodn. Supvr., San Marcos Daily Record, TX, San Marcos

Ray, Melanie
classified@lebanondemocrat.com, Adv. Mgr., Classified, The Lebanon Democrat, TN, Lebanon
classified@lebanondemocrat.com, Classified Mgr., The Hartsville Vidette, TN, Hartsville

Ray, Nancye ....(305) 361-3333 ext. 12

nray@islandernews.com, Ed. & Pub., Islander News, FL, Key Biscayne

Ray, Peter
pray@broadcastnews.ca, Quebec Correspondent, Broadcast News Limited, QC, Montreal

Ray, Yerby
onenews@observernewsonline.com, Mng. Ed., The Observer News Enterprise, NC, Newton

Raybon, Otis .... (706) 290-5265
oraybon@rn-t.com, Publisher, Rome News-Tribune, GA, Rome

Rayburn, Carver
crayburn@neshobademocrat.com, Assoc. Ed., The Neshoba Democrat, MS, Philadelphia

Raymer, Diana
draymer@dosmundos.com, Adv. Mgr., Dos Mundos, KS, Kansas City

Raymer, John .... (413) 585-5350
Prodn. Mgr., Pressroom, Daily Hampshire Gazette, MA, Northampton

Raymer, Marjory
marjory@mlive.com, Dir. of News, The Jackson Citizen Patriot, MI, Jackson

Raymond, L.
cartoonews@aol.com, Vice Pres., Sales, Cartoonews, Inc., New York

Raymond, Mark .... (541) 672-3321
mraymond@nrtoday.com, Pub., Umpqua Shopper, OR, Roseburg

Raymond, Mark .... (775) 283-5588
mraymond@nrtoday.com, Pub., Hot Sheet (OOB), NV, Carson City
mraymond@nrtoday.com, Pub., Nevada Appeal, NV, Carson City

Raymond, Mike .... (410) 704-5153
Towson Univ., MD, Towson

Rayos, Gail .... (407) 420-5582
grayos@orlandosentinel.com, Assoc. Mng. Ed., Bus., Orlando Sentinel, FL, Orlando

Razniewski, Chris
chris.razniewski@latimes.com, Dir., HR, Los Angeles Times, CA, Los Angeles

Razzano, Tiffany .... (727) 397-5563, ext. 306
trazzano@tbnweekly.com, Ed., Pinellas Park Beacon, FL, Seminole
trazzano@tbnweekly.com, Ed., Seminole Beacon, FL, Seminole

Re, Bernard .... (802) 447-2025
Interactive Media Dir., Bennington Banner, VT, Bennington

Rea, Bill
editor@caledoncitizen.com, Mng. Ed., Caledon Citizen, ON, Bolton

Rea, Doug
doug@nynewspapers.com, VP Adv., New York Press Association, NY, Cohoes

Rea, Glenn
glennrea@cuerorecord.com, Pub./Ed., The Cuero Record, TX, Cuero

Rea, Kim
krea@ncronline.org, Adv Mgr, National Catholic Reporter, MO, Kansas City

Rea, Lynn .... (757) 446-2097
lynn.rea@pilotonline.com, Nat'l Acct. Exec., The Virginian-Pilot, VA, Norfolk

Rea, Michelle
nypa@nynewspapers.com, Exec. Dir. , New York Press Association, NY, Cohoes

Read, Amy
aread@statesmanjournal.com, Digital Ed., Statesman Journal, OR, Salem

Read, Jeremy ....ext. 104
jeremy@samessenger.com, Adv. Dir., St. Albans Messenger, VT, Saint Albans

Read, Jeremy
jeremy@samessenger.com, Prodn. Mgr., Extra,

VT, Saint Albans

Read, Paul
paulr@spokanejournal.com, Pub., Spokane Journal of Business, WA, Spokane

Reader, Bill .... (740) 597-1294
Asst. Prof., Ohio University, OH, Athens

Reagan, Dann .... (325) 670-5213
reagand@reporternews.com, Online Dir., Abilene Reporter-News, TX, Abilene

Reagan, Joey
reagan@wsu.edu, Prof., Washington State University, WA, Pullman

Real, Kathy .... (508) 749-3166 x331
kreal@worcestermag.com, Pub. , Worcester Magazine, MA, Worcester

Ream, Amanda
aream@nassaucountyrecord.com, Editor, Nassau County Record, FL, Callahan

Reaman, Mark
editorial@crestedbuttenews.com, Ed., Crested Butte News, CO, Crested Butte

Reardon, Emily .... (508) 213-2275
emily.reardon@nichols.edu, Assistant Director of Admissions / International Students Counselor, Nichols College, MA, Dudley

Reardon, Frances
freardon@nothernpen.ca, Office/Circ Mgr, Northern Pen, NL, Saint Anthony

Reaska, Donna
dreaska@timestoday.com, Office Mgr., Washington Times Reporter, IL, Pekin
dreaska@timestoday.com, Office Mgr., Times News Group, IL, Pekin
dreaska@timestoday.com, Office Mgr., Woodford Times, IL, Pekin

Reaves, Gayle .... (817) 321-9787
Gayle.Reaves@fwweekly.com, Ed., Fort Worth Weekly, TX, Fort Worth

Reaves, Ron .... (256) 549-2048
ron.reaves@gadsdentimestoday.com, Exec. Ed., The Gadsden Times, AL, Gadsden

Reaves, Ron .... (256) 549-2048
ron.reaves@gadsdentimes.com, Executive Editor, Times2, AL, Gadsden

Rebele, Rowland .... (831) 688-0733
Paradise Post, CA, Paradise

Rebelo, Gina .... (212) 210-2052
grebelo@nydailynews.com, Sales Mgr., Real Estate & Travel, New York Daily News, NY, New York

Reber, Grata .... (806) 385-4481
ads@lambcountyleadernews.com, Adv. Dir., Lamb County Leader-News, TX, Littlefield

Rebman, Stephanie
(205) 443-5631, Mng. Ed., Birmingham Business Journal, AL, Birmingham

Rebmann, Dr. Richard
leserpost@stn.zgs.de, CEO, Filder-Zeitung, Stuttgart

Rebollo, Esther
efecol@efebogota.com.co, Rep., EFE News Services - Bogota, Colombia, Bogota

Rechenbach, Jeffrey
jrechenbach@cwa-union.org, Sec./Treasure, Communications Workers of America, DC, Washington

Recker, Pete .... (319) 335-5783
Univ. of Iowa, IA, Iowa City

Recore, Cassey
cassey@afcp.org, Administrative Assistant, Association of Free Community Papers, NY, Liverpool

Rector, Bill F.
wfr@ipa.net, Pub., The Daily Record, AR, Little Rock

Rector, Molly
sales@spectralogic.com, Dir., Cor. Mktg.,

Spectra Logic, CO, Boulder

Rector, Roger D.
roger@idacountycourier.com, Pub, Reminder, IA, Ida Grove

Rector, Roger D. .... (712) 364-3131
roger@idacountycourier.com, Pub., Ida County Courier, IA, Ida Grove

Rector, Todd .... (312) 222-4974
trector@tribune.com, Art Dir., TMS Specialty Products, IL, Chicago

Red, Phillip .... (918) 273-2446
nowatastar@sbcglobal.net, Pub., The Nowata Star, OK, Nowata

Red Corn, Louise .... (918) 847-2916
louise@bighearttimes.com, Owner/Pub/Ed, Bigheart Times, OK, Barnsdall

Redd, Teresa
tredd@herald-democrat.com, Prodn. Mgr., Composing, Herald Democrat, TX, Sherman

Redd, Teresa
tredd@heralddemocrat.com, Prodn. Mgr., The Herald Democrat Shopper Collin County, TX, Denison
tredd@heralddemocrat.com, Prodn. Mgr., The Herald Democrat Shopper Bryan County, TX, Denison

Reddell, Trace
trace.reddell@du.edu, Assoc. Prof./Dir., Digital Media Studies Grad. prog., University of Denver, CO, Denver

Reddell, Valerie .... (830) 672-2861
publisher@gonzalesinquirer.com, The Gonzales Inquirer, TX, Gonzales

Reddell, Valerie .... (936) 327-4357
Ed., Polk County Enterprise, TX, Livingston

Redder, Carl .... (231) 439-9379
credder@petoskeynews.com, Circ. Mgr., Northern Michigan Review, MI, Petoskey

Reddick, Randy
r.reddick@ttu.edu, Prof./Morris Professor and chair, Dept. of Journalism, Texas Tech University, TX, Lubbock

Redecker, Jerre .... (360) 754-5422
jredecker@theolympian.com, Sr. Ed., The Olympian, WA, Olympia

Redfearn, Dixie .... (310) 510-0500
editor@thecatalinaislander.com, Editor, The Catalina Islander, CA, Avalon

Redfearn, Kelly .... (605) 331-2356
kredfearn@argusleader.com, Advertising Director, Argus Leader, SD, Sioux Falls

Redfield, Jim
jimredfield@griffinchaseoliver.com, CEO, Griffin Chase Oliver, Inc., CA, Laguna Niguel

Redford, Brad ....ext. 217
sports@columbiabasinherald.com, Sports Ed., Columbia Basin Herald, WA, Moses Lake

Reding, Anita .... (918) 396-1616
anitar@skiatookjournal.com, Mng. Ed., Stigler News-Sentinel, OK, Stigler

Redlack, Darlainea .... (250) 445-2233
darlainea.redlack@boundarycreektimes.com, Circulation, The Boundary Creek Times, BC, Greenwood

Redlack, Darlainea
circulation@grandforksgazette.ca, Circ. Mgr., West Kootenay Advertiser, BC, Grand Forks

Redlack, Darlainea .... (250) 442-2191
darlainea.redlack@boundarycreektimes.com, Circulation, The Grand Forks Gazette, BC, Grand Forks

Redman, Janis
jredman@spooneradvocate.com, Prod. Mgr., Spooner Advocate, WI, Spooner

Redmer, Michelle .... (701) 377-2626
secretary, Burke County Tribune, ND, Bowbells

Redmon, Jeffrey .... (715) 749-3331

publisher@centralstcroixnews.com, Pub., Central St. Croix News, WI, Roberts

Redmond, Deborah........(916) 498-1234, ext 1373
deborahr@newsreview.com, Chief Operating Officer, Sacramento News & Review, CA, Sacramento

Redmond, Erin ....(408) 842-1694
eredmond@newsvmedia.com, Sports Ed, The Gilroy Dispatch, CA, Gilroy

Redmond, Keith.......................(208) 377-6455
kredmond@idahostatesman.com, Fin. Dir., Idaho Statesman, ID, Boise

Redshaw, Robert.....................(902) 563-3847
rredshaw@cbpost.com, Dir., Sales & Mktg., The Cape Breton Post, NS, Sydney

Reece, Gary
garyreece@aol.com, Owner, Reece & Associates, GA, Atlanta

Reece, Jeff
jeff.reece@pilotonline.com, Sr. Ed., The Virginian-Pilot, VA, Norfolk

Reece, Kelly
gcnews@embarqmail.com, Pub., Garden County News, NE, Oshkosh

Reece, Richard
reece@raldioc.org, Ed., The North Carolina Catholic, NC, Raleigh

Reed, Andy
andy.reed@lebanondemocrat.com, Sports Ed., The Lebanon Democrat, TN, Lebanon

Reed, Becky ....(360) 568-4121
Becky@snoho.com, Pub. / Adv. Mgr., Everett New Tribune, WA, Snohomish

Reed, Becky ....(360) 568-4121
becky@snoho.com, Pub. / Adv. Mgr., Snohomish County Tribune, WA, Snohomish

Reed, Cathy.................(724) 465-5555 ext. 206
creed@indianagazette.net, Adv. Dir., The Indiana Gazette, PA, Indiana

Reed, Chris
creed@ctimes.biz, Ad., Cherokee Chronicle Times, IA, Cherokee

Reed, Craig ....(541) 957-4210
creed@nrtoday.com, Features Ed., The News-Review, OR, Roseburg

Reed, Edwin H.
tribnews@otelco.net, Pub., The Arab Tribune, AL, Arab

Reed, Emily.......................(707) 464-2141
ereed@triplicate.com, Adv Acct Mgr, The Del Norte Triplicate, CA, Crescent City

Reed, Emily.................(205) 755-5747 ext. 613
emily.reed@clantonadvertiser.com, Staff Writer, The Clanton Advertiser, AL, Clanton

Reed, George R........................(904) 285-3239
redmsconsulting@cs.com, Mng. Dir., Media Services Group, Inc., FL, Ponte Vedra

Reed, Jennifer ....(585) 394-0770 Ext.330
jreed@messengerpostmedia.com, Digital Pub. Ed., Daily Messenger, NY, Canandaigua

Reed, John ....(217) 351-5230
jreed@news-gazette.com, Publisher, Rantoul Press, IL, Rantoul

Reed, John........................(217) 351-5230
jreed@news-gazette.com, CEO/Pub., The News-Gazette, IL, Champaign

Reed, K.........................(360) 394-5833
kreid@whidbeynewsgroup.com, Pub./Ed., Whidbey Crosswind, WA, Coupeville

Reed, Kevin
kevin.c.reed@medstar.net, Howard Univ., DC, Washington

Reed, Lisa ....(715) 735-7500 Ext. 146
staff writer, EagleHerald - ehextra.com, WI, Marinette

Reed, Marc
ezra.singer@verizon.com, Exec. Vice Pres.,

HR, Verizon Communications, Inc., NY, New York

Reed, Maryanne ....(304) 293-3505
pireed@mail.wvu.edu, Dean/Prof., West Virginia University, WV, Morgantown

Reed, Matt..............................(321) 242-3631
mreed@floridatoday.com, Public Interest Editor, Florida Today, FL, Melbourne

Reed, Michael E. ....(585) 598-0030
mreed@gatehousemedia.com, CEO, GateHouse Media, Inc., NY, Pittsford

Reed, Miles..........................(518) 395-3106
reed@dailygazette.com, Mng. Ed., The Daily Gazette, NY, Schenectady

Reed, Ray ....(254) 634-6666
ray.reed@forthoodsentinel.com, Gen. Mgr., Fort Hood Sentinel, TX, Fort Hood

Reed, Rick
ngsports@comcast.net, Mng. Ed./Sports Ed., The News-Gazette, IN, Winchester

Reed, Robert .... ext. 2483
bobbo.reed@scni.com, Prodn. Supvr., Pagination-Night, The Advocate, CT, Stamford

Reed, Roy
aa07298@uaccb.edu, Prof. Emer., University of Arkansas, AR, Fayetteville

Reed, Sarah ....(660) 463-7522
concordiannews@centurytel.net, The Concordian, MO, Concordia

Reed, Sheena
sheena.read@sunmedia.ca, Ed., The Nanton News, AB, Nanton

Reed, Steve ....(602) 444-4464
steve.reed@pni.com, Circ. Opns. Mgr., The Arizona Republic, AZ, Phoenix

Reed, Susanne
editor@hamiltoncountyherald.com, Gen. Mgr./ Adv. Dir., Hamilton County Herald, TN, Chattanooga

Reed, Terri
terri.reed@ruxton.com, Dir., West Coast Sales, Ruxton Group/VMG Advertising, AZ, Phoenix

Reed , Amanda..............(845) 252-7414 , ext 23
amanda@riverreporter.com, Prod. Mgr., The River Reporter, NY, Narrowsburg

Reedy, Jeffrey
jreedy@hearstnp.com, Circ. Dir., Opns., The Beaumont Enterprise, TX, Beaumont

Reedy, Jeffrey T.
jreedy@hearstnp.com, Pub., The Hardin County News, TX, Beaumont

Reeger, Barry.........................(724) 836-5454
breeger@tribweb.com, Chief of Photography, Opinion, Tribune-Review, PA, Greensburg

Reel, Guy ....(803) 323-4531
reelg@winthrop.edu, Asst. Prof., Winthrop University, SC, Rock Hill

Reel, Guy ....(803) 323-4531
reelg@winthrop.edu, Faculty Adviser, The Johnsonian, SC, Rock Hill

Reen, Christopher ....(405) 475-3311
creen@oklahoman.com, Pres. & Pub., The Oklahoman, OK, Oklahoma City

Reep, Keanon ....(870) 820-0131
kreep@whitehalljournal.com, Adv. Sales, White Hall Journal, AR, White Hall

Rees, David
reesd@missouri.edu, Chrmn., Kappa Alpha Mu Honorary Society in Photo Journalism, MO, Columbia

Rees, Jay ....(305) 347-6627
jrees@alm.com, Business Editor, Miami Daily Business Review, FL, Miami

Rees, Jay ....(305) 347-6627
jrees@alm.com, Business Editor, Palm Beach Daily Business Review, FL, Miami

Rees, Maurice.........................(902) 647-2968
maurice@theshorelinejournal.com, The Shoreline Journal, NS, Bass River

Rees, Michael W.
mrees@thepaperofwabash.com, Gen. Mgr., The Paper, IN, Wabash

Rees, Mike
mrees@thepaperofwabash.com, Pub., The News-Journal, IN, Wabash

Rees, Ryan
rrees@timescourier.com, Staff Writer, Times-Courier, GA, Ellijay

Rees, Wayne W. ....(260) 563-8326
ads@thepaperofwabash.com, OWNER, PUB. , The Paper, IN, Wabash

Reese, Donald
dreese@tnonline.com, Adv. Dir., Mktg., Times News, PA, Lehighton

Reese, Jody
jreese@hippopress.com, Publisher, The Hippo, NH, Manchester

Reese, Kaylie
kreese@bangordailynews.com, Copy Ed., Bangor Daily News, ME, Bangor

Reese, Lisa
lnelless@gannett.com, President & Publisher , Pensacola News Journal, FL, Pensacola
lnelless@gannett.com, Pub., Statesman Journal, OR, Salem

Reese, Lisa ....(724) 775-3200 ext. 120
lreese@timesonline.com, Pub., Beaver County Times, PA, Beaver

Reese, Lori ....(336) 727-7471
lreese@wsjournal.com, Advertising Sales Manager, Winston-Salem Journal, NC, Winston Salem

Reese, Mike
neoshopressoffice@sbcglobal.net, Prod. Mgr., Neosho Daily News, MO, Neosho

Reese, Nancy
nreece@kentuckynewera.com, Classified Mgr., Fort Campbell Courier, KY, Hopkinsville

Reese, Tallitha
rjeditor@centurytel.net, Ed., Republican Journal, WI, Darlington

Reese, Tammy ....(765) 213-5772
treese@muncie.gannett.com, Classified Supervisor, The Star Press, IN, Muncie

Reese Willey, Scott...................(281) 342-4474
swilley@fbherald.com, Managing Ed., Fort Bend Herald, TX, Rosenberg

Reeter-Brown, Laurie ....(972) 870-1992
laurier@ramblernewspapers.net, Office Mgr., The Irving Rambler, TX, Irving

Reetz, John
john.reetz@mediasolutionspartners.com, Gen. Mgr., COXnet, Cox Media Group, GA, Atlanta

Reeve, Debi
subscriptions@cheshireherald.com, Circ. Mgr., The Cheshire Herald, CT, Cheshire

Reeves, Amy
amy@goldendalesentinel.com, Advertising Representation, Goldendale Sentinel, WA, Goldendale

Reeves, Bill.........................(607) 432-1000
Hartwick College, NY, Oneonta

Reeves, Byron
reeves@stanford.edu, Edwards Prof., Stanford University, CA, Stanford

Reeves, Carla
sales@arenacindependent.com, Sales, Arenac County Independent, MI, Standish

Reeves, Cherri ....(615) 384-3567
creeves@mtcngroup.com, Staff Writer, Robertson County Times, TN, Clarksville

Reeves, Garth B. ....(305) 693-7093
garth@miamitimesonline.com, VP Business

Development, The Miami Times, FL, Miami

Reeves, Jeffrey ....(760) 754-2891
jreeves@u-bild.com, Features Ed., U-Bild Newspaper Features, Oceanside

Reeves, Jimmie
jimmie.reeves@ttu.edu, Assoc. Prof., Texas Tech University, TX, Lubbock

Reeves, John
bear78@cretenews.net, Pub., The Crete News, NE, Crete

Reeves, Julie.........................(931) 796-3191
lewisherald@bellsouth.net, Graphic Artist, Lewis County Herald, TN, Hohenwald

Reeves, Kathy
graphics@valleytimes-news.com, Graphics Ed., The Valley Times-News, AL, Lanett

Reeves, Laurenda
laurenda.reeves@lighthousenow.ca, Circ. Mgr., The Bulletin, NS, Bridgewater

Reeves, Laurenda
laurenda.reeves@lighthousenow.ca, Circ. Mgr., Lighthouse Now, NS, Bridgewater

Reeves, Rachel J.
info@miamitimesonline.com, Pub., The Miami Times, FL, Miami

Reeves, Stacey.........................(432) 333-7612
sreeves@oaoa.com, Nat'l Adv. Coord., Odessa American, TX, Odessa

Reeves, Stephanie
stephanie.reeves@selmatimesjournal.com, Acct. Dept Mgr, The Selma Times-Journal, AL, Selma

Reeves, Tim ....(601) 636-4545 ext. 122
tim.reeves@vicksburgpost.com, President/ Publisher, The Vicksburg Post, MS, Vicksburg

Reeves, Timothy
tim.reeves@vicksburgpost.com, Publisher, The Vicksburg Post, MS, Vicksburg

Reevs, James A......................(906) 228-2500
jreevs@miningjournal.net, Pub., The Mining Journal, MI, Marquette

Regan, Charles..............(805) 685-3100 ext. 124
reganc@maps.com, Exec. Vice Pres., Maps. com, CA, Santa Barbara

Regan, Myra.....................(386) 362-1734 x122
myra.regan@gaflnews.com, Pub., Jasper News, FL, Live Oak
myra.regan@gaflnews.com, Pub., Suwannee Democrat, FL, Live Oak
myra.regan@gaflnews.com, Publisher, Mayo Free Press, FL, Live Oak

Regan, Trace
tregan@cc.owu.edu, Chair/Prof., Ohio Wesleyan University, OH, Delaware

Regentin, Douglas
recorder@thumb.net, Ed., Tribune Recorder Leader, MI, Sandusky

Regimbald, Johanne ....(819) 425-8658
johanne.regimbald@quebecormedia.com, Information Du Nord Mont Tremblant, QC, Mont-Tremblant
johanne.regimbald@quebecormedia.com, Éditrice, Information Du Nord L'annonciation, QC, Mont-Tremblant

Regimbald, Johanne ....(819) 425-8658
info.nord@hebdosquebecor.com, Information Du Nord Sainte-agathe, QC, Mont Tremblant
info.nord@hebdosquebecor.com, Information Du Nord Vallee De La Rouge, QC, Mont-Tremblant

Register, Barb
bregister@pal-item.com, Classified Sales Rep., Palladium-Item, IN, Richmond

Register, Jim
jim.register@kinston.com, Circ. Dir., The Kinston Free Press, NC, Kinston

Register, Kathy ....(256) 840-3000 ext 120
kregister@sandmountainreporter.com,

Advertising Director, Sand Mountain Reporter, AL, Albertville

Rego, Gerry .... ext. 106
Adv. Rep., The Spectator, MA, New Bedford

Rego, Mike
mrego@eastbaynewspapers.com, Ed., The Post, RI, Bristol

Regt, Trina de
trina.deregt@sunmedia.ca, Circulation, Vermilion Standard, AB, Vermilion

Rehberg, Kevin
kevin.rehberg@auditedmedia.com, Dir., Client Dev., Alliance for Audited Media (AAM), IL, Arlington Heights

Reiber, Marge
mreiber@reporter-herald.com, HR Coord., Loveland Reporter-Herald, CO, Loveland

Reich, Sondra .... (812) 838-4811
advertising@mvdemocrat.com, Sales Rep, Mount Vernon Democrat, IN, Mount Vernon

Reichard, Mike .... (505) 428-7605
mreichard@sfnewmexican.com, Cir. Dir., The Santa Fe New Mexican, NM, Santa Fe

Reichard, Stacey .... (708) 608-4177
Moraine Valley Cmty. College, IL, Palos Hills

Reichbach, Emily .... (650) 255-1529
emily@makingit.com, Artists Representative , Making It Productions, Hermosa Beach

Reichblum, Charles
charles@knowledgeinanutshell.com, Contact, Century Features, Inc., PA, Pittsburgh

Reichenthal, Mark
markr@branfman.com, Assoc., Branfman Law Group, P.C., CA, Oceanside

Reichert, George .... (207) 504-8220
greichert@timesrecord.com, Subscriber Services Mgr., The Times Record, ME, Brunswick

Reichert, Susan
sreichert@readingeagle.com, Reading Eagle Company, PA, Reading

Reichman, Bob
breichman@sctnews.com, Ed., Sumter County Times, FL, Bushnell

Reid, Barry
kfrtimes@pldi.net, Pub., The Kingfisher Times & Free Press, OK, Kingfisher

Reid, Brandon .... (920) 686-2984
Sports Ed., The Sheboygan Press, WI, Sheboygan

Reid, Cathy
creid@postsignal.com, Adv. Mgr., Pilot Point Post Signal, TX, Pilot Point

Reid, Chris
art@cushingcitizen.com, Graphics, Cushing Citizen, OK, Cushing

Reid, Christine
editor@kingfisherpress.net, Sr. Ed., The Kingfisher Times & Free Press, OK, Kingfisher

Reid, David
davidreid@cushingcitizen.com, Owner/Pub., Cushing Citizen, OK, Cushing

Reid, Debbie
DReid@avtimes.net, Bus. Mgr. , Alberni Valley Times, BC, Port Alberni

Reid, Gary
kfrtimesgary@pldi.net, Pub. Emeritus, The Kingfisher Times & Free Press, OK, Kingfisher

Reid, Janice
sales@aldergrovestar.com, Adv. Sales Mgr., The Aldergrove Star, BC, Aldergrove

Reid, Jim .... (203) 354-1016
jreid@thehour.com, Advertising Manager, The Hour, CT, Norwalk

Reid, Kristen

kreid@gatehosuemedia.com, Digital Mktg. Specialist, Benton Evening News, IL, Benton

Reid, Lacey
echoads2@mrnews.ca, Advertising, The Echo-pioneer, AB, High Level

Reid, Macklin K. .... (203) 894-3351
mreid@acorn-online.com, News Ed., Ridgefield Press, CT, Ridgefield

Reid, Matt .... (978) 739-8509
mreid@wickedlocal.com, Ed., Stoneham Sun, MA, Somerville

Reid, Myra
accounting@cushingcitizen.com, Accounting, Cushing Citizen, OK, Cushing

Reid, Olive
oreid@umd.edu, Assoc. Dean/Dir., Undergrad. Studies, University of Maryland, MD, College Park

Reid, Phillip .... (580) 336-2222
wdn@wdnonline.com, Owner/Pub., The Perry Daily Journal, OK, Perry

Reid, Phillip R. .... (580) 772-3301
wdn@wdnonline.com, Pub., Weatherford Daily News, OK, Weatherford

Reid, Phillip R.
vdj@cableone.net, Pub. , The Vinita Daily Journal, OK, Vinita

Reid, Philip
vdj@cableone.net, Pub, The American, OK, Fairland

Reid, Rosalind
ros@casw.org, Exec. Dir., Council for the Advancement of Science Writing, Inc., WV, Hedgesville

Reigler, Hunter
hreigler@messenger-inquirer.com, News Ed., Messenger-Inquirer, KY, Owensboro

Reiher, Nick
nick.reiher@gmail.com, Ed., Farmers Weekly Review, IL, Joliet
nick.reiher@gmail.com, News Ed., Fox Valley Villages Sun, IL, Naperville

Reiling, Amanda
areiling@fayettepublishing.com, Prodn. Sup., The Elgin Echo, IA, West Union

Reilly, Jane .... (201) 612-0100
nyfwa@aol.com, Exec. Mgr., New York Financial Writers Association, Inc., NJ, Ridgewood

Reilly, John P. .... (203) 354-1048
Editor Emeritus, The Hour, CT, Norwalk

Reilly, Mike .... (402) 444-1277
mike.reilly@owh.com, Executive Editor, Omaha World-Herald, NE, Omaha

Reilly, Patrick
preilly@thedodgevillechronicle.com, Co-Pub./Ed., The Dodgeville Chronicle, WI, Dodgeville

Reilly, Tom .... (508) 236-0332
treilly@thesunchronicle.com, Sunday Ed., The Sun Chronicle, MA, Attleboro

Reily, Ann
areily@newburyportmagazine.com, Features Ed., The Daily News, MA, Newburyport

Reily, Emily
ereily@lowellsun.com, Copy Ed., The Sun, MA, Lowell

Reily, Ross
ross.reily@msbusiness.com, Editor, Mississippi Business Journal, MS, Jackson

Rein, Mark .... (308) 635-6057
mrein@wncc.net, Adv. Mgr., Western Nebraska Community College, NE, Scottsbluff

Reingold, Joyce
jreingold@pbdailynews.com, Pub., Palm Beach Daily News, FL, Palm Beach

Reinhardt, Andrew
andrew.reinhardt@startribune.com, Retail

Marketing Specialist
, Star Tribune, MN, Minneapolis

Reinhart, Amy .... (812) 488-2846
crescentmagazine@evansville.edu, Writing Director, Univ. of Evansville, IN, Evansville

Reinhart, Max
mreinhart@bryantimes.com, Asst. Ed. , The Bryan Times, OH, Bryan

Reinhart, Shannon
info@wideareaclassifieds.com, Exec. Dir., Wide Area Classified, MN, New Ulm

Reinholt Derr , Sonja .... (631) 354-8050
sderr@timesreview.com, Sales & Marketing Dir., The Suffolk Times, NY, Mattituck
sderr@timesreview.com, Sales & Marketing Dir., Riverhead News-Review, NY, Mattituck

Reinig, Pam
ccrnews@alpinecom.net, Ed., The Clayton County Register, IA, Elkader

Reinschmidt, Paul .... (605) 886-6901 ext. 110
paul.reinschmidt@thepublicopinion.com, Circ. Mgr., Coteau Shopper, SD, Watertown

Reinsel Cotter, Pamela .... (401) 277-7155
pcotter@providencejournal.com, Asst. Manag. Ed. Breaking News/Social Media, The Providence Journal, RI, Providence

Reis, Don
don.reis@latimes.com, Senior VP & Chief Rev. Officer, Los Angeles Times, CA, Los Angeles

Reis, Jerry .... ext. 112
Adv. Rep., The Spectator, MA, New Bedford

Reis, Mark .... (719) 636-0245
mark.reis@gazette.com, Photo/Video Director, The Gazette, CO, Colorado Springs

Reis, Vicky .... (785) 295-1125
vicky.reis@cjonline.com, Print Adv. Dir., The Topeka Capital-Journal, KS, Topeka

Reischel, Rob
robreischel@gmail.com, Sports Ed., Middleton Times-Tribune, WI, Black Earth

Reiste, Kenneth .... (605) 874-2499
clprint@itctel.com, Pub./Ed., Clear Lake Courier, SD, Clear Lake

Reiter, Wally
wreiter@ncronline.org, CFO/Bus. Mgr., National Catholic Reporter, MO, Kansas City

Reitknecht, Daria
dariareitknecht@gvpennysaver.com, Advertising Director, Genesee Valley Pennysaver, NY, Avon

Reitmeie, Deb
dreitmeier@reddeeradvocate.com, Circ. Mgr., Central Alberta Life, AB, Red Deer

Reitmeier, Debbie .... (403) 314-4302
dreitmeier@reddeeradvocate.com, Circulation Mgr, Friday Forward, AB, Red Deer

Reitsma-Bick, Angela
editor@christiancourier.ca, News Ed., Christian Courier, ON, Saint Catharine's

Relinger, Paul
prellinger@mykawartha.com, Special Pjcts. Ed., Peterborough This Week, ON, Peterborough

Relis, Jamie
jrelis@pubgroup.com, Acct. Mgr., Relish - Los Angeles, CA, Culver City

Relkow, Dan .... (403) 314-4312
drelkow@reddeeradvocate.com, Bus. Mgr., Red Deer Advocate, AB, Red Deer

Relph, Joseph .... (620) 378-4415
news@wilsoncountycitizen.com, Ed., Wilson County Citizen, KS, Fredonia

Rembe, Lorri
lrembe@pdclarion.com, Admin. Asst,, Princeton Daily Clarion, IN, Princeton

Remitz, Ed
sanmatean@smccd.net., College of San

Mateo, CA, San Mateo

Remmerie, Dirk
nvcrebactie@nieuwsblad.be, Ed., HET VOLK, Bagaarden

Rempp, Kerri .... (308) 432-5511
kerri.rempp@lee.net, Ed., The Chadron Record, NE, Chadron

Remy, Jon .... (714) 504-9437
jtremy@hotmail.com, General Manager, The Catalina Islander, CA, Avalon

Renard, Beth
beth.renard@daily-iberian.com, Admin. Secretary, The Daily Iberian, LA, New Iberia

Renaud, Endre
endre.renaud@hebdosquebecor.com, Gen. Mgr., Le Citoyen De La Vallee De L'or, QC, Val d'Or

Renaud, Jerry
jrenaud@unl.edu, Prof., University of Nebraska-Lincoln, NE, Lincoln

Renaud, John .... (573) 334-8626
jrenaud@semissourian.com, Concord Publishing House, Inc., MO, Cape Girardeau
jrenaud@semissourian.com, Prodn. Coord., Southeast Missourian, MO, Cape Girardeau

Renberg, Werner
werren@att.net, Self-Syndicator, Werner Renberg, Chappaqua

Rendall, Trevor
trevorr@inlander.com, Distribution Manager, The Pacific Northwest Inlander, WA, Spokane

Renderman, Michael
michael.renderman@cision.com, Vice Pres., Bus. Devel., Cision US, Inc., IL, Chicago

Rendleman, Raymond .... (503) 546-0742
rrendleman@clackamasreview.com, Ed, The Clackamas Review, OR, Portland
rrendleman@clackamasreview.com, Ed, Oregon City News, OR, Portland

Rendon, Dee .... (956) 585-4893
dee@sharylandtimes.com, Advertising Manager, Progress Times, TX, Mission

Reneau, Danny .... (409) 385-5278
Publisher@silsbeebee.com, Pub., Silsbee Bee, TX, Silsbee

Reneau, Danny .... (409) 385-5278
Publisher@silsbeebee.com, Pub, Kirbyville Banner, TX, Kirbyville

Reneau, Janet .... (409) 385-5278
publisher@silsbeebee.com, Adv. Dir., Silsbee Bee, TX, Silsbee

Reneau, Michael .... (423) 359-3138
michael.reneau@greenevillesun.com, Ed., The Greeneville Sun, TN, Greeneville

Renee, Yardley .... (514) 397-3926
renee.yardley@tembec.com, VP, Sales & Marketing, Tembec, ON, Etobicoke

Renfeld, Lori .... (406) 265-4112
Montana State Univ. Northern, MT, Havre

Renken, Brent .... (240) 215-8588
brenken@newspost.com, Dir. Adv. & Mrktg. , The Frederick News-Post, MD, Frederick

Renn, Linda .... (559) 591-4632
editor@thedinubasentinel.com, Ed., The Dinuba Sentinel, CA, Dinuba

Renner, Tara .... (740) 852-1616 Ext. 1623
trenner@civitasmedia.com, Acct. Exec. , The Madison Press, OH, London

Rennie, Doug .... (215) 898-7483
Univ. of Pennsylvania Law School, PA, Philadelphia

Reno, David .... (757) 446-2897
DAVID.RENO@PILOTONLINE.COM, Operations Director, Landmark Communications, Inc., VA, Norfolk

Reno, John
john.reno@molawyersmedia.com, Prod. Mgr.,

Missouri Lawyers Media, MO, Saint Louis

Reno, John
john.reno@molawyersmedia.com, Produ Mgr, St. Charles County Business Record, MO, Saint Charles

Reno, Steve
steve.reno@willcoxrangenews.com, Adv. Rep., Arizona Range News, AZ, Sierra Vista

Renois, Teddy .... (985) 857-2210
teddy.renois@houmatoday.com, Sports Writer, Daily Comet, LA, Thibodaux

Renollet, Jennifer .... (620) 257-2368
Office Asst., The Lyons News, KS, Lyons

Renouf-Farrell, Sharon .... (418) 752-5400
specs@globetrotter.net, Pub., Sea-coast Publications Inc./the Gaspe Spec, QC, New Carlisle

Renovitch, James
gaming@austinchronicle.com, Listings Ed, Austin Chronicle, TX, Austin

Rensberry, Steve .... (618) 667-3111
editor@wisperhome.com, Ed., Troy Times-Tribune, IL, Troy

Renstrom, Kim .... (760) 778-4646
kim.renstrom@desertsun.com, Advertising , Desert Post Weekly, CA, Palm Springs

Rentas, David
drentas@nypost.com, Ed. Dept./Photo, New York Post, NY, New York

Renteria, Mario .... (760) 337-3434
mrenteria@ivpressonline.com, Sports Ed., Imperial Valley Press, CA, El Centro

Rentner, Terry
trentne@bgsu.edu, Chair/Assoc. Prof., Bowling Green State University, OH, Bowling Green

Renuard, Lindsey
john.ferguson@baledger.com, Ed, Skiatook Journal, OK, Skiatook

Renze-Rhodes, Lisa
lrenze@bsu.edu, Publications Adviser, Ball State University, IN, Muncie

Reott, Krista
kreott@tribweb.com, Major/Nat'l Sales Asst., Leader Times, PA, Kittanning

Repath, Bill
brepath@thespec.com, Director of Operations, The Hamilton Spectator, ON, Hamilton

Repecki, Tiffany .... (239) 574-1110
trepecki@breezenewspapers.com, Assoc. ed., Cape Coral Breeze, FL, Cape Coral

Reppert, Jerry L.
editor@cairocitizen.com, Pub., The Cairo Citizen, IL, Cairo

Reppert, Jerry L.
reppert@midwest.net, Pub., The Gazette-Democrat, IL, Anna

Reppert, Jerry L.
reppert@midwest.net, Pub., Monday's Pub, IL, Anna

Resch, Alan D.
advertising@thechathamnews.com, Pub./Adv. Dir, The Chatham Record, NC, Pittsboro

Reschny, Delilah .... (306) 753-7179
Editor/Publisher, Macklin Mirror, SK, Macklin

Resmer, Cathy .... (802) 865-1020 x 14
cathy@sevendaysvt.com, Assoc. Pub., Seven Days, VT, Burlington

Resnek, Joshua .... (781) 284-2400
editor@chelsearecord.com, Vice Pres./ executive editor, Chelsea Record, MA, Revere

Ressler, Lora .... (503) 728-3350
lressler@countrymedia.net, Gen. Mgr., The Chief, OR, Clatskanie

Restino, Carey .... (907) 299-1172
crestino@reportalaska.com, News Ed., The Arctic Sounder, AK, Anchorage

crestino@reportalaska.com, News Ed., The Bristol Bay Times, AK, Anchorage

crestino@reportalaska.com, News Ed., The Dutch Harbor Fisherman, AK, Anchorage

Retherford, Aaron .... (802) 479-2582
editor@vt-world.com, Ed, The World, VT, Barre

Rethi, Donna .... (724) 465-5555 ext. 290
rethi@indianagazette.net, Prodn. Mgr., The Indiana Gazette, PA, Indiana

Retsinas, Greg .... (707) 526-8662
greg.retsinas@pressdemocrat.com, Digital Director, The Press Democrat, CA, Santa Rosa

Rettew, Robin
robin.rettew@targetbase.com, Mng. Dir., Targetbase, TX, Irving

Reuer, Wendy .... (701) 241-5530
wreuer@forumcomm.com, Assistant Ed., West Fargo Pioneer, ND, West Fargo
wreuer@forumcomm.com, Asst. Ed., W.F. Pioneer, InForum, ND, Fargo

Reuterfors, Roland .... (908) 216-8142
roland@motterstitch.com, Consultant, Motterstitch Company, Inc., RI, Carolina

Revis, Lee
editor@valdezstar.net, Ed., Valdez Star, AK, Valdez

Rex, Michael
mrex@cumberland.edu, Cumberland Univ., TN, Lebanon

Rexenes, Jonelle .... (603) 595-7000
Marketing Specialist, Presstek, Inc., NH, Hudson

Rey, Jay .... (727) 397-5563, ext. 313
jrey@tbnweekly.com, Adv. Mgr, Tarpon Springs Beacon, FL, Seminole
jrey@tbnweekly.com, Adv. Mgr, Belleair Bee, FL, Seminole
jrey@tbnweekly.com, Adv. Mgr, Beach Beacon, FL, Seminole
jrey@tbnweekly.com, Ad Sales Dir., Seminole Beacon, FL, Seminole
jrey@tbnweekly.com, Adv. Mgr, Largo Leader, FL, Seminole
jrey@tbnweekly.com, Adv. Mgr, Clearwater Beacon, FL, Seminole
jrey@tbnweekly.com, Adv. Dir., Tampa Bay Newspapers, Inc., FL, Seminole
jrey@tbnweekly.com, Adv. Mgr, Palm Harbor Beacon, FL, Seminole
jrey@tbnweekly.com, Adv. Mgr, Dunedin Beacon, FL, Seminole
jrey@tbnweekly.com, Ad. Sales Dir., Pinellas Park Beacon, FL, Seminole

Rey, Justo
jewishjournal@tribune.com, Gen. Mgr., Jewish Journal - Broward South, FL, Pompano Beach

Rey, Justo
jewishjournal@tribune.com, Vice Pres., Jewish Journal - Broward North, FL, Pompano Beach

Rey, Justo
jewishjournal@tribune.com, Gen. Mgr., Jewish Journal - Broward Central, FL, Fort Lauderdale

Rey, Justo
jewishjournal@tribune.com, Pres., Jewish Journal - Palm Beach North, FL, Pompano Beach

Reyes, Arlene .... (856) 528-4844
Adv. Dir., The Berlin Sun, NJ, Haddonfield
Adv. Dir., Burlington Township Sun, NJ, Haddonfield
Adv. Dir., Cherry Hill Sun, NJ, Haddonfield
Adv. Dir., Cinnaminson Sun, NJ, Haddonfield
Adv. Dir., Medford Sun, NJ, Haddonfield
Adv. Dir., Moorestown Sun, NJ, Haddonfield
Adv. Dir., Mt. Laurel Sun, NJ, Haddonfield
Adv. Dir., Palmyra Sun, NJ, Haddonfield
Adv. Dir., Shamong Sun, NJ, Haddonfield
Adv. Dir., Haddonfield Sun, NJ, Haddonfield
Adv. Dir., Sicklerville Sun, NJ, Haddonfield

Adv. Dir., Tabernacle Sun, NJ, Haddonfield
Adv. Dir., Voorhees Sun, NJ, Haddonfield
Adv. Dir., Marlton Sun, NJ, Haddonfield

Reyes, Art .... (951) 849-4586
areyes@recordgazette.net, Gen. Mgr., Record Gazette, CA, Banning

Reyes, Becci
breyes@aldiatx.com, Adv. Mgr., Nat'l Sales, Al Dia, TX, Dallas

Reyes, Clara
creyes@dosmundos.com, Ed., Dos Mundos, KS, Kansas City

Reyes, German
honduras@acan-efe.com, Rep., EFE News Services - Tegucigalpa, Honduras, Tegucigalpa

Reyes, Holly .... (956) 682-2423
hreyes@valleytowncrier.com, Business Manager, Valley Town Crier, TX, McAllen

Reyes, Manuel
newstaff@dosmundos.com, Pub., Dos Mundos, KS, Kansas City

Reyes, Richard .... (505) 863-6811 ext. 219
letters@gallupindependent.com, City Ed., Gallup Independent, NM, Gallup

Reyes, Stefany .... (516) 569-4000 x 236
dweingrad@liherald.com, Ed., East Meadow Herald, NY, Garden City

Reyes, William Jose
wjreyes@enfoquedeportivo.com, Pub., Enfoque Deportivo, TX, Houston

Reyes, Zuriel .... (770) 428-9411 ext. 359
Online Mgr., Marietta Daily Journal, GA, Marietta

Reynaud, Wilbur
karenenterprise@bellsouth.net, Pub., The Enterprise, LA, Vacherie

Reynebeau, Kim .... (920) 759-2000
sales@timesvillager.com, Sales, The Times-Villager, WI, Kaukauna

Reynolds, Bill .... (303) 954-5495
reynolds@denverpost.com, Senior VP Pres, Cir., The Denver Post, CO, Denver

Reynolds, Chris
chris@swarthmorean.com, Ed, The Swarthmorean, PA, Swarthmore

Reynolds, Darla .... (618) 239-2611
dreynolds@bnd.com, Adv., Belleville News-Democrat, IL, Belleville

Reynolds, Jaime .... (573) 248-2711
jreynolds@gatehousemedia.com, Reg. Ad. Dir, Hannibal Courier-Post, MO, Hannibal

Reynolds, Jaime
jreynolds@gatehousemedia.com, Sales Mgr., Benton Evening News, IL, Benton

Reynolds, Jennifer
jennifer.reynolds@galvnews.com, Photo Editor , The Galveston County Daily News, TX, Galveston

Reynolds, Jennifer
jennifer@adobe.com, Dir., Worldwide Adv., Adobe Systems, Inc., CA, San Jose

Reynolds, Jeremy
jeremy@ssecho.com, Adv. Sales Rep., Sulphur Springs News-Telegram, TX, Sulphur Springs

Reynolds, Kevin
reynolkj@jmu.edu, Assoc. Prof., James Madison University, VA, Harrisonburg

Reynolds, Larry
lreynolds@houstoncountycourier.com, Pub., Houston County Courier, TX, Crockett

Reynolds, Larry
larry@swdtimes.com, Pub., Shopper's Weekly, KS, Liberal

Reynolds, Lin .... (256) 740-5787
lin.reynolds@timesdaily.com, Prodn. Mgr., Pre Press, Times Daily, AL, Florence

Reynolds, Linda .... (478) 836-3195
gapostlegals@pstel.net, Assistant to the Publisher/Legals, The Georgia Post, GA, Roberta

Reynolds, Lynda
spartish@bellsouth.net, Office Mgr., Sparta Ishmaelite, GA, Sparta

Reynolds, Matt .... (318) 435-4521
matt@franklinsun.com, Sports Ed./Gen. Ed., The Franklin Sun, LA, Winnsboro

Reynolds, Megan .... (501) 548-1262
mreynolds@siftingsherald.com, GateHouse Media, Inc., NY, Pittsford

Reynolds, Megan
mreynolds@bentoncourier.com, Editor, The Saline Courier TMC, Benton

Reynolds, Monty C. .... (417) 256-9191
Commercial Printing, West Plains Daily Quill, MO, West Plains

Reynolds, Nick
editor@ithacatimes.com, Ed., Newfield News, NY, Ithaca
editor@ithacatimes.com, Ed., The Candor Chronicle, NY, Ithaca
editor@ithacatimes.com, Ed. , The Dryden Courier, NY, Ithaca

Reynolds, Pam .... (907) 486-3227
Business Manager, Kodiak Daily Mirror, AK, Kodiak

Reynolds, Paul .... (330) 364-8302
paul.reynolds@timesreporter.com, Gen. Mgr., The Times-Reporter, OH, New Philadelphia

Reynolds, Ray .... (843) 317-7362
rreynolds@florencenews.com, Prodn. Foreman, Mailroom, Morning News, SC, Florence

Reynolds, Rick .... (601) 833-6961
rick.reynolds@dailyleader.com, Pres./Pub., Prentiss Headlight, MS, Prentiss

Reynolds, Rick
rick.reynolds@dailyleader.com, Pub., Daily Leader, MS, Brookhaven

Reynolds, Vicki .... (316) 268-6529
VReynolds@wichitaeagle.com, News Editor, The Wichita Eagle, KS, Wichita

Reynolds , Nick
editor@ithacatimes.com, Mng. Ed. , The Interlaken Review, NY, Ithaca

Reynolds , Nick .... (607) 277-7000
editor@ithacatimes.com, Editor, Ithaca Times, NY, Ithaca

Reynolds-Soucie, Rachel .... (815) 937-3351
rsimpson@daily-journal.com, Dir. of Niche Publications, The Daily Journal, IL, Kankakee

Rezabek, James
info@mps-co.com, Pres., Midwest Publishers Supply Co., IL, Harwood Heights

Rezac, Chris .... (402) 444-1454
chris.rezac@owh.com, Adv. Mgr., Auto Sales , Omaha World-Herald, NE, Omaha

Reznick, Lynn .... (781) 665-4442
lynn@offthemarkcartoons.com, Mktg. Dir., Atlantic Feature Syndicate, Melrose

Rhaesa, Sean
srhaesa@journalgroup.com, Gen. Mgr., Associated Newspapers of Michigan, MI, Wayne

Rhea, Brooke .... (504) 865-5657
hullabaloo.advertising@gmail.com, Senior Business Manager, Tulane University, LA, New Orleans

Rhea, Stephanie .... (501) 337-7523 ext 206
compmdr@sbcglobal.net, Composition Mgr., Malvern Daily Record, AR, Malvern

Rhee, Minna
minna.rhee@sourcemedia.com, Chief Mktg. & Digital Officer, American Banker, NY, New York

Rhiley, Bill
newsbelleplaine@gmail.com, Publisher, The Belle Plaine News & The Oxford Register, KS, Belle Plaine

Rhiley, Bill
newsbelleplaine@gmail.com, Publisher, The Belle Plaine News, KS, Belle Plaine

Rhoades, Anthony .... (770) 227 - 3276 x238
anthony@griffindailynews.com, Asst. Mng. Ed., Griffin Daily News, GA, Griffin

Rhoades, Chris
crhoades@enterprisepub.com, Associate Publisher, Dakota County Star, NE, Blair

Rhoades, Chris
crhoades@enterprisepub.com, Associate Publisher, Washington County Enterprise, NE, Blair

Rhoades, John
Rhoades, Adv. Dir., The Daily Journal, CO, Denver

Rhoades, Mark
mrhoades@enterprisepub, Owner, Seward County Independent, NE, Seward

Rhoades, Mark .... (402) 426-2121 x102
mrhoades@enterprisepub.com, Pub., The Pilot Tribune / Enterprise, NE, Blair

Rhoades, Mark .... (404) 494-4264
mrhoades@enterprisepub.com, Owner/Pub., Dakota County Star, NE, Blair

Rhoades, Mark .... (402) 426-2121
mrhoades@enterprisepub.com, Pres., Enterprise Publishing Co., NE, Blair

Rhoades, Mark .... (402) 426-2121
mrhoades@enterprisepub.com, President, Missouri Valley Times-News, IA, Missouri Valley

Rhoades, Mark .... (402) 426-2121 x102
mrhoades@enterprise.com, Publisher, The Clipper, NE, Blair

Rhoades, Mark .... (402) 426-2121 x102
mrhoades@enterprisepub.com, Publisher/ Owner, Arlington Citizen, NE, Blair
mrhoades@enterprisepub.com, Pub., Hi-Line Enterprise, NE, Curtis

Rhoades, Mark .... (402) 426-2121
mrhoades@enterprisepub.com, Publisher, Washington County Enterprise, NE, Blair

Rhoades, Mark
mrhoades@enterprisepub.com, Pub., Seward County Connection, NE, Seward

Rhoades, Rex .... (207) 689-2886
rrhoades@sunjournal.com, Exec. Ed., Sun Journal, ME, Lewiston

Rhoads, David
davidr@pa-news.org, Pennsylvania NewsMedia Association, PA, Harrisburg

Rhodarmer, Mia
mia.rhodarmer@advocateanddemocrat. com, Ed., The Advocate & Democrat, TN, Sweetwater

Rhode, Amy........................(407) 656-2121
Wotimes@aol.com, The West Orange Times & Observer, FL, Winter Garden

Rhoden, Adam .... (256) 840-3000 ext 120
arhoden@sandmountainreporter.com, Adv. Exec., Sand Mountain Reporter, AL, Albertville

Rhoden, Russell J.
mail@tattnalljournal.com, Pub., The Journal Sentinel, GA, Reidsville

Rhodes, Charins .... (601) 364-1045
charina.rhodes@msbusiness.com, Circ. Mng., Mississippi Business Journal, MS, Jackson

Rhodes, Guy .... (334) 727-3020
guynrhodes@bellsouth.net, Editor/Publisher, The Tuskegee News, AL, Tuskegee

Rhodes, Mel .... ext. 3416
publisher@mineralwellsindex.com, Pub.,

Mineral Wells Index, TX, Mineral Wells

Rhodes, Melinda......................(740) 368-3517
mmrhodes@owu.edu, Advisor, Ohio Wesleyan University, OH, Delaware

Rhodes, Paul
prhodes@tsnews.com, Ed., Times Sentinel, KS, Cheney

Rhodes, Paul .... (901) 458-2911 ext. 4
prhodes@thebesttimes.com, Online Manager, The Best Times, TN, Memphis

Rhodes, Robin
rrhodes@mindspring.com, Exec. Dir. & Pub, Georgia Press Association, GA, Atlanta

Rhodes, Robin
rrhodes@minespring.com, Exec. Dir., Georgia Newspaper Service, Inc., GA, Atlanta

Rhodes, Sonny
cmrhodes@ualr.edu, The Forum, University of Arkansas at Little Rock, AR, Little Rock

Rhodes, Veronica......................(306) 781-5300
vrhodes@leaderpost.canwest.com, City Coord., The Leader-Post, SK, Regina

Rhodin, Tony...............(610) 258-7171 ext. 3465
arhodin@express-times.com, Asst. Mng. Ed., The Express-Times, PA, Easton

Rhoten, Jocelyn .... (336) 596-3349
jktolbert84@gmail.com, Editor-in-Chief, Florida State College at Jacksonville FL, Jacksonville

Rhymer, Karen ....(606) 248-1010 Ext. 1132
krhymer@civitasmedia.com, Contact, BlueCielo ECM Solutions, GA, Smyrna

Rhyne, Melanie
melanie.lrnews@gmail.com, Composing/ Layout, Little River News, AR, Ashdown

Rhyno, Crystal
crhyno@reddeeradvocate.com, Mng Ed, Friday Forward, AB, Red Deer

Rhyno, Crystal
crhyno@reddeeradvocate.com, Mng Ed, Central Alberta Life, AB, Red Deer

Ribbing, Jamie
jhewson@post-journal.com, Bus. Mgr., The Observer, NY, Dunkirk

Ricardi, Scott
sricardi@civitasmedia.com, Advertising Director and General Manager, Richmond County Daily Journal, NC, Rockingham

Ricardo, Larry .... (617) 779-3788
LRicardo@pilotcatholicnews.com, Adv. Mgr., The Pilot, MA, Braintree

Ricci, Paul
pricci@scansoft.com, Chrmn./CEO, Nuance Communications Inc., MA, Burlington

Ricciani, Geri
gricciani@imediainc.com, Dir., Pjct. Mgmt., Interactive Media Associates, NJ, Boonton

Riccioli, Jim .... (262) 446-6635
jim.riccioli@jrn.com, Reg. News Ed., Milwaukee Journal Sentinel, WI, Milwaukee

Riccioli, Jim
jriccioli@jrn.com, Ed., Bay View NOW, WI, Waukesha

Rice, Barry
brice@colum.edu, Acting Chair, Columbia College Chicago, IL, Chicago

Rice, Bob
editor@monahansnews.net, Adv. Dir., The Monahans News, TX, Monahans

Rice, Bobby
bobby@kentsspecialevents.com, Dir., Adv. Sales, Pensacola News Journal, FL, Pensacola

Rice, Brian........................(718) 260-4537
brice@cnglocal.com, Display/Online Adv., Flushing Times, NY, Bayside

Rice, Brian...........................(816) 637-6155

brian@leaderpress.com, Publisher, Editor, Town & Country Leader, MO, Excelsior Springs

Rice, Brian .... (718) 260-4537
brice@cnglocal.com, Display & Online Advertising , The Little Neck Ledger, NY, Bayside
brice@cnglocal.com, Display & Online Advertising , Queens Village Times (OOB), NY, BAYSIDE
brice@cnglocal.com, Display & Online Advertising, Jackson Heights Times, NY, Bayside
brice@cnglocal.com, Display & Online Advertising , Laurelton Times, NY, Bayside
brice@cnglocal.com, Display & Online Advertising , Ridgewood Ledger, NY, Bayside
brice@cnglocal.com, Display & Online Advertising , Fresh Meadows Times, NY, Bayside
brice@cnglocal.com, Display & Online Advertising , Jamaica Times, NY, Bayside

Rice, Chris
crice@osv.com, Prodn. Mgr., Our Sunday Visitor, IN, Huntington

Rice, Christina
info@newsrecordsentinel.com, Gen. Mgr./Ed., News-Record and Sentinel, NC, Marshall

Rice, Denasa
denasa@hpleader.com, Classified Adv. Mgr., The Leader & Times, KS, Liberal

Rice, Douglas
drice@call-post.com, Vice Pres., Mktg./Adv., King Media Enterprises, OH, Columbus

Rice, Frankie
frankierice@shelbystar.com, Prodn. Dir., Mailroom, The Star, NC, Shelby

Rice, Karri
comp@decaturdailydemocrat.com, Graphics, Decatur Daily Democrat, IN, Decatur

Rice, Linda
linda.rice@duncanbanner.com, Business Mgr. , The Duncan Banner, OK, Duncan

Rice, Lynn...............................(912) 427-3757
lsrice@bellsouth.net, Bus. Mgr., The Press-Sentinel, GA, Jesup

Rice, Micah...........................(360) 735-4548
micah.rice@columbian.com, Sports Editor, The Columbian, WA, Vancouver

Rice, Michelle.........................(609) 272-7100
MRice@pressofac.com, VP. of Sales / Mktg., The Press of Atlantic City, NJ, Pleasantville

Rice, Pat ....(386) 681-2222
Editor, Daytona Beach News-Journal, FL, Daytona Beach

Rice, Patricia...........................(702) 383-0262
price@reviewjournal.com, Office Mgr., Las Vegas Review-Journal, NV, Las Vegas

Rice, Patrick
publisher@wyopreview.com, Pub., Preview Real Estate Guide, WY, Cheyenne

Rice, Patrick
info@wyotraders.com, Pub., Trader's Shopper's Guide, WY, Cheyenne

Rice, Richard
richard@mygreeter.com, Pub., The Greeter, MT, Plentywood

Rice, Rob
robrice@otelco.net, Owner/Ed, The Blount Countian, AL, Oneonta

Rice, Sharon...........................(951) 244-1966
news@goldingpublications.com, Ed., The Friday Flyer, CA, Canyon Lake

Rice, Steve.................(519) 271-2220 ext. 205
srice@bowesnet.com, Sports Ed., The Stratford Beacon Herald, ON, Stratford

Rice, Valerie

news@henryettanewspaper.com, Mng. Ed., Henryetta Free-Lance, OK, Henryetta

Rice, Vicki .... (308) 233-9747
Educ. Ed., Kearney Hub, NE, Kearney

Rice , Brian .... (718) 260-4537
brice@cnglocal.com, Display & Online Advertising , The Whitestone Times, NY, Bayside

Rich, Andrea...................... (717) 272-5611 x147
andrearich@ldnews.com, Managing Ed., Lebanon Valley Review, PA, Lebanon
andrearich@ldnews.com, Managing Ed, The Lebanon Daily News, PA, Lebanon

Rich, John .... (559) 441-6663
jrich@fresnobee.com, Managing Ed, The Fresno Bee, CA, Fresno

Rich, Linda
lrich@pubgroup.com, Assoc. Ed., Direct Response, American Profile - New York, NY, New York

Rich, Linda
lrich@pubgorup.com, Assoc. Ed., Direct Response, Relish - New York, NY, New York

Richard, Clark
rclark@johnsoncitypress.com, Vice President, Sales, Kingsport Times-News, TN, Kingsport

Richard, Cody .... (318) 255-4353
cody@rustonleader.com, Gen. Mgr., Ruston (LA) Daily Leader, LA, Ruston

Richard, Dana
ccrads@alpinecom.net, Bus. Mgr., The Clayton County Register, IA, Elkader

Richard, Elizabeth
ericha11@slu.edu, Asst. Prof., Saint Louis University, MO, Saint Louis

Richard, Karen Carter
krichards@forwardtimes.com, Assoc. Pub., Houston Metro Weekender, TX, Houston

Richard, Michel
secom@quebectel.com, Ed., Le Portageur, QC, Natashquan

Richard, Sam
sam@lawattstimes.com, Mng. Ed., La Watts Times, CA, Los Angeles

Richards, Amy........................(708) 448-4000
arichards@regionalpublishing.com, Pub., The Reporter, IL, Palos Heights

Richards, Amy
arichards@regionalpublishing.com, Pub., The Regional News, IL, Palos Heights

Richards, Anthony .... (205) 755-5747, ext. 603
anthonyrichards@clantonadvertiser.com, Staff Writer, The Clanton Advertiser, AL, Clanton

Richards, Judy
jrichards@elpasotimes.com, El Paso Times, TX, El Paso

Richards, Kris
ijnews@centurytel.net, Adv. Mgr., The Independent-Journal, MO, Potosi

Richards, Neil
ijnews@centurytel.net, Ed., The Independent-Journal, MO, Potosi

Richards, Richard D. .... (218) 487-5255
richards@gvtel.com, Pub., McIntosh Times, MN, McIntosh

Richards, Richard D.
richards@gutel.com, Pub., Leader Record, MN, Gonvick

Richards, Richard D.
richards@gutel.com, Pub., The Oklee Herald, MN, Oklee

Richards, Robin......................(760) 326-2222
needlesdesertstar@citlink.net, Ed, Needles Desert Star, CA, Needles

Richards, Robin............(304) 752-6950 ex. 1726
rrichards@civitasmedia.com, Adv. Sales, The Logan Banner, WV, Logan

Richards, Samuel
ccsun@bayareanewsgroup.com, Ed.,
Lamorinda Sun, CA, Walnut Creek

Richards, Sherri ....(701) 241-5556
srichards@forumcomm.com, Features/
Business Editor, InForum, ND, Fargo

Richards, Steve ....(617) 244-3075
Cruise Columnist, Travel & Leisure Features,
MA, Newton
Corresp., New England News Service, Inc.,
Newton

Richards, Tommy ....(270) 783-3214
trichards@bgdailynews.com, Asst. Circ. Dir.,
Daily News, KY, Bowling Green

Richardson, Aaron
arichardson@dailyprogress.com, Ed., Rural
Virginian, VA, Charlottesville

Richardson, Bill
bricharson@lawdailyrecord.com, Sports Ed.,
Daily Record, IL, Lawrenceville

Richardson, Bob
brichardson@columbiabasinherald.com, Adv.
Dir., Columbia Basin Herald, WA, Moses
Lake

Richardson, Bob ....(509) 765-8549
publisher@suntribune.com, Publisher, The Sun
Tribune, WA, Othello

Richardson, Bruce ....(717) 891-0020
bruce.richardson@kba.com, National Sales
Manager, KBA North America, Inc. (Koenig &
Bauer AG), TX, Dallas

Richardson, Chad
crichardson@hastingsstargazette.com, Ed.,
Hastings Star Gazette, MN, Hastings

Richardson, Chad
crichardson@hastingsstargazette.com, Ed Dir,
New Richmond News, WI, New Richmond

Richardson, Chad
crichardson@hastingsstargazette.com, Adv.
Mgr., Trade Winds Shopping Guide, MN,
Hastings

Richardson, Charles ....(478) 744-4342
crichardson@macontel.com, Editorial
Columnist, The Telegraph, GA, Macon

Richardson, Cheryl
CRICHARD@lsj.com, HR Dir., Times Herald,
MI, Port Huron

Richardson, Christine ....(802) 479-2582
production@vt-world.com, Prodn. Mgr., The
World, VT, Barre

Richardson, Craig
craig@weirs.com, Circ. Mgr., The Weirs Times,
NH, Laconia

Richardson, Daniel ....(731) 986-2253
daniel@newsleaderonline.com, Pub, Carroll
County News-Leader, TN, Huntingdon

Richardson, Darrell G. ....(865) 482-1021
editor@oakridger.com, Publisher, The Oak
Ridger, TN, Oak Ridge

Richardson, Deb ....(480) 982-7799
drichardson@newszap.com, General Manager,
Apache Junction/Gold Canyon Independent,
AZ, Phoenix

Richardson, Deb
drichardson@newszap.com, Adv. Consultant,
Queen Creek Independent, AZ, Apache
Junction

Richardson, Dee ....(580) 569-2684
dee@kiowacountydemocrat.com, Owner/Ed./
Pub, Kiowa County Democrat, OK, Snyder

Richardson, Denise ....(607) 441-7211
drichardson@thedailystar.com, News Ed., The
Daily Star, NY, Oneonta

Richardson, Dennis
leaderads@bellsouth.net, Pub., Fulton
Shopper, KY, Fulton

Richardson, Dennis ....(270) 653-3381
gazette3322@bellsouth.net, Pub., The

Hickman County Gazette, KY, Clinton

Richardson, Dennis
fultonleader@bellsouth.net, Pub., Fulton
Leader, KY, Fulton

Richardson, Dennis ....(731) 694-2149
Dennisr@usit.net, Senior Associate-South,
Lewis Floyd- Grimes, W.B. & Co., AL, Gulf
Shores
Dennisr@usit.net, South/Southwest Assoc.,
Grimes, W.B. & Co., TN, Camden

Richardson, Dennis
bentonco@usit.net, Pub., The Camden
Chronicle, TN, Camden

Richardson, Dennis ....(731) 694-2149
Dennisr@usit.net, Sr. Associate-South, W.B.
Grimes & Company, MD, Gaithersburg

Richardson, Dennis M.
dennis@magicvalleypublishing.com, Owner,
Carroll County News-Leader, TN, Huntingdon

Richardson, Don
telfaireditor@windstream.net, Ed., The Telfair
Enterprise, GA, Mc Rae

Richardson, Jan ....(260) 347-0400 Ext. 1131
jrichardson@kpcmedia.com, Life Ed., The
News Sun, IN, Kendallville

Richardson, Julie
jrichardson@bonnersferryherald.com, Adv.
Rep., Bonners Ferry Herald, ID, Bonners
Ferry

Richardson, Ken ....(806) 828-6201
ken@slatonitenews.com, Ed./Pub., The
Slatonite, TX, Slaton
ken@slatonitenews.com, Publisher/Ed., The
Slatonite, TX, Slaton

Richardson, Lynn
lynn.richardson@elizabethton.com, Pub.,
Elizabethton Star, TN, Elizabethton

Richardson, Malva
malva@slatonitenews.com, Business Manager,
The Slatonite, TX, Slaton

Richardson, Matthew ....(731) 253-6666
matthew@magicvalleypublishing.com,
Gen. Mgr., The Lake County Banner, TN,
Tiptonville

Richardson, Pat ....(757) 446-2000
pat.richardson@pilotonline.com, Pub., The
Virginian-Pilot, VA, Norfolk

Richardson, Pat
prichardson@capgaznews.com, Pub., Crofton-
West County Gazette, MD, Annapolis

Richardson, Pat
prichardson@capgaznews.com, Pub., Bowie
Blade-News, MD, Annapolis

Richardson, Patricia
pat.richardson@carrollcountyonline.com, Pub.,
Mason-dixon Marketplace, MD, Westminster

Richardson, Scott ....(334) 727-3020
tuskegeenews@bellsouth.net, Assistant to the
Publisher, The Tuskegee News, AL, Tuskegee

Richardson, Stacy ....(618) 239-2648
srichardson@bnd.com, VP Finance, Belleville
News-Democrat, IL, Belleville

Richardson, Susan ....(336) 506-3004
srichardson@thetimesnews.com, Expeditor,
Union County Leader, NM, Clayton

Richardson, Terri ....(260) 461-8304
trich@jg.net, Features Ed., The Journal
Gazette, IN, FORT WAYNE

Richardson, Valerie ....(303) 470-7078
vrichardson@washingtontimes.com, Swift
Communications, Inc., NV, Carson City
vrichardson@washingtontimes.com, Denver
Bureau Chief, The Washington Times, DC,
Washington

Richardson, Wayne ....(609) 871-8060
wrichardson@calkins.com, Sports Ed.,
Burlington County Times, NJ, Willingboro

Richardson , Jim

jrichardson@gcnews-star.com, Sales, The
Garvin County News Star, OK, Maysville

Richcreek, Chris ....(407) 894-7300, Ext. 240
crichcreek@hearstsc.com, Senior Features
Editor, King Features Syndicate, NY, New
York

Richcreek, Chris ....(407) 894-7300 Ext. 240
crichcreek@hearstsc.com, Senior Features
Editor, North America Syndicate, New York

Richert, Chris ....(312) 369-8955
crichert@colum.edu, General Manager,
Columbia College Chicago, IL, Chicago

Richeson, Don ....(828) 743-5101
Editor@CrossroadsChronicle.com, Editor,
Crossroads Chronicle, NC, Cashiers

Richeson, Don
dricheson@madison-news.com, Ed., Madison
County Eagle, VA, Madison

Richey, Kelli ....(701) 223-6397
kelli@ndna.com, Mktg. Dir., North Dakota
Newspaper Association, ND, Bismarck

Richey, Theresa
circulation@mihomepaper.com, Circ. Mgr., The
County Press, MI, Lapeer

Richieri, Kenneth
kenneth.richieri@nytimes.com, Sr. Vice
Pres./Gen. Counsel & Sec., New England
Newspaper Group, NY, New York

Richieri, Kenneth A. ....(212) 556-1234
Vice Pres./Deputy Gen. Counsel, The New York
Times Co., NY, New York

Richmeier, Lisa
lrichmeier@publicitas.com, Contact, Publicitas
North America, Inc., AZ, Peoria

Richmond, Bill
ngeditor@comcast.net, City Ed., The News-
Gazette, IN, Winchester

Richmond, Della
natomanews@ruraltel.net, Ed., Natoma Luray
Independent, KS, Natoma

Richmond, Ron ....(317) 477-3244
rrichmond@greenfieldreporter.com, Circ.
District Mgr., Daily Reporter, IN, Greenfield

Richmond, Will ....(508) 676-2532
wrichmond@heraldnews.com, City Ed., The
Herald News, MA, Fall River

Richner, Clifford
nassaueditor@liherald.com, Pub., Nassau
Herald, NY, Garden City

Richner, Clifford ....(516) 569-4000 x229
crichner@liherald.com, Pub., Baldwin Herald,
NY, Garden City
crichner@liherald.com, Pub., Oyster Bay
Guardian, NY, Garden City
crichner@liherald.com, Pub., South Shore
Record (OOB) , NY, Garden City

Richner, Clifford
ahackmack@liherald.com, Pub., Malverne/
West Hempstead Herald, NY, Garden City

Richner, Clifford ....(516) 569-4000 x229
Pub., Lynbrook/East Rockaway Herald, NY,
Garden City

Richner, Clifford ....ext. 229
crichner@liherald.com, Pub., Primetime, NY,
Garden City

Richner, Clifford ....(516) 569-4000 ext. 229
crichner@liherald.com, Pub., Richner
Communications, Inc., NY, Garden City

Richner, Stuart ....(516) 569-4000 x230
Pub., Lynbrook/East Rockaway Herald, NY,
Garden City

Richner, Stuart
srichner@liherald.com, President, Richner
Communications, Inc., NY, Garden City

Richner, Stuart ....ext. 230
srichner@liherald.com, Pub., Primetime, NY,
Garden City

Richter, Adam
arichter@readingeagle.com, Reading Eagle
Company, PA, Reading

Richter, Corey ....(715) 365-6397 ext.388
corey@rivernewsonline.com, Circ. Mgr., The
Northwoods River News , WI, Rhinelander
corey@rivernewsonline.com, Circ. Mgr. ,
Northwoods Super Shopper, WI, Rhinelander

Richter, William
Richter@lrc.edu, Chair, Lenoir-Rhyne College,
NC, Hickory

Richwine, Hallie ....(575) 538-5893 Ext. 5807
hichwine@scsun-news.com, Off. Admin., Silver
City Sun-News, NM, Silver City

Rickard, Lois ....(217) 482-3276
btpublications@frontier.net, Ed., Mason City
Banner Times, IL, Mason City

Rickard, Mark
rickard.mark@victoriastar.ca, Ed. English, L'
Etoile Cataracte, NB, Grand Falls

Rickard, Mark ....(506) 473-3083
rickard.mark@victoriastar.ca, Ed., English,
Victoria County Star, NB, Grand Falls

Rickenbacher, Ted ....(214) 384-2779
rmedia@msn.com, Pres./Exec. Dir.,
Rickenbacher Media, TX, Dallas

Ricker, Fred ....(262) 656-6310
fricker@ucclocalmedia.com, Business
Manager, United Communications
Corporation, WI, Kenosha

Ricker, Peter ....(989) 839-4222
peter.ricker@mdn.net, Group Adv. Dir., Midland
Daily News, MI, Midland

Ricker, Shannon
sricker@bowesnet.com, Pub., Windsor Smart
Shopper, ON, Windsor

Rickers, Beth ....ext. 238
BRickers@dglobe.com, Features Ed.,
Worthington Daily Globe, MN, Worthington

Rickert, Janice ....(812) 331-4347
jrickert@heraldt.com, News Ed., The Herald
Times, IN, Bloomington

Ricketson, John E. ....(407) 886-2777
jr@theapopkachief..com, Pub., Apopka Chief
(The), FL, Apopka

Ricketson, John E. ....(407) 886-2777
jr@theapopkachief.com, Pub., The Planter,
FL, Apopka

Ricketts, Cathy ....(806) 323-6461
cathy@canadianrecord.com, News Ed, The
Canadian Record, TX, Canadian

Rickhoff, Kyle ....(406) 657-1468
krickhoff@billingsgazette.com, Digital Dir.,
Billings Gazette, MT, Billings

Rickman, Jim ....(406) 447-4020
Pub., The Whitefish Pilot, MT, Whitefish

Rickman, Jim ....(406) 443-2850
jim@mtnewspapers.com, Executive Director,
Montana Newspaper Association, MT,
Helena

Rickman, Karen ....(406) 447-4060
National Adv. Coord., Helena Independent
Record, MT, Helena

Rickman, Randall
rrickman@kenoshanews.com, Pub., Kenosha
News, WI, Kenosha

Rickman, Randy
rrickman@kenoshanews.com, Publisher-
Kenosha News, United Communications
Corporation, WI, Kenosha

Rickmond, Stewart ....(920) 426-6691
Gen. Mgr., Community Snapshot, WI, Oshkosh

Ricks, James
jricks@dmnmedia.com, General Manager:
Direct Marketing, Arts & Entertainment,
Health, Education, Sports, DMNLatino, The
Dallas Morning News, TX, Dallas

Ricks, Travis
travis@statenews.com, Creative Adviser, The State News/Michigan State University, MI, East Lansing

Rico, Damian .... **(219) 545-3980**
damian.rico@nwi.com, Community Dir., The Times of Northwest Indiana, IN, Munster

Rico, Dan .... **933-4375, ext 100**
courierads@gmail.com, Adv. Rep., County Courier, VT, Enosburg Falls

Rico-Sanchez, Sylvia .... **(310) 836-1372**
Ricosasy@elac.edu, Co-Adviser, East Los Angeles College, CA, Monterey Park

Riddell, Robert
briddell@heritage.com, Circ. Dir., Heritage Newspapers, Inc., MI, Southgate

Riddell, Vanessa
vanessa@sentinelnews.com, Classified Adv., Sentinel News Plus, KY, Shelbyville

Ridder, Lynn
lynn.ridder@scompapers.com, Production Director, Gwinnett Daily Post, GA, Lawrenceville

Ridder, Lynn .... **(229) 888-9387**
lynn.ridder@albanyherald.com, Director of Operations, The Albany Herald, GA, Albany

Riddick, Ken .... **(209) 578-2090**
kriddick@modbee.com, Pres./Pub., Merced Sun-Star, CA, Merced
kriddick@modbee.com, Pres./Pub., Los Banos Enterprise, CA, Los Banos
kriddick@modbee.com, Pres. & Pub., The Modesto Bee, CA, Modesto

Riddick, Ken .... **(805) 781-7825**
kriddick@thetribunenews.com, Pub., The Tribune, CA, San Luis Obispo

Riddings, Dean
fps-info@flpress.com, Pres./CEO, Florida Press Service, Inc., FL, Tallahassee

Riddle, Christina .... **(816) 218-6712**
christina.riddle@pitch.com, Production Manager, The Pitch, MO, Kansas City

Riddle, Phil
editor@weatherforddemocrat.com, Ed., Parker County Shopper, TX, Weatherford

Riddle, Susie
susie@adpakweekly.com, Prodn. Mgr., Ad Pak, NC, Wilmington

Ridenour, Shelley .... **(520) 423-8615**
sridenour@trivalleycentral.com, Assignment Ed., Casa Grande Dispatch, AZ, Casa Grande

Rideout, Brian
info@bkrstudio.com, Pres., BKR Studio, Inc., IN, South Bend

Rider, Joshua .... **(510) 655-3951**
Univ. of California-Berkeley Law School, CA, Berkeley

Rider, Priscilla
ads@basinbroadband.com, Adv. Dir., Andrews County News, TX, Andrews

Rider, Robert .... **(706) 376-8025**
robertrider@hartcom.net, Pub., The Hartwell Sun, GA, Hartwell

Ridgell, Rene
rridgell@chicoer.com, Classified Adv. Mgr., Chico Enterprise-Record, CA, Chico

Ridgeway, Marlene
news@boonvilledailynews.com, Pub., The Weekly, MO, Boonville

Ridgley, Darren .... **(204) 697-7098**
darren.ridgley@canstarnews.com, Deputy Ed., The Metro, MB, Winnipeg

Ridgley, Darren .... **(204) 697-7098**
darren.ridgley@canstarnews.com, Deputy Editor, The Lance, MB, Winnipeg

Ridings, Bill
newsdemocrat@bellsouth.net, Pub., Shopper's Guide, TN, Waverly

Ridings, Dean .... **(321) 283-5277**
deanr@flpress.com, Pres. & CEO, Florida Press Association, FL, Lake Mary

Ridings, Dean .... **(321) 283-5277**
dridings@mediagenius.com, Pres./CEO, Intersect Media Solutions, FL, Lake Mary

Ridler, Nancy .... **(320) 843-4111**
ads@monitor-news.com, Advertising, Swift County Monitor & News, MN, Benson

Ridley, Deb .... **(306) 662-2100**
dridley@maplecreeknews.com, Ad Sales, The Maple Creek News, SK, Maple Creek

Ridley, Jim
jridley@nashvillescene.com, Ed., Nashville Scene, TN, Nashville

Rieckman, Stewart .... **(920) 426-6691**
Exec. Ed., Community Snapshot, WI, Oshkosh

Riefler, Katja
katjar@aimgroup.com, Europe Director, Advanced Interactive Media Group, LLC, FL, Altamonte Springs

Rieg, Tiffany
thenickel@eotnet.net, The Nickel Want Ad Newspaper, OR, Hermiston

Rieger, Jamie .... **(403) 545-2258**
jrieger@bowislandcommentator.com, Ed., The 40-mile County Commentator, AB, Bow Island

Riegle, Richard
rriegle@newspapersfirst.com, Vice Pres./ Sales Mgr., Newspapers First, Inc., CA, Los Angeles

Riegler, Chad .... **(307) 672-2431**
chad@thesheridanpress.com , Production Manager, The Sheridan Press, WY, Sheridan

Riel, Kim
kriel@mykawartha.com, Office Mgr., Kawartha Lakes This Week, ON, Lindsay
kriel@mykawartha.com, Office Mgr, Brock Citizen, ON, Cannington

Riel, Tim .... **(401) 423-3200**
tim@jamestownpress.com, Ed., The Jamestown Press, RI, Jamestown

Riemerman, Paul
treditor@times-online.com, Ed., Valley City Times-Record, ND, Valley City

Ries, Julie .... **(812) 265-6313**
julie.ries@bigringwriting.com, Admin. Asst., Big Ring Media Team, Inc., Madison

Ries, Richard .... **(812) 265-6313**
rries@bigringwriting.com, Dir., Big Ring Media Team, Inc., Madison

Riese, Dustin .... **(920) 759-2000**
sports@timesvillager.com, Sports, The Times-Villager, WI, Kaukauna

Riess, Christoph
christoph.riess@wan-ifra.com, CEO, World Association of Newspapers and News Publishers (WAN-IFRA), Frankfurt

Rifanburg, Michael .... **(315) 253-5311**
michael.rifanburg@lee.net, Publisher, Auburn Publishers, Inc., NY, Auburn

Rifanburg, Michael
mrifanburg@gazettenet.com, Pub., Amherst Bulletin, MA, Northampton

Rifanburg, Michael .... **(413) 585-5335**
mrifanburg@gazettenet.com, Pub., The Recorder, MA, Greenfield

Rifanburg, Michael .... **(413) 585-5335**
mrifanburg@gazettenet.com, Pub., Daily Hampshire Gazette, MA, Northampton

Riffe, Daniel .... **(919) 962-4082**
Prof./Richard Cole Eminent Prof., University of North Carolina, NC, Chapel Hill

Riffle, Rich
rriffle@timesonline.com, Adv. Opns. Mgr., Beaver County Times, PA, Beaver

Rifkin, Marc
marc.rifkin@scala.com, Dir. Training/Servs., Scala, Inc., PA, Exton

Rigas, David .... **(606) 326-2628**
drigas@dailyindependent.com, Audience Development Director, The Daily Independent, KY, Ashland

Rigby, Mark
mark@adkpennysaver.com, Circ. Mgr., Pennysaver, NY, Plattsburgh

Rigby, Mark .... **(518) 563-0100**
pennysaver@westelcom.com, Pub., Adirondack Properties, NY, Plattsburgh

Rigby, Mark
mail@adkpennysaver.com, Pub., Real Estate Advertiser, NY, Plattsburgh

Rigdon, Terry
trigdon@peoplesdefender.com, Adv. Mgr., The People's Defender, OH, West Union

Riggenbach, Don .... **(402) 502-4367**
don@riggenbach.info, Mgr., Jandon Features, Omaha

Riggenbach, Jan .... **(402) 502-4367**
jan@riggenbach.info, Columnist, Jandon Features, Omaha

Riggers, Audra .... **(260) 356-6700 ext. 171**
ariggers@h-ponline.com, Pub. Gen. Mgr., Huntington Herald-Press, IN, Huntington

Riggin , Karen .... **(410) 968-1189**
smister@newszap.com, Adv. Consultant, Crisfield-Somerset County Times, MD, Crisfield

Riggs, Angel
riggsa@timesrecordnews.com, Bus./Oil Ed., Wichita Falls Times Record News, TX, Wichita Falls

Riggs, Ann .... **(614) 486-6677 ext. 1010**
ariggs@ohionews.org, Receptionist and Secretary, Ohio Newspaper Services, Inc., OH, Columbus
ariggs@ohionews.org, Admin. Asst., Ohio Newspaper Association, OH, Columbus

Riggs, Brett
riggs@gctelegram.com, Mng. Ed., La Semana en el Suroeste de Kansas, KS, Garden City

Riggs, Brett .... **ext. 234**
riggs@gctelegram.com, Mng. Ed., The Garden City Telegram, KS, Garden City

Riggs, Christopher M. .... **(316) 369-3965**
criggs@cdowk.org, Ed., The Catholic Advance, KS, Wichita

Riggs, Jeff
jriggs@athensreview.com, Ed., Athens Daily Review, TX, Athens

Righter, Julie
editor@fstribune.com, Pub., Countryside, KS, Fort Scott

Rigotti, Brenda
brigotti@sooeveningnews.com, Sunday Ed., Sault Ste. Marie Evening News, MI, Sault Sainte Marie

Rigsbee, Randall
rigsbee@thechathamnews.com, Ed., The Chatham Record, NC, Pittsboro

Rigsbee, Randall
rrigsbee@thechathamnews.com, Mng. Ed., The Chatham News, NC, Siler City

Riihl, Michelle
mriihl@windomnews.com, Office Mgr., Cottonwood County Citizen, MN, Windom

Rilea, Ted
tedrilea@suntimes.com, Vice Pres., Labor Rel. (Chicago Sun-Times/Chicago Grp.), Chicago Sun-Times, IL, Chicago

Riley, B.J. .... **(812) 231-4297**
bj.riley@tribstar.com, Pub., The Tribune Star, IN, Terre Haute

Riley, B.J.
bjriley@tribstar.com, Pub., Hometown, IN, Terre Haute

Riley, Brett .... **(563) 383-2255**
brett.riley@lee.net, Classified Adv. Dir., Bettendorf News, IA, Davenport
brett.riley@lee.net, Dir. Audience Development, Quad-City Times, IA, Davenport

Riley, Jackie
jriley@fnbwf.com, Mktg./Promo. Dir., Wichita Falls Times Record News, TX, Wichita Falls

Riley, Kerry
kriley@the-i.net, Pub./Ed., The Coastal Bend Herald, TX, Portland

Riley, Kevin .... **(404) 526-2161**
kriley@ajc.com, Ed., Atlanta Journal-Constitution, GA, Atlanta

Riley, Larry
larry.riley@shj.com, Publisher, Orland Press Register, CA, Willows
larry.riley@shj.com, Pub., Herald-Journal, SC, Spartanburg

Riley, Larry
lriley@cdapress.com, Pub., Coeur d'Alene Press, ID, Coeur D Alene

Riley, Linda .... **(215) 765-9000**
milestonesnews@pcaphl.org, Editor, Milestones, PA, Philadelphia

Riley, Norma .... **(618) 253-7146 eext 228**
nriley@dailyregister.com, Circ. Mgr., Eldorado Daily Journal, IL, Harrisburg
nriley@dailyregister.com, Circ Mgr, The Daily Register, IL, Harrisburg

Riley, Rachel
Gouvtribunepress@gmail.com, Ad., The Gouverneur Tribune-Press, NY, Gouverneur

Riley, Rachel
RRiley@tbo.com, Tampa Bay Times, FL, St Petersburg

Riley, Sid .... **(850) 526-1501**
sid@jacksoncountytimes.net, Managing Editor, Jackson County Times, FL, Marianna

Riley, Steve .... **(919) 836-4940**
sriley@newsobserver.com, Deputy Mng. Ed., The News & Observer, NC, Raleigh

Riley, Tom
triley@phillynews.com, Maintenance Manager, Philadelphia Inquirer, Daily News & Philly. com, PA, Philadelphia

Riley, Vic .... **(903) 564-3565**
news@whitesboronews.com, Sports writer, Whitesboro News-Record, TX, Whitesboro

Rimas, Andrew
a.rimas@northeastern.edu, Mng. Ed., The Improper Bostonian Magazine, MA, Boston

Rimas, Val
sales@rotoflex.com, Gen. Mgr./Vice Pres., Sales/Mktg., Rotoflex Mark Andy Canada, Inc., ON, Mississauga

Rinaldi, Sev .... **(203) 330-6309**
srinaldi@ctpost.com, Features Ed., Connecticut Post, CT, Bridgeport

Rinderer, Erin .... **(618) 239-2456**
erinderer@bnd.com, Adv., Belleville News-Democrat, IL, Belleville

Rindo, John Michael .... **(305) 347-6622**
jrindo@alm.com, Director of Creative Services, Miami Daily Business Review, FL, Miami

Rindock, Rob .... **(610) 258-7171, ext. 3445**
rrindock@express-times.com, Advertising Sales Manager, The Express-Times, PA, Easton

Rindos, Daniel F.
dan@bargainnews.com, Vice Pres., Communications Management Service, Inc., CT, Trumbull

Rinehart, Aly
aly.rinehart@nptelegraph.com, Copy Ed., The

North Platte Telegraph, NE, North Platte

Rinehart, Lorrie ....(334) 683-6318
lrinehart@centrevillepress.com, Pub., Marion
Times-Standard, AL, Marion

Rinehart, Lorrie ....(205) 926-9796
lorrie@centrevillepress.com, Pub., The
Centreville Press, AL, Centreville

Rinehart, Mick
mrinehart@decisionmark.com, Vice Pres.,
Pdct. Devel., Decisionmark Corp., IA, Cedar
Rapids

Rinehart, Renee
editor@signaturenewspaper.com, Ed., The
Signature, CO, La Veta

Rinek, Steve ....(760) 249-3245
steve@mtprogress.net, Pub., Mountaineer
Progress, CA, Wrightwood

Rinek, Vicky ....(760) 868-5757
vrinek@verizon.net, Ed., Mountaineer
Progress, CA, Wrightwood

Riner, Krystal ....(478) 987-1823
kriner@sunmulti.com, Managing Ed., The
Houston Home Journal, GA, Perry

Ringenberger, Michelle .... (309) 833-2114 ext. 258
mringenberger@mcdonoughvoice.com, Adv.
Mgr., Display, The McDonough County Voice,
IL, Macomb

Ringer, Diane ....(330) 541-9400 Ext. 4113
dringer@recordpub.com, Adv. Mgr., Stow
Sentry, OH, Kent

Ringer, Linda
lringer@usmd.edu, Asst. Dean/Dir., Bus.
Administration, University of Maryland, MD,
College Park

Ringness, Maureen ....(815) 526-4516
mringness@shawmedia.com, Group Sales Dir/
Major Nat'l Accts, Geneva Chronicle, IL, St
Charles
mringness@shawmedia.com, Major/Nat'l
Accts./Grp. Sales Dir., Naperville Reporter
(OOB), IL, Downers Grove
mringness@shawmedia.com, Group Sales
Dir/Major Nat'l Accts, Batavia Chronicle, IL,
St Charles
mringness@shawmedia.com, Major/Nat'l
Accts./Grp. Sales Dir., Huntley Farmside
(OOB), IL, Downers Grove
mringness@shawmedia.com, Major/Nat'l
Accts./Grp. Sales Dir., Warrenville Post
(OOB), IL, Downers Grove
mringness@shawmedia.com, Major/Nat'l
Accts./Grp. Sales Dir., Westchester Suburban
Life (OOB), IL, Downers Grove
mringness@shawmedia.com, Major/Nat'l
Accts./Grp. Sales Dir., Willowbrook Suburban
Life (OOB), IL, Downers Grove
mringness@shawmedia.com, Major/Nat'l
Accts./Grp. Sales Dir., The Winfield Press
(OOB), IL, Downers Grove
mringness@shawmedia.com, Major/Nat'l
Accts./Grp. Sales Dir., LaGrange Suburban
Life, IL, Downers Grove
mringness@shawmedia.com, Major/Nat'l
Accts./Grp. Sales Dir., Wood Dale Press
(OOB), IL, Downers Grove
mringness@shawmedia.com, Major/Nat'l
Accts./Grp. Sales Dir., The St. Charles Sun
(OOB), IL, Downers Grove
mringness@shawmedia.com, Major/Nat'l
Accts./Grp. Sales Dir., Glendale Heights
Press (OOB), IL, Downers Grove
mringness@shawmedia.com, Major/Nat'l
Accts./Grp. Sales Dir., Berwyn Suburban Life,
IL, Downers Grove
mringness@shawmedia.com, Major/Nat'l
Accts./Grp. Sales Dir., Riverside & Brookfield
Suburban Life, IL, Downers Grove
mringness@shawmedia.com, Major/Nat'l
Accts./Grp. Sales Dir., Elmhurst Suburban
Life, IL, Downers Grove
mringness@shawmedia.com, Major/Nat'l
Accts./Grp. Sales Dir., Carol Stream
Suburban Life, IL, Downers Grove
mringness@shawmedia.com, Major/Nat'l
Accts./Grp. Sales Dir., West Chicago

Suburban Life, IL, Downers Grove
mringness@shawmedia.com, Major/Nat'l
Accts./Grp. Sales Dir., Downers Grove
Suburban Life, IL, Downers Grove
mringness@shawmedia.com, Major/Nat'l
Accts./Grp. Sales Dir., Hinsdale Suburban
Life, IL, Downers Grove
mringness@shawmedia.com, Major/Nat'l
Accts./Grp. Sales Dir., Villa Park Suburban
Life, IL, Downers Grove
mringness@shawmedia.com, Major/Nat'l
Accts./Grp. Sales Dir., Westmont Suburban
Life, IL, Downers Grove
mringness@shawmedia.com, Major/Nat'l
Accts./Grp. Sales Dir., Bolingbrook Suburban
Life, IL, Downers Grove
mringness@shawmedia.com, Major/Nat'l
Accts./Grp. Sales Dir., Woodridge Suburban
Life, IL, Downers Grove
mringness@shawmedia.com, Major/Nat'l
Accts./Grp. Sales Dir., Lisle Suburban Life,
IL, Downers Grove
mringness@shawmedia.com, Major/Nat'l
Accts./Grp. Sales Dir., Addison Suburban
Life, IL, Downers Grove
mringness@shawmedia.com, Major/Nat'l
Accts./Grp. Sales Dir., Wheaton Suburban
Life, IL, Downers Grove
mringness@shawmedia.com, Major/Nat'l
Accts./Grp. Sales Dir., Lombard Suburban
Life, IL, Downers Grove
mringness@shawmedia.com, Major/Nat'l
Accts./Grp. Sales Dir., Lemont Suburban Life,
IL, Downers Grove
mringness@shawmedia.com, Group Sales Dir.,
Kane County Chronicle, IL, Saint Charles
mringness@shawmedia.com, Group Sales Dir.,
Northwest Herald, IL, Crystal Lake

Ringness, Tessa
tringness@kelownacapnews.com, Prodn. Mgr.,
Kelowna Capital News, BC, Kelowna

Rini, Alan ....(985) 850-1122
alan.rini@houmatoday.com, Adv. Sales, The
Courier, LA, Houma

Rinker, Rudy ....(417) 836-1204
rrinker@news-leader.com, Circ. Mgr., Single
Copy, Springfield News-Leader, MO,
Springfield

Rinks, J. Wayne
wrinks@usi.edu, Chair/Assoc. Prof., University
of Southern Indiana, IN, Evansville

Rinne, Diana
diana.rinne@sunmedia.ca, Ed., Daily Herald-
Tribune, AB, Grande Prairie

Rinne, Fred
fred.rinne@sunmedia.ca, City Ed., The
Record-gazette, AB, Peace River

Rinne, Fred
fred.rinne@sunmedia.ca, Reg. Mng. Ed., Daily
Herald-Tribune, AB, Grande Prairie

Riojas, Rudy .... 305-4181 Ext. 104
rudy@ourkidsmagazine.com, Pub., Our Kids
San Antonio, TX, San Antonio

Riojas-Aguero, Olga 806: 741-0371
Owner, El Editor-Lubbock, TX, Lubbock

Riopell, Mike ....(217) 782-6165
mriopell@dailyherald.com, Political Editor,
Daily Herald, IL, Arlington Heights

Rios, Armando
arios@baxterbulletin.com, The Baxter Bulletin,
AR, Mountain Home

Rios, Luis
lrios@lrmcpa.com, Dir., Photography, Herald
Values, FL, Miami

Rios, Luis
jrios@express-news.net, Dir. of Photography,
San Antonio Express-News, TX, San Antonio

Rioux, Bruce ....(207) 689-2915
brioux@sunjournal.com, Major Acc. Mgr., Sun
Journal, ME, Lewiston

Rioux, Caroline
caroline.rioux@monjournalexpress.com, Reg'l
Ed., Granby Express, QC, Granby

Rioux, Caroline
caroline.rioux@canadafrancais.com, Reg'l Ed.,
Le Guide De Cowansville, QC, Cowansville

Ripley, Catherine
ctnews@chillicothenews.com, News Ed, Salt
River Journal, MO, Hannibal

Ripley, Ken
shenterprise@embarqmail.com, Ed., Spring
Hope Enterprise & The Bailey News, NC,
Spring Hope

Ripperger, Nick ....(320) 677-2229
hcreview@frontiernet.net, Pub., Herman-
Hoffman Tribune, MN, Herman

Risch, Katie
katie.risch@centro.net, EVP, Customer
Experience, Centro Inc., IL, Chicago

Riscicar, Carla ....(979) 743-3450
stickerads@cmaaccess.com, Adv. Mgr., The
Schulenburg Sticker, TX, Schulenburg

Risdall, John ....(651) 286-6700
john.risdall@risdall.com, Chrmn./CEO, Risdall
Marketing Group, MN, New Brighton

Risdall, Ted ....(651) 286-6700
ted@risdall.com, Chrmn./Pres., Risdall
Marketing Group, MN, New Brighton

Riser, Darryl
driser@bellsouth.net, Mng. Ed., Richland
Beacon-News, LA, Rayville

Riser, Iva Gail
ivagail@eldoradonews.com, Prodn. Mgr., El
Dorado News-Times / Sunday News, AR,
El Dorado

Rishling, Vicki
rishling@uidaho.edu, Fac., University of Idaho,
ID, Moscow

Risinger, Dianna
timesads@centurytel.net, Office Mgr., Clay
County Times-Democrat, AR, Piggott

Risling, Catherine ....(310) 243-2313
California State Univ. Dominguez, CA, Carson

Rison, Robyn
rrison@heralddispatch.com, Features Ed., The
Herald-Dispatch, WV, Huntington

Ristano, Chuck ....(410) 245-5050
cristano@cecilwhig.com, Sports Ed., Cecil
Whig, MD, Elkton

Ritchey, Anna
advertising@tritownnews.com, Ad. Director, Tri-
Town News, NY, Sidney

Ritchey, Gretchen .... (501) 337-7523 ext 212
lifestyles@malvern-online.com, Lifestyles Ed.,
Malvern Daily Record, AR, Malvern

Ritchey, Tim
tritchey@modbee.com, Adv. Vice Pres., The
Modesto Bee, CA, Modesto

Ritchie, Alanna
aritchie@scpress.org, Adv. Dir., South Carolina
Press Services, Inc., SC, Columbia

Ritchie, Alanna
aritchie@scpress.org, Adv. Dir., South Carolina
Press Association, SC, Columbia

Ritchie, Bill
advertising@review-mirror.com, Adv. Mgr.,
Rideau Valley Mirror, ON, Westport
advertising@review-mirror.com, Manager of
Preprints
, Sun-Sentinel Co., FL, Fort Lauderdale

Ritchie, Bob
britchie@harding.edu, Instr., Harding
University, AR, Searcy

Ritchie, Brian ....(216) 999-5000
britchie@advancecentralservices.com, IT Prod
System Mgr, The Plain Dealer, OH, Brooklyn

Ritchie, Cinthia ....(907) 694-2727
cinthia.ritchie@alaskastar.com, Ed., Alaska
Star, AK, Eagle River

Ritchie, Donna ....(951) 244-1966

donna@goldingpublications.com, Editor, The
Friday Flyer, CA, Canyon Lake

Ritenburgh, Don
ritenbur@oakland.edu, Business Manager,
Oakland Univ., MI, Rochester

Ritschdorff, John
john.ritschdorff@marist.edu, Dean/Prof., Marist
College, NY, Poughkeepsie

Ritter, Geoffery
gritter@gatehousemedia.com, Ed., Benton
Evening News, IL, Benton

Ritter, Heather ....(847) 427-4391
hritter@dailyherald.com, Vice Pres./Director
Human Resources, Daily Herald, IL,
Arlington Heights

Ritter, Laura
laura@capegazette.com, Ed., Cape Gazette,
DE, Lewes

Ritter, Wes ....(615) 444-3952
wrriter@lebanonpublishing.com, Advertising
Director, The Lebanon Democrat, TN,
Lebanon

Ritz, Kama
publisher@stettlerindependent.com, Pub,
Stettler Independent, AB, Stettler

Rivard, Ray
editor@lakelandtimes.com, Assoc. Ed.,
Lakeland Times, WI, Minocqua

Rivard, Robert
rrivard@express-news.net, Ed., Bulverde
News, TX, San Antonio
rrivard@express-news.net, Ed., Fort Sam
News Leader, TX, San Antonio
rrivard@express-news.net, Ed., Kelly Observer,
TX, San Antonio
rrivard@express-news.net, Ed., Lackland
Talespinner, TX, San Antonio
rrivard@express-news.net, Ed., Medical
Patriot, TX, San Antonio
rrivard@express-news.net, Ed., North Central
News, TX, San Antonio
rrivard@express-news.net, Ed., Northeast
Herald, TX, San Antonio
rrivard@express-news.net, Ed., Randolph
Wingspread, TX, San Antonio
rrivard@express-news.net, Ed., Northwest
Weekly, TX, San Antonio

Riveiro, Jason
jriverio@tsjnews.com, La Jornada Latina, OH,
Blue Ash

Rivera, Adel
arivera@diocesecc.org, Administrative
Assistant, South Texas Catholic, TX, Corpus
Christi

Rivera, Brandi ....(805) 965-5205
brandi@independent.com, Publisher, Santa
Barbara Independent, CA, Santa Barbara

Rivera, Melissa
melissa.rivera@galvnews.com, News Editor,
The Galveston County Daily News, TX,
Galveston

Rivera, Patsy ....(602) 444-8133
patsy.rivera@pni.com, Admin. Asst., The
Arizona Republic, AZ, Phoenix

Rivera, Pauline ....(303) 936-8556
privera@lavozcolorado.com, Pub., La Voz
Newspaper, CO, Denver
privera@lavozcolorado.com, Pub./Adv. Dir., La
Voz Bilingue, CO, Thornton

Rivera, Ray ....(505) 983-3303
rrivera@sfnewmexican.com, Ed. , The Santa
Fe New Mexican, NM, Santa Fe

Rives, Jerry ....(903) 596-6219
jri@tylerpaper.com, Circ. Dir., Tyler Morning
Telegraph, TX, Tyler

Rives, John ....(301) 921-2680
jrives@gazette.net, Adv. Mgr., Joint Base
Journal, MD, Gaithersburg
jrives@gazette.net, Adv. Mgr., South Potomac
Pilot, MD, Gaithersburg
jrives@gazette.net, Adv. Mgr., Pentagon, MD,

Gaitherburg

Rives, John ....(301) 670-2680
jrives@gazette.net, Pub., The Bolling Aviator, MD, Gaithersburg

Rives, John
jrives@dcmilitary.com, Ed., Tester, MD, Gaithersburg

Rives, John ....(301) 670-2680
jrives@gazette.net, Pub., The Water Line, MD, Gaithersburg

Rives, John ....(301) 670-2680
jrives@gazette.net, Adv. Mgr., Fort Detrick Standard, MD, Gaithersburg

Rives, John ....(301) 670-2680
jrives@gazette.net, Adv. Mgr., Henderson Hall News, MD, Gaithersburg

Rives, John ....(301) 670-2680
jrives@gazette.net, Adv. Mgr., The NNMC Journal, MD, Gaithersburg

Rives, John
jrives@gazette.net, Pub., Capital Flyer, MD, Gaithersburg

Rivord, David ....(505) 880-0470
primeedit@swcp.com, Editor, Prime Time, NM, Albuquerque

Rizk, Chris
crizk@detroitnews.com, City Ed., Night, Detroit Free Press, MI, Detroit

Rizzi, Jim ....ext. 120
jimrizzi@slweekly.com, Pub., Salt Lake City Weekly, UT, Salt Lake City

Rizzo, Frank
frizzo@antonmediagroup.com, Ed. , Hicksville Illustrated News, NY, Mineola

Rizzo, Frank
frizzo@antonmediagroup.com, Ed., Farmingdale Observer, NY, Mineola

Rizzo, Mary Anne
marizzo@tribdem.com, Director Adv., The Tribune-Democrat, PA, Johnstown

Rizzuto, Robert
rrizzuto@repub.com, Asst. Online Ed., The Republican, MA, Springfield

Roach, Anita
circulation@woodwardnews.net, Cir. , Woodward News, OK, Woodward

Roach, Dan ....(231) 933-1439
droach@record-eagle.com, Advertising Department, Traverse City Record-Eagle, MI, Traverse City

Roach, Jyllian
editorinchief@dailylobo.com, Ed. in Chief, New Mexico Daily Lobo, NM, Albuquerque

Robb, Gary
grobb@santamariatimes.com, Online Ed., Santa Maria Times, CA, Santa Maria

Robb, Jack ....(334) 293-5800
jrobb@cnhi.com, Senior VP, Revenue, Community Newspaper Holdings, Inc., AL, Montgomery

Robberson, Tod ....(314) 340-8382
trobberson@post-dispatch.com, Editorial Page Ed., St. Louis Post-Dispatch, MO, Saint Louis

Robbins, Beth ....(252) 265-7849
brobbins@wilsontimes.com, Ad Rep, The Wilson Times, NC, Wilson

Robbins, Carolyn
letters@repub.com, Editorial Page Ed., The Republican, MA, Springfield

Robbins, Dana ....(905) 273-8230
dana.robbins@metroland.com, Pub., Mississauga News, ON, Mississauga

Robbins, Dana
dana.robbins@metroland.com, Pub, Brampton Guardian, ON, Mississauga

Robbins, Gayle ....(812) 316-5406
grobbins@suncommercial.com, Pub.,

Vincennes Sun-Commercial, IN, Vincennes

Robbins, Jae
sales@thecommunitypress.com, Sales, The Community Press, AB, Killam

Robbins, Len
lrobbins@theclinchcountynews.com, Ed./Pub., Clinch County News, GA, Homerville

Robbins, Ruth
rrobbins@metroparent.com, Assoc. Pub., Metro Parent Magazine, MI, Ferndale

Robbins, Tom
tom@robbinscpa.com, Sales Dir., World Features Syndicate, La Jolla

Robbs, Brett
robbs@spot.colorado.edu, Assoc. Prof., University of Colorado, CO, Boulder

Robers, Doug ....(919) 836-5658
drogers@newsobserver.com, Gen Mgr./ Adv. Dir., The Herald-Sun, NC, Durham

Roberson, Pegy ....(254) 583-7811
Adv. Dir., The Rosebud News, TX, Rosebud

Robert, Charlene ....(225) 388-0352
crobert@theadvocate.com, Marketing Dir., The Advocate, LA, Baton Rouge

Robert, Liette ....(819) 459-2222
general@lowdownonline.com, General Manager, The Low Down To Hull And Back News, QC, Wakefield

Robert Baker, Bishop
onevoice@bhmdiocese.org, Pub., One Voice, AL, Birmingham

Roberts, Angelia
advertising@guardonline.com, Adv. Ed. Mng. , Batesville Daily Guard, AR, Batesville

Roberts, Bill
broberts@bokf.com, Opns. Dir., Tulsa Pennysaver, OK, Tulsa

Roberts, Bobby Jean ....(775) 482-3365
broberts@tonopahtimes.com, Adv. Mgr., Tonopah Times-Bonanza and Goldfield News, NV, Tonopah

Roberts, Bradley
broberts@times-journal.com, Mng. Ed., The Times-Journal, AL, Fort Payne

Roberts, Cathy ....(610) 266-7903
cathy.roberts@us.mullermartini.com, Parts Mgr., Muller Martini Mailroom Systems, Inc., PA, Allentown

Roberts, Charles
Robertsc@etsu.edu, Chair, East Tennessee State University, TN, Johnson City

Roberts, Charles
editor@highlandnews.net, Ed., Highland Community News, CA, Highland

Roberts, Chris ....(505) 564-4624
croberts@daily-times.com, Ed., The Daily Times, NM, Farmington

Roberts, Christine
christine.roberts@teachforamerica.org, Ed., Mobile , New York Daily News, NY, New York

Roberts, Christopher ....(207) 563-3171
croberts@lcnme.com, Publisher, The Lincoln County News, ME, Newcastle

Roberts, Chuck ....(270) 678-5171
Prodn. Dir., Glasgow Daily Times, KY, Glasgow

Roberts, Churchill
clrobert@ufl.edu, Prof./Co-Dir., Documentary Institute, University of Florida, FL, Gainesville

Roberts, Cindy
cindy.l.roberts@us.abb.com, Office Mgr., Versailles Republican, IN, Versailles

Roberts, Colby ....(802) 865-1020 x 17
colby@sevendaysvt.com, Sales Dir./Assoc. Pub., Seven Days, VT, Burlington

Roberts, Connie
connie@huronhometownnews.com, Ed./Adv. Mgr., Huron Hometown News (OOB), OH,

Huron
connie@huronhometownnews.com, Adv. Mgr., The Beacon, OH, Port Clinton

Roberts, Courtney
courtneyroberts@my.unt.edu, Univ. of North Texas, TX, Denton

Roberts, Dan ....(734) 887-4400
droberts@mediaspangroup.com, President, MediaSpan, MI, Ann Arbor

Roberts, Darren ....(604) 892-9161
publisher@squamishchief.com, Pub, Squamish Chief, BC, Squamish

Roberts, Dave
sports@waynesvilledailyguide.com, Sports Ed., Daily Guide, MO, Waynesville

Roberts, Donnie
donnie.roberts@the-dispatch.com, Chief Photographer, The Dispatch, NC, Lexington

Roberts, Emily ....(501) 664-0125
eroberts@dolr.org, Prodn. Mgr., Arkansas Catholic, AR, Little Rock

Roberts, Gordon
editor@newsaegis.com, Ed., St. Clair News-Aegis, AL, Pell City

Roberts, H. Armstrong
info@robertstock.com, Pres., ClassicStock, ClassicStock / Robertstock, Philadelphia

Roberts, Jackie
news@haynesvillenews.com , Ed., Advertiser, LA, Homer

Roberts, Jackie
advertising@haynesvillenews.com, Ed., The Haynesville News, LA, Homer

Roberts, Jeremy
contact.us@quebecorusa.com, Dir. Cor. Commun., Quebecor World, QC, Montreal

Roberts, Jody
jody.roberts@lincolncourier.com, Adv. Mgr., Logan County Shopper, IL, Lincoln

Roberts, John
thtinc@tctelco.net, Pub., The Herington Times, KS, Herington

Roberts, Kathleen
robertskg@duq.edu, Asst. Prof., Duquesne University, PA, Pittsburgh

Roberts, Ken ....(205) 722-0211
ken.roberts@tuscaloosanews.com, City Ed., The Tuscaloosa News, AL, Tuscaloosa

Roberts, Kim
kim@livingstonnews.com, Sales Rep., The Livingston County News, NY, Geneseo

Roberts, Larry D.
lroberts@efn.org, Ed./Pub, Dead Mountain Echo, OR, Oakridge

Roberts, Lenny
editor@ojaivalleynews.com, Mng. Ed., Ojai Valley Shopper, CA, Ojai

Roberts, Marc
marc.roberts@sunmedia.ca, Circ., The Observer, ON, Sarnia

Roberts, Matt ....(307) 789-6560 ext. 110
editor@uintacountyherald.com, Ed., Uinta County Herald, WY, Evanston

Roberts, Megan
mroberts@ithaca.edu, Assoc. Prof., Ithaca College, NY, Ithaca

Roberts, Michele
michele.roberts@scripps.com, E. W. Scripps Co., OH, Cincinnati

Roberts, Mike ....(256) 740-5794
mike.roberts@timesdaily.com, Pressroom Mgr., Times Daily, AL, Florence

Roberts, Nancy
n.roberts@frontier.com, Sales Representative, Search Shopper, MN, Lindstrom

Roberts, Nancy L.
nroberts@albany.edu, Prof./Dir., Journ. Prog.,

State University of New York at Albany, NY, Albany

Roberts, Neal ....(212) 556-1234
Vice Pres., Orgn./Devel., The New York Times Co., NY, New York

Roberts, Nick ....(937) 259-2126
nick.roberts@cmgohio.com, VP of Marketing, Dayton Daily News, OH, Franklin

Roberts, Patricia
proberts@ocregister.com, Sales Mgr, The Orange County Register, CA, Santa Ana

Roberts, Patricia
proberts@deltastate.edu, Delta State Univ., MS, Cleveland

Roberts, Randy
randyroberts@thecourier.com, Photo Ed., The Courier, OH, Findlay

Roberts, Richard
sports@clevelandbanner.com, Sports Ed., Cleveland Daily Banner, TN, Cleveland

Roberts, Sam ....(336) 506-3048
sroberts@thetimesnews.com, Chief Photog., Times-News, NC, Burlington

Roberts, Stephen J. ....(312) 214-6141
sroberts@mpival.com, Vice Pres., Management Planning, Inc., IL, Chicago

Roberts, Steven
editor@nunatsiaq.com, Pub., Nunatsiaq News, NU, Iqaluit

Roberts, Tim ....(972) 392-0888
tim@wieck.com, Pres., Wieck, Richardson

Roberts, Toby
advertisinginfo@suntimes.com, Asst. to Ed., Chicago Sun-Times, IL, Chicago

Roberts, Tracey
publisher@quesnelobserver.com, Pub/Sales Mgr., Quesnel Cariboo Observer, BC, Quesnel

Roberts, Valeria ....(850) 526-3614
vroberts@jcfloridan.com, Pub./Adv. Dir., Jackson County Floridan, FL, Marianna

Roberts , Gina ....(541) 957-4288
groberts@nrtoday.com, Human resources , The News-Review, OR, Roseburg

Robertson, Alan
arobertson@bizjournals.com, Pub., Pittsburgh Business Times, PA, Pittsburgh

Robertson, Ashley ....(662) 846-4715
Delta State Univ., MS, Cleveland

Robertson, Brad ....(802) 660-1800
letters@bfp.burlingtonfreepress.com, Pub., Chittenden County Advertiser, VT, Burlington

Robertson, Charles
sales@robertsonpress.com, Pres., Robertson Press Machinery Co., Inc., MO, Joplin

Robertson, Dave
drobertson@t5datacenters.com, Chrmn., Georgia-Pacific Corp., GA, Atlanta

Robertson, Diane
cdjclass@clintondailyjournal.com, Classified Adv. Mgr., Clinton Journal, IL, Clinton

Robertson, Elizabeth
erobertson@phillynews.com, Staff Photographer, Philadelphia Inquirer, Daily News & Philly.com, PA, Philadelphia

Robertson, Greg ....(541) 992-1920
greg@oregoncoasttoday.com, Adv. Rep., Oregon Coast Today, OR, Lincoln City

Robertson, Jeff
jeff@torringtontelegram.com, Pub., The Platte County Record-Times, WY, Wheatland

Robertson, Jeff ....(307) 532-2184
jeff@luskherald.com, Pub., The Lusk Herald, WY, Lusk

Robertson, Jeff ....(307) 532-2184
jeff@torringtontelegram.com, Pub., The Torrington Telegram, WY, Torrington

MN, Edina

Rochelle, Kate
krochelle@gmnews.com, Promo. Coord., Suburban, NJ, Manalapan

Rochette, Marc
marc.rochette@lenouvelliste.qc.ca, Ed., Le Nouvelliste, QC, Trois-Rivieres

Rochford, Barry ....(260) 347-0400 Ext. 1135
brochford@kpcmedia.com, Managing Ed., The News Sun, IN, Kendallville

Rockeman, Olivia
copy@theaggie.org, Copy Chief, University of California, Davis, CA, Davis

Rocker, Av
avrocker@savpennysaver.com, Pub., Savannah Pennysaver, GA, Savannah

Rockley, Matt
mrockley@okotoks.greatwest.ca, Pub, Okotoks Western Wheel, AB, Okotoks

Rockley, Paul ....(403) 938-6397
prockley@greatwest.ca, Senior Advisor, Great West Newspapers LP, AB, St. Albert

Rockman, Craig ....(810) 240-8315
craig@rockmanpublishing.com, Publisher, Tri-County Times, MI, Fenton

Rockow, Joette ....(414) 229-4436
jrockow@uwm.edu, Senior Lecturer, University of Wisconsin-Milwaukee / Department of Journalism, Advertising, and Media Studies (JAMS), WI, Milwaukee

Rockstroh, Phillip G ....(202) 747-2077 x8092
prockstroh@washblade.com, Classified Advertising, Washington Blade, DC, Washington

Rockwell, J.V.
jvr@jvrhomes.com, Ed./Pub., Clay County Courier, AR, Corning

Rockwell, Jan V.
starherald@jvrhomes.com, Pub., Pocahontas Star Herald, AR, Pocahontas

Roda, Barbara Hough
broda@lnpnews.com, Community Liaison, LNP Media Group, Inc., PA, Lancaster
broda@lnpnews.com, Community Liaison, LNP, PA, Lancaster

Rodeffer, Dessa L.
quill@hcil.net, Adv. Mgr., The Hancock-Henderson Quill, IL, Stronghurst

Rodell, Valerie
vrodell@dioceseofgreensburg.org, Production Coordinator, The Catholic Accent, PA, Greensburg

Roden, Barbara ....(250) 453-2261
editorial@accjournal.ca, Editor, The Ashcroft-cache Creek Journal, BC, Ashcroft

Roden, Christopher ....(250) 453-2261
sales@accjournal.ca, Salesperson, The Ashcroft-cache Creek Journal, BC, Ashcroft

Rodgers, Carmen
carmen.rodgers@tallasseetribune.com, Reporter, The Tallassee Tribune, AL, Tallassee

Rodgers, Cheryl Kehoe ....ext. 209
City Ed., The Times Herald, PA, Lansdale

Rodgers, Mary Lou
editor@dcpostgazette.com, Ed., The Douglas County Post Gazette, NE, Elkhorn

Rodgers, Matt ....(740) 446-2342
mrodgers@civitasmedia.com, Sales, Tri-County Marketplace, OH, Gallipolis

Rodgers, Michael ....(256) 549-2087
michael.rodgers@gadsdentimes.com, Digital Prod, The Gadsden Times, AL, Gadsden

Rodgers, Robin ....(603) 880-1516
news@areanewsgroup.com, Ed., Hudson-Litchfield News, NH, Hudson

Rodgers, Scott

srodgers@northaugustastar.com, News Ed., The Star, SC, North Augusta

Rodgers, Tami
trodgers@kingstreenews.com, Pub./Ed., The News, SC, Kingstree

Rodgers, Traci
trodgers@kentuckynewera.com, Adv. Rep., Kentucky New Era, KY, Hopkinsville

Rodham, Luke
luke.rodham@wcinet.com, Adv. Sales Suprv., Telegraph Herald, IA, Dubuque

Rodi, Most Rev. Thomas J. ....(228) 702-2100
Pub., Gulf Pine Catholic, MS, Biloxi

Rodnick, Brian
brian.rodnick@sunmedia.ca, News Ed., The Barrie Examiner, ON, Barrie

Rodrick, Cathy
cathy.roderick@naplesnews.com, Mgr., IS/Pre Press, Naples Daily News, FL, Naples

Rodrick, Richard
rodrick.rich@uwlax.edu, Chair, University of Wisconsin-La Crosse, WI, La Crosse

Rodrigue, Darlene ....(985) 857-2220
darlene.rodrigue@houmatoday.com, Finance Dir., The Courier, LA, Houma

Rodrigue, Darlene ....(985) 857-2220
darlene.rodrigue@dailycomet.com, Finance Dir., Daily Comet, LA, Thibodaux

Rodrigue, George ....(216) 999-4373
grodrigue@plaind.com, President & Editor, The Plain Dealer, OH, Brooklyn

Rodrigues, Aaron ....(519) 598-4729
arodrigues@postmedia.com, Media Sales Mgr., Chatham This Week, ON, Chatham

Rodrigues, Hugo ....(613) 933-3160 ext. 225
Nat'l Dir., The Canadian Association of Journalists, ON, Cornwall

Rodrigues, Pradip
Pradip@CanIndia.com, Ed., Can-India News, ON, Mississauga

Rodriguez, Bonnie
editor_galtherald@herburger.net, Mng. Ed., The Galt Herald, CA, Galt
editor_galtherald@herburger.net, Mng. Ed., Galt Shopper, CA, Galt

Rodriguez, Brandi
brodriguez@ahwatukee.com, Circ. Mgr., East Valley Tribune, AZ, Tempe

Rodriguez, Cecil ....(505) 863-6811 ext. 214
Prod. Ed., Gallup Independent, NM, Gallup

Rodriguez, Codell ....(618) 351-5804
codell.rodriguez@thesouthern.com, Night Ed., The Southern Illinoisan, IL, Carbondale

Rodriguez, Jose ....(403) 250-4161
jose.rodriguez@sunmedia.ca, Ed.-in-Chief, The Calgary Sun, AB, Calgary

Rodriguez, Lizbeth
lizbeth.rodriguez@impremedia.com, Marketing Dir., El Diario La Prensa, NY, Brooklyn

Rodriguez, Manny
mrodriguez@sigconsult.com, Prodn. Mgr., Jewish Journal Palm Beach South, FL, Fort Lauderdale

Rodriguez, Miriam U.
usarmy.wsmr.atec.list.ranger@mail.mil, Ed., White Sands Missile Ranger, NM, White Sands Missile Range

Rodriguez, Nate ....(903) 893-8181
nrodriguez@heralddemocrat.com, Senior Group Publisher , Texoma marketing and media group, publisher of The Van Alstyne Leader, TX, Sherman

Rodriguez, Pablo
advertising@sweetwaterreporter.com, Composing Mgr., Sweetwater Reporter, TX, Sweetwater
advertising@sweetwaterreporter.com, Composing Mgr., Nolan County Shopper, TX,

Sweetwater

Rodriguez, Robert
rororodriguez@wphospital.org, Design Dir., The Journal News, NY, White Plains

Rodriguez, Teresa
teresar@capegazette.com, Prod., Cape Gazette, DE, Lewes

Rodriguez, Tony
rodriguez@trutest.com, Prodn. Mgr., The Catholic New World, IL, Chicago

Rodríguez, Ángel ....(787) 810-3377
opcpr@yahoo.com, Pres., Overseas Press Club of Puerto Rico (Established 1968), PR, San Juan

Roe, David
droe@certifiedaudit.com, Dir., Opns., Certified Audit of Circulations, Inc., NJ, Wayne

Roe, Eileen
subscribe@alconareview.com , Office/Circ. Mgr. , Alcona County Review, MI, Harrisville

Roe, John
jroe@therecord.com, Editorial Page Ed., The Record, ON, Kitchener

Roebke, Brian
broebke@timesvillager.com, Ed., The Times-Villager, WI, Kaukauna

Roeder, Larry
lroeder.ljrpublishing@gmail.com, Pub./Ed., Town and Country, PA, Pennsburg

Roegner, Kim ....(970) 224-7885
kimroegner@colorodoan.com, Pub., Colorado Connection, CO, Fort Collins

Roehl, Reagan
sports@taylorpress.net, Sports Ed., The Hutto News, TX, Taylor

Roehm, Carol ....(217) 477-5174
Newsroom, Commercial News, IL, Danville

Roehrman, Michael ....(316) 269-6753
MRoehrman@wichitaeagle.com, Deputy Ed./Pub. , The Wichita Eagle, KS, Wichita

Roemhildt, Scott
scott.roemhildt@mnsu.edu, Adj. Fac., Minnesota State University Mankato, MN, Mankato

Roenigk, Ron ....(773) 465-9800
insidepublicationschicago@gmail.com, Publisher, Inside-booster, IL, Chicago
insidepublicationschicago@gmail.com, Pub., News-Star, IL, Chicago
insidepublicationschicago@gmail.com, publisher, Inside Booster, IL, Chicago
insidepublicationschicago@gmail.com, Pub., Skyline, IL, Chicago

Roenna, Michael ....(312) 527-8422
mroenna@hoyllc.com, Sales Director, Hoy LLC, CA, Los Angeles

Roepke, Dave ....(701) 241-5542
droepke@forumcomm.com, News Dir., InForum, ND, Fargo

Roeske, Keith ....(847) 427-8800
kroeske@alfactp.com, VP Operations, alfa CTP Systems Inc., MA, Tewksbury
kroeske@alfactp.com, Vice President Of Operations, alfaQuest Technologies, IL, Lake Zurich

Roessler, Mark
mroessler@valleyadvocate.com, Mng. Ed., Valley Advocate, MA, Northampton

Roessner, Barbara
broessner@ctpost.com , Exec. Editor, Greenwich Time, CT, Old Greenwich

Rogala, Mary ....(906) 524-6194
sentinel1886@gmail.com, Ad Design/Graphic Artist, L'Anse Sentinel, MI, Lanse

Rogalsky, Carolyn
carolyn.rogalsky@parenthood.com, Calendar Ed., New York Family, KS, Overland Park

Rogers, Adam ....(330) 941-1807

Youngstown State Univ., OH, Youngstown

Rogers, Alan
arogers@harperimage.com, VP of Sales, Harper Corporation of America, NC, Charlotte

Rogers, Alex
arogers@indyweek.com, Bus. Mgr., Indy Week, NC, Durham

Rogers, Alice ....(713) 313-1976
Texas Southern Univ., TX, Houston

Rogers, Ally ....(502) 624-8728
ally.rogers@us.army.mil, Sports Ed., Turret, KY, Fort Knox

Rogers, Ben
mgelbman@sierrasun.com, Adv. Sales, Tahoe Daily Tribune, CA, South Lake Tahoe
mgelbman@sierrasun.com, Adv. Sales, The Record-Courier, NV, Gardnerville

Rogers, Benny
sportseditor@athensreview.com, Sports Ed., Athens Daily Review, TX, Athens

Rogers, Bill ....(803) 750-9561
brogers@scpress.org, Executive Director, South Carolina Press Association, SC, Columbia

Rogers, Brad ....(352) 867-4101
brad.rogers@starbanner.com, Editorial Page Ed., Ocala Star-Banner, FL, Ocala

Rogers, Chris
gcjads@bellsouth.net, Adv., Gilchrist County Journal, FL, Trenton

Rogers, Corey
crogers@oakdaleleader.com, Asst. Adv. Dir., Oakdale Leader, CA, Oakdale

Rogers, Craig
craig.rogers@thesouthern.com, Pub., The Southern Illinoisan, IL, Carbondale

Rogers, Cyndy ....(508) 529-4437
cyndyrogers@charter.net, Adv. Dir., Bellingham Bulletin, MA, Bellingham

Rogers, Don ....(530) 477-4299
drogers@theunion.com, Pub., The Union, CA, Grass Valley

Rogers, Don .... (616) 842-6400 ext. 236
drogers@grandhaventribune.com, Dir. of Op. Support, Grand Haven Tribune, MI, Grand Haven

Rogers, Donna .... (336) 722-8624 Ext 106
drogers@wschronicle.com, Ed, The Chronicle, NC, Winston Salem

Rogers, Doug
doug.rogers@investors.com, Mutual Funds/Personal Finance Ed., Investor's Business Daily, CA, Los Angeles

Rogers, Doug
newseditor@bellsouth.net, Ed., The Observer, SC, Holly Hill

Rogers, Doug ....(919) 836-5658
drogers@newsobserver.com, Adv. Dir., The Durham News, NC, Chapel Hill
drogers@newsobserver.com, Adv. Dir., Chapel Hill News, NC, Durham
drogers@newsobserver.com, Adv. Mgr., The News & Observer, NC, Raleigh

Rogers, Elizabeth ....(724) 222-2200
lrogers@observer-reporter.com, City/Metro Ed., Observer-Reporter, PA, Washington

Rogers, Helen ....(203) 789-5214
hrogers@nhregister.com, Credit Mgr., New Haven Register, CT, New Haven

Rogers, Jacob ....(860) 466-0187
jrogersa@stedwards.edu, Print EIC, St. Edwards Univ., TX, Austin

Rogers, Janis ....(954) 356-4700
jrogers@sunsentinel.com, Sun-Sentinel Co., FL, Fort Lauderdale

Rogers, Jeff ....(812) 379-5670
jrogers@aimmediaindiana.com, CFO, AIM

Media Indiana, IN, Columbus

Rogers, Laura ....(229) 244-3400 ext. 1253
laura.rogers@gaflnews.com, Adv. Mgr., Nat'l/
Major, Valdosta Daily Times, GA, Valdosta

Rogers, Laura ....(229) 269-4216
laura.rogers@gaflnews.com, Adv. Mgr., Nat'l/
Major Accts., The Moultrie Observer, GA,
Moultrie
laura.rogers@gaflnews.com, Nat'l Adv. Mgr.,
Jasper News, FL, Live Oak
laura.rogers@gaflnews.com, Major/Nat'l
Adv. Mgr., Americus Times-Recorder, GA,
Americus
laura.rogers@gaflnews.com, Adv. Mngr.,
Cordele Dispatch, GA, Cordele

Rogers, Laura
laura.rogers@gaflnews.com, Adv. Mgr., The
Tifton Gazette, GA, Tifton

Rogers, Mark
mark.rogers@miaminewsrecord.com, Adv.
Sales. Mgr., Miami News-record, OK, Miami

Rogers, Mark ....(662) 822-6687
markr328@gmail.com, Managing Ed., The
Columbian-Progress, MS, Columbia

Rogers, Meagan
wlarmon@ptsi.net, Classified Mgr., Perryton
Herald, TX, Perryton

Rogers, Michelle
editor@salinereporter.com, Ed., The Saline
Reporter, MI, Southgate

Rogers, Philip
oneads@observernewsonline.com, Prodn.
Mgr., The Observer News Enterprise, NC,
Newton

Rogers, Sandra .... x 294
Human Resources, The Daily Sentinel, CO,
Grand Junction

Rogers, Sean
srogers@republicmedia.com, Dir., Client
Strategy, The Arizona Republic, AZ, Phoenix

Rogers, Stephen
sarogers@advancemediany.com, Chairman,
The Post-Standard, NY, Syracuse

Rogers, Stephen A.
letters@syracuse.com, Pub./Ed., The Post-
Standard, NY, Syracuse

Rogers, Tony ....(215) 968-8165
rogerst@bucks.edu, Bucks County Cmty.
College, PA, Newtown

Rogers, William C.
brogers@scpress.org, Exec. Dir., South
Carolina Press Services, Inc., SC, Columbia

Rogge, Heather ....(414) 333-8635
hrogge@conleynet.com, Pub., The Hartford
Times Press, WI, West Bend
hrogge@conleynet.com, Pub./Adv. Mgr., The
Daily News, WI, West Bend
hrogge@conleynet.com, Conley Media LLC,
WI, Beaver Dam

Rogge, Heather
hrogge@conleynet.com, Pub./Adv. Dir., News
Graphic, WI, Cedarburg

Rogge, Heather ....(414) 333-8635
hrogge@conleynet.com, Pub & Adv Dir,
Washington County Post, WI, West Bend
hrogge@conleynet.com, Publisher, Weekend
Post, WI, West Bend

Roggen, Mark N. ....(413) 528-2300
mark.roggen@roggenconsultants.com, Pres.,
Roggen Management Consultants, Inc., MA,
North Egremont

Roggio, Armando
armando@practicalecommerce.com, Senior
Contributing Editor, Practical Ecommerce,
Traverse City

Roghaar, Brad ....(801) 625-4310
broghaar@standard.net, Adv. Dir., Hilltop
Times, UT, Ogden

Roghaar, Brad ....(801) 625-4558

Mgr., Creative, Standard-Examiner, UT, Ogden

Rognsvoog, Lynn ....(401) 272-1122
lynn@creativecirclemedia.com, Design
director, Creative Circle Media Solutions, RI,
East Providence

Rogo, Gary ....(203) 330-6223
grogo@ctpost.com, Sports Ed., Connecticut
Post, CT, Bridgeport

Rogoff, Alice
alice@alaskadispatch.com, Pub., Alaska
Dispatch News, AK, Anchorage

Rogoff, Lynn ....(212) 941-8461
director@amerikids.com, CEO, Amerikids
USA, NY, New York

Rogus, Mary ....(740) 593-2606
rogus@ohio.edu, Assoc. Prof., Ohio University,
OH, Athens

Roh, Shelly
ad@thedodgevillechronicle.com, Adv. Mgr., The
Dodgeville Chronicle, WI, Dodgeville

Rohde, Kathleen
kathleen@pacindex.com, Web edition editor,
Pacific Univ., OR, Forest Grove

Rohe, Bryan
brohe@cnaads.com, Acct. Exec., Customized
Newspaper Advertising (Iowa), IA, Des
Moines

Rohlik, Joel ....(520) 573-4277
jrohlik@tucson.com, VP Finance, Arizona Daily
Star, AZ, Tucson

Rohman, Katie ....(402) 426-2121
editor@enterprisepub.com, Managing Editor,
Arlington Citizen, NE, Blair

Rohman, Katie ....(402) 426-9860
mrhoades@enterprisepub.com, managing
editor, The Pilot Tribune / Enterprise, NE,
Blair

Rohman, Katie ....(402) 426-9860
editor@enterprisepub.com, Mng. Ed.,
Washington County Enterprise, NE, Blair

Rohman, Katie
editor@enterprisepub.com, Ed., Enterprise
Publishing Co., NE, Blair

Rohman, Katie ....(402) 426-2121 x128
editor@enterprisepub.com, Managing Editor,
The Clipper, NE, Blair

Rohr, Karen ....ext. 251
karen.rohr@rockdalecitizen, Features Ed.,
The Rockdale Citizen, GA, Conyers

Rohr, Rob ....(937) 225-6938
rob.rohr@coxinc.com, Senior Vice President &
General Manager, Dayton Daily News, OH,
Franklin
rob.rohr@coxinc.com, Sr. VP, Adv., Middletown
Journal, OH, Liberty Township
rob.rohr@coxinc.com, Sr. VP, Adv. / Gen. Mgr.,
Springfield News-Sun, OH, Springfield

Rohrman, Paul ....(215) 345-3125
Systems Mgr., The Intelligencer, PA,
Doylestown

Roiland, Heidi ....(320) 589-2525
hroiland@morrissuntribune.com, Bus. Mgr.,
Morris Sun Tribune, MN, Morris

Rojas, Fernando F.
rojas123@aol.com, Pub., Resumen
Newspaper, NY, Jamaica

Rojas, Javier ....(213) 800-9896
javier@agenciapi.com, Media Mgr., Agencia
Prensa Internacional Inc., Los Angeles

Roknick, Michael ....ext. 241
mroknick@sharonherald.com, Bus. Ed., The
Herald, PA, Sharon

Roland, Becky
broland@coastnewsgroup.com, Circ. Mgr, The
Coast News, CA, Encinitas
broland@coastnewsgroup.com, Circ. Mgr,
Rancho Santa Fe News, CA, Encinitas

Roldan, Kym ....(231) 796-4831 ext.349

comp@pioneergroup.com, Prod. Mgr., Lake
County Star, MI, Baldwin

Rolfe, Bruce ....(269) 746-4331
scribe@ctsmail.net, Ed., The Climax Crescent,
MI, Climax

Rolinson, Christopher
crolinson@pointpark.edu, Asst. Prof., Point
Park University, PA, Pittsburgh

Roll, Patrick ....(600) 248-5223
proll@fayettenews.com, The Fayette
Advertiser, MO, Fayette
proll@fayettenews.com, Publisher, Fayette
Advertiser, MO, Fayette

Rolle, Dijon ....(301) 677-6806
dijon.n.rolle.civ@mail.mil, Editor, Soundoff!,
MD, Fort Meade

Roller, Cindy
croller@Cooperreview.com, Ed., Cooper
Review, TX, Cooper

Rollins, Jason
jrollins@newsandsentinel.com, Ad. Mgr.,
Parkersburg News & Sentinel, WV,
Parkersburg

Rollins, Jess ....(417) 836-5272
jrollins@news-leader.com, Missouri State
Univ., MO, Springfield

Rollins, Nora ....(979) 732-6243
norar1@sbcglobal.net, Adv. Sales, The Banner
Press Newspaper, TX, Columbus

Rollins, Rebekah
rrollins@walkermessenger.com, Office Mgr./
Classifieds/Legals, Walker County Plus, GA,
La Fayette

Rollins, Ron ....(937) 225-2165
ron.rollins@coxinc.com, Associate Editor,
Dayton Daily News, OH, Franklin

Rollo, Brandi ....(504) 392-1619
ads@plaqueminesgazette.com, Graphic
Designer, Layout Artist, Plaquemines
Gazette, LA, Belle Chasse

Rollo, Brandi ....(504) 392-1619
ads@thestbernardvoice.com, Graphic
Designer , The St. Bernard Voice, LA, Arabi

Romaguera, Mike ....(318) 362-0214
mromaguera@gannett.com, Adv. Sales Leader,
The News-Star, LA, Monroe

Roman, William E. ....(617) 482-7501
broman@harriswilliams.com, Mng. Dir., Harris
Williams & Co., MA, Boston

Romanelli, Hollis ....(203) 245-1877 ext. 6114
h.romanelli@shorepublishing.com, Acct.
Manager, Valley Courier, CT, Madison

Romanoski, Matt
matt@phillyvoice.com, Exe. Ed., PhillyVoice.
com, PA, Philadelphia

Romanski, Stephanie ....(308) 381-5430
sromanski@theindependent.com, Web/Social
Media Ed., The Grand Island Independent,
NE, Grand Island

Romanus, Michelle
lfdnews@litchfieldil.com, Wire Ed., News-
Herald, IL, Litchfield

Rombel, Adam ....(315) 579-3902
arombel@cnybj.com, Ed.-in-Chief, The Central
New York Business Journal, NY, Syracuse

Rome, Chandler ....(225) 754-2070
crome35@gmail.com, Editor-in-Chief,
Louisiana State University, LA, Baton Rouge

Romens, Gary
asmith@dailyunion.com, Prodn. Mgr., Pre
Press, Daily Jefferson County Union, WI,
Fort Atkinson

Romeo, Karen ....(315) 661-2422
kromeo@wdt.net, Advertising Director,
Northern New York Pennysaver, NY,
Watertown

Romero, Marcela ....(305) 262-7575
mromero@efeame, Marketing Coordinator,

EFE News Services - Washington, DC,
Washington

Romero, Mike
romerom@eptrail.com, Pub., Estes Park Trail-
Gazette, CO, Estes Park

Romero-Salas, Thomas
sports@dailylobo.com, Sports Ed., New
Mexico Daily Lobo, NM, Albuquerque

Romey, Linda
lromey@ncronline.org, Adv. Mgr., National
Catholic Reporter, MO, Kansas City

Romine, Heather
bookkeeping@elgincourier.com, Circ. Mgr,
Elgin Courier, TX, Elgin

Romine, Latisha
legal@artesianews.com, Admin., Artesia Daily
Press, NM, Artesia

Romkey, Mike ....(309) 757-4988
romkey@qconline.com, Assoc. ME/Print &
Online Production, The Dispatch-Argus, IL,
Moline

Romo, Roberto ....(408) 938-1700
Graphics Design, El Observador, CA, San Jose

Ron, Ciani ....(816) 234-4440
rciani@kcstar.com, Adv., The Olathe News,
MO, Kansas City

Ron, Waite ....(330) 541-9452
rwaite@dixcom.com, General Manager,
Record Publishing Company, LLC, OH, Kent

Ronald, Jack
j.ronald@thecr.com, Pub., The Commercial
Review, IN, Portland

Ronald, John C. ....(260) 726-8141
Pub., Dunkirk News and Sun, IN, Dunkirk

Roncal, Rafael ....(202) 281-2442
rafael@elpreg.org, Ed., El Pregonero, MD,
Hyattsville

Rondeau, Andrea
news@cowichanvalleycitizen.com, Mng. Ed.,
Cowichan Valley Citizen, BC, Duncan

Rondeau, Mark .... (802) 447-7567 ext. 113
mrondeau@benningtonbanner.com, Local
News Ed., Bennington Banner, VT,
Bennington

Rone, Marvin ....(307) 266-0588
marvin.rone@trib.com, Outside Sales Rep,
Casper Star-Tribune, WY, Casper

Ronhovdee, Lisa
lronhovdee@sierranevadamedia.com,
Distribution, Sierra Sun, CA, Truckee
lronhovdee@sierranevadamedia.com,
Distribution, Tahoe Daily Tribune, CA, South
Lake Tahoe
lronhovdee@sierranevadamedia.com,
Distribution, The Record-Courier, NV,
Gardnerville

Ronquist, Neal
nronquist@duluthnews.com, Publisher, Duluth
News Tribune, MN, Duluth

Ronquist, Neal
nronquist@pinejournal.com, Pub., The Pine
Journal, MN, Duluth

Ronquist, Neal
publish@rivertowns.net, Pub., The Hudson
Star-Observer, WI, River Falls
publish@rivertowns.net, Publisher, River Falls
Journal, WI, River Falls

Ronquist, Neal
nronquist@lcnewschronicle.com, Pub., Lake
County News-Chronicle, MN, Two Harbors

Ronzio, Anthony ....(207) 990-8177
aronzio@bangordailynews.com, Exec. Dir.,
Bangor Daily News, ME, Bangor

Rood, Mark ....(800) 597-9798
mrood@toma.com, Pres., American Consulting
Services, WA, Camas

Rood, Mike ....(225) 344 - 9309 x106
mike@lapress.com, Communications Dir.,

Louisiana Press Association, LA, Baton Rouge

Roof, Don .... (515) 663-6934
droof@amestrib.com, Dir., Prodn., Story County Advertiser, IA, Ames

Rook, John
jrook@cheshireherald.com, Ed., The Cheshire Herald, CT, Cheshire

Rook, Lisa .... (301) 334-3963
lmrook@therepublicannews.com, Adv. Mgr., The Republican, MD, OAKLAND

Rook, Suzanne .... (507) 931-8561
srook@lecenter.com, Mng. Ed., The Le Center Leader, MN, Le Center

Rook, Suzanne .... (507) 931-8567
srook@wasecacountynews.com, Ed, Waseca County News, MN, Waseca
srook@wasecacountynews.com, Mng. Ed., St. Peter Herald, MN, Saint Peter

Rook, Suzanne .... (507) 333-3134
editor@faribault.com, Regional Managing Editor, Faribault Daily News, MN, Faribault

Rook, Suzanne .... (507) 665-3332
srook@lesueurnews-herald.com, Reg Mgr Ed, Le Sueur News-Herald, MN, Le Sueur

Rook, Suzanne .... (507) 333-3134
editor@northfieldnews.com, Lonsdale Area News-Review, MN, Lonsdale

Rooney, Donna
brightonparklife@aol.com, Ed., Brighton Park - McKinley Park Life, IL, Chicago

Rooney, Ed .... (847) 797-5125
rooney@pioneerlocal.com, Display Adv. Mgr., Arlington Heights Post, IL, Chicago

Rooney, Sean .... (403) 528-5688
srooney@medicinehatnews.com, Sports Ed., Medicine Hat News, AB, Medicine Hat

Roop, Jason
jason.roop@styleweekly.com, Editor, Style Weekly, VA, Richmond

Roos, Rob
rroos@sooeveningnews.com, Sports Ed., Sault Ste. Marie Evening News, MI, Sault Sainte Marie

Roosa, Julie
jkroosa@dmacc.edu, Des Moines Area Cmty. College, IA, Ankeny

Roosenraad, Jon A. .... (352) 392-1124
Prof./Asst. Dean, Student Servs., University of Florida, FL, Gainesville

Roosevelt, Pam .... (562) 947-8755
Southern California Univ. of Health Sciences, CA, Whittier

Root, Jeff .... (870) 245-4186
rootj@obu.edu, Ouachita Baptist Univ., AR, Arkadelphia

Root, Jon .... (508) 676-2575
jroot@heraldnews.com, Mng. Ed., Real Estate Guide, MA, Fall River

Root, Jon .... (508) 676-2575
jroot@heraldnews.com, Content Dir., Taunton Daily Gazette, MA, Taunton

Root, Kim
kroot@parsonssun.com, Classified Adv. Sales, Parsons Sun, KS, Parsons

Root, Steve .... (850) 449-7668
publisher@ThriftyNickelP.com, General Manager, Thrifty Nickel - Pensacola, FL, Pensacola

Root, Steve .... (850) 449-7668
publisher@ThriftyNickelP.com, Publisher, Thrifty Nickel - Ft. Walton Beach, FL, Fort Walton Beach

Roper, Nadine
nadine@rogueriverpress.com, d., Rogue River Press, OR, Grants Pass

Roper, Shannon

shannon.roper@marist.edu, Asst. Prof., Marist College, NY, Poughkeepsie

Ropp, Kathy
kathy.ropp@myhorrynews.com, Ed., The Horry Independent, SC, Conway

Roque, Justine
thereminderads@comcast.net, Prod. Mgr, Cumberland Reminder, NJ, Millville

Rorex, Dee
deanna.rorex@navy.mil, Ed., On Target, CA, Ridgecrest

Rosa, Catherine
kate195@aol.com, Bus. Mgr., Canarsie Courier, NY, Brooklyn

Rosa, Christopher
chris.rosa@vermiliontoday.com, Managing Ed., Abbeville Meridional, LA, Abbeville

Rosa, Rolando
rrosa@jcfloridan.com, Sports Editor, Jackson County Floridan, FL, Marianna

Rosado, Fernando
bohemio@ix.netcom.com, Ed., El Bohemio News, CA, San Francisco

Rosado, Rossana
rossana.rosado@eldiariony.com, CEO/Pub., El Diario La Prensa, NY, Brooklyn

Rosato-Taylor, Andrea .... (250) 729-4248
arosato-taylor@nanaimodailynews.com, Sales and Mktg. Mgr., Nanaimo Daily News, BC, Nanaimo

Roschewski, Marybeth .... (308) 345-4500
circmgr@mccookgazette.com, Circ. Mgr., McCook Daily Gazette, NE, Mc Cook

Rose, Bob .... (314) 340-8333
brose@post-dispatch.com, Deputy Managing Ed., St. Louis Post-Dispatch, MO, Saint Louis

Rose, Ed .... (503) 294-5026
erose@acsor.com, Dir. Cir. Audience, The Oregonian, OR, Portland

Rose, Ed
erose@mailtribune.com, Operations Director, The Ashland Daily Tidings, OR, Medford

Rose, Hope .... (757) 934-9604
hope.rose@suffolknewsherald.com, Adv. Rep., Suffolk News-Herald, VA, Suffolk

Rose, John Lemieux
john@media-enterprises.com, Principal, Media enterprises, CA, Tustin

Rose, Joyce .... (859) 624-6607
composing@richmondregister.com, The Richmond Register, KY, Richmond

Rose, Kelly .... (504) 826-3070
krose@nola.com, Vice Pres., Adv, The Times-Picayune, LA, New Orleans

Rose, Leslie .... (225) 473-3101
editor@donaldsonvillechief.com, Editor, The Donaldsonville Chief, LA, Donaldsonville

Rose, Mark
mrose@nola.com, VP Digital Solutions, The Times-Picayune, LA, New Orleans

Rose, Maureen .... (502) 624-1096
maureen.rose@us.army.mil, Assoc. Ed., Turret, KY, Fort Knox

Rose, Rachel .... (360) 735-4605
rachel.rose@columbian.com, Circ. Mgr., Promo./Sales, The Columbian Alternate Delivery Service, WA, Vancouver

Rose, Rachel .... (360) 735-4605
rachel.rose@columbian.com, Circ. Mgr., Promo./Sales, The Columbian, WA, Vancouver

Rose, Rick .... (318) 459-3493
Richard.Rose@shreveporttimes.com, Territory Sales Mgr., The Times, LA, Shreveport

Rose, Robert .... (404) 865-4350
robert.rose@thomsonreuters.com, Bureau Chief, Atlanta, The Wall Street Journal, NY,

New York

Rose, Rod .... (765) 482-4650 ext. 127
rod.rose@reporter.net, Farm Ed., The Reporter, IN, Lebanon

Rose, Ruth .... (606) 528-7898 Ext. 17
rrose@thetimestribune.com, Adv. Rep., Times-Tribune, KY, Corbin

Rose, Shayne
srose@clevescene.com, Adv. Dir., Cleveland Scene, OH, Cleveland

Rose, Steve
srose@semissourian.com, Prodn. Mgr., Southeast Missourian Plus, MO, Cape Girardeau

Rose, Tina
tina@independentnews.com, Adv. Mgr., The Independent, CA, Livermore

Rose, Wendy
wrose@thewesternstar.com, Adv., The Gulf News, NL, Port aux Basques

Roseberry, Bill .... (618) 656-4700 x48
broseberry@edwpub.net, Sports Ed., Edwardsville Intelligencer, IL, Edwardsville

Rosebush, Judson .... (212) 581-3000
judson@rosebush.com, Pres., Judson Rosebush Co., NY, Carmel

Rosen, Derek
drosen@uniondemocrat.com, Coord., Systems/Web, The Union Democrat, CA, Sonora

Rosen, Jay .... (212) 998-7980
jr3@nyu.edu, Chair, New York University, NY, New York

Rosen, Mark A. .... (914) 766-4773
rosenm@us.ibm.com, Vice Pres., Integrated Mktg. Commun., IBM Software Grp., IBM Corp., NY, Armonk

Rosen, Richard
richard.rosen@nielsen.com, Mng. Ed., Women's Wear Daily, NY, New York

Rosenauer, Ken
klr9015@griffon.mwsc.edu, Chair, Missouri Western State College, MO, Saint Joseph

Rosenberg, Alan .... (401) 277-7409
arosenbe@providencejournal.com, Managing Ed. Features, The Providence Journal, RI, Providence

Rosenberg, Marcy .... (541) 303-3336
mrosenberg@eastoregonian.com, Circulation Manager, East Oregonian, OR, Pendleton

Rosenberg, Tracy .... (510) 684-6853
tracy@media-alliance.org, Exec. Dir., Media Alliance, CA, San Francisco

Rosenberg, Wolf .... (916) 288-6036
wolf@cnpa.com, VP Adv., California News Publishers Association, CA, Sacramento

Rosenberg Amzallag, Kim .... (212) 453-9420
amzallag@forward.com, Adv. Dir., Forward Newspaper, NY, New York

Rosenberger, Barb
brosenbe@gannett.com, Prod. Mgr, Action Advertiser, WI, Fond Du Lac

Rosenberger, Paul
prosenberger@chespub.com, Gen. Mgr., The Dundalk Eagle, MD, Dundalk

Rosenberry, Dena .... (719) 636-0278
dena.rosenberry@gazette.com, Presentation Director, The Gazette, CO, Colorado Springs

Rosenblatt, Gary
gary@jewishweek.org, Ed., Jewish Week, NY, New York

Rosenblatt, Gary .... (212) 921-7822 x215
gary@jewishweek.org, Pub., The Jewish Week, NY, New York

Rosenblatt, Gary .... (212) 921-7822 x215
gary@jewishweek.org, Pub., The Westchester Jewish Week, NY, New York

gary@jewishweek.org, Ed. & Pub., Manhattan/Westchester Jewish Week, NY, New York

Rosenbluth, Susan L. .... (201) 569-2845
susan@jewishvoiceandopinion.com, Editor, Jewish Voice and Opinion, NJ, Englewood

Rosenburg, Kate
leader@lucernevalley.net, Ed., Lucerne Valley Leader, CA, Victorville

Rosenburgh, Scott .... (815) 459-4040
srosenburgh@nwherald.com, Vice Pres./Adv. Dir., Northwest Citizen Shopper, IL, Crystal Lake

Rosenbush, Rich
editor@drf.com, Ed. in Chief, Daily Racing Form, NY, New York

Rosener, Brian
brosener@dasrnews.com, Sports Ed., Daily American Republic, MO, Poplar Bluff

Rosenfeld, James .... (631) 843-2080
jrosenfeld@newsday.com, Local Mktg Sales Project Mgr, Newsday Hometown Shopper, NY, Melville

Rosenfeld, James .... (631) 843-2080
jrosenfeld@newsday.com, Research Project Mgr., Newsday's Marketeer, NY, Brooklyn
jrosenfeld@newsday.com, Newsday, NY, Melville

Rosengren, Peter .... (847) 427-4645
prosengren@dailyherald.com, Vice Pres./Director of Advertising
, Daily Herald, IL, Arlington Heights

Rosenkranz, David
misc@vassar.edu, Vassar College, NY, Poughkeepsie

Rosensteel, Mike
mike@sdcnn.com, Adv. Mgr., San Diego Uptown News, CA, San Diego
mike@sdcnn.com, Adv. Mgr, GAY San Diego, CA, San Diego

Rosenstiel, Thomas
tom.rosenstiel@pressinstitute.org, Executive Director, American Press Institute, VA, Arlington

Rosenthal, Cindy .... (212) 332-6406
cindy.rosenthal@journalismonline.com, Director of Public Affairs, Press+, NY, New York

Rosenthal, Dr. Robert
rrosenth@suffolk.edu, Chair, Suffolk University, MA, Boston

Rosenthal, Fary .... (770) 938-0003
atlasflags@mindspring.com, President, Atlas Flags, Inc., GA, Tucker

Rosenthal, Michele
publisher@pipestoneflyer.ca, Pub, Leduc-wetaskiwin Pipestone Flyer, AB, Millet
publisher@pipestoneflyer.ca, Pub, Rimbey Review, AB, Rimbey

Rosenthal, Michele .... (403) 783-1660
publisher@pipestoneflyer.com, publisher, Ponoka News, AB, Ponoka

Rosenthal, Ray
rrosenthal@newspress.com, Nat'l Adv. Sales Mgr., Santa Barbara News-Press, CA, Santa Barbara

Rosewag, Sandra .... (410) 857-8554
Post Press Mgr., Carroll County Times, MD, Westminster

Rosiek, Susan
srosiek@hometownlife.com, Executive Editor/Publisher, Westland Observer, MI, Detroit

Rosiek, Susan
srosiek@hometownlife.com, Exec. Ed./Pub., Northville Record, MI, Detroit

Rosiek, Susan
srosiek@hometownlife.com, Executive Editor/Publisher, Livonia Observer, MI, Detroit

Rosiek, Susan

srosiek@hometownlife.com, Pub./Gen. Mgr., The Livingston County Daily Press & Argus, MI, Howell

Rosiek, Susan
srosiek@hometownlife.com, Executive Editor/ Publisher, Redford Observer, MI, Detroit

Rosiek, Susan .... (734) 953-2100
srosiek@oe.homecomm.net, Exec. Ed., Lake Orion Eccentric, MI, Detroit

Rosiek, Susan
srosiek@hometownlife.com, Exec. Ed./Pub., Milford Times, MI, Detroit

Roslow, Jeff
jroslow@scmginc.com, Ed., The Polk County News and Democrat, FL, Winter Haven

Rosman, Mark .... ext. 8278
Mng. Ed., Tri-Town News, NJ, Manalapan

Rosman, Mark
gmntnews@gmnews.com, Ed., North/South Brunswick Sentinel, NJ, Manalapan

Rosman, Mark R. ....(732) 358-5200 ext. 8278
Mng. Ed., News Transcript, NJ, Manalapan

Rosner, Eric
erosner@mullermartinims.com, Dir., Regl. Sales (Mid-Atlantic States), Muller Martini Mailroom Systems, Inc., PA, Allentown

Rosner, Ron .... (845) 331-5000 Ext. 01225
rrosner@freemanonline.com, Sports Ed., Daily Freeman, NY, Kingston

Ross, Andrea ....(601) 981-3060
aross@mspress.org, Media Director, Mississippi Press Services, Inc., MS, Jackson

Ross, Andrea
aross@mspress.org, Media Dir., Mississippi Press Association, MS, Jackson

Ross, Chauncey ....(724) 465-5555 x 263
cross@indianagazette.net, The Indiana Gazette, PA, Indiana

Ross, Dave .... (973) 627-2427 #111
dross@fulcoinc.com, Client Services Director, Fulco, Inc., NJ, Denville

Ross, David ....(416) 364-0321
dross@cp.org, CFO, Broadcast News Limited, ON, Toronto
dross@cp.org, CFO, Canadian Press, The - Toronto, ON, ON, Toronto

Ross, David ....(760) 749-1112
editor@valleycenter.com, Ed, Valley Roadrunner, CA, Valley Center

Ross, David ....(760) 546-4000
Editor In Chief, Times-Advocate, CA, Escondido

Ross, Diane ....(217) 477-5110
Adv., Commercial News, IL, Danville

Ross, Donald M. ....(917) 368-8600
rstalzer@bankrate.com, Sr. Vice Pres./Chief Revenue Officer, Bankrate.com, North Palm Beach

Ross, Doug ....(219) 548-4360
doug.ross@nwi.com, Porter County Ed. , The Times of Northwest Indiana, IN, Munster

Ross, Janna
jross@gbpnews.com, Manager Ed., The Leader, IN, Charlestown

Ross, Jeannette ....(203) 894-3333
editor@wiltonbulletin.com, Ed., Wilton Bulletin, CT, Ridgefield
editor@wiltonbulletin.com, Ed, The Hour, CT, Norwalk

Ross, Jim ....(352) 671-6412
Assistant Managing Editor, Ocala Star-Banner, FL, Ocala

Ross, Jody
jody.ross@villanova.edu, Villanova Univ., PA, Villanova

Ross, Joe

abby.luby@marist.edu, Asst. Prof., Marist College, NY, Poughkeepsie

Ross, Julia ....(918) 793-3841
mrfields@stinternet.net, Ed, Shidler Review, OK, Shidler

Ross, Ken
editor@ctimes.biz, Mng. Ed., Area Advertiser, IA, Cherokee

Ross, Ken
kross@thesunchronicle.com, Asst. Mng. Ed., Features, The Sun Chronicle, MA, Attleboro

Ross, Ken
gaeditor@iowatelecom.net, Pub., The Lake City Graphic-Advocate, IA, Lake City

Ross, Ken ....(712) 297-7544
gaeditor@iowatelecom.net, Ed., The Graphic Advocate, IA, Rockwell City

Ross, Kendrick ....(201) 217-2460
KROSS@JJOURNAL.COM, PUBLISHER, The Jersey Journal, NJ, Secaucus

Ross, Kirby
kross@phillipscountyreview.com, Ed., Phillips County Review, KS, Phillipsburg

Ross, Paul ....(570) 501-3520
pross@standardspeaker.com, Adv. Dir., Hazleton Standard-Speaker, PA, Hazleton

Ross, Rhonda
lasso@twu.edu, Advisor, Texas Woman's Univ., TX, Denton

Ross, Richard ...(781) 255-7773, 1-(800) 783-5600
Syndicated Ad Features, Inc., MA, Walpole

Ross, Sharon ....(219) 852-4328
sharon.ross@nwi.com, Metro Ed., The Times of Northwest Indiana, IN, Munster

Ross, Shirley
circulation@newsdemocrat.com, Circ. Mgr., The News Democrat, OH, Georgetown

Ross, Susan
accessnw@wsu.edu, Assoc. Prof./Exec. Dir., Northwest Access, Washington State University, WA, Pullman

Ross, Vicki
advertising@coppercountrynews.com, Adv. Sales, Copper Country News, AZ, Globe

Ross-Polito, Kim
crestlineadvocate@midohio.twcbc.com, Ed., The Crestline Advocate, OH, Crestline

Rossano, Fred
frossano@heraldstaronline.com, News Ed., Herald-Star, OH, Steubenville

Rossetti, Mike
mrossetti@therepublic.com, Adv. Dir., The Republic, IN, Columbus

Rossi, Angelica
sales@el-observador.com, Acct. Rep., El Observador, CA, San Jose

Rossi, Angelica ....(408) 457-1192
angelica@el-observador.com, Pres./Pub., El Observador, CA, San Jose

Rossi, Jason
jrossi@shawmedia.com, Sports Ed. , Geneva Chronicle, IL, St Charles

Rossi, Justin ....(408) 457-1035
justin@el-observador.com, Sales, El Observador, CA, San Jose

Rossi, Lisa ....(515) 284-8293
lrossi@dmreg.com, Storytelling Coach, The Des Moines Register, IA, Des Moines

Rossi, Peter
news@wakefielditem.com, Ed., Wakefield Daily Item, MA, Wakefield

Rossi, Steven B.
srossi@bayareanewsgroup.com, CEO, Digital First Media, CO, Denver

Rossiter, David
david.rossiter@lethbridgeherald.com, Photo Dept. Mgr., The Lethbridge Herald, AB,

Lethbridge

Rossler, Mark
trucksales@lmh-na.com, Mktg. Dir., Linde Lift Truck Corp., SC, Summerville

Rossow, Jim ....(217) 351-5231
jrossow@news-gazette.com, Ed., The News-Gazette, IL, Champaign

Rossow, Marshel
marshel.rossow@mnsu.edu, Prof., Minnesota State University Mankato, MN, Mankato

Rostkoski, Tim
time@nickelsworth.com, Nickel's Worth Publications Inc, ID, Coeur D Alene
time@nickelsworth.com, Distribution Mgr., Nickels Worth, ID, Coeur D Alene

Rosts, Scott .... (905) 688-2444 ext. 268
srosts@niagarathisweek.com, Ed., The Grimsby Lincoln News, ON, Grimsby

Roszczyk, Steve ....(440) 953-8268
Pub., Lake County Kids, OH, Willoughby

Rotar, Chris ....(303) 566-4102
crotar@ourcoloradonews.com, Mng. Ed., Highlands Ranch Herald, CO, Highlands Ranch
crotar@ourcoloradonews.com, Mng. Ed., The Littleton Independent, CO, Highlands Ranch
crotar@ourcoloradonews.com, Mng. Ed., Parker Chronicle, CO, Highlands Ranch
crotar@ourcoloradonews.com, Mng. Ed., Centennial Citizen, CO, Highlands Ranch
crotar@ourcoloradonews.com, Mng. Ed., Lone Tree Voice, CO, Highlands Ranch
crotar@ourcoloradonews.com, Mng. Ed., Elbert County News, CO, Highlands Ranch
crotar@ourcoloradonews.com, Mng. Ed., Castle Rock News Press, CO, HIGHLANDS RANCH
crotar@ourcoloradonews.com, Ed., Douglas County News Press, CO, Highlands Ranch

Rotche, Jim ....(312) 401-1523
jrotche@chicagotribune.com, Gen. Mgr., Daily Southtown, IL, Aurora

Roth, Jack ....(732) 922-6000 ext. 3930
jroth@njpressmedia.com, VP/Prod., Asbury Park Press, NJ, Neptune

Roth, Marilyn
mroth@thedalleschronicle.com, Pub., The Dalles Daily Chronicle, OR, The Dalles

Roth, Pamela
editor@vicnews.com, Ed, Victoria News, BC, Victoria

Rothe, Deric ....(530) 852-0205
dericr@goldcountrymedia.com, Auburn Journal, CA, Auburn

Rotherham, Katherine ....(217) 747-1281
katherine.rotherham@sj-r.com, Multi-Media Sales Representative, Springfield Shopper, IL, Springfield

Rothman, William
rothman@miami.edu, Prof., University of Miami, FL, Coral Gables

Rothrock, Edwin ....(785) 832-7233
erothrock@ljworld.com, Lawrence Journal-World, KS, Lawrence

Rothseid, Ruth .... (212) 921-7822 x254
ruth@jewishweek.org, Sales Dir., Manhattan/ Westchester Jewish Week, NY, New York

Rothseid, Ruth
ruth@jewishweek.org, Sales Mgr., Jewish Week, NY, New York

Rothseid, Ruth ....(212) 997-2954
ruth@jewishweek.org, Sales Manager, The Jewish Week, NY, New York

Rothstein, Richard
rrothstein@newsusa.com, Vice Pres., Sales, NewsUSA, Inc., VA, Falls Church

Rotter, John ....(805) 437-0452
jrotter@vcstar.com, Circ. Dir., Home Delivery, Ventura County Star, CA, Camarillo

Rouch, Scott ....(706) 868-1222
scott.rouch@augustachronicle.com, Sports Writer, The Columbia County News-Times, GA, Evans

Rougeot, Melissa
mrougeot@starlocalnews.com, Circ. Mgr, Little Elm Journal, TX, Plano
mrougeot@starlocalnews.com, Circ. Mgr, Lake Cities Sun, TX, Plano
mrougeot@starlocalnews.com, Circ. Mgr, Carrollton Leader, TX, Plano
mrougeot@starlocalnews.com, Circ. Mgr, Coppell Gazette, TX, Plano
mrougeot@starlocalnews.com, Circ. Mgr, The Colony Courier Leader, TX, Plano
mrougeot@starlocalnews.com, Circ. Mgr, Allen American, TX, Plano
mrougeot@starlocalnews.com, Circ. Mgr, Rowlett Lakeshore Times, TX, Plano
mrougeot@starlocalnews.com, Circ. Mgr, Mesquite News, TX, Plano
mrougeot@starlocalnews.com, Circ. Mgr, Celina Record, TX, Plano
mrougeot@starlocalnews.com, Circ. Mgr, Frisco Enterprise, TX, Plano
mrougeot@starlocalnews.com, Circ. Mgr, McKinney Courier-Gazette, TX, Plano
mrougeot@starlocalnews.com, Circ. Mgr, Lewisville Leader, TX, Plano

Rought, Sue
srought@thedailyreview.com, Classified Advertising Manager, The Daily Review, PA, Towanda

Rouillard, Sebastien ....(418) 589-5900
sebastien.rouillard@hebdosquebecor.com; sebastian.rouillard@quebecormedia.com, Objectif Plein Jour, QC, Baie Comeau
sebastien.rouillard@hebdosquebecor.com; sebastian.rouillard@quebecormedia.com, Plein Jour Sur Manicouagan, QC, Baie Comeau
sebastien.rouillard@hebdosquebecor.com; sebastian.rouillard@quebecormedia.com, Plein Jour De Baie Comeau, QC, Baie Comeau

Roulston, Keith
info@northhuron.on.ca, Pub. , North Huron Publishing Inc., ON, Blyth

Roulston-Wilde, Dejah
auroranews@ns.aliantzinc.ca , Admin Clerk, The Aurora, NS, Greenwood

Rounce, Jeff
jrounce@businessexaminer.com, Pub./CEO, South Sound BIZ, WA, Tacoma

Rounds, David
drounds@bayareanewsgroup.com, Pub., The Montclarion, CA, Alameda

Rouner, Donna
donna.rouner@colostate.edu, Prof., Colorado State University, CO, Fort Collins

Rounsavall, Lesia ....(936) 687-2424
lrounsavall@messenger-news.com, Office Manager/Sales, The Messenger, TX, Grapeland

Rounsville, Teresa ....(607) 776-2121
trounsville@the-leader.com, Sales Mgr., Steuben Courier-Advocate, NY, Bath

Rountree, Mark
mrountree@leavenworthtimes.com, Managing Editor, The Leavenworth Times, KS, Leavenworth

Rourke, Jim
jorourke@digitalfirstmedia.com, Pub., Northeastern Shopper North, MI, Tawas City
jorourke@digitalfirstmedia.com, Pub., Northeastern Shopper South, MI, Tawas City

Rourke, Leigh
lrourke@simcoe.com, Adv. Mgr., The Mirror, ON, Midland

Rouse, Chip ....(443) 394-9781
chiprouse@stevenson.edu, Stevenson University, MD, Stevenson

Rouse, David ....(919) 739-7870

drouse@newsargus.com, Mgmt. Info Servs. Mgr., Goldsboro News-Argus, NC, Goldsboro

Rouse, Josh .... (785) 295-5660
joshua.rouse@cjonline.com, Copy Ed., The Topeka Capital-Journal, KS, Topeka

Rouse, Shelia .... (731) 285-4091 Ext. 111
srouse@stategazette.com, Publisher, State Gazette, TN, Dyersburg

Rouse, Shelia
srouse@stategazette.com, Pub./Gen. Mgr., Dyersburg News, TN, Dyersburg

Routh, Natalie
(425) 432-1209, Advertising Manager, Covington-Maple Valley-Black Diamond Reporter, WA, Kent

Routly, Paula .... (802) 865-1020 x 12
paula@sevendaysvt.com, Pub./Ed., Seven Days, VT, Burlington

Routon, Ralph .... (719) 634-5905
ralph.routon@csbj.com, Exec. Ed., Colorado Springs Business Journal, CO, Colorado Springs

Rovegno, Susan
srovegno@hcnonline.com, Sales Mgr., Cypress Creek Mirror, TX, Houston
srovegno@hcnonline.com, Sales Mgr., Tomball Potpourri, TX, Conroe
srovegno@hcnonline.com, Sales Mgr., Magnolia Potpourri, TX, Conroe

Rovere, Donna .... (732) 219-5788 ext. 206
trtredbank@aol.com, Gen. Mgr., The Two River Times, NJ, Red Bank

Rovira, Miguel Frau
manila@efe.com, Bureau Chief, EFE News Services - Manila, Philippines, Manila

Rovito, Diego A.
dierev@newstech.com, Vice Pres., Newstech Co. (Div. of Rovinter, Inc.), FL, Miami

Rovner, Michael .... (808) 529-4328
mrovner@staradvertiser.com, Managing Ed./Design, Honolulu Star-Advertiser, HI, Honolulu

Rowan, Andrew .... (718) 289-5314
Advisor, Bronx Cmty. College, NY, Bronx

Rowan, Janice
rowan@rowan.edu, Prof., Rowan Univ., NJ, Glassboro

Rowan, Toni .... (901) 853-2241
publisher@colliervilleherald.net, Pub., The Collierville Herald, TN, Collierville

Rowden, Tim
trowden@labortribune.com, Associate Editor, St. Louis/Southern Illinois Labor Tribune, MO, Saint Louis

Rowe, Ben .... (518) 565-4157
browe@pressrepublican.com, Night Editor, Press-Republican, NY, Plattsburgh

Rowe, Charles .... (843) 937-5528
crowe@postandcourier.com, Editorial Page Ed., The Post and Courier, SC, Charleston

Rowe, Clifford
rowecg@plu.edu, Area Head, Pacific Lutheran University, WA, Tacoma

Rowe, David
rowed@reporternews.com, Circ. Dir., Abilene Reporter-News, TX, Abilene

Rowe, Kermit .... (937) 328-0364
krowe@coxohio.com, Sports Ed., Springfield News-Sun, OH, Springfield

Rowe, Verna .... (316) 283-1500 x102
vrowe@thekansan.com, Business Asst., The Newton Kansan, KS, Newton

Rowe, Wanda .... (816) 637-6155
wanda@leaderpress.com, Sales Manager, Town & Country Leader, MO, Excelsior Springs

Rowe, Wes
wrowe@registercitizen.com, Pub., Better

Living, CT, Torrington

Rowell, Brian
browell@dailypress.net, Political/Gov't Ed., Daily Press, MI, Escanaba

Rowell, Michelle .... (256) 840-3000 ext 130
mrowell@sandmountainreporter.com, Business Manager, Sand Mountain Reporter, AL, Albertville

Rowell, Phil
prowell@ricentral.com, Circ. Mgr., Chariho Times, RI, Wakefield
prowell@ricentral.com, Circ. Mgr., Coventry Courier, RI, Wakefield
prowell@ricentral.com, Circ. Mgr., East Greenwich Pendulum, RI, Wakefield
prowell@ricentral.com, Circ. Mgr., Standard-Times, RI, Wakefield

Rowell, Phil .... (401) 821-7400 Ext. 231
prowell@ricentral.com, Circ. Mgr., Narragansett Times, RI, Wakefield
prowell@ricentral.com, Cir. Dir., Kent County Daily Times, RI, West Warwick

Rowell, Susan
sjjournal@shtc.net, Pub., Pageland Progressive-Journal, SC, Pageland

Rowell, Susan
news@thelancasternews.com, Pub., Lancaster News, SC, Lancaster

Rowell, Valerie .... (706) 868-1222 x 110
valerie.rowell@augustachronicle.com, Staff Writer, The Columbia County News-Times, GA, Evans

Rowen, Scott
srowan@eptrail.com, Mng. Ed., Estes Park Trail-Gazette, CO, Estes Park

Rowland, Brett
browland@shawmedia.com, News Editor, Daily Chronicle, IL, Dekalb

Rowland, Gordon
rowland@ithaca.edu, Assoc. Prof./ Organizational Communication, Learning, and Design Chair, Ithaca College, NY, Ithaca

Rowland, Lynette
editor@rollerskating.com, Ed., Indy's Child, IN, Indianapolis

Rowland, Mary ....(603) 742-4455 ext. 2931
mprowland@fosters.com, Mng. Ed., Foster's Daily Democrat, NH, Dover

Rowland, Steve
steve@tctrib.com, Pub, Tri-County News, OR, Junction City

Rowlee, Linda
lrowlee@townnews.com, Reg. Sales Mgr., TownNews.com, IL, Moline

Rowles, Shirley .... (814) 765-5535
classified@theprogressnews.com, Classified Advertising Manager, The Progress, PA, Clearfield

Rowlett, Richard .... (615) 859-6609
rowlettadvertising@att.net, Pres., Rowlett Advertising Service, Inc., TN, Goodlettsville

Rowley, Ben
ben@nvcmedia.com, Web. Ed. , Mineral County Independent News, NV, Hawthorne

Rowley, Ben
contact.lcrecord@gmail.com, Ed., Lincoln County Record, NV, Alamo

Rowley, Don .... (928) 556-2240
drowley@azdailysun.com, Pres./Pub., Arizona Daily Sun, Flagstaff, AZ, Flagstaff

Rowley, Sean .... (918) 456-8833
srowley@tahlequahdailypress.com, news editor, Tahlequah Daily Press, OK, Tahlequah

Roxbury, Rich
rroxbury@record-eagle.com, Circ. Dir., Traverse City Record-Eagle, MI, Traverse City

Roxbury, Rich
rroxbury@duluthnews.com, Circulation

Director, Superior Telegram, WI, Superior

Roxbury, Rich
rroxbury@duluthnews.com, Circulation Director, Duluth News Tribune, MN, Duluth

Roy, Bertrand .... (450) 667-4190
revueme@smelaval.org, Missions Etrangeres, QC, Laval

Roy, Bill
broy@bizjournals.com, Ed, Wichita Business Journal, KS, Wichita

Roy, Bobby
bobby.roy@sunmedia.ca, Ed, La Nouvelle Beaumont News, AB, Beaumont
bobby.roy@sunmedia.ca, Ed, Devon Dispatch News, AB, Devon
bobby.roy@sunmedia.ca, Ed, Leduc Representative, AB, Leduc

Roy, Brian .... (901) 433-9138
brian.roy@journalinc.com, Gen Mgr, The Bartlett Express, TN, Bartlett

Roy, Carolyn
carolyn@natchitochestimes.com, Ed., Natchitoches Times, LA, Natchitoches

Roy, Jean
editorial@thecanadianpress.com, Director , Canadian Press, The - Quebec City, QC, QC, Quebec City

Roy, Jean .... (514) 849-7693
Vice Pres., French Servs., Canadian Press, The - Toronto, ON, ON, Toronto

Roy, Mark
mark.roy@mx3.com, Gen. Mgr., Manney's Shopper, MN, Hibbing

Roy, Mark .... (218) 326-6623
mroy@grandrapidsheraldreview.net, Pub, Grand Rapids Herald-Review, MN, Grand Rapids

Roy, Matthew ....(978) 632-8000 ext. 23
mroy@thegardnernews.com, NIE Coord./Asst. Ed. , The Gardner News, MA, Gardner

Roy, Rebekah .... (207) 761-8379 ext. 341
rroy@mainebiz.biz, Mktg. Mgr., Mainebiz, ME, Portland

Roy, Richard .... (416) 947-7503
richard.roy@sunmedia.ca, VP & CIO, Info Serv., The Toronto Sun, ON, Toronto

Roy, Sandy
sandy.roy@monteregieweb.com, Sales Dir., Le Reflet, QC, Delson

Roy-Bornstein, Carolyn .... (978) 476-9121
pediatricpoints@comcast.net, MD, Pediatric Points, Newburyport

Royal, Cindy
croyal@txstate.edu, Asst. Prof., Texas State University-San Marcos, TX, San Marcos

Royal, James .... (918) 581-8394
james.royal@tulsaworld.com, Chief designer, Tulsa World, OK, Tulsa

Royer, Ike
tim@thenetwerx.com, Pres., Cachet Fine Art Photographic Paper, CA, Fountain Valley

Royer, Liz .... (778) 225-0032
sales@comoxvalleyrecord.com, Comox Valley Record, BC, Courtenay

Royer, Raymond
raymond.royer@domtar.com, Pres./CEO, Domtar, Inc., QC, Montreal

Royse, Pat
newsroom@dailystandard.com, Mng. Ed., The Daily Standard, OH, Celina

Royston, Wendy
wendy@dakotafire.net, Mng. Ed., Tripp Star-Ledger, SD, Tripp
wendy@dakotafire.net, Mng. Ed., The Parkston Advance, SD, Parkston
wendy@dakotafire.net, Mng. Ed., Tri County News, ND, Gackle

Rozak, Bill

brozak@uniondemocrat.com, Sports Ed., The Union Democrat, CA, Sonora

Rozen, Lee
lrozen@dnews.com, Managing Editor, Moscow-Pullman Daily News, ID, Moscow

Rozeski, John
circulation@rwpennysaver.com, Rw Publications - Akron / Corfu Pennysaver, NY, Orchard Park
circulation@rwpennysaver.com, Rw Publications - Attica Pennysaver, NY, Orchard Park
circulation@rwpennysaver.com, Rw Publications - East Aurora / Elma Pennysaver, NY, Orchard Park
circulation@rwpennysaver.com, Rw Publications - Orchard Park Pennysaver, NY, Orchard Park
circulation@rwpennysaver.com, Rw Publications - West Seneca Pennysaver, NY, Orchard Park

Rozier, Vanessa
rozierv@state.gov, Howard Univ., DC, Washington

Rozon, Peter
peter.rozon@monteregieweb.com, Adv. Rep., Le Soleil Du St-laurent, QC, Salaberry-de-Valleyfield

Rozum, Kay .... ext. 3418
circulation@mineralwellsindex.com, Circ. Mgr., Mineral Wells Index, TX, Mineral Wells

Rozycki, Bob
bobr@westfairinc.com, Mng. Ed., Fairfield County Business Journal, NY, White Plains
bobr@westfairinc.com, Mng. Ed., Westchester County Business Journal, NY, White Plains

Ruane, Gloria .... (724) 838-5143
gruane@tribweb.com, Metro Ed., Tribune-Review, PA, Greensburg

Rubbelke, Nathan
n.rubbelke@thecr.com, Reporter, The Commercial Review, IN, Portland

Rubel, Walter .... (575) 541-5441
wrubel@lcsun-news.com, Reg. Opinion Pg. Ed., Las Cruces Sun-News, NM, Las Cruces

Rubin, Saul .... (310) 434-3537
rubin_saul@smc.edu, Santa Monica College, CA, Santa Monica

Rubino, Mark .... (630) 844-1999
mrubino@industrialnoisecontrol.com, Pres., Industrial Noise Control, Inc., IL, North Aurora

Rubio, Enrique
efe@menara.ma, Rep., EFE News Services - Rabat, Morocco, Rabat

Ruble, Noukla .... (202) 495-8717
nouklar@rtdna.org, Meetings and Events Manager, Radio Television Digital News Association, DC, Washington

Ruby, Lillie
news.trib@timestribune.com, Adv. Dir., The Times Tribune, TX, Brookshire

Ruch, Melissa
melissa@crestedbuttenews.com, Circ. Mgr., Crested Butte News, CO, Crested Butte

Rucinski, Ed
ed.rucinski@nuance.com, Sr. Vice Pres./Gen. Mgr., Int'l/Commun. Recording Systems, Nuance Communications, Inc., MA, Burlington

Rucker, Bob .... (805) 546-8208
bob@newtimesslo.com, Publisher, New Times, CA, San Luis Obispo
bob@newtimesslo.com, Publisher, The Santa Maria Sun, CA, Santa Maria

Rucker, Joan .... (785) 295-5626
joan.rucker@cjonline.com, Sales Exec., The Topeka Capital-Journal, KS, Topeka

Rucker, Scott
scott@taylorpress.net, Adv., The Hutto News,

Russell, Richard
rrussell@sackvilletribunepost.com, Pub., The Sackville Tribune-post, NB, Sackville

Russell, Richard
rrussell@ngnews.ca, Pub., The Citizen-record, NS, Amherst

Russell, Sharon .... (708) 258-3473 ext. 623
Treasurer, Cornerstone Media, IL, Peotone

Russell, Wayne
wayne@ameliamonitor.com, Ed., The Amelia Bulletin Monitor, VA, Amelia Court House

Russin, Dean .... (607) 441-7215
drussin@thedailystar.com, Sports Ed., The Daily Star, NY, Oneonta

Russo, Danielle
achait@ndnu.edu, Notre Dame De Namur University, CA, Belmont

Russo, Michael .... (336) 506-3061
michael.russo@thetimesnews.com, Digital Director, Times-News, NC, Burlington

Russo, Robert
rob.russo@thecanadianpress.com, Bureau Chief, Broadcast News Limited, ON, Ottawa
rob.russo@thecanadianpress.com, Bureau Chief, Canadian Press, The - Washington, DC, Washington
rob.russo@thecanadianpress.com, Bureau Chief, Canadian Press, The - Ottawa, ON, ON, Ottawa

Russo, Ronald L.
Technical@LRADX.com, Pres., Direct Reproduction Corp., NY, Mount Vernon

Russo, Sandy .... (603) 880-1516
sandy@areanewsgroup.com, Sales Rep, Pelham/Windham News, NH, Hudson

Russo, Tom .... (317) 477-3210
trusso@greenfieldreporter.com, Photo Ed., Daily Reporter, IN, Greenfield

Rust, Jon
jrust@semissourian.com, Pub., Southeast Missourian Plus, MO, Cape Girardeau

Rust, Jon K. .... (573) 335-6611 ext. 103
jrust@semissourian.com, Co-Pres./Pub., Rust Communications, MO, Cape Girardeau

Rust, Jon K. .... (573) 335-6611 ext. 103
jrust@semissourian.com, Pub., Southeast Missourian, MO, Cape Girardeau

Rust, Melody
melodycitizen@gmail.com, Design Dir., Lovely County Citizen, AR, Eureka Springs

Rust, Rex D. .... (573) 335-6611 ext. 108
rrust@semissourian.com, Co-Pres., Rust Communications, MO, Cape Girardeau

Rustowski, Tom .... (61 2) 8272 4600
tomasz.rustowski@dowjones.com, Regl. Sales Mgr., Dow Jones Newswires - Sydney, Australia, Sydney

Rutberg, Fredric .... (413) 496-6380
frutberg@berkshireeagle.com, Pres., Brattleboro Reformer, VT, Brattleboro
frutberg@berkshireeagle.com, Pres., Manchester Journal, VT, Manchester Center

Rutgers, Stephen .... (202) 747-2077 x8077
srutgers@washblade.com, Dir Sales & Mktg, Washington Blade, DC, Washington

Ruth, Larry
lruth@theadvocate.com, Mgr., Customer Sales, The Advocate Newspaper, LA, Baton Rouge

Ruth, Pamela
rrads@rangerreview.com, Adv. Sales, Glendive Ranger-Review, MT, Glendive

Ruth, Roberth
editor@wallowa.com, Ed., Wallowa County Chieftain, OR, Enterprise

Ruthemeyer, Dan
druthemeyer@skagitpublishing.com, Sports Ed., Skagit Valley Herald, WA, Mount Vernon

Rutherford, Chris

crutherford@nwherald.com, Adv. Mgr., Northwest Citizen Shopper, IL, Crystal Lake

Rutherford, Chuck .... (217) 421-6943
Prodn. Mgr., Press, Herald & Review, Decatur, IL, Decatur

Rutherford, Joe .... (662) 678-1597
joe.rutherford@journalinc.com, Editorial Ed., Northeast Mississippi Daily Journal, MS, Tupelo

Rutherford, Kay .... (712) 654-2911
kayrmanillatimes@fmctc.com, Adv Mgr, Manilla Times, IA, Manilla

Rutherford, Tony .... (304) 544-8160
trutherford@huntingtonnews.net, Ed., HuntingtonNews.net, WV, Huntington

Ruthhart, Roger .... (309) 736-3517
riroger@qconline.com, Managing Editor, The Dispatch-Argus, IL, Moline

Rutkowski, Gary .... ext. 121
gary@samessenger.com, Mng. Ed., Extra, VT, Saint Albans

Rutkowski, Gary
gary@samessenger.com, Ed., St. Albans Messenger, VT, Saint Albans

Rutledge, Nancy .... ext. 28
Prodn. Mgr., Whiteside News Sentinel, IL, Morrison

Rutten, Jacques
publisher@lewistownnews.com, Pub., Lewistown News-Argus, MT, Lewistown

Rutten, Jacques .... (406) 566-2471
press@itstriangle.com, Pub., Judith Basin Press, MT, Lewistown

Rutter, Vicky .... (417) 256-9191
Customer Service Representative, West Plains Daily Quill, MO, West Plains

Ruttlen, Mable
mruttlen@eprisenow.com, Account Exec., The Enterprise Ledger, AL, Enterprise

Ruud, Candice .... (541) 737-2232
Oregon State Univ., OR, Corvallis

Ruvolo, Roger .... (951) 368-9419
rruvolo@pe.com, Asst. Managing Ed., The Press-Enterprise, CA, Riverside

Ruzgar, Michelle .... (561) 820-3912
mruzgar@pbpost.com, Internet Mktg. Mgr., The Palm Beach Post, FL, West Palm Beach

Ruzicka, Lora .... (308) 381-9461
lora.ruzicka@theindependent.com, Prepress Prod. Supervisor, The Grand Island Independent, NE, Grand Island

Ryall, Zach .... (512) 445-3685
zryall@statesman.com, Photo Dir., Austin American-Statesman, TX, Austin

Ryan, Charles
cryan@thechronicle.com , Ed., The Chronicle, CT, Willimantic

Ryan, Cherie .... (618) 487-5634
news@beechercityjournal.com, Mng. Ed., Beecher City Journal, IL, Beecher City

Ryan, Connor .... (616) 527-2100
cryan@sentinel-standard.com, Sports Editor, Ionia Sentinel-Standard, MI, Ionia

Ryan, Cy .... (775) 687-5032
cy@lasvegassun.com, Carson City Bureau Chief, Las Vegas Sun, NV, Henderson

Ryan, Debi .... (936) 564-8361
dryan@dailysentinel.com, Publisher, The Daily Sentinel, TX, Nacogdoches

Ryan, Elizabeth .... (601) 693-1551 ext 3230
eryan@themeridianstar.com, Skyline Advertising, Skyline, MS, Meridian
eryan@themeridianstar.com, Church Pages & Bus. Review, The Meridian Star, MS, Meridian

Ryan, Fred .... (819) 684-4755
abwqp@bulletinaylmer.com, Publisher , The

West-quebec Post, QC, Gatineau

Ryan, Jack
publisher@enterprise-journal.com, Pub./Ed./Gen. Mgr., Enterprise-Journal, MS, McComb

Ryan, Jack
publisher@enterprisejournal.com, Ed., Southwest Sun, MS, McComb

Ryan, Jamie
jryan@nectarcorp.com, Ed., South Bay's Neighbor, NY, Farmingdale
jryan@nectarcorp.com, Ed., The Neighbor Newspapers, NY, Farmingdale

Ryan, Jeremiah .... (401) 789-9744 Ext. 209
jryan@ricentral.com, Ed., Coventry Courier, RI, Wakefield
jryan@ricentral.com, Ed., Kent County Daily Times, RI, West Warwick

Ryan, John
jmryan@eiu.edu, Prof./Dir. Stud. Pubs., Eastern Illinois University, IL, Charleston

Ryan, Karen-Lee .... (210) 250-3161
klryan@mysa.com, Exec. Producer, San Antonio Express-News, TX, San Antonio

Ryan, Keith .... (585) 352-3411 x125
keith.ryan@westsidenewsny.com, Pub., Hamlin Clarkson Herald, NY, Spencerport
keith.ryan@westsidenewsny.com, Publisher, Suburban News South, NY, Spencerport
keith.ryan@westsidenewsny.com, Publisher and Adv. Mgr., Westside News, NY, Spencerport
keith.ryan@westsidenewsny.com, Publisher, Suburban News North, NY, Spencerport
keith.ryan@westsidenewsny.com, Publisher, Suburban News West, NY, Spencerport

Ryan, Lily .... (819) 684-4755
editor@westquebecpost.com, Editor, The West-quebec Post, QC, Gatineau

Ryan, Lily .... (819) 684-4755
info@bulletinaylmer.com, Ed. , Le Bulletin D'aylmer, QC, Gatineau

Ryan, Mark
cnads@crescent-news.com, Publisher, Crescent Extra, OH, Defiance

Ryan, Mark .... ext. 214
cnads@crescent-news.com, Adv. Mgr., Adams Publishing Group, LLC, MN, Virginia

Ryan, Mark .... (419) 784-5441 ext. 205
mryan@crescent-news.com , Pub., The Crescent-News, OH, Defiance

Ryan, Michael .... (706) 823-3366
michael.ryan@augustachronicle.com, Editorial Page Editor, The Augusta Chronicle, GA, Augusta

Ryan, Mike
mryan@merichem.com, Prof., University of Houston, TX, Houston

Ryan, Mike .... (602) 444-5810
mike.ryan@pni.com, Gen. Mgr., Scottsdale Republic, The Arizona Republic, AZ, Phoenix

Ryan, Mike .... (816) 218-6745
mike.ryan@pich.com, Circulation Director, The Pitch, MO, Kansas City

Ryan, Molly Howard
countian@otelco.net, Pub., The Blount Countian, AL, Oneonta

Ryan, Monette .... (714) 796-3845
mmichel@ocregister.com, Excelsior Los Angeles, CA, Los Angeles
mmichel@ocregister.com, Adv. Acc. Exec., La Prensa, CA, Riverside

Ryan, Robyn
robynryan@poncacitynews.com, Retail Adv. Mgr., The Ponca City News, OK, Ponca City

Ryan, Russ .... (740) 373-2121 Ext. 211
rryan@mariettatimes.com, Info. Systems Mgr., The Marietta Times, OH, Marietta

Ryan, Sarah
wdn@wdnonline.com, Class. Adv. Mgr. ,

Weatherford Daily News, OK, Weatherford

Ryan, Sharon
sryan@bayareanewsgroup.com, Pres./Pub., East Bay Times, CA, Walnut Creek
sryan@bayareanewsgroup.com, Pers./Pub., The Mercury News, CA, San Jose
sryan@bayareanewsgroup.com, Pub, Digital First Media, CO, Denver

Ryan, Sharon .... (408) 920-5576
SRyan@mercurynews.com, Pres./Pub., The Cupertino Courier, CA, San Jose
SRyan@mercurynews.com, Pres./Pub., Saratoga News, CA, San Jose
SRyan@mercurynews.com, Pres./Pub., Campbell Reporter, CA, San Jose
SRyan@mercurynews.com, Pres./Pub., Almaden Resident, CA, San Jose

Ryan, Shaun .... (904) 819-3503
shaun.ryan@staugustinerecord.com, Health Ed., The St. Augustine Record, FL, Saint Augustine

Ryan, Sophia .... (819) 684-4755
ventes.sales@bulletinaylmer.com, sales manager, The West-quebec Post, QC, Gatineau

Ryan, Stephanie
stephanie.ryan@kmbs.konicaminolta.us, Corporate Contact, Konica Minolta Business Solutions, AL, Mobile

Ryan, Steve .... (978) 371-5750
sryan@wickedlocal.com, Ed., Wakefield Observer, MA, Danvers

Ryan, Steve .... (978) 371-5750
sryan@wickedlocal.com, Ed., Reading Advocate, MA, Danvers

Ryan, Tim .... (203) 317-2430
tryan@record-journal.com, Sr. Vice Pres., Record-Journal, CT, Meriden

Ryan, Timothy
tryan@dailypress.com, Pres./CEO/Pub., Daily Press Porch Plus, VA, Newport News

Ryan, Timothy
timothy.ryan@latimes.com, Pub. & Chief Exec. Officer, Los Angeles Times, CA, Los Angeles

Ryan, Timothy .... (610) 820-6500
publisher@mcall.com, Publisher, President and CEO, The Morning Call, PA, Allentown

Ryan, Tom
carlson@carlson-dc.com, Vice Pres., Mktg, Carlson Design Construct, CA, Irvine

Ryan, Toni .... (574) 658-4111
tryan@the-papers.com, Advertising Representative, The Paper - Kosciusko Edition, IN, Milford

Ryan, Travis .... (478) 272-5522 ext. 210
graphics@courier-herald.com, Online Mgr., The Courier Herald, GA, Dublin

Ryan , Morgan
sports@adirondackdailyenterprise.com, Sports Ed., Adirondack Daily Enterprise, NY, Saranac Lake

Ryba, Andy
andy.ryba@nonpareilonline.com, Adv. Dir., The Daily Nonpareil, IA, Council Bluffs

Ryba, Jacki .... (785) 822-1493
jryba@salina.com, Bus./HR Dir., The Salina Journal, KS, Salina

Rybarcyk, Tony
trybarcyk@news-press.com, Gen. Mgr., The Commercial Appeal, TN, Memphis

Ryce, Walter .... (831) 394-5656
walter@mcweekly.com, Monterey County Weekly, CA, Seaside

Ryckman, Larry .... (303) 954-1829
lcolacioppo@denverpost.com, Senior Ed. News, The Denver Post, CO, Denver

Ryder, Donna
dryder@ucmessenger.com, Farm Ed., The Messenger, TN, Union City

Ryder, Phillip A. .... (850) 484-8622
thejoker@thefunnypages.com, Creator, The
Funny Pages, Pensacola

Rye, Beth................................. (605) 665-7811
beth.rye@yankton.net, New Media Director,
Yankton Daily Press & Dakotan, SD, Yankton

Ryker, Bill
bill.ryker@anygraaf.com, SALES DIR.,
Anygraaf USA, MD, Owings Mills

Ryoji, Sharon
sharon@shoom.com, Vice Pres., Customer
Serv., Shoom, Inc., CA, Incino

Ryzewicz, Keith .... (908) 243-6653
kryzewicz@gannettnj.com, Comm. Ed., Courier
News, NJ, Somerville

S

Saabye, David.......................... (212) 621-1500
Associated Press, The, New York

Saad, Nabil
expreso@interlog.com, Mng. Ed., El Expreso,
ON, Mississauga

Saal, Rich .... (217) 788-1475
rich.saal@sj-r.com, Photo Ed., The State
Journal-Register, IL, Springfield

Sabba, Sharilyn
SherilynSabba@WoodsideHerald.com, Prodn.
Mgr., Woodside Herald, NY, Sunnyside

Sabin, Jim .... (740) 681-4344
jsabin@nncogannett.com, Editorial Page Ed.,
Eagle-Gazette Media, OH, Lancaster

Sabljak, Mark
mark.waters@marquette.edu, Pub., Milwaukee
Business Journal, WI, Milwaukee

Sablynski, Christine
tribune.chris@gmail.com, Mng. Ed., West
Essex Tribune, NJ, Livingston

Sabourin, Jill
jill@luminanews.com, Account Exec., Lumina
News, NC, Wilmington

Sabrina, Stockrahm
westfallgcdw@gmail.com, Editor, Greene
County Daily World, IN, Linton

Sacash, David .... (843) 661-1682
dsacash@frmarion.edu, Francis Marion
University, SC, Florence

Sacco, James .... (540) 574-6291
jsacco@dnrecord.com, Sports Ed., Daily
News-Record, VA, Harrisonburg

Sacco, Jim .... (540) 932-3557
jsacco@newsvirginian.com, Sports Ed., The
News Virginian, VA, Waynesboro

Sachetti, James................ (570) 387-1234 1301
jim.sachetti@pressenterprise.net, Ed., Press
Enterprise, PA, Bloomsburg

Sachetti, Jim .... ext. 1301
Ed., Around The House, PA, Bloomsburg

Sachse, Claire
claire.sachse@tryondailybulletin.com,
Managing Ed., Tryon Daily Bulletin, NC, Tryon

Sackariason, Carolyn
sack@aspendailynews.com, Ed., Aspen Daily
News, CO, Aspen

Sackett, Jim
jsackett@wallowa.com, Adv Sales, Wallowa
County Chieftain, OR, Enterprise

Sackman, Dave
info@lrwonline.com, Chairman and CEO,
Lieberman Research Worldwide, CA, Los
Angeles

Sacks, Christy .... (423) 837-6312
composing@marioncountynews.net, Jasper
Journal, TN, South Pittsburg
composing@marioncountynews.net,
Composer, South Pittsburg Hustler, TN,
South Pittsburg

Sacks, Christy .... (423) 837-6312
composing@marioncountynews.net,
Composer, Sequatchie Valley Purchase, TN,
South Pittsburg

Sacks, Michael H. .... (713) 362-6025
mike.sacks@chron.com, Vice President,
Operations, Houston Chronicle, TX, Houston

Sadd, Randy
rsadd@hamilton.net, Ed., The Doniphan
Herald, NE, Doniphan

Sade, Vivian ..... (260) 241-7737 or (260) 693-2473
vsade8@gmail.com, Freelance writer/blogger
2017-18 WPCI President; WPCI
Communications Contest co-chair, Free
lance journalist/blogger, IN, Churubusco

Sadick, Rick
rsadick@estevanmercury.ca, Pub., Southeast
Lifestyles, SK, Estevan

Sadick, Rick .... (306) 634-2654
bkersey@estevanmercury.ca, Pub., Estevan
Mercury, SK, Estevan

Sadler, Barbara
bsadler@philly.com, Advertising Director,
Philadelphia Inquirer, Daily News & Philly.
com, PA, Philadelphia

Sadler, Cheryl .... (440) 951-0000
csadler@news-herald.com, Mobile/Digit. Ed.,
The News-Herald, OH, Willoughby

Sadler, Tom
info@owaa.org, Exec. Dir., Outdoor Writers
Association of America, Inc., MT, Missoula

Sadowski, Nick........................ (212) 594-2266
nick.outwater@gmail.com, EIC/Partner, Nowy
Dziennik, NJ, Garfield

Sadri, Farid .... (770) 416-7570 ext. 104
fsadri@atlantalatino.com, Adv. Mgr., Atlanta
Latino, GA, Atlanta

Saeed, Zanub.......................... (212) 803-8439
zanub.saeed@sourcemedia.com, Managing
Ed., American Banker Online, American
Banker, NY, New York

Saenz, Andrew
asaenz@gvnews.com, Adv. Mgr., Green Valley
News & Sahuarita Sn, AZ, Green Valley
asaenz@gvnews.com, Int. Gen. Mgr., Nogales
International, AZ, Nogales

Saenz, Vanessa
hebview@gmail.com, Adv. Dir., Hebbronville
View, TX, Hebbronville

Safa, Cindy .... (208) 639-3517
csuffa@idahobusinessreview.com, Assoc.
Pub., Idaho Business Review, ID, Boise

Safford, Dave
dssaffor@valassis.com, Sales Exec., Valassis,
MI, Livonia

Safford, Susan
ssafford@mvtimes.com, Production mgr.,
The Martha's Vineyard Times, MA, Vineyard
Haven

Sagan, Bruce .... (773) 358-3126
b.sagan@hpherald.com, Pub., Hyde Park
Herald, IL, Chicago

Sage, Mark
jsage@wythenews.com, Ed., Enterprise
Buyers Catalogue, VA, Wytheville

Sage, Mark .... (800) 655-1406
jsage@wythenews.com, Group Ed., The Floyd
Press, VA, Floyd
jsage@wythenews.com, Group Ed., Smyth
County News & Messenger, VA, Marion

Sage, Meagan........................ (401) 232-6896
Bryant College, RI, Smithfield

Sage, Robert .... (657) 278-4275
rlsage@fullerton.edu, Bus. Mgr., California
State Univ., Fullerton, CA, Fullerton

Sager, Pat .... (903) 509-2339
psager@tyler.net, OWNER/PUBLISHER,
Homes & Land of Tyler & East Texas, TX,
Tyler

Sager, Paul
argus@kkspc.com, Adv. Sales Rep., The
Astoria South Fulton Argus, IL, Astoria

Saggers, Ann .... (260) 347-0400 Ext. 1143
asaggars@kpcmedia.com, Creative Mgr., The
News Sun, IN, Kendallville

Sagona, Julie.......................... (225) 473-3101
jsagona@donaldsonvillechief.com, Office
manager, The Donaldsonville Chief, LA,
Donaldsonville

Saia, Pam
advertising1@helena-arkansas.com, Adv.
Rep., The Helena Arkansas Daily World, AR,
HELENA

Saia, Rick
rsaia@wbjournal.com, Ed., Worcester
Business Journal, MA, Worcester

Sailer, Linda........................... (701) 456-1209
lsailer@thedickinsonpress.com, Lifestyles Ed.,
The Dickinson Press, ND, Dickinson

Sailors, Jan
jan@rutherfordweekly.com, Prod. Mgr,
Rutherford Weekly, NC, Forest City

Saito, Laurie
laurie@thestranger.com, Gen. Mgr., The
Stranger, WA, Seattle

Saito, Sindy .... (818) 990-5945
editor@newscalendar.com, Editor, Hollywood
News Service, Sherman Oaks

Saiya, Veronique 478/471-7393
vsaiya@gmail.com, Mng. Ed., Georgia Family
Magazine, GA, Macon

Sakamoto, Penny
psakamoto@blackpress.ca, Pub., Goldstream
Gazette, BC, Victoria

Sakamoto, Penny
psakamoto@blackpress.ca, Group Pub.,
Victoria News, BC, Victoria

Sakellariou, Tony .... (845) 331-5000 Ext. 01226
tsakellariou@freemanonline.com, Controller,
Daily Freeman, NY, Kingston

Salaman, Mindy .... (770) 382-4545
Office Mgr., The Daily Tribune News, GA,
Cartersville

Salamone, Gary P...................... (858) 492-8696
continentalnewsservice@yahoo.com, Ed.
in-Chief, Continental Features/Continental
News Service, San Diego

Salapuddin, Robert
rsalapuddin@therecorder.com, The Recorder,
CA, San Francisco

Salata, Ronald .... (847) 427-4425
Rsalata@dailyherald.com, Director of Display
Advertising, Daily Herald, IL, Arlington
Heights

Salazar, Amelia .... (949) 660-6150 ext. 217
amelia@thelog.com, Circ. Dir., The Log
Newspaper, CA, Fountain Valley
amelia@thelog.com, Circulation Director, Editor
& Publisher Magazine, CA, Fountain Valley

Salcedo, myra .... (432) 288-2696
salcedo@utpb.edu, Advisor, Univ. of Texas
Permian Basin, TX, Odessa

Salcetti, Marianne
msalcetti@keene.edu, Asst. Prof., Keene State
College of the University System of New
Hampshire, NH, Keene

Saldivar, Olga .... (956) 982-6648
Bus. Mgr., The Brownsville Herald, TX,
Brownsville

Sale, Sharon........................... (970) 242-5555
Dist. Mgr., The Nickel, CO, Grand Junction

Salegna, Mary.............................. ext. 32
salegna@licatholic.org, Opns. Mgr., The Long
Island Catholic, NY, Roosevelt

Saleik, Brad .... (260) 461-8449
bsaleik@news-sentinel.com, Design Ed., The
News-Sentinel, IN, Fort Wayne

Salem, Zaina .... (330) 972-6184
editor-in-chief@buchtelite.com, Editor-in-Chief,
The University of Akron, OH, Akron

Salerno, Richard .... (718) 816-3162
salerno@siadvance.com, Circ. Mgr., Staten
Island Advance, NY, Staten Island

Sales, Ben
ben@newvoices.org, Jewish Student Press
Service, NY, New York

Salfino, Catherine .... (201) 939-7875
catherinesalfino@comcast.net, Pres.,
Meadowlands Media Group, Rutherford

Salfino, Michael .... (201) 939-7875
salfino@comcast.net, Columnist, Meadowlands
Media Group, Rutherford

Salfrank, Lori
lsalfrank@aberdeennews.com, Dir., Finance,
Aberdeen American News, SD, Aberdeen

Salfrank, Terry
tsalfrank@aberdeennews.com, Prod. Mgr.,
Aberdeen American News, SD, Aberdeen

Salierno, Rich .... (785) 832-7225
rsalierno@ljworld.com, Lawrence Journal-
World, KS, Lawrence

Salinas, Carlos
csalinas@catholicherald.com, Adv. Mgr.,
Arlington Catholic Herald, VA, Arlington

Salinas, Lisa
lsalinas@forsythnews.com, Circ. Mgr., Forsyth
County News, GA, Cumming
lsalinas@forsythnews.com, Circ. Dir., Dawson
County News, GA, Dawsonville

Salinas, Sara .... (858) 451-6200
SaraS@BrehmMail.com, Dir, Human
Resources, Brehm Communications, Inc.,
CA, San Diego

Salinas, Sergio H. .... (915) 546-6159
ssalinas@elpasotimes.com, CEO/Pres./Pub.,
El Paso Times, TX, El Paso
ssalinas@elpasotimes.com, CEO/President &
Publisher, El Paso y Mas, TX, El Paso

Salisbury, Phil......................... (781) 433-8322
psalisbury@wickedlocal.com, Ed. , Norwood
Transcript & Bulletin, MA, Needham
psalisbury@wickedlocal.com, Ed., The
Dedham Transcript, MA, Needham

Salkeld, Stu........................... (780) 460-5510
editor@pipestoneflyer.ca, Ed, Leduc-
wetaskiwin Pipestone Flyer, AB, Millet

Sall, Lyle
record@ctcweb.net, Pub., The Adams County
Record, ID, Council

Sallee, Steve .... (812) 277-7231
District Mgr., The Times-Mail, IN, Bedford

Sallo, Stewart .... (303) 494-5511
publisher@boulderweekly.com, Pub., Boulder
Weekly, CO, Boulder

Salomon, Kyle .... (405) 376-4571
ksalomon@mustangnews.info, Ed., The Yukon
Review, OK, Yukon

Saloway, Tony .... (780) 468-0170
tony.saloway@edm.sunpub.com, News Ed.,
The Edmonton Sun, AB, Edmonton

Saltas, John .... (801) 575-7003
john@cityweekly.net, Pub., Salt Lake City
Weekly, UT, Salt Lake City

Salter, French .... (256) 340-2463
French.Salter@theredstonerocket.com, Gen.
Mgr., Bulletin Board, AL, Montgomery
French.Salter@theredstonerocket.com, Gen.
Mgr., Redston Rocket, AL, Decatur

Salter, Justin .... (760) 297-2900
Publisher, Times-Advocate, CA, Escondido

Salter, Tracy
tracy.salter@greenvilleadvocate.com, Pub.,
The Greenville Advocate, AL, Greenville

tracy.salter@greenvilleadvocate.com, Pub., The Luverne Journal, AL, Luverne

Salter, Tracy
tracy.salter@greenvilleadvocate.com/, Adv. Mgr., Lowndes Signal, AL, Fort Deposit

Saltz, Howard ....(954) 356-4601
hsaltz@sunsentinel.com, Pub., The Gazette - Pembroke Pines & Miramar, FL, Fort Lauderdale
hsaltz@sunsentinel.com, Pub. & Editor in Chief, Sun-Sentinel Co., FL, Fort Lauderdale

Saltz, Howard ....(954) 356-4600
HSaltz@Sun-Sentinel.com, Ed., South Florida Sun-Sentinel, FL, Fort Lauderdale

Saltzgaver, Harry
hsalt@gazettes.com, Exec. Ed., Uptown Gazette, CA, Long Beach

Saltzgaver, Henry
hsalt@gazettes.com, Exec. Ed., Downtown Gazette, CA, Long Beach
hsalt@gazettes.com, Exec. Ed., Grunion Gazette, CA, Long Beach

Saltzman, Amy ....(617) 629-3382
asaltzman@wickedlocal.com, Ed., Cambridge Chronicle & TAB, MA, Somerville

Saltzman, Belinda
belinda@countrypeddlerbg.com, Country Peddler, KY, Bowling Green

Saltzman, Joe
saltzman@usc.edu, Prof., University of Southern California, CA, Los Angeles

Salvador, Michael
msalvador@wsu.edu, Assoc. Prof./Assoc. Dir., Opns. and Budget, Washington State University, WA, Pullman

Salvaterra, Neanda
neanda@blackstarnews.com, Assistant Web Ed., Black Star News, NY, New York

Salvati, Carmen
carman@circulation.net, Mktg. Dir., Circulation Development, Inc., MO, Wentzville

Salvner, Gary
gsalvner@ysu.edu, Chair, English, Youngstown State University, OH, Youngstown

Salyards, Candie
news@hfherald.com, Co-Pub./Own./Mng. Ed./ Adv. Rep., Haxtun-Fleming Herald, CO, Haxtun

Salyers, Sharon ....(423) 929-3111
srsalyers@johnsoncitypress.com, Johnson City Press, TN, Johnson City

Salzman, Gerald
gerald_salzman@dailyjournal.com, Pub., The Los Angeles Daily Journal, CA, Los Angeles

Salzman, Gerald L. ....(213) 229-5300
gerald_salzman@dailyjournal.com, Pub., Daily Commerce, CA, Los Angeles

Salzman, Jerry
daily_recorder@dailyjournal.com, Pres./Pub., The Daily Recorder, CA, Sacramento

Salzman, Jim
jim.salzman@thecash-book.com, Adv. Mgr., Cash-Book Journal/The Weekender, MO, Jackson

Sam, Metcalf
smetcalf@jrn.com, Manager, Digital Yield, Milwaukee Journal Sentinel, WI, Milwaukee

Samel, Samanhta
sam@brooklyneagle.com, Mng. Ed. , The Phoenix, NY, Brooklyn

Samet, Diana
dsamet@loyola.edu, Graphics, Loyola College, MD, Baltimore

Samford, Rhonda ....(936) 254-3618
ttnews@ttnewsinc.com, Adv. Mgr., Timpson & Tenaha News, TX, Timpson

Sammon, Kerry ....(613) 342-4441 Ext. 500267
ksammon@postmedia.com, Med. Sales Dir. ,

The Recorder & Times, ON, Brockville
ksammon@postmedia.com, Ed., Kemptville Advance Emc, ON, Smiths Falls

Sammons, Angela ....(208) 465-8136
asammons@idahopress.com, Media Sales Rep., Idaho Press, ID, Nampa
asammons@idahopress.com, Adv. Mgr., Idaho Press-Tribune, ID, Nampa

Sammons, Joyce ....(910) 653-7440
tribjoyce@tabor-loris.com, Adv./Reporter, Tabor-Loris Tribune, NC, Tabor City

Sample, George ....(814) 623-1151
Pres., The Bedford Gazette, PA, Bedford

Sample, George R. ....(814) 643-4040
aalexander@dailyherald.com, Pres./Pub., The Daily Herald, PA, Tyrone

Sample, Joe ....(713) 226-5574
samplej@uhd.edu, Associate Prof., Univ. of Houston Downtown, TX, Houston

Sample, Michael ....(814) 827-3634
msample@titusvilleherald.com, Pub./Adv. Dir., The Titusville Herald, PA, Titusville

Sampson, Keith
ksampson@lahontanvalleynews.com, Cir. Dir., Nevada Appeal, NV, Carson City
ksampson@lahontanvalleynews.com, Circ. Dir., Hot Sheet (OOB), NV, Carson City

Samrov, Adam .... (802) 447-7567 ext. 120
asamrov@benningtonbanner.com, Managing Ed., Bennington Banner, VT, Bennington

Sams, Beverly ....(574) 722-5000 Ext. 5165
beverly.sams@indianamedia.com, Regl. Adv. Dir., Pharos-Tribune, IN, Logansport

Sams, Beverly ....(765) 454-6707
beverly.sams@indianamediagroup.com, Rgl. Adv. Dir., Kokomo Tribune, IN, Kokomo

Samson, Michel
msamson@lesoleil.com, Online Ed., Le Soleil, QC, Quebec

Samson, Nancy
nsamson@ngnews.ca, Prod. Mgr., The News, NS, New Glasgow

Samuel, Pernice
samuel.pernice@kba.com, Executive Sales, KBA North America, Inc. (Koenig & Bauer AG), TX, Dallas

Samuels, Jeanne
jeannes@jhvonline.com, Pub./Ed., Jewish Herald-Voice, TX, Houston

Samuels, Jeanne F. ....(713) 630-0391
jeannes@jhvonline.com, Editor, Jewish Herald-Voice, TX, Houston

Samuels, Jeffrey
jsamuels@morrismultimedia.com, Vice Pres./ CFO, Morris Multimedia, Inc., GA, Savannah

Samuels, Jeffrey R. ....(912) 233-1281
info@morrismultimedia.com, Morris Multimedia, Inc., GA, Savannah

Samuels, Vicki ....(713) 305-2552
vicki@jhvonline.com, Adv. Dir., Jewish Herald-Voice, TX, Houston
vicki@jhvonline.com, Advertising Manager, Jewish Herald-Voice, TX, Houston

Samuelson, Josh
mcsports@midrivers.com, Sports Ed., Miles City Star, MT, Miles City

Samyn, Paul ....(204) 697-7292
Paul.Samyn@freepress.mb.ca, Editor, Winnipeg Free Press, MB, Winnipeg

San Filippo, Thom
t.sanfilippo@wsj.com, VP President, Customer Service, The Wall Street Journal, NY, New York

SanSoucie, Therese ....(603) 570-2116
tsansoucie@seacoastonline.com, Graphics Sup. , Portsmouth Herald, NH, Portsmouth

Sanak, Courtney ....(205) 443-5610
csanak@bizjournals.com, Events Mgr,

Birmingham Business Journal, AL, Birmingham

Sanborn, Deb ....(603) 224-5301 ext. 226
dsanborn@cmonitor.com, Sales Dir., Concord Monitor, NH, Concord

Sanborne, Mark ....(212) 803-8231
mark.sanborne@sourcemedia.com, Co-Chief, Copy Desk, American Banker, NY, New York

Sanca, Ruben
ruben_sanca@uml.edu, Univ. of Massachusetts Lowell Connector, MA, Lowell

Sancen, Silvia
ssancen@alinas.gannett.com, Ed., El Sol, CA, Salinas

Sanchez, Alex ....(469) 977-3602
asanchez@aldiatx.com, Gen. Mgr., Al Dia, TX, Dallas

Sanchez, Bianca
classified@egpnews.com, Circ. Mgr., Eastside Sun, CA, Los Angeles
classified@egpnews.com, Circ. Mgr., City Terrace Comet, CA, Los Angeles
classified@egpnews.com, Circ. Mgr., Commerce Comet, CA, Los Angeles
classified@egpnews.com, Circ. Mgr., Ela Brooklyn-Belvedere Comet, CA, Los Angeles
classified@egpnews.com, Circ. Mgr., Mexican American Sun, CA, Los Angeles
classified@egpnews.com, Circ. Mgr., Montebello Comet, CA, Los Angeles
classified@egpnews.com, Circ. Mgr., Monterey Park Comet, CA, Los Angeles
classified@egpnews.com, Circ. Mgr., Northeast Sun, CA, Los Angeles
classified@egpnews.com, Circ. Mgr., Vernon Sun, CA, Los Angeles
classified@egpnews.com, Circ. Mgr., Wyvernwood Chronicle, CA, Los Angeles
classified@egpnews.com, Circ. Mgr., Bell Gardens Sun, CA, Los Angeles

Sanchez, Carlos ....(956) 683-4066
csanchez@themonitor.com, Editor, The Monitor, TX, McAllen

Sanchez, Dolores
publisher@egpnews.com, Pub., Bell Gardens Sun, CA, Los Angeles
publisher@egpnews.com, Pub., City Terrace Comet, CA, Los Angeles
publisher@egpnews.com, Pub., Commerce Comet, CA, Los Angeles
publisher@egpnews.com, Pub., Eastside Sun, CA, Los Angeles
publisher@egpnews.com, Pub., Ela Brooklyn-Belvedere Comet, CA, Los Angeles
publisher@egpnews.com, Pub., Mexican American Sun, CA, Los Angeles
publisher@egpnews.com, Pub., Montebello Comet, CA, Los Angeles
publisher@egpnews.com, Pub., Monterey Park Comet, CA, Los Angeles
publisher@egpnews.com, Pub., Northeast Sun, CA, Los Angeles
publisher@egpnews.com, Pub., Vernon Sun, CA, Los Angeles
publisher@egpnews.com, Pub., Wyvernwood Chronicle, CA, Los Angeles

Sanchez, Dolores ....(313) 841-0100
elcentral1@aol.com, Ed., El Central, MI, Detroit

Sanchez, Dru
d.sanchez@gvnews.com, Pub., Green Valley News & Sahuarita Sn, AZ, Green Valley

Sanchez, Ernesto
neto@valleybargainbook.com, Circ. Mgr, Valley Town Crier, TX, McAllen

Sanchez, Isabel ....(505) 823-3884
isanchez@abqjournal.com, Asst. City Ed., Albuquerque Journal, NM, Albuquerque

Sanchez, John
john@queensledger.com, director of marketing, Brooklyn Downtown Star, NY, Woodside

Sanchez, John
john@queensledger.com, Director of marketing, The Queens Examiner, NY,

Woodside

Sanchez, John
john@queensledger.com, director of marketing, Long Island City/Astoria/Jackson Heights Journal, NY, Woodside

Sanchez, Jonathan M.
jmsanchez@egpnews.com, Adv. Mgr., Wyvernwood Chronicle, CA, Los Angeles
jmsanchez@egpnews.com, Adv. Mgr., City Terrace Comet, CA, Los Angeles
jmsanchez@egpnews.com, Adv. Mgr., Commerce Comet, CA, Los Angeles
jmsanchez@egpnews.com, Adv. Mgr., Ela Brooklyn-Belvedere Comet, CA, Los Angeles
jmsanchez@egpnews.com, Adv. Mgr., Mexican American Sun, CA, Los Angeles
jmsanchez@egpnews.com, Adv. Mgr., Montebello Comet, CA, Los Angeles
jmsanchez@egpnews.com, Adv. Mgr., Monterey Park Comet, CA, Los Angeles
jmsanchez@egpnews.com, Adv. Mgr., Northeast Sun, CA, Los Angeles
jmsanchez@egpnews.com, Adv. Mgr., Vernon Sun, CA, Los Angeles
jmsanchez@egpnews.com, Adv. Mgr., Bell Gardens Sun, CA, Los Angeles

Sanchez, Matilde
msanchez@clarin.com, Ed., Clarin Contenidos, CA, Buenos Aires

Sanchez, Rene ....(612) 673-1731
rene.sanchez@startribune.com, Ed. & Sr. VP, Star Tribune, MN, Minneapolis

Sanchez, Sharon ....(956) 585-4893
Office Mgr., Progress Times, TX, Mission

Sanchez, Tammy ....(718) 639-7000
wsanchez@queensledger.com, Gen. Mgr., The Queens Examiner, NY, Woodside

Sanchez, Tammy
ads@queensledger.com, Gen. Mgr., Greenpoint Star & Northside Weekly News, NY, Woodside

Sanchez, Vonne
Vonnie@thealpinesun.com, Pub., Alpine Sun, CA, Alpine

Sanchez, Walter H. ....(718) 639-7000
wsanchez@queensledger.com, Pub., BQE Publishing Inc., NY, Woodside
wsanchez@queensledger.com, Pub., Queens Ledger, NY, Maspeth
wsanchez@queensledger.com, Pub., Forest Hills/Rego Park Times, NY, Maspeth
wsanchez@queensledger.com, Ed., Glendale Register, NY, Maspeth
wsanchez@queensledger.com, Ed., The Leader-Observer of Woodhaven, NY, Maspeth
wsanchez@queensledger.com, Ed., Brooklyn Downtown Star, NY, Woodside
wsanchez@queensledger.com, Ed., Long Island City/Astoria/Jackson Heights Journal, NY, Woodside
wsanchez@queensledger.com, Ed., Greenpoint Star & Northside Weekly News, NY, Woodside
wsanchez@queensledger.com, Ed., The Queens Examiner, NY, Woodside

Sand, Barry
bsand@flagler.edu, Instr., Flagler College, FL, Saint Augustine

Sand, Linda ....(909) 537-5815
lsand@csusb.edu, California State Univ., CA, San Bernardino

Sandberg, Matt ....(970) 887-3334 x 13100
msandberg@skyhidailynews.com, Publisher, Summit Daily News, CO, Frisco

Sandberg, Sandy
ssandberg@summitdaily.com, Nat'l Acct. Mgr., Vail Daily, CO, Avon

Sandefur, Mona
msandefur@bentoneveningnews.com, Reporter, Benton Evening News, IL, Benton

Sander, Arron
printing@richmond-dailynews.com, Pressman/

Prod. Supervisor, Richmond News, MO, Richmond

Sanderford, Brian......................(479) 784-0466
bsanderford@swtimes.com, Sports Ed., Times Record, AR, Fort Smith

Sanders, Amy
asanders@startribune.com, Asst. Prof., University of Minnesota, MN, Minneapolis

Sanders, Annette ....(937) 548-3330
asanders@earlybirdpaper.com, Mkt Dir, The Early Bird, OH, Greenville

Sanders, Ashley
asanders@beaumontservices.com, Managing Editor, The Beaumont Enterprise, TX, Beaumont

Sanders, Bob Ray......................(817) 390-7775
bobray@star-telegram.com, Vice Pres./Assoc. Ed., Fort Worth Star-Telegram, TX, Fort Worth

Sanders, Casey
csanders@nashvillescene.com, Circ. Mgr., Nashville Scene, TN, Nashville

Sanders, Cody........................(417) 256-9191
news@wpdailyquill.net, Sports Editor, West Plains Daily Quill, MO, West Plains

Sanders, Connie
csanders@oskyherald.com, Bus. Mgr., Oskaloosa Herald, IA, Oskaloosa

Sanders, Curt
curt.sanders@westword.com, Circ. Mgr., Denver Westword, CO, Denver

Sanders, Douglas
pickenscnty@centurytel.net, Pub. / Ed., Pickens County Herald, AL, Carrollton

Sanders, Essie
essie@centrevillepress.com, Typist, The Centreville Press, AL, Centreville

Sanders, Gina
gina_sanders@teenvogue.com, Pres./CEO, Fairchild Fashion Grp., Women's Wear Daily, NY, New York

Sanders, Jack ....(203) 894-3350
newsroom@acorn-online.com, Exec. Ed., Ridgefield Press, CT, Ridgefield

Sanders, Keith P.
umcjourkta@missouri.edu, Exec. Dir./ Treasurer, Kappa Tau Alpha National Honor Society for Journalism & Mass Communication, MO, Columbia

Sanders, Matt ....(573) 388-3652
msanders@semissourian.com, Mng. Ed., Southeast Missourian, MO, Cape Girardeau

Sanders, Norm ....(618) 239-2454
nsanders@bnd.com, Sports, Belleville News-Democrat, IL, Belleville

Sanders, Peggy
psanders@examiner-enterprise.com, Class. Adv. Rep., Examiner-Enterprise, OK, Bartlesville

Sanders, Rick ....(631) 963-5589
rsanders@brainworks.com, Director of Sales, Brainworks Software Development Corp., NY, Sayville

Sanders, Robert
Robert_Sanders@tamu-commerce.edu, Prof., Texas A&M University-Commerce, TX, Commerce

Sanders, Roy
ads@bctribune.com, Ed., Burleson County Tribune, TX, Caldwell

Sanders, Taralisha....................(850) 877-0105
tsanders@capitaloutlook.com, General Manager, Capital Outlook, FL, Tallahassee

Sanderson, Bob
bsanderson@eclipsenet.com, Contract Admin., Martin Automatic, Inc., IL, Rockford

Sanderson, Cate
cate.sanderson@parenthood.com, Pub., New York Family, KS, Overland Park

Sanderson, Greta ....(765) 482-4650 Ext. 121
greta.sanderson@reporter.net, Pub, Zionsville Times Sentinel, IN, Zionsville
greta.sanderson@reporter.net, Pub., The Reporter, IN, Lebanon

Sandhu, Prab ....(215) 625-8501 ext 212
prab@epgn.com, Advertising Manager, Philadelphia Gay News, PA, Philadelphia

Sandlin, Cloie
cloie@pendantpublishing.com, Mgr Ed, Beacon Senior Newspaper, CO, Grand Junction

Sandlin, Darrell R. ....(256) 740-4711
darrell.sandlin@timesdaily.com, Pub., Times Daily, AL, Florence

Sandlin, Evelyn ....(865) 981-1152
evelyn.sandlin@thedailytimes.com, Adv. Dir., The Daily Times, TN, Maryville

Sandlin, Steve
steve.sandlin@miller-publications.com, Mng. Ed., Miamisburg News, OH, Miamisburg

Sandmeier, Bryan......................(865) 981-1196
bryan.sandmeier@thedailytimes.com, Circulation Director, The Daily Times, TN, Maryville

Sandoval, Madeline ....(786) 286-8787
patrianews@aol.com, Feature Editor, El Nuevo PATRIA, FL, Miami

Sandoval, Sam
sams@cskt.org, Asst. Ed., Char-Koosta News, MT, Pablo

Sandstrom, Carrie ....(701) 202-6496
carrie.sandstrom@my.und.edu, Editor-in-Chief, Univ. of North Dakota, ND, Grand Forks

Sandvig, Denise ....(360) 735-4441
denise.sandvig@columbian.com, HR Mgr., The Columbian, WA, Vancouver

Sandy, Brian ....(715) 833-7435
brian.sandy@ecpc.com, Mktg. / Promo Mgr., Leader-Telegram, WI, Eau Claire

Sandza, Richard
rsandza@navytimes.com, Ed., Army Times, VA, Vienna

Sanford, Gregg
sports@aransaspassprogress.com, The Ingleside Index, TX, Aransas Pass

Sanford, Harry
rjdel@gbpnews.com, Circ. Mgr., The Washington County Edition, IN, Salem
rjdel@gbpnews.com, Circ. Mgr., The Giveaway, IN, Scottsburg
rjdel@gbpnews.com, Circ. Mgr., The Leader, IN, Charlestown
rjdel@gbpnews.com, Circ. Mgr, The Banner-Gazette, IN, Pekin

Sanford, Jason ....(614) 486-6677 ext. 1014
jsanford@ohionews.org, Comm. Mgr., Ohio Newspaper Association, OH, Columbus
jsanford@ohionews.org, Manager of Communications & Content, Ohio Newspaper Services, Inc., OH, Columbus

Sanford, Karen ....(601) 792-4221
editor@prentissheadlight.com, Ed./Gen. Mgr., Prentiss Headlight, MS, Prentiss

Sanford, Keith
ksanford@nwaonline.net, Circ. Dir., The Free Weekly, AR, Fayetteville

Sanford, Kerri ....(403) 528-5691
ksandford@medicinehatnews.com, Mng. Ed., Medicine Hat News, AB, Medicine Hat

Sanford, Kurt
bill.pardue@lexisnexis.com, Pres./CEO, Cor. & Fed. Mkts., LexisNexis, CA, Los Angeles

Sanford, Richard D.
news@catskillmountainnews.com, Ed., Catskill Mountain News, NY, Arkville

Sanford, Terry
sales@wessan.com, Pres., Wessan Interactive, NE, Omaha

Sangiorgio, David ....(603) 224-5301 ext. 382
dsangiorgio@cmonitor.com , Pub., Concord Monitor, NH, Concord

Sanguinetti, Phillip A. ....(256) 235-9202
psanguinetti@annistonstar.com, Pres., Consolidated Publishing Co., AL, Anniston

Sanguinetti, Phillip A. ....(256) 235-9202
psanguinetti@annistonstar.com, Pres., The Anniston Star, AL, Anniston

Sanguinetti, Phillip A.
psanguinetti@annistonstar.com, Pub., The Jacksonville News, AL, Anniston

Sanner, Janet L. ....(440) 933-5100
jsanner@2presspapers.com, Adv. Mgr./Gen. Mgr., North Ridgeville Press, OH, Avon Lake
jsanner@2presspapers.com, Exec. Ed./Gen. Mgr., West Life, OH, Rocky River

Sans Werner, Claudia M. ....(202) 463-8777
csans@religionnews.com, Bus./Sales Mgr., Religion News Service, Washington

Sansalone, Nancy A.
nsansalone@sla.org, COO/CFO, Special Libraries Association, News Division, VA, Alexandria

Sansing, Leah ....(901) 528-8122
leah@memphisdailynews.com, Marketing Director, The Daily News, TN, Memphis

Sant, Robin
robins@milehighnews.com, Circ. Mgr., Arvada Press, CO, Golden

Santacruz, Daniel......................(973) 253-2707
santacruz@northjersey.com, Ed., Su Guia, NJ, Clifton

Santamaria, John......................(516) 589-1615
Editor in Chief, New York Institute of Technology, NY, Old Westbury

Santarelli, Denny ....(217) 351-5299
dsantare@news-gazette.com , Customer Care Center Manager, The News-Gazette, IL, Champaign

Santaularia, Ramon
viena@efe.com, Rep., EFE News Services - Vienna, Austria, Vienna

Santi, Pat
rhydowen@aol.com, Sec., Dog Writers' Association of America, PA, Coatesville

Santiago, Howard ....(209) 249-3575
Pressroom Manager, Manteca Bulletin, CA, Manteca

Santise, Nick ....(609) 989-5468
nsantise@njadvancemedia.com, Adv. Mgr., The Times, NJ, Trenton

Santoro, Peggy ....(775) 788-6310
psantoro@rgj.com, Senior Content Ed., Reno Gazette-Journal, NV, Reno

Santos, Andrea
sales@santronics.com, Dir., Mktg., Santronics Software, FL, Homestead

Santos, Carlos........................(434) 207-0224
carlos@fluvannareview.com, Pub./Ed./Circ. Mgr., Fluvanna Review, VA, Palmyra

Santos, Cuate
cuate@lmtonline.com, Photo Dept. Mgr., Laredo Morning Times, TX, Laredo

Santos, Debralee
editor@thebronxfreepress.com, Ed., The Bronx Free Press, NY, New York

Santos, Hector
hsantos@santronics.com, Pres., Santronics Software, FL, Homestead

Santos, Lisa ....(707) 527-1200 ext. 205
Adv. Dir., North Bay Bohemian, CA, Santa Rosa

Santos, Nelson ....(519) 733-2211
nsantos@postmedia.com, News Ed., The Kingsville Reporter, ON, Kingsville

Sanville, Connie
publisher@jonews.com, Owner/Pub., Journal Opinion, VT, Bradford

Sanz, Jose Manuel
bruselas@efe.com, Rep., EFE News Services - Brussels, Belgium, Brussels

Sanzick, Alice ....(215) 354-3055
asanzick@bsmphilly.com, Advertising Representative, Northeast Times, PA, Bensalem

Saperstein, Patricia
pat.saperstein@variety.com, Sr. Ed., Daily Variety, CA, Los Angeles

Sarabia, Daniel
sarabia@roanoke.edu, Roanoke College, VA, Salem

Saracco, Donna ....(203) 789-5726
editor@fairfieldminuteman.com, Ed., Fairfield Minuteman, CT, New Haven

Saracevic, Alan ....(415) 777-7928
asaracevic@sfchronicle.com, Sports Ed., San Francisco Chronicle, CA, San Francisco

Sardinia, Michele....................(315) 251-1831
msardinia@advanemediany.com, VP Digital Solutions, The Post-Standard, NY, Syracuse

Sargent, Bud
bsargent@miningjournal.net, Mng. Ed., The Mining Journal, MI, Marquette

Sargent, Jessica ....(205) 722-0128
jessica.sargent@tuscaloosanews.com, Cust. Serv Mgr, The Tuscaloosa News, AL, Tuscaloosa

Sargent, Karie ....(419) 521-7269
ksargent@gannett.com, Class. Sales Ctr. Mgr., News Journal, OH, Mansfield
ksargent@gannett.com, Class. Mgr., Chillicothe Gazette, OH, Chillicothe
ksargent@gannett.com, Class. Sales Ctr. Mgr., Times Recorder, OH, Zanesville
ksargent@gannett.com, Class. Sales Ctr. Mgr. , The Coshocton Tribune, OH, Coshocton
ksargent@gannett.com, Class. Sales Ctr. Mgr., The Advocate, OH, Newark
ksargent@gannett.com, Class. Sales Ctr. Mgr., The News-Messenger, OH, Fremont
ksargent@gannett.com, Class. Mgr., Eagle-Gazette Media, OH, Lancaster
ksargent@gannett.com, Class. Sales Ctr. Mgr., News Herald, OH, Fremont
ksargent@gannett.com, Class. Sales Ctr. Mgr., The Marion Star, OH, Marion

Sarkesian, Elijah
elijah@davidatlanta.com, Georgia State Univ., GA, Atlanta

Sarko, Daniel..........................(410) 332-6243
dsarko@baltsun.com, Digital/Interactive Manager, The Morning Call, PA, Allentown
dsarko@baltsun.com, Adv. Dir, The Record, MD, Bel Air

Sarkozy, Paul
psarkozy@ottawacitizen.com, VP Mktg. and Reader Sales, The Ottawa Citizen, ON, Ottawa

Sartwell, Matt ....(603) 668-4321
msartwell@unionleader.com, Managing Editor, New Hampshire Union Leader/New Hampshire Sunday News, NH, Manchester

Sarver, Jessika
preprints@americanpress.com, Preprints/Acct. Exec. , American Press, LA, Lake Charles

Sarver, Jody Stephenson
jsarver@wsjournal.com, Sales Agent, Star Watch, Winston Salem

Sarver, Jody Stephenson
jsarver@wsjournal.com, Sales Agent, Spotlight, Winston Salem

Sarwate, Becky
becky.sarwate@gmail.com, Pres., Illinois Woman's Press Association, Inc., IL, Chicago

Sass, Kathie

Citizen, KY, Berea

Schaaf-Wheeler, Judith
jschaaf@centurytel.net, Pub., Mountain Echo
X-tra, MO, Ironton

Schaal, Ashley .... (518) 290-3919
aschaal@digitalfirstmedia.com, Classified
Adv. Inside Sales/Customer Service, The
Saratogian, NY, Saratoga Springs

Schaap, Caitlyn .... (209) 223-8769
Ed., Amador Ledger-Dispatch, CA, Jackson

Schaben, Allen
allen.schaben@latimes.com, Staff
Photographer, Los Angeles Times, CA, Los
Angeles

Schable, Chris
cschable@thenewsdispatch.com, Exec. Ed.,
Herald News Review, IL, Decatur

Schacherer, Brent .... (320) 693-3266
schacherer@hutchinsonleader.com, Pub.,
Independent Review, MN, Litchfield

Schacherer, Brent .... (320) 234-4143
schacherer@hutchinsonleader.com, Pub,
Hutchinson Leader And Leader Shopper,
MN, Hutchinson

Schachleiter, Sharon
kynews@communitypress.com, Circ. Mgr.,
Florence Recorder, KY, Fort Mitchell

Schachleiter, Sharon
sschachleiter@communitypress.com, Circ.
Mgr, Union Recorder, KY, Fort Mitchell

Schachleiter, Sharon
sschachleiter@communitypress.com, Circ.
Mgr., Western Hills Press, OH, Cincinnati
sschachleiter@communitypress.com, Circ.
Mgr., Delhi Press, OH, Cincinnati
sschachleiter@communitypress.com, Circ.
Mgr., Hilltop Press, OH, Cincinnati
sschachleiter@communitypress.com, Circ.
Mgr., Price Hill Press, OH, Cincinnati

Schachleiter, Sharon .... (859) 442-3464
Circ. Mgr., Boone Community Recorder, KY,
Fort Mitchell

Schacht, Nicholas
uscourses@learningtree.com, Pres./CEO,
Learning Tree International, CA, El Segundo

Schading, Chuck .... (315) 789-3333
editor@fltimes.com, Managing Ed., Finger
Lakes Times, NY, Geneva

Schaechter, Joe .... (309) 797-0301
jschaechter@qconline.com, Asst Cir Dir/S &
Ret, Ad Extra, IL, Moline

Schaechter, Joe .... (309) 797-0301
jschaechter@qconline.com, Co-Director
Circulation/Sales & Marketing, The Dispatch-
Argus, IL, Moline

Schaefer, Diane .... (941) 726-6145
dschaefer@BusinessObserverFL.com, Assoc.
Pub./Adv. Dir., Business Observer-Collier,
FL, Naples
dschaefer@BusinessObserverFL.com, Assoc.
Pub., Adv., Business Observer, FL, Sarasota
dschaefer@BusinessObserverFL.com,
Assoc. Pub./Adv. Dir., Business Observer-
Hillsborough-Pasco, FL, Sarasota
dschaefer@BusinessObserverFL.com, Assoc.
Pub./Adv. Dir., Business Observer-Lee, FL,
Sarasota
dschaefer@BusinessObserverFL.com, Assoc.
Pub./Adv. Dir., Business Observer-Pinellas,
FL, Clearwater

Schaefer, Ernest
eschaferinc@aol.com, Pres., Ernest Schaefer,
Inc., NJ, Union

Schaefer, Heather .... (715) 365-6397
heather@rivernewsonline.com, Assoc. Ed.,
Northwoods Super Shopper, WI, Rhinelander
heather@rivernewsonline.com, Assoc. Ed., The
Northwoods River News , WI, Rhinelander

Schaefer, Kevin
klschaefer@mckendree.edu, Web/Design

Editor, McKendree University, IL, Lebanon

Schaefer, William
wschaefer@gvc.edu, Chair, Grand View
College, IA, Des Moines

Schaefer, Bonnie .... (610) 562-2267
BonnieS@WindsorPress.com, Display
Advertising Manager, Northern Berks
Merchandiser, PA, Hamburg
BonnieS@WindsorPress.com, Display
Advertising Manager, East Penn Valley
Merchandiser, PA, Hamburg

Schaeffer, Dave
info@congentco.com, Founder/CEO, Cogent
Communications, Inc., DC, Washington

Schaeffer, Denice .... (610) 371-5125
dschaeffer@readingeagle.com, Multimedia
Sales Manager, Reading Eagle, PA, Reading

Schaeffer, Denice .... (610) 970-3218 Ext. 632
denice@berksmontnews.com, Gen. Mgr., The
Boyertown Area Times, PA, Pottstown
denice@berksmontnews.com, Gen. Mgr., The
Kutztown Area Patriot, PA, Pottstown

Schaeffer, Denice .... (610) 371-5125
denice@berksmontnews.com, Adv. Mgr., Tri-
County Record, PA, Pottstown
denice@berksmontnews.com, Gen. Mgr, The
Community Connection, PA, Pottstown
denice@berksmontnews.com, Gen. Mgr,
Berksmont News, PA, Pottstown
denice@berksmontnews.com, Adv., South
Schuylkill News, PA, Schuylkill Haven

Schaeffer, Eric .... (610) 371-5129
eschaeffer@readingeagle.com, Senior
Information Technology Director, Reading
Eagle, PA, Reading
eschaeffer@readingeagle.com, Information
Technology Director, Reading Eagle
Company, PA, Reading

Schafer, Bob .... (612) 673-7155
bob.schafer@startribune.com, Asst. Mng. Ed.,
Admin., Star Tribune, MN, Minneapolis

Schafer, Liz
editor@hersamacornvt.com, Ed., Vermont
News Guide, VT, Manchester Center

Schaff, Jason
jschaff@the-signal.com, Executive Editor,
Connect SCV, CA, Santa Clarita

Schaff, Kevin
schaff@thoughtequity.com, Founder/CEO,
Thought Equity Management, Inc., CO,
Denver

Schaffer, Jim .... (402) 465-2352
Nebraska Wesleyan Univ., NE, Lincoln

Schaffer, Michael
iowegianeditor@mchsi.com, Ed., Ad Express,
IA, Centerville

Schaffer, Michael
mschaffer@dailyiowegian.com, Mng. Ed., Ad-
Express & Daily Iowegian, IA, Centerville

Schaffner, John
john@thebeacon.net, Pub., Huron Hometown
News (OOB), OH, Huron
john@thebeacon.net, Pub., The Beacon, OH,
Port Clinton

Schaible, Daniel
dschaible@burrellesluce.com, Senior VP,
Content Management, BurrellesLuce, NJ,
Florham Park

Schaible, Doris .... (815) 232-0102
dschaible@journalstandard.com, Circ. Mgr.,
The Journal-Standard, IL, Freeport

Schaible, Linda
linda.schaible@chron.com, Vice President,
Audience Development & Planning, Houston
Chronicle, TX, Houston

Schaible, Linda .... (407) 420-5776
lschaible@tribune.com, Vice Pres., Interactive,
Orlando Sentinel, FL, Orlando

Schamehorn, Mary
myrtlepointherald@gmail.com, Ed., Myrtle

Point Herald, OR, Myrtle Point

Schanen, William F. .... (262) 284-3494
bschanen3@ozaukeepress.com, Pub./Ed.,
Ozaukee Press, WI, Port Washington

Schanfelt, Jay .... (602) 889-7120
jschanfeldt@azcapitoltimes.com, Adv. Acc.
Exec., Arizona Capitol Times, AZ, Phoenix

Schankweiler, David
davids@journalmultimedia.com, CEO, Central
Penn Business Journal, PA, Harrisburg

Schankweiler, David A.
deniser@journalpub.com, Pub., Central Penn
Parent, PA, Harrisburg

Schanz, Chris
c.schanz@thecr.com, Sports Ed., The
Commercial Review, IN, Portland

Schardt, Doug
komori.american@attglobal.net, Pdct. Mgr.,
Komori America Corp., IL, Rolling Meadows

Scharf, Jenny
Jscharf@pinalcentral.com, Sr. Adv. Consultant,
Casa Grande Valley Newspapers Inc., AZ,
Casa Grande

Scharf, Rachel
williamsrecordeic@gmail.com, Editor-in-Chief,
Williams College, MA, Williamstown

Scharnow, Michael
mike@fhtimes.com, Ed., Let's Go, AZ, Fountain
Hills

Scharnow, Michael G.
mike@fhtimes.com, Ed., The Fountain Hill
Times, AZ, Fountain Hills

Schattner, Kyle .... (519) 662-1082 ext. 41
kschattner@newhamburgindependent.ca, Adv.
Rep., New Hamburg Independent, ON, New
Hamburg

Schau, Julie .... (306) 651-6305
Commun.Coord., Saskatchewan Weekly
Newspapers Association, SK, Saskatoon

Schaub, Kathy
kschaub@clackamasreview.com, Adv. Rep,
Oregon City News, OR, Portland
kschaub@clackamasreview.com, Adv. Rep.,
The Clackamas Review, OR, Portland

Schaub, Terry .... (281) 391-3141
tschaub@katytimes.com, Pub., The Katy
Times, TX, Katy

Schaub, Terry
tschaub@rrleader.com, Pub., The Pflugerville
Pflag, TX, Austin
tschaub@rrleader.com, Pub., Round Rock
Leader, TX, Round Rock

Schaumburg, Jason .... (815) 526-4414
jschaumburg@nwherald.com, Editor,
Northwest Herald, Northwest Herald, IL,
Crystal Lake

Schauppner, Kurt
kurts@deserttrail.com, Ed./Gen. Mgr., Desert
Trail, CA, Twentynine Palms

Schaus, Kim
kschaus@bizjournals.com, General Mgr.,
Buffalo Law Journal, NY, Buffalo

Schauseil, Robin D.
robins@nacm.org, Pres., National Association
of Credit Management, MD, Columbia

Schawb, Will .... (610) 377-2051
wschwab@tnonline.com, Digital/Interactive
Manager, Times News, PA, Lehighton

Schechtman, Cliff .... (207) 791-6693
cschechtman@pressherald.com, Exec. Ed.,
Portland Press Herald / Maine Sunday
Telegram, ME, Portland

Schecter, Joanne
jschecter@aaf.org, Sr. Vice Pres., AAF College
Chapters, DC, Washington

Schecter, Kelly .... (607) 324-1425
kellyschecter@eveningtribune.com, Regional
Advertising Director, Pennsaverplus, NY,

Hornell

Scheel, Patricia .... (262) 513-2690
pscheel@conleynet.com, Prepress Mgr., The
Freeman, WI, Waukesha

Scheffer, Richard
countytimes@sbcglobal.net, Ed., Mississippi
County Times, MO, Charleston

Scheibe, Bill
bscheibe@tribpub.com, Sports Ed., The
Courier-News, IL, Aurora
bscheibe@tribpub.com, Sports Ed., Daily
Southtown, IL, Aurora

Scheidecker, Cassie .... (406) 988-7987
art@dillontribune.com, Graphics Artist, Dillon
Tribune, MT, Dillon

Scheiner, Lowell
lscheine@poly.edu, Polytechnic Institute of
NYU, NY, Brooklyn

Scheitheir, Karl .... (716) 204-4948
karls@beenews.com, Prodn. Mgr., East Aurora
Bee, NY, Williamsville

Schell, Jeff
jschell@news-herald.com, Adv. Dir., The News-
Herald, OH, Willoughby

Schell, Jeff .... (440) 245-6901 Ext. 47159
publisher@morningjournal.com, Pub., The
Morning Journal, OH, Lorain

Schell, Jim
jschell@willowbend.com, VP Bus
Development, Willow Bend Communications,
Inc., TX, Dallas

Schell, Lisa .... (507) 285-7466
lschell@postbulletin.com, Adv Mgr., Agri News,
MN, Rochester

Schelle, Crystal .... (301) 791-7728
crystal.schelle@herald-mail.com, Lifestyle Ed.,
The Herald-Mail, MD, Hagerstown

Schelleberger, Harlan
vnh@onemain.com, Pub./Adv. Mgr., Spokane
Valley News Herald, WA, Spokane Valley

Schellenbach, Tricia .... (216) 368-6949
Case Western Reserve Univ., OH, Cleveland

Scheller, Fred
fscheller@dailyitem.com, Circ. Dir., The Daily
Item, MA, Lynn

Schenk, Fred
fred@columbusmessenger.com, Adv. Mgr.,
Westside Messenger, OH, Columbus
fred@columbusmessenger.com, Adv. Mgr.,
Eastside Messenger, OH, Columbus
fred@columbusmessenger.com, Adv. Mgr.,
Southwest Messenger, OH, Columbus
fred@columbusmessenger.com, Adv. Mgr.,
Madison Messenger, OH, Columbus
fred@columbusmessenger.com, Adv. Mgr.
, Southeast Messenger, OH, Columbus

Schenkler, Michael
publisher@queentribune.com, Pres./Pub.,
Tribco LLC, NY, Whitestone

Schepeler, Matt .... (517) 592-2122
news@theexponent.com, Ed., The Exponent,
MI, Brooklyn

Scherban, Debra .... (413) 585-5229
dscherban@gazettenet.com, Mng. Ed.,
Features, Daily Hampshire Gazette, MA,
Northampton

Scherer, Sally .... (859) 231-3303
sscherer1@herald-leader.com, Features Ed.,
Lexington Herald-Leader, KY, Lexington

Scherf, Scott
scottscherf@reviewtimes.com, Gen. Mgr., The
Review Times, OH, Fostoria

Schermann, B.J.
bunny@theecho.ca, Pub., The Echo, ON,
Manitouwadge

Schermer, Greg P. .... (563) 383-2100
VP, Strategy, Lee Enterprises, Inc., IA,
Davenport

Schertz, Jennifer
js@fdconsumernews.com, Consumer News, IA, Fort Dodge

Scheveers, Tracey
tscheveers@reddeerexpress.com, Pub, Red Deer Express, AB, Red Deer

Schexnaydre, Marie
mschexnaydre@weeklycitizen.com, Circ. Mgr., Gonzales Weekly Citizen, LA, Gonzales

Schexnaydre, Stephanie .... (225) 644-6397
sschexnaydre@gatehousemedia.com, General Manager/Bookkeeper, Gonzales Weekly Citizen, LA, Gonzales

Schexnyder, Caskey .... (318) 202-5871
caskey@rustonleader.com, Circ. Mgr., Ruston (LA) Daily Leader, LA, Ruston

Schey, Ray .... (602) 308-6500
Pub., The Business Journal, AZ, Phoenix

Schiavone , Georgia .... ext. 27
georgia@northcountrynow.com, Prodn. Mgr., North Country This Week, NY, Potsdam

Schiavoni, Marilyn .... (412) 462-0626
valleymirror@comcast.net, Pub./Ed., The Valley Mirror, PA, Munhall

Schiefelbein, Dave .... (719) 395-8621 x14
editor@chaffeecountytimes.com, Ed., The Chaffee County Times, CO, Buena Vista

Schiefelbein, Jack .... (308) 381-9436
jack.schiefelbein@theindependent.com, Controller, The Grand Island Independent, NE, Grand Island

Schiefelbein, Joseph .... (225) 388-0321
jschiefelbein@theadvocate.com, Exec. Sports Ed., The Advocate, LA, Baton Rouge

Schieffer, Gary .... (217) 788-1517
gary.schieffer@sj-r.com, Metro Ed., The State Journal-Register, IL, Springfield

Schieffer, Tom
hartshopper@hartel.net, Hartington Shopper, NE, Hartington

Schiekofer, Rich. .... (212) 856-6382
rich.schiekofer@naa.org, SVP Bus. Dev., News Media Alliance, VA, Arlington

Schier, Anna .... (630) 427-6248
aschier@shawmedia.com, Ed., Carol Stream Suburban Life, IL, Downers Grove
aschier@shawmedia.com, Ed., West Chicago Suburban Life, IL, Downers Grove
aschier@shawmedia.com, Ed., Wheaton Suburban Life, IL, Downers Grove
aschier@shawmedia.com, Lemont Suburban Life, IL, Downers Grove

Schier, Frank .... (815) 670-6440
contact@rockrivertimes.com, Pub./Ed./Adv., The Rock River Times, IL, Rockford

Schierhoff, Jo
jschierhoff@ncronline.org, Circ Mgr, National Catholic Reporter, MO, Kansas City

Schierhorn, Carl
cschierh@kent.edu, Kent State Univ., OH, Kent

Schievelbein, Micki .... (605) 624-4429
micki.schievelbein@yankton.net, Adv. Dir., Vermillion Plain Talk, SD, Vermillion

Schievelbein, Micki
michele.schievelbein@yankton.net, Adv. Dir., Yankton Daily Press & Dakotan, SD, Yankton

Schiferle, Holly
classified@beenews.com, Classifieds Mgr., Amherst Bee, NY, Williamsville

Schiff, Arlene D. .... ext. 12
Pub., Berkshire Jewish Voice, MA, Pittsfield

Schiff, Damien .... (619) 260-4600
Univ. of San Diego School of Law, CA, San Diego

Schiff, Fred .... (713) 742-1000
jamspamforever@gmail.com, Assoc. Prof., University of Houston, TX, Houston

Schiffer, David .... (212) 255-3464
david@dlsdesign.com, Pres., DLS Design, NY, New York

Schiffman, Marlene
marlene@newspubinc.com, Mt. Horeb Town And Country Shopper, WI, Mount Horeb

Schiffo, Robert
rschiffo@ledroit.com, Circ. Dir., Le Droit, ON, Ottawa

Schiffres, Jeremy .... (845) 331-5000 Ext. 01227
jschiffres@freemanonline.com, City Ed., Daily Freeman, NY, Kingston

Schild, Tonya
tonya.schild@yankton.net, Bus. Mgr., Yankton Daily Press & Dakotan, SD, Yankton

Schildkraut, Dana .... (914) 323-5447
Manhattanville College, NY, Purchase

Schiller, Alexander
alex@dorkstormpress.com, Office Mgr., Dork Storm Press/Shetland Productions, Madison

Schiller, Matthew
matthew.schiller@archny.org, Adv. Mgr., Catholic New York, NY, New York

Schilling, Betty
calumetadvertiser@charter.net, Adv. Mgr., Chilton Times-Journal, WI, Chilton

Schilousky, Kim
kimsfam@eaglecom.net, Location News Reporter, Cedar Rapids Press, NE, Cedar Rapids

Schindler, Anne
themail@folioweekly.com, Ed., Folio Weekly, FL, Jacksonville

Schindler, Paul .... (646) 452-2503
editor@gaycitynews.com, Ed. in Chief, Gay City News, NY, New York

Schipper, Becky
news@iafalls.com, Ed., Ackley World Journal, IA, Ackley

Schirmer, John
jrs@nashvilleleader.com, Ed., The Nashville News-Leader, AR, Nashville

Schiro, Barry .... (201) 414-5200
baschiro@cbaol.com, Pres., Cba Industries, NJ, Elmwood Park

Schiska, Amy
Schiska@RNA.org, Business Mgr., Religion News Association, MO, Columbia

Schisler, Barb
barb@pekintimes.com, Production Mgr., Pekin Daily Times, IL, Pekin

Schlager, Brandon .... (716) 598-1968
brandon.schlager@yahoo.com, Managing Editor, SUNY College/Buffalo, NY, Buffalo

Schlagheck, Carol
carol.schlagheck@emich.edu, Journ. Program Coord., Eastern Michigan University, MI, Ypsilanti

Schlagheck, Julie
jschlaghec@stcloud.gannett.com, Adv. Mgr., Online Devel., St. Cloud Times, MN, Saint Cloud

Schlagheck, Julie
jschlagheck@stcloud.gannett.com, Gen. Mgr., The Shopping News, MN, Saint Cloud

Schlander, John
schlander@sptimes.com, Digital General Mgr., Tampa Bay Times, FL, St Petersburg

Schlau, Mark
nstoday@aol.com, Pub., North Shore Today, NY, Syosset

Schlegel, Bradlwy .... (215) 679-5060
bschlegel.ljrpublishing@gmail.com, Staff Writer, Town and Country, PA, Pennsburg

Schlegel, Mary
mary.schlegel@kellyhart.com, Adv. Dir., Fort Worth Business Press, TX, Fort Worth

Schleier, Curt .... (201) 391-7135
writa1@me.com, Pres./Ed., Curt Schleier Reviews, River Vale

Schlemminger, Mandy
mschlemminger@anninstonstar.com, Customer Serv Mgr, The Anniston Star, AL, Anniston

Schlenker, Dave
scene@gvillesun.com, Amusements/Entertainment Ed., The Gainesville Sun, FL, Gainesville

Schleppenbach, Barbara
schleppb@quincy.edu, Chair of Fine Arts & Communication, Quincy Univ., IL, Quincy

Schlesinger, Mike
editor@dysartreporter.com, Pub., The Dysart Reporter, IA, Dysart

Schlesinger, Mike
mschlesinger@timesrepublican.com, Pub., Times-Republican, IA, Marshalltown

Schlesinger, Mike
trpub@timesrepublican.com, Pub., Reinbeck Courier, IA, Reinbeck

Schlesinger, Mike
trpup@timesrepublican.com, Pub., Pennysaver, IA, Marshalltown

Schlesman, Chance
cschlesman@orlandosentinel.com, Acct. Mgr., Orlando Sentinel, FL, Orlando

Schlichenmeyer, Terri .... (608) 782-2665
bookwormsez@yahoo.com, Book Reviewer, The Bookworm Sez, LLC, La Crosse

Schlicht, Suzanne .... (970) 871-4224
sschlicht@theworldco.net, COO, WorldWest LLC, KS, Lawrence

Schlicht, Suzanne .... (970) 871-4224
sschlicht@SteamboatToday.com, Pub., Steamboat Today, CO, Steamboat Springs
sschlicht@SteamboatToday.com, Pub., Steamboat Pilot, CO, Steamboat Springs

Schlichter, Jay .... (239) 213-6000
jschlichter@naplesnews.com, Ed, The Collier Citizen, FL, Naples
jschlichter@naplesnews.com, Editor, Marco Eagle, FL, Naples

Schlichtman, Lisa .... (970) 871-4221
lschlichtman@SteamboatToday.com, Ed., Craig Daily Press, CO, Craig

Schlichtman , Lisa .... (970) 871-4221
lschlichtman@SteamboatToday.com, Ed., Steamboat Today, CO, Steamboat Springs
lschlichtman@SteamboatToday.com, Ed., Steamboat Pilot, CO, Steamboat Springs

Schliepp, Russ
rschliepp@discoverhometown.com, Adv. Sales Rep., West Bend Express News, WI, Brown Deer
rschliepp@discoverhometown.com, Adv. Sales Rep., West Allis Express News, WI, Brown Deer
rschliepp@discoverhometown.com, Adv. Sales Rep., Sussex Express News, WI, Brown Deer
rschliepp@discoverhometown.com, Adv. Sales Rep., Slinger Express News, WI, Brown Deer
rschliepp@discoverhometown.com, Adv. Sales Rep., Milwaukee Express News, WI, Brown Deer
rschliepp@discoverhometown.com, Adv. Sales Rep., Menomonee Falls Express News, WI, Brown Deer
rschliepp@discoverhometown.com, Adv. Sales Rep., Jackson Express News, WI, Brown Deer
rschliepp@discoverhometown.com, Adv. Sales Rep., Hartford Express News, WI, Brown Deer
rschliepp@discoverhometown.com, Adv. Sales Rep., Germantown Express News, WI, Brown Deer
rschliepp@discoverhometown.com, Adv. Sales Rep., Wauwatosa Express News, WI, Brown Deer

Schlindwein, Diane
dschlindwein@dio.org, Reporter, Catholic Times, IL, Springfield

Schlitt, Jon .... (785) 864-7666
jschlitt@kansan.com, Sales and Marketing Adviser, The University Daily Kansan, KS, Lawrence

Schloss, David G.
newsroom@harrisonnewsherald.com, Pub., Harrison News-Herald, OH, Cadiz

Schlosser, Brian
bschlosser@thedailyreview.com, Regional Director of Production, The Daily Review, PA, Towanda

Schmal, Jeanne .... ext. 105
jeanne@pdsadnet.com, Gen. Mgr., Publishers Development Service, WI, Fond Du Lac
jeanne@pdsadnet.com, Gen. Mgr., Publishers Development Service, WI, Fond du Lac

Schmale, Angela .... (785) 562-2317
circulation@marysvilleonline.net, Circulation manager, business office, Marysville Advocate, KS, Marysville

Schmeckpeper, Sheryl ..... (402) 371-1020 ext. 241
living@norfolkdailynews.com, Living Page Ed., Norfolk Daily News, NE, Norfolk

Schmeid, Teresa .... (316) 942-5385
tschmeid@activeagingonline.com, Advertising Manager, The Active Age, KS, Wichita

Schmeltzer, Scott .... (701) 451-5561
sschmeltzer@forumcomm.com, Dir. of Adv., InForum, ND, Fargo

Schmeltzer, Scott .... (920) 743-3321
sschmeltze@doorcountyadvocate.com, General Manager / Ad Director, Door County Real Estate Guide, WI, Sturgeon Bay

Schmeltzer, Scott
scott.schmeltzer@albertleatribune.com, Pub., Tribune Shopping News, MN, Albert Lea

Schmid, Emily Mae
eschmid@diocesefwsb.org, Social Media Manager, Today's Catholic, TX, San Antonio

Schmid, Loydale
news@community-news.com, Adv. Dir., The Community News, TX, Aledo

Schmid, Pat .... (207) 633-4620, ext. 104
patschmid@boothbayregister.com, Bus. Mgr., Wiscasset Newspaper, ME, Boothbay Harbor

Schmidleithner, Rudi
Rudi_Schmidleithner@acer.com, Pres., Pan America Opns., Acer America, CA, San Jose

Schmidt, Al .... (214) 232-3385
Pres., Imagen, Inc., TX, Dallas

Schmidt, Debbie .... (605) 647-2284
publisher@lennoxnews.com, Co-Pub./Business manager, The Lennox Independent, SD, Lennox

Schmidt, Doris
doschmidt@fitchburgstate.edu, Fitchburg State College, MA, Fitchburg

Schmidt, Fred .... (304) 526-2816
fschmidt@heralddispatch.com, Herald Dispatch, CA, Los Angeles
fschmidt@heralddispatch.com, Bluefield Daily Telegraph, WV, Bluefield
fschmidt@heralddispatch.com, Circulation Director, The Herald-Dispatch, WV, Huntington

Schmidt, Fred 931 3885 6464
fSchmnidt@c-dh.net, Circulation Director, Columbia Daily Herald, TN, Columbia

Schmidt, Kim
k.schmidt@technologyintegrators.net, Acct. Exec., Technology Integrators, IL, Effingham

Schmidt, Liz
lizs@vcnewsreview.com, Circ. Mgr., Three Lakes News, WI, Eagle River

Schmidt, Margaret

margaret.schmidt@jjournal.com, VP & Ed., The Jersey Journal, NJ, Secaucus

Schmidt, Pat
wabnews@redred.com, Pub., Wabasso Standard, MN, Wabasso

Schmidt, Pat
publisher@redwoodfallsgazette.com, Pub., Redwood Falls Livewire, MN, Redwood Falls

Schmidt, Seth
balatonpublishing@yahoo.com, Ed., Balaton Press Tribune, MN, Balaton

Schmidt, Seth
tracypublishing@HeadlightHerald.com, Pub./ Gen. Mgr., Tracy Headlight-Herald, MN, Tracy

Schmidt, T.J.
mcnnews@hctc.net, Adv. Dir., Mason County News, TX, Mason

Schmidt, Thomas H....................(202) 281-2405
tom@cathstan.org, Gen. Mgr., Catholic Standard, DC, Washington

Schmidt, Tim ....(636) 528-9550
lcjpub@lcs.net, Gen Mgr, Troy Free Press, MO, Troy

Schmith, Mark
markschmith@siouxcityjournal.com, Mgmt. Info Servs. Mgr., Sioux City Journal, IA, Sioux City

Schmitt, Hannah
hannah@metrofamilymagazine.com, Editor, MetroFamily Magazine, OK, Oklahoma City

Schmitt, John
john.schmitt@pfizer.com, Accountant/CPA, Cartoonews, Inc., New York

Schmitt, Tom
tschmitt@nonpareilonline.com, Pub., The Daily Nonpareil, IA, Council Bluffs

Schmitz, Tina
tschmitz@ucclocalmedia.com, CFAO, United Communications Corporation, WI, Kenosha

Schmoldt, Pam......................(608) 755-8275
pschmoldt@gazettextra.com, VP Financial Operations, The Gazette - gazettextra.com, WI, Janesville

Schmoldt, Randy.....................(406) 443-2850
randy@mtnewspapers.com, Accounting Specialist, Montana Newspaper Advertising Service, Inc., MT, Helena

Schmucker, Jason
jason.schmucker@ecm-inc.com, Ed., The Laker, MN, Waconia
jason.schmucker@ecm-inc.com, Ed., Norwood Young America Times, MN, Waconia
jason.schmucker@ecm-inc.com, Ed., Carver County News, MN, Waconia
jason.schmucker@ecm-inc.com, Ed., The Pioneer, MN, Waconia
jason.schmucker@ecm-inc.com, Ed., The Waconia Patriot, MN, Waconia

Schnabel, Mark .... (316) 283-1500 x119
mschnabel@thekansan.com, Sports Ed., The Newton Kansan, KS, Newton

Schnarr, J.W...........................(403) 758-6911
editor@westwindweekly.com, Ed., Westwind Weekly News, AB, Magrath

Schnarrs, Bob
bobs@mansimedia.com, Pennsylvania NewsMedia Association, PA, Harrisburg

Schnars, Rich ....(561) 820-4657
rschnars@pbpost.com, Circ. Mgr., Opns., The Palm Beach Post, FL, West Palm Beach

Schnee, Laura
Shelby.stockton@wagonercountyat.com, Mktg., Wagoner Tribune, OK, Wagoner
Shelby.stockton@wagonercountyat.com, Mktg. Consult., Coweta American (OOB), OK, WAGONER

Schneider, Barbara ....(978) 745-4111
PUBLISHER@jewishjournal.org, Pub., North Shore Jewish Press, MA, Salem

Schneider, Bryan......................(216) 999-5474
bschneider@plaind.com, Dir. Circ Distribution & Transportation, The Plain Dealer, OH, Brooklyn

Schneider, Debbie Ann
ads2sell@aol.com, Adv. Mgr., Pennysaver, NY, Ozone Park

Schneider, Howard
howard.schneider@stonybrook.edu, Dean, Stony Brook University, NY, Stony Brook

Schneider, Jane
janes@memphisparent.com, Ed., Memphis Parent, TN, Memphis

Schneider, Jay
lrlife@frontiernet.net, Ed., Elysian Enterprise, MN, New Prague

Schneider, Jay.........................(507) 362-4495
news@newpraguetimes.com, Ed., Lake Region Life, MN, New Prague

Schneider, Kerry
sharry.smith@creativeloafing.com, Adv. Dir., Creative Loafing Atlanta, GA, Atlanta

Schneider, Melissa .... (239) 765-0400 ext. 103
mschneider@breezenewspapers.com, Ed., Fort Myers Beach Bulletin, FL, Fort Myers Beach

Schneider, Michael
michael@orangestreetstudio.com, Daily Variety, CA, Los Angeles

Schneider, Pat
pschneider@capitalnewspapers.com, The Capital Times, WI, Madison

Schneider, Roger
roger.schneider@goshennews.com, City Ed., The Goshen News, IN, Goshen

Schneider, Traci.................................ext. 180
Mktg. Dir., Pittsburgh City Paper, PA, Pittsburgh

Schnell, Judy ....(920) 563-5553
circ.renewal@dailyunion.com, Rural Rt. Mgr., Daily Jefferson County Union, WI, Fort Atkinson

Schnell, Klaudia
graphics@deltapublications.com, Prodn. Mgr., Tempo, WI, Kiel

Schnepf, Kevin ....(701) 241-5549
kschnepf@forumcomm.com, Sports Ed., InForum, ND, Fargo

Schnepp, Julie
accounting@thepaperofwabash.com, Circ. Mgr, The Paper, IN, Wabash

Schneps, Joshua ....(718) 238-6600
jschneps@brooklynreporter.com, Pub, The Brooklyn Spectator, NY, Brooklyn

Schneps-Yunis, Victoria
vschneps@qns.com, Pub., The Queens Courier, NY, Bayside
vschneps@qns.com, Pub. , Times Newsweekly, NY, Bayside

Schnier, Elaine
eschnier@lauterbachgroup.com, Bus. Mgr., Lauterbach Group, WI, Sussex

Schnoebelen, Jeff
nwopaper@poldi.net, Pub., Northwest Oklahoman, OK, Shattuck

Schnoebelen, Tim
leader2@pldi.net, Ed., Mooreland Leader, OK, Mooreland

Schoch, Joy..........................(701) 456-1203
jschoch@thedickinsonpress.com, Bus. Mgr., The Dickinson Press, ND, Dickinson
jschoch@thedickinsonpress.com, Bus. Mgr. , Advertizer, ND, Dickinson

Schoch, Phil ....(830) 693-4367
phil.schoch@highlandernews.com, Exec. Ed., The Highlander, TX, Marble Falls

Schock, Scott
sschock@sentco.net, Ed., Falls City Journal, NE, Falls City

Schoeberl, Marcia
Marcia@MadisonDailyLeader.com, Managing Ed., The Madison Daily Leader, SD, Madison

Schoen, Kevin F. ....(401) 380-2343
Schoen@NewportRI.com, Operations Mgr., The Newport Daily News, RI, Newport

Schoen, Scott.........................(631) 913-4228
Scott.Schoen@thedolancompany.com, Long Island Business News, NY, Ronkonkoma

Schoenbacher, Robert N.
roberts@metrosuburbia.com, Pres., Metro Suburbia, Inc./Newhouse Newspapers, NY, New York

Schoenberg, Jerry ....(707) 453-8123
jschoenberg@thereporter.com, Circ. Mgr., The Reporter, CA, Vacaville

Schofield, Barb.........................780- 332-2215
mznads1@mrnews.ca, Adv. Sales, The Mile Zero News, AB, High Level

Scholl, David J. ....(707) 678-8917
staff@independentvoice.com, Pub/Ed, Dixon's Independent Voice, CA, Dixon

Scholl, Paul..........................(916) 773-1111
Publisher@MPG8.com, Owner/Pub., Paul V Scholl, CA, Carmichael

Scholl, Paul..........................(916) 773-1111
Publisher@MPG8.com, Pub., Carmichael Times, CA, Carmichael

Scholl, Susan
editor@carrollcountycomet.com, Co-Publisher, Carroll County Comet, IN, Flora

Scholz, Charles
cscholz@nmsu.edu, Instr., New Mexico State University, NM, Las Cruces

School, Pat
pschool@conleynet.com, Production Manager, Oconomowoc Enterprise, WI, Waukesha

Schoonebeek, Ralph ....ext. 110
ralph@dckr.com, Prodn. Mgr., County Shopper, NY, Delhi

Schoonover, Jason
jason.schoonover@austindailyherald.com, Managing Ed., Austin Daily Herald, MN, Austin

Schoonover, Steve ....(530) 896-7750
sschoonover@chicoer.com, Local News Editor, Oroville Mercury - Register, CA, Oroville
sschoonover@chicoer.com, City Ed., Chico Enterprise-Record, CA, Chico

Schopf, Brian
bschopf@uta.edu, University of Texas at Arlington, TX, Arlington

Schott, Elizabeth
liz.schott@sourcemedia.net, The Gazette, IA, Cedar Rapids

Schott, Kate
kata.schott@sj-r.com, Editorial Ed., The State Journal-Register, IL, Springfield

Schott, Ron
tvlgenmgr@lcs.net, Gen. Mgr./Ed., The Vandalia Leader, MO, Vandalia

Schou, Nick
nschou@ocweekly.com, Mng. Ed., Oc Weekly, CA, Fountain Valley

Schowengerdt, Paula ....(660) 679-6126
butler@yoeurxgroup.com, Adv. Mgr., News-Xpress, MO, Butler

Schrader, Rusty .... (563) 263-2331 ext. 225
rusty.schrader@muscatinejournal.com, News Ed., Muscatine Journal, IA, Muscatine

Schrader, Rusty ....(563) 262-0532
News Ed., The Post, IA, Muscatine

Schrafel, Daniel........................(516) 299-2619
Long Island Univ./C.W.Post, NY, Brookville

Schrag, Jeff
jschrag@thedailyevents.com, Publisher, The Daily Events, MO, Springfield

Schrag, John ....(503) 357-3181
jschrag@pamplinmedia.com, Ed., Boom! Boomers and Beyond, OR, Gresham
jschrag@pamplinmedia.com, Ed., The Portland Tribune, OR, Portland

Schrag, Jonathan ....(847) 208-4521
jrschrag@knox.edu, Co-Editor-in-Chief, Knox College, IL, Galesburg

Schrag, Robert
editor@mennoweekly.org, Pub., Mennonite Weekly Review, KS, Newton

Schraum, Brian
bschraum@greenriver.edu, Adviser, Green River Community College, WA, Auburn

Schreiber, Glenn
daytonreview@lvcta.com, Pub., Dayton Review, IA, Dayton

Schreiber, Kathy ....(702) 895-5702
kathy.schreiber@unlv.edu, Business Manager, University of Nevada, Las Vegas, NV, Las Vegas

Schreiber, Tim.........................(715) 842-4424
tschreiber@mmclocal.com, Gen. Mgr., Foto News, WI, Merrill
tschreiber@mmclocal.com, Gen. Mgr., Wausau Times / Buyers' Guide, WI, Merrill

Schreppel, Ed ....(570) 628-6003
eschreppel@republicanherald.com, Asst. Mng. Ed., The Republican-Herald, PA, Pottsville

Schreuers, Jason
publisher@prpeak.com, Pub/Ed, Powell River Peak, BC, Powell River

Schrieber, Don
pnpaper@windstream.net, Pub., The Prospect-News, MO, Doniphan

Schrieber, Don
dschrieber@darnews.com, Publisher, Daily American Republic, MO, Poplar Bluff

Schrimpf, David
dschrimpf@vvdailypress.com, Online Mgr., Desert Dispatch, CA, Victorville

Schroder, Doug.......................(815) 239-1028
news@rvpublishing.com, Ed., The Tempo, IL, Byron

Schroder, Phil ....(360) 754-5441
pschroder@theolympian.com, VP Circ., The Olympian, WA, Olympia

Schroderous, Krista ....(780) 998-7070
krista.schroderous@sunmedia.ca, Advertising Consultant, The Fort Saskatchewan Record, AB, Fort Saskatchewan

Schroeder, Alan
a.schroeder@northeastern.edu, Assoc. Prof., Northeastern University, MA, Boston

Schroeder, Angela ....(218) 739-7288
Fergus Falls Cmty. College, MN, Fergus Falls

Schroeder, April .... (605) 224-7301 x120
april.schroeder@capjournal.com, Adv Consultant, Capital Journal, SD, Pierre

Schroeder, Bill ....(507) 533-4271
starnews@stewiestar.com, Pub, Stewartville Star, MN, Stewartville

Schroeder, Cheyenne ....(620) 241-2422
cderksen@mcphersonsentinel.com, Managing Editor, McPherson Sentinel, KS, McPherson

Schroeder, Clint ....(830) 367-3501
wkcurrent@classicnet.net, Pub./Ed., West Kerr Current, TX, Ingram

Schroeder, Heather ....ext. 486
heather.schroeder@aurora.org, Mount Mary College, WI, Milwaukee

Schroeder, Lynn ....(920) 743-3321
lschroeder@gannett.com, Circulation Operations Coordinator, Door County Advocate, WI, Sturgeon Bay

Schroeder, Lynn
editor@polarcomm.com, Ed., The Cavalier Chronicle, ND, Cavalier

Schroeder, Michael....................(860) 801-5099
mschroeder@centralctcommunications.com,
Pub., The Bristol Press, CT, Bristol
mschroeder@centralctcommunications.com,
Editor and Publisher, Rocky Hill Post (OOB),
CT, New Britain
mschroeder@centralctcommunications.com,
Pub/ed, Wethersfield Post (OOB), CT, New
Britain
mschroeder@centralctcommunications.com,
Owner and Publisher, Newington Town Crier,
CT, New Britain

Schroeder, Michael E. ....(860) 801-5099
Ed. & Pub, New Britain Herald, CT, New Britain

Schroeder, Nancy ....(830) 367-3501
wkcurrent@classicnet.net, Advertising Director,
West Kerr Current, TX, Ingram

Schroeder, Sheila
sheila.schroeder@du.edu, Asst. Prof.,
University of Denver, CO, Denver

Schroeder, Steve......................(800) 468-9568
Steve@pagecooperative.com, General
Manager, PAGE Cooperative, VA, Vienna

Schroeder, Tali
tschroeder@oglethorpe.edu, Ed., Oglethorpe
University, GA, Brookhaven

Schroeder, Theodore
tim@cavchronicle.com, Pub. Emeritus, The
Cavalier Chronicle, ND, Cavalier

Schryvers , Joan
Joan.Springfieldtimes@hotmail.com, Adv. Rep,
Springfield Times, OR, Springfield

Schubargo, Jim ....(419) 470-8600
jim.schubargo@toledolegalnews.com, V.P.
Finance, Toledo Legal News, OH, Toledo

Schuelke, Anne ....(507) 389-1079
anne.schuelke@mnsu.edu, Minnesota State
Univ. Mankato, MN, Mankato

Schueller, Nate
nschueller@wctrib.com, Circulation Manager,
West Central Tribune, MN, Willmar

Schueter, Roger......................(618) 239-2465
rschueter, Features, Belleville News-Democrat,
IL, Belleville

Schuey, Tammy ....(724) 282-8000
tschuey@butlereagle.com, Director of
Technology, Eagle Printing Co., PA, Butler

Schuhmann, G. Raymond
info@thetechnologyagency.com, Pres., Kinetic
Corporation, KY, Louisville

Schuler, Rory
rschuler@heraldnews.com, Exec. City. Ed.,
Taunton Daily Gazette, MA, Taunton

Schult, Eric ....(910) 609-0656
schulte@fayobserver.com, Operations Director,
Fayetteville Publishing Co., NC, Fayetteville

Schulte, Chris ....(715) 845-0701
cschulte@wdhprint.com, Sports Ed., The
Wausau Daily Herald, WI, Wausau

Schulte, Deborah ....(318) 487-6458
dschulte@thetowntalk.com, Distribution Mgr.,
The Town Talk, LA, Alexandria

Schulte, Tom
tschulte@georgiabulletin.org, Graphic Artist,
The Georgia Bulletin, GA, Smyrna

Schultz, Bernie ....(505) 986-3007
bschutz@sfnewmexican.com, Adv. Dir. , The
Santa Fe New Mexican, NM, Santa Fe

Schultz, Chris......................(320) 282-7865
cschultz@heraldjournal.com, Dassel-Cokato
Enterprise Dispatch, MN, Cokato

Schultz, Chris
hj@heraldjournal.com, Adv. Mgr., Herald
Journal, MN, Winsted

Schultz, Courtney ....(910) 893-1520
editor, Campbell Univ., NC, Buies Creek

Schultz, David
dschultz@mlinc.com, Press Mgr., Media Logic

USA, LLC, NY, Albany

Schultz, David
daves@news-banner.com, Asst. Ed., News-
Banner, IN, Bluffton

Schultz, Don
dschultz@northwestern.edu, Prof.,
Northwestern University, IL, Evanston

Schultz, Frank
fschultz@gazetteextra.com, Educ. Reporter,
The Janesville Gazette - GazetteXtra, WI,
Janesville

Schultz, Gary
info@mrgco.com, Pres., Multimedia Research
Group, Inc., AZ, Scottsdale

Schultz, Jan......................(308) 882-4453
Managing editor, Imperial Republican, NE,
Imperial

Schultz, Julia ....(740) 446-2342 Ext 2104
jschultz@civitasmedia.com, Adv. Dir. , The
Daily Sentinel, OH, Pomeroy
jschultz@civitasmedia.com, Adv. Mgr., Point
Pleasant Register, WV, Point Pleasant

Schultz, Linda ....(814) 765-5581
Treasurer/Controller, The Progress, PA,
Clearfield

Schultz, Mark......................(919) 829-8950
mschultz@heraldsun.com, Mng. Ed., The
Herald-Sun, NC, Durham

Schultz, Mark
editor@newsobserver.com, Ed, The Durham
News, NC, Chapel Hill

Schultz, Mark......................(919) 932-2030
mark.schultz@newsobserver.com, Pub.,
Chapel Hill News, NC, Durham

Schultz, Nikki
nschultz@cbaol.com, Midwest Regional Sales
Representative, Cba Industries, NJ, Elmwood
Park

Schultz, Olita ....(613) 232-5689
admin@loradiottawa.ca, Accounting, L'ora Di
Ottawa, ON, Ottawa

Schultz, Richard ....(630) 755-9370
richard.schultz@gossinternational.com, Sr.
Vice Pres., Global Sales, Goss International
Corporation, NH, Durham

Schultz, Shelly
sschultz@city.mankato.mn.us, Adj. Fac.,
Minnesota State University Mankato, MN,
Mankato

Schultz, Thomas L.
toms@wdtimes.com, Editorial Page Ed.,
Watertown Daily Times, WI, Watertown

Schultz, Tom
tom@firstlutheranwarren.com, City Editor,
Times Observer, PA, Warren

Schulz, Jena
jschulz@qni.biz, Dir., HR, Quincy Media, Inc.,
IL, Quincy

Schulz, Julia...............(740) 446-2342 Ext. 2104
jschultz@civitasmedia.com, Adv. Dir., Gallipolis
Daily Tribune, OH, Gallipolis

Schulz, Sally......................(707) 453-8109
sally@thereporter.com, Classified Mgr., Vallejo
Times-Herald, CA, Vallejo

Schulze, Peggy......................ext. 229
pschulze@leaderunion.com, Adv. Mgr., The
Leader-union Publishing Co., IL, Vandalia

Schumacher, Amber
Tribune@gwtc.net, Mng. Ed., Edgemont Herald
Tribune, SD, Edgemont

Schumacher, Chris
t.c.s@mchsi.com, Pub., The Tri-City Star, SD,
White

Schumacher, Chris
chris.rfdnews@mchsi.com, Pub., The Volga
Tribune, SD, Volga

Schumacher, Chris

rfdnews@mchsi.com, Pub., The Arlington Sun,
SD, Arlington

Schumacher, Dean....................(651) 345-3316
graphic@rconnect.com, Adv. Mgr., The Lake
City Graphic, MN, Lake City

Schumacher, Jeff
jeff.schumacher@vicksburgpost.com, Pub, The
Daily Post-Athenian, TN, Athens
jeff.schumacher@vicksburgpost.com, Pub.,
The Advocate & Democrat, TN, Sweetwater

Schumacher, Jeff
jeff@pdclarion.com, Pub./CEO, Princeton
Publishing Co., Inc., IN, Princeton

Schumacher, Jeff ....(812) 385-2525
jeff@pdclarion.com, Pub./CEO, Oakland City
Journal, IN, Princeton

Schumacher, Linda
lschumacher@theperrychief.com, Adv. Mgr.,
Chiefland Shopper, IA, Perry

Schumacher, Linda ....(605) 542-4831
ern@itctel.com, Pub./Ed., The Elkton Record,
SD, Elkton
ern@itctel.com, Co-Pub., The Arlington Sun,
SD, Arlington

Schumacher, Linda
ads@theperrychief.com, Adv. Mgr., Perry Chief,
IA, Perry

Schumacher, Megan ....(573) 882-3792
mschumacher@asne.org, Sr. Info. Specialist,
American Society of News Editors, MO,
Columbia

Schumacher, Michael ....(806) 345-3445
michael.schumacher@amarillo.com, Director
of Visual Content, Amarillo Globe-News, TX,
Amarillo

Schumacher, Tammy
tschumacher@ncnewspress.com, Ed./Adv. Dir.,
Hamburg Reporter, IA, Hamburg

Schumacher, Tammy
tschumacher@ncnewspress.com, Gen. Mgr.,
Nebraska City News-Press, NE, Nebraska
City
tschumacher@ncnewspress.com, Gen. Mgr.,
Syracuse Journal-Democrat, NE, Syracuse

Schumacher, Terry....................(651) 345-3316
graphic.terry@embarqmail.com, Pub., The
Lake City Graphic, MN, Lake City

Schumacher, Thomas ....(337) 349-2737
vermadvertising@gmail.com, Business
Manager, Univ. of Louisiana at Lafayette The
Vermilion, LA, Lafayette

Schumer, Lizz...............(716) 592-4550 ext 24
lschumer@springvillejournal.com, Ed. ,
Springville Journal, NY, Buffalo

Schumer, Lizz.................... 716/649-4040, x255
lschumer@thesunnews.net, Editor, The Sun
and Erie County Independent, NY, Hamburg

Schumm, Kip ....(574) 658-4111
kschumm@the-papers.com, Pub.,
Shopping Guide News, IN, Rochester
kschumm@the-papers.com, Adv. Mgr., The
Paper - Kosciusko Edition, IN, Milford

Schumm, Kip ....(574) 658-4111 ext. 2328
kschumm@the-papers.com, Dir., Mktg., The
Mail-Journal, IN, Milford

Schummers, Linda ....(410) 454-0524
lschummers@bizjournals.com, Business
Manager, Baltimore Business Journal, MD,
Baltimore

Schunk, Andrew...........(330) 541-9400 Ext. 4172
aschunk@recordpub.com, Ed., Twinsburg
Bulletin, OH, Kent

Schupp, Dennis .... (913) 888-0695 Ext: 135
dschupp@smithpressroomproducts.com,
Pres., Smith Pressroom Products, Inc., KS,
Overland Park

Schur, Cynthia ....(805) 739-2154
publisher@santamariatimes.com, Pub., Adobe
Press, CA, Santa Maria

Schur, Cynthia
oschur@santamariatimes.com, Pres./Pub.,
Santa Maria Times, CA, Santa Maria

Schur, Cynthia
cschur@santamariatimes.com, Pub., The
Lompoc Record, CA, Santa Maria

Schur, Cynthia ....(805) 739-2154
cschur@syvnews.com, Pub., Santa Ynez Valley
News/Extra, CA, Solvang

Schur, Hans
hsc@schur.com, Owner, Schur International
a/s, Dk-8700 Horsens

Schurkey, Steve ....(530) 477-4214
Sschurkey@theunion.com, Circ. Dir., The
Union, CA, Grass Valley

Schurman, Jean
editor@bitterrootstar.com, Adv. Sales
Consultant, Bitterroot Star, MT, Stevensville

Schurter, Ted ....(217) 788-1476
ted.schurter@sj-r.com, Asst. Photo Ed., The
State Journal-Register, IL, Springfield

Schurz, Scott
sschurz@schurz.com, VP of Human
Resources and Corporate Development,
Schurz Communications Inc, IN, Mishawaka

Schurz, Scott C. ....(812) 331-4250
htnews@heraldt.com, Pres. & Pub., The Herald
Times, IN, Bloomington

Schurz, Todd F. ....(574) 247-7222
tschurz@schurz.com, President and CEO,
Schurz Communications Inc, IN, Mishawaka

Schust, Mary
mary.schust@mediaprof.com, Sr. Vice Pres.,
Underwriting, Media Professional Insurance,
MO, Kansas City

Schuster, Margo
margo.schuster@investors.com, Vice Pres.,
Customer Rel., Investor's Business Daily, CA,
Los Angeles

Schuster, Roy......................(303) 566-4092
rschuster@coloradocommunitymedia.com,
Adv. Mgr., Lone Tree Voice, CO, Highlands
Ranch
rschuster@coloradocommunitymedia.com,
Adv. Rep., Parker Chronicle, CO, Highlands
Ranch

Schuttenberg, Mark .... ext. 2275
marks@newsreview.com, Circ. Mgr., Chico
News & Review, CA, Chico

Schutz, Bernie .... (719) 544-3520 ext. 510
Adv. Dir., Mktg./Online Publishing, The Pueblo
Chieftain, CO, Pueblo

Schutz, Gayle L.
arapmir@atcjet.net, Pub, Arapahoe Public
Mirror, NE, Arapahoe

Schutz, Roxanne
classad@ncnewspress.com, Classified Sales,
Hamburg Reporter, IA, Hamburg
classad@ncnewspress.com, Classified Adv.
Mgr., Nebraska City News-Press, NE,
Nebraska City

Schuver, Justin
justin.schuver@bogalusadailynews.com,
Publisher and Editor, Bogalusa Daily News,
LA, Bogalusa

Schuver, Justin
jschuver@mcduffieprogress.com, Ed., Dollar
Saver, GA, Thomson

Schuver, Michael F.
mschuver@lminews.com, Vice Pres.,
Lancaster Management, Inc., AL, Gadsden

Schuver, Mike
publisher@bransontrilakesnews.com, Pub.,
Branson Tri-Lakes News, MO, Hollister

Schuyler, Barbara ....(858) 451-6200
BSchuyler@BrehmMail.com, Real Estate Mgr,
Brehm Communications, Inc., CA, San Diego

Schuyler, Ryan .... **(858) 451-6200**
RyanS@BrehmMail.com, Interactive Media &
Technology Mgr, Brehm Communications,
Inc., CA, San Diego

Schuyler, Ryan .... **(916) 985-2581**
ryans@goldcountrymedia.com, Pub., Folsom
Telegraph, CA, Roseville

Schwab, Daphne .... **(212) 556-3861**
schwabd@nytimes.com, VP, Sales Dev., The
New York Times, NY, New York

Schwab, Misty
mschwab@lonsdalenewsreview.com, Reporter,
Lonsdale Area News-Review, MN, Lonsdale

Schwab, Patty
classifieds@devilslakejournal.com, Class. Ad.
Mgr., Devils Lake Journal, ND, Devils Lake

Schwachter, Jeff
editor@acweekly.com, Ed., Atlantic City
Weekly, NJ, Pleasantville

Schwachter, Jeffrey .... **(856) 327-8800**
jschwachter@snjtoday.com, Ed., SNJ Today
Newspaper, NJ, Millville

Schwadron, Harley .... **(734) 665-8272**
schwaboo@comcast.net, Ed., Schwadron
Cartoon & Illustration Service, Ann Arbor

Schwaller, Jeff .... **(906) 497-5652**
jschwaller@powersprinting.net, Prodn. Mgr.,
Pressroom, The Daily News, MI, Iron
Mountain

Schwalm, Connie .... **(306) 736-2535**
thecitizen@sasktel.net, Reporter, Kipling
Citizen, SK, Kipling

Schwanbeck, Brad .... **(419) 724-6320**
bschwanbeck@toledoblade.com, Circ. Mgr.,
Distr., The Blade, OH, Toledo

Schwans, Troy
tschwans@triotel.net, Ed., Bridgewater Tribune,
SD, Bridgewater

Schwans, Troy
tschwans@triotel.net, Pub./Ed., Salem Special,
SD, Salem

Schwanz, Rodolfo .... **(207) 256-2244**
rschwanz@napanews.com, Class. Adv. Dir,
Napa Valley Register, CA, Napa

Schwartskopf, Gary
gschwartzkopf@mediaspangroup.com, Dir. of
Sales, Western USA, MediaSpan, MI, Ann
Arbor

Schwartz, Alan .... **(973) 267-9292**
info@caprockdev.com, President, Caprock
Developments, Inc., NJ, Morris Plains

Schwartz, Ben .... **(308) 324-5511**
ben.schwartz@lexch.com, Editor, Lexington
Clipper-Herald, NE, Lexington

Schwartz, Colleen
Colleen.Schwartz@dowjones.com, VP.
President of Communications, The Wall
Street Journal, NY, New York

Schwartz, David
davidschwartz@augustana.edu, Advisor,
Augustana College, IL, Rock Island

Schwartz, Diane
dschwartz@accessintel.com, Vice Pres./Pub.,
PR & Marketing News, NY, New York

Schwartz, Eric .... **(360) 807-8224**
eshawartz@chronline.com, Editor, The
Chronicle, WA, Centralia

Schwartz, Howard
schwartzh@enigma.rider.edu, Chair, Rider
University, NJ, Lawrenceville

Schwartz, Jody
jschwartz@timesonline.com, Dir., Adv. Sales,
Beaver County Times, PA, Beaver

Schwartz, Michael
info@intercon.com, Pres., Intercontinental
Engineering Co., MI, Taylor

Schwartz, Sandy

sandy.schwartz@coxinc.com, Pres., Cox Media
Group, GA, Atlanta

Schwartz, Sid .... **(608) 755-8293**
sschwartz@gazettextra.com, Ed., The Gazette
- gazettextra.com, WI, Janesville
sschwartz@gazettextra.com, Ed., The
Janesville Gazette - GazetteXtra, WI,
Janesville

Schwartz, Stan .... **(217) 241-1400**
stan@nna.org, Comm. Dir., National
Newspaper Association Publishers' Auxiliary,
IL, Springfield

Schwartz, Stan .... **(573) 777-4981**
stan@nna.org, Comm. Dir., National
Newspaper Association, IL, Springfield

Schwartz, Thomas
schwartz.13@osu.edu, Assoc. Prof., Ohio
State University, OH, Columbus

Schwartzenberger, Terry
homestead@napoleonnd.com, Pub. / Ed.,
Napoleon Homestead, ND, Napoleon

Schwartzkopf, Karen
wjournal@ncn.net, Pub., Whittemore
Independent, IA, Whittemore

Schwartzkopf, Susan .... **(864) 298-4100**
sschwart@greenvillenews.com, VP Market
Devl and New Media, The Greenville News,
SC, Greenville

Schwarz, Kim .... **(740) 397-5333 Ext. 242**
kim242@mountvernonnews.com, Class. Mgr.,
Mount Vernon News, OH, Mount Vernon

Schwarz, Michael .... **(619) 463-5515**
mschwarz@sdjewishtimes.com, Dir., Sales,
San Diego Jewish Times, CA, La Mesa

Schwefel, Melissa .... **(608) 257-4990 ext. 132**
Acct. Exec., Start Renting Magazine, WI,
Madison

Schwegman, Marilyn .... **(812) 934-4343**
marilyn.schwegman@batesvilleheraldtribune.
com, advertising representative, The Herald-
Tribune, IN, Batesville

Schwegman, Rhonda .... **(317) 398-1264**
rhonda@shelbynews.com, Adv. Dir., The
Shelbyville News, IN, Shelbyville

Schweitzer, Alana
newsoptimist.alana@sasktel.net, Pub.,
Battlefords News-optimist, SK, North
Battleford
newsoptimist.alana@sasktel.net, Pub.,
Regional Optimist, SK, North Battleford

Schweitzer, Alana
newsoptimist.alana@sasktel.net, Pub.,
Advertiser-post, SK, North Battleford

Schweitzer, Oliver
oschweitzer@admediapartners.com, Principal,
AdMedia Partners, Inc., NY, New York

Schweitzer, Shaun .... **(330) 996-3614**
sschweitzer@thebeaconjournal.com, VP/
Circulation, Akron Beacon Journal, OH,
Akron

Schwensen, Dave .... **(440) 967-0293**
dave@northshorepublishing.com, Author/
Award-Winning Humor Columnist,
DSEntertainment/North Shore Publishing,
Vermilion

Schwien, Nick
nicks_news@dailynews.net, Managing Editor,
The Hays Daily News, KS, Hays

Schwing, John .... **(203) 330-6248**
jschwing@ctpost.com, Metro Ed., Connecticut
Post, CT, Bridgeport

Schwinghamer, Gord .... **(780) 468-0202**
gord.schwinghamer@sunmedia.ca, Adv. Dir.,
The Edmonton Sun, AB, Edmonton

Schwitek, Jessica .... **(250) 344-5251**
editor@thegoldenstar.net, Ed., Golden Star,
BC, Golden

Sciacca, Joseph .... **(617) 619-6305**

Joseph.Sciacca@bostonherald.com, Ed. in
Chief, Boston Herald, MA, Boston

Sciacqua, Toni .... **(310) 540-5511, ext 6436**
tsciacqua@scng.com, Managing Editor, Digital
Operations, The Facts (Redlands), CA,
Redlands

Sciacqua, Toni .... **(310) 543-6132**
toni.sciacqua@dailybreeze.com, Ed., Daily
Breeze, CA, Torrance

Sciacqua, Toni .... **(310) 543-6132**
toni.sciacqua@dailybreeze.com , Managing
Ed., Digital Op., Los Angeles Daily News,
CA, Woodland Hills

Sciacqua, Toni .... **(310) 543-6132**
toni.sciacqua@scng.com, Mng Digital Ed,
Press-Telegram, CA, Long Beach

Sciarillo, Phillip
messenger127e@aol.com, Pub., Brookhaven
Review, NY, Smithtown

Sciarillo, Phillip L.
messenger127e@aol.com, Pub., Smithtown
Messenger, NY, Smithtown

Sciarrotta, Samantha .... **(609) 396-1511 ext.121**
ssciarrotta@mercerspace.com, Ed.,
Bordentown Current, NJ, Lawrence
ssciarrotta@mercerspace.com, Ed. , Lawrence
Gazette - Community News Service, NJ,
Lawrence

Scibeck, Douglas .... **(617) 696-7758**
editor@miltontimes.com, Editor, Milton Times,
MA, Milton

Scibora, Marco
info@nicollet.com, Pres., Nicollet Technologies,
MN, Bloomington

Scibora, Marco
marco@acdstar.com, Pres./CEO, Advanced
Communication Design, Inc., MN,
Minneapolis

Scicchitano, Eric
escicchitano@dailyitem.com, Reporter, The
Daily Item, PA, Sunbury

Scione, George .... **(603) 594-1254**
gscione@nashvatelegraph.com, Asst. Sports
Reporter, The Telegraph, NH, Nashua

Sciotto, Tony .... **(812) 877-0685**
tony.sciotto@tribstar.com, Prod. Mgr., The
Tribune Star, IN, Terre Haute

Scobey, Michael
mscobey@calkins-media.com, COO, Calkins
Media, PA, Levittown

Scobey, Mike .... **(215) 345-3095**
mscobey@phillyburbs.com, Pub., The
Intelligencer, PA, Doylestown

Scobie, Jerry
jbscobie2@statesmanjournal.com, CFO,
Statesman Journal, OR, Salem

Scoder, Dennis Van .... **(419) 784-5441 ext. 225**
dvan@crescent-news.com, Ed., Adams
Publishing Group, LLC, MN, Virginia

Scofield, Dan
dscofield@ocregister.com, CFO, The Orange
County Register, CA, Santa Ana

Scofield, Dan .... **(818) 713-3562**
dscofield@scng.com, CFO, Southern California
News Group, CA, Woodland Hills
dscofield@scng.com, Chief Fin Officer, Press-
Telegram, CA, Long Beach

Scofield, Dan .... **(818) 713-3562**
dan.scofield@langnews.com , CFO, Los
Angeles Daily News, CA, Woodland Hills

Scoggins, Shane
sscoggins@franklincountycitizen.com, Pub.,
The News Leader, GA, Lavonia
sscoggins@franklincountycitizen.com, Pub.,
Franklin County Citizen Leader, GA, Lavonia

Scogin, Mike .... **(502) 863-1111**
mscogin@news-graphic.com, Pres./Pub.,
Georgetown News-Graphic, KY, Georgetown

Scogin, Mike
mscogin@news-graphic.com, Pres./Pub., The
Scott Shopper, KY, Georgetown

Scoles, Samantha .... **(740) 397-5333 Ext. 248**
samantha.scoles@mountvernonnews.com,
Mng. Ed. , Mount Vernon News, OH, Mount
Vernon

Scoppe, Cindi
cscoppe@thestate.com, Assoc. Ed., The State,
SC, Columbia

Scotchie, Joe
jscotchie@antonmediagroup.com, Ed. , Roslyn
News, NY, Mineola
jscotchie@antonmediagroup.com, Ed., New
Hyde Park Illustrated, NY, Mineola

Scott, Albert
gazette@midwest.net, Prodn. Mgr., Greene
County Shopper, IL, Carrollton
gazette@midwest.net, Prodn. Mgr., Jersey
County Shopper, IL, Carrollton
gazette@midwest.net, Ed., The Carrollton
Gazette-Patriot, IL, Carrollton

Scott, Alexis .... **(404) 761-1114 ext 18**
publisher@atlantadailyworld.com, Pub., Atlanta
Daily World, GA, Atlanta

Scott, Bob
bob.scott.b6vx@statefarm.com, Circ. Dir., The
Pantagraph, IL, Bloomington

Scott, Byron
scottb@missouri.edu, Prof., University of
Missouri, MO, Columbia

Scott, Charles
cscott@recordnet.com, CFO, The Record, CA,
Stockton

Scott, Chris .... **(978) 970-4648**
cscott@lowellsun.com, City Ed., The Sun, MA,
Lowell

Scott, Christine .... **(250) 478-9552**
cscott@goldstreamgazette.com, Pub.,
Goldstream Gazette, BC, Victoria

Scott, Clay .... **(615) 230-3361**
clay.scott@volstate.edu, Volunteer State Cmty.
College, TN, Gallatin

Scott, Danny .... **(575) 746-3524**
danny@artesianews.com, Pub., Artesia Daily
Press, NM, Artesia

Scott, Fred
fred.scott@selmatimesjournal.com, Prodn.
Mgr., The Selma Times-Journal, AL, Selma

Scott, Ian
ians@advancedtele.co.uk, Mng. Dir./Gen. Mgr.,
Advanced Telecom Services, Inc. (U.K.),
London

Scott, Ian .... **(902) 426-2811 ext. 2801**
iscott@herald.ca, VP Operations, The
Chronicle Herald, NS, Halifax

Scott, Karen
kws@freese.com, Prodn. Mgr., Wedgwood
Shopping News, TX, Fort Worth

Scott, Karla
scottkd@slu.edu, Assoc. Prof., Saint Louis
University, MO, Saint Louis

Scott, Kelli .... **(509) 665-1183**
scott@wenatcheeworld.com, Editorial Page
Ed., The Wenatchee World, WA, Wenatchee

Scott, Kelly Ann .... **(775) 327-6785**
kscott@rgj.com, Exec. Ed., Reno Gazette-
Journal, NV, Reno

Scott, Kraft
kraft.scott@latimes.com, Deputy Managing Ed.
, Los Angeles Times, CA, Los Angeles

Scott, Laura
agcommonwealth@sbcglobal.net, Pub., Ash
Grove Commonwealth, MO, Ash Grove

Scott, Laura
editor@crosscountrytimes.com, Ed., Cross
Country Times, MO, Willard

Scott, Mary .... **(515) 663-6951**

mscott@amestrib.com, Sales Mgr., Boone News-Republican, IA, Boone

Scott, Mary
mscott@gannett.com, Circ. Mgr., Green Sheet, MI, Howell

Scott, Maude
maudes@djc.com, Mng. Ed., Seattle Daily Journal of Commerce, WA, Seattle

Scott, Melanie.........................(514) 914-7007
editor.thelowdown@gmail.com, Ed., The Low Down To Hull And Back News, QC, Wakefield

Scott, Michael.........................(906) 483-2230
mscott@mininggazette.com, Pub., The Daily Mining Gazette, MI, Houghton

Scott, Michael
nnsladmin@nnsl.com, Gen. Mgr., Inuvik Drum, NT, Yellowknife

Scott, Michael
nnsladmin@nnsl.com, Gen. Mgr., Yellowknifer, NT, Yellowknife
nnsladmin@nnsl.com, Gen Mgr, Nunavut News/north, NU, Yellowknife

Scott, Michael
nnsladmin@nnsl.com, Gen. Mgr., News/north, NT, Yellowknife

Scott, Michelle ....(509) 493-2112
mscott@eaglenewspapers.com, Reporter, The Enterprise, WA, White Salmon

Scott, Mike
edinasentinel@centurytel.net, Ed., The Edina Sentinel, MO, Edina

Scott, Mike
themedia@thecenturytel.net, Pub., The Media, MO, Kahoka

Scott, Oostman.........................(219) 933-2179
scott.oostman@niw.com, Retail Adv. Mgr., The Times of Northwest Indiana, IN, Munster

Scott, Robb
rscott@dmg.gannett.com, Sales Dir., Somerset Herald, MD, Salisbury
rscott@dmg.gannett.com, Dir. of Sales, Delaware Coast Press, DE, Bethany Beach
rscott@dmg.gannett.com, Dir. Sales, The Delaware Wave, DE, Bethany Beach

Scott, Robb ....(607) 798-1132
rscott@stargazette.com, Adv. Dir., The Daily Times, MD, Salisbury
rscott@stargazette.com, Adv. Dir. , Star-Gazette, NY, Elmira
rscott@stargazette.com, Adv. Dir., Press & Sun-Bulletin, NY, Binghamton

Scott, Robb
rscott@delmarvanow.com, Adv. Dir., Chincoteague Beacon, VA, Accomac
rscott@delmarvanow.com, Adv. Dir., Eastern Shore News, VA, Tasley

Scott, Robie ....(843) 937-5766
rscott@postandcourier.com, Communications and Community Relations Mgr., The Post and Courier, SC, Charleston

Scott, Shelli
sscott@billingsgazette.com, Retail Advertising Manager, Billings Gazette, MT, Billings

Scott, Sherri
sobrien@lfpress.com, Circ. Dir., Reader Sales/ Serv./Mktg., The London Free Press, ON, London

Scott, Steve ....(815) 457-2556
rankinindependent@gmail.com, Ed., Rankin Independent, IL, Cissna Park

Scott, Teri ....(716) 649-4040 ext 229
tjs@hkpublications.com, Dist. Mgr, The Sun and Erie County Independent, NY, Hamburg
tjs@hkpublications.com, Circ. Mgr., Cottonwood County Citizen, MN, Windom

Scott, Terry ....(416) 507-2126
terry.scott@thecanadianpress.com, Gen. Exec./Client Liaison, Broadcast News Limited, ON, Toronto
terry.scott@thecanadianpress.com, Vice Pres.,

Broadcasting, Canadian Press, The - Toronto, ON, ON, Toronto

Scott, Tim ....ext. 122
tscott@k-f.com, Mktg. Coord., K & F International, Inc., IN, Granger

Scott, Tony ....(217) 241-1400
tony@nna.org, Assoc. Dir., National Newspaper Association, IL, Springfield

Scott, Tony
tscott@gatehousemedia.com, Gen. Mgr., Daily Review Atlas, IL, Monmouth

Scott, Tony ....(309) 342-5577
tscott@gatehousemedia.com, Gen. Mgr., Pennysaver, IL, Monmouth
tscott@gatehousemedia.com, Pub., The McDonough County Voice, IL, Macomb
tscott@gatehousemedia.com, Pub., The Register-Mail, IL, Galesburg

Scott, Tony ....(217) 241-1300
tscott@illinoispress.org, VP, Business Dev., Illinois Press Association, IL, Springfield

Scott, Wendell
operations@atlantadailyworld.com, Prodn. Mgr., Atlanta Daily World, GA, Atlanta

Scott, Will.........................(859) 231-3246
wscott@herald-leader.com, Copy Ed., Lexington Herald-Leader, KY, Lexington

Scott-Bertling, Terry.........................(210) 250-3000
tbertling@express-news.net, New Publications & Special Projects Ed., Brooks Discovery News, TX, San Antonio
tbertling@express-news.net, Asst. Mng. Ed., Features, Bulverde News, TX, San Antonio
tbertling@express-news.net, Asst. Mng. Ed., Features, Fort Sam News Leader, TX, San Antonio
tbertling@express-news.net, Asst. Mng. Ed., Features, Kelly Observer, TX, San Antonio
tbertling@express-news.net, Asst. Mng. Ed., Features, Lackland Talespinner, TX, San Antonio
tbertling@express-news.net, Asst. Mng. Ed., Features, Medical Patriot, TX, San Antonio
tbertling@express-news.net, Asst. Mng. Ed., Features, North Central News, TX, San Antonio
tbertling@express-news.net, Asst. Mng. Ed., Features, Northeast Herald, TX, San Antonio
tbertling@express-news.net, Asst. Mng. Ed., Features, Randolph Wingspread, TX, San Antonio
tbertling@express-news.net, Asst. Mng. Ed., Features, Northwest Weekly, TX, San Antonio

Scratch, Racheal
editor@russellbanner.com, Ed, Banner, MB, Russell

Screaux, Sarah.........................(781) 280-3769
Middlesex Cmty. College, MA, Bedford

Scripps, Lora
lora@athensnews-courier.com, News Editor, The News-Courier, AL, Athens

Scrivner, Christine.........................(760) 371-4301
Adv. Mgr., The News Review, CA, Ridgecrest

Scroggin, Doug.........................(954) 425-1553
dscroggin@sun-sentinel.com, Dir., Major Adv., South Florida Sun-Sentinel, FL, Fort Lauderdale

Scroggins, Josh.........................(207) 941-7016
jscroggins@emh.org, Husson College, ME, Bangor

Scruggs, Sue
sscruggs@newsadvance.com, Sales Support, The News & Advance, VA, Lynchburg

Scully, Sean ....(707) 256-2246
sscully@napanews.com, Ed., Napa Valley Register, CA, Napa
sscully@napanews.com, Dir of News Content, American Canyon Eagle, CA, Napa

Seabolt, Al.........................(517) 417-2005
district_managers@lenconnect.com, District

Mgr., The Daily Telegram, MI, Adrian

Seabolt, Peggy
peggy@therandolphleader.com, Adv. Mgr., The Randolph Leader, AL, Roanoke

Seabrook, Don ....(509) 661-5225
seabrook@wenatcheeworld.com, The Wenatchee World, WA, Wenatchee

Seagrave, Jane ....(508) 627-4311
jseagrave@mvgazette.com, Pub., Vineyard Gazette, MA, Edgartown

Sealander, John
john@sealander.com, Owner, Sealander & Co., TX, Dallas

Seals, Bob
bseals@progress-index.com, Circ. Dir., The Progress-Index, VA, Petersburg

Seals, Demario ....(901) 433-9138
demario.seals@journalinc.com, Produ Mgr, The Bartlett Express, TN, Bartlett

Seals, Laurie ....(919) 789-2089
laurie@ncpress.com, Office Manager , North Carolina Press Association, NC, Raleigh

Seals, Otis
omaha@amclassifieds.com, American Classifieds - Lincoln, NE, Lincoln

Seals, Tom ....(316) 268-6362
TSeals@wichitaeagle.com, Asst. Sports Ed. , The Wichita Eagle, KS, Wichita

Seaman, Cary
c.seaman@antonnews.com, Mng. Ed., Glen Cove Record-Pilot, NY, Mineola

Seaman, Cary ....(516) 747-8282
c.seaman@antonnews.com, Managing Editor, Anton Community Newspapers, NY, Mineola

Seaman, Eric ....(260) 225-4902
eseaman@wabashplaindealer.com, Managing Editor, Wabash Plain Dealer, IN, Wabash

Seamons, Necia
editor@prestoncitizen.com, Ed., Preston Citizen, ID, Preston

Searano, Gil ....(213) 736-8117
Loyola Marymount Univ., CA, Los Angeles

Searcy, Jessica
searcy@erau.edu, Advisor, Embry-Riddle Aeronautical University, FL, Daytona Beach

Searl, Scott ....(402) 444-1726
scott.searl@owh.com, BH Media Group, NE, Omaha
scott.searl@owh.com, Sr. VP/Gen. Counsel, Omaha World-Herald, NE, Omaha

Searle, Dave.........................(317) 997-6055
dsearle@nuvo.net, Sales Mgr., Nuvo, IN, Indianapolis

Searles, G.........................(229) 436-2156
aswgeorgian@att.net, Publisher, Albany Southwest Georgian, GA, Albany

Sears, Adam.........................(541) 617-7844
asears@bendbulletin.com, The Bulletin, OR, Bend

Sears, Lori ....(410) 332-6405
lori.sears@baltsun.com......., Events Mgr., The Baltimore Sun, MD, Baltimore

Sears, Patricia
pmsears@newportvermontdailyexpress. com, Pub., The Newport Daily Express, VT, Newport

Sears, Todd ....(217) 788-1326
Pub., Lincoln Courier, IL, Lincoln
Gen. Mgr., Wisconsin State Journal, Madison, WI, Madison

Sears, Todd ....(217) 788-1326
todd.sears@sj-r.com, Pub., The State Journal-Register, IL, Springfield

Searson, Joyce
ahpublisher@bellsouth.net, Pub./Gen. Mgr., The Advertizer-Herald, SC, Bamberg

Sease, Cindy ....(406) 582-2616

csease@dailychronicle.com, Adv. Dir., Bozeman Daily Chronicle, MT, Bozeman

Seat, Patricia
pseat@gazettevirginian.com, Adv. Mgr., Gazette Virginian Super Shopper, VA, South Boston
pseat@gazettevirginian.com, The Gazette-Virginian, VA, South Boston

Seaton, Clydell
clydell@cameronherald.com, Office Mgr., The Cameron Herald, TX, Cameron

Seaton, Dave
dseaton@winfieldcourier.com, Pub., The Arkansas City Traveler, KS, Arkansas City
dseaton@winfieldcourier.com, Chairman, Winfield Daily Courier, KS, Winfield

Seaton, David Allen .... (620) 442-4200 ext. 122
daseaton@arkcity.net, Pub., Winfield Daily Courier, KS, Winfield

Seaton, Donald R.
tribune@hastingstribune.com, Pub., Encore, NE, Hastings

Seaton, Donald R.
drs@hastingstribune.com, Owner/President, Hastings Tribune, NE, Hastings

Seaton, Edward .... (785) 776-2200 Ext. 250
eseaton@TheMercury.com, Seaton Group, KS, Manhattan
eseaton@TheMercury.com, Chairman, The Manhattan Mercury, KS, Manhattan

Seaton, Frederick D.
dseaton@winfieldcourier.com, Editorial Page Ed., Winfield Daily Courier, KS, Winfield

Seaton, Frederick D.
dseaton@winfieldcourier.com, Ed., The Leader, KS, Winfield

Seaton, Jay ....x 250
Jay.Seaton@gjsentinel.com, Pub., The Daily Sentinel, CO, Grand Junction

Seaton, Ned M. ....Ext. 255
nseaton@themercury.com, Pub./Ed. in Chief, The Manhattan Mercury, KS, Manhattan

Seats, Debbie ....(575) 546-2611 Ext. 2610
dseats@scsun-news.com, Off. Admin. , Deming Headlight, NM, Deming

Seay, Heather
hs@rtpublishinginc.com, Adv. Mgr., Mandarin NewsLine, FL, Jacksonville
hs@rtpublishinginc.com, Adv. Mgr., Southside NewsLine, FL, Jacksonville
hs@rtpublishinginc.com, Adv. Mgr., The CreekLine, FL, Jacksonville
hs@rtpublishinginc.com, Adv. Mgr., Players Journal, FL, Jacksonville
hs@rtpublishinginc.com, Adv. Mgr., Ocean Breeze, FL, Jacksonville

Sebastian, Kelly
kellys@warrensentinel.com, Sales Mgr., Warren Sentinel, WY, Cheyenne

Sebesta, Jeff
jeff.sebesta@startribune.com, Retail Marketing Manager
, Star Tribune, MN, Minneapolis

Sebring, Blake
bsebring@news-sentinel.com, The News-Sentinel, IN, Fort Wayne

Secrist, Mark
mscrist@uidaho.edu, Assoc. Prof., University of Idaho, ID, Moscow

Sedmak, Jay
snpj@snpj.com, Prodn. Mgr., Prosveta, PA, Imperial

See, Craig E. ....(304) 725-2046
sojpublisher@gmail.com, Pres./Pub., Spirit of Jefferson, WV, Charles Town

Seeber, Mike ....(920) 993-7138
mseeber@appleton.gannett.com, Vice Pres., Finance, Post-Crescent, WI, Appleton

Seeber, Steve

sseeber.eph@lnpnews.com, Assist. Ed., Lititz Record Express, PA, Ephrata

Seebold, Lori
lseebold@dailyitem.com, Adv. Services Mgr., The Daily Item, MA, Lynn
lseebold@dailyitem.com, Production Mgr., The Daily Item, PA, Sunbury

Seeburger, John
info@chapelhillmfg.com, Pres./Vice Pres., Mktg., Chapel Hill Manufacturing Co., PA, Oreland

Seeger, Mel .... (860) 442-2200 ext. 299
m.seeger@theday.com, Purchasing Agent, The Day, CT, New London

Seegers, Penny
penny.seegers@goshennews.com, Adv. Sales Rep., The Goshen News, IN, Goshen

Seeling, Paul .... (715) 778-4990
editor@mygatewaynews.com, Ed./Pub., Sun-Argus, WI, Spring Valley
editor@mygatewaynews.com, Ed./Pub., Woodville Leader, WI, Spring Valley

Seely, Jeri .... (574) 658-4111
jseely@the-papers.com, Ed. in Chief, The Paper - Kosciusko Edition, IN, Milford

Seely, Jeri .... (574) 658-4111 ext. 2317
jseely@the-papers.com, Ed., The Mail-Journal, IN, Milford

Seelye, Tracey
editor@whitmanhansonexpress.com, Ed., Plympton-Halifax Express, MA, Hanson
editor@whitmanhansonexpress.com, Ed., Whitman-Hanson Express, MA, Hanson

Segal, Mark .... (215) 625-8501
mark@epgn.com, Pub., Philadelphia Gay News, PA, Philadelphia

Segar, Pete
sales@ergotron.com, Pres., Ergotron, Inc., MN, Saint Paul

Seger, Jamie .... (316) 283-1500 x104
jseger@thakansan.com, Circ. Mgr., Wellington Daily News, KS, Wellington
jseger@thakansan.com, Circ. Supervisor, The Newton Kansan, KS, Newton

Segers, Art
asegers@messengergadsden.com, Banner Herald, AL, Oneonta
asegers@messengergadsden.com, Pubilsher/Editor, The Clarion, AL, Ashville
asegers@messengergadsden.com, Adv. Dir., Gadsden Messenger, AL, Gadsden

Segev, Sigal
sigal.segev@fiu.edu, Florida International University, FL, North Miami

Seghers, Diane
dseghers@newstrib.com, Online Mgr., News-Tribune, IL, La Salle

Seghezzo, Francisco
francisco.seghezzo@impremedia.com, CEO, El Diario La Prensa, NY, Brooklyn

Sehnert, Cady
adminassist@thenewsleaders.com, Administrative Assistant, St. Joseph Newsleader, MN, Saint Joseph

Sehnert, Cady
adminassist@thenewsleaders.com, Administrative Assistant, Sartell Newsleader, MN, Saint Joseph

Seib, Gerald F.
a.chai@wsj.com, Asst. Mng. Ed./Exec. Washington Ed., The Wall Street Journal, NY, New York

Seibert, Joseph
jseibert@kpmg.com, Sr. Vice Pres., New England Newspaper Group, NY, New York

Seible, Tara .... (319) 291-1403
Tara.Seible@wcfcourier.com, Adv. Dir., The Courier, IA, Waterloo

Seidel, Jay .... (714) 992-7155

jseidel@fullcoll.edu, Advisor, Fullerton College, CA, Fullerton

Seidensticker, Jeff .... (617) 328-6645
jeff@merlinone.com, VP of IT & Managed Services, MerlinOne, Inc., MA, Quincy

Seidman, Dan .... (847) 359-7860
Dan@GotInfluenceInc.com, Founder/Self-Syndicator/Columnist, Got Influence? Publishing, Inverness

Seidman, Steven
seidman@ithaca.edu, Assoc. Prof., Ithaca College, NY, Ithaca

Seifer, Trenda .... (308) 386-4617
suthcourier@gpcom.net, Ed., The Courier-Times, NE, Sutherland

Seifert, David .... (540) 458-4060
Washington and Lee Univ., VA, Lexington

Seifert, Elizabeth
eseifert@sleepyeyenews.com, Circ. Mgr., Sleepy Eye Herald-Dispatch, MN, Sleepy Eye

Seil, Jane .... (208) 336-6707
jane@gapubinc.com, Publisher/Owner, Idaho Senior News, ID, Eagle

Seil, Patrick .... (618) 445-2355
navigator@nwcable.net, Pub., The Prairie Post, IL, Albion

Seiler, Christina .... (574) 224-5327
christinas@rochsent.com, Mng. Ed., The Rochester Sentinel, IN, Rochester

Seiser, Lisa .... (956) 430-6215
lseiser@valleystar.com, Ed., Valley Morning Star, TX, Harlingen

Seitz, Virginia A.
tlnmain@buckeye-express.com, Pub., Toledo Legal News, OH, Toledo

Seivert, Tom
gshores@thehawkeye.com, Circ. Mgr., Hawk Eye Shopper, IA, Burlington

Selby, Kyle
kselby@thevalleychronicle.com, Journalist, The Valley Chronicle, CA, Hemet

Selby, Vicki .... (217) 245-6121
vselby@civitasmedia.com, Advertising manager, Jacksonville Journal-Courier, IL, Jacksonville

Selch, Jared .... (317) 272-5800 ext. 126
jared.selch@flyergroup.com, Adv. Mgr., Hendricks County Flyer, IN, Avon

Selch, Jared .... (765) 482-4650 x111
jared.selch@reporter.net, Sales Dir., The Reporter, IN, Lebanon

Self, Chelsea
cself@postindependent.com, Visual journalist, Glenwood Springs Post Independent, CO, Glenwood Springs

Self, Jennifer .... (661) 395-7434
jself@bakersfield.com, Lifestyles Ed., The Bakersfield Californian, CA, Bakersfield

Self, Robert R.
keyshoppersnews@embarqmail.com, Founder, The Key Shoppers' News, Inc., OH, Swanton

Selig, John L. .... (800) 676-3342
jselig@mediamonitors.com, Sales Executive, Media Monitors, Inc., NY, White Plains

Seligman, Carole .... (415) 824-8730
caroleseligman@sbcglobal.net, Editor, Socialist Viewpoint, CA, San Francisco

Sell, Beth .... (503) 364-4431
bsell@capitalpress.com, Adv. Dir., Capital Press, OR, Salem

Sell, Jeremy
jeremy@saxmayercorp.com, Process Supvr., Information Technology, Saxmayer Corp., MI, Blissfield

Sell, Lisa
admanager@HeadlightHerald.com, Adv. Mgr., Tracy Headlight-Herald, MN, Tracy

Sell, T.M. .... (206) 592-3292
tsell@highline.edu, Advisor, Highline College, WA, Des Moines

Sellers, Diana
classads@newszap.com, Class Op. Mgr., Dorchester Banner, MD, Cambridge
classads@newszap.com, Classified Ops. Mgr., Sussex Post, DE, Milford
classads@newszap.com, Classified Ops. Mgr., Crisfield-Somerset County Times, MD, Crisfield
classads@newszap.com, Classified Ops. Mgr., Milford Chronicle, DE, Milford

Sellers, Dianna .... (302) 741-8240
dsellers@newszap.com, Classified Manager, Delaware State News, DE, Dover

Sellers, Kristi
ksellers@walkermessenger.com, Editorial Asst., Walker County Plus, GA, La Fayette

Sellers, Laura .... (503) 325-3211
lsellers@dailyastorian.com, Managing Editor, The Daily Astorian, OR, Astoria

Sellers, Tammy Jo .... ext. 101
subscribetoday@samessenger.com, Circ. Mgr., Extra, VT, Saint Albans

Sellier, Tanya .... (225) 473-3101
tsellier@donaldsonvillechief.com, Classified Clerk, The Donaldsonville Chief, LA, Donaldsonville

Selman, Sheila
sheila.selman@goshennews.com, Regl. Ed., The Goshen News, IN, Goshen

Selvig, Dave .... (701) 952-8460
daves@jamestownsun.com, Sports Ed., The Jamestown Sun, ND, Jamestown

Selvy, Sandy
sselvy@cnhi.com, Pub., The Stanly News & Press, NC, Albemarle

Selvy, Sandy
sselvy@cnhi.com, Pub., Advantage, NC, Albemarle

Selzer, Ethan
ethan.selzer@washpost.com, Director of Advertising, MAU, The Washington Post, DC, Washington

Semerad, Tony
tsemerad@sltrib.com, Dir.-Tribune Solutions, NewsView Solutions, UT, Salt Lake City

Semerad, Tony .... (801) 257-8772
tsemerad@sltrib.com, Government - Computer Assisted Reporting, The Salt Lake Tribune, UT, Salt Lake City

Semeraro, Cathy
csemeraro@southphillyreview.com, Circ. Mgr, South Philly Review, NJ, Cherry Hill

Semeschuk, Darcy
dsemeschuk@gmail.com, Office Mgr., Souris Plaindealer, MB, Souris

Seminoff, Kirk .... (316) 268-6278
KSeminoff@wichitaeagle.com, Comm. Eng. Ed., The Wichita Eagle, KS, Wichita

Semler, Loren H.
semler@semlerindustries.com, Pres., Semler Industries, Inc. (Pressroom Fluids Equipment Div.), IL, Franklin Park

Semmler, Ed
esemmler@sbtinfo.com, Mng. Ed., Market Place, IN, South Bend

Semonian, Wendy .... (617) 859-1400 ext. 231
wendy@improper.com, Pub., The Improper Bostonian Magazine, MA, Boston

Semple, Elizabeth .... (252) 329-9513
esemple@reflector.com, Dir., Mktg./Bus. Devel./Customer Care, The Daily Reflector, NC, Greenville

Semple, Elizabeth .... (252) 329-9513
esemple@reflector.com, Director of Sales & Marketing, Cooke Communications North Carolina, LLC, NC, Greenville

Senat, Joey
joey.senat@okstate.edu, Assoc. Prof., Oklahoma State University, OK, Stillwater

Seneca, Mandy
mandy.seneca@daily-iberian.com, Bus. Mgr., The Daily Iberian, LA, New Iberia

Senger, John .... (317) 477-3208
jsenger@greenfieldreporter.com, Adv. Dir., New Palestine Press, IN, Greenfield

Senger, John .... (317) 477-3208
jsenger@greenfieldreporter.com, Ad. Director, Pendleton Times-Post, IN, Pendleton
jsenger@greenfieldreporter.com, Circ. Mgr., Daily Reporter, IN, Greenfield

Sengupta, Subir
subir.sengupta@marist.edu, Assoc. Prof./Asst. Dean, Marist College, NY, Poughkeepsie

Sennott, Robert F.
publisher@barnstablepatriot.com, Pub., Barnstable Patriot, MA, Hyannis

Sensyzcyzn, Irene .... ext. 1002
classifieds@thereview.ca, Classified Adv. Mgr., The Review, ON, Vankleek Hill

Seppala, Joan Kinney
editmail@compuserve.com, Pub., The Independent, CA, Livermore

Serafini, Ray
rserafini@gantdaily.com, Adv./Digital Media Sales, Gant Daily, PA, Clearfield

Seraita, Steven .... (646) 654-8400
sseraita@scarborough.com, Exec. Vice Pres./Dir., Sales, Scarborough Research, NY, New York

Serchuk, Arnold
arnold@betascreen.com, Pres., Beta Screen Corp., NJ, Carlstadt

Sercovich, Terri .... (504) 279-7488
terri@thestbernardvoice.com, Managing Editor, The St. Bernard Voice, LA, Arabi

Sercovich, Terri .... (504) 390-0068
terri@plaqueminesgazette.com, Managing Editor, Plaquemines Gazette, LA, Belle Chasse

Serfoss, Rod .... (580) 323-5151
rodserfoss@clintondailynews.com, Pub./Ed., The Clinton Daily News, OK, Clinton

Serfustini, John
john.serfustini@sunad.com, Assoc. Ed., Sun Advocate, UT, Price

Sergent, Beth .... (740) 446-2342 ext. 2102
bsergent@civitasmedia.com, Ed., Sunday Times-Sentinel, OH, Gallipolis
bsergent@civitasmedia.com, Adv. Mgr., Tri-County Marketplace, OH, Gallipolis

Serino, Michael .... (607) 274-1618
serino@ithaca.edu, Ithaca College, NY, Ithaca

Serino, Stephanie .... (212) 556-3780
serino@nytimes.com, Exec. Dir., Licensing & Syndication, The New York Times News Service & Syndicate, New York

Serino, Stephanie .... (212) 556-3780
serino@nytimes.com, Exec. Dir., Licensing & Syndication, The New York Times News Service & Syndicate, New York

Sernoe, Jim .... (940) 397-4391
jim.sernoe@mwsu.edu, Chair/Assoc. Prof., Midwestern State University, TX, Wichita Falls

Serpa, John .... (805) 685-3100 ext. 122
serpaj@maps.com, Pres., Maps.com, CA, Santa Barbara

Serpe, Dennis .... (262) 656-6255
dserpe@kenoshanews.com, Asst. Adv. Dir., Kenosha News, WI, Kenosha

Serraglio, Mike
mserraglio@herald-leader.com, Prodn. Mgr., Bus. Systems, Lexington Herald-Leader, KY, Lexington

Shapiro, Edward
es@shorelinepub.com, Adv. Mgr., Westchester Jewish Life, NY, Pelham

Shapiro, Jo Ann .... (914) 949-9241
jjohnson@metro-email.com, VP, Sales, Metro Editorial Services, NY, New York

Shapiro, Michael
michael.j.shapiro@pfizer.com, Prof., Columbia University, NY, New York

Shapiro, Sondra
sshapiro@fiftyplusadvocate.com, Exec. Ed., Fifty Plus Advocate, MA, Worcester

Shapiro, Sondra
chronicle.sales@verizon.net, Pub., The Jewish Chronicle, MA, Worcester

Shapleigh, Katherine .... (540) 374-5461
kshapleigh@freelancestar.com, Life Ed., The Free Lance-Star, VA, Fredericksburg

Shapley, Linda .... (303) 954-1800
lshapley@denverpost.com, Dir., News Ops, The Denver Post, CO, Denver

Sharar, Mark
mark.sharar@investors.com, Prodn. Ed., Investor's Business Daily, CA, Los Angeles

Sharkey, Sabrina .... (315) 829-8018
editor@ictmn.com, Circ. Mgr., Indian Country Today, NY, Canastota

Sharkey, Sabrina .... (315) 363-5100
ssharkey@oneidadispatch.com, Circulation Supervisor, The Oneida Daily Dispatch, NY, Oneida

Sharma, Gautam .... (905) 454-1535
gsharma@metroland.com, Publisher, South Asian Focus, ON, Brampton

Sharon, Gary A. .... (330) 539-5433 ext.117
gary@litco.com, Executive Vice President, Litco International, Inc., OH, Vienna

Sharp, Dave
dsharp@flintjournal.com, Pub., Grand Blanc News, MI, Flint

Sharp, Diana
bellvillestar@ohcommedia.com, Ed., Bellville Star & Tri-Forks Press, OH, Bellville

Sharp, Gabrielle .... (937) 512-2958
clarion@sinclair.edu, Exec Ed, Sinclair Community College, OH, Dayton

Sharp, Jeanny .... (620) 694-5700 Ex. 200
jsharp@hutchnews.com, Advertising Director, The Hutchinson News, KS, Hutchinson

Sharp, Josh ....(217) 241-1300 x 238
jsharp@illinoispress.org, Dir. Gov. Relations, Illinois Press Association, IL, Springfield

Sharp, Luann .... (419) 724-6217
luannsharp@theblade.com, Asst. Managing Ed., The Blade, OH, Toledo

Sharp, Matt
matts@mbusinessreview.com, Chief Digital Officer, The Grand Rapids Press, MI, Grand Rapids

Sharp, Rita
lusynews@gmail.com, Owner/Publisher, Lucas-Sylvan News, KS, Lucas

Sharp, Sharon .... (209) 533-1713
ssharp@uniondemocrat.com, Circulation Manager, The Union Democrat, CA, Sonora

Sharpe, Lee....................(828) 632-2532
time898@bellsouth.net, Pub., The Taylorsville Times, NC, Taylorsville

Sharpnack, Joe .... (313) 512-9705
sharptoons@yahoo.com, Self-Syndicator, Sharpnack, Joe, Iowa City

Shashack, Greg .... (618) 463-2565
Asst. Sports Ed., The Telegraph, IL, Alton

Shaske, Cindy .... (262) 306-5030
cshaske@conleynet.com, Call Center Dir., Washington County Post, WI, West Bend

Shasteen, Jerry

jshasteen@circlevilleherald.com, Adv. Mgr., The Circleville Herald, OH, Circleville

Shattil, Daniel .... (402) 472-1769
dshattil@unlnotes.unl.edu, Univ. of Nebraska-Lincoln, NE, Lincoln

Shattuck, Tom .... (617) 619-6400
Thomas.shattuck@bostonherald.com, Producer Herald Radio, Boston Herald, MA, Boston

Shatz, Sherry
sherry@starnews.ca, Sales & Promo, Wainwright Star Edge, AB, Wainwright

Shauf, Noel .... (850) 315-4475
nshauf@nwfdailynews.com, IT Dir., Northwest Florida Daily News, FL, Fort Walton Beach

Shaughnessy, John .... (317) 236-1554
jshaughnessy@archindy.org, Asst. Ed., The Criterion, IN, Indianapolis

Shaughnessy, Stacy .... (516) 307-1045 Ext. 211
sshaughnessy@theislandnow.com, Adv. Dir., New Hyde Park Herald Courier, NY, Williston Park

Shaver, Diane
dshaver@heraldnet.com, The Herald, WA, Everett

Shaver, Judi .... ext. 2099
jshaver@citizensvoice.com, Coord., The Citizens' Voice, PA, Wilkes Barre

Shaver, Lori
lmshaver@pal-item.com, District Mgr., Palladium-Item, IN, Richmond

Shaver, Mary Alice
mshaver@mail.ucf.edu, Prof., University of Central Florida, FL, Orlando

Shaver, Rick .... (613) 933-0014 ext. 226
rick.shaver@tc.tc, General Manager/ Publisher, Seaway News, ON, Cornwall

Shaw, Chris
sports@nypost.com, Ed. Dept./Sports, New York Post, NY, New York

Shaw, Dan .... (414) 225-1807
dshaw@dailyreporter.com, Managing Editor, The Daily Reporter, WI, Milwaukee

Shaw, David .... (202) 463-8777
david.shaw@religionnews.com, Bus. Coord., Religion News Service, Washington

Shaw, Deb .... (888) 486-2466
debshawlma@gmail.com, Local Media Today Editor, Local Media Association, MI, Lake City

Shaw, Diana .... (740) 852-1616 Ext.1614
dshaw@civitasmedia.com, Ed. Asst. , The Madison Press, OH, London

Shaw, Donald L. .... (919) 962-4087
Kenan Prof., University of North Carolina, NC, Chapel Hill

Shaw, Gary...........................(619) 955-8960
kevin@uptownexaminer.com, Pub., Uptown San Diego Examiner, CA, San Diego

Shaw, J. Tom .... (630) 427-6210
jtshaw@shawmedia.com, Pub., Gurnee Suburban Life (OOB), IL, Grayslake
jtshaw@shawmedia.com, Pub., Riverside & Brookfield Suburban Life, IL, Downers Grove
jtshaw@shawmedia.com, Pub., Elmhurst Suburban Life, IL, Downers Grove
jtshaw@shawmedia.com, Pub., Glendale Heights Press (OOB), IL, Downers Grove
jtshaw@shawmedia.com, Pub, Carol Stream Suburban Life, IL, Downers Grove
jtshaw@shawmedia.com, Pub., Berwyn Suburban Life, IL, Downers Grove
jtshaw@shawmedia.com, Pub., The St. Charles Sun (OOB), IL, Downers Grove
jtshaw@shawmedia.com, Pub., LaGrange Suburban Life, IL, Downers Grove
jtshaw@shawmedia.com, Pub., West Chicago Suburban Life, IL, Downers Grove
jtshaw@shawmedia.com, Pub., Downers Grove Suburban Life, IL, Downers Grove

jtshaw@shawmedia.com, Pub., Glen Ellyn Suburban Life, IL, Downers Grove
jtshaw@shawmedia.com, Pub., Naperville Reporter (OOB), IL, Downers Grove
jtshaw@shawmedia.com, Pub., Hinsdale Suburban Life, IL, Downers Grove
jtshaw@shawmedia.com, Pub., Villa Park Suburban Life, IL, Downers Grove
jtshaw@shawmedia.com, Pub., Warrenville Post (OOB), IL, Downers Grove
jtshaw@shawmedia.com, Pub., Westchester Suburban Life (OOB), IL, Downers Grove
jtshaw@shawmedia.com, Pub., Westmont Suburban Life, IL, Downers Grove
jtshaw@shawmedia.com, Pub., The Winfield Press (OOB), IL, Downers Grove
jtshaw@shawmedia.com, Pub., Bolingbrook Suburban Life, IL, Downers Grove
jtshaw@shawmedia.com, Pub., Wood Dale Press (OOB), IL, Downers Grove
jtshaw@shawmedia.com, Pub., Wheaton Suburban Life, IL, Downers Grove
jtshaw@shawmedia.com, Pub., Lombard Suburban Life, IL, Downers Grove
jtshaw@shawmedia.com, Pub., Lemont Suburban Life, IL, Downers Grove
jtshaw@shawmedia.com, Pub., Woodridge Suburban Life, IL, Downers Grove
jtshaw@shawmedia.com, Pub., Lisle Suburban Life, IL, Downers Grove
jtshaw@shawmedia.com, Pub., Willowbrook Suburban Life (OOB), IL, Downers Grove
jtshaw@shawmedia.com, Pub., Huntley Farmside (OOB), IL, Downers Grove

Shaw, J.Tom
jtshaw@shawsuburban.com, Vice Pres./ Mkt. Devel., Northwest Citizen Shopper, IL, Crystal Lake

Shaw, Joseph P.............. (631) 287-1500 ext. 125
joeshaw@pressnewsgroup.com, Ed., The Southampton Press, NY, Southampton

Shaw, Julie .... (515) 284-8226
jaharvey@dmreg.com , Gen. Mgr., The Des Moines Register, IA, Des Moines

Shaw, Kevin
kshaw@sbtinfo.com, VP, Operations, South Bend Tribune, IN, South Bend

Shaw, Kevin
kshaw@sbtinfo.com, Circ. Mgr., Market Place, IN, South Bend

Shaw, Kyle
editor@thecoast.ca, Ed, The Coast, NS, Halifax

Shaw, Mark
mark@ignitefoodservice.com, The Daily Journal, CO, Denver

Shaw, Richard........................... (435) 637-0732
gm@sunad.com, Pub., Sun Advocate, UT, Price

Shaw, Rick
shawrf@missouri.edu, Dir., Kappa Alpha Mu Honorary Society in Photo Journalism, MO, Columbia

Shaw, Slayton
sales@southeastsun.com, Prod. Mgr, Daleville Sun-courier, AL, Enterprise
sales@southeastsun.com, Prod. Mgr, Southeast Sun, AL, Enterprise

Shaw, Susanne....................... (785) 864-3986
sshaw@ku.edu, Exec. Dir., Accrediting Council on Education in Journalism and Mass Communications, KS, Lawrence

Shaw, Ted .... (519) 255-6849
tshaw@windsorstar.com, Entertainment Ed., The Windsor Star, ON, Windsor

Shaw, William
publisher@valleyrecord.com, Pub., Snoqualmie Valley Record, WA, Snoqualmie

Shay, James .... (203) 330-6242
jshay@ctpost.com, Facility Mgr., Connecticut Post, CT, Bridgeport

Shea, Bill
bshea@messengernews.net, City Ed, Messenger Extra, IA, Fort Dodge

bshea@messengernews.net, City Editor, The Messenger, IA, Fort Dodge

Shea, Cindy
cshea@okpress.com, Advertising Manager, Oklahoma Press Association, OK, Oklahoma City

Shea, Dan
dshea@theadvocate.com, Pres./COO, The Advocate, LA, Baton Rouge

Shea, Kevin............................. (609) 989-5731
kshea@njadvancemedia.com, Mng. Prod / Comm. Ed. , The Times, NJ, Trenton

Shea, Lorraine
jbarrett@timesonline.com, Mgr., Educ. Serv., Beaver County Times, PA, Beaver

Shealer, Sheldon
sshealer@msmary.edu, Mount St. Mary's Univ., MD, Emmitsburg

Shealy, Ralph B.
sentinel@saludasc.com, Pub./Ed., Standard Sentinel, SC, Saluda

Shealy, Teresa .... (803) 532-6203
twincitynews@pbtcomm.net, Office Mgr., The Twin-City News, SC, Batesburg Leesville

Shearer, Alan .... (202) 334-6377
william.shearer@washpost.com, Ed. Dir./Gen. Mgr., The Washington Post Writers Group, Washington

Shearer, Dan .... (520) 547-9770
dshearer@gvnews.com, Ed., Green Valley News & Sahuarita Sn, AZ, Green Valley

Shearer, Dan .... (520) 547-9770
dshearer@gvnews.com, Ed., Sahuarita Sun, AZ, Green Valley

Shearer, Ellen
shearer@northwestern.edu, Prof., Northwestern University, IL, Evanston

Shearer, Michael...................... (740) 328-8820
mshearer@nncogannett.com, Exec. Ed., The Granville Sentinel, OH, Newark
mshearer@nncogannett.com, Exec. Ed., The Pataskala Standard, OH, Newark
mshearer@nncogannett.com, Media Network of Central Ohio, OH, Newark

Shearer, Michael...................... (419) 521-7249
mshearer@mncogannett.com, Exec. Ed., News Journal, OH, Mansfield

Shearer, Teresa
tshearer@gt.rr.com, Production Manager, East Texas Review, TX, Longview

Shearlaw, Jay .... (403) 443-5133
info@threehillscapital.com, Produ Mgr, The Three Hills Capital, AB, Three Hills

Shearlaw, Timothy.................... (403) 443-5133
Ed., The Three Hills Capital, AB, Three Hills

Sheddy, Bob
bob@drumhellermail.com, Mng. Ed, Drumheller Mail, AB, Drumheller

Sheddy, Ossie .... (403) 823-2580
editor@drumhellermail.com, Pub., Drumheller Mail, AB, Drumheller

Sheedy, Daniel
sales@printsoftamericas.com, Nat'l Sales Mgr., Printsoft Americas, Inc., IL, Chicago

Sheedy, Jack
jsheedy@catholictranscript.org, News Ed., The Catholic Transcript, CT, Bloomfield

Sheehan, A.M. .... (207) 743-7011
asheehan@sunmediagroup.net, Ed, Advertiser Democrat, ME, Norway
asheehan@sunmediagroup.net, News Ed., The Daily Star, LA, Hammond

Sheehan, Gayle
gsheehan@gatehousemedia.com, Exec. Office Mgr., The Patriot Ledger, MA, Quincy

Sheehan, Mike .... (978) 970-4855
msheehan@lowellsun.com, Dir., Circ., The Dispatch News, MA, Lowell

Sheehan, Mike .... **(978) 970-4855**
msheehan@lowellsun.com , Circ. Dir. ,
Broadcaster, MA, Lowell

Sheehan, Mike .... **(978) 970-4855**
msheehan @lowellsun.com, VP Circulation,
The Sun, MA, Lowell

Sheets, David .... **(423) 743-4112**
ds@erwinrecord.net, Graphic Design, The
Erwin Record, TN, Erwin

Sheets, Jocelyn
jocelynsheets@yahoo.com, Photo Ed., The Iola
Register, KS, Iola

Sheets, Sherryl
slsheets@rgnews.biz, Office Mgr., The
Richwood Gazette, OH, Marysville

Sheets, Theda
circulation @newkirkherald.com, Circ./Office
Mgr. , The Newkirk Herald Journal, OK,
Newkirk

Sheff, Jean
jean.sheff@westchesterfamily.com , Ed./Co-
Pub, Westchester Family, NY, Braircliff Manor

Sheffield, Paulette
paulette@snpa.org, Office Mgr., Southern
Newspaper Publishers Association, GA,
Atlanta

Shefte, Whitney
president@whnpa.org, President, White House
News Photographers Association, Inc., DC,
Washington

Sheinman, Mort
mortone@aol.com, Membership Chairman,
Society of the Silurians, NY, New York

Shelby, Edmund .... **(606) 464-2444**
Ed., Beattyville Enterprise, KY, Beattyville

Shelby, Zack
wheel1@militarynews.com, Ed., The Wheel,
VA, Norfolk

Shelden, Darla
darla.shelden@yahoo.com, Reporter, The City
Sentinel, OK, Oklahoma City

Sheldon, Bob
bshelton@news-gazette.com, Prod. Mgr.,
Rantoul Press, IL, Rantoul

Shelhart, Cheri
editor@kvpost.net, Ed. , Kankakee Valley Post-
News, IN, Demotte

Shellabarger, Diana .... **(770) 683-1739**
diana @newnan.com, Controller, The Newnan
Times-Herald, GA, Newnan

Sheller, Joe
jsheller@mtmercy.edu, Mt. Mercy College, IA,
Cedar Rapids

Shelley, Dennis
dennis@eufaulatribune.com, Adv. Sales Rep.,
Eufaula Tribune, AL, Eufaula

Shelley, Rachel .... **(207) 386-5230**
editor@coastaljournal.com, Asst. Ed. , Coastal
Journal, ME, Bath

Shelly, Derek
derek.shelly@sunmedia.ca, Mng. Ed. , The
Kingston Whig-Standard, ON, Kingston

Shelton, Clint .... **(256) 340-2465**
clint.shelton @decaturdaily.com, Pub., The
Decatur Daily, AL, Decatur

Shelton, Clint
clint.shelton@decaturdaily.com, Gen. Mgr.,
Tennessee Valley Media Co., Inc., AL,
Decatur

Shelton, David .... **(336) 373-7206**
david.shelton@herald-citizen.com, Adv. Mgr.,
Herald-Citizen, TN, Cookeville

Shelton, Don .... **(206) 464-8284**
dshelton@seattletimes.com, Exec. Ed., The
Seattle Times, WA, Seattle

Shelton, Kate
kshelton@ottawaherald.com, Staff Writer, The

Ottawa Herald, KS, Ottawa

Shelton, Linda
gazette@gazettevirginian.com, Pub., The
Gazette-Virginian, VA, South Boston

Shelton, Melinda .... **(504) 520-5096**
mshelton@xula.edu, Advisor, Xavier Univ. of
Louisiana, LA, New Orleans

Shelton Jr., Barrett C.
barrett.shelton @decaturdaily.com, Pres./
Pub., Tennessee Valley Media Co., Inc., AL,
Decatur

Shemanske, Susan .... **(262) 634-3322**
sshemanske@journaltimes.com, Sports Ed.,
The Journal Times, WI, Racine

Shen, Jason .... **(650) 721-5801**
Stanford Univ., CA, Stanford

Shepard, Kim .... **ext. 111**
kim@dckr.com, Vice Pres., County Shopper,
NY, Delhi

Shepard, Liz .... **(810) 989-6273**
lshepard@thetimesherald.com, Local Content
Ed., Times Herald, MI, Port Huron

Shepard, Randy .... **(607) 746-2178**
r.shepard@dckr.com, County Shopper -
Catskill Park, NY, Delhi
r.shepard@dckr.com, County Shopper -
Delaware, NY, Delhi
r.shepard@dckr.com, Adv. Mgr., County
Shopper, NY, Delhi

Shepard, Randy
news@waltonreporter.com, Pub./Ed., The
Reporter, NY, Delhi

Shepard, Robin
rlshepar@wisc.edu, Assoc. Prof., University of
Wisconsin-Madison, WI, Madison

Shepard, Stephen
sshepard@nasft.org, Dean, CUNY Graduate
School of Journalism, NY, New York

Shepard III, T.R. .... **(212) 969-7547**
trshepard@hearst.com, Pres., King Features
Syndicate, NY, New York
trshepard@hearst.com, Pres., North America
Syndicate, New York

Shephard, Jen .... **(574) 296-5818**
jshephard@elkharttruth.com, Chief
Photographer, Elkhart Truth, IN, Elkhart

Shepherd, Allison .... **(270) 358-3118**
publisher@laruecountyherald.com, Pub, LaRue
County Herald News, KY, Hodgenville

Shepherd, Barb
barb@beacononlinenews.com, Co-Pub./Ed.,
The West Volusia Beacon, FL, Deland

Shepherd, Blake .... **(540) 568-1674**
shephebn@jmu.edu, Advertising and
Marketing Coordinator, James Madison
University, VA, Harrisonburg

Shepherd, Jana .... **(515) 244-2145 x 159**
jshepherd@inanews.com, Program Dir., Iowa
Newspaper Association, Inc., IA, Des Moines

Shepherd, Kevin .... **ext. 118**
kshep@steelcitymedia.com, Opns. Dir.,
Pittsburgh City Paper, PA, Pittsburgh

Shepherd, Linda .... **(617) 786-7050**
lshepherd@ledger.com, City Editor, The Patriot
Ledger, MA, Quincy

Shepherd, Polly
dbox5219@gmail.com, Pub., Covington-Maple
Valley-Black Diamond Reporter, WA, Kent

Sheppard, Anthony .... **(304) 752-6950**
asheppard@civitasmedia.com, Adv. Sales, The
Logan Banner, WV, Logan

Sheppard, Dick .... **(559) 875-2511**
SangerHerald@gmail.com, Editor, Sanger
Herald, CA, Sanger

Sheppard, Lesley .... **(306) 691-1262**
lsheppard@mjtimes.sk.ca, Mng. Ed., The
Moose Jaw Times-Herald, SK, Moose Jaw

Shepphard, Charles K.
fayettenews@hotmail.com, Ed., Fayette
Chronicle, MS, Fayette

Sher, Gerald .... **(617) 619-6229**
gerald.sher@bostonherald.com, Circ. Mgr.,
Home Delivery, Boston Herald, MA, Boston

Sher, Louis Y.
care@kaidy.com, Owner/Pres., The Witzzle
Co., Plano

Sherban, Keith .... **ext. 101**
keith@wwthayne.com, Gen. Mgr., Senior Times
South Central Michigan, MI, Battle Creek

Sherban, Sherii .... **(269) 979-1412 ext. 102**
sherii@wwthayne.com, Publisher / Exec. Ed.,
Senior Times South Central Michigan, MI,
Battle Creek

Sherberg, Ellen .... **(314) 421-8310**
esherberg@bizjournals.com, Pub., St. Louis
Business Journal, MO, Saint Louis

Sherblom, John C.
john@maine.edu, Chair/Prof., University of
Maine, ME, Orono

Sherburne, Michele
advertising@jonews.com, Adv. Mgr., Journal
Opinion, VT, Bradford

Sherer, Krista
Krista@sonomawest.com, Sonoma West
Times and News Ed, Sonoma West Times
and News, CA, Healdsburg

Sherer, Valerie .... **(256) 740-5755**
valerie.sherer@timesdaily.com, News Asst.,
Times Daily, AL, Florence

Sheridan, Brian
tricountynews@media-md.net, Mng. Ed., Tri-
County News, WI, Mondovi

Sheridan, Mark .... **(765) 213-5769**
msheridan@muncie.gannett.com, Retail Adv.
Mgr., The Star Press, IN, Muncie

Sheridan, Megan .... **(920) 356-6772**
msheridan@capitalnewspapers.com, Ed.,
Columbus Journal, WI, Beaver Dam

Sherlock, Don .... **(508) 375-4946**
dsherlock@wickedlocal.com, Sports Ed., The
Register, MA, Hyannis

Sherlock, Jake .... **(307) 778-1109**
jsherloc@lccc.wy.edu, Adviser, Laramie County
Cmty. College, WY, Cheyenne

Sherlock, Mark
mark@alliancetimes.com, Prodn. Mgr., T-h
Plus, NE, Alliance

Sherlock, Steve .... **(207) 689-2883**
ssherlock@sunjournal.com, Web Content Ed./
Regl. Ed., Sun Journal, ME, Lewiston

Sherman, Albert K.
prepress@newportri.com, Pub., Newport
Navalog, RI, Newport

Sherman, Anita .... **(540) 812-2282**
anita@culpepertimes.com, Ed, Culpeper
Times, VA, Culpeper

Sherman, Cindy
csherman@beauregarddailynews.net, Multi
Media Sales Executive, Beauregard Daily
News, LA, Deridder

Sherman, Darwin K. .... **(319) 653-2191**
darwink@lisco.com, President, The
Washington Evening Journal, IA, Washington

Sherman, David .... **(414) 225-1815**
david.sherman@dailyreporter.com, Pub., The
Daily Reporter, WI, Milwaukee

Sherman, David .... **(716) 204-4905 ext. 4905**
dsherman@beenews.com, Bee Group
Newspapers, NY, Williamsville
dsherman@beenews.com, Mng. Ed., East
Aurora Bee, NY, Williamsville

Sherman, James A.
shermanpub@aol.com, Pub., Clarkston News,
MI, Clarkston

Sherman, James A.
shermanpub@aol.com, Pub., Oxford Leader,
MI, Oxford

Sherman, James A.
shermanpub@aol.com, CEO/Pub., Sherman
Publications, Inc., MI, Oxford

Sherman, Jim
shermanpub@aol.com, Pub., The Lake Orion
Review, MI, Lake Orion

Sherman, Jim .... **(248) 628-4801**
shermanpub@aol.com, Pub, Citizen, MI,
Ortonville

Sherman, Jim
shermanpub@aol.com, Pub., Ad-vertiser, MI,
Oxford

Sherman, Jim
shermanpub@aol.com, Pub, Ortonville Citizen,
MI, Ortonville

Sherman, Katie .... **(815) 526-4418**
ksherman@shawmedia.com, Marketing Dir.,
Huntley Farmside (OOB), IL, Downers Grove
ksherman@shawmedia.com, Marketing
Dir., Willowbrook Suburban Life (OOB), IL,
Downers Grove
ksherman@shawmedia.com, Marketing Dir.,
Elmhurst Suburban Life, IL, Downers Grove
ksherman@shawmedia.com, Marketing Dir.,
Glendale Heights Press (OOB), IL, Downers
Grove
ksherman@shawmedia.com, Marketing Dir,
Carol Stream Suburban Life, IL, Downers
Grove
ksherman@shawmedia.com, Marketing Dir.,
West Chicago Suburban Life, IL, Downers
Grove
ksherman@shawmedia.com, Marketing Dir.,
Downers Grove Suburban Life, IL, Downers
Grove
ksherman@shawmedia.com, Marketing Dir.,
Glen Ellyn Suburban Life, IL, Downers Grove
ksherman@shawmedia.com, Marketing Dir.,
Naperville Reporter (OOB), IL, Downers
Grove
ksherman@shawmedia.com, Marketing Dir.,
Hinsdale Suburban Life, IL, Downers Grove
ksherman@shawmedia.com, Marketing Dir.,
Villa Park Suburban Life, IL, Downers Grove
ksherman@shawmedia.com, Marketing Dir.,
Warrenville Post (OOB), IL, Downers Grove
ksherman@shawmedia.com, Marketing
Dir., Westchester Suburban Life (OOB), IL,
Downers Grove
ksherman@shawmedia.com, Marketing Dir.,
Westmont Suburban Life, IL, Downers Grove
ksherman@shawmedia.com, Marketing Dir.,
The Winfield Press (OOB), IL, Downers
Grove
ksherman@shawmedia.com, Marketing Dir.,
Bolingbrook Suburban Life, IL, Downers
Grove
ksherman@shawmedia.com, Marketing Dir.,
Wood Dale Press (OOB), IL, Downers Grove
ksherman@shawmedia.com, Marketing Dir.,
Addison Suburban Life, IL, Downers Grove
ksherman@shawmedia.com, Marketing Dir.,
Wheaton Suburban Life, IL, Downers Grove
ksherman@shawmedia.com, Marketing Dir.,
Lombard Suburban Life, IL, Downers Grove
ksherman@shawmedia.com, Marketing Dir.,
Lemont Suburban Life, IL, Downers Grove
ksherman@shawmedia.com, Marketing Dir.,
Woodridge Suburban Life, IL, Downers Grove
ksherman@shawmedia.com, Marketing Dir.,
Lisle Suburban Life, IL, Downers Grove
ksherman@shawmedia.com, Marketing Dir.,
The St. Charles Sun (OOB), IL, Downers
Grove
ksherman@shawmedia.com, Marketing Dir.,
Berwyn Suburban Life, IL, Downers Grove
ksherman@shawmedia.com, Marketing Dir.,
Riverside & Brookfield Suburban Life, IL,
Downers Grove

Sherman, Lisa
lrs@grahamhanson.com, Pres. & Chief Exec.
Officer, The Advertising Council, Inc., NY,
New York

Sherman, Rodney

rsherman.theclarionnews@gmail.com, Ed., Clarion News, PA, Clarion

Sherman, Sherrill...................(217) 477-5185
Circ., Commercial News, IL, Danville

Shermeyer, Pam.....................(313) 222-2351
pshermeyer@detroitnews.com, Multi Media Editor, The Detroit News, MI, Detroit

Shermeyer, Pam
Pam.Shermeyer@detroitnews.com, Online Content Dir., Detroit Free Press, MI, Detroit

Sheroan, Ben.........................(502) 624-1095
Ed., The Gold Standard, KY, Fort Knox

Sheroan, Ben
wwheat@thenewsenterprise.com, Ed., Central Kentucky Homes Real Estate, KY, Elizabethtown

Sheroan, Ben.........................(270) 505-1764
bsheroan@thenewsenterprise.com, Ed., The News-Enterprise, KY, Elizabethtown

Sherrer, Pauline D.
psherrer@crossville-chronicle.com, Pub., Crossville Chronicle, TN, Crossville

Sherrick, Edward D..............(203) 661-3344
Sr. Vice Pres./CFO, White Birch Paper, CT, Greenwich

Sherrill, Greg..............(865) 584-5761, Ext. 106
gsherrill@tnpress.com, Exec. Dir., Tennessee Press Association, Inc., TN, Knoxville
gsherrill@tnpress.com, Exec. Dir., Tennessee Press Service, Inc., TN, Knoxville

Sherry, Mark
marks@deltapublications.com, Ed., Tempo, WI, Kiel

Shertizinger, Bailey.................(850) 561-1612
Editor-in-Chief, FSView & Florida Flambeau, FL, Tallahassee

Shertzer, Chris
cshertzer@mdpennysaver.com, Maryland Pennysaver, MD, Hanover

Sherwood, Linda
linda.sherwood@psavers.com, Display Sales Manager, West Volusia Pennysaver, FL, Deland

Sherwood, Mark
msherwood@avpress.com, Adv. Dir., Antelope Valley Press, CA, Palmdale

Sheumaker, Allyson
asheumaker@trinidadchroniclenews.com, Gen. Mgr., The Chronicle-News, CO, Trinidad

Shevlin, Tom
tom@newport-now.com, Web Pub., Newport This Week, RI, Newport

Shiba, Noriyuki
overseas@tks-net.co.jp, Pres., TKS Ltd., Tokyo

Shibla, Adam
ashibla@suntimes.com, Sr. Mgr. Retail Relationship, Chicago Sun-Times, IL, Chicago

Shields, Brandon
bjshields@jacksonsun.com, Sports Ed., The Jackson Sun, TN, Jackson

Shields, Grace.....................(248) 336-7300
gshields@rangerdata.com, Director of Marketing & Customer Service, Ranger Data Technologies Inc., MI, Troy

Shields, John
jcompton@journalregister.com, Pub., Shore Line Shopper, CT, Guilford

Shields, Lloyd..............(308) 345-4500 ext. 131
production@mccookgazette.com, Prodn. Mgr., Pre Press, McCook Daily Gazette, NE, Mc Cook

Shields, Shelby
shelby.shields@usmc.mil, Ed., Desert Warrior, AZ, Yuma

Shields, Susan.....................(707) 984-6223
susanshields@pacific.net, Adv. Mgr.,

Mendocino County Observer, CA, Laytonville

Shiffer, Alex
publisher@gunkjournal.com, Exec. Ed., Shawangunk Journal, NY, Ellenville

Shifflet, Mark L.
dt4@evansville.edu, Prof./Chair, University of Evansville, IN, Evansville

Shifflett, John.....................(434) 978-7250
jshifflett2@dailyprogress.com, Sports Ed., The Daily Progress, VA, Charlottesville

Shifflett, Trish.....................(940) 549-7800
admgr@grahamleader.com, Advertising Manager, Lake Country Shopper, TX, Graham

Shiflet, Denise.....................(304) 643-2221
gazette@zoominternet.net, Prodn. Mgr., Ritchie Gazette & Cairo Standard, WV, Harrisville

Shiflett, Lee
circulation@tbnweekly.com, Circ. Mgr, Belleair Bee, FL, Seminole
circulation@tbnweekly.com, Circ. Mgr, Beach Beacon, FL, Seminole
circulation@tbnweekly.com, Circ. Mgr, Largo Leader, FL, Seminole
circulation@tbnweekly.com, Circ. Mgr, Clearwater Beacon, FL, Seminole
circulation@tbnweekly.com, Circ. Mgr, Palm Harbor Beacon, FL, Seminole
circulation@tbnweekly.com, Circ. Mgr, Dunedin Beacon, FL, Seminole
circulation@tbnweekly.com, Circ. Mgr, Tarpon Springs Beacon, FL, Seminole
circulation@tbnweekly.com, Circ. Mgr, Seminole Beacon, FL, Seminole
circulation@tbnweekly.com, Circ. Mgr, Wesley Chapel Laker, FL, Land O Lakes
circulation@tbnweekly.com, Circ. Mgr, Zephyrhills Laker, FL, Land O Lakes
circulation@tbnweekly.com, Circ. Mgr, Land O Lakes Laker, FL, Land O Lakes
circulation@tbnweekly.com, Circ. Mgr, The Lutz News, FL, Land O Lakes

Shilander, Kellie.....................(231) 845-5181
kellie@ludingtondailynews.com, Circulation Manager, Ludington Shopper's Edition, MI, Ludington

Shillingburg, Dan
danshill@sourcenews.com, Vice Pres./Pub., The Daily Reporter, OH, Columbus

Shimabukuro, Betty.................(808) 529-4768
bshimabukuro@staradvertiser.com, Managing Ed./Prod., Honolulu Star-Advertiser, HI, Honolulu

Shimojima, Andy.....................(541) 826-4832
andys@argusobserver.com, Adv. Mgr., Retail, Argus Observer, OR, Ontario
andys@argusobserver.com, Adv. Mgr., Retail, Independent-Enterprise, ID, Payette

Shindlebower, John
editor@spencermagnet.com, Editor, Spencer Magnet, KY, Taylorsville

Shindledecker, Scott
sports@thecourierexpress.com, Sports Ed., The Courier Express, PA, Du Bois

Shine, Eve
info@atikokanprogress.ca, Circ. Mgr., Atikokan Progress, ON, Atikokan

Shine, James.....................(419) 993-2051
jshine@limanews.com, Pub./Gen. Mgr., The Lima News, OH, Lima

Shine, Tom.....................(316) 268-6268
TShine@wichitaeagle.com, Deputy Ed./Print, The Wichita Eagle, KS, Wichita

Shingler, Mark.....................(920) 261-4902
marks@wdtimes.com, Adv. Mgr., Classified, Watertown Daily Times, WI, Watertown

Shinske, Stuart.....................(845) 437-4802
sshinske@gannett.com, Exec. Ed., Poughkeepsie Journal, NY, Poughkeepsie

Shiosaki, Joanne.....................(509) 313-6875
shiosaki@gonzaga.edu, Student Publications

Manager, Gonzaga University, WA, Spokane

Shipley, Linda
lshipley1@unlnotes.unl.edu, Prof./Assoc. Dean, University of Nebraska-Lincoln, NE, Lincoln

Shipman, Cheri.....................(979) 458-1207
cshipman@tamhsc.edu, Texas A&M Univ., TX, College Station

Shipp, Glen.....................(416) 847-2004
mjohnston@bbm.ca, Exec. Vice Pres./CFO, BBM Canada, ON, Toronto

Shirey, Jessica
editor@gantdaily.com, Ed., Gant Daily, PA, Clearfield

Shirley, Andy.....................(985) 384-8370
andy@daily-review.com, Gen. Mgr., Morgan City Newspapers LLC, LA, Morgan City

Shirley, Candice
classified@punxsutawneyspirit.com, Adv. Mgr., Classified, Jefferson County Neighbors, PA, Punxsutawney
classified@punxsutawneyspirit.com, Adv. Mgr., Classified, The Punxsutawney Spirit, PA, Punxsutawney

Shirley, Daniel.....................(478) 744-4227
dshirley@macon.com, Sports Ed., The Telegraph, GA, Macon

Shirley, Julie
julie.shirley@bellinghamherald.com, Exec. Ed., The Bellingham Herald, WA, Bellingham

Shively, Maureen.....................(303) 566-4078
mshively@coloradocommunitymedia.com, Adv. Mgr., Castle Rock News Press, CO, HIGHLANDS RANCH
mshively@coloradocommunitymedia.com, Adv. Mgr., Highlands Ranch Herald, CO, Highlands Ranch

Shivley, Joanne.............(770) 428-9411 ext. 350
Accounting Mgr., Marietta Daily Journal, GA, Marietta

Shmase, Jeff
editor@weeklynews.net, Ed., Weekly News, MA, Peabody

Shmidheiser, Ken.....................(606) 451-4902
kshmidheiser@somerset-kentucky.com, Managing Ed., The Commonwealth-Journal, KY, Somerset

Shock Peters, Charmel...............(757) 446-2000
charmel.shock@pilotonline.com, Adv. Ops. Mgr., The Virginian-Pilot, VA, Norfolk

Shockley, Ted.....................ext. 125
tshockley@smgpo.gannett.com, Mng. Ed., Eastern Shore News, VA, Tasley

Shockley, Trudy
tshockley@hammondstar.com, Asst. Bus. Mgr., The Daily Star, LA, Hammond

Shoemaker, Gerald.....................(518) 395-3002
mailroom@dailygazette.net, Prodn. Foreman, Mailroom, The Daily Gazette, NY, Schenectady

Shoemaker, Jillian
editor@stillwatercountynews.com, Ed., The Stillwater County News, MT, Columbus

Shoemaker, John.....................(570) 928-8403
sully@epix.net, Pub., The Sullivan Review, PA, Dushore

Shoemaker, Will.....................(970) 641-1414
editor@gunnisontimes.com, Ed., Gunnison Country Times, CO, Gunnison

Shoen, Kevin
circulation@independentri.com, Circ. Mgr, The Independent, RI, Newport

Shofar, Cassandra
cassandra@geaugamapleleaf.com, News Ed., Geauga County Maple Leaf, OH, Chardon

Shoffner, Brenda.....................(850) 315-4430
bshoffner@nwfdailynews.com, Ent. Ed., Northwest Florida Daily News, FL, Fort Walton Beach

Shoffner, Jim.....................(850) 315-4407
jshoffner@nwfdailynews.com, Editorial Page Ed., Northwest Florida Daily News, FL, Fort Walton Beach

Shoopman, Danielle.................(415) 214-3945
danielle.shoopman@news-star.com, Asst. Cir. Mgr., Shawnee News-Star, OK, Shawnee

Shope, Ted.................(717) 766-0211 ext. 2400
info@frycomm.com, Circ. Mgr., Guide News, PA, Mechanicsburg

Shore, Vicki
vshore@thehj.com, Adv. Mgr., Herald Journal, IN, Monticello

Short, Alice
alice.short@latimes.com, Assistant Managing Editor, Los Angeles Times, CA, Los Angeles

Short, Alyssa
hbanner@rrv.net, Cir. Mgr., Hillsboro Banner, ND, Hillsboro

Short, Bill.....................(901) 872-2286
govtreporter@yahoo.com, Copy Ed., The Millington Star, TN, Memphis

Short, Cole
hbanner@rrv.net, Ed. , Hillsboro Banner, ND, Hillsboro

Short, David
dshort@sanmarcosrecord.com, Exec. Ed., San Marcos Daily Record, TX, San Marcos

Short, Evelyn.....................(215) 361-8810
eshort@thereporteronline.com, Night Ed., The Reporter, PA, Lansdale

Short, Hugh
hshort@iona.edu, Iona College, NY, New Rochelle

Short, James.....................(304) 367-2563
jeshort@timeswv.com, Prodn. Mgr., Times West Virginian, WV, Fairmont

Short, Judy
News1@FarmlandNews.com, Ed, Farmland News, OH, Archbold

Short, Mark
short@pdclarion.com, Prod. Specialist, Princeton Daily Clarion, IN, Princeton

Short, Nancy
satw@satw.org, Exec. Dir., Society of American Travel Writers, Inc., WI, Oak Creek

Short, Robbie.........................(580) 221-6525
robby.short@ardmoreite.com, Mng. Ed., The Ardmoreite, OK, Ardmore

Shortall, Matt..............(845) 887-5200 ext. 118
matt@sc-democrat.com, Co-Editor, Sullivan County Democrat, NY, Callicoon

Shortes, Sam
twinvpub@infinet.com, Pub./Ed., The Lewisburg Leader, OH, West Alexandria
twinvpub@infinet.com, Pub./Ed., The Twin Valley News, OH, West Alexandria
twinvpub@infinet.com, Pub./Ed., The Advertiser, OH, West Alexandria

Shortley, Vanessa
v.shortley@newsoforange.com, Ed., The News of Orange County, NC, Hillsborough

Shorts, T. Mark.....................(937) 538-4658
mshorts@civitasmedia.com, Reg. Cir. Mgr., The Sidney Daily News, OH, Sidney

Shortt, Ryan
rshort@ottawacitizen.com, VP, Adv. Sales, The Ottawa Citizen, ON, Ottawa

Shortt Goodyear, Celia...............(702) 586-9401
cgoodyear@bouldercityreview.com, Reporter, Boulder City Review, NV, Boulder City

Shortuse, Marcy
mshortuse@bocabeacon.com, Ed., Boca Beacon, FL, Boca Grande

Shoub, Zach.....................(905) 727-3300
zach@lpcmedia.ca, Adv. Sales, The Auroran, ON, Aurora

Showell, Brenda .... (918) 465-2321
lcntads@att.net, Office Mgr, Latimer County
News-Tribune, OK, Wilburton

Showell, Mark .... (918) 567-2390
tricountypubink@sbcglobal.net, Ed, Talihina
American, OK, Talihina

Showell, Mark .... (918) 465-2321
lcnt@att.net, Ed., Latimer County News-
Tribune, OK, Wilburton

Showell, Michael .... (304) 647-5724
publisher@mountainmessenger.com,
Publisher, Shinnston News & Harrison
County Journal, WV, Lewisburg

Shrader, Greg .... (936) 631-2602
gshrader@lufkindailynews.com, Pub., The
Lufkin Daily News, TX, Lufkin

Shrader, James E. .... (618) 208-6419
jshrader@civitasmedia.com, Pub., The
Telegraph, IL, Alton

Shrader, Jennifer .... (706) 884-7311 ext. 2153
jennifer.shrader@lagrangenews.com, Ed.,
LaGrange Daily News, GA, Lagrange

Shrefler, Carol .... (412) 320-7909
cshrefler@tribweb.com, Ops. Mgr., Tribune-
Review, PA, Greensburg

Shreve-Gilbert, Holly
shreve@oakland.edu, Co-Dir., Oakland
University, MI, Rochester

Shribman, David .... (412) 263-1890
DSHRIBMAN@POST-GAZETTE.COM, Exec.
Ed. & VP, Pittsburgh Post-Gazette, PA,
Clinton

Shrier, Kevin .... ext. 232
kshrier@bowesnet.com, Adv. Mgr., Focus, ON,
Goderich

Shroyer, Cindi
cshroyer@galioninquirer.com, Ed., Weekly Advisor, OH, Galion

Shrum, Rick
wtxcc@wtxcc.com, Pub./Ed./Adv. Dir., West
Texas County Courier, TX, Horizon City

Shtylla, Vjollca
vjollca@icfj.org, Vice Pres., Development,
International Center for Journalists, DC,
Washington

Shubert, Frank
frank@boernestar.com, Adv. Dir., Boerne Star,
TX, Boerne

Shubert, Frank .... (830) 693-4367
frank@highlandernews.com, Ed. / Pub., Burnet
Bulletin, TX, Burnet

Shuberynski, Shirley ......(613) 678-3327 ext. 2013
Advertising Sales, The Review, ON, Vankleek
Hill

Shugg, Beth
bshugg@carolinaparent.com, Editor, Carolina
Parent, NY, White Plains

Shuler, Brandon .... (406) 552—4049
brandon@owaa.org, Executive Director,
Outdoor Writers Association of America, Inc.,
MT, Missoula

Shuler, Matt
jcstar@yahoo.com, Ed./Pub., Jackson County
Star, CO, Walden

Shuler, Michelle
jcstar@yahoo.com, THE BOSS, Jackson
County Star, CO, Walden

Shulmister, Ross
sentry@shulmister.com, Ed., The Sentry, FL,
Pompano Beach

Shults, Lana Sweeten .... (940) 720-3462
lshults@wf.scripps.com, Radio/Television
Ed., Wichita Falls Times Record News, TX,
Wichita Falls

Shultz, Chris .... (320) 282-7865
cschultz@heraldjournal.com, Delano Herald
Journal, MN, Delano

Shultz, Harold .... (517) 279-9764
shopperads@cbpu.com, Pub., Shoppers
Guide, MI, Coldwater

Shultz, Jeff
publisher@gcnews-star.com, Co-Pub./Co-
Own./Ed., The Garvin County News Star,
OK, Maysville

Shultz, Nanette
news@gcnews-star.com, Co-Pub./Co-Own.,
The Garvin County News Star, OK, Maysville

Shultz, Susan .... (203) 656-4230
editor@darientimes.com, Ed., Darien Times,
CT, Darien

Shumacher, Jeff
jeff@pdclarion.com, Pub., Princeton Daily
Clarion, IN, Princeton

Shuman, Cary
cary@lynnjournal.com, Ed. in Chief, Chelsea
Record, MA, Revere

Shuman-Prins, Linda
lindas@goldcountrymedia.com, Business
Develop., Placer Herald, CA, Rocklin
lindas@goldcountrymedia.com, Business
Develop., Colfax Record, CA, Colfax
lindas@goldcountrymedia.com, Bus Develop.,
Lincoln News Messenger, CA, Lincoln
lindas@goldcountrymedia.com, Business
Develop., El Dorado Hills Telegraph, CA,
Roseville

Shumate, Anne .... (727) 451-3696
ashumate@businessobserverfl.com, Dir. Sales/
Mktg., Business Observer, FL, Sarasota

Shumway, Bill .... (315) 265-1000 ext. 21
bill@northcountrynow.com, Pub., North
Country This Week, NY, Potsdam

Shumway, Darla .... (406) 653-2222
herald@nemont.net, Publisher, The Herald-
News, MT, Wolf Point

Shumway, Darla
searchlight@nemont.net, Pub., The
Searchlight, MT, Culbertson

Shunney, Kate .... (304) 258-1800
editor@morganmessenger.com, Ed., The
Morgan Messenger, WV, Berkeley Springs

Shunney, Kate .... (304) 258-1800
editory@morganmessenger.com, Ed, The
Hancock News, MD, Hancock

Shupac, Mark
mshupac@ctcsoftware.com, Contact, Catalyst
International, Inc., WI, Milwaukee

Shupe, Erik
news@minneapolismessenger.net, Pub/Ed,
Minneapolis Messenger, KS, Minneapolis

Shurett, Ben
ben.shurett@sandmountainreporter.com, Pub.,
The Shopper, AL, Albertville
ben.shurett@sandmountainreporter.com, Pub.,
Sand Mountain Reporter, AL, Albertville

Shurett, Brad
brad.shurett@thedailysentinel.com, Pub., The
Daily Sentinel, AL, Scottsboro

Shurman, Mark .... (727) 445-4144
mshurman@tampabay.com, Adv. Mgr., Tampa
Bay Times, FL, St Petersburg

Shurtleff, Andrew .... (434) 978-7278
ashurtleff@dailyprogress.com, Chief
Photojournalist, The Daily Progress, VA,
Charlottesville

Shutes, Linda
lshutes@journalnet.com, General Sales Mgr.,
Idaho State Journal, ID, Pocatello

Shwanke, Bruce .... (306) 482-3252
gazettepost.news@sasktel.net, Pub., Gazette-
post News, SK, Carnduff

Sibaja, Jose
jsibaja@elespecial.com, Ed. Dir., El Especialito,
NJ, Union City

Sible, Nancy .... (260) 347-7211

nsible@kpcmedia.com, KPC Media Group,
Inc., IN, Kendallville

Sibley, Lori .... (316) 321-1120
lsibley@butlercountytimesgazette.com, Circ.
Mgr., The Butler County Times-Gazette, KS,
Augusta

Siburt, Debra .... (715) 845-0602
dsiburt@wdhprint.com, Librarian, The Wausau
Daily Herald, WI, Wausau

Siccardi, Joseph L.
revblt@rochester.rr.com, Pub., The Reveille/
Between The Lakes, NY, Waterloo

Sickels, David
dsickels@thepostnewspapers.com, Managing
Editor, The Post Newspapers - Medina, OH,
Medina

Sickle, David .... (570) 628-6150
dsickle@republicanherald.com, Dir., Circ., The
Republican-Herald, PA, Pottsville

Sickle, David .... (570) 628-6150
dsickle@republicanherald.com, Dir., Circ., The
News-Item, PA, Shamokin

Sickler, Ted
tsickler@lnpews.com, Managing Editor, LNP,
PA, Lancaster
tsickler@lnpews.com, Managing Editor, LNP
Media Group, Inc., PA, Lancaster

Sickles, Deanna .... (217) 774-2161 ext. 263
deanna.sickles@shelbyvilledailyunion.com,
Adv. Mgr, Daily Union, IL, Shelbyville

Sicliano, Sam
editors@app.com, Vice Pres., Addresses
Unlimited, NJ, Neptune

Siddall, Pam .... (205) 325-3126
President, The Birmingham News, AL,
Birmingham

Siddle, Ron .... (661) 267-4134
rsiddle@avpress.com, Photo Ed., Antelope
Valley Press, CA, Palmdale

Siddons, Brad
bsiddons@lewistownsentinel.com, Online Mgr.,
The Sentinel, PA, Lewistown

Siddons, Mary Beth
info@snaponbusinesssolutions.com, Pres.,
Snap-on Business Solutions, OH, Richfield

Sidel, Kent
kent.sidel@zu.ac.ae, Prof./Asst. Dean, Abu
Dhabi, Zayed University, Al Ruwayyah

Sides, John
john@codyenterprise.com, Prodn. Mgr., The
Cody Enterprise, WY, Cody

Sidham, Rochelle ....ext. 225
news@empiretribune.com, Pub., Cross
Timbers Trading Post, TX, Stephenville

Sidlo, Steve
ssidlo@coxohio.com, Pub., Springfield News-
Sun, OH, Springfield

Sidlo, Steve
ssidlo@coxohio.com, Pub., Tri-county
Shoppers News, OH, Springfield

Sidlow, Sarah .... (937) 222-8855 ext. 213
editor@daytoncitypaper.com, Ed., Dayton City
Paper, OH, Dayton

Sidna, Tom .... (508) 749-3166, ext. 154
Circ. Mgr., The Landmark, MA, Holden

Sieber, Mike
newsroom@harrisonnewsherald.com, Editor,
Harrison News-Herald, OH, Cadiz

Siebert, Mark .... (515) 263-6124
msiebert@grandview.edu, Grand View
University, IA, Des Moines

Sieble, Tara .... (319) 291-1403
tara.sieble@wcfcourier.com, Adv. Mgr, Insider,
IA, Waterloo

Siebrass, Travis .... (847) 427-4575
tsiebrass@dailyherald.com, Digital Editor /
Online Content, Daily Herald, IL, Arlington

Heights

Siedenberg, Ivan
De.Oroark@Verizon.Com, Chrmn./CEO, MCI,
VA, Ashburn

Siegel, Bette .... (315) 445-2040 ext. 116
jewishobservercny@gmail.com, Ed., The
Jewish Observer, NY, Syracuse

Siegel, Brad .... (630) 258-0955
bradsiegel@systems-technology-inc.com,
Sales. Dir., Systems Technology, Inc., CA,
San Bernardino

Siegel, Debbie
debbie@bba-la.com, Adv Sales Rep.,
American Profile - Los Angeles, CA, Los
Angeles

Siegel, Gary .... (212) 803-1560
gary.siegel@sourcemedia.com, Asst. Ed.,
American Banker Online, American Banker,
NY, New York

Siegel, Gary ....(724) 537-3351 ext. 19
garysiegel1@verizon.net, Pub., Adv. Dir., The
Latrobe Bulletin, PA, Latrobe

Siegel, Marshall .... (972) 238-6068
advertise@dcccd.edu, Adv. Mgr., Richland
College, TX, Dallas

Siegel, Randy ....(212) 450-0980 ext. 0980
randy_siegel@parade.com, Pres., Parade,
New York

Siegel, Stephen
sbsiegel@uvps.com, Pres., UV Process
Supply, Inc., IL, Chicago

Siegler, Lucille .... (207) 780-4084 Ext. 2
lucille@usmfreepress.org, Business Manager,
University of Southern Maine, ME, Portland

Sielski, Dave
dsielski@gannett.com, Circ. Mgr., De Pere
Journal, WI, Green Bay
dsielski@gannett.com, Circ. Mgr, Lakeshore
Chronicle, WI, Manitowoc

Siemers, Tom
tsiemers@mesabidailynews.net, Circ. Mgr.,
Mesabi Daily News, MN, Virginia

Siemers, Tom .... (270) 505-1440
tsiemers@thenewsenterprise.com, Circ. Mgr.,
The News-Enterprise, KY, Elizabethtown

Siemon, Holly .... (215) 336-2500
hsiemon@southphillyreview.com, Prod. Mgr.,
South Philly Review, NJ, Cherry Hill

Sienkiewicz, Joe .... (920) 426-6632
Chief Photographer, Oshkosh Northwestern,
WI, Oshkosh

Sierra, Juan Jose
bakerte@co.monterey.ca.us, CFO, The
Monterey County Herald, CA, Monterey

Sierra, Ric .... (813) 259-7473
Tampa Bay Times, FL, St Petersburg

Siete, Linda
lsiete@reflejos.com, Gen. Mgr., Reflejos
Bilingual Publications, IL, Arlington Heights

Sievertsen, Joleen .... (712) 654-2911
manillatimes@fmctc.com, Office Mgr, Manilla
Times, IA, Manilla

Sigal, Phyllis
sigal@news-register.net, Food/Women's Ed.,
The Intelligencer, WV, Wheeling

Sigel, Ellen .... (212) 313-9044
esigel@alm.com, Vice Pres., Licensing/Bus.
Devel., ALM, New York

Signa, Tom
tsigna@worcestermag.com, Adv. Mgr,
Leominster Champion, MA, Leominster

Sigurdson, Sarah
sarah.sigurdswon@thenownewspaper.com,
Ad Control/Admin, The Now Newspaper,
BC, Surrey

Sigvaldason, Jack .... (867) 873-4031
nnsladmin@nnsl.com, Pub., Inuvik Drum, NT,

Yellowknife

Sigvaldason, Jack
nnsladmin@nnsl.com, Pub., News/north, NT, Yellowknife

Sigvaldason, Jack .... (867) 766-8264
nnsladmin@nnsl.com, Pub., Yellowknifer, NT, Yellowknife

Sigvaldason, Jack
nnsladmin@nnsl.com, Pub., Deh Cho Drum, NT, Yellowknife

Sigvaldason , Jack..................... (867) 873-8507
nnsl@nnsl.com, Pub, Kivalliq News, NU, Yellowknife
nnsl@nnsl.com, Pub, Nunavut News/north, NU, Yellowknife

Sikkema, Lisa .... (574) 296-5965
lsikkema@elkharttruth.com, Advertising Director, Elkhart Truth, IN, Elkhart

Sikorski, Gary
gsikorski@lds.com, Vice Pres., Opns., Logical Design Solutions, Inc., NJ, Florham Park

Sikoutris, Sylvia
sylvia@westfairinc.com, Circ. Mgr., Fairfield County Business Journal, NY, White Plains
sylvia@westfairinc.com, Circ. Mgr., Westchester County Business Journal, NY, White Plains

Silberfeld, Eileen .... (410) 454-0530
esilberfeld@bizjournals.com, Audience Development Director, Baltimore Business Journal, MD, Baltimore

Silbernagel, Bob ....ext. 236
Editorial Page Ed., The Daily Sentinel, CO, Grand Junction

Siler, Steve J.
sales@hurletron.com, Gen. Mgr., Hurletron, Inc., IL, Libertyville

Silette, Lori
circulation@delphosherald.com, Cir. / Class., Delphos Daily Herald, OH, Delphos

Silinski, Albert H.
brightonparklife@aol.com, Circ. Mgr., Brighton Park - McKinley Park Life, IL, Chicago

Sillick, David .... (904) 265-2203
dsillick@bizjournals.com, President and Publisher, Jacksonville Business Journal, FL, Jacksonville

Silliman, Sue
ssilliman@wehco.com, Gen. Mgr., Camden News, AR, Camden

Sills, Jim .... (910) 609-0675
jsills@ncweeklies.com, Pub., Duplin Times, NC, Kenansville

Silow-Carroll, Andrew .... (973) 929-3141
asc@njjewishnews.com, Editor in Chief/CEO, New Jersey Jewish News, NJ, Whippany

Silva, Clarence
fsgsonny@flex.com, Pub., Hawaii Catholic Herald, HI, Honolulu

Silva, Dan .... (956) 683-4245
dsilva@rgvmedianetwork.com, Contact Center Manager, The Monitor, TX, McAllen

Silva, Emmy .... (214) 309-0990
emmysilva@elextranewspaper.com, Publisher/ Editor
Advertising Manager, El Extra Newspaper, TX, Dallas

Silva, Jim .... (209) 578-2279
jsilva@modbee.com, Digital Content Prod, Merced Sun-Star, CA, Merced

Silva, Melissa .... (806) 385-4481
classifieds@lambcountyleadernews.com, Classified Adv. Mgr./Circ. Mgr., Lamb County Leader-News, TX, Littlefield

Silva, Rick
rsilva@paradisepost.com, Mng. Ed., Paradise Post, CA, Paradise

Silva, Star

ssilva@bonnersferryherald.com, Ed., Bonners Ferry Herald, ID, Bonners Ferry

Silvas, Travis
tsilvas@county-journal.com, Circ. Mgr., The County Journal, MI, Charlotte
tsilvas@county-journal.com, Circ. Mgr, Flashes Advertising & News, MI, Charlotte

Silver, Lauren
lsilver@jewishmonmouth.org, Ed., Jewish Voice, NJ, Cherry Hill

Silver, Lorne
lsilver@thestar.ca, Dir., Creative Mktg., Toronto Star, ON, Toronto

Silver, Matt
chisago@citlink.net, Pub., Search Shopper, MN, Lindstrom

Silver, Matt .... (617) 257-5115
chisago@citlink.net, Pub., Chisago County Press, MN, Lindstrom

Silver, Sheryl .... (954) 647-5995
sheryl.silver@yahoo.com, Owner/Author, Career Source/Column, Birmingham

Silver, Steven....................... (203) 775-9122
steven@ctpennysaver.com, Pub., Yankee Pennysaver, CT, Brookfield

Silverman, Adam
asilverman@burlingtonfreepress.com, Content Strategist, The Burlington Free Press, VT, Burlington

Silverman, Amy
amy.silverman@newtimes.com, Mng. Editor, New Times, AZ, Phoenix

Silverman, Fran
fsilverman@fairfield.edu, Fac., Fairfield University, CT, Fairfield

Silverman, Rick .... (607) 255-0565
Cornell Law School, NY, Ithaca

Silverstein, Arthur .... (718) 816-3158
silverstein@siadvance.com, Controller, Staten Island Advance, NY, Staten Island

Silverstein, Brandon .... (410) 200-6469
bsilverstein@chespub.com , Adv. Dir. , The Star-Democrat, MD, Easton

Silvestri, Chris .... (856) 317-7829
csilvestri@gannettnj.com, Reg. Plan., The Courier-Post, NJ, Cherry Hill

Silvestri, Thomas A.................... (804) 649-6121
tsilvestri@timesdispatch.com, Pres./Pub., Richmond Times-Dispatch, VA, Richmond
tsilvestri@timesdispatch.com, Southern Newspaper Publishers Association, GA, Atlanta

Silvestrin, Debra
web@aan.org, Dir. of Meetings, Association of Alternative Newsmedia, DC, Washington

Silvia, Kerry
classified@hathawaypublishing.com, Classified Adv. Mgr., The Spectator, MA, New Bedford

Simard, Carolyn..................... (514) 985-3302
csimard@ledevoir.com, Circ. Dir., Le Devoir, QC, Montreal

Simard, Jean
jsimard@lequotidien.com, Prod./Circ. Mgr., Le Quotidien, QC, Saguenay

Simard, Martyne .... (450) 677-2556
info@marevueagricole.com, Revue De La Machinerie Agricole, QC, Longueuil

Simes, Libby .... (701) 250-8202
libby.simes@bismarcktribune.com, Pub, The Bismarck Tribune, ND, Bismarck

Simison, Cynthia...................... (413) 788-1214
csimison@repub.com, Managing Ed., The Republican, MA, Springfield

Simmins, Emma
Esimmins@skyhidailynews.com, Adv. Mgr., Sky-Hi News, CO, Granby

Simmonds, Bob

bsimmonds@indexjournal.com, Web Page Ed., The Index-Journal, SC, Greenwood

Simmons, Jason...................... (902) 432-8211
jpsports@journalpioneer.com, Sports Ed., The Journal Pioneer, PE, Summerside

Simmons, Amanda .... (318) 747-7900
amanda@bossierpress.com, Managing Editor, Bossier Press-Tribune, LA, Bossier City

Simmons, Amy .... (620) 241-2422
asimmons@mcphersonsentinel.com, Advertising Manager, McPherson Sentinel, KS, McPherson

Simmons, Barb
barbsimmons@reviewatlas.com, Prodn. Mgr., Daily Review Atlas, IL, Monmouth

Simmons, Beau .... (405) 372-5000
bsimmons@stwnewspress.com, Ed., Stillwater News Press, OK, Stillwater

Simmons, Bob........................ (636) 528-9550
Ed, Troy Free Press, MO, Troy

Simmons, Bob........................ (636) 528-9550
Editor, The Lincoln County Journal, MO, Troy

Simmons, Chere
chere@observernews.net, Prod. Mgr, Observer News, FL, Ruskin

Simmons, Derek .... (612) 673-7885
Derek.Simmons@startribune.com, Asst. Managing Ed., Visuals , Star Tribune, MN, Minneapolis

Simmons, Erin
esimmons@unionrecorder.com, Adv. Dir., The Union-Recorder, GA, Milledgeville

Simmons, Erin .... (478) 453-1436
kmertz@unionrecorder.com, Adv. Director, Lake Oconee Breeze, GA, Milledgeville

Simmons, Galen
gsimmons@postmedia.com, Reporter, The Stratford Beacon Herald, ON, Stratford

Simmons, Garrett..................... (403) 380-7595
gsimmons@lethbridgeherald.com, Ed., The Lethbridge Herald, AB, Lethbridge

Simmons, Jeff
jsimmons@wythenews.com, Mng. Ed., Enterprise Buyers Catalogue, VA, Wytheville

Simmons, Jennifer .... (815) 561-2151
news@rochellenews-leader.com, Managing Ed. , Farmer's Report, IL, Mendota
news@rochellenews-leader.com, Managing Ed., The Rochelle News Leader, IL, Rochelle

Simmons, Michael
msimmons@onlinemadison.com, Associate Ed/Pub, Madison County Journal, MS, Ridgeland

Simmons, Michel
a2smith@lbcc.edu, Long Beach City College, CA, Long Beach

Simmons, Rick
rick@pdclarion.com, Circl. Mgr., Princeton Daily Clarion, IN, Princeton

Simmons, Staci .... (972) 280-0050 ext. 407
mameen@unitedad.com, Mktg. Mgr., DallasChild, TX, Addison

Simmons, Teresa .... (309) 298-1426
TL-Simmons@wiu.edu, Assoc. Prof./Advisor, WAF, Western Illinois University, IL, Macomb

Simmons, Tony........................ (850) 747-5080
tsimmons@pcnh.com, Online Ed., The News Herald, FL, Panama City

Simmons, Victoria .... (478) 542-4187
vsimmons54@gmail.com, Publisher, The Georgia Post, GA, Roberta

Simms, Brian
bimmms@herald-leader.com, DESIGN DIRECTOR
, Lexington Herald-Leader, KY, Lexington

Simms, Deidre
dsimms@philadelphiaweekly.com, Adv. Mgr.,

Philadelphia Weekly, NJ, Cherry Hill

Simon, Carl .... (262) 634-3322
csimon@journaltimes.com, Prodn. Supvr., Pressroom, The Journal Times, WI, Racine

Simon, David
dsimon@gazette.net, Bowie Star, MD, Laurel

Simon, James
jsimon@mail.fairfield.edu, Chair/Fac., Fairfield University, CT, Fairfield

Simon, Jeff
sales@lithcoinc.com, President, Lithco Inc., CA, Culver City

Simon, Jim .... (206) 464-2480
jsimon@seattletimes.com, Managing Ed., The Seattle Times, WA, Seattle

Simon, Kathy .... (989) 774-1472
simon1k@cmich.edu, Advisor, Central Michigan University, MI, Mount Pleasant

Simon, Peggy
peggysimon@progress-index.com, Mgr., Accounting, The Progress-Index, VA, Petersburg

Simon, Terri .... (815) 875-4461, ext. 6330
tsimon@bcrnews.com, Ed., Tonica News, IL, Princeton
tsimon@bcrnews.com, Ed., Bureau County Republican, IL, Princeton

Simon, Val .... (239) 393-4991
val@coastalbreezenews.com, Pub, Coastal Breeze News, FL, Marco Island
val@coastalbreezenews.com, Pub., Coastal Breeze News, FL, Marco Island

Simonds, Sara
ssimonds@fstribune.com, Composition Mgr., The Fort Scott Tribune, KS, Fort Scott

Simoneau, Therese.................... (815) 694-2122
Ed., The Advocate, IL, Clifton

Simonian, Dick........................ (800) 631-3128
Sales Consultant, Pitman Co., NJ, Elmwood Park

Simonini, Dennis
chisrnews@aol.com, Mng. Ed., DenBar Publishing, Inc, IL, Dundee

Simons, Chris .... (765) 213-5853
csimons@muncie.gannett.com, Copy Ed., The Star Press, IN, Muncie

Simons, Dan
dsimons@ljworld.com, Owner, WorldWest LLC, KS, Lawrence

Simons, Dolph .... (785) 832-7159
simons@ljworld.com, Lawrence Journal-World, KS, Lawrence

Simons, Dolph C.
simons@ljworld.com, Co-Mgr., WorldWest LLC, KS, Lawrence

Simpkins, Dave
dave@mntrails.com, Mid-minnesota Shopper, MN, Sauk Centre

Simpkins, Jerry .... (760) 365-3725 X241
simpkins@tds.net, Hi-Desert Publishing Co., Inc., CA, Yucca Valley

Simpleman, Julie.......... (269) 429-2400 ext. 877
jsimpleman@thehp.com, Circ. Dir. , The Herald-Palladium, MI, Saint Joseph

Simpson, Althea .... (910) 506-3022
asimpson@civitasmedia.com, Bus. Devp. Mgr. , The Laurinburg Exchange, NC, Laurinburg

Simpson, Beau
bsimpson@thenownewspaper.com, Ed, The Now Newspaper, BC, Surrey

Simpson, Ferris
fsimpson@civitasmedia.com, Bus./Circ Mgr., Mount Airy News, NC, Mount Airy

Simpson, Gerie .... (618) 239-2471
gsimpson@bnd.com, HR Dir., Belleville News-Democrat, IL, Belleville

Simpson, Isaac

isimpson@hbu.edu, Instr./Opns. Mgr., Instructional TV, Houston Baptist University, TX, Houston

Simpson, Jennifer
jennifer@bgparent.com, Owner & Publisher, Bowling Green Parent, KY, Bowling Green

Simpson, Julie
jsimpson@nevadadailymail.com, Pub., Nevada News, MO, Nevada

Simpson, Larry......................(270) 783-3250
lsimpson@bgdailynews.com, Prodn. Mgr., Daily News, KY, Bowling Green

Simpson, Les
les.simpson@amarillo.com, Pub., Amarillo Globe-News, TX, Amarillo

Simpson, Marie......................(708) 488-5106
Dominican Univ., IL, River Forest

Simpson, Max......................(410) 751-5912
msimpson@carrollcountytimes.com, Online/ Multimedia Prod. , Carroll County Times, MD, Westminster

Simpson, Nancy......................(559) 674-8134
CFO, The Madera Tribune, CA, Madera

Simpson, Rande
rsimpson@merlinone.com, Merlin Sr. Acct. Rep., MerlinOne, Inc., MA, Quincy

Simpson, Richard......................(919) 962-5177
Prof., University of North Carolina, NC, Chapel Hill

Simpson, Ron..............(419) 668-3771 Ext. 1224
rsimpson@norwalkreflector.com, Asst. Cir. Mgr., Norwalk Reflector, OH, Norwalk

Simpson, Shannon
shannon.simpson@blackpress.ca, Pub, Penticton Western News, BC, Penticton
shannon.simpson@blackpress.ca, Pub, Summerland Review, BC, Summerland

Simpson, Steve
ssimpson@gannett.com, East Group VP, Mktg/Strategy, Democrat and Chronicle, NY, Rochester

Simpson, Theresa......................(559) 735-3316
tsimpson@timesdeltamediagroup.com, Circ. Mgr. , Tulare Advance-Register, CA, Visalia
tsimpson@timesdeltamediagroup.com, Media Group Rep., Visalia Times-Delta, CA, Visalia

Simpson Strange, Lisa.....(270) 678-5171 Ext. 292
lsstrange@glasgowdailytimes.com, News Ed., Glasgow Daily Times, KY, Glasgow

Sims, Bill
bsims@chespub.com, Reg, Dir., Circ., The Avenue News, MD, Dundalk

Sims, Edward H.......................(941) 366-2169
Ed./Pub., Editor's Copy Syndicate, Sarasota

Sims, Janeen
news@mexicoledger.com, Ed., Mexico Ledger, MO, Mexico

Sims, Kristyn
ksims@boonevilledemocrat.com, Pub., Charleston Express, AR, Greenwood
ksims@boonevilledemocrat.com, Pub., Booneville Democrat, AR, Booneville

Sims, Marcia......................(985) 748-7156
marcia.sims@tangilena.com, Circ. Mgr., Amite Tangi-Digest, LA, Amite

Sims, Patsy
patsy1@pitt.edu, Coord., University of Pittsburgh, PA, Pittsburgh

Sims, Rita
rsims@postmedia.com, Adv. Mgr., The Kingsville Reporter, ON, Kingsville

Sin, Raymond
production@cityshopperonline.com, Art Dir., City Shopper, MA, Boston

Sin, Tenny
sales@umaxcare.com, Vice Pres., Mktg., UMAX Technologies, Inc., TX, Dallas

Sincell, Donald
newsroom@therepublicannews.com, Pub., The Republican, MD, OAKLAND

Sinclair, Norman
nsinclair@dailyitem.com, Audience Dir, The Daily Item, PA, Sunbury

Sinclair, Paula......................(416) 869-4046
psinclair@torstar.ca, CIO, Metroland & Star Media Group, Group IT, Torstar Corporation, Toronto Star, ON, Toronto

Sinclair, Sarah......................(805) 453-2646
sarah@independent.com, Santa Barbara Independent, CA, Santa Barbara

Sindelar, Amanda
editor@holtindependent.com, Editor, Holt County Independent, NE, O' Neill

Sindleri, Steve......................(814) 532-5180
sindleri@tribdem.com, Prodn. Dir., The Tribune-Democrat, PA, Johnstown

Singer, David
dsinger@pbcommercial.com, Circ. Dir., Jacksonville Patriot, AR, North Little Rock
dsinger@pbcommercial.com, Circ. Dir., Maumelle Monitor, AR, North Little Rock
dsinger@pbcommercial.com, Circ. Dir., Sherwood Voice, AR, North Little Rock
dsinger@pbcommercial.com, Circ. Dir., The North Little Rock Times, AR, North Little Rock
dsinger@pbcommercial.com, Circ. Dir., Hot Springs Village Voice, AR, Hot Springs Village

Singer, Duke......................(940) 691-2200
Duke.Singer@gmail.com, Pub, American Classifieds - Wichita Falls, TX, Wichita Falls

Singer, Larry......................(502) 418-5845
lsinger@jewishlouisville.org, Adv Sales, Jewish Louisville Community, KY, Louisville

Singer, Phyllis
PSinger@davlermedia.com, Ed. Dir., Westchester Parent, NY, Briarcliff Manor

Singh, Alexis......................(760) 337-3406
asingh@ivpms.com, Adv. Dir., Adelante Valle, CA, El Centro

Singletary, Grady
gsingletary@mailtribune.com, Pub./Gen. Mgr., Medford Nickel, OR, Medford

Singletary, James Grady
gsingletary@mailtribune.com, Pub., Mail Tribune, OR, Medford

Singletary, James Grady......................ext. 3035
gsingletary@mailtribune.com, Pub., The Ashland Daily Tidings, OR, Medford

Singleton, Belinda
ads@smithcountyreformer.net, Ed., Smith County Reformer, MS, Raleigh

Singleton, Dan
dsingleton@olds.greatwest.ca, Ed, Carstairs Courier, AB, Olds
dsingleton@olds.greatwest.ca, Ed, Mountain View Gazette, AB, Olds
dsingleton@olds.greatwest.ca, Ed, Sundre Round-up, AB, Sundre

Singleton, Dean......................(801) 204-6701
Pub., The Salt Lake Tribune, UT, Salt Lake City

Singleton, Kellie............ (256) 332-1881, ext.16
kellie.singleton@franklincountytimes.com, Ed., Franklin County Times, AL, Russellville

Singleton, Rena......................(270) 422-2155
messenger@bbtel.com, Pub., The Meade County Messenger, KY, Brandenburg

Singley, Shea
ssingley@berksmontnews.com, Ed., The Hamburg Area Item, PA, Pottstown

Sink, Steve
ssink@democratandchronicle.com, Bus. Ed., Democrat and Chronicle, NY, Rochester

Sinkclear, Jill......................(618) 208-6437
jsinkclear@civitasmedia.com, Circ. Dir, The

Telegraph, IL, Alton

Sinkie, Kim
ksinkie@mitchelladvisor.com, The Advisor Advantage, SD, Mitchell

Sinno, Abdul Karim
abdul.sinno@clarke.edu, Chair, Clarke College, IA, Dubuque

Sipchen, Bob
bob.sipchen@latimes.com, Sr. Ed., Los Angeles Times, CA, Los Angeles

Sipe, Michael......................(605) 432-1000
midpub@midlandpublishing.com, Co-Owner/ Pub., The Valley Shopper, SD, Milbank

Sipka, Andrea
asipka@mlive.com, Small Business Dir., The Jackson Citizen Patriot, MI, Jackson

Siraco, Paolo......................(613) 232-5689
info@loradiottawa.ca, Managing Editor, L'ora Di Ottawa, ON, Ottawa

Sirany, Adrienne......................(612) 673-4076
adrienne.sirany@startribune.com, Sr. VP, HR, Star Tribune, MN, Minneapolis

Sirera, Joe
jsirera@news-record.com, Assistant Sports Editor, News & Record, NC, Greensboro

Sirons, Eric......................(937) 325-7041
esirons@coxohio.com, Media Consultant, Tri-county Shoppers News, OH, Springfield

Sirota, Michael
msirdta@sdjewishtimes.com, Ed., San Diego Jewish Times, CA, La Mesa

Sisak, Rich
rsisak@yourjpurnal.com, Circ. Mgr., North Side Journal, MO, Chesterfield

Sisk, Amy......................(406) 243-4101
editor@montanakaimin.com, Editor, University of Montana, MT, Missoula

Sissing, Mike......................ext. 260
woodstockcirc@bowesnet.com, Circ. Mgr, Woodstock Sentinel-Review, ON, Woodstock

Sisson, Susan......................(512) 847-2202
ssisson@wimberleyview.com, Sales Rep, Wimberley View, TX, Wimberley

Sistak, Tom
toms@mywebtimes.com, Photo Ed., The Times, IL, Ottawa

Sistrunk, Bobbi......................(508) 591-6613
bsistrun@cnc.com, Reporter, Carver Reporter, MA, Plymouth

Sitler, Jon
jsitler@timesobserver.com, Sports Ed., Times Observer, PA, Warren

Siudut, Gene......................(813) 248-3921
gsiudut@lagacetanewspaper.com, Circ. Mgr., La Gaceta, FL, Tampa

Sivaganesh, Ashwini............ (412) 648-7985
editor@pittnews.com, Univ. of Pittsburgh, PA, Pittsburgh

Sivitz, Adam......................(909) 607-1647
Claremont McKenna College, CA, Claremont

Siwicki, Richard
rsiwicki@screenusa.com, Application Support Mgr., SCREEN (USA), IL, Rolling Meadows

Sizemore, Jamie
jsizemore@kystandard.com, Pub., Kentucky Standard, KY, Bardstown

Sizemore, Nola............(606) 573-4510 Ext. 1166
nsizemore@civitasmedia.com, Staff Writer, The Harlan Daily Enterprise, KY, Harlan

Sizer, Karen A.
artent@neb-sandhills.net, Ed., The Arthur Enterprise, NE, Arthur

Sjoberg, Sarah......................(562) 587-7339
chimes.advertising@biola.edu, Advertising Manager, Biola University, CA, La Mirada

Sjogren, Erika......................(847) 317-8155

Trinity International Univ., IL, Deerfield

Sjuberg, Gail......................ext. 210
news@driftwoodgimedia.com, Mng. Ed., Gulf Islands Driftwood, BC, Salt Spring Island

Skaftun, Emily
emily@na-weekly.com, Editor-in-chief, Norwegian American Weekly, WA, Seattle

Skaggs, Angie.............. (765) 342-3311 ext. 210
askaggs@reportert.com, Front Desk Coord., The Reporter Times, IN, Martinsville

Skaggs, Mary......................(941) 206-1005
mskaggs@sun-herald.com, Mgr., HR, Charlotte Sun, FL, Punta Gorda

Skaggs, Steve......................(352) 365-8213
steve.skaggs@dailycommercial.com , South Lake Press, FL, Leesburg

Skaggs, Steve.............. (336) 249-3981 ext 210
steve.skaggs@the-dispatch.com, Pub., The Dispatch, NC, Lexington

Skeel, Joe
jskeel@spj.org, Executive Director, Society of Professional Journalists, IN, Indianapolis

Skeens, Lisa
lrowan@cnpapers.com, Nat'l Adv. Mgr., The Charleston Gazette-Mail, WV, Charleston

Skelton, Matt
press@wayneindependent.com, Production Mgr., The Wayne Independent, PA, Honesdale

Skelton Johnson, Peggy.............. (205) 722-0199
peggy.skelton@tuscaloosanews.com, News Clerk, The Tuscaloosa News, AL, Tuscaloosa

Skenadore , Keith......................(920) 833-0420
keith.s@adcommnews.com, Ed, Advertiser Community News, WI, Seymour

Skerritt, Andrew
andrew.skerritt@famu.edu, Asst. Prof., Florida A&M University, FL, Tallahassee

Skewes, Carol......................(936) 336-3611
publisher@thevindicator.com, Pub., The Vindicator, TX, Liberty

Skifter, Marciel......................(507) 754-5486
Ed, Meadow Area Shopper, MN, Grand Meadow

Skiles, Russel......................(806) 872-2177
publisher@pressreporter.com, Pub., Lamesa Press Reporter, TX, Lamesa

Skiles, Shary......................(308) 345-4500
sskiles@ocsmccook.com, Pub., Big Nickel, NE, McCook

Skiles, Sharyn......................(308) 345-4500
sskiles@ocsmccook.com, Pub., McCook Daily Gazette, NE, Mc Cook

Skindrud, Erik......................(209) 966-2500
erik@mariposagazette.com, Editor, Mariposa Gazette, CA, Mariposa

Skinner, Andy
rmcgrew@cmgms.com, Ed., Oceana's Herald-Journal, MI, Hart

Skinner, Dennis......................(903) 794-0996
dskinner101@aol.com, Publisher, American Classifieds, TX, Texarkana

Skinner, Linda............(937) 878-3993 Ext. 2119
lskinner@civitasmedia.com, Cir. Bus. Mgr., Fairborn Daily Herald, OH, Xenia
lskinner@civitasmedia.com, Cir., Xenia Daily Gazette, OH, Xenia

Skinner, Mary Ann......................(631) 843-2335
Asst. Mng. Ed., Admin., Newsday, NY, Melville

Skinner, Shelia
sskinner101@aol.com, American Classifieds - Fort Collins / Greeley / Denver, CO, Fort Collins

Skinner, Winston......................(770) 683-1723
winston@newnan.com, News Ed., The Newnan Times-Herald, GA, Newnan

Skipper, Debbie......................(601) 961-7101

dskipper@jackson.gannett.com, Asst. Managing Ed., The Clarion-Ledger, MS, Jackson

Sklar, Robert...........................**ext. 236**
rsklar@thejewishnews.com, Ed., The Detroit Jewish News, MI, Southfield

Sklarsky, Frank
fsklarsky@tbk.org, Exec. Vice Pres./CFO, Eastman Kodak Co., NY, Rochester

Skoch, Tom .... **(440) 245-6901 ext. 536**
letters@morningjournal.com, Ed., The Morning Journal, OH, Lorain

Skolos, Shirley
sskolos@cowichanvalleycitizen.com, Pub./Adv. Mgr., Cowichan Valley Citizen, BC, Duncan
sskolos@cowichanvalleycitizen.com, Pub, The Cowichan News Leader, BC, Duncan

Skonie, Marissa
mskonie@st.kishwaukeecollege.edu, Ed. In Chief, Kishwaukee College, IL, Malta

Skoog, Herb
sales@decisionmark.com, Vice Pres., Opns., Decisionmark Corp., IA, Cedar Rapids

Skovgaard, Alex..........................**(402) 444-1233**
alex.skovgaard@midlandsnewspapers.com, President and COO, Midlands Newspapers, Inc., NE, Omaha

Skovgaard, Alex..........................**(402) 444-1233**
alex.skovgaard@owh.com, VICE PRESIDENT, BH MEDIA MIDWEST GROUP, BH Media Group, NE, Omaha
alex.skovgaard@owh.com, Pres./COO Midlands Newsp., Omaha World-Herald, NE, Omaha

Skrdlant, Tammy ....**(308) 233-9728**
Regl. Ed., Kearney Hub, NE, Kearney

Skrehart, Tammy
skrehart@imse.uta.edu, University of Texas at Arlington, TX, Arlington

Skrivan, Joseph M.
bmonitor@yahoo.com, Ed., The Bloomfield Monitor, NE, Bloomfield

Skryp, Ken ....**(716) 439-9222 Ext. 2293**
Circ. Mgr., Tonawanda News (OOB), NY, North Tonawanda
Cir., Lockport Union-Sun & Journal, NY, Lockport

Skufca, Sherry..........................**(260) 461-8201**
sskufca@jg.net, Ed., The Journal Gazette, IN, FORT WAYNE

Skwarczek, David
streams@streams.com, Pres., Dunn Solutions Group, IL, Skokie

Skyberg, Carol ....**(865) 220-5540**
carol.skyberg@oakridger.com, Major Acct., The Oak Ridger, TN, Oak Ridge

Slaboda, Gregg
gslaboda@trentonian.com, Photo Ed., The Trentonian, NJ, Trenton

Slack, Chris............................**(217) 268-4950**
slackpub@consolidated.net, Pub., Ed., Arcola Record-Herald, IL, Arcola

Slack, John D................**(407) 628-1755 ext. 111**
js@mediadesigngroup.com, CEO, Media Design Group, CA, Santa Monica

Slade, Patricia C..........................**ext. 106**
news@cricketpress.com, Ed., The Manchester Cricket, MA, Manchester

Slade, Scott............................**(317) 477-3229**
sslade@greenfieldreporter.com, Community Ed., Daily Reporter, IN, Greenfield

Slade, Scott............................**(317) 477-3229**
sslade@ptlpnews.com, Ed., Pendleton Times-Post, IN, Pendleton

Slade, Scott............................**(317) 477-3229**
sslade@greenfieldreporter.com, Community Ed., New Palestine Press, IN, Greenfield

Slagle, Kerry ....**(941) 323-6499**

kslagle@amuniversal.com, Pres., Universal Uclick International Divison, Kansas City
kslagle@amuniversal.com, Pres., United Media, MO, Kansas City

Slagle, Steve ....**(972) 258-3090**
steves@ppa.org, Pres./CEO, Promotional Products Association International, TX, Irving

Slaman, Christy ....**(731) 986-2253**
msfclassifieds@gmail.com, Art Director, Carroll County News-Leader, TN, Huntingdon

Slanchik, John
inquire@kepes.com, Mktg. Mgr., Kepes, Inc., WI, Kenosha

Slapak, Trevor
news@passherald.ca, Ed., Crowsnest Pass Herald, AB, Blairmore

Slater, Brad ....**(719) 544-3522**
bslater@chieftain.com, Gen. Mgr., The Pueblo Chieftain, CO, Pueblo

Slater, Emily ....**(805) 925-2691 ext. 2217**
eslater@timespressrecorder.com, Mng. Ed., Adobe Press, CA, Santa Maria

Slater, Glenda
glendaslater@embarqmail.com, Adv. Exec., Monticello News, FL, Monticello

Slater, Jan
slaterj@illinois.edu, Prof./Head, Adv., University of Illinois, IL, Urbana

Slater, John ....**(203) 752-2700**
jslater@journalregister.com, Pres., Main Street News, CT, New Haven
jslater@journalregister.com, Gen. Mgr., Westport Minuteman, CT, New Haven

Slater, John
jslater@journalregister.com, Gen. Mgr., Shore Line Newspapers, CT, New Haven

Slater, John ....**(203) 752-2700**
jslater@newhavenregister.com, Gen. Mgr., Shoreline Times, CT, New Haven

Slater, John ....**(203) 752-2700**
jslater@21st-centurymedia.com, Gen. Mgr., Fairfield Minuteman, CT, New Haven

Slater, John ....**(203) 752-2700**
jslater@newhavenregister.com, Multi Media Sales Mgr, The Dolphin, CT, Groton

Slater, Kevin
kslater@valleynewstoday.com, Ed., Weekly Times, IA, Shenandoah

Slater, Michael
slater.59@osu.edu, Prof., Ohio State University, OH, Columbus

Slater, Monja ....**(386) 362-1734 x105**
monja.slater@gaflnews.com, Advertising Director, Suwannee Democrat, FL, Live Oak

Slater, Nathan
nslater@journalnet.com, Circ. Dir, Portneuf Valley Trader, ID, Pocatello

Slater, Nathan ....**(208) 239-3143**
nslater@journalnet.com, Circ. Dir., Idaho State Journal, ID, Pocatello

Slater, Nick ....**(847) 491-3924**
Kellogg Grad. School of Mgmt., IL, Evanston

Slattery, Jack
jacks@americanultraviolet.com, Sales Rep., American Ultraviolet Co., Inc., IN, Lebanon

Slaughter, Jeanne ....**ext. 204**
business@chesapeakefamily.com, Mktg. Mgr., Chesapeake Family Life, MD, Annapolis

Slaughter, Tom
tslaughter@inlandpress.org, Exec. Dir., Inland Press Association, IL, Des Plaines

Slavin, David ....**(201) 230-0848**
Dslavin@mediamergers.com, Senior Associate-Mid-Atlantic/Southeast, Lewis Floyd- Grimes, W.B. & Co., AL, Gulf Shores
Dslavin@mediamergers.com, Southeast/South/Mid-Atlantic Assoc., Grimes, W.B. & Co., NJ, Sparta

Dslavin@mediamergers.com, Senior Associate- Southeast/South, Grimes, McGovern & Associates, NY, New York

Slavin, David ....**(201) 230-0848**
dslavin@mediamergers.com, Senior Associate, Grimes, W.B. & Co., NJ, Sparta

Slayden, David
david.slayden@colorado.edu, Assoc. Prof./Head, Adv. Seq., University of Colorado, CO, Boulder

Slaymaker, Joy
joyslaymaker@hendersondailynews.com, Prodn. Mgr., Henderson Daily News, TX, Henderson

Slayton, Jack
jacks@xtn.net, Sports Ed., The Daily Post-Athenian, TN, Athens

Slayton, Jeremy.......................**(804) 521-7584**
JeremyS@vpa.net, Communications Manager, Virginia Press Association, Inc., VA, Glen Allen

Slechta, Ronald C.
rcs@kalonanews.net, Pub., Reporter, IA, Lone Tree

Slegl, Cathy
ads@barnesville.com, Adv., Pike County Journal and Reporter, GA, Zebulon

Slep, Dan ....**(814) 946-7426**
dslep@altoonamirror.com, Circ. Dir., Altoona Mirror, PA, Altoona

Sleppy, Diana ....**(937) 569-4302**
dsleppy@dailyadvocate.com, Cust. Sales / Serv. Rep., Daily Advocate, OH, Greenville

Slette, Trevor
trevors@windomnews.com, Pub., Cottonwood County Citizen, MN, Windom
trevors@windomnews.com, Gen. Mgr., Mountain Lake/Butterfield Observer-Advocate, MN, Mountain Lake
trevors@windomnews.com, Pres., Minnesota Free Paper Association, MN, Little Falls
trevors@windomnews.com, Pub., Windom Shopper, MN, Windom

Slette, Trevor ....**(334) 393-2969**
trevors@windomnews.com, The Shopper, MN, Windom

Slight, Kari
editor@anchoragepress.com, Pub., Anchorage Press, AK, Anchorage

Sliment, Dan
dsliment@bnd.com, Belleville News-Democrat, IL, Belleville

Slinkard, Caleb.......................**(405) 366-3543**
editor@@normantranscript.com, Ed. , Rockwall County Herald Banner, TX, Greenville
editor@@normantranscript.com, Royse City Herald Banner, TX, Greenville
editor@@normantranscript.com, Ed., Norman Transcript, OK, Norman

Slivka, Mac
mac.slivka@rutlandherald.com, Exec. Asst., The Times Argus, VT, Barre

Sloan, Debbie ....**(269) 673-1720**
debra.sloan@flashespublishers.com, Mgr., Senior Times, MI, Allegan

Sloan, Debbie ....**(269) 673-1720**
debra.sloan@flashespublishers.com, Editorial, West Michigan Senior Times, MI, Holland

Sloan, Isabel ....**(419) 724-6220**
isloan@toledoblade.com, Exec. Asst., The Blade, OH, Toledo

Sloan, Robert
rsloan@hartsvillemessenger.com, Pub./Ed., The Hartsville Messenger, SC, Hartsville

Sloan, Stephan.......................**(401) 454-3130**
scs@scsloan.com, Assoc., Media Services Group, FL, Ponte Vedra

Sloca, John ....**(262) 656-6321**
jsloca@kenoshanews.com, Asst. Mng. Ed.,

Nights, Kenosha News, WI, Kenosha

Slocum, Lyla............................**(585) 237-2212**
Gen. Mgr., Perry Shopper, NY, Perry

Sloggatt, Peter
info@longislandernews.com, Mng. Ed., The Northport Journal, NY, Huntington

Sloggatt, Peter ....**P: (631) 427-7000 x 11**
info@longislandernews.com, Pub./Mng. Ed., The Record, NY, Huntington
info@longislandernews.com, Pub./Mng.Ed. , The Long-Islander News, NY, Huntington

Slone, Chris ....**(740) 353-3101 Ext. 1927**
cslone@civitasmedia.com, Ed., The Portsmouth Daily Times, OH, Portsmouth

Slone, Diana
dslone@register-herald.com, Adv. Mgr., Classified, The Register Herald, WV, Beckley

Slone, Marlyn ....**(918) 847-2916**
marlyn@bighearttimes.com, Adv., Bigheart Times, OK, Barnsdall

Slossar, William ....**(201) 894-6715**
slossar@northjresey.com, Ed., Twin-Boro News, NJ, Cresskill

Slotkin, Jason ....**(360) 867-6213**
The Evergreen State College, WA, Olympia

Sloup, Tammy ....**(815) 431-4048**
tammies@mywebtimes.com, Managing Editor, The Times, IL, Ottawa

Slovak-Barton, Cyndy
csb@haysfreepress.com, Pub., The News-Dispatch, TX, Driftwood
csb@haysfreepress.com, Pub., Hays Free Press, TX, Kyle

Sluggett, Rod............................**(250) 642-5752**
publisher@sookenewsmirror.com, publisher, The Sooke News Mirror, BC, Sooke

Slusher, Jim ....**(847) 427-4542**
jslusher@dailyherald.com, Deputy Managing Editor/Opinion Page, Daily Herald, IL, Arlington Heights

Slusher, Patty
pslusher@inlandpress.org, Dir. of Membership and Programming, Inland Press Association, IL, Des Plaines

Slusher, Rodger
subscribe@thevindicator.com, Circ. Mgr, The Vindicator, TX, Liberty

Sly, Alysia
classifieds@madisondailyleader.com, Classifieds, The Madison Daily Leader, SD, Madison

Sly, Judy ....**(209) 578-2317**
jsly@modbee.com, Editorial Page Ed., The Modesto Bee, CA, Modesto

Sly, Tom
tom.sly@scripps.com, Senior Director, Digital Revenue, E. W. Scripps Co., OH, Cincinnati

Slykhous, Simone
sslykhous@creators.com, Editor, Creators, Hermosa Beach

Smagala, Casey
csmagala@apcc-chgo.org, North Park Univ., IL, Chicago

Small, Len Robert ....**(815) 937-3399**
Editor & Publisher, The Daily Journal, IL, Kankakee

Small, Len Robert ....**(815) 937-3399**
Pres., Small Newspaper Group, IL, Kankakee

Small, Maynard ....**(816) 474-1400**
Maynard@creativemarketingKC.com, Pres., Creative Marketing Associates, Inc., MO, Kansas City

Smalley, John ....**(608) 252-6104**
jsmalley@madison.com, Ed., Wisconsin State Journal, Madison, WI, Madison

Smalley, Kevin
kevin@stepsaver.com, Prodn. Mgr., The

Observer, CT, Southington

Smalley, Kevin
sales@stepsaver.com, Prodn. Mgr., Step
Saver, CT, Southington

Smalley, Richard .... (403) 314-4373
rsmalley@reddeeradvocate.com, Adv. Mgr.,
Major Accts., Red Deer Advocate, AB, Red
Deer

Smallman, Dr. Christine .... (419) 724-6157
csmallman@toledoblade.com, Newspaper
In Education Coordinator, The Blade, OH,
Toledo

Smallman, Peter
psmallman@imagezone.com, Creative Dir.,
Image Zone, Inc., NY, New York

Smallwood, David
dsmallwood@ndigo.com, Editor, N'digo, IL,
Chicago

Smart, Jim .... (909) 537-7429
California State Univ., CA, San Bernardino

Smart, Paul
paul@gunkjournal.com, Mgn. Ed.,
Shawangunk Journal, NY, Ellenville

Smart, Robb .... (800) 408-4726 x 2
rsmart@nhonews.com, Adv. Exec., Navajo-
Hopi Observer, AZ, Flagstaff

Smart, Waylon
waylon.smart@thefacts.com, Info Servs./Online
Mgr., The Facts, TX, Clute

Smathers, Dianna .... (318) 747-7900
dianna@snimedia.com, Sales Manager,
Bossier Press-Tribune, LA, Bossier City

Smelle, Nate
editor@thevoiceofpelham.co, Ed., Fonthill
Voice Of Pelham, ON, Fonthill

Smelser, Amy .... (765) 677-1818
amy.smelser@indwes.edu, Instructor, Indiana
Wesleyan University, IN, Marion

Smelser, Amy .... (765) 677-1818
amy.smelser@indwes.edu, Ed., Indiana
Wesleyan University, IN, Marion

Smeraglia, Traci
alamsgr@bellsouth.net, Mng. Ed., Alabama
Messenger, AL, Birmingham

Smidt, Mark .... (319) 372-6421
ddsmidt@dailydem.com, Publisher, Democrat
Co., IA, Fort Madison

Smigelski, David
smig@mvtvwireless.com, Pub., Tri County
News, MN, Cottonwood

Smiglewski, David
smig@mvtvwireless.com, Pub., Granite Falls-
Clarkfield Advocate-Tribune, MN, Granite
Falls

Smigrod, Dan .... (404) 303-7311
dan@greattv.com, CEO/Chief Creative Officer,
GREAT!, GA, Brookhaven

Smilie, Jim .... (318) 487-6348
jsmilie@thetowntalk.com, Engagement &
Community Content Editor, The Town Talk,
LA, Alexandria

Smillie, Joe .... (360) 374-3311
advertising@forksforum.com, Pub./Ed./Circ.
Mgr., Forks Forum, WA, Forks

Smilovitz, Jacob .... (734) 647-3336
Univ. of Michigan, MI, Ann Arbor

Smith, Adam
adam@athensnews-courier.com, Manag.
Editor, The News-Courier, AL, Athens

Smith, Al
al.smith@travelport.com, Vice Pres., Circ., Cox
Media Group, GA, Atlanta

Smith, Amy
asmith@atlantaparent.com, Bus. Devel. Mgr.,
Atlanta Parent, GA, Atlanta

Smith, Amy .... (540) 213-9173

asmith@newsleader.com, Adv. Servs. Mgr.,
The News Leader, VA, Staunton

Smith, Angela
asmith@newspapermediagroup.com, Mktg.
Dir., The Berlin Sun, NJ, Haddonfield
asmith@newspapermediagroup.com,
Mktg. Dir., Burlington Township Sun, NJ,
Haddonfield
asmith@newspapermediagroup.com, Mktg.
Dir., Cherry Hill Sun, NJ, Haddonfield
asmith@newspapermediagroup.com, Mktg.
Dir., Cinnaminson Sun, NJ, Haddonfield
asmith@newspapermediagroup.com, Mktg.
Dir., Medford Sun, NJ, Haddonfield
asmith@newspapermediagroup.com, Mktg.
Dir., Moorestown Sun, NJ, Haddonfield
asmith@newspapermediagroup.com, Mktg.
Dir., Mt. Laurel Sun, NJ, Haddonfield
asmith@newspapermediagroup.com, Mktg.
Dir., Palmyra Sun, NJ, Haddonfield
asmith@newspapermediagroup.com, Mktg.
Dir., Shamong Sun, NJ, Haddonfield
asmith@newspapermediagroup.com, Mktg.
Dir., Haddonfield Sun, NJ, Haddonfield
asmith@newspapermediagroup.com, Mktg.
Dir., Sicklerville Sun, NJ, Haddonfield
asmith@newspapermediagroup.com, Mktg.
Dir., Tabernacle Sun, NJ, Haddonfield
asmith@newspapermediagroup.com, Mktg.
Dir., Voorhees Sun, NJ, Haddonfield
asmith@newspapermediagroup.com, Mktg.
Dir., Marlton Sun, NJ, Haddonfield

Smith, Anne .... (317) 477-3226
asmith@greenfieldreporter.com, Copy Ed.,
Daily Reporter, IN, Greenfield

Smith, Anthony .... (309) 686-3258
asmith@pjstar.com, City Ed., Night, Journal
Star, IL, Peoria

Smith, Art .... (740) 373-2121 Ext. 281
asmith@mariettatimes.com, Online Mgr., The
Marietta Times, OH, Marietta

Smith, Barbara
bsmith@breezenewspapers.com, Circ. Mgr,
The Pine Island Eagle, FL, Bokeelia
bsmith@breezenewspapers.com, Circ. Mgr,
North Fort Myers Neighbor, FL, Cape Coral
bsmith@breezenewspapers.com, Circ. Mgr,
Sanibel-Captiva Islander, FL, Cape Coral
bsmith@breezenewspapers.com, Circ. Mgr,
Fort Myers Beach Observer, FL, Fort Myers
Beach

Smith, Barbara
basmith@messenger-inquirer.com, Adv. Mgr.,
Servs., Messenger-Inquirer, KY, Owensboro

Smith, Barry .... (775) 885-0866
barry@nevadapress.com, Exec. Dir., Nevada
Press Association, Inc., NV, Carson City

Smith, Bart
bsmith@greeleytribune.com, Pub., Greeley
Daily Tribune, CO, Greeley
bsmith@greeleytribune.com, Pub., Windsor
Now, CO, Windsor

Smith, Becky .... (937) 552-2291
bsmith@civitasmedia.com, Adv. Mgr., Piqua
Daily Call, OH, Piqua

Smith, Becky .... (937) 552-2131
bsmith@civitasmedia.com, Adv. Dir., Troy Daily
News, OH, Troy

Smith, Beth .... (209) 826-3831 ext. 552
bsmith@losbanosenterprise.com, Admin./
Sales Asst., Los Banos Enterprise, CA, Los
Banos

Smith, Betty .... (503) 325-3211 Ext. 238
bsmith@dailyastorian.com, Adv. Mgr., Seaside
Signal, OR, Seaside
bsmith@dailyastorian.com, Adv. Mgr., The
Daily Astorian, OR, Astoria

Smith, Brad
brsmith@21st-centurymedia.com, Adv. Mgr.,
Main Line Times, PA, Ardmore
brsmith@21st-centurymedia.com, Adv. Mgr.,
Main Line Suburban Life, PA, Ardmore
brsmith@21st-centurymedia.com, Adv. Mgr.,
King of Prussia Courier, PA, Wayne

Smith, Bredan .... (603) 366-8463 ext.316
Ed. , The Cocheco Times, NH, Laconia

Smith, Brendan
brendan@weirs.com, Ed., The Weirs Times,
NH, Laconia

Smith, Brian .... (907) 335-1240
brian.smith@peninsulaclarion.com, City Ed.
Reporter, Peninsula Clarion, AK, Kenai

Smith, Bruce K. .... (435) 752-2121
bsmith@hjnews.com, Pub., Quality Buys, UT,
Logan

Smith, Bryan .... (717) 436-8206
brysmith@juniata-sentinel.com, Circ. Mgr.,
Juniata Sentinel, PA, Mifflintown

Smith, Carol
ahill@americanpublicmedia.org, Adv. Mgr.,
Market Place, IN, South Bend

Smith, Carol .... (717) 436-8206
csmith@juniata-sentinel.com, Ed., Juniata
Sentinel, PA, Mifflintown

Smith, Carolyn .... (219) 326-3817
csmith@heraldargus.com, Acct. Exec., Herald-
Argus, IN, La Porte

Smith, Carolyn .... (618) 239-2503
csmith@bnd.com, Newsroom, Belleville News-
Democrat, IL, Belleville

Smith, Casey
jdnads@bellsouth.net, Prod. Mgr., Jennings
(LA) Daily News, LA, Jennings

Smith, Catherine .... (806) 659-3434
reporterstatesman@gmail.com, Pub./Ed./
Adv. Dir., The Hansford County Reporter-
Statesman, TX, Spearman

Smith, Charlene .... (617) 218-8211
charlene.smith@lawyersweekly.com, Ad. Dir,
Massachusetts Lawyers Weekly, MA, Boston
charlene.smith@lawyersweekly.com, Ad.
Director, Rhode Island Lawyers Weekly, MA,
Boston

Smith, Charlie .... (604) 730-7043
charlie@straight.com, Editor, Georgia Straight,
BC, Vancouver

Smith, Charlie .... (662) 887-2222
csmith@enterprise-tocsin.com, Editor/
Publisher, The Enterprise-Tocsin, MS,
Indianola

Smith, Charlotte
ads@bladenjournal.com, Adv. Sales Rep.,
Bladen Journal, NC, Elizabethtown
ads@bladenjournal.com, Features Reporter,
The Charleston Gazette-Mail, WV,
Charleston

Smith, Charlotte
composing@kilgorenewsherald.com, Prod.
Mgr., Kilgore News Herald, TX, Kilgore

Smith, Cheryl
penonfire@aol.com, Pub./Gen. Mgr., Garland
Journal News, TX, Dallas
penonfire@aol.com, Pub./Gen. Mgr., Texas
Metro News, TX, Dallas

Smith, Christina .... (770) 287-3798
commfeat@charter.net, Co-Owner, Community
Features, Gainesville

Smith, Christine .... (307) 455-2525
duboisfrontier@wyoming.com, Mng. Ed.,
Dubois Frontier, WY, Dubois
duboisfrontier@wyoming.com, Eastern
Connecticut State Univ., CT, Willimantic

Smith, Christine
smith@batavianews.com, Circ. Mgr., Drummer
Pennysaver, NY, Batavia

Smith, Christy .... (260) 225-4949
csmith@wabashplaindealer.com, Customer
Service Rep/Legals Clerk, Wabash Plain
Dealer, IN, Wabash

Smith, Cindy
tvads@timesvirginian.com, Adv. Mgr., Times-
Virginian, VA, Appomattox

Smith, Clark
clark@menastar.com, Pub./Ed., DeQueen Bee,
AR, De Queen

Smith, Clark
clark@menastar.com, Pub., The Mena Star,
AR, Mena

Smith, Clark
publisher@helena-arkansas.com, Pub., The
Helena Arkansas Daily World, AR, HELENA

Smith, Claudia .... (212) 969-7542
cmsmith@hearst.com, Dir., PR, King Features
Syndicate, NY, New York
cmsmith@hearst.com, PR Dir., North America
Syndicate, New York

Smith, Clifton S.
publisher@bhcourier.com, Pub., Beverly Hills
Courier, CA, Beverly Hills

Smith, Colleen .... (519) 284-2440
csmith@stmarys.com, Advertising/Circulation,
St. Mary's Journal Argus, ON, St Marys

Smith, Cory .... ext. 252
Sports Ed., Woodstock Sentinel-Review, ON,
Woodstock

Smith, Cory
cosmith@postmedia.com, Sports Editor, The
Stratford Beacon Herald, ON, Stratford

Smith, Craig A.
braxton@mountain.net, Pub., Braxton
Democrat-Central, WV, Sutton

Smith, Dan
dan@bradley.edu, Dir., Forensics, Bradley
University, IL, Peoria

Smith, Dan
danamclass@gmail.com, Circ. Mgr., American
Classifieds - Alexandria, LA, Alexandria

Smith, Dan .... (925) 302-1628
dan@royal-coach.com, Circ. Dir., Almaden
Resident, CA, San Jose

Smith, Dana
subscriptions@boernestar.com, Boerne Star,
TX, Boerne

Smith, Danielle
nationalads@semissourian.com, National
Account Coord., Southeast Missourian, MO,
Cape Girardeau

Smith, Darlene .... (440) 245-6901 Ext. 46944
darlenesmith@morningjournal.com, Sales
Mgr., The Morning Journal, OH, Lorain

Smith, Darrell .... (765) 825-0588 ext. 227
dsmith@newsexaminer.com, Reporter,
Connersville News-Examiner, IN,
Connersville

Smith, Dave
dsmith@pgcitizen.ca, Adv. Mgr., The Prince
George Citizen, BC, Prince George

Smith, David .... (508) 591-6610
dsmith@wickedlocal.com, Ed., Duxbury
Reporter, MA, Marshfield

Smith, David
dsmith@corsicanadailysun.com, Circ. Mgr.,
Star Shopper, TX, Corsicana

Smith, David
dsmith@corsicanadailysun.com, Circ. Mgr.,
Corsicana Daily Sun, TX, Corsicana

Smith, David
dsmith@thewesterlysun.com, Ed., Wood River
Press, RI, Westerly
dsmith@thewesterlysun.com, Ed., Charlestown
Press, RI, Westerly

Smith, Dean
dsmith@newsadvance.com, Gen. Mgr., Nelson
County Times, VA, Amherst
dsmith@newsadvance.com, Gen. Mgr.,
Amherst New Era-Progress, VA, Amherst
dsmith@newsadvance.com, Digital Sales, The
News & Advance, VA, Lynchburg

Smith, Debbie .... (716) 645-2152
SUNY/Buffalo, NY, Buffalo

Smith, Deirdre Parker.................(704) 792-4252
dp1@salisburypost.com, Books Ed., Salisbury
Post, NC, Salisbury

Smith, Deneen ....(262) 656-6287
dsmith@kenoshanews.com, Bus. Writer,
Kenosha News, WI, Kenosha

Smith, Denise
office@ominecaexpress.com, Office/Sales/
Circ, Vanderhoof Omineca Express, BC,
Vanderhoof

Smith, Dennis ....(606) 451-4926
Circ. Asst., The Commonwealth-Journal, KY,
Somerset

Smith, Diana ....(407) 894-7300 Ext. 223
dlsmith@hearstsc.com, Executive Editor, North
America Syndicate, New York

Smith, Diana ....(407) 894-7300, Ext. 224
dlsmith@hearstsc.com, Executive Editor, King
Features Syndicate, NY, New York

Smith, Dolores ....(573) 547-4567
Office Mgr., The Perry County Republic-
Monitor, MO, Perryville

Smith, Don.................(304) 342-1011, ext. 160
donsmith@wvpress.org, Exec. Dir., West
Virginia Press Association, Inc., WV,
Charleston

Smith, Dona H.........................(337) 824-3011
jdnpublisher@bellsouth.net, Pub., Jennings
(LA) Daily News, LA, Jennings

Smith, Dona H.........................(337) 824-3011
publisher@jenningsdailynews.net, Vice
President - Operations, Fackelman
Newspapers, LA, Jennings

Smith, Donald S.......................(308) 381-9410
donald.smith@theindependent.com, Pub./
Pres., The Grand Island Independent, NE,
Grand Island

Smith, Doug ....(573) 518-3615
dsmith@dailyjournalonline.com, Ed.,
Farmington Press, MO, Park Hills
dsmith@dailyjournalonline.com, Managing Ed.,
Daily Journal, Park Hills, MO, Park Hills

Smith, Doug
dssmithSDT@gmail.com, Graphic Artist/
Composing, The Sullivan Daily Times, IN,
Sullivan

Smith, Dylan
dylansmith@tucsonsentinel.com, Pub./Ed.,
TucsonSentinel.com, AZ, Tucson

Smith, Earl
esmith@thisweeknews.com, Dir., Sales,
Consumer News Service Inc., OH, Lewis
Center

Smith, Edward N. ....(260) 745-0552
frostads@aol.com, Pub., Frost Illustrated, IN,
Fort Wayne

Smith, Elizabeth
elizabeth.smith@pepperdine.edu, Pepperdine
Univ., CA, Malibu

Smith, Emily ....(580) 634-2159
esmith@civitasmedia.com, Adv., Durant Daily
Democrat, OK, Durant

Smith, Emily
esmith@nypost.com, Ed. Dept./Page Six, New
York Post, NY, New York

Smith, Emma
emma.smith@lighthousenow.ca, The Bulletin,
NS, Bridgewater
emma.smith@lighthousenow.ca, Lighthouse
Now, NS, Bridgewater

Smith, Esther
esmith@hoodrivernews.com, Circ. Mgr., Hood
River News, OR, Hood River

Smith, Evelyn...............(407) 894-7300 Ext. 234
evelynsmith@hearstsc.com, Senior Comics
Editor, King Features Syndicate, NY, New
York

Smith, Evelyn...............(407) 894-7300 Ext. 234

evelynsmith@hearstsc.com, Senior Comics
Editor`, North America Syndicate, New York

Smith, Fran
fsmith@repub.com, Adv. Sales Mgr., The
Republican, MA, Springfield

Smith, Frazier
jsmith3@udayton.edu, Advisor, Univ. of Dayton,
OH, Dayton

Smith, Gail M..........................(212) 807-0400
gsmith@impactony.com, Pub., Impacto Latin
News, NY, New York

Smith, Gary
gsmith@spearmanreporter.com, Pub., The
Hansford County Reporter-Statesman, TX,
Spearman

Smith, Gary ....(919) 836-5680
gsmith@newsobserver.com, VP, Classified
Advertising, The News & Observer, NC,
Raleigh

Smith, George
gsmith731@aol.com, Columnist, The Anniston
Star, AL, Anniston

Smith, Gillian
gillian@duxburyclipper.com, Ed., Duxbury
Clipper, MA, Duxbury

Smith, Glenda
glenda@athensnews-courier.com, Ad
Production, The News-Courier, AL, Athens

Smith, Greg
gsmith@iowacity.gannett.com, City Ed., Iowa
City Press-Citizen, IA, Iowa City

Smith, Greg
gsmith@admediapartners.com, Managing Dir.,
AdMedia Partners, Inc., NY, New York

Smith, J W
tcma@texascma.org, Secretary/Treasurer,
Texas Circulation Management Association,
TX, The Woodlands

Smith, Jaci ....(507) 333-3134
jsmith@faribault.com, Mng. Ed., Faribault Daily
News, MN, Faribault

Smith, Jaci ....(507) 645-1116
jsmith@northfieldnews.com, Mng. Ed., Kenyon
Leader, MN, Kenyon

Smith, Jackie ....(309) 833-2114 ext. 253
jsmith@mcdonoughvoice.com, Ed., The
McDonough County Voice, IL, Macomb

Smith, Jacky
production@crestonvalleyadvance.ca, Prod.
Department, Creston Valley Advance, BC,
Creston

Smith, Jacqueline ....(203) 731-3369
jsmith@newstimes.com, Managing Ed., The
News-Times, CT, Danbury

Smith, James.......................................ext. 282
Exec. Ed., Parkersburg News & Sentinel, WV,
Parkersburg

Smith, James
james.smith@sanantonio.gov, CRO - Digital,
San Antonio Express-News, TX, San Antonio

Smith, Jamie
jsmith@bcfm.com, Director of Operations,
Media Financial Management Association,
IL, Northfield

Smith, Jancey
janc@pdclarion.com, Creative Dept. Mgr.,
Princeton Daily Clarion, IN, Princeton

Smith, Jane...........................(503) 243-2122
Jsmith@wweek.com, Associate Publisher,
Willamette Week, OR, Portland

Smith, Jane ....(317) 77-3222
jsmith@greenfieldreporter.com, Ed. Asst., Daily
Reporter, IN, Greenfield

Smith, Janet...............(843) 706-8114 ext. 8114
jsmith@islandpacket.com, Editorial Page Ed.,
The Island Packet, SC, Bluffton

Smith, Janice..........................(815) 244-2411

jlsmith1@grics.net, Graphic Designer, Carroll
County Mirror-Democrat, IL, Mount Carroll

Smith, Jayna 454-3561
jsmith@thecalaisadvertiser.com, Advertising,
The Calais Advertiser, ME, Calais

Smith, Jean
editor@siskiyoudaily.com, Circ. Mgr., Siskiyou
Daily News, CA, Yreka

Smith, Jeff ....(818) 240-1000
jsmith@glendale.edu, Glendale Cmty. College,
CA, Glendale

Smith, Jeff
info@beltingindustries.com, Sales Mgr., Belting
Industries Co., Inc., NJ, Kenilworth

Smith, Jeff
jjsmith@cnhi.com, Production Mgr., The New
Berlin Gazette, NY, Norwich
jjsmith@cnhi.com, Pub., The Weatherford
Democrat, TX, Weatherford

Smith, Jeffery ....(414) 229-4436
jsmith@uwm.edu, Professor, University of
Wisconsin-Milwaukee / Department of
Journalism, Advertising, and Media Studies
(JAMS), WI, Milwaukee

Smith, Jennifer
jsmith@shoshonenewspress.com, Marketing
Consultant, Shoshone News-Press, ID,
Osburn

Smith, Jerry ....(507) 837-5446
jsmith@wasecacountynews.com, Mng. Ed.,
Lonsdale Area News-Review, MN, Lonsdale

Smith, Jill ....(503) 357-3181
jsmith@fgnewstimes.com, Editor, Forest Grove
News-Times, OR, Forest Grove

Smith, Jill ....(503) 357-3181
jrsmith@fgnewstimes.com, Assoc. Ed., Forest
Grove News-Times, OR, Forest Grove

Smith, Jim ....1-(800) 321-0350 EXT. 104
jsmith@scity.com, National Sales Mgr., Steel
City Corp., OH, Ashland

Smith, Jim ....(530) 406-6230
news@dailydemocrat.com, Ed., The Daily
Democrat, CA, Woodland

Smith, John ....(301) 784-2517
jsmith@times-news.com, Managing Editor, The
Garrett County Weekender, MD, Cumberland

Smith, John ....(301) 784-2517
jsmith@times-news.com, Managing Editor, The
Cumberland Times-News, MD, Cumberland

Smith, John B. .... ext. 13
jbsjr@atlinq.com, Ed., The Atlanta Inquirer,
GA, Atlanta

Smith, John L..........................(773) 752-2500
achicagocrusader@aol.com, Adv. Dir., Chicago
Crusader, IL, Chicago

Smith, Jon
smith_jo@suu.edu, Chair, Southern Utah
University, UT, Cedar City

Smith, Judi .... ext. 184
judismith@thealmanac.net, Circ. Mgr., The
Almanac, PA, Pittsburgh

Smith, Judy ....(317) 472-5221
judy.smith@ibj.com, Adv. Mgr., Court &
Commercial Record, IN, Indianapolis

Smith, Justin ....(208) 239-3150
jtsmith@journalnet.com, Dir., Info Tech Servs.,
Idaho State Journal, ID, Pocatello

Smith, Justin ....(208) 239-3150
jtsmith@journalnet.com, Dir., IT Services,
Portneuf Valley Trader, ID, Pocatello

Smith, Karlie ....(434) 292-3019
karlie@courier-record.com, Assistant Office
Manager, Courier-Record, VA, Blackstone

Smith, Kathy ....(325) 597-2959
ksmith@bradystandard.com , Office Mgr.,
Brady Standard-Herald, TX, Brady

Smith, Katie ....(250) 423-4666

editor@thefreepress.ca, Ed, The Free Press,
BC, Fernie

Smith, Kayanna ....(574) 722-5000 Ext. 5109
kayanna.smith@pharostribune.com ,
Customer Service Rep., Pharos-Tribune, IN,
Logansport

Smith, Ken ....(864) 562-7401
ken.smith@shj.com, Dir. of Cir., Herald-Journal,
SC, Spartanburg

Smith, Ken
klsmith@uwyo.edu, Chair, University of
Wyoming, WY, Laramie

Smith, Ken
ken_smith@cable.comcast.com, Philadelphia
Media Network Inc., PA, Philadelphia

Smith, Kenneth J.....................(814) 643-4040
ksmith@huntingdondailynews.com, Purchasing
Agent, The Huntingdon Daily News, PA,
Huntingdon

Smith, Kenneth P......................(800) 533-4579
kensmith@issisvs.com, Pres., Insurance
Specialties Services, Inc., PA, New Britain

Smith, Kevin
ksmith@salemnews.net, Cir. Mgr., Salem
News, OH, Salem
ksmith@salemnews.net, Adv. Dir., West Central
Tribune, MN, Willmar

Smith, Kevin...............(626) 962-8811 ext. 2701
kevin.smith@sgvn.com, Bus. Ed., The Whittier
Daily News, CA, Monrovia

Smith, Kevin
kevin@auburnembroidery.com, Asst. Prof.,
Auburn University, AL, Auburn

Smith, Kevin ....(434) 385-5462
ksmith@newsadvance.com, Regional Ad
Director , The News & Advance, VA,
Lynchburg

Smith, Kim ....(254) 729-5103
kimberly@groesbeckjournal.com, General
Manager, Groesbeck Journal, TX, Groesbeck

Smith, Kimberlee ....(406) 566-2471
Adv., Judith Basin Press, MT, Lewistown

Smith, Kris.....................................ext. 238
ksmith@rrdailyherald.com, News Ed., The
Revue, NC, Roanoke Rapids

Smith, Kris...........................(815) 987-1462
kasmith@rockford.gannett.com, Prodn. Dir.,
The Star Shopper, IL, Rockford

Smith, Kris
ksmith@rrdailyherald.com, News Ed., Daily
Herald, NC, Roanoke Rapids

Smith, Kristine
idahoenterprise@atcnet.net, Ed./Pub., Idaho
Enterprise, ID, Malad City

Smith, Lana............................(859) 355-1200
lsmith@winchestersun.com, Member Services
Rep./Adv. Rep., The Winchester Sun, KY,
Winchester

Smith, Larry ....(217) 477-5183
lsmith@dancomnews.com, Ed., Commercial
News, IL, Danville

Smith, Laura
lsmith@southsidefellowship.org, Mng. Ed.,
Delta Democrat Times, MS, Greenville

Smith, Leighton
leightonsmith@uvp.com, Pres., UVP, LLC, CA,
Upland

Smith, Les
lessmith@heralddispatch.com, Mng. Ed., The
Herald-Dispatch, WV, Huntington

Smith, Lewis
lasmith@pvamu.edu, Prairie View A&M Univ.,
TX, Prairie View

Smith, Linda.....................................ext. 245
lindasmith@rrdailyherald.com, Bus. Mgr., The
Revue, NC, Roanoke Rapids

Smith, Linda

lindas@rich.com, Prodn. Mgr., The Buffalo Press, TX, Buffalo

Smith, Linda .... (252) 537-2505 ext. 245
lindasmith@rrdailyherald.com, Office Mgr., Daily Herald, NC, Roanoke Rapids

Smith, Lindell
ccrnews@wabash.net, Ed., Clay County Republican, IL, Louisville

Smith, Lisa
lisa@app-printing.com, Adv. Mgr., Albion New Era, IN, Albion

Smith, Lori
ls61@evansville.edu, Instr., University of Evansville, IN, Evansville

Smith, Lori
lfsmith@mdanderson.org, Adv Mgr, The Shopper Plus, MS, Houston

Smith, Lynn .... (812) 231-4325
lynn.smith@tribstar.com, Adv. Sales Exec., The Tribune Star, IN, Terre Haute

Smith, Lynn A.
circulation@towntopics.com, Ed., Town Topics, NJ, Kingston

Smith, Maddy .... (716) 491-5285
mesmith108@gmail.com, Advisor, SUNY College at Geneseo, NY, Geneseo

Smith, Madonna
madonna@pdclarion.com, Graphic Designer, Princeton Daily Clarion, IN, Princeton

Smith, Maggie
msmith@brightstarschools.org, News America FSI, CT, Wilton
msmith@brightstarschools.org, News America FSI, GA, Atlanta
msmith@brightstarschools.org, News America FSI, CA, Los Angeles
msmith@brightstarschools.org, News America FSI, TX, Dallas
msmith@brightstarschools.org, Office Mgr., News America FSI, NY, New York
msmith@brightstarschools.org, News America FSI, MN, Minneapolis
msmith@brightstarschools.org, Office Mgr., News America FSI, IL, Chicago

Smith, Marcus .... (618) 262-5144
msmith@mtcarmelregister.com, News Editor, Mount Carmel Register, IL, Mount Carmel

Smith, Marg
production@stpaul.greatwest.ca, Prod., Elk Point Review, AB, Elk Point

Smith, Marianne
jilld@thetruecitizen.com Marianne Smith Classifieds & Legals tclegals@gmail.com, Class. & Legals, The True Citizen, GA, Waynesboro

Smith, Marie .... (910) 323-0349
marie@newspaperconsultants.com, Exec. Dir. of Sales, Advantage Newspaper Consultants, NC, Fayetteville

Smith, Mark .... (505) 823-3935
msmith@abqjournal.com, Journal Asst. Sports Ed., Albuquerque Journal, NM, Albuquerque

Smith, Mark .... (905) 358-5711 ext. 1181
mark.smith@sunmedia.ca, Adv. Mgr., Niagara Falls Review, ON, Niagara Falls

Smith, Mark
davenporttimes@centurytel.net, Ed., Davenport Times, WA, Davenport

Smith, Mark M. ... (830) 980-2860/(603) 444-7141/ (802) 748-8121
smithm@caledonian-record.com, Pres., The Caledonian-Record, VT, Saint Johnsbury

Smith, Marlene .... (864) 562-7471
marlene.smith@shj.com, Dir .of HR, Herald-Journal, SC, Spartanburg

Smith, Marsha .... (760) 379-3667 x 15
marshas@kvsun.com, Pub., Kern Valley Sun, CA, Lake Isabella

Smith, Martha

msmith@tribweb.com, Exec. Asst. to Pres., Tribune-Review, PA, Greensburg

Smith, Mary Beth
news@thewinthropnews.com, Ed., Winthrop News, IA, Winthrop

Smith, Matt
MattSmith@gannett.com, Mng. Ed., City Pages, MN, Minneapolis
MattSmith@gannett.com, Copy Desk Chief, The Livingston County Daily Press & Argus, MI, Howell

Smith, Meg
smithm@cowley.edu, Cowley County Cmty. College, KS, Arkansas City

Smith, Megan .... (928) 445-3333
Advertising, The Daily Courier, AZ, Prescott

Smith, Melissa .... (317) 398-1261
msmith@shelbynews.com, Adv. Acct. Exec., The Shelbyville News, IN, Shelbyville

Smith, Michael .... (843) 488-7259
michael.smith@myhorrynews.com, Ed., Carolina Forest Chronicle, SC, Myrtle Beach

Smith, Michael
moreinfo@talx.com, Vice Pres., Market Devel., TALX Corp., MO, Saint Louis

Smith, Michael
michael.smith@galvnews.com, Lifestyle Ed., The Galveston County Daily News, TX, Galveston

Smith, Michael A. .... (409) 683-5206
michael.smith@galvnews.com, Assoc. Ed., The Galveston County Daily News, TX, Galveston

Smith, Michael J. .... (865) 908-4368
mjsmith@xtn.net, Vice Pres., Tourism, APG Media of Tennessee/North Carolina, TN, Greeneville

Smith, Michael R.
smithm@campbell.edu, Chair, Campbell University, NC, Buies Creek

Smith, Michele ....(319) 273-2157. (319) 240-3725 cell
Michele.smith@uni.edu, Univ. of Northern Iowa, IA, Cedar Falls

Smith, Mike
msmith@hermitagelighting.com, Pub., Nashville Scene, TN, Nashville

Smith, Mike
advertising@guardonline.com, Gen. Mgr., Delta News Citizen, MO, Kennett

Smith, Mike .... (864) 562-7200
michael.smith@shj.com, Exec. Ed., Herald-Journal, SC, Spartanburg

Smith, Mike .... ext. 43
msmith@stategazette.com, Mng. Ed., State Gazette, TN, Dyersburg

Smith, Nicole .... (507) 389-5454
nicole.smith-2@mnsu.edu, Minnesota State Univ. Mankato, MN, Mankato

Smith, Pam
psmith@wmed.org, Pub., The Nashville News, IL, Nashville

Smith, Patrick J. .... ext. 15
Pub., Ballston Journal, NY, Ballston Spa

Smith, Patrick J.
psmith@crwnewspapers.com, Pub., The Pennysaver, NY, Round Lake
psmith@crwnewspapers.com, Capital Region Weekly Newspaper Group, NY, Clifton Park

Smith, Paul
psmith@timesuniononline.com, Advertising Manager, Times-Union, IN, Warsaw

Smith, Paula
psmith@ucadvocate.com, Ed, Union County Advocate, KY, Morganfield

Smith, Penny
psmith@hpu.edu, Asst. Prof., Hawaii Pacific University, HI, Honolulu

Smith, Peter .... (502) 582-4469
psmith@courier-journal.com, Religion Writer, The Courier-Journal, KY, Louisville

Smith, Polly
abennett@suntimes.com, Bus. Ed., Chicago Sun-Times, IL, Chicago

Smith, R. Scudder
scudder@thebee.com, Pub & Ed, Antiques & The Arts Weekly, CT, Newtown
scudder@thebee.com, Publisher, The Newtown Bee, CT, Newtown

Smith, Rachael
rachael.smith@news-jrnl.com, New York Univ., NY, New York
rachael.smith@news-jrnl.com, Ed., Daytona Beach News-Journal, FL, Daytona Beach

Smith, Randi
rsmith@osceolasun.com, Pub., Messenger, MN, Scandia

Smith, Rebecca .... (814) 623-1151
rsmith@bedfordgazette.com, Bus. Mgr., Bedford Gazette, PA, Bedford
rsmith@bedfordgazette.com, Bus. Mgr. , The Bedford Gazette, PA, Bedford

Smith, Renee .... (916) 288-6017
renee@cnpa.com, Director of Meetings, California News Publishers Association, CA, Sacramento

Smith, Renee ....(606) 528-7898 Ext. 14
rsmith@thetimestribune.com, Circ. Clerk, Times-Tribune, KY, Corbin

Smith, Rex .... (518) 454-5040
rsmith@timesunion.com, Ed., Times Union, NY, Albany

Smith, Rhonda .... (812) 883-3281
rhonda@salemleader.com, Gen. Mgr., The Salem Democrat, IN, Salem

Smith, Rick
rsnama@wi.rr.com, Owner, Nama Graphics E, LLC, IL, Homer Glen

Smith, Rick .... (419) 448-3213
rsmith@advertiser-tribune.com, Columnist, San Angelo Standard-Times, TX, San Angelo
rsmith@advertiser-tribune.com, Cir. Ops. Mgr., The Advertiser-Tribune, OH, Tiffin

Smith, Rick
rsmit201@csc.com, Pub., NewsUSA, Inc., VA, Falls Church

Smith, Robert .... (403) 653-4664
news@templecitystar.net, Owner/Pub., Temple City Star, AB, Cardston

Smith, Robert
circulation@bigspringherald.com, Circ. Mgr., Big Spring Herald, TX, Big Spring

Smith, Robert H.
route2@sover.net, Pub., Route 2 Travel, Dining and Shopping Guide, VT, Manchester Center

Smith, Robert W. .... (847) 427-4632
rwsmith@dailyherald.com, Major Retail Account Manager, Daily Herald, IL, Arlington Heights

Smith, Robin
rsmith@bnd.com, Belleville News-Democrat, IL, Belleville

Smith, Robyn .... (505) 823-3855
rsmith@abqjournal.com, Copy Ed., Albuquerque Journal, NM, Albuquerque

Smith, Roger
mountaincitizen@bellsouth.net, Pub., The Mountain Citizen, KY, Inez

Smith, Ron
rsmith@mail.ucf.edu, Prof., University of Central Florida, FL, Orlando

Smith, Ron
editor@recordgazette.net, Rgl. Ops. Dir., The News Herald, FL, Panama City

Smith, Ron .... (410) 845-4619
rsmith@dmg.gannett.com, Operations Dir.,

Delaware Coast Press, DE, Bethany Beach
rsmith@dmg.gannett.com, Op. Dir., The Delaware Wave, DE, Bethany Beach
rsmith@dmg.gannett.com, Ops. Dir., The Daily Times, MD, Salisbury

Smith, Ronald D.
smithrd@buffalostate.edu, Chair, Buffalo State College, NY, Buffalo

Smith, Rosie. (830) 980-2860/(603) 444-7141/(802) 748-8121
chalouxr@caledonian-record.com, Educ. Services Dir., The Caledonian-Record, VT, Saint Johnsbury

Smith, Roxanne
rsmith@freedomenc.com, Circ. Mgr., Windsock, NC, Havelock

Smith, Sandra .... (603) 224-5301 ext. 339
ssmith@concordnet.org, Sports Ed., Concord Monitor, NH, Concord

Smith, Sandra (Sissy) ....ext. 220
ssmith@t-g.com, Display Adv. Mgr., Shelbyville Times-Gazette, TN, Shelbyville

Smith, Sarah
ads.sdt@gmail.com , Adv. Rep., The Sullivan Daily Times, IN, Sullivan

Smith, Sarah
sarahsmithrm@gmail.com, Secretary, Washington Press Association, WA, Renton

Smith, Scott .... (508) 591-6605
scsmith@wickedlocal.com, Mng. Ed., Kingston Reporter, MA, Plymouth

Smith, Shannon
Graphics-pc@primetimesonline.com, Graphic Design, PrimeTimes, UT, Salt Lake City

Smith, Shannon .... (541) 957-4226
ssmith@nrtoday.com, Adv. Dir., The News-Review, OR, Roseburg

Smith, Sharry .... (404) 614-2533
sharry.smith@creativeloafing.com, Publisher, Creative Loafing Atlanta, GA, Atlanta

Smith, Sharry .... (404) 688-5623
sharry.smith@creativeloafing.com, Pub., Creative Loafing Atlanta, GA, Atlanta

Smith, Sheila .... (785) 899-2338
s.smith@nwkansas.com, Circ. Mgr., Country Advocate, KS, Colby

Smith, Sheila
jenningsnews@bellsouth.net, Asst. Ed., Jennings (LA) Daily News, LA, Jennings

Smith, Shelia .... (256) 340-2354
shelia.smith@decaturdaily.com, Major Accts Mgr, The Decatur Daily, AL, Decatur

Smith, Sheryl
sheryl.smith@theparisnews.com, Adv. Sales Rep., The Paris News, TX, Paris

Smith, Slim x148
ssmith@cdispatch.com, Reporter & Columnist, The Commercial Dispatch, MS, Columbus

Smith, Stephanie
slsmith@westga.edu, State Univ. of West Georgia, GA, Carrollton

Smith, Stephen D.
ssmith@repub.com, City Ed, Days, The Republican, MA, Springfield

Smith, Steve .... (334) 792-3141
ssmith@dothaneagle.com, Regional Publisher, The Dothan Eagle, AL, Dothan

Smith, Steve
ssmith@metrowestnewspapers.com, Sports Ed., Fort Lupton Press, CO, Brighton

Smith, Steve .... (417) 837-1937
Circ@news-leader.com, Prodn. Mgr., Pressroom, Springfield News-Leader, MO, Springfield

Smith, Steve
ssmith@pulaskicountymirror.com, Ed., Pulaski County Mirror, MO, Saint Robert

Smith, Steven
smithsm@msoe.edu, Chrmn. of the Bd., Milwaukee Journal Sentinel, WI, Milwaukee

Smith, Steven
news@thewinthropnews.com, Adv. Mgr., Winthrop News, IA, Winthrop

Smith, Sue
ads@tobermorypress.com, Graphic Artist, The Bruce Peninsula Press, ON, Tobermory

Smith, Susan
ssmith@arkansasnews.com, Adv. Mgr., Lonoke Democrat, AR, Lonoke
ssmith@arkansasnews.com, Adv. Mgr., Jacksonville Patriot, AR, North Little Rock
ssmith@arkansasnews.com, Adv. Mgr., Sherwood Voice, AR, North Little Rock
ssmith@arkansasnews.com, Adv. Mgr., Carlisle Independent, AR, Carlisle
ssmith@arkansasnews.com, Adv. Mgr., The North Little Rock Times, AR, North Little Rock
ssmith@arkansasnews.com, Adv. Mgr., The Maumelle Monitor, AR, North Little Rock

Smith, Susan L. .... (412) 263-1858
ssmith@post-gazette.com, Mng. Ed., Pittsburgh Post-Gazette, PA, Clinton

Smith, Taylor
tsmith@prairiepress.net, Pub./Pres., The Prairie Press, IL, Paris

Smith, Terri
editor@desotodesototimestribune.com, News Ed., DeSoto Times-Tribune, MS, Hernando

Smith, Terry
news@athensnews.com, Ed., Athens News, OH, Athens

Smith, Terry .... (740) 594-8219
news@athensnews.com, Ed. and Pub., Athens News, OH, Athens

Smith, Thomas C. .... (804) 775-2704
tsmith@timesdispatch.com, Circ. Mgr., Metro, Richmond Times-Dispatch, VA, Richmond

Smith, Tim .... (812) 331-4203
tsmith@heraldt.com, Circ. Mgr., The Mooresville-Decatur Times, IN, Martinsville

Smith, Tim D. .... (812) 331-4203
tsmith@heraldt.com, Circ. Dir., The Herald Times, IN, Bloomington

Smith, Tim D. .... (812) 331-4203
Circ. Dir., The Times-Mail, IN, Bedford

Smith, Tim D. .... (812) 331-4203
tsmith@heraldt.com, Circ. Dir., The Reporter Times, IN, Martinsville

Smith, Todd .... (802) 748-8121
smitht@caledonian-record.com, Pub./VP, The Caledonian-Record, VT, Saint Johnsbury

Smith, Todd
toddsmith@independent.com, CFO, Santa Barbara Independent, CA, Santa Barbara

Smith, Todd M.
news@caledonian-record.com, Pub., The Caledonian-Record, VT, Saint Johnsbury

Smith, Tom
tsmith@timesdispatch.com, Metro Home Delivery Mgr., Richmond Delivery Service, VA, Richmond

Smith, Tracy
tlsmith@punxsutawneyspirit.com, Pub./ Adv. Dir. , The Punxsutawney Spirit, PA, Punxsutawney

Smith, Tracy .... (828) 389-8431
ads@claycountyprogress.com, Adv. Mgr., Clay County Progress, NC, Hayesville

Smith, Travis .... (254) 897-2282
news@theglenrosereporter.com, Mng. Ed., Glen Rose Reporter, TX, Stephenville

Smith, Trisha
message@evdio.org, Assist. Ed., The Message, IN, Evansville

Smith, Tyson
tyson@readinghorizons.com, Pres., Reading Horizons, UT, Kaysville

Smith, Val .... (916) 278-5340
valsmith@saclink.csus.edu, Chair, California State University, Sacramento, CA, Sacramento

Smith, Vernon
vsmith@hometownnewsol.com, Managing Partner, Hometown News, FL, Fort Pierce

Smith, Walter
newyorkbeacon@yahoo.com, Ed. in Chief, New York Beacon, NY, New York

Smith, Wayne .... (902) 681-2121
Adv. Mgr., Mirror-examiner, NS, Middleton
Adv. Mgr., Monitor (OOB), NS, Bridgetown

Smith, Wes .... (810) 452-2622
wsmith@mihomepaper.com, Pub., The Davison Index, MI, Davison
wsmith@mihomepaper.com, Pub./Ed., Flint Township View, MI, Davison
wsmith@mihomepaper.com, Pub./Ed., Grand Blanc View, MI, Davison
wsmith@mihomepaper.com, Pub./Ed., LA View, MI, Lapeer
wsmith@mihomepaper.com, Pub./Ed., Swartz Creek View, MI, Davison
wsmith@mihomepaper.com, Pub./Ed., Township View, MI, Chesaning
wsmith@mihomepaper.com, Pub./Ed., Tri-County Citizen, MI, Sandusky
wsmith@mihomepaper.com, Pub./Ed., Banner, MI, Brown City
wsmith@mihomepaper.com, Adv. Dir., The County Press, MI, Lapeer

Smith, William .... (928) 556-2292
Prodn. Mgr., Pressroom, Arizona Daily Sun, Flagstaff, AZ, Flagstaff

Smith, William P. .... (540) 374-5470
bsmith@freelancestar.com, Adv. Dir., The Free Lance-Star, VA, Fredericksburg

Smith, Wyndol
van@circulationsolutions.com, Sec., Circulation Solutions, Inc., AL, Auburn

Smith, Zach .... (512) 259-4449
sports@hillcountrynews.com, Sports Editor, Hill Country News, TX, Cedar Park

Smith , Emily
emily.smith@latimes.com, SVP, Digital , Los Angeles Times, CA, Los Angeles

Smith , Janet Mackay .... (978) 739-1347
Mng. Ed. , Ipswich Chronicle, MA, Danvers

Smith , Sr., Mark .... (706) 485-3501
amsmith@msgr.com, Pub, The Eatonton Messenger, GA, Eatonton

Smith Brown, Linda .... (309) 686-3106
lsmithbrown@timestoday.com, Gen. Sales Mgr., Woodford Times, IL, Pekin

Smith-Cronk, Judy .... (585) 335-2271
judycronk@dansvilleonline.com, Multi-Media Sales Executive, Genesee Country Express, NY, Dansville

Smith-Howell, Deborah
deborahsmith-howell@unomaha.edu, Prof./ Grad. Dean/Assoc. Vice Chancellor, University of Nebraska at Omaha, NE, Omaha

Smith-Hupp, Karen .... (301) 934-2251
karens@csmd.edu, Ed., College of Southern Maryland, MD, La Plata

Smith-Wilson, Henrietta
hsmith@forwardtimes.com, Adv. Dir., Houston Metro Weekender, TX, Houston

Smithee, Mary L. .... (806) 323-6461
mary@canadianrecord.com, Bus. Mgr., The Canadian Record, TX, Canadian

Smitherman, Lamar
osmitherman@morganton.com, Pub., The McDowell News, NC, Marion

Smitherman, Lamar

osmitherman@morganton.com, Pub., The News Herald, NC, Morganton

Smitherman, Laura .... (410) 332-6677
laura.smitherman@baltsun.com, Asst. Managing Ed., The Baltimore Sun, MD, Baltimore

Smithson, Tony .... (608) 755-9455
tsmithson@gazettextra.com, Vice President Printing Operations, The Gazette - gazettextra.com, WI, Janesville

Smolarick, Tim .... (941) 207-1010
tsmolarick@venicegondolier.com, Publisher, Venice Gondolier Sun, Sun Coast Media Group Inc, FL, Punta Gorda

Smolarick, Timothy .... (941) 207-1010
tsmolarick@venicegondolier.com, Pub., Venice Gondolier Sun, FL, Venice

Smolinski, Kathleen .... (810) 227-1575
kathy@georgemosesco.com, Production Manager / Art Director, Marketeer, MI, Brighton

Smoots MD, Elizabeth S. .... (425) 486-9131
doctor@practicalprevention.com, Self-Syndicator, Elizabeth S. Smoots, Seattle

Smothers, Jim
jsmothers@dailyhome.com, Webpage Coord., The Daily Home, AL, Talladega

Smothers, William
wsmoth3193@aol.com, Ed., Speakin' Out Weekly, AL, Huntsville

Smurl, Paul
psmurl@theladders.com, Adv. Vice Pres., The New York Times, NY, New York

Smysnuik, Orest
osmysnuik@glaciermedia.com, CFO, Glacier Media Group, BC, Vancouver

Smyth, Joe
jsmyth@newszap.com, Chrmn. of the Bd./CEO, Independent Newsmedia Inc. Usa, DE, Dover

Smyth, Russell
russells@cortezjournal.com, Managing Ed., Mancos Times, CO, Cortez

Smythe, Harvey
info@htshealthcare.com, Mng. Dir./Vice Pres., HTS Interactive Health Care, OR, Portland

Snead, Brett .... (402) 444-1425
brett.snead@owh.com, Director of Local Sales, Omaha World-Herald, NE, Omaha

Sneed, Jo Ann .... (417) 837-1127
jsneed@news-leader.com, Prodn. Supvr., Composing (Day), Springfield News-Leader, MO, Springfield

Sneed, Mitch
msneed@alexcityoutlook.com, Managing Ed, Alexander City Outlook, AL, Alexander City

Sneed, Timothy .... (931) 261-1275
owner/publisher, The Peddler, TN, Cookeville

Sneider, Andrew .... (405) 878-5441
St. Gregory's College, OK, Shawnee

Snell, Carvy
csnell@metteradvertiser.com, Ed., The Metter Advertiser, GA, Metter

Snider, Betty .... (540) 374-5427
bsnider@freelancestar.com, Managing Editor, The Free Lance-Star, VA, Fredericksburg

Snider, Gary
gsnider@printinnovators.com, Ops. Dir., The Free Lance-Star, VA, Fredericksburg

Snider, Gary .... (843) 317-7388
gsnider@bhminc.com, Prod. Dir., Morning News, SC, Florence

Snider, Jerry
jsnider@bignickel.com, Classified Mgr./Dist. Mgr., Big Nickel, MO, Joplin

Snider, Robbie .... (405) 933-2356
Owner/Ed, The Cyril News, OK, Cyril

Snider, Wayne .... ext. 229

wayne.snider@sunmedia.ca, City Ed. , The Timmins Daily Press, ON, Timmins

Snider, Wes .... (717) 703-3056
wesleys@mansimedia.com, Dir. Client Solutions, MANSI Media, PA, Harrisburg

Snidle, Laurie .... (618) 262-5144
lsindle@mtcarmelregister.com, Advertising Consultant, Mount Carmel Register, IL, Mount Carmel

Snizek, Rick .... (401) 272-1010
rsnizek@thericatholic.com, Executive Editor, Rhode Island Catholic, RI, Providence

Snodgrass, David .... (812) 331-4365
dsnodgress@heraldt.com, Photo Mgr., The Herald Times, IN, Bloomington

Snow, Constance .... (804) 633-5005
cpeditor@lcs.net, Editor, The Caroline Progress, VA, Bowling Green

Snow, David .... (270) 887-3239
dsnow@theeaglepost.us, Ed., Eagle Post, KY, Hopkinsville

Snow, Jerry .... (704) 261-2225
jsnow@theej.com, Sports Ed., The Enquirer-Journal, NC, Monroe

Snow, John
infous@enigma.com, Vice Pres., Mktg., Enigma, MA, Needham

Snow, Scott
ssnow@cnicorp.com, CNI Corp., NH, Milford

Snow, Terri .... (620) 221-1050
classified@ctnewsonline.com, Classified, Winfield Daily Courier, KS, Winfield

Snow, Trayce
trayce@rapidesfoundation.org, Louisiana State Univ., LA, Alexandria

Snowden, William
wsnowden@thewakullanews.com, Ed, The Wakulla News, FL, Crawfordville

Snyder, Aaron .... (606) 326-2664
asnyder@dailyindependent.com, Sports Ed., The Daily Independent, KY, Ashland

Snyder, Becky
bsnyder@earlybirdpaper.com, Circ. Mgr, The Early Bird, OH, Greenville

Snyder, David L.
alfredsun.news@gmail.com, Ed. and Pub., The Alfred Sun, NY, Alfred

Snyder, Eric
esnyder@geofirmallc.com, Mng. Ed., Nashville Business Journal, TN, Nashville

Snyder, Frank .... (419) 586-2371
fsnyder@dailystandard.com, Editorial Page Ed., The Daily Standard, OH, Celina
fsnyder@dailystandard.com, Pub., The Standard Shopping News, OH, Celina

Snyder, Gib
gsnyder@observertoday.com, Lifestyles coordinator, The Observer, NY, Dunkirk

Snyder, James
jims@aboutfamiliespa.com, Adv. Mgr., About Families Parenting Newspaper, PA, Lebanon

Snyder, James
jims@themerchandiser.com, Adv. Mgr., Merchandiser, PA, Lebanon

Snyder, John .... (800) 468-9568
john.snyder@pagecooperative.com, CEO, PAGE Cooperative, VA, Vienna

Snyder, John
john.snyder@pagecooperative.com, CEO, PAGE, PA, King Of Prussia

Snyder, Patricia .... (515) 465-4666
psnyder@theperrychief.com, Publisher, Perry Chief, IA, Perry

Snyder, Patricia
psnyder@theperrychief.com, Publisher, Chiefland Shopper, IA, Perry

Snyder, Rebecca .... (855) 721-6332 x3

rsnyder@mddcpress.com, Exec. Dir., Maryland-Delaware-DC Press Association, MD, Annapolis

Snyder, Richard
dsnyder@evesun.com, Pres. & Pub., The New Berlin Gazette, NY, Norwich

Snyder, Richard .... (607) 334-4714
info@pennysaver.com, Pub., Sidney Pennysaver, NY, Norwich

Snyder, Richard .... (607) 334-4714
dsnyder@pennysaver.com, Pub., Snyder Communications, NY, Norwich

Snyder, Richard
production@pennysaveronline.com, Publisher, Norwich Pennysaver, NY, Norwich

Snyder, Richard
production@pennysaveronline.com, Pennysaver, NY, Richfield Springs
production@pennysaveronline.com, Ed., Hall Of Fame Pennysaver, NY, Richfield Springs

Snyder, Richard .... (607) 337-3000
dsnyder@evesun.com, Pres. , The Evening Sun, NY, Norwich

Snyder, Richard
dsnyder@circulars.com, My Shopper - Mohawk Valley, NY, Cobleskill
dsnyder@circulars.com, My Shopper - Schoharie Edition, NY, Cobleskill

Snyder, Richard
info@pennysaveronline.com, Pub., Wharton Valley Pennysaver, NY, Norwich

Snyder, Richard
production@pennysaveronline.com, Turnpike Pennysaver, NY, Richfield Springs

Snyder, Richard`
production@pennysaveronline.com, Oneonta-cooperstown Pennysaver, NY, Richfield Springs

Snyder, Robert .... (304) 725-2046
editor@spiritofjefferson.com, Ed., Spirit of Jefferson, WV, Charles Town

Snyder, Steve .... (254) 883-2554
publisher@marlindemocrat.com, Pub./Ed., The Marlin Democrat, TX, Marlin

Snyder, Steven R.
srsnyder@hbu.edu, Chair/Assoc. Prof./ Photography, Houston Baptist University, TX, Houston

Socas, Roberto .... (212) 866-0248
Asst. Treasurer, Foreign Press Association, NY, New York

Socha, Gary
garysocha@currentnewspapers.com, Adv. Dir., Dupont Current, DC, Washington
garysocha@currentnewspapers.com, Adv. Dir., Foggy Bottom Current, DC, Washington
garysocha@currentnewspapers.com, Adv. Mgr., Georgetown Current, DC, Washington
garysocha@currentnewspapers.com, Adv. Dir., Northwest Current, DC, Washington

Socia, Todd
sociats@nytimes.com, The New York Times, NY, New York

Sodini, Fran
midvalleypub@aol.com, CEO, Mid Valley Publishing, CA, Winton

Sodini, Fran
midvalleypub@aol.com, Pres., Hilmar Times, CA, Hilmar

Sodt, Evelina .... (973) 785-3000 ext. 124
esodt@certifiedaudit.com, Dir., Mktg., Certified Audit of Circulations, Inc., NJ, Wayne

Soebbing, Adam .... (563) 383-2361
asoebbing@qctimes.com, Sports Ed., Quad-City Times, IA, Davenport

Soenksen, Roger
soenksra@jmu.edu, Prof., James Madison University, VA, Harrisonburg

Sofaly, Bob
bsofaly@beaufortgazette.com, Photographer, The Beaufort Gazette, SC, Bluffton

Soforic, Joseph F. .... (724) 887-7400 ext. 211
lgpoffice@scottdale.com, Pub., The Advisor, PA, Scottdale
lgpoffice@scottdale.com, Pub., The Ligonier Echo, PA, Ligonier

Sofradzija, Omar .... (517) 295-1680
omar@statenews.com, Advisor, The State News/Michigan State University, MI, East Lansing

Soga, Aki
asoga@burlingt.gannett.com, Editorial Page Ed., The Burlington Free Press, VT, Burlington

Sohl, Ashley .... (515) 953-4822, ext. 303
ashley@dmcityview.com, Advertising Director, Cityview, IA, Johnston

Soifer, Claudia
winnet@panix.com, Vice Pres./Gen. Mgr., World Interactive Network, NY, New York

Sokerka, Richard
rsbeacon@patersondiocese.org, Ed., The Beacon, NJ, Clifton

Sokolove, Sam
news@nmjlink.org, Pub., New Mexico Jewish Link, NM, Albuquerque

Sokolowski, Tiffany .... (859) 355-1200
tsokolowski@schurz.com, Circ. Dir., The Winchester Sun, KY, Winchester

Sokolowski , Erik. .... (413) 496-6293
esokolowski@berkshireeagle.com, Editor, The Advocate Weekly, MA, North Adams
esokolowski@berkshireeagle.com, Digital News Ed., The Berkshire Eagle, MA, Pittsfield

Solan, Alan
asolan@dnews.com, News Ed., Moscow-Pullman Daily News, ID, Moscow

Soldwedel, Joseph E. ...... (928) 783-3311 ext. 102
jsoldwedel@westernnews.com, Pres./CEO, Western News&Info, Inc., AZ, Yuma

Soldwedel, Kelly
ksoldwedel@westernnews.com, Prescott Newspapers, Inc., AZ, Prescott
ksoldwedel@westernnews.com, Pub., Prescott Valley Tribune, AZ, Chino Valley
ksoldwedel@westernnews.com, Publisher/CEO, Smart Shopper Ash Fork, AZ, Prescott
ksoldwedel@westernnews.com, Publisher/CEO, Smart Shopper, AZ, Prescott

Solem, Brad .... (651) 796-1113
brad.solem@ecm-inc.com, Adv. Acct. Exec., Stillwater Gazette, MN, Stillwater

Solinsky, Kolby
ksolinsky@blackpress.ca, Online Editor, Lake Country Calendar, BC, Kelowna

Solinsky, Matt
matt.solinsky@thedesertsun.com, Sports Ed., The Desert Sun, CA, Palm Springs

Solis, Robin
robins@spotmagic.com, Founder, Pub. Rel., SpotMagic, Inc., CA, San Francisco

Soliz, Leonard .... (559) 674-8134
lsoliz@maderatribune.net, Dir., Opns., The Madera Tribune, CA, Madera

Solliday, Nancy .... (239) 335-0252
nsolliday@news-press.com, VP Adv. Sales, The Commercial Appeal, TN, Memphis

Solly, Sallie .... (409) 423-2696
Kbanner@sbcglobal.net, Reporter, Kirbyville Banner, TX, Kirbyville

Solmonson, Phil
ads@wakefielditem.com, Adv. Dir., The Lynnfield Villager, MA, Wakefield
ads@wakefielditem.com, Adv. Dir., North Reading Transcript, MA, Wakefield

Soloduik, Wendy

wendy@simcoeyorkprinting.com, Ed., The Times Of New Tecumseth, ON, Beeton
wendy@simcoeyorkprinting.com, Ed., The Scope Of Innisfil, ON, Beeton

Solomon, Betty
bsolomon@bju.edu, Bob Jones University, SC, Greenville

Solomon, Felix .... (510) 464-3460
Laney College, CA, Oakland

Solomon, Fran .... (813) 259-7376
Tampa Bay Times, FL, St Petersburg

Solomon, Goody L. .... (202) 723-2477
goody.solomon@verizon.net, Owner/Exec. Ed./ Author, Food Nutrition Health News Service, Washington

Solomon, Herbert
info@nysaver.com, Pres., Pennysaver, NY, Nanuet

Solon, Connie .... (717) 295-5065
csolon@lnpnews.com, Production Manager, LNP, PA, Lancaster
csolon@lnpnews.com, Production Manager, LNP Media Group, Inc., PA, Lancaster

Solsek, Tundra .... (603) 219-6065
tslosek@nnenews.com, Newspapers of New England, NH, Concord

Solt, Tim .... (877) 334-8613
Reg. Mgr., Church Rickards, Whitlock & Co., Inc., IL, Westchester

Solt, Tim .... (203) 789-5350
Circ. Mgr., New Haven Register, CT, New Haven

Somers, Hannah
adsales2@havredailynews.com, Adv. Consultant, The Havre Daily News, MT, Havre

Sommer, Brenda
bsommer@themexianews.com, Ed., The Mexia News, TX, Mexia

Sommer, Brenda .... (940) 549-7800
editor@grahamleader.com, Ed., The Graham Leader, TX, Graham

Sommer, Jason
jsommer@fontbonne.edu, Fontbonne College, MO, Clayton

Sommer, Jennifer .... (815) 539-9396
jsommer@mendotareporter.com, Ed., Farmer's Report, IL, Mendota

Sommer, Oliver
osommer@blackpress.ca, Pub, Saanich News, BC, Victoria

Sommers, Lee
lsommers@longislandpress.com, Mktg. Mgr., Long Island Press, NY, Syosset

Sommerson, Shellie
ssommers@advpubtech.com, Adv. Prod. Mgr., Advanced Publishing Technology, CA, Burbank

Sondag, William H.
sonbtp@aol.com, Ed., Lacon Home Journal, IL, Lacon

Sondegard, Mary .... (859) 231-3568
msondergard@herald-leader.com, Copy Ed., Lexington Herald-Leader, KY, Lexington

Sonderman, Jeff
jeff.sonderman@pressinstitute.org, Deputy Director, American Press Institute, VA, Arlington

Sondreal, Steven R.
freepres@amerytel.net, Pub./Gen. Mgr., Amery Free Press, WI, Amery

Sondrup, Brett
bsondrup@republicmedia.com, Dir., Class. Adv., The Arizona Republic, AZ, Phoenix

Sonier , Francis
francis.sonier @ acadiemedia.com, Pub./ General Manager, L'Acadie Nouvelle, NB, Caraquet

Sonka, Mark .... (859) 231-3108
msonka@herald-leader.com, Copy Ed., Lexington Herald-Leader, KY, Lexington

Sonmez, Sevil
sevil.sonmez@zu.ac.ae, Prof., Zayed University, Al Ruwayyah

Sonneman, Toby
tsonnema@whatcom.ctc.edu, Whatcom Cmty. College, WA, Bellingham

Sonnenfeld, Laura .... (212) 556-3512
sonnela@nytimes.com, VP, Adv., The New York Times, NY, New York

Sonnier, Tanya
classifieds@banner-tribune.com, Classifieds Adv. Mgr. , Franklin Banner-Tribune, LA, Franklin

Sonntag, Patti .... (212) 556-5135
sonntpe@nytimes.com, Managing Editor, Syndicate, The New York Times News Service & Syndicate, New York

Sonntag, Patti .... (212) 556-5135
sonntpe@nytimes.com, Managing Editor, Syndicate, The New York Times News Service & Syndicate, New York

Sonsteng, Stan
courier@glasgowcourier.com, Production manager, The Glasgow Courier, MT, Glasgow

Sontag, Robert .... (248) 643-9910 ext. 12
rsontag@anrinc.net, Exec. Vice Pres./COO, American Newspaper Representatives, MI, Troy

Sontag, Robert .... (248) 643-7766
rsontag@anrinc.net, Exec. Vice Pres./COO, American Newspaper Representatives, Inc., MI, Troy

Sopata, Todd .... (715) 842-4424
tsopata@mmlocal.com, Lead Sales, Wausau Times / Buyers' Guide, WI, Merrill

Soper, Mark .... (306) 770-2222
msoper@swbooster.com, Adv. Mgr., The Southwest Booster, SK, Swift Current

Soper, Shawn
ssoper@mdcoastdispatch.com, News Ed., Maryland Coast Dispatch, MD, Berlin

Sopland, Jeff .... (502) 477-2239 ext. 21
graphics@spencermagnet.com, graphics designer, Spencer Magnet, KY, Taylorsville

Soprano, Cathy
csoprano@verafast.com, Exec. Vice Pres., Ver-A-Fast Corporation, OH, Rocky River

Sora, Joseph
sora@duq.edu, Asst. Prof., Duquesne University, PA, Pittsburgh

Sorber, Greg .... (505) 823-3991
gsorber@abqjournal.com, Asst. Photo Ed., Albuquerque Journal, NM, Albuquerque

Sorensen, Chris .... (719) 438-5800
press@kiowacountypress.com, Pub., Kiowa County Press, CO, Eads

Sorensen, Ken .... (306) 752-5737
ken.sorensen@sunmedia.ca, Pub., The Melfort Journal, SK, Melfort
ken.sorensen@sunmedia.ca, North East Sun, SK, Melfort

Sorenson, Jennifer
jsorenson@greatfallstribune.com, Advertising Director
, Great Bend Tribune, KS, Great Bend

Sorenson, Jennifer .... (520) 515-4605
publisher@myheraldreview.com, Publisher, Wick Communications - Herald/Review, AZ, Sierra Vista

Sorenson, Michael
websterherald@empirestateweeklies.com, Empire State Weeklies, NY

Sorenson, Paul
paul.sorenson@oati.net, Univ. of Minnesota Inst. of Tech, MN, Minneapolis

Sorenson, Randy
rsorenson@osceolanewsgazette.com, Internet Systems Mgr., Osceola News-gazette, FL, Kissimmee

Sores, Patricia
spmofc@rit.edu, Admin. Chair, Rochester Institute of Technology, NY, Rochester

Sorg, Lisa
lsorg@indyweek.com, Ed., The Independent Weekly, NC, Durham

Sorg, Sharon
ssorg@sharonherald.com, Pub., New Castle News, PA, New Castle

Sorg, Sharon
ssorg@sharonherald.com, Pub., The Herald, PA, Sharon

Sorg, Sharon ....(724) 981-6100
ssorg@sharonherald.com, Publisher, Market Guide, PA, Grove City

Sorg, Sharon ....(724) 981-6100
ssorg@sharonherald.com, Pub, Allied News, PA, Grove City

Sorohan, Martha ....(440) 576-9125 x116
courier@gazettenews.com, Editor, The Courier, OH, Jefferson

Sorrell Burnside, Vanessa
vanessa@therandolphleader.com, News Ed., The Randolph Leader, AL, Roanoke

Sosa, Chris
chsosa@redeyechicago.com, Sports Ed., RedEye, IL, Chicago

Sosa, Linda ....(817) 292-4484
Sales Person, Wedgwood Shopping News, TX, Fort Worth

Sosniecki, Gary
gsosniecki.townnews.com, Reg. Sales Mgr., TownNews.com, IL, Moline

Sossamon, Abbie ....(864) 489-1131
abbie@gaffneyledger.com, Features/Lifestyles Editor, The Gaffney Ledger, SC, Gaffney

Sossamon, Cody
cody@gaffneyledger.com, Pub., The Gaffney Ledger, SC, Gaffney

Soto, Sylvia ....(575) 541-5480
ssoto@lcsun-news.com , Cust. Serv. Sup., Las Cruces Sun-News, NM, Las Cruces

Soucie, Christine ....(902) 426-1146
csoucie@herald.ca, Books Ed., The Chronicle Herald, NS, Halifax

Soucy, Daniel.........................(450) 964-4444
dsoucy@larevue.qc.ca, Mktg Dir, La Revue De Terrebonne, QC, Terrebonne

Soucy, Dave ....(763) 712-3562
dave.soucy@ecm-inc.com, Prodn. Mgr., Anoka County Shopper, MN, Coon Rapids

Soultanian, Gary
gsoultaniant@nusconsulting.com, Co-Pres., NUS Consulting Group, NJ, Park Ridge

Soultanian, Richard
rsoultanian@nusconsulting.com, Co-Pres., NUS Consulting Group, NJ, Park Ridge

Sounders, Eugene
efsounders@mccainprint.com, Owner, McCain Printing Co., VA, Danville

South, Whitney.........................(519) 527-0240
seaforth.news@sunmedia.ca, Multi Media Journalist, The Huron Expositor, ON, Seaforth

Southard, Doug
doug.southard@starherald.com, Adv. Dir., Star-Herald, NE, Scottsbluff

Southard, Doug ....(308) 632-9039
doug.southard@starherald.com, Adv. Mgr., Twin City Weekly, NE, Scottsbluff

Southards, Sandy ....(336) 888-3567
aloflin@hpe.com, Adv. Mgr., Major Accts., High Point Enterprise, NC, High Point

Southern, Bill.........................(412) 263-1309
Director of Finance, Pittsburgh Post-Gazette, PA, Clinton

Southern, William ....(419) 724-6289
bsouthern@toledoblade.com, Director of Finance and IT, The Blade, OH, Toledo

Southmayd, Jim
sports@wakefielditem.com, Sports Ed., Wakefield Daily Item, MA, Wakefield

Souza, Aubree
asouza@news-press.com, Exec. Asst. to the Pub., The Commercial Appeal, TN, Memphis

Souza, Mike ....(860) 495-8224
msouza@themysticriverpress.com, Assoc. Ed., The Westerly Sun, CT, Pawcatuck

Sovell, Jane ....(507) 537-1551 ext #105
jsovell@marshallindependent.com, Bus. Mgr., Independent, MN, Marshall

Sovinski, B. Jon.........................(231) 924-0630
jon@hi-lites.com, Pub., Hi-lites Shoppers Guide, MI, Fremont

Sow, Holly ....(928) 425-7121
news@silverbelt.com, Ed., Arizona Silver Belt, AZ, Globe

Sowards-Cerny, Debra ....(719) 589-2553
ads@alamosanews.com, Advertising Manager, Valley Courier, CO, Alamosa

Sowers, Laura ....(574) 267-3111 Ext 219
lsowers@timesuniononline.com, Classified Supervisor, Times-Union, IN, Warsaw

Spaar, Betty S.
spaar@iland.net, Owner, The Odessan, MO, Odessa

Spaar, Hannah ....(816) 230-5311
spaar@iland.net, news editor, The Odessan, MO, Odessa

Spade, Kyle
news@cherokeenewspaper.com, Ed, The Cherokee Messenger & Republican, OK, Cherokee

Spaeder, Jerry.........................(386) 754-0424
Mng. Ed., Lake City Reporter, FL, Lake City

Spahr, Andrew
andrew@toledocitypaper.com, Acct. Exec., Toledo Area Parent News, OH, Toledo

Spalding, Dan ....(574) 296-5813
dspalding@elkharttruth.com, Assistant Managing Editor - Print, Elkhart Truth, IN, Elkhart

Spalvieri, Dennis
dspalvieri@mojonews.com, Asst. Ed., Morning Journal, OH, Lisbon

Spangler, Ben
benjamin.spangler@goucher.edu, Goucher College, MD, Towson

Spangler, Christine ....(920) 563-5553
Cspangler@dailyunion.com, Managing Editor, Daily Jefferson County Union, WI, Fort Atkinson

Spangler, Lisa.................(812) 663-3111 x7401
lisa.spangler@indianamediagroup.com, Rgl. Controller, Rushville Republican, IN, Rushville

Spangler, Todd ....(313) 222-6521
spangler@freepress.com, Deputy Metro Ed., Detroit Free Press, MI, Detroit

Spanner, James T. ....(304) 485-1891
jspanner@newsandsentinel.com, Pub., Parkersburg News & Sentinel, WV, Parkersburg

Spanner, Jim
jspanner@newsandsentinel.com, Pub., Parkersburg News & Sentinel, WV, Parkersburg

Sparby, Amy ....(641) 472-4129
pub@ffledger.com, Pub, Fairfield Town Crier, IA, Fairfield

Spargur, Tom ....(540) 812-2282
tspargur@culpepertimes.com, Group Sales Dir, Culpeper Times, VA, Culpeper

Spargur , Tom ....(540) 825-0771 ext 102
tspargur@starexponent.com , GM/Sales mgr , Quantico Sentry, VA, Leesburg

Sparkman, Kaylee ....(806) 364-2030
lifestyles@herefordbrand.com, Lifestyles Writer, The Hereford Brand, TX, Hereford

Sparks, Adam
asparks@staradvertiser.com, Dig. Ed., Honolulu Star-Advertiser, HI, Honolulu

Sparks, Darrell...........................ext. 252
Circ. Mgr., Weekly Alibi, NM, Albuquerque

Sparks, Dwight
dsparks@enterprise-record.com, Ed., Davie County Enterprise-Record, NC, Mocksville

Sparks, Dwight
courier9@bellsouth.net, Vice Pres., Davie County Publishing, Inc., NC, Mocksville

Sparks, Martha
msparks@loganbanner.com, Webmaster, The Logan Banner, WV, Logan

Sparrow, Colleen ....(250) 960-2767
csparrow@pgcitizen.ca, Pub., The Prince George Citizen, BC, Prince George

Spaulding, Beth
tmartinez@swbell.net, Bus. Mgr, The Pryor Times, OK, Claremore

Spaulding, Joann ....(765) 659-4622
jspaulding@ftimes.com, Accounting Clerk, The Times, IN, Frankfort

Spaulding, Jon
jspaulding@palltimes.com, Pub., The Palladium-Times, NY, Oswego

Spaulding, Jon ....(315) 343-3800 ext. 2248
jspaulding@palltimes.com, Pub., The Palladium-Times, NY, Fulton

Spaulding, Joshua
baysider@salmonpress.com, Ed., The Baysider, NH, Wolfeboro Falls

Spaulding, Kameron
kspaulding@berkshirebeacon.com, Editorial Assistant, Berkshire Beacon, MA, Lenox Dale

Spaulding, Richard
richardspaulding@srfol.org, Real Estate Ed., The Daily Transcript, CA, San Diego

Spaw, Rod ....(812) 331-4338
rspaw@heraldt.com, News Ed., The Herald Times, IN, Bloomington

Speakes, Larry M.
lspeakes@email.usps.gov, Mgr., Product Mktg., United States Postal Service, DC, Washington

Spear, Glen ....(270) 783-3254
gwspear@bgdailynews.com, Prodn. Mgr., Pressroom, Daily News, KY, Bowling Green

Spear, Glenda ....(270) 783-3211
Accountant, Daily News, KY, Bowling Green

Spear, Howard JP.....................(845) 238-0287
ocpnews@frontiernet.net, Editor, Orange County Post, NY, Vails Gate

Spear, Joe.................(800) 657-4662 Ext. 382
jspear@mankatofreepress.com, Mng. Ed., The Free Press, MN, Mankato

Spear, Ryan
ryan@pdclarion.com, Computer Specialist, Princeton Daily Clarion, IN, Princeton

Spear, Tyrone.........................(937) 339-2616
info@roconex.com, Pres., Roconex Corp., OH, Troy

Spearman, Lewis
grafikstar@aol.com, Adv. Dir., Highlands Star / Crosby Courier, TX, Houston

Spears, Jim
jspears@timesanddemocrat.com, Prodn. Mgr., The Times and Democrat, SC, Orangeburg

Spears, Steven ....(660) 543-4050
muleskinner@ucmo.edu, Mgr Ed, University of Central Missouri, MO, Warrensburg

Spears III, R.E
res.spears@suffolknewsherald.com, Editor, Suffolk News-Herald, VA, Suffolk

Specht, David A.
dspecht@bossierpress.com, Vice President & Publisher, Bossier Press-Tribune, LA, Bossier City

Specht, Kevin.........................(619) 955-8960
kevin@uptownexaminer.com, Legal Notice Rep., Uptown San Diego Examiner, CA, San Diego

Speciale, Samuel ....(304) 348-4843
sam.speciale@wvgazettemail.com, Education Reporter , The Charleston Gazette-Mail, WV, Charleston

Speck, Amy
amy.speck@journalinc.com, Nat'l Agency Coord., Northeast Mississippi Daily Journal, MS, Tupelo

Speck, Mary
admin@caledoncitizen.com, Office Mgr, Caledon Citizen, ON, Bolton

Specktor, Mordecai
editor@ajwnews.com, Ed., American Jewish World, MN, Minneapolis

Spector, Joe
jspector@gannett.com, Bureau Chief, Gannett News Service - Albany, NY, Albany

Spector, Mike ....(602) 444-4348
mike.spector@pni.com, Dir., HR, The Arizona Republic, AZ, Phoenix

Speechley, Ronald....................(815) 834-2499
ronald.speechley@srds.com, Publisher, SRDS, a Kantar Media Company, IL, Des Plaines

Speed, Susan
shermanpub@aol.com, Prod. Mgr, Ortonville Citizen, MI, Ortonville

Speelman, Sindy.........................(212) 210-1970
sspeelman@nydailynews.com, Sales Mgr, Natl. Retail & Preprints, New York Daily News, NY, New York

Speer, Bill
bspeer@thealpenanews.com, Pub./Ed., The Alpena News, MI, Alpena

Speer, Chris
info@nmh.com, Pres., New Media Hollywood, CA, Los Angeles

Speer, Diane
lifestyles@thealpenanews.com, Lifestyles Ed., The Alpena News, MI, Alpena

Speer, Jeremy
jeremy@gaylordheraldtimes.com, Ed., Gaylord Herald Times, MI, Gaylord

Speer, Jeremy ....(231) 347-2544
Exec. Sports Ed. , Petoskey News-Review, MI, Petoskey

Speer, John
editor@tamatoledonews.com, Ed., Toledo Chronicle, IA, Tama

Speer, John
jspeer@tamatoledonews.com, Ed., Tama County Shopper, IA, Tama

Speer, John
editor@tamatoledonews.com, Ed., The Tama News-Herald, IA, Tama

Speicher, Barbara L.
bspeciche@depaul.edu, Chair, DePaul University, IL, Chicago

Speicher, Melanie ....(937) 538-4822
mspeicher@sidneydailynews.com, News Ed., The Sidney Daily News, OH, Sidney

Speidel, Karen ....(701) 642-8585
newsmonitor@wahpetondailynews.com,

Director, North Dakota Newspaper Association, ND, Bismarck

Speidel, Karen
newsmonitor@wahpetondailynews.com, Mng. ed. , News-Monitor, ND, Wahpeton

Speirs, Dan .... (308) 233-9721
dan.speirs@kearneyhub.com, News Ed., Kearney Hub, NE, Kearney

Speirs, Julie .... (308) 233-9790
julie.speirs@kearneyhub.com, Pres./Pub., Kearney Hub, NE, Kearney

Speirs, Miki
circulation@saanichnews.com, Circ Mgr, Saanich News, BC, Victoria

Speller, Cherie .... (252) 329-9569
cspeller@reflector.com, Asst. Mng. Ed., The Daily Reflector, NC, Greenville

Spence, Craig
editor@ladysmithchronicle.com, Ed, The Ladysmith Chronicle, BC, Ladysmith

Spence, Tony
cns@catholicnews.com, Director/Editor in Chief, Catholic News Service, Washington

Spence, Tracey
tspence@lfpress.com, Circ. Mgr., Pennysaver, ON, London

Spence, Wendy .... (519) 268-7337
w.spence@on.aibn.com, Ed. , The Signpost, ON, Dorchester

Spencer, Cynthia .... (706) 823-3306
cynthia.spencer@augustachronicle.com, HR Director, The Augusta Chronicle, GA, Augusta

Spencer, David .... (910) 997-3111 Ext: 27
dspencer@civitasmedia.com, Business Dev. Manager, Richmond County Daily Journal, NC, Rockingham

Spencer, Halinka .... (585) 586-2525
Nazareth College of Rochester, NY, Rochester

Spencer, Hawes
editor@readthehook.com, Editor, The Hook, VA, Charlottesville

Spencer, Jason .... (864) 562-7233
jason.spencer@shj.com, Assist.City Ed., Herald-Journal, SC, Spartanburg

Spencer, Nancy .... (419) 695-0015 Ext. 134
nspencer@delphosherald.com, Ed., Delphos Daily Herald, OH, Delphos

Spencer, Rich
abortle@thedailyreview.com, Prodn. Mgr., Mailroom (Day), The Daily Review, PA, Towanda

Spencer, Sam .... (860) 347-3331, ext. 131
sam@middletownpress.com, Class., The Middletown Press, CT, Middletown

Spensley, Mark
mexpress@n-connect.net, Adv. Mgr., Monticello Shoppers' Guide, IA, Monticello

Sperl, Cheryl .... (605) 835-8089
gregorynews@gregorynews.com, Pub./Ed., Gregory Times-Advocate, SD, Gregory

Sperry, Judy
judy@artvoice.com, Adv. Dir., Art Voice, NY, Buffalo

Speth, Brenda .... (707) 256-2234
bspeth@napanews.com, Pub., Distinctive Properties, CA, Napa

Speth, Brenda .... (707) 256-2234
bspeth@napanews.com, Pub., American Canyon Eagle, CA, Napa

Speth, Lisa .... (801) 853-5068
lisa.speth@newscycle.com, Marketing Communications Mgr., Newscycle Solutions, MN, Bloomington

Spetrini, Paul .... (401) 294-4576
pspetrini@ricentral.com, Ed., Standard-Times, RI, Wakefield

Spevak, Jeff .... (585) 258-2452
jspevak@democratandchronicle.com, Pop Music/Nite Scene Reporter, Democrat and Chronicle, NY, Rochester

Speziali, John
production@simcoeyorkprinting.com, Production Mgr., The Times Of New Tecumseth, ON, Beeton

Spicehandler, Lauren .... (203) 966-9541
lspicehandler@hersamacorn.com, Acct. Exec., Darien Times, CT, Darien

Spicer, Bill
bill.spicer@maps.com, Dir., Online Commerce, Maps.com, CA, Santa Barbara

Spicer, Frank L. .... (304) 645-1206
WVDN2@aol.com, Vice Pres./Pub., Moffitt Newspapers, VA, Roanoke

Spicer, Zach .... (812) 523-7080
ZSpicer@TribTown.com, Sports Ed., The Tribune, IN, Seymour

Spiegel, Alan .... (301) 949-9766
alan@thebeaconnewspapers.com, Sales Dir., The Beacon, MD, Kensington

Spiegel, Alan .... (301) 949-9766
alan@thebeaconnewspapers.com, Vice President Sales & Marketing, The Beacon, MD, Kensington

Spiegel, Andrea .... ext. 100
aspiegel@metrokids.com, Circ. Mgr., MetroKids Delaware, PA, Philadelphia

Spieker-Martin, Debbie .... (775) 850-2286
Cor. Dir., Swift Communications, Inc., NV, Carson City

Spielberger, Ronald
rsplbrgr@memphis.edu, Assoc. Prof., University of Memphis, TN, Memphis

Spielman, Karleen
kspielman@journal-news.net, Adv. Rep., The Shepherdstown Chronicle, WV, Shepherdstown

Spielman, Matt .... (716) 487-1111
editorial@post-journal.com, News Ed., The Post-Journal, NY, Jamestown

Spilak, Brent
bspilak@innisfail.greatwest.ca, Pub/Adv. Mgr., Innisfail Province, AB, Innisfail

Spiliotis, Shannon .... (603) 413-5135
sspiliotis@mcleancommunications.com, Circ. Mgr., Parenting New Hampshire, NH, Manchester

Spillers, Melissa .... (765) 825-0581 ext. 247
mspillers@newsexaminer.com, Adv. Dir., Connersville News-Examiner, IN, Connersville

Spillman, Mary
spillman@bsu.edu, Asst. Prof./Coord., News-Editorial, Ball State University, IN, Muncie

Spina, Anthony .... ext. 3588
aspina@civitasmedia.com, Media Dir., Abington Journal, PA, Clarks Summit

Spinella, Gregory
welchnews@frontiernet.net, Pub., The Welch News, WV, Welch
welchnews@frontiernet.net, Pub., The Industrial News, WV, Welch

Spiner, Trent .... (603) 668-4321 Ext. 160
tspiner@unionleader.com, Exec. Ed., New Hampshire Union Leader/New Hampshire Sunday News, NH, Manchester

Spinosa, Stephen .... (203) 731-3427
sspinosa@hearstmediact.com, Ad. Dir., New Milford Spectrum, CT, New Milford
sspinosa@hearstmediact.com, Adv. Dir., Darien Times, CT, Darien
sspinosa@hearstmediact.com, Multimedia Sales Director, The News-Times, CT, Danbury

Spiridigliozzi, Vincent .... (514) 983-3317
vspiridigliozzi@ledevoir.com, Asst. Sales Mgr.,

Le Devoir, QC, Montreal

Spitalnick, Melissa .... (516) 307-1045 EXT 213
mspitalnick@theislandnow.com , ACCT EXECUTIVE, Great Neck News, NY, Williston Park

Spitler, Pete .... (618) 826-2385
pspitler@randolphcountyheraldtribune.com, Ed., Randolph County Herald Tribune, IL, Du Quoin

Spitler, Pete
pspitler@randolphcountyheraldtribune.com, Ed., Steeleville Ledger, IL, Du Quoin

Spitz, Jill .... (520) 573-4177
jspitz@azstarnet.com, Ed., Arizona Daily Star, AZ, Tucson

Spitzack, Tim .... (651) 457-1177
tim@stpaulpublishing.com, Pub./Ed., The St. Paul Voice, Downtown St. Paul Voice, South St. Paul Voice and La Voz Latina, MN, West St Paul

Spitzer, Brad .... (580) 928-5540
sayrerecord@cableone.net, Co-Pub., The Beckham County Record, OK, Sayre

Spitzer, Dayva
sayrerecord@cableone.net, Ed., The Beckham County Record, OK, Sayre

Spitzer, Pam .... (719) 263-5311
pspitzer@ljtdmail.com, Fowler Tribune Office Mgr., The Fowler Tribune, CO, Fowler

Spivey, Lynne
lspivey@xtn.net, Circ. Mgr., The Herald-News, TN, Dayton

Spohr, George .... (570) 704-3989
gspohr@timesleader.com, Executive Editor, Times Leader, PA, Wilkes Barre

Spohr, George .... (765) 420-5242
Exec. Ed., Journal and Courier, IN, Lafayette

Spolar, Stephen .... (412) 263-3053
sspolar@post-gazette.com, Human Resources, Pittsburgh Post-Gazette, PA, Clinton

Sponsler, Lucas
sponsler@westernschools.org, Ed./Pub., County Press, MI, Parma

Spoon, Doug .... (909) 869-3540
The Poly Post, CA, Pomona

Spotleson, Bruce
lasvegasweekly@lasvegasweekly.com, Pub., Las Vegas Weekly, NV, Henderson

Spotser, Carla
bookkeeping@cantondailyledger.com, Publisher, Fulton County Shopper, IL, Canton

Spradlin, Derrick
dspradlin@fhu.edu, Freed-Hardeman Univ., TN, Henderson

Spragg, David
spragg.david@brunswicknews.com, Editor - Administration, New Brunswick Telegraph-Journal, NB, Saint John

Sprague, James .... (765) 825-0588 ext. 235
jsprague@newsexaminer.com, Ed., Connersville News-Examiner, IN, Connersville

Sprague, Mike
mike.sprague@sgvn.com, Reporter, The Whittier Daily News, CA, Monrovia

Spratt, Heather .... (419) 278-2816
dflagnews@embarqmail.com, Editor, The Deshler Flag, OH, Deshler

Sprayregen, Nick
nsprayregen@risingmediagroup.com, Pub., Yonkers Rising, NY, Yonkers

Sprengelmeyer, M.E. .... (575) 472-3555
comsilvercom@plateautel.net, Rep./Pub., The Guadalupe County Communicator, NM, Santa Rosa

Spriggs, Diane
dstriggs1107@comcast.net, Ed., Baptist

Trumpet, AR, Little Rock

Springberg, Kathy .... (715) 735-6611
kspringberg@eagleherald.com, Vice President & General Manager-EagleHerald, The Gazette - gazettextra.com, WI, Janesville

Springer, Bill
sales@alvareviewcourier.net, Ad Rep, Alva Review-Courier, OK, Alva

Springer, Craig .... (301) 784-2540
cspringer@times-news.com, Advertising Director, The Garrett County Weekender, MD, Cumberland

Springer, Dan
dan@thereportergroup.org, Bus. Mgr., The Reporter, NY, Vestal

Springer, Dan
dan@thereportergroup.org, Bus. Mgr., The Voice, NY, Vestal

Springer, Heidi .... (262) 728-3424
hspringer@communityshoppers.com, Sales Operations Manager, Walworth County Shopper Advertiser, WI, Elkhorn

Springer, Heidi
hspringer@communityshoppers.com, Adv. Sales Mgr., Janesville Messenger, WI, Delavan
hspringer@communityshoppers.com, Sales Mgr., Stateline News, WI, Elkhorn
hspringer@communityshoppers.com, Sales Mgr., Walworth County Sunday, WI, Elkhorn

Sprinkel-Hart, Cyndi
cyndi.sprinkel-hart@lee.net, Adv. Dir., Lebanon Express, OR, Lebanon

Sprinkle, Joey .... (620) 442-4200 ext 114
sports@arkcity.net, Sports Ed., The Arkansas City Traveler, KS, Arkansas City

Sprong, Deb
dsprong@elkharttruth.com, Copy Ed., Elkhart Truth, IN, Elkhart

Sprung, James .... (352) 753-1119
jim.sprung@thevillagesmedia.com, General Manager, The Villages Daily Sun, FL, The Villages

Spula, Frank
popmail@insnet.com, Pub., Dziennik Zwaizkowy, IL, Chicago

Spula, Frank J.
frank.spula@pna-znp.org, Pres., Zgoda, IL, Chicago

Spurgeon, Cheryl .... (812) 375-2819
circulation@therepublic.com, Circ. Mgr., The Republic, IN, Columbus

Spurgeon, Jessica
jessica.spurgeon@courierpost.com, Pub., Hannibal Courier-Post, MO, Hannibal

Spurgeon, Karen .... (641) 664-2334
karen@bdemo.com, Pub, Bloomfield Democrat, IA, Bloomfield

Spurgron, Jessica
jessica.spurgeon@courierpost.com, Gen. Mgr., Salt River Journal, MO, Hannibal

Spurling, Lori .... (828) 202-2926
lspurling@thedigitalcourier.com, Pub., The Daily Courier, NC, Forest City

Spurlock, Ashly .... (317) 398-1257
aspurlock@shelbynews.com, Adv. Acct. Exec., The Shelbyville News, IN, Shelbyville

Spurlock, Kathy
kspurlock2@gannett.com, Exec. Ed., The News-Star, LA, Monroe

Spurney, Blake
bspurney@TheClaytonTribune.com, Hesston Record, KS, Hesston

Spurrell, Ken
kspurrell@tacomadailyindex.com, Pub., Tacoma Daily Index, WA, Tacoma

Squillace, Scott
ssquillace@livent.net, Comptroller, Yellowstone

Communications, MT, Livingston

Squillace, Scott
ssquillace@livent.net, Controller, The Livingston Enterprise, MT, Livingston

Squire, Gary
gary.squire@sunmedia.ca, Prod. Mgr., The Observer, ON, Sarnia

Squires, Bonnie .... (610) 329-6826
squires@pjvoice.org, President, Philadelphia Jewish Voice, PA, Bala Cynwyd

Squires, Sarah .... (507) 452-1262 ext. 101
winpost@winonapost.com, Ed, Winona Post, MN, Winona

Sr., Edwin C.
thecalhountimes@windstream.net, Ed., The Calhoun Times, SC, Saint Matthews

St-Amand, Alain
alain.st-amand@hebdosquebecor.com, Gen. Mgr., Le Pharillon, QC, Gaspe

St-Amand, Alain
alain.st-amand@quebecormedia.com, Regl. Dir. Gen., L'avant-poste Gaspesien, QC, Amqui

St. Amand, Alain
alain.st-amand@hebdosquebecor.com, Pub., Le Progres-echo, QC, Rimouski

St. Amand, Alain
alain.st-amand@hebdosquebecor.com, Pub., Le Rimouskois, QC, Rimouski

St. Amand, Charles .... (978) 970-4638
cstamand@lowellsun.com, Mng. Ed., The Sun, MA, Lowell

St. Amand, Charles .... (978) 516-2274
cstamand@sentinelandenterprise.com, Ed., Sentinel & Enterprise, MA, Fitchburg

St. Amand, Lea .... (970) 728-9788 ext.10
lea@telluridenews.com, Mktg./Sales Coord., The Norwood Post, CO, Telluride

St. Charles, Anna
astcharles@gatehousemedia.com, Director, Major & National Accounts, GateHouse Media, Inc., NY, Pittsford

St. Clair, Ricky .... (518) 565-4124
rstclair@pressrepublican.com, Sports Editor, Press-Republican, NY, Plattsburgh

St. Clair, Tina .... (812) 231-4228
tina.stclair@tribstar.com, Ad. Director, Tribune-Star Publishing Co., Inc., IN, Terre Haute

St. Claire, Allison .... (303) 355-3882
clearmountain@tde.com, Pub./Ed., Senior Wire News Service, Denver

St. Cyr, Brian
bstcyr@mediaspace.com, VP of Business Development & Marketing, Mediaspace Solutions, MN, Hopkins

St. Germain, Brent .... (985) 857-2239
brent.stgermain@houmatoday.com, Sports Ed., The Courier, LA, Houma

St. Hilaire, William C.
hrslatercompany@aol.com, Office Mgr., H.R. Slater Co., Inc., IL, Chicago

St. John, John .... (909) 799-9950 x222
johnstjohn@systems-technology-inc.com, Pres., Systems Technology, Inc., CA, San Bernardino

St. John, Lance .... (605) 845-3646
web@mobridgetribune.com, Web Printing Mgr., Mobridge Tribune, SD, Mobridge

St. Lawrence, Joe .... (807) 343-6228
joe.stlawrence@chroniclejournal.com, Prodn. Foreman, Pressroom, The Chronicle-Journal, ON, Thunder Bay

St. Louis, Jill
editorial@thecanadianpress.com, Bureau Chief, Broadcast News Limited, BC, Vancouver

St. Louis, Patricia

news@epcan.com, Mng. Ed., El Paso County Advertiser & News, CO, Fountain

St. Pierre, Mary ....ext. 212
Serv. Mgr., Florida Catholic, FL, Orlando

St. Romain, Penny
penny@avoyelles.com, Gen. Mgr., Bunkie Record, LA, Bunkie

Staab, David J.
dstaab@myprogressnews.com, Pub./Ed., The Progress News, PA, Emlenton

Staas-Haught, Jerry .... (856) 563-5265
jhaught@gannettnj.com, Reg. Cont. Strategist, The Daily Journal, NJ, Vineland

Stabbert III, Fred .... (845) 887-5200 ext. 103
publisher@sc-democrat.com, Publisher, Sullivan County Democrat, NY, Callicoon

Stabell, Shawn
shawn.stabell@timesargus.com, Circ. Dir., The Times Argus, VT, Barre
shawn.stabell@timesargus.com, Circ. Dir., Rutland Herald, VT, Rutland

Stabnick, Pete .... (501) 664-0125
pstabnick@dolr.org, advertising manager, Arkansas Catholic, AR, Little Rock

Stace, Janet
jstace@edmontonexaminer.com, Prodn. Mgr., The Grove Examiner, AB, Spruce Grove

Stacey, Phil .... (978) 338-2650
pstacey@salemnews.com, Sports Ed., The Salem News, MA, Beverly

Stack, Emily
managing@theaggie.org, Managing Editor, University of California, Davis, CA, Davis

Stack, Noel .... (530) 344-5073
nstack@mtdemocrat.net, Editor, Mountain Democrat, CA, Placerville

Stack, Noel .... (530) 344-5073
editor@villagelife.com, Mng. Ed., Village Life, CA, Placerville

Stack, Richard
rstack@american.edu, Assoc. Prof., American University, DC, Washington

Stackpole, Kerry
kstackpole@nahp.org, Exec. Dir., National Association of Hispanic Publications, DC, Washington

Stacks, Don
don.stacks@miami.edu, Prof./Prog. Dir., PR, University of Miami, FL, Coral Gables

Stadnyk, Mary
mstadn@dioceseoftrenton.org, Associate Ed, The Monitor, NJ, Trenton

Stadther, Luke .... (320) 523-2032
editor@rencopub.com, Editor, Renville County Register, MN, Renville

Stafford, John
rfahey@recorder.com, Adv. Sales, Daily Hampshire Gazette, MA, Northampton

Stafford, Jon .... (413) 585-5279
jstafford@gazettenet.com, Adv. Dir., Daily Hampshire Gazette, MA, Northampton

Stafford, Rob .... ext. 3053
rstafford@staffordgroup.com, Pres./Gen. Mgr., Publications, The Daily News, MI, Greenville

Stafford, Robert .... (616) 754-9301
Ed., Buy Line, MI, Greenville

Stafford, Tom
tom@springfieldnewssun.com, Women's Ed., Springfield News-Sun, OH, Springfield

Stagley, Gina
gslagley@newportindependent.com, Ed./Pub., Newport Independent, AR, Newport

Stagner, Rick .... (719) 691-4805
rstagner@lamarledger.com, Advertising Consultant, The Lamar Ledger, CO, Lamar

Stahl, Beverly .... (419) 784-5441 ext. 215
bev@crescent-news.com, Prepress Mgr.,

Adams Publishing Group, LLC, MN, Virginia

Stahl, Brent
bstahl@moriresearch.com, Vice Pres., Research, Minnesota Opinion Research, Inc. (MORI), MN, Minneapolis

Stahl, Deborah
ads@tcadvertiser.com, Adv Mgr., Tuscola County Advertiser, MI, Caro

Stahl, Jeff .... (517) 417-2006
jstahl@lenconnect.com, Circ. Dir., The Daily Telegram, MI, Adrian

Stahl, Nick .... (501) 505-1245
nicolas.stahl@thecabin.net, Online Dir., Log Cabin Democrat, AR, Conway

Stahl, Robert
robert.stahl@bachmanmachine.com, Asst. Prof., Saint Louis University, MO, Saint Louis

Stahla, Jeff .... (970) 669-5050, ext. 691
JStahla@Reporter-Herald.com, Mng. Ed., Loveland Reporter-Herald, CO, Loveland

Stahlbrodt, Peter J.
peterstahlbrodt@yahoo.com, The Shopping Bag Advertiser, NY, East Rochester
peterstahlbrodt@yahoo.com, Ed., Shopping Bag & Advertiser (OOB), NY, East Rochester

Stahle, Howard .... (801) 250-5656
news@magnanews.com, Owner/Pub./Ed., Oquirrh Times, UT, Magna

Stahle, R. Gail
clippe59@mail.idt.net, Ed., The Davis Clipper, UT, Bountiful

Staiano, John .... (630) 572-7650
john.staiano@harlandsimon.com, Managing Director - Americas, Harland Simon, IL, Oak Brook

Staik, Paul
pstaik@heartlandnewspapers.com, The Polk County News and Democrat, FL, Winter Haven

Stainer, Maria .... (202) 636-3265
mstainer@washingtontimes.com, Asst. Mng. Ed, Universal Desk, The Washington Times, DC, Washington

Stains, Larry
lstains@temple.edu, Asst. Prof./Dir., Mag. seq., Temple University, PA, Philadelphia

Stalcup, Mark
mstalcup@vinu.edu, Dir., Journalism Program, Vincennes University, IN, Vincennes

Stalder, Bryan .... (816) 241-0765
northeastnews@socket.net, Creative Director, The Northeast News, MO, Kansas City

Staley, Kelly
kstaley@marketing.org, Membership Mgr., Business Marketing Association, IL, Naperville

Stalheim, Curt .... (815) 248-4407
volunteer@stateline-isp.com, Pub., Volunteer Plus, IL, Durand

Stallard, Jack .... (903) 237-7760
jstallard@news-journal.com, Sports Ed., Longview News-Journal, TX, Longview

Stallings, CeCelia .... (252) 639-2668
cstallings@freedomenc.com, Adv. Sales., The Shopper, NC, New Bern

Stallings, LeAnn .... (334) 682-4422
progressiveera@mchsi.com, Graphics/Adv. Mgr., Wilcox Progressive Era, AL, Camden

Stallings, Mark .... (847) 427-4890
mstallings@dailyherald.com, Manager Digital Ops., Daily Herald, IL, Arlington Heights

Stallone, Albert A. .... (610) 236-4745
astallone@readingeagle.com, Packaging/Distr. Dir., Reading Eagle, PA, Reading

Stallone, Steve
steve.stallone@ilwu.org, Pres., International Labor Communications Association AFL/CIO/ CLC, DC, Washington

Stallwitz, Steve .... (785) 776-2200 Ext. 230
adv@themercury.com, Adv./Prod. Dir., The Manhattan Mercury, KS, Manhattan

Staloch, Steve
sstaloch@mainstreetmg.com, Pub., The Gilroy Dispatch, CA, Gilroy

Staman, Brad
brad.staman@geringcourier.com, Pub., Gering Courier, NE, Scottsbluff

Stambaugh, Craig
craig.stambaugh@stockton.edu, Richard Stockton College, NJ, Galloway

Stambaugh, Drew
dstambaugh@civitasmedia.com, Ed., Fulton County Expositor, OH, Wauseon
dstambaugh@civitasmedia.com, Ed., Swanton Enterprise, OH, Wauseon

Stamm, John
john@mifflinburgtelegraph.com, Pub., Mifflinburg Telegraph, PA, Mifflinburg

Stamm, Patricia .... (403) 314-4318
prstamm@reddeeradvocate.com, Adv. Mgr., Classified, Red Deer Advocate, AB, Red Deer

Stamoulis, Chris
aphrodite@hellenicnews.com, Mktg. Mgr., Hellenic News of America, PA, Concordville

Stamper, Don .... (847) 427-5548
dstamper@dailyherald.com, Director of Production, Daily Herald, IL, Arlington Heights

Stamper, Judy .... (580) 326-3311
judy@hugonews.com, VP, Acct., Hugo News, OK, Hugo

Stamper, Stan .... (580) 326-3311
hugonews@sbcglobal.net, Pres./Pub./Ed., Hugo News, OK, Hugo

Stamper, Tom
tstamper@hcnonline.com, Prod. Mgr, The Rancher, TX, Conroe

Stamport, Shelly .... (512) 259-4449
classifieds@hillcountrynews.com, Classifieds, Hill Country News, TX, Cedar Park

Stancampiano, Lou
publisher@express-times.com, President and Publisher, The Express-Times, PA, Easton

Stancampiano, Louis .... (973) 192-4188
lstancampiano@starledger.com, Advertising Director, The Star-Ledger, NJ, Newark

Standfield, Mary .... (903) 455-4220
mbstandfield@cnhi.com, Bus. Mgr., Herald-Banner, TX, Greenville
mbstandfield@cnhi.com, Royse City Herald Banner, TX, Greenville

Standfield, Olene
ostandfield@t-g.com, Circ. Dir., Shelbyville Times-Gazette, TN, Shelbyville

Standley, Tracy
tstandley@mcneese.edu, Asst. Prof., McNeese State University, LA, Lake Charles

Standring, Chris .... (780) 429-5112
cstandring@thejournal.canwest.com, At Home/ Look Ed., Edmonton Journal, AB, Edmonton

Standring, Suzette .... (617) 697-6854
director@columnists.com, Executive Director (as of January 2017), The National Society of Newspaper Columnists, Inc., MA, Milton

Stanek, Marcy
mstanek@salmonpress.com, Prodn. Mgr., Salmon Press, NH, Meredith

Stanfield, David
dstanfield@wsjournal.com , Regional Controller, Winston-Salem Journal, NC, Winston Salem

Stanfill, Nick
nstanfill@cnhi.com, Director, Internal Audit, Community Newspaper Holdings, Inc., AL, Montgomery

Stanford, Bill ....(570) 494-6789
wildbill@wildbillsartshow.net, Creator, Wild
Bill's Cartoon Show!, Montoursville

Stanford, Christie ....(903) 536-2015
centervillenewspaper@gmail.com, Publisher,
Centerville News, TX, Centerville

Stanford, Scott ....(970) 871-4202
sstanford@SteamboatToday.com, General
Manager, Steamboat Today, CO, Steamboat
Springs
sstanford@SteamboatToday.com, General
Manager, Steamboat Pilot, CO, Steamboat
Springs

Stanford, Scott ....(785) 832-7277
sstanford@ljworld.com, Publisher, Lawrence
Journal-World, KS, Lawrence

Stanford, Scott
sstanford@ljworld.com, Pub., Shawnee
Dispatch, KS, Shawnee

Stanford, Scott ....(970) 871-4202
sstanford@steamboatpilot.com, General
Manager - Steamboat Pilot & Today,
WorldWest LLC, KS, Lawrence

Stanford, Todd
tstanford@dailyitem.com, Sports Ed., The Daily
Item, MA, Lynn
tstanford@dailyitem.com, The Daily Item, PA,
Sunbury

Stang, Catherine
stoughtonsales@wcinet.com, Ad. Sales, The
Fitchburg Star, WI, Verona

Stangl, Tom
tstangl@lemarscomm.net, Pub., Shoppers
Guide, IA, Le Mars

Stangl, Tom
tstangl@theameryfreepress.com, Publisher,
Burnett County Sentinel, WI, Grantsburg

Stangl, Tom ....(715) 268-8101
tstangl@theameryfreepress.com, Pub, The
Sun, WI, Osceola

Stanislowski, John
john.stanislowski@bloapco.com, Pres., Blower
Application Co., Inc., WI, Germantown

Stanko, Frank....................(701) 642-8585
franks@wahpetondailynews.com, Reporter,
The Daily News, ND, Wahpeton

Stanley, Anna....................(785) 822-1435
astanley@salina.com, Adv. Asst., The Salina
Journal, KS, Salina

Stanley, Cathryn
asdix@dixcom.com, Ed., Barnesville
Enterprise, OH, Barnesville

Stanley, Cathy ....(707) 964-5642 ext. 96092
cstanley@advocate-news.com, Office Mgr, The
Mendocino Beacon, CA, Fort Bragg

Stanley, Dave
dave.stanley@globegazette.com, Pub., Town &
Country Shopper, IA, Osage

Stanley, Dave....................(641) 394-2111
publisher@nhtrib.com, Pub, New Hampton
Tribune, IA, New Hampton

Stanley, George ....(414) 224-2248
gstanley@journalsentinel.com, Sr. VP/Ed.,
Milwaukee Journal Sentinel, WI, Milwaukee

Stanley, Jim
ledgersports@socket.net, Sports Ed., Mexico
Ledger, MO, Mexico

Stanley, Monica....................(231) 941-1574
Prodn. Mgr., Mailroom, Traverse City Record-
Eagle, MI, Traverse City

Stanley, Monty ....(325) 659-8204
mstanley@gosanangelo.com, HR Dir., San
Angelo Standard-Times, TX, San Angelo

Stanley, Roger ....(509) 577-7757
rstanley@yakimaherald.com, Op. Dir., Yakima
Herald-Republic, WA, Yakima
rstanley@yakimaherald.com, Prodn. Mgr.,
Opns., San Mateo County Times (OOB), CA,

San Jose

Stanley, Sherry....................(276) 779-4036
Sr. Adv. Rep., The Pilot, NC, Pilot Mountain
Adv. Mgr., The Carroll News, VA, Hillsville

Stanley, Stephanie
sstanley@newswatchman.com, Ed., The Pike
County News Watchman, OH, Waverly

Stanley, Time........................(765) 671-1275
tstanley@chronicle-tribune.com, Pressroom
Mgr., Chronicle-Tribune, IN, Marion

Stanphill, Aileen
cottoncountylegals@sbcglobal.net, Office Mgr.,
Walters Herald, OK, Walters

Stansbury, Sarah
registerdisplay@gmail.com, Adv. Rep., The Iola
Register, KS, Iola

Stansel, Benita
bstensel@northumberlandnews.com, Circ.
Mgr., The Brighton Independent, ON,
Brighton

Stanton, Edwin ....(205) 722-0226
edwin.stanton@tuscaloosanews.com, Mng.
Ed. (Sports), The Tuscaloosa News, AL,
Tuscaloosa

Stanton, Ilene ....(971) 204-7759
istanton@pamplinmedia.com, Sr. commercial
Sales Rep, Nickel Ads Portland, Oregon,
OR, Portland

Stanton, Jim
jim@weeklydig.com, Ed., Boston's Weekly Dig,
MA, Boston

Stanton, Kevin................(508) 228-0001 Ext. 33
kstanton@inkym.com, Circ. , Nantucket Today,
MA, Nantucket
kstanton@inkym.com, Circulation/Classified
Manager, The Inquirer and Mirror, MA,
Nantucket

Stanton, Marcie
cleartrib@cebridge.net, Pub., Clearwater
Tribune, ID, Orofino

Stanton, Marianne
mstanton@inkym.com, Ed., The Inquirer and
Mirror, MA, Nantucket

Stanton, Michael
michael.stanton@sourcemedia.com, Pub., The
Bond Buyer, NY, New York

Stanton, Stacie
Marie@qctonline.com , Editor and Publisher,
Quebec Chronicle-telegraph, QC, Quebec

Stanul, Laurie ....(610) 596-3563
lstanul@ottawacitizen.com, Sales Planning
Cord., The Ottawa Citizen, ON, Ottawa

Stapleford, Tom ....(717) 307-2441
tom.stapleford@mercersburgjournal.com, Mng
Ed., Mercersburg Journal, PA, Mercersburg

Staples , Barbara ....(567) 242-0356
bstaples@civitasmedia.com, Adv. Mgr., The
Lima News, OH, Lima
bstaples@civitasmedia.com, Adv. Mgr. , The
Vindicator, OH, Youngstown

Stapleton, Becky
lsncol@aol.com, Adv. Mgr., Caldwell
Watchman, LA, Columbia

Stapleton, Jean ....(323) 265-8875
Staplej@elac.edu, Advisor, East Los Angeles
College, CA, Monterey Park

Stapleton, Libby ....(936) 633-5288
lstapleton@angelina.edu, Advisor, Angelina
College, TX, Lufkin

Stapleton, O.J.
ostapleton@newsdemocratleader.com,
Ed., The News Democrat & Leader, KY,
Russellville

Stapleton, Sally 860/701-4256
s.stapleton@theday.com, Managing Editor/
Multimedia, The Day, CT, New London

Stapleton, Sally ....(412) 263-1858
sstapleton@post-gazette.com, Managing

Editor, Pittsburgh Post-Gazette, PA, Clinton

Stapley, Charles
chuck.stapley@sunmedia.ca, Prodn. Dir., The
Ottawa Sun, ON, Ottawa

Starck, Kenneth
kenneth.starck@zu.ac.ae, Dean, Zayed
University, Al Ruwayyah

Stark, Carol
cstark@joplinglobe.com, Ed., The Joplin Globe,
MO, Joplin

Stark, Chuck ....(360) 792-8566
cstark@kitsapsun.com, Sports Ed., Kitsap
Sun, WA, Bremerton

Stark, Darlene
dstark@thepilot.com, Circ. Dir., The Pilot, NC,
Southern Pines

Stark, Pam
trads.pam@gmail.com, Sales, Valley City
Times-Record, ND, Valley City

Stark, Patricia
pdstark@pipeline.sbcc.edu, Santa Barbara City
College, CA, Santa Barbara

Stark, Paula ....ext. 107
pstark@floridasunonline.net, Pub., Osceola
News-gazette, FL, Kissimmee

Stark, Paula
pstark@osceolanewsgazette.com, Pub.,
Osceola Homefinder, FL, Kissimmee

Stark, Ven ....(989) 673-8603
Circ. Mgr., Shopper's Advantage, MI, Caro
Circ. Mgr., Tuscola County Advertiser, MI, Caro

Stark , Andria
press@wunderground.com, Press & Media
, Weather Underground, Inc., The, San
Francisco
press@wunderground.com, Vice Pres. Sales/
Mktg., The Weather Underground, Inc., San
Francisco

Starkey, John
john@irvingrambler.com, Pub., The Irving
Rambler, TX, Irving

Starkey, Stacey
irving@irvingrambler.com, Ed., The Irving
Rambler, TX, Irving

Starkey, Vickie ....(770) 934-7380
vstarkey@wdfarmerplans.com, Pres., W.D.
Farmer Residence Designer, Inc., Lilburn

Starnes, Judy
judy.starnes@thefacts.com, Gen. Mgr., The
Facts, TX, Clute

Starnes, Kim....................(765) 362-1200 x 110
kstarnes@jrpress.com, Adv. Mgr., Journal
Review, IN, Crawfordsville

Starnes, Pat
starnesp@att.net, Adv. Dir., The Weaverville
Tribune, NC, Weaverville

Starr, Bernie
bstarr@kentuckynewera.com, Adv. Rep.,
Kentucky New Era, KY, Hopkinsville

Starr, Curtis H.
phillips_county_news@yahoo.com, Ed., The
Phillips County News, MT, Malta

Starr, Jason.................(802) 872-9000 ext. 117
editor@willistonobserver.com, Editor, Williston
Observer, VT, Williston

Starr, Tena ....(802) 525-3531
tenas@bartonchronicle.com, Ed., The
Chronicle, VT, Barton

Starsick, Jennifer
jennifer@cnpapers.com, Adv. Mgr., The
Charleston Gazette-Mail, WV, Charleston

Stasiowski, Jim ....(605) 716-0981
Managing Editor, Rapid City Journal, SD,
Rapid City

Stasney, Ted ....(813) 259-7766
Tampa Bay Times, FL, St Petersburg

Staszkow, Craig

cstaszkow@dnews.com, Adv. Mgr., Moscow-
Pullman Daily News, ID, Moscow

Statler, Erik ....(732) 922-6000 ext. 3310
estatler@app.com, VP/Fin., Asbury Park Press,
NJ, Neptune

Statler, Judith
ads@rallshe.com, Pub., Ralls County Herald-
Enterprise, MO, New London

Staton, Cindy ....(740) 532-1441 Ext. 213
cindyjo.staton@irontontribune.com, Cir. Clerk /
CSR, The Ironton Tribune, OH, Ironton

Statz, Mary
nclgnews@gmail.com, Ed., Nuckolls County
Locomotive-Gazette, NE, Nelson

Staudt, Jill
jstaudt@pbdailynews.com, Adv. Team Leader,
Palm Beach Daily News, FL, Palm Beach

Stauffer, Lauren
advertising@thenorthsidechronicle.com,
Advertising Manager, The Northside
Chronicle, PA, Pittsburgh

Stautberg, Timothy E. ....(513) 977-3826
stautberg@scripps.com, Sr. Vice Pres./
Newspapers, E. W. Scripps Co., OH,
Cincinnati

Stavrakas, Scott ....(815) 220-6945
vpsales@newstrib.com, Adv. Dir., News-
Tribune, IL, La Salle

Stay, Matt
matt.stay@mowercountyshopper.com, Gen.
Mgr., Mower County Shopper, MN, Austin

Stearley, Eric ....(260) 377-9032
eric@thepaperofwabash.com, The Paper, IN,
Wabash

Stebbins, Chad
stebbins-c@mssu.edu, Exec. Dir., International
Society of Weekly Newspaper Editors, MO,
Joplin

Stebens, Jim ....(316) 788-0191
jstebens@aol.com, Ed., Real Estate Book,
KS, Wichita

Stechschulte, Michael ....(313) 596-7109
Michael@aod.org, Managing Ed., The
Michigan Catholic, MI, Detroit

Steckler, Rebecca.....................(313) 222-6400
rsteckler@dnps.com, Sr. VP of Sales &
Marketing
, Detroit Free Press, MI, Detroit

Stedham, Mike ....(256) 782-5713
mstedham@jsu.edu, Jacksonville State Univ.,
AL, Jacksonville

Stedman, Bill ....(508) 543-4851
foxboronews@yahoo.com, Managing Ed., The
Foxboro Reporter, MA, Foxboro

Stedman, Frank
wilburregister@centurytel.net, Pub., Wilbur
Register, WA, Wilbur

Steed, Camille ....(712) 325-3725
Iowa Western Cmty. College, IA, Council Bluffs

Steel, Pamela
psteel@metrolandnorthmedia.com, Ed,
Bracebridge Examiner, ON, Bracebridge

Steele, Ashley.........................(803) 359-7633
ashley.lexchron@gmail.com, Associate
Publisher, Lexington County Chronicle & The
Dispatch-News, SC, Lexington

Steele, Billy
bsteele@calhountimes.com, Adv. Mgr.,
Calhoun Times and Gordon County News,
GA, Calhoun

Steele, Brian
bsteele@record-eagle.com, American
International College, MA, Springfield
bsteele@record-eagle.com, Ed. in Chief,
Traverse City Record-Eagle, MI, Traverse City

Steele, Bruce ....(828) 232-5848
bsteele@citizen-times.com, Planning Ed., The
Asheville Citizen-Times, NC, Asheville

culture - Reporter, The Salt Lake Tribune, UT, Salt Lake City

Stephenson, LeAnna .... **(903) 628-5801**
lstephenson@bowiecountynow.com, Class. & Circ., Bowie County Citizen Tribune, TX, New Boston

Stephenson, Thomas A.
tstephen@express-news.net, Pres./Pub., Bulverde News, TX, San Antonio
tstephen@express-news.net, Pres./Pub., Fort Sam News Leader, TX, San Antonio
tstephen@express-news.net, Pres./Pub., Kelly Observer, TX, San Antonio
tstephen@express-news.net, Pres./Pub., Lackland Talespinner, TX, San Antonio
tstephen@express-news.net, Pres./Pub., Medical Patriot, TX, San Antonio
tstephen@express-news.net, Pres./Pub., North Central News, TX, San Antonio
tstephen@express-news.net, Pres./Pub., Northeast Herald, TX, San Antonio
tstephen@express-news.net, Pres./Pub., Randolph Wingspread, TX, San Antonio
tstephen@express-news.net, Pres./Pub., Northwest Weekly, TX, San Antonio

Stephenson, Todd
webmaster@sentinelnews.com, Webmaster, Sentinel News Plus, KY, Shelbyville

Stephenson Sarver, Jodi .... **(800) 457-1156**
jsarver@wsjournal.com, Rep., Media General Syndication Services, Winston Salem

Stepleton, Ian .... **(920) 748-3017**
rcpnews@riponprinters.com, Ed., Ripon Commonwealth Press, WI, Ripon

Stepleton, Teri T. .... **(256) 740-5742**
teri.stepleton@timesdaily.com, Lifestyle Ed., Times Daily, AL, Florence

Stepniak, Dave .... **(519) 676-5023**
pr.tribune@southkent.net, Prod Mgr, Blenheim News-tribune, ON, Blenheim

Stepp, Sheila .... **(843) 229-3067**
pdrealestateweekly@sc.rr.com, Secretary/ Treasurer, National Association of Real Estate Publishers, SC, Florence

Sterkowicz, Laurie .... **(503) 624-6397 ext 35**
lauries@orenews.com, Accounting Assistant, Oregon Newspaper Publishers Association, OR, Lake Oswego

Sterling, Dick
Gouvtribunepress@gmail.com, Ed., The Gouverneur Tribune-Press, NY, Gouverneur

Sterling, Ed
edsterling@texaspress.com, Member Services Director, Texas Press Association, TX, Austin

Sterling, James
sterlingj@missouri.edu, Prof., University of Missouri, MO, Columbia

Sterling, Kathleen
wnrcnews@instanet.com, Pub. /Ed., Valley Vantage, CA, Woodland Hills

Stern, Albert
jfb.berkshirevoice@verizon.net, Ed., Berkshire Jewish Voice, MA, Pittsfield

Stern, Andrew L.
andy.stern@feiu.org, Int'l Pres., Service Employees International Union, CLC, DC, Washington

Stern, David
feedback@frontierspublishing.com, Frontiers in LA, CA, Los Angeles

Stern, Elliott
estern@santamariatimes.com, Sports Ed., Santa Maria Times, CA, Santa Maria

Stern, Elliott .... **(805) 739-2235**
estern@timespressrecorder.com, Sports Ed., The Lompoc Record, CA, Santa Maria

Stern, Jennifer .... **(718) 615-3802**
jstern@cnglocal.com, Circ. Mgr, Caribbean Life, NY, Brooklyn

Stern, Linda .... **(407) 376-2434**

lstern@turnstilemediagroup.com, Advt, Winter Park-Maitland Observer, FL, Orlando

Stern, Pamela .... **(718) 240-4554**
pstern@springcreektowers.com, Spring Creek Sun, NY, Brooklyn

Stern, Rivkie .... **(201) 805-9448**
info@rivkie.com, Advertising Manager, Jewish Voice and Opinion, NJ, Englewood

Stern, Robert
rstern@projectsinknowledge.com, Pres., Projects In Knowledge, Inc., NJ, Livingston

Stern, Sherry
sstern@ocregister.com, Mag., Asst. Managing Ed., The Orange County Register, CA, Santa Ana

Sternberg, Bill
bsternberg@usatoday.com, Editor, Editorial Page, USA TODAY, VA, Mc Lean

Sterner, Kim .... **(717) 637-3736 Ext. 146**
ksterner@eveningsun.com, Community Sun Ed., The Evening Sun, PA, Hanover

Sterner, Parry
sales.redpress@midconetwork.com, Adv. Sales Mgr., The Redfield Press, SD, Redfield

Sterner, Sandra
sandy.sterner@pressenterprise.net, Adv. Dir., Press Enterprise, PA, Bloomsburg

Sterner, Sandra J. .... **ext. 1216**
Adv. Dir., Around The House, PA, Bloomsburg

Stetson, Deborah
dstetson@barnstablepatriot.com, Ed., Barnstable Patriot, MA, Hyannis

Stettler, Andy
astettler@mainlinemedianews.com, Exec. Ed., Main Line Suburban Life, PA, Ardmore
astettler@mainlinemedianews.com, Exec. Ed., King of Prussia Courier, PA, Wayne

Stevens, Becky .... **(843) 488-7237**
hi6882@sccoast.net, Production Mgr., Horry News & Shopper, SC, Conway

Stevens, Bill .... **(727) 869-6250**
stevens@tampabay.com, Ed., North Suncoast, Tampa Bay Times, FL, St Petersburg

Stevens, Chris .... **(989) 839-4266**
stevens@mdn.net, Sports Ed., Midland Daily News, MI, Midland

Stevens, David .... **(575) 763-3431 Ext. 310**
Eastern New Mexico News, NM, Clovis

Stevens, David .... **(575) 763-3431**
dstevens@cnjonline.com, Ed., Eastern New Mexico News, NM, Clovis

Stevens, David
david_stevens@link.freedom.com, Ed., Cannon Connection, NM, Clovis

Stevens, Donna
dstevens@criernewspapers.com, Classified Adv. Mgr., Dunwoody Crier, GA, Dunwoody

Stevens, Elizabeth
estevens@ocregister.com, Dir. Recruitment, The Orange County Register, CA, Santa Ana

Stevens, Gavin
gavin@houmaweekly.com, Prod. Mgr, The Weekly Want Ads, LA, Houma
gavin@houmaweekly.com, Creative Dir., Point of Vue, LA, Houma

Stevens, Greg .... **(530) 737-5045**
gstevens@redbluffdailynews.com, Pub./Adv. Dir., Daily News, CA, Red Bluff

Stevens, Hope .... **(765) 575-4619**
hstevensthecouriertimes.com, Customer Service Specialist, The Courier-Times, IN, New Castle

Stevens, Joan
swtdaily@yahoo.com, Multimedia Acct. Specialist, Southwest Daily News, LA, Sulphur

Stevens, John

john_stevens@praxair.com, Vice Pres., Procuremenet/Materials Mgmt., Praxair, Inc., CT, Danbury

Stevens, Kathy .... **(973) 383-1203**
kstevens@njherald.com, News Ed., New Jersey Herald, NJ, Newton

Stevens, Lori .... **(814) 643-4040 x126**
lstevens@huntingdondailynews.com , Bus. Mng., The Huntingdon Daily News, PA, Huntingdon

Stevens, Mary Ann .... **(251) 434-1543**
Adv. Mgr., The Catholic Week, AL, Mobile

Stevens, Matthew
mstevens@sun-herald.com, Asst Sports Ed., Charlotte Sun, FL, Punta Gorda

Stevens, Mike .... **(360) 792-3350**
mstevens@kitsapsun.com, Dir., Adv./Mktg., Kitsap Sun, WA, Bremerton

Stevens, Peter .... **(401) 821-2216**
rireminder@aol.com, Pub./Adv. Mgr., The Reminder, RI, Coventry

Stevens, Peter
rireminder@aol.com, The Reminder, RI, Coventry

Stevens, Ray
rwstevens@greenbay.gannett.com, Nat'l Sales, Post-Crescent, WI, Appleton

Stevens, Richard
rstevens@theleafchronicle.com, Ed./Gen. Mgr., The Leaf-Chronicle, TN, Clarksville

Stevens, Robert .... **(435) 835-4241**
news@sanpetemessenger.cpm, Mng Ed, Sanpete Messenger, UT, Manti

Stevens, Thomas
argus@kkspc.com, Pub., The Astoria South Fulton Argus, IL, Astoria

Stevens, Vicki .... **(859) 236-2551 Ext. 357**
vicki@amnews.com, Asst. Managing Ed., The Advocate-Messenger, KY, Danville

Stevens II, J.L. .... **(251) 380-3067**
jstevens@shc.edu, Integrated Multimedia Center (IMC) Operations Mgr and Student Media adviser, Spring Hill College, AL, Mobile

Stevenson, Bill .... **ext. 226**
editor@columbiabasinherald.com, Mng. Ed., Columbia Basin Herald, WA, Moses Lake

Stevenson, Crystal .... **(337) 494-4083**
cstevenson@americanpress.com, Exec. Ed., American Press, LA, Lake Charles

Stevenson, Diane
stevenson@statesman.org, Photo Ed., Statesman Journal, OR, Salem

Stevenson, Gary W. .... **(307) 245-3763**
news@pinebluffspost.com, Owner, Pine Bluffs Post, WY, Pine Bluffs

Stevenson, Gary W.
saratogasun@union-tel.com, Pub./Owner, The Saratoga Sun, WY, Saratoga

Stevenson, George .... **(609) 403-7131**
gsteve@dioceseoftrenton.org, Bus. Dir., The Monitor, NJ, Trenton

Stevenson, Jan ....**(734) 293-7200 ext. 22**
janstevenson@pridesource.com, CFO, Q Syndicate, Livonia

Stevenson, Jan ....**(248) 615-7003 ext. 22**
janstevenson@pridesource.com, Adv. Dir., Between The Lines, MI, Livonia

Stevenson, Jeffrey T. .... **(212) 935-4990**
stevensonj@vss.com, Mng. Partner/Co-CEO, Veronis Suhler Stevenson, NY, New York

Stevenson, Jim .... **1-(248) 360-7355, x21**
jimstevenson@scnmail.com, Pub., Spinal Column Newsweekly, MI, Highland

Stevenson, John W.
john@therandolphleader.com, Ed. / Pub., The Randolph Leader, AL, Roanoke

Stevenson, Kayla
kayla@timesleader.net, Circulation/Advertising, Times Leader, KY, Princeton

Stevenson, Marilyn
mstevenson@ottawaherald.com, Circ. coordinator, The Ottawa Herald, KS, Ottawa

Stevenson, Robert .... **(864) 388-8210**
rstevenson@lander.edu, Lander Univ., SC, Greenwood

Stevenson, Sue
sue@northcountyoutlook.com, Co-Pub./Adv. Mgr., North County Outlook, WA, Marysville

Stevenson, Suzanne .... **(916) 774-7955**
sstevens@bizjournals.com, Ed, Business Journal of Portland, OR, Portland
sstevens@bizjournals.com, Auburn Journal, CA, Auburn

Steward, George .... **(270) 783-3253**
gstewart@bgdailynews.com, Packaging Mgr., Daily News, KY, Bowling Green

Stewart, Alasdair .... **ext. 272**
Asst. News Ed., Walla Walla Union-Bulletin, WA, Walla Walla

Stewart, Amy .... **(740) 452-3601**
astewart@adjustoveyor.com, Executive Vice President, Stewart Glapat Corp., OH, Zanesville

Stewart, Angela .... **(217) 788-1370**
angela.stewart@sj-r.com, Manager, Springfield Shopper, IL, Springfield
angela.stewart@sj-r.com, Classified Adv. Mgr., The State Journal-Register, IL, Springfield

Stewart, Betty
bstewart@c-dh.net, Office Mgr., Columbia Daily Herald, TN, Columbia
bstewart@c-dh.net, Office Mgr. of Columbia Basin Herald, WA, Moses Lake

Stewart, Bill .... **(207) 621-5640**
bstewart@centralmaine.com, Exec. Sports Ed., Kennebec Journal, ME, Augusta
bstewart@centralmaine.com, Exec. Sports Ed., Morning Sentinel, ME, Waterville

Stewart, Carole C. .... **(412) 787-2881**
carole.stewart@homeimprovementtime.com, President, Home Improvement Time, Inc., Oakdale

Stewart, Charles T. .... **(740) 452-3601**
cstewart@adjustoveyor.com, C.E.O and Chairman, Stewart Glapat Corp., OH, Zanesville

Stewart, Chuck
editor@hypress.net, Exec. Ed & Pub., Hudson Valley Press, NY, Newburgh

Stewart, Cindy
cindy@whiterivercurrent.com, Ed., White River Current, AR, Calico Rock

Stewart, Dave .... **ext. 111**
sports@ncadvertiser.com, Sports Ed., New Canaan Advertiser, CT, New Canaan

Stewart, David T. .... **(740) 452-3601**
dstewart@adjustoveyor.com, Sales Manager , Stewart Glapat Corp., OH, Zanesville

Stewart, Don
dstewart@fmarion.edu, Chair, Francis Marion University, SC, Florence

Stewart, Donna .... **(816) 842-3804**
dstewart@kccall.com, Pub., The Call, MO, Kansas City

Stewart, Elizabeth
liz.kmherald@gmail.com, Ed, Kings Mountain Herald, NC, Kings Mountain

Stewart, Fred
Fred_Stewart@tamu-commerce.edu, Instr./ Publications Advisor, Texas A&M University-Commerce, TX, Commerce

Stewart, Fred .... **(903) 886-5231**
Fred.Stewart@tamuc.edu, Fac. Advisor, Texas A&M Univ. Commerce, TX, Commerce

Stocking, Peg.................(610) 740-0944
mstocking@tnonline.com, Adv. Mgr.,
Catasauqua Press, PA, Allentown

Stocking, Peg.................(610) 740-0944
mstocking@tnonline.com, Adv. Mgr., East Penn
Press, PA, Allentown

Stockmier, Kathleen.............(972) 273-3498
North Lake College, TX, Irving

Stockton, Cindy.................(574) 936-3101
cstockton@thepilotnews.com, Pub., The
Bremen Enquirer, IN, Bremen
cstockton@thepilotnews.com, Publisher/
Advertising Mgr., Post And Mail Shopping
News, IN, Columbia City
cstockton@thepilotnews.com, Publisher/
Advertising Mgr., The Post and Mail
(Tuesday), IN, Columbia City

Stockton, Cindy
cstockton@thepilotnews.com, Adv. Mgr., The
Culver Citizen, IN, Plymouth

Stockton, Cindy.................(574) 936-3101
cstockton@thepilotnews.com, Adv. Mgr., Mktg.,
Pilot News, IN, Plymouth
cstockton@thepilotnews.com, Adv. Mgr., Mktg.,
The Shopper, IN, Plymouth

Stockton, Cindy
cstockton@thepilotnews.com, Adv. Mgr.,
Bourbon News-Mirror, IN, Plymouth

Stockton, Cindy
cstockton@thepilotnews.com, Adv. Mgr., The
Leader, IN, Plymouth

Stockton, Sandy.................(530) 852-0277
sandys@goldcountrymedia.com, National
Advert, Folsom Telegraph, CA, Roseville

Stockton, Sandy.................(530) 852-0238
sandys@goldcountrymedia.com, Auburn
Journal, CA, Auburn

Stockwell, Jamie.................(210) 250-3492
JStockwell@express-news.net, Mng. Ed.,
Southside Reporter, TX, San Antonio
JStockwell@express-news.net, Managing
Editor, San Antonio Express-News, TX, San
Antonio
JStockwell@express-news.net, Mng. Ed.,
Brooks Discovery News, TX, San Antonio

Stoddard, Phil.................(608) 252-6357
pstoddard@madison.com, Circ. Dir., Wisconsin
State Journal, Madison, WI, Madison

Stoddard, Scott
sstoddard@thedailycourier.com, Editor, Daily
Courier, OR, Grants Pass

Stoddard, Scott.................(425) 392-6434
sstoddard@newcastle-news.com, Editor,
Newcastle News, WA, Issaquah

Stoddard, Scott.................(425) 392-6434
sstoddard@isspress.com, Editor, The Issaquah
Press, WA, Issaquah

Stoecklin, Mark.................ext. 131
mstoecklin@certifiedaudit.com, CEO, Certified
Audit of Circulations, Inc., NJ, Wayne

Stoelk, Jolene
Jolene.Stoelk@bulletinreview.com, Circ. Mgr.,
Denison Bulletin & Review, IA, Denison

Stoess-Hack, Jacquelyn.................ext. 105
editor@oldhamera.com, Ed., Marketplace, KY,
La Grange

Stoetzer, Pat.................(410) 857-7894
pat.stoetzer@carrollcountytimes.com, Sports
Ed. , Carroll County Times, MD, Westminster

Stofer, Larry.................(864) 370-1800
lstofer@bju.edu, Campus Media Supervisor,
Bob Jones University, SC, Greenville

Stofle, Michelle
mstofle@bizjournals.com, Adv. Mgr., Pacific
Business News, HI, Honolulu

Stohlberg, Doug
hsoeditor@rivertowns.net, Ed., The Hudson
Star-Observer, WI, River Falls

Stohlberg, Douglas W.
hsoeditor@rivertowns.net, Ed., Hot Sheet
Shopper, WI, River Falls

Stok, Glenn
customerservice@stok.com, Pres./Founder,
Stok Software, Inc., NY, Hauppauge

Stokebrand, Amy.................(402) 223-5233
astokebrand@beatricedailysun.com, Sales TL,
Beatrice Daily Sun, NE, Beatrice

Stoker, Kevin L..................(801) 422-1222
Assoc. Prof./Assoc. Chair, Grad. Studies,
Brigham Young University, UT, Provo

Stokes, Catherine
catherine.stokes@sunmedia.ca, Mgr.,
Customer Contact Centre, The Edmonton
Sun, AB, Edmonton

Stokes, Donna.................(843) 283-1147
dstokes@thelancasternews.com, Sales
consultant, Pageland Progressive-Journal,
SC, Pageland

Stokes, Sara
ads.cnews@gmail.com, Adv. Mgr., Canby
News, MN, Canby

Stokes, Valerie.................(717) 273-8127
vals@themerchandiser.com, Kapp - Dauphin /
Schuylkill Area Merchandiser, PA, Lebanon
vals@themerchandiser.com, Gen. Mgr., Kapp
Advertising Service, Inc., PA, Lebanon
vals@themerchandiser.com, Kapp - Gettysburg
Area Merchandiser, PA, Lebanon
vals@themerchandiser.com, Kapp - Greater
Reading Merchandiser Eastern Edition, PA,
Lebanon
vals@themerchandiser.com, Kapp - Greater
Reading Merchandiser Northern Edition, PA,
Lebanon
vals@themerchandiser.com, Kapp - Greater
Reading Merchandiser Western Edition, PA,
Lebanon
vals@themerchandiser.com, Kapp -
Hampstead/manchester Area Merchandiser,
PA, Lebanon
vals@themerchandiser.com, Kapp - Hanover
Area Merchandiser, PA, Lebanon
vals@themerchandiser.com, Kapp - Hershey
Area Merchandiser, PA, Lebanon
vals@themerchandiser.com, Kapp - Lebanon
Valley Area Merchandiser, PA, Lebanon
vals@themerchandiser.com, Kapp - Myerstown
Area Merchandiser, PA, Lebanon
vals@themerchandiser.com, Kapp - Northern
Adams / York Area Merchandiser, PA,
Lebanon
vals@themerchandiser.com, Gen. Mgr.,
Merchandiser, PA, Lebanon

Stolar, David.................(814) 870-1745
dave.stolar@timesnews.com, Opns. Dir., Erie
Times-News, PA, Erie

Stolar, Rebecca.................(808) 529-4845
rstolar@staradvertiser.com, VP/HR, Honolulu
Star-Advertiser, HI, Honolulu

Stolar, Rebecca.................(808) 529-4845
rstolar@staradvertiser.com, VP/Human
Resources, MidWeek Oahu, HI, Honolulu
rstolar@staradvertiser.com, VP/Human
Resources, Kauai Midweek, HI, Honolulu

Stolarczyk, Stanislaw
redakcja@fakty.ca, Ed. in Chief, Zwiazkowiec,
ON, Toronto

Stolk, Vanessa
vanessa.stolk@dowjones.com, Rep., Dow
Jones Newswires - Brussels, Belgium,
Brussels

Stoll, Donald
stoll@rowan.edu, Assoc. Prof., Rowan Univ.,
NJ, Glassboro

Stoll, Ira
istoll@nysun.com, Mng. Ed., The New York
Sun, NY, New York

Stolley, Roger.................(507) 645-1150
rstolley@cannonvalleyprinting.com, Prodn.
Mgr., Northfield News, MN, Northfield

Stolley, Roger.................(507) 645-1150
rstolley@cannonvalleyprinting.com, Prodn.
Mgr., Owatonna People's Press, MN,
Owatonna

Stolley, Theresa
techts@dailydem.com, Democrat Co., IA, Fort
Madison

Stolte, Barb.................(303) 566-4125
bstolte@coloradocommunitymedia.com, Opns.
Mgr., Northglenn-Thornton Sentinel, CO,
Westminster
bstolte@coloradocommunitymedia.com, Adv.
Mgr., Arvada Press, CO, Golden

Stoltzfus, Duane
dstoltzfus@goshen.edu, Prof., Goshen
College, IN, Goshen

Stolz, Jen.................(402) 426-2121 x127
blairartdept@enterprisepub.com, Art Director,
The Clipper, NE, Blair

Stolz, Jen.................(402) 426-2121 x127
blairartdept@enterprisepub.com, Prodn. Mgr.,
The Pilot Tribune / Enterprise, NE, Blair

Stom, Caroline Aoyagi
editor@pacificcitizen.org, Ed., Japanese
American Citizens League, CA, Los Angeles

Stone, Adam
astone@theexaminernews.com, Pub., The
White Plains Examiner, NY, Mount Kisco
astone@theexaminernews.com, Pub., The
Putnam Examiner, NY, Mount Kisco
astone@theexaminernews.com, Pub., The
Northern Westchester Examiner, NY, Mount
Kisco
astone@theexaminernews.com, Pub., The
Examiner, NY, Mount Kisco

Stone, Colleen
cstone@mlive.com, Sr. Dir. for Digital Culture
and Innovation, The Jackson Citizen Patriot,
MI, Jackson

Stone, David.................(859) 355-1218
dstone@winchestersun.com, Editor , The
Winchester Sun, KY, Winchester

Stone, Dean.................(865) 981-1148
Editorial Page Ed., The Daily Times, TN,
Maryville

Stone, Del.................(850) 315-4433
dstone@nwfdailynews.com, Online Ed.,
Northwest Florida Daily News, FL, Fort
Walton Beach

Stone, Diana
dhamilton@sanpatpublishing.com, Ed.,
Portland News, TX, Portland

Stone, Elizabeth
elizabeth.stone@foxnews.com, Fordham Univ.
Lincoln Center, NY, New York

Stone, Glen
gstone@centralgatech.edu, Macon State
College, GA, Macon

Stone, Gretchen
atticaeditor@sbcglobal.net, Ed., The Review
Republican, IN, Attica

Stone, Justine
lifestyles@csceagle.com, Lifestyles Ed,
Chadron State College, NE, Chadron

Stone, Ken.................(859) 824-3343
kstone@grantky.com, Pub., Grant County
News and Express, KY, Williamstown

Stone, Ken.................(859) 803-5219
kstone@grantky.com, Publisher, Grant County
News and Express, KY, Williamstown

Stone, Kitty.................ext. 1910
kitty.stone@gaflnews.com, Adv. Mgr., Retail
Sales, The Tifton Gazette, GA, Tifton

Stone, Mark
timesargus@bellsouth.net, President, The
Times-Argus, KY, Central City

Stone, Richard.................(512) 352-8535
publisher@taylorpress.net, Pub./Ed., Taylor
Press, TX, Taylor

Stone, Scott.................(847) 427-4630
sstone@dailyherald.com, President/Chief
Operating Officer, Daily Herald, IL, Arlington
Heights

Stone, Sharon.................(810) 433-6786
sstone@tctimes.com, Editor, Tri-County Times,
MI, Fenton

Stone, Steve.................(602) 323-0490
steve.stone@masthead.net, Branch Mgr.,
Masthead International, Inc., AZ, Phoenix

Stoneberg, David.................(707) 967-6800
editor@sthelenastar.com , Editor, St Helena
Star, CA, Saint Helena

Stoneburner, Mary Lou
mstoneburner@courant.com, Adv. Sales,
Courant Community - East Hartford, CT,
Hartford
mstoneburner@courant.com, Adv. Sales,
Courant Community - Colchester, CT,
Hartford
mstoneburner@courant.com, Adv. Sales,
Courant Community - Killingly, CT, Hartford
mstoneburner@courant.com, Adv. Sales,
Courant Community - Enfield, CT, Hartford
mstoneburner@courant.com, Adv. Sales,
Courant Community - Glastonbury, CT,
Hartford
mstoneburner@courant.com, Adv. Sales,
Courant Community - Hebron, CT, Hartford
mstoneburner@courant.com, Adv. Sales,
Courant Community - Valley, CT, Hartford
mstoneburner@courant.com, Adv. Sales,
Courant Community - Manchester, CT,
Hartford
mstoneburner@courant.com, Adv. Sales,
Courant Community - Putnam, CT, Hartford
mstoneburner@courant.com, Adv. Sales,
Courant Community - South Windsor, CT,
Hartford
mstoneburner@courant.com, Adv. Sales,
Courant Community - Stafford, CT, Hartford
mstoneburner@courant.com, Adv. Sales,
Courant Community - Windham, CT, Hartford
mstoneburner@courant.com, Adv. Sales,
Courant Community - Windsor, CT, Hartford
mstoneburner@courant.com, Adv. Sales,
Courant Community - Windsor Locks, CT,
Hartford
mstoneburner@courant.com, Adv. Sales,
Courant Community - Vernon, CT, Hartford

Stoneburner, Mary Lou.................(860) 241-6241
mstoneburner@courant.com, VP of Adv.,
Courant Community - Wethersfield, CT,
Hartford
mstoneburner@courant.com, VP Adv., The
Hartford Courant, CT, Hartford
mstoneburner@courant.com, VP of Adv.,
Courant Community - Colchester, CT,
Hartford
mstoneburner@courant.com, VP of Adv.,
Courant Community - East Hartford, CT,
Hartford
mstoneburner@courant.com, VP of Adv.,
Courant Community - Enfield, CT, Hartford
mstoneburner@courant.com, VP of Adv.,
Courant Community - Glastonbury, CT,
Hartford
mstoneburner@courant.com, VP of Adv.,
Courant Community - Hebron, CT, Hartford
mstoneburner@courant.com, VP of Adv.,
Courant Community - Killingly, CT, Hartford
mstoneburner@courant.com, VP of Adv.,
Courant Community - Manchester, CT,
Hartford
mstoneburner@courant.com, VP of Adv.,
Courant Community - Putnam, CT, Hartford
mstoneburner@courant.com, VP of Adv.,
Courant Community - South Windsor, CT,
Hartford
mstoneburner@courant.com, VP of Adv.,
Courant Community - Stafford, CT, Hartford
mstoneburner@courant.com, VP of Adv.,
Courant Community - Valley, CT, Hartford
mstoneburner@courant.com, VP of Adv.,
Courant Community - Vernon, CT, Hartford
mstoneburner@courant.com, VP of Adv.,
Courant Community - West Hartford, CT,
Hartford
mstoneburner@courant.com, VP of Adv.,

Courant Community - Windham, CT, Hartford
mstoneburner@courant.com, VP of Adv.,
Courant Community - Windsor, CT, Hartford
mstoneburner@courant.com, VP of Adv.,
Courant Community - Windsor Locks, CT,
Hartford

Stonecipher, Christine ....(772) 221-4270
Jupiter Courier, FL, Stuart

Stoneman, Marty
marty@patentdodc.com, Registered Patent
Attorney, Stoneman Law Offices Ltd., AZ,
Phoenix

Stoner, Edward ....(970) 748-2929
estoner@vaildaily.com, Mng. Ed., Vail Daily,
CO, Avon

Stonestreet, Betty.....................(252) 639-2664
bstonestreet@theshopper.cc, Circ. Mgr., The
Shopper, NC, New Bern

Stoochnoff, Dyan.......................(250) 442-2191
advertising@grandforksgazette.ca, Advertising
, The Grand Forks Gazette, BC, Grand Forks

Stoochnoff, Dyan.......................(250) 443-2233
dyan.stoochnoff@boundarycreektimes.com,
Associate Publisher, The Boundary Creek
Times, BC, Greenwood

Stopka, Jamie
JamieStopka@SteubenCourier.com, Circ. Mgr.
, Steuben Courier-Advocate, NY, Bath

Storch, Dennis ....(212) 877-2622
dstorch@aol.com, President, Dennis Storch
Co., NY, New York

Storey, Ian
ian.storey@njc.edu, Northeastern Junior
College, CO, Sterling

Storey, Karen
karen.storey@jda.com, Sales Mgr., Intactix,
AZ, Scottsdale

Storey, Ronald
publisher@decaturdailydemocrat.com, Pub.,
Decatur Daily Democrat, IN, Decatur
publisher@decaturdailydemocrat.com, Pub.,
Berne Shopping News, IN, Decatur

Storey, Sandy
sstorey@canbyherald.com, Adv, The Canby
Herald, OR, Canby

Storie, Shawn ....(765) 362-1200 Ext. 143
shawn.storie@jrpress.com, Group Mgr./Pub.,
Journal Review, IN, Crawfordsville

Storm, Kelly ....(405) 325-2722
kstorm@ou.edu, Staff Asst., Advertising
Workshop, Norman

Storrusten, Jack.....................(909) 483-9349
jack.storrusten@inlandnewspapers.com, Adv.
Rep, Classified, The Facts (Redlands), CA,
Redlands

Story, Bob
bstory@eaglenewspapers.com, News Ed.,
Daily Sun News, WA, Sunnyside

Story, Linda
lstory@reporter-herald.com, Adv. Dir., Loveland
Reporter-Herald, CO, Loveland

Story, Shelly
shelly.story@baycitytribune.com, Ed., The Bay
City Tribune, TX, Bay City

Stottmeister, Janet
jstottmeister@thehawkeye.com, Adv. Mgr.,
Hawk Eye Shopper, IA, Burlington

Stouder, Jenny ....(580) 569-2684
jen@kiowacountydemocrat.com, Office
Mgr/Advertising Manager, Kiowa County
Democrat, OK, Snyder

Stouff, Roger
webmaster@banner-tribune.com, Managing
Ed. , Franklin Banner-Tribune, LA, Franklin

Stoughtenger, Constance ....(315) 651-4372
hmtown@hotmail.com, CFO, The Reveille/
Between The Lakes, NY, Waterloo

Stoughtenger, John ....(315) 224-2768
Pub, The Reveille/Between The Lakes, NY,
Waterloo

Stouse, Dennis
dstouse@ju.edu, Dir., Jacksonville University,
FL, Jacksonville

Stout, Annie ....(575) 763-3431
astout@thenews.email, Business Manager,
Eastern New Mexico News, NM, Clovis

Stout, Devon......................................ext. 231
dstout@sharonherald.com, Circ. Dir., The
Meadville Tribune, PA, Meadville
dstout@sharonherald.com, Dir of Audience
Development , The Herald, PA, Sharon

Stout, Jim ....(580) 327-2200
jimstout@alvareviewcourier.net, News Editor,
Alva Review-Courier, OK, Alva

Stout, Kari Beth
stout@pulaskijournal.com, Mng. Ed., The
Independent, IN, Winamac
stout@pulaskijournal.com, Creative Dir., The
Pulaski County Journal, IN, Winamac

Stout, Kim
circulation@washjrnl.com, Circ. Dir., The
Washington Evening Journal, IA, Washington
circulation@washjrnl.com, Circ. Mgr., Fairfield
Town Crier, IA, Fairfield

Stout, Steve.........................(937) 652-1337
sstout@civitasmedia.com, Sports Ed., Urbana
Daily Citizen, OH, Urbana

Stovall, Vincent
vincent.stovall@marymount.edu, Marymount
Univ., VA, Arlington

Stover, Bob.........................(321) 242-3607
bstover@floridatoday.com, Exec. Ed., Missileer,
FL, Melbourne

Stover, Bob.........................(321) 242-3607
bstover@floridatoday.com, Exec. Editor, Best -
Central, FL, Melbourne
bstover@floridatoday.com, Exec. Editor, Best -
North, FL, Melbourne
bstover@floridatoday.com, Exec. Editor, Best -
South, FL, Melbourne

Stover, Diana
diana.stover@sjsu.edu, Prof., San Jose State
University, CA, San Jose

Stover, Franklin
news@humboldtbeacon.com, Ed., The
Humboldt Beacon, CA, Eureka

Stowe, Michael ....(304) 647-5724
publisher@mountainmedia.com, Publisher, The
Fincastle Herald, VA, Fincastle

Stowell, Roger ....(208) 475-2400
rstowell@idahopress.com, Prodn. Dir., Idaho
Press, ID, Nampa

Strabala, Rob ....(608) 252-6316
rstrabala@madison.com, Ops. Dir., Wisconsin
State Journal, Madison, WI, Madison

Strachan, Jeannie
jstrachan@examiner-enterprise.com, Adv.,
Pawhuska Journal-Capital, OK, Pawhuska
jstrachan@examiner-enterprise.com, Team
Lead. , Examiner-Enterprise, OK, Bartlesville

Strahinich, John ....(617) 619-6487
john.strahinich@bostonherald.com, Managing
Editor, Boston Herald, MA, Boston

Strain, Mike ....(918) 581-8356
mike.strain@tulsaworld.com, Mng. Ed., Tulsa
World, OK, Tulsa

Strain, Scott ....(510) 323-5111
Laney College, CA, Oakland

Strait, Jan
jstrait@parsonssun.com, Display Adv. Sales,
Parsons Sun, KS, Parsons

Strait, Mel
mls015@shsu.edu, Lectr., Sam Houston State
University, TX, Huntsville

Strait, Rusty
rustystrait@gmail.com, Journalist, The Valley

Chronicle, CA, Hemet

Straka, Jerry ....(574) 658-4111
jstraka@the-papers.com, Circulation, Senior
Life (OOB), IN, Milford
jstraka@the-papers.com, Circulation, The
Paper - Kosciusko Edition, IN, Milford

Straley, Teresa
businessmanager@franklinshopper.com,
Business Manager, The Franklin Shopper,
PA, Chambersburg

Strand, David
david.strand@lcms.org, Executive Director,
Reporter, MO, Saint Louis

Strand, Matt ....(860) 767-7130 x 13
mstrand@epg-inc.com, Operations Mgr., Essex
Products Group, CT, Centerbrook

Strange, Jim.........................(217) 342-3918
j.strange@blmachinedesign.com, Prodn. Mgr.,
Mfg., B & L Machine & Design, IL, Effingham

Strasner, Jay
jstrasner@thedailycitizen.com, Ed., The Daily
Citizen, AR, Searcy

Strasner, Jay T.
publisher@leader-news.com, Pub./Ed., El
Campo Leader-News, TX, El Campo

Strassburg, Colette ....(928) 717-7678
Yavapai College, AZ, Prescott

Stratman, Barb ....(406) 271-5561
indobserv@3rivers.net, Production-Adv. Mgr.,
Independent Observer, MT, Conrad

Strattan, Lisa ....(617) 786-7022
lstrattan@ledger.com, Exec. Ed., The
Enterprise, MA, Brockton

Strattan, Lisa ....(508) 676-2524
pub@wickedlocal.com, Executive Editor, The
Patriot Ledger, MA, Quincy

Strattan, Lisa ....(508) 676-2534
editor@heraldnews.com, Pub., The Herald
News, MA, Fall River

Stratton, Jeff
shoppersreview@charter.net, Owner/Publisher,
Shopper's Review, IL, Highland

Stratton, Judy
stratton@mail.sum.edu, Administrator,
Southern Methodist University, TX, Dallas

Stratton, Lisa ....(508) 676-2524
publisher@heraldnews.com, Pub., Taunton
Daily Gazette, MA, Taunton

Stratton, Wesley ....(937) 538-4826
wstratton@civitasmedia.com, CSR, The Sidney
Daily News, OH, Sidney

Straub, Liisa ....(602) 261-7655 ext. 105
l.straub@ananews.com, Accounting Assist.,
Arizona Newspapers Association, AZ,
Phoenix
l.straub@ananews.com, Network Adv. Mgr.,
ANA Advertising Services, Inc. (Arizona
Newspaper Association), AZ, Phoenix

Straub, Matt ....(860) 225-4601 ext. 273
mstraub@newbritainherald.com, Sports Ed.,
New Britain Herald, CT, New Britain

Straughan, Dulcie ....(919) 962-9002
Prof./Sr. Assoc. Dean, University of North
Carolina, NC, Chapel Hill

Straumanis, Andris ....(715) 425-4645
andris.straumanis@uwrf.edu, Advisor,
University of Wisconsin-River Falls, WI,
River Falls

Straus, Jeanne ....(845) 469-9000
nyoffice@strausnews.com, Pres., Chelsea
Clinton News, NY, New York
nyoffice@strausnews.com, Pres., Photo News,
NY, Chester

Straus, Jeanne
njoffice@strausnews.com, Pub., Township
Journal, NJ, Sparta

Straus, Jeanne ....(845) 469-9000
nyoffice@strausnews.com, Pres., The

Westsider, NY, New York

Straus, Jeanne
nyoffice@strausnews.com, Pres., Warwick
Advertiser, NY, Chester

Straus, Jeanne ....(845) 469-9000
nyoffice@strausnews.com, Pres., Our Town
Eastside, NY, Pearl River

Straus, Jeanne ....(845) 469-9000
nyoffice@strausnews.com, Pres, West Side
Spirit, NY, New York

Straus, Jeanne ....(845) 469-9000
jeanne@strausnews.com, Pres., The
Advertiser-News (North), NY, Chester

Straus, Jeanne ....(845) 469-9000
jeanne.straus@strausnews.com, Pres. , Sparta
Independent, NJ, Sparta
jeanne.straus@strausnews.com, Pres & Pub,
Straus News, NY, Chester
jeanne.straus@strausnews.com, Pres.,
Advertiser News (South Edition), NJ, Sparta
jeanne.straus@strausnews.com, Pres.,
Advertiser News (North Edition), NJ, Sparta
jeanne.straus@strausnews.com, Pub., Dirt
Magazine, NY, Chester

Strauss, James.........................(406) 791-1435
jstrauss@greatfallstribune.com, Pres./Pub./Ed.,
Great Falls Tribune, MT, Great Falls

Strauss, John ....(765) 285-8218
Advisor, Ball State University, IN, Muncie

Strauss, Mariya
mstrauss@peoplesworld.org, Mng. Ed.,
People's World, IL, Chicago

Stravato, Peggy ....(716) 326-3163
pstravato@westfieldrepublican.com, Inside
Sales, Quality Guide, NY, Westfield

Stravelli, Gloria
hubeditor@gmnews.com, Mng. Ed., The
Independent, NJ, Manalapan

Stravelli, Gloria ....(732) 870-6070 ext. 201
aville@gmnews.com, Mng. Ed., Atlanticville,
NJ, Manalapan

Stravolemis, Jill......................(303) 473-1420
jill@dailycamera.com, Vice Pres.: Marketing
and Advertising, Prairie Mountain Publishing,
CO, Boulder
jill@dailycamera.com, Mgr., Mktg./Promo./New
Media, Daily Camera, CO, Boulder

Stravrakas, Scott ....(815) 223-3200 ext. 145
addir@newstrib.com, Adv., Illinois Valley
Shopper, IL, La Salle

Strawser, Justin
jstrawser@dailyitem.com, Reporter, The Daily
Item, PA, Sunbury

Strean, Linda ....(805) 564-5214
Mng. Ed., Santa Barbara News-Press, CA,
Santa Barbara

Streb, Edward
streb@rowan.edu, Prof., Rowan Univ., NJ,
Glassboro

Street, Buddy
buddy.street@eunicetoday.com, Circ. Mgr., The
Eunice News, LA, Eunice

Street, Jody
shelbynews@shelbynews.com, Adv. Mgr., The
Extra, IN, Shelbyville

Street, Oliver ....(304) 293-5874
oliver.street@mail.wvu.edu, Assistant Dean,
Student Services, West Virginia University,
WV, Morgantown

Street, Robin
rbstreet@olemiss.edu, Instr./Dir., MS
Scholastic Press, University of Mississippi,
MS, University

Streets, Nancy.........................(775) 748-2704
nstreets@elkodaily.com, Adv. Dir., Elko Daily
Free Press, NV, Elko

Streifler, Lori
lori@socalnews.com, Ed., City News Service,

Inc. - San Diego, CA, San Diego
lori@socalnews.com, Ed., City News Service,
Inc. - Los Angeles, CA, Los Angeles

Streitenberger, Keith ....(937) 328-0376
kstreitenberger@coxohio.com, Editorial Page
Ed., Springfield News-Sun, OH, Springfield

Strempel, Dan
dstrempel@marketresearch.com, Sr. Ed.,
Simba Information, CT, Stamford

Strength, Reed
alabamian@montevallo.edu, Editor, Univ. of
Montevallo, AL, Montevallo

Strescino, Peter............ (719) 544-3520 ext. 425
pstress@chieftain.com, Lifestyle Ed., The
Pueblo Chieftain, CO, Pueblo

Strett, Beth
production@florencenewsjournal.com, Prodn.
Mgr., The Florence News Journal, SC,
Florence

Strett, Beth
production@florencenewsjournal.com, Prod.
Mgr, Marion County News Journal, SC,
Marion
production@florencenewsjournal.com, Prodn.
Mgr., The Hartsville News Journal, SC,
Hartsville

Streuli, Ted ....(405) 235-3100
tstreuli@journalrecord.com, Editor and
Associate Publisher, The Journal Record,
OK, Oklahoma City

Strickbine, Steve
cheazecake@gmail.com, Pub., West Valley
View, AZ, Goodyear
cheazecake@gmail.com, Pub., Ahwatukee
Foothills News, AZ, Tempe

Stricker, Gary W. ....(618) 243-5563
press1@okawvilletimes.com, Pub., The
Okawville Times, IL, Okawville

Strickland, Bence 860/701-4254
b.strickland@theday.com, Classified
Advertising Manager, The Day, CT, New
London

Strickland, Bill ....(229) 438-3202
bill.strickland@albanyherald.com, IT Director,
The Albany Herald, GA, Albany

Strickland, Danny....................(912) 427-3757
Press Mgr., The Press-Sentinel, GA, Jesup

Strickland, Karen ....(724) 787-7432
kstrickland@tribweb.com, Cir. Mgr., Daily
Courier, PA, Connellsville

Strickland, Luke......................(770) 957-9161
lstrickland@henryherald.com, Sports Ed.,
Clayton News Daily, GA, Jonesboro

Strickland, Lynda
lstrickland@lakecityreporter.com, Adv. Dir.,
Lake City Reporter, FL, Lake City
lstrickland@lakecityreporter.com, Sr. Adv. Mgr.,
The Gainesville Sun, FL, Gainesville

Strickland, Margaret ....(251) 580-2100
mstrickland@faulknerstate.edu, James
Faulkner State Cmty. College, AL, Bay
Minette

Strickler, Dan
danstrickler@timesnews.net, Kingsport Times-
News, TN, Kingsport

Striessky, Patricia M.
patricia@forestcitynews.com, Pub./Ed., The
Forest City News, PA, Forest City

Strine, Chris ....(239) 574-1110
cstrine@breezenewspapers.com, Mng. Ed.,
Cape Coral Breeze, FL, Cape Coral

Stringer, David R.
dstringer@tylerpaper.com, Adv. Dir., Tyler
Morning Telegraph, TX, Tyler

Stringer, Holly........................(919) 821-9730
reece@raldioc.org, Adv. Mgr., The North
Carolina Catholic, NC, Raleigh

Stringfellow, Lee....................(251) 219-5070

lstringfellow@press-register.com, Dir., HR,
Press-Register, AL, Mobile

Strode, Dale ....(970) 925-3414
dstrode@aspentimes.com, Sports Ed., The
Aspen Times, CO, Aspen

Stroebel-Barichellow, Julie ....(815) 431-4072
julies@mywebtimes.com, Night Editor, The
Times, IL, Ottawa

Strogoff, Jody Hope
info@coloradostatesman.com, Ed., Colorado
Statesman, CO, Denver

Strohl, Lisa ....(717) 703-3071
lisas@pa-news.org, Communications Manager,
Pennsylvania NewsMedia Association, PA,
Harrisburg

Strohm, Gary ....(217) 826-3600
strohmnews@joink.com, Pub., Marshall
Advocate, IL, Marshall
strohmnews@joink.com, Pub., Casey Westfield
Reporter, IL, Marshall
strohmnews@joink.com, Pub., West Vigo
Times, IL, Marshall

Strohte, Kylah ....(509) 922-3456
Kylah@ExchangePublishing.com, Executive
Director of the Pacific Northwest Association
of Want Ad Newspapers (PNAWAN) &
Western Regional Advertising Program
(WRAP), Pacific Northwest Association of
Want Ad Newspapers (PNAWAN) & Western
Regional Advertising Program (WRAP), WA,
Spokane

Stromley, Michael
mstromley@greenwooddemocrat.com,
News Desk, Greenwood Democrat, AR,
Greenwood

Stromsodt, Kirsten....................(701) 241-5582
kstromsodt@agweek.com, Director, Agweek,
ND, Grand Forks

Stromsodt, Kirsten
kstromsodt@gfherald.com, Assigning Ed.,
Grand Forks Herald, ND, Grand Forks

Strong, Chris ....(513) 768-8201
cstrong@enquirer.com, VP of Sales, The
Cincinnati Enquirer, OH, Cincinnati

Strong, Donna
dstrong@delmar.edu, Del Mar College
Foghorn, TX, Corpus Christi

Strong, Gary ....(916) 321-1520
gstrong@sacbee.com, Sr. Vice Pres., Finance,
The Sacramento Bee, CA, Sacramento

Strother, Bill ....(812) 331-4265
bstrother@heraldt.com, Asst. Managing Ed.,
The Herald Times, IN, Bloomington

Strother, Sarah
sstrother@glaciermedia.ca, Pres., WPLP, The
Whistler Question, BC, Whistler
sstrother@glaciermedia.ca, Pub, Pique
Newsmagazine, BC, Whistler

Strother, William ....(812) 331-4361
bstrother@heraldt.com, Features/Lifestyle Ed.,
The Herald Times, IN, Bloomington

Stroud, James
jlstroud@spokesman-recorder.com, Adv.
Mgr., Minnesota Spokesman-recorder, MN,
Minneapolis

Stroud, Jessy ....(605) 996-5514
Internet/Systems Mgr., The Daily Republic,
SD, Mitchell

Stroud, John
jstroud@postindependent.com, Reporter,
Glenwood Springs Post Independent, CO,
Glenwood Springs

Stroud, Neva..........................(812) 865-3242
lmac1@blueriver.net, Adv. Mgr., The Progress
Examiner, IN, Orleans

Strouse, Chuck
chuck.strouse@miaminewtimes.com, Ed., New
Times Broward-Palm Beach, FL, Miami
chuck.strouse@miaminewtimes.com, Mng. Ed.,
Miami New Times, FL, Miami

Strub, Denise........................(662) 843-4241
news@bolivarcommercial.com, Mng. Ed., The
Bolivar Commercial, MS, Cleveland

Struck, Paul
pauls@ctimes.biz, Assc. Pub. & Ed. In Chief,
Cherokee Chronicle Times, IA, Cherokee

Struck, Paul
pauls@ctimes.biz, Pub., Area Advertiser, IA,
Cherokee

Strudler, Keith
keith.strudler@marist.edu, Asst. Prof., Marist
College, NY, Poughkeepsie

Struense, Stephanie..................(239) 574-1110
sstruense@breezenewspapers.com, National
& Major Account Sales Manager, Cape Coral
Breeze, FL, Cape Coral

Struglinski, Suzanne
president@rra.org, Pres., Regional Reporters
Association, DC, Washington

Strunk, Chris
news@arkvalleynews.com, Pub., Ark Valley
News, KS, Valley Center

Struth, Jay
news@killarneyguide.ca, Ed., Killarney Guide,
MB, Killarney

Struve, Lois
hstruve@gpcom.net, Ed., Deshler Rustler, NE,
Deshler

Stry, Bob Van
robert.vanstry@firstdata.com, Vice Pres.,
Sales, First Data Voice Services, NE, Omaha

Strzalka, Jim ....(937) 651-1126
jims@examiner.org, Adv. Sales. Rep.,
Bellefontaine Examiner, OH, Bellefontaine

Stuart, Bonnye
stuartb@winthrop.edu, Part-time Instr.,
Winthrop University, SC, Rock Hill

Stuart, Deanna
dstuart@atokaspeedynet.net, Ed, Atoka
County Times, OK, Atoka

Stuart, Lara
circulation@cowichannewsleader.com, Circ.
Mgr., The Cowichan News Leader, BC,
Duncan

Stuart, Laurie...............(845) 252-7414 ext. 33
publisher@riverreporter.com, Pub., The River
Reporter, NY, Narrowsburg

Stuart, Tosh
tosh.stuart@asu.edu, Arizona State Univ., AZ,
Tempe

Stubbe, Lori
lstubbe@gannett.com, Nat'l Adv. Rep.,
Oshkosh Northwestern, WI, Oshkosh

Stubbings, Donna
subscriptions@catholiccourier.com, Circ. Mgr.,
Catholic Courier, NY, Rochester

Stubblebine, Ray
ray@raystubblebine.com, Trustee, New York
Press Photographers Association, Inc., NY,
New York

Stubblefield, Dale
sports2@southernstandard.com, Circ. Mgr.,
Southern Standard, TN, McMinnville

Stubbs, Blake........................(712) 873-3141
blake@wiatel.net, Pub & Ed, The Record, IA,
Moville

Stubbs, Nick
thunderbolt@macdill.af.mil, Ed., Thunderbolt,
FL, Tampa

Stuckey, Anita ....(620) 694-5700 Ext. 222
astuckey@hutchnews.com, Adv. Supvr., Sales,
The Hutchinson News, KS, Hutchinson

Stuckey, Anita ....(620) 694-5700
astuckey@hutchnews.com, Mkt Solutions Mgr,
The Bee, KS, Hutchinson

Stuckey, John.........................(867) 667-4774
circulation@whitehorsestar.com, Circ. Mgr.,

Whitehorse Star, YT, Whitehorse

Stuckey, Patricia
composing@bentoncourier.com, Prodn. Mgr.,
The Saline Courier TMC, Benton
composing@bentoncourier.com, Composing
Manager, The Saline Courier, AR, Benton

Stuckly, Derrick
derrick.stuckly@brownwoodbulletin.com,
Assistant Editor/Sports Editor, Brownwood
Bulletin, TX, Brownwood

Stucky, Nancy
nvn@embarqmail.com, Pub.
, Ninnescah Valley News, KS, Pretty Prairie

Studer, Greg
webmaster@thepostnewspapers.com, Circ.
Mgr, The Post Newspapers - Strongsville,
OH, Medina
webmaster@thepostnewspapers.com, Circ.
Mgr, The Post Newspapers - Eastern Medina,
OH, Medina
webmaster@thepostnewspapers.com, Circ.
Mgr, The Post Newspapers - Medina, OH,
Medina
webmaster@thepostnewspapers.com, Circ.
Mgr, The Post Newspapers - Northern
Wayne, OH, Medina
webmaster@thepostnewspapers.com, Circ.
Mgr, The Post Newspapers - Southern
Medina, OH, Medina
webmaster@thepostnewspapers.com, Circ.
Mgr, The Post Newspapers - Wadsworth,
OH, Medina

Studinger, Matt.......................(815) 842-1153
mstudinger@pontiacdailyleader.com, Adv
Executive
, Livingston Shopping News, IL, Pontiac

Studley, Bridgette
bridgette@studleyprinting.com, Publisher, Lake
Champlain Weekly, NY, Plattsburgh

Studley, William ....(518) 563-1414
bill@studleyprinting.com, Publisher, Lake
Champlain Weekly, NY, Plattsburgh

Stuehmeier, John
info@theshoppersweekly.com, General
Manager, The Shoppers Weekly Papers, IL,
Centralia

Stuff, Jessica ....(334) 670-6301
jessica.stuff@troymessenger.com, Class. Mgr
and Bookkeeping, The Troy Messenger,
AL, Troy

Stukenberg, Les
lstukenberg@prescottaz.com, Photo Ed., The
Daily Courier, AZ, Prescott

Stull, Lora
lora@woodlink.net, Office Mgr, Mount Ayr
Record-News, IA, Mount Ayr

Stultz, Sarah
sarah.stultz@albertleatribune.com, Asst. Ed.,
Albert Lea Tribune, MN, Albert Lea

Stumb, Jeff
fincastle@ourvalley.org, Group Pub., The
Fincastle Herald, VA, Fincastle

Stumb, Jeff
jeffstumb@hotmail.com, Vice Pres., Main
Street Newspapers, Inc., VA, Salem

Stumbo, Betty E.
betty@tribune-courier.com, Treasurer, Tribune
Courier & Madison Tribune, OH, Ontario

Stumbo, Frank
frank@tribune-courier.com, Pub./Ed., Tribune
Courier & Madison Tribune, OH, Ontario

Stump, David
dstump@heraldprint.com, Pub./Ed., The New
Washington Herald, OH, New Washington

Stumpf, Daniel
dan@rochesterbg.com, Pub., Rochester
Buyers' Guide, MN, Rochester
dan@rochesterbg.com, Pub., St. Charles
Press, MN, Saint Charles
dan@rochesterbg.com, Owner, Stumpf
Publishing Co., Inc., MN, Plainview

Stumpf, Daniel J.
thebuyersexpress@centurytel.net, Adv. Mgr.,
Buyers Express, WI, La Crosse

Stumpf, Daniel Y.
scpress@hbcsc.net, Pub., Lewiston Journal,
MN, Saint Charles
scpress@hbcsc.net, Pub., Plainview News,
MN, Plainview

Stumpf, Michael
thewedge@nelson-tel.net, Pub., The Courier-
Wedge, WI, Durand

Stumpf, Rebecca
rstumpf@dallasnews.com, Metro Print Team
Leader, The Dallas Morning News, TX, Dallas

Stuntz, Scott
editor@tetonvalleynews.net, Mng. Ed., Teton
Valley News, ID, Driggs

Sturbaum, Erin
editor@idahoworld.com, Ed., Idaho World, ID,
Idaho City

Sturdefant, Anna ....(417) 935-2257
anna@webstercountycitizen.com, Gen. Mgr.,
Webster County Citizen, MO, Seymour

Sturgeon, Marty ....(517) 295-1680
gm@statenews.com, Gen. Mgr., The State
News/Michigan State University, MI, East
Lansing

Sturm, Lorraine ....(585) 237-6310
rsturm@frontiernet.net, Ed., Perry Herald,
NY, Perry

Sturm, Tom
listings@valleyadvocate.com, Listings. Ed.,
Valley Advocate, MA, Northampton

Stusse, Sue ....(712) 293-4292
sstusse@siouxcityjournal.com, Controller,
Sioux City Journal, IA, Sioux City

Stutsman, Beth ....(574) 237-4325
Indiana Univ., IN, South Bend

Stutzman, Jennifer ....(443) 260-3309
jstutzman@dmg.gannett.com, Customer
Service Rep., The Daily Times, MD, Salisbury

Styer, Norm
nstyer@acnpapers.com, Pub., Sun Gazette,
VA, Mc Lean

Styf, Jon ....(815) 280-4119
news@morrisherald-news.com, Morris Herald-
News, IL, MORRIS

Styf, Jon ....(815) 280-4119
jstyf@shawmedia.com, Ed., Herald Life, IL,
Morris
jstyf@shawmedia.com, Ed., The Herald-News,
IL, Joliet
jstyf@shawmedia.com, Ed., Morris Herald-
News, IL, MORRIS

Sublett, Kelly ....(501) 505-1213
kelly.sublett@thecabin.net, VP Audience, Log
Cabin Democrat, AR, Conway

Subramaniam, Anjali ....(646) 432-6000
anjalim@indiaabroad.com, Adv. Dir., India
Abroad, NY, New York

Sucher, Elizabeth ....(617) 929-8641
esucher@globe.com, Adv. Div. Mgr.,
Amusement, The Boston Globe, MA, Boston

Suchy, Scott
suchy@charlestoncitypaper.com, Arts Ed., The
Charleston City Paper, SC, Charleston

Sudbeck, Cheryl ....(402) 986-1777
howellsjournal@msn.com, Pub., Ed., Howells
Journal, NE, Howells

Sudbrook, Jeff
jsudbrook@morningjournal.com, Pub., El
Latino Expreso, OH, Lorain

Suddes, Linda
lsuddes@mykawartha.com, Bus. Admin./
Opns., Kawartha Lakes This Week, ON,
Lindsay

Sudeith, Robert ....(503) 687-1218
rsudeith@oregonlitho.com, Sale/Mktg. Dir,

News-Register, OR, McMinnville

Suderman, Nicole
nicole@hillsborofreepress.com, Circ. Mgr.,
Hillsboro Free Press, KS, Hillsboro
nicole@hillsborofreepress.com, Circ. Mgr.,
Buyer's Edge Of South Central Kansas, KS,
Newton

Suderok, Jeffery
letters@morningjournal.com, Pub., Express
Line, OH, Lorain

Sudes, Linda
lsuddes@mykawartha.com, Gen. Mgr.,
Peterborough This Week, ON, Peterborough

Suel, Bob ....(952) 345-6577
bsuel@swpub.com, Adv, Chaska Herald, MN,
Chaska

Suen, Eugene
esuen@fuller.edu, Fuller Theological Seminary,
CA, Pasadena

Suffolk, Ted E. ....(330) 747-1471
tsuffolk@vindy.com, Asst. Gen. Mgr., The
Vindicator, OH, Youngstown

Sugawara, Marianne
msugawara@creators.com, Vice President of
Operations, Creators, Hermosa Beach

Suggs, Donald
dsuggs@dancestlouis.org, Pub., St. Louis
American, MO, Saint Louis

Sugiura, Wataru
info@bishamon.com, Pres., Bishamon
Industries Corp., CA, Ontario

Suhl, Wayne
wsuhl.ljrpublishing@gmail.com, Adv. Mgr.,
Town and Country, PA, Pennsburg

Suhrbier, Regina
rsuhrbier@messengernews.net, Multi-Media
Sales Manager, The Messenger, IA, Fort
Dodge

Suits, Christy ....(406) 346-2149
ip-news@rangeweb.net, Managing Editor, The
Independent Press, MT, Forsyth

Suits, Mary ....(903) 596-6338
circulation@tylerpaper.com, Circ. Mgr., Tyler
Morning Telegraph, TX, Tyler

Suitt, Sande ....(615) 278-5160
suitt@dnj.com, News Ed., The Daily News
Journal, TN, Murfreesboro

Sukiennik, Greg ....(802) 490-6000
gsukiennik@manchesterjournal.com, Ed.,
Manchester Journal, VT, Manchester Center

Sukle, Joseph G. ....(717) 944-4628
joesukle@pressandjournal.com, Pub., Press
and Journal, PA, Middletown

Sulan, Daniel
dsulan@ksliga.ca, Chair, Business Committee,
Kanadsky Slovak / The Canadian Slovak,
ON, Mississauga

Sullens, David ....(570) 724-2287
dsullens@tiogapublishing.com, Ed./Pub., Free
Press-Courier, PA, Wellsboro

Sullens, David ....(570) 724-2287
dsullens@tiogapublishing.com, Ed./Pub., The
Wellsboro Gazette, PA, Wellsboro

Sullivan, Beth
thepress@in-motion.net, Ed., Speedway Town
Press, IN, Indianapolis

Sullivan, Bill
bsullivan@havertys.com, Nat'l Online Sales
Mgr., Cox Media Group, GA, Atlanta

Sullivan, Bill ....(916) 351-3750
bills@goldcountrymedia.com , Advert., Folsom
Telegraph, CA, Roseville

Sullivan, Dan
dan.sullivan@shj.com, Night Ed., Herald-
Journal, SC, Spartanburg

Sullivan, Dan
dan.sullivan@claconnect.com, Prof./Cowles

Chair, University of Minnesota, MN,
Minneapolis

Sullivan, Denver E. ....(812) 663-3111 x7005
denver.sullivan@nhimidwest.com, Rushville
Republican, IN, Rushville

Sullivan, Denver E. ....(812) 663-3111 x7005
denver.sullivan@nhimidwest.com, IT Dir.,
Greensburg Daily News, IN, Greensburg

Sullivan, Don ....(203) 838-2333
dsullivan@miles33.com, Sr. VP. Sales, Miles
33, CT, Norwalk

Sullivan, Don ....+1 (203) 838-2333
info@miles33.com, Sr. VP Sales, Tera Digital
Publishing, CT, Norwalk

Sullivan, Donna ....(785) 485-2290
countian@twinvalley.net, Editor/Publisher, Riley
Countian, KS, Riley

Sullivan, Donna ....(785) 539-7558
gandgeditor@agpress.com, Ed., Grass &
Grain, KS, Manhattan

Sullivan, Elizabeth
elizabeth.sullivan@olympus.com, Sr. PR Mgr.,
Olympus America, Inc., PA, Center Valley

Sullivan, Glenda ....(850) 747-5024
gsullivan@pcnh.com, Circ. Customer Service
Mgr., The News Herald, FL, Panama City

Sullivan, Joanna ....(410) 454-0512
jsullivan@bizjournals.com, Editor, Baltimore
Business Journal, MD, Baltimore

Sullivan, John ....(406) 222-2000
execoffice@livent.net, Pub., The Livingston
Enterprise, MT, Livingston

Sullivan, John
bkirk@ecnnews.com, Director of Online
Editorial Operations, Winnipeg Free Press,
MB, Winnipeg

Sullivan, John
execoffice@livent.net, Pub., Park County Super
Shopper, MT, Livingston

Sullivan, John
enterprise@livent.net, Pres., Yellowstone
Communications, MT, Livingston

Sullivan, John
loganrep@ruraltel.net, Ed., The Logan
Republican, KS, Logan

Sullivan, Joyce
jsullivan@pdpost.com, Gen. Mgr., Florida
Pennysaver, FL, West Palm Beach

Sullivan, Lynne ....(508) 676-2571
lsullivan@heraldnews.com, Editor-in-Chief, The
Herald News, MA, Fall River

Sullivan, Margaret
public@nytimes.com, Public Ed., The New York
Times, NY, New York

Sullivan, Michael ....(718) 960-4966
michael.sullivan@lehman.cuny.edu, CUNY
Schools, NY, Bronx

Sullivan, Michael
editor@vcreporter.com, Ed., Ventura County
Reporter, CA, Ventura

Sullivan, Mickie
mickie.sullivan@langnews.com, VP, Nat'l Sales/
Major Retail, The Sun, CA, San Bernardino
mickie.sullivan@langnews.com, VP, Nat'l Sales/
Major Retail, San Gabriel Valley Tribune, CA,
Monrovia
mickie.sullivan@langnews.com, VP, Nat'l
Sales/Major Retail, The Whittier Daily News,
CA, Monrovia

Sullivan, Mike ....(812) 231-4218
mike.sullivan@tribstar.com, Adv. Sales Exec.,
The Tribune Star, IN, Terre Haute

Sullivan, Nancy
nancy.sullivan@latimes.com, VP,
Communications, Los Angeles Times, CA,
Los Angeles

Sullivan, Patrick
psullivan@ptleader.com, Mng. Ed., Port

Townsend & Jefferson County Leader, WA,
Port Townsend

Sullivan, Randy
randy.sullivan@fujifilmgs.com, Reg'l Sales
Mgr., Fujifilm Graphic Systems USA, Inc.,
TX, Arlington

Sullivan, Ray ....(575) 763-3431
ray_sullivan@link.freedom.com, Pub., Cannon
Connection, NM, Clovis

Sullivan, Raymond E.
jemco2@comcast.net , Sales Mgr., Johnstone
Engineering & Machine Co., PA, Parkesburg

Sullivan, Shannon
shannon_sullivan@mccom.com, Vice
President, Account Supervisor, M/C/C, TX,
Dallas

Sullivan, Shawn ....(207) 324-5986
ssullivan@sanfordnews.com, Ed., Sanford
News, ME, Sanford

Sullivan, Stacy ....(602) 444-8749
stacy.sullivan@arizonarepublic.com, A & E
Rep. Ed., The Arizona Republic, AZ, Phoenix

Sullivan , Lynne ....(508) 967-3141
eic@tauntongazette.com, Editor-in-Chief,
Taunton Daily Gazette, MA, Taunton

Sully, Dan ....(306) 873-4515
adsrecorder@sasktel.net, Adv. Mgr., Parkland
Review, SK, Tisdale

Sulonen, Dana ....(334) 737-2513
dsulonen@oanow.com, Sports Ed, Opelika-
Auburn News, AL, Opelika

Sulouff, Steve
stevesulouff@nwherald.com, I.T. Director,
Northwest Herald, IL, Crystal Lake

Sulser, Shelley
shopper@j-adgraphics.com, Ed., Battle Creek
Shopper News, MI, Battle Creek

Sultze, Kimberly
ksultze@smcvt.edu, Chair/Assoc. Prof., St.
Michael's College, VT, Colchester

Sulzberger, Arthur O. ....(212) 556-1234
Chrmn., The New York Time Co./ Pub., The
New York Times, The New York Times Co.,
NY, New York

Sulzberger, Arthur Ochs
nytnews@nytimes.com, New England
Newspaper Group, NY, New York

Sulzberger Jr., Arthur
publisher@nytimes.com, Chairman & Pub., The
New York Times, NY, New York

Summerfelt, Darrell
production@nanaimobulletin.com, Prodn. Mgr.,
Nanaimo News Bulletin, BC, Nanaimo

Summerlin, Denise ....(903) 897-2281
Circ. Mgr., The Monitor, TX, Naples

Summerlin, James ....(985) 254-7821
sports@hammondstar.com, Sports Ed. , The
Daily Star, LA, Hammond

Summerlin, Ryan
rsummerlin@postindependent.com, Reporter,
Glenwood Springs Post Independent, CO,
Glenwood Springs

Summers, Danny
dannysummers@yourpeaknews.com, News/
Sports Reporter, The Tribune, CO, Monument

Summers, Danny
dannysummers@yourpeaknews.com, Sports/
News Reporter, The Pikes Peak Courier, CO,
Woodland Park

Summers, Denise ....(317) 781-0023
news@southsidervoice.com, Ed./Owner,
Southsider Voice, IN, Indianapolis

Summers, Nancy ....(813) 259-7984
nsummers@veranosresources.com, Tampa
Bay Times, FL, St Petersburg

Summers, Phil ....(618) 262-5144 ext. 135
psummers@mtcarmelregister.com, Publisher/

President, Mount Carmel Register, IL, Mount Carmel

Summit, Jodi
editor@timberjay.com, Adv. Mgr./Ed., Timberjay, MN, Tower

Sumner, Brent
sumnerbr@uvu.edu, Utah Valley University, UT, Orem

Sumner, Dan
dan.sumner@thepublicopinion.com, Prodn. Mgr., Coteau Shopper, SD, Watertown

Sumner, Dan .... (605) 886-6901
Prodn. Mgr., Press, Watertown Public Opinion, SD, Watertown

Sumner, Darrell
publisher@cj.kscoxmail.com, Owner/Pub., Coffeyville Journal, KS, Coffeyville

Sumner, Darren D. .... (918) 224-5185
publisher@sapulpaheraldonline.com, Pub., Sapulpa Daily Herald, OK, Sapulpa

Sumner, Josh .... (303) 566-4113
jjohnson@coloradocommunitymedia.com, Mng. Ed., Westminster Window, CO, Westminster
jjohnson@coloradocommunitymedia.com, Mng. Ed., Northglenn-Thornton Sentinel, CO, Westminster

Sumpter, Brian .... (707) 900-2016
bsumpter@record-bee.com, Sports Ed., Lake County Record-Bee, CA, Lakeport

Sumpter, Randall S.
r-sumpter@tamu.edu, Dir., Journ. Studies/ Assoc. Prof., Commun., Texas A&M University, TX, College Station

Sund, Nancy .... (641) 484-2841
editor@tamatoledonews.com, Gen. Mgr., The Tama News-Herald, IA, Tama

Sund, Nancy
nsund@tamatoledonews.com, Adv. Mgr., Tama County Shopper, IA, Tama

Sund, Nancy .... (641) 484-2841
editor@tamatoledonews.com, Adv. Mgr., Toledo Chronicle, IA, Tama

Sunderashan, K.
marketing@dt.co.in, Ed., DAILY THANTHI, Chennai, Tamil Nadu

Sundermeyer, Katie
ksundermeyer@skagitpublshing.com, Adv. Mgr., Co-op, Skagit Valley Herald, WA, Mount Vernon

Sundt, Gary
gws8@nau.edu, Northern Arizona Univ., AZ, Flagstaff

Sung, Amanda
asmug@metroland.com, Adv Mgr, Bradford & West Gwillimbury Topic, ON, Newmarket

Supanich, Andreas
asupanich@detroitnews.com, News Ed. , The Detroit News, MI, Detroit

Supin, Jeanne .... (828) 773-3481
hi@supin.com, Watauga Consulting, Inc., Boone

Sura, Lorna .... (203) 354-1020
lsura@thehour.com, Executive Assistant to the Publisher, The Hour, CT, Norwalk

Suraci, Frank .... (310) 543-6621
frank.suraci@dailybreeze.com, City Ed., Daily Breeze, CA, Torrance

Surber, Jim
advertising@vernonrecord.com, Adv. Dir., The Vernon Daily Record, TX, Vernon

Suri, Navin 233 17651
Ed. in Chief, DAILY MILAP, New Delhi

Suri, Punam
editor@milap.com, Mng. Ed., DAILY MILAP, New Delhi

Suro, Roberto
suro@usc.edu, Prof., University of Southern

California, CA, Los Angeles

Surso, Virginia
mtfw@macedonian.org, Ed., Macedonian Tribune, IN, Fort Wayne

Suss, Duncan .... (617) 619-6688
duncan.suss@bostonherald.com, Dir. of Publishing Systems, Boston Herald, MA, Boston

Sussang, Kathy .... (419) 448-3237
ksussang@advertiser-tribune.com, Nat'l Adv. Mgr., The Advertiser-Tribune, OH, Tiffin

Sussens, John
sales@midsys.co.uk, Mng. Dir., Midsystems Technology Ltd., London

Sustad, Keith
messenger@wiktel.com, Ed., Messenger Banner, MN, Stephen

Sutch, Nedra .... (724) 282-8000 ext. 211
nsutch@butlereagle.com, Adv. Mgr., Classified, Butler Eagle, PA, Butler

Sutcliffe, Andy .... (406) 543-6609 x119
asutcliffe@missoulanews.com, General Manager, Missoula Independent, MT, Missoula

Sutcliffe, Andy .... (406) 543-6609 x119
asutcliffe@missoulanews.com, General Manager, Missoula Independent, MT, Missoula

Sutherland, Anthony X.
editorjednota@yahoo.com, Ed., Jednota, PA, Middletown

Sutherland, Booke
newnews@grm.net, Managing Editor, Lamoni Chronicle, IA, Lamoni

Sutherland, Frank .... (615) 804-9377
fsutherland@gmail.com, The Tennessean, TN, Nashville
fsutherland@gmail.com, TN Media, TN, Nashville

Sutherland, John C. .... (352) 392-4046
Prof./Chair, Dept. of Adv., University of Florida, FL, Gainesville

Sutherland, Linda .... (845) 562-7066
lsutherland@gtilite.com, Sales/Mktg Coord., Graphic Technology, Inc. (GTI), NY, Newburgh

Sutherland, Patrick J.
psutherl@bethanywv.edu, Chair/Assoc. Prof., Bethany College, WV, Bethany

Sutherland, Tom .... (419) 724-6373
tsutherland@toledoblade.com, Advert. Sales Mgr/PrePress Sup, The Blade, OH, Toledo

Sutphen, Debra .... (603) 594-1216
news@nashuatelegraph.com, Senior Online Adv. Exec., The Telegraph, NH, Nashua

Sutton, Angie
addirector@brunswickbeacon.com, Adv. Mgr., The Brunswick Beacon, NC, Shallotte

Sutton, Ben .... (601) 584-3063
bsutton@hattiesburgamerican.com, Sports Producer, Hattiesburg American, MS, Hattiesburg

Sutton, Bob .... (336) 506-3050
Sports Ed., Times-News, NC, Burlington

Sutton, Dan .... ext. 1901
dan.sutton@gaflnews.com, Pub/Adv. Dir, The Tifton Gazette, GA, Tifton

Sutton, David .... (765) 883-5414
dsutton@townnews.com, Reg. Sales Mgr., TownNews.com, IL, Moline

Sutton, David .... (559) 735-3256
dwsutton@visaliatimesdelta.com, Prodn. Mgr., Opns., Visalia Times-Delta, CA, Visalia

Sutton, Doug
doug@scfree.net, Santa Clarita Gazette & Free Classifieds, CA, Canyon Country

Sutton, Marie .... (205) 873-5130

masutton@uab.edu, Director, Univ. of Alabama at Birmingham, AL, Birmingham

Sutton, Robert .... (205) 722-0234
robert.sutton@tuscaloosa.com, Photo Dept. Mgr., The Tuscaloosa News, AL, Tuscaloosa

Sutton, Teri
tsutton@townnews.com, Tech. Sales Rep., TownNews.com, IL, Moline

Sutton, Tim
tsutton@j-adgraphics.com, Prod. Mgr, Ad-Visor and Chronicle, MI, Marshall
tsutton@j-adgraphics.com, Prod. Mgr, Reminder, MI, Hastings

Suwalsky, Salomon
salomonsuwalsky@royal.com, Pres., Royal Consumer Information Products, Inc., NJ, Somerset

Svec, Andrew .... (540) 981-3203
andrew.svec@roanoke.com, Design and Presentation Editor, The Roanoke Times, VA, Roanoke

Svec, Joe .... (209) 223-8761
jsvec@ledger-dispatch.com, Circ. Coord., Amador Ledger-Dispatch, CA, Jackson

Svehlak, Lange
publisher@jacksonvilleprogress.com, Pub., Athens Daily Review, TX, Athens
publisher@jacksonvilleprogress.com, Pub., Jacksonville Daily Progress, TX, Jacksonville

Svehlak, Linge
lsvehlak@athensreview.com, Pub., The Star, TX, Athens

Sveikauskas, Geddy .... (845) 334-8200
geddy@ulsterpublishing.com, Pub., Ulster Publishing, NY, Kingston

Sveikauskas, Geddy
geddy@ulsterpublishing.com, Owner/Pub., New Paltz Times, NY, New Paltz

Svendgard, Brady
bsvendgard@journalstar.com, Circ. Mgr., Neighborhood Extra, NE, Lincoln

Svendgard, Brady .... (402) 473-7200
bsvendgard@journalstar.com, Operations Dir., Lincoln Journal Star, NE, Lincoln

Svidal, Kathy
ksvidal@devilslakejournal.com, Pub., Devils Lake Journal, ND, Devils Lake

Svihovec, Steve .... (715) 833-9257
steve.svihovec@ecpc.com, Prodn. Mgr., Entertainment Spotlight Saver, WI, Eau Claire

Svihovec, Travis .... (605) 845-3646
travis@mobridgetribune.com, Special Sections Ed., Mobridge Tribune, SD, Mobridge

Svingen, John
jsvingen@bemidjipioneer.com, Adv. Dir., The Bemidji Pioneer, MN, Bemidji

Svoboda, Kacie .... (605) 574-2538
prevailer@goldenwest.net, Ed., Hill City Prevailer-News, SD, Hill City

Svoboda, Nola
nola@telluridedailyplanet.com, Prodn. Mgr., Telluride Daily Planet; the Watch; The Norwood Post, CO, Telluride

Swafford, Chris
admanager@sapulpaheraldonline.com, Adv. Mgr., Sapulpa Daily Herald, OK, Sapulpa

Swafford, Maria .... (606) 546-9225
Advr Mgr, The Mountain Advocate, KY, Barbourville

Swaic, Debbie
dswaic@nevadadailymail.com, Circ. Mgr., Countryside, KS, Fort Scott

Swails, Steve .... (317) 444-4185
steven.swails@indystar.com, Circ. Mgr., Coverstory, WI, Madison

Swain, Bruce
bswain@uwf.edu, Chair, University of West

Florida, FL, Pensacola

Swalboski, Craig
swalbo@postbulletin.com, Sports Ed., Post-Bulletin, MN, Rochester

Swan, Brent
news@thepaperofwabash.com, Ed., The Paper, IN, Wabash

Swan, Darryl
dswan@spotlightnews.net, Pub., The South County Spotlight, OR, Scappoose

Swan, Jenna .... (403) 887-2331
editor@sylvanlakenews.com, Ed, Sylvan Lake News, AB, Sylvan Lake

Swan, Jenna .... (403) 887-2331
editor@sylvanlakenews.com, Ed, Eckville Echo, AB, Sylvan Lake

Swan, Laura .... (520) 432-7254
mail@thebisbeeobserver.com, Prodn. Mgr., The Bisbee Observer, AZ, Bisbee

Swaney, Casey .... (828) 236-8978
cswaney@citizen-times.com, Digital Producer , The Asheville Citizen-Times, NC, Asheville

Swaney, Kim .... (406) 675-3000
kimberlys@cskt.org, Ed., Char-Koosta News, MT, Pablo

Swank, Shonita .... (620) 792-1211, ext. 218
sfox@gbtribune.com, Circ. Dir. , Great Bend Tribune, KS, Great Bend

Swanson, Barbara .... (312) 222-4041
bswanson@oregonian.com, VP, Sales/ Multimedia, Forest Grove Leader, OR, Portland
bswanson@oregonian.com, Adv. Dir., Classified, Chicago Tribune, IL, Chicago

Swanson, Debbie .... (208) 459-5508
College of Idaho, ID, Caldwell

Swanson, Jack
editor@oelweindailyregister.com, Mng. Ed., The Oelwein Daily Register, IA, Oelwein

Swanson, Jack
editor@onlinedailyregister.com, Mng. Ed., Shopper's Reminder, IA, Oelwein

Swanson, Jim .... ext. 400
sports@princegeorgecitizen.com, Sports Ed., The Prince George Citizen, BC, Prince George

Swanson, Kathy
ads@resorter.com, Pub., Straitsland Resorter, MI, Indian River

Swanson, Lillian
lswanson@bsmphilly.com, Ed, Northeast Times, PA, Bensalem

Swanson, Lori .... (651) 228-5086
ljswanson@pioneerpress.com, Dir., Mktg., St. Paul Pioneer Press, MN, Saint Paul

Swanson, Miriam .... (541) 367-2135
mirian@sweethomenews.com, Adv. Dir, The New Era, OR, Sweet Home

Swanson, Paul .... (402) 444-1248
paul.swanson@owh.com, Mgr., Suburban Newspapers, Omaha World-Herald, NE, Omaha

Swanson, Paul .... (402) 444-1248
paul.swanson@bellevueleader.com, Special Projects Manager, Ralston Recorder, NE, Bellevue

Swanson, Paul .... (402) 444-1248
paul.swanson@owh.com, Mktg. Dir., Papillion Times, NE, Bellevue

Swanson, Paul .... (402) 444-1248
paul.swanson@owh.com, Adv. Mgr., Gretna Breeze, NE, Bellevue
paul.swanson@owh.com, Adv. Mgr., Bellevue Leader, NE, Bellevue

Swanson, Paul .... (402) 505-3602
paul.swanson@bellevueleader.com, Adv. Mgr., Air Pulse, NE, Bellevue

Swanson, Pete
sports@pdclarion.com, Sports Ed., Princeton Daily Clarion, IN, Princeton

Swanson, Sam ....(218) 855-5841
VP of Revenue Development, Brainerd Dispatch, MN, Brainerd

Swanson, Scott .... (541) 367-2135
news@sweethomenews.com, Pub, The New Era, OR, Sweet Home

Swanson, Steve
bpusczan@siix-usa.com, Mgr., Sales/ Engineering, Siix USA Corp., IL, Elk Grove Village

Swanton, Andy
aswanton@berkshireeagle.com, VP, Ops, The Berkshire Eagle, MA, Pittsfield

Swarner, Ken
swarnerkm@aol.com, Pub., Northwest Airlifter, WA, Lakewood

Swart, Russ ....(319) 360-3936
russ@tidbitpapers.com, Tidbits Of Linn County, IA, Cedar Rapids

Swartz, David
editor@esthervillenews.net, Sports Ed., Estherville News, IA, Estherville

Swartz, Don
publisher@florencenewsjournal.com, Pub., The Hartsville News Journal, SC, Hartsville
publisher@florencenewsjournal.com, Pub./Ed., Marion County News Journal, SC, Marion

Swartz, Don....................(843) 667-9656
publisher@florencenewsjournal.com , Pub., The Florence News Journal, SC, Florence

Swartz, Donna
thetimes@nmax.net, Owner/Ed., The Times, PA, Port Royal

Swartz, Judy
judy@smmirror.com, Sales Mgr., Westside Today, CA, Santa Monica
judy@smmirror.com, Sales Mgr., Santa Monica Mirror, CA, Santa Monica
judy@smmirror.com, Sales Mgr., Brentwood News, CA, Santa Monica
judy@smmirror.com, Sales Mgr., Yo Venice, CA, Santa Monica
judy@smmirror.com, Sales Mgr., Century City News, CA, Santa Monica
judy@smmirror.com, Sales Mgr., LA Pride, CA, Santa Monica

Swartz, Steven R.
sswartz@hearst.com, Pres., Hearst Newspapers, Hearst Communications, Inc., NY, New York

Swartz, Stewart
stew@wtr.com, Retail Adv. Mgr., Wichita Falls Times Record News, TX, Wichita Falls

Swartzentruber, David
tisun@gisco.net, Ed., Thousand Island Sun, NY, Alexandria Bay

Swartzlander, David ....(402) 826-8269
david.swartzlander@doane.edu, Doane College, NE, Crete

Swearengin, Matt ....(580) 634-2160
mswearengin@civitasmedia.com, Mng. Ed., Durant Daily Democrat, OK, Durant

Swearingen, Abby
abby.swearingen@therogersvillereview.com, Adv. Exec., The Rogersville Review, TN, Rogersville

Sweat, Dalton ....(512) 847-2202
dsweat@wimberleyview.com, GM/Ed., Wimberley View, TX, Wimberley

Sweat, Jimmye
jimmye@northsidesun.com, Ed., Northside Sun, MS, Jackson

Sweeney, Amy..................(978) 946-2243
asweeney@eagletribune.com, Photo Dir., The Eagle-Tribune, MA, North Andover

Sweeney, Anna ....(563) 588-7828

anna.sweeney@loras.edu, Loras College, IA, Dubuque

Sweeney, John ....(919) 962-4074
jsweeney@email.unc.edu, Distinguished Prof. in Sports Commun., University of North Carolina, NC, Chapel Hill

Sweeney, Kevin
editor@nujournal.com, Ed., The Journal, MN, New Ulm

Sweeney, Mike
msweeney@mojonews.com, Prodn. Mgr., Press, Morning Journal, OH, Lisbon

Sweeney, Tom..................(818) 965-0882
toms@a-americanpressparts.com, Vice Pres., Opns., A-American Machine & Assembly (Press Parts Div.), IL, Rockford

Sweet, Dennis
dennis.sweet@sunchemical.com, Gen. Mgr., Rycoline Products, Inc., IL, Chicago

Sweetapple, Ray ....(709) 637-4663
rsweetapple@thewesternstar.com, Editorial Page Ed., The Western Star, NL, Corner Brook

Sweetman, Keri ....(780) 429-5346
ksweetman@thejournal.canwest.com, Culture Ed., Edmonton Journal, AB, Edmonton

Sweetser, Kim ....(308) 381-9434
kim.sweetser@theindependent.com, Adv. Mgr., Retail, The Grand Island Independent, NE, Grand Island

Sweetwood, Mark..........(330) 747-1471 Ext. 1384
msweetwood@vindy.com, Mng. Ed., The Vindicator, OH, Youngstown

Sweetwood, Matthew
info@uniquephoto.com, COO, Unique Photo, NJ, Fairfield

Swegle, Terri
tswegle@shawmedia.com, CFO Treasurer, Shaw Media, IL, Sterling

Sweigard, Peter ....(410) 332-6169
pete.sweigard@baltsun.com . , Asst. Managing Ed. Digital, The Baltimore Sun, MD, Baltimore

Sweitzer, Judy
jsweitzer@pontiacdailyleader.com, Advertising Executive, Livingston Shopping News, IL, Pontiac

Swenson, Anne..................(218) 365-3141
thepub@elyecho.com, Pub., North Country Saver, MN, Ely

Swenson, Anne................(218) 365-3141 ext. 20
thepub@elyecho.com, Pub., The Ely Echo, MN, Ely

Swenson, Brad ....(712) 642-2791 ext. 1003
pub@missourivalleytimes.com, Publisher, Missouri Valley Times-News, IA, Missouri Valley

Swenson, Brad .. (712) 881-1101 or (712) 642-2791
pub@missourivalleytimes.com, Publisher, Mapleton Press, IA, Mapleton

Swenson, Brandi
bswenson@readingeagle.com , Web Designer, Reading Eagle, PA, Reading

Swenson, Charles R.
editor@coastalobserver.com, Ed., Coastal Observer, SC, Pawleys Island

Swenson, Coleen ....(208) 587-3331 ext. 14
cswenson@mountainhomenews.com, Mountain Home News, ID, Mountain Home

Swenson, Ian ....(253) 274-7388
ian.swenson@thenewstribune.com, Asst. Mng. Ed., Online, The News Tribune, WA, Tacoma

Swenson, Jim
jswenson@wcinet.com, Features Ed., Telegraph Herald, IA, Dubuque

Swenson, Melissa ....(218) 844-1451
MSWENSON@DLNEWSPAPERS.COM, Publisher, Detroit Lakes Tribune, MN, Detroit Lakes

Swenson, Melissa ....(218) 844-1451
mswenson@dlnewspapers.com, Publisher, Lake Area Press, MN, Detroit Lakes

Swenson, Melissa ....(218) 346-5900
mswenson@eotfocus.com, Pub. , Perham Focus, MN, Perham
mswenson@eotfocus.com, Adv. Mgr., Enterprise Bulletin, MN, Perham

Swenson, Sarah
sarah.swenson@sunmedia.ca, Ed, Lacombe Globe, AB, Lacombe
sarah.swenson@sunmedia.ca, Ed., Wetaskiwin Times, AB, Wetaskiwin

Swenson, Stacy ....(509) 424-7873
shpstacy@gmail.com, Pub. , Adams County Record, ND, Hettinger
shpstacy@gmail.com, Adv. Mgr., Hill City Prevailer-News, SD, Hill City

Swepton, Kevin
printing@iolaregister.com, Commercial Printing, The Iola Register, KS, Iola

Swibold, Dennis
dennis.swibold@umontana.edu, Prof., The University of Montana, MT, Missoula

Swider, Theresa..................(315) 792-5029
tswider@uticaod.com, Controller, The Observer-Dispatch, NY, Utica

Swift, Richard P.
rswift@bi.brant.allen.com, Gen. Sales Mgr., Newsprint Sales Co., VA, Charlottesville

Swift, Susan
susanswift@arkansasleader.com, Adv. Rep., The Leader, AR, Jacksonville

Swift, Todd
tswift@keynoter.com, Prodn. Mgr., The Reporter, FL, Tavernier

Swil, Warren
wiswil@pasadena.edu, Pasadena City College, CA, Pasadena

Swillo, Sara
sswillo@assumption.edu, Assumption College, MA, Worcester

Swinconeck, John
jswinconeck@timesrecord.com, Ed., The Times Record, ME, Brunswick

Swindler, Samantha
newsclerk@oregonian.com, Ed., Forest Grove Leader, OR, Portland

Swintek, Beth
beth.swintek@thefacts.com, Circ. Mgr., The Facts, TX, Clute

Swirko, Cindy
swirkoc@gvillesun.com, Educ. Writer, Lower, The Gainesville Sun, FL, Gainesville

Swisher, Michael
ktfpsports@gmail.com, Mng./Sports Ed., The Kingfisher Times & Free Press, OK, Kingfisher

Swiston, Jeff ....(715) 682-2313
Advertising, The Ashland Daily Press, WI, Ashland

Switalski, David
info@quipp.com, Vice Pres., Opns., Quipp System, Inc., FL, Miami Lakes

Switchenko, Katie ....(202) 725-8318
katies@rtdna.org, Awards, Membership and Programs Manager, Radio Television Digital News Association, DC, Washington

Switzer, Aaron
aaron@bendsource.com, Pub., Source Weekly, OR, Bend

Switzer, Jamie
jamie.switzer@colostate.edu, Assoc. Prof., Colorado State University, CO, Fort Collins

Swofford, Robert..................(707) 521-5251
bob.swofford@pressdemocrat.com, Mng. Ed., The Press Democrat, CA, Santa Rosa

Swygart, J.

j@decaturdailydemocrat.com, Features Ed., Berne Shopping News, IN, Decatur
j@decaturdailydemocrat.com, Managing Ed., Decatur Daily Democrat, IN, Decatur

Sydow, Carey ....(815) 987-1463
csydow@rockford.gannett.com, Prodn. Mgr., The Star Shopper, IL, Rockford

Sydow, Dena..................(231) 439-9313
dsydow@petoskeynews.com, Mktg. Mgr., Northern Michigan Review, MI, Petoskey

Syed, Hasanat Ahmad
humanrights@sympatico.ca, Mng. Ed., New Canada, ON, Toronto

Sygutek, Lisa
passherald@shaw.ca, Pub., Crowsnest Pass Herald, AB, Blairmore

Sykes, Bryan
editor@theaggie.org, Editor-in-Chief, University of California, Davis, CA, Davis

Sykes, Daniel..................(502) 513-1166
dsykes@lcni.com, Exec. VP., Landmark Community Newspapers, LLC, KY, Shelbyville

Sykes, Dave ....ext. 214
dsykes@bowesnet.com, Pub., Focus, ON, Goderich

Sykes, Deirdre ....(973) 569-7112
sykes@northjersey.com, The Record, NJ, Woodland Park
sykes@northjersey.com, Sr. Dir., Herald News, NJ, Rockaway

Sykes, Doreen..............(705) 445-4611 ext. 222
dsykes@theenterprisebulletin.com, Pub., The Enterprise-bulletin, ON, Collingwood

Sykes, Jack ....(703) 380-2808
bureauchief@winsphoto.com, CEO/Chief Photographer, World Images News Service, Centreville

Sykes, John..................(501) 918-4529
jsykes@arkansasonline.com, Chief Photographer, Arkansas Democrat-Gazette, AR, Little Rock

Sykes, Michael
msykes@hartfordadvocate.com, Sales Mgr., New Mass Media, Inc., CT, Hartford

Sylvester, Dan
dsylvester@ottumwacourier.com, Adv. Mgr., The Ottumwa Courier, IA, Ottumwa

Sylvester, Joe
jsylvester@dailyitem.com, Reporter, The Daily Item, PA, Sunbury

Sylvester, Maureen..................(978) 970-4880
msylvester@lowellsun.com, Circ. Mgr., Alternate Delivery, The Sun, MA, Lowell

Sylvester, Rebecca
rebecca.sylvester@uc.edu, Creative Director, Cincinnati Citybeat, OH, Cincinnati

Sylvester , Ron ....(620) 694-5700 ext. 300
rsylvester@hutchnews.com, Mng. Ed., The Hutchinson News, KS, Hutchinson

Symington, Pamela ....(540) 351-1166
psymington@virginianewsgroup.com, Gen. Mgr, Fauquier Times, VA, Warrenton

Symons, Allene
symons_allene@sac.edu, Santa Ana College, CA, Santa Ana

Symson, Adam ....(513) 977-3000
adam.symson@scripps.com, Pres. & CEO, E. W. Scripps Co., OH, Cincinnati

Synder, Holli
holli.snyder@nptelegraph.com, Bus. Mgr., The North Platte Telegraph, NE, North Platte

Synett, Lawrence
lsynett@shawmedia.com, Web Ed., Daily Chronicle, IL, Dekalb

Synyard, April ....(858) 258-2570
solutions@ democratandchronicle .com, Mktg. Mgr., Democrat and Chronicle, NY,

Rochester

Syse, Scarlett ....(317) 736-2749
ssyse@dailyjournal.net, Group Ed., Daily
Journal, IN, Franklin

Syversen, Jenny ....(770) 535-6323
jsyversen@gainesvilletimes.com, Director of
advertising and marketing, The Times, GA,
Gainesville

Syverson, Dave ....(605) 845-3646
dave@mobridgetribune.com, Sales Rep.,
Mobridge Tribune, SD, Mobridge

Szabrak, Rick
ohioclassified@nncogannett.com, Adv. Mgr.,
Lancaster/fairfield Advertiser, OH, Carroll

Szabrak, Rick ....(740) 681-4356
rszabrak@nncogannett.com, Group Publisher,
Eagle-Gazette Media, OH, Lancaster

Szadziewicz, Sherry ....(605) 331-2276
sszadzie@argusleader.com, Marketing
Director, Argus Leader, SD, Sioux Falls

Szefc, John ....(845) 291-7367
Jszefc@hvc.rr.com, Sr. Associate-Northeast/
News England, W.B. Grimes & Company,
MD, Gaithersburg

Szefc, John ....(845) 291-7367
Jszefc@hvc.rr.com, Northeast/New England
Regl. Mgr., Grimes, W.B. & Co., NY, Goshen
Jszefc@hvc.rr.com, Senior Associate-
Northeast, Lewis Floyd- Grimes, W.B. & Co.,
AL, Gulf Shores
Jszefc@hvc.rr.com, Senior Associate-
Northeast/New England, Grimes, McGovern
& Associates, NY, New York

Szefe, John ....(845) 291-7367
Grimes, McGovern & Associates, NY, New York

Szold, Charlie ....(202) 885-1409
American Univ., DC, Washington

Szollar, Mark
szollar@northjersey.com, Adv. Dir., The
Record, NJ, Woodland Park

Szozda, Jordan
jordan@presspublications.com, Circ. Mgr, The
Press, OH, Millbury

Szucs, Jennifer........................(216) 956-0210
jszucs@advancecentralservices.com, Bus. Sol.
Mgr., IT, The Plain Dealer, OH, Brooklyn

Szudlo, Betty ....(330) 721-4055
sports@medina-gazette.com, Sports Ed., The
Medina County Gazette, OH, Medina

Szymanski, Ed........................(308) 233-9718
Prodn. Mgr., Distr., Kearney Hub, NE, Kearney

T

Tabar, David
dt@durangoherald.com, IT Mgr., Durango
Herald, CO, Durango

Tabb, Lynne
ads@wetmountaintribune.com, Adv. Dir., Wet
Mountain Tribune, CO, Westcliffe

Taber, Kim ....(501) 337-7523
Bus. Mgr., Malvern Daily TMC, Malvern

Taber, Kim ....(501) 337-7523 ext 208
accounts@malvern-online.com, Business Mgr.,
Malvern Daily Record, AR, Malvern

Tabor, Betty
clydejournal@earthlink.net, Pub., Clyde
Journal, TX, Clyde
clydejournal@earthlink.net, Pub., Baird
Banner, TX, Clyde

Tabor, Daniel
clydejournal@earthlink.net, Ed, Clyde Journal,
TX, Clyde

Tabor, Danny........................(325) 893-4244
clydejournal@earthlink.net, Editor, Baird
Banner, TX, Clyde

Tabor, Daryl

thepress@the-press.com, Mng. Ed., The
Crittenden Press, KY, Marion

Tabor, Glen............................(423) 392-1333
gtabor@timesnews.net, Treasurer, Southern
Circulation Managers Association, TN,
Kingsport

Tabor, John ....(603) 570-2100
jtabor@seacoastonline.com, Pub., Portsmouth
Herald, NH, Portsmouth
jtabor@seacoastonline.com, Pub., Exeter
News-Letter, NH, Portsmouth
jtabor@seacoastonline.com, Pub., York County
Coast Star, NH, Portsmouth
jtabor@seacoastonline.com, Pres. & Pub. ,
Foster's Daily Democrat, NH, Dover

Tabor, John
jtabor@seacoastonline.com, Pub., The York
Weekly, NH, Portsmouth

Tabor, John ....(603) 570-2100
jtabor@seacoastonline.com, Seacoast Media
Group, NH, Portsmouth

Tabor, John ....(603) 610-1169
jtabor@seacoastonline.com, Pub., The
Hampton Union, NH, Portsmouth

Taborski, Michael....................(530) 283-0800
mtaborski@plumasnews.com, Pub., Feather
Publishing Co., Inc., CA, Quincy

Taborski, Michael ....(530) 283-0800
mtaborski@plumasnews.com, Pub, Portola
Reporter, CA, Portola

Taborski, Michael ....(530) 283-0800
mtaborski@plumasnews.com, Pub., Westwood
Pinepress, CA, Susanville

Taborski, Michael C. ....(530) 283-0800
mtaborski@plumasnews.com, Pub., Feather
River Bulletin, CA, Quincy

Taborski, Michael C. ....(530) 283-0800
mtaborski@plumasnews.com, Pub, Chester
Progressive, CA, Chester

Taborski, Michael C. ....(530) 283-0800
mtaborski@plumasnews.com, Pub, Lassen
County Times, CA, Susanville

Taborski, Michael C. ....(530) 283-0800
mtaborski@plumasnews.com, Pub., Indian
Valley Record, CA, Greenville

Tackett, Dan
dan.tackett@lincolncourier.com, News Ed.,
Logan County Shopper, IL, Lincoln

Tackett, Gary ....(928) 474-5251 x117
gtackett@payson.com, Director of Sales, The
Payson Roundup, AZ, Payson

Tafelski, Scott ....(312) 222-3159
shaimurphy@tribune.com, Dir., Technical
Devel., Chicago Tribune, IL, Chicago

Tafoya, Diane
dianet@chieftain.com, Mgr., Bus. Office/
Purchasing Agent, The Pueblo Chieftain,
CO, Pueblo

Taft, Susan............................(903) 645-3948
beenewspaper@etcnonline.com, Ed., The Bee,
TX, Daingerfield
beenewspaper@etcnonline.com, Ed., Pittsburg
Gazette, TX, Pittsburg

Taggart, Mark........................(920) 743-3321
mtaggart@gannett.com, Advertising Manager,
Door County Advocate, WI, Sturgeon Bay

Tai, Zixue
ztai2@uky.edu, Instr., Southern Illinois
University Edwardsville, IL, Edwardsville
ztai2@uky.edu, Asst. Prof., University of
Kentucky, KY, Lexington

Tait, Annette
star@westriv.com, Ed., Center Republican,
ND, Beulah

Taje, Leanne............................ext. 122
Circ. Mgr., The Camrose Booster, AB, Camrose

Takeuchi, Masashi
masashi.takeuchi@dowjones.com, Sales Mgr.,

Dow Jones Newswires - Tokyo, Japan, Tokyo

Talbert, Jeff ....(407) 894-7300 ext. 225
jtalbert@hearstsc.com, VP, Reed Brennan
Media Associates, Inc., FL, Orlando

Talbert, Jim ....(276) 963-1081
jtalbert@richlands-news-press.com, Ed.,
Richlands News-Press, VA, Richlands

Talbert, Lee ....ext. 349
ltalbert@johnsoncitypress.com, Photo Dept.
Mgr., Johnson City Press, TN, Johnson City

Talbert, Tia ....ext. 21
tjt@astech.intermedia.com, Dir., Client Servs.,
ASTech InterMedia, CO, Denver

Talbot, Josh ....(978) 249-3535 ext.653
sports@atholdailynews.com, Sports Ed., Athol
Daily News, MA, Athol

Talbot, Tom ....(508) 676-2554
ttalbot@wickedlocal.com, Adv. Dir., O Jornal,
MA, Fall River

Talbot, Veronick ....(450) 964-4444
redaction@larevue.qc.ca, News Dir, La Revue
De Terrebonne, QC, Terrebonne

Talbot, Véronick ....(450) 964-4444
redaction@larevue.qc.ca, Rédactrice en chef,
Le Trait D'union, QC, Terrebonne

Talbot, Warren ....(978) 946-2274
wtalbot@eagletribune.com, City Ed., The
Eagle-Tribune, MA, North Andover

Talbott, Michael
chapregister@embarqmail.com, Ed., Chappell
Register, NE, Chappell

Talent, Britt
ccherald@tds.net, Ed., Cleveland County
Herald, AR, Rison

Talent, Leslie ....(907) 335-1247
leslie.talent@peninsulaclarion.com, Adv. Dir,
Peninsula Clarion, AK, Kenai

Talerico, Matt........................(724) 225-2621
mtalerico@observer-reporter.com, Retail
Sales Mgr., Observer-Reporter, PA,
Washington

Talla, Donna
dtalla@nwfdailynews.com, The Polk County
News and Democrat, FL, Winter Haven

Talla, Donna ....(703) 230-6692
Northwest Florida Daily News, FL, Fort Walton
Beach

Talla, Donna ....(850) 315-4340
dtalla@nwfdailynews.com, Adv. Dir., The
Walton Sun, FL, Santa Rosa Beach

Tallent, Rebecca
rtallent@uidaho.edu, Asst. Prof., University of
Idaho, ID, Moscow

Talley, Caleb
newsroom@thnews.com, Reporter. /
Photographer, Times-Herald, AR, Forrest City

Talley, Edie
driftwoodeditor@uno.edu, Editor in Chief,
University of New Orleans, LA, New Orleans

Talley, Lucy ....(704) 869-1702
ltalley@gastongazette.com, Pub., The Gaston
Gazette, NC, Gastonia
ltalley@gastongazette.com, Pub., The Star,
NC, Shelby

Tallmadge, David ....(770) 428-9411 ext. 464
Prodn. Mgr., Marietta Daily Journal, GA,
Marietta

Tallman, Jeff
jtallman@mountainx.com, Distribution
Manager, Mountain Xpress, NC, Asheville

Tam, Shirley
stam@ottawacitizen.com, Dir. of Finance, The
Ottawa Citizen, ON, Ottawa

Tamayo, Guillermo ....(805) 739-2147
gtamayo@leecentralcoastnews.com, Circ. Mgr.,
Santa Maria Times, CA, Santa Maria

Tamayo, Vincenta........................(760) 337-3447

amapilis@ivpressonline.com, Designer. Copy
Ed, Imperial Valley Press, CA, El Centro

Tamborrino, Richard ....(305) 440-3225
rtamborrino@keynoter.com , Pub., The
Reporter, FL, Tavernier

Tamburina, Karen....................(503) 630-3241
email@estacadanews.com, Adv., Estacada
News, OR, Estacada

Tamburino, Tina ....(760) 789-1350
tina.tamburrino@ramonasentinel.com, Gen
Mgr, Ramona Sentinel, CA, Ramona

Tamke, Jon
blreview@arvig.net, Ed., Battle Lake Review,
MN, Battle Lake

Tamraz, Cathy Baron ....Pres./COO
Business Wire - San Francisco, CA, San
Francisco
Pres./COO, Business Wire - Boston, MA,
Boston

Tamucci, Laura
ltamucci@steamboattoday.com, Adv. Dir.,
Steamboat Today, CO, Steamboat Springs
ltamucci@steamboattoday.com, Adv. Dir.,
Steamboat Pilot, CO, Steamboat Springs

Tan, Alexis S.............................(509) 335-8535
Prof., Washington State University, WA,
Pullman

Tan, Jon ....(617) 779-3792
JTan@pilotcatholicnews.com, Coord., Mktg./
Circ., The Pilot, MA, Braintree

Tan, Whye-Ko..........................+65 6391 9622
whye-ko.tan@nytimes.com, Regional Director,
Asia Pacific, The New York Times News
Service & Syndicate, New York
whye-ko.tan@nytimes.com, Regional Director,
Asia Pacific, The New York Times News
Service & Syndicate, New York

Tandy, Mary B.
herald1@earthlink.net, Ed., Indiana Herald, IN,
Indianapolis

Taneja, Aanchal
ataneja6@iit.edu, Illinois Inst. of Technology,
IL, Chicago

Tang, Janice
jtang@therecorder.com, Controller, The
Recorder, CA, San Francisco

Tang, Yong ....(309) 298-1948
y-tang@wiu.edu, Asst Prof
Dir of Journalism, Western Illinois University,
IL, Macomb

Tangeman, Hannah
htangema@nebrwesleyan.edu, Editor,
Nebraska Wesleyan Univ., NE, Lincoln

Tangi, Daniel
dtangi@southphillyreview.com, Adv. Mgr.,
South Philly Review, NJ, Cherry Hill

Tankersley, Phil ....(314) 838-1469
Circ. Mgr., Independent News, MO, Florissant

Tanksley, Karen ....(912) 826-0847
ktanksley@effinghamherald.net, Pub.,
Effingham Herald, GA, Rincon

Tannahill, Carol ....(618) 842-2662
admanager@waycopress.com, Adv. Mgr.,
Wayne County Press, IL, Fairfield

Tanner, Adrienne....................(604) 605-2214
atanner@postmedia.com, Dep. Ed., The
Province, BC, Vancouver

Tanner, Hal H. ....(919) 739-7906
htanner3@newsargus.com, Publisher,
Goldsboro News-Argus, NC, Goldsboro

Tanner, James........................(800) 327-8463
jtanner@verafast.com, Mktg./Research
Specialist, Ver-A-Fast Corporation, OH,
Rocky River

Tanner, Jetty..............................ext. 200
jetty.tanner@gaflnews.com, Office Mgr., The
Tifton Gazette, GA, Tifton

Tanner, Rachel

dixiesun@dixie.edu, Dixie State College, UT, Saint George

Tannler, Nancy
examiner@inseportland.com, Pub./Circ. Mgr., The Southeast Examiner, OR, Portland

Tanquary, Bob .... (618) 262-5144
btanquary@mtcamelregister.com, Accounting Clerk, Mount Carmel Register, IL, Mount Carmel

Tant, Greg
greg.tant@coxinc.com, Dir., Newsprint Supply, Cox Media Group, GA, Atlanta

Tanzone, Daniel F.
sokol205@aol.com, Ed., Slovak Catholic Falcon, NJ, Passaic

Tapa, Clara .... (262) 656-6307
ctappa@ucclocalmedia.com, Chief Administrative Officer, United Communications Corporation, WI, Kenosha

Tapsell, Julie
julie.tapsell@sunmedia.ca, Office Mgr., St. Thomas Times-Journal, ON, Saint Thomas

Tarapacki, Thomas .... (800) 422-1275
Assistant Editor, Polish American Journal, NY, North Boston

Taraska, Morey .... (217) 224-3403
mtaraska@qni.biz, Asst. to Pres./CEO, Quincy Media, Inc., IL, Quincy

Tardif, Raymond
raymond.tardif@lenouvelliste.qc.ca, Pres./Ed., Le Nouvelliste, QC, Trois-Rivieres

Tardif, Richard .... (514) 697-6330
execdir@qcna.qc.ca, Executive Director, Quebec Community Newspapers Association, QC, Pointe-Claire

Tarica, Joe .... (805) 781-7911
jtarica@thetribunenews.com, Sr. Ed., The Tribune, CA, San Luis Obispo

Tarley, Amanda .... (718) 260-2555
classified@cnglocal.com, Classified Adv. Mgr., Brooklyn Courier, NY, Brooklyn
classified@cnglocal.com, Classified Advertising
, The Little Neck Ledger, NY, Bayside
classified@cnglocal.com, Classified Adv. Mgr., Bay Ridge Courier, NY, Brooklyn

Tarley, Amanda .... (718) 260-2500
atarley@cnglocal.com, Classified Advertising Director, Fresh Meadows Times, NY, Bayside
atarley@cnglocal.com, Classified Advertising Director, Jackson Heights Times, NY, Bayside
atarley@cnglocal.com, Classified Advertising Director, Jamaica Times, NY, Bayside
atarley@cnglocal.com, Classified Advertising Director, Laurelton Times, NY, Bayside
atarley@cnglocal.com, Classified Advertising Director, Ridgewood Ledger, NY, Bayside

Tarley , Amanda .... (718) 260-2555
classified@cnglocal.com, Classified Advertising
, The Whitestone Times, NY, Bayside

Tarlton, Brenda .... (618) 643-2387
brenda.tarlton@mcleansborotimesleader.com, Adv, The Times-Leader, IL, Mc Leansboro

Tarot, Gilles .... (202) 414-0637
gilles.tarot@afp.com, Mktg & Sales Dir., North America, Agence France-Presse - Washington, DC, Washington

Tarr, Ashley .... (607) 777-2244
SUNY/Binghamton, NY, Binghamton

Tarrant, Erica
erica@thestranger.com, Prodn. Mgr., The Stranger, WA, Seattle

Tarrant, James
newsrecorder@sasktel.net, Ed., The Tisdale Recorder, SK, Tisdale

Tarter, Steve .... (309) 686-3260
starter@pjstar.com, Bus. Ed., Journal Star, IL, Peoria

Tarulli, Christine
CTarulli@davlermedia.com, Mng. Ed., Westchester Parent, NY, Briarcliff Manor

Tarwater, deborah .... (601) 584-3056 ....
dtarwater@hattiesburgamerican.com, Circ. Mgr. , Hattiesburg American, MS, Hattiesburg

Tarzian, Donna
donna.tarzian@latimes.com, VP Brand Marketing, Los Angeles Times, CA, Los Angeles

Tasaka, Guy .... (215) 949-4012
gtasaka@calkins.com, Vice Pres./Chief Digital Officer, Calkins Media, PA, Levittown

Tash, Paul .... (727) 893-8887
ptash@sptimes.com, Chairman & CEO, Tampa Bay Times, FL, St Petersburg

Tasman, Marc .... (414) 229-4436
mtasman@uwm.edu, Senior Lecturer, University of Wisconsin-Milwaukee / Department of Journalism, Advertising, and Media Studies (JAMS), WI, Milwaukee

Tast, Lisa .... (309) 462-3189
abingdonargus@gmail.com, Adv. Mgr., Argus-Sentinel, IL, Galesburg

Tate, Bart
btate@bnd.com, Belleville News-Democrat, IL, Belleville

Tate, Byron .... (870) 534-1427
btate@pbcommercial.com, Pub., Cabot Star-Herald, AR, Cabot
btate@pbcommercial.com, Pub., Hot Springs Village Voice, AR, Hot Springs Village
btate@pbcommercial.com, Pub., Carlisle Independent, AR, Carlisle
btate@pbcommercial.com, Pub., Lonoke Democrat, AR, Lonoke
btate@pbcommercial.com, Pub., Maumelle Monitor, AR, North Little Rock
btate@pbcommercial.com, Pub., The North Little Rock Times, AR, North Little Rock
btate@pbcommercial.com, Pub., Jacksonville Patriot, AR, North Little Rock
btate@pbcommercial.com, Pub., Sherwood Voice, AR, North Little Rock

Tate, Byron .... (479) 784-0444
byron@thesheridanheadlight.com, Pub., Sheridan Headlight, AR, Sheridan

Tate, Grace
grace.tate@courierpost.com, Circ. Mgr, Hannibal Courier-Post, MO, Hannibal

Tate, Grady .... (765) 825-0588 ext. 229
gtate@newsexaminer.com, Sports Ed., Connersville News-Examiner, IN, Connersville

Tate, Jenay
jenay@coalfield.com, Pub., The Dickenson Star, VA, Clintwood

Tate, Jennifer .... (937) 229-3211
Univ. of Dayton Law School, OH, Dayton

Tate, Karen
ktate@coalfield.com, Account Exec., The Post, VA, Big Stone Gap
ktate@coalfield.com, Adv. Mgr., The Dickenson Star, VA, Clintwood
ktate@coalfield.com, Adv. Mgr., The Coalfield Progress, VA, Norton

Tate, Paula
ptate@coalfield.com, Mng. Ed., The Dickenson Star, VA, Clintwood

Tatom, Cecil .... (409) 787-2172
screporter@yahoo.com, Reporter, The Sabine County Reporter, TX, Hemphill

Tatum, Elinor .... (212) 932-7465
elinor.tatum@amsterdamnews.com, Publisher / Editor in Chief, New York Amsterdam News, NY, New York

Tatum, Kala .... (256) 232-2720
circulation@athens-news-courier.com, Audience Development Associate, The News-Courier, AL, Athens

Tatum, Rebekah .... (573) 225-6365
kpirebekah@gmail.com, Advertising Account Executive, The Huntingburg Press, IN, Huntingburg

Tatum, Shannon .... (601) 979-2167
shannon.d.tatum@jsums.edu, Publications Coordinator/Ad Manager, Jackson State University, MS, Jackson

Taufen, Amber .... (720) 635-9065
amber@inman.com, Ed. In Chief, Inman News, Emeryville

Taus, Rebecca .... (904) 886-4919
publisher@rtpublishinginc.com, Pub. Mgr, Mandarin NewsLine, FL, Jacksonville
publisher@rtpublishinginc.com, Pub., Ocean Breeze, FL, Jacksonville

Tauscher, William
bill.tauscher@vertical.com, CEO, Vertical Communications, Inc., AZ, Phoenix

Taves, Susan .... (715) 365-6397 ext.363
subscriptions@rivernewsonline.com, Subscriptions, The Northwoods River News , WI, Rhinelander
subscriptions@rivernewsonline.com, Subscriptions, Northwoods Super Shopper, WI, Rhinelander

Tavoularis, Ashley .... (212) 803-8323
ashley.tavoularis@sourcemedia.com, Mktg. Cord., American Banker, NY, New York

Taylor, Aeron
Aeron.Taylor@owassoreporter.com, Mktg., Owasso Reporter, OK, Owasso

Taylor, Alistair
editor@campbellrivermirror.com, Ed, The Campbell River Courier-islander, BC, Campbell River

Taylor, Andy
ataylor@record-eagle.com, Ed, Montgomery County Chronicle, KS, Caney
ataylor@record-eagle.com, Associate Ed., Traverse City Record-Eagle, MI, Traverse City

Taylor, Angela .... (409) 683-5239
angela.taylor@galvnews.com, Community News Editor, The Galveston County Daily News, TX, Galveston

Taylor, Ann Elise .... (574) 296-5826
ataylor@elkharttruth.com, Assistant Managing Editor - Digital, Elkhart Truth, IN, Elkhart

Taylor, Anne .... (425) 564-2434
Bellevue Cmty. College, WA, Bellevue

Taylor, Balkom
taylor.balkom@gmail.com, Editor in Chief, Louisiana State University, LA, Baton Rouge

Taylor, Baretta
btaylor@progress-index.com, Adv. Dir., The Daily Herald, PA, Tyrone
btaylor@progress-index.com, Adv. Dir., The Progress-Index, VA, Petersburg

Taylor, Beanie
beanietaylor@elkintribune.com, Staff Reporter, The Tribune, NC, Elkin

Taylor, Becky .... ext 1912
becky.taylor@gaflnews.com, Sports Ed., The Tifton Gazette, GA, Tifton

Taylor, Becky .... (765) 423-5511
btaylor@journalandcourier.com, Adv. Mgr., Classified, Journal and Courier, IN, Lafayette

Taylor, Beverly .... (806) 669-2525
classified1@thepampanews.com, Classified Mgr., The Pampa News, TX, Pampa

Taylor, Bill .... (850) 599-2337
btaylor@tallahassee.com, Gen. Manager , Tallahassee Democrat, FL, Tallahassee

Taylor, Bonnie
bonniet@thetruecitizen.com, Gen. Mgr., The Signal, GA, Waynesboro

Taylor, Brooks .... (319) 385-3131
news@mpnews.net, News Editor, Mt. Pleasant News, IA, Mount Pleasant

Taylor, Christine W. .... (860) 241-6275
cwolfram@courant.com, VP/Digital Platform , The Hartford Courant, CT, Hartford

Taylor, Cindi .... (806) 271-3381
cindi@thetexasspur.com, Pub., The Texas Spur, TX, Spur

Taylor, Dan
publisher@thestargroup.com, Pub., Joshua Star, TX, Burleson
publisher@thestargroup.com, Pub., Keene Star, TX, Burleson
publisher@thestargroup.com, Pub., Crowley Star, TX, Burleson
publisher@thestargroup.com, Pub., Alvarado Star, TX, Burleson
publisher@thestargroup.com, Pub., Burleson Star, TX, Burleson

Taylor, Daryl .... (765) 653-5151
dtaylor@bannergraphic.com, Gen. Mgr., Banner-Graphic, IN, Greencastle

Taylor, Dave
hancockclarion@bellsouth.net, Adv Mgr, The Hancock Clarion, KY, Hawesville

Taylor, David .... (281) 378-1919
dtaylor@hcnonline.com, Ed., Bellaire Examiner, TX, Houston

Taylor, Davis .... (559) 583-2400
dtaylor@hanfordsentinel.com, Pub., The Kingsburg Recorder, CA, Hanford

Taylor, Davis .... (559) 583-2400
publisher@hanfordsentinel.com, Pub., The Selma Enterprise, CA, Hanford

Taylor, Dean .... (337) 289-6351
dxtaylor@theadvertiser.com, Home Delivery Mgr., Daily World, LA, Opelousas

Taylor, Dee .... (803) 644-2371
dtaylor@aikensstandard.com, Adv. Dir., Evening Post Industries' Aiken Communications, SC, Aiken

Taylor, Diana
advertising@winfieldcourier.com, Adv. Sales, Winfield Daily Courier, KS, Winfield

Taylor, Emily .... (812) 888-4551
etaylor@vinu.edu, Jrnlsm Asst. Professor, Journalism Program, Vincennes University, IN, Vincennes

Taylor, Faye
ftaylor@sunherald.com, Coord., Credit, The Sun Herald, MS, Gulfport

Taylor, Gary .... (847) 866-6501
gtaylor@trustwave.com, Ed., Morton Grove Champion, IL, Chicago

Taylor, George
timesnews@tnonline.com, New Media Ed., Times News, PA, Lehighton

Taylor, George .... (610) 625-2121
gtaylor@tnonline.com, Ed., Bethlehem Press, PA, Allentown

Taylor, Gerald J. .... (309) 757-4924
gjtaylor@qconline.com, Pub., Ad Extra, IL, Moline
gjtaylor@qconline.com, Ed./Pub., The Dispatch-Argus, IL, Moline

Taylor, Heber .... (409) 683-5239
heber.taylor@galvnews.com, Ed., The Galveston County Daily News, TX, Galveston

Taylor, Helen .... (505) 823-3927
htaylor@abqjournal.com, Special Sec./Feat. Ed., Albuquerque Journal, NM, Albuquerque

Taylor, James .... (830) 796-3718
james@banderabulletin.com, Adv. Dir., Bandera Bulletin, TX, Bandera

Taylor, Janine
production@orangevillebanner.com, Prodn. Mgr., The Orangeville Banner, ON, Orangeville

Taylor, Jason
jtaylor@timesfreepress.com, Publisher, The Clarion-Ledger, MS, Jackson

Taylor, Jean
jtaylor@ldnews.com, HR
, The Lebanon Daily News, PA, Lebanon

Taylor, Jeff .... (313) 222-5150
jtaylor@freepress.com, Deputy Mng. Ed.,
Detroit Free Press, MI, Detroit

Taylor, Jennifer
jennifer@pikecountygeorgia.com, Office Mgr.,
Pike County Journal and Reporter, GA,
Zebulon

Taylor, Jody .... (574) 722-5000 ext. 5125
jody.taylor@pharostribune.com, Classified /
Expeditor, Pharos-Tribune, IN, Logansport

Taylor, John
jtaylor@theworldco.info, Pub, The Baldwin City
Signal, KS, Baldwin City

Taylor, Joyce .... (423) 472-5041
dmontgomery@bradleyco.net, Credit Mgr.,
Cleveland Daily Banner, TN, Cleveland

Taylor, Karen .... (615) 329-8706
Fisk Univ., TN, Nashville

Taylor, Karen Cord
ktaylor@beaconhilltimes.com, Ed. & Pub. , The
Beacon Hill Times, MA, Boston

Taylor, Kathy
taylornews@taylornews.org, Mng. Ed.,
Cherryvale Chronicle, KS, Cherryvale

Taylor, Kathy
kathy@taylornews.org, Prairie Star, KS, Sedan
kathy@taylornews.org, Co-Pub., Labette
Avenue, KS, Oswego
kathy@taylornews.org, Montgomery County
Chronicle, KS, Caney

Taylor, Keith .... (919) 739-7833
ktaylor@newsargus.com, Online Ed.,
Goldsboro News-Argus, NC, Goldsboro

Taylor, Kelly
kellyat@bgsu.edu, Instr., Bowling Green State
University, OH, Bowling Green

Taylor, Kevin .... (760) 754-2891
ktaylor@u-bild.com, Pres., U-Bild Newspaper
Features, Oceanside

Taylor, Kim .... (401) 423-3200
news@jamestownpress.com, Prod. Mgr., The
Jamestown Press, RI, Jamestown

Taylor, Krystle
editor@sbcglobal.net, Ed, Hugo News, OK,
Hugo

Taylor, Larry .... (205) 371-2488
larry@mound.net, Pub., Moundville Times, AL,
Moundville

Taylor, Linda .... (765) 998-5591
Linda_Taylor1@taylor.edu, Instructor in
Professional Writing, Taylor University, IN,
Upland

Taylor, Lorne
signal@smokylake.com, Ed/Pub/Owner,
Smoky Lake Signal, AB, Smoky Lake

Taylor, Lynn .... (204) 677-4534
generalmanager@thompsoncitizen.net, Gen.
Mgr., Thompson Citizen/nickel Belt News,
MB, Thompson

Taylor, Lynne
lynnet@rhodybeat.com, Credit Mgr., Warwick
Beacon, RI, Warwick

Taylor, Marcia
mataylor@nsu.edu, Asst. Prof., Norfolk State
University, VA, Norfolk

Taylor, Marcia .... (302) 857-6585
mtaylor@desu.edu, Advisor, Delaware State
Univ., DE, Dover

Taylor, Mark A. .... (513) 931-4050
mtaylor@standardpub.com, Pub., Christian
Standard, OH, Cincinnati

Taylor, Meredith .... (212) 279-2102
mtaylor@nrdc.org, Executive Director, College
Media Association, NY, New York

Taylor, Mike .... (352) 793-2161
mtaylor@sctnews.com, Sales Rep, Sumter
County Times, FL, Bushnell

Taylor, Molly
m.taylor@lgpfc.com, Circ. Coord., NIE, The
Kinston Free Press, NC, Kinston

Taylor, Mynette
mynette@mcgregormirror.com, Circ. Mgr./Bus.
Mgr., McGregor Mirror & Crawford Sun, TX,
Mc Gregor

Taylor, Pat
pat@thepilot.com, Adv. Dir, The Pilot, NC,
Southern Pines
pat@thepilot.com, Vice President, North
Carolina Press Association, NC, Raleigh

Taylor, Patty
sviad3@silverstar.com, Adv. Sales, Star Valley
Independent, WY, Afton

Taylor, Phil .... (402) 444-1111
phil.taylor@owh.com, General Manager,
Omaha World-Herald, NE, Omaha

Taylor, Ray .... (605) 224-7301 x102
ray.taylor@capjournal.com, Circ Mgr, Capital
Journal, SD, Pierre

Taylor, Rob .... (907) 561-1674
unicom@unicom-alaska.com, Vice Pres./Gen.
Mgr., Unicom, Inc., AK, Anchorage

Taylor, Ronald
retaylor@utk.edu, Prof./Dir., School of Adv.
& PR, The University of Tennessee, TN,
Knoxville

Taylor, Ross William
buckeye@archboldbuckeye.com, Pub.,
Archbold Buckeye, OH, Archbold

Taylor, Rudy
taylornews@sbcglobal.net, Mng. Ed., Prairie
Star, KS, Sedan

Taylor, Rudy
rudy@taylornews.org, Co-Pub., Labette
Avenue, KS, Oswego
rudy@taylornews.org, Montgomery County
Chronicle, KS, Caney

Taylor, Sam .... (904) 260-9770
staylor@folioweekly.com, Circ. Mgr., Folio
Weekly, FL, Jacksonville

Taylor, Sarah .... (405) 601-2081
sarah@metrofamilymagazine.com, Publisher,
MetroFamily Magazine, OK, Oklahoma City

Taylor, Sarah .... (765) 932-2222
staylor@saanichnews.com, Sales, Saanich
News, BC, Victoria

Taylor, Scott .... (801) 237-2110
taylor@deseretnews.com, Managing Ed.,
Deseret News, UT, Salt Lake City

Taylor, Shane
sales@gonzalesinquirer.com, Adv. Sales, The
Gonzales Inquirer, TX, Gonzales

Taylor, Stephanie
stephanie@salemleader.com, Ed., The Salem
Leader, IN, Salem

Taylor, Tara .... (415) 461-6006, ext. 209
ttaylor@verifiedaudit.com, Audit Mgr., Verified
Audit Circulation (VAC), CA, San Rafael

Taylor, Theresa .... (843) 937-4886
ttaylor@postandcourier.com, Feature's Ed.,
The Post and Courier, SC, Charleston

Taylor, Tom .... (562) 499-1203
tom.taylor@presstelegram.com, Retail Sales
Mgr., Press-Telegram, CA, Long Beach

Taylor, Vicki
vtaylor@civitasmedia.com, Pub., Galion
Inquirer, OH, Galion

Taylor, Vicki .... (567) 393-6220 ext 2042
vtaylor@civitasmedia.com, Gen. Mgr. , The
Morrow County Sentinel, OH, Mount Gilead
vtaylor@civitasmedia.com, Pub., Weekly Advisor, OH, Galion

Teague, Danny

dteague@tvcc.edu, Trinity Valley Cmty. College,
TX, Athens

Tears, Cheryl .... (315) 462-6411
mail@themerchandiser.net, Pres, The
Merchandiser, NY, Clifton Springs

Teasdale, Emilia .... (518) 392-1122
eteasdale@columbiapaper.com, Deputy Pub.,
The Columbia Paper, NY, Ghent

Teasdale, Parry .... (518) 392-1122
ads@columbiapaper.com, Ed. & Pub., The
Columbia Paper, NY, Ghent

Tebbe, Jay .... (618) 239-2100
Jtebbe@bnd.com, Pres./Pub., Belleville News-
Democrat, IL, Belleville
Jtebbe@bnd.com, Pres./Pub., O'Fallon
Progress, IL, Belleville

Techaira, Patricia
patricia.techaira@sddt.com, Mgr., HR, The
Daily Transcript, CA, San Diego

Tedder, Angie .... (336) 727-7470
atedder@wsjournal.com, Winston-Salem
Monthly Magazine Sales Manager, Winston-
Salem Journal, NC, Winston Salem

Tedeschi, George .... (202) 462-1400
gtedeschi@gciu.org, Pres., Graphic
Communications International, DC,
Washington

Tedesco, Antoine
atedesco@insidetoronto.com, Mng. Ed., The
Parkdale Villager, ON, Toronto

Tedesco, Antoine .... (416) 774-2367
atedesco@insidetoronto.com, Managing Ed. ,
City Centre Mirror, ON, Toronto

Tedford, Daniel
daniel.tedford@langnews.com, City Editor, The
Whittier Daily News, CA, Monrovia

Tedford, Daniel .... (626) 544-0816
daniel.tedford@langnews.com , Dig. News Dir.,
Daily Breeze, CA, Torrance

Tedford, Heather .... (902) 629-6026
htedford@theguardian.pe.ca , Adv. Dir., The
Guardian, PE, Charlottetown

Tedrick, Ben .... (979) 731-4679
william.tedrick@theeagle.com, Mgmt. Info
Servs. Mgr., The Eagle, TX, Bryan

Tedrick, Brian
btedrick@herald-mail.com, Circ. Dir., Herald-
mail Express, MD, Hagerstown

Teer, Dawn .... (870) 489-1082
dteer@whitehalljournal.com, Reporter and
Columnist, White Hall Journal, AR, White Hall

Teeters, Claire .... (909) 797-9101
cteeters@newsmirror.net, Ed., Yucaipa &
Calimesa News-Mirror, CA, Yucaipa

Tefft, Sally B.
news@greenwichjournalsalempress.com, Mng.
Ed., The Greenwich Journal-Salem Press,
NY, Greenwich

Teglas, Johnny
jteglas@roanecounty.com, Pub., Harriman
Record, TN, Kingston
jteglas@roanecounty.com, Gen. Mgr., Morgan
County News, TN, Wartburg

Teglas, Johnny .... (865) 376-3481
jteglas@roanecounty.com, Pub., The Shopper,
TN, Kingston

Teicher, Jim
jim@cybersmart.org, Exec. Dir., CyberSmart,
NJ, Bernardsville

Teichmann, Stephanie
castaatszeitung@earthlink.net, Pub.,
California-Staats Zeitung, CA, Los Angeles

Teigen, Tammy
tammy@buffalobulletin.com, Office Mgr.,
Buffalo Bulletin, WY, Buffalo

Telfer, Jack .... (989) 839-4240
jtelferii@mdn.net, Ed., Midland Daily News,
MI, Midland

Tell, Michael
lasvegasisraelite@cox.net, Prodn. Mgr., Las
Vegas Israelite, NV, Las Vegas

Telle, Brandon
btelle@creators.com, Head of development,
programming and technology, Creators,
Hermosa Beach

Telle, Sheila
stelle@creators.com, Sales Administrator,
Creators, Hermosa Beach

Tellez, Mila
mila@tma.net, Pub., EXTRA Bilingual
Community Newspaper, IL, Chicago
mila@tma.net, Extra Bilingual Community
Newspaper (OOB), IL, Chicago

Telli, Andy .... (615) 783-0771
andy.Telli@dioceseofnashville.com, Mng. Ed.,
Tennessee Register, TN, Nashville

Tempey, Nathan .... (718) 260-4504
NTempey@CNGLocal.com, Deputy Ed., The
Brooklyn Papers, NY, Brooklyn

Temple, Darlene .... (203) 354-1079
dtemple@thehour.com, Circ Manager, The
Wilton Villager, CT, Norwalk
dtemple@thehour.com, Asst. Circulation
Director, The Hour, CT, Norwalk

Temple, John .... (304) 293-6116
john.temple@mail.wvu.edu, Associate
Professor, West Virginia University, WV,
Morgantown

Temple, June L.
antwerpbeeargus@frontier.com, Pub./Ed.,
Antwerp Bee-Argus, OH, Antwerp

Tempus, Kent .... (920) 834-4242
editorial@goocontocounty.com, Editor, Lakes/
forest Beacon, WI, Oconto

Ten Broeck, Carolyn
editor@willistonpioneer.com, Ed., Williston
Pioneer Sun News, FL, Williston

TenEyck, Paul .... (952) 345-6675
pteneyck@swpub.com, Southwest Suburban
Publishing, MN, Shakopee

Tenenbaum, David M.
dmt@merlinone.com, Pres./CEO, MerlinOne,
Inc., MA, Quincy

Tennant, Brenda .... (403) 932-6588
btennant@cochrane.greatwest.ca, Pub./Adv.
Mgr, Cochrane Eagle, AB, Cochrane

Tenney, Matthew
marketing@jewishjournal.com, Circ. Mgr., The
Jewish Journal of Greater Los Angeles, CA,
Los Angeles

Tennyson, David
timesnews@osceolatimes.com, Pub., The
Osceola Times, AR, Osceola

Tennyson, David
dtennyson@couriernews.net, Pub., Blytheville
Courier News, AR, Blytheville

Tennyson, David
news@democratargus.com, Pub., The
Democrat Argus, MO, Caruthersville

Tennyson, Troy .... (517) 278-2318, ext. 20
ttennyson@thedailyreporter.com, Sports Ed. ,
The Daily Reporter, MI, Coldwater

Teofilo, Steve .... (920) 996-7215
steofilo@appleton.gannett.com, Digital
Manager, Post-Crescent, WI, Appleton

Teonnies, Daniel .... (619) 437-8800
daniel@eaglenewsca.com, Adv. Dir., Coronado
Eagle & Journal, CA, Coronado

Tepp, Norb
ntepp@pcgazette.com, CFO, The Portage
County Gazette, WI, Stevens Point

Ter Meer, Sheila K. .... ext. 221
sheila.termeer@tribstar.com, Online Ed., The
Tribune Star, IN, Terre Haute

Tergeoglou, Tim .... (845) 331-5000 Ext. 01099
ttergeoglou@freemanonline.com, Adv. Dir.,

Daily Freeman, NY, Kingston

Tergeoglou, Timothy ....(845) 400-1099
ttergeoglou@freemanonline.com, Reg. Adv.
Dir., The Saratogian, NY, Saratoga Springs

Tergeoglou, Timothy ....(845) 400-1099
ttergeoglou@freemanonline.com , Reg. Adv.
Dir., The Record, NY, Troy

Tergeoglou, Timothy ....(845) 400-1099
ttergeoglou@freemanonline.com, Regional
Advertising Director, Greenbush Life, NY,
Troy
ttergeoglou@freemanonline.com, Ad. Sales
Mgr., Latham Life, NY, Troy

Terhaar, Joyce ....(916) 321-1004
jterhaar@sacbee.com, Executive Editor &
Sr. VP News , The Sacramento Bee, CA,
Sacramento

Ternet, Lois
loisternet@yahoo.com, Ed., The Monroeville
News, IN, Monroeville

Terrazas, Chris ....(916) 498-7910, ext. 1397
christ@newsreview.com, Design Manager,
Sacramento News & Review, CA,
Sacramento

Terrell, Ryan ....(630) 427-6252
rterrell@shawmedia.com, Ed., Downers Grove
Suburban Life, IL, Downers Grove
rterrell@shawmedia.com, Ed., Westmont
Suburban Life, IL, Downers Grove
rterrell@shawmedia.com, Ed., Woodridge
Suburban Life, IL, Downers Grove
rterrell@shawmedia.com, Ed., Lisle Suburban
Life, IL, Downers Grove

Terrell, Scott
cweeks@skagitpublishing.com, Photo Ed.,
Skagit Valley Herald, WA, Mount Vernon

Terry, Bill ....(830) 995-3634
Features editor and photographer, The Comfort
News, TX, Comfort

Terry, Bob
bterry@thealabamabaptist.org, Pres., Alabama
Baptist, AL, BIRMINGHAM

Terry, Dan ....(805) 684-4428
dan@coastalview.com, Advertising Manager,
Coastal View News, CA, Carpinteria

Terry, Jim
jim_terry@mccom.com, SVP, Account Service,
M/C/C, TX, Dallas

Terry, Judy ....ext. 228
judy.terry@empiretribune.com, Adv. Mgr.,
Cross Timbers Trading Post, TX, Stephenville

Terry, Kukle
tkukle@metroland.com, Vice President,
Metroland Media Group Ltd., ON,
Mississauga

Terry, Mary
maryterry@bellsouh.net, Pub., The Delhi
Dispatch, LA, Rayville

Terry, Mary
maryterry@bellsouth.net, Pub., Richland
Beacon-News, LA, Rayville

Terry, Mary ....(318) 428-3207
wcarrollgazette@bellsouth.net, Pub./Gen. Mgr.,
The West Carroll Gazette, LA, Oak Grove

Terry, Merry
merryterry@bellsouth.net, Caldwell Watchman,
LA, Columbia

Terry, Michele ....(336) 506-3071
mterry@thetimesnews.com, Mgr., Mktg./
Promo., Times-News, NC, Burlington

Terry, Reese
rterry@dailycorinthian.com, Pub., Banner
Independent, MS, Booneville

Terry, Reese ....(662) 287-6111 ext 337
rterry@dailycorinthian.com, Pub., The Daily
Corinthian, MS, Corinth

Terry, Robert ....(703) 258-0821
rterry@bizjournals.com, Mng. Ed., Washington

Business Journal, VA, Arlington

Terwilliger, Cindy ....(989) 779-6107
cterwilliger@michigannewspapers.com,
Recruitment Specialist , Morning Sun, MI,
Alma

Terwilliger, Vicki ....(570) 682-9081
vicki-t@citizenstandard.com, Ed., The Citizen-
Standard, PA, Valley View

Terziyski, Jordan
jterziyski@perretta.com, Asst. Serv. Mgr.,
Perretta Graphics Corp., NY, Poughkeepsie

Terzotis, Judi ....(337) 289-6302
jterzotis@gannett.com, Pres./Pub., Daily World,
LA, Opelousas
jterzotis@gannett.com, Adv. Dir., The Clarion-
Ledger, MS, Jackson

Tesoro, Mark ....(307) 789-6560 ext 112
mtesoro@uintacountyherald.com, Pub., The
Kemmerer Gazette, WY, Kemmerer

Tesoro, Mark ....(307) 789-6560 ext. 112
mtesoro@uintacountyherald.com, Pub.,
Bridger Valley Pioneer, WY, Lyman

Tesoro, Mark ....(307) 789-6560 ext 112
mtesoro@uintacountyherald.com, Publisher ,
Sublette Examiner, WY, Pinedale
mtesoro@uintacountyherald.com, Pub., Uinta
County Herald, WY, Evanston

Tessier, Jean-Pierre
jeanpierre.tessier@monteregieweb.com, Adv.
Rep., Le Soleil Du St-laurent, QC, Salaberry-
de-Valleyfield

Tessier, Suzanne ....(613) 678-3327 ext. 1005
ads@thereview.ca, Prodn. Mgr., The Review,
ON, Vankleek Hill

Testa, Helen
circulation@lakevillejournal.com, Circ. Mgr.,
The Lakeville Journal, CT, Falls Village

Testa, Helen
htesta@lakevillejournal.com, Circ. Mgr., The
Winsted Journal, CT, Winsted

Testa, Keith ....(603) 224-5301 ext. 378
ktesta@theconcordinsider.com, Ed., The
Concord Insider, Concord Monitor, NH,
Concord

Tetrault, Denis
denis.tetreault@quebecormedia.com, VP,
Prodn., Le Journal de Montreal, QC,
Montreal

Tetrault, Shauna ....(320) 676-3123
stetrault@millelacsmessenger.com, Ed., Mille
Lacs Messenger, MN, Isle

Tetreault, Barbara
barbara@berlindailysun.com, Managing Ed.,
The Berlin Daily Sun, NH, BERLIN

Tetz, Debi ....(403) 235-8666
dtetz@calgaryherald.com, Local Ad. Service
Team Leader, Calgary Herald, AB, Calgary

Tetzman, Heidi
htetzman@forumcomm.com, Asst. Feautures
Ed., InForum, ND, Fargo

Teubner, Nellene ....(949) 492-4316
nteubner@ocregister.com, Ed., Sun-Post
News, CA, Santa Ana

Teufel, Brady
bteufel@calpoly.edu, Full-time Lectr., California
Polytechnic State Universtiy, CA, San Luis
Obispo

Teverbaugh, Rick
rick.teverbaugh@heraldbulletin.com, Sports
Ed., Madison County Direct, IN, Anderson

Texter, Lynne
texter@lasalle.edu, Chair, La Salle University,
PA, Philadelphia

Tezon, Anne L.
annelorenetezon@gmail.com, Publisher and
editor, The Caldwell County News, MO,
Hamilton

Tezon, Anne L.

news@llpublications.com, Ed., The Hamilton
Advocate, MO, Hamilton

Thacker, Brett
bthacker@express-news.net, Mng. Ed.,
Bulverde News, TX, San Antonio
bthacker@express-news.net, Mng. Ed., Fort
Sam News Leader, TX, San Antonio
bthacker@express-news.net, Mng. Ed., Kelly
Observer, TX, San Antonio
bthacker@express-news.net, Mng. Ed.,
Lackland Talespinner, TX, San Antonio
bthacker@express-news.net, Mng. Ed.,
Medical Patriot, TX, San Antonio
bthacker@express-news.net, Mng. Ed., North
Central News, TX, San Antonio
bthacker@express-news.net, Mng. Ed.,
Northeast Herald, TX, San Antonio
bthacker@express-news.net, Mng. Ed.,
Randolph Wingspread, TX, San Antonio
bthacker@express-news.net, Mng. Ed.,
Northwest Weekly, TX, San Antonio

Thaete, Kevin
kthaete@victoriaadvocate.com, Cir. Dir. ,
Victoria Advocate, TX, Victoria

Thal, Ian ....(617) 357-9100 ext. 147
IanT@thejewishadvocate.com, The Jewish
Advocate, MA, Boston

Thalmann, Dan ....(785) 325-2219
newseditor@nckcn.com, Ed., Washington
County News, KS, Washington

Thames, Rick
rthames@charlotteobserver.com, The
Charlotte Observer, NC, Charlotte

Thames, Rick ....(704) 358-5000
rthames@charlotteobserver.com, Editor/VP,
News, The Charlotte Observer, NC, Charlotte

Thanki, Juli
jthanki@tennessean.com, Music Reporter, TN
Media, TN, Nashville
jthanki@tennessean.com, Music Reporter, The
Tennessean, TN, Nashville

Thanos, Dino ....(630) 894-0934
dino@dollarwiseonline.com, Ed., Dollar Wise,
IL, Hoffman Estates

Thatch, Mary Alice Jervay
wilmjourn@aol.com, Pub./Ed., Wilmington
Journal, NC, Wilmington

Thatch, Shawn Jervay ....(910) 762-5502
wilmjourn@aol.com, Office Mgr., Wilmington
Journal, NC, Wilmington

Thayer, Autumn ....(805) 466-2585 x120
athayer@pasoroblespress.com, Circ. Mgr.,
Paso Robles Press, CA, Paso Robles
athayer@pasoroblespress.com, Office Mgr.,
Atascadero News, CA, Atascadero

Thayer, Cindy
hcjads@pinetel.com, Adv. Dir, Hells Canyon
Journal, OR, Halfway

Thayer, Frank
fthayer@nmsu.edu, Asst. Prof., New Mexico
State University, NM, Las Cruces

Theall, James ....(303) 440-7855
sales@immediate.com, Pres./CEO, Media
Marketing, Inc., CO, Westminster

Theall, Patti ....(303) 997-1350
Patti.theall@immediate.com, VP, Sales, Media
Marketing, Inc., CO, Westminster

Theall, Patti
ptheall@capenews.net, Sales Director, The
Falmouth Enterprise, MA, Falmouth

Theile, Ralph ....(954) 724-2181
theiler@graphline.com, Vice Pres.,Marketing/
Operations, GraphLine, FL, Sunrise

Thein, Jane
gbpress@alpinecom.net, Circ. Mgr.,
Guttenberg Press, IA, Guttenberg

Theis, Peter F.
sales@conservit.com, Pres., Conservit
Corporation, IL, Fox Lake

Thell, Magnus

magnus.thell@cision.com, Gen. Mgr., Cision
AB, Stockholm

Theriault, Mike ....(207) 689-2861
mtheriault@sunjournal.com, Circ. Dir., Sun
Journal, ME, Lewiston

Therrien, Denis ....(514) 636-7314
denis.therrien@tc.tc, General Manager, The
Chronicle, QC, Dorval
denis.therrien@tc.tc, Publisher, Cites
Nouvelles, QC, Dorval

Therrien, Ellen ....(203) 426-3141
ellen@thebee.com, Adv. Manager, The
Newtown Bee, CT, Newtown

Thesen, Pamela ....(780) 723-3301
pam.thesen@sunmedia.ca, Adv. Dir, Edson
Leader, AB, Edson

Thibault, Michel
m.thibault@cybersoleil.com, Ed., Le Soleil Du
St-laurent, QC, Chateauguay

Thibeault, Mario
mario.thibeault@hebdosquebecor.com, Mng.
Ed., Nordest Plus, QC, Sept-Iles

Thibodaux, Brad ....(985) 876-3008, ext. 14
Adv. Dir, Tri-Parish Times & Business News,
LA, Houma

Thibodaux, Mindy ....(985) 850-1123
lbachlet@gatehousemedia.com, Acct., Daily
Comet, LA, Thibodaux

Thibodaux, Mindy ....(985) 857-2221
mindy.thibodaux@houmatoday.com,
Accountant, The Courier, LA, Houma

Thibodeau, Wayne ....(902) 629-6038
wthibodeau@theguardian.pe.ca , News Ed.,
The Guardian, PE, Charlottetown

Thiel, Emily
ethiel@berksmontnews.com, Ed., Berksmont
News, PA, Pottstown

Thiel, Robyn ....(701) 843-7567
newsalemjournal@westriv.com, Pub. / Ed. ,
New Salem Journal, ND, New Salem

Thiemann, David ....(402) 472-1769
dn@unl.edu, Director of Sales and Marketing,
Univ. of Nebraska-Lincoln, NE, Lincoln

Thien Giao, Pham Phu
news@nguoi-viet.com, Nguoi Viet News, CA,
Westminster

Thill, Nicole ....(503) 543-6387
nthill@spotlightnews.net, News Reporter, The
South County Spotlight, OR, Scappoose

Thissen, Sherri
classifieds@austindailyherald.com, Classifieds
Sales Consultant, Austin Daily Herald, MN,
Austin

Thissen, Terry
terry.thissen@albertleatribune.com, Production
Dir., Albert Lea Tribune, MN, Albert Lea

Thistle, Scott ....(207) 689-2849
sthistle@sunjournal.com, REGL. ED.
, Sun Journal, ME, Lewiston

Thomann, Pat
kpieditor@gmail.com, Ed., Livingston Ledger,
KY, Smithland

Thomas, Angela ....(503) 274-8733
athomas@bizjournals.com, Adv. Coord.,
Business Journal of Portland, OR, Portland

Thomas, Ava
athomas@journalstar.com, Publisher,
Neighborhood Extra, NE, Lincoln

Thomas, Ava
athomas@journalstar.com, Pub, Lincoln
Journal Star, NE, Lincoln

Thomas, Barry R. ....(678) 778-2616
onewhirl@aol.com, Pub, St. Louis Evening
Whirl, MO, Saint Louis

Thomas, Bill
bthomas@thetomahawk.com, Pub., The
Tomahawk, TN, Mountain City

Thomas, Binoy
info@weeklyvoice.com, Editor-in-Chief, The Weekly Voice, ON, Mississauga

Thomas, Brenda
ourhomepaper@gmail.com, Office Mgr., The Home News, NC, Marshville

Thomas, Bruce
wabascafever4@shaw.ca, Pub., Wabasca Fever, AB, Wabasca

Thomas, Clarence
cwthomas@vcu.edu, Assoc. Prof., Virginia Commonwealth University, VA, Richmond

Thomas, Dan
dthomas@uptivity.com, Gen. Mgr., Heartland Delivery, Inc., NE, Columbus

Thomas, Dave .... (937) 743-6703
dave.thomas@coxinc.com, Senior Director, Technology & Operations, Dayton Daily News, OH, Franklin

Thomas, Debbie
dthomas@thedailycourier.com, Adv. Mgr., Carbondale Times, IL, Carbondale

Thomas, Don
Dthomas@theperrychief.com, Prodn. Mgr., Perry Chief, IA, Perry

Thomas, Donald
dthomas@theperrychief.com, Prodn. Mgr., Chiefland Shopper, IA, Perry

Thomas, Donna .... (662) 862-8244
dsthomas@iccms.edu, Dir., PR, Itawamba Cmty. College, MS, Fulton

Thomas, Dru
Dru@bhpioneer.com, Adv. Mgr., Nation's Center News, SD, Buffalo
Dru@bhpioneer.com, Adv. Sales, Black Hills Pioneer, SD, Spearfish

Thomas, Dru
dru@bhpioneer.com, Adv. Mgr., Weekly Prospector, SD, Spearfish

Thomas, Eric
pressinfo@lsoft.com, CEO, L-Soft International, Inc., MD, Landover

Thomas, Hal
hthomas@mullermartinims.com, Dir., Integrated Systems Engineering, Muller Martini Mailroom Systems, Inc., PA, Allentown

Thomas, Jason .... (812) 206-2127
jason.thomas@newsandtribune.com, Asst. Ed., News and Tribune, IN, Jeffersonville
jason.thomas@newsandtribune.com, Asst. Ed., Tribune, IN, New Albany

Thomas, Jason C. .... (618) 549-2799
jthomas@earthlink.net, Pub., Carbondale Times, IL, Carbondale

Thomas, Jay
oppnews@centurytel.net, Ed., The Opp News, AL, Opp

Thomas, Jill .... (937) 651-1133
subscriptions@examiner.org, Circ. Mgr., Bellefontaine Examiner, OH, Bellefontaine

Thomas, Joe
newsroom@tricityledger.com, Ed., The Tri-City Ledger, AL, Flomaton

Thomas, John .... (203) 435-1387
jthomas@penfieldcomm.com, CEO, Inner-city News, CT, New Haven

Thomas, Joshua
joshuathomas@courierstandardenterprise.com, Ed., Courier Standard Enterprise, NY, Amsterdam

Thomas, Karen
karent@dailyamerican.com, Office Mgr., Daily American, PA, Somerset

Thomas, Karin .... ext. 27
kthomas@bakercountypress.com, Bus. Mgr., The Baker County Press, FL, Macclenny

Thomas, Kelly

info@midvalleypub.com, Bookkeeper, Winton Times, CA, Winton

Thomas, Koshy
koshyvoa@aol.com, Publisher, Voice Of Asia, TX, Houston

Thomas, Lovan
lthomas@natchitochestimes.com, Pres./Pub., Natchitoches Times, LA, Natchitoches

Thomas, Lovan
news@natchitochestimes.com, Pres./Pub., Natchitoches Times Newspapers, LA, Natchitoches

Thomas, Lucas
lthomas@dvtnv.com, Reporter, Desert Valley Times, NV, Mesquite

Thomas, Maggie
m.thomas@tcu.edu, Assoc. Prof., Texas Christian University, TX, Fort Worth

Thomas, Mark
m.thomas@altavistajournal.com, Gen. Mgr./ Ed., The Journal (OOB), VA, KING GEORGE
m.thomas@altavistajournal.com, Ed./Gen. Mgr., Altavista Journal, VA, Altavista

Thomas, Mark .... (405) 499-0033
mthomas@okpress.com, Executive Vice President, Oklahoma Press Association, OK, Oklahoma City

Thomas, Mark .... (414) 224-2201
mark@thomasbuildingconsulting.com, Circ. Sr. Vice Pres., Milwaukee Journal Sentinel, WI, Milwaukee

Thomas, Mark
mthomas@okpress.com, Exec. Vice Pres., Oklahoma Press Service, OK, Oklahoma City

Thomas, Martha J.
mthomas@glasgowdailytimes.com, Newsroom Clerk, Glasgow Daily Times, KY, Glasgow

Thomas, Mary .... (412) 263-1925
mthomas@post-gazette.com, Arts Critic, Pittsburgh Post-Gazette, PA, Clinton

Thomas, Michelle .... (503) 357-3181
mthomas@fgnewstimes.com, Adv. Dir., Forest Grove News-Times, OR, Forest Grove

Thomas, Mike .... (508) 676-2531
sports@heraldnews.com, Sports Ed., The Herald News, MA, Fall River

Thomas, Mike .... (867) 667-6285 EXT 230
mthomas@yukon-news.com, Publisher, Yukon News, YT, Whitehorse

Thomas, Morrell
mthomas@newsandpressonline.com, Gen. Mgr., The News & Press, SC, Darlington

Thomas, Mr. Richard G.
info@voterama.info, Pub./Ed., Voterama in Congress - Thomas Voting Reports, Washington

Thomas, Ms. Rosalina .... (646) 223-4000 ext. 5457
rosalina.thomas@thomsonreuters.com, Vice Pres./Head of Sales - The Americas, Reuters News Agency, Thomson Reuters, Reuters Media, NY, New York

Thomas, Owen
othomas@sfchronicle.com, Business and Tech Ed., San Francisco Chronicle, CA, San Francisco

Thomas, Patricia .... (780) 891-2108
scopepub2@icloud.com, Adv. Mgr., Scope (OOB), AB, Slave Lake
scopepub2@icloud.com, Wabasca Fever, AB, Wabasca

Thomas, Paul .... (717) 255-8283
pthomas@acssyr.com, VP & General Manager, The Patriot-News, PA, Mechanicsburg

Thomas, Phyllis
gfreepress@sbcglobal.net, Adv. Dir., The Winkler County News, TX, Kermit

Thomas, Rob
rthomas@madison.com, The Capital Times,

WI, Madison

Thomas, Robert
sales@ashlandmotorcompany.com, Randolph-Macon College, VA, Ashland

Thomas, Russ
russ.thomas@traunerconsulting.com, Mgr., New Bus., Trauner Consulting Services, Inc., PA, Philadelphia

Thomas, Sean .... (209) 498-2076
Editor@calaverasenterprise.com, Ed, Calaveras Enterprise, CA, San Andreas

Thomas, Tameka .... (229) 246-2827 ext. 105
tameka@thepostsearchlight.com, Asst. Adv. Mgr., Post-searchlight Extra, GA, Bainbridge

Thomas, Tim .... (410) 280-5966
tjthomas@capgaznews.com, Publisher, The Capital, MD, Annapolis

Thomas, Timothy .... (419) 674-4066 Ext. 232
kteditor@kentontimes.com, News Ed. , The Kenton Times, OH, Kenton
kteditor@kentontimes.com, Nat'l Adv. Mgr., The Arizona Republic, AZ, Phoenix

Thomas, Vickie .... (706) 367-2486
ads@mainstreetnews.com, Prodn. Mgr., The Jackson Herald, GA, Jefferson

Thomas, Will .... (931) 433-9737
Pub., Exchange, TN, Fayetteville

Thomas, Will
will@exchange-inc.com, Pub., The Shopper, TN, Manchester
will@exchange-inc.com, Pub., Exchange - Madison County, TN, Fayetteville
will@exchange-inc.com, Exchange - Manchester (formerly Coffee County Shopper), TN, Fayetteville
will@exchange-inc.com, CEO, Exchange - Tullahoma, TN, Fayetteville
will@exchange-inc.com, Exchange - Winchester, TN, Fayetteville
will@exchange-inc.com, Pub., Exchange - Lincoln Co./fayetteville, TN, Fayetteville

Thomas , Debbie
dthomas@thedailycourier.com, Adv. Dir. , Daily Courier, OR, Grants Pass

Thomas-Anderson, Gloria .... (913) 433-3877
gloria@hearttones.com, Pres./Founder, Heart Tones, Lumberton

Thomas-Woods, Renee .... (314) 513-4465
St. Louis Cmty. College Florissant Valley, MO, Saint Louis

Thomason, Craig
cthomason@express-news.net, Asst. Mng. Ed., News, Bulverde News, TX, San Antonio
cthomason@express-news.net, Asst. Mng. Ed., News, Fort Sam News Leader, TX, San Antonio
cthomason@express-news.net, Asst. Mng. Ed., News, Kelly Observer, TX, San Antonio
cthomason@express-news.net, Asst. Mng. Ed., News, Lackland Talespinner, TX, San Antonio
cthomason@express-news.net, Asst. Mng. Ed., News, Medical Patriot, TX, San Antonio
cthomason@express-news.net, Asst. Mng. Ed., News, North Central News, TX, San Antonio
cthomason@express-news.net, Asst. Mng. Ed., News, Northeast Herald, TX, San Antonio
cthomason@express-news.net, Asst. Mng. Ed., News, Randolph Wingspread, TX, San Antonio
cthomason@express-news.net, Asst. Mng. Ed., News, Northwest Weekly, TX, San Antonio

Thomason, Ed
ed@weeklyrecord.net, Pub., The Weekly Record, MO, New Madrid

Thomason, Rick
thelog@link.freedom.com, Pub., Log Extra, FL, Destin

Thomason, Rick .... (910) 416-5867
rthomason@civitasmedia.com, Pub., The Robesonian, NC, Lumberton

Thomason, Rick .... (706) 407-2657
rick_thomason@link.freedom.com, Publisher, The Thomaston Times, GA, Lagrange

Thomasson, Jana M.
jmt@themountainpress.com, Pub., The Mountain Press, TN, Sevierville

Thomasson, Marianne .... (770) 253-1576
marianne@newnan.com, VP, The Newnan Times-Herald, GA, Newnan

Thomasson, William W. .... (770) 253-1576
Pres., The Newnan Times-Herald, GA, Newnan

Thome, John
sales@bstpromark.com, Vice Pres., Mktg., BST Pro Mark, IL, Elmhurst

Thome, Kevin
advertisers@cheesereporter.com, Mktg. Dir./Adv. Mgr., The Cheese Reporter, WI, Madison

Thomma, Steven .... (202) 266-7453
director@whca.net, Executive Director, White House Correspondents Association, DC, Washington

Thompason, Tony
info@ss8.com, VP of Marketing , SS8 Networks, CA, Milpitas

Thompkins, Kevin .... (317) 773-9960 ext. 122
kevin@thetimes24-7.com, Managing Editor, The Times, IN, Noblesville

Thompsen, Philip .... (610) 436-2283
pthompsen@wcupa.edu, West Chester University, PA, West Chester

Thompson, Adam .... (252) 635-5669
Adam.Thompson@newbernsj.com, Sports Ed. , The Sun Journal, NC, New Bern

Thompson, Alison .... (410) 332-6300
allison.thompson@baltsun.com, Retail Adv., Towson Times, MD, Baltimore

Thompson, Allison .... (410) 332-6850
allison.thompson@baltsun.com, Adv., Howard County Times, MD, Columbia

Thompson, Amanda
athompson@springfi.gannett.com, Adv. Sales, Springfield News-Leader, MO, Springfield

Thompson, Amie .... (406) 791-6536
athompson@greatfallstribune.com, Specialty Publication Editor, Great Falls Tribune, MT, Great Falls
athompson@greatfallstribune.com, Planning Editor Print & Digital , Great Bend Tribune, KS, Great Bend

Thompson, Amy
amy@bryantimes.com, Class. Adv. Mgr., The Bryan Times, OH, Bryan

Thompson, Andy .... (920) 729-6622
athompson@postcrescent.com, Editor/Local enterprise, Post-Crescent, WI, Appleton

Thompson, Bill
bthompson@readingeagle.com, Circulation Sales Specialist, Reading Eagle Company, PA, Reading

Thompson, Bishop Charles C.
message@evdio.org, Publisher, The Message, IN, Evansville

Thompson, Brad
bthomps@linfield.edu, Chair, Linfield College, OR, McMinnville

Thompson, Chad .... (352) 528-3343
Chad.Thompson@chieflandcitizen.com, Sales Representative, Williston Pioneer Sun News, FL, Williston

Thompson, Cheryl .... (417) 256-9191
Customer Service Representative, West Plains Daily Quill, MO, West Plains

Thompson, Chip .... (530) 737-5042
editor@redbluffdailynews.com, Ed., Daily News, CA, Red Bluff

Thompson, Connie M.
connie@phonographherald.com, Pub., The

Phonograph-Herald, NE, Saint Paul

Thompson, Connie M.
connie@phonographherald.com, Pub., The
Wolbach Messenger, NE, Wolbach

Thompson, Dave
polkcountynews@yahoo.com, Pub., Polk
County News, NE, Stromsburg

Thompson, David
dthompson@kypress.com, Exec. Dir., Kentucky
Press Service, Inc., KY, Frankfort

Thompson, David T. ....(502) 223-8821
dthompson@kypress.com, Exec. Dir., Kentucky
Press Association, Inc., KY, Frankfort

Thompson, Demetrius
dthompson@newtoncountyappeal.com,
Managing Editor, The Newton County
Appeal, MS, Union

Thompson, Dennis....................(603) 610-1121
dthompson@seacoastonline.com , Exeter
News-Letter, NH, Portsmouth
dthompson@seacoastonline.com , York County
Coast Star, NH, Portsmouth
dthompson@seacoastonline.com , Circ. Dir.,
Portsmouth Herald, NH, Portsmouth

Thompson, Dennis....................(603) 610-1188
Circ. Dir., The Hampton Union, NH, Portsmouth

Thompson, Diane ....(972) 248-0451 x 236
Dthompson@willowbend.com, CFO, Willow
Bend Communications, Inc., TX, Dallas

Thompson, Donna
trends@herkimertelegram.com, Trends Ed.,
The Herkimer Telegram, NY, Herkimer

Thompson, Greg ....(503) 221-8471
gthompson@oregonian.com, Dir. Local Retail,
The Oregonian, OR, Portland

Thompson, Guy ....(260) 463-2167
editor@lagrangepublishing.com, editor,
LaGrange Standard, IN, Lagrange

Thompson, Guy
editor@lagrangepublishing.com, LaGrange
News, IN, Lagrange

Thompson, Haley
hthompson@theglenrosereporter.com, Adv.
Exec., Glen Rose Reporter, TX, Stephenville

Thompson, Herman L.
morrisnews@windstream.net, Ed., The Morris
News, OK, Morris

Thompson, Howard....................(509) 826-1110
hthompson@omakchronicle.com, Mailroom
Manager, Omak-Okanogan County
Chronicle, WA, Omak

Thompson, J.R.
jr@rockyforddailygazette.com , Pub./Ed./Bus.
Mgr., Rocky Ford Daily Gazette, CO, Rocky
Ford

Thompson, Jackie L.
jackie@wcrecord.com, Pub., The Walsh County
Record, ND, Grafton

Thompson, James
jthompson@freedomforum.org, Vice Pres.,
Opns., Freedom Forum, DC, Washington

Thompson, Jenn
addirector@havredailynews.com, Adv. Dir., The
Havre Daily News, MT, Havre

Thompson, Jeri
Jeri.Thompson@thecharlottepost.com, Adv.
Dir., The Charlotte Post, NC, Charlotte

Thompson, Jim........................(706) 208-2222
jim.thompson@onlineathens.com, Editorial
Page Ed., Athens Banner-Herald, GA,
Athens

Thompson, Jody
jthompson@hoodrivernews.com, Adv. Mgr.,
Hood River News, OR, Hood River

Thompson, John
thompsonj@byui.edu, Brigham Young Univ.
Idaho, ID, Rexburg

Thompson, Jonathan
jonathan@hcn.org, Ed. in Chief, High Country
News, Paonia

Thompson, Joyce ....(336) 506-3003
jthompson@thetimesnews.com, HR Dir.,
Times-News, NC, Burlington

Thompson, Julia
julia.thompson@arizonarepublic.com, Digital
Content Dir., The Arizona Republic, AZ,
Phoenix

Thompson, Julia
juliathompson@freeborncountyshopper.com,
Gen. Mgr., Freeborn County Shopper, MN,
Albert Lea

Thompson, June ....(514) 987-2222
jthompson@montrealgazette.com, Newsroom
Administrator, Montreal Gazette, QC,
Montreal

Thompson, Karen Fox ....(812) 379-5679
kfox@aimmediaindiana.com, Dir., Info. Servs.
and human resources, AIM Media Indiana,
IN, Columbus

Thompson, Kate
"kthompson@algona.com ", Pub., County Line
(OOB), KS, Parsons
"kthompson@algona.com ", The Reminder,
IA, Algona

Thompson, Kate
kate.thompson@valleynewstoday.com,
Publisher, Essex Independent, IA,
Shenandoah

Thompson, Kate
kate.thompson@valleynewstoday.com, Pub.,
Valley News Today, IA, Shenandoah

Thompson, Kay ....(903) 473-2653
ads@rainscountyleader.com, Adv. Mgr., Rains
County Leader, TX, Emory

Thompson, Ken ....(765) 420-5229
kthompson@jconline.com, Planning Ed. ,
Journal and Courier, IN, Lafayette

Thompson, Kiley ....(540) 239-1180
kileyt71@gmail.com, General Manager,
Virginia Polytechnic Institute, VA, Blacksburg

Thompson, Laura
sales@rockyforddailygazette.com, Adv. Mgr.,
Rocky Ford Daily Gazette, CO, Rocky Ford

Thompson, Lynn
lynn@okemahnewsleader.com, Pub./Ed.,
Okemah News Leader, OK, Okemah

Thompson, Marc
marc.thompson@newscyclesolutions.com,
Rgl. Sales Dir., Newscycle Solutions, MN,
Bloomington

Thompson, Marcy....................(318) 435-4521
marcy@franklinsun.com, Community Ed.
General News, The Franklin Sun, LA,
Winnsboro

Thompson, Margie
mthompson@uniondemocrat.com, Mng. Ed.,
Features, The Union Democrat, CA, Sonora

Thompson, Mark
mark.thompson@ipreo.com, CEO, The New
York Times, NY, New York

Thompson, Martie
editor@rtpublishinginc.com, Ed., Mandarin
NewsLine, FL, Jacksonville
editor@rtpublishinginc.com, Ed., Southside
NewsLine, FL, Jacksonville
editor@rtpublishinginc.com, Ed., The
CreekLine, FL, Jacksonville
editor@rtpublishinginc.com, Ed., Players
Journal, FL, Jacksonville
editor@rtpublishinginc.com, Ed., Ocean
Breeze, FL, Jacksonville

Thompson, Michelle ....(901) 529-6471
michelle.thompson@commercialappeal.com,
Sales Manager-Territories, The Commercial
Appeal, TN, Memphis

Thompson, Mickey
info@caraustar.com, Vice Pres., The Newark

Group, GA, Cedartown

Thompson, Mike ....(905) 684-7251 ext. 1130
mike.thomson@sunmedia.ca, Adv. Mgr. , St.
Catharines Standard, ON, Saint Catharine's

Thompson, Mike ....(860) 633-4691 ext. 225
rivereast@snet.net, Ed., Rivereast News
Bulletin, CT, Glastonbury

Thompson, Nathan
vgnews@mchsi.com, Editor, Villa Grove News,
IL, Villa Grove

Thompson, Neil ....(812) 342-1056
nthompson@therepublic.com, Prodn. Mgr.,
Republic Extra, IN, Columbus

Thompson, Paul
lcollins@northeastnews.net, Managing Editor,
The Northeast News, MO, Kansas City

Thompson, Phil
philt@ksexpo.com, Online Mgr., The Topeka
Capital-Journal, KS, Topeka

Thompson, Randy
editor@hermistonherald.com, Ed., The
Hermiston Herald, OR, Hermiston

Thompson, Randy ....(800) 655-1406
rthompson@wythenews.com, Adv. Dir., Smyth
County News & Messenger, VA, Marion

Thompson, Rick ....(618) 463-2508
rthompson@civitasmedia.com, Controller, The
Telegraph, IL, Alton

Thompson, Rob
rthompson@portlandmercury.com, Pub.,
Portland Mercury, OR, Portland

Thompson, Roberta
printing@timesleader.net, Printing Rep, Times
Leader, KY, Princeton

Thompson, Roger
roger@okemahnewsleader.com, Ed./Adv. Dir.,
Okemah News Leader, OK, Okemah

Thompson, Rowland
anewspaper@aol.com, Exec. Dir., Allied Daily
Newspapers of Washington, WA, Olympia

Thompson, Roxanne
roxanne@clareaholmlocalpress.ca, Owner/
Pub., Clareaholm Local Press, AB,
Clareaholm

Thompson, Sandy
polkcountynews@yahoo.com, Pub., Polk
County News, NE, Stromsburg

Thompson, Sarah
sthompson@civitasmedia.com, Adv. Rep., The
Daily Sentinel, OH, Pomeroy

Thompson, Scott ....(561) 379-2635
sat@wingopromo.com, Pres., Wingo, LLC, FL,
Wellington

Thompson, Shannon
ads@thereminder.ca, Office Admin, Flin Flon
Reminder, MB, Flin Flon

Thompson, Sonya
customerservice@portlandleader.net, Ed., The
Portland Leader, TN, Portland

Thompson, Steve ....(785) 295-5609
steve.thompson@cjonline.com, Copy Ed., The
Topeka Capital-Journal, KS, Topeka

Thompson, Steve ....(972) 248-0451
info@willowbend.com, Pres, Willow Bend
Communications, Inc., TX, Dallas

Thompson, Terri......................(443) 524-8181
tthompson@thedailyrecord.com, Acc. Mgr.,
The Daily Record, MD, Baltimore

Thompson, Terry ....(813) 259-7435
Tampa Bay Times, FL, St Petersburg

Thompson, Terry
terry.thompson@sjsu.edu, Circ. Mgr., Viet
Mercury, CA, San Jose

Thompson, Tim........................(850) 747-5001
tthompson@pcnh.com, Publisher, News
Herald, OH, Fremont

Thompson, Tim........................(850) 747-5001
tthompson@pcnh.com, Publisher, The News
Herald, FL, Panama City

Thompson, Wendy
editor@gtgazette.com, Ed., Georgetown
Gazette, CA, Georgetown

Thompson , Shappelle
shappelle.thompson@nydailyrecord.com, Acct.
Mgr. , The Daily Record, NY, Rochester

Thomson, Chris ....(519) 662-1082 ext. 32
Reporter/photographer, New Hamburg
Independent, ON, New Hamburg

Thomson, Marie Ann ....(313) 222-2776
mathompson@detroitnews.com, Support Staff
Mgr., The Detroit News, MI, Detroit

Thomson, Richard
richard.g.thomson@pfizer.com, Bus. Ed., The
New York Sun, NY, New York

Thomson, Rick ....(204) 725-0209
rthomson@wheatcityjournal.ca, Sales Mgr,
Westman Journal, MB, Brandon

Thomson, Robert
robert.thomson@wsj.com, CEO, News Group,
The Wall Street Journal, NY, New York

Thomson, Robert
robert.thomson@dowjones.com, Ed. in Chief,
Dow Jones & Company, NY, New York

Thomson , Heather
hthomson@avtimes.net, Ed. , Alberni Valley
Times, BC, Port Alberni

Thoreson, Rod
tvtimes@tvutel.com, Mng. Ed., Twin Valley
Times/Gary Graphic, MN, Twin Valley

Thoreson, Rod
fertjou@gvtel.com, Ed., The Fertile Journal,
MN, Fertile

Thormaehlen, Mark ....(281) 342-8691
markt@hartmannews.com, Controller, Hartman
Newspapers LP, TX, Rosenberg

Thorn, Martha ....(410) 293-1536
marthat@admiralheights.org, US Naval
Academy, MD, Annapolis

Thornberry, David ....(419) 695-0015 Ext.138
dthornberry@delphosherald.com, Adv. ,
Delphos Daily Herald, OH, Delphos

Thornberry, David..........(419) 695-0015 ext. 130
dthornberry@delphosherald.com , Pub., The
Ada Herald, OH, Ada

Thornburg, Cheryl
business.mgr.pdn@gmail.com, Bus. Mgr.,
Poteau Daily News, OK, Poteau

Thornburg, Mike
jetrepub@fairpoint.net, Ed., Jetmore
Republican, KS, Jetmore

Thornburg, Ron ....(801) 625-4504
Circ. Dir., Standard-Examiner, UT, Ogden

Thornburgh, Tom ....(281) 449-9945
nenewsroom@aol.com, Ed, Northeast News,
TX, Houston

Thorne, Valerie
vthorne@statesmanjournal.com, Class. Mgr. ,
Statesman Journal, OR, Salem

Thornhill, Mike
sports@idacountycourier.com, Sports Ed., Ida
County Courier, IA, Ida Grove

Thornhill, Rachel
advertising@riversidereader.com, Adv. Sales,
Riverside Reader, LA, Port Allen

Thornley, Bill
bthornley@spooneradvocate.com, Assc. Ed.,
Spooner Advocate, WI, Spooner

Thornton, Carlinda
cthornton@woodwardnews.net, Adv.,
Woodward News, OK, Woodward

Thornton, Mark ....(601) 649-9388
editor@leader-call.net, Editor, Laurel Leader-
Call, MS, Laurel

Thornton, Terrance .... (623) 445-2774
tthornton@newszap.com, Ed., Town of
Paradise Valley Independent, AZ, Phoenix

Thornton, Terrance .... (623) 445-2774
tthornton@newszap.com, Ed., Scottsdale
Independent, AZ, Phoenix

Thorpe, Keith .... (360) 452-2345, ext 5058
kthorpe@peninsuladailynews.com, Photo
Chief, Peninsula Daily News, WA, Port
Angeles

Thorson, Bruce
bthorson2@unlnotes.unl.edu, Assoc. Prof.,
University of Nebraska-Lincoln, NE, Lincoln

Thorson, Esther
thorsone@missouri.edu, Prof./Assoc. Dean,
Grad. Studies/Research, University of
Missouri, MO, Columbia

Thorson, Todd .... (515) 733-4318
scherald@storycity.net, Ed., The Story City
Herald, IA, Ames

Thrams, Gregory J. .... (920) 261-4949
gregt@wdtimes.com, Prodn. Mgr., Watertown
Daily Times, WI, Watertown

Thrasher, Bonnie .... (870) 972-3075
bthrasher@astate.edu, Advisor, Arkansas
State Univ., AR, State University

Threadway, Bobbie .... (812) 331-4206
btreadway@schurz.com, The Herald Times, IN,
Bloomington

Threatt, Cathy .... (912) 384-2323
adsales@douglasenterprise.net, Adv. Mgr./
Sales Rep., The Douglas Enterprise, GA,
Douglas

Threatt, Loretta
loretta@thestewarthoustontimes.com, Pub.,
Stewart-Houston Times, TN, Dover

Thrift, Myra
society@wjhnews.com, Food/Garden Ed.,
Waycross Journal-Herald, GA, Waycross

Throne, Michael W. .... (740) 773-2111
mthrone@chillicothegazette.com, Ed.,
Chillicothe Gazette, OH, Chillicothe

Throne, Mike .... (740) 773-2111
mthrone@nncogannett.com, Gen. Mgr., Ross
County Advertiser, OH, Chillicothe

Thrower, Ann
a.mcginnis@murraystate.edu, Adj., Murray
State University, KY, Murray

Thulien, Yvonne
office@ecareview.com, Office Mgr., East
Central Alberta Review, AB, Coronation

Thurber, Beth
bthurber@reminderpublications.com, Prodn.
Mgr., Reminder Metrowest / Chicopee
Herald, MA, East Longmeadow
bthurber@reminderpublications.com, Prodn.
Mgr., The Reminder, MA, East Longmeadow
bthurber@reminderpublications.com, Prodn.
Mgr., Springfield Reminder, MA, East
Longmeadow

Thurlbeck, Edward .... (403) 527-5777
etrhurlbeck@shoppergroup.com, Adv. Mgr.,
The Lethbridge Shopper, AB, Lethbridge
etrhurlbeck@shoppergroup.com, Sales
Manager, The Medicine Hat Shopper, AB,
Medicine Hat

Thurlow, Rich
rthurlow@kdminer.com, Ed., Kingman Daily
Miner, AZ, Kingman

Thurman, Susan
sthurman@c-dh.net, Photo Dept. Mgr.,
Columbia Daily Herald, TN, Columbia

Thurman Terry Goad, Mary
circulation@newsadvance.com, Circ. Mgr., The
Eden Daily News, NC, Reidsville

Thurmond, Clark .... (512) 930-4824
clark@wilcosun.com, Pub., Sunday Sun, TX,
Georgetown
clark@wilcosun.com, Pub., The Williamson

County Sun, TX, Georgetown

Thurmond, Clark
clark@wilcosun.com, Pub., San Gabriel
Weekly, TX, Georgetown

Thurmond, Tina
tina.thurmond@thedailysentinel.com, Staff
Writer, The Daily Sentinel, AL, Scottsboro

Thurston, Steve .... (240) 567-7564
thurston@mcadvocate.com, Montgomery
College, MD, Rockville

Thusat, Peter
peter.thusat@thunderstone.com, CMO,
Thunderstone Software LLC, OH, Cleveland

Thwaites, Bob
bthwaites@windsorstar.com, Pub., The Tilbury
Times, ON, Tilbury
bthwaites@windsorstar.com, Dir., Audience
Development/Customer Service, The
Windsor Star, ON, Windsor

Thyken, Bill .... (509) 577-7710
bthyken@yakimaherald.com, Finance Director,
Yakima Herald-Republic, WA, Yakima

Thyken, Bill
wthyken@ubnet.com, Controller, Walla Walla
Union-Bulletin, WA, Walla Walla

Tibbals, Sam .... (203) 458-5769
stibbals@ctcentral.com, Circ. Mgr., Elm City
Newspapers, CT, Milford

Ticktin, Neil
press_releases@mactech.com, Pub., MacTech
Magazine, CA, Westlake Village

Tidewell, J.R.
jr@moultonadvertiser.com, Staff Writer, The
Moulton Advertiser, AL, Moulton

Tidrick, Dennis .... ext. 2216
dennis.tidrick@scni.com, Prodn. Mgr., Pre
Press, The Advocate, CT, Stamford

Tidwell, James
journal@eiu.edu, Chair/Prof., Eastern Illinois
University, IL, Charleston

Tidwell, Jerry
jtidwell@hcnews.com, Pub., Hood County
News, TX, Granbury

Tiernan, Erin .... (781) 837-4575
etiernan@wickedlocal.com , Editor, Norwell
Mariner, MA, Marshfield

Tiernan, Tom
ttiernan@thehj.com, Adv. Dir., Herald Journal,
IN, Monticello

Tierney, Justin
justin.tierney@lincolncourier.com, Sports Ed.,
Logan County Shopper, IL, Lincoln

Tierney, Kathie .... (423) 837-6312
mcnews@marioncountynews.net, Managing
Ed., South Pittsburg Hustler, TN, South
Pittsburg

Tierney, Kathie .... (423) 837-6312
mcnews@marioncountynews.net, Managing
Ed., Jasper Journal, TN, South Pittsburg

Tierney, Randall
randall.tierney@parentingoc.com, Ed. in Chief,
Parenting Magazine of Orange County, CA,
Orange

Tiffen, Stuart
editor@wdsrtimes.com, Ed, Sonoma West
Times and News, CA, Healdsburg
editor@wdsrtimes.com, Editor , The Windsor
Times, CA, Healdsburg

Tighe, Timothy 860/701-4242
t.tighe@theday.com, Press Manager, The Day,
CT, New London

Tijero, Zulema .... (703) 248-3668
zulyt@netscape.net, Adv. Mgr., El Tiempo
Latino, DC, Washington

Tilcock, Wayne .... (530) 747-8060
photo@davisenterprise.net, Photo Ed., The
Davis Enterprise, CA, DAVIS

Till, Martin K.
mtill@express-times.com, Pub, The US, PA,
Easton

Till, Traci .... (254) 796-4325
hiconews@gmail.com, Managing Editor,
Production Coordinator, Hico News Review,
TX, Hico

Tillbrook, Clive
clive@marketnews.com, Market News
International, New York

Tiller, Kathy
k.tiller@volusialiteracy.org, Community Rel.
Mgr., Daytona Beach News-Journal, FL,
Daytona Beach

Tiller, Martha .... (541) 633-2193
mtiller@bendbulletin.com, Special Projects
Mgr., The Bulletin, OR, Bend

Tiller, Sheila .... (770) 267-2901
composing@waltontribune.com, Composing
Mgr., The Walton Tribune, GA, Monroe

Tillotson, Dolph .... (713) 266-5481
dtillotson@sninews.com, Pres.
, Southern Newspapers Inc., TX, Houston

Tillotta, Steven
steven@houstonvoice.org, Co-Publisher,
Entertainment Editor, Houston Voice, TX,
Houston

Tim, Duguay
Tim.Duguay@rutlandherald.com, Adv. Sales
Mgr., Rutland Herald, VT, Rutland

Timble, Steve
mail@chicagoreader.com, Assoc. Pub.,
Reader, IL, Chicago

Timme, Shannon .... (203) 245-1877 ext 6156
s.timme@shorepublishing.com, Acct. Manager,
Harbor News, CT, Madison

Timmerman, Kelsey .... (937) 423-3517
kelsey@travelin-light.com, Writer/Photographer,
Travelin' Light, Muncie

Timmis, Lori .... (865) 675-6397
Lori@farragutpress.com, Receptionist, Farragut
Press, TN, Farragut

Timmons, Carol Brandon .... (502) 498-1958
ctimmons@bizjournals.com, Ed., Louisville
Business First, KY, Louisville

Timmons, Mandy
newspub@nwol.net, Adv. Dir., Crane News,
TX, Crane

Timmons, Tim .... (765) 361-0100
ttimmons@thepaper24-7.com , Pub.,
The Paper of Montgomery County, IN,
Crawfordsville

Timney, Mark
mtimney@keene.edu, Asst. Prof., Keene State
College of the University System of New
Hampshire, NH, Keene

**Timothy, larry.kilman@wan-ifra.org .... Dir., Global
Affairs**
Balding, World Association of Newspapers and
News Publishers (WAN-IFRA)

Timpe, Bob .... (904) 261-3696
btimpe@fbnewsleader.com, Circ. Mgr., News-
Leader, FL, Fernandina Beach

Timpe, Bob
btimpe@nassaucountyrecord.com, Circ. Dir.,
Nassau County Record, FL, Callahan

Timpone, Sonya
sonya@cuerorecord.com, Adv. Dir., The Cuero
Record, TX, Cuero

Timpone, Sonya
yorktownnews@sbcglobal.net, Adv. Dir.,
Yorktown News-View, TX, Yorktown

Tincher, Ron .... (208) 465-8191
rtincher@idahopress.com, Circ. Dir., Idaho
Press, ID, Nampa

Tiner, Stephanie
stiner@stuttgartdailyleader.com, Business
Mgr., Stuttgart Daily Leader, AR, Stuttgart

stiner @ stuttgartdailyleader.com, White Hall
Journal, AR, White Hall

Ting, Alice .... (212) 556-5967
alicet@nytimes.com, Vice President, Licensing
& Syndication, The New York Times News
Service & Syndicate, New York

Ting, Alice .... (212) 556-5967
alicet@nytimes.com, Vice President, Licensing
& Syndication, The New York Times News
Service & Syndicate, New York

Ting, Ching Yi
cyting@taipei.org, Contact, Taipei Economic
& Cultural Office, Press Division - New York,
NY, New York

Ting, Eva
circulation@pacificcitizen.org, Circ. Dept.,
Japanese American Citizens League, CA,
Los Angeles

Tingle, Bobby
btingle@panews.com, Cir. Dir., Port Arthur
News, TX, Port Arthur

Tingle, Bobby .... (409) 883-3572
bobby.tingle@orangeleader.com, Pub, The
Orange Leader, TX, Orange

Tingle, Shawntale .... (812) 265-3641, ext. 225
Carrier Mgr. , Madison Courier, Inc., IN,
Madison

Tingley, Michele .... (860) 647-5401
mtingley@courant.com, Adv. Dir., The Hartford
Courant, CT, Hartford

Tingwall, John
johnt@metrosuburbia.com, Adv. Sales Mgr.,
Metro Suburbia, Inc./Newhouse Newspapers,
NY, New York

Tinkel, Janice
jant_bus@dailynews.net, Bus. Mgr., The Hays
Daily News, KS, Hays

Tinker, Allan
gazette@westriv.com, Editor, McClusky
Gazette, ND, McClusky

Tinker, Allan
turtle@westriv.com, Ed., McLean County
Journal, ND, McClusky

Tinker, Alllan .... (701) 363-2492
gazette@westriv.com, Editor/Office Supervisor,
McClusky Gazette, ND, McClusky

Tinnen, Steven
publisher@clintoncountyleader.com, Pub, The
Clinton County Leader, MO, Plattsburg

Tinsley, Anita .... (337) 494-4033
atinsley@americanpress.com, Bus. Mgr.,
Shearman Corporation, LA, Lake Charles

Tinsley, Shannon
stinsley@thenews-gazette.com, Sales Mgr.,
The News-Gazette, VA, Lexington

Tippens, Dianne
dtippens@calhountimes.com, Adv. Rep.,
Calhoun Times and Gordon County News,
GA, Calhoun

Tipper, Stephen
stephen.tipper@sunmedia.ca, Editor, Vulcan
Advocate, AB, Vulcan
stephen.tipper@sunmedia.ca, Ed., The Nanton
News, AB, Nanton

Tippetts, Bruce
freemontnews@wyoming.com, Sports Ed., The
Riverton Ranger, WY, Riverton

Tipping, Joy
editor@richmond-dailynews.com, Mng. Ed.,
Richmond News, MO, Richmond

Tipton, Emily .... (256) 304-0041
legals@times-journal.com, Classified
Representative, The Times-Journal, AL, Fort
Payne

Tipton, Nancy .... (505) 823-3886
ntipton@abqpubco.com, ABQJournal.com,
Albuquerque Journal, NM, Albuquerque

Tipton, Virgil

virgil@newsengin.com, CTO, NewsEngin, Inc., MO, Chesterfield

Tischer, Bruce
pcnews@athenet.net, Circ. Mgr., Home Showcase, WI, Appleton

Tisdale, John
j.tisdale@tcu.edu, Assoc. Prof., Texas Christian University, TX, Fort Worth

Title, Debbie ....(908) 232-2913 ext. 104
debbie.title@njfamily.com, Office Mgr., New Jersey Family, NJ, Summit

Titone, Robert
rob.titone@sj-r.com, Circ. Mgr., Lincoln Courier, IL, Lincoln
rob.titone@sj-r.com, Circ. Mgr., Springfield Advertiser, IL, Springfield

Titterington, Kristin
editor@rockymountainpub.com, Ed., Rocky Mountain Parent Magazine, OH, Troy

Titus, Caroline
editor@ferndaleenterprise.us, Ed./Pub., The Ferndale Enterprise, CA, Ferndale

Titus, Cathleen ....(212) 969-7537
ctitus@hearst.com, VP, Int'l Syndication, King Features Syndicate, NY, New York
ctitus@hearst.com, VP., Int'l Syndication, North America Syndicate, New York

Titus, Sandra ....(603) 436-1800
stitus@seacoastonline.com, Adv. Mgr., Classified/Sales, Portsmouth Herald, NH, Portsmouth

Tloessl, Marty
woodwardprint@wcinet.com, Gen. Mgr., Woodward Printing Services, WI, Platteville

Toal, Holly ....(845) 628-8401
putnampress@aol.com, Ed-in-Chief, Putnam County Press, NY, Mahopac
putnampress@aol.com, Ed-in-Chief, Putnam County Times, NY, Mahopac

Toben, Angie...............(417) 866-0841
atoben@dioscg.org, Administrative Assistant/ Circulation Manager, The Mirror, MO, Springfield

Toberman, Wayne ....(312) 834-7228
President, International Press Club of Chicago (IPCC), IL, Chicago

Tobey, Kirk ....(989) 725-5136
circulation@argus-press.com, Circ. Mgr., The Argus-Press, MI, Owosso

Tobey, Steve
stobey@wickedlocal.com , Sports Ed., The Beacon-Villager, MA, Concord

Tobia, Chris
chris.tobia@newsday.com, Director, Major Retail Sales, Newsday, NY, Melville

Tobias, Eric M.
sales@tobiasinc.com, Vice Pres., Tobias Associates, Inc., PA, Ivyland

Tobias, Scott
retail@westword.com, Publisher, Denver Westword, CO, Denver

Tobin, Chuck ....(867) 667-4481
chuck@whitehorsestar.com, Reporter, Whitehorse Star, YT, Whitehorse

Tobin, Jeff...............(712) 293-4207
Mng. Ed., Sports, Sioux City Journal, IA, Sioux City

Tobin, Kathleen A. ....(715) 453-2151
news@tomahawkleader.com, Co-Pub./Ed., Tomahawk Leader, WI, Tomahawk

Tobin, Larry ....(715) 453-2151
Larry@tomahawkleader.com, Co-Publisher, Tomahawk Leader, WI, Tomahawk

Tobon, John...............(905) 732-2411 ext. 291
john.tobon@sunmedia.ca, Pub., Welland Tribune, ON, Welland
john.tobon@sunmedia.ca, In Port News, ON, Port Colborne

Toby, Stephen ....(978) 371-5741
stobey@wickedlocal.com, Sports Ed., Winchester Star, MA, Lexington

Tocci, Linda...............ext. 322
ltocci@cnylink.com, Adv. Mgr., Syracuse Parent, NY, Syracuse

Todd, Brenda
advertising@post-voice.com, Ad. Director, Pender-Topsail Post & Voice, NC, Burgaw

Todd, David
david.todd@flagshipnews.com, Prodn. Mgr., Journal And Guide, VA, Norfolk

Todd, Jeanette
tbotill@hotmail.com, Ed., The Corcoran Journal, CA, Corcoran

Todd, Keven ....(302) 346-5449
keven.todd@doverpost.com, Pres./ Pub., Hockessin Community News, DE, Middletown
keven.todd@doverpost.com, Pres./ Pub., Hockessin Community News, DE, Middletown
keven.todd@doverpost.com, Pres./Pub., Smyrna/Clayton Sun-Times, DE, Middletown
keven.todd@doverpost.com, Pres./Pub., The Middletown Transcript, DE, Middletown
keven.todd@doverpost.com, Pres./Pub., The Sussex Countian, DE, Dover
keven.todd@doverpost.com, Pres./Pub., Milford Beacon, DE, Dover

Todd, Matthews ....(253) 627-4853
editor@tacomadailyindex.com, Tacoma Daily Index, WA, Tacoma

Todd, Michael ....(801) 575-5600
mtodd@deseretnews.com, CFO, Deseret News, UT, Salt Lake City

Todd, Sarah ....(212) 803-8753
sarah.todd@sourcemedia.com, Deputy Editor, Bankthink, American Banker, NY, New York

Todd, Steve ....(609) 871-8022
stodd@calkins.com, Audience Development Director & GM, Calkins Media, PA, Levittown

Todd, Tommy ....(305) 292-7777 ext. 204
ttodd@keysnews.com, Director of Advertising, Cooke Communications Florida, LLC, FL, Key West
ttodd@keysnews.com, Adv. Dir., The Free Press, FL, Tampa

Todd, Wendy ....(309) 734-3176
wendytodd@reviewatlas.com, Adv. Mgr., Pennysaver, IL, Monmouth

Todor, Rob
rtodor@the-review.com, Ed., The News Leader, OH, Minerva

Todor, Robert ....(330) 821-1200
rtodor@the-review.com, The Alliance Review, OH
rtodor@the-review.com, Executive Editor, Alliance Publishing Co. LLC, OH, Alliance

Todor , Rob
rtodor@the-review.com, Ed., The Press-News, OH, Minerva

Toffey, Stephanie
stoffey@timesshamrock.com, The Times-Tribune, PA, Scranton

Tofoya, Jessica
circulation@rockyforddailygazette.com , Circ. Dir., Rocky Ford Daily Gazette, CO, Rocky Ford

Tokie, Terry ....(252) 635-5639
Terry.Tokie@newbernsj.com, Adv. Dir., The Sun Journal, NC, New Bern

Toler, James ....(540) 374-5416
jtoler@freelancestar.com, Editorial Page Editor, The Free Lance-Star, VA, Fredericksburg

Toler, Jim ....(518) 744-5211
james.toler@washpost.com, Marketing Representative/Northeast & South, Washington Post News Service with Bloomberg News, Washington

Toler, Jim ....(518) 744-5211
jtoler@unitedmedia.com, Regl. Sales Mgr., Newspaper Enterprise Association (Div. of United Media), NY, New York
jtoler@unitedmedia.com, Regl. Sales Mgr., United Feature Syndicate (Div. of United Media), New York

Toler, Jordan...............(859) 885-5381
jtoler@schurz.com, Digital Media Consultant, The Winchester Sun, KY, Winchester

Toler, Tammie
ttoler@bdtonline.net, Pub./Gen. Mgr., Princeton Times, WV, Princeton

Toles, Thomas...............(706) 367-2488
tommy@mainstreetnews.com, Bus./Printing Mgr., The Jackson Herald, GA, Jefferson

Toles, Thomas...............(706) 367-2488
tommy@mainstreetnews.com, Bus./Printing Mgr., The Madison County Journal, GA, Jefferson

Tolle, Tony ....(580) 548-8194
ttolle@enidnews.com, Pressroom Mgr., Enid News & Eagle, OK, Enid

Tollefson, Daniel J................(269) 651-5407
tollefson@sturgisjournal.com, Pub., Sturgis Journal, MI, Sturgis

Tollefson, Roger ....(308) 632-9019
Gen. Mgr., Twin City Weekly, NE, Scottsbluff

Tollefson, Roger ....(308) 632-9000
roger.tollefson@starherald.com, Gen. Mgr., Star-Herald, NE, Scottsbluff

Tollefson, Roger S.
tolly@star-herald.com, Pub., Luverne Announcer, MN, Luverne

Tolley, Brian
btolley@fayobserver.com, Exec. Ed., Carolina Flyer, NC, Fayetteville

Tolley, Brian ....(601) 961-7175
btolley@jackson.gannett.com , Madison County Herald, MS, Ridgeland

Tolliver, Preston
editor@mcrecordonline.com, Mng. Ed., The Madison County Record, AR, Huntsville

Tolliver, Sandra ....(412) 320-7829
stolliver@tribweb.com, Deputy Managing Ed., Tribune-Review, PA, Greensburg

Tolson, Dorma
dtolson@mojonews.com, Ed., Morning Journal, OH, Lisbon

Tolstrup, Kathleen ....(518) 792-9914 ext. 2200
kftolstrup@tribune.com, Gen. Mgr., Sales/ Mktg., Tribune Media Services Entertainment Products, Queensbury

Tolstrup, Kathleen
tvdata@tvdata.com, Sr. Vice Pres.-Sales, Tribune Media Services, NY, Glens Falls

Tolton, Jonathan
JTOLTON@SEATTLETIMES.COM, Vice Pres., American Newspaper Layout Managers Association (ANLOMA), FL, Fort Myers

Tom, Dempsey ....(518) 434-2193
tad@vdata.com, President, Vision Data Equipment Corp., NY, Rensselaer

Tom, Mike
e-dub@pomeroy-wa.com, Pub./Ed., East Washingtonian, WA, Pomeroy

Tomaselli, Gwen
gtomaselli@metro-email.com, Regional Sales Mgr., Metro Editorial Services, NY, New York

Tomaselli, Ralph...............(203) 317-2220
rtomaselli@record-journal.com, Sr. Vice President & Editor, The Record-Journal Publishing Co., CT, Meriden
rtomaselli@record-journal.com, Mng. Ed., Record-Journal, CT, Meriden

Tomasik, Mark...............(772) 221-4204
Ed., Jupiter Courier, FL, Stuart

Tomaske, Gordon

Gordon.tomaske@latimes.com, CFO, Times Community News (TCN), CA, Los Angeles

Tomaszewski, Lois
ltomaszewski@thepilotnews.com, Mng. Ed., Pilot News, IN, Plymouth
ltomaszewski@thepilotnews.com, Mng. Ed., The Shopper, IN, Plymouth

Tomaszewski, Lois...............(574) 216-0075
ltomaszewski@thepilotnews.com, Ed., The Culver Citizen, IN, Plymouth

Tomczak, Maureen...............(314) 340-8102
mtomczak@post-dispatch.com, Office Mgr., St. Louis Post-Dispatch, MO, Saint Louis

Tomich, Sebastian ....(212) 556-1416
sebastian.tomich@nytimes.com, VP, Ad Product & Plan. Senior VP, Adv., The New York Times, NY, New York

Tomlin, Jimmy ....(336) 888-3578
jtomlin@hpe.com, Columnist, High Point Enterprise, NC, High Point

Tomlin, Robyn ....(214) 977-8227
rtomlin@dallasnews.com, Vice President/ Managing Editor, The Dallas Morning News, TX, Dallas

Tomlinson, Andrew
andrew.tomlinson@hhs.gov, American Univ., DC, Washington

Tomlinson, Bruce ....(973) 383-1171
btomlinson@njherald.com, Exec. Ed., New Jersey Herald, NJ, Newton

Tomlinson, Harley
harley@rensselaerrepublican.com, Sports Ed., Rensselaer Republican, IN, Rensselaer

Tomlinson, Harley
harley@rensselaerrepublican.com, Sports Ed., Remington Press, IN, Rensselaer

Tomlinson, Harley
harley@rensselaerrepublican.com, Morocco Courier, IN, Kentland

Tompkins, Paula George
mediainquiries@channelnet.com, Founder/ CEO, ChannelNet, CA, Sausalito

Tompkins, Penne
editor@theotherpaperbvt.com, Ed., The Other Paper, VT, South Burlington

Tompkins, Peter ....(919) 836-5909
ptompkins@newsobserver.com, Adv. Dir., North Raleigh News, NC, Raleigh

Tompkins, Ted
ttompkins@ctpost.com, Co-Mng. Ed., Connecticut Post, CT, Bridgeport

Tompt, Brenda...............(701) 845-0463
troffice@times-online.com, Office Mgr., Valley City Times-Record, ND, Valley City

Toncray, Marla ....(606) 564-9091 ext. 275
Marla.Toncray@lee.net, News Ed., The Mayfield Messenger, KY, Mayfield
Marla.Toncray@lee.net, News Ed., The Advertiser, KY, Maysville

Tonderum, Penny ....(712) 859-3780
grtimes@rvtc.net, Pub., The Graettinger Times, IA, Graettinger

Toner, Bobbie...............(617) 666-4010
bobbie@thesomervillenews.com, Adv. Dir., The Somerville Times, MA, Somerville

Toney, David E................(979) 345-3127
gctribune@consolidated.net, Pub., The Gulf Coast Tribune, TX, Needville
gctribune@consolidated.net, Pub., The Brazoria County News, TX, West Columbia

Toney, Julian ....(662) 247-3373
editor@thebelzonibanner.com, Ed., The Belzoni Banner, MS, Belzoni

Toney, Karen...............(918) 653-2425
heavenerledger@windstream.net, Legals, The Heavener Ledger, OK, Heavener

Tonsing, Julie
jtonsing@fmtimes.com , Pub. , Fort Morgan

Times, CO, Fort Morgan
jtonsing@fmtimes.com , Pub., Morgan Times
Review, CO, Fort Morgan

Tonsing, Julie .... (970) 526-9299
jtonsing@journal-advocate.com, Pub., Journal-
Advocate, CO, Sterling

Tooker, Beth
MonteVistaClass@gmail.com, The Monte Vista
Journal, CO, Monte Vista
MonteVistaClass@gmail.com, Office Mgr., The
Mineral County Miner, CO, Monte Vista
MonteVistaClass@gmail.com, Office Mgr., The
South Fork Tines, CO, Monte Vista
MonteVistaClass@gmail.com, Class. Mgr., The
Conejos County Citizen, CO, Monte Vista
MonteVistaClass@gmail.com, Office Mgr., The
Del Norte Prospector, CO, Monte Vista

Toole, Betty Jo
terrytoole@bellsouth.net, Gen. Mgr., Miller
County Liberal, GA, Colquitt

Toole, Terry
terrytoole@bellsouth.net, Ed./Pub., Miller
County Liberal, GA, Colquitt

Tooley, Mike
www.theheraldtorc.com, Pub., The Herald, NM,
Truth Or Consequences

Tooley, Teresa .... (541) 447-6205
ttooley@centraloregonian.com, Gen. Mgr.,
Central Oregonian, OR, Prineville

Toomey, Carol .... (978) 371-2442
carolaction@aol.com, Publisher, Action
Unlimited, MA, Concord

Toomey, Joe
joe@actionunlimited.com, Circ. Mgr, Action
Unlimited, MA, Concord

Toone, Linda
manager@alvareviewcourier.net, Office
Manager, Alva Review-Courier, OK, Alva

Toops, Roger W. .... (623) 847-4603
rtoops@star-times.com, Bus. Mgr., The
Glendale Star, AZ, Glendale

Toops, William E. .... (623) 847-4602
wtoops@star-times.com, Pub./Gen. Mng.,
Peoria Times, AZ, Glendale
wtoops@star-times.com, Pub./Gen.Mng., The
Glendale Star, AZ, Glendale

Toothman, Melissa .... (304) 269-1600, ext. 104
news@westondemocrat.com, Editor, Weston
Democrat, WV, Weston

Topham, Renee
kanadakurier@mb.sympatico.ca, Pub., Kanada
Kurier, MB, Winnipeg

Toporek, Devin .... (212) 642-1707
dtoporek@inta.org, International Trademark
Association, NY, New York

Topp, Thomas
thomas.topp@heidelberg.com, Sr. Vice
Pres., Finance, Heidelberg USA, Inc., GA,
Kennesaw

Toppel, Ann
ann.t@hcnonline.com, Mgmt. Info Servs. Mgr.,
The Courier of Montgomery County, TX,
Conroe

Topping, Julie .... (313) 222-8850
jtopping@freepress.com, Deputy Mng. Ed.,
Detroit Free Press, MI, Detroit

Topping, Paul
pault@mathtype.com, Pres., Design Science,
Inc., CA, Long Beach

Torain, Sean .... (336) 506-3024
storain@thetimesnews.com, Representative,
Mid-Atlantic Circulation Managers
Association, NC, Roanoke Rapids

Torbett, Rob .... (509) 665-1170
torbett@wenatcheeworld.com, Controller, The
Wenatchee World, WA, Wenatchee

Torgerson, Lois
northernstar@mchsi.com, Mng. Ed., Northern
Star, MN, Clinton

Torpey, Mark .... (617) 786-7060
mtorpey@ledger.com, Sports Ed., The
Enterprise, MA, Brockton

Torregrosa, Aixa .... (215) 361-8824
atorregrosa@thereporteronline.com, Lifestyles
Ed., The Reporter, PA, Lansdale

Torregrossa, Susan
storregrossa@southcomm.com, Assoc. Pub.,
Nashville Scene, TN, Nashville

Torres, Brenda
holtvillenews@aol.com, Pub., Holtville Tribune,
CA, Holtville

Torres, Buffy
buffy.torres@therogersvillereview.com,
Adv. Exec., The Rogersville Review, TN,
Rogersville

Torres, Jose
sports@gonzalesinquirer.com, The Gonzales
Inquirer, TX, Gonzales

Torres, Julia .... (407) 767-0070 Ext. 122
Office Mgr., La Prensa, FL, Longwood

Torres, Lorena .... (213) 896-2153
lorena.torres@laopinion.com, Dir., Local Sales,
La Opinion, CA, Los Angeles

Torres, Moncho
india@efe.com, Correspondent, EFE News
Services - New Delhi, India, New Delhi

Torres, Sharon
sharon.torres@buckeyevalleynews.net, Editor,
CFO, Buckeye Valley News, AZ, Buckeye

Torrey, John
john.torrey@xpedx.com, Vice Pres./Gen. Mgr.,
Xpedx Printing Technologies, OH, Loveland

Torrez, Lisa
banner@srcaccess.net, Adv. Dir., Baylor
County Banner, TX, Seymour

Torrivio, Leona .... (505) 863-6811 ext. 204
independentcirc@gmail.com, Circ., Gallup
Independent, NM, Gallup

Tortolano, Jim .... (714) 895-8256
jtortolano@gwc.cccd.edu, Advisor, Golden
West College, CA, Huntington Beach

Tortorici, Leigh
leigh2@alabamapress.org, Senior Marketing
Rep., Alabama Press Association, AL,
Birmingham

Toscano, Bill
publisher@manchesternewspapers.com, Ed.,
Northshire Free Press, NY, Granville
publisher@manchesternewspapers.com, Ed.,
The Lakes Region Free Press, NY, Granville

Toth, Joe .... (405) 372-5000
jtoth@stwnewspress.com, Dir. of Audience
Dev., Stillwater News Press, OK, Stillwater

Toth, Larry .... (580) 585-5159
circulation@swoknews.com, Cir. Dir., The
Lawton Constitution, OK, Lawton

Toth, Sharon .... (979) 849-5407
sharon.bulletin@gmail.com, Co-Publisher /
Advertising Director, The Bulletin, TX,
Angleton

Totten, Kim
kjtotten@pocahontastimes.com, Adv. Mgr., The
Pocahontas Times, WV, Marlinton

Touby, Frank
deareditor@thebulletin.ca, Ed., The Bulletin -
Journal Of Downtown Toronto, ON, Toronto

Touby, Paulette
cbnews@yahoo.com, Pub., The Bulletin -
Journal Of Downtown Toronto, ON, Toronto

Touchet, Judy
classifieds@banner-tribune.com, Accounting,
Franklin Banner-Tribune, LA, Franklin

Touchette, Daniel
dtouchet@lavoixdelest.qc.ca, Adv. Mgr., La
Voix De L'est Plus, QC, Granby

Touchette, Jean

jean.touchette@transcontinental, Editeur,
Corriere Italiano, QC, Montreal

Touchette, Marty
sports@reviewatlas.com, Sports Ed.,
Pennysaver, IL, Monmouth

Tougas, Joe
aalishma.shrestha@mnsu.edu, Adj. Fac.,
Minnesota State University Mankato, MN,
Mankato

Tourangeau, Emilia-Larivee .... (514) 522-6142
emilie.larivee-Touraine@fpjq.org , Deputy Dir.,
Federation professionnelle des journalistes
du Quebec, QC, Montreal (Quebec)

Touvell, Jim .... (260) 461-8629
jtouvell@jg.net, Managing Ed., The Journal
Gazette, IN, FORT WAYNE

Tower, Jennifer .... (309) 686-3119
circulation@suncommunitynews.com, Circ.
Mgr, The Valley News Sun, NY, Elizabethtown
circulation@suncommunitynews.com, Circ.
Mgr, The Adirondack Journal Sun, NY,
Elizabethtown
circulation@suncommunitynews.com, Circ.
Mgr, The Times of Ti Sun, NY, Elizabethtown
circulation@suncommunitynews.com, Circ.
Mgr, The Burgh Sun, NY, Elizabethtown
circulation@suncommunitynews.com,
Circ. Mgr, The News Enterprise Sun, NY,
Elizabethtown
circulation@suncommunitynews.com, Circ.
Mgr, The North Countryman Sun, NY,
Elizabethtown
circulation@suncommunitynews.com,
Neighbors Ed., Journal Star, IL, Peoria

Towle, Mike .... (615) 575-7122
mtowle@mtcngroup.com, General Manager,
The Sumner County Shopper, TN, Gallatin

Towler, Mary Anna .... (585) 244-9073
matowler@rochester-citynews.com, co-
publisher/Editor, City Newspaper, NY,
Rochester

Towler, William .... (585) 244-3329 ext. 20
btowler@rochester-citynews.com, co-publisher,
City Newspaper, NY, Rochester

Towner, Jim
jtowner@timesshamrock.com, Gen. Mgr.,
Times-Shamrock Communications, PA,
Scranton

Townes, Brenda .... (859) 236-2551 Ext. 4
btownes@amnews.com, District Mgr., The
Advocate-Messenger, KY, Danville

Towns, Hollis .... (732) 922-6000 x 4210
htowns@gannettnj.com, Ed., Tuckerton
Beacon, NJ, Neptune

Towns, Hollis
htowns@njpressmedia.com, Exec. Ed./VP ,
The Lacey Beacon, NJ, Neptune

Towns, Hollis .... (732) 643-4210
htowns@gannettnj.com, Exec Ed. & VP News,
Home News Tribune, NJ, Somerville

Towns, Hollis .... (732) 922-6000
htowns@njpressmedia.com, Exec. Ed. & Vice
Pres./News, Asbury Park Press, NJ, Neptune

Towns, Stuart
townsws@appstate.edu, Chair, Appalachian
State University, NC, Boone

Towns , Hollis
htowns@njpressmedia.com, Exec. Ed./VP,
Beach Haven Times, NJ, Neptune

Townsend, Billy .... ext. 236
btownsend@hhjnews.com, Prodn. Mgr., Opns.,
The Houston Home Journal, GA, Perry

Townsend, Brian
news@precinctreporter.com, Ed., Precinct
Reporter, CA, San Bernardino

Townsend, C. Edward
hendersonind@frontiernet.net, Pub.,
Henderson Independent, MN, Henderson

Townsend, C. Edward .... (952) 873-2261
bpherald@frontiernet.net, Pub., Belle Plaine

Herald, MN, Belle Plaine

Townsend, Candace .... (337) 317-1009
ctownsen@mcneese.edu, McNeese State
Univ., LA, Lake Charles

Townsend, Debbie
debbie.townsend@bellinghamherald.com,
Managing Ed., The Bellingham Herald, WA,
Bellingham

Townsend, Jim
jimt@aimgroup.com, Editorial Director,
Advanced Interactive Media Group, LLC, FL,
Altamonte Springs

Townsend, Jimmy .... ext. 228
jtownsend@hhjnews.com, Prodn. Mgr.,
Mailroom, The Houston Home Journal, GA,
Perry

Townsend, Tom
tom.townsend@kybaptist.org, Mktg. Mgr.,
Western Recorder, KY, Louisville

Townshend, Carter
ctownshend@keynoter.com, Circ. Mgr., The
Reporter, FL, Tavernier

Townsley, Loren .... (818) 677-2915
editor@csun.edu, Editor, California State
University, Northridge, CA, Northridge

Townsley, Nancy .... (503) 357-3181
ntownsley@fgnewstimes.com, Ed, The
Hillsboro Tribune, OR, Forest Grove
ntownsley@fgnewstimes.com, Mng. Ed., Forest
Grove News-Times, OR, Forest Grove

Townsley, Steven .... (212) 597-5733
steven.townsley@dowjones.com, Dir., Sales,
The Wall Street Journal Sunday, New York

Townsley, Steven
stownsley@burrellesluce.com, Director of
Publisher Services, BurrellesLuce, NJ,
Florham Park

Townsley, Wes .... (260) 347-0400 Ext. 1166
wtownsley@kpcmedia.com, Circ. Acc. Mgr.,
Greater Fort Wayne Business Weekly, IN,
Fort Wayne

Trabitz, Adam .... (740) 328-8502
atrabitz@gannett.com, Sales Leader, The
Advocate, OH, Newark
atrabitz@gannett.com, Adv. Sales Dir. , Times
Recorder, OH, Zanesville

Trabitz, Adam .... (740) 328-8502
atrabitz@gannett.com, Adv. Dir., The Granville
Sentinel, OH, Newark
atrabitz@gannett.com, Adv. Dir., The Pataskala
Standard, OH, Newark
atrabitz@gannett.com, Adv. Sales Dir., The
News-Messenger, OH, Fremont
atrabitz@gannett.com, News Herald, OH,
Fremont
atrabitz@gannett.com, Sales Dir., The
Coshocton Tribune, OH, Coshocton
atrabitz@gannett.com, Adv. Sales Dir., The
Marion Star, OH, Marion
atrabitz@gannett.com, Sales Dir, News
Journal, OH, Mansfield

Trabitz, Adam .... (740) 328-8502
atrabitz@gannett.com, Adv. Sales Dir.,
Telegraph-Forum, OH, Mansfield

Tracey, Michael
michael.tracey@colorado.edu, Prof., University
of Colorado, CO, Boulder

Tracey IV, P.J. .... (870) 356-2111
gwherald@windstream.net, Ed., Glenwood
Herald, AR, Glenwood

Trachtenberg, Karen
livpaper@gmail.com, Prodn. Mgr., West Essex
Tribune, NJ, Livingston

Tracy, Ann .... (916) 798-2136
at@insidepublications.com, Acc. Rep., Inside
East Sacramento, CA, Sacramento

Tracy, Gregory .... (617) 779-3782
gtracy@pilotcatholicnews.com, Mng. Ed., The
Pilot, MA, Braintree

Tracy, James

editor@sanpatpublishing.com, Co-Pub./Ed., The Odem - Edroy Times, TX, Sinton

Tracy, James F.
jftracyjr@sanpatpublishing.com, Co-Pub./Ed., San Patricio County News, TX, Sinton

Tracy, James F.
jftracyjr@sanpatpublishing.com, Co-Pub., San Patricio Publishing Co., Inc., TX, Sinton

Tracy, John
advertising@sanpatpublishing.com, Co-Pub./Adv. Dir., The Odem - Edroy Times, TX, Sinton
advertising@sanpatpublishing.com, Co-Pub./Adv. Dir., San Patricio County News, TX, Sinton
advertising@sanpatpublishing.com, Co-Pub., Taft Tribune, TX, Taft

Tracy, John H. ....(361) 364-1270
Co-Pub./Adv. Mgr., Portland News, TX, Portland

Tracy, John H.
jhtracy@sanpatpublishing.com, Co-Pub., San Patricio Publishing Co., Inc., TX, Sinton

Tracy, Mike ....(613) 688-1487
mtracy@perfprint.ca, Publisher, The Stittsville News, ON, Ottawa

Tracy, Mike ....(613) 688-1487
mtracy@pefprint.ca, Pub., Kanata Kourier-standard Emc, ON, Ottawa
mtracy@pefprint.ca, Pub., The Renfrew Mercury Emc, ON, Renfrew
mtracy@pefprint.ca, Pub., Ottawa West Emc, ON, Ottawa
mtracy@pefprint.ca, Pub, Arnprior Chronicle Guide Emc, ON, Arnprior
mtracy@pefprint.ca, Pub., Orleans News Emc, ON, Ottawa
mtracy@pefprint.ca, Pub., Nepean-barrhaven News Emc, ON, Ottawa
mtracy@pefprint.ca, Pub., Ottawa South Emc, ON, Ottawa
mtracy@pefprint.ca, Pub., Manotick News Emc, ON, Ottawa
mtracy@pefprint.ca, West Carleton Review, ON, Arnprior
mtracy@pefprint.ca, Pub., Ottawa East Emc, ON, Ottawa

Tracy, Pat ....(604) 444-3030
editor@burnabynow.com, Ed., Burnaby Now, BC, Burnaby

Tracy, Pat ....(604) 444-3007
ptracy@newwestrecord.ca, Ed, New Westminster Record, BC, New Westminster
ptracy@newwestrecord.ca, Ed., The Record, BC, Burnaby

Tracy, Steffenson
ed.antlers.amer@sbcglobal.net, Pub/Ed/Gen. Mgr., Antlers American, OK, Antlers

Tracy, Wren .... (415) 461-6006, ext. 203
wtracy@verifieaudit.com, Audit Mgr., Verified Audit Circulation (VAC), CA, San Rafael

Traeger, Missy
missy@saukherald.com, Sales Mgr., Sauk Centre Herald, MN, Sauk Centre

Traeger, Missy.........................(320) 352-6577
missy@saukherald.com, Sales Mgr., Benton County News, MN, Foley

Trafford, Daniel ....(401) 767-8544
dtrafford@woonsocketcall.com, Ed., Neighbors Newspaper, RI, Woonsocket
dtrafford@woonsocketcall.com, Mng. Ed., Cumberland Lincoln Neighbors, RI, Woonsocket

Trafton, Margie
tnf@nb.aibn.com, Mng. Ed., The New Freeman, NB, Saint John

Trafton, Nancy Jo ....(765) 420-5265
ntrafton@journalandcourier.com, Dir., Market Devel., Journal and Courier, IN, Lafayette

Trager, Robert
robert.trager@colorado.edu, Prof., University of Colorado, CO, Boulder

Trahan, Brian
swdailyeditor@gmail.com, Rgl. Exec. Ed., Southwest Daily News, LA, Sulphur

Trahan, Candice ....(409) 883-3571
candice.trahan@orangeleader.com, Inside Sales, The Orange Leader, TX, Orange

Trahan, Claude
claude.trahan@tc.tc, Mng. Ed., Journal Le Coup D'oeil, QC, Napierville

Trahan, Lucien G. ....(603) 668-4321
ltrahan@unionleader.com , Circ. Dir., Opns., New Hampshire Union Leader/New Hampshire Sunday News, NH, Manchester

Trahan Jr., Terry
editor@povhouma.com, Ed., Point of Vue, LA, Houma

Trainor, John...........................(312) 527-8429
jtrainor@hoyllc.com, Gen. Mgr, Hoy LLC, CA, Los Angeles

Trainor, John
info@magnacom-inc.com, Pres., MagnaCom, Inc., AL, Huntsville

Trainor, Tim ....(541) 966-0835
ttrainor@eastoregonian.com, Opinion Page Editor, East Oregonian, OR, Pendleton

Trainque, Tom ....(978) 632-8000 ext. 21
ttrainque@thegardnernews.com, Sports Ed., The Gardner News, MA, Gardner

Trama, Anthony
trama@creatorsmedia.com, CEO, The Creators Media Group, NY, Pleasantville

Trammell, Curtis ....(949) 542-3520
ctrammell@hearst.com, West Coast Sales, North America Syndicate, New York

Trammell, Curtis ....(312) 222-8934
Sales manager, TMS Specialty Products, IL, Chicago

Trammell, Curtis ....(312) 961-2789
ctrammell@hearst.com, Western Region Sales, King Features Syndicate, NY, New York

Trammell, Jim
jtrammel@highpoint.edu, Asst. Prof., High Point Univ., NC, High Point

Trammell, Robby......................(405) 475-3311
Asst. Mng. Ed., The Oklahoman, OK, Oklahoma City

Tran, Christine
tran@sddt.com, Dir., Mktg., The Daily Transcript, CA, San Diego

Tran, Millie
millie.tran@pressinstitute.org, Editorial Coordinator, American Press Institute, VA, Arlington

Tran, Vi ....(626) 395-6154
California Inst. of Technology, CA, Pasadena

Tranchida, David ....(860) 495-8248
dtranchida@thewesterlysun.com, VP & Editor, The Westerly Sun, CT, Pawcatuck

Tranchida, David ....(860) 495-8248
dtranchida@thewesterlysun.com, Vice Pres./Ed., The Express, CT, Pawcatuck

Trang, Terry
design@glasgowcourier.com, Office manager, The Glasgow Courier, MT, Glasgow

Tranquill, Joseph ....(740) 373-2121 Ext. 253
jtranquill@newsandsentinel.com, Cir. Dir., The Marietta Times, OH, Marietta

Tranquill, Matthew ....(304) 485-1891
mtranquill@examiner-enterprise.com, Pub, Pawhuska Journal-Capital, OK, Pawhuska
mtranquill@examiner-enterprise.com, Pub., Examiner-Enterprise, OK, Bartlesville
mtranquill@examiner-enterprise.com, Adv. Dir., Parkersburg News & Sentinel, WV, Parkersburg

Trapani, Charlie ....(570) 628-6059

ctrapani@republicanherald.com, Sales Mgr., The Republican-Herald, PA, Pottsville

Trapp, Robert
rgsun@cybermesa.com, Publisher, Rio Grande Sun, NM, Espanola
rgsun@cybermesa.com, Pub./Co-owner, Rio Grande Sun, NM, Espanola

Trapp, Stella A.
seantrapp@transylvaniatimes.com, Pub., The Transylvania Times, NC, Brevard

Trappe, Renee......................(847) 427-4468
rtrappe@dailyherald.com, Group Editor / Southern Illinois Local Media Group, Daily Herald, IL, Arlington Heights

Trares, Chris.........................(919) 836-5737
ctrares@newsobserver.com, Digital Acct. Mgr., The News & Observer, NC, Raleigh

Traud, Steve ....(440) 998-2323 Ext. 138
straud@starbeacon.com, Circ. Dir., The Oak Ridger, TN, Oak Ridge
straud@starbeacon.com, Dir. of Aud. Dev. (Cir.), Star Beacon, OH, Ashtabula

Traud, Steve ....(812) 464-7503
stephen.traud@courierpress.com, Dir./Circ. Sales, Evansville Courier & Press, IN, Evansville

Traugott, Michael
mtrau@umich.edu, Chair, University of Michigan, MI, Ann Arbor

Trautman, Mike ....(502) 582-4226
mtroutman@courier-journal.com, Metro Ed., The Courier-Journal, KY, Louisville

Trautmann, Mike ....(515) 284-8546
mtrautmann@dmreg.com, Content Strategist , The Des Moines Register, IA, Des Moines

Trautner, Laurie
ltrautner@thehawkeye.com, Adv. Mgr., Classified, The Hawk Eye, IA, Burlington

Travin, Michael
michaelt@resident.com, Adv. Mgr., Midtown Resident, NY, New York

Travin, Michael
mtravin@resident.com, Pub., Upper East Side Resident, NY, New York

Travin, Michael
michaelt@incompassoutdoor.com, Co-Pub., Upper West Side Resident, NY, New York

Travis, Greg
editor@murrayledger.com, Managing Ed., The Murray Ledger & Times, KY, Murray

Traxler, Buck
buck@theindependentobserver.com, Ed., Independent Observer, MT, Conrad

Trayes, Edward
trayes@temple.edu, Prof./Dir., MJ Prog./Dir., Photojournalism seq., Temple University, PA, Philadelphia

Traylor, Catey......................(989) 774-3493
editor@cm-life.com, Editor, 2013-2014, Central Michigan University, MI, Mount Pleasant

Traylor, Hattie
hatraylor@mtsu.edu, Academic Advisor, Middle Tennessee State University, TN, Murfreesboro

Traynor, Michael
michael.traynor@blufftontoday.com, Pub., Bluffton Today, SC, Bluffton

Traynor, Michael
michael.traynor@savannahnow.com, Pub., Savannah Morning News, GA, Savannah

Treadway, Bobbie......................(812) 331-4206
btreadway@heraldt.com , The Herald Times, IN, Bloomington

Treadwell, Jaine ....(334) 670-6301
jaine.treadwell@troymessenger.com, Features Ed., The Troy Messenger, AL, Troy

Treadwell, Kent ....(405) 475-3311
ktreadwell@opubco.com, Financial Mgr., The

Oklahoman, OK, Oklahoma City

Treadwell, Michael .... (256) 840-3000 ext 115
htreadwell@sandmountainreporter.com, Managing Editor, Sand Mountain Reporter, AL, Albertville

Treanor, Pat............................(626) 351-8184
Owner, Paste-Up Supply, CA, Temple City

Trebilcock, Gary L. ....(330) 539-5433
President, Litco International, Inc., OH, Vienna

Trebisovsky, Barbara ....(612) 278-0240
barbaratrebisovsky@mna.org, Asst. Exec. Dir., Minnesota Newspaper Association, MN, Minneapolis

Trebuchon, Gail
gailt@thecolumbiastar.com, Adv. Mgr., The Columbia Star, SC, Columbia

Tredway, Joyce
jtredway@lawdailyrecord.com, Circ. Mgr., Daily Record, IL, Lawrenceville

Tredway, Wendy
wendy@thenews-journal.com, Sales, The News-Journal, NC, Raeford

Treece, Jenny ....(775) 283-5570
jtreece@sierranevadmedia.com, Bus. Dev. Mgr., Nevada Appeal, NV, Carson City

Trefcer, Jackie
jackie@apopkachief.fdn.com, Mktg. & Ad. Dir., Apopka Chief (The), FL, Apopka

Trefethen, Bill ....(978) 338-2640
btrefethen@salemnews.com, Retail Adv. Mgr., The Salem News, MA, Beverly

Trefethen, Bill ....(978) 961-3161
btrefethen@newburyportnews.com, Adv. Mgr. , The Daily News, MA, Newburyport

Treichler, Bruce
btreichler@acnpapers.com, Pub., Monticello Times, MN, Monticello

Treichler, Bruce
information@monticellotimes.com, Pub., Monticello Shopper, MN, Monticello

Treinen, Mark......................(715) 845-0655
mtreinen@wdhprint.com, Exec. Ed., The Wausau Daily Herald, WI, Wausau

Treise, Debbie ....(352) 392-6557
dtreise@jou.ufl.edu, Prof./Assoc. Dean, Grad. Studies/Research/Al and Effie Flanagan Prof. in Journalism & Communication, University of Florida, FL, Gainesville

Trejo, Anthony ....(469) 977-3696
atrejo@aldiatx.com, Online Ed., Al Dia, TX, Dallas

Tremaine, Kelly ....(860) 495-8277
ktremaine@thewesterlysun.com, Ass. Pub. , The Express, CT, Pawcatuck

Tremaine, Kelly ....(860) 495-8277
ktremaine@thewesterlysun.com, Display Adv. Dir., New Haven Register, CT, New Haven
ktremaine@thewesterlysun.com, Associate Publisher , The Westerly Sun, CT, Pawcatuck

Tremaine, Kelly ....(860) 495-8277
ktremaine@thewesterlysun.com, Associate Publisher, The Express, CT, Pawcatuck
ktremaine@thewesterlysun.com, Vice Pres./Adv. Dir., Wood River Press, RI, Westerly
ktremaine@thewesterlysun.com, Vice Pres./Adv. Dir., Charlestown Press, RI, Westerly

Tremaine, Pam
pam.tremaine@sunmedia.ca, Adv. Mgr., Wetaskiwin Times, AB, Wetaskiwin

Tremblay, Bob ....(508) 626-4409
robt@wickedlocal.com, Bus. Ed., Milford Daily News, MA, Milford
robt@wickedlocal.com, Bus. Ed., Metrowest Daily News, MA, Framingham

Tremblay, Hope
hopetremblay@thewestfieldnews.com, Longmeadow Ed., The Westfield News , MA,

Tryon, Thomas Lee .... (941) 361-4540
tom.tryon@heraldtribune.com, Editorial Page
Ed., Sarasota Herald-Tribune, FL, Sarasota

Tsang, Catarina
catarina@tsangseymour.com, Principal, Tsang
Seymour Design, Inc., NY, New York

Tshida, Jennifer
jennifer@thealpinesun.com, Adv. Mgr., Alpine
Sun, CA, Alpine

Tsoutsouris, Val .... (574) 224-5326
valsports@rochsent.com, Sports Ed.,
Compass, IN, Rochester
valsports@rochsent.com, Sports Ed., The
Rochester Sentinel, IN, Rochester

Tubbs, Susie
stubbs@journalnet.com, Classified Adv. Mgr.,
Idaho State Journal, ID, Pocatello

Tubbs, William F.
btubbs@northscottpress.com, Pub., The North
Scott Press, IA, Eldridge

Tubbs, William F. .... (563) 285-8111
btubbs@northscottpress.com, Pub, Eastern
Iowa Bizzzy Bee, IA, Eldridge

Tubs, Bill
adnews@netwtc.net, Adv. Mgr., Wilton-Durant
Advocate News, IA, Wilton

Tuccillo, Frederick .... (732) 223-0076, Ext. 27
ftuccillo@thecoaststar.com, Ed., The Coast
Star, NJ, Manasquan

Tuccio-Koonz, Linda .... (203) 731-3330
lkoonz@newstimes.com, Features Ed., The
News-Times, CT, Danbury

Tuccitto, Joe .... (631) 737-6020 x147
jtuccitto@flexography.org, Education Director,
Flexographic Technical Association, NY,
Bohemia

Tucibat, Sam
sam.tucibat@highland.edu, Highland Cmty.
College, IL, Freeport

Tuck, Deborah .... (252) 436-2821
dtuck@hendersondispatch.com, Adv. Dir., Daily
Dispatch, NC, Henderson

Tuck, Deborah
dtuck@hendersondispatch.com, Adv. Dir., Tri-
county Shopper, NC, Henderson

Tucker, Ben
btucker@wayneindependent.com, Advertising
Manager, The Wayne Independent, PA,
Honesdale

Tucker, Bill
btucker@edwpub.net, Editor, Edwardsville
Intelligencer, IL, Edwardsville

Tucker, Billy R. .... (478) 929-3636
publisher@seniornewsga.com, President/
Publisher, Senior News, GA, Warner Robins

Tucker, Cody .... (307) 358-2965
cody@douglas-budget.com, Office Mgr., The
Douglas Budget, WY, Douglas
cody@douglas-budget.com, Office Mgr., The
Daily Dunklin Democrat, MO, Kennett

Tucker, David .... (973) 392-1755
dtucker@starledger.com, Mng. Ed., The Star-
Ledger, NJ, Newark

Tucker, Diane Straus .... (202) 955-9010
dstraustucker@washingtonmonthly.com,
Publisher, Washington Monthly LLC,
Washington

Tucker, John
john.tucker@lakesunonline.com, Pub., Lake
Sun Leader, MO, Camdenton

Tucker, John
jtucker@gatehousemedia.com, Pub., The
Gurdon Times, AR, Arkadelphia

Tucker, Jordan .... (901) 529-2217
jordan.tucker@commercialappeal.com, Client
Strategy Manager, The Commercial Appeal,
TN, Memphis

Tucker, Larry .... (903) 763-4522

news@woodcountymonitor.com, News Editor,
Wood County Monitor, TX, Quitman

Tucker, Liz. .... (845) 887-5200 ext. 110
lizt@sc-democrat.com, Advertising Director,
Sullivan County Democrat, NY, Callicoon

Tucker, Lori .... (225) 388-0199
ltucker@theadvocate.com, Special Sections
Editor, The Advocate, LA, Baton Rouge

Tucker, Mark
mark.tucker@newhorizons.com, Vice. Pres.,
Mktg., New Horizons Computer Learning
Center, CA, Anaheim

Tucker, Marsha
chermessenger@att.net, Gen. Mgr., The
Cherokee Messenger & Republican, OK,
Cherokee

Tucker, Michael .... (406) 388-5101 x12
mtucker@belgrade-news.com, Ed., Belgrade
News, MT, Belgrade

Tucker, Michael .... (513) 768-8938
mtucker@gmti.gannett.com, Dir., Sales &
Marketing, Digital Collections, OH, Cincinnati

Tucker, Michael .... (781) 784-0932
mtucker@tuckergroup.com, Owner, The Tucker
Group, MA, Sharon

Tucker, Mike .... (814) 773-3161
mtucker@zitomedia.net, Prodn., Shop Right,
PA, Ridgway
mtucker@zitomedia.net, Production Mgr., The
Ridgway Record, PA, Ridgway

Tucker, Phillip .... (765) 342-1448 ext. 248
ptucker@reporter-times.com, District Mgr., The
Reporter Times, IN, Martinsville

Tucker, R.D. .... (209) 966-2500
rdtucker@mariposagazette.com, Pub.,
Mariposa Gazette, CA, Mariposa

Tucker, Robert M.
bob@beachbecky.com, Ed., Chilton County
News, AL, Clanton

Tucker, Robin .... (501) 372-1443
rtucker@abpg.com, Sales Dir, Little Rock
Family, AR, Little Rock

Tucker, Tim .... (618) 239-2610
ttucker@bnd.com, Adv., Belleville News-
Democrat, IL, Belleville

Tuckman, Ian .... (301) 459-5624
Circ. Mgr., Greenbelt News Review, MD,
Greenbelt

Tuermer-Lee, Kaelyn
city@theaggie.org, City Editor, University of
California, Davis, CA, Davis

Tuffin, Lois
ltuffin@mykawartha.com, Mng. Ed., Brock
Citizen, ON, Cannington

Tuffin, Lois
ltuffin@mykawartha.com, Ed. in Chief,
Peterborough This Week, ON, Peterborough

Tuffin, Lois .... (705) 749-3383
ltuffin@mykawartha.com, Ed. in Chief,
Kawartha Lakes This Week, ON, Lindsay
ltuffin@mykawartha.com, Ed-In-Chief,
Metroland Media Group Ltd., ON,
Mississauga

Tuggle, Charles A. .... (919) 962-5694
Prof., University of North Carolina, NC, Chapel
Hill

Tuley, Milissa .... (317) 624-4430
mtuley@hspa.com, Communications
Specialist, Hoosier State Press Association,
IN, Indianapolis

Tuli, Suneet
info@widecom.com, Vice Pres., Sales/Mktg.,
WideCom Group, Inc., NY, Buffalo

Tull, Chelsea
ads@spotlightnews.net, Graphic Designer, The
South County Spotlight, OR, Scappoose

Tullis, Candice .... (316) 978-6905
ctullis@wichitaeagle.com, Wichita State Univ.,

KS, Wichita

Tullos, Pat. .... (318) 281-4421
ptullos@bastropenterprise.com, Adv. Dir., The
Daily Citizen, AR, Searcy
ptullos@bastropenterprise.com, Adv. Sales,
Bastrop Daily Enterprise, LA, Bastrop

Tully, Mac .... (303) 954-5050
mtully@denverpost.com, Pub. Chief Exec.
Officer, The Denver Post, CO, Denver

Tully, Marcus
mtully@mykawartha.com, News Ed., Kawartha
Lakes This Week, ON, Lindsay

Tuma, David
david@beltonjournal.com, Pub., The Belton
Journal, TX, Belton

Tune, Amy. .... (580) 922-4296
dcpub@pldi.net, Asst. Ed & Office Mgr, The
Dewey County Record, OK, Seiling

Tungate, Anna .... (317) 398-1271
atungate@shelbynews.com, Single Copy Mgr.,
The Shelbyville News, IN, Shelbyville

Tungett, Lynne
news@newportthisweek.net, Pub., Newport
This Week, RI, Newport

Tunke, Adrienne
adrienne.tunke@mcall.com, Nat'l Adv. Mgr.,
The Morning Call, PA, Allentown

Tunke, Chris .... (403) 528-5766
ctunke@medicinehatnews.com, National &
Multi-Market Sales, Medicine Hat News, AB,
Medicine Hat
ctunke@medicinehatnews.com, Multi-Market/
National Adv. Sales, The Lethbridge Herald,
AB, Lethbridge

Tupa, Mike
mtupa@examiner-enterprise.com, Sports Ed.,
Examiner-Enterprise, OK, Bartlesville

Turbeville, Kevin
kturbeville@jonesborosun.com, Sports Ed.,
The Jonesboro Sun, AR, Jonesboro

Turbyfill, Diane .... (704) 669-3334
dturbyfill@shelbystar.com, managing editor,
The Star, NC, Shelby

Turck, Andrew
news@bighorncountynews.com, Ed., Big Horn
County News, MT, Hardin

Turcotte, Alain
alain.turcotte@lenouvelliste.qc.ca, Pres./Ed.,
Le Nouvelliste, QC, Trois-Rivieres

Turcotte, Claudia
claudia.turcotte@transcontinental.ca, Sales
manager, L'etoile Du Lac, QC, Roberval

Turcotte, Rita .... (413) 585-5288
rturcotte@gazettenet.com, Adv. Prodn. Mgr.,
Daily Hampshire Gazette, MA, Northampton

Turczyn, Coury .... (865) 342-6068
coury@metropulse.com, Ed., Metro Pulse, TN,
Knoxville

Tures, John
jtures@lagrange.edu, Advisor, LaGrange
College, GA, Lagrange

Turgeon, Gerry .... (403) 250-4172
gturgeon@calgaryherald.com, Dist. Mgr. ,
Calgary Herald, AB, Calgary

Turgeon, Kathy
classified@mininickel.com, Gen. Mgr., Mini
Nickle Classifieds, MT, Bozeman

Turk, Jeff .... ext. 234
jturk@sharonherald.com, Religion Ed., The
Herald, PA, Sharon

Turley, Patrick H.
wcnews@turley.com, Pub., West County News,
MA, Shelburne Falls

Turley, Patrick H.
ads@turley.com, Pub., Shopping Guide, MA,
Palmer

Turley, Patrick H.

editorial@turley.com, Pub., The Register, MA,
Wilbraham

Turley, Patrick H.
ads@turley.com, Pub., Buy Line, MA, Palmer

Turley, Patrick H.
pturley@turley.com, Pub., Agawam Advertiser
News, MA, Feeding Hills

Turley, Patrick H.
editorial@turley.com, Pub., Country Journal,
MA, Huntington

Turley, Patrick H.
pturley@turley.com, Pub., The Chicopee
Register, MA, Chicopee

Turley, Patrick H.
classifieds@turley.com, Owner, Barre Gazette,
MA, Barre

Turley, Patrick H.
editorial@turley.com, Pres., Turley Publications,
Inc., MA, Palmer

Turley, Patrick H.
cbennett@turley.com, Pub., Wilbraham-
Hampden Times, MA, Wilbraham

Turley, Patrick H.
pturley@turley.com, Pub., The Holyoke Sun,
MA, Chicopee

Turnbloom, Lucas .... (858) 490-8276
art@diocese-sdiego.org, Art Dir., The Southern
Cross, CA, San Diego

Turner, Alan .... (601) 364-1021
alan.turner@msbusiness.com, Mississippi
Business Journal, MS, Jackson

Turner, Anita
sales1@grenadastar.com, Adv. Sales, Grenada
Star, MS, Grenada

Turner, Carmen .... (318) 281-2699
cturner@bastropenterprise.com, Circ. Mgr.,
Bastrop Daily Enterprise, LA, Bastrop

Turner, Charles
turnercc@jmu.edu, Prof., James Madison
University, VA, Harrisonburg

Turner, Corey
cturner@hcnonline.com, Pub/Ad Dir, Dayton
News, TX, Conroe

Turner, Corey .... (281) 378-1071
cturner@hcnonline.com, Gen. Sales Mgr.,
Atascocita Observer, TX, Conroe
cturner@hcnonline.com, Pub/Ad Dir, East
Montgomery County Observer, TX, Humble
cturner@hcnonline.com, Gen. Sales Mgr.,
Humble Observer, TX, Conroe
cturner@hcnonline.com, Gen. Sales Mgr.,
Kingwood Observer, TX, Conroe
cturner@hcnonline.com, Gen. Sales Mgr., Lake
Houston Observer, TX, Conroe
cturner@hcnonline.com, Gen. Sales Mgr., The
Courier of Montgomery County, TX, Conroe

Turner, Corey
cturner@hcnonline.com, Pub/Ad Dir, Eastex
Advocate, TX, Cleveland

Turner, Dudley B.
dbturner@uakron.edu, Dir., University of
Akron, OH, Akron

Turner, Jerry
news@thesouthalabamian.com, Pub., The
South Alabamian, AL, Jackson

Turner, Jim
jimturner@loganjournal.com, The Logan
Journal, KY, Russellville

Turner, Joe
fayette1866@aol.com, Office Manager, Fayette
Chronicle, MS, Fayette

Turner, Julie
editor@lebanondailyrecord.com, Ed., The
Lebanon Daily Record, MO, Lebanon

Turner, K.A.
kturner@al.com, Bus./Finance Ed., Press-
Register, AL, Mobile

Turner, Kate .... (613) 279-3150

info@frontenacnews.ca, Advertising sales rep, The Frontenac News, ON, Sharbot Lake

Turner, Lynne
editor@mountforest.com, Ed., The Mount Forest Confederate, ON, Mount Forest

Turner, Marlene
bvalnews@qwestoffice.net, Owner,Publisher, Buckeye Valley News, AZ, Buckeye

Turner, Martha........................(202) 898-4825
Accounting, Press Associates, Inc., Washington

Turner, Molly..........................(312) 553-3191
mturner@ccc.edu, Faculty Advisor, Harold Washington College, IL, Chicago

Turner, Niki...............................(970) 878-4017
editor@theheraldtimes.com, Editor/Publisher, The Rio Blanco Herald Times, CO, Meeker

Turner, Nikki
niki@theheraldtimes.com, Ed., The Rio Blanco Herald Times, CO, Meeker

Turner, Pat
pat@theheraldtimes.com, Prod. Mgr., Melrose Beacon, MN, Melrose
pat@theheraldtimes.com, Adv. Acct. Exec., The Rio Blanco Herald Times, CO, Meeker

Turner, Robert
bturner@bradenton.com, Pub., Bradenton Herald, FL, Bradenton
bturner@bradenton.com, Editor&Publisher, The County Record, FL, Blountstown

Turner, Ronnie
ronnie.turner@chron.com, Univ. of Houston, TX, Houston

Turner, Russell
herald@tds.net, Ed., Greene County Herald, MS, Leakesville

Turner, Rusty..........................(479) 872-5001
rturner@nwaonline.net, Pub., Washington County Enterprise-Leader, AR, Farmington
rturner@nwaonline.net, Pub., Westside Eagle Observer, AR, Siloam Springs

Turner, Ryan
rturner@lethbridgeherald.com, Prod. & Systems Mgr., The Lethbridge Herald, AB, Lethbridge

Turner, Sally
aadom@eiu.edu, Assoc. Prof./Advisor, Yearbook, Eastern Illinois University, IL, Charleston

Turner, Scott
sturner@co.yellowstone.mt.gov, Editor & Publisher, Billings Times, MT, Billings

Turner, Scott
editorial@dchieftain.com, Pub./Ed. , El Defensor Chieftain, NM, Socorro

Turner, Scott
marketing@bowebellhowell.com, Vice Pres., Sales, Bowe Bell + Howell, NC, Durham

Turner, Steven
sturner@dnronline.com, Adv. Dir., Daily News-Record, VA, Harrisonburg

Turner, Tim
t.turner@afdb.org, Vice Pres./Gen. Mgr., Dow Jones Newswires - New York, NY, New York

Turner, Willis..........................(312) 893-0751
willis.turner@smei.org, Pres./CEO, Sales and Marketing Executives International, WA, Sumas

Turns, Alan
adsales@chestercounty.com, Adv. Mgr., Chester County Press, PA, West Grove

Turpin, Craig
cturpin@njnpublishing.com, Exec. Ed., The Warren Reporter, NJ, Flemington

Turpin, Craig
news@hcdemocrat.com, Exec. Ed., Star-Gazette, NJ, Flemington

Turro, Lyle a.....................(815) 937-3376

lturro@daily-journal.com, Sr. Sales Mgr., The Daily Journal, IL, Kankakee

Turtle, Charlotte........................(270) 745-3055
charlotte.turtle@wku.edu, Adviser, Talisman, Western Kentucky University, KY, Bowling Green

Tuthill, John T................(631) 475-1000 ext. 25
jttuthill3@optonline.net, Pub., Suffolk County News, NY, Patchogue

Tuthill, John T................(631) 475-1000, ext. 28
ttlia@optonline.net, Pub., Islip Bulletin, NY, Patchogue

Tuthill, John T................(631) 475-1000, ext. 28
advletters@optonline.com, Pub., Long Island Advance, NY, Patchogue

Tuthill, Terry.................(631) 475-1000 ext. 28
ttlia@optonline.net, Asst. Pub., Long Island Advance, NY, Patchogue
ttlia@optonline.net, Asst. Pub., Islip Bulletin, NY, Patchogue

Tutor, Phillip
ptutor@annistonstar.com, Commentary Ed., The Anniston Star, AL, Anniston

Tutt, Rosemary
rtutt@flagler.edu, Asst. Prof., Flagler College, FL, Saint Augustine

Tutterow, Ray
erads2@davie-enterprise.com, Adv. Dir., Davie County Enterprise-Record, NC, Mocksville

Tuttle, Amanda........................(614) 236-6011
Capital Univ. Law School, OH, Columbus

Tuttle, Mary...........................(812) 206-2133
mary.tuttle@newsandtribune.com, Adv. Mgr., News and Tribune, IN, Jeffersonville
mary.tuttle@newsandtribune.com, Adv. Mgr., Tribune, IN, New Albany

Tuttle, Regan
norwoodpost@yahoo.com, Ed., The Norwood Post, CO, Telluride

Tuttle, Roberta W.
rtuttle@catholictranscript.org, Mng. Ed., The Catholic Transcript, CT, Bloomfield

Tuz, Susan
stuz@newstimes.com, Ed. Dept., The News-Times, CT, Danbury

Tweddle, Stephen.....................(340) 778-9246
stevetweddle@cwc4webs.com, Pres., Canadian Web Consultants Ltd., ON, Port Sydney
stevetweddle@cwc4webs.com, Pres., Canadian Web Consultants Ltd., Christiansted

Tweedie, Sanford
tweedie@rowan.edu, Assoc. Prof., Rowan Univ., NJ, Glassboro

Twieg, Daniel
editor@insideuab.com, Ed. in Chief, Univ. of Alabama at Birmingham, AL, Birmingham

Twitty, Stephanie
stwitty@newsvirginian.com, Classifieds Adv. Mgr., The News Virginian, VA, Waynesboro

Tycz, Rebecca
times@gwtc.net, Pub./Adv. Dir., Springfield Times, SD, Springfield
times@gwtc.net, Pub., Ed., Tribune & Register, SD, Tyndall

Tyer, Brad.......................(406) 543-6609 x107
btyer@missoulanews.com, Editor, Missoula Independent, MT, Missoula

Tyer, Brad.......................(406) 543-6609 x107
editor@missoulanews.com, Editor, Missoula Independent, MT, Missoula

Tyers, William
biz@telegraph-nh.com, Prodn. Mgr., The Telegraph Publishing Co., NH, Hudson

Tykwinski, Becky...........(507) 359-2091 ext. 170
Adv. Mgr., New Ulm Shopper/post Review, MN, New Ulm

Tyler, David....................(315) 434-8889 x 302
dtyler@eaglenewsonline.com, Pres./Pub., Eagle Newspapers, NY, Syracuse
dtyler@eaglenewsonline.com, The Eagle, NY, Syracuse
dtyler@eaglenewsonline.com, Pres./Pub., The Madison Eagle, NY, Canastota
dtyler@eaglenewsonline.com, Adv. Mgr., Marcellus Observer, NY, Skaneateles
dtyler@eaglenewsonline.com, Pub., The Eagle, VT, Middlebury
dtyler@eaglenewsonline.com, Pub., Cazenovia Republican, NY, Syracuse
dtyler@eaglenewsonline.com, Pub., Eagle Bulletin, NY, Syracuse
dtyler@eaglenewsonline.com, Pub., Eagle Star Review, NY, Syracuse
dtyler@eaglenewsonline.com, Pub., Skaneateles Press, NY, Syracuse

Tyler, Gary.............................(502) 498-1946
gtyler@bizjournals.com, Adv. Dir., Louisville Business First, KY, Louisville

Tyler, Gary
gary.tyler@sj-r.com, Adv. Dir., Springfield Advertiser, IL, Springfield

Tyler, Scott
styler@palestineherald.com, Sports Ed., Palestine Herald-Press, TX, Palestine

Tyler , Dave.................(315) 434-8889 ext. 302
dtyler@eaglenewsonline.com, Pub. , Baldwinsville Messenger, NY, Syracuse

Tyler , David
dtyler@eaglenewsonline.com, Pub. , Eagle Observer, NY, Syracuse

Tym, Tina...............................(570) 628-6250
ttym@republicanherald.com, Features Ed., The Republican-Herald, PA, Pottsville

Tymon, Vicki
vicki@dailyjm.com, Graphics Coord., Daily Journal/Messenger, SC, Seneca

Tynan, Jack...........................(705) 746-2104
editor@parrysound.com, Mng. Ed., Parry Sound North Star, ON, Parry Sound

Tynan, Jack...........................(705) 789-5541
jtynan@metrolandnorthmedia.com, Huntsville Forester, ON, Huntsville

Tynan, Jack........................ (705) 789-5541
jtynan@metrolandnorthmedia.com, Adv. , The Gravenhurst Banner, ON, Gravenhurst

Tyner, Cindy...........................(765) 724-4469
alextribune@elwoodpublishing.com, Adv. Director, Alexandria Times-Tribune, IN, Elwood

Tyrrell, Beck
beckt@independentmail.com, Sales Support & Pagination, Anderson Independent-Mail, SC, Anderson

Tyrrell, Paul...........................(918) 581-8326
paul.tyrrell@tulsaworld.com, City editor, Tulsa World, OK, Tulsa

Tyson, Beckie..........................(479) 641-7161
news@atkinschronicle.com, Managing. Ed., Atkins Chronicle, AR, Atkins

Tyson, Ginnie.........................(479) 641-7161
news@atkinschronicle.com, Pub., Atkins Chronicle, AR, Atkins

Tyson, Melissa........................(785) 762-5000
m.tyson@thedailyunion.net, Publisher/ Advertising Manager, The Daily Union, KS, Junction City

Tyson, Van A...........................(479) 641-7161
news@atkinschronicle.com, Ed., Atkins Chronicle, AR, Atkins

Tyson, Van A.
dovertimes@hotmail.com, Pub., The Dover Times, AR, Atkins

Tytell, Lon
ads@wvdispatch.com, Adv. Mgr., Warwick Valley Dispatch, NY, Warwick

Tywoniuk, Barb...............(780) 842-4465 ext.116

barb@starnews.ca, Graphic Design Dept. Manager, Wainwright Star Edge, AB, Wainwright

U

Ubert, Ken
ubertk@discoverhometown.com, Pres./Pub., West Bend Express News, WI, Brown Deer
ubertk@discoverhometown.com, Pres./Pub., West Allis Express News, WI, Brown Deer
ubertk@discoverhometown.com, Pres./Pub., Sussex Express News, WI, Brown Deer
ubertk@discoverhometown.com, Pres./Pub., Slinger Express News, WI, Brown Deer
ubertk@discoverhometown.com, Pres./Pub., Milwaukee Express News, WI, Brown Deer
ubertk@discoverhometown.com, Pres./Pub., Menomonee Falls Express News, WI, Brown Deer
ubertk@discoverhometown.com, Pres./Pub., Jackson Express News, WI, Brown Deer
ubertk@discoverhometown.com, Pres./Pub., Hartford Express News, WI, Brown Deer
ubertk@discoverhometown.com, Pres./Pub., Germantown Express News, WI, Brown Deer
ubertk@discoverhometown.com, Pres./Pub., Wauwatosa Express News, WI, Brown Deer

Ude, Julie
ude@decorahnewspapers.com, Adv. Mgr., Decorah Public Opinion, IA, Decorah

Udero, Danny..............(575) 538-5893 ext. 5804
dudero@scsun-news.com, Sports Ed., Silver City Sun-News, NM, Silver City

Udo-O'Malley, Annabelle
events@aaja.org, Contact, Asian American Journalists Association, CA, San Francisco

Uebel, Cecilia........................(915) 546-6250
cuebel@elpasotimes.com, Adv. Dir. , El Paso Times, TX, El Paso
cuebel@elpasotimes.com, Senior VP of Advertising and Marketing, El Paso y Mas, TX, El Paso

Ueno, Katz
editor@entertainmenttoday.net, Pub., Entertainment Today Inc, CA, Los Angeles

Uffelman, Fred
khoyt@mediaonepa.com, Pub., The Evening Sun, PA, Hanover

Uffelman, Fred
news@eveningsun.com, Pub., Sun Marketplace, PA, Hanover
news@eveningsun.com, Pres./Pub., The York Dispatch, PA, York

Ugalde, Ana Maria....................(708) 652-6397
anamaria@eldianews.com, Ed., El Dia, IL, Cicero

Ugast, Tom
tom_ugast@harte-hanks.com, Gen. Mgr., Harte-Hanks, MD, Baltimore

Uhrich, Kevin
kevinu@pasadenaweekly.com, Ed., Pasadena Weekly, CA, Pasadena

Ukura, Kim...........................(320) 589-2525
kukura@morrissuntribune.com, Ed., Morris Sun Tribune, MN, Morris

Ulibarri, Romelia
classsales@lavozcolorado.com, Sales Mgr., La Voz Newspaper, CO, Denver
classsales@lavozcolorado.com, Classified Mgr., La Voz Bilingue, CO, Thornton

Ulicne, Luann
lulicne@altoonamirror.com, Nat'l/Classifieds Adv. Mgr., Altoona Mirror, PA, Altoona

Ulku, Jay
julku@forumcomm.com, News Ed., Bus., InForum, ND, Fargo

Ullmann, Mary
titonkatopic@netins.net, Ed., Titonka Topic, IA, Titonka

Ulloth, Dana

dulloth@bloomu.edu, Chair, Bloomsburg University - The Voice, PA, Bloomsburg

Ullrich, Tammi ....(518) 828-1616
tullrich@registerstar.com, Personnel Administrator, The Ravena News-Herald, NY, Ravena

Ullrich, Tammi ....(518) 828-1616 ext. 2402
tullrich@registerstar.com, Admin./Asst.to the Pub., The Daily Mail, NY, Hudson

Ullrich, Tammi ....(518) 828-1616 Ext. 2402
tullrich@registerstar.com, HR/Business Mgr., Register-Star, NY, Hudson

Ullyot, Russ
russ.ullyot@sunmedia.ca, Ed, Bow Valley Crag & Canyon, AB, Banff
russ.ullyot@sunmedia.ca, Editor(print), Banff Crag & Canyon OOB* (2013), AB, Banff

Ulm, Gerry ....(530) 344-5051
gulm@mtdemocrat.net, Circ. Mgr., Mountain Democrat, CA, Placerville

Ulman, Kart
toimetus@vabaeestisona.com, Ed., Vaba Eesti Sona, NY, New York

Ulmans, Kart
talitus@vabaeestisona.com, Ed., Free Estonian Word, NY, New York

Uloa, Sylvia...........................(575) 541-5438
sulloa@lcsun-news.com, Mng. Ed., Las Cruces Sun-News, NM, Las Cruces

Ulrich, Ronald........................(202) 334-5289
Ronald.Ulrich@washpost.com, Adv, Washington Post Express, DC, Washington

Umholtz, Josh
joshu@neighbornews.com, Pub., Independence Daily Reporter, KS, Independence

Umphrey, G.L...........................(800) 765-5377
bestroll@aol.com, Pres., Republic Roller Corp., MI, Three Rivers

Underberg, Larry
lunderberg@semo.edu, Assoc. Prof., Southeast Missouri State University, MO, Cape Girardeau

Underwood, Craig ....(516) 674-2500
cunderwood@gi.konicaminolta.us, Rgl. Mgr., Konica Minolta Business Solutions, AL, Mobile

Underwood, Roger...................(850) 747-5049
runderwood@pcnh.com, The News Herald, FL, Panama City

Underwood, Scott...................(765) 640-4845
scott.underwood@heraldbulletin.com, Ed., The Herald Bulletin, IN, Anderson

Ungar, Randi
rungar@starledger.com, Director, The Star-Ledger, NJ, Newark

Ungaro, Joe.........................(973) 428-6624
jungaro@gannettnj.com, General Manager/ Editor, Daily Record, NJ, Parsippany

Unger, David S. ....(201) 798-7800 ext. 601
dunger@hudsonreporter.com, Co-Pub., Bayonne Community News, NJ, Bayonne
dunger@hudsonreporter.com, Adv. Mgr., Mid Week Reporter (OOB), NJ, Hoboken
dunger@hudsonreporter.com, Pub., The Hoboken Reporter, NJ, Bayonne
dunger@hudsonreporter.com, Co-Pub., West New York/Union City Reporter, NJ, Hoboken
dunger@hudsonreporter.com, Pub., The North Bergen Reporter, NJ, Bayonne
dunger@hudsonreporter.com, Co-Pub, Secaucus Reporter, NJ, Bayonne
dunger@hudsonreporter.com, Adv. Dir., Mr., NJ, Bayonne
dunger@hudsonreporter.com, Co-Pub./Adv. Dir., Hudson Reporter Associates, Lp, NJ, Bayonne
dunger@hudsonreporter.com, Co-Pub., The Weehawken Reporter, NJ, Bayonne

Unger, Dawn.........................(708) 456-0300

Triton College, IL, River Grove

Unger, Robert
ungerr@umkc.edu, Prof., University of Missouri-Kansas City, MO, Kansas City

Ungerman Levy, Mellisa
mungermanlevy@mnpubs.com, Adv. Sales Mgr., Good Age, MN, Minneapolis

Ungs-Sogaard, Mary ....(563) 875-7131
mungs-sogaard@wcinet.com, Publisher, Dyersville Commercial, IA, Dyersville

Ungs-Sogaard, Mary
, Publisher/General Manager, Eastern Iowa Shopping News, IA, Dyersville

Ungs-Sogaard, Mary ....(563) 875-7131
mungs-sogaard@wcinet.com, Publisher, Cascade Pioneer, IA, Cascade

Unknown, Unknown ....(312) 503-4714
Northwestern Univ. School of Law, IL, Chicago

Unks, Walter..........................(336) 727-7250
wunks@wsjournal.com, Photo Editor, Winston-Salem Journal, NC, Winston Salem

Unsworth, Renee
renee.unsworth@staugustine.com, Compass Ed., The St. Augustine Record, FL, Saint Augustine

Uphues, Bob
buphues@wjinc.com, Ed., Landmark, IL, Oak Park

Upshaw, Lynn B.
upshaw@upshawmarketing.com, Principal, Upshaw & Associates, CA, Kentfield

Uptain, Greg
guptain@yourjournal.com, Ed., Illinois Suburban Journals, IL, Collinsville
guptain@yourjournal.com, Ed., St. Charles County Suburban Journals, IL, Collinsville

Upton, Chris ....(865) 992-3392
enewspaper@aol.com, Pub., The Union News Leader, TN, Maynardville

Upton, Rory........................(631) 475-1000 x15
Display Adv. Mgr., Long Island Advance, NY, Patchogue

Uranga, Rachel ....(562) 499-1263
rachel.uranga@langnews.com, Opinion/Ed, Press-Telegram, CA, Long Beach

Urayama, Yoshiko
emailishimpo@mc.net, Pub., Chicago Shimpo, IL, Chicago

Urban, Grant................(620) 442-4200 ext. 121
lifestyles@arkcity.net, Lifestyle/Action Ed., The Arkansas City Traveler, KS, Arkansas City

Urban, Jerry
jurban@paradisepost.com, Adv. Dir., Paradise Post, CA, Paradise

Urban, Ryan
editor@thechetekalert.com, News Ed., The Chetek Alert, WI, Chetek

Urbanec, Melissa
melissa@wayneherald.com, Gen. Mgr., The Wayne Herald, NE, Wayne

Urbanovsky, Chris
curbanovsky@sanmarcosrecord.com, Production Dir., San Marcos Daily Record, TX, San Marcos

Urbanski, Stephen ....(304) 293-6797
steve.urbanski@mail.wvu.edu, Director of Graduate Studies/Associate Professor, West Virginia University, WV, Morgantown

Urbigkeit, Ruth
rangerads@wyoming.com, Adv. Coord., The Riverton Ranger, WY, Riverton

Urciolo, Molly
molly.urciolo@washpost.com, Partner Program Manager, The Washington Post, DC, Washington

Urlaub, Mike...........................ext. 230
Prodn. Mgr., The News-Record, WY, Gillette

Urquhart, Bruce ....(519) 537-2341 ext. 248
bruce.urquhart@sunmedia.ca, Ed., Woodstock Sentinel-Review, ON, Woodstock

Urquhart, Bruce ....(519) 271-2220 ext. 202
bruce.urquhart@sunmedia.ca, Mng. Ed., The Stratford Beacon Herald, ON, Stratford

Ursery, Mike ....(600) 248-5223
mursery@fayettenews.com, Sports Editor, Fayette Advertiser, MO, Fayette

Ursini, Lisa
lursini@yourdailyglobe.com, Publisher, Daily Globe, Inc., MI, Ironwood

Ursprung, Kathy
kursprung@thedalleschronicle.com, Exec. Ed., The Dalles Daily Chronicle, OR, The Dalles

Ursua, Stephanie ....(661) 823-6361
sursua@tehachapinews.com, Bus. Mgr, Tehachapi News, CA, Tehachapi

Uruena, Eduardo ....(416) 531-2495
director@diarioelpopular.com, Mng. Ed., El Popular, ON, Toronto

Utecht, Jane
Jane@MadisonDailyLeader.com, Reporter, The Madison Daily Leader, SD, Madison

Uthe, Lloyd
lloyd@michelscom.com, General Manager, Ad Venture Classifieds, SD, Sioux Falls

Utley, Cathi
hacmgr@lcs.net, Gen. Mgr., The Hermann Advertiser-Courier, MO, Hermann

Utter, John
jutter@gannett.com, Retail Adv. Mgr., Green Sheet, MI, Howell

Uus, Peter............................ext. 106
puus@fairfieldweekly.com, Prodn. Mgr., Hartford Courant, CT, Hartford
puus@fairfieldweekly.com, Prodn. Mgr., Hartford Advocate, CT, Hartford

Uzal, Jose
ellatino@msn.com, Ed., El Latino Newspaper, FL, West Palm Beach

Uzkan, Sarp...........................(312) 222-6541
sarp@tribpub.com, Dir., Technical Opns./Help Desk, Chicago Tribune, IL, Chicago

V

Vacar, Vaughn ....ext. 244
vvacar@timesonline.com, Circ. Mgr., Mktg., Beaver County Times, PA, Beaver

Vaccarelli, Rick
rvaccarelli@bizjournals.com, Adv. Dir., Pittsburgh Business Times, PA, Pittsburgh

Vacchiano, Thomas J.
info@xrite.com, Pres./CEO/COO, X-Rite Inc., MI, Grand Rapids

Vachon, Dave...........(613) 962-9171 ext. 546226
dave.vachon@sunmedia.ca, News Ed. , The County Weekly News, ON, Picton

Vachon, Tom...........................(603) 323-5077
tvachon@merrsoft.com, Owner, Merrimac Software Associates, NH, South Tamworth

Vaci, Kathy......................(440) 576-9125 x 107
tribune@gazettenews.com, Editor, Lake County Tribune, OH, Jefferson

Vada, Snider..........................(316) 283-5231
vsnider@southwind.net, This Side of 60, North Newton

Vadner , Nicole ....(763) 241-3677
nicole.vadner@ecm-inc.com , Advertising Sales Rep, Star News, MN, Elk River

Vadnie, Michael
mvadnie@stcloudstate.edu, Prof./Coord., News Editorial, St. Cloud State University, MN, Saint Cloud

Vagun, Alice ....(608) 257-4712
editor@badgerherald.com, Editor-in-Chief,

University of Wisconsin Madison, WI, Madison

Vahey, Linda
lindav@cnc.com, Cir. Mgr., Georgetown Record, MA, Danvers

Vahlenkamp, John ....(303) 776-2244 ext. 239
jvahlenkamp@times-call.com, Ed., Longmont Weekly (OOB), CO, Longmont
jvahlenkamp@times-call.com, Mng. Ed., Longmont Times-Call, CO, Longmont

Vaillancourt, Sylvie ....(819) 623-7374
svaillancourt@lecourant.ca, Journal Le Courant Des Hautes-laurentides, QC, Mont-Laurier

Valade, Mary ....(705) 674-5271 ext. 271
Office Mgr., The Sudbury Star, ON, Sudbury

Valden, Diane
dvalden@columbiapaper.com, Associate Ed., The Columbia Paper, NY, Ghent

Valdes, Christina
cvaldes@parkecountysentinel.com, Circ. Mgr., Parke County Sentinel, IN, Rockville

Valdez, Carmen ....(626) 584-5430
Fuller Theological Seminary, CA, Pasadena

Valdez, Linda ....(520) 884-0148
Linda.Valdez@ArizonaRepublic.com, The Arizona Republic, AZ, Phoenix

Valdez, Monica
graphics@warrensentinel.com, Prodn. Mgr./ Graphics, Warren Sentinel, WY, Cheyenne

Valentine, Brenda
crosbycountynews@windstream.net, Adv. Dir., Crosby County News, TX, Ralls

Valentine, Donna ....(409) 828-2836
Advertising Director, The Beaumont Enterprise, TX, Beaumont

Valentine, Gerald P.
jvalentine@mpival.com, Vice Pres., Management Planning, Inc., NJ, Princeton

Valentine, Harry E.
dispatch@claycenter.com, Pub., Clay Center Saver, KS, Clay Center

Valentine, Harry E. ....(785) 632-2127
dispatch@claycenter.com, Pres./Pub./ Treasurer, The Clay Center Dispatch, KS, Clay Center

Valentine, Michael
michael.valentine@ubs.com, Vice Pres., HR, The New York Times, NY, New York

Valentine, Troy
troyv@ctimes.biz, Adv. Mgr., Area Advertiser, IA, Cherokee

Valentine, Troy
troyv@ctimes.biz, Assc. Pub./Adv. Mgr., Cherokee Chronicle Times, IA, Cherokee

Valentine-Marsh, Caron
caron@aaobserver.com, Creative Director, Ann Arbor Observer, MI, Ann Arbor

Valentini, Kyle
kvalentini@alonovus.com, Ed, The Bargain Hunter - Tuscarawas, OH, Millersburg
kvalentini@alonovus.com, Ed, Tuscarawas Bargain Hunter, OH, Millersburg

Valenze, Jennifer
circulation@denpubs.com, Circ. Mgr., The Eagle, VT, Middlebury

Valenzuela, Pamela
info@womcom.org, Exec. Dir., Association for Women in Communications, VA, Alexandria

Valero, Ralph..........................(888) 309-0639
ralph@miracomcomputer.com, Field Application Engineer, Miracom Computer Corp., NY, Eastchester

Valeskini, Gerhard.........................875 3333
gerhard.valeskini@kleinezeitung.at, Adv. Dir., KLEINE ZEITUNG, 8010 Graz

Valiante, Chet ....(203) 354-1010

cvaliante@thehour.com, Pub./COO, The Hour, CT, Norwalk

Valiante, Chet .... (203) 354-1010
cvaliante@thehour.com, Pub./COO, The Wilton Villager, CT, Norwalk

Valik, Gary .... (315) 661-2358
gvalik@wdt.net, Sales / Mktg. VP, Daily Courier-Observer/Advance News, NY, Massena

gvalik@wdt.net, Sales / Mktg. VP, Carthage Republican Tribune, NY, LOWVILLE

Valik, Gary .... (315) 661-2358
gvalik@wdt.net, Corp VP Sales & Mktg., Ogdensburg Journal/Advance News, NY, Ogdensburg

Valkaer, Jorgen .... (615) 495-7266
info@ccieurope.com, Sales, CCI Europe, Inc.-Georgia Branch, GA, Kennesaw

Valker, Jorgen
jv@ccieurope.com, Vice Pres., Project Sales, CCI Europe, Inc., GA, Kennesaw

Valko, Mike
circulation@waynesvilledailyguide.com, Circ. Mgr., Daily Guide, MO, Waynesville

Valko, Mike
mike.valko@lakesunonline.com, Circ. /Dist./ Subscriptions, Lake Sun Leader, MO, Camdenton

Valles, Marc .... (707) 441-0507
mvalles@times-standard.com, Mng. Ed. , Times-Standard , CA, Eureka

Valley, Emilie
emilie.vallee@transcontinental.ca, Ed., L'hebdo Journal, QC, Trois-Rivieres

Valli, Gail .... (330) 580-8438
gail.valli@cantonrep.com, Class. Adv. Mgr., The Repository, OH, Canton

Vallieu, Melody .... (937) 552-2131
mvallieu@civitasmedia.com, Ed., Troy Daily News, OH, Troy

Vallieu, Melody .... (937) 773-2721 Ext. 1341
mvallieu@civitasmedia.com, Ed., Piqua Daily Call, OH, Piqua

Valluzzo, Rocco .... (203) 894-3327
sports@thewestonforum.com, Sports Ed., Weston Forum, CT, Ridgefield

Valluzzo, Rocco .... (203) 894-3327
rocco@thereddingpilot.com, Sports Ed., Redding Pilot, CT, Ridgefield

Valpy, Bruce
editorial@nnsl.com, Mng. Ed., Inuvik Drum, NT, Yellowknife

Valpy, Bruce
editorial@nnsl.com, Mng. Ed., Deh Cho Drum, NT, Yellowknife

Valpy, Bruce
editorial@nnsl.com, Mng. Ed., Yellowknifer, NT, Yellowknife

Valpy, Bruce
editorial@nnsl.com, Ed., News/north, NT, Yellowknife

Van, Sandy .... (951) 827-3459
News Ed, Univ. of California, Riverside, CA, Riverside

Van Arnem, Harold
info@netvillage.com, CEO, netVillage.com, LLC., MD, Laurel

Van Baalen, Pete .... (574) 296-5963
pvanbaalen@elkharttruth.com, Pub., Elkhart Truth, IN, Elkhart

Van Beek, Rebecca .... (920) 533-8338
frontdesk@thecampbellsportnews.com, office/production, Campbellsport News, WI, Campbellsport

Van Camp, Lesa .... (701) 454-6333
valleynv@polarcomm.com, Editor/Owner, Valley News & Views, ND, Drayton

Van Dorn, Michael
mvandorn@lawdailyrecord.com, Mng. Ed. , Daily Record, IL, Lawrenceville

Van Dress, Veronica .... (330) 775-1126
veronica.vandress@indeonline.com, Editor, The Independent, OH, Massillon

Van Dusen, Jill
jill@nynewspapers.com, Mktg. Dir., New York Press Service, NY, Albany

Van Dyke, Marcia
mvandyke@@whidbeynewstimes.com, Pub., The Whidbey Classifieds, WA, Coupeville

Van Dyne, Nathan .... (719) 636-0195
nathan.vandyne@gazette.com, Features Editor, The Gazette, CO, Colorado Springs

Van Engelenhoven, Deb .... (641) 660-1571
debve@oskyherald.com, PUblisher, Oskaloosa Shopper, IA, Oskaloosa

Van Engelenhoven, Deb
debve@oskyherald.com, Pub./Adv. Sales./ Classified Adv. Mgr./Display Adv., Oskaloosa Herald, IA, Oskaloosa

Van Essen, Owen D. .... (505) 820-2700
owen@dirksvanessen.com, Pres., Dirks, Van Essen & Murray, NM, Santa Fe

Van Genderen, Gayle
sdmail@siouxvalley.net, Pub., South Dakota Mail, SD, Plankinton

Van Hise, Carol
carol@adkpennysaver.com, Adv. Mgr., Pennysaver, NY, Plattsburgh

Van Hoesen, Jill .... (315) 782-1000
jvanhoesen@wdt.net, Johnson Newspaper Corp., NY, Watertown

Van Hook, Bill .... (251) 219-5302
bvanhook@press-register.com, Circ. Mgr., Opns., Press-Register, AL, Mobile

Van Koevering, Kurt
kurt@zrgraphics.com, Ed., Zeeland Record, MI, Zeeland

Van Natter, Jim
inquiries@pti.com, Sales Vice Pres., PTI Marketing Technologies, Inc., CA, Solana Beach

Van Reed, Barbara .... (508) 943-8784
bvanreed@TheYankeeXpress.com, Publisher, The Yankee Xpress, MA, Webster

Van Reeuwyk, Christine .... (250) 480-3260
editor@oakbaynews.com, Editor, Oak Bay News, BC, Victoria

Van Schoyck, Mary .... (567) 242-0472
mvanschoyck@limanews.com, CS Mgr., The Lima News, OH, Lima

Van Scoder, Chris .... (419) 784-5441 ext 213
cvanscoder@crescent-news.com, Adv. Mgr., The Crescent-News, OH, Defiance

Van Scoder, Dennis
dvan@crescent-news.com, Mng. Ed., Crescent Extra, OH, Defiance

Van Scoder, Dennis .... (419) 784-5441 ext. 225
dvan@crescent-news.com , Ed., The Crescent-News, OH, Defiance

Van Sice, Ethan .... (334) 682-4422
ethanvansice@gmail.com, Editor in Chief, Wilcox Progressive Era, AL, Camden

Van Sickle, Sonya .... (803) 329-4085
svansickle@heraldonline.com, Adv. Mgr., The Herald, SC, Rock Hill

Van Slyke, Dirk
DVANSLYKE@THEGREENSHEET.COM, Greensheet, TX, Dallas

Van Slyke, Jim .... (757) 853-3969 ext. 3003
jim.vanslyke@militarynews.com, Ed., Soundings, VA, Norfolk

Van Stry, Michael .... (805) 684-4428
news@coastalview.com, Pub., Coastal View News, CA, Carpinteria

Van Treeck, Jane
jvantreeck@sheboygandaily.com, News Dir., MySheboygan.com, WI, Kohler

Van Tuyl, Aaron .... (360) 807-8229
avantuyl@chronline.com, Sports Ed., The Chronicle, WA, Centralia

Van Vonderen, Mary .... (920) 339-2787
mvanvonderen@megtec.com, Mktg. Mgr., MEGTEC Systems, WI, De Pere

Van Winkle, Irene .... (830) 367-3501
wkcurrent@classicnet.net, reporter, ad sales, West Kerr Current, TX, Ingram

Van Winkle, Jim
theqcn@gmail.com, Ed & Owner, Queen Central News, NY, Camden

Van Wyke, Jill .... (515) 271-2295
Drake Univ., IA, Des Moines

Van de Ventor, Barb .... (937) 372-4444
bvandeventer@brownpublishing.com, Adv. Mgr., Greene County Shopper, OH, Xenia

VanAernam, Tim
tim@lhprint.com, Prodn. Mgr., Mailroom, The Leader-Herald, NY, Gloversville

VanAirsdale, Stu .... (916) 278-6065
stvcsus@gmail.com, Faculty Adviser, Sacramento State, CA, Sacramento

VanArsdale, Emma
editor@journalpilot.com, Ed., Hancock County Journal-Pilot, IL, Carthage

VanAuker, Amanda .... (517) 278-2318, ext. 27
avanauker@thedailyreporter.com, Interim Ed., The Daily Reporter, MI, Coldwater
avanauker@thedailyreporter.com, News Ed., Hillsdale Daily News, MI, Hillsdale

VanAuker , Amanda .... (517) 369-5085
patriot@cbpu.com, Mng. Ed., Bronson Journal, MI, Coldwater

VanBrocklin, Lucretia .... (540) 463-3113
circulation@thenews-gazette.com, Circulation Manager, The News-Gazette, VA, Lexington

VanDeHoef, Chris .... (860) 541-6438
chris@ctcapitolgroup.com, Executive Director, Connecticut Daily Newspapers Association, CT, Hartford

VanDemark, Steve .... (419) 784-5441
vandemark@crescent-news.com, Gen. Mgr., Adams Publishing Group, LLC, MN, Virginia

VanEe, Marty .... (574) 583-5121
VP, The News Reminder, IN, Monticello

VanGilder, Scott .... 1-(800) 321-0350 EXT. 108
svangilder@scity.com, Operations Manager, Steel City Corp., OH, Ashland

VanGundy, Kevin .... (970) 243-8829
kevin@pendantpublishing.com, Pub., Beacon Senior Newspaper, CO, Grand Junction

VanHise, Carol .... (518) 563-0100 ext. 107
carol@adkpennysaver.com, Adv. Mgr., Real Estate Advertiser, NY, Plattsburgh

VanHoesen, Jill .... ext. 2571
jvanhoesen@wdt.net, CIO, Watertown Daily Times, NY, Watertown

VanHorn, Edward
edward@snpa.org, Exec. Dir., Southern Newspaper Publishers Association, GA, Atlanta

VanLandingham, Lou Ann .... (252) 792-1181
lavan@ncweeklies.com, Adv. , Enterprise & Weekly Herald, NC, Williamston

VanLaningham, Bill .... (818) 713-3501
bvanlaningham@scng.com, VP, Mktg, Southern California News Group, CA, Woodland Hills
bvanlaningham@scng.com, VP Mktg, Press-Telegram, CA, Long Beach

VanMatre, Kim .... (765) 361-0100
Kvanmatre@thepaper24-7.com, Adv. Mgr., The Paper of Montgomery County, IN, Crawfordsville

VanPelt, Jennifer .... (603) 224-5301 ext. 318
LiveWell Ed., Concord Monitor, NH, Concord

VanSkiver, Melissa .... (607) 324-1425 Ext 230
mvanskiver@gatehousemedia.com, Adv. Dir., Wellsville Daily Reporter, NY, Wellsville

VanSkiver, Melissa .... (607) 324-1425 ext. 230
mvanskiver@gatehousemedia.com, Advertising Director, Genesee Country Express, NY, Dansville

VanTassel, Mark
mvantassel@thenortheastgeorgian.com, Regl. Bus. Mgr., The Northeast Georgian, GA, Cornelia

VanVeld, Robert
vanveld@indyweek.com, Circ. Mgr., The Independent Weekly, NC, Durham

Vana, David .... (361) 594-2911
dvana@shorack.com, Customer Service, Kaspar Wire Works, Inc./Sho-Rack, TX, Shiner

Vanaver, Elissa
elissa@breakthroughmiami.org, Vice Pres., HR/Asst. to Pub., Herald Values, FL, Miami

Vance, Carolyn .... (217) 351-5228
cvance@news-gazette.com, Librarian, The News-Gazette, IL, Champaign

Vance, Dan
dvance@news-sentinel.com, Multimedia Specialist, The News-Sentinel, IN, Fort Wayne

Vance, Karina .... (360) 354-4444
subscribe@lyndentribune.com, Circulation Mgr, Lynden Tribune, WA, Lynden

Vance, Kathy
kvance@tampatrib.com, Clerk, South Shore News, FL, Tampa

Vance, Michael
michael@battsandassoc.com, Oakwood College, AL, Huntsville

Vancel, Ingraham .... 765/743-1111 ext. 111
production@purdueexponent.org, Prodn. Dir., The Purdue Exponent, IN, West Lafayette

Vanden Berge, Sara
sara.vandenberge@empiretribune.com, Ed., Cross Timbers Trading Post, TX, Stephenville

Vander Plas, Melissa .... (507) 886-2453
mvanderplas@bluffcountrynews.com, Ed., Bluff Country Reader, MN, Spring Valley

Vander Veen, Hank
ads@mantecabulletin.com, Group Pub., Manteca Bulletin, CA, Manteca

Vander Woude, Kari .... (712) 732-3130
kvanderwoude@stormlakepilottribune.com, Gen. Mgr., Storm Lake Pilot Tribune, IA, Storm Lake

Vander Zee, Leonard
lvanderzee@crcna.org, Interim Editor, The Banner, MI, Grand Rapids

VanderMey, Randy .... (805) 403-4251
vanderme@westmont.edu, Advisor, Randy VanderMey, CA, Santa Barbara

VanderWeert, Margaret .... (641) 594-3200
press@netins.net, Editor, Sully Hometown Press, IA, Sully

Vanderbeck, Jeff .... ext. 52
jvanderbeck@news-expressky.com, Pub., The Mountain Bargain Hunter, KY, Pikeville

Vanderbeck, Jeff .... ext. 52
jvanderbeck@news-expressky.com, Pub., The Appalachian News-Express, KY, Pikeville

Vanderhayden, Jutta
business@thestarnews.com, Business Mgr., The Star-News, CA, Chula Vista

Vanderhoof, Joe .... (570) 420-4311
jvanderhoof@th-record.com, Pres., Pocono Record Plus, PA, Stroudsburg

Vanderhoof, Joe .... (845) 346-3011

cveley@thetribunenews.com, Circulation Manager, The Tribune, CA, San Luis Obispo

Velilla, John F.
inter2003@embarqmail.com, Dir., Sales, Inter-Continental Graphics, Inc., FL, Fort Myers

Velin, Conrad
cvelin@rgj.com, Controller, Reno Gazette-Journal, NV, Reno

Vell, Brent
tribune@dellrapids.net, Ed., Baltic Beacon, SD, Dell Rapids

Vellucci, Amy
amy@yourneighborhoodnews.com, Pub./Sales Dir., Hooksett Banner, NH, Manchester

Velo, Fernando ....(714) 972-9912
aztecanews@aol.com, Pub., Azteca News, CA, Santa Ana

Velotta, Rick ....(702) 308-6851
rickv_unlv@gmail.com, Adviser, University of Nevada, Las Vegas, NV, Las Vegas

Velotta, Rick
rickv_unlv@yahoo.com, Adviser, University of Nevada, Las Vegas, NV, Las Vegas

Velthoven, Aaron
avelthoven@dnps.com, VP. of Marketing, Detroit Free Press, MI, Detroit

Veltri, Deborah ....(304) 626-1413
advertising@exponent-telegram.com, Adv. Dir., The Exponent Telegram, WV, Clarksburg

Velvin, Candace
publisher@cameronherald.com, Interim Pub., The Cameron Herald, TX, Cameron

Velvin, Randy
r.velvin@womackpublishing.com, Gen. Mgr., South Hill Enterprise, VA, South Hill
r.velvin@womackpublishing.com, Gen. Mgr., Mecklenburg Reporter, VA, South Hill
r.velvin@womackpublishing.com, Press Opns. Mgr., Womack Publishing Co., VA, Lynchburg

Vemillion, Jaime
aadams@republicservices.com, Classified Adv. Mgr., The Republic, IN, Columbus

Venema, Sheri ....(410) 777-1947
sbvenema@aacc.edu, Advisor, Anne Arundel Cmty. College Campus Current, MD, Arnold

Venis, Brian.........................(905) 475-2357
bvenis@graphicroller.com, Pres., Graphic Roll Coverings, ON, Richmond Hill

Vennekotter, Michael.................(517) 486-2164
michael@saxmayercorp.com, Pres., Mktg./ Sales, Saxmayer Corp., MI, Blissfield

Venneri, Laura ....(360) 687-5151
laura@thereflector.com, Pub, The Reflector, WA, Battle Ground

Venso, Mike ....(801) 257-8806
mvenso@newsviewsolutions.com, Dir.-Sales, NewsView Solutions, UT, Salt Lake City

Venter, Harry L. ....(303) 769-4646
rbell357@aol.com, Ed., Tri-County Tribune, CO, Deer Trail

Ventimiglia, Brandon ....(517) 432-3000
advertising@statenews.com, Advertising Manager, The State News/Michigan State University, MI, East Lansing

Veon, Greg
gveon@qctimes.com, Pub., Bettendorf News, IA, Davenport

Veon, Greg R. ....(563) 383-2200
VP, Publishing, Lee Enterprises, Inc., IA, Davenport

VerCamman, Adam ....(202) 636-3000
avercamman@washingtontimes.com, Dir. Adv. & Sales, The Washington Times, DC, Washington

Veraguth, Mary............(507) 452-+1262 ext. 105
circulation@winonapost.com, Circ. Dir, Winona Post, MN, Winona

Veraldi, Lorna
lorna.veraldi@fiu.edu, Assoc. Prof., Florida International University, FL, North Miami

Verdick, Glenda ....(563) 333-2633
gverdick@qctimes.com, Event Mgr., Bettendorf News, IA, Davenport

Verdon, Susan.........................(714) 796-7954
svardon@ocregister.com, Ed., Aliso Viejo News, CA, Santa Ana

Vered, Allie ....(804) 740-2000
editor@virginiajewishlife.com, Mng. Ed., Virginia Jewish Life, VA, Richmond

Vergara, Carmen...............................ext. 212
Adv. Coord., Weekend Balita/Midweek Balita, CA, Glendale

Verhoogen, Therese
tverhoogen@backbaysun.com, Ad. Director, The Back Bay Sun, MA, Revere

Vermillion, Peggy
newspapr@netins.net, Pub./GM, Villisca Review, IA, Villisca

Vermon, Cheril
cvernon@palestineherald.com, Features Ed., Palestine Herald-Press, TX, Palestine

Verna, Paul M. ....(215) 679-4133
upshopper@comcast.net, Pub., Upper Perk Shopper's Guide, PA, Pennsburg

Verner, Chris.........................(704) 797-4262
cverner@salisburypost.com, Editorial Page Ed., Salisbury Post, NC, Salisbury

Vernon, Cheril ....(936) 687-2424
news@messenger-news.com, Copy Editor / Composing, The Messenger, TX, Grapeland

Vernon, Dane
dvernon@vernonpublishing.com, Pub, The Versailles Leader-Statesman, MO, Versailles

Vernon, Dane
times@vernonpublishing.com, Pub., The Tipton Times, MO, Tipton

Vernon, Jerry
jvernon@connectionnewspapers.com, Exec. Vice Pres., Springfield Connection, VA, Alexandria
jvernon@connectionnewspapers.com, Exec. Vice Pres., Alexandria Gazette Packet, VA, Alexandria
jvernon@connectionnewspapers.com, Exec. Vice Pres., Arlington Connection, VA, Alexandria
jvernon@connectionnewspapers.com, Exec. Vice Pres., Burke Connection, VA, Alexandria
jvernon@connectionnewspapers.com, Exec. Vice Pres., Centre View, VA, Alexandria
jvernon@connectionnewspapers.com, Exec. Vice Pres., Fairfax Connection, VA, Alexandria
jvernon@connectionnewspapers.com, Exec. Vice Pres., Fairfax Station/Clifton/Lorton Connection, VA, Alexandria
jvernon@connectionnewspapers.com, Exec. Vice Pres., Great Falls Connection, VA, Alexandria
jvernon@connectionnewspapers.com, Exec. Vice Pres., McLean Connection, VA, Alexandria
jvernon@connectionnewspapers.com, Exec. Vice Pres., Potomac Almanac, VA, Alexandria
jvernon@connectionnewspapers.com, Exec. Vice Pres., Reston Connection, VA, Alexandria
jvernon@connectionnewspapers.com, Exec. Vice Pres., Vienna/Oakton Connection, VA, Alexandria
jvernon@connectionnewspapers.com, Exec. Vice Pres., Oak Hill/Herndon Connection, VA, Alexandria
jvernon@connectionnewspapers.com, Exec. Vice Pres., Mount Vernon Gazette, VA, Alexandria
jvernon@connectionnewspapers.com, Vice Pres., Connection Publishing, Inc., VA, Alexandria

Vernon, Lisa ....(517) 548-7060
LVernon@Michigan.com, Multimedia Sales Mgr., The Livingston County Daily Press & Argus, MI, Howell
LVernon@Michigan.com, Retail Adv. Mgr., Green Sheet, MI, Howell

Vernon, Trevor
tvernon@vernonpublishing.com, Pub., Miller County Autogram Sentinel, MO, Eldon
tvernon@vernonpublishing.com, Pub., The Index, MO, Hermitage
tvernon@vernonpublishing.com, Pub., Eldon Advertiser, MO, Eldon

Vernon, Trish ....(302) 645-7700
thv@capegazette.com, Ed., Cape Gazette, DE, Lewes

Veroba, Polly ....(306) 691-1253
pveroba@mjtimes.sk.ca, Bus. Mgr., The Moose Jaw Times-Herald, SK, Moose Jaw

Verrico, Kurt ....ext. 199
kverrico@timesonline.com, Circ. Mgr., Distr., Beaver County Times, PA, Beaver

Verstraete, Victor
victorv@birch.net, American Classifieds - Fort Worth-arlington, TX, River Oaks

Verticchio, Lu..........................(250) 960-2757
lverticchio@pgcitizen.ca, Sales Mgr., The Prince George Citizen, BC, Prince George

Vervaet, Linda...............................ext. 112
lvervaet@k-f.com, Coord., Int'l Sales, K & F International, Inc., IN, Granger

Veskerna, Julie ....(402) 941-1426
julie.veskerna@lee.net, Advertising Team Leader, Fremont Area Shopper, NE, Fremont

Veslany, Sarah
editor@psu.edu, Editor in Chief , Penn State Univ., PA, Erie

Vespoint, Cheryl
publisher@barbertonherald.com, Pub., The Barberton Herald, OH, Barberton

Vessels, Joe
circulation@pdclarion.com, Distribution Mgr., Princeton Daily Clarion, IN, Princeton

Vest, Kelly
kelly@newtondailynews.com, Prodn. Mgr., Newton Daily News, IA, Newton

Vest, Stephen
steve@kentuckymonthly.com, Pub/Ed, Kentucky Monthly, KY, Frankfort

Vestal, Kelly Brooks
kbrooks@ruidosonews.com, Mng. Ed. , The Ruidoso News, NM, Ruidoso

Vestal, Terrance............ (760) 873-3535 ext. 211
editor@inyoregister.com, Managing Editor, Inyo Register, CA, Bishop

Vestrich, Lee
leev@bulbtronics.com, Vice Pres., Sales, Bulbtronics, NY, Farmingdale

Vetter, Kathy ....(817) 390-7380
vetter@star-telegram.com, Mng. Ed., Enterprise, Fort Worth Star-Telegram, TX, Fort Worth

Vetter, Steven
svetter@i-70scout.com, Mng. Ed., Eastern Colorado News, CO, Strasburg

Veuleman, Amy
aveuleman@mcneese.edu, Instr., Speech Prog., McNeese State University, LA, Lake Charles

Veyera, Bob.........................(860) 867-6895
bveyera@fujifilm.com, Newspaper Acct. Mgr., NW Reg., Fujifilm North America Corporation, IL, Hanover Park

Vezza, Richard ....(973) 392-4161
publisher@starledger.com, Pub., The Star-Ledger, NJ, Newark

Viafore, Christina ....(607) 746-4753
viaforcs@delhi.edu, Advisor, SUNY College of Technology/Delhi, NY, Delhi

Viall, Elizabeth
ekviall@eiu.edu, Instr., Eastern Illinois University, IL, Charleston

Viau, Charles
production@bulletinaylmer.com, Prodn. Mgr., Le Bulletin D'aylmer, QC, Gatineau

Vice, Barbara
pub@drumrightgusher.com, news@ drumrightgusher.com, Pub./Ed., Drumright Gusher, OK, Drumright

Vick, Justin
editor@thecharlotteweekly.com, Ed., South Charlotte Weekly, NC, Charlotte
editor@thecharlotteweekly.com, Ed., The Union County Weekly, NC, Charlotte
editor@thecharlotteweekly.com, Ed., The Matthews-Mint Hill, NC, Charlotte

Vick, Patty ....(585) 387-0577
pvick@burnishine.com, Graphic Arts Customer Service, Burnishine Products, IL, Lake Villa

Vicker, Lauren
lvicker@sjfc.edu, Chair/Prof., St. John Fisher College, NY, Rochester

Vicker, Scott
svicker@crestonnews.com, Mng., Ed., Osceola Sentinel-Tribune, IA, Osceola
svicker@crestonnews.com, Mng., Ed., Creston News Advertiser, IA, Creston

Vickery, Jonathan.........................(803) 259-3501
jonathan.vickery@morris.com, Mng. Ed., The People-Sentinel, SC, Barnwell

Vickery, Peggy
peggyvickery@hartcom.net, Gen. Mgr., The Hartwell Sun, GA, Hartwell

Victor, Beaux ....(337) 462-0616
guardian@wnonline.net, Adv. Mgr., Guardian, LA, Fort Polk

Vidal-Sainio, Lisa
ads@elyecho.com, Advt Dir, The Ely Echo, MN, Ely

Vidmar, Dawn ....(312) 655-7110
dvidmar@catholicnewworld.com, Adv. Mgr., The Catholic New World, IL, Chicago

Vidos, Nikki
lifestyles@vermiliontoday.com, Lifestyles Ed., Abbeville Meridional, LA, Abbeville

Viechweg, Trevor
trevor.viechweg@scni.com, Prodn. Mgr., Transportation, The Advocate, CT, Stamford

Viehman, Rob ....(573) 885-7460
news@cubafreepress.com, Pub., The Cuba Free Press, MO, Cuba

Viehman, Rob ....(573) 885-7460
stvlstar@misn.com, Pub., Steelville Star-Crawford Mirror, MO, Steelville

Vierthaler, Bruce
spearcty@ucom.net, Pub., Spearville News, KS, Spearville

Viggiano, Kim
kim@metrosn.com, Senior VP, Operations, Metro Newspaper Advertising Services, Inc., NY, New York

Vigil, Vicki
vickiesue@avpsalida.com, Adv. Mgr., The Mountain Mail, CO, Salida

Vigil, Vickie
vickiesue@themountainmail.com, Adv. Dir., Mountain Guide, CO, Salida

Vigna, Cheri
cvigna@carolinaparent.com, Art Dir., Carolina Parent, NY, White Plains

Vilchis, Eric.........................(951) 368-9414
evilchis@pe.com, Photo-Visuals Ed., The Press-Enterprise, CA, Riverside

Vilencia, Bridget ....(724) 223-2635
bvilenica@observer-reporter.com, Circ. Dir., Observer-Reporter, PA, Washington

Villa, Marie .... (585) 385-7393
mvilla@sjfc.edu, Media Adviser, St. John
Fisher College, NY, Rochester

Villa, Mary Jo .... (608) 755-8228
mjvilla@gazettextra.com, VP Strategic
Operations., The Gazette - gazettextra.com,
WI, Janesville
mjvilla@gazettextra.com, The Janesville
Gazette - GazetteXtra, WI, Janesville

Villalobos, Pam .... (815) 273-2277
pvillalobos@grics.net, Times-Journal Office
Mgr./Adv. Rep., Carroll County Mirror-
Democrat, IL, Mount Carroll

Villalpando, Carlina .... (830) 257-0337
carlina.villalpando@dailytimes.com, Mng. Ed.,
Kerrville Daily Times, TX, Kerrville

Villalpando, Carlina
cvillalpando@tylerpaper.com, Editor, Tyler
Morning Telegraph, TX, Tyler

Villani, Dan .... (541) 338-2229
dan.villani@registerguard.com, Creative Servs.
Mgr., The Register-Guard, OR, Eugene

Villanueva, Derek .... (405) 475-3380
dvillanueva@oklahoman.com, National and
Majors Sales Manager, The Oklahoman, OK,
Oklahoma City

Villanueva, James .... (806) 828-6201
james@slatonitenews.com, Managing Editor,
The Slatonite, TX, Slaton

Villard, Charles
cvillard@bangordailynews.com, Prodn. Mgr.,
The Weekly, ME, Bangor

Villarosa, Linda
linda@cuny.edu, City College of New York, NY,
New York

Villarreal, Debra .... (361) 886-3604
Credit Mgr., Corpus Christi Caller-Times, TX,
Corpus Christi

Villarreal, Phil .... (520) 573-4130
prv@azstarnet.com, Film Critic, Arizona Daily
Star, AZ, Tucson

Villarreal, Ricardo .... (520) 415-1841
circulation@nogalesinternational.com, Circ.
Mgr., Nogales International, AZ, Nogales
circulation@nogalesinternational.com, Circ.
Mgr., Santa Cruz Valley Sun, AZ, Nogales

Villela, Veronica .... (602) 744-6546
veronica.villela@voicemediagroup.com,
Business Manager, Ruxton Group/VMG
Advertising, AZ, Phoenix

Villeneuve, Michel .... (514) 881-8583
abonnement.tp@videotron.ca, Tourisme Plus,
QC, Montreal

Villeneuve, Pierre
promotion@jdeq.com, Mgr., Promo., Le Journal
de Quebec, QC, Vanier

Villeneuve, Terry .... (306) 236-5353
pride.terry@sasktel.net, Pub, Northern Pride,
SK, Meadow Lake

Villicana Casati, Josefina .... (512) 445-3637
jcasati@ahorasi.com, Ed., ahora si!, TX, Austin

Villoch, Alexandra .... (305) 376-3212
avilloch@MiamiHerald.com, Pres./Pub., Miami
Herald, FL, Doral

Vina, Jose
jvina@communityshoppers.com, Adv. Mgr.,
Walworth County Sunday, WI, Elkhorn

Vincent, Angela
avincent@thelancasternews.com, Circ. Mgr.,
Lancaster News, SC, Lancaster

Vincent, Curt
cvincent@civitasmedia.com, Ed./Gen. Mgr.,
Bladen Journal, NC, Elizabethtown

Vincent, John .... (978) 632-8000 ext. 37
jvincent@thegardnernews.com, Asst.
Managing Ed. , The Gardner News, MA,
Gardner

Vinci, Mike

m.vinci@22ndcenturymedia.com, Sales Dir.,
The Tinley Junction, IL, Orland Park
m.vinci@22ndcenturymedia.com, Sales Dir.,
The Frankfort Station, IL, Orland Park
m.vinci@22ndcenturymedia.com, Sales Dir.,
The Lockport Legend, IL, Orland Park
m.vinci@22ndcenturymedia.com, Adv. Dir./
Nat'l Adv. Mgr., The Northbrook Tower, IL,
Northbrook
m.vinci@22ndcenturymedia.com, Nat'l Sales
Dir., The Wilmette Beacon, IL, Northbrook
m.vinci@22ndcenturymedia.com, Adv. Dir./
Nat'l Adv. Mgr., The Malibu Surfside News,
CA, Malibu
m.vinci@22ndcenturymedia.com, Sales Dir.,
The New Lenox Patriot, IL, Orland Park
m.vinci@22ndcenturymedia.com, Nat'l Sales
Dir., The Glenview Lantern, IL, Northbrook
m.vinci@22ndcenturymedia.com, Sales Dir.,
The Mokena Messenger, IL, Orland Park
m.vinci@22ndcenturymedia.com, Sales Dir.,
The Homer Horizon, IL, Orland Park
m.vinci@22ndcenturymedia.com, Sales Dir.,
The Orland Park Prairie, IL, Orland Park

Vinciguerra, Mark .... (518) 828-1616 ext. 2401
mvinciguerra@registerstar.com, Pub., Greene
County News, NY, Hudson
mvinciguerra@registerstar.com, Pub., The
Ravena News-Herald, NY, Ravena

Vinciguerra, Mark .... (518) 828-1616 ext. 2403
mvinciguerra@registerstar.com, Pub./Gen.
Mgr., The Daily Mail, NY, Hudson

Vinciguerra, Mark
mvinciguerra@registerstar.com, Pub., Chatham
Courier, NY, Hudson

Vinciguerra, Mark .... (518) 828-1616 Ext. 2401
mvinciguerra@registerstar.com, Pub., Register-
Star, NY, Hudson

Vinciguerra , Mark .... (518) 828-1616
mvinciguerra@registerstar.com , Pub.,
Mountain Eagle, NY, Stamford

Vineberg, Steve
svineberg@holycross.edu, College of the Holy
Cross, MA, Worcester

Viner, Aaron .... (319) 653-2191
sports@washjrnl.com, Sports Ed., The
Washington Evening Journal, IA, Washington

Vines, Mark .... (734) 953-2187
mvines@oe.homecomm.net, Prodn. Mgr., Lake
Orion Eccentric, MI, Detroit

Vines, Nikkole .... (870) 356-2111
gwbusiness@windstream.net, Office Mgr,
Glenwood Herald, AR, Glenwood

Vinikoor, Robert
bob@wntk.com, The Radio Shopper, NH, New
London

Vinson, Jamie
news@msadvocate.com, Ed., Mt. Sterling
Advocate, KY, Mount Sterling

Vinson, Larry
lvinson@mcneese.edu, Assoc. Prof., Speech
Prog., McNeese State University, LA, Lake
Charles

Viola, Francesca
fviola@temple.edu, Asst. Prof., Temple
University, PA, Philadelphia

Violi, Susan .... (402) 444-1486
sue.violi@owh.com, Dir Community Relations,
Omaha World-Herald, NE, Omaha

Virgen, Steve
steve.virgen@latimes.com, Sports Ed., Daily
Pilot, CA, Costa Mesa

Virgin, Bill
bill.virgin@yahoo.com, President, Washington
Press Association, WA, Renton

Virnig, Craig .... (956) 682-2423
Prodn. Mgr., Bargain Book, TX, Brownsville

Virnig, Sherid
sheriv@pa-news.org, Pennsylvania
NewsMedia Association, PA, Harrisburg

Vis, Matt
mvis@dougallmedia.com, Reporter, Thunder
Bay Source, ON, Thunder Bay

Visconte, Angela .... (585) 330-3080
avisconte@catholiccourier.com, Advertising,
Catholic Courier, NY, Rochester

Visic, Mark
mvisic@kubra.com, Sr. Vice Pres., Bus. Devel.,
Kubra, ON, Mississauga

Visotto, Bernie
class@mountaineer.bz, Office Mgr., The
Mountaineer, AB, Rocky Mountain House

Vit, Bruno
bruno.vit@sunmedia.ca, Dir., Reader Sales/
Serv., The Sault Star, ON, Sault Sainte Marie

Vitale, Gina
gina.vitale@thetriangle.org, Drexel Univ., PA,
Philadelphia

Vitale, Tim
tim.vitale@usu.edu, Adj. Instr., Utah State
University, UT, Logan

Vitek, Joe
jvitek@gatehosuemedia.com, Multi-Media Acct.
Exec., Benton Evening News, IL, Benton

Vitrano, David
david.vitrano@wickcommunications.com, Gen.
Mgr/Mng. Ed., L'Observateur, LA, La Place

Vives, Lisa .... (212) 244-3123
ipsgin@igc.org, Exec. Dir., Global Information
Network, New York

Vivian, Richard .... (519) 623-7395 ex. 215
rvivian@cambridgetimes.ca, Ed, Cambridge
Times, ON, Cambridge

Vivian, Robert
vivian@alma.edu, Alma College, MI, Alma

Vizer, Tim
tvizer@bnd.com, Belleville News-Democrat,
IL, Belleville

Vizer, Tim .... (618) 239-2470
tvizer@bnd.com, Photo, Belleville News-
Democrat, IL, Belleville

Vizzini, John .... (321) 242-3850
jvizzini@floridatoday.com, Opns. Dir., Missileer,
FL, Melbourne

Vizzini, John .... (321) 242-3850
jvizzini@floridatoday.com, Operations Dir.,
Florida Today, FL, Melbourne

Vobejda, Bill
bill.vobejda@lee.net, Pub., Columbus Area
Choice, NE, Columbus

Vocate, Donna R.
dvocate@atu.edu, Head/Prof., Arkansas Tech
University, AR, Russellville

Voccio, Chris .... (860) 425-4320
cvoccio@norwichbulletin.com, Pub., The
Bulletin, CT, Norwich

Voccio, Chris .... (716) 439-9222 Ext. 2280
cvoccio@cnhi.com, Pub., Tonawanda News
(OOB), NY, North Tonawanda
cvoccio@cnhi.com, Pub., Lockport Union-Sun
& Journal, NY, Lockport
cvoccio@cnhi.com, Pub., Niagara Gazette, NY,
Niagara Falls

Vodenichar, Ronald .... (724) 282-8000
rvodenichar@butlereagle.com, Publisher and
general manager, Eagle Printing Co., PA,
Butler

Vodopich, Becky
office@newslj.com, Office Mgr., News Letter
Journal, WY, Newcastle

Voerding, Brian .... (507) 453-3510
brian.voerding@lee.net, Ed, Winona Daily
News, MN, Winona

Vogel, Amber
amber@republictimes.net, Circ. Coord.,
Republic-times Shopper, IL, Waterloo

Vogel, Annette .... (603) 927-4028

info@intertownrecord.com, Pub./Gen. Mgr.,
InterTown Record, NH, North Sutton

Vogel, Rob
rvogel@scc.spokane.edu, Spokane Cmty.
College, WA, Spokane

Vogl-Bauer, Sally
voglbaus@uww.edu, Contact, University of
Wisconsin-Whitewater, WI, Whitewater

Vognar, Chris .... (214) 977-8142
cvognar@dallasnews.com, Critic, The Dallas
Morning News, TX, Dallas

Vogt, Nancy .... (218) 855-5877
nancy.vogt@ineandlakes.com, Editor, Echoland
Shopper, MN, Brainerd

Vogt, Rob
rob@claresholmlocalpress.ca, Ed., Claresholm
Local Press, AB, Claresholm

Vohden, Bonnie
bonnie.vohden@njfamily.com, Assoc. Pub.,
Union County Family, NJ, Mountainside

Vohden, Bonnie
bonnie.vohden@njfamily.com, Co-Pub., New
Jersey Family, NJ, Summit

Vohden, Bonnie
bonnie.vohden@njfamily.com, Assoc. Pub.,
Morris County Family, NJ, Mountainside

Void, Kelly .... (847) 427-4578
kvold@dailyherald.com, Digital Editor for
Engagement, Daily Herald, IL, Arlington
Heights

Voisine, Alison
alison.voisine@sjvalley-times.com, Print Shop
Customer Service Director, St. John Valley
Times, ME, Madawaska

Vojtasek, Karen .... (574) 224-5323
karenv@rochsent.com, Adv. Dir., The
Rochester Sentinel, IN, Rochester

Volcek, Joe
joe.volcek@nptelegraph.com, Circ. Dir., The
North Platte Telegraph, NE, North Platte

Volcsko, Jake .... (215) 345-3095
jvolcsko@calkins.com, General Manager,
Calkins Media, PA, Levittown

Volesky, Richard .... (701) 872-3755
Ed., Billings County Pioneer, ND, Beach

Volkert, Dennis
volkert@sturgisjournal.com, Feat. Ed., Sturgis
Journal, MI, Sturgis

Volland, Stan .... (813) 259-7876
Tampa Bay Times, FL, St Petersburg

Volosin, Beth .... (330) 332-4601
bvolosin@salemnews.net, Pub., Salem News,
OH, Salem

Volpe, Hermel .... (506) 735-5575
madproduction@brunswicknews.com, Pub., Le
Madawaska, NB, Edmundston

Von Kampen, Joan
joan.vonkampen@nptelegraph.com, Managing
Ed. , The North Platte Telegraph, NE, North
Platte

Von Kaenel, Jeff .... (916) 498-1234, ext. 1371
jeffv@newsreview.com, CEO, Reno News &
Review, NV, Reno
jeffv@newsreview.com, President, Sacramento
News & Review, CA, Sacramento

Von Ohlsen, Robin
rvonohlsen@njnpublishing.com, Adv. Dir., The
Warren Reporter, NJ, Flemington

Von Pinnon, Janelle .... (320) 363-7741
janellev@thenewsleaders.com, CEO/Owner/
Pub., The Newsleaders, MN, SAINT
JOSEPH
janellev@thenewsleaders.com, Publisher, St.
Joseph Newsleader, MN, Saint Joseph

Von Pinnon, Janelle .... (320) 363-7741
janellev@thenewsleaders.com, CEO/Owner/
Publisher, Sartell Newsleader, MN, Saint
Joseph

Wagner, Peter W. ....(712) 324-5347 ext. 5730
pww@iowainformation.com, Pres., Creative
House Print Media Consultants, IA, Sheldon
pww@iowainformation.com, Adv. Mgr., The
Golden Shopper, IA, Sheldon

Wagner, Peter W. ....ext. 5730
pww@iowainformation.com, Pub., N'West Iowa
Review, IA, Sheldon

Wagner, Sarah
swagner@alm.com, Office Mgr., Daily Report,
GA, Atlanta

Wagner, Vivian
vwagner@muskingum.edu, Muskingum
College, OH, New Concord

Wagoner, Rae
rwagoner@heraldledger.com, Pub., The
Herald-Ledger, KY, Eddyville

Wagster, Lynette Calhoun ....(731) 587-3144
lcwagster@wcpnews.com, Gen. Mgr., Weakley
County Press, TN, Martin

Wahl, Larry ....(251) 434-1544
thecatholicweek@bellsouth.net, Ed., The
Catholic Week, AL, Mobile

Wahl, Paul
paulw@montrosepress.com, Managing Ed,
The Montrose Daily Press, CO, Montrose

Wahl, T. Andrew ....(425) 388-9419
Adviser, Everett Community College, WA,
Everett

Wahler, Steve ....(270) 691-7282
swahler@messenger-inquirer.com , IT Mgr.,
Messenger-Inquirer, KY, Owensboro

Wahlheim, Dan ....(309) 757-4939
wahl@qconline.com, Production Director, The
Dispatch-Argus, IL, Moline

Waid, Machele ....(260) 665-3117 Ext. 2118
mwaid@kpcmedia.com, Acct. Exec., The
Herald Republican, IN, Angola

Waidelich, Audrey
info@heatandcontrol.com, Dir., Mktg., Heat
and Control, Inc., CA, Hayward

Wainer, Herb
herwai@horinc.com, Pres., Horizons, Inc., OH,
Cleveland

Wainwright, Nigel ....(780) 468-0344
nigel.wainwright@sunmedia.ca, Circ. Dir., The
Edmonton Sun, AB, Edmonton

Wainwright, Rachel
rachel.wainwright@gaflnews.com, Circ. Mgr.,
The Tifton Gazette, GA, Tifton

Wainwright, Rachel
rachel.wainwright@gaflnews.com, Circ. Dir.,
Cordele Dispatch, GA, Cordele

Wainwright, Rachel
rachel.wainwright@gaflnews.com, Circ. Mgr.,
Tifton Shopper, GA, Tifton

Wainwright, Rachel ....(229) 924-2751
rachel.wainwright@gaflnews.com , Circ. Dir.,
Americus Times-Recorder, GA, Americus

Wair, Cathy
cwair@lebanondemocrat.com, Sr. Exec. Mktg
Specialist, The Lebanon Democrat, TN,
Lebanon

Waisner, Judy ....(417) 723-5248
scrclassified@centurylink.net, Reception/
Classifieds, Crane Chronicle/Stone County
Republican, MO, Crane

Waite, Robert. ....(330) 821-1200
rwaite@dixcom.com, Gen. Mgr., The Review,
OH, Alliance

Waite, Ron ....(330) 541-9400 Ext. 4200
rwaite@dixcom.com, General Manager
, The Advantage, OH, Kent
rwaite@dixcom.com, Gen. Mgr., Twinsburg
Bulletin, OH, Kent

Waite, Ron ....(330) 541-9400 x 4200
rwaite@dixcom.com, Gen. Mgr., Stow Sentry,
OH, Kent

Waite, Ron ....(330) 541-9400 ex. 4200
rwaite@dixcom.com, Gen. Mgr., Hudson Hub-
Times, OH, Kent

Waite, Ron ....(330) 541-9400 x 4200
rwaite@dixcom.com, Pub., Sandusky Register,
OH, Sandusky
rwaite@dixcom.com, Gen. Mgr., Aurora
Advocate, OH, Kent

Waite, Sara ....(970) 526-9310
swaite@journal-advocate.com, Mng. Ed.,
Journal-Advocate, CO, Sterling

Waiters, Anna
awalters@beenews.com, Ed., Ken-Ton Bee,
NY, Williamsville

Waitkunas, Joe
editor@homesellermagazine.com, Ed.,
Homeseller Magazine, OH, Holmesville

Waits, Glenn.........................(501) 623-7711
GLENNW@HOTSR.COM, Circ. Dir., The
Sentinel-Record, AR, Hot Springs National
Park

Waitt, Robert D.............(732) 358-5200 ext. 8220
Adv. Dir., Tri-Town News, NJ, Manalapan

Waitt, Robert D.
bwaitt@gmnews.com, Adv. Director, North/
South Brunswick Sentinel, NJ, Manalapan

Wajsman, Beryl ....ext. 241
editor@thesuburban.com, Editor-in-chief, The
Suburban West Island, QC, Montreal
editor@thesuburban.com, The Suburban East
End Edition, QC, Saint Laurent

Walck, Pamela E......................(912) 652-0299
pamela.walck@savannahnow.com, Gov't/
Bus. Ed., Savannah Morning News, GA,
Savannah

Wald, Richard
richard.wald@baruch.cuny.edu, Prof.,
Columbia University, NY, New York

Walden, Dwain............. (229) 985-4545 ext. 214
dwain.walden@gaflnews.com, Pub., The
Moultrie Observer, GA, Moultrie

Walden, G.M.
info@truproof.co.uk, Mng. Dir., Truproof Ltd.,
London

Walden, Robert ....(571) 366-1140
robert@newsmediaalliance.org, CFO, News
Media Alliance, VA, Arlington

Walden, Ruth
nhtribune@mchsi.com, Circ. Mgr., New
Hampton Shopper, IA, New Hampton

Walden, Ruth ....(919) 962-4088
walden@unc.edu, James Howard & Hallie
McLean Parker Distinguished Prof.,
University of North Carolina, NC, Chapel Hill

Waldman, Diane
diane.waldman@du.edu, Assoc. Prof./Chair,
University of Denver, CO, Denver

Waldo, Luann
ciapub@netins.net, Ed., Scranton Journal, IA,
Scranton

Waldron, Al ....(505) 428-7630
awaldron@sfnewmexican.com, Com. Print
Sales / Mktg. Mgr. , The Santa Fe New
Mexican, NM, Santa Fe

Waldron, Danielle ....(574) 296-5902
dwaldron@elkharttruth.com, Copy Ed., Elkhart
Truth, IN, Elkhart

Waldron, Sandy ....(352) 245-3161
vosm@aol.com, Ed., Voice of South Marion,
FL, Belleview

Waldrop, Randy ....(915) 546-6327
rwaldrop@elpasotimes.com, Circ. Mgr.,
Transportation, El Paso Times, TX, El Paso
rwaldrop@elpasotimes.com, Circ. Mgr.,
Transportation, El Paso y Mas, TX, El Paso

Waldsmith, Jodi......................(816) 218-6701
jodi.waldsmith@pitch.com, Accounts
Receivable, The Pitch, MO, Kansas City

Walery, Debi.........................(503) 221-8327
dwalery@oregonian.com, Adv. Dir., The
Oregonian, OR, Portland

Wales, Cliff Ann ....(603) 672-9444
news@amherstcitizen.com, Pub./Ed., Amherst
Citizen, NH, Amherst

Wales, James
ads@amherstcitizen.com, Adv. Dir., Amherst
Citizen, NH, Amherst

Walk, Dan
sports@punxsutawneyspirit.com, Sports
Ed., Jefferson County Neighbors, PA,
Punxsutawney
sports@punxsutawneyspirit.com, Sports Ed.,
The Punxsutawney Spirit, PA, Punxsutawney

Walker, Andrew ....(574) 296-5913
awalker@etruth.com, Elkhart Truth, IN, Elkhart

Walker, Andrew
awalker@news-journal.com, Adv. Dir., Marshall
News Messenger, TX, Marshall

Walker, Barbara
barbarawalker@siouxcityjournal.com, City Ed.,
Sioux City Journal, IA, Sioux City

Walker, Bill ....(978) 772-0777
bwalker@mnprintingdevens.com, Director Of
Operations, The Sun, MA, Lowell

Walker, Bill
bwalker@mnprintingdevens.com, Opns. Dir.,
Townsend Times, MA, Devens

Walker, Caitlin
ads@theheraldtimes.com, Display Adv., The
Rio Blanco Herald Times, CO, Meeker

Walker, Chris ....(925) 943-8034
cwalker@bayareanewsgroup.com, Asst. Prof.,
Auburn University, AL, Auburn
cwalker@bayareanewsgroup.com, Reg. News
Ed., The Montclarion, CA, Alameda
cwalker@bayareanewsgroup.com, News Ed.,
Piedmonter, CA, Alameda
cwalker@bayareanewsgroup.com, Reg. News
Ed. , The Berkeley Voice, CA, Richmond
cwalker@bayareanewsgroup.com, News Ed.,
Alameda Journal, CA, Alameda

Walker, Chris ....(928) 453-4237
cwalker@havasunews.com, HR Mgr., Today's
News-Herald, AZ, Lake Havasu City

Walker, Dalton ....(304) 342-1011
dwalker@wvpress.org, Adv. Staff, West Virginia
Press Association, Inc., WV, Charleston

Walker, Daniel
editor@heraldbanner.com, Ed., Herald-Banner,
TX, Greenville

Walker, Darlene......................(256) 259-1020
darlene.walker@thedailysentinel.com,
Circulation Manager, The Daily Sentinel, AL,
Scottsboro

Walker, Dean ....(613) 332-2300
bancroft-times@sympatico.ca, Owner, The
Bancroft Times, ON, Bancroft

Walker, Deb ....1-(800) 321-0350 EXT 101
dwalker@scity.com, Customer Service, Steel
City Corp., OH, Ashland

Walker, Dianne
dianne@iowatelecom.net, Owner, Publisher/
Editor, Dunlap Reporter, IA, Dunlap

Walker, Donna ....(864) 298-4473
dwalker@greenvilleonline.com, City people
writer, The Greenville News, SC, Greenville

Walker, Elaine
ewalker@goanacortes.com, News Ed., Fidalgo
This Week, WA, Anacortes

Walker, Gregg ....(715) 356-5236
gm@lakelandtimes.com, Pub./Ed., The
Northwoods River News , WI, Rhinelander
gm@lakelandtimes.com, Pub./Ed., Northwoods
Super Shopper, WI, Rhinelander
gm@lakelandtimes.com, Gen. Mgr., Lakeland
Times, WI, Minocqua

Walker, Gregory......................(603) 352-1234

gwalker@keenesentinel.com, Press Frmn, The
Keene Sentinel, NH, Keene

Walker, Harold
harold.e.walker@usps.gov, Exec. Vice Pres./
CFO, United States Postal Service, DC,
Washington

Walker, James ....(740) 532-1441 Ext. 209
jim.walker@irontontribune.com, Sports Ed.,
The Ironton Tribune, OH, Ironton

Walker, James Herbert ....(512) 756-6136
james.walker@burnetbulletin.com, Burnet
Community Ed., Burnet Bulletin, TX, Burnet

Walker, Keith
kathy_may@westernlitho.com, Mktg. Mgr.,
Western LithoTech, MO, Springfield
kathy_may@westernlitho.com, Prodn. Mgr.,
Newspaper Product, Western LithoTech, MO,
Saint Louis

Walker, Ladele
ladele@foxbay.com, Pres., Fox Bay Industries,
Inc., WA, Auburn

Walker, Louise
lwalker@aspentimes.com, Adv. Acct. Mgr.,
Snowmass Sun, CO, Aspen

Walker, Lyn
clydejournal@earthlink.net, Ed./Adv. Dir., Baird
Banner, TX, Clyde
clydejournal@earthlink.net, Adv Dir, Clyde
Journal, TX, Clyde

Walker, Mark
mwalker@blackpress.ca, Director of Sales
and Marketing , Lake Country Calendar, BC,
Kelowna

Walker, Mark ....(859) 236-2551 Ext. 354
mwalker@amnews.com, Circ. Mgr., The
Advocate-Messenger, KY, Danville

Walker, Molly
micki@currycountyreporter.com, Co-Pub/Adv.,
Curry County Reporter, OR, Gold Beach

Walker, Pat ....(215) 949-4160
pwalker@calkins.com, Exec. Ed., Burlington
County Times, NJ, Willingboro
pwalker@calkins.com, Exec. Ed. , Bucks
County Courier Times, PA, Levittown
pwalker@calkins.com, Exec. Ed, The
Intelligencer, PA, Doylestown

Walker, Patricia ....(215) 949-4160
pwalker@calkins.com, Exec. Editor, Calkins
Media, PA, Levittown

Walker, Patricia S. Meagher ....ext. 4160
pwalker@phillyburbs.com, Executive Ed., The
Intelligencer, PA, Doylestown

Walker, Paul David
egazzette@valu-line.com, Pres., The Emporia
Gazette, KS, Emporia

Walker, Richard
rwalker@northkitsapherald.com, Ed., Kingston
Community News, WA, Poulsbo

Walker, Richard
rwalker@northkitsapherald.com, Ed., North
Kitsap Herald, WA, Poulsbo

Walker, Robin ....(843) 317-7232
rwalker@florencenews.com, Regional Adv. Dir.,
Morning News, SC, Florence

Walker, Rose
rose.walker@globegazette.com, Nat'l Adv.
Rep., Globe Gazette, Mason City, IA, Mason
City

Walker, Sherri ....(516) 667-4579
sherri.walker@sunmedia.ca, Dir., Reader
Sales, Service & Mktg., The London Free
Press, ON, London

Walker, Susan J. ....(773) 358-3128
s.walker@hpherald.com, VP/Gen. Mgr., Hyde
Park Herald, IL, Chicago

Walker, Tammy.................................Ext. 131
circulation@sandmountainreporter.com, Cir.
Mgr, Sand Mountain Reporter, AL, Albertville

Walter, Rick
rwalter@kmnewspaper.com, Vice Pres., Sales, K & M Newspaper Services, Inc., NY, Monroe

Walter, Timothy
twalter@catholicpress.org, Exec. Dir, Catholic Press Association, IL, Chicago

Walter, Veronica
ronnie.walter@mcall.com, The Morning Call, PA, Allentown

Walters, Barb .... (812) 523-7070
bwalters@tribtown.com, Adv. Admin., The Tribune, IN, Seymour

Walters, Bryan .... (740) 446-2342 Ext. 2101
bwalters@civitasmedia.com, Sports. Ed., Gallipolis Daily Tribune, OH, Gallipolis

Walters, Carla .... (765) 362-1200 Ext. 104
carla@jrpress.com, Cir. Mgr., Journal Review, IN, Crawfordsville

Walters, Jennifer .... (724) 779-7167
jwalters@tribweb.com, CFO, Trib Total Media, Inc., PA, Pittsburgh

Walters, Les
jrpaper@centurytel.net, Mgn. Ed., Journal Record, AL, Haleyville

Walters, Linda M.
linda@waubayclipper.com, Pub./Ed./Adv. Dir., Waubay Clipper, SD, Waubay

Walters, Mark .... (202) 650-6814
markwalters@cqrollcall.com, SVP, Advertising, Congressional Quarterly, Inc., DC, Washington

Walters, Ricky
sports@bentoncourier.com, Press Room Mgr., The Saline Courier, AR, Benton

Walters, Rob
rwalters@bristolnews.com, Mng. Ed., Bristol Herald Courier, VA, Bristol

Walters, Robert .... (718) 981-1234
bwalters@siadvance.com, Staten Island Advance, NY, Staten Island

Walters, Tanner
editor@media.ucla.edu, Ed. in Chief, University of California, Los Angeles, CA, Los Angeles

Walters, Tim .... (321) 242-3681
twalters@floridatoday.com, Visuals Editor, Florida Today, FL, Melbourne

Waltersdorf, Carrie .... (508) 693-6100 ext. 23
Adv. Dir., The Martha's Vineyard Times, MA, Vineyard Haven

Walther, Jim
jwalther@gulfcoastnewspapers.com, Pub., The Onlooker, AL, Foley

Waltner, Tim .... (605) 925-7033
courier@gwtc.net, Former publisher, The Freeman Courier, SD, Freeman

Walton, Charlie .... (304) 845-2260
mdsvecho@gmail.com, Pub./Gen. Mgr., Moundsville Daily Echo, WV, Moundsville

Walton, Cindy
cindy@pdclarion.com, Prod. Coord., Princeton Daily Clarion, IN, Princeton

Walton, Georgianne .... (803) 533-5518
gwalton@timesanddemocrat.com, Asst. Pub., The Times and Democrat, SC, Orangeburg

Walton, Jon
circulation@downriversundaytimes.com, Circ. Mgr., Dearborn Times-Herald, MI, Dearborn

Walton, Michael .... (302) 324-2638
miwalton@delawareonline.com, Sales Operations Director, The News Journal, DE, New Castle

Walton, Mike .... (920) 803-9945
mwalton@sheboygansun.com, The Sheboygan Sun, WI, Sheboygan

Walton, Shane .... (417) 334-3161
swalton@bransontrilakesnews.com, Advertising Manager, Branson Tri-Lakes

News, MO, Hollister

Waltzer, Carl
wdigital@nyc.rr.com, Pres., Carl Waltzer Digital Services, Inc., NY, New York

Waluszko, Alex
uvp@uvp.com, Vice Pres., Mktg./Sales, UVP, LLC, CA, Upland

Walz, Kent .... (505) 823-4444
kwalz@abqjournal.com, Ed-in-Chief, Albuquerque Journal, NM, Albuquerque

Walzak, Josh .... (814) 275-3131
jwalzak@thecourierexpress.com, Ed., The Leader-Vindicator, PA, New Bethlehem

Walzer, Robert
robert.walzer@wsj.com, Asst. Mng. Ed., The Daily Deal, NY, New York

Walzer, Steve .... (847) 486-7317
walzer@pioneerlocal.com, Regl./Nat'l Adv. Mgr., Morton Grove Champion, IL, Chicago

Walzer, Steve .... (847) 486-7317
walzer@pioneerlocal.com, Regl./Nat'l Adv. Mgr., Arlington Heights Post, IL, Chicago

Walzer, Steve .... (847) 486-7317
walzer@pioneerlocal.com, Regl./Nat'l Adv. Mgr., Niles Herald-Spectator, IL, Chicago

Walzer, Steve .... (847) 486-7317
walzer@pioneerlocal.com, Regl./Nat'l Adv. Mgr., Northbrook Star, IL, Chicago

Wambach, Jamie .... (262) 763-2575, ext. 150
jamiew@standardpress.com, Adv. Mgr., Burlington Standard Press, WI, Burlington

Wampler, Scotty .... (276) 935-2123
VirginiaMountaineer@gmail.com, Mng. Ed., The Virginia Mountaineer, VA, Grundy

Wamsley, Gary
gwamsley@hearstnp.com, Circ. Dir., Huron Daily Tribune, MI, Bad Axe

Wamsley, Gary .... (989) 839-4287
gwamsley@hearstnp.com, Circ. Dir., Midland Daily News, MI, Midland

Wamsley, Gary .... (970) 669-3272
editor@berthoudrecorder.com, Pub, ed, reporter, photographer, Colonel, CO, Loveland

Wamsley, Jay .... (435) 797-1757
jaywamsley@cc.usu.edu, Utah State Univ., UT, Logan

Wamsley, Patricia .... (740) 446-2342 Ext. 2093
pwamsley@civitasmedia.com, CSR, Gallipolis Daily Tribune, OH, Gallipolis

Wanbaugh, Michael .... (574) 533-2151 ext. 308
michael.wanbaugh@goshennews.com, Ed., Extra, IN, Goshen

Wandling, Barb
barb.Wandling@lee.net, Adv. Mgr., Jackson County Chronicle, WI, Black River Falls

Wandrei, Catherine
hr@berkshireeagle.com, HR, The Berkshire Eagle, MA, Pittsfield

Wane, Dena
dwane@btimes.com, Mng. Ed., The Baltimore Times, MD, Baltimore

Wanek, Robert
robertw@wahpetondailynews.com, Reporter, The Daily News, ND, Wahpeton

Wanfried, Kurt
kwanfried@oneidadispatch.com, Ed., Pennysaver, NY, Oneida

Wang, Emily
xwang14@uchicago.edu, Managing Editor, Univ. of Chicago, IL, Chicago

Wang, Frank .... (202) 895-1851
fywang@tecro.us, Dir. Press, Taipei Economic & Cultural Representative Office, Press Division - Washington, DC, Washington

Wang, Ming
ming@cypress.com, CFO, Acer America, CA,

San Jose

Wang, Weirui
weirui.wang@fiu.edu, Florida International University, FL, North Miami

Wang, Weiyan
aackerson@missouristate.edu, Assoc. Prof., Missouri State University, MO, Springfield

Wanlass, Don
dwanless@wavepublication.com, Mng. Ed., Wave Community Newspaper, CA, Los Angeles
dwanless@wavepublication.com, Ed, Los Angeles Wave, CA, Los Angeles

Wann, Chuck
lrlife@frontiernet.net, Pub., Lake Region Life, MN, New Prague

Wann, E. Charles .... (507) 364-8601
wade@montgomerymnnews.com, Pub., Montgomery Messenger, MN, Montgomery

Wann, E. Charles
cwann@newpraguetimes.com, Pub., The New Prague Times, MN, New Prague

Wanninger, Dawn
dawnw@thejewishchronicle.net, Prodn. Mgr., The Jewish Chronicle, PA, Pittsburgh

Waran, Lori
lori.waran@styleweekly.com, Publisher, Style Weekly, VA, Richmond

Warburton, Steven .... (613) 525-2020, ext.25
Mng. Ed., The Glengarry News, ON, Alexandria

Ward, Al
awward@gannett.com, Multimedia Ed., The Livingston County Daily Press & Argus, MI, Howell

Ward, Amelia Ashley
sundoc97@aol.com, Ed., Sun Reporter, CA, San Francisco

Ward, Amie
amie.ward@ttu.edu, Texas Tech University, TX, Lubbock

Ward, Barbara .... (315) 393-1003
bward@ogd.com, Adv. Mgr., Ogdensburg Journal/Advance News, NY, Ogdensburg

Ward, Brad .... (309) 743-0805
bward@townnews.com, CEO, TownNews, IL, Moline

Ward, Brian .... (902) 426-3088
brward@herald.ca, Assignment Ed., Day, The Chronicle Herald, NS, Halifax

Ward, Darryl D. .... (306) 842-7487
production@weyburnreview.com, Pub., Weyburn & Area Booster, SK, Weyburn

Ward, Don
pm.local@stpeters.sk.ca, Assoc. Ed., Order Of St. Benedict, SK, Muenster

Ward, Gary
gward@thestate.com, Managing Ed. for Online, The State, SC, Columbia

Ward, Heidi .... (262) 631-1742
heidi.ward@lee.net, Major/Nat'l Accts. Rep., The Journal Times, WI, Racine

Ward, Jennifer
jward@recordernewspapers.com, Advertising Sales Rep, New Jersey Hills Media Group, NJ, Whippany

Ward, Jennifer .... (810) 433-6822
jward@tctimes.com, General Manager, Tri-County Times, MI, Fenton

Ward, Jim .... (931) 329-1188
jward@marshalltribune.com, Adv. Mgr./Gen. Mgr., Marshall County Tribune, TN, Lewisburg

Ward, John .... (615) 259-8822
jajsward@gmail.com, VP, Sales, The Tennessean, TN, Nashville
jajsward@gmail.com, VP, Sales, TN Media, TN, Nashville

Ward, Katie .... (618) 374-4258

Principia College, IL, Elsah

Ward, Kelsi
kelsi.ward@my.und.edu, Features Editor, Univ. of North Dakota, ND, Grand Forks

Ward, Lee .... (606) 326-2661
lward@dailyindependent.com, Lifestyles Ed., The Daily Independent, KY, Ashland

Ward, Lucinda
buyer@iowatelecom.net, Pub., Bonny Buyer, IA, West Point

Ward, Mark .... (954) 574-5335
mward@tribune.com, Circ. Mgr., Margate / Coconut Creek Forum, FL, Fort Lauderdale
mward@tribune.com, Circ. Mgr., Delray Beach Forum, FL, Fort Lauderdale
mward@tribune.com, Royal Palm Forum (OOB), FL, Fort Lauderdale
mward@tribune.com, Circ. Mgr., Boynton Forum, FL, Fort Lauderdale
mward@tribune.com, Circ. Mgr., East Side Forum, FL, Fort Lauderdale
mward@tribune.com, Circ. Mgr., Deerfield and Pompano Forum, FL, Fort Lauderdale
mward@tribune.com, Circ. Mgr., Hi-Riser - Broward, FL, Pompano Beach
mward@tribune.com, Circ. Mgr., Boca Raton Forum, FL, Fort Lauderdale
mward@tribune.com, Circ. Mgr., The Forum - Sunrise & Tamarac, FL, Davie
mward@tribune.com, Circ. Mgr., Weston Gazette, FL, Fort Lauderdale
mward@tribune.com, Circ. Mgr., Oakland Park Gazette (OOB), FL, Fort Lauderdale
mward@tribune.com, Circ. Mgr., West Boca Forum, FL, Fort Lauderdale

Ward, Michael
michael@colliervilleherald.net, Ed., The Collierville Herald, TN, Collierville

Ward, Paul
pward@auroraadvertiser.net, Ad Manager, Big Aa Shopper, MO, Aurora

Ward, Richard
rward@hrblock.com, Pub., Wyandotte Daily News Weekly Print Edition, KS, Kansas City

Ward, Robin
rward@civitasmedia.com, Bus. Mgr./Adv. Rep., Amherst News-Times, OH, Oberlin
rward@civitasmedia.com, Bus. Mgr./Adv. Rep., Oberlin News-Tribune, OH, Oberlin
rward@civitasmedia.com, Bus. Mgr./Adv. Rep., Wellington Enterprise, OH, Oberlin

Ward, Terry .... (260) 347-0400
tward@kpcmedia.com, Chief Operating Officer, Smart Shopper, IN, Kendallville

Ward, Terry
tward@peninsuladailynews.com, Publisher, Peninsula Daily News, WA, Port Angeles

Ward, Terry .... (260) 426-2640 ext. 325
tward@kpcmedia.com, CEO, KPC Media Group, Inc., IN, Kendallville

Ward, Thomas V. .... (401) 334-9555 x 123
tward@valleybreeze.com, Pub., The Valley Breeze - Cumberland/Lincoln, RI, Lincoln

Ward, Tom .... (401) 334-9555 ext.123
tward@valleybreeze.com, Pub., The North Providence Breeze, RI, Lincoln
tward@valleybreeze.com, Pub., The Valley Breeze - Woonsocket/North Smithfield, RI, Lincoln
tward@valleybreeze.com, Pub., The Valley Breeze & Observer, RI, Lincoln
tward@valleybreeze.com, Pub., The Valley Breeze - Pawtucket, RI, Lincoln

Ward-Johnson, Frances
fward@elon.edu, Assoc. Prof., Elon University, NC, Elon

Wardeh, Dana
dwardeh@orlandosentinel.com, Nat'l Retail Dir., Orlando Sentinel, FL, Orlando

Wardell , Teresa
circulation@OKCTribune.com, Office Mgr., The Bethany Tribune, OK, Bethany

Warden, Don
wardpub@fidnet.com, Assoc., Gasconade County Republican, MO, Owensville

Wardle, Andrew .... **(229) 985-4545 x 1712**
andrew.wardle@gaflnews.com, Circ. Dir., The Moultrie Observer, GA, Moultrie

Wardle, Andrew ....(229) 244-3400 ext. 1286
andrew.wardle@gaflnews.com, VP Circ., Valdosta Daily Times, GA, Valdosta

Ware, Ashley
classified@threeriversnews.com, Classifieds, Three Rivers Commercial-News, MI, Three Rivers

Ware, Don
thetimes089@centurytel.net, Ed., The Times, OR, Brownsville

Ware, Janis L.
jlware4@aol.com, Pub., The Atlanta Voice, GA, Atlanta

Ware, Kim.................................**(817) 270-3340**
kimware@azlenews.net, Pub./Adv. Dir., Azle News, TX, Azle

Wareham Best, Jennifer ....**(707) 965-6437**
Chair, Pacific Union College, CA, Angwin

Warfel, Susan
susan.warfel@investors.com, Mng. Ed., Investor's Business Daily, CA, Los Angeles

Warg, Jean
jwarg@messengernews.net, Adv. Mgr., Class., The Messenger, IA, Fort Dodge

Wargo, John R.
jwargo@email.usps.gov, Sr. Vice Pres., Mktg. Devel., United States Postal Service, DC, Washington

Warmbir, Steve........................**(312) 321-3000**
swarmbir@suntimes.com, Dir of Dig. and Editorial Innovation, Chicago Sun-Times, IL, Chicago

Warnecke, Steve
swarnecke@newtonmedia.com, Director New Business Development, Newton Media Associates, Inc., VA, Chesapeake

Warneke, Deb ....**(402) 371-1020 ext. 2615**
dwarneke@norfolkdailynews.com, Bus. Mgr., Norfolk Daily News, NE, Norfolk

Warneke, Kent
editor@norfolkdailynews.com, Ed., Daily News Plus, NE, Norfolk

Warneke, Kent........................**(877) 371-1020**
editor@norfolkdailynews.com, Ed., Norfolk Daily News, NE, Norfolk

Warner, Bob
afitzpatrick@battlecreekenquirer.com, News Ed., Battle Creek Enquirer, MI, Battle Creek

Warner, Brooke
bwarner@nevadaappeal.com, Gen. Mgr. , Nevada Appeal, NV, Carson City

Warner, Byron
byron.warner@dioceseofnashville.com, Adv. Mgr., Tennessee Register, TN, Nashville

Warner, Charles
cwarner@civitasmedia.com, Mng. Ed., Union Daily Times, SC, Union

Warner, Daryl........................**(519) 823-6030**
dwarner@guelphmercury.com, Prodn. Mgr., The Guelph Mercury Tribune, ON, Guelph

Warner, David
david.warner@creativeloafing.com, Editor-in-Chief, Creative Loafing Tampa Bay, FL, Tampa

Warner, Gary ....**(479) 524-7255**
advocate@jbu.edu, John Brown Univ., AR, Siloam Springs

Warner, Gary ....**(785) 295-1138**
gary.warner@cjonline.com, Dir. of Circ. , Topeka Capital-Journal, KS, Topeka

Warner, Kathy

kathy@crossroadsnews.com, Adv. Mgr, CrossRoadsNews, GA, Decatur

Warner, Winnie
winnie.warner@bucknell.edu, Bucknell Univ., PA, Lewisburg

Warnick, Denny K.
galnews@eos.net, Pub., The Gallatin County News, KY, Warsaw

Warnimont, Charlie
sports@putnamsentinel.com, Sports Ed., Putnam County Sentinel, OH, Ottawa

Warnock, Dan ....**(813) 948-4227**
Tampa Bay Times, FL, St Petersburg

Warren, Carol ....**(859) 236-2551 Ext. 176**
cwarren@amnews.com, Classifieds Asst., The Advocate-Messenger, KY, Danville

Warren, Charles......................**(418) 665-1299**
hebdo@charlevoix.net, Hebdo Charlevoisien, QC, La Malbaie

Warren, Chris
cwarren@wickedlocal.com, Adv. Dir., Community Newspaper Co.-Metro, MA, Needham

Warren, Cindy
cwarren@thejournalnet.com, Daily Journal, IN, Franklin

Warren, Cris ....**(781) 433-8313**
cwarren@wickedlocal.com, Reg. Adv. Dir. , The Dedham Transcript, MA, Needham

Warren, Cris ....**(781) 433-8313**
cwarren@wickedlocal.com, Reg. Adv. Dir., Dover-Sherborn Press, MA, Needham

Warren, Cris
cwarren@wickedlocal.com, Reg. Adv. Dir. , Cambridge Chronicle & TAB, MA, Somerville

Warren, Cynthia......................**(770) 787-6397**
cbwarren@covnews.com, Adv. Mgr., The Covington News, GA, Covington

Warren, Dave........................**(603) 594-1270**
news@nashuatelegraph.com, IT Mgr., The Telegraph, NH, Nashua

Warren, Doug........................**(425) 347-5634**
artwork@mukilteobeacon.com, Graphics, Mukilteo Beacon, WA, Mukilteo

Warren, Doug...............................512232214
dwarren@austin.utexas.edu, Advisor, Texas Student Media, TX, Austin

Warren, Hillary........................**(614) 823-3377**
adviser@otterbein360.com, Advisor, Otterbein University, OH, Westerville

Warren, James
mail@chicagoreader.com, Pub., Reader, IL, Chicago

Warren, Joe
jwarren@countrymedia.net, Pub, Headlight-Herald, OR, Tillamook
jwarren@countrymedia.net, Pub./Ed., Lindsay Letter, TX, Lindsay

Warren, Joe
jwarren@countrymedia.net, Pub, The News Guard, OR, Lincoln City

Warren, Joe
joewarren@npgco.com, Pub/Ed, Hiawatha World, KS, Hiawatha
joewarren@npgco.com, Pub., The Daily Star-Journal, MO, Warrensburg

Warren, Joe..............**(913) 367-0583 ext. 20411**
joewarren@npgco.com, Pub./Ed., Atchison Globe, KS, Atchison

Warren, John
news@sdvoice.com, Ed., San Diego Voice & Viewpoint, CA, San Diego

Warren, Kira Lisa
liwarren@coxohio.com, Ed., JournalNews, OH, Hamilton

Warren, Mark........................**(586) 826-7499**
mwarren@hometownlife.com, Circ. Dir.,

Westland Observer, MI, Detroit

Warren, Mark........................**(734) 953-2199**
mwarren@oe.homecomm.net, Circ. Dir., Lake Orion Eccentric, MI, Detroit

Warren, Mark
mtwarren@hometownlife.com, Circ. Dir., Livonia Observer, MI, Detroit

Warren, Mark
mwarren@hometownlife.com, Circ. Dir., South Oakland Eccentric, MI, Detroit

Warren, Mark
mtwarren@hometownlife.com, Circ. Dir., Redford Observer, MI, Detroit

Warren, Mark........................**(586) 826-7499**
mwarren@hometownlife.com, Circ. Dir., Plymouth Observer, MI, Detroit

Warren, Richard J. ....**(207) 990-8221**
rwarren@bangordailynews.net, Pub., The Weekly, ME, Bangor

Warren, Richard J. ....**(207) 990-8220**
jluetjen@bangordailynews.com, Pub., Bangor Daily News, ME, Bangor

Warren, Stephanie
Stephanie.warren@tangilena.com, Ed, St. Helena Echo, LA, Greensburg

Warren, Timothy
twarren@thewarrengroup.com, CEO, Banker & Tradesman, MA, Boston

Warren, Troy..........................**(270) 783-3214**
twarren@bgdailynews.com, Circ. Mgr., Daily News, KY, Bowling Green

Warren, Wade
wwarren@cogdellhospital.com, Asst. Pub., Snyder Daily News, TX, Snyder

Warren-Till, Kelly....................**(757) 446-2000**
kelly.warren@pilotonline.com, Adv. Dir., The Virginian-Pilot, VA, Norfolk

Warshaw, Susan......................**(410) 554-8225**
Adv. Mgr., The Afro American Newspaper-washington, MD, Baltimore

Warsinskey, Eric
Editor@WatongaRepublican.com, Ed, Geary Star, OK, Geary
Editor@WatongaRepublican.com, Ed, Hinton Record, OK, Hinton
Editor@WatongaRepublican.com, Chief Ed, The Watonga Republican, OK, Watonga

Warsinskey, Tim ....**(216) 999-4370**
twarsinskey@plaind.com, Managing Editor, The Plain Dealer, OH, Brooklyn

Wartik, Maggie
mwartik@chicagotribune.com, Gen. Mgr. of Suburban Weeklies, Forest Leaves, IL, Chicago
mwartik@chicagotribune.com, Gen. Mgr. of Suburban Weeklies, Evanston Review, IL, Chicago
mwartik@chicagotribune.com, Gen. Mgr. of Suburban Weeklies, The Doings – Western Springs, IL, Chicago
mwartik@chicagotribune.com, Gen. Mgr. of Suburban Weeklies, The Doings – Oak Brook and Elmhurst, IL, Chicago
mwartik@chicagotribune.com, Gen. Mgr. of Suburban Weeklies, The Doings – La Grange, IL, Chicago
mwartik@chicagotribune.com, Gen. Mgr. of Suburban Weeklies, The Doings – Hinsdale, IL, Chicago
mwartik@chicagotribune.com, Gen. Mgr. of Suburban Weeklies, The Doings – Clarendon Hills, IL, Chicago
mwartik@chicagotribune.com, Gen. Mgr. of Suburban Weeklies, The Doings Weekly – Burr Ridge, IL, Chicago
mwartik@chicagotribune.com, Gen. Mgr. of Suburban Weeklies, Crown Point Star, IL, Chicago
mwartik@chicagotribune.com, Gen. Mgr. of Suburban Weeklies , Franklin Park Herald-Journal, IL, Chicago
mwartik@chicagotribune.com, Gen. Mgr. of

Suburban Weeklies, The Naperville Sun, IL, Chicago
mwartik@chicagotribune.com, Gen. Mgr. of Suburban Weeklies, Buffalo Grove Countryside, IL, Chicago
mwartik@chicagotribune.com, Gen. Mgr. of Suburban Weeklies, Deerfield Review, IL, Chicago
mwartik@chicagotribune.com, Gen. Mgr. of Suburban Weeklies, Chicago Tribune, IL, Chicago
mwartik@chicagotribune.com, Gen. Mgr. of Suburban Weeklies, Elmwood Park Leaves, IL, Chicago
mwartik@chicagotribune.com, Gen. Mgr. of Suburban Weeklies, Glencoe News, IL, Chicago
mwartik@chicagotribune.com, Gen. Mgr. of Suburban Weeklies, Glenview Announcements, IL, Chicago
mwartik@chicagotribune.com, Gen. Mgr. of Suburban Weeklies, Highland Park News, IL, Chicago
mwartik@chicagotribune.com, Gen. Mgr. of Suburban Weeklies, Arlington Heights Post, IL, Glenview
mwartik@chicagotribune.com, Gen. Mgr. of Suburban Weeklies, Lake Forester, IL, Chicago
mwartik@chicagotribune.com, Gen. Mgr. of Suburban Weeklies, Lake Zurich Courier, IL, Chicago
mwartik@chicagotribune.com, Gen. Mgr. of Suburban Weeklies, Libertyville Review, IL, Chicago
mwartik@chicagotribune.com, Gen. Mgr. of Suburban Weeklies, Lincolnshire Review, IL, Chicago
mwartik@chicagotribune.com, Gen. Mgr. of Suburban Weeklies, Lincolnwood Review, IL, Chicago
mwartik@chicagotribune.com, Gen. Mgr. of Suburban Weeklies, Morton Grove Champion, IL, Chicago
mwartik@chicagotribune.com, Gen. Mgr. of Suburban Weeklies, Mundelein Review, IL, Chicago
mwartik@chicagotribune.com, Gen. Mgr. of Suburban Weeklies, Niles Herald-Spectator, IL, Chicago
mwartik@chicagotribune.com, Gen. Mgr. of Suburban Weeklies, Norridge-Harwood Heights News, IL, Chicago
mwartik@chicagotribune.com, Gen. Mgr. of Suburban Weeklies, Northbrook Star, IL, Chicago
mwartik@chicagotribune.com, Gen. Mgr. of Suburban Weeklies, Oak Leaves, IL, Chicago
mwartik@chicagotribune.com, Gen. Mgr. of Suburban Weeklies, Park Ridge Herald Advocate, IL, Chicago
mwartik@chicagotribune.com, Gen. Mgr. of Suburban Weeklies, Skokie Review, IL, Chicago
mwartik@chicagotribune.com, Gen. Mgr. of Suburban Weeklies, Vernon Hills Review, IL, Chicago
mwartik@chicagotribune.com, Gen. Mgr. of Suburban Weeklies, Wilmette Life, IL, Chicago
mwartik@chicagotribune.com, Gen. Mgr. of Suburban Weeklies, Winnetka Talk, IL, Chicago
mwartik@chicagotribune.com, Gen. Mgr. of Suburban Weeklies, Barrington Courier-Review, IL, Glenview

Warwick, Dru
dru.warwick@sunmedia.ca, Prod. Mgr., The Edmonton Sun, AB, Edmonton

Wasch, Ken ....ext. 1310
ken.wasch@siia.net, Pres., Software & Information Industry Association, DC, Washington

Wash, Paul............................**(540) 949-8213**
pwash@newsvirginian.com, Circ. Dir., The News Virginian, VA, Waynesboro

Washburn, Carolyn
cwashburn@enquirer.com, Exec. Ed., Western Hills Press, OH, Cincinnati

cwashburn@enquirer.com, Ed., Northwest Press, OH, Cincinnati

cwashburn@enquirer.com, Exec. Ed., Price Hill Press, OH, Cincinnati

cwashburn@enquirer.com, Exec. Ed., Hilltop Press, OH, Cincinnati

cwashburn@enquirer.com, Exec. Ed., Delhi Press, OH, Cincinnati

Washburn, David
seniorvoice@gci.net, Mng Ed, Senior Voice, AK, Anchorage

Washburn, Diane .... (815) 942-3221
Adv. Dir., Morris Herald-News, IL, MORRIS

Washburn, Joel T. .... (731) 352-3323
washburn@mckenziebanner.com, Ed., McKenzie Banner, TN, Mc Kenzie

Washburn, Patrick .... (740) 593-2593
Prof., Ohio University, OH, Athens

Washington, Charles
pdxobserv@aol.com, Adv. Mgr., Portland Observer, OR, Portland

Washington, Isaac
scbnews@aol.com, Pres./CEO/Pub., Black News, SC, Columbia

Washington, James .... (214) 428-8958
jaws@dallasweekly.com, Pub., Dallas Weekly, TX, Dallas

Washington, James A.
swashington@theatlantavoice.com, Editor, The Atlanta Voice, GA, Atlanta

Washington, Linn
linn.washington@temple.edu, Assoc. Prof./ Dir., News-Ed. seq., Temple University, PA, Philadelphia

Washington, Mae .... (870) 543-1405
mwashington@bcommercial.com, Circ. Mgr. , Pine Bluff Commercial, AR, Pine Bluff

Washington, Romona .... (863) 386-5634
romona.washington@newssun.com, Exec. Ed., Highlands News-Sun, FL, Sebring

Washington, Taleen
washington@uhcl.edu, Univ. of Houston Clear Lake, TX, Houston

Wass, Douglas .... (780) 498-5716
Circ. Vice Pres., Reader Servs., Edmonton Journal, AB, Edmonton

Wasser, Scott .... (207) 791-6266
swasser@mainetoday.com, Exec. Ed., Saving Source, ME, Portland

Wasserman, Mark .... (215) 886-5662 x263
mwasserman@maned.com, Head of Global Sales and Marketing, Managing Editor, Inc., PA, Jenkintown

Wasson, Gale
busmgr@bedfordbulletin.com, Bus. Mgr., Bedford Bullet, VA, Bedford

Wataha, Jemie .... (785) 776-2200 Ext. 225
jwataha@themercury.com, Office Mgr., The Manhattan Mercury, KS, Manhattan

Waterhouse, Gordon
gwaterhouse@medicinehatnews.com, Circ. Dir., Medicine Hat News, AB, Medicine Hat

Waterloo, Michael ....
(717) 272-5611 x159
michaelwaterloo@ldnews.com, Features Ed., The Lebanon Daily News, PA, Lebanon

Waterman, Don
don.waterman@dowjones.com, Senior Vice President, Printing & Distribution , Dow Jones Local Media Group, NY, Middletown

Waterman, Ken
ken.waterman@sunmedia.ca, Prodn. Mgr., The Winnipeg Sun, MB, Winnipeg

Waterman, Sally
swaterman@minnpost.com, Ad. Director, MinnPost, MN, Minneapolis

Waters, Betty

advertising@tylerpaper.com, Educ. Ed., Tyler Morning Telegraph, TX, Tyler

Waters, Bill J. .... (775) 850-2285
Cor. Controller, Swift Communications, Inc., NV, Carson City

Waters, Bradley
bwaters@rny.com, Adv. Dir., Daily Sentinel, NY, Rome

Waters, Carla
nceeditor@centurylink.net, Pub, Morocco Courier, IN, Kentland

nceeditor@centurylink.net, Mng. Ed., The Newton County Enterprise, IN, Kentland

Waters, Carla
cwaters@intranix.com, Mng. Ed., Times-Republic, IL, Watseka

Waters, George
george@georgewaters.net, Humor Columnist, George Waters

Waters, Jana .... (870) 972-2961
Advertising Manager, Arkansas State Univ., AR, State University

Waters, Jeff .... (386) 362-1734 x131
jeff.waters@gaflnews.com, Editor, Mayo Free Press, FL, Live Oak

jeff.waters@gaflnews.com, Editor, Suwannee Democrat, FL, Live Oak

jeff.waters@gaflnews.com, Ed., Jasper News, FL, Live Oak

Waters, Jenee
jwaters@beenews.com, Ed., West Seneca Bee, NY, Williamsville

Waters, Jessica
jwaters@thetoccoarecord.com, News Ed., The Toccoa Record, GA, Toccoa

Waters, Russell .... (386) 754-0407
rwaters@lakecityreporter.com, Circ. Dir., Lake City Reporter, FL, Lake City

Waters, Sam
swaters@dailyrepublicannews.com, Circ. Dir. , Benton Evening News, IL, Benton

Waters, Stephen B.
sbwaters@rny.com, Pub., Daily Sentinel, NY, Rome

Waters, Thomas R. .... (214) 369-7570
tom@parkcitiesnews.com, Ed./Gen. Mgr., Park Cities News, TX, Dallas

Waters, Wendall
ipswich@wickedlocal.com, Ed., Ipswich Chronicle, MA, Danvers

Waterstone, Jared
jared.waterstone@advisorsource.com, Circ. Dir., Adviser & Source, MI, New Baltimore

Watkins, Bruce
news@coushattacitizen.com, Ed/Adv Rep, Coushatta Citizen Shopper, LA, Coushatta

Watkins, Candacee
csutherland@coalfield.com, Account Exec., The Dickenson Star, VA, Clintwood

Watkins, Dale .... (718) 636-9500
Marketing Director, New York Daily Challenge, NY, Brooklyn

Watkins, Haley .... (870) 946-3933
graphics@dewitt-ee.com, Graphic Designer, De Witt Era-Enterprise, AR, De Witt

Watkins, John
dipub@ridgecrestca.com, Pub., Daily Midway Driller, CA, Taft

Watkins, John
dipub@richcrustca.com, Pub., Bargain Hunter, CA, Taft

Watkins, John .... ext. 101
dipub@ridgecrestca.com, Pub., The Daily Independent, CA, Ridgecrest

Watkins, Lynne
lwatkins@dailyadvance.com, IS Manager, The Daily Advance, NC, Elizabeth City

Watkins, Pam .... (972) 480-8383
pam_watkins@mccom.com, SVP, Business and Media Strategy, M/C/C, TX, Dallas

Watkins, Pat
pwatkins@coastalcourier.com, Web Ed., The Coastal Courier, GA, Hinesville

Watkins, Pat
pwatkins@coastalcourier.com, Mng. Ed., Tri-county Pennysaver, GA, Hinesville

Watkins, Patsy .... (479) 575-3601
pwatkins@uark.edu, Chair/Assoc. Prof., University of Arkansas, AR, Fayetteville

Watkins, Thomas H.
challengegroup@yahoo.com, Pub., New York Daily Challenge, NY, Brooklyn

Watkins, Thomas H.
challengegroup@yahoo.com, Pub., Afro Times, NY, Brooklyn

Watkins, Thomas H.
challengegroup@yahoo.com, Pub., The New American, NY, Brooklyn

Watkins, Wendy
wendy@thegraftonnews.com, Graphic Designer, The Grafton Villager, MA, South Grafton

Watley, Sylvia .... (601) 979-2167
sylvia.t.watley@jsums.edu, Jackson State University, MS, Jackson

Watness, Philip .... (509) 427-8444
scpioneernews@gorge.net, Ed., Skamania County Pioneer, WA, Stevenson

Watson, Andrea
andrea.watson@ttu.edu, Asst Dir/Media Advisor, Texas Tech University, TX, Lubbock

Watson, Bettie .... (517) 629-0041
news@albionrecorder.com, Adv. Mgr., Mid Michigan Buyer's Guide, MI, Alma

Watson, Bettie
thesalesman@frontiernet.net, The Salesman, MI, Concord

Watson, Bob .... ext. 203
boosterads@swbooster.com, Pub., The Southwest Booster, SK, Swift Current

Watson, Brian .... (360) 8007-8219
bwatson@chronline.com, Sales Dir., The Chronicle, WA, Centralia

Watson, Chris .... (831) 423-4242 ext. 263
cwatson@santacruzsentinel.com, Books Ed., Santa Cruz Sentinel, CA, Scotts Valley

Watson, Crystal
advertising@tiogand.com, Ad. Mgr., Tioga Tribune, ND, Tioga

Watson, Deanna .... (940) 720-3491
watson@timesrecordnews.com, Ed., Wichita Falls Times Record News, TX, Wichita Falls

Watson, Debbie
debbiew@theheraldtimes.com, Front Office Mgr., The Rio Blanco Herald Times, CO, Meeker

Watson, Eric .... (484) 365-7524
ewatson@lincoln.edu, Lincoln Univ., PA, Lincoln University

Watson, George
g.watson@asu.edu, Prof., Arizona State University, AZ, Tempe

Watson, Greg .... (321) 242-3927
gwatson@floridatoday.com, Sales and Marketing Dir., Florida Today, FL, Melbourne

Watson, Jewell .... (336) 727-4080
jwatson@wsjournal.com, Sports Editor, Winston-Salem Journal, NC, Winston Salem

Watson, John
jwatson@american.edu, Assoc. Prof., American University, DC, Washington

Watson, John .... (716) 875-3380
jwatson@hfwindustries.com, Pres., HFW Industries, NY, Buffalo

Watson, Linda .... (563) 659-3121
observer@iowatelecom.net, News editor, The Observer, IA, De Witt

Watson, Mark
news@bhpioneer.com, Ed., Black Hills Pioneer, SD, Spearfish

Watson, Mark
news@bhpioneer.com, Ed., Weekly Prospector, SD, Spearfish

Watson, Mark
news@bhpioneer.com, Ed., Nation's Center News, SD, Buffalo

Watson, Mary Jo .... (940) 567-2616
advmgr@jacksboronewspapers.com, Ad manager, Jacksboro Herald-Gazette, TX, Jacksboro

Watson, Monica
monica@eacourier.com, Pub., The Copper Era, AZ, Safford

Watson, Rachel .... (706) 823-3360
rachel.watson@augustachronicle.com, Administrative Assistant to the President, The Augusta Chronicle, GA, Augusta

Watson, Randi .... (360) 405-9161
rwatson@kitsapsun.com, Pre Press Mgr., Kitsap Sun, WA, Bremerton

Watson, Rebecca .... (989) 269-6461
rwatson@hearstnp.com, General Manager, Huron Daily Tribune, MI, Bad Axe

Watson, Robert (Bob) .... (815) 244-2411
bwatson@grics.net, Ed./Pub./Owner, Carroll County Mirror-Democrat, IL, Mount Carroll

Watson, Robert W.
savtj@grics.net, Ed./Pub., Savanna Times-Journal, IL, Savanna

Watson, Roger .... (540) 213-9107
rwatson@newsleader.com, Pub., The News Leader, VA, Staunton

rwatson@newsleader.com, Gen. Mgr., Gallatin News Examiner, TN, Gallatin

Watson, Sam .... ext. 328
swatson@johnsoncitypress.com, Educ./School Ed., Johnson City Press, TN, Johnson City

Watson, Sean 1 (506) 343-4705
watson.sean@brunswicknews.com, Sr. Director of Distribution & Logistics, New Brunswick Telegraph-Journal, NB, Saint John

Watson, Sharon .... (913) 715-0725
sharon.watson@jocogov.org, Director of Public Affairs and Communications, The Best Times, KS, Olathe

Watson, Sioux
swatson@indyweek.com, Pub., The Independent Weekly, NC, Durham

Watson, Susan
nebpress@nebpress.com, Admin. Asst./ Press Release Coord., Nebraska Press Association/Nebraska Press Advertising Service, NE, Lincoln

Watson, Thomas
twatson@livent.net, Sports Editor, The Livingston Enterprise, MT, Livingston

Watson, Tom
tomwatson@csu.edu.au, Assoc. Prof./Head of School, Charles Stuart University, Bathurst

Watson, Vanessa 5208924
vanessam@marlexpress.co.nz, General Manager, THE MARLBOROUGH EXPRESS, Blenheim

Watson, Vickie .... (863) 386-5631
vickie.watson@newssun.com, Adv. Rep., Highlands News-Sun, FL, Sebring

Watt, Earl
earl@hpleader.com, Pub., The Leader & Times, KS, Liberal

Watt, Jenn
jenn@haliburtonpress.com, Managing Ed., The Bancroft Times, ON, Bancroft

Watt, Jenn
jenn@haliburtonpress.com, Mng. Ed, Bancroft
This Week, ON, Bancroft

Watt, Jenn .... (705) 457-1037
Ed., The Minden Times, ON, Minden

Watt, Peggy
peggy.watt@wvu.edu, Asst. Prof., Western
Washington University, WA, Bellingham

Wattenburger, Daniel .... (541) 278-2673
dwattenburger@eastoregonian.com, Managing
Editor, East Oregonian, OR, Pendleton

Watterson, Tonia
classified@thenews-gazette.com, Classified
Adv. Dir., The News-Gazette, VA, Lexington

Watts, Don .... (814) 368-3173
d.watts@bradfordera.com, Cir. Mng., The
Bradford Era, PA, Bradford

Watts, Michael
prodmgr@dailyjm.com, Pressroom Mgr., Daily
Journal/Messenger, SC, Seneca

Waugaman, Bill .... (330) 841-1600
wwaugaman@tribtoday.com, Cir. Dir., The
Tribune Chronicle, OH, Warren

Waugh, Diane
dwaugh@mikes.net, The Daily Clintonian , IN,
Clinton

Waugh, Margaret
leaderbeacon@qwestoffice.net, Adv. Mgr.,
Fremont-Mills Beacon-Enterprise, IA,
Malvern
leaderbeacon@qwestoffice.net, Adv. Mgr., The
Malvern Leader, IA, Malvern

Waugh, Tyler
news@hintonvoice.ca, Pub., The Hinton Voice,
AB, Hinton

Waxelbaum, Steve .... (561) 820-3405
swaxelbaum@pbpost.com, Adv. Mgr., Retail,
Bureau Offices, The Palm Beach Post, FL,
West Palm Beach

Way, Janet
Sdnadvertising@aol.com, Ad., Southern
Dutchess News, NY, Wappingers Falls

Way, Janet
Sdnadvertising@aol.com, Ad., Beacon Free
Press, NY, Wappingers Falls

Waybrant, Roxanne.............................. ex. 18
roxanne@richfieldreaper.com, reaperad@
richfieldreaper.com, Adv. Mgr., The Richfield
Shopper, UT, Richfield

Wayne, Robert N....................... (813) 259-7622
Tampa Bay Times, FL, St Petersburg

Wayt, Mary .... (252) 793-2123
beaconmary@mchsi.com, Pub./Ed., The
Roanoke Beacon, NC, Plymouth

Weafer, Mike .... (270) 691-7285
mweafer@messenger-inquirer.com, Ops. Mgr.,
Messenger-Inquirer, KY, Owensboro

Weakley, Laura............. (217) 698-8500 ext. 115
lweakley@dio.org, Circ. Mgr., Catholic Times,
IL, Springfield

Weakley, Nancy
nweakley@unitedad.com, Adv. Sales Mgr.,
DallasChild, TX, Addison

Wear, Jay .... (270) 691-7323
jwear@messenger-inquirer.com, Mailroom
Mgr., Messenger-Inquirer, KY, Owensboro

Weare, John ....(308) 762-3060 ext. 24
athnews@alliancetimes.com, Mng. Ed.,
Alliance Times-Herald, NE, Alliance

Weare, John E.
athnews@alliancetimes.com, Mng. Editor , T-h
Plus, NE, Alliance

Wearne, Dorothy
wearned@lanecc.edu, Lane Cmty. College,
OR, Eugene

Weasel Fat, Tracy
ad@templecitystar.net, Production Manager,
Temple City Star, AB, Cardston

Weatherford, Jillian
jweatherford@kentuckynewera.com, Adv. Rep.,
Kentucky New Era, KY, Hopkinsville

Weatherly, Mona
chiefnews@custercountychief.com, Exec Ed,
Custer County Chief, NE, Broken Bow

Weatherred, Jenna
mail@aspentimes.com, Pub., The Aspen
Times, CO, Aspen

Weaver, Amy .... (423) 335-2628
info@thenorthernlight.com, Southwest U.S.
Sales manager, Vision Data Equipment
Corp., NY, Rensselaer

Weaver, Barry
bweaver@kitsapsun.com, Classified Adv. Mgr.,
Kitsap Sun, WA, Bremerton

Weaver, Bill
bweaver@aliceechonews.com, Pub./Ed.,
Nueces County Record-Star, TX, Alice

Weaver, Bill................. (361) 664-6588 ext. 212
bweaver@aliceechonews.com, Adv. Dir., Alice
Echo-News Journal, TX, Alice
bweaver@aliceechonews.com, Adv. Dir., Freer
Press, TX, Alice

Weaver, Casey
cweaver@postindependent.com, Advertising
sales, Glenwood Springs Post Independent,
CO, Glenwood Springs

Weaver, Curt......................................ext. 207
production@columbiabasinherald.com, Prodn.
Supt., Columbia Basin Herald, WA, Moses
Lake

Weaver, David........................ (540) 981-3186
david.weaver@roanoke.com, Business
Manager, The Roanoke Times, VA, Roanoke

Weaver, David
dweaver@couriernews.com, Prod. Mgr., The
Courier, AR, Russellville

Weaver, Gordon .... (559) 583-2434
Circulation Manager, The Kingsburg Recorder,
CA, Hanford

Weaver, Kristen .... (830) 216-4519
kristen@wcn-online.com, Op. Dir., Wilson
County News, TX, Floresville

Weaver, Kristen .... (830) 216-4519
kristen@wcn-online.com, Adv. Dir., La Vernia
News, TX, La Vernia

Weaver, Mike.......................... (352) 563-3275
mweaver@chronicleonline.com, Prodn. Mgr.,
Pressroom, Citrus County Chronicle, FL,
Crystal River

Weaver, Mike.......................... (909) 866-3456
mweaver@bigbeargrizzly.net, Marketing
Director, Grizzly Weekender, CA, Big Bear
Lake

Weaver, Mike .... (909) 866-3456 x129
mweaver@bigbeargrizzly.net, Marketing
Director, Big Bear Grizzly, CA, Big Bear Lake

Weaver, Nate .... (620) 694-5700 Ext. 253
nweaver@hutchnews.com, Graphic Designer,
The Hutchinson News, KS, Hutchinson

Weaver, Penny .... (217) 238-6863
pweaver@jg-tc.com, Editor, Journal Gazette &
Times-Courier, IL, Mattoon

Weaver, Rebecca .... ext. 3611
rweaver@express-times.com, Credit Mgr., The
Express-Times, PA, Easton

Weaver, Rick .... (406) 755-7000
rvweaver@dailyinterlake.com, Publisher, Daily
Inter Lake, MT, Kalispell

Weaver, Rob........................... (419) 448-3251
rweaver@advertiser-tribune.com, Ed., The
Advertiser-Tribune, OH, Tiffin

Weaver, Sarah........................ (801) 204-6110
gerry@deseretnews.com, Church News Ed.,
Deseret News, UT, Salt Lake City

Weaver, Sherry
sherry.weaver@goshennews.com, Adv. Sales
Rep., The Goshen News, IN, Goshen

Weaver, Susan
scuc@ptd.net, Pres./Pub./Ed., Snyder County
Times, PA, Middleburg

Weaver, Taylor
tweaver@postmedia.com, Ed, Lloydminster
Meridian Booster, AB, Lloydminster

Weaver, Timothy J. .... (215) 345-3099
tweaver@phillyburbs.com, Controller, The
Intelligencer, PA, Doylestown

Weaver, Tom
sales@kiosk.com, Vice Pres., Sales/Mktg.,
Kiosk Information Systems, CO, Louisville

Weaver-Curran, Tracey
tcurran@bowesnet.com, Sales Mgr., Chatham
Pennysaver, ON, Chatham

Webb, Angie
ads@cseagle.com, Advt Dir, Chadron State
College, NE, Chadron

Webb, Cary
cwebb@northernnecknews.com, Pub.,
Northern Neck News, VA, Warsaw

Webb, Don
dwebb@epiphanydanville.org, Audiotex Mgr.,
Danville Register & Bee, VA, Danville

Webb, Gregg
sports@weatherforddemocrat.com, Sports Ed.,
The Weatherford Democrat, TX, Weatherford

Webb, James.......................... (252) 329-9665
Facilities Mgr., The Daily Reflector, NC,
Greenville

Webb, James A. Jr.
JWebb@webbweekly.com, Pub., Webb Weekly,
PA, South Williamsport

Webb, Joe
production@chippewa.com, Prodn. Mgr.,
Advertiser, WI, Chippewa Falls

Webb, Joe
production@chippewa.com, Prodn. Mgr., Your
Family Shopper, WI, Chippewa Falls

Webb, Kathi
kathi@thesheridanheadlight.com, Bus. Mgr.,
Sheridan Headlight, AR, Sheridan

Webb, Lynn .... (252) 265-7845
lynn@wilsontimes.com, Circ. Dir., The Wilson
Times, NC, Wilson

Webb, Marsha .... (601) 384-2484
advocate@telepak.net, Ed./Pub., Franklin
Advocate, MS, Meadville

Webb, Michael .... (919) 462-0900
michael@theromantic.com, Writer, The
RoMANtic Syndicated Column, Cary

Webb, Misty
mwebb@dothaneagle.com, Adv. Rep., Dothan
Progress, AL, Dothan

Webb, Renee
rwebb@catholicglobe.org, Ed., The Globe, IA,
Sioux City

Webb, Robin........................... (765) 213-5759
rwebb@muncie.gannett.com, Adv. Sales Exec.,
The Star Press, IN, Muncie

Webb, Tam .... (402) 444-3125
tam.webb@owh.com, Adv. Mgr., Custom
Publishing/Events, Omaha World-Herald,
NE, Omaha

Webb, Thomas K.
psaver@netsink.net, Pub., The Silver Creek
Pennysaver, NY, Fredonia

Webb, Thomas K.
psaver@netsink.net, Pub., Dunkirk/fredonia/
westfield Pennysaver, NY, Fredonia

Webb, Tim
twebb@bemidjipioneer.com, Home Delivery
Mgr., The Bemidji Pioneer, MN, Bemidji

Webb, Tom
mark@fredoniapennysaver.com, Fredonia
Pennysaver, NY, Fredonia

Webb, Travis....................(830) 379-5441 x 218
travis.webb@seguingazette.com, Managing
Editor, The Seguin Gazette, TX, Seguin

Webb, Victor
marwebint@cs.com, Pres., Marston Webb
International, NY, New York

Webb , Jessica .... (828) 488-2189
editor@thesmokymountaintimes.com, Ed., The
Smoky Mountain Times, NC, Bryson City

Webb Martin, Louise
lmartin@tampatrib.com, Tampa Bay Times, FL,
St Petersburg

Webber, Blake......................... (415) 297-8836
cwcma@imblake.com, Executive Director, Cal
Western Circulation Managers' Association,
CA, Novato

Webber, Karen .... (508) 793-9232
karen.webber@telegram.com, Exec. Ed.,
Telegram & Gazette, MA, Worcester

Webber, Kim
amckeehan@mycentraljersey.com, The Courier
News, TN, Clinton

Webber, Mark .... (952) 392-6807
mark.weber@ecm-inc.com, Gen. Mgr., Eden
Prairie Sun-Current, MN, Eden Prairie

Webber, Suzanne .... (219) 785-5213
Purdue Univ. North Central, IN, Westville

Weber, Bill .... (800) 399-4294
bill@bob-weber.com, Business Development
Director, Bob Weber, Inc., OH, Cleveland

Weber, Christine
chrisw@wyodaily.com, People Page Ed.,
Northern Wyoming Daily News, WY, Worland

Weber, Doris M.
comp.aps@newulmtel.net, Ed., Springfield
Advance-Press, MN, Springfield

Weber, Eric .... (918) 496-8103
sales@smartmax.com, Pres., SmartMax
Software, Inc., OK, Tulsa

Weber, Jeff
jeff@jeffweber.net, Pres., Weber Systems, Inc.,
OH, Beachwood

Weber, Jim S.
info@nwintl.com, Pres., Neasi-Weber
International, CA, Valencia

Weber, Joyce .... (780) 349-3033 Ext. 1
jweber@westlock.greatwest.ca, Adv., The
Westlock News, AB, Westlock

Weber, Kate .... (815) 526-4400
KWeber@ShawMedia.com, Publisher,
Northwest Herald, IL, Crystal Lake

Weber, Kenda .... (309) 757-8377
kweber@qconline.com, Media Sales Manager,
The Dispatch-Argus, IL, Moline

Weber, Mark
editor@reddeerexpress.com, Ed, Red Deer
Express, AB, Red Deer

Weber, Mark .... (952) 392-6807
mark.weber@ecm-inc.com, Gen. Mgr, The
Gold Miner, MN, Waconia

Weber, Mark.......................... (952) 392-6807
mark.weber@ecm-inc.com, Gen Mgr
Excelsior/Shorewood/Chanhassen Sun
Sailor, MN, Eden Prairie

Weber, Mark
mark.weber@ecm-inc.com, Gen. Mgr.,
Southwest Suburban Publishing, MN,
Shakopee
mark.weber@ecm-inc.com, Gen. Mgr.,
Champlin-Dayton Press, MN, Osseo
mark.weber@ecm-inc.com, Gen. Mgr., St.
Louis Park Sun Sailor, MN, Osseo
mark.weber@ecm-inc.com, Gen. Mgr., Osseo-
Maple Grove Press, MN, Osseo
mark.weber@ecm-inc.com, Gen. Mgr., South
Crow River News, MN, Osseo

mark.weber@ecm-inc.com, Gen. Mgr.,
Rockford Area News Leader, MN, Osseo
mark.weber@ecm-inc.com, Gen. Mgr.,
Brooklyn Center/Brooklyn Park Sun-Post,
MN, Osseo
mark.weber@ecm-inc.com, Gen. Mgr., North
Crow River News, MN, Osseo

Weber, Mark
mweber@diocesefwsb.org, News Specialist,
Today's Catholic, TX, San Antonio

Weber, Maureen
pm.canadian@stpeterspress.ca, Assoc. Ed.,
Order Of St. Benedict, SK, Muenster

Weber, Rob .... (412) 263-1693
rweber@post-gazette.com, Director of
Operations, Pittsburgh Post-Gazette, PA,
Clinton

Weber, Stephanie .... (719) 476-4857
stephanie.weber@gazette.com, VP of IT and
Digital Development, The Gazette, CO,
Colorado Springs

Weber, Tad .... (559) 441-6491
tweber@fresnobee.com, Metro Ed, The Fresno
Bee, CA, Fresno

Weber, Wade
wweber@moraminn.com, Pub., Kanabec
County Times, MN, Mora

Webster, Carol .... (780) 333-2100
sgazett@telusplanet.net, Ed., Grizzly Gazette,
AB, Swan Hills

Webster, Gordon
gordon@thebusinessjournal.com, Pub., The
Business Journal, CA, Fresno

Webster, Joyce .... (403) 578-4111
publisher@ECAreview.com, Pub, East Central
Alberta Review, AB, Coronation

Webster, Mark .... (843) 626-0251
mwebster@thesunnews.com, Pub., The Sun
News, SC, Myrtle Beach

Webster, Paige .... ((508) 967-3120
pwebster@wickedlocal.com, Adv. Dir. , Taunton
Daily Gazette, MA, Taunton

Webster, Pattie
pwebster@thevermontstandard.com, Office
Coordinator, The Vermont Standard, VT,
Woodstock

Webster, Tara
twebster@bnd.com, Belleville News-Democrat,
IL, Belleville

Weddell, Jim .... (915) 546-6370
jweddell@elpasotimes.com, VP of Online/
Digital, El Paso y Mas, TX, El Paso

Weddle, Chris .... (760) 778-4709
Christopher.Weddle@DesertSun.com, Prod.,
The Desert Sun, CA, Palm Springs

Weddle, Steve .... (540) 967-0368
vavp@thecentralvirginian.com, Publisher, The
Central Virginian, VA, Louisa

Weddle, Tim .... (816) 271-8510
tim.weddle@newspressnow.com, Adv. Dir., St.
Joseph News-Press, MO, Saint Joseph

Wedel, Channing
Channing.Wedel@wagonercountyat.com,
Class./Inside Sales, Wagoner Tribune, OK,
Wagoner

Wedel, Megan
mwedel@duluthnews.com, Advertising
Director, Duluth News Tribune, MN, Duluth

Wedel, Megan .... (218) 461-9256
mwedel@duluthnews.com, Adv. Dir., Superior
Telegram, WI, Superior

Wedge, Maureen
mwedge@sunjournal.com, Vice Pres., HR, Sun
Media Group, ME, Lewiston

Wee, Eric
ericw@ediwise.com, EDIWISE, ON,
Mississauga

Weedmark, Kevin
world_spectator@sasktel.net, Ed., World-
spectator, SK, Moosomin

Weekley, David
dcweekley@ualr.edu, Instr., University of
Arkansas at Little Rock, AR, Little Rock

Weeks, Birgit
bweeks@powhatantoday.com, Adv. Mgr.,
Powhatan Today, VA, Powhatan

Weeks, Colette
cweeks@skagitpublishing.com, Mng. Ed.,
Administration, Skagit Valley Herald, WA,
Mount Vernon

Weeks, Colette .... (360) 293-3122 x1040
cweeks@goanacortes.com, Ed. / Gen. Mgr,
Anacortes American, WA, Anacortes

Weeks, Ray .... (806) 323-6461
advertising@canadianrecord.com, Adv. Mgr.,
The Canadian Record, TX, Canadian

Weems, Amber
amber@thepicayune.com, COO/Pub., The
Picayune, TX, Marble Falls
amber@thepicayune.com, Pres./Pub./Adv.
Sales, DailyTrib.com, TX, MARBLE FALLS

Weese, Brad .... (785) 657-7417
thesheridansentinel@gmail.com, Owner/
Advertising & Journalist/Publisher, The
Sheridan Sentinel, KS, Hoxie

Weesner, Betty Jean .... (317) 745-2777
therepublican@sbcglobal.net, Pub., The
Republican, IN, Danville

Weetman, Cathy
cweetman@postmedia.com, Ed, Drayton Valley
Western Review, AB, Drayton Valley

Weets, Monica .... (320) 676-3123
mweets@millelacsmessenger.com, Adv., Mille
Lacs Messenger, MN, Isle

Wegner, Dale P. .... (712) 662-7161
sacsuneditor@frontiernet.net, Ed./Gen. Mgr.,
The Sac Sun, IA, Sac City

Wehenkel, Arthur D .... (423) 359-3160
artie.wehenkel@greenevillesun.com, Adv. Dir.,
The Greeneville Sun, TN, Greeneville

Wehking, Jakki
ppinews@me.com, Co-Pub/Ed., The Parkers
Prairie Independent, LLC, MN, Parkers
Prairie

Wehle, Greg
greg.wehle@bulletinreview.com, Pub., Denison
Bulletin & Review, IA, Denison

Wehle, Greg
greg.wehle@bulletinreview.com, Crawford
County Advisor, IA, Denison

Wehle, Lori
lori.wehle@bulletinreview.com, Adv. Sales
Rep., Denison Bulletin & Review, IA, Denison

Wehmer, Dan
citizen@webstercountycitizen.com, Ed.,
Webster County Citizen, MO, Seymour

Wehmer, Dan
citizen@webstercountycitizen.com, Ed.,
Webster County Advertiser, MO, Seymour

Wehmueller, John .... (301) 670-2052
Sports Ed., The Gazette - Damascus /
Clarksburg, MD, Gaithersburg
Sports Ed., The Gazette - Rockville / Aspen Hill
/ Wheaton (OOB), MD, Gaithersburg
Sports Ed., The Gazette - Silver Spring /
Takoma Park / Burtonsville (OOB), MD,
Gaithersburg
Sports Ed., The Gazette - Olney (OOB), MD,
Gaithersburg
Sports Ed., The Gazette - Germantown /
Poolsville / Boyds (OOB), MD, Gaithersburg
Sports Ed., The Gazette - Bethesda /
Chevy Chase / Kensington (OOB), MD,
Gaithersburg
Sports Ed., The Gazette - Gaithersburg / Mont.
Village (OOB), MD, Gaithersburg
Sports Ed., The Gazette - North / Central

Prince George Co. (OOB), MD, Gaithersburg
Sports Ed., The Gazette - South / Central
Prince George Co. (OOB), MD, Gaithersburg
Sports Ed., The Gazette - Potomac / North
Potomac, MD, Gaithersburg
Sports Ed., Business Gazette, MD,
Gaithersburg

Wehrhahn, Tom .... (419) 739-3515
editor@wapakwdn.com, Wapakoneta Daily
News, OH, Wapakoneta

Wehrman, Cecile .... (701) 965-6088
Past President, North Dakota Newspaper
Association, ND, Bismarck

Weibert, Will .... (660) 826-1000
will@sedaliademocrat.com , Publisher,
Whiteman Warrior, MO, Whiteman Afb

Weideman, Paul .... (505) 986-3043
reguide@sfnewmexican.com, Ed., HomelSanta
Fe Real Estate Guide, NM, Santa Fe

Weideman, Robert
robert.weideman@nuance.com, Sr. Vice Pres.,
Mktg., Nuance Communications Inc., MA,
Burlington

Weidenbener, Lesley .... (317) 472-5370
lweidenbener@ibj.com, Managing Ed.,
Indianapolis Business Journal, IN,
Indianapolis

Weidendorf, Dwayne
publisher@blackpress.ca, Pub, The Now
Newspaper, BC, Surrey

Weidman, Sheila M.
sweidman@gapac.com, Sr. Vice Pres.,
Commun. government and Pub. Aff.,
Georgia-Pacific Corp., GA, Atlanta

Weigel, Deb
debweigel@oelweindailyregister.com, Pub.,
Bremer County Independent, IA, Waverly
debweigel@oelweindailyregister.com, Pub.,
The Oelwein Daily Register, IA, Oelwein

Weigel, Deb
debweigel@oelweindailyregister.com, Pub.,
Bremer-butler Super Shopper, IA, Waverly

Weill, Susan
weill@txstate.edu, Assoc. Prof., Texas State
University-San Marcos, TX, San Marcos

Weimer, Harald
harald.weimer@heidelberg.com, President,
Heidelberg USA, Inc., GA, Kennesaw

Weinberg, Al
weinberg@hood.edu, Dir./Prof. of Journalism,
Hood College, MD, Frederick

Weinberg, Neil
Neil.Weinberg@sourcemedia.com, Ed. in
Chief, American Banker, NY, New York

Weinberg, Steve
weinbergs@missouri.edu, Prof., University of
Missouri, MO, Columbia

Weinberger, Larry Ross .... (914) 592-5222 ext. 209
sboering@nysaver.com, Pub., Pennysaver, NY,
Elmsford
sboering@nysaver.com, The Pennysaver
Group, NY, Pelham

Weinberger, Peter
peterw@advance.net, Pres., Advance Internet,
Inc., NJ, Jersey City

Weinberger, Peter .... (980) 428-1485
pweinberger@claremont-courier.com, Pub.,
Claremont Courier, CA, Claremont

Weiner, Caren .... (310) 904-6043
cweiner@pvnews.com, Sales Exec., Palos
Verdes Peninsula News, CA, Rolling Hills
Estates

Weiner, Jonathan
jonathan.weiner@eclerx.com, Prof., Columbia
University, NY, New York

Weinfurter, Roger
rweinfurter@alaskadispatch.com, VP, Audience
Engagement, Alaska Dispatch News, AK,
Anchorage

Weingarten, Randi
online@aft.org, Pres., American Federation of
Teachers, Washington

Weinholzer, Charles .... (651) 483-2300
weinholc@corp.inxintl.com, Sr. Vice Pres.-
Liquid Div., INX International Ink Co., IL,
Schaumburg

Weinmann, Darlene .... (215) 291-5560 ext. 108
dweinmann@metrokids.com, Adv. Mgr.,
Metrokids South Jersey, PA, Philadelphia

Weinmann, Darlene .... (215) 291-5560 ext. 108
dweinmann@metrokids.com, Adv. Mgr.,
MetroKids Delaware, PA, Philadelphia

Weinmann, Darlene .... (215) 291-5560 ext. 108
dweinmann@metrokids.com, Publisher,
Metrokids Magazine, TX, Addison

Weinreich, Marc .... (845) 208-0774
weinreich@halstonmedia.com, Ed., Mahopac
News, NY, Somers

Weinstein, Bonnie .... (415) 824-8730
info@socialistviewpoint.org, Editor, Socialist
Viewpoint, CA, San Francisco

Weinstock, C .... (805) 654-6400 ext. 1228
Ventura College, CA, Ventura

Weinstock, Kim
kweinstock@saukvalley.com, Customer
Service, The Telegraph, IL, Dixon

Weir, Brock
brock@auroran.com, Ed., The Auroran, ON,
Aurora

Weir, Duncan .... (613) 283-3182 ext.164
dweir@perfprint.ca, Pub. , The Perth Courier
Emc, ON, Smith Falls
dweir@perfprint.ca, Group Pub.l, The Carleton
Place-almonte Canadian Gazette Emc, ON,
Smith Falls
dweir@perfprint.ca, Pub., Smiths Falls Record
News Emc, ON, Smiths Falls
dweir@perfprint.ca, Group Pub., Kemptville
Advance Emc, ON, Smiths Falls

Weir, Jeremy .... (617) 482-6462
jweir@mpival.com, Reg'l Dir., Management
Planning, Inc., MA, Boston

Weir, Kathleen .... (318) 747-7900
composing@bossierpress.com, Composing
Director , Bossier Press-Tribune, LA, Bossier
City

Weir , Duncan
dweir@perfprint.ca, Pub., Frontenac Emc, ON,
Kingston

Weisbeck, Leonard A.
aldenadvertiser@rochester.com, Gen. Mgr. &
Ed., Alden Advertiser, NY, Alden

Weisbeck, Veronica .... (208) 879-4445
Office manager, The Challis Messenger, ID,
Challis

Weisberger, Luayne .... (308) 762-3060 ext. 25
lifestyles@alliancetimes.com, Lifestyles Ed.,
Alliance Times-Herald, NE, Alliance

Weisbrod, Cathy .... (519) 894-5552
cweisbrod@therecord.com, National Adv./
Admin. Supervisor, The Record, ON,
Kitchener

Weisburgh, Cecily .... ext. 1437
cweisburgh@keenesentinel.com, Dig. Content
Ed., The Keene Sentinel, NH, Keene

Weise, Becky
becky.fcr@verizon.net, Adv. Dir., The Fayette
County Record, TX, La Grange

Weisenberger, Cora .... (708) 296-8669
weisenbergercora@gmail.com, Pres., Illinois
Woman's Press Association, Inc., IL, Chicago

Weisenstein, Brad .... (618) 239-2510
bweisenstein@bnd.com, Photo Ed., Belleville
News-Democrat, IL, Belleville

Weisgerber, Luayne
lifestyles@alliancetimes.com, Lifestyles Ed.,
Alliance Times-Herald, NE, Alliance

Weisman, Janine
weisman@newportri.com, Ed., Newport Mercury, RI, Newport

Weismantle, Carmella ..... (412) 471-1252 ext. 225
cwiesmantle@stargate.net, Prodn. Mgr., Pittsburgh Catholic, PA, Pittsburgh

Weiss, Arnold .... (716) 854-2192
buffjewrev@aol.com, Pub., Buffalo Jewish Review, NY, Buffalo

Weiss, Arnold ....ext. 273
aweiss@cosmoscommunications.com, Pres., Cosmos Communications, Inc., NY, Long Island City

Weiss, Debra
dweiss@andreweshapirocancerfoundation.org, Exec. Vice Pres./Mktg. Dir., Metro Editorial Services, NY, New York

Weiss, John.................................. ext. 2806
jweiss@csindy.com, Pub., Colorado Springs Independent, CO, Colorado Springs

Weiss, John
jweiss@postbulletin.com, Environmental/ Ecology Ed., Post-Bulletin, MN, Rochester

Weiss, Marshall....................... (937) 610-1555
mweiss@jfgd.net, Ed./Pub., The Dayton Jewish Observer, OH, Dayton

Weiss, Rob............................ (541) 484-0519
rob@eugeneweekly.com, Director of Advertising, Eugene Weekly, OR, Eugene

Weiss, Ryan
rweiss@argus-press.com, Sports Ed., The Argus-Press, MI, Owosso

Weiss, Susan .... (718) 260-2587
Susan@NYParenting.com , Publisher/Exec. Editor, New York Parenting - Brooklyn Family/ Manhattan Family/Queens Family/Bronx-Riverdale Family/Westchester Family, NY, Brooklyn

Weiss, Vicky........................... (701) 250-8242
vicky.weiss@bismarcktribune.com, Librarian, The Bismarck Tribune, ND, Bismarck

Welbon, Yvonne....................... (336) 517-2306
Bennett College, NC, Greensboro

Welborn, Laura................. (812) 663-3111 x7001
laura.welborn@indianamediagroup.com, Rgl. Pub., Greensburg Daily News, IN, Greensburg

Welborn, Laura................. (812) 663-3111 x7001
laura.welborn@indianamediagroup.com, Rgl. Pub., Rushville Republican, IN, Rushville

Welborn, Laura................ (812) 663-3111
Laura.Welborn@indianamediagroup.com, publisher, The Herald-Tribune, IN, Batesville

Welborn, Laura .... (812) 663-3111 x7001
laura.welborn@indianamediagroup.com, Reg. Pub., The Greensburg Times, IN, Greensburg

Welborne, Anthony
adriana@ncat.edu, Asst. Prof., North Carolina A&T State University, NC, Greensboro

Welch, Bill .... (814) 824-3362
wwelch@mercyhurst..edu, Mercyhurst University, PA, Erie

Welch, Bob.................. (207) 282-1535 ext. 315
circmanager@journaltribune.com, Circ. Mgr., Journal-Tribune, ME, Biddeford

Welch, Bud
gwelch@statesville.com, Circ. Mgr., Mooresville Tribune, NC, Mooresville

Welch, Bud............................ (704) 761-2928
gwelch@statesville.com, Circ. Mgr., Statesville Record & Landmark, NC, Statesville

Welch, Chris
chris@theforumnews.com, Circ. Mgr, The Forum, LA, Shreveport

Welch, Debi
welchd@knews.com, Dir., HR, Knoxville News Sentinel, TN, Knoxville

Welch, Donnie.........................(760) 955-5345
dwelch@thespectrum.com, Pub., Daily Press, CA, Victorville

Welch, Geoffrey
gwelch@shelbypublishing.com, VP/Sales Mgr. Midwest, Shelby Publishing Co. Inc., GA, Gainesville

Welch, Hal
hal@upstatetoday.com, General Manager, Golden Corner Shopper, SC, Seneca

Welch, John B.
matt@welchpublishing.com, Pub., Perrysburg Messenger Journal, OH, Perrysburg
matt@welchpublishing.com, Pub., Rossford Record Journal, OH, Rossford
matt@welchpublishing.com, Pub., Holland-Springfield Journal, OH, Perrysburg
matt@welchpublishing.com, Pub., Point & Shoreland Journal, OH, Toledo

Welch, Matthew H.
matt@welchpublishing.com, Adv. Mgr., Perrysburg Messenger Journal, OH, Perrysburg
matt@welchpublishing.com, Adv. Mgr., Rossford Record Journal, OH, Rossford
matt@welchpublishing.com, Pres, Holland-Springfield Journal, OH, Perrysburg
matt@welchpublishing.com, Adv. Mgr., Point & Shoreland Journal, OH, Toledo

Welch, Richard........................(203) 574-3636
rwelch@rep-am.com, Mgr., Citizen's News, CT, Waterbury

Welch, Rick................(270) 824-3300 ext. 1007
rwelch@the-messenger.com, Pub., The Messenger, KY, Madisonville

Welch, Teresa
twelch@aledotimesrecord.com, Adv. Dir., The Times Record, IL, Aledo

Welchel, Darla
darla@newcastlepacer.com, Ed, Newcastle Pacer, OK, Newcastle

Welches, Mark........................(626) 544-0888
jim.maurer@sgvn.com, San Gabriel Valley Tribune, CA, Monrovia

Weld, Andy
aweld@couriernews.net, Ed., Blytheville Courier News, AR, Blytheville

Weldon, Luci
lweldon@warrenrecord.com, Asst. Ed., Warren Record, NC, Warrenton

Welker, Joel .... (205) 443-5617
jwelker@bizjournals.com, Pres./Pub., Birmingham Business Journal, AL, Birmingham

Welker, Sandy
swelker@cantondailyledger.com, Class., Daily Ledger, IL, Canton

Wellenkamp, Pat
stargazette@casscomm.com, Gen. Mgr., Stargazette Extra, IL, Beardstown

Wellenkamp, Patricia
pwell@casscomm.com, Adv. Mgr., Cass County Star-Gazette, IL, Beardstown

Weller, Friend
friend.weller@usu.edu, Adj. Instr., Utah State University, UT, Logan

Wells, Chris
cwells@newseum.org, Sr. Vice Pres., Int'l Programs, Freedom Forum, DC, Washington

Wells, Chuck
cwells@greenfieldreporter.com, Pub., Daily Reporter, IN, Greenfield
cwells@greenfieldreporter.com, Pub., New Palestine Press, IN, Greenfield

Wells, Chuck...........................(317) 462-5528
cwells@ptlpnews.com, Pub., Pendleton Times-Post, IN, Pendleton

Wells, Chuck .... (812) 379-5606
cwells@aimmediaindiana.com, Publisher, AIM Media Indiana, IN, Columbus

Wells, Chuck...........................(812) 523-7050
cwells@tribtown.com, Pub., The Tribune, IN, Seymour

Wells, Chuck .... (812) 379-5606
cwells@aimmediaindiana.com, Pub./Adv. Dir., Republic Extra, IN, Columbus

Wells, David............ (865) 584-5761 Ext. 108
dwells@tnpress.com, Director of Advertising, Tennessee Press Service, Inc., TN, Knoxville

Wells, David .... (865) 584-5761, Ext. 108
dwells@tnpress.com, Advertising Dir., Tennessee Press Association, Inc., TN, Knoxville

Wells, Don
a.parnell@pittsburghpennysaver.com, Prodn. Mgr., Penny Saver, NC, Charlotte

Wells, Douglas.............. (928) 635-4426 x 3604
dwells@williamsnews.com, Pub., Williams-Grand Canyon News, AZ, Williams

Wells, Ernie
redaction.rimouski@hebdosquebecor.com, Ed., Le Progres-echo, QC, Rimouski

Wells, Gina .... (951) 244-1966
gina@goldingpublications.com, Classified Mgr., The Friday Flyer, CA, Canyon Lake

Wells, Glynelle.........................(314) 421-8340
gwells@bizjournals.com, Adv. Dir., St. Louis Business Journal, MO, Saint Louis

Wells, Greg
editor@tjrcn.com, Mng. Ed., The Times Journal, KY, Russell Springs

Wells, Judy
deltimes@mts.net, Office Mgr., The Deloraine Times And Star, MB, Deloraine

Wells, Julia .... (508) 627-4311 ext. 124
jwells@mvgazette.com, Ed., Vineyard Gazette, MA, Edgartown

Wells, Karen
editor@pilotnl.ca, Ed., The Pilot, NL, Lewisporte

Wells, Keith.................. (812) 663-3111 x7017
keith.wells@indianamediagroup.com, Rgl. Adv. Dir., Rushville Republican, IN, Rushville

Wells, Ken
newsroom@sherbrookerecord.com, Pub., Brome County News, QC, Knowlton

Wells, Mary Kaye
mwells@palatkadailynews.com, Adv. Dir., Palatka Daily News, FL, Palatka

Wells, Michael .... (859) 231-3346
mwells@herald-leader.com, HR Dir., Lexington Herald-Leader, KY, Lexington

Wells, Pam
pwells@capitalnewspapers.com, The Capital Times, WI, Madison

Wells, Pam
pwells@madison.com, CFO, Capital Newspapers, WI, Madison

Wells, Patricia
knoxconews@gmail.com, The Star-Ledger, NJ, Newark

Wells, Richard
wells@unt.edu, Prof./Coord., Photo seq., University of North Texas, TX, Denton

Wells, Rob .... (202) 862-9272
rob.wells@dowjones.com, Bureau Chief, Dow Jones Newswires - Washington, DC, Washington

Wells, Ryan
rwells@shawmedia.com, Ed., The Elburn Herald, IL, St Charles
rwells@shawmedia.com, Gen. Mgr., Addison Suburban Life, IL, Downers Grove
rwells@shawmedia.com, Barrington Suburban Life (OOB), IL, Crystal Lake
rwells@shawmedia.com, Berwyn Suburban Life, IL, Downers Grove
rwells@shawmedia.com, Bolingbrook

Suburban Life, IL, Downers Grove
rwells@shawmedia.com, Riverside & Brookfield Suburban Life, IL, Downers Grove
rwells@shawmedia.com, Carol Stream Suburban Life, IL, Downers Grove
rwells@shawmedia.com, Downers Grove Suburban Life, IL, Downers Grove
rwells@shawmedia.com, Elmhurst Suburban Life, IL, Downers Grove
rwells@shawmedia.com, Glen Ellyn Suburban Life, IL, Downers Grove
rwells@shawmedia.com, Gurnee Suburban Life (OOB), IL, Grayslake
rwells@shawmedia.com, Hinsdale Suburban Life, IL, Downers Grove
rwells@shawmedia.com, LaGrange Suburban Life, IL, Downers Grove
rwells@shawmedia.com, Lake County Suburban Life, IL, Grayslake
rwells@shawmedia.com, Lemont Suburban Life, IL, Downers Grove
rwells@shawmedia.com, Lisle Suburban Life, IL, Downers Grove
rwells@shawmedia.com, Lombard Suburban Life, IL, Downers Grove
rwells@shawmedia.com, Main Line Suburban Life, PA, Ardmore
rwells@shawmedia.com, Northeast Suburban Life, OH, Loveland
rwells@shawmedia.com, Suburban Life Lake County Magazine, IL
rwells@shawmedia.com, Suburban Life Magazine, IL
rwells@shawmedia.com, Suburban Life Magazine, IL
rwells@shawmedia.com, Suburban Life Publications, IL, Downers Grove
rwells@shawmedia.com, Villa Park Suburban Life, IL, Downers Grove
rwells@shawmedia.com, West Chicago Suburban Life, IL, Downers Grove
rwells@shawmedia.com, Westchester Suburban Life (OOB), IL, Downers Grove
rwells@shawmedia.com, Westmont Suburban Life, IL, Downers Grove
rwells@shawmedia.com, Wheaton Suburban Life, IL, Downers Grove
rwells@shawmedia.com, Willowbrook Suburban Life (OOB), IL, Downers Grove
rwells@shawmedia.com, Woodridge Suburban Life, IL, Downers Grove

Wells, S. Kay Andrews
ghayes@flsentinel.com, Pub., Florida Sentinel-bulletin, FL, Tampa

Wells, Sadie
advocate@nntc.net, Ed., The Butte Gazette, NE, Butte

Wells, Sharon
indexpress@poka.com, Pub./Adv. Dir., O'Donnell Index-Press, TX, Odonnell

Wells, Terry
advertising@bunabeacon.com, Co-Pub./Adv. Dir., The Buna Beacon, TX, Buna

Wells, Veritta
vwells@overlandstorage.com, Vice Pres., HR, Overland Storage, Inc., CA, San Diego

Wells, Vinde...................(815) 732-6166 ext. 32
vwells@oglecountynews.com, Ed., Forreston Journal, IL, Dixon

Wells, Vinde...................(815) 732-6166, Ext. 5903
vwells@oglecountynews.com, Ed., Mt. Morris Times, IL, Dixon
vwells@oglecountynews.com, Ed., Ogle County Life, IL, Oregon
vwells@oglecountynews.com, Ed., Tri-County Press, IL, Dixon
vwells@oglecountynews.com, Ed., Oregon Republican Reporter, IL, Dixon

Wells-Lego, Pamela .... (812) 379-5649
wellslego@therepublic.com, Adv. Mgr., Republic Extra, IN, Columbus

Welsh, Ben
ben.welsh@latimes.com, Data Desk, Senior Dig. Ed., Los Angeles Times, CA, Los Angeles

Welsh, Kevin .... (318) 459-3363

kwelsh@gannett.com, Circ. Dir., The Times, LA, Shreveport

Welsh, Taylor
welsh@picayuneitem.com, Sports/News Writer, Picayune Item, MS, Picayune

Welter, Liz .... **(920) 743-3321**
lwelter@gannett.com, Reporter, Door County Advocate, WI, Sturgeon Bay

Welter, Tamara
tamara.welter@biola.edu, Asst. Prof., Biola University, CA, La Mirada

Welty, Cheryl .... **(937) 644-9111**
cw@marysvillejt.com, Pub., Marysville Journal-Tribune, OH, Marysville

Wendelken, Dave
wendeldh@jmu.edu, Assoc. Prof., James Madison University, VA, Harrisonburg

Wendland, Melissa
mwendland@messengernews.net, Office Manager, The Messenger, IA, Fort Dodge

Wendland, Melissa .... **(515) 573-2141 ext. 403**
mwendland@messengernews.net, Office Mgr., Messenger Extra, IA, Fort Dodge

Wendle, Scott .... **(830) 582-2048**
wscott@the-i.net, Pub./Ed./Owner, Cow Country Courier, TX, Nixon

Wendorf, Nile
nile@extranews.net, Assoc. Pub./Gen. Mgr., EXTRA Bilingual Community Newspaper, IL, Chicago

Wendzonka, Mary
mwendzonka@elkharttruth.com, Creative Services Mgr., Elkhart Truth, IN, Elkhart

Wenger, Harold
hwenger@snews.com, Pub./Gen. Mgr., The Shopping News of Lancaster County, PA, Ephrata

Wennerstrom, Karla
editor@edenprairienews.com, Ed., Eden Prairie News, MN, Eden Prairie

Wenrick, Laura .... **(360) 735-4474**
laura.wenrick@columbian.com, Advertising Sales Mgr., The Columbian, WA, Vancouver

Wensel, Diane
diane.wensel@sunmedia.ca, Mktg. Mgr., The Calgary Sun, AB, Calgary

Wenski, Thomas G.
info@thefloridacatholic.org, Pub., The Florida Catholic, FL, Orlando

Wensman, Tena .... **(320) 616-1932**
tena.wensman@ecm-inc.com, Sales Manager, Morrison County Record, MN, Little Falls

Wentz, Cheryl
cwentz@hcnonline.com, Advt Sales Mgr, Deer Park Broadcaster, TX, Webster

Wentz, Cheryl .... **(281) 378-1922**
cwentz@hcnonline.com, Advt Sales Mgr, Bay Area Citizen, TX, Webster

Wentz, Cheryl .... **(281) 378-1922**
cwentz@hcnonline.com, Advt Sales Mgr, Pasadena Citizen, TX, Webster

Wentz, Cheryl .... **(281) 378-1922**
cwentz@hcnonline.com, Advt Sales Mgr, Friendswood Journal, TX, Conroe

Wentz, Kathleen
kathleen.wentz@abilicorp.com, Mng. Ed., East Bay Express, CA, Oakland

Wenzel, Beth
beth@zanderpressinc, Brillion Lake To Lake Shopper, WI, Brillion
beth@zanderpressinc.com, Prodn. Mgr., Lake To Lake Shopper, WI, Brillion

Wenzel, Beth
beth@zanderpressinc.com, Pub., The Brillion News, WI, Brillion

Wenzel, Holly
review@lillienews.com, Ed., Maplewood

Review, MN, North Saint Paul

Wenzel, Judith E.
jw@intercontinentalweb.com, Pres., Inter-Continental Graphics, Inc., FL, Fort Myers

Wenzel, Korrie
dailynews@mitchellrepublic.com, Pub., The Advisor Advantage, SD, Mitchell

Wenzel, Korrie .... **(701) 780-1103**
Pub., Grand Forks Herald, ND, Grand Forks

Wenzel, Scott
swenzel@airadv.net, Ed., Frankenmuth News, MI, Frankenmuth

Wenzl, Tim .... **(620) 227-1556**
twenzl@dcdiocese.org, Adv Rep, The Southwest Kansas Catholic, KS, Dodge City

Werblin, Cathy .... **(714) 432-5094**
cwerblin@occ.cccd.edu, Orange Coast College, CA, Costa Mesa

Werda, Christie
cwerda@thealpenanews.com, Adv. Mgr., The Alpena News, MI, Alpena

Werder, Allison .... **(413) 731-1846**
awerder@masslive.com, Pres., The Republican, MA, Springfield

Werderman, Kathy .... **(309) 852-2181**
kwerderman@starcourier.com, Classified Adv. Mgr., Star-Courier, IL, Kewanee

Werley, Kris
kwerley@readingeagle.com, Reading Eagle Company, PA, Reading

Werling, Glen
glenw@news-banner.com, Mng. Ed., News-Banner, IN, Bluffton

Wermers, Jason .... **(912) 489-9431**
jwermers@statesboroherald.com, Editor, Statesboro Herald, GA, Statesboro

Werner, Debbie
dwerner@rvpublishing.com, Adv. Sales, The Belvidere Daily Republican, IL, Belvidere

Werner, Debbie .... **(815) 727-4811**
debbie@willcfb.com, Adv. Mgr., Farmers Weekly Review, IL, Joliet

Werner, George .... **(928) 282-7795 x 117**
GWerner@LarsonNewpapers.com, Copy Ed., Sedona Red Rock News, AZ, Sedona

Werner, Jeff .... **(215) 867-2064**
advance@buckslocalnews.com, Ed., Bristol Pilot, PA, Bristol
advance@buckslocalnews.com, Ed., Newtown Advance, PA, Lansdale

Werner, Jeff .... **(215) 648-1080**
advance@buckslocalnews.com, Ed, Montgomery Media, PA, Lansdale
advance@buckslocalnews.com, Ed., Advance of Bucks County, PA, Lansdale

Werner, Lori
loriwerner@diodecom.net, Pub., The Advisor, NE, Hebron

Werner, Michael
pitmanphoto@att.net, Pres., Pitman Photo Supply, FL, Miami

Wernicke, Carl
cwernicke@ihmc.us, Editorial Page Ed., Pensacola News Journal, FL, Pensacola

Werre, Suzanne
leadernews@bhgnews.com, Ed., Underwood News, ND, Underwood

Werrell, James .... **(803) 329-4081**
jwerrell@heraldonline.com, Editorial Page Ed., The Herald, SC, Rock Hill

Wert, Kevin .... **(717) 703-3049**
kevinw@mansimedia.com, Dir. Client Solutions, MANSI Media, PA, Harrisburg

Werth, Gina .... **(620) 792-1211 ext. 200**
gwerth@gbtribune.com, Classifieds, Great Bend Tribune, KS, Great Bend

Wertheimer, Doug .... **(847) 674-7827**

chicagojewishstar@comcast.net, Ed./Pub., Chicago Jewish Star, IL, Skokie

Wertin, Wren
wren@vaildaily.com, Circ. Mgr., Vail Daily, CO, Avon

Werts, Marcia .... **(316) 269-6762**
mwerts@wichitaeagle.com, Metro Ed., The Wichita Eagle, KS, Wichita

Wesa, David
davidwesa@circulation.net, Dir., Info. Servs., Circulation Development, Inc., MO, Wentzville

Wesche, Warren .... **ext. 2412**
Prodn. Mgr., West Point News, NE, West Point

Wesley, Tad .... **(812) 231-4264**
tad.wesley@tribstar.com, District Mgr., The Tribune Star, IN, Terre Haute

Wesner, Brett .... **(806) 385-4481**
wherald@sbcglobal.net, Pub., The Castro County News, TX, Dimmitt
wherald@sbcglobal.net, Pub., Lamb County Leader-News, TX, Littlefield

Wesner, Scott
tj2hts@yahoo.com, Pub., Mason County News, TX, Mason

Wesner, Scott
scottwesner@hotmail.com, Pub., Blanco County News, TX, Blanco

Wesner, Scott
thenews@verizon.net, Adv. Dir., The Llano News, TX, Llano

Wesner, Scott
jcnews@moment.net, Pub., Johnson City Record-Courier, TX, Johnson City

Wesolowski, Tim .... **(513) 977-3000**
tim.wesolowski@scripps.com, Sr. VP/CFO/Treasurer, E. W. Scripps Co., OH, Cincinnati

Wessel, Chris
cwessel@jonesborosun.com, Editor, The Jonesboro Sun, AR, Jonesboro

Wessel, Craig .... **(503) 274-8733**
cwessel@bizjournals.com, Pub, Business Journal of Portland, OR, Portland

Wessel, Tammy .... **(859) 654-3332**
copy@falmouthoutlook.com, Typesetter, The Shopper's Outlook (free Shopper), KY, Falmouth

Wesseler, Marsha
marsha@winfieldcourier.com, Adv. Dir., The Leader, KS, Winfield

Wesseler, Marsha .... **(620) 221-1050**
advertising@winfieldcourier.com, Adv. Dir., Winfield Daily Courier, KS, Winfield

Wessell, Rick
journalnews@mail.com, Adv. Dir., Glenview Journal, IL, Des Plaines
journalnews@mail.com, Adv. Dir., Park Ridge Journal, IL, Des Plaines
journalnews@mail.com, Adv. Dir., Prospect Heights Journal, IL, Des Plaines
journalnews@mail.com, Managing Ed., Arlington Heights/Buffalo Grove/Rolling Meadows/Wheeling Journal, IL, Des Plaines
journalnews@mail.com, Adv. Dir., Palatine Journal, IL, Des Plaines
journalnews@mail.com, Adv. Dir., Des Plaines Journal, IL, Des Plaines
journalnews@mail.com, Adv. Dir., Niles Journal, IL, Des Plaines
journalnews@mail.com, Adv. Dir., Elk Grove Journal, IL, Des Plaines
journalnews@mail.com, Adv. Dir., Mount Prospect Journal, IL, Des Plaines
journalnews@mail.com, Adv. Dir., Rosemont Journal, IL, Des Plaines

Wessell, Robert
journalnews@mail.com, Classified Mgr., Niles Journal, IL, Des Plaines
journalnews@mail.com, Classified Mgr., Elk Grove Journal, IL, Des Plaines
journalnews@mail.com, Classified Mgr.,

Rosemont Journal, IL, Des Plaines
journalnews@mail.com, Classified Mgr., Mount Prospect Journal, IL, Des Plaines
journalnews@mail.com, Classified Mgr., Glenview Journal, IL, Des Plaines
journalnews@mail.com, Classified Mgr., Prospect Heights Journal, IL, Des Plaines
journalnews@mail.com, Classified Mgr., Arlington Heights/Buffalo Grove/Rolling Meadows/Wheeling Journal, IL, Des Plaines
journalnews@mail.com, Classified Mgr., Des Plaines Journal, IL, Des Plaines
journalnews@mail.com, Classified Mgr., Palatine Journal, IL, Des Plaines
journalnews@mail.com, Classified Mgr., Park Ridge Journal, IL, Des Plaines

Wessell, Stefanie .... **(440) 576-9125 x107**
swessell@gazettenews.com, senior editor, The Gazette, OH, Jefferson

Wessell, Stefanie .... **(440) 576-9125 ext. 107**
swessell@gazettenews.com, Ed., The Shores News, OH, Jefferson

Wessell, Todd
journalnews@mail.com, Managing Ed. , Des Plaines Journal, IL, Des Plaines
journalnews@mail.com, Managing Ed., Palatine Journal, IL, Des Plaines
journalnews@mail.com, Managing Ed., Park Ridge Journal, IL, Des Plaines
journalnews@mail.com, Managing Ed., Elk Grove Journal, IL, Des Plaines
journalnews@mail.com, Managing Ed., Rosemont Journal, IL, Des Plaines
journalnews@mail.com, Managing Ed., Prospect Heights Journal, IL, Des Plaines
journalnews@mail.com, Ed./Pub., Arlington Heights/Buffalo Grove/Rolling Meadows/Wheeling Journal, IL, Des Plaines
journalnews@mail.com, Managing Ed., Glenview Journal, IL, Des Plaines
journalnews@mail.com, Managing Ed., Niles Journal, IL, Des Plaines
journalnews@mail.com, Managing Ed., Mount Prospect Journal, IL, Des Plaines

West, Amy S.
asw@capcomachinery.com, Vice Pres., Finance, Capco Machinery Systems, Inc., VA, Roanoke

West, Andrew .... **(302) 741-8204**
awest@newszap.com, Mng. Ed., Delaware State News, DE, Dover

West, Bert
bert.palaciosbeacon@gmail.com, Ed., Palacios Beacon, TX, Palacios

West, Carlton
dliebman@state-journal.com, Ed., The State Journal, KY, Frankfort

West, Debra .... **(203) 330-6377**
dwest@ctpost.com, Assistant Managing Editor, Connecticut Post, CT, Bridgeport

West, Dennis .... **(978) 516-2267**
dwest@sentinelandenterprise.com, Circ. Mgr., Sentinel & Enterprise, MA, Fitchburg

West, Francine
westf@bridgeportindex.com, Prod. Mgr., Chico Texan, TX, Bridgeport

West, Gary
gwest@hermistonherald.com, Ed, Hermiston Herald, OR, Hermiston

West, Gary .... **(541) 564-4532**
gwest@eastoregonian.com, Hermiston Ed., East Oregonian, OR, Pendleton

West, J. Lynn
lynn.west@journalinc.com, Editor, New Albany Gazette, MS, New Albany

West, John R.
pb@bannercorp.net, Pub./Ed., The Press & Banner, SC, Abbeville

West, Kenneth
tcherald@brmemc.net, Pub., Towns County Herald, GA, Hiawassee

West, Kenneth

info@nganews.com, Pub., North Georgia News, GA, Blairsville

West, Lamar
lamarbannercorp@charter.net, Prod. Mgr., The Press & Banner, SC, Abbeville

West, Mark D.
west@unca.edu, Chair, University of North Carolina-Asheville, NC, Asheville

West, Michael
west@lao.ten.fujitsu.com, Mktg., Dir., Fujitsu Ten Corp. of America, CA, Torrance

West, Nicholas M.
palaciosbeacon@gmail.com, Pub., Palacios Beacon, TX, Palacios

West, Ryan .... (361) 972-3009
palaciosbeacon@gmail.com, Palacios Beacon, TX, Palacios

West, Sharon
west.9@osu.edu, Assoc. Prof., Ohio State University, OH, Columbus

West, Sherry .... (270) 745-2651
sherry.west@wku.edu, Operations Mgr, Western Kentucky University, KY, Bowling Green

West, Tom .... (320) 616-1932
tom.west@mcrecord.com, Gen. Mgr., Morrison County Record, MN, Little Falls

West, Tom
brian.mccoy@ecm-inc.com, Gen. Mgr., Dairyland Peach, MN, Sauk Centre

West, Ty .... (205) 443-5637
twest@bizjournals.com, Ed.-in-chief, Birmingham Business Journal, AL, Birmingham

West-Ravenell, Barbara
bwestravenell@timesanddemocrat.com, Prodn. Mgr., Distr., The Times and Democrat, SC, Orangeburg

Westaby, Monique
mwestabynews@gmail.com, Cadott Mgr., Courier Sentinel, WI, Cornell

Westad, Denise .... (701) 473-5436
farmerspress@gondtc.com, Owner/Pub., Benson County Farmers Press, ND, Minnewaukan
farmerspress@gondtc.com, Pub. , Lakota American, ND, Lakota

Westberry, Theresa .... (229) 244-3400 Ext. 1243
theresa.westberry@gaflnews.com, Advertising Director, Valdosta Daily Times, GA, Valdosta

Westen, John-Henry ...... (888) 678-6008 ext 920
jhwesten@lifesitenews.com, Ed. & Chief, LifeSiteNews.com, VA, Front Royal

Wester, Milton .... (406) 628-4412
publisher@laureloutlook.com, Prodn. Mgr., Laurel Outlook, MT, Laurel

Westergaard, Neil .... (303) 803-9220
nwestergaard@bizjournals.com, Ed., Denver Business Journal, CO, Denver

Westerhold , Matt .... (419) 609-5866
mattwesterhold@sanduskyregister.com, Mng. Ed., Sandusky Register, OH, Sandusky

Westerholt, Robert
Robert.westerholt@riverfronttimes.com, Production Manager, The Riverfront Times, MO, Saint Louis

Westerkamp, Chris
cwesterkamp@jewishallianceri.org, Adv. Mgr., The Jewish Voice, RI, Providence

Westerman, Wanda .... (405) 214-3968
wanda.westerman@news-star.com, Class. Adv. Exec. , Shawnee News-Star, OK, Shawnee

Westfall, Patricia .... (740) 593-2595
westfall@ohio.edu, Prof., Ohio University, OH, Athens

Westjohn, Lara
l.westjohn@blmachinedesign.com, Mktg. Mgr., B & L Machine & Design, IL, Effingham

Westmoreland, Phillip
usa@lorentzen-wettre.com, Pres., Lorentzen & Wettre, GA, Alpharetta

Weston, Dallas
dallas@thenewsprogress.com, News Ed., Mecklenburg Reporter, VA, South Hill

Weston, Joe .... (406) 543-6609
jweston@missoulanews.com, Prodn. Dir., Missoula Independent, MT, Missoula

Weston, Lloyd .... (708) 696-3261
Ed., Niles Herald-Spectator, IL, Chicago

Weston, Ray .... (315) 661-2316
rweston@wdt.net, VP Finance, Watertown Daily Times, NY, Watertown

Weston-Elchert, Laura .... (260) 461-8468
lweston@news-sentinel.com, Multimedia Ed., The News-Sentinel, IN, Fort Wayne

Westphal, Steve
swestpha@mlive.com, Sr. Dir. for National Accounts, The Jackson Citizen Patriot, MI, Jackson

Westphal, Steve
ahop@kalamazoogazette.com, Sr. Dir. for National Accounts, The Kalamazoo Gazette, MI, Kalamazoo

Westwood, Sheena
sheena.westwood@zu.ac.ae, Assoc. Prof., Zayed University, Al Ruwayyah

Wetherington, Todd
twetherington@ncweeklies.com, Ed., Duplin Times, NC, Kenansville

Wethington, Paula .... (734) 240-5745
paula@monroenews.com, Reporter, Bedford Now, MI, Monroe

Wetterstrand, Katy .... (805) 238-3524
katy@westernquartz.com, CFO, Western Quartz Products, Inc., CA, Paso Robles

Wetton, Claire .... (519) 537-2341 x515268
cwetton@postmedia.com, Media sales, The Ingersoll Times, ON, Woodstock

Wetzel, Jay
rhads@therecordherald.com, Prodn. Supt., The Record Herald, PA, Waynesboro

Wetzel, Michael .... (256) 304-2462
mwetzel@decaturdaily.com, Asst. Sports Ed, The Decatur Daily, AL, Decatur

Weybret, Marty .... (209) 369-2761 ext. 205
martw@lodinews.com, Pub., Sentinel Express, CA, Lodi

Weyer, Jake
jweyer@mnpubs.com, Asst. Ed., Good Age, MN, Minneapolis

Weymouth, Bonnie
weymouthbo@wssu.edu, Part-time Staff, Winston-Salem State University, NC, Winston-Salem

Whalen, Cathy .... (315) 265-1000, ext. 32
CathyW@northcountrynow.com, Production Manager, North Country This Week, NY, Potsdam

Whalen, David .... (845) 451-1406
d_whalen@culinary.edu, Culinary Institute of America, NY, Hyde Park

Whalen, David
ads@lincnews.com, Gen. Mgr., Lincoln News, ME, Lincoln

Whalen, Ellen .... (507) 765-2151
news@fillmorecountyjournal.com, Asst. Ed., Fillmore County Journal, MN, Preston

Whalen, John .... (603) 668-4321
jwhalen@unionleader.com, Dir., Newspaper Sales & Marketing, New Hampshire Union Leader/New Hampshire Sunday News, NH, Manchester

Whalen, John R.
cryogen@cryogenesis-usa.com, Vice Pres., Sales, Cryogenesis (A Div. of WM & C Services, Inc.), OH, Cleveland

Whalen, Michael .... (617) 367-9100
michaelw@thejewishadvocate.com, Ed., The Jewish Advocate, MA, Boston

Whaley, Joi
jwhaley@themountainpress.com, Adv. Dir., The Mountain Press, TN, Sevierville

Whaley, Mary
mary@cheboygantribune.com, Circ. Mgr. , Mackinaw Journal, MI, Cheboygan
mary@cheboygantribune.com, Circ. Mgr., Cheboygan Daily Tribune, MI, Cheboygan

Whaley, Mike .... (603) 742-4455 ext. 2949
mwhaley@fosters.com, Sports Ed., Foster's Daily Democrat, NH, Dover

Whaley, Scott .... (731) 989-4624
swhaley@chestercountyindependent.com, Publisher, Chester County Independent, TN, Henderson

Wharton, Carin
carin.wharton@pressenterprise.net, Classifieds Adv. Mg., Press Enterprise, PA, Bloomsburg

Wheater, Richard C.
news@uncats.net, Ed., Fremont Times-Indicator, MI, Fremont

Wheatfall, LaGloria .... (713) 663-6996
lagloria@defendermediagroup.com, Multi-media Mgr., Houston Defender Media Group, Formerly Houston Defender, TX, Houston

Wheatley, Chris .... (509) 313-5865
wheatley@gonzaga.edu, Student Publications Assistant Manager, Gonzaga University, WA, Spokane

Wheeland, Christy .... (918) 486-4444
christy.wheeland@wagonercountyat.com, Ed, Wagoner Tribune, OK, Wagoner
christy.wheeland@wagonercountyat.com, Ed, Coweta American (OOB), OK, WAGONER

Wheeler, Andrew
awheeler@whcorp.com, President, Windmoeller and Hoelscher Corp., RI, Lincoln

Wheeler, Audrey
audrey.wheeler@gazcomm.com, Prodn. Mgr., Penny Saver, IA, Cedar Rapids

Wheeler, Dee .... (978) 249-3535 ext. 601
Classified Adv. , Athol Daily News, MA, Athol

Wheeler, Kelly .... (619) 231-9097
Bureau Chief, City News Service, Inc. - San Diego, CA, San Diego

Wheeler, Pamela .... (251) 434-1545
thecatholicweek@bellsouth.net, Production Manager, The Catholic Week, AL, Mobile

Wheeler, Vince .... (336) 888-3517
vwheeler@hpenews.com, Opinion Editor , High Point Enterprise, NC, High Point

Wheelock, Sharon M.
gcn@neb-sandhills.net, Ed., Grant County News, NE, Hyannis

Whelan, Mary Beth .... (631) 661-3131
marybethw@globephotos.com, Pres., Globe Photos, Inc., West Islip

Whelan, Marybeth
marybethw@globephotos.com, Globe Photos, Inc., West Islip

Whelan, Raymond D.
rayw@globephotos.com, Vice Pres., Globe Photos, Inc., West Islip

Whelan, Tom .... (888) 309-0639
twhelan@miracomcomputer.com, Director, Customer Service, Miracom Computer Corp., NY, Eastchester

Whelchel, Mary .... (540) 981-3252
mary.whelchel@roanoke.com, National and Majors Director, The Roanoke Times, VA, Roanoke

Whelchel, Sandy .... (303) 841-0246
authorsandy@hotmail.com, Exec. Dir., National Writers Association, CO, Parker

Wherry, Greg A.
editor@cottonwoodchronicle.com, Pub., Cottonwood Chronicle, ID, Cottonwood

Whetmore, Edward
ewhetmore@csudh.edu, Chair, California State University, Dominguez Hills, CA, Carson

Whetten, Bruce
bwhetten@douglasdispatch.com, Managing Ed., The Douglas Dispatch, AZ, Douglas

Whetton, Anita
anita.whetten@goshennews.com, Graphic Artist, The Goshen News, IN, Goshen

Whicher, Tami
twhicher@fdlreporter.com, Admin. Assistant, Action Advertiser, WI, Fond Du Lac
twhicher@fdlreporter.com, Admin. Assistant, Action Sunday, WI, Fond Du Lac

Whimes, Mark
tributeeditor@gmail.com, Co-Pub./Ed, Tyler Tribute, MN, Tyler

Whipkey, Brian
brianw@dailyamerican.com, Editorial Page Ed., Daily American, PA, Somerset

Whipple, Catherine .... (612) 722-3686
thecirclenews@gmail.com, Managing Editor, The Circle Corporation, MN, Minneapolis

Whipple, Sue
swhipple@argus-press.com, N.I.E., The Argus-Press, MI, Owosso

Whisenant, Charles
charleswhis@gmail.com, Ed., The Arab Tribune, AL, Arab

Whisler, David .... (304) 284-0319
oncoor@dominionpost.com, Online Coord., The Dominion Post, WV, Morgantown

Whisler, Kirk
kirk@whisler.com, Pres., Latino 247 Media Group, CA, Carlsbad

Whisnant, Gabe .... (704) 669-3334
gwhisnant@shelbystar.com, News Ed., The Star, NC, Shelby

Whiston, Julia
whca@starpower.net, Exec. Dir., White House Correspondents Association, DC, Washington

Whitacre, Tammy
editor@wayuga.com, Ed., Post-Herald, NY, Red Creek

Whitaker, Alanna .... (251) 421-1821
Managing Editor, University of South Alabama, AL, Mobile

Whitaker, Bill
bwhitaker@wacotrib.com, City Ed., Waco Tribune-Herald, TX, Waco

Whitaker, Cassidy
cassidy.whitaker@email.saintleo.edu, Editor-in-Chief, Saint Leo University, FL, Saint Leo

Whitaker, Cheryl
cheryl.whitaker@starnewsonline.com, Office Mgr. , StarNews, NC, Wilmington

Whitaker, John .... (209) 345-8090
johnwhitaker@midvalleypub.com, Ed., Merced County Times, CA, Merced

Whitaker, Sara .... (903) 665-2462
editor@jimplecute.com, Ed., Jefferson Jimplecute, TX, Jefferson

Whitaker, Sheila .... (843) 672-2358
swhitaker@pagelandprogressive.com, Office manager, Pageland Progressive-Journal, SC, Pageland

White, Allen
allen.white@murraystate.edu, Prof./Interim Chair, Murray State University, KY, Murray

White, Barney
news@chicotnewspapers.com, Pub., Eudora Enterprise, AR, Lake Village

LA, Natchitoches

Whitehead, W.R.
newsadvo@windstream.net, Ed., Fordyce
News-Advocate, AR, Fordyce

Whitehouse, Abigail
Abigail.whitehouse@theinteriorjournal.com,
Editor, The Interior Journal, KY, Stanford

Whitehouse, Virginia
gwhitehouse@whitworth.edu, Chair, Whitworth
University, WA, Spokane

Whitehurst, Tom .... (361) 886-3662
whitehurstt@caller.com, Bus. Ed., Corpus
Christi Caller-Times, TX, Corpus Christi

Whiteman, Rick .... (317) 873-6397 ext.24
rick.whiteman@timessentinel.com, Sales Mgr,
Zionsville Times Sentinel, IN, Zionsville

Whitesell, Amanda
awhitesell@gannett.com, Web Ed., The
Livingston County Daily Press & Argus, MI,
Howell

Whitfield, Dave
dwhitfield@rmoutlook.com, Ed, Rocky
Mountain Outlook, AB, Canmore

Whitfield, Janani
jwhitfield@stpaul.greatwest.ca, Pub, St. Paul
Journal, AB, Saint Paul

Whitfield, Jhonny
johnny.whitfield@nando.com, Mng. Ed.,
Eastern Wake News, NC, Raleigh

Whitfield, Johnny
jwhitfield@newsobserver.com, Ed., Garner-
Cleveland Record, NC, Raleigh

Whitfield, Kenneth
kwhitfield@jjournal.com, Pub., The Jersey
Journal, NJ, Secaucus

Whiting, Fred .... (630) 850-9680
fred@whitingtech.com, Pres., Whiting
Technologies, IL, La Grange

Whiting, Gail .... (336) 727-7335
gwhiting@wsjournal.com, VP Advertiisng
Sales, Winston-Salem Journal, NC, Winston
Salem

Whiting, Richard .... (864) 943-2522
rwhiting@indexjournal.com, Exec. News Ed.,
The Index-Journal, SC, Greenwood

Whiting, Vicki .... (707) 996-6077
vicki@kidscoop.com, Pres./CEO, Kid Scoop,
Sonoma

Whiting , Gail .... (845) 346-3080
gwhiting@th-record.com, Adv. Dir., The Times
Herald-Record, NY, Middletown

Whitley, Bob .... (912) 427-3757
Circ. Mgr., The Press-Sentinel, GA, Jesup

Whitley, Bonnie
bwhitley@theclinchcountynews.com, Prodn.
Mgr., Clinch County News, GA, Homerville

Whitley, Flora
courier@mrtc.com, Ed., Elliott County News,
KY, West Liberty

Whitley, Sheila
whitley@ncat.edu, Asst. Prof., North Carolina
A&T State University, NC, Greensboro

Whitley, William L. .... (972) 231-4500
whitleytx@cs.com, Dir., Media Services Group,
Inc., FL, Ponte Vedra

Whitley , Michael
michael.whitley@latimes.com, Asst. Managing
Ed., Los Angeles Times, CA, Los Angeles

Whitlock, Becky
bwhitlock@timesnews.net, Radio/Television
Ed., Kingsport Times-News, TN, Kingsport

Whitlock, John
jwhitlock@owentonnewsherald.com, News Ed.,
Owenton News-Herald, KY, Owenton

Whitlock, Kevin
kevin.whitlock@indeonline.com, Photographer,
The Independent, OH, Massillon

Whitlock, Mary Ann .... (310) 687-5800
whitlock@microtek.com, Dir., Mktg., Microtek,
CA, Santa Fe Springs

Whitlow, Roseanna
rwhitlow@semo.edu, Instr., Southeast Missouri
State University, MO, Cape Girardeau

Whitman, Barry .... (269) 429-2400
bwhitman@theHP.com, Circ. Dir., South Haven
Tribune, MI, South Haven

Whitman, David .... (250) 380-5289
dwhitman@timescolonist.com, Dir. Adv. ,
Victoria Times Colonist, BC, Victoria

Whitmire, Carol
editor@quanahtribunechief.com, Ed., Quanah
Tribune-Chief, TX, Quanah

Whitmire, Don .... ext. 1401
Circ. Mgr., Around The House, PA, Bloomsburg

Whitmore, Deanna .... (209) 578-2209
dwhitmore@modbee.com, Adv. Dir., The
Chowchilla News, CA, Merced
dwhitmore@modbee.com, Adv. Mgr., Inside
Sales, The Modesto Bee, CA, Modesto
dwhitmore@modbee.com, Adv. Dir., Los Banos
Enterprise, CA, Los Banos

Whitney, Andrea .... (409) 423-2696
kbanner@sbcglobal.net, Ed, Kirbyville Banner,
TX, Kirbyville

Whitney, Dan
sports@ctimes.biz, Staff Writer, Cherokee
Chronicle Times, IA, Cherokee

Whitney, Jamie
editor@pokyrd.com, Staff writer, Pocahontas
Record-Democrat, IA, Pocahontas

Whitney, Jonathan K.
webmaster@gocarrollcounty.com, Pub., Carroll
County Review, IL, Thomson

Whitney, Michael .... (360) 568-4121
michael@snoho.com, Editor, Everett New
Tribune, WA, Snohomish
michael@snoho.com, Editor, Snohomish
County Tribune, WA, Snohomish

Whitney, Stu .... (605) 977-3922
swhitney@argusleader.com, Sports Editor,
Argus Leader, SD, Sioux Falls

Whitney, Tara
twhitney@berkshireeagle.com, Circ. Dir., The
Berkshire Eagle, MA, Pittsfield

Whitsitt, Cheryl .... (417) 836-1115
cwhitsitt@news-leader.com, Mng. Ed.,
Springfield News-Leader, MO, Springfield

Whitson, Keith .... (423) 743-4112
kwhitson@erwinrecord.net, Publisher, The
Erwin Record, TN, Erwin

Whitson, Lisa
lisa.whitson@lincolncourier.com, Website Mgr.,
Logan County Shopper, IL, Lincoln

Whitson, Lyn .... (901) 433-9138
lyn.whitson@journalinc.com, Sales, The
Bartlett Express, TN, Bartlett

Whitt, Eric .... (336) 599-0162 ext. 102
circulation@roxboro-courier.com, Circ. Mgr.,
The Courier-Times, NC, Roxboro

Whitt, Jan
jan.whitt@colorado.edu, Assoc. Prof.,
University of Colorado, CO, Boulder

Whittaker, Dala .... (417) 962-4411
cabent@centurytel.net, Pub., Cabool
Enterprise, MO, Cabool

Whittaker, John
jwhittaker@post-journal.com, Ed., The Post-
Journal, NY, Jamestown

Whittaker, Misty
misty.whitaker@kokomotribune.com, Customer
Service Mgr., Kokomo Tribune, IN, Kokomo

Whittaker, Tim .... (905) 579-4400
twhittaker@durhamregion.com, Pub.,
Clarington This Week, ON, Oshawa

Whittaker, Tim
twhitacker@durhamregion.com, Pub., Uxbridge
Times-journal, ON, Uxbridge

Whittaker, Timothy J.
newsroom@durhamregion.com, Pub., Ajax-
pickering News Advertiser, ON, Oshawa

Whittaker, Timothy J. ..... (905) 215-0500 ext.2201
twhittaker@durhamregion.com, Pub., Canadian
Statesman, ON, Oshawa

Whittaker, Timothy J.
twhittaker@durhamregion.com, Pub.,
Northumberland News, ON, Cobourg

Whittaker, Timothy J. .... (905) 579-4400
twhittaker@durhamregion.com, Pub., Oshawa-
whitby This Week, ON, Oshawa

Whittington, Erika .... (317) 477-3205
ewhittington@greenfieldreporter.com, Sr. Adv.
Rep., Daily Reporter, IN, Greenfield

Whittle, Roger .... (605) 886-6901
rogerwhittle@thepublicopinion.com, Managing
Ed., Watertown Public Opinion, SD,
Watertown

Whitton, Brett .... (203) 354-1040
bwhitton@wiltonvillager.com, President, The
Hour, CT, Norwalk

Whitton, Dennis .... (978) 970-4628
dwhitton@lowellsun.com, Sports Ed. , The
Sun, MA, Lowell

Whittum, James
jwhittum@dothaneagle.com, Pub., Dothan
Progress, AL, Dothan

Whitworth, Claudia A. .... (540) 343-0326
Ed., The Roanoke Tribune, VA, Roanoke

Whitworth, Paul E. .... (956) 371-2728
chroniclenews@msn.com, Pub./Ed.,
Raymondville Chronicle & Willacy County
News, TX, Raymondville

Whitworth, Ray
ray@whitworthknifecompany.com, Owner,
Whitworth Knife Company, OH, Cincinnati

Whitworth, Richard
rwhitworth@gciu.org, Executive Assistant to
the President, Graphic Communications
International, DC, Washington

Whitworth, Scott
swhitworth@gainesvilletimes.com, Circ. Dir.,
The Times, GA, Gainesville

Whizan, Debra
debra@santacruz.com, Pub., Metro Santa
Cruz, CA, Santa Cruz

Whong, Jason .... (443) 524-8158
jwhong@thedailyrecord.com, Digital Ed. , The
Daily Record, MD, Baltimore

Whorton, Jay .... (770) 428-9411 ext. 510
jwhorton@mdjonline.com, Assoc. Pub.,
Marietta Daily Journal, GA, Marietta

Wick, Francis
francis.wick@wickcommunications.com, Pres. /
CEO, Wick Communications, AZ, Sierra Vista

Wick, Francis .... (520) 586-3382
francis.wick@svherald.com, Publisher, San
Pedro Valley News-Sun, AZ, Benson

Wick, Jeff .... (979) 968-3155
jeff@fayettecountyrecord.com, Ed., The Fayette
County Record, TX, La Grange

Wick, Pat .... (520) 515-4604
pat.wick@wickcommunications.com, Asst. Gen.
Mgr., Wick Communications - Herald/Review,
AZ, Sierra Vista
pat.wick@wickcommunications.com,
Columnist, Marion County Record, KS,
Marion

Wick, Patricia .... (520) 515-4604
pat.wick@wickcommunications.com, Dir.,
Mktg., Sierra Vista Herald - Sunday Bravo
Shopper, AZ, Sierra Vista

Wicke, Ulrich .... (469) 532-8000
ulrick.wicke@kba.com, Vice-President of Sales

& Service, KBA North America, Inc. (Koenig
& Bauer AG), TX, Dallas

Wickenberg, Ken .... (780) 429-5168
kwickenberg@thejournal.canwest.com, Vice
Pres., HR, Edmonton Journal, AB, Edmonton

Wicker, Beau .... (574) 722-5000 ext. 5180
beau.wicker@pharostribune.com, Sports Ed.,
Pharos-Tribune, IN, Logansport

Wicker, Neisah .... (765) 825-0581 ext. 225
nwicker@newsexaminer.com, District/Circ.
Mgr., Connersville News-Examiner, IN,
Connersville

Wickes, Sally .... (541) 338-2620
Mktg. Dir., The Register-Guard, OR, Eugene

Wickham, Sean .... (517) 372-2424 x 12
sean@michiganpress.org, Design &
Communications Specialist, Michigan Press
Association, MI, Lansing

Wicklund, Ida
ida@parentmap.com, Advertising &
Partnerships, Manager, ParentMap, WA,
Mercer Island

Wicklund, Joe
jwicklun@css.edu, College of St. Scholastica,
MN, Duluth

Wickwire, April .... (316) 321-1120
awickwire@butlercountytimesgazette.com, Adv.
Coord., The Butler County Times-Gazette,
KS, Augusta

Wickwire, Genia
info@ulsterpublishing.com, Ad. Dir., New Paltz
Times, NY, New Paltz

Wickwire, Genia
info@ulsterpublishing.com, Adv. Dir./Circ
Mgr./Classified Adv., Kingston Times, NY,
Kingston
info@ulsterpublishing.com, Ad. Dir., Saugerties
Times, NY, Kingston
info@ulsterpublishing.com, Ad. Director,
Woodstock Times, NY, Kingston

Wicoff, Mary .... (217) 477-6161
mwicoff@dacc.edu, City Ed., Commercial
News, IL, Danville

Wicoff, Reid .... (303) 954-5480
tmeskel@denverpost.com, VP Pres. of Dig.
Sales, The Denver Post, CO, Denver

Widdison, Eileen
ewiddison@thedailycourier.com, Circ. Mgr.,
Daily Courier, OR, Grants Pass

Widdle, Terri .... (816) 887-2414
terri@midamericagraphics.com, Sec., Mid-
America Graphics, Inc., MO, Harrisonville

Widener, Barbara .... (309) 697-1851
limestonenews@yahoo.com, Ed., Limestone
Independent News, IL, Bartonville

Widmer, Sherrie
s.widmer.valleyherald@gmail.com, Pub, Valley
Herald, OR, Milton Freewater

Widmer, Tessa .... Same as others
Office worker, The Garvin County News Star,
OK, Maysville

Widrick, Loren
lwidrick@townnews.com, Reg. Sales Mgr.,
TownNews.com, IL, Moline

Wiebe, Valorie .... (403) 223-2266
vwiebe@tabertimes.com, Pub, The Sunny
South News, AB, Coaldale
vwiebe@tabertimes.com, Pub., The Taber
Times, AB, Taber
vwiebe@tabertimes.com, Pub., Vauxhall
Advance, AB, Vauxhall

Wiebe, Valorie .... (403) 223-2266
vwiebe@tabertimes.com, Pub., Westwind
Weekly News, AB, Magrath

Wiechec, Nancy .... (928) 913-8668
nwiechec@azdailysun.com, Man. Ed., Flagstaff
Live!, AZ, Flagstaff

Wieck, James .... (972) 392-0888

jwieck@wieck.com, Chrmn., Wieck, Richardson

Wiederaenders, Tim ....(928) 445-3333
twiederaenders@prescottaz.com, Executive
Editor, Smart Shopper Ash Fork, AZ,
Prescott
twiederaenders@prescottaz.com, Executive
Editor, Smart Shopper, AZ, Prescott
twiederaenders@prescottaz.com, City Editor,
The Daily Courier, AZ, Prescott

Wiedmaier, Debbie
bookkeeper@mynwmo.com, Office Mgr., The
Citizen Observer, MO, Cameron

Wiegand, G. Robert
robert.wiegand@publicitas.com, Director
Hawaii/Pacific, Publicitas North America,
Inc., HI, Kailua

Wiegel, Robert ....(785) 628-1081
bobw@dailynews.net, Circ. Mgr., The Hays
Daily News, KS, Hays

Wiegel, Robert
bobw@dailynews.net, Circ. Mgr., The Hays
Daily News Extra, KS, Hays

Wiegenstein, Steve
swiegenstein@culver.edu, Journalism/PR
Head, Culver-Stockton College, MO, Canton

Wiegert, Lucas ....(620) 672-5511
Advertising Manager, Sunflower Shopper's
Guide, KS, Pratt

Wieland, Paul
pwieland@sbu.edu, Lectr./Coord., Broadcast,
St. Bonaventure University, NY, Saint
Bonaventure

Wiercinski, Sara
swiercinski@nronline.org, Aud Engagement
Dir, National Catholic Reporter, MO, Kansas
City

Wierman, Stephanie
info@thearthurgraphic.com; recordherald@
consolidated.net, Gen. Mgr./Adv. Mgr.,
Southern Piatt Record Herald, IL, Arthur

Wiers, Jack ....(808) 656-3157
Pau Hana Editor, Hawaii Army Weekly, HI,
Schofield Barracks

Wiese, Becky
rustler@jonesprint.com, Ed., Riesel Rustler,
TX, Waco

Wiese, Sharon
sweise@redoakexpress.com, Adv. Sales, Red
Oak Express, IA, Red Oak

Wiese, Tara
advertising@thenewsleaders.com, Production
Manager/Designer, Sartell Newsleader, MN,
Saint Joseph
advertising@thenewsleaders.com, Production
Manager/Designer, St. Joseph Newsleader,
MN, Saint Joseph
advertising@thenewsleaders.com, Prod. Mgr/
Designer, The Newsleaders, MN, SAINT
JOSEPH

Wieser, Charlie
tcvomaha@archomaha.org, Exec. Ed., The
Catholic Voice, NE, Omaha

Wiesner, Scot ....(262) 306-5089
swiesner@conleynet.com, Composing Mgr.,
The Daily News, WI, West Bend

Wiesner, Scott
swiesner@conleynet.com, Prod. Mgr, The
Hartford Times Press, WI, West Bend

Wiestm, Shawna ....(403) 654-2122
office@vauxhalladvance.com, Office/Sales,
Vauxhall Advance, AB, Vauxhall

Wiezalis, Pete ....(315) 829-8355
pwiezalis@indiancountry.com, Dir., Mktg.,
Indian Country Today, NY, Canastota

Wiford, Haley
hwiford@parsonssun.com, Display Adv. Sales,
Parsons Sun, KS, Parsons

Wiggins, Donna ....(843) 317-7219
dwiggins@hartsvillemessenger.com, Acct.

Exec., Lake City News & Post, SC, Florence
dwiggins@hartsvillemessenger.com, Account
Exec., The Hartsville Messenger, SC,
Hartsville

Wiggins, Gail
gwiggins@ncat.edu, Asst. Prof., North Carolina
A&T State University, NC, Greensboro

Wiggins, Gene
gwiggins@northeastlamarfire.com, Prof. Emer.,
University of Southern Mississippi, MS,
Hattiesburg

Wiggins, Mike .... x 252
Mike.Wiggins@gjsentinel.com, Managing
Editor, The Daily Sentinel, CO, Grand
Junction

Wiggins, Sammie
adsales@beacononlinenews.com, Co-Pub.,
The West Volusia Beacon, FL, Deland

Wiggins, Vickey
vwiggins@paris-express.com, Pub., Paris
Express, AR, Paris

Wigginton, Mosby ....(804) 798-9031
hpcppub@lcs.net, Publisher, The Caroline
Progress, VA, Bowling Green

Wight, Stacy ....(207) 504-8203
swight@timesrecord.com, Business Mgr., The
Times Record, ME, Brunswick

Wiginton, Ron ....(630) 617-3321
Elmhurst College, IL, Elmhurst

Wigley, Shelley
swigley@uta.edu, Asst. Prof., University of
Texas at Arlington, TX, Arlington

Wigton, Amelia
ameliaw@ccheadliner.com, Ed., Christian
County Headliner News, MO, Ozark

Wilbanks, George ....(410) 780-3303
wilbanks2005@comcast.net, Pub./Gen. Mgr.,
East County Times, MD, Baltimore

Wilbanks, Mike
m.wilbanks@comcast.net, Opns. Mgr., East
County Times, MD, Baltimore

Wilber, Melissa ....(715) 799-5167
mwilber@mitw.org, Administrative/Design
Assistant, Menominee Nation News, WI,
Keshena

Wilber, Rick
rwilber@cas.usf.edu, Asst. Prof., University of
South Florida, FL, Tampa

Wilborn, Charles ....(434) 791-7976
cwilborn@registerbee.com, Assistant Editor,
Danville Register & Bee, VA, Danville

Wilbur, Carol
cwilbur@record-bee.com, Production Dir., Lake
County Record-Bee, CA, Lakeport

Wilbur, Martin
mwilbur@theexaminernews.com, Ed., The
Examiner, NY, Mount Kisco

Wilcox, Amanda ....(903) 849-3333
sports@c-bstatesman.com, Circulation
/ Distribution, Chandler & Brownsboro
Statesman, TX, Chandler

Wilcox, Andy ....(605) 764-2000
svn@SiouxValleyNewsOnline.com, Pub./Ed.,
Sioux Valley News, SD, Canton

Wilcox, Dennis
dennis.wilcox@sjsu.edu, Prof., San Jose State
University, CA, San Jose

Wilcox, Dennis W.
wilcoxprinting@mchsi.com, Pub., Madrid
Register-News, IA, Madrid

Wilcox, Jim
jwilcox@snu.edu, Newspaper, Southern
Nazarene Univ., OK, Bethany

Wilcox, Justin ....(423) 722-0501
jwilcox@johnsoncitypress.com, Pub., Johnson
City Press, TN, Johnson City

Wilcox, Mike

wilcoxmike2@gmail.com, Publisher, owner,
Allegan County News, MI, Allegan

Wilcox, Mike
yourmarionpress@gmail.com, Publ, The
Marion Press, MI, Marion

Wilcox, Tom ....(781) 398-8007
twilcox@wickedlocal.com, Sports Ed.,
Wellesley Townsman, MA, Needham

Wild, Fredric M.
wild@lycoming.edu, Chair, Lycoming College,
PA, Williamsport

Wilder, Ed ....(954) 698-6397 ext. 305
EWilder@tribune.com, Circ. Mgr., Eastsider
FL, Tamarac

Wilder, Ed ....(954) 574-5305
ewilder@tribune.com, Circ. Mgr., The Forum -
Sunrise & Tamarac, FL, Davie

Wilder, Ed ....(954) 574-5304
ewilder@tribune.com, Circ. Mgr., The Forum -
Sunrise & Tamarac, FL, Davie

Wilder, Ed ....ext. 305
ewilder@tribune.com, Circ. Mgr., Jewish
Journal - Broward Central, FL, Fort
Lauderdale

Wilder, Ed ....ext. 305
ewilder@tribune.com, Circ. Mgr., Jewish
Journal - Miami Dade, FL, Pompano Beach

Wilder, Ed ....ext. 305
ewilder@tribune.com, Circ. Mgr., Jewish
Journal - Palm Beach North, FL, Pompano
Beach

Wilder, Ed
ewilder@tribune.com, Circ. Mgr., Coral Springs
Focus (OOB), FL, Coral Springs
ewilder@tribune.com, Plantation/Davie Forum,
FL, Fort Lauderdale
ewilder@tribune.com, Circ. Mgr., Shalom -
Broward, FL, Fort Lauderdale
ewilder@tribune.com, Circ. Mgr., Shalom -
Palm Beach, FL, Fort Lauderdale
ewilder@tribune.com, Circ. Mgr., South
Woodham Focus (OOB), FL, Fort Lauderdale

Wilder, Ed ....ext. 305
ewilder@tribune.com, Circ. Mgr., Jewish
Journal - Broward South, FL, Pompano
Beach

Wilder, Ed ....ext. 305
ewilder@tribune.com, Circ. Mgr., Jewish
Journal Palm Beach South, FL, Fort
Lauderdale

Wilder, Ed ....ext. 305
ewilder@tribune.com, Circ. Mgr., Jewish
Journal - Broward North, FL, Pompano
Beach

Wilder, Kelly
parentline@comcast.net, Pub., Parent Line,
MD, Lusby

Wilder, Kirstin
kirstin.wilder@variety.com, Asst. Mng. Ed.,
Daily Variety, CA, Los Angeles

Wilder, Marty Robacker
martyw@bradfordera.com, Mng. Ed., Bradford
Era, PA, Bradford

Wilder, Marty Robacker
martyw@bradfordera.com, Mng. Ed., The
Bradford Era, PA, Bradford

Wilder, Nancy
wilder@pdclarion.com, Accounting Mgr.,
Princeton Daily Clarion, IN, Princeton

Wilder, Paul J.
tricitynews@yahoo.com, Ed., The Tri-City
News, KY, Cumberland

Wilderman, Greg
greg.wilderman@globegazette.com, Adv. Mgr.,
Mitchell County Press-News, IA, Osage
greg.wilderman@globegazette.com, Adv. Mgr.,
Display, Globe Gazette, Mason City, IA,
Mason City

Wilderman, Melanie ....(580) 327-8481

mgwilderman@nwosu.edu, Northwestern
Oklahoma State Univ., OK, Alva

Wildsmith, Steven ....(865) 981-1165
Entertainment/Amusements Ed., The Daily
Times, TN, Maryville

Wile, Jaclyn
columbiajournaleditor@gmail.com, Columbia
Union College, MD, Takoma Park

Wile, Olivia
wile0@findlay.edu, Pulse Editor, The University
of Findlay, OH, Findlay

Wiley, Derek ....(706) 769-5175 x 30
sportseditor@oconeeenterprise.com, Sports
Ed., Oconee Enterprise, GA, Watkinsville

Wiley, Derek ....(503) 390-1051
news@keizertimes.com, Assoc. Ed.,
Keizertimes, OR, Keizer

Wiley, Tony
tonywiley@esko.com, Division Mgr., Printers
Systems, Esko-Graphics, OH, Vandalia

Wilford, Brian
bwilford@oceansidestar.com, Ed., The
Oceanside Star, BC, Parksville

Wilhelm, Kim
kimwilhelm@thecourier.com, Committee Chair,
Ohio Circulation Managers Association, OH,
Columbus

Wilhelm, Kim
kimfoos@thecourier.com, Readership and
Audience Dev. Dir., The Courier, OH, Findlay

Wilhelms, Christopher
wilhelms@communityshoppers.com, Circ. Mgr,
Janesville Messenger, WI, Delavan
wilhelms@communityshoppers.com, Circ. Mgr.,
Walworth County Sunday, WI, Elkhorn
wilhelms@communityshoppers.com, Circ. Mgr,
Stateline News, WI, Elkhorn

Wilhoite, Marion
mwilhoite@c-dh.net, Sports Ed., Columbia
Daily Herald, TN, Columbia

Wilken, Michelle ....(785) 456-2602
office@wamegonews.com, Co-Managing
Editor, The Wamego Times, KS, Wamego

Wilkerson, Bradley ....(325) 356-2636
bradley@thecomanchechief.com, Editor, The
Comanche Chief, TX, Comanche

Wilkerson, James ....(325) 356-2636
editor@thecomanchechief.com, Ed., The
Comanche Chief, TX, Comanche

Wilkerson, Judith ....(830) 281-2341
judithwm4530@yahoo.com, Pub., Pleasanton
Express, TX, Pleasanton

Wilkerson, Lance ....(325) 356-2636
Editor, The Comanche Chief, TX, Comanche

Wilkerson, Raymond ....(972) 721-4070
wilkerson@udallas.edu, Univ. of Dallas, TX,
Irving

Wilkerson, Scott ....(405) 499-0020
swilkerson@okpress.com, Front Office/Building
Manager , Oklahoma Press Association, OK,
Oklahoma City

Wilkerson, Shawn
newtonnews@valornet.com, Co-Pub./Adv. Dir.,
Newton County News, TX, Newton

Wilkerson Holmes, Noel ....(830) 281-2341
nwilkersonholmes@pleasantonexpress.com,
Associate Pub., Pleasanton Express, TX,
Pleasanton

Wilkes, Neal
ap@atlantaparent.com, Prodn. Mgr., Atlanta
Parent, GA, Atlanta

Wilkie, Jim ....(304) 457-6271
Alderson-Broaddus College, WV, Philippi

Wilkie, Trent
trent.wilkie@sunmedia.ca, Editor, The
Camrose Canadian, AB, Camrose

Wilkins, Denny

dwilkins@sbu.edu, Assoc. Prof./Coord., Print, St. Bonaventure University, NY, Saint Bonaventure

Wilkins, Nan ....(617) 779-3783
nwilkins@pilotcatholicnews.com, Prodn. Mgr., The Pilot, MA, Braintree

Wilkinson, Barb ....(780) 429-5374
bwilkinson@thejournal.canwest.com, Deputy Ed., Readership/Features, Edmonton Journal, AB, Edmonton

Wilkinson, Brian
editor@sierrastar.com, Ed., Sierra Star, CA, Oakhurst

Wilkinson, Darryl
darryl@GPCink.com, Owner/Pub., Gallatin North Missourian, MO, Gallatin

Wilkinson, Earl J.
inma@inma.org, Exec. Dir., International Newspaper Marketing Association, Inc., TX, Dallas

Wilkinson, Ed
ewilkinson@diobrook.org, Ed., The Tablet, NY, Brooklyn

Wilkinson, Jeffrey ....(281) 649-3034
Faculty Adviser, Houston Baptist Univ., TX, Houston

Wilkinson, Karen ....(627) 696-7758
karen.miltontimes@gmail.com, circulation manager, Milton Times, MA, Milton

Wilkinson, Kathy
k.wilkinson@postandcourier.com, Vice Pres., Evening Post Community Publications Grp., Evening Post Publishing Newspaper Group, SC, Charleston

Wilkinson, Liz ....(660) 663-2154
liz@GPCink.com, Owner/Pub., Gallatin North Missourian, MO, Gallatin

Wilkinson, Norm ....(801) 687-9191
nickelnorm@hotmail.com, Pub./Ed./Adv. Dir., Thrifty Nickel - Utah, UT, Orem

Wilkinson, Robyn
rwilkinson@caledonenterprise.com, Ed, Caledon Enterprise, ON, Bolton

Wilkison, Shelly ....(512) 778-5577
news@LHindependent.com, Pub./Owner, The Liberty Hill Independent, TX, Liberty Hill

Wilkosz, Gabrielle ....(512) 576-7240
Editor-In-Chief, St. Edwards Univ., TX, Austin

Wilks, Rick
rwilks@tampatrib.com, Tampa Bay Times, FL, St Petersburg

Wilks, Synquette ....(302) 494-7545
skwilks09@students.desu.edu, EIC, Delaware State Univ., DE, Dover

Will, Kristin ....(413) 536-5333
kwill@turley.com, Ed., The Holyoke Sun, MA, Chicopee
kwill@turley.com, Ed., Town Reminder, MA, South Hadley

Will, Roger ....972=398-4476
rwill@starlocalnews.com, Publisher, Star Community Newspapers, TX, Plano

Willard, George ....(248) 336-7300
gwillardsr@rangerdata.com, Sr. VP of Operations, Ranger Data Technologies Inc., MI, Troy

Willard, Terri
terri.willard@goshennews.com, Classified Sales Rep., The Goshen News, IN, Goshen

Willcox, Bob
bob.willcox@fbcpublishing.com, Pub., Wheel & Deal, AB, Irricana

Willcox, Suzanne ....(561) 820-4930
swillcox@pbpost.com, Mgr., Research/Sales Presentations, The Palm Beach Post, FL, West Palm Beach

Willems, Jennifer....................(309) 671-1550
cathpost@cdop.org, The Catholic Post, IL, Peoria

Willems, John ....(905) 853-8888
jwillems@metroland.com, General Manager, The Richmond Hill Liberal, ON, Markham

Willems, John ....(905) 853-8888
john.willems@metroland.com, Metroland Media Group Ltd., ON, Mississauga

Willems, John ....(905) 853-8888
jwillems@metroland.com, Gen. Mgr. , Markham Economist & Sun, ON, Markham

Willems, Will................(765) 482-4650 Ext. 128
will.willems@reporter.net, Sports Ed., The Reporter, IN, Lebanon

Willenbrink, Bob
bobw@mail.uca.edu, Chair, University of Central Arkansas, AR, Conway

Willenbrock, Fred J.....................(509) 447-2433
theminer@povn.com, Pub., The Gem State Miner, WA, Newport

Willenbrock, Fred J.
theminer@povn.com, Pub., Newport Miner, WA, Newport

Willerscheidt, Marcus
thorn-biz@rose-hulman.edu, Business Manager, Rose-Hulman Inst. of Technology, IN, Terre Haute

Willets, Sarah
swillets@civitasmedia.com, Managing Ed., The Robesonian, NC, Lumberton

Willett, Janet ....(573) 248-2700
janet.willett@courierpost.com, Controller/Dir., HR, Hannibal Courier-Post, MO, Hannibal

Willett, Susan ....(734) 467-1900
swillett@journalgroup.com, Pub., The Wayne Eagle, MI, Plymouth

Willett, Susan
swillett@journalgroup.com, Pub., Associated Newspapers of Michigan, MI, Wayne

Willett, Susan
swillett@journalgroup.com, Pub., The Westland Eagle, MI, Plymouth

Willett, Susan
swillett@journalgroup.com, Pub., The Inkster Ledger Star, MI, Plymouth

Willett, Susan
swillett@journalgroup.com, Pub., Northville Eagle, MI, Plymouth

Willett, Susan
swillett@journalgroup.com, Pub., Plymouth Eagle, MI, Plymouth

Willett, Susan ....(734) 467 1900
swillett@journalgroup.com, Ed./Pub., The Romulus Roman, MI, Plymouth

Willett, Susan
swillett@journalgroup.com, Pub., Canton Eagle, MI, Plymouth

Willey, Jamie
jwilley@parsonssun.com, Asst. Mng. Ed., Parsons Sun, KS, Parsons

Willgren, Charles
editor@blanconews.com, Ed., Blanco County News, TX, Blanco

Willhite, Greg ....(765) 762-2411
atticasales@sbcglobal.net, Gen. Mgr., Fountain County Neighbor, IN, Attica
atticasales@sbcglobal.net, Acct. Exec. , The Review Republican, IN, Attica

Willhite, Greg ....(765) 762-2411
atticasales@sbcglobal.net, Adv. Mgr./ Gen. Mgr., Messenger, IN, Attica

Williams, Aaron
awilliams@sfchronicle.com, Interactive Ed, San Francisco Chronicle, CA, San Francisco

Williams, Alan ....(813) 259-8234
awilliams@748inc.com, Tampa Bay Times, FL, St Petersburg

Williams, Ann
awilliams@es.marywood.edu, Marywood University, PA, Scranton

Williams, Bart ....(405) 475-3437
bwilliams@opubco.com, VP, Production, The Oklahoman, OK, Oklahoma City

Williams, Becky........................(352) 542-0131
adsdcadvocate@gmail.com, Ad. Rep., Dixie County Advocate, FL, Cross City

Williams, Betty ....(252) 329-9511
bwilliams@reflector.com, Display Adv. Dir., The Daily Reflector, NC, Greenville

Williams, Bob
bob.williams@lee.net, Pub., At Home With Flipside, IL, Carbondale

Williams, Bob ....(814) 665-8291 Ext 35
bwilliams@thecorryjournal.com, Pub., Corry Journal, PA, Corry

Williams, Bob
bwilliams@yourjournals.com, Pub., Chesterfield Journal, MO, Saint Louis

Williams, Brian ....(559) 784-5000 Ext. 1044
bwilliams@portervillerecorder.com, Mng. Ed./ Asst. Pub., The Porterville Recorder, CA, Porterville

Williams, Carey
editor@heraldjournal.net, Ed., Advocate Democrat, GA, Greensboro

Williams, Carla ....(541) 942-3325
legals@cgsentinel.com, Circ./Class. Mgr, Cottage Grove Sentinel, OR, Cottage Grove

Williams, Celeste....................(817) 390-7697
cxwilliams@star-telegram.com, Mng. Ed., Sports, Fort Worth Star-Telegram, TX, Fort Worth

Williams, Charean
cjwilliams@star-telegram.com, Editorial Dept, Fort Worth Star-Telegram, TX, Fort Worth

Williams, Charles
wilkesjp@charter.net, Ed., The Wilkes Journal-Patriot, NC, North Wilkesboro

Williams, Cheryl S. ....(912) 449-6693
cwilliams@theblacksheartimes.com, Assoc. Pub., The Blackshear Times, GA, Blackshear

Williams, Chris ....(250) 559-4680
chris.williams@haidagwaiiobserver.com, Sales Mgr., Haida Gwaii Observer, BC, Queen Charlotte

Williams, Clarissa
clarissa.williams@doverpost.com, Pub. Mgr. Smyrna/Clayton Sun-Times, DE, Middletown

Williams, Clarissa
daytona.pennysaver@psavers.com, Group General Manager, Volusia Pennysaver, Inc., FL, Ormond Beach
daytona.pennysaver@psavers.com, St. John's Pennysaver, FL, Palatka

Williams, Connie ....(623) 847-4601
sales@star-times.com, Adv. Mgr., Peoria Times, AZ, Glendale

Williams, Corey...........(251) 867-4876, Ext. 116
sports@brewtonstandard.com, Sports Ed, The Brewton Standard, AL, Brewton

Williams, Daniel
business@parispi.net, Office Mgr., The Paris Post-Intelligencer, TN, Paris
business@parispi.net, Director of Audience Development, The Day, CT, New London

Williams, Dave
dwilliams@yrmg.com, Retail Sales Mgr., The Newmarket Era-banner, ON, Newmarket

Williams, David........................(607) 735-1815
dwilliams@elmira.edu, Elmira College, NY, Elmira

Williams, Dawn ....(630) 531-1670
chgoeniornews@yahoo.com, Managing Editor, DenBar Publishing, Inc, IL, Dundee

Williams, Deb ....(715) 395-5007
dwilliams@superiortelegram.com, Human Resources Manager, Superior Telegram, WI, Superior

Williams, Denice ....(503) 221-8514
dwilliams@oregonian.com, Adv. Mgr., Verticals, The Oregonian, OR, Portland

Williams, Dennis ....(660) 699-2194
clarencecourier@centurytel.net, Pub., Ed., Clarence Courier, MO, Clarence

Williams, Dick
dwilliams@criernewspapers.com, Ed., Dunwoody Crier, GA, Dunwoody

Williams, Ed
ewilliams@lewistownsentinel.com, Circ. Mgr., The Sentinel, PA, Lewistown

Williams, Eileen ....(512) 404-2300
conference@voicetext.com, Pres., VoiceText Communications, TX, Austin

Williams, Evonne ....(731) 642-1162
ewilliams@parispi.net, Bus. Mgr., The Paris Post-Intelligencer, TN, Paris

Williams, Gene
g.williams@technologyintegrators.net, Sales Engineer, Technology Integrators, IL, Effingham

Williams, Glenn
glenn.williams@naplesnews.com, Mgr., Packaging, Naples Daily News, FL, Naples

Williams, Hannah
hwilliams1@vikings.northpark.edu, Online Editor, North Park Univ., IL, Chicago

Williams, Heather
hwilliams@ledger-enquirer.com, Circ. Mktg., Columbus Ledger-Enquirer, GA, Columbus

Williams, Herbert
a-graesser@memphis.edu, Prof. Emer., University of Memphis, TN, Memphis

Williams, Jack
daychron@bmi.net, Pub./Ed., Dayton Chronicle, WA, Dayton

Williams, Jennifer
heather.irwin@pressdemocrat.com, Digital Development Director, The Press Democrat, CA, Santa Rosa

Williams, Joanne
jwilliams@themeidianstar.com, Olivet College, MI, Olivet

Williams, Joe ....(314) 340-8000
joewilliams@post-dispatch.com, St. Louis Post-Dispatch, MO, Saint Louis

Williams, Joe
jwilliams@jcslumenchristi.org, Dir., Finance, The Clarion-Ledger, MS, Jackson

Williams, John ....(201) 933-7100
US Ink, NJ, Carlstadt

Williams, Josh
josh.williams@ipreo.com, The New York Times, NY, New York

Williams, Joyce........................(540) 665-4959
jwilliams@winchesterstar.com, Systems Mgr., The Winchester Star, VA, Winchester

Williams, Julian
jwilliams@claflin.edu, Asst. Prof., Claflin University, SC, Orangeburg

Williams, Julie................(928) 474-5251 x 107
jwantland@payson.com, Opns. Mgr., The Payson Roundup, AZ, Payson

Williams, Kevin ....(800) 245-7515
kwilliams@oasisnewsfeatures.com, Exec. Ed., Oasis Newsfeatures, Inc., Middletown

Williams, Kimberly
williams.kimberly@dailygleaner.com, Pub/Ed., The Oromocto Post-gazette, NB, Oromocto

Williams, Kristi
kwilliams@kentuckynewera.com, Adv. Rep., Kentucky New Era, KY, Hopkinsville

Williams, Kristie
kwilliams@socket.net, Membership Services

jwillis@statesgraphic.com, Editor, Brownsville States-Graphic, TN, Brownsville

Willis, Jerry .... **(918) 684-2932**
jwillis@muskogeephoenix.com, Ed., County Journal, IL, Percy
jwillis@muskogeephoenix.com, News / Photo Ed. , Muskogee Phoenix, OK, Muskogee

Willis, Katie .... **(410) 463-9883**
kwillis@chespub.com , Community Ed. , The Star-Democrat, MD, Easton

Willis, Larry .... **(618) 497-8272**
cjournal@egyptian.net, Co-Pub., County Journal, IL, Percy

Willis, Paula
homes@news-graphic.com, Prodn. Mgr., The Scott Shopper, KY, Georgetown

Willis, Robert
robert.willis@memphistn.gov, Instr., University of Memphis, TN, Memphis

Willis, Steven .... **(719) 589-2553**
advertising sales, Valley Courier, CO, Alamosa

Willis, Wayne
wayne.willis@sunmedia.ca, Prod. Supervisor, The Peterborough Examiner, ON, Peterborough

Williscraft, Mike
mwilliscraft@niagarathisweek.com, Editorial Dir., Niagara This Week, ON, Thorold

Williscraft, Mike
mwilliscraft@niagarathisweek.com, Editorial Mgr., The Grimsby Lincoln News, ON, Grimsby

Williston, Lorie
lwilliston@blackpress.ca, Pres., Cariboo Press, BC, Williams Lake
lwilliston@blackpress.ca, Pub, North Thompson Times, BC, Clearwater

Willmann, Teresa
columbine@evergreenco.com, Pub., Columbine Courier, CO, Evergreen

Wills, David .... **(501) 993-6284**
dwills@bentoncourier.com, Addvertising Director, The Saline Courier TMC, Benton

Wills, Jane .... **(310) 451-3307**
jhwills@fliinc.com, Vice President, FLI, Incorporated, CA, Santa Monica

Wills, John .... **(310) 451-3307**
jcwills@fliinc.com, President/CEO, FLI, Incorporated, CA, Santa Monica

Wills, Peter C.
peterwills@providenceamerican.com, Pub., The Providence American, RI, Providence

Wills, Rob
thenorthfieldnews@gmail.com, Adv. Dir., The Northfield News, VT, Northfield

Wilmes, Mychal .... **(507) 285-7659**
wilmes@agrinews.com, Mng. Ed., Agri News, MN, Rochester

Wilmoth, Tom
news@bedfordbulletin.com, Ed., Bedford Bullet, VA, Bedford

Wilmoth, Tom .... **(540) 586-8612**
news@bedfordbulletin.com, Ed., Bedford Bulletin, VA, Bedford

Wilner, Richard
rwilner@nypost.com, Ed. Dept./Business, New York Post, NY, New York

Wilson, Adam
adwilson@dmreg.com, Ed., Extra, IA, Indianola
adwilson@dmreg.com, Ed., Record-Herald and Indianola Tribune, IA, Indianola

Wilson, Alisha .... **(662) 862-3141 ext. 104**
itimes1@yahoo.com, Ed., The Itawamba County Times, MS, Fulton

Wilson, Allen .... **(406) 657-1471**
awilson@billingsgazette.com, Circ. Dir., Billings Gazette, MT, Billings

Wilson, Allison .... **(417) 256-9191**
editor@wpdailyquill.net, Managing Editor, West Plains Daily Quill, MO, West Plains

Wilson, Amy
editor@towncrieronline.com, Ed./Gen. Mgr., Austintown Town Crier, OH, Warren
editor@towncrieronline.com, Ed./Gen. Mgr., Canfield Town Crier, OH, Warren
editor@towncrieronline.com, Ed./Gen. Mgr., Poland Town Crier, OH, Warren
editor@towncrieronline.com, Ed./Gen. Mgr., Boardman Town Crier, OH, Warren

Wilson, Amy Leigh .... **(330) 629-6229**
editor@mvparentmagazine.com, Ed., Mahoning Valley Parent Magazine, OH, Warren

Wilson, Ann .... **(712) 792-3573**
management@carrollspaper.com, Gen Mgr., Carroll Daily Times Herald, IA, Carroll

Wilson, Barbara
bwilson@dailyhome.com, Business Mgr, The Daily Home, AL, Talladega

Wilson, Barbara
barbaraw@re-wa.org, Circ. Mgr., Weekend Advocate, OH, Greenville

Wilson, Betsy
reviewnews@gmail.com, Pub., Intercounty Newspaper Group, PA, Philadelphia

Wilson, Bradley .... **(940) 397-4704**
bradley.wilson@mwsu.edu, Advisor, Midwestern State University, TX, Wichita Falls

Wilson, Bradley .... **(919) 515-2411**
Advisor, North Carolina State Univ., NC, Raleigh

Wilson, Brett
brett.wilson@ml.com, Pub., Parade, New York

Wilson, Catherine .... **(305) 347-6611**
cwilson@alm.com, Law Editor, Miami Daily Business Review, FL, Miami

Wilson, Cathy .... **(305) 347-6611**
cwilson@alm.com, Law Editor, Palm Beach Daily Business Review, FL, Miami

Wilson, Cathy
cathy.wilson@flyergroup.com, Bus. Mgr., The Weekend Flyer, IN, Avon

Wilson, Cathy .... **(317) 272-5800 ext. 207**
cathy.wilson@flyergroup.com, Bus. Mgr., Hendricks County Flyer, IN, Avon

Wilson, Charles .... **(813) 259-7736**
Tampa Bay Times, FL, St Petersburg

Wilson, Chris
cbwilson@metlife.com, Pres/COO, Simmons Market Research Bureau, NY, New York

Wilson, Chris
chris.wilson@monroe360.com, Ed., Monroe County Journal, MS, Amory

Wilson, Christine .... **(808) 529-4778**
cwilson@staradvertiser.com, Today/Feat. Ed., Honolulu Star-Advertiser, HI, Honolulu

Wilson, Cindy .... **(217) 486-6496**
thesentinel@comcast.net, Ed./Pub., The Sentinel, IL, Illiopolis

Wilson, Cristy .... **(618) 936-2212**
sumpress@frontier.com, Advertising/Graphics Designer, The Sumner Press, IL, Sumner

Wilson, Cynthia .... **(361) 886-3719**
wilsonc@caller.com, Features Ed., Corpus Christi Caller-Times, TX, Corpus Christi

Wilson, Darrin
darrin.wilson@camillaga.net, Pub., The Pelham Journal, GA, Camilla

Wilson, Darrin .... **(229) 336-5265**
darrin.wilson@camillaga.net, Pub., Camilla Enterprise, GA, Camilla

Wilson, Dave .... **(305) 376-3685**
dwilson@miamiherald.com, Senior Editor / Administration, Miami Herald, FL, Doral

dwilson@miamiherald.com, Mng. Ed., News, Herald Values, FL, Miami

Wilson, Dennis .... **(973) 364-0605**
americanfootballnetworks@gmail.com, Pres., Metropolitan New York Football Writers Association, NJ, Roseland

Wilson, Derek .... **(415) 892-1516 x 13**
Central Marin Ed, Novato Advance, CA, Novato

Wilson, Don
don@llfs.com, Circ. Mgr., The Daily News, NC, Jacksonville

Wilson, Drew .... **(256) 840-3000 ext 121**
dwilson@sandmountainreporter.com, Adv , Sand Mountain Reporter, AL, Albertville

Wilson, Dylan .... **(252) 436-2833**
dwilson@hendersondispatch.com, Features Ed., Daily Dispatch, NC, Henderson

Wilson, Elizabeth
bwilson@journalregister.com, Pub., King of Prussia Courier, PA, Wayne

Wilson, Elizabeth .... **(215) 542-0200 ext. 222**
ewilson@montgomerynews.com, Pub., Souderton Independent, PA, Fort Washington

Wilson, Elizabeth .... **(215) 542-0200 ext. 222**
ewilson@montgomerynews.com, Pub., The Review, PA, Philadelphia

Wilson, Elizabeth .... **(215) 628-9300 ext. 230**
bwilson@montgomerynews.com, Pub., Montgomery Newspapers, PA, Fort Washington

Wilson, Eric .... **(304) 291-9417**
ewilson@dominionpost.com, Adv. Dir., The Dominion Post, WV, Morgantown

Wilson, Geordie
gwilson@newspost.com, Pub., The Frederick News-Post, MD, Frederick

Wilson, Geordie .... **(603) 224-5301 ext. 269**
Pub., Newspapers of New England, NH, Concord

Wilson, Gerald L. .... **(205) 380-2800**
glwilson@usouthal.edu, Prof./Chair, University of South Alabama, AL, Mobile

Wilson, Henrietta
forwardtimes@forwardtimes.com, Adv. Dir., Houston Forward Times, TX, Houston

Wilson, James
general@carrollspaper.com, Pub., Times Herald Advertiser, IA, Carroll

Wilson, Jay
jwilson@longbineauto.com, Adv. Mgr., Display/Nat'l, The Emporia Gazette, KS, Emporia

Wilson, Jennifer .... **(316) 321-1120**
jwilson@butlercountytimesgazette.com, Adv. Exec., The Butler County Times-Gazette, KS, Augusta

Wilson, Jim
jwilson@lindenwood.edu, Dean, Lindenwood University, MO, Saint Charles

Wilson, Joe
jwilson@kentuckynewera.com, Sports Ed., Fort Campbell Courier, KY, Hopkinsville

Wilson, Joe
jwilson@kentuckynewera.com, Sports Editor, Kentucky New Era, KY, Hopkinsville

Wilson, Joey
joeywilson@pittstoyota.com, Photo Ed., The Courier Herald, GA, Dublin

Wilson, John
john@quantumops.com, Pub., Chattanoogan.com, TN, Chattanooga

Wilson, Julie
julie@pennywiseads.com, Adv. Mgr., Pennywise, BC, Kaslo

Wilson, Kari .... **(785) 776-2200 Ext. 261**
kwilson@themercury.com, Customer Service Supervisor, The Manhattan Mercury, KS, Manhattan

Wilson, Kay
nodawaynews@socket.net, Pub./Owner, Nodaway News Leader, MO, Maryville

Wilson, Keith D. .... **(423) 246-8121**
kwilson@timesnews.net, Pub./Vice Pres./Treasurer, Kingsport Times-News, TN, Kingsport

Wilson, Kelli .... **(209) 634-9141**
kthreet@turlockjournal.com, Circ. Mgr., The Ceres Courier, CA, Turlock

Wilson, Ken .... **(912) 384-2323**
circulation@douglasenterprise.net, Circ. Mgr., The Douglas Enterprise, GA, Douglas

Wilson, Kevin
kevinw@wdtimes.com, Sports Ed., Watertown Daily Times, WI, Watertown

Wilson, Kevin .... **(575) 763-3431**
kwilson@thenews.email, Managing Editor, Eastern New Mexico News, NM, Clovis

Wilson, Kristin
kristinw@ndsc.org, Adv. Dir., Finder, ND, Bismarck

Wilson, Kristine .... **(847) 427-4369**
kwilson@dailyherald.com, Assistant Corporate Secretary, Daily Herald, IL, Arlington Heights

Wilson, Larry A.
news@therichtondispatch.com, Ed., The Richton Dispatch, MS, Richton

Wilson, Lisa .... **(705) 268-5050 ext. 222**
lisa.wilson@sunmedia.ca, Pub. , The Timmins Daily Press, ON, Timmins

Wilson, Lisa
lwilson@postmedia.com, Adv. Dir., Northern News, ON, Kirkland Lake

Wilson, Lisa Klem .... **(212) 293-8612**
lwilson@unitedmedia.com, Sr. Vice Pres./Gen. Mgr., Newspaper Enterprise Association (Div. of United Media), NY, New York
lwilson@unitedmedia.com, Sr. Vice Pres./Gen. Mgr., United Feature Syndicate (Div. of United Media), New York
lwilson@unitedmedia.com, Sales & Mktg. Contact/Sr. Vice Pres. & Gen. Mgr., United Media, Scripps Howard News Service, Washington

Wilson, Marc .... **(309) 743-0816**
mwilson@townnews.com, Exec Chairman, TownNews.com, IL, Moline

Wilson, Mark .... **(252) 407-9922**
mwilson@rmtelegram.com, Pub., Rocky Mount Telegram, NC, Rocky Mount
mwilson@rmtelegram.com, President, North Carolina Press Association, NC, Raleigh

Wilson, Mark .... **(252) 407-9967**
mwilson@rmtelegram.com, Publisher, Rocky Mount Telegram, Cooke Communications North Carolina, LLC, NC, Greenville
mwilson@rmtelegram.com, VP, Adv., Morning News, SC, Florence

Wilson, Mary .... **(816) 761-6200**
mwilson@jcadvocate.com, Editor, Jackson County Advocate, MO, Grandview

Wilson, Melissa
melissa.wilson@fastsigns.com, Adv. Dir., Tallapoosa Journal, GA, Carrollton

Wilson, Melissa .... **(770) 834-6631**
melissa@times-georgian.com, Reg. Adv. Dir., Times-Georgian, GA, Carrollton

Wilson, Melissa .... **(470) 729-3237**
melissa@times-georgian.com, Adv. Dir., Douglas County Sentinel, GA, Douglasville

Wilson, Michael .... **(255) 388-0190**
mwilson@theadvocate.com, VP, Digital Media, The Advocate, LA, Baton Rouge

Wilson, Michael .... **(512) 445-3715**
michaelwilson@statesman.com, VP, Digital Media, Capital City Press, LA

Wilson, Michael
michael.wilson1@state.co.us, Prodn. Mgr.,

Denver Westword, CO, Denver

Wilson, Mike ....(727) 892-2924
mwilson@tampabay.com, Mng. Ed., Enterprise,
Tampa Bay Times, FL, St Petersburg

Wilson, Mike ....(214) 977-8473
mikewilson@dallasnews.com, Editor, The
Dallas Morning News, TX, Dallas

Wilson, Mike ....(608) 478-2516
MWilson@hngnews.com, Adv. Sales Rep., The
Star, WI, Sun Prairie

Wilson, Neena ....(256) 845-1914
nwilson@goval.com, Mgr., Gerrard
Ovalstrapping, AL, Fort Payne

Wilson, Nick
nwilson@bannergraphic.com, Banner-Graphic,
IN, Greencastle

Wilson, Pat ....(867) 667-2013
pat@whitehorsestar.com, Accounts,
Whitehorse Star, YT, Whitehorse

Wilson, Patti ....(918) 259-7564
pattiw@ok.neighbornews.com, HR Mgr., The
Pioneer - Big Rapids, MI, Big Rapids

Wilson, Pete ....1-(800) 489-5090
wilson.braziltimes@gmail.com, Editor, The
Brazil Times, IN, Brazil

Wilson, Pete
mwilson@jcbipaper.com, Exec. Ed., The
Telegram, OH, Jackson

Wilson, Peter A.
valeader@valliant.com, Ed., The Valliant
Leader, OK, Valliant

Wilson, Randy ....(330) 287-1630
rwilson@the-daily-record.com, Nat'l Adv. Sales,
The Daily Record, OH, Wooster

Wilson, Randy ....(928) 556-2254
rwilson@azdailysun.com, Editorial Page Ed.,
Arizona Daily Sun, Flagstaff, AZ, Flagstaff

Wilson, Rebecca
rwilson@thearknewspaper.com, Asst. Ed., The
Ark, CA, Tiburon

Wilson, Rhonda
editor@sonoratx.net, Adv. Dir., Devil's River
News, TX, Sonora

Wilson, Robin ....(603) 668-4321
rwilson@unionleader.com, Adv. Servs.
Mgr., New Hampshire Union Leader/New
Hampshire Sunday News, NH, Manchester

Wilson, Robin ....(304) 636-2121, ext. 103
rwilson@theintermountain.com, Business
Office Mgr., The Inter-Mountain, WV, Elkins

Wilson, Robin
robin@newcastlepacer.com, Pub., Early Bird
Express, OK, Newcastle

Wilson, Sarah
editor@menastar.com, Ed., The Mena Star,
AR, Mena

Wilson, Sarah O. ....(574) 224-5331
show@rochsent.com, Pub., The Rochester
Sentinel, IN, Rochester

Wilson, Scott
swilson@ptleader.com, Pub., Port Townsend &
Jefferson County Leader, WA, Port Townsend

Wilson, Scott ....(270) 678-5171 Ext. 286
swilson@glasgowdailytimes.com, Sports Ed.,
Glasgow Daily Times, KY, Glasgow

Wilson, Scott ....(816) 218-6787
scott.wilson@pitch.com, Editor, The Pitch, MO,
Kansas City

Wilson, Steve
steve.wilson@htimes.com, Adv. Mgr., Retail,
The Huntsville Times, AL, Huntsville

Wilson, Steven D.
stevenwilson@glasgowdailytimes.com, Acct.
Exec., Glasgow Daily Times, KY, Glasgow

Wilson, Thomas G. ....(828) 264-3612
twilson@xtn.net, Vice Pres., Western North
Carolina Div., APG Media of Tennessee/

North Carolina, TN, Greeneville

Wilson, Todd ....(386) 754-0418
twilson@lakecityreporter.com, Publisher, Lake
City Reporter, FL, Lake City

Wilson, Todd
sales@pdisaneck.com, Exec. VP, PDI Plastics,
OH, Westerville

Wilson, Van
van@capitaloutlook.com, Circ.Mgr., Capital
Outlook, FL, Tallahassee

Wilson, William S. ....(574) 224-5329
wsw@rochsent.com, Exec. Ed., The Rochester
Sentinel, IN, Rochester

Wilson, Yumi
ywilson@linkedin.com, Asst. Prof., San
Francisco State University, CA, San
Francisco

Wilston, Dennis ....(301) 846-2105
dwilston@gazette.net, Pub., The Gazette Real
Estate Guide (OOB), MD, Frederick
dwilston@gazette.net, Corp. Adv. Dir., The
Gazette - Rockville / Aspen Hill / Wheaton
(OOB), MD, Gaithersburg
dwilston@gazette.net, Corp. Adv. Dir., The
Gazette - Germantown / Poolsville / Boyds
(OOB), MD, Gaithersburg
dwilston@gazette.net, Corp. Adv. Dir., The
Gazette - Olney (OOB), MD, Gaithersburg
dwilston@gazette.net, Corp. Adv. Dir., The
Gazette - Gaithersburg / Mont. Village (OOB),
MD, Gaithersburg
dwilston@gazette.net, Corp. Adv. Dir., The
Gazette - Damascus / Clarksburg, MD,
Gaithersburg
dwilston@gazette.net, Corp. Adv. Dir., The
Gazette - Bethesda / Chevy Chase /
Kensington (OOB), MD, Gaithersburg
dwilston@gazette.net, Corp. Adv. Dir., The
Gazette - Potomac / North Potomac, MD,
Gaithersburg
dwilston@gazette.net, Corp. Adv. Dir., The
Gazette - Silver Spring / Takoma Park /
Burtonsville (OOB), MD, Gaithersburg
dwilston@gazette.net, Corp. Adv. Dir., The
Gazette - North / Central Prince George Co.
(OOB), MD, Gaithersburg

Wimberley, Ashley ....(501) 374-1500
ashley@arkansaspress.org, Adv. & Mktg. Dir.,
Arkansas Press Services, AR, Little Rock

Wimmer, Maria
mwimmer@aspentimes.com, Distrib. Mgr.,
Snowmass Sun, CO, Aspen

Wimmer, Terry
terry.wimmer@arizona.edu, Prof., University of
Arizona, AZ, Tucson

Wimsatt, Richard
rwimsatt@kentuckynewera.com, Adv. Rep.,
Kentucky New Era, KY, Hopkinsville

Winchester, Susan ....(217) 477-5103
Class., Commercial News, IL, Danville

Windley, Denise ....(801) 465-9221
thepaysonchronicle@msn.com, Mng. Ed., The
Payson Chronicle, UT, Payson

Winegarden, Dave ....(209) 249-3503
Group Publisher, Manteca Bulletin, CA,
Manteca

Wineka, Mark ....(704) 797-4263
mwineka@salisburypost.com, Political Ed.,
Salisbury Post, NC, Salisbury

Wineman, Neil
nwineman@commgraphics.com, New Bus. Dir.,
CommGraphics Interactive, Inc., NE, Lincoln

Winer, Marlene
marlene@teletype.com, Mktg. Mgr., TeleType
Co., MA, Boston

Winfield, Betty
winfieldb@missouri.edu, Prof., University of
Missouri, MO, Columbia

Winfrey, Jake
jwinfrey@cullmantimes.com, Sports Ed., The
Cullman Times, AL, Cullman

Winfried, Schenker
winfried.schenker@kba.com, Sales Director
Web Presses, KBA North America, Inc.
(Koenig & Bauer AG), TX, Dallas

Wing, Anne C.
info@chaunceywing.com, President, Chauncey
Wing's Sons, Inc., MA, Marion

Wing, Chuck ....(801) 236-6004
wingnut@deseretnews.com, Photo Ed.,
Deseret News, UT, Salt Lake City

Wing, Jennifer ....(315) 434-8889 x320
Ed., The Eagle, NY, Syracuse

Wing, Jill
jwing@saratogian.com, Copy Ed., The
Saratogian, NY, Saratoga Springs

Wingert, Bridget ....(215) 794-1096
Bridget@BucksCountyHerald.com, Ed., Bucks
County Herald, PA, Lahaska

Wingert, Joseph
jgwingert@buckscountyherald.com, Associate
Pub, Bucks County Herald, PA, Lahaska

Wingert, Stephan ....(956) 683-4067
swingert@themonitor.com, Pub., The Monitor,
TX, McAllen

Winget, Cody
cwinget@cityweekly.net, Acctg. Mgr., Salt Lake
City Weekly, UT, Salt Lake City

Wingrove, RayeLynne
tribadss@otelco.net, Class. Ads Mgr, The Arab
Tribune, AL, Arab

Winings, Ruby
circulation@swpub.com, Circ. Mgr., Savage
Pacer, MN, Savage

Winjum, Kimberlly
kwinjum@whidbeynewstimes.com, Assc. Pub.,
South Whidbey Record, WA, Coupeville

Winjum, Kimberly
kimw@ferndalerecordjournal.com, Adv. Mgr.,
Whatcom County Shopper, WA, Ferndale

Wink, Shaun ....(806) 537-3634
shaun@panhandleherald.com, Ed./Pub./Adv.
Dir./Owner, Panhandle Herald / White Deer
News, TX, Panhandle

Winkeler, Les
les.winkeler@thesouthern.com, Sports Ed.,
The Southern Illinoisan, IL, Carbondale

Winkeler, Les ....ext. 5084
Les.Winkeler@TheSouthern.com, Sports Ed.,
At Home With Flipside, IL, Carbondale

Winkelman, Marge ....(763) 712-2402
marge.winkelman@ecm-inc.com, Pres./COO,
The Waconia Patriot, MN, Waconia
marge.winkelman@ecm-inc.com, Pres./
COO, Norwood Young America Times, MN,
Waconia

Winkelman, Max ....(250) 395-2219
newsroom@100milefreepress.net, Ed., 100
Mile House Free Press, BC, 100 Mile House

Winkler, Carol
carolwinkler@gsu.edu, Chair, Georgia State
University, GA, Atlanta

Winkler, Don
dwinkler@lethbridgeherald.com, Prodn. Mgr.,
Commercial Print, The Lethbridge Herald,
AB, Lethbridge

Winkler, Jay ....(615) 259-8389
jwinkler@tennessean.com, Vice Pres., Circ.,
TN Media, TN, Nashville
jwinkler@tennessean.com, Vice Pres., Circ.,
The Tennessean, TN, Nashville

Winnecke, Joycelynn ....(312) 222-3232
Associate Manger, Editor of National News,
Chicago Tribune, IL, Chicago

Winnemore, Amy
awinnemore@delconewsnetwork.com, Mng.
Ed., Springfield Press, PA, Swarthmore

Winnemuller, Diane ....(850) 315-4301
dwinnemuller@courier-tribune.com, Publisher,

Northwest Florida Daily News, FL, Fort
Walton Beach

Winningham, Daniel
dwinningha@enquirerdemocrat.com, Macoupin
County Enquirer Democrat, IL, Carlinville

Winquist, Kate ....(306) 672-3373
kate@advancesouthwest.com, Pub, Advance
Southwest (formerly Gull Lake Advance), SK,
Gull Lake

Winship, George ....(530) 365-2797
gwinship@andersonvalleypost.com, Ed.,
Anderson Valley Post, CA, Redding

Winskowski, Dennis
dennisw@dlnewspapers.com, Pub., The Detroit
Lakes Tribune, MN, Detroit Lakes

Winslow, Carmen
carmen.winslow@mtstandard.com, Mng. Ed.,
The Montana Standard, MT, Butte

Winslow, Susan ....(707) 427-6955
Copy Ed., Daily Republic, CA, Fairfield

Winsor, Deborah ....(941) 361-4994
deb.winsor@heraldtribune.com, Asst. Mng. Ed.,
Sarasota Herald-Tribune, FL, Sarasota

Winston, Diane
dianewin@usc.edu, Knight Chair in Media and
Religion/Assoc. Prof., University of Southern
California, CA, Los Angeles

Winter, Amy ....(765) 648-4255
amy.winter@heraldbulletin.com, Circ. Dir., The
Herald Bulletin, IN, Anderson
amy.winter@heraldbulletin.com, Pub.,
Commercial News, IL, Danville

Winter, Dixie
dixiewinter@nckcn.com, Adv. Sales, Concordia
Blade-Empire, KS, Concordia

Winter, Don
donw@encompassmediagroup.com, Adv. Mgr.,
Midtown Resident, NY, New York

Winter, Don
leadernews@westriv.com, Pub., Upper West
Side Resident, NY, New York
leadernews@westriv.com, Ed. , Leader-News,
ND, Washburn

Winter, Jacob ....(507) 553-3131
mirror.shopper@gmail.com, Staff Writer, Wells
Mirror, MN, Wells

Winter, Janice ....(218) 894-1112
jwinter@staplesworld.com, graphic designer/
photo tech, Staples World, MN, Staples

Winter, Ken ....(231) 347-2554
kwint@petoskeynews.com, Pres., Northern
Michigan Review, Inc., MI, Petoskey

Winter, Matt ....(423) 623-6171
matt.winter@newportplaintalk.com, News
Editor, The Newport Plain Talk, TN, Newport

Winter, Sabine ....(972) 860-7290
Eastfield College, TX, Mesquite

Winter, Shawn ....(231) 933-1413
swinter@record-eagle.com, Adv. Dir. , Traverse
City Record-Eagle, MI, Traverse City

Winterland, Barry ....(309) 820-3205
bwinterland@pantagraph.com, Gen. Mgr.,
Woodford Star, IL, Eureka

Winterland, Barry ....(309) 820-3205
bwinterland@pantagraph.com, Pub., The
Woodford County Journal, IL, Eureka

Winterland, Barry L. ....(309) 820-3205
bwinterland@pantagraph.com, Gen. Mgr., The
Pantagraph, IL, Bloomington

Winters, Amy
amy.winter@heraldbulletin.com, Circ. Mgr.,
Madison County Direct, IN, Anderson

Winters, Gordon
gwinters@journalstar.com, Editorial Page Ed.,
Lincoln Journal Star, NE, Lincoln

Winters, John ....(770) 683-1712
john@newnan.com, Pub., The Newnan Times-

Herald, GA, Newnan

Winters, Mary
mwinters@qni.biz, VP, Newspapers & Interactive, Quincy Media, Inc., IL, Quincy

Winters, Matt
mwinters@chinookobserver.com, Pub./Ed., Chinook Observer, WA, Long Beach

Winters, Melani .... (802) 254-2311, Ext. 161
mwinters@reformer.com, Night Mng. Ed., Brattleboro Reformer, VT, Brattleboro

Wipperman, Darin
courierreporter@salmonpress.com, The Coos County Democrat, NH, Lancaster
courierreporter@salmonpress.com, Ed., The Berlin Reporter, NH, Lancaster

Wipperman, Darin
courierreporter@salmonpress.com, Ed., Littleton Courier, NH, Littleton

Wippler, Charlotte
ads@stonecountyenterprise.com, Ad Sales, Stone County Enterprise, MS, Wiggins

Wirestone, Clay .... (603) 224-5301 ext. 305
Features Ed., Concord Monitor, NH, Concord

Wirt, Joe .... (916) 288-6021
joe@cnpa.com, Director of Affiliate Relations, California News Publishers Association, CA, Sacramento

Wirth, Eileen M.
emw@creighton.edu, Chair/Prof., Creighton Univ., NE, Omaha

Wirth, Hans .... (262) 785-3241
hans.wirth@us.abb.com, Mgr.-Sales Applications/Printing Drives Systems, ABB, Inc. (Printing Systems), WI, New Berlin

Wirth, Michael
mwirth@utk.edu, Dean/Prof., The University of Tennessee, TN, Knoxville

Wirth, Tim .... (412) 263-1589
twirth@post-gazette.com, Advertising Operation/System Manager, Pittsburgh Post-Gazette, PA, Clinton

Wirtz, Ralph E. .... (989) 839-4241
ralphewirtz@mdn.net, Editorial Page Ed., Midland Daily News, MI, Midland

Wisbith, Jody
jpowers@heraldstaronline.com, Metro Ed., Herald-Star, OH, Steubenville

Wisch, Susan
sharonwisch@gmail.com, VP Sales and Circ., Texas Jewish Post, TX, Dallas

Wischnowski, Stan
swischnowski@phillynews.com, Executive Editor, Philadelphia Inquirer, Daily News & Philly.com, PA, Philadelphia

Wise, Belinda .... (765) 575-4644
bwise@thecouriertimes.com, Adv. Sales Exec., The Courier-Times, IN, New Castle

Wise, Corby .... (740) 397-5333 Ext. 240
cwise@mountvernonnews.com, Adv. Mgr., Mount Vernon News, OH, Mount Vernon

Wise, Jerry
deqnewsman@yahoo.com, Ed., The DeQuincy News, LA, Dequincy

Wise, Linda
journal@ktc.com, Adv. Dir., Hill Country Community Journal, TX, Kerrville

Wise, Monica .... (580) 310-7505
mwise@theadanews.com, Class., The Ada News, OK, Ada

Wise, Sara .... (304) 462-7309
glenvillenews@gmail.com, Receptionist/Circulation Clerk, The Glenville Pathfinder, WV, Glenville

Wise, Sara .... (304) 462-7309
glenvillenews@gmail.com, Receptionist/Circulation Manager, The Glenville Democrat/Pathfinder, WV, Glenville

Wise, Sherrie
enterpriseads@atcnet.net, Adv. Exec., Idaho Enterprise, ID, Malad City

Wise, Stan .... (605) 622-2304
farmforum@aberdeennews.com, Ed, Farm Forum, SD, Aberdeen

Wise, Susan .... (309) 690-5342
swise@multiad.com, Business Development Manager, Local Search Association, IL, Peoria

Wise, T. Corby
cwise@mountvernonnews.com, Adv. Mgr., Shopper's Mart, OH, Mount Vernon

Wise-Chappuis, Larkin
Members@FarmlandNews.com, Circulation Mgr/Sales, Farmland News, OH, Archbold

Wiseman, Greg
greg.wiseman@sunmedia.ca, Managing Ed., Nipawin Journal, SK, Nipawin

Wiseman, Jerry
paper@netins.net, Pub., The Chronicle, IA, Odebolt

Wiseman, Mikayla
mikayla.wiseman@nptelegraph.com, Copy Ed., The North Platte Telegraph, NE, North Platte

Wiseman, Norman .... same
same, The Petersburg Observer, IL, Petersburg

Wiseman, Robert .... (330) 747-1471
bwiseman@vindy.com, HR Dir., The Vindicator, OH, Youngstown

Wiseman, Shoni
shoni.wiseman@lubbockonline.com, Retail Adv. Dir., Lubbock Avalanche-Journal, TX, Lubbock

Wiseman, Susan
swiseman@mtcamelregister.com, Classifieds, Mount Carmel Register, IL, Mount Carmel

Wisener, Robert
robert@hotsr.com, Sports Ed., The Sentinel-Record, AR, Hot Springs National Park

Wiskirchen, Brenda
bwiskirchen@qni.biz, Dir., Opns. Support, Quincy Media, Inc., IL, Quincy

Wisner, J'Aime .... (406) 548-3353
jaime.wisner@mininickel.com, Manager, Mini Nickel Classifieds, MT, Bozeman

Wisner, Rob .... (520) 573-4182
rwisner@tucson.com, Dir. Digital Innovation, Arizona Daily Star, AZ, Tucson

Wisner, Tedd
twisner@bemidjipioneer.com, Circ. Mgr., Buyline, MN, Bemidji

Wisniewski, Andrew .... (928) 913-8669
andyw@flaglive.com, Editor, Flagstaff Live!, AZ, Flagstaff

Wisniewski, David
circulation@windsorpress.com, Dist. Mgr., Northern Berks Merchandiser, PA, Hamburg

Wissinger, Bruce .... (814) 532-5076
bwissinger@tribdem.com, Editorial Page Ed., The Tribune-Democrat, PA, Johnstown

Witaschek, Sylvia .... (703) 318-1385
switaschek@thefamilymagazine.com, Associate Publisher, Washington FAMILY Magazine, VA, Woodbridge

Witherspoon, Mark .... (515) 294-4815
mark.witherspoon@iowastatedaily.com, Advisor, Iowa State University, IA, Ames

Witmer, Jessica .... (570) 682-9081
jessica-w@citizenstandard.com, Adv. Consultant, The Citizen-Standard, PA, Valley View

Witmyer, Christine
posteagle@aol.com, Ed., The Post Eagle, NJ, Clifton

Witt, G. Michael
witt@motioncity.com, Producing Dir., Motion

City Films, CA, Santa Monica

Witt, Jim .... (817) 390-7704
jwitt@star-telegram.com, Sr. Vice Pres./Exec. Ed., Fort Worth Star-Telegram, TX, Fort Worth

Witt, Leonard
lwitt@kennesaw.edu, Assoc. Prof./Eminent Scholar/Robert D. Fowler Distinguished Chair, Kennesaw State University, GA, Kennesaw

Witt, Marion
marionw@sunpubfl.com, Office Mgr., Triangle News Leader, FL, Mount Dora

Witte, Dan
spstar@newspubinc.com, Pub., Sauk Prairie Star, WI, Sauk City

Witte, Dan
nsa@newspubinc.com, Pub., News-Sickle-Arrow, WI, Black Earth

Witte, Daniel .... (608) 767-3655
Pub., The Marquette County Tribune, WI, Montello

Witte, David .... (209) 826-3831 ext. 565
sports@losbanosenterprise.com, Sports Reporter, Los Banos Enterprise, CA, Los Banos

Witte, Mark .... (608) 767-3655
Pub., The Marquette County Tribune, WI, Montello

Witte, Sully .... (843) 958-7482
editor@moultrienews.com, Ed., Moultrie News, SC, Charleston

Witten, Scott
switten@laurinburgexchange.com, Ed., Community News Advertiser, NC, Laurinburg

Witten, Scott .... (910) 276-2311 ext 12
switten@civitasmedia.com, Ed., The Laurinburg Exchange, NC, Laurinburg

Wittig, Ainslee
ainslee.wittig@willcoxrangenews.com, Mng. Ed., Arizona Range News, AZ, Sierra Vista

Wittland, Andrew
aww13@albion.edu, Albion College, MI, Albion

Wittsell, Lynn .... (608) 444-0654
Assoc. Editor, Dane County Kids, WI, Mc Farland

Witwer, Dianne
dwitwer@news-banner.com, Dir., Mktg, Treasurer, News-Banner, IN, Bluffton

Witwer, George O.
gowitwer@kpcnews.net, Principal Owner, KPC Media Group, Inc., IN, Kendallville

Wivoda , Tradie .... (763) 241-3659
tracie.wivoda@ecm-inc.com, Advertising Sales Rep, Star News, MN, Elk River

Woare, Karen .... (217) 421-6917
Data Processing Supvr., Herald & Review, Decatur, IL, Decatur

Wobbema, Amy
nrtranscript@gmail.com, Pub. /Ed., New Rockford Transcript, ND, New Rockford

Woehlk, Heinz D.
heinz@truman.edu, Contact, Truman State University, MO, Kirksville

Woelfel, Bob
bwoelfel@timesonline.com, Adv. Dir., Beaver County Times, PA, Beaver

Woerner, Tom .... (910) 893-5121
editor@harnettcountynews.com, Ed., Harnett County News, NC, Lillington

Wofford, Betty
betty@deleonfreepress.com, Adv. Mgr., De Leon Free Press, TX, De Leon

Wognum, Nick ....(218) 365-3141 ext. 19
Adv. Mgr., The Ely Echo, MN, Ely

Wohlford, Eric .... (812) 663-3111 x7003
sports@greensburgdailynews.com, Sports Ed.

, The Greensburg Times, IN, Greensburg
sports@greensburgdailynews.com, Sports, Greensburg Daily News, IN, Greensburg

Wohlfort, Craig .... (512) 445-3567
cwohlfort@statesman.com, Controller, Austin American-Statesman, TX, Austin

Wojciechowski, Linda
lwojciechowski@tnonline.com, Assoc. Ed., Catasauqua Press, PA, Allentown

Wojcik, John
jwojcik@peoplesworld.org, Ed.-in-Chief, People's World, IL, Chicago

Wojcik, Larry .... (440) 667-3011
lwojcik@hallcontractingservices.com, Director of Sales, Hall Contracting Services, Inc., OH, Avon Lake

Wojtalik, Stanley
stanleysadvertising@gmail.com, Pres., Stanley Advertising & Distributing Co., MI, Detroit

Wojtecki, Dennis B.
dennis@enescee.com, Mgr., North Shore Consultants, Inc., IL, Chicago

Wolber, Brian
bwolber@goldwindamerica.com, Illinois Inst. of Technology, IL, Chicago

Wolcott, Bill .... (716) 286-8512
Niagara Univ., NY, Niagara University

Wolcott, David .... (508) 591-6627
dwolcott@wickedlocal.com, Sports Ed., Old Colony Memorial, MA, Plymouth

Wolcott, Dottie .... (970) 429-9122
dwolcott@aspentimes.com, Bus. Mgr., The Aspen Times, CO, Aspen

Wolcott, Kimmie .... (585) 237-2212
ads@perryshopper.com, Office Mgr., Perry Shopper, NY, Perry

Woldoff, Leisah
leisah_woldoff@jewishaz.com, Mng. Ed., Jewish News, AZ, Phoenix

Wolf, Andrew .... (718) 543-5200
bxny@aol.com, Ed., Riverdale Review, NY, Bronx

Wolf, Andrew
bxny@aol.com, Pub., Bronx Press-Review, NY, Bronx

Wolf, Clint
cwolf@beloitdailynews.com, City Ed., Beloit Daily News, WI, Beloit

Wolf, Clint .... (608) 364-9225 ext. 139
cwolf@beloitdailynews.com, News Ed., My Stateline Shopper, WI, Beloit

Wolf, Gary L.
info@whitewaterpub.com, Pub., The Brookville American, IN, Brookville

Wolf, Gordon
gordon.wolf@bulletinreview.com, Ed., Denison Bulletin & Review, IA, Denison

Wolf, Mark .... (574) 296-5949
mwolf@elkharttruth.com, Circulation Director, Elkhart Truth, IN, Elkhart

Wolf, Philip .... (250) 729-4240
pwolf@nanaimodailynews.com, Ed., Harbour City Star (OOB), BC, Nanaimo
pwolf@nanaimodailynews.com, Deputy Ed., Nanaimo Daily News, BC, Nanaimo

Wolf, Susan .... (203) 894-3337
pilot@theredding pilot.com, Ed., Redding Pilot, CT, Ridgefield

Wolf, Ted
jeanann.miller@lincolncourier.com, Advertising Manager, Lincoln Courier, IL, Lincoln

Wolfcale, Joe .... (415) 892-1516 x 38
jwolfcale@marinscope.com, Ed., Ross Valley Reporter, CA, Sausalito
jwolfcale@marinscope.com, Ed., Ross Valley Reporter, CA, Novato

Wolfcale, Joe .... (415) 892-1516 x 38

Managing Ed, Novato Advance, CA, Novato

Wolfe, Adam......................(315) 312-3269
Editor-in-Chief, SUNY College/Oswego, NY, Oswego

Wolfe, Bradley
bradley.wolfe@parkbugle.org, Adv. Mgr., The Park Bugle, MN, Saint Paul

Wolfe, Charlotte ....(662) 678-1656
charlotte.wolfe@journalinc.com, Assc. Pub., Northeast Mississippi Daily Journal, MS, Tupelo

Wolfe, Cheryl
cwolfe@mtco.com, Ed., The Woodford County Journal, IL, Eureka

Wolfe, Colin ....(407) 377-0400
cwolfe@orlandoweekly.com, Web Ed., Orlando Weekly, FL, Orlando

Wolfe, Daniel.......................(212) 803-8397
daniel.wolfe@sourcemedia.com, Contributing Editor, American Banker, NY, New York

Wolfe, Deborah
amy@usfsp.edu, Adj. Fac., University of South Florida St. Petersburg, FL, Saint Petersburg

Wolfe, Jordan ....(503) 842-7535
jwolfe@countrymedia.net, News Ed, North Coast Citizen, OR, Manzanita
jwolfe@countrymedia.net, Ed, Headlight-Herald, OR, Tillamook

Wolfe, Lisa...........................(888) 678-6008
lwolfe@lifesitenews.com, Secretary & Treasurer, LifeSiteNews.com, VA, Front Royal

Wolfe, Ron
ron.wolfe@zu.ac.ae, Prof./Asst. Dean, Dubai, Zayed University, Al Ruwayyah

Wolfenbarger, Jolene ....(405) 388-4011
sleader@pldi.net, Pub./Ed., Sentinel Leader, OK, Sentinel

Wolff, Don...........................(707) 526-8525
barbara.mitchel@pressdemocrat.com, Adv. Mgr., Nat'l, The Press Democrat, CA, Santa Rosa

Wolff, Jeff............................(319) 398-5871
jwolff@wcinet.com, Dir., Market Research/Adv. Servs., The Gazette, IA, Cedar Rapids
jwolff@wcinet.com, Adv. Dir., Telegraph Herald, IA, Dubuque

Wolff, P.L............................(202) 234-1717
newsroom@intowner.com, Mng Ed, The InTowner, DC, Washington

Wolff, Sharon
selbyrec@venturecomm.net, Pub., Selby Record, SD, Selby

Wolfgang, Rachel.....................(607) 274-3208
Ithaca College, NY, Ithaca

Wolfington, Robert
rwolfington@frontiernet.net, Ed., Tyler Tribute, MN, Tyler

Wolfington, Robert
rwolfington@frontiernet.net, Ed., Southwestern Peach, MN, Tyler

Wolfram, Manfred K.
wolframk@uc.edu, Chair, University of Cincinnati, OH, Cincinnati

Wolfson, Bernard ....(714) 796-2440
bwolfson@ocregister.com, Bus. Ed., The Orange County Register, CA, Santa Ana

Wolfson, Jill
jill.wolfson@parenthood.com, Editor, Bay Area Parent, CA, Campbell

Wolk, Erv
wolkadv@earthlink.net, Pres., Wolk Advertising, Inc. (Retail Carpet Ad Service), MI, Birmingham

Wolman, Jonathan ....(313) 222-2110
jon.wolman@detroitnews.com, Editor and Publisher, Detroit Free Press, MI, Detroit
jon.wolman@detroitnews.com, Ed and Pub, The Detroit News, MI, Detroit

Wolse-Lloyd, Katie
katie@columbusalive.com, Pub., Alive, OH, Columbus

Wolsey, Michael ....(801) 257-8577
mwolsey@utahpress.com, Accounting, Utah Press Association, Inc., UT, Sandy

Wolstenholme, Iona
iwolstenholme@llb.greatwest.ca, Sales Mgr., Lac La Biche Post, AB, Lac La Biche

Wolszon, John
wolszonj@archspm.org, Prodn. Mgr., The Catholic Spirit, MN, Saint Paul

Wolterman, Beth ....(712) 364-3131 ext. 110
editor@idacountycourier.com, Ed., Ida County Courier, IA, Ida Grove

Wolters, Keith
marketing@convergys.com, Sr. Dir., Mktg., Convergys, OH, Cincinnati

Wolverton, Lee ....(540) 981-3207
lee.wolverton@roanoke.com, Managing Editor, The Roanoke Times, VA, Roanoke

Wolverton, Lee ....(806) 345-3365
lee.wolverton@amarillo.com, Ed., Amarillo Globe-News, TX, Amarillo

Womack, Charles ....(336) 316-1231
publisher@yesweekly.com, Pub., Yes! Weekly, NC, Greensboro

Womack, Charles A.
jamestownnews@northstate.net, Pub., Jamestown News, NC, Jamestown

Womack, Charles Zan........(434) 432-1654 ext. 15
zanwomack@womackpublishing.com, Chrmn., Womack Publishing Co., VA, Lynchburg

Womack, Deanna
dwomack@kennesaw.edu, Prof., Kennesaw State University, GA, Kennesaw

Womer, Jake.......................(301) 733-5131
jakew@herald-mail.com, Exec. Ed., The Herald-Mail, MD, Hagerstown

Womer, Jake
jwomer@herald-mail.com, Exec. Ed., Herald-mail Express, MD, Hagerstown

Won, Jiyoung.......................(573) 882-2430
jwon@asne.org, Comm. Mgr., American Society of News Editors, MO, Columbia

Wong, Corey.........................(208) 639-3526
cwong@idahobusinessreview.com, Acct. Exec., Idaho Business Review, ID, Boise

Wong, Hugo
reporter@peninsulanewsreview.com, The Peninsula News Review, BC, Sidney

Wong, Kam
kam.wong@ss8.com, CFO, SS8 Networks, CA, Milpitas

Wong, Ling-Mei
lingmeiwong@sampan.org, Ed., Sampan Newspaper, MA, Boston

Wong, Matt ....(212) 854-8396
matt.wong@sherry-lehmann.com, Columbia Univ. Bus. School, NY, New York

Wong, Ying
ying.wong@mccann.com, SVP, Human Resources/Office Management, American Banker, NY, New York

Woo, Linda............................(808) 529-4355
lwoo@staradvertiser.com, National Adv., USA Today Hawaii Edition , HI, Honolulu

Woo, Linda............................(808) 529-4355
lwoo@staradvertiser.com, National Adv., Honolulu Star-Advertiser, HI, Honolulu
lwoo@staradvertiser.com, National Advertising, West Hawaii Today, HI, Kailua Kona
lwoo@staradvertiser.com, National Advertising, Hawaii Tribune-Herald, HI, Hilo

Wood, Bruce M........................(909) 628-5501
bwood@championnewspapers.com, Pub./Adv. Dir., Chino Champion, CA, Chino
bwood@championnewspapers.com, Pub./Adv.

Dir., Chino Hills Champion, CA, Chino

Wood, Carol ....(303) 473-1362
cwood@prairiemountainmedia.com, Ed., Broomfield Enterprise, CO, Boulder

Wood, Carol ....(303) 473-1362
cwood@prairiemountainmedia.com, Editor, Colorado Hometown Weekly, CO, Boulder

Wood, Charles
elgincourier@elgincourier.com, Ed., Elgin Courier, TX, Elgin

Wood, Chris...........................(321) 242-3806
cwood@floridatoday.com, Adv. Dir., Missileer, FL, Melbourne

Wood, Chris
cwood06@harris.com, Adv. Dir, Florida Today, FL, Melbourne

Wood, Christine
christine@coastreporter.net, Circ. Mgr., Coast Reporter, BC, Sechelt

Wood, Christopher
cwood@republicmedia.com, Dir.; Automotive, The Arizona Republic, AZ, Phoenix

Wood, Christopher....................(212) 803-8437
christopher.wood@sourcemedia.com, Ed., American Banker Online, American Banker, NY, New York

Wood, Cy
news@valleytimes-news.com, Ed., The Valley Times-News, AL, Lanett

Wood, Darlene ....(651) 407-1208
marketing@presspubs.com, The Lowdown - St. Croix Valley Area, MN, White Bear Lake

Wood, Darlene ....(651) 407-1208
marketing@presspubs.com, Sales Mgr., Forest Lake Lowdown, MN, White Bear Lake

Wood, Dave.................................ext. 208
dwood@mmclocal.com, Pub./Gen. Mgr., Stevens Point Buyers' Guide/city Times, WI, Stevens Point
dwood@mmclocal.com, Pub./Gen. Mgr., Marshfield Hub City Times And Buyers' Guide, WI, Marshfield

Wood, Dave...........................(920) 217-3309
dwood@mmclocal.com, General Manager, Waupaca County Post, WI, Waupaca

Wood, Denise ....ext. 3135
COO, AIGA, the professional association for design, NY, New York

Wood, Derek
sacosageads@centurytel.net, Ad. Sales, St. Clair Co. Courier, MO, Osceola

Wood, Emily ....(540) 981-3302
emily.wood@roanoke.com, Controller , The Roanoke Times, VA, Roanoke

Wood, Frank
fwood@register-herald.com, Pub., The Fayette Tribune, WV, Oak Hill

Wood, Frank...........................(304) 442-4156
fwood@register-herald.com, Pub., Montgomery Herald, WV, Oak Hill

Wood, Frank
fwood@register-herald.com, Pub., The Register Herald, WV, Beckley
fwood@register-herald.com, Pub., Times West Virginian, WV, Fairmont

Wood, Gary
gary.wood@yankton.net, Ed./Pub., Yankton Daily Press & Dakotan, SD, Yankton

Wood, Gary ....(605) 624-4429
gary.wood@plaintalk.net, Pub./Ed., Vermillion Plain Talk, SD, Vermillion

Wood, Gary
gary.wood@yankton.net, Owner/Pub., The Broadcaster, SD, Vermillion

Wood, Gary
gary.wood@yankton.net, Ed., Missouri Valley Shopper, SD, Yankton

Wood, Hazel ....(419) 826-1010
hazelmwood@msn.com, Pres., The Key Shoppers' News, Inc., OH, Swanton

Wood, Jenna
circulation@otelco.net, Circ. Mgr., The Blount Countian, AL, Oneonta

Wood, Jesse
jesse@highcountrypress.com, News. Ed., High Country Press, NC, Boone

Wood, Jim
jw1email@aol.com, Pub., Warren Sentinel, WY, Cheyenne

Wood, Josh ....(316) 268-6413
JWood@wichitaeagle.com, Ed. in Chief, The Wichita Eagle, KS, Wichita

Wood, Karen..............(207) 781-3661 ext. 111
kwood@theforecaster.net, Publisher, The Forecaster, ME, Falmouth
kwood@theforecaster.net, Audit Coord., Circulation Verification Council, MO, Saint Louis

Wood, Kelly...........................(414) 224-2898
kwood@journalsentinel.com, VP Cir., Audience & Customer Care, Milwaukee Journal Sentinel, WI, Milwaukee

Wood, Kevin C.
kwood@byowner.com, Pub., FSBO, NY, Bohemia

Wood, Kim
kim@myspartanews.com, Ed., The Expositor, TN, Sparta

Wood, Leighton
lpwood@skagitpublishing.com, Pres., The Argus, WA, Mount Vernon

Wood, Leighton P.
lpwood@skagitpublishing.com, Pres., Skagit Valley Herald, WA, Mount Vernon

Wood, Len
lwood@santamariatimes.com, Asst. Mng. Ed., Santa Maria Times, CA, Santa Maria

Wood, Len ....(805) 564-5128
lwood@newspress.com, Photo/Graphics Ed., Santa Barbara News-Press, CA, Santa Barbara

Wood, Les
les@cfmedia.info, Circ. Mgr, Rutherford Weekly, NC, Forest City
les@cfmedia.info, Circ. Mgr, Shelby Shopper & Info, NC, Shelby

Wood, Linda
class@mvtimes.com, Classified Adv. Mgr., The Martha's Vineyard Times, MA, Vineyard Haven

Wood, Linda
readznews@aol.com, Bus. Mgr., Zephyrhills News, FL, Zephyrhills

Wood, Lisa ....(765) 569-2033
Lwood@parkecountysentinel.com, Business/ News Coordinator, Parke County Sentinel, IN, Rockville

Wood, Mike ....(402) 374-2225
mike.wood@lee.net, Pub., Midwest Messenger, NE, Tekamah

Wood, Patrick J. ....(715) 842-4424
publisher@mmlocal.com, Pub., Wausau Times / Buyers' Guide, WI, Merrill

Wood, Robert.........................(719) 784-6383
florencecitizen@aol.com, Ed., The Florence Citizen, CO, Florence

Wood, Sam ....(217) 732-2101 ext. 338
sam.wood@lincolncourier.com, Sports Ed., Lincoln Courier, IL, Lincoln

Wood, Samantha ....(413) 496-6243
swood@berkshireeagle.com, Managing Editor for News, The Berkshire Eagle, MA, Pittsfield

Wood, Scott
news@whitesboronews.com, Pub./Ed., Whitesboro News-Record, TX, Whitesboro

Worrall, David
adservices@localsource.com, Pub., Belleville Post, NJ, Union

Worrall, David......................(908) 686-7700
hankwebb@thelocalsource.com, Pub., Vailsburg Leader, NJ, Union

Worrall, David
ads@thelocalsource.com, Pub., Nutley Journal, NJ, Union

Worrall, David
wcn22@localsource.com, Pub., The Glen Ridge Paper, NJ, Union

Worrall, David......................(908) 686-7700
Pub., News-Record of Maplewood & South Orange, NJ, Union

Worrall, Nancy
nworrall@thelocalsource.com, Bus. Mgr., Irvington Herald, NJ, Union

Worrall, Nancy
nworrall@thelocalsource.com, Controller, Nutley Journal, NJ, Union

Worrall, Nancy
nworrall@thelocalsource.com, Controller, West Orange Chronicle, NJ, Union

Worrall, Nancy
nworrall@thelocalsource.com, Bus. Mgr., News-Record of Maplewood & South Orange, NJ, Union
nworrall@thelocalsource.com, Controller, The Glen Ridge Paper, NJ, Union

Worrall, Nancy
nworrall@thelocalsource.com, Controller, Record-Transcript of east orange and orange, NJ, Union
nworrall@thelocalsource.com, Bus. Mgr., The Independent Press of Bloomfield, NJ, Union
nworrall@thelocalsource.com, Controller, Vailsburg Leader, NJ, Union
nworrall@thelocalsource.com, Controller, Union County Local Source, NJ, Union

Worrall, Nancy.............(908) 686-7700 ext. 308
nworrall@thelocalsource.com, Vice Pres., Bookkeeping/Circ./Accts. Payable, Worrall Community Newspapers, Inc., NJ, Union
nworrall@thelocalsource.com, Controller, Belleville Post, NJ, Union

Worrall, Peter
ads@thelocalsource.com, IT / Production Manager
Circulation Manager, Belleville Post, NJ, Union

Worrall, Peter W. ....(908) 686-7700 ext. 330
spikew@thelocalsource.com, Vice Pres., Worrall Community Newspapers, Inc., NJ, Union

Worrall, Raymond ....(908) 686-7700 ext. 332
rsw@thelocalsource.com, Vice Pres., Editorial/Composing, Worrall Community Newspapers, Inc., NJ, Union

Worrall, Raymond
rsw@thelocalsource.com, Vice Pres., Editorial, The Independent Press of Bloomfield, NJ, Union
rsw@thelocalsource.com, General Manager, Union County Local Source, NJ, Union

Worrall, Raymond
rsw@thelocalsource.com, Gen. Mgr., Belleville Post, NJ, Union

Worrell, Allen ....(276) 779-4062
aworrel@civitasmedia.com, Ed., The Carroll News, VA, Hillsville

Worrell, Kris......................(609) 272-7277
KWorrell@pressofac.com, VP. News, The Press of Atlantic City, NJ, Pleasantville

Worrell, Kris......................(315) 792-5004
kworrell@uticaod.com, Ed., Your Valley, NY, Utica

Worrell, Rodney......................(402) 387-2844
ainsworthnews@ainsworthnews.com, Pub., Ainsworth Star-Journal, NE, Ainsworth

Worstell, Dave ....(406) 657-1352

dworstell@billingsgazette.com, Adv. Dir., Sales/Mktg., Billings Gazette, MT, Billings

Wortel, Gary ....(817) 390-7454
gwortel@star-telegram.com, Pres./Pub., Fort Worth Star-Telegram, TX, Fort Worth
gwortel@star-telegram.com, Pres. / Pub., The Keller Citizen, TX, Fort Worth

Worth, Gary
aalvord@nmsu.edu, Instr., New Mexico State University, NM, Las Cruces

Worth, Kevin
kworth@gellerco.com, Pres./Pub., The Daily Deal, NY, New York

Worthen, John......................(870) 534-3400
jworthen@pbcommercial.com, Mng. Ed., White Hall Journal, AR, White Hall
jworthen@pbcommercial.com, Mng. Ed., Pine Bluff Commercial, AR, Pine Bluff

Worthington, John D.
news@theaegis.com, Pub., The Weekender, MD, Bel Air

Worthington, John D.
ads@theaegis.com, Pub., Adams Publishing Group, LLC, MN, Virginia

Worthington, John D.
news@theaegis.com, Pub., The Record, MD, Bel Air

Worthington, Liz
liz.worthington@pressinstitute.org, Content Strategy Program Manager, American Press Institute, VA, Arlington

Worthington, Lonnie
lworthington@kansa.com, Chief Operating Officer, Kansa Technology, LLC, KS, Emporia

Worthington, Nancy
nancy.worthington@quinnipiac.edu, Assoc. Prof., Quinnipiac University, CT, Hamden

Wortsman, Marc
mwortsman@mardenkane.com, Exec. Vice Pres., Marden-Kane, INC, NY, Garden City

Woryk, Carrie
cawo@esko-graphics.com, Mktg. Commun. Mgr., Esko-Graphics, OH, Vandalia

Wozinsky, Jessica
jessica_wozinsky@parade.com, Social Media Editor, Parade, New York

Wraight, Rebecca......................(610) 377-2051
Mktg., Times News, PA, Lehighton

Wren, Megan ....(615) 560-2203
mwren@dicksonherald.com, Adv. Mgr., Fairview Observer, TN, Fairview
mwren@dicksonherald.com, Adv. Mgr., The Dickson Herald, TN, Dickson

Wriedt, George
ads@kirksvilledailyexpress.com, Adv. Dir., Kirksville Crier, MO, Kirksville

Wriedt, George
gwriedt@kirksvilledailyexpress.com, Adv. Mgr., Kirksville Daily Express, MO, Kirksville

Wrigh, Myra ....(336) 983-4789
editor@piedmontparent.com, Ed., Piedmont Parent, NC, King

Wright, Aaron
office@thebanner.com, Office Mgr., The Jackson County Banner, IN, Brownstown

Wright, Adam......................(209) 249-3555
I.T. Manager, Manteca Bulletin, CA, Manteca

Wright, Andy............................(212) 556-1050
wrighah@nytimes.com, Senior VP, Adv. & Pub., The New York Times, NY, New York

Wright, Angela ....(606) 248-1010 Ext. 1134
awright@civitasmedia.com, Trading Post Clerk, Middlesboro Daily News, KY, Middlesboro

Wright, Ann
electrastarnews@electratel.net, Adv. Dir., Electra Star-News, TX, Electra

Wright, Ashley

aswright@gannett.com, Automotive & Real Estate Mgr.
, Lansing State Journal, MI, Lansing

Wright, Bill ....(317) 472-5342
bwright@ibj.com, Circulation Manager, Court & Commercial Record, IN, Indianapolis
bwright@ibj.com, Circ. Mgr. , Indianapolis Business Journal, IN, Indianapolis

Wright, Brent
bwright@mymts.net, Adv. Mgr., Dauphin Herald, MB, Dauphin

Wright, Brian ....(520) 568-4198
bwright@copamonitor.com, News Ed., Maricopa Monitor, AZ, Maricopa

Wright, Chase ....(203) 354-1065
cwright@thehour.com, Ed., The Wilton Villager, CT, Norwalk

Wright, Chase ....(203) 354-1065
cwright@thehour.com, Regional Editor - Wilton Villager, Stamford Times, The Hour, CT, Norwalk

Wright, Claire
claire.wright@wne.edu, Springfield College, MA, Springfield

Wright, Clarence
clarence@newcastlepacer.com, Gen. Mgr., Newcastle Pacer, OK, Newcastle

Wright, Clero ....(478) 744-4252
cwright@macon.com, Adv. Mgr., Classified, The Telegraph, GA, Macon

Wright, Cliff
cwright@rimpublications.com, Pub., Kuna Melba News, ID, Kuna

Wright, Dalton
dwright@lebanondailyrecord.com, Pres., Lebanon Publishing Co., MO, Lebanon

Wright, Dalton C. ....(417) 532-9131
editor@lebanondailyrecord.com, Pres./Pub., The Lebanon Daily Record, MO, Lebanon

Wright, David
david.wright@drake.edu, Assoc. Prof./Asst. Dean, Drake University, IA, Des Moines

Wright, David A.
info@martinautomatic.com, Vice Pres., Sales, Martin Automatic, Inc., IL, Rockford

Wright, Debbie
dwright@dddnews.com, Office Mgr., Daily Dunklin Democrat Extra, MO, Kennett

Wright, Debbie
dwright@dddnews.com, Office Mgr., The Daily Dunklin Democrat, MO, Kennett

Wright, F. Eugene......................(845) 986-2216
editor@wvdispatch.com, Publisher/Owner, Warwick Valley Dispatch, NY, Warwick

Wright, Gary ....(978) 970-4882
grwright@lowellsun.com, Circ. Opns. Mgr., The Dispatch News, MA, Lowell

Wright, Gary ....(978) 970-4882
grwright@lowellsun.com, Circ. Mgr., Home Delivery, The Sun, MA, Lowell

Wright, Heidi ....(503) 385-4902
hwright@eomediagroup.com, COO, EO Media Group, OR, Salem

Wright, Jesse ....(662) 627-2201
jwright@pressregister.com, Managing Editor, The Clarksdale Press Register, MS, Clarksdale

Wright, Joan
nelighnews@frontiernet.com, Pub., Clearwater Record-Ewing News, NE, Neligh

Wright, Joan
jwright@mycarrollnews.com, Asst. Ed., River City Trading Post, KY, Carrollton

Wright, John
jwright@murrayledger.com, Ed., The Murray Ledger & Times, KY, Murray

Wright, John ....(865) 457-2515

jwright@mycouriernews.com, Publisher, The Courier News, TN, Clinton

Wright, John P.
jwright@heralddemocrat.com, Pub., Herald Democrat, TX, Sherman

Wright, Joye ....(580) 588-3862
wright@apachenews.com, Ed., The Apache News, OK, Apache

Wright, Kelly
kelly.wright@carolinashealthcare.org, Pub., The Matthews-Mint Hill, NC, Charlotte
kelly.wright@carolinashealthcare.org, Pub., The Union County Weekly, NC, Charlotte

Wright, Lili ....(765) 658-5977
editor@ddepauw.edu, DePauw Univ., IN, Greencastle

Wright, Lisa
lwright@thevermontstandard.com, Prodn. Mgr., The Vermont Standard, VT, Woodstock

Wright, Lorine ....(858) 876-8945
editor@delmartimes.net, Exec. Ed., Carmel Valley Leader (OOB), CA, Del Mar
editor@delmartimes.net, Exec. Ed., Carmel Valley News, CA, Solana Beach
editor@delmartimes.net, Exec. Ed., Rancho Santa Fe Review, CA, Solana Beach
editor@delmartimes.net, Exec. Ed., Solana Beach Sun, CA, Solana Beach
editor@delmartimes.net, Exec. Ed., Del Mar Times, CA, Solana Beach
editor@delmartimes.net, Exec. Ed., San Diego Suburban News (OOB), CA, La Jolla
editor@delmartimes.net, Executive Editor, Encinitas Advocate, CA, Solana Beach

Wright, Mark
mark.wright@targetbase.com, Pres./CEO, Targetbase, TX, Irving

Wright, Mark
dayglo@dayglo.com, Vice Pres., Sales, Day-Glo Color Corp., OH, Cleveland

Wright, Mary Beth
laferianews@aol.com, Ed., La Feria News, TX, La Feria

Wright, Monty ....(209) 754-3861
circulation@calaverasenterprise.com, Circ. Sup., Calaveras Enterprise, CA, San Andreas

Wright, Natalie........................(734) 677-5125
nkwright@wccnet.edu, Ed., Washtenaw Community College, MI, Ann Arbor

Wright, Nathan ....(903) 566-7131
editor@patriottalon.com, Editor in Chief, Univ. of Texas at Tyler, TX, Tyler

Wright, Richard
richard.wright@va.gov, Prof., Howard University, DC, Washington

Wright, Stewart ....(207) 791-6785
swright@mainetoday.com, Chief Information Officer, Portland Press Herald / Maine Sunday Telegram, ME, Portland

Wright, Tammie ....(336) 249-3981 ext 205
tammie.wright@the-dispatch.com, Adv. Mgr., The Dispatch, NC, Lexington

Wright, Tawana
twright@pressargus.com, Circ. Mgr., Alma Journal, AR, Van Buren

Wrightsman, Stacie ....(765) 575-4634
swrightsman@thecouriertimes.com, Adv. Dir., The Courier-Times, IN, New Castle

Wringert, Stephen
leader@lucernevalley.net, Pub., Lucerne Valley Leader, CA, Victorville

Wrinn, Stephen
smwrin2@email.uky.edu, Dir., University Press of Kentucky, KY, Lexington

Wroble, Jerre
jerre@slweekly.com, Ed., Salt Lake City Weekly, UT, Salt Lake City

Wroblewski, Andrew ....(631) 427-7000 x 15

@huntington.com, Adv. Mgr., Sales,
y Reporter, OH, Columbus

, Scott ....(920) 356-6726
nn@capitalnewspapers.com, Adv.
opping Reminder, WI, Columbus

, Scott ....(920) 356-6756
nn@capitalnewspapers.com, Monday
er, WI, Beaver Dam
nn@capitalnewspapers.com, Gen.
aily Citizen, Beaver Dam, WI, Beaver

nn, Scott
ann@madison.com, Shoppers View,
aver Dam

r, Ron
linger@jjournal.com, Sports Ed., The
y Journal, NJ, Secaucus

, Dan.............. (907) 486-3227 ext. 613
sing@kodiakdailymirror.com, Office
ager, Kodiak Daily Mirror, AK, Kodiak

, Courtney
ey.zellars@tribstar.com, Circ. Dir.,
hetown, IN, Terre Haute

s, Courtney ....(812) 231-4264
ney.zellars@tribstar.com, Mktg. Dir., The
une Star, IN, Terre Haute

r, Susan ....(717) 270-2742
nz@aboutfamiliespa.com, Ed., About
milies Parenting Newspaper, PA, Lebanon

r, Tom.............................(419) 724-6317
er@toleodblade.com, Audience
evelopment and Customer Service Mgr.,
he Blade, OH, Toledo

ers, Courtney ....(812) 231-4260
urtney.zellars@tribstar.com, Adv. Sales
Exec., The Tribune Star, IN, Terre Haute

man, Nancy
zeman@prairiepress.net, Ed./VP, The Prairie
Press, IL, Paris

eman, Robert ....ext. 205
/ice President, Norwood Paper, IL, Chicago

Zeman, Tim
news@metrowestnewspapers.com, Pub.,
Brighton Standard Blade, CO, Brighton

Zemenick, Rebecca .... (570) 682-9081
rebecca-z@citizenstandard.com, Mng. Ed., The
Citizen-Standard, PA, Valley View

Zeng, Lily
zengli@astate.edu, Asst. Prof., Arkansas State
University, AR, Jonesboro

Zeng, X.Y..............................(604) 869-4992
news@hopestandard.com, Ed., Hope
Standard, BC, Hope

Zenner, Brandon ....(816) 516-7030
brandonzennermedia@gmail.com, Editor-in-
Chief, Northwest Missouri State Univ., MO,
Maryville

Zenz, Barbara
bzenz@stephenz.com, Pres./CEO, The
Stephenz Group, CA, San Jose

Zepezauer, Keven.....................(252) 329-9630
kzepezaurer@reflector.com, First Vice
President, Mid-Atlantic Circulation Managers
Association, NC, Roanoke Rapids

Zepezauer, Keven ....(252) 265-7812
kzepezauer@wilsontimes.com, Gen Mngr, The
Wilson Times, NC, Wilson

Zerbey, Joseph H. ....(419) 263-1252
jzerbey@toledoblade.com, Gen. Mgr., The
Blade, OH, Toledo

Zeremski, Adam
eanews@eastaurorany.com, Mng. Ed., East
Aurora Advertiser, NY, East Aurora
eanews@eastaurorany.com, Ed., Elma Review,
NY, East Aurora

Zeringue, Jeff

jeff.zeringue@daily-iberian.com, Ed., The Daily
Iberian, LA, New Iberia

Zernechel, Denise
dzernechel@mankatofreepress.com, Circ. Dir.,
The Free Press, MN, Mankato

Zerr, Catherine ....(605) 845-3646
news@mobridgetribune.com, Ed, Monday
Reminder, SD, Mobridge

Zerr, Katie ....(605) 845-3646
news@mobridgetribune.com, Ed., Mobridge
Tribune, SD, Mobridge

Zesk, Richard.....................................ext. 285
r.zesk@theday.com, Adv. Mgr., Classified, The
Day, CT, New London

Zetterberg, Linda
lzetterberg@njnpublishing.com, Prodn. Mgr.,
The Warren Reporter, NJ, Flemington

Zeve, Bradley............... (831) 394-5656 ext. 103
bradley@mcweekly.com, Exec. Ed. & CEO,
Monterey County Weekly, CA, Seaside

Zewicky, David ....(734) 240-5025
dzewicky@monroenews.com, Circ. Mgr., The
Monroe News, MI, Monroe
dzewicky@monroenews.com, Circ. & Classified
Mgr., Bedford Now, MI, Monroe

Zezza, Peggy ....Ext. 3571
pzezza@pittsburghcatholic.org, Circ. Mgr.,
Pittsburgh Catholic, PA, Pittsburgh

Zhang, Julie
jzhang@eastwest.edu, Bus. Dir., Lawton Media
Inc., OK, Lawton

Zhao, Xinshu ....(919) 962-1465
Prof., University of North Carolina, NC, Chapel
Hill

Zharp, Rocky
rzharp@thevalleychronicle.com, Sales & Adv.,
The Valley Chronicle, CA, Hemet

Zhivago, Kristin
kristin@zhivago.com, Pres., Zhivago
Management Partners, RI, Jamestown

Zic, Valentina..........................(781) 433-8366
vzic@wickedlocal.com , Ed., Needham Times,
MA, Needham

Ziegler, Grant V.
nnr7420@dcccd.edu, Editor-in-Chief, North
Lake College, TX, Irving

Zienemann, Scott
szeinemann@capitalnewspapers.com, Adv.
Mgr., Monday-mini, WI, Beaver Dam

Zienemann, Scott
szeinemann@capitalnewspapers.com, Adv.
Mgr., Tri-county, WI, Beaver Dam

Zientara, Robert
editor.barron@chibardun.net, Ed., Barron
News-Shield, WI, Barron

Zier, Frank
fzier@pubgroup.com, Nashville/West Coast
Assoc. Pub., Relish - Franklin, TN, Franklin

Zier, Frank
fzier@pubgroup.com, Nashville/West Coast
Assoc. Pub., American Profile - Franklin, TN,
Franklin

Zikias, Robert ....(937) 225-6995
robert.zikias@coxinc.com, Vice President &
CFO, Dayton Daily News, OH, Franklin

Zilstra, David
david.zilstra@gmail.com, Pub/Adv Dir,
Bancroft This Week, ON, Bancroft

Zimanek, Brad........................(334) 261-1586
bzimanek@gannett.com, Consumer Exper.
Dir/Sports Ed, Montgomery Advertiser, AL,
Montgomery

Zimbalist, Michael ....(212) 556-3850
michaelz@nytimes.com, Senior VP, Ad
Products & Research & Dev., The New York
Times, NY, New York

Zimmer, Amanda

amanda@claresholmlocalpress.ca, Prod. Mgr.,
Claresholm Local Press, AB, Claresholm

Zimmer, Becky ....(306) 682-2561
rzimmer@humboldtjournal.ca, Ed. , The
Humboldt Journal, SK, Humboldt
rzimmer@humboldtjournal.ca, Ed. , East
Central Trader, SK, Humboldt

Zimmer, Gretchen............(614) 221-2449 ext. 90
Prodn. Mgr., Alive, OH, Columbus

Zimmerman, Chris ....(620) 429-2773
Pub., Cherokee County News-Advocate, KS,
Columbus

Zimmerman, Donald
a.siemers@colostate.edu, Prof./Dir., Center
for Writing and Communication Technology,
Colorado State University, CO, Fort Collins

Zimmerman, John
advertising@shipnewschronicle.com, Gen.
Mgr./Adv. Dir., The Shippensburg News-
Chronicle, PA, Shippensburg
advertising@shipnewschronicle.com, Gen.
Mgr./Adv. Dir., The Valley Times-Star, PA,
Shippensburg

Zimmerman, Neal
nzimmerman@tribune.com, Mgr., Tribune
Media Network, CA, San Francisco

Zimmerman, Rex ....(620) 825-4229
kionews@sctelcom.net, Ed., The Kiowa News,
KS, Kiowa

Zimmerman, Robert...................(212) 947-5100
mfaggiano@metro-email.com, Publisher, Metro
Editorial Services, NY, New York

Zimmerman, Shane
szimmerman@lnpnews.com, Sr. Vice President
of Administration, LNP, PA, Lancaster
szimmerman@lnpnews.com, Sr. Vice President
of Administration, LNP Media Group, Inc.,
PA, Lancaster

Zimmerman, Tammy ....(979) 731-4680
tammy.zimmerman@theeagle.com, Pre Press
Mgr., The Eagle, TX, Bryan

Zimmermann, Mark V. ....(202) 281-2412
mark@cathstan.org, Ed., Catholic Standard,
DC, Washington

Zines, Tricia .... (949) 388-7700 ext. 107
tzines@picketfencemedia.com, The Capistrano
Dispatch, CA, Capistrano Beach
tzines@picketfencemedia.com, Prod. and Circ.
Mgr., Dana Point Times, CA, Capistrano
Beach

Zink, Joe
joe.zink@lee.net, Gen. Mgr., Burt County
Plaindealer, NE, Tekamah
joe.zink@lee.net, Gen. Mgr., Midwest
Messenger, NE, Tekamah

Zins, Joanthan ....(401) 380-2351
zins@newportRI.com, Editor, The Newport
Daily News, RI, Newport

Zins, Jonathan ....(401) 380-2351
editor@newportri.com, Mng Ed, The Edward A.
Sherman Publishing Co., RI, Newport

Zinsmeyer, Cheryl
skyline@sulross.edu, Student Publications
Advisor, Sul Ross State Univ., TX, Alpine

Ziomek, Karl
editor@heritage.com, Ed., Heritage Sunday,
MI, Southgate

Zion, Cathy....................(502) 327-8855 ext. 11
cathy@todayspublications.com, Owner/
Publisher, Today's Family, KY, Louisville

Zionc, Ed
Ed@xyonicz.com, Pres./Mgr., Mktg., XYonicz,
NY, Rome

Zippert, Carol...........................(205) 372-0525
carolxzippert@aol.com, Co-Pub., Greene
County Democrat, AL, Eutaw

Zirkle, William
lgp@scottdale.com, Ed., The Times-Sun, PA,
West Newton

Zitis, Ellen
zitis@northjersey.com, Adv. Mgr., Community
News, NJ, Fair Lawn

Zitis, Ellen
zitis@northjersey.com, Adv. Mgr., Mahwah
Suburban News, NJ, Ridgewood
zitis@northjersey.com, Adv. Mgr., Midland Park
Suburban News, NJ, Ridgewood
zitis@northjersey.com, Adv. Mgr., Twin-Boro
News, NJ, Cresskill
zitis@northjersey.com, Adv. Mgr., Glen Rock
Gazette, NJ, Ridgewood

Zitis, Ellen
thegazette@northjersey.com, Ad. Director, The
Gazette, NJ, Fair Lawn

Zivanovic, Crista ....(219) 933-3250
crista.zivanovic@nwi.com, News Ed., The
Times of Northwest Indiana, IN, Munster

Zizzo, Judith ....(954) 596-5632
jzizzo@tribune.com, Managing Editor,
Deerfield and Pompano Forum, FL, Fort
Lauderdale
jzizzo@tribune.com, Managing Ed., Hi-Riser -
Broward, FL, Pompano Beach

Zizzo, Robert
rzizzo@greenbay.gannett.com, Exec Editor,
Green Bay Press-Gazette, WI, Green Bay

Zloza, Marlene ....(219) 769-9292
mzloza@dcgary.org, Staff writer, Northwest
Indiana Catholic, IN, Merrillville

Zmiyiwsky, Daria ....(204) 290-5353
daria.zmiyiwsky@sunmedia.ca, Pub., Kenora
Daily Miner & News, ON, Kenora
daria.zmiyiwsky@sunmedia.ca, Adv. Dir,
Central Plains Herald Leader, MB, Portage
La Prairie

Zmiyiwsky, Daria
daria.zmiyiwsky@sunmedia.ca, Reg. Promo.
& Comm. Relations Dir., St. Catharines
Standard, ON, Saint Catharine's

Zoch, Lynn
lzoch@radford.edu, Dir., Radford University,
VA, Radford

Zoebelein, Maureen..................(503) 357-3181
mzoebelein@fgnewstimes.com, Prodn. Mgr.,
Forest Grove News-Times, OR, Forest Grove

Zoeller, Chris ....(843) 937-2373
czoeller@postandcourier.com, Strategic Mktg.
Dir., The Post and Courier, SC, Charleston

Zogg, Michael ....(707) 464-2141
Sports Ed, The Del Norte Triplicate, CA,
Crescent City

Zohoori, Ali
zohoori@bradley.edu, Prof., Bradley University,
IL, Peoria

Zokal, Joseph ....(815) 220-6968
design@newstrib.com, Prodn. Mgr., Pre Press,
News-Tribune, IL, La Salle

Zoldan, Sheldon
szoldan@Fortmyer.gannett.com, Content
Strategist
, The Commercial Appeal, TN, Memphis

Zollinger, Robert C. ....(505) 863-6811
nmboof@hotmail.com, Vice Pres./Pub., Gallup
Independent, NM, Gallup

Zollman, Peter M. ....(321) 356-3182
pzollman@aimgroup.com, Founding Principal,
Advanced Interactive Media Group, LLC, FL,
Altamonte Springs

Zolotora, Irena ....(718) 368-2348
vechny@yahoo.com, COO, Vecherniy New
York, NY, Brooklyn

Zonars, Stephen C. ....(740) 548-1273
szonars@the.dispatch.com, Vice Pres., On
Target Marketing, The Bag, OH, Lewis
Center

Zoochi, Laura
editor@belleviewview.com, Ed., The View, MI,
Southgate

Zorich, David ....(563) 383-2367
cmccormick@qctimes.com, Controller, Quad-City Times, IA, Davenport

Zorichak, Maureen ....Adv. Dir.
Herald-Standard, PA, Uniontown

Zorn, Alex ....(970) 384-9114
azorn@citizentelegram.com, Ed., Citizen Telegram, CO, Glenwood Springs

Zotti, Ed
edzotti@gmail.com, Editor/General Mgr, Straight Dope - Wrapports/Sun-Times Media, Inc., Chicago

Zouain, Adalgiza ....(407) 767-0070
adalgiza.zouain@laprensaorlando.com,, Sales, La Prensa, FL, Longwood

Zoucha, Pam ....(402) 371-1020 ext. 225
pzoucha@norfolkdailynews.com, Retail Mgr., Norfolk Daily News, NE, Norfolk

Zoupaniotis, Apostolos
info@greeknewsonline.com, Ed., Greek News, NY, Astoria

Zucco, Debbie
deborah.zucco@latimes.com, Community Ed., Daily Pilot, CA, Costa Mesa

Zucco, Omar
ozucco@mcall.com, Dir. Major Accts./Nat'l Adv., The Morning Call, PA, Allentown

Zuchelli, Mark...................................ext. 224
mzuchelli@timesonline.com, Circ. Mgr., Home Delivery, Beaver County Times, PA, Beaver

Zuckerman, Mortimer B..............(212) 326-4010
Chrmn./Pub., New York Daily News, NY, New York

Zuegner, Carol
czuegner@creighton.edu, Assoc. Prof., Creighton Univ., NE, Omaha

Zuello, Lieah
sales@willistonpioneer.com, Adv. Sales, Williston Pioneer Sun News, FL, Williston

Zuerker, Dawn.........................(806) 742-3384
dawn.zuerker@ttu.edu, Asst. Dir./Adv. Mgr., Texas Tech University, TX, Lubbock

Zufelt, Jerome M.
jzufelt@dioceseofgreensburg.org, Editor, The Catholic Accent, The Catholic Accent, PA,

Greensburg

Zummo, Mike
njoffice@strausnews.com, Mng. Ed., Photo News, NY, Chester

Zummo, Mike
njoffice@strausnews.com, Mng. Ed, Dirt Magazine, NY, Chester

Zummo, Mike
njoffice@strausnews.com, Mng. Ed., Warwick Advertiser, NY, Chester

Zummo, Mike
njoffice@strausnews.com, Mng. Ed. , The West Milford Messenger, NJ, West Milford
njoffice@strausnews.com, Mng. Ed., Sparta Independent, NJ, Sparta
njoffice@strausnews.com, Mng. Ed., Advertiser News (South Edition), NJ, Sparta
njoffice@strausnews.com, Mng. Ed., Advertiser News (North Edition), NJ, Sparta

Zummo, Mike
njoffice@strausnews.com, Mng. Ed., The Advertiser-News (North), NY, Chester

Zumwalt, Barbara
azumwalt@recordnet.com, Metro Ed., The Record, CA, Stockton

Zunde, Steve ....(973) 589-7800
priscodigital@prisco.com, President, PriscoDigital LLC, Printers' Service/Prisco/PriscoDigital, NJ, Newark

Zuniga, Alex
azuniga@newtimesslo.com, Arts Dir., New Times, CA, San Luis Obispo
azuniga@newtimesslo.com, Arts Dir., The Santa Maria Sun, CA, Santa Maria

Zuniga, Michael
mike.zuniga@coxinc.com, Sr. Mgr., Cox Media Group, GA, Atlanta

Zupancic, Gary ....(512) 847-2202
Reporter, Wimberley View, TX, Wimberley

Zuppa, Tom ....(978) 970-4643
tzuppa@lowellsun.com, Mng. Ed., The Dispatch News, MA, Lowell

Zuppa, Tom ....(978) 970-4643
tzuppa@lowellsun.com, Asst. Mng. Ed., Local News-Weekend, The Sun, MA, Lowell

Zuraw, Cathy...........................(203) 330-6498

czuraw@ctpost.com, Photo/Graphics Ed., Connecticut Post, CT, Bridgeport

Zurcher, Anthony
azurcher@creators.com, Editor, Creators, Hermosa Beach

Zurek, Chester ....(815) 462-1129
czmccainbind@earthlink.net, National Service/Product Manager, McCain Bindery Systems, IL, New Lenox

Zurek, Jerome
zurek@cabrini.edu, Chair, Cabrini University Loquitur, PA, Radnor

Zurenda, Keith
kzurenda@gannett.com, Account Executive, Gannett News Service - Albany, NY, Albany

Zurn, Katie
kzurn@jcpgroup.com, Office Mgr., Lake Country Reporter, WI, Hartland
kzurn@jcpgroup.com, Office Mgr., Kettle Moraine Index, WI, Hartland
kzurn@jcpgroup.com, Office Mgr., Oconomowoc Focus, WI, Hartland
kzurn@jcpgroup.com, Office Mgr., Sussex Sun, WI, Hartland

Zurowski, Monica.....................(403) 235-7291
mzurowski@calgaryherald.com, Exec. Producer, Calgary Herald, AB, Calgary

Zusman, Mark........................(503) 243-2122
mzusman@wweek.com, Publisher, Willamette Week, OR, Portland

Zwart, Marg
oronotimes@rogers.com, Ed., Weekly Times, ON, Orono

Zweerink, Brad ....(707) 427-6991
Photo Ed., Daily Republic, CA, Fairfield

Zweifel, Dave
dzweifel@capitalnewspapers.com, Ed., The Capital Times, WI, Madison

Zwerling, Elizabeth ....(909) 593-3511 ext. 4293
zwerling@ulv.edu, University of La Verne, CA, La Verne

Zwetzig, Kelly
kelly.zwetzig@starherald.com, Mktg. & Dig. Med. Mgr., Star-Herald, NE, Scottsbluff

Zwez, Amy
circulation@theeveningleader.com, Cir. Mgr.,

The Evening Leader, OH, Saint Marys

Zwez, Deb.............................(419) 739-35
publisher@wapakwdn.com, Pub., Auglaize Merchandiser, OH, Wapakoneta

Zwez, Deb
publisher@nktelco.net, Pub., The Community Post, OH, Minster
publisher@nktelco.net, Pub., Merchandiser (OOB), OH, Minster

Zwez, Deborah ....(419) 738-212
publisher@wapakwdn.com, Pub., Wapakoneta Daily News, OH, Wapakoneta

Zwickel, Steven ....(608) 262-517
zwickel@engr.wisc.edu, Advisor, Wisconsin Engineer Magazine, WI, Madison

Zwiebel, Joe
jzwiebel@HartfordBusiness.com, Pres., Hartford Business Journal, CT, Hartford

Zwierzynski, Dan
dzwierzynski@batavianews.com, Prodn. Mgr., Drummer Pennysaver, NY, Batavia

Zygmont, Erik..........................(410) 732-6603
ezygmont@baltimoreguide.com, Ed., Baltimore Guide South, MD, Baltimore

Zygmont, Erik..........................(410) 732-6603
ezygmont@baltimoreguide.com, Editor, The Baltimore Guide, MD, Baltimore

Zygmunt, Elizabeth
ezygmunt@timesshamrock.com, Ed., Northeast Pennsylvania Business Journal, PA, Scranton

Zyla, Greg
gzyla@thedailyreview.com, Pub., Wyoming County Press Examiner, PA, Tunkhannock

Zyla, Greg.............................(570) 265-1600
gzyla@thedailyreview.com, Pub., The News Item, Shamokin
gzyla@thedailyreview.com, Pub., The Daily Review, PA, Towanda

Zynomirski, Jillian....................(905) 768-3111
jillian@haldimandpress.com, Pub., The Haldimand Press, ON, Hagersville

Zyskowski, Bob
zyskowski@archspm.org, Assoc. Pub., The Catholic Spirit, MN, Saint Paul